Stanley Gibbons SIMPLIFIED CATALOGUE

Stamps of the World 1994

An illustrated and priced three-volume guide to the postage stamps of the whole world, excluding changes of paper, perforation, shade and watermark

VOLUME 3

COMMONWEALTH COUNTRIES

STANLEY GIBBONS LTD
London and Ringwood

By Appointment to
Her Majesty the Queen
Stanley Gibbons Limited
London
Philatelists

60th Edition

Published in Great Britain by
Stanley Gibbons Ltd
Publications Editorial, Sales Offices and Distribution Centre
5, Parkside, Christchurch Road,
Ringwood, Hampshire BH24 3SH
Telephone 0425 472363

ISBN: 085259-381-3

Published as Stanley Gibbons Simplified Stamp Catalogue from 1934 to 1970, renamed Stamps of the World in 1971, and produced in two (1982–88) or three (from 1989) volumes as Stanley Gibbons Simplified Catalogue of Stamps of the World.
This volume published November 1994

S.G. Item No. 2883 (94)

Origination by BPC Whitefriars Ltd, Tunbridge Wells, Kent
Printed in Great Britain by Bemrose Security Printing, London & Derby

Stanley Gibbons
SIMPLIFIED CATALOGUE

Stamps of the World

This popular catalogue is a straightforward three-volume listing of the stamps that have been issued everywhere in the world since the very first–Great Britain's famous Penny Black in 1840.

This edition continues the three-volume format. Volume 1 (Foreign countries A–J) appeared in September, Volume 2 (Foreign countries K–Z) in October, and Volume 3 covering Commonwealth countries completes the trio.

Readers are reminded that the Catalogue Supplements, published in each issue of **Gibbons Stamp Monthly,** can be used to update the listings in **Stamps of the World** as well as our twenty-two part standard catalogue. To make the supplement even more useful the Type numbers given to the illustrations are now the same in the Stamps of the World as in the standard catalogues. The first Catalogue Supplement to this Volume appeared in the October 1994 issue of **Gibbons Stamp Monthly.**

Gibbons Stamp Monthly can be obtained through newsagents or on postal subscription from Stanley Gibbons Publications, 5, Parkside, Christchurch Road, Ringwood, Hants BH24 3SH.

The catalogue has many important features:

- As an indication of current values virtually every stamp is priced. Thousands of alterations have been made since the last edition.
- By being set out on a simplified basis that excludes changes of paper, perforation, shade, watermark, gum or printer's and date imprints it is particularly easy to use. (For its exact scope see "Information for users" pages following.)
- The thousands of illustrations and helpful descriptions of stamp designs make it of maximum appeal to collectors with thematic interests.
- Its catalogue numbers are the world-recognised Stanley Gibbons numbers throughout.
- Helpful introductory notes for the collector are included, backed by much historical, geographical and currency information.
- A very detailed index gives instant location of countries in this volume, and a cross-reference to those included in the other volumes.

Over 8,400 stamps and 2,175 new illustrations have been added to this 1994 edition. The 1994 three-volume edition contains over 312,400 stamps and 74,750 illustrations.

The listings in this edition are based on the standard catalogues: Part 1 British Commonwealth) (1994 edition), Part 2 (Austria & Hungary) (5th edition), Part 3 (Balkans) (3rd edition), Part 4 (Benelux) (3rd edition), Part 5 (Czechoslovakia & Poland) (4th edition), Part 6 (France) (3rd edition), Part 7 (Germany) (4th edition), Part 8 (Italy & Switzerland (4th edition), Part 9 (Portugal & Spain) (3rd edition), Part 10 (Russia) (4th edition), Part 11 (Scandinavia) (4th edition), Part 12 (Africa since Independence A-E) (2nd edition), Part 13 (Africa since Independence F-M) (1st edition), Part 14 (Africa since Independence N-Z) (1st edition), Part 15 (Central America) (2nd edition), Part 16 (Central Asia) (3rd edition), Part 17 (China) (4th edition), Part 18 (Japan & Korea) (3rd edition), Part 19 Middle East) (4th edition), Part 20 (South America) (3rd edition), Part 21 (South-East Asia) (2nd edition) and Part 22 (United States) (4th edition).

Stanley Gibbons Stamp Catalogue
Complete List of Parts

1 British Commonwealth
(Annual in two volumes)

Foreign Countries

2 Austria & Hungary (5th edition, 1994)
Austria · Bosnia & Herzegovina · U.N. (Vienna) · Hungary

3 Balkans (3rd edition, 1987)
Albania · Bulgaria · Greece & Islands · Rumania · Yugoslavia

4 Benelux (4th edition, 1993)
Belgium & Colonies · Netherlands & Colonies · Luxembourg

5 Czechoslovakia & Poland (4th edition, 1991)
Czechoslovakia · Bohemia & Moravia · Slovakia · Poland

6 France (4th edition, 1993)
France · Colonies · Andorra · Monaco

7 Germany (4th edition, 1992)
Germany · States · Colonies · Post Offices

8 Italy & Switzerland (4th edition, 1993)
Italy & Colonies · Fiume · San Marino · Vatican City · Trieste · Liechtenstein · Switzerland · U.N. (Geneva)

9 Portugal & Spain (3rd edition, 1991)
Andorra · Portugal & Colonies · Spain & Colonies

10 Russia (4th edition, 1991)
Russia · Baltic States · Mongolia · Tuva

11 Scandinavia (4th edition, 1994)
Aland Islands · Denmark · Faroe Islands · Finland · Greenland · Iceland · Norway · Sweden

12 Africa since Independence A-E (2nd edition, 1983)
Algeria · Angola · Benin · Bophuthatswana · Burundi · Cameroun · Cape Verde · Central African Republic · Chad · Comoro Islands · Congo · Djibouti · Equatorial Guinea · Ethiopia

13 Africa since Independence F-M (1st edition, 1981)
Gabon · Guinea · Guinea-Bissau · Ivory Coast · Liberia · Libya · Malagasy Republic · Mali · Mauritania · Morocco · Mozambique

14 Africa since Independence N-Z (1st edition, 1981)
Niger Republic · Rwanda · St. Thomas & Prince · Senegal · Somalia · Sudan · Togo · Transkei · Tunisia · Upper Volta · Venda · Zaire

15 Central America (2nd edition, 1984)
Costa Rica · Cuba · Dominican Republic · El Salvador · Guatemala · Haiti · Honduras · Mexico · Nicaragua · Panama

16 Central Asia (3rd edition, 1992)
Afghanistan · Iran · Turkey

17 China (4th edition, 1989)
China · Taiwan · Tibet · Foreign P.O.s

18 Japan & Korea (3rd edition, 1992)
Japan · Ryukyus · Korean Empire · South Korea · North Korea

19 Middle East (4th edition, 1990)
Bahrain · Egypt · Iraq · Israel · Jordan · Kuwait · Lebanon · Oman · Qatar · Saudi Arabia · Syria · U.A.E. · Yemen A.R. · Yemen P.D.R.

20 South America (3rd edition, 1989)
Argentina · Bolivia · Brazil · Chile · Colombia · Ecuador · Paraguay · Peru · Surinam · Uruguay · Venezuela

21 South-East Asia (2nd edition, 1985)
Bhutan · Burma · Indonesia · Kampuchea · Laos · Nepal · Philippines · Thailand · Vietnam

22 United States (4th edition, 1993)
U.S. & Possessions · Canal Zone · Marshall Islands · Micronesia · Palau · U.N. (New York, Geneva, Vienna)

Thematic Catalogues

Stanley Gibbons Catalogues for use with **Stamps of the World.**
Collect Aircraft on Stamps (forthcoming)
Collect Birds on Stamps (3rd edition, 1992)
Collect Butterflies and Other Insects on Stamps (1st edition, 1991)
Collect Chess on Stamps (1st edition, 1992)
Collect Fungi on Stamps (1st edition, 1991).
Collect Mammals on Stamps (1st edition, 1986)
Collect Railways on Stamps (2nd edition, 1990)
Collect Ships on Stamps (2nd edition, 1993)

Information for users

Aim

The aim of this catalogue is to provide a straightforward illustrated and priced guide to the postage stamps of the whole world to help you to enjoy the greatest hobby of the present day.

Arrangement

The catalogue lists countries in alphabetical order and there is a complete index at the end of each volume. For ease of reference country names are also printed at the head of each page.

Within each country, postage stamps are listed first. They are followed by separate sections for such other categories as postage due stamps, parcel post stamps, express stamps, official stamps, etc.

All catalogue lists are set out according to dates of issue of the stamps, starting from the earliest and working through to the most recent. New issues received too late for inclusion in the main lists will be found as "Addenda" at the end of each volume.

Scope of the Catalogue

The *Simplified Catalogue of Stamps of the World* contains listings of postage stamps only. Apart from the ordinary definitive, commemorative and air-mail stamps of each country – which appear first in each list – there are sections for the following where appropriate:

- postage due stamps
- parcel post stamps
- official stamps
- express and special delivery stamps
- charity and compulsory tax stamps
- newspaper and journal stamps
- printed matter stamps
- registration stamps
- acknowledgement of receipt stamps
- late fee and too late stamps
- military post stamps
- recorded message stamps
- personal delivery stamps

We receive numerous enquiries from collectors about other items which do not fall within the categories set out above and which consequently do not appear in the catalogue lists. It may be helpful, therefore, to summarise the other kinds of stamp that exist but which we deliberately exclude from this postage stamp catalogue.

We do *not* list the following:

Fiscal or revenue stamps: stamps used solely in collecting taxes or fees for non-postal purposes. Examples would be stamps which pay a tax on a receipt, represent the stamp duty on a contract or frank a customs document. Common inscriptions found include: Documentary, Proprietary, Inter. Revenue, Contract Note.

Local stamps: postage stamps whose validity and use are limited in area, say to a single town or city, though in some cases they provided, with official sanction, services in parts of countries not covered by the respective government.

Local carriage labels and Private local issues: many labels exist ostensibly to cover the cost of ferrying mail from one of Great Britain's offshore islands to the nearest mainland post office. They are not recognised as valid for national or international mail. Examples: Calf of Man, Davaar, Herm, Lundy, Pabay, Stroma. Items from some other places have only the status of tourist souvenir labels.

Telegraph stamps: stamps intended solely for the prepayment of telegraphic communication.

Bogus or "phantom" stamps: labels from mythical places or non-existent administrations. Examples in the classical period were Sedang, Counani, Clipperton Island and in modern times Thomond and Monte Bello Islands. Numerous labels have also appeared since the War from dissident groups as propaganda for their claims and without authority from the home governments. Common examples are labels for "Free Albania", "Free Rumania" and "Free Croatia" and numerous issues for Nagaland, Indonesia and the South Moluccas ("Republik Maluku Selatan").

Railway letter fee stamps: special stamps issued by railway companies for the conveyance of letters by rail. Example: Talyllyn Railway. Similar services are now offered by some bus companies and the labels they issue likewise do not qualify for inclusion in the catalogue.

Perfins ("perforated initials"): numerous postage stamps may be found with initial letters or designs punctured through them by tiny holes. These are applied by private and public concerns as a precaution against theft and do not qualify for separate mention.

Information for users

Labels: innumerable items exist resembling stamps but – as they do not prepay postage – they are classified as labels. The commonest categories are:

- propaganda and publicity labels: designed to further a cause or campaign;
- exhibition labels: particularly souvenirs from philatelic events;
- testing labels: stamp-size labels used in testing stamp-vending machines;
- Post Office training school stamps: British stamps overprinted with two thick vertical bars or SCHOOL SPECIMEN are produced by the Post Office for training purposes;
- seals and stickers: numerous charities produce stamp-like labels, particularly at Christmas and Easter, as a means of raising funds and these have no postal validity.

Cut-outs: items of postal stationery, such as envelopes, cards and wrappers, often have stamps impressed or imprinted on them. They may usually be cut out and affixed to envelopes, etc., for postal use if desired, but such items are not listed in this catalogue.

Collectors wanting further information about exact definitions are referred to *Philatelic Terms Illustrated,* published by Stanley Gibbons and containing many illustrations in colour (third edition price £7.50 plus £3 postage and packing).

There is also a priced listing of the postal fiscals of Great Britain in our Part 1 *(British Commonwealth)* Catalogue and in Volume 1 of the *Great Britain Specialised* Catalogue (5th and later editions).

Although, as stated, none of the above qualify for inclusion in this postage stamp catalogue, this does not imply that they are of no interest to certain collectors. Indeed, in the 1950s, a group was formed in Great Britain called the "Cinderella Stamp Club", whose object is the study of all those stamps which Stanley Gibbons do *not* list in their catalogues.

Catalogue Numbers

Stanley Gibbons catalogue numbers are recognised universally and any individual stamp can be identified by quoting the catalogue number (the one at the left of the column) prefixed by the name of the country and the letters "S.G.". Do not confuse the catalogue number with the type numbers which refer to illustrations.

Prices

Prices in the left-hand column are for unused stamps and those in the right-hand column for used. Prices are given in pence and pounds:

100 pence (p) = 1 pound (£1).

Prices are shown as follows:

10 means 10p (10 pence);
1.75 means £1.75 (1 pound and 75 pence);
For £100 and above, prices are in whole pounds.

Our prices are for stamps in fine average condition, and in issues where condition varies we may ask more for the superb and less for the sub-standard.

The minimum price quoted is 10p which represents a handling charge rather than a basis for valuing common stamps.

The prices quoted are generally for the cheapest variety of stamps but it is worth noting that differences of watermark, perforation, or other details, outside the scope of this catalogue, may often increase the value of the stamp.

Where prices are not given in either column it is either because the stamps are not known to exist in that particular condition, or, more usually, because there is no reliable information as to value.

All prices are subject to change without prior notice and we give no guarantee to supply all stamps priced. Prices quoted for albums, publications, etc. advertised in this catalogue are also subject to change without prior notice.

Unused Stamps

In the case of stamps from *Great Britain* and the *Commonwealth,* prices for unused stamps of Queen Victoria to King George V are for lightly hinged examples; unused prices of King Edward VIII to Queen Elizabeth II issues are for unmounted mint. The prices of unused *Foreign* stamps are for lightly hinged examples for those issued before 1946, thereafter for examples unmounted mint.

Used Stamps

Prices for used stamps generally refer to postally used examples, though for certain issues it is for cancelled-to-order.

Information for users

Guarantee

All stamps supplied by us are guaranteed originals in the following terms:

If not as described, and returned by the purchaser, we undertake to refund the price paid to us in the original transaction. If any stamp is certified as genuine by the Expert Committee of the Royal Philatelic Society, London, or by B.P.A. Expertising Ltd., the purchaser shall not be entitled to make any claim against us for any error, omission or mistake in such certificate.

Consumers' statutory rights are not affected by the above guarantee.

Currency

At the beginning of each country brief details give the currencies in which the values of the stamps are expressed. The dates, where given, are those of the earliest stamp issues in the particular currency. Where the currency is obvious, e.g. where the colony has the same currency as the mother country, no details are given.

Illustrations

Illustrations of stamps of Commonwealth countries (in Volume 3) and of any surcharges and overprints which are shown and not described are actual size; stamps of all foreign countries are reduced to $\frac{3}{4}$ linear, unless otherwise stated.

"Key-Types"

A number of standard designs occur so frequently in the stamps of the French, German, Portuguese and Spanish colonies that it would be a waste of space to repeat them. Instead these are all illustrated on page xii together with the descriptive names and letters by which they are referred to in the lists.

Type Numbers

These are the bold figures found below each illustration. References to "Type **6**", for example, in the lists of a country should therefore be understood to refer to the illustration below which the number **"6"** appears. These type numbers are also given in the second column of figures alongside each list of stamps, thus indicating clearly the design of each stamp. In the case of Key-Types – see above – letters take the place of the type numbers.

Where an issue comprises stamps of similar design, represented in this catalogue by one illustration, the corresponding type numbers should be taken as indicating this general design.

Where there are blanks in the type number column it means that the type of the corresponding stamps is that shown by the last number above in the type column of the same issue.

A dash (–) in the type column means that no illustration of the stamp is shown.

Where type numbers refer to stamps of another country, e.g. where stamps of one country are overprinted for use in another, this is always made clear in the text.

Stamp Designs

Brief descriptions of the subjects of the stamp designs are given either below or beside the illustrations, at the foot of the list of the issue concerned, or in the actual lists. Where a particular subject, e.g. the portrait of a well-known monarch, recurs frequently the description is not repeated, nor are obvious designs described.

Generally, the unillustrated designs are in the same shape and size as the one illustrated, except where otherwise indicated.

Surcharges and Overprints

Surcharges and overprints are usually described in the headings to the issues concerned. Where the actual wording of a surcharge or overprint is given it is shown in bold type.

Some stamps are described as being "Surcharged in words", e.g. **TWO CENTS,** and others "Surcharged in figures and words", e.g. **20 CENTS,** although of course many surcharges are in foreign languages and combinations of words and figures are numerous. There are often bars, etc., obliterating old values or inscriptions but in general these are only mentioned where it is necessary to avoid confusion.

No attention is paid in this catalogue to colours of overprints and surcharges so that stamps with the same overprints in different colours are not listed separately.

Numbers in brackets after the descriptions of overprinted or surcharged stamps are the catalogue numbers of the unoverprinted stamps.

Note – the words "inscribed" or "inscription" always refer to wording incorporated in the design of a stamp and not surcharges or overprints.

Coloured Papers

Where stamps are printed on coloured paper the description is given as e.g. "4 c. black on blue" – a stamp printed in black on blue paper. No attention is paid in this catalogue to differences in the texture of paper, e.g. laid, wove.

Information for users

Watermarks

Stamps having different watermarks, but otherwise the same, are not listed separately. No reference is therefore made to watermarks in this volume.

Stamp Colours

Colour names are only required for the identification of stamps, therefore they have been made as simple as possible. Thus "scarlet", "vermilion", "carmine" are all usually called red. Qualifying colour names have been introduced only where necessary for the sake of clearness.

Where stamps are printed in two or more colours the central portion of the design is in the first colour given, unless otherwise stated.

Perforations

All stamps are perforated unless otherwise stated. No distinction is made between the various gauges of perforation but early stamp issues which exist both imperforate and perforated are usually listed separately.

Where a heading states "Imperf. or perf." or "Perf. or rouletted" this does not necessarily mean that all values of the issue are found in both conditions.

Dates of Issue

The date given at the head of each issue is that of the appearance of the earliest stamp in the series. As stamps of the same design or issue are usually grouped together a list of King George VI stamps, for example, headed "1938" may include stamps issued from 1938 to the end of the reign.

Miniature Sheets

These are outside the scope of this catalogue but are listed in all other Stanley Gibbons catalogues.

"Appendix" Countries

We regret that, since 1968, it has been necessary to establish an Appendix (at the end of each country as appropriate) to which numerous stamps have had to be consigned. Several countries imagine that by issuing huge quantities of unnecessary stamps they will have a ready source of income from stamp collectors – and particularly from the less-experienced ones. Stanley Gibbons refuse to encourage this exploitation of the hobby and we do not stock the stamps concerned.

Two kinds of stamp are therefore given the briefest of mentions in the Appendix, purely for the sake of record. Administrations issuing stamps greatly in excess of true postal needs have the offending issues placed there. Likewise it contains stamps which have not fulfilled all the normal conditions for full catalogue listing.

These conditions are that the stamps must be issued by a legitimate postal authority, recognised by the government concerned, and are adhesives, valid for proper postal use in the class of service for which they are inscribed. Stamps, with the exception of such categories as postage dues and officials, must be available to the general public at face value with no artificial restrictions being imposed on their distribution.

The publishers of this catalogue have observed, with concern, the proliferation of 'artificial' stamp-issuing territories. On several occasions this has resulted in separately inscribed issues for various component parts of otherwise united states or territories.

Stanley Gibbons Publications have decided that where such circumstances occur, they will not, in the future, list these items in the SG catalogue without first satisfying themselves that the stamps represent a genuine political, historical or postal division within the country concerned. Any such issues which do not fulfil this stipulation will be recorded in the Catalogue Appendix only.

Stamps in the Appendix are kept under review in the light of any newly acquired information about them. If we are satisfied that a stamp qualifies for proper listing in the body of the catalogue it is moved there.

"Undesirable Issues"

The rules governing many competitive exhibitions – including the Melville Competition – are set by the Fédération Internationale de Philatelie and stipulate a downgrading of marks for stamps classed as "undesirable issues".

This catalogue can be taken as a guide to status. All stamps in the main listings and Addenda are acceptable. Stamps in the Appendix should not be entered for competition as these are the "undesirable issues".

Particular care is advised with Aden Protectorate States, Ajman, Bhutan, Chad, Fujeira, Khor Fakkan, Manama, Ras al Khaima, Sharjah, Umm al Qiwain and Yemen. Totally bogus stamps exist (as explained in Appendix notes) and these are to be avoided also for competition. As distinct from "undesirable stamps" certain categories are not covered in this catalogue purely by reason of its scope (see page v). Consult the particular competition rules to see if such are admissible even though not listed by us.

Information for users

Where to Look for More Detailed Listings

The present work deliberately omits details of paper, perforation, shade and watermark. But as you become more absorbed in stamp collecting and wish to get greater enjoyment from the hobby you may well want to study these matters.

All the information you require about any particular postage stamp will be found in the main Stanley Gibbons Catalogues.

Commonwealth countries in Volume 3 are covered by the Part 1 (British Commonwealth) Catalogue published annually in two volumes.

For foreign countries you can easily find which catalogue to consult by looking at the country headings in the present book.

To the right of each country name are code letters specifying which volume of our main catalogues contains that country's listing.

The code letters are as follows:

Pt. 2 Part 2
Pt. 3 Part 3 etc.

(See page iv for complete list of Parts.)

So, for example, if you want to know more about Chinese stamps than is contained in the *Simplified Catalogue of Stamps of the World* the reference to

CHINA Pt. 17

guides you to the Gibbons Part 17 *(China)* Catalogue listing for the details you require.

New editions of Parts 2 to 22 appear at irregular intervals.

Correspondence

Whilst we welcome information and suggestions we must ask correspondents to include the cost of postage for the return of any stamps submitted plus registration where appropriate. Letters should be addressed to The Catalogue Editor at Ringwood.

Where information is solicited purely for the benefit of the enquirer we regret we cannot undertake to reply unless stamps or reply coupons are sent to cover the postage.

Identification of Stamps

We regret we do not give opinions as to the genuineness of stamps, nor do we identify stamps or number them by our Catalogue.

Users of this catalogue are referred to our companion booklet entitled *Stamp Collecting — How to Identify Stamps.* It explains how to look up stamps in this catalogue, contains a full checklist of stamp inscriptions and gives help in dealing with unfamiliar scripts. It is available from Stanley Gibbons at £2.25, postage extra.

Stanley Gibbons would like to complement your collection

At Stanley Gibbons we offer a range of services which are designed to complement your collection.

Our modern stamp shop, the largest in Europe, together with our rare stamp department has one of the most comprehensive stocks of Great Britain in the world, so whether you are a beginner or an experienced philatelist you are certain to find something to suit your special requirements.

Alternatively through our Mail Order services you can control the growth of your collection from the comfort of your own home. Our Postal Sales Department regularly sends out mailings of Special Offers. We can also help with your wants list—so why not ask us for those elusive items?

And don't forget Stanley Gibbons Auctions which holds, on average, 8–10 sales each year. Come along in person or send in a written bid for the items you require. For details of current subscription rates for Auction catalogues write to Stanley Gibbons Auctions, 399 Strand, London WC2R 0LX.

Why not take advantage of the many services we have to offer? Visit our premises in the Strand or, for more information, write to the appropriate address on page x.

Stanley Gibbons Holdings Plc Addresses

Stanley Gibbons Limited, Stanley Gibbons Auctions

399 Strand, London WC2R 0LX
Telephone 071 836 8444 Fax 071 836 7342 for all departments.

Auction Room and Specialist Stamp Departments. Open Monday–Friday 9.30 a.m. to 5 p.m.

Shop. Open Monday–Friday 8.30 a.m. to 6 p.m. and Saturday 10 a.m. to 4.00 p.m.

Stanley Gibbons Publications

5 Parkside, Christchurch Road, Ringwood, Hants BH24 3SH.
Telephone 0425 472363 (24 hour answerphone service) Fax 0425 470247.

Publication Showroom (at above address). Open Monday–Friday 8.30 a.m. to 5 p.m.

Publications Mail Order. FREEPHONE 0800 611622. Monday–Friday 8.30 a.m. to 5 p.m.

Urch Harris & Co.

(a division of Stanley Gibbons Ltd),
1 Osprey Court, Hawkfield Way, Bristol BS14 0BE.
Telephone 0272 465656 Fax 0272 465225.

Monday–Friday 8.30 a.m. to 5 p.m.

U.H. New Issue Service, Osprey (Postal) Auctions, U.H. Digest.

Stanley Gibbons Publications Overseas Representation

Stanley Gibbons Publications are represented overseas by the following sole distributors (*), main distributors (**) or licensees (***).

Australia*
Lighthouse Philatelic (Aust.) Pty. Ltd., P.O. Box 763, Strawberry Hills, New South Wales, 2012 Australia.

Stanley Gibbons (Australia) Pty. Ltd.*** P.O. Box 863J, Melbourne 3001, Australia.

Belgium and Luxembourg**
Davo c/o Philac, Rue du Midi 48, Bruxelles, 1000 Belgium.

Canada*
Lighthouse Publications (Canada) Ltd., 255 Duke Street, Montreal, Quebec, Canada H3C 2M2

Denmark**
Davo c/o Lindner Falzlos, Gl Randers vej 28, 8450 Hammel, Denmark.

Finland**
Davo c/o Suomen Postimerkkeily Ludvingkatu 5 SF-00130 Helsinki, Finland.

France*
Davo France (Casteilla), 10, Rue Leon Foucault, 78184 St. Quentin Yvelines Cesex, France.

Germany and Austria*
Leuchtturm Albenverlag, Paul Koch KG Am Spakenberg 45, Postfach 1340, D-2054 Geesthacht, Germany.

Hong Kong**
Po-on Stamp Service, G.P.O. Box 2498, Hong Kong.

Israel**
Capital Stamps, P.O. Box 3769, Jerusalem 91036, Israel.

Italy*
Secrian Srl, Via Pantelleria 2, I-20156, Milan, Italy.

Japan**
Japan Philatelic Co. Ltd., P.O. Box 2, Suginami-Minami, Tokyo, Japan.

Netherlands*
Davo Publications, P.O. Box 411, 7400 AK Deventer, Netherlands.

New Zealand***
Stanley Gibbons (New Zealand) Ltd., P.O. Box 80, Wellington, New Zealand.

Norway**
Davo Norge A/S, P.O. Box 738 Sentrum, N-0105, Oslo, Norway.

Singapore***
Stanley Gibbons (Singapore) Pte Ltd., Raffles City P.O. Box 1689, Singapore 9117.

South Africa***
Philatelic Holdings (Pty) Ltd., P.O. Box 930, Parklands, RSA 2121.

Republic Coin and Stamp Accessories (Pty) Ltd.,** P.O. Box 11199, Johannesburg, RSA 2000.

Sweden*
Chr Winther Soerensen AB, Box 43, S-310 Knaered, Sweden.

Switzerland**
Phila Service, Burgstrasse 160, CH 4125, Riehen, Switzerland.

USA*
Lighthouse Publications Inc., P.O. Box 750, 274 Washington Avenue, Hackensack, New Jersey 07602–0705, U.S.A.

West Indies/Caribbean**
Hugh Dunphy, P.O. Box 413, Kingston 10, Jamaica, West Indies.

Abbreviations

Anniv.	denotes	Anniversary
Assn.	,,	Association
Bis.	,,	Bistre
Bl.	,,	Blue
Bldg.	,,	Building
Blk.	,,	Black
Br.	,,	British *or* Bridge
Brn.	,,	Brown
B.W.I.	,,	British West Indies
C.A.R.I.F.T.A.	,,	Caribbean Free Trade Area
Cent.	,,	Centenary
Chest.	,,	Chestnut
Choc.	,,	Chocolate
Clar.	,,	Claret
Coll.	,,	College
Commem.	,,	Commemoration
Conf.	,,	Conference
Diag.	,,	Diagonally
E.C.A.F.E.	,,	Economic Commission for Asia and Far East
Emer.	,,	Emerald
E.P.T. Conference	,,	European Postal and Telecommunications Conference
Exn.	,,	Exhibition
F.A.O.	,,	Food and Agriculture Organization
Fig.	,,	Figure
G.A.T.T.	,,	General Agreement on Tariffs and Trade
G.B.	,,	Great Britain
Gen.	,,	General
Govt.	,,	Government
Grn.	,,	Green
Horiz.	,,	Horizontal
H.Q.	,,	Headquarters
Imperf.	,,	Imperforate
Inaug.	,,	Inauguration
Ind.	,,	Indigo
Inscr.	,,	Inscribed or inscription
Int.	,,	International
I.A.T.A.	,,	International Air Transport Association
I.C.A.O.	,,	International Civil Aviation Organization
I.C.Y.	,,	International Co-operation Year
I.G.Y.	,,	International Geophysical Year
I.L.O.	,,	International Labour Office (or later, Organization)
I.M.C.O.	,,	Inter-Governmental Maritime Consultative Organization
I.T.U.	,,	International Telecommunication Union
Is.	,,	Islands
Lav.	,,	Lavender
Mar.	,,	Maroon
mm.	,,	Millimetres
Mult.	,,	Multicoloured
Mve.	denotes	Mauve
Nat.	,,	National
N.A.T.O.	,,	North Atlantic Treaty Organization
O.D.E.C.A.	,,	Organization of Central American States
Ol.	,,	Olive
Optd.	,,	Overprinted
Orge. *or* oran.	,,	Orange
P.A.T.A.	,,	Pacific Area Travel Association
Perf.	,,	Perforated
Post.	,,	Postage
Pres.	,,	President
P.U.	,,	Postal Union
Pur.	,,	Purple
R.	,,	River
R.S.A.	,,	Republic of South Africa
Roul.	,,	Rouletted
Sep.	,,	Sepia
S.E.A.T.O.	,,	South East Asia Treaty Organization
Surch.	,,	Surcharged
T.	,,	Type
T.U.C.	,,	Trades Union Congress
Turq.	,,	Turquoise
Ultram.	,,	Ultramarine
U.N.E.S.C.O.	,,	United Nations Educational, Scientific & Cultural Organization
U.N.I.C.E.F.	,,	United Nations Children's Fund
U.N.O.	,,	United Nations Organization
U.N.R.W.A.	,,	United Nations Relief and Works Agency for Palestine Refugees in the Near East
U.N.T.E.A.	,,	United Nations Temporary Executive Authority
U.N.R.R.A.	,,	United Nations Relief and Rehabilitation Administration
U.P.U.	,,	Universal Postal Union
Verm.	,,	Vermilion
Vert.	,,	Vertical
Vio.	,,	Violet
W.F.T.U.	,,	World Federation of Trade Unions
W.H.O.	,,	World Health Organization
Yell.	,,	Yellow

Arabic Numerals

As in the case of European figures, the details of the Arabic numerals vary in different stamp designs, but they should be readily recognised with the aid of this illustration:

٠	١	٢	٣	٤
0	1	2	3	4
٥	٦	٧	٨	٩
5	6	7	8	9

Key-Types

(see note on page vii)

French Group

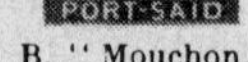

A. " Blanc." B. " Mouchon." C. " Merson." D. " Tablet."

" International Colonial Exhibition."

E. F. G. H.

I. " Faidherbe." J. " Palms." K. " Balay." L. " Natives." M. " Figure."

German Group

N. " Yacht." O. " Yacht."

Spanish Group

X. " Alfonso XII." Y. " Baby." Z. "Curly Head"

Portuguese Group

P. " Crown." Q. " Embossed." R. " Figures." S. " Carlos." T. " Manoel." U. " Ceres." V. " Newspaper." W. " Due."

STANLEY GIBBONS SIMPLIFIED CATALOGUE OF STAMPS OF THE WORLD—VOLUME 3 COMMONWEALTH COUNTRIES

ABU DHABI

The largest of the Trucial States in the Persian Gulf. Treaty relations with Great Britain expired on 31 December 1966, when the Abu Dhabi Post Office took over the postal services.

1964. 100 naye paise = 1 rupee.
1966. 1,000 fils = 1 dinar.

1. Shaikh Shakhbut bin Sultan.

3. Ruler's Palace.

1964.

1\. **1.** 5 n.p. green 80 70
2\. 15 n.p. brown .. .. 1·25 80
3\. 20 n.p. blue .. .. 1·40 65
4\. 30 n.p. orange .. .. 1·40 1·25
5\. – 40 n.p. violet .. .. 2·75 20
6\. – 50 n.p. bistre .. .. 2·50 65
7\. – 75 n.p. black .. .. 2·75 1·25
8\. **3.** 1 r. green .. .. 3·75 1·00
9\. 2 r. black .. .. 5·50 2·75
10\. – 5 r. red .. .. .. 13·00 7·00
11\. – 10 r. blue.. .. .. 18·00 14·00

DESIGNS—As Type **1**: 40 to 75 n.p. Mountain gazelle. As Type **3**: 5 , 10 r. Oil rig and camels.

5. Saker Falcon.

1965. Falconry.

12\. **5.** 20 n.p. brown and blue 7·00 1·25
13\. – 40 n.p. brown and blue 9·00 2·50
14\. – 2 r. sepia and turquoise 15·00 9·50

DESIGNS: 40 n.p., 2 r. Other types of Saker Falcon on gloved hand.

1966. Nos. 1/11 surch. in new currency ("Fils" only on Nos. 5/7) and ruler's portrait obliterated with bars.

15. 1. 5 f. on 5 n.p. green .. 6·50 5·00
16. 15 f. on 15 n.p. brown .. 6·50 2·25
17. 20 f. on 20 n.p. blue .. 6·50 3·75
18. 30 f. on 30 n.p. orange .. 8·00 8·00
19. – 40 f. on 40 n.p. violet .. 11·00 85
20. – 50 f. on 50 n.p. bistre .. 16·00 13·00
21. – 75 f. on 75 n.p. black .. 16·00 13·00
22. 3. 100 f. on 1 r. green .. 15·00 3·50
23. 200 f. on 2 r. black .. 18·00 12·00
24. – 500 f. on 5 r. red .. .. 30·00 35·00
25. – 1 d. on 10 r. blue .. 40·00 65·00

Independent Postal Administration issues are listed in volume 1.

ADEN

Peninsula on southern coast of Arabia. Formerly part of the Indian Empire. A Crown Colony from 1 April 1937 to 18 January 1963, when Aden joined the South Arabian Federation, whose stamps it then used.

1937. 16 annas = 1 rupee.
1951. 100 cents = 1 shilling.

1. Dhow.

1937.

1\. **1.** ½ a. green .. .. .. 3·00 1·40
2\. 9 p. green .. .. .. 3·00 1·60
3\. 1 a. brown .. .. 3·00 70
4\. 2 a. red .. .. .. 3·00 2·00
5\. 2½ a. blue .. .. .. 3·00 80
6\. 3 a. red .. .. .. 9·00 6·50
7\. 3½ a. blue .. .. .. 4·00 2·00
8\. 8 a. purple .. .. 19·00 5·50
9\. 1 r. brown.. .. .. 24·00 7·00
10\. 2 r. yellow .. .. 48·00 16·00
11\. 5 r. purple .. .. 90·00 60·00
12\. 10 r. olive £180 £170

2. King George VI and Queen Elizabeth.

1937. Coronation.

13\. **2.** 1 a. brown 75 80
14\. 2½ a. blue .. .. .. 1·25 1·40
15\. 3½ a. blue .. .. .. 1·50 2·50

3. Aidrus Mosque, Crater.

1939.

16\. **3.** ½ a. green 50 60
17\. – ¾ a. brown .. .. 1·25 2·50
18\. – 1 a. blue .. .. .. 1·00 1·25
19\. – 1½ a. red 45 60
20\. **3.** 2 a. brown 20 25
21\. – 2½ a. blue 30 30
22\. – 3 a. brown and red .. 50 25
23\. – 8 a. orange 35 40
23a. – 14 a. brown and blue .. 2·25 1·00
24\. – 1 r. green .. .. 1·75 1·50
25\. – 2 r. blue and mauve .. 4·75 1·75
26\. – 5 r. brown and olive .. 11·00 6·00
27\. – 10 r. brown and violet .. 26·00 11·00

DESIGNS: ¾ a., 5 r. Adenese Camel Corps. 1 a., 2 r. Harbour. 1½ a., 1 r. Adenese dhow. 2½ a., 8 a. Mukalla. 3 a., 14 a., 10 r. "Capture of Aden, 1839" (Capt. Rundle).

9. Houses of Parliament, London.

1946. Victory.

28\. **9.** 1½ a. red 15 50
29\. 2½ a. blue 15 30

10. King George VI and Queen Elizabeth. **11.**

1949. Royal Silver Wedding.

30\. **10.** 1½ a. red 40 80
31\. **11.** 10 r. purple .. .. 25·00 28·00

1949. 75th Anniv of U.P.U. As T **20/23** of Antigua surch with new values.

32\. 2½ a. on 20 c. blue .. 75 1·00
33\. 3 a. on 30 c. red .. 1·50 1·00
34\. 8 a. on 50 c. orange .. 1·60 1·00
35\. 1 r. on 1 s. blue .. 2·10 2·50

1951. Stamps of 1939 surch. in cents or shillings.

36\. 5 c. on 1 a. blue 15 40
37\. 10 c. on 2 a. brown 15 45
38\. 15 c. on 2½ a. blue .. .. 20 1·00
39\. 20 c. on 3 a. brown & red .. 25 40
40\. 30 c. on 8 a. orange .. 25 65
41 50 c. on 8 a. orange .. 25 35
42\. 70 c. on 14 a. brown & blue 1·00 1·25
43\. 1 s. on 1 r. green 35 30
44\. 2 s. on 2 r. blue and mauve 4·50 2·50
45\. 5 s. on 5 r. brown & olive .. 16·00 5·00
46\. 10 s. on 10 r. brown & violet 23·00 9·50

13. Queen Elizabeth II. **14.** Minaret.

15. Camel Transport.

1953. Coronation.

47\. **13.** 15 c. black and green .. 50 1·25

1953.

48 **14** 5 c. green 20 10
49a 5 c. turquoise .. 10 30
50 **15** 10 c. orange 40 10
51 10 c. red 10 30
52 – 15 c. turquoise .. 1·25 60
79 – 15 c. grey .. .. 30 2·50
80 – 25 c. red 30 40
81 – 35 c. blue .. .. 1·00 2·00
58 – 50 c. blue 20 10
60 – 70 c. grey 20 10
61a – 70 c. black 90 20
62 – 1 s. brown and violet 30 10
63 – 1 s. black and violet .. 80 10
64 – 1 s. 25 blue and black 2·25 60
65 – 2 s. brown and red .. 1·25 50
66 – 2 s. black and red .. 3·75 50
67 – 5 s. brown and blue .. 1·25 50
68 – 5 s. black and blue .. 2·50 50
69 – 10 s. brown and green 1·75 8·00
70 – 10 s. black and bronze 7·00 1·25
71 – 20 s. brown and lilac 6·50 10·00
72 – 20 s. black and lilac .. 35·00 13·00

DESIGNS—HORIZ. 15 c. Crater. 25 c. Mosque. 1 s. Dhow building. 20 s. (38 × 27 mm.). Aden in 1572. VERT. 35 c. Dhow. 50 c. Map. 70 c. Salt works. 1 s. 25, Colony's badge. 2 s. Aden Protectorate Levy. 5 s. Crater Pass. 10 s. Tribesmen.

1954. Royal Visit. As No. 62 but inscr. "ROYAL VISIT 1954".

73\. 1 s. sepia and violet .. 30 30

1959. Revised Constitution. Optd. **REVISED CONSTITUTION 1959** (in Arabic on No. 74).

74\. 15 c. green (No. 53) .. 20 1·00
75\. 1 s. 25 blue and blk. (No. 64) 55 1·00

28. Protein Foods.

1963. Freedom from Hunger.

76\. **28.** 1 s. 25 c. green .. .. 1·50 1·40

For later issues see **SOUTH ARABIAN FEDERATION.**

ADEN PROTECTORATE STATES

The states of the Eastern Aden Protectorate commonly known as the Hadhramaut.

The National Liberation Front took control on 1 October 1967, and full independence was granted by Great Britain on 30 November 1967 when the People's Republic of Southern Yemen (comprising the Protectorate States and the South Arabian Federation) was declared.

1937. 16 annas = 1 rupee.
1951. 100 cents = 1 shilling.
1966. 1,000 fils = 1 dinar.

SEIYUN

1. Sultan of Seiyun.

2. Seiyun.

1942.

1\. **1.** ½ a. green 15 35
2\. ¾ a. brown 15 35
3\. 1 a. blue 15 35
4\. **2.** 1½ a. red 20 40
5\. – 2 a. sepia 20 60
6\. – 2½ a. blue .. .. 30 1·00
7\. – 3 a. sepia and red .. 60 75
8\. – 8 a. red 30 50
9\. – 1 r. green 80 60
10\. – 2 r. blue and purple .. 6·50 8·50
11\. – 5 r. brown and green .. 16·00 12·00

DESIGNS—VERT. 2 a. Tarim. 2½ a. Mosque at Seiyun. 1 r. South Gate, Tarim. 5 r. Mosque Entrance, Tarim. HORIZ. 3 a. Fortress at Tarim. 8 a. Mosque at Seiyun. 2 r. A Kathiri House.

1946. Victory. Optd. **VICTORY ISSUE 8th JUNE 1946.**

12\. **2.** 1½ a. red 10 30
13\. – 2½ a. blue (No. 6) .. 10 10

1949. Silver Wedding. As T **10/11** of Aden.

14\. 1½ a. red .. .. .. 30 2·00
15\. 5 r. green .. .. .. 11·00 9·00

1949. 75th Anniv of U.P.U. As T **20/23** of Antigua surch with new values.

16\. 2½ a. on 20 c. blue .. 25 50
17\. 3 a. on 30 c. red 40 65
18\. 8 a. on 50 c. orange .. 40 75
19\. 1 r. on 1 s. blue 60 90

1951. 1942 stamps surch. in cents or shillings.

20. 1.	5 c. on 1 a. blue	15	20
21. –	10 c. on 2 a. sepia ..	30	20
22. –	15 c. on 2½ a. blue ..	15	20
23. –	20 c. on 3 a. sepia and red	15	30
24. –	50 c. on 8 a. red	15	20
25. –	1s. on 1 r. green	20	25
26. –	2s. on 2 r. blue and purple	2·00	9·50
27. –	5s. on 5 r. brown and green	9·00	25·00

1953. Coronation. As T 13 of Aden.

28.	15 c. black and green ..	30	1·40

14. Sultan Hussein.

Designs—vert. 35 c. Mosque at Selyun. 70 c. Qarn Adh Dhabi. 2 s. South Gate, Tarim. 10 s. Mosque entrance, Tarim horiz. 50 c. Fortress at Tarim 1 s. Mosque at Seiyun. 1 s. 25, Seiyun. 1 s. 50, Gheil Omer. 5 s. Kathiri house.

1954. As 1942 issue and new designs, but with portrait of Sultan Hussein as in T 14.

29. 14.	5 c. brown	10	10
30.	10 c. blue	15	10
31. 2.	15 c. green	15	10
32. –	25 c. red	15	10
33. –	35 c. blue	15	10
34. –	50 c. brown and red ..	15	10
39. –	70 c. black	85	65
35. –	1 s. orange	15	10
40. –	1 s. 25 green	85	4·25
41. –	1 s. 50 violet	85	4·25
36. –	2 s. green	4·00	1·50
37. –	5 s. blue and violet ..	5·00	3·00
38. –	10 s. brown and violet ..	6·00	6·50

1966. Nos. 29 etc. surch. **SOUTH ARABIA** in English and Arabic, with value and bar.

42 14	5 f. on 5 c.	15	10
43 –	5 f. on 10 c.	15	10
44 2	10 f. on 15 c.	15	20
45 –	15 f. on 25 c.	20	20
46 –	20 f. on 35 c.	15	20
47 –	25 f. on 50 c.	15	30
61 –	35 f. on 70 c.	60	30
49 –	50 f on 1 s.	20	15
50 –	65 f. on 1 s. 25	20	15
51 –	75 f. on 1 s. 50	20	30
65 –	100 f. on 2 s.	2·75	1·00
53 –	250 f. on 5 s.	1·40	3·75
54 –	500 f. on 10 s.	1·75	3·75

Each value has two similar surcharges.

1966. Nos. 57, 59, 61/7 variously optd. as given below, together with Olympic "rings".

68.	10 f. on 15 c. (**LOS ANGELES 1932**)	15	15
69.	20 f. on 35 c (**BERLIN 1936**)	20	20
70.	35 f. on 70 c. **INTERNATIONAL COOPERATION**, etc)	20	20
71.	50 f. on 1 s. (**LONDON 1948**)	25	25
72.	65 f. on 1 s. 25 (**HELSINKI 1952**)	35	60
73.	75 f. on 1 s. 50 (**MELBOURNE 1956**) ..	40	65
74.	100 f. on 2 s. (**ROME 1960**)	50	75
75.	250 f. on 5 s. (**TOKYO 1964**)	1·00	1·75
76.	500 f. on 10 s. (**MEXICO CITY 1968**)	1·40	2·75

1966. World Cup Football Championships. Nos. 57, 59, 61/2, 65/7 optd. **CHAMPIONS ENGLAND** (10 f., 50 f. and 250 f.) or **FOOTBALL 1966** (others). Both with football symbol.

77.	10 f. on 15 c.	50	30
78.	20 f. on 35 c.	70	40
79.	35 f. on 70 c.	80	40
80.	50 f. on 1 s.	90	40
81.	100 f. on 2 s.	3·25	1·75
82.	250 f. on 5 s.	7·00	4·50
83.	500 f. on 10 s.	9·00	7·00

29. " Telstar ".

1966. Cent. of I.T.U. (1965).

84. 29.	5 f. green, black & vio.	1·00	25
85. –	10 f. purple, black & green	1·10	30
86. –	15 f. blue, black & orange	1·50	40
87. 29.	25 f. green, black and red	2·25	50
88. –	35 f. purple, black & yell.	2·75	70
89. –	50 f. blue, black & brown	3·25	1·10
90. 29.	65 f. green, black & yellow	3·75	1·25

Designs: 10 f., 35 f. "Relay". 15 f., 50 f. "Ranger".

32. Churchill at Easel.

1966. Sir Winston Churchill's Paintings. Multicoloured.

91.	5 f. Type 32	1·25	15
92.	10 f. " Antibes "	1·50	15
93.	15 f. " Flowers "	1·50	20
94.	20 f. " Tapestries " ..	1·60	35
95.	25 f. " Village, Lake Lugano "	1·75	35
96.	35 f. " Church, Lake Como "	1·90	40
97.	50 f. " Flowers at Chartwell "	2·25	65
98.	65 f. Type 32	2·75	90

The 15, 35 and 50 f. are vert.

1967. "World Peace". Nos. 57, 59, 61/7 optd. **WORLD PEACE** and names as given below.

99.	10 f. on 15 c. (**PANDIT NEHRU**)	60	50
100.	20 f. on 35 c. (**WINSTON CHURCHILL**	4·50	1·75
101.	35 f. on 70 c (**DAG HAMMARSKJOLD**) ..	50	60
102.	50 f. on 1 s. (**JOHN F. KENNEDY**)	60	70
103.	65 f. on 1 s. 25 (**LUDWIG ERHARD**)	70	80
104.	75 f. on 1 s. 50 (**LYNDON JOHNSON**)	80	90
105.	100 f. on 2 s. (**ELEANOR ROOSEVELT**)	1·00	1·25
106.	250 f. on 5 s. (**WINSTON CHURCHILL**)	12·00	8·50
107.	500 f. on 10 s. (**JOHN F. KENNEDY**)	5·00	8·50

40. " Master Crewe as Henry VIII " (Sir Joshua Reynolds).

1967. Paintings.

108. 40.	5 f. multicoloured ..	30	25
109. –	10 f. multicoloured ..	35	30
110. –	15 f. multicoloured ..	40	35
111. –	20 f. multicoloured ..	45	40
112. –	25 f. multicoloured ..	50	45
113. –	35 f. multicoloured ..	70	65
114. –	50 f. multicoloured ..	85	75
115. –	65 f. multicoloured ..	1·10	1·00
116. –	75 f. multicoloured ..	1·40	1·25

Paintings: 10 f. " The Dancer " (Degas). 15 f. " The Fifer " (Manet). 20 f. " Stag at Sharkey's " (boxing-match, G. Burrows). 25 f. " Don Manuel Osorio " (Goya). 35 f. " St. Martin Distributing His Cloak " (A. van Dyck). 50 f. " The Blue Boy " (Gainsborough). 65 f " The White Horse " (Gauguin). (45 × 60 mm.): 75 f. " Mona Lisa " (Da Vinci).

1967. American Astronauts. Nos. 57, 59, 61/2 and 65/6 optd. as below, all with space capsule.

117.	10 f. on 15 c. (**ALAN SHEPARD, JR.**) ..	55	80
118.	20 f. on 35 c. (**VIRGIL GRISSOM**)	70	95
119.	35 f. on 70 c. (**JOHN GLENN JR.**)	95	1·40
120.	50 f. on 1 s. (**SCOTT CARPENTER**)	95	1·40
121.	100 f. on 2 s. (**WALTER SCHIRRA JR.**)	2·25	3·25
122.	250 f. on 5 s. (**GORDON COOPER JR.**)	3·50	5·00

50. Churchill Crown.

1967. Churchill Commem.

123. 50.	75 f. multicoloured ..	9·00	6·50

HADHRAMAUT

(a) Issues inscribed " SHIHR and MUKALLA "

1. Sultan of Shihr and Mukalla.

2. Mukalla Harbour.

1942.

1. 1.	½ a. green	20	30
2.	¾ a. brown	30	30
3.	1 a. blue	50	40
4. 2.	1½ a. red	55	30
5. –	2 a. sepia	55	40
6. –	2½ a. blue	40	30
7. –	3 a. sepia and red ..	60	30
8. –	8 a. red	40	40
9. –	1 r. green	60	70
10. –	2 r blue and purple ..	9·00	8·00
11. –	5 r. brown and green ..	12·00	8·50

Designs—vert. 2 a. Gateway of Shihr. 3 a. Outpost of Mukalla. 1 r. Du'an. horiz. 2½ a. Shibam. 8 a. 'Einat. 2 r. Mosque in Hureidha. 5 r. Meshed.

1946. Victory. Optd. **VICTORY ISSUE 8th JUNE 1946.**

12. 2.	1½ a. red	10	30
13. –	2½ a. blue	10	10

1949. Silver Wedding. As T 10/11 of Aden.

14.	1½ a. red	50	2·00
15.	5 r. green	12·00	9·00

1949. U.P.U. As T20/23 of Antigua surch.

16.	2½ a. on 20 c. blue	20	20
17.	3 a. on 30 c. red	55	50
18.	8 a. on 50 c. orange ..	55	60
19.	1 r. on 1 s. blue	60	50

1951. Stamps of 1942 surch. in cents or shillings.

20.	5 c. on 1 a. blue	15	15
21.	10 c. on 2 a. sepia	15	15
22.	15 c. on 2½ a. blue	15	15
23.	20 c. on 3 a. sepia and red	15	20
24.	50 c. on 8 a. red	15	40
25.	1 s. on 1 r. green	30	25
26.	2 s. on 2 r. blue and purple	4·00	5·50
27.	5 s. on 5 r. brown and green	6·50	9·00

1953. Coronation. As T 13 of Aden.

28.	15 c. black and blue ..	50	55

(b) Issues inscribed " HADHRAMAUT ".

11. Metal Work. 22.

1955. Occupations. Portrait as in T 11. Nos. 36/40 horiz. designs.

29. 11.	5 c. blue	10	10
30. –	10 c. black (Mat-making)	15	10
31. –	15 c. green (Weaving) ..	15	10
32. –	25 c. red (Pottery) ..	15	10
33. –	35 c. blue (Building) ..	15	10
34. –	50 c. orange (Date cultivation)	15	10
35. –	90 c. brown (Agriculture)	15	15
36. –	1 s. black & lilac (Fisheries)	20	10
37. –	1 s. 25 c. black and orange (Lime-burning)	30	45
38. –	2 s. black and blue (Dhow building)	3·00	60
39. –	5 s. black and green (Agriculture)	4·25	1·25
40. –	10 s. black & red (as No. 37)	4·50	3·00

1963. Occupations. As Nos. 29/40 but with inset portrait of Sultan Awadh bin Saleh el Qu'aiti, as in T 22.

41. 22.	5 c. blue	10	10
42. –	10 c. black	10	10
43. –	15 c. green	10	10
44. –	25 c. red	10	10
45. –	35 c. blue	10	10
46. –	50 c. orange	10	10
47. –	70 c. brown (As No. 35)	15	20
48. –	1 s. black and lilac ..	20	10
49. –	1 s. 25 black and orange	45	75
50. –	2 s. black and blue ..	2·75	1·00
51. –	5 s. black and green ..	10·00	10·00
52. –	10 s. black and red ..	10·00	12·00

1966. Nos. 41/52 surch. **SOUTH ARABIA** in English and Arabic, with value and bar.

53. 5.	5 f. on 5 c.	10	30
54. –	5 f. on 10 c.	10	30
55. –	10 f. on 15 c.	10	20
56. –	15 f. on 25 c.	10	30
57. –	20 f. on 35 c.	10	50
58. –	25 f. on 50 c.	10	30
59. –	35 f. on 70 c.	10	30
60. –	50 f. on 1 s.	10	15
61. –	65 f. on 1 s. 25	40	30
62. –	100 f. on 2 s.	55	75
63. –	250 f. on 5 s.	1·00	1·50
64. –	500 f. on 10 s.	15·00	3·00

1966. Churchill Commem. Nos. 54/6 optd. **1874-1965 WINSTON CHURCHILL.**

65.	5 f. on 10 c.	5·50	7·00
66.	10 f. on 15 c.	6·50	8·00
67.	15 f. on 25 c.	8·50	10·50

1966. Pres. Kennedy Commem. Nos. 57/9 optd. **1917-63 JOHN F. KENNEDY.**

68.	20 f. on 35 c.	1·75	5·00
69.	25 f. on 50 c.	2·00	5·50
70.	35 f. on 70 c.	3·00	6·50

25. World Cup Emblem. (Actual size 55 × 55 mm.)

1966. World Cup Football Championships.

71. 25.	5 f. purple and orange	1·75	25
72. –	10 f. violet and green ..	2·00	25
73. –	15 f. purple and orange	2·25	30
74. –	20 f. violet and green ..	2·50	40
75. 25.	25 f. green and red ..	2·75	55
76. –	35 f. blue and yellow ..	3·25	80
77. –	50 f. green and red ..	3·75	1·10
78. 25.	65 f. blue and yellow ..	4·50	1·40

Designs: 10 f., 35 f. Wembley Stadium. 15 f., 50 f. Footballers. 20 f. Jules Rimet Cup and football.

29. Mexican Hat and Blanket. (Actual size 63 × 63 mm.)

1966. Pre-Olympic Games, Mexico (1968).

79. 29.	75 f. sepia and green ..	1·25	1·25

30. Telecommunications Satellite.

1966. Int. Co-operation Year.

80 **30.** 5 f. mauve, purple & green 2·25 35
81. – 10 f. multicoloured .. 2·50 35
82. – 15 f. purple, blue and red 2·75 40
83. **30.** 20 f. blue, purple and red 3·00 45
84. – 25 f. multicoloured .. 3·25 50
85. **30.** 35 f. purple, red and blue 4·50 80
86. – 50 f. purple, green and red 6·00 1·25
87. **30.** 65 f. brown, violet and red 6·50 1·75

DESIGNS: 10 f. Olympic runner (inscr. " ROME 1960 "). 15 f. Fishes. 25 f. Olympic runner (inscr. " TOKIO 1964 "). 50 f. Tobacco plant.

MAHRA SULTANATE OF QISHN AND SOCOTRA

The National Liberation Front took control on 1 October 1967, and full independence was granted by Great Britain on 30 November 1967. Subsequently part of Southern Yemen.

1. Mahra Flag.

1967.

1. **1.** 5 f. multicoloured .. 1·10 10
2. 10 f. multicoloured .. 1·10 15
3. 15 f. multicoloured .. 1·10 15
4. 20 f. multicoloured .. 1·10 20
5. 25 f. multicoloured .. 1·10 25
6. 35 f. multicoloured .. 1·10 25
7. 50 f. multicoloured .. 1·10 25
8. 65 f. multicoloured .. 1·10 25
9. 100 f. multicoloured .. 1·10 25
10. 250 f. multicoloured .. 1·25 35
11. 500 f. multicoloured .. 1·50 50

APPENDIX

The following stamps have either been issued in excess of postal needs, or have not been made available to the public in reasonable quantities at face value.

SEIYUN

1967.

Hunting. 20 f.

Olympic Games, Grenoble. Postage 10, 25, 35, 50, 75 f.; Air 100, 200 f.

Scout Jamboree, Idaho. Air 150 f.

Paintings—Renoir. Postage 10, 35, 50, 65, 75 f.; Air 100, 200, 250 f.

Paintings—Toulouse-Lautrec. Postage 10, 35, 50, 65, 75 f.; Air 100, 200, 250 f.

Stated to have been occupied by the N.L.F. on 1st October, 1967.

HADHRAMAUT

1967.

Stampex, London. Postage 5, 10, 15, 20, 25 f.; Air 50, 65 f.

Amphilex International Stamp Exhibition, Amsterdam. Air 75 f.

Olympic Games, Mexico (1968). 75 f.

Paintings. Postage 5, 10, 15, 20, 25 f.; Air 50, 65 f.

Scout Jamboree, Idaho. Air 35 f.

Space Research. Postage 10, 25, 35, 50, 75 f.; Air 100, 250 f.

Stated to have been occupied by the N.L.F. on 17th September, 1967.

MAHRA

1967.

Scout Jamboree, Idaho. 15, 75, 100, 150 f.

President Kennedy, Commemoration Postage 10, 15, 25, 50, 75, 100, 150 f.; Air 250, 500 f.

Olympic Games, Mexico (1968). Postage 10, 25, 50 f.; Air 250, 500 f.

Stated to have been occupied by the N.L.F. on 1 October 1967.

Although the British Government did not officially relinquish control over Eastern Aden Protectorate (which comprises the above states) until 30 November 1967, to the National Liberation Front (later the Southern Yemen Republic), that Government claimed that the N.L.F. were in control of them on the dates given above and repudiated the contract under which the former rulers authorised some further new issues which were placed on the market. However, despite this claim there is some uncertainty as to whether any of these later issues were delivered and actually used for postal purposes.

For later issues see SOUTHERN YEMEN and YEMEN PEOPLE'S DEMOCRATIC REPUBLIC in volume 2.

AITUTAKI

Island in the S. Pacific.

1903. 12 pence = 1 shilling.
20 shillings = 1 pound.
1967. 100 cents = 1 dollar.

A. NEW ZEALAND DEPENDENCY.

The British Govt., who had exercised a protectorate over the Cook Islands group since the 1880's handed the islands, including Aitutaki to New Zealand administration in 1901. Cook Is. stamps were used from 1932 to 1972.

Stamps of New Zealand overprinted **AITUTAKI** and value in native language.

1903. Pictorial stamps.

1 **23** ½d. green .. .. .. 3·25 6·50
2 **42** 1d. red .. .. .. 4·75 5·50
4 **26** 2½d. blue .. .. .. 9·00 11·00
5 **28** 3d. brown .. .. 8·00 15·00
6 **31** 6d. red .. .. .. 24·00 25·00
7 **34** 1s. red .. .. .. 55·00 85·00

1911. King Edward VII stamps.

9 **51** ½d. green .. .. .. 75 2·50
10 **53** 1d. red .. .. .. 3·00 8·00
11 **51** 6d. red .. .. .. 35·00 70·00
12 1s. red .. .. .. 55·00 £120

1916. King George V stamps

13. **62.** 6d. red .. .. .. 7·50 23·00
14a. 1s. red .. .. .. 28·00 75·00

1917. King George V stamps optd. **AITUTAKI** only.

19 **62** ½d. green .. .. 1·00 4·25
20 **53** 1d. red .. .. 2·50 9·50
21 **62** 1½d. grey .. .. 3·50 26·00
22 1½d. brown .. .. 80 7·00
15 2½d. blue .. .. 1·40 12·00
16 3d. brown .. .. 1·25 14·00
17 6d. red .. .. 4·50 14·00
18 1s. red .. .. 12·00 23·00

1920. As 1920 pictorial stamps of Cook Is.

30 ½d. black and green .. 2·00 7·50
31 1d. black and red .. 2·75 6·50
26 1½d. black and brown .. 6·00 12·00
32 2½d. black and blue .. 7·50 42·00
27 3d. black and blue .. 2·00 12·00
28 6d. brown and grey .. 5·00 14·00
29 1s. black and purple .. 9·00 16·00

B. PART OF COOK ISLANDS.

On 9 August 1972. Aitutaki became a Port of Entry into the Cook Islands. Whilst remaining part of the Cook Islands, Aitutaki has a separate postal service.

1972. Nos. 227/8, 230, 233/4, 238, 240/1, 243 and 244 of Cook Islands optd. **Aitutaki.**

33 **79** ½ c. multicoloured .. 30 80
34 – 1 c. multicoloured .. 70 1·40
35 – 2½ c. multicoloured .. 3·50 8·00
36 – 4 c. multicoloured .. 70 85
37 – 5 c. multicoloured .. 4·50 8·50
38 – 10 c. multicoloured .. 4·50 6·50
39 – 20 c. multicoloured .. 70 1·00
40 – 25 c. multicoloured .. 70 1·00
41 – 50 c. multicoloured .. 3·75 3·25
42 – $1 multicoloured .. 6·50 6·50

1972. Christmas. Nos. 406/8 of Cook Islands optd. **Aitutaki.**

43. **130.** 1 c. multicoloured .. 10 10
44. – 5 c. multicoloured .. 15 15
45. – 10 c. multicoloured .. 15 25

1972. Royal Silver Wedding. As Nos. 413 and 415 of Cook Islands, but inscr. " COOK ISLANDS Aitutaki ".

46. **131.** 5 c. black and silver .. 4·75 2·75
47. – 15 c. black and silver .. 2·75 1·50

1972. No. 245 of Cook Islands optd. **AITUTAKI.**

48. $2 multicoloured .. .. 60 1·00

1972. Nos. 227/8, 230, 233, 234, 238, 240, 241, 243 and 244 of Cook Islands optd. **AITUTAKI** within ornamental oval.

49. **79.** ½ c. multicoloured .. 15 10
50. – 1 c. multicoloured .. 15 10
51. – 2½ c. multicoloured .. 20 10
52. – 4 c. multicoloured .. 25 15
53. – 5 c. multicoloured .. 25 15
54. – 10 c. multicoloured .. 35 25
55. – 20 c. multicoloured .. 70 50
56. – 25 c. multicoloured .. 70 55
57. – 50 c. multicoloured .. 1·25 90
58. – $1 multicoloured .. 1·75 1·75

13. " Christ Mocked " (Grunewald).

1973. Easter. Multicoloured.

59. 1 c. Type **13** 15 10
60. 1 c. " St. Veronica " (Van der Weyden) 15 10
61. 1 c. " The Crucified Christ with Virgin Mary, Saints and Angels " (Raphael) 15 10
62. 1 c. " Resurrection " (Piero della Francesca) 15 10
63. 5 c. " The Last Supper " (Master of Amiens) .. 20 15
64. 5 c. " Condemnation " (Holbein) 20 15
65. 5 c. " Christ on the Cross " (Rubens) .. 20 15
66. 5 c. " Resurrection " (El Greco) 20 15
67. 10 c. " Disrobing of Christ " (El Greco) 20 15
68. 10 c. " St. Veronica " (Van Oostsanen) 20 15
69. 10 c. " Christ on the Cross " (Rubens) 20 15
70. 10 c. " Resurrection " (Bouts) 20 15

1973. Silver Wedding Coinage. Nos. 417/23 of Cook Is. optd. **AITUTAKI.**

71. **132.** 1 c. black, red & gold .. 10 10
72. – 2 c. black. blue & gold 10 10
73. – 5 c. black, green & silver 10 10
74. – 10 c. black, blue & silver 15 10
75. – 20 c. black, green & silver 20 15
76. – 50 c. black, red & silver 40 30
77. – $1 black, blue & silver 65 45

1973. 10th Anniv. of Treaty Banning Nuclear Testing. Nos. 236, 238, 240 and 243 of Cook Is. optd. **AITUTAKI** within ornamental oval and **TENTH ANNIVERSARY CESSATION OF NUCLEAR TESTING TREATY.**

78. 8 c. multicoloured 15 15
79. 10 c. multicoloured 15 15
80. 20 c. multicoloured 30 20
81. 50 c. multicoloured 70 50

16. Red Hibiscus and Princess Anne.

1973. Royal Wedding. Multicoloured.

82. 25 c. Type **16** 25 10
83. 30 c. Capt. Mark Phillips and Blue Hibiscus .. 25 10

17. " Virgin and Child " (Montagna).

1973. Christmas. "Virgin and Child" paintings by artist listed below. Mult.

85. 1 c. Type **17** 10 10
86. 1 c. Crivelli 10 10
87. 1 c. Van Dyck 10 10
88. 1 c. Perugino 10 10
89. 5 c. Veronese (child on shoulder) 20 10
90. 5 c. Veronese (child on lap) 20 10
91. 5 c. Cima 20 10
92. 5 c. Memling 20 10
93. 10 c. Memling 20 10
94. 10 c. Del Colle 20 10
95. 10 c. Raphael 20 10
96. 10 c. Lotto 20 10

18. " Murex ramosus ".

1974. Sea-shells. Multicoloured.

97. ½ c. Type **18** 45 50
98. 1 c. " Nautilus macromphallus " .. 45 50
99. 2 c. " Harpa major " .. 45 50
100. 3 c. " Phalium strigatum " 45 50
101. 4 c. " Cypraea talpa " .. 45 50
102. 5 c. " Mitra stictica " .. 45 50
103. 8 c. " Charonia tritonis " .. 45 50
104. 10 c. " Murex triremis " .. 45 50
105. 20 c. " Oliva sericea " .. 60 50
106. 25 c. " Tritonalia rubeta " .. 70 50
107. 60 c. " Strombus latissimus " 2·50 1·25
108. $1 " Biplex perca " .. 1·75 1·40
109 $2 Queen Elizabeth II and " Terebra maculata " .. 6·00 8·50
110. $5 Queen Elizabeth II and " Cypraea hesitat " .. 27·00 10·00

The $2 and $5 are larger, 53 × 25 mm.

19. Bligh and H.M.S. "Bounty".

1974. William Bligh's Discovery of Aitutaki. Multicoloured

114. 1 c. Type **19** 25 10
115. 1 c. H.M.S. "Bounty" .. 25 10
116. 5 c. Bligh, and H.M.S. "Bounty" at Aitutaki .. 55 15
117. 5 c. Aitutaki chart of 1856 55 15
118. 8 c. Capt. Cook and H.M.S. "Resolution" 85 20
119. 8 c. Map of Aitutaki and inset location map .. 85 20

See also Nos. 123/8.

20. Aitutaki Stamps of 1903, and Map.

1974. Centenary of Universal Postal Union. Multicoloured.

120. 25 c. Type **20** 65 40
121. 50 c. Surcharged 1903, and 1920, and map .. 85 60

1974. Air. As Nos. 114/119 in larger size (46 × 26 mm.), additionally inscr. "AIR MAIL".

123. 10 c. Type **19** 55 15
124. 10 c. H.M.S. "Bounty" .. 55 15
125. 25 c. Bligh, and H.M.S. "Bounty" at Aitutaki .. 70 25
126. 25 c. Aitutaki chart of 1856 70 25
127. 30 c. Capt. Cook and H.M.S. "Resolution" .. 70 25
128. 30 c. Map of Aitutaki and inset location map .. 70 25

21. "Virgin and Child" (Hugo van der Goes).

1974. Christmas. "Virgin and Child" paintings by artists named. Mult.

129. 1 c. Type **21** 10 10
130. 5 c. G. Bellini 10 10
131. 8 c. G. David 10 10
132. 10 c. A. da Messina .. 10 10
133. 25 c. J. Van Cleve .. 20 20
134. 30 c. Master of the Life of St. Catherine 20 20

22. Churchill as Schoolboy.

1974. Birth Centenary of Sir Winston Churchill. Multicoloured.
136. 10 c. Type 22 .. .. 30 25
137. 25 c. Churchill as young man 60 50
138. 30 c. Churchill with troops 75 60
139. 50 c. Churchill painting .. 1·10 80
140. $1 Churchill giving "V"-sign .. .. .. 2·00 1·50

1974. Children's Christmas Fund. Nos. 129/34 surch.
142. 21. 1 c.+1 c. multicoloured 10 10
143. – 5 c.+1 c. multicoloured 10 10
144. – 8 c.+1 c. multicoloured 10 10
145. – 10 c.+1 c. multicoloured 10 10
146. – 25 c.+1 c. multicoloured 20 20
147. – 30 c.+1 c. multicoloured 20 20

24. Soviet and U.S. Flags.

1975. "Apollo-Soyuz" Space Project. Multicoloured.
148. 25 c. Type 24 .. .. 30 20
149. 50 c. Daedalus with space capsule 40 30

25. "Madonna and Child with Saints Francis and John" (Lorenzetti).

1975. Christmas. Multicoloured.
151. 6 c. } Type 25 .. .. 10 10
152. 6 c. } 10 10
153. 6 c. } 10 10
154. 7 c. } "Adoration of .. 10 10
155. 7 c. } the Kings" .. 10 10
156. 7 c. } (Van der Weyden) .. 10 10
157. 15 c. } "Madonna and .. 15 15
158. 15 c. } Child enthroned with Saints Onufrius and John the Baptist" .. 15 15
159. 15 c. } (Montagna) .. 15 15
160. 20 c. } "Adoration of .. 20 15
161. 20 c. } the Shepherds" .. 20 15
162. 20 c. } (Reni) .. 20 15
Type 25 shows the left-hand stamp of the 6 c. design.

1975. Children's Christmas Fund. Nos. 151/62 surch.
164. 25. 6 c.+1 c. multicoloured 15 10
165. – 6 c.+1 c. multicoloured 15 10
166. – 6 c.+1 c. multicoloured 15 10
167. – 7 c.+1 c. multicoloured 15 10
168. – 7 c.+1 c. multicoloured 15 10
169. – 7 c.+1 c. multicoloured 15 10
170. – 15 c.+1 c. multicoloured 20 15
171. – 15 c.+1 c. multicoloured 20 15
172. – 15 c.+1 c. multicoloured 20 15
173. – 20 c.+1 c. multicoloured 25 20
174. – 20 c.+1 c. multicoloured 25 20
175. – 20 c.+1 c. multicoloured 25 20

26. "The Descent" (detail, 15th cent. Flemish School).

1976. Easter. Multicoloured.
176. 15 c. Type 26 .. .. 15 10
177. 30 c. "The Descent" (detail) 20 15
178. 35 c. "The Descent" (detail) 25 20

27. "The Declaration of Independence" (detail).

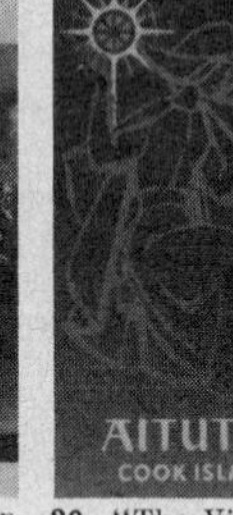

30. "The Visitation".

28. Cycling.

1976. Bicent. of American Revolution. Multicoloured.
180. 30 c. } Type 27 .. .. 60 30
181. 30 c. } 60 30
182. 30 c. } 60 30
183. 35 c. } "Surrender of Lord 70 40
184. 35 c. } Cornwallis at York- 70 40
185. 35 c. } town" (John Trumbull) 70 40
186. 50 c. } "The Resignation of 80 45
187. 50 c. } General Washington" 80 45
188. 50 c. } (John Trumbull) .. 80 45
Type 27 shows the left-hand stamp of the 30 c. design.

1976. Olympic Games, Montreal. Mult.
190. 15 c. Type 28 .. .. 20 15
191. 35 c. Sailing 40 20
192. 60 c. Hockey 55 25
193. 70 c. Sprinting 60 30

1976. Royal Visit to the U.S.A. Nos. 190/3 optd. **ROYAL VISIT JULY 1976.**
195. 28. 15 c. multicoloured .. 25 15
196. – 35 c. multicoloured .. 40 25
197. – 60 c. multicoloured .. 60 40
198. – 70 c. multicoloured .. 70 45

1976. Christmas. Multicoloured.
200. 6 c. } Type 30 .. .. 10 10
201. 6 c. } 10 10
202. 7 c. } "Angel and .. 10 10
203. 7 c. } Shepherds" .. 10 10
204. 15 c. } "The Holy Family" 10 10
205. 15 c. } 10 10
206. 20 c. } "The Magi" .. 15 15
207. 20 c. } 15 15
Type 30 shows the left-hand stamp of the 6 c. design.

1976. Children's Christmas Fund. Nos. 200/07 surch.
209. 30. 6 c.+1 c. multicoloured 10 10
210. – 6 c.+1 c. multicoloured 10 10
211. – 7 c.+1 c. multicoloured 10 10
212. – 7 c.+1 c. multicoloured 10 10
213. – 15 c.+1 c. multicoloured 15 15
214. – 15 c.+1 c. multicoloured 15 15
215. – 20 c.+1 c. multicoloured 15 15
216. – 20 c.+1 c. multicoloured 15 15

32. Alexander Graham Bell and First Telephone.

1977. Centenary of Telephone (1976).
218. 32. 25 c. black, gold and red 20 15
219. – 70 c. black, gold & lilac 40 40
DESIGN: 70 c. Satellite and Earth station.

33. "Christ on the Cross" (detail).

1977. Easter. 400th Birth Anniv. of Rubens. Multicoloured.
221. 15 c. Type 33 .. .. 45 15
222. 20 c. "Lamentation for Christ" 60 20
223. 35 c. "Christ with Straw" 75 25

34. Capt. Bligh, George III and H.M.S. "Bounty".

1977. Silver Jubilee. Multicoloured.
225. 25 c. Type 34 .. .. 50 45
226. 35 c. Rev. Williams, George IV and Aitutaki Church 60 50
227. 50 c. Union Jack, Queen Victoria and island map 75 75
228. $1 Balcony scene 1953 1·00 1·25

35. The Shepherds.

1977. Christmas. Multicoloured.
230. 6 c. Type 35 .. .. 10 10
231. 6 c. Angel 10 10
232. 7 c. Mary, Jesus and Ox .. 10 10
233. 7 c. Joseph and donkey .. 10 10
234. 15 c. Three kings 10 10
235. 15 c. Virgin and Child .. 10 10
236. 20 c. Joseph 10 10
237. 20 c. Mary and Jesus on donkey 10 10

1977. Children's Christmas Fund. Nos. 230/7 surch. +1 c.
239. 6 c.+1 c. } Type 35 .. 10 10
240. 6 c.+1 c. } .. 10 10
241. 7 c.+1 c. } The Holy 10 10
242. 7 c.+1 c. } Family 10 10
243. 15 c.+1 c. } Virgin and Child with the Three 15 10
244. 15 c.+1 c. } Kings 15 10
245. 20 c.+1 c. } "The Flight 15 10
246. 20 c.+1 c. } into Egypt" 15 10

37. Hawaiian Goddess.

1978. Bicent. of Discovery of Hawaii. Mult.
248. 35 c. Type 37 .. .. 45 25
249. 50 c. Figurehead of H.M.S. "Resolution" (horiz.) 75 40
250. $1 Hawaiian temple figure 1·00 70

38. "Christ on the way to Calvary" (Martini).

1978. Easter. Paintings from the Louvre, Paris. Multicoloured.
252. 15 c. Type 38 .. .. 10 10
253. 20 c. "Pieta of Avignon" (E. Quanton) 15 10
254. 35 c. "The Pilgrims at Emmaus" (Rembrandt) 20 15

39. The Yale of Beaufort.

40. "Adoration of the Infant Jesus".

1978. 25th Anniv. of Coronation. Mult.
257. $1 Type 39 .. .. 55 65
258. $1 Queen Elizabeth II .. 55 65
259. $1 Aitutaki ancestral statue 55 65

1978. Christmas. 450th Death Anniv. of Durer. Multicoloured.
261. 15 c. Type 40 .. .. 35 15
262. 17 c. "The Madonna with Child" 40 15
263. 30 c. "The Madonna with the Iris" 55 20
264. 35 c. "The Madonna of the Siskin" 60 25

41. "Captain Cook" (Nathaniel Dance).

1979. Death Bicent. of Captain Cook. Mult.
266. 50 c. Type 41 .. .. 1·00 80
267. 75 c. H.M.S. "Resolution" and "Adventure" at Matavai Bay, Tahiti (W. Hodges) .. .. .. 1·75 95

42. Girl with Flowers.

1979. International Year of the Child. Mult.
269. 30 c. Type 42 .. .. 15 15
270. 35 c. Boy playing guitar .. 20 20
271. 65 c. Children in canoe .. 30 30

43. "Man writing a Letter" (painting by Gabriel Metsu).

1979. Death Centenary of Sir Rowland Hill. Multicoloured.

273. 50 c. Type **43** 45 60
274. 50 c. Sir Rowland Hill with Penny Black, 1903 ½ d and 1911 1 d stamps .. 45 60
275. 50 c. "Girl in Blue reading a Letter" (Jan Vermeer) 45 60
276. 65 c. "Woman writing a Letter" (Gerard Terborch) 50 65
277. 65 c. Sir Rowland Hill, with Penny Black, 1903 3d and 1920 ½d stamps .. 50 65
278. 65 c. "Lady reading a Letter" (Jan Vermeer) .. 50 65

44. " The Burial of Christ (left detail) (Quentin Metsys).

1980. Easter. Multicoloured.

280. 20 c. Type **44** 40 25
281. 30 c. " The Burial of Christ " (centre detail) 50 35
282. 35 c. " The Burial of Christ " (right detail) 65 45

45. Einstein as a Young Man.

1980. 25th Death Anniv. of Albert Einstein (physicist). Multicoloured.

284. 12 c. Type **45** 50 50
285. 12 c. Atom and "E = mc² " equation 50 50
286. 15 c. Einstein in middle-age 55 55
287. 15 c. Cross over nuclear explosion (Test Ban Treaty, 1963) 55 55
288. 20 c. Einstein as an old man 65 65
289. 20 c. Hand preventing atomic explosion .. 65 65

46. Ancestor Figure, Aitutaki.

1980. Third South Pacific Festival of Arts. Multicoloured.

291. 6 c. Type **46** 10 10
292. 6 c. Staff god image Rarotonga 10 10
293. 6 c. Trade adze, Mangaia 10 10
294. 6 c. Carved image of Tangaroa, Rarotonga .. 10 10
295. 12 c. Wooden image Aitutaki 10 10
296. 12 c. Hand club, Rarotonga 10 10
297. 12 c. Carved mace " god ", Mangaia 10 10
298. 12 c. Fisherman's god, Rarotonga 10 10
299. 15 c. Ti'i image, Aitutaki 15 15
300. 15 c. Fisherman's god, Rarotonga (different) 15 15
301. 15 c. Carved mace " god ", Cook Islands 15 15
302. 15 c. Carved image of Tangaroa, Rarotonga (different) 15 15
303. 20c. Chief's headdress, Aitutaki 15 15
304. 20 c. Carved mace " god " Cook Islands, (different) 15 15
305. 20 c. Staff god image, Rarotonga (different) 15 15
306. 20 c. Carved image of Tangaroa, Rarotonga (different) 15 15

47. " The Virgin and Child " (13th century).

1980. Christmas. Sculptures of " The Virgin and Child ". Multicoloured.

308. 15 c. Type **47** 15 15
309. 20 c. 14th century .. 15 15
310. 25 c. 15th century .. 15 15
311. 35 c. 15th century (different) 20 20

48. " Mourning Virgin ".

1981. Easter. Details of Sculpture " Buria of Christ " by Pedro Roldan.

313. **48.** 30 c. gold and green .. 25 25
314. – 40 c. gold and lilac .. 30 30
315. – 50 c. gold and blue .. 30 30

DESIGNS: 40 c. " Christ ". 50 c. " Saint John ".

49. Gouldian Finch.

1981. Birds (1st series). Multicoloured.

317 1 c. Type **49** 45 30
318 1 c. Common starling .. 45 30
319 2 c. Golden whistler .. 50 30
320 2 c. Scarlet robin .. 50 30
321 3 c. Rufous fantail .. 60 30
322 3 c. Peregrine falcon .. 60 30
323 4 c. Java sparrow .. 70 30
324 4 c. Barn owl 70 30
325 5 c. Tahitian lory .. 70 30
326 5 c. White-breasted wood swallow 70 30
327 6 c. Purple swamphen .. 70 30
328 6 c. Rock dove 70 30
329 10 c. Chestnut-breasted mannikin 90 30
330 10 c. Zebra dove 90 30
331 12 c. Eastern reef heron .. 1·00 40
332 12 c. Common mynah .. 1·00 40
333 15 c. Whimbrel (horiz) .. 1·25 40
334 15 c. Black-browed albatross (horiz) .. 1·25 40
335 20 c. American golden plover (horiz) .. 1·50 55
336 20 c. White tern (horiz) .. 1·50 55
337 25 c. Spotbill duck (horiz) 1·75 70
338 25 c. Brown booby (horiz) 1·75 70
339 30 c. Great frigate bird (horiz) .. .. .. 2·00 85
340 30 c. Pintail (horiz) .. 2·00 85
341 35 c. Long-billed reed warbler .. .. 2·25 1·00
342 35 c. Pomarine skua .. 2·25 1·00
343 40 c. Banded rail .. .. 2·75 1·25
344 40 c. Spotted triller .. 2·75 1·25
345 50 c. Royal albatross .. 3·00 1·50
346 50 c. Stephen's lory .. 3·00 1·50
347 70 c. Red-headed parrot-finch .. .. .. 5·50 3·00
348 70 c. Orange dove .. 5·50 3·00
349 $1 Blue-headed flycatcher 6·50 3·75
350 $2 Red-bellied flycatcher 10·00 8·00
351 $4 Red munia .. .. 17·00 14·00
352 $5 Flat-billed kingfisher 19·00 16·00

See also Nos. 475/94.

50. Prince Charles.

1981. Royal Wedding. Multicoloured.

391. 60 c. Type **50** 40 55
392. 80 c. Lady Diana Spencer 50 65
393. $1.40 Prince Charles and Lady Diana (87 × 70 mm.) 80 1·00

1981. International Year for Disabled Persons. Nos. 391/3 surch. + **5c.**

394. 60 c. + 5 c. Type **50** .. 1·25 1·25
395. 80 c. + 5 c. Lady Diana Spencer .. .. .. 1·75 1·75
396. $1.40 + 5 c. Prince Charles and Lady Diana .. 3·25 3·25

52. Footballers.

1981. World Cup Football Championship, Spain (1982). Football Scenes. Mult.

397. 12 c. Ball to left of stamp 35 35
398. 12 c. Ball to right .. 35 35
399. 15 c. Ball to right .. 40 40
400. 15 c. Ball to left 40 40
401. 20 c. Ball to left 50 50
402. 20 c. Ball to right .. 50 50
403. 25 c. Type **52** 55 55
404. 25 c. " ESPANA 82 " inscription 55 55

53. " The Holy Family ".

1981. Christmas. Etchings by Rembrandt.

406. **53.** 15 c. brown and gold .. 40 40
407. – 30 c. brown and gold .. 65 65
408. – 40 c. brown and gold .. 85 85
409. – 50 c. brown and gold .. 1·10 1·10

DESIGNS—VERT. 30 c. " Virgin with Child ". HORIZ. 40 c. " Adoration of the Shepherds ". 50 c. " The Holy Family ".

54. Princess of Wales.

1982. 21st Birthday of Princess of Wales. Multicoloured.

411 70 c. Type **54** 60 60
412 $1 Prince and Princess of Wales 75 75
413 $2 Princess Diana (different) .. .. 1·25 1·50

1982. Birth of Prince William of Wales. (1st issue). Nos. 391/3 optd.

415. 60 c. Type **50** .. .. 1·50 1·25
416. 60 c. Type **50** .. .. 1·50 1·25
417. 80 c. Lady Diana Spencer 2·00 1·50
418. 80 c. Lady Diana Spencer 2·00 1·50
419. $1.40 Prince Charles and Lady Diana .. .. 3·50 2·25
420. $1.40 Prince Charles and Lady Diana .. .. 3·50 2·25

OPTS. Nos. 415, 417 and 419, **21 JUNE 1982. PRINCE WILLIAM OF WALES.** Nos. 416, 418 and 420, **COMMEMORATING THE ROYAL BIRTH.**

1982. Birth of Prince William of Wales. (2nd issue). As Nos. 411/13 but inscr. " ROYAL BIRTH 21 JUNE 1982 PRINCE WILLIAM OF WALES ".

421. 70 c. Type **54** 60 60
422. $1 Prince and Princess of Wales 75 75
423. $2 Princess Diana (different) .. .. 1·25 1·50

56. " Virgin and Child " (12th-century sculpture).

1982. Christmas. Religious Sculptures. Multicoloured.

425. 18 c. Type **56** 60 60
426. 36 c. " Virgin and Child " (12th-century) .. 75 75
427. 48 c. " Virgin and Child " (13th-century) .. 90 90
428. 60 c. " Virgin and Child " (15th-century) .. .. 1·25 1·25

57. Aitutaki Bananas.

1983. Commonwealth Day. Multicoloured.

430. 48 c. Type **57** .. .. 1·10 50
431. 48 c. Ancient Ti'i image .. 1·10 50
432. 48 c. Tourist canoeing .. 1·10 50
433. 48 c. Captain William Bligh and chart .. .. 1·10 50

58. Scouts around Campfire.

1983. 75th Anniv. of Boy Scout Movement. Multicoloured.

434. 36 c. Type **58** 50 45
435. 48 c. Scout saluting .. 60 55
436. 60 c. Scouts hiking .. 70 70

1983. 15th World Scout Jamboree, Alberta, Canada. Nos. 434/6 optd **15th WORLD SCOUT JAMBOREE.**

438. 36 c. Type **58** 80 45
439. 48 c. Scout saluting .. 1·00 55
440. 60 c. Scouts hiking .. 1·25 75

60. Modern Sport Balloon.

1983. Bicentenary of Manned Flight.

442. 18 c. multicoloured .. 35 20
443. 36 c. multicoloured .. 55 40
444. 48 c. multicoloured .. 70 50
445. 60 c. multicoloured .. 90 60

DESIGNS: 36 c. to 60 c. showing different modern sports balloons.

1983. Various stamps surch. (a) Nos. 335/48 and 352.

447. 18 c. on 20 c. American Golden Plover .. .. 1·25 50
448. 18 c. on 20 c. White tern .. 1·25 50
449. 36 c. on 25 c. Spotbill duck 1·75 75
450. 36 c. on 25 c. Brown booby 1·75 75
451. 36 c. on 30 c. Great frigate bird .. .. .. 1·75 75
452. 36 c. on 30 c. Pintail .. 1·75 75
453. 36 c. on 35 c. Long-billed reed warbler .. .. 1·75 75
454. 36 c. on 35 c. Pomarine skua .. .. .. 1·75 75
455. 48 c. on 49 c. Banded rail 2·50 85
456. 48 c. on 40 c. Spotted triller 2·50 85
457. 48 c. on 50 c. Royal Albatross .. .. .. 2·50 85
458. 48 c. on 50 c. Stephen's lory .. .. .. 2·50 85
459. 72 c. on 70 c. Red-headed parrot finch .. .. 4·50 1·50
460. 72 c. on 70 c. Orange dove 4·50 1·50
461. $5.60 on $5 Flat-billed kingfisher (vert.) .. 18·00 8·50

(b) Nos. 392/3 and 412/3.

462. 96 c. on 80 c. Lady Diana Spencer .. .. .. 4·00 2·50
463. 96 c. on $1 Prince and Princess of Wales .. 3·50 2·00
464. $1.20 on $1.40 Prince Charles and Lady Diana 4·00 2·50
465. $1.20 on $2 Princess Diana 3·50 2·00

63. International Mail.

1983. World Communications Year. Multicoloured.

466. 48 c. Type **63** 65 45
467. 60 c. Telecommunications 85 60
468. 96 c. Space satellite .. 1·25 90

64. " Madonna of the Chair ".

1983. Christmas. 500th Birth Anniv. of Raphael. Multicoloured.

470. 36 c. Type **64** 35 30
471. 48 c. " The Alba Madonna " 50 40
472. 60 c. "Conestabile Madonna" 70 55

65. Gouldian Finch.

1984. Birds (2nd series). Multicoloured.

475. 2 c. Type **65** 10 10
476. 3 c. Common Starling .. 10 10
477. 5 c. Scarlet Robin 10 10
478. 10 c. Golden Whistler .. 10 10
479. 12 c. Rufous Fantail .. 10 10
480. 18 c. Peregrine Falcon .. 15 20
481. 24 c. Barn Owl 15 20
482. 30 c. Java Sparrow 20 25
483. 36 c. White-breasted Wood Swallow 25 30
484. 48 c. Tahitian Lory 35 40
485. 50 c. Rock Dove 35 40
486. 60 c. Purple Swamphen .. 45 50
487. 72 c. Zebra Dove 50 55
488. 96 c. Chestnut-breasted Mannikin 70 75
489. $1.20 Common Mynah .. 90 95
490. $2.10 Eastern Reef Heron .. 1·50 1·60
491. $3 Blue-headed Flycatcher .. 2·25 2·40
492. $4.20 Red-bellied Flycatcher 3·00 3·25
493. $5.60 Red Munia .. .. 4·00 4·25
494. $9.60 Flat billed Kingfisher 7·00 7·25

66. Javelin throwing.

1984. Olympic Games, Los Angeles. Multicoloured.

495. 36 c. Type **66** 30 35
496. 48 c. Shot-putting 40 45
497. 60 c. Hurdling 45 55
498. $2 Basketball .. .. 1·10 1·50

DESIGNS: Show Memorial Coliseum and various events.

1984. Olympic Gold Medal Winners. Nos. 495/8 optd.

500. 36 c. Type **66** (optd. **"Javelin Throw Tessa Sanderson Great Britain"**) 30 35
501. 48 c. Shot-putting (optd. **"Shot Put Claudia Losch Germany"**) 40 45
502. 60 c. Hurdling (optd. **"Heptathlon Glynis Nunn Australia"**) 45 55
503. $2 Basketball (optd. **"Team Basketball United States"**) .. .. .. 1·10 1·50

67. Capt. William Bligh and Chart.

1984. "Ausipex" International Stamp Exhibition, Melbourne, Multicoloured.

504. 60 c. Type **67** .. .. 1·75 1·75
505. 96 c. H.M.S. "Bounty" and map .. .. .. 2·00 2·00
506. $1.40 Aitutaki stamps of 1974, 1979 and 1981 with map .. .. .. 3·00 3·00

1984. Birth of Prince Henry (1st issue). No. 391 optd. **"15-9-84 Birth Prince Henry"** and surch. also.

508. $3 on 60 c. Type **50** .. 4·00 3·00

69. The Annunciation.

1984. Christmas. Details from Altarpiece, St. Paul's Church, Palencia, Spain. Multicoloured.

509. 36 c. Type **69** 30 35
510. 48 c. The Nativity .. 40 45
511. 60 c. The Epiphany .. 45 50
512. 96 c. The Flight into Egypt 75 80

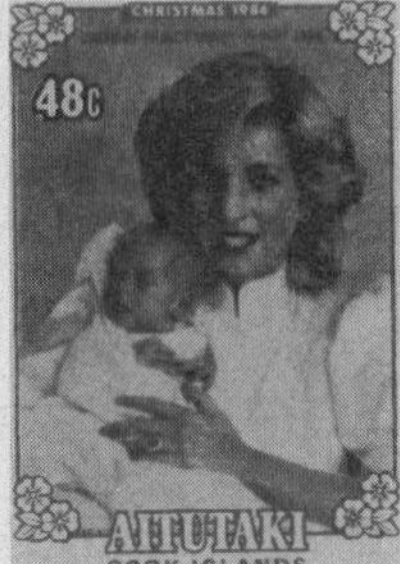

70. Princess Diana with Prince Henry.

1984. Birth of Prince Henry (2nd issue). Multicoloured.

514. 48 c. Type **70** 65 55
515. 60 c. Prince William with Prince Henry 75 60
516. $2.10 Prince and Princess of Wales with children .. 2·00 1·75

71. Grey Kingbird.

1985. Birth Bicentenary of John J. Audubon (ornithologist). Designs showing original paintings. Multicoloured.

518. 55 c. Type **71** 70 70
519. 65 c. Bohemian waxwing .. 75 75
520. 75 c. Summer tanager .. 85 85
521. 95 c. Common cardinal .. 1·00 1·00
522. $1.15 White-winged crossbill .. .. .. 1·25 1·25

72. The Queen Mother, aged Seven.

1985. Life and Times of Queen Elizabeth the Queen Mother. Multicoloured.

523. 55 c. Type **72** 45 50
524. 65 c. Engagement photograph, 1922 .. .. 50 55
525. 75 c. With young Princess Elizabeth 60 65
526. $1.30 With baby Prince Charles .. .. .. 1·00 1·10

73. "The Calmady Children" (T. Lawrence)

1985. International Youth Year. Mult.

528. 75 c. Type **73** .. 1·00 55
529. 90 c. "Madame Charpentier's Children" (Renoir) .. 1·25 65
530. $1.40 "Young Girls at Piano" (Renoir) .. 3·50 1·00

74. "Adoration of the Magi" (Giotto) and "Giotto" Spacecraft.

1985. Christmas. Appearance of Halley's Comet (1st issue). Multicoloured.

532. 95 c. Type **74** 75 80
533. 95 c. As Type **74** but showing "Planet A" spacecraft 75 80
534. $1.15 Type **74** 90 95
535. $1.15 As No. 533 .. .. 90 95

75. Halley's Comet, A.D. 684 (from "Nuremberg Chronicle").

1986. Appearance of Halley's Comet (2nd issue). Multicoloured.

537. 90 c. Type **75** 65 70
538. $1.25 Halley's Comet, 1066 (from Bayeux Tapestry) 85 90
539. $1.75 Halley's Comet, 1456 (from "Lucerne Chronicles") .. .. 1·25 1·40

76. Queen Elizabeth II on Coronation Day (from photo by Cecil Beaton).

1986. 60th Birthday of Queen Elizabeth II.

542. **76.** 95 c. multicoloured .. 85 85

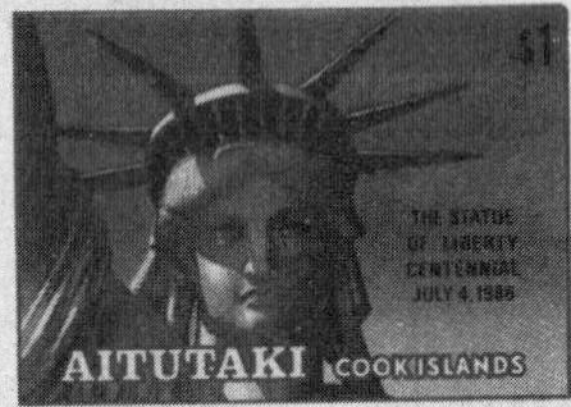

77. Head of Statue of Liberty.

1986. Centenary of Statue of Liberty. Multicoloured

544. $1 Type **77** 80 80
545. $2.75 Statue of Liberty at sunset .. .. .. 2·25 2·25

78. Prince Andrew and Miss Sarah Ferguson

1986. Royal Wedding.

547. **78.** $2 multicoloured .. 2·00 2·00

MORE DETAILED LISTS

are given in the Stanley Gibbons Catalogues referred to in the country headings.
For lists of current volumes see Introduction.

79. "St. Anne with Virgin and Child".

1986. Christmas. Paintings by Dürer. Mult.
551. 75 c. Type **79** .. .. 1·25 1·25
552. $1.35 "Virgin and Child" .. 1·75 1·75
553. $1.95 "The Adoration of the Magi" .. .. 2·25 2·25
554. $2.75 "Madonna of the Rosary" .. .. 2·75 2·75

1986. Visit of Pope John Paul II to South Pacific. Nos. 551/4 optd. **NOVEMBER 21–24 1986 FIRST VISIT TO SOUTH PACIFIC** and surch also.
556. 75 c.+10 c. Type **79** .. 1·75 1·75
557. $1.35+10 c. "Virgin and Child" .. .. .. 2·25 2·25
558. $1.95+10 c. "The Adoration of the Magi" .. 2·75 2·75
559. $2.75+10 c. "Madonna of the Rosary" .. .. 3·50 3·50

1987. Hurricane Relief Fund. Nos. 544/5, 547, 551/4 and 556/9 surch. **HURRICANE RELIEF + 50 c.**
561. 75 c.+50 c. Type **79** .. 1·75 1·75
562. 75 c.+10 c.+50 c. Type **79** 2·00 2·00
563. $1.+50 c. Type **77** .. 2·25 2·25
564. $1.35+50 c. "Virgin and Child" (Durer) .. .. 2·40 2·40
565. $1.35+10 c.+50 c. "Virgin and Child" (Durer) .. 2·50 2·50
566. $1.95+50 c. "The Adoration of the Magi" (Durer) 3·00 3·00
567. $1.95+10 c.+50 c. "The Adoration of the Magi" (Durer) .. .. .. 3·00 3·00
568. $2+59 c. Type **78** .. .. 3·00 3·00
569. $2.75+50 c. Statue of Liberty at sunset .. 3·50 3·50
570. $2.75+50 c. "Madonna of the Rosary" (Durer) .. 3·50 3·50
571. $2.75+10 c.+50 c. "Madonna of the Rosary" (Durer) .. 3·50 3·50

1987. Royal Ruby Wedding. Nos. 391/3 surch. **2.50 Royal Wedding 40th Anniv.**
572. $2.50 on 60 c. Type **50** .. 2·50 2·50
573. $2.50 on 80 c. Lady Diana Spencer .. .. .. 2·50 2·50
574. $2.50 on $1.40 Prince Charles and Lady Diana (87×70 mm.) .. .. 2·50 2·50

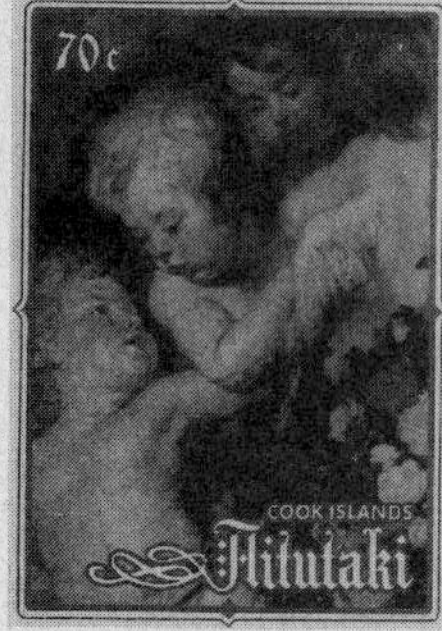

83. Angels.

1987. Christmas. Details of angels from "Virgin with Garland" by Rubens.
575. **83.** 70 c. multicoloured .. 1·10 1·10
576. – 85 c. multicoloured .. 1·25 1·25
577. – $1.50 multicoloured .. 2·00 2·00
578. – $1.85 multicoloured .. 2·25 2·25

84 Chariot racing and Athletics

1988. Olympic Games, Seoul. Ancient and modern Olympic sports. Multicoloured.
581 70 c. Type **84** 80 90
582 85 c. Greek runners and football .. .. 90 1·00
583 95 c. Greek wrestling and handball .. .. 1·00 1·10
584 $1.40 Greek hoplites and tennis .. .. .. 1·60 1·75

1988. Olympic Medal Winners, Los Angeles. Nos. 581/4 optd.
586 70 c. Type **84** (optd **"FLORENCE GRIFFTH JOYNER UNITED STATES 100 M AND 200 M"**) .. 80 90
587 85 c. Greek runners and football (optd **"GELINDO BORDIN ITALY MARATHON"**) .. 90 1·00
588 95 c. Greek wrestling and handball (optd **"HITOSHI SAITO JAPAN JUDO"**) .. 1·00 1·10
589 $1.40 Greek hoplites and tennis (optd **"STEFFI GRAF WEST GERMANY WOMEN'S TENNIS"**) 1·60 1·75

85 "Adoration of the Shepherds" (detail)

1988. Christmas. Paintings by Rembrandt. Multicoloured.
590 55 c. Type **85** 90 90
591 70 c. "The Holy Family" 1·00 1·00
592 85 c. "Presentation in the Temple" .. .. 1·10 1·10
593 95 c. "The Holy Family" (different) .. .. 1·40 1·40
594 $1.15 "Presentation in the Temple" (different) .. 1·60 1·60

86 H.M.S. "Bounty" leaving Spithead and Capt. Bligh

1989. Bicentenary of Discovery of Aitutaki by Capt. Bligh. Multicoloured.
596 55 c. Type **86** .. .. 1·10 1·10
597 65 c. Breadfruit plants .. 1·25 1·25
598 75 c. Old chart showing Aitutaki and Capt. Bligh 1·40 1·40
599 95 c. Native outrigger and H.M.S. "Bounty" off Aitutaki .. .. 1·90 1·90
600 $1.65 Fletcher Christian confronting Bligh .. 2·50 2·50

87 "Apollo 11" Astronaut on Moon

1989. 20th Anniv of First Manned Landing on Moon. Multicoloured.
602 75 c. Type **87** 60 60
603 $1.15 Conducting experiment on Moon 90 90
604 $1.80 Astronaut on Moon carrying equipment .. 1·50 1·50

88 Virgin Mary

1989. Christmas. Details from "Virgin in the Glory" by Titian. Multicoloured.
606 70 c. Type **88** 95 95
607 85 c. Christ Child .. .. 1·25 1·25
608 95 c. Angel .. .. 1·50 1·50
609 $1.25 Cherubs .. .. 2·00 2·00

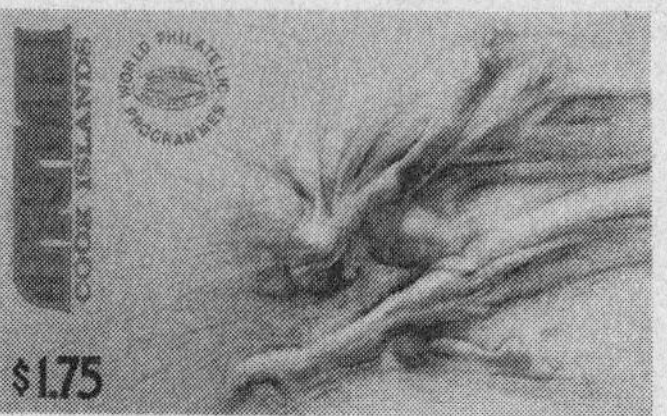

89 Human Comet striking Earth

1990. Protection of the Environment. Mult.
611 $1.75 Type **89** .. .. 1·50 1·50
612 $1.75 Comet's tail .. 1·50 1·50
Nos. 611/12 were printed together, se-tenant, forming a composite design.

91 "Madonna of the Basket" (Correggio)

1990. Christmas. Religious Paintings. Mult.
615 70 c. Type **91** 70 70
616 85 c. "Virgin and Child" (Morando) 80 80
617 95 c. "Adoration of the Child" (Tiepolo) .. 90 90
618 $1.75 "Mystic Marriage of St. Catherine" (Memling) 1·60 1·60

1990. "Birdpex '90" Stamp Exhibition, Christchurch, New Zealand. Nos. 349/50 optd **Birdpex'90** and bird's head.
620 $1 Blue-headed flycatcher 1·75 1·75
621 $2 Red-bellied flycatcher 2·50 2·50

1991. 65th Birthday of Queen Elizabeth II No. 352 optd **COMMEMORATING 65th BIRTHDAY OF H.M. QUEEN ELIZABETH II.**
622 $5 Flat-billed kingfisher 4·75 5·00

93 "The Holy Family" (A. Mengs)

1991. Christmas. Religious Paintings. Mult.
623 80 c. Type **93** 70 70
624 90 c. "Virgin and the Child" (Lippi) 80 80
625 $1.05 "Virgin and Child" (A. Durer) 95 95
626 $1.75 "Adoration of the Shepherds" (G. De La Tour) .. .. .. 1·60 1·60

94 Hurdling

1992. Olympic Games, Barcelona. Mult.
628 95 c. Type **94** 80 80
629 $1.25 Weightlifting .. 1·10 1·10
630 $1.50 Judo .. .. 1·40 1·40
631 $1.95 Football .. .. 1·75 1·75

95 Vaka Motu Canoe

1992. 6th Festival of Pacific Arts, Rarotonga. Sailing canoes. Multicoloured.
632 30 c. Type **95** 35 35
633 50 c. Hamatafua 50 50
634 95 c. Alia Kalia Ndrua .. 85 85
635 $1.75 Hokule'a Hawaiian 1·60 1·60
636 $1.95 Tuamotu Pani .. 2·00 2·00

1992. Royal Visit by Prince Edward. Nos. 632/6 optd **ROYAL VISIT.**
637 30 c. Type **95** 35 35
638 50 c. Hamatafua 50 50
639 95 c. Alia Kalia Ndrua .. 85 85
640 $1.75 Hokule'a Hawaiian 1·60 1·60
641 $1.95 Tuamotu Pahi .. 2·00 2·00

96 "Virgin's Nativity" (detail) (Reni)

1992. Christmas. Different details from "Virgin's Nativity" by Guido Reni.
642 **96** 80 c. multicoloured .. 75 75
643 – 90 c. multicoloured .. 85 85
644 – $1.05 multicoloured .. 1·00 1·00
645 – $1.75 multicoloured .. 1·60 1·60

97 The Departure from Palos

1992. 500th Anniv of Discovery of America by Columbus. Multicoloured.
647 $1.25 Type **97** .. .. 1·25 1·25
648 $1.75 Map of voyages .. 1·60 1·60
649 $1.95 Columbus and crew in New World .. .. 2·00 2·00

HAVE YOU READ THE NOTES AT THE BEGINNING OF THIS CATALOGUE?
These often provide answers to the enquiries we receive.

98 Queen Victoria and King Edward VII

1993. 40th Anniv of Coronation. Mult.

650	$1.75 Type **98**	1·60	1·60
651	$1.75 King George V and King George VI ..	1·60	1·60
652	$1.75 Queen Elizabeth II in 1953 and 1993	1·60	1·60

99 "Madonna and Child" (Nino Pisano)

1993. Christmas. Religious Sculptures. Mult.

653	80 c. Type **99**	60	65
654	90 c. "Virgin on Rosebush" (Luca della Robbia) ..	65	70
655	$1.15 "Virgin with Child and St. John" (Juan Francisco Rustici) ..	85	90
656	$1.95 "Virgin with Child" (Miguel Angel)	1·50	1·60
657	$3 "Madonna and Child" (Jacopo della Quercia) (32 × 47 mm)	2·25	2·40

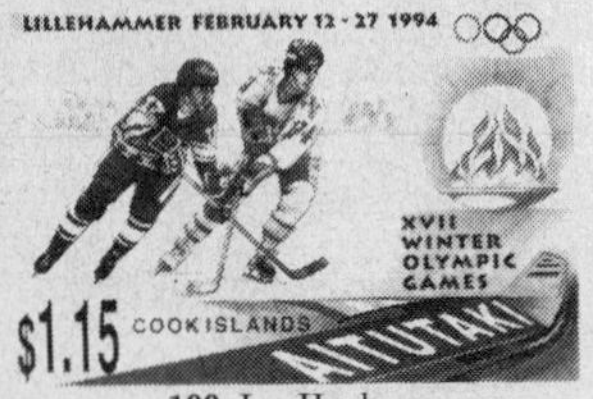

100 Ice Hockey

1994. Winter Olympic Games, Lillehammer. Multicoloured.

658	$1.15 Type **100**	85	90
659	$1.15 Ski-jumping ..	85	90
660	$1.15 Cross-country skiing	85	90

101 "Ipomoea pes-caprae"

1994. Flowers. Multicoloured.

661	5 c. Type **101**	10	10
662	10 c. "Plumeria alba" ..	10	10
663	15 c. "Hibiscus rosa-sinensis"	10	10
664	20 c. "Allamanda cathartica"	15	20
665	25 c. "Delonix regia" ..	20	25
666	30 c. "Gardenia taitensis"	20	25
667	50 c. "Plumeria rubra" ..	35	40
668	80 c. "Ipomoea littoralis"	60	65
669	85 c. "Hibiscus tiliaceus"	60	65
670	90 c. "Erythrina variegata"	65	70

OFFICIAL STAMPS

1978. Nos. 98/105, 107/10 and 227/8 optd. **O.H.M.S.** or surch also.

O 1.	1 c. multicoloured ..	90	10
O 2.	2 c. multicoloured ..	1·00	10
O 3.	3 c. multicoloured ..	1·00	10
O 4.	4 c. multicoloured ..	1·00	10
O 5.	5 c. multicoloured ..	1·00	10
O 6.	8 c. multicoloured ..	1·25	10
O 7.	10 c. multicoloured ..	1·50	15
O 8.	15 c. on 60 c. mult. ..	2·50	20
O 9.	18 c. on 60 c. mult. ..	2·50	20
O 10.	20 c. multicoloured ..	1·00	55
O 11.	50 c. multicoloured ..	7·00	70
O 12.	60 c. multicoloured ..	8·00	85
O 13.	$1 multicoloured (No. 108)	9·00	1·25
O 14.	$2 multicoloured ..		
O 15.	$4 on $1 multicoloured (No. 228)	2·50	1·75
O 16.	$5 multicoloured ..	11·00	3·00

1985. Nos. 351/2, 430/3, 475, 477/94 optd **O.H.M.S.** or surch also.

O17	2 c. Type **65** ..	10	10
O18	5 c. Scarlet robin ..	10	10
O19	10 c. Golden whistler ..	10	10
O20	12 c. Rufous fantail ..	10	10
O21	18 c. Peregrine falcon ..	15	20
O22	20 c. on 24 c. Barn owl	15	20
O23	30 c. Java sparrow ..	20	25
O24	40 c. on 36 c. White-breasted wood swallow	30	35
O25	50 c. Rock dove ..	35	40
O26	55 c. on 48 c. Tahitian lory	40	45
O27	60 c. Purple swamphen	45	50
O28	65 c. on 72 c. Zebra dove	45	50
O38	75 c. on 48 c. Type **57** ..	55	60
O39	75 c. on 48 c. Ancient Ti'i image ..	55	60
O40	75 c. on 48 c. Tourist canoeing ..	55	60
O41	75 c. on 48 c. Captain William Bligh and chart ..	55	60
O29	80 c. on 96 c. Chestnut-breasted mannikin ..	60	65
O30	$1.20 Common mynah	90	95
O31	$2.10 Eastern reef heron	1·50	1·60
O32	$3 Blue-headed fly-catcher ..	2·25	2·40
O33	$4.20 Red-bellied fly-catcher	3·00	3·25
O34	$5.60 Red munia ..	4·00	4·25
O35	$9.60 Flat-billied king-fisher	7·00	7·25
O36	$14 on $4 Red munia (35 × 48 mm) ..	10·00	11·00
O37	$18 on $5 Flat-billed king-fisher	13·00	13·50

ALWAR

A state of Rajputana N. India. Now uses Indian stamps.

12 pies = 1 anna; 16 annas = 1 rupee.

1. Native Dagger.

1877. Roul or perf.

1a **1.**	¼ a. blue	2·00	50
5	¼ a. green	2·00	1·60
2b	1 a. brown	1·40	60

ANGUILLA

St. Christopher, Nevis and Anguilla were granted Associated Statehood on 27 February 1967, but following a referendum Anguilla declared her independence and the St. Christopher authorities withdrew. On 7 July 1969, the Anguilla post office was officially recognised by the Government of St. Christopher, Nevis and Anguilla and normal postal communications via St. Christopher were resumed.

By the Anguilla Act of 27 July 1971, the island was restored to direct British control.

100 cents = 1 West Indian dollar.

1967. Nos. 129/44 of St. Kitts–Nevis optd. **Independent Anguilla** and bar.

1. –	½ c. sepia and blue ..	24·00	20·00
2. **33.**	1 c. multicoloured ..	25·00	6·50
3. –	2 c. multicoloured ..	26·00	1·25
4. –	3 c. multicoloured ..	26·00	4·50
5. –	4 c. multicoloured ..	26·00	5·50
6. –	5 c. multicoloured ..	95·00	18·00
7. –	6 c. multicoloured ..	45·00	9·00
8. –	10 c. multicoloured ..	26·00	6·50
9. –	15 c. multicoloured ..	55·00	11·00
10. –	20 c. multicoloured ..	90·00	12·00
11. –	25 c. multicoloured ..	75·00	20·00
12. –	50 c. multicoloured ..	—	£450
13. –	60 c. multicoloured ..	—	£850
14. –	$1 yellow and blue ..	—	£400
15. –	$2. 50 multicoloured ..	—	£300
16. –	$5 multicoloured ..	—	£300
	Set of 16	£8000	£2250

The above stamps were issued by the governing Council and have been accepted for international mail. Owing to the limited stocks available for overprinting, the sale of the stamps was personally controlled by the Post-master and no orders from the trade were accepted.

2. Mahogany Tree, The Quarter.

1967.

17. **2.**	1 c. green, brown and orge.	10	20
18. -	2 c. turquoise and black ..	10	20
19. -	3 c. black and green ..	10	10
20. -	4 c. blue and black ..	10	10
21. -	5 c. multicoloured ..	10	10
22. -	6 c. red and black ..	10	10
23. -	10 c. multicoloured ..	15	10
24. -	15 c. multicoloured ..	30	20
25. -	20 c. multicoloured ..	40	20
26. -	25 c. multicoloured ..	50	20
27. -	40 c. green, turq. and black	80	25
28. -	60 c. multicoloured ..	2·25	1·25
29. -	$1 multicoloured ..	1·75	2·25
30. -	$2·50 multicoloured ..	2·00	2·25
31. -	$5 multicoloured ..	3·50	3·75

DESIGNS: 2 c. Sombrero Lighthouse. 3 c. St. Mary's Church. 4 c. Valley Police Station. 5 c. Old Plantation House, Mt. Fortune. 6 c. Valley Post Office. 10 c. Methodist Church, West End 15 c. Wall-Blake Airport. 20 c. Aircraft over Sandy Ground. 25 c. Island Harbour. 40 c. Map of Anguilla. 60 c. Hermit Crab and Starfish. $1, Hibiscus. $2·50, Local scene. $5, Spiny Lobster.

On 9 January 1969, Anguilla reaffirmed her independence from St. Kitts and issued Nos. 17/31 optd. **INDEPENDENCE JANUARY, 1969.**

17. Yachts in Lagoon.

1968. Anguillan Ships. Multicoloured.

32.	10 c. Type **17**	20	10
33.	15 c. Boat on Beach ..	25	10
34.	25 c. Schooner "Warspite"	35	15
35.	40 c. Schooner "Atlantic Star"	45	20

18. Purple-throated Carib.

1968. Anguillan Birds. Multicoloured.

36.	10 c. Type **18**	75	15
37.	15 c. Bananaquit	95	20
38.	25 c. Black-necked stilt (horiz.)	1·25	20
39.	40 c. Royal tern (horiz.) ..	1·50	30

19. Guides' Badge and Anniversary Years.

1968. 35th Anniv. of Anguillan Girl Guides. Multicoloured.

40.	10 c. Type **19**	10	10
41.	15 c. Badge and Silhouettes of Guides (vert.) ..	15	10
42.	25 c. Guides Badge and Headquarters, Valley ..	20	15
43.	40 c. Association and Proficiency Badges (vert.) ..	25	15

20. The Three Kings.

1968. Christmas.

44. **20.**	1 c. black and red ..	10	10
45. –	10 c. black and blue ..	10	10
46. –	15 c. black and brown ..	15	10
47. –	40 c. black and blue ..	15	10
48. –	50 c. black and green ..	20	15

DESIGNS—VERT. 10 c. The Wise Men. 15 c. Holy Family and Manger. HORIZ. 40 c. The Shepherds. 50 c. Holy Family and Donkey.

21. Bagging Salt.

1969. Anguillan Salt Industry. Multicoloured.

49.	10 c. Type **21**	15	10
50.	15 c. Packing salt	20	10
51.	40 c. Salt pond	25	10
52.	50 c Loading salt	25	10

22. "The Crucifixion" (Studio of Massys).

1969. Easter Commem. Multicoloured.

53.	25 c. Type **22**	20	15
54.	40 c. "The Last Supper" (Ascr. to Roberti) ..	25	15

23. Amaryllis.

1969. Flowers of the Caribbean Mult.

55.	10 c. Type **23**	20	15
56.	15 c. Bougainvillea	25	15
57.	40 c. Hibiscus	50	30
58.	50 c. "Cattleya" Orchid ..	1·25	90

24. Turbans and Star Shells.

1969. Sea Shells. Multicoloured.

59.	10 c. Type **24**	20	10
60.	15 c. Spiny oysters ..	20	10
61.	40 c. Scotch, Royal and Smooth Scotch bonnets	30	15
62.	50 c. Triton trumpet ..	40	20

1969. Christmas. Nos. 17, 25/8 optd. with different seasonal emblems.

63.	1 c. multicoloured	10	10
64.	20 c. multicoloured ..	20	10
65.	25 c. multicoloured ..	20	10
66.	40 c. multicoloured ..	25	15
67.	60 c. multicoloured ..	40	20

30. Red Goatfish.

1969. Fishes. Multicoloured.

68.	10 c. Type **30**	30	15
69.	15 c. Blue Striped Grunts ..	45	15
70.	40 c. Mutton Grouper ..	55	20
71.	50 c. Banded Butterfly Fish	65	20

31. "Morning Glory".

1970. Flowers. Multicoloured.

72.	10 c. Type **31**	30	10
73.	15 c. Blue Petrea	45	10
74.	40 c. Hibiscus	70	20
75.	50 c. "Flame Tree" ..	80	25

32. "Deposition" (Rosso Fiorentino).

1970. Easter. Multicoloured.

76.	10 c. "The Ascent to Calvary" (Tiepolo)	20	10
77.	20 c. "Crucifixion" (Masaccio) ..	30	10
78.	40 c. Type **32** ..	35	15
79.	60 c. "The Ascent to Calvary" (Murillo) ..	40	15

Nos. 76 and 79 are horiz.

33. Scout Badge and Map.

1970. 40th Anniv. of Scouting in Anguilla. Multicoloured.

80.	10 c. Type **33**	15	10
81.	15 c. Scout camp, and cubs practising First Aid ..	20	10
82.	40 c. Monkey bridge ..	25	15
83.	50 c. Scout H.Q. building and Lord Baden-Powell	35	15

34. Boatbuilding.

1970. Multicoloured.

84.	1 c. Type **34**	20	30
85.	2 c. Road Construction ..	20	30
86.	3 c. Quay, Blowing Point ..	20	20
87.	4 c. Broadcaster, Radio Anguilla	20	40
88.	5 c. Cottage Hospital Extension	20	40
89.	6 c. Valley Secondary School	20	40
90.	10 c. Hotel Extension ..	20	30
91.	15 c. Sandy Ground ..	30	30
92.	20 c. Supermarket and Cinema	45	30
93.	25 c. Bananas and Mangoes	35	70
94.	40 c. Wall Blake Airport ..	60	90
95.	60 c. Sandy Ground Jetty ..	65	1·25
96.	$1 Administration Buildings	1·25	1·40
97.	$2·50 Livestock	1·50	3·50
98.	$5 Sandy Hill Bay	2·75	3·75

35. "The Adoration of the Shepherds" (Reni).

1970. Christmas. Multicoloured.

99.	1 c. Type **35**	10	10
100.	20 c. "The Virgin and Child" (Gozzoli)	30	15
101.	25 c. "Mystic Nativity" (detail, Botticelli)	30	15
102.	40 c. "The Santa Margherita Madonna" (detail, Mazzola)	40	20
103.	50 c. "The Adoration of the Magi" (detail, Tiepolo)	40	20

36. "Ecce Homo" (detail, Correggio).

1971. Easter. Paintings. Multicoloured.

104.	10 c. Type **36**	15	10
105.	15 c. "Christ appearing to St. Peter" (detail, Carracci)	25	10
106.	40 c. "Angels weeping over the Dead Christ" (detail, Guercino)	30	10
107.	50 c. "The Supper at Emmaus" (detail, Caravaggio)	30	15

The 40 c. and 50 c. designs are horiz.

37. "Hypolimnas misippus".

1971. Butterflies. Multicolourd.

108	10 c. Type **37**	80	70
109	15 c. "Junonia evarete" ..	1·00	80
110	40 c. "Agraulis vanillae"	1·60	1·25
111	50 c. "Danaus plexippus"	1·90	1·50

38. "Magnanime" and "Aimable" in Battle.

1971. Sea-battles of the West Indies. Multicoloured.

112.	10 c. Type **38**	70	70
113.	15 c. H.M.S. "Duke", "Glorieux" and H.M.S. "Agamemnon" ..	85	85
114.	25 c. H.M.S. "Formidable" and H.M.S. "Namur" against "Ville de Paris" ..	1·25	1·25
115.	40 c. H.M.S. "Canada" ..	1·40	1·40
116.	50 c. H.M.S. "St. Albans" and wreck of "Hector"	1·60	1·60

Nos. 112/116 were issued in horizontal se-tenant strips within the sheet to form a composite design.

39. "The Ansidei Madonna" (detail, Raphael).

1971. Christmas. Multicoloured.

117.	20 c. Type **39**	25	25
118.	25 c. "Mystic Nativity" (detail, Botticelli) ..	25	25
119.	40 c. "Adoration of the Shepherds" (detail, ascr. to Murillo) ..	40	40
120.	50 c. "The Madonna of the Iris" (detail, ascr. to Durer)	45	45

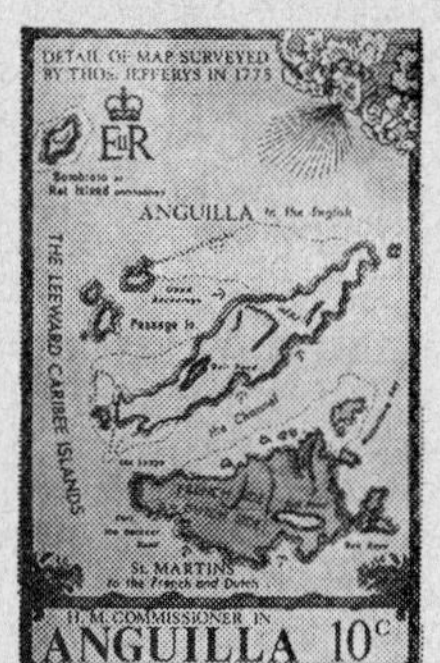

40. Map of Anguilla and St. Martin by Thomas Jefferys, 1775.

1972. Caribbean Maps depicting Anguilla. Multicoloured.

121.	10 c. Type **40**	25	10
122.	15 c. Samuel Fahlberg's Map, 1814	35	15
123.	40 c. Thomas Jefferys' Map, 1775 (horiz.) ..	50	25
124.	50 c. Capt. E. Barnett's Map, 1847 (horiz.)	60	25

41. "Jesus Buffeted".

1972. Easter. Multicoloured.

125.	10 c. Type **41**	25	25
126.	15 c. "The Way of Sorrows"	30	30
127.	25 c. "The Crucifixion" ..	30	30
128.	40 c. "Descent from the Cross"	35	35
129.	50 c. "The Burial" ..	40	40

42. Loblolly Tree.

1972. Multicoloured.

130.	1 c. Spear fishing	10	40
131.	2 c. Type **42**	10	40
132.	3 c. Sandy ground ..	10	40
133.	4 c. Ferry at Blowing Point	15	20
134	5 c. Agriculture	15	40
135.	6 c. St. Mary's Church ..	25	20
136.	10 c. St. Gerrard's Church	25	40
137.	15 c. Cottage hospital extension	25	30
138.	20 c. Public library ..	30	35
139.	25 c. Sunset at Blowing Point	40	70
140.	40 c. Boat building ..	1·50	1·50
141.	60 c. Hibiscus	4·00	3·50
142.	$1 Magnificent Frigate Bird	8·00	6·00
143.	$2·50 Frangipani ..	6·00	7·00
144.	$5 Brown Pelican ..	13·00	13·00
144a.	$10 Green-back turtle ..	18·00	18·00

1972. Royal Silver Wedding. As T. **52**, of Ascension, but with Schooner and Common dolphin in background.

145.	25 c. green	1·00	1·50
146.	40 c. brown	1·10	1·75

44. Flight into Egypt.

1972. Christmas. Multicoloured.

147.	1 c. Type **44**	10	10
148.	20 c. Star of Bethlehem	25	20
149.	25 c. Holy Family ..	25	20
150.	40 c. Arrival of the Magi	30	25
151.	50 c. Adoration of the Magi	30	25

MINIMUM PRICE

The minimum price quoted is 10p which represents a handling charge rather than a basis for valuing common stamps. For further notes about prices see introductory pages.

45. " The Betrayal of Christ ".

1973. Easter. Multicoloured.

152.	1 c. Type **45**	10	10
153.	10 c. " The Man of Sorrows "	10	10
154.	20 c. " Christ bearing the Cross "	15	15
155.	25 c. " The Crucifixion "	15	15
156.	40 c. " The Descent from the Cross "	15	15
157.	50 c. " The Resurrection "	20	20

46. " Santa Maria ".

1973. Columbus Discovers the West Indies. Multicoloured.

159.	1 c. Type **46**.	10	10
160.	20 c. Early map	75	75
161.	40 c. Map of voyages	90	90
162.	70 c. Sighting land	1·50	1·50
163.	$1·20 Landing of Columbus	2·25	2·25

47. Princess Anne and Captain Mark Phillips.

1973. Royal Wedding. Multicoloured. Background colours given.

165.	**47.**	60 c. green	20	15
166.		$1·20 mauve	30	15

48. " The Adoration of the Shepherds " (Reni).

1973. Christmas. Multicoloured.

167	1 c. Type **48**	10	10
168	10 c. "The Madonna and Child with Saints Jerome and Dominic" (Filippino Lippi)	10	10
169	20 c. "The Nativity" (Master of Brunswick)	15	15
170	25 c. "Madonna of the Meadow" (Bellini)	15	15
171	40 c. "Virgin and Child" (Cima)	20	20
172	50 c. "Adoration of the Kings" (Geertgen)	20	20

49. " The Crucifixion " (Raphael).

1974. Easter. Details of Raphael's " Crucifixion ".

174.	**49.**	1 c. multicoloured	10	10
175.	–	15 c. multicoloured	15	10
176.	–	20 c. multicoloured	20	15
177.	–	25 c. multicoloured	20	15
178.	–	40 c. multicoloured	20	15
179.	–	$1 multicoloured	25	25

50. Churchill Making " Victory " Sign.

1974. Birth Centenary of Sir Winston Churchill. Multicoloured.

181.	1 c. Type **50**	10	10
182.	20 c. Churchill with Roosevelt	30	20
183.	25 c. Wartime broadcast	30	20
184.	40 c. Birthplace, Blenheim Palace	40	30
185.	60 c. Churchill's statue	50	35
186.	$1·20 Country residence, Chartwell	70	55

51. U.P.U. Emblem.

1974. Centenary of U.P.U.

188.	**51.**	1 c. black and blue	10	10
189.		20 c. black and orange	15	15
190.		25 c. black and yellow	15	15
191.		40 c. black and mauve	25	25
192.		60 c. black and green	40	40
193.		$1·20 black and blue	60	60

52. Anguillan pointing to Star.

1974. Christmas. Multicoloured.

195.	1 c. Type **52**	10	10
196.	20 c. Child in Manger	15	15
197.	25 c. King's offering	15	15
198.	40 c. Star over map of Anguilla	15	15
199.	60 c. Family looking at Star	20	20
200.	$1·20 Angels of Peace	30	30

53. "Mary, John and Mary Magdalene" (Matthias Grunewald).

1975. Easter. Details from Isenheim Altarpiece, Colmar Museum. Multicoloured.

202.	1 c. Type **53**	10	10
203.	10 c. "The Crucifixion"	15	15
204.	15 c. "St. John the Baptist"	15	15
205.	20 c. "St. Sebastian and Angels"	20	20
206.	$1 "The Entombment" (horiz.)	35	35
207.	$1·50 "St. Anthony the Hermit"	45	45

54. Statue of Liberty.

1975. Bicent of American Revolution. Mult.

209.	1 c. Type **54**	10	10
210.	10 c. The Capitol	20	10
211.	15 c. " Congress voting for Independence " (Pine and Savage)	25	15
212.	20 c. Washington and map	25	15
213.	$1 Boston Tea Party	60	40
214.	$1·50 Bicentenary logo	70	60

55. " Madonna, Child and the Infant John the Baptist" (Raphael).

1975. Christmas. " Madonna and Child " paintings by artists named. Mult.

216.	1 c. Type **55**	10	10
217.	10 c. Cima	15	10
218.	15 c. Dolci	20	10
219.	20 c. Durer	20	15
220.	$1 Bellini	35	25
221.	$1·50 Botticelli	45	35

1976. New Constitution. Nos. 130 etc. optd. **NEW CONSTITUTION 1976**, or surch. also.

223.	1 c. Spear fishing	20	30
224.	2 c. on 1 c. Spear fishing	20	30
225.	2 c. Type **42**	2·25	90
226.	3 c. on 40 c. Boat building	40	30
227.	4 c. Ferry at Blowing Point	40	50
228.	5 c. on 40 c. Boat building	30	50
229.	6 c. St. Mary's Church	30	40
230.	10 c. on 20 c. Public Library	30	50
231.	10 c. St. Gerard's Church	3·00	1·00
232.	15 c. Cottage Hospital extension	30	50
233.	20 c. Public Library	30	40
234.	25 c. Sunset at Blowing Point	30	40
235.	40 c. Boat Building	45	40
236.	60 c. Hibiscus	70	70
237.	$1 Magnificent Frigate Bird	3·25	2·25
238.	$2·50 Frangipani	2·25	2·25
239.	$5 Brown Pelican	5·50	6·00
240.	$10 Green-back Turtle	4·00	6·00

57. Almond.

1976. Flowering Trees. Multicoloured.

241.	1 c. Type **57**	10	10
242.	10 c. Autograph	10	10
243.	15 c. Calabash	15	15
244.	20 c. Cordia	15	15
245.	$1 Papaya	35	45
246.	$1·50 Flamboyant	45	55

58. The Three Marys.

1976. Easter. Showing portions of the Altar Frontal Tapestry, Rheinau. Multicoloured.

248.	1 c. Type **58**	10	10
249.	10 c. The Crucifixion	10	10
250.	15 c. Two Soldiers	15	15
251.	20 c. The Annunciation	15	15
252.	$1 The complete tapestry (horiz.)	65	65
253.	$1·50 The Risen Christ	80	80

59. French Ships approaching Anguilla.

1976. Bicent of Battle of Anguilla. Mult.

255	1 c. Type **59**	10	10
256	3 c. "Margaret" (sloop) leaving Anguilla	70	35
257	15 c. Capture of "Le Desius"	1·00	55
258	25 c. "La Vaillante" forced aground	1·25	80
259	$1 H.M.S. "Lapwing"	1·75	1·25
260	$1.50 "Le Desius" burning	2·25	1·75

60. " Christmas Carnival " (A. Richardson).

1976. Christmas. Children's Paintings. Multicoloured.

262.	1 c. Type **60**	10	10
263.	3 c. "Dreams of Christmas Gifts" (J. Connor)	10	10
264.	15 c. "Carolling" (P. Richardson)	15	15
265.	25 c. "Candle-light Procession" (A. Mussington)	20	20
266.	$1 "Going to Church" (B. Franklin)	40	30
267.	$1.50 "Coming Home for Christmas" (E. Gumbs)	50	40

61. Prince Charles and H.M.S. "Minerva" (frigate).

1977. Silver Jubilee. Multicoloured.

269	25 c. Type **61**	15	10
270	40 c. Prince Philip landing by launch at Road Bay, 1964	20	15
271	$1.20 Coronation scene	35	25
272	$2.50 Coronation regalia and map of Anguilla	50	40

62. Yellow-crowned Night Heron.

1977. Multicoloured.

274. 1 c. Type **62** 20 40
275. 2 c. Great Barracuda .. 30 40
276. 3 c. Queen Conch .. 50 60
277. 4 c. Spanish Bayonet (flower) 40 30
278. 5 c. Trunkfish 50 20
279. 6 c. Cable and Wireless building 15 30
280. 10 c. American Kestrel .. 2·00 1·25
281. 15 c. Ground orchid .. 2·25 1·25
282. 20 c. Parrotfish .. .. 2·00 75
283. 22 c. Lobster fishing boat 35 45
284. 35 c. Boat race 60 55
285. 50 c. Sea bean 90 45
286. $1 Sandy Island 60 45
287. $2·50 Manchineel .. .. 1·00 1·00
288. $5 Ground Lizard .. 2·00 1·75
289. $10 Red-billed Tropic Bird 7·00 4·25

63. " The Crucifixion " (Massys).

1977. Easter. Paintings by Castagno ($1.50) or Ugolino (others). Multicoloured.

291. 1 c. Type **63** 10 10
292. 3 c. " The Betrayal " .. 10 10
293. 22 c. " The Way to Calvary " 20 20
294. 30 c. " The Deposition " .. 25 25
295. $1 " The Resurrection " .. 50 50
296. $1·50 " The Crucifixion " 65 65

1977. Royal Visit. Nos. 269/72 optd. **ROYAL VISIT TO WEST INDIES.**

298. 25 c. Type **61** 15 10
299. 40 c. Prince Philip landing at Road Bay, 1964 .. 20 20
300. $1.20 Coronation scene .. 30 30
301. $1.50 Coronation regalia and map of Anguilla .. 50 50

65. " Le Chapeau de Paille ".

1977. 400th Birth Anniv. of Rubens. Mult.

303. 25 c. Type **65** 15 15
304. 40 c. " Helen Fourment and her Two Children " 20 25
305. $1·20 " Rubens and his Wife " 60 65
306. $2·50 " Marchesa Brigida Spinola-Doria " .. 75 95

1977. Christmas. Nos. 262/7 optd. **1977** or surch. also.

308. 1 c. Type **60** 10 10
309. 5 c. on 3. c " Dreams of Christmas Gifts " .. 10 10
310. 12 c. on 15 c. " Carolling " 15 15
311. 18 c. on 25 c. " Candlelight Procession " 20 20
312. $1 " Going to Church on Christmas Eve " .. 45 45
313. $2·50 on $1·50 " Coming Home for Christmas " .. 90 90

1978. Easter. Nos. 303/6 optd. **EASTER 1978.**

315. 25 c. Type **65** 15 20
316. 40 c. " Helen Fourment with her Two Children " 15 20
317. $1·20 " Rubens and his Wife " 30 40
318. $2·50 " Marchesa Brigida Spinola-Doria " .. 40 60

68. Coronation Coach at Admiralty Arch.

1978. 25th Anniv. of Coronation. Mult.

320. 22 c. Buckingham Palace 10 10
321. 50 c. Type **68** 10 10
322. $1·50 Balcony Scene .. 15 15
323. $2·50 Royal coat of arms 25 25

1978. Anniversaries. Nos. 283/4 and 287 optd. **VALLEY SECONDARY SCHOOL 1953-1978** and Nos. 285/6 and 288 optd. **ROAD METHODIST CHURCH 1878-1978,** or surch. also.

325. 22 c. Lobster fishing boat 20 15
326. 35 c. Boat race 30 20
327. 50 c. Sea bean 40 30
328. $1 Sandy Island 50 40
329. $1·20 on $5 Ground Lizard 60 45
330. $1·50 on $2.50 Manchineel 75 55

71. Mother and Child.

1978. Christmas. Children's Paintings. Multicoloured.

331. 5 c. Type **71** 10 10
332. 12 c. Christmas masquerade 10 10
333. 18 c. Christmas dinner .. 10 10
334. 22 c. Serenading 10 10
335. $1 Child in manger .. 30 30
336. $2·50 Family going to Church 50 50

1979. International Year of the Child. As Nos. 331/6, but additionally inscr. **"1979 INTERNATIONAL YEAR OF THE CHILD "** and emblem. Borders in different colours

338. 5 c. Type **71** 10 10
339. 12 c. Christmas masquerade 10 10
340. 18 c. Christmas dinner .. 15 15
341. 22 c. Serenading 15 15
342. $1 Child in manger .. 60 60
343. $2.50 Family going to Church 90 90

1979. Nos. 274/7 and 279/80 surch.

345. 12 c. on 2 c. Great Barracuda 50 40
346. 14 c. on 4 c. Spanish Bayonet 40 40
347. 18 c. on 3 c. Queen Conch 70 45
348. 25 c. on 6 c. Cable and Wireless Building .. 50 40
349. 38 c. on 10 c. American Kestrel .. .. 1·00 60
350. 40 c. on 1 c. Type **62** .. 1·00 60

73. Valley Methodist Church.

1979. Easter. Church Interiors. Mult.

351. 5 c. Type **73** 10 10
352. 12 c. St. Mary's Anglican Church, The Valley .. 10 10
353. 18 c. St. Gerard's Roman Catholic Church, The Valley 15 15
354. 22 c. Road Methodist Church 15 15
355. $1·50 St. Augustine's Anglican Church, East End 60 60
356. $2·50 West End Methodist Church 75 75

HAVE YOU READ THE NOTES AT THE BEGINNING OF THIS CATALOGUE?
These often provide answers to the enquiries we receive.

74. Cape of Good Hope 1d. " Woodblock " of 1881.

1979. Death Centenary of Sir Rowland Hill. Multicoloured.

358. 1 c. Type **74** 10 10
359. 1 c. U.S.A. "inverted Jenny" of 1918 .. .. 10 10
360. 22 c. Penny Black ("V.R." Official) 15 15
361. 35 c. Germany 2 m, "Graf Zeppelin" of 1928 .. 20 20
362. $1.50 U.S.A. $5 "Columbus" of 1893 .. 60 60
363. $2.50 Great Britain £5 orange of 1882 .. .. 95 95

75. Wright " Flyer I " (1st powered Flight, 1903).

1979. History of Powered Flight. Mult.

365. 5 c. Type **75** 10 10
366. 12 c. Louis Bleriot at Dover after Channel crossing, 1909 .. .. .. 10 10
367. 18 c. Vickers " Vimy " (1st non-stop crossing of Atlantic, 1919) .. 15 15
368. 22 c. " Spirit of St. Louis " (1st solo Atlantic flight by Charles Lindbergh, 1927) 15 20
369. $1·50 LZ 127 " Graf Zeppelin ", 1928 .. 40 60
370. $2·50 " Concorde ", 1979 1·40 90

76. Sombrero Island.

1979. Outer Islands. Multicoloured.

372. 5 c. Type **76** 10 10
373. 12 c. Anguillita Island .. 10 10
374. 18 c. Sandy Island .. 15 15
375. 25 c. Prickly Pear Cays .. 15 15
376. $1 Dog Island 30 45
377. $2·50 Scrub Island .. 50 70

77. Red Poinsettia.

1979. Christmas. Multicoloured.

379. 22 c. Type **77** 40 30
380. 35 c. Kalanchoe 50 40
381. $1·50 Cream Poinsettia .. 90 80
382. $2·50 White Poinsettia .. 1·25 1·25

78. Exhibition Scene.

1979. " London 1980 " International Stamp Exhibition (1st issue). Mult.

384. 35 c. Type **78** 15 20
385. 50 c. Earls Court Exhibition Centre 20 25
386. $1·50 Penny Black and Two-penny Blue stamps 55 60
387. $2·50 Exhibition Logo .. 90 95

See also Nos. 407/9.

79. Games Site.

1980. Winter Olympic Games, Lake Placid, U.S.A. Multicoloured.

389. 5 c. Type **79** 10 10
390. 18 c. Ice hockey 10 10
391. 35 c. Ice skating 15 20
392. 50 c. Bobsleighing .. 15 20
393. $1 Skiing 30 35
394. $2·50 Luge-tobogganing 65 80

80. Salt ready for " Reaping ".

1980. Salt Industry. Multicoloured.

396. 5 c. Type **80** 10 10
397. 12 c. Tallying salt .. 10 10
398. 18 c. Unloading salt flats 15 15
399. 22 c. Salt storage heap .. 15 15
400. $1 Salt for bagging and grinding 30 40
401. $2·50 Loading salt for export 50 70

1980. Anniversaries. Nos. 280, 282 and 287/8 opted. **50th Anniversary Scouting 1980** (10 c., $2·50.) **75th Anniversary Rotary 1980** (others).

403. 10 c. American Kestrel. 50 10
404. 20 c. Parrotfish 55 15
405. $2·50 Manchineel .. 1·50 1·00
406. $5 Ground Lizard .. 2·25 1·90

83. Palace of Westminster and Great Britain 1970 9d. " Philympia " Commem.

1980. " London 1980 " International Stamps Exhibition (2nd issue). Multicoloured.

407. 50 c. Type **83** 40 40
408. $1·50 City Hall, Toronto and " Capex 1978 " stamp of Canada 70 70
409. $2·50 Statue of Liberty and 1976 " Interphil " stamp of U.S.A. .. 1·00 1·00

84. Queen Elizabeth the Queen Mother.

1980. 80th Birthday of The Queen Mother.

411. **84.** 35 c. multicoloured .. 30 25
412. 50 c. multicoloured .. 45 30
413. $1·50 multicoloured .. 90 75
414. $3 multicoloured .. 2·75 1·50

85. Brown Pelicans.

1980. Christmas. Birds. Multicoloured.

416. 5 c. Type **85** 30 10
417. 22 c. Great blue heron .. 75 20
418. $1.50 Barn swallow .. 1·75 60
419. $3 Ruby-throated hummingbird .. .. 2·25 1·40

1980. Separation from St. Kitts. Nos. 274, 277, 280/9, 334 and 418/19 optd. **SEPARATION 1980,** or surch. also.

421. 1 c. Type **62** 10 30
422. 2 c. on 4 c. Spanish bayonet 10 30
423. 5 c. on 15 c. Ground orchid 15 35
424. 5 c. on $1.50 Barn swallow 15 35
425. 5 c. on $3 Ruby-throated hummingbird 15 35
426. 10 c. American kestrel .. 20 50
427. 12 c. on $1 Sandy Island .. 20 50
428. 14 c. on $2.50 Manchineel 20 50
429. 15 c. Ground orchid .. 25 50
430. 18 c. on $5 Ground lizard 25 50
431. 20 c. Parrotfish 25 50
432. 22 c. Lobster fishing boat 25 50
433. 25 c. on 15 c. Ground orchid 30 55
434. 35 c. Boat race 30 55
435. 38 c. on 22 c. Seranading .. 30 55
436. 40 c. on 1 c. Type **62** .. 30 55
437. 50 c. Sea bean 35 65
438. $1 Sandy Island 50 90
439. $2.50 Manchineel .. .. 1·00 2·00
440. $5 Ground lizard .. .. 2·25 3·50
441. $10 Red-billed tropic bird 5·00 6·00
442. $10 on 6 c. Cable and Wireless Building .. 5·00 6·00

87. First Petition for Separation, 1825.

1980. Separation from St. Kitts. Multicoloured.

443. 18 c. Type **87** 15 10
444. 22 c. Referendum ballot paper, 1967 .. .. 15 10
445. 35 c. Airport blockade, 1967 20 15
446. 50 c. Anguillan flag .. 25 20
447. $1 Separation celebration, 1980 .. .. .. 40 35

88. " Nelson's Dockyard " (R. Granger Barrett).

1981. 175th Death Anniv. of Lord Nelson. Multicoloured.

449. 22 c. Type **88** 60 20
450. 35 c. " Ships in which Nelson Served " (Nicholas Pocock) 80 35
451. 50 c. " H.M.S. Victory " (Monamy Swaine) .. 1·00 45
452. $3 " Battle of Trafalgar " (Clarkson Stanfield) .. 2·00 2·00

89. Minnie Mouse being chased by Bees.

1981. Easter. Walt Disney Cartoon Characters. Multicoloured.

454 1 c. Type **89** 10 10
455 2 c. Pluto laughing at Mickey Mouse 10 10
456 3 c. Minnie Mouse tying ribbon round Pluto's neck 10 10
457 5 c. Minnie Mouse confronted by love-struck bird who fancies her bonnet 10 10
458 7 c. Dewey and Huey admiring themselves in mirror 10 10
459 9 c. Horace Horsecollar and Clarabelle Cow out for a stroll 10 10
460 10 c. Daisy Duck with hat full of Easter eggs .. 10 10
461 $2 Goofy unwrapping Easter hat .. .. 1·40 1·90
462 $3 Donald Duck in his Easter finery .. .. 1·60 1·60

90. Prince Charles, Lady Diana Spencer and St. Paul's Cathedral.

1981. Royal Wedding. Multicoloured.

464. 50 c. Type **90** 20 25
465. $2·50 Althorp 50 65
466. $3 Windsor Castle .. 55 75

91. Children playing in Tree.

1981. 35th Anniv. of U.N.I.C.E.F. Mult.

470. 5 c. Type **91** 15 15
471. 10 c. Children playing by pool 15 15
472. 15 c. Children playing musical instruments .. 15 15
473. $3 Children playing with pets .. .. .. 2·00 2·00

1981. Christmas. Designs as T **89** showing scenes from Walt Disney's cartoon film " The Night Before Christmas ".

475. 1 c. multicoloured .. 10 10
476. 2 c. multicoloured .. 10 10
477. 3 c. multicoloured .. 10 10
478. 5 c. multicoloured .. 10 10
479. 7 c. multicoloured .. 10 10
480. 10 c. multicoloured .. 10 10
481. 12 c. multicoloured .. 10 10
482. $2 multicoloured .. .. 1·90 1·25
483. $3 multicoloured .. .. 1·90 1·60

92. Red Grouper.

1982. Multicoloured.

485 1 c. Type **92** 15 20
486 5 c. Ferry service, Blowing Point 15 20
487 10 c. Island dinghies .. 15 20
488 15 c. Majorettes 15 20
489 20 c. Launching boat, Sandy Hill 30 20
490 25 c. Corals 75 30
491 30 c. Little Bay cliffs .. 30 25
492 35 c. Fountain Cave interior .. .. 1·25 50
493 40 c. Sunset over Sandy Island 30 30
494 45 c. Landing at Sombrero 50 40
495 60 c. Seine fishing .. 2·25 85
496 75 c. Boat race at sunset, Sandy Ground 70 65
497 $1 Bagging lobster at Island Harbour .. 1·75 1·00
498 $5 Brown pelicans .. 11·00 6·00
499 $7.50 Hibiscus .. .. 8·50 6·00
500 $10 Queen triggerfish .. 11·00 9·50

1982. No. 494 surch. **50 c.**

501. 50 c. on 45 c. Landing at Sombrero 35 35

94. Anthurium and "Heliconius charithonia"

1982. Easter. Flowers and Butterflies. Multicoloured.

502 10 c. Type **94** 15 10
503 35 c. Bird of Paradise and "Junonia evarete" .. 30 30
504 75 c. Allamanda and "Danaus plexippus" .. 55 55
505 $3 Orchid Tree and "Biblis hyperia" .. .. 1·75 2·00

95. Lady Diana Spencer in 1961.

1982. 21st Birthday of Princess of Wales. Multicoloured.

507. 10 c. Type **95** 10 10
508. 30 c. Lady Diana Spencer in 1968 .. .. .. 20 20
509. 40 c. Lady Diana in 1970 25 25
510. 60 c. Lady Diana in 1974 35 35
511. $2 Lady Diana in 1981 .. 1·10 1·10
512. $3 Lady Diana in 1981 (different) .. .. 1·40 1·40

96. Pitching Tent.

1982. 75th Anniv. of Boy Scout Movement. Multicoloured.

515. 10 c. Type **96** 45 20
516. 35 c. Scout band 85 50
517. 75 c. Yachting .. .. 1·25 90
518. $3 On parade .. .. 3·00 2·75

1982. World Cup Football Championship, Spain. Horiz. designs as T **89** showing scenes from Walt Disney's cartoon film " Bedknobs and Broomsticks ".

520. 1 c. multicoloured .. 10 10
521. 3 c. multicoloured .. 10 10
522. 4 c. multicoloured .. 10 10
523. 5 c. multicoloured .. 10 10
524. 7 c. multicoloured .. 10 10
525. 9 c. multicoloured .. 10 10
526. 10 c. multicoloured .. 10 10
527. $2.50 multicoloured .. 2·00 1·75
528. $3 multicoloured .. 2·00 2·00

1982. Commonwealth Games, Brisbane. Nos. 487, 495/6 and 498 optd **COMMONWEALTH GAMES 1982.**

530 10 c. Island dinghies .. 15 15
531 60 c. Seine fishing .. 45 45
532 75 c. Boat race at sunset, Sandy Ground 60 60
533 $5 Brown pelicans .. 3·25 3·25

1982. Birth Centenary of A. A. Milne (author). Designs as T **89.**

534. 1 c. multicoloured .. 10 10
535. 2 c. multicoloured .. 10 10
536. 3 c. multicoloured .. 10 10
537. 5 c. multicoloured .. 10 10
538. 7 c. multicoloured .. 15 10
539. 10 c. multicoloured .. 20 10
540. 12 c. multicoloured .. 20 10
541. 20 c. multicoloured .. 25 15
542. $5 multicoloured .. 3·50 3·75

DESIGNS—HORIZ. 1 c. to $5 Scenes from various " Winnie the Pooh " stories.

98. Culture.

1983. Commonwealth Day. Multicoloured.

544. 10 c. Type **98** 10 10
545. 35 c. Anguilla and British flags 30 30
546. 75 c. Economic co-operation 60 60
547. $2·50, Salt industry (salt pond) .. .. .. 3·00 2·50

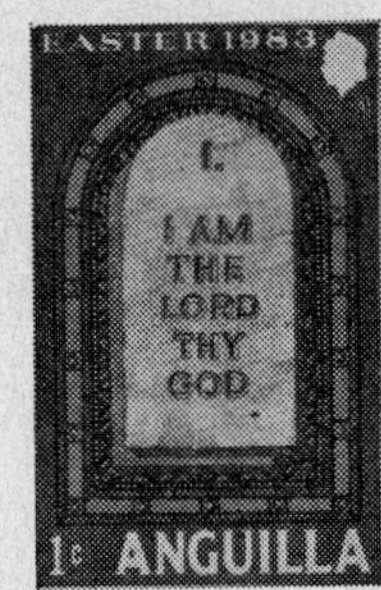

99. " I am the Lord Thy God ".

1983. Easter. The Ten Commandments. Multicoloured.

549 1 c. Type **99** 10 10
550 2 c. "Thou shalt not make any graven image" .. 10 10
551 3 c. "Thou shalt not take My Name in vain" .. 10 10
552 10 c. "Remember the Sabbath Day" 20 10
553 35 c. "Honour thy father and mother" 45 20
554 60 c. "Thou shalt not kill" 70 40
555 75 c. "Thou shalt not commit adultery" .. 80 50
556 $2 "Thou shalt not steal" 2·00 1·50
557 $2.50 "Thou shalt not bear false witness" .. .. 2·25 1·50
558 $5 "Thou shalt not covet" 3·50 2·75

100. Leatherback Turtle.

1983. Turtles. Multicoloured.

560. 10 c. Type **100** 55 25
561. 35 c. Hawksbill Turtle .. 1·00 55
562. 75 c. Green Turtle .. .. 1·50 90
563. $1 Loggerhead Turtle .. 1·75 1·40

101. Montgolfier Hot Air Balloon, 1783.

1983. Bicentenary of Manned Flight. Mult.

565. 10 c. Type **101** 25 10
566. 60 c. Blanchard and Jefferies crossing English Channel by balloon, 1785 .. 70 35
567. $1 Henri Giffard's steam driven airship, 1852 .. 90 50
568. $2·50, Otto Lillienthal and glider, 1890-96 .. .. 1·75 1·25

102. Boy's Brigade Band and Flag.

1983. Centenary of Boys' Brigade. Mult.

570. 10 c. Type **102** 15 15
571. $5 Brigade members marching .. .. 2·75 2·75

1983. 150th Anniv. of Abolition of Slavery. Nos. 487, 493 and 497/8 optd. **150TH ANNIVERSARY ABOLITION OF SLAVERY ACT.**

573 10 c. Island dinghies .. 10 10
574 40 c. Sunset over Sandy Island 25 25
575 $1 Bagging lobster at Island Harbour .. 50 50
576 $5 Brown pelicans .. 3·25 2·75

104. Jiminy on Clock ("Cricket on the Hearth").

1983. Christmas. Walt Disney Cartoon Characters. Multicoloured.

577. 1 c. Type **104** 10 10
578. 2 c. Jiminy with fiddle ("Cricket on the Hearth") 10 10
579. 3 c. Jiminy among toys ("Cricket on the Hearth") 10 10
580. 4 c. Mickey as Bob Crachit ("A Christmas Carol") 10 10
581. 5 c. Donald Duck as Scrooge ("A Christmas Carol") 10 10
582. 6 c. Mini and Goofy in "The Chimes" 10 10
583. 10 c. Goofy sees an imp appearing from bells ("The Chimes") .. 10 10
584. $2 Donald Duck as Mr. Pickwick ("The Pickwick Papers") .. .. 2·50 1·50
585. $3 Disney characters as Pickwickians ("The Pickwick Papers") .. .. 2·75 1·90

105. 100 Metres Race.

1984. Olympic Games, Los Angeles. Multicoloured.

A. Inscr. "1984 Los Angeles".
B. Inscr. "1984 Olympics Los Angeles" and Olympic emblem.

		A		B	
587.	1 c. Type **105** ..	10	10	10	10
588.	2 c. Long jumping ..	10	10	10	10
589.	3 c. Shot-putting ..	10	10	10	10
590.	4 c. High jumping ..	10	10	10	10
591.	5 c. 400 Metres race	10	10	10	10
592.	6 c. Hurdling ..	10	10	10	10
593.	10 c. Discus-throwing	10	10	10	10
594.	$1 Pole-vaulting ..	1·50	1·00	1·50	1·50
595.	$4 Javelin-throwing	4·00	3·00	4·00	3·00

106. "Justice".

1984. Easter. Multicoloured.

597. 10 c. Type **106** 15 10
598. 25 c. "Poetry" 20 20
599. 35 c. "Philosophy" .. 30 30
600. 40 c. "Theology" 30 30
601. $1 "Abraham and Paul" .. 85 85
602. $2 "Moses and Matthew" 1·60 1·60
603. $3 "John and David" .. 2·25 2·25
604. $4 "Peter and Adam" .. 2·50 2·50

Nos. 597/604 show details from "La Stanza della Segnatura" by Raphael.

1984. Nos. 485, 491, 498/500 surch.

606. 25 c. on $7.50 Hibiscus .. 35 35
607. 35 c. on 30 c. Little Bay cliffs 40 40
608. 60 c. on 1 c. Red grouper 45 45
609. $2.50 on $5 Brown pelicans 1·40 1·50
610. $2.50 on $10 Queen triggerfish .. .. .. 1·40 1·50

108. 1913 1d. Kangaroo Stamp.

1984. "Ausipex 84" International Stamp Exhibition. Multicoloured.

611. 10 c. Type **108** 20 20
612. 75 c. 1914 6d. Laughing Kookaburra 85 85
613. $1 1932 2d. Sydney Harbour Bridge .. .. 1·25 1·25
614. $2.50 1938 10s. King George VI .. .. .. 2·25 2·25

109. Thomas Fowell Buxton.

1984. 150th Anniv. of Abolition of Slavery. Multicoloured.

616. 10 c. Type **109** 10 10
617. 25 c. Abraham Lincoln .. 25 25
618. 35 c. Henri Christophe .. 35 35
619. 60 c. Thomas Clarkson .. 50 50
620. 75 c. William Wilberforce 60 60
621. $1 Olaudah Equiano .. 70 70
622. $2.50 General Charles Gordon .. .. .. 1·60 1·60
623. $5 Granville Sharp .. 3·00 3·00

1984. Universal Postal Union Congress, Hamburg. Nos. 486/7 and 498 optd. **U.P.U. CONGRESS HAMBURG 1984** or surch. also (No. 626).

625 5 c. Ferry service, Blowing Point 15 10
626 20 c. on 10 c. Island dinghies 20 15
627 $5 Brown pelicans .. 4·00 3·50

1984. Birth of Prince Henry. Nos. 507/12 optd. **BIRTH PRINCE HENRY 15.9.84.**

628. 10 c. Type **95** 10 10
629. 30 c. Lady Diana Spencer in 1968 .. .. .. 20 25
630. 40 c. Lady Diana in 1970 .. 25 30
631. 60 c. Lady Diana in 1974 .. 40 45
632. $2 Lady Diana in 1981 .. 1·25 1·40
633. $3 Lady Diana in 1981 (different) .. .. 1·50 2·25

112. Christmas in Sweden.

1984. Christmas. Walt Disney Cartoon Characters. National Scenes. Multicoloured.

636. 1 c. Type **112** 10 10
637. 2 c. Italy 10 10
638. 3 c. Holland 10 10
639. 4 c. Mexico 10 10
640. 5 c. Spain 10 10
641. 10 c. Disneyland, U.S.A. .. 10 10
642. $1 Japan .. .. .. 1·75 85
643. $2 Anguilla .. .. 2·25 1·50
644. $4 Germany .. .. 3·75 3·00

113. Icarus in Flight

1984. 40th Anniv. of International Civil Aviation Authority. Multicoloured

646 60 c. Type **113** 45 45
647. 75 c. "Solar Princess" (abstract) 60 60
648. $2.50, I.C.A.O. emblem (vert.) .. .. .. 1·75 2·00

114. Barn Swallow

1985. Birth Bicentenary of John J. Audubon (ornithologist). Multicoloured.

650. 10 c. Type **114** 15 10
651. 60 c. American Wood stork 45 40
652. 75 c. Roseate tern 50 45
653. $5 Osprey .. .. .. 2·75 3·00

115. The Queen Mother visiting King's College Hospital, London.

1985. Life and Times of Queen Elizabeth the Queen Mother. Multicoloured.

655. 10 c. Type **115** 10 10
656. $2 The Queen Mother inspecting Royal Marine Volunteer Cadets, Deal 90 1·25
657. $3 The Queen Mother outside Clarence House 1·40 1·75

116. White-tailed Tropic Bird.

1985. Birds. Multicoloured.

659. 5 c. Brown pelican .. 40 40
660. 10 c. Mourning dove .. 40 40
661. 15 c. Magnificent frigate bird (inscr. "Man-o-War") 50 50
662. 20 c. Antillean crested hummingbird 50 50
663. 25 c. Type **116** 50 50
664. 30 c. Caribbean elaenia .. 50 50
665. 35 c. Black-whiskered vireo 3·25 2·50
665a. 35 c. Lesser Antillean bullfinch 50 50
666. 40 c. Yellow-crowned night heron 60 60
667. 45 c. Pearly-eyed thrasher 50 50
668. 50 c. Laughing gull .. 50 50
669. 65 c. Brown booby .. 55 55
670. 80 c. Grey kingbird .. 1·00 1·00
671. $1 Audubon's shearwater 1·25 1·25
672. $1.35 Roseate tern .. 1·25 1·25
673. $2.50 Bananaquit .. .. 3·25 3·25
674. $5 Belted kingfisher .. 3·50 3·75
675. $10 Green heron .. .. 6·50 7·00

1985. 75th Anniv. of Girl Guide Movement. Nos. 486, 491, 496 and 498 optd. **GIRL GUIDES 75TH ANNIVERSARY 1910-1985.**

676. 5 c. Ferry service, Blowing Point 20 10
677. 30 c. Little Bay cliffs .. 40 25
678. 75 c. Boat race at sunset, Sandy Ground .. 60 70
679. $5 Brown Pelicans .. 4·25 3·50

118. Goofy as Huckleberry Finn Fishing.

1985. 150th Birth Anniv. of Mark Twain (author). Walt Disney cartoon characters in scenes from "Huckleberry Finn". Mult.

680. 10 c. Type **118** 20 15
681. 60 c. Pete as Pap surprising Huck 85 75
682. $1 "Multiplication tables" 1·40 1·10
683. $3 The Duke reciting Shakespeare .. .. 3·00 2·75

119. Hansel and Gretel (Mickey and Minnie Mouse) awakening in Forest.

1985. Birth Bicentenaries of Grimm Brothers (folklorists). Designs showing Walt Disney cartoon characters in scenes from "Hansel and Gretel". Multicoloured.

685. 5 c. Type **119** 10 10
686. 50 c. Hansel and Gretel find the gingerbread house 45 35
687. 90 c. Hansel and Gretel meeting the Witch .. 80 65
688. $4 Hansel and Gretel captured by the Witch 2·75 2·50

120. Statue of Liberty and "Danmark" (Denmark).

1985. Centenary of the Statue of Liberty (1986). The Statue of Liberty and Cadet ships.

690. 10 c. Type **120** 50 50
691. 20 c. "Eagle" (U.S.A.) .. 70 70
692. 60 c. "Amerigo Vespucci" (Italy) .. .. .. 1·25 1·25
693. 75 c. "Sir Winston Churchill" (Great Britain) .. .. .. 1·50 1·50
694. $2 "Nippon Maru" (Japan) 2·25 2·25
695. $2.50 "Gorch Fock" (West Germany) .. .. 2·50 2·50

1985. 80th Anniv of Rotary (10, 35 c.) and International Youth Year (others). Nos. 487, 491 and 497 optd or surch **80th ANNIVERSARY ROTARY 1985** and emblem (10, 35 c.) or **INTERNATIONAL YOUTH YEAR** and emblem ($1, 5).

697 10 c. Island dinghies .. 10 10
698 35 c. on 30 c. Little Bay cliffs 25 25
699 $1 Bagging lobster at Island Harbour .. 70 70
700 $5 on 30 c. Little Bay cliffs 3·50 3·50

123. Johannes Hevelius (astronomer) and Mayan Temple Observatory.

1986. Appearance of Halley's Comet Mult.

701. 5 c. Type **123** 25 25
702. 10 c. "Viking Lander" space vehicle on Mars, 1976 .. .. .. 25 25
703. 60 c. Comet in 1664 (from Theatri Cosmicum, 1668) 85 85
704. $4 Comet over Mississippi riverboat, 1835 (150th birth anniv. of Mark Twain) .. .. .. 3·50 3·50

124. "The Crucifixion".

1986. Easter.

706. **124.** 10 c. multicoloured .. 20 20
707. – 25 c. multicoloured .. 35 35
708. – 45 c. multicoloured .. 65 65
709. – $4 multicoloured .. 3·25 3·25

Designs: 25 c. to $4. Different stained glass windows from Chartres Cathedral.

125. Princess Elizabeth inspecting Guards, 1946.

1986. 60th Birthday of Queen Elizabeth II.

711. **125.** 20 c. black and yellow 15 15
712. – $2 multicoloured .. 1·25 1·25
713. – $3 multicoloured .. 1·75 1·75

Designs: $2 Queen at Garter ceremony. $3 At Trooping the Colour.

1986. "Ameripex" International Stamp Exhibition, Chicago. Nos. 659, 667, 671, 673 and 675 optd. **AMERIPEX 1986**.

715. 5 c. Brown pelican .. 10 10
716. 45 c. Pearly-eyed thrasher 35 35
717. $1 Audubon's shearwater 65 65
718. $2.50 Bananaquit .. .. 1·50 1·50
719. $10 Green heron .. .. 5·50 5·50

127. Prince Andrew and Miss Sarah Ferguson.

1986. Royal Wedding. Multicoloured.

720. 10 c. Type **127** 10 10
721. 35 c. Prince Andrew .. 20 25
722. $2 Miss Sarah Ferguson .. 1·00 1·10
723. $3 Prince Andrew and Miss Sarah Ferguson (different) .. .. 1·50 1·60

1986. International Peace Year. Nos. 616/23 optd. **INTERNATIONAL YEAR OF PEACE.**

725. 10 c. Type **109** 15 15
726. 25 c. Abraham Lincoln .. 25 25
727. 35 c. Henri Christophe .. 35 35
728. 60 c. Thomas Clarkson .. 55 55
729. 75 c. William Wilberforce 70 70
730. $1 Olaudah Equiano .. 80 80
731. $2.50 General Gordon .. 1·75 1·75
732. $5 Granville Sharp .. 3·00 3·00

129. Trading Sloop.

1986. Christmas. Ships. Multicoloured.

734 10 c. Type **129** 40 40
735 45 c. "Lady Rodney" (cargo liner) .. .. 1·00 1·00
736 80 c. "West Derby" (19th-century sailing ship) .. 1·40 1·40
737 $3 "Warspite" (local sloop) 3·25 3·25

130. Christopher Columbus with Astrolabe.

1986. 500th Anniv. (1992) of Discovery of America by Columbus. Multicoloured.

739. 5 c. Type **130** 15 15
740. 10 c. Columbus on board ship 20 20
741. 35 c. "Santa Maria" .. 75 75
742. 80 c. King Ferdinand and Queen Isabella of Spain (horiz.) 90 90
743. $4 Caribbean Indians smoking tobacco (horiz.) 3·00 3·00

131. "Danaus plexippus".

1987. Easter. Butterflies. Multicoloured.

745 10 c. Type **131** 30 30
746 80 c. "Anartia jatrophae" 1·40 1·40
747 $1 "Heliconius charithonia" .. .. 1·50 1·50
748 $2 "Junonia evarete" .. 2·50 2·50

132. Old Goose Iron and Modern Electric Iron (illustration reduced actual size 59 × 28 mm.).

1987. 20th Anniv. of Separation from St. Kitts-Nevis. Multicoloured.

750. 10 c. Type **132** 10 10
751. 35 c. Old East End School and Albena Lake-Hodge Comprehensive College 15 20
752. 45 c. Past and present markets 20 25
753. 80 c. Previous sailing ferry and new motor ferry, Blowing Point 35 40
754. $1 Original mobile office and new telephone exchange 45 50
755. $2 Open-air meeting, Burrowes Park and House of Assembly in session 90 95

1987. "Capex '87" International Stamp Exhibition, Toronto. Nos. 665a, 667, 670 and 675 optd. **CAPEX '87.**

757. 35 c. Lesser Antillean bullfinch 35 35
758. 45 c. Pearly-eyed thrasher 45 45
759. 80 c. Grey kingbird .. 70 70
760. $10 Green heron .. .. 6·00 6·00

1987. 20th Anniv. of Independence. Nos. 659, 661/4 and 665a/75 optd. **20 YEARS OF PROGRESS 1967–1987,** No. 762 surch. also.

761. 5 c. Brown pelican .. 20 20
762. 10 c. on 15 c. Magnificent frigate bird 20 30
763. 15 c. Magnificent frigate bird 20 30
764. 20 c. Antillean crested hummingbird 30 40
765. 25 c. Type **116** 30 40
766. 30 c. Caribbean elaenia .. 40 50
767. 35 c. Lesser Antillean bullfinch 45 55
768. 40 c. Yellow-crowned night heron 45 55
769. 45 c. Pearly-eyed thrasher 50 60
770. 50 c. Laughing gull .. 50 60
771. 65 c. Brown booby .. 55 70
772. 80 c. Grey kingbird .. 65 80
773. $1 Audubon's shearwater 80 90
774. $1.35 Roseate tern .. 1·00 1·25
775. $2.50 Bananaquit .. .. 1·50 2·00
776. $5 Belted kingfisher .. 2·75 3·50
777. $10 Green heron .. .. 5·50 7·00

135. Wicket Keeper and Game in Progress.

1987. Cricket World Cup. Multicoloured.

778. 10 c. Type **135** 35 30
779. 35 c. Batsman and local Anguilla team 65 50
780. 45 c. Batsman and game in progress 75 60
781. $2.50 Bowler and game in progress .. .. .. 2·25 2·50

136. West Indian Top Shell.

1987. Christmas. Sea Shells and Crabs. Multicoloured.

783. 10 c. Type **136** 20 20
784. 35 c. Ghost crab 45 45
785. 50 c. Spiny Caribbean vase 70 70
786. $2 Great Land crab .. 2·00 2·00

1987. Royal Ruby Wedding. Nos. 665a, 671/2 and 675 optd. **40TH WEDDING ANNIVERSARY H.M. QUEEN ELIZABETH II H.R.H. THE DUKE OF EDINBURGH.**

788. 35 c. Lesser Antillean bullfinch 15 20
789. $1 Audubon's shearwater 45 50
790. $1.35 Roseate tern .. 60 65
791. $10 Green heron .. .. 4·50 4·75

138 "Crinum erubescens"

1988. Easter. Lilies. Multicoloured.

792 30 c. Type **138** 15 15
793 45 c. Spider lily 25 25
794 $1 "Crinum macowanii" .. 50 50
795 $2.50 Day lily .. .. 1·25 1·25

139 Relay Racing

1988. Olympic Games, Seoul. Multicoloured.

797 35 c. Type **139** 35 30
798 45 c. Windsurfing 45 40
799 50 c. Tennis 75 60
800 80 c. Basketball .. 1·25 90

140 Common Sea Fan

1988. Christmas. Marine Life. Multicoloured.

802 35 c. Type **140** 20 20
803 80 c. Coral crab 50 50
804 $1 Grooved brain coral .. 60 60
805 $1.60 Queen triggerfish .. 90 90

1988. Visit of Princess Alexandra. Nos. 665a, 670/1 and 673 optd **H.R.H. PRINCESS ALEXANDRA'S VISIT NOVEMBER 1988.**

807 35 c. Lesser Antillean bullfinch 50 50
808 80 c. Grey kingbird .. 90 90
809 $1 Audubon's shearwater 1·10 1·10
810 $2.50 Bananaquit .. 2·25 2·25

142 Wood Slave

1989. Lizards. Multicoloured.

811 45 c. Type **142** 20 25
812 80 c. Slippery back .. 40 45
813 $2.50 "Iguana delicatissima" .. .. 1·25 1·40

143 "Christ Crowned with Thorns" (detail) (Bosch)

1989. Easter. Religious Paintings. Mult.

815 35 c. Type **143** 15 20
816 80 c. "Christ bearing the Cross" (detail) (Gerard David) 40 45
817 $1 "The Deposition" (detail) (Gerard David) 45 50
818 $1.60 "Pieta" (detail) (Rogier van der Weyden) 75 80

144 University Arms

1989. 40th Anniv of University of the West Indies.

820 **144** $5 multicoloured .. 2·40 2·50

1989. 20th Anniv of First Manned Landing on Moon. Nos. 670/2 and 674 optd **20th ANNIVERSARY MOON LANDING**.

821 80 c. Grey kingbird .. 40 45
822 $1 Audubon's shearwater 45 50
823 $1.35 Roseate tern .. 65 70
824 $5 Belted kingfisher .. 2·40 2·50

146 Lone Star (house), 1930

1989. Christmas. Historic Houses. Mult.

825 5 c. Type **146** 10 10
826 35 c. Whitehouse, 1906 .. 15 20
827 45 c. Hodges House .. 20 25
828 80 c. Warden's Place .. 40 45

147 Blear Eye

1990. Fishes. Multicoloured.

830 5 c. Type **147** 10 10
831 10 c. Redman 10 10
832 15 c. Speckletail 10 10
833 25 c. Grunt 10 15
834 30 c. Amber jack 10 15
835 35 c. Red hind 15 20
836 40 c. Goatfish 15 20
837 45 c. Old wife 20 25
838 50 c. Butter fish 25 30
839 65 c. Shell fish 30 35
840 80 c. Yellowtail snapper .. 40 45
841 $1 Katy 50 55
842 $1.35 Mutton grouper .. 65 70
843 $2.50 Doctor fish .. .. 1·25 1·40
844 $5 Angelfish .. .. 2·40 2·50
845 $10 Barracuda .. .. 5·00 5·25

148 The Last Supper

1990. Easter. Multicoloured.

846 35 c. Type **148** 15 20
847 45 c. The Trial 20 25
848 $1.35 The Crucifixion .. 55 60
849 $2.50 The Empty Tomb .. 1·00 1·10

149 G.B. 1840 Penny Black

1990. "Stamp World London 90" International Stamp Exhibition. Multicoloured

851 25 c. Type **149** 25 25
852 50 c. G.B. 1840 Twopenny Blue 40 40
853 $1.50 Cape of Good Hope 1861 1d. "woodblock" (horiz) .. .. 1·00 1·00
854 $2.50 G.B. 1882 £5 (horiz) .. 1·50 1·50

1990. Anniversaries and Events. Nos. 841/4 optd.

856 $1 Katy (optd **EXPO '90**) 70 70
857 $1.35 Mutton Grouper (optd **1990 INTERNATIONAL LITERACY YEAR**) .. 85 85
858 $2.50 Doctor fish (optd **WORLD CUP FOOTBALL CHAMPIONSHIPS 1990**) .. 1·75 1·75
859 $5 Angelfish (optd **90TH BIRTHDAY H.M. THE QUEEN MOTHER**) .. .. 2·75 2·75

151 Mermaid Flag

1990. Island Flags. Multicoloured.

860 50 c. Type **151** 25 25
861 80 c. New Anguilla official flag 40 40
862 $1 Three Dolphins flag .. 50 50
863 $5 Governor's official flag 2·40 3·25

152 Laughing Gulls

1990. Christmas. Sea Birds. Multicoloured.

864 10 c. Type **152** 25 25
865 35 c. Brown booby .. 40 40
866 $1.50 Bridled tern .. 1·00 1·00
867 $3.50 Brown pelican .. 2·00 2·00

1991. Easter. Nos. 846/9 optd **1991**.

869 35 c. Type **148** 35 35
870 45 c. The Trial 45 45
871 $1.35 The Crucifixion .. 1·00 1·00
872 $2.50 The Empty Tomb .. 1·75 1·75

154 Angel

1991. Christmas.

874 **154** 5 c. violet, brown & blk 15 15
875 – 35 c. multicoloured .. 35 35
876 – 80 c. multicoloured .. 70 70
877 – $1 multicoloured .. 90 90

DESIGNS—VERT. 35 c. Father Christmas. HORIZ. 80 c. Church and house; $1 Palm trees at night.

155 Angels with Palm Branches outside St. Gerard's Church

1992. Easter. Multicoloured.

879 35 c. Type **155** 25 25
880 45 c. Angels singing outside Methodist Church .. 35 35
881 80 c. Village (horiz) .. 60 60
882 $1 Congregation going to St. Mary's Church .. 75 75
883 $5 Dinghy regatta (horiz) 3·25 3·25

1992. No. 834 surch **$1.60**.

884 $1.60 on 30 c. Amber jack 1·00 1·00

157 Anguillan Flags

1992. 25th Anniv of Separation from St. Kitts–Nevis. Multicoloured.

885 80 c. Type **157** 50 50
886 $1 Present official seal .. 65 65
887 $1.60 Anguillan flags at airport 90 90
888 $2 Royal Commissioner's official seal .. .. 1·25 1·25

158 Dinghy Race

1992. Sailing Dinghy Racing.

890 **158** 20 c. multicoloured .. 20 20
891 – 35 c. multicoloured .. 30 30
892 – 45 c. multicoloured .. 35 35
893 – 80 c. multicoloured .. 60 60
894 – 80 c. black and blue .. 60 60
895 – $1 multicoloured .. 70 70

DESIGNS—VERT. 35 c. Stylized poster; 80 c. (No. 893) "Blue Bird" in race; 80 c. (No. 894) Construction drawings of "Blue Bird" by Douglas Pyle; $1 Stylized poster (different). HORIZ. 45 c. Dinghies on beach.

159 Mucka Jumbie on Stilts

1992. Christmas. Local Traditions. Mult.

897 20 c. Type **159** 15 15
898 70 c. Masqueraders .. 45 45
899 $1.05 Baking in old style oven 65 65
900 $2.40 Collecting presents from Christmas tree .. 1·25 1·40

160 Columbus landing in New World

1992. 500th Anniv of Discovery of America by Columbus.

902 **160** 80 c. multicoloured .. 55 55
903 – $1 black and brown .. 65 65
904 – $2 multicoloured .. 1·25 1·25
905 – $3 multicoloured .. 1·60 1·60

DESIGNS—VERT. $1 Christopher Columbus; HORIZ. $2 Fleet of Columbus; $3 "Pinta".

161 "Kite Flying" (Kyle Brooks)

1993. Easter. Children's Paintings. Mult.

No.	Description	Unused	Used
907	20 c. Type **161**	15	15
908	45 c. "Clifftop Village Service" (Kara Connor)	30	30
909	80 c. "Morning Devotion on Sombero" (Junior Carty)	55	55
910	$1.50 "Hill Top Church Service" (Leana Harris)	1·00	1·00

162 Salt Picking

1993. Traditional Industries. Multicoloured.

No.	Description	Unused	Used
912	20 c. Type **162**	15	15
913	80 c. Tobacco growing ..	55	55
914	$1 Cotton picking ..	70	70
915	$2 Harvesting sugar cane	1·25	1·25

163 Lord Great Chamberlain presenting Spurs of Chivalry to Queen

1993. 40th Anniv of Coronation. Mult.

No.	Description	Unused	Used
917	80 c. Type **163**	40	45
918	$1 The Benediction ..	50	55
919	$2 Queen Elizabeth II in Coronation robes	95	1·00
920	$3 St. Edward's Crown ..	1·40	1·50

164 Carnival Pan Player

1993. Anguilla Carnival. Multicoloured.

No.	Description	Unused	Used
922	20 c. Type **164**	10	10
923	45 c. Revellers dressed as pirates	20	25
924	80 c. Revellers dressed as stars	40	45
925	$1 Mas dancing	50	55
926	$2 Masked couple ..	95	1·00
927	$3 Revellers dressed as commandos	1·40	1·50

MINIMUM PRICE

The minimum price quoted is 10p which represents a handling charge rather than a basis for valuing common stamps. For further notes about prices see introductory pages.

ANTIGUA

One of the Leeward Is., Br. W. Indies. Used general issues for Leeward Is., concurrently with Antiguan stamps until 1 July 1956. Ministerial Government introduced on 1 January 1960. Achieved Associated Statehood on 3 March 1967 and Independence within the Commonwealth on 1 November 1981.

Nos. 718/22 and 733 onwards are inscribed "Antigua & Barbuda".

1862. 12 pence = 1 shilling.
20 shillings = 1 pound.
1951. 100 cents = 1 West Indian dollar.

1.

3.

1862.

No.	Type	Description	Unused	Used
5.	1.	1d. mauve	£110	42·00
25.		1d. red	80	2·25
29.		6d. green	55·00	£120

1879.

No.	Type	Description	Unused	Used
21.	3.	½d. green	1·40	10·00
22.		2½d. brown	£130	50·00
27.		2½d. blue	5·50	11·00
23.		4d. blue	£275	15·00
28.		4d. brown	1·25	2·00
30.		1s. mauve	£160	£120

4.

5.

8.

1903.

No.	Type	Description	Unused	Used
31	4	½d. black and green ..	2·50	4·25
41		½d. green	1·25	3·25
32		1d. black and red ..	4·00	40
43		1d. red	3·00	1·40
45		2d. purple and brown ..	3·75	21·00
34		2½d. black and blue ..	8·00	12·00
46		2½d. blue	7·00	15·00
47		3d. green and brown ..	6·50	17·00
48		6d. purple and black ..	7·50	29·00
49		1s. blue and purple ..	15·00	60·00
50		2s. green and violet ..	50·00	70·00
39		2s. 6d. black and purple..	17·00	48·00
40	5	5s. green and violet ..	70·00	80·00

1913. Head of King George V.

No.	Type	Description	Unused	Used
51.	5.	5s. green and violet ..	70·00	95·00

1916. Optd. **WAR STAMP.**

No.	Type	Description	Unused	Used
52.	4.	½d. green	40	75
54.		1½d. orange	35	75

1921.

No.	Type	Description	Unused	Used
62	8	½d. green	35	20
63		1d. red	75	20
64		1d. violet	1·25	1·50
67		1½d. orange	1·50	7·00
68		1½d. red	1·90	1·75
69		1½d. brown	1·50	60
70		2d. grey	1·00	75
72		2½d. blue	3·00	5·50
73		2½d. yellow	1·25	17·00
74		3d. purple on yellow ..	4·00	8·50
56		4d. black & red on yellow	1·25	5·00
75		6d. purple	2·75	5·50
57		1s. black on green ..	3·75	7·00
58		2s. purple & blue on blue	8·00	19·00
78		2s. 6d. black & red on blue	15·00	22·00
79		3s. green and violet ..	20·00	55·00
80		4s. black and red ..	48·00	50·00
60		5s. green & red on yellow	8·00	28·00
61		£1 purple and black on red	£170	£225

9. Old Dockyard, English Harbour.

12. Sir Thomas Warner and "Concepcion".

1932. Tercent. Designs with medallion portrait of King George V.

No.	Type	Description	Unused	Used
81.	9.	½d. green	1·75	4·25
82.		1d. red	2·50	2·75
83.		1½d. brown	3·00	4·25
84.	–	2d. grey	3·75	15·00
85.	–	2½d. blue	3·75	8·00
86.	–	3d. orange	3·75	12·00
87.	–	6d. violet	11·00	12·00
88.	–	1s. olive	14·00	25·00
89.	–	2s. 6d. purple	38·00	45·00
90.	12.	5s black and brown ..	70·00	£100

DESIGNS—HORIZ. 2d. to 3d. Government House, St. John's. 6d. to 2s. 6d. Nelson's "Victory".

13. Windsor Castle.

1935. Silver Jubilee.

No.	Type	Description	Unused	Used
91.	13.	1d. blue and red ..	2·00	1·00
92.		1½d. blue and grey ..	2·50	45
93.		2½d. brown and blue ..	4·75	1·00
94.		1s. grey and purple ..	8·50	11·00

1937. Coronation. As T **2** of Aden.

No.	Type	Description	Unused	Used
95.		1d red	50	55
96.		1½d. brown	60	35
97.		2½d. blue	1·75	75

15. English Harbour.

16. Nelson's Dockyard.

1938.

No.	Type	Description	Unused	Used
98	15	½d. green	20	50
99a	16	1d. red	1·25	65
100a		1½d. brown	2·00	85
101	15	2d. grey	30	40
102	16	2½d. blue	45	70
103	–	3d. orange	45	50
104	–	6d. violet	80	50
105	–	1s. black and brown ..	2·00	65
106a	–	2s. 6d. purple	20·00	5·50
107	–	5s. olive	12·00	7·00
108	16	10s. mauve	16·00	25·00
109	–	£1 green	25·00	32·00

DESIGNS: HORIZ. 3d., 2s. 6d., £1, Fort James, VERT. 6d., 1s. 5s., St. John's Harbour.

1946. Victory. As T **9** of Aden.

No.	Type	Description	Unused	Used
110.		1½d. brown	15	10
111.		3d. orange	15	30

1949. Silver Wedding. As T **10/11** of Aden.

No.	Type	Description	Unused	Used
112.		2½d. blue	30	50
113.		5s. green	8·00	4·25

20. Hermes, Globe and Forms of Transport.

21. Hemispheres, Aeroplane and Steamer.

22. Hermes and Globe.

23. U.P.U. Monument.

1949. 75th Anniv of U.P.U.

No.	Type	Description	Unused	Used
114	20	2½d. blue	40	50
115	21	3d. orange	80	85
116	22	6d. purple	80	85
117	23	1s. brown	80	75

24. Arms of University.

25. Princess Alice.

1951. Inaug of B.W.I. University College.

No.	Type	Description	Unused	Used
118	24	3 c. black and brown ..	45	40
119	25	12 c. black and violet ..	45	55

1953. Coronation. As T **13** of Aden.

No.	Type	Description	Unused	Used
120.		2 c. black and green ..	15	40

27. Martello Tower.

DESIGNS — HORIZ. ½ c., 6 c., 60 c., $4.80, Fort James. VERT. 12 c. 24 c., $1.20, St. John's Harbour.

1953. Designs as 1938 issues but with portrait of Queen Elizabeth II as in T **27**.

No.	Type	Description	Unused	Used
120a	–	½ c. brown	20	20
121	14	1 c. grey	20	40
122	16	2 c. green	15	10
123		3 c. black and yellow ..	40	15
153	14	4 c. red	30	20
154	16	5 c. black and lilac ..	20	10
155	–	6 c. yellow	50	30
156	27	8 c. blue	30	20
157	–	12 c. violet	30	20
158	–	24 c. black and brown..	1·00	70
130	27	48 c. purple and blue..	6·00	2·00
131	–	60 c. purple	6·50	80
132a	–	$1.20 olive	1·50	70
133	16	$2.40 purple	8·00	12·00
134	–	$4.80 slate	11·00	18·00

28. Federation Map.

1958. Inauguration of British Caribbean Federation.

No.	Type	Description	Unused	Used
135	28	3 c. green	1·00	30
136		6 c. blue	1·25	1·25
137		12 c. red	1·40	60

1960. New Constitution. Optd. **COMMEMORATION ANTIGUA CONSTITUTION.**

138.	**16.**	3 c. black and yellow ..	15	15
139.	–	12 c. violet (No. 128) ..	15	15

30. Nelson's Dockyard and Admiral Nelson.

1961. Restoration of Nelson's Dockyard.

140	**30**	20 c. purple and brown	80	60
141		30 c. green and blue ..	95	65

31. Stamp of 1862 and R.M.S.P. "Solent I" at English Harbour.

1962. Stamp Cent.

142	**31**	3 c. purple and green ..	50	10
143		10 c. blue and green ..	60	10
144		12 c. sepia and green ..	70	10
145		50 c. brown and green ..	1·25	1·25

1963. Freedom from Hunger. As T **28** of Aden.

146.		12 c. green	15	15

33. Red Cross Emblem.

1963. Centenary of Red Cross.

147	**33**	3 c. red and black ..	20	50
148		12 c. red and blue ..	50	1·00

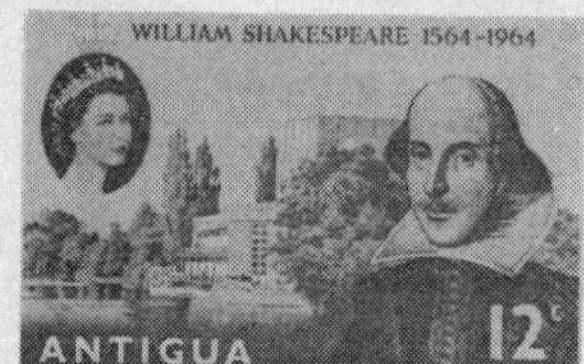

34. Shakespeare and Memorial Theatre, Stratford-upon-Avon.

1964. 400th Birth Anniv. of Shakespeare.

164	**34**	12 c. brown	15	10

1965. No. 157 surch **15c**.

165		15 c. on 12 c. violet ..	10	10

36. I.T.U. Emblem.

1965. Centenary of I.T.U.

166	**36**	2 c. blue and red ..	20	15
167		50 c. yellow and blue ..	1·25	80

37. I.C.Y. Emblem.

1965. Int. Co-operation Year.

168	**37**	4 c. purple & turquoise	15	10
169		15 c. green and lavender	25	20

38. Sir Winston Churchill, and St. Paul's Cathedral in Wartime.

1966. Churchill Commem. Designs in black, red and gold with background in colours given.

170	**38**	½ c. blue	10	30
171		4 c. green	30	10
172		25 c. brown	65	40
173		35 c. violet	75	45

39. Queen Elizabeth II and Duke of Edinburgh.

1966. Royal Visit.

174	**39**	6 c. black and blue ..	2·00	1·10
175		15 c. black and mauve ..	2·25	1·40

40. Footballer's Legs, Ball and Jules Rimet Cup.

1966. World Cup Football Championships.

176	**40**	6 c. multicoloured ..	15	15
177		35 c. multicoloured ..	50	25

41. W.H.O. Building.

1966. Inaug. of W.H.O. Headquarters, Geneva.

178	**41**	2 c. black, green & blue	15	15
179		15 c. black, pur. & brn.	70	25

42. Nelson's Dockyard.

1966.

180	**42**	½ c. green and turquoise	10	30
181	–	1 c. purple and red ..	10	30
182	–	2 c. slate and orange ..	10	15
183	–	3 c. red and black ..	10	15
238	–	4 c. violet and brown ..	15	15
185	–	5 c. blue and olive ..	10	10
186	–	6 c. salmon and purple ..	15	10
187	–	10 c. green and red ..	15	10
188	–	15 c. brown and blue ..	30	10
189	–	25 c. slate and sepia ..	35	20
244	–	35 c. red and brown ..	60	1·00
245	–	50 c. green and black ..	70	2·00
192	–	75 c. blue & ultramarine	1·50	2·50
246	–	$1 red and olive ..	1·25	3·50
194	–	$2.50 black and red ..	3·25	5·50
195	–	$5 green and violet ..	5·50	6·50

DESIGNS: 1 c. Old Post Office, St. John's. 2 c. Health Centre. 3 c. Teacher's Training College. 4 c. Martello Tower, Barbuda. 5 c. Ruins of Officers' Quarters, Shirley Heights. 6 c. Government House, Barbuda. 10 c. Princess Margaret School. 15 c. Air Terminal Building. 25 c. General Post Office. 35 c. Clarence House. 50 c. Government House, St. John's. 75 c. Administration Building. $1, Courthouse, St. John's. $2.50, Magistrates' Court. $5 St. John's Cathedral.

54. "Education".

55. "Science".

56. "Culture".

1966. 20th Anniv. of U.N.E.S.C.O.

196.	**54.**	4 c. violet, yell. & orge.	15	10
197.	**55.**	25 c. yellow, violet & ol.	35	10
198.	**56.**	$1 black, purple & orge.	1·75	1·75

57. State Flag and Maps.

1967. Statehood. Multicoloured.

199.		4 c. Type **57**	10	10
200.		15 c. State Flag	10	10
201.		25 c. Premier's Office and State Flag	10	20
202.		35 c. As 15 c.	15	25

60. Gilbert Memorial Church.

1967. Attainment of Autonomy by the Methodist Church.

203.	**60.**	4 c. black and red ..	10	10
204.	–	25 c. black and green ..	15	15
205.	–	35 c. black and blue ..	15	15

DESIGNS: 25 c. Nathaniel Gilbert's House. 35 c. Caribbean and Central American Map.

63. Coat of Arms.

1967. 300th Anniv. of Treaty of Breda and Grant of New Arms.

206.	**63.**	15 c. multicoloured ..	15	10
207.		35 c. multicoloured ..	15	10

64. "Susan Constant" (settlers' ship).

1967. 300th Anniv. of Barbuda Settlement.

208.	**64.**	4 c. blue	15	10
209.	–	6 c. purple	15	10
210.	**64.**	25 c. green	30	15
211.	–	35 c. black	30	20

DESIGN: 6 c., 35 c. Blaeu's Map of 1665.

66. Tracking Station.

1968. N.A.S.A. Apollo Project. Inauguration of Dow Hill Tracking Station.

212.	**66.**	4 c. blue, yellow & black	10	10
213.	–	15 c. blue, yell. & black	20	10
214.	–	25 c. blue, yell. & black	20	10
215.	–	50 c. blue, yell. & black	30	20

DESIGNS: 15 c. Antenna and Spacecraft taking off. 25 c. Spacecraft approaching Moon. 50 c. Re-entry of Space Capsule.

70. Limbo-dancing.

1968. Tourism. Multicoloured.

216.		½ c. Type **70**	10	10
217.		15 c. Water-skier & Bathers	20	10
218.		25 c. Yachts and beach ..	25	10
219.		35 c. Underwater swimming	25	10
220.		50 c. Type **70**	40	45

74. Old Harbour in 1768.

1968. Opening of St. John's Deep Water Harbour.

221.	**74.**	2 c. blue and red ..	10	10
222.	–	15 c. green and sepia ..	30	10
223.	–	25 c. yellow and blue ..	35	10
224.	–	35 c. Salmon and emer.	40	10
225.	**74.**	$1 black	80	70

DESIGNS: 15 c. Old Harbour in 1829. 25 c. Freighter and Chart of New Harbour. 35 c. New Harbour.

78. Parliament Buildings.

1969. Tercent. of Parliament. Multicoloured.

226.		4 c. Type **78**	10	10
227.		15 c. Antigua Mace and Bearer	20	10
228.		25 c. House of Representatives' Room ..	20	10
229.		50 c. Coat of arms and Seal of Antigua ..	30	50

82. Freight Transport.

1969. 1st Anniv. of Caribbean Free Trade Area.

230.	**82.**	4 c. black and purple ..	10	10
231.		15 c. black and blue ..	20	10
232.	–	25 c. brn., black & ochre	20	20
233.	–	35 c. choc., blk. and brn.	20	20

DESIGN—VERT. 25 c., 35 c. Crate of cargo.

84. Island of Redonda (Chart).

1969. Centenary of Redonda Phosphate Industry. Multicoloured.

249.	15 c. Type **84**	25	10
250.	25 c. View of Redonda from the sea	25	10
251.	50 c. Type **84**	55	65

86. "The Adoration of the Magi" (Marcillat).

1969. Christmas. Stained Glass Windows. Multicoloured.

252.	6 c. Type **86**	10	10
253.	10 c. "The Nativity" (unknown German artist, 15th cent.)	10	10
254.	35 c. Type **86**	25	10
255.	50 c. As 10 c.	50	30

1970. Surch. **20c.** and bars.

256.	20 c. on 25 c. (No. 189)	10	10

89. Coat of Arms.

1970. Coil Stamps.

257. **89.**	5 c. blue	10	10
258.	10 c. green	10	15
259.	25 c. red	20	25

90. Sikorski "S–38".

1970. 40th Anniv. of Antiguan Air Services. Multicoloured.

260.	5 c. Type **90**	30	10
261.	20 c. Dornier "DO–X"	60	10
262.	35 c. Hawker Siddeley "HS–748"	75	10
263.	50 c. Douglas "C–124C" (Globemaster II)	90	90
264.	75 c. Vickers "VC–10"	1·00	1·60

91. Dickens and Scene from "Nicholas Nickleby".

1970. Death Cent. of Charles Dickens.

265. **91.**	5 c. bistre, sepia & blk.	10	10
266. –	20 c. turquoise, sepia and black	20	10
267. –	35 c. blue, sepia & black	30	10
268. –	$1 red, sepia and black	75	50

DESIGNS: All stamps show Dickens and scene from: 20 c. "Pickwick Papers". 35 c. "Oliver Twist". $1, "David Copperfield".

92. Carib Indian and War Canoe.

1970. Multicoloured.

269	½ c. Type **92**	10	30
270	1 c. Columbus and "Nina"	25	30
271	2 c. Sir Thomas Warner's emblem and "Concepcion"	40	40
325	3 c. Viscount Hood and H.M.S. "Barfleur"	35	30
273	4 c. Sir George Rodney and H.M.S. "Formidable"	40	50
327	5 c. Nelson and H.M.S. "Boreas"	50	30
275	6 c. William IV and H.M.S. "Pegasus"	50	60
276	10 c. "Blackbeard" and pirate ketch	65	35
277	15 c. Collingwood and H.M.S. "Pelican"	2·50	1·00
278	20 c. Nelson and H.M.S. "Victory"	1·25	60
279	25 c. "Solent I" (paddle-steamer)	1·25	60
280	35 c. George V (when Prince George) and H.M.S. "Canada" (screw corvette)	1·60	70
281	50 c. H.M.S. "Renown" (battle cruiser)	4·00	2·25
331	75 c. "Federal Maple" (freighter)	5·50	3·00
332	$1 "Sol Quest" (yacht) and class emblem	4·50	1·75
333	$2.50 H.M.S. "London" (destroyer)	4·50	6·50
285	$5 "Pathfinder" (tug)	7·00	7·50

93. "The Small Passion" (detail) (Durer).

1970. Christmas.

286. **93.**	3 c. black and blue	10	10
287. –	10 c. purple and pink	10	10
288. **93.**	35 c. black and red	25	10
289. –	50 c. black and lilac	40	40

DESIGN: 10 c., 50 c. "Adoration of the Magi" (detail) (Durer).

94. 4th King's Own Regt., 1759.

1970. Military Uniforms (1st series) Multicoloured.

290.	½ c. Type **94**	10	10
291.	10 c. 4th West India Regt., 1804	50	10
292.	20 c. 60th Regt., The Royal American, 1809	1·00	25
293.	35 c. 93rd Regt., Sutherland Highlanders, 1826-34	1·40	30
294.	75 c. 3rd West India Regt., 1851	2·25	2·25

See also Nos. 303/7, 313/17, 353/7 and 380/4.

MORE DETAILED LISTS
are given in the Stanley Gibbons Catalogues referred to in the country headings.
For lists of current volumes see Introduction.

95. Market Woman casting Vote.

1971. 20th Anniv. of Adult Suffrage.

296. **95.**	5 c. brown	10	10
297. –	20 c. olive	10	10
298. –	35 c. purple	10	10
299. –	50 c. blue	15	30

DESIGNS: People voting: 20 c. Executive. 35 c. Housewife. 50 c. Artisan.

96. "The Last Supper".

1971. Easter. Works by Durer.

300. **96.**	5 c. black, grey & red	10	10
301. –	35 c. black, grey & violet	10	10
302. –	75 c. black, grey & gold	20	30

DESIGNS: 35 c. "The Crucifixion". 75 c. "The Resurrection".

1971. Military Uniforms (2nd series). As T **94**. Multicoloured.

303.	½ c. Private, 12th Regt., The Suffolk (1704)	10	10
304.	10 c. Grenadier, 38th Regt., South Staffs. (1751)	35	15
305.	20 c. Light Company, 5th Regt., Royal Northumberland Fusiliers (1778)	65	20
306.	35 c. Private, 48th Regt., The Northamptonshire (1793)	1·10	40
307.	75 c. Private, 15th Regt., East Yorks (1805)	2·25	2·75

97. "Madonna and Child" (detail, Veronese).

1971. Christmas. Multicoloured.

309.	3 c. Type **97**	10	10
310.	5 c. "Adoration of the Shepherds" (detail, Veronese)	10	10
311.	35 c. Type **97**	25	10
312.	50 c. As 5 c.	40	30

1972. Military Uniforms (3rd series). As T **94**. Multicoloured.

313.	½ c. Battalion Company Officer, 25th Foot, 1815	10	10
314.	10 c. Sergeant, 14th Foot, 1837	45	10
315.	20 c. Private, 67th Foot, 1853	85	15
316.	35 c. Officer, Royal Artillery, 1854	1·25	20
317.	75 c. Private, 29th Foot, 1870	1·75	2·00

98. Cowrie Helmet.

1972. Shells. Multicoloured.

319.	3 c. Type **98**	20	10
320.	5 c. Measeled Cowrie	20	10
321.	35 c. West Indian Fighting Conch	65	10
322.	50 c. Hawk Wing Conch	1·25	1·40

99. St. John's Cathedral, Side View.

1972. Christmas and 125th Anniv. of St. John's Cathedral. Multicoloured.

335.	35 c. Type **99**	20	10
336.	50 c. Cathedral interior	25	20
337.	75 c. St. John's Cathedral	30	50

1972. Royal Silver Wedding. As T **52**, of Ascension, but with floral background.

339.	20 c. blue	15	15
340.	35 c. blue	15	15

101. Batsman and Map.

1972. 50th Anniv. of Rising Sun Cricket Club. Multicoloured.

341.	5 c. Type **101**	45	25
342.	35 c. Batsman and wicket keeper	1·40	1·25
343.	$1 Club badge	2·75	3·50

102. Yacht and Map.

1972. Inaug. of Antigua and Barbuda Tourist Office in New York. Multicoloured.

345.	35 c. Type **102**	15	10
346.	50 c. Yachts	20	15
347.	75 c. St. John's G.P.O.	25	30
348.	$1 Statue of Liberty	30	35

103. "Episcopal Coat of Arms".

1973. Easter. Multicoloured.

350. **103.**	5 c. Type **103**	10	10
351. –	35 c. "The Crucifixion"	15	10
352. –	75 c. "Arms of 1st Bishop of Antigua"	25	30

Nos. 350/2 show different stained-glass windows from St. John's Cathedral.

1973. Military Uniforms (4th series). As T **94.** Multicoloured.
353. ½ c. Private, Zachariah Tiffin's Regt., of Foot, 1701 .. .. .. 10 10
354. 10 c. Private, 63rd Regt., of Foot, 1759 .. .. 30 10
355. 20 c. Light Company Officer, 35th Regt., of Foot, 1828 45 15
356. 35 c. Private, 2nd West India Regt., 1853 .. 75 15
357. 75 c. Sergeant, 49th Regt., 1858 .. .. .. 1·50 1·00

104. Butterfly Costumes

1973. Carnival. Multicoloured.
359. 5 c. Type **104** 10 10
360. 20 c. Carnival street scene 15 10
361. 35 c. Carnival troupe .. 20 10
362. 75 c. Carnival Queen .. 30 30

105. "Virgin of the Milk Porridge" (Gerard David).

1973. Christmas. Multicoloured.
364. 3 c. Type **105** 10 10
365. 5 c. "Adoration of the Magi" (Stomer) .. 10 10
366. 20 c. "The Granducal Madonna" (Raphael).. 20 10
367. 35 c. "Nativity with God the Father and Holy Ghost" (Battista) .. 30 10
368. $1 "Madonna and Child" (Murillo).. .. .. 60 60

106. Princess Anne and Captain Mark Phillips.

1973. Royal Wedding.
370. **106.** 35 c. multicoloured .. 15 10
371. – $2 multicoloured .. 35 25
The $2 is as Type **106** but has a different border.

1973. Nos. 370/1 optd. **HONEYMOON VISIT DECEMBER 16th 1973.**
373. 106. 35 c. multicoloured .. 15 10
374. – $2 multicoloured .. 40 40

108. Coat of Arms of Antigua and University.

1974. 25th Anniv. of University of West Indies. Multicoloured.
376. 5 c. Type **108** 10 10
377. 20 c. Extra-mural art .. 10 10
378. 35 c. Antigua campus .. 10 10
379. 75 c. Antigua chancellor 20 25

1974. Military Uniforms (5th series). As T **94.** Multicoloured.
380. ½ c Officer, 59th Foot, 1797 10 10
381. 10 c. Gunner, Royal Artillery, 1800 .. .. 45 10
382. 20 c. Private, 1st West India Regt., 1830 .. 70 10
383. 35 c. Officer, 92nd Foot, 1843 .. .. .. 85 10
384. 75 c. Private, 23rd Foot, 1846 .. .. .. 1·25 60

109. English Postman Mailcoach and Helicopter.

1974. Centenary of U.P.U. Multicoloured.
386. ½ c. Type **109** 10 10
387. 1 c. Bellman, mail steamer "Orinoco" and satellite 10 10
388. 2 c. Train guard, post-bus and hydrofoil 10 10
389. 5 c. Swiss messenger, Wells Fargo coach and "Concorde" 30 10
390. 20 c. Postillion, Japanese postmen and carrier pigeon 35 10
391. 35 c. Antiguan postman, flying-boat and tracking station 45 15
392. $1 Medieval courier, American express train and Boeing "747" .. 1·75 1·10
On the ½ c. English is spelt "Enlish" and on the 2 c. Postal is spelt "Fostal".

110. Traditional Player.

1974. Antiguan Steel Bands.
394.110. 5 c. dull red, red & black 10 10
395. – 20 c. brn. light brn. & blk. 10 10
396. – 35 c. light grn. grn. & blk. 10 10
397. – 75 c. blue, dull bl. & blk. 20 20
DESIGNS—HORIZ. 20 c. Traditional band. 35 c. Modern band. VERT. 75 c. Modern player.

111. Footballers.

1974. World Cup Football Championships.
399. **111.** 5 c. multicoloured .. 10 10
400. – 35 c. multicoloured .. 10 10
401. – 75 c. multicoloured .. 25 30
402. – $1 multicoloured .. 30 40
Nos. 400/2 show various footballing designs similar to Type **111.**

1974. Earthquake Relief Fund. Nos. 400/2 and 397 optd. or surch. **EARTHQUAKE RELIEF.**
404. 35 c. multicoloured .. 20 10
405. 75 c. multicoloured .. 30 25
406. $1 multicoloured 40 30
407. $5 on 75 c. dull blue, blue and black .. .. 1·50 2·00

113. Churchill as Schoolboy and School College Building, Harrow.

1974. Birth Centenary of Sir Winston Churchill. Multicoloured.
408. 5 c. Type **113.** 10 10
409. 35 c. Churchill and St. Paul's Cathedral .. 20 10
410. 75 c. Coat of arms and catafalque 30 35
411. $1 Churchill, "reward" notice and South African escape route 50 60

114. "Madonna of the Trees" (Bellini).

1974. Christmas. "Madonna and Child" paintings by named artists. Multicoloured.
413. ½ c. Type **114** 10 10
414. 1 c. Raphael 10 10
415. 2 c. Van der Weyden .. 10 10
416. 3 c. Giorgione 10 10
417. 5 c. Manaegna 10 10
418. 20 c. Vivarini 20 10
419. 35 c. Montagna 30 10
420. 75 c. Lorenzo Costa .. 55 60

1975. Nos. 390/2 and 282 surch.
422. 50 c. on 20 c. multicoloured 1·25 1·75
423. $2.50 on 35 c. mult. .. 3·00 5·00
424. $5 on $1 multicoloured .. 4·50 7·00
425. $10 on 75 c. mult. .. 4·50 7·50

116. Carib War Canoe, English Harbour, 1300.

1975. Nelson's Dockyard. Multicoloured.
427. 5 c. Type **116** 15 10
428. 15 c. Ship of the line, English Harbour, 1770 .. .. 60 10
429. 35 c. HMS "Boreas" at anchor, and Lord Nelson, 1787 .. .. .. 1·00 15
430. 50 c. Yachts during "Sailing Week", 1974 .. .. 1·25 40
431. $1 Yacht Anchorage, Old Dockyard, 1970.. .. 1·50 1·10

117. Lady of the Valley Church.

1975. Antiguan Churches. Multicoloured.
433. 5 c. Type **117.** 10 10
434. 20 c. Gilbert Memorial .. 10 10
435. 35 c. Grace Hill Moravian 15 10
436. 50 c. St. Phillips 20 20
437. $1 Ebenezer Methodist .. 35 50

118. Map of 1721 and Sextant of 1640.

1975. Maps of Antigua. Multicoloured.
439. 5 c. Type **118** 20 10
440. 20 c. Map of 1775 and galleon 45 10
441. 35 c. Maps of 1775 and 1955 55 15
442. $1 1973 maps of Antigua and English Harbour .. 1·40 1·50

119. Scout Bugler.

1975. World Scout Jamboree, Norway. Multicoloured.
444. 15 c. Type **119** 25 15
445. 20 c. Scouts in camp .. 30 15
446. 35 c. "Lord Baden-Powell" (D. Jagger) 50 20
447. $2 Scout dancers from Dahomey .. .. 1·50 1·75

120. "Eurema elathea".

1975. Butterflies. Multicoloured.
449 ½ c. Type **120** 10 10
450 1 c. "Danaus plexippus" .. 10 10
451 2 c. "Phoebis philea" .. 10 10
452 5 c. "Hypolimnas misippus" 15 10
453 20 c. "Eurema proterpia" 60 60
454 35 c. "Battus polydamas" 90 90
455 $2 "Cynthia cardui" .. 4·00 7·00
No. 452 is incorrectly captioned "Marpesia petreus thetys".

121. "Madonna and Child" (Correggio).

1975. Christmas. "Madonna and Child" paintings by artists named. **Mult.**
457. ½ c. Type **121** 10 10
458. 1 c. El Greco 10 10
459. 2 c. Durer 10 10
460. 3 c. Antonello 10 10
461. 5 c. Bellini.. .. .. 10 10
462. 10 c. Durer (different) .. 10 10
463. 35 c. Bellini (different) .. 40 10
464. $2 Durer (different again) 1·00 70

122. Vivian Richards.

1975. World Cricket Cup Winners. **Mult.**
466. 5 c. Type **122** .. .. 1·00 20
467. 35 c. Andy Roberts .. 2·50 60
468. $2 West Indies Team (horiz.) 5·50 7·50

123. Antillean Crested Hummingbird.

1976. Multicoloured.
469. ½ c. Type **123** 20 40
470. 1 c. Imperial Amazon .. 30 40
471. 2 c. Zenaida Dove .. 30 40
472. 3 c. Loggerhead Kingbird 30 40
473. 4 c. Red-necked Pigeon .. 30 40
474. 5 c. Rufous-throated Solitaire 50 10
475. 6 c. Orchid tree 30 40
476. 10 c. Bougainvillea .. 30 10
477. 15 c. Geiger tree 35 10
478. 20 c. Flamboyant 35 35
479. 25 c. Hibiscus 40 15
480. 35 c. Flame of the Wood 40 20
481. 50 c. Cannon at Fort James 55 50
482. 75 c. Premier's Office .. 60 65
483. $1 Potworks Dam .. 75 90
484. $2.50 Diamond irrigation scheme .. .. 2·00 2·25
485. $5 Government House .. 4·50 4·00
486. $10 Coolidge International Airport .. .. 4·50 6·00
Nos. 484/6 are larger, 44 × 28 mm.

124. Privates, Clark's Illinois. Regt.

1976. Bicent of American Revolution. Mult.

487 ½ c. Type **124** 10 10
488 1 c. Rifleman, Pennsylvania Militia 10 10
489 2 c. Powder horn 10 10
490 5 c. Water bottle 10 10
491 35 c. American flags .. 40 10
492 $1 "Montgomery" (American brig) .. 1·50 55
493 $5 "Ranger" (privateer sloop) .. .. .. 3·75 3·50

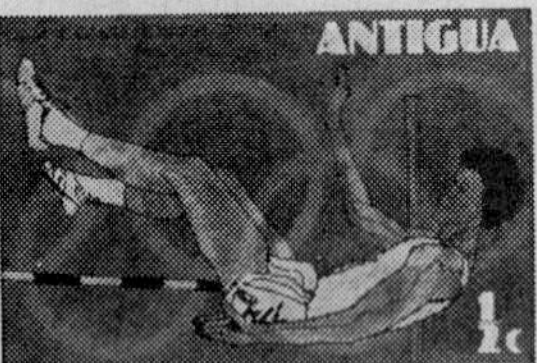

125. High Jump.

1976. Olympic Games, Montreal.

495. **125.** ½ c. brn., yell. & blk. 10 10
496. – 1 c. violet, bl. & blk. 10 10
497. – 2 c. green and black 10 10
498. – 15 c. blue and black .. 15 10
499. – 30 c. brn., yell. & blk. 20 15
500. – $1 orange, red & black 50 40
501. – $2 red and black .. 80 80

DESIGNS: 1 c. Boxing. 2 c. Pole vault. 15 c. Swimming. 30 c. Running. $1, Cycling. $2 Shot put.

126. Water Skiing.

1976. Water Sports. Multicoloured.

503. ½ c. Type **126** 10 10
504. 1 c. Sailing 10 10
505. 2 c. Snorkeling 10 10
506. 20 c. Deep sea fishing .. 15 10
507. 50 c. Scuba diving .. 35 35
508. $2 Swimming .. .. 1·00 1·25

127. French Angelfish.

1976. Fish. Multicoloured.

510. 15 c. Type **127** 40 15
511. 30 c. Yellowfin Grouper .. 60 30
512. 50 c. Yellowtail Snappers 80 50
513. 90 c. Shy Hamlet .. 1·00 80

128. The Annunciation.

1976. Christmas. Multicoloured.

514. 8 c. Type **128** 10 10
515. 10 c. The Holy Family .. 10 10
516. 15 c. The Magi 10 10
517. 50 c. The Shepherds .. 20 25
518. $1 Epiphany scene .. 30 50

129. Mercury and U.P.U. Emblem.

1976. Special Events, 1976. Multicoloured.

519. ½ c. Type **129** 10 10
520. 1 c. Alfred Nobel 10 10
521. 10 c. Space satellite .. 20 10
522. 50 c. Viv Richards and Andy Roberts .. .. 2·75 1·50
523. $1 Bell and telephones .. 2·00 2·00
524. $2 Yacht "Freelance" .. 3·00 3·50

130. Royal Family.

1977. Silver Jubilee. Multicoloured. (a) Perf.

526. 10 c. Type **130** 10 10
527. 30 c. Royal Visit, 1966 .. 10 10
528. 50 c. The Queen enthroned 15 15
529. 90 c. The Queen after Coronation 25 20
530. $2.50 Queen and Prince Charles 45 35

(b) Roul. × imperf. Self-adhesive.

532. 50 c. As 90 c. 35 60
533. $5 The Queen and Prince Philip .. .. 2·50 3·50

Nos. 532/3 come from booklets.

131. Making Camp.

1977. Caribbean Scout Jamboree, Jamaica. Multicoloured.

534. ½ c. Type **131** 10 10
535. 1 c. Hiking 10 10
536. 2 c. Rock-climbing 10 10
537. 10 c. Cutting logs .. 15 10
538. 30 c. Map and sign reading 30 10
539. 50 c. First aid 50 25
540. $2 Rafting .. .. 1·75 2·00

132. Carnival Costume.

1977. 21st Anniversary of Carnival. Mult.

542. 10 c. Type **132** 10 10
543. 30 c. Carnival Queen .. 20 10
544. 50 c. Butterfly costume .. 25 15
545. 90 c. Queen of the band .. 35 25
546. $1 Calypso King and Queen 35 30

1977. Royal Visit. Nos. 526/30 optd. **ROYAL VISIT 28th OCTOBER 1977.**

548. 10 c. Type **130** 10 10
549. 30 c. Royal Visit, 1966 .. 10 10
550. 50 c. The Queen enthroned 15 10
551. 90 c. The Queen after Coronation 25 20
552. $2·50 Queen and Prince Charles 45 35

134. "Virgin and Child Enthroned" (Tura).

1977. Christmas. Paintings by artists listed. Multicoloured.

554. ½ c. Type **134** 10 10
555. 1 c. Crivelli 10 10
556. 2 c. Lotto 10 10
557. 8 c. Pontormo 15 10
558. 10 c. Tura (different) .. 15 10
559. 25 c. Lotto (different) .. 30 10
560. $2 Crivelli (different) .. 85 60

135. Pineapple.

1977. 10th Anniv. of Statehood. Mult.

562. 10 c. Type **135** 10 10
563. 15 c. State flag 10 10
564. 50 c. Police band .. 1·50 60
565. 90 c. Premier V.C. Bird .. 55 60
566. $2 State Coat of Arms .. 90 1·00

136. "Glider III", 1902.

1978. 75th Anniv. of Powered Flight. Mult.

568. ½ c. Type **136** 10 10
569. 1 c. "Flyer I", 1903 .. 10 10
570. 2 c. Launch system and engine 10 10
571. 10 c. Orville Wright (vert.) 10 10
572. 50 c. "Flyer III", 1905 .. 55 15
573. 90 c. Wilbur Wright (vert.) 80 30
574. $2 Wright "Model B", 1910 .. .. .. 1·25 80

137. Sunfish Regatta.

1978. Sailing Week. Multicoloured.

576. 10 c. Type **137** 20 10
577. 50 c. Fishing and work boat race 45 20
578. 90 c. Curtain Bluff race .. 75 35
579. $2 Power boat rally .. 1·40 1·25

138. Queen Elizabeth and Prince Philip.

1978. 25th Anniv. of Coronation. Mult. (a) Perf.

581. 10 c. Type **138** 10 10
582. 30 c. Crowning 10 10
583. 50 c. Coronation procession 15 10
584. 90 c. Queen seated in St. Edward's Chair .. 20 15
585. $2·50 Queen wearing Imperial State Crown .. 40 40

(b) Roul. × imperf. Self-adhesive. Horiz designs as Type **138**

587. 25 c. Glass Coach .. 15 30
588. 50 c. Irish State Coach .. 25 50
589. $5 Coronation Coach .. 2·50 3·00

Nos. 587/9 come from booklets.

140. Player running with Ball.

1978. World Cup Football Championships, Argentina. Multicoloured.

590. 10 c. Type **140** 15 10
591. 15 c. Players in front of goal 15 10
592. $3 Referee and player .. 2·75 1·75

141. Petrea.

1978. Flowers. Multicoloured.

594. 25 c. Type **141** 25 10
595. 50 c. Sunflower 35 20
596. 90 c. Frangipani 60 30
597. $2 Passion Flower .. 1·25 1·10

142. "St. Ildefonso receiving the Chasuble from the Virgin".

1978. Christmas. Paintings by Rubens. Multicoloured.

599. 8 c. Type **142** 10 10
600. 25 c. "The Flight of St. Barbara" 20 10
601. $2 "Madonna and child, with St. Joseph, John the Baptist and Donor. 65 55

The painting shown on No. 601 is incorrectly attributed to Rubens on the stamp. The artist was Sebastiano del Piombo.

143. 1d. Stamp of 1863.

1979. Death Centenary of Sir Rowland Hill. Multicoloured.

603. 25 c. Type **143** 10 10
604. 50 c. 1840 Penny Black .. 25 15
605. $1 Mail coach and woman posting letter, c. 1840 .. 45 30
606. $2 Modern transport .. 1·50 75

144. " The Deposition from the Cross " (painting).

1979. Easter. Works by Durer.

608. 144. 10 c. multicoloured .. 10 10
609. – 50 c. multicoloured .. 35 20
610. – $4 black, mauve & yell. 1·75 90

DESIGNS: 50 c., " Christ on the Cross – The Passion " (wood engraving). $4, " Man of Sorrows with Hands Raised " (wood engraving).

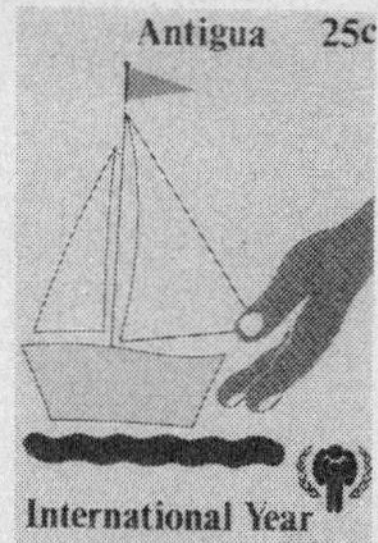

145. Toy Yacht and Child's Hand.

1979. International Year of the Child. Multicoloured.

612. 25 c. Type 145 .. .. 10 10
613. 50 c. Rocket 25 15
614. 90 c. Car 40 25
615. $2 Toy train .. .. 1·00 90

Nos. 612/15 also show the hands of children of different races.

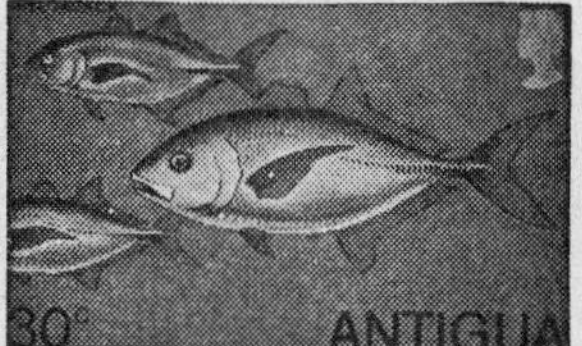

146. Yellowjack.

1979. Fish. Multicoloured.

617. 30 c. Type 146 .. .. 40 15
618. 50 c. Bluefin Tuna .. 50 25
619. 90 c. Sailfish 75 40
620. $3 Wahoo .. .. 2·25 1·75

147. Cook's Birthplace, Marton.

1979. Death Bicentenary of Captain Cook. Multicoloured.

622. 25 c. Type 147 .. .. 35 20
623. 50 c. H.M.S. "Endeavour 45 40
624. 90 c. Marine chronometer 60 60
625. $3 Landing at Botany Bay 1·50 2·25

148. The Holy Family.

1979. Christmas. Multicoloured.

627. 8 c. Type 148 .. .. 10 10
628. 25 c. Virgin and Child on ass 15 10
629. 50 c. Shepherd and star .. 30 35
630. $4 Wise Men with gifts .. 1·75 2·00

149. Javelin Throwing.

1980. Olympic Games, Moscow. Mult.

632. 10 c. Type 149 .. .. 15 10
633. 25 c. Running 20 10
634. $1 Pole vault 50 50
635. $2 Hurdles 80 95

150. Mickey Mouse and Aeroplane.

1980. International Year of the Child. Walt Disney Cartoon Characters. Multicoloured.

637. ½ c. Type 150 .. .. 10 10
638. 1 c. Donald Duck driving car (vert.) 10 10
639. 2 c. Goofy driving taxi .. 10 10
640. 3 c. Mickey and Minnie Mouse on motorcycle .. 10 10
641. 4 c. Huey, Dewey and Louie on a bicycle for three 10 10
642. 5 c. Grandma Duck and truck of roosters .. 10 10
643. 10 c. Mickey Mouse in jeep (vert.) 10 10
644. $1 Chip and Dale in Yacht 1·75 1·25
645. $4 Donald Duck riding toy train (vert.) .. 3·75 4·00

1980. " London 1980 " International Stamp Exhibition. Nos. 603/6 optd. **LONDON 1980.**

647. 25 c. 1d. stamp of 1863 .. 20 15
648. 50 c. Penny Black .. 30 20
649. $1 Stage-coach and woman posting letter, c. 1840 .. 55 40
650. $2 Modern mail transporting .. .. .. 2·25 2·25

152. " David " (statue, Donatello).

1980. Famous Works of Art. Multicoloured.

651. 10 c. Type 152 .. .. 10 10
652. 30 c. " The Birth of Venus " (painting, Botticelli) (horiz.) 30 15
653. 50 c. " Reclining Couple " (sarcophagus), Cerveteri (horiz.) 45 40
654. 90 c. " The Garden of Earthly Delights " (painting by Bosch) (horiz.) .. 65 65
655. $1 " Portinari Altarpiece " (painting, van der Goes) (horiz.) 75 75
656. $4 " Eleanora of Toledo and her son, Giovanni de'Medici (painting, Bronzino) .. .. 2·25 3·00

153. Anniversary Emblem and Headquarters, U.S.A.

1980. 75th Anniv. of Rotary International. Multicoloured.

658. 30 c. Type 153 .. .. 40 30
659. 50 c. Rotary anniversary emblem and Antigua Rotary Club banner .. 50 50
660. 90 c. Map of Antigua and Rotary emblem .. 70 70
661. $3 Paul P. Harris (founder) and Rotary emblem .. 2·25 2·75

154. Queen Elizabeth the Queen Mother.

1980. 80th Birthday of The Queen Mother.

663. 154. 10 c. multicoloured .. 20 10
664. $2·50 multicoloured 1·50 2·25

155. Ringed Kingfisher.

1980. Birds. Multicoloured.

666. 10 c. Type 155 .. .. 35 15
667. 30 c. Plain Pigeon .. 55 30
668. $1 Green-throated Carib .. 1·50 1·10
669. $2 Black-necked Stilt .. 1·75 2·00

1980. Christmas. Walt Disney's "Sleeping Beauty". As Type 150. Mult.

671. ½ c. The Bad Fairy with her raven 10 10
672. 1 c. The good fairies .. 10 10
673. 2 c. Aurora 10 10
674. 4 c. Aurora pricks her finger 10 10
675. 8 c. The prince 10 10
676. 10 c. The prince fights the dragon 15 10
677. 25 c. The prince awakens Aurora with a kiss .. 20 20
678. $2 The prince and Aurora's betrothal .. .. 2·25 2·25
679. $2·50 The prince and princess .. .. 2·50 2·50

156. Diesel Locomotive No. 15.

1981. Sugar Cane Railway Locomotives. Multicoloured.

681. 25 c. Type 156 .. .. 15 15
682. 50 c. Narrow-gauge steam locomotive 30 30
683. 90 c. Diesel locomotives Nos. 1 and 10 .. .. 55 55
684. $3 Steam locomotive hauling sugar cane .. 2·00 2·00

1981. Independence. Nos 475/6 and 478/86 optd. " **INDEPENDENCE 1981** ".

686. 6 c. Orchid Tree 10 10
687. 10 c. Bougainvillea .. 10 10
688. 20 c. Flamboyant 10 10
689. 25 c. Hibiscus 15 15
690. 35 c. Flame of the Wood .. 20 20
691. 50 c. Cannon at Fort James 35 35
692. 75 c. Premier's Office .. 40 40
693. $1 Potworks Dam .. 55 55
694. $2·50 Irrigation scheme, Diamond Estate .. 1·25 1·25
695. $5 Government House .. 2·50 2·50
696. $10 Coolidge International Airport .. .. 4·50 5·00

158. " Pipes of Pan ".

1981. Birth Centenary of Picasso. Mult.

697. 10 c. Type 158 .. .. 10 10
698. 50 c. " Seated Harlequin " 30 30
699. 90 c. " Paulo as Harlequin " 55 55
700. $4 " Mother and Child " 2·50 2·50

159. Prince Charles and Lady Diana Spencer.

1981. Royal Wedding (1st issue). Mult.

702. 25 c. Type 159 .. .. 15 10
703. 50 c. Glamis Castle .. 15 10
704. $4 Prince Charles skiing .. 90 1·10

160. Prince of Wales at Investiture, 1969.

1981. Royal Wedding (2nd issue). Mult. Roul. × imperf. self-adhesive.

706. 25 c. Type 160 .. .. 15 20
707. 25 c. Prince Charles as baby, 1948 .. .. 15 20
708. $1 Prince Charles at R.A.F. College, Cranwell, 1971 25 40
709. $1 Prince Charles attending Hill House School, 1956 .. .. .. 25 40
710. $2 Prince Charles and Lady Diana Spencer .. 50 75
711. $2 Prince Charles at Trinity College, 1967 .. .. 50 75
712. $5 Prince Charles and Lady Diana (different) .. 1·00 1·50

161. Irene Joshua (founder).

1981. 50th Anniv. of Antigua Girl Guide Movement. Multicoloured.

713. 10 c. Type 161 .. .. 10 10
714. 50 c. Campfire sing-song 35 35
715. 90 c. Sailing 65 65
716. $2.50 Animal tending .. 1·75 1·75

162. Antigua and Barbuda Coat of Arms.

1981. Independence. Multicoloured.

718. 10 c. Type **162** 10 10
719. 50 c. Pineapple, with Antigua and Barbuda flag and map 25 15
720. 90 c. Prime Minister Vere Bird 50 30
721. $2.50 St. John's Cathedral (38 × 25 mm.) .. .. 1·00 1·40

163. " Holy Night " (Jacques Stella).

1981. Christmas. Paintings. Multicoloured.

723. 8 c. Type **163** 15 10
724. 30 c. " Mary with Child " (Julius Schnorr von Carolfeld) 40 15
725. $1 " Virgin and Child " (Alonso Cano) .. .. 1·10 90
726. $3 " Virgin and Child " (Lorenzo di Credi) .. 2·75 3·75

164. Swimming.

1981. International Year of Disabled People. Sports for the Disabled. Mult.

728. 10 c. Type **164** 10 10
729. 50 c. Discus-throwing .. 30 30
730. 90 c. Archery 55 55
731. $2 Baseball .. .. 1·40 1·40

165. Scene from Football Match.

1982. World Cup Football Championship, Spain.

733. **165.** 10 c. multicoloured .. 20 10
734. – 50 c. multicoloured .. 50 35
735. – 90 c. multicoloured .. 80 70
736. – $4 multicoloured .. 3·50 3·50

DESIGNS: 50 c. to $4, Scenes from various matches.

166. European " A-300 (Airbus) ".

1982. Coolidge International Airport. Multicoloured.

738. 10 c. Type **166** 10 10
739. 50 c. Hawker-Siddeley " 748 " 30 30
740. 90 c. De Havilland " DCH6 " (Twin Otter) " .. 60 60
741. $2.50 Britten-Norman " Islander " .. .. 1·75 1·75

167. Cordia.

1982. Death Centenary of Charles Darwin. Fauna and Flora. Multicoloured.

743. 10 c. Type **167** 15 10
744. 50 c. Small Indian mongoose (horiz.) 45 40
745. 90 c. Corallita 75 75
746. $2 Mexican bulldog bat (horiz.) .. .. .. 2·00 3·25

168. Queen's House, Greenwich.

1982. 21st Birthday of Princess of Wales. Multicoloured.

748. 90 c. Type **168** 45 45
749. $1 Prince and Princess of Wales 50 50
750. $4 Princess Diana .. 2·00 2·00

170. Boy Scouts decorating Streets for Independence Parade.

1982. 75th Anniv of Boy Scout Movement. Multicoloured.

752 10 c. Type **170** 15 10
753 50 c. Boy Scout giving helping hand during street parade 40 40
754 90 c. Boy Scouts attending H.R.H. Princess Margaret at Independence Ceremony 75 75
755 $2.20 Cub Scout giving directions to tourists .. 1·75 2·75

1982. Birth of Prince William of Wales. Nos. 748/50 optd. **ROYAL BABY 21.6.82.**

757. 90 c. Type **168** 45 45
758. $1 Prince and Princess of Wales 50 50
759. $4 Princess Diana .. 2·00 2·00

172. Roosevelt in 1940.

1982. Birth Centenary of Franklin D. Roosevelt. (Nos. 761, 763 and 765/6) and George Washington. 250th Birth Anniv. (others). Multicoloured.

761. 10 c. Type **172** 20 10
762. 25 c. Washington as blacksmith 45 15
763. 45 c. Churchill, Roosevelt and Stalin at Yalta Conference .. .. 1·00 40
764. 60 c. Washington crossing the Delaware (vert.) .. 1·00 40
765. $1 "Roosevelt Special" train (vert.) .. 1·75 90
766. $3 Portrait of Roosevelt (vert.) .. .. .. 2·40 2·40

173. " Annunciation ".

1982. Christmas. Religious Paintings by Raphael. Multicoloured.

769. 10 c. Type **173** 10 10
770. 30 c. " Adoration of the Magi " 15 15
771. $1 " Presentation at the Temple " 50 50
772. $4 "Coronation of the Virgin" 2·10 2·25

174. Tritons and Dolphins.

1983. 500th Birth Anniv. of Raphael. Details from "Galatea" Fresco. Multicoloured.

774. 45 c. Type **174** 20 25
775. 50 c. Sea Nymph carried off by Triton 25 30
776. 60 c. Winged angel steering Dolphins (horiz.) .. 30 35
777. $4 Cupids shooting arrows (horiz.) .. .. 1·90 2·00

175. Pineapple Produce.

1983. Commonwealth Day. Multicoloured.

779. 25 c. Type **175** 15 15
780. 45 c. Carnival 20 25
781. 60 c. Tourism 30 35
782. $3 Airport .. .. 1·25 1·50

176. T.V. Satellite Coverage of Royal Wedding.

1983. World Communications Year. Mult.

783. 15 c. Type **176** 40 20
784. 50 c. Police communications 2·25 1·50
785. 60 c. House-to-train telephone call .. .. 2·25 1·50
786. $3 Satellite earth station with planets Jupiter and Saturn .. .. .. 4·75 5·00

177. Bottlenose Dolphin.

1983. Whales. Multicoloured.

788. 15 c. Type **177** 85 20
789. 50 c. Fin whale .. .. 1·75 1·25
790. 60 c. Bowhead whale .. 2·00 1·25
791. $3 Spectacled porpoise .. 3·75 4·25

178. Cashew Nut.

1983. Fruits and Flowers. Multicoloured.

793. 1 c. Type **178** 20 30
794. 2 c. Passion Fruit 20 30
795. 3 c. Mango 20 30
796. 5 c. Grapefruit 30 20
797. 10 c. Pawpaw 30 20
798. 15 c. Breadfruit 35 20
799. 20 c. Coconut 45 20
800. 25 c. Oleander 55 40
801. 30 c. Banana 60 40
802. 40 c. Pineapple 65 30
803. 45 c. Cordia 75 40
804. 50 c. Cassia 90 60
805. 60 c. Poui .. .. 1·00 65
806. $1 Frangipani .. .. 1·50 80
807. $2 Flamboyant .. .. 2·25 2·25
808. $2·50, Lemon .. .. 2·25 2·50
809. $5 Lignum Vitae .. .. 4·25 5·50
810. $10 National flag and coat of arms .. .. .. 8·00 11·00

179. Dornier " Do X " Flying Boat.

1983. Bicentenary of Manned Flight. Mult.

811. 30 c. Type **179** 75 30
812. 50 c. Supermarine " S.6B ", seaplane 90 60
813. 60 c. Curtiss " 9C " biplane and airship U.S.S. "Akron" 1·25 85
814. $4 " Pro Juventute " balloon .. .. .. 3·75 5·00

180. " Sibyls and Angels " (detail) (Raphael).

1983. Christmas. 500th Birth Anniv. of Raphael.

816. **180.** 10 c. multicoloured .. 30 20
817. – 30 c. multicoloured .. 65 35
818. – $1 multicoloured .. 1·50 1·25
819. – $4 multicoloured .. 4·00 5·00

DESIGNS—HORIZ. 10 c. to $4, Different details from " Sibyls and Angels ".

181. John Wesley (founder). **182.** Discus.

1983. Bicentenary of Methodist Church (1984). Multicoloured.

821. 15 c. Type **181** 25 15
822. 50 c. Nathaniel Gilbert (founder in Antigua) .. 70 50
823. 60 c. St. John Methodist Church steeple 75 65
824. $3 Ebenezer Methodist Church, St. John's .. 3·00 4·00

1984. Olympic Games, Los Angeles. Mult.

825. 25 c. Type **182** 20 15
826. 50 c. Gymnastics 35 30
827. 90 c. Hurdling 65 55
828. $3 Cycling .. .. 2·25 2·50

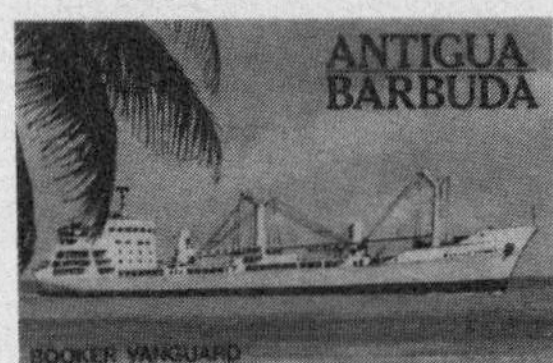

183. "Booker Vanguard" (freighter).

1984. Ships. Multicoloured.

830 45 c. Type **183** .. .. 1·25 55
831 50 c. S.S. "Canberra" (liner) 1·50 80
832 60 c. Sailing boats .. 1·75 1·00
833 $4 "Fairwind" (cargo liner) 5·00 6·50

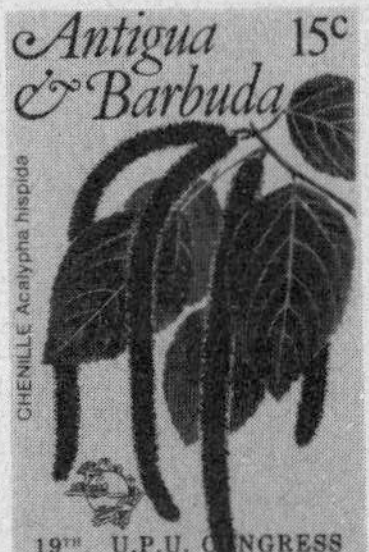

184. Chenille.

1984. Universal Postal Union Congress, Hamburg. Multicoloured.
835. 15 c. Type **184** 40 15
836. 50 c. Shell Flower .. .. 1·00 70
837. 60 c. Anthurium .. .. 1·10 90
838. $3 Angels Trumpet .. 4·00 5·00

1984. Various stamps surch.
(a) Nos. 702/4
840 $2 on 25 c. Type **159** .. 4·00 4·00
841 $2 on 50 c. Glamis Castle 4·00 4·00
842 $2 on $4 Prince Charles skiing .. .. .. 4·00 4·00
(b) Nos. 748/50
844 $2 on 90 c. Type **168** .. 3·00 2·25
845 $2 on $1 Prince and Princess of Wales .. 3·00 2·25
846 $2 on $4 Princess Diana .. 3·00 2·25
(c) Nos. 757/9
848 $2 on 90 c. Type **168** .. 3·00 2·25
849 $2 on $1 Prince and Princess of Wales .. 3·00 2·25
850 $2 on $4 Princess Diana .. 3·00 2·25
(d) Nos. 779/82
852 $2 on 25 c. Type **175** .. 1·25 1·25
853 $2 on 45 c. Carnival .. 1·25 1·25
854 $2 on 60 c. Tourism .. 1·25 1·25
855 $2 on $3 Airport .. 1·25 1·25

187. Abraham Lincoln.

1984. Presidents of the United States of America. Multicoloured.
856. 10 c. Type **187** 10 10
857. 20 c. Harry S. Truman .. 15 15
858. 30 c. Dwight D. Eisenhower 25 25
859. 40 c. Ronald W. Reagan .. 40 30
860. 90 c. Gettysburg Address, 1863 .. .. .. 80 65
861. $1.10 Formation of N.A.T.O. 1949 .. .. 1·10 75
862. $1.50 Eisenhower during the war .. .. .. 1·40 1·10
863. $2 Reagan and Caribbean Basin Initiative .. .. 1·60 1·40

188. View of Moravian Mission.

1984. 150th Anniv. of Abolition of Slavery. Multicoloured.
864. 40 c. Type **188** 80 50
865. 50 c. Antigua Courthouse, 1823 .. .. .. 90 65
866. 60 c. Planting sugar-cane, Monks Hill 95 75
867. $3 Boiling house, Delaps' estate .. .. .. 4·00 4·75

189. Rufous-sided Towhee.

1984. Songbirds. Multicoloured.
869. 40 c. Type **189** .. .. 1·25 65
870. 50 c. Parula warbler .. 1·40 80
871. 60 c. House wren .. .. 1·50 90
872. $2 Ruby-crowned kinglet 3·00 3·25
873. $3 Common flicker .. 4·00 4·50

190. Grass-skiing.

1984. "Ausipex" International Stamp Exhibition, Melbourne, Australian Sports. Multicoloured.
875. $1 Type **190** .. .. 1·75 1·50
876. $5 Australian Football .. 5·00 5·50

191. "The Virgin and Infant with Angels and Cherubs".

1984. 450th Death Anniv. of Correggio (painter). Multicoloured.
878 25 c. Type **191** 40 20
879 60 c. "The Four Saints" .. 80 50
880 90 c. "St. Catherine" .. 1·10 75
881 $3 "The Campori Madonna" .. .. .. 3·25 3·00

192. "The Blue Dancers".

1984. 150th Birth Anniv. of Edgar Degas (painter). Multicoloured.
883. 15 c. Type **192** 35 15
884. 50 c. "The Pink Dancers" 80 60
885. 70 c. "Two Dancers" .. 1·10 85
886. $4 "Dancers at the Bar" .. 4·00 4·75

193. Sir Winston Churchill.

1984. Famous People. Multicoloured.
888. 60 c. Type **193** .. .. 1·25 1·50
889. 60 c. Mahatma Gandhi .. 1·25 1·50
890. 60 c. John F. Kennedy .. 1·25 1·50
891. 60 c. Mao Tse-tung .. 1·25 1·50
892. $1 Churchill with General De Gaulle, Paris, 1944 (horiz.) .. .. .. 1·50 1·75
893. $1 Gandhi leaving London by train, 1931 (horiz.) .. 1·50 1·75
894. $1 Kennedy with Chancellor Adenauer and Mayor Brandt, Berlin, 1963 (horiz.) .. .. 1·50 1·75
895. $1 Mao Tse-tung with Lin Piao, Peking, 1969 (horiz.) .. .. .. 1·50 1·75

194. Donald Duck fishing.

1984. Christmas. Walt Disney Cartoon Characters. Multicoloured.
897. 1 c. Type **194** 10 10
898. 2 c. Donald Duck lying on beach 10 10
899. 3 c. Donald Duck and nephews with fishing rods and fishes 10 10
900. 4 c. Donald Duck and nephews in boat .. 10 10
901. 5 c. Wearing diving masks 10 10
902. 10 c. In deckchairs reading books 10 10
903. $1 With toy shark's fin .. 2·00 1·25
904. $2 In sailing boat .. .. 3·00 2·50
905. $5 Attempting to propel boat .. .. .. 5·00 5·00

195. Torch from Statue in Madison Square Park, 1885.

1985. Cent (1986) of Statue of Liberty. Mult.
907 25 c. Type **195** 20 20
908 30 c. Statue of Liberty and scaffolding ("Restoration and Renewal") (vert) .. 20 20
909 50 c. Frederic Bartholdi (sculptor) supervising construction, 1876 .. 30 30
910 90 c. Close-up of statue .. 55 55
911 $1 Statue and cadet ship ("Operation Sail", 1976) (vert) 60 60
912 $3 Dedication ceremony, 1886 .. .. .. 1·75 1·75

196. Arawak Pot Sherd and Indians making Clay Utensils.

1985. Native American Artefacts. Mult.
914. 15 c. Type **196** 15 10
915. 50 c. Arawak body design and Arawak Indians tattooing 30 30
916. 60 c. Head of the god "Yocahu" and Indians harvesting manioc .. 40 40
917. $3 Carib war club and Carib Indians going into battle .. .. .. 1·75 2·25

197. Triumph 2hp "Jap", 1903.

1985. Centenary of the Motorcycle. Mult.
919. 10 c. Type **197** 60 15
920. 30 c. "Indian Arrow", 1949 1·00 40
921. 60 c. BMW "R100RS" 1976 .. .. .. 1·50 1·00
922. $4 Harley-Davidson "Model II", 1916 .. 5·00 5·50

198. Slavonian Grebe.

1985. Birth Bicentenary of John J. Audubon (ornithologist) (1st issue). Multicoloured. Designs showing original paintings.
924. 90 c. Type **198** .. .. 1·50 90
925. $1 British storm petrel .. 1·75 1·00
926. $1.50 Great blue heron .. 2·25 2·00
927. $3 Double-crested cormorant .. .. 3·50 3·75
See also Nos. 990/3.

199. "Anaea cyanea".

1985. Butterflies. Multicoloured.
929 25 c. Type **199** .. .. 1·00 30
930 60 c. "Leodonta dysoni" 2·25 1·25
931 90 c. "Junea doraete" .. 2·75 1·50
932 $4 "Prepona pylene" .. 7·50 7·00

200. Cessna "172".

1985. 40th Anniv. of International Civil Aviation Organisation. Multicoloured.
934. 30 c. Type **200** .. .. 1·25 30
935. 90 c. Fokker "DVII" .. 2·75 1·25
936. $1.50 Spad "VII" .. .. 3·75 2·00
937. $3 Boeing "747" .. .. 5·50 5·50

201. Maimonides.

1985. 850th Birth Anniv. of Maimonides (physician, philosopher and scholar).
939. **201.** $2 green .. .. 3·75 3·00

202. Young Farmers with Produce.

1985. International Youth Year. Mult.
941. 25 c. Type **202** 15 20
942. 50 c. Hotel management trainees 25 30
943. 60 c. Girls with goat and boys with football ("Environment") .. 35 40
944. $3 Windsurfing ("Leisure") 1·60 1·75

MORE DETAILED LISTS
are given in the Stanley Gibbons Catalogues referred to in the country headings.
For lists of current volumes see Introduction.

203. The Queen Mother attending Church.

1985. Life and Times of Queen Elizabeth the Queen Mother. Multicoloured.

946. $1 Type **203** 55 60
947. $1.50 Watching children playing in London garden 70 85
948. $2.50 The Queen Mother in 1979 .. .. 1·00 1·40

Stamps as Nos. 946/8 but with face values of 90 c., $1 and $3 exists from additional sheetlets with changed background colours.

204. Magnificent Frigate Bird.

1985. Marine Life. Multicoloured.

950. 15 c. Type **204** 85 30
951. 45 c. Brain coral .. .. 1·75 95
952. 60 c. Cushion star .. .. 2·00 1·40
953. $3 Spotted moray eel .. 6·00 7·50

205. Girl Guides Nursing.

1985. 75th Anniv. of Girl Guide Movement. Multicoloured.

955. 15 c. Type **205** 75 20
956. 45 c. Open-air Girl Guide meeting .. .. 1·40 60
957. 60 c. Lord and Lady Baden-Powell .. .. 1·75 90
958. $3 Girl Guides gathering flowers .. .. 4·25 4·00

206. Bass Trombone.

1985. 300th Birth Anniv. of Johann Sebastian Bach (composer). Multicoloured.

960. 25 c. Type **206** .. .. 1·40 55
961. 50 c. English horn .. .. 1·75 1·10
962. $1 Violino piccolo .. .. 3·25 1·75
963. $3 Bass rackett .. .. 6·00 7·00

207. Flags of Great Britain and Antigua.

1985. Royal Visit. Multicoloured.

965. 60 c. Type **207** .. .. 1·25 45
966. $1 Queen Elizabeth II (vert.) .. .. 2·00 1·00
967. $4 Royal Yacht "Britannia" .. .. 4·75 3·75

1985. 150th Birth Anniv. of Mark Twain (author). As T **118** of Anguilla showing Walt Disney cartoon characters in scenes from "Roughing It". Multicoloured.

969. 25 c. Donald Duck and Mickey Mouse meeting Indians 35 20
970. 50 c. Mickey Mouse, Donald Duck and Goofy canoeing 55 45
971. $1.10 Goofy as Pony Express Rider .. 1·00 90
972. $1.50 Donald Duck and Goofy hunting buffalo .. 1·40 1·10
973. $2 Mickey Mouse and silver mine .. .. 1·90 1·75

1985. Birth Bicentenaries of Grimm Brothers (folklorists). As T **119** of Anguilla showing Walt Disney cartoon characters in scenes from "Spindle, Shuttle and Needle". Multicoloured.

975. 30 c. The Prince (Mickey Mouse) searches for a bride) 70 35
976. 60 c. The Prince finds the Orphan Girl (Minnie Mouse) .. .. .. 1·00 70
977. 70 c. The Spindle finds the Prince .. .. .. 1·25 80
978. $1 The Needle tidies the Girl's House .. .. 1·75 1·50
979. $3 The Prince proposes .. 3·75 4·25

208. Benjamin Franklin and U.N. (New York) 1953 U.P.U. 5 c. Stamp.

1985. 40th Anniv. of United Nations Organization. Multicoloured.

981. 40 c. Type **208** .. .. 1·00 55
982. $1 George Washington Carver (agricultural chemist) and 1982 Nature Conservation 28 c. stamp .. .. 2·00 1·75
983. $3 Charles Lindbergh (aviator) and 1978 I.C.A.O. 25 c. stamp .. 4·25 4·75

Nos. 975/7 each include a United Nations (New York) stamp design.

209. "Madonna and Child" (De Landi).

1985. Christmas. Religious Paintings. Mult.

985. 10 c. Type **209** 25 15
986. 25 c. "Madonna and Child" (Berlinghiero) 50 25
987. 60 c. "The Nativity" (Fra Angelico) 80 50
988. $4 "Presentation in the Temple" (Giovanni di Paolo) .. .. .. 3·75 4·25

1986. Birth Bicentenary of John J. Audubon (ornithologist) (2nd issue). Designs as T **198** showing original paintings. Multicoloured.

990. 60 c. Mallard .. .. 1·50 90
991. 90 c. North American black duck .. .. 2·00 1·25
992. $1.50 Pintail .. .. 3·00 3·00
993. $3 American wigeon .. 4·25 4·75

210. Football, Boots and Trophy.

1986. World Cup Football Championship, Mexico. Multicoloured.

995. 30 c. Type **210** 85 40
996. 60 c. Goalkeeper (vert.) .. 1·25 75
997. $1 Referee blowing whistle (vert.) .. .. .. 1·75 1·40
998. $4 Ball in net .. .. 5·50 5·50

1986. Appearance of Halley's Comet (1st issue). As T **123** of Anguilla. Multicoloured.

1000. 5 c. Edmond Halley and Old Greenwich Observatory 15 10
1001. 10 c. "Me 163B Komet" (fighter aircraft), 1944 20 10
1002. 60 c. Montezuma (Aztec Emperor) and Comet in 1517 (from "Historias de las Indias de Neuva Espana") .. .. 1·00 55
1003. $4 Pocahontas saving Capt. John Smith and Comet in 1607 .. .. 4·00 3·50

See also Nos. 1047/50.

1986. 60th Birthday of Queen Elizabeth II. As T **125** of Anguilla.

1005. 60 c. black and yellow .. 35 35
1006. $1 multicoloured .. 55 55
1007. $4 multicoloured .. 2·10 2·10

DESIGNS: 60 c. Wedding photograph, 1947; $1 Queen at Trooping the Colour. $4 In Scotland.

211. Tug.

1986. Local Boats. Multicoloured.

1009. 30 c. Type **211** 25 20
1010. 60 c. Game fishing boat 45 35
1011. $1 Yacht 75 60
1012. $4 Lugger with auxiliary sail .. .. .. 2·50 3·00

212. "Hiawatha Express".

1986. "Ameripex '86" International Stamp Exhibition, Chicago. Famous American Trains. Multicoloured,

1014. 25 c. Type **212** .. .. 1·00 40
1015. 50 c. "Grand Canyon Express" .. .. 1·60 75
1016. $1 "Powhattan Arrow Express" .. .. 2·00 1·50
1017. $3 "Empire State Express" .. .. 5·00 5·00

213. Prince Andrew and Miss Sarah Ferguson.

1986. Royal Wedding. Multicoloured.

1019. 45 c. Type **213** 45 35
1020. 60 c. Prince Andrew .. 50 45
1021. $4 Prince Andrew with Prince Philip .. .. 2·50 3·00

214. Fly-specked Cerith.

1986. Sea Shells. Multicoloured.

1023. 15 c. Type **214** 75 30
1024. 45 c. Smooth Scotch Bonnet .. .. 1·75 90
1025. 60 c. West Indian Crown Conch .. .. .. 2·00 1·25
1026. $3 Murex Ciboney .. 6·50 7·00

215. Water Lily.

1986. Flowers. Multicoloured.

1028. 10 c. Type **215** 15 15
1029. 15 c. Queen of the Night 20 15
1030. 50 c. Cup of Gold .. 55 40
1031. 60 c. Beach Morning Glory 70 45
1032. 70 c. Golden Trumpet .. 80 55
1033. $1 Air Plant .. .. 1·10 75
1034. $3 Purple Wreath .. 2·50 2·50
1035. $4 Zephyr Lily .. .. 3·00 3·25

1986. World Cup Football Championship Winners, Mexico. Nos. 995/8 optd. **WINNERS Argentina 3 W. Germany 2.**

1037 30 c. Type **210** 50 35
1038 60 c. Goalkeeper (vert) .. 80 60
1039 $1 Referee blowing whistle (vert) .. .. 1·10 85
1040 $4 Ball in net .. .. 4·25 4·00

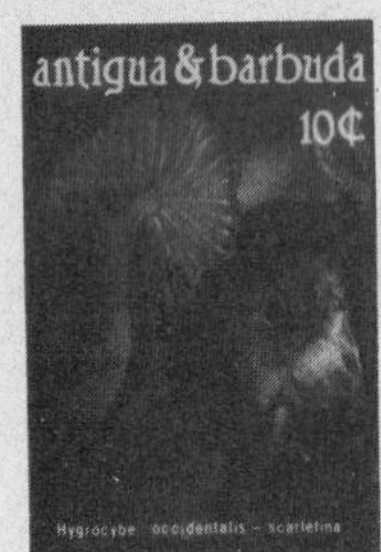

217. "Hygrocybe occidentalis var. scarletina".

1986. Mushrooms. Multicoloured.

1042. 10 c. Type **217** 30 20
1043. 50 c. "Trogia buccinalis" 70 55
1044. $1 "Collybia subpruinosa" .. .. 1·25 1·00
1045. $4 "Leucocoprinus brebissonii" .. .. 3·00 4·00

(**218**).

1986. Appearance of Halley's Comet (2nd issue). Nos. 1000/3 optd. with T **218**.

1047. 5 c. Edmond Halley and Old Greenwich Observatory 15 10
1048. 10 c. "Me 163B Komet" (fighter aircraft), 1944 20 10
1049. 60 c. Montezuma (Aztec emperor) and comet in 1517 (from "Historias de las Indias de Neuva Espana") .. 1·00 65
1050. $4 Pocahontas saving Capt. John Smith and comet in 1607 .. .. 4·50 4·00

219. Auburn "Speedster" (1933).

1986. Centenary of First Benz Motor Car. Multicoloured.

1052. 10 c. Type **219** 15 10
1053. 15 c. Mercury "Sable" (1986) 20 10
1054. 50 c. Cadillac (1959) .. 55 30
1055. 60 c. Studebaker (1950) .. 70 45
1056. 70 c. Lagonda "V-12" (1939) 80 55
1057. $1 Adler "Standard" (1930) .. .. .. 1·10 75
1058. $3 DKW (1956) .. .. 2·50 2·50
1059. $4 Mercedes "500K" (1936) .. .. .. 3·00 3·00

220. Young Mickey Mouse playing Santa Claus.

1986. Christmas. Designs showing Walt Disney cartoon characters as babies. Mult.

1061. 25 c. Type **220** 45 35
1062. 30 c. Mickey and Minnie Mouse building snowman 50 40
1063. 40 c. Aunt Matilda and Goofy baking 55 45
1064. 60 c. Goofy and Pluto .. 80 65
1065. 70 c. Pluto, Donald and Daisy Duck carol singing 95 75
1066. $1.50 Donald Duck, Mickey Mouse and Pluto stringing popcorn .. .. 1·60 1·50
1067. $3 Grandma Duck and Minnie Mouse .. .. 3·00 3·00
1068. $4 Donald Duck and Pete .. .. .. 3·25 3·25

221. Arms of Antigua. **222.** "Canada I" (1981).

1986.

1070. **221.** 10 c. blue 20 20
1071. 25 c. red 30 35

DESIGN: 25 c. Flag of Antigua.

1987. America's Cup Yachting Championship. Multicoloured.

1072. 30 c. Type **222** 30 20
1073. 60 c. "Gretel II" (1970) .. 45 40
1074. $1 "Sceptre" (1958) .. 85 75
1075. $3 "Vigilant" (1893) .. 2·25 2·50

223. Bridled Burrfish.

1987. Marine Life. Multicoloured.

1077. 15 c. Type **223** 50 20
1078. 30 c. Common noddy .. 80 35
1079. 40 c. Nassau grouper .. 85 45
1080. 50 c. Laughing gull .. 1·25 70
1081. 60 c. French angelfish .. 1·40 75
1082. $1 Porkfish .. .. 1·60 1·40
1083. $2 Royal tern .. .. 3·00 3·00
1084. $3 Sooty tern .. .. 3·75 3·75

Nos. 1078, 1080 and 1083/4 are without the World Wildlife Fund logo shown on Type **223**.

224. Handball.

1987. Olympic Games, Seoul (1988) (1st issue). Multicoloured.

1086. 10 c. Type **224** 15 10
1087. 60 c. Fencing 35 35
1088. $1 Gymnastics 60 65
1089. $3 Football .. .. 1·75 2·25

See also Nos. 1222/5.

225. "The Profile".

1987. Birth Centenary of Marc Chagall (artist). Multicoloured.

1091. 10 c. Type **225** 10 10
1092. 30 c. "Portrait of the Artist's Sister" .. 15 15
1093. 40 c. "Bride with Fan" 20 25
1094. 60 c. "David in Profile" 25 30
1095. 90 c. "Fiancee with Bouquet" 40 45
1096. $1 "Self Portrait with Brushes" 45 50
1097. $3 "The Walk" .. .. 1·40 1·75
1098. $4 "Three Candles" .. 1·75 2·00

226. "Spirit of Australia" (fastest powerboat), 1978.

1987. Milestones of Transportation. Mult.

1100 10 c. Type **226** 25 15
1101 15 c. Siemen's electric locomotive, 1879 .. 40 20
1102 30 c. U.S.S. "Triton" (first submerged circumnavigation), 1960 45 25
1103 50 c. Trevithick's steam carriage (first passenger-carrying vehicle), 1801 .. .. 60 40
1104 60 c. U.S.S. "New Jersey" (battleship), 1942 .. 70 45
1105 70 c. Draisaine bicycle, 1818 .. .. .. 70 50
1106 90 c. "United States" (liner) (holder of Blue Riband), 1952 .. .. 1·00 65
1107 $1.50 Cierva "C.4" (first autogiro), 1923 .. 1·40 1·00
1108 $2 Curtiss "NC.4" (first transatlantic flight), 1919 .. .. .. 1·50 1·25
1109 $3 "Queen Elizabeth 2" (liner), 1969 .. .. 2·50 2·00

227. Lee Iacocca at Unveiling of Restored Statue.

1987. Centenary of Statue of Liberty (1986) (2nd issue). Multicoloured.

1110. 15 c. Type **227** 15 15
1111. 30 c. Statue at sunset (side view) 20 20
1112. 45 c. Aerial view of head 30 30
1113. 50 c. Lee Iacocca and torch 35 35
1114. 60 c. Workman inside head of Statue (horiz.) 35 35
1115. 90 c. Restoration work (horiz.) 50 50
1116. $1 Head of Statue .. 55 55
1117. $2 Statue at sunset (front view) .. .. .. 1·00 1·25
1118. $3 Inspecting restoration work (horiz.) .. .. 1·60 1·75
1119. $5 Statue at night .. 2·50 3·00

228. Grace Kelly.

1987. Entertainers. Multicoloured.

1120. 15 c. Type **228** 50 20
1121. 30 c. Marilyn Monroe .. 60 35
1122. 45 c. Orson Welles .. 65 40
1123. 50 c. Judy Garland .. 65 45
1124. 60 c. John Lennon .. 1·10 65
1125. $1 Rock Hudson .. 1·25 75
1126. $2 John Wayne .. .. 2·00 1·40
1127. $3 Elvis Presley .. .. 3·00 2·25

229. Scouts around Camp Fire and Red Kangaroo.

1987. 16th World Scout Jamboree, Australia. Multicoloured.

1128. 10 c. Type **229** 25 10
1129. 60 c. Scouts canoeing and blue-winged kookaburra 70 40
1130. $1 Scouts on assault course and ring-tailed rock wallaby .. .. 1·00 80
1131. $3 Field kitchen and koala .. .. .. 2·00 2·25

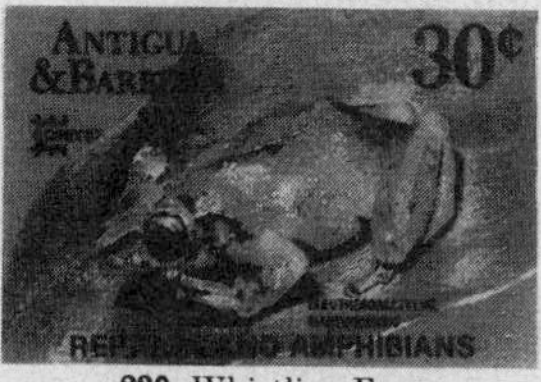

230. Whistling Frog.

1987. "Capex '87" International Stamp Exhibition, Toronto. Reptiles and Amphibians. Multicoloured.

1133. 30 c. Type **230** 15 15
1134. 60 c. Croaking lizard .. 25 30
1135. $1 Antiguan anole .. 45 50
1136. $3 Red-footed tortoise .. 1·40 1·75

1987. 10th Death Anniv. of Elvis Presley (entertainer). No. 1127 optd. **10th ANNIVERSARY 16th AUGUST 1987.**

1138. $3 Elvis Presley .. .. 2·50 2·25

232. House of Burgesses, Virginia ("Freedom of Speech")

1987. Bicentenary of U.S. Constitution. Multicoloured.

1139. 15 c. Type **232** 10 10
1140. 45 c. State Seal, Connecticut 20 25
1141. 60 c. State Seal, Delaware 25 30
1142. $4 Governor Morris (Pennsylvania delegate) (vert.) .. 1·75 1·90

233. "Madonna and Child" (Bernardo Daddi). **234.** Wedding Photograph, 1947.

1987. Christmas. Religious Paintings. Mult.

1144. 45 c. Type **233** 20 25
1145. 60 c. St. Joseph (detail, "The Nativity" (Sano di Pietro)) 25 30
1146. $1 Virgin Mary (detail, "The Nativity" (Sano di Pietro)) 45 50
1147. $4 "Music-making Angel" (Melozzo da Forli) .. .. .. 1·75 2·25

1988. Royal Ruby Wedding.

1149. **234.** 25 c. brn., blk. & bl. 15 15
1150. – 60 c. multicoloured .. 30 30
1151. – $2 brn., blk. & grn. 90 95
1152. – $3 multicoloured .. 1·40 1·50

DESIGNS: 60 c. Queen Elizabeth II. $2 Princess Elizabeth and Prince Philip with Prince Charles at his Christening, 1948. $3 Queen Elizabeth (from photo by Tim Graham), 1980.

235 Great Blue Heron

1988. Birds of Antigua. Multicoloured.

1154 10 c. Type **235** 20 15
1155 15 c. Ringed kingfisher (horiz) 20 15
1156 50 c. Bananaquit (horiz) 40 30
1157 60 c. Purple gallinule (horiz) 40 30
1158 70 c. Blue-hooded euphonia (horiz) .. 50 35
1159 $1 Brown-throated conure ("Caribbean Parakeet") 70 55
1160 $3 Troupial (horiz) .. 2·00 2·25
1161 $4 Purple-throated carib (horiz) .. .. 2·25 2·75

236 First Aid at Daycare Centre, Antigua

1988. Salvation Army's Community Service. Multicoloured.

1163 25 c. Type **236** 45 35
1164 30 c. Giving penicillin injection, Indonesia .. 45 35
1165 40 c. Children at daycare centre, Bolivia .. 55 45
1166 45 c. Rehabilitation of the handicapped, India .. 55 45
1167 50 c. Training blind man, Kenya 70 70
1168 60 c. Weighing baby, Ghana 70 70
1169 $1 Training typist, Zambia .. .. 1·25 1·25
1170 $2 Emergency food kitchen, Sri Lanka .. 1·90 2·00

237 Columbus's Second Fleet, 1493

1988. 500th Anniv (1992) of Discovery of America by Columbus (1st issue). Mult.

1172 10 c. Type **237** 15 10
1173 30 c. Painos Indian village and fleet 20 15
1174 45 c. "Santa Mariagalante" (flagship) and Painos village 25 25
1175 60 c. Painos Indians offering Columbus fruit and vegetables .. 30 30
1176 90 c. Painos Indian and Columbus with scarlet macaw 45 45
1177 $1 Columbus landing on island 50 50
1178 $3 Spanish soldier and fleet .. .. 1·40 1·50
1179 $4 Fleet under sail .. 1·75 2·00

See also Nos. 1267/70, 1360/7, 1503/10, 1654/9 and 1670/1.

238 "Bust of Christ"

1988. Easter. 500th Birth Anniv of Titian (artist). Multicoloured.

1181 30 c. Type **238** 15 15
1182 40 c. "Scourging of Christ" 20 25
1183 45 c. "Madonna in Glory with Saints" 20 25
1184 50 c. "The Averoldi Polyptych" (detail) .. 25 30
1185 $1 "Christ Crowned with Thorns" 45 50
1186 $2 "Christ Mocked" .. 90 95
1187 $3 "Christ and Simon of Cyrene" .. .. 1·40 1·50
1188 $4 "Crucifixion with Virgin and Saints" .. 1·75 2·00

239 Two Yachts rounding Buoy

1988. Sailing Week. Multicoloured.

1190 30 c. Type **239** 25 15
1191 60 c. Three yachts 40 30
1192 $1 British yacht under way 60 50
1193 $3 Three yachts (different) .. .. 1·50 2·00

240 Mickey Mouse and Diver with Porpoise

1988. Disney EPCOT Centre, Orlando, Florida. Designs showing cartoon characters and exhibits. Multicoloured.

1195 1 c. Type **240** 10 10
1196 2 c. Goofy and Mickey Mouse with futuristic car (vert) 10 10
1197 3 c. Mickey Mouse and Goofy as Atlas (vert) .. 10 10
1198 4 c. Mickey Mouse and "Edaphosaurus" (prehistoric reptile) .. 10 10
1199 5 c. Mickey Mouse at Journey into Imagination exhibit .. 10 10
1200 10 c. Mickey Mouse collecting vegetables (vert) 10 10
1201 25 c. Type **240** 20 20
1202 30 c. As 2 c. 20 20
1203 40 c. As 3 c. 25 25
1204 60 c. As 4 c. 40 40
1205 70 c. As 5 c. 45 45
1206 $1.50 As 10 c. 95 95
1207 $3 Goofy and Mickey Mouse with robot (vert) 1·75 1·75
1208 $4 Mickey Mouse and Clarabelle at Horizons exhibit .. .. 2·00 2·00

1988. Stamp Exhibitions. Nos. 1083/4 optd.

1210 $2 Royal tern (optd **Praga '88**, Prague) .. 90 95
1211 $3 Sooty tern (optd **INDEPENDENCE 40**, Israel) .. .. 1·40 1·50

242 Jacaranda

1988. Flowering Trees. Multicoloured.

1213 10 c. Type **242** 20 15
1214 30 c. Cordia 25 20
1215 50 c. Orchid tree .. 40 40
1216 90 c. Flamboyant .. 50 50
1217 $1 African tulip tree .. 55 55
1218 $2 Potato tree .. .. 1·10 1·10
1219 $3 Crepe myrtle .. .. 1·40 1·60
1220 $4 Pitch apple .. .. 1·75 2·25

243 Gymnastics

1988. Olympic Games, Seoul (2nd issue). Mult.

1222 40 c. Type **243** 20 25
1223 60 c. Weightlifting .. 25 30
1224 $1 Water polo (horiz) .. 45 50
1225 $3 Boxing (horiz) .. 1·40 1·50

244 "Danaus plexippus"

1988. Caribbean Butterflies. Multicoloured.

1227 1 c. Type **244** 10 10
1228 2 c. "Greta diaphanus" 10 10
1229 3 c. "Calisto archebates" 10 10
1230 5 c. "Hamadryas feronia" 10 10
1231 10 c. "Mestra dorcas" .. 10 10
1232 15 c. "Hypolimnas misippus" 10 10
1233 20 c. "Dione juno" .. 10 10
1234 25 c. "Heliconius charithonia" 10 15
1235 30 c. "Eurema pyro" .. 15 20
1236 40 c. "Papilio androgeus" 20 25
1237 45 c. "Anteos maerula" 20 25
1238 50 c. "Aphrissa orbis" .. 25 30
1239 60 c. "Astraptes xagua" 30 35
1240 $1 "Heliopetes arsalte" 50 55
1241 $2 "Polites baracoa" .. 95 1·00
1242 $2.50 "Phocides pigmalion" .. .. .. 1·25 1·40
1243 $5 "Prepona amphitoe" 2·40 2·50
1244 $10 "Oarisma nanus" .. 5·00 5·25
1244a $20 "Parides lycimenes" 9·50 9·75

245 President Kennedy and Family

1988. 25th Death Anniv of John F. Kennedy (American statesman). Multicoloured.

1245 1 c. Type **245** 10 10
1246 2 c. Kennedy commanding "PT109" 10 10
1247 3 c. Funeral cortege .. 10 10
1248 4 c. In motorcade, Mexico City 10 10
1249 30 c. As 1 c. 15 15
1250 60 c. As 4 c. 25 30
1251 $1 As 3 c. 45 50
1252 $4 As 2 c. .. .. 1·60 1·75

246 Minnie Mouse carol singing

1988. Christmas. "Mickey's Christmas Chorale". Designs showing Walt Disney cartoon characters. Multicoloured

1254 10 c. Type **246** 10 10
1255 25 c. Pluto 15 15
1256 30 c. Mickey Mouse playing ukelele .. 15 15
1257 70 c. Donald Duck and nephew 35 35
1258 $1 Mordie and Ferdie carol singing .. 45 50
1259 $1 Goofy carol singing .. 45 50
1260 $1 Chip n'Dale sliding off roof 45 50
1261 $1 Two of Donald Duck's nephews at window 45 50
1262 $1 As 10 c. 45 50
1263 $1 As 25 c. 45 50
1264 $1 As 30 c. 45 50
1265 $1 As 70 c. 45 50

Nos. 1258/65 were printed together, se-tenant, forming a composite design.

247 Arawak Warriors

1989. 500th Anniv of Discovery of America by Columbus (1992) (2nd issue). Pre-Columbian Arawak Society. Multicoloured.

1267 $1.50 Type **247** 65 70
1268 $1.50 Whip dancers .. 65 70
1269 $1.50 Whip dancers and chief with pineapple .. 65 70
1270 $1.50 Family and camp fire 65 70

Nos. 1267/70 were printed together, se-tenant, forming a composite design.

248 De Havilland "Comet 4" Airliner

1989. 50th Anniv of First Jet Flight. Mult.

1272 10 c. Type **248** 10 10
1273 30 c. Messerschmitt "Me 262" fighter .. 10 15
1274 40 c. Boeing "707" airliner 15 20
1275 60 c. Canadair "F-86 Sabre" fighter .. 25 30
1276 $1 Lockheed "F-104 Starfighter" fighters .. 40 45
1277 $2 McDonnell Douglas "DC-10" airliner .. 85 90
1278 $3 Boeing "747" airliner 1·25 1·40
1279 $4 McDonnell "F-4 Phantom" fighter .. 1·75 1·90

249 "Festivale"

1989. Caribbean Cruise Ships. Multicoloured.

1281 25 c. Type **249** .. 20 15
1282 45 c. "Southward" .. 35 25
1283 50 c. "Sagafjord" .. 35 25
1284 60 c. "Daphne" 35 30
1285 75 c. "Cunard Countess" 40 40
1286 90 c. "Song of America" 55 55
1287 $3 "Island Princess" .. 1·50 1·75
1288 $4 "Galileo" .. 2·00 2·25

250 "Fish swimming by Duck half-submerged in Stream"

1989. Japanese Art. Paintings by Hiroshige. Multicoloured.

1290 25 c. Type **250** 10 15
1291 45 c. "Crane and Wave" 20 25
1292 50 c. "Sparrows and Morning Glories" .. 20 25
1293 60 c. "Crested Blackbird and Flowering Cherry" 25 30
1294 $1 "Great Knot sitting among Water Grass" .. 40 45
1295 $2 "Goose on a Bank of Water" 85 90
1296 $3 "Black Paradise Flycatcher and Blossoms" .. .. 1·25 1·40
1297 $4 "Sleepy Owl perched on a Pine Branch" .. 1·75 1·90

251 Mickey and Minnie Mouse in Helicopter over River Seine

1989. "Philexfrance 89" International Stamp Exhibition, Paris. Walt Disney cartoon characters in Paris. Multicoloured.

1299 1 c. Type **251** 10 10
1300 2 c. Goofy and Mickey Mouse passing Arc de Triomphe 10 10
1301 3 c. Mickey Mouse painting picture of Notre Dame 10 10
1302 4 c. Mickey and Minnie Mouse with Pluto leaving Metro station 10 10
1303 5 c. Minnie Mouse as model in fashion show 10 10
1304 10 c. Daisy Duck, Minnie Mouse and Clarabelle as Folies Bergere dancers 10 10
1305 $5 Mickey and Minnie Mouse shopping in street market .. .. 2·75 3·00
1306 $6 Mickey and Minnie Mouse, Jose Carioca and Donald Duck at pavement cafe .. 3·25 3·50

252 Goalkeeper

1989. World Cup Football Championship, Italy (1990). Multicoloured.

1308 15 c. Type **252** 15 10
1309 25 c. Goalkeeper moving towards ball 20 15
1310 $1 Goalkeeper reaching for ball 60 60
1311 $4 Goalkeeper saving goal 2·00 2·25

253 "Mycena pura"

1989. Fungi. Multicoloured.

1313 10 c. Type **253** 15 10
1314 25 c. "Psathyrella tuberculata" 20 15
1315 50 c. "Psilocybe cubensis" 35 25
1316 60 c. "Leptonia caeruleocapitata" .. 35 30
1317 75 c. "Xeromphalina tenuipes" 45 40
1318 $1 "Chlorophyllum molybolites" 55 55
1319 $3 "Marasmius haematocephalus" .. 1·75 1·75
1320 $4 "Cantharellus cinnabarinos" .. 2·00 2·25

254 Desmarest's Hutia

1989. Local Fauna. Multicoloured.

1322 25 c. Type **254** 20 15
1323 45 c. Caribbean monk seal 35 30
1324 80 c. Mustache bat (vert) 45 40
1325 $4 American manatee (vert) .. .. .. 2·25 2·40

255 Goofy and Old Printing Press

1989. "American Philately". Walt Disney cartoon characters with stamps and the logo of the American Philatelic Society. Mult.

1327 1 c. Type **255** 10 10
1328 2 c. Donald Duck cancelling first day cover for Mickey Mouse .. 10 10
1329 3 c. Donald Duck's nephews reading recruiting poster for Pony Express riders .. 10 10
1330 4 c. Morty and Ferdie as early radio broadcasters 10 10
1331 5 c. Donald Duck and water buffalo watching television 10 10
1332 10 c. Donald Duck with stamp album 10 10
1333 $4 Daisy Duck with computer system .. 2·00 2·25
1334 $6 Donald's nephews with stereo radio, trumpet and guitar .. .. 3·00 3·25

256 Mickey Mouse and Donald Duck with Locomotive "John Bull", 1831

1989. "World Stamp Expo '89" International Stamp Exhibition, Washington. Walt Disney cartoon characters and locomotives. Mult.

1336 25 c. Type **256** 20 20
1337 45 c. Mickey Mouse and friends with "Atlantic", 1832 .. .. .. 30 30
1338 50 c. Mickey Mouse and Goofy with "William Crooks", 1861 .. .. 30 30
1339 60 c. Mickey Mouse and Goofy with "Minnetonka", 1869 .. .. 35 35
1340 $1 Chip n'Dale with "Thatcher Perkins", 1863 .. .. .. 50 50
1341 $2 Mickey and Minnie Mouse with "Pioneer", 1848 .. .. .. 95 1·00
1342 $3 Mickey Mouse and Donald Duck with cog railway locomotive "Peppersass", 1869 .. 1·40 1·60
1343 $4 Mickey Mouse with Huey, Dewey and Louie aboard N.Y. World's Fair "Gimbels Flyer", 1939 .. .. 1·75 2·00

258 Launch of "Apollo 11"

1989. 20th Anniv of First Manned Landing on Moon. Multicoloured.

1346 10 c. Type **258** 15 10
1347 45 c. Aldrin on Moon .. 30 25
1348 $1 Module "Eagle" over Moon (horiz) 60 55
1349 $4 Recovery of "Apollo 11" crew after splashdown (horiz) .. .. 2·25 2·40

259 "The Small Cowper Madonna" (Raphael)

260 Star-eyed Hermit Crab

1989. Christmas. Paintings by Raphael and Giotto. Multicoloured.

1351 10 c. Type **259** 10 10
1352 25 c. "Madonna of the Goldfinch" (Raphael) 15 15
1353 30 c. "The Alba Madonna" (Raphael) .. 15 15
1354 50 c. Saint (detail, "Bologna Altarpiece") (Giotto) 30 30
1355 60 c. Angel (detail, "Bologna Altarpiece") (Giotto) 35 35
1356 70 c. Angel slaying serpent (detail, "Bologna Altarpiece") (Giotto) 40 40
1357 $4 Evangelist (detail, "Bologna Altarpiece") (Giotto) .. .. 2·00 2·25
1358 $5 "Madonna of Foligno" (detail) (Raphael) .. 2·50 2·75

1990. 500th Anniv (1992) of Discovery of America by Columbus (3rd issue). New World Natural History—Marine Life. Mult.

1360 10 c. Type **260** 10 10
1361 20 c. Spiny lobster .. 10 10
1362 25 c. Magnificent banded fanworm 10 15
1363 45 c. Cannonball jellyfish 20 25
1364 60 c. Red-spiny sea star 30 35
1365 $2 Peppermint shrimp .. 95 1·00
1366 $3 Coral crab .. .. 1·40 1·50
1367 $4 Branching fire coral .. 2·00 2·10

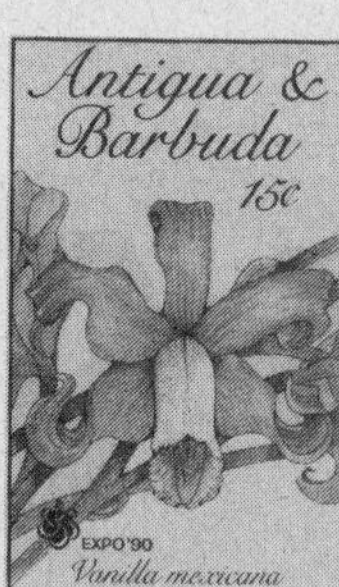

261 "Vanilla mexicana"

1990. "Expo '90" International Garden and Greenery Exhibition, Osaka. Orchids. Mult.

1369 15 c. Type **261** 10 10
1370 45 c. "Epidendrum ibaguense" 20 25
1371 50 c. "Epidendrum secundum" 25 30
1372 60 c. "Maxillaria conferta" 30 35
1373 $1 "Oncidium altissimum" 50 55
1374 $2 "Spiranthes lanceolata" .. .. 95 1·00
1375 $3 "Tonopsis utricularioides" .. 1·40 1·50
1376 $5 "Epidendrum nocturnum" .. .. 2·40 2·50

262 Queen Victoria and Queen Elizabeth II

1990. 150th Anniv of the Penny Black.

1378 **262** 45 c. green 20 25
1379 – 60 c. mauve 30 35
1380 – $5 blue .. .. 2·40 2·50

DESIGNS: 60 c., $5 As Type **262**, but with different backgrounds.

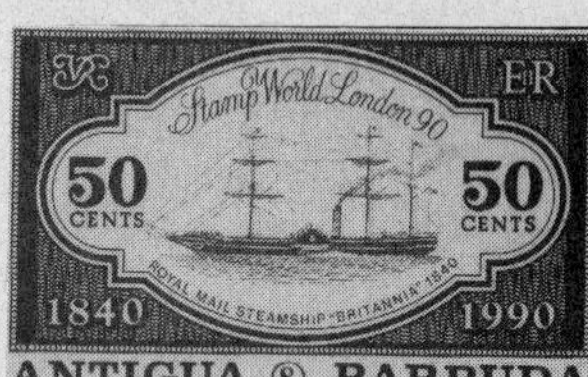

263 "Britannia" (mail steamer), 1840

1990. "Stamp World London 90" International Stamp Exhibition.

1382 **263** 50 c. green and red .. 25 30
1383 – 75 c. brown and red 35 40
1384 – $4 blue and red .. 2·00 2·10

DESIGNS: 75 c. Railway sorting carriage, 1892; $4 Imperial Airways flying boat "Centaurus", 1938.

264 Flamefish

1990. Reef Fishes. Multicoloured.

1386 10 c. Type **264** 10 10
1387 15 c. Coney 10 10
1388 50 c. Squirrelfish .. 25 30
1389 60 c. Sergeant major .. 30 35
1390 $1 Yellowtail snapper .. 50 55
1391 $2 Rock beauty .. .. 95 1·00
1392 $3 Spanish hogfish .. 1·40 1·50
1393 $4 Striped parrotfish .. 2·00 2·10

265 "Voyager 2" passing Saturn

1990. Achievements in Space. Multicoloured.

1395 45 c. Type **265** 20 25
1396 45 c. "Pioneer 11" photographing Saturn 20 25
1397 45 c. Astronaut in transporter 20 25
1398 45 c. Space shuttle "Columbia" 20 25
1399 45 c. "Apollo 10" command module on parachutes 20 25
1400 45 c. "Skylab" space station 20 25
1401 45 c. Astronaut Edward White in space .. 20 25
1402 45 c. "Apollo" spacecraft on joint mission .. 20 25
1403 45 c. "Soyuz" spacecraft on joint mission .. 20 25

1404	45 c. "Mariner 1" passing Venus	20	25
1405	45 c. "Gemini 4" capsule	20	25
1406	45 c. "Sputnik 1" ..	20	25
1407	45 c. Hubble space telescope	20	25
1408	45 c. "X-15" rocket plane	20	25
1409	45 c. "Bell X-1" aircraft	20	25
1410	45 c. "Apollo 17" astronaut and lunar rock formation ..	20	25
1411	45 c. Lunar Rover ..	20	25
1412	45 c. "Apollo 14" lunar module	20	25
1413	45 c. Astronaut Buzz Aldrin on Moon ..	20	25
1414	45 c. Soviet "Lunokhod" lunar vehicle ..	20	25

266 Queen Mother in Evening Dress

1990. 90th Birthday of Queen Elizabeth the Queen Mother.

1415	**266**	15 c. multicoloured ..	10	10
1416	–	35 c. multicoloured ..	15	20
1417	–	75 c. multicoloured ..	35	40
1418	–	$3 multicoloured ..	1·40	1·50

DESIGNS: Nos. 1416/18, Recent photographs of the Queen Mother.

267 Mickey Mouse as Animator

1990. Mickey Mouse in Hollywood. Walt Disney cartoon characters. Multicoloured.

1420	25 c. Type **267**	10	15
1421	45 c. Minnie Mouse learning lines while being dressed ..	20	25
1422	50 c. Mickey Mouse with clapper board	25	30
1423	60 c. Daisy Duck making-up Mickey Mouse ..	30	35
1424	$1 Clarabelle Cow as Cleopatra	50	55
1425	$2 Mickey Mouse directing Goofy and Donald Duck	95	1·00
1426	$3 Mickey Mouse directing Goofy as birdman ..	1·40	1·50
1427	$4 Donald Duck and Mickey Mouse editing film	2·00	2·25

268 Men's 20 Kilometres Walk

1990. Olympic Games, Barcelona (1992). Mult.

1429	50 c. Type **268**	25	30
1430	75 c. Triple jump ..	35	40
1431	$1 Men's 10,000 metres ..	50	55
1432	$5 Javelin	2·40	2·50

269 Huey and Dewey asleep ("Christmas Stories")

1990 International Literacy Year. Walt Disney cartoon characters illustrating works by Charles Dickens. Multicoloured.

1434	15 c. Type **269**	10	10
1435	45 c. Donald Duck as Poor Jo looking at grave ("Bleak House")	20	25
1436	50 c. Dewey as Oliver asking for more ("Oliver Twist") ..	25	30
1437	60 c. Daisy Duck as The Marchioness ("Old Curiosity Shop") ..	30	35
1438	$1 Little Nell giving nosegay to her grand-father ("Little Nell") ..	50	55
1439	$2 Scrooge McDuck as Mr. Pickwick ("Pickwick Papers")	95	1·00
1440	$3 Minnie Mouse as Florence and Mickey Mouse as Paul ("Dombey and Son")	1·40	1·50
1441	$5 Minnie Mouse as Jenny Wren ("Our Mutual Friend")	2·40	2·50

1990. World Cup Football Championship Winners, Italy. Nos. 1308/11 optd **Winners West Germany 1 Argentina 0**.

1443	15 c. Type **252**	10	10
1444	25 c. Goalkeeper moving towards ball ..	10	10
1445	$1 Goalkeeper reaching for ball	50	55
1446	$4 Goalkeeper saving goal	2·00	2·10

271 Pearly-eyed Thrasher

1990. Birds. Multicoloured.

1448	10 c. Type **271**	10	10
1449	25 c. Purple-throated carib	10	15
1450	50 c. Yellowthroat ..	25	30
1451	60 c. American kestrel ..	30	35
1452	$1 Yellow-bellied sapsucker	50	55
1453	$2 Purple gallinule ..	95	1·00
1454	$3 Yellow-crowned night heron	1·40	1·50
1455	$4 Blue-hooded euphonia	2·00	2·10

272 "Madonna and Child with Saints" (detail, Sebastiano del Piombo)

1990. Christmas. Paintings by Renaissance Masters. Multicoloured.

1457	25 c. Type **272**	10	15
1458	30 c. "Virgin and Child with Angels" (detail, Grunewald) (vert) ..	15	20
1459	40 c. "The Holy Family and a Shepherd" (detail, Titian) ..	20	25
1460	60 c. "Virgin and Child" (detail, Lippi) (vert) ..	30	35
1461	$1 "Jesus, St. John and Two Angels" (Rubens)	50	55
1462	$2 "Adoration of the Shepherds" (detail, Vincenzo Catena) ..	95	1·00
1463	$4 "Adoration of the Magi" (detail, Giorgione)	2·00	2·10
1464	$5 "Virgin and Child adored by Warrior" (detail, Vincenzo Catena)	2·40	2·50

273 "Rape of the Daughters of Leucippus" (detail)

1991. 350th Death Anniv of Rubens. Mult.

1466	25 c. Type **273**	10	15
1467	45 c. "Bacchanal" (detail)	20	25
1468	50 c. "Rape of the Sabine Women" (detail) ..	25	30
1469	60 c. "Battle of the Amazons" (detail) ..	30	35
1470	$1 "Rape of the Sabine Women" (different detail)	50	55
1471	$2 "Bacchanal" (different detail)	95	1·00
1472	$3 "Rape of the Sabine Women" (different detail)	1·40	1·50
1473	$4 "Bacchanal" (different detail)	2·00	2·10

274 U.S. Troops cross into Germany, 1944

1991. 50th Anniv of Second World War. Mult.

1475	10 c. Type **274**	10	10
1476	15 c. Axis surrender in North Africa, 1943 ..	10	10
1477	25 c. U.S. tanks invade Kwalajalein, 1944 ..	10	15
1478	45 c. Roosevelt and Churchill meet at Casablanca, 1943 ..	20	25
1479	50 c. Marshal Badoglio, Prime Minister of Italian anti-fascist government, 1943 ..	25	30
1480	$1 Lord Mountbatten, Supreme Allied Commander South-east Asia, 1943	50	55
1481	$2 Greek victory at Koritza, 1940 ..	95	1·00
1482	$4 Anglo-Soviet mutual assistance pact, 1941 ..	2·00	2·10
1483	$5 Operation Torch landings, 1942	2·40	2·50

275 Locomotive "Prince Regent", Middleton Colliery, 1812

1991. Cog Railways. Multicoloured.

1485	25 c. Type **275**	10	10
1486	30 c. Snowdon Mountain Railway	10	10
1487	40 c. First railcar at Hell Gate, Manitou & Pike's Peak Railway, U.S.A.	15	20
1488	60 c. Pnka rack railway, Amberawa, Java ..	30	35
1489	$1 Green Mountain Railway, Maine, 1883 ..	50	55
1490	$2 Cog locomotive "Pike's Peak", 1891	95	1·00
1491	$4 Vitznau–Rigi Railway, Switzerland, and Mt Rigi hotel local post stamp	2·00	2·10
1492	$5 Leopoldina Railway, Brazil	2·40	2·50

276 "Heliconius charithonia"

1991. Butterflies. Multicoloured.

1494	10 c. Type **276**	10	10
1495	35 c. "Marpesia petreus"	15	20
1496	50 c. "Anartia amathea"	25	30
1497	75 c. "Siproeta stelenes"	35	40
1498	$1 "Battus polydamas"	50	55
1499	$2 "Historis odius" ..	95	1·00
1500	$4 "Hypolimnas misippus"	2·00	2·10
1501	$5 "Hamadryas feronia"	2·40	2·50

277 Hanno the Phoenician, 450 B.C.

1991. 500th Anniv (1992) of Discovery of America by Columbus (4th issue). History of Exploration.

1503	10 c. Type **277**	10	10
1504	15 c. Pytheas the Greek, 325 B.C.	10	10
1505	45 c. Erik the Red discovering Greenland, 985 A.D.	20	25
1506	60 c. Leif Eriksson reaching Vinland, 1000 A.D.	30	35
1507	$1 Scylax the Greek in the Indian ocean, 518 A.D.	50	55
1508	$2 Marco Polo sailing to the Orient, 1259 A.D. ..	95	1·00
1509	$4 Ship of Queen Hatshepsut of Egypt, 1493 B.C.	2·00	2·10
1510	$5 St. Brendan's coracle, 500 A.D.	2·40	2·50

278 "Camille Roulin" (Van Gogh)

1991. Death Cent of (1990) Vincent van Gogh (artist). Multicoloured.

1512	5 c. Type **278**	10	10
1513	10 c. "Armand Roulin" ..	10	10
1514	15 c. "Young Peasant Woman with Straw Hat sitting in the Wheat"	10	10
1515	25 c. "Adeline Ravoux"	10	10
1516	30 c. "The Schoolboy" ..	15	20
1517	40 c. "Doctor Gachet" ..	20	25
1518	50 c. "Portrait of a Man"	25	30
1519	75 c. "Two Children" ..	35	40
1520	$2 "The Postman Joseph Roulin"	95	1·00
1521	$3 "The Seated Zouave"	1·40	1·50
1522	$4 "L'Arlesienne" ..	2·00	2·10
1523	$5 "Self-Portrait, November/December 1888"	2·40	2·50

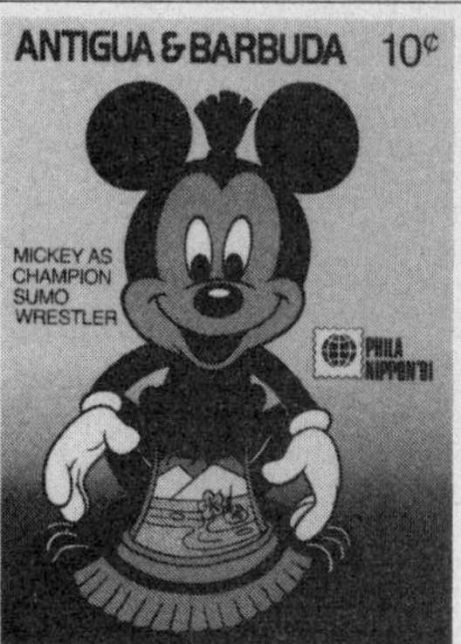

279 Mickey Mouse as Champion Sumo Wrestler

1991. "Philanippon '91" International Stamp Exhibition, Tokyo. Walt Disney cartoon characters participating in martial arts. Multicoloured.

1525	10 c. Type **279**	10	10
1526	15 c. Goofy using the tonfa (horiz)	10	10
1527	45 c. Donald Duck as a Ninja (horiz)	20	25
1528	60 c. Mickey armed for Kung fu	30	35
1529	$1 Goofy with Kendo sword	50	55
1530	$2 Mickey and Donald demonstrating Aikido (horiz)	95	1·00
1531	$4 Mickey and Donald in Judo bout (horiz) ..	2·00	2·10
1532	$5 Mickey performing Yabusame (mounted archery)	2·40	2·50

280 Queen Elizabeth and Prince Philip in 1976

1991. 65th Birthday of Queen Elizabeth II. Multicoloured.

1534	15 c. Type **280**	10	10
1535	20 c. The Queen and Prince Philip in Portugal, 1985 ..	10	10
1536	$2 Queen Elizabeth II ..	95	1·00
1537	$4 The Queen and Prince Philip at Ascot, 1986 ..	2·00	2·10

1991. 10th Wedding Anniv of Prince and Princess of Wales. As T **280**. Mult.

1539	10 c. Prince and Princess of Wales at party, 1986	10	10
1540	40 c. Separate portraits of Prince, Princess and sons	20	25
1541	$1 Prince Henry and Prince William ..	50	55
1542	$5 Princess Diana in Australia and Prince Charles in Hungary ..	2·40	2·50

281 Daisy Duck teeing-off

1991. Golf. Walt Disney cartoon characters. Multicoloured.

1544	10 c. Type **281**	10	10
1545	15 c. Goofy playing ball from under trees ..	10	10
1546	45 c. Mickey Mouse playing deflected shot	20	25
1547	60 c. Mickey hacking divot out of fairway ..	30	35
1548	$1 Donald Duck playing ball out of pond ..	50	55
1549	$2 Minnie Mouse hitting ball over pond ..	95	1·00
1550	$4 Donald in a bunker ..	2·00	2·10
1551	$5 Goofy trying snooker shot into hole ..	2·40	2·50

282 Moose receiving Gold Medal

1991. 50th Anniv of Archie Comics, and Olympic Games, Barcelona (1992). Mult.

1553	10 c. Type **282**	10	10
1554	25 c. Archie playing polo on a motorcycle (horiz)	10	10
1555	40 c. Archie and Betty at fencing class	20	25
1556	60 c. Archie joining girls' volleyball team ..	30	35
1557	$1 Archie with tennis ball in his mouth	50	55
1558	$2 Archie running marathon	95	1·00
1559	$4 Archie judging women's gymnastics (horiz)	2·00	2·10
1560	$5 Archie watching the cheer-leaders	2·40	2·50

283 Presidents De Gaulle and Kennedy, 1961

1991. Birth Centenary of Charles de Gaulle (French statesman). Multicoloured.

1562	10 c. Type **283**	10	10
1563	15 c. General De Gaulle with Pres. Roosevelt, 1945 (vert)	10	10
1564	45 c. Pres. De Gaulle with Chancellor Adenauer, 1962 (vert)	20	25
1565	60 c. De Gaulle at Arc de Triomphe, Liberation of Paris, 1944 (vert) ..	30	35
1566	$1 General De Gaulle crossing the Rhine, 1945	50	55
1567	$2 General De Gaulle in Algiers, 1944	95	1·00
1568	$4 Presidents De Gaulle and Eisenhower, 1960	2·00	2·10
1569	$5 De Gaulle returning from Germany, 1968 (vert)	2·40	2·50

284 Parliament Building and Map

1991. 10th Anniv of Independence.

1571	284	10 c. multicoloured ..	10	10

285 Germans celebrating Reunification

1991. Anniversaries and Events. Mult.

1573	25 c. Type **285**	10	10
1574	75 c. Cubs erecting tent ..	35	40
1575	$1.50 "Don Giovanni" and Mozart	75	80
1576	$2 Chariot driver and Gate at night	95	1·00
1577	$2 Lord Baden-Powell and members of 3rd Antigua Methodist cub pack (vert)	95	1·00
1578	$2 Lilienthal's signature and glider "Flugzeug Nr. 5"	95	1·00
1579	$2.50 Driver in modern locomotive (vert) ..	1·25	1·40
1580	$3 Statues from podium	1·40	1·50
1581	$3.50 Cubs and camp fire	1·60	1·75
1582	$4 St. Peter's Cathedral, Salzburg	2·00	2·10

ANNIVERSARIES AND EVENTS: Nos. 1573, 1576, 1580, Bicentenary of Brandenburg Gate, Germany; 1574, 1577, 1581, 17th World Scout Jamboree, Korea; 1575, 1582, Death bicentenary of Mozart (composer); 1578, Centenary of Otto Lilienthal's gliding experiments; 1579, Centenary of Trans-Siberian Railway.

286 "Nimitz" Class Carrier and "Ticonderoga" Class Cruiser

1991. 50th Anniv of Japanese Attack on Pearl Harbor. Multicoloured.

1585	$1 Type **286**	50	55
1586	$1 Tourist launch ..	50	55
1587	$1 U.S.S. "Arizona" memorial	50	55
1588	$1 Wreaths on water and aircraft	50	55
1589	$1 White tern	50	55
1590	$1 Japanese torpedo bombers over Pearl City	50	55
1591	$1 Zeros attacking ..	50	55
1592	$1 Battleship Row in flames	50	55
1593	$1 U.S.S. "Nevada" (battleship) underway	50	55
1594	$1 Zeros returning to carriers	50	55

287 "The Annunciation"

1991. Christmas. Religious Paintings by Fra Angelico. Multicoloured.

1595	10 c. Type **287**	10	10
1596	30 c. "Nativity" ..	15	20
1597	40 c. "Adoration of the Magi"	20	25
1598	60 c. "Presentation in the Temple"	30	35
1599	$1 "Circumcision" ..	50	55
1600	$3 "Flight into Egypt" ..	1·40	1·50
1601	$4 "Massacre of the Innocents"	2·00	2·10
1602	$5 "Christ teaching in the Temple"	2·40	2·50

288 Queen Elizabeth II and Bird Sanctuary

1992. 40th Anniv of Queen Elizabeth II's Accession. Multicoloured.

1604	10 c. Type **288**	10	10
1605	30 c. Nelson's Dockyard	15	20
1606	$1 Ruins on Shirley Heights	50	55
1607	$5 Beach and palm trees	2·40	2·50

289 Mickey Mouse awarding Swimming Gold Medal to Mermaid

1992. Olympic Games, Barcelona. Walt Disney cartoon characters. Multicoloured.

1609	10 c. Type **289**	10	10
1610	15 c. Huey, Dewey and Louie with kayak ..	10	10
1611	30 c. Donald Duck and Uncle Scrooge in yacht	15	20
1612	50 c. Donald and horse playing water polo ..	25	30
1613	$1 Big Pete weightlifting	50	55
1614	$2 Donald and Goofy fencing	95	1·00
1615	$4 Mickey and Donald playing volleyball ..	2·00	2·10
1616	$5 Goofy vaulting ..	2·40	2·50

290 Pteranodon

1992. Prehistoric Animals. Multicoloured.

1618	10 c. Type **290**	10	10
1619	15 c. Brachiosaurus ..	10	10
1620	30 c. Tyrannosaurus Rex	15	20
1621	50 c. Parasaurolophus ..	25	30
1622	$1 Deinonychus (horiz) ..	50	55
1623	$2 Triceratops (horiz) ..	95	1·00
1624	$4 Protoceratops hatching (horiz)	2·00	2·10
1625	$5 Stegosaurus (horiz) ..	2·40	2·50

291 "Supper at Emmaus" (Caravaggio)

1992. Easter. Religious Paintings. Mult.

1627	10 c. Type **291**	10	10
1628	15 c. "The Vision of St. Peter" (Zurbaran) ..	10	10
1629	30 c. "Christ driving the Money Changers from the Temple" (Tiepolo)	15	20
1630	40 c. "Martyrdom of St. Bartholomew" (detail) (Ribera)	20	25
1631	$1 "Christ driving the Money Changers from the Temple" (detail) (Tiepolo)	50	55
1632	$2 "Crucifixion" (detail) (Altdorfer)	95	1·00
1633	$4 "The Deposition" (detail) (Fra Angelico)	2·00	2·10
1634	$5 "The Deposition" (different detail) (Fra Angelico)	2·40	2·50

292 "The Miracle at the Well" (Alonso Cano)

1992. "Granada '92" International Stamp Exhibition, Spain. Spanish Paintings. Mult.

1636	10 c. Type **292**	10	10
1637	15 c. "The Poet Luis de Gongora y Argote" (Velazquez)	10	10
1638	30 c. "The Painter Francisco Goya" (Vincente Lopez Portana)	15	20
1639	40 c. "Maria de las Nieves Michaela Fourdinier" (Luis Paret y Alcazar)	20	25
1640	$1 "Carlos III eating before his Court" (Alcazar) (horiz) ..	50	55
1641	$2 "Rain Shower in Granada" (Antonio Munoz Degrain) (horiz)	95	1·00
1642	$4 "Sarah Bernhardt" (Santiago Rusinol i Prats)	2·00	2·10
1643	$5 "The Hermitage Garden" (Joaquim Mir Trinxet)	2·40	2·50

293 "Amanita caesarea"

1992. Fungi. Multicoloured.

1645	10 c. Type **293**	10	10
1646	15 c. "Collybia fusipes" ..	10	10
1647	30 c. "Boletus aereus" ..	15	20
1648	40 c. "Laccaria amethystina"	20	25
1649	$1 "Russula virescens" ..	50	55
1650	$2 "Tricholoma auratum"	95	1·00
1651	$4 "Calocybe gambosa"	2·00	2·10
1652	$5 "Panus tigrinus" ..	2·40	2·50

294 Memorial Cross and Huts, San Salvador

1992. 500th Anniv of Discovery of America by Columbus (5th issue). World Columbian Stamp "Expo '92", Chicago. Multicoloured.

1654	15 c. Type **294**	10	10
1655	30 c. Martin Pinzon with telescope	15	20
1656	40 c. Christopher Columbus	20	25
1657	$1 "Pinta"	50	55
1658	$2 "Nina"	95	1·00
1659	$4 "Santa Maria" ..	2·00	2·10

295 Antillean Crested Hummingbird and Wild Plantain

1992. "Genova '92" International Thematic Stamp Exhibition. Hummingbirds and Plants. Multicoloured.

1661	10 c. Type **295**	10	10
1662	25 c. Green mango and parrot's plantain ..	10	10
1663	45 c. Purple-throated carib and lobster claws	20	25
1664	60 c. Antillean mango and coral plant	30	35
1665	$1 Vervain hummingbird and cardinal's guard ..	50	55
1666	$2 Rufous-breasted hermit and heliconia ..	95	1·00
1667	$4 Blue-headed hummingbird and red ginger ..	2·00	2·10
1668	$5 Green-throated carib and ornamental banana	2·40	2·50

296 Columbus meeting Amerindians

1992. 500th Anniv of Discovery of America by Columbus (6th issue). Organization of East Caribbean States. Multicoloured.

1670	$1 Type **296**	50	55
1671	$2 Ships approaching island	95	1·00

297 Ts'ai Lun and Paper

1992. Inventors and Inventions. Mult.

1672	10 c. Type **297**	10	10
1673	25 c. Igor Sikorsky and four-engined biplane ..	10	10
1674	30 c. Alexander Graham Bell and early telephone	15	20
1675	40 c. Johannes Gutenberg and early printing press	20	25
1676	60 c. James Watt and stationary steam engine	30	35
1677	$1 Anton van Leeuwenhoek and early microscope	50	55
1678	$4 Louis Braille and hands reading braille	2·00	2·10
1679	$5 Galileo and telescope	2·40	2·50

298 Elvis looking Pensive

1992. 15th Death Anniv of Elvis Presley. Multicoloured.

1681	$1 Type **298**	50	55
1682	$1 Wearing black and yellow striped shirt ..	50	55
1683	$1 Singing into microphone	50	55
1684	$1 Wearing wide-brimmed hat	50	55
1685	$1 With microphone in right hand	50	55
1686	$1 In Army uniform ..	50	55
1687	$1 Wearing pink shirt ..	50	55
1688	$1 In yellow shirt ..	50	55
1689	$1 In jacket and bow tie	50	55

300 "Virgin and Child with Angels" (detail) (School of Piero della Francesca)

1992. Christmas. Details of the Holy Child from various paintings. Multicoloured.

1691	10 c. Type **300**	10	10
1692	25 c. "Madonna degli Alberelli" (Giovanni Bellini)	10	10
1693	30 c. "Madonna and Child with St. Anthony Abbot and St. Sigismund" (Neroccio)	15	20
1694	40 c. "Madonna and the Grand Duke" (Raphael)	20	25
1695	60 c. "The Nativity" (Georges de la Tour) ..	30	35
1696	$1 "Holy Family" (Jacob Jordaens)	50	55
1697	$4 "Madonna and Child Enthroned" (Magaritone)	2·00	2·10
1698	$5 "Madonna and Child on a Curved Throne" (Byzantine school) ..	2·40	2·50

301 Russian Cosmonauts

1992. Anniversaries and Events. Mult.

1700	10 c. Type **301**	10	10
1701	40 c. "Graf Zeppelin" (airship), 1929	20	25
1702	45 c. Bishop Daniel Davis	20	25
1703	75 c. Konrad Adenauer making speech ..	35	40
1704	$1 Bus Mosbacher and "Weatherly" (yacht) ..	50	55
1705	$1.50 Rain forest ..	75	80
1706	$2 Tiger	95	1·00
1707	$2 National flag, plant and emblem (horiz) ..	95	1·00
1708	$2 Members of Community Players company (horiz) ..	95	1·00
1709	$2.25 Women carrying pots	1·00	1·10
1710	$3 Lions Club emblem ..	1·40	1·50
1711	$4 Chinese rocket on launch tower	2·00	2·10
1712	$4 West German and N.A.T.O. flags ..	2·00	2·10
1713	$6 Hugo Eckener (airship pioneer)	3·00	3·25

ANNIVERSARIES AND EVENTS: Nos. 1700, 1711, International Space Year; Nos. 1701, 1713, 75th death anniv of Count Ferdinand von Zeppelin; No. 1702, 150th anniv of Anglican Diocese of North-eastern Caribbean and Aruba; Nos. 1703, 1712, 25th death anniv of Konrad Adenauer (German statesman); No. 1704, Americas Cup yachting championship; Nos. 1705/6, Earth Summit '92, Rio; No. 1707, 50th anniv of Inter-American Institute for Agricultural Co-operation; No. 1708, 40th anniv of Cultural Development; No. 1709, United Nations World Health Organization Projects; No. 1710, 75th anniv of International Association of Lions Clubs.

302 Boy Hiker resting

1993. Hummel Figurines. Multicoloured.

1715	15 c. Type **302**	10	10
1716	30 c. Girl sitting on fence	15	20
1717	40 c. Boy hunter ..	20	25
1718	50 c. Boy with umbrella	25	30
1719	$1 Hikers at signpost ..	50	55
1720	$2 Boy hiker with pack and stick	95	1·00
1721	$4 Girl with young child and goat	2·00	2·10
1722	$5 Boy whistling ..	2·40	2·50

303 Goofy playing Golf

1993. Opening of Euro-Disney Resort, Paris. Multicoloured.

1724	10 c. Type **303**	10	10
1725	25 c. Chip and Dale at Davy Crockett's campground	10	10
1726	30 c. Donald Duck at the Cheyenne Hotel	15	20
1727	40 c. Goofy at the Santa Fe Hotel	20	25
1728	$1 Mickey and Minnie Mouse at the New York Hotel	50	55
1729	$2 Mickey, Minnie and Goofy in car	95	1·00
1730	$4 Goofy at Pirates of the Caribbean	2·00	2·10
1731	$5 Donald at Adventureland	2·40	2·50

304 Cardinal's Guard

1993. Flowers. Multicoloured.

1733	15 c. Type **304**	10	10
1734	25 c. Giant granadilla ..	10	10
1735	30 c. Spider flower ..	15	20
1736	40 c. Gold vine ..	20	25
1737	$1 Frangipani ..	50	55
1738	$2 Bougainvillea ..	95	1·00
1739	$4 Yellow oleander ..	2·00	2·10
1740	$5 Spicy jatropha ..	2·40	2·50

305 "The Destiny of Marie de' Medici" (upper detail)

1993. Bicentenary of the Louvre, Paris. Paintings by Peter Paul Rubens. Mult.

1742 $1 Type **305** 50 55
1743 $1 "The Birth of Marie de' Medici" 50 55
1744 $1 "The Education of Marie de' Medici" .. 50 55
1745 $1 "The Destiny of Marie de' Medici" (lower detail) 50 55
1746 $1 "Henry VI receiving the Portrait of Marie" 50 55
1747 $1 "The Meeting of the King and Marie at Lyons" 50 55
1748 $1 "The Marriage by Proxy" 50 55
1749 $1 "The Birth of Louis XIII" 50 55
1750 $1 "The Capture of Juliers" 50 55
1751 $1 "The Exchange of the Princesses" 50 55
1752 $1 "The Regency" 50 55
1753 $1 "The Majority of Louis XIII" 50 55
1754 $1 "The Flight from Blois" 50 55
1755 $1 "The Treaty of Angouleme" 50 55
1756 $1 "The Peace of Angers" 50 55
1757 $1 "The Reconciliation of Louis and Marie de' Medici" 50 55

Nos. 1742/57 depict details from "The Story of Marie de' Medici".

306 St. Lucia Amazon

1993. Endangered Species. Multicoloured.

1759 $1 Type **306** 50 55
1760 $1 Cahow 50 55
1761 $1 Swallow-tailed kite .. 50 55
1762 $1 Everglade kite .. 50 55
1763 $1 Imperial amazon .. 50 55
1764 $1 Humpback whale .. 50 55
1765 $1 Plain pigeon .. 50 55
1766 $1 St. Vincent amazon .. 50 55
1767 $1 Puerto Rican amazon 50 55
1768 $1 Leatherback turtle .. 50 55
1769 $1 American crocodile .. 50 55
1770 $1 Hawksbill turtle .. 50 55

Nos.1759/70 were printed together, se-tenant, with the background forming a composite design.

307 Queen Elizabeth II at Coronation (photograph by Cecil Beaton)

1993. 40th Anniv of Coronation (1st issue).

1772 **307** 30 c. multicoloured .. 15 20
1773 – 40 c. multicoloured .. 20 25
1774 – $2 blue and black .. 95 1·00
1775 – $4 multicoloured .. 2·00 2·10

DESIGNS: 40 c. Imperial State Crown; $2 Procession of heralds; $4 Queen Elizabeth II and Prince Edward.

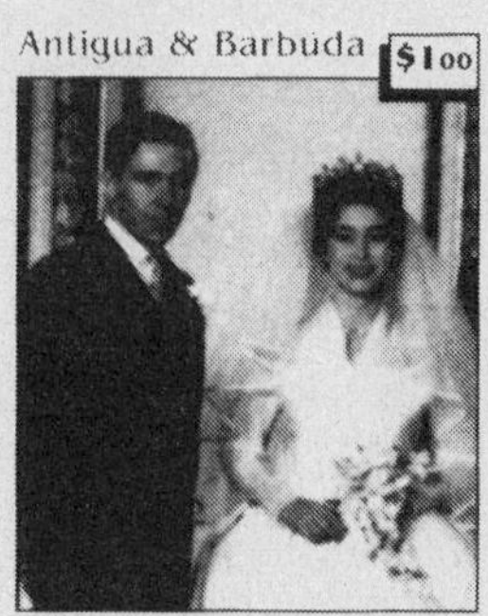

308 Princess Margaret and Antony Armstrong-Jones

1993. 40th Anniv of Coronation (2nd issue).

1777/1808 $1 x 32 either grey and black or mult .. 14·50 16·00

DESIGNS: Various views from each decade of the reign.

309 Edward Stanley Gibbons and Catalogue of 1865

1993. Famous Professional Philatelists.

1809 **309** $1.50 brn, blk & grn 75 80
1810 – $1.50 multicoloured .. 75 80
1811 – $1.50 multicoloured .. 75 80
1812 – $1.50 multicoloured .. 75 80
1813 – $1.50 multicoloured .. 75 80
1814 – $1.50 multicoloured .. 75 80

DSEIGNS: No. 1810, Theodore Champion and France 1849 1 f. stamp; No. 1811, J. Walter Scott and U.S.A. 1918 24 c. "Inverted Jenny" error; No. 1812, Hugo Michel and Bavaria 1849 1 k. stamp; No. 1813, Alberto and Giulio Bolaffi with Sardinia 1851 5 c. stamp; No. 1814, Richard Borek and Brunswick 1865 1 gr. stamp.

310 Paul Gascoigne

1993. World Cup Football Championship, U.S.A. English players. Multicoloured.

1816 $2 Type **310** .. .. 95 1·00
1817 $2 David Platt .. .. 95 1·00
1818 $2 Martin Peters .. 95 1·00
1819 $2 John Barnes .. .. 95 1·00
1820 $2 Gary Lineker .. 95 1·00
1821 $2 Geoff Hurst .. .. 95 1·00
1822 $2 Bobby Charlton .. 95 1·00
1823 $2 Bryan Robson .. 95 1·00
1824 $2 Bobby Moore .. 95 1·00
1825 $2 Nobby Stiles .. 95 1·00
1826 $2 Gordon Banks .. 95 1·00
1827 $2 Peter Shilton .. 95 1·00

MINIMUM PRICE

The minimum price quoted is 10p which represents a handling charge rather than a basis for valuing common stamps. For further notes about prices see introductory pages.

311 Grand Inspector W. Heath

1993. Anniversaries and Events. Mult.

1829 10 c. Type **311** 10 10
1830 15 c. Rodnina and Oulanov (U.S.S.R.) (pairs figure skating) (horiz) 10 10
1831 30 c. Present Masonic Hall, St. John's (horiz) 15 20
1832 30 c. Willy Brandt with Helmut Schmidt and George Leber (horiz) .. 15 20
1833 30 c. "Cat and Bird" (Picasso) (horiz) .. 15 20
1834 40 c. Previous Masonic Hall, St. John's (horiz) 20 25
1835 40 c. "Fish on a Newspaper" (Picasso) (horiz) 20 25
1836 40 c. Early astronomical equipment 20 25
1837 40 c. Prince Naruhito and engagement photographs (horiz) .. 20 25
1838 60 c. Grand Inspector J. Jeffery 30 35
1839 $1 "Woman Combing her Hair" (W. Slewinski) (horiz) 50 55
1840 $3 Masako Owada and engagement photographs (horiz) .. 1·40 1·50
1841 $3 "Artist's Wife with Cat" (Konrad Kryzanowski) (horiz) 1·40 1·50
1842 $4 Willy Brandt and protest march (horiz) 2·00 2·10
1843 $4 Galaxy .. .. 2·00 2·10
1844 $5 Alberto Tomba (Italy) (giant slalom) (horiz) 2·40 2·50
1845 $5 "Dying Bull" (Picasso) (horiz) .. .. 2·40 2·50
1846 $5 Pres. Clinton and family (horiz) .. 2·40 2·50

ANNIVERSARIES AND EVENTS: Nos. 1829, 1831, 1834, 1838, 150th anniv of St. John's Masonic Lodge No. 492; Nos. 1830, 1844, Winter Olympic Games '94, Lillehammer; Nos. 1832, 1842, 80th birth anniv of Willy Brandt (German politician); Nos. 1833, 1835, 1845, 20th death anniv of Picasso (artist); Nos.1836, 1843, 450th death anniv of Copernicus (astronomer); Nos. 1837, 1840, Marriage of Crown Prince Naruhito of Japan; Nos. 1839, 1841, "Polska '93" International Stamp Exhibition, Poznan; No. 1846, Inaugration of U.S. President William Clinton.

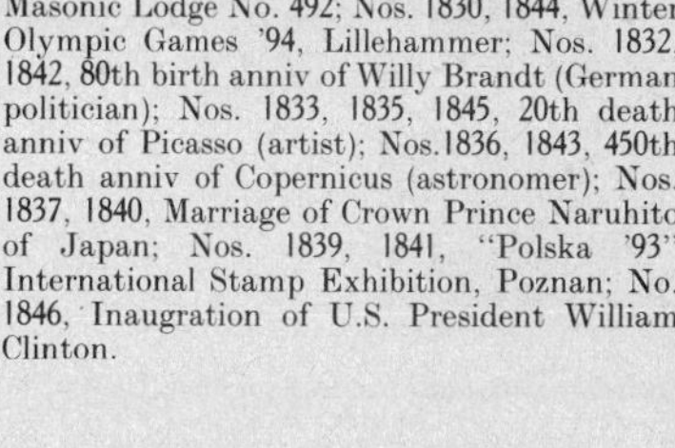

312 Hugo Eckener and Dr. W. Beckers with Zeppelin over Lake George, New York

1993. Aviation Anniversaries. Multicoloured.

1848 30 c. Type **312** 15 20
1849 40 c. Chicago World's Fair from "Graf Zeppelin" 20 25
1850 40 c. Gloster E.28/39, 1941 20 25
1851 40 c. George Washington writing balloon mail letter (vert) 20 25
1852 $4 Pres. Wilson and biplane .. .. 2·00 2·10
1853 $5 "Hindenburg" over Ebbets Field baseball stadium, 1937 .. .. 2·40 2·50
1854 $5 Gloster Meteor in dogfight .. .. 2·40 2·50

ANNIVERSARIES: Nos. 1848/9, 1853, 125th birth anniv of Hugo Eckener (airship commander); Nos. 1850, 1854, 75th anniv of Royal Air Force; Nos. 1851/2, Bicentenary of first airmail flight.

313 Lincoln Continental

1993. Centenaries of Henry Ford's First Petrol Engine (Nos. 1856, 1858,) and Karl Benz's First Four-wheeled Car (others). Mult.

1856 30 c. Type **313** 15 20
1857 40 c. Mercedes racing car, 1914 .. .. 20 25
1858 $4 Ford "GT40", 1966 .. 2·00 2·10
1859 $5 Mercedes Benz "gull-wing" coupe, 1954 .. 2·40 2·50

314 "The Musical Farmer", 1932

1993. Mickey Mouse Film Posters. Mult.

1861 10 c. Type **314** 10 10
1862 15 c. "Little Whirlwind", 1941 .. .. 10 10
1863 30 c. "Pluto's Dream House", 1940 .. .. 15 20
1864 40 c. "Gulliver Mickey", 1934 .. .. 20 25
1865 50 c. "Alpine Climbers", 1936 .. .. 25 30
1866 $1 "Mr. Mouse Takes a Trip", 1940 .. .. 50 55
1867 $2 "The Nifty Nineties", 1941 .. .. 95 1·00
1868 $4 "Mickey Down Under", 1948 .. .. 2·00 2·10
1869 $5 "The Pointer", 1939 2·40 2·50

315 Marie and Fritz with Christmas Tree

1993. Christmas. Mickey's Nutcracker. Walt Disney cartoon characters in scenes from "The Nutcracker". Multicoloured.

1871 10 c. Type **315** 10 10
1872 15 c. Marie recieves Nutcracker from Godfather Drosselmeir 10 10
1873 20 c. Fritz breaks Nutcracker 10 10
1874 30 c. Nutcracker with sword 15 20
1875 40 c. Nutcracker and Marie in the snow .. 20 25
1876 50 c. Marie and the Prince meet Sugar Plum Fairy 25 30
1877 60 c. Marie and Prince in Crystal Hall .. 30 35
1878 $3 Huey, Dewey and Louie as Cossack dancers .. .. 1·40 1·50
1879 $6 Mother Ginger and her puppets .. .. 3·00 3·25

ALBUM LISTS

Write for our latest list of albums and accessories. This will be sent free on request.

316 "Hannah and Samuel" (Rembrandt)

1993. Famous Paintings by Rembrandt and Matisse. Multicoloured.

1881	15 c. Type **316**	10	10
1882	15 c. "Guitarist" (Matisse)	10	10
1883	30 c. "The Jewish Bride" (Rembrandt)	15	20
1884	40 c. "Jacob wrestling with the Angel" (Rembrandt)	20	25
1885	60 c. "Interior with a Goldfish Bowl" (Matisse)	30	35
1886	$1 "Mlle Yvonne Landsberg" (Matisse)	50	55
1887	$4 "The Toboggan" (Matisse)	2·00	2·10
1888	$5 "Moses with the Tablets of the Law" (Rembrandt)	2·40	2·50

ASCENSION

An island in S. Atlantic. A dependency of St. Helena.

1922. 12 pence = 1 shilling.
20 shilling = 1 pound.
1971. 100 pence = 1 pound.

1922. Stamps of St. Helena, optd. **ASCENSION.**

1.	½d. black and green	3·25	8·50
2.	1d. green	3·75	8·50
3.	1½d. red	14·00	35·00
4.	2d. black and slate	12·00	12·00
5.	3d. blue	12·00	15·00
6.	8d. black and purple ..	24·00	32·00
9.	1s. black on green	26·00	32·00
7.	2s. black and blue on blue..	80·00	£100
8.	3s. black and violet	£120	£140

2. Badge of St. Helena.

1924.

10.	**2.**	½d. black	2·50	7·00
11.		1d. black and green ..	4·00	5·00
12.		1½d. red	6·00	17·00
13.		2d. black and grey ..	6·00	4·00
14.		3d. blue	4·75	9·00
15.		4d. black on yellow ..	38·00	65·00
15d.		5d. purple and green ..	10·00	20·00
16.		6d. black and purple ..	45·00	70·00
17.		8d. black and violet ..	11·00	29·00
18.		1s. black and brown ..	18·00	35·00
19.		2s. black & blue on blue..	55·00	80·00
20.		3s. black on blue	80·00	85·00

3. Georgetown.

4. Ascension Island.

DESIGNS—HORIZ. 1½d. The Pier. 3d. Long Beach. 5d. Three Sisters. 1s. Sooty Tern. 5s. Green mountain.

1934. Medallion portrait of King George V. (except 1s.).

21.	**3.**	½d. black and violet ..	90	80
22.	**4.**	1d. black and green ..	1·75	1·25
23.	–	1½d. black and red ..	1·75	2·25
24.	**4.**	2d. black and orange ..	1·75	2·25
25.	–	3d. black and blue ..	1·75	1·50
26.	–	5d. black and blue ..	2·25	3·25
27.	**4.**	8d. black and brown ..	4·25	4·75
28.	–	1s. black and red.. ..	16·00	6·00
29.	**4.**	2s. 6d. black and purple..	32·00	32·00
30.	–	5s. black and brown ..	45·00	55·00

1935. Silver Jubilee. As T **13** of Antigua.

31.	1½d. blue and red ..	3·50	4·50
32.	2d. blue and grey ..	11·00	18·00
33.	5d. green and blue ..	14·00	18·00
34.	1s. grey and purple ..	20·00	25·00

1937. Coronation. As T **2** of Aden.

35.	1d. green	50	50
36.	2d. orange	1·50	40
37.	3d. blue	1·50	50

10. The Pier.

1938.

38b	**A.**	½d. black and violet ..	50	90
39	**B.**	1d. black and green ..	48·00	8·50
39b		1d. black and orange ..	45	60
39d	**C.**	1d. black and green ..	30	30
40b	**10.**	1½d. black and red ..	70	80
40d		1½d. black and pink ..	45	80
41a	**B.**	2d. black and orange ..	80	40
41c		2d. black and red ..	40	50
42	D	3d. black and blue ..	£100	26·00
42b		3d. black and grey ..	70	80
42d	B	4d. black and blue ..	4·50	3·00
43	C	6d. black and blue ..	8·00	70
44a	A	1s. black and brown ..	4·50	2·00
45	**10**	2s. 6d. black and red ..	35·00	7·50
46a	D	5s. black and brown ..	45·00	26·00
47a	C	10s. black and purple ..	65·00	55·00

DESIGNS: A, Georgetown. B, Green Mountain C, Three Sisters. D, Long Beach.

1946. Victory. As T **9** of Aden.

48.	2d. orange	40	30
49.	4d. blue	40	30

1948. Silver Wedding. As T **10/11** of Aden.

50.	3d. black	50	30
51.	10s. mauve..	45·00	38·00

1949. U.P.U. As T **20/23** of Antigua.

52.	3d. red	1·40	1·00
53.	4d. blue	5·50	1·10
54.	6d. olive	6·00	2·00
55.	1s. black	6·00	1·50

1953. Coronation. As Type **13** of Aden.

56.	3d. black and grey ..	1·25	1·50

15. Water Catchment.

1956.

57.	**15.**	½d. black and brown ..	10	30
58.	–	1d. black and mauve ..	90	50
59.	–	1½d. black and orange ..	30	50
60.	–	2d. black and red ..	1·00	50
61.	–	2½d. black and brown ..	75	70
62.	–	3d. black and blue ..	2·00	1·00
63.	–	4d. black and turquoise..	1·25	1·25
64.	–	6d. black and blue ..	1·25	90
65.	–	7d. black and olive ..	1·00	1·00
66.	–	1s. black and red ..	1·00	90
67.	–	2s. 6d. black and purple	27·00	6·50
68.	–	5s. black and green ..	35·00	17·00
69.	–	10s. black and purple ..	48·00	35·00

DESIGNS: 1d. Map of Ascension. 1½d. Georgetown. 2d. Map showing Atlantic cables. 2½d. Mountain Road. 3d. White-tailed Tropic Bird. 4d. Long-finned Tunny. 6d. Rollers on seashore. 7d. Turtles. 1s. Land Crab. 2s. 6d. Sooty Tern. 5s. Perfect Crater. 10s. View of Ascension.

28. Brown Booby.

1963. Birds. Multicoloured.

70.	1d. Type **28**	40	20
71.	1½d. White-capped Noddy	70	40
72.	2d. White Tern	70	30
73.	3d. Red-billed Tropic Bird	75	30
74.	4½d. Common Noddy ..	75	30
75.	6d. Sooty Tern	70	30
76.	7d. Ascension Frigate-Bird	70	30
77.	10d. Blue-faced Booby ..	70	30
78.	1s. White-tailed Tropic Bird	70	30
79.	1s. 6d. Red-billed Tropic Bird	3·50	1·75
80.	2s. 6d. Madeiran Storm Petrel	4·75	4·00
81.	5s. Red-footed Booby (brown phase)	6·00	3·50
82.	10s. Ascension Frigate-Birds	12·00	4·75
83.	£1 Red-footed Booby (white phase)	22·00	7·00

1963. Freedom from Hunger. As T **28** of Aden.

84.	1s. 6d. red	2·25	40

1963. Cent of Red Cross. As T **33** of Antigua.

85.	3d. red and black	3·50	60
86.	1s. 6d. red and blue ..	7·50	2·00

1965. Cent of I.T.U. As T **36** of Antigua.

87.	3d. mauve and violet ..	1·25	25
88.	6d. turquoise and brown..	1·50	30

1965. I.C.Y. As T **37** of Antigua.

89.	1d. purple and turquoise ..	50	20
90.	6d. green and lavender ..	1·50	50

1966. Churchill Commemoration. As T **38** of Antigua.

91.	1d. blue	50	25
92.	3d. green	2·75	70
93.	6d. brown	3·50	75
94.	1s. 6d. violet	4·50	1·25

1966. World Cup Football Championship. As T **40** of Antigua.

95.	3d. multicoloured	1·25	30
96.	6d. multicoloured	1·50	40

1966. Inauguration of W.H.O. Headquarters, Geneva. As T **41** of Antigua.

97.	3d. black, green and blue..	1·75	40
98.	1s. 6d. black, purple & ochre	4·25	1·10

42. Satellite Station.

1966. Opening of Apollo Communication Satellite Earth Station.

99.	**42.**	4d. black and violet ..	15	20
100.		8d. black and green ..	20	20
101.		1s. 3d. black and brown	25	25
102.		2s. 6d. black and blue..	35	70

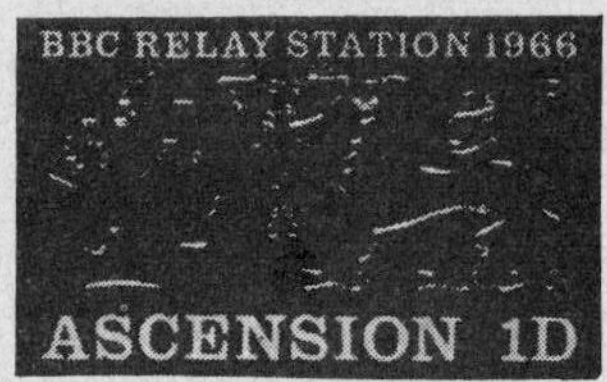

43. B.B.C. Emblem.

1966. Opening of B.B.C. Relay Station.

103.	**43.**	1d. gold and blue ..	15	15
104.		3d. gold and green ..	20	20
105.		6d. gold and violet ..	25	20
106.		1s. 6d. gold and red ..	25	25

1967. 20th Anniv. of U.N.E.S.C.O. As T **54/56** of Antigua.

107.	3d. multicoloured ..	2·25	80
108.	6d. yellow, violet and olive	3·50	1·00
109.	1s. 6d. black, pur. & orge.	5·50	1·40

44. Human Rights Emblem and Chain Links.

1968. Human Rights Year

110.	**44.**	6d. orge., red and blk..	20	10
111.		1s. 6d. blue, red & blk..	30	15
112.		2s. 6d. grn., red & blk..	35	20

45. Ascension Black-Fish.

1968. Fishes (1st series).

113.	**45.**	4d. black and blue ..	50	20
114.	–	8d. multicoloured ..	60	35
115.	–	1s. 9d. multicoloured ..	80	40
116.	–	2s. 3d. multicoloured ..	90	45

DESIGNS: 8d. Leather-jacket. 1s. 9d. Tunny. 2s. 3d. Mako Shark.

See also Nos. 117/120 and 126/9.

1969. Fishes (2nd series). As T **45**. Mult.

117.	4d. Sailfish	1·00	60
118.	6d. Old Wife	1·25	80
119.	1s. 6d. Yellowtail ..	2·25	1·50
120.	2s. 11d. Jack	3·75	2·25

46. H.M.S. "Rattlesnake".

1969. Royal Naval Crests (1st series).
121. **46.** 4d. multicoloured .. 50 15
122. – 9d. multicoloured .. 70 15
123. – 1s. 9d. blue and gold .. 1·25 25
124. – 2s. 3d. multicoloured .. 1·50 30
DESIGNS: 9d. H.M.S. "Weston". 1s. 9d. H.M.S. "Undaunted", 2s. 3d. H.M.S. "Eagle".
See also Nos. 130/3, 149/52, 154/7 and 166/9.

1970. Fishes (3rd series). As T **45.** **Mult.**
126. 4d. Wahoo .. .. 4·00 1·50
127. 9d. Coal-fish .. .. 4·00 1·50
128. 1s. 9d. Dolphin .. .. 5·50 2·25
129. 2s. 3d. Soldier fish .. 5·50 2·25

1970. Royal Naval Crests (2nd series). As T **46.** Multicoloured.
130. 4d. H.M.S. "Penelope" 1·50 35
131. 9d. H.M.S. "Carlisle" .. 1·75 60
132. 1s. 6d. H.M.S. "Amphion" 2·25 85
133. 2s. 6d. H.M.S. "Magpie" 2·75 1·25

50. Early Chinese Rocket.

1971. Decimal Currency. Evolution of Space Travel. Multicoloured.
135. ½p. Type **50** 15 15
136. 1p. Medieval Arab astronomers 20 15
137. 1½p. Tycho Brahe's observatory, quadrant and supernova 30 30
138. 2p. Galileo, Moon and telescope 40 30
139. 2½p. Isaac Newton, instruments and apple .. 1·00 60
140. 3½p. Harrison's chronometer and ship .. 1·25 55
141. 4½p. Space rocket taking off 1·25 50
142. 5p. World's largest telescope, Palomar .. 1·00 60
143. 7½p. World's largest radio telescope, Jodrell Bank 4·50 1·40
144. 10p. "Mariner VII" and Mars .. .. 3·50 1·75
145. 12½p. "Sputnik II" and Space dog, Laika .. 7·00 2·00
146. 25p. Walking in Space .. 8·00 2·25
147. 50p. "Apollo XI" crew on Moon .. .. 5·00 2·50
148. £1 Future Space Research station .. .. 5·50 4·50
Nos. 137/40, 142/5 and 147/8 are horiz.

1971. Royal Naval Crests (3rd series). As T **46.** Multicoloured.
149. 2p. H.M.S. "Phoenix" .. 1·25 30
150. 4p. H.M.S. "Milford" .. 1·75 55
151. 9p. H.M.S. "Pelican" .. 2·00 80
152. 15p. H.M.S. "Oberon" .. 2·25 1·00

1972. Royal Naval Crests (4th series). As T **46.** Multicoloured.
154. 1½p. H.M.S. "Lowestoft" 65 50
155. 3p. H.M.S. "Auckland" 85 75
156. 6p. H.M.S. "Nigeria" .. 1·10 1·25
157. 17½p. H.M.S. "Bermuda" 2·25 2·50

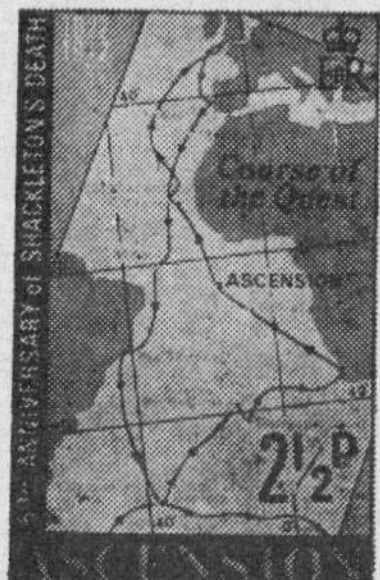

51. Course of the "Quest".

1972. 50th Anniv. of Shackleton's Death. Multicoloured.
159. 2½p. Type **51** .. .. 1·00 60
160. 4p. Shackleton and "Quest" (horiz.) .. 1·10 70
161. 7½p. Shackleton's cabin and "Quest" (horiz.) .. 1·25 75
162. 11p. Shackleton's statue and memorial .. .. 1·40 1·00

INDEX

Countries can be quickly located by referring to the index at the end of this volume.

52. Land Crab and Mako Shark.

1972. Royal Silver Wedding. Multicoloured
164. **52.** 2p. violet 15 10
165. 16p. red 35 30

1973. Royal Naval Crests (5th series) As T **46.** Multicoloured
166. 2p. H.M.S. "Birmingham" 2·50 1·00
167. 4p. H.M.S. "Cardiff" .. 3·00 1·00
168. 9p. H.M.S. "Penzance" 4·00 1·25
169. 13p. H.M.S. "Rochester" 4·50 1·50

53. Green Turtle.
(Illustration reduced. Actual size 53 × 27 mm.).

1973. Turtles. Multicoloured.
171. 4p. Type **53** .. .. 3·75 1·00
172. 9p. Loggerhead turtle .. 4·00 1·50
173. 12p. Hawksbill turtle .. 4·25 1·50

54. Sergeant, R.M. Light Infantry, 1900.

1973. 50th Anniv. of Departure of Royal Marines from Ascension. Multicoloured.
174. 2p. Type **54** .. .. 2·50 1·25
175. 6p. R.M. Private, 1816 .. 3·50 1·75
176. 12p. R.M. Light Infantry Officer, 1880 .. .. 4·00 2·25
177. 20p. R.M. Artillery Colour Sergeant, 1910 .. .. 4·50 2·50

1973. Royal Wedding. As T **47** of Anguilla. Multicoloured. Background colours given.
178. 2p. brown 15 10
179. 18p. green 25 15

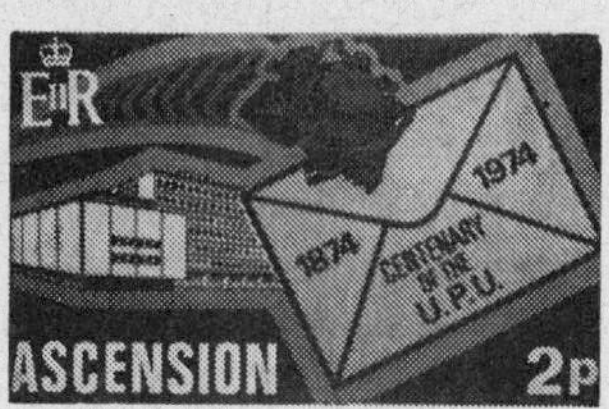

55. Letter and H.Q., Berne.

1974. Cent. of Universal Postal Union. Mult.
180. 2p. Type **55** 25 30
181. 9p. Hermes and U.P.U. monument 40 45

56. Churchill as a Boy, and Birthplace, Blenheim Palace.

1974. Birth Centenary of Sir Winston Churchill. Multicoloured.
182. 5p. Type **56** 40 40
183. 25p. Churchill as statesman, and U.N. Building .. 1·00 1·00

57. "Skylab 3" and Photograph of Ascension.

1975. Space Satellites. Multicoloured.
185. 2p. Type **57** 40 30
186. 18p. "Skylab 4" Command module and photograph 50 40

58. U.S.A.F. "Starlifter".

1975. Wideawake Airfield. **Multicoloured.**
187. 2p. Type **58** .. .. 1·50 65
188. 5p. R.A.F. "Hercules" .. 2·00 85
189. 9p. Vickers "VC-10" .. 2·25 1·40
190. 24p. U.S.A.F. "Galaxy" 3·50 3·00

1975. "Apollo-Soyuz" Space Link. Nos. 141 and 145/6 optd. **APOLLO-SOYUZ LINK 1975.**
192. 4½p. multicoloured .. 25 15
193. 12½p. multicoloured .. 35 20
194. 25p. multicoloured .. 45 35

60. Arrival of Royal Navy, 1815.

1975. 160th Anniv. Occupation. Mult.
195. 2p. Type **60** 35 25
196. 5p. Water supply, Dampiers Drip 50 40
197. 9p. First landing, 1815 .. 60 60
198. 15p. The garden on Green Mountain 75 85

61. Yellow Canaries.

1976. Multicoloured
199. 1p Type **61** 40 65
200. 2p. White Tern (vert.) .. 45 75
201. 3p. Common Waxbill .. 45 80
202. 4p. White-capped Noddy (vert.) 50 80
203. 5p. Common Noddy .. 70 95
204. 6p. Common Mynah .. 70 95
205. 7p. Madeiran Storm Petrel (vert.) .. .. 70 1·00
206. 8p. Sooty Tern .. .. 70 1·00
207. 9p. Blue-faced Booby (vert.) 70 1·00
208. 10 p. Red-footed Booby .. 70 1·00
209. 15 p. Bare-throated Francolin (vert.) .. .. 1·25 1·75
210. 18p. Brown Booby (vert.) 1·25 1·75
211. 25p. Red-billed Bo'sun Bird 1·40 1·75
212. 50p. Yellow-billed Tropic Bird .. .. .. 2·25 2·50
213. £1 Ascension Frigate-Bird (vert.) .. .. 2·75 3·25
214. £2 Boatswain Bird Island Sanctuary .. .. 5·50 7·50
No. 214 is larger, 50 + 38 mm.

63. G.B. Penny Red with Ascension Postmark.

1976. Festival of Stamps, London.
215. **63.** 5p. red, black & brown 20 15
216. – 9p. green, black & brn. 30 20
217. – 25p. multicoloured .. 50 45
DESIGNS—VERT. 9p. ½d. stamp of 1922. HORIZ. 25p. "Southampton Castle" (liner).

64. U.S. Base. Ascension.

1976. Bicent. of American Revolution. Mult.
219. 8p. Type **64** .. .. 1·00 40
220. 9p. NASA Station at Devils Ashpit .. .. .. 1·00 45
221. 25p. "Viking" landing on Mars .. .. .. 1·50 80

65. Visit of Prince Philip, 1957.

1977. Silver Jubilee. **Multicoloured.**
222. 8p. Type **65** 15 15
223. 12p. Coronation Coach leaving Buckingham Palace (horiz.) 25 20
224. 25p. Coronation Coach (horiz.) 45 40

66. Tunnel carrying Water Pipe.

1977. Water Supplies. **Multicoloured.**
225. 3p. Type **66** 25 15
226. 5p. Breakneck Valley wells 35 20
227. 12p. Break tank (horiz.) .. 65 35
228. 25p. Water catchment (horiz.) .. .. .. 1·00 65

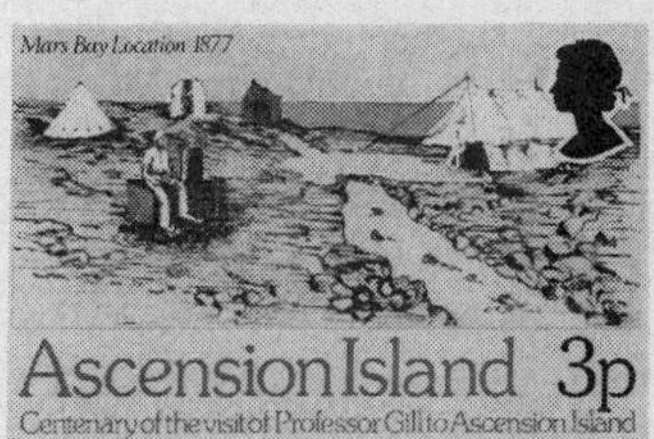

67. Mars Bay Location, 1877.

1977. Centenary of Visit of Professor Gill (astronomer). Multicoloured.
229. 3p. Type **67** 30 20
230. 8p. Instrument sites, Mars Bay 45 25
231. 12p. Sir David and Lady Gill 65 40
232. 25p. Maps of Ascension .. 1·10 70

68. Lion of England.

1978. 25th Anniv. of Coronation.

233. **68.**	25p. yell., brn. & silver	60	65
234. –	25p. multicoloured ..	60	65
235. –	25p. yell., brn. & silver	60	65

DESIGNS: No. 234, Queen Elizabeth II. No. 235, Green Turtle.

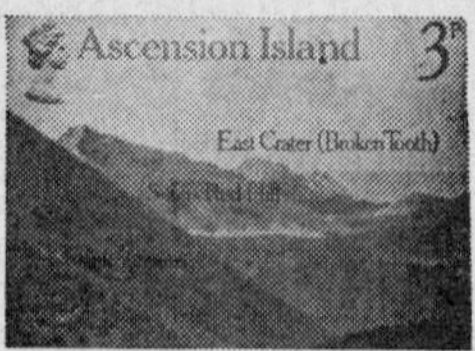

70. Flank of Sisters, Sisters' Red Hill and East Crater.

1978. Ascension Island Volcanic Rock Formations. Multicoloured.

236.	3p. Type **70**	20	20
237.	5p. Holland's Crater (Hollow Tooth) ..	30	30
238.	12p. Street Crater, Lower Valley Crater and Bear's Back	40	40
239.	15p. Butt Crater, Weather post and Green Mountain	45	45
240.	25p. Flank of Sisters, Thistle Hill and Two Boats Village	50	50

Nos. 236/40 were issued as a se-tenant strip within the sheet, forming a composite design.

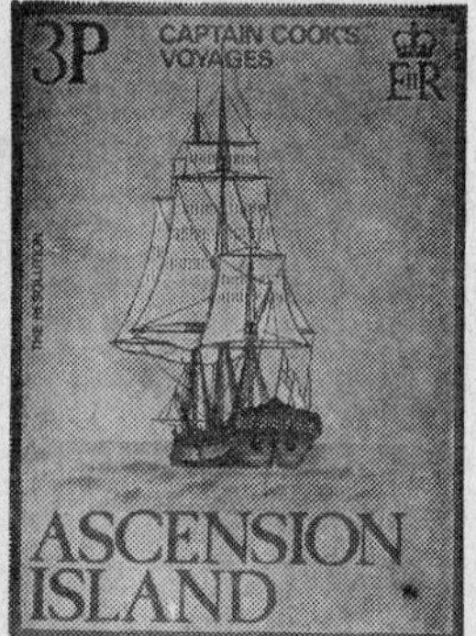

71. "The Resolution" (H. Roberts).

1979. Bicentenary of Captain Cook's Voyages, 1768–79. Multicoloured.

242.	3p. Type **71**	45	25
243.	8p. Cook's chronometer ..	65	40
244.	12p. Green Turtle ..	75	50
245.	25p. Flaxman/Wedgwood medallion of Cook ..	1·00	70

72. St. Mary's Church, Georgetown.

1979. Ascension Day. Multicoloured.

246.	8p. Type **72**	20	20
247.	12p. Map of Ascension ..	30	30
248.	50p. "The Ascension" (painting by Rembrandt)	80	90

73. Landing Cable, Comfortless Cove.

1979. 80th Anniv. Eastern Telegraph Company's Arrival on Ascension.

249. **73.**	3p. black and red ..	15	10
250. –	8p. black and green ..	25	20
251. –	12p. black and yellow..	30	25
252. –	15p. black and violet ..	35	35
253. –	25p. black and brown..	50	50

DESIGNS—HORIZ. 8p. C.S. "Anglia", 15p. C.S. "Seine", 25p. Cable and wireless earth station. VERT. 12p. Map of Atlantic cable network.

74. 6d. 1938 Stamp.

1979. Death Centenary of Sir Rowland Hill.

254. **74.**	3p. black and blue ..	15	10
255. –	8p. black, green and pale green	20	20
256. –	12p. black, blue and pale blue	25	25
257. –	50p. black and red ..	80	90

DESIGNS—HORIZ. 8p. 1956 5s. definitive. VERT. 12p. 1924 3s. stamp. 50p. Sir Rowland Hill.

75. "Anogramma ascensionis".

1980. Ferns and Grasses. Multicoloured.

258.	3 p. Type **75**	10	10
259.	6p. "Xiphopteris ascensionense"	20	15
260.	8p. "Sporobolus caespitosus"	20	15
261.	12p. "Sporobolus durus" (vert.)	30	25
262.	18p. "Dryopteris ascensionis" (vert.)	40	35
263.	24p. "Marattia purpurascens" (vert.)	50	50

76. 17th Century, Bottle Post.

1980. "London 1980" International Stamp Exhibition. Multicoloured.

264	8p. Type **76**	20	20
265	12p. 19th-century chance calling ship	25	25
266	15p. "Garth Castle" (regular mail service from 1863)	25	30
267	50p. "St Helena" (mail services, 1980)	70	90

77. H.M. Queen Elizabeth the Queen Mother.

1980. 80th Birthday of the Queen Mother.

269. **77.**	15p. multicoloured ..	40	40

78. Lubbock's Yellowtail.

1980. Fishes. Multicoloured.

270.	3p. Type **78**	30	15
271.	10p. Resplendent Angelfish	45	25
272.	25p. Hedgehog Butterflyfish	75	50
273.	40p. Marmalade Razorfish	1·00	65

79. H.M.S. "Tortoise".

1980. 150th Anniv. of Royal Geographical Society. Multicoloured.

274.	10p. Type **79**	45	40
275.	15p. "Wideawake Fair" ..	55	45
276.	60p. Mid-Atlantic Ridge (38 × 48 mm.)	1·10	1·25

80. Green Mountain Farm, 1881.

1981. Green Mountain Farm. Multicoloured.

277.	12p. Type **80**	35	35
278.	15p. Two Boats, 1881 ..	40	40
279.	20p. Green Mountain and Two Boats, 1981 ..	50	50
280.	30p. Green Mountain Farm, 1981	70	70

81. Cable and Wireless Earth Station.

1981. "Space Shuttle" Mission and Opening of 2nd Earth Station.

281. **81.**	15p. black, blue and pale blue	30	35

82. Poinsettia.

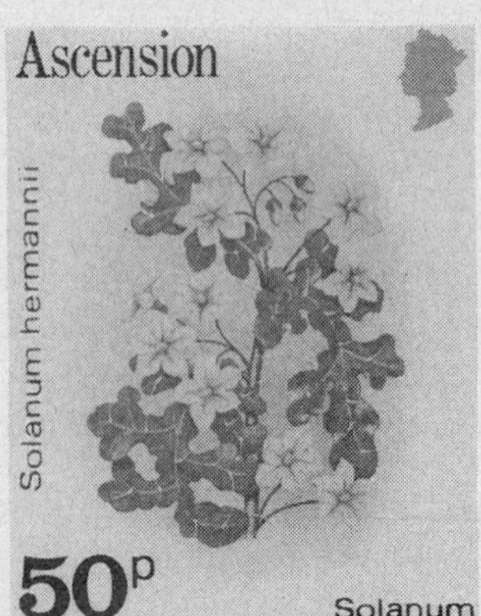

83. Solanum.

1981. Flowers. Multicoloured.

282.	1p. Type **82**	70	60
283.	2p. Clustered Wax Flower	50	65
284.	3p. Kolanchoe (vert.) ..	50	65
285.	4p. Yellow Pops	80	65
286.	5p. Camels Foot Creeper..	80	65
287.	8p. White Oleander ..	80	70
288.	10p. Ascension Lily (vert.)	45	60
289.	12p. Coral Plant (vert.) ..	1·25	75
290.	15p. Yellow Allamanda ..	50	65
291.	20p. Ascension Euphorbia	1·00	70
292.	30p. Flame of the Forest (vert.)	1·25	1·10
293.	40p. Bougainvillea "King Leopold"	1·25	1·75
294.	50p. Type **83**	1·25	2·00
295	£1 Ladies Petticoat ..	2·00	2·75
296.	£2 Red Hibiscus	3·75	4·75

Nos. 294/6 are as Type 83.

84. Map by Maxwell, 1793.

1981. Early Maps of Ascension.

297. **84.**	10p. blk., gold and blue	30	35
298. –	12p. blk., gold and grn.	30	35
299. –	15p. blk., gold and stone	35	40
300. –	40p. blk., gold and yell.	70	85

DESIGNS: 12p. Maxwell, 1793 (different). 15p. Ekeberg and Chapman, 1811. 40p. Campbell, 1819.

85. Wedding Bouquet from Ascension.

1981. Royal Wedding. Multicoloured.

302.	10p. Type **85**	25	25
303.	15p. Prince Charles in Fleet Air Arm flying kit ..	30	30
304.	50p. Prince Charles and Lady Diana Spencer ..	85	85

87. "Interest".

1981. 25th Anniv. of Duke of Edinburgh Award Scheme. Multicoloured.

305.	5p Type **87**..	15	15
306.	10p. "Physical acitivities"	20	20
307.	15p. "Service"	25	25
308.	40p. Duke of Edinburgh ..	70	70

88. Scout crossing Rope Bridge.

1982. 75th Anniv. of Boy Scout Movement.

309. **88.**	10 p. black, blue and light blue	45	35
310. –	15 p. black, brown and yellow	55	50
311. –	25 p. black, mauve and light mauve ..	75	60
312. –	40 p. black, red and orange	1·10	85

DESIGNS: 15 p. 1st Ascension Scout Group flag. 25 p. Scouts learning to use radio. 40 p. Lord Baden-Powell.

89. Charles Darwin.

1982. 150th Anniv. of Charles Darwin's Voyage. Multicoloured.

314.	10 p. Type **89**	50	40
315.	12 p. Darwin's pistols ..	55	50
316.	15 p. Rock Crab	60	55
317.	40 p. H.M.S. "Beagle" ..	1·10	95

90. Fairey "Swordfish".

1982. 40th Anniv. of Wideawake Airfield. Multicoloured.
318. 5 p. Type **90** 70 35
319. 10 p. North American "B-25C (Mitchell)" .. 90 40
320. 15 p. Boeing "EC-135N (Aria)" .. .. 1·25 55
321. 50 p. Lockheed "Hercules" 1·75 1·10

91. Ascension Coat of Arms.

1982. 21st Birthday of Princess of Wales. Multicoloured.
322. 12 p. Type **91** 30 30
323. 15 p. Lady Diana Spencer in Music Room, Buckingham Palace 35 35
324. 25 p. Bride and Earl Spencer leaving Clarence House 55 55
325. 50 p. Formal portrait .. 1·00 1·00

1982. Commonwealth Games, Brisbane. Nos. 290/1 optd. **1st PARTICIPATION COMMONWEALTH GAMES 1982.**
326. 15p. Yellow Allamanda .. 30 40
327. 20p. Ascension Euphorbia 40 45

94. Bush House, London.

1982. Christmas. 50th Anniv of B.B.C. External Broadcasting. Multicoloured.
328. 5p. Type **94** 25 25
329. 10p. Atlantic relay station 35 35
330. 25p. Lord Reith, first Director-General .. 75 75
331. 40p. King George V making his first Christmas broadcast, 1932 .. .. .. 1·00 1·00

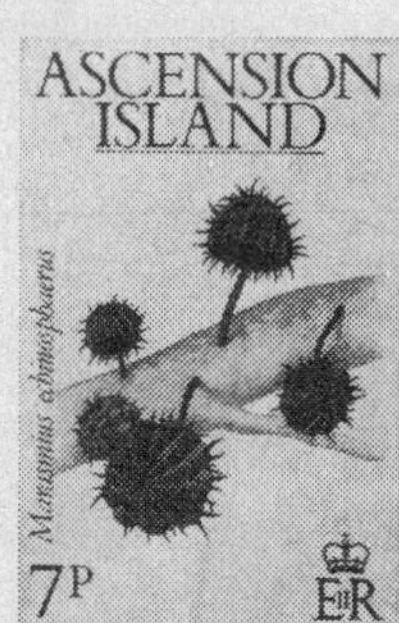

95. "Marasmius echinosphaerus".

1983. Fungi. Multicoloured.
332 7p. Type **95** 55 30
333 12p. "Chlorophyllum molybdites" 75 45
334 15p. "Leucocoprinus cepaestripes" 90 50
335 20p. "Lycoperdon marginatum" .. .. 1·10 65
336 50p. "Marasmiellus distantifolius" .. .. 1·75 1·25

96. Aerial View of Georgetown.

1983. Island Views (1st series). Multicoloured.
337. 12p. Type **96** 25 30
338. 15p. Green Mountain farm 30 35
339. 20p. Boatswain Bird Island 40 45
340. 60p. Telemetry Hill by night .. .. .. 1·25 1·40
See also Nos. 367/70.

97. "Wessex 5" Helicopter of No. 845 Naval Air Squadron.

1983. Bicentenary of Manned Flight. British Military Aircraft. Multicoloured.
341. 12p. Type **97** 75 40
342. 15p. "Vulcan B2" of No. 44 Squadron 85 50
343. 20p. "Nimrod MR2P" of No. 120 Squadron .. 95 60
344. 60p. "Victor K2" of No. 55 Squadron .. .. 2·00 1·75

98. Iguanid.

1983. Introduced Species. Multicoloured.
345. 12p. Type **98** 30 30
346. 15p. Common rabbit .. 35 35
347. 20p. Cat 45 45
348. 60p. Donkey .. .. 1·40 1·40

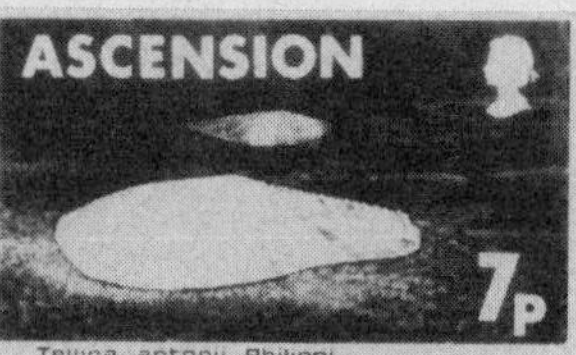

99. "Tellina antonii Philippi".

1983. Sea Shells. Multicoloured.
349. 7p. Type **99** 20 20
350. 12p. "Nodipecten nodosus" 30 30
351. 15p. "Cypraea lurida oceanic Sch" 35 35
352. 20p. "Nerita ascensionis Gmelin" 45 45
353. 50p. "Micromelo undatus (Bruguiere)" .. .. 1·10 1·10

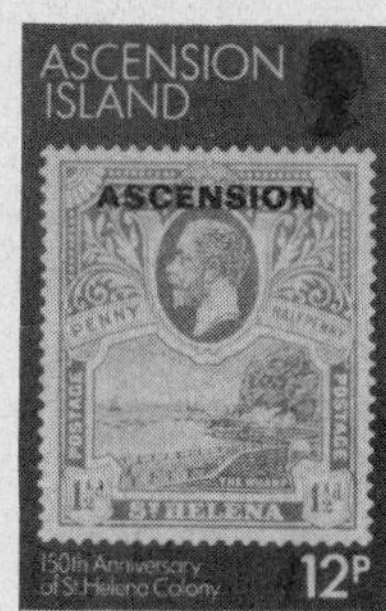

100. 1922 1½d. Stamp.

1984. 150th Anniv. of St. Helena as a British Colony. Multicoloured.
354. 12p. Type **100** 45 45
355. 15p. 1922 2d. stamp .. 50 50
356. 20p. 1922 8d. stamp .. 55 55
357. 60p. 1922 1s. stamp .. 1·40 1·40

102. Naval Semaphore.

1984. 250th Anniv of "Lloyd's List" (newspaper). Multicoloured.
359 12p. Type **102** 30 30
360 15p. "Southampton Castle" (liner) 35 35
361 20p. Pier head 45 45
362 70p. "Dane" (screw steamer) .. .. 1·50 1·50

103. Penny Coin and Yellowfin Tuna.

1984. New Coinage. Multicoloured.
363. 12p. Type **103** 50 35
364. 15p. Twopenny coin and donkey 60 40
365. 20p. Fifty pence coin and Green Turtle 75 50
366. 70p. Pound coin and Sooty Tern .. .. .. 2·00 1·75

1984. Island Views (2nd series). As T **96**. Multicoloured.
367. 12p. The Devil's Riding-school 30 30
368. 15p. St. Mary's Church .. 35 35
369. 20p. Two Boats Village .. 45 45
370. 70p. Ascension from the sea .. .. .. 1·50 1·50

104. Bermuda Cypress.

1985. Trees. Multicoloured.
371. 7p. Type **104** 55 20
372. 12p. Norfolk Island Pine .. 65 30
373. 15p. Screwpine 75 35
374. 20p. Eucalyptus 90 45
375. 65p. Spore Tree .. .. 2·25 1·40

105. The Queen Mother with Prince Andrew at Silver Jubilee Service.

1985. Life and Times of Queen Elizabeth the Queen Mother. Multicoloured.
376. 12p. With the Duke of York at Balmoral, 1924 30 30
377. 15p. Type **105** 35 35
378. 20p. The Queen Mother at Ascot 45 45
379. 70p. With Prince Henry at his christening (from photo by Lord Snowdon) 1·50 1·50

106. 32 Pdr. Smooth Bore Muzzle-loader, *c.* 1820, and Royal Marine Artillery Hat Plate, *c.* 1816.

1985. Guns on Ascension Island. Mult.
381. 12p. Type **106** 70 55
382. 15p. 7 inch rifled muzzle-loader c. 1866 and Royal Cypher on barrel 80 65
383. 20p. 7 pdr rifled muzzle-loader, c. 1877, and Royal Artillery Badge .. 90 85
384. 70p. 5.5 inch gun, 1941, and crest from H.M.S. "Hood" .. .. .. 2·50 2·50

107. Guide Flag.

1985. 75th Anniv. of Girl Guide Movement and International Youth Year. Multicoloured.
385. 12p. Type **107** 75 45
386. 15p. Practising first aid .. 85 40
387. 20p. Camping 95 50
388. 70p. Lady Baden-Powell .. 2·75 2·00

108. "Clerodendrum fragrans".

1985. Wild Flowers. Multicoloured.
389. 12p. Type **108** 45 45
390. 15p. Shell ginger 55 55
391. 20p. Cape daisy 65 65
392. 70p. Ginger lily .. .. 2·00 2·00

109. Newton's Reflector Telescope.

1986. Appearance of Halley's Comet. Mult.
393. 12p. Type **109** 75 60
394. 15p. Edmond Halley and Old Greenwich Observatory 85 70
395. 20p. Short's Gregorian telescope and comet, 1759 .. 95 80
396. 70p. Ascension satellite tracking station and ICE spacecraft .. .. 2·75 2·50

110. Princess Elizabeth in 1926.

1986. 60th Birthday of Queen Elizabeth II. Multicoloured.
397. 7p. Type **110** 15 20
398. 15p. Queen making Christmas broadcast, 1952 .. 30 35
399. 20p. At Garter ceremony, Windsor Castle, 1983 .. 40 45
400. 35p. In Auckland, New Zealand, 1981 .. .. 70 75
401. £1 At Crown Agents' Head Office, London, 1983 .. 2·00 2·10

111. 1975 Space Satellites 2p. Stamp.

1986. "Ameripex '86" International Stamp Exhibition, Chicago. Designs showing previous Ascension stamps. Multicoloured.
402. 12p. Type **111** 40 40
403. 15p. 1980 "London 1980" International Stamp Exhibition 50p 50 50
404. 20p. 1976 Bicentenary of American Revolution 8p. 65 65
405. 70p. 1982 40th Anniv. of Wideawake Airfield 10p. 1·75 1·75

112. Prince Andrew and Miss Sarah Ferguson.

1986. Royal Wedding. Multicoloured.
407. 15p. Type **112** 45 35
408. 35p. Prince Andrew aboard H.M.S. "Brazen" 95 75

113. H.M.S. "Ganymede" (c. 1811).

1986. Ships of the Royal Navy. Mult.
409. 1p. Type **113** 55 55
410. 2p. H.M.S. "Kangaroo" (c. 1811) 60 60
411. 4p. H.M.S. "Trinculo" (c. 1811) 60 60
412. 5p. H.M.S. "Daring" (c. 1811) 60 60
413. 9p. H.M.S. "Thais" (c. 1811) 70 70
414. 10p. H.M.S. "Pheasant" (1819) 70 70
415. 15p. H.M.S. "Myrmidon" (1819) 80 80
416. 18p. H.M.S. "Atholl" (1825) 90 90
417. 20p. H.M.S. "Medina" (1830) 90 90
418. 25p. H.M.S. "Saracen" (1840) .. .. .. 1·00 1·00
419. 30p. H.M.S. "Hydra" (c. 1845) .. .. .. 1·00 1·00
420. 50p. H.M.S. "Sealark" (1849) .. .. .. 1·25 1·75
421. 70p. H.M.S. "Rattlesnake" (1868) .. .. 1·75 2·25
422. £1 H.M.S. "Penelope" (1889) .. .. .. 2·40 3·00
423. £2 H.M.S. "Monarch" (1897) .. .. .. 5·00 6·50

114. Cape Gooseberry.

1987. Edible Bush Fruits. Multicoloured.
424. 12p. Type **114** 65 65
425. 15p. Prickly pear 75 75
426. 20p. Guava 85 85
427. 70p. Loquat .. .. 2·00 2·00

115. Ignition of Rocket Motors.

1987. 25th Anniv. of First American Manned Earth Orbit. Multicoloured.
428. 15p. Type **115** 45 45
429. 18p. Lift-off 50 50
430. 25p. Re-entry 65 65
431. £1 Splashdown .. .. 2·25 2·25

116. Captains in Full Dress raising Red Ensign.

1987. 19th-century Uniforms (1st series). Royal Navy, 1815–20. Multicoloured.
433. 25p. Type **116** 60 60
434. 25p. Surgeon and seamen 60 60
435. 25p. Seaman with water-carrying donkey .. 60 60
436. 25p. Midshipman and gun 60 60
437. 25p. Commander in undress uniform surveying 60 60
See also Nos. 478/82.

117. "Cynthia cardui".

1987 Insects (1st series). Multicoloured.
438 15p. Type **117** 55 65
439 18p. "Danaus chrysippus" 60 75
440 25p. "Hypolimnas misippus" 75 85
441 £1 "Lampides boeticus" .. 2·25 2·50
See also Nos. 452/5 and 483/6.

118. Male Ascension Frigate Birds.

1987. Sea Birds (1st series). Multicoloured.
442 25p. Type **118** 80 90
443 25p. Juvenile Ascension frigate bird, brown booby and blue-faced boobies 80 90
444 25p. Male Ascension frigate bird and blue-faced boobies 80 90
445 25p. Female Ascension frigate bird 80 90
446 25p. Adult male feeding juvenile Ascension frigate bird 80 90
Nos. 442/6 were printed together, se-tenant, forming a composite design.
See also Nos. 469/73.

1987. Royal Ruby Wedding. Nos. 397/401 optd. **40TH WEDDING ANNIVERSARY.**
447. 7p Type **110** 15 20
448. 15p Queen making Christmas broadcast, 1952 .. .. .. 30 35
449. 20p. At Garter ceremony, Windsor Castle, 1983 .. 40 45
450. 35p. In Auckland, New Zealand, 1981 .. .. 70 75
451. £1 At Crown Agents' Head Office, London, 1983 .. 2·00 2·10

1988. Insects (2nd series). As T **117**. Mult.
452 15p. "Gryllus bimaculatus" (field cricket) 50 50
453 18p. "Ruspolia differeus" (bush cricket) 55 55
454 25p. "Chilomenus lunata" (ladybird) 70 70
455 £1 "Diachrysia orichalcea" (moth) .. .. .. 2·25 2·25

120. Bate's Memorial, St. Mary's Church.

1988. 150th Death Anniv. of Captain William Bate (garrison commander, 1828–38). Mult.
456. 9p. Type **120** 35 35
457. 15p. Commodore's Cottage 45 45
458. 18p. North East Cottage .. 50 50
459. 25p. Map of Ascension .. 70 70
460. 70p. Captain Bate and marines .. .. .. 1·75 1·75

121 H.M.S. "Resolution" (ship of the line), 1667

1988. Bicentenary of Australian Settlement. Ships of the Royal Navy. Multicoloured.
461 9p. Type **121** 65 35
462 18p. H.M.S. "Resolution" (Captain Cook), 1772 .. 90 55
463 25p. H.M.S. "Resolution" (battleship), 1892 .. 1·25 75
464 65p. H.M.S. "Resolution" (battleship), 1916 .. 2·25 1·50

1988. "Sydpex '88" National Stamp Exhibition, Sydney. Nos. 461/4 optd **SYDPEX 88 30.7.88 -7.8.88.**
465 9p. Type **121** 25 25
466 18p. H.M.S. "Resolution" (Captain Cook), 1772 .. 40 40
467 25p. H.M.S. "Resolution" (battleship), 1892 .. 55 55
468 65p. H.M.S. "Resolution" (battleship), 1916 .. 1·40 1·40

1988. Sea Birds (2nd series). Sooty Tern. As T **118**. Multicoloured.
469 25p. Pair displaying .. 90 90
470 25p. Turning egg 90 90
471 25p. Incubating egg .. 90 90
472 25p. Feeding chick .. 90 90
473 25p. Immature sooty tern 90 90
Nos. 469/73 were printed together, se-tenant, forming a composite design of a nesting colony.

123 Lloyd's Coffee House, London, 1688

1988. 300th Anniv of Lloyd's of London. Mult.
474 8p. Type **123** 25 25
475 18p. "Alert IV" (cable ship) (horiz) 50 50
476 25p. Satellite recovery in space (horiz) 70 70
477 65p. "Good Hope Castle" (cargo liner) on fire off Ascension, 1973 .. 1·50 1·50

1988. 19th-century Uniforms (2nd series). Royal Marines 1821-34. As T **116**. Mult.
478 25p. Marines landing on Ascension, 1821 .. 1·10 1·25
479 25p. Officer and Marine at semaphore station, 1829 1·10 1·25
480 25p. Sergeant and Marine at Octagonal Tank, 1831 1·10 1·25
481 25p. Officers at water pipe tunnel, 1833 .. .. 1·10 1·25
482 25p. Officer supervising construction of barracks, 1834 .. .. .. 1·10 1·25

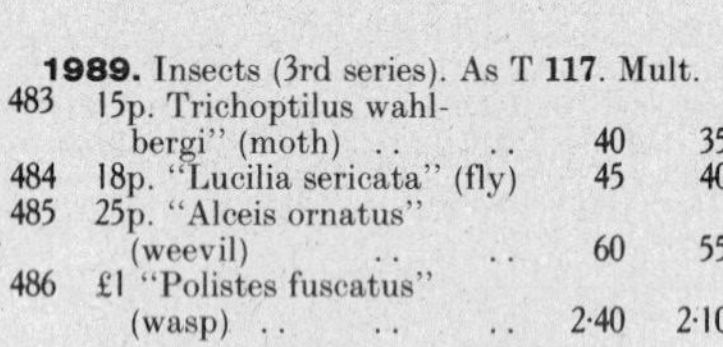

1989. Insects (3rd series). As T **117**. Mult.
483 15p. "Trichoptilus wahlbergi" (moth) 40 35
484 18p. "Lucilia sericata" (fly) 45 40
485 25p. "Alceis ornatus" (weevil) 60 55
486 £1 "Polistes fuscatus" (wasp) .. .. .. 2·40 2·10

124 Two Land Crabs

1989. Ascension Land Crabs. Multicoloured.
487 15p. Type **124** 40 40
488 18p. Crab with claws raised 45 45
489 25p. Crab on rock .. 60 60
490 £1 Crab in surf .. .. 2·25 2·25

126 "Apollo 7" Tracking Station, Ascension

1989. 20th Anniv of First Manned Landing on Moon. Multicoloured.
493 15p. Type **126** 30 35
494 18p. Launch of "Apollo 7" (30 × 30 mm) 35 40
495 25p. "Apollo 7" emblem (30 × 30 mm) 50 55
496 70p. "Apollo 7" jettisoning expended Saturn rocket 1·40 1·50

127 "Queen Elizabeth 2" (liner) and U.S.S. "John F. Kennedy" (aircraft carrier) in New York Harbour

1989. "Philexfrance 89" International Stamp Exhibition, Paris, and "World Stamp Expo '89", Washington. Designs showing Statue of Liberty and Centenary celebrations. Multicoloured.

498 15p. Type **127** 35 35
499 15p. Cleaning statue .. 35 35
500 15p. Statue of Liberty .. 35 35
501 15p. Crown of statue .. 35 35
502 15p. Warships and New York skyline 35 35
503 15p. "Jean de Vienne" (French destroyer) and skyscrapers 35 35

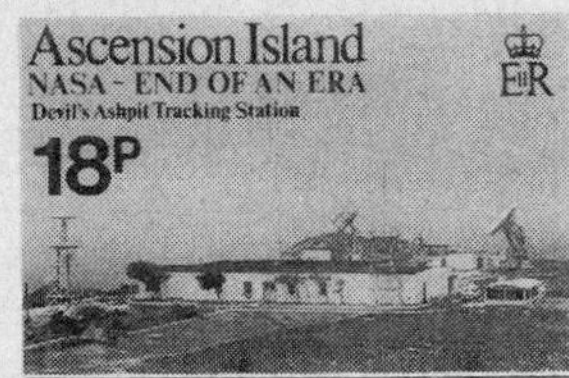

128 Devil's Ashpit Tracking Station

1989. Closure of Devil's Ashpit Tracking Station, Ascension. Multicoloured.

504 18p. Type **128** 60 50
505 25p. Launch of shuttle "Atlantis" 80 55

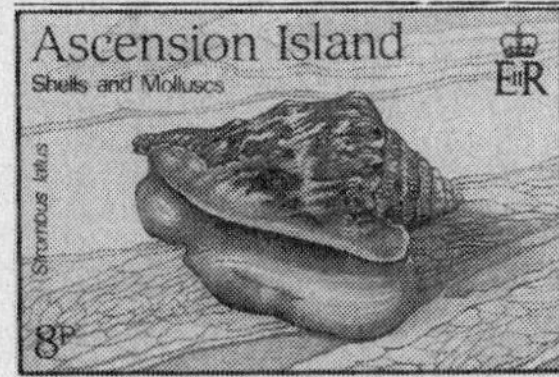

129 "Strombus latus"

1989. Sea Shells. Multicoloured.

506 8p. Type **129** 25 20
507 18p. "Tonna galea" .. 45 40
508 25p. "Harpa doris" .. 60 55
509 £1 "Charonia variegata" .. 2·25 2·25

130 Donkeys

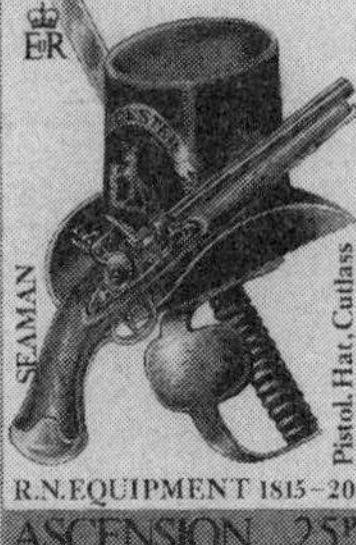

131 Seaman's Pistol, Hat and Cutlass

1989. Multicoloured.

510 18p. Type **130** 35 40
511 25p. Green turtle 50 55

1990. Royal Navy Equipment, 1815–20. Mult.

512 25p. Type **131** 60 60
513 25p. Midshipman's belt plate, button, sword and hat 60 60
514 25p. Surgeon's hat, sword and instrument chest .. 60 60
515 25p. Captain's hat, telescope and sword .. 60 60
516 25p. Admiral's epaulette, megaphone, hat and pocket 60 60

See also Nos. 541/5.

132 Pair of Ascension Frigate Birds with Young

1990. Ascension Frigate Bird. Multicoloured.

517 9p. Type **132** 30 30
518 10p. Fledgeling 35 35
519 11p. Adult male in flight .. 35 35
520 15p. Female and immature birds in flight 40 40

133 Penny Black and Twopence Blue

1990. "Stamp World London 90" International Stamp Exhibition. Multicoloured.

521 9p. Type **133** 30 30
522 18p. Ascension postmarks used on G.B. stamps .. 50 50
523 25p. Unloading mail at Wideawake Airfield .. 75 75
524 £1 Mail van and Main Post Office .. .. .. 2·25 2·25

134 "Queen Elizabeth, 1940" (Sir Gerald Kelly)

1990. 90th Birthday of Queen Elizabeth the Queen Mother.

525 **134** 25p. multicoloured .. 75 75
526 – £1 black and lilac .. 2·25 2·25

DESIGN—(29 × 37 mm) £1 King George VI and Queen Elizabeth with Bren-gun carrier.

136 "Madonna and Child" (sculpture, Dino Felici)

1990. Christmas. Works of Art. Multicoloured.

527 8p. Type **136** 40 30
528 18p. "Madonna and Child" (anon) 80 60
529 25p. "Madonna and Child with St. John" (Johann Gebhard) .. .. 1·25 85
530 65p. "Madonna and Child" (Giacomo Gritti) .. 2·50 2·00

137 "Garth Castle" (mail steamer), 1910

1990. Maiden Voyage of "St. Helena II". Multicoloured.

531 9p. Type **137** 50 35
532 18p. "St. Helena I" during Falklands Islands campaign, 1982 .. 75 55
533 25p. Launch of "St. Helena II" 95 75
534 70p. Duke of York launching "St. Helena II" .. 2·50 2·00

1991. 175th Anniv of Occupation. Nos. 418, 420 and 422 optd **BRITISH FOR 175 YEARS**.

536 25p. H.M.S. "Saracen" (1840) .. .. .. 1·00 75
537 50p. H.M.S. "Sealark" (1849) .. .. .. 1·75 1·50
538 £1 H.M.S. "Penelope" (1889) .. .. .. 2·75 2·50

139 Queen Elizabeth II at Trooping the Colour

1991. 65th Birthday of Queen Elizabeth II and 70th Birthday of Prince Philip. Mult.

539 25p. Type **139** 75 80
540 25p. Prince Philip in naval uniform 75 70

1991. Royal Marines Equipment, 1821–44. As T **131**. Multicoloured.

541 25p. Officer's shako, epaulettes, belt plate and button .. .. 1·00 1·00
542 25p. Officer's cap, sword, epaulettes and belt plate 1·00 1·00
543 25p. Drum major's shako and staff .. .. 1·00 1·00
544 25p. Sergeant's shako, chevrons, belt plate and canteen .. .. 1·00 1·00
545 25p. Drummer's shako and side-drum .. .. 1·00 1·00

140 B.B.C. World Service Relay Station

1991. 25th Anniv of B.B.C. Atlantic Relay Station. Multicoloured.

546 15p. Type **140** 50 50
547 18p. Transmitters at English Bay 60 60
548 25p. Satellite receiving station (vert) 75 75
549 70p. Antenna support tower (vert) .. .. 2·00 2·25

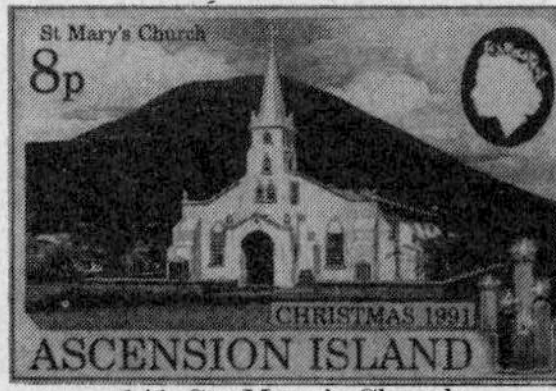

141 St. Mary's Church

1991. Christmas. Ascension Churches. Mult.

550 8p. Type **141** 30 30
551 18p. Interior of St. Mary's Church 60 60
552 25p. Our Lady of Ascension Grotto .. 80 80
553 65p. Interior of Our Lady of Ascension Grotto .. 2·25 2·40

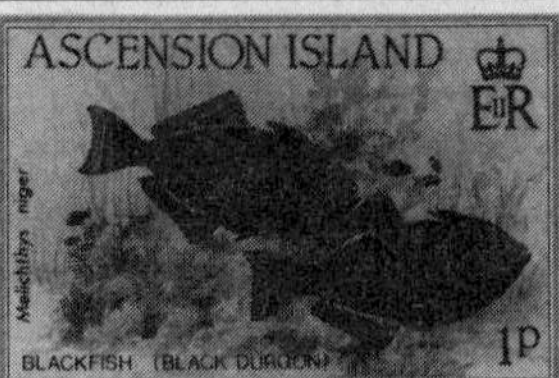

142 Blackfish

1991. Fishes. Multicoloured.

554 1p. Type **142** 10 10
555 2p. Five finger 10 10
556 4p. Resplendent angelfish 10 10
557 5p. Silver fish 10 15
558 9p. Gurnard 20 25
559 10p. Blue dad 20 25
560 15p. Cunning fish .. 30 35
561 18p. Grouper 35 40
562 20p. Moray eel 40 45
563 25p. Hardback soldierfish 50 55
564 30p. Blue marlin 60 65
565 50p. Wahoo .. .. 1·00 1·10
566 70p. Yellowfin tuna .. 1·40 1·50
567 £1 Blue shark .. .. 2·00 2·10
568 £2.50 Bottlenose dolphin .. 5·00 5·25

143 Holland's Crater

1992. 40th Anniv of Queen Elizabeth II's Accession. Multicoloured.

569 9p. Type **143** 30 30
570 15p. Green Mountain .. 50 50
571 18p. Boatswain Bird Island 60 60
572 25p. Three portraits of Queen Elizabeth .. 80 80
573 70p. Queen Elizabeth II .. 2·00 2·00

The portraits shown on the 25p. are repeated from the three lower values of the set.

144 Compass Rose and "Eye of the Wind" (cadet brig)

1992. 500th Anniv of Discovery of America by Columbus and Re-enactment Voyages. Multicoloured.

574 9p. Type **144** 40 40
575 18p. Map of re-enactment voyages and "Soren Larsen" (cadet brigantine) 70 70
576 25p. "Santa Maria", "Pinta" and "Nina" .. 90 90
577 70p. Columbus and "Santa Maria" .. .. .. 2·00 2·00

145 Control Tower, Wideawake Airfield

1992. 50th Anniv of Wideawake Airfield. Multicoloured.

578 15p. Type **145** 55 55
579 18p. Nose hangar .. 60 60
580 25p. Site preparation by U.S. Army engineers .. 80 80
581 70p. Laying fuel pipeline 2·25 2·25

146 Nimrod Mk.2

1992. 10th Anniv of Liberation of Falkland Islands. Aircraft. Multicoloured.

582	15p. Type **146**	60	60
583	18p. VC.10 landing at Ascension	65	65
584	25p. Wessex HU Mk.5 helicopter lifting supplies ..	80	80
585	65p. Vulcan B2 over Ascension	2·10	2·10

147 "Christmas in Great Britain and Ascension"

1992. Christmas. Children's Paintings. Mult.

587	8p. Type **147**	25	25
588	18p. "Santa Claus riding turtle"	55	55
589	25p. "Nativity"	75	75
590	65p. "Nativity with rabbit"	2·00	2·00

148 Male Canary Singing

1993. Yellow Canary. Multicoloured.

591	15p. Type **148**	50	50
592	18p. Adult male and female	60	60
593	25p. Young birds calling for food	75	75
594	70p. Adults and young birds on the wing ..	2·25	2·25

149 Sopwith Snipe

1993. 75th Anniv of Royal Air Force. Mult.

595	20p. Type **149**	60	60
596	25p. Supermarine Southampton	65	65
597	30p. Avro Anson	75	75
598	70p. Vickers Wellington 1c	1·75	1·75

150 Map of South Atlantic Cable

1993. 25th Anniv of South Atlantic Cable Company. Multicoloured.

600	20p. Type **150**	70	70
601	25p. "Vercors" laying cable	80	80
602	30p. Map of Ascension ..	90	90
603	70p. "Vercors" (cable ship) off Ascension	2·00	2·00

151 Lanatana Camara

1993. Local Flowers. Multicoloured.

604	20p. Type **151**	60	60
605	25p. Moonflower	65	65
606	30p. Hibiscus	75	75
607	70p. Frangipani	1·75	1·75

152 Posting Christmas Card to Ascension

1993. Christmas. Multicoloured.

608	12p. Type **152**	30	35
609	20p. Loading mail onto R.A.F. Tristar at Brize Norton	50	55
610	25p. Tristar over South Atlantic	60	65
611	30p. Unloading mail at Wideawake Airfield ..	70	75
612	65p. Receiving card and Georgetown Post Office	1·50	1·60

153 Ichthyosaurus

1994. Prehistoric Aquatic Reptiles. Mult.

614	12p. Type **153**	25	30
615	20p. Metriorhynchus ..	40	45
616	25p. Mosasaurus	50	55
617	30p. Elasmosaurus ..	60	55
618	65p. Plesiosaurus	1·25	1·40

1994. "Hong Kong '94" International Stamp Exhibition. Nos. 614/18 optd **HONG KONG '94** and emblem.

619	12p. Type **153**	25	30
620	20p. Metriorhynchus ..	40	45
621	25p. Mosasaurus	50	55
622	30p. Elasmosaurus ..	60	65
623	65p. Plesiosaurus	1·25	1·40

155 Young Green Turtles heading towards Sea

1994. Green Turtles. Multicoloured.

624	20p. Type **155**	40	45
625	25p. Turtle digging nest ..	50	55
626	30p. Turtle leaving sea ..	60	65
627	65p. Turtle swimming ..	1·25	1·40

POSTAGE DUE STAMPS

D 1. Outline Map of Ascension.

1986.

D1.	D 1	1p. dp. brown & brn.	10	10
D2.		2p. brown and orange	10	10
D3.		5p. brown and orange	10	10
D4.		7p. black and violet ..	15	20
D5.		10p. black and blue ..	20	25
D6.		25p. black and green ..	50	55

AUSTRALIA

An island continent to the S.E. of Asia. A Commonwealth consisting of the states of New S. Wales, Queensland, S. Australia, Tasmania, Victoria and W. Australia.

1913. 12 pence = 1 shilling.
20 shillings = 1 pound.
1966. 100 cents = 1 dollar.

1. Eastern Grey Kangaroo.

1913.

1	1	½d. green	5·00	2·00
2cb		1d. red	7·00	75
3		2d. grey	25·00	2·75
36		2½d. blue	22·00	8·50
37		3d. green	27·00	3·00
6		4d. orange	48·00	22·00
8		5d. brown	40·00	28·00
38		6d. blue	55·00	6·00
73		6d. brown	22·00	1·25
133		9d. violet	23·00	1·00
40a		1s. green	35·00	2·50
41		2s. brown	£150	9·00
134		2s. red	5·00	45
135		5s. grey and yellow ..	£110	12·00
136		10s. grey and red ..	£250	£100
44		£1 brown and blue ..	£1300	£700
137		£1 grey	£425	£150
138		£2 black and red ..	£1600	£325

3.

4. Laughing Kookaburra.

1913.

29a	3	½d green	3·50	70
94		½d. orange	1·75	90
17		1d. red	2·50	4·50
57		1d. violet	6·00	70
125		1d. green	1·50	10
59		1½d. brown	6·00	30
61		1½d. green	2·50	25
97		1½d. red	1·50	40
62		2d. orange	15·00	45
127		2d. red	1·75	10
99b		2d. brown	9·00	40
128		3d. blue	16·00	60
32		4d. orange	40·00	2·25
64		4d. violet	11·00	11·00
65		4d. blue	48·00	6·50
129		4d. green	16·00	80
92		4½d. violet	17·00	3·25
130		5d. brown	14·00	15
131		1s. 4d. blue	60·00	3·50

1913.

19.	4.	6d. red	70·00	38·00

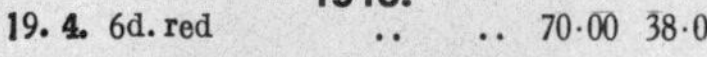

8. Parliament House, Canberra.

1927. Opening of Parliament House.

105.	8.	1½d. red	80	50

1928. National Stamp Exhibition, Melbourne.

106.	4.	3d. blue	4·25	4·50

9. "DH66" Biplane and Pastoral Scene.

1929. Air.

115.	9.	3d. green..	10·00	3·25

10. Black Swan.

1929. Centenary Western Australia.

116.	10.	1½d. red	1·00	1·25

11. Capt. Chas. Sturt. 17. Superb Lyrebird.

13. The "Southern Cross" above Hemispheres.

1930. Centenary of Sturt's Exploration of River Murray.

117.	11.	1½d. red	1·00	55
118.		3d. blue	4·00	5·50

1930. Surch. in words.

119.	5a.	2d. on 1½d. red	1·00	40
120.		5d. on 4½d. violet ..	7·50	7·50

1931. Kingsford Smith's Flights.

121.	13.	2d. red (postage) ..	75	60
122.		3d. blue	5·50	4·50
123.		6d. purple (air)	10·00	10·00

1931. Air. As T 13 but inscr. "AIR MAIL SERVICE".

139.	–	6d. brown	16·00	12·00

1931. Air. No. 139 optd. **O.S.**

139a.	–	6d. brown	35·00	45·00

1932.

140.	17.	1s. green	40·00	1·00

18. Sydney Harbour Bridge.

1932.

144	18.	2d. red	2·75	1·00
142		3d. blue..	4·50	7·50
143		5s. green	£375	£180

19. Laughing Kookaburra.

1932.

146.	19.	6d. red	25·00	55

20. Melbourne and R. Yarra.

1934. Centenary of Victoria.

147.	20.	2d. red	2·50	1·75
148.		3d. blue..	6·00	5·50
149.		1s. black	45·00	18·00

21. Merino Ram.

1934. Death Centenary of Capt. John MacArthur.

150.	21.	2d. red	4·00	1·50
151.		3d. blue..	10·00	8·00
152.		9d. purple	35·00	35·00

22. Hermes.

1934.

153b **22** 1s. 6d. purple .. .. 8·50 90

23. Cenotaph, Whitehall. **24.** King George V on "Anzac".

1935. 20th Anniv. of Gallipoli Landing.

154. **23.** 2d. red 80 30
155. 1s. black .. .. 48·00 38·00

1935. Silver Jubilee.

156. **24.** 2d. red .. .. .. 1·50 30
157. 3d. blue .. .. .. 7·00 7·00
158. 2s. violet .. .. 45·00 38·00

25. Amphitrite and Telephone Cable.

1936. Opening of Submarine Telephone Cable to Tasmania.

159. **25.** 2d. red 75 50
160 3d. blue .. .. .. 2·75 3·50

26. Site of Adelaide, 1836. Old Gum Tree Glenelg; King William St., Adelaide.

1936. Centenary of South Australia.

161. **26.** 2d. red .. .. 1·25 40
162. 3d. blue .. .. 6·00 5·00
163. 1s. green .. .. 11·00 8·00

27. Wallaroo. **28.** Queen Elizabeth.

29. King George VI. **30.**

31. King George VI. **33.** Merino Ram.

38. Queen Elizabeth.

Designs—As Type **28.** 4d. Koala. 6d. Kookaburra, 1s. Lyre Bird. As Type **33**: 9d. Platypus. As Type **38**: 10s. K. George VI.

40. King George VI and Queen Elizabeth.

1937.

228 **27.** ½d. orange 20 10
165 **28.** 1d. green 30 10
180 – 1d. green .. .. 1·50 10
181 – 1d. purple .. .. 1·25 10
182 **29.** 1½d. purple .. .. 4·50 7·50
183 1½d. green .. .. 1·00 40
167 **30.** 2d. red 30 10
184 – 2d. red .. .. .. 2·50 10
185 **30.** 2d. purple 50 50
186 **31.** 3d. blue .. .. .. 45·00 2·25
187 3d. brown 30 10
188 – 4d. green .. .. 1·50 10
188a **33.** 5d. purple .. .. 45 1·50
189a – 6d. brown .. .. 1·75 10
190 – 9d. brown 80 20
191 – 1s. green .. .. 1·00 10
175a **31.** 1s 4d. mauve .. .. 1·50 1·50
176a **38.** 5s. red .. .. .. 7·00 1·75
177 – 10s. purple .. .. 38·00 12·00
178 **40.** £1 slate .. .. 60·00 30·00

Nos. 180 and 184 are as Types **28 and 30** but with completely shaded background.

41. Governor Phillip at Sydney Cove. (J. Allcot).

1937. 150th Anniv. of New South Wales.

193. **41.** 2d. red .. .. 2·25 15
194. 3d. blue .. .. 10·00 2·75
195. 9d. purple .. .. 22·00 9·50

42. A.I.F. and Nurse.

1940. Australian Imperial Forces.

196. **42.** 1d. green .. .. 1·50 95
197. 2d. red .. .. .. 1·50 30
198. 3d. blue .. .. .. 11·00 7·50
199. 6d. purple .. .. 21·00 13·00

1941. Surch. with figures and bars.

200. **30.** 2½d. on 2d. red .. 1·25 30
201. **31.** 3½d. on 3d. blue .. 1·50 1·50
202. **33.** 5½d. on 5d. purple .. 7·50 3·75

46a. Queen Elizabeth. **47.** King George VI.

48. King George VI. **49.**

50. Emu. **52.** Duke and Duchess of Gloucester.

1942.

203. **46a.** 1d. purple 20 10
204. 1½d. green 20 10
204a. **47.** 2d. purple 40 30
205. **48.** 2½d. red 20 10
206. **49.** 3½d. blue 25 10
207. **50.** 5½d. grey 65 10

1945. Royal Visit.

209. **52.** 2½d. red 10 10
210. 3½d. blue 15 40
211. 5½d. grey 20 40

53. Star and Wreath.

1946. Victory. Inscr. "PEACE 1945".

213. **53.** 2½d. red 10 10
214. – 3½d. blue 25 75
215. – 5½d. green 30 50

Designs—horiz. 3½d. Flag and dove. vert. 5½d. Angel.

56. Sir Thomas Mitchell and Queensland.

1946. Centenary of Mitchell's Central Queensland Exploration.

216. **56.** 2½d. red 10 10
217. 3½d. blue 20 60
218. 1s. green 25 25

57. Lt. John Shortland, R.N. **58.** Steel Foundry.

1947. 150th Anniv. of City of Newcastle.

219. **57.** 2½d. lake 10 10
220. **58.** 3½d. blue 20 45
221. – 5½d. green 20 35

Design—As Type **58**: horiz. 5½d. Coal carrier Cranes.

60. Queen Elizabeth II when Princess.

1947. Wedding of Princess Elizabeth.

222 **60** 1d. purple 15 10

61. Hereford Bull. **61a.** Hermes and Globe.

62. Aboriginal Art. **62a.** Commonwealth Coat of Arms.

1948.

223. **61.** 1s. 3d. brown .. .. 1·75 85
223a. **61a.** 1s. 6d. brown .. .. 1·75 10
224. **62.** 2s. brown .. .. 2·00 10
224a. **62a.** 5s. red .. .. .. 6·00 10
224b. 10s. purple .. .. 24·00 45
224c. £1 blue .. .. 40·00 3·00
224d. £2 green .. .. £110 14·00

63. William J. Farrer. **64.** Ferdinand von Mueller.

1948. W. J. Farrer (wheat research).

225. **63.** 2½d. red 10 10

1948. Sir Ferdinand von Mueller (botanist).

226. **64.** 2½d. red 10 10

65. Boy Scout. **66.** "Henry Lawson". (Sir Lionel Lindsey).

1948. Pan-Pacific Scout Jamboree, Wonga Park.

227. **65.** 2½d. lake 10 10

For 3½d. value dates "1952–53", see No. 254.

1949. Birth Anniv. of Henry Lawson (poet).

231. **66.** 2½d. purple 15 10

67. Mounted Postman and Aeroplane.

1949. 75th Anniversary of U.P.U.

232. **67.** 3½d. blue 20 25

68. Lord Forrest of Bunbury.

1949. Lord Forrest (explorer and politician).

233. **68.** 2½d. red 15 10

69. King George VI. **70.** Queen Elizabeth.

81. King George VI. **80.**

71. Aborigine. **82.** King George VI.

1950.

236 **70** 1½d. green 15 10
237 2d. green 15 10
234 **69** 2½d. red 10 10
235a 2½d. brown 15 15
235 3d. red 15 10
235b 3d. green 15 10
248 **81** 3½d. purple 10 10
249 4½d. red 15 60
250 6½d. brown 15 55
251 6½d. green 10 15
247 **80** 7½d. blue 15 45
238 **71** 8½d. brown 15 40
252 **82** 1s. 0½d. blue 35 30
253 **71** 2s. 6d. brown (21 × 25½ mm) .. .. 2·50 35

72. **73.** Reproduction of First Stamps of N.S.W. and Victoria.

1950. Centenary of Australian States Stamps.

239. **72.** 2½d. purple 10 10
240. **73.** 2½d. purple 10 10

DESIGNS—As Type **70:** No. 242, Sir Edmund Barton. As Type **77:** No. 243. Opening first Federal Parliament.

75. Sir Henry Parkes.

77. Federal Parliament House, Canberra.

1951. 50th Anniv. of Commonwealth. Inscr. as in T **75** and **77**.

241.	**75.**	3d. lake ..	30	10
242.	–	3d. lake ..	30	10
243.	–	5½d. blue	20	1·50
244.	**77.**	1s. 6d. brown ..	35	50

78. E. H. Hargraves. **79.** C. J. Latrobe.

1951. Cent. of Discovery of Gold in Australia.

245.	**78.**	3d. purple	30	10

1951. Centenary of Responsible Government in Victoria.

246.	**79.**	3d. purple	30	10

1952. Pan-Pacific Scout Jamboree, Greystanes. As T **65** but dated "1952–53".

254.	**65.**	3½d. lake	10	10

83. Butter. **86.** Queen Elizabeth II.

1953. Food Production. Inscr. "PRODUCE FOOD!".

255.	**83.**	3d. green	30	10
256.	–	3d. green (Wheat)	30	10
257.	–	3d. green (Beef)	30	10
258.	**83.**	3½d. red ..	30	10
259.	–	3½d. red (Wheat)	30	10
260.	–	3½d. red (Beef) ..	30	10

1953.

261.	**86.**	1d. purple	15	10
261a.		2½d. blue	20	10
262.		3d. green	20	10
263.		3½d. red	20	10
263a.		6½d. orange	1·50	10

87. Queen Elizabeth II.

1953. Coronation.

264.	**87.**	3½d. red ..	35	10
265.		7½d. violet	1·25	65
266.		2s. turquoise	5·00	40

88. Young Farmers and Calf.

1953. 25th Anniv. of Australian Young Farmers' Clubs.

267.	**88.**	3½d. brown and green ..	10	10

89. Lt.-Gov. D. Collins.

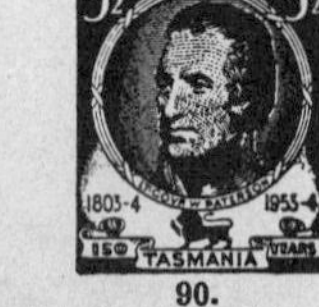

90. Lt.-Gov. W. Paterson.

91. Sullivan Cove, Hobart, 1804.

1953. 150th Anniversary of Settlement in Tasmania.

268.	**89.**	3½d. purple	30	10
269.	**90.**	3½d. purple	30	10
270.	**91.**	2s. green	2·00	2·50

92. Stamp of 1853.

1953. 1st Cent. of Tasmania Postage Stamps.

271.	**92.**	3d. red ..	10	20

93. Queen Elizabeth II and Duke of Edinburgh.

94. Queen Elizabeth II.

95. "Telegraphic Communications".

1954. Royal Visit.

272.	**93.**	3½d. red	20	10
273.	**94.**	7½d. purple	35	1·00
274.	**93.**	2s. green	85	60

1954. Centenary of Telegraph.

275.	**95.**	3½d. brown	10	10

96. Red Cross and Globe.

1954. 40th Anniv. Australian Red Cross Society.

276.	**96.**	3½d. blue and red	10	10

97. Mute Swan.

1954. Cent. of Western Australian Stamp.

277.	**97.**	3½d. black	15	10

98. Locomotives of 1854 and 1954.

1954. Centenary of Australian Railways.

278.	**98.**	3½d. purple	30	10

99. Territory Badge.

100. Olympic Games Symbol.

1954. Australian Antarctic Research.

279.	**99.**	3½d. black	15	10

1954. Olympic Games Propaganda.

280.	**100.**	2s. blue ..	70	40
280a.		2s. green	1·75	1·25

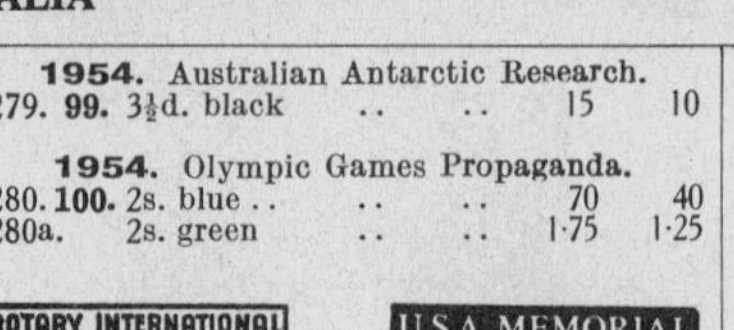

101. Rotary Symbol, Globe and Flags. **103.** American Memorial, Canberra.

1955. 50th Anniv. of Rotary International.

281.	**101.**	3½d. red	10	10

1955. Australian-American Friendship.

283.	**103.**	3½d. blue	10	10

113. Queen Elizabeth II. **102.**

1955.

294	**113.**	4d. lake ..	30	10
294a		7½d. violet	1·25	1·25
295		10d. blue	1·50	55
282	**102.**	1s. 0½d. blue	3·25	50
282a		1s. 7d. brown ..	3·50	15

104. Cobb & Co. Coach (from dry-print by Sir Lionel Lindsey).

1955. Mail-coach Pioneers Commem.

284.	**104.**	3½d. sepia	25	10
285.		2s. brown	75	1·40

105. Y.M.C.A. Emblem and Map of the World.

1955. World Cent. of Y.M.C.A.

286.	**105.**	3½d. green and red	10	10

106. Florence Nightingale, and Young Nurse.

107. Queen Victoria.

1955. Nursing Profession Commemoration.

287.	**106.**	3½d. lilac	10	10

1955. Centenary of South Australian Postage Stamp.

288.	**107.**	3½d. green	10	10

108. Badges of N.S.W., Victoria and Tasmania.

1956. Centenary of Responsible Govt. in N.S.W., Victoria and Tasmania.

289.	**108.**	3½d. lake	10	10

109. Arms of Melbourne.

110. Olympic Torch and Symbol.

111. Collins Street, Melbourne.

1956. Olympic Games, Melbourne.

290.	**109.**	4d. red	25	10
291.	**110.**	7½d. blue	40	70
292.	**111.**	1s. multicoloured	40	20
293.	–	2s. multicoloured	50	70

DESIGN: As Type **111:** 2s. Melbourne across R. Yarra.

115. S. Australia Coat of Arms.

1957. Centenary of Responsible Government in South Australia.

296	**115**	4d. brown	10	10

116. Map of Australia and Caduceus.

1957. Royal Flying Doctor Service of Australia.

297	**116**	7d. blue	15	10

117. "The Spirit of Christmas" (Child) (after Sir Joshua Reynolds).

1957. Christmas.

298	**117**	3½d. red	10	10
299		4d. purple	10	10

118. Super-Constellation Airliner.

1958. Inaug. of Australian "Round-the-World" Air Service.

301.	**118.**	2s. blue	85	85

119. Hall of Memory, Sailor and Airmen.

1958.

302.	**119.**	5½d. lake	55	30
303.	–	5½d. lake	55	30

No. 303 shows a soldier and servicewoman instead of the sailor and airman.

120. Sir Charles Kingsford Smith and the "Southern Cross".

122. The Nativity.

121. Silver Mine, Broken Hill.

1958. 30th Anniv. of 1st Air Crossing of the Tasman Sea.
304. **120.** 8d. blue 60 85

1958. 75th Anniv. of Founding of Broken Hill.
305. **121.** 4d. brown 30 10

1958. Christmas Issue.
306. **122.** 3½d. red 20 10
307. 4d. violet 20 10

124. Queen Elizabeth II.

126. Queen Elizabeth II. 127.

128. Queen Elizabeth II. 129.

1959.
308. – 1d. purple 10 10
309. **124.** 2d. brown 30 15
311. **126.** 3d. turquoise .. 15 10
312. **127.** 3½d. green 15 15
313. **128.** 4d. red .. .. 1·75 10
314. **129.** 5d. blue 90 10
No. 308 shows a head and shoulders portrait as in Type **128** and is vert.

131. Numbat.

137. Christmas Bells.

142. Aboriginal Stockman.

1959.
316. **131.** 6d. brown .. .. 1·75 10
317. – 8d. red 75 10
318. – 9d. sepia .. .. 2·50 35
319. – 11d. blue .. .. 1·25 15
320. – 1s. green .. .. 4·75 30
321. – 1s. 2d. purple .. 1·00 15
322. **137.** 1s. 6d. red on yellow 2·50 80
323. – 2s. blue .. .. 1·25 10
324. – 2s. 3d. green on yellow .. .. 1·75 10
324a. – 2s. 3d. green .. .. 7·00 1·50
325. – 2s. 5d. brown on yellow .. .. 7·00 45
326. – 3s red .. .. .. 2·00 10
327. **142.** 5s. brown .. .. 20·00 75
DESIGNS—As Type **131**—VERT. 8d. Tiger Cat. 9d. Eastern grey kangaroo. 11d. Common rabbit bandicoot. 1s. Platypus. HORIZ. 1s. 2d. Thylacine. As Type **137**. 2s. Flannel Flower 2s. 3d. Wattle. 2s. 5d. Banksia (plant). 3s. Waratah.

143. Postmaster Isaac Nichols boarding the Brig "Experiment".

1959 150th Anniv. of Australian P.O.
331. **143.** 4d. slate 15 10

144. Parliament House, Brisbane and Arms of Queensland.

145. "The Approach of the Magi".

1959. Cent. of Queensland Self-Government.
332. **144.** 4d. lilac and green .. 10 10

1959. Christmas.
333. **145.** 5d. violet 10 10

146. Girl Guide and Lord Baden-Powell.

1960. Golden Jubilee of Girl Guide Movement.
334. **146.** 5d. blue 30 15

147. "The Overlanders" (after Sir Daryl Lindsay).

1960. Centenary of Northern Territory Exploration.
335. **147.** 5d. mauve 30 15

148. "Archer" and Melbourne Cup.

149 Queen Victoria.

1960. 100th Melbourne Cup Race Commem.
336. **148.** 5d. sepia 20 10

1960. Centenary of Queensland Stamps.
337. **149.** 5d. green 25 10

150. Open Bible and Candle.

1960. Christmas Issue.
338. **150.** 5d. lake 10 10

151. Colombo Plan Bureau Emblem.

152. Melba (after bust by Sir Bertram Mackennal).

1961. Colombo Plan.
339. **151.** 1s. brown 10 10

1961. Birth Centenary of Dame Nellie Melba (singer).
340. **152.** 5d. blue 30 15

153. Open Prayer Book and Text.

1961. Christmas issue.
341. **153.** 5d. brown 10 10

154. J. M. Stuart.

155. Flynn's Grave and Nursing Sister.

1962. Centenary of Stuart's South to North Crossing of Australia.
342. **154.** 5d. red.. .. .. 15 10

1962. 50th Anniv. of Australian Inland Mission.
343. **155.** 5d. multicoloured .. 30 15

156. "Woman".

157. "Madonna and Child".

1962. "Associated Country Women of the World" Conference, Melbourne.
344. **156.** 5d. green 10 10

1962. Christmas.
345. **157.** 5d. violet 15 10

158. Perth and Kangaroo Paw (plant).

1962. British Empire and Commonwealth Games, Perth. Multicoloured.
346. 5d. Type **158** 40 10
347. 2s. 3d. Arms of Perth and running track .. .. 3·25 2·50

160. Queen Elizabeth II.

163. Centenary Emblem.

162. Arms of Canberra and W. B. Griffin (architect).

1963. Royal Visit.
348. **160.** 5d. green 35 10
349. – 2s. 3d. lake .. .. 2·25 3·50
DESIGN: 2s. 3d. Queen Elizabeth II and Duke of Edinburgh.

1963. 50th Anniversary of Canberra.
350. **162.** 5d. green 15 10

1963. Centenary of Red Cross
351. **163.** 5d. red, grey and blue 30 10

164. Blaxland, Lawson and Wentworth on Mt. York.

1963. 150th Anniv. of First Crossing of Blue Mountains.
352. **164.** 5d. blue 15 10

165. "Export".

1963. Export Campaign.
353. **165.** 5d. red 10 10

1963. As T **160** but smaller (17½ × 21½ mm.) "5D" at top right replacing "ROYAL VISIT 1963" and oak leaves omitted.
354 5d. green 65 10
354c 5d. red 55 10

167. Tasman and "Heemskerk".

1963. Navigators.
355. **167.** 4s. blue .. .. 4·50 55
356. – 5s. brown .. .. 6·00 75
357. – 7s. 6d. olive .. .. 19·00 16·00
358. – 10s. purple .. .. 42·00 4·25
359. – £1 violet .. .. 48·00 14·00
360. – £2 sepia .. .. 85·00 75·00
DESIGNS—As Type **167**: 7s. 6d. Captain Cook. 10s. Flinders and "Investigator". 20½ × 25½ mm: 5s. Dampier and "Roebuck". £1, Bass and whale boat. £2, Admiral King and "Mermaid" (survey cutter).

173. "Peace on Earth . . .".

176. Black-backed Magpie.

174. "Commonwealth Cable.

1963. Christmas.
361. **173.** 5d. blue 10 10

1963. Opening of COMPAC (Trans-Pacific Telephone Cable).
362. **174.** 2s. 3d. multicoloured 3·25 4·00

1964.

363. – 6d. multicoloured .. 60 25
364. 176. 9d. black, grey & green 1·50 3·25
365. – 1s. 6d. multicoloured .. 1·00 1·40
366. – 2s. yellow, black & pink 2·50 50
367. – 2s. 5d. multicoloured .. 7·00 3·50
368. – 2s. 6d. multicoloured .. 4·75 3·00
369. – 3s. multicoloured .. 5·00 1·50

BIRDS—HORIZ. 6d. Yellow-tailed Thornbill. 2s. 6d. Scarlet Robin. VERT. 1s. 6d. Galah (cockatoo). 2s. Golden Whistler (Thickhead). 2s. 5d. Blue Wren. 3s. Straw-necked Ibis.

182. "Bleriot" Aircraft (type flown by M. Guillaux, 1914).

1964. 50th Anniv. of 1st Australian Airmail Flight.

370. 182. 5d. green 40 10
371. 2s. 3d. red .. .. 3·00 2·00

183. Child looking at Nativity Scene. **184.** "Simpson and his Donkey".

1964. Christmas.

372. 183. 5d. red, blue, buff & blk. 10 10

1965. 50th Anniv. of Gallipoli Landing.

373. 184. 5d. brown 65 10
374. 8d. blue .. .. 1·00 2·25
375 2s. 3d. purple .. .. 1·75 2·25

185. "Telecommunications". **186.** Sir Winston Churchill.

1965. Centenary of I.T.U.

376. 185. 5d. black, brown & blue 30 10

1965. Churchill Commem.

377. 186. 5d. black, grey & blue 15 10

187. General Monash. **189.** I.C.Y. Emblem.

188. Hargrave and "Seaplane" (1902).

1965. Birth Centenary of General Sir John Monash (engineer and soldier).

378. 187. 5d. multicoloured .. 15 10

1965. 50th Death Anniv. of Lawrence Hargrave (aviation pioneer).

379. 188. 5d. multicoloured .. 15 10

1965. Int. Co-operation Year.

380. 189. 2s. 3d. green and blue 1·75 2·00

190. "Nativity Scene".

1965. Christmas.

381. 190. 5d. multicoloured .. 15 10

191. Queen Elizabeth II. **192.** Blue-faced Honeyeater.

1966. Decimal currency. As earlier issues but with values in cents and dollars as in T 191/2. Also some new designs.

382. 191. 1 c. brown 25 10
383. 2 c. green 70 10
384. 3 c. green 70 10
404. 3 c. blk., pink & grn. 20 40
385. 4 c. red 20 10
405. 4 c. blk., brn. & red 45 20
405a. 5 c. blk., brn. & bl. 60 10
386. – 5 c. mult. (as 363) .. 25 10
386c. 191. 5 c. blue .. 1·75 10
387. 192. 6 c. multicoloured .. 70 40
387a. 6 c. orange 55 10
388. – 7 c. multicoloured .. 1·50 10
388a. 191. 7 c. purple .. .. 1·10 15
389. – 8 c. multicoloured .. 1·50 25
390. – 9 c. multicoloured .. 1·50 15
391. – 10 c. multicoloured .. 1·50 10
392. – 13 c. multicoloured .. 3·25 25
393. – 15 c. mult. (as 365) .. 2·50 50
394. – 20 c. yell. blk. & pink (as 366) .. .. 6·00 15
395. – 24 c. multicoloured .. 90 55
396. – 25 c. mult. (as 368) .. 5·00 20
397. – 30 c. mult. (as 369) .. 24·00 45
398. 167. 40 c. blue .. 8·50 10
399. – 50 c. brown (as 356) 11·00 10
400. – 75 c. olive (as 357) .. 1·00 1·50
401. – $1 purple (as 358) .. 3·25 15
402. – $2 violet (as 359) .. 8·00 30
403. – $4 brown (as 360) .. 7·50 5·50

DESIGNS—VERT. 7 c. Humbug fish. 8 c. Coral fish. 9 c. Hermit crab. 10 c. Anemone fish. 13 c. Red-necked Avocet. HORIZ. 24 c. Azure Kingfisher.

200. "Saving Life".

1966. 75th Anniv. Royal Life Saving Society.

406. 200. 4 c. black, bright blue and blue 15 10

201. "Adoration of the Shepherds".

1966. Christmas.

407. 201. 4 c. black and olive .. 10 10

202. "Eendracht". **203.** Open Bible.

1966. 350th Anniv. of Dirk Hartog's Landing in Australia.

408. 202. 4 c. multicoloured .. 10 10

1967. 150th Anniv. of British and Foreign Bible Society in Australia.

409. 203. 4 c. multicoloured .. 10 10

204. Ancient Keys and Modern Lock.

1967. 150th Anniv. of Australian Banking.

410. 204. 4 c. black, blue & green 10 10

205. Lions Badge and 50 Stars.

1967. 50th Anniversary of Lions Int.

411. 205. 4 c. black, gold & blue 10 10

206. Y.W.C.A. Emblem.

1967. World Y.W.C.A. Council Meeting, Monash University, Victoria.

412. 206. 4 c. multicoloured .. 10 10

207. Anatomical Figures.

1967. 5th World Gynaecology and Obstetrics Congress, Sydney.

413. 207. 4 c. black, blue & violet 10 10

1967. No. 385 surch.

414. 191. 5 c. on 4 c. red .. 70 10

209. Christmas Bells and Gothic Arches.

1967. Christmas. Multicoloured.

415. 5 c. Type 209 .. .. 20 10
416. 25 c. Religious symbols (vert.) .. .. 1·25 1·75

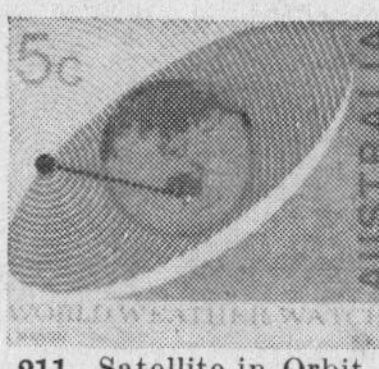

211. Satellite in Orbit.

1968. World Weather Watch. Multicoloured.

417. 5 c. Type 211 .. .. 30 10
418. 20 c. World Weather Map 1·75 3·75

213. Radar Antenna. **214.** Kangaroo Paw (Western Australia).

1968. World Telecommunications Intelsat II.

419. 213. 25 c. blue, black & grn. 3·00 5·50

1968. State Floral Emblems. Multicoloured.

420. 6 c. Type 214 .. .. 55 65
421. 13 c. Pink Heath (Victoria) 65 40
422. 15 c. Tasmanian Blue Gum (Tasmania) .. .. 1·50 20
423. 20 c. Sturt's Desert Pea (South Australia) .. 7·50 40
424. 25 c. Cooktown Orchid (Queensland) .. .. 4·00 50
425. 30 c. Waratah (New South Wales) .. .. .. 1·00 10

220. Soil Sample Analysis.

1968. Int. Soil Science Congress and World Medical Assn. Assembly. Multicoloured.

426. 5 c. Type 220 .. .. 10 10
427. 5 c. Rubber-gloved hands syringe and head of Hippocrates. 10 10

222. Athlete carrying Torch, and Sunstone Symbol. **224.** Houses and Dollar Signs.

1968. Olympic Games, Mexico City. Mult.

428 5 c. Type 222 .. .. 30 10
429 25 c. Sunstone Symbol and Mexican Flag .. .. 45 1·50

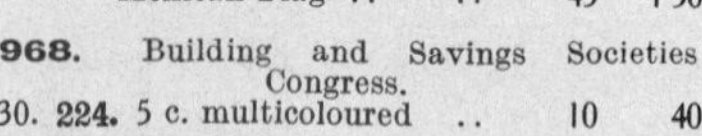

1968. Building and Savings Societies Congress.

430. 224. 5 c. multicoloured .. 10 40

225. Church Window and View of Bethlehem. **226.** Edgeworth David (geologist).

1968. Christmas.

431. 225. 5 c. multicoloured .. 10 10

1968. Famous Australians. (1st series).

432. 226. 5 c. green on myrtle .. 75 20
433. – 5 c. black on blue .. 75 20
434. – 5 c. brown on buff .. 75 20
435. – 5 c. violet on lilac .. 75 20

DESIGNS: No. 433, A. B. Paterson (poet). No. 434, Albert Namatjira (artist). No. 435, Caroline Chrisholm (social worker).

Nos. 432/5 were only issued in booklets and exist with one or two sides imperf.

See also Nos. 446/9, 479/82, 505/8, 537/40, 590/5, 602/7 and 637/40.

230. Macquarie Lighthouse.

1968. 150th Anniv. of Macquarie Lighthouse.

436. 230. 5 c. black on yellow .. 10 30

231. Pioneers and Modern Building, Darwin.

1969. Centenary of Northern Territory Settlement.

437. 231. 5 c. brn. olive & ochre 10 10

232. Melbourne Harbour.

1969. 6th Biennial Conference of International Association of Ports and Harbours.
438. **232.** 5 c. multicoloured .. 15 10

233. Concentric Circles (Symbolising Management, Labour and Government).

1969. 50th Anniv. of I.L.O.
439. **233.** 5 c. multicoloured .. 15 10

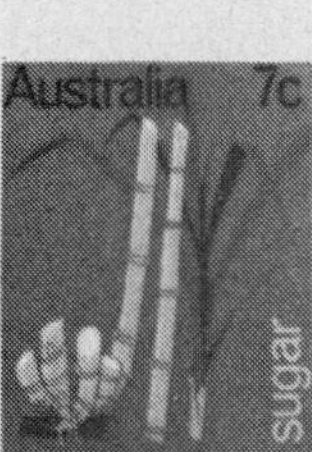

234. Sugar Cane.

238. "The Nativity" (stained glass window).

1969. Primary Industries. Multicoloured.
440. 7 c. Type **234** .. .. 1·25 2·50
441. 15 c. Timber .. .. 4·00 6·00
442. 20 c. Wheat .. .. 1·25 80
443. 25 c. Wool .. .. 2·50 2·25

1969. Christmas. Multicoloured.
444. 5 c. Type **238** 20 10
445. 25 c. "Tree of Life", Christ in crib and Christmas Star (abstract).. .. 1·00 2·00

240. Edmund Barton.

244. Capt. Ross Smith's Vickers "Vimy", 1919.

1969. Famous Australians (2nd series). Prime Ministers.
446. **240.** 5 c. black on green .. 90 20
447. – 5 c. black on green .. 90 20
448. – 5 c. black on green .. 90 20
449. – 5 c. black on green .. 90 20
DESIGNS: No 447, Alfred Deakin. No. 448, J. C. Watson. No. 449, G. H. Reid.
Nos. 446/9 were only issued in booklets and only exist with one or two adjacent sides imperf.

1969. 50th Anniv. of 1st England–Australia Flight.
450. **244.** 5 c. multicoloured .. 15 10
451. – 5 c. red, black & green 15 10
452. – 5 c. multicoloured .. 15 10
DESIGNS: No. 451, Lt. H. Fysh and Lt. P. McGinness 1919 Survey with Ford car. No. 452, Capt. Wrigley and Sgt. Murphy in "BE 2E" take off to meet the Smiths.

247. Symbolic Track and Diesel Locomotive.

1970. Sydney-Perth Standard Gauge Railway Link.
453. **247.** 5 c. multicoloured .. 15 10

248. Australian Pavilion, Osaka.

1970. World Fair, Osaka. Expo. 70.
454. **248.** 5 c. multicoloured .. 15 10
455. – 20 c. red and black .. 35 65
DESIGN: 20 c. "Southern Cross" and "from the Country of the south with warm feelings" (message).

251. Australian Flag.

1970. Royal Visit.
456. – 5 c. black and ochre .. 25 15
457. **251.** 30 c. multicoloured .. 1·25 2·00
DESIGN: 5 c. Queen Elizabeth II and Duke of Edinburgh.

252. Lucerne Plant, Bull and Sun.

1970. 11th Int. Grasslands Congress.
458. **252.** 5 c. multicoloured .. 10 40

253. Captain Cook and H.M.S. "Endeavour".

259. Sturt's Desert Rose.

1970. Bicentenary Captain Cook's Discovery of Australia's East Coast. Multicoloured.
459. 5 c. Type **253** 50 10
460. 5 c. Sextant and H.M.S. "Endeavour" 50 10
461. 5 c. Landing at Botany Bay 50 10
462. 5 c. Charting and exploring 50 10
463. 5 c. Claiming possession .. 50 10
464. 30 c. Captain Cook, H.M.S. "Endeavour", Sextant, Aborigines and Kangaroo (63 × 30 mm.) 1·75 2·75
Nos. 459/63 were issued together se-tenant in horiz. strips of five, forming a composite design.

1970. Coil Stamps. Multicoloured.
465a 2 c. Type **259** 35 20
466 4 c. Type **259** .. .. 70 1·25
467 5 c. Golden Wattle .. 20 10
468 6 c. Type **259** .. .. 1·25 1·00
468b 7 c. Sturt's Desert Pea .. 40 30
468d 10 c. As 7 c. 30 25

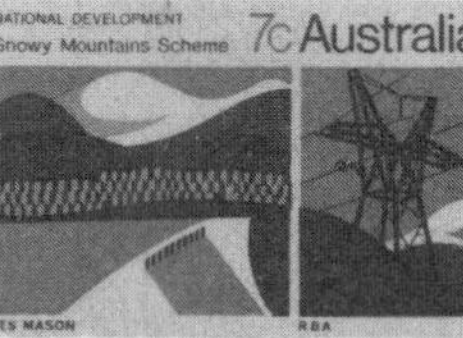

264. Snowy Mountains Scheme.

1970. National Development (1st series). Multicoloured.
469. 7 c. Type **264** 30 80
470. 8 c. Ord River scheme .. 15 15
471. 9 c. Bauxite to aluminium 15 15
472. 10 c. Oil and natural gas .. 40 10
See also Nos. 541/4.

265. Rising Flames.

1970. 16th Commonwealth Parliamentary Association Conference, Canberra.
473. **265.** 6 c. multicoloured .. 10 10

266. Milk Analysis and Dairy Herd.

1970. 18th Int. Dairy Congress, Sydney.
474. **266.** 6 c. multicoloured .. 10 10

267. "The Nativity".

268. U.N. "Plant" and Dove of Peace.

1970. Christmas.
475. **267.** 6 c. multicoloured .. 10 10

1970. 25th Anniv. of United Nations.
476. **268.** 6 c. multicoloured .. 15 10

269. Boeing "707" and Avro "504".

1970. 50th Anniv. of QANTAS Airline.
477. **269.** 6 c. multicoloured .. 35 10
478. – 30 c. multicoloured .. 90 1·50
DESIGN: 30 c. Avro "504" and Boeing "707".

1970. Famous Australians (3rd series). As T **226**.
479 6 c. blue .. .. .. 1·50 20
480 6 c. black on brown .. 1·50 20
481 6 c. purple on pink .. 1·50 20
482 6 c. red on pink .. .. 1·50 20
DESIGNS: No. 479, The Duigan brothers (pioneer aviators). 480, Lachlan Macquarie (Governor of New South Wales). 481, Adam Lindsay Gordon (poet). 482, E. J. Eyre (explorer).

271. "Theatre".

1971. "Australia-Asia". Multicoloured.
483. 7 c. Type **271** 45 60
484. 15 c. "Music" .. .. 70 1·00
485. 20 c. "Sea Craft" 65 90

272. The Southern Cross.

1971. Cent. of Australian Natives' Assoc.
486. **272.** 6 c. black, red and blue 10 10

273. Market "Graph".

1971. Cent. of Sydney Stock Exchange.
487. **273.** 6 c. multicoloured .. 10 10

274. Rotary Emblem.

1971. 50th Anniv. of Rotary International in Australia.
488. **274.** 6 c. mutlicoloured .. 15 10

275. "Mirage" Jets and "D.H.9a" Biplane.

276. Draught-horse, Cat and Dog.

1971. 50th Anniversary of R.A.A.F.
489. **275.** 6 c. multicoloured .. 15 10

1971. Animals. Multicoloured.
490. 6 c. Type **276** 20 10
491. 12 c. Vet and lamb ("Animal Science") .. 45 45
492. 18 c. Red Kangaroo ("Fauna Conservation") 60 75
493. 24 c. Guide-dog ("Animals Aid to Man") .. .. 1·50 2·25
The 6 c. commemorates the Centenary of the Australian R.S.P.C.A.

277. Bark Painting.

1971. Aboriginal Art. Multicoloured.
494. 20 c. Type **277** 20 20
495. 25 c. Body decoration .. 20 50
496. 30 c. Cave painting (vert.) 30 20
497. 35 c. Grave posts (vert.) 30 15

278. The Three Kings and the Star.

1971. Christmas. Colours of star and colour of "AUSTRALIA" given.
498. **278.** 7 c. blue, mve. & brn. 1·00 15
499. 7 c. mve., brn. & white 1·00 15
500. 7 c. mve., white & blk. 6·00 80
501. 7 c. blk., green & blk. 1·00 15
502. 7 c. lilac, green & mve. 1·00 15
503. 7 c. blk., brn. & white 1·00 15
504. 7 c. blue, mve. & green 25·00 2·25

1972. Famous Australians. (4th series). As Type **240**. Prime Ministers.
505. 7 c. blue 70 20
506. 7 c. blue 70 20
507. 7 c. red 70 20
508. 7 c. red 70 20
DESIGNS: No. 505, Andrew Fisher. No. 506, W. M. Hughes. No. 507, Joseph Cook. No. 508, S. M. Bruce.

280. Cameo Brooch.

1972. 50th Anniv. of Country Women's Assn.
509. **280.** 7 c. multicoloured .. 20 10

281. Fruit.

1972. Primary Industries. Multicoloured.
510. 20 c. Type **281** .. .. 3·00 4·00
511. 25 c. Rice .. .. .. 3·00 5·50
512. 30 c. Fish .. .. .. 3·00 3·00
513. 35 c. Beef .. .. .. 7·00 1·75

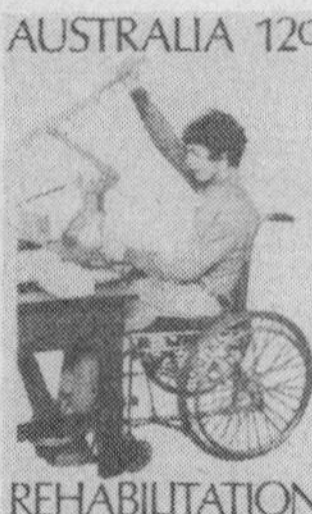

282. Worker in Wheelchair. **284.** Athletics.

283. Telegraph Line.

1972. Rehabilitation of the Disabled.
514. **282.** 12 c. brown and green 10 10
515. – 18 c. green and orange 50 35
516. – 24 c. blue and brown .. 15 10
DESIGNS—HORIZ. 18 c. Patient and teacher. VERT. 24 c. Boy playing with ball.

1972. Cent. of Overland Telegraph Line.
517. **283.** 7 c. multicoloured .. 15 15

1972. Olympic Games, Munich. Mult.
518. 7 c. Type **284** 30 30
519. 7 c. Rowing 30 30
520. 7 c. Swimming 30 30
521. 35 c. Equestrian .. .. 2·50 4·75

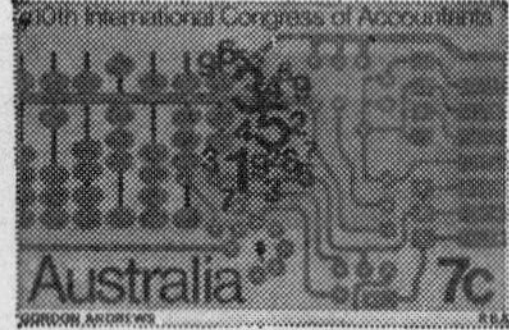

285. Numerals and Computer Circuit.

1972. 10th Int. Congress of Accountants, Sydney.
522. **285.** 7 c. multicoloured .. 15 15

286. Australian-built Harvester.

1972. Pioneer Life. Multicoloured.
523. 5 c. Pioneer Family (vert.) 15 10
524. 10 c. Water-pump (vert.) .. 40 10
525. 15 c. Type **286** 15 10
526. 40 c. House 30 60
527. 50 c. Stage Coach 80 20
528. 60 c. Morse key (vert.) .. 60 1·00
529. 80 c. "Gem" (paddle-steamer) .. .. .. 60 1·00

287. Jesus with Children.

1972. Christmas. Multicoloured.
530. 7 c. Type **287** 30 10
531. 35 c. Dove and spectrum motif (vert.) .. .. 7·00 8·50

288. " Length ".

1973. Metric Conversion. Multicoloured.
532. 7 c. Type **288** 40 40
533. 7 c. " Volume " 40 40
534. 7 c. " Mass " 40 40
535. 7 c. " Temperature " (horiz.) 40 40

289. Caduceus and Laurel Wreath.

1973. 25th Anniv. of World Health Organization.
536. **289.** 7 c. multicoloured .. 30 15

1973. Famous Australians (5th series). As Type **226**.
537. 7 c. brown and black .. 50 35
538. 7 c. lilac and black .. 50 35
539. 7 c. brown and black .. 50 35
540. 7 c. lilac and black .. 50 35
PORTRAITS: No. 537, William Wentworth (statesman and explorer). No. 538, Isaac Isaacs (1st Australian-born Governor-General). No. 539, Mary Gilmore (writer). No. 540, Marcus Clarke (author).

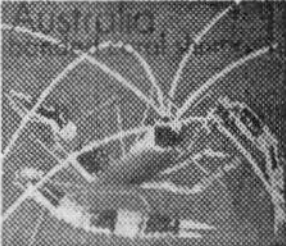

291. Shipping. **292.** Banded Coral Shrimp.

1973. National Development (2nd series). Multicoloured.
541. 20 c. Type **291** .. .. 4·00 4·25
542. 25 c. Iron ore and steel .. 4·00 4·50
543. 30 c. Beef roads .. .. 4·00 4·50
544. 35 c. Mapping .. .. 3·50 4·50

1973. Marine Life and Gemstones. Mult.
545. 1 c. Type **292** 10 10
546. 2 c. Fiddler crab 10 10
547. 3 c. Coral crab 10 10
548. 4 c. Mauve stinger .. 30 55
549. 6 c. Chrysoprase (vert.) .. 30 10
550. 7 c. Agate (vert.) 30 10
551. 8 c. Opal (vert.) 30 10
552. 9 c. Rhodonite (vert.) .. 60 15
552a. 10 c. Star sapphire (vert.) 30 10

293. Children at Play.

1973. 50th Anniv. of Legacy (Welfare Organization).
553. **293.** 7 c. brown, red & green 30 10

294. John Baptising Jesus.

1973. Christmas. Multicoloured.
554. 7 c. Type **294** 35 10
555. 30 c. The Good Shepherd 1·75 1·75

295. Sydney Opera House.

1973. Architecture.
556. **295.** 7 c. blue and pale blue 30 15
557. – 10 c. ochre and brown 80 70
558. – 40 c. grey, brown & blk. 1·00 1·50
559. – 50 c. multicoloured .. 1·25 2·50
DESIGNS—HORIZ. 10 c. Buchanan's Hotel, Townsville. 40 c. Como House, Melbourne. VERT. 50 c. St. James' Church, Sydney.

296. Wireless Receiver and Speaker.

1973. 50th Anniv. of Regular Radio Broadcasting.
560. **296.** 7 c. blue, red and black 15 10

297. Common Wombat. **298.** " Sergeant of Light Horse" (G. Lambert).

1974. Animals. Multicoloured.
561. 20 c. Type **297** 35 10
562. 25 c. Short-nosed echidna 75 60
563. 30 c. Brush-tailed possum 40 15
564. 75 c. Pygmy glider .. 1·00 85

1974. Australian Paintings. Multicoloured.
565. $1 Type **298** .. .. 1·00 10
566. $2 " Red Gums of the Far North " (H. Heysen) .. 1·50 25
566a. $4 " Shearing the Rams " (Tom Roberts) .. 3·00 2·25
567. $5 " McMahon's Point " (Sir Arthur Streeton) .. 6·00 2·25
567a. $10 " Coming South " (Tom Roberts) .. 8·50 3·50
The $2 and $4 are horiz. designs.

299. Supreme Court Judge.

1974. 150th Anniv. of Australia's Third Charter of Justice.
568. **299.** 7 c. multicoloured .. 20 10

300. Rugby Football.

1974. Non-Olympic Sports. Multicoloured.
569. 7 c. Type **300** 55 35
570. 7 c. Bowls 55 35
571. 7 c. Australian football (vert.) 55 35
572. 7 c. Cricket (vert.) .. 55 35
573. 7 c. Golf (vert.) 55 35
574. 7 c. Surfing (vert.) .. 55 35
575. 7 c. Tennis (vert.) .. 55 35

301. " Transport of Mails ".

1974. Centenary of U.P.U. Multicoloured.
576. 7 c. Type **301** 40 20
577. 30 c. Three-part version of Type **301** (vert.) .. 1·25 1·90

302. Letter " A " and W. C. Wentworth (co-founder). **304.** "The Adoration of the Magi ".

1974. 150th Anniv. of First Independent Newspaper. "The Australian".
578. **302.** 7 c. black and brown 30 30

1974. No. 551 surch.
579. 9 c. on 8 c. multicoloured 15 15

1974. Christmas. Woodcuts by Durer.
580. **304.** 10 c. black on cream .. 25 10
581. – 35 c. black on cream .. 80 1·00
DESIGN: 35 c. " The Flight into Egypt ".

305. " Pre-School Education ".

1974. Education in Australia. Multicoloured.
582. 5 c. Type **305** 50 40
583. 11 c. " Correspondence Schools " 50 25
584. 15 c. " Science Education " 80 40
585. 60 c. " Advanced Education " (vert.) .. .. 2·00 2·75

306. "Road Safety". **307.** Australian Women's Year Emblem.

1975. Environmental Dangers. Multicoloured.
586. 10 c. Type **306** 40 40
587. 10 c. " Pollution " (horiz.) 40 40
588. 10 c. " Bush Fires " (horiz.) 40 40

1975. International Women's Year.
589. **307.** 10 c. bl., grn. & vio. .. 20 15

308. J. H. Scullin.

1975. Famous Australians (6th series). Prime Ministers. Multicoloured.
590. 10 c. Type **308** 25 30
591. 10 c. J. A. Lyons 25 30
592. 10 c. Earle Page 25 30
593. 10 c. Arthur Fadden .. 25 30
594. 10 c. John Curtin 25 30
595. 10 c. J. B. Chifley .. 25 30

309. Atomic Absorption Spectrophotometry.

1975. Scientific Development. Multicoloured.

596.	11 c. Type **309**	60	40
597.	24 c. Radio astronomy ..	1·40	1·90
598.	33 c. Immunology ..	1·75	2·50
599.	48 c. Oceanography ..	2·50	2·75

310. Logo of Australian Postal Commission.

1975. Inauguration of Australian Postal and Telecommunications Commissions.

600.	**310.**	10 c. blk., red & grey	25	10
601.	–	10 c. blk., orge. & grey	25	10

DESIGN: No. 601a, Logo of Australian Telecommunications Commission.

311. Edith Cowan. **312.** "Helichrysum thomsonii".

1975. Famous Australians (7th series). Australian Women. Multicoloured.

602.	10 c. Type **311**	35	55
603.	10 c. Louisa Lawson ..	35	55
604.	10 c. "Henry Richardson" (pen-name of Ethel Richardson)	35	55
605.	10 c. Catherine Spence	35	55
606.	10 c. Constance Stone ..	50	55
607.	10 c. Truganini	35	55

1975. Wild Flowers. Mult.

608.	18 c. Type **312**	25	10
609.	45 c. "Callistemon teretifolius" (horiz.)	50	10

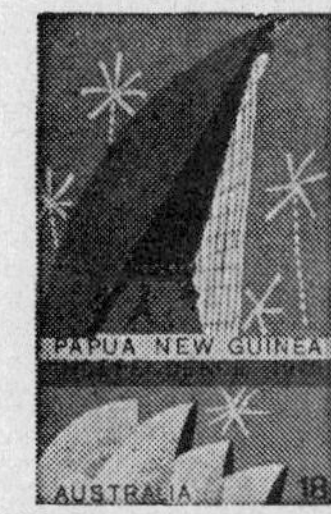

313. "Tambaran" House and Sydney Opera House. **314.** Epiphany Scene.

1975. Independence of Papua New Guinea. Multicoloured.

610.	18 c. Type **313**	35	10
611.	25 c. "Freedom" (bird in flight) (horiz.)	70	1·25

1975. Christmas.

612.	**314.**	15 c. multicoloured ..	25	10
613.	–	45 c. vio., bl. & silver	1·00	2·40

DESIGN—HORIZ. 45 c. "Shining Star".

315. Australian Coat of Arms.

1976. 75th Anniversary of Nationhood.

614.	**315.**	18 c. multicoloured ..	35	20

316. Telephone-user, circa 1878.

1976. Centenary of Telephone.

615.	**316.**	18 c. multicoloured ..	20	15

317. John Oxley.

1976. 19th Century Explorers. Mult.

616.	18 c. Type **317**	30	40
617.	18 c. Hume and Hovell ..	30	40
618.	18 c. John Forrest ..	30	40
619.	18 c. Ernest Giles ..	30	40
620.	18 c. William Gosse ..	30	40
621.	18 c. Peter Warburton ..	30	40

318. Measuring Stick, Graph and Computer Tape.

1976. 50th Anniv. of Commonwealth Scientific and Industrial Research Organization.

622.	**318.**	18 c. multicoloured ..	20	15

319. Football.

1976. Olympic Games, Montreal. Mult.

623.	18 c. Type **319**	30	20
624.	18 c. Gymnastics (vert.) ..	30	20
625.	25 c. Diving (vert.) ..	50	50
626.	40 c. Cycling	70	70

320. Richmond Bridge, Tasmania.

1976. Australian Scenes. Multicoloured.

627.	5 c. Type **320**	15	10
628.	25 c. Broken Bay, N.S.W.	40	20
629.	35 c. Wittenoom Gorge, W.A.	35	20
630.	50 c. Mt. Buffalo, Victoria (vert.)	70	30
631.	70 c. Barrier Reef ..	1·00	1·25
632.	85 c. Ayers Rock, N.T. ..	1·00	1·75

321. Blamire Young (designer of first Australian stamp).

1976. National Stamp Week.

633.	**321.**	18 c. multicoloured ..	15	15

322. "Virgin and Child" (detail, Simone Contarini).

1976. Christmas.

635.	**322.**	15 c. mauve and blue	25	10
636.	–	45 c. multicoloured ..	70	80

DESIGN: Toy koala bear and decorations.

323. John Gould.

1976. Famous Australians. (8th series). Scientists. Multicoloured.

637.	18 c. Type **323**	35	45
638.	18 c. Thomas Laby ..	35	45
639.	18 c. Sir Baldwin Spencer	35	45
640.	18 c. Griffith Taylor ..	35	45

324. "Music". **325.** Queen Elizabeth II.

1977. Performing Arts. Multicoloured.

641.	20 c. Type **324**	25	25
642.	30 c. Drama	40	35
643.	40 c. Dance	55	40
644.	60 c. Opera	1·00	1·75

1977. Silver Jubilee. Multicoloured.

645.	18 c. Type **325**	20	10
646.	45 c. The Queen and Duke of Edinburgh	50	80

326. Fielder and Wicket Keeper.

1977. Centenary of Australia–England Test Cricket.

647.	18 c. Type **326**	35	45
648.	18 c. Umpire and batsman	35	45
649.	18 c. Fielders	35	45
650.	18 c. Batsman and umpire	35	45
651.	18 c. Bowler and fielder ..	35	45
652.	45 c. Batsman facing bowler	75	1·10

327. Parliament House.

1977. 50th Anniv. of Opening of Parliament House, Canberra

653.	**327.**	18 c. multicoloured ..	15	10

328. Trade Union Workers.

1977. 50th Anniv. of Australian Council of Trade Unions.

654.	**328.**	18 c. multicoloured ..	15	10

329. Surfing Santa.

1977. Christmas. Multicoloured.

655.	15 c. Type **329**	25	10
656.	45 c. Madonna and Child ..	1·00	90

330. National Flag.

1978. Australia Day.

657.	**330.**	18 c. multicoloured ..	20	15

331. Harry Hawker and Sopwith "Camel".

1978. Early Australian Aviators. Mult.

658.	18 c. Type **331**	35	45
659.	18 c. Bert Hinkler and Avro "Avian" ..	35	45
660.	18 c. Sir Charles Kingsford Smith and "Southern Cross"	35	45
661.	18 c. Charles Ulm and "Southern Cross" ..	35	45

332. Beechcraft "Baron" landing at Station Airstrip.

1978. 50th Anniv. of Royal Flying Doctor Service.

663.	**332.**	18 c. multicoloured ..	20	15

333. Illawarra Flame Tree. **334.** Sturt's Desert Rose and Map.

1978. Trees. Multicoloured.

664.	18 c. Type **333**	30	15
665.	25 c. Ghost Gum	50	1·40
666.	40 c. Grass Tree	80	2·00
667.	45 c. Cootamundra Wattle	80	90

1978. Establishment of Government for the Northern Territory.

668.	**334.**	18 c. multicoloured ..	20	15

335. Hooded Plover.

1978. Australian Birds (1st series). Mult.

669.	1 c. Spotted-sided Finch	10	20
670.	2 c. Crimson Finch ..	10	20
671.	5 c. Type **335**	15	10
672.	15 c. Forest Kingfisher (vert.)	20	20
673.	20 c. Australian Dabchick	50	10
674.	20 c. Eastern Yellow Robin	20	10
675.	22 c. White-tailed Kingfisher 22 × 29 mm. ..	30	10
676.	25 c. Masked Plover ..	70	35
677.	30 c. Oystercatcher ..	80	25
678.	40 c. Variegated Wren (vert.	30	45
679.	50 c. Flame Robin (vert.)	40	50
680.	55 c. Comb-crested Jacana	85	60

See also Nos. 734/40.

336. 1928 3d. National Stamp Exhibition Commemorative.

1978. 50th Anniv. of National Stamp Week. and National Stamp Exhibition.

694.	**336.**	20 c. multicoloured ..	15	15

Christmas 1978
AUSTRALIA 15c

337. " The Madonna and the Child " (after van Eyck).

1978. Christmas. Multicoloured.
696. 15 c. Type **337** 30 10
697. 25 c. " The Virgin and Child " (Marmion) .. 45 55
698. 55 c. " The Holy Family " (del Vaga) 70 90

338. " Tulloch ".

1978. Horse-Racing. Multicoloured.
699. 20 c. Type **338** 35 10
700. 35 c. " Bernborough " (vert.) 60 70
701. 50 c. " Phar Lap " (vert.) 85 1·00
702. 55 c. " Peter Pan " .. 90 1·00

339. Raising the Flag, Sydney Cove, 26th January, 1788.

1979. Australia Day.
703. **339.** 20 c. multicoloured .. 15 15

340. P.S. " Canberra ".

1979. Ferries and Murray River Steamers. Multicoloured.
704. 20 c. Type **340** 35 10
705. 35 c. M.V. " Lady Denman " 60 85
706. 50 c. P.S. " Murray River Queen " .. .. 80 1·25
707. 55 c. H.V. " Curl Curl " .. 90 1·25

341. Port Campbell, Victoria.

1979. National Parks. Multicoloured.
708. 20 c. Type **341** 25 25
709. 20 c. Uluru, Northern Territory 25 25
710. 20 c. Royal, New South Wales 25 25
711. 20 c. Flinders Ranges, South Australia .. 25 25
712. 20 c. Nambung, Western Australia 25 25
713. 20 c. Girraween, Queensland (vert.) 25 25
714. 20 c. Mount Field, Tasmania (vert.) 25 25

342. " Double Fairlie " Type Locomotive, Western Australia.

1979. Steam Railways. Multicoloured.
715. 20 c. Type **342** 30 10
716. 35 c. Locomotive "Puffing Billy", Victoria 55 70
717. 50 c. Locomotive, Pichi Richi Line, South Australia .. .. 80 1·10
718. 55 c. Locomotive, Zig Zag Railway, New South Wales .. .. .. 90 1·25

343. Symbolic Swan.

1979. 150th Anniv. of Western Australia.
719. **343.** 20 c. multicoloured .. 15 15

344. Children playing on Slide.

1979. International Year of the Child.
720. **344.** 20 c. multicoloured .. 15 10

345. Letters and Parcels.

1979. Christmas. Multicoloured.
721. 15 c. " Christ's Nativity " (Eastern European icon) 15 10
722. 25 c. Type **345** 25 50
723. 55 c. " Madonna and Child " (Buglioni) 40 75

346. Fly-Fishing.

1979. Fishing.
724. **346.** 20 c. multicoloured .. 20 10
725. – 35 c. blue and violet 35 70
726. – 50 c. multicoloured .. 40 90
727. – 55 c. multicoloured .. 45 85

DESIGNS: 35 c. Spinning. 50 c. Deep sea game fishing. 55 c. Surf fishing.

347. Matthew Flinders.

1980. Australia Day.
728. **347.** 20 c. multicoloured .. 20 10

348. Dingo.

1980. Dogs. Multicoloured.
729. 20 c. Type **348** 35 10
730. 25 c. Border Collie .. 35 40
731. 35 c. Australian Terrier .. 50 70
732. 50 c. Australian Cattle Dog 1·10 1·75
733. 55 c. Australian Kelpie .. 1·00 1·40

1980. Birds (2nd series). As T **335**. Mult.
734. 10 c. Golden shouldered parrot (vert.) 30 10
734b. 18 c. Spotted catbird (vert.) .. .. .. 70 1·10
735. 28 c. Australian bee eater (vert.) 50 30
736. 35 c. Regent bower bird (vert.) 35 10
737. 45 c. Masked wood swallow 40 10
738. 60 c. Australian king parrot (vert.) 50 15
739. 80 c. Rainbow pitta .. 85 75
740. $1 Black-backed magpie (vert.) 85 10

349. Queen Elizabeth II. **350.** " Once a jolly Swagman camp'd by a Billabong ".

1980. Birthday of Queen Elizabeth II.
741. **349.** 22 c. multicoloured .. 30 20

1980. Folklore. " Waltzing Matilda ". Mult.
742. 22 c. Type **350** 40 10
743. 22 c. " And he sang as he shoved that jumbuck in his tuckerbag " .. 40 10
744. 22 c. " Up rode the squatter mounted on his thoroughbred " 40 10
745. 22 c. " Down came the troopers one, two, three " 40 10
746. 22 c. " And the ghost may be heard as you pass by that billabong " .. 40 10

351. High Court Building, Canberra.

1980. Opening of High Court Building.
747. **351.** 22 c. multicoloured .. 20 20

352. Salvation Army.

1980. Community Welfare. Multicoloured.
748. 22 c. Type **352** 40 40
749. 22 c. St. Vincent de Paul Society (vert.) 40 40
750. 22 c. Meals on Wheels (vert.) 40 40
751. 22 c. " Life. Be in it " .. 40 40

353. Postbox, c. 1900. **354.** " Holy Family " (painting, Prospero Fontana).

1980. National Stamp Week. Multicoloured.
752. 22 c. Type **353** 30 10
753. 22 c. Postman, facing left 30 10
754. 22 c. Mail van 30 10
755. 22 c. Postman, facing right 30 10
756. 22 c. Postman and postbox 30 10

1980. Christmas. Multicoloured.
758. 15 c. "The Virgin Enthroned" (Justin O'Brien) (detail) 15 10
759. 28 c. Type **354** 25 40
760. 60 c. "Madonna and Child" (Sculpture by School of M. Zuern) .. .. 50 1·10

355. " Wackett ", 1941.

1980. Australian Aircraft. Multicoloured.
761. 22 c. Type **355** 35 10
762. 40 c. " Winjeel ", 1955 .. 60 85
763. 45 c. " Boomerang ", 1944 70 95
764. 60 c. " Nomad ", 1975 .. 90 1·25

356. Flag in shape of Australia.

1981. Australia Day.
765. **356.** 22 c. multicoloured .. 20 20

357. Caricature of Darby Munro (jockey) **358.** 1931 Kingsford Smith's Flights 6d. Commemorative.

1981. Sporting Personalities. Caricatures. Mult.
766. 22 c. Type **357** 30 10
767. 35 c. Victor Trumper (cricket) 65 70
768. 55 c. Sir Norman Brookes (tennis) .. .. .. 85 1·00
769. 60 c. Walter Lindrum (billiards) .. .. 90 1·25

1981. 50th Anniv. of Official Australia–U.K. Airmail Service.
770. **358.** 22 c. lilac, red and blue 20 10
771. – 60 c. lilac, red and blue 50 90

DESIGN—HORIZ. 60 c. As T **358**, but format changed.

359. Apex Emblem and Map of Australia.

1981. 50th Anniv. of Apex (young men's service club).
772. **359.** 22 c. multicoloured .. 20 20

360. Queen's Personal Standard for Australia.

1981. Birthday of Queen Elizabeth II.

773. 360.	22 c. multicoloured ..	20	20

361. " Licence Inspected ".

1981. Gold Rush Era. Sketches by S. T. Gill. Multicoloured.

774.	22 c. Type **361**	20	25
775.	22 c. " Puddling " ..	20	25
776.	22 c. " Quality of washing stuff "	20	25
777.	22 c. " On route to deposit gold "	20	25

362. "On the Wallaby Track" (Fred McCubbin).

1981. Paintings. Multicoloured.

778.	$2 Type **362**	1·75	30
779.	$5 "A Holiday at Mentone 1888" (Charles Conder) ..	4·75	1·25

363. Thylacine.

363a. Blue Mountain Tree Frog.

363b. "Papilio ulysses" (butterfly).

1981. Wildlife. Multicoloured.

781	1 c. Lace monitor ..	10	20
782	3 c. Corroboree frog ..	10	10
783	4 c. "Euschemon rafflesia" (butterfly) (vert)	55	30
784	5 c. Queensland hairy-nosed wombat (vert) ..	10	10
785	10 c. "Ornithoptera priamus" (butterfly) (vert)	60	10
786	15 c. Eastern snake-necked tortoise ..	20	30
787	20 c. "Graphium macleayanus" (butterfly) (vert)	80	35
788	24 c. Type **363**	35	10
789	25 c. Common rabbit-bandicoot (vert) ..	35	10
790	27 c. Type **363a**	35	20
791	27 c. Type **363b**	90	30
792	30 c. Bridle nail-tailed wallaby (vert) ..	40	15
792a	30 c. "Pseudalmenus chlorinda" (butterfly) (vert)	1·00	20
793	35 c. "Danaus hamata" (butterfly) (vert) ..	1·00	30
794	40 c. Smooth knob-tailed gecko	45	30
795	45 c. "Cressida cressida" (butterfly) (vert) ..	1·00	30
796	50 c. Leadbeater's possum	50	10
797	55 c. Stick-nest rat (vert)	50	30
798	60 c. "Delias aganippe" (butterfly) (vert) ..	1·10	30
799	65 c. Yellow-faced whip snake	80	30
800	70 c. Crucifix toad ..	65	1·00
801	75 c. Eastern water dragon	80	40
802	80 c. "Ogyris amaryllis" (butterfly) (vert) ..	1·40	1·25
803	85 c. Centralian blue-tongued lizard ..	1·10	1·25
804	90 c. Freshwater crocodile	1·10	1·25
805	95 c. Thorny devil ..	1·00	1·40
806	$1 "Tisiphone abeona" (butterfly) (vert) ..	1·40	30

364. Prince Charles and Lady Diana Spencer.

1981. Royal Wedding.

821. 364.	24 c. multicoloured ..	25	10
822.	60 c. multicoloured ..	75	1·00

365. " Cortinarius cinnabarinus ".

1981. Australian Fungi. Multicoloured.

823.	24 c. Type **365**	35	10
824.	35 c. " Coprinus comatus "	50	60
825.	55 c. " Armillaria luteobubalina "	70	85
826.	60 c. " Cortinarius austrovenetus "	80	1·00

366. Disabled People playing Basketball.

1981. International Year for Disabled Persons.

827. 366.	24 c. multicoloured ..	20	20

367. " Christmas Bush for His Adorning ".

1981. Christmas. Scenes and Verses from Carols by W. James and J. Wheeler. Mult.

828.	18 c. Type **367** ..	25	10
829.	30 c. " The Silver Stars are in the Sky " ..	35	25
830.	60 c. " Noeltime " ..	60	70

368. Globe depicting Australia.

369. Ocean Racing Yacht.

1981. Commonwealth Heads of Government Meeting, Melbourne.

831. 368.	24 c. black, blue & gold	20	10
832.	60 c. blk., blue & silver	50	75

1981. Yachts. Multicoloured.

833	24 c. Type **369**	35	10
834	35 c. "Sharpie"	50	50
835	55 c. "12 Metre"	75	85
836	60 c. "Sabot"	1·00	1·00

370. Aborigine, Governor Phillip (founder of N.S.W. 1788) and Post World War II Migrant.

1982. Australia Day. " Three Great Waves of Migration ".

837. 370.	24 c. multicoloured ..	35	25

371. Humpback Whale.

1982. Whales. Multicoloured.

838.	24 c. Sperm whale	40	10
839.	35 c. Black right whale (vert.)	60	60
840.	55 c. Blue whale (vert.) ..	1·10	1·25
841.	60 c. Type **371**	1·25	1·40

372. Queen Elizabeth II.

373. " Marjorie Atherton ".

1982. Birthday of Queen Elizabeth II.

842. 372.	27 c. multicoloured ..	35	15

1982. Roses. Multicoloured.

843.	27 c. Type **373**	40	15
844.	40 c. " Imp "	55	70
845.	65 c. " Minnie Watson " ..	95	1·40
846.	75 c. " Satellite " ..	1·10	1·50

374. Radio Announcer and 1930-style Microphone.

1982. 50th Anniv. of ABC (Australian Broadcasting Commission.) Multicoloured.

847.	27 c. Type **374**	30	40
848.	27 c. ABC logo	30	40

375. Forbes Post Office.

1982. Historic Australian Post Offices. Multicoloured.

849.	27 c. Type **375**	40	35
850.	27 c. Flemington Post Office	40	35
851.	27 c. Rockhampton Post Office	40	35
852.	27 c. Kingston S.E. Post Office (horiz.)	40	35
853.	27 c. York Post Office (horiz.)	40	35
854.	27 c. Launceston Post Office	40	35
855.	27 c. Old Post and Telegraph Station, Alice Springs (horiz.) ..	40	35

376. Early Australian Christmas Card.

1982. Christmas. Multicoloured.

856.	21 c. Bushman's Hotel with Cobb's coach arriving (horiz.)	30	10
857.	35 c. Type **376**	50	60
858.	75 c. Little girl offering Christmas pudding to swagman	75	1·40

377. Boxing.

1982. Commonwealth Games, Brisbane.

859. 377.	27 c. stone, yellow and red	25	20
860. –	27 c. yellow, stone and green	25	20
861. –	27 c. stone, yellow and brown	25	20
862. –	75 c. multicoloured ..	75	90

DESIGNS: No. 860, Archery. No. 861, Weightlifting. No. 862, Pole-vaulting.

378. Sydney Harbour Bridge 5s. Stamp of 1932

1982. National Stamp Week.

864. 378.	27 c. multicoloured ..	35	30

379. " Yirawala " Bark Painting.

1982. Opening of Australian National Gallery.

865. 279.	27 c. multicoloured ..	30	25

380. Mimi Spirits Dancing.

1982. Aboriginal Culture. Music and Dance.

No.	Type	Description	Mint	Used
866.	380.	27 c. multicoloured ..	25	10
867.	–	40 c. multicoloured ..	40	50
868.	–	65 c. multicoloured ..	70	80
869.	–	75 c. multicoloured ..	80	1·10

DESIGNS: 40 c. to 75 c. Aboriginal Bark Paintings of Mimi Spirits.

381. "Eucalyptus calophylla" 'Rosea'.

1982. Eucalyptus Flowers. Multicoloured.

No.	Description	Mint	Used
870.	1 c. Type **381**	10	20
871.	2 c. "Eucalyptus casia" ..	10	20
872.	3 c. "Eucalyptus ficifolia"	50	75
873.	10 c. "Eucalyptus globulus"	50	75
874.	27 c. "Eucalyptus forrestiana"	35	40

382. Shand Mason Steam Fire Engine, 1891.

1983. Historic Fire Engines. Multicoloured.

No.	Description	Mint	Used
875.	27 c. Type **382**	35	10
876.	40 c. Hotchkiss fire engine, 1914	50	60
877.	65 c. Ahrens-Fox PS2 fire engine, 1929	90	1·25
878.	75 c. Merryweather manual fire appliance, 1851 ..	1·00	1·40

383. H.M.S. "Sirius".

1983. Australia Day. Multicoloured.

No.	Description	Mint	Used
879.	27 c. Type **383**	40	50
880.	27 c. H.M.S. "Supply" ..	40	50

384. Stylised Kangaroo and Kiwi. 385. Equality and Dignity.

1983. Closer Economic Relationship Agreement with New Zealand.

No.	Type	Description	Mint	Used
881.	384.	27 c. multicoloured ..	30	30

1983. Commonwealth Day. Multicoloured.

No.	Description	Mint	Used
882.	27 c. Type **385**	25	25
883.	27 c. Liberty and Freedom	25	25
884.	27 c. Social Justice and Co-operation	25	25
885.	75 c. Peace and Harmony	70	1·10

386. R.Y. "Britannia" passing Sydney Opera House.

1983. Birthday of Queen Elizabeth II.

No.	Type	Description	Mint	Used
886.	386.	27 c. multicoloured ..	45	30

387. "Postal and Telecommunications Services".

1983. World Communications Year.

No.	Type	Description	Mint	Used
887.	387.	27 c. multicoloured ..	30	30

388. Badge of the Order of St. John.

1983. Centenary of St. John Ambulance in Australia.

No.	Type	Description	Mint	Used
888.	388.	27 c. black and blue ..	35	30

389. Jaycee Members and Badge.

1983. 50th Anniversary of Australian Jaycees.

No.	Type	Description	Mint	Used
889.	389.	27 c. multicoloured ..	30	30

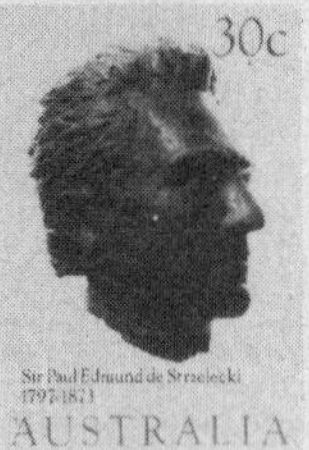

390. "The Bloke". 392. Sir Paul Edmund de Strzelecki.

391. Nativity Scene.

1983. Folklore. "The Sentimental Bloke" (humorous poem by C. J. Dennis). Mult.

No.	Description	Mint	Used
890.	27 c. Type **390**	45	45
891.	27 c. "Doreen–The Intro"	45	45
892.	27 c. "The Stror 'at Coot"	45	45
893.	27 c. "Hitched"	45	45
894.	27 c. "The Mooch o' Life"	45	45

1983. Christmas. Children's Paintings. Multicoloured.

No.	Description	Mint	Used
895.	24 c. Type **391**	20	10
896.	35 c. Kookaburra	35	45
897.	85 c. Father Christmas in sleigh over beach ..	90	1·10

1983. Explorers of Australia. Multicoloured.

No.	Description	Mint	Used
898.	30 c. Type **392**	35	40
899.	30 c. Ludwig Leichhardt ..	35	40
900.	30 c. William John Wills and Robert O'Hara Burke	35	40
901.	30 c. Alexander Forrest ..	35	40

393. Cook Family Cottage, Melbourne.

1984. Australia Day.

No.	Type	Description	Mint	Used
902.	393.	30 c. black and stone	30	35

394. Charles Ulm, "Faith in Australia" and Trans-Tasman Cover.

1984. 50th Anniv. of First Official Airmail Flights, New Zealand–Australia and Australia–Papua New Guinea. Mult.

No.	Description	Mint	Used
903.	45 c. Type **394**	1·00	1·25
904.	45 c. As Type **394** but showing flown cover to Papua New Guinea ..	1·00	1·25

395. Thomson "Steamer", 1898.

1984. Veteran and Vintage Cars. Mult.

No.	Description	Mint	Used
905.	30 c. Type **395**	45	60
906.	30 c. Tarrant, 1906 ..	45	60
907.	30 c. Gordon & Co. "Australian Six", 1919 ..	45	60
908.	30 c. Summit, 1923 ..	45	60
909.	30 c. Chic, 1924	45	60

396. Queen Elizabeth II.

1984. Birthday of Queen Elizabeth II.

No.	Type	Description	Mint	Used
910.	396.	30 c. multicoloured ..	30	35

397. "Cutty Sark".

1984. Clipper Ships. Multicoloured.

No.	Description	Mint	Used
911.	30 c. Type **397**	40	25
912.	45 c. "Orient" (horiz.) ..	70	70
913.	75 c. "Sobraon" (horiz.) ..	1·25	1·50
914.	85 c. "Thermopylae" ..	1·25	1·50

398. Freestyle.

1984. Skiing. Multicoloured.

No.	Description	Mint	Used
915.	30 c. Type **398**	40	45
916.	30 c. Downhill racer ..	40	45
917.	30 c. Slalom (horiz.) ..	40	45
918.	30 c. Nordic (horiz.) ..	40	45

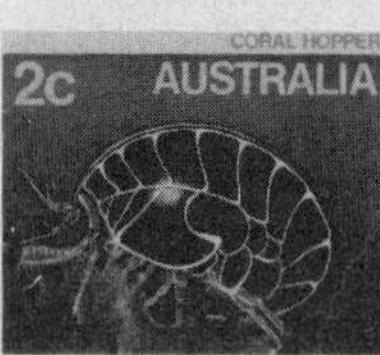

399. Coral Hopper.

1984. Marine Life. Multicoloured.

No.	Description	Mint	Used
919.	2 c. Type **399**	10	20
920.	3 c. Jimble	10	20
921.	5 c. Tasselled angler fish ..	10	10
922.	10 c. Stonefish	20	10
923.	20 c. Red handfish ..	45	30
924.	25 c. Orange-tipped cowrie	45	30
925.	30 c. Choat's wrasse ..	45	40
926.	33 c. Leafy sea-dragon ..	45	10
927.	40 c. Red velvet fish ..	65	50
928.	45 c. Textile cone	80	50
929.	50 c. Blue-lined surgeon fish	80	40
930.	55 c. Bennett's nudibranch	80	50
931.	60 c. Lionfish	90	70
932.	65 c. Stingaree	90	70
933.	70 c. Blue-ringed octopus	90	65
934.	80 c. Pineapple fish ..	1·25	70
935.	85 c. Regal angel fish ..	90	50
936.	90 c. Crab-eyed goby ..	1·00	75
937.	$1 Crown of thorns starfish	1·50	80

400. Before the Event.

1984. Olympic Games. Los Angeles. Multicoloured.

No.	Description	Mint	Used
941.	30 c. Type **400**	35	35
942.	30 c. During the Event ..	35	35
943.	30 c. After the Event (vert.)	35	35

401. Australian 1913 1 d. Kangaroo Stamp. 402. "Angel" (stained-glass window St. Francis' Church. Melbourne).

1984. "Ausipex 84" International Stamp Exhibition, Melbourne.

No.	Type	Description	Mint	Used
944.	401.	30 c. multicoloured ..	35	30

1984. Christmas. Stained-glass Windows. Multicoloured.

No.	Description	Mint	Used
946.	24 c. "Angel and Child" (Holy Trinity Church, Sydney)	30	20
947.	30 c. "Veiled Virgin and Child" (St. Mary's Catholic Church, Geelong) ..	45	30
948.	40 c. Type **402**	60	60
949.	50 c. "Three Kings" (St. Mary's Cathedral, Sydney)	80	80
950.	85 c. "Madonna and Child" (St. Bartholomew's Church, Norwood) ..	1·00	1·25

403. "Stick Figures". (Cobar Region).

1984. Bicentenary (1988) of Australian Settlement. (1st issue). The First Australians. Multicoloured.

No.	Description	Mint	Used
951.	30 c. Type **403**	45	45
952.	30 c. "Bunjil" (large figure), Grampians	45	45
953.	30 c. "Quikans" (tall figures), Cape York ..	45	45
954.	30 c. "Wandjina Spirit and Baby Snakes" (Gibb River)	45	45
955.	30 c. "Rock Python" (Gibb River)	45	45
956.	30 c. "Silver Barramundi" (fish) (Kakadu National Park)	45	45
957.	30 c. Bicentenary emblem	45	45
958.	85 c. "Rock Possum" (Kakadu National Park)	1·10	1·25

See also Nos. 972/5, 993/6, 1002/7, 1019/22, 1059/63, 1064/6, 1077/81, 1090/2, 1110, 1137/41, 1145/8 and 1149.

404. Yellow-tufted Honeyeater.

1984. 150th Anniv. of Victoria.

959.	30 c. Type **404**	35	55
960.	30 c. Leadbeater's Possum	35	55

405. "Musgrave Ranges" (Sidney Nolan).

1985. Australia Day. Birth Bicentenary of Dorothea Mackellar (author of poem "My Country"). Multicoloured.

961.	30 c. Type **405**	45	65
962.	30 c. "The Walls of China" (Russell Drysdale) ..	45	65

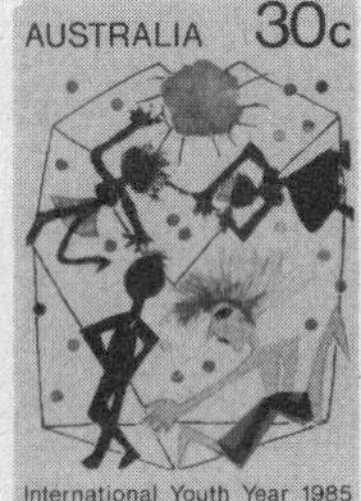

406. Young People of Different Races and Sun.

1985. International Youth Year.

963.	**406.**	30 c. multicoloured ..	35	30

407. Royal Victorian Volunteer Artillery.

1985. 19th-Century Australian Military Uniforms. Multicoloured.

964.	33 c. Type **407**	60	60
965.	33 c. Western Australian Pinjarrah Cavalry ..	60	60
966.	33 c. New South Wales Lancers	60	60
967.	33 c. New South Wales Contingent to the Sudan	60	60
968.	33 c. Victorian Mounted Rifles	60	60

408. District Nurse of early 1900s.

1985. Centenary of District Nursing Services.

969.	**408.**	33 c. multicoloured ..	40	35

409. Sulphur-crested Cockatoos.

1985. Multicoloured, background colour given.

970.	**409.**	1 c. flesh	1·50	2·00
971.		33 c. turquoise ..	45	55

410. Abel Tasman and Journal Entry.

1985. Bicentenary (1988) of Australian Settlement (2nd issue). Navigators. Mult.

972.	33 c. Type **410**	45	35
973.	33 c. Dirk Hartog's "Eendracht" (detail, Aert Anthonisz) ..	45	35
974.	33 c. "William Dampier" (detail, T. Murray) ..	45	35
975.	90 c. Globe and hand with extract from Dampier's journal	1·10	1·50

411. Sovereign's Badge of Order of Australia.

412. Tree, and Soil running through Hourglass ("Soil")

1985. Queen Elizabeth II's Birthday.

977.	**411.**	33 c. multicoloured ..	35	30

1985. Conservation. Multicoloured.

978.	33 c. Type **412**	45	20
979.	50 c. Washing on line and smog ("air")	70	85
980.	80 c. Tap and flower ("water")	1·10	1·40
981.	90 c. Chain encircling flames ("energy") ..	1·25	1·75

413. "Elves and Fairies" (Annie Rentoul and Ida Rentoul Outhwaite).

1985. Classic Australian Children's Books. Multicoloured.

982.	33 c. Type **413**	50	65
983.	33 c. "The Magic Pudding" (Norman Lindsay) ..	50	65
984.	33 c. "Ginger Meggs" (James Charles Bancks)	50	65
985.	33 c. "Blinky Bill" (Dorothy Wall)	50	65
986.	33 c. "Snugglepot and Cuddlepie" (May Gibbs)	50	65

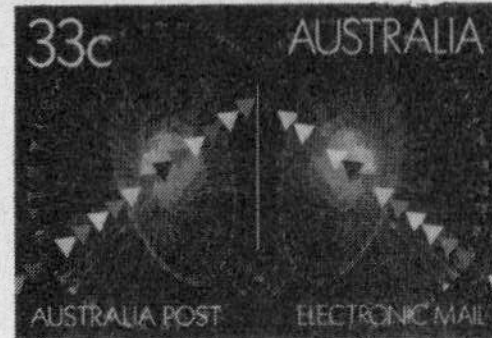

414. Dish Aerials.

1985. Electronic Mail Service.

987.	**414.**	33 c. multicoloured ..	35	30

415. Angel in Sailing Ship.

1985. Christmas. Multicoloured.

988.	27 c. Angel with holly wings	30	15
989.	33 c. Angel with bells ..	35	15
990.	45 c. Type **415**	50	50
991.	55 c. Angel with star ..	65	70
992.	90 c. Angel with Christmas tree bauble	1·00	1·25

416. Astrolabe ("Batavia", 1629).

1985. Bicentenary (1988) of Australian Settlement (3rd issue). Relics from Early Shipwrecks. Multicoloured.

993.	33 c. Type **416**	40	15
994.	50 c. German beardman jug ("Vergulde Draeck", 1656)	70	75
995.	90 c. Wooden bobbins ("Batavia", 1629) and encrusted scissors ("Zeewijk", 1727) ..	1·40	1·60
996.	$1 Silver and brass buckle ("Zeewijk", 1727) ..	1·60	1·60

417. Aboriginal Wandjina Spirit, Map of Australia and Egg.

418. AUSSAT Satellite, Moon and Earth's Surface.

1986. Australia Day.

997.	**417.**	33 c. multicoloured ..	40	30

1986. AUSSAT National Communications Satellite System. Multicoloured.

998.	33 c. Type **418**	50	15
999.	80 c. AUSSAT satellite in orbit	1·50	2·00

419. H.M.S. "Buffalo".

1986. 150th Anniv. of South Australia. Multicoloured.

1000	33 c. Type **419**	70	90
1001	33 c. "City Sign" sculpture (Otto Hajek), Adelaide	70	90

Nos. 1000/1 were printed together se-tenant the background of each horizontal pair showing an extract from the colony's Letters Patent of 1836.

420. "Banksia serrata".

1986. Bicentenary of Australian Settlement (1988) (4th issue). Cook's Voyage to New Holland. Multicoloured.

1002.	33 c. Type **420**	60	35
1003.	33 c. "Hibiscus meraukensis"	60	35
1004.	50 c. "Dillenia alata" ..	90	80
1005.	80 c. "Correa reflexa" ..	1·60	1·60
1006.	90 c. "Joseph Banks" (botanist) (Reynolds) and Banks with Dr. Solander	2·00	2·00
1007.	90 c. "Sydney Parkinson" (self-portrait) and Parkinson drawing	2·00	2·00

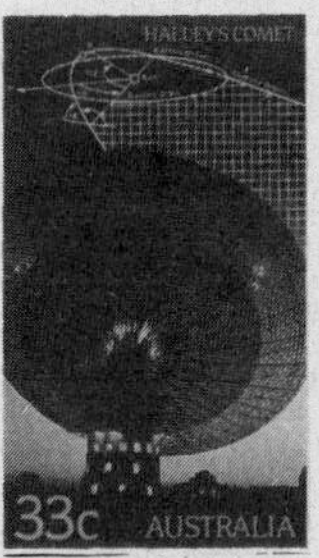

421. Radio Telescope, Parkes, and Diagram of Comet's Orbit.

422. Queen Elizabeth II.

1986. Appearance of Halley's Comet.

1008.	**421.**	33 c. multicoloured ..	50	35

1986. 60th Birthday of Queen Elizabeth.

1009.	**422.**	33 c. multicoloured ..	45	35

423. Brumbies (wild horses).

1986. Australian Horses. Multicoloured.

1010.	33 c. Type **423**	60	15
1011.	80 c. Mustering	1·50	1·50
1012.	90 c. Show-jumping ..	1·75	1·75
1013.	$1 Child on pony ..	2·00	2·00

424. "The Old Shearer stands".

1986. Folklore. Scenes and Verses from the Folksong "Click go the Shears". Mult.

1014. 33 c. Type **424** 65 75
1015. 33 c. "The ringer looks around" 65 75
1016. 33 c. "The boss of the board".. .. .. 65 75
1017. 33 c. "The tar-boy is there" 65 75
1018. 33 c. "Shearing is all over" 65 75

Nos. 1014/18 were printed together, se-tenant, forming a composite design.

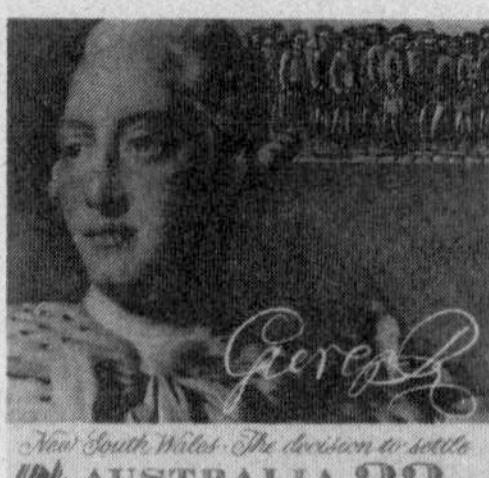

425. "King George III" (A. Ramsay) and Convicts.

1986. Bicentenary of Australian Settlement (1988) (5th issue). Convict Settlement in New South Wales. Multicoloured.

1019. 33 c. Type **425** 80 50
1020. 33 c. "Lord Sydney" (Gilbert Stuart) and convicts 80 50
1021. 33 c. "Captain Arthur Phillip" (F. Wheatley) and ship 80 50
1022. $1 "Captain John Hunter" (W. B. Bennett) and aborigines .. .. 3·25 3·75

426. Red Kangaroo. **427.** Royal Bluebell.

1986. Australian Wildlife (1st series). Multicoloured

1023. 36 c. Type **426** 55 60
1024. 36 c. Emu 55 60
1025. 36 c. Koala 55 60
1026. 36 c. Laughing kookaburra 55 60
1027. 36 c. Platypus 55 60

See also Nos. 1072/6.

1986. Alpine Wildflowers. Multicoloured.

1028. 3 c. Type **427** 25 25
1029. 5 c. Alpine Marsh Marigold .. .. 1·25 1·40
1030. 25 c. Mount Buffalo Sunray .. .. 1·25 1·40
1031. 36 c. Silver Snow Daisy 60 30

428. Pink Enamel Orchid.

1986. Native Orchids. Multicoloured.

1032. 36 c. Type **428** 70 20
1033. 55 c. "Dendrobium nindii".. .. .. 1·25 1·00
1034. 90 c. Duck Orchid .. 1·90 2·00
1035. $1 Queen of Sheba Orchid .. .. .. 2·00 2·00

429. "Australia II" crossing Finishing Line.

1986. Australian Victory in America's Cup, 1983. Multicoloured.

1036. 36 c. Type **429** 65 55
1037. 36 c. Boxing kangaroo flag of winning syndicate 65 55
1038. 36 c. America's Cup trophy 65 55

430. Dove with Olive Branch and Sun.

1986. International Peace Year.

1039. **430.** 36 c. multicoloured .. 65 35

431. Mary and Joseph.

1986. Christmas. Scenes from children's nativity play. Multicoloured.

1040a 30 c. Type **431** 30 30
1041 36 c. Three Wise Men leaving gifts 50 45
1042 60 c. Angels (horiz.) .. 90 1·50

432. Australian Flag on Printed Circuit Board.

1987. Australia Day. Multicoloured.

1044. 36 c. Type **432** 35 35
1045. 36 c. "Australian Made" Campaign logos .. 35 35

433. Aerial View of Yacht.

1987. America's Cup Yachting Championship. Multicoloured.

1046. 36 c. Type **433** 40 20
1047. 55 c. Two yachts tacking 80 1·00
1048. 90 c. Two yachts turning 1·25 1·60
1049. $1 Two yachts under full sail .. .. .. 1·40 1·75

434. Grapes and Melons.

1987. Australian Fruit. Multicoloured.

1050. 36 c. Type **434** 40 20
1051. 65 c. Tropical and sub-tropical fruits .. .. 85 1·25
1052. 90 c. Citrus fruit, apples and pears .. .. 1·25 1·60
1053. $1 Stone and berry fruits 1·40 1·60

435. Livestock.

1987. Agricultural Shows. Multicoloured.

1054. 36 c. Type **435** 60 20
1055. 65 c. Produce .. .. 1·25 1·60
1056. 90 c. Sideshows .. .. 1·75 2·10
1057. $1 Competitions .. .. 1·90 2·10

436. Queen Elizabeth in Australia, 1986.

1987. Queen Elizabeth II's Birthday.

1058. **436.** 36 c. multicoloured .. 50 40

437. Convicts on Quay.

1987. Bicentenary of Australian Settlement (1988) (6th issue). Departure of the First Fleet. Multicoloured.

1059. 36 c. Type **437** 70 85
1060. 36 c. Royal Marines officer and wife .. 70 85
1061. 36 c. Sailors loading supplies 70 85
1062. 36 c. Officers being ferried to ships .. 70 85
1063. 36 c. Fleet in English Channel 70 85

See also Nos. 1064/6, 1077/81 and 1090/2.

1987. Bicentenary of Australian Settlement (1988) (7th issue). First Fleet at Tenerife. As T **437**. Multicoloured.

1064. 36 c. Ferrying supplies, Santa Cruz 65 75
1065. 36 c. Canary Islands fishermen and departing fleet 65 75
1066. $1 Fleet arriving at Tenerife .. .. 1·40 1·60

Nos. 1064/5 were printed together, se-tenant, forming a composite design.

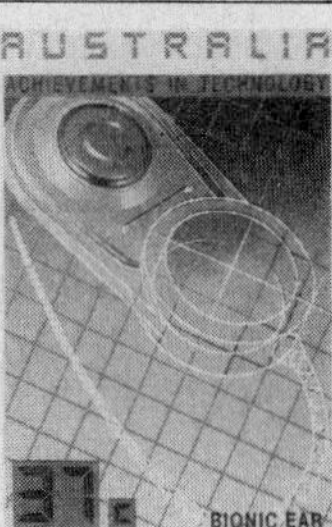

438. "At the Station". **439.** Bionic Ear.

1987. Folklore. Scenes and Verses from Poem "The Man from Snowy River". Mult.

1067. 36 c. Type **438** 70 85
1068. 36 c. "Mountain bred" .. 70 85
1069. 36 c. "That terrible descent" 70 85
1070. 36 c. "At their heels" .. 70 85
1071. 36 c. "Brought them back" 70 85

Nos. 1067/71 were printed together, se-tenant, forming a composite background design of mountain scenery.

1987. Australian Wildlife (2nd series). As T **426**. Multicoloured.

1072. 37 c. Common brushtail possum 50 50
1073. 37 c. Sulphur-crested cockatoo 50 50
1074. 37 c. Common wombat .. 50 50
1075. 37 c. Crimson rosella .. 50 50
1076. 37 c. Echidna 50 50

1987. Bicentenary of Australian Settlement (1988) (8th issue). First Fleet at Rio de Janeiro. As T **437**. Multicoloured.

1077. 37 c. Sperm whale and fleet 70 85
1078. 37 c. Brazilian coast .. 70 85
1079. 37 c. British officers in market 70 85
1080. 37 c. Religious procession 70 85
1081. 37 c. Fleet leaving Rio .. 70 85

Nos. 1077/81 were printed together, se-tenant, forming a composite design.

1987. Australian Achievements in Technology, Multicoloured.

1082. 37 c. Type **439** 40 35
1083. 53 c. Microchips 65 60
1084. 63 c. Robotics 75 70
1085. 68 c. Ceramics 80 75

440. Catching Crayfish.

1987. "Aussie Kids". Multicoloured.

1086. 37 c. Type **440** 35 35
1087. 55 c. Playing cat's cradle 75 65
1088. 90 c. Young football supporters .. .. 1·10 95
1089. $1 Children with kangaroo .. .. 1·25 1·10

1987. Bicentenary of Australian Settlement (1988) (9th issue). First Fleet at Cape of Good Hope. As T **437**. Multicoloured.

1090. 37 c. Marine checking list of livestock 50 65
1091. 37 c. Loading livestock .. 50 65
1092. $1 First Fleet at Cape Town .. .. .. 1·25 1·40

Nos. 1090/1 were printed together, se-tenant, forming a composite design.

441. Detail of Spearthrower, Western Australia.

1987. Aboriginal Crafts. Multicoloured

1093. 3 c. Type **441** .. .. 90 1·10
1094. 15 c. Shield pattern, New South Wales .. .. 2·00 2·75
1095. 37 c. Basket weave, Queensland .. .. 90 1·10
1096. 37 c. Bowl design Central Australia .. 90 1·10
1097. 37 c. Belt pattern Northern Territory .. 90 1·10

442. Grandmother and Granddaughters with Candles.

1987. Christmas. Designs showing carol singing by candlelight. Multicoloured.

1098. 30 c. Type **442** 40 40
1099. 30 c. Father and daughters 40 40
1100. 30 c. Four children .. 40 40
1101. 30 c. Family 40 40
1102. 30 c. Six teenagers .. 40 40
1103. 37 c. Choir (horiz.) .. 45 45
1104. 63 c. Father and two children (horiz.) .. 75 75

1988. Bicentenary of Australian Settlement (10th issue). Arrival of First Fleet. As T **437**. Multicoloured.

1105. 37 c. Aborigines watching arrival of Fleet, Botany Bay .. 70 80
1106. 37 c. Aborigine family and anchored ships .. 70 80
1107. 37 c. Fleet arriving at Sydney Cove 70 80
1108. 37 c. Ship's boat .. 70 80
1109. 37 c. Raising the flag, Sydney Cove, 26 January 1788 .. 70 80

Nos. 1105/9 were printed together, se-tenant, forming a composite design.

443. Koala with Stockman's Hat and Eagle dressed as Uncle Sam.

1988. Bicentenary of Australian Settlement (11th issue). Joint issue with U.S.A.

1110. **443.** 37 c. multicoloured .. 60 35

444 "Religion" (A. Horner)

1988. "Living Together". Designs showing cartoons. Multicoloured (except 30 c.).

1111 1 c. Type **444** .. 20 20
1112 2 c. "Industry" (P. Nicholson) 20 20
1113 3 c. "Local Government" (A. Collette) 20 20
1114 4 c. "Trade Unions" (Liz Honey) .. 20 20
1115 5 c. "Parliament" (Bronwyn Halls) .. 20 20
1116 10 c. "Transport" (Meg Williams) 20 10
1117 15 c. "Sport" (G. Cook) 20 30
1118 20 c. "Commerce" (M. Atcherson) 45 30
1119 25 c. "Housing" (C. Smith) 30 30
1120 30 c. "Welfare" (R. Tandberg) (black and lilac) 30 35
1121 37 c. "Postal Services" (P. Viska) 60 50
1121b 39 c. "Tourism" (J. Spooner) 60 50
1122 40 c. "Recreation" (R. Harvey) 45 40
1123 45 c. "Health" (Jenny Coopes) 55 50
1124 50 c. "Mining" (G. Haddon) 55 50
1125 53 c. "Primary Industry" (S. Leahy) 1·00 85
1126 55 c. "Education" (Victoria Roberts) .. 75 55
1127 60 c. "Armed Forces" (B. Green) 55 60
1128 63 c. "Police" (J. Russell) .. .. 1·50 75
1129 65 c. "Telecommunications" (B. Petty) 85 75
1130 68 c. "The Media" (A. Langoulant) .. 1·25 75
1131 70 c. "Science and Technology" (J. Hook) .. .. 1·50 90
1132 75 c. "Visual Arts" (G. Dazeley) .. .. 1·00 90
1133 80 c. "Performing Arts" (A. Stitt) .. 1·00 1·00
1134 90 c. "Banking" (S. Billington) .. .. 1·10 90
1135 95 c. "Law" (C. Aslanis) .. .. 85 1·00
1136 $1 "Rescue and Emergency" (M. Leunig) .. .. 1·10 90

445 "Government House, Sydney, 1790" (George Raper)

1988. Bicentenary of Australian Settlement (12th issue). "The Early Years, 1788 -1809". Multicoloured.

1137 37 c. Type **445** 60 60
1138 37 c. "Government Farm, Parramatta, 1791" ("The Port Jackson Painter") 60 60
1139 37 c. "Parramatta Road, 1796" (attr Thomas Watling) 60 60
1140 37 c. "View of Sydney Cove, c. 1800" (detail) (Edward Dayes) .. 60 60
1141 37 c. "Sydney Hospital, 1803", (detail) (George William Evans) .. 60 60

Nos. 1137/41 were printed together, se-tenant, forming a composite background design from the painting, "View of Sydney from the East Side of the Cove, c. 1808" by John Eyre.

446 Queen Elizabeth II (from photo by Tim Graham)

1988. Queen Elizabeth II's Birthday.

1142 **446** 37 c. multicoloured .. 50 40

447 Expo '88 Logo

1988. "Expo '88" World Fair, Brisbane.

1143 **447** 37 c. multicoloured .. 50 40

448 New Parliament House

1988. Opening of New Parliament House, Canberra.

1144 **448** 37 c. multicoloured .. 50 40

449 Early Settler and Sailing Clipper

1988. Bicentenary of Australian Settlement (13th issue). Multicoloured.

1145 37 c. Type **449** .. .. 75 1·00
1146 37 c. Queen Elizabeth II with British and Australian Parliament Buildings .. .. 75 1·00
1147 $1 W. G. Grace (cricketer) and tennis racquet .. 2·00 2·25
1148 $1 Shakespeare, John Lennon (entertainer) and Sydney Opera House .. .. .. 2·00 2·25

Stamps in similar designs were also issued by Great Britain.

450 Kiwi and Koala at Campfire

1988. Bicentenary of Australian Settlement (14th issue).

1149 **450** 37 c. multicoloured .. 65 40

A stamp in a similar design was also issued by New Zealand.

451 "Bush Potato Country" (Turkey Tolsen Tjupurrula and David Corby Tjapaltjarri)

1988. Art of the Desert. Aboriginal Paintings from Central Australia. Multicoloured.

1150 37 c. Type **451** 40 40
1151 55 c. "Courtship Rejected" (Limpi Puntungka Tjapangati) 60 60
1152 90 c. "Medicine Story" (artist unknown) .. 1·00 1·10
1153 $1 "Ancestor Dreaming" (Tim Leura Tjapaltjarri) .. 1·10 1·25

452 Basketball

1988. Olympic Games, Seoul. Multicoloured.

1154 37 c. Type **452** 40 40
1155 65 c. Athlete crossing finish line .. 70 70
1156 $1 Gymnast with hoop .. 1·10 1·25

453 Rod and Mace

1988. 34th Commonwealth Parliamentary Conference, Canberra.

1157 **453** 37 c. multicoloured .. 50 60

454 Necklace by Peter Tully

1988. Australian Crafts. Multicoloured.

1158 2 c. Type **454** 70 90
1159 5 c. Vase by Colin Levy 70 90
1160 39 c. Teapot by Frank Bauer .. 40 35

455 Pinnacles Desert

1988. Panorama of Australia. Mult.

1161 39 c. Type **455** 55 40
1162 55 c. Flooded landscape, Arnhem Land .. 70 60
1163 65 c. Twelve Apostles, Victoria 85 70
1164 70 c. Mountain Ash Wood 95 90

456 "The Nativity" (Danielle Hush)

1988. Christmas. Multicoloured.

1165 32 c. Type **456** 40 35
1166 39 c. "Koala as Father Christmas" (Kylie Courtney) 45 40
1167 63 c. "Christmas Cockatoo" (Benjamin Stevenson) 75 85

457 Sir Henry Parkes

1989. Australia Day. Centenary of Federation Speech by Sir Henry Parkes (N.S.W. Prime Minister).

1168	**457** 39 c. multicoloured	35	40

458 Bowls

1989. Sports. Multicoloured.

1169	1 c. Type **458**	10	10
1170a	2 c. Tenpin-bowling	20	20
1171	3 c. Australian football	15	10
1172	5 c. Kayaking and canoeing	10	10
1174	10 c. Sailboarding	10	15
1176	20 c. Tennis	15	20
1179	39 c. Fishing	35	40
1180	41 c. Cycling	40	35
1181	43 c. Skateboarding	35	40
1184	55 c. Kite-flying	45	50
1186a	65 c. Rock-climbing	60	65
1187	70 c. Cricket	60	65
1188	75 c. Netball	65	70
1189	80 c. Squash	70	75
1190	85 c. Diving	75	80
1191	90 c. Soccer	75	80
1192	$1 Fun-run	95	1·00
1193	$1.10 Golf	95	1·00
1194	$1.20 Hang-gliding	1·00	1·10

459 Merino

1989. Sheep in Australia. Multicoloured.

1195	39 c. Type **459**	55	40
1196	39 c. Poll Dorset	55	40
1197	85 c. Polwarth	90	1·00
1198	$1 Corriedale	1·10	1·25

460 Adelaide Botanic Garden

1989. Botanic Gardens. Multicoloured.

1199	$2 Noroo, New South Wales	2·00	90
1200	$5 Mawarra, Victoria	4·75	2·50
1201	$10 Type **460**	9·50	5·00
1201a	$20 "A View of the Artist's House and Garden in Mills Plains, Van Diemen's Land" (John Glover)	19·00	14·00

461 "Queen Elizabeth II" (sculpture, John Dowie)

1989. Queen Elizabeth II's Birthday.

1202	**461** 39 c. multicoloured	35	40

462 Arrival of Immigrant Ship, 1830's

1989. Colonial Development (1st issue). Pastoral Era 1810–1850. Multicoloured.

1203	39 c. Type **462**	45	45
1204	39 c. Pioneer cottage and wool dray	45	45
1205	39 c. Squatter's homestead	45	45
1206	39 c. Shepherd with flock (from Joseph Lycett's "Views of Australia")	45	45
1207	39 c. Explorer in desert (after watercolour by Edward Frome)	45	45

See also Nos. 1254/8 and 1264/8.

463 Gladys Moncrieff and Roy Rene

1989. Australian Stage and Screen Personalities. Multicoloured.

1208	39 c. Type **463**	40	40
1209	85 c. Charles Chauvel and Chips Rafferty	85	85
1210	$1 Nellie Stewart and J. C. Williamson	1·00	1·00
1211	$1.10 Lottie Lyell and Raymond Longford	1·10	1·10

464 "Impression" (Tom Roberts)

1989. Australian Impressionist Paintings. Multicoloured.

1212	41 c. Type **464**	45	45
1213	41 c. "Impression for Golden Summer" (Sir Arthur Streeton)	45	45
1214	41 c. "All on a Summer's Day" (Charles Conder) (vert)	45	45
1215	41 c. "Petit Dejeuner" (Frederick McCubbin)	45	45

465 Freeways

1989. The Urban Environment.

1216	**465** 41 c. black, pur & grn	65	80
1217	– 41 c. blk, pur & mve	65	80
1218	– 41 c. black, pur & bl	65	80

DESIGNS: No. 1217, City buildings, Melbourne; No. 1218, Commuter train at platform.

466 Hikers outside Youth Hostel

1989. 50th Anniv of Australian Youth Hostels.

1219	**466** 41 c. multicoloured	45	45

467 Horse Tram, Adelaide, 1878

1989. Historic Trams. Multicoloured.

1220	41 c. Type **467**	50	50
1221	41 c. Steam tram, Sydney, 1884	50	50
1222	41 c. Cable tram, Melbourne, 1886	50	50
1223	41 c. Double-deck electric tram, Hobart, 1893	50	50
1224	41 c. Combination electric tram, Brisbane, 1901	50	50

468 "Annunciation" (15th-century Book of Hours)

1989. Christmas. Illuminated Manuscripts. Multicoloured.

1225	36 c. Type **468**	35	40
1226	41 c. "Annunciation to the Shepherds" (Wharncliffe Book of Hours, c. 1475)	45	45
1227	80 c. "Adoration of the Magi" (15th-century Parisian Book of Hours)	95	95

469 Radio Waves and Globe

1989. 50th Anniv of Radio Australia.

1228	**469** 41 c. multicoloured	45	45

470 Golden Wattle

471 Australian Wildflowers

1990. Australia Day.

1229	**470** 41 c. multicoloured	45	45

1990. Greetings Stamp.

1230	**471** 41 c. multicoloured	45	45
1231	43 c. multicoloured	35	40

472 Dr. Constance Stone (first Australian woman doctor), Modern Doctor and Nurses

1990. Cent of Women in Medical Practice.

1232	**472** 41 c. multicoloured	45	45

473 Greater Glider

1990. Animals of the High Country. Mult.

1233	41 c. Type **473**	55	45
1234	65 c. Tiger cat ("Spotted-tailed Quoll")	80	75
1235	70 c. Mountain pygmy-possum	85	80
1236	80 c. Brush-tailed rock-wallaby	95	90

474 "Stop Smoking"

1990. Community Health. Multicoloured.

1237	41 c. Type **474**	55	45
1238	41 c. "Drinking and driving don't mix"	55	45
1239	41 c. "No junk food, please"	55	45
1240	41 c. "Guess who's just had a checkup?"	55	45

475 Soldiers from Two World Wars

476 Queen at Australian Ballet Gala Performance, London, 1988

1990. "The Anzac Tradition". Multicoloured.

1241	41 c. Type **475**	45	40
1242	41 c. Fighter pilots and munitions worker	45	40
1243	65 c. Veterans and Anzac Day parade	75	80
1244	$1 Casualty evacuation, Vietnam, and disabled veteran	1·10	1·25
1245	$1.10 Letters from home and returning troopships	1·25	1·40

1990. Queen Elizabeth II's Birthday.

1246	**476** 41 c. multicoloured	50	45

477 New South Wales 1861 5s. Stamp

1990. 150th Anniv of the Penny Black. Designs showing stamps. Multicoloured.

1247 41 c. Type **477** 45 60
1248 41 c. South Australia 1855 unissued 1s. 45 60
1249 41 c. Tasmania 1853 4d. .. 45 60
1250 41 c. Victoria 1867 5s. .. 45 60
1251 41 c. Queensland 1897 unissued 6d. 45 60
1252 41 c. Western Australia 1855 4d. with inverted frame 45 60

478 Gold Miners on way to Diggings

1990. Colonial Development (2nd issue). Gold Fever. Multicoloured.

1254 41 c. Type **478** 45 45
1255 41 c. Mining camp .. 45 45
1256 41 c. Panning and washing for gold 45 45
1257 41 c. Gold Commissioner's tent 45 45
1258 41 c. Moving gold under escort 45 45

479 Glaciology Research

1990. Australian–Soviet Scientific Co-operation in Antarctica. Multicoloured.

1261 41 c. Type **479** 45 40
1262 $1.10 Krill (marine biology research) .. 1·25 1·25

Stamps in similar designs were also issued by Russia.

480 Auctioning Building Plots

1990. Colonial Development (3rd series). Boomtime. Multicoloured.

1264 41 c. Type **480** 45 45
1265 41 c. Colonial mansion .. 45 45
1266 41 c. Stock exchange .. 45 45
1267 41 c. Fashionable society 45 45
1268 41 c. Factories 45 45

481 "Salmon Gums" (Robert Juniper)
482 "Adelaide Town Hall" (Edmund Gouldsmith)

1990. "Heidelberg and Heritage" Art Exhibition. Multicoloured.

1269 28 c. Type **481** 60 60
1270 43 c. "The Blue Dress" (Brian Dunlop) .. 45 45

1990. 150th Anniv of Local Government.

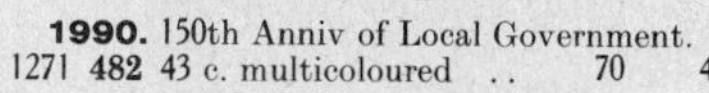

1271 **482** 43 c. multicoloured .. 70 40

483 Laughing Kookaburras and Gifts

1990. Christmas. Multicoloured.

1272 38 c. Type **483** 50 40
1273 43 c. Baby Jesus with koalas and wallaby (vert) 50 40
1274 80 c. Possum on Christmas tree .. 1·25 1·00

484 National Flag

1991. Australia Day. 90th Anniv of Australian Flag.

1275 **484** 43 c. blue, red & grey 50 40
1276 – 90 c. multicoloured .. 1·10 1·25
1277 – $1 multicoloured .. 1·25 1·40
1278 – $1.20 red, blue & grey 1·60 1·75

DESIGNS: 90 c. Royal Australian Navy ensign; $1 Royal Australian Air Force standard; $1.20, Australian merchant marine ensign.

485 Black-necked Stork

1991. Waterbirds. Multicoloured.

1279 43 c. Type **485** 60 40
1280 43 c. Black swan (horiz) 60 40
1281 85 c. Cape Barren goose 1·25 1·50
1282 $1 Chestnut-breasted teal (horiz) .. .. 1·40 1·60

486 Recruitment Poster (Women's Services)

1991. Anzac Day. 50th Anniversaries.

1283 **486** 43 c. multicoloured .. 50 40
1284 – 43 c. black, grn & brn 50 40
1285 – $1.20 multicoloured .. 1·75 2·00

DESIGNS: 43 c. (No. 1284) Patrol (Defence of Tobruk); $1.20, "V-P Day Canberra" (Harold Abbot) (Australian War Memorial).

487 Queen Elizabeth at Royal Albert Hall, London
489 "Bondi" (Max Dupain)

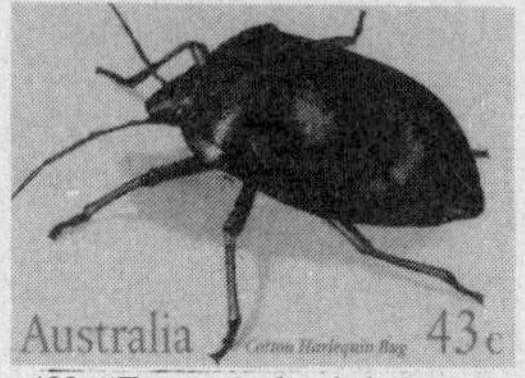

488 "Tectocris diophthalmus" (bug)

1991. Queen Elizabeth II's Birthday.

1286 **487** 43 c. multicoloured .. 60 45

1991. Insects. Multicoloured.

1287 43 c. Type **488** 50 45
1288 43 c. "Cizara ardeniae" (hawk moth) 50 45
1289 80 c. "Petasida ephippigera" (grasshopper) 1·00 1·25
1290 $1 "Castiarina producta" (beetle) .. .. 1·25 1·50

1991. 150 Years of Photography in Australia.

1291 **489** 43 c. black, brn & blue 50 50
1292 – 43 c. black, grn & brn 50 50
1293 – 70 c. black, grn & brn 90 90
1294 – $1.20 black, brn & grn 1·50 1·50

DESIGNS: No. 1292, "Gears for the Mining Industry, Vickers Ruwolt, Melbourne" (Wolfgang Sievers); 1293, "The Wheel of Youth" (Harold Cazneaux); 1294, "Teacup Ballet" (Olive Cotton).

490 Singing Group

1991. Australian Radio Broadcasting. Designs showing listeners and scenes from radio programmes. Multicoloured.

1295 43 c. Type **490** 50 45
1296 43 c. "Blue Hills" serial 50 45
1297 85 c. "The Quiz Kids" .. 1·10 1·25
1298 $1 "Argonauts' Club" children's programme .. 1·25 1·40

491 Puppy
492 George Vancouver (1791) and Edward Eyre (1841)

1991. Domestic Pets. Multicoloured.

1299 43 c. Type **491** 55 45
1300 43 c. Kitten 55 45
1301 70 c. Pony 90 90
1302 $1 Sulphur-crested cockatoo .. .. 1·25 1·25

1991. Exploration of Western Australia.

1303 **492** $1.05 multicoloured .. 1·25 1·25

493 "Seven Little Australians" (Ethel Turner)

1991. Australian Writers of the 1890s. Mult.

1305 43 c. Type **493** 50 45
1306 75 c. "On Our Selection" (Steele Rudd) 80 75
1307 $1 "Clancy of the Overflow" (poem, A. B. Paterson) (vert) .. 1·10 95
1308 $1.20 "The Drover's Wife" (short story, Henry Lawson) (vert) 1·25 1·40

494 Shepherd

1991. Christmas. Multicoloured.

1309 38 c. Type **494** 40 40
1310 43 c. Infant Jesus .. 45 45
1311 90 c. Wise Man .. .. 1·10 1·25

495 Parma Wallaby

1992. Threatened Species. Multicoloured.

1312 45 c. Type **495** 40 45
1313 45 c. Ghost bat 40 45
1314 45 c. Long-tailed dunnart 40 45
1315 45 c. Little pygmy-possum 40 45
1316 45 c. Dusky hopping-mouse 40 45
1317 45 c. Squirrel glider .. 40 45

496 Basket of Wild Flowers

1992. Greetings Stamp.

1318 **496** 45 c. multicoloured .. 40 45

497 Noosa River, Queensland

1992. Wetlands and Waterways. Mult.

1319 20 c. Type **497** .. .. 80 1·00
1320 45 c. Lake Eildon, Victoria 40 45

498 "Young Endeavour" (brigantine)

1992. Australia Day. Sailing Ships. Mult.

1333	45 c. Type **498**	60	45
1334	45 c. "Britannia" (yacht) (vert)	60	45
1335	$1.05 "Akarana" (cutter) (vert)	1·40	1·50
1336	$1.20 "John Louis" (pearling lugger) ..	1·60	1·75

499 Bombing of Darwin

1992. 50th Anniv of Second World War Battles. Multicoloured.

1338	45 c. Type **499**	60	45
1339	75 c. Anti-aircraft gun and fighters, Milne Bay	1·00	1·00
1340	75 c. Infantry on Kokoda Trail	1·00	1·00
1341	$1.05 H.M.A.S. "Australia" (cruiser) and American carrier, Coral Sea	1·25	1·50
1342	$1.20 Australians advancing, El Alamein	1·40	1·60

500 "Helix Nebula"

1992. International Space Year. Mult.

1343	45 c. Type **500**	50	45
1344	$1.05 "The Pleiades" ..	1·25	1·25
1345	$1.20 "Spiral Galaxy, NGC 2997"	1·50	1·50

501 Hunter Valley, New South Wales

1992. Vineyard Regions. Multicoloured.

1347	45 c. Type **501**	60	50
1348	45 c. North East Victoria	60	50
1349	45 c. Barossa Valley, South Australia ..	60	50
1350	45 c. Coonawarra, South Australia	60	50
1351	45 c. Margaret River, Western Australia ..	60	50

502 3½d. Stamp of 1953

1992. Queen Elizabeth II's Birthday.

1352	**502** 45 c. multicoloured ..	55	50

503 Salt Action

1992. Land Conservation. Multicoloured.

1353	45 c. Type **503**	55	55
1354	45 c. Farm planning ..	55	55
1355	45 c. Erosion control ..	55	55
1356	45 c. Tree planting ..	55	55
1357	45 c. Dune care	55	55

504 Cycling

1992. Olympic Games and Paralympic Games (No. 1359), Barcelona. Multicoloured.

1358	45 c. Type **504**	60	45
1359	$1.20 High jumping ..	1·50	1·60
1360	$1.20 Weightlifting ..	1·50	1·60

505 Echidna

1992. Australian Wildlife. Multicoloured.

1361	30 c. Saltwater crocodile	30	35
1362	35 c. Type **505**	35	40
1363	40 c. Platypus	35	40
1364	50 c. Koala	45	50
1365	60 c. Common bushtail possum	55	60
1366	70 c. Kookaburra ..	65	70
1367	85 c. Pelican	80	85
1368	90 c. Eastern grey kangaroo	85	90
1369	95 c. Common wombat ..	90	95
1370	$1.20 Pink cockatoo ..	1·25	1·40
1371	$1.35 Emu	1·25	1·40

506 Sydney Harbour Tunnel (value at left)

1992. Opening of Sydney Harbour Tunnel. Multicoloured.

1375	45 c. Type **506**	75	75
1376	45 c. Sydney Harbour Tunnel (value at right)	75	75

Nos. 1375/6 were printed together, se-tenant, forming a composite design.

507 Warden's Courthouse, Coolgardie

1992. Centenary of Discovery of Gold at Coolgardie and Kalgoorlie. Multicoloured.

1377	45 c. Type **507**	60	45
1378	45 c. Post Office, Kalgoorlie	60	45
1379	$1.05 York Hotel, Kalgoorlie	1·40	1·50
1380	$1.20 Town Hall, Kalgoorlie	1·50	1·75

508 Bowler of 1892

1992. Centenary of Sheffield Shield Cricket Tournament. Multicoloured.

1381	45 c. Type **508**	60	45
1382	$1.20 Batsman and wicket-keeper	1·40	1·60

509 Children's Nativity Play

1992. Christmas. Multicoloured.

1383	40 c. Type **509**	55	40
1384	45 c. Child waking on Christmas Day ..	60	45
1385	$1 Children carol singing	1·50	1·60

510 "Ghost Gum, Central Australia" (Namatjira)

1993. Australia Day. Paintings by Albert Namatjira. Multicoloured.

1386	45 c. Type **510**	65	65
1387	45 c. "Across the Plain to Mount Giles"	65	65

511 "Wild Onion Dreaming" (Pauline Nakamarra Woods)

1993. "Dreamings". Paintings by Aboriginal Artists. Multicoloured.

1388	45 c. Type **511**	60	45
1389	75 c. "Yam Plants" (Jack Wunuwun) (vert) ..	95	95
1390	85 c. "Goose Egg Hunt" (George Milpurrurru) (vert)	1·10	1·25
1391	$1 "Kalumpiwarra-Ngulalintji" (Rover Thomas)	1·25	1·40

512 Uluru (Ayers Rock) National Park

1993. World Heritage Sites. Multicoloured.

1392	45 c. Type **512**	55	45
1393	85 c. Rain forest, Fraser Island	1·00	1·00
1394	95 c. Beach, Shark Bay ..	1·25	1·25
1395	$2 Waterfall, Kakadu ..	2·50	2·50

513 Queen Elizabeth II on Royal Visit, 1992

1993. Queen Elizabeth II's Birthday.

1396	**513** 45 c. multicoloured ..	60	60

514 H.M.A.S. "Sydney" (cruiser, launched 1934) in Action

1993. Second World War Naval Vessels. Mult.

1397	45 c. Type **514**	55	45
1398	85 c. H.M.A.S. "Bathurst" (mine-sweeper)	1·10	1·10
1399	$1.05 H.M.A.S. "Arunta" (destroyer)	1·25	1·25
1400	$1.20 "Centaur" (hospital ship) and tug ..	1·50	1·60

515 "Work in the Home"

1993. Working Life in the 1890s. Mult.

1401	45 c. Type **515**	55	45
1402	45 c. "Work in the Cities"	55	45
1403	$1 "Work in the Country"	1·10	1·10
1404	$1.20 Trade Union banner	1·50	1·75

516 Centenary Special Train, Tasmania, 1971

1993. Australian Trains. Multicoloured.

1405	45 c. Type **516**	40	45
1406	45 c. "Spirit of Progress", Victoria	40	45
1407	45 c. "Western Endeavour", Western Australia, 1970 ..	40	45
1408	45 c. "Silver City Comet", New South Wales ..	40	45
1409	45 c. Kuranda tourist train, Queensland ..	40	45
1410	45 c. "The Ghan", Northern Territory ..	40	45

Nos. 1405/10 also come self-adhesive.

517 "Black Cockatoo Feather" (Fiona Foley)

1993. International Year of Indigenous Peoples. Aboriginal Art. Multicoloured.

1417	45 c. Type **517**	40	45
1418	75 c. "Ngarrgooroon Country" (Hector Jandany) (horiz) ..	70	75
1419	$1 "Ngak Ngak" (Ginger Riley Munduwalawala) (horiz)	95	1·00
1420	$1.05 "Untitled" (Robert Cole)	1·00	1·10

518 Conference Emblem

1993. Inter-Parliamentary Union Conference and 50th Anniv of Women in Federal Parliament. Multicoloured.

1421	45 c. Type **518**	40	45
1422	45 c. Dame Enid Lyons and Senator Dorothy Tangney	40	45

519 Ornithocheirus

1993. Prehistoric Animals. Multicoloured.

1423	45 c. Type **519**	40	45
1424	45 c. Leaellynasaura (25 × 30 mm)	40	45
1425	45 c. Timimus (26 × 33 mm)	40	45
1426	45 c. Allosaurus (26 × 33 mm)	40	45
1427	75 c. Muttaburrasaurus (30 × 50 mm)	70	75
1428	$1.05 Minmi (50 × 30 mm)	1·00	1·10

Nos. 1423/4 also come self-adhesive.

520 "Goodwill"

1993. Christmas. Multicoloured.

1432	40 c. Type **520**	40	45
1433	45 c. "Joy"	40	45
1434	$1 "Peace"	95	1·00

521 "Shoalhaven River Bank—Dawn" (Arthur Boyd)

1994. Australia Day. Landscape Paintings. Multicoloured.

1435	45 c. Type **521**	40	45
1436	85 c. "Wimmera" (Sir Sidney Nolan) ..	80	85
1437	$1.05 "Lagoon, Wimmera" (Nolan) ..	1·00	1·10
1438	$2 "White Cockatoos with Flame Trees" (Boyd) (vert)	2·00	2·10

522 Teaching Lifesaving Techniques

1994. Centenary of Organised Life Saving in Australia. Multicoloured.

1439	45 c. Type **522**	40	45
1440	45 c. Lifeguard on watch	40	45
1441	95 c. Lifeguard team ..	90	95
1442	$1.20 Lifeguards' surf boards	1·25	1·40

Nos. 1439/40 also come self-adhesive.

523 Rose

1994. Greetings Stamps. Flower photographs by Lariane Fonseca. Multicoloured.

1445	45 c. Type **523**	40	45
1446	45 c. Tulips	40	45
1447	45 c. Poppies	40	45

524 Bridge and National Flags

1994. Opening of Friendship Bridge between Thailand and Laos.

1448	**524**	95 c. multicoloured ..	90	95

525 "Queen Elizabeth II" (Sir William Dargie)

1994. Queen Elizabeth II's Birthday.

1449	**525**	45 c. multicoloured ..	40	45

526 "Family in Field" (Bobbie-Lea Blackmore)

1994. International Year of the Family. Children's Paintings. Multicoloured.

1450	45 c. Type **526**	40	45
1451	75 c. "Family on Beach" (Kathryn Teoh)	65	70
1452	$1 "Family around Fire" (Maree McCarthy) ..	95	1·00

OFFICIAL STAMPS

1931. Overprinted **O.S.**

(a) Kangaroo issue.

O 133.	**1.**	6d. brown ..	25·00	20·00

(b) King George V issue.

O 128	**5a.**	½d. orange	6·00	1·50
O 129		1d. green	4·00	45
O 130		2d. red	6·00	55
O 131		3d. blue	7·50	5·00
O 126		4d. olive	20·00	3·75
O 132		5d. brown	40·00	25·00

(c) Various issues.

O 123.	**13.**	2d. red	55·00	16·00
O 134.	**18.**	2d. red	5·00	2·00
O 124.	**13.**	3d. blue	£200	38·00
O 135.	**18.**	3d. blue	15·00	7·00
O 136.	**17.**	1s. green	50·00	35·00

POSTAGE DUE STAMPS

D 1.

D 3.

1902. White space below value at foot

D 1.	D 1.	½d. green	2·75	3·00
D 2.		1d. green	9·50	4·50
D 3.		2d. green	25·00	4·00
D 4.		3d. green	25·00	17·00
D 5.		4d. green	38·00	10·00
D 6.		6d. green	55·00	9·00
D 7.		8d. green	95·00	70·00
D 8.		5s. green	£180	70·00

1902. White space filled in.

D 22	D **3.**	½d. green	5·00	3·00
D 23		1d. green	5·00	1·25
D 24		2d. green	20·00	2·50
D 25		3d. green	42·00	4·25
D 26		4d. green	38·00	3·75
D 17		5d. green	35·00	9·00
D 28		6d. green	50·00	8·50
D 29		8d. green	95·00	27·00
D 18		10d. green	65·00	14·00
D 19		1s. green	48·00	10·00
D 20		2s. green	£100	16·00
D 33		5s. green	£160	18·00
D 43		10s. green	£2000	£1300
D 44		20s. green	£3750	£2250

1908. As Type D **3**, but stroke after figure of value, thus " 5/– ".

D 58.	D **3.**	1s. green	75·00	8·00
D 60.		2s. green	£950	£1200
D 59.		5s. green	£200	48·00
D 61.		10s. green	£2000	£2250
D 62.		20s. green	£5000	£6000

D 7.

D 10.

1909.

D 132	D **7.**	½d. red and green ..	1·00	1·75
D 120		1d. red and green ..	90	60
D 93		1½d. red and green ..	1·50	9·00
D 121		2d. red and green ..	4·50	95
D 134		3d. red and green ..	1·75	2·50
D 109		4d. red and green ..	3·75	2·25
D 124		5d. red and green ..	8·00	2·50
D 137		6d. red and green ..	2·75	2·75
D 126		7d. red and green ..	4·25	8·50
D 127		8d. red and green .	10·00	25·00
D 139		10d. red and green ..	5·50	3·25
D 128		1s. red and green .	18·00	1·25
D 70		2s. red and green ..	70·00	16·00
D 71		5s. red and green ..	80·00	17·00
D 72		10s. red and green ..	£225	£150
D 73		£1 red and green ..	£475	£250

1953.

D 140	D **10.**	1s. red and green ..	3·75	3·50
D 130		2s. red and green ..	18·00	12·00
D 131a		5s. red and green ..	12·00	70

AUSTRALIAN ANTARCTIC TERRITORY

By an order in Council of 7 February 1933, the territory S. of latitude 60°S. between 160th and 145th meridians of East longtitude (excepting Adelie Land) was placed under Australian administration. Until 1957 stamps of Australia were used from the bases.

1966. 100 cents = 1 dollar.

1. 1954 Expedition at Vestfold Hills and Map.

1957.

1	1	2s. blue	1·75	80

2. Members of Shackleton Expedition at S. Magnetic Pole 1909.

DESIGNS—As Type **3**—VERT. 1s. Dog-team and iceberg. 2s. 3d. Map of Antarctica and Emperor Penguins.

3. Weazel and Team.

1959.

2.	**2.**	5d on 4d. black and sepia ..	60	15
3.	**3.**	8d on 7d. black and blue ..	5·00	2·00
4.	–	1s. myrtle	4·50	1·75
5.	–	2s. 3d. green	12·00	4·00

6.

7. Sir Douglas Mawson (Expedition leader).

1961.

6.	**6.**	5d. blue	1·50	20

1961. 50th Anniv. of 1911–14 Australian Antarctic Expedition.

7.	**7.**	5d. myrtle	35	20

8. Aurora and Camera Dome.

1966. Multicoloured.

8	1 c. Type 8	70	30
9	2 c. Emperor penguins ..	2·25	80
10	4 c. Ship and iceberg ..	70	90
11	5 c. Banding southern elephant-seals	2·75	1·75
12	7 c. Measuring snow strata	80	80
13	10 c. Wind gauges ..	1·00	90
14	15 c. Weather balloon ..	4·00	2·00
15	20 c. Helicopter (horiz) ..	4·25	2·25
16	25 c. Radio operator (horiz)	5·00	3·75
17	50 c. Ice-compression tests (horiz)	17·00	9·00
18	$1 Parahelion ("mock sun") (horiz)	42·00	16·00

11. Sastrugi (Snow Ridges).

1971. 10th Anniv. of Antarctic Treaty.

19. **11.** 6 c. blue and black .. 1·25 1·00
20. – 30 c. multicoloured .. 6·50 7·00

DESIGN: 30 c. Pancake ice.

12. Capt. Cook, Sextant and Compass.

1972. Bicentenary of Cook's Circumnavigation of Antarctica. Mult.

21. 7 c. Type **12** .. .. 3·00 75
22. 35 c. Chart and H.M.S. "Resolution" .. .. 9·00 6·00

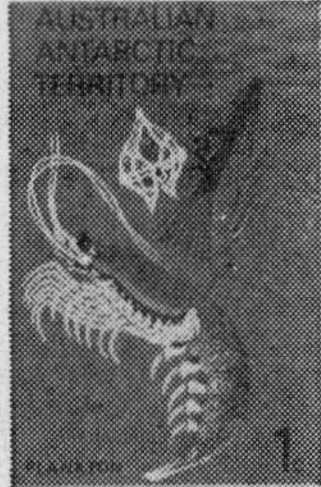

13. Plankton.

1973. Multicoloured.

23. 1 c. Type **13** 30 15
24. 5 c. Mawson's "Gipsy Moth", 1931 .. .. 30 50
25. 7 c. Adelie Penguin .. 2·25 70
26. 8 c. Rymill's "Fox Moth", 1934-7 .. .. 40 50
27. 9 c. Leopard seal (horiz.) .. 40 50
28. 10 c. Killer whale (horiz.) .. 5·50 1·75
29. 20 c. Wandering Albatross (horiz.) 90 80
30. 25 c. Wilkins' Lockheed "Vega", 1928 (horiz.) .. 60 80
31. 30 c. Ellsworth's Northrop "Gamma", 1935 .. 60 80
32. 35 c. Christensen's Avro "Avian", 1934 (horiz.) .. 60 80
33. 50 c. Byrd's "Tri-Motor" 1929 .. .. 70 80
34. $1 Sperm whale .. .. 1·25 1·40

14. Admiral Byrd (expedition leader), Aircraft and Map of South Pole.

1979. 50th Anniv. of First Flight over South Pole. Multicoloured.

35. 20 c. Type **14** 50 50
36. 55 c. Admiral Byrd, aircraft and Antarctic terrain 1·25 1·75

15. "Thala Dan" (supply ship).

1979. Ships. Multicoloured.

37 1 c. "Aurora" (horiz) .. 15 10
38 2 c. "Penola" (Rymill's ship) 40 10
39 5 c. Type **15** 30 40
40 10 c. H.M.S. "Challenger" (survey ship) (horiz) .. 50 10
41 15 c. "Morning" (bow view) (whaling ship) (horiz) .. 2·00 2·00
42 15 c. "Nimrod" (stern view) (Shackleton's ship) (horiz) 1·40 40
43 20 c. "Discovery II" (supply ship) (horiz) .. .. 50 1·25
44 22 c. "Terra Nova" (Scott's ship) .. .. .. 90 1·25
45 25 c. "Endurance" (Shackleton's ship) .. 60 1·00
46 30 c. "Fram" (Amundsen's ship) (horiz) .. .. 60 1·25
47 35 c. "Nella Dan" (supply ship) (horiz) .. .. 80 1·25
48 40 c. "Kista Dan" (supply ship) .. .. .. 1·25 60
49 45 c. "L'Astrolabe" (D'Urville's ship) (horiz) 70 70
50 50 c. "Norvegia" (supply ship) (horiz) 70 70
51 55 c. "Discovery" (Scott's ship) .. .. .. 85 2·00
52 $1 H.M.S. "Resolution" (Cook's ship) .. .. 1·75 2·25

No. 41 is incorrectly inscribed "S.Y. Nimrod".

16. Sir Douglas Mawson in Antarctic Terrain.

1982. Birth Centenary of Sir Douglas Mawson (Antarctic explorer). Multicoloured.

53. 27 c. Type **16** 50 30
54. 75 c. Sir Douglas Mawson and map of Australian Antarctic Territory .. 1·50 2·25

17. Light-mantled Sooty Albatross.

1983. Regional Wildlife. Multicoloured.

55. 27 c. Type **17** 80 90
56. 27 c. King cormorant .. 80 90
57. 27 c. Southern elephant seal 80 90
58. 27 c. Royal penguin .. 80 90
59. 27 c. Dove prion 80 90

18. Antarctic Scientist.

1983. 12th Antarctic Treaty Consultative Meeting. Canberra.

60. **18.** 27 c. milticoloured .. 75 75

19. Prismatic Compass and Lloyd-Creak Dip Circle.

1984. 75th Anniv. of Magnetic Pole Expedition. Multicoloured.

61. 30 c. Type **19** 85 60
62. 85 c. Aneroid barometer and theodolite .. .. 1·90 1·75

20. Dog Team pulling Sledge.

1984. Antarctic Scenes. Multicoloured.

63. 2 c. Summer afternoon Mawson station 10 10
64. 5 c. Type **20** 10 10
65. 10 c. Late summer evening, MacRobertson Land .. 10 15
66. 15 c. Prince Charles Mountains 15 20
67. 20 c. Summer morning Wilkesland 15 20
68. 25 c. Sea-ice and iceberg .. 20 25
69. 30 c. Mount Coates 25 30
70. 33 c. "Iceberg Alley", Mawson 25 30
71. 36 c. Early winter evening, Casey Station 30 35
72. 45 c. Brash ice (vert.) .. 60 70
73. 60 c. Midwinter shadows, Casey Station 50 55
74. 75 c. Coastline .. .. 1·25 1·50
75. 85 c. Landing strip .. .. 1·50 1·75
76. 90 c. Pancake ice (vert.) .. 75 80
77. $1 Emperor penguins .. 85 90

21. Prince Charles Mountains near Mawson Station.

1986. 25th Anniv. of Antarctic Treaty.

78. **21.** 36 c. multicoloured .. 1·25 50

22 Hourglass Dolphins and "Nella Dan"

1988. Environment, Conservation and Technology. Multicoloured.

79 37 c. Type **22** 90 85
80 37 c. Emperor penguins and Davis Station 90 85
81 37 c. Crabeater seal and helicopter 90 85
82 37 c. Adelie penguins and tracked vehicle .. 90 85
83 37 c. Grey-headed albatross and photographer .. 90 85

23 "Antarctica"

1989. Antarctic Landscape Paintings by Sir Sidney Nolan. Multicoloured.

84 39 c. Type **23** .. 80 50
85 39 c. "Iceberg Alley" .. 80 50
86 60 c. "Glacial Flow" .. 1·40 75
87 80 c. "Frozen Sea" .. 1·90 1·00

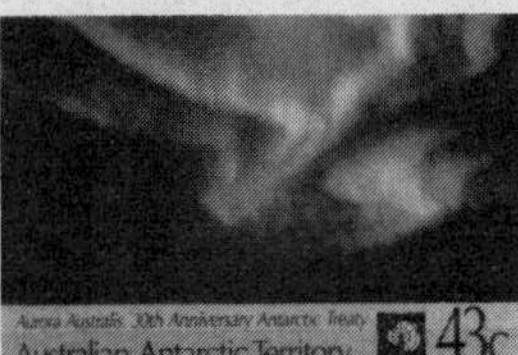

24 "Aurora Australis"

1991. 30th Anniv of Antarctic Treaty (43 c.) and maiden voyage of "Aurora Australis" (research ship) ($1.20). Multicoloured.

88 43 c. Type **24** 75 50
89 $1.20 "Aurora Australis" off Heard Island .. .. 2·00 2·00

25 Adelie Penguin and Chick

1992. Antarctic Wildlife. Multicoloured.

90 45 c. Type **25** 40 45
91 75 c. Elephant seal with pup 70 75
92 85 c. Northern giant petrel on nest with fledgeling .. 80 85
93 95 c. Weddell seal and pup 90 95
94 $1 Royal penguin .. .. 95 1·00
95 $1.20 Emperor penguins with chicks (vert) .. 1·25 1·40
96 $1.40 Fur seal .. .. 1·40 1·50
97 $1.50 King penguin (vert) .. 1·40 1·50

AUSTRALIAN ANTARCTIC TERRITORY

26 Head of Husky

1994. Departure of Huskies from Antarctica. Multicoloured.

104 45 c. Type **26** 40 45
105 75 c. Dogs pulling sledge (horiz) 70 75
106 85 c. Husky in harness .. 80 85
107 $1.05 Dogs on leads (horiz) 1·00 1·10

BAHAMAS

A group of islands in the Br. W. Indies, S.E. of Florida. Self-Government introduced on 7 January 1964. The islands became an independent member of the British Commonwealth on 10 July 1973.

1859. 12 pence = 1 shilling.
20 shillings = 1 pound
1966. 100 cents = 1 dollar.

1.

2.

1859. Imperf.
2 1 1d. rose .. .. .. 42·00 £1500

3.

5.

1860. Perf.
40 1 1d. red .. .. .. 38·00 12·00
27 2 4d. red .. .. .. £225 60·00
30 6d. violet .. .. .. £160 60·00
39a 3 1s. green .. .. .. 7·50 7·00

1883. Surch. **FOURPENCE.**
45. 2. 4d. on 6d. violet £550 £400

1884.
48. 5. 1d. red .. .. .. 4·75 1·75
52. 2½d. blue.. .. .. 9·00 1·75
53. 4d. yellow .. .. 9·00 4·00
54. 6d. mauve .. .. 4·50 26·00
56. 5s. green .. .. 65·00 75·00
57. £1 red £300 £225

6. Queen's Staircase, Nassau.

1901.
111 6 1d. black and red .. 80 1·00
76a 3d. purple on buff .. 3·75 4·50
77 3d. black and brown .. 70 2·25
59 5d. black and orange .. 8·00 40·00
78 5d. black and mauve .. 2·75 5·50
113 2s. black and blue .. 15·00 28·00
61 3s. black and green .. 25·00 48·00

7.

8.

1902.
71 7 ½d. green .. .. .. 3·75 1·75
62 1d. red .. .. .. 1·50 1·50
63 2½d. blue .. .. .. 6·50 1·25
64 4d. yellow .. .. 12·00 38·00
66 6d. brown .. .. 5·50 13·00
67 1s. black and red.. .. 14·00 35·00
69 5s. purple and blue .. 50·00 70·00
70 £1 green and black .. £250 £300

1912.
115 8 ½d. green.. .. .. 30 40
116 1d. red .. .. .. 1·00 15
117 1½d. brown .. .. 1·10 1·00
118 2d. grey .. .. 85 2·75
119 2½d. blue.. .. .. 80 2·75
120a 3d. purple on yellow .. 5·00 15·00
121 4d. yellow .. .. 70 5·00
122 6d. brown .. .. 60 1·25
123 1s. black and red .. 2·50 5·50
124 5s. purple and blue .. 27·00 48·00
125 £1 green and black .. £150 £250

1917. Optd. **1.1.17** and Red Cross.
90 6 1d. black and red .. 40 95

1918. Optd **WAR TAX** in one line.
96 8 ½d. green.. .. .. 40 1·40
97 1d. red 40 35
93 6 1d. black and red .. 2·00 2·75
98 3d. purple on yellow .. 40 1·50
100 3d. black and brown .. 45 4·00
99 8 1s. black and red .. 3·50 2·75

1919. Optd. **WAR CHARITY 3.6.18.**
101 6 1d. black and red .. 30 2·50

1919. Optd. **WAR TAX** in two lines.
102 8 ½d. green.. .. .. 30 1·25
103 1d. red .. .. .. 40 1·50
105 6 3d. black and brown .. 55 5·50
104 8 1s. black and red 6·00 21·00

16.

1920. Peace Celebration.
106 16 ½d. green .. .. 55 3·50
107 1d. red .. .. 2·75 70
108 2d. grey .. .. 2·75 6·50
109 3d. brown .. .. 2·75 9·00
110 1s. green .. .. 10·00 29·00

17. Seal of the Colony.

1930. Tercentenary of the Colony.
126 17 1d. black and red .. 2·00 2·50
127 3d. black and brown .. 3·50 12·00
128 5d. black and violet .. 3·50 12·00
129 2s. black and blue .. 18·00 38·00
130 3s. black and green .. 38·00 60·00

1931. As T **17**, but without dates at top.
131 2s. black and blue .. 2·00 50
132 3s. black and green .. 2·00 85

1935. Silver Jubilee. As T **13** of Antigua.
141. 1½d. blue and red .. 70 1·25
142. 2½d. brown and blue .. 3·00 3·75
143. 6d. blue and olive .. 6·00 6·50
144. 1s. grey and purple .. 6·00 8·00

19. Greater Flamingo (in flight).

1935.
145. 19. 8d. blue and red .. 4·50 2·75

1937. Coronation. As T **2** of Aden.
146. ½d. green 15 15
147. 1½d. brown 30 45
148. 2½d. blue 50 75

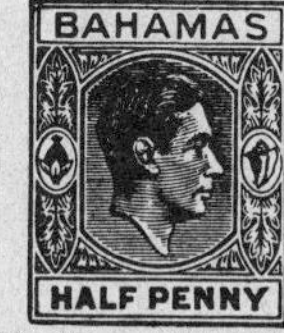
20. King George VI.

DESIGNS—As Type **15**. HORIZ. 6d. Fort Charlotte. 8d. Flamingoes.

21. Sea Garden, Nassau.

1938.
149 20. ½d. green 15 60
149c ½d. purple .. .. 50 2·50
150 1d. red .. .. 8·50 4·75
150a 1d. grey 30 50
151 1½d. brown 75 75
152 2d. grey .. .. 17·00 9·00
152b 2d. red 60 55
152c 2d. green 30 80
153 2½d. blue .. .. 3·25 2·00
153a 20 2½d. violet 75 60
154 3d. violet .. .. 16·00 5·00
154a 3d. blue 30 90
154b 3d. red .. .. 50 2·75
158 21 4d. blue and orange .. 1·00 40
159 – 6d. green and blue .. 60 40
160 – 8d. blue and red .. 4·50 1·40
154c 20 10d. orange .. .. 2·00 20
155a 1s. black and red .. 3·75 30
156b 5s. purple and blue .. 22·00 5·00
157a £1 green and black .. 55·00 40·00

1940. Surch.
161. 20. 3d. on 2½d. blue .. 40 40

1942. 450th Anniv. of Landing of Columbus. Optd. **1492 LANDFALL OF COLUMBUS 1942.**
162 20 ½d. green 30 60
163 1d. grey 30 60
164 1½d. brown 40 60
165 2d. red 30 65
166 2½d. blue 30 65
167 3d. blue 30 65
168 21 4d. blue and orange .. 40 90
169 – 6d. grn. & blue (No. 159) 40 1·75
170 – 8d. blue & red (No. 160) 90 70
171 20 1s. black and red .. 2·50 1·00
172 17 2s. black and blue .. 7·00 9·00
173a 3s. black and green .. 4·50 6·50
174a 20 5s. purple and blue .. 18·00 9·50
175a £1 green and black .. 26·00 23·00

1946. Victory. As T **9** of Aden.
176. 1½d. brown 10 10
177. 3d. blue.. .. .. 10 10

26. Infant Welfare Clinic.

1948. Tercentenary of Settlement of Island of Eleuthera. Inscr. as in T **26**.
178. 26. ½d. orange 20 50
179. – 1d. olive 20 35
180. – 1½d. yellow 25 80
181. – 2d. red 30 40
182. – 2½d. brown 35 75
183. – 3d. blue.. .. .. 50 85
184. – 4d. black 50 70
185. – 6d. green .. .. 1·50 80
186. – 8d. violet 50 70
187. – 10d. red.. .. .. 50 35
188. – 1s. brown 75 50
189. – 2s. purple .. .. 4·00 8·50
190. – 3s. blue.. .. .. 7·00 8·50
191. – 5s. mauve .. .. 4·00 4·50
192. – 10s. grey .. .. 9·00 9·00
193. – £1 red .. .. .. 13·00 13·00
DESIGNS: 1d. Agriculture. 1½d., Sisal. 2d. Straw work. 2½d., Dairy. 3d. Fishing fleet. 4d. Island settlement. 6d. Tuna fishing. 8d. Paradise Beach. 10d. Modern hotels. 1s. Yacht racing. 2s. Water sports — skiing. 3s. Shipbuilding. 5s. Transportation. 10s. Salt production. £1, Parliament Buildings.

1948. Silver Wedding. As T **10/11** of Aden.
194. 1½d. brown 20 25
195. £1 grey .. .. .. 32·00 30·00

1949. 75th Anniv of U.P.U. As T **20/23** of Antigua.
196. 2½d. violet 35 40
197. 3d. blue .. .. .. 1·00 1·00
198. 6d. blue .. .. .. 1·00 1·00
199. 1s. red .. .. .. 1·00 75

1953. Coronation. As T **13** of Aden.
200. 6d. black and blue .. 15 35

42. Infant Welfare Clinic.

1954. Designs as Nos. 178/93 but with portrait of Queen Elizabeth II and without commemorative inscr. as in T **42**.
201. 42. ½d. black and red .. 10 60
202. – 1d. olive and brown .. 10 10
203. – 1½d. blue and black .. 15 40
204. – 2d. brown and green .. 15 15
205. – 3d. black and red .. 45 45
206. – 4d. turquoise and purple 30 30
207. – 5d. brown and blue .. 1·40 2·25
208. – 6d. blue and black .. 30 10
209. – 8d. black and lilac .. 60 40
210. – 10d. black and blue .. 30 10
211. – 1s. blue and brown .. 60 10
212. – 2s. orange and black .. 2·00 70
213. – 2s. 6d. black and blue.. 3·50 2·00
214. – 5s. green and orange .. 17·00 75
215. – 10s. black and slate .. 10·00 1·75
216. – £1 black and violet .. 17·00 6·00
DESIGNS: 1½d., Island settlement. 4d. Water sports—Skiing. 5d. Dairy. 6d. Transportation. 2s. Sisal. 2s. 6d. Shipbuilding. 5s. Tuna fishing. Other values the same as for the corresponding values in Nos. 178/93.

43. Queen Elizabeth II.

1959. Centenary of Bahamas Stamp.
217. 43. 1d. black and red .. 35 15
218. 2d. black and green .. 35 70
219. 6d. black and blue .. 45 30
220. 10d. black and brown.. 50 80

44. Christ Church Cathedral.

1962. Centenary of Nassau.
221. 44. 8d. green 45 45
222. – 10d. violet 45 25
DESIGN 10d. Nassau Public Library.

1963. Freedom from Hunger. As T **28** of Aden.
223. 8d. sepia 40 35

1963. Bahamas Talks. Nos. 209/10 optd. **BAHAMAS TALKS 1962.**
224. 8d. black and lilac .. 40 60
225. 10d. black and blue .. 50 65

1963. Cent of Red Cross. As T **33** of Antigua.
226. 1d red and black .. 40 30
227. 10d. red and blue .. 1·40 2·25

1964. New Constitution. Nos. 201/16 optd. **NEW CONSTITUTION 1964.**
228. 42. ½d. black and red .. 10 30
229. – 1d. olive and brown .. 10 15
230. – 1½d. blue and black .. 60 30
231. – 2d. brown and green .. 10 20
232. – 3d. black and red .. 60 30
233. – 4d. turquoise and purple 40 45
234. – 5d. brown and blue .. 40 65
235. – 6d. blue and black .. 40 30
236. – 8d. black and lilac .. 60 30
237. – 10d. black and blue .. 30 15
238 – 1s. blue and brown .. 55 15
239. – 2s. brown and black .. 1·50 1·75
240. – 2s. 6d. black and blue.. 2·00 2·50
241. – 5s. green and orange .. 4·50 3·25
242. – 10s. black and slate .. 4·00 5·50
243. – £1 black and violet .. 8·50 15·00

1964. 400th Birth Anniv of Shakespeare. As T **34** of Antigua.
244 6d. turquoise 10 10

1964. Olympic Games, Tokyo. No. 211 surch. with Olympic "rings" symbol and value.
245. 8d. on 1s. blue and brown 30 15

49. Colony's Badge.

1965.
247. 49. ½d. multicoloured .. 15 80
248. – 1d. slate, blue & orange 30 30
249. – 1½d. red, green & brown 15 80
250. – 2d. slate, green & blue.. 15 10
251. – 3d. red, blue and purple 90 20
252. – 4d. green, blue & brown 70 1·40
253. – 6d. green, blue and red 30 10
254. – 8d. purple, blue & bronze 50 30
255. – 10d. brown, grn. & violet 25 10
256a. – 1s. multicoloured .. 30 10
257. – 2s. brown, blue & green 1·00 1·00
258. – 2s. 6d. olive, blue & red 2·00 2·50
259. – 5s. brown, blue & green 2·75 1·00
260. – 10s. red, blue and brown 10·00 2·50
261. – £1 brown, blue and red 10·00 6·50
DESIGNS: 1d. Out Island Regatta. 1½d. Hospital. 2d. High School. 3d. Greater Flamingo. 4d. R.M.S. "Queen Elizabeth". 6d. "Development". 8d. Yachting. 10d. Public Square. 1s. Sea Garden. 2s. Old Cannon at Fort Charlotte. 2s. 6d. Sikorsky "S-38" Seaplane (1929) and Boeing "707" Airliner. 5s. Williamson Film Project (1914) and Undersea Post Office (1939). 10s. Conch Shell. £1, Columbus' Flagship.

1965. Cent of I.T.U. As T **36** of Antigua.
262. 1d. green and orange .. 15 10
263. 2s. purple and olive .. 65 45

1965. No. 254 surch.

264.	–	9d. on 8d. purple, blue and bronze	20	10

1965. I.C.Y. As T **37** of Antigua.

265.	½d. purple and turquoise	10	50
266.	1s. green and lavender ..	30	40

1966. Churchill Commem. As T **38** of Antigua.

267.	½d. blue	10	40
268.	2d. green	30	30
269.	10d. brown	65	85
270.	1s. violet	75	1·40

1966. Royal Visit. As T **39** of Antigua, but inscr. "to the Caribbean" omitted.

271.	6d. black and blue ..	90	50
272.	1s. black and mauve ..	1·60	1·25

1966. Decimal currency. Nos. **247/61 surch.**

273.	**49.**	1 c. on ½d. multicoloured	10	20
274.	–	2 c. on 1d. slate, blue and orange	10	20
275.	–	3 c. on 2d. slate, green and blue	10	10
276.	–	4 c. on 3d. red, bl. & pur.	45	10
277.	–	5 c. on 4d. green, blue and brown	15	60
278.	–	8 c. on 6d. grn., bl. & red	15	20
279.	–	10 c. on 8d. purple, blue and bronze	30	60
280.	–	11 c. on 1½d. red, green and brown	15	30
281.	–	12 c. on 10d. brown, grn. and violet	15	10
282.	–	15 c. on 1s. multicoloured	25	10
283.	–	22 c. on 2s. brown, blue and green	60	80
284.	–	50 c. on 2s. 6d. olive, blue and red ..	90	1·40
285.	–	$1 on 5s. brown, blue and green	1·25	1·50
286.	–	$2 on 10s. red, bl. & brn.	5·00	4·25
287.	–	$3 on £1 brn., bl. & red	5·00	4·25

1966. World Cup Football Championships. As T **40** of Antigua.

288.	8 c. multicoloured ..	15	15
289.	15 c. multicoloured ..	25	25

1966. Inauguration of W.H.O. Headquarters, Geneva. As T **41** of Antigua.

290.	11 c. black, green and blue	25	20
291.	15 c. black, purple & ochre	30	25

1966. 20th Anniv. of U.N.E.S.C.O. As T **54/6** of Antigua.

292.	3 c. multicoloured ..	15	10
293.	15 c. yellow, violet & olive	35	30
294.	$1 black, purple & orange	1·50	2·25

1967. As Nos. 247/51, 253/9 and 261 but values in decimal currency, and new designs for 5 c. and $2.

295.	**49.**	1 c. multicoloured ..	10	90
296.	–	2 c. slate, blue & green	15	15
297.	–	3 c. slate, green & violet	10	10
298.	–	4 c. red, lt. blue & blue	4·00	30
299.	–	5 c. black, blue & purple	60	60
300.	–	8 c. green, blue & brown	25	10
301.	–	10 c. pur., blue & red ..	30	60
302.	–	11 c. red, green and blue	25	60
303.	–	12 c. brown, grn. & olive	25	10
304.	–	15 c. multicoloured ..	55	10
305.	–	22 c. brown, blue & red	70	65
306.	–	50 c. olive, blue & grn.	2·00	75
307.	–	$1 maroon, blue & pur.	2·00	60
308.	–	$2 multicoloured ..	9·00	2·50
309.	–	$3 brown, blue & pur.	3·75	2·00

New Designs: 5 c. "Oceanic". $2, Conch Shell (different).

69. Bahamas Crest.

1967. Diamond Jubilee of World Scouting. Multicoloured.

310.	3 c. Type **69**	35	15
311.	15 c. Scout badge.. ..	40	15

71. Globe and Emblem.

1968. Human Rights Year. Multicoloured.

312.	3 c. Type **71**	10	10
313.	12 c. Scales of Justice and Emblem	20	10
314.	$1 Bahamas Crest & Emblem	70	80

HAVE YOU READ THE NOTES AT THE BEGINNING OF THIS CATALOGUE?
These often provide answers to the enquiries we receive.

74. Golf.

1968. Tourism. Multicoloured.

315.	5 c. Type **74**	75	40
316.	11 c. Yachting	1·00	30
317.	15 c. Horse-racing ..	1·00	35
318.	50 c. Water-skiing ..	2·25	3·50

78. Racing Yacht and Olympic Monument.

1968. Olympic Games, Mexico City.

319.	**78.**	5 c. brn., yell. and grn.	25	15
320.	–	11 c. multicoloured ..	35	25
321.	–	50 c. multicoloured ..	80	1·40
322.	**78.**	$1 grey, blue and violet	1·75	3·00

Designs: 11 c. Long jumping and Olympic Monument. 50 c. Running and Olympic Monument.

81. Legislative Building.

1968. 14th Commonwealth Parliamentary Conf. Multicoloured.

323.	3 c. Type **81**	10	10
324.	10 c. Bahamas Mace and Westminster Clock Tower	15	20
325.	12 c. Local Straw Market	15	25
326.	15 c. Horse drawn Surrey	20	30

Nos. 324/5 are vert.

85. Obverse and reverse of $100 Gold Coin.

1968. Gold Coins Commemorating the first General Election under the New Constitution.

327.	**85.**	3 c. red on gold ..	20	25
328.	–	12 c. green on gold ..	35	50
329.	–	15 c. purple on gold ..	40	60
330.	–	$1 black on gold ..	1·75	2·50

Obverse and Reverse of: 12 c. $50 Gold Coin. 15 c. $20 Gold Coin. $1, $10 Gold Coin.

89. First Flight Postcard of 1919.

1969. 50th Anniv. of Bahamas Airmail Services.

331.	**89.**	12 c. multicoloured ..	65	50
332.	–	15 c. multicoloured ..	75	1·10

Design: 15 c. Sikorsky "S-38" Seaplane of 1929.

91. Game-Fishing Boats.

1969. Tourism. One Millionth Visitor to Bahamas. Multicoloured.

333.	3 c. Type **91**	35	10
334.	11 c. Paradise Beach ..	50	15
335.	"Sunfish" sailing boats ..	50	15
336.	15 c. Rawson Square and parade	60	25

92. "The Adoration of the Shepherds" (Louis le Nain).

1969. Christmas. Multicoloured.

338.	3 c. Type **92**	10	10
339.	11 c. "The Adoration of the Shepherds" (Poussin) ..	15	15
340.	12 c. "The Adoration of the Kings" (Gerard David)	15	15
341.	15 c. "The Adoration of the Kings" (Vincenzo Foppa)	20	25

93. Badge of Girl Guides.

1970. Diamond Jubilee of Girl Guides' Association. Multicoloured.

342.	3 c. Type **93**	30	10
343.	12 c. Badge of Brownies	45	20
344.	15 c. Badge of Rangers	50	35

94. New U.P.U. Headquarters and Emblem.

1970. New U.P.U. Headquarters Building.

345.	**94.**	3 c. multicoloured ..	10	10
346.		15 c. multicoloured ..	20	30

95. Coach and Globe.

1970. "Goodwill Caravan". Multicoloured.

347.	3 c. Type **95**	40	10
348.	11 c. Train and globe ..	1·00	20
349.	12 c. "Canberra" (liner), yacht & globe	1·00	30
350.	15 c. Airliner and globe ..	1·00	70

96. Nurse, Patients and Greater Flamingo.

1970. Cent. of British Red Cross. Mult.

352.	3 c. Type **96**	60	20
353.	15 c. Hospital and dolphin	65	90

97. "The Nativity" (detail, Pittoni).

1970. Christmas. Multicoloured.

354.	3 c. Type **97**	15	10
355.	11 c. "The Holy Family" (detail, Anton Raphael Mengs)	20	15
356.	12 c. "The Adoration of the Shepherds" (detail, Giorgione)	20	15
357.	15 c. "The Adoration of the Shepherds" (detail, School of Seville) ..	30	30

98. International Airport.

1971. Multicoloured.

359	1 c. Type **98**	10	30
360	2 c. Breadfruit	15	35
361	3 c. Straw Market ..	15	30
362	4 c. Hawksbill turtle ..	1·50	4·50
363	5 c. Grouper	45	40
364	6 c. As 4 c.	35	1·00
365	7 c. Hibiscus	1·75	2·00
464	8 c. Yellow Elder.. ..	2·25	30
367	10 c. Bahamian sponge boat	40	30
368	11 c. Greater Flamingoes	1·75	85
369	12 c. As 7 c.	2·00	3·00
370	15 c. Bonefish	40	55
466	16 c. As 7 c.	70	35
371	18 c. Royal Poinciana ..	55	65
467a	21 c. As 2 c.	80	1·25
372	22 c. As 18 c.	2·75	7·50
468	25 c. As 4 c.	90	40
469	40 c. As 10 c.	2·00	75
470	50 c. Post Office, Nassau	1·75	1·75
471	$1 Pineapple (vert.) ..	2·25	2·50
472	$2 Crawfish (vert.) ..	3·75	6·00
525	$3 Junkanoo (vert.) ..	4·50	7·00

99. Snowflake.

1971. Christmas.

377.	**99.**	3 c. pur., orge. and gold	10	10
378.	–	11 c. blue and gold ..	20	15
379.	–	15 c. multicoloured ..	20	20
380.	–	18 c. blue, ultram. & gold	25	25

Designs: 11 c. "Peace on Earth" (doves). 15 c. Arms of Bahamas and holly. 18 c. Starlit lagoon.

100. High jumping.

1972. Olympic Games, Munich. Multicoloured.

382.	10 c. Type **100**	30	30
383.	11 c. Cycling	35	30
384.	15 c. Running	40	45
385.	18 c. Sailing	70	80

101. Shepherd.

1972. Christmas. Multicoloured.

387.	3 c. Type **101**	10	10
388.	6 c. Bells	10	10
389.	15 c. Holly and Cross ..	15	20
390.	20 c. Poinsettia	25	45

1972. Royal Silver Wedding. As T **52**, of Ascension, but with Mace and Galleon in background.

393.	11 c. pink	15	15
394.	18 c. violet	15	20

104. Weather Satellite.

1973. Cent. of I.M.O./W.M.O. Mult.

410.	15 c. Type **104**	50	25
411.	18 c. Weather radar ..	60	35

105. C. A. Bain (national hero).

1973. Independence. Multicoloured.

412.	3 c. Type **105**	10	10
413.	11 c. Coat of arms ..	15	10
414.	15 c. Bahamas flag ..	20	15
415.	$1 Governor-General, M. B. Butler	90	1·00

106. "The Virgin in Prayer" (Sassoferrato).

1973. Christmas. Multicoloured.

417.	3 c. Type **106**	10	10
418.	11 c. "Virgin and Child with St. John" (Filippino Lippi) ..	15	15
419.	15 c. "A Choir of Angels" (Simon Marmion) ..	15	15
420.	18 c. "The Two Trinities" (Murillo)	25	25

107. "Agriculture and Sciences".

1974. 25th Anniv. of University of West Indies. Multicoloured.

422.	15 c. Type **107**	20	25
423.	18 c. "Arts, Engineering and General Studies" ..	25	30

108. U.P.U. Monument, Berne.

1974. Centenary of U.P.U.

424. **108.**	3 c. multicoloured ..	10	10
425. –	13 c. multicoloured (vert.)	20	25
426. –	14 c. multicoloured ..	20	30
427. –	18 c. multicoloured (vert.)	25	35

DESIGNS: As Type **108** but showing different arrangements of the U.P.U. Monument.

109. Roseate Spoonbills.

1974. 15th Anniv. of Bahamas National Trust. Multicoloured.

429.	13 c. Type **109**	85	75
430.	14 c. White-crowned Pigeon	85	75
431.	21 c. White-tailed Tropic Birds	1·25	1·25
432.	36 c. Cuban Amazon ..	1·60	1·75

110. "The Holy Family" (Jacques de Stella).

1974. Christmas. Multicoloured.

434.	8 c. Type **110**	10	10
435.	10 c. "Madonna and Child" (16th Century Brescian School)	15	15
436.	12 c. "Virgin and Child with St. John the Baptist and St. Catherine" (Previtali)	15	15
437.	21 c. "Virgin and Child with Angels" (Previtali) ..	25	30

111. "Anteos maerula".

1975. Butterflies. Multicoloured.

439	3 c. Type **111**	25	15
440	14 c. "Eurema nicippe" ..	80	50
441	18 c. "Papilio andraemon"	95	65
442	21 c. "Euptoieta hegesia"	1·10	85

112. Sheep Husbandry.

1975. Economic Diversification. Mult.

444.	3 c. Type **112**	10	10
445.	14 c. Electric-reel fishing (vert.)	20	15
446.	18 c. Farming	25	20
447.	21 c. Oil Refinery (vert.)	45	35

113. Rowena Rand (evangelist).

1975. International Women's Year.

449. **113.**	14 c. brn., light bl. & bl.	20	25
450. –	18 c. yell., grn. & brn...	25	30

DESIGN: 18 c. I.W.Y. symbol and Harvest symbol.

114. "Adoration of the Shepherds" (Perugino).

1975. Christmas. Multicoloured.

451.	3 c. Type **114**	15	15
452.	8 c. "Adoration of the Magi" (Ghirlandaio)	20	10
453.	18 c. As 8 c.	50	55
454.	21 c. Type **114**	60	75

115. Telephones, 1876 and 1976.

1976. Centenary of Telephone. Multicoloured.

456.	3 c. Type **115**	10	10
457.	16 c. Radio-telephone link, Deleporte	25	30
458.	21 c. Alexander Graham Bell	35	45
459.	25 c. Satellite	40	55

116. Map of North America.

1976. Bicent. of American Revolution. Multicoloured.

475.	16 c. Type **116**	30	30
476.	$1 John Murray, Earl of Dunmore	1·50	1·75

117. Cycling.

1976. Olympic Games, Montreal.

478. **117.**	8 c. mauve, blue and light blue	20	10
479. –	16 c. orange, brown and light blue	25	15
480. –	25 c. blue, mauve and light blue	30	25
481. –	40 c. brown, orange and light blue	50	55

DESIGNS: 16 c. Jumping. 25 c. Sailing. 40 c. Boxing.

118. "Virgin and Child" (detail, Lippi).

1976. Christmas. Multicoloured.

483.	3 c. Type **118**	10	10
484.	21 c. "Adoration of the Shepherds" (School of Seville)	15	15
485.	25 c. "Adoration of the Kings" (detail, Foppa)	15	20
486.	40 c. "Virgin and Child" (detail, Vivarini) ..	25	40

119. Queen beneath Cloth of Gold Canopy.

1977. Silver Jubilee. Multicoloured.

488.	8 c. Type **119**	10	10
489.	16 c. The Crowning ..	15	15
490.	21 c. Taking the Oath ..	15	15
491.	40 c. Queen with sceptre and orb	25	30

120. Featherduster.

1977. Marine Life. Multicoloured.

493.	3 c. Type **120**	15	15
494.	8 c. Pork Fish and cave ..	30	20
495.	16 c. Elkhorn Coral ..	55	40
496.	21 c. Soft Coral and sponge	65	55

121. Scouts around Campfire and Home-made Shower.

1977. 6th Caribbean Scout Jamboree. **Mult.**

498.	16 c. Type **121**	65	20
499.	21 c. Boating scenes ..	75	25

1977. Royal Visit. Nos. 488/91 optd. **Royal Visit October 1977.**

500.	8 c. Type **119**	15	10
501.	16 c. The Crowning ..	20	15
502.	21 c. Taking the Oath ..	25	25
503.	40 c. Queen with Sceptre and Orb	30	40

123. Virgin and Child.

1977. Christmas. Multicoloured.

505.	3 c. Type **123**	10	10
506.	16 c. The Magi	20	25
507.	21 c. Nativity Scene ..	25	40
508.	25 c. The Magi and star ..	30	45

124. Public Library, Nassau (Colonial).

1978. Architectural Heritage.

510. **124.**	3 c. black and green ..	10	10
511. –	8 c. black and blue ..	15	10
512. –	16 c. black and mauve	20	20
513. –	18 c. black and pink ..	25	30

DESIGNS: 8 c. St. Matthew's Church. 16 c. Government House. 18 c. The Hermitage, Cat Island.

125. Sceptre, St. Edward's Crown and Orb.

1978. 25th Anniv. of Coronation. Mult.

515.	16 c. Type **125**	15	10
516.	$1 Queen in Coronation regalia	50	65

126. Coat of Arms within Wreath and Three Ships.

1978. Christmas.

532. **126.**	5 c. gold, lake and red	20	10
533. –	21 c. gold, deep blue and blue	55	25

DESIGN: 21 c. Three angels with trumpets.

127. Child reaching for Adult.

1979. International Year of the Child. Multicoloured.

535.	5 c. Type **127**	20	15
536.	16 c. Boys playing leap-frog	40	45
537.	21 c. Girls skipping ..	50	60
538.	25 c. Bricks with I.Y.C. emblem	50	75

128. Sir Rowland Hill and Penny Black.

1979. Death Centenary of Sir Rowland Hill. Multicoloured.

540.	10 c. Type **128**	30	10
541.	21 c. Printing press, 1840 and 6d. stamp of 1862 ..	45	30
542.	25 c. Great Britain 1856 6d. with "A 05" (Nassau) cancellation, and 1840 2d. Blue	50	50
543.	40 c. Early mailboat and 1d. stamp of 1859	65	70

129. Commemorative Plaque and Map of Bahamas.

1979. 250th Anniv. of Parliament. Mult.

545.	16 c. Type **129**	20	10
546.	21 c. Parliament buildings	25	15
547.	25 c. Legislative Chamber	25	15
548.	$1 Senate Chamber ..	70	80

130. Goombay Carnival Headdress.

1979. Christmas.

550. **130.**	5 c. multicoloured ..	10	10
551. –	10 c. multicoloured ..	10	10
552. –	16 c. multicoloured ..	15	10
553. –	21 c. multicoloured ..	20	20
554. –	25 c. multicoloured ..	20	20
555. –	40 c. multicoloured ..	30	35

DESIGNS: 10 c. to 40 c. Various Carnival costumes.

131. Landfall of Columbus, 1492.

1980. Multicoloured.

557	1 c. Type **131**	30	70
558	3 c. Blackbeard the pirate	30	70
559	5 c. Eleutheran Adventurers (Articles and Orders, 1647)	30	30
560	10 c. Ceremonial mace ..	20	30
561	12 c. The Loyalists, 1783–1788	20	60
562	15 c. Slave trading, Vendue House	4·50	50
563	16 c. Wrecking in the 1800's	30	50
564	18 c. Blockade running (American Civil War) ..	40	80
565	21 c. Bootlegging, 1919–1929	40	80
566	25 c. Pineapple cultivation	40	80
567	40 c. Sponge clipping ..	70	85
568	50 c. Tourist development	75	75
569	$1 Modern agriculture ..	1·40	3·00
570	$2 Modern air and sea transport	3·00	3·50
571	$3 Banking (Central Bank)	3·00	4·00
572	$5 Independence, 10 July 1973	4·75	6·00

132. Virgin and Child.

1980. Christmas Straw-work. Multicoloured.

573.	5 c. Three Kings	10	10
574.	21 c. Type **132**	25	10
575.	25 c. Angel	25	15
576.	$1 Christmas Tree ..	75	70

133. Disabled Person with Walking Stick.

1981. International Year of Disabled People. Multicoloured.

578.	5 c. Type **133**	10	10
579.	$1 Disabled person in wheel-chair	1·25	1·25

134. Grand Bahama Tracking Site.

1981. Space Exploration. Multicoloured.

581.	10 c. Type **134**	20	15
582.	20 c. Satellite view of Bahamas (vert.) ..	45	45
583.	25 c. Satellite view of Eleuthera	50	60
584.	50 c. Satellite view of Andros and New Province (vert.)	75	1·00

135. Prince Charles and Lady Diana Spencer.

1981. Royal Wedding. Multicoloured.

586.	30 c. Type **135**	75	25
587.	$2 Prince Charles and Prime Minister Pindling ..	3·75	1·75

136. Bahama Pintail.

1981. Wildlife (1st series). Birds. Mult.

589.	5 c. Type **136**	60	15
590.	20 c. Reddish Egret ..	1·00	50
591.	25 c. Brown Booby ..	1·10	55
592.	$1 Black-billed Whistling Duck	2·50	3·50

See also Nos. 626/9, 653/6 and 690/3.

1981. Commonwealth Finance Ministers' Meeting. Nos. 559/60, 566 and 568 optd. **COMMONWEALTH FINANCE MINISTER'S MEETING 21-23 SEPTEMBER 1981.**

594.	5 c. Eleutheran Adventurers (Articles and Orders, 1647)	10	15
595.	10 c. Ceremonial Mace ..	10	20
596.	25 c. Pineapple cultivation	40	60
597.	50 c. Tourist development	75	1·50

138. Poultry.

1981. World Food Day. Multicoloured.

598.	5 c. Type **138**.	10	10
599.	20 c. Sheep	30	35
600.	30 c. Lobsters	40	50
601.	50 c. Pigs	75	1·50

139. Father Christmas.

1981. Christmas. Multicoloured.

603.	5 c. Type **139**	35	45
604.	5 c. Mother and child ..	35	45
605.	5 c. St. Nicholas, Holland	35	45
606.	25 c. Lussibruden, Sweden	65	70
607.	25 c. Mother and child (different)	65	70
608.	25 c. King Wenceslas, Czechoslovakia ..	65	70
609.	30 c. Mother with child on knee	65	70
610.	30 c. Mother carrying child	65	70
611.	$1 Christkindl Angel, Germany	1·25	1·50

140. Robert Koch.

1982. Centenary of Discovery of Tubercle Bacillus by Robert Koch.

612. **140.**	5 c. blk., brn. & lilac ..	30	15
613. –	16 c. blk., brn. & orge...	65	40
614. –	21 c. multicoloured ..	75	45
615. –	$1 multicoloured ..	2·50	4·50

DESIGNS: 16 c. Stylised infected person. 21 c. Early and modern microscopes. $1 Mantoux test.

141. Greater Flamingo (male).

1982. Greater Flamingoes. Multicoloured.

617.	25 c. Type **141**	65	90
618.	25 c. Female	65	90
619.	25 c. Female with nestling	65	90
620.	25 c. Juvenile	65	90
621.	25 c. Immature bird ..	65	90

142. Lady Diana Spencer at Ascot, June 1981.

1982. 21st Birthday of Princess of Wales. Multicoloured

622.	16 c. Bahamas coat of arms	20	10
623.	25 c. Type **142**	35	15
624.	40 c. Bride and Earl Spencer arriving at St. Paul's	50	20
625.	$1 Formal portrait ..	1·00	1·25

1982. Wildlife (2nd series). Mammals. As Type **136**. Multicoloured.

626.	10 c. Buffy flower bat ..	30	15
627.	16 c. Bahaman hutia ..	50	25
628.	21 c. Common racoon ..	65	55
629.	$1 Common dolphin ..	1·90	1·75

143. House of Assembly Plaque.

1982. 28th Commonwealth Parliamentary Association Conference. Multicoloured.

631.	5 c. Type **143**.	15	10
632.	25 c. Association coat of arms	45	35
633.	40 c. Coat of arms ..	70	60
634.	50 c. House of Assembly ..	85	75

INDEX
Countries can be quickly located by referring to the index at the end of this volume.

144. Wesley Methodist Church, Baillou Hill Road.

1982. Christmas. Churches. Multicoloured.

635. 5 c. Type **144** 10 10
636. 12 c. Centreville Seventh Day Adventist Church 20 20
637. 15 c. The Church of God of Prophecy, East Street.. 25 25
638. 21 c. Bethel Baptist Church, Meeting Street 30 30
639. 25 c. St. Francis Xavier Catholic Church, Highbury Park 35 50
640. $1 Holy Cross Anglican Church, Highbury Park 1·50 2·50

145. Prime Minister Lyndon O. Pindling.

1983. Commonwealth Day. Multicoloured.

641. 5 c. Type **145** 10 10
642. 25 c. Bahamian and Commonwealth flags .. 40 40
643. 35 c. Map showing position of Bahamas 50 50
644. $1 Ocean liner .. .. 1·40 1·40

1983. Nos. 562/5 surch.

645. 20 c. on 15 c. Slave, Trading Vendue House 50 35
646. 31 c. on 21 c. Bootlegging, 1919-29 .. .. 60 55
647. 35 c. on 16 c. Wrecking in the 1800's 70 60
648. 80 c. on 18 c. Blockade running (American Civil War) 1·50 1·40

147. Customs Officers and Liner.

1983. 30th Anniv. of Customs Co-operation Council. Multicoloured.

649. 31 c. Type **147** .. .. 1·50 45
650. $1 Customs officers and airliner .. .. .. 3·00 2·00

148. Raising the National Flag. **149.** " Loyalist Dreams ".

1983. 10th Anniv. of Independence.

651. **148.** $1 multicoloured .. 1·25 1·40

1983. Wildlife (3rd series). Butterflies. As T **136**.

653. 5 c. multicoloured .. 40 10
654. 25 c. multicoloured .. 85 40
655. 31 c. black, yellow & red.. 95 45
656. 50 c. multicoloured .. 1·25 70

DESIGNS: 5 c. "Atalopedes carteri". 25 c. "Ascia monuste". 31 c. "Phoebis agarithe". 50 c. "Dryas julia".

1983. Bicentenary of Arrival of American Loyalists in the Bahamas. Multicoloured.

658. 5 c. Type **149** 10 10
659. 31 c. New Plymouth, Abaco (horiz.) 45 50
660. 35 c. New Plymouth Hotel (horiz.) 50 70
661. 50 c. " Island Hope " .. 65 90

150. Consolidated " Catalina ".

1983. Air. Bicentenary of Manned Flight. Multicoloured.

663. 10 c. Type **150** 15 15
664. 25 c. Avro " Tudor IV " .. 35 30
665. 31 c. Avro " Lancastrian " 40 45
666. 35 c. Consolidated " Commodore " 45 50

For these stamps without the Manned Flight logo, see Nos. 699/702.

151. " Christmas Bells " (Monica Pinder). **152.** 1861 4d. Stamp.

1983. Christmas. Children's Paintings. Multicoloured.

667. 5 c. Type **151** 10 10
668. 20 c. " Flamingo " (Cory Bullard) 25 30
669. 25 c. " Yellow Hibiscus with Christmas Candle " (Monique Bailey) .. 35 40
670. 31 c. " Santa goes a-sailing " (Sabrina Seiler) (horiz.) 40 45
671. 35 c. " Silhouette scene with Palm Trees " (James Blake) 45 50
672. 50 c. " Silhouette scene with Pelicans " (Erik Russell) (horiz.) 65 70

1984. 125th Anniv. of First Bahamas Postage Stamp. Multicoloured.

673. 5 c. Type **152** 25 10
674. $1 1859 1d. stamp .. 1·75 1·50

153. "Trent I" (paddle-steamer).

1984. 250th Anniv of "Lloyd's List" (newspaper). Multicoloured.

675 5 c. Type **153** 15 10
676 31 c. "Orinoco II" (mail ship), 1886 .. .. 65 60
677 35 c. Cruise liners in Nassau harbour .. 75 75
678 50 c. "Oropesa" (container ship) .. .. .. 1·10 1·25

154. Running.

1984. Olympic Games, Los Angeles.

679. **154.** 5 c. green, black and gold 10 10
680. – 25 c. blue, black and gold 45 50
681. – 31 c. red, black and gold 55 60
682. – $1 brown, black and gold 1·75 2·25

DESIGNS: 25 c. Shot-putting. 31 c. Boxing. $1 Basketball.

155. Bahamas and Caribbean Community Flags.

1984. 5th Conference of Caribbean Community Heads of Government.

684. **155.** 50 c. multicoloured .. 90 95

156. Bahama Woodstar.

1984. 25th Anniv. of National Trust. Mult.

685 31 c. Type **156** .. .. 1·50 1·60
686 31 c. Belted kingfishers, greater flamingos and "Eleutherodactylus planirostris" (frog) .. 1·50 1·60
687 31 c. Black-necked stilts, greater flamingos and "Phoebis sennae" (butterfly) .. .. 1·50 1·60
688 31 c. "Urbanus proteus" (butterfly) and "Chelonia mydas" (turtle) .. .. .. 1·50 1·60
689 31 c. Osprey and greater flamingos .. .. 1·50 1·60

Nos. 685/9 were printed together in horizontal strips of 5 forming a composite design.

1984. Wildlife (4th series). Reptiles and Amphibians. As T **136**.

690. 5 c. Allens' Cay Iguana .. 25 10
691. 25 c. Curly-tailed Lizard .. 75 50
692. 35 c. Greenhouse Frog .. 90 65
693. 50 c. Atlantic Green Turtle.. 1·40 95

157. "The Holy Virgin with Jesus and Johannes" (19th-century porcelain plaque after Titian)

1984. Christmas. Religious Paintings. Multicoloured.

695. 5 c. Type **157** 10 10
696. 31 c. "Madonna with Child in Tropical Landscape" (aquarelle, Anais Colin) 55 60
697. 35 c. The Holy Virgin with the "Child" (miniature on ivory, Elena Caula) .. 60 65

1985. Air. As Nos. 663/6, but without Manned Flight Logo.

699 10 c. Type **150** .. 25 20
700 25 c. Avro "Tudor IV" .. 45 40
701 31 c. Avro "Lancastrian" 45 45
702 35 c. Consolidated "Commodore" 65 45

158. Brownie Emblem and Conch.

1985. International Youth Year. 75th Anniv. of Girl Guide Movement. Multicoloured.

703. 5 c. Type **158**. 20 15
704. 25 c. Tents and coconut palm 75 60
705. 31 c. Guide salute and greater flamingos .. 1·00 60
706. 35 c. Ranger emblem and marlin .. .. .. 1·10 80

159. Killdeer.

1985. Birth Bicentenary of John J. Audubon (ornithologist). Multicoloured.

708. 5 c. Type **159** 50 10
709. 31 c. Mourning Dove (vert.) .. .. .. 1·25 55
710. 35 c. "Mourning Dove" (John J. Audubon) (vert.) .. .. .. 1·40 60
711. $1 "Killdeer" (John J. Audubon) .. .. 2·00 1·60

160. The Queen Mother at Christening of Peter Phillips, 1977.

1985. Life and Times of Queen Elizabeth the Queen Mother. Multicoloured.

712. 5 c. Visiting Auckland, New Zealand, 1927 .. 10 10
713. 25 c. Type **160** 40 40
714. 35 c. The Queen Mother attending church .. 55 55
715. 50 c. With Prince Henry at his christening (from photo by Lord Snowdon) 75 75

161. Ears of Wheat and Emblems.

1985. 40th Anniv. of U.N.O. and F.A.O.

717. **161.** 25 c. multicoloured .. 60 50

162. Queen Elizabeth II.

1985. Commonwealth Heads of Government Meeting, Nassau. Multicoloured.
718. 31 c. Type **162** .. .. 1·50 1·40
719. 35 c. Bahamas Prime Minister's flag and Commonwealth emblem 1·75 1·60

163. "Grandma's Christmas Bouquet" (Alton Roland Lowe)

1985. Christmas. Paintings by Alton Roland Lowe. Multicoloured.
736. 5 c. Type **163** 20 10
737. 25 c. "Junkanoo Romeo and Juliet" (vert.) .. 75 65
738. 31 c. "Bunce Gal" (vert.) 95 90
739. 35 c. "Home for Christmas" .. .. 1·25 1·10

1986. 60th Birthday of Queen Elizabeth II. As T **110** of Ascension. Multicoloured.
741. 10 c. Princess Elizabeth, aged one, 1927 .. .. 15 20
742. 25 c. The Coronation, 1953 35 40
743. 35 c. Queen making speech at Commonwealth Banquet, Bahamas, 1985 50 55
744. 40 c. In Djakova, Yugoslavia, 1972 .. 55 60
745. $1 At Crown Agents Head Office, London, 1983 .. 1·40 1·50

164. 1980 1 c. and 18 c. Definitive Stamps.

1986. "Ameripex '86" International Stamp Exhibition, Chicago.
746. **164.** 5 c. multicoloured .. 20 15
747. – 25 c. multicoloured .. 60 50
748. – 31 c. multicoloured .. 70 60
749. – 50 c. multicoloured .. 1·00 1·00
750. – $1 blk., grn. & bl. .. 1·75 2·25

DESIGNS:—HORIZ. (showing Bahamas stamps)—25 c. 1969 50th Anniversary of Bahamas Airmail Service pair. 31 c. 1976 Bicentenary of American Revolution 16 c., 50 c. 1981 Space Exploration miniature sheet. VERT—$1 Statue of Liberty. No. 750 also commemorates the Centenary of the Statue of Liberty.

1986. Royal Wedding. As T **112** of Ascension. Multicoloured.
756. 10 c. Prince Andrew and Miss Sarah Ferguson .. 20 20
757. $1 Prince Andrew .. .. 1·60 1·90

165. Rock Beauty (juvenile).

1986. Fishes. Multicoloured.
791 5 c. Type **165** 20 40
759 10 c. Stoplight Parrotfish 40 30
793 15 c. Jackknife Fish .. 45 45
761 20 c. Flamefish .. 70 60
762 25 c. Swissguard Basslet .. 90 65
763 30 c. Spotfin Butterflyfish 70 65
764 35 c. Queen Triggerfish .. 75 65
765 40 c. Four-eyed Butterflyfish 80 80
766 45 c. Fairy Basslet .. 85 85
767 50 c. Queen Angelfish .. 90 90
797 60 c. Blue Chromis .. 1·40 1·75
769 $1 Spanish Hogfish .. 2·00 2·00
799 $2 Harlequin Bass .. 2·50 4·00
771 $3 Blackbar Soldier Fish .. 4·50 5·00
772 $5 Pygmy Angelfish .. 6·00 7·00
773 $10 Red Hind .. .. 12·00 15·00

166. Christ Church Cathedral, Nassau, 1861.

1986. 125th Annivs. of City of Nassau, Diocese and Cathedral. Multicoloured.
774. 10 c. Type **166** 15 20
775. 40 c. Christ Church Cathedral, 1986 .. .. 55 60

167. Man and Boy looking at Crib.

1986. Christmas. International Peace Year. Multicoloured.
777. 10 c. Type **167** 15 20
778. 40 c. Mary and Joseph journeying to Bethlehem 55 65
779. 45 c. Children praying and Star of Bethlehem .. 65 85
780. 50 c. Children exchanging gifts .. .. .. 70 1·10

168. Great Isaac Lighthouse.

1987. Lighthouses. Multicoloured.
782. 10 c. Type **168** 75 30
783. 40 c. Bird Rock lighthouse 2·25 1·25
784. 45 c. Castle Island lighthouse .. .. 2·25 1·25
785. $1 "Hole in the Wall" lighthouse .. .. 3·25 4·50

169. Anne Bonney.

1987. Pirates and Privateers of the Caribbean. Multicoloured.
786. 10 c. Type **169** 65 30
787. 40 c. Edward Teach ("Blackbeard") .. .. 2·00 1·25
788. 45 c. Captain Edward England .. .. 2·00 1·25
789. 50 c. Captain Woodes Rogers .. .. 2·00 1·50

170. Bahamasair Boeing "737".

1987. Air. Aircraft. Multicoloured.
800 15 c. Type **170** 40 40
801 40 c. Eastern airlines Boeing "757" 90 90
802 45 c. Pan Am Airbus "A300" .. .. .. 1·00 1·00
803 50 c. British Airways Boeing "747" .. .. 1·25 1·25

171. "Norway" (liner) and Catamaran.

1987. Tourist Transport. Multicoloured.
804. 40 c. Type **171** 85 85
805. 40 c. Liners and speedboat 85 85
806. 40 c. Game fishing boat and cruising yacht .. 85 85
807. 40 c. Game fishing boat and racing yachts .. 85 85
808. 40 c. Fishing boat and schooner 85 85
809. 40 c. Bahamasair airliner 85 85
810. 40 c. Bahamasair and Pan Am Boeing airliners .. 85 85
811. 40 c. Light aircraft and radio beacon 85 85
812. 40 c. Aircraft and Nassau control tower 85 85
813. 40 c. Helicopter and parked aircraft 85 85

Nos. 804/8 and 809/13 were each printed together, se-tenant, forming a composite design.

172. "Cattleyopsis lindenii".

1987. Christmas. Orchids. Multicoloured.
814. 10 c. Type **172** 40 10
815. 40 c. "Encyclia lucayana" 1·10 70
816. 45 c. "Encyclia hodgeana" 1·25 80
817. 50 c. "Encyclia lleidae" .. 1·50 90

173. King Ferdinand and Queen Isabella of Spain.

1988. 500th Anniv. (1992) of Discovery of America by Columbus (1st issue). Mult.
819. 10 c. Type **173** 40 20
820. 40 c. Columbus before Talavera Committee .. 1·25 85
821. 45 c. Lucayan village .. 1·40 95
822. 50 c. Lucayan potters .. 1·50 1·40

See also Nos. 844/7, 870/3, 908/11 and 933/6.

174 Whistling Ducks in Flight

1988. Black-billed Whistling Duck. Mult.
824 5 c. Type **174** 55 25
825 10 c. Whistling duck in reeds 75 25
826 20 c. Pair with brood .. 1·40 65
827 45 c. Pair wading .. 2·25 1·50

175 Grantstown Cabin, c. 1820

1988. 150th Anniv of Abolition of Slavery. Multicoloured.
828 10 c. Type **175** 15 15
829 40 c. Basket-making, Grantstown 50 55

176 Olympic Flame, High Jumping, Hammer throwing, Basketball and Gymnastics

1988. Olympic Games, Seoul. Designs taken from painting by James Martin. Mult.
830 10 c. Type **176** 15 15
831 40 c. Athletics, archery, swimming, long jumping, weightlifting and boxing .. 50 55
832 45 c. Javelin throwing, gymnastics, hurdling and shot put .. 55 60
833 $1 Athletics, hurdling, gymnastics and cycling 1·25 1·40

1988. 300th Anniv of Lloyd's of London. As T **123** of Ascension. Multicoloured.
835 10 c. "Lloyd's List" of 1740 20 15
836 40 c. Freeport Harbour (horiz) 60 55
837 45 c. Space shuttle over Bahamas (horiz) .. 65 60
838 $1 "Yarmouth Castle" (freighter) on fire .. 1·40 1·40

177 "Oh Little Town of Bethlehem"

1988. Christmas. Carols. Multicoloured.
839 10 c. Type **177** 15 15
840 40 c. "Little Donkey" .. 50 55
841 45 c. "Silent Night" .. 55 60
842 50 c. "Hark the Herald Angels Sing" .. 60 65

1989. 500th Anniv (1992) of Discovery of America by Columbus (2nd issue). As T **173**. Multicoloured.
844 10 c. Columbus drawing chart 35 20
845 40 c. Types of caravel .. 1·25 85
846 45 c. Early navigational instruments .. .. 1·40 90
847 50 c. Arawak artefacts .. 1·50 1·10

178 Cuban Emerald

1989. Hummingbirds. Multicoloured.

849 10 c. Type **178** 40 20
850 40 c. Ruby-throated hummingbird .. 1·00 1·10
851 45 c. Bahama woodstar .. 1·10 1·25
852 50 c. Rufous hummingbird 1·25 1·50

179 Teaching Water Safety

1989. 125th Anniv of International Red Cross. Multicoloured.

853 10 c. Type **179** 30 20
854 $1 Henri Dunant (founder) and Battle of Solferino 2·00 2·10

1989. 20th Anniv of First Manned Landing on Moon. As T **126** of Ascension. Multicoloured.

855 10 c. "Apollo 8" Communications Station, Grand Bahama 15 20
856 40 c. Crew of "Apollo 8" (30 × 30 mm) 50 55
857 45 c. "Apollo 8" emblem (30 × 30 mm) 55 60
858 $1 The Earth seen from "Apollo 8" .. .. 1·25 1·40

180 Church of the Nativity, Bethlehem

1989. Christmas. Churches of the Holy Land. Multicoloured.

860 10 c. Type **180** 25 20
861 40 c. Basilica of the Annunciation, Nazareth 65 55
862 45 c. Tabgha Church, Galilee 70 60
863 $1 Church of the Holy Sepulchre, Jerusalem .. 1·50 1·60

181 1974 U.P.U. Centenary 13 c. Stamp and Globe

1989. "World Stamp Expo '89" International Stamp Exhibition, Washington. Multicoloured.

865 10 c. Type **181** 30 20
866 40 c. 1970 New U.P.U. Headquarters Building 3 c. and building .. 90 65
867 45 c. 1986 "Ameripex '86" $1 and Capitol, Washington 95 80
868 $1 1949 75th anniversary of U.P.U. 2½d. and Bahamasair airliner .. 2·50 2·75

1990. 500th Anniv (1992) of Discovery of America by Columbus (3rd issue). As T **173**. Multicoloured.

870 10 c. Launching caravel .. 40 20
871 40 c. Provisioning ship .. 1·25 1·00
872 45 c. Shortening sail .. 1·40 1·10
873 50 c. Lucayan fishermen .. 1·50 1·25

182 Bahamas Flag, O.A.S. Headquarters and Centenary Logo

1990. Centenary of Organization of American States.

875 **182** 40 c. multicoloured .. 90 90

184 Teacher with Boy

1990. International Literacy Year. Mult.

877 10 c. Type **184** 30 20
878 40 c. Three boys in class .. 90 1·00
879 50 c. Teacher and children with books .. .. 1·00 1·25

1990. 90th Birthday of Queen Elizabeth the Queen Mother. As T **134** of Ascension.

880 40 c. multicoloured .. 50 50
881 $1.50 black and ochre .. 2·00 2·00

DESIGNS—21 × 36 mm. 40 c. "Queen Elizabeth 1938" (Sir Gerald Kelly). 29 × 37 mm. $1.50, Queen Elizabeth at garden party, France, 1938.

185 Cuban Amazon preening

1990. Cuban Amazon (Bahamian Parrot). Multicoloured.

882 10 c. Type **185** 30 20
883 40 c. Pair in flight .. 80 70
884 45 c. Cuban amazon's head 90 80
885 50 c. Perched on branch .. 1·10 1·25

186 The Annunciation

1990. Christmas. Multicoloured.

887 10 c. Type **186** 20 15
888 40 c. The Nativity .. 55 55
889 45 c. Angel appearing to Shepherds 65 65
890 $1 The three Kings .. 1·60 1·75

187 Green Heron

1991. Birds. Multicoloured.

892 5 c. Type **187** 10 10
975 10 c. Turkey vulture .. 15 20
894 15 c. Osprey 20 25
895 20 c. Clapper rail 25 30
978 25 c. Royal tern 30 35
979 30 c. Key West quail dove 40 45
898 40 c. Smooth-billed ani .. 50 55
899 45 c. Burrowing owl .. 60 65
900 50 c. Hairy woodpecker .. 85 85
901 55 c. Mangrove cuckoo .. 70 75
902 60 c. Bahama mockingbird 80 85
903 70 c. Red-winged blackbird 90 95
904 $1 Thick-billed vireo .. 1·25 1·40
905 $2 Bahama yellowthroat 2·50 2·75
988 $5 Stripe-headed tanager 6·50 6·75
907 $10 Greater Antillean bullfinch .. .. 13·00 13·50

1991. 500th Anniv (1992) of Discovery of America by Columbus (4th issue). As T **173**. Multicoloured.

908 15 c. Columbus navigating by stars 40 25
909 40 c. Fleet in mid-Atlantic 90 1·00
910 55 c. Lucayan family worshipping at night .. 1·10 1·40
911 60 c. Map of First Voyage 1·50 1·75

1991. 65th Birthday of Queen Elizabeth II and 70th Birthday of Prince Philip. As T **139** of Ascension. Multicoloured.

913 15 c. Prince Philip .. 75 75
914 $1 Queen Elizabeth II .. 1·50 1·50

188 Radar Plot of Hurricane Hugo

1991. International Decade for Natural Disaster Reduction. Multicoloured.

915 15 c. Type **188** 30 20
916 40 c. Diagram of hurricane 70 70
917 55 c. Flooding caused by Hurricane David, 1979 90 1·00
918 60 c. U.S. Dept of Commerce weather reconnaissance Lockheed WP-3D Orion .. .. 1·40 1·50

189 The Annunciation

1991. Christmas. Multicoloured.

919 15 c. Type **189** 30 20
920 55 c. Mary and Joseph travelling to Bethlehem 85 85
921 60 c. Angel appearing to the shepherds 90 90
922 $1 Adoration of the kings 1·75 2·00

190 First Progressive Liberal Party Cabinet

1992. 25th Anniv of Majority Rule. Mult.

924 15 c. Type **190** 30 20
925 40 c. Signing of Independence Constitution .. 70 70
926 55 c. Prince of Wales handing over Constitutional Instrument (vert) 90 90
927 60 c. First Bahamian Governor-General, Sir Milo Butler (vert) .. 1·25 1·40

1992. 40th Anniv of Queen Elizabeth II's Accession. As T **143** of Ascension. Mult.

928 15 c. Queen Elizabeth with bouquet 30 20
929 40 c. Queen Elizabeth with flags 70 70
930 55 c. Queen Elizabeth at display 90 90
931 60 c. Three portraits of Queen Elizabeth .. 1·00 1·00
932 $1 Queen Elizabeth II .. 1·50 1·75

1992. 500th Anniv of Discovery of America by Columbus (5th issue). As T **173**. Mult.

933 15 c. Lucayans sighting fleet 30 20
934 40 c. "Santa Maria" and dolphins 70 70
935 55 c. Lucayan canoes approaching ships .. 90 90
936 60 c. Columbus giving thanks for landfall .. 1·25 1·40

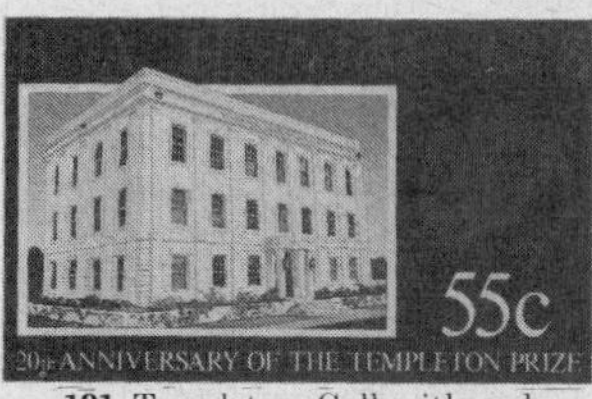

191 Templeton, Galbraith and Hansberger Ltd Building

1992. 20th Anniv of Templeton Prize for Religion.

938 **191** 55 c. multicoloured .. 90 90

192 Pole Vaulting

1992. Olympic Games, Barcelona. Mult.

939 15 c. Type **192** 30 20
940 40 c. Javelin 70 70
941 55 c. Hurdling 90 90
942 60 c. Basketball .. .. 1·25 1·40

193 Arid Landscape and Starving Child

1992. International Conference on Nutrition, Rome. Multicoloured.

944 15 c. Type **193** 30 25
945 55 c. Seedling, cornfield and child .. .. 95 1·00

194 Mary visiting Elizabeth

1992. Christmas. Multicoloured.

No.	Description	Unused	Used
947	15 c. Type **194**	25	20
948	55 c. The Nativity ..	90	90
949	60 c. Angel and shepherds	1·00	1·00
950	70 c. Wise Men and star ..	1·25	1·40

196 Flags of Bahamas and U.S.A. with Agricultural Worker

1993. 50th Anniv of The Contract (U.S.A.–Bahamas farm labour programme). Each including national flags. Multicoloured.

No.	Description	Unused	Used
953	15 c. Type **196**	30	25
954	55 c. Onions	1·10	1·10
955	60 c. Citrus fruit	1·10	1·10
956	70 c. Apples	1·25	1·25

1993. 75th Anniv of Royal Air Force. As T **149** of Ascension. Multicoloured.

No.	Description	Unused	Used
957	15 c. Westland Wapiti ..	30	25
958	40 c. Gloster Gladiator ..	75	75
959	55 c. DeHavilland Vampire	1·00	1·00
960	70 c. English Electric Lightning	1·25	1·25

197 1978 Coronation Anniversary Stamps

1993. 40th Anniv of Coronation. Mult.

No.	Description	Unused	Used
962	15 c. Type **197**	20	20
963	55 c. Two examples of 1953 Coronation stamp	90	90
964	60 c. 1977 Silver Jubilee 8 c. and 16 c. stamps ..	1·00	1·00
965	70 c. 1977 Silver Jubilee 21 c. and 40 c. stamps ..	1·25	1·25

198 "Lignum vitae" (national tree)

1993. 20th Anniv of Independence. Mult.

No.	Description	Unused	Used
966	15 c. Type **198**	20	20
967	55 c. Yellow elder (national flower)	90	90
968	60 c. Blue marlin (national fish)	1·00	1·00
969	70 c. Flamingo (national bird)	1·40	1·40

199 Cordia

1993. Environment Protection. Wildflowers. Multicoloured.

No.	Description	Unused	Used
970	15 c. Type **199**	20	25
971	55 c. Seaside morning glory	90	90
972	60 c. Poinciana	1·00	1·00
973	70 c. Spider lily	1·25	1·25

200 The Annunciation

1993. Christmas. Multicoloured.

No.	Description	Unused	Used
990	15 c. Type **200**	20	25
991	55 c. Angel and shepherds	90	90
992	60 c. Holy Family ..	1·00	1·00
993	70 c. Three Kings ..	1·25	1·25

201 Family

1994. "Hong Kong '94" International Stamp Exhibition. International Year of the Family. Multicoloured.

No.	Description	Unused	Used
995	15 c. Type **201**	20	25
996	55 c. Children doing homework	65	70
997	60 c. Grandfather and grandson fishing ..	80	85
998	70 c. Grandmother teaching grandchildren the Lord's Prayer ..	90	95

202 Flags of Bahamas and Great Britain

1994. Royal Visit. Multicioloured.

No.	Description	Unused	Used
999	15 c. Type **202**	20	25
1000	55 c. Royal Yacht "Britannia" ..	65	70
1001	60 c. Queen Elizabeth II	80	85
1002	70 c. Queen Elizabeth and Prince Philip ..	90	95

203 Yachts

1994. 40th Anniv of National Family Island Regatta. Multicoloured.

No.	Description	Unused	Used
1003	15 c. Type **203** ..	20	25
1004	55 c. Dinghy racing ..	65	70
1005	60 c. Working boats ..	80	85
1006	70 c. Sailing sloop ..	90	95

SPECIAL DELIVERY STAMPS

1916. Optd **SPECIAL DELIVERY**.

No.	Type	Description	Unused	Used
S2	6	5d. black and orange ..	45	4·00
S3		5d. black and mauve ..	30	1·25

MINIMUM PRICE

The minimum price quoted is 10p which represents a handling charge rather than a basis for valuing common stamps. For further notes about prices see introductory pages.

BAHAWALPUR

A former state of Pakistan, now merged in West Pakistan.

12 pies = 1 anna, 16 annas = 1 rupee.

(1.)

1947. Nos. 265/8, 269a/77 and 259/62 of India optd. with Type **1**.

No.	Type	Description	Unused
1.	**100a.**	3 p. slate..	8·00
2.		½ a. purple	8·00
3.		9 p. green	8·00
4.		1 a. red	8·00
5.	**101.**	1½ a. violet	8·50
6.		2 a. red	8·50
7.		3 a. violet	8·50
8.		3½ a. blue	8·50
9.	**102.**	4 a. brown	9·00
10.		6 a. green	9·00
11.		8 a. violet	9·00
12.		12 a. lake	9·00
13.	–	14 a. purple	40·00
14.	**93.**	1 r. grey and brown ..	18·00
15.		2 r. purple and brown..	£450
16.		5 r. green and blue ..	£475
17.		10 r. purple and red ..	£500

2. Amir Muhammad Bahwal Khan I Abbasi.

1948. Bicentenary Commem.

No.	Type	Description	Unused	Used
18.	**2.**	½ a. black and red ..	30	1·25

4. H.H. the Amir of Bahawalpur.

5. The Tombs of the Amirs.

1948.

No.	Type	Description	Unused	Used
19.	**4.**	3 p. black and blue ..	20	8·50
20.		½ a. black and red ..	20	8·50
21.		9 p. black and green ..	20	8·50
22.		1 a. black and red ..	20	8·50
23.		1½ a. black and violet ..	20	8·50
24.	**5.**	2 a. green and red ..	20	10·00
25.	–	4 a. orange and brown ..	30	11·00
26.	–	6 a. violet and blue ..	30	12·00
27.	–	8 a. red and violet ..	30	12·00
28.	–	12 a. green and red ..	35	13·00
29.	–	1 r. violet and brown ..	6·00	22·00
35.	–	1 r. green and orange ..	30	10·00
30.	–	2 r. green and red ..	16·00	28·00
36.	–	2 r. black and red ..	30	13·00
31.	–	5 r. black and violet ..	20·00	40·00
37.	–	5 r. brown and blue ..	30	22·00
32.	–	10 r. red and black ..	25·00	55·00
38.	–	10 r. brown and green ..	35	27·00

DESIGNS—HORIZ. 2 a. As Type **5**. 6 a. Fort Derawar from the Lake. 8 a. Nur-Mahal Palace. 12 a. Sadiq-Garh Palace. Larger (46 × 32 mm.): 10 r. Three generations of Rulers. VERT. As Type **5**: 4 a. Mosque in Sadiq-Gerh. 1 r., 2 r., 5 r. H.H. the Amir of Bahawalpuf.

12. H.H. the Amir of Bahawalpur and Mohammed Ali Jinnah.

1948. 1st Anniv. of Union with Pakistan.

No.	Type	Description	Unused	Used
33.	**12.**	1½ a. red and green ..	15	1·00

13. Soldiers of 1848 and 1948.

1948. Centenary of Multan Campaign.

No.	Type	Description	Unused	Used
34.	**13.**	1½ a. black and red ..	30	6·00

14. Irrigation.

1949. Silver Jubilee of Accession of H.H. the Amir of Bahawalpur.

No.	Type	Description	Unused	Used
39.	**14.**	3 p. black and blue ..	10	6·00
40.	–	½ a. black and orange ..	10	6·00
41.	–	9 p. black and green ..	10	6·00
42.	–	1 a. black and red ..	10	6·00

DESIGNS: ½ a. Wheat. 9 p. Cotton. 1 a. Sahiwal bull.

17. U.P.U. Monument, Berne.

1949. 75th Anniv. of U.P.U.

No.	Type	Description	Unused	Used
43.	**17.**	9 p. black and green ..	20	2·00
44.		1 a. black and mauve ..	20	2·00
45.		1½ a. black and orange ..	20	2·00
46.		2½ a. black and blue ..	20	2·00

OFFICIAL STAMPS

O 4. Eastern White Pelicans.

1945. As Type **O 4** with Arabic opt.

No.	Type	Description	Unused	Used
O 1.	–	½ a. black and green ..	1·25	5·00
O 2.	–	1 a. black and red ..	1·75	3·50
O 7.	–	1 a. black and brown..	23·00	45·00
O 3.	–	2 a. black and violet ..	2·75	5·00
O 4.	**O 4.**	4 a. black and olive ..	6·50	13·00
O 5.	–	8 a. black and brown..	10·00	7·50
O 6.	–	1 r. black and orange..	10·00	7·50

DESIGNS: ½ a. Panjnad Weir. 1 a. (No. O2), Camel and calf. 1 a. (No. O3), Baggage camels. 2 a. Blackbuck antelopes. 8 a. Juma Masjid Mosque, Fort Derawar. 1 r. Temple at Pattan Munara.

(O 8.)

1945. Types as Nos. O 1, etc., in new colours and without Arabic opt. (a) Surch. as Type **O 8.**

No.	Description	Unused	Used
O 11.	½ a. on 8 a. black and purple (as No. O 5) ..	4·25	2·00
O 12.	1½ a. on 1 r. black and orange (as No. O 6) ..	18·00	5·00
O 13.	1½ a. on 2 r. black and blue (as No. O 1) ..	70·00	6·50

(b) Optd. **SERVICE** and Arabic inscription.

No.	Description	Unused	Used
O 14.	½ a. black and red (as No. O 1)	1·25	7·50
O 15.	1 a. black and red (as No. O 2)	1·75	8·00
O 16.	2 a. black and orange (as No O 3)	3·00	23·00

1945. As Type **4** but inscr. "**SERVICE**" at left.

No.	Description	Unused	Used
O 17.	3 p. black and blue ..	1·00	4·00
O 18.	1½ a. black and violet ..	8·00	4·75

O 11. Allied Banners.

1946. Victory.
O 19. **O 11.** 1½ a. green and grey 1·75 2·00

1948. Stamps of 1948 with Arabic opt. as in Type O 4.
O 20. **4.** 3 p. black and blue .. 20 5·50
O 21. 1 a. black and red .. 20 4·50
O 22. **5.** 2 a. green and red .. 20 6·00
O 23. – 4 a. orange and brown .. 20 8·00
O 24. – 1 r. green and orange .. 20 9·00
O 25. – 2 r. black and red .. 20 11·00
O 26. – 5 r. chocolate and blue 30 19·00
O 27. – 10 r. brown and green .. 30 24·00

1949. 75th Anniv. of U.P.U. Optd. as in Type O 4.
O 28. **17.** 9 p. black and green .. 15 4·50
O 29. 1 a. black and mauve .. 15 4·50
O 30. 1½ a. black and orange .. 15 4·50
O 31. 2½ a. black and blue .. 15 4·50

BAHRAIN

An archipelago in the Persian Gulf on the Arabian coast. An independent shaikhdom with Indian and, later, British postal administration. The latter was closed on 1 January 1966, when the Bahrain Post Office took over.

1933. 12 pies = 1 anna; 16 annas = 1 rupee.
1957. 100 naye paise = 1 rupee.

Stamps of India overprinted **BAHRAIN**.

1933. King George V.
1 **55.** 3 p. grey .. .. 2·00 45
2 **56.** ½ a. green .. .. 6·50 3·25
15 **79.** ½ a. green .. .. 3·00 55
3 **80.** 9 p. green .. .. 3·25 80
4 **57.** 1 a. brown .. .. 5·50 2·50
16 **81.** 1 a. brown .. .. 6·00 40
5 **82.** 1 a. 3 p. mauve .. 3·00 45
6 **70.** 2 a. orange .. .. 8·50 4·50
17 **59.** 2 a. orange .. .. 19·00 7·50
7 **62.** 3 a. blue .. .. 19·00 35·00
18 3 a. red .. .. 4·75 30
8 **83.** 3 a. 6 p. blue .. 3·25 30
9 **71.** 4 a. green .. .. 18·00 35·00
19 **63.** 4 a. olive .. .. 3·00 30
10 **65.** 8 a. mauve .. .. 3·50 25
11 **66.** 12 a. red .. .. 4·75 70
12 **67.** 1 r. brown and green .. 15·00 7·50
13 2 r. red and orange .. 30·00 35·00
14 5 r. blue and violet .. 85·00 £110

1938. King George VI.
20. **91.** 3 p. slate .. .. 4·50 1·00
21. ½ a. brown .. .. 1·25 10
22. 9 p. green .. .. 1·50 60
23. 1 a. red .. .. 1·25 10
24. **92.** 2 a. red .. .. 4·50 50
26. – 3 a. green (No. 253) 42·00 3·75
27. – 3½ a. blue (No. 254) 3·50 2·25
28. – 4 a. brown (No. 255) £110 50·00
30. – 8 a. violet (No. 257) £130 35·00
31. – 12 a. red (No. 258) 90·00 48·00
32. **93.** 1 r. slate and brown 2·50 1·25
33. 2 r. purple and brown .. 15·00 1·75
34. 5 r. green and blue 30·00 13·00
35. 10 r. purple and red 65·00 20·00
36. 15 r. brown and green .. 42·00 42·00
37 25 r. slate and purple .. 95·00 70·00

1942. King George VI.
38. **100a** 3 p. slate 30 30
39. ½ a. mauve .. .. 2·00 70
40. 9 p. green .. .. 6·50 7·00
41. 1 a. red .. .. 2·75 20
42. **101.** 1 a. 3 p. bistre .. 6·00 8·50
43. 1½ a. violet .. .. 4·75 2·00
44. 2 a. red .. .. 2·00 1·25
45. 3 a. violet .. .. 8·50 3·00
46. 3½ a. blue .. .. 3·00 9·00
47. **102.** 4 a. brown .. .. 1·25 60
48. 6 a. green .. .. 7·00 5·50
49. 8 a. violet .. .. 1·25 75
50. 12 a. purple .. .. 2·25 1·75

Stamps of Great Britain surcharged **BAHRAIN** and new value in Indian currency.

1948. King George VI.
51. **128.** ½ a. on ½d. pale green .. 40 30
71. ½ a. on ½d. orange .. 30 30
52. 1 a. on 1d. pale red .. 40 45
72. 1 a. on 1d. blue .. 70 10
53. 1½ a. on 1½d. pale brown 40 50
73. 1½ a. on 1½d. green .. 70 6·50
54. 2 a. on 2d. pale orange 40 20
74. 2 a. on 2d. brown .. 40 30
55. 2½ a. on 2½d. light blue 50 1·10
75. 2½ a. on 2½d. red .. 70 6·50
56. 3 a. on 3d. pale violet .. 40 10
76. **129.** 4 a. on 4d. blue .. 50 1·25
57. 6 a. on 6d. purple .. 40 10
58. **130.** 1 r. on 1s. brown .. 1·25 10
59. **131.** 2 r. on 2s. 6d. green .. 5·00 4·00
60. 5 r. on 5s. red .. 5·50 4·50
60a. – 10 r. on 10s. bright blue (No. 478a) .. .. 60·00 40·00

1948. Silver Wedding.
61. **137.** 2½ a. on 2½d. blue .. 30 30
62. **138.** 15 r. on £1 blue .. 40·00 45·00

1948. Olympic Games.
63. **139.** 2½ a. on 2½d. blue .. 55 55
64. **140.** 3 a. on 3d. violet .. 55 1·00
65. – 6 a. on 6d. purple .. 1·50 1·75
66. – 1 r. on 1s. brown .. 1·50 2·25

1949. U.P.U.
67. **143.** 2½ a. on 2½d. blue .. 40 1·50
68. **144.** 3 a. on 3d. violet .. 75 2·00
69. – 6 a. on 6d. purple .. 75 2·25
70. – 1 r. on 1s. brown .. 1·40 1·50

1951. Pictorial stamps (Nos. 509/11).
77. **147.** 2 r. on 2s. 6d. green .. 18·00 4·25
78. – 5 r. on 5s. red .. 13·00 3·50
79. – 10 r. on 10s. blue .. 25·00 6·50

1952. Queen Elizabeth II.
80 **154** ½ a. on ½d. orange .. 10 10
81 1 a. on 1d. blue .. 10 10
82 1½ a. on 1½d. green .. 10 10
83 2 a. on 2d. brown .. 20 10
84 **155** 2½ a. on 2½d. red .. 20 30
85 3 a. on 3d. lilac .. 30 10
86 4 a. on 4d. blue .. 6·50 20
99 **157** 6 a. on 6d. purple .. 50 50
88 **160** 12 a. on 1s. 3d. green .. 3·00 20
89 1 r. on 1s. 6d. blue .. 3·00 10

1953. Coronation.
90. **161.** 2½ a. on 2½d. red .. 1·25 75
91. – 4 a. on 4d. blue .. 2·25 1·50
92. **163.** 12 a. on 1s. 3d. green .. 3·25 1·50
93. – 1 r. on 1s. 6d. blue .. 7·50 50

1955. Pictorial stamps (Nos. 595a/598a).
94 **166** 2 r. on 2s. 6d. brown .. 5·50 1·25
95 – 5 r. on 5s. red .. 11·00 2·75
96 – 10 r. on 10s. blue .. 20·00 2·75

1957. Queen Elizabeth II.
102. **157.** 1 n.p. on 5d. brown .. 10 10
103. **154.** 3 n.p. on ½d. orange .. 30 55
104. 6 n.p. on 1d. blue .. 30 55
105. 9 n.p. on 1½d. green .. 30 40
106. 12 n.p. on 2d. pale brn. 30 30
107. **155.** 15 n.p. on 2½d. red .. 30 15
108. 20 n.p. on 3d. lilac .. 30 10
109. 25 n.p. on 4d. blue .. 75 90
110. **157.** 40 n.p. on 6d. purple 40 10
111. 50 n.p. on 9d. olive .. 3·50 4·00
112. 75 n.p. on 1s. 3d. green 2·25 50

1957. World Scout Jubilee Jamboree.
113. **170.** 15 n.p. on 2½d. red .. 25 35
114. **171.** 25 n.p. on 4d. blue .. 30 35
115. – 75 n.p. on 1s. 3d. green 40 45

16. Shaikh Sulman bin Hamed al-Khalifa.

1960.
117. **16.** 5 n.p. blue 10 10
118. 15 n.p. orange 10 10
119. 20 n.p. violet 10 10
120. 30 n.p. bistre 10 10
121. 40 n.p. grey 15 10
122. 50 n.p. green 15 10
123. 75 n.p. brown 25 15
124. – 1 r. black .. .. 1·00 20
125. – 2 r. red .. .. 2·75 60
126. – 5 r. blue .. .. 4·50 1·75
127. – 10 r. green .. .. 11·00 2·50

The rupee values are larger (27×32½ mm.)

18. Shaikh Isa bin Sulman al-Khalifa.

19. Air Terminal Muharraq.

1964.
128. **18.** 5 n.p. blue 10 10
129. 15 n.p. orange 10 10
130. 20 n.p. violet 10 10
131. 30 n.p. bistre 10 10
132. 40 n.p. slate 15 10
133. 50 n.p. green 15 10
134. 75 n.p. brown 25 10
135. **19.** 1 r. black .. .. 1·25 40
136. 2 r. red .. .. 7·00 40
137. – 5 r. blue .. .. 8·50 6·00
138. – 10 r. myrtle .. .. 12·00 6·00

DESIGNS—As Type **19**: 5 r., 10 r. Deep water harbour.

For later issues see Volume 1.

INDEX

Countries can be quickly located by referring to the index at the end of this volume.

BAMRA

A state in India. Now uses Indian stamps.

12 pies = 1 anna; 16 annas = 1 rupee.

BAMRA
postage

1.

8.

1888.
1. **1.** ¼ a. black on yellow .. £160
2. ½ a. black on red .. .. 70·00
3. 1 a. black on blue .. 42·00
4. 2 a. black on green .. 65·00 £160
5. 4 a. black on yellow .. 48·00 £160
6. 8 a. black on red .. .. 38·00

1890. Imperf.
27 **8.** ¼ a. black on red 70 85
11 ½ a. black on green .. 1·10 1·25
13 1 a. black on yellow .. 1·90 1·25
16 2 a. black on red .. .. 1·60 2·00
19 4 a. black on red .. .. 4·00 2·50
22 8 a. black on red .. .. 7·50 8·50
25 1 r. black on red .. .. 15·00 18·00

BANGLADESH

Formerly the Eastern wing of Pakistan. Following a landslide victory in the Pakistan General Election in December 1970 by the Awami League party, the National Assembly was suspended. Unrest spread throughout the eastern province culminating in the intervention of India on the side of the East Bengalis. The new state became effective after the surrender of the Pakistan army in December 1971.

1971. 100 paisa = 1 rupee.
1972. 100 paisa = 1 taka.

1. Map of Bangladesh.

3. "Martyrdom".

1971.
1. **1.** 10 p. indigo, orange & blue 10 10
2. – 20 p. multicoloured .. 10 10
3. – 50 p. multicoloured .. 10 10
4. – 1 r. multicoloured 10 10
5. – 2 r. turquoise, blue and red 25 35
6 – 3 r. light-green, grn. & blue 30 45
7. – 5 r. multicoloured 50 75
8. – 10 r. gold, red and blue .. 1·00 1·75

DESIGNS: 20 p. "Dacca University Massacre". 50 p. "75 Million People". 1 r. Flag of Independence. 2 r. Ballot box. 3 r. Broken chain. 5 r. Shaikh Majibur Rahman. 10 r. "Support Bangla Desh" and map.

1971. Liberation. Nos. 1 and 7/8 optd. **BANGLADESH LIBERATED.**
9. 10 p. indigo, orge. and blue 10 10
10. 5 r. multicoloured .. 1·50 1·50
11. 10 r. gold, red and blue .. 2·00 2·25

The remaining values of the original issue were also overprinted and placed on sale in Great Britain but were not issued in Bangladesh.

On the 1 February 1972 the Agency placed on sale a further issue in the flag, map and Sheikh Mujib designs in new colours and new currency (100 paisa = 1 taka). This issue proved to be unacceptable to the Bangladesh authorities who declared them to be invalid for postal purposes, no supplies being sold within Bangladesh. The values comprise 1, 2, 3, 5, 7, 10, 15, 20, 25, 40, 50, 75 p., 1, 2 and 5 t.

1972. In Memory of the Martyrs.
12. **3.** 20p. green and red .. 30 30

4. Flames of Independence.

1972. 1st Anniv. of Independence.
13. **4.** 20p. lake and red .. 15 10
14. 60p. blue and red .. 20 25
15. 75p. violet and red .. 25 40

5. Doves of Peace.

1972. Victory Day.
16. **5.** 20 p. multicoloured .. 15 10
17. 60 p. multicoloured .. 20 30
18. 75 p. multicoloured .. 20 30

6. "Homage to Martyrs".

7. Embroidered Quilt.

8. Court of Justice.

1973. In Memory of the Martyrs.
19. **6.** 20 p. multicoloured .. 15 10
20. 60 p. multicoloured .. 30 35
21. 1 t. 35 multicoloured .. 65 1·25

1973.
22. **7.** 2 p. black 10 30
23. – 3 p. green 20 30
24. – 5 p. brown 20 10
25. – 10 p. black 20 10
26. – 20 p. green 50 10
27. – 25 p. mauve .. .. 2·00 10
28. – 50 p. purple .. .. 1·50 20
29. – 60 p. grey 75 30
30. – 75 p. orange 80 30
31. – 90 p. brown 90 40
32. **8.** 1 t. violet .. .. .. 3·50 10
33. – 2 t. green .. .. 4·00 40
34. – 5 t. blue .. .. 4·50 1·25
35. – 10 t. pink .. .. 5·00 2·75

DESIGNS—VERT. As Type **7**. 3 p. Jute field. 5 p. Jack fruit. 10 p. Bullocks ploughing. 20 p. Rakta jaba (flower). 25 p. Tiger. 60 p. Bamboo grove. 75 p. Plucking tea. 90 p. Handicrafts. As Type **8**. 2 t. Date tree. HORIZ. (28×22 mm.). 50 p. Hilsa (fish). As Type **8**. 5 t Fishing boat. 10 t. Sixty-dome mosque, Bagerhat.

See also Nos. 49/51a. and 64 etc.

9. Flame Emblem.

1973. 25th Anniv. of Declaration of Human Rights.
36. **9.** 10 p. multicoloured .. 10 10
37. 1 t. 25 multicoloured .. 20 20

10. Family, Map and Graph.

1974. First Population Census.

38. **10.**	20 p. multicoloured ..	10	10
39.	25 p. multicoloured ..	10	10
40.	75 p. multicoloured ..	20	20

11. Copernicus and Heliocentric System.

1974. 500th Birth Anniv. of Copernicus.

41. **11.**	25 p. orge., viol. & blk.	10	10
42.	75 p. orge., grn. & blk. ..	25	40

12. U.N. H.Q. and Bangladesh Flag.

1974. Bangladesh's Admission to the U.N.

43. **12.**	25 p. multicoloured ..	10	10
44.	1 t. multicoloured ..	35	40

13. U.P.U. Emblem.

1974. Centenary of Universal Postal Union. Multicoloured.

45.	25 p. Type **13**	10	10
46.	1 t. 25 Mail runner	20	15
47.	1 t. 75 Type **13**	25	25
48.	5 t. As 1 t. 25	80	1·40

14. Courts of Justice.

1974. As Nos. 32/5 with revised inscriptions.

49. **14.**	1 t. violet	1·50	10
50. –	2 t. olive	2·00	70
51. –	5 t. blue	3·00	70
51a. –	10 t. pink	8·00	4·00

MORE DETAILED LISTS are given in the Stanley Gibbons Catalogues referred to in the country headings. For lists of current volumes see Introduction.

15. Tiger. **16.** Symbolic Family.

1974. Wildlife Preservation. Multicoloured.

52.	25 p. Type **15**	70	10
53.	50 p. Tiger cub	1·25	60
54.	2 t. Tiger in stream ..	2·75	3·25

1974. World Population Year. "Family Planning for All". Multicoloured.

55.	25p. Type **16**	15	10
56.	70 p. Village family	25	40
57.	1 t. 25 Heads of family (horiz.)	40	85

17. Radar Antenna.

1975. Inauguration of Betbunia Satellite Earth Station.

58. **17.**	25 p. black, silver and red	10	10
59.	1 t. black, silver and blue	20	40

18. Woman's Head.

1975. International Women's Year.

60. **18.**	50 p. multicoloured ..	10	10
61.	2 t. multicoloured ..	25	55

1976. As Nos 24/31 and 49/51a but redrawn in smaller size.

64. –	5 p. green	20	10
65. –	10 p. black	20	10
66. –	20 p. green	70	10
67. –	25 p. mauve	1·50	10
68. –	50 p. purple	1·75	10
69. –	60 p. grey	40	20
70. –	75 p. green	1·25	70
71. –	90 p. brown	40	20
72. **14.**	1 t. violet	2·00	10
73. –	2 t. green	2·75	10
74. –	5 t. blue	2·75	1·25
75. –	10 t. red	5·00	1·25

Nos. 64/71 are 23×18 mm (50p) or 18×23 mm. (others) and Nos 72/75 are 20×32 mm (2 t.) or 32×20 mm. (others).

19. Telephones of 1876 and 1976.

1976. Centenary of Telephone.

76. **19.**	2 t. 25 multicoloured ..	25	20
77. –	5 t. red, green and black	55	65

DESIGN: 5 t. Alexander Graham Bell.

20. Eye and Nutriments.

1976. Prevention of Blindness

78. **20.**	30 p. multicoloured ..	40	10
79.	2 t. 25 multicoloured ..	1·10	1·25

21. Liberty Bell.

1976. Bicent. of American Revolution. Mult.

80.	30 p. Type **21**	10	10
81.	2 t. 25 Statue of Liberty ..	30	25
82.	5 t. "Mayflower"	80	50
83.	10 t. Mount Rushmore ..	80	80

22. Industry, Science, Agriculture and Education.

1976. 25th Anniv. of Colombo Plan.

85. **22.**	30 p. multicoloured ..	15	10
86.	2 t. 25 multicoloured ..	35	35

23. Hurdling.

1976. Olympic Games, Montreal. Mult.

87.	25 p. Type **23**	10	10
88.	30 p. Running (horiz.) ..	10	10
89.	1 t. Pole vaulting	10	10
90.	2 t. 25 Swimming (horiz.) ..	30	30
91	3 t. 50 Gymnastics	60	70
92.	5 t. Football	1·00	1·25

24. The Blessing.

1977. Silver Jubilee. Multicoloured.

93.	30 p. Type **24**	10	10
94.	2 t. 25 Queen Elizabeth II	35	35
95.	10 t. Queen Elizabeth and Prince Philip	1·00	1·00

25. Qazi Nazrul Islam (poet).

1977. Qazi Nazrul Islam. Commemoration.

97. **25.**	40 p. green and black ..	10	10
98. –	2 t. 25 brn., red & light brn.	30	30

DESIGN—HORIZ. 2 t. 25, Head and shoulders portrait.

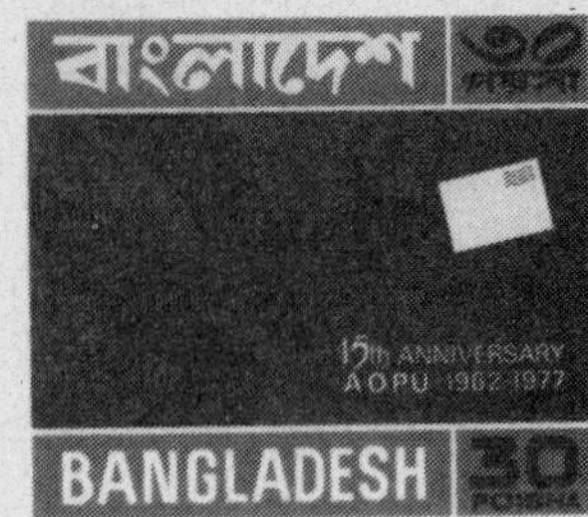

26. Bird with Letter.

1977. 15th Anniv. of Asian-Oceanic Postal Union.

99. **26.**	30 p. red, blue and grey	10	10
100.	2 t. 25 red, blue & grey	20	25

27. Sloth Bear.

1977. Animals. Multicoloured.

101.	40 p. Type **27**	20	10
102.	1 t. Spotted deer	30	10
103.	2 t. 25 Leopard (horiz.) ..	85	20
104.	3 t. 50 Gaur (horiz.) ..	90	35
105.	4 t. Indian elephant (horiz.)	1·75	50
106.	5 t. Tiger (horiz.)	2·00	75

The Bengali numerals on the 40p. resemble "80", and that on the 4 t. resembles "8".

28. Camp Fire and Tent.

1978. First National Scout Jamboree.

107. **28.**	40 p. red, blue & pale blue	30	10
108. –	3 t. 50 lilac, grn. & blue	1·25	30
109. –	5 t. grn., blue & red ..	1·40	45

DESIGNS—HORIZ. 3 t. 50, Scout stretcher-team. VERT. 5 t. Scout salute.

29. "Michelia champaca".

1978. Flowers. Multicoloured.

110.	40 p. Type **29**	30	10
111.	1 t. "Cassia fistula" ..	55	15
112.	2 t. 25 "Dedonix regia"	85	30
113.	3 t. 50 "Nymphaea nouchali"	1·00	60
114.	4 t. "Butea monosperma"	1·10	80
115.	5 t. "Anthocephalus indicus"	1·25	85

30. St. Edward's Crown and Sceptres.

1978. 25th Anniv. of Coronation. Mult.

116. 40 p. Type **30** 10 10
117. 3 t. 50 Balcony scene .. 25 35
118. 5 t. Queen Elizabeth and Prince Philip 40 55
119. 10 t. Coronation portrait by Cecil Beaton .. 80 1·00

31. Sir Alan Cobham's " DH 50 ".

1978. 75th Anniv. of Powered Flight.

121. **31.** 40 p. multicoloured .. 15 10
122. – 2 t. 25 brown and blue .. 50 40
123. – 3 t. 50 brown and yellow 65 60
124. – 5 t. multicoloured .. 4·00 3·00

DESIGNS: 2 t. 25, Captain Hans Bertram's seaplane " Atlantis ". 3 t. 50, Wright brothers' " Flyer I ". 5 t. " Concorde ".

32. Fenchuganj Fertiliser Factory.

33. Tawaf-E-Ka'aba, Mecca.

1978.

125. – 5 p. brown 10 10
126. **32.** 10 p. blue 10 10
127. – 15 p. orange 10 10
128. – 20 p. red 10 10
129. – 25 p. blue 15 10
130. – 30 p. green 75 10
131. – 40 p. purple 30 10
132. – 50 p. black .. .. 1·75 80
134. – 80 p. brown 20 10
136. – 1 t. violet .. .. 2·00 10
137. – 2 t. blue 50 85

DESIGNS–HORIZ. 5 p. Lalbag Fort. 25 p. Jute on a boat. 40 p., 50 p. Baitul Mukarram Mosque. 1 t. Dotara (musical instrument). 2 t. Karnaphuli Dam. VERT. 15 p. pineapple. 20 p. Bangladesh gas. 30 p. Banana Tree. 80 p. Mohastan Garh.

1978. Pilgrimage to Mecca. Multicoloured

140. 40 p. Type **33** 20 10
141. 3 t. Pilgrims in Wuquf, Arafat (horiz.) 60 45

34. Jasim Uddin.

1979. 3rd Death Anniv. of Jasim Uddin (poet).

142. **34.** 40 p. multicoloured .. 20 20

35. Moulana Abdul Hamid Khan Bhashani.

1979. 3rd Death Anniv. of Moulana Abdul Hamid Khan Bhashani (national leader).

143. **35.** 40 p. multicoloured .. 40 20

36. Sir Rowland Hill.

1979. Death Centenary of Sir Rowland Hill.

144. **36.** 40 p. blue, red and pale blue 10 10
145. – 3 t. 50 multicoloured .. 35 30
146. – 10 t. multicoloured .. 80 1·00

DESIGNS: 3 t. 50, Sir Rowland Hill and first Bangladesh stamp. 10 t. Sir Rowland Hill and Bangladesh U.P.U. stamp.

37. Children with Hoops.

1979. International Year of the Child. Mult.

148. 40 p. Type **37** 10 10
149. 3 t. 50 Boy with kite .. 35 35
150. 5 t. Children jumping .. 50 50

38. Rotary International Emblem.

1980. 75th Anniv. of Rotary International.

152. **38.** 40 p. black, red & yellow 20 10
153. – 5 t. gold and blue .. 65 45

DESIGN: 5 t. Rotary emblem (different).

39. Canal Digging.

1980. Mass Participation in Canal Digging.

154. **39.** 40 p. multicoloured .. 40 30

40. A. K. Fazlul Huq.

1980. 18th Death Anniv. of A. K. Fazlul Huq (national leader).

155. **40.** 40 p. multicoloured .. 30 30

41. Early Forms of Mail Transport.

1980. " London 1980 " International Stamp Exhibition. Multicoloured.

156. 1 t. Type **41** 15 10
157. 10 t. Modern forms of mail transport .. .. 1·25 85

42. Dome of the Rock.

1980. Palestinian Warfare.

159. **42.** 50 p. lilac 70 30

43. Outdoor Class.

1980. Education.

160. **43.** 50 p. multicoloured .. 40 30

44. Beach Scene.

1980. World Tourism Conference, Manila. Multicoloured.

161. 50 p. Type **44** 30 30
162. 5 t. Beach scene (different) 60 70

45. Mecca.

1980. Moslem Year 1400 A.H. Commem.

164. **45.** 50 p. multicoloured .. 20 20

46. Begum Roquiah.

1980. Birth Centenary of Begum Roquiah (campaigner for women's rights).

165. **46.** 50 p. multicoloured .. 10 10
166. 2 t. multicoloured .. 35 20

47. Spotted Deer and Scout Emblem.

1981. 5th Asia-Pacific and 2nd Bangladesh Scout Jamboree.

167. **47.** 50 p. multicoloured .. 30 15
168. 5 t. multicoloured .. 1·10 1·10

1981. Second Population Census. Nos. 38/40 optd. **2ND CENSUS 1981.**

169. **10.** 20 p. multicoloured .. 10 10
170. 25 p. multicoloured .. 10 10
171. 75 p. multicoloured .. 20 30

49. Queen Elizabeth the Queen Mother.

1981. 80th Birthday of The Queen Mother.

172. **49.** 1 t. multicoloured .. 15 15
173. 15 t. multicoloured .. 3·00 2·50

50. Revolutionary with Flag and Submachine-gun.

1981. 10th Anniv. Independence. Mult.

175. 50p. Type **50** 15 10
176. 2 t. Figures on map symbolising Bangladesh lifestyle 25 30

51. Bangladesh Village and Farm Scenes.

1981. U.N. Conference on Least Developed Countries, Paris.

177. **51.** 50 p. multicoloured .. 35 15

52. Kemal Ataturk in Civilian Dress.

1981. Birth Centenary of Kemal Ataturk (Turkish statesman).

178. 50 p. Type **52** 40 20
179. 1 t. Kemal Ataturk in uniform 70 40

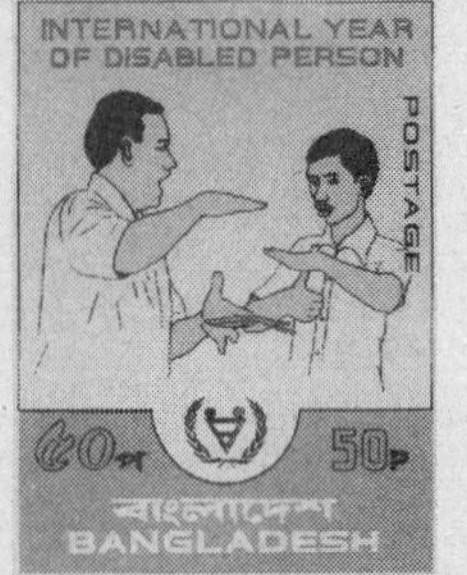

53. Deaf People using Sign Language.

1981. International Year for Disabled Persons. Multicoloured.

180. 50 p. Type **53** 30 15
181. 2 t. Disabled person writing (horiz.) .. .. .. 1·10 75

54. Farm Scene and Wheat Ear.

1981. World Food Day.

182. **54.** 50 p. multicoloured .. 50 40

55. River Scene.

1982. 10th Anniv. Human Environment Conference.

183. **55.** 50 p. multicoloured .. 50 40

56. Dr. M. Hussain.

1982. 1st Death Anniv of Dr. Motahar Hussain (educationist).

184 **56** 50 p. multicoloured .. 50 40

57. Knotted Rope surrounding Bengali " 75 ".

1982. 75th Anniv. of Boy Scout Movement and 125th Birth Anniv. of Lord Baden-Powell. Multicoloured.

185. 50 p. Type **57** .. .. 1·00 30
186. 2 t. Lord Baden-Powell. (vert.) .. .. .. 3·00 3·25

সম্মিলিত
সশস্ত্র বাহিনী দিবস
২১ নভেম্বর,৮২

58.

1982. Armed Forces' Day. No. 175 optd with T **58**.

187. 50 p. Type **50** .. .. 1·25 85

59. Captain Mohiuddin Jahangir.

1983. Heroes and Martyrs of the Liberation. Multicoloured, background colour of commemorative plaque given.

188. 50 p. Type **59** (orange) .. 25 25
189. 50 p. Sepoy Hamidur Rahman (green) .. 25 25
190. 50 p. Sepoy Mohammed Mustafa Kamal (red) .. 25 25
191. 50 p. Muhammed Ruhul Amin (yellow) 25 25
192. 50 p. Flt. Lt. M. Matiur Rahman (brown) .. 25 25
193. 50 p. Lance-Naik Munshi Abdur Rob (brown) .. 25 25
194. 50 p. Lance-Naik Nur Mouhammad (green) .. 25 25

60. Metric Scales.

1983. Introduction of Metric Weights and Measures. Multicoloured.

195. 50 p. Type **60** 40 30
196. 2 t. Weights, jug and tape measure (horiz.) .. 1·50 2·00

61. Dr. Robert Koch.

1983. Centenary (1982) of Robert Koch's Discovery of Tubercle Bacillus. Mult.

197. 50 p. Type **61** 75 40
198. 1 t. Microscope, slide and X-ray .. .. .. 2·00 2·25

62. Open Stage Theatre.

1983. Commonwealth Day. Multicoloured.

199. 1 t. Type **62** 10 15
200. 3 t. Boat race 20 30
201. 10 t. Snake dance 65 90
202. 15 t. Picking tea .. .. 1·00 1·50

63. Dr. Muhammed Shahidulla.

1983. Dr. Muhammed Shahidulla (Bengali scholar). Commemoration.

203. **63.** 50 p. multicoloured .. 75 50

64. Magpie Robin.

1983. Birds of Bangladesh. Multicoloured.

204. 50 p. Type **64** .. .. 1·25 40
205. 2 t. White-breasted Kingfisher (vert.) .. .. 2·25 2·25
206. 3 t. 75 Lesser Golden-backed Woodpecker (vert.) .. .. .. 3·00 3·00
207. 5 t. White-winged Wood Duck .. .. .. 3·50 3·50

65. "Macrobrachium rosenbergii".

1984. Fishes. Multicoloured.

209. 50 p. Type **65** 70 30
210. 2 t. "Stromateus cinereus" 1·75 1·60
211. 3 t. 75 "Labeo rohita" .. 2·25 2·00
212. 5 t. "Anaba testudineus" 2·75 2·75

1983. Visit of Queen Elizabeth II, No. 95 optd. **Nov '83 Visit of Queen.**

214. 10 t. Queen Elizabeth and Prince Philip .. .. 3·00 3·25

67. Conference Hall, Dhaka.

1983. 14th Islamic Foreign Ministers' Conference. Dhaka. Multicoloured.

215. 50 p. Type **67** 40 30
216. 5 t. Old Fort, Dhaka .. 1·50 2·00

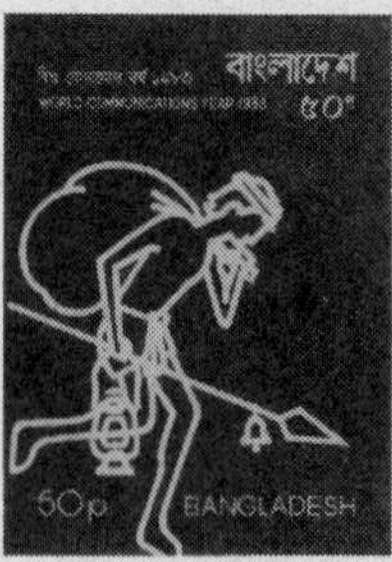

68. Early Mail Runner.  **69.** Carrying Mail by Boat.

1983. World Communications Year. Mult.

217. 50 p. Type **68.** 30 15
218. 5 t. Sailing ship, steam train and jet airliner .. 1·75 1·00
219. 10 t. Mail runner and dish aerial (horiz.) .. .. 2·50 1·90

1983. Postal Communications.

220. **69.** 5 p. blue 10 10
221. – 10 p. purple 10 10
222. – 15 p. blue 10 10
223. – 20 p. black 10 10
224. – 25 p. grey 10 10
225. – 30 p. brown 10 10
226. – 50 p. brown 10 10
227. – 1 t. blue 10 10
228. – 2 t. green 20 10
228a. – 3 t. brown 10 10
229. – 5 t. purple 30 20

DESIGNS—HORIZ. (22 × 17 mm.) 10 p. Counter, Dhaka G.P.O. 15 p. I.W.T.A. Terminal, Dhaka. 20 p. Inside railway travelling post office. 30 p. Emptying pillar box. 50 p. Mobile post office van (30 × 19 mm.) 1 t. Kamalapur Railway Station, Dhaka. 2 t. Zia International Airport. 3 t. Sorting mail by machine. 5 t. Khulna G.P.O. VERT. (17 × 22 mm.) 25 p. Delivering a letter.

প্রথম বাংলাদেশ জাতীয় ডাকটিকিট প্রদর্শনী-১৯৮৪

(**70**).

1984. 1st National Stamp Exhibition (1st issue). Nos 161/2 optd with T **70** (5 t.) or "First Bangladesh National Philatelic Exhibition—1984" (50 p.).

230 **44.** 50 p. multicoloured .. 50 70
231. – 5 t. multicoloured .. 75 1·00

71. Girl with Stamp Album. (Illustration reduced. Actual size 67 × 34 mm).

1984. 1st National Stamp Exhibition (2nd issue). Multicoloured.

232. 50 p. Type **71** 50 70
233. 7 t. 30 Boy with stamp album .. .. .. 1·00 1·25

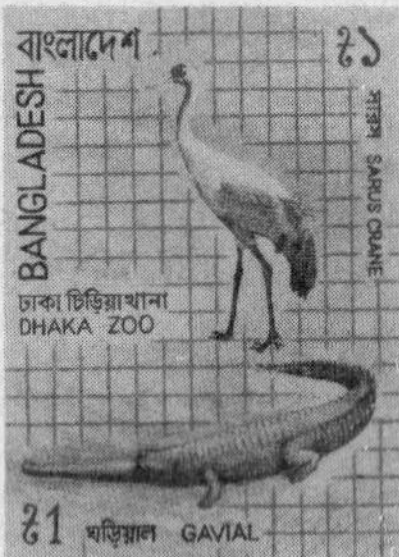

72. Sarus Crane and Gavial.

1984. Dhaka Zoo. Multicoloured.

235. 1 t. Type **72** .. .. 1·25 75
236. 2 t. Common peafowl and tiger .. .. .. 2·00 2·50

73. Eagle attacking Hen with Chicks.

1984. Centenary of Postal Life Insurance. Multicoloured.

237. 1 t. Type **73** 50 20
238. 5 t. Bangladesh family and postman's hand with insurance cheque .. 1·10 80

খুলনাপেক্স—৮৪

74. Abbasuddin Ahmad (singer).

(**75**).

1984. Abbasuddin (Ahmad (singer) Commemoration.

239. **74.** 3 t. multicoloured .. 60 30

1984. "Khulnapex-84" Stamp Exhibition. No. 86 optd. with T **75**.

240 **22** 2 t. 25 multicoloured .. 60 45

76. Cycling.

1984. Olympic Games, Los Angeles. Mult.

241. 1 t. Type **76** 45 20
242. 5 t. Hockey .. .. 1·50 1·50
243. 10 t. Volleyball .. .. 2·00 2·25

77. Farmer with Rice and Sickle.

1985. 9th Annual Meeting of Islamic Development Bank, Dhaka. Multicoloured.

244. 1 t. Type **77** 30 15
245. 5 t. Citizens of four races 95 70

78. Mother and Baby.

1985. Child Survival Campaign. Mult.

246. 1 t. Type **78** 30 10
247. 10 t. Young child and growth graph .. .. 1·75 1·25

উপজেলা নির্বাচন ১৯৮৫

(**79**).

1985. Local Elections. Nos 110/15 optd. with T **79**.

248 40 p. Type **29** 10 15
249 1 t. "Cassia fistula" .. 10 20
250 2 t.25 "Delonix regia" .. 15 35
251 3 t.50 "Nymphaea nouchali" 20 45
252 4 t. "Butea monosperma" 20 45
253 5 t. "Anthocephalus indicus" 30 55

80. Women working at Traditional Crafts.

1985. United Nations Decade for Women. Multicoloured.

254. 1 t. Type **80** 25 10
255. 10 t. Women with microscope, computer terminal and in classroom 1·00 85

81. U.N. Building, New York, Peace Doves and Flags.

1985. 40th Anniv. of United Nations Organization and 11th Anniv. of Bangladesh Membership. Multicoloured.

256. 1 t. Type **81** 10 10
257. 10 t. Map of world and Bangladesh flag .. 80 90

82. Head of Youth, Flowers and Symbols of Commerce and Agriculture.

1985. International Youth Year. Mult.

258. 1 t. Type **82** 10 10
259. 5 t. Head of youth, flowers and symbols of industry 40 60

83. Emblem and Seven Doves.

1985. 1st Summit Meeting of South Asian Association for Regional Co-operation, Dhaka. Multicoloured.

260. 1 t. Type **83** 10 10
261. 5 t. Flags of member nations and lotus blossom 40 60

84. Zainul Abedin.

1985. 10th Death Anniv. of Zainul Abedin (artist).

262. **84.** 3 t. multicoloured .. 65 30

তৃতীয় বাংলাদেশ জাতীয় জাম্বুরী ১৯৮৫-৮৬

(**85**).

1985. Third National Scout Jamboree. No. 109 optd. with T **85**.

263. 5 t. green, blue and red .. 1·25 60

86. "Fishing Net" (Safiuddin Ahmed).

1986. Bangladesh Paintings. Multicoloured.

264 1 t. Type **86** 15 10
265. 5 t. "Happy Return" (Quamrul Hassan) .. 40 50
266. 10 t. "Levelling the Ploughed Field" (Zainul Abedin) 70 80

87. Two Players competing for Ball.

1986. World Cup Football Championship, Mexico. Multicoloured.

267. 1 t. Type **87** 30 10
268. 10 t. Goalkeeper and ball in net .. .. .. 1·50 1·00

88. General M. A. G. Osmani.

1986. General M. A. G. Osmani (army commander-in-chief) Commemoration.

270. **88.** 3 t. multicoloured. .. 80 40

1986. South Asian Association for Regional Co-operation Seminar. No. 183 optd. **SAARC SEMINAR '86.**

271. **55.** 50 p. multicoloured .. 90 90

90. Butterflies and Nuclear Explosion.

1986. International Peace Year. Mult.

272. 1 t. Type **90** 50 25
273. 10 t. Flowers and ruined buildings .. .. 2·50 2·75

1987. Conference for Development. Nos. 152/3 optd **CONFERENCE FOR DEVELOPMENT '87**, No. 275 surch also.

275. **38.** 1 t. on 40 p. black, red and yellow 10 15
276. – 5 t. gold and blue .. 30 60

92. Demonstrators with Placards.

1987. 35th Anniv. of Bangla Language Movement. Multicoloured.

277. 3 t. Type **92** 65 85
278. 3 t. Martyrs' Memorial .. 65 85

Nos. 277/8 were printed together, se-tenant, forming a composite design.

93. Nurse giving Injection.

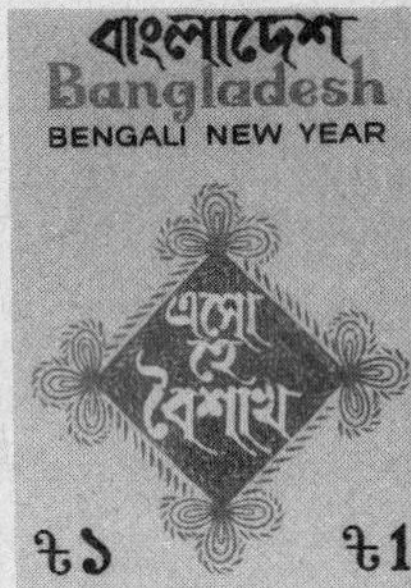

94. Pattern and Bengali Script.

1987. World Health Day.

279. **93.** 1 t. black and blue .. 1·40 90

See also No. 295.

1987. Bengali New Year. Multicoloured.

280. 1 t. Type **94** 10 10
281. 10 t. Bengali woman .. 40 60

95. Jute Shika.

1987. Export Products. Multicoloured.

282. 1 t. Type **95** 10 10
283. 5 t. Jute carpet (horiz.) .. 20 30
284. 10 t. Cane table lamp .. 40 60

96. Ustad Ayet Ali Khan and Surbahar.

1987. 20th Death Anniv. of Ustad Ayet Ali Khan (musician and composer).
285. **96.** 5 t. multicoloured .. 40 40

97. Palanquin.

1987. Transport. Multicoloured.
286. 2 t. Type **97** 15 15
287. 3 t. Bicycle rickshaw .. 20 20
288. 5 t. River steamer .. 30 35
289. 7 t. Express diesel train .. 40 50
290. 10 t. Bullock cart 45 75

98. H. S. Suhrawardy.

1987. Hossain Shahid Suhrawardy (politician) Commem.
291. **98.** 3 t. multicoloured .. 20 30

99. Villagers fleeing from Typhoon.

1987. International Year of Shelter for the Homeless. Multicoloured.
292. 5 t. Type **99** 20 30
293. 5 t. Villagers and modern houses 20 30

100. President Ershad addressing Parliament.

1987. 1st Anniv. of Return to Democracy.
294. **100.** 10 t. multicoloured .. 40 60

1988. World Health Day. As T **93**.
295 25 p. brown 30 20
Design: 25 p. Oral rehydration.

101. Woman planting Palm Saplings.

1988. I.F.A.D. Seminar on Agricultural Loans for Rural Women. Multicoloured.
296. 3 t. Type **101** 15 20
297. 5 t. Village woman milking cow 20 40

102 Basketball

1988. Olympic Games, Seoul. Multicoloured.
298 5 t. Type **102** 20 25
299 5 t. Weightlifting .. 20 25
300 5 t. Tennis 20 25
301 5 t. Rifle-shooting .. 20 25
302 5 t. Boxing 20 25

103 Interior of Shait Gumbaz Mosque, Bagerhat

1988. Historical Buildings. Multicoloured.
303 1 t. Type **103** 10 10
304 4 t. Paharpur Monastery 10 10
305 5 t. Kantanagar Temple, Dinajpur 10 10
306 10 t. Lalbag Fort, Dhaka 15 15

104 Henri Dunant (founder), Red Cross and Crescent

1988. 125th Anniv of International Red Cross and Red Crescent. Multicoloured.
307 5 t. Type **104** 20 25
308 10 t. Red Cross workers with patient .. 40 45

105 Dr. Qudrat-i-Khuda in Laboratory

1988. Dr. Qudrat-i-Khuda (scientist) Commemoration.
309 **105** 5 t. multicoloured .. 20 25

106 Wicket-keeper

1988. Asia Cup Cricket. Multicoloured.
310 1 t. Type **106** 50 80
311 5 t. Batsman 70 95
312 10 t. Bowler .. .. 75 1·25

107 Labourers, Factory and Technician

1988. 32nd Meeting of Colombo Plan Consultative Committee, Dhaka.
313 **107** 3 t. multicoloured .. 10 10
314 10 t. multicoloured .. 40 45

108 Dhaka G.P.O. Building (Illus reduced, actual size 55 × 31 mm)

1988. 25th Anniv of Dhaka G.P.O. Building. Multicoloured.
315 1 t. Type **108** 10 10
316 5 t. Post Office counter .. 20 25

৫ম জাতীয় রোভার মুট
১৯৮৮-৮৯
(**109**)

1988. 5th National Rover Scout Moot. No. 168 optd with T **109**.
317 **47** 5 t. multicoloured .. 30 30

110 Bangladesh Airport

1989. Bangladesh Landmarks.
318 **110** 3 t. black and blue .. 10 10
318a – 4 t. blue 10 10
319 – 5 t. black and brown 15 20
320 – 10 t. red 30 35
321 – 20 t. multicoloured .. 65 70
Designs—Vert. (22 × 33 mm) 5 t. Curzon Hall. (19½ × 31½ mm) 10 t. Fertiliser Factory, Chittagong. Horiz. (33 × 23 mm) 4 t. Chittagong Port. 20 t. Postal Academy, Rajshahi.

চতুর্থ দ্বিবার্ষিক এশীয়
চারুকলা প্রদর্শনী
বাংলাদেশ ১৯৮৯
(**111**)

1989. 4th Biennial Asian Art Exhibition. No. 266 optd with T **111**.
322 10 t. "Levelling the Ploughed Field" (Zainul Abedin) 40 45

112 Irrigation Methods and Student with Telescope

1989. 12th National Science and Technology Week.
323 **112** 10 t. multicoloured .. 40 45

113 Academy Logo

1989. 75th Anniv of Police Academy, Sardah.
324 **113** 10 t. multicoloured .. 40 45

114 Rejoicing Crowds, Paris, 1789

1989. Bicent of French Revolution. Mult.
325 17 t. Type **114** 70 75
326 17 t. Storming the Bastille, 1789 .. .. .. 70 75

115 Sowing and Harvesting

1989. 10th Anniv of Asia–Pacific Integrated Rural Development Centre. Multicoloured.
329 5 t. Type **115** 45 45
330 10 t. Rural activities .. 50 50
Nos. 329/30 were printed together, se-tenant, forming a composite design.

116 Helper and Child playing with Baby

1989. 40th Anniv of S.O.S International Children's Village. Multicoloured.
331 1 t. Type **116** 15 10
332 10 t. Foster mother with children 55 55

117 U.N. Soldier on Watch

1989. 1st Anniv of Bangladesh Participation in U.N. Peace-keeping Force. Multicoloured.
333 4 t. Type **117** 40 30
334 10 t. Two soldiers checking positions 85 70

118 Festival Emblem

1989. 2nd Asian Poetry Festival, Dhaka.
335 **118** 2 t. red, dp red & green 15 10
336 – 10 t. multicoloured .. 60 65
DESIGN: 10 t. Festival emblem and hall.

119 State Security Printing Press

1989. Inauguration of State Security Printing Press, Gazipur.
337 **119** 10 t. multicoloured .. 65 65

120 Water Lilies and T.V. Emblem

1989. 25th Anniv of Bangladesh Television. Multicoloured.
338 5 t. Type **120** 30 30
339 10 t. Central emblem and water lilies 65 80

121 Gharial in Shallow Water

1990. Endangered Wildlife. Gharial. Mult.
340 50 p. Type **121** 45 30
341 2 t. Gharial feeding .. 60 40
342 4 t. Gharials basking on sand bank 80 55
343 10 t. Two gharials resting 1·40 95

122 Symbolic Family

1990. Population Day.
344 **122** 6 t. multicoloured .. 45 35

123 Justice S.M. Murshed

1990. 10th Death Anniv of Justice Syed Mahbub Murshed.
345 **123** 5 t. multicoloured .. 70 35

124 Boy learning Alphabet

1990. International Literacy Year. Mult.
346 6 t. Type **124** 75 40
347 10 t. Boy teaching girl to write .. .. .. 1·25 85

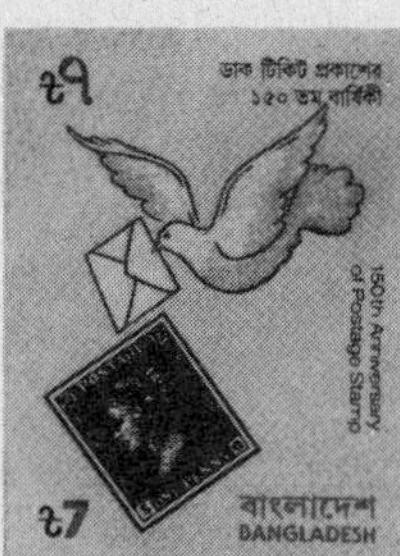

125 Penny Black with "Stamp World London 90" Exhibition Emblem

1990. 150th Anniv of the Penny Black. Mult.
348 7 t. Type **125** .. .. 1·00 50
349 10 t. Penny Black, 1983 World Communications Year stamp and Bengali mail runner .. .. 1·40 90

126 Goalkeeper and Ball

1990. World Cup Football Championship, Italy. Multicoloured.
350 8 t. Type **126** .. .. 1·10 70
351 10 t. Footballer with ball 1·40 90

127 Mango

1990. Fruit. Multicoloured.
353 1 t. Type **127** 20 10
354 2 t. Guava 20 10
355 3 t. Water melon 25 15
356 4 t. Papaya 30 25
357 5 t. Bread fruit 50 45
358 10 t. Carambola 90 90

128 Man gathering Wheat

1990. U.N. Conference on Least Developed Countries, Paris.
359 **128** 10 t. multicoloured .. 1·00 75

129 Map of Asia with Stream of Letters

1990. 20th Anniv of Asia–Pacific Postal Training Centre. Multicoloured.
360 2 t. Type **129** 40 20
361 6 t. Map of Pacific with stream of letters .. 50 30
Nos. 360/1 were printed together, se-tenant, forming a composite map design.

130 Canoe Racing

1990. Asian Games, Beijing. Multicoloured.
362 2 t. Type **130** 30 10
363 4 t. Kabaddi 45 25
364 8 t. Wrestling 80 50
365 10 t. Badminton .. .. 1·00 80

131 Lalan Shah

1990. 1st Death Anniv of Lalan Shah (poet).
366 **131** 6 t. multicoloured .. 75 35

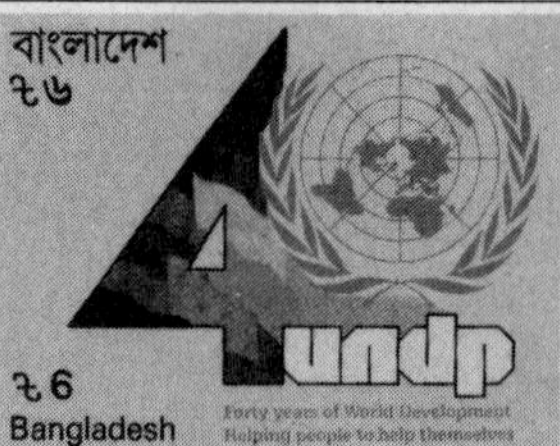

132 U.N. Logo and "40"

1990. 40th Anniv of United Nations Development Programme.
367 **132** 6 t. multicoloured .. 65 35

133 Immunization

1990.
368 **133** 2 t. brown 10 10
369 – 6 t. blue and yellow .. 20 25
DESIGN—HORIZ (30 × 19 mm). 6 t. Salimullah Hall.

135 "Danaus chrysippus"

1990. Butterflies. Multicoloured.
376 6 t. Type **135** 90 90
377 6 t. "Precis almana" .. 90 90
378 10 t. "Ixias pyrene" .. 1·10 1·10
379 10 t. "Danaus plexippus" 1·10 1·10

136 Drugs attacking Bangladesh

1991. U.N. Anti-Drugs Decade. Mult.
380 2 t. Type **136** 50 25
381 4 t. "Drug" snake around globe 60 35

137 Silhouetted People on Map

1991. 3rd National Census.
382 **137** 4 t. multicoloured .. 30 30

138 "Invincible Bangla" (statue)

1991. 20th Anniv of Independence. Mult.

No.	Description	Unused	Used
383	4 t. Type **138**	35	35
384	4 t. "Freedom Fighter" (statue)	35	35
385	4 t. Mujibnagar Memorial	35	35
386	4 t. Eternal flame ..	35	35
387	4 t. National Martyrs' Memorial	35	35

Nos. 383/7 were issued together, se-tenant, forming a omposite design.

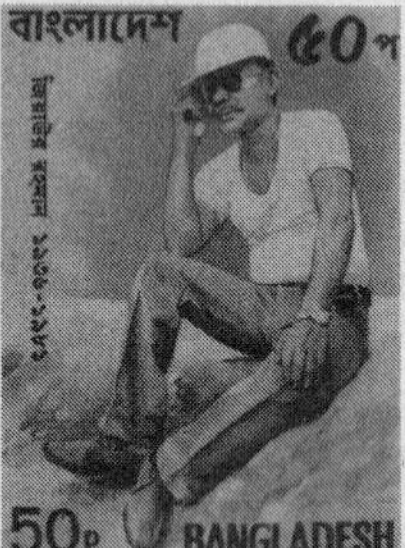

139 Pres. Rahman Seated

1991. 10th Death Anniv of President Ziaur Rahman. Multicoloured.

No.	Description	Unused	Used
388	50 p. Type **139**	10	10
389	2 t. Pres. Rahman's head in circular decoration ..	40	40

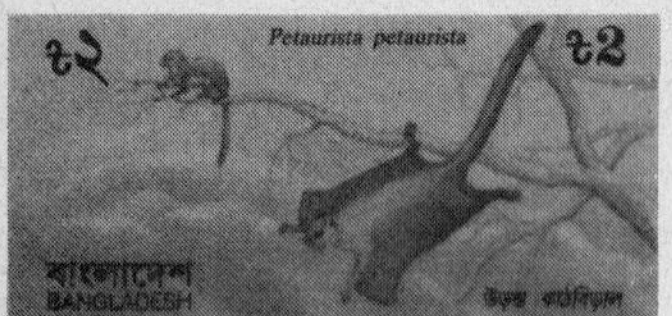

140 Red Giant Flying Squirrel

1991. Endangered Species. Multicoloured.

No.	Description	Unused	Used
391	2 t. Type **140**	40	40
392	4 t. Black-faced monkey (vert)	40	40
393	6 t. Great Indian hornbill (vert)	55	55
394	10 t. Armoured pangolin ..	80	80

141 Kaikobad

1991. 40th Death Anniv of Kaikobad (poet).

No.	Description	Unused	Used
395 **141**	6 t. multicoloured ..	40	40

142 Rabindranath Tagore and Temple

1991. 50th Death Anniv of Rabindranath Tagore (poet).

No.	Description	Unused	Used
396 **142**	4 t. multicoloured ..	30	30

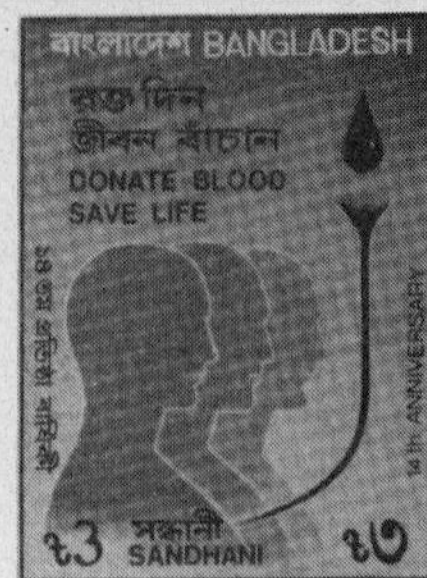

143 Voluntary Blood Donation Programme

1991. 14th Anniv of "Sandhani" (medical students' association).

No.	Description	Unused	Used
397 **143**	3 t. black and red ..	35	35
398 –	5 t. multicoloured ..	45	45

DESIGN: 5 t. Blind man and eye

144 Shahid Naziruddin and Crowd

1991. 1st Death Anniv of Shahid Naziruddin Jahad (democrat).

No.	Description	Unused	Used
399 **144**	2 t. black, green & brn	30	30

145 Shaheed Noor Hossain with Slogan on Chest

1991. 4th Death Anniv of Shaheed Noor Hossain (democrat).

No.	Description	Unused	Used
400 **145**	2 t. multicoloured ..	30	30

146 Bronze Stupa

1991. Archaeological Relics from Mainamati. Multicoloured.

No.	Description	Unused	Used
401	4 t. Type **146**	45	45
402	4 t. Earthenware and bronze pitchers ..	45	45
403	4 t. Remains of Salban Vihara Monastery ..	45	45
404	4 t. Gold coins	45	45
405	4 t. Terracotta plaque ..	45	45

147 Demonstrators

1991. 1st Anniv of Mass Uprising.

No.	Description	Unused	Used
406 **147**	4 t. multicoloured ..	30	30

148 Munier Chowdhury

1991. 20th Anniv of Independence. Martyred Intellectuals (1st series). Each black and brown.

No.	Description	Unused	Used
407	2 t. Type **148**	10	10
408	2 t. Ghyasuddin Ahmad ..	10	10
409	2 t. Rashidul Hasan ..	10	10
410	2 t. Muhammad Anwar Pasha	10	10
411	2 t. Dr. Muhammad Mortaza	10	10
412	2 t. Shahid Saber ..	10	10
413	2 t. Fazlur Rahman Khan	10	10
414	2 t. Ranada Prasad Saha	10	10
415	2 t. Adhyaksha Joges Chandra Ghose ..	10	10
416	2 t. Santosh Chandra Bhattacharyya ..	10	10
417	2 t. Dr. Gobinda Chandra Deb	10	10
418	2 t. A. Muniruzzaman ..	10	10
419	2 t. Mufazzal Haider Chaudhury	10	10
420	2 t. Dr. Abdul Alim Choudhury	10	10
421	2 t. Sirajuddin Hossain ..	10	10
422	2 t. Shahidulla kaiser ..	10	10
423	2 t. Altaf Mahmud ..	10	10
424	2 t. Dr. Jyotirmay Guha Thakurta	10	10
425	2 t. Dr. Muhammad Abul Khair	10	10
426	2 t. Dr. Serajul Haque Khan	10	10
427	2 t. Dr. Mohammad Fazle Rabbi	10	10
428	2 t. Mir Abdul Quyyum ..	10	10
429	2 t. Golam Mostafa ..	10	10
430	2 t. Dhirendranath Dutta	10	10
431	2 t. S. Mannan	10	10
432	2 t. Nizamuddin Ahmad ..	10	10
433	2 t. Abul Bashar Chowdhury	10	10
434	2 t. Selina Parveen ..	10	10
435	2 t. Dr. Abul Kalam Azad	10	10
436	2 t. Saidul Hassan ..	10	10

See also Nos. 483/92.

149 "Penaeus monodon"

1991. Shrimps. Multicoloured.

No.	Description	Unused	Used
437	6 t. Type **149**	70	70
438	6 t. "Metapenaeus monoceros"	70	70

150 Death of Raihan Jaglu

1992. 5th Death Anniv of Shaheed Mirze Abu Raihan Jaglu.

No.	Description	Unused	Used
439 **150**	2 t. multicoloured ..	40	30

151 Rural and Urban Scenes

1992. World Environment Day. Mult.

No.	Description	Unused	Used
440	4 t. Type **151**	25	15
441	10 t. World Environment Day logo (horiz) ..	65	75

152 Nawab Sirajuddaulah

1992. 235th Death Anniv of Nawab Sirajuddaulah of Bengal.

No.	Description	Unused	Used
442 **152**	10 t. multicoloured ..	50	50

153 Syed Ismail Hossain Sirajee

1992. 61st Death Anniv of Syed Ismail Hossain Sirajee.

No.	Description	Unused	Used
443 **153**	4 t. multicoloured ..	30	20

154 Couple planting Seedling

1992. Plant Week. Multicoloured.

No.	Description	Unused	Used
444	2 t. Type **154**	25	25
445	4 t. Birds on tree (vert) ..	25	25

155 Canoe Racing

1992. Olympic Games, Barcelona. Mult.

No.	Description	Unused	Used
446	4 t. Type **155**	25	25
447	6 t. Hands holding torch with Olympic rings ..	35	35
448	10 t. Olympic rings and doves	60	60
449	10 t. Olympic rings and multiracial handshake ..	60	60

1992. "Banglapex '92", National Philatelic Exhibition (1st issue). No. 290 optd **Banglapex '92**.

No.	Description	Unused	Used
450	10 t. Bullock cart ..	60	60

See also Nos. 452/3.

157 Masnad-e-Ala Isa Khan

1992. 393rd Death Anniv of Masnad-e-Ala Isa Khan.

451 **157** 4 t. multicoloured .. 30 20

158 Ceremonial Elephant (19th-century ivory carving)

1992. "Banglapex '92", National Philatelic Exhibition (2nd issue). Multicoloured.

452 10 t. Type **158** 65 70

453 10 t. Victorian pillarbox between early and modern postmen .. 65 70

159 Star Mosque

1992. Star Mosque, Dhaka.

455 **159** 10 t. multicoloured .. 50 50

160 Meer Nisar Ali Titumeer and Fort

1992. 161st Death Anniv of Meer Nisar Ali Titumeer.

456 **160** 10 t. multicoloured .. 50 50

161 Terracotta Head and Seal

1992. Archaeological Relics from Mahasthangarh. Multicoloured.

457 10 t. Type **161** 50 50

458 10 t. Terracotta panel showing swan 50 50

459 10 t. Terracotta statue of Surya 50 50

460 10 t. Gupta stone column 50 50

162 Young Child and Food

1992. International Conference on Nutrition, Rome.

461 **162** 4 t. multicoloured .. 20 20

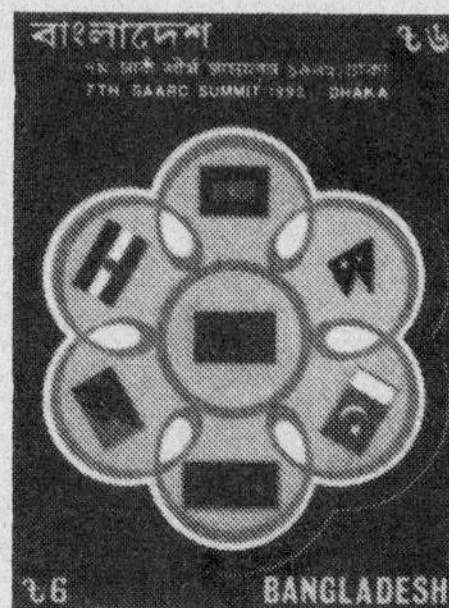

163 National Flags

1992. 7th South Asian Association for Regional Co-operation Summit Conference, Dhaka. Multicoloured.

462 6 t. Type **163** 30 30

463 10 t. S.A.A.R.C. emblem .. 50 50

164 Syed Abdus Samad

1993. Syed Abdus Samad (footballer) Commemoration.

464 **164** 2 t. multicoloured .. 20 20

165 Haji Shariat Ullah

1993. Haji Shariat Ullah Commemoration.

465 **165** 2 t. multicoloured .. 20 20

166 People digging Canal

1993. Irrigation Canals Construction Project. Multicoloured.

466 2 t. Type **166** 20 20

467 2 t. Completed canal and paddy-fields 20 20

167 Accident Prevention

1993. World Health Day. Multicoloured.

468 6 t. Type **167** 30 30

469 10 t. Satellite photograph and symbols of trauma (vert) 50 50

168 National Images

1993. 1400th Year of Bengali Solar Calendar.

470 **168** 2 t. multicoloured .. 20 20

169 Schoolchildren and Bengali Script

1993. Compulsory Primary Education. Mult.

471 2 t. Type **169** 20 20

472 2 t. Books and slate (horiz) 20 20

170 Nawab Sir Salimullah and Palace

1993. 122nd Birth Anniv of Nawab Sir Salimullah.

473 **170** 4 t. multicoloured .. 20 20

171 Fish Production

1993. Fish Fortnight.

474 **171** 2 t. multicoloured .. 10 10

172 Sunderban

1993. Natural Beauty of Bangladesh. Mult.

475 10 t. Type **172** 30 35

476 10 t. Kuakata beach .. 30 35

477 10 t. Madhabkunda waterfall (vert) 30 35

478 10 t. River Piyain, Jaflang (vert) 30 35

173 Exhibition Emblem

1993. 6th Asian Art Biennale.

480 **173** 10 t. multicoloured .. 30 35

174 Foy's Lake

1993. Tourism Month.

481 **174** 10 t. multicoloured .. 30 35

175 Burdwan House

1993. Foundation Day Bangla Academy.

482 **175** 2 t. brown and green .. 10 10

1993. Martyred Intellectuals (2nd series). As T **148**. Each black and brown.

483 2 t. Lt. Cdr. Moazzam Hussain 10 10

484 2 t. Muhammad Habibur Rahman 10 10

485 2 t. Khandoker Abu Taleb 10 10

486 2 t. Moshiur Rahman .. 10 10

487 2 t. Md Abdul Muktadir .. 10 10

488 2 t. Nutan Chandra Sinha 10 10

489 2 t. Syed Nazmul Haque 10 10

490 2 t. Dr. Mohammed Amin Uddin 10 10

491 2 t. Dr. Faizul Mohee .. 10 10

492 2 t. Sukha Ranjan Somaddar 10 10

176 Tomb of Sultan Ghiyasuddin Azam Shah

1993. Muslim Monuments.

493 **176** 10 t. multicoloured .. 30 35

177 Scouting Activities and Jamboree Emblem

1994. 14th Asian-Pacific and 5th Bangladesh National Scout Jamboree.

494	**177**	2 t. multicoloured ..	10	10

OFFICIAL STAMPS

1973. Nos. 22, etc. optd. **SERVICE.**

O 1.	**7.**	2 p. black	10	30
O 2.	–	3 p. green	10	30
O 3.	–	5 p. brown	15	10
O 4.	–	10 p. black	15	10
O 5.	–	20 p. green	90	10
O 6.	–	25 p. mauve	2·25	10
O 7.	–	60 p. grey	2·50	75
O 8.	–	75 p. orange	90	20
O 9.	**8.**	1 t. violet	8·00	3·50
O 10.	–	5 t. blue	4·00	5·00

1974. Nos. 49/51 optd. **SERVICE.**

O 11.	**14.**	1 t. violet	2·50	30
O 12.	–	2 t. olive	3·50	1·25
O 13.	–	5 t. blue	5·00	4·50

1976. Nos. 64/70 and 72/4 optd. **SERVICE.**

O 14.	–	5 p. green	30	20
O 15.	–	10 p. black	60	20
O 16.	–	20 p. green	85	20
O 17.	–	25 p. mauve	2·00	20
O 18.	–	50 p. purple	2·00	20
O 19.	–	60 p. grey	30	50
O 20.	–	75 p. olive	30	50
O 21.	**14.**	1 t. blue	1·75	30
O 22.	–	2 t. green	35	70
O 23.	–	5 t. blue	30	70

1981. Nos. 125/9 and 131/7 optd **SERVICE**.

O24	–	5 p. brown	40	40
O25	**32**	10 p. blue	40	40
O26	–	15 p. orange	50	50
O27	–	20 p. red	30	40
O28	–	25 p. blue	80	1·00
O29	–	30 p. green	80	70
O30	–	40 p. purple	50	15
O31	–	50 p. black	30	10
O32	–	80 p. brown	60	15
O33	–	1 t. violet	30	15
O34	–	2 t. blue	35	80

1983. Nos. 220/9 and 318a optd **Service**.

O35	**69**	5 p. blue	10	10
O36	–	10 p. purple	10	10
O37	–	15 p. blue	10	10
O38	–	20 p. black	10	10
O39	–	25 p. grey	10	10
O40	–	30 p. brown	10	10
O41	–	50 p. brown	10	10
O43	–	2 t. green	10	10
O44	–	4 t. blue	10	10
O45	–	5 t. purple	15	20

সার্ভিস (O **5**)

সার্ভিস (O **6**)

1990. Nos. 368/9 optd with Type O **5**.

O46	**133**	2 t. brown	10	10
O47		6 t. blue and yellow ..	20	25

1992. No. 227 optd with Type O **6**.

O48		1 t. blue	10	10

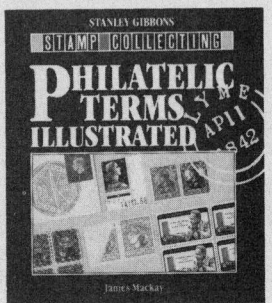

BARBADOS

An island in the Br. W. Indies, E. of the Windward Is., attained self-government on 16th October, 1961 and achieved independence within the Commonwealth on 30 November 1966.

1950. 100 cents = 1 Barbados dollar.

1. Britannia. 2.

1852. Imperf.

8	1	(½d.) green	85·00	£200
10		(1d.) blue	21·00	50·00
4a		(2d.) slate	£200	£1100
5		(4d.) red	50·00	£300
11	2	6d. red	£700	£110
12a		1s. black	£140	70·00

1860. Perf.

21	1.	(½d.) green	7·50	7·50
24		(1d.) blue	21·00	3·00
25		(4d.) red	60·00	25·00
32	2.	6d. red	55·00	11·00
33		6d. orange	70·00	22·00
35		1s. black	32·00	6·00

1873. Perf.

72	2	½d. green	6·00	50
74		1d. blue	28·00	30
63		3d. brown	£325	£110
75		3d. mauve	75·00	3·50
76		4d. red	70·00	7·00
79		6d. yellow	90·00	1·00
81		1s. purple	£100	2·75

3. 4.

1873.

64.	3.	5s. red	£950	£300

1878. Half of No. 64 surch. **1 D.**

86.	3.	1d. on half 5s. red	£3250	£600

1882.

90	4.	½d. green	5·00	90
92		1d. red	4·50	25
93		2½d. blue	50·00	70
96		3d. purple	3·25	9·00
97		4d. grey	£170	2·00
99		4d. brown	2·75	60
100		6d. brown	55·00	28·00
102		1s. brown	19·00	21·00
103		5s. bistre	£140	£170

1892. Surch. **HALF-PENNY.**

104.	4.	½d. on 4d. brown	50	1·50

6. Seal of Colony. 7.

1892.

105	6	¼d. grey and red	70	10
163		¼d. brown	60	30
106		½d. green	40	10
107		1d. red	1·50	10
108		2d. black and orange	6·00	65
166		2d. grey	4·00	8·50
139		2½d. blue	5·00	15
110		5d. olive	4·75	4·50
111		6d. mauve and red	6·00	2·00
168		6d. purple	4·50	14·00
112		8d. orange and blue	2·50	17·00
113		10d. green and red	4·75	6·50
169		1s. black on green	7·50	14·00
114		2s. 6d. black and orange	40·00	40·00
144		2s. 6d. violet and green	26·00	60·00

1897. Diamond Jubilee.

116.	7.	¼d. grey and red	75	15
117.		½d. green	1·75	15
118.		1d. red	2·25	10
119.		2½d. blue	4·00	40
120.		5d. brown	10·00	10·00
121.		6d. mauve and red	14·00	14·00
122.		8d. orange and blue	4·75	16·00
123.		10d. green and red	30·00	35·00
124.		2s. 6d. black and orange	35·00	45·00

8. Nelson Monument.

1906. Death Centenary of Nelson.

145	8	¼d. black and grey	3·00	60
146		½d. black and green	5·00	15
147		1d. black and red	5·00	15
148		2d. black and yellow	1·75	3·50
149		2½d. black and blue	3·75	1·00
150		6d. black and mauve	16·00	20·00
151		1s. black and red	18·00	35·00

9. "Olive Blossom", 1650. 11.

1906. Tercent. of Annexation of Barbados.

152.	9.	1d. black, blue and green	10·00	25

1907. Surch. **Kingston/Relief/Fund 1d.**

153.	6.	1d. on 2d. blk. & orge.	1·25	4·25

1912.

170.	11.	¼d. brown	50	40
171.		½d. green	1·50	10
172.		1d. red	2·00	10
173.		2d. grey	2·00	8·00
174.		2½d. blue	1·25	30
175.		3d. purple on yellow	1·25	6·00
176.		4d. red & black on yellow	1·25	11·00
177.		6d. purple	6·00	7·50

Larger type, with portrait at top centre.

178.		1s. black on green	4·75	7·50
179.		2s. blue and pur. on blue	28·00	38·00
180.		3s. violet and green	50·00	55·00

14.

1916.

181	14.	¼d. brown	55	20
182		½d. green	1·10	15
183a		1d. red	2·00	15
184		2d. grey	3·50	9·00
185		2½d. blue	1·00	50
186		3d. purple on yellow	1·75	2·50
187		4d. red on yellow	70	9·00
199		4d. black and red	80	3·00
188		6d. purple	2·50	3·25
189		1s. black on green	7·00	5·50
190		2s. purple on blue	16·00	7·50
191		3s. violet	35·00	75·00
200		3s. green and violet	16·00	40·00

1917. Optd. **WAR TAX.**

197.	11.	1d. red	15	15

16.

1920. Victory. Inscr. "VICTORY 1919".

201.	16.	¼d. black and brown	20	60
202.		½d. black and green	80	15
203.		1d. black and red	1·50	10
204.		2d. black and grey	1·75	6·00
205.		2½d. indigo and blue	2·75	6·50
206.		3d. black and purple	1·60	3·00
207.		4d. black and green	1·75	3·50
208.		6d. black and orange	2·50	6·00
209.	–	1s. black and green	6·00	15·00
210.	–	2s. black and brown	13·00	18·00
211.	–	3s. black and orange	16·00	22·00

The 1s. to 3s. show Victory full-face.

18. 19.

1921.

217.	18.	¼d. brown	15	10
219.		½d. green	70	15
220.		1d. red	70	10
221.		2d. grey	1·60	20
222.		2½d. blue	1·50	4·00
213.		3d. purple on yellow	1·75	4·50
214.		4d. red on yellow	1·75	7·00
225.		6d. purple	2·50	4·50
215.		1s. black on green	4·50	11·00
227.		2s. purple on blue	10·00	18·00
228.		3s. violet	13·00	38·00

1925. Inscr. "POSTAGE & REVENUE".

229	19.	¼d. brown	10	10
230		½d. green	10	10
231		1d. red	25	10
231ba		1½d. orange	90	75
232		2d. grey	40	2·00
233		2½d. blue	50	60
234		3d. purple on yellow	50	35
235		4d. red on yellow	60	85
236		6d. purple	60	50
237		1s. black on green	1·50	3·50
238		2s. purple on blue	6·50	6·50
238a		2s. 6d. red on blue	16·00	20·00
239		3s. violet	11·00	13·00

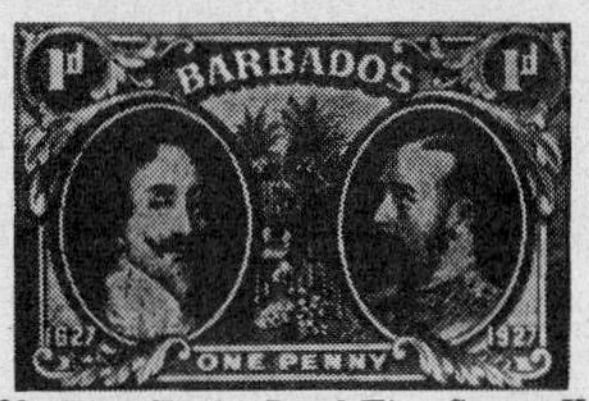

20. King Charles I and King George V.

1927. Tercent. of Settlement of Barbados.

240.	20.	1d. red	75	40

1935. Silver Jubilee. As T **13** of Antigua.

241.		1d. blue and red	30	20
242.		1½d. blue and grey	2·25	3·50
243.		2½d. brown and blue	2·25	1·50
244.		1s. grey and purple	13·00	14·00

1937. Coronation. As T **2** of Aden.

245.		1d. red	30	15
246.		1½d. brown	40	30
247.		2½d. blue	70	45

21. Badge of the Colony.

1938. "POSTAGE & REVENUE" omitted.

248.	21.	½d. green	3·75	15
248b.		½d. yellow	15	15
249a.		1d red	14·00	10
249c.		1d. green	15	10
250.		1½d. orange	15	10
250b.		2d. mauve	35	90
250c.		2d. red	15	10
251.		2½d. blue	50	30
252b.		3d. brown	15	20
252c.		3d. blue	20	50
253.		4d. black	15	10
254.		6d. violet	50	10
254a.		8d. mauve	45	1·10
255a.		1s. olive	30	10
256.		2s. 6d. purple	4·00	85
256a.		5s. blue	3·25	4·00

22. Kings Charles I, George VI. Assembly Chamber and Mace.

1939. Tercentenary of General Assembly.

257.	22.	½d. green	1·50	30
258.		1d. red	1·50	30
259.		1½d. orange	1·50	60
260.		2½d. blue	1·50	1·50
261.		3d. brown	1·60	2·00

1946. Victory. As T **9** of Aden.

262.		1½d. orange	10	10
263.		3d. brown	10	10

1947. Surch. **ONE PENNY.**

264.	17.	1d. on 2d. red	30	1·10

1948. Silver Wedding. As T **10/11** of Aden.

265.		1½d. orange	25	10
266.		5s. blue	9·00	5·00

1949. U.P.U. As T **20/23** of Antigua.

267.		1½d. orange	30	30
268.		3d. blue	40	35
269.		4d. grey	70	70
270.		1s. olive	80	60

24. Dover Fort.

35. Seal of Barbados.

1950.

271.	24.	1 c. blue	15	1·40
272.	–	2 c. green	15	80
273.	–	3 c. brown and green	15	70
274.	–	4 c. red	15	20
275.	–	6 c. blue	15	80
276.	–	8 c. blue and purple	55	70
277.	–	12 c. blue and olive	90	40
278.	–	24 c. red and black	80	30
279.	–	48 c. violet	8·00	4·50
280.	–	60 c. green and lake	6·00	5·50
281.	–	$1.20 c. red and olive	8·50	2·50
282.	35.	$2.40 c. black	15·00	8·50

DESIGNS—As Type **24:** HORIZ. 2 c. Sugar cane breeding. 3 c. Public buildings. 6 c. Casting net. 8 c. "Frances W. Smith" (schooner). 12 c. Flying fish. 24 c. Old Main Guard Garrison. 60 c. Careenage. VERT. 4 c. Statue of Nelson. 48 c. St. Michael's Cathedral. $1.20 c. Map and wireless mast.

1951. Inauguration of B.W.I. University College. As T **24/25** of Antigua.

283	3 c. brown and blue	30	30
284	12 c. blue and olive	55	70

36. King George VI and Stamp of 1852.

1952. Centenary of Barbados Stamp.

285.	36.	3 c. green and slate	15	25
286.		4 c. blue and red	15	25
287.		12 c. slate and green	15	25
288.		24 c. brown and sepia	15	25

37. Harbour Police.

1953. As 1950 issue but with portrait or cypher (No. 301) of Queen Elizabeth II as in T **37**.

289	24.	1 c. blue	10	40
290	–	2 c. orange & turquoise	15	30
291	–	3 c. black and green	15	30
292	–	4 c. black and orange	20	20
293	37.	5 c. blue and red	20	30
294	–	6 c. brown	15	30
295	–	8 c. black and blue	90	30
315	–	12 c. blue and olive	60	50
297	–	24 c. red and black	45	10
298	–	48 c. violet	2·00	1·00
299	–	60 c. green and purple	9·00	2·00
300	–	$1.20 red and olive	19·00	2·00
301	35.	$2.40 black	7·50	1·25

1953. Coronation. As T **13** of Aden.

302.	4 c. black and orange	15	10

1958. British Caribbean Federation. As T **28** of Antigua.

303.	3 c. green	30	15
304.	6 c. blue	40	1·00
305.	12 c. red	40	20

38. Deep Water Harbour, Bridgetown.

1961. Opening of Deep Water Harbour.

306.	38.	4 c. black and orange	10	15
307		8 c. black and blue	10	20
308.		24 c. red and black	15	20

39. Scout Badge and Map of Barbados.

1962. Golden Jubilee of Barbados Boy Scout Association.

309.	39.	4 c. black and orange	30	10
310.		12 c. blue & brown ..	60	15
311.		$1.20 red & green	1·25	2·25

1965. Cent of I.T.U. As T 36 of Antigua.

320.	2 c. lilac and red	25	15
321.	48 c. yellow and drab. ..	1·00	1·25

40. Deep Sea Coral.

1965.

342	40.	1 c. black, pink and blue	10	15
323	–	2 c. brown, yell. & mauve	20	15
324	–	3 c. brown and orange..	45	60
344	–	3 c. brown and orange	30	90
325	–	4 c. blue and green ..	15	10
326	–	5 c. sepia, red and lilac	30	15
327	–	6 c. multicoloured ..	45	20
328	–	8 c. multicoloured ..	25	10
329	–	12 c. multicoloured ..	35	10
330	–	15 c. black, yellow & red	80	70
331	–	25 c. blue and ochre ..	95	75
332	–	35 c. red and green ..	1·50	15
333	–	50 c. blue and green ..	2·00	40
334	–	$1 multicoloured ..	2·75	1·25
335	–	$2.50 multicoloured ..	2·75	1·25
355a	–	$5 multicoloured ..	10·00	7·00

DESIGNS: 2 c. Lobster (wrongly inscr. "Panulirus" for "Palinurus"). 3 c. (No. 324) Sea Horse (wrongly inscr. "Hippocanpus"). 3 c. (No. 344) (correctly inscr. "Hippocampus"). 4 c. Sea Urchin. 5 c. Staghorn Coral. 6 c. Butterfly Fish. 8 c. File Shell. 12 c. Balloon Fish. 15 c. Angel Fish. 25 c. Brain Coral. 35 c. Brittle Star. 50 c. Flying Fish. $1, Queen Conch Shell. $2·50, Fiddler Crab. VERT. $5, Dolphin.

1966. Churchill Commem. As T 38 of Antigua.

336.	1 c. blue	10	10
337.	4 c. green	30	10
338.	25 c. brown	70	40
339.	35 c. violet	80	60

1966. Royal Visit. As T 39 of Antigua.

340.	3 c. black and blue ..	40	25
341.	35 c. black and mauve ..	1·60	80

54. Arms of Barbados.

1966. Independence. Multicoloured.

356.	4 c. Type 54	10	10
357.	25 c. Hilton Hotel (horiz.)	15	10
358.	35 c. G. Sobers (Test cricketer)	60	20
359.	50 c. Pine Hill Dairy (horiz)	60	20

1967. 20th Anniv. of U.N.E.S.C.O. As T 54/56 of Antigua.

360.	4 c. multicoloured ..	30	10
361.	12 c. yellow, violet & olive	70	55
362.	25 c. black, purple & orange	1·00	1·40

MORE DETAILED LISTS
are given in the Stanley Gibbons Catalogues referred to in the country headings.
For lists of current volumes see Introduction.

58. Policeman and Anchor.

1967. Cent. of Harbour Police. Multicoloured.

363.	4 c. Type 58	10	10
364.	25 c. Policeman with telescope	20	10
365.	35 c. "BPI" (police launch) (horiz.)	20	10
366.	50 c. Policeman outside H.Q.	25	25

The 25 c. and 50 c. are horiz.

62. Governor-General Sir Winston Scott, G.C.M.G.

67. Radar Antenna.

66. U.N. Building, Santiago, Chile.

1967. 1st Anniv. of Independence. Mult.

367.	4 c. Type 62	10	10
368.	25 c. Independence Arch..	15	10
369.	35 c. Treasury Building ..	15	10
370.	50 c. Parliament Building	15	20

Nos. 368/70 are horiz.

1968. 20th Anniv. of Economic Commission for Latin America.

371. 66.	15 c. multicoloured ..	10	10

1968. World Meteorological Day. Mult.

372.	3 c. Type 67	10	10
373.	25 c. Meteorological Institute (horiz.)	25	10
374.	50 c. Harp Gun and Coat of Arms	30	20

70. Lady Baden-Powell and Guide at Camp Fire.

1968. Golden Jubilee of Girl Guiding in Barbados.

375.	70.	3 c. blue, blk. & gold	25	20
376.	–	25 c. blue, blk. & gold	50	25
377.	–	35 c. yell., blk. & gold	65	25

DESIGNS: 25 c. Lady Baden-Powell and Pax Hill. 35 c. Lady Baden-Powell and Guides' Badge.

73. Hands breaking Chain, and Human Rights Emblem.

1968. Human Rights Year.

378.	73.	4 c. violet, brown & grn.	10	10
379.	–	25 c. blk., blue & yellow	10	10
380.	–	35 c. multicoloured ..	10	10

DESIGNS: 25 c. Human Rights Emblem and family enchained. 35 c. Shadows of refugees beyond opening fence.

76. Racehorses in the Paddock.

1969. Horse-Racing. Multicoloured.

381.	4 c. Type 76	20	10
382.	25 c. Starting-Gate ..	35	10
383.	35 c. On the flat	35	10
384.	50 c. The Winning-post ..	45	60

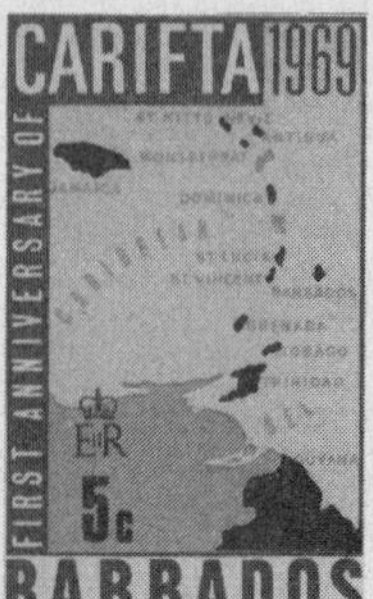

80. Map showing "CARIFTA" Countries.

1969. 1st Anniv. of "CARIFTA". Mult.

386.	5 c. Type 80	10	10
387.	12 c. "Strength in Unity"	10	10
388.	25 c. Type 80 (horiz.) ..	10	10
389.	50 c. As 12 c.	15	20

82. I.L.O. Emblem and "1919-1969".

1969. 50th Anniversary of I.L.O.

390.	82.	4 c. black, green & blue	10	10
391.		25 c. blk, mauve & red	20	10

1969. No. 363 surch ONE CENT.

392. 58.	1 c. on 4 c. mult. ..	10	10

84. National Scout Badge.

1969. Independence of Barbados Boy Scouts Assn., and 50th Anniv. of Barbados Sea Scouts. Multicoloured.

393.	5 c. Type 84	10	10
394.	25 c. Sea Scouts rowing ..	35	10
395.	35 c. Scouts around campfire	45	10
396.	50 c. Scouts and National Scout H.Q.	60	40

1970. No. 346 surch 4.

398.	4 c. on 5 c. sepia, red & lilac	10	10

89. Lion at Gun Hill.

1970. Multicoloured.

399.	1 c. Type 89	10	30
400.	2 c. Trafalgar Fountain ..	30	40
401.	3 c. Montefiore Drinking Fountain	10	40
402.	4 c. St. James' Monument	10	10
403.	5 c. St. Ann's Fort ..	10	10
404.	6 c. Old Sugar Mill, Morgan Lewis	35	2·00
405.	8 c. The Cenotaph ..	10	10
406.	10 c. South Point Lighthouse	85	15
407.	12 c. Barbados Museum..	40	10
408.	15 c. Sharon Moravian Church	30	15
409.	25 c. George Washington House	25	15
410.	35 c. Nicholas Abbey ..	30	75
411.	50 c. Bowmanston Pumping Station	40	85
412.	$1 Queen Elizabeth Hospital	70	2·50
413.	$2.50 Sugar Factory ..	2·00	4·00
467.	$5 Seawell Int. Airport ..	4·00	5·50

The 12 c. to $5 are horiz.

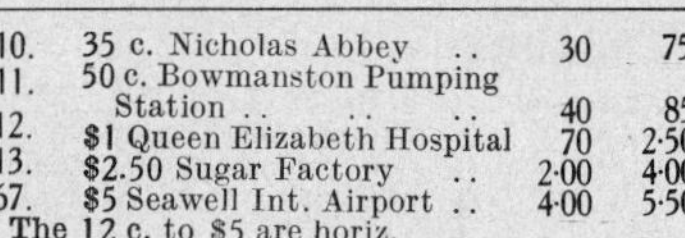

105. Primary Schoolgirl.

1970. 25th Anniv. of U.N. Multicoloured.

415.	4 c. Type 105	10	10
416.	5 c. Secondary Schoolboy	10	10
417.	25 c. Technical Student ..	35	10
418.	50 c. University Building	55	45

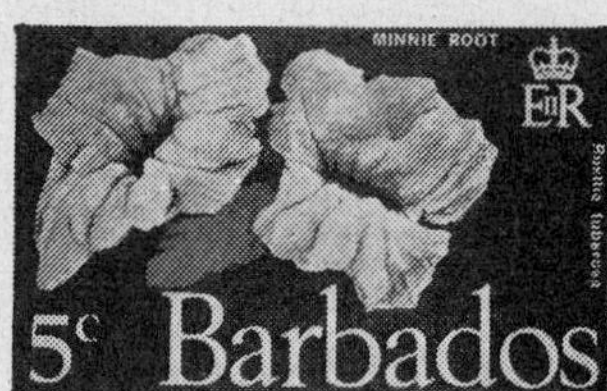

106. Minnie Root.

1970. Flowers of Barbados. Multicoloured.

419.	1 c. Barbados Easter Lily	10	20
420.	5 c. Type 106 ..	40	10
421.	10 c. Eyelash Orchid ..	1·00	10
422.	25 c. Pride of Barbados ..	1·10	55
423.	35 c. Christmas Hope ..	1·25	70

The 1 c. and 25 c. are vert.

107. "Via Dolorosa" Window, St. Margaret's Church, St. John.

1971. Easter. Multicoloured.

425.	4 c. Type 107	10	10
426.	10 c. "The Resurrection" (Benjamin West) ..	10	10
427.	35 c. Type 107	15	10
428.	50 c. As 10 c.	30	60

108. "Sailfish" Craft.

1971. Tourism. Multicoloured.

429.	1 c. Type 108	10	10
430.	5 c. Tennis	15	10
431.	12 c. Horse-riding ..	20	10
432.	25 c. Water-skiing ..	30	20
433.	50 c. Scuba-diving ..	50	65

109. S. J. Prescod (politician).

1971. Death Cent. of Samuel Jackman Prescod.

434.	109.	3 c. multicoloured ..	10	10
435.		35 c. multicoloured ..	15	10

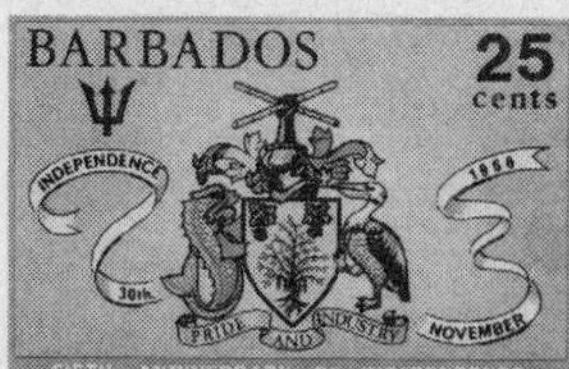

110. Arms of Barbados.

1971. 5th Anniv. of Independence. Mult.

436. 4 c. Type **110** 15 10
437. 15 c. National flag and map 25 10
438. 25 c. Type **110** 35 10
439. 50 c. As 15 c. 70 55

111. Transmitting "Then and Now".

1972. Cent. of Cable Link. Multicoloured.

440. 4 c. Type **111** 10 10
441. 10 c. Cable Ship "Stanley Angwin" 15 10
442. 35 c. Barbados Earth Station and "Intelsat 4" .. 35 15
443. 50 c. Mt. Misery and Tropospheric Scatter Station .. 50 80

112. Map and Badge.

1972. Diamond Jubilee of Scouts. Mult.

444. 5 c. Type **112** 10 10
445. 15 c. Pioneers of Scouting 15 10
446. 25 c. Scouts 30 15
447. 50 c. Flags 50 75

Nos. 445/7 are horiz.

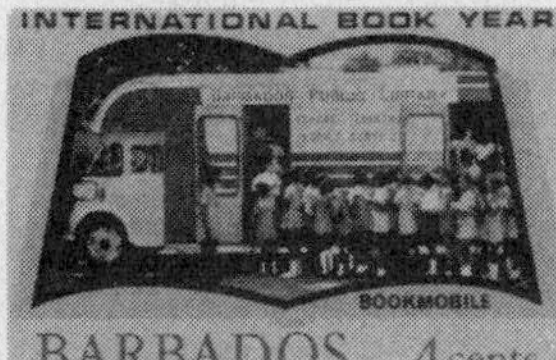

113. Mobile Library.

1972. Int. Book Year. Multicoloured.

448. 4 c. Type **113** 10 10
449. 15 c. Visual-aids van .. 10 10
450. 25 c. Public Library .. 20 10
451. $1 Codrington College .. 1·25 1·50

114. Potter's Wheel.

1973. Pottery in Barbados. Mult.

468. 5 c. Type **114** 10 10
469. 15 c. Kilns 20 10
470. 25 c. Finished products .. 25 10
471. $1 Market scene .. .. 90 1·10

115. First Flight, 1911.

1973. Aviation.

472.**115.** 5 c. multicoloured .. 15 10
473. – 15 c. multicoloured .. 60 10
474. – 25 c. blue, blk. & cobalt 85 20
475. – 50 c. multicoloured .. 1·50 1·90

DESIGNS: 15 c. First flight to Barbados, 1928. 25 c. Passenger aircraft, 1939. 50 c. "VC-10" airliner, 1973.

116. University Chancellor.

1973. 25th Anniv. of University of West Indies. Multicoloured.

476. 5 c. Type **116** 10 10
477. 25 c. Sherlock Hall .. 25 15
478. 35 c. Cave Hill Campus .. 30 25

1974. No. 462 surch.

479. 4 c. on 25 c. multicoloured 10 10

118. Old Sail Boat.

1974. Fishing Boats of Barbados. Mult.

480. 15 c. Type **118** 20 15
481. 35 c. Rowing-boat .. 45 25
482. 50 c. Motor fishing-boat .. 60 60
483. $1 "Calamar" (fishing boat) .. .. .. 1·00 1·10

119. "Cattleya Gaskelliana Alba".

1974. Orchids. Multicoloured.

485 1 c. Type **119** 15 70
486 2 c. "Renanthera storiei" 20 70
512 3 c. "Dendrobium" "Rose Marie" 15 80
546 4 c. "Epidendrum ibaguense" 45 2·00
514 5 c. "Schomburgkia humboldtii" 35 15
490 8 c. "Oncidium ampliatum" 1·00 80
515 10 c. "Arachnis maggie oei" 35 10
492 12 c. "Dendrobium aggregatum" 45 70
517 15 c. "Paphiopedilum puddle" 70 15
493a 20 c. "Spathoglottis" "The Gold" .. .. 4·75 4·50
518 25 c. "Epidendrum ciliare" (Eyelash) 70 10
495 35 c. "Bletia patula" 2·00 1·50
519 45 c. "Phalaenopsis schilleriana" "Sunset Glow" 60 15
496 50 c. As 45 c. .. .. 4·00 2·00
497 $1 "Ascocenda" "Red Gem" 4·00 3·25
498 $2.50 "Brassolaeliocattleya" "Nugget" .. .. 3·50 3·25
499 $5 "Caularthron bicornatum" .. .. 3·50 6·00
500 $10 "Vanda" "Josephine Black" .. .. .. 4·00 12·00

The 1 c., 20 c., 25 c., $2.50 and $5 are horiz. the rest are vert.

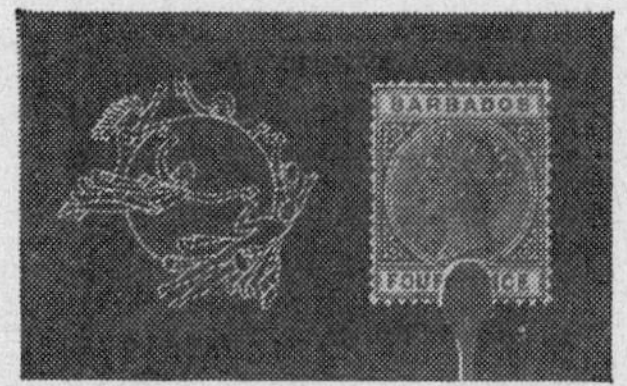

120. 4d. Stamp of 1882, and U.P.U. Emblem.

1974. Centenary of Universal Postal Union.

501.**120.** 8 c. mauve, orge. & grn. 10 10
502. – 35 c. red, orge. & brown 20 10
503. – 50 c. ultram., bl. & silver 25 30
504. – $1 blue, brown & black 55 80

DESIGNS: 35 c. Letters encircling the globe. 50 c. U.P.U. emblem and arms of Barbados. $1, Map of Barbados, sailing-ship and aeroplane.

121. Royal Yacht "Britannia".

1975. Royal Visit. Multicoloured.

506. 8 c. Type **121** 20 15
507. 25 c. Type **121** 50 25
508. 35 c. Sunset and palms .. 60 30
509. $1 As 35 c. .. .. 1·75 2·00

122. St. Michael's Cathedral.

1975. 150th Anniv. of Anglican Diocese. Mult.

526. 5 c. Type **122** 10 10
527. 15 c. Bishop Coleridge .. 15 10
528. 50 c. All Saints' Church .. 45 50
529. $1 "Archangel Michael and Satan" (Stained-glass window, St. Michael's Cathedral, Bridgetown) 70 80

123. Pony Float.

1975. Crop-over Festival. Multicoloured.

531. 8 c. Type **123** 10 10
532. 25 c. Man on stilts .. 10 10
533. 35 c. Maypole dancing .. 15 10
534. 50 c. Cuban dancers .. 30 45

124. Barbados Coat of Arms. **125.** 17th-Century Sailing Ship.

1975. Coil Definitives.

536.**124.** 5 c. blue 15 60
537. 25 c. violet .. .. 25 1·00

1975. 350th Anniv. of First Settlement. Mult.

538. 4 c. Type **125** 25 10
539. 10 c. Bearded fig tree and fruit 30 15
540. 25 c. Ogilvy's 17-century map 50 30
541. $1 Captain John Powell .. 2·00 3·00

126. Map of the Caribbean.

1976. West Indian Victory in World Cricket Cup.

559.**126.** 25 c. multicoloured .. 1·00 1·00
560. – 45 c. black and purple .. 1·25 1·75

DESIGN—VERT 45 c. The Prudential Cup.

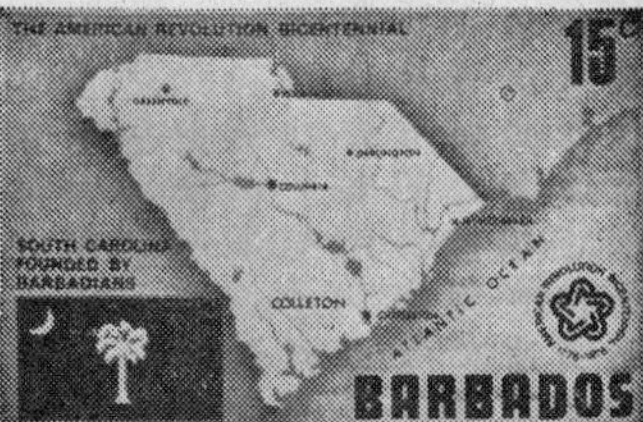

127. Flag and Map of South Carolina.

1976. Bicent. of American Revolution. Mult.

561. 15 c. Type **127** 40 15
562. 25 c. George Washington and map of Bridgetown 45 15
563. 50 c. Independence Declaration 70 80
564. $1 Prince Hall .. .. 95 2·00

128. Early Postman.

1976. 125th Anniv. of Post Office Act. Mult.

565. 8 c. Type **128** 10 10
566. 35 c. Modern postman .. 25 10
567. 50 c. Early letter 30 25
568. $1 Delivery van 50 75

129. Coast Guard Launches.

1976. 10th Anniv. of Independence. Mult.

569. 5 c. Type **129** 15 10
570. 15 c. Reverse of currency note 15 10
571. 25 c. Barbados national anthem 20 20
572. $1 Independence Day parade .. .. .. 55 1·25

130. Arrival of Coronation Coach at Westminster Abbey.

1977. Silver Jubilee. Multicoloured.

574. 15 c. Queen knighting Garfield Sobers 1975 .. 60 25
575. 50 c. Type **130** 75 40
576. $1 Queen entering Abbey 1·10 70

131. Underwater Park.

1977. Natural Beauty of Barbados. Mult.

577. 5 c. Type **131** 15 10
578. 35 c. Royal Palms (vert.) 30 10
579. 50 c. Underwater caves .. 40 35
580. $1 Stalagmite in Harrison's Cave (vert.) .. 70 1·00

132. Maces of the House of Commons.

1977. 13th Regional Conference of Commonwealth Parliamentary Association.

582. **132.** 10 c. orge., yell. & brn. 10 10
583. – 25 c. green, orange and dark green 10 10
584. – 50 c. multicoloured .. 20 20
585. – $1 blue, orange and deep blue 55 75

DESIGNS—VERT. 25 c. Speaker's Chair. 50 c. Senate Chamber. HORIZ. $1, Sam Lord's Castle.

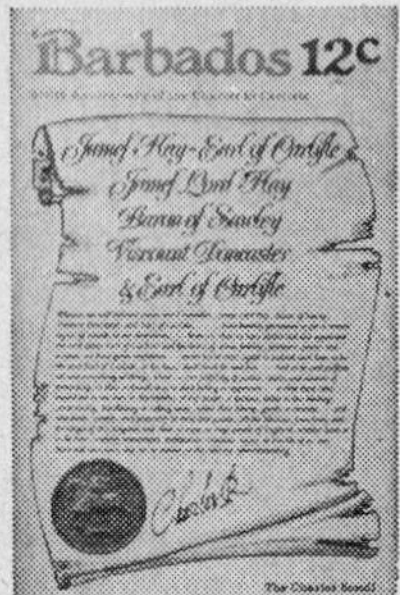

133. The Charter Scroll.

1977. 350th Anniv. of Granting of Charter to Earl of Carlisle. Multicoloured.

586. 12 c. Type **133** 15 10
587. 25 c. The earl receiving charter 15 10
588. 45 c. The earl and Charles I (horiz.) 30 35
589. $1 Ligon's map, 1657 (horiz.) .. .. .. 50 1·00

1977. Royal Visit. As Nos. 574/6 but inscr. "SILVER JUBILEE ROYAL VISIT".

590. 15 c. Garfield Sobers being knighted, 1975 .. .. 40 40
591. 50 c. Type **130** 60 50
592. $1 Queen entering Abbey 90 75

134. Gibson's Map of Bridgetown, 1766.

1978. 350th Anniv. of Founding of Bridgetown.

593. **134.** 12 c. multicoloured .. 15 10
594. – 25 c. black, green & gold 20 10
595. – 45 c. multicoloured .. 25 15
596. – $1 multicoloured .. 40 60

DESIGNS: 25 c. "A Prospect of Bridgetown in Barbados" (engraving by S. Copens, 1695). 45 c. "Trafalgar Square, Bridgetown" (drawing by J. M. Carter, 1835). $1, The Bridges, 1978.

135. Pelican.

1978. 25th Anniv. of Coronation.

597. – 50 c. olive, black & blue 25 50
598. – 50 c. multicoloured .. 25 50
599. **135.** 50 c. olive, black & blue 25 50

DESIGNS: No. 597, Griffin of Edward III. No. 598, Queen Elizabeth II.

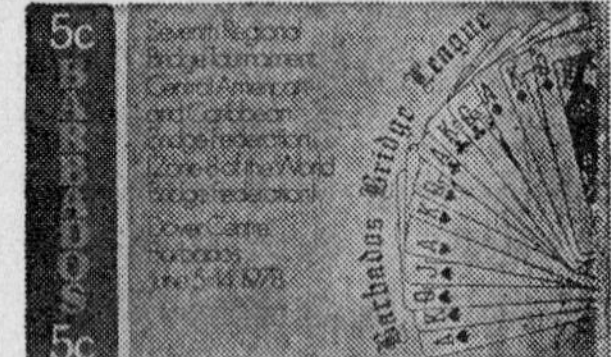

136. Barbados Bridge League Logo.

1978. 7th Regional Bridge Tournament, Barbados. Multicoloured.

600. 5 c. Type **136** 10 10
601. 10 c. Emblem of World Bridge Federation .. 15 10
602. 45 c. Central American and Caribbean Bridge Federation emblem 25 10
603. $1 Playing cards on map of Caribbean 40 60

137. Camp Scene.

(Illustration reduced. Actual size 60×35mm).

1978. Diamond Jubilee of Guiding. Mult.

605. 12 c. Type **137** 25 15
606. 28 c. Community work .. 40 15
607. 50 c. Badge and "60" (vert.) 55 30
608. $1 Guide badge (vert.) .. 75 1·00

138. Garment Industry.

1978. Industries of Barbados. Multicoloured.

609. 12 c. Type **138** 15 10
610. 28 c. Cooper (vert.) .. 25 25
611. 45 c. Blacksmith (vert.) .. 35 55
612. 50 c. Wrought iron working 40 55

139. Early Mail Steamer.

1979. Ships. Multicoloured.

613. 12 c. Type **139** 35 10
614. 25 c. "Queen Elizabeth 2" in Deep Water Harbour 55 15
615. 50 c. "Ra II" nearing Barbados 75 80
616. $1 Early mail steamer (different) .. .. .. 1·00 1·75

140. 1953 1 c. Definitive Stamp.

1979. Death Centenary of Sir Rowland Hill. Multicoloured.

617. 12 c. Type **140** 20 15
618. 28 c. 1975 350th Anniv. of first settlement 25 c. commemorative (vert.) 25 30
619. 45 c. Penny Black with Maltese Cross postmark (vert.) 40 45

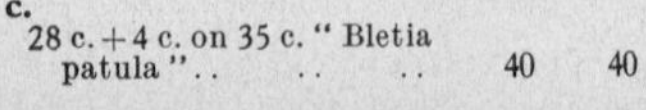

1979. St. Vincent Relief Fund. No. 495 surch. **ST. VINCENT RELIEF FUND 28 c. + 4 c.**

621. 28 c.+4 c. on 35 c. "Bletia patula" 40 40

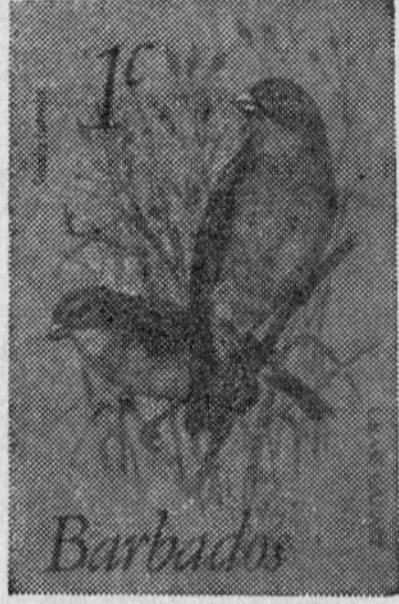

142. Grassland Yellow Finch.

1979. Birds. Multicoloured.

622 1 c. Type **142** 10 60
623 2 c. Grey Kingbird .. 10 60
624 5 c. Lesser Antillean Bullfinch 10 60
625 8 c. Magnificent Frigate Bird (Cobbler) 10 40
626 10 c. Cattle Egret .. 10 30
627 12 c. Green Heron .. 15 45
627a 15 c. Carib Grackle .. 4·50 2·50
628 20 c. Antillean Crested Hummingbird .. 20 45
629 25 c. Scaly-breasted Ground Dove 20 50
630 28 c. As 15 c. 50 60
631 35 c. Green-throated Carib 30 60
631b 40 c. Red necked Pigeon 4·50 2·50
632 45 c. Zenaida Dove .. 35 60
633 50 c. As 40 c. 55 80
633a 55 c. American Golden Plover .. .. 3·50 2·25
633b 60 c. Bananaquit .. .. 4·50 3·25
634 70 c. As 60 c. .. .. 55 1·40
635 $1 Caribbean Elaenia .. 1·00 1·50
636 $2·50 American Redstart 2·00 4·50
637 $5 Belted Kingfisher .. 3·25 8·00
638 $10 Moorhen .. .. 6·50 14·00

143. Unloading H.A.R.P. Gun on Railway Wagon at Foul Bay.

1979. Space Projects Commemorations. Mult.

639. 10 c. Type **143** 15 10
640. 12 c. H.A.R.P. gun on railway wagon under tow (vert.) 20 15
641. 20 c. Firing launcher (vert.) 20 20
642. 28 c. Bath Earth Station and "Intelsat" 30 30
643. 45 c. "Intelsat" over Caribbean 45 50
644. 50 c. "Intelsat" over Atlantic (vert.) .. 45 60

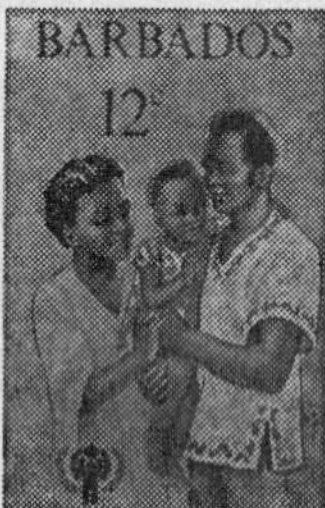

144. Family.

1979. International Year of the Child. Mult.

646. 12 c. Type **144** 10 10
647. 28 c. Ring of children and map of Barbados .. 15 15
648. 45 c. Child with teacher 20 20
649. 50 c. Children playing .. 20 20
650. $1 Children and kite .. 35 45

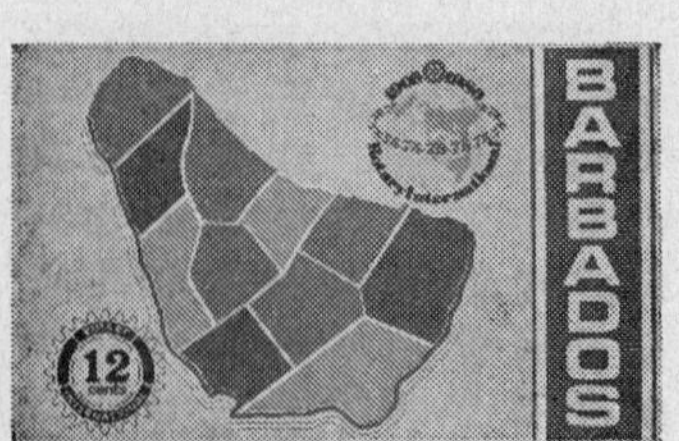

145. Map of Barbados.

1980. 75th Anniv. of Rotary International. Multicoloured.

651. 12 c. Type **145** 15 10
652. 28 c. Map of Caribbean .. 20 15
653. 50 c. Globe (anniversary emblem) 25 35
654. $1 Paul P. Harris (founder) 40 95

146. Private, Artillery Company, Barbados Volunteer Force, circa 1909.

1980. Barbados Regiment. Multicoloured.

655. 12 c. Type **146** 25 10
656. 35 c. Drum Major, Zouave uniform 45 15
657. 50 c. Sovereign's and Regimental Colours 50 30
658. $1 Barbados Regiment Corps of Women .. 75 70

148. Underwater Scenery.

1980. Underwater Scenery.

660. **148.** 12 c. multicoloured .. 15 10
661. – 28 c. multicoloured .. 25 15
662. – 50 c. multicoloured .. 40 25
663. – $1 multicoloured .. 65 70

Nos. 661/3 show various underwater scenes.

149. Bathsheba Railway Station.

1981. Early Transport. Multicoloured.

665. 12 c. Type **149** 10 10
666. 28 c. Cab stand in The Green 20 15
667. 45 c. Animal-drawn tram 30 25
668. 70 c. Horse-drawn bus .. 45 50
669. $1 Railway Station, Fairchild Street 60 85

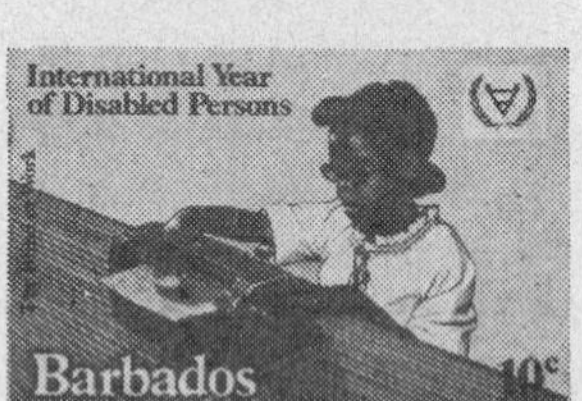

150. The Blind at Work.

1981. International Year for Disabled Persons. Multicoloured.

670. 10 c. Type **150** 20 10
671. 25 c. Sign language (vert.) 40 20
672. 45 c. "Be alert to the white cane" (vert.) 70 40
673. $2·50 Children at play .. 2·25 3·25

151. Prince Charles dressed for Polo.

1981. Royal Wedding. Multicoloured.

674. 28 c. Wedding bouquet from Barbados 20 10
675. 50 c. Type **151** 25 15
676. $2·50 Prince Charles and Lady Diana Spencer .. 80 1·25

152. Landship Manoeuvre.

1981. Carifesta (Caribbean Festival of Arts), Barbados. Multicoloured.

677. 15 c. Type **152** 20 15
678. 20 c. Yoruba dancers .. 20 15
679. 40 c. Tuk band 30 25
680. 55 c. Sculpture by Frank Collymore 45 35
681. $1 Harbour scene .. 70 75

1981. Nos. 630, 632 and 634 surch.

682. 15 c. on 28 c. Carib Grackle 15 15
683. 40 c. on 45 c. Zenaida Dove 20 35
684. 60 c. on 70 c. Bananaquit .. 30 45

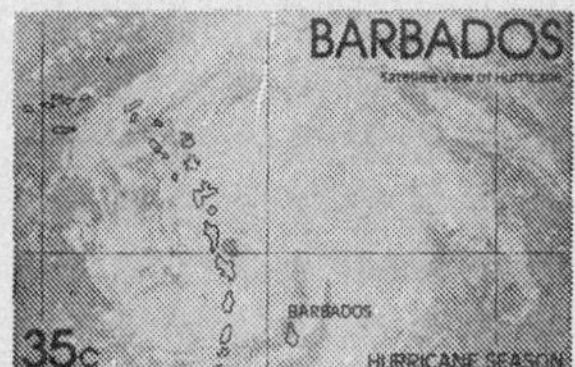

154. Satellite view of Hurricane.

1981. Hurricane Season.

685. **154.** 35 c. black and blue .. 30 20
686. – 50 c. multicoloured .. 40 35
687. – 60 c. multicoloured .. 50 50
688. – $1 multicoloured .. 75 90

DESIGNS: 50 c. Hurricane "Gladys" from "Apollo 7". 60 c. Police Department on hurricane watch. $1, Hurricane hunter (McDonnell "F2H-2P (Banshee)" jet aircraft).

155. Twin Falls.

1981. Harrison's Cave. Multicoloured.

689. 10 c. Type **155** 10 10
690. 20 c. Stream in Rotunda Room 20 15
691. 55 c. Formations in Rotunda Room 40 50
692. $2.50 Cascade Pool .. 1·25 2·25

156. Black Belly Ram.

1982. Black Belly Sheep. Multicoloured.

693. 40 c. Type **156** 30 30
694. 50 c. Black belly ewe .. 30 35
695. 60 c. Ewe with lambs .. 40 60
696. $1 Ram and ewe, with map of Barbados .. .. 65 1·50

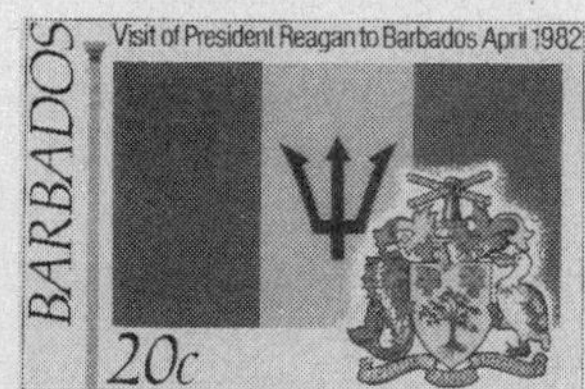

157. Barbados Coat of Arms and Flag.

1982. President Reagan's Visit. Mult.

697. 20 c. Type **157** .. .. 80 1·00
698. 20 c. U.S.A. coat of arms and flag .. .. 80 1·00
699. 55 c. Type **157** .. .. 1·25 1·50
700. 55 c. As No. 698 .. .. 1·25 1·50

158. Lighter.

1982. Early Marine Transport. Mult.

701. 20 c. Type **158** 20 15
702. 35 c. Rowing boat .. 35 25
703. 55 c. Speightstown schooner 50 40
704. $2.50 Inter-colonial schooner .. .. 2·00 2·25

159. Bride and Earl Spencer Proceeding up the Aisle.

1982. 21st Birthday of Princess of Wales. Multicoloured.

705. 20 c. Barbados coat of arms 20 15
706. 60 c. Princess at Llanelwedd, October, 1981 .. 55 50
707. $1.20 Type **159** .. .. 90 1·10
708. $2.50 Formal portrait .. 1·50 1·90

160. "To Help other People".

1982. 75th Anniv. of Boy Scout Movement. Multicoloured.

709. 15 c. Type **160** 60 10
710. 40 c. "I Promise to do my Best" (horiz.) .. .. 1·00 30
711. 55 c. "To do my Duty to God, the Queen and my Country" (horiz.) .. 1·25 55
712. $1 National and Troop flags .. .. 1·75 1·50

161. Arms of George Washington.

1982. 250th Birth Anniv. of George Washington. Multicoloured.

714. 10 c. Type **161** 10 10
715. 55 c. Washington House, Barbados 45 45
716. 60 c. Washington with troops 50 50
717. $2. 50 Washington taking Oath .. .. 1·60 1·60

162. "Agraulis vanillae".

1983. Butterflies. Multicoloured.

718 20 c. Type **162** 70 15
719 40 c. "Danaus plexippus" 1·00 40
720 55 c. "Hypolimnas misippus" .. .. 1·10 45
721 $2·50 "Hemiargus hanno" 2·75 2·00

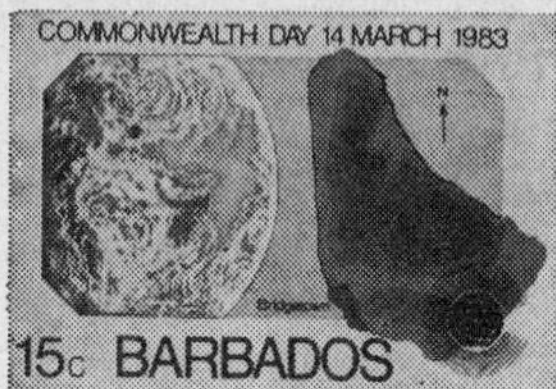

163. Map of Barbados and Satellite View.

1983. Commonwealth Day. Multicoloured.

722. 15 c. Type **163** 25 10
723. 40 c. Tourist beach .. 40 20
724. 60 c. Sugar cane harvesting 60 40
725. $1 Cricket match .. .. 1·50 1·10

164. U.S. Navy Dirigible.

1983. Bicentenary of Manned Flight.

726. 20 c. Type **164** 60 10
727. 40 c. Douglas "DC3" .. 85 30
728. 55 c. Vickers "Viscount" 95 70
729. $1 Lockheed "Tristar" .. 1·75 2·25

165. Nash "600", 1941.

1983. Classic Cars. Multicoloured.

730. 25 c. Type **165** 40 20
731. 45 c. Dodge, 1938 .. .. 50 30
732. 75 c. Ford "Model AA", 1930 .. .. .. 70 85
733. $2·50 Dodge "Four", 1918 .. .. .. 2·00 2·75

166. Game in Progress.

167. Angel playing Lute (detail "The Virgin and Child") (Masaccio).

1983. Table Tennis World Cup Competition. Multicoloured.

734. 20 c. Type **166** 25 20
735. 65 c. Map of Barbados .. 50 55
736. $1 World Table Tennis Cup 75 1·00

1983. Christmas. 50th Anniv. of Barbados Museum.

737. **167.** 10 c. multicoloured .. 30 10
738. – 25 c. multicoloured .. 55 20
739. – 45 c. multicoloured .. 80 40
740. – 75 c. black and gold .. 1·25 1·40
741. – $2·50 multicoloured .. 3·75 5·00

DESIGNS—HORIZ. 45 c. "The Barbados Museum" (Richard Day). 75 c. "St. Ann's Garrison" (W. S. Hedges). $2.50 Needham's Point, Carlisle Bay. VERT. 25 c., $2 Different details from "The Virgin and Child" (Masaccio).

168. Track and Field Events.

1984. Olympic Games, Los Angeles.

745. **168.** 50 c. green, black and brown 60 45
746. – 65 c. orange, black and brown 80 60
747. – 75 c. blue, black and deep blue 90 70
748. – $1 brown, black and yellow .. .. .. 1·25 90

DESIGNS: 65 c. Shooting. 75 c. Sailing. $1 Cycling.

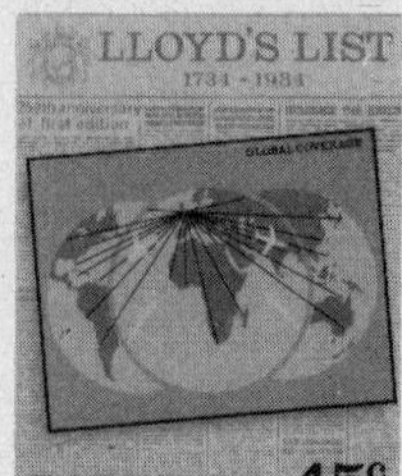

169. Global Coverage.

1984. 250th Anniv of "Lloyd's List" (newspaper). Multicoloured.

750 45 c. Type **169** 70 40
751 50 c. Bridgetown harbour 80 50
752 75 c. "Philosopher" (full-rigged ship), 1857 .. 1·10 70
753 $1 "Sea Princess" (liner), 1984 .. .. .. 1·25 95

171. Local Junior Match.

1984. 60th Anniv of International Chess Federation. Multicoloured.

755 25 c. Type **171** .. .. 1·00 25
756 45 c. Staunton and 19th-century knights .. 1·40 45
757 65 c. Staunton queen and 18th-century queen from Macao .. .. 1·60 70
758 $2 Staunton and 17th-century rooks .. .. 3·25 3·50

172. Poinsettia.

1984. Christmas. Flowers. Multicoloured.

759. 50 c. Type **172** .. .. 1·50 70
760. 65 c. Snow-on-the-Mountain .. .. 1·75 90
761. 75 c. Christmas Candle .. 2·00 2·00
762. $1 Christmas Hope .. 2·25 2·75

173. Pink-tipped Anemone.

1985. Marine Life. Multicoloured.

794 1 c. Bristle Worm 20 30
795 2 c. Spotted Trunkfish .. 20 30
796 5 c. Coney 30 15
797 10 c. Type **173** 30 15
798 20 c. Christmas Tree Worm 30 30
799 25 c. Hermit Crab 40 40
800 35 c. Animal Flower .. 60 35
801 40 c. Vase Sponge 50 50
802 45 c. Spotted Moray .. 60 50
803 50 c. Ghost Crab 60 60
804 65 c. Flamingo Tongue Snail 65 70
805 75 c. Sergeant Major .. 70 75
806 $1 Caribbean Warty Anemone 85 85
807 $2.50 Green Turtle .. 2·00 1·75
808 $5 Rock Beauty (fish) .. 4·50 3·25
809 $10 Elkhorn Coral .. .. 9·00 8·00

174. The Queen Mother at Docks.

1985. Life and Times of Queen Elizabeth the Queen Mother. Multicoloured.

No.	Description	Unused	Used
779.	25 c. In the White Drawing Room, Buckingham Palace, 1930s	15	20
780.	65 c. With Lady Diana Spencer at Trooping the Colour, 1981	45	50
781.	75 c. Type **174**	55	60
782.	$1 With Prince Henry at his christening (from photo by Lord Snowdon)	70	75

175. Peregrine Falcon.

1985. Birth Bicentenary of John J. Audubon (ornithologist). Designs showing original paintings. Multicoloured.

No.	Description	Unused	Used
784.	45 c. Type **175**	1·25	55
785.	65 c. Prairie Warbler (vert.)	1·50	90
786.	75 c. Great Blue Heron (vert.)	1·75	2·00
787.	$1 Yellow Warbler (vert.)	2·00	4·25

176. Intelsat Satellite orbiting Earth.

1985. 20th Anniv. of Intelsat Satellite System.

No.	Description	Unused	Used
788.	**176.** 75 c. multicoloured	75	60

177. Traffic Policeman.

1985. 150th Anniv. of Royal Barbados Police. Multicoloured.

No.	Description	Unused	Used
789.	25 c. Type **177**	1·00	20
790.	50 c. Police Band on bandstand	1·75	70
791.	65 c. Dog handler	2·25	1·10
792.	$1 Mounted policeman in ceremonial uniform	2·50	2·00

1986. 60th Birthday of Queen Elizabeth II. As T **110** of Ascension. Multicoloured.

No.	Description	Unused	Used
810.	25 c. Princess Elizabeth aged two, 1928	15	20
811.	50 c. At University College of West Indies, Jamaica, 1953	35	40
812.	65 c. With Duke of Edinburgh, Barbados, 1985	45	50
813.	75 c. At banquet in Sao Paulo, Brazil, 1968	55	60
814.	$2 At Crown Agents Head Office, London, 1983	1·40	1·50

178. Trans-Canada "North Star DC-472" Airliner.

1986. "Expo '86" World Fair, Vancouver. Multicoloured.

No.	Description	Unused	Used
815	50 c. Type **178**	50	40
816	$2.50 "Lady Nelson" (cargo liner)	2·00	1·90

1986. "Ameripex '86" International Stamp Exhibition, Chicago. As T **164** of Bahamas, showing Barbados stamps. Multicoloured.

No.	Description	Unused	Used
817.	45 c. 1976 Bicentenary of American Revolution 25 c.	75	35
818.	50 c. 1976 Bicentenary of American Revolution 25 c.	85	40
819.	65 c. 1981 Hurricane Season $1	95	50
820.	$1 1982 Visit of President Reagan 55 c. × 2	1·25	75

1986. Royal Wedding. As T **112** of Ascension. Multicoloured.

No.	Description	Unused	Used
822.	45 c. Prince Andrew and Miss Sarah Ferguson	60	35
823.	$1 Prince Andrew in Midshipman's uniform	1·00	75

179. Transporting Electricity Poles, 1923.

1986. 75th Anniv. of Electricity in Barbados. Multicoloured.

No.	Description	Unused	Used
824.	10 c. Type **179**	15	10
825.	25 c. Heathman Ladder, 1935 (vert.)	25	20
826.	65 c. Transport fleet, 1941	60	50
827.	$2 Bucket truck, 1986 (vert.)	1·60	1·75

180. "Alpinia purpurata" and Church Window.

1986. Christmas. Multicoloured.

No.	Description	Unused	Used
828.	25 c. Type **180**	20	20
829.	50 c. "Anthurium andraeanum"	45	45
830.	75 c. "Heliconia rostrata"	75	70
831.	$2 "Heliconia × psittacorum	1·50	2·25

181. Shot Putting.

1987. 10th Anniv. of Special Olympics. Multicoloured.

No.	Description	Unused	Used
832.	15 c. Type **181**	25	15
833.	45 c. Wheelchair racing	45	30
834.	65 c. Long jumping	60	50
835.	$2 Logo and slogan	1·75	2·00

182. Barn Swallow.

1987. "Capex '87" International Stamp Exhibition, Toronto. Birds. Multicoloured.

No.	Description	Unused	Used
836.	25 c. Type **182**	1·00	40
837.	50 c. Yellow warbler	1·25	80
838.	65 c. Audubon's shearwater	1·50	1·50
839.	75 c. Black-whiskered vireo	1·75	2·00
840.	$1 Scarlet tanager	1·90	2·50

183. Sea Scout saluting.

1987. 75th Anniv. of Scouting in Barbados. Multicoloured.

No.	Description	Unused	Used
841.	10 c. Type **183**	20	10
842.	25 c. Scout jamboree	30	20
843.	65 c. Scout badges	65	45
844.	$2 Scout band	1·60	1·75

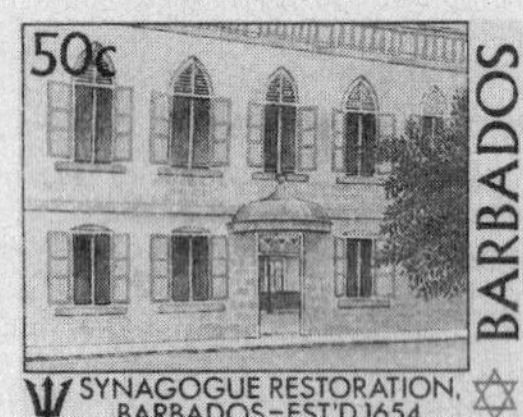

184. Bridgetown Synagogue.

1987. Restoration of Bridgetown Synagogue. Multicoloured.

No.	Description	Unused	Used
845.	50 c. Type **184**	1·25	1·25
846.	65 c. Interior of Synagogue	1·50	1·50
847.	75 c. Ten Commandments (vert.)	1·75	2·75
848.	$1 Marble laver (vert.)	2·00	2·50

185. Arms and Colonial Seal.

1987. 21st Anniv. of Independence. Mult.

No.	Description	Unused	Used
849.	29 c. Type **185**	30	20
850.	45 c. Flags of Barbados and Great Britain	40	30
851.	65 c. Silver dollar and one penny coins	70	45
852.	$2 Colours of Barbados Regiment	1·50	1·40

186. Herman C. Griffith.

1988. West Indian Cricket. Each showing portrait, cricket equipment and early belt buckle. Multicoloured.

No.	Description	Unused	Used
854	15 c. E. A. Manny Martindale	1·00	40
855	45 c. George Challenor	1·75	75
856	50 c. Type **186**	2·00	95
857	75 c. Harold Austin	2·25	2·25
858	$2 Frank Worrell	3·75	4·50

187 "Kentropyx borckianus"

1988. Lizards of Barbados. Multicoloured.

No.	Description	Unused	Used
859	10 c. Type **187**	40	10
860	50 c. "Hemidactylus mabouia"	1·00	35
861	65 c. "Anolis extremus"	1·25	55
862	$2 "Gymnophthalmus underwoodii"	2·75	2·00

188 Cycling

1988. Olympic Games, Seoul. Multicoloured.

No.	Description	Unused	Used
863	25 c. Type **188**	20	20
864	45 c. Athletics	30	30
865	75 c. Relay swimming	55	55
866	$2 Yachting	2·25	2·25

1988. 300th Anniv of Lloyd's of London. As T **123** of Ascension.

No.	Description	Unused	Used
868	40 c. multicoloured	55	30
869	50 c. multicoloured	65	35
870	65 c. multicoloured	90	45
871	$2 blue and red	2·00	2·00

DESIGNS: VERT—40 c. Royal Exchange, 1774; $2 Sinking of "Titanic", 1912. HORIZ—50 c. Early sugar mill; 65 c. "Author" (container ship).

189 Harry Bayley and Observatory

1988. 25th Anniv of Harry Bayley Observatory. Multicoloured.

No.	Description	Unused	Used
872	25 c. Type **189**	50	20
873	65 c. Observatory with North Star and Southern Cross constellations	90	45
874	75 c. Andromeda galaxy	1·10	50
875	$2 Orion constellation	2·50	2·25

190 LIAT BAe "748"

1989. 50th Anniv of Commercial Aviation in Barbados. Multicoloured.

876 25 c. Type **190** 70 20
877 65 c. Panam Douglas "DC-8" .. .. 1·25 50
878 75 c. British Airways "Concorde" at Grantley Adams Airport .. 1·40 60
879 $2 Caribbean Air Cargo Boeing "707-351c" .. 2·75 2·25

191 Assembly Chamber

1989. 350th Anniv of Parliament.

880 **191** 25 c. multicoloured .. 40 20
881 – 50 c. multicoloured .. 60 35
882 – 75 c. blue and black .. 85 50
883 – $2.50 multicoloured .. 2·00 2·00

DESIGNS: 50 c. The Speaker; 75 c. Parliament Buildings, c. 1882; $2.50, Queen Elizabeth II and Prince Philip in Parliament.

192 Brown Hare

1989. Wildlife Preservation. Multicoloured.

884 10 c. Type **192** 30 10
885 50 c. Red-footed tortoise (horiz) 75 35
886 65 c. Savanna ("Green") monkey 85 45
887 $2 "Bufo marinus" (toad) (horiz) .. .. 2·25 2·00

193 Bread 'n Cheese

1989. Wild Plants. Multicoloured.

921 2 c. Type **193** 10 10
891 5 c. Scarlet cordia .. 10 10
892 10 c. Columnar cactus .. 10 10
893 20 c. Spiderlily 10 10
925 25 c. Rock balsam .. 15 20
895 30 c. Hollyhock 20 25
895a 35 c. Red sage 25 30
927 45 c. Yellow shak-shak .. 30 35
928 50 c. Whitewood .. 30 35
898 55 c. Bluebell 35 40
930 65 c. Prickly sage .. 45 50
900 70 c. Seaside samphire .. 45 50
901 80 c. Flat-hand dildo .. 50 55
901a 90 c. Herringbone .. 65 70
902 $1.10 Lent tree 70 75
934 $2.50 Rodwood .. .. 1·60 1·75
935 $5 Cowitch .. .. 3·25 3·50
936 $10 Maypole .. .. 6·50 6·75

194 Water Skiing

1989. "World Stamp Expo '89" International Stamp Exn, Washington. Watersports. Mult.

906 25 c. Type **194** 45 25
907 50 c. Yachting 80 75
908 65 c. Scuba diving .. 1·00 1·00
909 $2.50 Surfing .. .. 3·75 4·50

195 Barbados 1852 1d. Stamp

1990. 150th Anniv of the Penny Black and "Stamp World London 90" International Stamp Exhibition.

910 **195** 25 c. green, blk & yell 45 20
911 – 50 c. multicoloured .. 75 25
912 – 65 c. multicoloured .. 85 75
913 – $2.50 multicoloured 2·75 3·50

DESIGNS: 50 c. 1d. 1882 Queen Victoria stamp; 65 c. 1899 2d. stamp; $2.50 1912 3d. stamp.

196 Bugler and Jockeys

1990. Horse Racing. Multicoloured.

915 25 c. Type **196** 35 25
916 45 c. Horse and jockey in parade ring 50 45
917 75 c. At the finish .. 75 65
918 $2 Leading in the winner (vert) .. .. .. 2·00 2·25

1990. 90th Birthday of Queen Elizabeth the Queen Mother. As T **134** of Ascension.

919 75 c. multicoloured .. 60 45
920 $2.50 black and green .. 1·90 2·10

DESIGNS—21 × 36 mm. 75 c. Lady Elizabeth Bowes-Lyon, April 1923 (from painting by John Lander). 29 × 37 mm. $2.50, Lady Elizabeth Bowes-Lyon on her engagement, January 1923.

197 "Orthemis ferruginea" (dragonfly)

1990. Insects. Multicoloured.

937 50 c. Type **197** 55 40
938 65 c. "Ligyrus tumulosus" (beetle) 75 65
939 75 c. "Neoconocephalus sp." (grasshopper) .. 85 85
940 $2 "Bostra maxwelli" (stick-insect) .. 1·75 2·00

1990. Visit of the Princess Royal. Nos. 925, 901 and 903 optd **VISIT OF HRH THE PRINCESS ROYAL OCTOBER 1990.**

941 25 c. Rock balsam .. 20 15
942 80 c. Flat-hand dildo .. 60 60
943 $2.50 Rodwood .. 1·90 2·00

199 Star

1990. Christmas. Multicoloured.

944 20 c. Type **199** 20 15
945 50 c. Figures from crib .. 40 35
946 $1 Stained glass window .. 70 65
947 $2 Angel (statue) .. 1·25 1·50

200 Adult Male Yellow Warbler

1991. Endangered Species. Yellow Warbler. Multicoloured.

948 10 c. Type **200** 20 15
949 20 c. Pair feeding chicks in nest 25 20
950 45 c. Female feeding chicks in nest 45 35
951 $1 Male with fledgeling .. 95 95

201 Sorting Daily Catch

1991. Fishing in Barbados. Multicoloured.

952 5 c. Type **201** 20 15
953 50 c. Line fishing (horiz) .. 70 65
954 75 c. Fish cleaning (horiz) 1·00 1·00
955 $2.50 Game fishing .. 2·50 3·00

202 Masonic Building, Bridgetown

1991. 250th Anniv of Freemasonry in Barbados (1990).

956 **202** 25 c. multicoloured .. 40 25
957 – 65 c. multicoloured .. 80 65
958 – 75 c. black, yell & brn ·90 75
959 – $2.50 multicoloured .. 3·00 3·50

DESIGNS: 65 c. Compass and square (masonic symbols); 75 c. Royal Arch jewel; $2.50, Ceremonial apron, columns and badge.

203 "Battus polydamus"

1991. "Philanippon '91" International Stamp Exhibition, Tokyo. Butterflies. Mult.

960 20 c. Type **203** 20 15
961 50 c. "Urbanus proteus" (vert) 45 35
962 65 c. "Phoebis sennae" .. 60 50
963 $2.50 "Junonia evarete" (vert) .. .. .. 2·10 2·40

204 School Class

1991. 25th Anniv of Independence. Mult.

965 10 c. Type **204** 10 10
966 25 c. Barbados Workers' Union Labour college .. 15 20
967 65 c. Building a house .. 45 50
968 75 c. Sugar cane harvesting 50 60
969 $1 Health clinic 80 55

205 Jesus carrying Cross

1992. Easter. Multicoloured.

971 35 c. Type **205** 40 25
972 70 c. Crucifixion .. 70 65
973 90 c. Descent from the Cross 85 85
974 $3 Risen Christ .. .. 2·75 3·00

206 Cannon Ball

1992. Conservation. Flowering Trees. Mult.

975 10 c. Type **206** 15 10
976 30 c. Golden shower tree .. 30 30
977 80 c. Frangipani 80 80
978 $1.10 Flamboyant .. 1·00 1·10

207 "Epidendrum Costa Rica"

1992. Orchids. Multicoloured.

979 55 c. Type **207** 45 35
980 65 c. "Cattleya guttaca" .. 60 60
981 70 c. "Laeliacattleya Splashing Around" .. 60 60
982 $1.40 "Phalaenopsis Kathy Saegert" .. .. 1·10 1·40

208 Mini Moke and Gun Hill Signal Station, St. George

1992. Transport and Tourism. Multicoloured.

983	5 c. Type **208**	15	15
984	35 c. Tour bus and Bathsheba Beach, St. Joseph	40	25
985	90 c. BWIA McDonnell Douglas MD 83 over Grantley Adams Airport	90	90
986	$2 "Festivale" (liner) and Bridgetown harbour ..	1·50	1·75

209 Barbados Gooseberry

1993. Cacti and Succulents. Multicoloured.

987	10 c. Type **209**	10	10
988	35 c. Night-blooming cereus	35	35
989	$1.40 Aloe	1·25	1·25
990	$2 Scrunchineel	1·75	1·75

1993. 75th Anniv of Royal Air Force. As T **149** of Ascension. Multicoloured.

991	10 c. Hawker Hunter	15	15
992	30 c. Handley Page Vvictor	30	30
993	70 c. Hawker Typhoon ..	65	65
994	$3 Hawker Hurricane ..	2·40	2·40

1993. 14th World Orchid Conference, Glasgow. Nos. 979/82 optd **WORLD ORCHID CONFERENCE 1993**.

996	55 c. Type **207**	55	55
997	65 c. "Cattleya guttaca" ..	65	65
998	70 c. "Laeliacattleya" "Splashing Around" ..	65	65
999	$1.40 "Phalaenopsis" "Kathy Saegert" ..	1·25	1·25

211 18 pdr Culverin of 1625, Denmark Fort

1993. 17th-century English Cannon. Mult.

1000	5 c. Type **211**	10	10
1001	45 c. 6 pdr of 1649–60, St. Ann's Fort	50	50
1002	$1 9 pdr demi-culverin of 1691, The Main Guard	1·10	1·10
1003	$2.50 32 pdr demi-cannon of 1693–94, Charles Fort	2·00	2·25

212 Sailor's Shell-work Valentine and Carved Amerindian

1993. 60th Anniv of Barbados Museum. Multicoloured.

1004	10 c. Type **212**	10	10
1005	75 c. "Barbados Mulatto Girl" (Agostino Brunias)	60	60
1006	90 c. Morris Cup and soldier of West India Regiment, 1858 ..	80	80
1007	$1.10 Ogilby's map of Barbados, 1679, and Ashanti gold weights	1·10	1·10

213 Plesiosaurus

1993. Prehistoric Aquatic Animals. Mult.

1008	90 c. Type **213**	90	90
1009	90 c. Ichthyosaurus ..	90	90
1010	90 c. Elasmosaurus ..	90	90
1011	90 c. Mosasaurus ..	90	90
1012	90 c. Archelon	90	90

Nos. 1008/12 were printed together, se-tenant, with the background forming a composite design.

214 Cricket

1994. Sports and Tourism. Multicoloured.

1013	10 c. Type **214**	10	10
1014	35 c. Rally driving ..	25	30
1015	50 c. Golf	30	35
1016	70 c. Long distance running	45	50
1017	$1.40 Swimming	80	85

215 Whimbrel

1994. "Hong Kong '94" International Stamp Exhibition. Migratory Birds. Mult.

1018	10 c. Type **215**	10	10
1019	35 c. American golden plover	25	30
1020	70 c. Turnstone	45	50
1021	$3 Louisiana heron ("Tricoloured Heron")	1·90	2·00

POSTAGE DUE STAMPS

D 1.

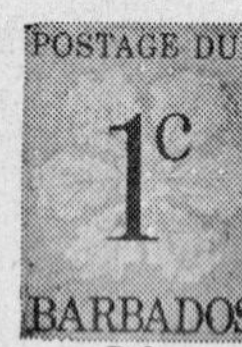

D 2.

1934.

D 1.	**D 1.** ½d. green	50	2·75
D 2.	1d. black	70	70
D 3.	3d. red	16·00	16·00

1950. Values in cents.

D 7	D 1 1 c. green	30	3·50
D 5a	2 c. black	40	2·50
D 9	6 c. red	50	4·00

1976.

D 14a.	**D 2.** 1 c. mauve & pink	10	10
D 15a.	– 2 c. blue & lt. blue	10	10
D 16a.	– 5 c. brown & yell.	10	10
D 17a.	– 10 c. blue & lilac ..	10	10
D 18a.	– 25 c. deep green & green	15	20
D 19.	– $1 red & deep red	60	65

DESIGNS: Nos. D15/19 show different floral backgrounds.

BARBUDA

One of the Leeward Is., Br. W. Indies. Dependency of Antigua. Used stamps of Antigua and Leeward Is. concurrently. The issues from 1968 are also valid for use in Antigua. From 1971 to 1973 the stamps of Antigua were again used.

1922. 12 pence = 1 shilling.
20 shillings = 1 pound.
1951. 100 cents = 1 West Indian dollar.

1922. Stamps of Leeward Islands optd. **BARBUDA.**

1.	**11.** ½d. green	1·00	7·50
2.	1d. red	1·00	7·50
3.	2d. grey	1·00	7·50
4.	2½d. blue	1·00	7·50
9.	3d. purple on yellow ..	1·00	8·00
5.	6d. purple	1·50	14·00
10.	1s. black on green ..	1·50	8·00
6.	2s. purple and blue on blue	9·00	42·00
7.	3s. green and violet ..	29·00	75·00
8.	4s. black and red	38·00	75·00
11.	5s. green & red on yellow	65·00	£130

2. Map of Barbuda.

1968.

12.	**2.** ½ c. brown, black and pink	20	10
13.	1 c. orange, black and flesh	30	10
14.	2 c. brown, red and rose ..	30	10
15.	3 c. brown, yellow & lemon	30	10
16.	4 c. black, green and light green	30	10
17.	5 c. turquoise and black ..	30	10
18.	6 c. black, purple and lilac	40	10
19.	10 c. black, blue & cobalt	30	10
20.	15 c. black, green & turq.	30	40

3. Great Amberjack.

1968. Fishes. Multicoloured.

20a.	20 c. Great Barracuda ..	1·50	2·00
21.	25 c. Type **3**	60	25
22.	35 c. French Angelfish ..	60	25
23.	50 c. Porkfish	60	45
24.	73 c. Striped Parrotfish ..	70	80
25.	$1 Longspine Squirrelfish	85	2·00
26.	$2·50 Catalufa	1·50	5·00
27.	$5 Blue Chromis	3·75	7·50

10. Sprinting and Aztec Sun-stone.

1968. Olympic Games, Mexico. Multicoloured.

28.	25 c. Type **10**	25	25
29.	35 c. High-jumping and Aztec statue	30	25
30.	75 c. Yachting and Aztec lion mask	45	45

14. "The Ascension" (Orcagna).

1969. Easter Commem.

32.	**14.** 25 c. black and blue ..	15	45
33.	35 c. black and red ..	15	50
34.	75 c. black and lilac ..	15	55

15. Scout Enrolment Ceremony.

1969. 3rd Caribbean Scout Jamboree. Mult.

35.	25 c. Type **15**	35	55
36.	35 c. Scouts around camp fire	55	65
37.	75 c. Sea Scouts rowing boat	70	85

18. "Sistine Madonna" (Raphael).

1969. Christmas.

38.	**18.** ½ c. multicoloured ..	10	10
39.	25 c. multicoloured ..	10	15
40.	35 c. multicoloured ..	10	20
41.	35 c. multicoloured ..	20	35

19. William I (1066–87).

1970. English Monarchs. Multicoloured.

42.	35 c. Type **19**	30	15
43.	35 c. William II (1087-1100)	10	15
44.	35 c. Henry I (1100-35) ..	10	15
45.	35 c. Stephen (1135-54) ..	10	15
46.	35 c. Henry II. (1154-89) ..	10	15
47.	35 c. Richard I (1189-99) ..	10	15
48.	35 c. John (1199-1216) ..	10	15
49.	35 c. Henry III (1216-72) ..	10	15
50.	35 c. Edward I (1272-1307)	10	15
51.	35 c. Edward II (1307-27) ..	10	15
52.	35 c. Edward III (1327-77)	10	15
53.	35 c. Richard II (1377-99) ..	10	15
54.	35 c. Henry IV (1399-1413)	10	15
55.	35 c. Henry V (1413-22) ..	10	15
56.	35 c. Henry VI (1422-61) ..	10	15
57.	35 c. Edward IV (1462-83) ..	10	15
58. 56.	35 c. Edward V (April-June 1483)	10	15
59.	35 c. Richard III (1483-85)	10	15
60.	35 c. Henry VII (1485-1509)	10	15
61.	35 c. Henry VIII (1509-47)	10	15
62.	35 c. Edward VI (1547-53) ..	10	15
63.	35 c. Lady Jane Grey (1553)	10	15
64.	35 c. Mary I (1553-8) ..	10	15
65.	35 c. Elizabeth I (1558-1603)	10	15
66.	35 c. James I (1603-25) ..	10	15
67.	35 c. Charles I (1625-49) ..	10	15
68.	35 c. Charles II (1649-1685)	10	15
69.	35 c. James II (1685-1688) ..	10	15
70.	35 c. William III (1689-1702)	10	15
71.	35 c. Mary II (1689-1694) ..	10	15
72.	35 c. Anne (1702-1714) ..	15	15
73.	35 c. George I (1714-1727) ..	15	15
74.	35 c. George II (1727-1760)	15	15
75.	35 c. George III (1760-1820)	15	15
76.	35 c. George IV (1820-1830)	15	15
77.	35 c. William IV (1830-1837)	15	15
78.	35 c. Victoria (1837-1901) ..	15	15

See also Nos. 710/15.

1970. No. 12 surch.

79.	**2.** 20 c. on ½ c. brn., blk. & pink	10	20

21. "The Way to Calvary" (Ugolino).

1970. Easter. Paintings. Multicoloured.
80. 25 c. Type 21 .. .. 15 30
81. 35 c. "The Deposition from the Cross" (Ugolino) .. 15 30
82. 75 c. Crucifix (The Master of S. Francesco) 15 35

22. Oliver is introduced to Fagin ("Oliver Twist").

1970. Death Centenary of Charles Dickens. Multicoloured.
83. 20 c. Type 22 .. .. 10 15
84. 75 c. Dickens and scene from "The Old Curiosity Shop" 20 40

23. "Madonna of the Meadows" (G. Bellini).

1970. Christmas. Multicoloured.
85. 20 c. Type 23 .. .. 10 25
86. 50 c. "Madonna, Child and Angels" (from Wilton diptych) 15 30
87. 75 c. "The Nativity" (della Francesca) 15 35

24. Nurse with Patient in Wheelchair.

1970. Cent. of British Red Cross. Mult.
88. 20 c. Type 24 .. .. 15 30
89. 35 c. Nurse giving Patient Magazines (horiz.) .. 20 40
90. 75 c. Nurse and Mother weighing Baby (horiz.) .. 25 70

25. "Angel with Vases".

1971. Easter. "Mond" Crucifixion by Raphael. Multicoloured.
91. 35 c. Type 25 .. .. 15 65
92. 50 c. "Christ crucified" .. 15 75
93. 75 c. "Angel with vase" .. 15 80

26. Martello Tower.

1971. Tourism. Multicoloured.
94. 20 c. Type 26 .. .. 10 25
95. 25 c. Sailing boats 10 30
96. 50 c. Hotel bungalows .. 15 35
97. 75 c. Government House and Mystery Stone 20 40

27. "The Granducal Madonna" (Raphael).

1971. Christmas. Multicoloured.
98. ½ c. Type 27 .. .. 10 10
99. 35 c. "The Asidei Madonna" (Raphael) .. 10 20
100. 50 c. "The Madonna and Child" (Botticelli) .. 15 25
101. 75 c. "The Madonna of the Trees" (Bellini) .. 15 30

Four stamps to commemorate the 500th Birth Anniv. of Durer were prepared in late 1971, but their issue was not authorised by the Antigua Government.

1973. Royal Wedding. Nos. 370/1 of Antigua optd. **BARBUDA** twice.
102. 106. 35 c. multicoloured .. 10·00 4·25
103. $2 multicoloured .. 5·00 2·25

1973. Ships. Nos. 269/85 of Antigua optd. **BARBUDA.**
116. 92. ½ c. multicoloured .. 15 20
104. – 1 c. multicoloured .. 15 20
105. – 2 c. multicoloured .. 25 25
117. – 3 c. multicoloured .. 25 25
106. – 4 c. multicoloured .. 30 30
107. – 5 c. multicoloured .. 40 40
108. – 6 c. multicoloured .. 40 40
109. – 10 c. multicoloured .. 45 45
118. – 15 c. multicoloured .. 35 50
110. – 20 c. multicoloured .. 55 60
111. – 25 c. multicoloured .. 55 60
112. – 35 c. multicoloured .. 55 70
113. – 50 c. multicoloured .. 55 70
114. – 75 c. multicoloured .. 55 70
119. – $1 multicoloured .. 55 70
115. – $2·50 multicoloured .. 1·25 1·50
121. – $5 multicoloured .. 1·40 2·50

1973. Military Uniforms. Nos. 353, 355 and 357 of Antigua optd. **BARBUDA.**
122. ½ c. multicoloured .. 10 10
123. 20 c. multicoloured .. 15 10
124. 75 c. multicoloured .. 40 15

1973. Carnival. Nos. 360/2 of Antigua optd. **BARBUDA.**
126. 20 c. multicoloured .. 10 10
127. 35 c. multicoloured .. 10 10
128. 75 c. multicoloured .. 20 25

1973. Christmas. Nos. 364/68 of Antigua optd. **BARBUDA.**
130. 105. 3 c. multicoloured .. 10 10
131. – 5 c. multicoloured .. 10 10
132. – 20 c. multicoloured .. 10 10
133. – 35 c. multicoloured .. 15 15
134. – $1 multicoloured .. 30 30

1973. Honeymoon Visit. Nos. 373/4 of Antigua additionally optd. **BARBUDA.**
136. 35 c. multicoloured .. 40 20
137. $2 multicoloured .. 1·25 60

1974. University of West Indies. Nos. 376/9 of Antigua optd. **BARBUDA.**
139. 5 c. multicoloured .. 10 10
140. 20 c. multicoloured .. 10 10
141. 35 c. multicoloured .. 15 15
142. 75 c. multicoloured .. 15 15

1974. Military Uniforms. Nos. 380/4 of Antigua optd. **BARBUDA.**
143. ½ c. multicoloured .. 10 10
144. 10 c. multicoloured .. 10 10
145. 20 c. multicoloured .. 20 10
146. 35 c. multicoloured .. 25 10
147. 75 c. multicoloured .. 45 25

1974. Centenary of U.P.U. (1st issue). Nos. 386/92 of Antigua optd. with either a or b.
(a). **BARBUDA 13 JULY 1922.**
148. ½ c. multicoloured .. 10 10
150. 1 c. multicoloured .. 10 10
152. 2 c. multicoloured .. 15 15
154. 5 c. multicoloured .. 15 15
156. 20 c. multicoloured .. 40 70
158. 35 c. multicoloured .. 80 1·50
160. $1 multicoloured .. 2·25 4·00

(b). **BARBUDA 15 SEPT. 1874 G.P.U.** ("General Postal Union").
149. ½ c. multicoloured .. 10 10
151. 1 c. multicoloured .. 10 10
153. 2 c. multicoloured .. 15 15
155. 5 c. multicoloured .. 15 15
157. 20 c. multicoloured .. 40 70
159. 35 c. multicoloured .. 80 1·50
161. $1 multicoloured .. 2·25 4·00

1974. Antiguan Steel Bands. Nos. 394/97 of Antigua optd. **BARBUDA.**
163. 5 c. dull red, red & blk. .. 10 10
164. 20 c. brn., light brn. & blk. 10 10
165. 35 c. light grn., grn. & blk. 10 10
166. 75 c. dull blue, blue & blk. 20 20

39. Footballers.

1974. World Cup Football Championships (1st issue).
168. 39. 35 c. multicoloured .. 10 10
169. – $1·20 multicoloured .. 25 35
170. – $2·50 multicoloured .. 35 50
DESIGNS: $1·20, $2·50, Footballers in action similar to Type 39.

1974. World Cup Football Championships (2nd issue). Nos. 399/402 of Antigua optd. **BARBUDA.**
172. 111. 5 c. multicoloured .. 10 10
173. – 35 c. multicoloured .. 10 10
174. – 75 c. multicoloured .. 15 15
175. – $1 multicoloured .. 20 25

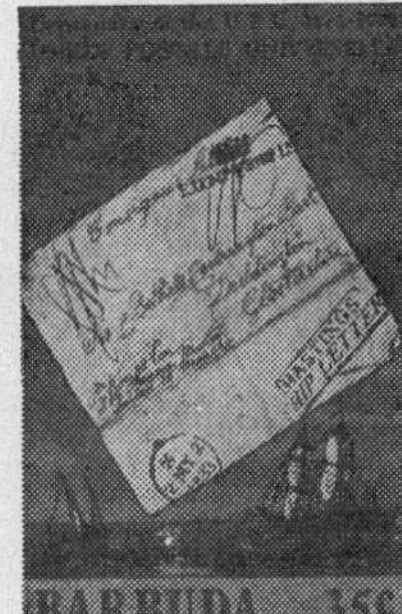

41. Ship Letter of 1833.

1974. Centenary of Universal Postal Union. (2nd issue). Multicoloured.
177. 35 c. Type 41 .. .. 10 10
178. $1·20 Stamps and postmark of 1922 .. .. 30 50
179. $2·50 Mailplane over map of Barbuda 55 75

42. Greater Amberjack.

1974. Multicoloured.
181. ½ c. Oleander, Rose Bay .. 10 40
182. 1 c. Blue Petrea .. 15 40
183. 2 c. Poinsettia .. 15 40
184. 3 c. Cassia tree .. 15 40
185. 4 c. Type 42 .. 50 40
186. 5 c. Holy Trinity School .. 15 15
187. 6 c. Snorkeling .. 15 30
188. 10 c. Pilgrim Holiness Church 15 20
189. 15 c. New Cottage Hospital 15 20
190. 20 c. Post Office and Treasury 15 20
191. 25 c. Island jetty and boats 30 30
192. 35 c. Martello Tower .. 30 30
193. 50 c. Warden's House .. 30 30
194. 75 c. Inter-island aircraft 75 1·00
195. $1 Tortoise 70 80
196. $2·50 Spiny lobster .. 1·50 2·25
197. $5 Magnificent Frigate Bird 11·00 5·50
197b. $10 Hibiscus .. .. 9·00 9·50

The 50 c. to $1 are 39 × 25 mm., $2.50 and $5 45 × 29 mm., $10 34 × 48 mm.
The ½ to 3 c., 25 c. and $10 are vert.

1974. Birth Cent. of Sir Winston Churchill. (1st issue). Nos. 408/11 of Antigua optd. **BARBUDA.**
198. 113. 5 c. multicoloured .. 10 10
199. – 35 c. multicoloured .. 20 15
200. – 75 c. multicoloured .. 35 45
201. – $1 multicoloured .. 55 70

43. Churchill making Broadcast.

1974. Birth Centenary of Sir Winston Churchill. (2nd issue). Multicoloured.
203. 5 c. Type 43 .. .. 10 10
204. 35 c. Churchill and Chartwell 10 10
205. 75 c. Churchill painting .. 20 20
206. $1 Churchill making "V"-sign 25 30

1974. Christmas. Nos. 413/20 of Antigua optd. **BARBUDA.**
208. 114. ½ c. multicoloured .. 10 10
209. – 1 c. multicoloured .. 10 10
210. – 2 c. multicoloured .. 10 10
211. – 3 c. multicoloured .. 10 10
212. – 5 c. multicoloured .. 10 10
213. – 20 c. multicoloured .. 10 10
214. – 35 c. multicoloured .. 15 15
215. – 75 c. multicoloured .. 30 30

1975. Nelson's Dockyard. Nos. 427/31 of Antigua optd. **BARBUDA.**
217. 116. 5 c. multicoloured .. 15 15
218. – 15 c. multicoloured .. 30 25
219. – 35 c. multicoloured .. 45 35
220. – 50 c. multicoloured .. 60 50
221. – $1 multicoloured .. 80 80

45. Ships of the Line.

1975. Sea Battles. Battle of the Saints, 1782. Multicoloured.
223. 35 c. Type 45 .. .. 1·50 85
224. 50 c. H.M.S. "Ramillies" .. 1·50 1·00
225. 75 c. Ships firing broadsides 1·75 1·25
226. 95 c. Sailors fleeing burning ship .. .. 1·75 1·50

1975. "Apollo-Soyuz" Space Project. No. 197 optd. **U.S.A.-U.S.S.R. SPACE CO-OPERATION 1975** with **APOLLO** (No. 227) and **SOYUZ** (No. 228).
227. $5 multicoloured .. .. 6·50 9·00
228. $5 multicoloured .. .. 6·50 9·00

47. Officer, 65th Foot, 1763.

1975. Military Uniforms. Multicoloured.
229. 35 c. Type 47 .. .. 75 75
230. 50 c. Grenadier, 27th Foot 1701-10 .. .. 90 90
231. 75 c. Officer, 21st Foot, 1793-6 .. .. 1·00 1·00
232. 95 c. Officer, Royal Regt. of Artillery, 1800 .. 1·25 1·25

1975. 25th Anniv. of United Nations. Nos. 203/6 optd. **30th ANNIVERSARY UNITED NATIONS 1945–1975.**
233. 43. 5 c. multicoloured .. 10 10
234. – 35 c. multicoloured .. 10 15
235. – 75 c. multicoloured .. 15 20
236. – $1 multicoloured .. 20 30

1975. Christmas. Nos. 457/64 of Antigua optd. **BARBUDA.**
237. 121. ½ c. multicoloured .. 10 10
238. – 1 c. multicoloured .. 10 10
239. – 2 c. multicoloured .. 10 10
240. – 3 c. multicoloured .. 10 10
241. – 5 c. multicoloured .. 10 10
242. – 10 c. multicoloured .. 10 10
243. – 35 c. multicoloured .. 15 20
244. – $2 multicoloured .. 60 1·00

1975. World Cup Cricket Winners Nos. 466/8 of Antigua optd. **BARBUDA.**
246. 122. 5 c. multicoloured .. 75 1·00
247. – 35 c. multicoloured .. 1·50 2·00
248. – $2 multicoloured .. 3·25 4·25

51. Surrender of Cornwallis at Yorktown (Trumbull).

1976. Bicent. of American Revolution. Mult.
249. 15 c. } Type 51 .. .. 15 15
250. 15 c. 15 15
251. 15 c. 15 15
252. 35 c. } The 15 15
253. 35 c. } Battle of 15 15
254. 35 c. } Princetown 15 15
255. $1 } Surrender of .. 35 35
256. $1 } General Burgoyne .. 35 35
257. $1 } at Saratoga .. 35 35
258. $2 } Jefferson presenting .. 50 50
259. $2 } Declaration of .. 50 50
260. $2 } Independence .. 50 50
Type 51 shows the left-hand stamp of the 15 c. design.

52. Bananaquits.

1976. Birds. Multicoloured.
262 35 c. Type 52 .. .. 1·50 70
263 50 c. Blue-hooded euphonia 2·00 80
264 75 c. Royal tern .. .. 2·25 90
265 90 c. Killdeer .. .. 2·75 1·25
266 $1.25 Common cowbird .. 3·25 1·50
267 $2 Purple gallinule .. 4·00 2·25

1976. Royal Visit to the U.S.A. Nos. 249/60 additionally inscr. " H.M. QUEEN ELIZABETH ROYAL VISIT 6th JULY. H.R.H. DUKE OF EDINBURGH ".
268. 15 c. multicoloured .. 15 15
269. 15 c. multicoloured .. 15 15
270. 15 c. multicoloured .. 15 15
271. 35 c. multicoloured .. 20 30
272. 35 c. multicoloured .. 20 30
273. 35 c. multicoloured .. 20 30
274. $1 multicoloured 60 40
275. $1 multicoloured 60 40
276. $1 multicoloured 60 40
277. $2 multicoloured 70 90
278. $2 multicoloured 70 90
279. $2 multicoloured 70 90

1976. Christmas. Nos. 514/8 of Antigua optd. **BARBUDA.**
281. 128. 8 c. multicoloured .. 10 10
282. – 10 c. multicoloured .. 10 10
283. – 15 c. multicoloured .. 10 10
284. – 50 c. multicoloured .. 15 15
285. – $1 multicoloured .. 25 30

1976. Olympic Games, Montreal. Nos. 495/501 of Antigua optd. **BARBUDA.**
286. 125. ½ c. brn., yell. and blk. 10 10
287. – 1 c. violet and black .. 10 10
288. – 2 c. green and black .. 10 10
289. – 15 c. blue and black .. 10 10
290. – 30 c. brn., yell. and blk. 10 10
291. – $1 orge., red and black 20 20
292. – $2 rd and black .. 35 35

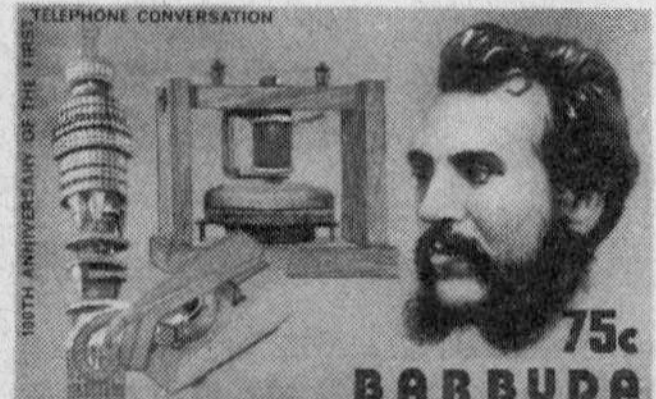

55. P.O. Tower, Telephones and Alexander Graham Bell.

1977. Centenary of First Telephone Transmission. Multicoloured.
294. 75 c. Type 55 .. .. 30 35
295. $1.25 T.V. Transmission by Satellite 45 55
296. $2 Globe showing satellite transmission scheme .. 65 75

56. St. Margaret's Church, Westminster.

1977. Silver Jubilee (1st issue). Multicoloured.
298. 75 c. Type 56 .. .. 15 15
299. 75 c. Street decorations .. 15 15
300. 75 c. Westminster Abbey 15 15
301. $1.25 Part of Coronation procession 25 25
302. $1.25 Coronation Coach .. 25 25
303. $1.25 Postillions 25 25

1977. Nos. 469/86 of Antigua optd. **BARBUDA.**
305. ½ c. Antillean crested hummingbird 20 20
306. 1 c. Imperial amazon .. 30 20
307. 2 c. Zenaida dove 30 20
308. 3 c. Loggerhead kingbird 30 20
309. 4 c. Red-necked pigeon .. 30 20
310. 5 c. Rufous-throated solitaire 30 20
311. 6 c. Orchid tree 25 20
312. 10 c. Bougainvillea .. 25 20
313. 15 c. Geiger tree 25 25
314. 20 c. Flamboyant 30 25
315. 25 c. Hibiscus 30 25
316. 35 c. Flame of the Wood .. 35 30
317. 50 c. Cannon at Fort James 40 40
318. 75 c. Premier's Office .. 40 40
319. $1 Potworks Dam 50 60
320. $2.50 Irrigation scheme .. 1·25 1·60
321. $5 Government House .. 2·75 3·25
322. $10 Coolidge Airport .. 5·50 7·50

1977. Silver Jubilee (2nd issue). Nos. 526/30 of Antigua optd. **BARBUDA.** (a) Perf.
323. 10 c. Royal Family .. 20 25
324. 30 c. Royal visit, 1966 .. 40 45
325. 50 c. The Queen enthroned 60 70
326. 90 c. The Queen after Coronation .. .. 1·10 1·40
327. $2.50 The Queen and Prince Charles .. .. 3·00 3·75
(b) Roul. × imperf. Self-adhesive.
329. 50 c. Queen after Coronation 40 70
330. $5 The Queen and Prince Philip .. .. .. 10·00 13·00
Nos. 329/30 come from booklets.

1977. Caribbean Scout Jamboree, Jamaica. Nos. 534/40 of Antigua optd. **BARBUDA.**
331. ½ c. Type 131 .. .. 10 10
332. 1 c. Hiking 10 10
333. 2 c. Rock-climbing .. 10 10
334. 10 c. Cutting logs .. 10 10
335. 30 c. Map and sign reading 40 40
336. 50 c. First aid 55 55
337. $2 Rafting .. .. 2·00 2·00

1977. 21st Anniv. of Carnival. Nos. 542/46 of Antigua optd. **BARBUDA.**
339. 10 c. Type 312 .. .. 10 10
340. 30 c. Carnival Queen .. 10 10
341. 50 c. Butterfly costume .. 15 20
342. 90 c. Queen of the Band .. 20 30
343. $1 Calypso King and Queen 25 40

61. Royal Yacht " Britannia ".

1977. Royal Visit (1st issue). Multicoloured.
345. 50 c. Type 61 .. .. 25 20
346. $1·50 Jubilee emblem .. 40 35
347. $2·50 Union Jack and flag of Antigua 60 50

1977. Royal Visit (2nd issue). Nos. 548/52 of Antigua optd. **BARBUDA.**
349. 10 c. Royal Family .. 15 10
350. 30 c. Queen Elizabeth and Prince Philip in car .. 30 15
351. 50 c. Queen enthroned .. 40 20
352. 90 c. Queen after Coronation 70 30
353. $2·50 The Queen and Prince Charles .. .. 1·75 80

1977. Christmas. Nos. 554/60 of Antigua optd. **BARBUDA.**
355. ½ c. Type 134 .. .. 10 10
356. 1 c. Crivelli 10 10
357. 2 c. Lotto 10 10
358. 8 c. Pontormo 10 10
359. 10 c. Tura (different) .. 10 10
360. 25 c. Lotto (different) .. 15 10
361. $2 Crivelli (different) .. 45 45

64. Zeppelin " LZ 1 ".

1977. Special Events, 1977. Multicoloured.
363. 75 c. Type 64 .. .. 30 30
364. 75 c. German Battleship and Naval Airship " L 31 " 30 30
365. 75 c. " Graf Zeppelin " in hangar 30 30
366. 75 c. Military Airship gondola 30 30
367. 95 c. Sputnik 1 .. .. 50 35
368. 95 c. Vostok rocket .. 50 35
369. 95 c. Voskhod rocket .. 50 35
370. 95 c. Space walk 50 35
371. $1·25 Fuelling for flight .. 70 45
372. $1·25 Leaving New York 70 45
373. $1·25 " Spirit of St. Louis" 70 45
374. $1·25 Welcome in England 70 45
375. $2 Lion of England .. 1·25 70
376. $2 Unicorn of Scotland .. 1·25 70
377. $2 Yale of Beaufort .. 1·25 70
378. $2 Falcon of Plantagenets 1·25 70
379. $5 } .. .. .. 1·40 1·25
380. $5 } " Daniel in the Lions 1·40 1·25
381. $5 } Den " (Rubens) .. 1·40 1·25
382. $5 } .. .. .. 1·40 1·25
EVENTS: 75 c. 75th Anniv. of Navigable Airships. 95 c. 20th Anniv. of U.S.S.R. Space Programme. $1·25, 50th Anniv. of Lindbergh's Transatlantic Flight. $2, Silver Jubilee of Queen Elizabeth II. $5, 400th Birth Anniv. of Rubens.
Nos. 379/82 form a composite design.

1978. 10th Anniv. of Statehood. Nos. 562/6 of Antigua optd. **BARBUDA.**
384. 10 c. Type 135 .. .. 10 10
385. 15 c. State flag 10 10
386. 50 c. Police band 20 15
387. 90 c. Premier V. C. Bird .. 20 20
388. $2 State Coat of Arms .. 40 40

66. " Pieta " (sculpture) (detail).

1978. Easter. Paintings and Sculptures by Michelangelo. Multicoloured.
390. 75 c. Type 66 .. .. 15 15
391. 95 c. " The Holy Family " 20 20
392. $1·25 " Libyan sibyl " (from the Sistine Chapel) 25 25
393. $2 " The Flood " (from the Sistine Chapel) 30 35

1978. 75th Anniv. of Powered Flight. Nos. 568/74 of Antigua optd. **BARBUDA.**
395. ½ c. " Glider III ", 1902 .. 10 10
396. 1 c. " Flyer I ", 1903 .. 10 10
397. 2 c. Launch system and engine 10 10
398. 10 c. Orville Wright (vert.) 10 10
399. 50 c. " Flyer III ", 1905 .. 25 15
400. 90 c. Wilbur Wright (vert.) 35 15
401. $2 Wright " Model B ", 1910 .. .. .. 60 45

1978. Sailing Week. Nos. 576/79 of Antigua optd. **BARBUDA.**
403. 10 c. Sunfish regatta .. 20 10
404. 50 c. Fishing and work boat race 40 25
405. 90 c. Curtain Bluff race .. 55 35
406. $2 Power boat rally .. 85 75

68. St. Edward's Crown.

1978. 25th Anniv. of Coronation. (1st issue). Multicoloured.
408. 75 c. Type 68 .. .. 15 15
409. 75 c. Imperial State Crown 15 15
410. $1.50 Queen Mary's Crown 25 25
411. $1.50 Queen Mother's Crown 25 25
412. $2.50 Queen Consort's Crown 45 45
413. $2.50 Queen Victoria's Crown 45 45

1978. 25th Anniv. of Coronation. (2nd issue). Nos. 581/5 of Antigua optd. **BARBUDA.**
415. 10 c. Queen Elizabeth and Prince Philip 10 10
416. 30 c. The Crowning .. 10 10
417. 50 c. Coronation procession 15 15
418. 90 c. Queen seated in St. Edward's Chair .. 20 20
419. $2.50 Queen wearing Imperial State Crown .. 50 60

1978. 25th Anniv. of Coronation. (3rd issue). As Nos. 587/9 of Antigua additionally inscr. "BARBUDA".
421. 25 c. Glass Coach .. 40 70
422. 50 c. Irish State Coach .. 40 70
423. $5 Coronation Coach .. 1·50 2·25

1978. World Cup Football Championship, Argentina. Nos. 590/2 of Antigua optd. **BARBUDA.**
424. 10 c. Player running with ball 10 10
425. 15 c. Players in front of goal 10 10
426. $3 Referee and player .. 1·00 1·25

1978. Flowers. As Nos. 594/7 of Antigua optd. **BARBUDA.**
428. 25 c. Petrea 25 35
429. 50 c. Sunflower 50 70
430. 90 c. Frangipani 70 90
431. $2 Passion Flower .. 1·25 1·75

1978. Christmas. As Nos. 599/601 of Antigua optd. **BARBUDA.**
433. 8 c. " St. Idefonso receiving the Chasuble from the Virgin " 10 10
434. 25 c. " The Flight of St. Barbara " 15 15
435. $2 " Madonna and child, with St. Joseph, John the Baptist and Donor " 60 1·25

70. Blackbar Soldierfish.

1978. Flora and Fauna. Multicoloured.
437 25 c. Type 70 .. .. 1·50 1·50
438 50 c. "Cynthia cardui" (butterfly) .. .. 2·25 2·25
439 75 c. Dwarf poinciana .. 2·75 2·75
440 95 c. "Heliconius charithonia" (butterfly) 3·75 3·75
441 $1.25 Bougainvillea .. 3·75 3·75

71. Footballers and World Cup. 72. Sir Rowland Hill.

1978. Anniversaries and Events
442. 75 c. Type 71 .. .. 50 50
443. 95 c. Wright Brothers and " Flyer I " (horiz.) .. 60 70
444. $1.25 " Double Eagle II " and map of Atlantic (horiz.) 70 80
445. $2 Prince Philip paying homage to the Queen .. 1·25 1·60
EVENTS: 75 c. Argentina—Winners of World Cup Football Championship. 95 c. 75th anniv. of powered flight. $1.25, First Atlantic Crossing by balloon. $2, 25th anniv. of Coronation.

1979. Death Centenary of Sir Rowland Hill. (1st issue). Multicoloured.
447. 75 c. Type 72 .. .. 45 50
448. 95 c. Mail coach, 1840 (horiz.) 55 60
449. $1.25, London's first pillar box, 1855 (horiz.) .. 60 70
450. $2 Mail leaving St. Martin's Le Grand Post Office, London 90 95

1979. Death Centenary of Sir Rowland Hill. (2nd issue). Nos. 603/6 of Antigua optd. **BARBUDA.**
452. 25 c. 1d. Stamp of 1863 .. 15 15
453. 50 c. Penny Black .. 20 20
454. $1 Stage-coach and woman posting letter, c. 1840 .. 35 30
455. $2 Modern mail transport 80 60

1979. Easter. Works of Durer. Nos. 608/10 of Antigua optd. **BARBUDA.**
457. 10 c. multicoloured .. 10 10
458. 50 c. multicoloured .. 20 20
459. $4 black, mauve & yellow 90 1·10

74. Passengers alighting from British Airways Boeing " 747 ".

1979. 30th Anniv. of International Civil Aviation Organization. Multicoloured.
461. 75 c. Type 74 .. .. 35 60
462. 95 c. Air traffic control .. 40 70
463. $1.25 Ground crew-man directing Boeing " 707 " on runway 40 75

1979. International Year of the Child (1st issue). Nos. 612/15 of Antigua optd. **BARBUDA.**
464. 25 c. Yacht 20 15
465. 50 c. Rocket 35 25
466. 90 c. Car 50 35
467. $2 Toy train .. .. 1·25 60

1979. Fishes. Nos. 617/20 of Antigua optd. **BARBUDA.**

469. 30 c. Yellowjack 20 15
470. 50 c. Bluefin Tuna 30 20
471. 90 c. Sailfish 40 30
472. $3 Wahoo .. .. 1·10 1·10

1979. Death Bicent. of Captain Cook. Nos. 622/5 of Antigua optd. **BARBUDA.**

474. 25 c. Cook's Birthplace, Marton 30 30
475. 50 c. H.M.S. "Endeavour" 50 45
476. 90 c. Marine chronometer 65 60
477. $3 Landing at Botany Bay 1·75 1·50

77. "Virgin with the Pear"

1979. International Year of the Child (2nd issue). Paintings by Durer. Multicoloured.

479. 25 c. Type **77** 15 15
480. 50 c. "Virgin with the Pink" (detail) 25 25
481. 75 c. "Virgin with the Pear" (different detail) 30 30
482. $1.25 "Nativity" (detail) 40 40

1979. Christmas. Nos. 627/630 of Antigua optd. **BARBUDA.**

484. 8 c. The Holy Family .. 10 10
485. 25 c. Mary and Jesus on donkey 20 10
486. 50 c. Shepherd looking at star 35 15
487. $4 The Three Kings .. 1·25 80

1980. Olympic Games, Moscow. Nos. 632/5 of Antigua optd. **BARBUDA.**

489. 10 c. Javelin 10 10
490. 25 c. Running 10 10
491. $1 Pole vault 30 20
492. $2 Hurdles 55 40

1980. "London 1980" International Stamp Exhibition. Nos. 452/5 optd. **LONDON 1980.**

494. 25 c. 1d. stamp of 1863 .. 35 20
495. 50 c. Penny Black .. 45 40
496. $1 Stage-coach and woman posting letter, c. 1840 .. 85 65
497. $2 Modern mail transport 2·75 1·50

80. "Apollo II" Crew Badge.

1980. 10th Anniv. of "Apollo II" Moon Landing. Multicoloured.

498. 75 c. Type **80** 25 25
499. 95 c. Plaque left on Moon 30 30
500. $1.25 Rejoining the mother-ship 40 40
501. $2 "Lunar Module" .. 65 65

81. American Widgeon.

1980. Birds. Multicoloured.

503. 1 c. Type **81** 30 30
504. 2 c. Snowy plover 35 20
505. 4 c. Rose-breasted grosbeak 40 30
506. 6 c. Mangrove cuckoo .. 40 30
507. 10 c. Adelaide's warbler .. 40 30
508. 15 c. Scaly-breasted thrasher 45 30
509. 20 c. Yellow-crowned night heron 45 30
510. 25 c. Bridled quail dove .. 45 30
511. 35 c. Carib grackle .. 55 40
512. 50 c. Northern pintail .. 65 35
513. 75 c. Black-whispered vireo 80 45
514. $1 Blue-winged teal .. 1·00 70
515. $1.50 Green-throated carib (vert.) .. .. .. 1·25 80
516. $2 Red-necked pigeon (vert.) .. .. 2·00 1·25
517. $2.50 Wied's crested fly-catcher (vert.) .. 2·50 1·50
518. $5 Yellow-bellied sap-sucker (vert.) .. .. 3·25 2·50
519. $7.50 Caribbean elaenia (vert.) .. .. .. 4·25 5·00
520. $10 Great egret (vert.) .. 5·00 5·00

1980. Famous Works of Art. Nos. 651/7 of Antigua optd. **BARBUDA.**

521. 10 c. "David" (statue, Donatello) 10 10
522. 30 c. "The Birth of Venus" (painting, Sandro Botticelli) 15 15
523. 50 c. "Reclining Couple" (sarcophagus), Cerveteri 20 20
524. 90 c. "The Garden of Earthly Delights" (painting, Hieronymus Bosch) .. 25 25
525. $1 "Portinari Altarpiece" (painting, Hugo van der Goes) 25 25
526. $4 "Eleanora of Toledo and her Son Giovanni de'Medici (painting, Agnolo Bronzino) 80 80

1980. 75th Anniv. of Rotary International. Nos. 651/4 of Antigua optd. **BARBUDA.**

528. 30 c. Rotary Headquarters 15 15
529. 50 c. Antigua Rotary banner 20 20
530. 90 c. Map of Antigua .. 25 25
531. $3 Paul P. Harris (founder) 65 65

1980. 80th Birthday of The Queen Mother. Nos. 663/4 of Antigua optd. **BARBUDA.**

533. 10 c. multicoloured .. 50 15
534. $2.50 multicoloured .. 3·25 1·50

1980. Birds. Nos. 666/9 of Antigua optd. **BARBUDA.**

536. 10 c. Ringed Kingfisher .. 85 50
537. 30 c. Plain Pigeon .. 1·25 70
538. $1 Green-throated Carib 2·25 1·75
539. $2 Black necked Stilt .. 3·00 3·50

1981. Sugar Cane Railway Locomotives. Nos. 681/4 of Antigua optd. **BARBUDA**

541. 25 c. Diesel locomotive No. 15 .. .. 1·00 25
542. 50 c. Narrow-gauge steam locomotive .. .. 1·25 35
543. 90 c. Diesel locomotive Nos. 1 and 10 .. 1·50 45
544. $3 Steam locomotive hauling sugar cane .. .. 2·75 1·40

84. Florence Nightingale.

1981. Famous Women.

546. **84.** 50 c. multicoloured .. 30 30
547. – 90 c. multicoloured .. 55 55
548. – $1 multicoloured .. 60 60
549. – $4 black, brown & lilac 1·75 1·75

DESIGNS: 90 c. Marie Curie. $1 Amy Johnson. $4 Eleanor Roosevelt.

85. Goofy in Motor-boat.

1981. Walt Disney Cartoon Characters. Multicoloured.

550. 10 c. Type **85** 25 10
551. 20 c. Donald Duck reversing car into sea 30 15
552. 25 c. Mickey Mouse asking tug-boat to take on more than it can handle .. 40 20
553. 30 c. Porpoise turning tables on Goofy 50 25
554. 35 c. Goofy in sailing boat 50 25
555. 40 c. Mickey Mouse and boat being lifted out of water by fish 60 30
556. 75 c. Donald Duck fishing for flying-fish with butterfly net 75 45
557. $1 Minnie Mouse in brightly decorated sailing boat .. 85 55
558. $2 Chip and Dale on floating ship-in-bottle .. 1·60 1·10

1981. Birth Centenary of Picasso. Nos. 697/700 of Antigua optd. with **BARBUDA.**

560. 10 c. "Pipes of Pan" .. 10 10
561. 50 c. "Seated Harlequin" 25 25
562. 90 c. "Paulo as Harlequin" 45 45
563. $4 "Mother and Child" 1·60 1·60

87. Buckingham Palace. 88.
(Illust. reduced. Actual size 65 mm × 26 mm)

1981. Royal Wedding (1st issue). Buildings. Each printed in black on either pink, green or lilac backgrounds.

565. $1 } Type **87/8** 70 70
566. $1 } 70 70
567. $1.50 } Caernarvon Castle 85 85
568. $1.50 } 85 85
569. $4 } Highgrove House .. 1·75 1·75
570. $4 } 1·75 1·75

Same prices for any background colour. The two versions of each value form composite designs.

1981. Royal Wedding (2nd issue). Nos. 702/5 of Antigua optd. **BARBUDA.**

572. 25 c. Prince Charles and Lady Diana Spencer .. 25 25
573. 50 c. Glamis Castle .. 35 35
574. $4 Prince Charles skiing .. 1·00 1·40

89. "Integration and Travel".

1981. International Year of Disabled Persons.

576. **89.** 50 c. multicoloured .. 40 25
577. – 90 c. black, orange and green 60 40
578. – $1 black, blue and green 65 45
579. – $4 black yell. and brown 1·25 1·75

DESIGNS: 90 c. Braille and sign language. $1 "Helping hands". $4 "Mobility aids for disabled".

1981. Royal Wedding (3rd issue). Booklet stamps. Nos. 706/12 of Antigua optd. **BARBUDA.**

580. 25 c. Prince of Wales at Investiture, 1969 .. 25 25
581. 25 c. Prince Charles as baby, 1948 .. .. 25 25
582. $1 Prince Charles at R.A.F. College, Cranwell, 1971 45 45
583. $1 Prince Charles attending Hill House School, 1956 .. .. .. 45 45
584. $2 Prince Charles and Lady Diana Spencer .. 80 80
585. $2 Prince Charles at Trinity College, 1967 .. 80 80
586. $5 Prince Charles and Lady Diana .. .. 2·25 3·00

1981. Independence. No. 686/96 of Antigua additionally optd. **BARBUDA.**

587. 6 c. Orchid Tree 50 15
588. 10 c. Bougainvillea .. 55 15
589. 20 c. Flamboyant 70 20
590. 25 c. Hibiscus 80 25
591. 35 c. Flame of the Wood .. 90 30
592. 50 c. Cannon at Fort James 1·10 45
593. 75 c. Premier's Office .. 1·25 60
594. $1 Potworks Dam .. 1·50 65
595. $2.50 Irrigation scheme, Diamond Estate .. 3·50 2·00
596. $5 Government House and Gardens .. .. 4·25 2·75
597. $10 Coolidge International Airport .. .. 6·00 4·75

1981. 50th Anniv. of Antigua Girl Guide Movement. Nos. 713/16 of Antigua optd. **BARBUDA.**

598. 10 c. Irene Joshua (founder) 45 10
599. 50 c. Campfire sing-song .. 1·00 30
600. 90 c. Sailing .. .. 1·40 45
601. $2.50 Animal tending .. 2·75 1·40

1981. International Year of Disabled People. Sport for the Disabled. Nos. 728/31 of Antigua optd. **BARBUDA.**

603. 10 c. Swimming 30 15
604. 50 c. Discus throwing .. 65 35
605. 90 c. Archery 90 60
606. $2 Baseball .. .. 2·25 1·60

1981. Christmas. Paintings. No. 726/6 of Antigua optd. **BARBUDA.**

608. 8 c. "Holy Night" (Jacques Stella) .. 10 10
609. 30 c. "Mary with Child" (Julius Schnorr von Carolfeld) 20 20
610. $1 "Virgin and Child" (Alonso Cano) 40 40
611. $3 "Virgin and Child" (Lorenzo di Credi) .. 1·10 1·10

93. Princess of Wales.

1982. Birth of Prince William of Wales (1st issue).

613. **93.** $1 multicoloured .. 50 50
614. $2.50 multicoloured .. 1·10 1·10
615. $5 multicoloured .. 2·25 2·25

1982. South Atlantic Fund. Booklet stamps. Nos 580/6 surch. **S. Atlantic Fund + 50 c.**

617. 25 c.+50 c. Prince of Wales at Investiture, 1969 .. 20 20
618. 25 c.+50 c. Prince Charles as baby, 1948 .. .. 20 20
619. $1+50 c. Prince Charles at R.A.F. College, Cranwell,1971 .. .. 45 45
620. $1+50 c. Prince Charles attending Hill House School, 1956 .. .. 45 45
621. $2+50 c. Prince Charles and Lady Diana Spencer 75 75
622. $2+50 c. Prince Charles at Trinity College, 1967 75 75
623. $5+50 c. Prince Charles and Lady Diana .. 2·00 2·00

1982. 21st Birthday of Princess of Wales. (1st issue). As Nos. 613/16 but inscr. "Twenty First Birthday Greetings to H.R.H. The Princess of Wales."

624. $1 multicoloured .. 65 45
625. $2.50 multicoloured .. 1·50 1·25
626. $5 multicoloured .. 2·75 2·40

1982. 21st Birthday of Princess of Wales (2nd issue). Nos. 748/51 of Antigua optd. **BARBUDA MAIL.**

628. 90 c. Queen's House, Greenwich 45 45
629. $1 Prince and Princess of Wales 50 50
630. $4 Princess of Wales .. 1·50 1·50

1982. Birth of Price William of Wales (2nd issue). Nos. 757/9 of Antigua optd. **ROYAL BABY 21.6.82.**

632. 90 c. Queen's House, Grenwich 55 45
633. $1 Prince and Princess of Wales 60 50
634. $4 Princess of Wales .. 2·25 2·00

1982. Birth Centenary of Franklin D. Roosevelt and 250th Birth Anniv. of George Washington. Nos. 761/6 of Antigua optd. **BARBUDA MAIL.**

636. 10 c. Roosevelt in 1940 .. 15 10
637. 25 c. Washington as blacksmith 20 15
638. 45 c. Churchill, Roosevelt and Stalin at Yalta Conference 35 25
639. 60 c. Washington crossing Delaware 45 35
640. $1 "Roosevelt Special" train 65 55
641. $3 Portrait of Roosevelt .. 1·75 1·75

1982. Christmas. Religious Paintings by Raphael. Nos. 769/72 of Antigua optd. **BARBUDA MAIL.**

644. 10 c. "Annunciation" .. 10 10
645. 30 c. "Adoration of the Magi" 15 15
646. $1 "Presentation in the Temple" 40 40
647. $4 "Coronation of the Virgin" .. .. 1·75 1·75

1983. 500th Birth Anniv. of Raphael. Details from "Galatea" Fresco. Nos. 774/7 of Antigua optd. **BARBUDA MAIL.**

649. 45 c. Tritons and Dolphins 20 20
650. 50 c. Sea Nymph carried off by Triton 25 25
651. 60 c. Winged angel steering Dolphins (horiz.) .. 30 30
652. $4 Cupids shooting arrows 1·60 1·60

1983. Commonwealth Day. Nos. 779/82 of Antigua optd. **BARBUDA MAIL.**

654. 25 c. Pineapple produce .. 50 60
655. 45 c. Carnival 80 90
656. 60 c. Tourism .. .. 1·25 1·40
657. $3 Airport .. .. 2·75 3·50

1983. World Communications Year. Nos. 783/6 of Antigua optd. **BARBUDA MAIL.**

658. 15 c. T.V. satellite coverage of Royal Wedding .. 55 20
659. 50 c. Police communications 1·75 80
660. 60 c. House-to-diesel train telephone call .. .. 1·75 85
661. $3 Satellite earth station with planets Jupiter and Saturn .. .. .. 3·50 2·25

97. Vincenzo Lunardi's Balloon Flight, London, 1785.

1983. Bicentenary of Manned Flight (1st issue). Multicoloured.

663. $1 Type **97** 35 35
664. $1.50, Montgolfier brothers' balloon flight, Paris, 1783 55 55
665. $2.50, Blanchard and Jeffries' Cross-Channel balloon flight, 1785 .. .. 90 90

See also Nos. 672/5.

1983. Whales, Nos. 788/92 of Antigua optd. **BARBUDA MAIL.**

667. 15 c. Bottlenose Dolphin .. 80 40
668. 50 c. Finback Whale .. 2·75 1·60
669. 60 c. Bowhead Whale .. 3·00 1·75
670. $3 Spectacled Porpoise .. 5·00 4·25

1983. Bicentenary of Manned Flight. (2nd issue). Nos. 811/15 of Antigua optd. **BARBUDA MAIL.**

672. 30 c. Dornier "Do X" flying boat 65 35
673. 50 c. Supermarine "S.6B" seaplane 85 60
674. 60 c. Curtiss "9C" biplane and airship U.S.S. "Akron" 95 70
675. $4 Pro Juventute balloon 4·00 4·00

1983. Nos. 565/70 surch.

677. 45 c. on $1 Type **87** .. 65 65
678. 45 c. on $1 Type **88** .. 65 65
679. 50 c. on $1.50 Caernarvon Castle 70 70
680. 50 c. on $1.50 Caernarvon Castle 70 70
681. 60 c. on $4 Highgrove House (left) 80 80
682. 60 c. on $4 Highgrove House (right) 80 80

1983. Nos. 793/810 of Antigua optd. **BARBUDA MAIL.**

683. 1 c. Cashew Nut 10 10
684. 2 c. Passion Fruit 10 10
685. 3 c. Mango 10 10
686. 5 c. Grapefruit 10 10
687. 10 c. Pawpaw 10 10
688. 15 c. Breadfruit 20 10
689. 20 c. Coconut 25 15
690. 25 c. Oleander 25 15
691. 30 c. Banana 30 20
692. 40 c. Pineapple 35 25
693. 45 c. Cordia 40 30
694. 50 c. Cassia 50 30
695. 60 c. Poui 50 30
696. $1 Frangipani 70 50
697. $2 Flamboyant .. .. 1·50 1·25
698. $2.50 Lemon .. .. 2·00 1·75
699. $5 Lignum Vitae .. .. 3·25 2·75
700. $10 National Flag and coat of arms .. .. .. 5·50 5·50

1983. Christmas. 500th Birth Anniv. of Raphael. Nos. 816/20 of Antigua optd. **BARBUDA MAIL.**

701. 10 c. multicoloured .. 10 10
702. 30 c. multicoloured .. 15 20
703. $1 multicoloured 45 50
704. $4 multicoloured .. .. 1·50 1·75

1983. Bicentenary (1984) of Methodist Church. Nos. 821/4 of Antigua optd. **BARBUDA MAIL.**

706. 15 c. Type **181** 25 15
707. 50 c. Nathaniel Gilbert (founder in Antigua) .. 50 30
708. 60 c. St. John Methodist Church steeple 55 35
709. $3 Ebenezer Methodist Church, St. John's .. 2·00 1·75

INDEX

Countries can be quickly located by referring to the index at the end of this volume.

100. Edward VII.

1984. Members of British Royal Family. Multicoloured.

710. $1 Type **100** .. .. 90 1·25
711. $1 George V .. .. 90 1·25
712. $1 George VI .. .. 90 1·25
713. $1 Elizabeth II .. .. 90 1·25
714. $1 Charles, Prince of Wales 90 1·25
715. $1 Prince William of Wales 90 1·25

1984. Olympic Games, Los Angeles (1st issue). Nos. 825/8 of Antigua optd **BARBUDA MAIL.**

716 25 c. Discus 15 20
717 50 c. Gymnastics 35 40
718 90 c. Hurdling 50 60
719 $3 Cycling .. .. 1·25 1·50

1984. Ships. Nos. 830/3 of Antigua optd **BARBUDA MAIL.**

721 45 c. "Booker Vanguard" (freighter) .. .. 1·50 45
722 50 c. "Canberra" (liner) .. 1·50 50
723 60 c. Sailing boats .. 1·75 60
724 $4 "Fairwind" (cargo liner) 4·25 2·75

1984. Universal Postal Union Congress, Hamburg. Nos. 835/8 of Antigua optd. **BARBUDA MAIL.**

726. 15 c. Chenille 35 15
727. 50 c. Shell Flower 75 50
728. 60 c. Anthurium 90 60
729. $3 Angels Trumpet .. 2·25 2·00

101. Olympic Stadium, Athens, 1896.

1984. Olympic Games, Los Angeles (2nd issue). Multicoloured.

731. $1.50 Type **101** .. 1·00 1·10
732. $2.50 Olympic stadium, Los Angeles, 1984 .. 1·50 1·75
733. $5 Athlete carrying Olympic torch .. .. 2·50 2·75

1984. Presidents of the United States of America. Nos. 856/63 of Antigua optd. **BARBUDA MAIL.**

735. 10 c. Abraham Lincoln .. 10 10
736. 20 c. Harry Truman .. 15 15
737. 30 c. Dwight Eisenhower .. 20 25
738. 40 c. Ronald Reagan .. 25 30
739. 90 c. Gettysburg Address, 1863. .. .. .. 50 55
740. $1.10 Formation of N.A.T.O., 1949 .. .. 60 65
741. $1.50 Eisenhower during Second World War .. 80 85
742. $2 Reagan and Caribbean Basin Initiative .. .. 1·00 1·25

1984. Abolition of Slavery. Nos. 864/7 of Antigua optd. **BARBUDA MAIL.**

743. 40 c. View of Moravian Mission 30 30
744. 50 c. Antigua Courthouse, 1823. .. .. .. 40 40
745. 60 c. Planting sugar-cane, Monks Hill 45 45
746. $3 Boiling house, Delaps' Estate .. .. .. 1·90 1·90

1984. Songbirds. Nos. 869/73 of Antigua optd. **BARBUDA MAIL.**

748. 40 c. Rufous-sided towhee 45 45
749. 50 c. Parula warbler .. 50 50
750. 60 c. House wren 55 55
751. $2 Ruby-crowned kinglet 1·50 1·50
752. $3 Common flicker .. 2·25 2·25

1984. 450th Death Anniv. of Correggio (painter). Nos. 878/81 of Antigua optd. **BARBUDA MAIL.**

754. 25 c. "The Virgin and Infant with Angels and Cherubs" 15 20
755. 60 c. "The Four Saints" .. 40 45
756. 90 c. "St. Catherine" .. 60 65
757. $3 "The Campori Madonna" 1·75 2·25

1984. 'Ausipex' International Stamp Exhibition, Melbourne. Australian Sports Nos. 875/6 of Antigua optd. **BARBUDA MAIL.**

759. $1 Grass-skiing 70 75
760. $5 Ausralian Football .. 3·00 3·75

1984. 150th Birth Anniv. of Edgar Degas (painter). Nos. 883/6 of Antigua optd. **BARBUDA MAIL.**

762. 15 c. "The Blue Dancers" 10 10
763. 50 c. "The Pink Dancers" 30 40
764. 70 c. "Two Dancers" .. 45 55
765. $4 "Dancers at the Bar" .. 2·40 3·50

1985. Famous People. Nos. 888/96 of Antigua optd. **BARBUDA MAIL.**

767. 60 c. Winston Churchill .. 1·50 80
768. 60 c. Mahatma Gandhi .. 1·50 80
769. 60 c. John F. Kennedy .. 1·50 80
770. 60 c. Mao Tse-tung .. 1·50 80
771. $1 Churchill with General De Gaulle, Paris, 1944 (horiz.) .. .. .. 2·00 1·00
772. $1 Gandhi leaving London by train, 1931 (horiz.) .. 2·00 1·00
773. $1 Kennedy with Chancellor Adenauer and Mayor Brandt, Berlin, 1963 (horiz.) .. 2·00 1·00
774. $1 Mao Tse-tung with Lin Piao, Peking, 1969 (horiz.) .. .. .. 2·00 1·00

103. Lady Elizabeth Bowes-Lyon, 1907. and Camellias.

1985. The Life and Times of Queen Elizabeth the Queen Mother. Multicoloured.

776. 15 c. Type **103** 10 10
777. 45 c. Duchess of York, 1926, and "Elizabeth of Glamis" roses 20 25
778. 50 c. The Queen Mother after the Coronation, 1937 .. .. .. 20 25
779. 60 c. In Garter robes, 1971, and Dog Roses 25 30
780. 90 c. Attending Royal Variety show, 1967, and red Hibiscus 40 45
781. $2 The Queen Mother in 1982, and blue Plumbago 80 1·10
782. $3 Receiving 82nd birthday gifts from children, and Morning Glory .. .. 1·40 1·60

104. Roseate Tern.

1985. Birth Bicentenary of John J. Audubon (ornithologist) (1st issue). Designs showing original paintings. Multicoloured.

783. 45 c. Type **104** 25 30
784. 50 c. Mangrove Cuckoo .. 25 30
785. 60 c. Yellow-crowned Night Heron 30 40
786. $5 Brown Pelican .. .. 2·25 3·25

See also Nos. 794/7 and 914/17.

1985. Centenary (1986) of Statue of Liberty (1st issue). Nos. 907/13 of Antigua optd **BARBUDA MAIL.**

787. 25 c. Torch from statue in Madison Square Park, 1885 .. .. .. 15 20
788. 30 c. Statue of Liberty and scaffolding ("Restoration and Renewal") (vert.) 15 20
789. 50 c. Frederic Bartholdi (sculptor) supervising construction, 1876 .. 25 30
790. 90 c. Close-up of Statue .. 50 55
791. $1 Statue and sailing ship ("Operation Sail", 1976) (vert.) 55 60
792. $3 Dedication ceremony, 1886 (vert.) .. .. 1·60 1·75

See also Nos. 987/96.

1985. Birth Bicentenary of John J. Audubon (ornithologist) (2nd issue). Nos 924/8 of Antigua optd. **BARBUDA MAIL.**

794. 90 c. Slavonian grebe .. 2·25 2·00
795. $1 British storm petrel .. 2·50 2·25
796. $1.50 Great blue heron .. 3·00 2·75
797. $3 Double-crested cormorant .. .. 4·25 4·00

1985. Butterflies. Nos. 929/33 of Antigua optd. **BARBUDA MAIL.**

799 25 c. "Anaea cyanea" .. 1·50 90
800 60 c. "Leodonta dysoni" .. 2·75 1·50
801 90 c. "Junea doraete" .. 3·25 2·00
802 $4 "Prepona pylene" .. 7·00 6·00

1985. Centenary of Motorcycle. Nos 919/23 of Antigua optd. **BARBUDA MAIL.**

804. 10 c. Triumph 2hp "Jap", 1903 .. .. .. 40 10
805. 30 c. Indian "Arrow", 1949 70 20
806. 60 c. BMW "R100RS", 1976 .. .. .. 1·10 40
807. $4 Harley-Davidson "Model II", 1916 .. 3·50 2·75

1985. 85th Birthday of Queen Elizabeth the Queen Mother. Nos. 776/82 optd. **4th Aug 1900–1985.**

809. 15 c. Type **103** 45 10
810. 45 c. Duchess of York, 1926, and "Elizabeth of Glamis" roses 75 30
811. 50 c. The Queen Mother after the Coronation, 1937 .. .. .. 75 30
812. 60 c. In Garter robes, 1971, and Dog Roses 85 40
813. 90 c. Attending Royal Variety show, 1967, and red Hibiscus .. .. 1·25 55
814. $2 The Queen Mother in 1982, and blue Plumbago 2·00 1·25
815. $3 Receiving 82nd birthday gifts from children, and Morning Glory .. .. 2·75 1·75

1985. Native American Artefacts. Nos. 914/18 of Antigua optd. **BARBUDA MAIL.**

816. 15 c. Arawak pot sherd and Indians making clay utensils 15 10
817. 50 c. Arawak body design and Arawak Indians tattooing 30 30
818. 60 c. Head of the god "Yocahu" and Indians harvesting manioc .. 40 40
819. $3 Carib war club and Carib Indians going into battle .. .. .. 1·60 1·75

1985. 40th Anniv. of International Civil Aviation Organization. Nos. 934/8 of Antigua optd. **BARBUDA MAIL.**

821. 30 c. Cessna "172" .. 20 20
822. 90 c. Fokker "DVII" .. 55 55
823. $1.50 Spad "VII" 85 85
824. $3 Boeing "747" .. 1·75 1·75

1985. Life and Times of Queen Elizabeth the Queen Mother (2nd series). Nos. 946/8 of Antigua optd. **BARBUDA MAIL.**

826. $1 The Queen Mother attending church .. 1·75 1·75
827. $1.50 Watching children playing in London garden .. .. .. 2·00 2·00
828. $2.50 The Queen Mother in 1979 .. .. .. 2·75 2·75

1985. 850th Birth Anniv. of Maimonides (physician, philosopher and scholar). No. 939 of Antigua optd. **BARBUDA MAIL.**

830. $2 green .. .. 3·75 3·50

1985. (25 Nov). Marine Life. Nos. 950/3 of Antigua optd. **BARBUDA MAIL.**

832. 15 c. Magnificent Frigate Bird .. .. .. 1·25 40
833. 45 c. Brain Coral .. 1·50 70
834. 60 c. Cushion Star .. .. 1·75 85
835. $3 Spotted Moray Eel .. 4·25 3·25

1986. International Youth Year. Nos. 941/5 of Antigua optd. **BARBUDA MAIL.**

837. 25 c. Young farmers with produce 15 15
838. 50 c. Hotel management trainees 25 30
839. 60 c. Girls with goat and boys with football ("Environment") .. 30 35
840. $3 Windsurfing ("Leisure") 1·50 1·60

1986. Royal Visit. Nos. 965/8 of Antigua optd. **BARBUDA MAIL.**

842 60 c. Flags of Great Britain and Antigua 60 35
843 $1 Queen Elizabeth II (vert.) 80 55
844 $4 Royal Yacht "Britannia" .. .. 2·50 2·10

1986. 75th Anniv. of Girl Guide Movement. Nos. 955/8 of Antigua optd. **BARBUDA MAIL.**

846. 15 c. Girl Guides nursing .. 70 50
847. 45 c. Open-air Girl Guide meeting .. .. .. 1·75 1·50
848. 60 c. Lord and Lady Baden-Powell .. .. 2·00 1·75
849. $3 Girl Guides gathering flowers .. .. .. 4·50 4·50

1986. 300th Birth Anniv. of Johann Sebastian Bach (composer). Nos 960/3 of Antigua optd. **BARBUDA MAIL.**

851. 25 c. multicoloured .. 1·00 70
852. 50 c. multicoloured .. 1·50 1·40
853. $1 multicoloured .. .. 2·25 2·00
854. $3 multicoloured .. .. 4·75 4·75

1986. Christmas. Religious Paintings. Nos. 985/8 of Antigua optd. **BARBUDA MAIL.**

856. 10 c. "Madonna and Child" (De Landi) 40 20
857. 25 c. "Madonna and Child" (Berlinghiero) 80 50
858. 60 c. "The Nativity" (Fra Angelico) .. .. 1·50 85
859. $4 "Presentation in the Temple" (Giovanni di Paolo) .. .. .. 4·00 5·00

108. Queen Elizabeth II meeting Members of Legislature.

1986. 60th Birthday of Queen Elizabeth II (1st issue). Multicoloured.

861. $1 Type **108** .. .. 1·00 1·00
862. $2 Queen with Headmistress of Liberta School .. .. .. 1·10 1·10
863. $2.50 Queen greeted by Governor-General of Antigua .. .. .. 1·25 1·50

See also Nos. 872/4.

109. Halley's Comet over Barbuda Beach.

1986. Appearance of Halley's Comet (1st issue). Multicoloured.

865. $1 Type **109** 80 80
866. $2.50 Early telescope and dish aerial (vert.) .. 1·50 1·75
867. $5 Comet and World map 2·50 2·75

See also Nos. 886/89.

1986. 40th Anniv. of United Nations Organization. Nos. 981/3 of Antigua optd. **BARBUDA MAIL.**

868. 40 c. Benjamin Franklin and U.N. (New York) 1953 U.P.U. 5 c. stamp 1·25 85
869. $1 George Washington Carver (agricultural chemist) and 1982 Nature Conservation 28 c. stamp .. 2·00 1·60
870. $3 Charles Lindbergh (aviator) and 1978 I.C.A.O. 25 c. stamp .. 3·75 3·50

1986. 60th Birthday of Queen Elizabeth II (2nd issue). Nos. 1005/7 of Antigua optd. **BARBUDA MAIL.**

872. 60 c. black and yellow .. 1·25 1·00
873. $1 multicoloured .. .. 1·75 1·60
874. $4 multicoloured .. .. 3·50 3·50

1986. World Cup Football Championship, Mexico. Nos. 995/8 of Antigua optd. **BARBUDA MAIL.**

876. 30 c. Football, boots and trophy .. .. .. 1·50 1·00
877. 60 c. Goalkeeper (vert.) .. 2·50 1·60
878. $1 Referee blowing whistle (vert.) .. .. .. 2·75 2·00
879. $4 Ball in net .. .. 6·00 5·00

1986. "Ameripex '86" International Stamp Exhibition, Chicago. Famous American Trains. Nos. 1014/17 of Antigua optd. **BARBUDA MAIL.**

881. 25 c. "Hiawatha Express" 1·60 1·00
882. 50 c. "Grand Canyon Express" .. .. 2·50 1·60
883. $1 "Powhattan Arrow Express" .. .. 3·00 2·40
884. $3 "Empire State Express" 6·00 5·00

1986. Appearance of Halley's Comet (2nd issue). Nos. 1000/3 of Antigua optd. **BARBUDA MAIL.**

886. 5 c. Edmond Halley and Old Greenwich Observatory 55 35
887. 10 c. "Me 163B Komet" (fighter aircraft), 1944 .. 55 35
888. 60 c. Montezuma (Aztec Emperor) and Comet in 1517 (from "Historias de las Indias de Neuva Espana") .. .. 2·00 1·25
889. $4 Pocahontas saving Capt. John Smith and Comet in 1607 .. .. 6·00 5·00

1986. Royal Wedding. Nos. 1019/21 of Antigua optd. **BARBUDA MAIL.**

891. 45 c. Prince Andrew and Miss Sarah Ferguson .. 65 45
892. 60 c. Prince Andrew .. 75 55
893. $4 Prince Andrew with Prince Philip .. .. 3·50 3·25

1986. Sea Shells. Nos. 1023/6 of Antigua optd. **BARBUDA MAIL.**

895. 15 c. Fly-specked Cerith .. 1·50 85
896. 45 c. Smooth Scotch Bonnet .. .. .. 2·00 1·60
897. 60 c. West Indian Crown Conch .. .. .. 2·50 2·25
898. $3 Murex Ciboney .. .. 7·50 6·50

1986. Flowers. Nos. 1028/35 of Antigua optd. **BARBUDA MAIL.**

900. 10 c. "Nymphaea ampla" (water lily) 20 20
901. 15 c. Queen of the Night .. 30 30
902. 50 c. Cup of Gold 50 50
903. 60 c. Beach Morning Glory 55 55
904. 70 c. Golden Trumpet .. 70 70
905. $1 Air Plant 85 85
906. $3 Purple Wreath .. .. 2·25 2·25
907. $4 Zephyr Lily .. .. 2·75 2·75

1986. Mushrooms. Nos. 1042/5 of Antigua optd. **BARBUDA MAIL.**

909 10 c. "Hygrocybe occidentalis var scarletina" .. 55 30
910 50 c. "Trogia buccinalis" 2·00 1·50
911 $1 "Collybia subpruinosa" 3·25 2·25
912 $4 "Leucocoprinus brebissonii" .. .. 8·00 5·50

1986. Birth Bicentenary of John J. Audubon (ornithologist) (3rd issue). Nos. 990/3 of Antigua optd. **BARBUDA MAIL.**

914. 60 c. Mallard 85 60
915. 90 c. North American black duck .. .. 1·25 85
916. $1.50 American pintail .. 2·00 1·50
917. $3 Wigeon .. .. 3·25 3·00

1987. Local Boats. Nos. 1009/12 of Antigua optd. **BARBUDA MAIL.**

918. 30 c. Tugboat 30 30
919. 60 c. Game fishing boat .. 45 45
920. $1 Yacht 75 75
921. $4 Lugger with auxiliary sail .. .. .. 2·50 2·50

1987. Centenary of First Benz Motor Car. Nos. 1052/9 of Antigua optd. **BARBUDA MAIL.**

923. 10 c. Auburn "Speedster" (1933) 20 15
924. 15 c. Mercury "Sable" (1986) 25 20
925. 50 c. Cadillac (1959) .. 55 45
926. 60 c. Studebaker (1950) .. 55 45
927. 70 c. Lagonda "V-12" (1939) 60 50
928. $1 Adler "Standard" (1930) 80 65
929. $3 DKW (1956) .. .. 2·00 1·75
930. $4 Mercedes "500K" (1936) 2·50 2·25

1987. World Cup Football Championship Winners, Mexico. Nos. 1037/40 of Antigua optd. **BARBUDA MAIL.**

932. 30 c. Football, boots and trophy 60 40
933. 60 c. Goalkeeper (vert.) .. 90 60
934. $1 Referee blowing whistle (vert.) .. .. .. 1·40 80
935. $4 Ball in net .. .. 3·25 2·50

1987. America's Cup Yachting Championship. Nos. 1072/5 of Antigua optd. **BARBUDA MAIL.**

936. 30 c. "Canada I" (1981) .. 20 20
937. 60 c. "Gretel II" (1970) .. 35 35
938. $1 "Sceptre" (1958) .. 60 60
939. $3 "Vigilant" (1893) .. 1·75 1·75

1987. Marine Life. Nos. 1077/84 of Antigua optd. **BARBUDA MAIL.**

941. 15 c. Bridled burrfish .. 25 20
942. 30 c. Common noddy .. 50 35
943. 40 c. Nassau grouper .. 50 35
944. 50 c. Laughing gull .. 75 55
945. 60 c. French angelfish .. 75 55
946. $1 Porkfish 75 65
947. $2 Royal tern .. 2·00 1·50
948. $3 Sooty tern .. .. 2·25 2·00

1987. Milestones of Transportation. Nos. 1100/9 of Antigua optd **BARBUDA MAIL.**

950 10 c. "Spirit of Australia" (fastest powerboat), 1978 35 25
951 15 c. Siemen's electric locomotive, 1879 .. 60 45
952 30 c. U.S.S. "Triton" (first submerged circumnavigation), 1960 .. .. 75 75
953 50 c. Trevithick's steam carriage (first passenger-carrying vehicle), 1801 .. 85 70
954 60 c. U.S.S. "New Jersey" (battleship), 1942 .. 1·00 75
955 70 c. Draisine bicycle, 1818 1·00 80
956 90 c. "United States" (liner) (holder of Blue Riband), 1952 .. 1·25 1·00
957 $1.50 Cierva "C.4" (first autogiro), 1923 .. 1·75 1·50
958 $2 Curtiss "NC.4" (first transatlantic flight), 1919 2·00 1·75
959 $3 "Queen Elizabeth 2" (liner), 1969 .. 3·00 2·50

110. Shore Crab.

1987. Marine Life. Multicoloured.

960. 5 c. Type **110** 20 30
961. 10 c. Sea cucumber .. 20 30
962. 15 c. Stop light parrotfish 25 40
963. 25 c. Banded coral shrimp 30 40
964. 35 c. Spotted drum .. 35 45
965. 60 c. Thorny starfish .. 50 65
966. 75 c. Atlantic trumpet triton 60 75
967. 90 c. Feather star and yellow beaker sponge .. 70 90
968. $1 Blue gorgonian (vert.) 70 90
969. $1.25 Slender filefish (vert.) 90 1·25
970. $5 Barred hamlet (vert.) .. 2·00 2·75
971. $7.50 Fairy basslet (vert.) 3·50 4·50
972. $10 Fire coral and butterfly fish (vert.) .. .. 4·00 5·00

1987. Olympic Games, Seoul (1988). Nos. 1086/9 of Antigua optd. **BARBUDA MAIL.**

973. 10 c. Handball 25 10
974. 60 c. Fencing 45 40
975. $1 Gymnastics 80 70
976. $3 Football .. .. 1·90 2·25

1987. Birth Centenary of Marc Chagall (artist). Nos. 1091/8 of Antigua optd. **BARBUDA MAIL.**

978. 10 c. "The Profile" .. 10 10
979. 30 c. "Portrait of the Artist's Sister" 15 15
980. 40 c. "Bride with Fan" .. 20 25
981. 60 c. "David in Profile" .. 25 30
982. 90 c. "Fiancee with Bouquet" 40 45
983. $1 "Self Portrait with Brushes" 45 50
984. $3 "The Walk" .. 1·40 1·50
985. $4 "Three Candles" .. 1·75 1·90

1987. Centenary (1986) of Statue of Liberty (2nd issue). Nos. 1110/19 of Antigua optd. **BARBUDA MAIL.**

987. 15 c. Lee Iacocca at unveiling of restored statue 10 10
988. 30 c. Statue at sunset (side view) 15 15
989. 45 c. Aerial view of head .. 20 25
990. 50 c. Lee Iacocca and torch 25 30
991. 60 c. Workmen inside head of statue (horiz.) .. 25 30
992. 90 c. Restoration work (horiz.) 40 45
993. $1 Head of statue 45 50
994. $2 Statue at sunset (front view) 90 95
995. $3 Inspecting restoration work (horiz.) .. .. 1·40 1·50
996. $5 Statue at night .. 2·25 2·40

1987. Entertainers. Nos. 1120/7 of Antigua optd. **BARBUDA MAIL.**

997. 15 c. Grace Kelly .. 40 40
998. 30 c. Marilyn Monroe .. 55 55
999. 45 c. Orson Welles .. 65 65
1000. 50 c. Judy Garland .. 75 75
1001. 60 c. John Lennon .. 1·25 1·10
1002. $1 Rock Hudson .. 1·40 1·25
1003. $2 John Wayne .. .. 2·25 2·00
1004. $3 Elvis Presley .. .. 3·00 2·75

1987. "Capex '87" International Stamp Exhibition, Toronto. Reptiles and Amphibians. Nos. 1133/6 of Antigua optd. **BABUDA MAIL.**

1005. 30 c. Whistling frog .. 35 35
1006. 60 c. Croaking lizard .. 60 60
1007. $1 Antiguan anole .. 85 85
1008. $3 Red-footed tortoise .. 2·00 2·00

1988. Christmas. Religious Paintings. Nos. 1144/7 of Antigua optd. **BARBUDA MAIL.**

1010. 45 c. "Madonna and Child" (Bernardo Daddi) 20 25
1011. 60 c. St. Joseph (detail, "The Nativity" (Sano di Pietro)) 25 30
1012. $1 Virgin Mary (detail, "The Nativity" (Sano di Pietro)) 45 50
1013. $4 "Music-making Angel" (Melozzo da Forli) .. .. .. 1·75 1·90

1988. Salvation Army's Community Service. Nos.1163/70 of Antigua optd **BARBUDA MAIL.**

1015 25 c. First aid at daycare centre, Antigua .. 55 55
1016 30 c. Giving penicillin injection, Indonesia .. 55 55
1017 40 c. Children at daycare centre, Bolivia .. 65 65
1018 45 c. Rehabilitation of the handicapped, India .. 65 65
1019 50 c. Training blind man, Kenya 80 80
1020 60 c. Weighing baby, Ghana 80 80
1021 $1 Training typist, Zambia .. .. 1·25 1·25
1022 $2 Emergency food kitchen, Sri Lanka .. 1·75 1·75

1988. Bicentenary of U.S. Constitution. Nos. 1139/42 of Antigua optd **BARBUDA MAIL.**

1024 15 c. House of Burgesses, Virginia ("Freedom of Speech") 10 10
1025 45 c. State Seal, Connecticut 20 25
1026 60 c. State Seal, Delaware 25 30
1027 $4 Gouverneur Morris (Pennsylvania delegate) (vert) .. .. 1·75 1·90

1988. Royal Ruby Wedding. Nos. 1149/52 of Antigua optd **BARBUDA MAIL.**

1029 25 c. brown, black & blue 30 20
1030 60 c. multicoloured .. 55 35
1031 $2 brown, black and green 1·40 1·25
1032 $3 multicoloured .. 1·75 1·75

1988. Birds of Antigua. Nos. 1154/61 of Antigua optd **BARBUDA MAIL.**

1034 10 c. Great blue heron .. 45 30
1035 15 c. Ringed kingfisher (horiz) 50 30
1036 50 c. Bananaquit (horiz) 85 70
1037 60 c. Purple gallinule (horiz) 85 70
1038 70 c. Blue-hooded euphonia (horiz) .. 1·00 85
1039 $1 Brown-throated conure ("Caribbean Parakeet") 1·25 1·00
1040 $3 Troupial (horiz) .. 2·50 2·50
1041 $4 Purple-throated carib (horiz) .. .. 2·75 2·75

1988. 500th Anniv (1992) of Discovery of America by Columbus (1st issue). Nos. 1172/9 of Antigua optd **BARBUDA MAIL**.

1043 10 c. Columbus's second fleet, 1493 .. .. 15 15
1044 30 c. Painos Indian village and fleet 20 20
1045 45 c. "Santa Mariagalante" (flagship) and Painos village 35 35
1046 60 c. Painos Indians offering Columbus fruit and vegetables .. 35 35
1047 90 c. Painos Indian and Columbus with scarlet macaw 60 60
1048 $1 Columbus landing on island 65 65
1049 $3 Spanish soldier and fleet 1·50 1·50
1050 $4 Fleet under sail .. 2·00 2·00

See also Nos. 1112/15, 1177/84, 1285/92, 1374/9 and 1381/2.

1988. 500th Birth Anniv of Titian. Nos. 1181/8 of Antigua optd **BARBUDA MAIL**.

1052 30 c. "Bust of Christ" .. 15 15
1053 40 c. "Scourging of Christ" 20 25
1054 45 c. "Madonna in Glory with Saints" 20 25
1055 50 c. "The Averoldi Polyptych" (detail) .. 25 30
1056 $1 "Christ Crowned with Thorns" 45 50
1057 $2 "Christ Mocked" .. 90 95
1058 $3 "Christ and Simon of Cyrene" .. .. 1·40 1·50
1059 $4 "Crucifixion with Virgin and Saints" .. 1·75 2·00

1988. 16th World Scout Jamboree, Australia. Nos. 1128/31 of Antigua optd **BARBUDA MAIL**.

1061 10 c. Scouts around camp fire and red kangaroo 15 15
1062 60 c. Scouts canoeing and blue-winged kookaburra 45 45
1063 $1 Scouts on assault course and ring-tailed rock wallaby .. 70 70
1064 $3 Field kitchen and koala .. .. .. 1·75 1·75

1988. Sailing Week. Nos. 1190/3 of Antigua optd **BARBUDA MAIL**.

1066 30 c. Two yachts rounding buoy 20 20
1067 60 c. Three yachts .. 45 45
1068 $1 British yacht under way 70 70
1069 $3 Three yachts (different) 1·60 1·60

1988. Flowering Trees. Nos. 1213/20 of Antigua optd **BARBUDA MAIL**.

1071 10 c. Jacaranda 10 10
1072 30 c. Cordia 15 15
1073 50 c. Orchid tree .. 20 25
1074 90 c. Flamboyant .. 40 45
1075 $1 African tulip tree .. 45 50
1076 $2 Potato tree 80 85
1077 $3 Crepe myrtle .. .. 1·25 1·40
1078 $4 Pitch apple .. .. 1·60 1·75

1988. Olympic Games, Seoul. Nos. 1222/5 of Antigua optd **BARBUDA MAIL**.

1080 40 c. Gymnastics .. 20 25
1081 60 c. Weightlifting .. 25 30
1082 $1 Water polo (horiz) .. 45 50
1083 $3 Boxing (horiz) .. 1·25 1·40

1988. Caribbean Butterflies. Nos. 1227/44 of Antigua optd **BARBUDA MAIL**.

1085 1 c. "Danaus plexippus" 10 10
1086 2 c. "Greta diaphanus" 10 10
1087 3 c. "Calisto archebates" 10 10
1088 5 c. "Hamadryas feronia" 10 10
1089 10 c. "Mestra dorcas" .. 10 10
1090 15 c. "Hypolimnas misippus" 10 10
1091 20 c. "Dione juno" .. 10 10
1092 25 c. "Heliconius charithonia" 10 15
1093 30 c. "Eurema pyro" .. 10 15
1094 40 c. "Papilio androgeus" 20 25
1095 45 c. "Anteos maerula" 20 25
1096 50 c. "Aphrissa orbis" .. 25 30
1097 60 c. "Astraptes xagua" 30 35
1098 $1 "Heliopetes arsalte" 50 55
1099 $2 "Polites baracoa" .. 95 1·00
1100 $2.50 "Phocides pigmalion" .. .. .. 1·25 1·40
1101 $5 "Prepona amphitoe" 2·40 2·50
1102 $10 "Oarisma nanus" .. 5·00 5·25
1102a $20 "Parides lycimenes" 9·50 9·75

1989. 25th Death Anniv of John F. Kennedy (American statesman). Nos. 1245/52 of Antigua optd **BARBUDA MAIL**.

1103 1 c. President Kennedy and family 10 10
1104 2 c. Kennedy commanding "PT109" 10 10
1105 3 c. Funeral cortege .. 10 10
1106 4 c. In motorcade, Mexico 10 10
1107 30 c. As 1 c. 15 20
1108 60 c. As 4 c. 30 35
1109 $1 As 3 c. 45 50
1110 $4 As 2 c. .. .. 1·90 2·00

1989. 500th Anniv (1992) of Discovery of America by Columbus (2nd issue). Pre-Columbian Arawak Society. Nos. 1267/70 of Antigua optd **BARBUDA MAIL**.

1112 $1.50 Arawak warriors .. 75 75
1113 $1.50 Whip dancers .. 75 75
1114 $1.50 Whip dancers and chief with pineapple .. 75 75
1115 $1.50 Family and camp fire 75 75

1989. 50th Anniv of First Jet Flight. Nos. 1272/9 of Antigua optd **BARBUDA MAIL**.

1117 10 c. De Havilland "Comet 4" airliner .. 15 15
1118 30 c. Messerschmitt "Me 262" fighter 25 25
1119 40 c. Boeing "707" airliner 30 30
1120 60 c. Canadair "F-86 Sabre" fighter .. 40 40
1121 $1 Lockheed "F-104 Starfighter" fighters .. 60 60
1122 $2 McDonnell Douglas "DC-10" airliner .. 1·25 1·25
1123 $3 Boeing "747" airliner 1·75 1·75
1124 $4 McDonnell "F-4 Phantom" fighter .. 2·25 2·25

1989. Caribbean Cruise Ships. Nos. 1281/8 of Antigua optd **BARBUDA MAIL**.

1126 25 c. "Festivale" .. 20 20
1127 45 c. "Southward" .. 35 35
1128 50 c. "Sagafjord" .. 40 40
1129 60 c. "Daphne" .. 45 45
1130 75 c. "Cunard Countess" 55 55
1131 90 c. "Song of America" 60 60
1132 $3 "Island Princess" .. 2·00 2·00
1133 $4 "Galileo" .. .. 2·50 2·50

1989. Japanese Art. Paintings by Hiroshige. Nos. 1290/7 of Antigua optd **BARBUDA MAIL**.

1135 25 c. "Fish swimming by Duck half-submerged in Stream" 10 15
1136 45 c. "Crane and Wave" 20 25
1137 50 c. "Sparrows and Morning Glories" .. 25 30
1138 60 c. "Crested Blackbird and Flowering Cherry" 30 35
1139 $1 "Great Knot sitting among Water Grass" .. 45 50
1140 $2 "Goose on a Bank of Water" .. .. 95 1·00
1141 $3 "Black Paradise Flycatcher and Blossoms" 1·50 1·60
1142 $4 "Sleepy Owl perched on a Pine Branch" .. 1·90 2·00

1989. World Cup Football Championship, Italy (1990). Nos. 1308/11 of Antigua optd **BARBUDA MAIL**.

1144 15 c. Goalkeeper .. 10 10
1145 25 c. Goalkeeper moving towards ball 10 15
1146 $1 Goalkeeper reaching for ball 45 50
1147 $4 Goalkeeper saving goal 1·90 2·00

1989. Christmas. Paintings by Raphael and Giotto. Nos. 1351/8 of Antigua optd **BARBUDA MAIL**.

1149 10 c. "The Small Cowper Madonna" (Raphael) .. 10 10
1150 25 c. "Madonna of the Goldfinch" (Raphael) 10 15
1151 30 c. "The Alba Madonna" (Raphael) .. 15 20
1152 50 c. Saint (detail, "Bologna Altarpiece") (Giotto) 25 30
1153 60 c. Angel (detail, "Bologna Altarpiece") (Giotto) 30 35
1154 70 c. Angel slaying serpent (detail, "Bologna Altarpiece") (Giotto) .. 35 40
1155 $4 Evangelist (detail, "Bologna Altarpiece") (Giotto) .. .. 1·90 2·00
1156 $5 "Madonna of Foligno" (Raphael) .. .. 2·40 2·50

1990. Fungi. Nos. 1313/20 of Antigua optd **BARBUDA MAIL**.

1158 10 c. Lilac fairy helmet .. 40 30
1159 25 c. Rough psathyrella (vert) 60 30
1160 50 c. Golden tops .. 95 75
1161 60 c. Blue cap (vert) .. 1·00 80
1162 75 c. Brown cap (vert) .. 1·25 85
1163 $1 Green gill (vert) .. 1·40 90
1164 $3 Red pinwheel .. 3·25 3·00
1165 $4 Red hanterelle .. 3·50 3·25

1990. Local Fauna. Nos. 1322/5 optd **BARBUDA MAIL**.

1167 25 c. Desmarest's hutia .. 25 25
1168 45 c. Caribbean monk seal 45 45
1169 60 c. Mustache bat (vert) 55 55
1170 $4 American manatee (vert) .. .. 2·25 2·25

1990. 20th Anniv of First Manned Landing on Moon. Nos. 1346/9 optd **BARBUDA MAIL**.

1172 10 c. Launch of "Apollo 11" 25 20
1173 45 c. Aldrin on Moon .. 55 45
1174 $1 Module "Eagle" over Moon (horiz) .. .. 1·00 90
1175 $4 Recovery of "Apollo 11" crew after splashdown (horiz) .. .. .. 3·25 3·50

1990. 500th Anniv (1992) of Discovery of America by Columbus (3rd issue). New World Natural History—Marine Life. Nos. 1360/7 of Antigua optd **BARBUDA MAIL**.

1177 10 c. Star-eyed hermit crab 20 20
1178 20 c. Spiny lobster .. 25 25
1179 25 c. Magnificent banded fanworm 25 25
1180 45 c. Cannonball jellyfish 40 40
1181 60 c. Red-spiny sea star 55 55
1182 $2 Peppermint shrimp .. 1·25 1·25
1183 $3 Coral crab .. .. 1·60 1·60
1184 $4 Branching fire coral .. 1·75 1·75

1990. "EXPO 90" International Garden and Greenery Exhibition, Osaka. Orchids. Nos.1369/76 of Antigua optd **BARBUDA MAIL**.

1186 15 c. "Vanilla mexicana" 40 30
1187 45 c. "Epidendrum ibaguense" 75 55
1188 50 c. "Epidendrum secundum" 75 55
1189 60 c. "Maxillaria conferta" 85 70
1190 $1 "Onicidium altissimum" .. .. 1·25 1·00
1191 $2 "Spiranthes lanceolata" .. .. 2·00 2·00
1192 $3 "Tonopsis utricularioides" .. 2·75 2·75
1193 $5 "Epidendrum nocturnum" .. .. 4·50 4·50

1990. Reef Fishes. Nos. 1386/93 of Antigua optd **BARBUDA MAIL**.

1195 10 c. Flamefish 20 20
1196 15 c. Coney 25 25
1197 50 c. Squirrelfish .. 55 55
1198 60 c. Sergeant major .. 60 60
1199 $1 Yellowtail snapper .. 85 85
1200 $2 Rock beauty .. .. 1·50 1·50
1201 $3 Spanish hogfish .. 1·75 1·75
1202 $4 Striped parrotfish .. 2·00 2·00

1990. 1st Anniv of Hurricane Hugo. Nos. 971/2 surch **1st Anniversary Hurricane Hugo 16th September, 1989–1990.**

1204 $5 on $7.50 Fairy basslet (vert) .. .. .. 2·25 2·25
1205 $7.50 on $10 Fire coral and butterfly fish (vert) 3·25 3·25

1990. 90th Birthday of Queen Elizabeth the Queen Mother. Nos. 1415/18 of Antigua optd **BARBUDA MAIL**.

1206 15 c. multicoloured .. 15 15
1207 35 c. multicoloured .. 20 20
1208 75 c. multicoloured .. 35 35
1209 $3 multicoloured .. 1·25 1·25

1990. Achievements in Space. Nos. 1395/1414 of Antigua optd **BARBUDA MAIL**.

1211 45 c. "Voyager 2" passing Saturn 25 25
1212 45 c. "Pioneer 11" photographing Saturn .. 25 25
1213 45 c. Astronaut in transporter 25 25
1214 45 c. Space shuttle "Columbia" 25 25
1215 45 c. "Apollo 10" command module on parachutes 25 25
1216 45 c. "Skylab" space station 25 25
1217 45 c. Astronaut Edward White in space .. 25 25
1218 45 c. "Apollo" spacecraft on joint mission .. 25 25
1219 45 c. "Soyuz" spacecraft on joint mission .. 25 25
1220 45 c. "Mariner 1" passing Venus 25 25
1221 45 c. "Gemini 4" capsule 25 25
1222 45 c. "Sputnik 1" .. 25 25
1223 45 c. Hubble space telescope 25 25
1224 45 c. "X-15" rocket plane 25 25
1225 45 c. "Bell X-1" aircraft 25 25
1226 45 c. "Apollo 17" astronaut and lunar rock formation .. 25 25
1227 45 c. Lunar rover .. 25 25
1228 45 c. "Apollo 14" lunar module 25 25
1229 45 c. Astronaut Buzz Aldrin on Moon .. 25 25
1230 45 c. Soviet "Lunokhod" lunar vehicle 25 25

1990. Christmas. Paintings by Renaissance Masters. Nos. 1457/64 of Antigua optd **BARBUDA MAIL**.

1231 25 c. "Madonna and Child with Saints (detail, Sebastiano del Piombo) 10 10
1232 30 c. "Virgin and Child with Angels" (detail, Grunewald) (vert) .. 10 15
1233 40 c. "The Holy Family and a Shepherd" (detail, Titian) .. 15 20
1234 60 c. "Virgin and Child" (detail, Lippi) (vert) .. 25 30
1235 $1 "Jesus, St. John and Two Angels" (Rubens) 40 45
1236 $2 "Adoration of the Shepherds" (detail, Vincenzo Catena) .. 80 85
1237 $4 "Adoration of the Magi" (detail, Giorgione) .. .. 1·60 1·75
1238 $5 "Virgin and Child adored by Warrior" (detail, Vincenzo Catena) .. .. 2·00 2·10

1991. 150th Anniv of the Penny Black. Nos. 1378/80 of Antigua optd **BARBUDA MAIL**.

1240 45 c. green 35 35
1241 60 c. mauve 40 40
1242 $5 blue .. .. .. 2·75 2·75

1991. "Stamp World London 90" International Stamp Exhibition. Nos. 1382/4 of Antigua optd **BARBUDA MAIL**.

1244 50 c. green and red .. 35 35
1245 75 c. brown and red .. 45 45
1246 $4 blue and red .. .. 2·40 2·40

119 Troupial

1991. Wild Birds. Multicoloured.

1248 60 c. Type **119** .. 40 40
1249 $2 Adelaide's warbler ("Christmas Bird") .. 1·25 1·25
1250 $4 Rose-breasted grosbeak 2·50 2·50
1251 $7 Wied's crested flycatcher .. .. 4·25 4·25

1991. Olympic Games, Barcelona (1992). Nos. 1429/32 of Antigua optd **BARBUDA MAIL**.

1252 50 c. Men's 20 kilometres walk 20 25
1253 75 c. Triple jump .. 30 35
1254 $1 Men's 10,000 metres .. 40 45
1255 $5 Javelin .. .. 2·10 2·25

1991. Birds. Nos. 1448/55 of Antigua optd **BARBUDA MAIL**.

1257 10 c. Pearly-eyed thrasher 20 10
1258 25 c. Purple-thorated carib 25 25
1259 50 c. Yellowthroat .. 45 45
1260 60 c. American kestrel .. 55 55
1261 $1 Yellow-bellied sapsucker 75 75
1262 $2 Purple gallinule .. 1·40 1·40
1263 $3 Yellow-crowned night heron .. .. .. 2·00 2·00
1264 $4 Blue-hooded euphonia 2·50 2·50

1991. 350th Death Anniv of Rubens. Nos. 1466/73 of Antigua optd **BARBUDA MAIL**.

1266 25 c. "Rape of the Daughters of Leucippus" (detail) 10 10
1267 45 c. "Bacchanal" (detail) 20 25
1268 50 c. "Rape of the Sabine Women" (detail) .. 20 25
1269 60 c. "Battle of the Amazons" (detail) .. 25 30
1270 $1 "Rape of the Sabine Women" (different detail) 40 45
1271 $2 "Bacchanal" (different detail) 85 90
1272 $3 "Rape of the Sabine Women" (different detail) .. .. 1·25 1·40
1273 $4 "Bacchanal" (different detail) .. .. 1·75 1·90

1991. 50th Anniv of Second World War. Nos. 1475/83 of Antigua optd **BARBUDA MAIL**.

1275 10 c. U.S. troops cross into Germany, 1944 .. 15 15
1276 15 c. Axis surrender in North Africa, 1943 .. 20 20
1277 25 c. U.S. tanks invade Kwalajalein, 1944 .. 30 30

1278 45 c. Roosevelt and Churchill meet at Casablanca, 1943 45 45
1279 50 c. Marshall Badoglio, Prime Minister of Italian anti-facist government, 1943 45 45
1280 $1 Lord Mountbatten, Supreme Allied Commander South-east Asia, 1943 80 80
1281 $2 Greek victory at Koritza, 1940 1·50 1·50
1282 $4 Anglo-Soviet mutual assistance pact, 1941 2·75 2·75
1283 $5 Operation Torch landings, 1942 3·00 3·00

1991. 500th Anniv (1992) of Discovery of America by Columbus (4th issue). History of Exploration. Nos. 1503/10 of Antigua optd **BARBUDA MAIL.**
1285 10 c. multicoloured 10 10
1286 15 c. multicoloured 15 15
1287 45 c. multicoloured 30 30
1288 60 c. multicoloured 40 40
1289 $1 multicoloured 55 55
1290 $2 multicoloured 1·00 1·00
1291 $4 multicoloured 1·90 2·00
1292 $5 multicoloured 2·50 2·75

1991. Butterflies. Nos. 1494/1501 of Antigua optd **BARBUDA MAIL.**
1294 10 c. "Heliconius charithonia" 20 20
1295 35 c. "Marpesia petreus" 40 40
1296 50 c. "Anartia amathea" 50 50
1297 75 c. "Siproeta stelenes" 65 65
1298 $1 "Battus polydamas" 80 80
1299 $2 "Historis odius" 1·40 1·40
1300 $4 "Hypolimnas misippus" 2·75 2·75
1301 $5 "Hamadryas feronia" 3·00 3·00

1991. 65th Birthday of Queen Elizabeth II. Nos. 1534/7 of Antigua optd **BARBUDA MAIL.**
1303 15 c. Queen Elizabeth and Prince Philip in 1976 10 10
1304 20 c. The Queen and Prince Philip in Portugal, 1985 10 10
1305 $2 Queen Elizabeth II 85 90
1306 $4 The Queen and Prince Philip at Ascot, 1986 1·75 1·90

1991. 10th Wedding Anniv of Prince and Princess of Wales. Nos. 1539/42 of Antigua optd **BARBUDA MAIL.**
1308 10 c. Prince and Princess of Wales at party, 1986 10 10
1309 40 c. Separate portraits of Prince, Princess and sons 15 20
1310 $1 Prince Henry and Prince William 45 50
1311 $5 Princess Diana in Australia and Prince Charles in Hungary 2·25 2·40

1991. Christmas. Religious Paintings by Fra Angelico. Nos. 1595/1602 of Antigua optd **BARBUDA MAIL.**
1313 10 c. "The Annunciation" 10 10
1314 30 c. "Nativity" 15 20
1315 40 c. "Adoration of the Magi" 15 20
1316 60 c. "Presentation in the Temple" 25 30
1317 $1 "Circumcision" 45 50
1318 $3 "Flight into Egypt" 1·25 1·40
1319 $4 "Massacre of the Innocents" 1·75 1·90
1320 $5 "Christ teaching in the Temple" 2·25 2·40

1992. Death Centenary (1990) of Vincent van Gogh (artist). Nos. 1512/23 of Antigua optd **BARBUDA MAIL.**
1321 5 c. "Camille Roulin" 10 10
1322 10 c. "Armand Roulin" 10 10
1323 15 c. "Young Peasant Woman with Straw Hat sitting in the Wheat" 10 10
1324 25 c. "Adeline Ravoux" 10 10
1325 30 c. "The Schoolboy" 15 20
1326 40 c. "Doctor Gachet" 15 20
1327 50 c. "Portrait of a Man" 20 25
1328 75 c. "Two Children" 35 40
1329 $2 "The Postman Joseph Roulin" 85 90
1330 $3 "The Seated Zouave" 1·25 1·40
1331 $4 "L'Arlesienne" 1·75 1·90
1332 $5 "Self-Portrait, November/December 1888" 2·25 2·40

1992. Birth Centenary of Charles de Gaulle (French statesman). Nos. 1562/9 of Antigua optd **BARBUDA MAIL.**
1334 10 c. Presidents De Gaulle and Kennedy, 1961 10 10
1335 15 c. General De Gaulle with Pres. Roosevelt, 1945 (vert) 15 15
1336 45 c. Pres. De Gaulle with Chancellor Adenauer, 1962 (vert) 30 30
1337 60 c. De Gaulle at Arc de Triomphe, Liberation of Paris, 1944 (vert) 40 40
1338 $1 General De Gaulle crossing the Rhine, 1945 65 65
1339 $2 General De Gaulle in Algiers, 1944 1·10 1·10
1340 $4 Presidents De Gaulle and Eisenhower, 1960 1·90 1·90
1341 $5 De Gaulle returning from Germany, 1968 (vert) 2·40 2·40

1992. Easter. Religious Paintings. Nos. 1627/34 of Antigua optd **BARBUDA MAIL.**
1343 10 c. "Supper at Emmaus" (Caravaggio) 10 10
1344 15 c. "The Vision of St. Peter" (Zurbaran) 10 10
1345 30 c. "Christ driving the Money-changers from the Temple" (Tiepolo) 15 20
1346 40 c. "Martyrdom of St. Bartholomew" (detail) (Ribera) 20 25
1347 $1 "Christ driving the Money-changers from the Temple" (detail) (Tiepolo) 50 55
1348 $2 "Crucifixion" (detail) (Altdorfer) 95 1·00
1349 $4 "The Deposition" (detail) (Fra Angelico) 2·00 2·10
1350 $5 "The Deposition" (different detail) (Fra Angelico) 2·40 2·50

1992. Anniversaries and Events. Nos. 1573/82 of Antigua optd **BARBUDA MAIL.**
1352 25 c. Germans celebrating Reunification 10 10
1353 75 c. Cubs erecting tent 35 40
1354 $1.50 "Don Giovanni" and Mozart 75 80
1355 $2 Chariot driver and Gate at night 95 1·00
1356 $2 Lord Baden-Powell and members of the 3rd Antigua Methodist cub pack (vert) 95 1·00
1357 $2 Lilienthal's signature and glider "Flugzeug Nr. 5" 95 1·00
1358 $2.50 Driver in modern locomotive (vert) 1·25 1·40
1359 $3 Statues from podium 1·40 1·50
1360 $3.50 Cubs and campfire 1·60 1·75
1361 $4 St. Peter's Cathedral, Salzburg 2·00 2·10

1992. 50th Anniv of Japanese Attack on Pearl Harbor. Nos. 1585/94 of Antigua optd **BARBUDA MAIL.**
1364 $1 "Nimitz" class carrier and "Ticonderoga" class cruiser 50 55
1365 $1 Tourist launch 50 55
1366 $1 U.S.S. "Arizona" memorial 50 55
1367 $1 Wreaths on water and aircraft 50 55
1368 $1 White tern 50 55
1369 $1 Japanese torpedo bombers over Pearl City 50 55
1370 $1 Zeros attacking 50 55
1371 $1 Battleship Row in flames 50 55
1372 $1 U.S.S. "Nevada" (battleship) underway 50 55
1373 $1 Zeros returning to carriers 50 55

1992. 500th Anniv of Discovery of America by Columbus (5th issue). World Columbian Stamp "Expo '92", Chicago. Nos. 1654/9 of Antigua optd **BARBUDA MAIL.**
1374 15 c. Memorial cross and huts, San Salvador 10 10
1375 30 c. Martin Pinzon with telescope 15 20
1376 40 c. Christopher Columbus 20 25
1377 $1 "Pinta" 50 55
1378 $2 "Nina" 95 1·00
1379 $4 "Santa Maria" 2·00 2·10

1992. 500th Anniv of Discovery of America by Columbus (6th issue). Organization of East Caribbean States. Nos. 1670/1 of Antigua optd **BARBUDA MAIL.**
1381 $1 Columbus meeting Amerindians 50 55
1382 $2 Ships approaching island 95 1·00

1992. 40th Anniv of Queen Elizabeth II's Accession. Nos. 1604/7 of Antigua optd **BARBUDA MAIL.**
1384 10 c. Queen Elizabeth II and bird sanctuary 10 10
1385 30 c. Nelson's Dockyard 15 20
1386 $1 Ruins on Shirley Heights 50 55
1387 $5 Beach and palm trees 2·40 2·50

1992. Prehistoric Animals. Nos. 1618/25 of Antigua optd **BARBUDA MAIL.**
1389 10 c. Pteranodon 10 10
1390 15 c. Brachiosaurus 10 10
1391 30 c. Tyrannosaurus Rex 15 20
1392 50 c. Parasaurolophus 25 30
1393 $1 Deinonychus (horiz) 50 55
1394 $2 Triceratops (horiz) 95 1·00
1395 $4 Protoceratops hatching (horiz) 2·00 2·10
1396 $5 Stegosaurus (horiz) 2·40 2·50

1992. Christmas. Nos. 1691/8 of Antigua optd **BARBUDA MAIL.**
1398 10 c. "Virgin and Child with Angels" (School of Piero della Francesca) 10 10
1399 25 c. "Madonna degli Alberelli" (Giovanni Bellini) 10 10
1400 30 c. "Madonna and Child with St. Anthony Abbot and St. Sigismund" (Neroccio) 15 20
1401 40 c. "Madonna and the Grand Duke" (Raphael) 20 25
1402 60 c. "The Nativity" (Georges de la Tour) 30 35
1403 $1 "Holy Family" (Jacob Jordaens) 50 55
1404 $4 "Madonna and Child Enthroned" (Magaritone) 2·00 2·10
1405 $5 "Madonna and Child on a Curved Throne" (Byzantine school) 2·40 2·50

1993. Fungi. Nos. 1645/52 of Antigua optd **BARBUDA MAIL.**
1407 10 c. "Amanita caesarea" 10 10
1408 15 c. "Collybia fusipes" 10 10
1409 30 c. "Boletus aereus" 15 20
1410 40 c. "Laccaria amethystina" 20 25
1411 $1 "Russula virescens" 50 55
1412 $2 "Tricholoma auratum" 95 1·00
1413 $4 "Calocybe gambosa" 2·00 2·10
1414 $5 "Panus tigrinus" 2·40 2·50

1993. "Granada '92" International Stamp Exhibition, Spain. Spanish Paintings. Nos. 1636/43 of Antigua optd **BARBUDA MAIL.**
1416 10 c. "The Miracle at the Well" (Alonzo Cano) 10 10
1417 15 c. "The Poet Luis de Gongora y Argote" (Velazquez) 10 10
1418 30 c. "The Painter Francisco Goya" (Vincente Lopez Portana) 15 20
1419 40 c. "Maria de las Nieves Michaela Fourdinier" (Luis Paret y Alcazar) 20 25
1420 $1 "Carlos III eating before his Court" (Alcazar) (horiz) 50 55
1421 $2 "Rain Shower in Granada" (Antonio Munoz Degrain) (horiz) 95 1·00
1422 $4 "Sarah Bernhardt" (Santiago Ruisnol i Prats) 2·00 2·10
1423 $5 "The Hermitage Garden" (Joaquim Mir Trinxet) 2·40 2·50

1993. "Genova '92" International Thematic Stamp Exhibition. Hummingbirds and Plants. Nos. 1661/8 of Antigua optd **BARBUDA MAIL.**
1425 10 c. Antillean crested hummingbird and wild plantain 10 10
1426 25 c. Green mango and parrot's plantain 10 10
1427 45 c. Purple-throated carib and lobster claws 20 25
1428 60 c. Antillean mango and coral plant 30 35
1429 $1 Vervain hummingbird and cardinal's guard 50 55
1430 $2 Rufous-breasted hermit and heliconia 95 1·00
1431 $4 Blue-headed hummingbird and reed ginger 2·00 2·10
1432 $5 Green-throated carib and ornamental banana 2·40 2·50

1993. Inventors and Inventions. Nos. 1672/9 of Antigua optd **BARBUDA MAIL.**
1434 10 c. Ts'ai Lun and paper 10 10
1435 25 c. Igor Sikorsky and four-engined biplane 10 10
1436 30 c. Alexander Graham Bell and early telephone 15 20
1437 40 c. Johannes Gutenberg and early printing press 20 25
1438 60 c. James Watt and stationary steam engine 30 35
1439 $1 Anton van Leeuwenhoek and early microscope 50 55
1440 $4 Louis Braille and hands reading braille 2·00 2·10
1441 $5 Galileo and telescope 2·40 2·50

1993. Anniversaries and Events. Nos. 1700/13 of Antigua optd **BARBUDA MAIL.**
1443 10 c. Russian cosmonauts 10 10
1444 40 c. "Graf Zeppelin" (airship), 1929 20 25
1445 45 c. Bishop Daniel Davis 20 25
1446 75 c. Konrad Adenauer making speech 35 40
1447 $1 Bus Mosbacher and "Weatherly" (yacht) 50 55
1448 $1.50 Rain forest 75 80
1449 $2 Tiger 95 1·00
1450 $2 National flag, plant and emblem (horiz) 95 1·00
1451 $2 Members of Community Players company (horiz) 95 1·00
1452 $2.25 Women carrying pots 1·00 1·10
1453 $3 Lions Club emblem 1·40 1·50
1454 $4 Chinese rocket on launch tower 2·00 2·10
1455 $6 Hugo Eckener (airship pioneer) 3·00 3·25

1993. Flowers. Nos. 1733/40 of Antigua optd **BARBUDA MAIL.**
1457 15 c. Cardinal's guard 10 10
1458 25 c. Giant granadilla 10 10
1459 30 c. Spider flower 15 20
1460 40 c. Gold vine 20 25
1461 $1 Frangipani 50 55
1462 $2 Bougainvillea 95 1·00
1463 $4 Yellow oleander 2·00 2·10
1464 $5 Spicy jatropha 2·40 2·50

1993. World Bird Watch. Nos. 1248/51 optd **WORLD BIRDWATCH 9-10 OCTOBER 1993.**
1466 60 c. Type **119** 30 35
1467 $2 Adelaide's warbler 95 1·00
1468 $4 Rose-breasted grosbeak 2·00 2·10
1469 $7 Wied's Crested flycatcher 3·50 3·75

1993. Endangered Species. Nos. 1759/70 of Antigua optd **BARBUDA MAIL.**
1470 $1 St. Lucia amazon 50 55
1471 $1 Cahow 50 55
1472 $1 Swallow-tailed kite 50 55
1473 $1 Everglade kite 50 55
1474 $1 Imperial amazon 50 55
1475 $1 Humpback whale 50 55
1476 $1 Plain pigeon 50 55
1477 $1 St. Vincent amazon 50 55
1478 $1 Puerto Rican amazon 50 55
1479 $1 Leatherback turtle 50 55
1480 $1 American crocodile 50 55
1481 $1 Hawksbill turtle 50 55

1994. Bicentenary of the Louvre, Paris. Paintings by Peter Paul Rubens. Nos. 1742/9 of Antigua optd **BARBUDA MAIL.**
1483 $1 "The Destiny of Marie de' Medici" (upper detail) 50 55
1484 $1 "The Birth of Marie de' Medici" 50 55
1485 $1 "The Education of Marie de' Medici" 50 55
1486 $1 "The Destiny of Marie de' Medici" (lower detail) 50 55
1487 $1 "Henry VI receiving the Portrait of Marie" 50 55
1488 $1 "The Meeting of the King and Marie at Lyons" 50 55
1489 $1 "The Marriage by Proxy" 50 55
1490 $1 "The Birth of Louis XIII" 50 55

1994. World Cup Football Championship 1994, U.S.A. Nos. 1816/27 of Antigua optd **BARBUDA MAIL.**
1492 $2 Paul Gascoigne 95 1·00
1493 $2 David Platt 95 1·00
1494 $2 Martin Peters 95 1·00
1495 $2 John Barnes 95 1·00
1496 $2 Gary Lineker 95 1·00
1497 $2 Geoff Hurst 95 1·00
1498 $2 Bobby Charlton 95 1·00
1499 $2 Bryan Robson 95 1·00
1500 $2 Bobby Moore 95 1·00
1501 $2 Nobby Stiles 95 1·00
1502 $2 Gordon Banks 95 1·00
1503 $2 Peter Shilton 95 1·00

BARWANI

A state of Central India. Now uses Indian stamps.

12 pies = 1 anna; 16 annas = 1 rupee

1. Rana Ranjitsingh. 2.

1921.

3	1	¼ a. green	12·00	48·00
28b		¼ a. blue	1·40	6·50
37		¼ a. black	2·75	16·00
18		¼ a. pink	90	6·50
4		½ a. blue	17·00	70·00
14		½ a. green	1·25	11·00
10	2	1 a. red	1·50	11·00
39		1 a. brown	9·00	14·00
11		2 a. purple	1·90	11·00
41		2 a. red	21·00	65·00
31		4 a. orange	50·00	85·00
42a		4 a. green	10·00	22·00

DESIGN: 4 a. Another portrait of Rana Ranjitsingh.

4. Rana Devi Singh. 5.

1932.

32.	4.	¼ a. slate	90	9·00
33.		½ a. green	1·75	9·00
34.		1 a. brown	1·75	9·00
35.		2 a. purple	3·25	15·00
36.		4 a. olive	6·00	20·00

1938.

43.	5.	1 a. brown	20·00	38·00

BASUTOLAND

An African territory under Br. protection, N.E. of Cape Province. Self-Government introduced on 1 April 1965. Attained independence on 4 October 1966, when the country was renamed Lesotho.

1961. 100 cents = 1 rand.

1. King George V, Nile Crocodile and Mountains.

1933.

1.	1.	½d. green	60	1·00
2.		1d. red	60	45
3.		2d. purple	70	35
4.		3d. blue	70	60
5.		4d. grey	2·50	6·50
6.		6d. yellow	3·00	1·50
7.		1s. orange	3·75	4·50
8.		2s. 6d. brown	20·00	42·00
9.		5s. violet	42·00	60·00
10.		10s. olive	£100	£110

1935. Silver Jubilee. As T **13** of Antigua.

11.	1d. blue and red	45	25
12.	2d. blue and grey ..	55	75
13.	3d. brown and blue ..	3·50	1·25
14.	6d. grey and purple ..	3·75	1·25

1937. Coronation. As T **2** of Aden.

15.	1d. red	35	10
16.	2d. purple	70	85
17.	3d. blue	90	85

1938. As T **1**, but portrait of King George VI.

18.	½d. green	30	50
19.	1d. red	50	15
20.	1½d. blue	40	40
21.	2d. purple	30	30
22.	3d. blue	30	50
23.	4d. grey	1·50	2·25
24.	6d. yellow	50	50
25.	1s. orange	50	80
26.	2s. 6d. brown	8·00	8·50
27.	5s. violet	22·00	8·50
28.	10s. olive	22·00	15·00

1945. Victory. Stamps of South Africa optd. **Basutoland.** Alternate stamps inscr. in English or Afrikaans.

29.	55.	1d. brown and red ..	30	30
30.		2d. blue and violet ..	30	30
31.		3d. blue	30	60

Prices are for bi-lingual pairs.

5. King George VI and Queen Elizabeth.

1947. Royal Visit.

32.	–	1d. red	10	10
33.	5.	2d. green	10	10
34.	–	3d. blue	10	10
35.	–	1s. mauve	15	10

DESIGNS–VERT. 1d. King George VI. HORIZ. 3d. Queen Elizabeth II as Princess and Princess Margaret. 1s. The Royal Family.

1948. Silver Wedding. As T **10/11** of Aden.

36.	1½d. blue	20	10
37.	10s. green	30·00	24·00

1949. U.P.U. As T **20/23** of Antigua.

38.	1½d. blue	30	30
39.	3d. blue	1·40	70
40.	6d. orange	1·50	90
41.	1s. brown	1·25	90

1953. Coronation. As T **13** of Aden.

42.	2d. black and purple ..	20	50

8. Qiloane.

9. Mohair (Shearing Goats).

DESIGNS — HORIZ. 1d. Orange River. 2d. Mosuto horseman. 3d. Basuto household. 4½d. Maletsunyane Falls. 6d. Herd-boy with lesiba. 1s. Pastoral scene. 1s. 3d. 'Plane over Lancers' Gap. 2s. 6d. Old Fort, Leribe. 5s. Mission cave house.

1954.

43.	8.	½d. black and sepia ..	10	10
44.	–	1d. black and green ..	10	10
45.	–	2d. blue and orange ..	60	10
46.	–	3d. sage and red	80	20
47.	–	4½d. indigo and blue ..	70	15
48.	–	6d. brown and green ..	1·25	15
49.	–	1s. bronze and purple ..	1·25	20
50.	–	1s. 3d. brown & turquoise	9·00	4·50
51.	–	2s. 6d. blue and red ..	6·50	5·50
52.	–	5s. black and red	4·75	8·50
53.	9.	10s. black and purple ..	18·00	23·00

1959. Surch. **½d.** and bar.

54.	½d. on 2d. blue and orange (No. 45)	10	15

20. "Chief Moshoeshoe I" (engraving by Delangle).

DESIGNS: 1s. Council House. 1s. 3d. Mosuto horseman.

1959. Inauguration National Council.

55.	20.	3d. black and olive ..	30	10
56.	–	1s. red and green	30	20
57.	–	1s. 3d. blue and orange ..	45	55

1961. Nos. 43/53 surch.

58	8.	½ c. on ½d. black and sepia	10	10
59	–	1 c. on 1d. black & green	10	10
60	–	2 c. on 2d. blue & orange	10	10
61	–	2½ c. on 3d. green and red	10	10
62	–	3½ c. on 4½d. indigo & blue	10	10
63	–	5 c. on 6d. brown & green	10	10
64	–	10 c. on 1s. green & purple	10	10
65a	–	12½c. on 1s. 3d. brown and turquoise	20	10
66	–	25 c. on 2s. 6d. blue & red	20	30
67a	–	50 c. on 5s. black and red	90	1·25
68b	9.	1 r. on 10s. black & purple	4·00	4·00

26 Basuto Household.

1961. As 1954 but value in new currency as in T **26**.

69	8	½ c. black and brown ..	10	20
70	–	1 c. black & green (as 1d.)	10	40
71	–	2 c. blue & orge (as 2d.)	50	95
86	26	2½ c. green and red ..	15	15
73	–	3½ c. indigo & bl (as 4½d.)	30	1·25
88	–	5 c. brown & grn (as 6d.)	30	40
75	–	10 c. green & pur (as 1s.)	20	30
90	–	12½ c. brown and green (as 1s. 3d.) ..	2·25	1·50
77	–	25 c. bl & red (as 2s. 6d.)	3·00	6·00
78	–	50 c. black & red (as 5s.)	5·50	8·50
79	9	1 r. black and purple ..	15·00	9·00

1963. Freedom from Hunger. As T **28** of Aden.

80.	12½ c. violet	40	15

1963. Cent of Red Cross. As T **33** of Antigua.

81.	2½ c. red and black ..	20	10
82.	12½ c. red and blue ..	60	60

27. Mosotho Woman and Child.

1965. New Constitution. Inscr. "SELF GOVERNMENT 1965". Multicoloured.

94.	2½ c. Type **27**	20	10
95.	3½ c. Maseru Border Post	25	20
96.	5 c. Mountain Scene ..	25	20
97.	12½ c. Legislative Buildings	45	70

1965. Cent of I.T.U. As T **36** of Antigua.

98	1 c. red and purple ..	15	10
99	20 c. blue and brown ..	35	30

1965. I.C.Y. As T **37** of Antigua.

100	½ c. purple and turquoise	10	10
101	12½ c. green and lavender	45	35

1966. Churchill Commem. As T **38** of Antigua.

102	1 c. blue	15	30
103	2½ c. green	45	10
104	10 c. brown	70	30
105	22½ c. violet	90	60

OFFICIAL STAMPS

1934. Nos. 1/3 and 6 optd **OFFICIAL.**

O 1	1	½d. green	£2000	£2000
O 2		1d. red	£1300	£1000
O 3		2d. purple	£750	£550
O 4		6d. yellow	£10000	£4500

POSTAGE DUE STAMPS

1933. As Type D **1** of Barbados.

D 1b.	1d. red	30	50
D 2a.	2d. violet	30	1·50

D 2.

1956.

D 3.	D 2.	1d. red	30	1·50
D 4.		2d. violet	30	2·50

1961. Surch.

D 5.	D 2.	1 c. on 1d. red ..	10	30
D 6.		1 c. on 2d. violet ..	10	30
D 7.		5 c. on 2d. violet ..	15	30
D 8.	–	5 c. on 2d. vio.(No.D2a)	1·50	6·50

1964. As Type D **2**, but values in decimal currency.

D 9.	1 c. red	1·75	7·50
D 10.	5 c. violet	1·75	7·50

For later issues see **LESOTHO.**

BATUM

Batum, a Russian port on the Black Sea, had been taken by Turkish troops during the First World War. Following the Armistice British Forces occupied the town on 1 December 1918. Batum was handed over to the National Republic of Georgia on 7 July 1920.

100 kopeks = 1 rouble.

1.

БАТУМ. ОБ.

Руб 10 Руб

(2.)

1919.

1.	1.	5 k. green	3·00	3·75
2.		10 k. blue	3·00	3·75
3.		50 k. yellow	80	1·00
4.		1 r. brown	1·25	1·50
5.		3 r. violet	5·00	5·50
6.		5 r. brown	6·00	6·50

1919. Arms types of Russia surch. as T **2.**

7.	10 r. on 1 k. orange ..	18·00	20·00
8.	10 r. on 3 k. red	11·00	13·00
9.	10 r. on 5 k. purple ..	£180	£180
10.	10 r. on 10 on 7 k. blue ..	£160	£160

1919. T 1 optd. **BRITISH OCCUPATION.**

11	1.	5 k. green	5·00	5·50
12		10 k. blue	5·00	5·50
13		25 k. yellow	4·50	5·00
14		1 r. blue	3·00	3·50
15		2 r. pink	80	1·00
16		3 r. violet	80	1·00
17		5 r. brown	1·10	1·40
18		7 r. red	2·50	3·00

1919. Arms type of Russia surch. with Russian inscription, **BRITISH OCCUPATION** and new value.

19	10 r. on 3 k. red	8·50	9·50
20a	15 r. on 1 k. orange ..	23·00	23·00
29	25 r. on 5 k. purple ..	20·00	20·00
30a	25 r. on 10 on 7 k. blue ..	32·00	32·00
31a	25 r. on 20 on 14 k. red and blue	32·00	32·00
32a	25 r. on 25 k. purple & grn	48·00	48·00
33	25 r. on 50 k. green & pur	32·00	32·00
21	50 r. on 1 k. orange ..	£160	£160
34	50 r. on 2 k. green ..	48·00	48·00
35	50 r. on 3 k. red ..	48·00	48·00
36	50 r. on 4 k. red ..	45·00	45·00
37	50 r. on 5 k. purple ..	32·00	32·00
27	50 r. on 10 k. blue ..	£700	£700
28	50 r. on 15 k. blue and brown	£250	£250

1920. Romanov type of Russia surch with Russian inscr, **BRITISH OCCUPATION** and new value.

41	50 r. on 4 k. red	28·00	32·00

1920. Nos. 11, 13 and 3 surch with new value (50 r. with **BRITISH OCCUPATION** also).

42	1.	25 r. on 5 k. green ..	14·00	14·00
43		25 r. on 25 k. yellow ..	12·00	12·00
44a		50 r. on 50 k. yellow ..	7·50	7·50

1920. T 1 optd. **BRITISH OCCUPATION.**

45	1.	1 r. brown	30	1·40
46		2 r. blue	40	1·40
47		3 r. pink	40	1·40
48		5 r. black	40	1·40
49		7 r. yellow	40	1·40
50		10 r. green	40	1·40
51		15 r. violet	70	2·50
52		25 r. red	60	1·90
53		50 r. blue	85	3·00

BECHUANALAND

A colony and protectorate in Central S. Africa. British Bechuanaland (colony) was annexed to Cape of Good Hope in 1895. Internal Self-Government in the protectorate introduced on 1st March, 1965. Attained independence on 30th September, 1966, when the country was renamed Botswana.

1885. 12 pence = 1 shilling.
20 shillings = 1 pound.
1961. 100 cents = 1 rand.

A. BRITISH BECHUANALAND

British
Bechuanaland
(1.)

BRITISH
BECHUANALAND
(2.)

1885. Stamps of Cape of Good Hope ("Hope" seated) optd. with T **1.**

4.	6.	½d. black	7·00	11·00
5.		1d. red	9·00	9·00
6.		2d. brown	28·00	12·00
2.		3d. red	32·00	35·00
3.		4d. blue	55·00	60·00
7.		6d. purple	60·00	32·00
8.		1s. green	£200	£130

1887. Stamps of Gt. Britain (Queen Victoria) optd. with T **2.**

9.	71.	½d. red	70	1·00

3.

4.

1887.

10.	**3.**	1d. lilac and black ..	12·00	1·25
11.		2d. lilac and black ..	45·00	80
12.		3d. lilac and black ..	3·25	4·75
13.		4d. lilac and black ..	38·00	2·75
14.		6d. lilac and black ..	42·00	3·25
15.	**4.**	1s. green and black ..	28·00	4·50
16.		2s. green and black ..	45·00	35·00
17.		2s. 6d. green and black ..	60·00	42·00
18.		5s. green and black ..	80·00	£100
19.		10s. green and black ..	£170	£275
20.	–	£1 lilac and black ..	£900	£800
21.	–	£5 lilac and black ..	£2750	£1300

Nos. 20/1 are as Type **4** but larger, 23 × 39½ mm.

1888. Surch.

22.	**3.**	" 1d." on 1d. lilac & black	7·50	5·00
23.		" 2d." on 2d. lilac & black	15·00	2·50
25.		" 4d." on 4d. lilac & black	£150	£170
26.		" 6d. " on 6d. lilac & black	70·00	17·00
28.	**4.**	" 1s. " on 1s. green & black	£100	55·00

1888. Surch. **ONE HALF-PENNY** and bars.

29.	**3.**	½d. on 3d. lilac and black	£110	£130

British

Bechuanaland.

(9.)

British Bechuanaland

(10.)

1889. Stamp of Cape of Good Hope (" Hope" seated) optd. with T **9.**

30.	**6.**	½d. black	3·25	17·00

1891. Stamps of Cape of Good Hope ("Hope" seated) optd with T **10**, reading up or down.

38	6	1d. red	2·25	2·25
32		2d. brown	3·25	2·25

1891. Stamps of Gt. Britain (Queen Victoria) optd. **BRITISH BECHUANALAND.**

33.	**57.**	1d lilac	6·00	75
34.	**73.**	2d. green and red ..	3·50	2·75
35.	**76.**	4d. green and brown ..	2·50	50
36.	**79.**	6d. purple on red ..	3·00	2·00
37.	**82.**	1s. green	13·00	16·00

B. BECHUANALAND PROTECTORATE.

1888. No. 9 to 19 optd. **Protectorate** or surch. also.

40.	**71.**	½d. red	2·75	20·00
41.	**3.**	1d. on 1d. lilac and black	6·50	12·00
42.		2d. on 2d. lilac and black	19·00	17·00
43.		3d. on 3d. lilac and black	80·00	£110
51.		4d. on 4d. lilac and black	55·00	32·00
45.		6d. on 6d. lilac and black	55·00	40·00
46.	**4.**	1s. green and black ..	55·00	48·00
47.		2s. green and black ..	£450	£650
48.		2s. 6d. green and black ..	£500	£650
49.		5s. green and black ..	£1100	£1500
50.		10 s. green and black ..	£3000	£4000

1889. Stamp of Cape of Good Hope ("Hope" seated) optd. **Bechuanaland Protectorate.**

52.	**6.**	½d. black	2·75	25·00

1889. No. 9 surch. **Protectorate Fourpence.**

53.	**71.**	4d. on ½d. red	16·00	3·25

1897. Stamp of Cape of Good Hope ("Hope" seated) optd. as T **2.**

56.	**6.**	½d. green	2·50	7·00

Stamps of Gt. Britain overprinted **BECHUANALAND PROTECTORATE.**

1897. Queen Victoria.

59.	**71.**	½d. red	85	1·50
60.		½d. green	1·40	2·00
61.	**57.**	1d. lilac	3·75	45
62.	**73.**	2d. green and red ..	2·25	4·50
63.	**75.**	3d. purple on yellow ..	5·50	8·50
64.	**76.**	4d. green and brown ..	11·00	11·00
65.	**79.**	6d. purple on red ..	18·00	11·00

1904. King Edward VII.

66	83	½d. turquoise	80	90
68		1d. red	4·50	25
69		2½d. blue	3·50	5·00
70	–	1 s. green & red (No. 314)	29·00	70·00

1912. King George V.

73	**105.**	½d. green	1·10	1·75
72	**102.**	1d. red	55	60
92	**104.**	1d. red	1·00	70
75	**105.**	1½d. brown	1·75	3·00
93	**106.**	2d. orange	1·50	1·00
78	**104.**	2½d. blue	3·00	15·00
79	**106.**	3d. violet	5·50	12·00
80		4d. grey	6·00	14·00
81	**107.**	6d. purple	6·50	16·00
82	**108.**	1s. brown	7·50	18·00
88	**109.**	2s. 6d. brown	80·00	£150
89		5s. red	£110	£225

22. King George V, Baobab Tree and Cattle drinking.

1932.

99.	**22.**	½d. green	75	30
100.		1d. red	75	25
101.		2d. brown	75	30
102.		3d. blue	1·00	50
103.		4d. orange	1·00	4·00
104.		6d. purple	2·75	2·00
105.		1s. black and olive ..	5·00	7·00
106.		2s. black and orange ..	24·00	38·00
107.		2s. 6d. black and red ..	19·00	30·00
108.		3s. black and purple ..	35·00	42·00
109.		5s. black and blue ..	45·00	45·00
110.		10s. black and brown ..	90·00	£100

1935. Silver Jubilee. As T **13** of Antigua.

111.		1d. blue and red ..	30	90
112.		2d. blue and black ..	1·00	1·10
113.		3d. brown and blue ..	1·00	1·10
114.		6d. grey and purple ..	2·50	1·10

1937. Coronation. As T **2** of Aden.

115.		1d. red	45	40
116.		2d. brown	85	65
117.		3d. blue	85	80

1938. As T **22**, but portrait of King George VI

118b		½d. green	1·00	2·25
119		1d. red	15	40
120a		1½d. blue	30	70
121		2d. brown	20	40
122		3d. blue	30	1·00
123		4d. orange	90	2·00
124a		6d. purple	2·50	2·50
125		1s. black and olive ..	2·75	2·50
126		2s. 6d. black and red ..	14·00	8·50
127		5s. black and blue ..	80·00	8·50
128		10s. black and brown ..	14·00	16·00

1945. Victory. Stamps of South Africa optd. **Bechuanaland.** Alternate stamps inscr. in English or Afrikaans.

129.	**55.**	1d. brown and red ..	40	25
130.		2d. blue & vio. (No. 109)	40	35
131.		3d. blue (No. 110) ..	40	35

Prices for bi-lingual pairs.

1947. Royal Visit. As Nos. 32/5 of Basutoland.

132.		1d. red	10	10
133.		2d. green	10	10
134.		3d. blue	10	10
135.		1s. mauve	10	10

1948. Silver Wedding. As T **10/11** of Aden.

136.		1½d. blue	30	10
137.		10s. grey	27·00	30·00

1949. U.P.U. As T **20/23** of Antigua.

138.		1½d. blue	45	30
139.		3d. blue	80	60
140.		6d. mauve	90	80
141.		1s. olive	95	80

1953. Coronation. As T **13** of Aden.

142.		2d. black and brown ..	15	30

1955. As T **22** but portrait of Queen Elizabeth II, facing right.

143		½d. green	40	30
144		1d. red	65	10
145		2d. brown	1·25	30
146		3d. blue	3·00	60
146b		4d. orange	5·50	6·00
147		4½d. blue	1·50	35
148		6d. purple	1·25	60
149		1s. black and olive ..	1·25	70
150		1s. 3d. black and lilac ..	8·00	9·50
151		2s. 6d. black and red ..	8·50	9·50
152		5s. black and blue ..	10·00	8·50
153		10s. black and brown ..	16·00	15·00

26. Queen Victoria. Queen Elizabeth II and Landscape.

1960. 75th Anniv. of Protectorate.

154.	**26.**	1d. sepia and black ..	30	40
155.		3d. mauve and black ..	30	20
156.		6d. blue and black ..	30	40

1961. Stamps of 1955 surch.

157a		1 c. on 1d. red	20	10
158		2 c. on 2d. brown ..	20	10
159		2½ c. on 2d. brown ..	30	10
160		2½ c. on 3d. blue	2·00	2·00
161d		3½ c. on 4d. orange ..	20	20
162a		5 c. on 6d. purple ..	20	10
163		10 c. on 1s. black and olive	20	10
164		12½ c. on 1s. 3d. blk. & lilac	50	20
165		25 c. on 2s. 6d. black & red	1·75	50
166		50 c. on 5s. black and blue	2·50	1·50
167b		1 r. on 10s. black & brown	3·50	2·00

28. African Golden Oriole.

1961.

168.	**28.**	1 c. multicoloured ..	60	30
169.	–	2 c. orange, black & olive	60	90
170.	–	2½ c. multicoloured ..	60	10
171.	–	3½c. multicoloured ..	60	70
172.	–	5 c. multicoloured ..	1·25	80
173.	–	7½ c. multicoloured ..	60	60
174.	–	10 c. multicoloured ..	75	50
175.	–	12½ c. multicoloured ..	13·00	3·25
176.	–	20 c. brown and drab ..	50	70
177.	–	25 c. sepia and lemon ..	50	75
178.	–	35 c. blue and orange ..	80	1·50
179.	–	50 c. sepia and olive ..	1·00	2·25
180.	–	1 r. black and brown ..	3·00	2·50
181.	–	2 r. brown and turquoise	18·00	8·50

DESIGNS—VERT. 2 c. Hoopoe. 2½ c. Scarlet-chested Sunbird. 3½ c. Yellow-rumped Bishop. 5 c. Swallow-tailed Bee Eater. 7½ c. African Grey Hornbill. 10 c. Red-headed Weaver. 12½ c. Brown-hooded Kingfisher. 20 c. Woman musician. 35 c. Woman grinding maize. 1 r. Lion. 2 r. Police Camel Patrol. HORIZ. 25 c. Baobab tree. 50 c. Bechuana Ox.

1963. Freedom from Hunger. As T **28** of Aden.

182.		12½ c. green	30	15

1963. Cent of Red Cross. As T **33** of Antigua.

183.		2½ c. red and black ..	20	10
184.		12½ c. red and blue ..	40	40

1964. 400th Birth Anniv of Shakespeare. As T **34** of Antigua.

185.		12½ c. brown	15	15

C. BECHUANALAND

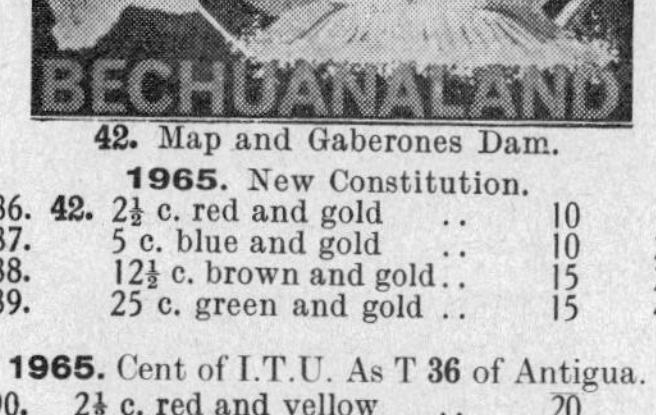

42. Map and Gaberones Dam.

1965. New Constitution.

186.	**42.**	2½ c. red and gold ..	10	10
187.		5 c. blue and gold ..	10	20
188.		12½ c. brown and gold ..	15	20
189.		25 c. green and gold ..	15	40

1965. Cent of I.T.U. As T **36** of Antigua.

190.		2½ c. red and yellow ..	20	10
191.		12½ c. mauve and brown ..	45	30

1965. I.C.Y. As T **37** of Antigua.

192.		1 c. purple and turquoise	10	10
193.		12½ c. green and lavender	60	55

1966. Churchill Commem. As T **38** of Antigua.

194.		1 c. blue	15	20
195.		2½ c. green	35	10
196.		12½ c. brown	70	20
197.		20 c. violet	75	40

43. Haslar Smoke Generator.

1966. Bechuanaland Royal Pioneer Corps.

198.	**43.**	2½ c. blue, red and green	20	10
199.	–	5 c. brown and blue ..	20	20
200.	–	15 c. blue, red and green	30	10
201.	–	35 c. multicoloured ..	30	70

DESIGNS: 5 c. Bugler. 15 c. Gun-site. 35 c. Regimental Cap Badge.

POSTAGE DUE STAMPS

1926. Postage Due stamps of Gt. Britain optd. **BECHUANALAND PROTECTORATE.**

D 1.	**D 1.**	½d. green	3·25	50·00
D 2.		1d. red	3·25	42·00
D 3.		2d. black	6·00	75·00

D 3.

1932.

D4	D 3	½d. green	5·00	23·00
D5a		1d. red	30	7·50
D6b		2d. violet	60	11·00

1961. Surch.

D 7.	**D 3.**	1 c. on 1d. red ..	25	50
D 8.		2 c. on 2d. violet ..	25	1·50
D 9.		5 c. on ½d. green ..	20	60

1961. As Type D **3** but values in decimal currency.

D 10.		1 c. red	15	80
D 11.		2 c. violet	15	90
D 12.		5 c. green	30	1·10

For later issues see **BOTSWANA.**

BELIZE

British Honduras was renamed Belize on the 1st June 1973 and the country became independent within the Commonwealth on 21 September 1981.

100 cents = 1 dollar.

1973. Nos. 256/66 and 277/8 of British Honduras optd. **BELIZE** and two stars.

347.	–	½ c. Multicoloured. ..	10	10
348.	**63.**	1 c. black, brn. & yell.	10	10
349.	–	2 c. black, green & yell.	10	10
350.	–	3 c. black, brown & lilac	10	10
351.	–	4 c. multicoloured ..	10	10
352.	–	5 c. black and red ..	10	10
353.	–	10 c. multicoloured ..	15	15
354.	–	15 c. multicoloured ..	20	20
355.	–	25 c. multicoloured ..	35	35
356.	–	50 c. multicoloured ..	55	55
357.	–	$1 multicoloured ..	90	1·25
358.	–	$2 multicoloured ..	1·75	2·00
359.	–	$5 multicoloured ..	2·50	3·75

1973. Royal Wedding. As T **47** of Anguilla. Background colours given. Multicoloured.

360.		26 c. blue	15	10
361.		50 c. brown	15	20

82. Crana.

1974. As Nos. 256/66 and 276/78 of British Honduras. Multicoloured.

362.		½ c. Type **82**	10	10
363.		1 c. Jew Fish	10	10
364.		2 c. White-lipped peccary	10	10
365.		3 c. Grouper	10	10
366.		4 c. Collared anteater ..	10	10
367.		5 c. Bone Fish	10	10
368.		10 c. Paca	15	15
369.		15 c. Dolphin	20	20
370.		25 c. Kinkajou	35	35
371.		50 c. Mutton Snapper ..	60	70
372.		$1 Tayra	1·00	1·50
373.		$2 Great Barracuda ..	1·50	2·00
374.		$5 Puma	5·50	3·50

83. Deer.

1974. Mayan Artefacts (1st series). Pottery Motifs. Multicoloured.

375.		3 c. Type **83**	10	10
376.		6 c. Jaguar deity	15	10
377.		16 c. Sea monster ..	20	10
378.		26 c. Cormorant	40	10
379.		50 c. Scarlet macaw ..	60	40

See also Nos 398/402.

84. " Parides arcas ".

1974. Butterflies of Belize. Multicoloured.

380	½ c. Type **84**	60	90
381	1 c. "Evenus regalis" ..	80	80
405	2 c. "Colobura dirce" ..	50	70
383	3 c. "Catonephele numilia"	90	90
384	4 c. "Battus belus" ..	1·10	1·00
385	5 c. "Callicore patelina" ..	1·50	1·00
386	10 c. "Diaethria astala" ..	1·00	50
410	15 c. "Nessaea aglaura" ..	75	70
388	16 c. "Prepona pseudo-joiceyi"	3·00	3·00
412	25 c. "Papilio thoas" ..	95	40
390	26 c. "Hamadryas arethusa"	2·50	4·25
413	35 c. Type **84**	7·00	4·50
391	50 c. "Panthiades bathilildis"	2·00	65
392	$1 "Caligo uranus" ..	5·50	2·25
393	$2 "Heliconius sapho" ..	3·50	1·25
394	$5 "Eurytides philolaus"	4·00	4·00
395	$10 "Philaethria dido" ..	10·00	4·00

85. Churchill when Prime Minister, and Coronation Scene.

1974. Birth Centenary of Sir Winston Churchill. Multicoloured.

396. 50 c. Type **85** 20 20
397. $1 Churchill in stetson, and Williamsburg Liberty Bell 30 30

86. The Actun Balam Vase.

1975. Mayan Artefacts (2nd series). Multicoloured.

398. 3 c. Type **86** 10 10
399. 6 c. Seated figure 10 10
400. 16 c. Costumed priest .. 25 10
401. 26 c. Head with headdress 35 20
402. 50 c. Layman and priest .. 45 60

87. Musicians.

1975. Christmas. Multicoloured.

435. 6 c. Type **87** 10 10
436. 26 c. Children and "crib" 20 10
437. 50 c. Dancer and drummers (vert.) 30 25
438. $1 Family and map (vert.) 55 70

88. William Wrigley Jr. and Chicle Tapping.

1976. Bicent. of American Revolution. Mult.

439. 10 c. Type **88** 10 10
440. 35 c. Charles Lindbergh .. 25 40
441. $1 J. L. Stephens (archaeologist) .. .. .. 60 1·00

89. Cycling.

1976. Olympic Games, Montreal. Mult.

442. 35 c. Type **89** 15 10
443. 45 c. Running 20 15
444. $1 Shooting 35 50

1976. No. 390 surch.

445. 20 c. on 26 c. multicoloured 1·25 80

1976. West Indian Victory in World Cricket Cup. As Nos. 559/60 of Barbados.

446. 35 c. multicoloured .. 50 50
447. $1 black and purple .. 1·10 1·75

1976. No. 426 surch.

448. 5 c. on 15 c. multicoloured 1·50 2·00

92. Queen and Bishops.

1977. Silver Jubilee. Multicoloured.

449. 10 c. Royal Visit, 1975 .. 10 10
450. 35 c. Queen and Rose Window 30 20
451. $2 Type **92** .. .. 80 1·25

93. Red-capped Manakin.

1977. Birds (1st series). Multicoloured.

452. 8 c. Type **93** 75 20
453. 10 c. Hooded Oriole .. 90 25
454. 25 c. Blue-crowned Motmot 1·25 55
455. 35 c. Slaty-breasted Tinamou 1·50 75
456. 45 c. Ocellated Turkey .. 1·75 1·10
457. $1 White Hawk .. .. 3·00 3·25

See also Nos. 467/72, 486/91 and 561/6.

94. Laboratory Workers.

1977. 75th Anniv. of Pan-American Health Organization. Multicoloured.

459. 35 c. Type **94** 20 20
460. $1 Mobile medical unit .. 40 65

1978. Nos. 386 and 413 optd **BELIZE DEFENCE FORCE 1ST JANUARY 1978**.

462 10 c. "Diaethria astala" .. 65 20
463 35 c. Type 84 .. .. 1·10 60

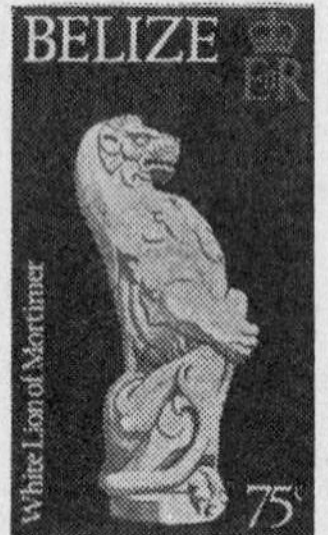

96. White Lion of Mortimer.

1978. 25th Anniversary of Coronation.

464. **96.** 75 c. brn., red and silver 25 30
465. – 75 c. multicoloured .. 25 30
466. – 75 c. brn., red and silver 25 30

DESIGNS: No. 465, Queen Elizabeth II. No. 466, Jaguar (Maya god of Day and Night).

1978. Birds (2nd series). As T **93**. Mult.

467. 10 c. White-capped Parrot 35 30
468. 25 c. Crimson-collared Tanager 80 45
469. 35 c. Citreoline Trogon .. 1·00 55
470. 45 c. American Finfoot .. 1·25 1·40
471. 50 c. Muscovy Duck .. 1·40 1·60
472. $1 King Vulture .. .. 1·90 3·00

97. "Russelia sarmentosa".

1978. Christmas. Wild Flowers and Ferns. Multicoloured.

474. 10 c. Type **97** 15 10
475. 15 c. "Lygodium polymorphum" 20 10
476. 35 c. "Heliconia aurantiaca" 30 15
477. 45 c. "Adiantum tetraphyllum" 35 30
478. 50 c. "Angelonia ciliaris" 35 40
479. $1 "Thelypteris obliterata" 60 80

98. Internal Airmail Service, 1937.

1979. Centenary of U.P.U. Membership. Mult.

480 5 c. Type **98** 10 10
481 10 c. "Heron H" (mail boat), 1949 .. .. 15 10
482 35 c. Internal mail service, 1920 (canoe) 20 20
483 45 c. Steam Creek Railway mail, 1910 .. .. 55 55
484 50 c. Mounted mail courier, 1882 .. .. .. 40 50
485 $2 "Eagle" (mail boat), 1856 .. .. .. 1·10 1·75

1979. No. 413 surch.

487. 15 c. on 35 c. Type **84** .. 65 1·50

1979. Birds (3rd series). As T **93**. Mult.

488. 10 c. Boat-billed Heron .. 40 10
489. 25 c. Grey-necked Wood Rail 65 20
490. 35 c. Lineated Woodpecker 75 30
491. 45 c. Blue-grey Tanager .. 80 40
492. 50 c. Laughing Falcon .. 80 80
493. $1 Long-tailed Hermit .. 1·25 1·60

101. Paslow Building, Belize G.P.O.

1979. 25th Anniv. of Coronation. Mult.

495. 25 c. Type **101** 20 10
496. 50 c. Houses of Parliament 35 10
497. 75 c. Coronation State Coach 55 10
498. $1 Queen on horseback (vert.) 70 10
499. $2 Prince of Wales (vert.) .. 1·40 15
500. $3 Queen and Duke of Edinburgh (vert.) .. 2·10 20
501. $4 Portrait of Queen (vert.) 2·75 25
502. $5 St. Edward's Crown .. 3·50 30

102. Safety Aeroplane (1909).

1979. Death Centenary of Sir Rowland Hill. 60th Anniv of I.C.A.O. (International Civil Aviation Organization), previously Int Commission for Air Navigation. Mult.

504. 4 c. Type **102** 15 10
505. 25 c. Boeing "707-720" .. 40 20
506. 50 c. "Concorde" 90 30
507. 75 c. Handley Page "W8b" (1922) 75 30
508. $1 Avro "F" (1912) .. 90 30
509. $1.50 Cody (1910) .. .. 1·50 30
510. $2 Triplane II (1909) .. 1·75 40
511. $3 Santos Dumont's aeroplane (1906) .. .. 2·50 45
512. $4 First motorized flight, Wright brothers (1903) .. 3·00 65

103. Handball.

1979. Olympic Games, Moscow (1980). Multicoloured.

514. 25 c. Type **103** 20 10
515. 50 c. Weightlifting .. 35 10
516. 75 c. Athletics 55 10
517. $1 Football 70 10
518. $2 Yachting .. .. 1·40 15
519. $3 Swimming .. .. 1·75 20
520. $4 Boxing .. .. 2·00 25
521. $5 Cycling .. .. 2·50 30

104. Olympic Torch.

1979. Winter Olympic Games, Lake Placid (1980). Multicoloured.

523. 25 c. Type **104** 20 10
524. 50 c. Giant Slalom .. 45 15
525. 75 c. Figure-skating .. 65 15
526. $1 Slalom skiing 80 15
527. $2 Speed-skating .. .. 1·60 20
528. $3 Cross-country skiing .. 2·50 30
529. $4 Shooting .. .. 3·00 40
530. $5 Gold, Silver and Bronze medals .. .. .. 3·50 45

105. "Cypraea zebra".

1980. Shells. Multicoloured.

532. 1 c. Type **105** 10 10
533. 2 c. "Macrocallista maculata" 10 10
534. 3 c. "Arca zebra" (vert.) 15 10
535. 4 c. "Chama macerophylla" (vert.) 20 10
536. 5 c. "Latirus cariniferus" 20 10
537. 10 c. "Conus spurius" (vert.) 30 10
538. 15 c. "Murex cabritii" (vert.) 40 10
539. 20 c. "Atrina rigida" .. 45 10
540. 25 c. "Chlamys imbricata" (vert.) 45 10
541. 35 c. "Conus granulatus" (vert.) 60 10
542. 45 c. "Tellina radiata" (vert.) 75 10
543. 50 c. "Leucozonia nassa leucozonalis" 85 10
544. 85 c. "Tripterotyphis triangularis" .. .. 1·25 10
545. $1 "Strombus gigas" (vert.) 1·50 10
546. $2 "Strombus gallus" (vert.) .. .. .. 2·75 30
547. $5 "Fasciolaria tulipa" .. 5·00 75
548. $10 "Arene cruentata" .. 8·00 1·25

106. Girl and Flower Arrangement.

1980. International Year of the Child. Multicoloured.

550. 25 c. Type **106** 20 10
551. 50 c. Boy holding football 30 10
552. 75 c. Boy with butterfly .. 45 10
553. $1 Girl holding doll .. 60 10
554. $1.50 Boy carrying basket of fruit 95 15
555. $2 Boy holding shell .. 1·25 20
556. $3 Girl holding posy .. 1·90 25
557. $4 Boy and girl wrapped in blanket .. .. 2·50 30

1980. No. 412 surch.

560. 10 c. on 25 c. "Papilio thoas" 65 85

108. Jabiru.

1980. Birds (4th series). Multicoloured.

561. 10 c. Type **108** .. .. 4·00 2·25
562. 25 c. Barred antshrike .. 4·25 2·25
563. 35 c. Northern royal flycatcher .. .. 4·25 2·50
564. 45 c. White-necked puffbird .. .. .. 4·50 2·75
565. 50 c. Ornate hawk-eagle .. 4·50 3·00
566. $1 Golden-masked tanager 5·00 3·50

109. Speed Skating.

1980. Winter Olympic Games, Lake Placid. Medal Winners. Multicoloured.

568. 25 c. Type **109** 30 15
569. 50 c. Ice-hockey 50 15
570. 75 c. Figure-skating .. 60 15
571. $1 Alpine-skiing 85 15
572. $1.50 Giant slalom (women) .. .. .. 1·25 25
573. $2 Speed-skating (women) 1·50 30
574. $3 Cross-country skiing .. 2·25 40
575. $5 Giant slalom .. .. 3·50 55

1980. "ESPAMER" International Stamp Exhibition. Madrid. Nos. 560/5 optd. **BELIZE ESPAMER '80 MADRID 3–12 OCT 1980** (Nos. 577/9) or surch. also.

577. 10 c. Type **107** .. .. 2·00 2·00
578. 25 c. Barred antshrike .. 2·25 2·25
579. 35 c. Northern royal flycatcher .. .. .. 2·50 2·50
580. 40 c. on 45 c. White-necked puffbird .. .. .. 2·75 2·75
581. 40 c. on 50 c. Ornate hawk-eagle .. .. .. 2·75 2·75
582. 40 c. on $1 Golden-masked tanager .. .. .. 2·75 2·75

111. Witch in Sky.

1980. Fairy Tales. "Sleeping Beauty".

583. 25 c. multicoloured .. 30 15
584. 40 c. multicoloured .. 40 15
585. 50 c. multicoloured .. 55 15
586. 75 c. multicoloured .. 70 15
587. $1 multicoloured 80 20
588. $1.50 multicoloured .. 1·25 30
589. $3 multicoloured .. .. 2·40 35
590. $4 multicoloured .. .. 3·00 45

DESIGNS: Illustrations from the story.

112. H.M. Queen Elizabeth the Queen Mother

1980. 80th Birthday of H.M. Queen Elizabeth the Queen Mother.

592. **112.** $1 multicoloured .. 1·25 40

113. The Annunciation.

1980. Christmas. Multicoloured.

594. 25 c. Type **113** 20 10
595. 50 c. Bethlehem 35 10
596. 75 c. The Holy Family .. 55 10
597. $1 The Nativity 70 10
598. $1.50 The Flight into Egypt 90 15
599. $2 Shepherds following the Star .. .. .. 1·10 20
600. $3 Virgin, Child & Angel 1·60 25
601. $4 Adoration of the Kings 1·90 30

1981. "WIPA" International Stamp Exhibition, Vienna. Nos. 598 and 601 surch.

603. $1 on $1.50 The Flight into Egypt 60 65
604. $2 on $4 Adoration of the Kings .. .. 1·25 1·40

115. Paul Harris (founder).

1981. 75th Anniv. of Rotary International. Multicoloured.

606. 25 c. Type **115** 20 25
607. 50 c. Emblems of Rotary activities 35 35
608. $1 75th Anniversary emblem 70 65
609. $1.50 Educational scholarship programme .. 1·10 1·00
610. $2 "Project Hippocrates" 1·40 1·40
611. $3 Emblems .. .. 2·10 2·00
612. $5 Emblem & handshake 3·50 3·25

Nos 609 and 612 are horiz.

116. Coat of Arms of Prince of Wales.

1981. Royal Wedding. Multicoloured.
(a) Size 22 × 38 mm.

614. 50 c. Type **116** 35 40
615. $1 Prince Charles in military uniform .. 70 75
616. $1.50 Royal couple .. 1·10 1·25

(b) Size 25 × 42 mm. with gold borders.

617. 50 c. Type **116** 35 15
618. $1 As No. 615 .. .. 70 35
619. $1·50 As No. 616 .. .. 1·10 45

1981. No. 538 surch.

621. 10 c. on 15 c. "Murex cabritii" .. .. 1·75 1·90

118. Athletics.

1981. History of the Olympics. Mult.

622. 85 c. Type **118** 60 10
623. $1 Cycling 70 10
624. $1·50 Boxing .. .. 1·10 10
625. $2 1984 Games—Los Angeles & Sarajevo .. 1·40 20
626. $3 Baron Pierre de Coubertin 2·10 30
627. $5 Olympic Flame .. 3·50 40

1981. Independence Commemoration (1st issue). Optd. **Independence 21 Sept., 1981.**
(a) On Nos. 532/44 and 546/8.

629. 1 c. Type **105** 10 10
630. 2 c. "Macrocallista maculata" 10 10
631. 3 c. "Arca zebra" (vert.) 10 10
632. 4 c. "Chama macerophylla" (vert.) 10 10
633. 5 c. "Latirus cariniferus" 10 10
634. 10 c. "Conus spurius" (vert.) 15 10
635. 15 c. "Murex cabritii" (vert.) 25 10
636. 20 c. "Atrina rigida" .. 25 15
637. 25 c. "Chlamys imbricata" (vert.) 35 25
638. 35 c. "Conus granulatus" 45 30
639. 45 c. "Tellina radiata" (vert.) 60 40
640. 50 c. "Leucozonia nassa leucozonalis" 60 40
641. 85 c. "Tripterotyphis triangularis" 85 70
642. $2 "Strombus gallus" (vert.) .. .. .. 2·25 2·00
643. $5 "Fasciolaria tulipa" .. 4·50 4·50
644. $10 "Arene cruentata" .. 8·50 8·50

(b) On Nos. 606/12.

646. 25 c. Type **115** 20 25
647. 50 c. Emblems of Rotary activities 35 35
648. $1 75th Anniversary emblem 70 65
649. $1·50 Educational scholarship programme .. 1·10 1·00
650. $2 "Project Hippocrates" 1·40 1·40
651. $3 Emblems .. .. 2·10 2·00
652. $5 Emblems and handshake 3·50 3·25

See also Nos. 657/62.

1981. "ESPAMER" International Stamp Exhibition, Buenos Aires. No. 609 surch.

654. $1 on $1.50 Educational scholarship programme .. 1·00 1·00

122. Black Orchid.

1981. Independence Commemoration (2nd issue). Multicoloured.

657. 10 c. Belize Coat of Arms (horiz.) 30 10
658. 35 c. Map of Belize .. 65 30
659. 50 c. Type **122** .. .. 1·50 35
660. 85 c. Baird's Tapir (horiz.) 1·40 60
661. $1 Mahogany Tree .. 1·50 65
662. $2 Keel-billed Toucan (horiz.) .. .. .. 3·00 1·40

123. Uruguayan Footballer.

1981. World Cup Football Championship, Spain (1st issue). Multicoloured.

664. 10 c. Type **123** 50 10
665. 25 c. Italian footballer .. 80 15
666. 50 c. German footballer .. 1·00 20
667. $1 Brazilian footballer .. 1·75 30
668. $1·50 Argentinian footballer 2·25 50
669. $2 English footballer .. 2·75 65

See also Nos. 721/6.

124. British 19th-century Warship.

1981. Sailing Ships. Multicoloured.

671. 10 c. Type **124** 60 20
672. 25 c. "Madagascar" (1837) 1·25 35
673. 35 c. Brig "Whitby" (1838) 1·50 35
674. 55 c. "China" (1838) .. 1·75 50
675. 85 c. "Swiftsure" (1850) .. 2·50 70
676. $2 "Windsor Castle" (1857) 4·50 95

1982. "ESSEN '82" International Stamp Exhibition. West Germany. Nos. 662 and 669 optd. **ESSEN 82** and surch. also.

678. $1 on $2 Keel-billed toucan 1·50 75
679. $1 on $2 English footballer 1·50 75

126. Princess Diana.

1982. 21st Birthday of Princess of Wales.
(a) Size 22 × 38 mm.

680. **126.** 50 c. multicoloured .. 25 35
681. $1 multicoloured .. 35 65
682. $1.50 multicoloured .. 50 1·00

(b) Size 25 × 43 mm.
683. 50 c. multicoloured .. 35 10
684. $1 multicoloured .. 70 20
685. $1.50 multicoloured .. 1·10 30

DESIGNS: Portraits of Princess of Wales with different backgrounds.

127. Lighting Camp-fire.

1982. 125th Birth Anniv. of Lord Baden-Powell. Multicoloured.
687. 10 c. Type **127** 30 10
688. 25 c. Bird watching .. 60 25
689. 35 c. Three scouts, one playing guitar 70 30
690. 50 c. Hiking 85 35
691. 85 c. Scouts with flag .. 1·25 60
692. $2 Saluting .. .. 2·25 1·40

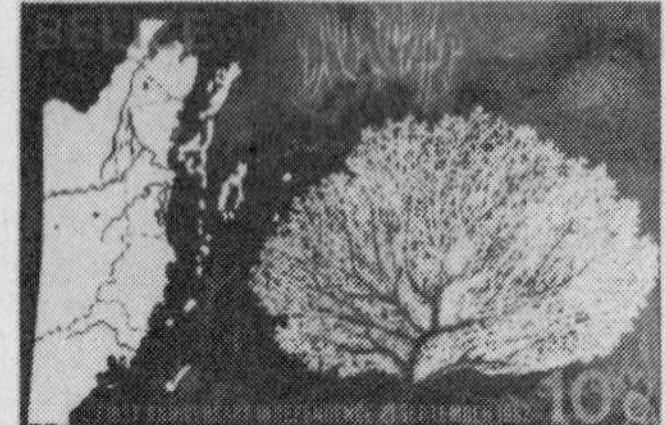

128. "Gorgonia ventalina".

1982. 1st Anniv. of Independence. Marine Life.
694. 10 c. Type **128** 45 10
695. 35 c. "Carpiuis corallinus" 1·10 15
696. 50 c. "Plexaura flexuasa" 1·40 20
697. 85 c. "Candylactis gigantea" 2·00 25
698. $1 "Stenopus hispidus" .. 2·25 45
699. $2 "Abudefduf saxatilus" 2·75 70

1982. "BELGICA 82" International Stamp Exhibition, Brussels. Nos. 687/92 optd. **BELGICA 82 INT YEAR OF THE CHILD 1975. SIR ROWLAND HILL 1879 CENTENARY OF BIRTH.**
701. 10 c. Type **127** 50 30
702. 25 c. Bird watching .. 1·40 75
703. 35 c. Three scouts, one playing guitar .. .. 1·75 1·00
704. 50 c. Hiking .. .. 2·25 1·50
705. 85 c. Scouts with flag .. 3·75 2·50
706. $2 Saluting .. .. 9·00 6·50

1982. Birth of Prince William of Wales (1st issue). Nos. 680/5 optd. **BIRTH OF H.R.H. PRINCE WILLIAM ARTHUR PHILIP LOUIS 21ST JUNE 1982.**

(a) Size 22 × 38 mm.
707. 50 c. multicoloured .. 25 35
708. $1 multicoloured .. 35 50
709. $1.50 multicoloured .. 50 75

(b) Size 25 × 43 mm.
710. 50 c. multicoloured .. 25 35
711. $1 multicoloured .. 35 50
712. $1.50 multicoloured .. 50 75

1982. Birth of Prince William of Wales (2nd issue). Nos. 614–19 optd. **BIRTH OF H.R.H. PRINCE WILLIAM ARTHUR PHILIP LOUIS 21ST JUNE 1982** in gold.

(a) Size 22 × 38 mm.
714 50 c. Type **116** .. .. 2·50 1·00
715 $1 Prince Charles in military uniform .. 5·00 2·00
716 $1.50 Royal couple .. 7·50 3·00

(b) Size 25 × 42 mm.
717. 50 c. Type **116** 35 35
718. $1 As No. 715 .. 70 70
719. $1.50 As No. 716 .. 1·10 1·10

131. Scotland v New Zealand.

1982. World Cup Football Championship, Spain (2nd issue). Multicoloured.
721. 20 c. + 10 c. Type **131** .. 60 50
722. 30 c. + 15 c. Scotland v New Zealand (different) .. 70 50
723. 40 c. + 20 c. Kuwait v France 80 50
724. 60 c. + 50 c. Italy v Brazil 1·25 70
725. $1 + 50 c. France v Northern Ireland .. .. 2·00 85
726. $1.50 + 75 c. Austria v Chile 2·50 1·10

133. Belize Cathedral.

1983. Visit of Pope John Paul II.
729. **133.** 50 c. multicoloured .. 2·00 90

134. Map of Belize.

1983. Commonwealth Day. Multicoloured.
731. 35 c. Type **134** 35 35
732. 50 c. "Maya Stella" from Lamanai Indian church (horiz.) 50 50
733. 85 c. Supreme Court Building (horiz.) 75 75
734. $2 University Centre, Belize (horiz.) .. .. 1·75 2·00

1983. No. 658 surch.
735. 10 c. on 35 c. Map of Belize

136. Lana's "Flying boat" 1670.

1983. Bicentenary of Manned Flight. Mult.
736. 10 c. Type **136** 30 20
737. 25 c. Barthelemy Lourenco's flying machine, 1709 .. 60 40
738. 50 c. Guyton de Morveau's airship 85 55
739. 85 c. Early dirigible .. 1·25 85
740. $1 The "Clement Bayard" 1·40 1·00
741. $1.50 "R-34" airship .. 1·90 1·40

1983. Nos. 662 and 699 surch.
743. $1.25 on $2 Keel-billed Toucan .. .. 3·50 4·00
744. $1.25 on $2 "Abudefduf saxatilus" .. .. 5·50 5·50

1983. No. 541 surch.
746. 10 c. on 35 c. "Conus granulatus" .. .. 20·00

141. Altun Ha.

1983. Maya Monuments. Multicoloured.
747. 10 c. Type **141** 10 10
748. 15 c. Xunantunich .. 10 10
749. 75 c. Cerros 30 40
750. $3 Lamanal 70 80

142. Belmopan Earth Station.

1983. World Communications Year. Mult.
752. 10 c. Type **142** 30 10
753. 15 c. "Telstar 2" .. 40 20
754. 75 c. U.P.U. logo .. 1·25 1·10
755. $2 M.V. "Heron H" Mail Service .. .. 2·75 3·00

143. Jaguar Cub.

1983. The Jaguar. Multicoloured.
756. 5 c. Type **143** 20 10
757. 10 c. Adult Jaguar .. 25 10
758. 85 c. Jaguar in river .. 1·50 1·10
759. $1 Jaguar on rock .. 1·75 1·50

144. Pope John Paul II.

1983. Christmas.
761. **144.** 10 c. multicoloured .. 25 10
762. 15 c. multicoloured .. 30 10
763. 75 c. multicoloured .. 80 60
764. $2 multicoloured .. 1·75 1·40

145. Foureye Butterflyfish.

1984. Marine Life from the Belize Coral Reef. Multicoloured.
766. 1 c. Type **145** .. 15 10
767. 2 c. Cushion Star .. 15 10
768. 3 c. Flower Coral .. 15 10
769. 4 c. Fairy Basslet .. 15 10
770. 5 c. Spanish Hogfish .. 15 10
771. 6 c. Star-Eyed Hermit Crab 20 10
772. 10 c. Sea Fans and Fire Sponge 25 15
773. 15 c. Blueheads .. 30 30
774. 25 c. Blue Striped Grunt .. 35 30
775. 50 c. Coral Crab .. 60 60
776. 60 c. Tube Sponge .. 75 65
777. 75 c. Brain Coral .. 85 60
778. $1 Yellow-tail Snapper .. 1·25 1·00
779. $2 Common Lettuce Slug 2·25 2·25
780. $5 Yellow Damselfish .. 4·00 4·50
781. $10 Rock Beauty .. 7·50 10·00

1984. Visit of the Archbishop of Canterbury. Nos. 772 and 775 optd. **VISIT OF THE LORD ARCHBISHOP OF CANTERBURY 8th–11th MARCH 1984.**
782. 10 c. Sea Fans and Fire Sponge 60 30
783. 50 c. Coral Crab .. 1·00 70

147. Shooting.

1984. Olympic Games, Los Angeles. Mult.

(a) Sheet Stamps.
784. 25 c. Type **147** .. 30 25
785. 75 c. Boxing .. 70 60
786. $1 Marathon .. 90 80
787. $2 Cycling .. 1·75 1·60

(b) Booklet stamps. Similar designs to T **147** but Royal cypher replaced by Queen's head.
789. 5 c. Marathon .. 15 30
790. 20 c. Sprinting .. 25 50
791. 25 c. Shot-putting .. 25 50
792. $2 Olympic torch .. 35 80

148. British Honduras 1866 1s. Stamp.

1984. "Ausipex" International Stamp Exhibition, Melbourne. Multicoloured.
793. 15 c. Type **148** .. 15 15
794. 30 c. Bath mail coach, 1784 25 25
795. 65 c. Sir Rowland Hill and Penny Black .. 55 55
796. 75 c. British Honduras railway locomotive, 1910 .. 65 65
797. $2 Royal Exhibition buildings, Melbourne .. 1·50 1·75

149. Prince Albert.

1984. 500th Anniv. (1985) of British Royal House of Tudor. Multicoloured.
799. 50 c. Type **149** .. 25 35
800. 50 c. Queen Victoria .. 25 35
801. 75 c. King George VI .. 35 45
802. 75 c. Queen Elizabeth the Queen Mother .. 35 45
803. $1 Princess of Wales .. 50 70
804. $1 Prince of Wales .. 50 70

150. White-fronted Amazon.

1984. Parrots. Multicoloured.
806. $1 Type **150** .. 1·50 1·25
807. $1 White-capped parrot (horiz.) .. 1·50 1·25
808. $1 Mealy amazon (horiz.) 1·50 1·25
809. $1 Red-lored amazon .. 1·50 1·25

Nos 806/9 were issued together, se-tenant forming a composite design.

151. Effigy Censer, 1450 (Santa Rita Site).

1984. Maya Artefacts. Multicoloured.
811. 25 c. Type **151** .. 25 25
812. 75 c. Vase, 675 (Actun Chapat) .. 60 60
813. $1 Tripod vase, 500 (Santa Rita site) .. 80 80
814. $2 Sun god Kinich Ahau, 600 (Altun Ha site) .. 1·75 1·75

152. Governor-General inspecting Girl Guides.

1985. International Youth Year and 75th Anniv. of Girl Guide Movement. Multicoloured.

815. 25 c. Type **152** 25 30
816. 50 c. Girl Guides camping 40 45
817. 90 c. Checking map on hike 55 65
818. $1.25 Students in laboratory 65 80
819. $2 Lady Baden-Powell (founder) .. .. 85 1·10

153. White-tailed Kite.

1985. Birth Bicentenary of John J. Audubon (ornithologist). Designs showing original paintings. Multicoloured.

820. 10 c. Type **153** 60 15
821. 15 c. Cuvier's Kinglet (horiz.) 70 20
822. 25 c. Painted Bunting .. 90 40
822a. 60 c. As 25 c. (1988) 1·50 1·25
823. 75 c. Belted Kingfisher .. 1·50 1·00
824. $1 Northern Cardinal .. 1·75 1·25
825. $3 Long-billed Curlew (horiz.) .. .. .. 3·00 3·00

154. The Queen Mother with Princess Elizabeth, 1928

1985. Life and Times of Queen Elizabeth the Queen Mother. Multicoloured.

827. 10 c. Type **154** 10 10
828. 15 c. The Queen Mother, 1980 .. .. .. 10 10
829. 75 c. Waving to the crowd, 1982 .. .. .. 40 40
830. $5 Four generations of Royal Family at Prince William's Christening .. 2·50 2·75

1985. Inauguration of New Government. Nos. 772/3 and 775 optd. **INAUGURATION OF NEW GOVERNMENT—21st DECEMBER 1984.**

832. 10 c. Sea Fans and Fire Sponge 25 15
833. 15 c. Blueheads 30 20
834. 50 c. Coral Crab 80 60

156. British Honduras 1935 Silver Jubilee 25 c. stamp and King George V with Queen Mary in Carriage. (Illustration reduced, actual size 68 × 32 mm.).

1985. 50th Anniv. of First Commonwealth Omnibus Issue. Designs showing British Honduras/Belize stamps. Multicoloured.

835. 50 c. Type **156** 35 40
836. 50 c. 1937 Coronation 3 c., and King George VI and Queen Elizabeth in Coronation robes .. 35 40
837. 50 c. 1946 Victory 3 c. and Victory celebrations .. 35 40
838. 50 c. 1948 Royal Silver Wedding 4 c. and King George VI and Queen Elizabeth at Westminster Abbey service 35 40
839. 50 c. 1953 Coronation 4 c. and Queen Elizabeth II in Coronation robes .. 35 40
840. 50 c. 1966 Churchill 25 c., Sir Winston Churchill and fighter aircraft .. 35 40
841. 50 c. 1972 Royal Silver Wedding 50 c. and 1948 Wedding photograph .. 35 40
842. 50 c. 1973 Royal Wedding 50 c. and Princess Anne and Capt. Mark Phillips at their Wedding .. 35 40
843. 50 c. 1977 Silver Jubilee $2 and Queen Elizabeth II during tour 35 40
844. 50 c. 1978 25th anniv. of Coronation 75 c. and Imperial Crown 35 40

157. Mounted Postboy and Early Letter to Belize.

1985. 350th Anniv of British Post Office. Mult.

846 10 c. Type **157** 40 10
847 15 c. "Hinchinbrook II" (sailing packet) engaging "Grand Turk" (American privateer) .. 55 15
848 25 c. "Duke of Marlborough II" (sailing packet) 70 25
849 75 c. "Diana" (packet) .. 1·25 60
850 $1 Falmouth packet ship 1·50 1·00
851 $3 "Conway" (mail paddle-steamer) .. .. 3·75 3·00

1985. Commonwealth Heads of Govenment Meeting, Nassau, Bahamas. Nos. 827/30 optd **COMMONWEALTH SUMMIT CONFERENCE, BAHAMAS 16th-22nd OCTOBER 1985.**

852 10 c. Type **154** 10 10
853 15 c. The Queen Mother, 1980 .. .. .. 10 15
854 75 c. Waving to the crowd, 1982 .. .. .. 40 40
855 $5 Four generations of Royal Family at Prince William's Christening .. 2·50 2·75

1985. 80th Anniv of Rotary International. Nos. 815/9 optd **80th ANNIVERSARY OF ROTARY INTERNATIONAL.**

857 25 c. Type **152** 45 25
858 50 c. Girl Guides camping 70 40
859 90 c. Checking map on hike 1·00 70
860 $1.25 Students in laboratory .. .. 1·50 95
861 $2 Lady Baden-Powell (founder) .. .. 2·25 1·50

160. Royal Standard and Belize Flag.

1985. Royal Visit. Multicoloured.

862. 25 c. Type **160** 55 65
863. 75 c. Queen Elizabeth II .. 1·25 1·40
864. $4 Royal Yacht "Britannia" (81 × 39 mm.) .. .. 3·00 3·00

161. Mountie in Canoe (Canada).

1985. Christmas. 30th Anniv. of Disneyland, U.S.A. Designs showing dolls from "It's a Small World" exhibition. Multicoloured.

866. 1 c. Type **161** 10 10
867. 2 c. Indian chief and squaw (U.S.A.) 10 10
868. 3 c. Incas climbing Andes (South America) .. 10 10
869. 4 c. Africans beating drums (Africa) 10 10
870. 5 c. Snake-charmer and dancer (India and Far East) 10 10
871. 6 c. Boy and girl with donkey (Belize) 10 10
872. 50 c. Musician and dancer (Balkans) 70 50
873. $1.50, Boys with camel (Egypt and Saudi Arabia) .. .. 1·75 1·40
874. $3 Woman and girls playing with kite (Japan) .. .. 3·00 2·50

1985. World Cup Football Championship, Mexico (1986) (1st issue). Nos. 835/44 optd. **PRE "WORLD CUP FOOTBALL" MEXICO 1986.**

876. 50 c. Type **156** 60 40
877. 50 c. 1937 Coronation 3 c., and King George VI and Queen Elizabeth in Coronation robes .. 60 40
878. 50 c. Victory 3 c., and Victory celebrations .. 60 40
879. 50 c. 1948 Royal Silver Wedding 4 c., and King George VI and Queen Elizabeth at Westminister Abbey service 60 40
880. 50 c. 1953 Coronation 4 c. and Queen Elizabeth II in Coronation robes .. 60 40
881. 50 c. 1966 Churchill 25 c., Sir Winston Churchill and fighter aircraft .. 60 40
882. 50 c. 1972 Royal Silver Wedding 50 c., and 1948 wedding photograph .. 60 40
883. 50 c. 1973 Royal Wedding 50 c., and Princess Anne and Capt. Mark Phillips at their Wedding .. 60 40
884. 50 c. 1977 Silver Jubilee $2, and Queen Elizabeth II during tour 60 40
885. 50 c. 1978 25th anniv. of Coronation 75 c., and Imperial Crown 60 40

See also Nos. 936/9.

163. Indian Costume.

1986. Costumes of Belize. Multicoloured.

887. 5 c. Type **163** 50 15
888. 10 c. Maya 60 15
889. 15 c. Garifuna 75 20
890. 25 c. Creole 95 30
891. 50 c. Chinese .. .. 1·40 70
892. 75 c. Lebanese .. .. 1·75 1·10
893. $1 European c 1900 .. 2·00 1·50
894. $2 Latin .. .. .. 2·75 2·25

164. Pope Pius X.

1986. Easter. 20th-century Popes. Mult.

896. 50 c. Type **164** .. .. 1·00 1·00
897. 50 c. Benedict XV .. .. 1·00 1·00
898. 50 c. Pius XI .. .. 1·00 1·00
899. 50 c. Pius XII .. .. 1·00 1·00
900. 50 c. John XXIII .. .. 1·00 1·00
901. 50 c. Paul VI .. .. 1·00 1·00
902. 50 c. John Paul I .. .. 1·00 1·00
903. 50 c. John Paul II .. .. 1·00 1·00

165. Princess Elizabeth aged Three.

1986. 60th Birthday of Queen Elizabeth II. Multicoloured.

905. 25 c. Type **165** 15 20
906. 50 c. Queen wearing Imperial State Crown .. 35 40
907. 75 c. At Trooping the Colour 50 55
908. $3 Queen wearing diadem 2·10 2·25

166. Halley's Comet and Japanese "Planet A" Spacecraft.

1986. Appearance of Halley's Comet. Mult.

910. 10 c. Type **166** 20 20
911. 15 c. Halley's Comet, 1910 30 30
912. 50 c. Comet and European "Giotto" spacecraft .. 40 40
913. 75 c. Belize Weather Bureau 70 70
914. $1 Comet and U.S.A. space telescope 95 95
915. $2 Edmond Halley .. 1·50 1·50

167. George Washington.

1986. United States Presidents. Mult.

917. 10 c. Type **167** 35 35
918. 20 c. John Adams 40 40
919. 30 c. Thomas Jefferson .. 45 45
920. 50 c. James Madison .. 60 60
922. $1.50 James Monroe .. 1·25 1·25
922. $2 John Quincy Adams .. 1·50 1·50

168. Auguste Bartholdi (sculptor) and Statue's Head.

1986. Centenary of Statue of Liberty. Multicoloured.

924. 25 c. Type **168** 40 40
925. 50 c. Statue's head at U.S. Centennial Celebration, Philadelphia, 1876 .. 50 60
926. 75 c. Unveiling Ceremony, 1886 .. .. .. 60 70
927. $3 Statue of Liberty and flags of Belize and U.S.A. .. .. .. 1·75 2·00

169. British Honduras 1866 1 s. Stamp.

1986. "Ameripex" International Stamp Exhibition, Chicago. Multicoloured.

929.	10 c. Type **169**	40	40
930.	15 c. 1981 Royal Wedding $1.50 stamp	55	55
931.	50 c. U.S.A. 1918 24 c. air-mail inverted centre error	75	75
932.	75 c. U.S.S. "Constitution" (frigate)	1·00	1·00
933.	$1 Liberty Bell	1·25	1·25
934.	$2 White House	1·60	1·60

170. English and Brazilian Players.

1986. World Cup Football Championship, Mexico (2nd issue). Multicoloured.

936.	25 c. Type **170**	1·00	75
937.	50 c. Mexican player and Maya statues	1·40	1·10
938.	75 c. Two Belizean players	1·75	1·50
939.	$3 Aztec stone calendar ..	3·00	2·50

171. Miss Sarah Ferguson.

1986. Royal Wedding. Multicoloured.

941.	25 c. Type **171**	40	25
942.	75 c. Prince Andrew ..	90	65
943.	$3 Prince Andrew and Miss Sarah Ferguson (92 × 41 mm)	2·25	2·25

1986. World Cup Football Championship Winners, Mexico. Nos. 936/9 optd. **ARGENTINA–WINNERS 1986.**

945.	25 c. Type **170**	90	60
946.	50 c. Mexican player and Maya statues	1·25	1·00
947.	75 c. Two Belizean players	1·60	1·40
948.	$3 Aztec stone calendar ..	2·75	2·50

1986. "Stockholmia '86" International Stamp Exhibition, Sweden. Nos. 929/34. optd. **STOCKHOLMIA 86** and emblem.

950.	10 c. Type **169**	40	40
951.	15 c. 1981 Royal Wedding $1.50 stamp	50	50
952.	50 c. U.S.A. 1918 24 c. airmail inverted centre error	70	70
953.	75 c. U.S.S. "Constitution"	90	90
954.	$1 Liberty Bell	1·10	1·10
955.	$2 White House	1·60	1·60

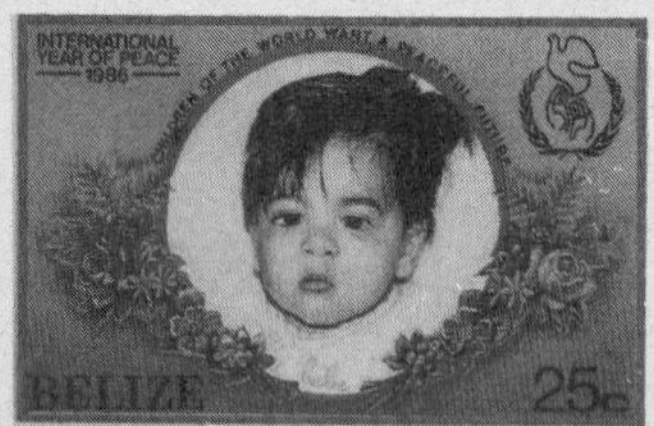

174. Amerindian Girl.

1986. International Peace Year. Mult.

957.	25 c. Type **174**	45	45
958.	50 c. European boy and girls	70	70
959.	75 c. Japanese girl ..	1·00	1·00
960.	$3 Indian boy and European girl	2·25	2·25

175. "Amanita lilloi".

1986. Fungi and Toucans. Multicoloured.

962.	5 c. Type **175**	75	75
963.	10 c. Keel-billed toucan ..	90	90
964.	25 c. "Boletellus cubensis"	1·25	1·25
965.	25 c. Collared aracari ..	1·25	1·25
966.	75 c. "Psilocybe caerulescens"	1·50	1·50
967.	$1 Emerald toucanet ..	1·50	1·50
968.	$1.25 Crimson-rumped toucanet	1·50	1·50
969.	$2 "Russula puiggarii" ..	2·00	2·00

176. Jose Carioca.

1986. Christmas. Designs showing Walt Disney cartoon characters in scenes from "Saludos Amigos". Multicoloured.

970.	2 c. Type **176**	20	10
971.	3 c. Jose Carioca, Panchito and Donald Duck ..	20	10
972.	4 c. Daisy Duck as Rio Carnival dancer	20	10
973.	5 c. Mickey and Minnie Mouse as musician and dancer	20	10
974.	6 c. Jose Carioca using umbrella as flute ..	20	10
975.	50 c. Donald Duck and Panchito	1·00	85
976.	65 c. Jose Carioca and Donald Duck playing hide and seek	1·25	1·10
977.	$1.35 Donald Duck playing maracas	2·00	1·75
978.	$2 Goofy as matador ..	2·75	2·50

177. Princess Elizabeth in Wedding Dress, 1947.

1987. Royal Ruby Wedding. Multicoloured.

980.	25 c. Type **177**	20	20
981.	75 c. Queen and Duke of Edinburgh, 1972 ..	35	40
982.	$1 Queen on her 60th birthday	40	50
983.	$4 in Garter robes	1·00	1·25

178. "America II", 1983.

1987. America's Cup Yachting Championship. Multicoloured.

985.	25 c. Type **178**	20	25
986.	75 c. "Stars and Stripes", 1987	35	40
987.	$1 "Australia II", 1983 ..	40	50
988.	$4 "White Crusader" ..	1·00	1·50

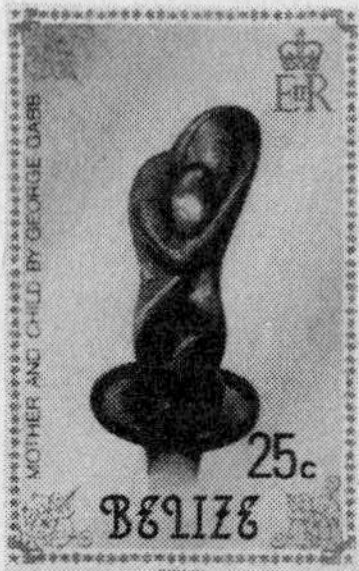

179 "Mother and Child"

1987. Wood Carvings by George Gabb. Mult.

990	25 c. Type **179**	15	20
991	75 c. "Standing Form" ..	35	40
992	$1 "Love-doves" ..	40	50
993	$4 "Depiction of Music"	1·10	1·60

180 Black-handed Spider Monkey

1987. Primates. Multicoloured.

995	25 c. Type **180**	25	20
996	75 c. Black howler monkey	40	45
997	$1 Spider monkeys with baby	45	55
998	$4 Two black howler monkeys	1·10	1·60

181 Guides on Parade

1987. 50th Anniv of Girl Guide Movement in Belize. Multicoloured.

1000	25 c. Type **181**	25	20
1001	75 c. Brownie camp ..	55	60
1002	$1 Guide camp	75	80
1003	$4 Olave, Lady Baden-Powell	2·75	3·00

182 Indian Refugee Camp

1987. International Year of Shelter for the Homeless. Multicoloured.

1005	25 c. Type **182**	35	20
1006	75 c. Filipino family and slum	70	50
1007	$1 Family in Middle East shanty town	90	70
1008	$4 Building modern house in Belize ..	3·00	3·00

183 "Laelia euspatha"

1987. Christmas. Orchids. Illustrations from Sanders's "Reichenbachia". Multicoloured.

1009	1 c. Type **183**	45	30
1010	2 c. "Cattleya citrina" ..	45	30
1011	3 c. "Masdevallia backhousiana" ..	45	30
1012	4 c. "Cypripedium tautzianum" ..	45	30
1013	5 c. "Trichopilia suavis alba"	45	30
1014	6 c. "Odontoglossum hebraicum"	45	30
1015	7 c. "Cattleya trianaei schroederiana" ..	45	30
1016	10 c. "Saccolabium giganteum"	75	45
1017	30 c. "Cattleya warscewiczii"	90	60
1018	50 c. "Chysis bractescens"	1·25	80
1019	70 c. "Cattleya rochellensis"	1·40	90
1020	$1 "Laelia elegans schilleriana"	1·50	1·00
1021	$1.50 "Laelia anceps percivaliana"	1·60	1·40
1022	$3 "Laelia gouldiana" ..	2·25	1·90

184 Christ condemned to Death

1988. Easter. The Stations of the Cross. Mult.

1024	40 c. Type **184**	30	30
1025	40 c. Christ carrying the Cross	30	30
1026	40 c. Falling for the first time	30	30
1027	40 c. Christ meets Mary ..	30	30
1028	40 c. Simon of Cyrene helping to carry the Cross	30	30
1029	40 c. Veronica wiping the face of Christ ..	30	30
1030	40 c. Christ falling a second time ..	30	30
1031	40 c. Consoling the women of Jerusalem ..	30	30
1032	40 c. Falling for the third time	30	30
1033	40 c. Christ being stripped	30	30
1034	40 c. Christ nailed to the Cross	30	30
1035	40 c. Dying on the Cross	30	30
1036	40 c. Christ taken down from the Cross ..	30	30
1037	40 c. Christ being laid in the sepulchre	30	30

185 Basketball

1988. Olympic Games, Seoul. Multicoloured.
1038 10 c. Type **185** 10 10
1039 25 c. Volleyball 15 20
1040 60 c. Table tennis 35 40
1041 75 c. Diving 45 50
1042 $1 Judo 60 65
1043 $2 Hockey 1·25 1·40

186 Public Health Nurse, c. 1912

1988. 125th Anniv of International Red Cross. Multicoloured.
1045 60 c. Type **186** 70 50
1046 75 c. Hospital ship and ambulance launch, 1937 90 65
1047 $1 Ambulance at hospital tent, 1956 1·25 85
1048 $2 Ambulance plane, 1940 1·75 1·75

187 Collared Anteater ("Ants Bear")

1989. Small Animals of Belize. Multicoloured.
1049 10 c. Paca ("Gibnut") 45 45
1049a 25 c. Four-eyed opossum (vert) 60 60
1051 50 c. Type **187** 1·00 1·00
1052 60 c. As 10 c. 1·25 1·25
1053 75 c. Red brocket 1·40 1·40
1054 $2 Collared peccary 2·75 2·75

1989. 20th Anniv of First Manned Landing on Moon. As T **126** of Ascension. Multicoloured.
1055 25 c. Docking of "Apollo 9" modules 15 20
1056 50 c. "Apollo 9" command service module in Space (30 × 30 mm) 30 35
1057 75 c. "Apollo 9" emblem (30 × 30 mm) 45 50
1058 $1 "Apollo 9" lunar module in space 60 65

1989. No. 771 surch.
1060 5 c. on 6 c. Star-eyed hermit crab 3·50 85

190 Wesley Church

1989. Christmas. Belize Churches.
1062 **190** 10 c. blk, pink & brn 15 10
1063 – 25 c. blk, lilac & mve 20 20
1064 – 60 c. black, turq & bl 40 40
1065 – 75 c. blk, grn & lt grn 55 60
1066 – $1 black, pale yellow and yellow 70 75
DESIGNS: 25 c. Baptist Church; 60 c. St. John's Anglican Cathedral; 75 c. St. Andrew's Presbyterian Church; $1 Holy Redeemer Roman Catholic Cathedral.

191 White-winged Tanager and "Catonephele numilia"

1990. Birds and Butterflies. Multicoloured.
1067 5 c. Type **191** 10 10
1068 10 c. Keel-billed toucan and "Nessaea aglaura" 10 10
1069 15 c. Magnificent frigate bird and "Eurytides philolaus" 10 10
1070 25 c. Jabiru and "Heliconius sapho" 15 20
1071 30 c. Great blue heron and "Colobura dirce" 20 25
1072 50 c. Northern oriole and "Hamadryas arethusia" 30 35
1073 60 c. Scarlet macaw and "Evenus regalis" 40 45
1074 75 c. Red-legged honey-creeper and "Callicore patelina" 50 55
1075 $1 Spectacled owl and "Caligo uranus" 65 70
1076 $2 Green jay and "Philaethria dido" 1·25 1·40
1077 $5 Turkey vulture and "Battus belus" 3·25 3·50
1078 $10 Osprey and "Papilio thoas" 6·00 6·25

1990. First Belize Dollar Coin. No. 1075 optd **FIRST DOLLAR COIN 1990**.
1079 $1 Spectacled owl and "Caligo uranus" 1·50 1·25

193 Green Turtle

1990. Turtles. Multicoloured.
1080 10 c. Type **193** 20 15
1081 25 c. Hawksbill turtle 30 25
1082 60 c. Saltwater loggerhead turtle 60 50
1083 75 c. Freshwater loggerhead turtle 75 65
1084 $1 Bocatora turtle 95 95
1085 $2 Hicatee turtle 1·75 1·75

194 Fairey Battle

1990. 50th Anniv of the Battle of Britain. Multicoloured.
1086 10 c. Type **194** 30 15
1087 25 c. Bristol Beaufort 50 30
1088 60 c. Bristol Blenheim IV 1·00 70
1089 75 c. Armstrong-Whitworth Whitley 1·10 75
1090 $1 Vickeers-Armstrong Wellington 1·25 90
1091 $2 Handley-Page Hampden 1·75 1·75

195 "Cattleya bowringiana"

1990. Christmas. Orchids. Multicoloured.
1092 25 c. Type **195** 25 20
1093 50 c. "Rhyncholaelia digbyana" 35 35
1094 60 c. "Sobralia macrantha" 45 40
1095 75 c. "Chysis bractescens" 60 55
1096 $1 "Vanilla planifolia" 70 70
1097 $2 "Epidendrum polyanthum" 1·25 1·40

196 Common Iguana

1991. Reptiles and Mammals. Multicoloured.
1098 25 c. Type **196** 45 35
1099 50 c. Morelet's crocodile 70 70
1100 60 c. American manatee 80 80
1101 75 c. Boa constrictor 90 90
1102 $1 Baird's tapir 1·25 1·25
1103 $2 Jaguar 2·00 2·00

1991. 65th Birthday of Queen Elizabeth II and 70th Birthday of Prince Philip. As T **139** of Ascension. Multicoloured.
1104 $1 Queen Elizabeth II wearing tiara 90 90
1105 $1 Prince Philip wearing panama 90 90

197 Weather Radar

1991. International Decade for Natural Disaster Reduction.
1106 **197** 60 c. multicoloured 55 55
1107 – 75 c. multicoloured 65 65
1108 – $1 blue and black 80 80
1109 – $2 multicoloured 1·40 1·40
DESIGNS: 75 c. Weather station; $1 Floods in Belize after Hurricane Hattie, 1961; $2 Satellite image of Hurricane Gilbert.

198 Thomas Ramos and Demonstration

1991. 10th Anniv of Independence. Famous Belizians (1st series). Multicoloured.
1110 25 c. Type **198** 25 20
1111 60 c. Sir Isaiah Morter and palm trees 55 55
1112 75 c. Antonio Soberanis and political meeting 70 70
1113 $1 Santiago Ricalde and cutting sugar-cane 95 95
See also Nos. 1126/9 and 1148/51.

199 "Anansi the Spider"

1991. Christmas. Folklore. Multicoloured.
1114 25 c. Type **199** 25 20
1115 50 c. "Jack-o-Lantern" 50 50
1116 60 c. "Tata Duende" (vert) 60 60
1117 75 c. "Xtabai" 70 70
1118 $1 "Warrie Massa" (vert) 90 90
1119 $2 "Old Heg" 1·60 1·60

200 "Gongora quinquenervis"

1992. Easter. Orchids. Multicoloured.
1120 25 c. Type **200** 30 20
1121 50 c. "Oncidium sphacelatum" 60 50
1122 60 c. "Encyclia bratescens" 70 70
1123 75 c. "Epidendrum ciliare" 80 80
1124 $1 "Psygmorchis pusilla" 1·00 1·00
1125 $2 "Galeandra batemanii" 1·90 1·90

1992. Famous Belizeans (2nd series). As T **198**, but inscr "EMINENT BELIZEANS". Multicoloured.
1126 25 c. Gwendolyn Lizarraga (politician) and High School 25 20
1127 60 c. Rafael Fonseca (civil servant) and Government Offices, Belize 50 50
1128 75 c. Vivian Seay (health worker) and nurses 65 65
1129 $1 Samuel Haynes (U.N.I.A. worker) and words of National Anthem 85 85

201 Xunantunich and National Assembly

1992. 500th Anniv of Discovery of America by Columbus. Mayan sites and modern buildings. Multicoloured.
1130 25 c. Type **201** 25 20
1131 60 c. Altun Ha and Supreme Court 50 50
1132 75 c. Santa Rita and Tower Hill Sugar Factory 65 65
1133 $5 Lamanai and Citrus Company works 3·50 3·50

202 Hashishi Pampi

1992. Christmas. Folklore. Multicoloured.
1134 25 c. Type **202** 25 20
1135 60 c. Cadejo 45 45
1136 $1 La Sucia (vert) 80 80
1137 $5 Sisimito 3·25 3·50

1993. 75th Anniv of Royal Air Force. As T **149** of Ascension. Multicoloured.
1138 25 c. Aerospatiale Puma 25 20
1139 50 c. British Aerospace Harrier 45 45
1140 60 c. DeHavilland Mosquito 55 55
1141 75 c. Avro Lancaster 70 70
1142 $1 Consolidated Liberator 85 85
1143 $3 Short Stirling 2·50 2·50

203 "Lycaste aromatica"

1993. 14th World Orchid Conference, Glasgow. Multicoloured.

1144	25 c. Type **203**	25	20
1145	60 c. "Sobralia decora" ..	60	60
1146	$1 "Maxillaria alba" ..	90	90
1147	$2 "Brassavola nodosa"	1·75	1·75

1993. Famous Belizeans (3rd series). As T **198**, but inscr "EMINENT BELIZEANS" at top. Multicoloured.

1148	25 c. Herbert Watkin Beaumont, Post Office and postmark ..	20	20
1149	60 c. Dr. Selvyn Walford Young and score of National Anthem ..	50	50
1150	75 c. Cleopatra White and health centre	65	65
1151	$1 Dr. Karl Heusner and early car	85	85

204 Boom and Chime Band

1993. Christmas. Local Customs. Mult.

1152	25 c. Type **204**	15	20
1153	60 c. John Canoe dance ..	40	45
1154	75 c. Cortez dance ..	50	55
1155	$2 Maya musical group ..	1·25	1·40

1994. "Hong Kong '94" International Stamp Exhibition. No. 1075 optd **HONG KONG '94** and emblem.

1156	$1 Spectacled owl and "Caligo uranus" ..	65	70

1994. Royal Visit. As T **202** of Bahamas. Multicoloured.

1157	25 c. Flags of Belize and Great Britain ..	15	20
1158	60 c. Queen Elizabeth II in yellow coat and hat	40	45
1159	75 c. Queen Elizabeth in evening dress	50	55
1160	$1 Queen Elizabeth, Prince Philip and Yeomen of the Guard	65	70

POSTAGE DUE STAMPS

D 2.

1976.

D 6.	D 2.	1 c. red and green ..	10	55
D 7.	–	2 c. purple and violet	10	55
D 8.	–	5 c. green and brown	15	65
D 9.	–	15 c. green and red ..	25	90
D 10.	–	25 c. orange & green	40	1·00

DESIGNS: Nos. D 7/10 as Type D **2** but with different frames.

BERMUDA

A group of islands in the W. Atlantic, E. of N. Carolina. Usually regarded by collectors as part of the Br. W. Indies group, though this is not strictly correct.

1865. 12 pence = 1 shilling.
20 shillings = 1 pound.
1970. 100 cents = 1 dollar (U.S).

9. Queen Victoria.

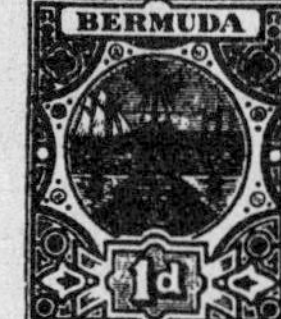

13. Dry Dock.

1865. Portrait. Various frames.

19	9	½d. stone	1·90	3·75
21a		½d. green	1·90	70
24a		1d. red	5·00	20
25		2d. blue	42·00	3·25
26a		2d. purple	2·75	1·25
27a		2½d. blue	4·25	40
10		3d. yellow	£150	60·00
28		3d. grey	20·00	5·50
20		4d. red	15·00	1·75
34		4d. brown	26·00	38·00
7		6d. mauve	22·00	12·00
11		1s. green	11·00	£100
29a		1s. brown	13·00	11·00

1874. Surch. in words

15.	**9.**	1d. on 2d. blue	£700	£350
16.		1d. on 3d. yellow	£450	£350
17.		1d. on 1s. green	£500	£250
12.		3d. on 1d. red	£8000	
14.		3d. on 1s. green	£1200	£650

1901. Surch. **ONE FARTHING** and bar.

30.	**9.**	¼d. on 1s. grey	40	40

1902.

34a	**13.**	¼d. brown and violet ..	50	2·00
31		½d. black and green ..	9·00	1·25
41		½d. green	7·50	2·50
32		1d. brown and red ..	8·00	10
42		1d. red	16·00	10
37		2d. grey and orange ..	7·50	10·00
38		2½d. brown and blue ..	8·50	12·00
43		2½d. blue	12·00	5·75
33		3d. mauve and green ..	1·75	1·75
39		4d. blue and brown ..	3·00	11·00

14. Badge of the Colony.

15.

1910.

76b	**14.**	¼d. brown	1·00	1·25
77		½d. green	70	15
79		1d. red	8·50	30
79b		1½d. brown	3·75	35
80		2d. grey	1·50	1·50
82a		2½d. blue	1·75	35
81a		2½d. green	1·00	1·50
84		3d. purple on yellow ..	1·00	1·00
83		3d. blue	15·00	26·00
85		4d. red on yellow ..	1·00	1·25
86		6d. purple	80	80
51		1s. black on green ..	2·25	3·75
51b	**15.**	2s. purple & blue on blue	14·00	38·00
52		2s. 6d. black & red on bl.	22·00	55·00
52b		4s. black and red ..	60·00	75·00
53c		5s. green & red on yell.	38·00	55·00
92c		10s. green & red on green	£120	£170
93		12s. 6d. black & orange	£300	£350
55		£1 purple & black on red	£350	£550

1918 Optd. **WAR TAX.**

56.	**14.**	1d. red	45	40

18.
Tercent. of Representative Institutions.

(a) **1920.** 1st Issue.

59.	**18.**	¼d. brown	1·00	9·00
60.		½d. green	1·25	7·00
65.		1d. red	1·00	30
61.		2d. grey	8·50	24·00
66.		2½d. blue	6·50	8·00
62.		3d. purple on yellow ..	8·00	22·00
63.		4d. black & red on yellow	8·50	20·00
67.		6d. purple	16·00	45·00
64.		1s. black on green ..	16·00	45·00

19.

(b) **1921.** 2nd Issue.

74.	**19.**	¼d. brown	35	2·75
75.		½d. green	2·75	6·00
76.		1d. red	2·00	35
68.		2d. grey	4·50	15·00
69.		2½d. blue	9·00	3·00
70.		3d. purple on yellow ..	4·00	13·00
71.		4d. red on yellow ..	14·00	18·00
72.		6d. purple	9·00	32·00
73.		1s. black on green ..	21·00	35·00

1935. Silver Jubilee. As T **13** of Antigua.

94.	1d. blue and red	45	55
95.	1½d. blue and grey ..	70	1·40
96.	2½d. brown and blue ..	1·40	90
97.	1s. grey and purple ..	9·50	17·00

20. Hamilton Harbour.

22. "Lucie" (yacht).

1936.

98.	**20.**	½d. green	10	10
99.	–	1d. black and red ..	15	15
100.	–	1½d. black and brown ..	75	15
101.	**22.**	2d. black and blue ..	4·50	2·00
102.	–	2½d. blue	80	25
103.	–	3d. black and red ..	2·25	90
104.	–	6d. red and violet ..	80	10
105.	–	1s. green	3·25	6·00
106.	**20.**	1s. 6d. brown	40	10

DESIGNS—HORIZ. 1d., 1½d. South Shore, nr. Spanish Rock. 3d. Point House, Warwick Parish. VERT. 2½d., 1s. Grape Bay, Paget Parish. 6d. House at Par-la-Ville, Hamilton.
The 1d., 1½d., 2½d. and 1s. values include a portrait of King George V.

1937. Coronation. As T **2** of Aden.

107.	1d. red	50	50
108.	1½d. brown	60	95
109.	2½d. blue	1·10	1·50

26. Ships in Hamilton Harbour.

DESIGNS—VERT. 3d. St. David's Lighthouse. The 2½d. and 1s. are as 1935, but with King George VI portrait.

28. White-tailed Tropic Bird, Arms of Bermuda and Native Flower.

1938.

110	**26**	1d. black and red ..	50	20
111b		1½d. blue and brown ..	1·50	35
112	**22**	2d. blue and black ..	40·00	5·00
112a	–	2d. blue and red ..	1·50	80
113	–	2½d. blue	11·00	1·25
113c	–	2½d. blue and sepia ..	2·25	1·50
114	–	3d. black and red ..	11·00	90
114a	–	3d. black and blue ..	1·50	40
114c	**28**	7½d. blk., blue & green	4·50	2·25
115	–	1s. green	2·00	50

As T **15**, but King George VI portrait.

116b	2s. purple & blue on blue	7·00	1·50
117d	2s. 6d. blk. & red on blue	16·00	10·00
118f	5s. green and red on yell.	15·00	11·00
119f	10s. green & red on grn.	23·00	35·00
120b	12s. 6d. grey and orange	85·00	50·00
121c	£1 purple & black on red	48·00	65·00

1940. Surch. **HALFPENNY XX.**

122.	**26.**	½d. on 1d. black and red	40	45

1946. Victory. As T **9** of Aden.

123.	1½d. brown	15	15
124.	3d. blue	15	15

1948. Silver Wedding. As T **10** and **11** of Aden.

125.	1½d. brown ..	30	50
126.	£1 red	48·00	48·00

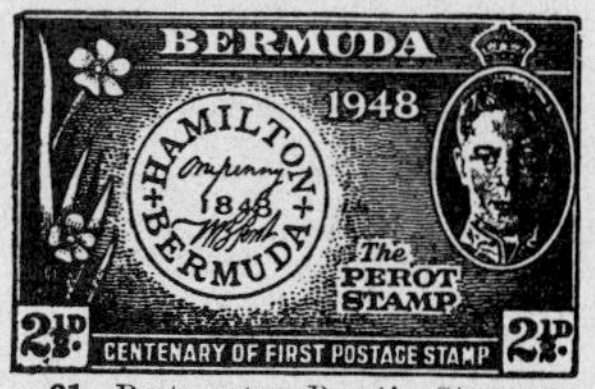

31. Postmaster Perot's Stamp.

1949. Cent. of Postmaster Perot's Stamp.

127.	**31.**	2½d. blue and brown ..	15	15
128.		3d. black and blue ..	15	15
129.		6d. violet and green ..	15	15

1949. U.P.U. As T **20/23** of Antigua.

130.	2½d. black	75	75
131.	3d. blue	90	75
132.	6d. purple	1·00	75
133.	1s. green	1·00	75

1953. Coronation. As T **13** of Aden.

134.	1½d. black and blue ..	35	15

34. Easter Lily.

43. Hog Coin.

1953.

135a	–	½d. olive	20	60
136a	–	1d. black and red ..	50	30
137	**34.**	1½d. green	30	10
138	–	2d. blue and red ..	40	40
139	–	2½d. red	1·50	50
140	–	3d. purple	30	10
141	–	4d. black and blue ..	30	40
142	–	4½d. green	45	1·00
143	–	6d. black and turquoise	5·00	60
156	–	6d. black and mauve ..	50	15
143a	–	8d. black and red ..	2·25	30
143b	–	9d. violet	6·50	2·50
144	–	1s. orange	50	15
145	–	1s. 3d. blue	3·25	30
146	–	2s. brown	3·00	85
147	–	2s. 6d. red	3·50	45
148	**43.**	5s. red	15·00	85
149	–	10s. blue	12·00	5·00
150	–	£1 multicoloured ..	20·00	21·00

DESIGNS—HORIZ. ½d. Easter lilies, 1d., 4d. Postmaster Perot's stamp. 2d. "Victory II" (racing dinghy). 2½d. Sir George Somers and "Sea Venture". 3d., 1s. 3d. Map of Bermuda, 4½d., 9d. "Sea Venture" inter-island boat, coin and Perot stamp. 6d. (No. 143), 8d. White-tailed Tropic Bird. 6d. (No. 156), Perot's Post Office. 1s. Early Bermuda coins. 2s. Arms of St. George's 10s. Obverse and reverse of hog coin. £1 Arms of Bermuda. VERT. 2s. 6d. Warwick Fort. No. 156 commemorates the restoration and reopening of Perot's Post Office.

1953. Royal Visit. As No. 143a but inscr "ROYAL VISIT 1953".

151.	6d. black and turquoise	30	20

1953. Three Power Talks. Nos. 140 and 145 optd **Three Power Talks December, 1953.**

152.	3d. purple	10	10
153.	1s. 3d. blue	10	10

1956. 50th Anniv of United States–Bermuda Yacht Race. Nos. 143a and 145 optd **50th ANNIVERSARY US–BERMUDA OCEAN RACE 1956.**

154.	8d. black and red	20	40
155.	1s. 3d. blue	20	55

49. Arms of King James I and Queen Elizabeth II.

1959. 350th Anniv. of Settlement. Arms in red, yellow and blue. Frame colours given.

157. **49.** 1½d. blue 25 10
158. 3d. grey 30 40
159. 4d. purple 35 50
160. 8d. violet 35 15
161. 9d. olive .. .. 35 1·00
162. 1s 3d. brown 35 30

50. The Old Rectory, St. George's, c. 1730.

1962.

163. **50.** 1d. purple, blk. & orge. 10 35
164. – 2d. multicoloured .. 10 15
165. – 3d. brown and blue .. 10 10
166. – 4d. brown and mauve 20 40
167. – 5d. blue and red .. 1·50 2·25
168. – 6d. blue, grn. & bl. .. 20 30
169. – 8d. blue, green & orge. 30 35
170. – 9d. blue and brown .. 25 30
197. – 10d. violet and ochre .. 75 60
171. – 1s. multicoloured .. 20 10
172. – 1s. 3d. lake, grey & bistre 75 15
173. – 1s 6d. violet and ochre 2·25 2·50
199. – 1s 6d. blue and red .. 3·25 1·75
174. – 2s. brown and orange 2·50 1·25
175. – 2s 3d. sepia and green 2·00 6·00
176. – 2s 6d. sep., grn. & yell. 55 35
177. – 5s. purple and green .. 1·25 1·50
178. 10s. mve, grn. & buff .. 4·00 5·00
179. – £1 blk., olive & orge... 14·00 14·00

DESIGNS: 2d. Church of St. Peter, St. George's. 3d. Government House, 1892. 4d. The Cathedral, Hamilton, 1894. 5d., 1s. 6d. (No. 199) H.M. Dockyard, 1811. 6d. Perot's Post Office, 1848. 8d. G.P.O., Hamilton, 1869. 9d. Library, Par-la-Ville. 10d., 1s. 6d. (No. 173) Bermuda cottage, c. 1705. 1s. Christ Church, Warwick, 1719. 1s. 3d. City Hall, Hamilton, 1960. 2s. Town of St. George. 2s. 3d. Bermuda house, c. 1710. 2s. 6d. Bermuda house, early 18th century. 5s. Colonial Secretariat, 1833. 10s. Old Post Office, Somerset, 1890. £1. The House of Assembly, 1815.

1963. Freedom from Hunger. As T **28** of Aden.

180. 1s. 3d. sepia 80 35

1963. Cent of Red Cross. As T **33** of Antigua.

181. 3d. red and black .. 75 25
182. 1s. 3d. red and blue .. 2·00 2·25

67. "Tsotsi in the Bundu". (Finn class yacht.).

1964. Olympic Games, Tokyo.

183. **67.** 3d. red, violet and blue 10 10

1965. Cent of I.T.U. As T **36** of Antigua.

184. 3d. blue and green .. 75 25
185. 2s. yellow and blue .. 1·50 1·25

68. Scout Badge and St. Edward's Crown.

1965. 50th Anniv. of Bermuda Boy Scouts Association.

186. **68.** 2s. multicoloured .. 50 50

1965. I.C.Y. As T **37** of Antigua.

187. 4d. purple and turquoise .. 50 20
188. 2s. 6d. green and lavender 1·50 80

1966. Churchill Commem. As T **38** of Antigua.

189. 3d. blue 50 20
190. 6d. green .. .. .. 1·00 45
191. 10d. brown .. .. .. 1·25 75
192. 1s. 3d. violet .. .. 1·50 2·00

1966. World Cup Football Championship. As T **40** of Antigua.

193. 10d. multicoloured .. 50 15
194. 2s. 6d. multicoloured .. 75 65

1966. 20th Anniv. of U.N.E.S.C.O. As T **54/56** of Antigua.

201. 4d. multicoloured .. 60 15
202. 1s. 3d. yellow, violet & olive 1·25 65
203. 2s. black, purple & orange 2·00 1·25

69. G.P.O. Building.

1967. Opening of New General Post Office.

204. **69.** 3d. multicoloured .. 10 10
205. 1s. multicoloured .. 10 10
206. 1s. 6d. multicoloured .. 15 20
207. 2s. 6d. multicoloured .. 15 30

70. "Mercury" (cable ship) and Chain Links.

1967. Inauguration of Bermuda–Tortola Telephone Service. Multicoloured.

208. 3d. Type **70** 10 10
209. 1s. Map, telephone and microphone 10 10
210. 1s. 6d. Telecommunications media 20 25
211. 2s. 6d. "Mercury" (cable ship) and Marine Fauna 25 40

74. Human Rights Emblem and Doves.

1968. Human Rights Year.

212. **74.** 3d. indigo, blue & green 10 10
213. 1s. brown, blue & lt. bl. 10 10
214. 1s. 6d. black, blue & red 10 10
215. 2s. 6d. grn., bl. & yellow 15 15

75. Mace and Queen's Profile.

1968. New Constitution.

216. **75.** 3d. multicoloured .. 10 10
217. 1s. multicoloured .. 10 10
218. – 1s. 6d. yell., blk. & bl. 10 20
219. – 2s. 6d. lilac, black and yellow 15 30

DESIGN: 1s. 6d., 2s. 6d., Houses of Parliament, and House of Assembly, Bermuda.

MINIMUM PRICE

The minimum price quoted is 10p which represents a handling charge rather than a basis for valuing common stamps. For further notes about prices see introductory pages.

77. Football, Athletics and Yachting.

1968. Olympic Games, Mexico.

220. **77.** 3d. multicoloured .. 10 10
221. 1s. multicoloured .. 15 10
222. 1s. 6d. multicoloured .. 20 20
223. 2s. 6d. multicoloured .. 20 30

78. Brownie and Guide.

1969. 50th Anniv. of Girl Guides. Mult.

224. 3d. Type **78** 10 10
225. 1s. Type **78** 20 10
226. 1s. 6d. Guides and Badge 25 30
227. 2s. 6d. As 1s. 6d... .. 35 65

80 Emerald-studded Gold Cross and Seaweed.

1969. Underwater Treasure. Multicoloured.

228. 4d. Type **80** 20 10
229. 1s. 3d. Emerald-studded gold cross and sea-bed .. 35 15
230. 2s. As Type **80** 45 70
231. 2s. 6d. As 1s. 3d. .. .. 45 1·10

1970. Decimal Currency. Nos. 163/79 surch.

232. 1 c. on 1d. pur., blk. & orge. 10 70
233. 2 c. on 2d. multicoloured .. 10 10
234. 3 c. on 3d. brown and blue 10 10
235. 4 c. on 4d. brown & mauve 10 10
236. 5 c. on 8d. blue, grn. & orge. 15 60
237. 6 c. on 6d. grey, grn. & blue 15 50
238. 9 c. on 9d. blue and brown 30 75
239. 10 c. on 10d. violet & ochre 30 25
240. 12 c. on 1s. multicoloured 30 15
241. 15 c. on 1s. 3d. lake, grey and bistre .. .. 1·50 1·00
242. 18 c. on 1s. 6d. blue & red 80 65
243. 24 c. on 2s. brown & orange 85 75
244. 30 c. and 2s. 6d. sepia, green and yellow .. .. 1·00 1·25
245. 36 c. on 2s. 3d. sepia & grn. 1·75 3·00
246. 60 c. on 5s. purple & green 2·25 2·75
247. $1.20 on 10s. mauve, green and buff .. .. .. 4·00 12·00
248. $2.40 on £1 black, olive and orange .. .. 7·00 17·00

83. Spathiphyllum.

1970. Flowers. Multicoloured.

249. 1 c. Type **83** 10 20
250. 2 c. Bottlebrush 20 25
251. 3 c. Oleander (vert.) .. 15 10
252. 4 c. Bermudiana 15 10
253. 5 c. Poinsettia 30 20
254. 6 c. Hibiscus 30 30
255. 9 c. Cereus 20 45
256. 10 c. Bougainvillea (vert.) 20 15
257. 12 c. Jacaranda 80 60
258. 15 c. Passion Flower .. 90 1·40
258a. 17 c. As 15 c. .. .. 2·75 2·75
259. 18 c. Coralita .. .. 2·25 2·25
259a. 20 c. As 18 c. .. .. 2·75 2·75
260. 24 c. Morning Glory .. 1·50 3·50
260a. 25 c. As 24 c. .. .. 2·75 3·00
261. 30 c. Tecoma .. .. 1·00 1·25
262. 36 c. Angel's Trumpet .. 1·25 2·25
262a. 40 c. as 36 c. .. .. 2·75 3·50
263. 60 c. Plumbago .. .. 1·75 1·75
263a. $1 As 60 c. .. .. 3·25 4·50

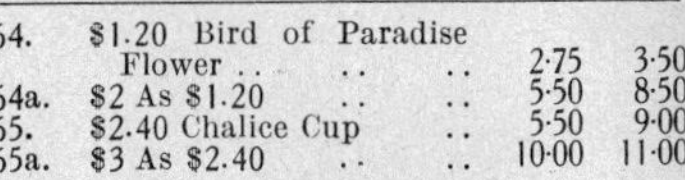

264. $1.20 Bird of Paradise Flower .. .. .. 2·75 3·50
264a. $2 As $1.20 .. .. 5·50 8·50
265. $2.40 Chalice Cup .. 5·50 9·00
265a. $3 As $2.40 .. .. 10·00 11·00

1970. 350th Anniv. of Bermuda Parliament. Multicoloured.

266. 4 c. Type **84** 10 10
267. 15 c. The Sessions House, Hamilton 25 15
268. 18 c. St. Peter's Church, St. George's 25 20
269. 24 c. Town Hall, Hamilton 35 45

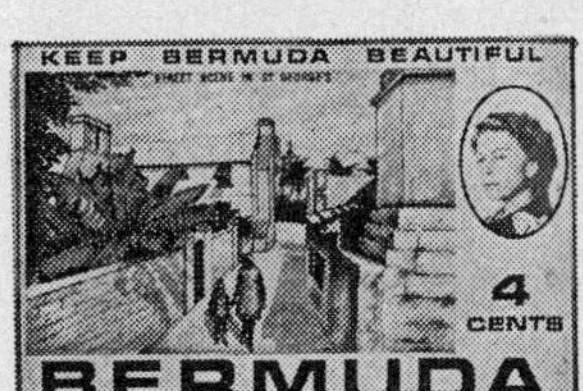

85. Street Scene, St. George's.

1971. "Keep Bermuda Beautiful". Mult.

271. 4 c. Type **85** 20 10
272. 15 c. Horseshoe Bay .. 55 45
273. 18 c. Gibbs Hill Lighthouse 1·00 1·10
274. 24 c. Hamilton Harbour .. 1·25 1·75

86. Building of the "Deliverance".

1971. Voyage of the "Deliverance". Mult.

275. 4 c. Type **86** 50 20
276. 15 c. "Deliverance" and "Patience" at Jamestown (vert.) .. .. 1·50 1·75
277. 18 c. Wreck of the "Sea Venture" (vert.) .. 1·75 2·25
278. 24 c. "Deliverance" and "Patience" on high seas 1·90 2·50

87. Green overlooking Ocean View.

1971. Golfing in Bermuda. Multicoloured.

279. 4 c. Type **87** 35 10
280. 15 c. Golfers at Port Royal 65 60
281. 18 c. Castle Harbour .. 75 60
282. 24 c. Belmont .. .. 1·00 85

1971. Anglo-American Talks. Nos. 252, 258, 259 and 260 optd. **HEATH-NIXON DECEMBER 1971.**

283. 4 c. Bermudiana 10 10
284. 15 c. Passion Flower .. 10 20
285. 18 c. Coralita 15 55
286. 24 c. Morning Glory .. 20 70

89. Bonefish.

1972. World Fishing Records. Multicoloured.

287. 4 c. Type **89** 30 10
288. 15 c. Wahoo 35 30
289. 18 c. Yellowfin Tuna .. 40 45
290. 24 c. Greater Amberjack 45 70

1972. Royal Silver Wedding. As T **52** of Ascension, but with "Admiralty Oar" and Mace in background.

291. 4 c. violet 15 10
292. 15 c. red 15 40

91. Palmetto.

1973. Tree Planting Year. Multicoloured.

293. 4 c. Type **91** 30 10

294. 15 c. Olivewood Bark .. 90 75

295. 18 c. Bermuda Cedar .. 1·00 1·00

296. 24 c. Mahogany .. .. 1·10 1·40

1973. Royal Wedding. As T **47** of Anguilla. Background colour given. Mult.

297. 15 c. mauve 15 15

298. 18 c. blue 15 15

92. Bernard Park, Pembroke, 1973.

1973. Centenary of Lawn Tennis. Mult.

299. 4 c. Type **92** 30 10

300. 15 c. Clermont Court, 1873 60 50

301. 18 c. Leamington Spa Court, 1872 .. .. 70 1·00

302. 24 c. Staten Island Courts, 1874 .. .. .. 85 1·25

93. Weather Vane, City Hall.

1974. 50th Anniv. of Rotary in Bermuda. Multicoloured.

320. 5 c. Type **93** 15 10

321. 17 c. St. Peter's Church, St. George's 45 35

322. 20 c. Somerset Bridge .. 50 1·00

323. 25 c. Map of Bermuda, 1626 60 1·60

94. Jack of Clubs and "good bridge hand".

1975. World Bridge Championships, Bermuda. Multicoloured.

324. 5 c. Type **94** 25 10

325. 17 c. Queen of Diamonds and Bermuda Bowl .. 65 50

326. 20 c. King of Hearts and Bermuda Bowl .. .. 70 1·75

327. 25 c. Ace of Spades and Bermuda Bowl .. .. 80 2·00

95. Queen Elizabeth II and the Duke of Edinburgh.

1975. Royal Visit.

328. **95.** 17 c. multicoloured .. 60 65

329. 20 c. multicoloured .. 65 1·75

96. Short S23 "C" Class Flying-boat "Cavalier", 1937.

1975. 50th Anniv. of Air-mail Service. Mult.

330. 5 c. Type **96** 40 10

331. 17 c. Airship "Los Angeles", 1925 .. .. .. 1·25 75

332. 20 c. Lockheed "Constellation", 1946 .. .. 1·40 2·50

333. 25 c. Boeing "747", 1970 1·50 3·25

97. Supporters of American Army raiding Royal Magazine.

1975. Bicentenary of Gunpowder Plot, St. George's. Multicoloured.

335. 5 c. Type **97** 20 10

336. 17 c. Setting off for raid .. 40 30

337. 20 c. Loading gunpowder aboard American ship .. 45 70

338. 25 c. Gunpowder on beach 50 80

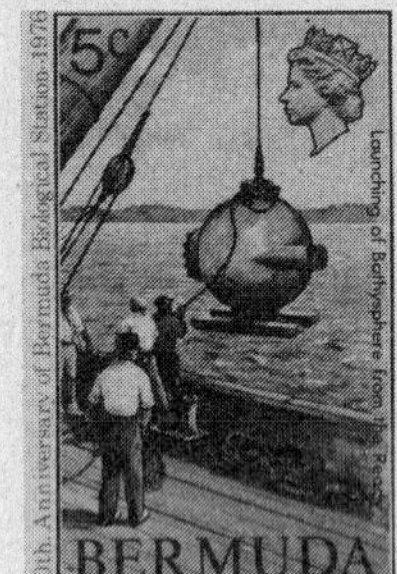

98. Launching "Ready" (bathysphere).

1976. 50th Anniv. of Bermuda Biological Station. Multicoloured.

357. 5 c. Type **98** 35 10

358. 17 c. View from the sea (horiz.) 70 60

359. 20 c. H.M.S. "Challenger", 1873 (horiz.) .. .. 75 2·25

360. 25 c. Beebe's Bathysphere descent, 1934 .. .. 1·00 2·50

99. "Christian Radich" (cadet ship).

1976. Tall Ships Race. Multicoloured.

361 5 c. Type **99** 60 20

362 12 c. "Juan Sebastian de Elcano" (Spanish cadet schooner) .. .. 1·00 1·75

363 17 c. "Eagle" (U.S. coastguard cadet ship) 1·25 1·75

364 20 c. "Sir Winston Churchill" (cadet schooner) .. .. 1·40 2·50

365 40 c. "Kruzenshtern" (Russian cadet barque) 2·00 3·00

366 $1 "Cutty Sark" trophy .. 3·00 7·00

100. Silver Trophy and Club Flags.

1976. 75th Anniv. of St. George's v. Somerset Cricket Cup Match. Multicoloured.

367. 5 c. Type **100** 35 10

368. 17 c. Badge and Pavilion, St. George's Club .. 75 55

369. 20 c. Badge and Pavilion, Somerset Club .. 1·00 2·50

370. 25 c. Somerset playing field 1·50 3·50

101. Royal Visit, 1975.

1977. Silver Jubilee. Multicoloured.

371. 5 c. Type **101** 15 10

372. 20 c. St. Edward's Crown 25 20

373. $1 The Queen in Chair of Estate .. .. .. 80 1·25

102. Stockdale House, St. George's, 1784–1812.

1977. Centenary of U.P.U. Membership. Multicoloured.

374. 5 c. Type **102** 15 10

375. 15 c. Perot Post Office and stamp 35 50

376. 17 c. St. George's P.O. c. 1860 .. .. .. 35 50

377. 20 c. Old G.P.O., Hamilton, c. 1935 .. .. .. 45 60

378. 40 c. New G.P.O., Hamilton, 1967 .. .. 75 1·10

103. 17th-Century Ship approaching Castle Is.

1977. Piloting. Multicoloured.

379. 5 c. Type **103** 30 10

380. 15 c. Pilot leaving ship, 1795 .. .. .. 60 50

381. 17 c. Pilots rowing out to paddle-steamer 70 50

382. 20 c. Pilot gigs and brig "Harvest Queen" .. 75 1·75

383. 40 c. Modern pilot cutter and R.M.S. "Queen Elizabeth 2" .. .. 1·25 2·75

104. Great Seal of Queen Elizabeth I.

1978. 25th Anniv. of Coronation. Mult.

384. 8 c. Type **104** 10 10

385. 50 c. Great Seal of Queen Elizabeth II 30 30

386. $1 Queen Elizabeth II .. 60 75

105. White-tailed Tropic Bird.

1978. Wildlife. Multicoloured.

387 3 c. Type **105** .. .. 1·50 80

388 4 c. White-eyed vireo .. 1·25 80

389 5 c. Eastern bluebird .. 1·25 70

390 7 c. Whistling frog .. 50 70

391 8 c. Common cardinal (Redbird) .. .. 1·25 45

392 10 c. Spiny lobster .. 20 10

393 12 c. Land crab 30 60

394 15 c. Lizard (Skink) .. 30 15

395 20 c. Foureye butterfly fish 30 30

396 25 c. Red hind 30 20

397 30 c. "Danaus plexippus" (butterfly) .. .. 2·25 2·25

398 40 c. Rock beauty .. 45 1·50

399 50 c. Banded butterfly fish 55 75

400 $1 Blue angelfish .. 95 1·75

401 $2 Humpback whale .. 2·00 2·75

402 $3 Green turtle .. .. 2·75 3·00

403 $5 Cahow .. .. .. 6·50 6·00

106. Map by Sir George Somers, 1609.

1979. Antique Maps. Multicoloured.

404. 8 c. Type **106** 15 10

405. 15 c. Map by John Seller, 1685 .. .. .. 20 15

406. 20 c. Map by H. Moll, 1729–40 (vert.) .. 25 25

407. 25 c. Map by Desbruslins, 1740 .. .. .. 30 30

408. 50 c. Map by Speed, 1626 45 70

107. Policeman and Policewoman.

1979. Centenary of Police. Multicoloured.

409 8 c. Type **107** 20 10

410 20 c. Policeman directing traffic (horiz) 45 50

411 25 c. "Blue Heron" (police launch) (horiz) .. 50 60

412 50 c. Police car and motor cycle .. .. .. 90 1·25

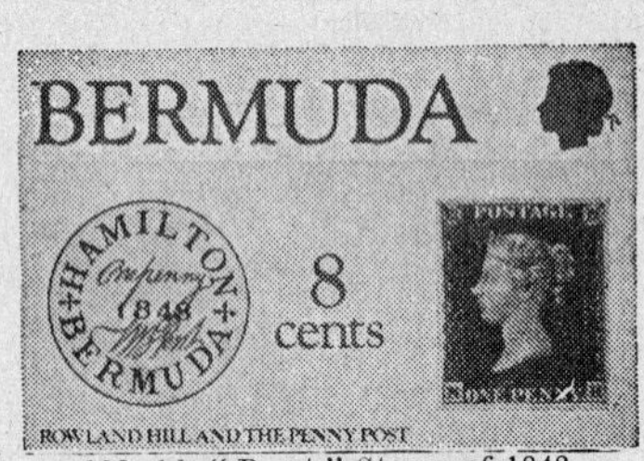

108. 1d. "Perot" Stamp of 1848 and 1840 Penny Black.

1980. Death Cent. of Sir Rowland Hill. Mult.

413. 8 c. Type **108** 10 10

414. 20 c. "Perot" and Sir Rowland Hill 15 25

415. 25 c. "Perot" and early letter 15 30

416. 50 c. "Perot" and "Paid 1" cancellation .. 25 70

109. British Airways "Tristar 500" approaching Bermuda.

1980. "London 1980" International Stamp Exhibition. Multicoloured.

417	25 c. Type **109**	30	15
418	50 c. "Orduna I" (liner) at Grassy Bay, 1926 ..	45	35
419	$1 "Delta" (screw steamer) at St. George's Harbour, 1856	85	1·00
420	$2 "Lord Sidmouth" (sailing packet) in Old Ship Channel, St. George's	1·40	1·75

110. Gina Swainson (" Miss World 1979–80 ").

1980. " Miss World 1979–80 " Commemoration. Multicoloured.

421.	8 c. Type **110**	15	10
422.	20 c. Miss Swainson after crowning ceremony ..	20	20
423.	50 c. Miss Swainson on Peacock Throne ..	35	35
424.	$1 Miss Swainson in Bermuda carriage	70	90

111. Queen Elizabeth the Queen Mother.

1980. 80th Birthday of The Queen Mother.

425. **111.**	25 c. multicoloured ..	30	50

112. Bermuda from Satellite.

1980. Commonwealth Finance Ministers Meeting. Multicoloured.

426.	8 c. Type **112**	10	10
427.	20 c. " Camden "	20	40
428.	25 c. Princess Hotel, Hamilton	20	50
429.	50 c. Government House ..	35	1·25

113. Kitchen, 18th-century.

1981. Heritage Week. Multicoloured.

430.	8 c. Type **113**	15	10
431.	25 c. Gathering Easter lilies, 20th-century ..	40	50
432.	30 c. Fishing, 20th-century	50	70
433.	40 c. Stone cutting, 19th-century	55	1·00
434.	50 c. Onion shipping, 19th-century	75	1·25
435.	$1 Privateering, 17th-century	1·60	2·75

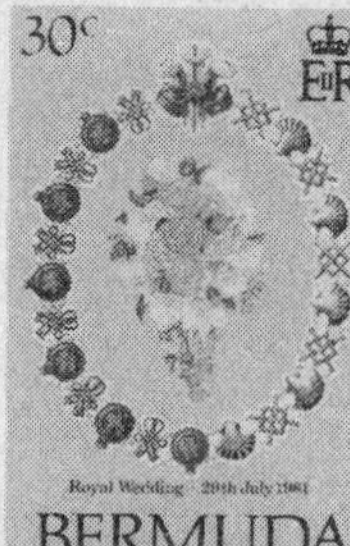

114. Wedding Bouquet from Bermuda.

115. " Service ", Hamilton.

1981. Royal Wedding. Multicoloured.

436.	30 c. Type **114**	30	30
437.	50 c. Prince Charles as Royal Navy Commander ..	50	55
438.	$1 Prince Charles and Lady Diana Spencer	90	1·25

1981. 25th Anniv. of Duke of Edinburgh Award Scheme. Multicoloured.

439.	10 c. Type **115**	15	10
440.	25 c. " Outward Bound ", Paget Island	25	20
441.	30 c. " Expedition ", St. David's Island	25	30
442.	$1 Duke of Edinburgh ..	80	1·25

116 " Conus species ".

1982. Sea-Shells. Multicoloured.

443.	10 c. Type **116**	30	10
444.	25 c. " Bursa finlayi " ..	70	75
445.	30 c. " Sconsia striata " ..	75	85
446.	$1 " Murex pterynotus lightbourni "	2·00	3·00

117. Regimental Colours and Colour Party.

1982. Bermuda Regiment. Multicoloured.

447.	10 c. Type **117**	45	10
448.	25 c. Queen's Birthday Parade	90	80
449.	30 c. Governor inspecting Guard of Honour	1·00	1·25
450.	40 c. Beating the Retreat	1·25	1·50
451.	50 c. Ceremonial gunners	1·40	1·75
452.	$1 Guard of Honour, Royal visit, 1975	2·25	3·25

118. Charles Fort.

1982. Historic Bermuda Forts. Multicoloured.

453.	10 c. Type **118**	20	20
454.	25 c. Pembroke Fort ..	50	85
455.	30 c. Southampton Fort (horiz.)	60	1·25
456.	$1 Smiths Fort and Pagets Fort (horiz.)	1·75	3·75

119. Arms of Sir Edwin Sandys.

1983. Coats of Arms (1st series). Multicoloured.

457.	10 c. Type **119**	45	15
458.	25 c. Arms of the Bermuda Company	1·40	1·00
459.	50 c. Arms of William Herbert, Earl of Pembroke	2·25	2·75
460.	$1 Arms of Sir George Somers	3·00	4·25

See also Nos. 482/5 and 499/502.

120. Early Fitted Dinghy.

1983. Fitted Dinghies. Multicoloured.

461.	12 c. Type **120**	20	15
462.	30 c. Modern Dinghy inshore	45	75
463.	40 c. Early Dinghy (different)	60	90
464.	$1 Modern dinghy with red and white spinnaker ..	1·50	3·25

121. Curtiss " Jenny " Seaplane.

1983. Bicentenary of Manned Flight. Mult.

465.	12 c. Type **121** (First Flight over Bermuda)	40	15
466.	30 c. Pilot Radio, " Stinson " seaplane (First completed flight between U.S. and Bermuda)		
467.	40 c. Short "Empire" flying boat "Cavalier" (First scheduled passenger flight)	75	1·00
468.	$1 U.S.S. " Los Angeles " (airship) moored to U.S.S. " Patoka "	1·00	1·50
		2·00	3·50

122. Joseph Stockdale.

1984. Bicentenary of Bermuda's First Newspaper and Postal Service. Mult.

469.	12 c. Type **122**	20	15
470.	30 c. " The Bermuda Gazette "	50	80
471.	40 c. Stockdale's postal service (horiz.)	70	1·10
472.	$1 " Lady Hammond " (mail boat) (horiz.) ..	2·00	3·25

123. Sir Thomas Gates and Sir George Somers.

1984. 375th Anniv. of First Settlement in Bermuda. Multicoloured

473.	12 c. Type **123**	20	15
474.	30 c. Jamestown, Virginia ..	50	85
475.	40 c. Wreck of "Sea Venture"	90	1·10
476.	$1 Fleet leaving Plymouth, Devon	2·00	3·50

124. Swimming.

1984. Olympic Games, Los Angeles. Multicoloured.

478.	12 c. Type **124**	25	15
479.	30 c. Track and field events (horiz.)	60	75
480.	40 c. Equestrian	80	1·00
481.	$1 Sailing (horiz.)	2·25	3·25

1984. Coats of Arms (2nd series). As T **119.** Multicoloured.

482.	12 c. Arms of Henry Wriothesley, Earl of Southampton	50	15
483.	30 c. Arms of Sir Thomas Smith	1·00	85
484.	40 c. Arms of William Cavendish Earl of Devonshire	1·25	1·25
485.	$1 Town arms of St. George	2·75	3·00

125. Buttery.

1985. Bermuda Architecture. Multicoloured.

486.	12 c. Type **125**	35	15
487.	30 c. Limestone rooftops (horiz.)	80	70
488.	40 c. Chimneys (horiz.) ..	95	85
489.	$1.50 Entrance archway ..	3·00	3·25

126. Osprey.

1985. Birth Bicentenary of John J. Audubon (ornithologist). Designs showing original drawings. Multicoloured.

490.	12 c. Type **126**	90	25
491.	30 c. Yellow-crowned night heron	1·40	65
492.	40 c. Great egret (horiz.) ..	1·60	85
493.	$1.50 Eastern bluebird ..	3·25	3·25

127. The Queen Mother with Grandchildren, 1980.

1985. Life and Times of Queen Elizabeth the Queen Mother. Multicoloured.

494.	12 c. Queen Consort, 1937	25	15
495.	30 c. Type **127**	50	50
496.	40 c. At Clarence House on 83rd birthday	60	60
497.	$1.50 With Prince Henry at his christening (from photo by Lord Snowdon)	2·25	2·75

1985. Coats of Arms (3rd series). Designs as T **119**. Multicoloured.

499.	12 c. Hamilton	65	15
500.	30 c. Paget	1·25	80
501.	40 c. Warwick	1·50	1·25
502.	$1.50 City of Hamilton ..	3·50	3·75

128. Halley's Comet and Bermuda Archipelago.

1985. Appearance of Halley's Comet. Multicoloured

503.	15 c. Type **128**	85	25
504.	40 c. Halley's Comet, A.D. 684 (from Nuremberg Chronicles, 1493) ..	1·60	1·60
505.	50 c. "Halley's Comet, 1531" (from Peter Apian woodcut, 1532)	1·90	2·00
506.	$1.50, "Halley's Comet, 1759" (Samuel Scott) ..	3·50	4·25

129. "Constellation" (schooner), 1943.

1986. Ships Wrecked on Bermuda. Mult.

507	3 c. Type **129**	10	10
508	5 c. "Early Riser" (pilot boat), 1876	10	10
509	7 c. "Madiana" (screw steamer), 1903 ..	50	50
664	10 c. "Curlew" (sail/steamer), 1856 ..	15	20
511	12 c. "Warwick" (galleon), 1619	60	60
665	15 c. H.M.S. "Vixen" (gunboat), 1890 ..	20	25
512c	18 c. As 7 c.	20	25
667	20 c. "San Pedro" (Spanish galleon), 1594	25	30
668	25 c. "Alert" (fishing sloop), 1877	30	35
515	40 c. "North Carolina" (barque), 1880 ..	50	55
516	50 c. "Mark Antonie" (Spanish privateer), 1777	1·25	1·25
672	60 c. "Mary Celestia" (Confederate paddle-steamer), 1864 ..	80	85
517c	70 c. "Caesar" (brig), 1818	90	95
518	$1 "L'Herminie" (French frigate), 1839	1·25	1·40
519	$1.50 As 70 c.	3·00	3·00
520	$2 "Lord Amherst" (transport), 1778 ..	2·25	2·40
521	$3 "Minerva" (sailing ship), 1849	4·00	4·25
522	$5 "Caraquet" (cargo liner), 1923	6·50	6·75
523	$8 H.M.S. "Pallas" (frigate), 1783	10·50	11·00

1986. 60th Birthday of Queen Elizabeth II. As T **110** of Ascension. Multicoloured.

524.	15 c. Princess Elizabeth aged three, 1929 ..	30	30
525.	40 c. With Earl of Rosebery at Oaks May Meeting, Epsom, 1954 ..	60	60
526.	50 c. With Duke of Edinburgh, Bermuda, 1975	75	75
527.	60 c. At British Embassy, Paris, 1972	90	90
528.	$1.50 At Crown Agents Head Office, London, 1983	2·25	2·50

1986. "Ameripex '86" International Stamp Exhibition, Chicago. As T **164** of Bahamas, showing Bermuda stamps. Multicoloured.

529.	15 c. 1984 375th Anniv. of Settlement miniature sheet	65	30
530.	40 c. 1973 Lawn Tennis Centenary 24 c.	1·00	70
531.	50 c. 1983 Bicentenary of Manned Flight 12 c. ..	1·25	1·00
532.	$1 1976 Tall Ships Race 17 c.	2·25	2·50

1986. 25th Anniv. of World Wildlife Fund. No. 402 surch.

534.	90 c. on $3 Green turtle ..	2·00	2·50

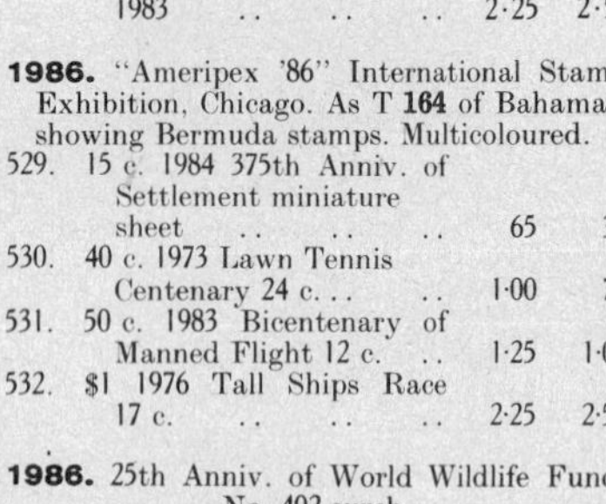

131. Train in Front Street, Hamilton, 1940.

1987. Transport (1st series). Bermuda Railway. Multicoloured.

535.	15 c. Type **131**	60	25
536.	40 c. Train crossing Springfield Trestle ..	1·10	90
537.	50 c. "St. George Special" at Bailey's Bay Station	1·40	1·50
538.	$1.50 Boat train at St. George	2·50	3·50

See also Nos. 557/60, 574/7 and 624/9.

132. "Bermuda Settlers", 1901.

1987. Paintings by Winslow Homer. Multicoloured.

539.	15 c. Type **132**	25	25
540.	30 c. "Bermuda", 1900 ..	45	45
541.	40 c. "Bermuda Landscape", 1901 (buff frame)	55	55
544.	40 c. Type **132**	90	1·10
545.	40 c. As No. 540	90	1·10
546.	40 c. As No. 541 (grey frame)	90	1·10
547.	40 c. As No. 542	90	1·10
548.	40 c. As No. 543	90	1·10
542.	50 c. "Inland Water", 1901	70	70
543.	$1.50 "Salt Kettle", 1899 ..	2·25	2·50

133. Pan Am Sikorsky "S-42B" "Bermuda Clipper" Flying Boat at Mooring.

1987. 50th Anniv. of Inauguration of Bermuda—U.S.A. Air Service. Multicoloured.

549.	15 c. Type **133**	75	15
550.	40 c. Imperial Airways Short "S-23" "Cavalier" flying boat at mooring ..	1·40	70
551.	50 c. "Bermuda Clipper" in flight over signpost ..	1·60	80
552.	$1.50 "Cavalier" on apron and "Bermuda Clipper" in flight	3·75	3·00

134. 19th-century Wagon carrying Telephone Poles.

1987. Centenary of Bermuda Telephone Company. Multicoloured.

553.	15 c. Type **134**	45	15
554.	40 c. Early telephone exchange	1·00	60
555.	50 c. Early and modern telephones	1·25	70
556.	$1.50 Communications satellite orbiting Earth	2·50	2·50

135. Mail Wagon, c. 1869.

1988. Transport (2nd series). Horse-drawn Carts and Wagons. Multicoloured.

557.	15 c. Type **135**	25	15
558.	40 c. Open cart, c. 1823 ..	55	55
559.	50 c. Closed cart, c. 1823 ..	65	65
560.	$1.50 Two-wheeled wagon, c. 1930	2·00	2·50

136 "Old Blush"

1988. Old Garden Roses (1st series). Mult.

561	15 c. Type **136**	25	25
562	30 c. "Anna Olivier" ..	40	40
563	40 c. "Rosa chinensis semperflorens" (vert) ..	55	55
564	50 c. "Archduke Charles"	65	65
565	$1.50 "Rosa chinensis viridiflora" (vert) ..	1·75	1·90

See also Nos. 584/8 and, for designs with the royal cypher instead of the Queen's head, Nos. 589/98.

1983. 300th Anniv of Lloyd's of London. As T **123** of Ascension. Multicoloured.

566	18 c. Loss of H.M.S. "Lutine" (frigate), 1799	25	25
567	50 c. "Sentinel" (cable ship) (horiz) ..	70	65
568	60 c. "Bermuda" (liner), Hamilton, 1931 (horiz)	80	75
569	$2 Loss of H.M.S. "Valerian" (sloop) in hurricane, 1926 ..	2·75	3·00

137 Devonshire Parish Militia, 1812

1988. Military Uniforms. Multicoloured.

570	18 c. Type **137**	30	25
571	50 c. 71st (Highland) Regiment, 1831–34 ..	70	65
572	60 c. Cameron Highlanders, 1942	80	75
573	$2 Troop of horse, 1774 ..	2·75	3·00

138 "Corona" (ferry)

1989. Transport (3rd series). Ferry Services. Multicoloured.

574	18 c. Type **138**	25	25
575	50 c. Rowing boat ferry ..	65	65
576	60 c. St. George's barge ferry	75	75
577	$2 "Laconia"	2·50	2·75

139 Morgan's Island

1989. 150 Years of Photography. Mult.

578	18 c. Type **139**	25	25
579	30 c. Front Street, Hamilton	40	45
580	50 c. Waterfront, Front Street, Hamilton ..	70	85
581	60 c. Crow Lane from Hamilton Harbour ..	80	1·00
582	70 c. Shipbuilding, Hamilton Harbour ..	95	1·25
583	$1 Dockyard	1·25	2·00

1989. Old Garden Roses (2nd series). As T **136**. Multicoloured.

584	18 c. "Agrippina" (vert) ..	30	25
585	30 c. "Smith's Parish" (vert)	45	50
586	50 c. "Champney's Pink Cluster"	80	95
587	60 c. "Rosette Delizy" ..	90	1·25
588	$1.50 "Rosa bracteata" ..	2·00	3·00

1989. Old Garden Roses designs as Nos. 561/5 and 584/8, but with royal cypher at top left instead of Queen's head. Multicoloured.

589	50 c. As No. 565 (vert) ..	90	1·00
590	50 c. As No. 563 (vert) ..	90	1·00
591	50 c. Type **136**	90	1·00
592	50 c. As No. 562	90	1·00
593	50 c. As No. 564	90	1·00
594	50 c. As No. 585 (vert) ..	90	1·00
595	50 c. As No. 584 (vert) ..	90	1·00
596	50 c. As No. 586	90	1·00
597	50 c. As No. 587	90	1·00
598	50 c. As No. 588	90	1·00

140 Main Library, Hamilton

1989. 150th Anniv of Bermuda Library. Mult.

599	18 c. Type **140**	20	25
600	50 c. The Old Rectory, St. George's	60	65
601	60 c. Somerset Library, Springfield	70	75
602	$2 Cabinet Building, Hamilton	2·40	2·75

141 1865 1d. Rose

1989. Commonwealth Postal Conf. Mult.
603 141 18 c. grey, pink & red 20 25
604 – 50 c. grey, blue & lt bl 60 65
605 – 60 c. grey, pur & mve 70 75
606 – $2 grey, green and emerald .. .. 2·40 2·75
DESIGNS: 50 c. 1866 2d. blue; 60 c. 1865 6d. purple; $2, 1865 1s. green.

142 "Fairylands, c. 1890" (Ross Turner)

1990. Bermuda Paintings (1st series). Mult.
607 18 c. Type **142** 30 25
608 50 c. "Shinebone Alley, c. 1953" (Ogden Pleissner) .. .. 75 1·00
609 60 c. "Salt Kettle, 1916" (Prosper Senate) .. 85 1·25
610 $2 "St. George's, 1934" (Jack Bush) .. .. 2·75 4·00
See also Nos. 630/3.

1990. "Stamp World London 90" International Stamp Exhibition. Nos. 603/6 optd **Stamp World London 90** and logo.
611 18 c. grey, pink and red .. 30 25
612 50 c. grey, blue and lt blue 75 85
613 60 c. grey, purple & mauve 85 1·00
614 $2 grey, green and emerald 2·75 3·25

1990. Nos. 511, 516 and 519 surch.
615 30 c. on 12 c. "Warwick" (galleon), 1619 .. .. 35 40
616 55 c. on 50 c. "Mark Antonie" (Spanish privateer), 1777 .. 65 70
617 80 c. on $1.50 "Caesar" (brig), 1818 .. .. 95 1·00

145 The Halifax and Bermudas Cable Company Office, Hamilton

1990. Centenary of Cable and Wireless in Bermuda.
618 145 20 c. brown and black 35 25
619 – 55 c. brown and black 85 1·00
620 – 70 c. multicoloured .. 1·10 1·25
621 – $2 multicoloured .. 2·75 3·25
DESIGNS: 55 c. "Westmeath" (cable ship), 1890; 70 c. Wireless transmitter station, St. George's, 1928; $2 "Sir Eric Sharp" (cable ship).

1991. President Bush-Prime Minister Major Talks, Bermuda. Nos. 618/19 optd **BUSH-MAJOR 16 MARCH 1991**.
622 145 20 c. brown and black 70 50
623 – 55 c. brown and black 1·40 1·75

147 Two-seater Pony Cart, 1805

1991. Transport (4th series). Horse-drawn Carriages. Multicoloured.
624 20 c. Type **147** 35 25
625 30 c. Varnished rockaway, 1830 .. .. .. 45 45
626 55 c. Vis-a-Vis victoria, 1895 .. .. .. 85 1·00
627 70 c. Semi-formal phaeton, 1900 .. .. .. 1·10 1·40
628 80 c. Pony runabout, 1905 1·25 1·60
629 $1 Ladies phaeton, 1910 1·50 1·90

148 "Bermuda, 1916" (Prosper Senat)

1991. Bermuda Paintings (2nd series). Mult.
630 20 c. Type **148** 40 30
631 55 c. "Bermuda Cottage", 1930 (Frank Allison) (horiz) .. .. .. 1·00 1·25
632 70 c. "Old Maid's Lane", 1934 (Jack Bush) .. 1·25 1·75
633 $2 "St. George's", 1953 (Ogden Pleissner) (horiz) 2·75 3·25

1991. 65th Birthday of Queen Elizabeth II and 70th Birthday of Prince Philip. As T **139** of Ascension. Multicoloured.
634 55 c. Prince Philip in tropical naval uniform 90 1·25
635 70 c. Queen Elizabeth II in Bermuda .. .. 1·10 1·25

149 H.M.S. "Argonaut" (cruiser) in Floating Dock

1991. 50th Anniv of Second World War. Mult.
636 20 c. Type **149** 40 30
637 55 c. Kindley airfield .. 85 90
638 70 c. Boeing "314" flying boat and map of Atlantic route .. 1·25 1·50
639 $2 Censored trans-Atlantic mail .. .. .. 2·75 3·25

1992. 40th Anniv of Queen Elizabeth II's Accession. As T **143** of Ascension. Mult.
640 20 c. Old fort on beach .. 35 30
641 30 c. Public gardens .. 45 45
642 55 c. Cottage garden .. 80 80
643 70 c. Beach and hotels .. 1·00 1·25
644 $1 Queen Elizabeth II .. 1·40 1·75

150 Rings and Medallion

1992. 500th Anniv of Discovery of America by Columbus. Spanish Artifacts. Mult.
645 25 c. Type **150** 50 35
646 35 c. Ink wells 70 65
647 60 c. Gold ornaments .. 1·00 1·00
648 75 c. Bishop buttons and crucifix .. .. 1·25 1·40
649 85 c. Earrings and pearl buttons .. .. 1·40 1·60
650 $1 Jug and bowls .. 1·75 2·00

151 "Wreck of 'Sea Venture' "

1992. Stained Glass Windows. Multicoloured.
651 25 c. Type **151** 35 35
652 60 c. "Birds in tree" .. 80 90
653 75 c. "St. Francis feeding bird" .. .. 95 1·10
654 $2 "Shells" .. .. 2·40 2·75

152 German Shepherd

1992. 7th World Congress of Kennel Clubs. Multicoloured.
655 25 c. Type **152** 55 40
656 35 c. Irish setter 70 65
657 60 c. Whippet (vert) .. 1·25 1·25
658 75 c. Border terrier (vert) 1·40 1·40
659 85 c. Pomeranian (vert) .. 1·90 2·00
660 $1 Schipperke (vert) .. 2·25 2·40

153 Policeman, Cyclist and Cruise Liner

1993. Tourism Posters by Adolph Treidler. Multicoloured.
679 25 c. Type **153** 45 35
680 60 c. Seaside golf course .. 1·25 1·25
681 75 c. Deserted beach .. 1·50 1·50
682 $2 Dancers in evening dress and cruise liner .. 3·50 3·75

154 "Duchesse de Brabant" Rose and Bee

1993.
683 154 10 c. multicoloured .. 15 20
684 25 c. multicoloured .. 35 40
685 50 c. multicoloured .. 65 70
686 60 c. multicoloured .. 80 85

1993. 75th Anniv of Royal Air Force. As T **149** of Ascension. Multicoloured.
687 25 c. Consolidated Catalina 45 35
688 60 c. Supermarine Spitfire 1·25 1·25
689 75 c. Bristol Beaufighter .. 1·40 1·40
690 $2 Handley Page Halifax 3·25 3·50

155 Hamilton from the Sea

1993. Bicentenary of Hamilton. Mult.
691 25 c. Type **155** 40 35
692 60 c. Waterfront .. .. 1·00 1·10
693 75 c. Barrel warehouse .. 1·25 1·25
694 $2 Sailing ships off Hamilton .. .. 2·75 3·00

156 "Queen of Bermuda" (liner) at Hamilton

1994. 75th Anniv of Furness Line's Bermuda Cruises. Adolphe Treidler Posters. Mult.
695 25 c. Type **156** 30 35
696 60 c. "Queen of Bermuda" entering port (horiz) .. 80 85
697 75 c. "Queen of Bermuda" and "Ocean Monarch" (liners) (horiz) .. 95 1·00
698 $2 Passengers on promenade deck at night 2·50 2·75

157 Queen Elizabeth II in Bermuda

1994. Royal Visit. Multicoloured.
699 25 c. Type **157** 30 35
700 60 c. Queen Elizabeth and Prince Philip in open carriage 80 85
701 75 c. Royal Yacht "Britannia" .. .. 95 1·00

BHOPAL

A state of C. India. Now uses Indian stamps.

12 pies = 1 anna; 16 annas = 1 rupee.

3.

4.

1876. Imperf.

5	3	$\frac{1}{4}$ a. black	2·75	5·50
4		$\frac{1}{2}$ a. red	11·00	20·00

1878. Imperf. or perf.

6	4	$\frac{1}{4}$ a. green	6·50	10·00
15		$\frac{1}{4}$ a. red	1·75	1·00
8		$\frac{1}{2}$ a. red	3·75	6·00
9		$\frac{1}{2}$ a. brown	20·00	28·00

1881. As T **3.** but larger. Imperf. or perf.

29	$\frac{1}{4}$ a. black	60	70
37	$\frac{1}{2}$ a. red	90	1·40
46	$\frac{1}{2}$ a. black	80	1·40
30	1 a. brown	95	2·00
31	2 a. blue	75	1·00
32	4 a. yellow	1·25	1·90

14.

16.

1884. Perf.

49.	14.	$\frac{1}{4}$ a. green	1·60	4·25
76.		$\frac{1}{4}$ a. black	50	60

1884. Imperf. or perf.

63.	16.	$\frac{1}{4}$ a. green	30	30
65.		$\frac{1}{4}$ a. black	30	30
52.		$\frac{1}{2}$ a. black	70	60
59.		$\frac{1}{2}$ a. red	40	50

17.

1890. Imperf. or perf.

71	17	8 a. greenish black	14·00	15·00

19.

20. State arms.

1902. Imperf.

90	19.	$\frac{1}{4}$ a. red	65	1·50
91		$\frac{1}{2}$ a. black	55	2·25
92		1 a. brown	1·00	3·00
94		2 a. blue	2·50	12·00
96		4 a. yellow	14·00	38·00
97		8 a. lilac	32·00	70·00
98		1 r. red	45·00	85·00

1908. Perf.

100.	20.	1 a. green	1·50	1·25

OFFICIAL STAMPS

1908. As T **20.** but inscr. " H.H. BEGUM'S SERVICE " optd. **SERVICE.**

O301	$\frac{1}{2}$ a. green	1·25	10
O302	1 a. red	1·90	30
O307	2 a. blue	3·00	30
O304	4 a. brown	8·00	15

O 4.

1930. Type O **4** optd. **SERVICE.**

O309.	O 4.	$\frac{1}{2}$ a. green	3·25	30
O310.		1 a. red	4·25	15
O311.		2 a. blue	3·75	15
O312.		4 a. brown	3·50	20

1932. As T **20,** but inscr " POSTAGE " at left and " BHOPAL STATE " at right, optd. **SERVICE.**

O313.	–	$\frac{1}{4}$ a. orange	1·90	30

1932. As T **20,** but inscr. " POSTAGE " at left and " BHOPAL GOVT " at right, optd. **SERVICE.**

O314.	–	$\frac{1}{2}$ a. green	2·25	10
O315.	–	1 a. red	4·25	10
O316.	–	2 a. blue	4·75	45
O317.	–	4 a. brown	3·75	60

1935. Nos. O 314, etc., surch.

O318	–	$\frac{1}{4}$ a. on $\frac{1}{2}$ a. green	13·00	6·50
O319	–	3 p. on $\frac{1}{2}$ a. green	1·60	1·50
O320	–	$\frac{1}{4}$ a. on 2 a. blue	12·00	7·00
O321	–	3 p. on 2 a. blue	1·00	1·25
O323	–	$\frac{1}{4}$ a. on 4 a. brown	29·00	12·00
O325	–	3 p. on 4 a. brown	1·90	1·25
O326	–	1 a. on $\frac{1}{2}$ a. green	1·00	1·25
O328	–	1 a. on 2 a. blue	60	65
O329	–	1a. on 4 a. brown	1·90	2·25

O 8.

1935.

O330.	O 8.	1 a. 3 p. blue and red	80	20
O331.		1 a. 6 p. blue and red	80	20
O332.		1 a. 6 p. red	1·75	30

Nos. O331/2 are similar to Type O **8,** but inscr. " BHOPAL STATE POSTAGE ".

O 9.

1936. Type O **9** optd. **SERVICE.**

O334.	O 9.	$\frac{1}{4}$ a. yellow	80	10
O335.		1 a. red	80	10

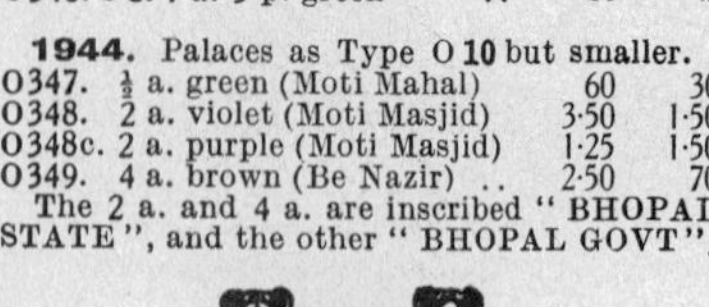

O **10** The Moti Mahal.

1936. As Type O **4** optd. **SERVICE.**

O336.	O 10.	$\frac{1}{2}$ a. purple and green	60	30
O337.	–	2 a. brown and blue	70	20
O338.	–	2 a. green and violet	3·00	20
O339.	–	4 a. blue and brown	1·50	50
O340.	–	8 a. purple and blue	2·25	65
O341.	–	1 r. blue and purple	5·50	2·75

DESIGNS: 2 a. The Moti Masjid. 4 a. Taj Mahal and Be-Nazir Palaces. 8 a. Ahmadabad Palace. 1 r. Rait Ghat.

No. O336 is inscribed " BHOPAL GOVT " below the arms, other values have " BHOPAL STATE ".

1940. Animal designs, as Type O **10** but inscr. "SERVICE" in bottom panel.

O344.	–	$\frac{1}{4}$ a. blue (Tiger)	2·00	40
O345.	–	1 a. purple (Spotted deer)	10·00	45

1941. As Type O **8** but " SERVICE " inscr. instead of optd.

O346.	O 8.	1 a. 3 p. green	60	45

1944. Palaces as Type O **10** but smaller.

O347.	$\frac{1}{2}$ a. green (Moti Mahal)	60	30
O348.	2 a. violet (Moti Masjid)	3·50	1·50
O348c.	2 a. purple (Moti Masjid)	1·25	1·50
O349.	4 a. brown (Be Nazir)	2·50	70

The 2 a. and 4 a. are inscribed " BHOPAL STATE ", and the other " BHOPAL GOVT ".

O 14 Arms of Bhopal.

1944.

O350	O 14.	3 p. blue	50	20
O351b		9 p. brown	2·00	2·00
O352		1 a. purple	2·50	30
O352b		1 a. violet	3·50	1·10
O353		$1\frac{1}{2}$ a. red	1·10	30
O354		3 a. yellow	4·50	2·75
O354d		3 a. brown	42·00	38·00
O355		6 a. red	7·50	21·00

1949. Surch. **2 As.** and bars.

O356.	O 14.	2 a. on $1\frac{1}{2}$ a. red	1·75	3·50

1949. Surch. **2 As.** and ornaments.

O357.	O 14.	2 a. on $1\frac{1}{2}$ a. red	£300	£350

BHOR

A state of W. India, Bombay district. Now uses Indian stamps.

12 pies = 1 anna; 16 annas = 1 ruppee.

1.

3. Pant Sachiv Shankarro Chimnaji.

1879. Imperf.

1.	1.	$\frac{1}{2}$ a. red	1·75	3·25

Similar to T **3,** but rectangular.

2.		1 a. red	2·50	4·50

1901. Imperf.

3.	3.	$\frac{1}{2}$ a. red	6·00	28·00

BIAFRA

The following stamps were issued by Biafra (the Eastern Region of Nigeria) during the civil war with the Federal Government, 1967–70.

They were in regular use within Biafra from the time when supplies of Nigerian stamps were exhausted, and towards the end of the conflict they began to be used on external mail carried by air via Libreville.

Biafra was overrun by Federal troops on 10 January, 1970, and surrender took place on 15 January.

12 pence = 1 shilling.
20 shillings = 1 pound.

1. Map of Republic.

5. Weapon Maintenance.

1968. Independence. Multicoloured.

1.	2d. Type **1**	10	40
2.	4d. Arms, Flag and Date of Independence	10	50
3.	1s. Mother and Child (17 × 22 mm.)	15	1·10

1968. Nos. 172/5 and 176/85 of Nigeria optd. with Arms and **SOVEREIGN BIAFRA.**

4.	$\frac{1}{2}$d. mult. (No. 172)	90	2·25
5.	1d. mult. (No. 173)	1·25	3·50
6.	$1\frac{1}{2}$d. mult. (No. 174)	3·75	7·00
7.	2d. mult. (No. 175)	17·00	45·00
8.	4d. mult. (No. 177)	17·00	45·00
9.	6d. mult. (No. 178)	3·50	6·00
10.	9d. blue & red (No. 179)	1·75	2·50
11.	1s. mult. (No. 180)	50·00	90·00
12.	1s. 3d. mult. (No. 181)	32·00	50·00
13.	2s. 6d. mult. (No. 182)	1·75	5·50
14.	5s. mult. (No. 183)	1·75	5·50
15.	10s. mult. (No. 184)	10·00	25·00
16.	£1 mult. (No. 185)	10·00	25·00

1968. 1st Anniv. of Independence. Mult.

17.	4d. Type **5**	15	10
18.	1s. Victim of Atrocity	20	20
19.	2s. 6d Nurse and Refugees	45	1·50
20.	5s. Biafran Arms and Banknote	60	2·25
21.	10s. Orphaned Child	1·00	3·25

16. Child in chains, and Globe.

1969. 2nd Anniv. of Independence. Multicoloured; frame colours given.

35.	16.	2d. orange	1·00	3·00
36.		4d. red	1·00	3·00
37.		1s. blue	1·25	4·25
38.		2s. 6d. green	2·00	9·50

17. Pope Paul VI, Africa, and Papal Arms.

1969. Visit of Pope Paul to Africa. Multicoloured; background colours given.

39.	17.	4d. orange	40	2·25
40.	–	6d. blue	55	4·50
41.	–	9d. green	75	6·00
42.	–	3s. mauve	2·25	12·00

DESIGNS: Pope Paul VI, map of Africa and—6d. Arms of Vatican. 9d. St. Peter's Basilica. 3s. Statue of St. Peter.

BIJAWAR

A state of Central India. Now uses Indian stamps.

12 pies = 1 anna; 16 annas = 1 rupee.

1. Maharaja Sir Sarwant Singh Bahadur. 2.

1935.

6	1	3 p. brown	1·00	1·60
2		6 p. red	2·00	1·60
3		9 p. violet	2·00	2·25
4		1 a. blue	2·75	2·75
5		2 a. green	3·00	4·00

1937.

11.	2.	4 a. orange	5·00	45·00
12.		6 a. lemon	5·00	45·00
13.		8 a. green	5·50	55·00
14.		12 a. blue	6·00	60·00
15.		1 r. violet	25·00	90·00

BOTSWANA

Formerly Bechuanaland Protectorate, attained independence on 30 September 1966, and changed its name to Botswana.

1966. 100 cents = 1 rand.
1976. 100 thebe = 1 pula.

47. National Assembly Building.

1966. Independence. Multicoloured.

202.	$2\frac{1}{2}$ c. Type, **47**	15	10
203.	5 c. Abattoir Lobatsi	20	10
204.	15 c. National Airways " Dakota "	40	10
205.	35 c. State House, Gaberones	40	20

1966. Nos. 168/81 of Bechuanaland optd. **REPUBLIC OF BOTSWANA.**

206.	28.	1 c. multicoloured	25	10
207.	–	2 c. orange, black & olive	30	10
208.	–	$2\frac{1}{2}$ c. multicoloured	30	10
209.	–	$3\frac{1}{2}$ c. multicoloured	40	15
210.	–	5 c. multicoloured	40	50
211.	–	$7\frac{1}{2}$ c. multicoloured	40	60
212.	–	10 c. multicoloured	60	20
213.	–	$12\frac{1}{2}$ c. multicoloured	3·75	1·75
214.	–	20 c. brown and drab	75	45
215.	–	25 c. sepia and lemon	75	1·00
216.	–	35 c. blue and orange	85	1·10
217.	–	50 c. sepia and olive	50	70
218.	–	1 r. black and brown	75	1·25
219.	–	2 r. brown and turquoise	1·50	2·50

52. Golden Oriole.

1967. Multicoloured.

No.	Description	Unused	Used
220.	1 c. Type **52**	30	15
221.	2 c. Hoopoe	40	10
222.	3 c. Groundscraper Thrush	55	10
223.	4 c. Cordon-bleu	55	10
224.	5 c. Secretary Bird ..	55	10
225.	7 c. Yellow-billed Hornbill	60	90
226.	10 c. Burchell's Gonolek ..	60	15
227.	15 c. Malachite Kingfisher	6·00	1·50
228.	20 c. African Fish Eagle ..	6·00	80
229.	25 c. Go-away Bird ..	3·25	70
230.	35 c. Scimitar-bill	6·00	1·25
231.	50 c. Comb Duck	3·25	1·50
232.	1 r. Levaillant's Barbet ..	7·00	3·25
233.	2 r. Didric Cuckoo ..	9·50	13·00

66. Students and University.

1967. 1st Conferment of University Degrees.

No.	Description	Unused	Used
234. **66.**	3 c. sepia, blue & orange	10	10
235.	7 c. sepia, blue & turquoise	10	10
236.	15 c. sepia, blue and red	10	10
237.	35 c. sepia, blue & violet	20	10

67. Bushbuck.

1967. Chobe Game Reserve. Multicoloured.

No.	Description	Unused	Used
238.	3 c. Type **67**	10	20
239.	7 c. Sable Antelope ..	15	20
240.	35 c. Fishing on the Chobe River	70	95

70. Arms of Botswana and Human Rights Emblem.

1968. Human Rights Year.

No.	Description	Unused	Used
241. **70.**	3 c. multicoloured ..	10	10
242. –	15 c. multicoloured ..	25	30
243. –	25 c. multicoloured ..	25	40

The designs of Nos. 242/3 are similar, but are arranged differently.

73. Eland and Giraffe Rock Paintings, Tsodilo Hills.

1968. Opening of National Museum and Art Gallery. Multicoloured.

No.	Description	Unused	Used
244.	3 c. Type **73**	35	20
245.	7 c. Girl wearing ceremonial beads ..	45	20
246.	10 c. "Baobab Trees" (Thomas Baines) ..	45	25
247.	15 c. National Museum and art gallery (72 × 19 mm)	60	1·10

No. 245 is vert. and the size is **31 × 48 mm.**

77. African Family, and Star over Village.

1968. Christmas.

No.	Description	Unused	Used
249. **77.**	1 c. multicoloured ..	10	10
250.	2 c. multicoloured ..	10	10
251.	5 c. multicoloured ..	10	10
252.	25 c. multicoloured ..	15	40

78. Scout, Lion and Badge in frame.

1969. 22nd World Scout Conf., Helsinki. Multicoloured.

No.	Description	Unused	Used
253.	3 c. Type **78**	50	15
254.	15 c. Scouts cooking over open fire	1·00	75
255.	25 c. Scouts around camp fire	1·10	90

The 15 c. is vert.

81. Woman, Child and Christmas Star.

1969. Christmas.

No.	Description	Unused	Used
256. **81.**	1 c. blue and brown ..	10	10
257.	2 c. olive and brown ..	10	10
258.	4 c. yellow and brown ..	10	10
259.	35 c. brown and violet ..	20	20

82. Diamond Treatment Plant, Orapa.

1970. Developing Botswana. Multicoloured.

No.	Description	Unused	Used
261.	3 c. Type **82**	70	20
262.	7 c. Copper-nickel mining	95	20
263.	10 c. Copper-nickel mine, Selebi-Pikwe (horiz.) ..	1·25	·25
264.	35 c. Orapa Diamond mine and diamonds (horiz.) ..	2·75	1·60

83. Mr. Micawber ("David Copperfield").

1970. Death Centenary of Charles Dickens. Multicoloured.

No.	Description	Unused	Used
265.	3 c. Type **83**	25	10
266.	7 c. Scrooge ("A Christmas Carol")	35	10
267.	15 c. Fagin ("Oliver Twist")	60	40
268.	25 c. Bill Sykes ("Oliver Twist")	90	60

84. U.N. Building and Emblem. (Illustration reduced. Actual size 59 × 21 mm.)

1970. 25th Anniv. of United Nations.

No.	Description	Unused	Used
270. **84.**	15 c. blue, brown & silver	50	30

85. Crocodile.

1970. Christmas. Multicoloured.

No.	Description	Unused	Used
271.	1 c. Type **85**	10	10
272.	2 c. Giraffe	10	10
273.	7 c. Elephant	15	10
274.	25 c. Rhinoceros	60	70

86. Sorghum.

1971. Important Crops. Multicoloured.

No.	Description	Unused	Used
276.	3 c. Type **86**	15	10
277.	7 c. Millet	20	10
278.	10 c. Maize	20	10
279.	35 c. Groundnuts	70	40

87. Map and Head of Cow.

1971. Fifth Anniv. of Independence.

No.	Description	Unused	Used
280. **87.**	3 c. black, brown & grn.	10	10
281. –	4 c. black, lt. bl. & bl.	10	10
282. –	7 c. black & orange ..	20	15
283. –	10 c. multicoloured ..	25	15
284. –	20 c. multicoloured ..	80	1·40

DESIGNS: 4 c. Map and cogs. 7 c. Map and common zebra. 10 c. Map and sorghum stalk crossed by tusk. 20 c. Arms and map of Botswana.

88. King bringing Gift of Gold.

1971. Christmas. Multicoloured.

No.	Description	Unused	Used
285.	2 c. Type **88**	10	10
286.	3 c. King bringing frankincense	10	10
287.	7 c. King bringing myrrh	10	10
288.	20 c. Three Kings behold the star	35	50

INDEX

Countries can be quickly located by referring to the index at the end of this volume.

89. Orion.

1972. "Night Sky".

No.	Description	Unused	Used
290. **89.**	3c. blue, blk. and red ..	40	20
291. –	7c. blue, black and yell.	75	60
292. –	10c. grn., blk. and orge.	85	75
293. –	20c. blue, blk. and green	1·60	1·60

CONSTELLATIONS: 7c. The Scorpion. 10c. The Centaur. 20c. The Cross.

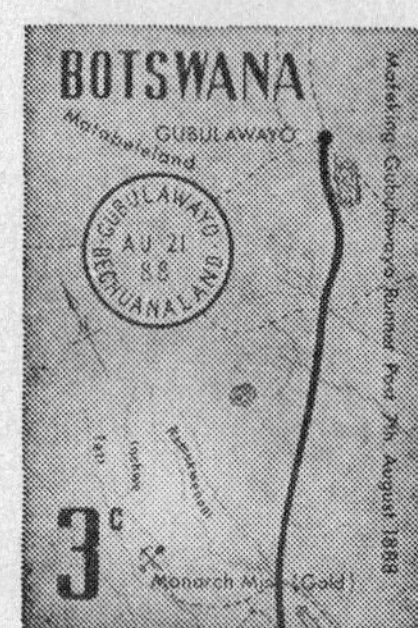

90. Postmark and Map.

1972. Mafeking-Gubulawayo Runner Post. Multicoloured.

No.	Description	Unused	Used
294.	3 c. Type **90**	30	10
295.	4 c. Bechuanaland stamp and map	30	35
296.	7 c. Runners and map ..	45	50
297.	20 c. Mafeking postmark and map	1·10	1·25

For these designs with change inscription see Nos. 652/5.

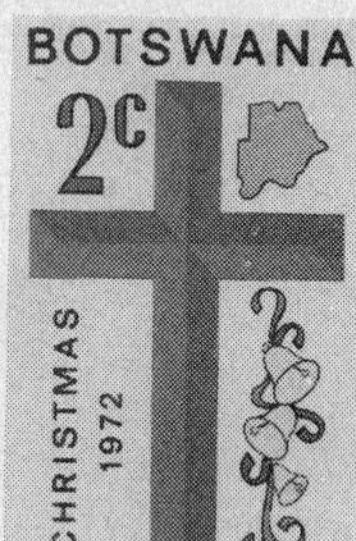

91. Cross, Map and Bells.

1972. Christmas. Each with Cross and Map. Multicoloured.

No.	Description	Unused	Used
299.	2 c. Type **91**	10	20
300.	3 c. Cross, map and candle	10	10
301.	7 c. Cross, map and Christmas tree	15	20
302.	20 c. Cross, map, star and holly	40	65

92. Thor.

1973. Centenary of I.M.O./W.M.O. Norse myths. Multicoloured.

No.	Description	Unused	Used
304.	3 c. Type **92**	25	10
305.	4 c. Sun God's chariot (horiz.)	30	15
306.	7 c. Ymir, the frost giant ..	40	15
307.	20 c. Odin and Sleipnir (horiz.)	1·00	70

93. Livingstone and River Scene.

1973. Death Centenary of Dr. Livingstone. Multicoloured.

308.	3 c. Type **93**	10	10
309.	20 c. Livingstone meeting Stanley	50	60

94. Donkey and Foal at Village Trough.

1973. Christmas. Multicoloured.

310.	3 c. Type **94**	10	10
311.	4 c. Shepherd and flock (horiz.)	10	10
312.	7 c. Mother and child ..	10	10
313.	20 c. Kgotla meeting (horiz.)	40	60

95. Gaborone Campus.

1974. 10th Anniv. of University of Botswana, Lesotho and Swaziland. Multicoloured.

314.	3 c. Type **95**	10	10
315.	7 c. Kwaluseni Campus ..	10	10
316.	20 c. Roma Campus ..	15	20
317.	35 c. Map and flags of the three countries	20	35

96. Methods of Mail Transport. (Illustration reduced. Actual size 58 × 21 mm.).

1974. Centenary of U.P.U. Multicoloured.

318.	2 c. Type **96**	45	35
319.	3 c. Post Office, Palapye, circa 1889	45	35
320.	7 c. Bechuanaland Police Camel Post, circa 1900	70	70
321.	20 c. Mail-planes of 1920 and 1974	2·50	2·50

97. Amethyst.

1974. Botswana Minerals. Multicoloured.

322.	1 c. Type **97**	60	70
323.	2 c. Agate—"Botswana Pink"	60	70
324.	3 c. Quartz	65	70
325.	4 c. Copper nickel ..	70	60
326.	5 c. Moss agate	70	75
327.	7 c. Agate..	80	60
328.	10 c. Stilbite	1·40	65
329.	15 c. Moshaneng Banded Marble	2·00	2·00
330.	20 c. Gem diamonds ..	4·00	2·00
331.	25 c. Chrysotile	4·50	1·50
332.	35 c. Jasper	4·25	2·25
333.	50 c. Moss quartz ..	4·50	4·50
334.	1 r. Citrine	7·50	9·00
335.	2 r. Chalcopyrite	20·00	18·00

98. "Stapelia variegata".

1974. Christmas. Multicoloured.

336.	2 c. Type **98**	20	30
337.	7 c. "Hibiscus lunarifolius"	50	20
338.	15 c. "Ceratotheca triloba"	1·10	1·25
339.	20 c. "Nerine laticoma"	1·25	1·50

99. President Sir Seretse Khama.

1975. 10th Anniv. of Self-Government.

341. **99.**	4 c. multicoloured ..	10	10
342.	10 c. multicoloured ..	15	10
343.	20 c. multicoloured ..	25	15
344.	35 c. multicoloured ..	45	35

100. Ostrich.

1975. Rock Paintings, Tsodilo Hills. Mult.

346.	4 c. Type **100**	30	10
347.	10 c. White rhinoceros ..	70	10
348.	25 c. Spotted hyena ..	1·75	55
349.	35 c. Scorpion	2·00	1·10

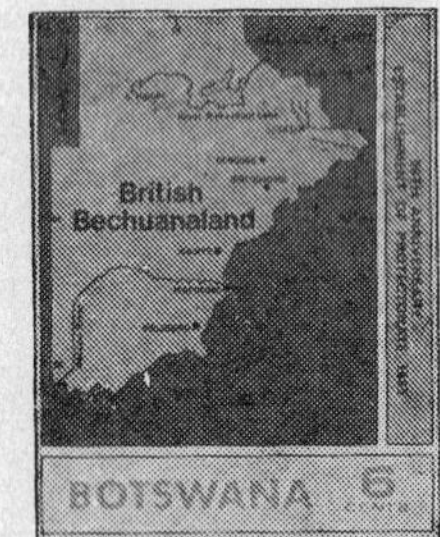

101. Map of British Bechuanaland, 1885.

1975. Anniversaries. Multicoloured.

351.	6 c. Type **101**	30	20
352.	10 c. Chief Khama, 1875..	40	15
353.	25 c. Chiefs Sebele, Bathoen and Khama, 1895 (horiz.)	80	75

EVENTS: 6 c. 90th Anniv. of Protectorate. 10 c. Centenary of Khama's Accession. 25 c. 80th Anniv. of Chiefs' visit to London.

102. "Aloe marlothii".

1975. Christmas. Aloes. Multicoloured.

354.	3 c. Type **102**	30	10
355.	10 c. "Aloe lutescens" ..	75	35
356.	15 c. "Aloe zebrina" ..	1·40	1·75
357.	25 c. "Aloe littoralis" ..	1·60	2·00

103. Drum.

1976. Traditional Musical Instruments. Mult.

358.	4 c. Type **103**	15	10
359.	10 c. Hand Piano ..	25	10
360.	15 c. Segankuru (violin)..	30	30
361.	25 c. Kudu Signal Horn..	40	55

104. One Pula Note.

1976. First National Currency. Mult.

362.	4 c. Type **104**	15	10
363.	10 c. Two pula note ..	20	10
364.	15 c. Five pula note ..	35	20
365.	25 c. Ten pula note ..	45	45

1976. Nos. 322/35 surch. in new currency.

367.	1 t. on 1 c. multicoloured..	85	55
368.	2 t. on 2 c. multicoloured..	85	40
369.	3 t. on 3 c. multicoloured..	85	40
370.	4 t. on 4 c. multicoloured..	1·25	40
371.	5 t. on 5 c. multicoloured..	1·25	30
372.	7 t. on 7 c. multicoloured..	1·00	70
373.	10 t. on 10 c. multicoloured	1·00	70
374.	15 t. on 15 c. multicoloured	3·25	80
375.	20 t. on 20 c. multicoloured	6·00	65
376.	25 t. on 25 c. multicoloured	4·50	1·25
377.	35 t. on 35 c. multicoloured	4·50	1·75
378.	50 t. on 50 c. multicoloured	6·00	3·25
379.	1 p. on 1 r. multicoloured	7·00	3·50
380.	2 p. on 2 r. multicoloured	10·00	8·00

106. Botswanan Cattle.

1976. 10th Anniv. of Independence. Mult.

381.	4 t. Type **106**	15	10
382.	10 t. Deer, Okavango Delta (vert.)	30	10
383.	15 t. School and pupils ..	40	30
384.	25 t. Rural weaving (vert.)	55	40
385.	35 t. Miner (vert.) ..	1·25	75

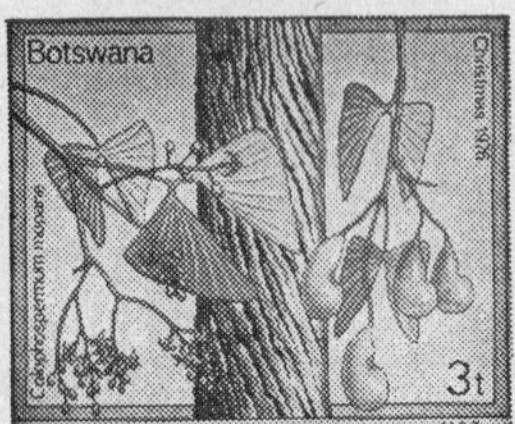

107. "Colophosphermum mopane".

1976. Christmas Trees. Multicoloured.

386.	3 t. Type **107**	15	10
387.	4 t. "Baikiaea plurijuga"	15	10
388.	10 t. "Sterculia rogersii"	40	15
389.	25 t. "Acacia nilotica"..	80	50
390.	40 t. "Kigelia africana"	1·25	1·25

108. Coronation Coach.

1977. Silver Jubilee. Multicoloured.

391.	4 t. The Queen and Sir Seretse Khama ..	10	10
392.	25 t. Type **108**	20	15
393.	40 t. The Recognition ..	35	45

109. African Clawless Otter.

1977. Diminishing Species. Multicoloured.

394.	3 t. Type **109**	35	30
395.	4 t. Serval	35	30
396.	10 t. Bat-eared fox ..	90	40
397.	25 t. Temminck's ground pangolin	2·00	1·25
398.	40 t. Brown hyena ..	3·00	2·50

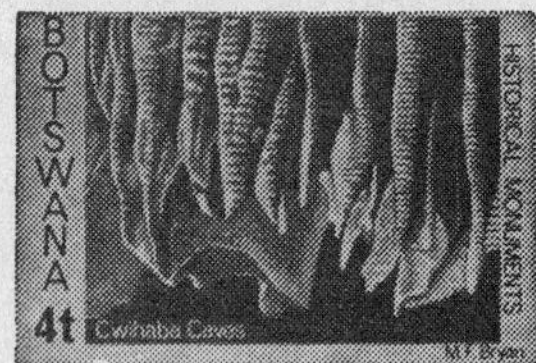

110. Cwihaba Caves.

1977. Historical Monuments. Multicoloured.

399.	4 t. Type **110**	25	10
400.	5 t. Khama Memorial ..	25	10
401.	15 t. Green's Tree ..	55	40
402.	20 t. Mmajojo Ruins ..	55	45
403.	25 t. Ancient morabaraba board	55	50
404.	35 t. Matsieng's footprint	70	60

111. "Hypoxij nitida".

112. Little Black Bustard.

1977. Christmas. Lilies. Multicoloured.

406.	3 t. Type **111**	15	10
407.	5 t. "Haemanthus magnificus"	15	10
408.	10 t. "Boophane disticha"	35	10
409.	25 t. "Vellozia retinervis"	75	40
410.	40 t. "Ammocharis coranica"	1·00	1·00

1978. Birds. Multicoloured.

411.	1 t. Type **112**	30	65
412.	2 t. Marabou stork ..	30	65
413.	3 t. Green wood hoopoe ..	30	65
414.	4 t. Carmine bee eater ..	30	50
415.	5 t. African jacana ..	30	40
416.	7 t. African paradise flycatcher	40	50
417.	10 t. Bennett's woodpecker	1·00	50
418.	15 t. Red bishop	60	1·25
419.	20 t. Crowned plover ..	60	1·25
420.	25 t. Giant kingfisher ..	60	1·25
421.	30 t. White-faced whistling duck	60	60
422.	35 t. Green heron	60	1·25
423.	45 t. Black-headed heron..	65	1·50
424.	50 t. Spotted eagle owl ..	3·00	2·25
425.	1 p. Gabar goshawk ..	1·25	2·25
426.	2 p. Martial eagle	2·00	5·50
427.	5 p. Saddle-bill stork ..	11·00	12·00

113. Tawana making Kaross.

1978. Okavango Delta. Multicoloured.

428.	4 t. Type **113**	10	10
429.	5 t. Tribe localities ..	10	10
430.	15 t. Bushman collecting roots	30	30
431.	20 t. Herero woman milking	35	35
432.	25 t. Yei poling "mokoro" (canoe)	40	40
433.	35 t. Mbukushu fishing ..	55	55

114. " Caralluma lutea ".

1978. Christmas. Flowers. Multicoloured.

435.	5 t. Type **114**	35	10
436.	10 t. " Hoodia lugardii "	50	15
437.	15 t. " Ipomoea transvaalensis "	90	55
438.	25 t. " Ansellia gigantea "	1·10	70

115. Sip Well.

1979. Water Development. Multicoloured.

439.	3 t. Type **115**	10	10
440.	5 t. Watering pit	15	10
441.	10 t. Hand dug well ..	15	10
442.	22 t. Windmill	40	30
443.	50 t. Modern drilling rig ..	75	55

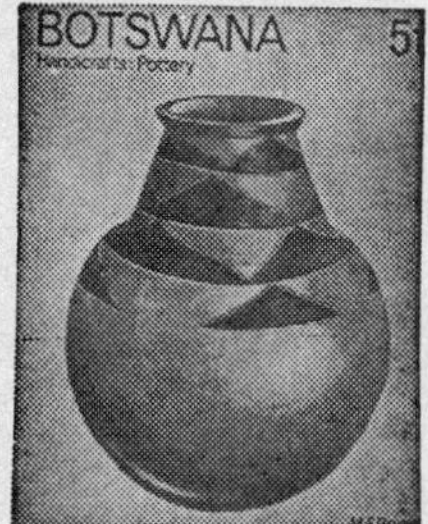

116. Pottery.

1979. Handicrafts. Multicoloured.

444.	5 t. Type **116**	10	10
445.	10 t. Clay modelling ..	15	10
446.	25 t. Basketry	30	25
447.	40 t. Beadwork	50	50

117. British Bechuanaland 1885 1d. Stamp and Sir Rowland Hill.

1979. Death Centenary of Sir Rowland Hill. Multicoloured.

449.	5 t. Type **117**	30	10
450.	25 t. Bechuanaland Protectorate 1932 2d. stamp	65	40
451.	45 t. 1967 Hoopoe 2 c. definitive stamp ..	75	65

118. Children Playing.

1979. International Year of the Child. Multicoloured.

452.	5 t. Type **118**	20	10
453.	10 t. Child playing with doll (vert.)	30	20

119. " Ximenia caffra ".

1979. Christmas. Flowers. Multicoloured.

454.	5 t. Type **119**	10	10
455.	10 t. " Sclerocarya caffra "	20	20
456.	15 t. " Hexalobus monopetalus "	35	35
457.	25 t. " Ficus soldanella "	45	45

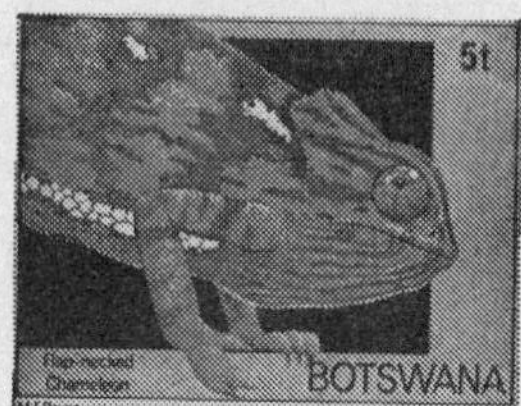

120. Flap-necked Chameleon.

1980. Reptiles. Multicoloured.

458.	5 t. Type **120**	20	10
459.	10 t. Leopard Tortoise ..	25	15
460.	25 t. Puff Adder	75	40
461.	40 t. White-throated Monitor	1·00	60

121. Rock Breaking.

1980. Early Mining. Multicoloured.

462.	5 t. Type **121**	25	15
463.	10 t. Ore hoisting ..	30	15
464.	15 t. Ore transport ..	70	55
465.	20 t. Ore crushing ..	75	65
466.	25 t. Smelting	80	80
467.	35 t. Tool and products ..	1·00	1·00

122. " Chiwele and the Giant ".

1980. Folktales. Multicoloured.

468.	5 t. Type **122**	10	10
469.	10 t. " Kgori is not deceived " (vert.)	15	10
470.	30 t. " Nyambi's wife and Crocodile " (vert.) ..	45	45
471.	45 t. " Clever Hare " (horiz.)	60	60

The 10 t. and 30 t. are 28 × 37 mm. and the 45 t. 44 × 27 mm.

123. Game watching, Makgadikgadi Pans. (Illustration reduced. Actual size 58 × 22 mm.).

1980. World Tourism Conference, Manila.

472. **123.**	5 t. multicoloured ..	45	20

124. " Acacia gerrardii ".

126. "Anax imperator" (dragonfly).

125. Heinrich von Stephan and Botswana 3d. and 3 c. U.P.U. Stamps.

1980. Christmas. Multicoloured.

473.	6 t. Type **124**	10	10
474.	10 t. "Acacia nilotica" ..	20	10
475.	25 t. "Acacia erubescens"	45	30
476.	40 t. "Dichrostachys cinerea"	70	70

1981. 150th Birth Anniv. of Heinrich von Stephan (founder of Universal Postal Union). Multicoloured.

477.	6 t. Type **125**	60	30
478.	20 t. 6d. and 7 c. U.P.U. stamps	1·40	1·50

1981. Insects. Multicoloured.

479	6 t. Type **126**	15	10
480	7 t. "Sphodromantis gastrica" (mantid) ..	15	20
481	10 t. "Zonocerus elegans" (grasshopper)	20	20
482	20 t. "Kheper nigroaeneus" (beetle)	35	45
483	30 t. "Papilio demodocus" (butterfly)	70	60
484	45 t. "Acanthocampa belina" (moth larva) ..	80	90

127. Camphill Community Rankoromane, Otse.

1981. International Year for Disabled Persons. Multicoloured.

486.	6 t. Type **127**	20	10
487.	20 t. Resource Centre for the Blind, Mochudi ..	55	35
488.	30 t. Tlamelong Rehabilitation Centre, Tlokweng	75	45

128. Woman reading Letter.

1981. Literacy Programme. Multicoloured.

489.	6 t. Type **128**	20	10
490.	7 t. Man filling in form ..	20	15
491.	20 t. Boy reading newspaper	50	35
492.	30 t. Child being taught to read	70	45

129. Sir Seretse Khama and Building.

1981. 1st Death Anniv. of Sir Seretse Khama (former President). Multicoloured.

493.	6 t. Type **129**	10	10
494.	10 t. Seretse Khama and building (different) ..	15	15
495.	30 t. Seretse Khama and Botswana flag	45	45
496.	45 t. Seretse Khama and building (different) ..	70	70

1981. Nos. 417 and 422 surch.

497.	25 t. on 35 t. Green heron	1·75	1·75
498.	30 t. on 10 t. Bennett's woodpecker	1·75	1·75

131. Traditional Ploughing.

1981. Cattle Industry. Multicoloured.

499.	6 t. Type **131**	10	10
500.	20 t. Agricultural show ..	35	45
501.	30 t. Botswana Meat Commission	45	55
502.	45 t. Vaccine Institute, Botswana	70	90

132. " Nymphaea caerulea ".

1981. Christmas. Flowers. Multicoloured.

503.	6 t. Type **132**	20	10
504.	10 t. " Nymphoides indica "	30	10
505.	25 t. " Nymphaea lotus "	70	70
506.	40 t. " Ottelia kunenensis "	1·00	1·40

133. " Cattle Post Scene " (Boitumelo Golaakwena).

1982. Children's Art. Multicoloured.

507.	6 t. Type **133**	40	10
508.	10 t. " Kgotla Meeting " (Reginald Klinck) ..	50	15
509.	30 t. " Village Water Supply " (Keromemang Matswiri)	1·50	55
510.	45 t. " With the Crops " (Kennedy Balemoge) ..	1·75	1·25

134. Common Type.

1982. Traditional Houses. Multicoloured.

511.	6 t. Type **134**	40	15
512.	10 t. Kgatleng type ..	50	15
513.	30 t. North Eastern type	1·75	1·00
514.	45 t. Sarwa type	2·00	2·50

135. African Masked Weaver.

1982. Birds. Multicoloured.

515.	1 t. Type **135**	60	65
516.	2 t. Lesser double-collared sunbird	70	70
517.	3 t. Red-throated bee eater	70	70
518.	4 t. Ostrich	70	70
519.	5 t. Grey-headed gull ..	70	70
520.	6 t. African pygmy goose	70	40
521.	7 t. Cattle egret	70	15
522.	8 t. Lanner falcon	1·00	90

523. 10 t. Yellow-billed stork .. 1·00 15
524. 15 t. Red-billed pintail (horiz.) .. .. .. 1·25 20
525. 20 t. Barn owl (horiz.) .. 3·25 1·75
526. 25 t. Hammerkop (horiz.) 2·00 70
527. 30 t. South African stilt (horiz.) .. .. .. 2·50 80
528. 35 t. Blacksmith plover (horiz.) .. .. .. 2·50 80
529. 45 t. Senegal wattled plover (horiz.) .. .. 2·75 1·00
530. 50 t. Helmet guineafowl (horiz.) .. .. .. 3·25 2·50
531. 1 p. Cape vulture (horiz.) 5·50 7·50
532. 2 p. Augur buzzard (horiz.) 8·50 11·00

136. " Coprinus comatus ".

1982. Christmas. Fungi. Multicoloured.
533 7 t. Type **136** .. .. 1·00 15
534 15 t. "Lactarius deliciosus" 1·75 45
535 35 t. "Amanita pantherina" .. .. 3·00 1·25
536 50 t. "Boletus edulis" .. 4·25 4·00

137. President Quett Masire.

1983. Commonwealth Day. Multicoloured.
537. 7 t. Type **137** 10 10
538. 15 t. Native Dancers .. 15 20
539. 35 t. Melbourne conference centre 45 55
540. 45 t. Meeting of Heads of State, Melbourne 55 80

138. Wattled Crane.

1983. Endangered Species. Multicoloured.
541. 7 t. Type **138** .. .. 1·00 20
542. 15 t. "Aloe lutescens" .. 1·25 65
543. 35 t. Roan Antelope .. 1·60 1·75
544. 50 t. Ivory Palm .. .. 1·75 2·50

139. Wooden Spoons.

1983. Traditional Artifacts. Multicoloured.
545. 7 t. Type **139** 20 10
546. 15 t. Personal ornaments .. 35 30
547. 35 t. Ox-hide Milk Bag .. 65 65
548. 50 t. Decorated Knives .. 85 1·10

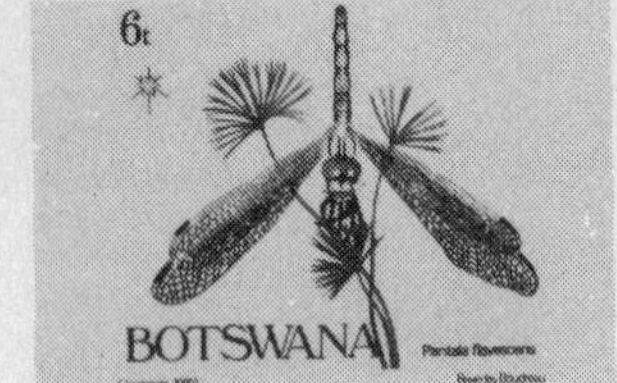

140. " Patntala flavescens ".

1983. Christmas. Dragonflies. Multicoloured.
550 6 t. Type **140** 30 10
551 15 t. "Anax imperator" .. 55 25
552 25 t. "Trithemis arteriosa" .. 75 55
553 45 t. "Chlorolestes elegans" 1·10 1·40

141. Sorting Diamonds.

1984. Mining Industry. Multicoloured.
554. 7 c. Type **141** 75 20
555. 15 c. Lime kiln .. .. 1·10 55
556. 35 c. Copper-nickel smelter plant (vert.) .. .. 1·75 1·10
557. 50 c. Stockpiled coal (vert.) 2·25 2·75

142. Riding Cattle.

1984. Traditional Transport. Multicoloured.
558. 7 t. Type **142** 15 10
559. 25 t. Sledge 35 40
560. 35 t. Wagon 50 60
561. 50 t. Two-wheeled donkey cart 75 90

143. Avro "504" Aircraft.

1984. 40th Anniv. of International Civil Aviation Organization. Multicoloured.
562. 7 t. Type **143** 40 10
563. 10 t. Westland "Wessex" 55 15
564. 15 t. Junkers "Ju 52/3M" 90 55
565. 25 t. De Havilland "Dragon Six" .. .. .. 1·10 85
566. 35 t. Douglas "DC3 Dakota" 1·25 1·25
567. 50 t. Fokker "F27 Friendship" .. .. .. 1·60 2·25

144. "Papilio demodocus".

1984. Christmas. Butterflies. Multicoloured.
568 7 t. Type **144** 75 15
569 25 t. "Byblia anvatara" .. 1·40 80
570 35 t. "Danaus chrysippus" 1·60 1·25
571 50 t. "Graphium taboranus" .. .. 1·75 2·75

No. 570 is incorrectly inscribed "Hypolimnas misippus".

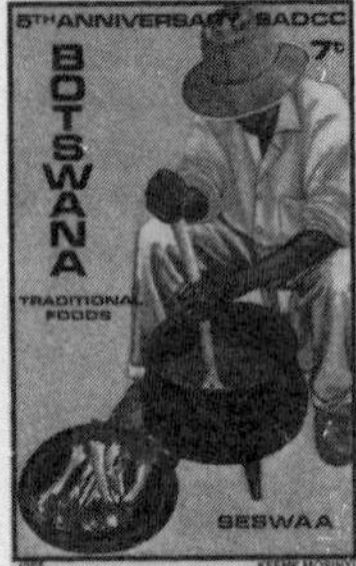

145. Seswaa (meat dish).

1985. 5th Anniv. of Southern African Development Co-ordination Conference. Traditional Foods. Multicoloured.
572. 7 t. Type **145** 20 10
573. 15 t. Bogobe (cereal porridge) 35 25
574. 25 t. Madila (soured coagulated cow's milk) 50 35
575. 50 t. Phane (caterpillars) .. 85 90

146. 1885 British Bechuanaland Overprint on Cape of Good Hope ½d.

1985. Centenary of First Bechuanaland Stamps.
577. **146.** 7 t black, grey-black and red 40 10
578. – 15 t. black, brown and yellow 60 30
579. – 25 t. black and red .. 85 55
580. – 35 t. black, blue and gold 95 70
581. – 50 t. multicoloured .. 1·10 1·50

DESIGNS—VERT—15 t. 1897 Bechuanaland Protectorate overprint on G.B. 3d.; 25 t. Bechuanaland Protectorate 1932 1d. definitive. HORIZ.—35 t. Bechuanaland 1965 Internal Self-Government 5 c.; 50 t. Botswana 1966 Independence 2½ c.

147. Bechuanaland Border Police, 1885–95.

1985. Centenary of Botswana Police. Mult.
582. 7 t. Type **147** .. .. 1·25 30
583. 10 t. Bechuanaland Mounted Police, 1895–1902 1·50 30
584. 25 t. Bechuanaland Protectorate Police, 1903–66 .. .. .. 2·00 1·50
585. 50 t. Botswana Police, from 1966 .. .. 3·00 3·50

148. "Cucumis metuliferus".

1985. Christmas. Edible Wild Cucumbers. Multicoloured.
586. 7 t. Type **148** 45 10
587. 15 t. "Acanthosicyos naudinianus" 70 50
588. 25 t. "Coccinia sessifolia" 1·00 85
589. 50 t. "Momordica balsamina" .. .. .. 1·75 2·50

149. Mr. Shippard and Chief Gaseitsiwe of the Bangwaketse.

1985. Centenary of Declaration of Bechuanaland Protectorate. Multicoloured.
590. 7 t. Type **149** 30 10
591. 15 t. Sir Charles Warren and Chief Sechele of the Bakwena 45 60
592. 25 t. Rev. Mackenzie and Chief Khama of the Bamangwato 70 70
593. 50 t. Map showing Protectorate .. .. 1·25 1·75

150. Halley's Comet over Serowe.

1986. Appearance of Halley's Comet. Multicoloured.
595. 7 t. Type **150** 50 10
596. 15 t. Comet over Bobonong at sunset 85 45
597. 35 t. Comet over Gomare at dawn .. .. 1·25 90
598. 50 t. Comet over Thamaga and Letlhakeng .. .. 1·50 2·00

151. Milk Bag.

1986. Traditional Milk Containers. Mult.
599. 8 t. Type **151** 10 10
600. 15 t. Clay pot and calabashes 20 25
601. 35 t. Wooden milk bucket 45 55
602. 50 t. Milk churn 60 80

153. "Ludwigia stogonifera".

1986. Christmas. Flowers of Okavango. Multicoloured.
604. 8 t. Type **153** 75 10
605. 15 t. "Sopubia mannii" .. 1·60 80
606. 35 t. "Commelina diffusa" 2·50 1·50
607. 35 t. "Hibiscus diversifolius" .. .. 3·00 4·00

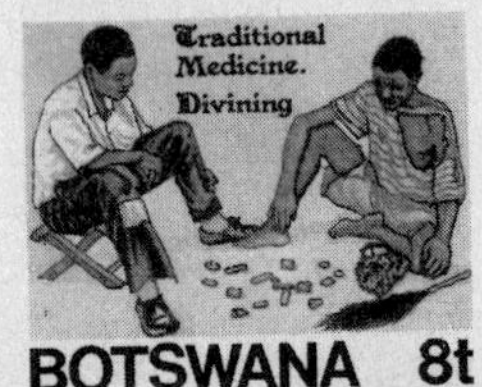

154. Divining.

1987. Traditional Medicine. Multicoloured.

608. 8 t. Type **154** 50 10
609. 15 t. Lightning prevention 85 55
610. 35 t. Rain making .. 1·50 1·25
611. 50 t. Blood letting .. 1·75 2·25

1987. Nos. 520, 523 and 530 surch.

612. 3 t. on 6 t. African pygmy goose 30 30
613. 5 t. on 10 t. Yellow-billed stork 30 30
614. 20 t. on 50 t. Helmet guineafowl (horiz.) .. 70 70

156. Oral Rehydration Therapy.

1987. U.N.I.C.E.F. Child Survival Campaign. Multicoloured.

615. 8 t. Type **156** 20 10
616. 15 t. Growth monitoring .. 35 30
617. 35 t. Immunization .. 75 80
618. 50 t. Breast feeding .. 1·10 1·40

157. Cape Fox.

1987. Animals of Botswana. Multicoloured.

619. 1 t. Type **157** 10 15
620. 2 t. Lechwe 10 15
621. 3 t. Zebra 10 15
622. 4 t. Duiker 10 15
623. 5 t. Banded mongoose .. 15 15
624. 6 t. Rusty-spotted genet .. 15 15
625. 8 t. Hedgehog 20 10
626. 10 t. Scrub hare 20 10
627. 12 t. Hippopotamus .. 30 30
628. 15 t. Suricate 30 15
629. 20 t. Caracal 40 30
630. 25 t. Steenbok 40 30
631. 30 t. Gemsbok 40 30
632. 35 t. Square-lipped rhinoceros 60 30
633. 40 t. Mountain reedbuck .. 55 35
634. 50 t. Rock Dassie 55 55
635. 1 p. Giraffe .. .. .. 1·00 1·25
636. 2 p. Tsessebe .. .. 1·75 2·00
637. 3 p. Side-striped jackal .. 3·00 3·50
638. 5 p. Hartebeest .. .. 5·50 6·00

158. "Cyperus articulatus".

1987. Christmas. Grasses and Sedges of Okavango. Multicoloured.

639. 8 t. Type **158** 20 10
640. 15 t. Broomgrass 30 25
641. 30 t. "Cyperus alopurcides" 55 55
642. 1 p. Bulrush sedge .. 1·40 1·60

159. Planting Seeds with Digging Stick.

1988. Early Cultivation. Multicoloured.

644. 8 t. Type **159** 20 10
645. 15 t. Using iron hoe 30 25
646. 35 t. Wooden ox-drawn plough 50 60
647. 50 t. Villagers using lesotlas 70 85

160 Red Lechwe at Water-hole

1988. Red Lechwe. Multicoloured.

648 10 t. Type **160** 30 10
649 15 t. Red lechwe and early morning sun .. 45 25
650 35 t. Female and calf .. 75 45
651 75 t. Herd on the move .. 1·40 1·60

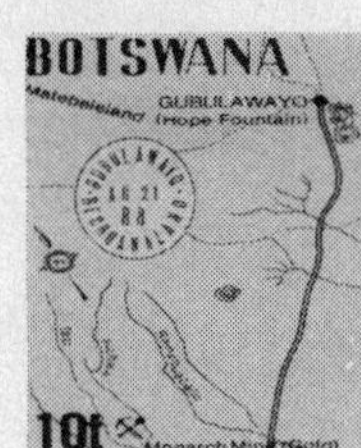

161 Gubulawayo Postmark and Route Southwards to Tati

1988. Centenary of Mafeking–Gubalawayo Runner Post. Designs as Nos. 294/7, but redrawn smaller with changed inscription as in T **161**. Multicoloured.

652 10 t. Type **161** 30 10
653 15 t. Bechuanaland 1888 6d. on 6d. stamp and route from Tati southwards 45 25
654 30 t. Runners and twin routes south from Shoshong 80 70
655 60 t. Mafeking postmark and routes to Bechuanaland and Transvaal .. .. 1·40 1·60

162 Pope John Paul II and Outline Map of Botswana

1988. Visit of Pope John Paul II. Mult.

657 10 t. Type **162** 25 10
658 15 t. Pope John Paul II .. 35 25
659 30 t. Pope giving blessing and outline map .. 55 60
660 80 t. Pope John Paul II (different) .. 1·40 1·60

163 National Museum and Art Gallery, Gaborone

1988. 20th Anniv of National Museum and Art Gallery, Gaborone. Multicoloured.

661 8 t. Type **163** 15 10
662 15 t. Pottery 20 25
663 30 t. Blacksmith's buffalo bellows 35 40
664 60 t. Children and mobile museum van 60 80

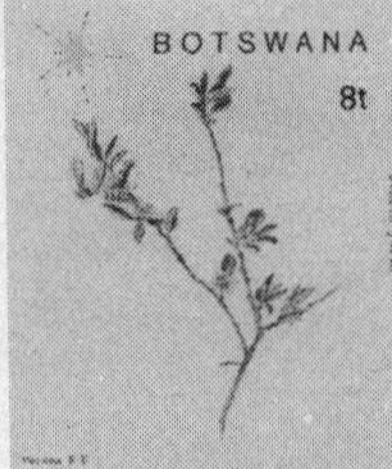

164 "Grewia flava"

1988. Flowering Plants of South-eastern Botswana. Multicoloured.

665 8 t. Type **164** 15 10
666 15 t. "Cienfuegosia digitata" 20 20
667 40 t. "Solanum seaforthianum" .. 45 45
668 75 t. "Carissa bispinosa" .. 75 85

165 Basket Granary

1989. Traditional Grain Storage. Mult.

669 8 t. Type **165** 20 10
670 15 t. Large letlole granary 35 20
671 30 t. Pot granary .. 55 40
672 60 t. Two types of serala .. 90 75

166 Female with Eggs

1989. Red-throated Heron ("Slaty Egret"). Multicoloured.

673 8 t. Type **166** 25 10
674 15 t. Chicks in nest .. 40 15
675 30 t. In flight 55 40
676 60 t. Pair building nest .. 85 75

167 "My Work at Home" (Ephraim Seeletso)

1989. Children's Paintings. Multicoloured.

678 10 t. Type **167** 30 10
679 15 t. "My Favourite Game" (hopscotch) (Neelma Bhatia) (vert) 40 30
680 30 t. "My Favourite Toy" (clay animals) (Thabo Habana) 65 65
681 1 p. "My School Day" (Thabo Olesitse) .. 1·75 2·00

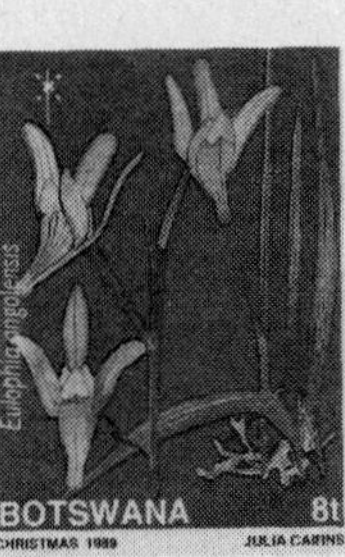

168 "Eulophia angolensis"

171 Telephone Engineer

169 Bechuanaland 1965 New Constitution 25 c. Stamp (25th anniv of Self Government)

1989. Christmas. Orchids. Multicoloured.

682 8 t. Type **168** 40 10
683 15 t. "Eulophia hereroensis" 70 35
684 30 t. "Eulophia speciosa" 1·10 85
685 60 t. "Eulophia petersii" 1·90 2·25

1990. Anniversaries.

686 **169** 8 t. multicoloured .. 30 10
687 – 15 t. multicoloured .. 45 30
688 – 30 t. multicoloured .. 70 70
689 – 60 t. black, blue & yell 1·10 1·50

DESIGNS: 15 t. Casting vote in ballot box (25th anniv of First Elections); 30 t. Outline map and flags of Southern African Development Co-ordination Conference countries (10th anniv); 60 t. Penny Black (150th anniv of first postage stamp).

1990. Nos. 619, 624 and 627 surch.

690 10 t. on 1 t. Type **157** .. 25 15
691 20 t. on 6 t. Rusty-spotted genet 35 35
692 50 t. on 12 t. Hippopotamus 75 75

1990. "Stamp World London 90" International Stamp Exhibition. Multicoloured.

693 8 t. Type **171** 15 10
694 15 t. Transmission pylon .. 25 20
695 30 t. Public telephone .. 40 35
696 2 p. Testing circuit board 1·75 2·00

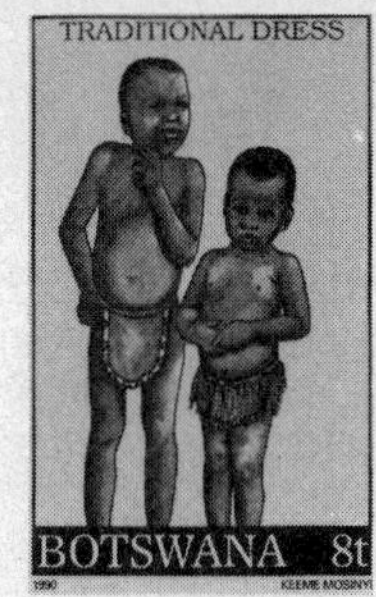

172 Young Children

1990. Traditional Dress. Multicoloured.

697 8 t. Type **172** 15 10
698 15 t. Young woman .. 25 25
699 30 t. Adult man 40 40
700 2 p. Adult woman .. 1·75 2·00

173 "Acacia nigrescens"

1990. Christmas. Flowering Trees. Mult.

702 8 t. Type **173** 20 10
703 15 t. "Peltophorum africanum" 35 20
704 30 t. "Burkea africana" .. 40 35
705 2 p. "Pterocarpus angolensis" .. .. 1·90 2·25

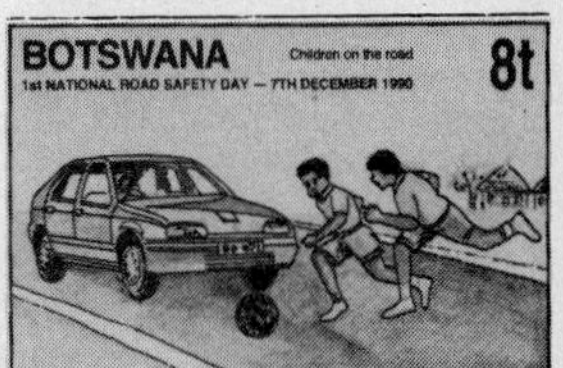

174 Children running in front of Car

1990. 1st National Road Safety Day. Mult.

706	8 t. Type **174**	30	15
707	15 t. Careless overtaking ..	55	30
708	30 t. Cattle on road ..	1·10	1·25

175 Cattle

1991. Rock Paintings. Multicoloured.

709	8 t. Type **175**	20	15
710	15 t. Cattle, drying frames and tree	35	25
711	30 t. Animal hides ..	55	55
712	2 p. Family herding cattle	1·90	2·25

176 Children

1991. National Census. Multicoloured.

713	8 t. Type **176**	15	10
714	15 t. Village	30	25
715	30 t. School	40	35
716	2 p. Hospital	1·50	2·00

177 Tourists viewing Elephants

1991. African Tourism Year. Okavango Delta. Multicoloured.

717	8 t. Type **177**	35	20
718	15 t. Crocodiles basking on river bank	45	30
719	35 t. Fish eagles and aircraft	75	65
720	2 p. Okavango wildlife (26 × 44 mm)	2·50	3·00

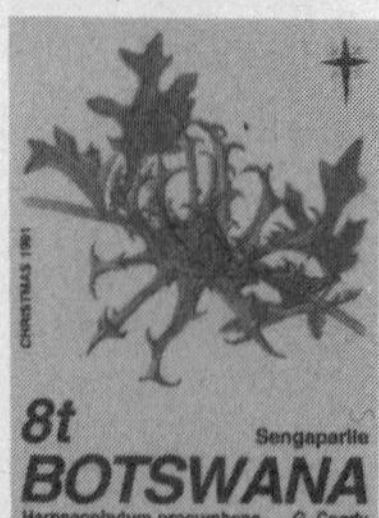

178 "Harpagophytum procumbens"

1991. Christmas. Seed Pods. Multicoloured.

721	8 t. Type **178**	15	10
722	15 t. "Tylosema esculentum"	25	20
723	30 t. "Abrus precatorius"	35	30
724	2 p. "Kigelia africana" ..	1·40	1·75

1992. Nos. 621, 624 and 627 surch.

725	8 t. on 12 t. Hippopotamus	20	15
726	10 t. on 12 t. Hippopotamus	20	20
727	25 t. on 6 t. Rusty-spotted genet	45	45
728	40 t. on 3 t. Zebra ..	70	80

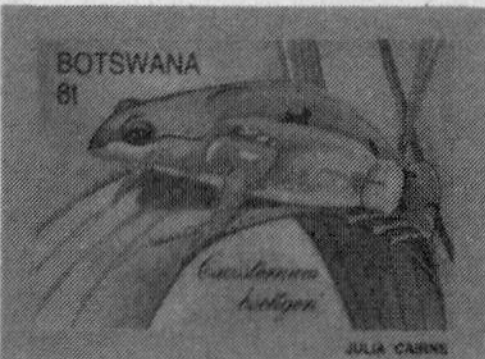

179 "Cacosternum boettgeri"

1992. Climbing Frogs. Multicoloured.

729	8 t. Type **179**	20	15
730	10 t. "Hyperolius marmoratus angolensis" (vert)	20	15
731	40 t. "Bufo fenoulheti" ..	75	60
732	1 p. "Hyperolius sp." (vert)	1·40	1·60

180 Air-conditioned Coaches

1992. Deluxe Railway Service. Multicoloured.

733	10 t. Type **180**	20	10
734	25 t. Diesel locomotive No. BD001 (vert) ..	40	35
735	40 t. Coach interior (vert)	65	60
736	2 p. Diesel locomotive No. BD028	2·25	2·50

181 Cheetah

1992. Animals. Multicoloured.

738	1 t. Type **181**	10	10
739	2 t. Spring hare	10	10
740	4 t. Blackfooted cat ..	10	10
741	5 t. Striped mouse ..	10	10
742	10 t. Oribi	10	10
743	12 t. Pangolin	10	10
744	15 t. Aardwolf	10	10
745	20 t. Warthog	10	10
746	25 t. Ground squirrel ..	15	20
747	35 t. Honey badger ..	20	25
748	40 t. Common mole rat ..	20	25
749	45 t. Wild dog	25	30
750	50 t. Water mongoose ..	25	30
751	80 t. Klipspringer ..	40	45
752	1 p. Lesser bushbaby ..	50	55
753	2 p. Bushveld elephant shrew	1·00	1·10
754	5 p. Zorilla	2·50	2·75
755	10 p. Vervet monkey ..	5·00	5·50

182 Boxing

183 "Adiantum incisum"

1992. Olympic Games, Barcelona. Mult.

756	10 t. Type **182**	15	10
757	50 t. Running	40	40
758	1 p. Boxing (different) ..	75	85
759	2 p. Running (different) ..	1·40	1·75

1992. Christmas. Ferns. Multicoloured.

761	10 t. Type **183**	20	10
762	25 t. "Actiniopteris radiata"	35	30
763	40 t. "Ceratopteris cornuta"	45	40
764	1 p. 50 "Pellaea calomelanos"	1·50	1·60

184 Helping Blind Person (Lions Club International)

1993. Charitable Organizations in Botswana. Multicoloured.

765	10 t. Type **184**	10	10
766	15 t. Nurse carrying child (Red Cross Society) (horiz)	15	15
767	25 t. Woman watering seedling (Ecumenical Decade)	25	25
768	35 t. Deaf children (Round Table) (horiz)	35	35
769	40 t. Crowd of people (Rotary International)	40	45
770	50 t. Hands at prayer (Botswana Christian Council) (horiz) ..	50	55

185 Bechuanaland Railways Class "6" Locomotive No. 1

1993. Railway Centenary. Multicoloured.

771	10 t. Type **185**	15	10
772	40 t. Class "19" locomotive No. 317	35	35
773	50 t. Class "12" locomotive No. 256	45	45
774	1 p. 50 Class "7" locomotive No. 71	1·10	1·25

186 Long-crested Eagle

1993. Endangered Eagles. Multicoloured.

776	10 t. Type **186**	15	10
777	25 t. Snake eagle	25	25
778	50 t. Bateleur	50	50
779	1 p. 50 Secretary bird ..	1·25	1·40

187 "Aloe zebrina"

1993. Christmas. Flora. Multicoloured.

780	12 t. Type **187**	15	10
781	25 t. "Croton megalobotrys"	25	20
782	50 t. "Boophane disticha"	40	40
783	1 p. "Euphoria davyi" ..	75	85

188 Boy with String Puppet

1994. Traditional Toys. Multicoloured.

784	10 t. Type **188**	10	10
785	40 t. Boys with clay cattle	20	25
786	50 t. Boy with spinner ..	25	30
787	1 p. Girls playing in make-believe houses ..	50	55

POSTAGE DUE STAMPS

1967. Nos. D 10/2 of Bechuanaland optd. **REPUBLIC OF BOTSWANA.**

D 13.	D 1.	1 c. red	15	1·75
D 14.		2 c. violet	15	2·00
D 15.		5 c. green	20	2·00

D 5. African Elephant.

D 6. Common Zebra.

1971.

D 16.	D 5.	1 c. red	55	2·00
D 17.		2 c. violet	1·25	2·25
D 18.		6 c. brown	1·60	3·25
D 19.		14 c. green	2·00	4·00

1977.

D 25	D 6.	1 t. black and red ..	10	10
D 26		2 t. black and green ..	10	10
D 27		4 t. black and red ..	10	10
D 28		10 t. black and blue ..	10	10
D 29		16 t. black & brown ..	10	10

BRITISH ANTARCTIC TERRITORY

Constituted in 1962 comprising territories south of latitude 60° S., from the former Falkland Is. Dependencies.

1963. 12 pence = 1 shilling.
20 shillings = 1 pound.
1971. 100 (new) pence = 1 pound.

1. M.V. "Kista Dan".

1963.

1. 1. ½d. blue .. .. .. 45 1·00
2. – 1d. brown 70 60
3. – 1½d. red and purple .. 70 60
4. – 2d. purple .. .. .. 1·00 60
5. – 2½d. myrtle .. .. 1·00 60
6. – 3d. turquoise .. .. 2·00 60
7. – 4d. sepia .. .. .. 1·50 1·00
8. – 6d. olive and blue .. 2·50 1·25
9. – 9d. green .. .. .. 2·50 1·00
10. – 1s. turquoise .. .. 1·75 60
11. – 2s. violet and brown .. 14·00 5·00
12. – 2s. 6d. blue .. .. 14·00 5·50
13. – 5s. orange and red .. 20·00 8·50
14. – 10s. blue and green .. 45·00 23·00
15. – £1 black and blue .. 75·00 48·00
15a.– £1 red and black .. £150 £120

DESIGNS: 1d. Manhauling. 1½d. Muskeg (tractor). 2d. Skiing. 2½d. Beaver (aircraft). 3d. R.R.S. "John Biscoe". 4d. Camp scene. 6d. H.M.S. "Protector". 9d. Sledging. 1s. Otter (aircraft). 2s. Huskies. 2s. 6d. Helicopter. 5s. Snocat (tractor). 10s. R.R.S. "Shackleton". £1 (No. 15), Antarctic map. £1 (No. 15a.), H.M.S. "Endurance".

1966. Churchill Commemoration. As T 38 of Antigua.

16. ½d. blue .. .. .. 80 2·00
17. 1d. green .. .. .. 3·00 2·00
18. 1s. brown .. .. .. 21·00 5·50
19. 2s. violet .. .. .. 24·00 6·00

17. Lemaire Channel and Icebergs.

1969. 25th Anniv. of Continuous Scientific Work.

20. 17. 3½d. black, blue & ultram. 3·50 2·00
21. – 6d. multicoloured .. 3·50 2·00
22. – 1s. black, blue and red .. 3·50 2·00
23. – 2s. black, orange and turq. 4·25 2·75

DESIGNS: 6d. Radio Sonde balloon. 1s. Muskeg pulling tent equipment. 2s. Surveyors with theodolite.

1971. Decimal Currency. Nos. 1/14 surch.

24. ½p. on ½d. blue .. .. 60 2·00
25. 1p. on 1d. brown .. .. 1·00 60
26. 1½p. on 1½d. red and purple 1·25 50
27. 2p. on 2d. purple .. .. 1·25 30
28. 2½p. on 2½d. green .. .. 1·75 40
29. 3p. on 3d. blue .. .. 2·50 55
30. 4p. on 4d. brown .. .. 2·25 55
31. 5p. on 6d. green and blue 4·25 2·50
32. 6p. on 9d. green .. .. 9·00 5·00
33. 7½p. on 1s. blue .. .. 9·00 5·50
34. 10p. on 2s. violet & brown 16·00 11·00
35. 15p. on 2s. 6d. blue .. 16·00 11·00
36. 25p. on 5s. orange & red .. 22·00 15·00
37. 50p. on 10s. blue & green 60·00 35·00

19. Setting up Camp.

1971. 10th Anniv. of Antarctic Treaty. Multicoloured.

38. 1½p. Type 19 .. .. 5·50 3·50
39. 4p. Snow Petrels .. .. 11·00 5·50
40. 5p. Weddell Seals .. .. 9·50 5·50
41. 10p. Adelie Penguins .. 16·00 8·00

Nos. 38/41 each include Antarctic Map and Queen Elizabeth in their design.

1972. Royal Silver Wedding. As Type 52 of Ascension, but with Kerguelen fur seals and Emperor penguins in background.

42. 5p. brown .. .. .. 3·75 2·50
43. 10p. green .. .. .. 3·75 2·50

21. James Cook and H.M.S. "Resolution".

1973. Multicoloured.

64a ½p. Type 21 .. .. 75 1·00
65 1p. Thaddeus Von Bellingshausen and "Vostok" .. .. 60 1·25
66 1½p. James Weddell and "Jane" .. .. .. 60 1·25
67 2p. John Biscoe and "Tula" .. .. .. 1·50 80
68 2½p. J. S. C. Dumont d'Urville and "L'Astrolabe" .. 1·50 80
49 3p. James Clark Ross and H.M.S. "Erebus" .. 95 1·75
70 4p. C. A. Larsen and "Jason" .. .. .. 55 2·00
51 5p. Adrien de Gerlache and "Belgica" .. .. 1·00 1·75
72 6p. Otto Nordenskjold and "Antarctic" .. .. 80 2·00
73 7½p. W. S. Bruce and "Scotia" .. .. .. 1·50 2·25
74a 10p. Jean-Baptiste Charcot and "Pourquoi Pas?" .. 1·00 2·75
75 15p. Ernest Shackleton and "Endurance" .. .. 1·25 1·50
76 25p. Hubert Wilkins and "San Francisco" .. 1·25 1·50
77a 50p. Lincoln Ellsworth and "Polar Star" .. .. 1·25 2·75
78a £1 John Rymill and "Penola" .. .. 2·00 4·00

The 25p. and 50p. show aircraft; the rest show ships.

1973. Royal Wedding. As Type 47 of Anguilla. Background colour given. Mult.

59. 5p. brown 40 20
60. 15p. blue 70 30

22. Churchill and Churchill Peninsula, B.A.T.

1974. Birth Centenary of Sir Winston Churchill. Multicoloured.

61. 5p. Type 22 .. .. 1·75 1·50
62. 15p. Churchill and "Trepassey" .. .. 2·25 2·00

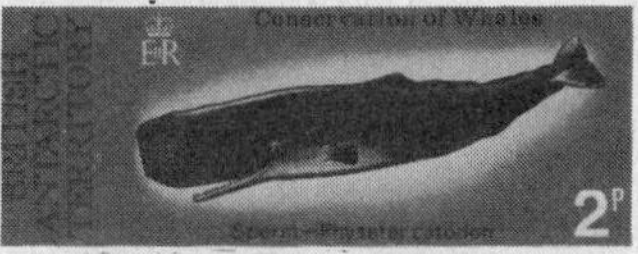

23. Sperm Whale. (Illustration reduced, actual size 58 × 21 mm).

1977. Conservation of Whales. Mult.

79. 2p. Type 23 .. .. 4·25 1·75
80. 8p. Fin Whale .. .. 5·50 2·25
81. 11p. Humpback Whale .. 6·00 2·25
82. 25p. Blue Whale .. .. 7·50 3·00

24. The Queen Before Taking the Oath.

1977. Silver Jubilee. Multicoloured.

83. 6p. Prince Philip's visit, 1956/7 .. .. .. 95 20
84. 11p. The Coronation Oath 1·25 30
85. 33p. Type 24 .. .. 1·50 45

25. Emperor Penguin.

1978. 25th Anniv. of Coronation.

86. – 25p. green, deep green and silver .. .. .. 1·10 75
87. – 25p. multicoloured .. 1·10 75
88. 25. 25p. green, deep green and silver .. .. .. 1·10 75

DESIGNS: No. 86, Black Bull of Clarence. No. 87, Queen Elizabeth II.

26. Macaroni Penguins.

1979. Penguins. Multicoloured.

89. 3p. Type 26 .. .. 7·00 6·50
90. 8p. Gentoo penguins .. 2·75 2·25
91. 11p. Adelie penguins .. 3·00 2·50
92. 25p. Emperor penguins .. 4·00 3·25

27. Sir John Barrow and "Tula".

1980. 150th Anniv of Royal Geographical Society. Former Presidents. Multicoloured.

93 3p. Type 27 .. .. 20 10
94 7p. Sir Clement Markham and "Discovery" 25 25
95 11p. Lord Curzon and whale-boat "James Caird" .. 30 30
96 15p. Sir William Goodenough 35 35
97 22p. Sir James Wordie .. 50 55
98 30p. Sir Raymond Priestley 60 65

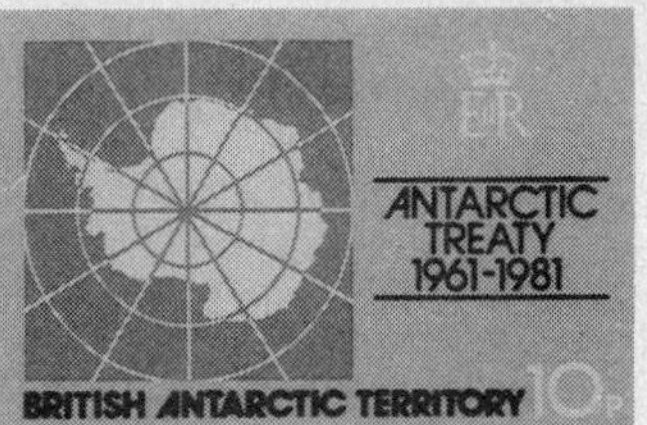

28. Map of Antarctic.

1981. 20th Anniv. of Antarctic Treaty.

99. 28. 10p. blk., blue & light blue 30 70
100. – 13p. blk., blue and grn. 35 80
101. – 25p. blk., blue & mauve 50 90
102. – 26p. blk., brn. and red 50 90

DESIGNS: 13p. Conservation research ("scientific co-operation"). 25p. Satellite image mapping ("technical co-operation"). 26p. Global geophysics ("scientific co-operation").

29. Map of Gondwana 280 million years ago and Contemporary Landscape Scene.

1982. Gondwana—Continental Drift and Climatic Change. Maps of Gondwana showing position of continents, and contemporary landscapes. Multicoloured.

103. 3p. Type 29 .. .. 20 40
104. 6p. 260 million years ago 25 50
105. 10p. 230 million years ago 30 60
106. 13p. 175 million years ago 35 70
107. 25p. 50 million years ago 55 75
108. 26p. Present day .. 55 75

30. British Antarctic Territory Coat of Arms.

1982. 21st Birthday of Princess of Wales. Multicoloured.

109. 5p. Type 30 .. .. 20 20
110. 17p. Princess of Wales (detail of painting by Bryan Organ) 45 50
111. 37p. Wedding ceremony 85 1·00
112. 50p. Formal portrait .. 95 1·40

31. Leopard Seal.
(Illustration reduced. Actual size 57 × 22mm.)

1983. 10th Anniv. of Antarctic Seal Conservation Convention. Multicoloured.

113. 5p. Type 31 .. .. 35 35
114. 10p. Weddell seals .. 40 40
115. 13p. Southern elephant seals 45 45
116. 17p. Kerguelen fur seals .. 55 55
117. 25p. Ross seals 65 65
118. 34p. Crabeater seals .. 85 85

32. De Havilland "Twin Otter".

1983. Bicentenary of Manned Flight. Mult.

119. 5 p. Type 32 .. .. 25 20
120. 13 p. De Havilland "Single Otter" 40 35
121. 17 p. Consolidated "Canso" 55 45
122. 50 p. Lockheed "Vega" .. 1·10 1·10

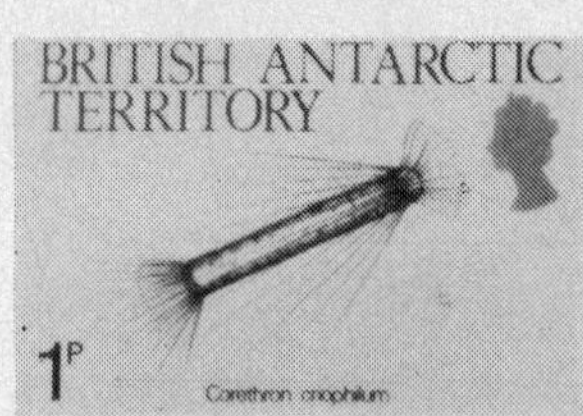

33. "Corethron criophilum".

1984. Marine Life. Multicoloured.

123. 1p. Type 33 .. .. 40 65
124. 2p. "Desmonema gaudichaudi" 45 65
125. 3p. "Tomopteris carpenteri" 45 75
126. 4p. "Pareuchaeta antarctica" 50 80
127. 5p. "Antarctomysis maxima" 50 80
128. 6p. "Antarcturus signiensis 55 90
129. 7p. "Serolis cornuta" .. 55 90
130. 8p. "Parathemisto gaudichaudii" .. .. .. 60 1·00
131. 9p. "Bovallia gigantea" .. 60 1·00
132. 10p. "Euphausia superba" 60 1·00
133. 15p. "Colossendeis australis" .. .. .. 70 1·25
134. 20p. "Todarodes sagittatus" .. .. .. 75 1·50
135. 25p. "Notothenia neglecta" 80 1·50
136. 50p. "Chaenocephalus aceratus" .. .. .. 1·25 1·75
137. £1 Crabeater seal .. .. 1·75 2·25
138. £3 Antarctic marine food chain .. .. .. 5·00 6·00

34. M.Y. "Penola" in Stella Creek.

1985. 50th Anniv. of British Graham Land Expedition. Multicoloured.

139. 7p. Type **34** 30 45
140. 22p. Northern Base, Winter Island 60 90
141. 27p. D. H. "Fox Moth" at Southern Base, Barry Island .. .. .. 70 1·00
142. 54p. Dog Team near Ablation Point, George VI Sound .. .. 1·25 1·75

35. Robert McCormick and McCormick's Skua.

1985. Early Naturalists. Multicoloured.

143. 7p. Type **35** .. .. 1·25 1·25
144. 22p. Sir Joseph Dalton Hooker and "Deschampsia antarctica" .. .. 1·75 2·00
145. 27p. Jean René C. Quoy and Hourglass Dolphin 1·90 2·00
146. 54p. James Weddell and Weddell Seal .. .. 2·75 3·00

36. Dr. Edmond Halley.

1986. Appearance of Halley's Comet. Mult.

147. 7p. Type **36** .. .. 1·00 65
148. 22p. Halley Station, Antarctica .. .. 1·75 1·10
149. 27p. "Halley's Comet, 1531" (from Peter Apian woodcut, 1532) .. .. 2·00 1·25
150. 54p. "Giotto" spacecraft .. 3·50 1·75

37. Snow Crystal.

1986. 50th Anniv. of International Glaciological Society. Snow crystals.

151. **37.** 10p. light blue and blue 50 50
152. – 24p. green & deep green 80 80
153. – 29p. mauve & dp. mve. 90 90
154. – 58p. blue and violet .. 1·25 1·75

MORE DETAILED LISTS
are given in the Stanley Gibbons Catalogues referred to in the country headings.
For lists of current volumes see Introduction.

38. Captain Scott, 1904.

1987. 75th Anniv. of Captain Scott's Arrival at South Pole. Multicoloured.

155. 10p. Type **38** 45 60
156. 24p. Hut Point and "Discovery", Ross Island, 1902–4 .. .. 80 1·10
157. 29p. Cape Evans Hut, 1911–13 .. .. .. 95 1·40
158. 58p. Scott's expedition at South Pole, 1912 .. 1·60 2·25

39. I.G.Y. Logo.

1987. 30th Anniv. of International Geophysical Year.

159. **39.** 10p. black and green .. 30 60
160. – 24p. multicoloured .. 60 1·10
161. – 29p. multicoloured .. 75 1·40
162. – 58p. multicoloured .. 1·40 2·25

DESIGNS: 24p. Port Lockroy. 29p. Argentine Islands. 58p. Halley Bay.

40. Aurora over South Ice Plateau Station.

1988. 30th Anniv. of Commonwealth Trans-Antarctic Expedition. Multicoloured.

163. 10p. Type **40** 30 30
164. 24p. "Otter" aircraft at Theron Mountains .. 60 60
165. 29p. Seismic ice-depth sounding 70 70
166. 58p. "Sno-cat" over crevasse .. .. .. 1·25 1·40

41 "Xanthoria elegans"

1989. Lichens. Multicoloured.

167 10p. Type **41** 45 50
168 24p. "Usnea aurantiaco-atra" .. 90 1·00
169 29p. "Cladonia chlorophaea" .. .. .. 1·00 1·10
170 58p. "Umbilicaria antarctica" .. .. 1·75 2·00

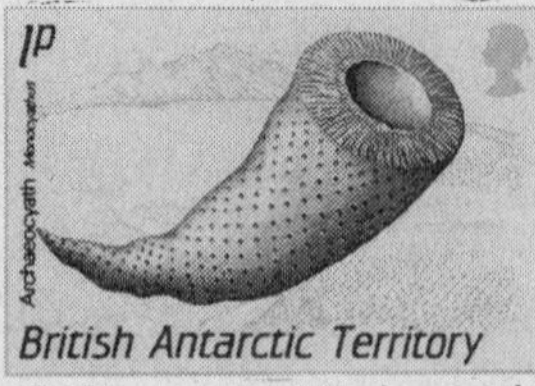

42 "Monocyathus" (archaeocyath)

1990. Fossils. Multicoloured.

171 1p. Type **42** 10 10
172 2p. "Lingulella" (brachiopod) 10 10
173 3p. "Triplagnoslus" (trilobite) 10 10
174 4p. "Lyriaspis" (trilobite) 10 10
175 5p. "Glossopteris" leaf (gymnosperm) 10 10
176 6p. "Gonatosorus" (fern) 10 10
177 7p. "Belemnopsis" (belemnite) 15 20
178 8p. "Sanmartinoceras" (ammonite) 15 20
179 9p. "Pinna" (mussel) .. 20 25
180 10p. "Aucellina" (mussel) 20 25
181 20p. "Trigonia" (mussel) .. 40 45
182 25p. "Perissoptera" (conch shell) 50 55
183 50p. "Ainoceras" (ammonite) .. .. .. 1·00 1·10
184 £1 "Gunnarites" (ammonite) .. .. .. 2·00 2·10
185 £3 "Hoploparia" (crayfish) 6·00 6·25

1990. 90th Birthday of Queen Elizabeth the Queen Mother. As T **134** of Ascension.

186 26p. multicoloured .. 1·25 1·50
187 £1 black and brown .. 3·25 3·50

DESIGNS—21 × 36 mm. 26p. Wedding of Prince Albert and Lady Elizabeth Bowes-Lyon, 1923. 29 × 37 mm. £1 The Royal Family, 1940.

43 Late Cretaceous Forest and Southern Beech Fossil

1991. Age of the Dinosaurs. Multicoloured.

188 12p. Type **43** 60 60
189 26p. Hypsilophodont dinosaurs and skull .. 1·25 1·25
190 31p. Frilled Sharks and tooth .. .. .. 1·50 1·50
191 62p. Mosasaur, Plesiosaur, and Mosasaur vertebra 2·50 2·50

44 Launching Meteorological Balloon, Halley IV Station

1991. Discovery of Antarctic Ozone Hole. Multicoloured.

192 12p. Type **44** 45 50
193 26p. Measuring ozone with Dobson spectrophotometer 85 95
194 31p. Satellite map showing ozone hole .. .. 95 1·10
195 62p. ER-2 aircraft and graph of chlorine monoxide and ozone levels .. .. .. 1·60 2·00

45 Researching Dry Valley

1991. 30th Anniv of Antarctic Treaty.

196 **45** 12p. multicoloured .. 45 50
197 – 26p. multicoloured .. 85 95
198 – 31p. black and green .. 95 1·10
199 – 62p. multicoloured .. 1·60 2·00

DESIGNS: 26p. Relief map of ice sheet; 31p. BIOMASS logo; 62p. Ross seal.

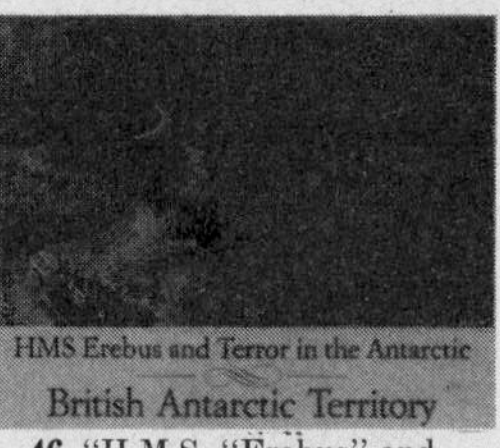

46 "H.M.S. "Erebus" and H.M.S. "Terror" in the Antarctic" (J. Carmichael)

1991. Maiden Voyage of "James Clark Ross" (research ship). Multicoloured.

200 12p. Type **46** 45 50
201 26p. Launch of "James Clark Ross" 85 95
202 31p. "James Clark Ross" in Antarctica .. .. 95 1·10
203 62p. Scientific research .. 1·60 2·00

1991. Birth Bicent of Michael Faraday (scientist). Nos. 200/3 additionally inscr "200th Anniversary M. Faraday 1791–1867".

204 12p. Type **46** 45 50
205 26p. Launch of "James Clark Ross" 85 95
206 31p. "James Clark Ross" in Antarctica .. .. 95 1·10
207 62p. Scientific research .. 1·60 2·00

47 Ross Seals

1992. Endangered Species. Seals and Penguins. Multicoloured.

208 4p. Type **47** 15 15
209 5p. Adelie penguins .. 15 15
210 7p. Weddell seal with pup 20 20
211 29p. Emperor penguins with chicks 90 90
212 34p. Crabeater seals with pup .. .. .. 1·10 1·10
213 68p. Chinstrap penguins with young .. .. 1·90 1·90

48 Sun Pillar at Faraday

1992. Lower Atmospheric Phenomena. Mult.

214 14p. Type **48** 50 50
215 29p. Halo over iceberg .. 90 90
216 34p. Lee Wave cloud .. 1·10 1·10
217 68p. Nacreous clouds .. 1·90 1·90

49 "Fitzroy"

1993. Antarctic Ships. Multicoloured.

218 1p. Type **49** 10 10
219 2p. "William Scoresby" .. 10 10
220 3p. "Eagle" 10 10
221 4p. "Trepassey" 10 10
222 5p. "John Biscoe I" .. 10 10
223 10p. "Norsel" 20 25
224 20p. H.M.S. "Protector" .. 40 45
225 30p. "Oluf Sven" 60 65
226 50p. "John Biscoe II" and "Shackleton" .. .. 1·00 1·10
227 £1 "Tottan" .. .. 2·00 2·10
228 £3 "Perla Dan" .. .. 6·00 6·25
229 £5 H.M.S. "Endurance I" 10·00 10·50

1994. "Hong Kong '94", International Stamp Exhibition. Nos. 240/5 optd **HONG KONG '94** and emblem.

230 15p. Type **51** 30 35
231 24p. Single-engined aircraft 50 55
232 31p. Single-engined aircraft and dog team 60 65
233 36p. Twin-engined aircraft and dog team 70 75
234 62p. Four-engined aircraft over landing strip .. 1·25 1·40
235 72p. Four-engined aircraft on runway .. .. 1·40 1·50

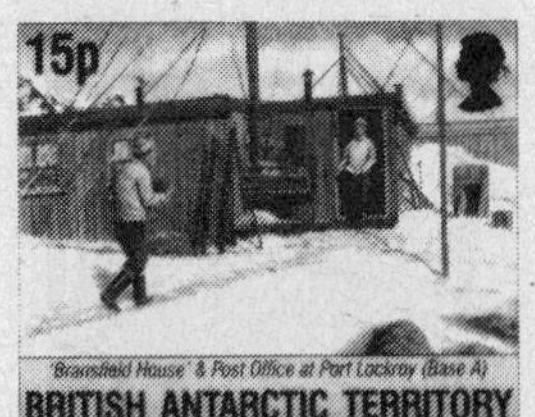

50 Bransfield House Post Office, Port Lockroy

1994. 50th Anniv of Operation Tabarin. Multicoloured.

236 15p. Type **50** 30 35
237 31p. Survey team, Hope Bay 60 65
238 36p. Dog team, Hope Bay 70 75
239 72p. "Fitzroy" (supply ship) and H.M.S. "William Scoresby" (minesweeper) .. .. 1·40 1·50

51 Huskies and Sledge

1994. Forms of Transportation. Mult.

240 15p. Type **51** 30 35
241 24p. Single-engined aircraft 50 55
242 31p. Single-engined aircraft and dog team 60 65
243 36p. Twin-engined aircraft and dog team 70 75
244 62p. Four-engined aircraft over landing strip .. 1·25 1·40
245 72p. Four-engined aircraft on runway .. .. 1·40 1·50

BRITISH COLUMBIA AND VANCOUVER ISLAND

1860. 12 pence = 1 shilling.
20 shillings = 1 pound.
1865. 100 cents = 1 dollar.

Former British colonies, now a Western province of the Dominion of Canada, whose stamps are now used.

1.

1860. Imperf. or perf.

2. **1.** 2½d. pink £275 £180

VANCOUVER ISLAND

2.

1865. Imperf. or perf.. Various frames.

13. **2.** 5 c. red £200 £130
14. – 10 c. blue £200 £140

BRITISH COLUMBIA

4. Emblems of United Kingdom.

1865.

21. **4.** 3d. blue .. .. .. 70·00 60·00

1868. Surch. in words or figures and words.

28 4 2 c. brown .. .. 75·00 75·00
29 5 c. red .. .. .. 90·00 90·00
24 10 c. red £400 £400
31 25 c. yellow £110 £110
26 50 c. mauve £400 £350
27 $1 green £600 £700

BRITISH COMMONWEALTH OCCUPATION OF JAPAN

Stamps used by British Commonwealth Occupation Forces, 1946–49.

12 pence = 1 shilling.
20 shillings = 1 pound.

1946. Stamps of Australia optd. **B.C.O.F JAPAN 1946.**

J 1. **27.** ½d. orange .. .. 2·50 4·25
J 2. **46.** 1d. purple .. .. 2·00 1·50
J 3. **31.** 3d. brown .. .. 1·40 1·75
J 4. – 6d. brown (No. 189a) .. 12·00 8·50
J 5. – 1s. green (No. 191) .. 12·00 9·50
J 6. **1.** 2s. red .. .. .. 40·00 45·00
J 7. **38.** 5s. red £110 £130

BRITISH EAST AFRICA

Now incorporated in Kenya and Uganda.

16 annas = 100 cents = 1 rupee.

1890. Stamps of Gt. Britain (1881) surch. **BRITISH EAST AFRICA COMPANY** and value in annas.

1. **57.** ½ a. on 1d. lilac £300 £200
2. **73.** 1 a. on 2d. green & red .. £400 £275
3. **78.** 4 a. on 5d. purple & blue £425 £275

3. Arms of the Company.

11.

1890. Nos. 16/19 are larger (24 × 25 mm.).

4b 3 ½ a. brown .. .. 70 2·00
5 1 a. green .. .. 3·00 3·75
6 2 a. red .. .. 2·75 3·25
7b 2½ a. black on yellow .. 3·75 4·00
8a 3 a. black on red .. 1·25 2·50
9 4 a. brown .. .. 2·50 4·50
11a 4½ a. purple .. .. 2·50 12·00
29 5 a. black on blue .. 1·25 9·50
30 7½ a. black .. .. 1·25 9·50
12 3 8 a. blue .. .. 5·50 7·00
13 8 a. grey £250 £225
14 1 r. red .. .. .. 6·00 9·00
15 1 r. grey £225 £225
16 – 2 r. red .. .. .. 11·00 15·00
17 – 3 r. purple .. .. 8·00 20·00
18 – 4 r. blue .. .. 12·00 26·00
19 – 5 r. green .. .. 30·00 48·00

1891. With handstamped or pen surcharges. Initialled in black.

20. **3.** ½ a. on 2 a. red £2750 £750
31. ½ a. on 3 a. black on red .. £250 45·00
32. 1 a. on 3 a. black on red .. £2500 £1200
26. 1 a. on 4 a. brown £2750 £900

1894. Surch. in words and figures

27. **3.** 5 a. on 8 a. blue .. .. 55·00 75·00
28. 7½ a. on 1 r. red .. .. 55·00 75·00

1895. Optd. **BRITISH EAST AFRICA.**

33. **3.** ½ a. brown .. .. 60·00 20·00
34. 1 a. green .. .. 65·00 65·00
35. 2 a. red .. .. .. £130 90·00
36. 2½ a. black on yellow .. £100 48·00
37. 3 a. black on red .. .. 48·00 38·00
38. 4 a. brown .. .. 38·00 35·00
39. 4½ a. purple .. .. £120 80·00
40. 5 a. black on blue .. £140 90·00
41. 7½ a. black .. .. 80·00 75·00
42. 8 a. blue .. .. .. 80·00 65·00
43. 1 r. red .. .. .. 48·00 42·00
44. – 2 r. red £225 £180
45. – 3 r. purple £130 £100
46. – 4 r. blue £130 £120
47. – 5 r. green £300 £250

1895. Surch. with large **2½.**

48. **3.** 2½ a. on 4½ a. purple .. 85·00 60·00

1895. Stamps of India (Queen Victoria) optd. **British East Africa.**

49. **23.** ½ a. turquoise .. .. 3·50 3·50
50. – 1 a. purple .. .. 3·25 3·50
51. – 1½ a. brown .. .. 3·75 3·25
52. – 2 a. blue .. .. 3·75 2·50
53. – 2½ a. green .. .. 5·50 2·5C
54. – 3 a. orange .. .. 7·50 8·00
55a. – 4 a. green (No. 96) .. 22·00 16·00
56. – 6 a. brown (No. 80) .. 24·00 30·00
57c. – 8 a. mauve .. .. 28·00 38·00
58. – 12 a. purple on red .. 20·00 26·00
59. – 1 r. grey (No. 101) .. 48·00 48·00
60. **37.** 1 r. green and red .. 32·00 50·00
61. **38.** 2 r. red and orange .. 48·00 80·00
62. 3 r. brown and green .. 60·00 90·00
63. 5 r. blue and violet .. 80·00 £110

1895. No. 51 surch. with small **2½.**

64. "2½" on 1½ a. brown .. 45·00 32·00

1896.

65 11 ½ a. green 85 60
66a 1 a. red .. .. 2·00 40
67 2 a. brown .. .. 1·50 3·25
68 2½ a. blue .. .. 4·50 1·10
69 3 a. grey .. .. 2·50 5·00
70 4 a. green .. .. 5·50 2·75
71 4½ a. yellow .. .. 3·50 8·50
72 5 a. brown .. .. 7·50 4·00
73 7½ a. mauve .. .. 5·00 20·00
74 8 a. grey .. .. 2·50 4·50
75 1 r. blue .. .. 26·00 20·00
76 2 r. orange .. .. 50·00 25·00
77 3 r. violet .. .. 50·00 27·00
78 4 r. red .. .. 50·00 48·00
79 5 r. brown .. .. 50·00 40·00

1897. Stamps of Zanzibar. 1896, optd. **British East Africa.**

80. **3.** ½ a green and red .. .. 40·00 38·00
81. 1 a. blue and red .. .. 70·00 70·00
82. 2 a. brown and red .. 26·00 20·00
83. 4½ a. orange and red .. 38·00 25·00
84. 5 a. brown and red .. 40·00 30·00
85. 7½ a. mauve and red .. 40·00 35·00

1897. As last, surch. **2½.**

86. **3.** "2½" on 1 a. blue and red 70·00 50·00
89. "2½" on 3 a. grey and red 65·00 48·00

1897. As Type **11,** but larger.

92a. 1 r. blue .. .. .. 28·00 18·00
93. 2 r. orange .. .. .. 48·00 48·00
94. 3 r. violet .. .. 48·00 70·00
95. 4 r. red £120 £160
96. 5 r. brown £110 £160
97. 10 r. brown £160 £225
98. 20 r. green £500 £1000
99. 50 r. mauve £1600 £2750

BRITISH FORCES IN EGYPT

SPECIAL SEALS AND STAMPS FOR THE USE OF BRITISH FORCES IN EGYPT

A. SEALS

A 1.

1932. (a) Inscr. "POSTAL SEAL".

A 1. A **1.** 1 p. blue and red .. 50·00 2·50

(b) Inscr. "LETTER SEAL".

A 2. A **1.** 1 p. blue and red .. 17·00 55

A 2.

1932. Christmas Seals.

A 3. A **2.** 3 m. black on blue .. 40·00 50·00
A 4. 3 m. lake .. .. 6·00 32·00
A 5. 3 m. blue .. .. 7·00 17·00
A 6. 3 m. red .. .. 1·25 16·00

A 3.

1934.

A 9. A **3.** 1 p. red 90 85
A 8. 1 p. green .. .. 3·00 3·00

1935. Silver Jubilee. Optd. **JUBILEE COMMEMORATION 1935.**

A 10. A **3.** 1 p. blue £200 £180

1935. Provisional Christmas Seal. Optd. **Xmas 1935 3 Milliemes.**

A 11. A **3.** 3 m. on 1 p. red .. 15·00 60·00

B. POSTAGE STAMPS

A **6.** King Fuad I.

A **7.** King Farouk.

1936.

A 12. A **6.** 3 m. green .. 1·00 60
A 13. 10 m. red .. .. 1·00 10

1939.

A 14. A **7.** 3 m. green .. .. 70 2·25
A 15. 10 m. red 80 10

BRITISH GUIANA

Situated on the N.E. coast of S. America. A British colony granted full internal self-Government in August, 1951. Attained independence on 26th May, 1966, when the country was renamed Guyana.

100 cents = 1 dollar.

1.

1850. Imperf. Used

1. **1.** 2 c. black on red .. .. — £55000
2. 4 c. black on orange .. — £2750
4. 8 c. black on green .. — £2000
5. 12 c. black on blue .. — £1700

Prices are for used stamps cut round. Stamps cut square are worth much more.

2.

3. Seal of the Colony.

1852. Imperf.

9. **2.** 1 c. black on magenta .. £8500 £4250
10. 4 c. black on blue .. £10000 £4500

1853. Imperf.

12. **3.** 1 c. red £2250 £800
20. 4 c. blue £850 £325

GUIANA.
6.

1856. Imperf.

23. 6. 1 c. black on magenta ..
24. 4 c. black on magenta .. — £5500
26. 4 c. black on blue .. — £32000

7. 9.

1860. Perf.

29 1 c. red .. £950 £180
40 1 c. brown .. £275 80·00
85 1 c. black .. 7·50 2·25
87 2 c. orange .. 16·00 1·50
89 4 c. blue .. 60·00 11·00
92 6 c. blue .. £100 26·00
95 8 c. red .. £100 13·00
98 12 c. lilac .. £130 13·00
99 12 c. grey .. £120 16·00
64 24 c. green .. £140 50·00
78 24 c. green .. £110 9·50
82 48 c. red .. £150 42·00

The prices quoted for Nos. 29/82 are for fine copies with four margins. Medium specimens can be supplied at much lower rates.

10. 16.

1862. Various borders. Roul.

116. 10 1 c. black on red .. £1500 £300
119. 2 c. black on yellow .. £1500 £250
122. 4 c. black on blue .. £1600 £325

The above prices are for stamps signed in the centre by the Postmaster. Unsigned stamps are worth considerably less.

1876.

126 16 1 c. grey .. 2·75 1·40
171 2 c. orange .. 20·00 15
172 4 c. blue .. 80·00 5·00
173 6 c. brown .. 5·00 6·50
174 8 c. red .. 80·00 40
131 12 c. violet .. 50·00 1·25
132 24 c. green .. 60·00 3·00
133 48 c. brown .. £110 18·00
134 96 c. olive .. £450 £250

1878. Optd. with thick horiz. or horiz. and vert. bars. (a) On postage stamps.

137. 16. 1 c. on 6 c. brown .. 38·00 80·00
141. 9. 1 c. on 6 c. blue .. £130 75·00

(b) On official stamps of 1875 and 1877.

138. 7. 1 c. black .. £130 70·00
139. 16. 1 c. grey .. £110 50·00
140. 2 c. orange .. £200 65·00
144. 4 c. blue .. £150 80·00
145. 6 c. brown .. £170 80·00
146. 7. 8 c. red .. £450 £170
148. 16. 8 c. red .. £250 85·00

1881. Surch. with figure. Old value barred out in ink. (a) On postage stamps.

152. 9. "1" on 48 c. red .. 32·00 5·00
149. 16. "1" on 96 c. olive .. 3·50 5·00
150. "2" on 96 c. olive .. 4·00 8·50

(b) On stamps optd. **OFFICIAL.**

153 7. "1" on 12 c. lilac £110 70·00
154 16. "1" on 48 c. brown £120 90·00
155 "2" on 12 c. violet 60·00 24·00
157 "2" on 24 c. green 70·00 35·00

26. 30.

1882.

162 26 1 c. black on red .. 35·00 28·00
165 2 c. black on yellow .. 50·00 40·00

Each stamp is perforated with the word "SPECIMEN".

1888. T 16 without value in bottom tablet, surch. **INLAND REVENUE** and value.

175. 16. 1 c. purple .. 75 20
176. 2 c. purple .. 1·25 30
177. 3 c. purple .. 60 20
178. 4 c. purple .. 3·00 30
179. 6 c. purple .. 2·50 1·75
180. 8 c. purple .. 1·50 25
181. 10 c. purple .. 6·00 2·50
182. 20 c. purple .. 19·00 10·00
183. 40 c. purple .. 20·00 17·00
184. 72 c. purple .. 35·00 38·00
185. $1 green .. £400 £400
186. $2 green .. £180 £180
187. $3 green .. £110 £110
188. $4 green .. £350 £350
189. $5 green .. £225 £200

1889. No. 176 surch. with additional **2.**

192. 16. "2" on 2 c. purple .. 75 15

1889.

193 30 1 c. purple and grey .. 2·00 90
213 1 c. green .. 40 10
194 2 c. purple and orange 1·50 10
234 2 c. purple and red .. 3·25 25
241a 2 c. purple & black on red 2·50 10
253a 2 c. red .. 7·00 10
195 4 c. purple and blue .. 4·00 1·50
254 4 c. brown and purple .. 2·25 60
214 5 c. blue .. 2·75 10
243a 5 c. pur. and blue on blue 3·50 4·50
198 6 c. purple and brown 6·00 4·75
236 6 c. black and blue 6·50 11·00
256 6 c. grey and black 13·00 7·00
199 8 c. purple and red 8·00 60
215 8 c. purple and black .. 2·75 2·25
200a 12 c. purple and mauve 8·50 2·00
257 12 c. orange and purple 4·00 4·00
246a 24 c. purple and green .. 3·75 4·50
202 48 c. purple and red .. 14·00 9·00
247a 48 c. grey and brown .. 13·00 20·00
248a 60 c. green and red .. 14·00 65·00
203 72 c. purple and brown 26·00 32·00
205 96 c. purple and red .. 65·00 70·00
250 96 c. blk. & red on yell. 35·00 45·00

1890. Nos. 185/8 surch. **ONE CENT.**

207. 16. 1 cent on $1 green .. 90 35
208. 1 cent on $2 green .. 60 60
209. 1 cent on $3 green .. 1·40 1·25
210. 1 cent on $4 green .. 2·00 4·50

32. Mount Roraima.

33. Kaieteur Falls. 37.

1898. Jubilee.

216. 32. 1 c. black and red .. 3·00 30
217. 33. 2 c. brown and blue .. 5·00 90
219. 32. 5 c. green and brown .. 25·00 2·00
220. 33. 10 c. black and red .. 15·00 20·00
221. 32. 15 c. brown and blue .. 25·00 16·00

1899. Nos. 219/21 surch. **TWO CENTS.**

222. 32. 2 c. on 5 c. grn. & brn. 2·00 1·25
223. 33. 2 c. on 10 c. blk. & red 70 1·60
224. 32. 2 c. on 15 c. brn. & blue 1·25 1·25

1905. T 30, but inscr. "REVENUE", optd. **POSTAGE AND REVENUE.**

251. 30. $2.40 green and violet £160 £275

1913.

259 37. 1 c. green .. 1·00 70
260 2 c. red .. 50 10
274 2 c. violet .. 1·00 10
261 4 c. brown and purple 1·75 25
262 5 c. blue .. 70 85
263 6 c. grey and black .. 85 85
276 6 c. blue .. 2·25 25
264 12 c. orange and violet 70 90
278 24 c. purple and green 1·50 4·50
279 48 c. grey and purple 8·50 3·50
280 60 c. green and red 7·00 40·00
281 72 c. purple and brown 9·00 38·00
282 96 c. black & red on yell. 14·00 35·00

1918. Optd. **WAR TAX** in two lines.

271. 37. 2 c. red .. 30 15

INDEX
Countries can be quickly located by referring to the index at the end of this volume.

39. Ploughing a Rice Field.

40. Indian shooting Fish. 41. Kaieteur Falls.

42. Public Buildings, Georgetown.

1931. Centenary of County Union.

283. 39. 1 c. green .. 1·25 75
284. 40. 2 c. brown .. 1·25 10
285. 41. 4 c. red .. 1·75 45
286. 42. 6 c. blue .. 1·25 2·50
287. 41. $1 violet .. 19·00 35·00

43. Ploughing a Rice Field.

44. Gold Mining. 53. South America.

1934.

288. 43. 1 c. green .. 50 30
289. 40. 2 c. brown .. 1·50 20
290. 44. 3 c. red .. 30 10
291. 41. 4 c. violet .. 1·75 45
292. – 6 c. blue .. 2·50 1·75
293. – 12 c. orange .. 10 10
294. – 24 c. purple .. 1·75 2·50
295. – 48 c. black .. 7·00 8·00
296. 41. 50 c. green .. 10·00 16·00
297. – 60 c. brown .. 26·00 27·00
298. – 72 c. purple .. 1·25 80
299. – 96 c. black .. 20·00 30·00
300. – $1 violet .. 32·00 26·00

DESIGNS—HORIZ. 6 c. Shooting logs over falls. 12 c. Stabroek Market. 24 c. Sugar canes in punts. 48 c. Forest road. 60 c. Victoria Regia lilies. 72 c. Mt. Roraima. $1, Botanical Gardens. VERT. 96 c. Sir Walter Raleigh and his son.

The 2 c., 4 c. and 50 c. are without the dates shown in Types 40/44 and the 12 c., 48 c., 72 c. and 96 c. have no portrait.

1935. Silver Jubilee. As Type **13** of Antigua.

301. 2 c. blue and grey .. 15 10
302. 6 c. brown and blue .. 80 30
303. 12 c. green and blue .. 1·50 4·75
304. 24 c. grey and purple .. 4·75 4·75

1937. Coronation. As Type **2** of Aden.

305. 2 c. brown .. 15 10
306. 4 c. grey .. 65 15
307. 6 c. blue .. 85 85

1938. Designs as for same values of 1934 issue (except where indicated) but with portrait of King George VI (as in T **53**) where portrait of King George V previously appeared.

308aa 43. 1 c. green .. 20 10
309a – 2 c. violet (As 4 c.) .. 30 10
310b 53. 4 c. red and black .. 45 15
311 – 6 c. blue (As 2 c.) .. 40 10
312a – 24 c. green .. 1·25 10
313 – 36 c. violet (As 4 c.) .. 1·75 20
314 – 48 c. orange .. 60 40
315 – 60 c. brown (As 6 c.) .. 10·00 3·50
316 – 96 c. purple .. 2·50 2·50
317 – $1 violet .. 10·00 35
318 – $2 purple (As 72 c.) 4·50 11·00
319 – $3 brown .. 27·00 25·00

DESIGN—HORIZ. $3, Victoria Regia lilies.

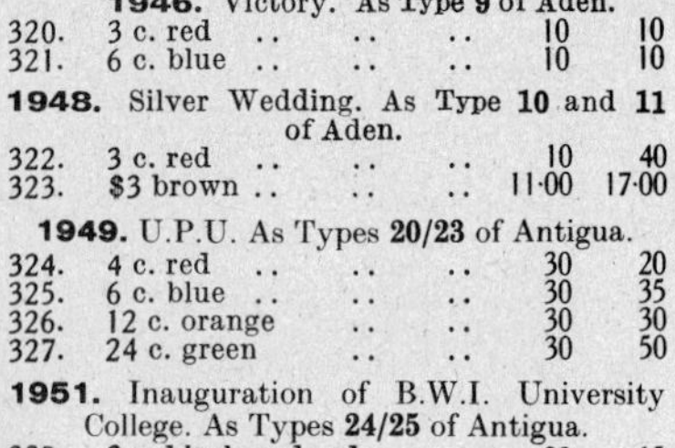

1946. Victory. As Type **9** of Aden.

320. 3 c. red .. 10 10
321. 6 c. blue .. 10 10

1948. Silver Wedding. As Type **10** and **11** of Aden.

322. 3 c. red .. 10 40
323. $3 brown .. 11·00 17·00

1949. U.P.U. As Types **20/23** of Antigua.

324. 4 c. red .. 30 20
325. 6 c. blue .. 30 35
326. 12 c. orange .. 30 30
327. 24 c. green .. 30 50

1951. Inauguration of B.W.I. University College. As Types **24/25** of Antigua.

328. 3 c. black and red .. 30 15
329. 6 c. black and blue .. 30 30

1953. Coronation. As Type **13** of Aden.

330. 4 c. black and red .. 15 10

55. G.P.O., Georgetown.

1954.

331. 55. 1 c. black .. 10 10
332. – 2 c. myrtle .. 10 10
333. – 3 c. olive and brown .. 3·00 10
334. – 4 c. violet .. 10 10
335. – 5 c. red and black .. 20 10
336. – 6 c. green .. 10 10
337. – 8 c. blue .. 10 10
338a. – 12 c. black and brown 15 10
360. – 24 c. black and orange 1·75 10
340. – 36 c. red and black .. 65 40
341a. – 48 c. blue and brown .. 40 40
342. – 72 c. red and green .. 9·00 2·75
364. – $1 multicoloured .. 7·00 90
344. – $2 mauve .. 11·00 3·50
345. – $5 blue and black .. 12·00 15·00

DESIGNS—HORIZ. 2 c. Botanical Gardens. 3 c. Victoria Regia lilies. 5 c. Map of Caribbean. 6 c. Rice combine-harvester. 8 c. Sugar cane entering factory. 24 c. Bauxite mining. 36 c. Mt. Roraima. $1, Channel-billed Toucan. $2, Dredging gold. VERT. 4 c. Amerindian shooting fish. 12 c. Felling Greenheart. 48 c. Kaieteur Falls, 72 c. Arapaimia (fish). $5, Arms, British Guiana.

70.

1961. History and Culture Week.

346. 70. 5 c. sepia and red .. 10 10
347. 6 c. sepia and green .. 10 10
348. 30 c. sepia and orange 20 20

1963. Freedom from Hunger. As T **28** of Aden.

349. 20 c. violet .. 30 10

1963. Cent of Red Cross. As T **33** of Antigua.

350. 5 c. red and black .. 10 15
351. 20 c. red and blue .. 35 25

71. Weightlifting.

1964. Olympic Games, Tokyo.

367. 71. 5 c. orange .. 10 10
368. 8 c. blue .. 10 10
369. 25 c. mauve .. 20 30

1965. Cent of I.T.U. As T **36** of Antigua.

370. 5 c. green and olive .. 10 15
371. 25 c. blue and mauve .. 20 15

1965. I.C.Y. As T **37** of Antigua.

372. 5 c. purple and turquoise 10 10
373. 25 c. green and lavender .. 25 20

72. St. George's Cathedral, Georgetown.

1966. Churchill Commem.
374. 72. 5 c. black, red and gold 30 10
375. 25 c. black, blue & gold 1·10 40

1966. Royal Visit. As T **39** of Antigua.
376. 3 c. black and blue .. 50 15
377. 25 c. black and mauve .. 1·50 60

OFFICIAL STAMPS

1875. Optd. **OFFICIAL.**
O 1. 7. 1 c. black .. .. 30·00 12·00
O 2. 2 c. orange .. .. £110 14·00
O 3. 8 c. red £275 £110
O 4. 12 c. lilac £1100 £450
O 5. 9. 24 c. green £750 £200

1877. Optd. **OFFICIAL.**
O 6. 16. 1 c. grey .. .. £160 55·00
O 7. 2 c. orange .. .. 75·00 13·00
O 8. 4 c. blue .. .. 75·00 20·00
O 9. 6 c. brown £2000 £500
O 10. 8 c. red £1700 £425

POSTAGE DUE STAMPS

1940. As Type D **1** of Barbados, but inscr. "BRITISH GUIANA".
D1a 1 c. green .. .. 1·25 5·00
D2a 2 c. black .. .. 1·50 3·00
D3 4 c. blue .. .. 30 5·00
D4a 12 c. red .. .. 10·00 18·00

For later issues see GUYANA.

BRITISH HONDURAS

A Br. colony on the E. coast of Central America. Self-government was granted on 1 Jan. 1964. The country was renamed Belize from 1 June 1973.

1866. 12 pence = 1 shilling.
20 shillings = 1pound.
1888. 100 cents = 1 dollar.

1.

2 CENTS (2.) 2 CENTS (4.)

1866.
17. 1. 1d. blue .. .. .. 38·00 13·00
18. 1d. red .. .. .. 18·00 11·00
13. 3d. brown .. .. 85·00 16·00
20. 4d. mauve .. .. 70·00 3·00
9. 6d red .. .. .. £170 27·00
21. 6d. yellow £275 £170
16. 1s. green .. .. .. £160 11·00
22. 1s. grey £250 £140

1888. Surch. as T **2.**
27. 1. 2 c. on 1d. red .. .. 8·00 15·00
25. 2 c. on 6d. red .. .. 70·00 65·00
26. 3 c. on 3d. brown .. 55·00 55·00
28. 10 c. on 4d. mauve .. 32·00 15·00
29. 20 c. on 6d. yellow .. 27·00 30·00
30. 50 c. on 1s. grey £325 £450

No. 30 surch. **TWO.**
35. 1. "TWO" on 50 c. on 1s. grey .. .. .. 38·00 75·00

1888. Surch. as T **4.**
36. 1. 1 c. on 1d. green.. .. 30 85
37. 2 c. on 1d. red .. .. 20 1·25
38. 3 c. on 3d. brown .. 1·25 1·25
39. 6 c. on 3d. blue .. .. 1·40 7·50
40. 10 c. on 4d. mauve .. 2·25 40
41. 20 c. on 6d. yellow .. 8·50 14·00
42. 50 c. on 1s. grey .. .. 19·00 55·00

1891. No. 40 surch. **6** and bar.
43. 1. "6" on 10 c. on 4d. mauve 40 1·50
Nos. 38 and 39 surch.
49. 1. "FIVE" on 3 c. on 3d. brown .. .. .. 40 1·40
50. "15" on 6 c. on 3d. blue 7·00 20·00

8.

NOTE: 10 c. (A) inscr. "POSTAGE POSTAGE"; (B) inscr. "POSTAGE & REVENUE".

1891.
51. 8. 1 c. green 80 40
52. 2 c. red 75 10
53. 2 c. brown .. .. 3·75 1·50
54. 5 c. blue .. .. .. 12·00 30
55. 5 c. black & blue on blue.. 7·50 1·40
56. 6 c. blue .. .. .. 3·25 75
57. 8 10 c. mauve and green (A) 8·50 8·00
58. 10 c. purple and green (B) 6·00 7·00
59a. 12 c. mauve and green .. 2·50 2·00
60. 24 c. yellow and blue .. 5·50 14·00
61. 25 c. brown and green .. 32·00 60·00
62. 50 c. green and red .. 19·00 40·00
63. $1 green and red .. .. 38·00 70·00
64. $2 green and blue .. 55·00 85·00
65. $5 green and black .. £190 £250

1899. Optd. **REVENUE.**
66. 8. 5 c. blue .. .. .. 4·00 2·00
67. 10 c. mauve and green .. 3·00 11·00
68. 25 c. brown and green .. 2·75 25·00
69. 1. 50 c. on 1s. grey £120 £275

14.

16.

1902.
84a 14 1 c. green 50 90
85a 2 c. purple & black on red 50 10
96 2 c. red .. .. .. 4·00 10
86 5 c. black & blue on blue 1·75 20
97 5 c. blue .. .. .. 1·75 10
87 10 c. purple and green .. 5·00 11·00
83 20 c. purple .. .. 3·50 14·00
89 25 c. purple and orange 7·00 32·00
100 25 c. black on green .. 2·75 38·00
90 50 c. green and red .. 14·00 50·00
91 $1 green and red .. 32·00 60·00
92 $2 green and blue .. 65·00 £110
93 $5 green and black .. £180 £250

1913.
101. 16. 1 c. green .. .. 1·25 30
102a. 2 c. red .. .. .. 1·75 25
103. 3 c. orange 30 15
104. 5 c. blue .. .. .. 2·00 40
105. 10 c. purple and green .. 2·75 6·50
106. 25 c. black on green .. 1·25 10·00
107. 50 c. purple & blue on blue 5·50 9·50
108. $1 black and red .. 10·00 23·00
109. $2 purple and green .. 55·00 60·00
110. $5 purple & black on red £180 £200

1915. Optd. with pattern of wavy lines.
111a. 16. 1 c. green .. .. 25 7·00
112. 2 c. red 85 50
113. 5 c. blue .. .. 25 2·75

1916. Optd. **WAR** in small letters.
114 16 1 c. green (No. 111a) .. 10 30
116 1 c. green (No. 101) .. 20 1·25
118 3 c. orange (No. 103) .. 40 2·00

1918. Optd. **WAR** in large letters 3 mm. high.
119. 16. 1 c. green 10 25
120. 3 c. orange 10 75

21.

22.

1921. Peace.
121. 21. 2 c. red .. .. .. 1·50 30
As last, but without word "PEACE"
123. 4 c. grey .. .. .. 2·25 30

1922.
126. 22 1 c. green .. .. .. 1·50 3·00
127. 2 c. brown 45 15
128. 2 c. red .. .. .. 1·00 15
129. 3 c. orange .. .. 7·50 3·00
130. 4 c. grey .. .. 1·75 20
131. 5 c. blue .. .. .. 1·25 55
132. 10 c. purple and olive .. 85 30
133. 25 c. black on green .. 1·00 5·50
134. 50 c. purple & blue on blue 4·50 11·00
136. $1 black and red .. 6·50 17·00
137. $2 green and purple .. 32·00 65·00
125. $5 purple and black on red £170 £190

1932. Optd. **BELIZE RELIEF FUND PLUS** and value.
138. 22. 1 c.+1 c. green .. .. 70 5·00
139. 2 c.+2 c. red .. .. 75 5·50
140. 3 c.+3 c. orange .. 85 6·50
141. 4 c.+4 c. grey .. .. 3·00 12·00
142. 5 c.+5 c. blue .. .. 4·75 13·00

1935. Silver Jubilee. As T **13** of Antigua.
143. 3 c. blue and black .. 35 45
144. 4 c. green and blue .. 1·50 90
145. 5 c. brown and blue .. 1·50 60
146. 25 c. grey and purple .. 1·60 1·75

1937. Coronation. As T **2** of Aden.
147. 3 c. orange 30 25
148. 4 c. grey .. .. 1·10 25
149. 5 c. blue .. .. 1·10 60

24. Maya figures.

1938.
150. 24. 1 c. purple and green .. 10 70
151. – 2 c. black and red .. 15 60
152. – 3 c. purple and brown .. 15 35
153. – 4 c. black and green .. 20 40
154. – 5 c. purple and blue .. 30 30
155. – 10 c. green and brown .. 45 45
156. – 15 c. brown and blue .. 45 40
157. – 25 c. blue and green .. 1·10 80
158. – 50 c. black and purple .. 9·00 3·00
159. – $1 red and olive .. 19·00 6·50
160. – $2 blue and purple .. 20·00 16·00
161. – $5 red and brown .. 21·00 23·00
DESIGNS—VERT. 2 c. Chicle tapping. 3 c. Cohune palm. $1, Court House, Belize. $2, Mahogany felling. $5, Arms of Colony. HORIZ. 4 c. Local products. 5 c. Grapefruit. 10 c. Mahogany logs in river. 15 c. Sergeant's Cay. 25 c. Dorey. 50 c. Chicle industry.

1946. Victory. As T **9** of Aden.
162. 3 c. brown.. .. .. 10 5
163. 5 c. blue 10 10

1948. Silver Wedding. As T **10** and **11** of Aden.
164. 4 c. green 15 20
165. $5 brown .. .. .. 15·00 32·00

36. Island of St. George's Cay.

1949. 150th Anniv. of Battle of St. George's Cay.
166. 36. 1 c. blue and green .. 10 30
167. 3 c. blue and brown .. 10 40
168. 4 c. olive and violet .. 10 40
169. – 5 c. brown and blue .. 40 20
170. – 10 c. green and brown 40 30
171. – 15 c. green and blue .. 40 20
DESIGNS: 5, 10 and 15 c. H.M.S. "Merlin".

1949. U.P.U. As T **20/23** of Antigua.
172. 4 c. green 40 20
173. 5 c. blue 55 20
174. 10 c. brown 70 55
175. 25 c. blue 85 50

1951. Inauguration of B.W.I. University College. As T **24/25** of Antigua.
176. 3 c. violet and brown .. 65 40
177. 10 c. green and brown 45 30

1953. Coronation. As T **13** of Aden.
178 4 c. black and green .. 20 30

39. Baird's Tapir

49. Mountain Orchid.

1953.
179 – 1 c. green and black .. 10 40
180a 39. 2 c. brown and black .. 50 10
181a – 3 c. lilac and mauve .. 10 10
182 – 4 c. brown and green.. 40 30
183 – 5 c. olive and red .. 10 10
184 – 10 c. slate and blue .. 10 10
185 – 15 c. green and violet.. 15 10
186 – 25 c. blue and brown.. 5·00 1·75
187 – 50 c. brown and purple 4·00 1·75
188 – $1 slate and brown .. 4·25 4·00
189 – $2 red and grey .. 6·50 4·50
190 49. $5 purple and slate .. 30·00 16·00
DESIGNS—HORIZ. 1 c. Arms of British Honduras Legislative. 3 c. Mace and Council Chamber. 4 c. Pine industry. 5 c. Spiny lobster. 10 c. Stanley Field Airport. 15 c. Maya Frieze. 25 c. "Morpho peleides" (butterfly). $1, Nine-banded armadillo. $2, Hawkesworth Bridge. VERT. 50 c. Maya Indian.

50. "Belize from Fort George, 1842." (C. J. Hullmandel).

1960. Post Office Centenary.
191. 50. 2 c. green 20 30
192. – 10 c. red 20 10
193. – 15 c. blue 25 25
DESIGNS: 10 c. Public Seals, 1860 and 1960. 15 c. Tamarind tree, Newtown Barracks.

1961. New Constitution. Stamps of 1953 optd. **NEW CONSTITUTION 1960.**
194. 39. 2 c. brown and black .. 20 10
195. – 3 c. lilac and mauve .. 25 10
196. – 10 c. slate and blue .. 25 10
197. – 15 c. green and violet.. 25 10

1962. Hurricane Hattie Relief Fund. Stamps of 1953 optd. **HURRICANE HATTIE.**
198. 1 c. green and black .. 10 30
199. 10 c. slate and blue .. 15 10
200. 25 c. blue and brown .. 90 50
201. 50 c. brown and purple .. 50 55

55. Great Curassow.

1962. Birds in natural colours; portrait and inscr. in black; background colours given.
239 55. 1 c. yellow 10 20
240 – 2 c. grey 30 40
204 – 3 c. green .. .. 1·50 75
241 – 4 c. pale grey .. .. 1·50 60
242 – 5 c. buff.. .. .. 40 10
243 – 10 c. stone 50 10
244 – 15 c. stone 60 10
209 – 25 c. slate .. .. 3·50 30
210 – 50 c. grey .. .. 4·00 35
211 – $1 blue .. .. .. 7·50 75
212 – $2 stone .. .. 8·00 3·00
213 – $5 grey .. .. .. 24·00 14·00
BIRDS: 2 c. Red-legged Honeycreeper. 3 c. Northern Jacana. 4 c. Great Kiskadee. 5 c. Scarlet-rumped Tanager. 10 c. Scarlet Macaw. 15 c. Slaty-tailed Trogon. 25 c. Red-footed Booby. 50 c. Keel-billed Toucan. $1, Magnificent Frigate Bird. $2, Rufous-tailed Jacamar. $5, Montezuma Oropendola.

1963. Freedom from Hunger. As T **28** of Aden.
214. 22 c. green 30 15

1963. Cent of Red Cross. As T **33** of Antigua.
215. 4 c. red and black.. .. 15 15
216. 22 c. red and blue.. .. 35 50

1964. New Constitution. Nos. 202, 204, 205 207 and 209 optd. **SELF GOVERNMENT 1964.**
217. 55. 1 c. yellow 10 15
218. – 3 c. green 25 15
219. – 4 c. pale grey 25 15
220. – 10 c. stone 25 10
221. – 25 c. slate 30 30

1965. Cent of I.T.U. As T **36** of Antigua.
222. 2 c. red and green .. 10 10
223. 50 c. yellow and purple .. 35 25

1965. I.C.Y. As T **37** of Antigua.
224. 1 c. purple and turquoise.. 10 10
225. 22 c. green and lavender.. 20 10

1966. Churchill Commem. As T **38** of Antigua.
226. 1 c. blue 10 10
227. 4 c. green 15 10
228. 22 c. brown 35 10
229. 25 c. violet 40 35

1966. Dedication of new Capital Site. Nos. 202, 204/5, 207 and 209 optd. **DEDICATION OF SITE NEW CAPITAL 9th OCTOBER 1965.**
230. 55. 1 c. yellow 10 15
231. – 3 c. green 20 15
232. – 4 c. pale grey 20 15
233. – 10 c. stone 25 10
234. – 25 c. slate 35 30

58. Citrus Grove.

1966. Stamp Cent. Multicoloured.
235. 5 c. Type **58** 10 10
236. 10 c. Half Moon Cay .. 10 10
237. 22 c. Hidden Valley Falls 10 10
238. 25 c. Maya Ruins, Xunantunich 15 15

59. Sailfish.

1967. Int. Tourist Year.

No.	Type	Description	Unused	Used
246.	59.	5 c. blue, black & yellow	15	15
247.	–	10 c. brown, black & red	15	10
248.	–	22 c. orge., blk. and grn.	25	10
249.	–	25 c. blue, black & yell.	25	35

DESIGNS: 10 c. Red brocket. 22 c. Jaguar. 25 c Tarpon.

60. "Schomburgkia tibicinis." 61. Monument of Belizean Patriots.

1968. 20th Anniv. of Economic Commission for Latin America. Multicoloured.

No.	Description	Unused	Used
250.	5 c. Type **60**	20	10
251.	10 c. "Maxillaria tenuifolia"	25	10
252.	22 c. "Bletia purpurea"	30	10
253.	25 c. "Sobralia macrantha"	40	20

1968. Human Rights Year. Multicoloured.

No.	Description	Unused	Used
254.	22 c. Type **61**	10	10
255.	50 c. Monument at Site of New Capital	10	10

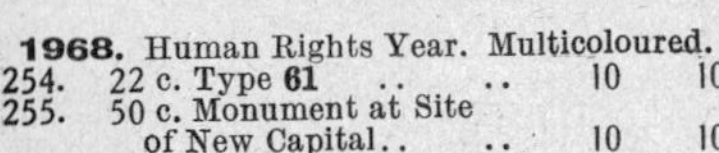

63. Jew Fish.

1968. Wildlife.

No.	Type	Description	Unused	Used
276.	–	½ c. mult. and blue	10	10
277.	–	½ c. mult. and yellow	50	75
256.	63.	1 c. blk., brn. and yell.	10	10
257.	–	2 c. blk., grn. and yell.	10	10
258.	–	3 c. blk., brn. and lilac	10	10
259.	–	4 c. multicoloured	10	30
260.	–	5 c. black and red	10	30
261.	–	10 c. multicoloured	15	10
262.	–	15 c. multicoloured	30	25
263.	–	25 c. multicoloured	30	25
264.	–	50 c. multicoloured	70	1·00
265.	–	$1 multicoloured	2·50	1·25
266.	–	$2 multicoloured	2·50	2·00
267.	–	$5 multicoloured	13·00	6·50

DESIGNS: ½ c. (Nos. 276 and 277) Crana Fish. 2 c. White-lipped peccary. 3 c. Grouper. 4 c. Collared anteater. 5 c. Bonefish. 10 c. Paca. 15 c. Dolphin. 25 c. Kinkajou. 50 c. Mutton Snapper. $1, Tayra. $2, Great Barracuda. $5, Puma.

64. "Rhyncholaelia digbyana".

1969. "Orchids of Belize" (1st series). Multicoloured.

No.	Description	Unused	Used
268.	5 c. Type **64**	50	15
269.	10 c. "Cattleya bowringiana"	55	15
270.	22 c. "Lycaste cochleatum"	85	15
271.	25 c. "Coryanthes speciosum"	1·10	95

See also Nos. 287/90.

65. Ziricote Tree.

1969. Indigenous Hardwoods (1st series). Multicoloured.

No.	Description	Unused	Used
272.	5 c. Type **65**	10	10
273.	10 c. Rosewood	10	10
274.	22 c. Mayflower	20	10
275.	25 c. Mahogany	20	30

See also Nos. 291/4, 315/8 and 333/7.

66. "The Virgin and Child" (Bellini). 69. Santa Maria.

1969. Christmas. Paintings. Multicoloured.

No.	Description	Unused	Used
279.	5 c. Type **66**	10	10
280.	15 c. Type **66**	10	10
281.	22 c. "The Adoration of the Magi" (Veronese)	10	10
282.	25 c. As No. 281	10	20

1970. Population Census. Nos. 260/3 optd. **POPULATION CENSUS 1970**

No.	Description	Unused	Used
283.	5 c. multicoloured	10	10
284.	10 c. multicoloured	10	10
285.	15 c. multicoloured	15	10
286.	25 c. multicoloured	15	15

1970. "Orchids of Belize" (2nd series). As T **64**. Multicoloured.

No.	Description	Unused	Used
287.	5 c. Black Orchid	35	10
288.	15 c. White Butterfly Orchid	50	10
289.	22 c. Swan Orchid	70	10
290.	25 c. Butterfly Orchid	70	30

1970. Indigenous Hardwoods (2nd series). Multicoloured.

No.	Description	Unused	Used
291.	5 c. Type **69**	25	10
292.	15 c. Nargusta	35	10
293.	22 c. Cedar	40	10
294.	25 c. Sapodilla	40	35

70. "The Nativity" (A. Hughes).

1970. Christmas. Multicoloured.

No.	Description	Unused	Used
295.	½ c. Type **70**	10	10
296.	5 c. "The Mystic Nativity" (Botticelli)	10	10
297.	10 c. Type **70**	10	10
298.	15 c. As 5 c.	15	10
299.	22 c. Type **70**	20	10
300.	50 c. As 5 c.	30	40

71. Legislative Assembly House.

1971. Establishment of New Capital Belmopan. Multicoloured.

No.	Description	Unused	Used
301.	5 c. Old Capital, Belize	10	10
302.	10 c. Government Plaza	10	10
303.	15 c. Type **71**	10	10
304.	22 c. Magistrates' Court	15	10
305.	25 c. Police H.Q.	15	15
306.	50 c. New G.P.O.	25	40

The 5 c. and 10 c. are larger, 60 × 22 mm.

72. "Tabebuia chrysantha".

1971. Easter. Flowers. Multicoloured.

No.	Description	Unused	Used
307.	½ c. Type **72**	10	10
308.	5 c. "Hymenocallis littorallis"	10	10
309.	10 c. "Hippeastrum equestre"	10	10
310.	15 c. Type **72**	15	10
311.	22 c. As 5 c.	15	10
312.	25 c. As 10 c.	20	30

1971. Racial Equality Year. Nos. 261 and 264 optd. **RACIAL EQUALITY YEAR-1971.**

No.	Description	Unused	Used
313.	10 c. multicoloured	20	10
314.	50 c. multicoloured	40	20

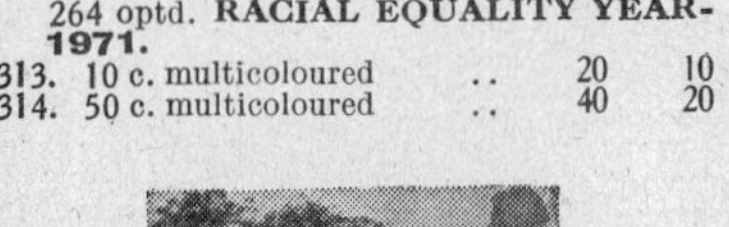

74. Tubroos.

1971. Indigenous Hardwoods (3rd series). Multicoloured.

No.	Description	Unused	Used
315.	5 c Type **74**	35	10
316.	15 c. Yemeri	50	30
317.	26 c. Billywebb	75	35
318.	50 c. Logwood	1·40	1·25

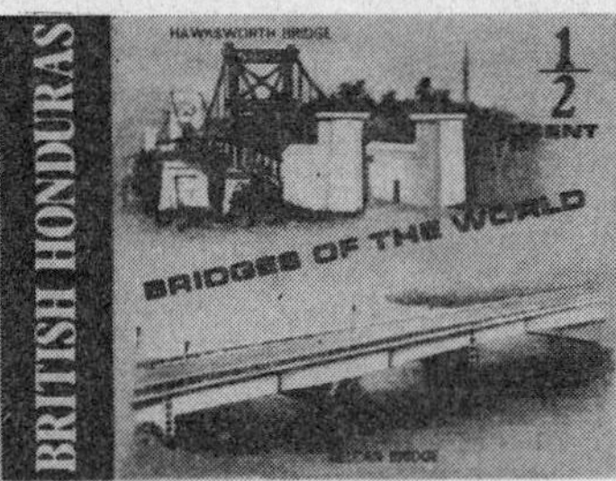

75. Hawksworth and Belcan Bridges.

1971. Bridges of the World. Multicoloured.

No.	Description	Unused	Used
320.	½ c. Type **75**	10	10
321.	5 c. Narrows Bridge, N.Y. and Quebec Bridge	10	10
322.	26 c. London Bridge (1871) and reconstructed, Arizona (1971)	30	10
323.	50 c. Belize Mexican Bridge and Swing Bridge	35	35

76. "Petrae volubis". 77. Seated Figure.

1972. Easter. Wild Flowers. Multicoloured.

No.	Description	Unused	Used
324.	6 c. Type **76**	15	10
325.	15 c. Yemeri	25	30
326.	26 c. Mayflower	50	45
327.	50 c. Tiger's Claw	80	70

1972. Mayan Artefacts. Multicoloured.

No.	Description	Unused	Used
328.	3c. Type **77**	15	10
329.	6c. Priest in "dancing" pose	20	10
330.	16 c. Sun God's Head (horiz.)	35	15
331.	26c. Priest and Sun God	50	20
332.	50c. Full-front figure	1·00	2·00

78. Banak.

1972. Indigenous Hardwoods (4th series). Multicoloured

No.	Description	Unused	Used
333.	3 c. Type **78**	15	10
334.	5 c. Quamwood	15	10
335.	16 c. Waika Chewstick	35	15
336.	26 c. Mamee-Apple	65	25
337.	50 c. My Lady	1·10	1·75

1972. Royal Silver Wedding. As T **52** of Ascension, but with Orchids of Belize in background.

No.	Description	Unused	Used
341.	26 c. green	25	10
342.	50 c. violet	40	40

80. Baron Bliss Day.

1973. Festivals of Belize. Multicoloured.

No.	Description	Unused	Used
343	3 c. Type **80**	15	10
344	10 c. Labour Day	15	10
345	26 c. Carib Settlement Day	25	10
346	50 c. Pan American Day	35	70

POSTAGE DUE STAMPS

D 1.

1923.

No.	Type	Description	Unused	Used
D 1	D 1.	1 c. black	80	7·50
D 4		2 c. black	1·50	3·75
D 5		4 c. black	50	4·25

For later issues see **BELIZE.**

BRITISH INDIAN OCEAN TERRITORY

A Crown Colony, established 8th November 1965, comprising the Chagos Archipelago (previously administered by Mauritius) and Aldabra, Farquhar and Desroches, previously administered by Seychelles to which country they were returned on 29th June 1976.

The Chagos Archipelego has no indigenous population, but stamps were provided from 1990 for use by civilian workers at the U.S. Navy base on Diego Garcia.

1968. 100 cents = 1 rupee.
1990. 100 pence = 1 pound.

1968. Nos. 196/200, 202/4 and 206/12 of Seychelles optd. **B.I.O.T.**

No.	Type	Description	Unused	Used
1.	24.	5 c. multicoloured	10	10
2.	–	10 c. multicoloured	10	10
3.	–	15 c. multicoloured	10	15
4.	–	20 c. multicoloured	15	15
5.	–	25 c. multicoloured	15	15
6.	–	40 c. multicoloured	15	20
7.	–	45 c. multicoloured	20	30
8.	–	50 c. multicoloured	20	30
9.	–	75 c. multicoloured	20	35
10.	–	1 r. multicoloured	40	35
11.	–	1 r. 50 multicoloured	1·75	1·50
12.	–	2 r. 25 multicoloured	3·75	3·75
13.	–	3 r. 50 multicoloured	4·00	4·50
14.	–	5 r. multicoloured	5·50	7·50
15.	–	10 r. multicoloured	18·00	20·00

2. Lascar.

1968. Marine Life. Multicoloured.

16.	5 c. Type **2**	30	1·00
17.	10 c. Hammerhead Shark (vert.)	30	1·00
18.	15 c. Tiger Shark	30	1·00
19.	20 c. Bat Ray	30	65
20.	25 c. Butterfly Fish (vert.)	80	1·00
20a.	30 c. Robber Crab	3·50	2·75
21.	40 c. Caranx	40	40
22.	45 c. Garfish (vert.)	2·25	2·50
23.	50 c. Barracuda	45	30
23a.	60 c. Spotted Pebble Crab	3·50	3·25
24.	75 c. Parrot Fish	2·50	2·75
24a.	85 c. Dorade (" Elegatis bipinnulatus ")	6·00	3·50
25.	1 r. Giant Hermit Crab	1·50	35
26.	1 r. 50 Humphead	2·50	2·50
27.	2 r. 25 Rock Cod	7·00	8·50
28.	3 r. 50 Black Marlin	4·00	3·75
29.	5 r. black, green and blue (Whale Shark) (vert.)	9·00	7·50
30.	10 r. Lion Fish	9·00	8·00

3. Sacred Ibis and Aldabra Coral Atoll.

1969. Coral Atolls.

31. **3.**	2 r. 25 multicoloured	1·25	35

4. Outrigger Canoe.

1969. Ships of the Islands. Multicoloured

32.	45 c. Type **4**	65	75
33.	75 c. Pirogue	65	80
34.	1 r. M.V. " Nordvaer "	70	90
35.	1 r. 50 " Isle of Farquhar "	80	1·00

5. Giant Land Tortoise.

1971. Aldabra Nature Reserve. Mult.

36.	45 c. Type **5**	2·50	2·00
37.	75 c. Aldabra Lily	3·00	2·50
38.	1 r. Aldabra Snail	3·50	2·75
39.	1 r. 50 Western Reef Heron	8·50	5·00

6. Arms of Royal Society and White-throated Rail.

1971 Opening of Royal Society Research Station, Aldabra.

40. **6.**	3 r. 50 multicoloured	13·00	8·50

7. Staghorn Coral.

1972. Coral. Multicoloured.

41.	40 c. Type **7**	3·00	2·00
42.	60 c. Brain coral	3·50	2·50
43.	1 r. Mushroom coral	3·50	3·00
44.	1 r. 75 Organ Pipe coral	4·50	4·00

1972. Royal Silver Wedding. As T **52** of Ascension, but with White-throated Rail and Sacred Ibis in background.

45.	95 c. green	65	40
46.	1 r. 50 violet	65	40

9. " Christ on the Cross ".

1973. Easter. Multicoloured.

47.	45 c. Type **9**	25	40
48.	75 c. " Joseph and Nicodemus burying Jesus "	35	55
49.	1 r. Type **9**	35	60
50.	1 r. 50 As 75 c.	40	70

10. Upsidedown Jellyfish.

1973. Wildlife (1st series). Multicoloured.

53	50 c. Type **10**	3·00	3·00
54	1 r. "Hypolimnas misippus" and "Belenois aldabrensis" (butterflies)	3·00	3·00
55	1 r. 50 "Nephila Madagascarienis" (spider)	3·50	3·00

See also Nos. 58/61, 77/80 and 86/9.

11. M.V. "Nordvaer".

1974. 5th Anniv. of "Nordvaer" Travelling Post Office. Multicoloured.

56.	85 c. Type **11**	50	75
57.	2 r. 50 "Nordvaer" off shore	75	1·25

12. Auger Shells.

1974. Wildlife (2nd series). Shells. Mult.

58.	45 c. Type **12**	1·75	1·00
59.	75 c. Green Turban	1·90	1·25
60.	1 r. Drupe Snail	2·25	1·50
61.	1 r. 50 Helmet Shell	2·50	1·75

13. Aldabra Drongo.

1975. Birds. Multicoloured.

62.	5 c. Type **13**	1·00	2·25
63.	10 c. Black coucal	1·00	2·25
64.	20 c. Mascarene fody	1·00	2·25
65.	25 c. White tern	1·00	2·50
66.	30 c. Crested tern	1·00	2·50
67.	40 c. Brown booby	1·00	2·50
68.	50 c. Common noddy (horiz.)	1·00	2·75
69.	60 c. Grey heron	1·00	3·00
70.	65 c. Blue-faced booby (horiz.)	1·00	3·00
71.	95 c. Madagascar white eye (horiz.)	1·00	3·00
72.	1 r. Green heron (horiz.)	1·25	3·00
73.	1 r. 75 Lesser frigate bird (horiz.)	2·00	3·75
74.	3 r. 50 White-tailed tropic bird (horiz.)	2·75	3·75
75.	5 r. Souimanga sunbird (horiz.)	4·00	5·00
76.	10 r. Madagascar turtle-dove (horiz.)	8·00	9·00

14. " Grewia salicifola ".

1975. Wildlife (3rd series). Seashore Plants. Multicoloured.

77.	50 c. Type **14**	40	80
78.	65 c. " Cassia aldabrensis "	45	90
79.	1 r. " Hypoestes aldabrensis "	60	1·10
80.	1 r. 60 " Euphorbia pyrifolia "	75	1·25

15. Map of Aldabra.

1975. 10th Anniv. of Territory. Maps. Mult.

81.	50 c. Type **15**	60	65
82.	1 r. Desroches	75	85
83.	1 r. 50 Farquhar	85	1·00
84.	2 r. Diego Garcia	95	1·25

16. "Utetheisa pulchella"(moth).

1976. Wildlife (4th series). Mult.

86	65 c. Type **16**	60	1·10
87	1 r. 20 "Dysdercus fasciatus" (bug)	75	1·25
88	1 r. 50 "Sphex torridus" (wasp)	80	1·40
89	2 r. "Oryctes rhinoceros" (beetle)	85	1·40

17 White-tailed Tropic Bird

1990. Birds. Multicoloured.

90	15p. Type **17**	30	35
91	20p. Madagascar turtle dove	40	45
92	24p. Great frigate bird	50	55
93	30p. Green heron	60	65
94	34p. Great sand plover	70	75
95	41p. Crab plover	80	85
96	45p. Crested tern	90	95
97	54p. Lesser crested tern	1·10	1·25
98	62p. White tern	1·25	1·40
99	71p. Red-footed booby	1·40	1·50
100	80p. Common mynah	1·60	1·75
101	£1 Madagascar red fody	2·00	2·10

18 1974 Wildlife 1 r. 50 Stamp

1990. "Stamp World London 90" International Stamp Exhibition. Multicoloured.

102	15p. Type **18**	75	75
103	20p. 1976 Wildlife 2 r. stamp	90	90
104	34p. 1975 Diego Garcia map 2 r. stamp	1·60	1·60
105	54p. 1969 "Nordvaer" 1 r. stamp	2·25	2·25

1990. 90th Birthday of Queen Elizabeth the Queen Mother. As T **134** of Ascension.

106	24p. multicoloured	1·25	1·25
107	£1 black and ochre	3·25	3·25

DESIGNS—21 × 36 mm. 24p. Lady Elizabeth Bowes-Lyon, 1923. 29 × 37 mm. £1 Queen Elizabeth and her daughters, 1940.

19 Territory Flag

1990. 25th Anniv of British Indian Ocean Territory. Multicoloured.

108	20p. Type **19**	1·25	1·25
109	24p. Coat of Arms	1·50	1·50

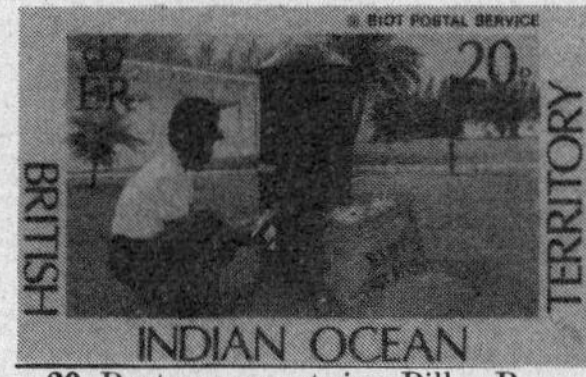
20 Postman emptying Pillar Box

1991. British Indian Ocean Territory Administration. Multicoloured.

111	20p. Type **20**	1·00	1·00
112	24p. Commissioner inspecting guard of Royal Marines	1·25	1·25
113	34p. Policemen outside station	1·75	1·75
114	54p. Customs officers boarding yacht	2·50	2·50

21 "Experiment" (E.I.C. survey brig), 1786

1991. Visiting Ships. Multicoloured.

115	20p. Type **21**	70	70
116	24p. "Pickering" (American brig), 1819 ..	85	85
117	34p. "Emden" (German cruiser), 1914	1·25	1·25
118	54p. H.M.S. "Edinburgh" (destroyer), 1988 ..	1·75	1·75

1992. 40th Anniv of Queen Elizabeth II's Accession. As T **143** of Ascension. Mult.

119	15p. Catholic chapel, Diego Garcia	60	60
120	20p. Planter's house, Diego Garcia	70	70
121	24p. Railway tracks on wharf, Diego Garcia ..	85	85
122	34p. Three portraits of Queen Elizabeth ..	1·10	1·10
123	54p. Queen Elizabeth II	1·60	1·60

22 R.A.F. Catalina (flying boat)

1992. Visiting Aircraft. Multicoloured.

124	20p. Type **22**	70	70
125	24p. R.A.F. Nimrod (maritime reconnaissance aircraft)	75	75
126	34p. P-3 Orion (transport aircraft)	1·10	1·10
127	54p. U.S.A.A.F. B-52 Stratofortress (heavy bomber)	1·60	1·60

23 "The Mystical Marriage of St. Catherine" (Correggio)

1992. Christmas. Religious Paintings. Mult.

128	5p. Type **23**	20	20
129	24p. "Madonna" (anon) ..	75	75
130	34p. "Madonna" (anon) (different) ..	1·10	1·10
131	54p. "The Birth of Jesus" (Kaspar Jele)	1·60	1·60

24 Coconut Crab and Rock

1993. Endangered Species. Coconut Crab. Multicoloured.

132	10p. Type **24**	30	35
133	10p. Crab on beach ..	30	35
134	10p. Two crabs	30	35
135	15p. Crab climbing coconut tree	45	50

1993. 75th Anniv of Royal Air Force. As T **149** of Ascension. Multicoloured.

136	20p. Vickers Virginia ..	55	60
137	24p. Bristol Bulldog ..	60	65
138	34p. Short Sunderland ..	75	90
139	54p. Bristol Blenheim IV	1·40	1·60

25 "Stachytarpheta urticifolia"

1993. Christmas. Flowers. Multicoloured.

141	20p. Type **25**	40	45
142	24p. "Ipomea pes-caprae"	50	55
143	34p. "Sida pusilla" ..	70	75
144	54p. "Catharanthus roseus"	1·10	1·25

1994. "Hong Kong '94" International Stamp Exhibition. Nos. 92 and 101 optd **HONG KONG '94** and emblem.

145	24p. Great frigate bird ..	50	55
146	£1 Madagascar red fody ..	2·00	2·10

BRITISH LEVANT

Stamps used at Br. post offices in the Turkish Empire. These offices closed in 1914. The stamps were again in use after 1918, during the British Occupation of Turkey.

Stamps of Great Britain surcharged or overprinted.

I. TURKISH CURRENCY.

40 paras = 1 piastre.

80 PARAS
(1.)

1885. Surch as T **1.**

1.	**64.**	40 par. on 2½d. purple ..	70·00	75
2.	**62.**	80 par. on 5d. green ..	£180	9·50
3a	**58.**	12 pi. on 2s. 6d. lilac ..	38·00	22·00

1887. Surch as T **1.**

4	**74**	40 par. on 2½d. pur. on bl.	1·75	10
5	**78**	80 par. on 5d. pur. & blue	9·00	25
6	**81**	4 pi. on 10d. pur. & red..	30·00	8·00

1893. Handstamped surcharge.

7.	**71.**	40 par. on ½d. red ..	£400	£100

1902. Surch. as T **1.**

29	–	30 par. on 1½d. pur. & grn.	4·25	55
8	**86.**	40 par. on 2½d. blue ..	4·75	10
9	–	80 par. on 5d. pur. & blue	3·00	85
13	**86.**	1 pi. on 2½d. blue ..	3·25	10
30	–	2 pi. on 5d. purple & blue	3·25	1·50
10	–	4 pi. on 10d. purple & red	8·50	4·00
21	–	5 pi. on 1s. green and red	3·75	6·50
11	–	12 pi. on 2s. 6d. purple..	25·00	32·00
12	–	24 pi. on 5s red	30·00	40·00

1906. Surch. **1 Piastre.**

15.	-	1 pi. on 2d. green and red	£1300	£600

1 PIASTRE
10 PARAS
(6.)

1909. Surch. as T **6.**

17.	–	1 pi. 10 par. on 3d. purple on yellow	8·00	20·00
18.	–	1 pi. 30 par. on 4d. green and brown	6·00	14·00
19.	–	1 pi. 30 par. on 4d. orge.	9·50	24·00
20.	**83.**	2 pi. 20 par. on 6d. purple	15·00	40·00

1910. Surch. in two lines.

22.	–	1¼ pi. on 3d. pur. on yell.	40	1·00
23.	–	1¾ pi. on 4d. orange ..	40	60
24.	**83.**	2½ pi. on 6d. purple ..	90	65

1913. Surch. in one or two lines.

41	**105.**	30 par. on ½d. green ..	30	5·50
35		30 par. on 1½d. brown	3·00	7·50
36a	**104.**	1 pi. on 2½d. blue ..	1·00	15
37.	**106.**	1¼ pi. on 3d. violet ..	2·00	4·25
42.	**104.**	1½ pi. on 1d. red ..	50	10
38b.	**106.**	1¾ pi. on 4d. grey-grn.	2·50	5·00
43.	**104.**	3¾ pi on 2½d. blue ..	70	25
39.	**108.**	4 pi. on 10d. blue ..	5·00	12·00
44.	**106.**	4½ pi. on 3d. violet ..	1·50	2·75
40.	**108.**	5 pi. on 1s. brown ..	20·00	48·00
45.	**107.**	7½ pi. on 5d. brown ..	30	10
46.	**108.**	15 pi. on 10d. blue ..	45	15
47.		18¾ pi. on 1s. brown..	3·75	3·75
48.	**109.**	45 pi. on 2s 6d. brown	20·00	40·00
49.		90 pi. on 5s. red ..	25·00	30·00
50.		180 pi. on 10s blue ..	45·00	40·00

II. BRITISH CURRENCY.

1905. Optd. **LEVANT.**

L 1.	**83.**	½d. green	2·25	15
L 2.		1d. red	2·00	15
L 3.		1½d. purple and green	4·50	1·50
L 4a.		2d. green and red ..	2·00	6·00
L 5.		2½d. blue	7·50	18·00
L 6.		3d. purple and yellow	5·50	11·00
L 7.		4d. green and brown ..	7·00	18·00
L 8		5d. purple and blue ..	14·00	25·00
L 9	**83.**	6d. purple ..	11·00	25·00
L 10.		1s green and red ..	25·00	32·00

1911. Optd. **LEVANT.**

L12	**98.**	½d. green	40	90
L14	**101.**	½d. green	25	10
L16	**105.**	½d. green	15	25
L13	**99.**	1d. red	40	3·75
L15	**102.**	1d. red	25	40
L17	**104.**	1d. red	15	2·00
L18	**106.**	2d. orange ..	1·25	18·00
L19		3d. violet	7·50	10·00
L20		4d. green	4·25	13·00
L21	**107.**	5d. brown.. ..	9·00	23·00
L22a		6d. purple.. ..	16·00	8·50
L23	**108.**	1s. brown	10·00	7·00
L24	**109.**	2s. 6d. brown ..	35·00	65·00

BRITISH FIELD OFFICE IN SALONICA

Levant
(S 1.)

1916. King George V stamps of Great Britain optd. with S **1.**

S 1.	**105.**	½d. green	27·00	£100
S 2.	**104.**	1d. red	27·00	£100
S 3.	**106.**	2d. orange	£100	£200
S 4.		3d. violet	80·00	£200
S 5.		4d. green	£100	£200
S 6.	**107.**	6d. purple	60·00	£160
S 7.	**108.**	9d. black	£250	£450
S 8.		1s. brown	£200	£400

The above stamps were overprinted at Salonica during the war of 1914–18.

BRITISH OCCUPATION OF ITALIAN COLONIES

Issues for use in Italian colonies occupied by British Forces. Middle East Forces overprints were used in Cyrenaica, Dodecanese Islands, Eritrea, Italian Somaliland and Tripolitania.

MIDDLE EAST FORCES

12 pence = 1 shilling.
20 shillings = 1 pound.

1942. Stamps of Gt. Britain optd. **M.E.F.**

M 1	**128**	1d. red	35	45
M12		2d. orange	90	10
M 3		2½d. blue	15	15
M 4		3d. violet	15	10
M 5	**129**	5d. brown	15	15
M16		6d. purple	30	10
M17	**130**	9d. olive	85	15
M18		1s. brown	50	10
M19	**131**	2s. 6d.	7·00	30
M20		5s. red	11·00	17·00
M21		10s. blue (No. 478a) ..	14·00	10·00

Prices. Our prices for Nos. M1/21 in used condition are for stamps with identifiable postmarks of the territories in which they were issued. These stamps were also used in the United Kingdom with offical sanction, from the summer of 1950 onwards, and with U K. postmarks are worth about 25 per cent less.

POSTAGE DUE STAMPS.

1942. Postage Due stamps of Gt. Britain overprinted **M.E.F.**

MD 1.	**D 1.**	½d. green	25	3·50
MD 2.		1d. red	30	1·25
MD 3.		2d. black	1·25	1·00
MD 4.		3d. violet	50	3·50
MD 5.		1s. blue	3·00	6·50

CYRENAICA

1000 milliemes = 1 Egyptian pound.

24. Mounted Warrior. 25.

1950.

136.	**24.**	1 m. brown	30	60
137.		2 m. red	50	60
138.		3 m. yellow	50	60
139.		4 m. green	1·25	2·50
140.		5 m. grey	50	70
141.		8 m. orange	50	55
142.		10 m. violet	60	50
143.		12 m. red	60	55
144.		20 m. blue	60	60
145.	**25.**	50 m. blue and brown..	1·90	3·00
146.		100 m. red and black ..	6·00	9·00
147.		200 m. violet and blue..	10·00	25·00
148.		500 m. yellow and green	38·00	60·00

POSTAGE DUE STAMPS

D 26.

1950.

D 149.	**D 26.**	2 m. brown.. ..	45·00	60·00
D 150.		4 m. green	45·00	60·00
D 151.		8 m. red	45·00	60·00
D 152.		10 m. orange ..	45·00	60·00
D 153.		20 m. yellow ..	45·00	60·00
D 154.		40 m. blue	45·00	60·00
D 155.		100 m. brown ..	45·00	60·00

ERITREA

100 cents = 1 shilling.

BRITISH MILITARY ADMINISTRATION

1948. Stamps of Great Britain surch. **B.M.A. ERITREA** and value in cents or shillings.

E 1.	**128.**	5 c. on ½d. green ..	40	65
E 2.		10 c. on 1d. red ..	50	1·75
E 3.		20 c. on 2d. orange..	45	2·25
E 4.		25 c. on 2½d. blue ..	30	60
E 5.		30 c. on 3d. violet ..	1·00	3·75
E 6.	**129.**	40 c. on 5d. brown ..	30	3·50
E 7.		50 c. on 6d. purple..	30	60
E 7a.	**130.**	65 c. on 8d. red ..	6·50	2·00
E 8.		75 c. on 9d. olive ..	50	75
E 9.		1 s. on 1s. brown ..	50	50
E 10.	**131.**	2 s. 50 on 2s. 6d. green	6·00	10·00
E 11.		5 s. on 5s. red ..	6·00	16·00
E 12.	–	10 s. on 10s. bright blue (No. 478a).. ..	13·00	19·00

BRITISH ADMINISTRATION

1950. Stamps of Great Britain surch. **B.A. ERITREA** and value in cents or shillings.

E 13.	128.	5 c. on ½d. green ..	30	5·50
E 26.		5 c. on ½d. orange ..	30	50
E 14.		10 c. on 1d. red ..	30	2·50
E 27.		10 c. on 1d. blue ..	30	35
E 15.		20 c. on 2d. orange ..	30	70
E 28.		20 c. on 2d. brown ..	30	30
E 16.		25 c. on 2½d. blue ..	30	60
E 29.		25 c. on 2½d. red ..	30	30
E 17.		30 c. on 3d. violet ..	30	90
E 18.	129.	40 c. on 5d. brown ..	40	90
E 19.		50 c. on 6d. purple ..	30	20
E 20.	130.	65 c. on 8d. red ..	40	1·00
E 21.		75 c. on 9d. olive ..	30	25
E 22.		1 s. on 1s. brown ..	30	15
E 23.	**131.**	**2 s. 50 on 2s. 6d. green**	3·25	4·50
E 24.		**5 s. on 5s. red** ..	5·50	9·00
E 25.	**–**	**10 s. on 10s. blue** (No. 478a) ..	38·00	40·00

1951. Nos. 509/11 of Great Britain surch. **B.A. ERITREA** and value in cents or shillings.

E 30.	**147.**	**2 s. 50 on 2s. 6d. green**	5·50	10·00
E 31.	**–**	**5 s. on 5s. red** ..	17·00	17·00
E 32.	**–**	**10 s. on 10s. blue** ..	18·00	17·00

POSTAGE DUE STAMPS

1948. Postage Due stamps of Great Britain surch. **B.M.A. ERITREA** and new value in cents or shillings.

ED 1.	D 1.	5 c. on ½d. green ..	9·00	18·00
ED 2.		10 c. on 1d. red ..	7·50	18·00
ED 3.		20 c. on 2d. black ..	7·00	13·00
ED 4.		30 c. on 3d. violet ..	8·00	12·00
ED 5.		1s. on 1s. blue ..	15·00	22·00

1950. Postage Due stamps of Great Britain surch. **B.A. ERITREA** and new value in cents or shillings.

ED 6.	D 1.	5 c. on ½ d. green	11·00	27·00
ED 7.		10 c. on 1d. red ..	8·00	14·00
ED 8.		20 c. on 2d. black	9·50	13·00
ED 9.		30 c. on 3d. violet	9·50	13·00
ED 10.		1s. on 1s. blue ..	15·00	22·00

SOMALIA

BRITISH OCCUPATION

1943. Stamps of Gt. Britain optd. **E.A.F.** (East African Forces).

S 1.	128.	1d. pale red ..	60	40
S 2.		2d. pale orange ..	80	90
S 3.		2½d. light blue ..	30	2·50
S 4.		3d. pale violet ..	40	15
S 5.	129.	5d. brown ..	40	40
S 6.		6d. purple ..	30	90
S 7.	130.	9d. olive ..	60	2·25
S 8.		1s. brown ..	80	15
S 9.	131.	2s. 6d. green ..	5·50	4·50

PRICES. Our prices for Nos. S 1/9 in used condition are for stamps with identifiable postmarks of the territories in which they were issued. These stamps were also used in the United Kingdom, with official sanction, from the summer of 1950, and with U.K. postmarks are worth about 25 per cent less.

BRITISH MILITARY ADMINISTRATION.

1948. Stamps of Great Britain surch. **B.M.A. SOMALIA** and new value in cents and shillings.

S 10.	128.	5 c. on ½d. pale green	20	1·25
S 11.		15 c. on 1½d. pale brn.	55	8·50
S 12.		20 c. on 2d. pale orge.	20	2·75
S 13.		25 c. on 2½d. light blue	20	3·00
S 14.		30 c. on 3d. pale violet	1·75	9·00
S 15.	129.	40 c. on 5d. brown ..	30	20
S 16.		50 c. on 6d. purple ..	30	2·00
S 17.	130.	75 c. on 9d. olive ..	2·00	11·00
S 18.		1s. on 1s. brown ..	1·25	20
S 19.	131.	2s. 50 c. on 2s. 6d. grn.	3·00	15·00
S 20.		5s. on 5s. red ..	7·00	23·00

BRITISH ADMINISTRATION

1950. Stamps of Great Britain surch. **B.A. SOMALIA** and value in cents and shillings.

S 21.	128.	5 c. on ½d. pale green	20	1·25
S 22.		15 c. on 1½d. pale brn.	60	10·00
S 23.		20 c. on 2d. pale orge.	60	3·25
S 24.		25 c. on 2½d. light blue	40	3·50
S 25.		30 c. on 3d. pale violet	1·00	3·00
S 26.	129.	40 c. on 5d. brown ..	55	85
S 27.		50 c. on 6d. purple ..	40	1·00
S 28.	130.	75 c. on 9d. olive ..	1·00	4·50
S 29.		1s. on 1s. brown ..	60	1·50
S 30.	131.	2s. 50 on 2s. 6d. grn.	4·00	16·00
S 31.		5s. on 5s. red ..	7·50	20·00

TRIPOLITANIA

BRITISH MILITARY ADMINISTRATION

1948. Stamps of Great Britain surch. **B.M.A. TRIPOLITANIA** and value in " **M.A.L.** " (Military Administration lire).

T 1.	128.	1 l. on ½d. pale green	30	80
T 2.		2 l. on 1d. pale red ..	20	25
T 3.		3 l. on 1½d. pale brown	20	50
T 4.		4 l. on 2d. pale orange	25	50
T 5.		5 l. on 2½d. light blue	30	20
T 6.		6 l. on 3d. pale violet	20	40
T 7.	129.	10 l. on 5d. brown ..	20	25
T 8.		12 l. on 6d. purple ..	30	20
T 9.	130.	18 l. on 9d. olive ..	50	65
T 10.		24 l. on 1s. brown ..	50	65
T 11.	131.	60 l. on 2s. 6d. green ..	2·00	4·50
T 12.		120 l. on 5s. red ..	8·00	14·00
T 13.	–	240 l. on 10s. bright blue (No. 478a)	16·00	65·00

BRITISH ADMINISTRATION

1950. As Nos. T1/13 but surch. **B.A. TRIPOLITANIA** and value in **M.A.L.**

T 14.	128.	1 l. on ½d. pale green	70	5·50
T 27.		1 l. on ½d. orange ..	20	2·50
T 15.		2 l. on 1d. pale red ..	85	40
T 28.		2 l. on 1d. blue ..	20	90
T 16.		3 l. on 1½d. pale brn.	35	5·00
T 29.		3 l. on 1½d. green ..	30	4·50
T 17.		4 l. on 2d. pale orange	25	4·50
T 30.		4 l. on 2d. brown ..	25	1·25
T 18.		5 l. on 2½d. light blue	25	70
T 31.		5 l. on 2½d. red ..	30	4·50
T 19.		6 l. on 3d. pale violet	50	1·50
T 20.	129.	10 l. on 5d. brown ..	30	1·75
T 21.		12 l. on 6d. purple ..	30	50
T 22.	130.	18 l. on 9d. olive ..	35	1·60
T 23.		24 l. on 1s. brown ..	45	3·50
T 24.	131.	60 l. on 2s. 6d. green	3·75	10·00
T 25.		120 l. on 5s. red ..	14·00	21·00
T 26.	–	240 l. on 10s. bright blue (No. 478a) ..	17·00	32·00

1951. Nos. 509/11 of Great Britain surch. **B.A. TRIPOLITANIA** and value in **M.A.L.**

T 32.	147.	60 l. on 2s. 6d. green	3·50	13·00
T 33.	–	120 l. on 5s. red ..	7·50	16·00
T 34.	–	240 l. on 10s. blue ..	19·00	27·00

POSTAGE DUE STAMPS

1948. Postage Due stamps of Great Britain surch. **B.M.A. TRIPOLITANIA** and value in M.A.L.

TD 1.	D 1.	1 l. on ½d. green ..	4·00	27·00
TD 2.		2 l. on 1d. red ..	2·50	27·00
TD 3.		4 l. on 2d. black ..	6·50	17·00
TD 4.		6 l. on 3d. violet ..	7·50	20·00
TD 5.		24 l. on 1s. blue ..	26·00	75·00

1950. As Nos. TD 1/5 but surch. **B.A. TRIPOLITANIA** and value in M.A.L.

TD 6.	D 1.	1 l. on ½d. green ..	7·00	38·00
TD 7.		2 l. on 1d. red ..	2·50	19·00
TD 8.		4 l. on 2d. black ..	2·75	20·00
TD 9.		6 l. on 3d. violet ..	15·00	60·00
TD 10.		24 l. on 1s. blue ..	32·00	80·00

BRITISH POSTAL AGENCIES IN EASTERN ARABIA

British stamps were surcharged for use in the area of the Persian Gulf.

The stamps were used in Muscat from 1st April 1948 to 29th April 1966; in Dubai from 1st April 1948 to 6th January 1961; In Qatar: Doha from August 1950, Umm Said from February 1956 to 31st March 1957; and in Abu Dhabi from 30th March 1963 (Das Island from December 1960) to 29th March 1964.

Certain of them were placed on sale in Kuwait Post Offices in 1951 and in 1953 due to shortages of stamps with "KUWAIT" overprint; and they can all be found commercially used from that state and from Bahrain.

1948. 12 pies = 1 anna; 16 annas = 1 rupee.
1957. 100 naye paise = 1 rupee.

Stamps of Great Britain surcharged in Indian currency.

1948. King George VI.

16.	128.	½ a. on ½d. pale green ..	1·00	1·75
35.		½ a. on ½d. orange ..	30	3·50
17.		1 a. on 1d. pale red ..	1·00	20
36.		1 a. on 1d. blue ..	30	1·75
18.		1½ a. on 1½d. pale brown	1·00	20
37.		1½ a. on 1½d. green ..	1·50	10·00
19.		2 a. on 2d. pale orange ..	80	45
38.		2 a. on 2d. brown ..	30	4·25
20.		2½ a. on 2½d. light blue	1·25	2·00
39.		2½ a. on 2½d. red ..	30	10·00
21.		3 a. on 3d. pale violet ..	1·25	10
40.	129.	4 a. on 4d. blue ..	30	1·75
22.		6 a. on 6d. purple ..	1·25	10
23.	130.	1 r. on 1s. brown ..	3·00	50
24.	131.	2 r. on 2s. 6d. green ..	6·50	20·00

1948. Royal Silver Wedding.

25.	137.	2½ a. on 2½d. blue ..	1·00	50
26.	138.	15 r. on £1 blue ..	28·00	35·00

1948. Olympic Games.

27.	139.	2½ a. on 2½d. blue ..	35	1·00
28.	140.	3 a. on 3d. violet ..	45	1·40
29.	–	6 a. on 6d. purple ..	45	1·40
30.	–	1 r. on 1s. brown ..	1·25	1·75

1949. 75th Anniv. of U.P.U.

31.	143.	2½ a. on 2½d. blue ..	60	1·75
32.	144.	3 a. on 3d. violet ..	60	1·75
33.	–	6 a. on 6d. purple ..	60	1·50
34.	–	1 r. on 1s. brown ..	2·50	2·00

1951. Pictorial.

41.	147.	2 r. on 2s. 6d. green ..	22·00	5·00

1952. Queen Elizabeth.

42	154.	½ a. on ½d. orange ..	10	40
43		1 a. on 1d. blue ..	10	40
44		1½ a. on 1½d. green ..	10	10
45		2 a. on 2d. brown ..	10	10
46	155.	2½ a. on 2½d. red ..	10	10
47		3 a. on 3d. lilac ..	20	10
48		4 a. on 4d. blue ..	55	1·25
49	157.	6 a. on 6d. purple ..	35	10
50	160.	12 a. on 1s. 3d. green ..	2·00	30
51		1 r. on 1s. 6d. blue ..	2·00	10

1953. Coronation.

52.	161.	2½ a. on 2½d. red ..	1·75	95
53.	–	4 a. on 4d. blue ..	1·75	95
54.	163.	12 a. on 1s. 3d. green ..	3·25	95
55.	–	1 r. on 1s. 6d. blue ..	4·50	45

1955. Pictorials.

56.	166.	2 r. on 2s. 6d. brown ..	3·25	70
57.	–	5 r. on 5s. red ..	9·00	2·00

1957. Value in naye paise, Queen Elizabeth II stamps surch **NP** twice (once only on 75 n. p.) and value.

65.	157.	1 n.p. on 5d. brown ..	10	30
66.	154.	3 n.p. on ½d. orange ..	20	85
81.		5 n.p. on 1d. blue ..	50	40
67.		6 n.p. on 1d. blue ..	20	85
68.		9 n.p. on 1½d. green ..	20	50
83.		10 n.p. on 1½d. green ..	50	40
69.		12 n.p. on 2d. pale brown	30	50
85.	155.	15 n.p. on 2½d. red ..	25	10
71.		20 n.p. on 3d. lilac ..	20	10
72.		25 n.p. on 4d. blue ..	70	2·25
87.		30 n.p. on 4½d. brown ..	40	40
73.	157.	40 n.p. on 6d. purple ..	30	10
89.	158.	50 n.p. on 9d. olive ..	80	80
90.	160.	75 n.p. on 1s. 3d. green	1·75	90

1957. World Scout Jubilee Jamboree.

76.	170.	15 n.p. on 2½d. red ..	25	75
77.	171.	25 n.p. on 4d. blue ..	30	75
78.	–	75 n.p. on 3d. green ..	35	75

BRITISH POST OFFICES IN CHINA

Stamps for use in Weihaiwei, and the neighbouring islands, leased to Great Britain from 1898 to 1 October 1930, when they were returned to China. The stamps were also used in the Treaty ports from 1917 until 1922.

100 cents = 1 dollar.

1917. Stamps of Hong Kong (King George V) optd. **CHINA.**

1	24.	1 c. brown	1·25	1·00
2		2 c. green	40	15
3		4 c. red	1·75	10
4		6 c. orange	1·25	45
5		8 c. grey	3·50	70
6		10 c. blue	2·75	10
7		12 c. purple on yellow ..	2·25	2·00
8		20 c. purple and olive ..	4·50	40
9		25 c. purple ..	4·00	12·00
11		30 c. purple and orange ..	14·00	3·50
12b		50 c. black on green ..	11·00	2·75
13		$1 purple and blue on blue	35·00	1·75
14		$2 red and black ..	85·00	35·00
15		$3 green and purple ..	£140	£100
16		$5 green and red on green	£160	£120
17		$10 purple & black on red	£450	£250

BRITISH POST OFFICES IN CRETE

40 paras = piastre.

1.

2.

1898.

1.	1.	20 par. violet	£375	£225

1898.

2.	2.	10 par. blue	8·00	12·00
4.		10 par. brown	8·00	17·00
3.		20 par. green	10·00	12·00
5.		20 par. red	14·00	15·00

BRITISH POST OFFICE IN SIAM

Used at Bangkok. Stamps of Straits Settlements, specially overprinted, were used for a time.

100 cents = 1 dollar.

1882. Stamps of Straits Settlements optd. **B**

On issue of 1867.

1.	19.	32 c. on 2 a. yellow ..	£30000	£40000

On issues of 1867–83.

14	5.	2 c. brown	£250	£200
13	9.	2 c. on 32 c. red (No. 60)	£1800	£1900
15	5.	2 c. red	40·00	35·00
16		4 c. red	£300	£180
17		4 c. brown	60·00	55·00
4	18	5 c. brown	£170	£180
18		5 c. blue	£190	£140
5	5	6 c. lilac	£130	90·00
20		8 c. orange	£100	60·00
21	19	10 c. grey	£110	80·00
8	5	12 c. blue	£700	£375
22		12 c. purple	£200	£140
9		24 c. green	£400	£120
10	8	30 c. red	£20000	£15000
11	9	96 c. grey	£3000	£1700

BRITISH VIRGIN ISLANDS

A group of the Leeward Is., Br. W. Indies. Used general issues for Leeward Is. concurrently with Virgin Is. stamps until 1st July, 1956. A Crown Colony.

1951. 100 cents = 1 West Indian dollar.
1962. 100 cents = 1 U.S. dollar.

1. St. Ursula.

2.

3.

4.

1866.

1.	1.	1d. green	45·00	60·00
16.	3.	4d. red	40·00	60·00
7.	2.	6d. red	60·00	90·00
11.	4.	1s. black and red ..	£200	£275

1867. With heavy coloured border.

18.	4.	1s. black and red	48·00	60·00

6.

8.

1880.

26.	6.	½d. yellow	75·00	80·00
27.		½d. green	3·25	8·00
24.		1d. green	55·00	85·00
29.		1d. red	20·00	25·00
25.		2½d. brown	85·00	£120
31.		2½d. blue	2·50	10·00

1887.

32	1.	1d. red	2·00	7·00
35	3.	4d. brown	40·00	75·00
38	2.	6d. violet	15·00	48·00
41	4.	1s. brown	50·00	80·00

1888. No. 18 surch. **4D.**

42.	4.	4d. on 1s. black and red ..	£110	£150

1899.

43.	8.	½d. green	60	55
44.		1d. red	2·25	2·50
45.		2½d. blue	12·00	4·00
46.		4d. brown	5·00	12·00
47.		6d. violet	4·50	4·50
48.		7d. green	7·00	8·00
49.		1s. yellow	18·00	32·00
50.		5s. blue	65·00	80·00

9.

11.

1904.

54.	9.	½d. purple and green ..	50	40
55.		1d. purple and red ..	85	35
56.		2d. purple and brown ..	3·25	4·50
57.		2½d. purple and blue ..	1·75	2·00
58.		3d. purple and black ..	2·75	3·00
59.		6d. purple and brown ..	2·75	3·00
60.		1s. green and red ..	2·75	4·75
61.		2s. 6d. green and black ..	18·00	45·00
62.		5s. green and blue ..	42·00	65·00

1913.

63	11	½d. green	1·00	1·75
68		1d. red	1·75	10·00
70		2d. grey	3·75	12·00
72		2½d. blue	4·00	6·50
73		3d. purple on yellow ..	1·60	4·75
74		6d. purple	3·00	3·75
75		1s. black on green ..	3·25	4·00
76		2s. 6d. blk. & red on blue	40·00	40·00
77		5s. green & red on yellow	32·00	85·00

1917. Optd. **WAR STAMP.**

78c	11	1d. red	20	2·25
79		3d. purple on yellow ..	25	8·50

14.

15. King George VI and Badge of Colony.

1922.

86 14 ½d. green .. .. 30 1·25
87 1d. red 30 50
88 1d. violet .. .. 70 2·50
90 1½d. red .. .. .. 1·25 2·25
92 2d. grey .. .. 60 3·50
95 2½d. blue .. .. 80 3·50
94 2½d. orange .. .. 1·25 1·25
96 3d. purple on yellow .. 1·50 5·50
97 5d. purple and olive .. 5·00 35·00
98 6d. purple .. .. 1·25 4·75
99 1s. black on green .. 1·25 8·50
84 2s. 6d. blk. & red on blue 3·75 9·00
101 5s. green & red on yellow 19·00 48·00

1935. Silver Jubilee. As T **13** of Antigua.

103. 1d. blue and red .. 65 1·25
104. 1½d. blue and grey .. 65 1·25
105. 2½d. brown and blue .. 65 1·25
106. 1s. grey and purple .. 5·00 8·50

1937. Coronation. As T **2** of Aden.

107. 1d. red 20 50
108. 1½d. brown .. .. 40 1·25
109. 2½d. blue 45 80

1938.

110a 15 ½d. green 30 60
111a 1d. red 30 40
112a 1½d. brown 65 85
113a 2d. grey 40 70
114a 2½d. blue 60 90
115a 3d. orange 40 70
116a 6d. mauve .. .. 1·50 70
117a 1s. brown .. .. 1·25 60
118a 2s. 6d. brown .. .. 11·00 3·00
119a 5s. red .. .. 12·00 4·00
120 10s. blue .. .. 7·00 8·00
121 £1 black .. .. 11·00 20·00

1946. Victory. As T **9** of Aden.

122. 1½d. brown 10 10
123. 3d. orange 10 10

1949. Silver Wedding. As T **10/11** of Aden.

124. 2½d. blue 10 10
125. £1 grey .. .. .. 9·00 12·00

1949. 75th Anniv of U.P.U. As T **20/23** of Antigua.

126. 2½d. blue 30 30
127. 3d. orange 50 55
128. 6d. mauve 50 30
129. 1s. olive 50 35

1951. Inauguration of B.W.I. University College. As T **24/25** of Antigua.

130. 3 c. black and red .. 40 15
131. 12 c. black and violet .. 40 25

16. Map.

1951. Restoration of Legislative Council.

132. 16. 6 c. orange 20 50
133. 12 c. purple 20 50
134. 24 c. olive 20 50
135. $1.20 red 45 75

18. Map of Jost Van Dyke.

1952.

136. – 1 c. black 30 60
137. 18. 2 c. green 35 30
138. – 3 c. black and brown .. 30 60
139. – 4 c. red 35 60
140. – 5 c. red and black .. 75 50
141. – 8 c. blue 35 30
142. – 12 c. violet 35 30
143. – 24 c. brown 35 30
144. – 60 c. green and blue .. 2·25 9·50
145. – $1.20 black and blue .. 3·75 8·00
146. – $2.40 green and brown 10·00 6·50
147. – $4.80 blue and red .. 10·00 11·00

DESIGNS—VERT. 1 c. Sombrero lighthouse. 24 c. Badge of Presidency. HORIZ. VIEWS: 3 c. Sheep Industry. 5 c. Cattle Industry. 60 c. Dead Man's Chest (Is.). $1.20, Sir Francis Drake Channel. $2.40, Road Town. HORIZ. MAPS: 4 c. Anegada Is. 8 c. Virgin Gorda Is. 12 c. Tortola Is. $4.80, Virgin Is.

1953. Coronation. As T **13** of Aden.

148. 2 c. black and green .. 15 45

29. Map of Tortola.

30. Brown Pelican.

1956.

149. 29. ½ c. black and purple .. 30 20
150. – 1 c. turquoise and slate 1·50 65
151. – 2 c. red and black .. 30 10
152. – 3 c. blue and olive .. 30 30
153. – 4 c. brown and turq. .. 35 30
154. – 5 c. black 45 10
155. – 8 c. orange and blue .. 45 40
156. – 12 c. blue and red .. 1·60 75
157. – 24 c. green and brown .. 80 50
158. – 60 c. blue and orange .. 6·50 6·00
159. – $1.20 green and red .. 1·25 3·75
160. 30. $2.40 yellow and purple 22·00 12·00
161. – $4.80 sepia & turquoise 22·00 13·00

DESIGNS—HORIZ. As Type **13**: 1 c. Virgin Islands sloop. 2 c. Nelthrop Red Poll bull. 3 c. Road Harbour. 4 c. Mountain Travel. 5 c. Badge of the Presidency. 8 c. Beach scene. 12 c. Boat launching. 24 c. White Cedar Tree. 60 c. Bonito (fish). $1.20, Treasury Square. As Type **30**: $4.80, Magnificent Frigate Bird.

1962. New Currency. Nos. 149/53, 155/61 surch. in U.S. Currency.

162. 29. 1 c. on ½ c. blk. & purple 30 10
163. – 2 c. on 1 c. turquoise and violet 55 10
164. – 3 c. on 2 c. red and black 30 10
165. – 4 c. on 3 c. blue & olive 30 10
166. – 5 c. on 4 c. brn. & turq. 30 10
167 – 8 c. on 8 c. orange & blue 30 10
168. – 10 c. on 12 c. blue & red 30 10
169. – 12 c. on 24 c. grn. & brn. 30 10
170. – 25 c. on 60 c. blue & orge. 1·25 45
171. – 70 c. on $1.20 grn. & red 35 45
172. 30. $1.40 on $2.40 lemon & purple .. .. 6·50 3·00
173. – $2.80 on $4.80 sepia and turquoise .. .. 7·00 3·00

1963. Freedom from Hunger. As T **28** of Aden.

174. 25 c. violet 20 10

1963. Cent of Red Cross. As T **33** of Antigua.

175. 2 c. red and black 10 10
176. 25 c. red and blue 25 20

1964. 400th Birth Anniv of Shakespeare. As T **34** of Antigua.

177. 10 c. blue 10 10

43. Bonito.

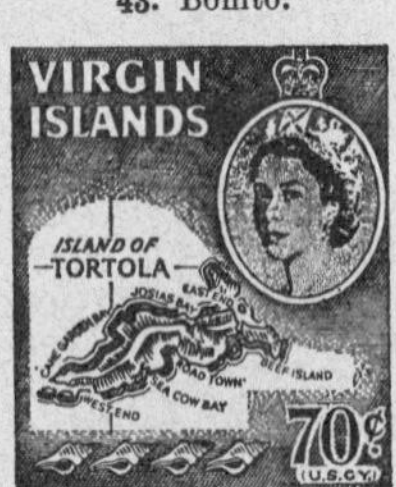

44. Map of Tortola.

1964.

178. 43. 1 c. blue and olive .. 30 60
179. – 2 c. olive and red .. 15 30
180. – 3 c. sepia & turquoise .. 2·50 90
181. – 4 c. black and red .. 60 70
182. – 5 c. black and green .. 55 55
183. – 6 c. black and orange .. 30 70
184. – 8 c. black and mauve .. 30 40
185. – 10 c. lake and lilac .. 85 20
186. – 12 c. green and blue .. 1·25 1·00
187. – 15 c. green and black .. 35 80
188. – 25 c. green and purple .. 9·50 1·40
189. 44. 70 c. black and brown .. 3·00 1·50
190. – $1 green and brown .. 3·00 1·50
191. – $1.40 blue and red .. 14·00 5·50
192. – $2.80 black and purple 14·00 8·00

DESIGNS—HORIZ. As Type **43**: 2 c. Soper's Hole 3 c. Brown Pelican. 4 c. Dead Man's Chest. 5 c. Road Harbour. 6 c. Fallen Jerusalem. 8 c. The Baths, Virgin Gorda. 10 c. Map of Virgin Islands. 12 c. "Youth of Tortola" (Tortola–St. Thomas ferry). 15 c. The Towers, Tortola. 25 c. Beef Island Airfield. VERT. As Type **44**: $1, Virgin Gorda. $1.40, Yachts at anchor. $2.80, Badge of the Colony (27½ × 37½ mm.).

1965. Cent of I.T.U. As T **36** of Antigua.

193. 4 c. yellow and turquoise 10 10
194. 25 c. blue and buff .. 20 20

1965. I.C.Y. As T **37** of Antigua.

195. 1 c. purple and turquoise .. 10 15
196. 25 c. green and lavender .. 30 15

1966. Churchill Commem. As T **38** of Antigua.

197. 1 c. blue 10 10
198. 2 c. green 15 10
199. 10 c. brown 30 10
200. 25 c. violet 60 25

1966. Royal Visit. As T **39** of Antigua.

201. 4 c. black and blue .. 30 10
202. 70 c. black and mauve .. 1·10 45

58. "Atrato I" (paddle-steamer), 1866.

1966. Stamp Centenary. Multicoloured.

203. 5 c. Type **58** 20 10
204. 10 c. 1d. and 6d. stamps of 1866 .. .. .. 30 10
205. 25 c. Mail transport, Beef Island, and 6d. stamp of 1866 .. .. .. 45 10
206. 60 c. Landing mail at Road-town, 1866 and 1d. stamp of 1866 .. .. .. 85 75

1966. Nos. 189 and 191/2 surch.

207. 44. 50 c. on 70 c. blk. & brn. 70 70
208. – $1·50 on $1·40 blue & red 2·00 2·00
209. – $3 on $2·80 blk. & pur. 2·50 2·75

1966. 20th Anniv. of U.N.E.S.C.O. As T **54/6** of Antigua.

210. 2 c. multicoloured .. 10 10
211. 12 c. yellow, violet & olive 20 10
212. 60 c. black, purple & orge. 50 30

63. Map of Virgin Islands.

1967. New Constitution.

213. 63. 2 c. multicoloured .. 10 10
214. 10 c. multicoloured .. 15 10
215. 25 c. multicoloured .. 15 10
216. $1 multicoloured .. 55 25

64. "Mercury" (cable ship) and Bermuda–Tortola Link.

1967. Inauguration of Bermuda–Tortola Telephone Service. Multicoloured.

217. 4 c. Type **64** 10 10
218. 10 c. Chalwell Telecommunications Station 10 10
219. 50 c. "Mercury" (cable ship) 30 20

67. Blue Marlin.

1968. Game Fishing. Multicoloured.

220. 2 c. Type **67** 10 40
221. 10 c. Cobia 25 10
222. 25 c. Wahoo 55 10
223. 40 c. Fishing launch and map 85 45

1968. Human Rights Year. Nos. 185 and 188 optd. **1968 INTERNATIONAL YEAR FOR HUMAN RIGHTS.**

224. 10 c. lake and lilac 15 10
225. 25 c. green and purple .. 25 30

72. Dr. Martin Luther King, Bible, Sword and Armour Gauntlet.

1968. Martin Luther King. Commem.

226. 72. 4 c. multicoloured .. 20 15
227. 25 c. multicoloured .. 30 15

73. DHC-6 Twin Otter.

1968. Opening of "Beef Island" Airport Extension. Multicoloured.

228. 2 c. Type **73** 15 40
229. 10 c. HS "748" Airliner 20 10
230. 25 c. HS "Heron" .. 55 10
231. $1 Royal Engineers' Cap badge .. .. .. 1·10 1·40

77. Long John Silver and Jim Hawkins.

1969. 75th Death Anniv. of Robert Louis Stevenson.

232. 77. 4 c. blue, yellow & red .. 25 10
233. – 10 c. multicoloured .. 30 10
234. – 40 c. brown, black & blue 50 20
235. – $1 multicoloured .. 75 1·00

DESIGNS—HORIZ. 10 c. Jim Hawkins escaping from the Pirates. $1, Treasure Trove. VERT. 40 c. The Fight with Israel Hands.

82. Yachts in Road Harbour, Tortola.

1969. Tourism. Multicoloured.

236. 2 c. Tourist and Rock Grouper (fish) 15 40
237. 10 c. Type **82** 30 10
238. 20 c. Sun-bathing at Virgin Gorda National Park .. 40 15
239. $1 Tourist and Pipe Organ cactus, at Virgin Gorda 90 1·25

Nos. 236 and 239 are vert.

85. Carib Canoe.

1970.

240. 85.	½ c. buff, brn. and sepia	10	55
241. –	1 c. blue and green ..	15	30
242. –	2 c. orge., brn. and slate	40	70
243. –	3 c. red, blue and sepia	30	60
244. –	4 c. turq., blue and brn.	30	50
245. –	5 c. green, pink & black	30	10
246. –	6 c. violet, mauve & grn.	40	75
247. –	8 c. green, yellow & sepia	50	1·40
248. –	10 c. blue and brown ..	50	15
249. –	12 c. yellow, red & brn.	65	75
250. –	15 c. grn., orge. and brn.	4·00	85
251. –	25 c. grn., blue and pur.	6·00	1·50
252. –	50 c. mauve, grn. & brn.	2·25	1·50
253. –	$1 salmon, grn. & brn.	3·50	4·00
254. –	$2 buff, slate and grey	6·50	7·50
255. –	$3 ochre, blue and sepia	5·00	6·50
256. –	$5 violet and grey ..	8·00	9·00

DESIGNS: 1 c. "Santa Maria" (Columbus's flagship). 2 c. "Elizabeth Bonaventure" (Drake's flagship). 3 c. Dutch buccaneer, c. 1660. 4 c. "Thetis", 1827 (after etching by E. W. Cooke). 5 c. Henry Morgan's ship (17th century). 6 c. H.M.S. "Boreas" (Captain Nelson, 1784). 8 c. H.M.S. "Eclair", 1804. 10 c. H.M.S. "Formidable", 1782. 12 c. H.M.S. "Nymph", 1778. 15 c. "Windsor Castle" (sailing packet) engaging "Jeune Richard" (French brig), 1807. 25 c. H.M.S. "Astrea", 1808. 50 c. Wreck of R.M.S. "Rhone", 1867. $1, Tortola sloop. $2, H.M.S. "Frobisher". $3, "Booker Viking" (cargo liner), 1967. $5, Hydrofoil "Sun Arrow".

102. "A Tale of Two Cities".

1970. Death Cent. of Charles Dickens.

257. 102.	5 c. black, red and grey	10	10
258. –	10 c. black, blue & green	20	10
259. –	25 c. blk., grn. and yell.	30	30

DESIGNS: 10 c. "Oliver Twist". 25 c. "Great Expectations".

103. Hospital Visit.

1970. Cent. of British Red Cross. Mult.

260.	4 c. Type 103	20	10
261.	10 c. First Aid class	30	10
262.	25 c. Red Cross and Coat of arms	60	30

104. Mary Read.

1970. Pirates. Multicoloured.

263.	½ c. Type 104	10	10
264.	10 c. George Lowther ..	35	10
265.	30 c. Edward Teach (Blackbeard)	85	20
266.	60 c. Henry Morgan ..	1·25	60

105. Children and "UNICEF".

1971. 25th Anniv. of U.N.I.C.E.F.

267. 105.	15 c. multicoloured ..	10	10
268.	30 c. multicoloured ..	20	25

1972. Royal Visit of Princess Margaret. Nos. 244 and 251 optd. **VISIT OF H.R.H. THE PRINCESS MARGARET 1972.**

269.	4 c. bl. chalky bl. and brn.	15	10
270.	25 c. green, blue and plum	25	30

107. Seamen of 1800.

1972. "Interpex" Stamp Exhib., New York. Naval Uniforms. Multicoloured.

271.	½ c. Type 107	10	10
272.	10 c. Boatswain, 1787-1807	35	10
273.	30 c. Captain, 1795-1812	85	45
274.	60 c. Admiral, 1787-95 ..	1·50	1·25

1972. Royal Silver Wedding. As T 52 of Ascension, but with Sailfish and "Sir Winston Churchill" (cadet schooner) in background.

275	15 c. blue	20	15
276	25 c. blue	20	15

109. Blue Marlin.

1972. Game Fish. Multicoloured.

277.	½ c. Type 109	10	20
278.	½ c. Wahoo	15	20
279.	15 c. Allison Tuna ..	55	25
280.	25 c. White Marlin ..	60	30
281.	50 c. Sailfish	1·25	90
282.	$1 Dolphin	2·00	2·00

110. J. C. Lettsom.

1973. "Interpex 1973" (Quakers). Mult.

284.	½ c. Type 110	10	10
285.	10 c. Lettsom house (horiz.)	15	10
286.	15 c. Dr. W. Thornton ..	20	10
287.	30 c. Dr. Thornton and Capitol, Washington (horiz.)	25	20
288.	$1 William Penn (horiz.) ..	70	85

111. Green-throated Carib and Antillean Crested Hummingbird.

1973. 1st Issue of Coinage. Coins and local scenery. Multicoloured.

289.	1 c. Type 111	10	10
290.	5 c. "Zenaida Dove" (5 c. coin)	50	10
291.	10 c. "Ringed Kingfisher" (10 c. coin)	65	10
292.	25 c. "Mangrove Cuckoo" (25 c. coin)	85	15
293.	50 c. "Brown Pelican" (50 c. coin)	95	1·00
294.	$1 "Magnificent Frigatebird ($1 coin) ..	1·40	1·75

1973. Royal Wedding. As T 47 of Anguilla. Multicoloured. Background colours given.

301.	5 c. brown	10	10
302.	50 c. blue	20	20

112. "Virgin and Child" (Pintoricchio).

1973. Christmas. Multicoloured.

303.	½ c. Type 112	10	10
304.	3 c. "Virgin and Child" (Lorenzo di Credi) ..	10	10
305.	25 c. "Virgin and Child" (Crivelli)	15	10
306.	50 c. "Virgin and Child with St. John" (Luini)	30	40

113. Crest of the "Canopus" (French).

1974. "Interpex 1974" (Naval Crests). Mult.

307.	5 c. Type 113	20	10
308.	18 c. U.S.S. "Saginaw"	35	25
309.	25 c. H.M.S. "Rothesay"	40	30
310.	50 c. H.M.C.S. "Ottawa"	60	60

114. Christopher Columbus.

1974. Historical Figures.

312. 114.	5 c. orange and black ..	20	10
313. –	10 c. blue and black ..	35	10
314. –	25 c. violet and black ..	50	25
315. –	40 c. brn. & deep brn.	70	75

PORTRAITS: 10 c. Sir Walter Raleigh. 25 c. Sir Martin Frobisher. 40 c. Sir Francis Drake.

115. Trumpet Triton.

1974. Seashells. Multicoloured.

317.	5 c. Type 115	30	15
318.	18 c. West Indian Murex ..	60	30
319.	25 c. Bleeding Tooth ..	75	35
320.	75 c. Virgin Islands Latirus	1·75	1·75

116. Churchill and St. Mary, Aldermanbury, London.

1974. Birth Centenary of Sir Winston Churchill. Multicoloured.

322.	10 c. Type 116	15	10
323.	50 c. St. Mary, Fulton, Missouri	35	50

117. H.M.S. "Boreas".

1975. "Interpex 1975" Stamp Exhibition, New York. Ships' Figure-heads. Mult.

325.	5 c. Type 117	20	10
326.	18 c. "Golden Hind" ..	50	15
327.	40 c. H.M.S. "Superb" ..	70	20
328.	85 c. H.M.S. "Formidable"	1·50	1·00

118. Rock Beauty.

1975. Fishes. Multicoloured.

330.	½ c. Type 118	15	30
331.	1 c. Squirrelfish	30	50
332.	3 c. Queen Triggerfish ..	60	40
333.	5 c. Blue Angelfish ..	30	20
334.	8 c. Stoplight Parrotfish ..	30	25
335.	10 c. Queen Angelfish ..	30	25
336.	12 c. Nassau Grouper ..	40	30
337.	13 c. Blue Tang	40	30
338.	15 c. Sergeant Major ..	40	35
339.	18 c. Jewfish	70	70
340.	20 c. Bluehead Wrasse ..	60	70
341.	25 c. Grey Angelfish ..	1·00	60
342.	60 c. Glasseye Snapper ..	1·25	2·00
343.	$1 Blue Chromis	1·75	1·75
344.	$2·50 French Angelfish ..	3·50	4·50
345.	$3 Queen Parrotfish ..	4·25	5·00
346.	$5 Four-eye Butterfly Fish	8·00	7·50

119. St. George's Parish School (First meeting-place, 1950).

1975. 25th Anniv. of Legislative Council Restoration. Multicoloured.

347.	5 c. Type 119	10	10
348.	25 c. Legislative Council Building	25	10
349.	40 c. Mace and gavel ..	35	15
350.	75 c. Commemorative scroll	55	65

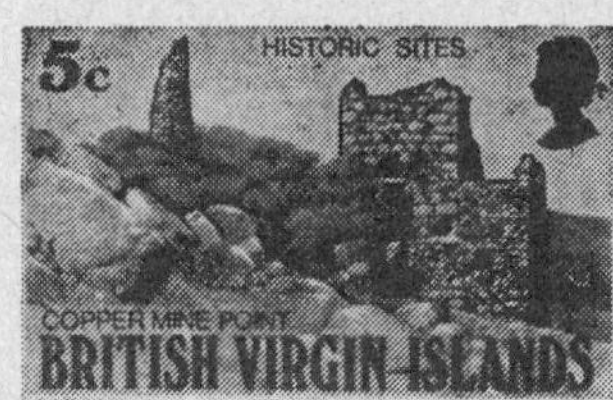

120. Copper Mine Point.

1976. Historic Sites. Multicoloured.

351.	5 c. Type 120	10	10
352.	18 c. Pleasant Valley ..	20	10
353.	50 c. Callwood Distillery ..	40	30
354.	75 c. The Dungeon ..	60	65

121. Massachusetts Brig "Hazard".

1976. Bicent of American Revolution. Mult.

355 8 c. Type **121** 60 15
356 22 c. American privateer "Spy" .. .. .. 1·10 45
357 40 c. "Raleigh" (American frigate) .. .. .. 1·60 1·00
358 75 c. Frigate "Alliance" and H.M.S. "Trepassy" 2·00 1·90

122. Government House, Tortola.

1976. Fifth Anniv. of Friendship Day with U.S. Virgin Is. Multicoloured.

360. 8 c. Type **122** 10 10
361. 15 c. Government House, St. Croix (vert.) .. 10 10
362. 30 c. Flags (vert.) 15 10
363. 75 c. Government seals .. 30 40

123. Royal Visit, 1966.

1977. Silver Jubilee. Multicoloured.

364. 8 c. Type **123** 10 10
365. 30 c. The Holy Bible .. 15 15
366. 60 c. Presentation of Holy Bible 25 40

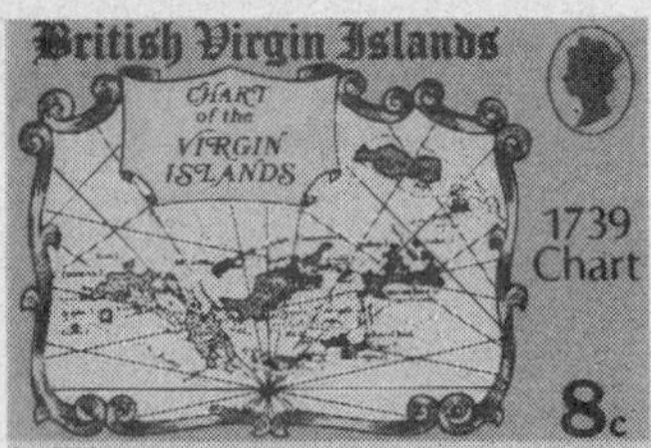

124. Chart of 1739.

1977. 18th-Century Maps. Multicoloured.

367. 8 c. Type **124** 40 10
368. 22 c. French Map, 1758 .. 75 30
369. 30 c. Map from English and Danish surveys, 1775 .. 1·00 65
370. 75 c. Map of 1779 .. 1·50 1·50

1977. Royal Visit. As Nos. 364/6 inscr. "SILVER JUBILEE ROYAL VISIT".

371. 5 c. Type **123** 10 10
372. 25 c. The Holy Bible .. 20 10
373. 50 c. Presentation of Holy Bible 35 25

125. Divers checking Equipment.

1978. Tourism. Multicoloured.

374. ½ c. Type **125** 10 10
375. 5 c. Cup coral on wreck of "Rhone" 15 10
376. 8 c. Sponge formation on wreck of "Rhone" .. 20 10
377. 22 c. Cup coral and sponges 50 15
378. 30 c. Sponges inside cave .. 60 20
379. 75 c. Marine life .. .. 1·10 85

126. Fire Coral.

1978. Corals. Multicoloured.

380. 8 c. Type **126** 25 15
381. 15 c. Staghorn coral .. 40 30
382. 40 c. Brain coral 75 85
383. 75 c. Elkhorn coral .. 1·50 1·60

127. Iguana.

1978. 25th Anniv. of Coronation.

384. – 50 c. brown, green and silver 25 40
385. – 50 c. multicoloured .. 25 40
386. **127.** 50 c. brown, green and silver 25 40

DESIGNS: No. 384, Plantagenet Falcon. No. 385, Queen Elizabeth II.

128. Lignum Vitae.

1978. Flowering Trees. Multicoloured.

387. 8 c. Type **128** 15 10
388. 22 c. Ginger Thomas .. 25 15
389. 40 c. Dog Almond .. 35 20
390. 75 c. White Cedar .. 60 70

129. " Eurema lisa ".

1978. Butterflies. Multicoloured.

392 5 c. Type **129** 25 10
393 22 c. "Agraulis vanillae" .. 75 20
394 30 c. "Heliconius charithonia" 85 30
395 75 c. "Hemiargus hanno" 1·25 1·25

130. Spiny Lobster.

1978. Wildlife Conservation. Multicoloured.

397. 5 c. Type **130** 15 10
398. 15 c. Large Iguana (vert.) 30 10
399. 22 c. Hawksbill Turtle .. 50 15
400. 75 c. Black Coral (vert.) .. 1·10 90

131. Strawberry Cactus.

1979. Native Cacti. Multicoloured.

402. ½ c. Type **131** 10 10
403. 5 c. Snowy cactus .. 15 10
404. 13 c. Barrel cactus .. 25 20
405. 22 c. Tree cactus 40 35
406. 30 c. Prickly Pear .. 45 40
407. 75 c. Dildo cactus .. 80 1·00

132. West Indian Girl.

1979. International Year of the Child. Multicoloured.

408. 5 c. Type **132** 10 10
409. 10 c. African boy 10 10
410. 13 c. Asian girl 10 10
411. $1 European boy .. 50 85

133. 1956 Road Harbour 3 c. Definitive Stamp.

1979. Death Centenary of Sir Rowland Hill.

413. **133.** 5 c. deep blue, blue and green 10 10
414. – 13 c. blue and mauve .. 10 10
415. – 75 c. blue and purple .. 45 50

DESIGN—HORIZ. 13 c. 1880 2½d. red-brown. 75 c. Great Britain 1910 unissued 2d. Tyrian plum.

134. Pencil Urchin.

1979. Underwater Life. Multicoloured.

417 ½ c. Calcified Algae .. 30 65
418 1 c. Purple-tipped Sea Anemone 40 65
419 3 c. Common Starfish .. 50 65
420 5 c. Type **134** 50 40
421 8 c. Triton's Trumpet .. 75 50
422 10 c. Christmas Tree Worms 30 50
423a 13 c. Flamingo Tongue Snail .. .. .. 1·25 75
424 15 c. Spider Crab 40 50
425 18 c. Sea Squirts .. .. 1·00 1·25
426 20 c. True Tulip 55 75
427 25 c. Rooster Tail Conch .. 1·25 1·75
428 30 c. Fighting Conch .. 1·25 1·00
429 60 c. Mangrove Crab .. 1·75 2·00
430 $1 Coral Polyps .. .. 2·50 3·50
431 $2.50 Peppermint Shrimp 3·50 6·00
432 $3 West Indian Murex .. 4·00 7·00
433 $5 Carpet Anemone .. 7·75 9·00

135. Rotary Athletics Meeting, Tortola.

1980. 75th Anniv. of Rotary International. Multicoloured.

434. 8 c. Type **135** 10 10
435. 22 c. Paul P. Harris (founder) 15 10
436. 60 c. Mount Sage, Tortola ("Creation of National Park") 40 40
437. $1 Rotary anniversary emblem 70 75

136. Brown Booby.

1980. "London 1980" International Stamp Exhibition. Birds. Multicoloured.

439. 20 c. Type **136** 20 20
440. 25 c. Magnificent Frigate-Bird 25 25
441. 50 c. White-tailed Tropic-Bird 40 40
442. 75 c. Brown Pelican .. 55 55

1980. Caribbean Commonwealth Parliamentary Association Meeting, Tortola. Nos. 414/15 optd. **CARIBBEAN COMMONWEALTH PARLIAMENTARY ASSOCIATION MEETING, TORTOLA, 11—19 JULY 1980.**

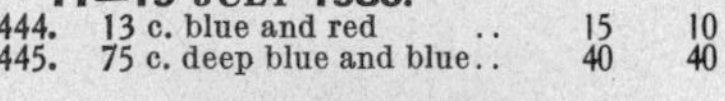

444. 13 c. blue and red .. 15 10
445. 75 c. deep blue and blue .. 40 40

138. Sir Francis Drake.

1980. Sir Francis Drake Commemoration. Multicoloured.

446. 8 c. Type **138** 50 10
447. 15 c. Queen Elizabeth I .. 70 15
448. 30 c. Drake receiving knighthood 90 30
449. 75 c. "Golden Hind" and coat of arms .. .. 1·75 95

139. Jost Van Dyke.

1980. Island Profiles. Multicoloured.

451. 2 c. Type **139** 10 10
452. 5 c. Peter Island 15 10
453. 13 c. Virgin Gorda .. 20 10
454. 22 c. Anegada 25 10
455. 30 c. Norman Island .. 35 15
456. $1 Tortola .. .. 90 1·00

MINIMUM PRICE

The minimum price quoted is 10p which represents a handling charge rather than a basis for valuing common stamps. For further notes about prices see introductory pages.

140. Dancing Lady.

1981. Flowers. Multicoloured.

458. 5 c. Type **140** 15 10
459. 20 c. Love in the Mist .. 40 25
460. 22 c. " Pitcairnia angustifolia " 40 25
461. 75 c. Dutchman's Pipe .. 1·40 1·40
462. $1 Maiden Apple .. 1·60 1·60

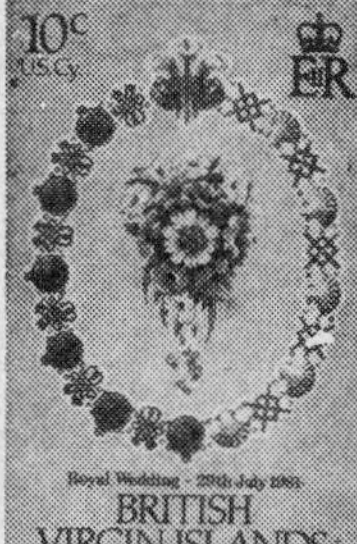

141. Wedding Bouquet from British Virgin Islands.

1981. Royal Wedding. Multicoloured.

463. 10 c. Type **141** 10 10
464. 35 c. Prince Charles and Queen Elizabeth the Queen Mother in Garter robes 30 15
465. $1.25 Prince Charles and Lady Diana Spencer .. 80 80

142. Stamp Collecting.

1981. 25th Anniv. of Duke of Edinburgh Award Scheme. Multicoloured.

466. 10 c. Type **142** 10 10
467. 15 c. Athletics 10 10
468. 50 c. Camping 25 25
469. $1 Duke of Edinburgh .. 40 45

143. " Development through Education ".

1981. International Year for Disabled Persons. Multicoloured.

470. 15 c. Type **143** 20 20
471. 20 c. Fort Charlotte Children's Centre 30 30
472. 30 c. " Developing cultural awareness " 40 40
473. $1 Fort Charlotte Children's Centre " (different) .. 1·25 1·25

144. Detail from " The Adoration of the Shepherds " (Rubens).

1981. Christmas.

474. **144.** 5 c. multicoloured .. 15 10
475. – 15 c. multicoloured .. 25 10
476. – 30 c. multicoloured .. 45 15
477. – $1 multicoloured .. 1·10 1·10

DESIGNS: 15 c. to $1. Further details from "The Adoration of the Shepherds" by Rubens.

145. Green-throated Caribs and Erythrina.

1982. Hummingbirds. Multicoloured.

479. 15 c. Type **145** 50 15
480. 30 c. Green-throated Carib and Bougainvillea .. 75 45
481. 35 c. Antillean Crested Hummingbirds and " Granadilla passiflora " 85 55
482. $1.25 Antillean Crested Hummingbirds and Hibiscus .. .. 2·50 2·75

146. " People caring for People ".

1982. 10th Anniv. of Lions Club of Tortola. Multicoloured.

483. 10 c. Type **146** 25 15
484. 20 c. Tortola Headquarters 45 20
485. 30 c. " We Serve " .. 65 30
486. $1.50 " Lions " Symbol .. 2·25 1·75

147. Princess at Victoria and Albert Museum, November, 1981.

1982. 21st Birthday of Princess of Wales. Multicoloured.

488. 10 c. British Virgin Islands coat of arms 15 10
489. 35 c. Type **147** 30 30
490. 50 c. Bride and groom proceeding into Vestry 50 50
491. $1.50 Formal portrait .. 1·25 1·60

148. Douglas " DC–3 ".

1982. 10th Anniv. of Air BVI. Multicoloured.

492. 10 c. Type **148** 20 15
493. 15 c. Britten-Norman " Islander " 25 20
494. 60 c. Hawker Siddeley " 748 " 90 75
495. 75 c. Runway scene .. 1·10 90

149. Scouts Raising Flag.

1982. 75th Anniv. of Boy Scout Movement and 50th Anniv. of Scouting in B.V.I. Multicoloured.

496. 8 c. Type **149** 20 10
497. 20 c. Cub Scout 45 25
498. 50 c. Sea Scout 85 55
499. $1 First camp, Brownsea Island, and portrait of Lord Baden-Powell .. 1·50 1·50

150. Legislature in Session.

1983. Commonwealth Day. Mult.

500. 10 c. Type **150** 10 10
501. 30 c. Tourism 25 20
502. 35 c. Satellite view of Earth showing Virgin Islands .. 25 25
503. 75 c. B.V.I. and Commonwealth flags 70 90

151. Florence Nightingale.

1983. Nursing Week. Multicoloured.

504. 10 c. Type **151** 50 15
505. 30 c. Staff nurse and assistant nurse 90 45
506. 60 c. Public Health nurses testing blood pressure (horiz.) .. .. .. 1·75 95
507. 75 c. Peebles Hospital (horiz.) 1·90 1·25

152. Frame Construction.

1983. Traditional Boat-building. Multicoloured.

508. 15 c. Type **152** 35 25
509. 25 c. Planking 55 40
510. 50 c. Launching 90 70
511. $1 Maiden Voyage .. 1·50 1·40

153. Grumman " Goose " Seaplane.

1983. Bicentenary of Manned Flight. Mult.

513. 10 c. Type **153** 20 15
514. 30 c. De Havilland "Heron" 45 45
515. 60 c. EMB " 110P1 Bandeirante " 85 85
516. $1.25, British Aerospace " HS 748 " .. .. 1·50 1·60

154. " Madonna and Child with the Infant Baptist ".

1983. Christmas. 500th Birth Anniv. of Raphael. Multicoloured.

517. 8 c. Type **154** 10 10
518. 15 c. "La Belle Jardiniere" 20 25
519. 50 c. " Madonna del Granduca " 65 70
520. $1 "The Terranuova Madonna " .. .. 1·25 1·40

155. Local Tournament.

1984. 60th Anniv of International Chess Federation. Multicoloured.

522 10 c. Type **155** .. .. 1·00 40
523 35 c. Staunton king, rook and pawn (vert) .. 2·00 1·25
524 75 c. Karpov's winning position against Jakobsen in 1980 Olympiad (vert) .. 3·75 3·25
525 $1 B.V.I. Gold Medal won by Bill Hook at 1980 Chess Olympiad .. 4·25 4·00

156. Port Purcell.

1984. 250th Anniv of "Lloyd's List" (newspaper). Multicoloured.

526 15 c. Type **156** 25 30
527 25 c. Boeing "747" .. 45 50
528 50 c. Wreck of "Rhone" (mail steamer), 1867 .. 90 95
529 $1 "Booker Viking" (cargo liner) .. .. .. 1·50 1·60

158. Running.

1984. Olympic Games, Los Angeles. Mult.

531. 15 c. Type **158** 40 30
532. 15 c. Runner 40 30
533. 20 c. Wind-surfing .. 45 35
534. 20 c. Surfer 45 35
535. 30 c. Sailing 65 50
536. 30 c. Yacht 65 50

159. Steel Band.

1984. 150th Anniv. of Abolition of Slavery. Multicoloured.

538. 10 c. Type **159** 20 25
539. 10 c. Dancing girls .. 20 25
540. 10 c. Men in traditional costumes 20 25
541. 10 c. Girl in traditional costume 20 25
542. 10 c. Festival Queen .. 20 25
543. 30 c. Green and yellow dinghies 40 45
544. 30 c. Blue and red dinghies 40 45
545. 30 c. White and blue dinghies 40 45
546. 30 c. Red and yellow dinghies 40 45
547. 30 c. Blue and white dinghies 40 45

DESIGNS: Various aspects of Emancipation Festival.

Nos. 543/7 form a composite design, the sail colours of the dinghies being described.

160. Sloop.

1984. Boats. Multicoloured.

548. 10 c. Type **160** 40 20
549. 35 c. Fishing boat .. .. 1·25 65
550. 60 c. Schooner .. .. 1·75 1·10
551. 75 c. Cargo boat .. .. 1·75 1·40

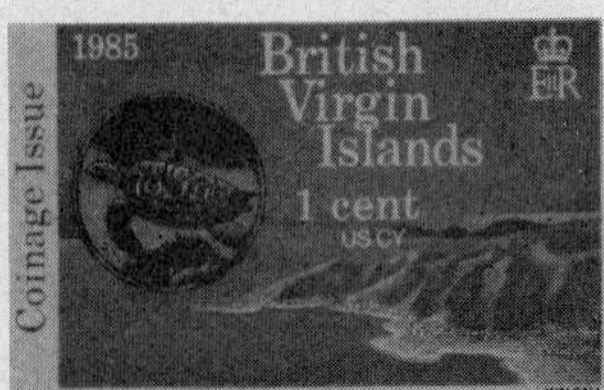

161. One Cent Coin and Aerial View.

1985. New Coinage. Coins and Local Scenery. Multicoloured.

553. 1 c. Type **161** 10 10
554. 5 c. Five cent coin and boulders on beach .. 10 10
555. 10 c. Ten cent coin and scuba diving 20 20
556. 25 c. Twenty-five cent coin and yachts 45 45
557. 50 c. Fifty cent coin and jetty .. .. .. 90 1·00
558. $1 One dollar coin and beach at night .. .. 1·75 2·00

162. Red-billed Tropic Bird.

1985. Birds of the British Virgin Islands. Multicoloured

560 1 c. Type **162** 10 10
561 2 c. Yellow-crowned night heron 10 10
562 5 c. Mangrove cuckoo .. 10 10
563 8 c. Northern mockingbird 10 10
647 10 c. Grey kingbird .. 15 20
565 12 c. Red-necked pigeon .. 15 20
566 15 c. Least bittern .. 20 25
567 18 c. Smooth-billed ani .. 25 30
568 20 c. Clapper rail 25 30
569 25 c. American kestrel .. 30 35
570 30 c. Pearly-eyed thrasher 40 45
571 35 c. Bridled quail dove .. 45 50
572 40 c. Green heron 50 55
573 50 c. Scaly-breasted ground dove 65 70
574 60 c. Little blue heron .. 80 85
658 $1 Audubon's shearwater 1·25 1·40
576 $2 Blue-faced booby .. 2·50 2·75
660 $3 Cattle egret .. .. 4·00 4·25
578 $5 Zenaida dove .. .. 6·50 6·75

163. The Queen Mother at Festival of Remembrance.

1985. Life and Times of Queen Elizabeth the Queen Mother. Multicoloured.

579. 10 c. Type **163** 15 20
580. 10 c. At Victoria Palace Theatre, 1984 .. .. 15 20
581 25 c. At the engagement of the Prince of Wales, 1981 35 40
582. 25 c. Opening Celia Johnson Theatre, 1985 .. 35 40
583. 50 c. The Queen Mother on her 82nd birthday .. 60 70
584. 50 c. At the Tate Gallery, 1983 .. .. .. 60 70
585. 75 c. At the Royal Smithfield Show, 1983 .. .. 90 1·00
586. 75 c. Unveiling Mountbatten Statue, 1983 .. 90 1·00

164. Seaside Sparrow.

1985. Birth Bicentenary of John J. Audubon (ornithologist). Designs showing original paintings. Multicoloured.

588. 5 c. Type **164** 50 20
589. 30 c. Passenger Pigeon .. 1·25 70
590. 50 c. Yellow-breasted Chat 1·50 1·50
591. $1 American Kestrel .. 2·25 2·50

165. S.V. "Flying Cloud".

1986. Visiting Cruise Ships. Multicoloured.

592. 35 c. Type **165** .. .. 1·75 85
593. 50 c. M.V. "Newport Clipper" .. .. .. 2·25 1·25
594. 75 c. M.V. "Cunard Countess' .. .. 2·75 2·00
595. $1 M.V. "Sea Goddess.. .. 3·25 2·50

1986. Inaugural Flight of Miami–Beef Island Air Service. Nos. 581/2 and 585/6 optd. **MIAMI B.V.I. INAUGURAL FLIGHT.**

596. 25 c. At the engagement of the Prince of Wales, 1981 50 50
597. 25 c. Opening Celia Johnson theatre, 1985 .. 50 50
598. 75 c. At the Royal Smithfield Show, 1983 .. 1·50 1·50
599. 75 c. Unveiling Mountbatten statue, 1983 .. .. .. 1·50 1·50

167. Queen Elizabeth II in 1958. (Illustration reduced, actual size 60 × 40 mm.).

1986. 60th Birthday of Queen Elizabeth II. Multicoloured.

600. 12 c. Type **167** 15 20
601. 35 c. At a Maundy Service 40 45
602. $1.50 Queen Elizabeth .. 1·40 1·75
603. $2 During a visit to Canberra, 1982 (vert.) .. 1·60 2·25

168. Miss Sarah Ferguson.

1986. Royal Wedding. Multicoloured.

605. 35 c. Type **168** 40 55
606. 35 c. Prince Andrew and Miss Sarah Ferguson .. 40 55
607. $1 Prince Andrew in morning dress (horiz.) .. 1·00 1·25
608. $1 Miss Sarah Ferguson (different) (horiz.) .. 1·00 1·25

169. Harvesting Sugar Cane.

1986. History of Rum Making. Multicoloured.

610. 12 c. Type **169** 80 40
611. 40 c. Bringing sugar cane to mill .. .. .. 1·50 1·25
612. 60 c. Rum distillery .. 2·00 2·00
613. $1 Delivering barrels of rum to ship .. .. 3·25 3·50

170. C.S. "Sentinel".

1986. 20th Anniv. of Cable and Wireless Caribbean Headquarters, Tortola. Mult.

615. 35 c. Type **170** 70 70
616. 35 c. C.S. "Retriever" (1961) 70 70
617. 60 c. C.S. "Cable Enterprise" (1964) .. 1·25 1·25
618. 60 c. C.S. "Mercury" (1962) 1·25 1·25
619. 75 c. C.S. "Recorder" (1955) .. .. .. 1·50 1·40
620. 75 c. C.S. "Pacific Guardian" (1984) .. 1·50 1·40
621. $1 S.S. "Great Eastern" (1860's) .. .. .. 1·75 1·75
622. $1 C.S. "Cable Venture" .. 1·75 1·75

172. 18th-century Spanish Galleon.

1987. Shipwrecks. Multicoloured.

625 12 c. Type **172** 75 35
626 35 c. H.M.S. "Astrea" (frigate), 1808 .. .. 1·50 1·10
627 75 c. "Rhone" (mail steamer), 1867 .. .. 2·50 2·50
628 $1.50 "Captain Rokos" (freighter), 1929 .. 4·25 4·75

173. Outline Map and Flag of Montserrat.

1987. 11th Meeting of Organisation of Eastern Caribbean States. Each showing outline map and flag. Multicoloured.

630. 10 c. Type **173** 40 40
631. 15 c. Grenada 50 50
632. 20 c. Dominica 55 55
633. 25 c. St. Kitts-Nevis .. 60 60
634. 35 c. St. Vincent and Grenadines 85 85
635. 50 c. British Virgin Islands 1·25 1·25
636. 75 c. Antigua and Barbuda 1·50 1·50
637. $1 St. Lucia .. .. 2·00 2·00

174. Spider Lily.

1987. Opening of Botanical Gardens. Multicoloured.

638. 12 c. Type **174** 80 35
639. 35 c. Barrel cactus .. 1·50 1·00
640. $1 Wild plantain .. 2·75 3·00
641. $1.50 Little butterfly orchid .. .. .. 7·00 6·50

175. Early Mail Packet and 1867 1s. Stamp.

1987. Bicentenary of Postal Services. Multicoloured.

662 10 c. Type **175** 60 30
663 20 c. Map and 1889 1d. stamp .. .. .. 1·25 75
664 35 c. Road Town Post Office and Customs House, c. 1913, and 1867 4d. stamp .. .. 1·75 1·25
665 $1.50 Mail plane and 1964 25 c. definitive .. .. 4·50 5·50

1988. 500th Birth Anniv of Titian (artist). As T **238** of Antigua. Multicoloured.

667 10 c. "Salome" 35 35
668 12 c. "Man with the Glove" 40 40
669 20 c. "Fabrizio Salvaresio" 60 60
670 25 c. "Daughter of Roberto Strozzi" 70 70
671 40 c. "Pope Julius II" .. 1·00 1·00
672 50 c. "Bishop Ludovico Beccadelli" .. .. 1·10 1·10
673 60 c. "King Philip II" .. 1·25 1·25
674 $1 "Empress Isabella of Portugal" .. .. 1·75 1·75

176 Aircraft over Sir Francis Drake Channel and Staunton Pawn

1988. 1st British Virgin Islands Open Chess Tournament. Multicoloured.
676 35 c. Type **176** .. .. 2·00 1·25
677 $1 Jose Capablanca (former World Champion) and Staunton king .. .. .. 5·00 5·00

177 Hurdling

1988. Olympic Games, Seoul. Multicoloured.
679 12 c. Type **177** 30 40
680 20 c. Windsurfing .. 45 40
681 75 c. Basketball .. 1·40 1·50
682 $1 Tennis .. .. 2·00 2·25

178 Swimmer ("Don't Swim Alone")

1988. 125th Anniv of International Red Cross.
684 **178** 12 c. black, red & blue 50 30
685 – 30 c. black, red & blue 85 70
686 – 60 c. black, red & blue 1·50 1·75
687 – $1 black, red and blue 2·25 2·75
DESIGNS: 30 c. Swimmers ("No swimming during electrical storms"); 60 c. Beach picnic ("Don't eat before swimming"); $1 Boat and equipment ("Proper equipment for boating").

179 Princess Alexandra

1988. Visit of Princess Alexandra. Designs showing different portraits.
689 **179** 40 c. multicoloured .. 1·50 75
690 – $1.50 multicoloured 3·50 4·00

180 Brown Pelican in Flight

1988. Wildlife (1st series). Aquatic Birds. Multicoloured.
692 10 c. Type **180** 70 30
693 12 c. Brown pelican perched on post .. 80 50
694 15 c. Brown pelican .. 90 75
695 35 c. Brown pelican swallowing fish .. 2·00 2·25

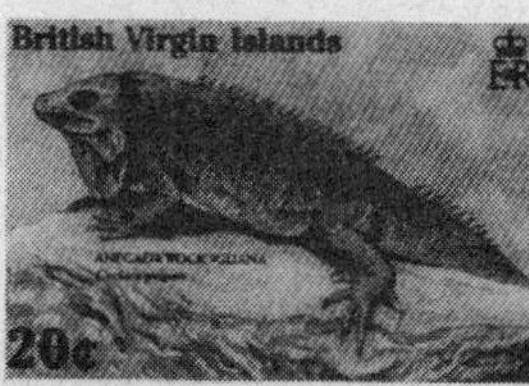

181 Anegada Rock Iguana

1988. Wildlife (2nd series). Endangered Species. Multicoloured.
697 20 c. Type **181** 65 45
698 40 c. Virgin gorda dwarf gecko .. .. .. 1·25 1·00
699 60 c. Hawksbill turtle .. 1·75 2·00
700 $1 Humpback whale .. 3·25 3·50

182 Yachts at Start

1989. Spring Regatta. Multicoloured.
702 12 c. Type **182** 35 25
703 40 c. Yacht tacking (horiz) 80 70
704 75 c. Yachts at sunset .. 1·40 1·60
705 $1 Yachts rounding buoy (horiz) .. .. .. 1·75 2·25

1989. 500th Anniv (1992) of Discovery of America by Columbus (1st issue). Pre-Columbian Arawak Society. As T **247** of Antigua. Multicoloured.
707 10 c. Arawak in hammock 25 20
708 20 c. Making fire .. 45 40
709 25 c. Making implements 50 45
710 $1.50 Arawak family .. 2·50 3·00
See also Nos. 741/4, 793/6 and 818/26.

183 "Apollo 11" Emblem

1989. 20th Anniv of First Manned Landing on Moon. Multicoloured.
712 15 c. Type **183** 40 30
713 30 c. Edwin Aldrin deploying scientific experiments 80 60
714 65 c. Aldrin and U.S. flag on Moon .. .. 1·40 1·60
715 $1 "Apollo 11" capsule after splashdown .. 2·00 2·25

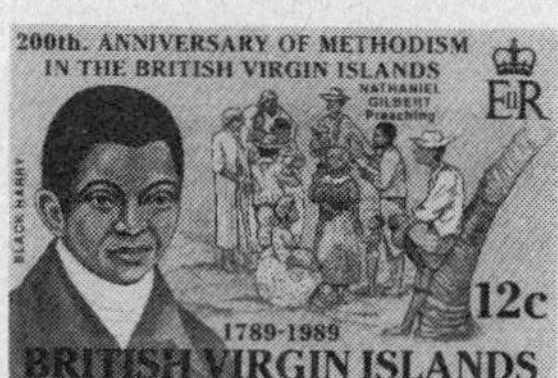

184 Black Harry and Nathaniel Gilbert preaching to Slaves

1989. Bicentenary of Methodist Church in British Virgin Islands. Multicoloured.
717 12 c. Type **184** 35 25
718 25 c. Methodist school exercise book 55 45
719 35 c. East End Methodist Church, 1810 .. .. 65 55
720 $1.25 Revd. John Wesley (founder of Methodism) and church youth choir 2·25 2·75

185 Player tackling

1989. World Cup Football Championship, Italy, 1990. Multicoloured.
722 5 c. Type **185** 30 20
723 10 c. Player dribbling ball 30 20
724 20 c. Two players chasing ball 55 45
725 $1.75 Goalkeeper diving for ball .. .. .. 3·75 4·25

186 Princess Alexandra and Sunset House

1990. "Stamp World London 90" Int. Stamp Exhibition. Royal Visitors. Mult.
727 50 c. Type **186** 65 70
728 50 c. Princess Margaret and Government House .. 65 70
729 50 c. Hon. Angus Ogilvy and Little Dix Bay Hotel 65 70
730 50 c. Princess Diana with Princes William and Harry and Necker Island Resort 65 70

187 Audubon's Shearwater

1990. Birds. Multicoloured.
732 5 c. Type **187** 10 10
733 12 c. Red-necked pigeon .. 15 20
734 20 c. Moorhen 25 30
735 25 c. Green heron .. 30 35
736 40 c. Yellow warbler .. 50 55
737 60 c. Smooth-billed ani .. 80 85
738 $1 Antillean crested hummingbird .. .. 1·25 1·40
739 $1.25 Black-faced grassquit 1·60 1·75

1990. 500th Anniv (1992) of Discovery of America by Columbus (2nd issue). New World Natural History–Fishes. As T **260** of Antigua. Multicoloured.
741 10 c. Blue tang (horiz) .. 15 20
742 35 c. Glasseye (horiz) .. 45 50
743 50 c. Slippery dick (horiz) 65 70
744 $1 Porkfish (horiz) .. 1·25 1·40

188 Queen Elizabeth the Queen Mother

1990. 90th Birthday of Queen Elizabeth the Queen Mother.
746 **188** 12 c. multicoloured .. 15 20
747 – 25 c. multicoloured .. 30 35
748 – 60 c. multicoloured .. 80 85
749 – $1 multicoloured .. 1·25 1·40
DESIGNS: 25, 60 c., $1 Recent photographs.

189 Footballers

1990. World Cup Football Championship, Italy.
751 **189** 12 c. multicoloured .. 15 20
752 – 20 c. multicoloured .. 25 30
753 – 50 c. multicoloured .. 65 70
754 – $1.25 multicoloured .. 1·60 1·75
DESIGNS: 20, 50 c., $1.25 Footballers.

190 Judo

1990. Olympic Games, Barcelona (1992). Mult.
756 12 c. Type **190** 15 20
757 40 c. Yachting 50 55
758 60 c. Hurdling 80 85
759 $1 Show jumping .. 1·25 1·40

191 Tree-fern, Sage Mountain National Park

192 Haiti Haiti

1991. 30th Anniv of National Parks Trust. Multicoloured.
761 10 c. Type **191** 15 20
762 25 c. Coppermine ruins, Virgin Gorda (horiz) .. 30 35
763 35 c. Ruined windmill, Mount Healthy .. 45 50
764 $2 The Baths (rock formation), Virgin Gorda (horiz) .. .. .. 2·50 2·75

1991. Flowers. Multicoloured.
765 1 c. Type **192** 10 10
766 2 c. Lobster claw .. 10 10
767 5 c. Frangipani .. 10 10
768 10 c. Autograph tree .. 15 20
769 12 c. Yellow allamanda .. 20 25
770 15 c. Lantana 20 25
771 20 c. Jerusalem thorn .. 25 30
772 25 c. Turk's cap 30 35
773 30 c. Swamp immortelle .. 40 45
774 35 c. White cedar .. 45 50
775 40 c. Mahoe tree .. 50 55
776 45 c. Pinguin 60 65
777 50 c. Christmas orchid .. 65 70
778 70 c. Lignum vitae .. 90 95
779 $1 African tulip tree .. 1·25 1·40
780 $2 Beach morning glory .. 2·50 2·75
781 $3 Organ pipe cactus .. 4·00 4·25
782 $5 Tall ground orchid .. 6·50 6·75
783 $10 Ground orchid .. 13·00 13·50

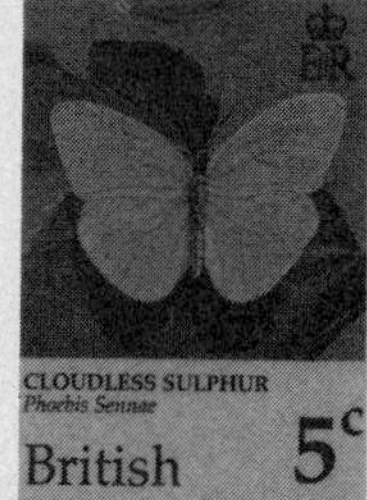

193 "Phoebis sennae"

1991. Butterflies. Multicoloured.
784 5 c. Type **193** 10 10
785 10 c. "Dryas iulia" .. 15 20
786 15 c. "Junonia evarete" .. 20 25
787 20 c. "Dione vanillae" .. 25 30
788 25 c. "Battus polydamus" 30 35
789 30 c. "Eurema lisa" .. 40 45
790 35 c. "Heliconius charitonius" 45 50
791 $1.50 "Siproeta stelenes" 2·00 2·10

1991. 500th Anniv (1992) of Discovery of America by Columbus (3rd issue). History of Exploration. As T **277** of Antigua. Mult.

793 12 c. "Vitoria" in Pacific (Magellan, 1519–21) .. 15 20
794 50 c. La Salle on the Mississippi, 1682 .. 65 70
795 75 c. John Cabot landing in Nova Scotia, 1497–98 .. 95 1·00
796 $1 Cartier discovering the St. Lawrence, 1534 .. 1·25 1·40

1991. Death Centenary (1990) of Vincent van Gogh (artist). As T **278** of Antigua. Mult.

798 15 c. "Cottage with Decrepit Barn and Stooping Woman" (horiz) 20 25
799 30 c. "Paul Gauguin's Armchair" 40 45
800 75 c. "Breton Women" (horiz) .. .. .. 95 1·00
801 $1 "Vase with Red Gladioli" .. .. 1·25 1·40

1991. Christmas. Religious Paintings by Quinten Massys. As T **291** of Antigua. Mult.

803 15 c. "The Virgin and Child Enthroned" (detail) .. 20 25
804 30 c. "The Virgin and Child Enthroned" (different detail) 40 45
805 60 c. "Adoration of the Magi" (detail) 80 85
806 $1 "Virgin in Adoration" .. 1·25 1·40

194 "Agaricus bisporus"

1992. Fungi. Multicoloured.

808 12 c. Type **194** 15 20
809 30 c. "Lentinus edodes" (horiz) 40 45
810 45 c. "Hyrocybe acutoconica" 60 65
811 $1 "Gymnopilus chrysopellus" (horiz) .. .. 1·25 1·40

1992. 40th Anniv of Queen Elizabeth II Accession. As T **292** of Antigua. Mult.

813 12 c. Little Dix Bay, Virgin Goda 15 20
814 45 c. Deadchest Bay, Peter Island 60 65
815 60 c. Pond Bay, Virgin Goda 80 85
816 $1 Cane Garden Bay, Tortola .. .. 1·25 1·40

195 Queen Isabella of Spain

1992. 500th Anniv of Discovery of America by Columbus (4th issue). Multicoloured.

818 10 c. Type **195** 15 20
819 15 c. Fleet of Columbus (horiz) 20 25
820 20 c. Arms awarded to Columbus 25 30
821 30 c. Landing Monument, Watling Island and Columbus's signature (horiz) 40 45
822 45 c. Christopher Columbus 60 65
823 50 c. Landing in New World and Spanish royal standard (horiz) .. 65 70
824 70 c. Convent at La Rabida .. .. 90 1·00
825 $1.50 Replica of "Santa Maria" and Caribbean Pavilion, New York World's Fair (horiz) .. 2·00 2·10

196 Basketball

1992. Olympic Games, Barcelona. Mult.

827 15 c. Type **196** 20 25
828 30 c. Tennis 40 45
829 60 c. Volleyball 80 85
830 $1 Football .. .. 1·25 1·40

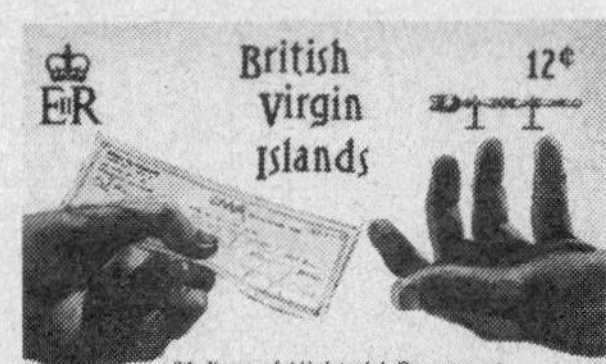

197 Issuing Social Security Cheque

1993. 25th Anniv of Ministerial Government. Multicoloured.

832 12 c. Type **197** 15 20
833 15 c. Map of British Virgin Islands 20 25
834 45 c. Administration building 60 65
835 $1.30 International currency abbreviations 1·60 1·75

198 Cruising Yacht and Swimmers, The Baths, Virgin Gorda

1993. Tourism. Multicoloured.

836 15 c. Type **198** 15 20
837 30 c. Cruising yacht under sail (vert) 40 45
838 60 c. Scuba diving .. 80 85
839 $1 Cruising yacht at anchor and snorklers (vert) .. .. .. 1·25 1·40

199 Queen Elizabeth II at Coronation (photograph by Cecil Beaton)

1993. 40th Anniv of Coronation.

841 **199** 12 c. multicoloured .. 15 20
842 – 45 c. multicoloured .. 60 65
843 – 60 c. grey and black .. 80 85
844 – $1 multicoloured .. 1·25 1·40

DESIGNS: 45 c. Orb; 60 c. Queen with Prince Philip, Queen Mother and Princess Margaret, 1953; $1 Queen Elizabeth II on official visit.

200 Columbus with King Ferdinand and Queen Isabella

1993. 500th Anniv of Discovery of Virgin Islands by Columbus. Multicoloured.

846 3 c. Type **200** 10 10
847 12 c. Columbus's ship leaving port 15 20
848 15 c. Blessing the fleet .. 20 25
849 25 c. Arms and flag of B.V.I. 30 35
850 30 c. Columbus and "Santa Maria" 40 45
851 45 c. Ships of second voyage 60 65
852 60 c. Columbus in ship's boat 80 85
853 $1 Landing of Columbus .. 1·25 1·40

201 Library Services Publications

1993. 50th Anniv of Secondary Education and Library Services. Multicoloured.

855 5 c. Type **201** 10 10
856 10 c. Secondary school sports 15 20
857 15 c. Stanley Nibbs (school teacher) (vert) 20 25
858 20 c. Mobile library .. 25 30
859 30 c. Dr. Norwell Harrigan (adminstrator and lecturer) (vert) 40 45
860 35 c. Children in library .. 45 50
861 70 c. Commemorative inscription on book .. 90 95
862 $1 B.V.I. High School .. 1·25 1·40

202 Anegada Ground Iguana

1994. Endangered Species. Anegada Ground Iguana.

863 **202** 5 c. multicoloured .. 10 10
864 – 10 c. multicoloured .. 15 20
865 – 15 c. multicoloured .. 20 25
866 – 45 c. multicoloured .. 60 65

DESIGNS: 10 c. to 45 c. Different iguanas.

OFFICIAL STAMPS

1985. Nos. 418/21 and 423/33 optd. **OFFICIAL.**

O 1. 1 c. Purple-tipped Sea Anemone 30 50
O 2. 3 c. Common Starfish .. 45 50
O 3. 5 c. Type **134** 45 30
O 4. 8 c. Triton's Trumpet (shell) 55 30
O 5. 13 c. Flamingo Tongue Snail 80 50
O 6. 15 c. Spider Crab 85 70
O 7. 18 c. Sea Squirts 90 80
O 8. 20 c. True Tulip (shell) .. 90 80
O 9. 25 c. Rooster Tail Conch (shell) .. .. .. 1·25 90
O10. 30 c. Fighting Conch (shell) 1·40 1·00
O11. 60 c. Mangrove Crab .. 2·50 2·50
O12. $1 Coral Polyps .. 3·75 3·75
O13. $2.50 Peppermint Shrimp .. 6·00 7·00
O14. $3 West Indian Murex (shell) .. .. .. 8·00 9·00
O15. $5 Carpet Anemone .. 11·00 15·00

1986. Nos. 560/78 optd. **OFFICIAL.**

O 16 1 c. Type **162** 10 10
O 17 2 c. Yellow-crowned night heron 10 10
O 18 5 c. Mangrove cuckoo .. 10 10
O 19 8 c. Northern mocking-bird 10 10
O 20 10 c. Grey kingbird .. 15 20
O 21 12 c. Red-necked pigeon 15 20
O 22 15 c. Least bittern .. 20 25
O 23 18 c. Smooth-billed ani .. 25 30
O 24 20 c. Clipper rail .. 25 30
O 25 25 c. American kestrel .. 30 35
O 26 30 c. Pearly-eyed thrasher 40 45
O 27 35 c. Bridled quail dove 45 50
O 28 40 c. Green heron .. 50 55
O 29 50 c. Scaly-breasted ground dove 65 70
O 30 60 c. Little blue heron .. 80 85
O 31 $1 Audubon's shear-water .. .. .. 1·25 1·40
O 32 $2 Blue-faced booby .. 2·50 2·75
O 33 $3 Cattle egret .. .. 4·00 4·25
O 34 $5 Zenaida dove .. 6·50 6·75

1991. Nos. 767/8, 771, 773/9 and 781 optd **OFFICIAL.**

O35 5 c. Frangipani 10 10
O36 10 c. Autograph tree 15 20
O37 20 c. Jerusalem thorn 25 30
O38 30 c. Swamp immortelle 40 45
O39 35 c. White cedar 45 50
O40 40 c. Mahoe tree 50 55
O41 45 c. Pinguin 60 65
O42 50 c. Christmas orchid 65 70
O43 70 c. Lignum vitae 90 1·00
O44 $1 African tulip tree 1·25 1·40
O45 $3 Organ pipe cactus 4·00 4·25

Nos. O35/45 were used on mail from the Philatelic Bureau and were not sold unused.

BRUNEI

A Sultanate on the N. Coast of Borneo.
100 cents = 1 dollar.

1. Star and Local Scene.

1895.

1.	1.	½ c. brown	1·25	14·00
2.		1 c. brown	1·25	12·00
3.		2 c. black	3·50	12·00
4.		3 c. blue	3·00	11·00
5.		5 c. green	6·00	13·00
6.		8 c. purple	6·00	16·00
7.		10 c. red	7·50	19·00
8.		25 c. green	28·00	42·00
9.		50 c. green	18·00	60·00
10.		$1 green	20·00	80·00

1906. Stamps of Labuan optd. **BRUNEI**, or surch. also.

11.	18.	1 c. black and purple	20·00	35·00
12.		2 c. on 3 c. black & brown	1·50	5·00
13.		2 c. on 8 c. black & orange	22·00	60·00
14.		3 c. black and brown	22·00	60·00
15.		4 c. on 12 c. black & yellow	1·50	4·75
16.		5 c. on 16 c. green & brown	30·00	48·00
17.		8 c. black and orange	8·50	18·00
18.		10 c. on 16 c. green & brn.	6·50	17·00
19.		25 c. on 16 c. green & brn.	90·00	£120
20.		30 c. on 16 c. green & brn.	80·00	£110
21.		50 c. on 16 c. green & brn.	80·00	£110
22.		$1 on 8 c. black & orange	80·00	£110

5. View on Brunei River.

1907.

23.	5.	1 c. black and green	2·25	8·00
24.		2 c black and red	2·50	4·50
25.		3 c. black and brown	10·00	18·00
26.		4 c. black and mauve	7·50	10·00
27.		5 c. black and blue	35·00	65·00
28.		8 c. black and orange	7·50	23·00
29.		10 c. black and green	4·50	7·00
30.		25 c. blue and brown	25·00	40·00
31.		30 c. violet and black	15·00	22·00
32.		50 c. green and brown	15·00	22·00
33.		$1 red and grey	50·00	80·00

1908.

35	5	1 c. green	40	95
60		1 c black	45	35
79		1 c. brown	50	80
36		2 c. black and brown	1·00	1·25
61		2 c. brown	90	3·00
62		2 c. green	45	30
80		2 c. grey	90	75
37		3 c. red	1·90	1·00
63		3 c. green	80	4·50
39		4 c. red	1·00	75
65		4 c. orange	1·00	50
40		5 c. black and orange	7·00	7·00
82		5 c. orange	80	80
67		5 c. grey	8·50	5·00
68		5 c. brown	2·25	15
41		8 c. blue and indigo	7·00	11·00
71		8 c. blue	6·00	5·00
72		8 c. black	2·50	55
84		8 c. red	40	60
42		10 c. purple on yellow	1·50	85
85		10 c. violet	60	20
86		15 c. blue	40	50
87		25 c. lilac	75	60
76		30 c. purple and orange	5·50	14·00
88		30 c. black and orange	75	70
77		50 c. black on green	7·00	15·00
89		50 c. black	1·25	40
46		$1 black and red on blue	20·00	48·00
90		$1 black and red	2·25	60
47		$5 red on green	85·00	£150
91		$5 green and red	16·00	14·00
92		$10 black and purple	35·00	32·00
48		$25 black on red	£450	£850

1922. Optd. **MALAYA-BORNEO EXHIBITION 1922.**

51.	5.	1 c. green	1·75	18·00
52.		2 c. black and brown	3·75	23·00
53.		3 c. red	5·00	35·00
54.		4 c. red	4·00	42·00
55.		5 c. orange	7·50	55·00
56.		10 c. purple on yellow	6·50	55·00
57.		25 c. lilac	14·00	80·00
58.		50 c. black on green	45·00	£150
59.		$1 black and red on blue	70·00	£190

7. Native Houses, Water Village.

1924.

81.	7.	3 c. green	1·00	1·75
83.		6 c. black	1·00	2·25
70.		6 c. red	3·75	10·00
74.		12 c. blue	4·50	9·00

8. Sultan Ahmed Tajudin and Water Village.

1949. Silver Jubilee of H.H. the Sultan.

93.	8.	8 c. black and red	55	60
94.		25 c. purple and orange	55	70
95.		50 c. black and blue	70	80

1949. 75th Anniv of U.P.U. As T **20/23** of Antigua.

96.		8 c. red	1·50	1·00
97.		15 c. blue	1·50	1·00
98.		25 c. mauve	1·50	1·00
99.		50 c. black	1·75	1·00

9. Sultan Omar Ali Saifuddin.

1952. Dollar values as T **8**, but with **arms** instead of portrait inset.

118ab	9	1 c. black	15	30
119a		2 c. black and orange	40	10
102		3 c. black and brown	10	30
103		4 c. black and green	10	20
104		6 c. black and grey	10	10
123		8 c. black and red	50	10
106		10 c. black and sepia	15	10
125		12 c. black and violet	1·50	10
126		15 c. black and blue	55	10
109		25 c. black and purple	1·75	10
110		50 c. black and blue	70	10
111	–	$1 black and green	1·25	85
112	–	$2 black and red	4·50	2·25
113a	–	$5 black and purple	10·00	3·25

11. Brunei Mosque and Sultan Omar.

1958. Opening of the Brunei Mosque.

114.	11.	8 c. black and green	20	50
115.		15 c. black and red	25	15
116.		35 c. black and lilac	30	80

12. "Protein Foods".

1963. Freedom from Hunger.

117.	12.	12 c. sepia	2·75	90

13. I.T.U. Emblem.

1965. Centenary of I.T.U.

132.	13.	4 c. mauve and brown	35	10
133.		75 c. yellow and green	1·00	75

14. I.C.Y. Emblem.

1965. Int. Co-operation Year.

134.	14.	4 c. purple and turquoise	20	10
135.		15 c. green and lavender	55	35

15. Sir Winston Churchill and St. Paul's Cathedral in Wartime.

1966. Churchill Commem. Designs in black, red and gold and with background in colours given.

136.	15.	3 c. blue	30	15
137.		10 c. green	1·50	20
138.		15 c. brown	1·75	35
139.		75 c. violet	3·75	2·00

16. Footballer's Legs, Ball and Jules Rimet Cup.

1966. World Cup Football Championships.

140.	16.	4 c. multicoloured	20	15
141.		75 c. multicoloured	75	60

17. W.H.O. Building.

1966. Inauguration of W.H.O. Headquarters, Geneva.

142.	17.	12 c. black, grn. & blue	35	25
143.		25 c. blk., pur. & ochre	55	45

18. "Education".

1966. 20th Anniv. of U.N.E.S.C.O.

144.	18.	4 c. multicoloured	35	10
145.	–	15 c. yell., violet & olive	75	50
146.	–	75 c. blk., pur. and orge.	2·25	3·50

DESIGNS: 15 c. "Science". 75 c. "Culture".

21. Religious Headquarters Building.

1967. 1400th Anniv. of Revelation of the Koran.

147.	21.	4 c. multicoloured	10	10
148.		10 c. multicoloured	15	10
149.	–	25 c. multicoloured	20	20
150.	–	50 c. multicoloured	35	70

Nos. 149/50 have sprigs of laurel flanking the main design (which has a smaller circle) in place of flagpoles.

22. Sultan of Brunei, Mosque and Flags.

1968. Installation of Y.T.M. Seri Paduka Duli Pengiran Temenggong. Multicoloured.

151.	4 c. Type 22	15	25
152.	12 c. Sultan of Brunei, Mosque and Flags (different)	40	65
153.	25 c. Type 22	50	1·10

No. 152 is horiz.

23. Sultan of Brunei.

1968. Birthday of Sultan

154.	23.	4 c. multicoloured	10	15
155.		12 c. multicoloured	20	35
156.		25 c. multicoloured	30	60

24. Sultan of Brunei.

1968. Coronation of Sultan of Brunei.

157.	24.	4 c. multicoloured	15	15
158.		12 c. multicoloured	25	45
159.		25 c. multicoloured	40	65

25. New Building and Sultan's Portrait.

1968. Opening of Hall of Language and Literature Bureau. Multicoloured.

160. 10 c. Type **25** 20 75
161. 15 c. New Building and Sultan's portrait (48½ × 22 mm.) .. 20 35
162. 30 c. As 15 c. 45 85

27. Human Rights Emblem and struggling Man.

1968. Human Rights Year.

163. **27.** 12 c. blk., yell. & grn... 10 20
164. 25 c. blk. yell. & bl. .. 15 25
165. 75 c. blk., yell. & pur... 45 1·50

28. Sultan of Brunei and W.H.O. Emblem.

1968. 20th Anniv. of World Health Organization.

166. **28.** 4 c. yell., blk. and blue.. 25 35
167. 15 c. yell., blk. & violet 45 55
168. 25 c. yell., blk. & olive.. 55 1·10

29. Deep Sea Oil-Rig, Sultan of Brunei and inset portrait of Pengiran Di-Gadong.

1969. Installation (9th May, 1968) of Pengiran Shar-bandar as Y.T.M. Seri Paduka Duli Pengiran Di-Gadong Sahibol Mal.

169. **29.** 12 c. multicoloured .. 50 30
170. 40 c. multicoloured .. 90 1·10
171. 50 c. multicoloured .. 1·10 1·40

30. Aerial View of Parliament Buildings.

1969. Opening of Royal Audience Hall and legislative Council Chamber.

172. **30.** 12 c. multicoloured .. 20 20
173. 25 c. multicoloured .. 30 40
174. – 50 c. red and violet .. 60 90

DESIGN: 50 c. Elevation of new buildings.

32. Youth Centre and Sultan's Portrait.

1969. Opening of New Youth Centre.

175. **32.** 6 c. multicoloured .. 20 30
176. 10 c. multicoloured .. 25 10
177. 30 c. multicoloured .. 70 60

33. Soldier, Sultan and Badge.

1971. 10th Anniv. of Royal Brunei Malay Regiment. Multicoloured.

178. 10 c. Type **33** 45 30
179. 15 c. Helicopter, Sultan and Arms (horiz.) .. 55 55
180. 75 c. "Pahlawan" (patrol boat), Sultan and Arms (horiz.) .. .. .. 2·50 4·50

34. Badge, and Officer in Full-dress Uniform.

1971. 50th Anniv. of Royal Brunei Police Force. Multicoloured.

181. 10 c. Type **34** 50 30
182. 15 c. Badge and Patrol Constable 70 80
183. 50 c. Badge and Traffic Constable .. .. 2·25 4·25

35. Perdana Wazir, Sultan of Brunei and View of Water Village.

1971. Installation of the Yang Teramat Malia as the Perdana Wazir.

184. **35.** 15 c. multicoloured .. 40 50
185. – 25 c. multicoloured .. 70 1·00
186. – 50 c. multicoloured .. 1·40 3·00

Nos. 185/6 show various views of Brunei Town.

36. Pottery.

1972. Opening of Brunei Museum. Mult.

187. 10 c. Type **36** 30 10
188. 12 c. Straw-work.. .. 40 20
189. 15 c. Leather-work .. 45 20
190. 25 c. Gold-work .. .. 1·25 1·10
191. 50 c. Museum Building (58 × 21 mm.) .. .. 2·25 2·50

37. Modern Building, Queen Elizabeth and Sultan of Brunei.

1972. Royal Visit. Each design with portrait of Queen and Sultan. Multicoloured.

192. 10 c. Type **37** 30 20
193. 15 c. Native houses .. 45 35
194. 25 c. Mosque .. .. 95 1·25
195. 50 c. Royal Assembly Hall 2·40 3·50

38. Secretariat Building.

1972. Renaming of Brunei Town as Bandar Seri Begawan.

196. **38.** 10 c. multicoloured .. 25 15
197. – 15 c. green, yell. & blk. 30 15
198. – 25 c. blue, yell. & black 50 50
199. – 50 c. red, blue and black 90 1·40

VIEWS: 15 c. Darul Hana Palace. 25 c. Old Brunei Town. 50 c. Town and Water Village.

39. Blackburn "Beverley" parachuting supplies.

1972. Opening of R.A.F. Museum, Hendon. Multicoloured.

200. 25 c. Type **39** .. .. 1·75 1·25
201. 75 c. Blackburn "Beverley" landing .. .. .. 3·25 3·75

1972. Royal Silver Wedding. As T **52** of Ascension, but with Girl with Traditional Flower-pot, and Boy with Bowl and Pipe in background.

210. 12 c. red 10 10
211. 75 c. green 20 50

41. Interpol H.Q., Paris.

1973. 50th Anniv. of Interpol.

212. **41.** 25 c. grn., pur. & black 1·50 1·25
213. – 50 c. blue, ultramarine and red .. .. 1·50 1·25

DESIGN: 50 c. Different view of the H.Q.

42. Sultan, Princess Anne and Capt. Phillips.

1973. Royal Wedding.

214. **42.** 25 c. multicoloured .. 15 10
215. 50 c. multicoloured .. 15 25

43. Churchill Painting.

44. Sultan Sir Hassanal Bolkiah Mu'izzaddin Waddaulah.

1973. Opening of Churchill Memorial Building. Multicoloured.

216. 12 c. Type **43** 10 20
217. 50 c. Churchill statue .. 30 1·40

1975. Multicoloured. Background colours given.

218 **44** 4 c. green 10 10
219 5 c. blue 10 10
220 6 c. green 40 40
221 10 c. lilac 10 10
222 15 c. brown 20 10
223 20 c. stone 20 20
224 25 c. green 30 15
225 30 c. blue 30 15
226 35 c. grey 35 20
227 40 c. purple 35 20
228 50 c. brown 40 20
229 75 c. green .. .. 60 1·50
256 $1 orange .. .. 1·25 1·75
257 $2 yellow .. .. 3·50 5·00
258 $5 silver .. .. 5·00 11·00
233 $10 gold .. .. 8·00 22·00

45. Aerial View of Airport.

1974. Inauguration of Brunei Int. Airport. Multicoloured

234. 50 c. Type **45** .. .. 1·00 1·00
235. 75 c. Sultan in Army uniform, and airport .. (48 × 36 mm.) 1·50 1·50

46. U.P.U. Emblem and Sultan.

1974. Cent. Universal Postal Union.

236. **46.** 12 c. multicoloured .. 20 20
237. 50 c. multicoloured .. 40 1·25
238. 75 c. multicoloured .. 50 1·40

47. Sir Winston Churchill.

1974. Birth. Cent. of Sir Winston Churchill.

239. **47.** 12 c. blk., blue and gold 25 20
240. – 75 c. blk., grn. & gold.. 45 90

DESIGN: 75 c. Churchill smoking cigar (profile).

48. Boeing "737" and R.B.A. Crest.

1975. Inauguration of Royal Brunei Airlines. Multicoloured.

241. 12 c. Type 48 .. .. 40 25
242. 35 c. ' 737 ' over Bander Seri Begawan Mosque .. 1·00 1·00
243. 75 c. ' 737 ' in flight .. 2·00 2·25

1976. Surch.

263. **44.** 10 c. on 6 c. brown .. 1·50 50

50. Royal Coat of Arms.

1977. Silver Jubilee. Multicoloured.

264. 10 c. Type **50** 15 20
265. 20 c. Imperial State Crown 20 35
266. 75 c. Queen Elizabeth (portrait by Annigoni) .. 45 75

51. The Moment of Crowning.

1978. 25th Anniv. of Coronation. Mult.

267. 10 c. Type **51** 15 10
268. 20 c. Queen in Coronation regalia 20 20
269. 75 c. Queen's departure from Abbey 55 80

52. Royal Crest.

1978. 10th Anniv. of Coronation of Sultan.

270. **52.** 10 c. black, red & yellow 15 10
271. – 20 c. multicoloured .. 25 25
272. – 75 c. multicoloured .. 70 1·00

DESIGNS: 20 c. Coronation. 75 c. Sultan's Crown.

53. Human Rights Emblem and Struggling Man.

1978. Human Rights Year.

274. **53.** 10 c. blk., yell. and red 10 10
275. 20 c. blk., yell. & violet 20 25
276. 75 c. blk., yell. & bistre 50 1·00

Type **53** is similar to the design used for the previous Human Rights issue in 1968.

54. Smiling Children.

1979. International Year of the Child.

277. **54.** 10 c. multicoloured .. 20 10
278. – $1 black and green .. 1·25 1·50

DESIGN: $1, I.Y.C. emblem.

55. Earth Satellite Station.

1979. Telisai Earth Satellite Station Multicoloured.

279. 10 c. Type **55** 15 15
280. 20 c. Satellite and antenna 25 30
281. 75 c. Television camera, telex machine and telephone .. .. .. 60 1·50

56. Hegira Symbol.

1979. Moslem Year 1400 A.H. Commemoration.

282. **56.** 10 c. black, yell. & green 10 15
283. 20 c. black, yell. & blue 15 25
284. 75 c. black, yell. & lilac 45 1·25

57. Installation Ceremony. **58.** Royal umbrella and sash

1980. 1st Anniv. of Prince Sufri Bolkiah's Installation as First Wazir. Multicoloured. Blue borders.

286. 10 c. Type **57** 15 10
287. 75 c. Wazir Sufri 65 80

1980. 1st Anniv. of Prince Jefri Bolkiah's Installation as Second Wazir. Designs similar to T **57** Multicoloured. Green borders.

288. 10 c. Installation ceremony 15 10
289. 75 c. Wazir Jefri 45 60

1981. Royal Regalia (1st series). Mult.

290. 10 c. Type **58** 20 15
291. 15 c. Sword and shield .. 25 20
292. 20 c. Lance and sheath .. 30 35
293. 30 c. Betel leaf container 40 70
294. 50 c. Coronation Crown (39 × 22 mm.) .. .. 70 2·25

See Nos. 298/303, 314/19 and 320/5.

59. I.T.U. and W.H.O. Emblems.

1981. World Telecommunciations and Health Day.

296. **59.** 10 c. black and red .. 40 20
297. 75 c. black, blue & violet 2·00 3·00

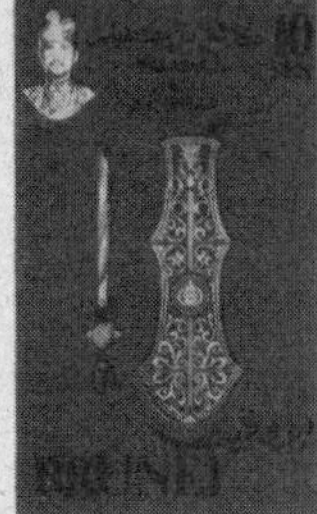

60. Shield and Broadsword.

1981. Royal Regalia (2nd series). Mult.

298. 10 c. Type **60** 10 10
299. 15 c. Blunderbuss and Pouch 15 15
300. 20 c. Crossed lances and sash 20 20
301. 30 c. Sword, shield and sash 30 50
302. 50 c. Forked lance .. 50 1·25
303. 75 c. Royal Drum (29 × 45 mm.) .. .. .. 70 2·00

61. Prince Charles as Colonel of the Welsh Guards.

1981. Royal Wedding. Multicoloured.

304. 10 c. Wedding bouquet from Brunei 35 15
305. $1 Type **61** .. .. 1·10 1·50
306. $2 Prince Charles and Lady Diana Spencer .. 1·40 2·25

62. Fishing.

1981. World Food Day. Multicoloured.

307. 10 c. Type **62** 50 15
308. $1 Farm produce and machinery .. .. 3·50 4·00

63. Blind Man and Braille Alphabet.

1981. International Year for Disabled Persons. Multicoloured.

309. 10 c. Type **63** 50 15
310. 20 c. Deaf people and sign language .. .. 1·25 65
311. 75 c. Disabled person and wheelchairs .. .. 2·75 3·75

64. Drawing of Infected Lungs.

1982. Centenary of Robert Koch's Discovery of Tubercle Bacillus. Multicoloured.

312. 10 c. Type **64** 50 25
313. 75 c. Magnified tubercle bacillus and microscope 2·50 3·25

1982. Royal Regalia (3rd series). As T **60**. Multicoloured.

314. 10 c. Ceremonial Ornament 10 10
315. 15 c. Silver Betel caddy .. 20 20
316. 20 c. Traditional Flower-pot 25 25
317. 30 c. Solitary Candle .. 40 60
318. 50 c. Golden Pipe.. .. 60 1·60
319. 75 c. Royal Chin Support (28 × 45mm.) .. .. 80 2·50

1982. Royal Regalia (4th series). As T **60**. Multicoloured.

320. 10 c. Royal Mace 25 10
321. 15 c. Ceremonial Shield and Spears 35 20
322. 20 c. Embroidered Ornament 45 30
323. 30 c. Golden-tasseled Cushion .. .. .. 65 1·00
324. 50 c. Ceremonial Dagger and Sheath .. .. .. 1·10 2·50
325. 75 c. Religious Mace (28 × 45 mm.) .. .. .. 1·50 3·25

65. Brunei Flag.

1983. Commonwealth Day.

326. **65.** 10 c. multicoloured .. 15 15
327. – 20 c. blue, black & buff 20 20
328. – 75 c. blue, black & green 45 55
329. – $2 blue, black & yellow 1·10 1·75

DESIGNS: 20 c. Brunei Mosque. 75 c. Machinery. $2 Sultan of Brunei.

66. " Postal Service ".

1983. World Communications Year.

330. **66.** 10 c. multicoloured .. 15 10
331. – 75 c. yellow, brn. & blk. 60 75
332. – $2 multicoloured .. 1·75 2·25

DESIGNS: 75 c. " Telephone Service "; $2 " Communications ".

67. Football.

1983. Official Opening of the Negara Hassanal Bolkiah Stadium. Multicoloured.

333. 10 c. Type **67** 55 15
334. 75 c. Athletics .. .. 1·90 1·50
335. $1 View of stadium (44 × 27 mm.) .. .. .. 2·50 2·50

68. Fishermen and Crustacea.

1983. Fishery Resources. Multicoloured.
336. 10 c. Type **68** 35 15
337. 50 c. Fishermen with net .. 1·00 70
338. 75 c. Fishing Trawler .. 1·25 1·40
339. $1 Fishing with hook and tackle .. .. .. 1·75 1·90

69. Royal Assembly Hall.

1984. Independence.
340. **69.** 10 c. brown & orange .. 20 10
341. – 20 c. pink and red .. 25 20
342. – 35 c. pink and purple .. 50 50
343. – 50 c. lt. blue and blue .. 65 70
344. – 75 c. lt. green & green .. 85 1·00
345. – $1 grey and brown .. 1·25 1·50
346. – $3 multicoloured .. 3·00 4·50

DESIGNS—(34 × 25 mm.). 20 c. Government Secretariat Building. 35 c. New Supreme Courts. 50 c. Natural gas well. 75 c. Omar Ali Saifuddin Mosque. $1 Sultan's Palace. (68 × 29 mm.). $3 Brunei flag and map of South-East Asia.

70. Natural Forests and Enrichment Planting.

1984. Forestry Resources. Multicoloured.
349. 10 c. Type **70** 55 25
350. 50 c. Forests and water resources .. .. 1·25 1·50
351. 75 c. Recreation forests .. 1·75 2·25
352. $1 Forests and wildlife .. 2·50 3·00

71. Sultan Omar Saifuddin 50 c. Stamp of 1952.

1984. "Philakorea" International Stamp Exhibition, Seoul. Multicoloured.
353. 10 c. Type **71** 20 10
354. 75 c. Brunei River view 10 c. stamp of 1907 .. 90 1·25
355. $2 Star and view ½ c. stamp of 1895 .. .. 2·00 3·00

72. United Nations Emblem.

1985. Admission of Brunei to World Organizations (1st issue)
357. **72.** 50 c. black, gold & blue 50 70
358. – 50 c. multicoloured .. 50 70
359. – 50 c. multicoloured .. 50 70
360. 50 c. multicoloured .. 50 70

DESIGNS: No. 358, Islamic Conference Organization logo. 359, Commonwealth logo. 360, A.S.E.A.N. emblem.

See also Nos. 383/6.

73. Young People and Brunei Flag.

1985. International Youth Year. Mult.
362. 10 c. Type **73** 45 20
363. 75 c. Young people at work 2·25 2·75
364. $1 Young people serving the community .. .. 2·75 3·25

74. Palestinian Emblem.

1985. International Palestinian Solidarity Day.
365. **74.** 10 c. multicoloured .. 40 20
366. 50 c. multicoloured .. 1·25 1·40
367. $1 multicoloured .. 2·00 2·25

75. Early and Modern Scout Uniforms.

1985. National Scout Jamboree. Mult.
368. 10 c. Type **75** 20 10
369. 20 c. Scout on tower signalling with flag .. 30 35
370. $2 Jamboree emblem .. 1·75 3·00

76. Sultan Sir Hassanal Bolkiah Mu'izzaddin Waddaulah.

1985.
371. **76.** 10 c. multicoloured .. 10 15
372. 15 c. multicoloured .. 10 15
373. 20 c. multicoloured .. 15 20
374. 25 c. multicoloured .. 20 25
375. 35 c. multicoloured .. 30 35
376. 40 c. multicoloured .. 30 35
377. 50 c. multicoloured .. 40 45
378. 75 c. multicoloured .. 60 65
379. $1 multicoloured .. 80 85
380. $2 multicoloured .. 1·60 1·75
381. $5 multicoloured .. 4·00 4·25
382. $10 multicoloured .. 8·25 8·50

Nos. 379/82 are larger, size 32 × 39 mm.

1986. Admission of Brunei to World Organizations (2nd issue). As T **72**.
383. 50 c. black, gold and green 40 60
384. 50 c. black, gold & mauve 40 60
385. 50 c. black, gold and red .. 40 60
386. 50 c. black, gold and blue 40 60

DESIGNS: No. 383, World Meteorological Organization emblem. 384, International Telecommunication Union emblem. 385, Universal Postal Union emblem. 386, International Civil Aviation Organization emblem.

78. Soldiers on Assault Course and Helicopter.

1986. 25th Anniv. of Brunei Armed Forces. Multicoloured.
388. 10 c. Type **78** .. .. 1·40 1·40
389. 20 c. Operating computer 1·60 1·60
390. 50 c. Anti-aircraft missile, helicopter and missile boat .. .. .. 2·25 2·25
391. 75 c. Army commanders and parade .. .. 2·50 2·50

Nos. 388/91 were printed together, se-tenant, forming a composite design.

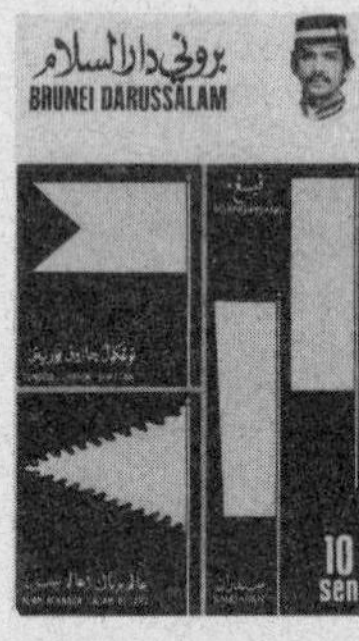

79. Tunggul Charok Buritan, Alam Bernaga (Alam Besar), Pisang-Pisang and Sandaran.

1986. Royal Ensigns (1st series).
392. **79.** 10 c. blk., yell. & red 30 10
393. – 75 c. multicoloured .. 1·00 1·00
394. – $2 blk., yell. & grn. .. 2·00 2·50

DESIGNS: 75 c. Ula-Ula Besar, Sumbu Layang and Payong Haram. $2 Panji-Panji, Chogan Istiadat (Chogan Di-Raja) and Chogan Ugama.

1986. Royal Ensigns (2nd series). As T **79**.
395. 10 c. multicoloured .. 30 10
396. 75 c. black, red and yellow 1·00 1·00
397. $2 multicoloured .. .. 2·00 2·50

DESIGNS: 10 c. Dadap, Tunggul Kawan, Ambal, Payong Ubor-Ubor, Sapu-Sapu Ayeng and Rawai Lidah. 75 c. Payong Tinggi and Payong Ubor-Ubor Tiga Ringkat. $2 Lambang Duli Yang Maha Mulia and Mahligai.

80. Stylised Peace Doves.

1986. International Peace Year. Multicoloured.
398. 50 c. Type **80** 75 75
399. 75 c. Stylised hands and "1986" .. .. .. 1·00 1·00
400. $1 International Peace Year emblem and arms of Brunei .. .. 1·25 1·25

81. Drug Addict in Cage and Syringe (poster by Othman bin Ramboh).

1987. National Anti-drug Campaign. Children's Posters. Multicoloured.
401. 10 c. Type **81** 55 20
402. 75 c. Drug addict and noose (Arman bin Mohd. Zaman) .. .. .. 1·75 1·75
403. $1 Blindfolded drug addict and noose (Abidin bin Hj. Rashid) .. .. 2·25 2·50

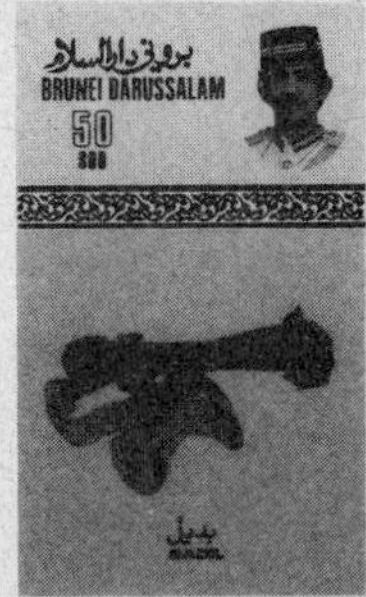

82. Cannon ("badil").

1987. Brassware (1st series). Multicoloured.
404. 50 c. Type **82** 50 50
405. 50 c. Lamp ("pelita") .. 50 50
406. 50 c. Betel container ("langguai") 50 50
407. 50 c. Water jug ("kiri") .. 50 50

See also Nos. 434/7.

83. Map showing Member Countries.

1987. 20th Anniv. of Association of South East Asian Nations. Multicoloured.
408. 20 c. Type **83** 20 20
409. 50 c. Dates and figures "20" 40 50
410. $1 Flags of member states 90 1·00

84. Brunei Citizens.

1987. 25th Anniv. (1986) of Language and Literature Bureau. Multicoloured.
411. 10 c Type **84** 25 25
412. 50 c. Flame emblem and hands holding open book 50 50
413. $2 Scenes of village life .. 1·50 1·50

Nos. 411/13 were printed together, se-tenant, forming a composite design taken from a mural.

85. "Artocarpus odoratissima".

1987. Local Fruits (1st series). Multicoloured.
414. 50 c. Type **85** 45 45
415. 50 c. "Canarium odontophyllum mig" 45 45
416. 50 c. "Litsea garciae" .. 45 45
417. 50 c. "Mangifera foetida lour" 45 45

See also Nos 421/4, 459/62 and 480/2.

86. Modern House.

1987. International Year of Shelter for the Homeless.
418. **86.** 50 c. multicoloured .. 40 50
419. – 75 c. multicoloured .. 55 65
420. – $1 multicoloured .. 80 90

DESIGNS: 75 c., $1 Modern Brunei housing projects.

1988. Local Fruits (2nd series). As T **85**. Multicoloured.

No.	Description	Unused	Used
421.	50 c. "Durio spp."	40	40
422.	50 c. "Durio oxleyanus"	40	40
423.	50 c. "Durio graveolens" (blue background)	40	40
424.	50 c. "Durio graveolens" (white background)	40	40

87. Wooden Lathe.

1988. Opening of Malay Technology Museum. Multicoloured.

No.	Description	Unused	Used
425.	10 c. Type **87**	15	10
426.	75 c. Crushing sugar cane	55	60
427.	$1 Bird scarer	70	70

88 Patterned Cloth.

1988. Handwoven Material (1st series). Mult.

No.	Description	Unused	Used
428	10 c. Type **88**	10	10
429	20 c. Jong Sarat cloth	15	15
430	25 c. Si Pugut cloth	20	20
431	40 c. Si Pugut Bunga Berlapis cloth	30	30
432	75 c. Si Lobang Bangsi Bungs Belitang Kipas cloth	55	60

See also Nos 442/6.

1988. Brassware (2nd series). As T **82**. Mult.

No.	Description	Unused	Used
434	50 c. Lidded two-handled pot ("periok")	40	40
435	50 c. Candlestick ("lampong")	40	40
436	50 c. Shallow circular dish with stand ("gangsa")	40	40
437	50 c. Repousse box with lid ("celapa")	40	40

89 Sultan reading Proclamation

1988. 20th Anniv of Sultan's Coronation. Multicoloured.

No.	Description	Unused	Used
438	20 c. Type **89**	10	10
439	75 c. Sultan reading from Koran	45	50
440	$2 In Coronation robes (26 × 63 mm)	1·25	1·40

1988. Handwoven Material (2nd series). As T **88**. Multicoloured.

No.	Description	Unused	Used
442	10 c. Beragi cloth	10	10
443	20 c. Bertabur cloth	10	10
444	25 c. Sukma Indra cloth	15	20
445	40 c. Si Pugut Bunga cloth	25	30
446	75 c. Beragi Si Lobang Bangsi Bunga Cendera Kesuma cloth	45	50

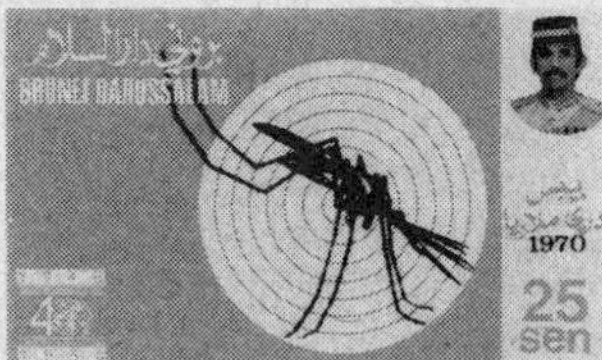

90 Malaria-carrying Mosquito

1988. 40th Anniv of W.H.O. Multicoloured.

No.	Description	Unused	Used
448	25 c. Type **90**	30	70
449	35 c. Man with insecticide spray and sample on slide	35	35
450	$2 Microscope and magnified malaria cells	1·75	1·75

91 Sultan and Council of Ministers

1989. 5th Anniv of National Day. Mult.

No.	Description	Unused	Used
451	20 c. Type **91**	20	15
452	30 c. Guard of honour	30	25
453	60 c. Firework display (27 × 55 mm)	50	40
454	$2 Congregation in mosque	1·50	1·75

92 Dove escaping from Cage

1989. "Freedom of Palestine". Multicoloured.

No.	Description	Unused	Used
456	20 c. Type **92**	20	20
457	75 c. Map and Palestinian flag	75	75
458	$1 Dome of the Rock, Jerusalem	1·00	1·00

1989. Local Fruits (3rd series). As T **85**. Multicoloured.

No.	Description	Unused	Used
459	60 c. "Daemonorops fissa"	1·10	1·25
460	60 c. "Eleiodoxa conferta"	1·10	1·25
461	60 c. "Salacca zalacca"	1·10	1·25
462	60 c. "Calamus ornatus"	1·10	1·25

93 Oil Pump

1989. 60th Anniv of Brunei Oil and Gas Industry. Multicoloured.

No.	Description	Unused	Used
463	20 c. Type **93**	30	30
464	60 c. Loading tanker	85	85
465	90 c. Oil well at sunset	1·25	1·25
466	$1 Pipe laying	1·40	1·40
467	$2 Oil terminal	2·25	2·75

94 Museum Building and Exhibits

1990. 25th Anniv of Brunei Museum. Mult.

No.	Description	Unused	Used
468	30 c. Type **94**	40	40
469	60 c. Official opening, 1965	75	85
470	$1 Brunei Museum	1·25	1·40

INDEX

Countries can be quickly located by referring to the index at the end of this volume.

95 Letters from Malay Alphabet

1990. International Literacy Year. Mult.

No.	Description	Unused	Used
471	15 c. Type **95**	25	10
472	90 c. English alphabet	1·25	1·50
473	$1 Literacy Year emblem and letters	1·50	2·00

96 Tarsier in Tree

1990. Endangered Species. Western Tarsier. Multicoloured.

No.	Description	Unused	Used
474	20 c. Western Tarsier on branch	35	35
475	60 c. Western Tarsier feeding	90	1·00
476	90 c. Type **96**	1·60	2·00

97 Symbolic Family

1990. Worldwide Campaign against AIDS. Multicoloured.

No.	Description	Unused	Used
477	20 c. Type **97**	40	40
478	30 c. Sources of infection	70	70
479	90 c. "AIDS" headstone surrounded by skulls	2·25	2·25

1990. Local Fruits (4th series). As T **85**. Multicoloured.

No.	Description	Unused	Used
480	60 c. "Willoughbea" sp. (brown fruit)	1·00	1·25
481	60 c. Ripe "Willoughbea" sp. (yellow fruit)	1·00	1·25
482	60 c. "Willoughbea angustifolia"	1·00	1·25

98 Proboscis Monkey on Ground

1991. Endangered Species. Proboscis Monkey. Multicoloured.

No.	Description	Unused	Used
483	15 c. Type **98**	35	35
484	20 c. Head of monkey	45	45
485	50 c. Monkey sitting on branch	1·10	1·10
486	60 c. Female monkey with baby climbing tree	1·25	1·40

99 Junior School Classes

1991. Teachers' Day. Multicoloured.

No.	Description	Unused	Used
487	60 c. Type **99**	1·00	1·25
488	90 c. Secondary school class	1·40	1·75

100 Young Brunei Beauty

1991. Fishes. Brunei Beauty. Multicoloured.

No.	Description	Unused	Used
489	30 c. Type **100**	65	65
490	60 c. Female fish	1·25	1·40
491	$1 Male fish	2·00	2·25

101 Graduate with Family

1991. Happy Family Campaign. Mult.

No.	Description	Unused	Used
492	20 c. Type **101**	40	40
493	60 c. Mothers with children	1·00	1·25
494	90 c. Family	1·60	1·75

102 Symbolic Heart and Trace

1992. World Health Day.

No.	Type	Description	Unused	Used
495	**102**	20 c. multicoloured	45	35
496	–	50 c. multicoloured	1·00	1·10
497	–	75 c. multicoloured	1·60	1·75

DESIGNS: 50 c., 70 c. (48 × 27 mm) Heart and heartbeat trace.

103 Map of Cable System

1992. Launching of Singapore–Borneo–Philippines Fibre Optic Submarine Cable System. Multicoloured.

No.	Description	Unused	Used
498	20 c. Type **103**	40	30
499	30 c. Diagram of Brunei connection	70	65
500	90 c. Submarine cable	1·75	2·00

104 Modern Sculptures

1992. Visit A.S.E.A.N. Year. Multicoloured.

501	20 c. Type **104**	55	55
502	60 c. Traditional martial arts	1·00	1·00
503	$1 Modern sculptures (different)	1·40	1·40

Nos. 501/3 were printed together, se-tenant, the backgrounds forming a composite design.

105 "A.S.E.A.N. 25" and Logo

1992. 25th Anniv of A.S.E.A.N (Association of South East Asian Nations). Multicoloured.

504	20 c. Type **105**	40	30
505	60 c. Headquarters building	1·00	1·25
506	90 c. National landmarks	1·60	1·75

106 Sultan in Procession

1992. 25th Anniv of Sultan's Accession. Mult.

507	25 c. Type **106**	50	55
508	25 c. Airport	50	55
509	25 c. Sultan's Palace	50	55
510	25 c. Docks and Brunei University	50	55
511	25 c. Mosque	50	55

Nos. 507/11 were printed together, se-tenant, forming a composite design.

107 Crested Wood Partridge

1992. Birds (1st series). Multicoloured.

512	30 c. Type **107**	40	30
513	60 c. Asiatic paradise flycatcher	90	75
514	$1 Great argus pheasant	1·50	1·5C

See also Nos. 515/17 and 518/20.

1993. Birds (2nd series). As T **107**. Mult.

515	30 c. Long-tailed parakeet	30	25
516	60 c. Magpie robin	80	70
517	$1 Blue-crowned hanging parrot	1·40	1·25

1993. Birds (3rd series). As T **107**. Mult.

518	30 c. Chesnut-breasted malkoha	35	30
519	60 c. White-rumped shama	65	65
520	$1 Black and red broadbill (vert)	95	95

JAPANESE OCCUPATION OF BRUNEI

These stamps were valid throughout British Borneo (i.e Brunei, Labuan, North Borneo and Sarawak.

100 cents = 1 dollar.

府政国帝本日大

(**1**) ("Imperial Japanese Government")

1942. Stamps of Brunei optd with T **1**.

J 1	**5**	1 c. black	5·00	19·00
J 2		2 c. green	32·00	90·00
J 3		2 c. orange	2·50	8·00
J 4		3 c. green	25·00	70·00
J 5		4 c. orange	3·00	12·00
J 6		5 c. brown	3·00	12·00
J 7	**7**	6 c. grey	50·00	£140
J 8		6 c. red	£550	£550
J 9	**5**	8 c. black	£650	£850
J10	**7**	8 c. red	3·00	12·00
J11	**5**	10 c. purple on yellow	8·00	24·00
J12	**7**	12 c. blue	12·00	24·00
J13		15 c. blue	8·50	24·00
J14	**5**	25 c. lilac	20·00	38·00
J15		30 c. purple and orange	90·00	£180
J16		50 c. black on green	35·00	50·00
J17		$1 black and red on blue	55·00	70·00
J18		$5 red on green	£800	£1200
J19		$25 black on red	£850	£1200

1944. Stamps of Brunei surch with Japanese characters reading "Imperial Japanese Post $3".

J20	**5**	$3 on 1 c. black	£4500	£4000

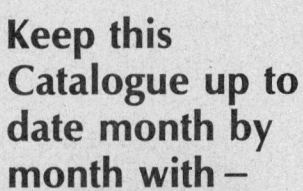

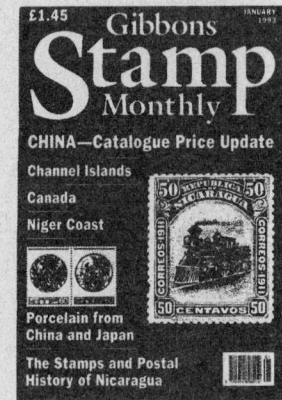

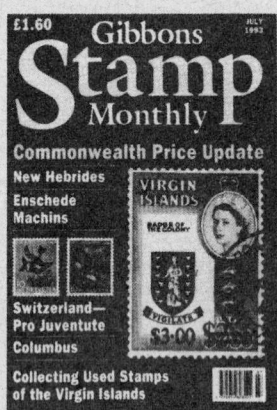

BUNDI

A state of Rajasthan, India. Now uses Indian stamps.

12 pies = 1 anna; 16 annas = 1 rupee.

8. Native Dagger.

11. Raja protecting Sacred Cows.

1894. Imperf.

12 8 ½ a. grey .. .. .. 1·60 1·75
13 1 a. red .. .. .. 1·40 1·50
14 2 a. green .. .. 6·50 8·50
8 4 a. green .. .. 28·00 38·00
15 8 a. red .. .. .. 4·50 8·50
16a 1 r. yellow on blue .. 7·50 18·00

1898. As T 8, but dagger point to left.
17a.**8.** 4 a. green .. .. 7·00 11·00

1914. Roul. or perf.

26 11 ¼ a. blue .. .. 1·75 4·25
38 ½ a. black .. .. 1·40 3·50
28a 1 a. red .. .. 5·00 7·00
20a 2 a. green .. .. 1·60 8·00
21 2½ a. yellow .. .. 5·00 18·00
31 3 a. brown .. .. 4·50 18·00
32 4 a. green .. .. 3·50 21·00
33 6 a. blue .. .. 8·00 42·00
42 8 a. orange .. .. 9·00 38·00
43 10 a. olive .. .. 16·00 45·00
44 12 a. green .. .. 6·00 45·00
25 1 r. lilac .. .. 15·00 60·00
46 2 r. brown and black .. 42·00 90·00
47 3 r. blue and brown .. 70·00 £140
48 4 r. green and red .. £150 £250
49 5 r. red and green .. £160 £275

20.

21. Maharao Rajah Bahadur Singh.

1941. Perf.

79.**20.** 3 p. blue .. .. .. 75 2·75
80. 6 p. blue .. .. .. 1·25 3·25
81. 1 a. red .. .. .. 1·50 3·50
82. 2 a. brown .. .. 4·00 9·00
83. 4 a. green .. .. 6·00 26·00
84. 8 a. green .. .. 10·00 80·00
85. 1 r. blue .. .. .. 22·00 £110

1947.

86.**21.** ¼ a. green .. .. 65 16·00
87. ½ a. violet .. .. 65 16·00
88. 1 a. green .. .. 65 16·00
89. – 2 a. red .. .. 1·00 30·00
90. – 4 a. orange .. .. 1·25 42·00
91. – 8 a. blue .. .. 2·25
92. – 1 r. brown .. .. 12·00

DESIGNS: 2 a., 4 a. Rajah in Indian dress. 8 a., 1 r. View of Bundi.

OFFICIAL STAMPS

बूंदी

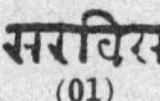

सरविस
(01)

A. Type O 1

B/C Optd. **BUNDI SERVICE.**

1918. Optd.

			A.	B/C
O 6	**11.**	¼ a. blue	1·25	1·60
O 16		½ a. black	4·00	2·75
O 8b		1 a. red	9·00	9·00
O 18		2 a. green	4·50	9·50
O 2		2½ a. yellow ..	2·00	6·00
O 3		3 a. brown	2·50	14·00
O 19		4 a. green	8·00	38·00
O 11		6 a. blue	11·00	70·00
O 20		8 a. orange	14·00	24·00
O 21		10 a. olive	32·00	48·00
O 22		12 a. green	32·00	50·00
O 5		1 r. lilac	35·00	35·00
O 24		2 r. brown and black ..	£250	£160
O 25		3 r. blue and brown ..	£275	£180
O 26		4 r. green and red ..	£275	£300
O 27		5 r. red and green ..	£275	£300

Prices for Nos. O 1/27 are for unused examples. Used examples are generally worth a small premium over the prices quoted.

1941. Optd. **SERVICE.**

O 53. **20.** 3 p. blue .. .. 2·25 5·00
O 54. 6 p. blue .. .. 6·50 6·00
O 55. 1 a. red .. .. 6·00 7·00
O 56. 2 a. brown .. .. 7·00 8·50
O 57. 4 a. green .. .. 24·00 65·00
O 58. 8 a. green .. .. 75·00 £180
O 59. 1 r. blue .. .. 95·00 £200

For later issues see **RAJASTHAN**.

BURMA

A territory in the east of India. Formerly part of the Indian Empire, but separated from it on 1 April 1937. Japanese forces were in occupation from 1942 to 1945 and Independence was established in 1948.

1937. 12 pies = 1 anna. 16 annas = 1 rupee.
1953. 100 pyas = 1 kyat (rupee).

1937. Stamps of India (King George V) optd. **BURMA.**

1. **55.** 3 p. grey 30 10
2. **79.** ½ a. green 30 10
3. **80.** 9 p. green 50 10
4. **81.** 1 a. brown 30 10
5. **59.** 2 a. red 30 10
6. **61.** 2½ a. orange 30 10
7. **62.** 3 a. red 65 30
8. **83.** 3½ a. blue 65 10
9. **63.** 4 a. olive 70 10
10. **64.** 6 a. bistre 60 35
11. **65.** 8 a. mauve .. .. 1·50 10
12. **66.** 12 a. red .. .. .. 2·25 85
13. **67.** 1 r. brown and green .. 9·50 90
14. 2 r. red and orange .. 14·00 6·50
15. 5 r. blue and violet .. 30·00 9·00
16. 10 r. green and red .. 48·00 35·00
17. 15 r. blue and olive .. £150 80·00
18. 25 r. orange and blue .. £300 £150

2. King George VI and "Chinthes".

3. King George VI and "Nagas".

4. Royal Barge.

8. King George VI and Peacock.

1938. King George VI.

18a. **2.** 1 p. orange .. .. 2·00 70
19. 3 p. violet 10 30
20. 6 p. blue 10 10
21. 9 p. green .. .. 1·00 80
22. **3.** 1 a. brown 10 10
23. 1½ a. green 20 60
24. 2 a. red 45 10
25. **4.** 2 a. 6 p. red .. .. 1·75 70
26. – 3 a. mauve .. .. 4·50 70
27. – 3 a. 6 p. blue .. .. 1·25 3·50
28. **3.** 4 a. blue 35 10
29. – 8 a. green .. .. 2·00 30
30. **8.** 1 r. purple and blue .. 7·00 20
31. 2 r. brown and purple .. 8·00 1·50
32. – 5 r. violet and red .. 45·00 18·00
33. – 10 r. brown and green .. 60·00 38·00

DESIGNS—HORIZ. As Type **4**: 3 a. Burma teak. 3 a. 6 p. Burma Rice. 8 a. Irrawaddy. VERT. As Type **3**: 5 r., 10 r. King George VI and "Nats".

1940. Cent. of First Adhesive Postage Stamp. Surch. **COMMEMORATION POSTAGE STAMP 6TH MAY, 1840,** and value in figures and letters.

34. **4.** 1 a. on 2 a. 6 p. red .. 2·00 70

For Japanese issues see "Japanese Occupation of Burma".

1945. British Military Administration. Stamps of 1938 optd. **MILY ADMN.**

35. **2.** 1 p. orange 10 10
36. 3 p. violet 10 30
37. 6 p. blue 10 30
38. 9 p. green 10 30
39. **3.** 1 a. brown 10 10
40. 1½ a. green 10 15
41. 2 a. red 10 15
42. **4.** 2 a. 6 p. red 60 60
43. – 3 a. mauve .. .. 1·50 20
44. – 3 a. 6 p. blue 10 70
45. **3.** 4 a. blue 10 25
46. – 8 a. green 10 40
47. **8.** 1 r. purple and blue .. 30 50
48. 2 r. brown and purple .. 30 90
49. – 5 r. violet and red .. 30 90
50. – 10 r. brown and green .. 50 90

1946. British Civil Administration. As 1938, but colours changed.

51. **2.** 3 p. brown 10 80
52. 6 p. violet 10 30
53. 9 p. green 10 90
54. **3.** 1 a. blue 10 10
55. 1½ a. orange 10 10
56. 2 a. red 10 40
57. **4.** 2 a. 6 p. blue .. .. 10 1·25
57a.– 3 a. blue .. .. .. 4·50 1·50
57b.– 3 a. 6 p. black and blue .. 10 1·00
58. **3.** 4 a. purple 10 30
59. – 8 a. mauve .. .. 1·75 90
60. **8.** 1 r. violet and mauve .. 75 20
61. 2 r. brown and orange .. 4·50 1·50
62. – 5 r. green and brown .. 4·50 6·00
63. – 10 r. red and violet .. 4·50 9·00

14. Burman.

1946. Victory.

64. **14.** 9 p. green 20 20
65. – 1½ a. vio. (Burmese woman) 20 10
66. – 2 a. red (Chinthe) 20 10
67. – 3 a. 6 p. blue (Elephant) 20 20

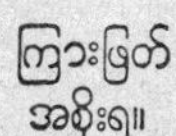

(18. Trans. "Interim Government").

1947. Stamps of 1946 optd. with T **18** or with larger opt. on large stamps.

68. **2.** 3 p. brown 50 65
69. 6 p. violet 10 30
70. 9 p. green 10 30
71. **3.** 1 a. blue 10 30
72. 1½ a. orange 70 10
73. 2 a. red 30 15
74. **4.** 2 a. 6 p. blue .. .. 1·25 85
75. – 3 a. blue .. .. .. 1·75 1·25
76. – 3 a. 6 p. black and blue .. 30 60
77. **3.** 4 a. purple .. .. 1·00 30
78. – 8 a. mauve .. .. 1·10 75
79. **8.** 1 r. violet and mauve .. 1·40 30
80. 2 r. brown and orange .. 2·00 2·25
81. – 5 r. green and brown .. 2·25 3·25
82. – 10 r. red and violet .. 2·25 3·25

OFFICIAL STAMPS

1937. Stamps of India (King George V) optd. **BURMA SERVICE.**

O 1. **55.** 3 p. grey 30 10
O 2. **79.** ½ a. green .. .. 1·00 10
O 3. **80.** 9 p. green .. .. 1·00 30
O 4. **81.** 1 a. brown 75 10
O 5. **59.** 2 a. red .. .. 1·00 35
O 6. **61.** 2½ a. orange .. .. 1·75 95
O 7. **63.** 4 a. olive .. .. 1·00 10
O 8. **64.** 6 a. bistre .. .. 2·00 3·75
O 9. **65.** 8 a. mauve .. .. 1·25 65
O 10. **66.** 12 a. red .. .. 1·50 2·50
O 11. **67.** 1 r. brown and green 11·00 3·00
O 12. 2 r. red and orange .. 20·00 17·00
O 13. 5 r. blue and violet .. 60·00 32·00
O 14. 10 r. green and red .. £170 80·00

1939. Stamps of 1938 optd. **SERVICE.**

O 15. **2.** 3 p. violet 10 20
O 16. 6 p. blue 10 20
O 17. 9 p. green .. .. 5·00 75
O 18. **3.** 1 a. brown 10 15
O 19. 1½ a. green .. .. 4·50 50
O 20. 2 a. red .. .. .. 1·00 20
O 21. **4.** 2 a. 6 p. red .. .. 15·00 4·50
O 22. **3.** 4 a. blue .. .. 5·50 45
O 23. – 8 a. green (No. 29) .. 20·00 3·50
O 24. **8.** 1 r. purple and blue .. 26·00 3·25
O 25. 2 r. brown and purple .. 30·00 5·00
O 26. – 5 r. violet & red (No. 32) 48·00 28·00
O 27. – 10 r. brn. & grn. (No. 33) £120 38·00

1946. Stamps of 1946 optd. **SERVICE.**

O 28. **2.** 3 p. brown 30 90
O 29. 6 p. violet 35 75
O 30. 9 p. green .. .. 10 1·75
O 31. **3.** 1 a. blue .. .. 10 1·25
O 32. 1½ a. orange 10 20
O 33. 2 a. red .. .. 10 1·25
O 34. **4.** 2 a. 6 p. blue .. .. 45 2·25
O 35. **3.** 4 a. purple 10 70
O 36. – 8 a. mauve (No. 59) .. 15 1·50
O 37. **8.** 1 r. violet and mauve .. 50 2·00
O 38. 2 r. brown and orange 5·00 15·00
O 39. – 5 r. green & brn. (No. 62) 9·00 23·00
O 40. – 10 r. red and violet (No. 63) .. .. 15·00 40·00

1947. Interim Govt. Nos. O 28, etc., optd. with T **18** or with large opt. on larger stamps.

O 41. **2.** 3 p. brown 15 40
O 42. 6 p. violet 30 10
O 43. 9 p. green 30 90
O 44. **3.** 1 a. blue .. .. 1·50 80
O 45. 1½ a. orange .. .. 2·50 20
O 46. 2 a. red .. .. 1·25 15
O 47. **4.** 2 a. 6 p. blue .. .. 6·00 2·50
O 48. **3.** 4 a. purple .. .. 2·25 35
O 49. – 8 a. mauve .. .. 2·75 1·75
O 50. **8.** 1 r. violet and mauve .. 6·50 1·75
O 51. 2 r. brown and orange .. 14·00 12·00
O 52. – 5 r. green and brown .. 14·00 17·00
O 53. – 10 r. red and violet .. 14·00 24·00

For issues after Independence see Volume 1.

JAPANESE OCCUPATION OF BURMA

1942. 12 pies = 1 anna; 16 annas = 1 rupee.
1942. 100 cents = 1 rupee.

(1.)

(3.)

Note.—There are various types of the Peacock overprint. Our prices, as usual in this Catalogue, are for the cheapest type.

1942. Postage stamps of Burma of 1937 (India types) optd. as T **1.**

J 22. **55.** 3 p. grey .. .. 3·00 14·00
J 23. **80.** 9 p. green .. .. 20·00 50·00
J 24. **59.** 2 a. red .. .. 75·00 £130
J 2. **83.** 3½ a. blue .. .. 38·00

1942. Official stamp of Burma of 1937 (India type) optd. as T **1.**

J 3. **64.** 6 a. bistre .. .. 60·00

1942. Postage stamps of Burma, 1938, optd. as T 1 or with T **3** (rupee values).

J 25 **1.** 1 p. orange £110 £160
J 12 3 p. violet .. .. 18·00 40·00
J 27 6 p. blue .. .. 21·00 45·00
J 14 9 p. green .. .. 13·00 35·00
J 29 **3.** 1 a. brown .. .. 8·00 22·00
J 30 1½ a. green .. .. 16·00 40·00
J 16 2 a. red .. .. 12·00 35·00
J 17 4 a. blue .. .. 26·00 48·00
J 18 **8.** 1 r. purple and blue .. £200
J 19 2 r. brown and purple .. £130

1942. Official stamps of Burma of 1939 optd. with T **1.**

J 7. **1.** 3 p. violet .. .. 15·00 45·00
J 8. 6 p. blue .. .. 11·00 32·00
J 9. **3.** 1 a. brown .. .. 10·00 24·00
J 35. 1½ a. green .. .. 80·00 £140
J 10. 2 a. red .. .. 16·00 45·00
J 11. 4 a. blue .. .. 15·00 40·00

(6a.) ("Yon Thon" = "Official use".)

1942. Official stamp of Burma of 1939 optd. with T **6a.**

J 44. – 8a. green (No. O 23) .. 65·00

7.

1942. Yano Seal.

J 45. **7.** (1a.) red .. .. 35·00 55·00

8. Farmer.

1942.

J 46. **8.** 1 a. red .. .. .. 14·00 14·00

1942. Stamps of Japan surch. in figures.

J 47. – ¼ a. on 1 s. brn. (No. 317) 18·00 23·00
J 48. **84.** ½ a. on 2 s. red .. 18·00 23·00
J 49. – ¾ a. on 3 s. grn. (No. 319) 38·00 40·00
J 50. – 1 a. on 5 s. red No. 396) 28·00 32·00
J 51. – 3 a. on 7 s. grn. (No. 323) 55·00 65·00
J 52. – 4 a. on 4 s. grn. (No. 320) 30·00 35·00
J 53. – 8 a. on 8 s. vio. (No. 324) £130 £140
J 54. – 1 r. on 10 s. red (No. 325) 15·00 22·00
J 55. – 2 r. on 20 s. blue (No. 328) 38·00 38·00
J 56. – 5 r. on 30 s. bl. (No. 330) 12·00 25·00

1942. No. 386 of Japan commemorating the fall of Singapore, surch. in figures.

J 56g. – 4 a. on 4 s. + 2 s. green and red £120 £130

(New currency. 100 cents = 1 rupee.)

1942. Handstamped with new value.

J 57. **5.** 5 c. on 1 a. red (No. J 46) 9·00 13·00

1942. Nos. J 47/53 with anna surcharges obliterated, and handstamped with new value in figures.

J 58. – 1 c. on ¼ a. on 1 s. brown 32·00 32·00
J 59. **84.** 2 c. on ½ a. on 2 s. red .. 32·00 32·00
J 60. – 3 c. on ¾ a. on 3 s. green 35·00 35·00
J 61. – 5 c. on 1 a. on 5 s. red 45·00 50·00
J 62. – 10 c. on 3 a. on 7 s. green 70·00 75·00
J 63. – 15 c. on 4 a. on 4 s. green 25·00 27·00
J 64. – 20 c. on 8 a. on 8 s. violet £160 £140

1942. Stamps of Japan surch. in cents only in figures.

J 65. – 1 c. on 1 s. brn. (No. 317) 15·00 18·00
J 66. **84.** 2 c. on 2 s. red .. 28·00 28·00
J 67. – 3 c. on 3 s. grn. (No. 319) 26·00 28·00
J 68. – 5 c. on 5 s. red (No. 396) .. .. 32·00 32·00
J 69. – 10 c. on 7 s. grn. (No. 323) 30·00 35·00
J 70. – 15 c. on 4 s. grn. (No. 320) 13·00 18·00
J 71. – 20 c. on 8 s. vio. (No. 324) 90·00 75·00

14. Burma State Crest.

1943. Perf. or Imperf.

J 72. **14.** 5 c. red .. .. 11·00 13·00

15. Farmer.

1943.

J 73. **15.** 1 c. orange .. .. 70 1·50
J 74. 2 c. green 60 90
J 75. 3 c. blue 60 75
J 77. 5 c. red .. .. 85 1·75
J 78. 10 c. brown .. .. 1·75 2·00
J 79. 15 c. mauve 30 70
J 80. 20 c. lilac 30 65
J 81. 30 c. green 30 70

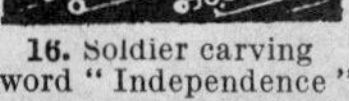
16. Soldier carving word " Independence ".

17. Rejoicing Peasant.

18. Boy with National Flag.

1943. Independence Day. Perf. or roul.

J 82a. **16.** 1 c. orange .. .. 1·00 1·50
J 83a. **17.** 3 c. blue .. .. 1·00 1·50
J 84a. **18.** 5 c. red .. .. 1·00 1·50

19. Burmese Woman.

20. Elephant carrying Log.

21. Watch Tower, Mandalay.

1943.

J 85. **19.** 1 c. orange .. .. 9·00 11·00
J 86. 2 c. green .. .. 40 1·25
J 87. 3 c. violet .. .. 50 1·75
J 88. **20.** 5 c. red 45 50
J 89. 10 c. blue 55 75
J 90. 15 c. orange .. .. 55 1·25
J 91. 20 c. green .. .. 50 1·50
J 92. 30 c. brown .. .. 50 1·50
J 93. **21.** 1 r. orange .. .. 30 1·25
J 94. 2 r. violet .. .. 30 2·25

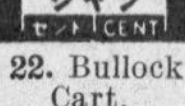
22. Bullock Cart.

23. Shan Woman.

ဗမာနိုင်ငံတော်

၂၀ ဆင့်။

(**24.** " Burma State " and value).

1943. Shan States issue.

J 95. **22.** 1 c. brown .. .. 13·00 19·00
J 96. 2 c. green .. .. 13·00 19·00
J 97. 3 c. violet .. .. 2·75 4·50
J 98. 5 c. blue .. .. 2·00 4·50
J 99. **23.** 10 c. blue .. .. 8·00 15·00
J 100. 20 c. red .. .. 15·00 12·00
J 101. 30 c. brown .. .. 12·00 19·00

1944. Optd. with T **24.**

J 102. **22.** 1 c. brown .. .. 1·25 3·00
J 103. 2 c. green 30 75
J 104. 3 c. violet .. .. 1·00 3·00
J 105. 5 c. blue 65 75
J 106. **23.** 10 c. blue .. .. 1·60 1·60
J 107. 20 c. red .. .. 30 1·25
J 108. 30 c. brown .. .. 30 1·25

BUSHIRE

An Iranian seaport. Stamps issued during the Br. occupation in the 1914–18 War.

20 chahis = 1 kran, 10 krans = 1 toman.

1915. Portrait stamps of Iran (1911) optd. **BUSHIRE Under British Occupation.**

1. **57.** 1 ch. orange and green .. 22·00 27·00
2. 2 ch. brown and red .. 22·00 21·00
3. 3 ch. green and grey .. 27·00 35·00
4. 5 ch. red and brown .. £250 £250
5. 6 ch. lake and green .. 21·00 18·00
6. 9 ch. lilac and brown .. 22·00 26·00
7. 10 ch. brown and red .. 24·00 24·00
8. 12 ch. blue and green .. 30·00 35·00
9. 24 ch. green & purple .. 45·00 35·00
10. 1 kr. red and blue .. 45·00 25·00
11. 2 kr. red and green .. £150 £120
12. 3 kr. black and lilac .. £140 £150
13. 5 kr. blue and red .. 70·00 65·00
14. 10 kr. red and brown .. 60·00 60·00

1915. Coronation issue of Iran optd. **BUSHIRE Under British Occupation.**

15. **66.** 1 ch. blue and red .. £300 £300
16. 2 ch. red and blue .. £5000 £5500
17. 3 ch. green £375 £400
18. 5 ch. red £3750 £4000
19. 6 ch. red and green .. £3000 £3250
20. 9 ch. violet and brown .. £475 £500
21. 10 ch. brown and green £800 £850
22. 12 ch. blue £900 £1000
23. 24 ch. black and brown .. £375 £400
24. **67.** 1 kr. black, brn. & silver £350 £375
25. 2 kr. red, blue and silver £300 £325
26. 3 kr. black, lilac & silver £425 £450
27. 5 kr. slate, brown & silver £400 £425
28. – 1 t. black, violet and gold £350 £400
29. – 3 t. red, lake and gold .. £2250 £2250

BUSSAHIR (BASHAHR)

A state in the Punjab, India. Now uses Indian stamps.

12 pies = 1 anna; 16 annas = 1 rupee.

1.

1895. Various frames. Imperf., perf, or roul.

9 **1.** ¼ a. pink .. .. .. 23·00 75·00
10 ½ a. grey .. .. .. 14·00 75·00
11 1 a. red .. .. .. 14·00 70·00
12 2 a. yellow .. .. 21·00 70·00
13 4 a. violet .. .. .. 15·00 75·00
14 8 a. brown .. .. 15·00 75·00
15 12 a. green .. .. 45·00 85·00
16 1 r. blue .. .. .. 25·00 80·00

1896. Similar types, but inscriptions on white ground and inscr. " **POSTAGE** " instead of " **STAMP** ".

27. **1.** ¼ a. violet .. .. .. 8·00 9·00
31. ¼ a. red .. .. .. 2·00 4·00
25. ½ a. blue .. .. .. 3·00 10·00
26. 1 a. olive .. .. .. 9·00 18·00
38. 1 a. red .. .. .. 2·00 6·00
41. 2 a. yellow .. .. 22·00 38·00
36. 4 a. red .. .. .. 23·00 60·00

CAICOS ISLANDS

Separate issues for these Islands, part of the Turks and Caicos Islands group, appeared from 1981 to 1985.

100 cents = 1 dollar.

1981. Nos. 514, 518, 520, 523 and 525/7 of Turks and Caicos Islands optd. **CAICOS ISLANDS.**

1. 1 c. Indigo Hamlet 10 10
2. 5 c. Spanish Grunt 10 10
3. 8 c. Foureye Butterflyfish .. 10 10
4. 20 c. Queen Angelfish .. 25 30
5. 50 c. Fairy Basslet 65 70
6. $1 Clown Wrasse .. .. 1·00 1·25
7. $2 Stoplight Parrotfish .. 2·50 2·75

1981. Royal Wedding. Nos. 653/5 of Turks and Caicos Islands optd. A. **Caicos Islands.** B. **CAICOS ISLANDS.**

		A		B	
8.	35 c. Prince Charles and Lady Diana Spencer	25	25	65	75
9.	65 c. Kensington Palace	40	40	85	1·00
10.	90 c. Prince Charles as Colonel of Welsh Guards	50	50	1·25	1·50

1981. Royal Wedding. Booklet stamps. As Nos. 657/9 of Turks and Caicos Islands, but each inscr. " Caicos Islands ". Mult. Self-adhesive.

12. 20 c. Lady Diana Spencer .. 80 60
13. $1 Prince Charles .. .. 80 1·25
14. $2 Prince Charles and Lady Diana Spencer .. .. 6·50 5·50

4. Conch and Lobster Fishing, South Caicos.

1983. Multicoloured.

15. 8 c. Type **4** 20 20
16. 10 c. Hawksbill Turtle, East Caicos 30 30
17. 20 c. Arawak Indians and idol, Middle Caicos .. 40 50
18. 35 c. Boat-building, North Caicos 70 80
19. 50 c. Marine biologist at work, Pine Cay 85 90
20. 95 c. Boeing " 707 " airliner at new airport, Providenciales .. .. .. 2·00 2·25
21. $1.10 Columbus's " Pinta ", West Caicos .. .. 2·50 2·50
22. $2 Fort George Cay .. .. 3·50 3·00
23. $3 Pirates Anne Bonny and Calico Jack at Parrot Cay 6·00 4·75

5. Goofy and Patch.

1983. Christmas. Multicoloured.

30. 1 c. Type **5** 10 10
31. 1 c. Chip and Dale 10 10
32. 2 c. Morty 10 10
33. 2 c. Morty and Ferdie .. 10 10
34. 3 c. Goofy and Louie .. 10 10
35. 3 c. Donald Duck, Huey, Dewey and Louie 10 10
36. 50 c. Uncle Scrooge .. .. 1·50 90
37. 70 c. Mickey Mouse and Ferdie .. .. .. 2·00 1·25
38. $1.10 Pinocchio, Jiminy Cricket and Figaro .. 2·50 1·90

6. "Leda and the Swan".

1984. 500th Birth. Anniv. of Raphael. Multi.

40. 35 c. Type **6** 75 50
41. 50 c. "Study of Apollo for Parnassus" .. .. 1·00 70
42. 95 c. "Study of two figures for the battle of Ostia" .. 2·00 1·25
43. $1.10 "Study for the Madonna of the Goldfinch" 2·00 1·50

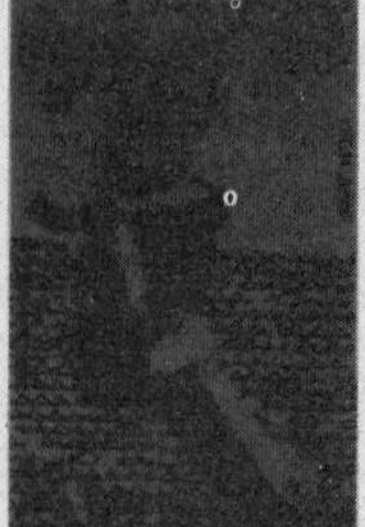
7. High Jump.

1984. Olympic Games, Los Angeles.

45. **7.** 4 c. multicoloured .. 10 10
46. – 25 c. multicoloured .. 20 20
47. – 65 c. blk., deep bl. & bl. 50 50
48. – $1.10 multicoloured .. 85 85

DESIGNS: 25 c. Archery. 65 c. Cycling. $1.10 Football.

8. Horace Horsecollar and Clarabelle Cow.

1984. Easter. Walt Disney Cartoon Characters. Multicoloured.
50. 35 c. Type **8** 60 60
51. 45 c. Mickey and Minnie Mouse, and Chip 75 75
52. 75 c. Gyro Gearloose, Chip 'n Dale .. .. .. 1·25 1·25
53. 85 c. Mickey Mouse, Chip 'n Dale .. .. .. 1·40 1·40

1984. Universal Postal Union Congress Hamburg. Nos. 20/1 optd. **UNIVERSAL POSTAL UNION 1874–1984** and emblem.
55. 95 c. Boeing "707" airliner at new airport, Providenciales .. .. .. 1·00 1·25
56. $1.10 Columbus's "Pinta", West Caicos .. .. 1·25 1·50

1984. "Ausipex" International Stamp Exhibition, Melbourne. No. 22 optd. **AUSIPEX 1984.**
57. $2 Fort George Cay .. 2·40 2·50

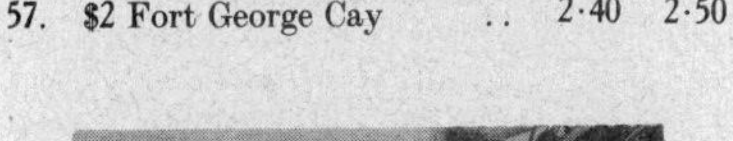

11. Seamen sighting American Manatees.

1984. 492nd Anniv. of Columbus's First Landfall. Multicoloured.
58. 10 c. Type **11** 40 30
59. 70 c. Columbus's fleet .. 2·00 1·40
60. $1 First landing in West Indies .. .. .. 2·50 2·00

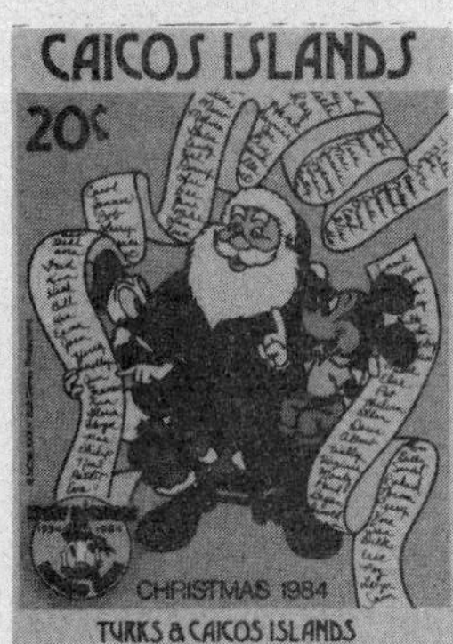

12. Donald Duck and Mickey Mouse with Father Christmas.

1984. Christmas. Walt Disney Cartoon Characters. Multicoloured.
62. 20 c. Type **12** 70 40
63. 35 c. Donald Duck opening refrigerator .. .. 1·00 65
64. 50 c. Mickey Mouse, Donald Duck and toy train .. 1·25 90
65. 75 c. Donald Duck and parcels .. .. 1·75 1·25
66. $1.10 Donald Duck and carol singers .. .. 2·25 1·75

13. Thick-billed Vireo.

1985. Birth Bicentenary of John J. Audubon (ornithologist). Multicoloured.
68. 20 c. Type **13** .. .. 1·00 40
69. 35 c. Black-faced Grassquit 1·40 65
70. 50 c. Pearly-eyed Thrasher 1·75 90
71. $1 Greater Antillean Bullfinch .. .. .. 2·25 1·75

14. Two Children learning to Read and Write (Education)

1985. International Youth Year. 40th Anniv. of United Nations. Multicolour.
73. 16 c. Type **14** 20 25
74. 35 c. Two children on playground swings (Health) .. 50 55
75. 70 c. Boy and girl (Love) .. 1·00 1·10
76. 90 c. Three children (Peace) 1·25 1·40

15. Air Caicos "DC-3" on Ground

1985. 40th Anniv. of International Civil Aviation Organization. Multicoloured.
78. 35 c. Type **15** 85 55
79. 75 c. Air Caicos Convair "440" .. .. .. 1·25 1·25
80. 90 c. TCNA "Islander" .. 2·00 1·40

16. The Queen Mother visiting Foundation for the Disabled, Leatherhead

1985. Life and Times of Queen Elizabeth the Queen Mother. Multicoloured.
82. 35 c Type **16** 50 55
83. 65 c. With Princess Anne (horiz) 90 95
84. 95 c. At Epsom, 1961 .. 1·40 1·60

1985. 150th Birth Anniv. of Mark Twain (author). Designs as T **118** of Anguilla, showing Walt Disney cartoon characters in scenes from "Tom Sawyer, Detective". Multicoloured.
86. 8 c. Huckleberry Finn (Goofy) and Tom Sawyer (Mickey Mouse) reading reward notice 30 10
87. 35 c. Huck and Tom meeting Jake Dunlap .. .. 1·00 55
88. 95 c. Huck and Tom spying on Jubiter Dunlap .. 2·00 1·40
89. $1.10 Huck and Tom with hound (Pluto) .. .. 2·25 1·60

1985. Birth Bicentenaries of Grimm Brothers (folklorists). Designs as T **119** of Anguilla, showing Walt Disney cartoon characters in scenes from "Six Soldiers of Fortune". Mult.
91. 16 c. The Soldier (Donald Duck) with his meagre pay 20 25
92. 25 c. The Soldier meeting the Strong Man (Horace Horsecollar) 30 35
93. 65 c. The Soldier meeting the Marksman (Mickey Mouse) 85 90
94. $1.35 The Fast Runner (Goofy) winning the race against the Princess (Daisy Duck) .. .. 1·75 1·90

CAMEROONS

BRITISH OCCUPATION

12 pence = 1 shilling;
20 shillings = 1 pound.

Former German colony occupied by British and French troops during 1914–16. The country was divided between them and the two areas were administered under the League of Nations mandate from 1922. The British section was administered as part of Nigeria until 1960. (see Southern Cameroons). For German and French issues see Volume 1.

1915. "Yacht" key-types of German Kamerun surch. **C.E.F.** and value in English currency.
1. N. ½d. on 3 pf. brown .. 6·00 16·00
2. ½d. on 5 pf. green .. 1·60 7·00
3. 1d. on 10 pf. red .. 1·25 5·00
4. 2d. on 20 pf. blue .. 3·50 15·00
5. 2½d. on 25 pf. black and red on yellow .. 11·00 30·00
6. 3d. on 30 pf. black and orange on buff .. 11·00 30·00
7. N. 4d. on 40 pf. black & red 11·00 30·00
8. 6d. on 50 pf. black and purple on buff .. 11·00 30·00
9. 8d. on 80 pf. black and red on rose .. .. 11·00 30·00
10. O. 1s. on 1 m. red .. £130 £425
11. 2s. on 2 m. blue .. £130 £425
12. 3s. on 3 m. black .. £130 £425
13. 5s. on 5 m. red & black £160 £425

CANADA

A British dominion consisting of the former province of Canada with Br. Columbia, New Brunswick, Newfoundland, Nova Scotia, and Prince Edward Is.

1851. 12 pence = 1 shilling (Canadian).
1859. 100 cents = 1 dollar.

4.

1. Beaver.

2. Prince Albert.

5.

6. Jacques Cartier.

3.

1851. Imperf.
17 **4.** ½d. red £600 £375
5 **1.** 3d. red £1000 £160
2 **2.** 6d. purple £7500 £900
12 **5.** 7½d. green £7000 £1500
14 **6.** 10d. blue £6500 £1100
4 **3.** 12d. black £60000 £40000

1858. Perf.
25 **4.** ½d. red £1300 £550
26 **1.** 3d. red £2250 £300
27a **2.** 6d. purple £5500 £1700

1859. Values in cents. Perf.
29 **4.** 1 c. red .. .. .. £180 22·00
44. 2 c. red £375 £120
31 **1.** 5 c. red .. .. .. £190 10·00
37. **2.** 10 c. violet .. .. £500 38·00
36. 10 c. brown .. .. £550 38·00
41. **5.** 12½ c. green .. .. £475 42·00
42. **6** 17 c. blue .. .. .. £600 60·00

DOMINION OF CANADA

13.

14.

1868. Various frames.
54 13 ½ c. black .. .. 38·00 30·00
55 14 1 c. brown .. .. £300 38·00
56 1 c. yellow .. .. £650 70·00
48 2 c. green .. .. £300 35·00
49 3 c. red .. .. .. £600 20·00
72 5 c. olive .. .. £700 65·00
59b 6 c. brown .. .. £600 32·00
60 12½ c. blue .. .. £375 35·00
83 15 c. purple .. .. 60·00 16·00
76b 15 c. blue .. .. £130 25·00

27.

21.

1870. Various frames.
77 **27.** ½ c. black .. .. 6·00 4·00
62d **21.** 1 c. yellow .. .. 17·00 15
78a 2 c. green .. .. 28·00 30
79 3 c. red .. .. .. 20·00 10
80 5 c. grey .. .. 50·00 45
81 6 c. brown .. .. 28·00 7·00
117 – 8 c. grey .. .. 65·00 3·00
82b **21.** 10 c. mauve .. .. £120 14·00
On 8 c. head is to left.

28.

1893.
115. **28.** 20 c. red .. .. £160 40·00
116. 50 c. blue .. .. £225 24·00

30. 31.

1897. Jubilee.
121. **30.** ½ c. black .. .. 48·00 48·00
122. 1 c. orange .. .. 8·00 2·00
124. 2 c. green .. .. 12·00 5·00
126. 3 c. red .. .. .. 8·00 80
128. 5 c. blue .. .. 27·00 10·00
129. 6 c. brown .. .. 85·00 85·00
130. 8 c. violet .. .. 32·00 25·00
131. 10 c. purple .. .. 50·00 38·00
132. 15 c. slate .. .. 85·00 85·00
133. 20 c. red .. .. 85·00 85·00
134. 50 c. blue .. .. £120 95·00
136. $1 red £400 £400
137. $2 violet £700 £300
138. $3 bistre £800 £600
139. $4 violet £800 £600
140. $5 green £800 £600

1897. Maple-leaves in four corners.
141. **31.** ½ c. black .. .. 4·75 3·00
143. 1 c. green .. .. 16·00 50
144. 2 c. violet .. .. 15·00 70
145. 3 c. red .. .. 20·00 35
146. 5 c. blue .. .. 60·00 1·50
147. 6 c. brown .. .. 55·00 16·00
148. 8 c. orange .. .. 70·00 5·00
149. 10 c. purple .. .. £120 55·00

1898. As T **31** but figures in lower corners.
150. ½ c. black .. .. 2·00 85
151. 1 c. green .. .. 20·00 15
154. 2 c. purple .. .. 22·00 10
155. 2 c. red .. .. 27·00 10
156. 3 c. red .. .. 32·00 30
157. 5 c. blue .. .. 75·00 70
159. 6 c. brown .. .. 75·00 38·00
160. 7 c. yellow .. .. 48·00 10·00
161. 8 c. orange .. .. 85·00 19·00
163. 10 c. purple .. .. £160 11·00
165. 20 c. olive .. .. £325 48·00

33. 35. King Edward VII.

1898. Imperial Penny Postage.
168 **33** 2 c. black, red and blue 22·00 3·00

1899. Surch. **2 CENTS.**
171. 2 c. on 3 c. red (No. 145) .. 11·00 5·00
172. 2 c. on 3 c. red (No. 156) .. 15·00 2·50

1903.
175 **35.** 1 c. green .. .. 15·00 15
176 2 c. red .. .. 15·00 10
178 5 c. blue .. .. 60·00 90
180 7 c. olive .. .. 55·00 1·25
182 10 c. purple .. .. £100 5·00
185 20 c. olive .. .. £225 18·00
187 50 c. mauve .. .. £350 65·00

36. King George V and Queen Mary, when Prince and Princess of Wales.

1908. Tercent. of Quebec. Dated "1608 1908".
188. **36.** ½ c. brown .. .. 3·25 2·50
189. – 1 c. green .. .. 8·00 1·50
190. – 2 c. red .. .. 14·00 60
191. – 5 c. blue .. .. 40·00 13·00
192. – 7 c. olive .. .. 48·00 32·00
193. – 10 c. violet .. .. 55·00 40·00
194. – 15 c. orange .. .. 75·00 50·00
195. – 20 c. brown .. .. £100 60·00

DESIGNS: 1 c. Cartier and Champlain. 2 c. King Edward VII and Queen Alexandra. 5 c. Champlain's House in Quebec. 7 c. Gen. Montcalm and Wolfe. 10 c. Quebec in 1700. 15 c. Champlain's departure for the West. 20 c. Cartier's arrival before Quebec.

44.

1912.
197 **44** 1 c. green .. .. 5·50 20
200 2 c. red .. .. 4·50 10
224 3 c. brown .. .. 5·00 30
205b 5 c. blue .. .. 60·00 50
209 7 c. yellow .. .. 20·00 1·50
211 10 c. purple .. .. 80·00 1·25
212 20 c. olive .. .. 28·00 85
215 50 c. deep brown .. 45·00 2·25

1915. Optd. **WAR TAX** diagonally.
225. **44.** 5 c. blue £100 £160
226. 20 c. olive .. .. 50·00 75·00
227. 50 c. deep brown .. 80·00 £110

46. 47.

1915.
228. **46.** 1 c. green .. .. 5·00 10
229. 2 c. red .. .. 5·00 20

1916.
233 **47** 2 c.+1 c. red .. .. 8·50 55
239 2 c.+1 c. brown .. .. 3·25 10

48. Quebec Conference, 1864, from painting "The Fathers of the Confederation", by Robert Harris.

1917. 50th Anniv. of Confederation.
244. **48.** 3 c. brown .. .. 16·00 55

1922.
246. **44.** 1 c. yellow .. .. 2·50 15
247. 2 c. green .. .. 2·25 10
248. 3 c. red .. .. 3·75 10
249. 4 c. yellow .. .. 8·00 2·00
250. 5 c. violet .. .. 5·00 75
251. 7 c. brown .. .. 12·00 6·00
252. 8 c. blue .. .. 17·00 7·00
253. 10 c. blue .. .. 20·00 1·00
254. 10 c. brown .. .. 18·00 1·00
255. $1 orange .. .. 50·00 3·75

1926. Surch. **2 CENTS** in one line.
264. **44.** 2 c. on 3 c. red .. 29·00 48·00

1926. Surch. **2 CENTS** in two lines.
265. **44.** 2 c. on 3 c. red .. 11·00 18·00

51. Sir J. A. Macdonald.

DESIGNS — HORIZ. As Type **52**: 3 c. Parliament Buildings, Ottawa. 12 c. Map of Canada, 1867–1927. VERT. As Type **51**: 5 c. Sir W. Laurier.

52. "The Fathers of the Confederation".

1927. 60th Anniv. of Confederation. I. Commemoration Issue. Dated "1867 1927".
266. **51.** 1 c. orange .. .. 2·00 85
267. **52.** 2 c. green .. .. 1·75 10
268. – 3 c. red .. .. 5·50 2·75
269. – 5 c. violet .. .. 3·25 2·50
270. – 12 c. blue .. .. 14·00 3·25

56. Darcy McGee.

57. Sir W. Laurier and Sir J. A. Macdonald.

II. Historical Issue.
271 **56** 5 c. violet .. .. 3·00 1·00
272 **57** 12 c. green .. .. 12·00 4·00
273 – 20 c. red .. .. 14·00 7·00

DESIGN—As Type **57**: 20 c. R. Baldwin and L. H. Lafontaine.

59.

1928. Air.
274. **59.** 5 c. brown .. .. 3·00 1·25

60. King George V.

DESIGNS—HORIZ. 12 c. Quebec Bridge. 20 c. Harvesting with horses. 50 c. "Bluenose" (fishing schooner). $1 Parliament Buildings, Ottawa.

61. Mt. Hurd and Indian Totem Poles.

1928.
275. **60.** 1 c. orange .. .. 1·60 30
276. 2 c. green 75 10
277. 3 c. red .. .. 13·00 9·00
278. 4 c. yellow .. .. 13·00 4·00
279. 5 c. violet .. .. 4·50 1·75
280. 8 c. blue .. .. 7·50 2·75
281. **61.** 10 c. green .. .. 7·00 40
282. – 12 c. black .. .. 15·00 4·50
283. – 20 c. red .. .. 27·00 5·50
284. – 50 c. blue .. .. £100 30·00
285. – $1 olive .. .. £110 38·00

66. **67.** Parliamentary Library, Ottawa.

68. The Old Citadel, Quebec.

1930.
288 **66.** 1 c. orange 45 45
300 1 c. green 80 10
289 2 c. green 80 10
301 2 c. red 70 30
302b 2 c. brown 70 10
303 3 c. red 90 10
290 4 c. yellow .. .. 6·00 1·50
291 5 c. violet .. .. 2·50 2·00
304 5 c. blue .. .. 5·00 10
292 8 c. blue .. .. 6·00 9·00
305 8 c. red .. .. 5·50 2·75
293 **67.** 10 c. olive .. .. 9·00 30
294 **68.** 12 c. black .. .. 9·00 1·75
325 13 c. violet .. .. 32·00 1·50
295 – 20 c. red .. .. 19·00 20
296 – 50 c. blue .. .. 80·00 13·00
297 – $1 olive .. .. 95·00 19·00

DESIGNS—HORIZ. 20 c. Harvesting with tractor. 50 c. Acadian Memorial Church, Grand Pre, Nova Scotia. $1, Mt. Edith Cavell.

72. Mercury and Western Hemisphere.

1930. Air.
310. **72.** 5 c. brown .. .. 14·00 15·00

73. Sir Georges Etienne Cartier.

1931.
312 **73** 10 c. green .. .. 2·75 10

1932. Air. Surch. **6** and bars
313. **59.** 6 c. on 5 c. brown .. 1·50 1·50

1932. Surch. **3** between bars.
314a. **66.** 3 c. on 2 c. red .. 1·00 10

76. King George V. **77.** Duke of Windsor when Prince of Wales.

78. Allegory of British Empire.

1932. Ottawa Conf. (a) Postage.
315. **76.** 3 c. red 70 50
316. **77.** 5 c. blue .. .. 6·00 2·00
317. **78.** 13 c. green .. .. 8·50 5·00

(b) Air. Surch. **6 OTTAWA CONFERENCE 6 1932** between bars.
318. **72.** 6 c. on 5 c. brown .. 10·00 10·00

80. King George V.

1932.
319. **80.** 1 c. green 60 10
320. 2 c. brown 70 10
321b. 3 c. red 85 10
322. 4 c. brown .. .. 35·00 6·00
323. 5 c. blue .. .. 10·00 10
324. 8 c. orange .. .. 22·00 2·25

81. Parliament Buildings, Ottawa.

1933. U.P.U. Congress (Preliminary Meeting).
329. **81.** 5 c. blue .. .. 5·00 1·75

1933. Optd. **WORLD'S GRAIN EXHIBITION & CONFERENCE REGINA 1933.**
330. – 20 c. red (No. 295) .. 20·00 5·50

83. S.S. "Royal William" (after S. Skillett).

1933. Cent. of 1st Transatlantic Steamboat Crossing.
331. **83.** 5 c. blue .. .. 6·00 1·75

84. Jacques Cartier approaching Land.

1934. 4th Cent. of Discovery of Canada.
332. **84.** 3 c. blue .. .. 2·00 1·00

85. U.E.L. Statue, Hamilton.

1934. 150th Anniv. of Arrival of United Empire Loyalists.
333. **85.** 10 c. olive .. .. 10·00 4·00

86. Seal of New Brunswick.

1934. 150th Anniv. of New Brunswick.
334. **86.** 2 c. brown .. .. 75 1·00

87. Queen Elizabeth II when Princess.

88. King George VI when Duke of York.

89. King George V and Queen Mary.

1935. Silver Jubilee. Dated " 1910–1935 ".

No.	Type	Description	Unused	Used
335.	87.	1 c. green	55	40
336.	88.	2 c. brown	60	30
337.	89.	3 c. red	1·75	15
338.	–	5 c. blue	3·50	2·75
339.	–	10 c. green	3·25	2·75
340.	–	13 c. blue	5·50	2·50

DESIGNS—VERT. 5 c. Duke of Windsor when Prince of Wales. HORIZ. 10 c. Windsor Castle. 13 c. " Britannia ".

93. King George V.

DESIGNS—HORIZ. 13 c. Confederation, Charlottetown, 1864. 20 c. Niagara Falls. 50 c. Parliament Buildings, Victoria, B.C. $1, Champlain Monument, Quebec.

94. Royal Canadian Mounted Policeman.

1935.

No.	Type	Description	Unused	Used
341.	93.	1 c. green	30	10
342.		2 c. brown	50	10
343.		3 c. red	60	10
344.		4 c. yellow	1·75	60
345.		5 c. blue	1·25	10
346.		8 c. orange	1·25	1·75
347.	94.	10 c. red	5·00	15
348.	–	13 c. violet	4·75	30
349.	–	20 c. green	15·00	50
350.	–	50 c. violet	25·00	4·00
351.	–	$1 blue	42·00	6·00

99. Daedalus.

1935. Air.

No.	Type	Description	Unused	Used
355.	99.	6 c. brown	1·75	60

100. King George VI and Queen Elizabeth.

1937. Coronation.

No.	Type	Description	Unused	Used
356.	100.	3 c. red	85	30

101. King George VI.

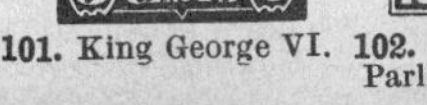

102. Memorial Chamber Parliament Buildings, Ottawa.

104. Fort Garry Gate, Winnipeg.

1937.

No.	Type	Description	Unused	Used
357.	101.	1 c. green	1·25	10
358.		2 c. brown	1·50	10
359.		3 c. red	2·00	10
360.		4 c. yellow	3·50	1·10
361.		5 c. blue	3·50	10
362.		8 c. orange	3·50	1·10
363.	102.	10 c. red	6·00	10
364.	–	13 c. blue	14·00	55
365.	104.	20 c. brown	22·00	20
366.	–	50 c. green	45·00	5·00
367.	–	$1 violet	65·00	5·50

DESIGNS—HORIZ. 13 c. Halifax Harbour. 50 c. Vancouver Harbour. $1, Chateau de Ramezay, Montreal.

107. Seaplane over S.S. " Distributor " on Mackenzie River.

1938. Air.

No.	Type	Description	Unused	Used
371.	107.	6 c. blue	7·00	30

108. Queen Elizabeth II when Princess and Princess Margaret.

1939. Royal Visit.

No.	Type	Description	Unused	Used
372.	108.	1 c. black and green	90	10
373.	–	2 c. black and brown	50	30
374.	–	3 c. black and red	40	10

DESIGNS—HORIZ. 3 c. King George VI and Queen Elizabeth. VERT. 2 c. National War Memorial, Ottawa.

111. King George VI in naval uniform. **112.** King George VI in military uniform.

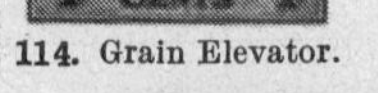

114. Grain Elevator. **115.** Farm Scene.

121. Air Training Camp.

1942. War Effort.

No.	Type	Description	Unused	Used
375.	111.	1 c. green (postage)	1·00	10
376.	112.	2 c. brown	1·75	10
377.	–	3 c. red	1·25	30
378.	–	3 c. purple	70	10
379.	114.	4 c. grey	4·50	60
380.	112.	4 c. red	55	10
381.	111.	5 c. blue	2·75	10
382.	115.	8 c. sepia	5·00	60
383.	–	10 c. brown	4·50	10
384.	–	13 c. green	4·00	4·25
385.	–	14 c. green	11·00	30
386.	–	20 c. brown	12·00	15
387.	–	50 c. violet	20·00	1·75
388.	–	$1 blue	55·00	4·00
399.	121.	6 c. blue (air)	8·00	2·75
400.		7 c. blue	1·50	10

DESIGNS—As Type 112: 3 c. King George VI. As Type 121. VERT. 10 c. Parliament Buildings. HORIZ. 13 c., 14 c. Ram tank. 20 c. Corvette. 50 c. Munitions factory. $1, H.M.S. Cossack" (destroyer).

122. Ontario Farm Scene.

1946. Re-conversion to Peace-time.

No.	Type	Description	Unused	Used
401.	122.	8 c. brown (postage)	1·25	90
402.	–	10 c. green	1·50	10
403.	–	14 c. brown	3·75	50
404.	–	20 c. grey	3·00	10
405.	–	50 c. green	15·00	1·50
406.	–	$1 purple	30·00	1·50
407.	–	7 c. blue (air)	3·00	10

DESIGNS: 10 c. Great Bear Lake. 14 c. St. Maurice River Power station. 20 c. Combine harvester. 50 c. Lumbering in Br. Columbia. $1, "Abegweit" (train ferry). 7 c. Canada Geese in flight.

129. Alexander Graham Bell and " Fame ".

130. " Canadian Citizenship ".

1947. Birth Cent. of Graham Bell (inventor of the telephone).

No.	Type	Description	Unused	Used
408.	129.	4 c. blue	10	10

1947. Advent of Canadian Citizenship and 80th Anniv. of Confederation.

No.	Type	Description	Unused	Used
409.	130.	4 c. blue	10	10

131. Queen Elizabeth II when Princess.

1948. Princess Elizabeth's Wedding.

No.	Type	Description	Unused	Used
410.	131.	4 c. blue	10	10

132. Queen Victoria, Parliament Building, Ottawa, and King George VI.

1948. Cent. of Responsible Government.

No.	Type	Description	Unused	Used
411.	132.	4 c. grey	10	10

133. Cabot's Ship " Matthew ".

1949. Entry of Newfoundland into Canadian Confederation.

No.	Type	Description	Unused	Used
412.	133.	4 c. green	10	10

134. "Founding of Halifax, 1749" (after C. W. Jeffries).

1949. Halifax Bicent.

No.	Type	Description	Unused	Used
413.	134.	4 c. violet	10	10

135. King George VI.

1949. Portraits of King George VI.

No.	Type	Description	Unused	Used
414	135	1 c. green	10	10
415	–	2 c. brown	15	20
415a	–	2 c. green	30	10
416	–	3 c. purple	30	10
417	–	4 c. red	20	10
418	–	5 c. blue	1·25	10

1950. As Nos. 414/8 but without " POSTES POSTAGE ".

No.	Type	Description	Unused	Used
424.		1 c. green	10	30
425.		2 c. brown	10	40
426.		3 c. purple	10	70
427.		4 c. red	10	10
428.		5 c. blue	25	1·25

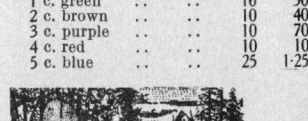

142. Drying Furs.

141. Oil Wells in Alberta.

1950.

No.	Type	Description	Unused	Used
432	142	10 c. purple	50	10
441	–	20 c. grey	75	10
431	141	50 c. green	7·50	90
433	–	$1 blue	45·00	3·50

DESIGNS: 20 c. Forestry products. $1, Fisherman.

145. Mackenzie King.

1951. Canadian Prime Ministers.

No.	Type	Description	Unused	Used
434.	–	3 c. green (Borden)	10	40
444.	–	3 c. purple (Abbott)	15	10
435.	145.	4 c. red	10	10
445.	-	4 c. red (A. Mackenzie)	15	10
475.	-	4 c. violet (Thompson)	15	10
483.	-	4 c. violet (Bennett)	10	15
476.	-	5 c. blue (Bowell)	15	10
484.	-	5 c. blue (Tupper)	10	10

146. Mail Trains, 1851 and 1951.

149. Reproduction of 3d., 1851.

DESIGNS—As Type 146: 5 c. S.S. "City of Toronto" and S.S. " Prince George ". 7 c. Mail coach and aeroplane.

1951. Centenary of First Canadian Postage Stamp. Dated " 1851 1951 ".

No.	Type	Description	Unused	Used
436.	146.	4 c. black	35	10
437.	–	5 c. violet	65	1·50
438.	–	7 c. blue	35	45
439.	149.	15 c. red	35	10

150. Queen Elizabeth II when Princess and Duke of Edinburgh.

1951. Royal Visit.

No.	Type	Description	Unused	Used
440.	150.	4 c. violet	10	10

152. Red Cross Emblem.

1952. 18th Int. Red Cross Conf., Toronto.
442. 152. 4 c. red and blue .. 15 10

153. Canada Goose.

1952.
443 153 7 c. blue 30 10

165. Eskimo Hunter.

160. Textile Industry.

164. Northern Gannet.

154. Pacific Coast Indian House and Totem Pole.

1953.
477. 165. 10 c. brown 15 10
474. 164. 15 c. black 40 10
488. – 20 c. green 30 10
489. – 25 c. red 35 10
462. 160. 50 c. green .. .. 1·25 10
446. 154. $1 black .. .. 7·50 20
DESIGNS—As Type 160—HORIZ. 20 c. Pulp and paper industry. VERT. 25 c. Chemical industry.

155. Polar Bear.

158. Queen Elizabeth II.

1953. National Wild Life Week.
447. 155. 2 c. blue 10 10
448. – 3 c. sepia (Elk) .. 10 10
449. – 4 c. slate (American Bighorn) 15 10

1953.
450. 158. 1 c. brown 10 10
451. 2 c. green 15 10
452. 3 c. red 15 15
453. 4 c. violet 20 10
454. 5 c. blue 20 10

159. Queen Elizabeth II.

161.

1953. Coronation.
461. 159. 4 c. violet 10 10

1954.
463. 161. 1 c. brown 10 10
464. 2 c. green 20 10
465. 3 c. red 50 10
466. 4 c. violet 30 10
467. 5 c. blue 30 10
468. 6 c. orange .. .. 1·00 30

1954. National Wild Life Week. As T 155.
472. 4 c. slate (Walrus) .. 35 10
473. 5 c. blue (American Beaver) 35 10

166. Musk-ox.

168. Dove and Torch.

167. Whooping Cranes.

1955. National Wild Life Week.
478. 166. 4 c. violet 30 10
479. 167. 5 c. blue 70 10

1955. 10th Anniv. of I.C.A.O.
480. 168. 5 c. blue 10 10

169. Pioneer Settlers.

1955. 50th Anniv. of Alberta and Saskatchewan Provinces.
481. 169. 5 c. blue 15 15

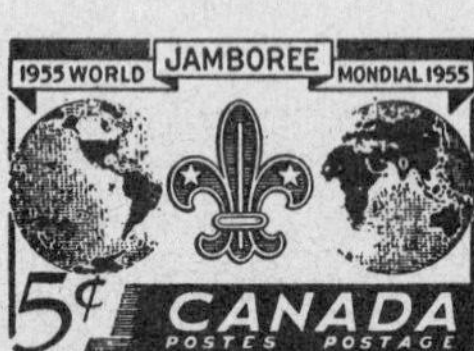
170. Scout Badge and Globe.

1955. 8th World Scout Jamboree.
482. 170. 5 c. brown and green.. 20 10

173. Ice-Hockey Players.

1956. Ice-hockey Commem.
485. 173. 5 c. blue 15 15

1956. National Wild Life Week. As T 155.
486. 4 c. violet (Reindeer) .. 20 15
487. 5 c. blue (Mountain goat) 20 10

178.

183. Great Northern Diver.

181. Hunting.

1956. Fire Prevention Week.
490. 178. 5 c. red and black .. 30 10

1957. Outdoor Recreation.
491. – 5 c. blue (Fishing) .. 25 10
492. – 5 c. blue (Swimming) 25 10
493. 181. 5 c. blue 25 10
494. – 5 c. blue (Skiing) .. 25 10

1957. National Wild Life Week.
495. 183. 5 c. black 20 10

184. Thompson with Sextant, and North American Map.

1957. Death Cent. of David Thompson (explorer).
496. 184. 5 c. blue 15 30

185. Parliament Buildings, Ottawa.

187. Miner.

1957. 14th U.P.C. Congress, Ottawa.
497. 185. 5 c. slate 15 10
498. – 15 c. slate .. .. 45 1·50
DESIGN—HORIZ. ($33\frac{1}{2} \times 22$ mm.): 15 c. Globe within posthorn.

1957. Mining Industry.
499. 187. 5 c. black 35 10

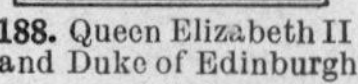
188. Queen Elizabeth II and Duke of Edinburgh.

190. Microscope.

189. "A Free Press".

1957. Royal Visit.
500. 188. 5 c. black 30 10

1958. The Canadian Press.
501. 189. 5 c. black 15 30

1958. Int. Geophysical Year.
502. 190. 5 c. blue 20 10

191. Miner Panning for Gold.

1958. Centenary of British Columbia.
503. 191. 5 c. turquoise .. 20 10

192. La Verendrye statue.

1958. La Verendrye (explorer). Commem.
504. 192. 5 c. blue 20 10

193. Samuel de Champlain and Heights of Quebec.

1958. 350th Anniv. of Founding of Quebec by Samuel de Champlain.
505. 193. 5 c. brown and green 30 10

194. Nurse.

1958. National Health.
506. 194. 5 c. purple 30 10

195. "Petroleum 1858-1958".

1958. Cent. of Canadian Oil Industry.
507. 195. 5 c. red and olive .. 30 10

196. Speaker's Chair and Mace.

1958. Bicent. of First Elected Assembly.
508. 196. 5 c. slate 30 10

197. The "Silver Dart".

1959. 50th Anniv. of First Flight of the "Silver Dart" in Canada.
509. 197. 5 c. black and blue .. 30 10

198. Globe showing N.A.T.O. Countries.

1959. 10th Anniv. of N.A.T.O.

510. **198.** 5 c. blue 40 10

199. 200.

1959. "Associated Country Women of the World" Commem.

511. **199.** 5 c. black & olive .. 15 10

1959. Royal Visit.

512. **200.** 5 c. red 30 10

201. Maple Leaf linked with American Eagle.

1959. Opening of St. Lawrence Seaway.

513. **201.** 5 c. blue and red .. 20 10

202. Maple Leaves.

1959. Bicentenary of Battle of Quebec.

514. **202.** 5 c. green and red .. 30 10

203. Girl Guides Badge. **204.** Dollard des Ormeaux.

1960. Golden Jubilee of Canadian Girl Guides Movement.

515. **203.** 5 c. blue and brown.. 20 10

1960. Tercent. of Battle of Long Sault.

516. **204.** 5 c. blue and brown.. 20 10

205. Surveyor, Bulldozer and Compass Rose. **206.** E. Pauline Johnson.

1961. Northern Development.

517. **205.** 5 c. green and red .. 15 10

1961. Birth Centenary of E. Pauline Johnson (Mohawk poetess).

518. **206.** 5 c. green and red .. 15 10

207. Arthur Meighen (statesman).

1961. Arthur Meighen Commem.

519. **207.** 5 c. blue 15 10

208. Engineers and Dam.

1961. Colombo Plan.

520. **208.** 5 c. brown and blue .. 30 10

209. "Resources for Tomorrow". **210.** "Education".

1961. Natural Resources.

521. **209.** 5 c. green and brown.. 15 10

1962. Education Year.

522. **210.** 5 c. black and brown 15 10

211. Lord Selkirk and Farmer.

1962. 150th Anniv. of Red River Settlement.

523. **211.** 5 c. brown & green .. 20 10

212. Talon bestowing gifts on married couple. **213.** British Columbia and Vancouver Is. 2½d. stamp of 1860, and Parliament Bldgs., B.C.

1962. Jean Talon Commem.

524. **212.** 5 c. blue 20 10

1962. Centenary of Victoria, B.C.

525. **213.** 5 c. red and black .. 30 10

214. Highway (map version) and Provincial Arms.

1962. Opening of Trans-Canada Highway.

526. **214.** 5 c. black and brown 15 10

215. Queen Elizabeth II and Wheat (agriculture) Symbol. **216.** Sir Casimir Gzowski.

1962. Different symbols in top left corner.

527. **215.** 1 c. brown	10	10
528. 2 c. green	15	10
529. 3 c. violet	15	10
530. 4 c. red	15	10
531. 5 c. blue	15	10

SYMBOLS: 1 c. Crystals (Mining). 2 c. Tree (Forestry). 3 c. Fish (Fisheries). 4 c. Electricity pylon (Industrial power). 5 c. Wheat (Agriculture).

1963. 150th Birth Anniv. of Sir Casimir Gzowski (engineer).

535. **216.** 5 c. purple 10 10

217. "Export Trade".

1963.

536. **217.** $1 red .. .. .. 6·50 1·75

218. Frobisher and barque "Gabriel".

1963. Sir Martin Frobisher Commem.

537. **218.** 5 c. blue 20 10

219. Horseman and Map.

1963. Bicent. of Quebec—Trois-Rivieres—Montreal Postal Service.

538. **219.** 5 c. brown and green 15 10

220. Canada Geese. **221.** Jet Airliner (composite) and Uplands Airport, Ottawa.

1963.

540. **221.** 7 c. blue	35	70
540a. 8 c. blue	50	30
539. **220.** 15 c. blue	1·25	10

222. "Peace on Earth".

1964. "Peace".

541. **222.** 5 c. ochre, blue & turq. 15 10

223. Maple Leaves.

1964. "Canadian Unity".

542. **223.** 5 c. lake and blue .. 10 10

224. White Trillium and Arms of Ontario.

1964. Provincial Badges.

543. **224.** 5 c. green, brown & orge.	40	20
544. – 5 c. green, brown & yell.	40	20
545. – 5 c. red, green & violet	30	20
546. – 5 c. blue, red & green..	30	20
547. – 5 c. purple, green & brn.	30	20
548. – 5 c. brown, green & mve.	30	20
549. – 5 c. lilac, green & pur.	50	20
550. – 5 c. green, yellow & red	30	20
551. – 5 c. sepia, orange & grn.	30	20
552. – 5 c. black, red & green	30	20
553. – 5 c. drab, green & yell.	30	20
554. – 5 c. blue, green and red	30	20
555. – 5 c. red and blue ..	30	20

FLOWERS AND ARMS OF: No. 544, Madonna Lily, Quebec. No. 545, Purple Violet, New Brunswick. No. 546, Mayflower, Nova Scotia. No. 547, Dogwood, British Columbia. No. 548, Prairie Crocus, Manitoba. No. 549, Lady's Slipper, Prince Edward Island. No. 550, Wild Rose, Alberta. No. 551, Prairie Lily, Saskatchewan. No. 552, Pitcher Plant, Newfoundland. No. 553, Mountain Avens, Northwest Territories. No. 554, Fireweed, Yukon Territory. No. 555, Maple Leaf, Canada.

1964. Surch.

556. **221.** 8 c. on 7 c. blue .. 15 15

238. Fathers of the Confederation Memorial, Charlottetown.

1964. Cent. of Charlottetown Conf.

557. **238.** 5 c. black 10 10

239. Maple Leaf and Hand with Quill Pen.

1964. Cent. of Quebec Conf.

558. **239.** 5 c. red and brown 15 10

240. Queen Elizabeth II. **241.** "Canadian Family".

1964. Royal Visit.

559. **240.** 5 c. purple 15 10

1964. Christmas.

560. **241.** 3 c. red	10	10
561. 5 c. blue	10	10

242. Co-operation.

1965. Int. Co-operation Year.

562. **242.** 5 c. green 35 10

243. Sir W. Grenfell.

1965. Birth Centenary of Sir Wilfred Grenfell (missionary).

563. **243.** 5 c. green 20 10

244. National Flag.

1965. Inauguration of National Flag.

564. **244.** 5 c. red and blue .. 15 10

245. Sir Winston Churchill.

246. Peace Tower, Parliament Bldgs., Ottawa.

1965. Churchill Commem.
565. **245.** 5 c. brown 15 10

1965. Inter-Parliamentary Union Conf., Ottawa.
566. **246.** 5 c. green 10 10

247. Parliament Buildings, Ottawa, 1865.

1965. Centenary of Proclamation of Ottawa as Capital.
567. **247.** 5 c brown 10 10

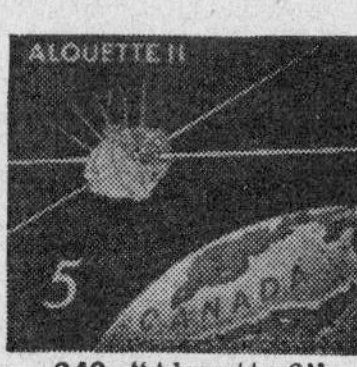

248. "Gold, Frankincense and Myrrh".

249. "Alouette 2" over Canada.

1965. Christmas.
568. **248.** 3 c. green 10 10
569. 5 c. blue 10 10

1966. Launching of Canadian Satellite, "Alouette 2".
570. **249.** 5 c. blue 15 10

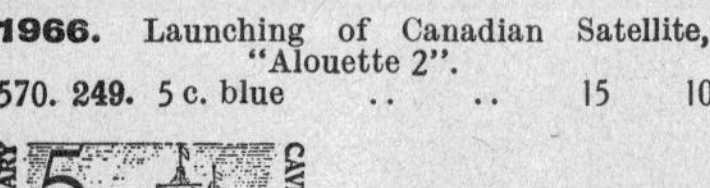

250. La Salle.

251. Road Signs.

1966. 300th Anniv. of La Salle's Arrival in Canada.
571. **250.** 5 c. green 15 10

1966. Highway Safety.
572. **251.** 5 c. yellow, blue & blk. 15 10

252. Canadian Delegation and Houses of Parliament.

1966. Cent. of London Conference.
573. **252.** 5 c. brown 10 10

253. Douglas Point Nuclear Power Station.

1966. Peaceful Uses of Atomic Energy.
574. **253.** 5 c. blue 10 10

254. Parliamentary Library, Ottawa.

255. " Praying Hands ", after Dürer.

1966. Commonwealth Parliamentary Assn. Conf., Ottawa.
575. **254.** 5 c. purple 10 10

1966. Christmas.
576. **255.** 3 c. red 10 10
577. 5 c. orange 10 10

256. Flag, and Canada on Globe.

257. Queen Elizabeth, Northern Lights and Dog-team.

262. " Alaska Highway " (A. Y. Jackson).

1967. Canadian Centennial.
578. **256.** 5 c. red and blue .. 10 10

1967.

579	**257.**	1 c. brown	10	10
580	–	2 c. green	10	10
581	–	3 c. purple	30	10
582	–	4 c. red	20	10
583	–	5 c. blue	20	10
601	–	6 c. red	45	10
607	–	6 c. black	30	10
609	–	7 c. green	30	10
584	**262.**	8 c. purple	35	30
610	–	8 c. black	30	10
585	–	10 c. olive	30	10
586	–	15 c. purple	30	10
587	–	20 c. blue	80	10
588	–	25 c. green	1·50	10
589	–	50 c. brown	1·75	10
590	–	$1 red	4·00	65

DESIGNS—As Type **257**—Queen Elizabeth and: 2 c. Totem Pole. 3 c. Combine-harvester and Oil Derrick. 4 c. Ship in Lock. 5 c. (No. 583), Harbour Scene. 6 c. (Nos. 606/7), 7 c. " Transport ". 8 c. (No. 610), Library of Parliament. As Type **262.** 10 c. " The Jack Pine " (T. Thomson). 15 c. " Bylot Island " (L. Harris). 20 c. " Quebec Ferry " (J. W. Morrice). 25 c. " The Solemn Land " (J. E. H. MacDonald). 50 c. " Summer's Stores " (Grain elevators, J. Ensor). $1, " Oilfield " (near Edmonton, H. G. Glyde).

269. Canadian Pavilion.

1967. World Fair, Montreal.
611. **269.** 5 c. blue and red .. 10 10

270. Allegory of " Womanhood " on Ballot-box.

271. Queen Elizabeth. II and Centennial Emblem.

1967. 50th Anniv. of Women's Franchise.
612. **270.** 5 c. purple and black 10 10

1967. Royal Visit.
613. **271.** 5 c. plum and brown .. 15 10

272. Athlete.

1967. Pan-American Games, Winnipeg.
614. **272.** 5 c. red 10 10

273. " World News ".

1967. 50th Anniv. of Canadian Press.
615. **273.** 5 c blue 10 10

274. Governor-General Vanier.

1967. Vanier Commem.
616. **274.** 5 c. black 10 10

275. People of 1867, and Toronto, 1967.

1967. Cent. of Toronto as Capital City of Ontario.
617. **275.** 5 c. green and red .. 10 10

276. Carol Singers.

277. Grey Jays.

1967. Christmas.
618. **276.** 3 c. red 10 10
619. 5 c. green 10 10

1968. Wild Life.
620. **277.** 5 c. multicoloured .. 30 10
See also Nos. 638/40.

278. Weather Map and Instruments.

1968. 20th Anniversary of First Meteorological Readings.
621. **278.** 5 c. multicoloured. .. 15 10

279. Narwhal.

1968. Wild Life.
622. **279.** 5 c. multicoloured .. 15 10

280. Globe, Maple Leaf and Rain Gauge.

1968. Int. Hydrological Decade.
623. **280.** 5 c. multicoloured .. 15 10

281. The " Nonsuch ".

1968. 300th Anniversary of Voyage of the "Nonsuch".
624. **281.** 5 c. multicoloured .. 20 10

282. Lacrosse Players.

1968. Lacrosse.
625. **282.** 5 c. multicoloured .. 15 10

283. Front Page of " The Globe ", George Brown and Legislative Building.

1968. 150th Birth Anniversary of George Brown (politician and journalist).
626. **283.** 5 c. multicoloured .. 10 10

284. H. Bourassa (politician and journalist).

286. Armistice Monument, Vimy.

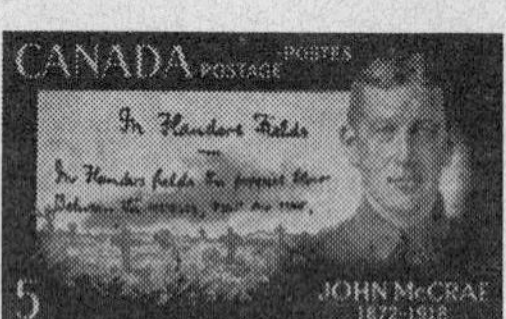

285. John McCrae, Battlefield and First Lines of "In Flanders Fields".

1968. Birth Centenary of Henri Bourassa.
627. **284.** 5 c. blk, red & cream 10 10

1968. 50th Death Anniv of John McCrae (soldier and poet).
628 **285** 5 c. multicoloured .. 10 10

1968. 50th Anniversary of 1918 Armistice.
629. **286.** 15 c. black 30 40

287. Eskimo Family (carving).

1968. Christmas.
630. **287.** 5 c. black and blue .. 10 10
631. – 6 c. black and ochre .. 10 10
DESIGN: 6 c. " Mother and Child " (carving).

289. Curling.

1969. Curling.
632. **289.** 6 c. black, blue and red 15 10

290. Vincent Massey. **292.** Globe and Tools.

291. "Return from the Harvest Field" (Suzor-Cote).

1969. Vincent Massey, First Canadian-born Governor-General.
633. **290.** 6 c. sepia and ochre .. 10 10

1969. Birth Centenary of Marc Aurele de Foy Suzor-Cote (painter).
634. **291.** 50 c. multicoloured .. 70 2·00

1969. 50th Anniversary of Int. Labour Organization.
635. **292.** 6 c. green 10 10

293. Vickers Vimy Aircraft over Atlantic Ocean.

1969. 50th Anniversary of 1st Non-stop Transatlantic Flight.
636. **293.** 15 c. brn., grn. & blue 40 55

294. Sir William Osler (J. S. Sargent). **295.** White-throated Sparrow.

1969. 50th Death Anniversary of Sir William Osler (physician).
637. **294.** 6 c. blue and brown .. 20 10

1969. Birds. Multicoloured.
638. 6 c. Type **295** 25 10
639. 10 c. Savannah Sparrow .. 65 80
640. 25 c. Hermit Thrush .. 1·90 2·50
The 10 c. and 25 c. are horiz.

298. Flags of Winter and Summer Games. **300.** Sir Isaac Brock and Memorial Column.

299. Outline of Prince Edward Island showing Charlottetown.

1969. Canadian Games.
641. **298.** 6 c. green, red & blue .. 10 10

1969. Bicent. of Charlottetown as Capital of Prince Edward Is.
642. **299.** 6 c. brown, blk. & blue 20 10

1969. Birth Bicent. of Sir Isaac Brock.
643. **300.** 6 c. orge., bis. & brn. 10 10

301. Children of the World in Prayer.

1969. Christmas.
644. **301.** 5 c. multicoloured .. 10 10
645. 6 c. multicoloured .. 10 10

302. Stephen Butler Leacock, Mask and "Mariposa".

1969. Birth Centenary of Stephen Butler Leacock (humorist).
646. **302.** 6 c. multicoloured .. 10 10

303. Symbolic Cross-roads.

1970. Centenary of Manitoba.
647. **303.** 6 c. blue, yellow & red 15 10

304. "Enchanted Owl" (Kenojuak).

1970. Centenary of Northwest Territories.
648. **304.** 6 c. red and black .. 10 10

305. Microscopic View of Inside of Leaf.

1970. Int. Biological Programme.
649. **305.** 6 c. green, yellow & blue 15 10

306. Expo 67 Emblem and stylized Cherry Blossom.

1970. World Fair, Osaka. Expo 70. Mult.
650. 25 c. Type **306** (red) .. 1·40 1·25
651. 25 c. Dogwood (violet) .. 1·40 1·25
652. 25 c. White Trillium (grn.) 1·40 1·25
653. 25 c. White Garden Lily (bl.) 1·40 1·25
NOTE: Each stamp shows a stylized Cherry Blossom, in a different colour, given above in brackets.

310. Henry Kelsey.

1970. 300th Birth Anniversary of Henry Kelsey (explorer).
654. **310.** 6 c. multicoloured .. 10 10

311. "Towards Unification".

1970. 25th Anniversary of U.N.
655. **311.** 10 c. blue 30 30
656. 15 c. mauve and lilac 40 35

312. Louis Riel (Metis leader). **313.** Mackenzie's Inscription, Dean Channel.

1970. Louis Riel Commem.
657. **312.** 6 c. blue and red .. 10 10

1970. Sir Alexander Mackenzie (explorer).
658. **313.** 6 c. brown 15 10

314. Sir Oliver Mowat (statesman).

1970. Sir Oliver Mowat Commem.
659. **314.** 6 c. red and black .. 10 10

315. "Isles of Spruce" (A. Lismer).

1970. 50th Anniversary of "Group of Seven" (artists).
660. **315.** 6 c. multicoloured .. 10 10

316. "Horse-drawn Sleigh" (D. Niskala). **328.** Sir Donald A. Smith.

1970. Christmas. Multicoloured.
661. 5 c. Type **316** 50 20
662. 5 c. "Stable and Star of Bethlehem" 50 20
663. 5 c. "Snowmen" 50 20
664. 5 c. "Skiing" 50 20
665. 5 c. "Santa Claus" .. 50 20
666. 6 c. "Santa Claus" (different) 50 20
667. 6 c. "Christ in Manger" .. 50 20
668. 6 c. "Toy Shop" 50 20
669. 6 c. "Christmas Tree" .. 50 20
670. 6 c. "Church" 50 20
671. 10 c. "Christ in Manger" (37×20 mm.) 30 30
672. 15 c. "Trees and Sledge" (37×20 mm.) .. 45 60

1970. 150th Birth Anniversary of Sir Donald Alexander Smith.
673. **328.** 6 c. yell., brn & grn. 15 10

329. "Big Raven" (E. Carr). **330.** Laboratory Equipment.

1971. Birth Centenary of Emily Carr (painter).
674. **329.** 6 c. multicoloured .. 20 20

1971. 50th Anniv. of Discovery of Insulin.
675. **330.** 6 c. multicoloured .. 30 20

331. "The Atom".

1971. Birth Centenary of Lord Rutherford (scientist).
676. **331.** 6 c. yellow, red & brn. 20 10

332. Maple "Keys". **333.** Louis Papineau.

1971. "The Maple Leaf in Four Seasons". Multicoloured.
677. 6 c. Type **332** (spring) .. 20 15
678. 6 c. Green leaves (summer) 20 15
679. 7 c. Autumn leaves .. 20 15
680. 7 c. Withered leaves and snow (winter) .. 20 15

1971. Death Centenary of Louis-Joseph Papineau (politician).
681. **333.** 6 c. multicoloured .. 15 15

334. Chart of Coppermine River.

1971. Bicentenary of Samuel Hearne's Expedition to the Coppermine River.
682 **334** 6 c. brown, red & buff 40 40

335. "People" and Computer Tapes.

1971. Centenary of 1st Canadian Census.
683. **335.** 6 c. blue, red & black 30 10

336. Maple Leaves.

1971. Radio Canada International.
684. **336.** 15 c. red, yell. & blk. 50 1·00

HAVE YOU READ THE NOTES AT THE BEGINNING OF THIS CATALOGUE?
These often provide answers to the enquiries we receive.

337. "B. C.".

1971. Centenary of British Columbia's Entry into the Confederation.

685.	**337.**	7 c. multicoloured ..	15	10

338. "Indian Encampment on Lake Huron" (Kane).

1971. Death Cent. of Paul Kane (painter).

686.	**338.**	7 c. multicoloured ..	20	10

339. "Snowflake".

340. Pierre Laporte (Quebec Cabinet Minister).

1971. Christmas.

687.	**339.**	6 c. blue	10	10
688.		7 c. green	15	10
689.	–	10 c. silver and red ..	55	1·00
690.	–	15 c. silver, pur. & lav.	85	1·40

Design: 10 c., 15 c. "Snowflake" design similar to Type **339** but square (26×26 mm.)

1971. 1st Anniversary of Assassination of Pierre Laporte.

691.	**340.**	7 c. black on buff ..	15	10

341. Skaters.

1972. World Figure Skating Championships, Calgary.

692.	**341.**	8 c. purple	15	10

342. J. A. MacDonald.

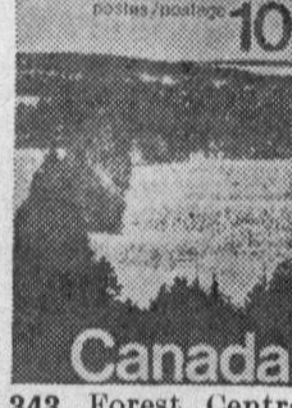

343. Forest, Central Canada.

344. Vancouver.

1972.

693	**342**	1 c. orange	10	10
694	–	2 c. green	10	10
695	–	3 c. brown	10	10
696	–	4 c. black	10	10
697	–	5 c. mauve	10	10
698	–	6 c. red	10	10
699	–	7 c. brown	10	15
700	–	8 c. blue	15	10
701	–	10 c. brown	40	10
702b	**343**	10 c. green, turquoise and orange ..	30	10
703b	–	15 c. blue and brown	30	10
704a	–	20 c. orge., vio. & bl.	30	10
705b	–	25 c. ultram. & bl. ..	60	10
706b	–	50 c. grn., bl. & brn.	40	10
709a	**344**	$1 multicoloured ..	70	30
708	–	$2 multicoloured ..	1·50	2·00

Designs: As Type **342** (1 to 7 c. show Canadian Prime Ministers). 2 c. W. Laurier. 3 c. R. Borden. 4 c. W. L. Mackenzie King. 5 c. R. B. Bennett. 6 c. L. B. Pearson. 7 c. Louis St. Laurent. 8 and 10 c. Queen Elizabeth II. As Type **343.** 15 c. American bighorn. 20 c. Prairie landscape from the air. 25 c. Polar Bears. 50 c. Seashore, Eastern Canada. As Type **344.** $2 Quebec.

345. Heart.

1972. World Health Day.

719.	**345.**	8 c. red	30	10

346. Frontenac and Fort Saint-Louis, Quebec.

1972. 300th Anniversary of Governor Frontenac's Appointment to New France.

720.	**346.**	8 c. red, brown & blue	15	15

347. Plains Indians' Artefacts.

347a. Buffalo Chase.

348. Thunderbird and Tribal Pattern.

348a. Dancer in Ceremonial Costume.

1972. Canadian Indians.

(a) Horiz. designs showing Artefacts as T **347** or Scenes from Indian Life as T **347a.**

721.	**347.**	8 c. multicoloured ..	40	10
722.	**347a.**	8 c. brn., yell. and blk.	40	10
723.	–	8 c. multicoloured ..	40	10
724.	–	8 c. multicoloured ..	40	10
725.	–	8 c. multicoloured ..	40	10
726.	–	8 c. brn., yell. and blk.	40	10
727.	–	8 c. multicoloured ..	40	10
728.	–	8 c. multicoloured ..	40	10
729.	–	10 c. multicoloured ..	40	20
730.	–	10 c. red, brown and black	40	20

Tribes: Nos. 721/2, Plains Indians. Nos. 723/4, Algonkians. Nos. 725/6, Pacific Coast Indians. Nos. 727/8, Subarctic Indians. Nos. 729/30, Iroquoians.

(b) Vert designs showing Costumes as T **348a** or Thunderbird and pattern as T**348**.

731.	**348a.**	8 c. orange, red & black	40	15
732.	**348.**	8 c. multicoloured ..	40	15
733.	–	8 c. red, violet & black	40	10
734.	–	8 c. green, brn. & blk.	40	10
735.	–	8 c. red and black ..	40	10
736.	–	8 c. multicoloured ..	40	10
737.	–	8 c. green, brn. & blk.	40	10
738.	–	8 c. multicoloured ..	40	10
739.	–	10 c. brn., orge. & blk.	40	20
740.	–	10 c. multicoloured ..	40	20

Tribes: Nos. 731/2, Plains Indians. Nos. 733/4, Algonkians. Nos. 735/6, Pacific Coast Indians. Nos. 737/8, Subarctic Indians. Nos. 739/40, Iroquoians.

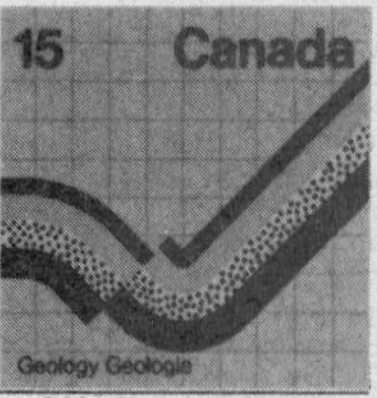

349. Earth's Crust.

350. Candles.

1972. Earth Sciences.

741.	–	15 c. multicoloured ..	1·00	1·50
742.	–	15 c. grey, blue & blk.	1·00	1·50
743.	**349.**	15 c. multicoloured ..	1·00	1·50
744.	–	15 c. grn., orge. & blk	1·00	1·50

Designs and events: No. 741 Photogrammetric surveying (12th Congress of Int. Society of Photogrammetry). No. 742, "Siegfried" lines (6th Conf. of Int. Cartographic Assn). No. 743 (24th Int. Geological Congress). No. 744, Diagram of village at road-intersection (22nd Int. Geographical Congress).

1972. Christmas. Multicoloured.

745.	6 c. Type **350**	15	10
746.	8 c. Type **350**	20	10
747.	10 c. Candles with fruits and pine boughs (horiz.)	60	75
748.	15 c. Candles with prayer-book, caskets and vase (horiz.)	80	1·00

Nos. 747/8 are size 36×20 mm.

351. "The Blacksmith's Shop" (Krieghoff).

1972. Death Centenary of Cornelius Krieghoff (painter).

749.	**351.**	8 c. multicoloured ..	30	15

352. F. de Montmorency-Laval.

1973. 350th Birth Anniversary of Monsignor de Laval (1st Bishop of Quebec).

750.	**352.**	8 c. blue, gold & silver	20	40

353. Commissioner French and Route of the March West.

1973. Centenary of Royal Canadian Mounted Police.

751.	**353.**	8 c. brn., orge. & red ..	35	20
752.	–	10 c. multicoloured ..	1·25	1·75
753.	–	15 c. multicoloured ..	2·00	2·50

Designs: 10 c. Spectrograph. 15 c. Mounted policeman.

354. Jeanne Mance.

1973. 300th Death Anniv. of Jeanne Mance (nurse).

754.	**354.**	8 c. multicoloured ..	20	40

355. Joseph Howe.

356. "Mist Fantasy" (MacDonald).

1973. Death Centenary of Joseph Howe (Nova Scotian politician).

755.	**355.**	8 c. gold and black ..	20	40

1973. J. E. H. MacDonald (artist). Birth Cent.

756.	**356.**	15 c. multicoloured ..	30	55

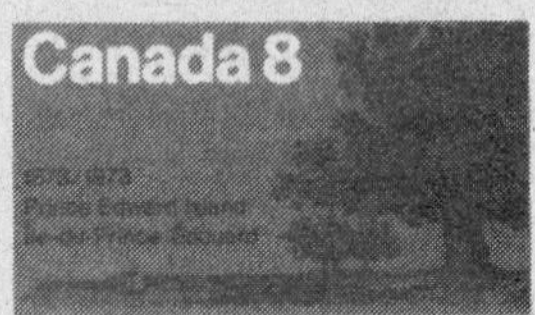

357. Oaks and Harbour.

1973. Centenary of Prince Edward Island's Entry into the Confederation.

757.	**357.**	8 c. orange and red ..	20	30

358. Scottish Settlers.

1973. Bicentenary of Arrival of Scottish Settlers at Pictou, Nova Scotia.

758.	**358.**	8 c. multicoloured ..	25	20

359. Queen Elizabeth II.

1973. Royal Visit and Commonwealth Heads of Government Meeting, Ottawa.

759.	**359.**	8 c. multicoloured ..	25	20
760.		15 c. multicoloured ..	1·00	1·90

360. Nellie McClung.

361. Emblem of 1976 Olympics.

1973. Birth Centenary of Nellie McClung (feminist).

761. **360.** 8 c multicoloured .. 20 40

1973. 1976 Olympic Games, Montreal (1st issue).

762. **361.** 8 c. multicoloured .. 20 15
763. 15 c. multicoloured .. 35 1·25

See also Nos. 768/71, 772/4, 786/9, 798/802, 809/11, 814/16, 829/32, 833/7 and 842/4.

362. Ice-skate.

1973. Christmas. Multicoloured.

764. 6 c. Type **362** 15 10
765. 8 c. Bird decoration .. 20 10
766. 10 c. Santa Claus (20×36 mm.) .. .. .. 70 1·40
767. 15 c. Shepherd (20×36 mm.) 80 1·75

363. Diving.

1974. 1976 Olympic Games, Montreal. (2nd issue). " Summer Activities ". **Each blue.**

768. 8 c. Type **363** 25 40
769. 8 c. " Jogging " 25 40
770. 8 c. Cycling 25 40
771. 8 c. Hiking 25 40

1974. 1976 Olympic Games, Montreal. (3rd issue). As Type **361** but smaller (20×36½ mm.).

772. **361.** 8 c.+2 c. multicoloured 15 40
773. 10 c.+5 c. multicoloured 25 80
774. 15 c.+5 c. multicoloured 30 1·25

364. Winnipeg Signpost, 1872.

1974. Winnipeg Centennial.

775. **364.** 8 c. multicoloured .. 20 15

365. Postmaster and Customer.

1974. Centenary of Canadian Letter Carrier Delivery Service. Multicoloured.

776. 8 c. Type **365** 60 70
777. 8 c. Postman collecting mail 60 70
778. 8 c. Mail handler 60 70
779. 8 c. Mail sorters 60 70
780. 8 c. Postman making delivery 60 70
781. 8 c. Rural delivery by car 60 70

366. "Canada's Contribution to Agriculture".

1974. Centenary of "Agricultural Education". Ontario Agricultural College.

782. **366.** 8 c. multicoloured .. 20 20

367. Telephone Development.

1974. Centenary of Invention of Telephone by Alexander Graham Bell.

783. **367.** 8 c. multicoloured .. 20 20

368. Bicycle Wheel.

1974. World Cycling Championships, Montreal.

784. **368.** 8 c. black, red & silver 20 30

369. Mennonite Settlers.

1974. Centenary of Arrival of Mennonites in Manitoba.

785. **369.** 8 c. multicoloured 20 20

1974. 1976 Olympic Games, Montreal (4th issue). " Winter Activities ". As T **363.** Each red.

786. 8 c. Snow-shoeing .. 50 50
787. 8 c. Skiing 50 50
788. 8 c. Skating 50 50
789. 8 c. Curling 50 50

370. Mercury, Winged Horses and U.P.U. Emblem.

1974. Centenary of U.P.U.

790. **370.** 8 c. violet, red & blue 15 15
791. 15 c. red, violet & blue 50 1·50

371. "The Nativity" (J. P. Lemieux).

1974. Christmas. Multicoloured.

792. 6 c. Type **371** 10 10
793. 8 c. "Skaters in Hull" (H. Masson) 10 10
794. 10 c. "The Ice Cone, Montmorency Falls" (R. C. Todd) 20 75
795. 15 c. "Village in the Laurentian Mountains" (C. A. Gagnon) 30 1·10

No. 793 is smaller 34×31 mm.

372. Marconi and St. John's Harbour, Newfoundland.

1974. Birth Centenary of Guglielmo Marconi (radio pioneer).

796. **372.** 8 c. multicoloured .. 20 20

373. Merritt and Welland Canal.

1974. William Merritt Commemoration.

797. **373.** 8 c. multicoloured .. 20 30

374. Swimming.

1975. 1976 Olympic Games, Montreal (5th issue). Multicoloured.

798. 8 c.+2 c. Type **374** .. 25 40
799. 10 c.+5 c. Rowing .. 30 80
800. 15 c.+5 c. Sailing .. .. 35 1·00

375. "The Sprinter".

1975. 1976 Olympic Games, Montreal (6th issue). Multicoloured.

801. $1 Type **375** .. .. 2·25 3·25
802. $2 "The Diver" (vert.) .. 2·75 4·75

376. " Anne of Green Gables " (Lucy Maud Montgomery).

1975. Canadian Writers (1st series). **Mult.**

803. 8 c. Type **376** 20 10
804. 8 c. " Maria Chapdelaine " (Louis Hemon) .. 20 10

See also Nos. 846/7, 940/1 and 1085/6.

377. Marguerite Bourgeoys (founder of the Order of Notre Dame).

378. S. D. Chown (founder of United Church of Canada).

1975. Canadian Celebrities.

805. **377.** 8 c. multicoloured .. 50 40
806. – 8 c. multicoloured .. 50 40
807. **378.** 8 c. multicoloured .. 30 50
808. – 8 c. multicoloured .. 30 50

DESIGNS—As Type **377**. No. 806, Alphonse Desjardins (leader of Credit Union movement). As Type **378**. No. 808, Dr. J. Cook (first moderator of Presbyterian Church in Canada).

MINIMUM PRICE

The minimum price quoted is 10p which represents a handling charge rather than a basis for valuing common stamps. For further notes about prices see introductory pages.

379. Pole-vaulting.

1975. 1976 Olympics (7th issue). **Mult.**

809. 20 c. Type **379** 35 50
810. 25 c. Marathon-running .. 50 80
811. 50 c. Hurdling .. .. 60 1·25

380. " Untamed " (photo by Walt Petrigo).

1975. Centenary of Calgary.

812. **380.** 8 c. multicoloured .. 20 30

381. I.W.Y. Symbol. **382.** Fencing

1975. International Women's Year.

813. **381.** 8 c. grey, brn. and blk. 20 30

1975. Olympic Games, Montreal (1976) (8th issue). Multicoloured.

814. 8 c.+2 c. Type **382** .. 30 45
815. 10 c.+5 c. Boxing .. .. 35 1·00
816. 15 c.+5 c. Judo .. .. 40 1·25

383. " Justice-Justitia " (Statue by W. S. Allward).

1975. Centenary of Canadian Supreme Court.

817. **383.** 8 c. multicoloured .. 20 30

384. "William D. Lawrence" (full-rigged ship).

1975. Canadian Ships (1st series). Coastal Vessels.

818 **384** 8 c. brown and black 75 65
819 – 8 c. green and black .. 75 65
820 – 8 c. green and black .. 75 65
821 – 8 c. brown and black 75 65

DESIGNS: No. 819, "Neptune" (steamer). 820, "Beaver" (paddle-steamer). 821, "Quadra" (steamer).

See also Nos. 851/4, 902/5 and 931/4.

385. " Santa Claus " (G. Kelly).

1975. Christmas. Multicoloured.

822. 6 c. Type **385** 15 10
823. 6 c. "Skater" (B. Cawsey) 15 10
824. 8 c. "Child" (D. Hebert) 15 10
825. 8 c. "Family" (L. Caldwell) 15 10
826. 10 c. "Gift" (D. Lovely) 30 50
827. 15 c. "Trees" (R. Kowalski) (horiz.) 40 75

386. Text, Badge and Bugle.

1975. Royal Canadian Legion. 50th Anniv.

828. **386.** 8 c. multicoloured .. 20 20

387. Basketball. **388.** Games Symbol and Snow Crystal.

1976. Olympic Games, Montreal (9th issue). Multicoloured.

829. 8 c.+2 c. Type **387** .. 40 55
830. 10 c.+5 c. Gymnastics .. 45 1·25
831. 20 c.+5 c. Soccer .. 55 1·50

1976. 12th Winter Olympic Games, Innsbruck.

832. **388.** 20 c. multicoloured .. 20 40

389. "Communications Arts".

1976. Olympic Games, Montreal (10th issue). Multicoloured.

833. 20 c. Type **389** 25 25
834. 25 c. Handicrafts .. 35 65
835. 50 c. Performing Arts .. 40 1·40

390. Place Ville Marie and Notre-Dame Church.

1976. Olympic Games, Montreal (11th issue). Multicoloured.

836. $1 Type **390** .. .. 2·50 5·50
837. $2 Olympic stadium and flags .. .. .. 3·00 6·50

391. Flower and Urban Sprawl.

1976. HABITAT. U.N. Conf. on Human Settlements, Vancouver.

838. **391.** 20 c. multicoloured .. 20 30

392. Benjamin Franklin and Map.

1976. Bicent. of American Revolution.

839. **392.** 10 c. multicoloured .. 20 35

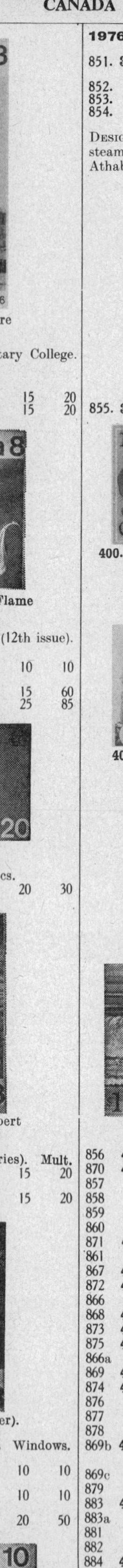

393. Wing Parade before Mackenzie Building.

1976. Centenary of Royal Military College. Multicoloured.

840. 8 c. Colour party and Memorial Arch .. 15 20
841. 8 c. Type **393** 15 20

394. Transfer of Olympic Flame by Satellite.

1976. Olympic Games, Montreal (12th issue). Multicoloured.

842. 8 c. Type **394** 10 10
843. 20 c. Carrying the Olympic flag 15 60
844. 25 c. Athletes with medals 25 85

395. Archer.

1976. Disabled Olympics.

845. **395.** 20 c. multicoloured .. 20 30

396. "Sam McGee" (Robert W. Service).

1976. Canadian Writers (2nd series). Mult.

846. 8 c. Type **396** 15 20
847. 8 c. "Le Survenant" (Germaine Guevremont) 15 20

397. "Nativity" (F. Mayer).

1976. Christmas. Stained-glass Windows. Multicoloured.

848. 8 c. Type **397** 10 10
849. 10 c. "Nativity" (G. Maile & Son) 10 10
850. 20 c. "Nativity" (Yvonne Williams) 20 50

398. "Northcote" (paddle-steamer).

1976. Canadian Ships (2nd series). Inland Vessels.

851. **398.** 10 c. light brown, brown and black 30 40
852. – 10 c. blue and black .. 30 40
853. – 10 c. blue and black .. 30 40
854. – 10 c. light green, green and black 30 40

DESIGNS: No. 852, "Passport" (paddle-steamer). 853, "Chicora" (paddle-steamer). 854, Athabasca" (steamer).

399. Queen Elizabeth II.

1977. Silver Jubilee.

855. **399.** 25 c. multicoloured .. 25 50

400. Bottle Gentian. **401.** Queen Elizabeth II (bas-relief by J. Huta).

402. Houses of Parliament. **403.** Trembling Aspen.

404. Prairie Town Main Street.

405. Fundy National Park.

1977.

856	**400.**	1 c. multicoloured ..	10	10
870	**402.**	1 c. blue	1·25	2·25
857	–	2 c. multicoloured ..	10	10
858	–	3 c. multicoloured ..	10	10
859	–	4 c. multicoloured ..	10	10
860	–	5 c. multicoloured ..	10	10
871	**402.**	5 c. lilac	45	30
861	–	10 c. multicoloured ..	15	10
867	**401.**	12 c. bl., grey & blk.	15	10
872	**402.**	12 c. blue	30	10
866	–	12 c. multicoloured ..	15	30
868	**401.**	14 c. red, grey & blk.	20	10
873	**402.**	14 c. red	15	10
875	**403.**	15 c. multicoloured ..	15	10
866a	–	15 c. multicoloured ..	15	15
869	**401.**	17 c. blk., grey & grn.	50	10
874	**402.**	17 c. green	30	10
876	–	20 c. multicoloured ..	15	10
877	–	25 c. multicoloured ..	15	10
878	–	30 c. multicoloured ..	20	10
869b	**401.**	30 c. deep purple, grey and purple ..	50	50
869c	–	32 c. blk., grey & bl.	45	45
879	–	35 c. multicoloured ..	25	10
883	**404.**	50 c. multicoloured ..	85	60
883a	–	60 c. multicoloured ..	65	45
881	–	75 c. multicoloured ..	85	90
882	–	80 c. multicoloured ..	85	60
884	**405.**	$1 multicoloured ..	90	50
884b	–	$1 multicoloured ..	85	45
884c	–	$1.50 multicoloured	2·50	2·25
885	–	$2 multicoloured ..	1·50	45
885b	–	$2 multicoloured ..	3·50	90
885c	–	$5 multicoloured ..	5·50	2·00
885d	–	$5 multicoloured ..	6·00	3·25

DESIGNS: As Type **400**, 2 c. Red Columbine. 3 c. Canada Lily. 4 c. Hepatica. 5 c. Shooting Star. 10 c. Franklin's Lady's Slipper Orchid. 12 c. Jewelweed. 15 c. (No. 866a) Canada Violet. As Type **403**, 20 c. Douglas Fir. 25 c. Sugar Maple. 30 c. Red Oak. 35 c. White Pine. As Type **404**. 60 c. Ontario City street. 75 c. Eastern City street. 80 c. Maritimes street. As Type **405**. $1 Glacier. $1.50 Waterton Lakes. $2 (No. 885) Kluane. $2 (No. 885b) Banff. $5 (No. 885c) Point Pelee. $5 (No. 885d) La Mauricie.

406. Puma.

1977. Endangered Wildlife (1st series).

886. **406.** 12 c. multicoloured .. 20 20

See also Nos. 906, 936/7, 976/7 and 1006/7.

407. "April in Algonquin Park".

1977. Birth Centenary of Tom Thomson (painter). Multicoloured.

887. 12 c. Type **407** 15 10
888. 12 c. "Autumn Birches" 15 10

408. Crown and Lion.

1977. Anniversaries. Multicoloured.

889. 12 c. Type **408** .. 15 15
890. 12 c. Order of Canada .. 15 15

EVENTS: No. 889, First Canadian-born Governor-General 25th Anniversary. No. 890, Order of Canada. 10th Anniv.

409. Peace Bridge, Niagara River.

1977. 50th Anniv. of Opening of Peace Bridge.

891. **409.** 12 c. multicoloured .. 15 15

410. Sir Sandford Fleming (engineer).

1977. Famous Canadians.

892. **410.** 12 c. blue 15 10
893. – 12 c. brown 15 10

DESIGN: No. 893, Joseph E. Bernier (explorer) and "Arctic" (survey ship).

411. Peace Tower, Parliament Buildings, Ottawa.

1977. 23rd Commonwealth Parliamentary Conf. Centre.

894. **411.** 25 c. multicoloured 20 30

412. Hunter Braves following Star.

1977. Christmas. Canada's first carol "Jesous Ahatonhia". Multicoloured.

895. 10 c. Type **412** 10 10
896. 12 c. Angelic choir .. 10 10
897. 25 c. Christ Child and "Chiefs from afar" .. 20 45

413. Seal Hunter (soapstone sculpture).

1977. Canadian Eskimos "Inuits" (1st series). Hunting. Multicoloured.
898. 12 c. Type **413** 15 15
899. 12 c. "Fisherman's Dream" (Pitaloosee) 15 15
900. 12 c. "Disguised Hunter" (L. Pitsiulak and S. Karpik 15 15
901. 12 c. "Hunters of Old" (Parr) 15 15
See also Nos. 924/7, 958/61 and 989/92.

414. Pinky (fishing boat).

1977. Canadian Ships (3rd series). Sailing Craft. Multicoloured.
902 12 c. Type **414** 15 25
903 12 c. "Malahat" (schooner) 15 25
904 12 c. Tern schooner .. 15 25
905 12 c. Mackinaw boat .. 15 25

415. Peregrine Falcon.

1978. Endangered Wildlife (2nd series).
906. **415.** 12 c. multicoloured .. 30 20

416. Pair of 1851 12 d. Black Stamps.

1978. "CAPEX '78" International Philatelic Exhibition, Toronto.
907. **416.** 12 c. black and sepia .. 10 10
914. – 14 c. blue, grey & pale grey 15 10
915. – 30 c. red, grey & pale grey 20 35
916. – $1.25 violet, grey and pale grey .. 80 1·10
DESIGNS: 14 c. Pair of 1855 10d. Cartier stamps. 30 c. Pair of 1857 ½d. red stamps. $1.25, Pair of 1851 6d. Prince Albert stamps.

417. Games Emblem.

1978. 11th Commonwealth Games, Edmonton (1st issue). Multicoloured.
908. 14 c. Type **417** 10 10
909. 30 c. Badminton 20 40
See Nos. 918/21.

418. "Captain Cook". (Nathaniel Dance).

1978. Bicent. of Cook's 3rd Voyage. Mult.
910. 14 c. Type **418** 20 15
911. 14 c. "Nootka Sound" (J. Webber) 20 15

419. Hardrock Silver Mine, Cobalt, Ontario.

1978. Resource Development. Mult.
912. 14 c. Type **419** 15 15
913. 14 c. Giant excavators, Athabasca Tar Sands .. 15 15

1978. 11th Commonwealth Games, Edmonton (2nd issue). As T **417.** Multicoloured.
918. 14 c. Games stadium .. 10 15
919. 14 c. Running 10 15
920. 30 c. Alberta legislature building 25 30
921. 30 c. Bowls 25 30

420. Prince's Gate (Exhibition entrance).

1978. Centenary of National Exhibition.
922. **420.** 14 c. multicoloured .. 15 30

421. Marguerite d'Youville.

1978. Marguerite d'Youville (founder of Grey Nuns) Commem.
923. **421.** 14 c. multicoloured .. 15 30

1978. Canadian Eskimos ("Inuits") (2nd series). Travel. As T **413.** Multicoloured.
924. 14 c. Woman on foot (painting by Pitseolak) .. 15 15
925. 14 c. "Migration" (soapstone sculpture of sailing umiak by Joe Talurinili) 15 15
926. 14 c. Aeroplane (stonecut and stencil print by Pudlo) 15 15
927. 14 c. Dogteam and dogsled (ivory sculpture by Abraham Kingmeatook) .. 15 15

422. "The Madonna of the Flowering Pea" (Cologne School).

1978. Christmas. Paintings. Multicoloured.
928. 12 c. Type **422** 10 10
929. 14 c. "The Virgin and Child with St. Anthony and Donor" (detail, Hans Memling) 10 10
930. 30 c. "The Virgin and Child" (Jacopo di Cione) .. 25 50

423. "Chief Justice Robinson" (paddle-steamer).

1978. Canadian Ships (4th series). Ice Vessels. Multicoloured.
931 14 c. Type **423** 40 50
932 14 c. "St. Roch" (steamer) 40 50
933 14 c. "Northern Light" (steamer) 40 50
934 14 c. "Labrador" (steamer) 40 50

424. Carnival Revellers.

1978. Quebec Carnival.
935. **424.** 14 c. multicoloured .. 20 20

425. Eastern Spiny Soft-shelled Turtle.

1979. Endangered Wildlife (3rd series). Multicoloured.
936. 17 c. Type **425** 20 10
937. 35 c. Bowhead Whale .. 40 70

426. Knotted Ribbon round Woman's Finger.

1979. Postal Code Publicity. Multicoloured.
938. 17 c. Type **426** 15 10
939. 17 c. Knotted string round man's finger 15 10

427. Scene from "Fruits of the Earth" by Frederick Philip Grove.

1979. Canadian Writers (3rd series). Multicoloured.
940. 17 c. Type **427** 15 15
941. 17 c. Scene from "Le Vaisseau d'Or" by Emile Nelligan.. .. 15 15

428. Charles-Michel de Salaberry (military hero).

1979. Famous Canadians. Multicoloured.
942. 17 c. Type **428** 25 15
943. 17 c. John By (engineer).. 25 15

430. Paddling Kayak.

1979. Canoe-Kayak Championships.
956. **430.** 17 c. multicoloured .. 15 30

431. Hockey Players.

1979. Women's Field Hockey Championship, Vancouver.
957. **431.** 17 c. black, yell. & green 15 30

1979. Canadian Eskimos (3rd series). Shelter and the Community. As T **413.** Multicoloured.
958. 17 c. "Summer Tent" (print by Kiakshuk) .. 15 15
959. 17 c. "Five Eskimos building an Igloo" (soapstone sculpture by Abraham) 15 15
960. 17 c. "The Dane" (print by Kalvak) .. 15 15
961. 17 c. "Inuit drum dance" (soapstone sculptures by Madeleine Isserkut and Jean Mapsalak) .. 15 15

432. Toy Train.

1979. Christmas. Multicoloured.
962. 15 c. Type **432** 10 10
963. 17 c. Hobby-horse .. 10 10
964. 35 c. Rag doll (vert.) .. 25 50

433. Child watering Tree of Life (painting by Marie-Annick Viatour).

1979. International Year of the Child.
965. **433.** 17 c. multicoloured .. 15 30

434. Canadair "CL-215".

1979. Canadian Aircraft (1st series). Flying Boats. Multicoloured.
966. 17 c. Type **434** 15 15
967. 17 c. Curtiss "HS-2L" .. 15 15
968. 35 c. Vickers "Vedette" 30 35
969. 35 c. Consolidated "Canso" 30 35
See also Nos. 996/9, 1050/3 and 1026/9.

435. Map of Arctic Islands.

1980. Centenary of Arctic Islands Acquisition.
970. **435.** 17 c. multicoloured .. 15 30

436. Skier.

1980. Winter Olympic Games, Lake Placid.
971. **436.** 35 c. multicoloured .. 30 65

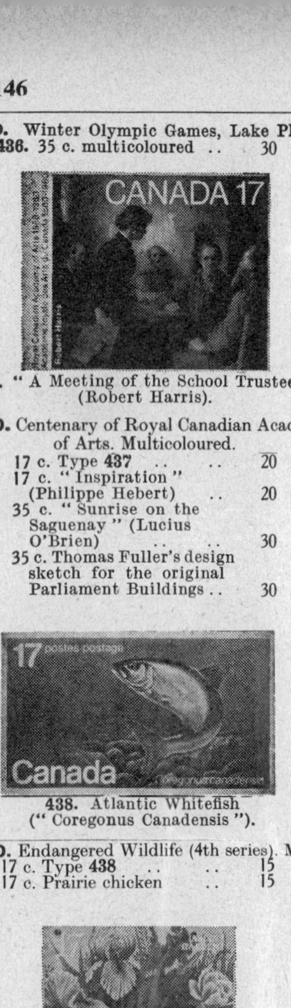

437. " A Meeting of the School Trustees " (Robert Harris).

1980. Centenary of Royal Canadian Academy of Arts. Multicoloured.
972. 17 c. Type **437** 20 15
973. 17 c. " Inspiration " (Philippe Hebert) .. 20 15
974. 35 c. " Sunrise on the Saguenay " (Lucius O'Brien) 30 35
975. 35 c. Thomas Fuller's design sketch for the original Parliament Buildings .. 30 35

438. Atlantic Whitefish (" Coregonus Canadensis ").

1980. Endangered Wildlife (4th series). Mult.
976 17 c. Type **438** 15 15
977 17 c. Prairie chicken .. 15 15

439. Garden Flowers.

1980. International Flower Show, Montreal.
978. **439.** 17 c. multicoloured .. 15 20

440. " Helping Hand ".

1980. Rehabilitation.
979. **440.** 17 c. gold and blue .. 15 20

441. Opening Bars of " O Canada ".

1980. Centenary of "O Canada" (national song). Multicoloured.
980 17 c. Type **441** 15 15
981 17 c. Calixa Lavallee (composer), Adolphe-Basile Routhier (original writer) and Robert Stanley Weir (writer of English version) .. 15 15

442. John G. Diefenbaker (statesman).

1980. John G. Diefenbaker Commemoration.
982. **442.** 17 c. blue 15 20

443. Emma Albani (singer).

1980. Famous Canadians. Multicoloured.
983. 17 c. Type **443** 15 15
984. 17 c. Healy Willan (composer 15 15
985. 17 c. Ned Hanlan (oarsman) (horiz.) 15 15

444. Alberta.

1980. 75th Anniv. of Alberta and Saskatchewan (provinces). Multicoloured.
986. 17 c. Type **444** 15 15
987. 17 c. Wheat fields, Saskatchewan 15 15

445. Uraninite Molecular Structure.

1980. Uranium Resources.
988. **445.** 35 c. multicoloured .. 30 30

1980. Canadian Eskimos (" Inuits ") (4th series). Spirits. Designs as T **413**. Mult.
989. 17 c. " Return of the Sun " (print, Kenojouak) .. 15 15
990. 17 c. " Sedna " (sculpture, Ashoona Kiawak) .. 15 15
991. 35 c. " Shaman " (print, Simon Tookoome) .. 25 30
992. 35 c. " Bird Spirit " (sculpture, Doris Hagiolok) .. 25 30

446. " Christmas Morning " (J. S. Hallam).

1980. Christmas. Multicoloured.
993. 15 c. Type **446** 10 10
994. 17 c. " Sleigh Ride " (Joseph Hallam) .. 15 10
995. 35 c. " McGill Cab Stand " (Kathleen Morris) .. 30 45

447. Avro Canada " CF-100 ".

1980. Canadian Aircraft (2nd series). Mult.
996. 17 c. Type **447** 15 15
997. 17 c. Avro " Lancaster " 15 15
998. 35 c. Curtiss " JN-4 Canuck " 30 35
999. 35 c. Hawker " Hurricane " 30 35

448. Emmanuel-Persillier Lachapelle.

1980. Dr. E.-P. Lachapelle (founder, Notre-Dame Hospital, Montreal) Commemoration.
1000. **448.** 17 c. brown, deep brown and blue 15 15

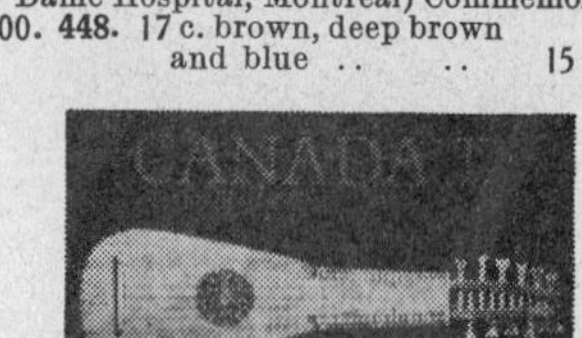

449. Mandora (18th century).

1981. " The Look of Music " Exhibition, Vancouver.
1001. **449.** 17 c. multicoloured .. 15 15

450. Henrietta Edwards.

1981. Feminists. Multicoloured.
1002. 17 c. Type **450** 15 15
1003. 17 c. Louise McKinney .. 15 15
1004. 17 c. Idola Saint-Jean .. 15 15
1005. 17 c. Emily Stowe .. 15 15

451. Vancouver Marmot.

1981. Endangered Wildlife (5th series). Multicoloured.
1006. 17 c. Type **451** 15 10
1007. 35 c. American bison .. 35 30

452. Kateri Tekawitha.

1981. 17th-century Canadian Women. Statues by Emile Brunet.
1008. **452.** 17 c. brown and green 15 15
1009. – 17 c. dark blue & blue 15 15
DESIGN: No. 1009, Marie de l'Incarnation.

453. " Self Portrait " (Frederick H. Varley).

1981. Canadian Paintings. Multicoloured.
1010. 17 c. Type **453** 15 10
1011. 17 c. " At Baie Saint-Paul " (Marc-Aurele Fortin) (horiz.) 15 10
1012. 35 c. " Untitled No. 6 " (Paul-Emile Borduas) 30 30

454. Canada in 1867.

1981. Canada Day. Maps showing evolution of Canada from Confederation to present day. Multicoloured.
1013. 17 c. Type **454** 15 15
1014. 17 c. Canada in 1873 .. 15 15
1015. 17 c. Canada in 1905 .. 15 15
1016. 17 c. Canada since 1949 15 15

355. Frere Marie-Victorin.

1981. Canadian Botanists. Multicoloured.
1017. 17 c. Type **455** 15 15
1018. 17 c. John Macoun .. 15 15

456. The Montreal Rose.

1981. Montreal Flower Show.
1019. **456.** 17 c. multicoloured .. 15 20

457. Drawing of Niagara-on-the-Lake.

1981. Bicent. of Niagara-on-the-Lake (town).
1020. **457.** 17 c. multicoloured .. 15 20

458. Acadian Community.

1981. Centenary of First Acadia (community) Convention.
1021. **458.** 17 c. multicoloured .. 15 20

459. Aaron R. Mosher.

1981. Birth Centenary of Aaron R. Mosher (founder of Canadian Labour Congress).
1022. **459.** 17 c. multicoloured .. 15 20

460. Christmas Tree, 1781.

1981. Christmas. Bicentenary of First Illuminated Christmas Tree in Canada.

1023. 15 c. Type **460** 20 15
1024. 15 c. Christmas Tree, 1881 20 15
1025. 15 c. Christmas Tree, 1981 20 15

461. De Havilland "Tiger Moth".

1981. Canadian Aircraft (3rd series). Mult.

1026. 17 c. Type **461** 20 15
1027. 17 c. Canadair "CL–41 (Tutor)" 20 15
1028. 35 c. Avro "Canada" jetliner 35 35
1029. 35 c. De Havilland Canada "Dash 7" 35 35

462. Canadian Maple Leaf Emblem.

1981.

1030a **462** A (30 c.) red .. 20 25

No. 1030 was printed before a new first class domestic letter rate had been agreed, "A" representing the face value of the stamp, later decided to be 30 c.

1982. As T **462** but including face values.

1033 **462** 5 c. red 10 10
1033d 8 c. blue .. .. 1·00 1·00
1034 10 c. green .. .. 1·00 65
1036 30 c. red 35 30
1032 30 c. red, grey & blue 30 30
1036a 32 c. red .. .. 1·25 1·25
1032b 32 c. red, brn. & stone 45 45

463. 1851 3 d. Stamp.

1982. "Canada 82" International Philatelic Youth Exhibition, Toronto. Stamps on Stamps. Multicoloured.

1037. 30 c. Type **463** 25 25
1038. 30 c. 1908 Centenary of Quebec 15 c. commemorative 25 25
1039. 35 c. 1935 10 c. 25 30
1040. 35 c. 1928 10 c. 25 30
1041. 60 c. 1929 50 c. 50 75

464. Jules Leger.

1982. Jules Leger (politician) Commemoration.

1043. **464.** 30 c. multicoloured .. 20 20

465. Stylised drawing of Terry Fox.

1982. Cancer victim Terry Fox's "Marathon of Hope" (Trans-Canada fund-raising run) Commemoration.

1044. **465.** 30 c. multicoloured .. 20 20

466. Stylised Open Book.
(Illustration reduced. Actual size 57 × 20 mm.)

1982. Patriation of Constitution.

1045. **466.** 30 c. multicoloured .. 20 20

467. Male and Female Salvationists with Street Scene.

1982. Centenary of Salvation Army in Canada.

1046. **467.** 30 c. multicoloured .. 20 20

469. Regina Legislature Building.

1982. Centenary of Regina.

1048. **469.** 30 c. multicoloured .. 20 20

470. Finish of Race.

1982. Centenary of Royal Canadian Henley Regatta.

1049. **470.** 30 c. multicoloured .. 20 25

471. Fairchild "FC–2W1".

1982. Bush Aircraft. Multicoloured.

1050. 30 c. Type **471** 35 20
1051. 30 c. De Havilland Canada "Beaver" .. 35 20
1052. 60 c. Fokker "Super Universal" .. 65 75
1053. 60 c. Noorduyn "Norseman" 65 75

472. Decoy.

475. Mary, Joseph and Baby Jesus.

1982. Heritage Artefacts.

1054. **472.** 1 c. black, light brn. and brown .. 10 10
1055. – 2 c. black, blue and green 10 10
1056. – 3 c. black, blue and deep blue .. 10 10
1057. – 5 c. black, pink and brown 10 10
1058. – 10 c. black, blue and turquoise .. 10 10
1059. – 20 c. black, light brn. and brown .. 20 10
1060. – 25 c. multicoloured .. 35 10
1061. – 37 c. black, green & deep green .. 50 40
1062. – 39 c. black, grey and violet .. .. 1·25 30
1063. – 42 c. multicoloured .. 45 25
1064. – 48 c. dp. brown, brn. and pink .. 70 40
1065. – 50 c. black, light blue and blue .. 1·25 20
1066. – 55 c. multicoloured .. 55 30
1067. – 64 c. deep grey, black and grey 80 50
1068. – 68 c. black, light brown and brown 1·25 50
1069. – 72 c. multicoloured .. 75 45

DESIGNS—VERT. 2 c. Fishing Spear. 3 c. Stable Lantern. 5 c. Bucket. 10 c. Weathercock. 20 c. Skates. 25 c. Butter stamp. HORIZ. 37 c. Plough. 39 c. Settle-bed. 42 c. Linen chest. 48 c. Cradle. 50 c. Sleigh. 55 c. Iron kettle. 64 c. Kitchen Stove. 68 c. Spinning Wheel. 72 c. Hand-drawn cart.

1982. Christmas. Nativity Scenes.

1080. 30 c. Type **475** 20 10
1081. 35 c. The Shepherds .. 25 35
1082. 60 c. The Three Wise Men 45 70

476. Globes forming Symbolic Designs.

1983. World Communications Year.

1083. **476.** 32 c. multicoloured .. 30 25

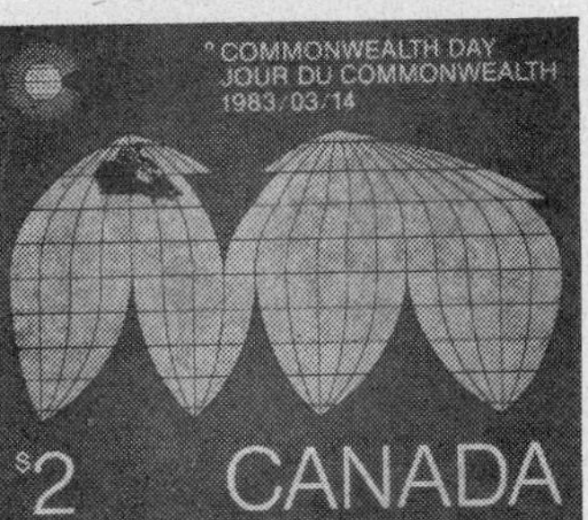

477. Map of World showing Canada.

1983. Commonwealth Day.

1084. **477.** $2 multicoloured .. 2·00 2·75

478. Scene from Novel "Angeline de Montbrun" by "Laure Conan" (Felicite Angers).

1983. Canadian Writers (4th series).

1085. 32 c. Type **478** 30 40
1086. 32 c. Woodcut illustrating "Sea-gulls" (poem by E. J. Pratt) 30 40

479. St. John Ambulance Badge and "100".

1983. Cent. of St. John Ambulance in Canada.

1087. **479.** 32 c. red, yell. & brn. 30 20

480. Victory Pictogram.

1983. "Universiade 83" World University Games, Edmonton.

1088. **480.** 32 c. multicoloured .. 25 15
1089. – 64 c. multicoloured .. 50 70

481. Fort William, Ontario.

1983. Canada Day. Forts (1st series). Mult.

1090. 32 c. Fort Henry, Ontario (44 × 22 mm.) .. 35 50
1091. 32 c. Type **481** 35 50
1092. 32 c. Fort Rodd Hill, British Columbia .. 35 50
1093. 32 c. Fort Wellington, Otnario (28 × 22 mm.) 35 50
1094. 32 c. Fort Prince of Wales, Manitoba (28 × 22 mm.) 35 50
1095. 32 c. Halifax Citadel, Nova Scotia (44 × 22 mm.) .. 35 50
1096. 32 c. Fort Chambly, Quebec 35 50
1097. 32 c. Fort No. 1, Point Levis, Quebec .. 35 50
1098. 32 c. Coteau-du-Lac Fort, Quebec (28 × 22 mm.) 35 50
1099. 32 c. Fort Beausejour, New Brunswick (28 × 22 mm.) 35 50

See also Nos. 1163/72.

482. Scouting Poster by Marc Fournier (aged 12).

1983. Scouting in Canada (75th Anniv.) and World Scout Jamboree, Alberta, (15th Anniversary).

1100. **482.** 32 c. multicoloured .. 30 30

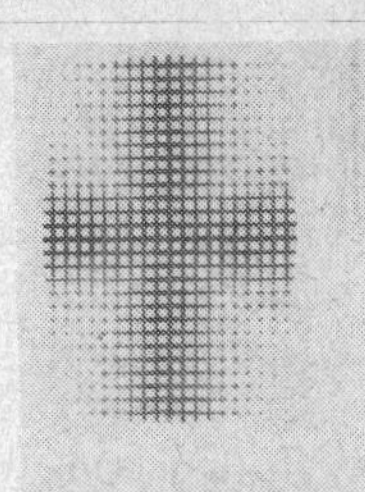

483. Cross Symbol.

1983. 6th Assembly of the World Council of Churches, Vancouver.

1101. **483.** 32 c. green & lilac .. 30 20

484. Sir Humphrey Gilbert (founder).

1983. 400th Anniv. of Newfoundland.

1102. **484.** 32 c. multicoloured .. 30 20

485. "NICKEL" Deposits.

1983. Centenary of Discovery of Sudbury Nickel Deposits.

1103. **485.** 32 c. multicoloured .. 30 20

486. Josiah Henson and Escaping Slaves.

1983. Nineteenth-century Social Reformers. Multicoloured.

1104. 32 c. Type **486** 25 25

1105. 32 c. Father Antoine Labelle and rural village (32 × 26 mm.) 25 25

487. Type 0–4–0, "Dorchester" Locomotive.

1983. Railway Locomotives (1st series). Mult.

1106. 32 c. Type **487** 80 80

1107. 32 c. Type 4–4–0, "Toronto" 80 80

1108. 37 c. Type 0–6–0, "Samson" 80 80

1109. 64 c. Type 4–4–0, "Adam Brown" .. 1·25 1·75

See also Nos. 1132/5, 1185/8 and 1223/6.

488. School Coat of Arms.

1983. Centenary of Dalhousie Law School.

1110. **488.** 32 c. multicoloured .. 30 30

489. City Church.

1983. Christmas. Churches. Multicoloured.

1111. 32 c. Type **489** 40 10

1112. 37 c. Family walking to Church 55 55

1113. 64 c. Country Chapel .. 90 1·60

490. Royal Canadian Regiment and British Columbia Regiment.

1983. Canadian Army Regiments. Mult.

1114. 32 c. Type **490** 65 70

1115. 32 c. Royal Winnipeg Rifles & Royal Canadian Dragoons 65 70

491. Gold Mine in Prospecting Pan.

1984. 50th Anniversary of Yellowknife.

1116. **491.** 32 c. multicoloured .. 30 30

492. Montreal Symphony Orchestra.

1984. 50th Anniversary of Montreal Symphony Orchestra.

1117. **492.** 32 c. multicoloured .. 35 30

493. Jacques Cartier.

1984. 450th Anniversary of Jacques Cartier's Voyage to Canada.

1118. **493.** 32 c. multicoloured .. 35 30

494. U.S.C.S. "Eagle".

1984. Tall Ships Visit.

1119. **494.** 32 c. multicoloured .. 35 30

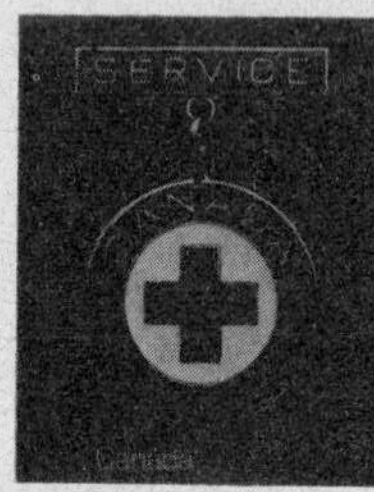

495. Service Medal.

1984. 75th Anniversary of Canadian Red Cross Society.

1120. **495.** 32 c. multicoloured .. 35 30

496. Oared Galleys.

1984. Bicentenary of New Brunswick.

1121. **496.** 32 c. multicoloured .. 35 30

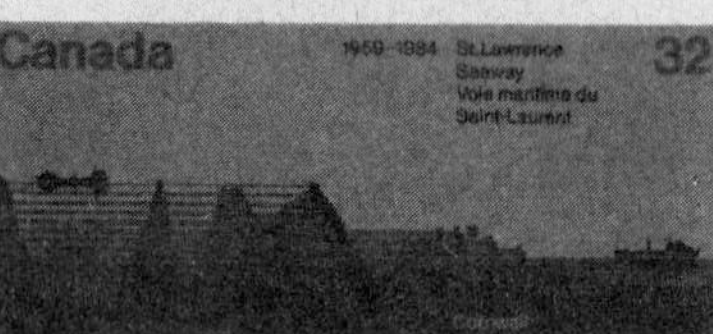

497. St. Lawrence Seaway. (Illustration reduced. Actual size 52 × 22mm.).

1984. 25th Anniv. of St. Lawrence Seaway.

1122. **497.** 32 c. multicoloured .. 45 30

499. Loyalists of 1784.

1984. Bicentenary of Arrival of United Empire Loyalists.

1124. **499.** 32 c. multicoloured .. 30 30

500. St. John's Basilica.

1984. Bicentenary of Roman Catholic Church in Newfoundland.

1125. **500.** 32 c. multicoloured .. 30 25

501. Coat of Arms of Pope John Paul II.

1984. Papal Visit.

1126. **501.** 32 c. multicoloured .. 40 20

1127. 64 c. multicoloured .. 85 1·10

502. Louisbourg Lighthouse, 1734.

1984. Canadian Lighthouses (1st series). Multicoloured.

1128. 32 c. Type **502** 85 90

1129. 32 c. Fisgard Lighthouse, 1860 .. .. .. 85 90

1130. 32 c. Ile Verte Lighthouse, 1809 .. .. 85 90

1131. 32 c. Gibraltar Point Lighthouse, 1808 .. 85 90

See also Nos. 1176/9.

503. Type 0–6–0, "Scotia", Locomotive.

1984. Railway Locomotives (2nd series). Mult.

1132. 32 c. Type **503** 75 75

1133. 32 c. Type 4-4-0, "Countess of Dufferin" .. 75 75

1134. 37 c. Type 2-6-0, GT Class "E3" .. .. 80 1·25

1135. 64 c. Type 4-6-0, CP Class "D10a" .. .. 1·25 1·75

See also Nos. 1185/8 and 1223/6.

504. "The Annunciation" (Jean Dallaire).

1984. Christmas. Religious Paintings. Mult.

1137. 32 c. Type **504** 30 10

1138. 37 c. "The Three Kings" (Simone Bouchard) .. 35 35

1139. 64 c. "Snow in Bethlehem" (David Milne) .. 60 80

505. Pilots of 1914–18, 1939–45 and 1984.

1984. 60th Anniv. of Royal Canadian Air Force.

1140. **505.** 32 c. multicoloured .. 35 30

506. Treffle Berthiaume (editor).

1984. Centenary of "La Presse" (newspaper).

1141. **506.** 32 c. brown, red and light brown .. 35 30

507. Heart and Arrow.

1985. International Youth Year.

1142. **507.** 32 c. multicoloured .. 30 30

508. Astronaut in Space, and Planet Earth.

1985. Canadian Space Programme.

1143. **508.** 32 c. multicoloured .. 40 30

509. Emily Murphy.

1985. Women's Rights Activists. Multicoloured.

1144. 32 c. Type **509** .. 40 40

1145. 32 c. Therese Casgrain .. 40 40

510. Gabriel Dumont (Métis leader) and Battle of Batoche, 1885.

1985. Centenary of the North-West Rebellion.

1146. **510.** 32 c. blue, red and grey 30 30

511. Rear View, Parliament Building, Ottawa.

512. Queen Elizabeth II.

512a. Queen Elizabeth II in 1984 (from photo by Karsh).

1985.

No.	Type	Description	Mint	Used
1147b	–	1 c. green	50	70
1148	–	2 c. green	10	30
1149	–	5 c. brown ..	20	40
1150a	–	6 c. brown ..	50	30
1150b	–	6 c. purplle ..	50	60
1151	511	34 c. black ..	85	1·00
1155		34c. multicoloured	50	10
1158		34 c. brown ..	1·75	1·75
1161	512	34 c. black and blue	45	30
1152	511	36 c. purple ..	1·75	80
1156		36 c. multicoloured	30	40
1159		36 c. red	80	80
1162	512	36 c. purple ..	1·25	60
1153	511	37 c. blue	75	20
1157	–	37 c. multicoloured	75	20
1162a	512a	37 c. multicoloured	1·25	20
1154	511	38 c. blue	60	75
1157c	–	38 c. multicoloured	35	20
1162b	512a	38 c. multicoloured	35	20
1160b	511	38 c. green ..	40	30
1162c	512a	39 c. multicoloured	1·00	20
1162d		40 c. multicoloured	40	20
1162e		42 c. multicoloured	40	20
1162f		43 c. multicoloured	45	30

DESIGNS: 1 c, 5 c, 6 c. (1150b) East Block, Parliament Building. 2, 6 c. (1150) West Block, Parliament Building. 37 c. (1157) Front view Parliament Building. 38 c. (1157c) Side view, Parliament Building.

1985. Canada Day. Forts (2nd series). As T **481**. Multicoloured.
1163. 34 c. Lower Fort Garry, Manitoba 50 55
1164. 34 c. Fort Anne, Nova Scotia 50 55
1165. 34 c. Fort York, Ontario 50 55
1166. 34 c. Castle Hill, Newfoundland 50 55
1167. 34 c. Fort Whoop Up, Alberta 50 55
1168. 34 c. Fort Erie, Ontario 50 55
1169. 34 c. Fort Walsh, Saskatchewan 50 55
1170. 34 c. Fort Lennox, Quebec 50 55
1171. 34 c. York Redoubt, Nova Scotia .. 50 55
1172. 34 c. Fort Frederick, Ontario 50 55
Nos. 1163 and 1168 measure 44 × 22 mm. and Nos. 1166/7 and 1171/2 28 × 22 mm.

513. Louis Hébert (apothecary).

514. Parliament Buildings and Map of World.

1985. 45th International Pharmaceutical Sciences Congress of Pharmaceutical Federation, Montreal.
1173. **513.** 34 c. multicoloured .. 45 35

1985. 74th Conference of Inter-Parliamentary Union, Ottawa.
1174. **514.** 34 c. multicoloured .. 45 35

515. Guide and Brownie Saluting.

1985. 75th Anniv. of Girl Guide Movement.
1175. **515.** 34 c. multicoloured .. 45 35

516. Sisters Islets Lighthouse.

1985. Canadian Lighthouses (2nd series). Multicoloured.
1176. 34 c. Type **516** .. .. 1·10 1·25
1177. 34 c. Pelee Passage Lighthouse .. .. 1·10 1·25
1178. 34 c. Haut-fond Prince Lighthouse .. .. 1·10 1·25
1179. 34 c. Rose Blanche Lighthouse, Cains Island .. .. .. 1·10 1·25

517. Santa Claus in Reindeer-drawn Sleigh.

1985. Christmas. Santa Claus Parade. Mult.
1181. 32 c. Canada Post's parade float 45 20
1182. 34 c. Type **517** 60 10
1183. 39 c. Acrobats and horse-drawn carriage .. 70 70
1184. 68 c. Christmas tree pudding and goose on float .. .. .. 1·25 1·25

1985. Railway Locomotives (3rd series). As T **503**. Multicoloured.
1185. 34 c. Class "K2" .. 70 75
1186. 34 c. Class "P2a" .. 70 75
1187. 39 c. Class "O10a" .. 85 85
1188. 68 c. Class "H4D" .. 1·40 1·50

518. Naval Personnel of 1910, 1939–45 and 1985.

1985. 75th Anniv. of Royal Canadian Navy.
1189. **518.** 34 c. multicoloured .. 65 35

519. "The Old Holton House, Montreal" (James Wilson Morrice).

1985. 125th Anniv. of Montreal Museum of Fine Arts.
1190. **519.** 34 c. multicoloured .. 40 35

520. Map of Alberta showing Olympic Sites. (Illustration reduced, actual size 52 × 25 mm.).

1986. Winter Olympic Games, Calgary (1988) (1st issue).
1191. **520.** 34 c. multicoloured .. 40 40
See also Nos. 1216/17, 1236/7, 1258/9 and 1281/4.

521. Canada Pavilion.

1986. "Expo '86" World Fair, Vancouver (1st issue). Multicoloured.
1192. 34p. Type **521** 80 45
1193. 39p. Early telephone, dish aerial and satellite 1·10 1·40
See also Nos. 1196/7.

522. Molly Brant.

523. Aubert de Gaspé and Scene from "Les Anciens Canadiens"

1986. 250th Birth Anniv. of Molly Brant (Iroquois leader).
1194. **522.** 34 c. multicoloured .. 40 40

1986. Birth Bicentenary of Philippe Aubert de Gaspé (author).
1195. **523.** 34 c. multicoloured .. 40 40

1986. "Expo '86" World Fair, Vancouver (2nd issue). As T **521**. Multicoloured.
1196. 34 c. Expo Centre, Vancouver (vert.) .. 45 40
1197. 68 c. Early and modern trains .. 1·00 1·10

524. Canadian Field Post Office and Cancellation, 1944.

1986. 75th Anniv. of Canadian Forces Postal Service.
1198. **524.** 34 c. multicoloured .. 75 40

525. Great Blue Heron.

1986. Birds of Canada. Multicoloured.
1199. 34 c. Type **525** .. .. 85 1·10
1200. 34 c. Snow goose .. 85 1·10
1201. 34 c. Great horned owl .. 85 1·10
1202. 34 c. Spruce grouse .. 85 1·10

526. Railway Rotary Snowplough.

1986. Canada Day. Science and Technology. Canadian Inventions (1st series). Mult.
1203. 34 c. Type **526** .. .. 90 1·00
1204. 34 c. Space shuttle "Challenger" launching satellite with Canadarm .. ..
1205. 34 c. Pilot wearing anti-gravity flight suit and "Spitfire" .. .. 90 1·00
1206. 34 c. Variable-pitch propeller and Avro "504K" airplane .. 90 1·00
See also Nos. 1241/4 and 1292/5. 90 1·00

527. C.B.C. Logos over Map of Canada.

1986. 50th Anniv. of Canadian Broadcasting Corporation.
1207. **527.** 34 c. multicoloured .. 40 45

528. Ice Age Artefacts, Tools and Settlement.

1986. Exploration of Canada (1st series). Discoverers. Multicoloured.
1208. 34 c. Type **528** 35 55
1209. 34 c. Viking ships .. 35 55
1210. 34 c. John Cabot's "Matthew" 1497, compass and fish .. 35 55
1211. 34 c. Henry Hudson cast adrift, 1611 .. .. 35 55
See also Nos. 1232/5, 1285/8 and 1319/22.

529. Crowfoot (Blackfoot Chief) and Indian Village.

1986. Founders of the Canadian West. Multicoloured.
1213. 34 c. Type **529** 35 55
1214. 34 c. James Macleod of the North West Mounted Police and Fort Macleod 35 55

530. Peace Dove and Globe.

1986. International Peace Year.
1215. **530.** 34 c. multicoloured .. 40 45

531. Ice Hockey. **532.** Angel with Crown.

1986. Winter Olympic Games, Calgary (1988) (2nd issue). Multicoloured.
1216. 34 c. Type **531** .. .. 1·00 1·25
1217. 34 c. Biathlon .. .. 1·00 1·25

1986. Christmas. Multicoloured.
1218. 29 c. Angel singing carol (36 × 22 mm.) 40 15
1219. 34 c. Type **532** 50 25
1220. 39 c. Angel playing lute 70 70
1221. 68 c. Angel with ribbon 1·00 1·75

533. John Molson with Theatre Royal, Montreal, "Accommodation" (paddle-steamer) and Railway Train.

1986. 150th Death Anniv. of John Molson (businessman).
1222. **533.** 34 c. multicoloured .. 50 50

1986. Railway Locomotives (4th series). As T **503**, but size 60 × 22 mm. Multicoloured

1223.	34 c. Class "V-1-a" ..	90	1·00
1224.	34 c. Class "Tla" ..	90	1·00
1225.	39 c. Class "U-2-a" ..	1·00	1·00
1226.	68 c. Class "Hlc" ..	1·75	2·25

534. Toronto's First Post Office.

1987. "Capex '87" International Stamp Exhibition, Toronto. Post Offices.

1227.	34 c. Type **534**	50	20
1228.	36 c. Nelson-Miramichi, New Brunswick ..	60	45
1229.	42 c. Saint-Ours, Quebec	70	65
1230.	72 c. Battleford, Saskatchewan ..	1·00	1·25

535. Etienne Brule exploring Lake Superior.

1987. Exploration of Canada (2nd series). Pioneers of New France. Multicoloured.

1232.	34 c. Type **535**	75	45
1233.	34 c. Radisson and Des Groseilliers with British and French flags	75	45
1234.	34 c. Jolliet and Father Marquette on the Mississippi ..	75	45
1235.	34 c. Jesuit missionary preaching to Indians	75	45

1987. Winter Olympic Games, Calgary (1988) (3rd issue). As T **531.** Multicoloured.

1236.	36 c. Speed skating ..	50	40
1237.	42 c. Bobsleighing ..	75	60

536. Volunteer Activities.

1987. National Volunteer Week.

1238. **536.**	36 c. multicoloured ..	30	35

537. Canadian Coat of Arms.

1987. 5th Anniv. of Canadian Charter of Rights and Freedoms.

1239. **537.**	36 c. multicoloured ..	35	35

538. Steel Girder, Gear Wheel and Microchip.

1987. Centenary of Engineering Institute of Canada.

1240. **538.**	36 c. multicoloured ..	35	40

539. R. A. Fessenden (AM Radio).

1987. Canada Day. Science and Technology. Canadian Inventors (2nd series). Mult.

1241.	36 c. Type **539**	50	35
1242.	36 c. C. Fenerty (newsprint pulp)	50	35
1243.	36 c. G.-E. Desbarats and W. Leggo (halftone engraving) ..	50	35
1244.	36 c. F. N. Gisborne (first North American undersea telegraph) ..	50	35

540. "Segwun".

1987. Canadian Steamships. Multicoloured.

1245.	36 c. Type **540**	1·25	1·50
1246.	36 c. "Princess Marguerite" (52 × 22 mm.)	1·25	1·50

541. Figurehead from "Hamilton", 1813.

1987. Historic Shipwrecks. Multicoloured.

1247.	36 c. Type **541**	45	45
1248.	36 c. "Hull of San Juan", 1565	45	45
1249.	36 c. Wheel from "Breadalbane", 1853 ..	45	45
1250.	36 c. Bell from "Ericsson", 1892 ..	45	45

542. Air Canada Boeing "767" and Globe.

1987. 50th Anniv. of Air Canada.

1251. **542.**	36 c. multicoloured ..	45	35

543. Summit Symbol.

1987. 2nd International Francophone Summit, Quebec.

1252. **543.**	36 c. multicoloured ..	30	35

544. Commonwealth Symbol.

1987. Commonwealth Heads of Government Meeting, Vancouver.

1253. **544.**	36 c. multicoloured ..	35	40

545. Poinsettia.

1987. Christmas. Christmas Plants. Mult.

1254	31 c. Decorated Christmas tree and presents (36 × 20 mm)	30	35
1255	36 c. Type **545**	35	40
1256	42 c. Holly wreath ..	40	45
1257	72 c. Mistleotoe and decorated tree ..	65	70

1987. Winter Olympic Games, Calgary (1988) (4th issue). As T **531.** Multicoloured.

1258.	36 c. Cross-country skiing	40	40
1259.	36 c. Ski-jumping ..	40	40

546. Football, Grey Cup and Spectators.

547. Flying Squirrel.

548a. Runnymede Library, Toronto.

1987. 75th Grey Cup Final (Canadian football championship), Vancouver.

1260. **546.**	36 c. multicoloured ..	35	40

1988. Canadian Mammals and Architecture. Multicoloured.

(a) As T **547.**

1261	1 c. Type **547** ..	10	10
1262	2 c. Porcupine	10	10
1263	3 c. Muskrat	10	10
1264	5 c. Varying hare ..	10	10
1265	6 c. Red fox	10	10
1266	10 c. Striped skunk ..	10	10
1267	25 c. American beaver ..	30	15
1268	43 c. Lynx (26 × 20 mm)	1·25	35
1269	44 c. Walrus (27 × 21 mm)	45	30
1270	45 c. Pronghorn (27 × 21 mm)	35	30
1270c	46 c. Wolverine (27 × 21 mm)	45	40
1271	57 c. Killer whale (26 × 20 mm)	1·75	55
1272	59 c. Musk ox (27 × 21 mm)	75	45
1273	61 c. Wolf (27 × 21 mm)	60	40
1273b	63 c. Harbour porpoise (27 × 21mm)	65	45
1274	74 c. Wapiti (26 × 20 mm)	1·40	50
1275	76 c. Brown bear (27 × 21 mm)	80	50
1276	78 c. White whale (27 × 21 mm)	90	55
1276c	80 c. Peary caribou (27 × 21)	80	60

(b) As T **548a.**

1277a	$1 Type **548a**	1·00	1·10
1278a	$2 McAdam Railway Station, New Brunswick	2·00	2·10
1279	$5 Bonsecours Market, Montreal	5·00	4·00

1988. Winter Olympic Games, Calgary (5th issue). As T **531.** Multicoloured.

1281.	37 c. Slalom skiing ..	65	40
1282.	37 c. Curling ..	65	40
1283.	43 c. Figure skating ..	75	45
1284.	74 c. Luge	1·25	70

549. Trade Goods, Blackfoot Encampment and Page from Anthony Henday's Journal.

1988. Exploration of Canada (3rd series). Explorers of the West. Multicoloured.

1285.	37 c. Type **549**	50	40
1286.	37 c. Discovery and map of George Vancouver's voyage	50	40
1287.	37 c. Simon Fraser's expedition portaging canoes	50	40
1288.	37 c. John Palliser's surveying equipment and view of prairie ..	50	40

550 "The Young Reader" (Ozias Leduc)

1988. Canadian Art (1st series).

1289 **550**	50 c. multicoloured ..	50	70

See also Nos. 1327, 1384, 1421, 1504 and 1539.

551 Mallard landing on Marsh

1988. Wildlife and Habitat Conservation. Multicoloured.

1290	37 c. Type **551**	50	40
1291	37 c. Moose feeding in marsh	50	40

552 Kerosene Lamp and Diagram of Distillation Plant

1988. Canada Day. Science and Technology. Canadian Inventions (3rd series). Mult.

1292	37 c. Type **552**	35	40
1293	37 c. Ears of Marquis wheat	35	40
1294	37 c. Electron microscope and magnified image ..	35	40
1295	37 c. Patient under "Cobalt 60" cancer therapy	35	40

553 "Papilio brevicauda"

1296	37 c. Type 553	60	40
1297	37 c. "Lycaeides idas" ..	60	40
1298	37 c. "Oeneis macounii"	60	40
1299	37 c. "Papilio glaucus" ..	60	40

554 St. John's Harbour Entrance and Skyline

1988. Centenary of Incorporation of St. John's, Newfoundland.

1300 554 37 c. multicoloured .. 35 40

555 Club Members working on Forestry Project and Rural Scene

1988. 75th Anniv of 4-H Clubs.

1301 555 37 c. multicoloured .. 35 40

556 Saint-Maurice Ironworks

1988. 250th Anniv of Saint-Maurice Ironworks, Quebec.

1302 556 37 c. black, orge & brn 35 40

557 Tahltan Bear Dog

1988. Canadian Dogs. Multicoloured.

1303	37 c. Type 557	60	40
1304	37 c. Nova Scotia duck tolling retriever ..	60	40
1305	37 c. Canadian eskimo dog	60	40
1306	37 c. Newfoundland ..	60	40

558 Baseball, Glove and Pitch

1988. 150th Anniv of Baseball in Canada. Multicoloured.

1307 558 37 c. multicoloured .. 35 40

559 Virgin with Inset of Holy Child

1988. Christmas. Icons. Multicoloured.

1308	32 c. Holy Family (36×21 mm)	35	35
1309	37 c. Type 559	35	40
1310	43 c. Virgin and Child ..	40	45
1311	74 c. Virgin and Child (different)	70	75

On No. 1308 the left-hand third of the design area is taken up by the bar code.

No. 1309 also commemorates the Millenium of Ukrainian Christianity.

560 Bishop Inglis and Nova Scotia Church

1988. Bicentenary of Consecration of Charles Inglis (first Canadian Anglican bishop) (1987).

1312 560 37 c. multicoloured .. 35 40

561 Frances Ann Hopkins and "Canoe Manned by Voyageurs"

1988. 150th Birth Anniv of Frances Ann Hopkins (artist).

1313 561 37 c. multicoloured .. 35 40

562 Angus Walters and "Bluenose" (yacht)

1988. 20th Death Anniv of Angus Walters (yachtsman).

1314 562 37 c. multicoloured .. 35 40

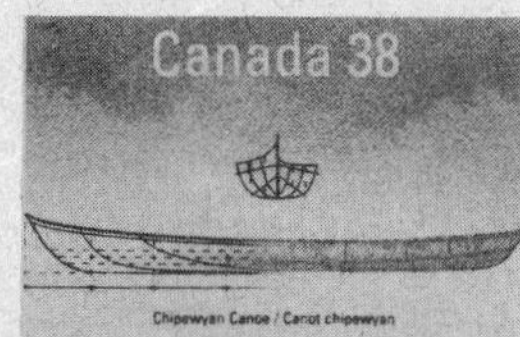

563 Chipewyan Canoe

1989. Small Craft of Canada (1st series). Native Canoes. Multicoloured.

1315	38 c. Type 563	50	50
1316	38 c. Haida canoe ..	50	50
1317	38 c. Inuit kayak ..	50	50
1318	38 c. Micmac canoe ..	50	50

See also Nos. 1377/80 and 1428/31.

564 Matonabbee and Hearne's Expedition

1989. Exploration of Canada (4th issue). Explorers of the North. Multicoloured.

1319	38 c. Type 564	55	55
1320	38 c. Relics of Franklin's expedition and White Ensign	55	55
1321	38 c. Joseph Tyrrell's compass, hammer and fossil	55	55
1322	38 c. Vilhjalmur Stefansson, camera on tripod and sledge dog team	55	55

565 Construction of Victoria Bridge, Montreal and William Notman

1989. Canada Day. "150 Years of Canadian Photography". Designs showing early photograph and photographer. Multicoloured.

1323	38 c. Type 565	50	50
1324	38 c. Plains Indian village and W. Hanson Boorne	50	50
1325	38 c. Horse-drawn sleigh and Alexander Henderson	50	50
1326	38 c. Quebec street scene and Jules-Ernest Livernois	50	50

566 Tsimshian Ceremonial Frontlet, c. 1900

1989. Canadian Art (2nd issue).

1327 566 50 c. multicoloured .. 55 60

567 Canadian Flag and Forest

1989. Self-adhesive. Multicoloured.

1328	38 c. Type 567	90	1·25
1328b	39 c. Canadian flag and prairie	80	1·00
1328c	40 c. Canadian flag and sea	80	1·00
1328d	42 c. Canadian flag over mountains	40	45
1328e	43 c. Canadian flag over lake	45	50

568 Archibald Lampman

1989. Canadian Poets. Multicoloured.

1329	38 c. Type 568	40	45
1330	38 c. Louis-Honore Frechette	40	45

569 "Clavulinopsis fusiformis"

1989. Mushrooms. Multicoloured.

1331	38 c. Type 569	50	50
1332	38 c. "Boletus mirabilis"	50	50
1333	38 c. "Cantharellus cinnabarinus" ..	50	50
1334	38 c. "Morchella esculenta"	50	50

570 Night Patrol, Korea

1989. 75th Annivs of Canadian Regiments. Multicoloured.

1335	38 c. Type 570 (Princess Patricia's Canadian Light Infantry) ..	70	70
1336	38 c. Trench raid, France, 1914–18 (Royal 22e Regiment)	70	70

571 Globe in Box

1989. Canada Export Trade Month.

1337 571 38 c. multicoloured .. 40 45

572 Film Director

1989. Arts and Entertainment.

1338	572	38 c. brown, deep brown and violet ..	40	45
1339	–	38 c. brown, deep brown and green ..	40	45
1340	–	38 c. brown, deep brown and mauve	40	45
1341	–	38 c. brown, deep brown and blue ..	40	45

DESIGNS: No. 1339, Actors; No. 1340, Dancers; No. 1341, Musicians.

573 "Snow II" (Lawren S. Harris)

1989. Christmas. Paintings of Winter Landscapes. Multicoloured.

1342 33 c. "Champ-de-Mars, Winter" (William Brymner) (35 × 21 mm) 35 40
1343 38 c. "Bend in the Gosselin River" (Marc-Aurele Suzor-Cote) (21 × 35 mm) 40 45
1344 44 c. Type **573** 45 50
1345 76 c. "Ste. Agnes" (A. H. Robinson) 80 85

On No. 1342 the left-hand third of the design area is taken up by a bar code.

574 Canadians listening to Declaration of War, 1939

1989. 50th Anniv of Outbreak of Second World War (1st issue).

1346 **574** 38 c. blk, silver & pur 40 45
1347 – 38 c. black, silver and grey 40 45
1348 – 38 c. blk, silver & grn 40 45
1349 – 38 c. black, silver & bl 40 45

DESIGNS: No. 1347, Army mobilization; No. 1348, British Commonwealth air crew training; See also Nos. 1409/12, 1456/9, 1521/4 and 1576/9.

575 Canadian Flag

576

1989.

1350 **575** 1 c. multicoloured .. 20 20
1351 – 5 c. multicoloured .. 20 20
1352 – 39 c. multicoloured .. 80 35
1354 **576** 39 c. multicoloured .. 40 20
1358 – 39 c. purple 60 75
1353 – 40 c. multicoloured .. 75 75
1355 – 40 c. multicoloured .. 40 20
1359 – 40 c. blue 40 45
1356 – 42 c. multicoloured .. 40 30
1360 – 42 c. red 40 45
1357 – 43 c. multicoloured .. 45 50
1361 – 43 c. green 45 50

DESIGNS: Nos. 1351/3, 1358/61, As T **575** but different folds in flag. As T **576**: No. 1355, Flag over forest; 1356, Flag over mountains; 1357, Flag over prairie.

577 Norman Bethune in 1937, and performing Operation, Montreal

1990. Birth Centenary of Dr. Norman Bethune (surgeon). Multicoloured.

1375 39 c. Type **577** 45 50
1376 39 c. Bethune in 1939, and treating wounded Chinese soldiers .. 45 50

1990. Small Craft of Canada (2nd series). Early Work Boats. As T **563**. Multicoloured.

1377 39 c. Fishing dory .. 50 55
1378 39 c. Logging pointer .. 50 55
1379 39 c. York boat .. 50 55
1380 39 c. North canoe .. 50 55

578 Maple Leaf Mosaic

1990. Multiculturalism.

1381 **578** 39 c. multicoloured .. 35 40

579 Mail Van (facing left)

1990. "Moving the Mail". Multicoloured.

1382 39 c. Type **579** 45 55
1383 39 c. Mail van (facing right) 45 55

1990. Canadian Art (3rd series). As T **550**. Multicoloured.

1384 50 c. "The West Wind" (Tom Thomson) .. 55 65

580 Amerindian and Inuit Dolls

1990. Dolls. Multicoloured.

1385 39 c. Type **580** 55 60
1386 39 c. 19th-century settlers' dolls 55 60
1387 39 c. Commercial dolls, 1917–36 .. .. 55 60
1388 39 c. Commercial dolls, 1940–60 .. .. 55 60

581 Canadian Flag and Fireworks

1990. Canada Day.

1389 **581** 39 c. multicoloured .. 45 50

582 "Stromatolites" (fossil algae)

1990. Prehistoric Canada (1st series). Primitive Life. Multicoloured.

1390 39 c. Type **582** 60 60
1391 39 c. "Opabinia regalis" (soft invertebrate) .. 60 60
1392 39 c. "Paradoxides davidis" (trilobite) .. 60 60
1393 39 c. "Eurypterus remipes" (sea scorpion) 60 60

See also Nos. 1417/20 and 1568/71.

583 Acadian Forest

1990. Canadian Forests. Multicoloured.

1394 39 c. Type **583** 60 60
1395 39 c. Great Lakes-St. Lawrence forest .. 60 60
1396 39 c. Pacific Coast forest 60 60
1397 39 c. Boreal forest .. 60 60

584 Clouds and Rainbow

1990. 150th Anniv of Weather Observing in Canada.

1398 **584** 39 c. multicoloured .. 40 50

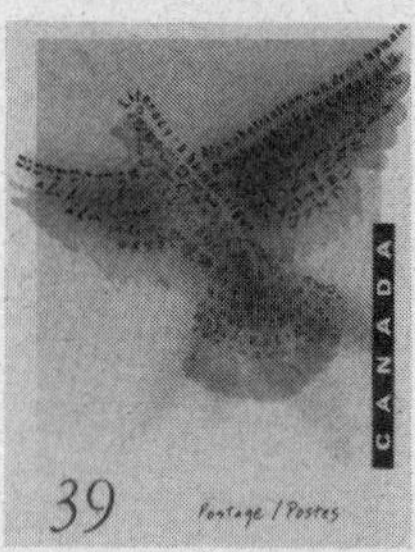

585 "Alphabet" Bird

1990. International Literacy Year.

1399 **585** 39 c. multicoloured .. 40 50

586 Sasquatch

1990. Legendary Creatures. Multicoloured.

1400 39 c. Type **586** 60 60
1401 39 c. Kraken 60 60
1402 39 c. Werewolf 60 60
1403 39 c. Ogopogo 60 60

587 Agnes Macphail

588 "Virgin Mary with Christ Child and St. John the Baptist" (Norval Morrisseau)

1990. Birth Centenary of Agnes Macphail (first woman elected to Parliament).

1404 **587** 39 c. multicoloured .. 40 50

1990. Christmas. Native Art.

1405 – 34 c. multicoloured .. 30 35
1406 **588** 39 c. multicoloured .. 35 40
1407 – 45 c. multicoloured .. 40 45
1408 – 78 c. black, red & grey 70 75

DESIGNS—35 × 21 mm. 34 c. "Rebirth" (Jackson Beardy). As T **588**. 45 c. "Mother and Child" (Inuit sculpture, Cape Dorset); 78 c. "Children of the Raven" (Bill Reid).

No. 1405 includes a bar code in the design.

1990. 50th Anniv of Second World War (2nd issue). As T **574**.

1409 39 c. black, silver & green 55 55
1410 39 c. black, silver & brown 55 55
1411 39 c. black, silver & brown 55 55
1412 39 c. black, silver & mve 55 55

DESIGNS: No. 1409, Canadian family at home, 1940; 1410, Packing parcels for the troops; 1411, Harvesting; 1412, Testing anti-gravity flying suit.

589 Jennie Trout (first woman physician) and Women's Medical College, Kingston

1991. Medical Pioneers. Multicoloured.

1413 40 c. Type **589** 50 50
1414 40 c. Wilder Penfield (neurosurgeon) and Montreal Neurological Institute 50 50
1415 40 c. Frederick Banting (discoverer of insulin) and University of Toronto medical faculty 50 50
1416 40 c. Harold Griffith (anesthesiologist) and Queen Elizabeth Hospital, Montreal .. 50 50

1991. Prehistoric Canada (2nd series). Primitive Vertebrates. As T **582**. Mult.

1417 40 c. "Eusthenopteron foordi" (fish fossil) .. 75 75
1418 40 c. "Hylonomus lyelli" (land reptile) 75 75
1419 40 c. Fossil conodonts .. 75 75
1420 40 c. "Archaeopteris halliana" (early tree) .. 75 75

1991. Canadian Art (4th series). As T **550**. Multicoloured.

1421 50 c. "Forest, British Columbia" (Emily Carr) 70 80

590 Blue Poppies and Butchart Gardens, Victoria

1991. Public Gardens. Multicoloured.

1422 40 c. Type **590** 55 55
1423 40 c. Marigolds and International Peace Garden, Boissevain .. 55 55
1424 40 c. Lilac and Royal Botanical Gardens, Hamilton 55 55
1425 40 c. Roses and Montreal Botanical Gardens .. 55 55
1426 40 c. Rhododendrons and Halifax Public Gardens 55 55

591 Maple Leaf

1991. Canada Day.

1427 **591** 40 c. multicoloured .. 50 60

1991. Small Craft of Canada (3rd series). As T **563**. Multicoloured.

1428 40 c. Verchere rowboat .. 60 65
1429 40 c. Touring kayak .. 60 65
1430 40 c. Sailing dinghy .. 60 65
1431 40 c. Cedar strip canoe .. 60 65

592 South Nahanni River

1991. Canadian Rivers (1st series). Mult.

1432	40 c. Type **592**	70	70
1433	40 c. Athabasca River ..	70	70
1434	40 c. Boundary Waters, Voyageur Waterway ..	70	70
1435	40 c. Jacques-Cartier River	70	70
1436	40 c. Main River ..	70	70

See also Nos. 1492/6, 1558/62 and 1584/8.

593 "Leaving Europe"

1991. Centenary of Ukrainian Immigration. Panels from "The Ukrainian Pioneer" by William Kurelek. Multicoloured.

1437	40 c. Type **593**	60	60
1438	40 c. "Canadian Winter"	60	60
1439	40 c. "Clearing the Land"	60	60
1440	40 c. "Harvest" ..	60	60

594 Ski Patrol rescuing Climber

1991. Emergency Services. Multicoloured.

1441	40 c. Type **594**	70	80
1442	40 c. Police at road traffic accident	70	80
1443	40 c. Firemen on extending ladder ..	70	80
1444	40 c. Rescue helicopter and lifeboat	70	80

595 "The Witched Canoe"

1991. Canadian Folktales. Multicoloured.

1445	40 c. Type **595**	60	60
1446	40 c. "The Orphan Boy"	60	60
1447	40 c. "Chinook"	60	60
1448	40 c. "Buried Treasure"	60	60

596 Grant Hall Tower

1991. 150th Anniv of Queen's University, Kingston.

1449 **596**	40 c. multicoloured ..	50	55

597 North American Santa Claus

1991. Christmas. Multicoloured.

1450	35 c. British Father Christmas (35 × 21 mm)	45	40
1451	40 c. Type **597**	55	45
1452	46 c. French Bonhomme Noel	65	70
1453	80 c. Dutch Sinterklaas ..	1·25	1·50

598 Players Jumping for Ball

1991. Basketball Centenary. Multicoloured.

1454 **598**	40 c. multicoloured ..	70	65

1991. 50th Anniv of Second World War (3rd issue). As T **574**.

1456	40 c. black, silver and blue	50	55
1457	40 c. black, silver & brown	50	55
1458	40 c. black, silver and lilac	50	55
1459	40 c. black, silver & brown	50	55

DESIGNS: No. 1456, Women's services, 1941; 1457, Armament factory; 1458, Cadets and veterans; 1459, Defence of Hong Kong.

599 Blueberry

600 McIntosh Apple

1991. Multicoloured. (a) Edible Berries.

1460	1 c. Type **599**	10	10
1461	2 c. Wild strawberry ..	10	10
1462	3 c. Black crowberry ..	10	10
1463	5 c. Rose hip	10	10
1464	6 c. Black raspberry ..	10	10
1465	10 c. Kinnikinnick ..	10	10
1466	25 c. Saskatoon berry ..	25	30

(b) Fruit and Nut Trees

1467	48 c. Type **600**	50	55
1468	49 c. Delicious apple ..	50	55
1469	65 c. Black walnut ..	70	70
1470	67 c. Beaked hazelnut ..	65	70
1471	84 c. Stanley plum ..	90	95
1472	86 c. Bartlett pear ..	85	90

Nos. 1460/6 were issued together, se-tenant, forming a composite design.

601 Ski Jumping

1992. Winter Olympic Games, Albertville. Multicoloured.

1482	42 c. Type **601**	50	55
1483	42 c. Figure skating ..	50	55
1484	42 c. Ice hockey	50	55
1485	42 c. Bobsleighing ..	50	55
1486	42 c. Alpine skiing ..	50	55

602 Ville-Marie in 17th Century

1992. "CANADA 92" International Youth Stamp Exhibition, Montreal. Mult.

1487	42 c. Type **602**	50	55
1488	42 c. Modern Montreal ..	50	55
1489	48 c. Compass rose, snow shoe and crow's nest of Cartier's ship "Grande Hermine"	55	60
1490	84 c. Atlantic map, Aztec "calendar stone" and navigational instrument	1·10	1·25

1992. Canadian Rivers (2nd series). As T **592** but horiz. Multicoloured.

1492	42 c. Magaree River ..	50	55
1493	42 c. West (Eliot) River	50	55
1494	42 c. Ottawa River ..	50	55
1495	42 c. Niagara River ..	50	55
1496	42 c. South Saskatchewan River	50	55

603 Road Bed Construction and Route Map

1992. 50th Anniv of Alaska Highway.

1497 **603**	42 c. multicoloured ..	50	60

1992. Olympic Games, Barcelona. As T **601**. Multicoloured.

1498	42 c. Gymnastics ..	50	55
1499	42 c. Athletics	50	55
1500	42 c. Diving	50	55
1501	42 c. Cycling	50	55
1502	42 c. Swimming	50	55

1992. Canadian Art (5th series). As T **550**. Multicoloured.

1504	50 c. "Red Nasturtiums" (David Milne) ..	60	70

605 Jerry Potts (scout)

1992. Folk Heroes. Multicoloured.

1505	42 c. Type **605**	40	45
1506	42 c. Capt. William Jackman and wreck of "Sea Clipper", 1867 ..	40	45
1507	42 c. Laura Secord (messenger)	40	45
1508	42 c. Jos Montferrand (lumberjack)	40	45

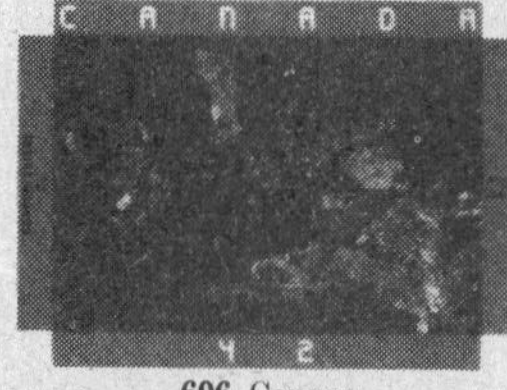

606 Copper

1992. 150th Anniv of Geological Survey of Canada. Minerals. Multicoloured.

1509	42 c. Type **606**	40	45
1510	42 c. Sodalite	40	45
1511	42 c. Gold	40	45
1512	42 c. Galena	40	45
1513	42 c. Grossular	40	45

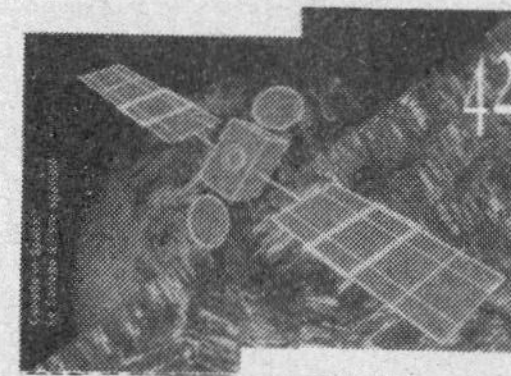

607 Satellite and Photographs from Space

1992. Canadian Space Programme. Mult.

1514	42 c. Type **607**	40	45
1515	42 c. Space shuttle over Canada (hologram) (32 × 26 mm)	40	45

608 Babe Siebert, Skates and Stick

1992. 75th Anniv of National Ice Hockey League. Multicoloured.

1516	42 c. Type **608**	40	45
1517	42 c. Claude Provost, Terry Sawchuck and team badges	40	45
1518	42 c. Hockey mask, gloves and modern player ..	40	45

609 Companion of the Order of Canada Insignia

1992. 25th Anniv of the Order of Canada and Daniel Roland Michener (former Governor-General) Commemoration. Multicoloured.

1519	42 c. Type **609**	40	45
1520	42 c. Daniel Roland Michener	40	45

1992. 50th Anniv of Second World War (4th issue). As T **574**.

1521	42 c. black, silver & brown	40	45
1522	42 c. black, silver & green	40	45
1523	42 c. black, silver & brown	40	45
1524	42 c. black, silver and blue	40	45

DESIGNS: No. 1521, Reporters and soldier, 1942; 1522, Liberator bombers over Newfoundland; 1523, Dieppe raid; 1524, U-boat sinking merchant ship.

610 Estonian Jouluvana

1992. Christmas. Multicoloured.

1525 37 c. North American Santa Claus (35 × 21 mm) 35 40
1526 42 c. Type **610** 40 45
1527 48 c. Italian La Befana .. 50 55
1528 84 c. German Weihnachtsmann 80 85

611 Adelaide Hoodless (women's movement pioneer)

1993. Prominent Canadian Women. Mult.

1529 43 c. Type **611** 45 50
1530 43 c. Marie-Josephine Gerin-Lajoie (social reformer) 45 50
1531 43 c. Pitseolak Ashoona (Inuit artist) 45 50
1532 43 c. Helen Kinnear (lawyer) 45 50

612 Ice Hockey Players with Cup

1993. Centenary of Stanley Cup.

1533 **612** 43 c. multicoloured .. 45 50

613 Coverlet, New Brunswick

1993. Hand-crafted Textiles. Multicoloured.

1534 43 c. Type **613** 45 50
1535 43 c. Pieced quilt, Ontario 45 50
1536 43 c. Doukhobor bed-cover, Saskatchewan .. 45 50
1537 43 c. Ceremonial robe, Kwakwaka'wakw .. 45 50
1538 43 c. Boutonne coverlet, Quebec 45 50

1993. Canadian Art (6th series). As T **550**. Multicoloured.

1539 86 c. "The Owl" (Kenojuak Ashevak) .. 85 90

614 Empress Hotel, Victoria

1993. Historic Hotels. Multicoloured.

1540 43 c. Type **614** 45 50
1541 43 c. Banff Springs Hotel 45 50
1542 43 c. Royal York Hotel, Toronto 45 50
1543 43 c. Le Chateau Frontenac, Quebec .. 45 50
1544 43 c. Algonquin Hotel, St. Andrews 45 50

615 Algonquin Park, Ontario

1993. Canada Day. Provincial and Territorial Parks. Multicoloured.

1545 43 c. Type **615** 45 50
1546 43 c. De La Gaspesie Park, Quebec 45 50
1547 43 c. Cedar Dunes Park, Prince Edward Island 45 50
1548 43 c. Cape St. Mary's Seabird Reserve, Newfoundland .. 45 50
1549 43 c. Mount Robson Park, British Columbia .. 45 50
1550 43 c. Writing-on-Stone Park, Alberta 45 50
1551 43 c. Spruce Woods Park, Manitoba 45 50
1552 43 c. Herschel Island Park, Yukon 45 50
1553 43 c. Cypress Hills Park, Saskatchewan .. 45 50
1554 43 c. The Rocks Park, New Brunswick .. 45 50
1555 43 c. Blomidon Park, Nova Scotia 45 50
1556 43 c. Katannilik Park, Northwest Territories 45 50

616 Toronto Skyscrapers

1993. Bicentenary of Toronto.

1557 **616** 43 c. multicoloured .. 45 50

1993. Canadian Rivers (3rd series). As T **592**. Multicoloured.

1558 43 c. Fraser River .. 45 50
1559 43 c. Yukon River .. 45 50
1560 43 c. Red River 45 50
1561 43 c. St. Lawrence River 45 50
1562 43 c. St. John River .. 45 50

618 "The Alberta Homesteader"

1993. Folk Songs. Multicoloured.

1564 43 c. Type **618** 45 50
1565 43 c. "Les Raftmans" (Quebec) 45 50
1566 43 c. "I'se the B'y that Builds the Boat" (Newfoundland) .. 45 50
1567 43 c. "Onkwa:ri Tenhanonniahkwe" (Mohawk Indian) .. 45 50

1993. Prehistoric Canada (3rd series). Dinosaurs. As T **582** but 40 × 28 mm. Mult.

1568 43 c. Massospondylus .. 45 50
1569 43 c. Stryacosaurus .. 45 50
1570 43 c. Albertosaurus .. 45 50
1571 43 c. Platecarpus .. 45 50

619 Polish Swiety Mikolaj

1993. Christmas. Multicoloured.

1572 38 c. North American Santa Claus (35 × 22 mm) 40 45
1573 43 c. Type **619** 45 50
1574 49 c. Russian Ded Moroz 50 55
1575 86 c. Australian Father Christmas 85 90

1993. 50th Anniv of Second World War (5th issue). As T **574**.

1576 43 c. black, silver & green 45 50
1577 43 c. black, silver and blue 45 50
1578 43 c. black, silver and blue 45 50
1579 43 c. black, silver & brown 45 50

DESIGNS: No. 1576, Loading munitions for Russia, 1943; No. 1577, Loading bombs on Lancaster; No. 1578, Escorts attacking U-boat; No. 1579, Infantry advancing, Italy.

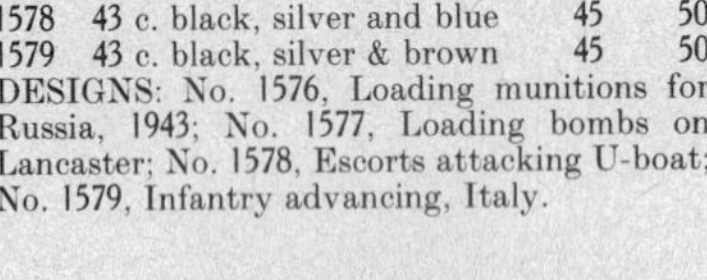

620 (face value at right) (¾-size illustration)

1994. Self-adhesive Greetings stamps. Mult.

1580 43 c. Type **620** 45 50
1581 43 c. As Type **620** but face value at left .. 45 50

It was intended that the sender should insert an appropriate greetings label into the circular space on each stamp before use.

621 Jeanne Sauve

1994. Jeanne Sauve (former Governor-General) Commemoration.

582 **621** 43 c. multicoloued .. 45 50

622 Timothy Eaton, Toronto Store of 1869 and Merchandise

1994. 125th Anniv of T. Eaton Company Ltd (department store group).

1583 **622** 43 c. multicoloured .. 45 50

1994. Canadian Rivers (4th series). As T **592** but horiz. Multicoloured.

1584 43 c. Saguenay River .. 45 50
1585 43 c. French River .. 45 50
1586 43 c. Mackenzie River .. 45 50
1587 43 c. Churchill River .. 45 50
1588 43 c. Columbia River .. 45 50

OFFICIAL STAMPS

1949. Optd **O.H.M.S.**

O162 **111** 1 c. green (postage) 1·00 1·75
O163 **112** 2 c. brown .. .. 9·50 11·00
O164 – 3 c. purple (No. 378) 1·00 1·10
O165 **112** 4 c. red .. .. 1·25 70
O166 – 10 c. green (No. 402) 3·75 15
O167 – 14 c. brown (No. 403) 4·25 1·00
O168 – 20 c. grey (No. 404) .. 11·00 60
O169 – 50 c. green (No. 405) £160 £100
O170 – $1 purple (No. 406) .. 50·00 45·00
O171 – 7 c. blue (No. 407) (air) .. .. 24·00 6·50

1949. Optd **O.H.M.S.**

O172 **135** 1 c. green 40 50
O173 – 2 c. brown (No. 415) 1·00 1·25
O174 – 3 c. purple (No. 416) 50 60
O175 – 4 c. red (No. 417) .. 75 10
O176 – 5 c. blue (No. 418) .. 2·00 1·25
O177 **141** 50 c. green .. .. 29·00 26·00

1950. Optd **G.**

O178 **135** 1 c. green (postage) 40 10
O179 – 2 c. brown (No. 415) 1·00 90
O180 – 2 c. green (No. 415a) 1·25 10
O181 – 3 c. purple (No. 416) 1·25 10
O182 – 4 c. red (No. 417) .. 1·25 20
O184 – 5 c. blue (No. 418) .. 2·50 30
O193 **153** 7 c. blue .. .. 1·25 80
O185 – 10 c. green (No. 402) 2·00 10
O191 **142** 10 c. purple .. .. 1·00 10
O186 – 14 c. brown (No. 403) 8·00 2·25
O187 – 20 c. grey (No. 404) .. 10·00 20
O194 – 20 c. grey (No. 441) .. 1·00 10
O188 **141** 50 c. green .. .. 8·50 7·00
O189 – $1 purple (No. 406) .. 60·00 48·00
O192 – $1 blue (No. 433) .. 55·00 55·00
O190 – 7 c. blue (No. 407) (air) .. .. 20·00 9·00

1953. 1st Queen Elizabeth II stamps optd **G.**

O196 **158** 1 c. brown 15 10
O197 2 c. green 20 10
O198 3 c. red 20 10
O199 4 c. violet 30 10
O200 5 c. blue 30 10

1953. Pictorial stamps optd **G.**

O206 **165** 10 c. brown 30 10
O207 – 20 c. green (No. 488) 60 10
O201 **160** 50 c. green .. .. 2·75 50
O195 **154** $1 black .. .. 7·00 8·00

1955. 2nd Queen Elizabeth II stamps optd **G.**

O202 **161** 1 c. brown 15 20
O203 2 c. green 15 10
O204 4 c. violet 30 10
O205 5 c. blue 15 10

1963. 3rd Queen Elizabeth II stamps optd **G.**

O208 **215** 1 c. brown .. .. 40 3·00
O209 2 c. green .. .. 40 2·50
O210 4 c. red .. .. 40 1·75
O211 5 c. blue 40 55

OFFICIAL SPECIAL DELIVERY STAMPS

1950. Optd **O.H.M.S.**

OS20 – 10 c. green (No. S15) .. 16·00 16·00

1950. Optd **G.**

OS21 – 10 c. green (No. S15) .. 21·00 22·00

POSTAGE DUE STAMPS

D 1.

D 2.

1906.

D 1 **D 1.** 1 c. violet .. .. 6·00 2·50
D 4 2 c. violet .. .. 8·50 1·00
D 5 4 c. violet .. .. 45·00 50·00
D 6 5 c. violet .. .. 16·00 1·75
D 8 10 c. violet .. .. 28·00 14·00

1930.

D 9. **D 2.** 1 c. violet .. .. 8·00 10·00
D 10. 2 c. violet .. .. 7·00 85
D 11. 4 c. violet .. .. 15·00 8·00
D 12. 5 c. violet .. .. 13·00 22·00
D 13. 10 c. violet .. .. 65·00 26·00

D 3.

D 4.

1933.

D 14. **D 3.** 1 c. violet .. .. 7·00 11·00
D 15. 2 c. violet .. .. 5·00 3·00
D 16. 4 c. violet .. .. 10·00 8·50
D 17. 10 c. violet .. .. 19·00 22·00

1935.

D 18. D 4. 1 c. violet 40 10
D 19. 2 c. violet 40 10
D 20. 3 c. violet .. .. 2·50 5·00
D 21. 4 c. violet 80 10
D 22. 5 c. violet .. .. 1·50 35
D 23. 6 c. violet .. .. 1·50 3·00
D 24. 10 c. violet 60 10

D 5.

1967.

(a) Size 21 × 17 mm.

D 25. D 5. 1 c. red .. .. 1·25 3·00
D 26. 2 c. red .. .. 1·00 80
D 27. 3 c. red .. .. 1·00 4·00
D 28. 4 c. red .. .. 2·25 1·25
D 29. 5 c. red .. .. 3·50 3·25
D 30. 6 c. red .. .. 1·60 3·75
D 31. 10 c. red .. .. 2·00 2·50

(b) Size 20 × 15½ mm.

D 32 D 5. 1 c. red 30 30
D 33 2 c. red .. .. 30 2·00
D 34 3 c. red .. .. 1·50 2·00
D 35 4 c. red 85 75
D 36a 5 c. red .. .. 50 2·25
D 37 6 c. red .. .. 1·75 3·25
D 38 8 c. red 75 60
D 39a 10 c. red 60 90
D 40 12 c. red .. .. 1·25 65
D 41 16 c. red .. .. 70 2·50
D 42 20 c. red .. .. 60 1·75
D 43 24 c. red .. .. 60 2·50
D 44 50 c. red .. .. 1·00 2·75

REGISTRATION STAMPS

R 1.

1875.

R 1. R 1. 2 c. orange .. .. 55·00 1·00
R 6. 5 c. green .. .. 75·00 1·00
R 8. 8 c. blue £325 £225

SPECIAL DELIVERY STAMPS

S 1.

1898.

S2 S 1 10 c. green .. .. 40·00 4·50

S 2.

1922.

S 4. S 2. 20 c. red .. .. 30·00 2·50

S 3. Mail-carrying, 1867 and 1927.

1927. 60th Anniversary of Confederation.

S 5. S 3. 20 c. orange .. .. 8·00 7·50

S 4.

1930.

S 6. S 4. 20 c. red .. .. 35·00 4·00

1932. As Type S 4, but inscr. "CENTS" instead of "TWENTY CENTS".

S 7. – 20 c. red .. .. .. 42·00 11·00

S 5. Allegory of Progress.

1935.

S 8. S 5. 20 c. red .. .. 3·50 1·25

S 6. Canadian Coat of Arms.

1938.

S 9. S 6. 10 c. green .. .. 13·00 55
S 10. 20 c. red .. .. 42·00 23·00

1939. Surch. **10 10** and bars.

S 11. S 6. 10 c. on 20 c. red .. 6·50 7·50

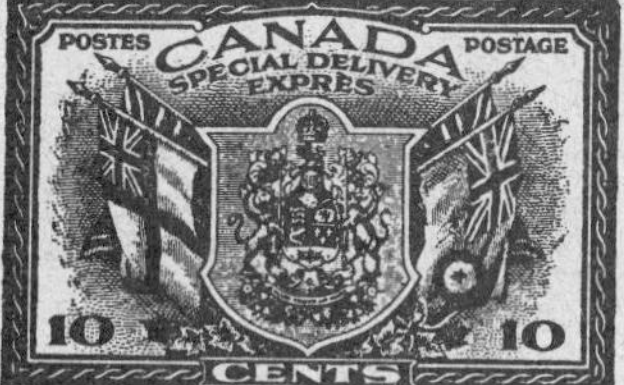

S 8. Coat of Arms and Flags.

S 9. Trans-Canada Plane.

1942.

S 12. S 8. 10 c. green (postage) .. 2·25 20
S 13. S 9. 16 c. blue (air) .. 2·00 20
S 14. 17 c. blue .. .. 2·50 30

1946.

S 15. 10 c. green (postage) .. 1·50 20
S 17. 17 c. blue (air) .. 4·00 3·25

DESIGNS: 10 c. as Type S 8, but with wreath of leaves. 17 c. as Type S 9, but with four-engined transatlantic 'plane.

CAPE OF GOOD HOPE

Formerly a Br. Colony, later the southernmost province of the Union of S. Africa.

12 pence = 1 shilling;
20 shillings = 1 pound.

1. "Hope".

1853. Imperf.

18 1. 1d. red £100 £225
19 4d. blue .. .. .. £100 42·00
20 6d. lilac £150 £450
8a 1s. green £225 £500

3.

1861. Imperf.

13. 3. 1d. red £13000 £2000
14. 4d. blue £9000 £1500

4. "Hope" seated, with vine and ram. (with outer frame-line).

6. (No outer frame-line).

1864. With outer frame line. Perf.

23a 4 1d. red .. .. .. 75·00 12·00
24 4d. blue .. .. .. 90·00 2·00
52a 6d. purple .. .. .. 2·75 15
53a 1s. green .. .. .. 35·00 30

1868. Surch.

32. 4. 1d. on 6d. violet .. .. £275 50·00
33. 1d. on 1s. green .. .. 38·00 23·00
34. 6. 3d. on 4d. blue .. .. 70·00 90
27. 4. 4d. on 6d. violet .. .. £130 12·00

1880. No outer frame line.

48. 6. ½d. black .. .. .. 1·25 10
49. 1d. red .. .. .. 1·25 10
36. 3d. pink .. .. .. £150 14·00
40. 3d. claret .. .. .. 5·50 90
51. 4d. blue .. .. .. 3·50 15
66. 5s. orange .. .. .. 48·00 3·50

1880. Surch. **THREEPENCE.**

35. 6. 3d. on 4d. red .. .. 42·00 1·50

1880. Surch. **3.**

37. 6. "3" on 3d. red .. .. 38·00 75

1882. Surch. **One Half-penny** and bar.

42. 6. ½d. on 3d. red .. .. 6·00 2·00

1882.

59. 6. ½d. green .. .. .. 1·50 10
60. 2d. brown .. .. .. 2·00 10
56. 2½d. olive .. .. .. 3·00 10
61a. 2½d. blue .. .. .. 2·25 10
62. 3d. mauve .. .. .. 2·25 40
63. 4d. olive .. .. .. 3·50 60
64. 1s. green .. .. .. 28·00 1·00
65. 1s. yellow .. .. .. 6·50 60

On the 2½d. stamps the value is in a white square at upper right-hand corner as well as at foot.

1891. Surch. **2½d.**

55a. 6. 2½d. on 3d. mauve .. 1·00 20

1893. Surch. **ONE PENNY** and bar.

57a. 6. 1d. on 2d. brown .. .. 1·10 10

17. "Hope" standing. Table Bay in background.

1893.

67 17 ½d. green 30 10
58a 1d. red 30 10
68 3d. mauve .. .. .. 4·00 60

18. Table Mountain and Bay and Arms of the Colony.

19.

1900.

69. 18. 1d. red 65 10

1902. Various frames.

70. 19. ½d. green 50 10
71. 1d. red 50 10
72. 2d. brown .. .. .. 3·25 55
73. 2½d. blue .. .. .. 2·50 5·50
74. 3d. purple .. .. .. 3·25 30
75. 4d. green .. .. .. 3·25 55
76. 6d. mauve .. .. .. 3·75 30
77. 1s. yellow .. .. .. 7·00 50
78. 5s. orange .. .. .. 45·00 6·50

CAYES OF BELIZE

A chain of several hundred islands, coral atolls, reefs and sandbanks stretching along the eastern seaboard of Belize.

The following issues for the Cayes of Belize fall outside the criteria for full listing as detailed on page viii.

100 cents = 1 dollar.

1984.

Marine Life, Map and Views, 1, 2, 5, 10, 15, 25, 75 c., $3, $5.
Lloyd's List (newspaper). 250th Anniv. 25, 75 c., $1, $2.
Olympic Games, Los Angeles. 10, 15, 75 c., $2.
90th Anniv. of "Caye Service" Local Stamps. 10, 15, 75 c., $2.

1985.

Birth Bicentenary of John J. Audubon (ornithologist). 25, 75 c., $1, $3.
Shipwrecks. $1 × 4.

CAYMAN ISLANDS

A group of islands in the Br. W. Indies. A dependency of Jamaica until August 1962, when it became a Crown Colony.

1900. 12 pence = 1 shilling;
20 shillings = 1 pound.
1969. 100 cents = 1 Jamaica dollar.

1.

2.

1900.

1a. 1. ½d. green .. .. .. 2·00 9·00
2. 1d. red .. .. .. 2·50 90

1902.

8 2 ½d. green .. .. .. 1·50 3·75
4 1d. red .. .. .. 5·50 6·50
10 2½d. blue .. .. .. 3·50 2·75
13 4d. brown and blue .. 20·00 32·00
11 6d. brown .. .. 16·00 35·00
14 6d. olive and red .. .. 20·00 45·00
12 1s. orange .. .. 32·00 48·00
15 1s. violet and green .. 35·00 50·00
16 5s. red and green £170 £250

1907. Surch. **One Halfpenny.**

17. 2. ½d. on 1d. red .. .. 30·00 55·00

1907. Surch.

18. 2. "½d." on 5s. red & green £225 £300
19. "1d." on 5s. red & green £225 £300
35. "2½d." on 4d. brn. & blue £1400 £2000

11.

8.

1907.

38. 11. ¼d. brown 40 30
25. 8. ½d. green .. .. .. 1·00 2·00
26. 1d. red 80 65
27. 2½d. blue .. .. .. 2·75 3·50
28. 3d. purple on yellow .. 2·25 6·50
29. 4d. black & red on yellow 48·00 50·00
30. 6d. purple .. .. 4·50 25·00
31. 1s. black on green .. 4·50 17·00
32. 5s. green & red on yellow 35·00 55·00
34. 10 s. green & red on green £160 £225

12.

19.

1912.

40 12 ¼d. brown 40 30
41 ½d. green .. .. 1·00 2·75
42 1d. red .. .. 2·25 90
43 2d. grey .. .. 70 3·50
44 2½d. blue .. .. 7·00 7·50
45a 3d. purple on yellow .. 2·00 4·50
46 4d. black & red on yell 75 4·00
47 6d. purple .. .. 2·25 5·00
48a 1s. black on green .. 2·00 2·75
49 2s. purple & blue on bl 8·50 35·00
50 3s. green and violet .. 19·00 55·00
51 5s. green & red on yell 70·00 £110
52a 10s. green & red on grn 80·00 £120

1917. Surch **1½d.** with **WAR STAMP** in two lines.

54 12 1½d. on 2½d. blue .. 50 3·25

1917. Optd. or surch as last, but with **WAR STAMP** in one line.

57. 12. ½d. green 20 95
58. 1½d. on 2d. grey .. 1·00 4·25
56. 1½d. on 2½d. blue .. 20 40
59. 1½d. on 2½d. orange .. 25 80

1921.

69 19 ¼d. brown 30 60
70 ½d. green 40 25
71 1d. red 70 85
72 1½d. brown .. .. 1·75 20
73 2d. grey .. .. .. 1·75 3·25
74 2½d. blue 50 45
75 3d. purple on yellow .. 50 1·25
62 4d. red on yellow .. 80 3·75
76 4½d. green.. .. .. 1·25 3·00
77 6d. red .. .. .. 5·50 24·00
63 1s. black on green .. 1·25 7·50
80 2s. violet on blue.. .. 9·00 15·00
81 3s. violet .. .. .. 18·00 15·00
82 5s. green on yellow .. 23·00 38·00
83 10s. red on green .. 48·00 65·00

20. Kings William IV and George V.

1932. Centenary of "Assembly of Justices and Vestry".

84. 20. ¼d. brown 60 90
85. ½d. green .. .. .. 1·50 5·00
86. 1d. red .. .. .. 1·75 4·00
87. 1½d. orange .. .. 1·50 1·00
88. 2d. grey .. .. .. 1·50 1·75
89. 2½d. blue .. .. .. 1·50 1·00
90. 3d. green .. .. .. 1·75 2·75
91. 6d. purple.. .. .. 6·00 14·00
92. 1s. black and brown .. 14·00 23·00
93. 2s. black and blue .. 38·00 60·00
94. 5s. black and green .. 80·00 £110
95. 10s. black and red .. £250 £350

1935. Silver Jubilee. As T **13** of Antigua.

96. ½d. black and green .. 15 20
97. 2½d. brown and blue .. 60 1·00
98. 6d. blue and olive .. 1·00 1·50
99. 1s. grey and purple .. 4·25 4·00

21. Cayman Islands.

1935.

100. 21. ¼d. black and brown .. 30 70
101. – ½d. blue and green .. 1·00 50
102. – 1d. blue and red .. 2·25 75
103. – 1½d. black and orange .. 1·50 1·10
104. – 2d. blue and purple .. 2·25 80
105. – 2½d. blue and black .. 3·00 75
106. 21. 3d. black and green .. 2·00 1·25
107. – 6d. purple and black .. 8·50 3·00
108. – 1s. blue and orange .. 4·00 4·50
109. – 2s. blue and black .. 45·00 30·00
110. – 5s. green and black .. 48·00 48·00
111. – 10s. black and red .. 65·00 75·00

DESIGNS—HORIZ. ½d., 2d., 1s. Cat boat. 1d., 2s. Red-footed Booby birds. 2½d., 6d., 5s. Hawksbill turtles. VERT. 1½d., 10s. Conch shells and coconut palms.

1937. Coronation. As T **2** of Aden.

112. ½d. green.. .. .. 30 20
113. 1d. red 50 20
114. 2½d. blue.. .. .. 95 40

26. Beach View.

30. Hawksbill Turtles.

DESIGNS—HORIZ. ¼d., 1s. Caribbean Dolphin. 1d., 3d. Map of Islands. 2½d., 5s. "Rembro" (schooner).

1938.

115a 26 ¼d. orange 10 45
116 – ½d. green 35 55
117 – 1d. red 20 65
118 26 1½d. black 20 10
119a 30 2d. violet 50 30
120 – 2½d. blue 20 20
120a – 2½d. orange .. .. 1·50 50
121 – 3d. orange 20 15
121a – 3d. blue .. .. 1·50 30
122a 30 6d. olive .. .. 1·25 70
123a – 1s. brown .. .. 2·75 1·25
124a 26 2s. green .. .. 23·00 9·00
125 – 5s. red .. .. .. 30·00 15·00
126a 30 10s. brown .. .. 21·00 9·00

1946. Victory. As T **9** of Aden.

127. 1½d. black.. .. .. 10 10
128. 3d. yellow.. .. .. 10 10

1948. Silver Wedding. As T **10/11** of Aden.

129. ½d. green 10 10
130. 10s. blue .. .. .. 10·00 6·50

1949. U.P.U. As T **20/23** of Antigua.

131. 2½d. orange 20 20
132. 3d. blue 70 40
133. 6d. olive 75 45
134. 1s. brown 75 30

31. Cat Boat.

1950.

135. 31. ¼d. blue and red .. 15 60
136. – ½d. violet and green .. 15 1·25
137. – 1d. olive and blue .. 60 75
138. – 1½d. green and brown.. 30 75
139. – 2d. violet and red .. 1·00 1·50
140. – 2½d. blue and black .. 50 60
141. – 3d. green and blue .. 1·40 1·50
142. – 6d. brown and blue .. 2·00 1·25
143. – 9d. red and green .. 2·25 2·00
144. – 1s. brown and orange .. 3·25 2·75
145. – 2s. violet and purple .. 7·50 7·00
146. – 5s. olive and violet .. 9·00 7·00
147. – 10s. black and red .. 13·00 11·00

DESIGNS: ½d. Coconut grove, Cayman Brac. 1d. Green turtle. 1½d. Making thatch rope. 2d. Cayman seamen. 2½d. Map. 3d. Parrot fish. 6d. Bluff, Cayman Brac. 9d. Georgetown Harbour. 1s. Turtle in "crawl". 2s. "Ziroma" (schooner). 5s. Boat-building. 10s. Government offices, Grand Cayman.

44. South Sound Lighthouse, Grand Cayman.

Portrait faces right on ¼d., 2d., 2½d., 4d., 1s. and 10s. values and left on others. The £1 shows a larger portrait of the Queen (vert.).

1953. As 1950 issue but with portrait of Queen Elizabeth II as in T **44**.

148 ¼d. blue and red .. 60 50
149 ½d. violet and green .. 20 50
150 1d. olive and blue .. 70 40
151 1½d. green and brown .. 40 20
152 2d. violet and red .. 3·00 85
153 2½d. blue and black .. 3·50 80
154 3d. green and blue .. 4·00 60
155 4d. black and blue .. 2·00 40
156 6d. brown and blue .. 1·75 30
157 9d. red and green .. 2·00 30
158 1s. brown and orange .. 3·25 20
159 2s. violet and purple .. 8·00 7·00
160 5s. olive and violet .. 10·00 4·00
161 10s. black and red .. 13·00 7·50
161a £1 blue .. .. .. 27·00 10·00

1953. Coronation. As T **13** of Aden.

162. 1d. black and green .. 20 80

46. Arms of the Cayman Is.

1959. New Constitution.

163. 46. 2½d. black and blue .. 30 55
164. 1s. black and orange .. 40 20

48. Cat Boat.

1962. Portrait as in T **48**.

165. – ¼d. green and red .. 15 55
166. 48. 1d. black and olive .. 20 20
167. – 1½d. yellow and purple 2·75 80
168. – 2d. blue and brown .. 60 30
169. – 2½d. violet & turquoise 75 70
170. – 3d. blue and red .. 30 10
171. – 4d. green and purple .. 80 60
172. – 6d. turquoise and sepia 3·25 30
173. – 9d. blue and purple .. 1·25 30
174. – 1s. sepia and red .. 60 10
175. – 1s. 3d. turq. and brown 2·00 1·50
176. – 1s. 9d. turquoise & violet 8·50 95
177. – 5s. plum and green .. 5·00 3·50
178. – 10s. olive and blue .. 10·00 8·00
179. – £1 red and black .. 17·00 15·00

DESIGNS—VERT. ¼d. Cuban Amazon. 9d. Angler with Kingfish. 10s. Arms. £1, Queen Elizabeth II. HORIZ. 1½d. "Schomburgkia thomsoniana" (orchid). 2d. Cayman Is. map. 2½d. Fisherman casting net. 3d. West Bay Beach. 4d. Green Turtle. 6d. "Lydia E. Wilson" (schooner). 1s. Iguana. 1s 3d. Swimming pool, Cayman Brac. 1s 9d. Water Sports. 5s. Fort George.

1963. Freedom from Hunger. As T **28** of Aden.

180. 1s. 9d. red.. .. .. 30 15

1963. Cent of Red Cross. As T **33** of Antigua.

181. 1d. red and black 15 30
182. 1s 9d. red and blue .. 70 1·25

1964. 400th Birth Anniv of Shakespeare. As T **34** of Antigua.

183. 6d. purple 10 10

1965. Cent of I.T.U. As T **36** of Antigua.

184. 1d. blue and purple .. 15 10
185. 1s 3d. purple and green .. 40 25

1965. I.C.Y. As T **37** of Antigua.

186. 1d. purple and turquoise 10 10
187. 1s. green and lavender .. 40 25

1966. Churchill Commem. As T **38** of Antigua.

188. ¼d. blue 10 50
189. 1d. green 20 10
190. 1s. brown 50 10
191. 1s. 9d. violet 70 50

1966. Royal Visit. As T **39** of Antigua.

192. 1d. black and blue .. 50 10
193. 1s. 9d. black and mauve.. 1·75 45

1966. World Cup Football Championship. As T **40** of Antigua.

194. 1½d. multicoloured .. 10 10
195. 1s. 9d. multicoloured .. 40 25

1966. Inauguration of W.H.O. Headquarters, Geneva. As T **41** of Antigua.

196. 2d. black, green and blue 30 15
197. 1s 3d. blk., pur. & ochre .. 70 60

62. Telephone and Map.

1966. Int. Telephone Links.

198. 62. 4d. multicoloured .. 20 15
199. 9d. multicoloured .. 20 15

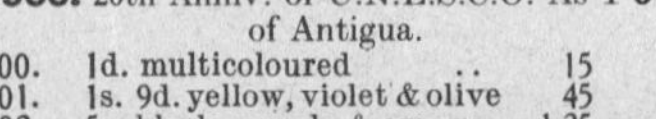

1966. 20th Anniv. of U.N.E.S.C.O. As T **54/6** of Antigua.

200. 1d. multicoloured .. 15 10
201. 1s. 9d. yellow, violet & olive 45 10
202. 5s. black, purple & orange 1·25 55

63. BAC 1-11 Airliner over Cayman Schooner.

1966. Opening of Cayman Jet Service.

203. 63. 1s. black, blue and green 40 20
204. 1s. 9d. purple, bl. & grn. 40 25

64. Water-skiing.

1967. Int. Tourist Year. Multicoloured.

205. 4d. Type **64** 30 10
206. 6d. Skin diving 30 20
207. 1s. Sport fishing 30 20
208. 1s. 9d. Sailing 45 45

68. Former Slaves and Emblem.

1968. Human Rights Year.

209. 68. 3d. green, black & gold 10 10
210. 9d. brown, gold & green 10 10
211. 5s. ultram., gold & green 30 45

69. Long-Jumping.

1968. Olympic Games, Mexico. Multicoloured.

212. 1s. Type **69** 10 10
213. 1s. 3d. High-jumping .. 15 20
214. 2s. Pole-vaulting 15 25

72. "The Adoration of the Shepherds" (Fabritius).

1968. Christmas. Multicoloured.

215. ¼d. Type **72** 10 20
221. ¼d. Type **72** 10 20
216. 1d. "The Adoration of the Shepherds" (Rembrandt).. .. .. 10 10
217. 6d. Type **72** 25 15
218. 8d. As 1d. 25 15
219. 1s. 3d. Type **72** 30 30
220. 2s. As 1d. 35 40

No. 215 has brown background and No. 221 a bright purple one.

74. Grand Cayman Thrush.

1969. Multicoloured.

No.	Description		
237	¼d. Type **74**	20	40
223	1d. Brahmin Cattle ..	10	10
224	2d. Blowholes on the coast	10	10
225	2½d. Map of Grand Cayman	15	10
226	3d. Georgetown scene ..	15	10
227	4d. Royal "Poinciana" ..	30	10
228	6d. Cayman Brac and Little Cayman on Chart ..	30	10
229	8d. Motor vessels at berth	30	10
230	1s. Basket making ..	20	10
231	1s. 3d. Beach scene ..	35	1·00
232	1s. 6d. Straw rope making	40	1·00
233	2s. Barracuda	1·00	80
234	4s. Government House ..	35	80
235	10s. Arms of the Cayman Islands	1·00	1·75
236	£1 black, ochre and red (Queen Elizabeth II) ..	2·00	2·50

Nos. 235/6 are vert.

1969. Decimal Currency. Nos. 222/36 **surch.** Multicoloured.

No.	Type	Description		
238.	**74.**	¼ c. on ¼d.	10	40
239.	–	1 c. on 1d.	10	10
240.	–	2 c. on 2d.	10	10
241.	–	3 c. on 4d.	10	10
242.	–	4 c. on 2½d.	10	10
243.	–	5 c. on 6d.	10	10
244.	–	7 c. on 8d.	10	10
245.	–	8 c. on 3d.	15	10
246.	–	10 c. on 1s.	25	10
247.	–	12 c. on 1s. 3d. ..	35	50
248.	–	15 c. on 1s. 6d. ..	45	50
249.	–	20 c. on 2s.	1·25	1·50
250.	–	40 c. on 4s.	45	80
251.	–	$1 on 10s.	1·50	1·60
252.	–	$2 on £1	2·00	3·25

90. "Madonna and Child" (Vivarini).

1969. Christmas. Multicoloured. Background colours given.

No.	Type	Description		
253.	**90.**	¼ c. red	10	10
254.		¼ c. mauve	10	10
255.		¼ c. green	10	10
256.		¼ c. blue	10	10
257.	–	1 c. blue	10	10
258.	**90.**	5 c. red	10	10
259.	–	7 c. green	10	10
260.	**90.**	12 c. green	15	15
261.	–	20 c. purple	20	25

DESIGNS: 1 c., 7 c., 20 c. "The Adoration of the Kings" (Gossaert).

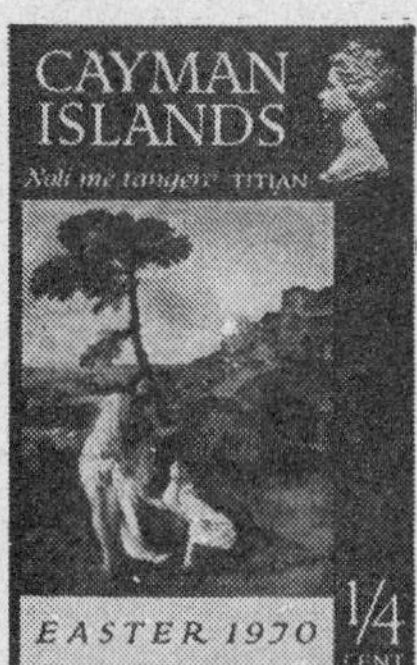

92. "Noli me tangere" (Titian).

1970. Easter. Multicoloured; frame colours given.

No.	Type	Description		
262.	**92.**	¼ c. red	10	10
263.		¼ c. green	10	10
264.		¼ c. brown	10	10
265.		¼ c. violet	10	10
266.		10 c. blue	25	10
267.		12 c. brown	25	10
268.		40 c. plum	35	35

93. Barnaby ("Barnaby Rudge").

1970. Death Centenary of Charles Dickens.

No.	Type	Description		
269.	**93.**	1 c. blk., grn. & yellow	10	10
270.	–	12 c. black, brown & red	10	10
271.	–	20 c. black, brn. & gold	15	10
272.	–	40 c. black, ultram. & blue	20	25

DESIGNS: 12 c. Sairey Gamp ("Martin Chuzzlewit"). 20 c. Mr. Micawber and David ("David Copperfield"). 40 c. The "Marchioness" ("The Old Curiosity Shop").

97. Grand Cayman Thrush.

1970. Decimal Currency. Designs as Nos. 222/36, but with values inscr. in decimal currency as in T **97.**

No.	Description		
273.	¼ c. multicoloured ..	10	10
274.	1 c. multicoloured ..	10	10
275.	2 c. multicoloured ..	10	10
276.	3 c. multicoloured ..	20	10
277.	4 c. multicoloured ..	20	10
278.	5 c. multicoloured ..	35	10
279.	7 c. multicoloured ..	30	10
280.	8 c. multicoloured ..	30	10
281.	10 c. multicoloured ..	30	10
282.	12 c. multicoloured ..	90	45
283.	15 c. multicoloured ..	1·25	1·25
284.	20 c. multicoloured ..	2·50	1·25
285.	40 c. multicoloured ..	85	75
286.	$1 multicoloured ..	1·75	3·00
287.	$2 black, ochre and red	2·75	4·00

98. The Three Wise Men.

1970. Christmas.

No.	Type	Description		
288.	**98.**	¼ c. green, grey and emer.	10	10
289.	–	1 c. black, yell. and grn.	10	10
290.	**98.**	5 c. grey, orange and red	10	10
291.	–	10 c. black, yell. and red	10	10
292.	**98.**	12 c. grey, green and blue	15	10
293.	–	20 c. black, yell. and grn.	20	15

DESIGN: 1 c., 10 c., 20 c. Nativity Scene and Globe.

100. Grand Cayman Terrapin.

1971. Turtles. Multicoloured.

No.	Description		
294.	5 c. Type **100**	30	25
295.	7 c. Green turtle	35	25
296.	12 c. Hawksbill turtle ..	55	30
297.	20 c. Turtle farm	1·00	1·40

101. "Dendrophylax fawcetti". **102.** "Adoration of the Kings" (French 15th cent.).

1971. Orchids. Multicoloured.

No.	Description		
298.	¼ c. Type **101**	10	45
299.	2 c. "Schomburgkia thomsoniana"	40	55
300.	10 c. "Vanilla claviculata"	90	70
301.	40 c "Oncidium variegatum"	3·00	3·50

1971. Christmas. Multicoloured.

No.	Description		
302.	¼ c. Type **102**	10	10
303.	1 c. "The Nativity" (Parisian, 14th cent.) ..	10	10
304.	5 c. "Adoration of the Magi" (Burgundian, 15th cent.)	10	10
305.	12 c. Type **102**	20	10
306.	15 c. As 1 c.	20	20
307.	20 c. As 5 c.	25	30

103. Turtle and Telephone Cable.

1972. Co-Axial Telephone Cable.

No.	Type	Description		
309.	**103.**	2 c. multicoloured ..	10	10
310.		10 c. multicoloured ..	10	10
311.		40 c. multicoloured ..	25	40

104. Court House Building.

1972. New Government Buildings. **Mult.**

No.	Description		
312.	5 c. Type **104**	10	10
313.	15 c. Legislative Assembly Building	10	10
314.	25 c. Type **104**	15	15
315.	40 c. As 15 c.	20	30

1972. Royal Silver Wedding. As T **52** of Ascension but with Hawksbill Turtle and Conch Shell in background.

No.	Description		
317.	12 c. violet	15	10
318.	30 c. green	15	20

106. $1 Coin and Note.

1972. 1st Issue of Currency. **Multicoloured.**

No.	Description		
319.	3 c. Type **106**	15	10
320.	6 c. $5 Coin and note ..	15	10
321.	15 c. $10 Coin and note ..	40	20
322.	25 c. $25 Coin and note ..	50	35

107. "The Way of Sorrow".

1973. Easter. Stained-Glass Windows. Multicoloured.

No.	Description		
324.	10 c. Type **107**	10	10
325.	12 c. "Christ Resurrected"	15	10
326.	20 c. "The Last Supper" (horiz.)	20	15
327.	30 c. "Christ on the Cross" (horiz.)	25	25

108. "The Nativity" (Storza Book of Hours).

1973. Christmas.

No.	Type	Description		
329.	**108.**	3 c. multicoloured ..	10	10
330.	–	5 c. multicoloured ..	10	10
331.	**108.**	9 c. multicoloured ..	15	10
332.	–	12 c. multicoloured ..	15	10
333.	**108.**	15 c. multicoloured ..	15	15
334.	–	25 c. multicoloured ..	20	25

DESIGN: 5, 12, 25 c. "The Adoration of the Magi" (Breviary of Queen Isabella).

1973. Royal Wedding. As Type **47** of Anguilla. Background colour given. **Mult.**

No.	Description		
335.	10 c. green	10	10
336.	30 c. mauve	15	10

109. White-winged Dove.

1974. Birds (1st series). **Multicoloured.**

No.	Description		
337.	3 c. Type **109**	1·40	20
338.	10 c. Vitelline Warbler ..	2·00	20
339.	12 c. Antillean Grackle	2·00	25
340.	20 c. West Indian Red-bellied Woodpecker ..	3·25	65
341.	30 c. Stripe-headed Tanager	5·00	1·50
342.	50 c. Yucatan Vireo ..	7·00	2·75

See also Nos. 383/8.

110. Old School Building.

1974. 25th Anniv. of University of West Indies. Multicoloured.

No.	Description		
343.	12 c. Type **110**	10	10
344.	20 c. New Comprehensive School	15	10
345.	30 c. Creative Arts Centre, Mona	15	25

111. Hermit Crab and Staghorn Coral.

1974. Size 41½ × 27 mm or 27 × 41½ mm. Mult.

No.	Description		
364	1 c Type **111**	1·25	1·50
412	3 c. Treasure-chest and lion's paw	85	1·50
348	4 c. Treasure and spotted scorpion-fish	50	70
349	5 c. Flintlock pistol and brain coral	2·25	60
350	6 c. Blackbeard and green turtle	35	1·00
415	8 c. As 9 c	2·50	1·75
351	9 c. Jewelled pomander and pork-fish	3·00	4·25
416	10 c. Spiny lobster & treasure	1·25	2·25
353	12 c. Jewelled sword and dagger and sea-fan ..	35	70
354	15 c. Cabrit's murex and treasure	40	1·00
417	20 c. Queen Conch & treasure	3·25	3·00
356	25 c. Hogfish and treasure	45	70
357	40 c. Gold chalice and sea-whip	2·00	1·00
358	$1 Coat of arms	2·75	3·25
359	$2 Queen Elizabeth II ..	4·00	9·00

For smaller designs see Nos. 445/52.

112. Sea Captain and Ship (Shipbuilding).

1974. Local Industries. Multicoloured.
360. 8 c. Type 112 .. .. 15 10
361. 12 c. Thatcher and cottage 15 10
362. 20 c. Farmer and plantation 25 20

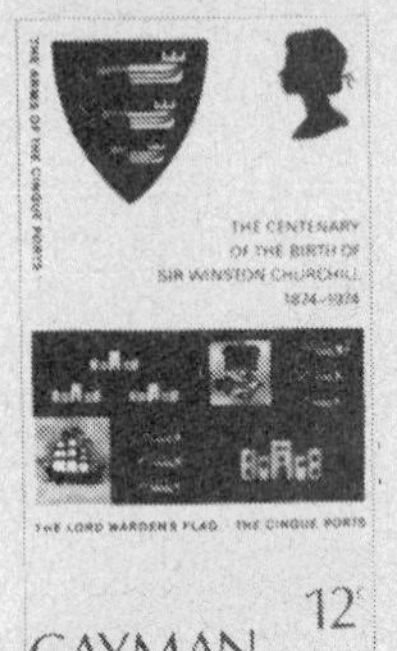

113. Arms of Cinque Ports and Lord Warden's Flag.

1974. Birth Centenary of Sir Winston Churchill. Multicoloured.
380. 12 c. Type 113 .. .. 15 10
381. 50 c. Churchill's coat of arms 45 70

1975. Birds (2nd series). As T 109. Mult.
383 3 c. Common flicker .. 70 45
384 10 c. Black-billed whistling duck .. .. 1·25 45
385 12 c. Yellow warbler .. 1·40 65
386 20 c. White-bellied dove .. 2·00 2·00
387 30 c. Magnificent frigate bird .. .. 3·25 3·50
388 50 c. Cuban amazon .. 3·75 5·00

114. "The Crucifixion".

1975. Easter. French Pastoral Staffs.
389. 114. 15 c. multicoloured .. 10 15
390. – 35 c. multicoloured .. 20 30
DESIGN: 35 c. Pastoral staff similar to Type 114.

115. Israel Hands.

1975. Pirates. Multicoloured.
392. 10 c. Type 115 .. .. 20 10
393. 12 c. John Fenn 20 10
394. 20 c. Thomas Anstis .. 40 35
395. 30 c. Edward Low .. 55 55

1975. Christmas. "Virgin and Child with Angels". As T 114.
396. 12 c. multicoloured .. 10 10
397. 50 c. multicoloured .. 30 30

116. Registered Cover, Government House and Sub-Post Office.

1975. 75th Anniv. of First Cayman Islands Postage Stamp. Multicoloured.
399. 10 c. Type 116 .. .. 10 10
400. 20 c. ½d. stamp and 1890–94 postmark .. 15 15
401. 30 c. 1d. stamp and 1908 surcharge 25 25
402. 50 c. ½d. and 1d. stamps .. 40 50

117. Seals of Georgia, Delaware and New Hampshire. (Illustration reduced. Actual size 58 × 22 mm.).

1976. Bicent. of American Revolution. Mult.
404. 10 c. Type 117 .. .. 50 15
405. 15 c. S.Carolina, New Jersey and Maryland seals .. 65 20
406. 20 c. Virginia, Rhode Is. and Massachusetts seals 75 25
407. 25 c. New York, Connecticut and N. Carolina seals 75 35
408. 30 c. Pennsylvania seal, Liberty Bell and U.S. Great Seal 90 40

118. Racing Dinghies.

1976. Olympic Games, Montreal. Mult.
410. 20 c. Type 118 .. .. 20 10
411. 50c. Racing dinghy .. 50 50

119. Queen Elizabeth II and Westminster Abbey.

1977. Silver Jubilee. Multicoloured.
427. 8 c. The Prince of Wales' visit, 1973 .. .. 10 20
428. 30 c. Type 119 .. .. 15 40
429. 50 c. Preparation of the Anointing (horiz.) .. 30 75

120. Scuba Diving.

1977. Tourism. Multicoloured.
430. 5 c. Type 120 .. .. 10 10
431. 10 c. Exploring a wreck .. 15 10
432. 20 c. Fairy Basslet (fish) .. 45 20
433. 25 c. Sergeant majors (fish) 55 35

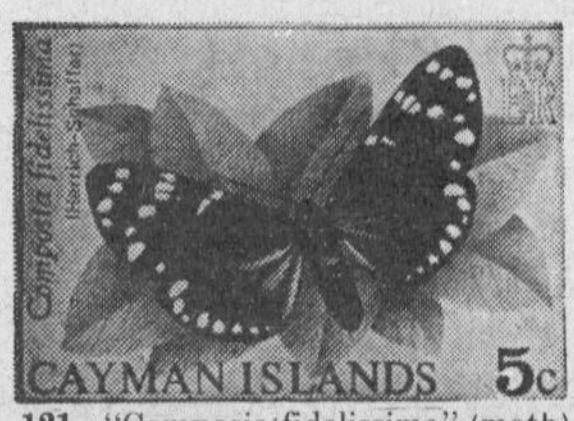

121. "Composia fidelissima" (moth).

1977. Butterflies and Moths. Multicoloured.
435 5 c. Type 121 .. .. 40 10
436 8 c. "Heliconius charithonia" 45 15
437 10 c. "Danaus gilippus" .. 45 15
438 15 c. "Agraulis vanillae" .. 80 40
439 20 c. "Junonia evarete" .. 1·00 45
440 30 c. "Anartia jatrophae" 1·25 70

122. Cruise Liner "Southward".

1978. New Harbour and Cruise Ships. Mult.
441. 3 c. Type 122 .. .. 15 10
442. 5 c. Cruise liner "Renaissance" 20 10
443. 30 c. New harbour (vert.) 70 25
444. 50 c. Cruise liner "Daphne" (vert.) 90 55

1978. As Nos. 346/59, 349, 352, 355, and 357/9, but designs smaller, 40 × 26 mm. or 26 × 40 mm.
445. 1 c. Type 111 .. .. 80 90
446. 3 c. Treasure chest and lion's paw 80 50
447. 5 c. Flintlock pistol and brain coral .. .. 1·50 2·25
448. 10 c. Spiny lobster and treasure .. .. .. 1·60 60
449. 20 c. Queen Conch and treasure .. .. .. 3·25 1·25
450. 40 c. Gold chalice and sea-whip .. .. .. 15·00 20·00
451. $1 Coat of arms (vert.) .. 8·00 8·00
452. $2 Queen Elizabeth II (vert.) .. .. 7·00 16·00

123. "The Crucifixion" (Durer).

1978. Easter and 450th Death Anniv. of Durers.
459. 123. 10 c. mauve and black .. 15 10
460. – 15 c. yellow and black .. 25 15
461. – 20 c. turquoise & black 30 20
462. – 30 c. lilac and black .. 45 35
DESIGNS: 15 c. "Christ at Emmaus". 20 c. "The Entry into Jerusalem". 30 c. "Christ washing Peter's Feet".

124. "Explorers" Singing Game.

125. Yale of Beaufort.

1978. 3rd International Council Meeting of Girls' Brigade. Multicoloured.
464. 3 c. Type 124 .. .. 15 10
465. 10 c. Colour party .. 25 10
466. 20 c. Girls and Duke of Edinburgh Award interests 50 20
467. 50 c. Girls using domestic skills .. .. .. 1·00 80

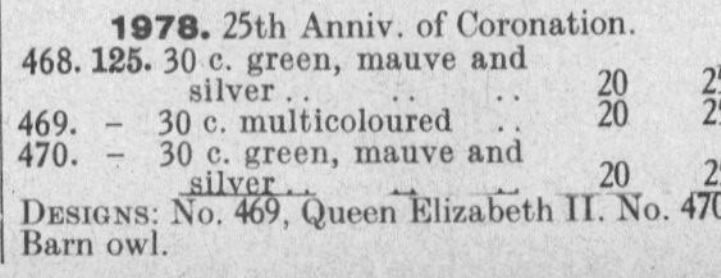

1978. 25th Anniv. of Coronation.
468. 125. 30 c. green, mauve and silver 20 25
469. – 30 c. multicoloured .. 20 25
470. – 30 c. green, mauve and silver 20 25
DESIGNS: No. 469, Queen Elizabeth II. No. 470, Barn owl.

126. Four Eyed Butterfly Fish.

1978. Fish (1st series). Multicoloured.
471. 3 c. Type 126 .. 15 10
472. 5 c. Grey Angel Fish .. 20 10
473. 10 c. Squirrel Fish 35 10
474. 15 c. Parrot Fish .. 45 30
475. 20 c. Spanish Hogfish .. 50 35
476. 30 c. Queen Angel Fish .. 60 50

127. Lockheed "Lodestar".

1979. 25th Anniv. of Owen Roberts Airfield. Multicoloured.
477. 3 c. Type 127 .. 15 10
478. 5 c. Consolidated "PBY" 15 10
479. 10 c. Vickers "Viking" .. 20 10
480. 15 c. B.A.C. "1-11" on tarmac 35 20
481. 20 c. Piper "Cheyenne" HS "125" and Bell "47" 45 30
482. 30 c. B.A.C. "1-11" over airfield 70 45

128. Trumpetfish.

1979. Fishes (2nd series). Multicoloured.
483. 1 c. Type 128 .. 10 10
484. 3 c. Nassau Grouper .. 15 10
485. 5 c. French Angelfish .. 15 10
486. 10 c. Schoolmaster Snappers 20 10
487. 20 c. Banded Butterflyfish 35 25
488. 50 c. Blackbar Soldierfish 70 70

129. 1900 1d. Stamp.

1979. Death Centenary of Sir Rowland Hill.
489. 129. 5 c. blk., carm. and blue 10 10
490. – 10 c. multicoloured .. 10 10
491. – 20 c. multicoloured .. 20 20
DESIGNS: 10 c. Great Britain 1902 3d. purple on lemon. 20 c. 1955 £1 blue.

130. The Holy Family and Angels.

1979. Christmas. Multicoloured.
493. 10 c. Type 130 .. .. 15 10
494. 20 c. Angels appearing to Shepherds 20 10
495. 30 c. Nativity 30 20
496. 40 c. The Magi .. 40 30

131. Local Rotary Project.

1980. 75th Anniv. of Rotary International.

497. 131. 20 c. blue, black & yell. 20 15
498. – 30 c. blue, black & yell. 25 20
499. – 50 c. blue, yell. & black 35 30

DESIGNS—VERT: 30 c. Paul P. Harris (founder). 50 c. Rotary anniversary emblem.

132. Walking Mail Carrier.

1980. " London 1980 " International Stamp Exhibition. Multicoloured.

500. 5 c. Type **132** 10 10
501. 10 c. Delivering mail by cat boat 15 10
502. 15 c. Mounted mail carrier 20 10
503. 30 c. Horse-drawn wagonette 30 15
504. 40 c. Postman on bicycle 30 15
505. $1 Motor transport .. 65 55

133. Queen Elizabeth the Queen Mother at the Derby, 1976.

1980. 80th Birthday of The Queen Mother.

506. **133.** 20 c. multicoloured .. 20 25

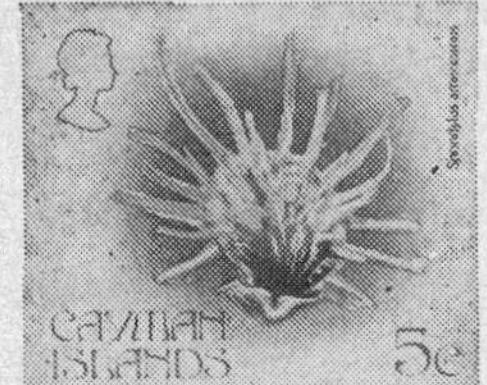

134. Atlantic Spiny Oyster.

1980. Shells. (1st series). Multicoloured.

507. 5 c. Type **134** 25 10
508. 10 c. West Indian Murex .. 25 10
509. 30 c. Triton 60 40
510. 50 c. Murex-line vase shell 75 80

See also Nos. 565/8 and 582/5.

135. Lantana.

1980. Flowers (1st series). Multicoloured.

511. 5 c. Type **135** 10 10
512. 15 c. " Bauhinia " .. 25 10
513. 30 c. " Hibiscus Rosa " .. 35 10
514. $1 " Milk and Wine Lily " 1·00 75

See also Nos. 541/4.

136. Juvenile Tarpon and Fire Sponge.

1980. Multicoloured.

515 3 c. Type **136** 40 50
516 5 c. Mangrove root oyster 50 50
517 10 c. Mangrove crab .. 40 40
518 15 c. Lizard and "Phycio-des phaon" (butterfly) 50 60
519 20 c. Louisiana heron .. 1·50 1·25
520 30 c. Red mangrove flower 70 80
521 40 c. Red mangrove seeds 75 80
522 50 c. Waterhouse's leaf-nosed bat .. .. 1·25 1·50
523 $1 Black-crowned night heron .. .. 4·00 4·25
524 $2 Coat of Arms .. .. 3·00 3·75
525 $5 Queen Elizabeth II .. 5·00 6·50

137. Eucharist.

1981. Easter. Multicoloured.

526. 3 c. Type **137** 10 10
527. 10 c. Crown of thorns .. 10 10
528. 20 c. Crucifix 20 10
529. $1 Lord Jesus Christ .. 70 80

138. Wood Slave.

1981. Reptiles and Amphibians. Multicoloured.

530. 20 c. Type **138** 30 20
531. 30 c. Cayman Iguana .. 45 35
532. 40 c. Lion Lizard 55 45
533. 50 c. Terrapin ("Hickatee") 65 55

139. Prince Charles.

1981. Royal Wedding. Multicoloured.

534. 20 c. Wedding bouquet from Cayman Islands .. 25 10
535. 30 c. Type **139** 40 10
536. $1 Prince Charles and Lady Diana Spencer .. .. 1·00 1·00

140. Disabled Scuba Divers.

1981. International Year of Disabled Persons. Multicoloured.

537. 5 c. Type **140** 10 10
538. 15 c. Old School for the Handicapped 30 20
539. 20 c. New School for the Handicapped 35 25
540. $1 Disabled people in wheelchairs, by the sea .. 1·60 1·25

1981. Flowers (2nd series). As T **135**. Mult.

541. 3 c. " Bougainvillea " .. 10 10
542. 10 c. " Morning Glory " 20 10
543. 20 c. " Wild Amaryllis " 45 25
544. $1 " Cordia " .. .. 1·75 1·75

141. Dr. Robert Koch and Microscope.

1982. Centenary of Robert Koch's Discovery of Tubercle Bacillus. Multicoloured.

545. 15 c. Type **141** 25 25
546. 30 c. Koch looking through microscope (vert). .. 45 45
547. 40 c. Microscope (vert.) .. 70 70
548. 50 c. Dr. Robert Koch (vert.) 80 80

142. Bride and Groom walking down Aisle.

1982. 21st Birthday of Princess of Wales. Multicoloured.

549. 20 c. Cayman Islands coat of arms 35 35
550. 30 c. Lady Diana Spencer in London, June, 1981 .. 45 45
551. 40 c. Type **142** 55 55
552. 50 c. Formal portrait .. 65 70

143. Pitching Tent.

1982. 75th Anniv. of Boy Scout Movement. Multicoloured.

553. 3 c. Type **143** 10 10
554. 20 c. Scouts camping .. 40 40
555. 30 c. Cub Scouts and Leaders 55 55
556. 50 c. Boating skills .. 85 85

144. " Madonna and Child with the Infant Baptist ".

1982. Christmas. Raphael Paintings. Mult.

557. 3 c. Type **144** 10 10
558. 10 c. " Madonna of the Tower " 20 20
559. 20 c. " Ansidei Madonna " 35 35
560. 30 c. " Madonna and Child " 50 50

145. Mace.

1982. 150th Anniv. of Representative Government. Multicoloured.

561. 3 c. Type **145** 10 10
562. 10 c. Old Courthouse .. 20 20
563. 20 c. Commonwealth Parliamentary Association coat of arms 35 35
564. 30 c. Legislative Assembly building 50 60

1983. Shells (2nd series). As T **134**. Mult.

565. 5 c. "Natica canrena" .. 15 10
566. 10 c. "Cassis tuberosa" .. 25 20
567. 20 c. "Strombus gallus" .. 45 40
568. $1 "Cypraecaissis testiculus" .. .. .. 1·75 1·75

146. Legislative Building, Cayman Brac.

1983. Royal Visit. Multicoloured.

569. 20 c. Type **146** 45 35
570. 30 c. Legislative Building, Grand Cayman 60 50
571. 50 c. Duke of Edinburgh (vert.) .. .. .. 1·25 90
572. $1 Queen Elizabeth II (vert.) .. .. .. 2·00 2·00

147. Satellite View of Earth.

1983. Commonwealth Day. Multicoloured.

574. 3 c. Type **147** 10 10
575 15 c. Cayman Islands and Commonwealth flags .. 25 30
576. 20 c. Fishing 30 35
577. 40 c. Portrait of Queen Elizabeth II 60 65

148. MRCU " Cessna " Aircraft.

1983. Bicentenary of Manned Flight. Multicoloured.

578. 3 c. Type **148** 20 15
579. 10 c. Consolidated " PBY Catalina " 35 20
580. 20 c. Boeing " 727-200 " .. 70 65
581. 40 c. Hawker Siddeley " HS 748 " .. .. 1·00 1·40

1984. Shells (3rd series). As Type **134**. Mult.

582. 3 c. " Natica floridana " .. 30 20
583. 10 c. " Conus austini " .. 55 25
584. 30 c. " Colubraia obscura " 1·10 80
585. 50 c. " Turbo cailletii " .. 1·40 1·50

149. "Song of Norway" (cruise liner).

1984. 250th Anniv of "Lloyd's List" (newspaper). Multicoloured.

586 5 c. Type **149** 20 10
587 10 c. View of old harbour 30 25
588 25 c. Wreck of "Ridgefield" (freighter) 80 65
589 50 c. "Goldfield" (schooner) .. .. 1·40 1·40

1984. Universal Postal Union Congress, Hamburg. No. 589 optd. **U.P.U. CONGRESS HAMBURG 1984.**

591. 50 c. Schooner "Goldfield" 1·00 1·50

151. Snowy Egret.

1984. Birds of the Cayman Islands (1st series). Multicoloured.

592. 5 c. Type **151** 55 15
593. 10 c. Bananaquit 65 25
594. 35 c. Belted kingfisher .. 2·00 1·25
595. $1 Brown booby .. .. 4·00 4·25

See also Nos. 627/30.

152. Couple on Beach at Sunset.

1984. Christmas. Local Festivities. Mult.

596.	5 c. Type **152**	15	25
597.	5 c. Family and schooner	15	25
598.	5 c. Carol singers	15	25
599.	5 c. East End bonfire	15	25
600.	25 c. Yachts	55	60
601.	25 c. Father Christmas in power-boat	55	60
602.	25 c. Children on beach	55	60
603.	25 c. Beach party	55	60

Nos 596/9 and 600/3 were each printed together, se-tenant, the four designs of each value forming a composite picture of a beach scene at night (5 c.) or in the daytime (25 c.).

153. "Schomburgkia thomsoniana (var. minor)".

1985. Orchids. Multicoloured.

605.	5 c. Type **153**	40	10
606.	10 c. "Schomburgkia thomsoniana"	65	20
607.	25 c. "Encyclia plicata"	1·40	70
608.	50 c. "Dendrophylax fawcettii"	1·60	2·00

154. Freighter Aground.

1985. Shipwrecks. Multicoloured.

609.	5 c. Type **154**	50	20
610.	25 c. Submerged sailing ship	1·50	85
611	35 c. Wrecked trawler	1·75	1·75
612	40 c. Submerged wreck on its side	1·90	2·25

155. Athletics.

1985. International Youth Year. Mult.

613.	5 c. Type **155**	10	10
614.	15 c. Students in library	25	30
615.	25 c. Football (vert.)	45	50
616.	50 c. Netball (vert.)	85	90

156. Morse Key (1935).

1985. 50th Anniv. of Telecommunications System. Multicoloured.

617.	5 c. Type **156**	15	10
618.	10 c. Hand cranked telephone	25	20
619.	25 c. Tropospheric scatter dish (1966)	55	60
620.	50 c. Earth station dish aerial (1979)	1·00	1·40

1986. 60th Birthday of Queen Elizabeth II. As T **110** of Ascension. Multicoloured.

621.	5 c. Princess Elizabeth at wedding of Lady May Cambridge, 1931	10	10
622.	10 c. In Norway, 1955	15	20
623.	25 c. Queen inspecting Royal Cayman Islands Police, 1983	45	50
624.	50 c. During Gulf tour, 1979	85	90
625.	$1 At Crown Agents Head Office, London, 1983	1·75	1·90

157. Magnificent Frigate Bird.

1986. Birds of the Cayman Islands (2nd series). Multicoloured.

627.	10 c. Type **157**	40	20
628.	25 c. Black-billed whistling duck (vert.)	85	85
629.	35 c. La Sagra's flycatcher (vert.)	95	1·25
630.	40 c. Yellow-faced grass-quit	1·10	1·75

1986. Royal Wedding. As T **112** of Ascension. Multicoloured.

633.	5 c. Prince Andrew and Miss Sarah Ferguson	20	10
634.	50 c. Prince Andrew aboard H.M.S. "Brazen"	1·10	1·00

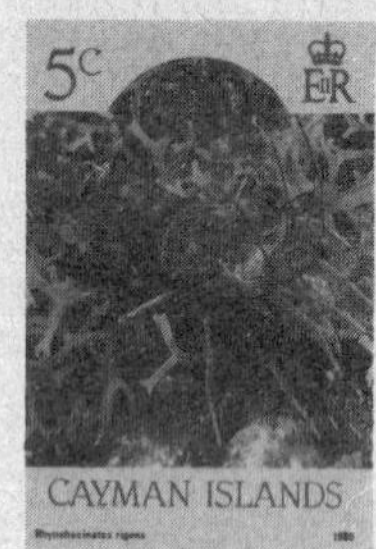

158. Red Coral Shrimp.

1986. Marine Life. Multicoloured.

635	5 c. Type **158**	30	40
636	10 c. Yellow crinoid	40	40
637	15 c. Hermit crab	35	50
638	20 c. Tube dwelling anemone	35	50
639	25 c. Christmas tree worm	45	60
640	35 c. Spiny puffer fish	70	80
641	50 c. Orangeball anemone	80	1·25
642	60 c. Basket starfish	80	1·40
643	75 c. Flamingo tongue snail	1·00	1·75
644	$1 Sea anemone	1·40	2·00
645	$2 Diamond blenny	2·75	3·50
646	$4 Flaming scallop	5·50	6·00

159. Golf.

1987. Tourism. Multicoloured.

647.	10 c. Type **159**	50	30
648.	15 c. Sailing	70	40
649.	25 c. Snorkelling	85	60
650.	35 c. Paragliding	95	85
651.	$1 Game fishing	2·50	3·50

HAVE YOU READ THE NOTES AT THE BEGINNING OF THIS CATALOGUE?
These often provide answers to the enquiries we receive.

160. Ackee.

1987. Cayman Islands Fruits. Multicoloured.

652.	5 c. Type **160**	10	10
653.	25 c. Breadfruit	45	45
654.	35 c. Pawpaw	60	60
655.	$1 Soursop	1·60	2·50

161. Lion Lizard.

1987. Lizards. Multicoloured.

656.	10 c. Type **161**	30	20
657.	50 c. Iguana	1·10	90
658.	$1 Anole	2·00	1·75

162. Poinsettia.

1987. Flowers. Multicoloured.

659.	5 c. Type **162**	30	10
660.	25 c. Periwinkle	90	50
661.	35 c. Yellow allamanda	1·00	80
662.	75 c. Blood lily	2·00	2·25

163. "Hemiargus ammon" and "Strymon martialis".

1988. Butterflies. Multicoloured.

663	5 c. Type **163**	50	20
664	25 c. "Phocides pigmalion"	1·10	55
665	50 c. "Anaea troglodyta"	1·60	1·50
666	$1 "Papilio andraemon"	2·00	2·50

164 Green Heron

1988. Herons. Multicoloured.

667	5 c. Type **164**	40	15
668	25 c. Louisiana Heron	1·00	50
669	50 c. Yellow-crowned night heron	1·40	1·40
670	$1 Little blue heron	1·75	2·25

165 Cycling

1988. Olympic Games, Seoul. Multicoloured.

671	10 c. Type **165**	15	20
672	50 c. Cayman Airways airliner and national team	70	75
673	$1 Sailing	1·40	1·50

166 Princess Alexandra

1988. Visit of Princess Alexandra. Mult.

675	5 c. Type **166**	30	10
676	$1 Princess Alexandra in evening dress	2·50	1·90

167 Georgetown Post Office and Cayman Postmark on Jamaica 1d., 1889

1989. Centenary of Cayman Islands Postal Service. Multicoloured.

677	**167**	5 c. multicoloured	20	20
678	–	25 c. green, black & bl	65	65
679	–	35 c. multicoloured	80	80
680	–	$1 multicoloured	2·00	2·00

DESIGNS: 25 c. "Orinoco" (mail steamer) and 1900 ½d. stamp; 35 c. G.P.O., Grand Cayman and "London 1980" $1 stamp; $1 Cayman Airways plane and 1966 1s. Jet Service stamp.

168 Captain Bligh ashore in West Indies

1989. Captain Bligh's Second Breadfruit Voyage, 1791-93. Multicoloured.

681	50 c. Type **168**	1·90	2·00
682	50 c. H.M.S. "Providence" (sloop) at anchor	1·90	2·00
683	50 c. Breadfruit in tubs and H.M.S. "Assistant" (transport)	1·90	2·00
684	50 c. Sailors moving tubs of breadfruit	1·90	2·00
685	50 c. Midshipman and stores	1·90	2·00

Nos. 681/5 were printed together, se-tenant, forming a composite design.

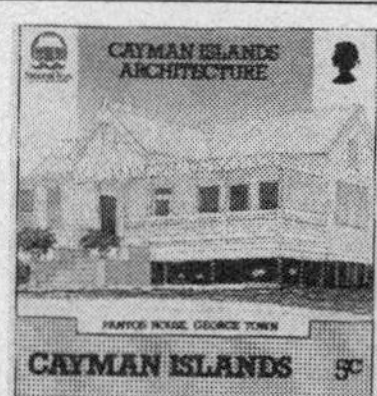

169 Panton House

1989. Architecture. Designs showing George Town buildings. Multicoloured.
686 5 c. Type **169** 10 15
687 10 c. Town hall and clock tower 15 20
688 25 c. Old Court House .. 40 50
689 35 c. Elmslie Memorial Church 55 65
690 $1 Post Office .. .. 1·50 2·00

170 Map of Grand Cayman, 1773, and Surveying Instruments

1989. Island Maps and Survey Ships. Mult.
691 5 c. Type **170** 30 30
692 25 c. Map of Cayman Islands, 1956, and surveying instruments 1·00 90
693 50 c. H.M.S. "Mutine", 1914 .. .. .. 1·75 1·75
694 $1 H.M.S. "Vidal", 1956 2·75 3·00

171 French Angel Fish

1990. Angel Fishes. Multicoloured.
707 10 c. Type **171** 40 30
708 25 c. Grey angel fish .. 80 60
709 50 c. Queen angel fish .. 1·60 1·60
710 $1 Rock beauty .. .. 2·25 2·50

1990. 90th Birthday of Queen Elizabeth the Queen Mother. As T **134** of Ascension.
711 50 c. multicoloured .. 1·00 1·00
712 $1 black and blue .. 2·00 2·25
DESIGNS—21 × 36 mm. 50 c. Silver Wedding photograph, 1948. 29 × 37 mm. $1 King George VI and Queen Elizabeth with Winston Churchill, 1940.

172 "Danaus eresimus"

1990. "Expo 90" International Garden and Greenery Exhibition, Osaka. Butterflies. Multicoloured.
713 5 c. Type **172** 30 25
714 25 c. "Brephidium exilis" 85 85
715 35 c. "Phyciodes phaon" 1·00 1·00
716 $1 "Agraulis vanillae" .. 2·50 2·75

173 Goes Weather Satellite

1991. International Decade for Natural Disaster Reduction. Multicoloured.
717 5 c. Type **173** 25 20
718 30 c. Meteorologist tracking hurricane .. 80 80
719 40 c. Damaged buildings .. 95 95
720 $1 U.S. Dept of Commerce weather reconnaisance Lockheed WP-3D Orion 2·75 3·00

174 Angels and "Datura candida"

1991. Christmas. Multicoloured.
721 5 c. Type **174** 15 15
722 30 c. Mary and Joseph going to Bethlehem and "Allamanda cathartica" 60 60
723 40 c. Adoration of the Kings and "Euphorbia pulcherrima" 75 75
724 60 c. Holy Family and "Guaiacum officinale" 95 95

175 Coconut Palm

1991. Island Scenes. Multicoloured.
725 5 c. Type **175** 10 10
726 15 c. Beach scene (horiz) .. 15 20
727 20 c. Poincianas in bloom (horiz) 30 35
728 30 c. Blowholes (horiz) .. 45 50
729 40 c. Police band (horiz) .. 60 65
730 50 c. "Song of Norway" (liner) at George Town 80 85
731 60 c. The Bluff, Cayman Brac (horiz) .. .. 95 1·00
732 80 c. Coat of arms .. 1·25 1·40
733 90 c. View of Hell (horiz) 1·40 1·50
734 $1 Game fishing (horiz) 1·50 1·60
735 $2 "Nieuw Amsterdam" (1983) and "Holiday" (liners) in harbour .. 3·00 3·25
736 $8 Queen Elizabeth II .. 12·50 13·00

1992. 40th Anniv of Queen Elizabeth II's Accession. As T **143** of Ascension. Mult.
737 5 c. Cayman's house .. 15 15
738 20 c. Sunset over islands .. 45 40
739 30 c. Beach 60 55
740 40 c. Three portraits of Queen Elizabeth .. 80 75
741 $1 Queen Elizabeth II .. 1·90 2·00

176 Single Cyclist

1992. Olympic Games, Barcelona. Cycling. Multicoloured.
742 15 c. Type **176** 40 30
743 40 c. Two cyclists .. 85 85
744 60 c. Cyclist's legs .. 1·40 1·50
745 $1 Two pursuit cyclists .. 1·60 1·90

177 Woman and Donkey with Panniers

1992. Island Heritage. Multicoloured.
746 5 c. Type **177** 15 10
747 30 c. Fisherman weaving net 55 55
748 40 c. Maypole dancing .. 70 70
749 60 c. Basket making .. 1·25 1·40
750 $1 Cooking on caboose .. 1·75 2·00

178 Yellow Sting-ray

1993. Rays. Multicoloured.
751 5 c. Type **178** 15 10
752 30 c. Southern sting-ray .. 60 60
753 40 c. Spotted eagle ray .. 80 80
754 $1 Manta ray .. .. 2·00 2·25

179 Turtle and Sailing Dinghies

1993. Tourism. Multicoloured.
755 15 c. Type **179** 40 45
756 15 c. Tourist boat, fishing launch and scuba diver 40 45
757 15 c. Golf 40 45
758 15 c. Tennis 40 45
759 15 c. Pirates and ship .. 40 45
760 30 c. Liner, tourist launch and yacht 75 85
761 30 c. Georgetown street .. 75 85
762 30 c. Tourist submarine .. 75 85
763 30 c. Motor scooter riders and cyclist 75 85
764 30 c. Cayman Airways aircraft 75 85

180 Grand Cayman Parrot with Wings spread

1993. Endangered Species. Grand Cayman Parrot. Multicoloured.
765 5 c. Type **180** 15 10
766 5 c. On branch with wings folded 15 10
767 30 c. Head of parrot .. 75 80
768 30 c. Pair of parrots .. 75 80

181 "Ionopsis utricularioides" and Manger

1993. Christmas. Orchids. Multicoloured.
769 5 c. Type **181** 10 10
770 40 c. "Encyclia cochleata" and shepherd 60 65
771 60 c. "Vanilla pompona" and wise men .. .. 95 1·00
772 $1 "Oncidium caymanense" and Virgin Mary 1·50 1·60

183 Flags of Great Britain and Cayman Islands

1994. Royal Visit. Multicoloured.
774 5 c. Type **183** 10 10
775 15 c. Royal Yacht "Britannia" .. 25 30
776 30 c. Queen Elizabeth II .. 45 50
777 $2 Queen Elizabeth and Prince Philip disembarking .. .. 3·00 3·25

184 Black-billed Whistling Duck

1994. Black-billed Whistling Duck ("West Indian Whistling Duck"). Multicoloured.
778 5 c. Type **184** 10 10
779 15 c. Duck landing on water (horiz) 25 30
780 20 c. Duck preening (horiz) 30 35
781 80 c. Duck flapping wings 1·25 1·40
782 $1 Adult and duckling .. 1·50 1·60

CEYLON

An island to the S. of India formerly under British administration, then a self-governing Dominion. The island became a Republic within the Commonwealth on 22 May 1972 and was renamed Sri Lanka (q.v.).

1857. 12 pence = 1 shilling;
20 shillings = 1 pound.
1872. 100 cents = 1 rupee.

2.

3.

1.

8.

1857. Imperf.

4. 2. ½d. lilac £160 £150
5. 1. 1d. blue .. .. .. £600 19·00
7. 2d. green .. .. .. £150 50·00
9. 3. 4d. red £50000 £4500
10. 1. 5d. brown £1500 £150
11. 6d. brown £1800 £130
13. 3. 8d. brown £20000 £1500
14. 9d. brown £30000 £900
15. 1. 10d. orange £800 £250
16. 1s. violet £4500 £200
17. 3. 1s. 9d. green £700 £800
19. 2s. blue £5000 £1200

The prices of these imperf. stamps vary greatly according to condition. The above prices are for fine copies with four margins. Poor to medium specimens are worth much less.

1861. Perf.

71 2 ½d. lilac .. .. 19·00 19·00
94 1 1d. blue .. .. 60·00 4·00
78 2d. green .. .. 35·00 6·00
98 2d. yellow .. .. 29·00 5·00
100 3 4d. red .. .. 29·00 11·00
27 1 5d. brown .. .. 75·00 8·00
101 5d. green .. .. 38·00 6·50
104 6d. brown .. .. 40·00 8·50
89 3 8d. brown .. .. 45·00 23·00
110 9d. brown .. .. 23·00 6·00
111a 1 10d. orange .. .. 25·00 5·00
114 1s. violet .. .. 60·00 5·50
117 3 2s. blue .. .. 65·00 11·00

1866. The 3d. has portrait in circle.

119. 8. 1d. blue .. .. .. 11·00 4·75
120. – 3d. red .. .. .. 45·00 22·00

9.

10.

30.

1872. Various frames.

256 9 2 c. brown .. .. 1·25 30
147 2 c. green .. .. 1·40 15
122 10 4 c. grey .. .. 27·00 1·25
148 4 c. purple .. .. 1·60 30
246 4 c. red .. .. 7·50 7·50
258 4 c. yellow .. .. 1·50 2·75
150 – 8 c. yellow .. .. 3·00 7·00
126 – 16 c. violet .. .. 60·00 2·75
127 – 24 c. green .. .. 30·00 2·00
128 – 32 c. grey .. .. 95·00 14·00
129 – 36 c. blue .. .. 80·00 16·00
130 – 48 c. red .. .. 60·00 5·00
131 – 64 c. brown .. .. £180 55·00
132 – 96 c. grey .. .. £150 26·00
201 30 1 r. 12 red .. .. 18·00 17·00
138 2 r. 50 red £450 £300
249 2 r. 50 purple on red .. 22·00 45·00

1882. Nos. 127 and 131 surch. in words and figures.

142. – 16 c. on 24 c. green .. 18·00 6·50
143. – 20 c. on 64 c. brown .. 9·00 3·50

1885. As Nos. 148/132 surch **Postage & Revenue** and value in words.

178. 5 c. on 4 c. red .. .. 13·00 3·25
179. 5 c. on 8 c. yellow .. 38·00 6·00
180. 5 c. on 16 c. violet .. 50·00 8·50
154. 5 c. on 24 c. green .. £1200 £100
182. 5 c. on 24 c. purple .. — £500
155. 5 c. on 32 c. grey .. 50·00 15·00
156. 5 c. on 36 c. blue .. £110 8·00
157. 5 c. on 48 c. red .. £450 32·00
158. 5 c. on 64 c. brown .. 50·00 4·50
159. 5 c. on 96 c. grey .. £275 55·00

1885. As Nos. 126/249 surch. with new value in words.

184 10 c. on 16 c. violet .. £2750 £600
162 10 c. on 24 c. green .. £275 75·00
185 10 c. on 24 c. purple .. 9·50 5·00
163 10 c. on 36 c. blue .. £300 £150
174 10 c. on 64 c. brown .. 40·00 65·00
186 15 c. on 16 c. violet .. 8·00 5·50
165 20 c. on 24 c. green .. 35·00 13·00
166 20 c. on 32 c. grey .. 28·00 25·00
167 25 c. on 32 c. grey .. 10·00 4·25
168 28 c. on 48 c. red .. 30·00 5·00
169 30 c. on 36 c. blue .. 8·50 7·50
170 56 c. on 96 c. grey .. 15·00 11·00
176 1 r. 12 on 2 r. 50 red .. 60·00 35·00

1885. Surch. **REVENUE AND POSTAGE 5 CENTS.**

187. – 5 c. on 8 c. lilac (as No. 150a) .. 7·50 1·00

1885. As Nos. 126/32 surch. in words and figures.

188. 10 c. on 24 c. purple .. 8·50 4·50
189. 15 c. on 16 c. yellow .. 38·00 5·00
190. 28 c. on 32 c. grey .. 13·00 2·50
191. 30 c. on 36 c. olive .. 27·00 14·00
192. 56 c. on 96 c. grey .. 32·00 8·00

1885. Surch. **1 R. 12 C.**

193. 30. 1 r. 12 on 2 r. 50 red .. 29·00 70·00

39.

28.

43.

1886.

245 39 3 c. brown and green .. 1·75 45
257 3 c. green .. .. 1·25 55
195 28 5 c. purple .. .. 1·50 10
259 39 6 c. red and black .. 75 45
260 12 c. olive and red .. 3·00 6·50
197 15 c. olive .. .. 3·25 80
261 15 c. blue .. .. 4·75 1·25
198 25 c. brown .. .. 2·25 1·00
199 28 c. grey .. .. 12·00 1·40
247 30 c. mauve and brown 4·00 1·75
262 75 c. black and brown .. 4·25 4·50
263 43 1 r. 50 red .. .. 15·00 35·00
264 2 r. 25 blue .. .. 28·00 35·00

1887. Nos. 148/9 surch.

A. Surch. **TWO CENTS.**

202. 10. 2 c. on 4 c. purple .. 1·00 50
203. 2 c. on 4 c. red 75 35

B. Surch. **TWO.**

204. 10. 2 c. on 4 c. purple .. 60 20
205. 2 c. on 4 c. red .. .. 2·50 20

C. Surch. **2 Cents** and bar.

206. 10. 2 c. on 4 c. purple .. 38·00 26·00
207. 2 c. on 4 c. red .. .. 2·00 75

D. Surch. **Two Cents** and bar.

208. 10. 2 c. on 4 c. purple .. 40·00 16·00
209. 2 c. on 4 c. red .. .. 2·00 80

E. Surch. **2 Cents** without bar.

210. 10. 2 c. on 4 c. purple .. 35·00 22·00
211. 2 c. on 4 c. red .. .. 6·00 60

1890. Surch. **POSTAGE Five Cents REVENUE.**

233. 39. 5 c. on 15 c. olive .. 1·25 1·50

1891. Surch. **FIFTEEN CENTS.**

239. 39. 15 c. on 25 c. brown .. 7·50 10·00
240. 15 c. on 28 c. grey .. 6·50 8·50

1892. Surch. **3 Cents** and bar.

241. 10. 3 c. on 4 c. purple .. 75 2·00
242. 3 c. on 4 c. red .. .. 1·50 5·50
243. 39. 3 c. on 28 c. grey .. 1·75 2·00

1898. Surch **Six Cents.**

250 39 6 c. on 15 c. green .. 55 45

1898. Surch with new value.

254 30 1 r. 50 on 2 r. 50 grey .. 20·00 40·00
255 2 r. 25 on 2 r. 50 yellow 28·00 70·00

44.

45.

1903. Various frames.

277. 44. 2 c. brown 55 10
278. 45. 3 c. green (A) 75 15
293. 3 c. green (B) .. .. 1·00 85
279. 4 c. orange and blue .. 65 55
268. – 5 c. purple } see footnote .. 1·50 30
289. – 5 c. purple } 2·00 10
281. – 6 c. red .. } 1·10 15
291. – 6 c. red .. } .. 70 10
294. 45. 10 c. olive and red .. 1·50 1·25
282. 12 c. olive and red .. 1·50 1·75
283. 15 c. blue 90 60
284. 25 c. brown .. .. 6·00 3·75
295. 25 c. grey .. .. 2·50 80
285. 30 c. violet and green .. 2·50 1·50
296. 50 c. brown .. .. 4·00 7·50
286. 75 c. blue and orange .. 5·25 8·00
297. 1 r. purple on yellow .. 7·50 10·00
287. 1 r. 50 grey .. .. 15·00 10·00
298. 2 r. red on yellow .. 15·00 27·00
288. 2 r. 25 brown and green 18·00 29·00
299. 5 r. black on green .. 35·00 65·00
300. 10 r. black on red .. 65·00 £160

(A) has value in shaded tablet; (B) in white tablet as in Type **45.**

Nos. 268 and 281 have the value in words; Nos. 289 and 291 in figures.

52. 57.

1912.

301 52. 1 c. brown 70 10
308 2 c. orange 30 20
339 3 c. green 55 75
355 3 c. grey 30 20
340 5 c. purple 30 15
341 6 c. red 55 75
356 6 c. violet 30 15
357 9 c. red on yellow .. 40 35
343 10 c. olive 60 40
360d 12 c. red .. .. 80 1·50
315 15 c. blue .. .. 1·50 1·25
359 15 c. green on yellow .. 1·25 1·25
360f 20 c. blue .. .. 1·00 45
346 25 c. yellow and blue .. 80 1·25
360h 30 c. green and violet 1·60 1·25
348 50 c. black and red .. 1·00 80
322a 1 r. purple on yellow 1·40 3·25
323a 2 r. black & red on yell. 2·25 8·50
324a 5 r. black on green .. 11·00 26·00
325 10 r. pur. & blk. on red 48·00 60·00
352 20 r. blk. & red on blue 75·00 75·00

Large type, as Bermuda T **15.**

327. 50 r. purple £300
328. 100 r. black £1300
360. 100 r. purple and blue .. £1300

1918. Optd. **WAR STAMP** or surch. **ONE CENT** and bar also

335. 52. 1 c. on 5 c. purple .. 50 30
330. 2 c. orange 20 40
331. 3 c. green 15 20
333. 5 c. purple 30 30

1918. Surch. **ONE CENT** and bar.

337. 52. 1 c. on 5 c. purple .. 15 25

1926. Surch. with new value and **bar.**

361. 52. 2 c. on 3 c. grey .. 70 1·00
362. 5 c. on 6 c. violet .. 50 40

1927.

363. 57. 1 r. purple .. .. 1·75 1·25
364. 2 r. green and red .. 3·75 2·75
365. 5 r. green and purple .. 12·00 18·00
366. 10 r. green and orange .. 28·00 75·00
367. 20 r. purple and blue .. 70·00 £160

60. Adam's Peak.

1935. King George V.

368. – 2 c. black and red .. 30 40
369. 60. 3 c. black and green .. 35 40
370. – 6 c. black and blue .. 30 30
371. – 9 c. green and orange .. 1·00 50
372. – 10 c. black and purple .. 1·25 1·25
373. – 15 c. brown and green .. 1·00 50
374. – 20 c. black and blue .. 1·75 1·75
375. – 25 c. blue and brown .. 1·40 1·25
376. – 30 c. red and green .. 3·00 1·25
377. – 50 c. black and violet .. 6·50 1·25
378. – 1 r. violet and brown .. 9·00 8·50

DESIGNS—VERT. 2 c. Tapping rubber. 6 c, Colombo Harbour. 9 c. Plucking tea. 20 c. Coconut palms. HORIZ. 10 c. Hill paddy (rice). 15 c. River scene. 25 c. Temple of the Tooth, Kandy. 30 c. Ancient irrigation tank. 50 c. Indian elephants. 1 r. Trincomalee.

1935. Silver Jubilee. As T **13** of **Antigua.**

379. 6 c. blue and grey .. 45 30
380. 9 c. green and blue .. 70 50
381. 20 c. brown and blue .. 4·25 2·00
382. 50 c. grey and purple .. 5·25 4·50

1937. Coronation. As T **2** of Aden.

383. 6 c. red 65 15
384. 9 c. green .. .. 2·50 2·00
385. 20 c. blue .. .. 3·50 3·75

70. Sigiriya (Lion Rock).

1938. As 1935 issue but with portrait of King George VI and "POSTAGE & REVENUE" omitted.

386b – 2 c. black and red .. 30 10
387e 60. 3 c. black and green .. 30 15
387f – 5 c. green and orange .. 30 10
388 – 6 c. black and blue .. 30 10
389 70. 10 c. black and blue .. 1·25 10
390 – 15 c. green and brown 1·25 10
391 – 20 c. black and blue .. 2·75 10
392a – 25 c. blue and brown .. 2·00 10
393 – 30 c. red and green .. 11·00 90
394e – 50 c. black and violet .. 2·50 20
395 – 1 r. blue and brown .. 12·00 45
396 – 2 r. black and red .. 6·50 1·50
396a – 2 r. black and violet .. 1·50 85

DESIGNS—VERT. 5 c. Coconut palms. 20 c. Plucking tea. 2 r. Ancient Guard-stone, Anuradhapura. Others, same as for corresponding values of 1935 issue.

1938. As T **57,** but head of King George VI to right.

397a. 5 r. green and purple .. 11·00 2·00

1940. Surch. with new value and bars.

398. – 3 c. on 6 c. black & blue (No. 388) 10 10
399. – 3 c. on 20 c. black & blue (No. 391) .. .. 1·50 1·00

1946. Victory. As T **9** of Aden.

400. 6 c. blue 10 10
401. 15 c. brown 10 40

75. Parliament Building.

1947. New Constitution.

402. 75. 6 c. black and blue .. 10 15
403. – 10 c. black, orge. & red 10 20
404. – 15 c. green and purple .. 10 30
405. – 25 c. yellow and green .. 10 15

DESIGNS—VERT. 10 c. Adam's Peak. 25 c. Anuradhapura. HORIZ. 15 c. Temple of the Tooth.

79. Lion Flag of Dominion.

80. D. S. Senanayake.

1949. 1st Anniv. of Independence.

406. 79. 4 c. red, yellow & brown 10 20
407. 80. 5 c. brown and green .. 10 10
408. 79. 15 c. red, yellow & orge. 25 15
409. 80. 25 c. brown and blue .. 15 20

No. 408 is larger (28×22 mm.).

82. Globe and Forms of Transport.

1949. 75th Anniv. of U.P.U. Inscr. as in T **45**. Designs show globe.

No.	Type	Description	Unused	Used
410.	**82.**	5 c. brown and green ..	75	10
411.	–	15 c. blk. & red (horiz.)	1·40	85
412.	–	25 c. blk. & blue (vert.)	1·40	75

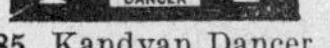

85. Kandyan Dancer. **88.** Sigiriya (Lion Rock).

90. Ruins at Madirgiriya.

1950.

No.	Type	Description	Unused	Used
413.	**85.**	4 c. purple and red ..	10	10
414.	–	5 c. green	10	10
415.	–	15 c. green and violet ..	1·50	30
416.	**88.**	30 c. red and yellow ..	30	40
417.	–	75 c. blue and orange ..	1·00	10
418.	**90.**	1 r. blue and brown ..	1·75	10

DESIGNS—VERT. As Types **85** and **88**: 5 c. Kiri Vehera, Polonnaruwa. 15 c. Vesak orchid. As Type **90**: 75 c. Octagon Library, Temple of the Tooth.

94. Coconut Trees. **99.** Tea Plantation.

1951.

No.	Type	Description	Unused	Used
419	–	2 c. brown & turquoise	10	30
420	–	3 c. black and violet ..	10	50
421	–	6 c. sepia and green ..	10	20
422	**94**	10 c. green and grey ..	75	40
423	–	25 c. orange and blue	10	20
424	–	35 c. red and green ..	1·50	1·25
425	–	40 c. brown	3·00	70
426	–	50 c. slate	30	10
427	**99**	85 c. black & turquoise	50	10
428	–	2 r. blue and brown ..	4·50	60
429	–	5 r. brown and orange	4·75	70
430	–	10 r. brown and buff ..	16·00	5·50

DESIGNS—As Type **94**. VERT. 2 c. Sambars, Ruhuna National Park. 3 c. Ancient Guard-stone, Anuradhapura. 6 c. Harvesting rice. 25 c. Sigiriya fresco. 35 c. Star orchid. HORIZ. 40 c. Rubber plantation. 50 c. Outrigger canoe. As Type **99**. HORIZ. 2 r. River Gal Dam. VERT. 5 r. Bas-relief, Anuradhapura. 10 r. Harvesting rice.

103. Ceylon. Mace and Symbols of Progress.

1952. Colombo Plan Exn.

No.	Type	Description	Unused	Used
431.	**103.**	5 c. green	10	10
432.		15 c. blue	20	40

104. Queen Elizabeth II. **106.** King Coconuts.

105. Ceremonial Procession.

1953. Coronation.

No.	Type	Description	Unused	Used
433.	**104.**	5 c. green	80	10

1954. Royal Visit.

No.	Type	Description	Unused	Used
434.	**105.**	10 c. blue	15	10

1954.

No.	Type	Description	Unused	Used
435.	**106.**	10 c. orge., brn. & buff	10	10

107. Farm Produce.

1955. Royal Agricultural and Food Exn.

No.	Type	Description	Unused	Used
436.	**107.**	10 c. brown and orange	10	10

108. Sir John Kotelawala and House of Representatives.

1956. Prime Minister's 25 years of Public Service.

No.	Type	Description	Unused	Used
437.	**108.**	10 c. green	10	10

109. Arrival of Vijaya in Ceylon.

110. Lampstand and Dharmachakra.

DESIGNS—VERT. 10 c. Hand of Peace and Dharmachakra. HORIZ. 15 c. Dharmachakra encircling the globe.

1956. Buddha Jayanti. Inscr. "2500".

No.	Type	Description	Unused	Used
438.	**109.**	3 c. blue and grey ..	15	10
439.	**110.**	4 c.+2 c. yellow & blue	20	50
440.	–	10 c.+5 c. red, yellow and grey	20	40
441.	–	15 c. blue	25	10

113. Mail Transport. **114.** Stamp of 1857.

1957. Stamp Centenary.

No.	Type	Description	Unused	Used
442.	**113.**	4 c. red and turquoise ..	60	30
443.		10 c. red and blue ..	60	10
444.	**114.**	35 c. brn., yell. and blue	30	30
445.		85 c. brn., yell. and grn.	70	1·10

1958. Nos. 439/40 with premium obliterated with bars.

No.	Type	Description	Unused	Used
446.	**110.**	4 c. yellow and blue ..	10	10
447.	–	10 c. red, yellow & grey	10	10

117. Kandyan Dancer.

1958. As Nos. 413 and 419, etc., and 435, but with inscriptions changed as in T **117**.

No.	Description	Unused	Used
448	2 c. brown and turquoise ..	10	40
449	3 c. black and violet ..	10	50
450	4 c. purple and red ..	10	10
451	5 c. green	10	10
452	6 c. sepia and green ..	10	55
453	10 c. orange, brown & buff	10	10
454	15 c. green and violet ..	3·50	60
455	25 c. orange and blue ..	10	10
456	30 c. red and yellow ..	15	70
457	35 c. red and green ..	4·50	15
459	50 c. slate	30	10
460a	75 c. blue and orange ..	2·00	70
461	85 c. black and turquoise	3·75	3·00
462	1 r. blue and brown ..	60	10
463	2 r. blue and brown ..	75	10
464	5 r. brown and orange ..	1·50	10
465	10 r. brown and buff ..	4·50	85

118 "Human Rights".

1958. 10th Anniv. of Declaration of Human Rights.

No.	Type	Description	Unused	Used
466.	**118.**	10 c. red, brn. and pur.	10	10
467.		85 c. red, turq. and grn. ..	30	45

119. Portraits of Founders and University Buildings.

1959. Institution of Pirivona Universities.

No.	Type	Description	Unused	Used
468.	**119.**	10 c. orange and blue ..	10	10

120. "Uprooted Tree". **121.** S.W.R.D. Bandaranaike.

1960. World Refugee Year.

No.	Type	Description	Unused	Used
469.	**120.**	4 c. brown and gold ..	10	50
470.		25 c. violet and gold ..	10	15

1961. Prime Minister Bandaranaike Commem.

No.	Type	Description	Unused	Used
471.	**121.**	10 c. blue & turquoise	10	10

See also Nos. 479 and 481.

122. Ceylon Scout Badge. **123.** Campaign Emblem.

1962. Golden Jubilee of Ceylon Boy Scouts Association.

No.	Type	Description	Unused	Used
472.	**122.**	35 c. buff and blue ..	15	10

1962. Malaria Eradication.

No.	Type	Description	Unused	Used
473.	**123.**	25 c. red and drab ..	10	10

124 "DH85 Leopard-Moth" and "Comet" Airliner

1963. Airmail Services. 25th Anniv.

No.	Type	Description	Unused	Used
474.	**124.**	50 c. black and blue ..	20	40

125. "Produce" and Campaign Emblem.

1963. Freedom from Hunger.

No.	Type	Description	Unused	Used
475.	**125.**	5 c. red and blue ..	30	1·00
476.		25 c. brown and olive ..	1·50	30

(**126.**)

1963. No. 450 surch. with T **126**.

No.	Description	Unused	Used
477.	2 c. on 4 c. purple and red	10	10

127. "Rural Life".

1963. Golden Jubilee of Ceylon Co-operative Movement (1962)

No.	Type	Description	Unused	Used
478.	**127.**	60 c. red and black ..	40	40

1963. Design similar to T **121**, but smaller (21 × 26 mm.) and with inscription rearranged at top.

No.	Description	Unused	Used
479.	10 c. blue	10	10
481.	10 c. violet and grey ..	10	10

No. 481 has a decorative pattern at foot instead of the inscription.

129. Terrain, Indian Elephant and Tree.

1963. National Conservation Week.

No.	Type	Description	Unused	Used
480.	**129.**	5 c. sepia and blue ..	40	40

131. Anagarika Dharmapala (Buddhist missionary).

1964. Birth Cent. of A. Dharmapala (founder of Maha Bodhi Society).

No.	Type	Description	Unused	Used
482.	**131.**	25 c. sepia and yellow	10	10

135. D. S. Senanayake. **143.** Ceylon Jungle Fowl.

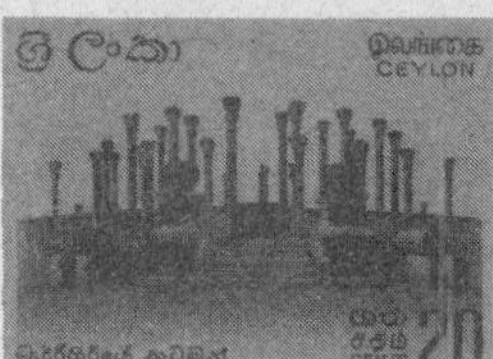

138. Ruins at Madirigiriya.

1964.
485. – 5 c. multicoloured .. 60 1·00
486. **135.** 10 c. green 10 10
487. – 10 c. green 10 10
488. – 15 c. multicoloured .. 90 30
489. **138.** 20 c. purple and buff .. 10 15
494. **143.** 60 c. multicoloured .. 1·25 70
495. – 75 c. multicoloured .. 1·25 50
497. – 1 r. brown and green .. 1·00 30
499. – 5 r. multicoloured .. 2·75 2·50
500. – 10 r. multicoloured .. 12·00 2·50

DESIGNS: As Type **143**. HORIZ. 5 c. Grackle. 15 c. Peacock. 75 c. Asian Black-headed Oriole. 5 r. Girls transplanting Rice (23×36 mm.). VERT. As Type **135**. 10 c. (No. 487). Similar portrait; but larger head and smaller inscriptions. 1 r. Tea Plantation (as Type **99**, but larger, 21×35 mm.). 10 r. Map of Ceylon (23×36 mm.).

150. Exhibition Buildings and Cogwheels.

1964. Industrial Exn.
501. – 5 c. multicoloured .. 10 60
502. **150.** 5 c. multicoloured .. 10 60

No. 501 is inscribed "INDUSTRIAL EXHIBITION" in Sinhala and Tamil, No. 502 in Sinhala and English.

151. Trains of 1864 and 1964.

1964. Centenary of Ceylon Railways.
503. – 60 c. blue, purple & green 1·75 40
504. **151.** 60 c. blue, purple & green 1·75 40

No. 503 is inscribed "RAILWAY CENTENARY" in Sinhala and Tamil, No. 504 in Sinhala and English.

152. I.T.U. Emblem and Symbols.

1965. Centenary of I.T.U.
505. **152.** 2 c. blue and red .. 20 1·10
506. 30 c. brown and red .. 1·75 45

153. I.C.Y. Emblem.

1965. Int. Co-operation Year.
507. **153.** 3 c. blue and red .. 30 1·00
508. 50 c. black, red & gold .. 2·25 50

154. Town Hall, Colombo.

1965. Cent. of Colombo Municipal Council.
509. **154.** 25 c. green and sepia 10 10

1965. No. 481 surch.
510. 5 c. on 10 c. violet and grey 10 30

157. Kandy and Council Crest.

1966. Cent. of Kandy Municipal Council.
512. **157.** 25 c. multicoloured .. 10 10

158. W.H.O. Building.

1966. Inaug. of W.H.O. Headquarters, Geneva.
513. **158.** 4 c. multicoloured .. 1·25 2·00
514. 1 r. multicoloured .. 5·25 1·50

160. Rice Paddy and Map of Ceylon.

1966. Int. Rice Year. Multicoloured.
515. 6 c. Type **160** 20 75
516. 30 c. Rice Paddy and Globe 30 15

161. U.N.E.S.C.O. Emblem.

1966. 20th Anniv. of U.N.E.S.C.O.
517. **161.** 3 c. multicoloured .. 75 1·00
518. 50 c. multicoloured .. 2·75 30

162. Water-resources Map.

1966. Int. Hydrological Decade.
519. **162.** 2 c. brown, yellow & blue 15 85
520. 2 r. multicoloured .. 60 1·60

163. Devotees at Buddhist Temple.

1967. Poya Holiday System. Multicoloured.
521. 5 c. Type **163** 10 40
522. 20 c. Mihintale 10 10
523. 35 c. Sacred Bo-tree Anuradhapura 10 15
524. 60 c. Adam's Peak 10 10

167. Galle Fort and Clock Tower.

1967. Cent. of Galle Municipal Council.
525. **167.** 25 c. multicoloured .. 30 20

168. Field Research.

1967. Cent. of Ceylon Tea Industry. Mult.
526. 4 c. Type **168** 30 80
527. 40 c. Tea-tasting equipment 75 70
528. 50 c. Leaves and bud .. 75 40
529. 1 r. Shipping tea .. .. 1·25 10

172. Elephant Ride.

1967. Int. Tourist Year.
530. **172.** 45 c. multicoloured .. 90 50

173. Ranger, Jubilee Emblem and Flag.

1967. Golden Jubilee of Ceylon Girl Guides' Assn.
532. **173.** 3 c. multicoloured .. 10 10
533. 25 c. multicoloured .. 25 10

174. Col. Olcott and Buddhist Flag.

1967. 60th Death Anniv. of Colonel Olcott (theosophist).
534. **174.** 15 c. multicoloured .. 20 20

175. Independence Hall.

1968. 20th Anniv. of Independence. Mult.
535. 5 c. Type **175** 10 55
536. 1 r. Lion Flag and Sceptre 20 10

177. Sir D. B. Jayatilleke.

1968. Birth Centenary of Sir Baron Jayatilleke (scholar and statesman)
537. **177.** 25 c. brown 10 10

178. Institute of Hygiene.

1968. 20th Anniv. of World Health Organization.
538. **178.** 50 c. multicoloured .. 10 10

179. Aircraft over Terminal Building.

1968. Opening of Colombo Airport.
539. **179.** 60 c. multicoloured .. 10 10

181. Open Koran and "1400".

1968. 1400th Anniv. of Koran.
541. **181.** 25 c. multicoloured .. 10 10

182. Human Rights Emblem.

1968. Human Rights Year.
542. **182.** 2 c. multicoloured .. 10 15
543. 20 c. multicoloured .. 10 10
544. 40 c. multicoloured .. 10 10
545. 2 r. multicoloured .. 55 2·75

183. All Ceylon Buddhist Congress Headquarters.

1968. Golden Jubilee of All Ceylon Buddhist Congress.
546. **183.** 5 c. multicoloured .. 10 40

184. E. W. Perera (patriot).

185. Symbols of Strength in Savings.

1969. Perera Commem.
547. **184.** 60 c. brown 10 30

1969. Silver Jubilee of National Savings Movement.
548. **185.** 3 c. multicoloured .. 10 10

186. Seat of Enlightenment under Sacred Bodhi Tree.

188. A. E. Goonesinghe.

1969. Vesak Day. Inscr. "Wesak".
549. **186.** 4 c. multicoloured .. 10 40
550. – 6 c. multicoloured .. 10 40
551. **186.** 35 c. multicoloured .. 10 10

DESIGN: 6 c. Buduresmala (Six-fold Buddha-Rays).

1969. Goonesinghe Commem.
552. **188.** 15 c. multicoloured .. 10 10

189. I.L.O. Emblem.

1969. 50th Anniv. of Int. Labour Organization.

553. **189.** 5 c. black and blue .. 10 10
554. 25 c. black and red .. 10 10

190. Convocation Hall, University of Ceylon.

1969. Educational Cent. Multicoloured.

555. 4 c. Type **190** 10 70
556. 35 c. Lamp of learning, globe and flags (horiz.) 10 10
557. 50 c. Uranium atom .. 15 10
558. 60 c. Symbols of scientific education 15 10

194. Ath Pana (Elephant Lamp).

1969. Archaeological Cent. Multicoloured.

559. 6 c. Type **194** 15 70
560. 1 r. Rock fortress of Sigiriya 25 10

196. Leopard.

1970. Wild Life Conservation. Multicoloured.

561. 5 c. Water buffalo .. .. 20 1·25
562. 15 c. Slender loris 60 30
563. 50 c. Spotted deer .. .. 80 1·25
564. 1 r. Type **196** .. .. 90 1·75

197. Emblem and Symbols.

1970. Asian Productivity Year.

565. **197.** 60 c. multicoloured .. 10 10

198. New U.P.U. H.Q. Building.

1970. New U.P.U. Headquarters Building.

566. **198.** 50 c. orge., blk. & blue 20 10
567. 1 r. 10 red, black and blue .. .. .. 1·10 30

199. Oil Lamp and Caduceus.

1970. Cent. of Colombo Medical School.

568 **199** 5 c. multicoloured .. 30 60
569 45 c. multicoloured .. 30 60

200. Victory March and S.W.R.D. Bandaranaike.

1970. Establishment of United Front Government.

570. **200.** 10 c. multicoloured .. 10 10

201. U.N. Emblem and Dove of Peace.

1970. 25th Anniv. of United Nations.

571. **201.** 2 r. multicoloured .. 1·50 2·25

202. Keppetipola Dissawa.

1970. 152nd Death Anniv. of Keppetipola Dissawa (Kandyan patriot).

572. **202.** 25 c. multicoloured .. 10 10

203. Ola Leaf Manuscript.

1970. Int. Education Year.

573. **203.** 15 c. multicoloured .. 65 1·00

204. C. H. De Soysa.

205. D. E. H. Pedris (patriot).

1971. 135th Birth Anniv. of C. H. De Soysa (philanthropist).

574. **204.** 20 c. multicoloured .. 15 40

1971. D. E. H. Pedris. Commemoration.

575. **205.** 25 c. multicoloured .. 15 50

206. Lenin.

207. Ananda Rajakaruna

1971. Lenin Commemoration.

576. **206.** 40 c. multicoloured .. 15 40

1971. Poets and Philosophers.

577. **207.** 5 c. blue 10 15
578. – 5 c. brown 10 15
579. – 5 c. orange 10 15
580. – 5 c. blue 10 15
581. – 5 c. brown 10 15

PORTRAITS: No. 578, Arumuga Navalar. No. 579, Rev. S. Mahinda. No. 580, Ananda Coomaraswamy. No. 581, Cumaratunga Munidasa.

1971. Surch. in figures.

582. **186.** 5 c. on 4 c. multicoloured 2·75 1·75
583. **190.** 5 c. on 4 c. multicoloured 10 1·00
584. **200.** 15 c. on 10 c. mult. .. 10 20
585. – 25 c. on 6 c. multicoloured (No. 550) 30 60
586. **194.** 25 c. on 6 c. mult. .. 30 80

209. Colombo Plan Emblem and Ceylon.

1971. 20th Anniv. of Colombo Plan.

587. **209.** 20 c. multicoloured .. 15 30

210. Globe and C.A.R.E. Package.

1971. 20th Anniv. of Co-operative for American Relief Everywhere.

588. **210.** 50 c. blue, violet & lilac 35 30

211. W.H.O. Emblem and Heart.

1972. World Health Day.

589. **211.** 25 c. multicoloured .. 90 60

212. Map of Asia and U.N. Emblem.

1972. 25th Anniv. of E.C.A.F.E.

590. **212.** 85 c. multicoloured .. 2·75 2·75

OFFICIAL STAMPS

1895. Stamps of Queen Victoria optd. **On Service.**

O 1. **9.** 2 c. green .. .. 6·00 25
O 8. 2 c. brown .. .. 3·50 60
O 2. **39.** 3 c. brown and green 9·00 40
O 9. 3 c. green .. .. 8·00 70
O 3. **28.** 5 c. purple .. .. 1·50 20
O 4. **29.** 15 c. olive .. .. 11·00 30
O 10. 15 c. blue .. .. 15·00 60
O 5. 25 c. brown .. .. 10·00 90
O 6. 30 c. mauve and brown 12·00 30
O 11. 75 c. black and brown 5·50 4·00
O 7. **30.** 1 r. 12 red .. .. 50·00 45·00

1903. Stamps of King Edward VII optd. **On Service.**

O 12. **44.** 2 c. brown .. .. 7·00 70
O 13. **45.** 3 c. green .. .. 4·25 2·00
O 14. – 5 c. purple (No. 268) 11·00 1·25
O 15. **45.** 15 c. blue .. .. 22·00 2·50
O 16. 25 c. brown .. .. 20·00 18·00
O 17. 30 c. violet and green 7·00 1·50

For later issues see **SRI LANKA.**

CHAMBA

An Indian "convention" state of the Punjab. Stamps of India optd.

12 pies = 1 anna; 16 annas = 1 rupee.

1886. Queen Victoria. Optd **CHAMBA STATE** in two lines.

1 **23.** ½ a. turquoise 10 30
2 – 1 a. purple 20 50
4 – 1½ a. brown .. .. 60 5·00
5 – 2 a. blue 60 75
7 – 2½ a. green .. .. 18·00 50·00
9 – 3 a. orange .. .. 50 2·75
10 – 4 a. green (No. 96) .. 1·00 3·00
12 – 6 a. brown (No. 80) .. 1·00 4·50
15 – 8 a. mauve .. .. 1·50 6·00
16 – 12 a. purple on red .. 2·00 4·75
17 – 1 r. grey (No. 101) .. 20·00 65·00
18 **37.** 1 r. green and red .. 1·90 5·50
19 **38.** 2 r. red and brown .. 55·00 £140
20 3 r. brown and green .. 55·00 £120
21 5 r. blue and violet .. 70·00 £200

1900. Queen Victoria. Optd **CHAMBA STATE** in two lines.

22 **40.** 3 p. red 10 20
23 3 p. grey 15 90
25 **23.** ½ a. green 10 30
26 – 1 a. red 10 20
27 – 2 a. lilac .. .. .. 5·00 15·00

1903. King Edward VII. Optd **CHAMBA STATE** in two lines.

28 **41.** 3 p. grey 10 75
30 – ½ a. green (No. 122) .. 10 20
31 – 1 a. red (No. 123) .. 15 20
32 – 2 a. lilac 30 90
34 – 3 a. orange .. .. 80 2·25
35 – 4 a. olive .. .. .. 1·10 5·00
36 – 6 a. bistre .. .. 1·50 7·50
37 – 8 a. mauve .. .. 1·50 6·00
39 – 12 a. purple on red .. 2·00 8·00
40 – 1 r. green and red .. 2·25 9·00

1907. King Edward VII. Optd **CHAMBA STATE** in two lines.

41. – ½ a. green (No. 149) .. 20 1·25
42. – 1 a. red (No. 150) .. 25 1·25

1913. King George V. Optd **CHAMBA STATE** in two lines.

43 **55.** 3 p. grey 10 30
44 **56.** ½ a. green 10 30
46 **57.** 1 a. red 15 70
55 1 a. brown .. .. 20 1·00
56 **58.** 1½ a. brown (No. 163) .. 14·00 55·00
57 1½ a. brown (No. 165) .. 30 2·25
58 1½ a. red .. .. .. 60 6·50
47 **59.** 2 a. lilac .. .. .. 45 2·50
59 **61.** 2½ a. blue .. .. 50 2·75
60 2½ a. orange .. .. 70 4·50
48 **62.** 3 a. orange .. .. 75 3·00
61 3 a. blue .. .. .. 1·10 5·50
49 **63.** 4 a. olive .. .. .. 70 2·00
50 **64.** 6 a. bistre .. .. 70 2·25
51 **65.** 8 a. mauve .. .. 1·00 4·25
52 **66.** 12 a. red .. .. 1·40 8·50
53 **67.** 1 r. brown and green .. 4·50 8·50

1921. No. 192 of India optd. **CHAMBA.**

54. **57.** 9 p. on 1 a. red .. .. 80 9·00

1927. Stamps of India (King George V) optd. **CHAMBA STATE** in one line.

62. **55.** 3 p. grey 10 40
63. **56.** ½ a. green 10 50
76. **79.** ½ a. green .. .. 35 2·75
64. **80.** 9 p. green .. .. 55 3·00
65. **57.** 1 a. brown 60 10
77. **81.** 1 a. brown 40 40
66. **82.** 1¼ a. mauve .. .. 35 1·40
67. **58.** 1½ a. red .. .. .. 1·25 1·75
68. **70.** 2 a. lilac 35 55
78. **59.** 2 a. red .. .. .. 30 8·00
69. **61.** 2½ a. orange .. .. 45 5·00
70. **62.** 3 a. blue .. .. .. 65 4·25
80. 3 a. red .. .. .. 1·00 3·25
71. **71.** 4 a. green .. .. 45 1·60
81. **63.** 4 a. olive .. .. .. 80 3·50
72. **64.** 6 a. bistre .. .. 24·00 90·00
73. **65.** 8 a. mauve .. .. 65 4·25
74. **66.** 12 a. red .. .. .. 90 5·50
75. **67.** 1 r. brown and green .. 2·75 9·50

1938. Stamps of India (King George VI Nos. 247/64) optd. **CHAMBA STATE.**

82. **91.** 3 p. slate .. .. .. 2·25 4·50
83. ½ a. brown .. .. 80 2·75
84. 9 p. green .. .. 2·25 12·00
85. 1 a. red 90 70
86. **92.** 2 a. red .. .. .. 1·60 4·25
87. – 2½ a. violet .. .. 1·90 9·50
88. – 3 a. green .. .. 4·00 10·00
89. – 3½ a. blue .. .. 2·75 12·00
90. – 4 a. brown .. .. 8·00 5·50
91. – 6 a. green .. .. 8·00 24·00
92. – 8 a. violet .. .. 8·00 20·00
93. – 12 a. red .. .. .. 3·50 24·00
94. **93.** 1 r. slate and brown .. 20·00 30·00
95. 2 r. purple and brown .. 32·00 £120
96. 5 r. green and blue .. 60·00 £200
97. 10 r. purple and red .. £120 £375
98. 15 r. brown and green .. £250 £550
99. 25 r. slate and purple .. £350 £650

1942. Stamps of India (King George VI) optd. **CHAMBA.**

(a) On issue of 1938.

100. **91.** ½ a. brown .. .. 9·00 10·00
101. 1 a. red .. .. .. 13·00 10·00
102. **93.** 1 r. slate and brown .. 21·00 32·00
103. 2 r. purple and brown .. 28·00 £120
104. 5 r. green and blue .. 60·00 £150
105. 10 r. purple and red .. 95·00 £300
106. 15 r. brown and green .. £250 £475
107. 25 r. slate and purple .. £325 £550

(b) On issue of 1940.

108.100a.	3 p. slate	40	1·90
109.	½ a. mauve	60	1·10
110.	9 p. green	50	4·75
111.	1 a. red	90	1·25
112.101.	1½ a. violet	70	3·50
113.	2 a. red	1·40	4·25
114.	3 a. violet	3·00	8·00
115.	3½ a. blue	3·00	16·00
116.102.	4 a. brown	3·00	4·75
117.	6 a. green	9·50	22·00
118.	8 a. violet	10·00	28·00
119.-	12 a. purple	19·00	38·00
120. –	14 a. purple (No. 277)	4·00	3·00

OFFICIAL STAMPS

Stamps of India optd.

1886. Queen Victoria. Optd **SERVICE CHAMBA STATE.**

O 1 **23.**	½ a. turquoise	10	10
O 3 –	1 a. purple	30	10
O 5 –	2 a. blue	50	70
O 7 –	3 a. orange	1·40	4·50
O 8 –	4 a. green (No. 96)	60	1·75
O 10 –	6 a. brown (No. 80)	1·50	4·25
O 13 –	8 a. mauve	70	1·25
O 14 –	12 a. purple on red	7·00	20·00
O 15 –	1 r. grey (No. 101)	11·00	55·00
O 16 **37.**	1 r. green and red	4·75	14·00

1902. Queen Victoria. Optd **SERVICE CHAMBA STATE.**

O 17. **40.**	3 p. grey	15	40
O 18. **23.**	½ a. green	15	1·60
O 20. –	1 a. red	30	40
O 21. –	2 a. lilac	6·00	16·00

1903. King Edward VII. Optd **SERVICE CHAMBA STATE.**

O 22. **41.**	3 p. grey	15	15
O 24.	½ a. green (No. 122)	10	10
O 25.	1 a. red (No. 123)	15	20
O 27. –	2 a. lilac	40	40
O 28. –	4 a. olive	1·50	6·50
O 29. –	8 a. mauve	1·60	6·50
O 31. –	1 r. green and red	1·25	3·75

1907. King Edward VII. Optd **SERVICE CHAMBA STATE.**

O 32. –	½ a. green (No. 149)	20	60
O 33. –	1 a. red (No. 150)	70	40

1913. King George V Official stamps optd **CHAMBA STATE.**

O 34. **55.**	3 p. grey	20	50
O 36. **56.**	½ a. green	10	10
O 38. **57.**	1 a. red	10	10
O 47.	1 a. brown	50	40
O 40. **59.**	2 a. lilac (No. O 83)	85	5·00
O 41. **63.**	4 a. olive (No. O 86)	85	3·25
O 42. **65.**	8 a. mauve	1·25	4·50
O 43. **67.**	1 r. brown and green	3·00	11·00

1914. King George V Official stamps optd. **SERVICE CHAMBA STATE.**

O 44. **59.**	2 a. lilac (No. 166)	7·00	
O 45. **63.**	4 a. olive (No. 210)	9·00	

1921. No. O 97 of India optd. **CHAMBA.**

O 46. **57.**	9 p. on 1 a. red	15	2·25

1927. King George V Postage stamps optd. **CHAMBA STATE SERVICE.**

O 48. **55.**	3 p. grey	30	25
O 49. **56.**	½ a. green	30	15
O 61. **79.**	½ a. green	40	30
O 50. **80.**	9 p. green	45	3·50
O 51. **57.**	1 a. brown	10	10
O 62. **81.**	1 a. brown	70	30
O 52. **82.**	1¼ a. mauve	2·25	40
O 53. **70.**	2 a. lilac	40	40
O 63. **59.**	2 a. red	1·40	80
O 54. **71.**	4 a. olive	40	50
O 65. **63.**	4 a. green	1·40	1·10
O 55. **65.**	8 a. mauve	1·50	5·00
O 56. **66.**	12 a. red	1·40	9·00
O 57. **67.**	1 r. brown and green	6·50	15·00
O 58.	2 r. red and orange	13·00	£100
O 59.	5 r. blue and violet	32·00	£150
O 60.	10 r. green and red	42·00	£140

1938. King George VI Postage stamps of India optd. **CHAMBA STATE SERVICE.**

O 66. **91.**	9 p. green	4·25	15·00
O 67.	1 a. red	3·25	1·10
O 68. **93.**	1 r. slate and brown	£750	£800
O 69.	2 r. purple and brown	50·00	£200
O 70.	5 r. green and blue	80·00	£275
O 71.	10 r. purple and red	£140	£450

1940. Official stamps of India optd. **CHAMBA.**

O 72. O **20.**	3 p. grey	60	40
O 73.	½ a. brown	8·00	1·50
O 74.	½ a. purple	60	70
O 75.	9 p. green	1·40	2·00
O 76.	1 a. red	60	50
O 77.	1 a. 3 p. brown	27·00	10·00
O 78.	1½ a. violet	3·50	2·00
O 79.	2 a. orange	2·75	1·60
O 80.	2½ a. violet	1·40	10·00
O 81.	4 a. brown	3·25	5·00
O 82.	8 a. violet	6·00	20·00

1942. King George VI Postage stamps of India optd. **CHAMBA SERVICE.**

O 83. **93.**	1 r. slate and brown	32·00	£100
O 84.	2 r. purple and brown	50·00	£160
O 85.	5 r. green and blue	85·00	£250
O 86.	10 r. purple and red	£140	£450

CHARKHARI

A state of Central India. Now uses Indian stamps.

12 pies = 1 anna; 16 annas = 1 rupee.

1.

2.

1894. Imperf. No gum.

5a **1.**	¼ a. purple	1·75	2·50
6	½ a. purple	2·25	3·50
7a	1 a. green	4·00	4·50
8a	2 a. green	7·00	8·00
9a	4 a. green	6·00	9·00

1909. Perf. or imperf.

15a. **2.**	1 p. brown	1·75	38·00
16.	1 p. blue	30	45
33.	1 p. violet	12·00	75·00
32.	1 p. green	35·00	95·00
25.	½ a. red	70	80
35.	½ a. brown	1·90	19·00
34.	½ a. olive	30	8·00
36.	½ a. black	40·00	95·00
18a.	1 a. green	1·25	1·10
40.	1 a. brown	2·75	19·00
41.	1 a. red	55·00	55·00
19.	2 a. blue	2·00	3·00
43.	2 a. grey	30·00	45·00
20.	4 a. green	2·75	4·00
44.	4 a. red	4·00	13·00
21.	8 a. red	4·50	12·00
22.	1 r. brown	8·00	20·00

4.

1912. Imperf.

28. **4.**	1 p. violet	7·00	5·00

5.

1922. Imperf.

29. **5.**	1 a. violet	60·00	75·00

6. Imlia Palace.

DESIGNS—HORIZ. ½ a. The Lake. 2 a. Industrial school. 4 a. Bird's-eye view of city. 8 a. Fort. 1 r. Guest House. 2 r. Palace Gate. 3 r. Temples at Rainpur. 5 r. Goverdhan Temple.

1931. Perf.

45. –	½ a. green	50	10
46. **7.**	1 a. sepia	50	10
47. –	2 a. violet	35	10
48. –	4 a. olive	40	10
49. –	8 a. mauve	45	10
50. –	1 r. green and red	1·25	15
51. –	2 r. red and brown	1·40	20
52. –	3 r. brown and green	4·00	25
53. –	5 r. blue and lilac	4·50	45

1940. Nos. 21/2 surch.

54. **2.**	½ a. on 8 a. red	25·00	85·00
55.	1 a. on 1 r. brown	65·00	£160
56.	"1 ANNA" on 1 r. brown	£375	£425

MORE DETAILED LISTS
are given in the Stanley Gibbons Catalogues referred to in the country headings.
For lists of current volumes see Introduction.

CHINA EXPEDITIONARY FORCE

Stamps used by Indian military forces in China.

12 pies = 1 anna; 16 annas = 1 rupee.
Stamps of India optd. **C.E.F.**

1900. Queen Victoria.

C 1. **40.**	3 p. red	30	60
C 2. **23.**	½ a. green	30	30
C 3. –	1 a. purple	2·00	85
C 11. –	1 a. red	22·00	6·50
C 4. –	2 a. blue	2·25	4·25
C 5. –	2½ a. green	2·50	8·00
C 6. –	3 a. orange	2·50	12·00
C 7. –	4 a. green (No. 96)	2·25	6·00
C 8. –	8 a. mauve	2·25	9·00
C 9. –	12 a. purple on red	7·50	13·00
C 10. **37.**	1 r. green and red	8·00	11·00

1904. King Edward VII.

C 12. **41.**	3 p. grey	2·00	3·25
C 13. –	1 a. red (No. 123)	2·00	70
C 14. –	2 a. lilac	9·50	1·75
C 15. –	2½ a. blue	2·75	5·00
C 16. –	3 a. orange	3·25	4·00
C 17. –	4 a. olive	7·50	11·00
C 18. –	8 a. mauve	6·50	7·50
C 19. –	12 a. purple on red	9·00	19·00
C 20. –	1 r. green and red	10·00	24·00

1909. King Edward VII.

C 21.	½ a. green (No. 149)	1·40	60
C 22.	1 a. red (No. 150)	1·00	30

1913. King George V.

C 23. **55.**	3 p. grey	1·40	10·00
C 24. **56.**	½ a. green	1·10	2·75
C 25. **57.**	1 a. red	1·75	1·50
C 26. **58.**	1½ a. brown (No. 163)	15·00	45·00
C 27. **59.**	2 a. lilac	6·00	30·00
C 28. **61.**	2½ a. blue	6·50	15·00
C 29. **62.**	3 a. orange	18·00	£110
C 30. **63.**	4 a. olive	17·00	£110
C 32. **65.**	8 a. mauve	15·00	£225
C 33. **66.**	12 a. red	15·00	90·00
C 34. **67.**	1 r. brown and green	48·00	£180

BRITISH RAILWAY ADMINISTRATION

1901. No. 121 of China surch **B.R.A. 5 Five Cents.**

BR133b **32**	5 c. on ½ c. brown	£170	£110

CHRISTMAS ISLAND

Situated in the Indian Ocean about 600 miles south of Singapore. Formerly part of the Straits Settlements and then of the Crown Colony of Singapore, Christmas Island was occupied by the Japanese from 31 March 1942 until September 1945. It reverted to Singapore after liberation but subsequently became an Australian territory on 15 October 1958.

1958. 100 cents = 1 Malayan dollar.
1968. 100 cents = 1 Australian dollar.

1. Queen Elizabeth II.

2. Map.

1958. Type of Australia with opt. and value in black.

1. **1.**	2 c. orange	55	50
2.	4 c. brown	60	30
3.	5 c. mauve	60	30
4.	6 c. blue	1·50	30
5.	8 c. sepia	3·50	50
6.	10 c. violet	2·50	30
7.	12 c. red	3·75	1·50
8.	20 c. blue	3·00	1·50
9.	50 c. green	4·50	1·50
10.	$1 turquoise	6·00	1·50

1963.

11. **2.**	2 c. orange	90	40
12. –	4 c. brown	50	20
13. –	5 c. purple	50	20
14. –	6 c. blue	40	30
15. –	8 c. black	3·75	40
16. –	10 c. violet	40	20
17. –	12 c. red	40	30
18. –	20 c. blue	1·00	35
19. –	50 c. green	2·00	35
20. –	$1 yellow	5·50	60

DESIGNS—VERT. 4 c. Moonflower. 5 c. Robber Crab. 8 c. Phosphate train. 10 c. Raising phosphate. HORIZ. 6 c. Island scene. 12 c. Flying Fish cove. 20 c. Loading cantilever. 50 c. Christmas Island Frigate bird. LARGER. (35 × 21 mm.): $1, White-tailed Tropic bird.

1965. 50th Anniv. of Gallipoli Landing. As T **184** of Australia, but slightly larger (22 × 34½ mm.).

21.	10 c. brown, blk. & green	30	50

12. Golden Striped Grouper.

1968. Fishes. Multicoloured.

22.	1 c. Type **12**	45	30
23.	2 c. Moorish Idol	60	20
24.	3 c. Forceps Fish	60	30
25.	4 c. Queen Triggerfish	60	20
26.	5 c. Regal Angelfish	75	20
27.	9 c. Surgeon Fish	2·00	40
28.	10 c. Scorpion Fish	1·50	20
28a.	15 c. Saddleback Butterfly	12·00	7·00
29.	20 c. Clown Butterfly	4·00	55
29a.	30 c. Ghost Pipefish	12·00	7·00
30.	50 c. Blue Lined Surgeon	10·00	3·00
31.	$1 Meyers Butterfly	15·00	5·00

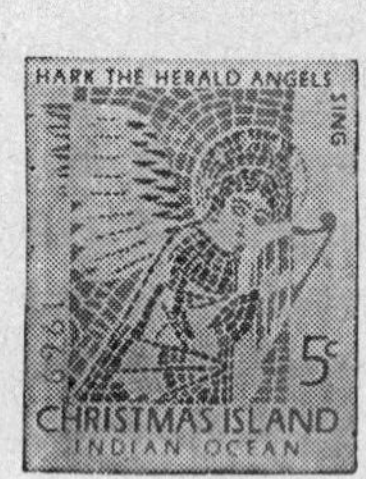

13. "Angel" (Mosaic). 14. "The Ansidei Madonna" (Raphael).

1969. Christmas.

32. **13.**	5 c. multicoloured	20	20

1970. Christmas. Paintings. Multicoloured.

33.	3 c. Type **14**	20	15
34.	5 c. "The Virgin and Child, St. John the Baptist and an Angel" (Morando)	20	15

15. "The Adoration of the Shepherds" (ascr. to the School of Seville).

1971. Christmas. Multicoloured.

35.	6 c. Type **15**	50	50
36.	20 c. "The Adoration of the Shepherds" (Reni)	1·00	1·00

16. H.M.S. "Flying Fish", 1887.

1972. Ships. Multicoloured.

37	1 c. "Eagle", 1714	25	50
38	2 c. H.M.S. "Redpole", 1890	30	60
39	3 c. M.V. "Hoi Houw", 1959	30	60
40	4 c. "Pigot", 1771	40	65
41	5 c. S.S. "Valetta", 1968	40	65
42	6 c. Type **16**	40	65
43	7 c. "Asia", 1805	40	65
44	8 c. T.S.S. "Islander", 1929–60	45	70
45	9 c. H.M.S. "Imperieuse", 1888	65	70
46	10 c. "Cyclops" class coast defence turret ship, 1871	55	70
47	20 c. "Thomas", 1615	85	80
48	25 c. Royal Navy sail sloop, 1864	1·25	1·00
49	30 c. "Cygnet", 1688	1·50	1·00
50	35 c. S.S. "Triadic", 1958	1·75	1·00
51	50 c. H.M.S. "Amethyst", 1857	2·25	2·00
52	$1 "Royal Mary", 1643	3·00	2·25

No. 45 is inscribed "H.M.S. Imperious", No. 46 "H.M.S. Egeria" and No. 48 "H.M.S. Gordon", all in error.

17. Angel of Peace.

1972. Christmas. Multicoloured.

53. 3 c. Type **17** 65 65
54. 3 c. Angel of Joy 65 65
55. 7 c. Type **17** 75 75
56. 7 c. As No. 54 .. .. 75 75

18. Virgin and Child, and Map.

1973. Christmas.

57. **18.** 7 c. multicoloured .. 1·00 35
58. 25 c. multicoloured .. 3·25 1·25

19. Mary and Holy Child within Christmas Star.

1974. Christmas.

59. **19.** 7 c. mauve and grey .. 60 75
60. 30 c. orge., yell. & grey .. 1·75 2·75

20. " The Flight into Egypt ".

1975. Christmas.

61. **20.** 10 c. yell., brn. & gold .. 50 35
62. 35 c. pink, blue & gold .. 1·50 1·40

21. Dove of Peace and Star of Bethlehem.

1976. Christmas.

63. **21.** 10 c. red, yellow & mauve 40 80
64. – 10 c. red, yellow & mauve 40 80
65. **21.** 35 c. violet, blue & green 70 90
66. – 35 c. violet, blue & green 70 90

DESIGNS: Nos. 64 and 66 are " mirror-images " of Type 21.

22. William Dampier (explorer).

1977. Famous Visitors. Multicoloured.

67 1 c. Type **22** 15 40
68 2 c. Capt. de Vlamingh (explorer) 20 40
69 3 c. Vice-Admiral MacLear 30 40
70 4 c. Sir John Murray (oceanographer) .. 30 50
71 5 c. Admiral Aldrich .. 30 40
72 6 c. Andrew Clunies Ross (first settler) 30 50
73 7 c. J. J. Lister (naturalist) 30 40
74 8 c. Admiral of the Fleet Sir William May 35 50
75 9 c. Henry Ridley (botanist) 40 40
76 10 c. George Clunies Ross (phosphate miner) .. 55 40
77 20 c. Capt. Joshua Slocum (yachtsman) 50 55
78 45 c. Charles Andrews (naturalist) 85 45
79 50 c. Richard Hanitsch (biologist) 95 60
80 75 c. Victor Purcell (scholar) 85 85
81 $1 Fam Choo Beng (educator) .. .. 1·25 1·25
82 $2 Sir Harold Spencer-Jones (astronomer) .. .. 2·50 2·25

23. Australian Coat of Arms on Map of Christmas Island.

1977. Silver Jubilee.

83. **23.** 45 c. multicoloured .. 60 70

24. " A Partridge in A Pear Tree ".

1977. Christmas. " The Twelve Days of Christmas ". Multicoloured.

84. 10 c. Type **24** 15 25
85. 10 c. " Two turtle doves " 15 25
86. 10 c. " Three French hens " 15 25
87. 10 c. " Four calling birds " 15 25
88. 10 c. " Five gold rings " .. 15 25
89. 10 c. " Six geese a-laying " 15 25
90. 10 c. " Seven swans a-swimming " 15 25
91. 10 c. " Eight maids a-milking " 15 25
92. 10 c. " Nine ladies dancing " 15 25
93. 10 c. " Ten Lords a-leaping " 15 25
94. 10 c. " Eleven pipers piping " 15 25
95. 10 c. " Twelve drummers drumming " 15 25

25. Abbott's Booby.

1978. 25th Anniv. of Coronation.

96. – 45 c. black and blue .. 60 95
97. – 45 c. multicoloured .. 60 95
98. **25.** 45 c. black and blue .. 60 95

DESIGNS: No. 96, White Swan of Bohun. No. 97, Queen Elizabeth II.

26. " Christ Child ".

1978. Christmas. Scenes from " The Song of Christmas ". Multicoloured.

99. 10 c. Type **26** 15 20
100. 10 c. " Herald Angels " .. 15 20
101. 10 c. " Redeemer " .. 15 20
102. 10 c. " Israel " 15 20
103. 10 c. " Star " 15 20
104. 10 c. " Three Wise Men " 15 20
105. 10 c. " Manger " 15 20
106. 10 c. " All He Stands For " 15 20
107. 10 c. " Shepherds Come " 15 20

27. Chinese Children.

1979. International Year of the Child. Children of different races. Multicoloured, colours of inscr. given.

108. 20 c. green (Type **27**) .. 45 45
109. 20 c. turquoise (Malay children) 45 45
110. 20 c. lilac (Indian children) 45 45
111. 20 c. red (European children) 45 45
112. 20 c. yellow (" Oranges and Lemons ") 45 45

28. 1958 2 c. Definitive.

1979. Death Centenary of Sir Rowland Hill. Multicoloured.

113. 20 c. Type **28** 30 40
114. 20 c. 1963 2 c. Map definitive 30 40
115. 20 c. 1965 50th Anniv. of Gallipoli Landing 10 c. commemorative 30 40
116. 20 c. 1968 4 c. Queen Triggerfish definitive .. 30 40
117. 20 c. 1969 Christmas 5 c. value 30 40

29. Wise Men following Star.

1979. Christmas. Multicoloured.

118. 20 c. Type **29** 20 30
119. 55 c. Virgin and Child .. 45 70

30. 9th Green.

1980. 25th Anniv. of Christmas Island Golf Club. Multicoloured.

120. 20 c. Type **30** 60 50
121. 55 c. Clubhouse .. .. 70 1·00

31. Surveying.

1980. Phosphate Industry (1st series). Multicoloured.

122. 15 c. Type **31** 15 25
123. 22 c. Drilling for samples 20 30
124. 40 c. Sample analysis .. 30 45
125. 55 c. Mine planning .. 40 55

See also Nos. 126/9, 136/9 and 140/3.

1980. Phosphate Industry (2nd series). As T **31**. Multicoloured.

126. 15 c. Jungle clearing .. 15 15
127. 22 c. Overburden removal 20 20
128. 40 c. Open cut mining .. 30 25
129. 55 c. Restoration 35 30

32. Angel with Harp.

1980. Christmas. Multicoloured.

130. 15 c. Type **32** 15 25
131. 15 c. Angel with wounded soldier 15 25
132. 22 c. Virgin and Child .. 20 30
133. 22 c. Kneeling couple .. 20 30
134. 60 c. Angel with harp (different) 45 45
135. 60 c. Angel with children 45 45

1981. Phosphate Industry (3rd series). As T **31**. Multicoloured.

136. 22 c. Screening and Stockpiling 20 20
137. 28 c. Train loading .. 25 25
138. 40 c. Railing 40 40
139. 60 c. Drying 55 55

1981. Phosphate Industry (4th series). As T **31**. Multicoloured.

140 22 c. Crushing 30 20
141 28 c. Conveying 40 25
142 40 c. Bulk storage .. 60 40
143 60 c. "Consolidated Venture" (bulk carrier) loading 70 55

33. " Cryptoblepharus egeriae ".

1981. Reptiles. Multicoloured.

144. 24 c. Type **33** 25 25
145. 30 c. " Emoia Nativitata " 30 30
146. 40 c. " Lepidodactylus listeri " 45 45
147. 60 c. " Cyrtodactylus sp. nov." 65 65

34. Scene from Carol " Away in a Manger ".

1981. Christmas.

148. **34.** 18 c. silver, dp. bl. and bl. 50 50
149. – 24 c. multicoloured .. 55 55
150. – 40 c. multicoloured .. 65 65
151. – 60 c. multicoloured .. 75 75

DESIGNS: 24 c. to 60 c. show various scenes from carol " Away in a Manger ".

35. Eastern Reef Heron.

1982 Birds. Multicoloured.

152. 1 c. Type **35** 35 30
153. 2 c. Common Noddy .. 35 30
154. 3 c. White-bellied Swiftlet .. 35 60
155. 4 c. Christmas Island Imperial Pigeon 35 60
156. 5 c. Christmas Island White eye 40 60
157. 10 c. Island Thrush 35 60
158. 25 c. Red-tailed Tropic Bird 75 50
159. 30 c. Emerald Dove 50 50
160. 40 c. Brown Booby 60 55
161. 50 c. Red-footed Booby .. 55 55
162. 65 c. Christmas Island Frigate Bird 55 55
163. 75 c. White-tailed Tropic Bird 65 65
164. 80 c. Australian Kestrel (vert.) .. .. .. 1·00 65
165. $1 Indonesian Hawk-Owl (vert.) .. .. .. 1·50 90
166. $2 Australian Goshawk .. 1·50 3·50
167. $4 Abbott's Booby (vert.) .. 3·00 3·25

36. Joseph.

1982. Christmas. Origami Paper Sculptures. Multicoloured.

168. 27 c. Type **36** 30 30
169. 50 c. Angel 45 45
170. 75 c. Mary and baby Jesus 65 65

37. "Mirror" Dinghy and Club House.

1983. 25th Anniv. of Christmas Island Boat Club. Multicoloured.

171. 27 c. Type **37** 35 35
172. 35 c. Ocean-going yachts .. 40 40
173. 50 c. Fishing launch and cargo ship (horiz.) .. 50 50
174. 75 c. Dinghy-racing and cantilever (horiz.) .. 70 70

38. Maps of Christmas Island and Australia, Eastern Grey Kangaroo and Whitetailed Tropic Bird.

1983. 25th Anniv. of Australian Territory. Multicoloured.

175. 24 c. Type **38** 20 20
176. 30 c. Christmas Island and Australian flag 30 30
177. 85 c. Maps of Christmas Island and Australia, and Boeing "727" .. 70 70

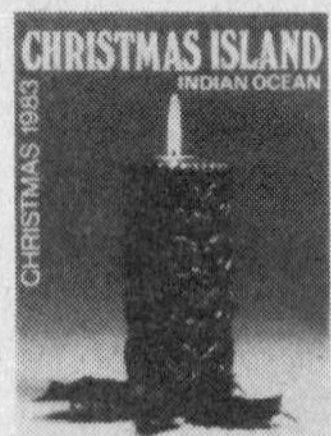

39. Candle and Holly.

1983. Christmas. Candles. Multicoloured.

178. 24 c. Type **39** 20 20
179. 30 c. Six gold candles .. 30 30
180. 85 c. Candles 70 70

40. Feeding on Leaf.

1984. Red Land Crab. Multicoloured.

181. 30 c. Type **40** 30 30
182. 40 c. Migration 40 40
183. 55 c. Development stages 50 50
184. 85 c. Adult female and young 70 70

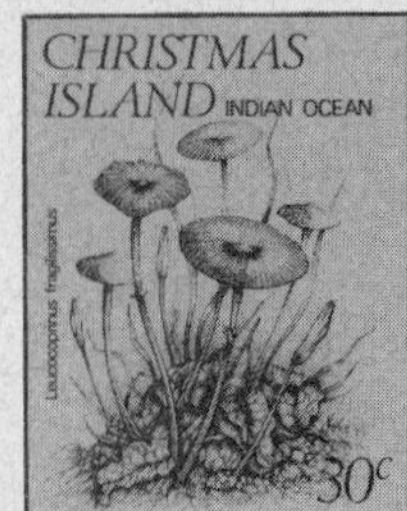

41. "Leucocoprinus fragilissimus".

1984. Fungi. Multicoloured.

185. 30 c. Type **41** 55 55
186. 40 c. "Microporus xanthopus" 65 65
187. 45 c. "Trogia anthidepas" 75 75
188. 55 c. "Haddowia longipes" 85 85
189. 85 c. "Phillipsia domingensis" .. .. .. 1·00 1·00

42. Run-out.

1984. 25th Anniv. of Cricket on Christmas Island. Multicoloured.

190. 30 c. Type **42** 75 80
191. 40 c. Bowled-out 85 90
192. 50 c. Batsman in action .. 1·10 1·25
193. 85 c. Fielder diving for catch .. .. .. 1·25 1·40

44. Robber Crab.

1985. Crabs (1st series). Multicoloured.

195. 30 c. Type **44** 65 50
196. 40 c. Horn-eyed ghost crab 75 60
197. 55 c. Purple hermit crab .. 90 75
198. 85 c. Little nipper .. .. 1·25 1·00

1985. Crabs (2nd Series). As T **44**. Mult.

199. 33 c. Blue crab 70 40
200. 45 c. Tawny hermit crab .. 80 60
201. 60 c. Red nipper 95 75
202. 90 c. Smooth-handed ghost crab .. .. 1·40 1·10

1985. Crabs (3rd series). As T **44**. Mult.

203. 33 c. Red crab 70 55
204. 45 c. Mottled crab 85 95
205. 60 c. Rock hopper crab .. 1·10 1·40
206. 90 c. Yellow nipper .. 1·50 2·00

45. "Once in Royal David's City"

1985. Christmas Carols. Multicoloured.

207. 27 c. Type **45** 70 80
208. 33 c. "While Sheperds Watched Their Flocks by Night" .. .. 80 1·00
209. 45 c. "Away in a Manger" 95 1·25
210. 60 c. "We Three Kings of Orient Are" .. .. 1·10 1·40
211. 90 c. "Hark the Herald Angels Sing .. .. 1·40 1·50

46. Halley's Comet over Christmas Island.

1986. Appearance of Halley's Comet. Mult.

212 33 c. Type **46** 65 65
213 45 c. Edmond Halley .. 80 1·00
214 60 c. Comet and "Consolidated Venture" (bulk carrier) loading phosphate .. .. 1·00 1·40
215 90 c. Comet over Flying Fish Cove .. .. 1·50 1·75

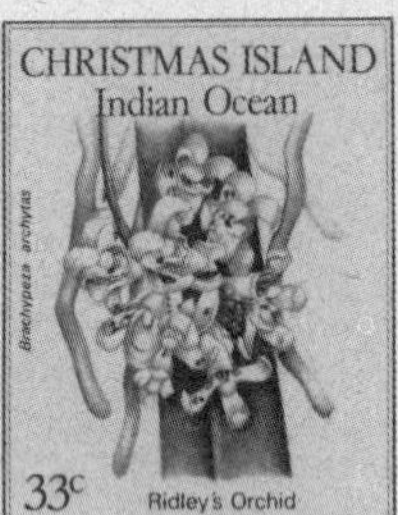

47. Ridley's Orchid.

1986. Native Flowers. Multicoloured.

216. 33 c. Type **47** 50 50
217. 45 c. Hanging flower .. 65 80
218. 60 c. Hoya .. .. .. 75 1·00
219. 90 c. Sea hibiscus .. .. 1·10 1·50

1986. Royal Wedding. As T **112** of Ascension. Multicoloured.

220. 33 c. Prince Andrew and Miss Sarah Ferguson .. 45 40
221. 90 c. Prince Andrew piloting helicopter, Digby, Canada, 1985 .. 95 1·60

48. Father Christmas and Reindeer in Speed Boat.

1986. Christmas. Multicoloured.

222. 30 c. Type **48** 65 50
223. 36 c. Father Christmas and reindeer on beach .. 75 60
224. 55 c. Father Christmas fishing .. .. .. 1·25 1·40
225. 70 c. Playing golf .. .. 1·75 2·25
226. $1 Sleeping in hammock .. 2·00 2·50

49. H.M.S. "Flying Fish" and Outline Map of Christmas Island.

1987. Centenary of Visits by H.M.S. "Flying Fish" and H.M.S. "Egeria". Mult.

227. 36 c. Type **49** 80 60
228. 90 c. H.M.S. "Egeria" and outline map .. .. 1·60 2·40

50. Blind Snake.

1987. Wildlife. Multicoloured.

229 1 c. Type **50** 40 50
230 2 c. Blue-tailed skink .. 40 50
231 3 c. Insectivorous bat .. 50 60
232 5 c. Grasshopper .. 50 60
233 10 c. Christmas Island fruit bat 50 60
234 25 c. Gecko 60 70
235 30 c. "Mantis religiosa" (mantid) 70 80
236 36 c. Indonesian hawk owl 1·25 1·40
237 40 c. Bull mouth helmet shell 65 75
237a 41 c. Nudibranch ("Phidiana sp.") .. 60 70
238 50 c. Textile cone shell .. 75 85
239 65 c. Brittle stars .. 75 85
240 75 c. Royal angelfish .. 75 85
241 90 c. "Appias paulina" (butterfly) .. .. 2·25 2·25
242 $1 "Hypolimnas misippus" (butterfly) .. 2·25 2·25
243 $2 Shrew .. .. 2·75 3·25
244 $5 Green turtle .. .. 4·50 5·50

1988. Bicentenary of Australian Settlement. Arrival of First Fleet. As Nos. 1105/9 of Australia, but each inscribed "CHRISTMAS ISLAND Indian Ocean" and "AUSTRALIA BICENTENARY".

246. 37 c. Aborigines watching arrival of Fleet, Botany Bay .. .. .. 1·25 1·40
247. 37 c. Aboriginal family and anchored ships .. .. 1·25 1·40
248. 37 c. Fleet arriving at Sydney Cove .. .. 1·25 1·40
249. 37 c. Ship's boat .. .. 1·25 1·40
250. 37 c. Raising the flag, Sydney Cove, 26 January 1788 .. .. .. 1·25 1·40

Nos. 246/50 were printed together, se-tenant, forming a composite design.

52 Captain William May

1988. Cent of British Annexation. Mult.

251 37 c. Type **52** 35 40
252 53 c. Annexation ceremony 50 55
253 95 c. H.M.S. "Imperieuse" (armoured cruiser) firing salute 90 95
254 $1.50 Building commemorative cairn .. 1·40 1·50

53 Pony and Trap, 1910

1988. Cent of Permanent Settlement. Mult.

255 37 c. Type **53** 45 40
256 55 c. Phosphate mining, 1910 .. .. .. 60 55
257 70 c. Steam locomotive, 1914 .. .. .. 85 70
258 $1 Arrival of first aircraft, 1957 .. .. .. 1·25 1·00

54 Beach Toys

1988. Christmas. Toys and Gifts. Mult.

259 32 c. Type **54** 40 35
260 39 c. Flippers, snorkel and mask 50 40
261 90 c. Model soldier, doll and soft toys .. 1·10 90
262 $1 Models of racing car, lorry and jet aircraft .. 1·25 1·00

55 Food on Table ("Good Harvesting")

1989. Chinese New Year. Multicoloured.
263 39 c. Type **55** 45 40
264 70 c. Decorations ("Prosperity") 80 70
265 90 c. Chinese girls ("Good Fortune") .. .. 1·10 90
266 $1 Lion dance ("Progress Every Year") .. .. 1·25 1·00

56 Sir John Murray

1989. 75th Death Anniv of Sir John Murray (oceanographer). Multicoloured.
267 39 c. Type **56** 50 50
268 80 c. Map of Christmas Island showing Murray Hill 95 95
269 $1 Oceanographic equipment .. .. .. 1·25 1·25
270 $1.10 H.M.S. "Challenger" (survey ship), 1872 .. 1·50 1·50

57 Four Children

1989. Malay Hari Raya Festival. Mult.
271 39 c. Type **57** 50 50
272 55 c. Man playing tambourine 70 70
273 80 c. Girl in festival costume .. .. 1·00 1·00
274 $1.10 Christmas Island Mosque .. .. 1·40 1·40

58 "Huperzia phlegmaria"

1989. Ferns. Multicoloured.
275 41 c. Type **58** 40 45
276 65 c. "Asplenium polydon" 60 65
277 80 c. Common bracken .. 75 80
278 $1.10 Birds-nest fern .. 1·00 1·10

MINIMUM PRICE

The minimum price quoted is 10p which represents a handling charge rather than a basis for valuing common stamps. For further notes about prices see introductory pages.

59 Virgin Mary and Star

61 First Sighting, 1615

1989. Christmas. Multicoloured.
279 36 c. Type **59** 35 40
280 41 c. Christ Child in manger 40 45
281 80 c. Shepherds and star 75 80
282 $1.10 Three Wise Men following star .. .. 1·00 1·10

1989. "Melbourne Stampshow '89". Nos. 237a and 242 optd with Stampshow logo.
283 41 c. Nudibranch ("Phidiana" sp.) .. 40 45
284 $1 "Hypolimnas misippus" (butterfly) .. .. 1·00 1·00

1990. 375th Anniv of Discovery of Christmas Island. Multicoloured.
285 41 c. Type **61** 50 50
286 $1.10 Second sighting and naming, 1643 .. .. 1·40 1·40

62 Miniature Tractor pulling Phosphate

1990. Christmas Island Transport. Mult.
287 1 c. Type **62** 15 20
288 2 c. Phosphate train .. 30 30
289 3 c. Diesel railcar (vert) .. 20 20
290 5 c. Loading road train .. 30 30
291 10 c. Trishaw (vert) .. 30 30
292 15 c. Terex truck 50 50
293 25 c. Articulated bus .. 30 30
294 30 c. Railway passenger rake (vert) .. 30 35
295 40 c. Passenger barge (vert) 35 40
296 50 c. Kolek (outrigger canoe) 55 55
297 65 c. Flying Doctor aircraft and ambulance .. 1·25 1·25
298 75 c. Commercial van .. 1·25 1·25
299 90 c. Vintage lorry .. 1·50 1·50
300 $1 Water tanker .. .. 1·50 1·50
301 $2 Traction engine .. 3·00 3·00
302 $5 Steam locomotive and flat car .. .. .. 4·50 4·75

63 Male Abbott's Booby

1990. Abbott's Booby. Multicoloured.
303 10 c. Type **63** 30 30
304 20 c. Juvenile male .. 50 50
305 29 c. Female with egg .. 55 55
306 41 c. Pair with chick .. 70 70

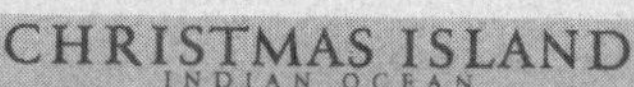

64 1977 Famous Visitors 9 c. Stamp

1990. Centenary of Henry Ridley's Visit. Multicoloured.
308 41 c. Type **64** 55 65
309 75 c. Ridley (botanist) in rainforest .. .. 85 1·40

65 "Corymborkus veratrifolia"

1990. Christmas. Flowers. Multicoloured.
311 38 c. Type **65** 60 60
312 43 c. "Hoya aldrichii" .. 65 65
313 80 c. "Quisqualis indica" 1·25 1·10
314 $1.20 "Barringtonia racemosa" .. .. 1·75 1·60

66 "Islander" (freighter), 1898

1991. Centenary of First Phosphate Mining Lease. Multicoloured.
316 43 c. Type **66** 60 60
317 43 c. Miners loading rail wagons, 1908 .. .. 60 60
318 85 c. Shay steam locomotive No. 4, 1925 .. 1·00 1·00
319 $1.20 Extracting phosphate, 1951 .. 1·40 1·40
320 $1.70 Land reclamation, 1990 .. .. .. 1·90 1·90

Nos. 316/20 were printed together, se-tenant, forming a composite forest design.

67 Teaching Children Road Safety

1991. Christmas Island Police Force. Mult.
321 43 c. Type **67** 60 60
322 43 c. Traffic control .. 60 60
323 90 c. Airport customs .. 1·40 1·40
324 $1.20 Police launch "Fregata Andrews" towing rescued boat .. 1·75 1·75

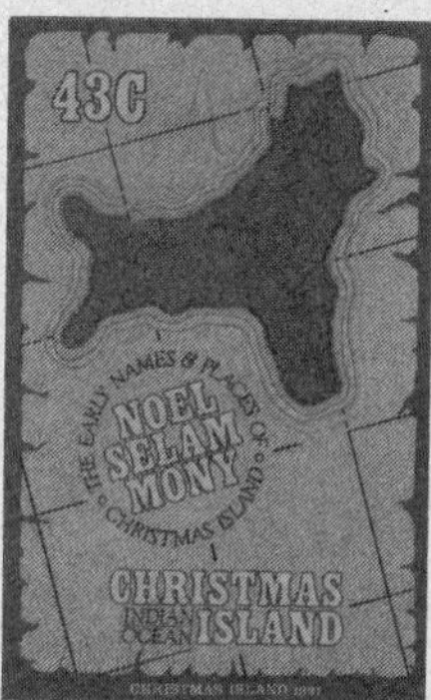

68 Map of Christmas Island, 1991

1991. Maps of Christmas Island. Mult.
326 43 c. Type **68** 65 65
327 75 c. Goos Atlas, 1666 .. 1·10 1·10
328 $1.10 De Manevillette, 1745 1·60 1·60
329 $1.20 Comberford, 1667 .. 1·75 1·90

HAVE YOU READ THE NOTES AT THE BEGINNING OF THIS CATALOGUE?

These often provide answers to the enquiries we receive.

69 "Bruguiera gymnorrhiza"

1991. Local Trees. Multicoloured.
330 43 c. Type **69** 65 65
331 70 c. "Syzygium operculatum" .. .. 1·00 1·00
332 85 c. "Ficus microcarpa" 1·25 1·25
333 $1.20 "Arenga listeri" .. 1·60 1·60

70 "Family round Christmas Tree" (S'ng Yen Luiw)

1991. Christmas. Children's Paintings. Mult.
334 38 c. Type **70** 45 50
335 38 c. "Opening Presents" (Liew Ann Nee) .. 45 50
336 38 c. "Beach Party" (Foo Pang Chuan) 45 50
337 38 c. "Christmas Walk" (Too Lai Peng) .. 45 50
338 38 c. "Santa Claus and Christmas Tree" (Jesamine Wheeler) .. 45 50
339 43 c. "Santa Claus fishing" (Ho Puay Ha) 50 60
340 $1 "Santa Claus in Boat" (Ng Hooi Hua) .. 1·10 1·25
341 $1.20 "Santa Claus surfing" (Yani Kawi) .. 1·25 1·50

71 Discussing Evacuation, 1942

1992. 50th Anniv of Partial Evacuation. Multicoloured.
342 45 c. Type **71** 55 55
343 45 c. Families waiting to embark 55 55
344 $1.05 Ferrying evacuees to "Islander" .. .. 1·40 1·40
345 $1.20 Departure of "Islander" (freighter) 1·60 1·60

72 "Cypraea caputserpentis"

1992. Shells. Multicoloured.
346 5 c. "Cypraea tigris" .. 10 10
347 10 c. Type **72** 10 10
348 15 c. "Lambis scorpius" .. 15 20
349 20 c. "Chlamys pallium" .. 15 20
350 25 c. "Engina mendicaria" 20 25
351 30 c. "Drupa ricinus" .. 30 35
352 40 c. "Distorsio reticulata" 40 45
353 45 c. "Turbo petholatus" 40 45
354 50 c. "Cantharus pulcher" 45 50
355 60 c. "Conus capitaneus" 60 65
356 70 c. "Turbo lajonkairii" 65 70
357 80 c. "Lambis chiragra" .. 75 80
358 90 c. "Angaria delphinus" 85 90
359 $1 "Vasum ceramicum" 95 1·00
360 $2 "Tonna perdix" .. 2·00 2·10
361 $5 "Drupa rubusidaea" .. 4·75 5·00

73 Torpedoing of "Eidsvold"

1992. 50th Anniv of Sinkings of "Eidsvold" and "Nissa Maru". Multicoloured.

362 45 c. Type **73** 55 55
363 80 c. "Eidsvold" sinking .. 90 90
364 $1.05 "Nissa Maru" under attack .. .. .. 1·40 1·40
365 $1.20 "Nissa Maru" beached .. .. 1·50 1·50

1992. "Kuala Lumpur '92" International Philatelic Exhibition. No. 361 optd with exhibition symbol.

366 $5 "Drupa rubusidaea" .. 5·50 6·00

75 Jungle

1992. Christmas. Multicoloured.

367 40 c. Type **75** 50 50
368 40 c. Seabirds over rock .. 50 50
369 45 c. Boobies on headland 55 55
370 $1.05 Seabirds and cliffs .. 1·25 1·25
371 $1.20 Cliffs .. .. 1·40 1·40

Nos. 367/71 were printed together, se-tenant, forming a composite coastal design.

76 Abbott's Booby

1993. Seabirds. Multicoloured.

372 45 c. Type **76** 55 55
373 45 c. Christmas Island frigate bird 55 55
374 45 c. Common noddy .. 55 55
375 45 c. Golden bosunbird .. 55 55
376 45 c. Brown booby .. 55 55

Nos. 372/6 were printed together, se-tenant, forming a composite design.

77 Dolly Beach

1993. Scenic Views of Christmas Island. Multicoloured.

378 85 c. Type **77** .. .. 1·00 1·00
379 95 c. Blow Holes .. .. 1·25 1·25
380 $1.05 Merrial Beach .. 1·40 1·40
381 $1.20 Rainforest .. .. 1·50 1·50

78 Turtle on Beach

1993. Christmas. Multicoloured.

382 40 c. Type **78** 40 45
383 45 c. Crabs and wave .. 40 45
384 $1 Christmas Island frigate bird and rainforest .. 95 1·00

79 Map of Christmas Island

1993. 350th Anniv of Naming of Christmas Island.

385 **79** $2 multicoloured .. 2·00 2·10

80 Pekingese

1994. Chinese New Year ("Year of the Dog"). Multicoloured.

386 45 c. Type **80** 40 45
387 45 c. Mickey (Christmas Island dog) 40 45

COCHIN

A state of S.W. India. Now uses Indian stamps.

1892. 6 puttans = 5 annas. Later as India.

1. Emblems of State.

1892. Value in "puttans".

1a **1.** ½ put. orange .. .. 1·25 1·25
2 1 put. purple .. .. 1·50 1·00
3 2 put. violet .. .. 1·00 1·40

3.  5.

1983. Value in "pies" or "puttans". With or without gum.

16. **3.** 3 pies, blue 30 10
17. ½ put. green (smaller) .. 75 10
18. **5.** 1 put. red .. .. 1·25 10
19. **3.** 2 put. violet .. .. 1·40 20

1909. Surch. **2.** No gum.

22. **3.** "2" on 3 pies, mauve .. 15 30

8. Raja Sir Sri Rama Varma I. **10.** Maharaia Sir Sri Rama Varma II.

1911. Value in "pies" or "annas".

26. **8.** 2 p. brown 30 10
27. 3 p. blue 30 10
28. 4 p. green 90 10
29. 9 p. red .. .. .. 1·10 10
30. 1 a. orange .. .. 1·60 10
31. 1½ a. purple .. .. 3·75 40
32. 2 a. grey .. .. .. 7·50 40
33. 3 a. red .. .. .. 28·00 32·00

1918. Various frames.

35b. **10.** 2 p. brown 75 10
36. 4 p. green 95 10
37. 6 p. brown .. .. 1·00 10
38. 8 p. brown .. .. 1·40 10
39. 9 p. red .. .. .. 8·50 15
40. 10 p. blue .. .. 1·40 10
41. 1 a. orange .. .. 6·50 40
42. 1½ a. purple .. .. 2·25 10
43. 2 a. grey .. .. 3·75 10
44. 2¼ a. green .. .. 3·75 90
45. 3 a. red .. .. .. 11·00 35

1922. Surch. with figure and words.

46. **8.** 2 p. on 3 p. blue .. 40 30

1928. Surch. in words in English and native characters and **ANCHAL & REVENUE.**

50. **10.** 1 a. on 2¼ a. green .. 5·00 12·00

1932. Surch. in figures and words both in English and in native characters.

51. **10.** 3 p. on 4 p. green .. 1·00 75
52. 3 p. on 8 p. brown .. 1·00 1·60
53. 9 p. on 10 p. blue .. 1·50 1·75

18. Maharaja Sir Sri Rama Varma III. **26.** Maharaja Sri Kerala Varma I.

1933.

54. **18.** 2 p. brown 50 15
55. 4 p. green 60 10
56. 6 p. red 70 10
57. 1 a. orange 70 10
58. 1 a. 8 p. red .. .. 3·00 2·50
59. 2 a. grey .. .. .. 2·25 20
60. 2¼ a. green .. .. 1·50 10
61. 3 a. orange .. .. 3·50 90
62. 3 a. 4 p. violet .. .. 1·50 1·40
63. 6 a. 8 p. sepia .. .. 1·75 5·50
64. 10 a. blue .. .. .. 3·00 7·50

1934. Surch. with figure and words.

65. **10.** 6 p. on 8 p. brown .. 75 50
66. 6 p. on 10 p. blue .. 1·75 75

1939. Optd. **ANCHAL.**

75. **18.** 1 a. orange .. .. 1·50 20

1939. Surch. in words only.

72. **18.** 3 p. on 1 a. 8 p. red .. £130 60·00
74. 6 p. on 1 a. 8 p. red .. 2·00 14·00

1943. Surch. **SURCHARGED** and value in words.

77. **18.** 3 p. on 4 p. green .. 5·00 1·75
73. 3 p. on 1 a. 8 p. red .. 2·00 5·50
76. 1 a. 3 p. on 1 a. 8 p. red .. 1·00 30

1943. Surch. **ANCHAL SURCHARGED NINE PIES.**

82. **18.** 9 p. on 1 a. orange .. 12·00 2·00

1943. Surch. **ANCHAL** and **value in words.**

79. **18.** 6 p. on 1 a. orange .. 55·00 29·00
80. 9 p. on 1 a. orange .. 70·00 80·00

1943.

85. **26.** 2 p. brown .. .. 1·00 50
87. 4 p. green .. .. 3·00 1·75
88. 6 p. brown .. .. 1·25 10
89. 9 p. blue .. .. .. 16·00 1·00
90. 1 a. orange .. .. 20·00 30·00
91. 2¼ a. green .. .. 13·00 50

1944. Surch. with value in **words only.**

93. **26.** 2 p. on 6 p. brown .. 75 1·50
94. 3 p. on 4 p. green .. 1·25 10
96. 3 p. on 6 p. brown .. 80 20
97. 4 p. on 6 p. brown .. 2·00 5·50

1944. Surch. **SURCHARGED and value in** words.

95. **26.** 3 p. on 4 p. green .. 1·60 10
92c. 1 a. 3 p. on 1 a. orange .. — £2500

1944. Surch. **ANCHAL NINE PIES.**

92a. **26.** 9 p. on 1 a. orange .. 4·00 65

1944. Surch. **ANCHAL SURCHARGED NINE PIES.**

92b. **26.** 9 p. on 1 a. orange .. 1·25 1·40

28. Maharaja Sri Ravi Varma.  **29.** Maharaja Sri Ravi Varma.

1944.

98a. **28.** 9 p. blue .. .. 4·00 6·00
99. 1 a. 3 p. mauve .. 6·00 4·50
100. 1 a. 9 p. blue . .. 11·00 6·00

1946. No gum.

101. **29.** 2 p. brown 75 10
102. 3 p. red 50 10
103. 4 p. green .. .. £1100 80·00
104. 6 p. brown .. .. 18·00 2·25
105. 9 p. blue 50 10
106. 1 a. orange .. .. 5·00 18·00
107. 2 a. black .. .. 65·00 3·00
108. 3 a. red .. .. .. 40·00 45

For No. 106, overprinted **"U.S.T.C."** or "T.-C." with or without surcharge, see Travancore–Cochin.

30. Maharaja Sri Kerala Varma II.

1948.

109. **30.** 2 p. brown 75 10
110. 3 p. red 75 10
111. 4 p. green .. .. 4·50 30
112. 6 p. brown .. .. 7·00 10
113. 9 p. blue .. .. 1·25 10
114. 2 a. black .. .. 26·00 30
115. 3 a. orange .. .. 35·00 35
116. 3 a. 4 p. violet £110 £325

31. Chinese Nets.

1949.
117. 31. 2 a. black .. .. 1·00 3·00
118. – 2¼ a. green (Dutch palace) 70 2·50

SIX PIES

ആറു പൈ
(33.)

1949. Surch. as T 33.
121. 29. 3 p. on 9 p. blue .. 4·00 10·00
125. 30. 3 p. on 9 p. blue .. 2·50 1·00
126. 6 p. on 9 p. blue .. 75 40
119. 28. 6 p. on 1 a. 3 p. mauve 1·25 1·50
122. 29. 6 p. on 1 a. 3 p. mauve 6·00 7·00
120. 29. 1 a. on 1 a. 9 p. blue .. 75 60
123. 29. 1 a. on 1 a. 9 p. blue 3·00 60

1949. Surch. SIX PIES or NINE PIES only.
127. 29. 6 p. on 1 a. orange .. 50·00 90·00
128. 9 p. on 1 a. orange .. 35·00 90·00

OFFICIAL STAMPS

1913. Optd. ON G C S.
O 1. 8. 3 p. blue £100 10
O 2. 4 p. green .. .. 8·00 10
O 3a. 9 p. red .. .. 13·00 10
O 4. 1½ a. purple .. .. 24·00 10
O 5. 2 a. grey .. .. 13·00 10
O 6. 3 a. red .. .. 32·00 15
O 7. 6 a. violet .. .. 28·00 2·00
O 8. 12 a. blue .. .. 26·00 5·00
O 9. 1½ r. green .. .. 22·00 32·00

1919. Optd. ON C G S.
O 10. 10. 4 p. green .. .. 3·25 10
O 11. 6 p. brown .. .. 5·00 10
O 26. 8 p. brown .. .. 6·00 10
O 13. 9 p. red .. .. 30·00 10
O 27. 10 p. blue .. .. 6·00 10
O 15. 1½ a. purple .. .. 5·50 10
O 28. 2 a. grey .. .. 16·00 10
O 17. 2¼ a. green .. .. 9·00 10
O 29. 3 a. red .. .. 8·00 15
O 19. 6 a. violet .. .. 26·00 50
O 19a. 12 a. blue .. .. 15·00 2·75
O 19b. 1½ r. green .. .. 22·00 55·00

1923. Official stamps surch. in figures and words.
O 32 10. 6 p on 8 p. brown .. 1·75 10
O 33 6 p. on 10 p. blue .. 4·00 10
O 20b 8. 8 p. on 9 p. red .. £120 15
O 21 10. 8 p. on 9 p. red .. 70·00 10
O 23 8. 10 p. on 9 p. red .. £475 7·00
O 22 10. 10 p. on 9 p. red .. 65·00 50

1933. Optd. ON C G S.
O 34. 18. 4 p. green .. .. 1·90 10
O 35. 6 p. red .. .. 1·90 10
O 52. 1 a. orange .. .. 1·00 10
O 37. 1 a. 8 p. red .. .. 2·00 20
O 50. 2 a. grey .. .. 7·50 40
O 39. 2¼ a. green .. .. 4·00 10
O 53. 3 a. orange .. .. 2·75 40
O 41. 3 a. 4 p. violet .. 1·50 15
O 42. 6 a. 8 p. sepia .. 1·50 20
O 43. 10 a. blue .. .. 1·50 25

1943. Official stamp surch. NINE PIES.
O 57. 10. 9 p. on 1½ a. purple .. £250 15·00

1943. Official stamps surch. SURCHARGED and value in words.
O 63. 18. 3 p. on 4 p. green .. 65·00 38·00
O 58. 3 p. on 1 a. 8 p. red .. 1·75 30
O 66. 1 a. 3 p. on 1 a. orange .. £160 80·00
O 61. 1 a. 9 p. on 1 a. 8 p. red 70 30

1943. Official stamps surch. in words.
O 62. 18. 3 p. on 4 p. green .. 11·00 3·00
O 64. 3 p. on 1 a. orange .. 1·75 1·00
O 65. 9 p. on 1 a. orange .. £160 40·00
O 59. 9 p. on 1 a. 8 p. red .. 95·00 24·00
O 60. 1 a. 9 p. on 1 a. 8 p. red 90 1·25

1944. Optd. ON C G S.
O 68 26. 4 p. green .. .. 10·00 90
O 69b 6 p. brown 70 10
O 70 1 a. orange .. .. £1200 40·00
O 71 2 a. black .. .. 1·75 30
O 72 2¼ a. green .. .. 1·50 30
O 73 3 a. red .. .. 2·50 40

1944. Official stamps surch. SURCHARGED and value in words.
O 75. 26. 3 p. on 4 p. green .. 3·00 30
O 78. 9 p. on 6 p. brown .. 1·50 20
O 80. 1 a. 3 p. on 1 a. orange 2·25 10

1944. Official stamps surch in words.
O 74 26 3 p. on 4 p. green .. 1·00 10
O 76 3 p. on 1 a. orange .. 8·50 1·75
O 77 9 p. on 6 p. brown .. 4·00 50
O 80 1 a. 3 p. on 1 a. orange 2·25 10

1944. Optd. ON C G S.
O 81. 28. 9 p. blue 80 10
O 82. 1 a. 3 p. mauve .. 55 20
O 83. 1 a. 9 p. blue .. 40 20

1948. Optd. ON C.G.S.
O 84. 29. 3 p. red 35 10
O 85. 4 p. green .. .. 14·00 4·00
O 86. 6 p. brown .. .. 3·25 25
O 87. 9 p. blue 75 10
O 88. 1 a. 3 p. mauve .. 1·25 20
O 89. 1 a. 9 p. blue .. 1·40 40
O 90. 2 a. black .. .. 12·00 1·50
O 91. 2¼ a. green .. .. 12·00 1·50

1949. Optd. ON C.G.S.
O 92. 30. 3 p. red 30 10
O 93. 4 p. green 50 15
O 94. 6 p. brown .. .. 1·00 10
O 95. 9 p. blue 75 10
O 96. 2 a. black 60 15
O 97. 2¼ a. green .. .. 1·40 2·25
O 98. 3 a. orange .. .. 1·10 30
O 99. 3 a. 4 p. violet .. 15·00 17·00

1949. Official stamps surch. as T 12.
O 103. 30. 6 p. on 3 p. red .. 35 40
O 104. 9 p. on 4 p. green .. 50 75
O 100. 28. 1 a. on 1 a. 9 p. blue 60 30
O 101. 29. 1 a. on 1 a. 9 p. blue 9·50 7·50

1949. Optd. SERVICE.
O 105. 30. 3 p. on 9 p. (No. 125) 60 45
For later issues see under Travancore-Cochin

COCOS (KEELING) ISLANDS

Islands in the Indian Ocean formerly administered by Singapore and transferred to Australian administration on 23 November 1955.

1963. 12 pence = 1 shilling;
12 shillings = 1 pound.
1966. 100 cents = 1 dollar (Australia).

5. Jukong (sailboat).

6. White Tern.

1963.
1. – 3d. brown .. .. .. 1·75 1·25
2. – 5d. blue .. .. .. 1·50 65
3. – 8d. red .. .. .. 4·50 1·75
4. – 1s. green .. .. .. 3·00 55
5. 5. 2s. purple .. .. .. 11·00 3·25
6. 6. 2s. 3d. green .. .. 42·00 3·25

DESIGNS—As Type 5. HORIZ. 3d. Copra industry. 1s. Palms. VERT. 8d. Map of islands. As Type 6: 5d. Super Constellation airliner.

1965. 50th Anniv. of Gallipoli Landing. As T 184 of Australia, but slightly larger (22×34½ mm.).
7. 5d. brown, black and green 60 45

With the introduction of decimal currency on 14th February, 1966, Australian stamps were used in Cocos Islands until the 1969 issue.

7. Reef Clam.

1969. Decimal Currency. Multicoloured.
8 1 c. Lajonkaines turbo shell (vert) .. 30 50
9 2 c. Crocus giant clam (vert) 1·00 70
10 3 c. Type 7 .. .. 30 20
11 4 c. "Petroscirtes mitrattus" (fish) .. 30 40
12 5 c. "Porites cocosensis" (coral) 35 20
13 6 c. Greater spotted flying fish 75 45
14 10 c. Banded rail .. .. 1·50 60
15 15 c. Java sparrow .. .. 1·00 30
16 20 c. Red-tailed tropic bird 1·00 30
17 30 c. Sooty tern .. .. 1·25 30
18 50 c. Eastern reef heron (vert) .. .. 2·00 30
19 $1 Great frigate bird (vert) 5·00 1·00

9. "Dragon", 1609.

1976. Ships. Multicoloured.
20. 1 c. Type 9 .. .. .. 30 40
21. 2 c. H.M.S. "Juno", 1857 (horiz.) 30 40
22. 5 c. H.M.S. "Beagle", 1836 (horiz.) 30 40
23. 10 c. H.M.A.S. "Sydney", 1914 (horiz.) 35 40
24. 15 c. S.M.S. "Emden", 1914 (horiz.) .. .. 1·00 55
25. 20 c. "Ayesha", 1907 (horiz.) 1·00 65
26. 25 c. T.S.S. "Islander", 1927 1·00 1·00
27. 30 c. M.V. "Cheshire", 1951 1·00 1·00
28. 35 c. Jukong (sailboat) (horiz.) .. .. 1·00 1·00
29. 40 c. C.S. "Scotia", 1900 (horiz.) .. .. 1·00 1·00
30. 50 c. R.M.S. "Orontes", 1929 .. .. 1·40 1·10
31. $1 Royal Yacht "Gothic", 1954 .. .. .. 2·00 1·40

10. Map of Cocos (Keeling) Islands, Union Flag, Stars and Trees.

1979. Inauguration of Independent Postal Service and First Statutory Council. Multicoloured.
32. 20 c. Type 10 .. .. 25 30
33. 50 c. Council seal and jukong (sailboat) .. 35 50

11. Bright Yellow Long-nosed Butterfly Fish.

1979. Fishes. Multicoloured.
34. 1 c. Type 11 .. .. 30 70
35. 2 c. Clown Butterfly Fish 30 30
36. 5 c. "Anthias sp." .. 40 80
37. 10 c. Meyer's Butterfly Fish 30 30
38. 15 c. Wrasse 30 30
39. 20 c. Charles' Clown Fish 45 30
39a. 22 c. Yellow-striped Emerald Triggerfish .. 30 30
40. 25 c. "Cheilinus fasciatus" 45 35
40a. 28 c. "Macropharyngodon meleagris" 35 35
41. 30 c. "Chaetodon madagascariensis" 65 45
42. 35 c. Angel Fish .. .. 65 1·25
43. 40 c. Hog Fish 70 90
44. 50 c. Wrasse (different) .. 85 75
45. 55 c. "Anampses meleagrides" 75 75
45a. 60 c. Grouper 75 75
46. $1 Surgeon fish .. .. 1·75 3·25
47. $2 Three-banded Butterflly Fish .. .. .. 2·00 3·25

12. "Peace on Earth".

1979. Christmas. Multicoloured.
48. 25 c. Type 12 .. .. 25 35
49. 55 c. Atoll seascape ("Goodwill") 40 55

13. Star, Map of Cocos (Keeling) Islands and Island Landscape.

1980. Christmas. Multicoloured.
50. 15 c. Type 13 .. .. 10 10
51. 28 c. The Three Kings .. 15 15
52. 60 c. Adoration 40 40

14. "Administered by the British Government, 1857".

1980. 25th Anniv. of Territorial Status under Australian Administration. Multicoloured.
53. 22 c. Type 14 .. .. 15 15
54. 22 c. Arms of Ceylon .. 15 15
55. 22 c. Arms of Straits Settlements 15 15
56. 22 c. Arms of Singapore .. 15 15
57. 22 c. Arms and flag of Australia .. 15 15

15. "Eye of the Wind" and Map of Cocos (Keeling) Islands.

1980. "Operation Drake" (round the world expedition) and 400th Anniv of Sir Francis Drake's Circumnavigation of the World. Multicoloured.
58 22 c. Type 15 .. .. 20 15
59 28 c. Routes map (horiz) .. 20 15
60 35 c. Sir Francis Drake and "Golden Hind" 20 15
61 60 c. Prince Charles (patron) and "Eye of the Wind" (brigantine) 35 30

16. Aerial view of Animal Quarantine Station.

1981. Opening of Animal Quarantine Station. Multicoloured.
62. 22 c. Type 16 .. .. 15 15
63. 45 c. Unloading livestock .. 30 30
64. 60 c. Livestock in pen .. 35 35

17. Consolidated " Catalina " " Guba II " Flying Boat.

1981. Aircraft. Multicoloured.

65. 22 c. Type **17** 25 25
66. 22 c. Consolidated "Liberator" and Avro "Lancastrian" 25 25
67. 22 c. Douglas " DC 4 (Skymaster) " and Lockheed " Constellation " .. 25 25
68. 22 c. Lockheed " Electra " 25 25
69. 22 c. Boeing " 727 " airliners 25 25

18. Prince Charles and Lady Diana Spencer.

1981. Royal Wedding.

70. **18.** 24 c. multicoloured .. 40 20
71. 60 c. multicoloured .. 85 60

19. " Angels we have heard on High ".

1981. Christmas. Scenes and Lines from Carol " Angels we have heard on High ". Mult.

72. 18 c. Type **19** 10 10
73. 30 c. " Shepherds why this Jubilee? " .. 20 20
74. 60 c. " Come to Bethlehem and see Him " 35 35

20. " Pachyseris speciosa " and " Heliofungia actiniformis " (corals).

1981. 150th Anniv. of Charles Darwin's Voyage. Multicoloured.

75. 24 c. Type **20** 35 15
76. 45 c. Charles Darwin in 1853 and " Pavona cactus " (coral) 55 30
77. 60 c. H.M.S. " Beagle ", 1832, and " Lobophyllia hemprichii " (coral) .. 70 35

21. Queen Victoria.

1982. 125th Anniv. of Annexation of Cocos (Keeling) Islands to British Empire. Mult.

79. 24 c. Type **21** 20 15
80. 45 c. Union flag 35 25
81. 60 c. Capt. S. Fremantle (annexation visit, 1857) .. 40 35

22. Lord Baden-Powell.

1982. 75th Anniv. of Boy Scout Movement. Multicoloured.

82. 27 c. Type **22** 30 15
83. 75 c. " 75 " and map of Cocos (Keeling) Islands (vert.) .. .. 1·10 60

23. " Precis villida ".

1982. Butterflies and Moths. Multicioloured.

84 1 c. Type **23** 90 45
85 2 c. "Cephonodes picus" (horiz) 40 40
86 5 c. "Macroglossom corythus" (horiz) .. 1·25 50
87 10 c. "Chasmina candida" 40 40
88 20 c. "Nagia linteola" (horiz) 40 55
89 25 c. "Eublemma rivula" .. 40 65
90 30 c. "Eurrhyparodes tricoloralis" 40 55
91 35 c. "Hippotion boerhaviae" (horiz) .. .. 1·50 65
92 40 c. "Euploea core" .. 40 70
93 45 c. "Psara hipponalis" (horiz) 50 70
94 50 c. "Danaus chrysippus" (horiz) .. .. 55 1·25
95 55 c. "Hypolimas misippus" 60 70
96 60 c. "Spodoptera litura" .. 65 1·50
97 $1 "Achaea janata" .. 2·25 2·50
98 $2 "Panacra velox" (horiz) 2·00 2·75
99 $3 "Utetheisa pulchelloides" (horiz) .. .. .. 2·75 2·75

24 " Call His Name Immanuel ".

1982. Christmas. Multicoloured.

100. 21 c. Type **24** 20 20
101. 35 c. " I bring you good tidings " 35 35
102. 75 c. " Arise and flee into Egypt " 80 80

25. " God will look after us " (Matt. 1:20).

1983. Christmas. Extracts from New Testament. Multicoloured.

103. 24 c. Type **25** 30 30
104. 24 c. " Our baby King, Jesus " (Matthew. 2:2) .. 30 30
105. 24 c. " Your Saviour is born " (Luke. 2:11) .. 30 30
106. 24 c. " Wise men followed the Star " (Matthew. 2:9–10) 30 30
107. 24 c. " And worship the Lord " (Matthew. 2:11) 30 30

26. Hari Raya Celebration.

1984. Cocos-Malaya Culture. Multicoloured.

108. 45 c. Type **26** 45 25
109. 75 c. Melenggok dancing .. 65 50
110. 85 c. Cocos-Malaya wedding 75 55

27. Unpacking Barrel.

1984. 75th Anniv. of Cocos Barrel Mail. Mult.

111. 35 c. Type **27** 35 25
112. 55 c. Jukong awaiting mail ship 60 50
113. 70 c. P & O mail ship "Morea" 70 55

28. Captain William Keeling.

1984. 375th Anniv. of Discovery of Cocos (Keeling) Islands. Multicoloured.

115. 30 c. Type **28** 70 40
116. 65 c. "Hector" .. .. 1·50 90
117. 95 c. Mariner's astrolabe .. 1·75 1·25
118. $1.10 Map "circa" 1666 .. 1·90 1·50

29. Malay Settlement, Home Island.

1984. "Ausipex" International Stamp Exhibition, Melbourne. Multicoloured.

119. 45 c. Type **29** 65 50
120. 55 c. Airstrip, West Island 75 60

30. "Rainbow" Fish.

1984. Christmas. Multicoloured.

122. 24 c. Type **30** 40 25
123. 35 c. "Rainbow" butterfly 70 40
124. 55 c. "Rainbow" bird .. 85 70

32. Jukong-building.

1985. Cocos-Malay Culture (2nd series). Handicrafts. Multicoloured.

126. 30 c. Type **32** 65 25
127. 45 c. Blacksmithing .. 90 50
128. 55 c. Woodcarving .. 1·10 60

33. C.S. "Scotia".

1985. Cable-laying Ships. Multicoloured.

129. 33 c. Type **33** .. .. 1·00 35
130. 65 c. C.S. "Anglia" .. 1·60 90
131. 80 c. C.S. "Patrol" .. 2·00 1·25

34. Red-footed Booby.

1985. Birds of Cocos (Keeling) Islands. Multicoloured.

132. 33 c. Type **34** .. .. 1·50 85
133. 60 c. Rufous night heron (juvenile) (horiz.) .. 1·75 1·10
134. $1 Banded rail (horiz.) .. 2·25 1·50

Nos. 132/4 were issued together se-tenant, forming a composite design.

35. "Trochus maculatus".

1985. Shells and Molluscs. Multicoloured.

135. 1 c. Type **35** 30 45
136. 2 c. "Smaragdia rangiana" 40 55
137. 3 c. "Chama sp." 45 60
138. 4 c. "Cypraea moneta" .. 45 60
139. 5 c. "Drupa morum" .. 45 60
140. 10 c. "Conus miles" .. 50 65
141. 15 c. "Terebra maculata" 60 85
142. 20 c. "Fragum fragum" .. 70 90
143. 30 c. "Turbo lajonkaini" 85 1·10
144. 33 c. "Mitra fissurata" .. 85 1·10
145. 40 c. "Lambis lambis" .. 95 1·25
146. 50 c. "Tridacna squamosa" 1·10 1·50
147. 60 c. "Cypraea histrio" .. 1·40 1·75
148. $1 "Phillidia varicosa" .. 2·25 2·75
149. $2 "Halgerda tessellata" .. 3·50 4·00
150. $3 "Harminoea cymbalum" .. .. 4·25 4·75

37. Charles Darwin, c 1840.

1986. 150th Anniv. of Charles Darwin's Visit. Multicoloured.

152. 33 c. Type **37** 70 50
153. 60 c. Map of H.M.S. "Beagle's" route, Australia to Cocos Islands .. .. 1·25 1·50
154. $1 H.M.S. "Beagle" .. 1·75 2·25

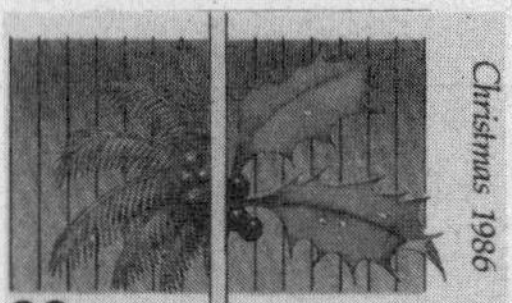

38. Coconut Palm and Holly Sprigs.

1986. Christmas. Multicoloured.

155. 30 c. Type **38** 45 40
156. 90 c. Sea shell and Christmas tree bauble .. 1·25 1·75
157. $1 Tropical fish and bell .. 1·50 2·00

INDEX

Countries can be quickly located by referring to the index at the end of this volume.

39. Jukong.

1987. Sailing Craft. Multicoloured.
158 36 c. Type **39** .. .. 1·10 1·25
159 36 c. Ocean racing yachts 1·10 1·25
160 36 c. "Sarimanok" (replica of early dhow) .. .. 1·10 1·25
161 36 c. "Ayesha" (schooner) 1·10 1·25
Nos. 158/61 were printed together, se-tenant, each strip forming a composite background design.

40. Beach, Direction Island.

1987. Cocos Islands Scenes. Multicoloured.
162. 70 c. Type **40** .. .. 1·25 1·25
163. 90 c. Palm forest, West Island .. .. .. 1·50 1·75
164. $1 Golf course .. .. 2·50 2·75

41. Radio Transmitter and Palm Trees at Sunset.

1987. Communications. Multicoloured.
165. 70 c. Type **41** .. .. 1·25 1·50
166. 75 c. Air liner at terminal 1·50 1·75
167. 90 c. "Intelsat 5" satellite 1·75 2·00
168. $1 Airmail letter and globe 2·00 2·25

42. Batik Printing.

1987. Cocos (Keeling) Islands Malay Industries. Multicoloured.
169. 45 c. Type **42** .. .. 1·25 1·50
170. 65 c. Jukong building 1·50 1·75
171. 75 c. Copra production .. 1·75 2·00

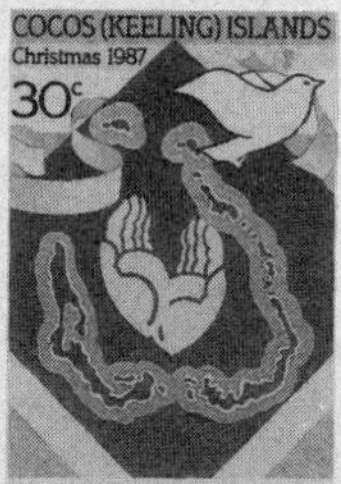

43. Hands releasing Peace Dove and Map of Islands.

1987. Christmas. Multicoloured.
172. 30 c. Type **43** 40 30
173. 90 c. Local children at Christmas party .. 1·25 1·00
174. $1 Island family and Christmas star .. .. 1·50 1·10

1988. Bicentenary of Australian Settlement. Arrival of First Fleet. As Nos. 1105/9 of Australia but each inscribed "COCOS (KEELING) ISLANDS" and "AUSTRALIA BICENTENARY".
175. 37 c. Aborigines watching arrival of Fleet, Botany Bay .. .. .. 1·40 1·40
176. 37 c. Aboriginal family and anchored ships .. .. 1·40 1·40
177. 37 c. Fleet arriving at Sydney Cove .. .. 1·40 1·40
178. 37 c. Ship's boat .. .. 1·40 1·40
179. 37 c. Raising the flag, Sydney Cove, 26 January 1788 .. .. 1·40 1·40
Nos. 175/9 were printed together, se-tenant, forming a composite design.

44 Coconut Flower

1988. Life Cycle of the Coconut. Mult.
180 37 c. Type **44** 50 40
181 65 c. Immature nuts .. 75 65
182 90 c. Coconut palm and mature nuts .. .. 1·10 90
183 $1 Seedlings .. .. 1·25 1·00

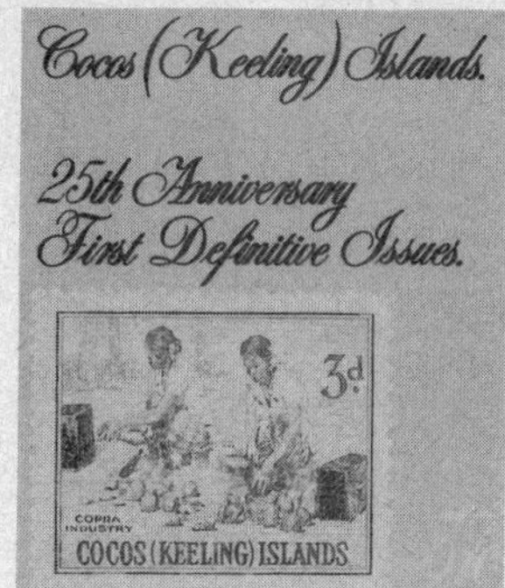

45 Copra 3d. Stamp of 1963

1988. 25th Anniv of First Cocos (Keeling) Islands Stamps. Each showing stamp from 1963 definitive set.
185 **45** 37 c. green, black & blue 70 70
186 – 55 c. green, black & brn 1·10 1·10
187 – 65 c. blue, black & lilac 1·25 1·25
188 – 70 c. red, black and grey 1·40 1·40
189 – 90 c. purple, blk & grey 1·60 1·60
190 – $1 green, black & brown 1·75 1·75
DESIGNS: 55 c. Palms 1s.; 65 c. "Super Constellation" 5d.; 70 c. Map 8d.; 90 c. "Jukong" (sailboat) 2s.; $1 White tern 2s. 3d.

46 "Pisonia grandis"

1988. Flora. Multicoloured.
191 1 c. Type **46** 10 20
192 2 c. "Cocos nucifera" .. 15 20
193 5 c. "Morinda citrifolia" .. 30 30
194 10 c. "Cordia subcordata" 30 30
195 30 c. "Argusia argentea" 50 50
196 37 c. "Calophyllum inophyllum" 50 50
197 40 c. "Barringtonia asiatica" 65 65
198 50 c. "Caesalpinia bonduc" 70 70
199 90 c. "Terminalia catappa" 1·00 1·00
200 $1 "Pemphis acidula" .. 1·10 1·10
201 $2 "Scaevola sericea" .. 2·00 2·25
202 $3 "Hibiscus tiliaceus" .. 3·50 3·75

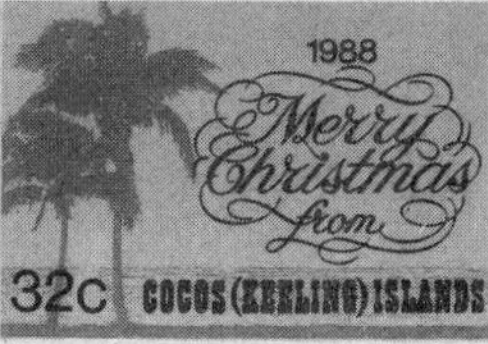

47 Beach at Sunset

1988. Christmas.
204 **47** 32 c. multicoloured .. 70 35
205 90 c. multicoloured .. 1·50 1·25
206 $1 multicoloured .. 1·25 1·25

48 Capt. P. G. Taylor

49 Jukong and Star

1989. 50th Anniv of First Indian Ocean Aerial Survey.
207 **48** 40 c. multicoloured .. 40 45
208 – 70 c. multicoloured .. 65 70
209 – $1 multicoloured .. 95 1·00
210 – $1.10 blue, lilac & black 1·00 1·10
DESIGNS: 70 c. Consolidated Catalina "PBY2" "Guba II" and crew; $1 "Guba II" over Direction Island; $1.10, Unissued Australia 5s. stamp commemorating flight.

1989. Christmas.
211 **49** 35 c. multicoloured .. 45 40
212 80 c. multicoloured .. 90 1·00
213 $1.10 multicoloured .. 1·10 1·25

50 H.M.A.S. "Sydney" (cruiser)

1989. 75th Anniv of Destruction of German Cruiser "Emden". Multicoloured.
214 40 c. Type **50** .. .. 1·10 1·10
215 70 c. "Emden" .. .. 1·40 1·40
216 $1 Emden's steam launch 1·75 1·75
217 $1.10 H.M.A.S. "Sydney" (1914) and crest .. 1·75 1·75

51 Xanthid Crab

1990. Cocos Islands Crabs. Multicoloured.
219 45 c. Type **51** 70 70
220 75 c. Ghost crab .. .. 1·00 1·00
221 $1 Red-backed mud crab 1·25 1·25
222 $1.30 Coconut crab (vert) 1·50 1·50

52 Captain Keeling and "Hector", 1609

1990. Navigators of the Pacific.
223 **52** 45 c. mauve .. .. 1·00 75
224 – 75 c. mauve and blue .. 1·40 1·40
225 – $1 mauve and stone .. 1·75 1·75
226 – $1.30 mauve and buff .. 2·00 2·25
DESIGNS: 75 c. Captain Fitzroy and H.M.S. "Beagle", 1836; $1 Captain Belcher and H.M.S. "Samarang", 1846; $1.30 Captain Fremantle and H.M.S. "Juno", 1857.

1990. "New Zealand 1990" International Stamp Exhibition, Auckland. No. 188 optd with logo and **NEW ZEALAND 1990 24 AUG 2 SEP AUCKLAND**.
228 70 c. red, black and grey .. 1·50 1·50

1990. No. 187 surch **$5**.
230 $5 on 65 c. blue, blk & lilac 5·00 5·00

55 Cocos Atoll from West and Star

1990. Christmas. Multicoloured.
231 40 c. Type **55** 45 50
232 70 c. Cocos atoll from south .. .. .. 80 1·00
233 $1.30 Cocos atoll from east 1·40 2·00

1990. Nos. 140/1, 143 and 146/7 surch **POSTAGE PAID** plus additional words as indicated.
235 (1 c.) on 30 c. "Turbo lajonkaini" (**LOCAL**) .. 30 30
234 (43 c.) on 10 c. "Conus miles" (**MAINLAND**) 60 60
237 70 c. on 60 c. "Cypraea histrio" (**ZONE 1**) .. 1·25 1·25
238 80 c. on 50 c. "Tridacna squamosa" (**ZONE 2**) 1·50 1·50
239 $1.20 on 15 c. "Terebra maculata" (**ZONE 5**) 1·75 1·75

58 Beaded Sea Star

1991. Starfish and Sea Urchins. Mult.
240 45 c. Type **58** 60 60
241 75 c. Feather star .. 1·10 1·10
242 $1 Slate pencil urchin .. 1·40 1·40
243 $1.30 Globose sea urchin .. 1·60 1·60

59 Cocos Islands

1991. Malay Hari Raya Festival. Mult.
244 45 c. Type **59** 60 60
245 75 c. Island house .. 1·10 1·10
246 $1.30 Islands scene .. 1·60 1·60

60 Child praying

1991. Christmas. Multicoloured.
247 38 c. Type **60** 50 45
248 43 c. Child dreaming of Christmas Day .. 60 55
249 $1 Child singing .. 1·25 1·10
250 $1.20 Child fascinated by decorations .. .. 1·25 1·25

61 "Lybia tessellata"

1992. Crustaceans. Multicoloured.
252 5 c. Type **61** 10 10
253 10 c. "Pilodius areolatus" 10 10
254 20 c. "Trizopagurus strigatus" 20 25
255 30 c. "Lophozozymus pulchellus" 30 35
256 40 c. "Thalamitoides quadridens" 35 40
257 45 c. "Calcinus elegans" (vert) 40 45
258 50 c. "Clibarius humilis" .. 45 50
259 60 c. "Trapezia rufopunctata" (vert) .. 55 60
260 80 c. "Pylopaguropsis magnimanus" (vert) .. 75 80
261 $1 "Trapezia ferruginea" (vert) .. .. .. 95 1·00
262 $2 "Trapezia guttata" (vert) .. .. .. 2·00 2·10
263 $3 "Trapezia cymodoce" (vert) .. .. .. 3·00 3·25

62 Banded Rail searching for Food

1992. Endangered Species. Banded Rail. Multicoloured.
264 10 c. Type **62** 20 20
265 15 c. Banded rail with chick 30 30
266 30 c. Two rails drinking .. 40 40
267 45 c. Rail and nest .. 50 50

63 "Santa Maria"

1992. 500th Anniv of Discovery of America by Columbus.
269 **63** $1.05 multicoloured .. 1·50 1·50

64 R.A.F. Spitfires on Island Airstrip

1992. 50th Anniv of Second World War. Mult.
270 45 c. Type **64** 55 55
271 85 c. Japanese aircraft bombing Kampong .. 1·00 1·00
272 $1.20 R.A.F. Sunderland (flying boat) .. .. 1·50 1·50

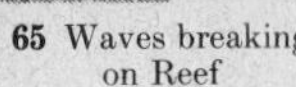

65 Waves breaking on Reef

66 "Lobophyllia hemprichii"

1992. Christmas. Multicoloured.
273 40 c. Type **65** 50 50
274 80 c. Direction Island .. 95 95
275 $1 Moorish idols (fish) and coral .. .. .. 1·25 1·25

1993. Corals. Multicoloured.
276 45 c. Type **66** 55 55
277 85 c. "Pocillopora eydouxi" .. .. 1·00 1·00
278 $1.05 "Fungia scutaria" .. 1·40 1·40
279 $1.20 "Sarcophyton sp" .. 1·50 1·50

67 Plastic 5 r. Token

1993. Early Cocos (Keeling) Islands Currency. Multicoloured.
280 45 c. Type **67** 55 55
281 85 c. 1968 1 r. plastic token 1·00 1·00
282 $1.05 1977 150 r. commemorative gold coin .. 1·40 1·40
283 $1.20 1910 plastic token .. 1·50 1·50

68 Primary School Pupil

1993. Education. Multicoloured.
284 5 c. Type **68** 10 10
285 45 c. Secondary school pupil 50 50
286 85 c. Learning traditional crafts 90 90
287 $1.05 Learning office skills 1·25 1·25
288 $1.20 Seaman training .. 1·40 1·40

69 Lifeboat and Crippled Yacht

1993. Air-Sea Rescue. Multicoloured.
289 45 c. Type **69** 55 55
290 85 c. "Westwind Seascan" (aircraft) .. .. 1·00 1·00
291 $1.05 "R.J. Hawke" (ferry) 1·25 1·25

70 Peace Doves

1993. Christmas.
293 **70** 40 c. multicoloured .. 40 45
294 80 c. multicoloured .. 75 80
295 $1 multicoloured .. 95 1·00

OFFICIAL STAMPS

1991. No. 182 surch **OFFICIAL PAID MAINLAND**.
O1 (43 c.) on 90 c. Coconut palm and mature nuts † 60

No. O1 was not sold to the public in unused condition.

COOK ISLANDS

A group of islands in the S. Pacific under New Zealand control, including Aitutaki, Niue, Penrhyn and Rarotonga. Granted Self-Government in 1965.

See also issues for Aitutaki and Penrhyn Island.

1892. 12 pence = 1 shilling.
20 shillings = 1 pound.
1967. 100 cents = 1 dollar.

1.

1892.
1. **1.** 1d. black .. .. .. 26·00 26·00
2. 1½d. mauve .. .. .. 38·00 38·00
3. 2½d. blue .. .. .. 38·00 38·00
4. 10d. red £140 £130

2. Queen Makea Takau.

3. White Tern or Torea.

1893.
11ba **3.** ½d. blue .. .. .. 3·50 4·75
28 ½d. green .. .. .. 1·40 3·25
13 **2.** 1d. brown .. .. .. 9·50 12·00
6 1d. blue .. .. .. 6·00 1·50
29 1d. red .. .. .. 2·25 3·00
43 1½d. mauve .. .. 5·50 3·50
15a **3.** 2d. brown .. .. 6·50 6·50
16a **2.** 2½d. red .. .. .. 9·50 9·00
32 2½d. blue .. .. .. 3·75 6·50
9 5d. black .. .. .. 14·00 13·00
18a **3.** 6d. purple .. .. 16·00 19·00
19 **2.** 10d. green .. .. 15·00 27·00
46 **3.** 1s. red .. .. .. 27·00 60·00

1899. Surch. **ONE HALF PENNY.**
21. **2.** ½d. on 1d. blue .. .. 32·00 38·00

1901. Optd. with crown.
22. **2.** 1d. brown £150 £140

1919. New Zealand stamps (King George V.) surch. **RAROTONGA** and value in native language in words.
56 **62** ½d. green 20 60
47 **53** 1d. red .. .. .. 40 1·00
57 **62** 1½d. brown 30 75
58 2d. yellow 30 80
48 2½d. blue .. .. .. 95 2·25
49 3d. brown .. .. 1·00 1·50
50 4d. violet .. .. 1·00 4·00
51 4½d. green .. .. 1·25 6·00
52 6d. red .. .. .. 1·50 5·00
53 7½d. brown .. .. 1·25 5·50
54 9d. green .. .. .. 1·75 8·00
55 1s. red .. .. .. 2·75 11·00

9. Captain Cook Landing.

17. Harbour, Rarotonga and Mt. Ikurangi.

1920. Inscr. " RAROTONGA ".
81. **9.** ½d. black and green .. 4·50 5·00
82. – 1d. black and red .. 5·00 1·50
72. – 1½d. black and blue .. 7·50 8·50
83. – 2½d. brown and blue .. 3·00 14·00
73. – 3d. black and brown .. 2·25 5·50
84. **17.** 4d. green and violet .. 4·50 14·00
74. – 6d. brown and orange .. 1·75 8·00
75. – 1s. black and violet .. 5·00 17·00

DESIGNS—VERT. 1d. Wharf at Avarua. 1½d. Capt. Cook (Dance). 2½d. Te Po, Rarotongan chief. 3d. Palm tree. HORIZ. 6d. Huts at Arorangi. 1s. Avarua Harbour.

1921. New Zealand stamps optd. **RAROTONGA.**
76 **F 4.** 2s. blue .. .. .. 26·00 48·00
77 2s. 6d. brown .. .. 18·00 45·00
78 5s. green .. .. 26·00 50·00
79 10s. red .. .. .. 48·00 65·00
80 £1 red .. .. .. 75·00 £100

1926. "Admiral" type of New Zealand optd. **RAROTONGA.**
90 **71.** 2s. blue .. .. .. 10·00 38·00
92 3s. mauve .. .. 16·00 40·00

1931. No. 77 surch. **TWO PENCE.**
94. 2d. on 1½d. black & blue 1·50 4·50

1931. Arms type of New Zealand optd. **RAROTONGA.**
95. **F 6** 2s. 6d. brown .. .. 9·00 18·00
96. 5s. green .. .. .. 16·00 42·00
97. 10s. red .. .. .. 32·00 70·00
98. £1 pink .. .. .. 65·00 £100

20. Captain Cook landing.

22. Double Maori Canoe.

1932. Inscr. " COOK ISLANDS ".
106. **20.** ½d. black and green .. 40 1·25
107. – 1d. black and red .. 45 1·25
108. **22.** 2d. black and brown .. 35 30
109. – 2½d. black and blue .. 30 1·75
110. – 4d. black and blue .. 30 35
142. – 6d. black and orange .. 1·00 80
105. – 1s. black and violet .. 7·00 18·00

DESIGNS—VERT. 1d. Capt. Cook. HORIZ. 2½d. Natives working cargo. 4d. Port of Avarua. 6d. R.M.S. " Monowai ". 1 s. King George V.

1935. Jubilee. As 1932, optd. **SILVER JUBILEE OF KING GEORGE V 1910-1935.**
113. 1d. red 60 70
114. 2½d. blue .. .. 75 1·00
115. 6d. green and orange .. 3·25 4·50

1936. Stamps of New Zealand optd **COOK ISLANDS**.
116 **71** 2s. blue .. .. 12·00 35·00
131 **F 6** 2s. 6d. brown .. .. 7·00 9·00
117 **71** 3s. mauve .. .. 13·00 48·00
132 **F 6** 5s. green .. .. 5·50 14·00
133 10s. red .. .. 30·00 48·00
134 £1 pink .. .. 32·00 48·00
135 £3 green .. .. 50·00 £150
98b £5 blue £170 £275

1937. Coronation T **106** of New Zealand optd. **COOK IS'DS.**
124. **106.** 1d. red 40 10
125. 2½d. blue 80 20
126. 6d. orange 80 20

29. King George VI.

30. Native Village.

1938.
143 **29** 1s. black and violet .. 1·00 1·50
128 **30** 2s. black and orange .. 11·00 7·00
145 – 3s. blue and green .. 19·00 15·00

DESIGN—HORIZ. 3s. Native canoe.

32. Tropical Landscape.

1940.
130. **32.** 3d. on 1½d. black & pur. 10 20

1946. Peace. Peace stamps of New Zealand of 1946 optd. **COOK ISLANDS.**
146. **132.** 1d. green 10 10
147. – 2d. purple 10 15
148. – 6d. brown and red .. 15 15
149. **139.** 8d. black and red .. 15 15

34. Ngatangila Channel, Rarotonga.

1949.
150. **34.** ½d. violet and brown .. 10 75
151. – 1d. brown and green .. 1·75 1·75
152. – 2d. brown and red .. 60 1·75
153. – 3d. green and blue .. 50 1·75
154. – 5d. green and violet .. 1·00 1·25
155. – 6d. black and red .. 2·00 2·25
156. – 8d. olive and orange .. 40 3·50
157. – 1s. blue and brown .. 4·25 3·50
158. – 2s. brown and red .. 3·00 7·50
159. – 3s. blue and green .. 4·75 9·00

DESIGNS–HORIZ. 1d. Capt. Cook and map of Hervey Is. 2d. Rarotonga and Rev. John Williams. 3d. Aitutaki and palm trees. 5d. Rarotonga Airfield. 6d. Penrhyn village. 8d. Native hut. VERT. 1s. Map and statue of Capt. Cook. 2s. Native hut and palms. 3s. "Matua" (inter-island freighter).

1953. Coronation. As Types of New Zealand but inscr. "COOK ISLANDS".
160. **164.** 3d. brown .. .. 1·00 55
161. **166.** 6d. grey .. .. 1·25 95

1960. No. 154 surch. **1/6.**
162. 1s. 6d. on 5d. green & violet 30 30

45. Tiare Maori.

52. Queen Elizabeth II.

55. Rarotonga.

1963.
163. **45.** 1d. green and yellow .. 35 20
164. – 2d. red and yellow .. 10 30
165. – 3d. yell., green & violet 55 30
166. – 5d. blue and black .. 4·50 30
167. – 6d. red, yellow and green 1·00 20
168. – 8d. black and blue .. 1·50 60
169. – 1s. yellow and green .. 40 20
170. **52.** 1s. 6d. violet .. .. 2·75 2·00
171. – 2s. brown and blue .. 75 75
172. – 3s. black and green .. 1·25 1·00
173. **55.** 5s. brown and blue .. 8·50 3·25
DESIGNS—As Type **45.** VERT. 2d. Fishing God. 8d. Skipjack Tuna. HORIZ. 3d. Frangipani (plant). 5d. Love tern. 6d. Hibiscus. 1s. Oranges. As Type **55:** 2s. Island scene. 3s. Administration Centre, Mangalia.

56. Eclipse and Palm.

1965. Solar Eclipse Observation, Manuae Island.
174. **56.** 6d. black, yellow & blue 15 10

57. N.Z. Ensign and Map.

1965. Internal Self-Government.
175. **57.** 4d. red and blue .. 10 10
176. – 10d. multicoloured .. 10 10
177. – 1s. multicoloured .. 10 10
178. – 1s. 9d. multicoloured .. 30 50
DESIGNS: 10d. London Missionary Society Church. 1s. Proclamation of Cession, 1900. 1s. 9d. Nikao School.

1966. Churchill Commem. Nos. 171/3 and 175/7 optd. **In Memoriam SIR WINSTON CHURCHILL 1874-1965.**
179. **57.** 4d. red and blue .. 75 30
180. – 10d. multicoloured .. 1·50 45
181. – 1s. multicoloured .. 1·50 65
182. – 2s. brown and blue .. 1·50 1·25
183. – 3s. black and green .. 1·50 1·25
184. **55.** 5s. brown and blue .. 2·00 1·75

1966. Air. Various stamps optd. **Airmail** and aeroplane or surch. in addition.
185. – 6d. red, yellow & green (No. 167) .. .. 1·25 20
186. – 7d. on 8d. black & blue (No. 168) .. .. 1·25 25
187. – 10d. on 3d. green & violet (No. 165) .. .. 1·00 15
188. – 1s. yellow and green (No. 169) .. .. 1·00 15
189. **52.** 1s. 6d. violet .. .. 1·25 1·25
190. – 2s. 3d. on 3s. black and green (No. 172) .. 1·00 65
191. **55.** 5s. brown and blue .. 1·50 1·50
192. – 10s. on 2s. brown and blue (No. 171) .. 1·75 7·50
193. – £1 pink (No. 143) .. 9·00 16·00

63. "Adoration of the Magi" (Fra Angelico).

1966. Christmas. Multicoloured.
194. 1d. Type **63** 10 10
195. 2d. "The Nativity" (Memling) 20 10
196. 4d. "Adoration of the Wise Men" (Velazquez) .. 20 15
197. 10d. "Adoration of the Wise Men" (H. Bosch) .. 20 20
198. 1s. 6d. "Adoration of the Shepherds" (J. de Ribera) 30 25

68. Tennis and Queen Elizabeth II.

1967. 2nd South Pacific Games, Noumea. Multicoloured.
199. ½d. Type **68** (postage) .. 10 10
200. 1d. Basketball and Games Emblem 10 10
201. 4d. Boxing and Cook Islands Team Badge 10 10
202. 7d. Football and Queen Elizabeth II 10 10
203. 10d. Running and Games Emblem (air) 10 10
204. 2s. 3d. Running and Cook Islands' Team Badge .. 15 10

1967. Decimal currency. Various stamps surch.
205. **45.** 1 c. on 1d. .. .. 45 1·10
206. – 2 c. on 2d. (No. 164) .. 10 10
207. – 2½ c. on 3d. (No. 165) .. 20 10
209. **57.** 3 c. on 4d. 15 10
210. – 4 c. on 5d. (No. 166) .. 1·40 20
211. – 5 c. on 6d. (No. 167) .. 15 10
212. **56.** 5 c. on 6d. .. .. 3·00 40
213. – 7 c. on 8d. (No. 168) .. 15 10
214. – 10 c. on 1s. (No. 169) .. 15 10
215. **52.** 15 c. on 1s. 6d... .. 2·00 1·00
216. – 30 c. on 3s. (No. 172) .. 14·00 4·50
217. **55.** 50 c. on 5s. .. .. 3·50 1·25
218. – $1 and 10s. on 10d. (No. 176) .. .. .. 14·00 6·50
219. – $2 on £1 (No. 134) .. 50·00 70·00
220. – $6 on £3 (No. 135) .. 95·00 £110
221. – $10 on £5 (No. 136) .. £120 £140

75. Village Scene, Cook Islands 1d. Stamp of 1892 and Queen Victoria (from "Penny Black").

1967. 75th Anniv. of 1st Cook Island Stamps. Multicoloured.
222. 1 c. (1d.) Type **75** 10 10
223. 3 c. (4d.) Post Office, Avarua, Rarotonga and Queen Elizabeth II 15 10
224. 8 c. (10d.) Avarua, Rarotonga, and Cook Islands 10d. stamp of 1892 .. 30 10
225. 18 c. (1s. 9d.) S.S. "Moana Roa", "DC-3" aircraft, map and Captain Cook 1·40 25

The face values are expressed in decimal currency and in the sterling equivalent.

79. Hibiscus.

81. Queen Elizabeth and Flowers.

1967. Flowers. Multicoloured.
227. ½ c. Type **79** 10 10
228. 1 c. "Hibiscus syriacus" 10 10
229. 2 c. Frangipani 10 10
230. 2½ c. "Clitoria ternatea" 20 10
231. 3 c. "Suva Queen .. 55 10
232. 4 c. Water Lily (wrongly inscr. "Walter Lily") 55 70
233. 4 c. Water Lily .. .. 2·00 10
234. 5 c. "Bauhinia bipinnata rosea" 35 10
235. 6 c. Yellow Hibiscus .. 30 10
236. 8 c. "Allamanda cathartica" 30 10
237. 9 c. Stephanotis 30 10
238. 10 c. "Poinciana regia flamboyant" 30 10
239. 15 c. Frangipani .. 40 10
240. 20 c. Thunbergia .. 2·25 85
241. 25 c. Canna Lily .. 1·00 15
242. 30 c. "Euphorbia pulcherrima poinsettia" 65 50
243. 50 c. "Gardenia taitensis' 1·00 55
244. $1 Queen Elizabeth II 1·75 80
245. $2 Queen Elizabeth II 3·50 1·50
246. $4 Type **81** .. .. 3·00 3·50
247. $6 As No. 246 .. 3·50 5·00
247c. $8 As No. 246 .. .. 8·00 13·00
248. $10 As No. 246 .. .. 8·00 12·00

97. "Ia Orana Maria".

1967. Gaugin's Polynesian Paintings.
249. **97.** 1 c. multicoloured .. 10 10
250. – 3 c. multicoloured .. 15 10
251. – 5 c. multicoloured .. 15 10
252. – 8 c. multicoloured .. 20 10
253. – 15 c. multicoloured .. 40 10
254. – 22 c. multicoloured .. 50 15
DESIGNS: 3 c. "Riders on the Beach". 5 c. "Still Life with Flowers" and inset portrait of Queen Elizabeth. 8 c. "Whispered Words". 15 c. "Maternity". 22 c. "Why are you angry?".

98. "The Holy Family" (Rubens).

1967. Christmas. Renaissance Paintings.
256. **98.** 1 c. multicoloured .. 10 10
257. – 3 c. multicoloured .. 10 10
258. – 4 c. multicoloured .. 10 10
259. – 8 c. multicoloured .. 15 10
260. – 15 c. multicoloured .. 30 10
261. – 25 c. multicoloured .. 35 10
DESIGNS: 3 c. "The Epiphany" (Durer). 4 c. "The Lucca Madonna" (J. Van Eyck). 8 c. "The Adoration of the Shepherds" (J. da Bassano). 15 c. "The Nativity" (El Greco). 25 c. "The Madonna and Child" (Correggio).

1968. Hurricane Relief. Nos. 231, 233, 251, 238, 241 and 243/4 optd. **HURRICANE RELIEF** plus value.
262. 3 c.+1 c. multicoloured .. 15 10
263. 4 c.+1 c. multicoloured .. 15 10
264. 5 c.+2 c. multicoloured .. 15 10
265. 10 c.+2 c. multicoloured 15 10
266. 25 c.+5 c. multicoloured 25 10
267. 50 c.+10 c. multicoloured 35 15
268. $1+10 c. multicoloured .. 60 30
On No. 264 silver blocking obliterates the design area around the lettering.

100. "Matavai Bay, Tahiti" (J. Barralet).

1968. Bicentenary of Captain Cook's 1st Voyage of Discovery.
269. **100.** ½ c. multicoloured (post.) 10 10
270. – 1 c. multicoloured .. 15 10
271. – 2 c. multicoloured .. 40 35
272. – 4 c. multicoloured .. 40 35
273. – 6 c. multicoloured (air) 90 65
274. – 10 c. multicoloured .. 1·25 75
275. – 15 c. multicoloured .. 1·50 90
276. – 25 c. multicoloured .. 1·75 1·25
DESIGNS—VERT. 1 c. "Island of Huaheine" (John Cleveley). 2 c. "Town of St. Peter and St. Paul, Kamchatka" (J. Webber). 4 c. "The Ice Islands" (Antarctica: W. Hodges). HORIZ. 6 c. "Resolution and Discovery" (J. Webber). 10 c. "The Island of Tahiti" (W. Hodges). 15 c. "Karakakooa, Hawaii" (J. Webber). 25 c. "The Landing at Middleburg" (W. Hodges).

102. Sailing.

1968. Olympic Games, Mexico. Multicoloured.
277. 1 c. Type **102.** 10 10
278. 5 c. Gymnastics 10 10
279. 15 c. High-jumping .. 15 10
280. 20 c. High-diving .. 15 10
281. 30 c. Cycling 15 10
282. 50 c. Hurdling 20 15

103. "Madonna and Child" (Titian).

1968. Christmas. Multicoloured.
283. 1 c. Type **103.** 10 10
284. 4 c. "The Holy Family of the Lamb" (Raphael) 10 10
285. 10 c. "The Madonna of the Rosary" (Murillo) .. 25 10
286. 20 c. "Adoration of the Magi" (Memling) .. 30 10
287. 30 c. "Adoration of the Magi" (Ghirlandaio) .. 35 10

104. Camp-fire Cooking.

1969. Diamond Jubilee of New Zealand Scout Movement and 5th National (New Zealand) Jamboree. Multicoloured.
289. ½ c. Type **104** 10 10
290. 1 c. Descent by rope .. 10 10
291. 5 c. Semaphore 10 10
292. 10 c. Tree-planting .. 15 10
293. 20 c. Constructing a shelter 25 10
294. 30 c. Lord Baden-Powell and island scene .. 40 15

105. High Jumping.

1969. 3rd. South Pacific Games, Port Moresby. Multicoloured.

295. ½ c. Type **105** 10 10
296. ½ c. Footballer 10 10
297. 1 c. Basketball 20 15
298. 1 c. Weightlifter 20 15
299. 4 c. Tennis-player 30 20
300 4 c. Hurdler 30 20
301. 10 c. Javelin-thrower .. 40 30
302. 10 c. Runner 40 30
303. 15 c. Golfer 75 55
304. 15 c. Boxer 75 55

106. Flowers, Map and Captain Cook. (Illustration reduced. Actual size 72 × 26 mm.).

1969. South Pacific Conf., Noumea. Mult.

306. 5 c. Premier Albert Henry 75 20
307. 10 c. Type **106** .. .. 1·40 60
308. 25 c. Flowers, map and arms of New Zealand .. 1·40 85
309. 30 c. Queen Elizabeth II, map and flowers .. 1·40 95

107. " Virgin and Child with Saints Jerome and Dominic " (Lippi).

1969. Christmas. Multicoloured.

310. 1 c. Type **107** 10 10
311. 4 c. " The Holy Family " (Fra. B. Della Porta) .. 10 10
312. 10 c. " Virgin and Child with Saints " (Memling) .. 15 10
313. 20 c. " Virgin and Child with Saints" (Robert Campin) 25 10
314. 30 c. " Virgin and Child " (Corregio) 25 20

108. "The Resurrection of Christ " (Raphael).

1970. Easter.

316. **108.** 4 c. multicoloured .. 10 10
317. – 8 c. multicoloured .. 10 10
318. – 20 c. multicoloured .. 15 10
319. – 25 c. multicoloured .. 20 10

DESIGNS: " The Resurrection of Christ " by Dirk Bouts (8 c.), Altdorfer (20 c.), Murillo (25 c.).

1970. "Apollo 13". Nos. 233, 236, 239/40, 242, and 245/6, optd. **KIA ORANA APOLLO 13 ASTRONAUTS Te Atua to Tatou Irinakianga.**

321. 4 c. multicoloured .. 10 10
322. 8 c. multicoloured .. 10 10
323. 15 c. multicoloured .. 10 10
324. 20 c. multicoloured .. 15 15
325. 30 c. multicoloured .. 20 20
326. $2 multicoloured .. 60 90
327. $4 multicoloured .. .. 1·25 2·75

110. The Royal Family.

1970. Royal Visit to New Zealand. **Mult.**

328. 5 c. Type **110** 65 30
329. 30 c. Captain Cook and H.M.S. " Endeavour " 2·75 1·75
330. $1 Royal Visit Commem. Coin .. .. .. 4·00 3·00

1970. 5th Anniv. of Self-Government Nos. 328/30, optd. **FIFTH ANNIVERSARY SELF-GOVERNMENT AUGUST 1970.**

332. **110.** 5 c. multicoloured .. 40 15
333. – 30 c. multicoloured .. 1·25 35
334. – $1 multicoloured .. 2·00 90

On No. 332, the opt. is arranged in one line around the frame of the stamp.

1970. Surch.

335. **81.** $4 on $8 multicoloured 3·50 3·00
336. $4 on $10 multicoloured 1·50 1·75

115. Mary, Joseph, and Christ in Manger.

1970. Christmas. Multicoloured.

337. 1 c. Type **115** 10 10
338. 4 c. Shepherds and Apparition of the Angel 10 10
339. 10 c. Mary showing Child to Joseph 15 10
340. 20 c. The Wise Men bearing Gifts 20 10
341. 30 c. Parents wrapping Child in swaddling clothes 25 15

1971. Surch. **PLUS 20c. UNITED KINGDOM SPECIAL MAIL SERVICE.**

343. 30 c. + 20 c. (No. 242) .. 40 50
344. 50 c. + 20 c. (No. 243) .. 1·50 1·75

The premium of 20 c. was to prepay a private delivery service fee in Great Britain during the postal strike. The mail was sent by air to a forwarding address in the Netherlands. No. 343 was intended for ordinary airmail ½ oz. letters, and No. 344 included registration fee.

117. Wedding of Princess Elizabeth and Prince Philip.

1971. Royal Visit of Duke of Edinburgh. Multicoloured.

345. 1 c. Type **117** 30 50
346. 4 c. Queen Elizabeth, Prince Philip, Prince Charles and Princess Anne at Windsor 75 1·10
347. 10 c. Prince Philip sailing 1·00 1·25
348. 15 c. Prince Philip in polo gear .. .. .. 1·00 1·25
349. 25 c. Prince Philip in Naval uniform, and Royal Yacht "Britannia" .. .. 1·50 2·00

1971. Fourth South Pacific Games, Tahiti, Nos. 238, 241 and 242 optd. **Fourth South Pacific Games Papeete** and emblem or surch. also.

351. 10 c. multicoloured .. 10 10
352. 10 c. + 1 c. multicoloured .. 10 10
353. 10 c. + 3 c. multicoloured .. 10 10
354. 25 c. multicoloured .. 15 10
355. 25 c. + 1 c. multicoloured .. 15 10
356. 25 c. + 3 c. multicoloured .. 15 10
357. 30 c. multicoloured .. 15 10
358. 30 c. + 1 c. multicoloured .. 15 10
359. 30 c. + 3 c. multicoloured .. 15 10

The stamps additionally surcharged 1 c. or 3 c. helped to finance the Cook Islands' team at the games.

1971. Nos. 230, 233, 236/7 and 239 surch.

360. 10 c. on 2½ c. multicoloured 15 25
361. 10 c. on 4 c. multicoloured 15 25
362. 10 c. on 8 c. multicoloured 15 25
363. 10 c. on 9 c. multicoloured 15 25
364. 10 c. on 15 c. multicoloured 15 25

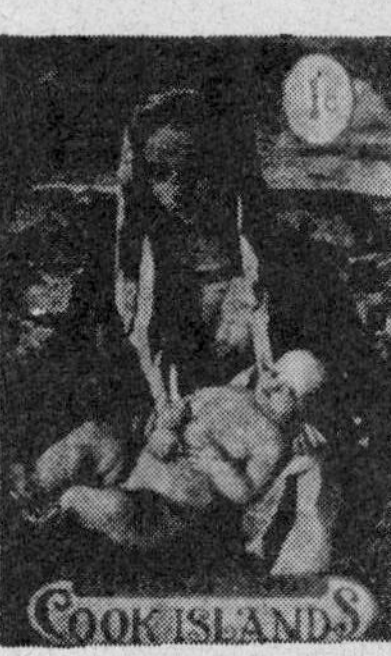

121. " Virgin and Child " (Bellini).

123. St. John.

1971. Christmas.

365. **121.** 1 c. multicoloured .. 10 10
366. – 4 c. multicoloured .. 10 10
367. – 10 c. multicoloured .. 25 10
368. – 20 c. multicoloured .. 50 10
369. – 30 c. multicoloured .. 50 20

DESIGNS: Various paintings of the " Virgin and Child " by Bellini. Similar to Type **121.**

1972. 25th Anniv. of South Pacific Commission. No. 244 optd. **SOUTH PACIFIC COMMISSION FEB. 1947–1972.**

372. $1 multicoloured 40 75

1972. Easter. Multicoloured.

373. 5c. Type **123** 10 10
374. 10c. Christ on the Cross .. 10 10
375. 30c. Mary, Mother of Jesus 25 25

1972. Hurricane Relief.

(a). Nos. 239, 241 and 243 optd. **HURRICANE RELIEF PLUS** premium.

379. 15c. + 5c. multicoloured .. 20 20
380. 25c. + 5c. multicoloured .. 20 20
382. 50c. + 10c. multicoloured .. 25 25

(b). Nos. 373/5 optd. **Hurricane Relief Plus** premium.

377. 5c. + 2c. multicoloured .. 10 10
378. 10c. + 2c. multicoloured .. 15 15
381. 30c. + 5c. multicoloured .. 20 20

126. Rocket heading for Moon. **127.** (Illustration reduced. Actual size 62 × 30 mm.)

1972. The Apollo Moon Exploration Flights. Multicoloured.

383. 5 c. Type **126** 15 10
384. 5 c. Type **127** 15 10
385. 10 c. } Astronauts on Moon 20 10
386. 10 c. } 20 10
387. 25 c. } Moon Rover and 25 15
388. 25 c. } astronauts working 25 15
389. 30 c. } Splashdown and 25 15
390. 30 c. } helicopter 25 15

These were issued in horizontal se-tenant pairs of each value, forming one composite design.

1972. Hurricane Relief. Nos. 383/390 surch. **HURRICANE RELIEF Plus** and premium.

392. 5 c. + 2 c. multicoloured .. 10 10
393. 5 c. + 2 c. multicoloured .. 10 10
394. 10 c. + 2 c. multicoloured 10 10
395. 10 c. + 2 c. multicoloured 10 10
396. 25 c. + 2 c. multicoloured 15 15
397. 25 c. + 2 c. multicoloured 15 15
398. 30 c. + 2 c. multicoloured 15 15
399. 30 c. + 2 c. multicoloured 15 15

129. High-jumping.

1972. Olympic Games, Munich. **Mult.**

401. 10 c. Type **129** 15 10
402. 25 c. Running 30 15
403. 30 c. Boxing 30 20

130. " The Rest on the flight into Egypt " (Caravaggio).

1972. Christmas. Multicoloured.

406. 1 c. Type **130** 10 10
407. 5 c. " Madonna of the Swallow " (Guercino) .. 25 10
408. 10 c. " Madonna of the Green Cushion " (Solario) 30 10
409. 20 c. " Madonna and Child " (di Credi) .. 45 20
410. 30 c. " Madonna and Child " (Bellini) .. 70 30

131. Marriage Ceremony.

1972. Royal Silver Wedding. Each black and silver.

413. 5 c. Type **131** 25 15
414. 10 c. Leaving Westminster Abbey 60 40
415. 15 c. Bride and Bridegroom (40 × 41 mm.) .. 75 50
416. 30 c. Family group (67 × 40 mm.) .. .. 1·10 80

132. Taro Leaf.

1973. Silver Wedding Coinage.

417. **132** 1 c. gold, mauve & black 10 10
418. – 2 c. gold, blue & black .. 10 10
419. – 5 c. silver, green & black 10 10
420. – 10 c. silver, blue & black 25 10
421. – 20 c. silver, grn. & black 35 10
422. – 50 c. silver, mauve & blk. 65 15
423. – $1 silver, blue & black .. 1·10 30

DESIGNS—HORIZ. (37 × 24 mm.). 2 c. Pineapple. 5 c. Hibiscus. (46 × 30 mm.). 10 c. Oranges. 20 c. White Tern. 50 c. Skipjack Tuna. VERT. (32 × 55 mm.). $1, Tangaroa.

133. " Noli me Tangere " (Titian).

1973. Easter. Multicoloured.

424. 5 c. Type **133** 15 10
425. 10 c. " The Descent from the Cross " (Rubens) .. 20 10
426. 30 c. " The Lamentation of Christ " (Durer) .. 25 10

134. Queen Elizabeth II in Coronation Regalia.

1973. 20th Anniversary of Queen Elizabeth's Coronation.

429. **134.** 10 c. multicoloured .. 65 1·25

1973. 10th Anniv. of Treaty Banning Nuclear Testing. Nos. 234, 236, 238 and 240/42 optd. **TENTH ANNIVERSARY CESSATION OF NUCLEAR TESTING TREATY.**

431. 5 c. multicoloured 10 10
432. 8 c. multicoloured 10 10
433. 10 c. multicoloured .. 10 10
434. 20 c. multicoloured .. 15 15
435. 25 c. multicoloured .. 20 15
436. 30 c. multicoloured .. 20 15

136. Tipairua.

1973. Maori Exploration of the Pacific. Sailing Craft. Multicoloured.

437. ½ c. Type **136** 10 10
438. 1 c. Wa'a Kaulua .. 10 10
439. 1½ c. Tainui 15 10
440. 5 c. War canoe .. 40 10
441. 10 c. Pahi .. 60 15
442. 15 c. Amatasi .. 1·10 45
443. 25 c. Vaka .. .. 1·40 65

137. The Annunciation.

1973. Christmas. Scenes from a 15th-cent. Flemish "Book of Hours". Multicoloured.

444. 1 c. Type **137** 10 10
445. 5 c. The Visitation .. 10 10
446. 10 c. Annunciation to the Shepherds 10 10
447. 20 c. Epiphany 15 10
448. 30 c. The Slaughter of the Innocents 20 15

138. Princess Anne.

1973. Royal Wedding. Multicoloured.

450. 25 c. Type **138** 20 10
451. 30 c. Capt. Mark Phillips 25 10
452. 50 c. Princess Anne and Capt. Phillips 30 15

139. Running.

1974. British Commonwealth Games, Christchurch. Multicoloured.

455. 1 c. Diving (vert.) .. 10 10
456. 3 c. Boxing (vert.) .. 10 10
457. 5 c. Type **139** 10 10
458. 10 c. Weightlifting .. 10 10
459. 30 c. Cycling 20 25

140. " Jesus carrying the Cross " (Raphael).

1974. Easter. Multicoloured.

461. 5 c. Type **140** 10 10
462. 10 c. " The Holy Trinity " (El Greco) 15 10
463. 30 c. " The Deposition of Christ " (Caravaggio) .. 25 20

141. Helmet Shell.

142. Queen Elizabeth II.

1974. Sea-shells. Multicoloured.

466. ½ c. Type **141** 30 10
467. 1 c. Vase Shell 30 10
468. 1½ c. Cockle Shell 30 10
469. 2 c. "Terebellum terebellum" 30 10
470. 3 c. Bat Volutes 45 10
471. 4 c. Conch Shell 50 10
472. 5 c. Triton Shell 50 10
473. 6 c. Snake-head (ovries) .. 50 60
474. 8 c. Helmet Shell (different) 60 10
475. 10 c. Auger Shell 60 10
476. 15 c. Mitre Shell 70 20
477. 20 c. Naticacid Shell .. 1·00 20
478. 25 c. Scallop Shell .. .. 1·00 30
479. 30 c. Soldier Cone Shell .. 1·00 30
480. 50 c. Cloth of Gold Cone Shell .. .. 7·00 3·00
481. 60 c. Olive Shell .. .. 7·00 3·00
482. $1 Type **142** .. .. 2·50 3·75
483. $2 Type **142** .. .. 2·50 2·25
484. $4 Queen Elizabeth II and sea shells .. .. 3·50 5·00
485. $6 As $4 .. .. 13·00 7·00
486. $8 As $4 .. .. 13·00 8·50
487. $10 As $4 .. .. 16·00 9·00

Nos. 484/7 are larger, 60 × 39 mm.

MINIMUM PRICE

The minimum price quoted is 10p which represents a handling charge rather than a basis for valuing common stamps. For further notes about prices see introductory pages.

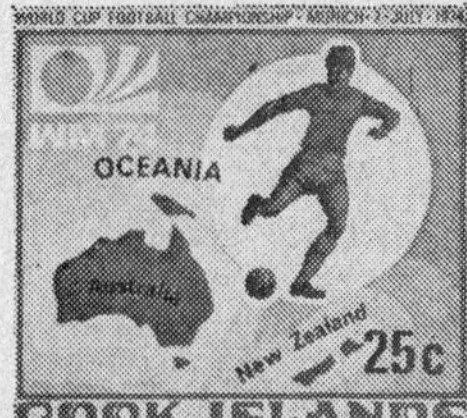

143. Footballer and Australasian Map.

1974. World Cup Football Championships, West Germany. Multicoloured.

488. 25 c. Type **143** 15 10
489. 50 c. Map and Munich Stadium 30 25
490. $1 Footballer, stadium and World Cup 50 45

144. Obverse and Reverse of Commemorative $2.50 Silver Coin.

1974. Bicentenary of Capt. Cook's Second Voyage of Discovery.

492. **144.** $2.50 silver, blk. & vio. 13·00 7·00
493. – $7.50 silver, blk. & grn. 27·00 13·00

DESIGN: $7.50, As Type **144** but showing $7.50 coin.

145. Early Stamps of Cook Islands.

1974. Centenary of U.P.U. Multicoloured.

495. 10 c. Type **145** 15 15
496. 25 c. Old landing strip, Rarotonga, and stamp of 1898 .. .. 30 40
497. 30 c. Post Office, Rarotonga, and stamp of 1920 .. 30 40
498. 50 c. U.P.U. emblem and stamps 40 65

146. "Madonna of the Goldfinch" (Raphael).

1974. Christmas. Multicoloured.

500. 1 c. Type **146** 10 10
501. 5 c. " The Sacred Family " (Andrea del Sarto) .. 15 10
502. 10 c. " The Virgin adoring the Child " (Correggio) 20 10
503. 20 c. " The Holy Family " (Rembrandt) 30 20
504. 30 c. " The Virgin and Child " (Rogier Van Der Weyden) 35 30

147. Churchill and Blenheim Palace.

1974. Birth Centenary of Sir Winston Churchill. Multicoloured.

506. 5 c. Type **147** 25 15
507. 10 c. Churchill and Houses of Parliament 40 15
508. 25 c. Churchill and Chartwell 80 30
509. 30 c. Churchill and Buckingham Palace 90 35
510. 50 c. Churchill and St. Paul's Cathedral .. .. 1·25 65

148. Vasco Nunez de Balboa and Discovery of Pacific Ocean (1513).

1975. Pacific Explorers. Multicoloured.

513 1 c. Type **148** 15 10
514 5 c. Fernando de Magallanes and map (1520) 55 20
515 10 c. Juan Sebastian del Cano and "Vitoria" (1520) .. .. .. 1·00 20
516 25 c. Friar Andres de Urdaneta and ship (1564–67) .. .. 2·00 75
517 30 c. Miguel Lopez de Legazpi and ship (1564–67) .. .. 2·00 80

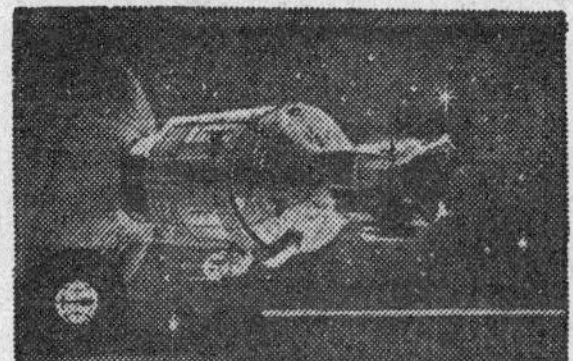

149. " Apollo " Capsule.

1975. " Apollo-Soyuz " Space Project. Mult.

518. 25 c. Type **149** 30 15
519. 25 c. " Soyuz " capsule .. 30 15
520. 30 c. " Soyuz " crew .. 35 15
521. 30 c. " Apollo " crew .. 35 15
522. 50 c. Cosmonaut within " Soyuz " 40 25
523. 50 c. Astronauts within " Apollo " 40 25

These were issued in horiz. se-tenant pairs of each value, forming one composite design.

150. $100 Commemorative Gold Coin.

1975. Bicent. of Captain Cook's 2nd Voyage.

525. **150.** $2 brown, gold & vio. 6·50 2·75

151. Cook Island's Flag and Map.

1975. 10th Anniv. of Self-Government.

526. 5 c. Type **151** 20 10
527. 10 c. Premier Sir Albert Henry and flag (vert.) .. 30 10
528. 25 c. Rarotonga and flag .. 70 30

152. " Madonna by the Fireside " (R. Campin).

1975. Christmas. Multicoloured.

529. 6 c. Type **152** 10 10
530. 10 c. " Madonna in the Meadow " (Raphael) .. 15 10
531. 15 c. " Madonna of the Oak " (atrib. Raphael) 20 10
532. 20 c. " Adoration of the Shepherds" (J. B. Maino) 25 15
533. 35 c. " The Annunciation " (Murillo) 30 20

153. " Entombment of Christ " (Raphael).

1976. Easter. Multicoloured.

536. 7 c. Type **153** 20 10
537. 15 c. " Pieta " (Veronese) 30 15
538. 35 c. " Pieta " (El Greco) 40 25

154. Benjamin Franklin and H.M.S. "Resolution".

1976. Bicent. of American Revolution. Mult.

541. $1 Type **154** .. .. 6·50 1·50
542. $2 Capt. Cook and H.M.S. "Resolution" .. .. 8·50 2·50

1976. Visit of Queen Elizabeth to U.S.A. Nos. 541/2 optd. **Royal Visit July 1976.**

544. **154.** $1 multicoloured .. 3·50 1·50
545. – $2 multicoloured .. 5·50 2·50

156. Hurdling.

1976. Olympic Games, Montreal. Mult.

547. 7 c. } Type **156** 10 10
548. 7 c. } 10 10
549. 15 c. } Hockey 15 15
550. 15 c. } 15 15
551. 30 c. } Fencing 25 15
552. 30 c. } 25 15
553. 35 c. } Football 30 20
554. 35 c. } 30 20

157. " The Visitation ".

1976. Christmas. Renaissance sculptures. Multicoloured.

556. 6 c. Type **157** 10 10
557. 10 c. " Adoration of the Shepherds " 10 10
558. 15 c. " Adoration of the Shepherds " (different) 15 10
559. 20 c. " The Epiphany " .. 20 20
560. 35 c. " The Holy Family " 25 25

158. Obverse and Reverse of $5 Mangaia Kingfisher Coin.

1976. National Wildlife and Conservation Day.

563. **158.** $1 multicoloured .. 3·50 1·25

159. Imperial State Crown.

1977. Silver Jubilee. Multicoloured.

564. 25 c. Type **159** 70 70
565. 25 c. The Queen with regalia 70 70
566. 50 c. Westminster Abbey 1·10 1·10
567. 50 c. Coronation coach .. 1·10 1·10
568. $1 The Queen and Prince Philip .. .. 2·00 2·00
569. $1 Royal Visit, 1974 .. 2·00 2·00

160. " Christ on the Cross ".

1977. Easter. 400th Birth Anniv. of Rubens. Multicoloured.

571. 7 c. Type **160** 35 10
572. 15 c. " Christ on the Cross " 55 15
573. 35 c. " The Deposition of Christ " .. .. .. 1·10 30

161. " Virgin and Child " (Memling).

1977. Christmas. Multicoloured.

576. 6 c. Type **161** 15 10
577. 10 c. " Madonna and Child with Saints and Donors " (Memling) 15 10
578. 15 c. " Adoration of the Kings " (Geertgen) .. 25 10
579. 20 c. " Virgin and Child with Saints " (Crivelli) .. 30 15
580. 35 c. " Adoration of the Magi " (16th Cent. flemish school) 40 20

162. Obverse and Reverse of $5 Cook Islands Swiftlet Coin.

1977. National Wildlife and Conservation Day.

583. **162.** $1 multicoloured .. 3·50 1·75

163. Captain Cook and H.M.S. " Resolution " (from paintings by N. Dance and H. Roberts).

1978. Bicentenary of Discovery of Hawaii. Multicoloured.

584. 50 c. Type **163** .. .. 1·50 60
585. $1 Earl of Sandwich and Cook landing at Owhyhee (from paintings by Thomas Gainsborough and J. Cleveley) .. .. 2·00 1·00
586. $2 Obverse and reverse of $200 coin and Cook monument, Hawaii .. .. 3·25 1·75

164. " Pieta " (Van der Weyden).

1978. Easter. Paintings from the National Gallery, London. Multicoloured.

588. 15 c. Type **164** 40 15
589. 35 c. " The Entombment " (Michelangelo) 50 30
590. 75 c. " The Supper at Emmaus " (Caravaggio) 75 55

165. Queen Elizabeth II.

1978. 25th Anniv. of Coronation. Mult.

593. 50 c. Type **165** 30 30
594. 50 c. The Lion of England 30 30
595. 50 c. Imperial State Crown 30 30
596. 50 c. Statue of Tangaroa (god) 30 30
597. 70 c. Type **165** 35 35
598. 70 c. Sceptre with Cross .. 35 35
599. 70 c. St. Edward's Crown 35 35
600. 70 c. Rarotongan staff god 35 35

1978. Nos. 466, 468, 473/4 and 478/82 surch.

602. 5 c. on 1½ c. " Corculum cardissa " 30 10
603. 7 c. on ½ c. Type **141** .. 35 15
604. 10 c. on 6 c. " Cypraea caputserpentis " .. 40 15
605. 10 c. on 8 c. " Bursa granularis " 40 15
606. 15 c. on ½ c. Type **141** .. 40 20
607. 15 c. on 25 c. " Gloripallium pallium " 40 20
608. 15 c. on 30 c. " Conus miles " 40 20
609. 15 c. on 50 c. " Conus textile " 40 20
610. 15 c. on 60 c. " Oliva sericea " 40 20
611. 17 c. on ½ c. Type **141** .. 70 25
612. 17 c. on 50 c. " Conus textile " 70 25

1978. 250th Birth Anniv. of Captain James Cook. Nos. 584/6 optd. **1728. 250th ANNIVERSARY OF COOK'S BIRTH. 1978.**

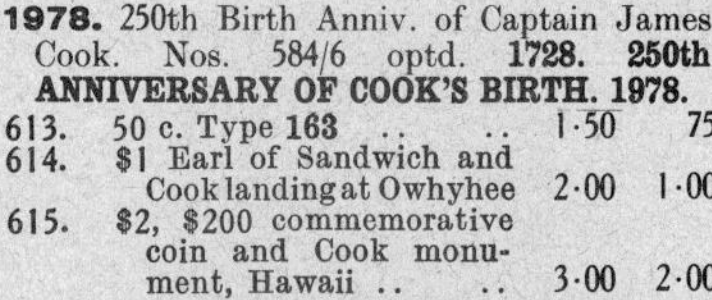

613. 50 c. Type **163** .. .. 1·50 75
614. $1 Earl of Sandwich and Cook landing at Owhyhee 2·00 1·00
615. $2, $200 commemorative coin and Cook monument, Hawaii .. .. 3·00 2·00

168. Obverse and Reverse of Pitcairn Warblers $5 Coin.

1978. National Wildlife and Conservation Day.

617. **168.** $1 multicoloured .. 2·00 1·00

169. " The Virgin and Child " (Van Der Weyden).

1978. Christmas. Paintings. Multicoloured.

618. 15 c. Type **169** 35 10
619. 17 c. " The Virgin and Child " (Crivelli) .. 35 15
620. 35 c. " The Virgin and Child " (Murillo) .. 65 30

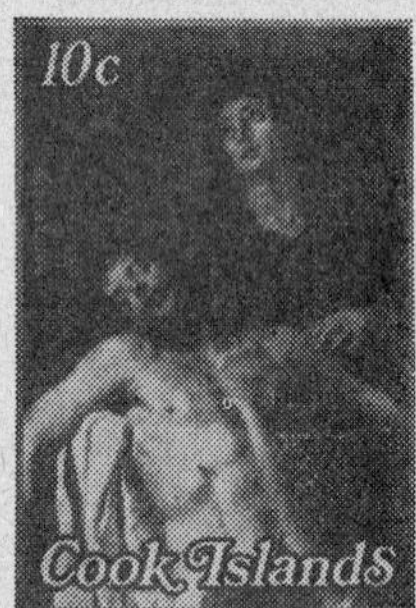

170. Virgin with Body of Christ.

1979. Easter. Details of Painting " Descent " by Gasper de Crayer. Multicoloured.

623. 10 c. Type **170** 20 10
624. 12 c. St. John 25 15
625. 15 c. Mary Magdalene .. 30 20
626. 20 c. Weeping angels .. 30 20

171. " Captain Cook " (James Weber).

1979. Death Bicent of Captain Cook. Mult.

628 20 c. Type **171** 50 20
629 30 c. H.M.S. "Resolution" 80 35
630 35 c. H.M.S. "Royal George" (ship of the line) 90 45
631 50 c. "Death of Captain Cook" (George Carter) 95 60

172. Post-Rider.

1979. Death Cent of Sir Rowland Hill. Mult.

633	30 c. Type **172**	35	25
634	30 c. Mail coach	35	25
635	30 c. Automobile	35	25
636	30 c. Railway train ..	35	25
637	35 c. "Cap-Hornier" (full-rigged ship)	40	25
638	35 c. River steamer ..	40	25
639	35 c. "Deutschland" (liner)	40	25
640	35 c. "United States" (liner)	40	25
641	50 c. Balloon "Neptune"	50	30
642	50 c. Junkers "F13" (airplane)	50	30
643	50 c. "Graf Zeppelin" ..	50	30
644	50 c. "Concorde"	50	30

1979. Nos. 466, 468 and 481 **surch.**

646.	6 c. on ½ c. Type **141** ..	15	15
647.	10 c. on 1½ c. " Corculum cardissa "	20	20
648.	15 c. on 60 c. " Oliva sericea "	30	30

174. Brother and Sister.

1979. International Year of the Child. Multicoloured.

649.	30 c. Type **174**	25	25
650.	50 c. Boy with tree drum	40	40
651.	65 c. Children dancing ..	50	50

175. "Apollo 11" Emblem.

1979. 10th Anniv. of "Apollo 11" Moon Landing. Multicoloured.

653.	30 c. Type **175**	35	40
654.	50 c. " Apollo 11 " crew..	45	60
655.	60 c. Neil Armstrong on the Moon	55	70
656.	65 c. Splashdown recovery	60	75

176. Obverse and reverse of $5 Rarotongan Fruit Dove Coin.

1979. National Wildlife and Conservation Day.

658. **176.**	$1 multicoloured ..	3·00	2·50

177. Glass Christmas Tree Ornaments.

1979. Christmas. Multicoloured.

659.	6 c. Type **177** (postage) ..	10	10
660.	10 c. Hibiscus and star ..	10	10
661.	12 c. Poinsettia, bells and candle	15	10
662.	15 c. Poinsettia leaves and Tiki (god)	15	15
663.	20 c. Type **177** (air) ..	20	15
664.	25 c. As No. 660 ..	25	20
665.	30 c. As No. 661	30	25
666.	35 c. As No. 662	35	30

1980. Christmas. As Nos. 659/66 but with charity premium.

667.	6 c.+2 c. Type **177** (postage)	10	10
668.	10 c.+2 c. Hibiscus and star	15	15
669.	12 c.+2 c. Flower, bells and candle ..	15	20
670.	15 c.+2 c. Flowers and carving	15	20
671.	20 c.+4 c. Type **177** (air)	15	25
672.	25 c.+4 c. As No. 660 ..	15	25
673.	30 c.+4 c. As No. 661 ..	20	30
674.	35 c.+4 c. As No. 662 ..	25	35

178. " Flagellation ".

1980. Easter. Illustrations by Gustav Dore. Each gold and brown.

675.	20 c. Type **178**	15	20
676.	20 c. " Crown of Thorns "	15	20
677.	30 c. " Jesus Insulted " ..	25	30
678.	30 c. " Jesus Falls " ..	25	30
679.	35 c. " The Crucifixion "	25	30
680.	35 c. " The Descent from the Cross "	25	30

179. Dove with Olive Twig.

1980. 75th Anniv. of Rotary International. Multicoloured.

683.	30 c. Type **179**	35	35
684.	35 c. Hibiscus flower ..	40	40
685.	50 c. Ribbons	50	50

1980. " Zeapex 80 " International Stamp Exhibition, Auckland. Nos. 633/44 optd. **ZEAPEX STAMP EXHIBITION — AUCKLAND 1980** and New Zealand 1865 1s. Stamp.

687	30 c. Type **172**	30	30
688	30 c. Mail coach	30	30
689	30 c. Automobile	30	30
690	30 c. Railway train ..	30	30
691	35 c. "Cap-Hornier" (full-rigged ship)	35	35
692	35 c. River steamer ..	35	35
693	35 c. "Deutschland" (liner)	35	35
694	35 c. "United States" (liner)	35	35
695	50 c. Balloon "Neptune"	65	45
696	50 c. Junkers "F13" (airplane)	65	45
697	50 c. "Graf Zeppelin" ..	65	45
698	50 c. "Concorde"	65	45

181. Queen Elizabeth the Queen Mother.

1980. 80th Birthday of The Queen Mother.

701. **181.**	50 c. multicoloured ..	1·40	90

182. Satellites orbiting Moon.

1980. 350th Death Anniv. of Johannes Kepler (astronomer) and 75th Death Anniv. of Jules Verne (writer). Multicoloured.

703.	12 c. Type **182**	50	35
704.	12 c. " Apollo " orbiting Moon	50	35
708.	20 c. ⎧ Jules Verne and dif-	45	35
709.	20 c. ⎨ ferent scenes from	45	35
710.	30 c. ⎨ " From the Earth	55	45
711.	30 c. ⎩ to the Moon " (vert.)	55	45
705.	50 c. Space station ..	1·00	80
706.	50 c. Astronaut on Moon..	1·00	80

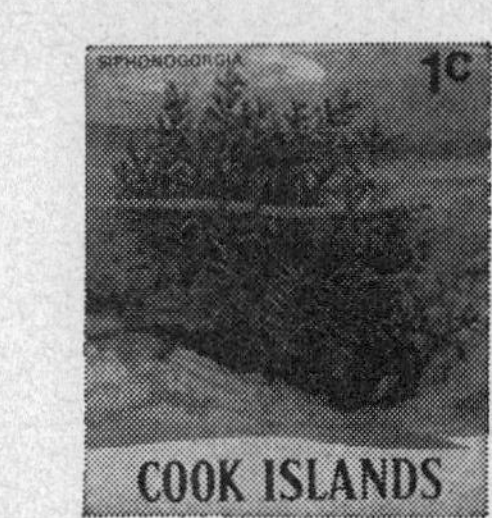

184. " Siphonogorgia ".

1980. Corals (1st series). Multicoloured.

713.	1 c. Type **184**	20	20
714.	1 c. " Pavona praetorta "	20	20
715.	1 c. " Stylaster echinatus "	20	20
716.	1 c. " Tubastraea " ..	20	20
717.	3 c. " Millepora alcicornis "	25	20
718.	3 c. "Junceella gemmacea "	25	20
719.	3 c. " Fungia fungites " ..	25	20
720.	3 c. "Heliofungia actiniformi	25	20
721.	4 c. " Distichopora violacea"	25	20
722.	4 c. " Stylaster "	25	20
723.	4 c. " Gonipora "	25	20
724.	4 c. " Caulastraea echinuata'	25	20
725.	5 c. " Ptilosarcus gurneyi "	25	20
726.	5 c. " Stylophora pistillata "	25	20
727.	5 c. " Melithaea squamata "	25	20
728.	5 c. " Porites andrewsi "	25	20
729.	6 c. "Lobophyllia bemprichii	25	20
730.	6 c. "Palauastrea ramosa"	25	20
731.	6 c. " Bellonella indica "	25	20
732.	6 c. " Pectinia alcicornis"	25	20
733.	8 c. "Sarcophyton digitatum "	25	20
734.	8 c. " Melithaea albitincta "	25	20
735.	8 c. " Plerogyra sinuosa "	25	20
736.	8 c. " Dendrophyllia gracilis "	25	20
737.	10 c. As Type **184** ..	30	20
738.	10 c. As No. 714	30	20
739.	10 c. As No. 715	30	20
740.	10 c. As No. 716	30	20
741.	12 c. As No. 717	30	20
742.	12 c. As No. 718	30	20
743.	12 c. As No. 719	30	20
744.	12 c. As No. 720	30	20
745.	15 c. As No. 721	30	20
746.	15 c. As No. 722	30	20
747.	15 c. As No. 723	30	20
748.	15 c. As No. 724	30	20
749.	20 c. As No. 725	35	30
750.	20 c. As No. 726	35	30
751.	20 c. As No. 727	35	30
752.	20 c. As No. 728	35	30
753.	25 c. As No. 729	35	30
754.	25 c. As No. 730	35	30
755.	25 c. As No. 731	35	30
756.	25 c. As No. 732	35	30
757.	30 c. As No. 733	40	30
758.	30 c. As No. 734	40	30
759.	30 c. As No. 735	40	30
760.	30 c. As No. 736	40	30
761.	35 c. Type **184**	45	35
762.	35 c. As No. 714	45	35
763.	35 c. As No. 715	45	35
764.	35 c. As No. 716	45	35
765.	50 c. As No. 717	65	55
766.	50 c. As No. 718	65	55
767.	50 c. As No. 719	65	55
768.	50 c. As No. 720	65	55
769.	60 c. As No. 721	75	65
770.	60 c. As No. 722	75	65
771.	60 c. As No. 723	75	65
772.	60 c. As No. 724	75	65
773.	70 c. As No. 725	2·00	75
774.	70 c. As No. 726	2·00	75
775.	70 c. As No. 727	2·00	75
776.	70 c. As No. 728	2·00	75
777.	80 c. As No. 729	2·00	80
778.	80 c. As No. 730	2·00	80
779.	80 c. As No. 731	2·00	80
780.	80 c. As No. 732	2·00	80
781.	$1 As No. 733	2·75	1·00
782.	$1 As No. 734	2·75	1·00
783.	$1 As No. 735	2·75	1·00
784.	$1 As No. 736	2·75	1·00
785.	$2 As No. 723	10·00	5·00
786.	$3 As No. 720	10·00	5·00
787.	$4 As No. 726	4·50	7·00
788.	$6 As No. 715	6·00	9·00
789.	$10 As No. 734	25·00	26·00

Nos. 761/74 are 30×40 mm., and Nos. 785/9, which include a portrait of Queen Elizabeth II in each design, are 55×35 mm.

See also Nos. 966/94.

185. Annunciation.

1980. Christmas. Scenes from 13th-century French Prayerbook. Multicoloured.

801.	15 c. Type **185**	25	15
802.	30 c. The Visitation ..	35	25
803.	40 c. The Nativity ..	45	30
804.	50 c. The Epiphany ..	60	40

186. " The Crucifixion " (from book of Saint-Amand).

1981. Easter. Illustrations from 12th-century French Prayer Books. Multicoloured.

807.	15 c. Type **186**	20	20
808.	25 c. " Placing in Tomb " (from book of Ingeburge)	30	30
809.	40 c. " Mourning at the Sepulchre " (from book of Ingeburge)	40	40

187. Prince Charles.

1981. Royal Wedding. Multicoloured.

812.	$1 Type **187**	1·50	1·50
813.	$2 Prince Charles and Lady Diana Spencer	2·75	2·75

188. Footballers.

1981. World Cup Football Championship, Spain (1982). Designs showing footballers. Multicoloured.

815.	20 c. Type **188**	40	20
816.	20 c. Figures to right of stamps	40	20
817.	30 c. Figures to left ..	50	30
818.	30 c. Figures to right ..	50	30
819.	35 c. Figures to left ..	50	35
820.	35 c. Figures to right ..	50	35
821.	50 c. Figures to left ..	65	45
822.	50 c. Figures to right ..	65	45

The two designs of each value were printed together, se-tenant, in horizontal pairs throughout the sheet, forming composite designs.

1981. International Year for Disabled Persons. Nos. 812/13 surch **+5 c.**

824.	$1+5 c. Type **187** ..	2·50	2·50
825.	$2+5 c. Prince Charles and Lady Diana Spencer ..	4·50	5·00

190. " Holy Virgin with Child ".

1982. Christmas. Details of Paintings by Rubens. Multicoloured.

827. 8 c. Type **190** 45 15
828. 15 c. " Coronation of St. Catherine " 55 25
829. 40 c. " Adoration of the Shepherds " 80 70
830. 50 c. " Adoration of the Magi " 85 80

191. Princess of Wales (inscr. " 21st Birthday ").

1982. 21st Birthday of Princess of Wales. Multicoloured.

833. $1.25 Type **191** .. .. 1·25 1·25
834. $1.25 As Type **191**, but inscr. " 1 July 1982 " .. 1·25 1·25
835. $2.50 Princess (inscr. " 21st Birthday ") (different) .. 1·75 1·75
836. $2.50 As No. 835, but inscr. " 1 July 1982 " .. 1·75 1·75

1982. Birth of Prince William of Wales (1st issue). Nos. 812/13 optd.

838. $1 Type **187** .. .. 3·50 2·25
839. $1 Type **187** .. .. 3·50 2·25
840. $2 Prince Charles and Lady Diana Spencer .. .. 6·00 5·00
841. $2 Prince Charles and Lady Diana Spencer .. .. 6·00 5·00

OPTS: Nos. 838 and 840, **" ROYAL BIRTH 21 JUNE 1982 "**. Nos. 839 and 841, **" PRINCE WILLIAM OF WALES "**.

1982. Birth of Prince William of Wales (2nd issue). As Nos. 833/6 but with changed inscriptions. Multicoloured.

843. $1.25 As Type **191**, inscr. " Royal Birth " .. 1·25 1·25
844. $1.25 As Type **191**, inscr. " 21 June 1982 " .. 1·25 1·25
845. $2.50 As No. 835, inscr. " Royal Birth " .. 1·75 1·75
846. $2.50 As No. 835, inscr. " 21 June 1982 " .. 1·75 1·75

193. " Serenade ".

1982. Norman Rockwell (painter) Commem. Multicoloured.

848. 5 c. Type **193** 35 10
849. 10 c. " The Hikers " .. 35 15
850. 20 c. " The Doctor and the Doll " 60 25
851. 30 c. " Home from Camp " 65 30

194. Franklin D. Roosevelt.

1982. Air. American Anniversaries. Mult.

852. 60 c. Type **194** .. .. 1·50 70
853. 80 c. Benjamin Franklin 1·75 80
854. $1·40 George Washington 2·00 1·25

ANNIVERSARIES: 60 c. Roosevelt birth centenary. 80 c. "Articles of Peace" negotiations bicentenary. $1.40, Washington 250th birth anniv.

195. " Virgin with Garlands " (detail Rubens) and Princess Diana with Prince William.

1982. Christmas.

856. **195.** 35 c. multicoloured .. 85 50
857. – 48 c. multicoloured .. 1·25 75
858. – 60 c. multicoloured .. 1·50 1·00
859. – $1.70 multicoloured .. 2·25 2·25

DESIGNS: 48 c. to $1.70, Different details from Ruben's painting " Virgin with Garlands ".

197. Statue of Tangaroa.

1983. Commonwealth Day. Multicoloured.

862. 60 c. Type **197** 55 60
863. 60 c. Rarotonga oranges .. 55 60
864. 60 c. Rarotonga airport .. 55 60
865. 60 c. Prime Minister Sir Thomas Davis 55 60

198. Scouts using Map and Compass.

1983. 75th Anniv. of Boy Scout Movement and 125th Birth Anniv. of Lord Baden-Powell (founder). Multicoloured.

866. 12 c. Type **198** 50 20
867. 12 c. Hiking 50 20
868. 36 c. Campfire cooking .. 80 40
869. 36 c. Erecting tent .. 80 40
870. 48 c. Hauling on rope .. 95 55
871. 48 c. Using bos'n's chair .. 95 55
872. 60 c. Digging hole for sapling .. .. 1·00 70
873. 60 c. Planting sapling .. 1·00 70

1983. 15th World Scout Jamboree, Alberta, Canada. Nos. 866/73 optd **XV WORLD JAMBOREE** (Nos. 875, 877, 879, 881) or optd **" ALBERTA, CANADA 1983 "** (others).

875. 12 c. Type **198** 20 20
876. 12 c. Hiking 20 20
877. 36 c. Campfire cooking .. 40 40
878. 36 c. Erecting tent .. 40 40
879. 48 c. Hauling on rope .. 55 55
880. 48 c. Using bos'n's chair .. 55 55
881. 60 c. Digging hole for sapling 70 70
882. 60 c. Planting sapling .. 70 70

1983. Various stamps surch.

884 – 18 c. on 8 c. mult (No. 733) 60 50
885 – 18 c. on 8 c. mult (No. 734) 60 50
886 – 18 c. on 8 c. mult (No. 735) 60 50
887 – 18 c. on 8 c. mult (No. 736) 60 50
888 – 36 c. on 15 c. mult (No. 745) .. .. 1·00 85
889 – 36 c. on 15 c. mult (No. 746) .. .. 1·00 85
890 – 36 c. on 15 c. mult (No. 747) .. .. 1·00 85
891 – 36 c. on 15 c. mult (No. 748) .. .. 1·00 85
892 – 36 c. on 30 c. mult (No. 757) .. .. 1·00 85
893 – 36 c. on 30 c. mult (No. 758) .. .. 1·00 85
894 – 36 c. on 30 c. mult (No. 759) .. .. 1·00 85
895 – 36 c. on 30 c. mult (No. 760) .. .. 1·00 85
896 **184** 36 c. on 35 c. mult .. 1·00 85
897 – 36 c. on 35 c. mult (No. 762) .. .. 1·00 85
898 – 36 c. on 35 c. mult (No. 763) .. .. 1·00 85
899 – 36 c. on 35 c. mult (No. 764) .. .. 1·00 85
900 – 48 c. on 25 c. mult (No. 753) .. .. 1·25 1·25
901 – 48 c. on 25 c. mult (No. 754) .. .. 1·25 1·25
902 – 48 c. on 25 c. mult (No. 755) .. .. 1·25 1·25
903 – 48 c. on 25 c. mult (No. 756) .. .. 1·25 1·25
904 – 72 c. on 70 c. mult (No. 773) .. .. 2·00 1·75
905 – 72 c. on 70 c. mult (No. 774) .. .. 2·00 1·75
906 – 72 c. on 70 c. mult (No. 775) .. .. 2·00 1·75
907 – 72 c. on 70 c. mult (No. 776) .. .. 2·00 1·75
908 – 96 c. on $1.40 mult (No. 854) .. .. 2·00 2·00
909 – 96 c. on $2 mult (No. 813) .. .. 8·50 8·50
910 – 96 c. on $2.50 mult (No. 835) .. .. 3·00 3·00
911 – 96 c. on $2.50 mult (No. 836) .. .. 3·00 3·00
912 – $5.60 on $6 mult (No. 788) .. .. 21·00 16·00
913 – $5.60 on $10 mult (No. 789) .. .. 21·00 16·00

202. Union Flag.

1983. Cook Islands Flags and Ensigns. Mult.

914. 6 c. Type **202** (postage) .. 20 10
915. 6 c. Group Federal flag .. 20 10
916. 12 c. Rarotonga ensign .. 20 10
917. 12 c. Flag of New Zealand 20 10
918. 15 c. Cook Islands' flag (1973–79) 25 15
919. 15 c. Cook Islands' National flag 25 15
920. 20 c. Type **202** (air) .. 35 25
921. 20 c. Group Federal flag .. 35 25
922. 30 c. Rarotonga ensign .. 50 30
923. 30 c. Flag of New Zealand 50 30
924. 35 c. Cook Islands' flag .. 55 35
925. 35 c. Cook Islands' National flag 55 35

203. Dish Aerial, Satellite Earth Station.

1983. World Communications Year.

927. 36 c. multicoloured .. 30 35
928. 48 c. multicoloured .. 45 45
929. 60 c. multicoloured .. 55 60
930. 96 c. multicoloured .. 85 90

DESIGNS: 48 to 96 c. Various satellites.

204. " La Belle Jardiniere ".

1983. Christmas. 500th Birth Anniv. of Raphael. Multicoloured.

932. 12 c. Type **204** 40 30
933. 18 c. " Madonna and Child with five Saints " .. 60 50
934. 36 c. " Madonna and Child with St. John " .. .. 1·25 1·25
935. 48 c. " Madonna of the Fish " .. .. .. 1·40 1·40
936. 60 c. " Madonna of the Baldacchino " .. .. 1·75 1·75

205. Montgolfier Balloon, 1783.

1984. Bicentenary (1983) of Manned Flight. Multicoloured.

939. 36 c. Type **205** 30 35
940. 48 c. Ascent of Adorne, Strasbourg 1784 .. 40 45
941. 60 c. Balloon driven by sails, 1785 .. .. 55 60
942. 72 c. Ascent of man on horse, 1798 .. .. 70 75
943. 96 c. Aerial acrobatics of Godard, 1850 .. .. 85 90

206. Cuvier's Beaked Whale.

1984. Save the Whale. Multicoloured.

946. 10 c. Type **206** 50 50
947. 18 c. Risso's Dolphin .. 75 75
948. 20 c. True's Beaked Whale 75 75
949. 24 c. Long Finned Pilot Whale 80 80
950. 30 c. Narwhal 90 90
951. 36 c. White Whale .. 1·10 1·10
952. 42 c. Common Dolphin .. 1·40 1·40
953. 48 c. Commerson's Dolphin 1·60 1·60
954. 60 c. Bottle-Nosed Dolphin 1·90 1·90
955. 72 c. Sowerby's Beaked Whale .. .. .. 2·00 2·00
956. 96 c. Common Porpoise .. 2·50 2·50
957. $2 Boutu .. .. .. 3·25 3·25

207. Athens, 1896.

1984. Olympic Games, Los Angeles. Mult.

958. 18 c. Type **207** 15 20
959. 24 c. Paris, 1900 .. .. 20 25
960. 36 c. St. Louis, 1904 .. 30 35
961. 48 c. London, 1948 .. 40 45
962. 60 c. Tokyo, 1964 .. 45 50
963. 72 c. Berlin, 1936 .. 55 60
964. 96 c. Rome, 1960 .. 75 80
965. $1.20 Los Angeles, 1930 .. 90 95

INDEX

Countries can be quickly located by referring to the index at the end of this volume.

208. " Siphonogorgia ".

1984. Corals (2nd series). Multicoloured.

966. 1 c. Type **208** 10 10
967. 2 c. "Millepora alcicornis" .. 10 10
968. 3 c. "Distichopora violacea" 15 10
969. 5 c. "Ptilosarcus gurneyi" 20 10
970. 10 c. "Lobophyllia bemprichii" 20 10
971. 12 c. "Sarcophyton digitatum" 20 15
972. 14 c. "Pavona praetorta" 20 15
973. 18 c. "Junceella gemmacea" 30 20
974. 20 c. "Stylaster" 30 20
975. 24 c. "Stylophora pistillata" 35 20
976. 30 c. "Palauaster ramosa" 50 25
977. 36 c. "Melithaea albitincta" 60 30
978. 40 c. "Stylaster echinatus" 60 30
979. 42 c. "Fungia fungites" .. 60 35
980. 48 c. "Gonipora" 65 35
981. 50 c. "Melithaea squamata" 70 45
982. 52 c. "Bellonella indica" .. 70 45
983. 55 c. "Plerogyra sinuosa" 75 50
984. 60 c. "Tubastraea" .. 85 60
985. 70 c. "Heliofungia actiniformis" 90 70
986. 85 c. "Caulastraea echinulata" 1·10 75
987. 96 c. "Porites andrewsi" .. 1·25 85
988. $1.10 "Pectinia alcicornis" 1·40 1·00
989. $1.20 "Dendrophyllia gracilis" 1·50 1·10
990. $3.60 on $2 "Gonipora" (55 × 35 mm) .. .. 3·75 2·75
991. $4.20 on $3 "Heliofungia actiniformis" (55 × 35 mm) .. .. .. 4·25 3·25
992. $5 on $4 "Stylophora pistillata" (55 × 35 mm) 4·50 3·75
993. $7.20 on $6 "Stylaster echinatus" (55 × 35 mm) 6·50 5·50
994. $9.60 on $10 "Melithaea albitincta" (55 × 35 mm) 8·00 7·50

1984. Olympic Gold Medal Winners. Nos. 963/5 optd.

995. 72 c. Berlin, 1936 (optd. **Equestrian Team Dressage Germany**) 60 65
996. 96 c. Rome, 1960 (optd. **Decathlon Daley Thompson Great Britain**) .. 80 85
997. $1.20 Los Angeles, 1930 (optd. **Equestrian Team Dressage Germany**) .. 1·00 1·10

211. Capt. Cook's Cottage, Melbourne.

1984. "Ausipex" International Stamp Exhibition, Melbourne. Multicoloured.

998. 36 c. Type **211** 90 90
999. 48 c. "H.M.S. 'Endeavour' careened for Repairs" (Sydney Parkinson) .. 1·40 1·40
1000. 60 c. "Cook's landing at Botany Bay" (E. Phillips Fox) .. .. 2·00 2·00
1001. $2 "Capt. James Cook" (John Webber) .. .. 3·25 3·25

1984. Birth of Prince Henry. Nos. 812 and 833/6 variously optd. or surch also (No. 1007).

1003. $1.25 Optd. **Commemorating-15 Sept. 1984** (No. 833) .. .. 1·75 1·10
1004. $1.25 Optd. **Birth H.R.H. Prince Henry** (No. 834) 1·75 1·10
1005. $2.50 Optd. **Commemorating-15 Sept. 1984** (No. 835) .. .. 3·00 2·00
1006. $2.50 Optd. **Birth H.R.H. Prince Henry** (No. 836) 3·00 2·00
1007. $3 on $1 Optd. **Royal Birth Prince Henry 15 Sept. 1984** (No. 812) .. .. 6·00 4·00

213. "Virgin on Throne with Child" (Giovanni Bellini)

1984. Christmas. Multicoloured

1008. 36 c. Type **213** 50 35
1009. 48 c. "Virgin and Child" (anonymous, 15th century) 60 45
1010. 60 c. "Virgin and Child with Saints" (Alvise Vivarini) 75 50
1011. 96 c. "Virgin and Child with Angels" (H. Memling) 95 80
1012. $1.20 "Adoration of Magi" (G. Tiepolo) .. .. 1·10 95

214. Downy Woodpecker.

1985. Birth Bicentenary of John J. Audubon (ornithologist). Designs showing original paintings. Multicoloured.

1015. 30 c. Type **214** .. .. 1·50 60
1016. 55 c. Black-throated Blue Warbler .. .. 1·75 1·00
1017. 65 c. Yellow-throated Warbler .. .. 2·00 1·25
1018. 75 c. Chestnut-sided Warbler .. .. 2·25 1·50
1019. 95 c. Dickcissel .. .. 2·40 1·60
1020. $1.15 White-crowned Sparrow .. .. 2·50 1·75

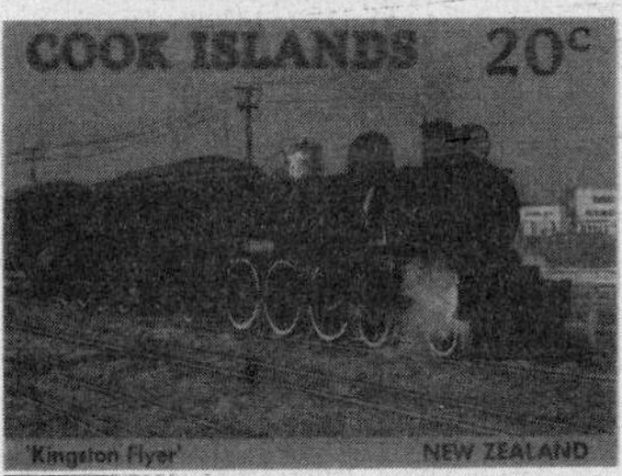

215. "The Kingston Flyer" (New Zealand).

1985. Famous Trains. Multicoloured.

1022. 20 c. Type **215** 85 50
1023. 55 c. Class "640" (Italy) 1·25 85
1024. 65 c. "Gotthard" type (Switzerland) .. .. 1·50 90
1025. 75 c. Union Pacific No. 6900 (U.S.A.) .. .. 1·75 1·10
1026. 95 c. "Super Continental" type (Canada) .. 2·00 1·25
1027. $1.15 "TGV" type (France) .. .. 2·25 1·50
1028. $2.20 "The Flying Scotsman" (Great Britain) 3·25 2·50
1029. $3.40 "The Orient Express" .. .. .. 3·50 3·75

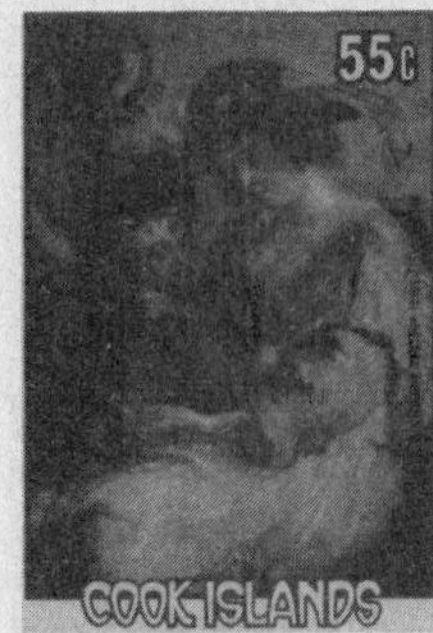

216. "Helena Fourment". (Peter Paul Rubens)

1985. International Youth Year. Mult.

1030. 55 c. Type **216** .. .. 1·25 1·25
1031. 65 c. "Vigee-Lebrun and Daughter" (E. Vigee-Lebrun) .. .. 1·60 1·60
1032. 75 c. "On the Terrace" (Renoir) .. .. 1·75 1·75
1033. $1.30 "Young Mother Sewing" (M. Cassatt) 2·25 2·25

217. "Lady Elizabeth, 1908". (Mabel Hankey)

1985. Life and Times of Queen Elizabeth the Queen Mother. Designs showing paintings. Multicoloured.

1035. 65 c. Type **217** 40 50
1036. 75 c. "Duchess of York, 1923" (Savely Sorine) 50 60
1037. $1.15 "Duchess of York, 1925" (Philip de Laszlo) 75 85
1038. $2.80 "Queen Elizabeth, 1938" (Sir Gerald Kelly) .. .. .. 1·90 2·25

218 Albert Henry (Prime Minister, 1965–78).

1985. 20th Anniv. of Self-Government. Multicoloured.

1040. 30 c. Type **218** 40 30
1041. 50 c. Sir Thomas Davis (Prime Minister, 1978–Apr. 1983 and from Nov. 1983) 65 45
1042. 65 c. Geoffrey Henry (Prime Minister, Apr.–Nov. 1983) 75 55

219. Golf.

1985. South Pacific Mini Games, Rarotonga. Multicoloured.

1044. 55 c. Type **219** .. .. 2·75 2·75
1045. 65 c. Rugby .. .. 2·75 2·75
1046. 75 c. Tennis .. .. 3·25 3·25

220. Sea Horse, Gearwheel and Leaves.

1985. Pacific Conferences, Rarotonga.

1048. **220.** 55 c. blk., gold & red 45 50
1049. 65 c. blk., gold & vio. 50 55
1050. 75 c. blk., gold & grn. 60 65

No. 1048 shows the South Pacific Bureau for Economic Co-operation logo and is inscribed "S.P.E.C. Meeting, 30 July–1 Aug 1985, Rarotonga". No. 1049 also shows the S.P.E.C. logo, but is inscribed "South Pacific Forum, 4–6 Aug 1985, Rarotonga". No. 1050 shows the Pacific Islands Conference logo and the inscription "Pacific Islands Conference, 7–10 Aug 1985, Rarotonga".

221. "Madonna of the Magnificat".

1985. Christmas. Virgin and Child Paintings by Botticelli. Multicoloured.

1052. 55 c. Type **221** .. .. 1·00 60
1053. 65 c. "Madonna with Pomegranate" .. 1·10 65
1054. 75 c. "Madonna and Child with Six Angels" 1·25 75
1055. 95 c. "Madonna and Child with St. John" 1·60 95

222. "The Eve of the Deluge" (John Martin).

1986. Appearance of Halley's Comet. Paintings. Multicoloured.

1058. 55 c. Type **222** .. .. 1·25 1·25
1059. 65 c. "Lot and his Daughters" (Lucas van Leyden) .. .. 1·40 1·40
1060. 75 c. "Auspicious Comet" (from treatise c 1857) .. .. 1·50 1·50
1061. $1.25 "Events following Charles I" (Herman Saftleven) .. .. 2·25 2·25
1062. $2 "Ossian receiving Napoleonic Officers" (Anne Louis Girodet-Trioson) .. .. 3·00 3·00

223. Queen Elizabeth II.

1986. 60th Birthday of Queen Elizabeth II. Designs showing formal portraits.

1065. **223.** 95 c. multicoloured .. 1·25 1·25

1066. – $1.25 multicoloured 1·50 1·50

1067. – $1.50 multicoloured 1·75 1·75

224. U.S.A. 1847 Franklin 5 c. Stamp and H.M.S. "Resolution" at Rarotonga.

1986. "Ameripex '86" International Exhibition, Chicago. Multicoloured.

1069. $1 Type **224** .. .. 2·75 2·75

1070. $1.50 Chicago .. .. 3·00 3·00

1071. $2 1975 definitive $2, Benjamin Franklin and H.M.S. "Resolution" .. .. .. 3·75 3·75

225. Head of Statue of Liberty.

1986. Centenary of Statue of Liberty. Multicoloured.

1072. $1 Type **225** 75 75

1073. $1.25 Hand and torch of Statue 90 90

1074. $2.75 Statue of Liberty 2·00 2·00

226. Miss Sarah Ferguson.

1986. Royal Wedding. Multicoloured.

1075. $1 Type **226** .. .. 1·00 1·00

1076. $2 Prince Andrew .. 1·75 1·75

1077. $3 Prince Andrew and Miss Sarah Ferguson (57 × 31 mm.) .. .. 2·50 2·50

228. "Holy Family with St. John the Baptist and St. Elizabeth".

1986. Christmas. Paintings by Rubens. Multicoloured.

1080. 55 c. Type **228** 70 70

1081. $1.30 "Virgin with the Garland" .. .. 1·50 1·50

1082. $2.75 "Adoration of the Magi" (detail).. .. 3·00 3·00

1986. Visit of Pope John Paul II to South Pacific. Nos. 1080/2 surch. **FIRST PAPAL VISIT TO SOUTH PACIFIC POPE JOHN PAUL II NOV 21–24 1986.**

1085 55 c.+10 c. Type **228** .. 1·50 1·50

1086 $1.30+10 c. "Virgin with the Garland" .. .. 2·00 2·00

1087 $2.75+10 c. "Adoration of the Magi" (detail) .. 3·50 3·50

1987. Various stamps surch.

(a) On Nos. 741/56, 761/76, and 787/8

1090. 10 c. on 15 c. "Distichopora violacea" .. 10 10

1091. 10 c. on 15 c. "Stylaster" 10 10

1092. 10 c. on 15 c. "Gonipora" 10 10

1093. 10 c. on 15 c. "Caulastraea echinulata" .. 10 10

1094. 10 c. on 25 c. "Lobophyllia bemprichii" .. 10 10

1095. 10 c. on 25 c. "Palauastrea ramosa" .. 10 10

1096. 10 c. on 25 c. "Bellonella indica" 10 10

1097. 10 c. on 25 c. "Pectinia alcicornis" 10 10

1098. 18 c. on 12 c. "Millepora alcicornis" 15 15

1099. 18 c. on 12 c. "Junceella gemmacea" 15 15

1100. 18 c. on 12 c. "Fungia fungites" 15 15

1101. 18 c. on 12 c. "Heliofungia actiniformis" .. 15 15

1102. 18 c. on 20 c. "Ptilosarcus qurneyi" .. 15 15

1103. 18 c. on 20 c. "Stylophora pistillata" .. 15 15

1104. 18 c. on 20 c. "Melithaea squamata" 15 15

1105. 18 c. on 20 c. "Porites andrewsi" .. 15 15

1106. 55 c. on 35 c. Type **184** .. 40 45

1107. 55 c. on 35 c. "Pavona praetorta" .. 40 45

1108. 55 c. on 35 c. "Stylaster echinatus" 40 45

1109. 55 c. on 35 c. "Tubastraea" 40 45

1110. 65 c. on 50 c. As No. 1098 45 50

1111. 65 c. on 50 c. As No. 1099 45 50

1112. 65 c. on 50 c. As No. 1100 45 50

1113. 65 c. on 50 c. As No. 1101 45 50

1114. 65 c. on 60 c. As No. 1090 45 50

1115. 65 c. on 60 c. As No. 1091 45 50

1116. 65 c. on 60 c. As No. 1092 45 50

1117. 65 c. on 60 c. As No. 1093 45 50

1118. 75 c. on 70 c. As No. 1102 55 60

1119. 75 c. on 70 c. As No. 1103 55 60

1120. 75 c. on 70 c. As No. 1104 55 60

1121. 75 c. on 70 c. As No. 1105 55 60

1122. $6.40 on $4 "Stylophora pistillata" .. .. 4·50 4·75

1123. $7.20 on $6 "Stylaster echinatus" .. .. 5·00 5·25

(b) On Nos. 812/13.

1124. $9.40 on $1 Type **187** .. 15·00 16·00

1125. $9.40 on $2 Prince Charles and Lady Diana Spencer .. 15·00 16·00

(c) On Nos. 835/6.

1126. $9.40 on $2.50 Princess of Wales (inscr. "21st Birthday") .. .. 15·00 16·00

1127. $9.40 on $2.50 As No. 1126, but inscr. "1 July 1982" .. .. 15·00 16·00

(d) On Nos. 966/8, 971/2, 975, 979/80, 982 and 987/9.

1128. 5 c. on 1 c. Type **208** .. 10 10

1129. 5 c. on 2 c. "Millepora alcicornis" 10 10

1130. 5 c. on 3 c. "Distichopora violacea" 10 10

1131. 5 c. on 12 c. "Sarcophyton digitatum" .. 10 10

1132. 5 c on 14 c. "Pavona praetorta" 10 10

1133. 18 c. on 24 c. "Stylophora pistillata" .. 15 15

1134. 55 c. on 52 c. "Bellonella indica" .. 40 45

1135. 65 c. on 42 c. "Fungia fungites" 45 50

1136. 75 c. on 48 c. "Gonipora" 55 60

1137. 95 c. on 96 c. "Porites andrewsi" 70 75

1138. 95 c. on $1.10 "Pectinia alcicornis" 70 75

1139. 95 c. on $1.20 "Dendrophyllia gracilis" .. 70 75

(e) On Nos. 998/1001.

1140. $1.30 on 36 c. Type **211** 1·40 1·50

1141. $1.30 on 48 c. "The 'Endeavour' careened for Repairs" (Sydney Parkinson) .. .. 1·40 1·50

1142. $1.30 on 60 c. "Cook's landing at Botany Bay" (E. Phillips Fox) 1·40 1·50

1143. $1.30 on $2 "Capt. James Cook" (John Webber) 1·40 1·50

(f) On Nos. 1065/7.

1144. **223.** $2.30 on 95 c. mult. 7·00 7·50

1145. – $2.80 on $1.25 mult. 7·00 7·50

1146. – $2.80 on $1.50 mult. 7·00 7·50

(g) On Nos. 1075/7.

1147. $2.80 on $1 Type **226** .. 6·00 6·50

1148. $2.80 on $2 Prince Andrew .. .. 6·00 6·50

1149. $2.80 on $3 Prince Andrew and Miss Sarah Ferguson (57 × 31 mm.) .. .. 6·00 6·50

1987. Various stamps surch.

1150. $2.80 on $2 "Gonipora" (No. 785) .. .. 2·10 2·25

1151. $5 on $3 "Heliofungia actiniformis" (No. 786) 4·00 4·25

1152. $9.40 on $10 "Melithaea albitincta" (No. 789) .. 7·50 7·75

1153. $9.40 on $1 Type **187** (No. 838) .. .. 7·50 7·75

1154. $9.40 on $1 Type **187** (No. 839) .. .. 7·50 7·75

1155. $9.40 on $2 Prince Charles and Lady Diana Spencer (No. 840) .. .. .. 7·50 7·75

1156. $9.40 on $2 Prince Charles and Lady Diana Spencer (No. 841) .. .. .. 7·50 7·75

1987. Hurricane Relief. Various stamps surch. **HURRICANE RELIEF + 50c.**

(a) On Nos. 1035/8.

1158. 65 c.+50 c. Type **217** .. 80 85

1159. 75 c.+50 c. "Duchess of York, 1923" (Savely Sorine).. .. .. 85 90

1160. $1.15+50 c. "Duchess of York, 1925" (Philip de Laszlo) .. .. 1·10 1·25

1161. $2.80+50 c. "Queen Elizabeth, 1938" (Sir Gerald Kelly) .. .. 2·25 2·40

(b) On Nos. 1058/62.

1163. 55 c.+50 c. Type **222** .. 75 80

1164. 65 c.+50 c. "Lot and his Daughters" (Lucas van Leyden) 80 85

1165. 75 c.+50 c. "Auspicious Comet" (from treatise c. 1587) 85 90

1166. $1.50+50 c. "Events following Charles I" (Herman Saftleven) .. 1·25 1·40

1167. $2+50 c. "Ossian receiving Napoleonic Officers" (Anne Louis Girodet-Trioson) .. 1·75 2·00

(c) On Nos. 1065/7.

1168. **223.** 95 c.+50 c. mult. .. 1·00 1·10

1169. – $1.25+50 c. mult. .. 1·25 1·40

1170. – $1.50+50 c. mult. .. 1·40 1·50

(d) On Nos. 1069/71.

1172. $1+50 c. Type **224** .. 1·00 1·10

1173. $1.50+50 c. Chicago .. 1·40 1·50

1174. $2+50 c. 1975 definitive $2, Benjamin Franklin and H.M.S. "Resolution" .. .. .. 1·75 1·90

(e) On Nos. 1072/4.

1175. $1+50 c. Type **225** .. 1·00 1·10

1176. $1.25+50 c. Hand and torch of Statue .. 1·25 1·40

1177. $2.75+50 c. Statue of Liberty .. .. 2·25 2·40

(f) On Nos. 1075/7.

1178. $1+50 c. Type **226** .. 1·00 1·25

1179. $2+50 c. Prince Andrew 1·75 1·90

1180. $3+50 c. Prince Andrew and Miss Sarah Ferguson (57 × 31 mm.) 2·40 2·50

(g) On Nos. 1080/2.

1181. 55 c.+50 c. Type **228** .. 75 80

1182. $1.30+50 c. "Virgin with the Garland" .. .. 1·25 1·40

1183. $2.75+50 c. "The Adoration of the Magi" (detail) .. 2·25 2·40

(h) On Nos. 1122, 1134/7 and

1186. 55 c.+25 c. on 52 c. "Bellonella indica" .. 55 60

1187. 65 c.+25 c. on 42 c. "Fungia fungites" .. 65 70

1188. 75 c.+25 c. on 48 c. "Gonipora" 70 75

1189. 95 c.+25 c. on 96 c. "Porites andrewsi" .. 85 90

1190. $2.80+50 c. on $2 "Gonipora" .. .. 2·25 2·40

1191. $5+50 c. on $3 "Heliofungia actiniformis" .. 3·75 4·00

1192. $6.40+50 c. on $4 "Stylophora pistillata" 4·75 5·00

1987. Royal Ruby Wedding. Nos. 484 and 787 optd. **ROYAL WEDDING FORTIETH ANNIVERSARY.**

1193. $4 Queen Elizabeth II and sea shells .. .. 4·50 4·50

1194. $4 Queen Elizabeth II and "Stylophora pistillata" .. .. 4·50 4·50

233. "The Holy Family" (Rembrandt).

1987. Christmas. Different paintings of the Holy Family by Rembrandt.

1195. **233.** $1.25 multicoloured 1·75 1·75

1196. – $1.50 multicoloured 2·00 2·00

1197. – $1.95 multicoloured 2·75 2·75

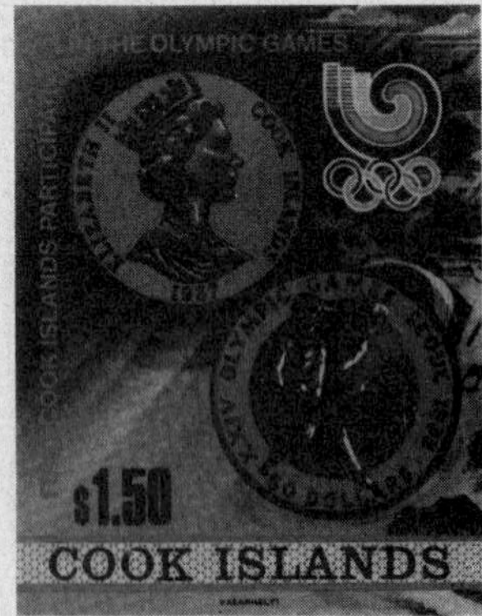

234 Olympic Commemorative $50 Coin

1988. Olympic Games, Seoul. Multicoloured.

1200 $1.50 Type **234** .. .. 1·75 1·75

1201 $1.50 Olympic torch and Seoul Olympic Park .. 1·75 1·75

1202 $1.50 Steffi Graf playing tennis and Olympic medal .. .. .. 1·75 1·75

Nos. 1200/2 were printed together, se-tenant, forming a composite design.

1988. Olympic Tennis Medal Winners, Seoul. Nos. 1200/2 optd.

1204 $1.50 Type **234** (optd **MILOSLAV MECIR CZECHOSLOVAKIA GOLD MEDAL WINNER MEN'S TENNIS**) 1·40 1·40

1205 $1.50 Olympic torch and Seoul Olympic Park (optd **TIM MAYOTTE UNITED STATES GABRIELA SABATINI ARGENTINA SILVER MEDAL WINNERS**) .. 1·40 1·40

1206 $1.50 Steffi Graf playing tennis and Olympic medal (optd **GOLD MEDAL WINNER STEFFI GRAF WEST GERMANY**) 1·40 1·40

236 "Virgin and Child"

1988. Christmas.

1208 **236** 70 c. multicoloured .. 1·25 1·25
1209 – 85 c. multicoloured .. 1·50 1·50
1210 – 95 c. multicoloured .. 1·75 1·75
1221 – $1.25 multicoloured .. 2·00 2·00

DESIGNS: 85 c.; 95 c.; $1.25 Various versions of the "Virgin and Child" by Durer.

237 "Apollo 11" leaving Earth

1989. 20th Anniv of First Manned Landing on Moon. Multicoloured.

1213 40 c. Type **237** 50 50
1214 40 c. Lunar module over Moon 50 50
1215 55 c. Aldrin stepping onto Moon 70 70
1216 55 c. Astronaut on Moon 70 70
1217 65 c. Working on lunar surface 80 80
1218 65 c. Conducting experiment 80 80
1219 75 c. "Apollo 11" leaving Moon 90 90
1220 75 c. Splashdown in South Pacific 90 90

238 Rarotonga Flycatcher

1989. Endangered Birds of the Cook Islands. Multicoloured.

1222 15 c. Type **238** 75 75
1223 20 c. Pair of Rarotonga flycatchers 75 75
1224 65 c. Pair of Rarotongan fruit doves .. .. 1·75 1·75
1225 70 c. Rarotongan fruit dove .. .. .. 1·75 1·75

239 Villagers

1989. Christmas. Details from "Adoration of the Magi" by Rubens. Mult.

1227 70 c. Type **239** 75 75
1228 85 c. Virgin Mary .. 90 90
1229 95 c. Christ Child .. 1·10 1·10
1230 $1.50 Boy with gift .. 1·75 1·75

240 Revd. John Williams and L.M.S. Church

1990. Christianity in the Cook Islands. Multicoloured.

1232 70 c. Type **240** 65 65
1233 85 c. Mgr. Bernardine Castanie and Roman Catholic Church .. 80 80
1234 95 c. Elder Osborne Widstoe and Mormon Church 85 85
1235 $1.60 Dr. J. E. Caldwell and Seventh Day Adventist Church .. 1·50 1·50

241 "Woman writing a Letter" (Terborch)

1990. 150th Anniv of the Penny Black. Designs showing paintings. Multicoloured.

1237 85 c. Type **241** .. .. 1·00 1·00
1238 $1.15 "George Gisze" (Holbein the Younger) 1·40 1·40
1239 $1.55 "Mrs. John Douglas" (Gainsborough) .. .. 1·75 1·75
1240 $1.85 "Portrait of a Gentleman" (Durer) .. 2·00 2·00

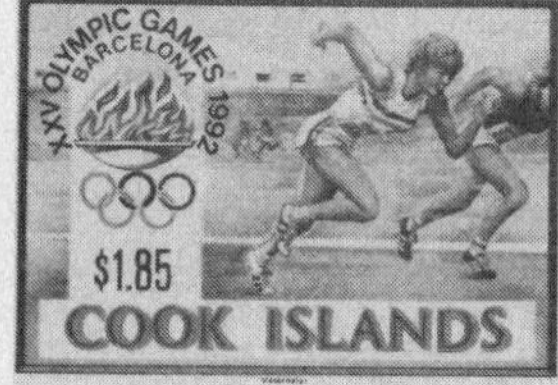

242 Sprinting

1990. Olympic Games, Barcelona, and Winter Olympic Games, Albertville (1992) (1st issue). Multicoloured.

1242 $1.85 Type **242** .. .. 2·50 2·50
1243 $1.85 Cook Islands $50 commemorative coin 2·50 2·50
1244 $1.85 Skiing .. .. 2·50 2·50

See also Nos. 1304/9.

243 Queen Elizabeth the Queen Mother

1990. 90th Birthday of Queen Elizabeth the Queen Mother.

1245 **243** $1.85 multicoloured .. 2·50 2·50

244 "Adoration of the Magi" (Memling)

1990. Christmas. Religious Paintings. Mult.

1248 70 c. Type **244** 75 75
1249 85 c. "Holy Family" (Lotto) 85 85
1250 95 c. "Madonna and Child with Saints John and Catherine" (Titian) .. 1·00 1·00
1251 $1.50 "Holy Family" (Titian) .. .. 1·50 1·50

246 Columbus (engraving by Theodoro de Bry)

1991. 500th Anniv (1992) of Discovery of America by Columbus.

1254 **246** $1 multicoloured .. 1·25 1·25

1991. 65th Birthday of Queen Elizabeth II. No. 789 optd **65TH BIRTHDAY**.

1255 $10 "Melithaea albitincta" 10·00 11·00

248 "Adoration of the Child" (G. delle Notti)

1991. Christmas. Religious Paintings. Mult.

1256 70 c. Type **248** 65 65
1257 85 c. "The Birth of the Virgin" (B. Murillo) .. 85 85
1258 $1.15 "Adoration of the Shepherds" (Rembrandt) .. .. 1·25 1·25
1259 $1.50 "Adoration of the Shepherds" (L. le Nain) 1·75 1·75

249 Red-breasted Maori Wrasse

1992. Reef Life. Multicoloured.

1261 5 c. Type **249** 10 10
1262 10 c. Blue sea star .. 10 10
1263 15 c. Black and gold angelfish 10 10
1264 20 c. Spotted pebble crab 15 20
1265 25 c. Black-tipped cod .. 20 25
1266 30 c. Spanish dancer .. 25 30
1267 50 c. Royal angelfish .. 35 40
1268 80 c. Squirrel fish .. 60 65
1269 85 c. Red pencil sea urchin .. 60 65
1270 90 c. Red-spot rainbow fish 65 70
1271 $1 Black-lined maori wrasse 70 75
1272 $2 Longnose butterfly fish 1·50 1·60
1273 $3 Red-spot rainbow fish 2·25 2·40
1274 $5 Blue sea-star .. .. 3·75 4·00
1275 $7 "Pygoplites diacanthus" .. 5·00 5·25
1276 $10 Spotted pebble crab 7·25 7·50

250 Tiger

1992. Endangered Wildlife. Multicoloured.

1279 $1.15 Type **250** .. .. 1·00 1·00
1280 $1.15 Indian elephant .. 1·00 1·00
1281 $1.15 Brown bear .. 1·00 1·00
1282 $1.15 Black rhinoceros .. 1·00 1·00
1283 $1.15 Chimpanzee .. 1·00 1·00
1284 $1.15 Argali .. .. 1·00 1·00
1285 $1.15 Heaviside's dolpin .. 1·00 1·00
1286 $1.15 Eagle owl .. .. 1·00 1·00
1287 $1.15 Bee hummingbird .. 1·00 1·00
1288 $1.15 Puma .. .. 1·00 1·00
1289 $1.15 European otter .. 1·00 1·00
1290 $1.15 Red kangaroo .. 1·00 1·00
1291 $1.15 Jackass penguin .. 75 80
1292 $1.15 Asian lion .. 75 80
1293 $1.15 Peregrine falcon .. 75 80
1294 $1.15 Persian fallow deer 75 80
1295 $1.15 Key deer 75 80
1296 $1.15 Alpine ibex .. 75 80
1297 $1.15 Mandrill 80 85
1298 $1.15 Gorilla 80 85
1299 $1.15 "Vanessa atalanta" (butterfly) 80 85
1300 $1.15 Takin 80 85
1301 $1.15 Ring-tailed lemur .. 80 85

251 Columbus and Landing in New World ($\frac{3}{4}$-size illustration)

1992. 500th Anniv of Discovery of America by Columbus.

1302 **251** $6 multicoloured .. 5·75 6·00

252 Football and $50 Commemorative Coin

1992. Olympic Games, Barcelona (2nd issue). Multicoloured.

1304 $1.75 Type **252** .. .. 1·40 1·40
1305 $1.75 Olympic gold medal 1·40 1·40
1306 $1.75 Basketball and $10 coin .. .. .. 1·40 1·40
1307 $2.25 Running .. .. 1·90 1·90
1308 $2.25 $10 and $50 coins .. 1·90 1·90
1309 $2.25 Cycling .. .. 1·90 1·90

253 Festival Poster

1992. 6th Festival of Pacific Arts, Rarotonga. Multicoloured.

No.	Description		
1311	80 c. Type **253**	70	70
1312	85 c. Seated Tangaroa carving	70	70
1313	$1 Seated Tangaroa carving (different) ..	85	85
1314	$1.75 Standing Tangaroa carving	1·60	1·60

1992. Royal Visit by Prince Edward. Nos. 1311/14 optd **ROYAL VISIT**.

No.	Description		
1315	80 c. Type **253**	70	70
1316	85 c. Seated Tangaroa carving	70	70
1317	$1 Seated Tangaroa carving (different) ..	85	85
1318	$1.75 Standing Tangaroa carving	1·60	1·60

255 "Worship of Shepherds" (Parmigianino)

1992. Christmas. Religious Paintings by Parmigianino. Multicoloured.

No.	Description		
1319	70 c. Type **255**	65	65
1320	85 c. "Virgin with Long Neck"	70	70
1321	$1.15 "Virgin with Rose"	95	95
1322	$1.90 "St. Margaret's Virgin"	1·60	1·60

256 Queen in Garter Robes

1992. 40th Anniv of Queen Elizabeth II's Accession. Multicoloured.

No.	Description		
1324	80 c. Type **256**	70	75
1325	$1.15 Queen at Trooping the Colour	1·10	1·10
1326	$1.50 Queen in evening dress	1·50	1·50
1327	$1.95 Queen with bouquet	1·75	1·75

257 Coronation Ceremony (¾-size illustration)

1993. 40th Anniv of Coronation. Mult.

No.	Description		
1328	$1 Type **257**	90	90
1329	$2 Coronation photograph by Cecil Beaton ..	1·75	1·75
1330	$3 Royal family on balcony	2·50	2·50

MINIMUM PRICE

The minimum price quoted is 10p which represents a handling charge rather than a basis for valuing common stamps. For further notes about prices see introductory pages.

258 "Virgin with Child" (Filippo Lippi)

1993. Christmas. Religious Paintings. Mult.

No.	Description		
1331	70 c. Type **258**	50	55
1332	85 c. "Bargellini Madonna" (Lodovico Carracci)	60	65
1333	$1.15 "Virgin of the Curtain" (Rafael Sanzio)	85	90
1334	$2.50 "Holy Family" (Agnolo Bronzino) ..	1·75	1·90
1335	$4 "Saint Zachary Virgin" (Parmigianino) (32 × 47 mm)	3·00	3·25

259 Skiing, Flags and Ice Skating (½-size illustration)

1994. Winter Olympic Games, Lillehammer.

No.	Description		
1336 **259**	$5 multicoloured ..	3·75	4·00

OFFICIAL STAMPS

1975. Nos. 228, etc., optd. **O H.M.S.** or surch. also.

No.	Description		
O 1.	1 c. multicoloured ..		
O 2.	2 c. multicoloured ..		
O 3.	3 c. multicoloured ..		
O 4.	4 c. multicoloured ..		
O 5.	5 c. on 2½ c. multicoloured		
O 6.	8 c. multicoloured ..		
O 7.	10 c. on 6 c. multicoloured		
O 8.	18 c. on 20 c. multicoloured		
O 9.	25 c. on 9 c. multicoloured		
O 10.	30 c. on 15 c. multicoloured		
O 11.	50 c. multicoloured ..		
O 12.	$1 multicoloured		
O 13.	$2 multicoloured		
O 14.	$4 multicoloured		
O 15.	$6 multicoloured		
O 1/15	.. .. Set of 15	†	25·00

These stamps were only sold to the public cancelled-to-order and not in unused condition.

1978. Nos. 466/7, 474, 478/81, 484/5, 542 and 568/9 optd. **O.H.M.S.** or surch also.

No.	Description		
O 16. –	1 c. multicoloured (No. 467)	30	10
O 17. **141.**	2 c. on ½ c. multicoloured	30	10
O 18.	5 c. on ½ c. multicoloured	30	10
O 19. –	10 c. on 8 c. multicoloured (No. 474)	35	10
O 20. –	15 c. on 50 c. multicoloured (No. 480) ..	45	10
O 21. –	18 c. on 60 c. multicoloured (No. 481) ..	45	15
O 22. –	25 c. multicoloured (No. 478)	50	20
O 23. –	30 c. multicoloured (No. 479)	50	25
O 24. –	35 c. on 60 c. multicoloured (No. 481) ..	65	30
O 25. –	50 c. multicoloured (No. 480)	1·00	35
O 26. –	60 c. multicoloured (No. 481)	1·10	45
O 27. –	$1 multicoloured (No. 568)	3·75	1·25
O 28. –	$1 multicoloured (No. 569)	3·75	1·25
O 29. –	$2 multicoloured (No. 542)	5·50	3·00
O 30. –	$4 multicoloured (No. 484)	8·50	3·25
O 31. –	$6 multicoloured (No. 485)	11·00	6·00

These stamps were only sold to the public cancelled to order and not in unused condition. They were made available to overseas collectors in mint condition during 1980.

1985. Nos. 786/8, 862/5, 969/74, 976, 978, 981, 984/6 and 988/9 optd **O.H.M.S.** or surch also.

No.	Description		
O32	5 c. "Ptilosarcus gurneyi"	10	10
O33	10 c. "Lobophyllia bemprichii"	10	10
O34	12 c. "Sarcophyton digitatum"	10	10
O35	14 c. "Pavona praetorta"	10	10
O36	18 c. "Junceella gemmacea"	15	20
O37	20 c. "Stylaster"	15	20
O38	30 c. "Palauastrea ramosa"	20	25
O39	40 c. "Stylaster echinatus"	30	35
O40	50 c. "Melithaea squamata"	35	40
O41	55 c. on 85 c. "Caulastraea echinulata"	40	45
O42	60 c. "Tubastraea" ..	45	50
O43	70 c. "Heliofungia actiniformis"	50	55
O46	75 c. on 60 c. Type **197** ..	55	60
O47	75 c. on 60 c. Rarotonga oranges	55	60
O48	75 c. on 60 c. Rarotonga airport	55	60
O49	75 c. on 60 c. Prime Minister Sir Thomas Davis	55	60
O44	$1.10 "Pectinia alcicornis"	80	85
O45	$2 on $1.20 "Dendrophyllia gracilis" ..	1·50	1·60
O50	$5 on $3 "Heliofungia actiniformis"	3·75	4·00
O51	$9 on $4 "Stylophora pistillata"	6·50	7·00
O52	$14 on $6 "Stylaster echinatus"	10·50	11·00
O53	$18 on $10 "Melithaea albitincta"	13·00	13·50

CYPRUS

An island in the E. Mediterranean. A Br. colony which became a republic within the Br. Commonwealth in 1960.

1880. 12 pence = 1 shilling.
1881. 40 paras = 1 piastre. 180 piastres = 1 pound.
1955. 1000 mils = 1 pound.
1983. 100 cents = 1 pound.

1880. Stamps of Gt. Britain (Queen Victoria) optd. **CYPRUS.**

No.	Description		
1. **7.**	½d. red	£100	£100
2. **5.**	1d. red	7·50	27·00
3. **41.**	2½d. mauve	1·75	5·00
4. –	4d. green (No. 153) ..	£120	£200
5. –	6d. grey (No. 161) ..	£500	£650
6. –	1s. green (No. 150) ..	£650	£450

1881. Stamps of Gt. Britain (Queen Victoria), surch. with new values.

No.	Description		
9 **5**	½d. on 1d. red	45·00	65·00
10	30 par. on 1d. red ..	95·00	80·00

7.

13.

1881.

No.	Description		
31 **7.**	½ pi. green	2·50	30
40	½ pi. green and red ..	4·00	50
32	30 par. mauve ..	3·00	2·25
41	30 par. mauve and green	2·00	55
33	1 pi. red	7·00	90
42	1 pi. red and blue ..	4·00	50
34	2 pi. blue	10·00	90
43	2 pi. blue and purple ..	4·50	55
35a	4 pi. olive	16·00	15·00
44	4 pi. olive and purple ..	9·50	3·25
21	6 pi. grey	35·00	16·00
45	6 pi. olive and green ..	6·50	7·50
46	9 pi. brown and red ..	15·00	8·00
22	12 pi. brown	£160	32·00
47	12 pi. brown and black ..	12·00	48·00
48	18 pi. grey and brown ..	48·00	40·00
49	45 pi. purple and blue ..	£110	£120

1882. Surch.

No.	Description		
25. **7.**	½ pi. on ½ pi. green ..	£120	6·50
24.	30 par. on 1 pi. red ..	£1400	£100

1903. As T 7 but portrait of King Edward VII.

No.	Description		
60.	5 par. brown and black ..	30	20
61.	10 par. orange and green ..	1·50	25
62.	½ pi. green and red ..	2·50	15
51.	30 par. violet and green ..	3·25	80
64.	1 pi. red and blue	1·50	50
65.	2 pi. blue and purple ..	4·25	70
66.	4 pi. olive and purple ..	9·00	6·00
67.	6 pi. olive and green ..	8·50	6·00
68.	9 pi. brown and red ..	18·00	6·50
57.	12 pi. brown and black ..	12·00	28·00
70.	18 pi. black and brown ..	27·00	8·00
71.	45 pi. purple and blue ..	65·00	£100

1912. As T 7 but portrait of King George V.

No.	Description		
74b.	10 par. orange and green	2·25	40
86.	10 par. grey and yellow ..	9·50	9·50
75.	½ pi. green and red ..	1·50	20
76.	30 par. violet and green ..	1·50	20
88.	30 par. green	4·25	40
77.	1 pi. red and blue	3·75	1·25
90	1 pi. violet and red ..	3·00	2·75
91.	1½ pi. yellow and black ..	3·25	3·75
78.	2 pi. blue and purple ..	4·75	90
93.	2 pi. red and blue	9·00	22·00
94.	2¾ pi. blue and purple ..	8·50	14·00
79.	4 pi. olive and purple ..	2·75	2·75
80.	6 pi. olive and green ..	2·75	6·00
81.	9 pi. brown and red ..	19·00	14·00
82.	12 pi. brown and black ..	9·00	15·00
83.	18 pi. black and brown .	22·00	18·00
84.	45 pi. purple and blue ..	60·00	90·00
100.	10s. green and red on yell.	£350	£550
101.	£1 purple and black on red	£1000	£1300

1924.

No.	Description		
103. **13.**	¼ pi. grey and brown ..	30	15
104.	½ pi. black	1·25	4·25
118.	½ pi. green	1·75	1·25
105.	¾ pi. green	1·00	60
119.	¾ pi. black	1·75	10
106.	1 pi. purple and brown ..	65	20
107.	1½ pi. orange and black	90	4·25
120.	1½ pi. red	2·25	30
108.	2 pi. red and green ..	1·75	6·00
121.	2 pi. yellow and black ..	4·25	3·25
122.	2½ pi. blue	1·75	30
109.	2¾ pi. blue and purple ..	2·00	1·75
110.	4 pi. olive and purple ..	2·00	1·50
111.	4½ pi. blk. & orge. on grn.	2·25	3·00
112.	6 pi. brown and green ..	2·25	3·50
113.	9 pi. brown and purple ..	2·75	3·00
114.	12 pi. brown and black ..	5·00	35·00
115.	18 pi. black and orange	17·00	4·50
116.	45 pi. purple and blue ..	28·00	32·00
117.	90 pi. green & red on yell.	70·00	£110
102.	£1 purple & black on red	£300	£500
117a.	£5 black on yellow ..	£3000	£5000

14. Silver coin of Amathus, 6th-Cent. BC.

1928. 50th Anniv. of British Rule. Dated "1878 1928".

123.	14.	¾ pi. violet	1·25	40
124.	–	1 pi. black and blue	1·50	65
125.	–	1½ pi. red	3·25	2·00
126.	–	2½ pi. blue	1·75	2·00
127.	–	4 pi. brown	5·00	7·00
128.	–	6 pi. blue	5·00	15·00
129.	–	9 pi. purple	5·00	10·00
130.	–	18 pi. black and brown	16·00	17·00
131.	–	45 pi. violet and blue	32·00	45·00
132.	–	£1 blue and brown	£225	£300

DESIGNS—VERT. 1 pi. Philosophor Zeno. 2½ pi. Discovery of body of St. Barnabas. 4 pi. Cloister, Abbey of Bella Paise. 9 pi. Tekke of Umm Haram. 18 pi. Statue of Richard I, Westminster. 45 pi. St. Nicholas Cathedral, Famagusta (now Lala Mustafa Pasha Mosque). £1 King George V. HORIZ. 1½ pi. Map of Cyprus. 6 pi. Badge of Cyprus.

24. Ruins of Vouni Palace.

30. St. Sophia Cathedral, Nicosia (now Selimiye Mosque).

1934.

133.	24.	¼ pi. blue and brown	30	50
134.	–	½ pi. green	45	50
135.	–	¾ pi. black and violet	70	10
136.	–	1 pi. black and brown	70	80
137.	–	1½ pi. red	70	55
138.	–	2½ pi. blue	1·25	80
139.	30.	4½ pi. black and red	3·00	2·25
140.	–	6 pi. black and blue	7·00	12·00
141.	–	9 pi. brown and violet	4·00	3·50
142.	–	18 pi. black and green	38·00	27·00
143.	–	45 pi. green and black	55·00	45·00

The ¼ pi. to 2½ pi. values have a medallion portrait of King George V.

DESIGNS—HORIZ. ½ pi. Small Marble Forum, Salamis. ¾ pi. Church of St. Barnabas and St. Hilarion, Peristerona. 1 pi. Roman theatre, Soli; 1½ pi. Kyrenia Harbour. 2½ pi. Kolossi Castle. 45 pi. Forest scene, Troodos. VERT. 6 pi. Bayraktar Mosque, Nicosia. 9 pi. Queen's Window. St. Hilarion Castle. 18 pi. Buyuk Kahn, Nicosia.

1935. Silver Jubilee. As T 13 of Antigua.

144.	¾ pi. blue and grey	65	15
145.	1½ pi. blue and red	2·75	2·50
146.	2½ pi. brown and blue	3·75	1·50
147.	9 pi. grey and purple	13·00	9·00

1937. Coronation. As T 2 of Aden.

148.	¾ pi. grey	75	20
149.	1½ pi. red	1·25	80
150.	2½ pi. blue	3·50	1·75

36. Map of Cyprus.

37. Othello's Tower, Famagusta. 38. King George VI.

1938.

151.	–	¼ pi. blue and brown	20	20
152.	–	½ pi. green	30	10
152a.	–	½ pi. violet	1·75	20
153.	–	¾ pi. black and violet	8·00	40
154.	–	1 pi. orange	40	10
155.	–	1½ pi. red	5·00	1·50
155a.	–	1½ pi. violet	30	30
155ab.	–	1½ pi. green	2·00	35
155b.	–	2 pi. black and red	30	10
156.	–	2½ pi. blue	12·00	4·00
156a.	–	3 pi. blue	55	15
156b.	–	4 pi. blue	3·00	30
157.	36.	4½ pi. grey	40	10
158.	–	6 pi. black and blue	55	80
159.	37.	9 pi. black and purple	1·75	20
160.	–	18 pi. black and olive	5·00	85
161.	–	45 pi. green and black	13·00	2·50
162.	38.	90 pi. mauve and black	24·00	4·50
163.	–	£1 red and blue	45·00	20·00

DESIGNS: 2 pi. Peristerona Church. 3 pi., 4 pi. Kolossi Castle. All other values except 4½ pi., 9 pi., 90 pi. and £1 have designs as 1934 issue but portrait of King George VI.

1946. Victory. As T 9 of Aden.

164.	1½ pi. violet	15	10
165.	3 pi. blue	15	15

1948. Silver Wedding. As T 10/11 of Aden.

166.	1½ pi. violet	30	20
167.	£1 blue	42·00	40·00

1949. U.P.U. As T 20/23 of Antigua.

168.	1½ pi. violet	90	70
169.	2 pi. red	1·25	90
170.	3 pi. blue	1·25	1·00
171.	9 pi. purple	1·75	1·10

1953. Coronation. As Type 13 of Aden.

172.	1½ pi. black and green	55	10

39. Carobs. 42. Copper Pyrites Mine.

49. St. Hilarion Castle.

53. Arms of Byzantium, Lusignan, Ottoman Empire and Venice.

1955.

173.	39.	2 m. brown	10	40
174.	–	3 m. violet	10	15
175.	–	5 m. orange	10	10
176.	42.	10 m. brown and green	40	10
177.	–	15 m. olive and blue	2·00	45
178.	–	20 m. brown and blue	30	15
179.	–	25 m. turquoise	50	50
180.	–	30 m. black and lake	45	10
181.	–	35 m. brown & turquoise	30	40
182.	–	40 m. green and brown	50	60
183.	49.	50 m. blue and brown	30	30
184.	–	100 m. mauve and green	8·00	60
185.	–	250 m. blue and brown	8·00	4·25
186.	–	500 m. slate and purple	26·00	11·00
187.	53.	£1 lake and slate	26·00	24·00

DESIGNS—As Type 39: 3 m. Grapes. 5 m. Oranges. As Type 42: 15 m. Troodos Forest. 20 m. Beach of Aphrodite. 25 m. Ancient coin of Paphos. 30 m. Kyrenia. 35 m. Harvest in Messaoria. 40 m. Famagusta harbour. As Type 49: 100 m. Hala Sultan Tekke. 250 m. Kanakaria Church. As Type 53: 500 m. Coins of Salamis Paphos, Citium and Idalium.

ΚΥΠΡΙΑΚΗ ΔΗΜΟΚΡΑΤΙΑ KIBRIS CUMHURIYETI (54.)

55. Map of Cyprus.

1960. Nos 173/87 optd. as T 54 ("CYPRUS REPUBLIC" in Greek and Turkish).

188.	39.	2 m. brown	20	20
189.	–	3 m. violet	20	15
190.	–	5 m. orange	70	10
191.	42.	10 m. brown and green	45	10
192.	–	15 m. olive and blue	75	10
193.	–	20 m. brown and blue	40	40
194.	–	25 m. turquoise	1·00	45
195.	–	30 m. black and lake	1·25	10
196.	–	35 m. brown & turquoise	1·50	20
197.	–	40 m. green and brown	2·00	65
198.	49.	50 m. blue and brown	2·00	40
199.	–	100 m. mauve & green	9·00	40
200.	–	250 m. blue and brown	25·00	2·00
201.	–	500 m. slate and purple	40·00	15·00
202.	53.	£1 lake and slate	60·00	48·00

1960. Constitution of Republic.

203.	55.	10 m. sepia and green	30	10
204.		30 m. blue and brown	65	10
205.		100 m. purple and slate	2·00	1·25

56. Doves.

1962. Europa.

206.	56.	10 m. purple and mauve	10	10
207.		40 m. blue and cobalt	20	15
208.		100 m. emerald & green	20	20

57. Campaign Emblem.

1962. Malaria Eradication.

209.	57.	10 m. black and green	20	15
210.		30 m. black and brown	40	15

63. St Barnabas' Church.

1962.

211.	–	3 m. brown and orange	10	30
212.	–	5 m. purple and green	10	10
213.	–	10 m. black and green	15	10
214.	–	15 m. black and purple	20	15
215.	63.	25 m. brown & chestnut	30	20
216.	–	30 m. dp. blue & lt. blue	20	10
217.	–	35 m. green and blue	35	10
218.	–	40 m. black and blue	1·25	1·50
219.	–	50 m. bronze and bistre	50	10
220.	–	100 m. brown and bistre	3·50	30
221.	–	250 m. black and brown	8·00	2·00
222.	–	500 m. brown and green	17·00	10·00
223.	–	£1 bronze and grey	22·00	24·00

DESIGNS—VERT. 3 m. Iron Age jug. 5 m. Grapes. 10 m. Bronze head of Apollo. 15 m. Selimiye Mosque, Nicosia. 35 m. Head of Aphrodite. 100 m. Hala Sultan Tekke. 500 m. Mouflon. HORIZ. 30 m. Temple of Apollo Hylates. 40 m. Skiing, Troodos. 50 m. Salamis Gymnasium. 250 m. Bella Paise Abbey. £1, St. Hilarion Castle.

72. Europa "Tree".

1963. Europa.

224.	72.	10 m. blue and black	75	20
225.		40 m. red and black	3·75	2·25
226.		150 m. green and black	16·00	8·00

73. Harvester. 75. Wolf Cub in Camp.

1963. Freedom from Hunger.

227.	73.	25 c. ochre, sepia & blue	50	25
228.	–	75 m. grey, black & lake	2·75	1·00

DESIGN: 75 m. Demeter, Goddess of Corn.

1963. 50th Anniv. of Cyprus Scout Movement and 3rd Commonwealth Scout Conference, Platres. Multicoloured.

229.	3 m. Type 75	10	15
230.	20 m. Sea Scout	35	10
231.	150 m. Scout with Mouflon	1·25	2·00

The 10 m. is vert.

79. Children's Centre, Kyrenia.

1963. Centenary of Red Cross. Multicoloured.

232.	10 m. Nurse tending child	50	15
233.	100 m. Type 79	3·75	3·50

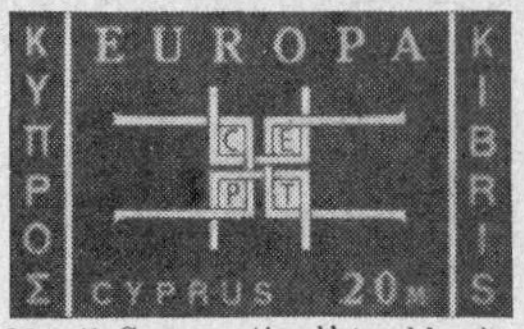

80. "Co-operation" (emblem).

1963. Europa.

234.	80.	20 m. buff, blue & violet	2·00	40
235.		30 m. grey, yell. & blue	3·50	40
236.		150 m. buff, blue & brown	12·00	10·00

1964. U.N. Security Council's Cyprus Resolutions, March, 1964. Nos. 213, etc., optd. with U.N. emblem and **1964.**

237.	10 m. black and green	20	10
238.	30 m. deep blue & light blue	20	10
239.	40 m. black and blue	20	20
240.	50 m. bronze and bistre	20	10
241.	100 m. brown and bistre	25	50

82. Soli Theatre.

1964. 400th Birth Anniv. of Shakespeare. Multicoloured.

242.	15 m. Type 82	45	15
243.	35 m. Curium Theatre	45	15
244.	50 m. Salamis Theatre	45	15
245.	100 m. Othello Tower, and scene from "Othello"	1·50	2·00

86. Running. 89. Europa "Flower".

1964. Olympic Games, Tokyo.

246.	86.	10 m. brown, blk. & yell.	15	10
247.	–	25 m. brown, bl. & slate	35	10
248.	–	75 m. brn., blk. & chest.	50	65

DESIGNS—HORIZ. 25 m. Boxing. 75 m. Charioteers.

1964. Europa.
249. **89.** 20 m. brown and ochre 75 10
250. 30 m. ultramarine & bue 1·50 10
251. 150 m. olive and green .. 7·00 6·50

90. Dionysus and Acme.

1964. Cyprus Wines. Multicoloured.
252. 10 m. Type **90** 25 10
253. 40 m. Silenus (satyr) .. 75 50
254. 50 m. Commandaria Wine 1·00 10
255. 100 m. Wine factory .. 3·00 1·60
Nos. 253/4 are vert.

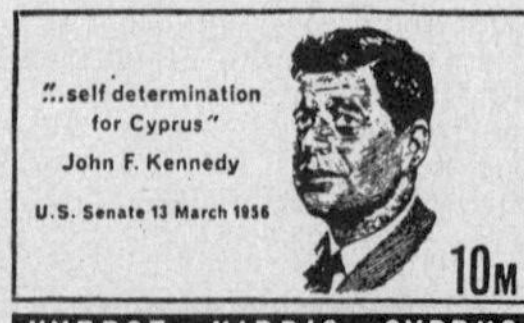

94. Pres. Kennedy.

1965. Pres. Kennedy Commem.
256. **94.** 10 m. blue 10 10
257. 40 m. green 25 20
258. 100 m. red 30 20

95. "Old Age".

DESIGNS—As Type **95**: 45 m. "Accident". LARGER (23×48 mm.): 75 m. "Maternity".

1965. Introduction of Social Insurance Law.
259 **95** 30 m. drab and green .. 20 10
260 – 45 m. green, bl & ultram 30 10
261 – 75 m. brown and flesh 1·00 1·75

98. I.T.U. Emblem and Symbols.

1965. Centenary of I.T.U.
262. **98.** 15 m. black, brn. & yell. 60 20
263. 60 m. blk., grn. & lt.-grn. 3·25 1·75
264. 75 m. blk., indigo & blue 3·75 3·00

99. I.C.Y. Emblem.

1965. Int. Co-operation Year.
265. **99.** 50 m. brown and green 1·00 10
266. 100 m. purple and green 1·50 70

100. Europa "Sprig".

1965. Europa.
267. **100.** 5 m. black, brn. & orge. 20 10
268. 45 m. black, brown & grn. 1·75 1·50
269. 150 m. black, brn. & grey 4·00 3·75

1966. U.N. General Assembly's Cyprus Resolution, Nos. 211, 213, 216 and 221 optd. **U.N. Resolution on Cyprus 18 Dec. 1965.**
270. 3 m. brown and orange .. 10 25
271. 10 m. black and green .. 15 10
272. 30 m. dp. blue and lt. blue 20 15
273. 250 m. black and brown .. 55 1·75

102. Discovery of St. Barnabas' Body.

1966. 1900th Death Anniv. of St Barnabas.
274. **102.** 15 m. multicoloured .. 15 10
275. – 25 m. drab, blk. & blue 20 10
276. – 100 m. multicoloured .. 45 1·25
DESIGNS—HORIZ. 25 m. St. Barnabas' Chapel. VERT. 100 m. St. Barnabas (icon).

1966. No. 211 surch.
278. – 5 m. on 3 m. brown and orange 10 10

107. General K. S. Thimayya and U.N. Emblem.

1966. Gen. Thimayya Commem.
279. **107.** 50 m. black and brown 30 10

108. Europa "Ship". **113.** Silver Coin of Evagoras I.

109. Stavrovouni Monastery.

1966. Europa.
280. **108.** 20 m. green and blue .. 40 10
281. 30 m. purple and blue 50 10
282. 150 m. bistre and blue 2·25 3·00

1966. Multicoloured.
283 3 m. Type **109** 40 40
284 5 m. Church of St. James, Trikomo 10 10
285 10 m. Zeno of Citium (marble bust) 15 30
286 15 m. Minoan wine ship of 700 B.C. (painting) .. 15 10
287 20 m. Type **113** .. .. 1·25 90
288 25 m. Sleeping Eros (marble statue) .. 30 10
289 30 m. St Nicholas's Cathedral, Famagusta 50 50
290 35 m. Gold sceptre from Curium .. 50 60
291 40 m. Silver dish from 7th century 70 50
292 50 m. Silver coin of Alexander the Great .. 90 10
293 100 m. Vase, 7th Century B.C. .. .. 3·25 15
294 250 m. Bronze ingot-stand 2·00 20
295 500 m. "The Rape of Ganymede" (mosaic) .. 3·00 70
296 £1 Aphrodite (marble statue) .. 6·50 6·00
DESIGNS—As Type **109**—VERT. 5 m. and 10 m. As Type **113**—HORIZ. 15 m., 25 m. and 50 m. VERT. 30 m., 35 m., 40 m. and 100 m. Nos. 294/6 are as Type **113** but larger, 28×40 mm.

123. Power Station, Limassol. **124.** Cogwheels.

1967. 1st Development Programme. Mult.
297. 10 m. Type **123** 10 10
298. 15 m. Arghaka-Maghounda Dam 20 10
299. 35 m. Troodos Highway .. 25 10
300. 50 m. Hilton Hotel, Nicosia 25 10
301. 100 m. Famagusta Harbour 30 70
Nos. 298/301 are vert.

1967. Europa.
302. **124.** 20 m. olive, green and light green 40 10
303. 30 m. violet, lilac & mve. 40 10
304. 150 m. sepia, brn. & chest. 1·40 2·00

125. Throwing the Javelin.

1967. Athletic Games, Nicosia. Multicoloured.
305. 15 m. Type **125** 25 10
306. 35 m. Running 25 30
307. 100 m. High-jumping .. 40 65

127. Ancient Monuments.

1967. Int. Tourist Year. Multicoloured.
309. 10 m. Type **127** 10 10
310. 40 m. Famagusta Beach 15 60
311. 50 m. "Comet" at Nicosia Airport 15 10
312. 100 m. Skier and Youth Hostel 20 65

128. St. Andrew Mosaic.

1967. Cent. of St. Andrew's Monastery.
313. **128.** 25 m. multicoloured .. 10 10

129. "The Crucifixion" (icon).

1967. Cyprus Art Exn., Paris.
314. **129.** 50 m. multicoloured .. 10 10

130. The Three Magi.

1967. 20th Anniv. of U.N.E.S.C.O.
315. **130.** 75 m. multicoloured .. 20 20

131. Human Rights Emblem over Stars.

1968. Human Rights Year. Multicoloured.
316. 50 m. Type **131** 10 10
317. 90 m. Human Rights and U.N. Emblems .. 30 60

134. Europa "Key".

1968. Europa.
319. **134.** 20 m. multicoloured .. 20 10
320. 30 m. multicoloured .. 30 10
321. 150 m. multicoloured .. 85 1·75

135. U.N. Children's Fund. Symbol and Boy drinking Milk.

1968. 21st Anniv. of U.N.I.C.E.F.
322. **135.** 35 m. brn., red & blk. 10 10

136. Aesculapius. **137.** Throwing the Discus.

1968. 20th Anniv. of W.H.O.
323. **136.** 50 m. blk., grn. & olive 10 10

1968. Olympic Games, Mexico. Multicoloured.
324. 10 m. Type **137** 10 10
325. 25 m. Sprint finish .. 10 10
326. 100 m. Olympic Stadium (horiz.) 20 75

138. I.L.O. Emblem.

1969. 50th Anniv. of Int. Labour Organization.
327. **138.** 50 m. brown and blue 15 10
328. 90 m. brn., blk. & grey 15 25

139. Mercator's Map of Cyprus, 1554.

1969. 1st Int. Congress of Cypriot Studies.
329. **139.** 35 m. multicoloured .. 20 30
330. – 50 m. multicoloured .. 20 10
DESIGN: 50 m. Blaeu's map of Cyprus, 1635.

141. Europa Emblem.

1969. Europa.
331. **141.** 20 m. multicoloured .. 25 10
332. 30 m. multicoloured .. 30 10
333. 150 m. multicoloured .. 1·10 2·00

142. Common Roller.

1969. Birds of Cyprus. Multicoloured.
334. 5 m. Type **142** 50 15
335. 15 m. Audouin's gull .. 70 15
336. 20 m. Cyprus warbler .. 75 15
337. 30 m. Jay 80 15
338. 40 m. Hoopoe .. .. 1·00 30
339. 90 m. Eleonora's falcon .. 2·75 5·00
Nos. 337/339 are vert.

143. "The Nativity", (12th-century wall painting).

1969. Christmas. Multicoloured.
340. 20 m. Type **143** 15 10
341. 45 m. "The Nativity" (14th cent. wall paintings) .. 15 20

146. Mahatma Gandhi.

1970. Birth Cent. of Mahatma Gandhi.
343. **146.** 25 m. bl., drab & blk. 15 10
344. 75 m. brown, drab and black 20 55

147. " Flaming Sun ".

1970. Europa.
345. **147.** 20 m. brown, yell. & orge. 20 10
346. 30 m. blue, yell. & orge. 30 10
347. 150 m. pur., yell. & orge. 1·00 2·25

148. Gladioli.

1970. Nature Conservation Year. Mult.
348. 10 m. Type **148** 10 10
349. 50 m. Poppies 20 10
350. 90 m. Giant Fennel .. 65 1·75

149. I.E.Y. Emblem. **152.** Virgin and Child.

1970. Anniversaries and Events.
351. **149.** 5 m. black and brown .. 10 10
352. – 15 m. multicoloured .. 10 10
353. – 75 m. multicoloured .. 15 35
DESIGNS AND EVENTS: 5 m. Int. Education Year. HORIZ. 15 m. Mosaic (50th General Assembly of Int. Vine and Wine Office). 75 m. Globe, Dove and U.N. Emblem (United Nations 25th Anniv.).

1970. Christmas. Wall-painting from Church of Panayia Podhythou, Galaba. Mult.
354. 25 m. Archangel (facing right) 20 20
355. 25 m. Type **152** 20 20
356. 25 m. Archangel (facing left) 20 20
357. 75 m. Virgin and Child between Archangels (42 × 30 mm.) 25 45

153. Cotton Napkin.

1971. Multicoloured.
358 3 m. Type **153** 30 55
359 5 m. St. George and Dragon (19th-cent bas-relief) 10 10
360 10 m. Woman in festival costume 15 30
361 15 m. Archaic Bichrome Kylix (cup) (horiz) .. 20 10
362 20 m. A pair of donors (St. Mamas Church) .. 35 40
363 25 m. "The Creation" (6th-cent mosaic) 30 10
364 30 m. Athena and horse-drawn chariot (4th-cent B.C. terracotta) (horiz) 30 10
365 40 m. Shepherd playing pipe (14th-cent fresco) .. 1·00 90
366 50 m. Hellenistic head (3rd-cent B.C.) 80 10
367 75 m. "Angel" (mosaic detail), Kanakaria Church .. .. .. 1·75 1·00
368 90 m. Mycenaean silver bowl (horiz) .. .. 2·50 1·25
369 250 m. Moufflon (detail of 3rd-cent mosaic) (horiz) 2·75 55
370 500 m. Ladies and sacred tree (detail 6th-cent amphora) (horiz) .. 1·25 70
371 $1 Horned god from Emkomi (12th-cent bronze statue) .. .. 3·00 1·60
SIZES: 24 × 37 or 37 × 24 10 m. to 90 m., 41 × 28 or 28 × 41 250 m. to £1.

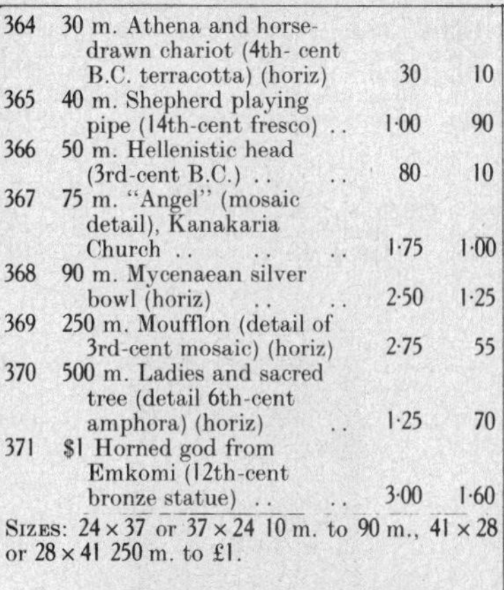

154. Europa Chain.

1971. Europa.
372. **154.** 20 m. blue, ultram. & blk. 20 10
373. 30 m. grn., myrtle & blk. 25 10
374. 150 m. yell., grn. & blk. 1·25 2·00

155. Archbishop Kyprianos.

1971. 150th Anniv. of Greek War of Independence. Multicoloured.
375. 15 m. Type **155** 10 10
376. 30 m. "Taking the Oath" (horiz.) 10 10
377. 100 m. Bishop Germanos, flag and freedom-fighters 20 50

156. Kyrenia Castle.

1971. Tourism. Multicoloured.
378. 15 m. Type **156** 10 10
379. 25 m. Gourd on sunny beach (vert.) 10 10
380. 60 m. Mountain scenery (vert.) 20 60
381. 100 m. Church of St. Evalios, Lambousa .. 20 65

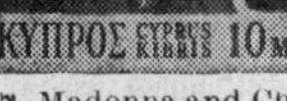

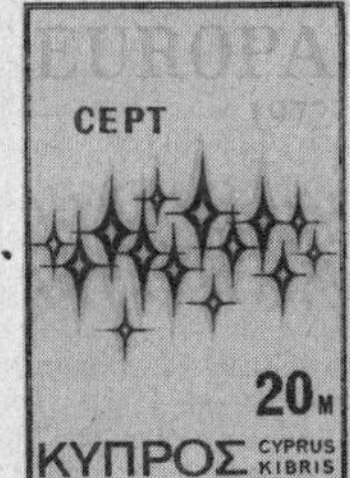

157. Madonna and Child in Stable. **159.** "Communications".

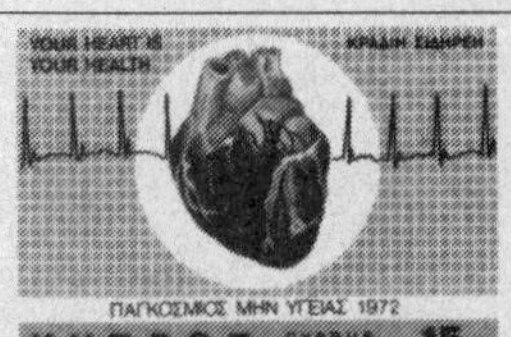

158. Heart.

1971. Christmas. Multicoloured.
382. 10 m. Type **157** 10 10
383. 50 m. The Three Wise Men 15 35
384. 100 m. The Shepherds .. 20 35

1972. World Heart Month.
385. **158.** 15 m. multicoloured .. 10 10
386. 50 m. multicoloured .. 20 45

1972. Europa.
387. **159.** 20 m. orge., brn. & brn. 30 15
388. 30 m. orge., ultram. & bl. 35 15
389. 150 m. orange, myrtle and green .. .. 2·50 3·25

160. Archery.

1972. Olympic Games, Munich. Mult.
390. 10 m. Type **160** 10 10
391. 40 m. Wrestling 15 10
392. 100m. Football 35 70

161. Stater of Marion.

1972. Ancient Coins of Cyprus (1st series).
393. **161.** 20 m. blue, blk. & silver 20 10
394. – 30 m. blue, blk. & silver 25 10
395. – 40 m. brn., blk. & silver 30 20
396. – 100 m. pink, blk. & silver 90 1·00
COINS: 30 m. Stater of Paphos. 40 m. Stater of Lapithos. 100 m. Stater of Idalion.
See also Nos. 486/9.

162. Bathing the Child Jesus.

1972. Christmas. Detail of mural in Holy Cross Church, Agiasmati. Multicoloured.
397. 10 m. Type **162** 10 10
398. 20 m. The Magi 10 10
399. 100 m. The Nativity .. 15 30

163. Mount Olympus, Troodos.

1973. 29th Int. Ski Federation Congress. Multicoloured.
401. 20 m. Type **163** 10 10
402. 100 m. Congress emblem .. 25 35

INDEX

Countries can be quickly located by referring to the index at the end of this volume.

164. Europa "Posthorn".

1973. Europa.
403. **164.** 20 m. multicoloured .. 35 10
404. 30 m. multicoloured .. 35 10
405. 150 m. multicoloured .. 2·00 3·00

165. Archbishop's Palace, Nicosia.

1973. Traditional Architecture. Mult.
406. 20 m. Type **165** 10 10
407. 30 m. House of Hajigeorgajis Cornessios, Nicosia (vert.) 10 10
408. 50 m. House at Gourri, 1850 (vert.) 15 10
409. 100 m. House at Rizokarpaso, 1772 .. .. .. 40 75

1973. No. 361 surch.
410. 20 m. on 15 m. multicoloured 15 15

167. Scout Emblem.

1973. Anniversaries and Events.
411. **167.** 10 m. green and brown 20 10
412. – 25 m. blue and lilac .. 20 10
413. – 35 m. grn., cream & grn. 25 25
414. – 50 m. blue and indigo .. 30 10
415. – 100 m. brown & sepia .. 70 80

DESIGNS AND EVENTS—VERT. 10 m. (Cyprus Boy Scouts. 60th anniv.). 50 m. Airline emblem (Cyprus Airways. 25th anniv.). 100 m. Interpol emblem (Interpol. 50th anniv.). HORIZ. 25 m. Outlines of Cyprus and the E.E.C. (Association of Cyprus with "Common Market"). 35 m. F.A.O. emblem (F.A.O. 10th anniv.).

168. Archangel Gabriel.

1973. Christmas. Murals from Araka Church. Multicoloured.
416. 10 m. Type **168** 10 10
417. 20 m. Madonna and Child 10 10
418. 100 m. Araka Church (horiz.) 45 65

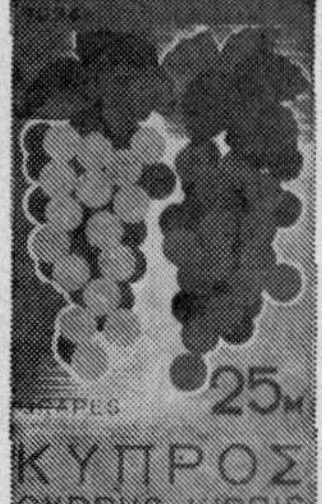

169. Grapes.

170. "The Rape of Europa" (Silver Stater of Marion).

1974. Products of Cyprus. Multicoloured
419. 25 m. Type **169** 10 15
420. 50 m. Grapefruit 20 50
421. 50 m. Oranges 20 50
422. 50 m. Lemons 20 50

1974. Europa.
423. **170.** 10 m. multicoloured .. 15 10
424. 40 m. multicoloured .. 65 30
425. 150 m. multicoloured .. 2·00 3·00

171. Title Page of A. Kyprianos' "History of Cyprus" (1788).

1974. 2nd Int. Congress of Cypriot Studies. Multicoloured.
426. 10 m. Type **171** 10 10
427. 25 m. Solon (philosopher) in mosaic (horiz.) .. 15 10
428. 100 m. "St. Neophytos" (wall painting) 60 75

1974. Obligatory Tax. Refugee Fund. No. 359 surch. **REFUGEE FUND** in English, Greek and Turkish.
430. 10 m. on 5 m. multicoloured 10 10

1974. U.N. Security Council Resolution 353. Nos. 360, 365, 366 and 369 optd. with **SECURITY COUNCIL RESOLUTION 353 20 JULY 1974.**
431. 10 m. multicoloured .. 20 10
432. 40 m. multicoloured .. 40 50
433. 50 m. multicoloured .. 40 10
434. 250 m. multicoloured .. 70 2·50

174. "Refugees".

1974. Obligatory Tax. Refugee Fund.
435. **174.** 10 m. black and grey 10 10

175. "Virgin and Child between Two Angels" Stavios Church.

1974. Christmas. Church Wall-paintings. Multicoloured.
436. 10 m. Type **175** 10 10
437. 50 m. "Adoration of the Magi", Ayios Neophytos Monastery (vert.) .. 20 10
438. 100 m. "Flight into Egypt", Ayios Neophytos Monastery .. 25 45

176. Larnau–Nicosia Mail-coach, 1878.

1975. Anniversaries and Events.
439. **176.** 20 m. multicoloured .. 40 10
440. – 30 m. blue and orange .. 45 75
441. **176.** 50 m. multicoloured .. 45 15
442. – 100 m. multicoloured .. 75 1·60

DESIGNS AND EVENTS—HORIZ. 20 m., 50 m. Universal Postal Union. Cent. VERT. 30 m. "Disabled Persons" (8th European Meeting of International Society for the Rehabilitation of Disabled Persons). 100 m. Council flag (25th Anniv. of Council of Europe).

177. "The Distaff" (M. Kashalos).

1975. Europa. Multicoloured.
443. 20 m. Type **177** 35 50
444. 30 m. "Nature Morte" (C. Savva) 35 60
445. 150 m. "Virgin and Child of Liopetri" (G. P. Georghiou) .. .. 50 1·00

178. Red Cross Flag over Map.

1975. Anniversaries and Events. Mult.
446. 25 m. Type **178** 25 10
447. 30 m. Nurse and Lamp (horiz.) 25 10
448. 75 m. Woman's Steatite idol (horiz.) 35 90

EVENTS: 25 m. 25th anniv. of Red Cross. 30 m. International Nurses' Day. 75 m. International Women's Year.

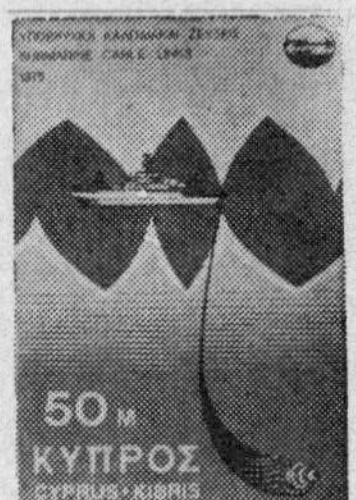

179. Submarine Cable Links.

1976. Telecommunications Achievements.
449. **179.** 50 m. multicoloured .. 40 10
450. – 100 m. yell., vio. & lilac 50 90

DESIGN—HORIZ. 100 m. International subscriber dialling.

1976. Surch.
451. **153.** 10 m. on 3 m. mult. .. 15 10

181. Human-figured Vessel, 19th-Century.

1976. Europa. Ceramics. Multicoloured.
452. 20 m. Type **181** 25 10
453. 60 m. Composite vessel, 2100–2000 B.C. .. 70 80
454. 100 m. Byzantine goblet .. 1·25 1·75

182. Self-help housing.

1976. Economic Reactivation. Mult.
455. 10 m. Type **182** 10 10
456. 25 m. Handicrafts .. 20 20
457. 30 m. Reafforestation .. 20 20
458. 60 m. Air Communications 35 55

183. Terracotta Statue of Youth.

184. Olympic Symbol.

1976. Cypriot Treasures.
459. **183.** 5 m. multicoloured .. 10 40
460. – 10 m. multicoloured .. 15 40
461. – 20 m. red, yell. & blk. 30 40
462. – 25 m. multicoloured .. 30 10
463. – 30 m. multicoloured .. 30 10
464. – 40 m. grn., brn. & blk. 45 45
465. – 50 m. light brown, brown and black 45 10
466. – 60 m. multicoloured .. 45 20
467. – 100 m. multicoloured 50 30
468. – 250 m. blue, grey & blk. 80 1·25
469. – 500 m blk., brn. & grn. 80 1·75
470. – £1 multicoloured .. 1·25 2·25

DESIGNS—VERT. 10 m. Limestone head (23 × 34 mm.). 20 m. Gold necklace from Lambousa (24 × 37 mm.). 25 m. Terracotta warrior (24 × 37 mm.). 30 m. Statue of a priest of Aphrodite (24 × 37 mm.). 250 m. Silver dish from Lambousa (28 × 41 mm.). 500 m. Bronze stand (28 × 41 mm.). £1, Statue of Artemis (28 × 41 mm.). HORIZ. 40 m. Bronze tablet (37 × 24 mm.). 50 m. Mycenaean crater (37 × 24 mm.). 60 m. Limestone sarcophagus (37 × 24 mm.). 100 m. Gold bracelet from Lambousa. (As Type **183**).

1976. Olympic Games, Montreal.
471. **184.** 20 m. red, blk. & yell. 10 10
472. – 60 m. multicoloured (horiz.) 20 30
473. – 100 m. multicoloured (horiz.) 30 35

DESIGNS: 60 m. and 100 m. Olympic Symbols (different).

185. "George Washington" (G. Stuart).

1976. Bicent. of American Revolution.
474. **185.** 100 m. multicoloured 40 30

186. Children in Library.

1976. Anniversaries and Events.
475. **186.** 40 m. multicoloured .. 20 15
476. – 50 m. brown and black 20 10
477. – 80 m. multicoloured .. 45 60

DESIGNS AND EVENTS: 40 m. Type **186.** (Promotion of Children's Books). 50 m. Low-cost housing (HABITAT Conference, Vancouver). 80 m. Eye protected by hands (World Health Day).

187. Archangel Michael.

188. "Cyprus 74", (wood engraving by A. Tassos).

1976. Christmas. Multicoloured.
478. 10 m. Type **187** 15 10
479. 15 m. Archangel Gabriel.. 15 10
480. 150 m. The Nativity .. 60 80
Designs show icons from Ayios Neophytis Monastry.

1977. Refugee Fund.
481. **188.** 10 m. black 20 10
See also Nos. 634 and 807 (see after No. 728).

189. "View of Prodhrornos" (A. Diamantis).

1977. Europa. Paintings. Multicoloured.
482. 20 m. Type **189** 20 10
483. 60 m. "Springtime at Monagroulli" (T. Kanthos) 40 55
484. 120 m. "Old Port, Limassol" (V. Ioannides) 70 1·25

190. Overprinted 500 m. Stamp of 1960.

1977. Silver Jubilee.
485. **190.** 120 m. multicoloured 30 30

191. Bronze Coin of Emperor Trajan.

1977. Ancient Coins of Cyprus (2nd series).
486. **191.** 10 m. blk., gold & blue 15 10
487. – 40 m. blk., silver & blue 30 30
488. – 60 m. blk., silver & orge. 35 35
489. – 100 m. blk., gold & grn. 50 95
Designs: 40 m. Silver tetradrachm of Demetrios Poliorcetes. 60 m. Silver tetradrachm of Ptolemy VIII. 100 m. Gold Octadrachm of Arsinoe II.

192. Archbishop Makarios in Ceremonial Robes.

1977. Death of Archbishop Makarios. Mult.
490. 20 m. Type **192** 15 10
491. 60 m. Archbishop in doorway 20 10
492. 250 m. Head and shoulders portrait .. .. .. 50 1·10

193. Embroidery, Pottery and Weaving.

1977. Anniversaries and Events. Mult.
493. 20 m. Type **193** 10 10
494. 40 m. Map of Mediterranean 15 20
495. 60 m. Gold medals .. 20 20
496. 80 m. Sputnik 20 85
Designs commemorate: 20 m. Revitalisation of handicrafts. 40 m. "Man and the Biosphere" Programme in the Mediterranean region. 60 m. Gold medals won by Cypriot students in the Orleans Gymnasiade. 80 m. 60th Anniv. of Russian Revolution.

194. "Nativity".

1977. Christmas. Children's Paintings. Mult.
497. 10 m. Type **194** 10 10
498. 40 m. "The Three Kings" 10 10
499. 150 m. "Flight into Egypt" 25 80

195. Demetrios Libertis.

1978. Cypriot Poets.
500. **195.** 40 m. brown & bistre 10 10
501. – 150 m. grey, blk. & red 30 80
Design: 150 m. Vasilis Michaelides.

196. Chrysorrhogiatissa Monastery Courtyard.

1978. Europa. Architecture. Multicoloured.
502. 25 m. Type **196** 20 10
503. 75 m. Kolossi Castle .. 40 35
504. 125 m. Municipal Library, Paphos .. .. .. 60 1·25

197. Archbishop of Cyprus, 1950–1977.

1978. Archbishop Makarios Commem. Mult.
505. 15 m. Type **197** 15 20
506. 25 m. Exiled in Seychelles, 9 March 1956—28 March 1957 .. .. .. 15 20
507. 50 m. President of the Republic 1960–1977 .. 20 25
508. 75 m. "Soldier of Christ" 20 30
509. 100 m. "Fighter for Freedom" 25 35

198. Affected Blood Corpuscles (Prevention of Thalassaemia).

199. Icon Stand.

1978. Anniversaries and Events.
511. **198.** 15 m. multicoloured .. 10 10
512. – 35 m. multicoloured .. 15 10
513. – 75 m. black and grey .. 20 30
514. – 125 m. multicoloured 35 80
Designs—vert. 35 m. Aristotle (sculpture) (2300th Death Anniv.). horiz. 75 m. "Heads" (Human Rights). 125 m. Wright brothers and "Flyer" (75th Anniv. of Powered Flight).

1978. Christmas.
515. **199.** 15 m. multicoloured .. 10 10
516. – 35 m. multicoloured .. 15 10
517. – 150 m. multicoloured 40 60
Designs: 35 m., 150 m. Different icon stands.

200. Aphrodite (statue from Soli).

1979. Goddess Aphrodite (1st issue). Mult.
518. 75 m. Type **200** 25 10
519. 125 m. Aphrodite on shell (detail from Botticelli's "Birth of Venus") .. 35 25
See also Nos. 584/5.

201. Van, Larnaca–Nicosia Mail-coach and Envelope.

1979. Europa. Communications. Multicoloured.
520. 25 m. Type **201** 20 10
521. 75 m. Radar, satellite and early telephone .. 45 20
522. 125 m. Aircraft, ship and envelopes .. .. 1·00 80

202. Peacock wrasse.

1979. Flora and Fauna. Multicoloured.
523. 25 m. Type **202** 15 10
524. 50 m. Black partridge. (vert.) 45 20
525. 75 m. Cedar (vert.) .. 45 20
526. 125 m. Mule. 50 60

203. I.B.E. and U.N.E.S.C.O. Emblems.

1979. Anniversaries and Events.
527. **203.** 15 m. multicoloured .. 10 10
528. – 25 m. multicoloured .. 10 10
529. – 50 m. blk., brn. & ochre 20 15
530. – 75 m. multicoloured .. 25 10
531. – 100 m. multicoloured 30 20
532. – 125 m. multicoloured 30 60
Designs and commemorations—vert. 15 m. Type **203** (International Bureau of Education. 50th anniv.). 125 m. Rotary International emblem and "75" (75th anniv.). horiz. 25 m. Graphic design of dove and stamp album (Cyprus Philatelic Society. 20th anniv.). 50 m. Lord Kitchener and map of Cyprus (Cyprus Survey Cent.). 75 m. Child's face (International Year of the Child). 100 m. Graphic design of footballers (U.E.F.A. European Football Association) (25th anniv.).

HAVE YOU READ THE NOTES AT THE BEGINNING OF THIS CATALOGUE?
These often provide answers to the enquiries we receive.

204. "Jesus" (from Church of the Virgin Mary, Arakas, Lagoudhera).

1979. Christmas. Icons. Multicoloured.
533. 15 m. Type **204** 10 10
534. 35 m. "Nativity" (Church of St. Nicholas, Famagusta District) (29×41 mm.) 10 10
535. 150 m. "Holy Mary" (Church of the Virgin Mary, Arakas) 25 30

205. 1880 ½d. Stamp with "969" (Nicosia) Postmark.

1980. Centenary of Cyprus Stamp. Multicoloured.
536. 40 m. Type **205** 10 10
537. 125 m. 1880 2½ d. stamp with "974" (Kyrenia) postmark 15 15
538. 175 m. 1880 1s. stamps with "942" (Larnaca) postmark 15 20

206. St. Barnabas (patron saint of Cyprus).

208. Gold Necklace, Arsos (7th cent. BC).

207. Sailing.

1980. Europa. Personalities. Multicoloured.
540. 40 m. Type **206** 10 10
541. 125 m. Zeno of Citium (founder of Stoic philosophy) 20 20

1980. Olympic Games, Moscow. Multicoloured.
542. 40 m. Type **207** 10 10
543. 125 m. Swimming .. 20 20
544. 200 m. Gymnastics .. 25 25

1980. Archaeological Treasures.
545. **208.** 10 m. multicoloured .. 30 35
546. – 15 m. multicoloured .. 30 35
547. – 25 m. multicoloured .. 30 10
548. – 40 m. multicoloured .. 40 30
549. – 50 m. multicoloured .. 40 10
550. – 75 m. multicoloured .. 50 40
551. – 100 m. multicoloured 75 15
552. – 125 m. multicoloured 75 15
553. – 150 m. multicoloured 90 15
554. – 175 m. multicoloured 90 40
555. – 200 m. multicoloured 90 30
556. – 500 m. multicoloured 1·50 1·00
557. – £1 multicoloured .. 2·00 1·25
558. – £2 multicoloured .. 3·75 2·00
Designs—horiz. 15 m. Bronze Cow, Vouni Palace (5th cent. BC). 40 m. Gold finger-ring, Enkomi (13th cent. BC). 500 m. Stone Bowl, Khirokitia (6th millennium BC). vert. 25 m. Amphora, Salamis (6th cent. BC). 50 m. Bronze Cauldron, Salamis (8th cent. BC), 75 m. Funerary Stele, Marion (5th cent. BC).

100 m. Jug (15–14th cent. BC). 125 m. Warrior (Terracotta) (6–5th cent. BC). 150 m. Lions attacking Bull (bronze relief), Vouni Palace (5th cent. BC). 175 m. Faience Rhyton, Kition (13th cent. BC). 200 m. Bronze statue of Ingot God, Enkomi (12th cent. BC). £1, Ivory Plaque, Salamis (7th cent. BC). £2, "Leda and the Swan" (mosaic), Kouklia (3rd cent. AD).

209. Cyprus Flag.

1980. 20th Anniv. of Republic of Cyprus. Multicoloured.

559. 40 m. Type **209** 10 10
560. 125 m. Signing Treaty of Establishment (41 × 29 mm.) 20 15
561. 175 m. Archbishop Makarios 35 25

210. Head and Peace Dove.

1980. International Day of Solidarity with Palestinian People.

562. **210.** 40 m. black and grey . . 20 20
563. – 125 m. black and grey 35 35

DESIGN: 125 m. Head and dove with olive branch.

211. Pulpit, Tripiotis Church, Nicosia. **212.** Folk Dancing.

1980. Christmas. Multicoloured.

564. 25 m. Type **211** 10 10
565. 100 m. Holy Doors, Panayia Church Paralimni 15 15
565. 125 m. Pulpit, Ayios Lazaros Church, Larnaca 15 15

1981. Europa. Folklore, showing folk-dancing from painting by T. Photiades.

567. **212.** 40 m. multicoloured . . 40 10
568. – 175 m. multicoloured 1·00 60

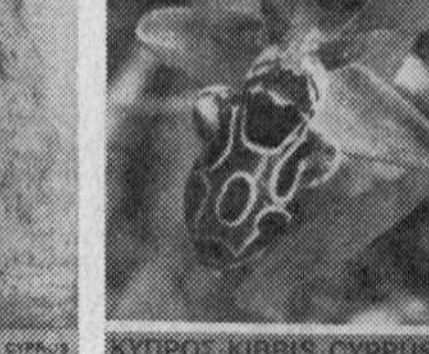

213. Self-portrait. **214.** "Ophrys kotschyi".

1981. 500th Anniv. of Leonardo da Vinci's Visit. Multicoloured.

569. 50 m. Type **213** 40 10
570. 125 m. "The Last Supper" (50 × 25 mm.) 70 40
571. 175 m Lace (Cyprus) and Milan Cathedral . . 95 60

1981. Cypriot Wild Orchids. Multicoloured.

572. 25 m. Type **214** 60 60
573. 50 m. "Orchis punctulata" 70 70
574. 75 m. "Ophrys argolica elegans" 80 80
575. 150 m. "Epipactis veratrifolia" . . . . 1·00 1·00

215. Heinrich von Stephan.

1981. Anniversaries and Events.

576. **215.** 25 m. dark green, green and blue 20 10
577. – 40 m. multicoloured . . 25 10
578. – 125 m. blk., red & grn. 50 25
579. – 150 m. multicoloured 60 30
580. – 200 m. multicoloured 60 35

DESIGNS AND COMMEMORATIONS: 25 m., Type **137** (150th birth anniv. of Heinrich von Stephan (founder of U.P.U.). 40 m. Stylised man holding dish of food (World Food Day). 125 m., Stylised hands (International Year for Disabled People). 150 m. Stylised building and flower (European Campaign for Urban Renaissance). 200 m. Prince Charles, Lady Diana Spencer and St. Paul's Cathedral (Royal Wedding).

216. "The Lady of the Angels" (from Church of the Transfiguration of Christ, Palekhori).

1981. Christmas. Murals from Nicosia District Churches. Multicoloured.

581. 25 m. Type **216** 20 10
582. 100 m. "Christ Pantokrator" (Church of Madonna of Arakas, Lagoudera) (vert.) . . 60 20
583. 125 m. "Baptism of Christ" (Church of Our Lady of Assinou, Nikitari) . . 70 30

217. "Louomene" (Aphrodite bathing) (statue, 250 B.C.).

1982. Aphrodite (Greek goddess of love and beauty) Commemoration. (2nd issue). Mult.

584. 125 m. Type **217** 80 45
585. 175 m. "Anadyomene" (Aphrodite emerging from the waters) (Titian) . . 95 65

218. Naval Battle with Greek Fire, 985 A.D.

1982. Europa. Historic Events. Multicoloured.

586. 40 m. Type **218** 60 10
587. 175 m. Conversion of Roman Proconsul Sergius Paulus to Christianity, Paphos, 45 A.D. . . . . 1·50 2·00

219. "XP" (monogram of Christ) (mosaic).

1982. World Cultural Heritage. Mult.

588. 50 m. Type **219** 30 10
589. 125 m. Head of priest-king of Paphos (sculpture) (24 × 37 mm.) 60 25
590. 225 m. Theseus (Greek god) (mosaic) . . . . 1·00 95

1982. No. 550 surch. **100.**

591. 100 m. on 75 m. Funerary stele, Marion (5th-century B.C.) 50 40

221. Cyprus and Stylised "75".

1982. 75th Anniv. of Boy Scout Movement. Multicoloured.

592. 100 m. Type **221** . . 40 20
593. 125 m. Lord Baden-Powell 45 30
594. 175 m. Camp-site 55 55

222. Holy Communion, The Bread.

1982. Christmas.

595. **222.** 25 m. multicoloured . . 10 10
596. – 100 m. gold and black 30 15
597. – 250 m. multicoloured 70 75

DESIGN—VERT. 100 m. Holy Chalice. HORIZ. 250 m. Holy Communion, The Wine.

223. Cyprus Forest Industries' Sawmill.

1983. Commonwealth Day. Multicoloured.

598. 50 m. Type **223** 10 10
599. 125 m. "Ikarios and the Discovery of Wine" (3rd-cent. mosaic) . . 25 25
600. 150 m. Folk-dancers, Commonwealth Film and Television Festival, 1980 30 35
601. 175 m. Royal Exhibition Building, Melbourne (Commonwealth Heads of Government Meeting, 1981) 35 40

224. Cyprosyllabic Inscription (6th cent. B.C.).

1983. Europa. Multicoloured.

602. 50 m. Type **224** 60 10
603. 200 m. Copper ore, ingot (Enkomi 1400–1250 B.C.) and bronze jug (2nd cent. A.D.) . . . . 1·75 2·00

225. "Pararge aegeria".

1983. Butterflies. Multicoloured.

604 60 m. Type **225** 25 20
605 130 m. "Aricia agestis" . . 45 25
606 250 m. "Glaucopsyche melanops" . . . . 85 1·25

1983. Nos. 545/56 surch.

607. 1 c. on 10 m. Type **208** . . 35 40
608. 2 c. on 15 m. Bronze cow, Vouni Palace (5th-cent. B.C.) (horiz.) 35 40
609. 3 c. on 25 m. Amphora, Salamis (16th-cent. B.C.) 35 20
610. 4 c. on 40 m. Gold finger-ring, Enkomi (13th-cent. B.C.) (horiz.) 40 20
611. 5 c. on 50 m. Bronze cauldron, Salamis (8th-cent. B.C.) 50 50
612. 6 c. on 75 m. Funerary stele, Marion (5th-cent. B.C.) . . 50 20
613. 10 c. on 100 m. Jug (15–14th-cent. B.C.) . . 60 40
614. 13 c. on 125 m. Warrior (Terracotta) (6–5th-cent. B.C.) 70 50
615. 15 c. on 150 m. Lions attacking bull (bronze relief), Vouni Palace 5th-cent. B.C.) (horiz.) . . 85 55
616. 20 c. on 200 m. Bronze statue of Ingot God, Enkomi (12th-cent. B.C.) . . 85 65
617. 25 c. on 175 m. Faience rhyton, Kition (13th-cent. B.C.) . . 95 1·10
618. 50 c. on 500 m. Stone bowl, Khirokitia (6th-millennium B.C.) (horiz.) . . 1·50 2·00

227. View of Power Station.

1983. Anniversaries and Events. Mult.

619. 3 c. Type **227** 10 20
620. 6 c. W.C.Y. logo 20 15
621. 13 c. "Sol Olympia" (liner) and "Polys" (tanker) . . 40 35
622. 15 c. Human Rights emblem and map of Europe 45 25
623. 20 c. Nicos Kazantzakis . . 55 65
624. 25 c. Makarios in church . . 65 65

COMMEMORATIONS: 3 c. 30th anniv. of Cyprus Electricity Authority. 6 c. World Communications Year. 13 c. 25th anniv. of International Maritime Organization. 15 c. 35th anniv. of Universal Declaration of Human Rights. 20 c. Birth centenary. 25 c. 70th birth anniv.

228. St. Lazaros Church, Larnaca.

1983. Christmas. Church Towers. Mult.

625. 4 c. Type **228** 20 10
626. 13 c. St. Varvara church, Kaimakli, Nicosia . . 55 35
627. 20 c. St. Ioannis church, Larnaca 90 90

229. Waterside Cafe, Larnaca.

1984. Old Engravings. Each brown and black.

628. 6 c. Type **229** 15 10
629. 20 c. Bazaar at Larnaca (39 × 25 mm.) 50 85
630. 30 c. Famagusta Gate, Nicosia (39 × 25 mm.) . . 80 1·25

230. C.E.P.T. 25th Anniversary Logo.

1984. Europa.

632. **230.** 6 c. light green, green and black 75 10
633. 15 c. light blue, blue and black .. .. 1·50 2·00

1984. Obligatory Tax. Refugee Fund. As T **188** but new value and dated "1984".

634. 1 c. black 10 10

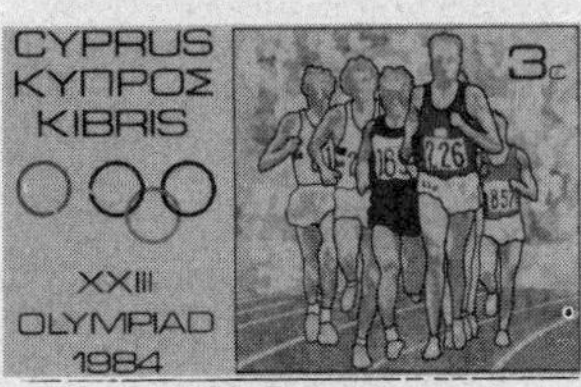
231. Running.

1984. Olympic Games, Los Angeles. Multicoloured.

635. 3 c. Type **231** 20 10
636. 4 c. Olympic column .. 20 20
637. 13 c. Swimming 55 75
638. 20 c. Gymnastics .. .. 80 1·00

232. Prisoners-of-War.

1984. 10th Anniv. of Turkish Landings in Cyprus. Multicoloured.

639. 15 c. Type **232** 40 45
640. 20 c. Map and burning buildings 50 55

233. Open Stamp Album (25th Anniv. of Cyprus Philatelic Society).

1984. Anniversaries and Events. Mult.

641. 6 c. Type **233** 40 20
642. 10 c. Football in motion (horiz.) (Cyprus Football Association—50th anniv.) 55 30
643. 15 c. "Dr. George Papanicolaou" (medical scientist—birth cent.) .. 75 50
644. 25 c. Antique map of Cyprus and ikon (horiz.) (International Symposia on Cartography and Medieval Paleography) 1·25 2·00

234. St. Mark (miniature from 11th-century Gospel).

1984. Christmas. Illuminated Gospels. Multicoloured.

645. 4 c. Type **234** 35 10
646. 13 c. Beginning of St. Mark's Gospel .. .. 1·00 50
647. 20 c. St. Luke (miniature from 11th-cent. Gospel) 1·50 2·00

235. Autumn at Platania, Troodos Mountains.

1985. Cyprus Scenes and Landscapes. Multicoloured.

648. 1 c. Type **235** 20 40
649. 2 c. Ayia Napa Monastery 20 40
650. 3 c. Phini Village—panoramic view .. 20 30
651. 4 c. Kykko Monastery .. 20 30
652. 5 c. Beach at Makronissos, Ayia Napa 20 20
653. 6 c. Village street, Omodhos (vert.) .. 30 20
654. 10 c. Panoramic sea view 45 30
655. 13 c. Windsurfing .. 55 25
656. 15 c. Beach at Protaras .. 65 25
657. 20 c. Forestry for development (vert.) 80 50
658. 25 c. Sunrise at Protaras (vert.) .. .. .. 1·00 1·00
659. 30 c. Village house, Pera .. 1·25 1·25
660. 50 c. Apollo Hylates Sanctuary, Curium .. 2·00 1·75
661. £1 Snow on Troodos Mountains (vert.) .. 3·50 3·00
662. £5 Personification of Autumn, House of Dionysos, Paphos (vert.) 13·00 15·00

236. Clay Idols of Musicians (7/6th Century B.C.)

1985. Europa. European Music Year. Mult.

663. 6 c. Type **236** .. .. 1·25 35
664. 15 c. Violin, lute, flute and score from the "Cyprus Suite" .. .. .. 2·00 2·00

237. Cyprus Coat of Arms (25th Anniv. of Republic).

238. "The Visit of the Madonna to Elizabeth" (Lambadistis Monastery, Kalopanayiotis).

1985. Anniversaries and Events.

665. **237.** 4 c. multicoloured .. 40 15
666. – 6 c. multicoloured .. 45 15
667. – 13 c. multicoloured .. 1·00 1·25
668. – 15 c. black olive-black and orange .. 1·50 1·25
669. – 20 c. multicoloured .. 1·50 2·00

DESIGNS—HORIZ. (43×30 mm) 6 c. "Barn of Liopetri" (detail) (Pol. Georghiou) (30th Anniv. of EOKA Campaign). 13 c. Three profiles (International Youth Year). 15 c. Solon Michaelides (composer and conductor) (European Music Year). VERT. (as T **237**)—20 c. U.N. Building, New York, and flags (40th Anniv. of United Nations Organisation).

1985. Christmas. Frescoes from Cypriot Churches. Multicoloured.

670. 4 c. Type **238** 35 10
671. 13 c. "The Nativity" (Lambadistis Monastery, Kalopanayiotis) .. 1·25 65
672. 20 c. "Candlemas-day" (Asinou Church) .. 1·75 2·00

239. Figure from Hellenistic Spoon Handle.

1986. New Archaeological Museum Fund. Multicoloured.

673. 15 c. Type **239** .. .. 1·00 45
674. 20 c. Pattern from early Ionian helmet and foot from statue .. .. 1·25 75
675. 25 c. Roman statue of Eros and Psyche .. .. 1·50 95
676. 30 c. Head of statue .. 1·75 1·10

No. 676 also commemorates the 50th anniversary of the Department of Antiquities.

240. Cyprus Mouflon and Cedars.

1986. Europa. Protection of Nature and the Environment. Multicoloured.

678. 7 c. Type **240** .. .. 1·00 30
679. 17 c. Greater flamingos at Larnaca Salt Lake .. 2·50 2·50

241. "Chlamys pesfelis".

1986. Sea Shells. Multicoloured.

680. 5 c. Type **241** 40 15
681. 7 c. "Charonia variegata" 45 15
682. 18 c. "Murex brandaris" .. 1·00 70
683. 25 c. "Cypraea spurca" .. 1·50 2·00

1986. Nos. 653 and 655 surch.

684. 7 c. on 6 c. Village street, Omodhos (vert.) .. 50 30
685. 18 c. on 13 c. Windsurfing 1·40 60

243. Globe, Outline Map of Cyprus and Swallows (Overseas Cypriots' Year).

1986. Anniversaries and Events. Mult.

686. 15 c. Type **243** .. .. 1·25 45
687. 18 c. Halley's Comet over Cyprus beach (40×23 mm.) .. .. 1·50 2·00
688. 18 c. Comet's tail over sea and Edmond Halley (40×23 mm.) .. .. 1·50 2·00

Nos. 687/8 were printed together, se-tenant, forming a composite design.

244. Pedestrian Crossing.

1986. Road Safety Campaign. Multicoloured.

689. 5 c. Type **244** .. .. 1·00 30
690. 7 c. Motor cycle crash helmet .. .. .. 1·10 30
691. 18 c. Hands fastening car seat belt .. .. .. 2·25 3·00

245. "The Nativity" (Church of Panayia tou Araka).

1986. Christmas. International Peace Year. Details of Nativity frescoes from Cypriot churches. Multicoloured.

692. 5 c. Type **245** 45 15
693. 15 c. Church of Panayia tou Moutoulla .. .. 1·50 30
694. 17 c. Church of St. Nicholas tis Steyis .. 1·75 2·00

246. Church of Virgin Mary, Asinou.

1987. Troodos Churches on the World Heritage List. Multicoloured.

695. 15 c. Type **246** .. .. 1·00 1·00
696. 15 c. Fresco of Virgin Mary, Moutoulla's Church .. .. .. 1·00 1·00
697. 15 c. Church of Virgin Mary, Podithou .. 1·00 1·00
698. 15 c. Fresco of Three Apostles, St. Ioannis Lampadistis Monastery 1·00 1·00
699. 15 c. Annunciation fresco, Church of the Holy Cross, Pelentriou .. 1·00 1·00
700. 15 c. Fresco of Saints, Church of the Cross, Ayiasmati .. .. 1·00 1·00
701. 15 c. Fresco of Archangel Michael and Donor, Pedoula's Church of St. Michael .. .. .. 1·00 1·00
702. 15 c. Church of St. Nicolaos, Steyis.. .. 1·00 1·00
703. 15 c. Fresco of Prophets, Church of Virgin Mary, Araka .. .. .. 1·00 1·00

247. Proposed Central Bank of Cyprus Building.

1987. Europa. Modern Architecture.

704. **247.** 7 c. multicoloured .. 1·00 30
705. – 18 c. blk., grey & grn. 2·00 1·75

DESIGN: 18 c. Headquarters complex, Cyprus Telecommunications Authority.

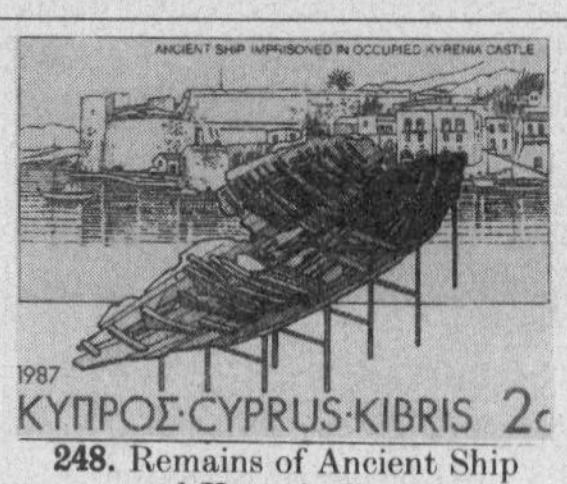

248. Remains of Ancient Ship and Kyrenia Castle.

1987. Voyage of "Kyrenia II" (replica of ancient ship). Multicoloured.

706. 2 c. Type **248** 30 20
707. 3 c. "Kyrenia II" under construction, 1982–5 .. 30 75
708. 5 c. "Kyrenia II" at Paphos, 1986 .. .. 55 20
709. 17 c. "Kyrenia II" at New York, 1986 .. .. 1·40 75

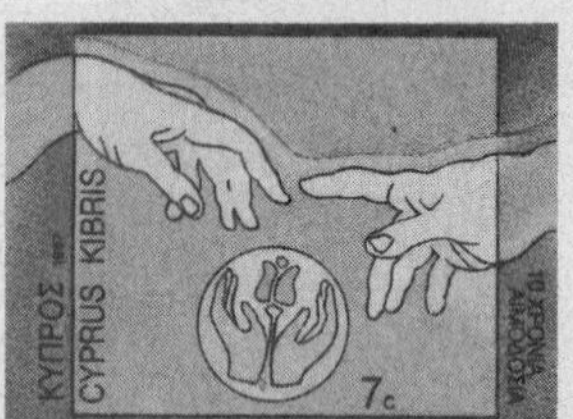

249. Hands (from Michelangelo's "Creation") and Emblem.

1987. Anniversaries and Events. Mult.

710. 7 c. Type **249** (10th anniv. of Blood Donation Co-ordinating Committee) 60 20
711. 15 c. Snail with flowered shell and countryside (European Countryside Campaign) .. .. 1·40 35
712. 20 c. Symbols of ocean bed and Earth's crust ("Troodos '87" Ophiolites and Oceanic Lithosphere Symposium) 1·75 3·00

250. Nativity Crib.

1987. Christmas. Traditional Customs. Mult.

713. 5 c. Type **250** 35 15
714. 15 c. Door knocker decorated with foliage .. 1·10 35
715. 17 c. Bowl of fruit and nuts 1·25 1·60

251 Flags of Cyprus and E.E.C.

1988. Cypriot–E.E.C. Customs Union. Mult.

716 15 c. Type **251** .. 1·10 1·50
717 18 c. Outline maps of Cyprus and E.E.C. countries .. .. 1·10 1·10

252 Intelpost Telefax Terminal (Illustration reduced, actual size 48 × 33 mm)

1988. Europa. Transport and Communications. Multicoloured.

718 7 c. Type **252** 65 65
719 7 c. Car driver using mobile telephone .. 65 65
720 18 c. Nose of Cyprus Airways airliner and greater flamingos .. 1·25 1·25
721 18 c. Airliner in flight and greater flamingos .. 1·25 1·25

253 Sailing

1988. Olympic Games, Seoul. Multicoloured.

722 5 c. Type **253** 30 20
723 7 c. Athletes at start .. 35 40
724 10 c. Shooting 40 70
725 20 c. Judo .. .. 90 1·40

254 Conference Emblem

1988. Non-Aligned Foreign Ministers' Conference, Nicosia.

726 **254** 1 c. black, blue & grn 10 10
727 – 10 c. multicoloured .. 45 60
728 – 50 c. multicoloured .. 2·25 2·25

DESIGNS: 10 c. Emblem of Republic of Cyprus; 50 c. Nehru, Tito, Nasser and Makarios.

255 "Cyprus 74" (wood engraving by A. Tassos)

1988. Obligatory Tax. Refugee Fund. Variously dated.

807 **255** 1 c. black and grey .. 10 10

1988. No. 651 surch **15 c.**

730 15 c. on 4 c. Kykko Monastery 70 60

256 "Presentation of Christ at the Temple" (Church of Holy Cross tou Agiasmati)

1988. Christmas. Designs showing frescoes from Cypriot churches. Multicoloured

731 5 c. Type **256** 35 20
732 15 c. "Virgin and Child" (St. John Lampadistis Monastery) 90 25
733 17 c. "Adoration of the Magi" (St. John Lampadistis Monastery) 1·25 1·40

257 Human Rights Logo

1988. 40th Anniv of Universal Declaration of Human Rights.

734 **257** 25 c. lt blue, dp bl & bl 90 1·25

258 Basketball

1989. 3rd Small European States' Games, Nicosia. Multicoloured.

735 1 c. Type **258** 10 15
736 5 c. Javelin 20 15
737 15 c. Wrestling 45 20
738 18 c. Athletics .. .. 60 1·00

259 Lingri Stick Game

1989. Europa. Children's Games. Mult.

740 7 c. Type **259** 40 45
741 7 c. Ziziros 40 45
742 18 c. Sitsia 65 80
743 18 c. Leapfrog 65 80

260 "Universal Man"

1989. Bicentenary of the French Revolution.

744 **260** 18 c. multicoloured .. 60 60

261 Stylized Human Figures

1989. Centenary of Interparliamentary Union (15 c.) and 9th Non-Aligned Summit Conference, Belgrade (30 c.). Multicoloured.

745 15 c. Type **261** 50 40
746 30 c. Conference logo .. 1·00 1·10

262 Worker Bees tending Larvae

1989. Bee-keeping. Multicoloured.

748 3 c. Type **262** 15 20
749 10 c. Bee on rock-rose flower 40 40
750 15 c. Bee on lemon flower 60 40
751 18 c. Queen and worker bees 65 70

263 Outstretched Hand and Profile (aid for Armenian earthquake victims)

1989. Anniversaries and Events. Mult.

752 3 c. Type **263** 15 20
753 5 c. Airmail envelope (Cyprus Philatelic Society F.I.P. membership) 25 10
754 7 c. Crab symbol and daisy (European Cancer Year) 45 65
755 17 c. Vegetables and fish (World Food Day) .. 75 65

264 Winter (detail from "Four Seasons")

1989. Roman Mosaics from Paphos. Mult.

756 1 c. Type **264** 10 10
757 2 c. Personification of Crete (32 × 24 mm) .. 10 10
758 3 c. Centaur and Maenad (24 × 32 mm) 10 10
759 4 c. Poseidon and Amymone (32 × 24 mm) 10 15
760 5 c. Leda 15 20
761 7 c. Apollon 20 25
762 10 c. Hermes and Dionysos (24 × 32 mm) 30 35
763 15 c. Cassiopeia 40 45
764 18 c. Orpheus (32 × 24 mm) 50 55
765 20 c. Nymphs (24 × 32 mm) 55 60
766 25 c. Amazon (24 × 32 mm) 70 75
767 40 c. Doris (32 × 24 mm) .. 1·10 1·25
768 50 c. Heracles and the Lion (39 × 27 mm) .. .. 1·40 1·50
769 £1 Apollon and Daphne (39 × 27 mm) .. .. 2·75 3·00
770 £3 Cupid (39 × 27 mm) .. 8·50 8·75

265 Hands and Open Book (International Literacy Year)

1990. Anniversaries and Events. Mult.

771 15 c. Type **265** 55 50
772 17 c. Dove and profiles (83rd Inter-Parliamentary Conference, Nicosia) 65 70
773 18 c. Lions International emblem (Lions Europa Forum, Limassol) .. 75 70

266 District Post Office, Paphos

1990. Europa. Post Office Buildings. Mult.

774 7 c. Type **266** 45 25
775 18 c. City Centre Post Office, Limassol .. 80 1·25

267 Symbolic Lips (25th anniv of Hotel and Catering Institute) (¾ size illustration)

1990. European Tourism Year. Multicoloured.

776 5 c. Type **267** 20 20
777 7 c. Bell tower, St. Lazarus Church (1100th anniv) .. 25 25
778 15 c. Butterflies and woman 65 30
779 18 c. Birds and man .. 85 95

268 Sun (wood carving)

1990. 30th Anniv of Republic. Multicoloured.

780 15 c. Type **268** 55 45
781 17 c. Bulls (pottery design) 65 50
782 18 c. Fishes (pottery design) 75 60
783 40 c. Tree and birds (wood carving) .. .. 1·40 1·25

269 "Chionodoxa lochiae"

1990. Endangered Wild Flowers. Book illustrations by Elektra Megaw. Mult.

785 2 c. Type **269** 15 20
786 3 c. "Pancratium maritimum" 15 20
787 5 c. "Paeonia mascula" .. 25 20
788 7 c. "Cyclamen cyprium" .. 30 25
789 15 c. "Tulipa cypria" .. 55 30
790 18 c. "Crocus cyprius" .. 80 1·25

270 "Nativity"

1990. Christmas. 16th-Century Icons. Mult.

791 5 c. Type **270** 20 20
792 15 c. "Virgin Hodegetria" 50 25
793 17 c. "Nativity" (different) 70 95

271 Archangel

1991. 6th-century Mosaics from Kanakaria Church. Multicoloured.

794 5 c. Type **271** 15 15
795 15 c. Christ Child .. 45 20
796 17 c. St. James 70 90
797 18 c. St. Matthew .. 70 1·00

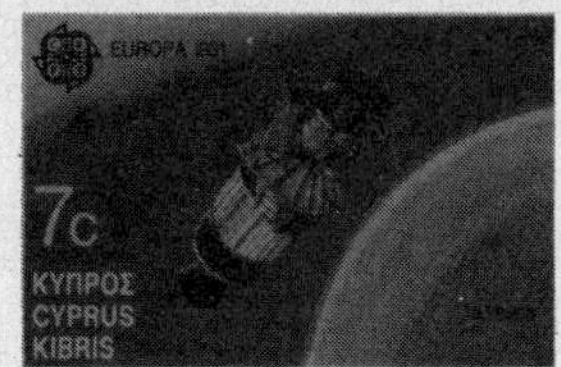

272 "Ulysses" Spacecraft

1991. Europa. Europe in Space. Mult.

798 7 c. Type **272** 25 20
799 18 c. "Giotto" and Halley's Comet 70 80

273 Young Pied Wheatear

1991. Pied ("Cyprus") Wheatear. Mult.

800 5 c. Type **273** 20 20
801 7 c. Adult bird in autumn plumage 25 20
802 15 c. Adult male in breeding plumage .. 45 35
803 30 c. Adult female in breeding plumage .. 1·10 1·50

274 Mother and Child with Tents

1991. 40th Anniv of U.N. Commission for Refugees. Each dp brown, brown and silver.

804 5 c. Type **274** 20 15
805 15 c. Three pairs of legs .. 70 40
806 18 c. Three children .. 90 1·25

275 The Nativity

1991. Christmas. Multicoloured.

808 5 c. Type **275** 15 15
809 15 c. Saint Basil 40 40
810 17 c. Baptism of Jesus .. 65 75

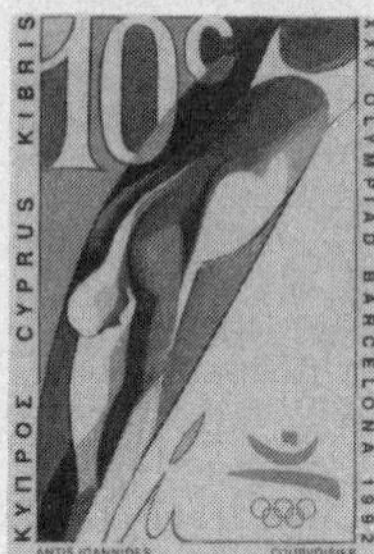

276 Swimming

1992. Olympic Games, Barcelona. Mult.

811 10 c. Type **276** 40 35
812 20 c. Long jump 70 60
813 30 c. Running .. .. 1·10 90
814 35 c. Discus .. .. 1·25 1·50

277 World Map and Emblem ("EXPO '92" Worlds Fair, Seville)

1992. Anniversaries and Events. Mult.

815 20 c. Type **277** 65 60
816 25 c. European map and football (10th under-16 European Football Championship) .. 80 75
817 30 c. Symbols of learning (inauguration of University of Cyprus) .. 1·00 1·50

278 Compass Rose and Map of Voyage

1992. Europa. 500th Anniv of Discovery of America by Columbus. Multicoloured.

818 10 c. Type **278** 65 65
819 10 c. "Departure from Palos" (R. Balaga) .. 65 65
820 30 c. Fleet of Columbus .. 1·00 1·00
821 30 c. Christopher Columbus .. 1·00 1·00

Nos. 818/9 and 820/1 were each issued together, se-tenant, forming composite designs.

279 "Chamaeleo chamaeleon"

1992. Reptiles. Multicoloured.

822 7 c. Type **279** 35 25
823 10 c. "Lacerta laevis troodica" (lizard) .. 40 35
824 15 c. "Mauremys caspica" (turtle) 65 75
825 20 c. "Coluber cypriensis" (snake) 75 80

280 Minoan Wine Ship of 7th Century B.C. and Modern Tanker

1992. 7th International Maritime and Shipping Conference, Nicosia.

826 **280** 50 c. multicoloured .. 2·00 2·00

281 "Visitation of the Virgin Mary to Elizabeth", Church of the Holy Cross, Pelendri

1992. Christmas. Church Fresco Paintings. Multicoloured.

827 7 c. Type **281** 35 25
828 15 c. "Virgin and Child Enthroned", Church of Panayia tou Araka 65 65
829 20 c. "Virgin and Child", Ayios Nicolaos tis Stegis Church 90 75

282 School Building and Laurel Wreath

1993. Centenary of Pancyprian Gymnasium (secondary school).

830 **282** 10 c. multicoloured .. 40 40

283 "Motherhood" (bronze sculpture, Nicos Dymiotis)

1993. Europa. Comtemporary Art. Mult.

831 10 c. Type **283** 40 40
832 30 c. "Motherhood" (painting, Christoforos Savva) (horiz) .. .. 1·10 1·10

284 Women Athletes (13th European Cup for Women)

1993. Anniversaries and Events. Mult.

No.	Description	Unused	Used
833	7 c. Type **284**	25	25
834	10 c. Scout symbols (80th anniv of Scouting in Cyprus) (vert) ..	35	35
835	20 c. Water-skier, dolphin and seabird (Moufflon Encouragement Cup) (inscr "Mufflon") ..	65	70
835a	20 c. Water-skier, dolphin and seabird (inscr "Moufflon")	65	70
836	25 c. Archbishop Makarios III and monastery (80th birth anniv) ..	80	85

285 Red Soldier Fish

1993. Fishes. Multicoloured.

No.	Description	Unused	Used
837	7 c. Type **285**	30	25
838	15 c. Red scorpion fish ..	55	50
839	20 c. Painted comber ..	65	65
840	30 c. Triggerfish	1·10	1·10

286 Conference Emblem

1993. 12th Commonwealth Summit Conf.

No.	Type	Description	Unused	Used
841	**286**	35 c. brown and ochre	1·10	1·10
842		40 c. brown and ochre	1·25	1·40

287 Ancient Sailing Ship and Modern Coaster

1993. "Maritime Cyprus '93" International Shipping Conference, Nicosia.

No.	Type	Description	Unused	Used
843	**287**	25 c. multicoloured ..	80	85

288 Cross from Stavrovouni Monastery

1993. Christmas. Church Crosses. Mult.

No.	Description	Unused	Used
844	7 c. Type **288**	20	25
845	20 c. Cross from Lefkara ..	55	60
846	25 c. Cross from Pedoulas (horiz)	70	75

289 Copper Smelting

1994. Europa. Discoveries. Ancient Copper Industry. Multicoloured.

No.	Description	Unused	Used
847	10 c. Type **289**	30	35
848	30 c. Ingot, ancient ship and map of Cyprus ..	75	80

290 Symbols of Disability (Persons with Special Needs Campaign)

1994. Anniversaries and Events. Mult.

No.	Description	Unused	Used
849	7 c. Type **290**	20	25
850	15 c. Olympic rings in flame (Centenary of International Olympic Committee)	40	45
851	20 c. Peace doves (World Gymnasiade, Nicosia) ..	55	60
852	25 c. Adults and unborn baby in tulip (International Year of the Family)	70	75

TURKISH CYPRIOT POSTS

After the inter-communal clashes during December 1963, a separate postal service was established on 6 January 1964, between some of the Turkish Cypriot areas, using handstamps inscribed "KIBRIS TURK POSTALARI". During 1964, however, an agreement was reached between representatives of the two communities for the restoration of postal services. This agreement, to which the United Nations representatives were a party, was ratified in November 1966 by the Republic's Council of Ministers. Under the scheme postal services were provided for the Turkish Cypriot communities in Famagusta, Limassol, Lefka and Nicosia, staffed by Turkish Cypriot employees of the Cypriot Department of Posts.

On 8 April 1970, 5 m. and 15 m. locally-produced labels, originally designated "Social Aid Stamps", were issued by the Turkish Cypriot community and these can be found on commercial covers. These local stamps are outside the scope of this catalogue.

On 29 October 1973 Nos. 1/7 were placed on sale, but were again used only on mail between the Turkish Cypriot areas.

Following the intervention by the Republic of Turkey in July 1974 these stamps replaced issues of the Republic of Cyprus in that part of the island, north and east of the Attila Line, controlled by the Autonomous Turkish Cypriot Administration.

1974. 1000 mhls = 1 pound.
1978. 100 kurus = 1 lira.

1. 50th Anniversary Emblem.

1974. 50th Anniv. of Republic of Turkey.

No.	Type	Description	Unused	Used
1.	–	3 m. multicoloured ..	30·00	30·00
2.	–	5 m. multicoloured ..	60	40
3.	–	10 m. multicoloured ..	50	20
4.	1.	15 m. red and black ..	2·50	1·50
5.	–	20 m. multicoloured ..	70	20
6.	–	50 m. multicoloured ..	2·00	1·50
7.	–	70 m. multicoloured ..	16·00	16·00

DESIGNS—VERT. 3 m. Woman sentry. 10 m. Man and woman with Turkish flags. 20 m. Ataturk statue, Kyrenia Gate, Nicosia. 50 m. "The Fallen". HORIZ. 5 m. Military parade, Nicosia. 70 m. Turkish flag and map of Cyprus.

These were first issued in 1973 for local use.

1975. Proclamation of the Turkish Federated State of Cyprus. Nos. 3 and 5 surch. **KIBRIS TURK FEDERE DEVLETI 13.2.1975.**

No.	Description	Unused	Used
8.	30 m. on 20 m. multicoloured	1·00	1·00
9.	100 m. on 10 m. multicoloured	1·50	2·25

3. Namik Kemal's Bust, Famagusta.

1975. Multicoloured.

No.	Description	Unused	Used
10.	3 m. Type **3**	15	30
11.	10 m. Ataturk Statue, Nicosia	15	10
12.	15 m. St. Hilarion Castle ..	25	20
13.	20 m. Ataturk Square, Nicosia	35	20
14.	25 m. Famagusta Beach ..	35	30
15.	30 m. Kyrenia Harbour ..	45	10
16.	50 m. Lala Mustafa Pasha Mosque, Famagusta (vert.)	60	10
17.	100 m. Interior, Kyrenia Castle	1·25	90
18.	250 m. Castle walls, Kyrenia	2·25	2·50
19.	500 m. Othello Tower, Famagusta (vert.) ..	4·50	4·50

See also Nos. 36/8.

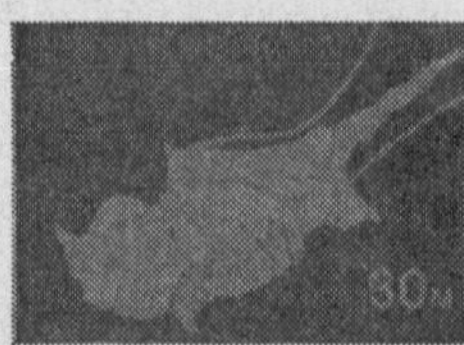

4. Map of Cyprus.

1975. "Peace in Cyprus". Multicoloured.

No.	Description	Unused	Used
20.	30 m. Type **4**	75	15
21.	50 m. Map, laurel and broken chain	85	20
22.	150 m. Map and laurel-sprig on globe (vert.)	2·25	1·00

MINIMUM PRICE

The minimum price quoted is 10p which represents a handling charge rather than a basis for valuing common stamps. For further notes about prices see introductory pages.

5. "Pomegranates" (I. V. Guney).

1975. Europa. Paintings. Multicoloured.

No.	Description	Unused	Used
23.	90 m. Type **5**	1·10	60
24.	100 m. "Harvest Time" (F. Direkoglu)	1·25	60

1976. Nos. 16/17 surch.

No.	Description	Unused	Used
25.	10 m. on 50 m. multicoloured	50	70
26.	30 m. on 100 m. multicoloured	50	80

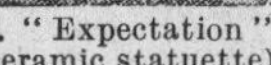

7. "Expectation" (ceramic statuette). **9.** Olympic Symbol "Flower".

8. Carob.

1976. Europa. Multicoloured.

No.	Description	Unused	Used
27.	60 m. Type **7**	65	70
28.	120 m. "Man in Meditation"	75	80

1976. Export Products. Fruits. **Mult.**

No.	Description	Unused	Used
29.	10 m. Type **8**	30	10
30.	25 m. Mandarin	50	10
31.	40 m. Strawberry	60	20
32.	60 m. Orange	75	50
33.	80 m. Lemon	80	1·60

1976. Olympic Games, Montreal. **Mult.**

No.	Description	Unused	Used
34.	60 m. Type **9**	25	20
35.	100 m. Olympic symbol and doves	35	25

10. Kyrema Harbour.

1976. Multicoloured.

No.	Description	Unused	Used
36.	5 m. Type **10**	55	15
37.	15 m. St. Hilarion Castle ..	55	15
38.	20 m. Ataturk Square, Nicosia	55	15

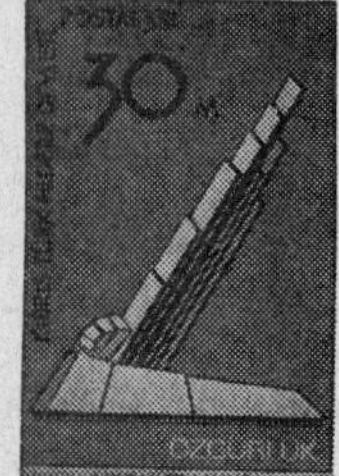

11. Liberation Monument, Karaeglanoglu (Ay. Georghios).

1976. Liberation Monument.

No.	Type	Description	Unused	Used
47.	**11.**	30 m. blue, pink and black	15	20
48.	–	150 m. red, pink and black	35	45

DESIGN: 150 m. Liberation Monument (different view).

12. Hotel, Salamis Bay.

1977. Europa. Multicoloured.

49. 80 m. Type 12 .. .. 50 80

50. 100 m. Kyrenia Port .. 60 80

13. Pottery.

1977. Handicrafts. Multicoloured.

51. 15 m. Type 13 .. .. 10 10

52. 30 m. Pottery (vert.) .. 10 10

53. 125 m. Basketware .. 30 50

14. Arap Ahmet Pasha Mosque, Nicosia.

1977. Turkish Buildings in Cyprus. Mult.

54. 20 m. Type 14 .. .. 10 10

55. 40 m. Paphos Castle (horiz.) 10 10

56. 70 m. Bekir Pasha aqueducts (horiz.) 15 20

57. 80 m. Sultan Mahmut library (horiz.) 15 25

15. Namik Kemal (bust) and House, Famagusta.

1977. Namik Kemal (patriotic poet). Mult.

58. 30 m. Type 15 .. .. 15 15

59. 140 m. Namik Kemal (portrait) (vert.) 35 60

16. Old Man and Woman.  17. Oratory in Buyuk Han, Nicosia.

1978. Social Security.

60. 16. 150 k. black, yell. & blue 10 10

61. – 275 k. blk., orge. and grn. 15 15

62. – 375 k. black, blue & orge. 25 20

DESIGNS: 275 k. Injured man with crutch. 375 k. Woman with family.

1978. Europa. Multicoloured.

63. 225 k. Type 17 .. .. 45 30

64. 450 k. Cistern in Selimiye Mosque, Nicosia .. 80 70

18. Motorway Junction.

1978. Communications. Multicoloured.

65. 75 k. Type 18 .. .. 15 10

66. 100 k. Hydrofoil "Ugur" .. 15 10

67. 650 k. Boeing "720" at Ercan Airport 50 35

19. Dove with laurel branch.

1978. National Oath.

68. 19. 150 k. yell., violet & blk. 10 10

69. – 225 k. black, red & yellow 10 10

70. – 725 k. black, blue & yell. 20 20

DESIGNS—VERT. 225 k. "Taking the Oath". HORIZ. 725 k. Symbolic dove.

20. Kemal Ataturk.

1978. Ataturk Commemoration.

71. 20. 75 k. pale turquoise and deep turquoise .. 10 10

72. 450 k. pink and brown .. 15 15

73. 650 k. blue and light blue 20 25

1979. Nos. 30/3 surch.

74. 50 k. on 25 m. Mandarin .. 10 10

75. 1 l. on 40 m. Strawberry .. 15 10

76. 3 l. on 60 m. Orange .. 15 10

77. 5 l. on 80 m. Lemon .. 35 15

23. Postage Stamp and Map of Cyprus.

1979. Europa. Communications. Mult.

79. 2 l. Type 23 .. .. 10 10

80. 3 l. Postage stamps, building and map 10 10

81. 8 l. Telephones, Earth and satellite 20 30

24. Microwave Antenna.

1979. 50th Anniversary of International Consultative Radio Committee.

82. 24. 2 l. multicoloured .. 20 10

83. 5 l. multicoloured .. 20 10

84. 6 l. multicoloured .. 25 15

25. School Children. 26. Lala Mustafa Pasha Mosque, Magusa.

1979. International Year of the Child. Multicoloured.

85. 1½ l. Type 25 .. .. 25 15

86. 4½ l. Children and globe (horiz.) 40 20

87. 6 l. College children .. 60 20

1980. Islamic Commemorations. Multicoloured.

88. 2½ l. Type 26 .. .. 10 10

89. 10 l. Arap Ahmet Pasha Mosque, Lefkosa .. 30 15

90. 20 l. Mecca and Medina .. 50 20

COMMEMORATIONS: 2½ l. 1st Islamic Conference in Turkish Cyprus. 10 l. General Assembly of World Islam Congress. 20 l. Moslem Year 1400 AH.

27. Ebu-Su'ud Efendi (philosopher).

1980. Europa. Personalities. Multicoloured.

91. 5 l. Type 27 .. .. 30 10

92. 30 l. Sultan Selim II .. 1·10 40

28. Omer's Shrine, Kyrenia.

1980. Ancient Monuments.

93. 28. 2½ l. blue and stone .. 10 10

94. – 3½ l. green and pink .. 10 10

95. – 5 l. brown on green .. 15 10

96. – 10 l. mauve and green .. 30 10

97. – 20 l. blue and yellow .. 50 25

DESIGNS: 3½ l. Entrance gate, Famagusta. 5 l. Funerary monuments (16th-cent.), Famagusta. 10 l. Bella Paise Abbey, Kyrenia. 20 l. Selimiye Mosque, Nicosia.

29. Cyprus 1880 6d. Stamp. 30. Dome of the Rock.

1980. Cyprus Stamp Centenary.

98. 29. 7½ l. blk., brn. and grn. 15 10

99. – 15 l. brown, dull blue and blue 20 15

100. – 50 l. black, red and grey 60 55

DESIGNS—HORIZ: 15 l. Cyprus 1960 Constitution of the Republic 30 m. commemorative stamp. VERT. 50 l. Social Welfare stamp, 1970.

1980. Palestinian Solidarity. Multicoloured.

101. 15 l. Type 30 .. .. 25 15

102. 35 l. Dome of the Rock (horiz.) 65 30

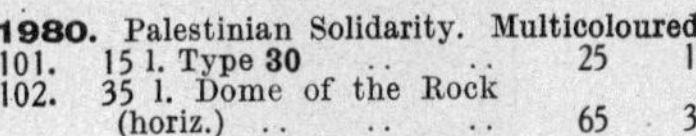

31. Extract from World Muslim Congress Statement in Turkish.

1981. Day of Solidarity with Islamic Countries.

103. 31. 1 l. buff, red and brown 15 15

104. – 35 l. pale grn., blk. & grn. 55 75

DESIGN: 35 l. Extract in English.

32. "Ataturk".

1981. Ataturk Stamp Exhibition, Lefkosa.

105. 32. 10 l. multicoloured .. 25 35

33. Folk-dancing.

1981. Europa. Folklore. Multicoloured.

106. 10 l. Type 33 .. .. 35 15

107. 30 l. Folkdancing (different) 60 35

35. Wild Convolvulus.

1981. Flowers. Multicoloured.

109. 1 l. Type 35 .. .. 10 10

110. 5 l. Persian cyclamen (horiz.) 10 10

111. 10 l. Spring mandrake (horiz.) 10 10

112. 25 l. Corn poppy 15 10

113. 30 l. Wild arum (horiz.) .. 20 10

114. 50 l. Sage-leaved rock rose 40 20

115. 100 l. "Cistus salviaefolius L." 75 30

116. 150 l. Giant fennel (horiz.) 1·40 90

36. Stylised Disabled Person in Wheelchair.

1981. Commemorations. Multicoloured.

117. 7½ l. Type 36 .. .. 30 35

118. 10 l. Heads of people of different races, peace dove and barbed wire (vert.) 50 55

119. 20 l. People of different races reaching out from globe, with dishes (vert.) 75 85

COMMEMORATIONS: 7½ l. International Year for Disabled Persons. 10 l. Anti-apartheid publicity. 20 l. World Food Day.

37. Turkish Cypriot and Palestinian Flags.

1981. Palestinian Solidarity.

120. 37. 10 l. multicoloured .. 30 40

38. Prince Charles and Lady Diana Spencer.

1981. Royal Wedding.
121. **38.** 50 l. multicoloured .. 1·00 85

40. Buffavento Castle.

1982. Tourism. Multicoloured.
123. 5 l. Type **40** 10 10
124. 10 l. Windsurfing 15 10
125. 15 l. Kantara Castle .. 25 15
126. 30 l. Shipwreck (300 B.C.) 50 40
Nos. 124/6 are horiz.

41. " Wedding " (A. Orek).

1982. Paintings (1st series). Multicoloured.
127. 30 l. Type **41** 15 30
128. 50 l. "Carob Pickers" (O. Nazim Selenge) (vert.) .. 30 70
See also Nos. 132/3, 157/8, 176/7, 185/6, 208/9, 225/7, 248/50, 284/5, 315/16 and 328/9.

42. Cross of Lorraine, Koch and Bacillus (Cent. of Koch's Discovery of Tubercle Bacillus).

1982. Anniversaries and Events. Mult.
129. 10 l. Type **42** 45 30
130. 30 l. Spectrum on football pitch (World Cup Football Championships, Spain 90 75
131. 70 l. "75" and Lord Baden-Powell (75th Anniv. of Boy Scout movement and 125th birth anniv.) (vert.) .. 1·60 1·75

43. " Calloused Hands " (Salih Oral).

1983. Paintings (2nd series). Multicoloured.
132. 30 l. Type **43** .. .. 90 1·25
133. 35 l. " Malya-Limassol Bus " (Emin Cizenel) .. .. 90 1·25

45. First Turkish Cypriot 10 m. Stamp.

1983. Anniversaries and Events. Mult.
135. 15 l. Type **45** 40 40
136. 20 l. " Turkish Achievements in Cyprus " (horiz.) 40 40
137. 25 l. " Liberation Fighters " 50 50
138. 30 l. Dish aerial and telegraph pole (horiz.) .. 60 60
139. 50 l. Dove and envelopes (horiz.) .. .. .. 1·25 1·25
EVENTS: 15, 20, 25 l. T.M.T. (Turkish Cypriot Resistance Organization) 25th Anniv. 30, 50 l. World Communications Year.

46. European Bee Eater.

1983. Birds of Cyprus. Multicoloured.
140. 10 l. Type **46** 80 80
141. 15 l. Goldfinch .. .. 1·00 1·00
142. 50 l. European Robin .. 1·25 1·25
143. 65 l. Golden Oriole .. 1·40 1·40

1983. Establishment of Republic. Nos. 109, 111/12 and 116 optd. **Kuzey Kibris Turk Cumhuriyeti 15.11.1983,** or surch. also.
144. 10 l. " Mandragara officinarum " 20 15
145. 15 l. on 1 l. " Convolvulus althaeoides " 30 15
146. 25 l. " Papaver rhoeas " .. 40 25
147. 150 l. " Ferula communis " 1·50 2·25

48. C.E.P.T. 25th Anniversary Logo.

1984. Europa.
148. **48.** 50 l. yellow, brown and black .. .. 2·25 2·25
149. 100 l. light blue, blue and black .. .. 2·25 2·25

49. Olympic Flame.

1984. Olympic Games, Los Angeles. Mult.
150. 10 l. Type **49** 15 10
151. 20 l. Olympic events within rings (horiz.) 25 25
152. 70 l. Martial arts event (horiz.) .. .. .. 50 1·25

50. Ataturk Cultural Centre.

1984. Opening of Ataturk Cultural Centre, Lefkosa.
153. **50.** 120 l. stone, black and brown .. .. 1·25 1·50

52. Turkish Cypriot Flag and Map.

1984. 10th Anniv. of Peace Operation. Mult.
154. 20 l. Type **52** 50 25
155. 70 l. Turkish Cypriot flag within book .. .. 1·00 1·50

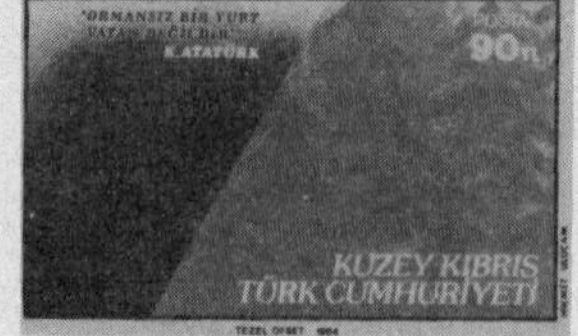

53. Burnt and Replanted Forests.

1984. World Forestry Resources.
156. **53.** 90 l. multicoloured .. 1·25 1·50

54. "Old Turkish Houses, Nicosia" (Cevdet Cagdas).

1984. Paintings (3rd series). Multicoloured.
157. 20 l. Type **54** 50 40
158. 70 l. "Scenery" (Olga Rauf) .. .. .. 1·10 1·50
See also Nos. 176/7, 185/6, 208/9, 225/7, 248/50, 284/5, 315/16 and 328/9.

55. Kemal Ataturk, Flag and Crowd.

1984. 1st Anniv. of Turkish Republic of Northern Cyprus. Multicoloured.
159. 20 l. Type **55** 30 25
160. 70 l. Legislative Assembly voting for Republic (horiz.) .. .. .. 80 1·00

56. Taekwondo Bout.

1984. International Taekwondo Championship, Girne.
161. **56.** 10 l. black, brown and grey 40 15
162. – 70 l. multicoloured .. 1·60 2·00
DESIGN: 70 l. Emblem and flags of competing nations.

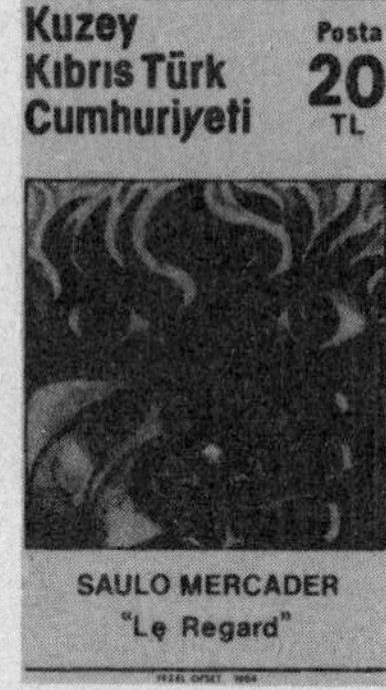

57. "Le Regard".

1984. Exhibition by Saulo Mercader (artist). Multicoloured.
163. 20 l. Type **57** 30 25
164. 70 l. "L'equilibre de L'esprit" (horiz.) .. 1·10 1·75

58. Musical Instruments and Music.

1984. Visit of Nurnberg Chamber Orchestra.
165. **58.** 70 l. multicoloured .. 1·50 2·00

59. Dr. Fazil Kucuk (politician). **61.** George Frederick Handel.

60. Goat.

1985. 1st Death Anniv. of Dr. Fazil Kucuk (politician). Multicoloured.
166. 20 l. Type **59** 30 25
167. 70 l. Dr. Fazil Kucuk reading newspaper .. .. 95 1·40

1985. Domestic Animals. Multicoloured.
168. 100 l. Type **60** 55 30
169. 200 l. Cow and calf .. 90 80
170. 300 l. Ram .. .. .. 1·25 1·50
171. 500 l. Donkey .. .. 2·00 2·75

1985. Europa. Composers.
172. **61.** 20 l. purple, green and light green .. .. 2·00 2·00
173. – 20 l. pur., brn. & pink 2·00 2·00
174. – 100 l. purple, blue and light blue .. .. 2·50 2·50
175. – 100 l. purple, brown and light brown .. 2·50 2·50
DESIGNS: No. 173, Giuseppe Domenico Scarlatti. 174, Johann Sebastian Bach. 175, Buhurizade Mustafa Itri Efendi.

1985. Paintings (4th series). As T **54.** Multicoloured.
176. 20 l. "Village Life" (Ali Atakan) 60 40
177. 50 l. "Woman carrying Water" (Ismet V. Güney) .. .. .. 1·40 2·00

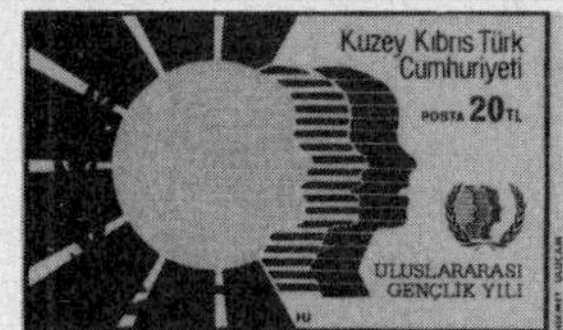

62. Heads of Three Youths.

1985. International Youth Year. Mult.

178. 20 l. Type **62** 50 20
179. 100 l. Dove and globe .. 2·00 2·50

63. Parachutist (Aviation League).

1985. Anniversaries and Events.

180. **63.** 20 l. multicoloured .. 45 20
181. – 50 l. black, brn. & bl. 90 75
182. – 100 l. brown .. .. 1·50 1·60
183. – 100 l. multicoloured .. 1·50 1·60
184. – 100 l. multicoloured .. 1·50 1·60

DESIGNS:—VERT. No. 181, Louis Pasteur (Centenary of Discovery of Rabies vaccine); 182, İsmet İnönü (Turkish statesman) (birth centenary (1984)). HORIZ.—183, "40" in figures and symbolic flower (40th anniv of United Nations Organization); 184, Patient receiving blood transfusion (Prevention of Thalassaemia).

1986. Paintings (5th series) As T **54**. Multicoloured.

185. 20 l. "House with Arches" (Gonen Atakol) 50 30
186. 100 l. "Ataturk Square" (Yalkin Muhtaroglu) .. 1·75 1·75

65. Karagoz Show Puppets.

1986. Karagoz Folk Puppets.

188. **65.** 100 l. multicoloured .. 1·25 1·00

66. Old Bronze Age Composite Pottery.

1986. Archaeological Artefacts. Cultural Links with Anatolia. Multicoloured.

189. 10 l. Type **66** 35 10
190. 20 l. Late Bronze Age bird jug (vert.) 65 20
191. 50 l. Neolithic earthenware pot .. .. 1·00 75
192. 100 l. Roman statue of Artemis (vert.) .. .. 1·50 1·75

67. Soldiers, Defence Force Badge and Ataturk (10th anniv. of Defence Forces).

1986. Anniversaries and Events. Mult.

193. 20 l. Type **67** 50 20
194. 50 l. Woman and two children (40th anniv. of Food and Agriculture Organization) 80 70
195. 100 l. Football and world map (World Cup Football Championship, Mexico) (horiz.) .. .. 1·75 1·75
196. 100 l. Orbit of Halley's Comet and "Giotto" space probe (horiz.) .. 1·75 1·75

68. Guzelyurt Dam and Power Station.

1986. Modern Development (1st series). Mult.

197. 20 l. Type **68** 80 20
198. 50 l. Low cost housing project, Lefkosa .. 1·10 90
199. 100 l. Kyrenia Airport .. 1·75 1·75

See also Nos. 223/4 and 258/63.

69. Prince Andrew and Miss Sarah Ferguson.

1986. 60th Birthday of Queen Elizabeth II and Royal Wedding. Multicoloured.

200. 100 l. Queen Elizabeth II 1·00 80
201. 100 l. Type **69** .. .. 1·00 80

70. Locomotive No. 11 and Trakhoni Station.

1986. Cyprus Railway. Multicoloured.

202. 50 l. Type **70** .. .. 2·00 1·50
203. 100 l. Locomotive No. 1 .. 2·50 2·50

1987. Nos. 94, 96/7 and 113 optd. **Kuzey Kibris Turk Cumhuriyeti** or surch also (No. 205).

204. 10 l. mauve and green .. 35 45
205. 15 l. on 3½ l. green and pink 35 45
206. 20 l. blue and yellow .. 35 45
207. 30 l. multicoloured .. 40 50

1987. Paintings (6th series). As T **54**. Mult.

208. 50 l. "Shepherd" (Feridun Isiman) .. .. .. 1·00 1·00
209. 125 l. "Pear Woman" (Mehmet Uluhan) .. 1·50 1·75

72. Modern House (architect A. Vural Behaeddin).

1987. Europa. Modern Architecture. Mult.

210. 50 l. Type **72** 60 30
211. 200 l. Modern house (architect Necdet Turgay) .. .. .. 1·75 2·00

73. Kneeling Folk Dancer.

74. Regimental Colour (1st Anniv. of Infantry Regiment).

1987. Folk Dancers. Multicoloured.

212. 20 l. Type **73** 20 10
213. 50 l. Standing male dancer 35 20
214. 200 l. Standing female dancer 90 75
215. 1000 l. Woman's headdress 3·25 3·75

1987. Anniversaries and Events. Mult.

216. 50 l. Type **74** 65 50
217. 50 l. Pres. Denktash and Turgut Ozal (1st anniv. of Turkish Prime Minister's visit) (horiz.) 65 50
218. 200 l. Emblem and Crescent (5th Islamic Summit Conference, Kuwait) .. .. .. 1·50 1·75
219. 200 l. Emblem and laurel leaves (Membership of Pharmaceutical Federation) (horiz.) .. 1·50 1·75

75. Ahmet Belig Pasha (Egyptian judge).

1987. Turkish Cypriot Personalities.

220. **75.** 50 l. brown and yellow 45 30
221. – 50 l. multicoloured .. 45 30
222. – 125 l. multicoloured .. 1·10 1·40

DESIGNS: 50 l. (No. 221) Mehmet Emin Pasha (Ottoman Grand Vizier). 125 l. Mehmet Kamil Pasha (Ottoman Grand Vizier).

76. Tourist Hotel, Girne.

1987. Modern Development (2nd series). Mult.

223. 150 l. Type **76** .. .. 1·00 75
224. 200 l. Dogu Akdeniz University .. .. 1·50 1·25

1988. Paintings (7th series). As T **54**. Mult.

225 20 l. "Woman making Pastry" (Ayhan Mentes) (vert) 35 15
226 50 l. "Chair Weaver" (Osman Guvenir) .. 55 50
227 150 l. "Woman weaving a Rug" (Zekai Yesiladali) (vert) .. .. .. 1·25 1·60

77 "Piyale Pasha" (tug)

1988. Europa. Transport and Communications. Multicoloured.

228 200 l. Type **77** .. .. 1·25 75
229 500 l. Dish aerial and antenna tower, Selvilitepe (vert) .. 2·00 2·50

No. 229 also commemorates the 25th anniv of Bayrak Radio and Television Corporation.

78 Lefkosa

1988. Tourism. Multicoloured.

230 150 l. Type **78** 55 55
231 200 l. Gazi-Magusa .. 65 65
232 300 l. Girne .. .. 90 1·00

79 Bulent Ecevit

1988. Turkish Prime Ministers. Multicoloured.

233 50 l. Type **79** 30 30
234 50 l. Bulent Ulusu .. 30 30
235 50 l. Turgut Ozal 30 30

80 Red Crescent Members on Exercise

1988. Civil Defence.

236 **80** 150 l. multicoloured .. 65 65

81 Hodori the Tiger (Games mascot) and Fireworks

1988. Olympic Games, Seoul. Multicoloured.

237 200 l. Type **81** 50 60
238 250 l. Athletics 60 70
239 400 l. Shot and running track with letters spelling "SEOUL" .. 85 1·10

82 Sedat Simavi (journalist)

85 Girl with Doll

1988. Anniversaries and Events.

240 **82** 50 l. green 20 20
241 – 100 l. multicoloured .. 30 30
242 – 300 l. multicoloured .. 60 60
243 – 400 l. multicoloured .. 80 80
244 – 400 l. multicoloured .. 80 80
245 – 600 l. multicoloured .. 1·25 1·25

DESIGNS: HORIZ—No. 241, Stylised figures around table and flags of participating countries (International Girne Conferences); 244, Presidents Gorbachev and Reagan signing treaty (Summit Meeting). VERT—No. 242, Cogwheels as flowers (North Cyprus Industrial Fair); 243, Globe (125th anniv of International Red Cross); 245, "Medical Services" (40th anniv of W.H.O.).

1989. Paintings (8th series). As T **54**. Mult.

248 150 l. "Dervis Pasa Mansion, Lefkosa" (Inci Kansu) 50 35
249 400 l. "Gamblers' Inn, Lefkosa" (Osman Gvenir) .. .. 1·00 1·00
250 600 l. "Mosque, Paphos" (Hikmet Ulucam) (vert) 1·50 1·60

1989. Europa. Children's Games. Mult.

251 600 l. Type **85** .. .. 1·25 1·00
252 1000 l. Boy with kite .. 1·75 2·00

86 Meeting of Presidents Vassiliou and Denktash

1989. Cyprus Peace Summit, Geneva, 1988.

253 **86** 500 l. red and black .. 75 75

87 Chukar Partridge

1989. Wildlife. Multicoloured.

254 100 l. Type **87** 20 15
255 200 l. Cyprus hare .. 30 25
256 700 l. Black partridge .. 1·25 80
257 2000 l. Red fox .. .. 2·25 2·25

88 Road Construction

1989. Modern Development (3rd series). Mult.

258 100 l. Type **88** 15 15
259 150 l. Laying water pipeline (vert) 20 20
260 200 l. Seedling trees (vert) 30 25
261 450 l. Modern telephone exchange (vert) .. 75 75
262 650 l. Steam turbine power station (vert) .. .. 1·00 1·00
263 700 l. Irrigation reservoir 1·25 1·25

89 Unloading Freighter at Quayside (15th anniv of Gazi Magusa Free Port)

1989. Anniversaries.

264 **89** 100 l. multicoloured .. 15 15
265 – 450 l. black, blue & red 55 55
266 – 500 l. black, yell & grey 60 60
267 – 600 l. black, red & blue 70 70
268 – 1000 l. multicoloured .. 1·25 1·25

DESIGNS—VERT (26 × 47 mm). 450 l. Airmail letter and stylized bird (25th anniv of Turkish Cypriot postal service). HORIZ (as T **89**). 500 l. Newspaper and printing press (centenary of "Saded" newspaper); 600 l. Statue of Aphrodite, lifebelt and seabird (30th anniv of International Maritime Organization); 1000 l. Soldiers (25th anniv of Turkish Cypriot resistance).

90 Erdal Inonu

1989. Visit of Professor Erdal Inonu (Turkish politician).

269 **90** 700 l. multicoloured .. 15 20

91 Mule-drawn Plough

1989. Traditional Agricultural Implements. Multicoloured.

270 150 l. Type **91** 15 20
271 450 l. Ox-drawn threshing sledge 50 55
272 550 l. Olive press (vert) .. 60 65

92 Smoking Ashtray and Drinks

1990. World Health Day. Multicoloured.

273 200 l. Type **92** 20 20
274 700 l. Smoking cigarette and heart 45 45

93 Yenierenkoy Post Office

1990. Europa. Post Office Buildings. Mult.

275 1000 t. Type **93** 50 50
276 1500 t. Ataturk Meydani Post Office 75 75

94 Song Thrush

96 Amphitheatre, Soli

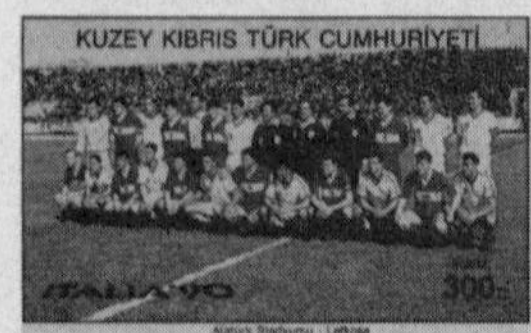

95 Two Football Teams

1990. World Environment Day. Birds. Multicoloured.

278 150 l. Type **94** 20 20
279 300 l. Blackcap 30 30
280 900 l. Black redstart .. 80 80
281 1000 l. Chiff-chaff .. 90 90

1990. World Cup Football Championship, Italy. Multicoloured.

282 300 l. Type **95** 40 25
283 1000 l. Championship symbol, globe and ball 1·10 1·25

1990. Paintings (9th series). As T **54**. Mult.

284 300 l. "Abstract" (Filiz Ankacc) 25 20
285 1000 l. Wooden sculpture (S. Tekman) (vert) .. 70 90

1990. Tourism. Multicoloured.

286 150 l. Type **96** 15 15
287 1000 l. Swan mosaic, Soli 70 70

97 Kenan Evren and Rauf Denktas

1990. Visit of President Kenan Evren of Turkey.

288 **97** 500 l. multicoloured .. 55 55

98 Road Signs and Heart wearing Seat Belt

1990. Traffic Safety Campaign. Mult.

289 150 l. Type **98** 20 15
290 300 l. Road signs, speeding car and spots of blood .. 30 20
291 1000 l. Traffic lights and road signs 90 65

99 Yildirim Akbulut

100 "Rosularia cypria"

1990. Visit of Turkish Prime Minister Yildirim Akbulut.

292 **99** 1000 l. multicoloured .. 50 50

1990. Plants. Multicoloured.

293 150 l. Type **100** 15 15
294 200 l. "Silene fraudratrix" 20 20
295 300 l. "Scutellaria sibthorpii" 25 25
296 600 l. "Sedum lampusae" 30 30
297 1000 l. "Onosma caespitosum" 50 50
298 1500 l. "Arabis cypria" .. 80 80

101 Kemal Ataturk at Easel (wood carving)

1990. International Literacy Year. Mult.

299 300 l. Type **101** 20 20
300 750 l. Globe, letters and books 45 45

1991. Nos. 189, 212 and 293 surch.

301 **66** 250 l. on 10 l. mult .. 15 15
302 **73** 250 l. on 20 l. mult .. 15 15
303 **100** 500 l. on 150 l. mult .. 25 25

103 "Ophrys lapethica"

1991. Orchids (1st series). Multicoloured.

304 250 l. Type **103** 25 25
305 500 l. "Ophrys kotschyi" 40 40

See also Nos. 311/14.

105 Kucuk Medrese Fountain, Lefkosa

1991. Fountains. Multicoloured.

307 250 l. Type **105** 10 10
308 500 l. Cafer Pasa fountain, Magusa 10 15
309 1500 l. Sarayonu Square fountain, Lefkosa .. 15 20
310 5000 l. Arabahmet Mosque fountain, Lefkosa .. 50 55

1991. Orchids (2nd series). As T **103**. Multicoloured.

311 100 l. "Serapias levantina" 10 10
312 500 l. "Dactylorhiza romana" 25 25
313 2000 l. "Orchis simia" .. 75 75
314 3000 l. "Orchis sancta" .. 1·10 1·10

1991. Paintings (10th series). As T **54**. Multicoloured.

315 250 l. "Hindiler" (S. Cizel) (vert) 20 20
316 500 l. "Dusme" (A. Mene) (vert) 30 30

106 Symbolic Roots (Year of Love to Yunus Emre)

1991. Anniversaries and Events.

317 **106** 250 l. yell, blk & mve 15 15
318 – 500 l. multicoloured .. 25 25
319 – 500 l. multicoloured .. 25 25
320 – 1500 l. multicoloured .. 70 70

DESIGNS—VERT. No. 318, Mustafa Cagatay commemoration; 319, University building (5th anniv of Eastern Mediterranean University). HORIZ. No. 320, Mozart (death bicent).

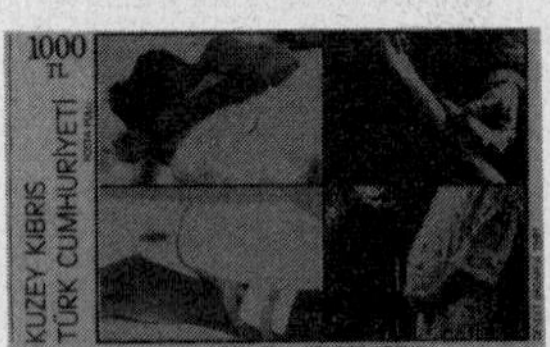

107 Four Sources of Infection

1991. "AIDS" Day.

321 **107** 1000 l. multicoloured .. 50 50

108 Lighthouse, Gazimagusa

1991. Lighthouses. Multicoloured.

322 250 l. Type **108** 15 15
323 500 l. Ancient lighthouses, Girne harbour 20 20
324 1500 l. Modern lighthouse, Girne harbour 55 55

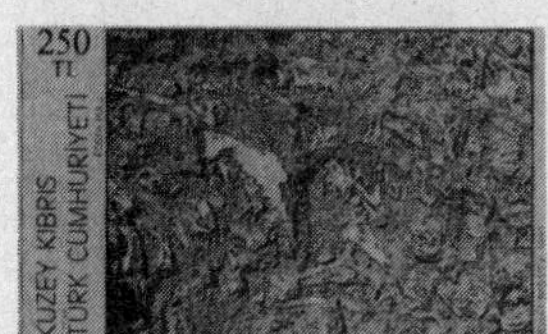

109 Elephant and Hippopotamus Fossils, Karaoglanoglu

1991. Tourism (1st series). Multicoloured.

325 250 l. Type **109** 15 15
326 500 l. Roman fish ponds, Lambusa 20 20
327 1500 l. Roman remains, Lambusa 55 55

See also Nos. 330/3 and 351/2.

1992. Paintings (11th series). As T **54**, but 31 × 49 mm. Multicoloured.

328 500 l. "Ebru" (A. Kandulu) 20 20
329 3500 l. "Street in Lefkosa" (I. Tatar) .. .. 1·25 1·25

1992. Tourism (2nd series). As T **109**. Mult.

330 500 l. Bugday Camii, Gazimagusa 20 20
331 500 l. Clay pigeon shooting 20 20
332 1000 l. Salamis Bay Hotel, Gazimagusa 40 40
333 1500 l. Casino, Girne (vert) 60 60

112 Gymnastics

1992. Olympic Games, Barcelona. Mult.

336 500 l. Type **112** 20 20
337 500 l. Tennis 20 20
338 1000 l. High jumping (horiz) 40 40
339 1500 l. Cycling (horiz) .. 65 65

113 New Generating Station, Girne

1992. Anniversaries and Events (1st series). Multicoloured.

340 500 l. Type **113** 20 20
341 500 l. Symbol of Housing Association (15th anniv) 20 20
342 1500 l. Domestic animals and birds (30th anniv of Veterinary Service) .. 60 60
343 1500 l. Cat (International Federation of Cat Societies Conference) .. 60 60

114 Airliner over Runway

1992. Anniversaries and Events (2nd series). Multicoloured.

344 1000 l. Type **114** (17th anniv of civil aviation) 35 35
345 1000 l. Meteorological instruments and weather (18th anniv of Meteorological Service) 35 35
346 1200 l. Surveying equipment and map (14th anniv of Survey Department) 50 50

115 Zubiye

1992. International Conference on Nutrition, Rome. Turkish Cypriot Cuisine. Mult.

347 2000 l. Type **115** 40 40
348 2500 l. Cicek Dolmasi .. 50 50
349 3000 l. Tatar Boregi .. 60 60
350 4000 l. Seftali Kebabi .. 75 75

1993. Tourism (3rd series). As T **109**. Multicoloured.

351 500 l. St. Barnabas Church and Monastery, Salamis 15 15
352 10000 l. Ancient pot .. 1·60 1·60

117 Olive Tree, Girne

1993. Ancient Trees. Multicoloured.

354 500 l. Type **117** 10 10
355 1000 l. River red gum, Kyrenia Gate, Lefkosa 10 10
356 3000 l. Oriental plane, Lapta 30 35
357 4000 l. Calabrian pine, Cinarli 40 45

118 Traditional Houses

1993. Arabahmet District Conservation Project, Lefkosa. Multicoloured.

358 1000 l. Type **118** 10 10
359 3000 l. Arabahmet street .. 30 35

119 National Flags turning into Doves

KUZEY KIBRIS TÜRK CUMHURİYETİ 500 TL

120 Kemal Ataturk

1993. 10th Anniv of Proclamation of Turkish Republic of Northern Cyprus.

360 **119** 500 l. red, black & blue 10 10
361 – 500 l. red and blue .. 10 10
362 – 1000 l. red, black & bl 10 10
363 – 5000 l. multicoloured .. 50 55

DESIGNS—HORIZ. No. 361, National flag forming figure "10"; No. 362, Dove carrying national flag; No. 363, Map of Cyprus and figure "10" wreath.

1993. Anniversaries. Multicoloured.

364 500 l. Type **120** (55th death anniv) 10 10
365 500 l. Stage and emblem (30th anniv of Turkish Cypriot theatre) (horiz) 10 10
366 1500 l. Branch badges (35th anniv of T.M.T. organization) (horiz) .. 15 20
367 2000 l. World map and computer (20th anniv of Turkish Cypriot news agency) (horiz) .. 20 25
368 5000 l. Ballet dancers and Caykovski'nin (death centenary) (horiz) .. 50 55

DHAR

A state of Central India. Now uses Indian stamps.

4 pice = 1 anna.

1.

2.

1897. Imperf.

1. **1.** ½ pice black on red .. 1·00 80
3. ¼ a. black on orange .. 1·10 2·25
4. ½ a. black on mauve .. 1·25 2·50
5. 1 a. black on green .. 3·00 6·00
6. 2 a. black on yellow .. 16·00 30·00

1898. Perf.

7b. **2.** ½ a. red .. .. 1·25 2·75
8. 1 a. purple .. .. 1·40 3·00
10. 2 a. green .. .. 3·25 13·00

DOMINICA

Until 31 December, 1939, one of the Leeward Is., but then transferred to the Windward Is. Used Leeward Is. stamps concurrently with Dominican issues from 1903 to above date.

1874. 12 pence = 1 shilling;
20 shillings = 1 pound.
1949. 100 cents = 1 West Indian dollar.

1.

1874.

15 1 ½d. yellow .. .. 1·00 4·75
20 ½d. green .. .. .. 50 3·25
5 1d. lilac .. .. .. 4·50 1·50
22a 1d. red .. .. .. 2·75 3·00
16 2½d. brown .. .. £130 2·00
23 2½d. blue .. .. .. 3·75 3·25
7 4d. blue .. .. .. 95·00 2·50
24 4d. grey .. .. .. 2·00 2·75
8 6d. green .. .. .. £140 20·00
25 6d. orange .. .. 5·50 20·00
9 1s. mauve .. .. £120 40·00

1882. No. 5 bisected and surch. with small ½.

10. **1.** ½(d.) on half 1d. lilac .. £140 32·00

1882. No. 5 bisected and surch. with large ½.

11. **1.** ½(d.) on half 1d. lilac .. 28·00 12·00

1883. No. 5 bisected and surch. **HALF PENNY** vert.

14. **1.** ½d. on half 1d. lilac .. 38·00 20·00

1886. Nos. 8 and 3 surch. in words and bar.

17. **1.** ½d. on 6d. green .. .. 4·00 3·50
18. 1d. on 6d. green £16000 £11000
19. 1d. on 1s. mauve .. .. 13·00 13·00

9. View of Roseau from the Sea.

10.

1903.

37 **9.** ½d. green .. .. .. 1·25 2·00
38 1d. grey and red .. .. 2·00 30
29 2d. green and brown .. 2·50 4·00
30 2½d. grey and blue .. 4·50 3·50
31 3d. purple and black .. 8·00 2·75
32 6d. grey and brown .. 4·25 13·00
43 1s. mauve and green .. 3·75 32·00
34 2s. black and purple .. 18·00 25·00
45 2s. 6d. green and orange 20·00 55·00
46 **10.** 5s. black and brown .. 55·00 75·00

1908.

48a 9. 1d. red .. .. .. 1·00 40
64 1½d. orange .. .. .. 3·50 8·50
65 2d. grey .. .. .. 2·75 3·25
66 2½d. blue .. .. .. 1·25 8·50
51 3d. purple on yellow .. 1·75 4·50
52a 6d. purple .. .. 3·50 16·00
53a 1s. black on green .. 1·60 2·75
53b 2s. pur. and blue on blue 24·00 55·00
53c 2s. 6d. black & red on blue 25·00 65·00

1914. As T 10, but portrait of King George V.
54. 5 s. red and green on yellow 50·00 70·00

1916. Surch. WAR TAX ONE HALF-PENNY.
55. 9. ½d. on ½d. green .. 10 75

1918. Optd. WAR TAX in small letters.
56. 9. ½d. green .. .. .. 50 4·00

1918. Optd. WAR TAX in large letters.
57. 9. ½d. green 10 30
58. 3d. purple on yellow .. 20 2·25

1919. Surch. WAR TAX 1½D.
59. 9. 1½d. on 2½d. orange .. 10 55

1920. Surch. 1½D.
60. 9. 1½d. on 2½d. orange .. 1·25 3·75

16.

1923.

71. 16. ½d. black and green .. 80 30
72. 1d. black and violet .. 1·25 50
73. 1d. black and red .. 7·50 80
74. 1½d. black and red .. 1·00 30
75. 1½d. black and brown .. 7·50 50
76. 2d. black and grey .. 85 40
77. 2½d. black and yellow .. 70 7·00
78. 2½d. black and blue .. 2·25 1·00
79. 3d. black and blue .. 70 9·00
80. 3d. black & red on yellow 1·00 1·00
81. 4d. black and brown .. 85 4·00
82. 6d. black and mauve .. 1·75 3·50
83. 1s. black on green .. 1·40 2·25
84. 2s. black & blue on blue.. 3·50 11·00
85. 2s. 6d. blk. & red on blue 12·00 14·00
86. 3s. black & purple on yell. 2·75 8·00
87. 4s. black and red on green 6·00 13·00
90. 5s. black & green on yell. 7·50 38·00
91. £1 black and purple on red £225 £275

1935. Silver Jubilee. As T 13 of Antigua.
92. 1d. blue and red 75 20
93. 1½d. blue and grey .. 1·00 45
94. 2½d. brown and blue .. 1·40 1·25
95. 1s. grey and purple .. 1·50 3·25

1937. Coronation. As T 2 of Aden.
96. 1d. red 40 10
97. 1½d. brown 40 10
98. 2½d. blue 60 85

17. Fresh Water Lake. 21. King George VI.

1938.

99. 17. ½d. brown and green .. 10 15
100. – 1d. black and red .. 20 20
101. – 1½d. green and purple .. 20 65
102. – 2d. red and black .. 40 60
103a.– 2½d. purple and blue .. 20 75
104. – 3d. olive and brown .. 30 40
104a.– 3½d. blue and mauve .. 1·50 45
105. 17. 6d. green and violet .. 1·00 70
105a. 7d. green and brown .. 1·50 70
106. – 1s. violet and olive .. 2·00 50
106a.– 2s. grey and purple .. 4·50 5·00
107. 17. 2s. 6d. black and red .. 11·00 4·75
108. – 5s. blue and brown .. 7·00 4·50
108a.– 10s. black and orange .. 12·00 14·00
DESIGNS—As Type 17: 1d., 3d., 2s., 5s. Layou River. 1½d., 2½d., 3½d. Picking Limes. 2d., 1s., 10s. Boiling Lake.

1940.

109a 21 ¼d. brown 10 10

1946. Victory. As Type 9. of Aden.
110. 1d. red 10 10
111. 3½d. blue 10 10

1948. Silver Wedding. As T 10/11 of Aden.
112. 1d. red 15 10
113. 10s. brown .. .. 6·00 16·00

1949. U.P.U. As T 20/23 of Antigua.
114. 5 c. blue 15 15
115. 6 c. brown 30 20
116. 12 c. purple 30 30
117. 24 c. olive 30 30

1951. Inauguration of B.W.I. University College. As T 24/25 of Antigua.
118. 3 c. green and violet .. 75 30
119. 12 c. green and red .. 75 20

23. Drying Cocoa.

1951. New Currency.
120. – ½ c. brown 10 15
121. 23. 1 c. black and red .. 10 30
122. – 2 c. brown and green .. 10 20
123. – 3 c. green and purple .. 10 50
124. – 4 c. orange and sepia .. 30 30
125. – 5 c. black and red .. 75 20
126. – 6 c. olive and brown .. 80 30
127. – 8 c. green and blue .. 50 45
128. – 12 c. black and green .. 45 1·00
129. – 14 c. blue and purple .. 85 1·00
130. – 24 c. purple and red .. 50 30
131. – 48 c. green and orange .. 1·50 4·25
132. – 60 c. red and black .. 1·50 2·50
133. – $1.20 green and black .. 4·00 2·75
134. – $2.40 orange and black 22·00 23·00
DESIGNS: ½c. As Type 21, but with portrait as Type 22. HORIZ. (as Type 22). 2 c., 60 c. Carib baskets. 3 c., 48 c. Lime plantation. 4 c. Picking oranges. 5 c. Bananas. 6 c. Botanical Gardens. 8 c. Drying vanilla beans. 12 c., $1.20, Fresh Water Lake. 14 c. Layou River, 24 c. Boiling Lake. VERT. $2.40, Picking oranges.

1951. New Constitution. Stamps of 1951 optd. NEW CONSTITUTION 1951.
135. 3 c. green and violet .. 15 40
136. 5 c. black and red .. 15 40
137. 8 c. green and blue .. 15 15
138. 14 c. blue and violet .. 15 15

1953. Coronation. As T 13 of Aden.
139. 2 c. black and green .. 15 10

1954. As Nos. 120/34 but with portrait of Queen Elizabeth II.
140 ½ c. brown 10 20
141 1 c. black and red .. 10 10
142 2 c. brown and green .. 15 40
143 3 c. green and purple .. 1·00 30
144 3 c. black and red .. 2·25 90
145 4 c. orange and brown .. 15 10
146 5 c. black and red .. 1·00 30
147 5 c. blue and brown .. 8·50 90
148 6 c. green and brown .. 20 10
149 8 c. green and blue .. 20 10
150a 10 c. green and brown .. 1·50 75
151 12 c. black and green .. 50 10
152 14 c. blue and purple .. 30 10
153 24 c. purple and red .. 30 10
154 48 c. green and orange .. 1·25 5·50
155 48 c. brown and violet .. 1·25 80
156 60 c. red and black .. 70 1·25
157 $1.20 green and black .. 12·00 6·00
158 $2.40 orange and black .. 13·00 12·00
DESIGNS (New)—HORIZ. Nos. 144, 155, Matmaking. No. 147, Canoe making. No. 150, Bananas.

1958. British Caribbean Federation. As T 25 of Antigua.
159. 3 c. green 35 10
160. 6 c. blue 50 40
161. 12 c. red 70 10

40. Seashore at Rosalie.

1963.

162 40. 1 c. green, blue and sepia 10 20
163 – 2 c. blue 30 10
164 – 3 c. brown and blue .. 30 20
165 – 4 c. grn., sep. & violet .. 10 10
166 – 5 c. mauve 30 10
167 – 6 c. green, bistre & violet 10 10
168 – 8 c. green, sepia & black 10 10
169 – 10 c. sepia and pink .. 10 10
170 – 12 c. green, blue & sepia 10 10
171 – 14 c. multicoloured .. 40 10
172 – 15 c. yellow, green & brn. 70 10
173 – 24 c. multicoloured .. 4·00 10
174 – 48 c. green, blue & black 75 25
175 – 60 c. orange, green & blk. 1·00 50
176 – $1.20 multicoloured .. 6·50 70
177 – $2.40 blue, turq. & brown 3·25 2·00
178 – $4.80 green, blue & brown 9·00 16·00
DESIGNS—VERT. 2 c., 5 c. Queen Elizabeth II (after Annigoni). 14 c. Traditional costume. 24 c. Imperial amazon. $2.40, Trafalgar Falls. $4.80, Coconut palm. HORIZ.. 3 c. Sailing canoe. 4 c. Sulphur springs. 6 c. Road making. 8 c. Dug-out canoe. 10 c. Crapaud (frog). 12 c. Scotts Head. 15 c. Bananas. 48 c. Goodwill. 60 c. Cocoa tree. $1.20, Coat of Arms.

1963. Freedom from Hunger. As T 28 of Aden.
179. 15 c. violet 15 10

1963. Cent of Red Cross. As T 33 of Antigua.
180. 5 c. red and black .. 15 10
181. 15 c. red and blue .. 30 55

1964. 400th Birth Anniv of Shakespeare. As T 34 of Antigua.
182. 15 c. purple 10 10

1965. Cent of I.T.U. As T 36 of Antigua.
183. 2 c. green and blue .. 10 10
184. 48 c. turquoise and grey .. 30 20

1965. I.C.Y. As T 37 of Antigua.
185. 1 c. purple and turquoise.. 10 20
186. 15 c. green and lavender .. 20 10

1966. Churchill Commem. As T 38 of Antigua.
187. 1 c. blue 10 10
188. 5 c. green 10 10
189. 15 c. brown 20 10
190. 24 c. violet 30 20

1966. Royal Visit. As T 39 of Antigua.
191. 5 c. black and blue .. 1·00 10
192. 15 c. black and mauve .. 1·50 20

1966. World Cup Football Championship. As T 40 of Antigua.
193. 5 c. multicoloured .. 20 15
194. 24 c. multicoloured .. 65 15

1966. Inauguration of W.H.O. Headquarters, Geneva. As T 41 of Antigua.
195. 5 c. black, green and blue.. 10 15
196. 24 c. black, purple & ochre 20 15

1966. 20th Anniv. of U.N.E.S.C.O. As T 54/6 of Antigua.
197. 5 c. red, yellow and orange 10 15
198. 15 c. yellow, violet & olive 25 10
199. 24 c. black, purple & orge. 25 15

56. Children of Three Races.

1967. National Day. Multicoloured.
205. 5 c. Type 56 .. .. 10 10
206. 10 c. The "Santa Maria" and Motto 10 10
207. 15 c. Hands holding Motto Ribbon 10 15
208. 24 c. Belaire Dancing .. 15 15

57. John F. Kennedy.

1968. Human Rights Year. Multicoloured.
209. 1 c. Type 57 .. .. 10 10
210. 10 c. Cecil E. A. Rawle .. 10 10
211. 12 c. Pope John XXIII .. 30 15
212. 48 c. Florence Nightingale 30 20
213. 60 c. Albert Schweitzer .. 30 20

1968. Associated Statehood. Nos. 162, etc. optd. ASSOCIATED STATEHOOD.
214. 1 c. grn., blue and sepia.. 10 10
215. 2 c. blue .. 10 10
216. 3 c. brown and blue .. 10 10
217. 4 c. green, sepia and violet 10 10
218. 5 c. mauve .. 10 10
219. 6 c. green, bistre and violet 10 10
220. 8 c. green, sepia and black 10 10
221. 10 c. sepia and pink .. 45 10
222. 12 c. green, blue and brown 10 10
224. 14 c. multicoloured .. 10 10
225. 15 c. yellow, green & brn. 10 10
226. 24 c. multicoloured .. 1·75 10
227. 48 c. green, blue and black 55 90
228. 60 c. orange, green and blk. 90 70
229. $1.20 multicoloured .. 1·00 1·75
230. $2.40 blue, turq. & brown 2·00 2·25
231. $4.80 green blue & brown 2·00 4·25

1968. National Day. Nos. 162/4, 171a and 176 optd. NATIONAL DAY 3 NOVEMBER 1968.
232. 1 c. grn., blue and sepia.. 10 10
233. 2 c. blue .. 10 10
234. 3 c. brown and blue .. 10 10
235. 14 c. multicoloured .. 10 10
236. $1.20 multicoloured .. 30 40

60. Forward shooting at Goal.

1968. Olympic Games, Mexico. Multicoloured.
237. 1 c. Type 60 .. 10 10
238. 1 c. Goalkeeper attempting to save ball .. 10 10
239. 5 c. Swimmers preparing to dive .. 10 10
240. 5 c. Swimmers diving .. 10 10
241. 48 c. Javelin-throwing .. 15 15
242. 48 c. Hurdling .. 15 15
243. 60 c. Basketball .. 15 15
244. 60 c. Basketball players 15 15

61. "The Small Cowper Madonna" (Raphael).

1968. Christmas.
245. 61. 5 c. multicoloured .. 10 10

62. "Venus and Adonis" (Rubens).

1969. 20th Anniv. of World Health Organization.
246. 62. 5 c. multicoloured .. 15 10
247. – 15 c. multicoloured .. 25 10
248. – 24 c. multicoloured .. 25 10
249. – 50 c. multicoloured .. 40 40
DESIGNS: 15 c. "The Death of Socrates" (J.—L. David). 24 c. "Christ and the Pilgrims of Emmaus" (Velasquez). 50 c. "Pilate washing his hands" (Rembrandt).

66. Picking Oranges.

1969. Tourism. Multicoloured.
250. 10 c. Type 66 .. 10 10
251. 10 c. Woman, child and ocean scene .. 10 10
252. 12 c. Fort Yeoung Hotel.. 15 10
253. 12 c. Red-necked Amazon 15 10
254. 24 c. Calypso band .. 15 10
255. 24 c. Women dancing .. 15 15
256. 48 c. Underwater life .. 20 25
257. 48 c. Skin-diver and turtle 20 25

67. "Strength in Unity" Emblem and Fruit trees.

1969. 1st Anniv. of C.A.R.I.F.T.A (Caribbean Free Trade Area). Multicoloured.
258. 5 c. Type 67 .. 10 10
259. 8 c. "HS 748" aircraft, emblem and island .. 10 10
260. 12 c. Chart of Caribbean Sea and emblem .. 15 10
261. 24 c. Steamship unloading, tug and emblem .. 20 10

71. "Spinning" (J. Millet).

1969. 50th Anniv. of International Labour Organization. Multicoloured.

262.	15 c. Type **71**	10	10
263.	30 c. "Threshing" (J. Millet)	15	15
264.	38 c. "Flax-pulling" (J. Millet)	15	15

72. Mahatma Gandhi weaving and Clock Tower, Westminster.

1969. Birth Cent. of Mahatma Gandhi. Mult.

265.	6 c. Type **72**	30	10
266.	38 c. Gandhi, Nehru and Mausoleum	50	15
267.	$1.20 Gandhi and Taj Mahal	1·40	40

NOTE: All stamps are incorrectly inscribed "Ghandi".

75. "Saint Joseph".

1969. National Day. Multicoloured.

268.	6 c. Type **75**	10	10
269.	8 c. "Saint John" ..	10	10
270.	12 c. "Saint Peter" ..	10	10
271.	60 c. "Saint Paul" ..	30	50

79. Queen Elizabeth II.

80. Purple-throated Carib and Flower.

1969. Centres multicoloured; colours of "D" given.

272.	**79.**	½ c. black and silver ..	10	50
273.	**80.**	1 c. black and yellow ..	30	50
274.	–	2 c. black and yellow ..	15	10
275.	–	3 c. black and yellow ..	1·25	1·00
276.	–	4 c. black and yellow ..	1·25	1·00
277.	–	5 c. black and yellow ..	1·25	30
278.	–	6 c. black and brown ..	1·25	1·50
279.	–	8 c. black and brown ..	20	10
280.	–	10 c. black and yellow ..	20	10
281.	–	12 c. black and yellow ..	20	10
282.	–	15 c. black and blue ..	20	10
283.	–	25 c. black and red ..	30	10
284.	–	30 c. black and olive ..	1·50	70
285.	–	38 c. black and purple ..	7·00	1·75
286.	–	50 c. black and brown ..	50	45
287.	–	60 c. black and yellow ..	55	80
288.	–	$1.20 black and yellow	1·00	1·75
289.	–	$2.40 black and gold ..	1·75	3·00
290.	–	$4.80 black and gold ..	3·00	6·00

DESIGNS—HORIZ. As Type **80**: 2 c. Poinsettia. 3 c. Red-necked pigeon. 4 c. Imperial amazon. 5 c. "Battus polydamas" (butterfly). 6 c. "Dryas julia" (butterfly). 8 c. Shipping bananas. 10 c. Portsmouth Harbour. 12 c. Copra processing plant. 15 c. Straw workers. 25 c. Timber plant. 30 c. Pumice mine. 38 c. Grammar school and playing fields. 50 c. Roseau Cathedral. 60 c. Government Headquarters (38 × 26½ mm). $1.20, Melville Hall airport (40 × 27 mm). $2.40, Coat of arms (39½ × 26 mm). VERT. $4.80, As Type **79** but larger (26 × 39 mm).

99. "The Virgin and the Child with St. John" (Perugino).

1969. Christmas. Paintings. Multicoloured.

291.	6 c. "Virgin and Child with St John" (Lippi) ..	10	10
292.	10 c. "Holy Family with Lamb" (Raphael) ..	10	10
293.	15 c. Type **99**	10	10
294.	$1.20 "Madonna of the Rose Hedge" (Botticelli)	35	40

101. Astronaut's First Step onto the Moon.

1970. Moon Landing. Multicoloured.

296.	½ c. Type **101**	10	10
297.	5 c. Scientific experiment on the Moon and flag ..	10	10
298.	8 c. Astronauts collecting rocks	10	10
299.	30 c. Module over Moon ..	20	15
300.	50 c. Moon plaque	30	25
301.	60 c. Astronauts	30	30

107. Giant Green Turtle.

1970. Flora and Fauna. Multicoloured.

303.	6 c. Type **107**	30	15
304.	24 c. Flying fish ..	60	45
305.	38 c. Anthurium lily ..	70	65
306.	60 c. Imperial and Red-necked parrots ..	2·50	2·25

108. 18th-Century National Costume.

1970. National Day. Multicoloured.

308.	5 c. Type **108**	10	10
309.	8 c. Carib basketry ..	10	10
310.	$1 Flag and Chart of Dominica	30	40

109. Scrooge and Marley's Ghost.

1970. Christmas and Death Cent. of Charles Dickens. Scenes from "A Christmas Carol". Multicoloured.

312.	2 c. Type **109**	10	10
313.	15 c. Fezziwig's Ball ..	15	10
314.	24 c. Scrooge and his Nephew's Party ..	15	10
315.	$1.20 Scrooge and the Ghost of Christmas Present	60	60

110. "The Doctor" (Sir Luke Fildes).

1970. Cent. of British red Cross. Mult.

317.	8 c. Type **110** ..	10	10
318.	10 c. Hands and Red Cross	10	10
319.	15 c. Flag of Dominica and Red Cross Emblem ..	15	10
320.	50 c. "The Sick Child" (E. Munch)	50	35

111. Marigot School.

1971. Int. Education Year. Multicoloured.

322.	5 c. Type **111**	10	10
323.	8 c. Goodwill Junior High School	10	10
324.	14 c. University of West Indies (Jamaica) ..	10	10
325.	$1 Trinity College, Cambridge	25	30

112. Waterfall.

1971. Tourism. Multicoloured.

327.	5 c. Type **112**	10	10
328.	10 c. Boat-building ..	10	10
329.	30 c. Sailing	20	10
330.	50 c. Yacht and motor launch	35	30

113. U.N.I.C.E.F. Symbol in "D".

1971. 25th Anniv. of U.N.I.C.E.F.

332.	**113.**	5 c. violet, blk., & gold	10	10
333.		10 c. yell., blk., & gold ..	10	10
334.		38 c. grn., blk. & gold ..	10	10
335.		$1.20 orge., blk. & gold	30	45

114. German Boy Scout.

1971. World Scout Jamboree, Asagiri, Japan. Various designs showing Boy Scouts from the nations listed. Multicoloured.

337.	20 c. Type **114** ..	15	10
338.	24 c. Great Britain ..	20	10
339.	30 c. Japan	25	10
340.	$1 Dominica	50	40

115. Groyne at Portsmouth.

1971. National Day. Multicoloured.

342.	8 c. Type **115**	10	10
343.	15 c. Carnival scene	10	10
344.	20 c. Carifta Queen (vert.)	10	10
345.	50 c. Rock of Atkinson (vert.)	20	25

116. Eight Reals Piece, 1761.

1972. Coins.

347.	**116.**	10 c. black, sil. & vio.	10	10
348.	–	30 c. black, sil. & grn. ..	15	15
349.	–	35 c. black, sil. & blue ..	20	20
350.	–	50 c. black, silver & red	40	60

DESIGNS—HORIZ. 30 c. Eleven and three bitt pieces, 1798. VERT. 35 c. Two reals and two bitt pieces, 1770. 50 c. Mocos, Pieces-of-eight and eight reals-eleven bitts piece, 1798.

117. Common Opossum.

1972. U.N. Conf. on the Human Environment, Stockholm. Multicoloured.

352.	½ c. Type **117**	10	10
353.	35 c. Brazilian agouti (rodent)	40	15
354.	60 c. Orchid	2·50	50
355.	$1·20 Hibiscus	2·50	1·60

118. Sprinter.

1972. Olympic Games, Munich. **Mult.**

357.	30 c. Type **118**	10	10
358.	35 c. Hurdler	15	15
359.	58 c. Hammer-thrower (vert.)	20	20
360.	72 c. Long-jumper (vert.) ..	40	40

119. General Post Office.

1972. National Day. Multicoloured.

362.	10 c. Type **119** ..	10	10
363.	20 c. Morne Diablotin ..	10	10
364.	30 c. Rodney's Rock ..	15	15

1972. Royal Silver Wedding. As T **52** of Ascension, but with Bananas and Sisserou Parrot in background.

366.	5 c. green	10	10
367.	$1 green	40	40

121. "The Adoration of the Shepherds" (Caravaggio).

1972. Christmas. Multicoloured.

368.	8 c. Type **121**	10	10
369.	14 c. "The Myosotis Virgin" (Rubens)	10	10
370.	30 c. "Madonna and Child" with St. Francesca Romana" (Gentileschi)	15	10
371.	$1 "Adoration of the Kings" (Mostaert)	40	70

122. Launching of Weather Satellite.

1973. Cent. of I.M.O./W.M.O. Multicoloured.

373.	½ c. Type **122**	10	10
374.	1 c. Nimbus satellite	10	10
375.	2 c. Radiosonde balloon	10	10
376.	30 c. Radarscope (horiz.)	15	15
377.	35 c. Diagram of pressure zones (horiz.)	20	20
378.	50 c. Hurricane shown by satellite (horiz.)	30	35
379.	$1 Computer weather-map (horiz.)	60	65

123. Going to Hospital.

1973. 25th Anniv. W.H.O. Multicoloured.

381.	½ c. Type **123**	10	10
382.	1 c. Maternity care	10	10
383.	2 c. Smallpox inoculation	10	10
384.	30 c. Emergency service	30	15
385.	35 c. Waiting for the doctor	35	15
386.	50 c. Medical examination	45	25
387.	$1 Travelling doctor	65	60

124. Cyrique Crab.

1973. Flora and Fauna. Multicoloured.

389.	½ c. Type **124**	10	10
390.	22 c. Blue Land-crab	35	10
391.	25 c. Bread Fruit	35	15
392.	$1.20 Sunflower	1·50	2·00

125. Princess Anne and Captain Mark Philips.

1973. Royal Wedding.

394. **125**	25 c. multicoloured	10	10
395. –	$2 multicoloured	30	30

DESIGN: $2 As Type **125**, but with different frame.

126. "Adoration of the Kings" (Brueghel).

1973. Christmas. "The Adoration of the Shepherds" by the artists listed. Mult.

397.	½ c. Type **126**	10	10
398.	1 c. Botticelli "Adoration of the Magi"	10	10
399.	2 c. Durer "Adoration of the Magi"	10	10
400.	12 c. Botticelli "Mystic Nativity"	20	10
401.	22 c. Rubens "Adoration of the Magi"	25	10
402.	35 c. Durer "The Nativity"	25	10
403.	$1 Giorgione "Adoration of the Shepherds"	90	55

127. Carib Basket-weaving.

1973. National Day. Multicoloured.

405.	5 c. Type **127**	10	10
406.	10 c. Staircase of the Snake	10	10
407.	50 c. Miss Caribbean Queen 1973	15	15
408.	60 c. Miss Carifta Queen 1973	15	15
409.	$1 Dance Group	25	30

Nos. 407/8 are vert.

128. University Centre Dominica.

1973. 25th Anniv. West Indies University. Multicoloured.

411.	12 c. Type **128**	10	10
412.	30 c. Graduation ceremony	10	10
413.	$1 University coat of arms	25	35

129. Dominica 1d. Stamp of 1874 and Map.

1974. Stamp Centenary. Multicoloured.

415.	½ c. Type **129**	10	10
416.	1 c. 6d. stamp of 1874 and posthorn	10	10
417.	2 c. 1d. stamp of 1874 and arms	10	10
418.	10 c. Type **129**	20	10
419.	50 c. As 1 c.	75	30
420.	$1.20 As 2 c.	1·00	70

130. Footballer and Flag of Brazil.

1974. World Cup Football Championship, West Germany. Multicoloured.

422.	½ c. Type **130**.	10	10
423.	1 c. West Germany	10	10
424.	2 c. Italy	10	10
425.	30 c. Scotland	40	10
426.	40 c. Sweden	40	10
427.	50 c. Netherlands	45	15
428.	$1 Yugoslavia	70	40

131. Indian Hole.

1974. National Day. Multicoloured.

430.	10 c. Type **131**	10	10
431.	40 c. Teachers' Training College	10	10
432.	$1 Bay Oil distillery plant, Petite Savanne	50	45

132. Churchill with "Colonist".

1974. Birth Cent. of Sir Winston Churchill. Multicoloured.

434.	½ c. Type **132**	10	10
435.	1 c. Churchill and Eisenhower	10	10
436.	2 c. Churchill and Roosevelt	10	10
437.	20 c. Churchill and troops on assault-course	15	10
438.	45 c. Painting at Marrakesh	25	10
439.	$2 Giving the "V" sign	80	1·00

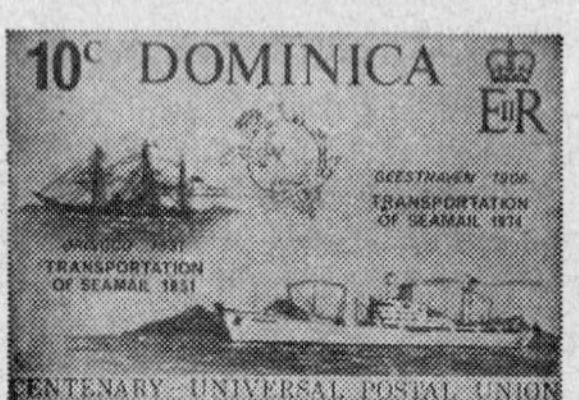

133. Mailboats "Orinoco" (1851) and "Geesthaven" (1974).

1974. Cent. of Universal Postal Union. Mult.

441.	10 c. Type **133**	15	10
442.	$2 Mailplanes—De Havilland "4" (1918) and Boeing "747" (1974)	65	1·00

134. "The Virgin and Child" (Tiso).

1974. Christmas. Multicoloured.

444.	½ c. Type **134**	10	10
445.	1 c. "Madonna and Child" (Costa)	10	10
446.	2 c. "The Nativity" (school of Rimini, 14th Cent.)	10	10
447.	10 c. "The Rest on the flight into Egypt" (Romanelli)	20	10
448.	25 c. "The Adoration of the Shepherds" (de Sermoneta)	35	10
449.	45 c. "The Nativity" (Guido Reni)	45	10
450.	$1 "The Adoration of the Magi" (Caselli)	65	40

135. Trigger Fish.

1975. Fishes. Multicoloured.

452.	½ c. Type **135**	10	10
453.	1 c. Cola	10	10
454.	2 c. Sailfish	10	10
455.	3 c. Vayway	10	10
456.	20 c. Bechine	1·00	50
457.	$2 Grouper	4·25	2·75

136. "Myscelia antholia".

1975. Dominican Butterflires. Multicoloured.

459	½ c. Type **136**	10	20
460	1 c. "Lycorea ceres"	10	20
461	2 c. "Anaea manthesia" ("Sierone nemesis")	15	20
462	6 c. "Battus polydamas"	60	30
463	30 c. "Anartia lytrea"	1·75	70
464	40 c. "Morpho peleides"	2·00	75
465	$2 "Dryas julia"	3·75	4·75

137. "Yare" (cargo liner).

1975. "Ships tied to Dominica's History". Multicoloured.

467	½ c. Type **137**	10	10
468	1 c. "Thames II" (liner), 1890	10	10
469	2 c. "Lady Nelson" (cargo liner)	10	10
470	20 c. "Lady Rodney" (cargo liner)	45	35
471	45 c. "Statesman" (freighter)	70	75
472	50 c. "Geestcape" (freighter)	80	65
473	$2 "Geeststar" (freighter)	4·50	3·25

138. "Women in Agriculture".

1975. International Women's Year. Mult.

475.	10 c. Type **138**	10	10
476.	$2 "Women in Industry and Commerce"	40	60

139. Miss Caribbean Queen, 1975.

1975. National Day. Multicoloured.

477.	5 c. Type **139**	10	10
478.	10 c. Public Library (horiz.)	10	10
479.	30 c. Citrus Factory (horiz.)	10	10
480.	$1 National Day Trophy	25	50

140. "Virgin and Child" (Mantegna).

1975. Christmas. "Virgin and Child" paintings by artists named. Multicoloured.

482. ½ c. Type **140** 10 10
483. 1 c. Fra Filippo Lippi .. 10 10
484. 2 c. Bellini 10 10
485. 10 c. Botticelli 10 10
486. 25 c. Bellini 10 10
487. 45 c. Correggio 15 10
488. $1 Durer 30 50

141. Hibiscus.

1975. Multicoloured.

490. ½ c. Type **141** 10 40
491. 1 c. African tulip 15 40
492. 2 c. Castor-oil tree .. 15 40
493. 3 c. White cedar flower .. 15 40
494. 4 c. Egg plant 15 40
495. 5 c. Gare 20 40
496. 6 c. Ochro 20 50
497. 8 c. Zenaida dove .. .. 1·00 50
498. 10 c. Screw pine 20 15
499. 20 c. Mango longue .. 30 15
500. 25 c. Crayfish 35 15
501. 30 c. Common opossum .. 90 70
502. 40 c. Bay leaf groves .. 90 70
503. 50 c. Tomatoes 55 40
504. $1 Lime factory 75 55
505. $2 Ram distillery .. .. 3·00 3·25
506. $5 Bay oil distillery .. 4·25 4·50
507. $10 Queen Elizabeth II (vert.) .. .. .. 10·00 15·00

Nos. 502/7 are larger, 28 × 44 mm. ($10) or 44 × 28 (others).

142. American Infantry.

1976. Bicent. of American Revolution. Mult.

508. ½ c. Type **142** 10 10
509. 1 c. British three-decker, 1782 .. .. .. 10 10
510. 2 c. George Washington .. 10 10
511. 45 c. British sailors .. 75 30
512. 75 c. British ensign .. 1·25 65
513. $2 Admiral Hood .. .. 3·00 2·00

143. Rowing.

1976. Olympic Games, Montreal. Mult.

515. ½ c. Type **143** 10 10
516. 1 c. Shot putting 10 10
517. 2 c. Swimming 10 10
518. 40 c. Relay 15 10
519. 45 c. Gymnastics 15 10
520. 60 c. Sailing 20 20
521. $2 Archery 55 80

144. Ringed Kingfisher.

1976. Wild Birds. Multicoloured.

523. ½ c. Type **144** 10 15
524. 1 c. Mourning dove .. 15 15
525. 2 c. Green heron 15 15
526. 15 c. Blue-winged hawk (vert.) .. .. .. 1·25 45
527. 30 c. Blue-headed hummingbird (vert.) .. .. 1·75 70
528. 45 c. Bananaquit (vert.) .. 2·50 1·00
529. $2 Imperial amazon (vert.) 9·00 8·50

1976. West Indian Victory in World Cricket Cup. As Nos. 559/60 of Barbados.

531. 15 c. Map of the Caribbean 1·00 1·25
532. 25 c. Prudential Cup .. 1·00 1·50

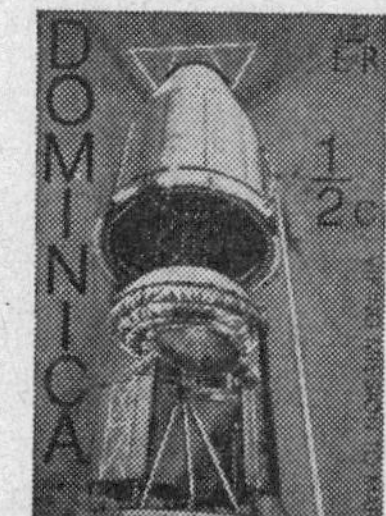

145. Viking Spacecraft System.

1976. Viking Space Mission. Multicoloured.

533. ½ c. Type **145** 10 10
534. 1 c. Launching pad (horiz.) 10 10
535. 2 c. Titan IIID and Centaur DII 10 10
536. 3 c. Orbiter and lander capsule 10 10
537. 45 c. Capsule, parachute unopened 30 15
538. 75 c. Capsule, parachute opened 50 25
539. $1 Lander descending (horiz.) 60 35
540. $2 Space vehicle on Mars (horiz.) 90 80

146. "Virgin and Child with Saints Anthony of Padua and Roch" (Giorgione).

1976. Christmas. "Virgin and Child" paintings by artists named. Multicoloured.

542. ½ c. Type **146** 10 10
543. 1 c. Bellini 10 10
544. 2 c. Mantegna 10 10
545. 6 c. Mantegna (different) .. 10 10
546. 25 c. Memling 10 10
547. 45 c. Correggio 15 10
548. $3 Raphael .. .. 70 1·00

147. Island Craft Co-operative.

1976. National Day. Multicoloured.

550. 10 c. Type **147** 10 10
551. 50 c. Harvesting Bananas 15 10
552. $1 Boxing Plant 30 35

148. Common Sundial.

1976. Shells. Multicoloured.

554. ½ c. Type **148** 10 10
555. 1 c. Flame Helmet .. 10 10
556. 2 c. Mouse Cone 10 10
557. 20 c. Caribbean Vase .. 45 10
558. 40 c. West Indian Fighting Conch 70 25
559. 50 c. Short Coral Shell .. 70 25
560. $3 Apple Murex .. .. 3·50 2·75

149. The Queen Crowned and Enthroned.

1977. Silver Jubilee. Multicoloured.

562. ½ c. Type **149** 10 10
563. 1 c. Imperial State Crown 10 10
564. 45 c. The Queen and Princess Anne 15 10
565. $2 Coronation Ring .. 25 30
566. $2.50 Ampulla and Spoon 30 40

150. Joseph Haydn.

1977. 150th Death Anniv. of Ludwig van Beethoven. Multi.

568. ½ c. Type **150** 10 10
569. 1 c. Scene from "Fidelio" 10 10
570. 2 c. Maria Casentini (dancer) 10 10
571. 15 c. Beethoven and pastoral scene 25 10
572. 30 c. "Wellington's Victory" 35 10
573. 40 c. Henriette Sontag (singer) 45 10
574. $2 The young Beethoven 1·50 1·50

151. Hiking.

1977. Caribbean Scout Jamboree, Jamaica. Multicoloured.

576. ½ c. Type **151** 10 10
577. 1 c. First-aid 10 10
578. 2 c. Camping 10 10
579. 45 c. Rock climbing .. 35 15
580. 50 c. Canoeing 40 20
581. $3 Sailing .. .. .. 2·00 1·75

152. Holy Family.

1977. Christmas. Multicoloured.

583. ½ c. Type **152** 10 10
584. 1 c. Angel and Shepherds 10 10
585. 2 c. Holy Baptism .. 10 10
586. 6 c. Flight into Egypt .. 15 10
587. 15 c. Three Kings with gifts 15 10
588. 45 c. Holy Family in the Temple 30 10
589. $3 Flight into Egypt (different) .. .. .. 1·25 70

1977. Royal Visit. Nos. 562/66 optd. **ROYAL VISIT W.I. 1977.**

591. ½ c. Type **149** 10 10
592. 1 c. Imperial State Crown 10 10
593. 45 c. The Queen and Princess Anne 15 10
594. $2 Coronation Ring .. 30 30
595. $2·50 Ampulla and Spoon 35 35

154. "Sousouelle Souris".

1978. "History of Carnival". Multicoloured.

597. ½ c. Type **154** 10 10
598. 1 c. Sensay costume .. 10 10
599. 2 c. Street musicians .. 10 10
600. 45 c. Douiette band .. 15 10
601. 50 c. Pappy Show wedding 15 10
602. $2 Masquerade band .. 45 60

155. Colonel Charles Lindbergh and "Spirit of St. Louis".

1978. Aviation Annivs. Multicoloured.

604. 6 c. Type **155** 15 10
605. 10 c. "Spirit of St. Louis", New York, 20th May 1927 20 10
606. 15 c. Lindbergh and map of Atlantic 30 10
607. 20 c. Lindbergh reaches Paris, 21st May 1927 .. 40 10
608. 40 c. "LZ1", Lake Constance, 1900 .. .. 50 20
609. 60 c. Count F. von Zeppelin and "LZ 2" 1906 .. 60 30
610. $3 "LZ127 Graf Zeppelin" 1928 .. .. .. 1·40 1·10

156. Queen receiving Homage.

1978. 25th Anniv. of Coronation. Multi.

612. 45 c. Type **156** 15 10
613. $2 Balcony scene .. 30 30
614. $2.50 Queen and Prince Philip 40 40

157. Wilbur Wright's Aeroplane.

1978. 75th Anniv. of First Powered Flight. Multicoloured.

616. 30 c. Type **157** 15 15
617. 40 c. "Flyer", 1908 .. 20 20
618. 60 c. "Flyer I" 25 25
619. $2 "Flyer I" (different) 85 85

158. "Two Apostles".

1978. Christmas. Paintings by Rubens. Multicoloured.

621. 20 c. Type **158** 10 10
622. 45 c. "Descent from the Cross" 15 10
623. 50 c. "St. Ildefonso receiving the Chasuble" .. 15 10
624. $3 "Assumption of the Virgin" 35 80

MINIMUM PRICE

The minimum price quoted is 10p which represents a handling charge rather than a basis for valuing common stamps. For further notes about prices see introductory pages.

159. Map showing Parishes.

1978. Independence. Multicoloured.

No.	Description	Unused	Used
626.	10 c. Type **159**	10	10
627.	25 c. "Sabinea carinalis" (national flower) ..	15	10
628.	45 c. New National flag ..	25	15
629.	50 c. Coat of arms ..	25	15
630.	$2 Prime Minister Patrick John	70	70

1978. Nos. 490/507 optd. **INDEPENDENCE 3rd NOVEMBER 1978.**

No.	Description	Unused	Used
632.	½ c. Type **57**	40	10
633.	1 c. African tulip	45	10
634.	2 c. Castor-oil tree ..	45	10
635.	3 c. White cedar flower ..	50	15
636.	4 c. Egg plant	50	15
637.	5 c. Gare	50	15
638.	6 c. Ochro	50	15
639.	8 c. Zenaida dove	1·25	20
640.	10 c. Screw pine	50	15
641.	20 c. Mango longue ..	60	15
642.	25 c. Crayfish	70	20
643.	30 c. Common opossum ..	70	20
644.	40 c. Bay leaf groves ..	70	25
645.	50 c. Tomatoes	1·00	30
646.	$1 Lime Factory	1·00	65
647.	$2 Rum distillery	1·25	1·00
648.	$5 Bay oil distillery ..	2·50	2·25
649.	$10 Queen Elizabeth II ..	5·50	4·50

161. Sir Rowland Hill.

1979. Death Cent. of Sir Rowland Hill. Multicoloured.

No.	Description	Unused	Used
650.	25 c. Type **161**	10	10
651.	45 c. G.B. 1840 Twopenny Blue	15	10
652.	50 c. Dominica 1874 1d. stamp	15	10
653.	$2 Maltese Cross handstamps	35	65

162. Children and Canoe.

1979. International Year of the Child. Multicoloured.

No.	Description	Unused	Used
655.	30 c. Type **162**	15	15
656.	40 c. Children with bananas	15	15
657.	50 c. Children playing cricket	50	40
658.	$3 Child feeding rabbits ..	1·00	1·50

163. Grouper.

1979. Marine Wildlife. Multicoloured.

No.	Description	Unused	Used
660.	10 c. Type **163**	30	10
661.	30 c. Striped dolphin ..	60	20
662.	50 c. White-tailed Tropic-Bird	1·50	40
663.	60 c. Brown Pelican ..	1·50	50
664.	$1 Long-finned pilot whale	2·00	70
665.	$2 Brown Booby	2·75	1·50

164. H.M.S. "Endeavour".

1979. Death Bicentenary of Captain Cook. Multicoloured.

No.	Description	Unused	Used
667.	10 c. Type **164**	45	10
668.	50 c. H.M.S. "Resolution" (Second Voyage) ..	1·00	60
669.	60 c. H.M.S. "Discovery" (Third Voyage) ..	1·10	70
670.	$2 Detail of Cook's chart of New Zealand, 1770 ..	1·60	1·50

165. Cooking at Camp-fire.

1979. 50th Anniv. of Girl Guide Movement in Dominica. Multicoloured.

No.	Description	Unused	Used
672.	10 c. Type **165**	25	10
673.	20 c. Pitching emergency rain tent	30	10
674.	50 c. Raising Dominican flag	45	10
675.	$2.50 Singing and dancing to accordian	1·25	80

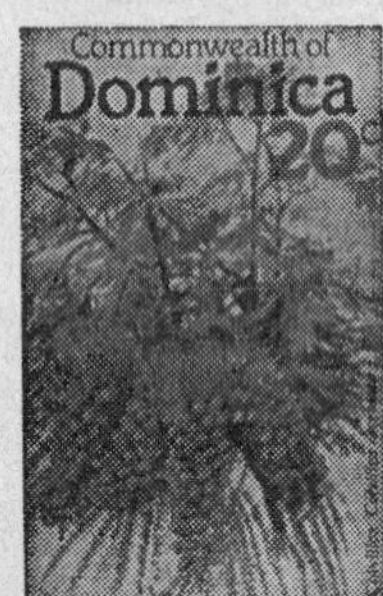

166. Colvillea.

1979. Flowering Trees. Multicoloured.

No.	Description	Unused	Used
677.	20 c. Type **166**	15	10
678.	40 c. "Lignum Vitae" ..	20	15
679.	60 c. Dwarf Poinciana ..	30	25
680.	$2 Fern Tree	70	90

167. Cathedral of the Assumption, Roseau.

1979. Christmas. Cathedrals. Multicoloured.

No.	Description	Unused	Used
682.	6 c. Type **167**	10	10
683.	45 c. St. Paul's, London (vert.)	15	10
684.	60 c. St. Peter's, Rome ..	15	10
685.	$3 Notre Dame, Paris (vert.)	55	60

1979. Hurricane Relief. Nos. 495, 502 and 506/7 optd. **HURRICANE RELIEF.**

No.	Description	Unused	Used
687.	5 c. Gare	10	10
688.	40 c. Bay Leaf Groves ..	10	10
689.	$5 Bay Oil Distillery ..	1·25	1·50
690.	$10 Queen Elizabeth II ..	2·00	2·25

169. Mickey Mouse and Octopus playing Xylophone.

1979. International Year of the Child. Walt Disney Characters. Multicoloured.

No.	Description	Unused	Used
691.	½ c. Type **169**	10	10
692.	1 c. Goofy playing guitar on rocking-horse ..	10	10
693.	2 c. Mickey Mouse playing violin and Goofy on bag-pipes	10	10
694.	3 c. Donald Duck playing drum with a pneumatic drill	10	10
695.	4 c. Minnie Mouse playing saxophone	10	10
696.	5 c. Goofy one-man band	10	10
697.	10 c. Horace Horsecollar blowing Dale from French horn	10	10
698.	$2 Huey, Dewey and Louie playing bass	2·75	1·50
699.	$2.50 Donald Duck at piano and Huey playing trumpet	3·00	1·75

170. Hospital Ward.

1980. 75th Anniv. of Rotary International. Multicoloured.

No.	Description	Unused	Used
701.	10 c. Type **170**	10	10
702.	20 c. Electro-cardiogram	15	10
703.	40 c. Mental hospital site	20	15
704.	$2.50 Paul Harris (founder)	55	70

1980. "London 1980" International Stamp Exhibition. Optd. **LONDON 1980.**

No.	Type	Description	Unused	Used
706.	**161.**	25 c. multicoloured ..	25	10
707.	–	45 c. multicoloured ..	30	15
708.	–	50 c. brown, blue & red	30	15
709.	–	$2 brown, red & yellow	80	60

171. Shot Putting.

1980. Olympic Games, Moscow. Mult.

No.	Description	Unused	Used
710.	30 c. Type **171**	20	10
711.	40 c. Basketball	35	15
712.	60 c. Swimming	35	20
713.	$2 Gymnastics	70	65

172. "Supper at Emmaus" (Caravaggio).

1980. Famous Paintings. Multicoloured.

No.	Description	Unused	Used
715.	20 c. Type **172**	10	10
716.	25 c. "Portrait of Charles I Hunting" (Van Dyck) (vert.)	10	10
717.	30 c. "The Maids of Honour" (Velazquez) (vert.)	15	10
718.	45 c. "The Rape of the Sabine Women" (Poussin)	15	10
719.	$1 "Embarkation for Cythera" (Watteau) ..	35	35
720.	$5 "Girl before a Mirror" (Picasso) (vert.) ..	1·50	1·50

173. Scene from "Peter Pan".

1980. Christmas. Scenes from "Peter Pan". Multicoloured.

No.	Description	Unused	Used
722.	½ c. Type **173** (Tinker Bell)	10	10
723.	1 c. Wendy sewing back Peter's shadow ..	10	10
724.	2 c. Peter introduces the mermaids	10	10
725.	3 c. Wendy and Peter with lost boys	10	10
726.	4 c. Captain Hook, Pirate Smee and Tiger Lily ..	10	10
727.	5 c. Peter with Tiger Lily and her father	10	10
728.	10 c. Captain Hook captures Peter and Wendy	10	10
729.	$2 Peter fights Captain Hook	1·50	1·10
730.	$2.50 Captain Hook in crocodile's jaws ..	1·75	1·25

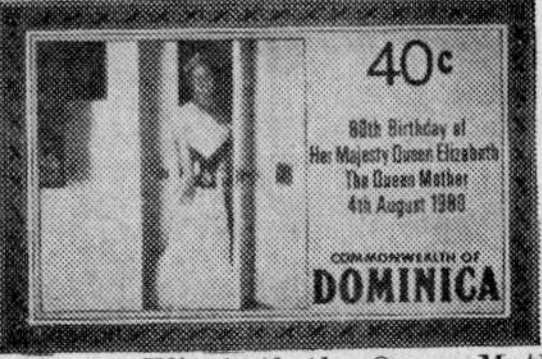

174. Queen Elizabeth the Queen Mother in Doorway.

1980. 80th Birthday of The Queen Mother.

No.	Type	Description	Unused	Used
732.	**174.**	40 c. multicoloured ..	15	15
733.		$2.50 multicoloured ..	60	60

175. Douglas Bay.

1981. "Dominica Safari". Multicoloured.

No.	Description	Unused	Used
735.	20 c. Type **175**	10	10
736.	30 c. Valley of Desolation	10	10
737.	40 c. Emerald Pool (vert.)	10	10
738.	$3 Indian River (vert.) ..	75	1·10

1981. Walt Disney's Cartoon Character, Pluto. As T **169**. Multicoloured.

No.	Description	Unused	Used
740.	$2 Pluto and Fifi	1·25	1·50

176. Forest Thrush.

1981. Birds. Multicoloured.

No.	Description	Unused	Used
742.	20 c. Type **176**	55	30
743.	30 c. Wied's crested fly-catcher	65	35
744.	40 c. Blue-hooded euphonia	75	45
745.	$5 Lesser Antillean pewee	3·50	4·75

177. Windsor Castle.

1981. Royal Wedding. Multicoloured.

No.	Description	Unused	Used
747.	40 c. Prince Charles and Lady Diana Spencer ..	10	10
748.	60 c. Type **177**	15	15
749.	$4 Prince Charles flying helicopter	50	75

178. Lady Diana Spencer.

1981. Royal Wedding. Multicoloured.

751.	25 c. Type **178** ..	20	35
752.	$2 Prince Charles ..	70	1·00
753.	$5 Prince Charles and Lady Diana Spencer	1·75	2·50

1981. Christmas. Scenes from Walt Disney's cartoon film "Santa's Workshop". As T **169**.

754.	½ c. multicoloured ..	10	10
755.	1 c. multicoloured ..	10	10
756.	2 c. multicoloured ..	10	10
757.	3 c. multicoloured ..	10	10
758.	4 c. multicoloured ..	10	10
759.	5 c. multicoloured ..	10	10
760.	10 c. multicoloured ..	10	10
761.	45 c. multicoloured ..	75	30
762.	$5 multicoloured	3·50	3·00

179. Ixora.

1981. Plant Life. Multicoloured.

764	1 c. Type **179**	10	30
765	2 c. Flamboyant	10	30
766	4 c. Poinsettia	15	10
767	5 c. Bois Caribe (national flower of Dominica) ..	15	10
768	8 c. Annatto or Roucou ..	20	10
769	10 c. Passion Fruit ..	30	10
770	15 c. Breadfruit or Yampain	55	15
771	20 c. Allamanda or Buttercup	40	15
772	25 c. Cashew Nut ..	40	15
773	35 c. Sousop or Couassol ..	45	30
774	40 c. Bougainvillea ..	45	30
775	45 c. Anthurium ..	50	35
776	60 c. Cacao or Cocoa ..	1·00	35
777	90 c. Pawpaw Tree or Papay	70	60
778	$1 Coconut Palm ..	1·00	80
779	$2 Coffee Tree or Cafe ..	1·00	2·00
780	$5 Heliconia or Lobster Claw	3·25	4·00
781	$10 Banana/Fig	5·00	8·00

Nos. 769, 770, 776, 778, 780 and 781 come with or without imprint date.

180. Curb Slope for Wheelchairs.

1981. International Year of Disabled People. Multicoloured.

782.	45 c. Type **180**	70	25
783.	60 c. Bus with invalid step	80	35
784.	75 c. Motor car controls adapted for handicapped	90	40
785.	$4 Bus with wheelchair ramp	2·50	2·50

181. "Olga Picasso in an Armchair".

1981. Birth Centenary of Picasso. Mult.

787.	45 c. Type **181** ..	75	25
788.	60 c. "Bathers"	85	35
789.	75 c. "Woman in Spanish Costume"	1·00	40
790.	$4 "Detail of Dog and Cock"	2·50	2·50

HAVE YOU READ THE NOTES AT THE BEGINNING OF THIS CATALOGUE?

These often provide answers to the enquiries we receive.

1982. World Cup Football Championship, Spain. Walt Disney Cartoon Characters. As T **169**. Multicoloured.

792.	½ c. Goofy chasing ball with butterfly net ..	10	10
793.	1 c. Donald Duck with ball in beak	10	10
794.	2 c. Goofy as goalkeeper ..	10	10
795.	3 c. Goofy looking for ball	10	10
796.	4 c. Goofy as park attendant puncturing ball with litter spike	10	10
797.	5 c. Pete and Donald Duck playing	10	10
798.	10 c. Donald Duck after kicking rock instead of ball	10	10
799.	60 c. Donald Duck feeling effects of a hard game and Daisy Duck dusting ball	85	60
800.	$5 Goofy hiding ball under his jersey from Mickey Mouse	3·75	3·75

182. "Golden Days".

1982. Norman Rockwell (painter) Commemoration. Multicoloured.

802.	10 c. Type **182**	10	10
803.	25 c. "The Morning News"	15	10
804.	45 c. "The Marbles Champ"	30	30
805.	$1 "Speeding Along" ..	55	55

183. Elma Napier (first woman elected to B.W.I. Legislative Council).

1982. Decade for Women. Multicoloured.

806.	10 c. Type **183**	10	10
807.	45 c. Margaret Mead (anthropologist) ..	30	30
808.	$1 Mabel (Cissy) Caudeiron (folk song composer and historian)	55	55
809.	$4 Eleanor Roosevelt ..	2·25	2·25

184. George Washington and Independence Hall, Philadelphia.

1982. 250th Birth Anniv. of George Washington. Birth Centenary of Franklin D. Roosevelt. Multicoloured.

811.	45 c. Type **184**	40	25
812.	60 c. Franklin D. Roosevelt and Capitol Washington D.C.	50	35
813.	90 c. Washington at Yorktown (detail "The Surrender of Corwallis" by Trumbull)	70	55
814.	$2 Construction of dam from W. Groppers' mural commemorating Roosevelt's "New Deal" ..	1·50	1·60

185. "Anaea dominicana".

1982. Butterflies. Multicoloured.

816	15 c. Type **185**	1·00	35
817	45 c. "Heliconius charithonia"	1·75	65
818	60 c. "Hypolimnas misippus"	2·00	1·25
819	$3 "Biblis hyperia" ..	4·50	5·00

186. Prince and Princess of Wales.

1982. 21st Birthday of Princess of Wales. Multicoloured.

821.	45 c. Buckingham Palace	30	15
822.	$2 Type **186**	70	80
823.	$4 Princess of Wales ..	1·10	1·25

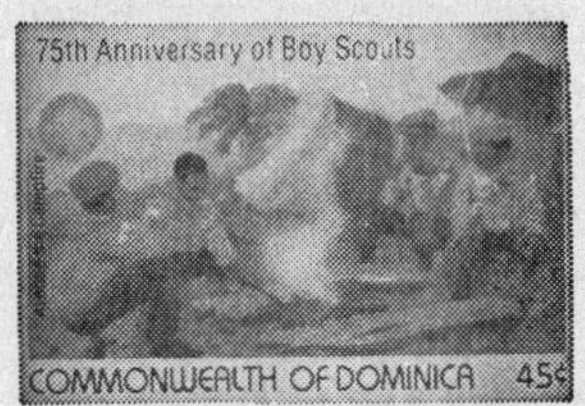

187. Scouts around Campfire.

1982. 75th Anniv. of Boy Scout Movement. Multicoloured.

825.	45 c. Type **187**	1·25	50
826.	60 c. Temperature study, Valley of Desolation ..	1·75	1·25
827.	75 c. Learning about native birds	2·25	1·50
828.	$3 Canoe trip along Indian River	4·25	5·00

1982. Birth of Prince William of Wales. Nos. 821/3 optd. **ROYAL BABY 21.6.82.**

830.	45 c. Buckingham Palace	30	30
831.	$2 Type **186**	90	1·10
832.	$4 Princess of Wales ..	1·60	1·90

188. "Holy Family of Francis I".

1982. Christmas. Raphael Paintings. Mult.

834.	25 c. Type **188**	15	10
835.	30 c. "Holy Family of the Pearl"	20	15
836.	90 c. "Canigiani Holy Family"	55	55
837.	$4 "Holy Family of the Oak Tree"	1·90	1·90

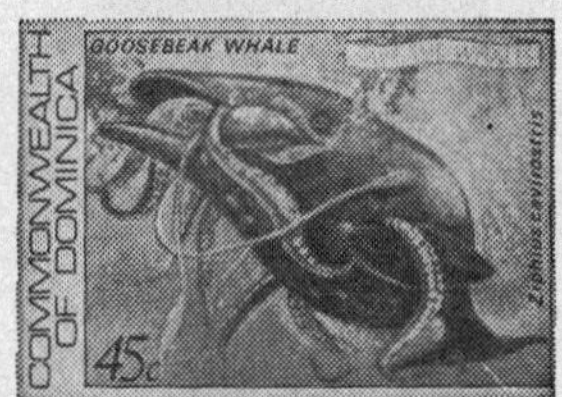

189. Cuvier's Beaked Whale.

1983. Save the Whales. Multicoloured.

839.	45 c. Type **189**	1·25	65
840.	60 c. Humpback Whale ..	1·50	1·25
841.	75 c. Black Right Whale ..	1·75	1·50
842.	$3 Melon-headed Whale ..	3·75	5·00

190. Banana Export.

1983. Commonwealth Day. Multicoloured.

844.	25 c. Type **190**	15	15
845.	30 c. Road building ..	15	20
846.	90 c. Community nursing	40	45
847.	$3 Tourism–handicrafts ..	1·00	1·50

191. Map and Satellite Picture of Hurricane.

1983. World Communications Year. Mult.

848.	45 c. Type **191**	20	25
849.	60 c. Aircraft-to-ship transmission	30	35
850.	90 c. Satellite communications	40	45
851.	$2 Shortwave radio ..	95	1·00

192. "Mayo-Mercury" Composite.

1983. Bicentenary of Manned Flight. Multi.

853.	45 c. Type **192**	50	30
854.	60 c. Macchi "M.39" seaplane	75	75
855.	90 c. Fairey "Swordfish" biplane	1·10	1·25
856.	$4 Zeppelin "LZ3" ..	3·25	4·25

193. Duesenberg "SJ", 1935.

1983. Classic Motor Cars. Multicoloured.

858.	10 c. Type **193**	10	10
859.	45 c. Studebaker "Avanti", 1962	25	25
860.	60 c. Cord "812" ..	35	35
861.	75 c. MG "TC", 1945 ..	40	40
862.	90 c. Camaro "350 SS", 1967	45	45
863.	$3 Porsch "356", 1948 ..	1·40	1·50

194. "Charity".

1983. Christmas. 500th Birth Anniv. of Raphael. Multicoloured.

865.	45 c. Type **194**	55	30
866.	60 c. "Hope"	70	50
867.	90 c. "Faith"	80	60
868.	$4 "The Cardinal Virtues"	2·50	3·00

195. Plumbeous Warbler.

1984. Birds. Multicoloured.

870	5 c. Type **195**	75	45
871	45 c. Imperial amazon ..	1·75	55
872	60 c. Blue-headed hummingbird	2·00	1·60
873	90 c. Red-necked amazon	2·50	3·00

196. Donald Duck.

1984. Easter. Multicoloured.

875.	½ c. Type **196**	10	10
876.	1 c. Mickey Mouse	10	10
877.	2 c. Tortoise and Hare	10	10
878.	3 c. Brer Rabbit and Brer Bear	10	10
879.	4 c. Donald Duck (different)	10	10
880.	5 c. White Rabbit	10	10
881.	10 c. Thumper	10	10
882.	$2 Pluto	3·00	2·75
883.	$4 Pluto (different)	4·25	4·00

197. Gymnastics.

1984. Olympic Games, Los Angeles. Multicoloured.

885.	30 c. Type **197**	20	25
886.	45 c. Javelin-throwing	30	35
887.	60 c. High diving	40	45
888.	$4 Fencing	2·00	2·50

198. "Atlantic Star".

1984. Shipping. Multicoloured.

890.	45 c. Type **198**	1·25	60
891.	60 c. "Atlantic" (liner)	1·50	1·25
892.	90 c. Carib fishing boat	2·00	1·50
893.	$4 "Norway" (liner)	4·25	6·00

1984. Universal Postal Union Congress, Hamburg. Nos. 769 and 780 optd. **19th UPU CONGRESS HAMBURG.**

895.	10 c. Passion Fruit	10	10
896.	$5 Heliconia or Lobster Claw	3·25	3·50

200. "Guzmania lingulata".

1984. "Ausipex" International Stamp Exhibition, Melbourne. Bromeliads. Mult.

897	45 c. Type **200**	30	35
898	60 c. "Pitcairnia angustifolia"	40	55
899	75 c. "Tillandsia fasciculata"	50	75
900	$3 "Aechmea smithiorum"	2·00	3·25

201. "The Virgin and Child with Young St. John" (Correggio).

1984. 450th Death Anniv. of Correggio (painter). Multicoloured.

902.	25 c. Type **201**	55	20
903.	60 c. "Christ bids Farewell to the Virgin Mary"	90	40
904.	90 c. "Do not Touch Me"	1·40	60
905.	$4 "The Mystical Marriage of St. Catherine"	3·25	2·75

202. "Before the Start" (Edgar Degas).

1984. 150th Birth Anniv. of Edgar Degas (painter). Multicoloured.

907.	30 c. Type **202**	55	25
908.	45 c. "Race on the Racecourse"	75	35
909.	$1 "Jockeys at the Flagpole"	1·50	75
910.	$3 "Racehorses at Longchamp"	2·75	2·50

203. Tabby.

1984. Cats. Multicoloured.

912	10 c. Type **203**	20	10
913	15 c. Calico shorthair	25	10
914	20 c. Siamese	35	15
915	25 c. Manx	40	20
916	45 c. Abyssinian	65	30
917	60 c. Tortoise-shell longhair	80	55
918	$1 Cornish rex	1·40	90
919	$2 Persian	2·00	2·25
920	$3 Himalayan	2·75	3·50
921	$5 Burmese	3·75	6·00

204. Avro "748".

1984. 40th Anniv. of International Civil Aviation Organisation. Multicoloured.

923.	30 c. Type **204**	75	20
924.	60 c. Twin "Otter"	1·50	40
925.	$1 "Islander"	2·00	80
926.	$3 "Casa"	3·50	3·00

MORE DETAILED LISTS

are given in the Stanley Gibbons Catalogues referred to in the country headings.

For lists of current volumes see Introduction.

205. Donald Duck, Mickey Mouse and Goofy with Father Christmas.

1984. Christmas. Walt Disney Cartoon Characters. Multicoloured.

928.	45 c. Type **205**	1·00	30
929.	60 c. Donald Duck as Father Christmas with toy train	1·25	70
930.	90 c. Donald Duck as Father Christmas in sleigh	1·75	1·25
931.	$2 Donald Duck and nephews in sledge	3·00	3·00
932.	$4 Donald Duck in snow with Christmas tree	4·00	4·25

206. Mrs. M. Bascom presenting Trefoil to Chief Guide Lady Baden-Powell.

1985. 75th Anniv. of Girl Guide Movement. Multicoloured.

934.	35 c. Type **206**	50	30
935.	45 c. Lady Baden-Powell inspecting Dominican brownies	70	35
936.	60 c. Lady Baden-Powell with Mrs. M. Bascom and Mrs. A. Robinson (guide leaders)	85	55
937.	$3 Lord and Lady Baden-Powell (vert.)	2·25	2·75

1985. Birth Bicentenary of John J. Audubon (ornithologist) (1st issue). As T **198** of Antigua. Multicoloured.

939.	45 c. Clapper rail	65	30
940.	$1 Black and white warbler (vert.)	1·25	80
941.	$2 Broad-winged hawk (vert.)	1·75	2·00
942.	$3 Ring-necked duck	2·25	2·50

See also Nos. 1013/16.

207. Student with Computer.

1985. Duke of Edinburgh's Award Scheme. Multicoloured.

944.	45 c. Type **207**	35	30
945.	60 c. Assisting doctor in hospital	55	40
946.	90 c. Two youths hiking	75	65
947.	$4 Family jogging	2·75	3·25

208. The Queen Mother visiting Sadlers Wells Opera.

1985. Life and Times of Queen Elizabeth the Queen Mother. Multicoloured.

949.	60 c. Type **208**	50	40
950.	$1 Fishing in Scotland	70	60
951.	$3 On her 84th birthday	1·90	2·00

209. Cricket Match ("Sports").

1985. International Youth Year. Mult.

953.	45 c. Type **209**	2·75	1·10
954.	60 c. Bird-watching "Environmental Study"	3·00	1·50
955.	$1 Stamp collecting ("Education")	3·25	2·50
956.	$3 Boating ("Leisure")	5·00	5·00

1985. 300th Birth Anniv. of Johann Sebastian Bach (composer). As T **206** of Antigua. Mult.

958.	45 c. Cornet	1·25	40
959.	60 c. Coiled trumpet	1·50	60
960.	$1 Piccolo	2·00	1·00
961.	$3 Violoncello piccolo	4·00	3·50

1985. Royal Visit. As T **207** of Antigua. Multicoloured.

963.	60 c. Flags of Great Britain and Dominica	1·00	55
964.	$1 Queen Elizabeth II (vert.)	1·75	1·50
965.	$4 Royal Yacht "Britannia"	4·50	5·00

1985. 150th Birth Anniv. of Mark Twain (author). As T **118** of Anguilla showing Walt Disney cartoon characters in scenes from "Tom Sawyer". Multicoloured.

967.	20 c. "The glorious whitewasher"	35	15
968.	60 c. "Aunt Polly's home dentistry"	85	50
969.	$1 "Aunt Polly's pain killer"	1·25	90
970.	$1.50, Mickey Mouse balancing on fence	1·75	1·50
971.	$2 "Lost in the cave with Becky"	2·25	1·75

1985. Birth Bicentenaries of Grimm Brothers (folklorists). Designs as T **119** of Anguilla showing Walt Disney cartoon characters in scenes from "Little Red Cap". Mult.

973.	10 c. Little Red Cap (Daisy Duck) meeting the Wolf	15	10
974.	45 c. The Wolf at the door	50	30
975.	90 c. The Wolf in Grandmother's bed	1·00	1·00
976.	$1 The Wolf lunging at Little Red Cap	1·25	1·25
977.	$3 The Woodsman (Donald Duck) chasing the Wolf	3·00	3·75

1985. 40th Anniv. of United Nations Organization. Designs as T **208** of Antigua showing United Nations (New York) stamps. Multicoloured.

979.	45 c. Lord Baden-Powell and 1984 International Youth Year 35 c.	1·00	40
980.	$2 Maimonides (physician) and 1966 W.H.O. Building 11 c.	4·00	2·25
981.	$3 Sir Rowland Hill (postal reformer) and 1976 25th anniv. of U.N. Postal Administration 13 c.	4·00	2·50

210. Two Players competing for Ball.

1986. World Cup Football Championship, Mexico. Multicoloured.

983.	45 c. Type **210**	1·25	35
984.	60 c. Player heading ball	1·40	70
985.	$1 Two players competing for ball (different)	1·75	1·25
986.	$3 Player with ball	3·75	3·75

211. Police in Rowing Boat pursuing River Pirates, 1890.

1986. Centenary of Statue of Liberty. Multicoloured.

988. 15 c. Type **211** .. .. 1·00 40
989. 25 c. Police patrol launch, 1986 .. .. .. 1·40 50
990. 45 c. Hoboken Ferry Terminal c 1890 .. .. 1·60 55
991. $4 Holland Tunnel entrance and staff, 1986 3·75 4·25

1986. Appearance of Halley's Comet (1st issue). As T **123** of Anguilla. Multicoloured.

993. 5 c. Nasir al Din al Tusi (Persian astronomer) and Jantal Mantar Observatory, Delhi .. 10 10
994. 10 c. Bell "X-1" Rocket Plane breaking sound barrier for first time, 1947 .. .. .. 10 10
995. 45 c. Halley's Comet of 1531 (from "Astronomicum Caesareum", 1540) 35 30
996. $4 Mark Twain and quotation, 1910 .. 2·25 2·50

See also Nos. 1032/5.

1986. 60th Birthday of Queen Elizabeth II. As T **125** of Anguilla. Mult.

998. 2 c. Wedding photograph, 1947 .. 10 15
999. $1 Queen meeting Pope John Paul II, 1982 .. 70 70
1000. $4 Queen on Royal Visit, 1971 .. .. .. 2·00 2·40

212. Mickey Mouse and Pluto mounting Stamps in Album.

1986. "Ameripex" International Stamp Exhibition, Chicago. Showing Walt Disney cartoon characters. Multicoloured.

1002. 25 c. Type **212** 60 40
1003. 45 c. Donald Duck examining stamp under magnifying glass 80 65
1004. 60 c. Chip n'Dale soaking and drying stamps .. 1·10 85
1005. $4 Donald Duck as scoutmaster awarding merit badges to Nephews .. .. 3·50 4·00

213. William I. **214.** "Virgin at Prayer".

1986. 500th Anniv. (1985) of Succession of House of Tudor. to English throne. Mult.

1007. 10 c. Type **213** 40 20
1008. 40 c. Richard II 80 45
1009. 50 c. Henry VIII 90 55
1010. $1 Charles II .. .. 1·75 1·25
1011. $2 Queen Anne .. .. 2·75 2·75
1012. $4 Queen Victoria .. .. 3·75 4·00

1986. Birth Bicentenary (1985) of John J. Audubon (ornithologist) (2nd issue). As T **198** of Antigua showing original paintings. Multicoloured.

1013. 25 c. Black-throated diver .. .. .. 1·00 45
1014. 60 c. Great blue heron (vert.) .. .. .. 1·50 95
1015. 90 c. Yellow-crowned night heron (vert.) .. 1·75 1·25
1016. $4 Common shoveler .. 4·00 5·00

1986. Royal Wedding. As T **213** of Antigua. Multicoloured.

1018. 45 c. Prince Andrew and Miss Sarah Ferguson 35 30
1019. 50 c. Prince Andrew .. 45 35
1020. $4 Prince Andrew climbing aboard aircraft .. .. 2·00 2·50

1986. World Cup Football Championship Winners, Mexico. Nos. 983/6 optd. **WINNERS Argentina 3 W. Germany 2.**

1022. 45 c. Type **210** .. .. 1·25 45
1023. 60 c. Player heading ball 1·50 1·10
1024. $1 Two players competing for ball .. .. 2·00 1·75
1025. $3 Player with ball .. 4·50 5·50

1986. Christmas. Paintings by Dürer. Multicoloured.

1027. 45 c. Type **214** 75 35
1028. 60 c. "Madonna and Child" .. .. .. 1·25 70
1029. $1 "Madonna of the Pear" .. .. .. 1·50 1·25
1030. $3 "Madonna and Child with St. Anne" .. 4·25 4·75

1986. Appearance of Halley's Comet (2nd issue). Nos. 993/6 optd. as T **218** of Antigua.

1032. 5 c. Nasir al Din al Tusi (Persian astronomer) and Jantal Mantar Observatory, Delhi .. 10 10
1033. 10 c. Bell "X-1" Rocket Plane breaking sound barrier for first time, 1947 .. .. .. 10 10
1034. 45 c. Halley's Comet of 1531 (from "Astronomicum Caesareum", 1540) 20 30
1035. $4 Mark Twain and quotation, 1910 .. 1·75 2·25

215. Broad-winged Hawk.

1987. Birds of Dominica. Multicoloured

1037 1 c. Type **215** 10 10
1241 2 c. Ruddy quail dove .. 10 10
1242 5 c. Red-necked pigeon .. 10 10
1243 10 c. Green heron .. 10 10
1244 15 c. Moorhen 10 10
1245 20 c. Ringed kingfisher .. 10 10
1246 25 c. Brown pelican .. 10 10
1247 35 c. White-tailed tropic bird 15 20
1248 45 c. Red-legged thrush .. 20 25
1249 60 c. Purple-throated carib 30 35
1047 90 c. Magnificent frigate bird 45 50
1251 $1 Brown trembler .. 50 55
1252 $2 Black-capped petrel .. 95 1·00
1253 $5 Barn owl .. .. 2·40 2·50
1254 $10 Imperial amazon .. 5·00 5·25

1987. America's Cup Yachting Championship. As T **222** of Antigua. Multicoloured.

1052. 45 c. "Reliance", 1903 .. 40 25
1053. 60 c. "Freedom", 1980 .. 45 40
1054. $1 "Mischief", 1881 .. 65 65
1055. $3 "Australia", 1977 .. 1·75 2·25

1987. Birth Centenary of Marc Chagall (artist). As T **225** of Antigua. Multicoloured.

1057. 25 c. "Artist and His Model" 20 15
1058. 35 c. "Midsummer Night's Dream" .. 20 20
1059. 45 c. "Joseph the Shepherd" .. 25 25
1060. 60 c. "The Cellist" .. 30 30
1061. 90 c. "Woman with Pigs" 50 50
1062. $1 "The Blue Circus" .. 55 55
1063. $3 "For Vava" .. 1·60 1·75
1064. $4 "The Rider" .. 1·90 2·25

216. Morch Poulsen's Triton.

1987. Sea Shells.

1066. **216.** 35 c. multicoloured .. 20 20
1067. – 45 c. vio., blk. & red 25 25
1068. – 60 c. multicoloured .. 30 30
1069. – $5 multicoloured .. 2·40 2·40

DESIGNS: 45 c. Swainson globe purple sea snail. 60 c. Banded tulip. $5 Lamarck deltoid rock shell.

No. 1066 is inscribed "TIRITON" in error.

217. "Cantharellus cinnabarinus".

1987. "Capex '87" International Stamp Exhibition, Toronto. Mushrooms of Dominica. Multicoloured.

1071. 45 c. Type **217** 75 50
1072. 60 c. "Boletellus cubensis" .. .. 1·10 90
1073. $2 "Eccilia cystiophorus" .. 3·50 2·75
1074. $3 "Xerocomus guadelupae" .. 4·00 3·50

218. Discovery of Dominica, 1493.

1987. 500th Anniv (1992) of Discovery of America by Columbus (1st issue). Mult.

1076. 10 c. Type **218** 35 20
1077. 15 c. Caribs greeting Columbus's fleet .. 40 20
1078. 45 c. Claiming the New World for Spain .. 55 35
1079. 60 c. Wreck of "Santa Maria" 70 40
1080. 90 c. Fleet leaving Spain 85 70
1081. $1 Sighting the New World 95 80
1082. $3 Trading with Indians 2·00 2·50
1083. $5 Building settlement .. 3·00 3·75

See also Nos. 1221/5, 1355/62, 1406/13, 1547/53 and 1612/13.

1987. Milestones of Transportation. As T **226** of Antigua. Multicoloured.

1085 10 c. H.M.S. "Warrior" (first ironclad warship), 1860 .. .. .. 40 40
1086 15 c. "MAGLEV-MLU 001" (fastest passenger train), 1979 .. .. 50 50
1087 25 c. "Flying Cloud" (fastest clipper passage New York–San Francisco) (vert) .. 60 60
1088 35 c. First elevated railway, New York, 1868 (vert) 70 70
1089 45 c. "Tom Thumb" (first U.S. passenger locomotive), 1830 .. .. 70 70
1090 60 c. "Spray" (Slocum's solo circumnavigation), 1895–98 (vert) 75 75
1091 90 c. "Sea-Land Commerce" (fastest Pacific passage), 1973 (vert) .. .. .. 1·00 1·00
1092 $1 First cable cars, San Francisco, 1873 .. 1·10 1·10
1093 $3 "Orient" Express", 1883 .. .. .. 2·75 2·75
1094 $4 "Clermont" (first commercial paddle-steamer), 1807 3·00 3·00

219. "Virgin and Child with St. Anne" (Durer).

1987. Christmas. Religious Paintings. Mult.

1095. 20 c. Type **219** 30 15
1096. 25 c. "Virgin and Child" (Murillo) 30 15
1097. $2 "Madonna and Child" (Foppa) .. .. 1·50 1·50
1098. $4 "Madonna and Child" (Da Verona) .. .. 2·75 3·25

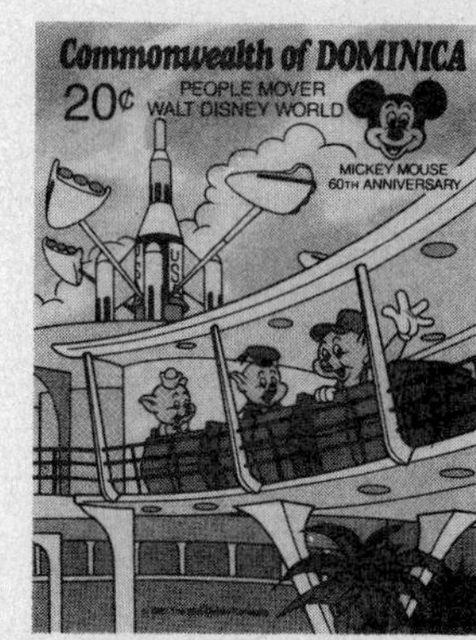

220. Three Little Pigs in People Mover, Walt Disney World.

1987. 60th Anniv. of Mickey Mouse (Walt Disney cartoon character). Multicoloured. Showing cartoon characters in trains.

1100. 20 c. Type **220** 30 30
1101. 25 c. Goofy driving horse tram, Disneyland .. 30 30
1102. 45 c. Donald Duck in "Roger E. Broggie", Walt Disney World .. 55 55
1103. 60 c. Goofy, Mickey Mouse, Donald Duck and Chip n'Dale aboard "Big Thunder Mountain" train, Disneyland 65 65
1104. 90 c. Mickey Mouse in "Walter E. Disney", Disneyland .. .. 1·00 1·00
1105. $1 Mickey and Minnie Mouse, Goofy, Donald and Daisy Duck in monorail, Walt Disney World .. .. .. 1·10 1·10
1106. $3 Dumbo flying over "Casey Jr" .. .. 2·75 2·75
1107. $4 Daisy Duck and Minnie Mouse in "Lilly Belle", Walt Disney World .. .. .. 3·25 3·25

1988. Royal Ruby Wedding. As T **234** of Antigua.

1109 45 c. multicoloured .. 65 25
1110 60 c. brown, black & green 80 50
1111 $1 multicoloured .. 1·00 90
1112 $3 multicoloured .. 2·25 2·75

DESIGNS: 45 c. Wedding portrait with attendants, 1947; 60 c. Princess Elizabeth with Prince Charles, c. 1950; $1 Princess Elizabeth and Prince Philip with Prince Charles and Princess Anne, 1950; $3 Queen Elizabeth.

221 Kayak Canoeing

1988. Olympic Games, Seoul. Multicoloured.
1114 45 c. Type **221** 55 35
1115 60 c. Taekwon-do 65 50
1116 $1 High diving 90 85
1117 $3 Gymnastics on bars 2·00 2·50

222 Carib Indian

1988. "Reunion '88" Tourism Programme. Multicoloured.
1119 10 c. Type **222** 10 10
1120 25 c. Mountainous interior (horiz) 10 10
1121 35 c. Indian River 10 10
1122 60 c. Belaire dancer and tourists 15 25
1123 90 c. Boiling Lake 20 35
1124 $3 Coral reef (horiz) 60 1·50

1988. Stamp Exhibitions. Nos. 1092/3 optd.
1126 $1 First cable cars, San Francisco, 1873 (optd **FINLANDIA 88**, Helsinki) 45 50
1127 $3 "Orient Express", 1883 (optd **INDEPENDENCE 40**, Israel) 1·25 1·40

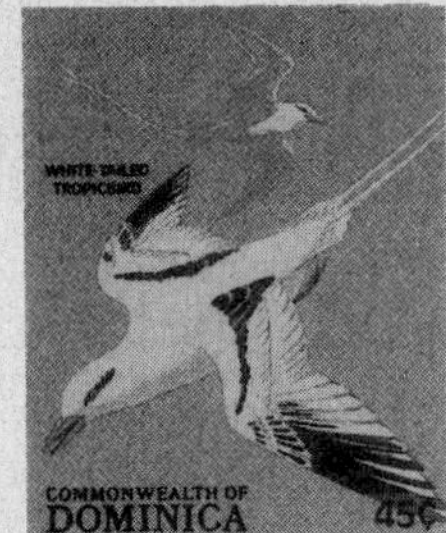

223 White-tailed Tropic Bird

1988. Dominica Rain Forest Flora and Fauna. Multicoloured.
1129 45 c. Type **223** 40 40
1130 45 c. Blue-hooded euphonia 40 40
1131 45 c. Smooth-billed ani 40 40
1132 45 c. Scaly-breasted thrasher 40 40
1133 45 c. Purple-throated carib 40 40
1134 45 c. "Marpesia petreus" and "Strymon maesites" (butterflies) 40 40
1135 45 c. Brown trembler 40 40
1136 45 c. Imperial amazon 40 40
1137 45 c. Mangrove cuckoo 40 40
1138 45 c. "Dynastes hercules" (beetle) 40 40
1139 45 c. "Historis odius" (butterfly) 40 40
1140 45 c. Red-necked amazon 40 40
1141 45 c. Tillandsia (plant) 40 40
1142 45 c. Bananaquit and "Polystacha luteola" (plant) 40 40
1143 45 c. False chameleon 40 40
1144 45 c. Iguana 40 40
1145 45 c. "Hypolimnas misippus" (butterfly) 40 40
1146 45 c. Green-throated carib 40 40
1147 45 c. Heliconia (plant) 40 40
1148 45 c. Agouti 40 40

Nos. 1129/48 were printed together, se-tenant, forming a composite design.

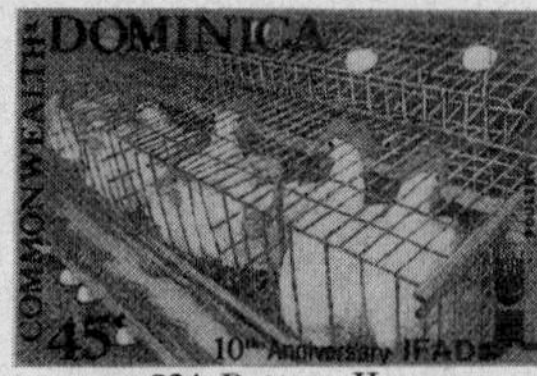

224 Battery Hens

1988. 10th Anniv of International Fund for Agricultural Development. Mult.
1149 45 c. Type **224** 50 30
1150 60 c. Pig 70 55
1151 90 c. Cattle 95 90
1152 $3 Black belly sheep 2·25 2·50

225 Gary Cooper

1988. Entertainers. Multicoloured.
1154 10 c. Type **225** 30 20
1155 35 c. Josephine Baker 40 35
1156 45 c. Maurice Chevalier 45 35
1157 60 c. James Cagney 50 40
1158 $1 Clark Gable 70 60
1159 $2 Louis Armstrong 1·10 1·10
1160 $3 Liberace 1·60 1·75
1161 $4 Spencer Tracy 2·00 2·50

1988. Flowering Trees. As T **242** of Antigua. Multicoloured.
1163 15 c. Sapodilla 10 10
1164 20 c. Tangerine 10 10
1165 25 c. Avocado pear 10 10
1166 45 c. Amherstia 20 25
1167 90 c. Lipstick tree 40 45
1168 $1 Cannonball tree 45 50
1169 $3 Saman 1·25 1·40
1170 $4 Pineapple 1·60 1·75

1988. 500th Birth Anniv of Titian (artist). As T **238** of Antigua. Multicoloured.
1172 25 c. "Jacopo Strada" 10 15
1173 35 c. "Titian's Daughter Lavinia" 15 20
1174 45 c. "Andrea Navagero" 20 25
1175 60 c. "Judith with Head of Holoferenes" 25 30
1176 $1 "Emilia di Spilimbergo" 45 50
1177 $2 "Martyrdom of St. Lawrence" 80 85
1178 $3 "Salome" 1·25 1·40
1179 $4 "St. John the Baptist" 1·60 1·75

226 Imperial Amazon

1988. 10th Anniv of Independence. Mult.
1181 20 c. Type **226** 55 20
1182 45 c. Dominica 1874 1d. stamp and landscape (horiz) 65 25
1183 $2 1978 Independence 10 c. stamp and landscape (horiz) 1·25 1·50
1184 $3 Carib Wood (national flower) 1·60 2·25

227 Pres. and Mrs. Kennedy

1988. 25th Death Anniv of John F. Kennedy (American statesman). Multicoloured.
1186 20 c. Type **227** 10 10
1187 25 c. Kennedy sailing 10 10
1188 $2 Outside Hyannis Port house 80 1·00
1189 $4 Speaking in Berlin (vert) 1·60 2·00

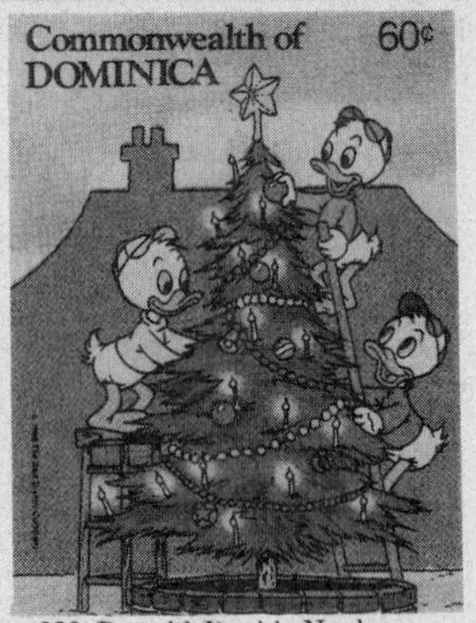

228 Donald Duck's Nephews decorating Christmas Tree

1988. Christmas. "Mickey's Christmas Mall". Walt Disney Cartoon Characters. Mult.
1191 60 c. Type **228** 35 35
1192 60 c. Daisy Duck outside clothes shop 35 35
1193 60 c. Winnie the Pooh in shop window 35 35
1194 60 c. Goofy with parcels 35 35
1195 60 c. Donald Duck as Father Christmas 35 35
1196 60 c. Mickey Mouse contributing to collection 35 35
1197 60 c. Minnie Mouse 35 35
1198 60 c. Chip n'Dale with peanut 35 35

Nos. 1191/8 were printed together, se-tenant, forming a composite design.

229 Raoul Wallenberg (diplomat) and Swedish Flag

1988. 40th Anniv of Universal Declaration of Human Rights.
1200 **229** $3 multicoloured 1·25 1·40

230 Greater Amberjack

1988. Game Fishes. Multicoloured.
1202 10 c. Type **230** 15 10
1203 15 c. Blue marlin 15 10
1204 35 c. Cobia 25 20
1205 45 c. Dolphin fish 35 25
1206 60 c. Cero 45 40
1207 90 c. Mahogany snapper 65 55
1208 $3 Yellowfin tuna 2·00 2·50
1209 $4 Rainbow parrotfish 2·50 3·00

231 Leatherback Turtle

1988. Insects and Reptiles. Multicoloured.
1211 10 c. Type **231** 35 15
1212 25 c. "Danaus plexippus" (butterfly) 1·00 35
1213 60 c. Green anole (lizard) 1·40 75
1213 $3 "Mantis religiosa" (mantid) 3·50 4·00

1989. Olympic Medal Winners, Seoul. Nos. 1114/17 optd.
1216 45 c. Type **221** (optd **Men's c-1,500m O. Heukrodt DDR**) 20 25
1217 60 c. Taekwon-do (optd **Women's Flyweight N. Y. Choo S. Korea**) 25 30
1218 $1 High diving (optd **Women's Platform Y. Xu China**) 40 45
1219 $3 Gymnastics on bars (optd **V. Artemov USSR**) 1·25 1·40

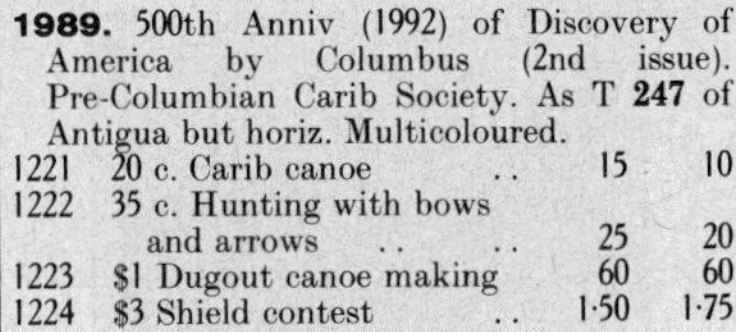
1989. 500th Anniv (1992) of Discovery of America by Columbus (2nd issue). Pre-Columbian Carib Society. As T **247** of Antigua but horiz. Multicoloured.
1221 20 c. Carib canoe 15 10
1222 35 c. Hunting with bows and arrows 25 20
1223 $1 Dugout canoe making 60 60
1224 $3 Shield contest 1·50 1·75

233 Map of Dominica, 1766

1989. "Philexfrance '89" International Stamp Exhibition, Paris. Multicoloured.
1226 10 c. Type **233** 15 10
1227 35 c. French coin of 1653 (horiz) 25 20
1228 $1 French warship, 1720 (horiz) 60 60
1229 $4 Coffee plant (horiz) 1·75 2·10

1989. Japanese Art. Paintings by Taikan. As T **250** of Antigua but vert. Multicoloured.
1231 10 c. "Lao-tzu" (detail) 10 10
1232 20 c. "Red Maple Leaves" (panels 1 and 2) 10 10
1233 45 c. "King Wen Hui learns a Lesson from his Cook" (detail) 20 25
1234 60 c. "Red Maple Leaves" (panels 3 and 4) 25 30
1235 $1 "Wild Flowers" (detail) 40 45
1236 $2 "Red Maple Leaves" (panels 5 and 6) 85 90
1237 $3 "Red Maple Leaves" (panels 7 and 8) 1·25 1·40
1238 $4 "Indian Ceremony of Floating Lamps on the River" (detail) 1·75 1·90

234 "Papilio homerus"

1989. Butterflies. Multicoloured.
1255 10 c. Type **234** 20 15
1256 15 c. "Morpho peleides" 20 15
1257 25 c. "Dryas julia" 30 25
1258 35 c. "Parides gundlachianus" 40 30
1259 60 c. "Danaus plexippus" 55 55
1260 $1 "Agraulis vanillae" 70 70
1261 $3 "Phoebis avellaneda" 1·90 2·00
1262 $5 "Papilio andraemon" 3·00 3·25

235 "Oncidium pusillum"

1989. Orchids. Multicoloured.

1264	10 c. Type **235**	20	15
1265	35 c. "Epidendrum cochleata"	40	30
1266	45 c. "Epidendrum ciliare"	50	40
1267	60 c. "Cyrtopodium andersonii"	60	60
1268	$1 "Habenaria pauciflora"	90	90
1269	$2 "Maxillaria alba" ..	1·50	1·60
1270	$3 "Selenipedium palmifolium" ..	2·00	2·25
1271	$4 "Brassavola cucullata"	2·50	2·75

236 "Apollo 11" Command Module in Lunar Orbit

1989. 20th Anniv of First Manned Landing on Moon. Multicoloured.

1273	10 c. Type **236**	15	10
1274	60 c. Neil Armstrong leaving lunar module ..	35	35
1275	$2 Edwin Aldrin at Sea of Tranquillity	1·10	1·10
1276	$3 Astronauts Armstrong and Aldrin with U.S. flag	1·50	1·50

237 Brazil v. Italy Final, 1970

1989. World Cup Football Championship, Italy. Multicoloured.

1278	$1 Type **237**	75	75
1279	$1 England v. West Germany, 1966 ..	75	75
1280	$1 West Germany v. Holland, 1974 ..	75	75
1281	$1 Italy v. West Germany, 1982 ..	75	75

Nos. 1278/81 were printed together, se-tenant, forming a composite central design of a football surrounded by flags of competing nations.

238 George Washington and Inauguration, 1789

1989. "World Stamp Expo '89" International Stamp Exhibition, Washington. Bicentenary of the U.S. Presidency. Multicoloured.

1283	60 c. Type **238**	35	35
1284	60 c. John Adams and Presidential Mansion, 1800	35	35
1285	60 c. Thomas Jefferson, Graff House, Philadelphia and Declaration of Independence	35	35
1286	60 c. James Madison and U.S.S. "Constitution" defeating H.M.S. "Guerriere", 1812 ..	35	35
1287	60 c. James Monroe and freed slaves landing in Liberia	35	35
1288	60 c. John Quincy Adams and barge on Erie Canal	35	35
1289	60 c. Millard Fillmore and Perry's fleet off Japan	35	35
1290	60 c. Franklin Pierce, Jefferson Davis and San Xavier Mission, Tucson	35	35
1291	60 c. James Buchanan, "Buffalo Bill" Cody carrying mail and Wells Fargo Pony Express stamp	35	35
1292	60 c. Abraham Lincoln and U.P.U. Monument, Berne	35	35
1293	60 c. Andrew Johnson, polar bear and Mt. McKinley, Alaska ..	35	35
1294	60 c. Ulysses S. Grant and Golden Spike Ceremony, 1869 ..	35	35
1295	60 c. Theodore Roosevelt and steam shovel excavating Panama Canal	35	35
1296	60 c. William H. Taft and Admiral Peary at North Pole	35	35
1297	60 c. Woodrow Wilson and Curtis "Jenny" on first scheduled airmail flight, 1918	35	35
1298	60 c. Warren G. Harding and airship U.S.S. "Shenandoah" at Lakehurst	35	35
1299	60 c. Calvin Coolidge and Lindbergh's "Spirit of St. Louis" on trans-Atlantic flight ..	35	35
1300	60 c. Mt. Rushmore National Monument ..	35	35
1301	60 c. Lyndon B. Johnson and Earth from Moon as seen by "Apollo 8" crew	35	35
1302	60 c. Richard Nixon and visit to Great Wall of China	35	35
1303	60 c. Gerald Ford and "Gorch Fock" (German cadet barque) at Bicentenary of Revolution celebrations	35	35
1304	60 c. Jimmy Carter and Pres. Sadat of Egypt with Prime Minister Begin of Israel ..	35	35
1305	60 c. Ronald Reagan and space shuttle "Columbia"	35	35
1306	60 c. George Bush and Grumman "Avenger" (fighter-bomber) ..	35	35

1989. Mickey Mouse in Hollywood (Walt Disney cartoon characters). As T **267** of Antigua. Multicoloured.

1308	20 c. Mickey Mouse reading script	20	20
1309	35 c. Mickey Mouse giving interview ..	35	35
1310	45 c. Mickey and Minnie Mouse with newspaper and magazines ..	40	40
1311	60 c. Mickey Mouse signing autographs ..	50	50
1312	$1 Trapped in dressing room	75	75
1313	$2 Mickey and Minnie Mouse with Pluto in limousine	1·40	1·40
1314	$3 Arriving at Awards ceremony	1·75	1·75
1315	$4 Mickey Mouse accepting award ..	2·25	2·25

1989. Christmas. Paintings by Botticelli. As T **259** of Antigua. Multicoloured.

1317	20 c. "Madonna in Glory with Seraphim" ..	15	15
1318	25 c. "The Annunciation" ..	20	20
1319	35 c. "Madonna of the Pomegranate" ..	30	30
1320	45 c. "Madonna of the Rosegarden"	35	35
1321	60 c. "Madonna of the Book"	50	50
1322	$1 "Madonna under a Baldachin"	65	65
1323	$4 "Madonna and Child with Angels"	2·25	2·25
1324	$5 "Bardi Madonna" ..	2·75	2·75

240 Lady Olave Baden-Powell and Agatha Robinson (Guide leaders)

1989. 60th Anniv of Girl Guides in Dominica.

1326 **240**	60 c. multicoloured ..	70	70

241 Jawaharlal Nehru

1989. Birth Centenary of Jawaharlal Nehru (Indian statesman).

1328 **241**	60 c. multicoloured ..	70	70

242 Cocoa Damselfish

1990. Tropical Fishes. Multicoloured.

1330	45 c. Type **242**	20	25
1331	45 c. Stinging jellyfish ..	20	25
1332	45 c. Dolphin fish ..	20	25
1333	45 c. Queen angelfish ..	20	25
1334	45 c. French angelfish ..	20	25
1335	45 c. Blue-striped grunt ..	20	25
1336	45 c. Pork fish	20	25
1337	45 c. Hammerhead shark	20	25
1338	45 c. Spadefish ..	20	25
1339	45 c. Great barracuda ..	20	25
1340	45 c. Stingray	20	25
1341	45 c. Black grunt ..	20	25
1342	45 c. Two-spotted butter-flyfish	20	25
1343	45 c. Dog snapper ..	20	25
1344	45 c. Southern puffer ..	20	25
1345	45 c. Four-eyed butter-flyfish	20	25
1346	45 c. Lane snapper ..	20	25
1347	45 c. Green moray ..	20	25

Nos. 1330/47 were printed together, se-tenant, forming a composite design.

243 St. Paul's Cathedral, London, c. 1840

1990. 150th Anniv of the Penny Black and "Stamp World London 90" International Stamp Exhibition.

1348 **243**	45 c. green and black	20	25
1349 –	50 c. blue and black	25	30
1350 –	60 c. blue and black	30	35
1351 –	90 c. green and black	45	50
1352 –	$3 blue and black ..	1·40	1·50
1353 –	$4 blue and black ..	2·00	2·10

DESIGNS: 50 c. British Post Office "accelerator" carriage, 1830; 60 c. St. Paul's and City of London; 90 c. Travelling post office, 1838; $3 "Hen and chickens" delivery cycle, 1883; $4 London skyline.

1990. 500th Anniv (1992) of Discovery of America by Columbus (3rd issue). New World Natural History—Seashells. As T **260** of Antigua. Multicoloured.

1355	10 c. Reticulated cowrie-helmet	10	10
1356	20 c. West Indian chank	10	10
1357	35 c. West Indian fighting conch	15	20
1358	60 c. True tulip ..	30	35
1359	$1 Sunrise tellin ..	50	55
1360	$2 Crown cone ..	95	1·00
1361	$3 Common dove shell ..	1·40	1·50
1362	$4 Atlantic fig shell ..	2·00	2·10

244 Blue-headed Hummingbird

1990. Birds. Multicoloured.

1364	10 c. Type **244**	10	10
1365	20 c. Black-capped petrel	10	10
1366	45 c. Red-necked amazon	20	25
1367	60 c. Black swift ..	30	35
1368	$1 Troupial	50	55
1369	$2 Common noddy ..	95	1·00
1370	$4 Lesser Antillean pewee	2·00	2·10
1371	$5 Little blue heron ..	2·40	2·50

1990. 90th Birthday of Queen Elizabeth the Queen Mother. As T **266** of Antigua.

1373	20 c. multicoloured ..	10	10
1374	45 c. multicoloured ..	20	25
1375	60 c. multicoloured ..	30	35
1376	$3 multicoloured ..	1·40	1·50

DESIGNS: 20 c. to $3 Recent photographs of Queen Mother.

1990. Olympic Games, Barcelona (1992) (1st issue). As T **268** of Antigua. Multicoloured.

1378	45 c. Type **245**	20	25
1379	60 c. Fencing	30	35
1380	$2 Swimming	95	1·00
1381	$3 Yachting	1·40	1·50

See also Nos. 1603/11.

245 Barnes, England

1990. World Cup Football Championship, Italy. Multicoloured.

1383	15 c. Type **245**	10	10
1384	45 c. Romario, Brazil ..	20	25
1385	60 c. Franz Beckenbauer, West Germany manager	30	35
1386	$4 Lindenberger, Austria	2·00	2·10

246 Mickey Mouse riding Herschell-Spillman Frog

1990. Christmas. Walt Disney cartoon characters and American carousel animals. Multicoloured.

1388	10 c. Type **246**	10	10
1389	15 c. Huey, Duey and Louie on Allan Herschell elephant ..	10	10
1390	25 c. Donald Duck on Allan Herschell polar bear	10	15
1391	45 c. Goofy on Dentzel goat	20	25
1392	$1 Donald Duck on Zalar giraffe	50	55
1393	$2 Daisy Duck on Herschell-Spillman stork	95	1·00
1394	$4 Goofy on Dentzel lion	2·00	2·10
1395	$5 Daisy Duck on Stein and Goldstein palomino stander	2·40	2·50

1991. Cog Railways. As T **275** of Antigua. Multicoloured.

1397 10 c. Glion–Roches De Naye locomotive, 1890 .. 10 10
1398 35 c. Electric railcar on Mt Pilatus 15 20
1399 45 c. Cog railway line to Schynige Platte .. 20 25
1400 60 c. Bugnli Viaduct, Furka–Oberalp line (vert) 30 35
1401 $1 Jungfrau train, 1910 .. 50 55
1402 $2 Testing Pike's Peak railcar, Switzerland, 1983 .. .. 95 1·00
1403 $4 Brienz–Rothorn steam train, 1991 .. .. 2·00 2·10
1404 $5 Arth–Rigi steam locomotive, 1890 .. .. 2·40 2·50

1991. 500th Anniv (1992) of Discovery of America by Columbus (4th issue). History of Exploration. As T **277** of Antigua. Mult.

1406 10 c. Gil Eannes sailing south of Cape Bojador, 1433–34 .. .. 10 10
1407 25 c. Alfonso Baldaya sailing south to Cape Blanc, 1436 .. .. 10 10
1408 45 c. Bartolomeu Dias in Table Bay, 1487 .. 20 25
1409 60 c. Vasco da Gama on voyage to India, 1497–99 .. .. 30 35
1410 $1 Vallarte the Dane off African coast 50 55
1411 $2 Aloisio Cadamosto in Cape Verde Islands, 1456–58 .. .. 45 1·00
1412 $4 Diogo Gomes on River Gambia, 1457 .. .. 2·00 2·10
1413 $5 Diogo Cao off African coast, 1482–85 .. .. 2·40 2·50

1991. "Phila Nippon '91" International Stamp Exhibition, Tokyo. As T **279** of Antigua. Multicoloured.

1415 10 c. Donald Duck as Shogun's guard (horiz) 10 10
1416 15 c. Mickey Mouse as Kabuki actor (horiz) .. 10 10
1417 25 c. Minnie and Mickey Mouse as bride and groom (horiz) 10 10
1418 45 c. Daisy Duck as geisha 20 25
1419 $1 Mickey Mouse in Sokutai court dress .. 50 55
1420 $2 Goofy as Mino farmer 95 1·00
1421 $4 Pete as Shogun .. 2·00 2·10
1422 $5 Donald Duck as Samurai (horiz) .. 2·40 2·50

247 "Craterellus cornucopioides"

1991. Fungi. Multicoloured.

1424 10 c. Type **247** 10 10
1425 15 c. "Coprinus comatus" 10 10
1426 45 c. "Morchella esculenta" 20 25
1427 60 c. "Cantharellus cibarius" 30 35
1428 $1 "Lepista nuda" .. 50 55
1429 $2 "Suillus luteus" .. 95 1·00
1430 $4 "Russula emetica" .. 2·00 2·10
1431 $5 "Armillaria mellea" .. 2·40 2·50

1991. 65th Birthday of Queen Elizabeth II. As T **280** of Antigua. Multicoloured.

1433 10 c. Queen and Prince William on Buckingham Palace Balcony, 1990 .. .. 10 10
1434 60 c. The Queen at Westminster Abbey, 1988 .. 30 35
1435 $2 The Queen and Prince Philip in Italy, 1990 .. 95 1·00
1436 $4 The Queen at Ascot, 1986 .. .. .. 2·00 2·10

1991. 10th Wedding Anniv of the Prince and Princess of Wales. As T **280** of Antigua. Multicoloured.

1438 15 c. Prince and Princess of Wales in West Germany, 1987 .. 10 10
1439 40 c. Separate photographs of Prince, Princess and sons .. 20 25
1440 $1 Separate photographs of Prince William and Prince Henry 50 55
1441 $5 Prince Charles at Caister and Princess Diana in Thailand .. 2·40 2·50

1991. Death Centenary (1990) of Vincent van Gogh (artist). As T **278** of Antigua. Mult.

1443 10 c. "Thatched Cottages" (horiz) 10 10
1444 25 c. "The House of Pere Eloi" (horiz) 10 10
1445 45 c. "The Midday Siesta" (horiz) 20 25
1446 60 c. "Portrait of a Young Peasant" 30 35
1447 $1 "Still Life: Vase with Irises against a Yellow Background" 50 55
1448 $2 "Still Life: Vase with Irises" (horiz) .. 95 1·00
1449 $4 "Blossoming Almond Tree" (horiz) .. .. 2·00 2·10
1450 $5 "Irises" (horiz) .. 2·40 2·50

1991. International Literacy Year (1990). Scenes from Disney cartoon film "The Little Mermaid". As T **269** of Antigua. Mult.

1452 10 c. Arial, Flounder and Sebastian (horiz) .. 10 10
1453 25 c. King Triton (horiz) 10 10
1454 45 c. Sebastian playing drums (horiz) 20 25
1455 60 c. Flotsam and Jestsam taunting Arial (horiz) 30 35
1456 $1 Scuttle, Flounder and Arial with pipe (horiz) 50 55
1457 $2 Arial and Flounder discovering book (horiz) 95 1·00
1458 $4 Prince Eric and crew (horiz) .. .. 2·00 2·25
1459 $5 Ursula the Sea Witch (horiz) .. .. 2·40 2·50

248 Empire State Building, New York

1991. World Landmarks. Multicoloured.

1461 10 c. Type **248** 10 10
1462 25 c. Kremlin, Moscow (horiz) 10 10
1463 45 c. Buckingham Palace, London (horiz) .. 20 25
1464 60 c. Eiffel Tower, Paris 30 35
1465 $1 Taj Mahal, Agra (horiz) 50 55
1466 $2 Opera House, Sydney (horiz) .. .. 95 1·00
1467 $4 Colosseum, Rome (horiz) .. .. 2·00 2·10
1468 $5 Pyramids, Giza (horiz) 2·40 2·50

249 Japanese Aircraft leaving Carrier "Akagi"

1991. 50th Anniv of Japanese Attack on Pearl Harbor. Multicoloured.

1470 10 c. Type **249** 10 10
1471 15 c. U.S.S. "Ward" (destroyer) and flying boat attacking midget submarine 10 10
1472 45 c. Second wave of aircraft leaving carriers 20 25
1473 60 c. Japanese Zero attacking Kaneche naval airfield 30 35
1474 $1 U.S.S. "Breeze", "Medusa" and "Curtiss" (destroyers) sinking midget submarine 50 55
1475 $2 U.S.S. "Nevada" (battleship) under attack .. .. 95 1·00
1476 $4 U.S.S. "Arizona" (battleship) sinking .. 2·00 2·10
1477 $5 Japanese aircraft .. 2·40 2·50

250 "Eurema venusta"

1991. Butterflies. Multicoloured.

1479 1 c. Type **250** 10 10
1480 2 c. "Agraulis vanillae" .. 10 10
1481 5 c. "Danaus plexippus" 10 10
1482 10 c. "Biblis hyperia" .. 10 10
1483 15 c. "Dryas julia" .. 10 10
1484 20 c. "Phoebis agarithe" 10 10
1485 25 c. "Junonia genoveva" 10 10
1486 35 c. "Battus polydamas" 15 20
1487 45 c. "Leptotes cassius" 20 25
1478a 55 c. "Ascia monuste" .. 25 30
1488 60 c. "Anaea dominicana" .. 30 35
1488a 65 c. "Hemiargus hanno" .. 30 35
1489 90 c. "Hypolimnas misippus" 45 50
1490 $1 "Urbanus proteus" .. 50 55
1490a $1.20 "Historis odius" .. 60 65
1491 $2 "Phoebis sennae" .. 95 1·00
1492 $5 "Cynthia cardui" ("Vanessa cardui") .. 2·40 2·50
1493 $10 "Marpesia petreus" 5·00 5·25
1494 $20 "Anartia jatrophae" 9·50 9·75

1991. Birth Centenary (1990) of Charles De Gaulle (French statesman). As T **283** of Antigua.

1495 45 c. brown 20 25

DESIGN—VERT. 45 c. De Gaulle in uniform.

251 Symbolic Cheque

1992. 40th Anniv of Credit Union Bank.

1497 **251** 10 c. grey and black 10 10
1498 – 60 c. multicoloured .. 30 35

DESIGN—HORIZ. 60 c. Credit Union symbol.

252 "18th-Century Creole Dress" (detail) (Agostino Brunias)

1991. Creole Week. Multicoloured.

1499 45 c. Type **252** 20 25
1500 60 c. Jing Ping band .. 30 35
1501 $1 Creole dancers .. 50 55

253 Island Beach

1991. Year of Environment and Shelter. Mult.

1503 15 c. Type **253** 10 10
1504 60 c. Imperial amazon .. 30 35

1991. Christmas. Religious Paintings by Jan van Eyck. As T **287** of Antigua. Mult.

1506 10 c. "Virgin Enthroned with Child" (detail) .. 10 10
1507 20 c. "Madonna at the Fountain" 10 10
1508 35 c. "Virgin in a Church" 15 20
1509 45 c. "Madonna with Canon van der Paele" 20 25
1510 60 c. "Madonna with Canon van der Paele" (detail) 30 35
1511 $1 "Madonna in an Interior" 50 55
1512 $3 "The Annunciation" .. 1·40 1·50
1513 $5 "The Annunciation" (different) .. .. 2·40 2·50

1992. 40th Anniv of Queen Elizabeth II's Accession. As T **288** of Antigua. Mult.

1515 10 c. Coastline 10 10
1516 15 c. Mountains overlooking small village .. 10 10
1517 $1 River estuary 50 55
1518 $5 Waterfall .. 2·40 2·50

254 Cricket Match

1992. Centenary (1991) of Botanical Gardens. Multicoloured.

1520 10 c. Type **254** 10 10
1521 15 c. Scenic Entrance .. 10 10
1522 45 c. Traveller's Tree .. 20 25
1523 60 c. Bamboo House .. 30 35
1524 $1 The Old Pavilion .. 50 55
1525 $2 "Ficus benjamina" .. 95 1·00
1526 $4 Cricket match (different) .. .. 2·00 2·10
1527 $5 Thirty-five Steps .. 2·40 2·50

1992. Easter. Religious Paintings. As T **291** of Antigua. Multicoloured.

1529 10 c. "The Supper at Emmaus" (Van Honthorst) 10 10
1530 15 c. "Christ before Caiaphas" (Van Honthorst) (vert) .. 10 10
1531 45 c. "The Taking of Christ" (De Boulogne) 20 25
1532 60 c. "Pilate washing his Hands" (Preti) (vert) 30 35
1533 $1 "The Last Supper" (detail) (Master of the Church of S. Francisco d'Evora) 50 55
1534 $2 "The Three Marys at the Tomb" (detail) (Bouguereau) (vert) .. 95 1·00
1535 $3 "Denial of St. Peter" (Terbrugghen) .. 1·40 1·50
1536 $5 "Doubting Thomas" (Strozzi) .. .. 2·40 2·50

1992. "Granada '92" International Stamp Exhibition, Spain. Art of Diego Rodriguez Velasquez. As T **292** of Antigua. Mult.

1538 10 c. "Pope Innocent X" (detail) 10 10
1539 15 c. "The Forge of Vulcan" (detail) .. 10 10
1540 45 c. "The Forge of Vulcan" (different detail) 20 25
1541 60 c. "Queen Mariana of Austria" (detail) .. 30 35
1542 $1 "Pablo de Valladolid" 50 55
1543 $2 "Sebastian de Morra" 95 1·00
1544 $3 "King Felipe IV" (detail) .. .. 1·40 1·50
1545 $4 "King Felipe IV" .. 2·00 2·10

255 Columbus and "Dynastes hercules" (beetle)

1992. 500th Anniv of Discovery of America by Columbus (5th issue). World Columbian Stamp "Expo '92", Chicago. Multicoloured.

1547 10 c. Type **255** 10 10
1548 25 c. Columbus and "Leptodactylus fallax" (frog) 10 10
1549 75 c. Columbus and red-necked amazon (bird) 35 40
1550 $2 Columbus and "Ameiva fuscata" (lizard) .. .. 95 1·00
1551 $4 Columbus and "Gramma loreto" (fish) 2·00 2·10
1552 $5 Columbus and "Rosa sinensis" (flower) .. 2·40 2·50

1992. "Genova '92" International Thematic Stamp Exhibition. Hummingbirds. As T **295** of Antigua. Multicoloured.

1554 10 c. Female purple-throated carib .. 10 10
1555 15 c. Female rufous-breasted hermit .. 10 10
1556 45 c. Male Puerto Rican emerald 20 25
1557 60 c. Female Antillean mango 30 35
1558 $1 Male green-throated carib 50 55
1559 $2 Male blue-headed hummingbird .. .. 95 1·00
1560 $4 Female eastern streamertail .. .. 2·00 2·10
1561 $5 Female Antillean crested hummingbird .. 2·40 2·50

1992. Prehistoric Animals. As T **290** of Antigua, but horiz. Multicoloured.

1563 10 c. Head of camptosaurus .. 10 10
1564 15 c. Edmontosaurus .. 10 10
1565 25 c. Corythosaurus .. 10 10
1566 60 c. Stegosaurus .. 30 35
1567 $1 Torosaurus 50 55
1568 $3 Euoplocephalus .. 1·40 1·50
1569 $4 Tyrannosaurus .. 2·00 2·10
1570 $5 Parasaurolophus .. 2·40 2·50

256 Trumpetfish and Blue Chromis

1992. Marine Life.

1572/1601 65 c. × 30 mult .. 8·00 8·25

1992. Olympic Games, Barcelona (2nd issue). As T **268** of Antigua. Multicoloured.

1603 10 c. Archery 10 10
1604 15 c. Two-man canoeing 10 10
1605 25 c. Men's 110 metres hurdles 10 10
1606 60 c. Men's high jump .. 30 35
1607 $1 Greco-Roman wrestling 50 55
1608 $2 Men's gymnastics—rings .. .. .. 95 1·00
1609 $4 Men's gymnastics—parallel bars .. .. 2·00 2·10
1610 $5 Equestrian dressage .. 2·40 2·50

1992. 500th Anniv of Discovery of America by Columbus (6th issue). Organization of East Caribbean States. As Nos. 1670/1 of Antigua. Multicoloured.

1612 $1 Columbus meeting Amerindians 50 55
1613 $2 Ships approaching island .. .. .. 95 1·00

1992. Hummel Figurines. As T **302** of Antigua. Multicoloured.

1614 20 c. Angel playing violin 10 10
1615 25 c. Angel playing recorder 10 10
1616 55 c. Angel playing lute .. 25 30
1617 65 c. Seated angel playing trumpet 30 35
1618 90 c. Angel on cloud with lantern 45 50
1619 $1 Angel with candle .. 50 55
1620 $1.20 Flying angel with Christmas tree .. 55 60
1621 $6 Angel on cloud with candle .. .. 3·00 3·25

257 Brass "Reno" Locomotive, Japan (1963)

1992. Toy Trains from Far Eastern Manufacturers. Multicoloured.

1623 15 c. Type **257** 10 10
1624 25 c. Union Pacific "Golden Classic" locomotive, China (1992) 10 10
1625 55 c. L.M.S. third class brake coach, Hong Kong (1970s) 25 30
1626 65 c. Brass Wabash locomotive, Japan (1958) .. 30 35
1627 75 c. Pennsylvania "Duplex" type locomotive, Korea (1991) .. 35 40
1628 $1 Streamlined locomotive, Japan (post 1945) 50 55
1629 $3 Japanese National Railways Class "C62" locomotive, Japan (1960) .. .. .. 1·40 1·50
1630 $5 Tinplate friction driven trains, Japan (1960s) .. 2·40 2·50

258 Goofy in "Two Weeks Vacation", 1952

1992. 60th Anniv of Goofy (Disney cartoon character). Designs showing sports from cartoon films. Multicoloured.

1632 10 c. Type **258** 10 10
1633 15 c. "Aquamania", 1961 10 10
1634 25 c. "Goofy Gymnastics", 1949 .. 10 10
1635 45 c. "How to Ride a Horse", 1941 .. .. 20 25
1636 $1 "Foul Hunting", 1947 50 55
1637 $2 "For Whom the Bulls Toil", 1953 .. .. 95 1·00
1638 $4 "Tennis Racquet", 1949 .. .. .. 2·00 2·10
1639 $5 "Double Dribble", 1946 2·40 2·50

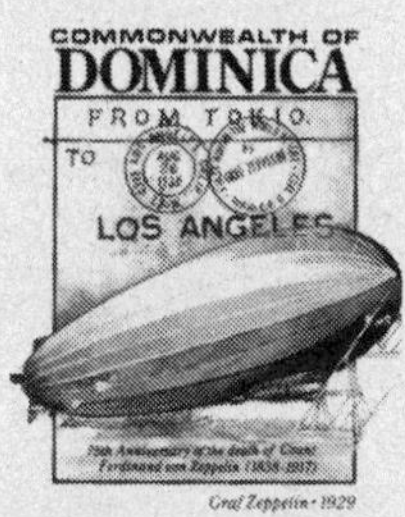

259 "Graf Zeppelin", 1929

1992. Anniversaries and Events. Mult.

1641 25 c. Type **259** 10 10
1642 45 c. Elderly man on bike 20 25
1643 45 c. Elderly man with seedling 20 25
1644 45 c. Elderly man and young boy fishing .. 20 25
1645 90 c. Space Shuttle "Atlantis" 45 50
1646 90 c. Konrad Adenauer (German statesman) .. 45 50
1647 $1.20 Sir Thomas Lipton and "Shamrock N" (yacht) 55 60
1648 $1.20 Snowy egret (bird) 55 60
1649 $1.20 Wolfgang Amadeus Mozart 55 60
1650 $2 Pulling fishing net ashore .. .. 95 1·00
1651 $3 Helen Keller (lecturer) 1·40 1·50
1652 $4 Eland (antelope) .. 2·00 2·10
1653 $4 Map of Allied Zones of Occupation, Germany, 1949 .. .. 2·00 2·10
1654 $4 Earth resources satellite .. .. 2·00 2·10
1655 $5 Count von Zeppelin .. 2·40 2·50

ANNIVERSARIES AND EVENTS: Nos. 1641, 1655, 75th death anniv of Count Ferdinand von Zeppelin; Nos. 1642/4, International Day of the Elderly; Nos. 1645, 1654, International Space Year; Nos. 1646, 1653, 25th death anniv of Konrad Adenauer; No. 1647, Americas Cup Yachting Championship; Nos. 1648, 1652, Earth Summit '92, Rio; No. 1649, Death bicent of Mozart; No. 1650, International Conference on Nutrition, Rome; No. 1651, 75th Anniv of International Association of Lions Clubs.

1993. Bicentenary of the Louvre, Paris. As T **305** of Antigua. Multicoloured.

1657 $1 "Madonna and Child with St. Catherine and a Rabbit" (left detail) (Titian) 50 55
1658 $1 "Madonna and Child with St. Catherine and a Rabbit" (right detail) (Titian) 50 55
1659 $1 "Women at her Toilet" (Titian) 50 55
1660 $1 "The Supper at Emmaus" (left detail) (Titian) 50 55
1661 $1 "The Supper at Emmaus" (right detail) (Titian) 50 55
1662 $1 "The Pastoral Concert" (Titian) .. 50 55
1663 $1 "An Allegory, perhaps of Marriage" (detail) (Titian) 50 55
1664 $1 "An Allegory, perhaps of Marriage" (different detail) (Titian) .. 50 55

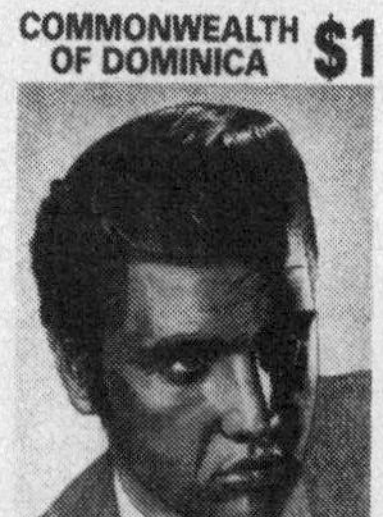

260 Elvis Presley

1993. 15th Death Anniv of Elvis Presley (singer). Multicoloured.

1666 $1 Type **260** 50 55
1667 $1 Elvis with guitar .. 50 55
1668 $1 Elvis with microphone 50 55

261 Plumbeous Warbler

1993. Birds. Multicoloured.

1669 90 c. Type **261** 45 50
1670 90 c. Black swift .. 45 50
1671 90 c. Blue-hooded euphonia 45 50
1672 90 c. Rufous-throated solitaire 45 50
1673 90 c. Ringed kingfisher .. 45 50
1674 90 c. Blue-headed hummingbird 45 50
1675 90 c. Bananaquit .. 45 50
1676 90 c. Brown trembler .. 45 50
1677 90 c. Forest thrush .. 45 50
1678 90 c. Purple-throated carib 45 50
1679 90 c. Ruddy quail dove .. 45 50
1680 90 c. Least bittern .. 45 50

Nos. 1669/80 were printed together, se-tenant, forming a composite design.

262 School Crest

1993. Centenary of Dominica Grammar School. Multicoloured.

1682 25 c. Type **262** 10 10
1683 30 c. V. Archer (first West Indian headmaster) .. 15 20
1684 65 c. Hubert Charles (first Dominican headmaster) 30 35
1685 90 c. Present school buildings 45 50

263 Leatherback Turtle on Beach

1993. Turtles. Multicoloured.

1686 25 c. Type **263** 10 10
1687 55 c. Hawksbill turtle swimming 25 30
1688 65 c. Atlantic ridley turtle 30 35
1689 90 c. Green turtle laying eggs 45 50
1690 $1 Green turtle swimming 50 55
1691 $2 Hawksbill turtle swimming (different) .. 95 1·00
1692 $4 Loggerhead turtle .. 2·00 2·10
1693 $5 Leatherback turtle swimming .. .. 2·40 2·50

264 Ford "Model A", 1928

1993. Centenaries of Henry Ford's First Petrol Engine (90 c., $5) and Karl Benz's First Four-wheeled Car (others). Multicoloured.

1695 90 c. Type **264** 45 50
1696 $1.20 Mercedes Benz car winning Swiss Grand Prix, 1936 .. .. 55 60
1697 $4 Mercedes Benz car winning German Grand Prix, 1935 .. .. 2·00 2·10
1698 $5 Ford "Model T", 1915 2·40 2·50

1993. 40th Anniv of Coronation. As T **307** of Antigua.

1700 20 c. multicoloured .. 10 10
1701 25 c. brown and black .. 10 10
1702 65 c. multicoloured .. 30 35
1703 $5 multicoloured .. 2·40 2·50

DESIGNS: 20 c. Queen Elizabeth II at Coronation (photograph by Cecil Beaton); 25 c. Queen wearing King Edward's Crown during Coronation ceremony; 65 c. Coronation coach; $5 Queen and Queen Mother in carriage.

265 New G.P.O. and Duke of Edinburgh

1993. Anniversaries and Events. Each brown, deep brown and black (Nos. 1707, 1717) or multicoloured (others).

1705 25 c. Type **265** 10 10
1706 25 c. "Bather with Beach Ball" (Picasso) (vert) .. 10 10
1707 65 c. Willy Brandt and Pres. Eisenhower, 1959 30 35
1708 90 c. As Type **265** but portrait of Queen Elizabeth II 45 50
1709 90 c. "Portrait of Leo Stein" (Picasso) (vert) 45 50
1710 90 c. Monika Holzner (Germany) (speed skating) (vert) .. 45 50
1711 90 c. "Self-portrait" (Marian Szczyrbula) (vert) 45 50
1712 90 c. Prince Naruhito and engagement photographs 45 50
1713 $1.20 16th-century telescope (vert) .. 55 60
1714 $3 "Bruno Jasienski" (Tyrus Czyzewski) (vert) .. .. .. 1·40 1·50
1715 $3 Modern observatory (vert) .. .. .. 1·40 1·50
1716 $4 Ray Leblanc and Tim Sweeney (U.S.A.) (ice hockey) (vert) .. 2·00 2·10
1717 $5 "Wilhelm Unde" (Picasso) (vert) .. 2·40 2·50
1718 $5 Willy Brandt and N.K. Winston at World's Fair, 1964 .. .. 2·40 2·50
1719 $5 Masako Owada and engagement photographs .. .. 2·40 2·50
1720 $5 Pres. Clinton and wife applauding .. .. 2·40 2·50

ANNIVERSARIES AND EVENTS: Nos. 1705, 1708, Opening of New General Post Office Building; Nos. 1706, 1709, 1717, 20th death anniv of Picasso (artist); Nos. 1707, 1718, 80th birth anniv of Willy Brandt (German politician); Nos. 1710, 1716, Winter Olympic Games '94, Lillehammer; Nos. 1711, 1714, "Polska '93" International Stamp Exhibition, Poznan; Nos. 1712, 1719, Marriage of Crown Prince Naruhito of Japan; Nos. 1713, 1715, 450th death anniv of Copernicus (astronomer); Nos. 1720, Inauguration of U.S. President William Clinton.

266 Hugo Eckener in New York Parade, 1928

1993. Aviation Anniversaries. Multicoloured.

1722 25 c. Type **266** 10 10
1723 55 c. BAC Lightning F.2 (fighter) 25 30
1724 65 c. "Graf Zeppelin" over Egypt, 1929 .. .. 30 30
1725 $1 Boeing 314 (flying boat) on transatlantic mail flight 50 55
1726 $2 Astronaut carrying mail to the Moon .. 95 1·00
1727 $4 "Viktoria Luise" over Kiel harbour, 1912 .. 2·00 2·10
1728 $5 Supermarine Spitfire (vert) .. .. 2·40 2·50

ANNIVERSARIES: Nos. 1722, 1724, 1727, 125th birth anniv of Hugo Eckener (airship commander); Nos. 1723, 1728, 75th Anniv of Royal Air Force; Nos. 1725/6, Bicentenary of first airmail flight.

267 Maradona (Argentina) and Buchwald (Germany)

1993. World Cup Football Championship, U.S.A (1994). Multicoloured.

1730 25 c. Type **267** 10 10
1731 55 c. Ruud Gullit (Netherlands) .. 30 35
1732 65 c. Chavarria (Costa Rica) and Bliss (U.S.A.) 30 35
1733 90 c. Diego Maradona (Argentina) 45 50
1734 90 c. Leonel Alvares (Colombia) 45 50
1735 $1 Altobelli (Italy) and Yong-hwang (South Korea) 50 55
1736 $2 Stopyra (France) .. 95 1·00
1737 $5 Renquin (Belgium) and Yaremtchuk (Russia) 2·40 2·50

268 Ornate Chedi, Wat Phra Boromathat Chaiya

1993. Asian International Stamp Exhibitons. Multicoloured. (a) "Indopex '93", Surabaya, Indonesia.

1739 25 c. Type **268** 10 10
1740 55 c. Temple ruins, Sukhothai 30 35
1741 90 c. Prasat Hin Phimai, Thailand .. 45 50
1742 $1.65 Arjuna and Prabu Gilling Wesi puppets .. 80 85
1743 $1.65 Loro Blonyo puppet 80 85
1744 $1.65 Yogyanese puppets 80 85
1745 $1.65 Wayang gedog puppet, Ng Setro .. 80 85
1746 $1.65 Wayang golek puppet 80 85
1747 $1.65 Wayang gedog puppet, Raden Damar Wulan .. 80 85
1748 $5 Main sanctuary, Prasat Phanom Rung, Thailand .. 2·40 2·40

(b) "Taipei '93", Taiwan

1750 25 c. Aw Boon Haw Gardens, Causeway Bay 10 10
1751 65 c. Observation building, Kenting Park 30 35
1752 90 c. Tzu-en pagoda on lakeshore, Taiwan .. 45 50
1753 $1.65 Chang E kite .. 80 85
1754 $1.65 Red Phoenix and Rising Sun kite .. 80 85
1755 $1.65 Heavenly Judge kite 80 85
1756 $1.65 Monkey King kite 80 85
1757 $1.65 Goddess of Luo River kite .. 80 85
1758 $1.65 Heavenly Maiden kite 80 85
1759 $5 Villa, Lantau Island 2·40 2·50

(c) "Bangkok '93", Thailand

1761 25 c. Tugu Monument, Java 10 10
1762 55 c. Candi Cangkuang mon, West Java .. 30 35
1763 90 c. Merus, Pura Taman Ayun, Mengwi .. 45 50
1764 $1.65 Hun Lek puppets of Rama and Sita .. 80 85
1765 $1.65 Burmese puppet .. 80 85
1766 $1.65 Burmese puppets .. 80 85
1767 $1.65 Demon puppet at Wat Phra Kaew .. 80 85
1768 $1.65 Hun Lek puppet performing Khun Chang 80 85
1769 $1.65 Hun Lek puppets performing Ramakien 80 85
1770 $5 Stone mosaic, Ceto .. 2·40 2·50

269 Willie

1993. "Willie the Operatic Whale". Scenes from Walt Disney's cartoon film. Mult.

1772 $1 Type **269** 50 55
1773 $1 Willie's pelican friend 50 55
1774 $1 Willie singing to seals 50 55
1775 $1 Willie singing "Lucia" 50 55
1776 $1 Willie in "Pagliacci" 50 55
1777 $1 Willie as Mephistopheles .. 50 55
1778 $1 Tetti Tatti searching for Willie 50 55
1779 $1 Whalers listening to Willie 50 55
1780 $1 Tetti Tatti with harpoon gun 50 55

APPENDIX

The following stamps have either been issued in excess of postal needs, or have not been made available to the public in reasonable quantities at face value.

1978-79.

History of Aviation. $16 × 30, each embossed on gold foil.

DUNGARPUR

A state of Rajasthan. Now uses Indian stamps.

12 pies = 1 anna, 16 annas = 1 rupee.

1. State Arms.

1933.

1. **1.** ¼ a. yellow .. .. — 75·00
2. ¼ a. red .. .. .. — £200
3. ¼ a. brown .. .. — £150
4. 1 a. blue .. .. — 75·00
5. 1 a. red .. .. .. — £650
6. 1 a. 3 p. violet .. .. — £100
7. 2 a. green .. .. — £130
8. 4 a. red .. .. .. — £225

2. Maharawal Sir Shri Lakshman Singh Bahadur.

1932. T **2** (various frames).

9. **2.** ¼ a. orange .. .. £225 30·00
10. ½ a. red .. .. .. £140 27·00
11. 1 a. blue .. .. £130 19·00
12. 1 a. 3 p. mauve .. £275 90·00
13. 1½ a. violet .. .. £300 95·00
14. 2 a. green £350 £170
15. 4 a. brown .. .. £275 75·00

DUTTIA (DATIA)

A state of Central India. Now uses Indian stamps.

12 pies = 1 anna, 16 annas = 1 rupee.

1. Ganesh.

2.

1893. Imperf.

1. **1.** ¼ a. black on orange .. £2000
2. ½ a. black on green .. £2500
4. 2 a. black on yellow .. £1700
5. 4 a. black on red .. £1300

Stamps of Type **1** come with the circular handstamp as shown on Type **2**. Examples of Nos. 1/2 without handstamp are worth slightly less than the prices quoted.

1893. Imperf.

6. **2.** ½ a. black on green .. 13·00 £100
3. 1 a. red £2000
7. 1 a. black .. .. .. 50·00 £120
8. 2 a. black on yellow .. 17·00 £110
10. 4 a. black on red .. .. 15·00 95·00

1896. Imperf.

5a. **2.** ½ a. black on green .. £4000
5b. 2 a. blue on yellow .. £2500

Nos. 5a/b are as Type **2**, but have rosettes in lower corners.

3.

4.

1897. Imperf.

12. **3.** ½ a. black on green .. 55·00
13. 1 a. black £120
14. 2 a. black on yellow .. 65·00
15. 4 a. black on red .. 60·00

1899. Imperf., roul. or perf.

16c. 4.	¼ a. red	1·75	6·50
38.	¼ a. blue	1·00	6·50
37.	¼ a. black	3·50	10·00
17.	½ a. black on green	1·40	6·50
30.	½ a. green	2·75	12·00
35.	½ a. blue	1·50	7·00
39.	½ a. pink	1·25	8·00
18.	1 a. black	1·40	6·50
31.	1 a. purple	3·50	13·00
36.	1 a. pink	1·40	8·00
19b.	2 a. black on yellow	1·75	8·50
32.	2 a. brown	8·50	19·00
33.	2 a. lilac	5·00	21·00
20.	4 a. black on red	1·50	5·50
34.	4 a. brown	65·00	

FALKLAND ISLANDS

A Br. colony in the S. Atlantic.

1878. 12 pence = 1 shilling;
20 shillings = 1 pound.
1971. 100 (new) pence = 1 pound.

3.

6.

1878.

17a 3.	½d. green	2·00	1·50
23	1d. red to brown	5·00	1·40
26	2d. purple	5·00	11·00
30	2½d. blue	20·00	7·50
32	4d. black	12·00	21·00
3	6d. green	45·00	45·00
34	6d. yellow	27·00	32·00
35	9d. red	23·00	55·00
38	1s. brown	30·00	35·00
41 –	2s. 6d. blue	£200	£250
42 6.	5s. red	£180	£200

DESIGN: 2s. 6d. As Type 6, but different frame.

1891. No. 11 bisected diagonally and each half surch. ½d.

14. 3.	½d. on half of 1d. brown	£450	£225

7.

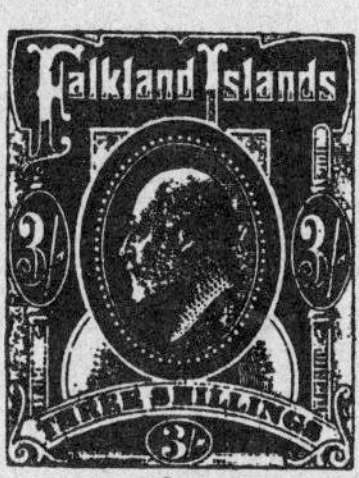

8.

1904.

43 7	½d. green	3·75	1·00
44a	1d. red	90	2·00
45	2d. purple	9·50	25·00
46	2½d. blue	29·00	7·50
47	6d. orange	35·00	48·00
48	1s. brown	40·00	30·00
49 8	3s. green	£130	£120
50	5s. red	£140	£140

1912. As T 7/8 but portrait of King George V.

60	½d. green	1·75	2·50
74	1d. red	5·00	80
75b	2d. purple	7·50	3·00
63c	2½d. blue	6·50	16·00
77	2½d. purple on yellow	4·00	32·00
64	6d. orange	12·00	18·00
65	1s. brown	28·00	28·00
66	3s. green	55·00	70·00
67	5s. red	60·00	85·00
67b	5s. purple	65·00	85·00
68	10s. red on green	£140	£200
69	£1 black on red	£300	£350

1918. As 1912, optd. WAR STAMP.

70b.	½d. green	50	6·50
71c.	1d. red	50	3·50
72a.	1s. brown	6·00	35·00

1928. No. 75b surch 2½d.

115	2½d. on 2d. purple	£650	£700

13. Fin Whale and Gentoo Penguins.

1929.

116.13.	½d. green	70	1·75
117.	1d. red	1·00	35
118.	2d. grey	1·25	1·00
119.	2½d. blue	1·25	1·75
120.	4d. orange	7·50	12·00
121.	6d. purple	7·50	7·00
122.	1s. black on green	14·00	18·00
123.	2s. 6d. red on blue	27·00	28·00
124.	5s. green on yellow	50·00	60·00
125.	10s. red on green	85·00	£110
126.	£1 black on red	£300	£400

15. Romney Marsh Ram.

1933. Centenary of British Occupation. Inscr. "1833–1933".

127.15.	½d. black and green	1·50	4·00
128. –	1d. black and red	3·50	1·25
129. –	1½d. black and blue	7·00	8·00
130. –	2d. black and brown	7·50	16·00
131. –	3d. black and violet	9·00	8·00
132. –	4d. black and orange	10·00	13·00
133. –	6d. black and grey	48·00	50·00
134. –	1s. black and olive	35·00	50·00
135. –	2s. 6d. black and violet	£100	£130
136. –	5s. black and yellow	£500	£650
137. –	10s. black and brown	£500	£600
138. –	£1 black and red	£1300	£1800

DESIGNS—HORIZ. 1d. Iceberg. 1½d. Whale-catcher. 2d. Port Louis. 3d. Map of Falkland Is. 4d. S. Georgia. 6d. Fin Whale. 1s. Government House, Stanley. VERT. 2s. 6d. Battle Memorial. 5s. King Penguin. 10s. Arms. £1. King George V.

1935. Silver Jubilee. As T 13 of Antigua.

139.	1d. blue and red	2·00	40
140.	2½d. brown and blue	5·00	1·25
141.	4d. green and blue	5·00	1·50
142.	1s. grey and purple	5·50	1·75

1937. Coronation. As T 2 of Aden.

143.	½d. green	30	10
144.	1d. red	40	45
145.	2½d. blue	80	45

27. Whales' Jaw Bones.

1938.

146	27	½d. black and green	20	75
147a	A	1d. black and red	3·00	75
148	B	1d. black and violet	1·40	1·75
149		2d. black and violet	1·00	50
150a	A	2d. black and red	75	50
151	C	2½d. black and blue	45	30
152	D	2½d. black and blue	2·75	3·75
153a	C	3d. black and blue	3·50	1·40
154	D	4d. black and purple	1·75	50
155	E	6d. black and brown	4·50	3·50
156		6d. black	3·25	4·50
157	F	9d. black and blue	8·00	50
158a	G	1s. blue	9·50	2·50
159	H	1s. 3d. black and red	1·50	1·40
160	I	2s. 6d. black	50·00	7·50
161	J	5s. blue and orange	£100	40·00
162	K	10s. black and orange	55·00	27·00
163	L	£1 black and violet	£110	48·00

DESIGNS—HORIZ. A, Black-necked swan. B, Battle memorial. C, Flock of sheep. D, Magellan goose. E, "Discovery II" (polar supply vessel). F, "William Scoresby" (research ship). G, Mount Sugar Top. H, Turkey vultures. I, Gentoo penguins. J, Southern sealion. K, Deception Is. L, Arms of Falkland Islands.

1946. Victory. As T 9 of Aden.

164.	1d. mauve	30	15
165.	3d. blue	30	15

1948. Silver Wedding. As T 10/11 of Aden.

166.	2½d. blue	2·00	70
167.	£1 mauve	90·00	55·00

1949. U.P.U. As T 20/23 of Antigua.

168.	1d. violet	1·50	75
169.	3d. blue	4·50	2·00
170.	1s. 3d. green	5·50	2·25
171.	2s. blue	5·50	6·50

39. Sheep.

1952.

172. 39.	½d. green	70	70
173. –	1d. red	80	40
174. –	2d. violet	3·25	1·50
175. –	2½d. black and blue	95	50
176. –	3d. blue	1·00	1·00
177. –	4d. purple	6·50	2·50
178. –	6d. brown	12·00	1·00
179. –	9d. yellow	7·50	4·50
180. –	1s. black	12·00	80
181. –	1s. 3d. orange	6·50	12·00
182. –	2s. 6d. olive	15·00	10·00
183. –	5s. purple	7·00	7·00
184. –	10s. grey	15·00	30·00
185. –	£1 black	25·00	30·00

DESIGNS—HORIZ. 1d. "Fitzroy" (supply ship). 2d. Magellan goose. 2½d. Map. 4d. Auster aircraft. 6d. "John Biscoe I" (research ship). 9d. View of the Two Sisters. 1s. 3d. Kelp goose and gander. 10s. Southern sealion and South American fur seal. £1, Hulk of "Great Britain". VERT. 3d. Arms. 1s. Gentoo penguins. 2s. 6d. Sheep shearing. 5s. Battle Memorial.

1953. Coronation. As T 13 of Aden.

186.	1d. black and red	1·00	1·25

1955. As 1952 issue but with portrait of Queen Elizabeth II.

187.	½d. green	70	1·25
188.	1d. red	1·25	60
189.	2d. violet	2·75	4·50
190.	6d. brown	5·50	60
191.	9d. yellow	23·00	17·00
192.	1s. black	3·50	1·25

54. Austral Thrush.

1960. Birds.

227. 54.	½d. black and green	30	30
194. –	1d. black and red	1·25	40
195. –	2d. black and blue	2·75	80
196. –	2½d. black and bistre	1·50	20
197. –	3d. black and olive	80	15
198. –	4d. black and red	1·25	60
199. –	5½d. black and violet	1·50	1·25
200. –	6d. black and sepia	1·50	15
201. –	9d. black and red	1·50	80
202. –	1s. black and purple	80	15
203. –	1s. 3d. black and blue	9·00	10·00
204. –	2s. black and brown	27·00	1·50
205. –	5s. black and turquoise	25·00	9·50
206. –	10s. black and purple	45·00	12·00
207. –	£1 black and yellow	48·00	27·00

BIRDS: 1d. Southern black-backed gull. 2d. Gentoo penguins. 2½d. Long-tailed meadow lark. 3d. Magellan goose. 4d. Falkland Is. flightless steamer ducks. 5½d. Rock-hopper penguins. 6d. Black-browed albatross. 9d. Silver grebe. 1s. Magellanic oystercatcher. 1s. 3d. Chilean teal. 2s. Kelp geese. 5s. King cormorants. 10s. Common Caracara. £1 Black-necked swan.

69. Morse Key.

1962. 50th Anniversary of Establishment of Radio Communication.

208. 69.	6d. red and orange	1·00	30
209. –	1s. green and olive	1·25	35
210. –	2s. violet and blue	1·25	90

DESIGNS: 1s. One-valve receiver. 2s. Rotary Spark transmitter.

1963. Freedom from Hunger. As T 28 of Aden.

211.	1s. blue	13·00	85

1963. Cent of Red Cross. As T 33 of Antigua.

212.	1d. red and black	5·00	50
213.	1s. red and blue	20·00	4·50

1964. 400th Birth Anniv of Shakespeare. As T 34 of Antigua.

214.	6d. black	1·00	30

72. H.M.S. "Glasgow".

1964. 50th Anniv. of Battle of the Falkland Islands.

215. 72.	2½d. black and red	6·50	2·75
216. –	6d. black and blue	1·00	25
217. –	1s. black and red	2·50	75
218. –	2s. black and blue	2·00	75

DESIGNS—HORIZ. 6d. H.M.S. "Kent". 1s. H.M.S. "Invincible". VERT. 2s. Battle Memorial.

1965. Cent of I.T.U. As T 36 of Antigua.

219.	1d. light blue & deep blue	85	20
220.	2s. lilac and yellow	12·00	1·50

1965. I.C.Y. As T 37 of Antigua.

221.	1d. purple and turquoise	1·50	20
222.	1s. green and lavender	7·50	1·10

1966. Churchill Commem. As T 38 of Antigua.

223.	½d. blue	65	40
224.	1d. green	2·25	15
225.	1s. brown	6·50	1·00
226.	2s. violet	8·00	1·25

76. Globe and Human Rights Emblem.

1968. Human Rights Year.

228. 76.	2d. multicoloured	50	20
229.	6d. multicoloured	55	20
230.	1s. multicoloured	60	20
231.	2s. multicoloured	70	30

77. Dusty Miller.

1968. Flowers Multicoloured.

232.	½d. Type 77	15	70
233.	1½d. Pig Vine	20	15
234.	2d. Pale Maiden	30	15
235.	3d. Dog Orchid	2·00	15
236.	3½d. Sea Cabbage	30	15
237.	4½d. Vanilla Daisy	50	70
238.	5½d. yellow, brown and grn. (Arrowleaf Marigold)	50	90
239.	6d. red, black and green (Diddle Dee)	50	20
240.	1s. Scurvy Grass	60	50
241.	1s. 6d. Prickly Burr	4·50	8·50
242.	2s. Fachine	5·50	6·50
243.	3s. Lavender	9·00	5·50
244.	5s. Felton's Flower	24·00	13·00
245.	£1 Yellow Orchid	13·00	2·00

Nos. 233, 236, 238/40 and 244 are horiz.

91. DHC—2 Beaver Floatplane.

1969. 21st Anniv. of Government Air Services. Multicoloured.

246.	2d. Type 91	35	30
247.	6d. "Norseman"	40	35
248.	1s. "Auster"	50	35
249.	2s. Arms of the Falkland Islands	1·75	70

92. Holy Trinity Church, 1869.

1969. Centenary of Bishop Stirling's Consecration.

250. 92.	2d. black, grey & green	40	30
251. –	6d. black, grey and red	50	30
252. –	1s. black, grey & lilac	55	30
253. –	2s. multicoloured	80	55

DESIGNS: 6d. Christ Church Cathedral, 1969. 1s. Bishop Stirling. 2s. Bishop's Mitre.

96. Mounted Volunteer.

1970. Golden Jubilee of Defence Force. Multicoloured.

254. 2d. Type **96** .. .. 1·90 60
255. 6d. Defence Post .. .. 2·00 60
256. 1s. Corporal in No. 1 Dress uniform .. .. .. 2·25 60
257. 2s. Badge .. .. .. 4·00 75

Nos. 255 and 257 are horiz.

97. S.S. "Great Britain" (1843).

1970. S.S. "Great Britain" Restoration. Stamps show S.S. "Great Britain" in year given Multicoloured.

258. 2d. Type **97** .. .. 1·75 40
259. 4d. 1845 .. .. .. 2·00 90
260. 9d. 1876 .. .. .. 2·00 90
261. 1s. 1886 .. .. .. 2·00 90
262. 2s. 1970 .. .. .. 2·75 90

1971. Decimal Currency. Nos. 232/44 surch.

263. ½p. on ½d. multicoloured 25 20
264. 1p. on 1½d. multicoloured 30 15
265. 1½p. on 2d. multicoloured 30 15
266. 2p. on 3d. multicoloured 50 20
267. 2½p. on 3½d. multicoloured 30 20
268. 3p. on 4½d. multicoloured 30 20
269. 4p. on 5½d. yellow, brown and green 30 20
270. 5p. on 6d. red, blk. & grn. 30 20
271. 6p. on 1s. multicoloured.. 5·50 2·50
272. 7½p. on 1s. 6d. mult. .. 8·00 3·25
273. 10p. on 2s. multicoloured.. 8·50 3·00
274. 15p. on 3s. multicoloured.. 6·50 2·75
275. 25p. on 5s. multicoloured.. 7·00 3·25

1972. Decimal Currency. Nos. 232/44 inscr. in decimal currency.

276. ½p. multicoloured .. 35 2·50
277. 1p. multicoloured .. 30 40
278. 1½p. multicoloured .. 30 1·50
279. 2p. multicoloured .. 13·00 1·25
280. 2½p. multicoloured .. 35 1·75
281. 3p. multicoloured .. 35 1·25
282. 4p. yellow, brown & green 40 50
283. 5p. red, black and green .. 40 55
295. 6p. multicoloured .. 2·00 2·25
285. 7½p. multicoloured .. 1·50 4·00
286. 10p. multicoloured .. 7·50 4·50
287. 15p. multicoloured .. 4·50 5·00
288. 25p. multicoloured .. 4·50 6·00

1972. Royal Silver Wedding. As T **52** of Ascension but with Romney Marsh Sheep and Giant Sea Lions in background.

289. 1p. green 30 25
290. 10p. blue 70 85

1973. Royal Wedding. As Type **47** of Anguilla. Background colour given. Mult.

291. 5p. mauve 25 10
292. 15p. brown 40 20

101. South American Fur Seal.

1974. Tourism. Multicoloured.

296. 2p. Type **101** .. .. 2·25 1·00
297. 4p. Trout-fishing .. .. 3·00 1·25
298. 5p. Rockhopper penguins 9·00 2·25
299. 15p. Long-tailed meadow lark .. .. .. 12·00 3·25

MORE DETAILED LISTS
are given in the Stanley Gibbons Catalogues referred to in the country headings.
For lists of current volumes see Introduction.

102. 19th-century Mail-coach.

1974. U.P.U. Multicoloured.

300. 2p. Type **102** 25 25
301. 5p. Packet ship, 1841 .. 35 45
302. 8p. First U.K. aerial post, 1911 .. .. .. 40 55
303. 16p. Ship's catapult mail, 1920's 60 75

103. Churchill and Houses of Parliament.

1974. Birth Centenary of Sir Winston Churchill. Multicoloured.

304 16p. Type **103** .. .. 1·40 1·40
305 20p. Churchill with H.M.S. "Inflexible" and H.M.S. "Invincible", 1914 .. 1·90 1·60

104. H.M.S. "Exeter".

1974. 35th Anniv. of Battle of the River Plate. Multicoloured.

307. 2p. Type **104** .. .. 3·00 1·60
308. 6p. H.M.N.Z. "Achilles" 4·50 3·50
309. 8p. "Admiral Graf Spee" 5·00 4·50
310. 16p. H.M.S. "Ajax" .. 8·50 12·00

105. Seal and Flag Badge.

1975. 50th Anniv. of Heraldic Arms. Mult.

311. 2p. Type **105** 50 35
312. 7½p. Coat of arms, 1925 .. 1·00 1·10
313. 10p. Coat of arms, 1948 .. 1·10 1·25
314. 16p. Arms of the Dependencies, 1952 .. .. 1·75 2·00

106. ½p Coin and Trout.

1975. New Coinage. Multicoloured.

316. 2p. Type **106** 85 45
317. 5½p. 1p Coin and Gentoo penguin .. .. 1·00 90
318. 8p 2p Coin and Magellan goose .. .. .. 1·40 1·25
319. 10p. 5p Coin and Black-browed albatross .. 1·60 1·40
320. 16p. 10p Coin and Southern sealion .. 1·75 1·75

107. Gathering Sheep.

1976. Sheep Farming Industry. Mult.

321. 2p. Type **107** 45 35
322. 7½p. Shearing .. .. 1·10 1·00
323. 10p. Dipping .. .. 1·40 1·40
324. 20p. Shipping .. .. 2·00 2·25

108. The Queen Awaiting Anointment.

1977. Silver Jubilee. Multicoloured.

325. 6p. Visit of Prince Philip 1957 1·50 95
326. 11p. The Queen, ampulla and anointing spoon .. 80 75
327. 33p. Type **108** .. .. 1·00 1·25

109. Map of Falkland Islands.

1977. Telecommunications. Multicoloured.

328. 3p. Type **109** 35 15
329. 11p. Ship to shore communications 75 40
330. 40p. Telex and telephone service .. .. .. 2·50 1·40

110. "A.E.S.". 1957–74.

1978. Mail Ships. Multicoloured.

331. 1p. Type **110** 20 20
332. 2p. "Darwin" 1957–73 .. 30 20
333. 3p. "Merak-N" 1951–52 .. 25 40
334. 4p. "Fitzroy" 1936–57 .. 20 30
335. 5p. "Lafonia" 1936–41 .. 30 30
336. 6p. "Fleurus" 1924–33 .. 30 30
337. 7p. "Falkland" 1914–34 .. 30 70
338. 8p. "Oravia" 1900–12 .. 35 50
339. 9p. "Memphis" 1890–97 .. 35 50
340. 10p. "Black Hawk" 1873–80 .. .. 35 50
341. 20p. "Foam" 1863–72 .. 1·25 1·75
342. 25p. "Fairy" 1857–61 .. 1·25 2·50
343. 50p. "Amelia" 1852–54 .. 2·25 3·00
344. £1 "Nautilus" 1846–48 .. 2·50 4·50
345. £3 "Hebe" 1842–46 .. 5·50 9·50

Nos. 331/45 come with and without date imprint.

111. Short "Hythe" at Stanley.

1978. 26th Anniv. of 1st Direct Flight, Southampton–Port Stanley. Multicoloured.

346. 11p. Type **111** .. .. 2·00 1·25
347. 33p. Route map and Short flying boat .. .. 2·50 1·75

112. Red Dragon of Wales.

113. First Fox Bay P.O. and 1d. Stamp of 1878.

1978. 25th Anniv. of Coronation. Mult.

348. **112.** 25p. brn., blue & silver 1·00 1·00
349. – 25p. multicoloured .. 1·00 1·00
350. – 25p. brn., blue & silver 1·00 1·00

DESIGNS: No. 349, Queen Elizabeth II No. 350, Hornless ram.

1978. Centenary of First Falkland Is. Postage Stamp. Multicoloured.

351. 3p. Type **113** 20 20
352. 11p. Second Stanley P.O. and 4d. stamp of 1878 35 40
353. 15p. New Island P.O. and 6d. stamp of 1878 .. 40 50
354. 22p. First Stanley P.O. and 1s. stamp of 1878 .. 70 65

114. "Macrocystis pyrifera".

1979. Kelp and Seaweed. Multicoloured.

355. 3p. Type **114** 20 15
356. 7p. "Durvillea sp." .. 40 25
357. 11p. "Lessonia sp." (horiz.) 50 30
358. 15p. "Callophyllis sp." (horiz.) 70 35
359. 25p. "Iradaea sp." .. 90 55

115. Britten-Norman "Islander" over Falkland Islands.

1979. Opening of Stanley Airport. Mult.

360. 3p. Type **115** 30 20
361. 11p. Fokker "F27" over South Atlantic 70 60
362. 15p. Fokker "28" over Airport 80 60
363. 25p. Cessna "172 (Skyhawk)", Britten-Norman "Islander", Fokker "F27" and "F28" over runway .. .. 1·50 80

116. Sir Rowland Hill and 1953 Coronation 1d. commemorative.

1979. Death Centenary of Sir Rowland Hill. Multicoloured.

364. 3p. Type **116** 25 25
365. 11p. 1878 1d. stamp (vert.) 50 70
366. 25p. Penny Black .. 75 85

117. Mail Drop by "Beaver" Aircraft.

1979. Centenary of Accession to the U.P.U. Multicoloured.

368.	3 p. Type **117**	20	20
369.	11p. Mail by horseback ..	45	55
370.	25p. Mail by schooner " Gwendolin "	75	1·00

118. Peale's Porpoise.

1980. Dolphins and Porpoises. Multicoloured.

371.	3p. Type **118**	30	25
372.	6p. Commerson's Dolphin (horiz.)	40	40
373.	7p. Hour-glass Dolphin (horiz.)	40	40
374.	11p. Spectacled Porpoise	70	65
375.	15p. Dusky Dolphin (horiz.)	80	75
376.	25p. Killer Whale (horiz.)	1·25	1·25

119. 1878 Falkland Islands Postmark.

1980. " London 1980 " International Stamp Exhibition.

377. 119.	11p. blk., gold and blue	30	35
378. –	11p. blk., gold and yell.	30	35
379. –	11p. blk., gold and green	30	35
380. –	11p. blk., gold and pur.	30	35
381. –	11p. black, gold and red	30	35
382. –	11p. blk., gold and flesh	30	35

POSTMARKS: No. 378, 1915 New Island. No. 379, 1901 Falkland Islands. No. 380, 1935 Port Stanley. No. 381, 1952 Port Stanley first overseas airmail. No. 382, 1934 Fox Bay.

120. Queen Elizabeth the Queen Mother at Ascot, 1971.

1980. 80th Birthday of Queen Mother.

383.	**120.** 11p. multicoloured ..	40	30

121. Forster's Caracara.

1980. Birds of Prey. Multicoloured.

384.	3p. Type **121**	30	25
385.	11p. Red-backed buzzard	70	60
386.	15p. Common caracara ..	85	75
387.	25p. Peregrine falcon ..	1·25	1·00

122. Stanley.

1981. Early Settlements. Multicoloured.

388.	3p. Type **122**	20	15
389.	11p. Port Egmont ..	40	35
390.	25p. Port Louis	80	65
391.	33p. Mission House, Keppel Island	1·10	80

123. Sheep.

1981. Farm Animals. Multicoloured.

392.	3p. Type **123**	20	25
393.	11p. Cattle	35	55
394.	25p. Horse	70	95
395.	33p. Dogs	1·00	1·25

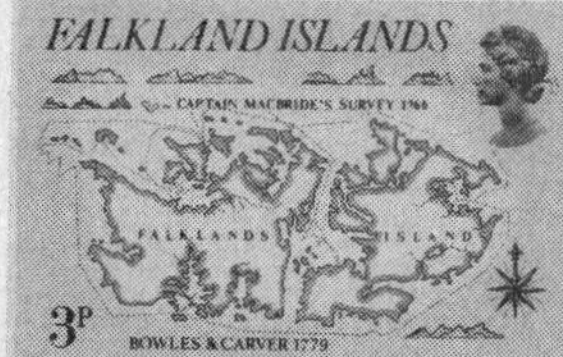

124. Bowles and Carver, 1779.

1981. Early Maps.

396. **124.**	3p. multicoloured ..	20	20
397. –	10p. multicoloured ..	40	45
398. –	13p. multicoloured ..	55	60
399. –	15p. multicoloured ..	55	65
400. –	25p. multicoloured ..	70	75
401. –	26p. black, pink & stone	70	75

MAPS: 10p. J. Hawkesworth, 1773. 13p. Eman Bowen, 1747. 15p. T. Boutflower, 1768. 25p. Philippe de Pretot, 1771. 26p. Bellin " Petite Atlas Maritime ", Paris, 1764.

125. Wedding Bouquet from Falkland Islands.

1981. Royal Wedding. Multicoloured.

402.	10p. Type **125**	45	40
403.	13p. Prince Charles riding	55	50
404.	52p. Prince Charles and Lady Diana Spencer ..	1·00	1·00

126. " Handicrafts ".

1981. 25th Anniv. of Duke of Edinburgh Award Scheme. Multicoloured.

405.	10p. Type **126**	30	20
406.	13p. " Camping "	50	30
407.	15p. " Canoeing "	55	40
408.	26p. Duke of Edinburgh	75	60

127. " The Adoration of the Holy Child " (16th-century Dutch Artist).

1981. Christmas. Paintings. Multicoloured.

409.	3p. Type **127**	20	20
410.	13p. " The Holy Family in an Italian Landscape " (17th-century Genoan artist)	35	45
411.	26p. " The Holy Virgin " (Reni)	55	75

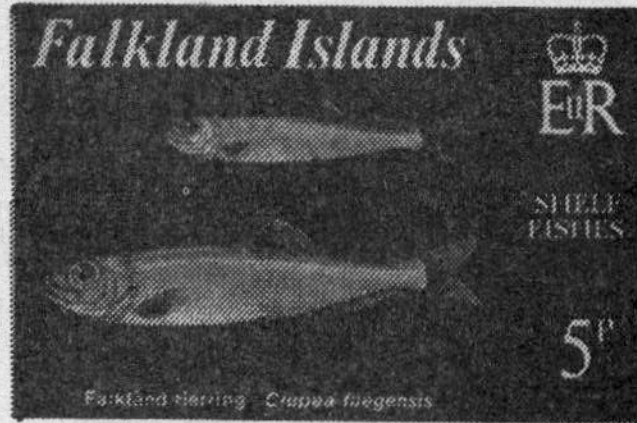

128. Falkland Herring.

1981. Shelf Fishes. Multicoloured.

412.	5p. Type **128**	15	15
413.	13p. Rock Cod (vert.) ..	30	30
414.	15p. Patagonian Hake ..	35	35
415.	25p. Southern Blue Whiting	60	65
416.	26p. Grey-tailed Skate (vert.)	60	65

129. " Lady Elizabeth, " 1913.

1982. Shipwrecks. Multicoloured.

417.	5p. Type **129**	30	50
418.	13p. " Capricorn ", 1882	40	70
419.	15p. " Jhelum ", 1870 ..	45	85
420.	25p. " Snowsquall ", 1864	75	1·10
421.	26p. " St. Mary ", 1890 ..	75	1·10

130. Charles Darwin.

1982. 150th Anniv. of Charles Darwin's Voyage. Multicoloured.

422.	5p. Type **130**	20	20
423.	17p. Darwin's microscope	50	55
424.	25 p. Falkland Islands Wolf	65	75
425.	34p. H.M.S. "Beagle" ..	85	95

131. Falkland Islands Coat of Arms.

1982. 21st Birthday of Princess of Wales. Multicoloured.

426.	5p. Type **131**	15	20
427.	17p. Princess at Royal Opera House, Covent Garden, November 1981	40	60
428.	37p. Bride and groom in doorway of St. Paul's ..	75	1·10
429.	50p. Formal portrait ..	1·00	1·25

132. Map of Falkland Islands. (Illustration reduced. Actual size 60 × 35 mm).

1982. Rebuilding Fund.

430. **132.**	£1+£1 multicoloured ..	3·50	4·75

1982. Commonwealth Games, Brisbane. Nos. 335 and 342 optd. **1st PARTICIPATION COMMONWEALTH GAMES 1982.**

431.	5p. " Lafonia ", 1936–41	15	30
432.	25p. " Fairy ", 1857–61 ..	60	1·10

134. Blackish Cinclodes.

1982. Birds of the Passerine Family. Mult.

433.	5p. Type **134**	15	15
434.	10p. Black-chinned siskin	25	25
435.	13p. Short-billed marsh wren	30	30
436.	25p. Black-throated finch	35	35
437.	25p. Correndera pipit ..	50	50
438.	34p. Dark-faced ground-tyrant	65	65

135. Raising Flag, Port Louis, 1833.

1983. 150th Anniv. of British Administration. Multicoloured.

439.	1p. Type **135**	20	20
440.	2p. Chelsea pensioners and barracks, 1849 (horiz.) ..	30	30
441.	5p. Development of wool trade, 1874	30	30
442.	10p. Ship-repairing trade, 1850–1890 (horiz.) ..	60	60
443.	15p. Government House, early 20th century (horiz.) ..	70	70
444.	20p. Battle of Falkland Islands, 1914 ..	90	90
445.	25p. Whalebone Arch (horiz.)	90	90
446.	40p. Contribution to War effort, 1939–45 ..	1·40	1·40
447.	50p. Duke of Edinburgh's visit, 1957 (horiz.) ..	1·75	1·75
448.	£1 Royal Marine uniforms	2·50	2·50
449.	£2 Queen Elizabeth II ..	3·75	4·50

136. 1933 British Administration Centenary 3d. Commemorative.

1983. Commonwealth Day. Multicoloured.

450.	5p. Type **136**	15	15
451.	17p. 1933 British Administration Centenary ½d. commemorative ..	35	45
452.	34p. 1933 British Administration Centenary 10s. commemorative (vert.)	70	80
453.	50p. 1983 British Administration 150th anniversary £2 commemorative (vert.)	1·00	1·25

137. British Army advancing across East Falkland.

1983. First Anniv. of Liberation. Mult.
454. 5p. Type **137** 15 25
455. 13p. S.S. "Canberra" and M.V. "Norland" at San Carlos 30 50
456. 17p. R.A.F. Hawker "Harrier" fighter .. 35 60
457. 50p. H.M.S. "Hermes" (aircraft carrier) .. 1·00 1·40

138. Diddle Dee.

1983. Native Fruits. Multicoloured.
459. 5p. Type **138** 20 20
460. 17 p. Tea Berry 45 50
461. 25p. Mountain Berry .. 70 65
462. 34p. Native Strawberry .. 85 80

139. Britten-Norman "Islander."

1983. Bicentenary of Manned Flight. Multicoloured.
463. 5p. Type **139** 15 20
464. 13p. "DHC-2 Beaver" .. 35 45
465. 17p. "Noorduyn Norseman" 40 50
466. 50p. "Auster" .. 1·00 1·25

1984. Nos. 443 and 445 surch.
467. 17p. on 15p. Government House, early 20th century 60 45
468. 22p. on 25p. Whalebone Arch, 1933 .. .. 65 55

141. "Araneus cinnabarinus" (juvenile spider).

1984. Insects and Spiders. Multicoloured.
469 1p. Type **141** 20 40
470 2p. "Alopophion occidentalis" (fly) .. .. 1·00 1·00
471 3p. "Pareuxoina falklandica" (moth) 40 45
472 4p. "Lissopterus quadrinotatus" (beetle) .. 30 45
473 5p. "Issoria cytheris" (butterfly) 30 45
474 6p. "Araneus cinnabarinus" (adult spider) 30 45
475 7p. "Trachysphyrus penai" (fly) 30 45
476 8p. "Caphornia ochricraspia" (moth) .. 30 45
477 9p. "Caneorhinus biangulatus" (weevil) .. 30 45
478 10p. "Syrphus octomaculatus" (fly) .. 30 45
479 20p. "Malvinius compressiventris" (weevil) 2·25 75
480 25p. "Metius blandus" (beetle) 75 90
481 50p. "Parudenus falklandicus" (cricket) .. 1·00 1·50
482 £1 "Emmenomma beauchenieus" (spider) 1·75 2·25
483 £3 "Cynthia carye" (butterfly) .. .. 5·00 6·00

No. 470 comes with or without imprint date.

142. "Wavertree" (sail merchantman).

1984. 250th Anniv. of "Lloyd's List" (newspaper). Multicoloured.
484 6p. Type **142** 45 25
485 17p. "Bjerk" (whale catcher) at Port Stanley 90 50
486 22p. "Oravia" (liner) stranded 95 55
487 52p. "Cunard Countess" (liner) .. .. .. 1·50 1·50

143. Ship, Aircraft and U.P.U. Logo.

1984. Universal Postal Union Congress, Hamburg.
488. **143.** 22p. multicoloured .. 55 65

144. Great Grebe.

1984. Grebes. Multicoloured.
489. 17p. Type **144** .. .. 1·00 1·00
490. 22p. Silver grebe .. .. 1·10 1·25
491. 52p. White-tufted grebe .. 2·50 3·00

145. Black-browed Albatross.

1984. Nature Conservation. Multicoloured.
492. 6p. Type **145** 90 80
493. 17p. Tussock grass .. 1·10 1·10
494. 22p. Dusky Dolphin and Southern Sea Lion .. 1·40 1·40
495. 52p. "Notothenia" (fish) and krill .. .. .. 2·00 3·00

146. Technical Drawing of "Wren" Class Locomotive.

1985. 70th Anniv. of Camber Railway. Each black, brown and light brown.
497. 7p. Type **146** 35 30
498. 22p. Sail-propelled trolley 70 90
499. 27p. Locomotive at work 85 1·25
500. 54p. "Falkland Islands Express" passenger train (76 × 25 mm.) .. .. 1·50 2·00

147. Construction Workers' Camp.

1985. Opening of Mount Pleasant Airport. Multicoloured.
501. 7p. Type **147** 50 30
502. 22p. Building construction 1·00 90
503. 27p. Completed airport .. 1·25 1·10
504. 54p. Airliner over runway 1·60 2·10

148. The Queen Mother on 84th Birthday.

1985. Life and Times of Queen Elizabeth the Queen Mother. Multicoloured.
505 7p. Attending reception at Lancaster House .. 25 20
506 22p. With Prince Charles, Mark Phillips and Princess Anne at Falklands Memorial Service 60 50
507 27p. Type **148** 70 60
508 54p. With Prince Henry at his christening (from photo by Lord Snowdon) 1·25 1·25

149. Captain J. McBride and H.M.S. "Jason", 1765.

1985. Early Cartographers. Multicoloured.
510. 7p. Type **149** 70 30
511. 22p. Commodore J. Byron and H.M.S. "Dolphin" and "Tamar", 1765 .. 1·00 70
512. 27p. Vice-Admiral R. FitzRoy and H.M.S. "Beagle", 1831 .. .. 1·10 75
513. 54p. Admiral Sir B. J. Sullivan and H.M.S. "Philomel", 1842 .. 1·75 1·50

1985. Early Naturalists. As T **35** of British Antarctic Territory. Multicoloured.
514. 7p. Philibert Commerson and Commerson's dolphin 75 35
515. 22p. Rene Primevere Lesson and "Lessonia" sp. (kelp) .. .. 1·25 1·00
516. 27p. Joseph Paul Gaimard and Common diving petrel 1·60 1·75
517. 54p. Charles Darwin and "Calceolaria darwinii" .. 1·90 2·50

150. Painted Keyhole Limpet.

1986. Seashells. Multicoloured.
518. 7p. Type **150** 65 35
519. 22p. Magellanic Volute .. 1·25 1·00
520. 27p. Patagonian Scallop .. 1·40 1·75
521. 54p. Rough Thorn Drupe 2·25 2·50

1986. 60th Birthday of Queen Elizabeth II. As T **110** of Ascension. Multicoloured.
522 10p. With Princess Margaret at St. Paul's, Walden Bury, Welwyn, 1932 .. .. .. 35 25
523 24p. Queen making Christmas television broadcast, 1958 .. .. 65 55
524 29p. In robes of Order of the Thistle, St. Giles Cathedral, Edinburgh, 1962 .. .. .. 75 60
525 45p. Aboad Royal Yacht "Britannia", U.S.A., 1976 .. .. .. 1·25 95
526 58p. At Crown Agents Head Office, London, 1983 .. .. .. 1·40 1·25

151. S.S. "Great Britain" crossing Atlantic, 1845.

1986. "Ameripex '86" International Stamp Exhibition, Chicago. Centenary of Arrival of S.S. "Great Britain" in Falkland Islands. Multicoloured.
527. 10p. Type **151** 40 30
528. 24p. Beached at Sparrow Cove, 1937 .. .. 75 65
529. 29p. Refloated on pontoon, 1970 .. .. 85 70
530. 58p. Undergoing restoration, Bristol, 1986 .. 1·40 1·25

152. Head of Rockhopper Penguin.

1986. Rockhopper Penguins. Multicoloured.
532. 10p. Type **152** 75 50
533. 24p. Rockhopper Penguins at sea .. .. 1·25 1·10
534. 29p. Courtship display .. 1·40 1·25
535. 58p. Adult with chick .. 2·00 2·00

153. Prince Andrew and Miss Sarah Ferguson presenting Polo Trophy, Windsor.

1986. Royal Wedding. Multicoloured.
536. 17p. Type **153** 65 40
537. 22p. Prince Andrew and Duchess of York on wedding day 75 55
538. 29p. Prince Andrew in battledress at opening of Fox Bay Mill 90 80

154. Survey Party, Sapper Hill.

1987. Bicentenary of Royal Engineers' Royal Warrant. Multicoloured.
539. 10p. Type **154** .. .. 1·00 50
540. 24p. Mine clearance by robot .. .. .. 1·60 1·25
541. 29p. Boxer Bridge, Stanley 1·75 1·50
542. 58p. Unloading mail, Mount Pleasant Airport 2·50 2·00

155. Southern Sea Lion.

1987. Seals. Multicoloured.

543.	10p. Type **155**	40	25
544.	24p. Falkland fur seal ..	1·00	55
545.	29p. Southern elephant seal	1·10	65
546.	58p. Leopard seal	1·90	1·25

156. "Suillus luteus".

1987. Fungi. Multicoloured.

547.	10p. Type **156**	1·40	75
548.	24p. "Mycena" sp. ..	2·25	1·75
549.	29p. "Camarophyllus adonis"	2·50	2·50
550.	58p. "Gerronema schusteri"	3·50	3·75

157. Victoria Cottage Home, c. 1912.

1987. Local Hospitals. Multicoloured.

551.	10p. Type **157**	30	25
552.	24p. King Edward VII Memorial Hospital, c 1914	65	55
553.	29p. Churchill Wing, King Edward VII Memorial Hospital, c. 1953 ..	75	60
554.	58p. Prince Andrew Wing, New Hospital, 1987 ..	1·25	1·25

158 Morris Truck, Fitzroy, 1940

1988. Early Vehicles. Multicoloured.

555	10p. Type **158**	30	25
556	24p. Citroen "Kegresse" half-track, San Carlos, 1929	65	55
557	29p. Ford one ton truck, Port Stanley, 1933 ..	75	60
558	58p. Ford "Model T" car, Darwin, 1935	1·25	1·25

159 Kelp Goose

1988. Falkland Islands Geese. Multicoloured.

559	10p. Type **159**	70	35
560	24p. Magellan ("Upland") goose	1·10	70
561	29p. Ruddy-headed goose	1·25	80
562	58p. Ashy-headed goose ..	1·75	1·75

1988. 300th Anniv of Lloyd's of London. Multicoloured. As T **123** of Ascension.

563	10p. Silver from Lloyd's Nelson Collection ..	25	25
564	24p. Falkland Islands hydroponic market garden (horiz)	55	55
565	29p. "A.E.S." (mail ship) (horiz)	60	60
566	58p. "Charles Cooper" (full-rigged ship), 1866	1·25	1·25

160 "Padua" (barque)

1989. Cape Horn Sailing Ships. Multicoloured

567	1p. Type **160**	10	10
613	2p. "Priwall" (barque) (vert)	10	10
614	3p. "Passat" (barque) ..	10	10
570	4p. "Archibald Russell" (barque) (vert) ..	10	10
571	5p. "Pamir" (barque) (vert)	10	15
617	6p. "Mozart" (barquentine)	10	15
573	7p. "Pommern" (barque)	15	20
574	8p. "Preussen" (full-rigged ship)	15	20
620	9p. "Fennia" (barque) ..	20	25
576	10p. "Cassard" (barque) ..	20	25
577	20p. "Lawhill" (barque) ..	40	45
578	25p. "Garthpool" (barque)	50	55
579	50p. "Grace Harwar" (full-rigged ship) ..	1·00	1·10
625	£1 "Criccieth Castle" (full-rigged ship) ..	2·00	2·10
581	£3 "Cutty Sark" (full-rigged ship) (vert)	6·00	6·25
582	£5 "Flying Cloud" (full-rigged ship)	10·00	10·50

161 Southern Right Whale

1989. Baleen Whales. Multicoloured.

583	10p. Type **161**	55	40
584	24p. Minke whale ..	1·00	85
585	29p. Humpback whale ..	1·25	1·00
586	58p. Blue whale	2·25	1·75

162 "Gymkhana" (Sarah Gilding)

1989. Sports Associations' Activities. Children's drawings. Multicoloured.

587	5p. Type **162**	20	20
588	10p. "Steer Riding" (Karen Steen)	30	30
589	17p. "Sheep Shearing" (Colin Shepherd) ..	45	45
590	24p. "Sheepdog Trials" (Rebecca Edwards) ..	60	70
591	29p. "Horse Racing" (Dilys Blackley) ..	70	80
592	45p. "Sack Race" (Donna Newell)	1·00	1·10

163 Vice-Admiral Sturdee and H.M.S. "Invincible" (battle cruiser)

1989. 75th Anniv of Battle of the Falkland Islands and 50th Anniv of Battle of the River Plate. Multicoloured.

593	10p. Type **163**	30	30
594	24p. Vice-Admiral Graf von Spee and "Scharnhorst" (German cruiser) ..	70	75
595	29p. Commodore Harwood and H.M.S. "Ajax" (cruiser)	80	85
596	58p. Captain Langsdorff and "Admiral Graf Spee" (German pocket battleship)	1·50	1·60

164 Southern Sea Lions on Kidney Island

1990. Nature Reserves and Sanctuaries. Mult.

597	12p. Type **164**	35	35
598	26p. Black-browed albatrosses on Beauchene Island	70	70
599	31p. Penguin colony on Bird Island	80	80
600	62p. Tussock grass on Elephant Jason Island	1·40	1·40

165 Spitfire Mk. I "Falkland Islands I"

1990. "Stamp World London 90" International Stamp Exhibition, London. Presentation Spitfires. Multicoloured.

601	12p. Type **165**	40	35
602	26p. Spitfire Mk. I "Falkland Islands VII"	80	70
603	31p. Cockpit and wing of "Falkland Islands I" ..	90	80
604	62p. Squadron scramble, 1940	1·40	1·40

1990. 90th Birthday of Queen Elizabeth the Queen Mother. As T **134** of Ascension.

606	26p. multicoloured	75	65
607	£1 black and red ..	2·50	2·75

DESIGNS—21 × 36 mm. 26p. Queen Mother in Dover. 29 × 37 mm. £1 On bridge of liner "Queen Elizabeth", 1946.

166 Black-browed Albatrosses

1990. Black-browed Albatross. Multicoloured.

608	12p. Type **166**	45	45
609	26p. Female with egg ..	90	90
610	31p. Adult and chick ..	1·25	1·25
611	62p. Black-browed albatross in flight	2·00	2·00

MINIMUM PRICE

The minimum price quoted is 10p which represents a handling charge rather than a basis for valuing common stamps. For further notes about prices see introductory pages.

167 "Gavilea australis"

1991. Orchids. Multicoloured.

629	12p. Type **167**	50	50
630	26p. Dog orchid	85	85
631	31p. "Chlorea gaudichaudii"	1·00	1·00
632	62p. Yellow orchid ..	2·00	2·00

168 Heads of Two King Penguins

1991. Endangered Species. King Penguin. Multicoloured.

633	2p. Type **168**	20	15
634	6p. Female incubating egg	30	25
635	12p. Female with two chicks	50	40
636	20p. Penguin underwater	75	70
637	31p. Parents feeding their chick	1·00	95
638	62p. Courtship dance ..	1·90	1·75

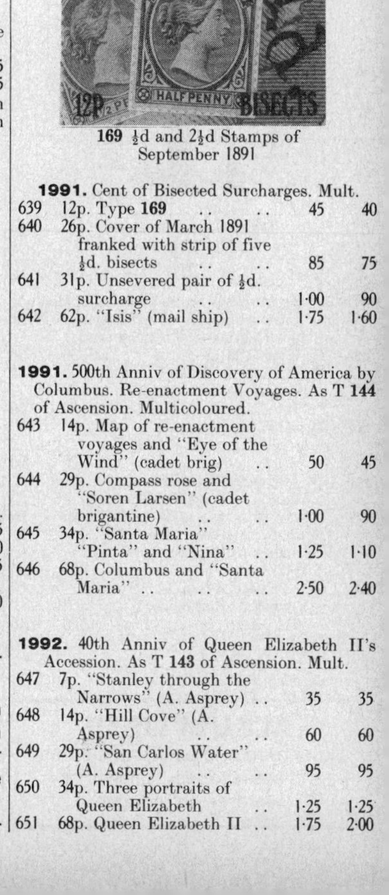

169 ½d and 2½d Stamps of September 1891

1991. Cent of Bisected Surcharges. Mult.

639	12p. Type **169**	45	40
640	26p. Cover of March 1891 franked with strip of five ½d. bisects	85	75
641	31p. Unsevered pair of ½d. surcharge	1·00	90
642	62p. "Isis" (mail ship) ..	1·75	1·60

1991. 500th Anniv of Discovery of America by Columbus. Re-enactment Voyages. As T **144** of Ascension. Multicoloured.

643	14p. Map of re-enactment voyages and "Eye of the Wind" (cadet brig) ..	50	45
644	29p. Compass rose and "Soren Larsen" (cadet brigantine)	1·00	90
645	34p. "Santa Maria" "Pinta" and "Nina" ..	1·25	1·10
646	68p. Columbus and "Santa Maria"	2·50	2·40

1992. 40th Anniv of Queen Elizabeth II's Accession. As T **143** of Ascension. Mult.

647	7p. "Stanley through the Narrows" (A. Asprey) ..	35	35
648	14p. "Hill Cove" (A. Asprey)	60	60
649	29p. "San Carlos Water" (A. Asprey)	95	95
650	34p. Three portraits of Queen Elizabeth ..	1·25	1·25
651	68p. Queen Elizabeth II ..	1·75	2·00

170 Laying Foundation Stone, 1890

1992. Centenary of Christ Church Cathedral, Stanley. Multicoloured.

652 14p. Type **170** 55 55
653 29p. Interior of Cathedral, 1920 .. .. .. 1·00 1·00
654 34p. Bishop's chair .. 1·25 1·25
655 68p. Cathedral in 1900 (horiz) .. .. .. 1·90 1·90

1992. 10th Anniv of Liberation. As T **146** of Ascension. Multicoloured.

656 14p. + 6p. San Carlos Cemetery 75 75
657 29p. + 11p. War Memorial, Port Stanley .. .. 1·40 1·40
658 34p. + 16p. South Atlantic medal .. .. .. 1·60 1·60
659 68p. + 32p. Government House, Port Stanley .. 2·75 2·75

The premiums on Nos. 656/9 were for the S.S.A.F.A.

171 Captain John Davis and Backstaff

1992. 400th Anniv of First Sighting of the Falkland Islands. Multicoloured.

661 22p. Type **171** 75 75
662 29p. Capt. John Davis .. 90 90
663 34p. Queen Elizabeth I and Queen Elizabeth II .. 1·25 1·25
664 68p. "Desire" sighting Falkland Islands .. 2·00 2·25

172 Private, Falkland Islands Volunteers, 1892

1992. Centenary of Falkland Islands Defence Force and 50th Anniv of Affiliation to West Yorkshire Regiment. Multicoloured.

665 7p. Type **172** 30 30
666 14p. Officer, Falkland Islands Defence Corps, 1914 .. .. .. 50 50
667 22p. Officer, Falkland Islands Defence Force, 1920 .. .. .. 70 70
668 29p. Private, Falkland Islands Defence Force, 1939–45 .. .. .. 90 90
669 34p. Officer, West Yorkshire Regiment, 1942 .. .. .. 1·25 1·25
670 68p. Private, West Yorkshire Regiment, 1942 .. .. .. 2·00 2·10

173 South American Tern

1993. Gulls and Terns. Multicoloured.

671 15p. Type **173** 50 50
672 31p. Brown-hooded gull ("Pink breasted gull") 95 95
673 36p. Dolphin gull .. 1·25 1·25
674 72p. Southern black-backed gull ("Dominican gull") .. .. .. 2·25 2·25

1993. 75th Anniv of Royal Air Force. As T **149** of Ascension. Multicoloured.

676 15p. Avro Vulcan .. 45 50
677 15p. Lockheed Hercules .. 45 50
678 15p. Boeing Vertol Chinook 45 50
679 15p. Lockheed Tri-Star .. 45 50

175 Short-finned Squid

1993. Fisheries. Multicoloured.

681 15p. Type **175** 45 45
682 31p. Catch of whiptailed hake 90 90
683 36p. "Falklands Protector" (fisheries patrol vessel) 1·25 1·25
684 72p. Britten-Norman "Islander" patrol aircraft and fish factory ship .. .. .. 1·90 2·00

176 "Great Britain" in Drydock, Bristol

1993. 150th Anniv of Launch of "Great Britain" (liner). Multicoloured.

685 8p. Type **176** 30 30
686 £1 "Great Britain" at sea 2·50 2·75

177 "Explorer" (liner)

1993. Tourism. Multicoloured.

687 16p. Type **177** 40 40
688 34p. Rockhopper penguins 85 85
689 39p. "World Discoverer" (liner) .. .. 1·00 1·00
690 78p. "Columbus Caravelle" (liner) .. .. .. 1·75 2·00

178 Pony

1993. Pets. Multicoloured.

691 8p. Type **178** 15 20
692 16p. Lamb 30 35
693 34p. Puppy and cat .. 70 75
694 39p. Kitten (vert) .. 80 85
695 78p. Collie dog (vert) .. 1·50 1·60

1994. "Hong Kong '94" International Stamp Exhibition. Nos. 691/5 optd **HONG KONG '94** and emblem.

696 8p. Type **178** 15 20
697 16p. Lamb 30 35
698 34p. Puppy and cat .. 70 75
699 39p. Kitten (vert) .. 80 85
700 78p. Collie dog (vert) .. 1·50 1·60

179 Goose Barnacles

1994. Inshore Marine Life. Multicoloured.

701 1p. Type **179** 10 10
702 2p. Painted shrimp (horiz) 10 10
703 8p. Common limpet (horiz) 15 15
704 9p. Mullet (horiz) .. 20 20
705 10p. Sea anemones (horiz) 20 20
706 20p. Rock eel (horiz) .. 40 40
707 25p. Spider crab (horiz) .. 50 50
708 50p. Lobster krill .. 1·00 1·00
709 80p. Falkland skate (horiz) 1·60 1·60
710 £1 Centollon crab (horiz) 2·00 2·00
711 £3 Rock cod (horiz) .. 6·00 6·00
712 £5 Octopus .. .. 10·00 10·00

POSTAGE DUE STAMPS

D 1 King Penguin

1991.

D1 D 1 1p. red and mauve .. 10 10
D2 2p. orange & lt orange 10 10
D3 3p. ochre and yellow .. 10 10
D4 4p. green & light green 10 10
D5 5p. blue and light blue 10 15
D6 10p. deep blue and blue 20 25
D7 20p. violet and lilac .. 40 45
D8 50p. green & lt green 1·00 1·10

FALKLAND ISLANDS DEPENDENCIES

Four groups of Islands situated between the Falkland Is. and the South Pole. In 1946 the four groups ceased issuing separate issues which were replaced by a single general issue. From 1963 the stamps of Br. Antarctic Territory were used in all these islands except South Georgia and South Sandwich for which separate stamps were issued inscribed "SOUTH GEORGIA" from 1963 until 1980.

Under the new constitution effective on 3 October 1985, South Georgia and South Sandwich Islands ceased to be dependencies of the Falkland Islands.

1944. 12 pence = 1 shilling.
20 shillings = 1 pound.
1971. 100 (new) pence = 1 pound.

GRAHAM LAND

1944. Stamps of Falkland Is. of 1938 optd **GRAHAM LAND DEPENDENCY OF.**

A 1. 27. ½d. black and green .. 30 1·00
A 2. – 1d. black and violet .. 30 1·00
A 3. – 2d. black and red .. 40 1·00
A 4. – 3d. black and blue .. 30 1·00
A 5. – 4d. black and purple .. 2·75 1·75
A 6. – 6d. black and brown .. 10·00 2·25
A 7. – 9d. black and blue .. 1·50 1·25
A 8. – 1s. blue .. .. 1·50 1·25

SOUTH GEORGIA

1944. Stamps of Falkland Is. of 1938 optd. **SOUTH GEORGIA DEPENDENCY OF.**

B 1. 27. ½d. black and green .. 30 1·00
B 2. – 1d. black and violet .. 30 1·00
B 3. – 2d. black and red .. 40 1·00
B 4. – 3d. black and blue .. 30 1·00
B 5. – 4d. black and purple .. 2·75 1·75
B 6. – 6d. black and brown .. 10·00 2·25
B 7. – 9d. black and blue .. 1·50 1·25
B 8. – 1s. blue .. .. .. 1·50 1·25

SOUTH ORKNEYS

1944. Stamps of Falkland Is. of 1938 optd. **SOUTH ORKNEYS DEPENDENCY OF.**

C 1. 27. ½d. black and green .. 30 1·00
C 2. – 1d. black and violet .. 30 1·00
C 3. – 2d. black and red .. 40 1·00
C 4. – 3d. black and blue .. 30 1·00
C 5. – 4d. black and purple .. 2·75 1·75
C 6. – 6d. black and brown .. 10·00 2·25
C 7. – 9d. black and blue .. 1·50 1·25
C 8. – 1s. blue .. .. 1·50 1·25

SOUTH SHETLANDS

1944. Stamps of Falkland Is. of 1938 optd. **SOUTH SHETLAND DEPENDENCY OF.**

D 1. 27. ½d. black and green .. 30 1·00
D 2. – 1d. black and violet .. 30 1·00
D 3. – 2d. black and red .. 40 1·00
D 4. – 3d. black and blue .. 30 1·00
D 5. – 4d. black and purple .. 2·75 1·75
D 6. – 6d. black and brown .. 10·00 2·25
D 7. – 9d. black and blue .. 1·50 1·25
D 8. – 1s. blue .. .. 1·50 1·25

GENERAL ISSUES

G 1.

1946.

G 1 G 1. ½d. black and green .. 1·00 2·00
G 2 1d. black and violet .. 1·25 1·75
G 3 2d. black and red .. 1·25 2·50
G 11a 2½d. black and blue .. 9·50 7·00
G 4 3d. black and blue .. 1·25 3·50
G 5 4d. black and red .. 2·25 4·25
G 6 6d. black and orange .. 3·25 4·50
G 7 9d. black and brown .. 2·00 2·75
G 8 1s. black and purple .. 2·00 4·00

1946. Victory. As T **9** of Aden.

G 17. 1d. violet 50 15
G 18. 3d. blue 75 15

1949. Silver Wedding. As T **10/11** of Aden.

G 19. 2½d. blue .. .. 1·00 75
G 20. 1s. blue .. .. .. 5·50 1·75

1949. U.P.U. As T **20/23** of Antigua.

G 21. 1d. violet .. .. 2·00 1·50
G 22. 2d. red .. .. 6·50 2·50
G 23. 3d. blue .. .. 8·00 1·25
G 24. 6d. orange .. 12·00 3·00

1953. Coronation. As T **13** of Aden.

G 25. 1d. black and violet .. 1·50 1·25

G 3. "Trepassey", 1945-47.

1954. Ships.

No.	Type	Description	Mint	Used
G 26.	–	½d. black and green ..	30	85
G 27.	G 3.	1d. black and sepia	75	85
G 28.	–	1½d. black and olive	75	85
G 29.	–	2d. black and red ..	90	20
G 30.	–	2½d. black and yellow	90	15
G 31.	–	3d. black and blue ..	90	15
G 32.	–	4d. black and purple	2·50	30
G 33.	–	6d. black and lilac ..	2·50	35
G 34.	–	9d. black	2·50	55
G 35.	–	1s. black and brown ..	2·50	55
G 36.	–	2s. black and red	15·00	9·00
G 37.	–	2s. 6d. black & turq.	15·00	6·00
G 38.	–	5 s. black and violet	35·00	6·50
G 39.	–	10s. black and blue ..	48·00	18·00
G 40.	–	£1 black	£110	48·00

SHIPS—VERT. ½d. "John Biscoe". 6d. "Discovery". 9d. "Endurance". 2s. 6d. "Francais". 5s. "Scotia". £1, "Belgica". HORIZ. 1½d. "Wyatt Earp". 2d. "Eagle". 2½d. "Penola". 3d. "Discovery II". 4d. "William Scoresby". 1s. "Deutschland". 2s. "Pourquoi pas?". 10s. "Antarctic".

1956. Trans-Antarctic Expedition. Nos. G 27, G 30/1 and G 33 optd. **TRANS-ANTARCTIC EXPEDITION 1955-1958.**

No.	Type	Description	Mint	Used
G 41.	G 3.	1d. black and sepia ..	10	30
G 42.	–	2½d. black and yellow	40	30
G 43.	–	3d. black and blue ..	40	30
G 44.	–	6d. black and lilac ..	40	30

For later issues see **BRITISH ANTARCTIC TERRITORIES** and **SOUTH GEORGIA.**

ISSUES FOR SOUTH GEORGIA AND SOUTH SANDWICH ISLANDS.

In 1980 stamps were again inscribed "FALKLAND ISLANDS DEPENDENCIES" for use in the above area.

14. Map of Falkland Islands Dependencies.

1980. Multicoloured.

No.	Description	Mint	Used
74	1p. Type **14**	30	30
75	2p. Shag Rocks	30	30
76	3p. Bird and Willis Islands	30	30
77	4p. Gulbrandsen Lake ..	30	30
78	5p. King Edward Point ..	30	30
79	6p. Sir Ernest Shackleton's Memorial Cross, Hope Point	30	60
80	7p. Sir Ernest Shackleton's grave, Grytviken ..	30	60
81	8p. Grytviken Church ..	30	60
82	9p. Coaling Hulk "Louise" at Grytviken	30	60
83	10p. Clerke Rocks	50	60
84	20p. Candlemas Island ..	2·00	1·50
85	25p. Twitcher Rock and Cook Island, Southern Thule	2·00	2·25
86	50p. R.R.S. "John Biscoe II" in Cumberland Bay	1·50	2·00
87	£1 R.R.S. "Bransfield" in Cumberland Bay ..	2·00	2·75
88	£3 H.M.S. "Endurance" in Cumberland Bay ..	5·00	6·50

These stamps come with or without date imprint.

15. Magellanic Clubmoss.

1981. Plants. Multicoloured.

No.	Description	Mint	Used
89.	3p. Type **15**	25	25
90.	6p. Alpine Cat's-tail ..	30	30
91.	7p. Greater Burnet ..	30	30
92.	11p. Antarctic Bedstraw ..	50	40
93.	15p. Brown Rush	70	55
94.	25p. Antarctic Hair Grass	1·00	80

16. Wedding Bouquet from Falkland Islands Dependencies.

1981. Royal Wedding. Multicoloured.

No.	Description	Mint	Used
95.	10p. Type **16**	30	40
96.	13p. Prince Charles dressed for Skiing	40	50
97.	52p. Prince Charles and Lady Diana Spencer	1·00	1·00

17. Introduced Reindeer during Calving, Spring.

1982. Reindeer. Multicoloured.

No.	Description	Mint	Used
98.	5p. Type **17**	45	65
99.	13p. Bull at rut, Autumn	65	85
100.	25p. Reindeer and mountains, Winter	1·10	1·40
101.	26p. Reindeer feeding on tussock, late Winter ..	1·10	1·40

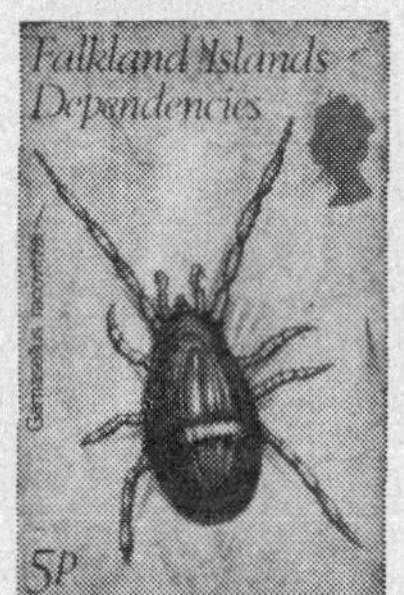

18. "Gamasellus racovitzai" (tick).

1982. Insects. Multicoloured.

No.	Description	Mint	Used
102	5p. Type **18**	20	25
103	10p. "Alaskozetes antarcticus" (mite) ..	30	35
104	13p. "Cryptopygus antarcticus" (spring-tail) ..	35	40
105	15p. "Notiomaso australis" (spider)	40	45
106	25p. "Hydromedion sparsutum" (beetle) ..	65	70
107	26p. "Parochlus steinenii" (midge)	65	70

19. Lady Diana Spencer at Tidworth, Hampshire, July 1981.

1982. 21st Birthday of Princess of Wales. Multicoloured.

No.	Description	Mint	Used
108.	5p. Falkland Islands Dependencies coat of arms	10	15
109.	17p. Type **19**	30	35
110.	37p. Bride and groom on steps of St. Pauls ..	75	80
111.	50p. Formal portrait ..	1·00	1·10

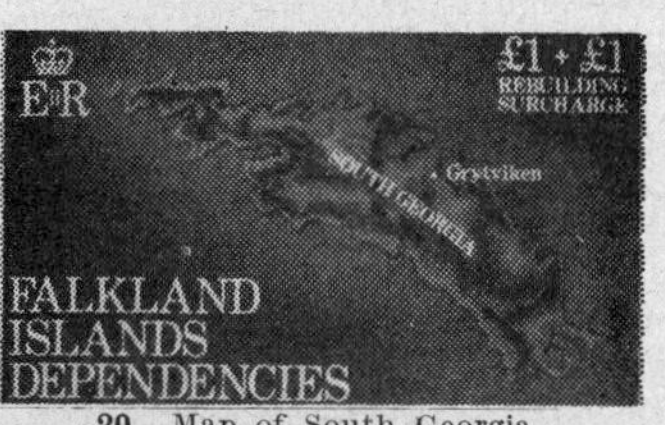

20. Map of South Georgia. (Illustration reduced. Actual size 60 × 35 mm).

1982. Rebuilding Fund.

No.	Type	Description	Mint	Used
112.	20.	£1 + £1 multicoloured ..	3·50	4·50

21. Westland "Whirlwind".

1983. Bicentenary of Manned Flight. Mult.

No.	Description	Mint	Used
113	5p. Type **21**	30	20
114	13p. Westland "Wasp" ..	55	45
115	17p. Supermarine "Walrus"	60	50
116	50p. Auster	1·40	1·25

22. "Euphausia superba".

1983. Crustacea. Multicoloured.

No.	Description	Mint	Used
117.	5p. Type **22**	20	20
118.	17p. "Glytonotus antarcticus"	50	50
119.	25p. "Epimeria monodon"	60	60
120.	34p. "Serolis pagenstecheri"	90	80

23. Zavodovski Island.

1984. Volcanoes of South Sandwich Islands. Multicoloured.

No.	Description	Mint	Used
121.	6p. Type **23**	70	60
122.	17p. Mt Michael, Saunders Island	1·50	1·00
123.	22p. Bellingshausen Island	1·60	1·25
124.	52p. Bristol Island ..	2·25	2·00

24. Grey-headed Albatross.

1985. Albatrosses. Multicoloured.

No.	Description	Mint	Used
125.	7p. Type **24**	85	55
126.	22p. Black-browed Albatross	1·50	85
127.	27p. Wandering Albatross	1·60	1·00
128.	54p. Light-mantled Sooty Albatross	2·00	1·60

25. The Queen Mother.

1985. Life and Times of Queen Elizabeth the Queen Mother. Multicoloured.

No.	Description	Mint	Used
129.	7p. At Windsor Castle on Princess Elizabeth's 14th Birthday, 1940	20	25
130.	22p. With Princess Anne, Lady Sarah Armstrong-Jones and Prince Edward at Trooping the Colour	50	60
131.	27p. Type **25**	60	70
132.	54p. With Prince Henry at his christening (from photo by Lord Snowdon)	1·25	1·25

1985. Early Naturalists. As T **35** of British Antarctic Territory. Multicoloured.

No.	Description	Mint	Used
134.	7p. Dumont d'Urville and "Durvillea antarctica" (kelp)	75	50
135.	22p. Johann Reinhold Forster and King Penguin	1·50	1·00
136.	27p. Johann Georg Adam Forster and Tussock Grass	1·60	1·25
137.	54p. Sir Joseph Banks and Dove Prion	2·25	2·25

For later issues see **SOUTH GEORGIA** and **SOUTH SANDWICH ISLANDS.**

FARIDKOT

A state of the Punjab, India. Now uses Indian stamps.

1 folus = 1 paisa = ¼ anna. Later, as India.

N 1. (1 folus).

N 2. (1 paisa).

1879. Imperf.

No.	Type	Description	Mint	Used
N 5.	1.	1 f. blue	1·00	1·75
N 6.	2.	1 p. blue	1·60	4·00

1887. Stamps of India (Queen Victoria) optd. **FARIDKOT STATE.**

No.	Type	Description	Mint	Used
17	40	3 p. red	50	20·00
1	23	½ a. turquoise	30	35
3	–	1 a. purple	50	60
4	–	2 a. blue	1·75	2·50
7	–	3 a. orange	1·00	1·75
8	–	4 a. green (No. 96) ..	2·50	6·50
11	–	6 a. brown (No. 80) ..	1·75	7·00
12	–	8 a. mauve	4·00	16·00
14	–	12 a. purple on red ..	25·00	£200
15	–	1 r. grey	22·00	£180
16	37	1 r. green and red ..	22·00	35·00

OFFICIAL STAMPS

1886. Stamps of India (Queen Victoria) optd. **SERVICE FARIDKOT STATE.**

No.	Type	Description	Mint	Used
O 1	23.	½ a. turquoise	15	30
O 3	–	1 a. purple	45	65
O 5	–	2 a. blue	70	6·00
O 6	–	3 a. orange	3·25	3·50
O 8	–	4 a. green (No. 96) ..	1·50	7·00
O 11	–	6 a. brown (No. 80) ..	10·00	13·00
O 12	–	8 a. mauve	2·50	9·00
O 14	–	1 r. grey	26·00	80·00
O 15	37.	1 r. green and red ..	50·00	£225

FEDERATED MALAY STATES

A Br. protectorate in S.E. Asia, comprising the States of Negri Sembilan (with Sungei Ujong), Pahang, Perak and Selangor.

Separate issues for each of these states appeared in 1936.

100 cents = $1 (Straits).

1900. Stamps of Negri Sembilan optd. **FEDERATED MALAY STATES** and bar.

No.	Type	Description	Mint	Used
1.	3.	1 c. purple and green ..	1·60	3·00
2.		2 c. purple and brown ..	22·00	48·00
3.		3 c. purple and black ..	1·90	3·25
4.		5 c. purple and yellow ..	65·00	£130
5.		10 c. purple and orange ..	2·50	14·00
6.		20 c. green and olive ..	50·00	75·00
7.		25 c. green and red ..	£150	£190
8.		50 c. green and black ..	60·00	90·00

1900. Stamps of Perak optd. **FEDERATED MALAY STATES** and bar.

No.	Type	Description	Mint	Used
9.	31.	5 c. purple and yellow ..	10·00	48·00
10.		10 c. purple and orange ..	55·00	60·00
11.	32.	$1 green	£100	£140
12.		$2 green and red	90·00	£130
13.		$5 green and blue ..	£200	£300
14.		$25 green and orange ..	£3750	

3.

4.

1900.

No.	Type	Description	Unused	Used
15a	3.	1 c. black and green ..	60	30
29		1 c. green	1·50	20
30		1 c. brown	2·25	90
53		1 c. black	50	20
55		2 c. green	55	10
54		2 c. brown	4·00	2·25
16b		3 c. black and brown ..	1·25	20
58		3 c. brown	60	40
34		3 c. red	2·00	10
35		3 c. grey	1·25	20
57		3 c. green	1·50	1·75
36d		4 c. black and red ..	4·00	25
38		4 c. red	80	15
60		4 c. orange	65	10
18		5 c. green & red on yellow	1·50	2·00
61		5 c. mauve on yellow ..	85	20
62		5 c. brown	1·75	10
63		6 c. orange	55	45
64		6 c. red	90	10
41b		8 c. black and blue ..	5·00	3·50
42		8 c. blue	13·00	90
43b		10 c. black and mauve ..	10·00	30
44		10 c. blue	6·00	80
66		10 c. black and blue ..	2·00	75
67		10 c. purple on yellow ..	3·50	40
68		12 c. blue	1·25	10
45		20 c. mauve and black ..	2·25	30
70		25 c. purple and mauve ..	2·50	75
71		30 c. purple and orange ..	3·25	1·50
72		35 c. red on yellow ..	3·75	14·00
73		35 c. red and purple ..	12·00	12·00
74		50 c. black and orange ..	13·00	4·50
75		50 c. black on green ..	4·00	1·50
76a	4.	$1 green	12·00	26·00
77	3.	$1 black and red on blue..	10·00	2·75
78	4.	$2 green and red ..	12·00	55·00
79	3.	$2 green & red on yellow	28·00	26·00
80	4.	$5 green and blue ..	60·00	95·00
81	3.	$5 green and red on green	£120	£130
82	4.	$25 green and orange ..	£650	£350

POSTAGE DUE STAMPS

D 1.

1924.

No.	Type	Description	Unused	Used
D 1.	D 1.	1 c. violet	3·50	9·50
D 2.		2 c. black	1·75	2·00
D 3.		4 c. green	2·25	4·25
D 4.		8 c. red	4·50	14·00
D 5.		10 c. orange	7·75	11·00
D 6.		12 c. blue	8·50	16·00

FIJI

A Br. colony in the S. Pacific which became independent within the Commonwealth during October 1970.

1870. 12 pence = 1 shilling;
20 shillings = 1 pound.
1969. 100 cents = 1 dollar.

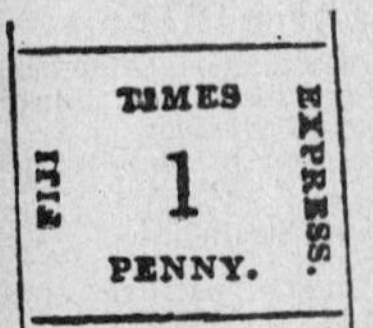

1.

2.

1870.

No.	Type	Description	Unused	Used
5.	1.	1d. black on pink	£750	£1400
6.		3d. black on pink	£1200	£1800
7.		6d. black on pink	£800	£1500
8.		9d. black on pink	£1300	£2000
9.		1s. black on pink	£800	£1000

1871.

No.	Type	Description	Unused	Used
10.	2.	1d. blue	50·00	£120
11.		3d. green	£110	£350
12.		6d. red	£120	£275

1872. Surch. in words.

No.	Type	Description	Unused	Used
13a	2.	2 c. on 1d. blue	25·00	40·00
14		6 c. on 3d. green	65·00	65·00
15		12 c. on 6d. red	85·00	75·00

V.R. (5.) (8.)

1874. Optd. as T 5.

No.	Type	Description	Unused	Used
16.	2.	2 c. on 1d. blue	£650	£180
17.		6 c. on 3d. green	£950	£450
18.		12 c. on 6d. red	£470	£170

1875. Nos. 17 and 18 surch. **2d.**

No.	Type	Description	Unused	Used
22.	2.	2d. on 6 c. on 3d. green ..	£375	£130
27.		2d. on 12 c. on 6d. red ..	£1000	£475

1876. Optd. with T 8, and the 3d. surch. in words also.

No.	Type	Description	Unused	Used
31.	2.	1d. blue	13·00	23·00
29.		2d. on 3d. green ..	35·00	48·00
34.		4d. on 3d. mauve ..	70·00	30·00
33.		6d. red	48·00	27·00

10.

12.

1878. Surcharges on Nos. 36 and 41/2 in words.

No.	Type	Description	Unused	Used
35	10	1d. blue	4·00	4·25
40		2d. green..	8·00	90
36		2d. on 3d. green ..	4·00	9·00
54		4d. mauve	6·00	7·00
41		4d. on 1d. mauve ..	23·00	13·00
42		4d. on 2d. mauve ..	60·00	9·00
59a		6d. red	6·00	4·50
67	12	1s. brown	24·00	8·50
69		5 s. red and black ..	50·00	35·00

1891. Surch. in figures or words.

No.	Type	Description	Unused	Used
72a.	10.	½d. on 1d. blue	35·00	60·00
70.		2½d. on 2d. green ..	40·00	48·00
73.		5d. on 4d. mauve ..	45·00	65·00
74a.		5d. on 6d. red	55·00	60·00

20.

21. Native Canoe.

1891.

No.	Type	Description	Unused	Used
99	20	½d. grey	1·00	2·50
87	21	1d. black..	2·50	3·00
101		1d. mauve	3·50	50
89		2d. green..	4·75	80
103a	10	2½d. brown	5·00	5·00
85	21	5d. blue	7·00	7·50

23.

1903.

No.	Type	Description	Unused	Used
104	23.	½d. green..	2·25	1·50
105		1d. purple & black on red	8·50	55
119		1d. red	3·25	10
106		2d. purple and orange ..	2·00	1·25
107		2½d. purple & blue on blue	14·00	15·00
120		2½d. blue..	4·25	6·00
108		3d. purple	1·50	4·25
109		4d. purple and black ..	1·50	2·50
110		5d. purple and green ..	1·50	5·00
111		6d. purple and red ..	1·50	2·50
121		6d. purple	6·00	14·00
112		1s. green and red ..	10·00	24·00
122		1s. black on green ..	4·00	10·00
113		5s. green and black ..	29·00	70·00
123		5s. green and red on yell.	38·00	48·00
114		£1 black and blue ..	£325	£350
124		£1 purple and blk. on red	£325	£375

1912. As T 23, but portrait of King George V.

No.	Type	Description	Unused	Used
125		¼d. brown..	45	30
126		½d. green	60	60
127		1d. red	2·00	10
231		1d. violet	1·00	10
232		1½d. red	4·00	3·25
128		2d. grey	1·00	10
129		2½d. blue	3·50	3·50
130		3d. purple on yellow ..	3·00	3·50
234		3d. blue	1·25	1·25
235		4d. black & red on yellow	5·00	7·00
236		5d. purple and olive ..	1·50	2·00
237		6d. purple..	2·00	1·25
238		1s. black on green ..	3·00	6·00
239		2s. purple and blue on blue	28·00	50·00
240		2s. 6d. black & red on blue	11·00	32·00
136		5s. green and red on yellow	29·00	40·00
137		£1 purple and black on red	£250	£275

1916. Nos. 126/7 optd WAR STAMP.

No.	Type	Description	Unused	Used
138.		½d. green	35	1·75
139a.		1d. red	60	75

1935. Silver Jubilee. As T 13 of Antigua.

No.	Type	Description	Unused	Used
242.		1½d. blue and red ..	80	3·25
243.		2d. blue and grey ..	1·50	35
244.		3d. brown and blue ..	2·50	2·75
245.		1s. grey and purple ..	4·50	3·50

1937. Coronation. As T 2 of Aden.

No.	Type	Description	Unused	Used
246.		1d. violet	70	45
247.		2d. grey	80	55
248.		3d. blue	80	55

28. Natives Sailing Canoe.

29. Native Village.

32. Government Offices.

1938.

No.	Type	Description	Unused	Used
249	28.	½d. green	10	30
250	29.	1d. brown and blue ..	30	20
252c	–	1½d. red..	90	1·25
254	–	2d. brown and green ..	18·00	16·00
255	32.	2d. green and mauve ..	40	50
256a	–	2½d. brown and green..	40	40
257	–	3d. blue..	85	30
258	–	5d. blue and red ..	50·00	10·00
259	–	5d. green and red ..	20	30
261b	–	6d. black	1·50	40
261c	–	8d. red	60	25
262	–	1s. black and yellow ..	75	30
263	–	1s. 5d. black and red ..	15	10
263a	–	1s. 6d. blue	4·50	1·50
264	–	2s. violet and orange ..	1·75	40
265	–	2s. 6d. green and brown	2·00	90
266	–	5s. green and purple ..	2·25	1·25
266a	–	10s. orange and green..	35·00	40·00
266b	–	£1 blue and red ..	55·00	50·00

DESIGNS—HORIZ. As Type **32**: 1½d. Canakan (canoe). 2d. (No. 254), 2½d., 6d. Map of Fiji Is. HORIZ. As Type **29**: 3d. Canoe and Arms. 8d., 1s. 5d., 1s. 6d. Arms. 2 s. Suva Harbour. 2s. 6d. River scene. 5s. Chief's hut. VERT. As Type **29**: 5d. (Nos. 258/9) Sugar cane. 1s. Spearing fish. 10s. Paw-Paw tree. £1, Police bugler.

1941. No. 254 surch.

No.	Type	Description	Unused	Used
267.	–	2½d. on 2d. brn. & green	40	20

1946. Victory. As T 9 of Aden.

No.	Type	Description	Unused	Used
268.		2½d. green..	10	20
269.		3d. blue	10	10

1948. Silver Wedding. As T 10/11 of Aden.

No.	Type	Description	Unused	Used
270.		2½d. green..	40	60
271.		5s. blue	14·00	5·00

1949. U.P.U. As T 20/23 of Antigua.

No.	Type	Description	Unused	Used
272.		2d. purple..	55	30
273.		3d. blue	90	1·25
274.		8d. red	90	1·00
275.		1s. 6d. blue	1·10	1·00

43. Children Bathing.

1951. Health stamps. Inscr. "HEALTH".

No.	Type	Description	Unused	Used
276.	43.	1d.+1d. brown ..	10	40
277.	–	2d.+1d. green ..	30	40

DESIGN—VERT. 2d. Rugby footballer.

1953. Coronation. As T 13 of Aden.

No.	Type	Description	Unused	Used
278.		2½d. black and green ..	50	30

1953. Royal Visit. As No. 261c but with portrait of Queen Elizabeth II and inscr "ROYAL VISIT 1953".

No.	Type	Description	Unused	Used
279		8d. red	15	15

46. Queen Elizabeth II (after Annigoni).

48. Loading Copra.

1954. Queen Elizabeth II. (I) inscr. "FIJI". (II) inscr. "Fiji".

No.	Type	Description	Unused	Used
280	28.	½d. green	15	60
298	46.	½d. green	15	30
281		1d. turquoise (I) ..	50	10
299		1d. blue (II)	1·00	60
282		1½d. sepia (I) ..	50	20
300		1½d. sepia (II)	1·00	30
283	32.	2d. green and mauve ..	1·25	30
312	46.	2d. red (I)	45	15
284		2½d. violet (I) ..	70	10
302		2½d. orange brown (I)..	1·50	2·25
285	48.	3d. brown and purple..	1·25	20
287	–	6d. black (As No. 261)	1·25	50
303	A.	6d. red and black ..	1·25	10
288	–	8d. red (As No. 261d)	1·00	1·25
316	B.	10d. brown and red ..	60	50
289	–	1s. black & yell. (As 262)	1·50	10
306	C.	1s. blue	1·50	10
290	D.	1s. 6d. blue and green	15·00	90
291	E.	2s. black and red ..	5·50	20
292a	–	2s. 6d. grn. & brn. (As 265)	1·00	10
320	F.	2s. 6d. black and purple	1·50	25
293	G.	5s. ochre and blue ..	24·00	1·25
294	–	10s. orange and green (As 266a)	11·00	20·00
309	H.	10s. green and sepia ..	8·50	3·50
295	–	£1 blue and red (As 266b)	42·00	18·00
325	I.	£1 black and orange ..	18·00	11·00

DESIGNS—HORIZ. As Type **48**: A, Fijian beating lali. B, Yaqona ceremony. C, Location map. D, Sugar cane train. E, Preparing bananas for export. F, Nadi Airport. G, Gold industry. H, Cutting sugar-cane. I, Arms of Fiji.

52. River Scene.

1954. Health stamps.

No.	Type	Description	Unused	Used
296.	52.	1½d.+½d. brown & grn.	10	40
297.	–	2½d.+½d. orge. & black	10	10

DESIGN: 2½d. Queen's portrait and Cross of Lorraine inscr. "FIJI WAR MEMORIAL" and "ANTI-TUBERCULOSIS CAMPAIGN".

56. Hibiscus.

DESIGNS — HORIZ. 1s. 6d. International date line. 4s. Kandavu parrot. 5s. Orange dove. VERT. 2s. White orchid. SMALLER (23 × 28 mm.): 3d. Queen Elizabeth II.

1959.

No.	Type	Description	Unused	Used
313	–	3d. multicoloured ..	25	10
304	56	8d. multicoloured ..	50	25
315	–	9d. multicoloured ..	90	65
318	–	1s. 6d. multicoloured ..	3·50	90
319	–	2s. yell., grn. & copper	15·00	2·00
308	–	4s. multicoloured ..	1·75	1·75
323	–	5s. red, yellow and grey	14·00	35

1963. Royal Visit. Optd. **ROYAL VISIT 1963.**

No.	Type	Description	Unused	Used
326.	–	3d. mult. (No. 313) ..	10	10
327.	C.	1s. blue (No. 317) ..	10	10

1963. Freedom from Hunger. As T 28 of Aden.

No.	Type	Description	Unused	Used
328.	–	2s. blue	4·75	70

69. Running.

1963. 1st South Pacific Games, Suva, Inscr. as in T **69**.
329. **19.** 3d. brn., yellow & black .. 25 10
330. – 9d. brown, violet & black .. 35 35
331. – 1s. brown, green & black .. 35 10
332. – 2s. 6d. brown, blue & blk. .. 90 50
DESIGNS—VERT. 9d. Throwing the discus. 1s. Hockey. HORIZ. 2s. 6d. High-jumping.

1963. Cent of Red Cross. As T **33** of Antigua.
333. 2d. red and black 50 10
334. 2s. red and blue .. .. 2·50 1·50

1963. Opening of COMPAC (Trans-Pacific Telephone Cable). No. 317 optd. **COMPAC CABLE IN SERVICE DECEMBER 1963** and ship.
335. C. 1s. blue 30 10

74. Jamborette Emblem.

76. Flying-boat "Aotearoa".

1964. 50th Anniv. of Fijian Scout Movement.
336. **74.** 3d. multicoloured .. 10 20
337. – 1s. violet and brown .. 10 25
DESIGN: 1s. Scouts of three races.

1964. 25th Anniv. of 1st Fiji–Tonga Airmail Service.
338. **76.** 3d. black and red .. 30 10
339. – 6d. red and blue .. 40 40
340. – 1s. black and turquoise .. 40 40
DESIGNS—VERT. 6d. Fiji Airways "Heron". HORIZ. (37½ × 25 mm.): 1s. "Aotearoa" and map.

1965. Cent of I.T.U. As T **36** of Antigua.
341. 3d. blue and red 50 10
342. 2s. yellow and bistre .. 1·25 25

1965. I.C.Y. As T **37** of Antigua.
343. 2d. purple and turquoise .. 30 10
344. 2s. 6d. green and lavender .. 70 25

1966. Churchill Commem. As T **38** of Antigua.
345. 3d. blue 70 10
346. 9d. green 90 40
347. 1s. brown 90 10
348. 2s. 6d. violet .. .. 1·00 50

1966. World Cup Football Championship. As T **40** of Antigua.
349. 2d. multicoloured 20 10
350. 2s. multicoloured 50 20

79. H.M.S. "Pandora" approaching Split Island, Rotuma.

1966. 175th Anniv. of Discovery of Rotuma. Multicoloured.
351. 3d. Type **79** 15 10
352. 10d. Rotuma Chiefs .. 15 10
353. 1s. 6d. Rotumans welcoming H.M.S. "Pandora" .. 25 20

1966. Inauguration of W.H.O. Headquarters, Geneva. As T **41** of Antigua.
354. 6d. black, green and blue .. 1·00 20
355. 2s. 6d. black, pur. & ochre .. 2·50 55

82. Running.

1966. 2nd South Pacific Games.
356. **82.** 3d. black, brown & green .. 10 10
357. – 9d. black, brown & blue .. 15 15
358. – 1s. multicoloured .. 15 15
DESIGNS: VERT. 9d. Putting the shot. HORIZ. 1s. Diving.

85. Military Forces Band.

1967. Int. Tourist Year. Multicoloured.
360. 3d. Type **85** 15 10
361. 9d. Reef diving 15 10
362. 1s. Beqa Fire Walkers .. 15 10
363. 2s. "Oriana" (cruise liner) at Suva 45 15

89. Bligh (bust), H.M.S. "Providence" and Chart.

1967. 150th Death Anniv. of Admiral Bligh.
364. **89.** 4d. multicoloured .. 10 10
365. – 1s. multicoloured .. 10 10
366. – 2s. 6d. multicoloured .. 15 15
DESIGNS—(As Type **89**): 2s. 6d. Bligh's Tomb. (54 × 20 mm.) 1s. "Bounty's longboat being chased in Fiji waters".

92. Simmonds "Spartan" Seaplane.

1968. 40th Anniv. of Kingsford Smith's Pacific Flight via Fiji.
367. **92.** 2d. black and green .. 15 10
368. – 6d. blue, black and lake .. 15 10
369. – 1s. violet and green .. 20 10
370. – 2s. brown and blue .. 30 15
DESIGNS: 6d. HS "748" and airline insignias. 1s. "Southern Cross" and Crew. 2s. Lockheed "Altair" Monoplane.

96. Bure Huts.

1968.
371. ½d. multicoloured 10 10
372. 1d. blue, red & yellow .. 10 10
373. 2d. blue, brown & ochre .. 10 10
374. 3d. green, blue & ochre .. 35 10
375. 4d. multicoloured 80 15
376. 6d. multicoloured 25 10
377. 9d. multicoloured 15 15
378. 10d. blue, orange & brown 1·25 20
379. 1s. blue and red 20 10
380. 1s. 6d. multicoloured .. 4·25 3·75
381. 2s. turq., black & red .. 1·00 2·00
382. 2s. 6d. multicoloured .. 1·00 1·00
383. 3s. multicoloured .. .. 4·50 6·00
384. 4s. ochre, black and olive 6·50 2·75
385. 5s. multicoloured .. .. 4·00 2·50
386. 10s. brown, black & ochre 3·50 3·50
387. £1 multicoloured .. .. 3·50 7·50
DESIGNS—HORIZ. (As T **96**) ½d. Type **96**. 1d. Passion flowers. 2d. Pearly nautilus. 4d. "Psilogramma jordana" (moth). 6d. Angel fish 9d. Bamboo raft. 10d. "Asota woodfordi" (moth). 3s. Golden cworie shell (33 × 22 mm). 2s. Sea snake. 2s. 6d. Outrigger canoes. 5s. Bamboo orchids. £1, Queen Elizabeth and Arms of Fiji. VERT. (23 × 33 mm). 3d. Eastern reef heron. 1s. Black marlin. 1s. 6d. Orangebreasted honeyeaters. 4s. Mining industry. 10s. Ceremonial whale's tooth.

HAVE YOU READ THE NOTES AT THE BEGINNING OF THIS CATALOGUE?
These often provide answers to the enquiries we receive.

113. Map of Fiji, W.H.O. Emblem and Nurses.

1968. 20th Anniv. of W.H.O. Multicoloured.
388. 3d. Type **113**. 15 10
389. 9d. Transferring Patient to Medical Ship "Vuniwai" 20 10
390. 3s. Recreation 25 20

116. Passion Flowers.

1969. Decimal Currency. Designs as T **96** etc., but with values inscr. in decimal currency as in T **116**.
391. **116.** 1 c. bl., red & yell. .. 10 10
392. – 2 c. bl., brn. & ochre (As 373) 10 10
393. – 3 c. green, blue & ochre (As 374) 30 10
394. – 4 c. multicoloured (As 375) .. .. 1·50 10
395. – 5 c. multicoloured (As 376) 20 10
396. **96.** 6 c. multicoloured .. 10 10
397. – 8 c. multicoloured (As 377) 10 10
398. – 9 c. blue, orange and brown (As 378) .. 1·50 80
399. – 10 c. blue & red (As 379) 20 10
400. – 15 c. mult. (As 380) .. 8·00 3·25
401. – 20 c. turq., blk. & red (As 381) .. .. 1·00 80
402. – 25 c. mult. (As 382) .. 1·00 30
403. – 30 c. mult. (As 383) .. 6·50 2·25
404. – 40 c. ochre, blk. & olive (As 384) .. .. 5·50 3·50
405. – 50 c. mult. (As 385) .. 4·50 30
406. – $1 brn., blk. & ochre (As 386) .. .. 4·00 60
407. – $2 mult. (As 387) .. 4·00 5·00

117. Fijian Soldiers overlooking the Solomon Islands.

1969. 25th Anniv. of Fijian Military Forces' Solomons Campaign.
408. **117.** 3 c. multicoloured .. 15 10
409. – 10 c. multicoloured .. 20 10
410. – 25 c. multicoloured .. 30 20
DESIGNS: 10 c. Regimental flags and soldiers in full dress and battledress. 25 c. Sofanaia Sukanaivala and Victoria Cross.

120. Javelin Throwing.

1969. 3rd South Pacific Games, Port Moresby.
411. **120.** 4 c. blk., brown & red .. 10 10
412. – 8 c. black, grey & blue .. 10 10
413. – 20 c. multicoloured .. 20 20
DESIGNS: 8 c. Yachting. 20 c. Games medal and winner's rostrum.

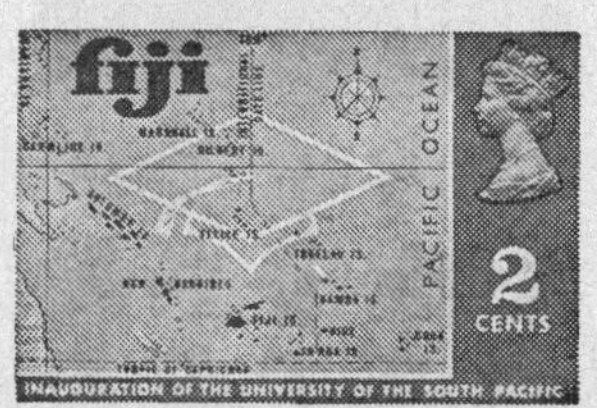

123. Map of South Pacific and "Mortar-board."

1969. Inauguration of University of the South Pacific. Multicoloured.
414. 2 c. Type **123** 10 15
415. 8 c. R.N.Z.A.F. Badge and "Sunderland" Flying-Boat over Laucala Bay (Site of University) .. 15 10
416. 25 c. Science Students at work 25 15

1970. Royal Visit. Nos. 392, 399 and 402 optd. **ROYAL VISIT 1970.**
417. 2 c. blue, brown and ochre 10 20
418. 10 c. blue and red .. 10 10
419. 25 c. multicoloured .. 20 10

127. Chaulmugra Tree, Makogai.

1970. Closing of Leprosy Hospital, Makogai.
420. **127.** 2 c. multicoloured .. 10 10
421. – 10 c. green and black .. 10 10
422. – 10 c. blue, blk. & mauve 10 10
423. – 30 c. multicoloured .. 20 40
DESIGNS: 10 c. (No. 421) "Cascade" (Semisi Maya). 10 c. (No. 422) "Sea urchins" (Semisi Maya). 30 c. Makogai Hospital.
Nos. 421/2 are vert.

131. Abel Tasman and Log, 1643.

1970. Explorers and Discoverers.
424. **131.** 2 c. blk., brn. & turq. 40 25
425. – 3 c. multicoloured .. 1·00 25
426. – 8 c. multicoloured .. 1·00 15
427. – 25 c. multicoloured .. 1·00 15
DESIGNS: 3 c. Captain Cook and H.M.S. "Endeavour", 1774. 8 c. Captain Bligh and Longboat, 1789. 25 c. Fijian and Ocean-going Canoe.

135. King Cakobau and Cession Stone.

1970. Independence. Multicoloured.
428. 2 c. Type **135**. 10 10
429. 3 c. Children of the World 10 10
430. 10 c. Prime Minister and Fijian Flag 10 10
431. 25 c. Dancers in Costume 20 20

139. 1d. and 6d. Stamps of 1870.

1970. Stamp Cent. Multicoloured.
432. 4 c. Type **139** 10 10
433. 15 c. Fijian Stamps of all Reigns (61 × 21 mm.) .. 15 15
434. 20 c. "Fiji Times" Office and modern G.P.O. .. 15 15

140. Grey-backed White-eye.

142. Women's Basketball.

1971. Birds and Flowers. Multicoloured.
435 1 c. "Cirrhopetalum umbellatum" 15 20
436 2 c. Cardinal honeyeater .. 10 10
437 3 c. "Calanthe furcata" .. 45 20

438 4 c. "Bulbophyllum sp. nov." 60 30
439 5 c. Type **140** 35 10
510 6 c. "Phaius tancarvilliae" 1·75 20
441 8 c. Blue-headed flycatcher 35 10
442 10 c. "Acanthephippium vitiense" 40 10
513 15 c. "Dendrobium tokai" 1·75 60
444 20 c. Slaty flycatcher 90 30
445 25 c. Yellow-faced honey-eater .. .. .. 1·50 20
516 30 c. "Dendrobium gordonii" .. .. 6·00 95
517 40 c. Masked shining parrot .. .. .. 3·25 60
518 50 c. White-throated pigeon .. .. .. 3·25 65
449 $1 Collared lory .. .. 4·00 1·25
520 $2 "Dendrobium platygastrium" .. .. 5·50 3·50

The 25c. to $2 are larger ($22\frac{1}{2} \times 35\frac{1}{2}$ mm.).

1971. 4th South Pacific Games, Tahiti.
451. **142.** 8 c. multicoloured .. 10 10
452. – 10 c. blue, blk. and brn. 10 10
453. – 25 c. grn., blk. and brn. 30 25
DESIGNS: 10 c. Running. 25 c. Weightlifting.

143. Community Education.

1972. 25th Anniv. of South Pacific Commission. Multicoloured.
454. 2 c. Type **143** 10 10
455. 4 c. Public Health 10 10
456. 50 c. Economic Growth .. 35 65

144. "Native Canoe".

1972. South Pacific Festival of Arts, Suva.
457. **144.** 10 c. blk., orge. and bl. 10 10

145. Flowers, Conch and Ceremonial Whale's Tooth.

1972. Royal Silver Wedding. Multicoloured. Background colours given.
474. **145.** 10 c. green 20 10
475. 25 c. purple 30 10

1972. Hurricane Relief. Nos. 400 and 403 surch. **HURRICANE RELIEF +** and premium.
476. 15 c. + 5 c. multicoloured .. 15 15
477. 30 c. + 10 c. multicoloured 15 15

147. Line Out.

1973. Diamond Jubilee of Rugby Union. Multicoloured.
478. 2 c. Type **147** 15 25
479. 8 c. Body tackle 25 10
480. 25 c. Conversion 65 40

148. Forestry Development.

1973. Development Projects. Multicoloured.
481. 5 c. Type **148** 10 10
482. 8 c. Rice irrigation scheme 10 10
483. 10 c. Low income housing 10 10
484. 25 c. Highway construction 20 30

149. Christmas.

1973. Festivals of Joy. Multicoloured.
485. 3 c. Type **149** 10 10
486. 10 c. Diwali 10 10
487. 20 c. Id-ul-Fitar 15 15
488. 25 c. Chinese New Year .. 15 15

150. Athletics.

1974. Commonwealth Games, Christchurch, New Zealand. Multicoloured.
489. 3 c. Type **150** 15 10
490. 8 c. Boxing 15 10
491. 50 c. Bowling 50 75

151. Bowler.

1974. Centenary of Cricket. Multicoloured.
492. 3 c. Type **151** 50 25
493. 25 c. Batsman and wicket-keeper .. .. 1·75 35
494. 40 c. Fielder (horiz.) .. 2·50 90

152. Fiji Postman.

1974. Cent. of Universal Postal Union. Multicoloured.
495. 3 c. Type **152** 10 10
496. 8 c. Loading mail onto "Fijian Princess" .. 10 10
497. 30 c. Fijian post office and mailbus 20 20
498. 50 c. Modern aircraft .. 35 60

153. Cubs lighting Fire.

1974. 1st National Scout Jamboree, Lautoka. Multicoloured.
499. 3 c. Type **153** 15 10
500. 10 c. Scouts reading map 20 10
501. 40 c. Scouts and Fijian flag (vert.) .. .. .. 65 1·00

154. Cakobau Club and Flag.

1974. Cent. of Deed of Cession and 4th Anniv. of Independence. Multicoloured.
502. 3 c. Type **154** 10 10
503. 8 c. King Cakobau and Queen Victoria 10 10
504. 50 c. Raising the Royal Standard at Nasova Ovalau 30 55

155. "Diwali" (Hindu Festival).

1975. "Festivals of Joy". Multicoloured.
521. 3 c. Type **155** 10 10
522. 15 c. "Id-Ul-Fitar" (Muslim Festival) 10 10
523. 25 c. Chinese New Year .. 15 15
524. 30 c. Christmas 20 30

156. Steam Locomotive No. 21.

1976. Sugar Trains. Multicoloured.
526 4 c. Type **156** 25 10
527 15 c. Diesel loco No. 8 .. 75 30
528 20 c. Diesel loco No. 1 .. 85 40
529 30 c. Free passenger train 1·10 85

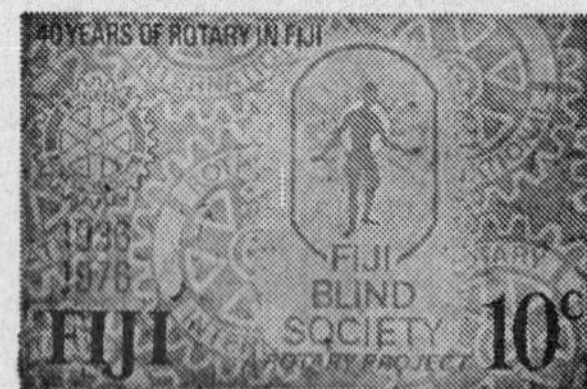

157. Fiji Blind Society and Rotary Symbols.

1976. 40th Anniv. of Rotary in Fiji.
530. **157.** 10 c. blue, grn. & blk. 15 10
531. – 25 c. multicoloured .. 40 50
DESIGN: 25 c. Ambulance and Rotary Symbol.

158. D.H. "Drover".
(Illustration reduced, Actual size 57 × 21 mm).

1976. 25th Anniv. of Air Services. Mult.
532. 4 c. Type **158** 40 20
533. 15 c. B.A.C. "1–11" .. 1·00 1·50
534. 25 c. H.S. "748" .. 2·00 1·75
535. 30 c. Britten-Norman "Trislander" .. .. 2·25 3·25

159. The Queen's Visit to Fiji, 1970.

1977. Silver Jubilee. Multicoloured.
536. 10 c. Type **159** 10 10
537. 25 c. King Edward's Chair 15 10
538. 30 c. The Queen wearing cloth of gold supertunica 25 15

160. Map of the World.

1977. E.E.C./A.C.P.* Council of Ministers Conference. Multicoloured.
539. 4 c. Type **160** 10 10
540. 30 c. Map of Fiji group .. 30 65
* A.C.P. = African, Caribbean, Pacific Group.

161. "Hibiscus rosa-sinensis".

1977. 21st Anniversary of Fiji Hibiscus Festival.
541. **161** 4 c. multicoloured .. 10 10
542. – 15 c. multicoloured .. 15 10
543. – 30 c. multicoloured .. 25 15
544. – 35 c. multicoloured .. 40 35
Nos. 542/44 show different varieties of "Hibiscus rosa-sinensis".

162. Drua.

1977. Canoes. Multicoloured.
545. 4 c. Type **162** 10 10
546. 15 c. Tabilai 20 20
547. 25 c. Takai 25 25
548. 40 c. Camakua 35 80

163. White Hart of Richard II.

1978. 25th Anniv. of Coronation. Mult.
549. **163.** 25 c. brn., green & silver 20 25
550. – 25 c. multicoloured .. 20 25
551. – 25 c. brn., green & silver 20 25
DESIGNS: No. 550, Queen Elizabeth II. No. 551, Banded iguana.

164. Defence Force surrounding Plane, Suva.

1978. Aviation Annivs. Multicoloured.

552.	4 c. Type **164**	15	10
553.	15 c. " Southern Cross " prior to leaving Naselai Beach	25	30
554.	25 c. Wright " Flyer " ..	50	55
555.	30 c. Bristol " F2B " ..	50	70

The 25 c. value commemorates the 75th Anniv. of Powered Flight, the 30 c. the 60th Anniv. of R.A.F. and the other values the 50th Anniv. of First Trans-Pacific Flight by Kingsford-Smith.

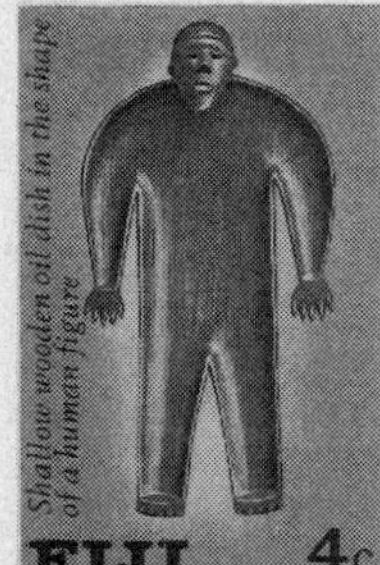

165. Shallow Wooden Oil Dish in Shape of Human Figure.

1978. Fijian Artifacts. Multicoloured.

556	4 c. Type **165**	10	10
557.	15 c. Necklace of cachalot teeth (horiz.) ..	10	10
558.	25 c. Double water bottle (horiz.)	15	10
559.	30 c. Finely carved Ula or throwing club	15	15

166. Advent Crown with Candles (Christmas).

1978. Festivals. Multicoloured.

560.	4 c. Type **166**	10	10
561.	15 c. Lamps (Diwali) ..	10	10
562.	25 c. Coffee pot, cups and fruit (Id-Ul-Fitar) ..	10	10
563.	40 c. Lion (Chinese New Year)	25	40

167. Banded Iguana.

1979. Endangered Wildlife. Multicoloured.

564.	4 c. Type **167**	10	10
565.	15 c. Tree Frog	30	10
566.	25 c. Long-legged Warbler	60	20
567.	30 c. Pink-billed Parrot Finch	75	70

168. Women with Dholak.

1979. Centenary of Arrival of Indians. Multicoloured.

568.	4 c. Type **168**	10	10
569.	15 c. Men sitting round tanoa	10	10
570.	30 c. Farmer and sugar cane plantation ..	15	10
571.	40 c. Sailing ship " Leonidas "	40	25

169. Soccer.

1979. 6th South Pacific Games. Multicoloured.

572.	4 c. Type **169**	10	10
573.	15 c. Rugby Union ..	25	10
574.	30 c. Lawn tennis ..	55	35
575.	40 c. Weightlifting ..	60	45

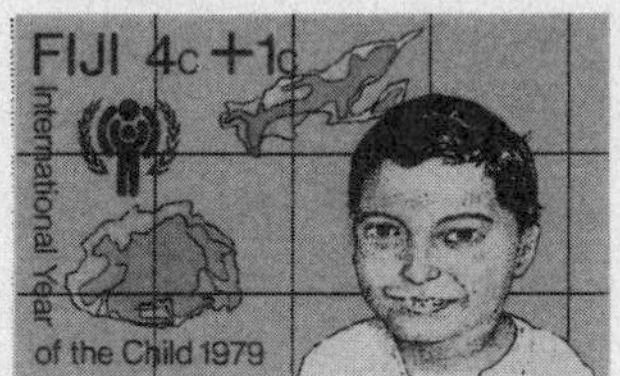

170. Indian Child and Map of Fiji.

1979. International Year of the Child. Multicoloured.

576.	4 c.+1 c. Type **170** ..	10	10
577.	15 c.+2 c. European child	15	15
578.	30 c.+3 c. Chinese child ..	15	15
579.	40 c.+4 c. Fijian child ..	15	20

171. Old Town Hall, Suva.

1979. Architecture. Multicoloured.

719	1 c. Type **171**	10	10
720a	2 c. Dudley Church, Suva	20	20
721	3 c. Fiji International Telecommunications Building, Suva ..	20	20
582c	4 c. Lautoka Mosque ..	10	10
583	5 c. As 4 c.	10	10
584	6 c. General Post Office, Suva	10	10
724	8 c. Public School, Levuka	30	30
725	10 c. Fiji Visitors Bureau, Suva	20	30
586	12 c. Public School, Levuka	15	15
587a	15 c. Colonial War Memorial Hospital, Suva	10	15
588	18 c. Labasa sugar mill ..	15	20
730	20 c. Rewa Bridge, Nausori	30	50
590a	30 c. Sacred Heart Cathedral, Suva (vert)	25	30
732	35 c. Grand Pacific Hotel, Suva	30	35
592	45 c. Shiva Temple, Suva	35	40
593	50 c. Serua Island Village	40	40
735	$1 Solo Rock lighthouse (30 × 46 mm)	85	90
595	$2 Baker Memorial Hall, Nausori (46 × 30 mm) ..	1·75	1·90
595a	$5 Government House (46 × 30 mm)	4·25	4·50

Nos. 582c/95a come with or without date imprint.

172. " Southern Cross ", 1873.

1980. " London 1980 " International Stamp Exhibition. Multicoloured.

596.	6 c. Type **172**	15	10
597.	20 c. " Levuka ", 1910 ..	20	10
598.	45 c. " Matua ", 1936 ..	35	40
599.	50 c. " Oronsay ", 1951 ..	40	55

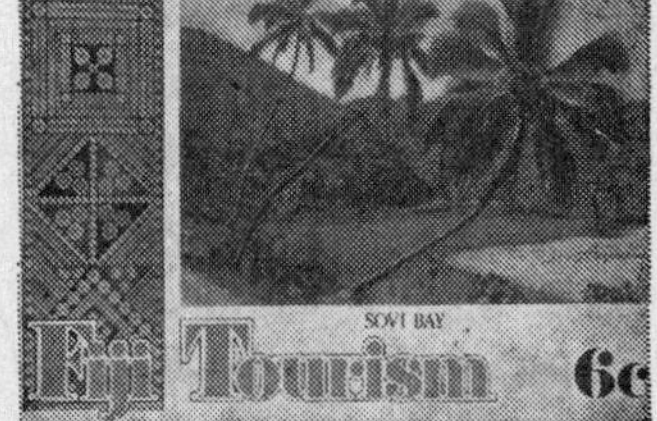

173. Sovi Bay.

1980. Tourism. Multicoloured.

600.	6 c. Type **173**	10	10
601.	20 c. Evening scene, Yanuca Island	15	15
602.	45 c. Dravuni Beach ..	20	40
603.	50 c. Wakaya Island ..	20	45

174. Official Opening of Parliament 1979.

1980. 10th Anniv. of Independence. Multi.

604.	6 c. Type **174**	10	10
605.	20 c. Fiji coat of arms (vert.)	15	10
606.	45 c. Fiji flag	20	20
607.	50 c. Queen Elizabeth II (vert.)	25	35

175. " Coastal Scene " (painting, Semisi Maya).

1981. International Year for Disabled Persons. Multicoloured.

608.	6 c. Type **175**	10	10
609.	35 c. " Underwater Scene " (Semisi Maya)	45	30
610.	50 c. Semisi Maya (disabled artist) at work (vert.) .	55	40
611.	60 c. " Peacock " (Semisi Maya) (vert.) ..	60	45

176. Prince Charles Sailing.

1981. Royal Wedding. Multicoloured.

612.	6 c. Wedding bouquet from Fiji	10	10
613.	45 c. Type **176**	45	15
614.	$1 Prince Charles and Lady Diana Spencer ..	75	60

177. Operator Assistance Centre.

1981. Telecommunications. Multicoloured.

615.	6 c. Type **177**	10	10
616.	35 c. Microwave station	55	50
617.	50 c. Satellite earth station	75	75
618.	60 c. Cable ship " Retriever "	90	90

178. " Eat Fiji Foods ".

1981. World Food Day.

619. **178.**	20 c. multicoloured ..	30	15

179. Ratu Sir Lala Sukuna (first Speaker, Legislative Council).

1981. Commonwealth Parliamentary Association Conference, Suva.

620. **179.**	6 c. black, buff and brown	10	10
621. –	35 c. multicoloured ..	30	30
622. –	50 c. multicoloured ..	45	45

DESIGNS: 35 c. Mace of the House of Representatives. 50 c. Suva Civic Centre.

180. Bell " P–39 (Airacobra) ".

1981. World War II Aircraft. Multicoloured.

624.	6 c. Type **180**	50	10
625.	18 c. Consolidated " PBY–5 " (Catalina)	1·10	35
626.	35 c. Curtiss " P–40 (Warhawk) "	1·60	75
627.	60 c. Short " Singapore "	2·00	2·00

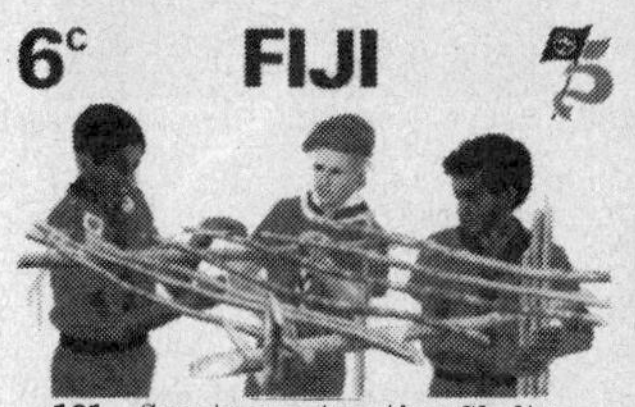

181. Scouts constructing Shelter.

1982. 75th Anniv. of Boy Scout Movement. Multicoloured.

628.	6 c. Type **181**	15	10
629.	20 c. Scouts sailing (vert.)	50	30
630.	45 c. Scouts by campfire ..	85	50
631.	60 c. Lord Baden-Powell (vert.)	1·00	1·00

182. Fiji Soldiers at U.N. Checkpoint.

1982. Disciplined Forces. Multicoloured.

632.	12 c. Type **182**	25	10
633.	30 c. Soldiers engaged on rural development ..	50	45
634.	40 c. Police patrol	70	60
635.	70 c. "Kiro" (minesweeper)	1·00	1·10

183. Footballers and Fiji Football Association Logo.

1982. World Cup Football Championship, Spain.

636. **183.**	6 c. red, black and yel.	10	10
637. –	18 c. multicoloured ..	25	20
638. –	50 c. multicoloured ..	70	60
639. –	90 c. multicoloured ..	1·10	1·25

DESIGNS: 18 c. Footballers and World Cup emblem. 50 c. Football and Bernabeu Stadium. 90 c. Footballers and Naranjito (mascot.)

184. Bride and Groom leaving St. Paul's.

1982. 21st Birthday of Princess of Wales. Multicoloured.

640.	20 c. Fiji coat of arms ..	25	25
641.	35 c. Lady Diana Spencer at Broadlands, May 1981	35	35
642.	45 c. Type **184**	50	50
643.	$1 Formal portrait ..	1·25	1·75

185. Prince Philip.

1982. Royal Visit. Multicoloured.

644.	6 c. Type **185**	10	10
645.	45 c. Queen Elizabeth II ..	65	1·75

186. Baby Jesus with Mary and Joseph.

1982. Christmas. Multicoloured.

647.	6 c. Type **186**	10	10
648.	20 c. Three Wise Men presenting gifts	30	20
649.	35 c. Carol-singing ..	45	35

187. Red-throated Lorikeet.

1983. Parrots. Multicoloured.

651.	20 c. Type **187**	1·00	15
652.	40 c. Blue-crowned Lory ..	1·40	40
653.	55 c. Masked Shining Parrot	1·60	80
654.	70 c. Red Shining Parrot ..	1·75	1·50

188. Bure in Traditional Village.

1983. Commonwealth Day. Multicoloured.

655.	8 c. Type **188**	10	10
656.	25 c. Barefoot firewalkers	20	15
657.	50 c. Sugar industry ..	30	35
658.	80 c. Kava "Yagona" ceremony	55	70

189. First Manned Balloon Flight, 1783.

1983. Bicentenary of Manned Flight. Mult.

659.	8 c. Type **189**	10	10
660.	20 c. Wright brothers' "Flyer"	25	30
661.	25 c. Douglas "Super DC 3"	35	40
662.	40 c. De Havilland "Comet"	55	60
663.	50 c. Boeing "747" ..	65	70
664.	58 c. Space Shuttle ..	75	80

190. Nawanawa.

1983. Flowers (1st series). Multicoloured.

665.	8 c. Type **190**	10	10
666.	25 c. Rosawa	35	30
667.	40 c. Warerega	55	50
668.	$1 Saburo	1·25	1·40

See also Nos. 680/3.

191. Fijian beating Lali and Earth Satellite Station.

1983. World Communications Year.

669.	**191.** 50 c. multicoloured ..	50	70

192. "Dacryopinax spathularia".

1984. Fungi. Multicoloured.

670.	8 c. Type **192**	50	10
671.	15 c. "Podoscypha involula"	75	25
672.	40 c. "Lentinus squarrosulus"	1·25	80
673.	50 c. "Scleroderma flavidum" (horiz.) ..	1·50	90
674.	$1 "Phillipsia domingensis" (horiz.)	1·75	2·25

193. "Tui Lau" (freighter) on Reef.

1984. 250th Anniv. of "Lloyd's List" (newspaper). Multicoloured.

675	8 c. Type **193**	30	10
676	40 c. "Tofua" (cargo liner)	85	65
677	55 c. "Canberra" (liner)	1·00	85
678	60 c. "Nedlloyd Madras" (freighter) at Suva wharf	1·10	95

1984. Flowers (2nd series). As T **190**. Mult.

680.	15 c. Drividrivi	25	25
681.	20 c. Vesida	35	35
682.	50 c. Vuga	80	80
683.	70 c. Qaiqi	1·10	1·10

INDEX

Countries can be quickly located by referring to the index at the end of this volume.

195. Prize Bull, Yalavou Cattle Scheme.

1984. "Ausipex" International Stamp Exhibition, Melbourne. Multicoloured.

684.	8 c. Type **195**	15	10
685.	25 c. Wailoa Power Station	40	40
686.	40 c. Air Pacific Boeing "737" airliner	65	65
687.	$1 Container ship "Fua Kavenga"	1·60	1·60

196. The Stable at Bethlehem.

1984. Christmas. Children's Paintings. Multicoloured.

688.	8 c. Type **196**	10	10
689.	20 c. Outrigger canoe ..	30	20
690.	25 c. Father Christmas and Christmas tree	35	25
691.	40 c. Going to church ..	60	60
692.	$1 Decorating Christmas tree (vert.)	1·50	1·60

197. "Danaus plexippus".

1985. Butterflies. Multicoloured.

693	8 c. Type **197**	60	10
694	25 c. "Hypolimnas bolina"	1·10	60
695	40 c. "Lampides boeticus" (vert)	1·50	90
696	$1 "Precis villida" (vert)	2·00	3·50

198. Outrigger Canoe off Toberua Island.

1985. "Expo '85" World Fair, Japan. Mult.

697.	20 c. Type **198**	50	30
698.	25 c. Wainivula Falls ..	85	40
699.	50 c. Mana Island	95	70
700.	$1 Sawa-I-Lau Caves ..	1·25	1·40

199. With Prince Charles at Garter Ceremony.

1985. Life and Times of Queen Elizabeth the Queen Mother. Multicoloured.

701.	8 c. With Prince Andrew on her 60th Birthday ..	10	10
702.	25 c. Type **199**	35	40
703.	40 c. The Queen Mother at Epsom Races	50	80
704.	50 c. With Prince Henry at his christening (from photo by Lord Snowdon)	65	1·25

200. Horned Squirrel Fish.

1985. Shallow Water Marine Fishes. Multicoloured.

706.	40 c. Type **200**	85	55
707.	50 c. Yellow-banded Goatfish	1·00	70
708.	55 c. Fairy Cod	1·00	85
709.	$1 Peacock Rock Cod ..	1·75	2·50

201. Collared Petrel.

1985. Seabirds. Multicoloured.

710.	15 c. Type **201**	95	30
711.	20 c. Lesser Frigate Bird ..	1·00	35
712.	50 c. Brown Booby ..	2·25	2·00
713.	$1 Crested Tern	3·50	4·50

1986. 60th Birthday of Queen Elizabeth II. As T **110** of Ascension. Multicoloured.

714.	20 c. With Duke of York at Royal Tournament, 1936	30	30
715.	25 c. Royal Family on Palace balcony after Princess Margaret's wedding, 1960	35	35
716.	40 c. Queen inspecting guard of honour, Suva, 1982	55	55
717.	50 c. In Luxembourg, 1976	65	85
718.	$1 At Crown Agents Head Office, London, 1983 ..	1·10	1·60

202. Children and "Peace for Fiji and the World" Slogan

1986. International Peace Year. Mult.

736.	8 c. Type **202**	15	10
737.	40 c. Peace dove and houses	60	75

203. Halley's Comet in Centaurus Constellation and Newton's Reflector.

1986. Appearance of Halley's Comet. Multicoloured.

738.	25 c. Type **203**	1·00	40
739.	40 c. Halley's Comet over Lomaiviti	1·25	75
740.	$1 "Giotto" spacecraft photographing comet nucleus	2·50	3·25

204. Ground Frog.

1986. Reptiles and Amphibians. Mult.

741.	8 c. Type **204**	45	10
742.	20 c. Burrowing snake ..	70	30
743.	25 c. Spotted gecko ..	80	35
744.	40 c. Crested iguana ..	1·00	80
745.	50 c. Blotched skink ..	1·25	2·00
746.	$1 Speckled skink	1·75	3·25

205. Gatawaka. **206.** Weasel Cone.

1986. Ancient War Clubs. Multicoloured.

747.	25 c. Type **205**	70	35
748.	40 c. Siriti	90	60
749.	50 c. Bulibuli	1·10	1·25
750.	$1 Culacula	1·90	2·50

1987. Cone Shells of Fiji. Multicoloured.

751.	15 c. Type **206**	70	25
752.	20 c. Pertusus cone ..	80	30
753.	25 c. Admiral cone ..	85	35
754.	40 c. Leaden cone	1·25	70
755.	50 c. Imperial cone ..	1·40	1·25
756.	$1 Geography cone ..	1·90	2·25

209. Traditional Fijian House.

1987. International Year of Shelter for the Homeless. Multicoloured.

759.	55 c. Type **209**	45	50
760.	70 c. Modern bungalows ..	55	60

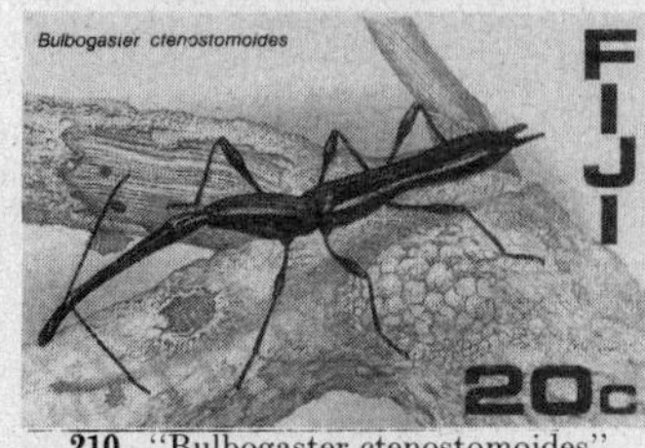

210. "Bulbogaster ctenostomoides" (stick-inscet).

1987. Fijian Insects. Multicoloured.

761	20 c. Type **210**	50	30
762	25 c. "Paracupta flaviventris" (beetle) ..	55	35
763	40 c. "Cerambyrhynchus schoenherri" (beetle) ..	70	50
764	50 c. "Rhinoscapha lagopyga" (weevil) ..	80	80
765	$1 "Xixuthrus heros" (beetle)	1·40	1·75

POSTAGE DUE STAMPS

D 1. D 3.

1917.

D 5a	D 1.	½d. black	£450	£225
D 2		1d. black	£250	65·00
D 3		2d. black	£200	55·00
D 4		3d. black	£250	70·00
D 5		4d. black	£600	£325

1918.

D 6.	D 3.	½d. black	2·50	13·00
D 7.		1d. black	2·75	4·50
D 8.		2d. black	2·75	7·50
D 9.		3d. black	3·25	28·00
D 10.		4d. black	5·50	19·00

D 4.

1940.

D 11.	D 4.	1d. green	4·50	40·00
D 12.		2d. green	6·00	40·00
D 13.		3d. green	8·50	50·00
D 14.		4d. green	11·00	50·00
D 15.		5d. green	12·00	50·00
D 16.		6d. green	14·00	60·00
D 17.		1s. red	19·00	80·00
D 18.		1s. 6d. red ..	20·00	£120

Fiji left the Commonwealth in 1987. Subsequent issues are listed in volume 1.

GAMBIA

A Br. colony and protectorate on the W. coast of Africa. Granted full internal self-government on 4 October 1963, and achieved independence on 18 February 1965. Became a republic within the Commonwealth on 24 April 1970.

1869. 12 pence = 1 shilling;
20 shillings = 1 pound.
1971. 100 bututs = 1 dalasy.

1. 2.

1869. Imperf.

5	1	4d. brown..	£350	£180
8		6d. blue	£300	£180

1880. Perf.

11	1.	½d. orange..	4·00	9·00
12		1d. purple	2·50	4·50
13		2d. red	18·00	9·50
14b		3d. blue	42·00	25·00
30		4d. brown..	2·50	2·00
17		6d. blue	70·00	45·00
19		1s. green	£180	£100

1886.

21	1	½d. green	1·00	1·00
23		1d. red	3·50	4·00
25		2d. orange	1·40	5·00
27		2½d. blue	1·75	1·50
29		3d. grey	2·00	10·00
34		6d. green	10·00	30·00
35		1s. violet	3·00	14·00

1898.

37.	2.	½d. green	1·75	1·75
38.		1d. red	1·25	75
39.		2d. orange and mauve ..	3·00	3·50
40.		2½d. blue	1·40	1·50
41.		3d. purple and blue ..	6·50	12·00
42.		4d. brown and blue ..	5·00	18·00
43.		6d. green and red ..	8·00	15·00
44.		1s. mauve and green ..	17·00	38·00

1902. As T **2**, but portrait of King Edward VII.

57	½d. green	1·75	25
46	1d. red	1·00	55
47	2d. orange and mauve ..	3·25	2·00
74	2d. grey	1·40	4·00
60	2½d. blue	2·00	3·25
61	3d. purple and blue ..	4·75	2·00
75	3d. purple on yellow ..	2·75	1·50
50	4d. brown and blue ..	3·00	17·00
76	4d. black and red on yellow	80	65
63	5d. grey and black ..	9·50	12·00
77	5d. orange and purple ..	1·00	1·25
51	6d. green and red ..	3·25	9·50
78	6d. purple	1·50	2·25
65	7½d. green and red ..	5·00	19·00
79	7½d. brown and blue ..	1·25	2·50
80	10d. green and red ..	1·75	6·50
67	1s. mauve nad green ..	15·00	45·00
81	1s. black on green ..	2·00	9·50
53	1s. 6d. green & red on yell	5·50	15·00
82	1s. 6d. violet and green ..	8·50	28·00
54	2s. grey and orange ..	30·00	48·00
83	2s. purple and blue on blue	6·00	17·00
55	2s. 6d. purple & brn on yell	15·00	48·00
84	2s. 6d. black & red on blue	21·00	18·00
56	3s. red and green on yellow	17·00	48·00
85	3s. yellow and green ..	22·00	40·00

1906. Surch. in words.

69.	½d. on 2s. 6d. (No. 55) ..	40·00	60·00
70.	1d. on 3s. (No. 56) ..	55·00	35·00

1912. As T 2, but portrait of King George V.

86	½d. green..	45	70
87a	1d. red	90	30
88	1½d. olive and green ..	30	30
89	2d. grey	45	1·25
112	2½d. blue..	50	3·50
91	3d. purple on yellow ..	30	30
92c	4d. black & red on yellow	1·50	6·00
93	5d. orange and purple ..	50	1·25
94	6d. purple	50	90
95	7½d. brown and blue ..	80	4·00
96a	10d. green and red ..	1·50	15·00
97	1s. black on green ..	60	1·00
98	1s. 6d. violet and green..	5·00	9·00
99	2s. purple & blue on blue	2·25	6·00
100	2s. 6d. black & red on blue	2·50	11·00
101	3s. yellow and green ..	7·50	17·00
117	4s. black and red ..	40·00	70·00
102	5s. green & red on yellow	48·00	70·00

9. 10.

1922.

122.	9.	½d. blk. and green ..	55	40
124.		1d. black and brown ..	70	10
125.		1½d. black and red ..	80	10
126.		2d. black and grey ..	1·00	90
127.		2½d. black and orange	90	6·00
128.		3d. black and blue ..	85	10
118.		4d. black & red on yell.	1·75	1·50
130.		5d. black and olive ..	2·00	10·00
131.		6d. black and red ..	1·25	20
119.		7½d. black & pur. on yell.	1·75	6·50
133.		10d. black and blue ..	4·50	17·00
134.	10.	1s. black & pur. on yell.	2·25	30
135.		1s. 6d. black and blue..	9·00	12·00
136.		2s. black & pur. on blue	3·25	3·00
137.		2s. 6d. black and green	3·75	9·50
138.		3s. black and purple ..	11·00	32·00
140.		4s. black and brown ..	4·00	16·00
141.		5s. black & grn. on yell.	9·50	28·00
142.		10s. black and olive ..	65·00	85·00

1935. Silver Jubilee. As T **13** of **Antigua.**

143.	1½d. blue and red ..	50	30
144.	3d. brown and blue ..	55	70
145.	6d. blue and olive ..	90	90
146.	1s. grey and purple ..	2·25	1·25

1937. Coronation. As T **2** of Aden.

147.	1d. brown	30	15
148.	1½d. red	30	30
149.	3d. blue	80	45

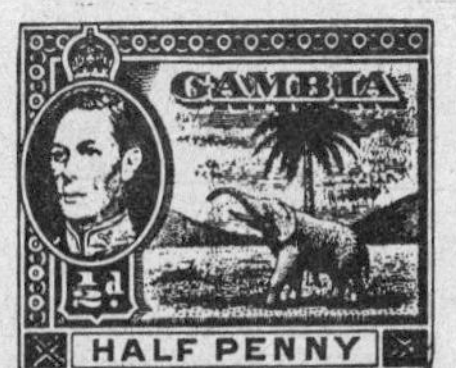

11. Elephant (from Colony Badge).

1938.

150	11	½d. black and green ..	15	40
151		1d. purple and brown	20	30
152b		1½d. pink and red ..	30	60
152c		1½d. blue and black ..	30	70
153		2d. blue and black ..	80	1·75
153a		2d. pink and red ..	40	60
154		3d. blue..	30	10
154a		5d. green and purple ..	45	45
155		6d. olive and red ..	85	35
156		1s. blue and purple ..	1·25	10
156a		1s. 3d. purple and blue	1·50	1·25
157		2s. red and blue ..	4·25	3·25
158		2s. 6d. brown and green	11·00	2·00
159		4s. red and purple ..	17·00	2·50
160		5s. blue and red ..	17·00	4·00
161		10s. orange and black ..	17·00	9·00

1946. Victory. As T **9** of Aden.

162.	1½d. black	10	10
163.	3d. blue	10	10

1948. Silver Wedding. As T **10/11** of Aden.

164.	1½d. black	25	10
165.	£1 mauve	12·00	12·00

1949. U.P.U. As T **20/23** of Antigua.

166.	1½d. black	40	30
167.	3d. blue	80	30
168.	6d. mauve	80	30
169.	1s. violet..	80	30

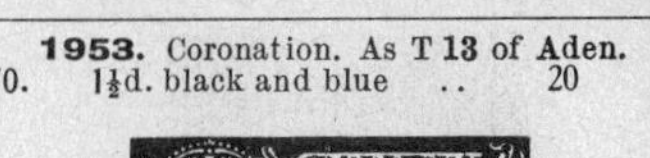

1953. Coronation. As T **13** of Aden.

170.	1½d. black and blue ..	20	30

12. Tapping for Palm Wine.

1953. Queen Elizabeth II.

171.	12.	½d. red and green ..	30	20
172.	–	1d. blue and brown ..	40	20
173.	–	1½d. brown and black ..	20	50
174.	–	2½d. black and red ..	45	70
175.	–	3d. blue and lilac ..	35	10
176.	–	4d. black and blue ..	60	1·75
177.	12.	6d. brown and purple ..	35	15
178.	–	1s. brown and green ..	60	15
179.	–	1s. 3d. ultram. and blue	8·00	40
180.	–	2s. blue and red ..	5·00	3·00
181.	–	2s. 6d. green and brown	3·50	1·25
182.	–	4s. blue and brown ..	4·50	1·50
183.	–	5s. brown and blue ..	2·50	1·50
184.	–	10s. blue and green ..	11·00	6·50
185.	–	£1 green and black ..	11·00	9·50

DESIGNS—HORIZ. 1d., 1s. 3d. Cutter (sailing ship). 1½d., 5s. Wollof woman. 2½d., 2s. Barra canoe. 3d., 10s. S.S. "Lady Wright". 4d., 4s. James Island. 1s., 2s. 6d. Woman hoeing. £1 as Type **11**.

20. Queen Elizabeth II and Palm.

1961. Royal Visit.

186.	20.	2d. green and purple ..	15	15
187.	–	3d. turquoise and sepia	35	15
188.	–	6d. blue and red ..	35	30
189.	20.	1s. 3d. violet and green	35	90

DESIGN: 3d., 6d. Queen Elizabeth II and West African map.

1963. Freedom from Hunger. As T **28** of Aden.

190.	1s. 3d. red	40	15

1963. Cent of Red Cross. As T **33** of Antigua.

191.	2d. red and black ..	15	10
192.	1s. 3d. red and blue ..	40	35

22. Beautiful Sunbird.

1963. Queen Elizabeth II. Multicoloured.

193.	½d. Type **22**	20	40
194.	1d. Yellow-mantled Whydah	30	30
195.	1½d. Cattle Egret	1·00	60
196.	2d. Senegal Parrot ..	1·00	50
197.	3d. Rose-ringed Parakeet..	1·40	30
198.	4d. Violet Starling ..	75	60
199.	6d. Village Weaver ..	1·40	10
200.	1s. Rufous-crowned Roller	60	10
201.	1s. 3d. Red-eyed Dove ..	10·00	1·40
202.	2s. 6d. Double-spurred Francolin	8·00	2·25
203.	5s. Palm-nut Vulture ..	6·00	2·75
204.	10s. Orange-cheeked Waxbill	12·00	7·00
205.	£1 African Emerald Cuckoo	24·00	14·00

1963. New Constitution. Nos. 194, 197 and 200/1 optd. **SELF GOVERNMENT 1963.**

206.	1d. multicoloured ..	10	20
207.	3d. multicoloured ..	20	10
208.	1s. multicoloured.. ..	20	10
209.	1s. 3d. multicoloured ..	25	35

1964. 400th Birth Anniv of Shakespeare. As T **34** of Antigua.

210.	6d. blue	10	10

36. Gambia Flag and River.

1965. Independence. Multicoloured.

211.	½d. Type **36**	10	15
212.	2d. Arms	10	10
213.	7½d. Type **36**	20	20
214.	1s. 6d. Arms	25	20

1985. Nos. 193/205 optd. **INDEPENDENCE 1965.** Multicoloured.

215	½d. Type **22**	30	30
216	1d. Yellow-mantled whydah	30	10
217	1½d. Cattle egret	60	30
218	2d. Senegal parrot ..	70	15
219	3d. Rose-ringed parakeet	70	15
220	4d. Violet starling ..	70	30
221	6d. Village weaver ..	70	10
222	1s. Rufous-crowned roller	70	10
223	1s. 3d. Red-eyed dove ..	70	10
224	2s. 6d. Double-spurred francolin	70	15
225	5s. Palm-nut vulture ..	70	40
226	10s. Orange-cheeked waxbill	1·60	1·50
227	£1 African emerald cuckoo	4·00	6·00

39. I.T.U. Emblem and Symbols.

1965. Centenary of I.T.U.

228.	**39.**	1d silver and blue ..	15	10
229.		1s 6d. gold and violet	55	15

40. Sir Winston Churchill and Houses of Parliament.

1966. Churchill Commem.

230.	**40.**	1d. multicoloured ..	10	10
231.		6d. multicoloured ..	20	10
232.		1s. 6d. multicoloured ..	40	30

41. Red-cheeked Cordon-bleu.

1966. Birds. Multicoloured.

233.	½d. Type **41** ..	50	20
234.	1d. White-faced Whistling Duck	30	15
235	1½d. Red-throated Bee Eater	30	20
236.	2d. Lesser Pied Kingfisher	3·25	30
237.	3d. Golden Bishop ..	30	10
238.	4d. African Fish Eagle ..	50	30
239.	6d. Yellow-bellied Green Pigeon	40	10
240.	1s. Blue-bellied Roller ..	40	10
241.	1s. 6d. African Pigmy Kingfisher	85	30
242.	2s. 6d. Spur-winged Goose	95	70
243.	5s. Cardinal Woodpecker ..	1·00	75
244.	10s. Violet Turaco	1·25	2·75
245.	£1 Pin-tailed Whydah (Size 25 × 39½ mm.) ..	1·25	5·50

54. Arms, Early Settlement and Modern Buildings.

1966. 150th Anniversary of Bathurst.

246.	**54.**	1d. silver, brown & orge.	10	10
247.		2d. silver, brown & blue	10	10
248.		6d. silver, brown & grn.	10	10
249.		1s. 6d. silver, brn. & pur.	15	15

55. I.T.Y. Emblem and Hotels.

1967. Int. Tourist Year.

250.	**55.**	2d. silver, brown & green	10	10
251.		1s. silver, brown & orge.	10	10
252.		1s. 6d. silver, brn. & mve.	15	15

56. Handcuffs.

1968. Human Rights Year. Multicoloured.

253.	1d. Type **56**	10	10
254.	1s. Fort Bullen	10	10
255.	5s. Methodist Church ..	30	30

59. Queen Victoria, Queen Elizabeth II and 4d. stamp of 1869.

1969. Gambia Stamp Centenary.

256.	**59.**	4d. sepia and ochre ..	20	10
257.		6d. blue and green ..	20	10
258.	–	2s. 6d. multicoloured ..	70	55

DESIGN: 2s. 6d. Queen Elizabeth II with 4d. and 6d. stamps of 1869.

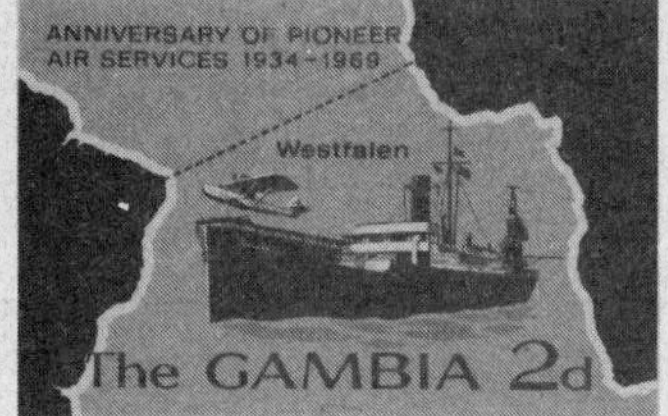

61. Catapult-Ship "Westfalen" launching Dornier "Wal".

1969. 35th Anniv. of Pioneer Air Service. Multicoloured.

259.	2d. Type **61**	55	20
260.	1s. Dornier "Wal" flying-boat	65	20
261.	1s. 6d. "Graf Zeppelin" airship	80	1·00

63. Athlete and Gambian Flag.

1970. 9th British Commonwealth Games, Edinburgh.

262.	**63.**	1d. multicoloured ..	10	10
263.		1s. multicoloured ..	10	10
264.		5s. multicoloured ..	30	30

64. President Sir Dawda Kairaba Jawara and State House.

1970. Republic Day. Multicoloured.

265.	2d. Type **64**	10	10
266.	1s. President Sir Dawda Jawara	15	10
267.	1s. 6d. President and flag of Gambia	30	20

The 1s. and 1s. 6d. are both vertical designs.

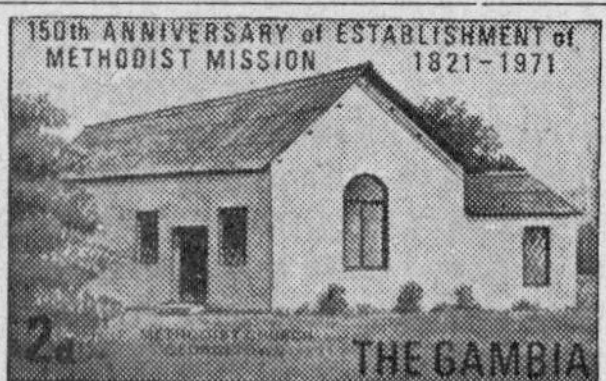

65. Methodist Church, Georgetown.

1971. 150th Anniversary of Establishment of Methodist Mission. Multicoloured.

268.	2d. Type **65**	10	10
269.	1s. Map of Africa and Gambian flag (vert.) ..	15	10
270.	1s. 6d. John Wesley and scroll	15	20

66. Yellowfin Tunny.

1971. New Currency. Fishes. Multicoloured.

271.	2 b. Type **66**	10	40
272.	4 b. Peters' Mormyrid ..	10	15
273.	6 b. Tropical Flying Fish	15	40
274.	8 b. African Sleeper Goby	15	40
275.	10 b. Yellowtail Snapper	20	15
276.	13 b. Rock Hind	20	40
277.	25 b. Gymnallabes ..	35	40
278.	38 b. Tiger Shark ..	55	45
279.	50 b. Electric Catfish ..	70	55
280.	63 b. Black Synbranchus	80	1·50
281.	1 d. 25 Smalltooth Sawfish	1·75	2·50
282.	2 d. 50 Barracuda ..	4·00	4·50
283.	5 d. Brown Bullhead ..	5·50	7·00

67. Mungo Park in Scotland.

1971. Birth Cent. of Mungo Park. Mult.

284.	4 b. Type **67**	20	10
285.	25 b. Dug-out canoe ..	35	25
286.	37 b. Death of Mungo Park, Busa Rapids	55	75

68. Radio Gambia.

1972. 10th Anniv. of Radio Gambia.

287.	**68.**	4 b. brown and black ..	10	10
288.	–	25 b. blue, orge. & blk.	10	25
289.	**68.**	37 b. green and black ..	20	50

DESIGN: 25 b. Broadcast-area map.

69. High-jumping.

1972. Olympic Games, Munich.

290.	**69.**	4 b. multicoloured ..	10	10
291.		25 b. multicoloured ..	15	15
292.		37 b. multicoloured ..	15	20

70. Manding Woman.

1972. Int. Conf. on Manding Studies. **Mult.**

293.	2 b. Type **70**	10	10
294.	25 b. Musician playing the Kora	15	15
295.	37 b. Map of Mali Empire	25	25

71. Children carrying Fanal.

1972. Fanals (Model Boats). **Multicoloured.**

296.	2 b. Type **71**	10	10
297.	1 d. 25 Fanal with lanterns	30	45

72. Groundnuts.

1973. Freedom from Hunger Campaign.

298.	**72.**	2 b. multicoloured ..	10	10
299.		25 b. multicoloured ..	15	10
300.		37 b. multicoloured ..	25	20

73. Planting and Drying Rice.

1973. Agriculture (1st series). **Multicoloured.**

301.	2 b. Type **73**	10	10
302.	25 b. Guinea Corn ..	20	15
303.	37 b. Rice	25	25

74. Oil Palm.

1973. Agriculture (2nd series). Mult.

304.	2 b. Type **74**	10	10
305.	25 b. Limes	30	30
306.	37 b. Oil Palm (fruits) ..	40	40

75. Cassava.

1973. Agriculture (3rd series). Multicoloured.
307. 2 b. Type **75** 10 10
308. 50 b. Cotton 40 25

76. O.A.U. Emblem.

1973. 10th Anniversary of O.A.U.
309. **76.** 4 b. multicoloured 10 10
310. 25 b. multicoloured 15 10
311. 37 b. multicoloured 15 20

77. Red Cross.

1973. 25th Anniv. of Gambian Red Cross.
312. **77.** 4 b. red and black 10 10
313. 25 b. red black & blue 15 15
314. 37 b. red, black & green 20 20

78. Arms of Banjul.

1973. Change of Bathurst's Name to Banjul.
315. **78.** 4 b. multicoloured 10 10
316. 25 b. multicoloured 15 15
317. 37 b. multicoloured 15 20

79. U.P.U. Emblem.

1974. Centenary of U.P.U.
318. **79.** 4 b. multicoloured 10 10
319. 37 b. multicoloured 20 30

80. Churchill as Harrow Schoolboy.

1974. Birth Centenary of Sir Winston Churchill. Multicoloured.
320. 4 b. Type **80** 10 10
321. 37 b. Churchill as 4th Hussars officer 25 15
322. 50 b. Churchill as Prime Minister 40 50

81. " Different Races ".

1974. World Population Year. Multicoloured.
323. 4 b. Type **81** 10 10
324. 37 b. " Multiplication and Division of Races " 15 15
325. 50 b. " World Population " 20 25

82. Dr. Schweitzer and River Scene.

1975. Birth Centenary of Dr. Albert Schweitzer. Multicoloured.
326. 10 b. Type **82** 20 10
327. 50 b. Surgery scene 55 25
328. 1 d. 25 River journey 1·00 55

83. Dove of Peace.

1975. 10th Anniv. of Independence. Mult.
329. 4 b. Type **83** 10 10
330. 10 b. Gambian flag 10 10
331. 50 b. Gambian arms 15 10
332. 1 d. 25 Map of The Gambia 35 40

84. Development Graph.

1975. 10th Anniversary of African Development Bank. Multicoloured.
333. 10 b. Type **84** 10 10
334. 50 b. Symbolic plant 20 15
335. 1 d. 25 Bank emblem and symbols 55 60

85. " Statue of David " (Michelangelo).

1975. 500th Birth Anniv. of Michelangelo. Multicoloured.
336. 10 b. Type **85** 15 10
337. 50 b. " Madonna of the Steps " 35 10
338. 1 d. 25 " Battle of the Centaurs " (horiz.) 60 60

86. School Building.

1975. Centenary of Gambia High School. Multicoloured.
339. 10 b. Type **86** 10 10
340. 50 b. Pupil with scientific apparatus 15 10
341. 1 d. 50 School crest 35 35

87. " Teaching ".

1975. International Women's Year. Mult.
342. 4 b. Type **87** 10 10
343. 10 b. " Planting rice " 10 10
344. 50 b. " Nursing " 35 15
345. 1 d. 50 " Directing traffic " 85 35

88. Woman playing Golf.

1975. 11th Anniversary of Independence. Multicoloured.
346. 10 b. Type **88** 30 10
347. 50 b. Man playing golf 1·10 20
348. 1 d. 50 President playing golf 2·00 70

89. American Militiaman.

1976. Bicent. of American Revolution. Mult.
349. 25 b. Type **89** 30 10
350. 50 b. Soldier of the Continental Army 50 20
351. 1 d. 25 Independence Declaration 80 60

90. Mother and Child.

1976. Christmas.
353. **90.** 10 b. multicoloured 10 10
354. 50 b. multicoloured 15 10
355. 1 d. 25 multicoloured 50 45

91. Serval Cat.

1976. Abuko Nature Reserve (1st series). Multicoloured.
356. 10 b. Type **91** 60 10
357. 20 b. Bushbuck 1·00 20
358. 50 b. Sitatunga (deer) 1·75 40
359. 1 d. 25 Leopard 3·00 1·25

See also Nos. 400/3, 431/4 and 460/3.

92. Festival Emblem and Gambian Weaver.

1977. 2nd World Black and African Festival of Arts and Culture, Nigeria.
361. **92.** 25 b. multicoloured 15 10
362. 50 b. multicoloured 20 15
363. 1 d. 25 multicoloured 50 70

93. The Spurs and Jewelled Sword.

1977. Silver Jubilee. Multicoloured.
365. 25 b. The Queen's visit, 1961 50 50
366. 50 b. Type **93** 30 30
367. 1 d. 25 Oblation of the Sword 60 60

94. Stone Circles, Kuntaur.

1977. Tourism. Multicoloured.
368. 25 b. Type **94** 10 10
369. 50 b. Ruined Fort, James Island 20 20
370. 1 d. 25 Mungo Park Monument 70 70

95. Widow of Last Year.

1977. Flowers and Shrubs. Multicoloured.
371 2 b. Type **95** 10 15
372 4 b. White Water-lily 10 30
373 6 b. Fireball Lily 10 30
374 8 b. Cocks-comb 10 15
375 10 b. Broad Leaved Ground Orchid 1·50 30
376 13 b. Fibre Plant (yellow background) 15 40
376a 13 b. Fibre Plant (grey background) 3·50 3·00
377 25 b. False Kapok 15 15
378 38 b. Baobab 25 55
379 50 b. Coral Tree 35 35
380 63 b. Gloriosa Lily 40 70
381 1 d. 25 Bell-flowered Mimosa 70 1·25
382 2 d. 50 Kindin Dolo 75 1·25
383 5 d. African Tulip Tree 1·25 2·00

Nos. 373/78 and 381/2 are vert. designs.

96. Endangered Animals.

1977. Banjul Declaration.

384. 96.	10 b. black and blue ..	15	10
385. –	25 b. multicoloured ..	40	10
386. –	50 b. multicoloured ..	65	20
387. –	1 d. 25 black and red ..	1·40	75

DESIGNS: 25 b. Extract from Declaration. 50 b. Declaration in full. 1 d. 25, Endangered insects and flowers.

97. " Flight into Egypt ".

1977. 400th Birth Anniv. of Rubens. Mult.

388.	10 b. Type 97	15	10
389.	25 b. " The Education of the Virgin "	25	10
390.	50 b. " Clara Serena Rubens "	50	30
391.	1 d. " Madonna with Saints "	90	90

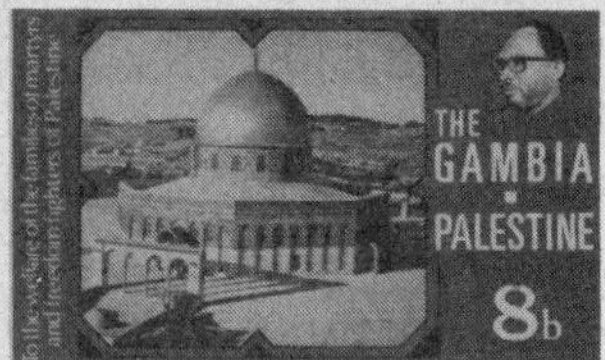

98. Dome of the Rock, Jerusalem.

1978. Palestinian Welfare.

392. 98.	8 b. multicoloured ..	50	15
393.	25 b. multicoloured ..	2·00	85

99. Walking on a Greasy Pole.

1978. 13th Anniv. of Independence. Mult.

394.	10 b. Type 99	10	10
395.	50 b. Pillow fighting ..	15	10
396.	1 d. Long boat rowing ..	35	45

100. Lion.

1978. 25th Anniversary of Coronation.

397. –	1 d. black, brown & yell.	35	60
398. –	1 d. multicoloured ..	35	60
399. 100.	1 d. black, brn. & yell	35	60

DESIGNS: No. 397, White Greyhound of Richmond. No. 398, Queen Elizabeth II.

101. Verreaux's Eagle Owl.

1978. Abuko Nature Reserve (2nd series). Multicoloured.

400.	20 b. Type 101	2·00	30
401.	25 b. Lizard buzzard ..	2·00	30
402.	50 b. African Harrier hawk	3·50	1·75
403.	1 d. 25 Long-crested eagle	6·00	6·00

102. M.V. " Lady Wright ".

1978. Launching of River Vessel " Lady Chilel Jawara ". Multicoloured.

404.	8 b. Type 102	15	10
405.	25 b. Sectional view of " Lady Chilel Jawara "	40	25
406.	1 d. " Lady Chilel Jawara "	1·25	1·10

103. Police Service.

1979. 14th Anniv. of Independence. Mult.

407.	10 b. Type 103	60	10
408.	50 b. Fire Service ..	1·10	25
409.	1 d. 25 Ambulance Service	1·40	80

1979. Nos. 376 and 380/1 surch.

410.	25 b. on 13 b. Fibre Plant	20	35
411.	25 b. on 63 b. Gloriosa Lily	15	20
412.	25 b. on 1 d. 25, Bell-flowered Mimosa ..	15	20

105. " Ramsgate Sands " (detail showing children playing on beach).

1979. International Year of the Child. " Ramsgate Sands " (William Powell Frith). Multicoloured.

413.	10 b. Type 105	10	10
414.	25 b. Detail showing child paddling (vert.) ..	20	10
415.	1 d. Complete painting (60 × 23 mm.)	60	60

106. 1883 2½d. Stamp.

1979. Death Centenary of Sir Rowland Hill. Multicoloured.

416.	10 b. Type 106	10	10
417.	25 b. 1869 4d. stamp ..	15	10
418.	50 b. 1965 Independence 7½d. commemorative ..	20	20
419.	1 d. 25 1935 Silver Jubilee 1½d. commemorative ..	40	50

107. Satellite Earth Station under Construction.

1979. Abuko Satellite Earth Station. Mult.

421.	25 b. Type 107	20	10
422.	50 b. Satellite Earth Station (completed) ..	30	20
423.	1 d. " Intelsat " satellite	65	60

108. " Apollo 11 " leaving Launch Pad.

1979. 10th Anniv. of Moon Landing. Mult.

424.	25 b. Type 108	20	10
425.	38 b. " Apollo 11 " in Moon orbit	25	20
426.	50 b. Splashdown ..	30	40
430.	2 d. Lunar module on Moon	1·50	1·75

Nos. 424/6 also exist self-adhesive from booklet panes. No. 430 only exists in this form.

109. "Acraea zetes".

1980. Abuko Nature Reserve (3rd series). Butterflies. Multicoloured.

431	25 b. Type 109	35	20
432	50 b. "Precis hierta" ..	55	40
433	1 d. "Graphium leonidas"	85	80
434	1 d. 25 "Charaxes jasius"	90	85

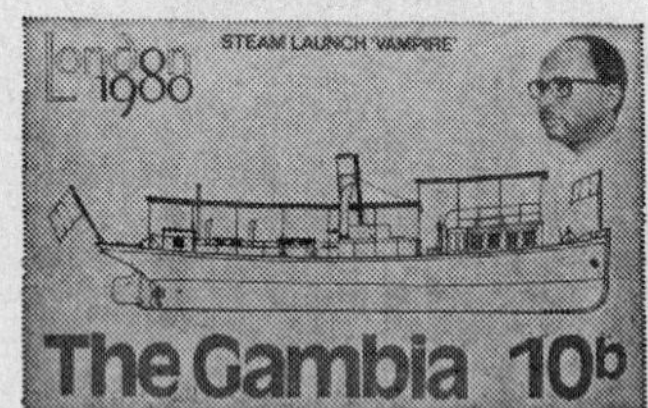

110. Steam Launch " Vampire ".

1980. " London 1980 " International Stamp Exhibition. Multicoloured.

436.	10 b. Type 110	15	10
437.	25 b. T.S.S. " Lady Denham "	20	10
438.	50 b. T.S.C.M.Y. " Mansa Kila Ba "	30	20
439.	1 d. 25 T.S.S. " Prince of Wales "	50	60

Nos. 438 and 439 are larger, 50 × 28 mm.

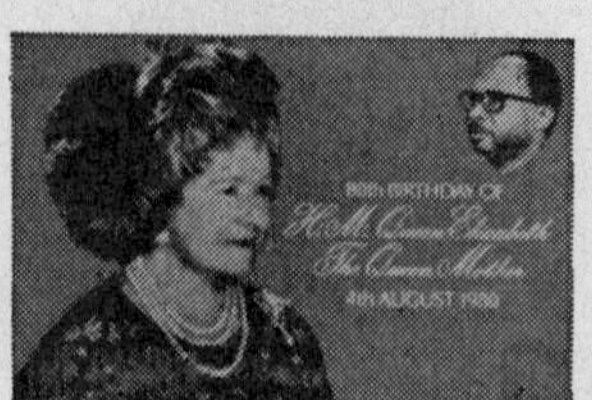

111. Queen Elizabeth the Queen Mother.

1980. 80th Birthday of The Queen Mother.

440. 111.	67 b. multicoloured ..	30	35

INDEX

Countries can be quickly located by referring to the index at the end of this volume.

112. Phoenician Trading Vessel.

1980. Early Sailing Vessels. Multicoloured.

441.	8 b. Type 112	10	10
442.	67 b. Egyptian sea-going vessel	30	20
443.	75 b. Portuguese caravel ..	40	30
444.	1 d. Spanish galleon ..	65	50

113. " Madonna and Child " (Francesco de Mura).

1980. Christmas. Multicoloured.

445.	8 b. Type 113	10	10
446.	67 b. " Praying Madonna with Crown of Stars " (workshop of Correggio)	25	25
447.	75 b. " La Zingarella " (workshop replica of Correggio painting) ..	25	30

114. New Atlantic Hotel.

1981. World Tourism Conference, Manila. Multicoloured.

448.	25 b. Type 114	15	10
449.	75 b. Ancient stone circles	40	40
450.	85 b. Conference emblem	50	50

115. 1979 Abuko Satellite Earth Station 50 b. Commemorative.

1981. World Telecommunications Day.

451. 115.	50 b. multicoloured ..	55	30
452. –	50 b. multicoloured ..	55	30
453. –	85 b. black and brown	80	55

DESIGNS: No. 452, 1975 Schweitzer Birth Cent. 50 b. Commemorative. No. 453, I.T.U. and W.H.O. emblems.

116. Prince Charles in Naval Uniform.

1981. Royal Wedding. Multicoloured.

454.	75 b. Wedding bouquet from Gambia	30	20
455.	1 d. Type 116	35	30
456.	1 d. 25 Prince Charles and Lady Diana Spencer ..	40	35

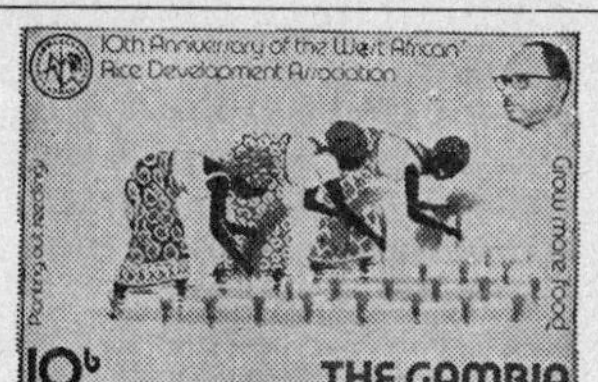

117. Planting-out Seedlings.

1981. 10th Anniversary of West African Rice Development Association. Mult.

457. 10 b. Type **117** 10 10
458. 50 b. Care of the Crops .. 35 35
459. 85 b. Winnowing and drying 55 55

118. Bosc's Monitor.

1981. Abuko Nature Reserve (4th series). Reptiles. Mult.

460. 40 b. Type **118** 60 20
461. 60 b. Dwarf Crocodile .. 90 45
462. 80 b. Royal Python .. 1·40 75
463. 85 b. Chameleon .. .. 1·50 80

119. Examination Room.

1982. 30th Anniversary of West African Examinations Council. Multicoloured.

464. 60 b. Type **119** 50 30
465. 85 b. First High School .. 65 45
466. 1 d. 10 Council's office .. 85 55

1982. No. 454 surch. **60 B.**

467. 60 b. on 75 b. Wedding bouquet from Gambia .. 2·00 2·50

121. Tree-planting (" Conservation ").

1982. 75th Anniv. of Boy Scout Movement. Multicoloured.

468. 85 b. Type **121** .. .. 1·75 1·25
469. 1 d. 25 Woodworking .. 2·00 2·25
470. 1 d. 27 Lord Baden-Powell 2·25 2·75

122. Gambia Football Team.

1982. World Cup Football Championship, Spain. Multicoloured.

471. 10 b. Type **122** 15 10
472. 1 d. 10 Gambian team practice 85 70
473. 1 d. 25 Bernabeu Stadium, Madrid 90 75
474. 1 d. 55 FIFA World Cup .. 95 80

123. Gambia Coat of Arms.

1982. 21st Birthday of Princess of Wales. Multicoloured.

476. 10 b. Type **123** 10 10
477. 85 b. Princess at City Hall, Cardiff, October 1981 .. 35 30
478. 1 d. 10 Bride and groom returning to Buckingham Palace 45 45
479. 2 d. 50 Formal portrait .. 90 1·25

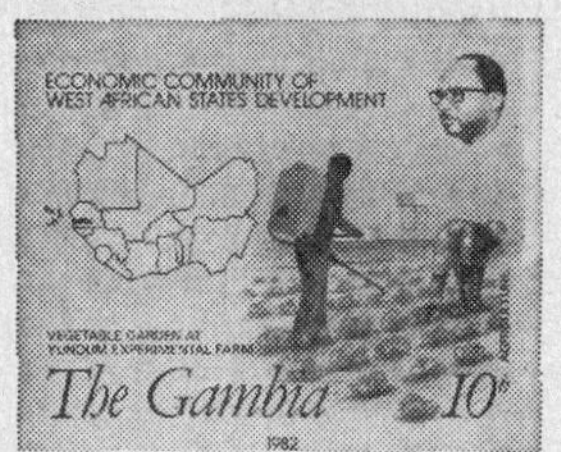

124. Vegetable Garden at Yundum Experimental Farm.

1982. Economic Community of West African States Development. Multicoloured.

480. 10 b. Type **124** 30 15
481. 60 b. Banjul/Kaolack microwave tower .. .. 1·50 1·50
482. 90 b. Soap factory, Denton Bridge, Banjul .. .. 1·75 2·00
483. 1 d. 25 Control tower, Yundum Airport .. 1·90 2·50

125. " Kassina cassinoides ".

1982. Frogs. Multicoloured.

484. 10 b. Type **125** 50 15
485. 20 b. " Hylarana galamensis " 80 25
486. 85 b. " Euphlyctis occipitalis " .. .. .. 1·50 1·40
487. 2 d. " Kassina senegalensis " 2·75 3·75

126. Satellite View of Gambia.

1983. Commonwealth Day. Multicoloured.

488. 10 b. Type **126** 10 10
489. 60 b. Batik cloth 30 45
490. 1 d. 10 Bagging groundnuts 50 65
491. 2 d. 10 Gambia flag .. 90 1·25

127. Blessed Anne Marie Javouhey (foundress of Order).

1983. Centenary of Sisters of St. Joseph of Cluny's Work in Gambia. Multicoloured.

492. 10 b. Type **127** 10 10
493. 85 b. Bathurst Hospital, nun and school children (horiz.) 45 50

128. Canoes.

1983. River Craft. Multicoloured.

494 1 b. Type **128** 15 30
495 2 b. Upstream ferry .. 20 30
496 3 b. Dredger 20 30
497 4 b. "Sir Dawda" (harbour launch) 30 30
498 5 b. Cargo liner 30 30
499 10 b. "Lady Dale" (60 ft. launch) 30 10
500 20 b. "Shonga" (container ship) 45 30
501 30 b. Large sailing canoe 45 30
502 40 b. "Lady Wright" (river steamer) 65 45
503 50 b. Container ship (different) 65 45
504 75 b. Fishing boats .. 75 45
505 1 d. Tug with groundnut barges 90 55
506 1 d. 25 Groundnut canoe 1·00 75
507 2 d. 50 "Banjul" (car ferry) 1·75 2·25
508 5 d. "Bintang Bolong" (freighter) .. .. 2·50 3·50
509 10 d. "Lady Chilel Jawara" (river vessel) .. .. 4·00 5·50

129. Osprey in Tree.

1983. The Osprey. Multicoloured.

510. 10 b. Type **129** 85 20
511. 60 b. Osprey .. .. 1·75 1·50
512. 85 b. Osprey with catch .. 2·00 2·00
513. 1 d. 10 In flight .. .. 2·25 3·00

130. Local Ferry.

1983. World Communications Year. Mult.

514. 10 b. Type **130** 10 10
515. 85 b. Telex operator .. 45 50
516. 90 b. Radio Gambia .. 45 50
517. 1 d. 10 Loading mail into aircraft 60 65

131. " St. Paul preaching at Athens " (detail).

1983. 500th Birth Anniversary of Raphael.

518. 131. 60 b. multicoloured .. 35 40
519. – 85 b. multicoloured .. 45 50
520. – 1 d. multicoloured .. 50 55

Nos. 519/20 show different details of " St. Paul preaching at Athens ".

132. Early Balloon and Siege of Paris Cover.

1983. Bicentenary of Manned Flight. Mult.

522. 60 b. Type **132** 35 40
523. 85 b. Lufthansa aircraft and flown cover .. 45 50
524. 90 b. Junkers aircraft and Hans Bertram cover .. 45 50
525. 1 d. 25 Lunar Module and H.E. Sieger's space cover 65 70
526. 4 d. "Graf Zeppelin" (airship) .. .. .. 2·00 2·50

133. Shot-putting.

1984. Olympic Games Los Angeles (1st issue). Multicoloured.

527. 60 b. Type **133** 25 30
528. 85 b. High jumping (horiz.) 35 40
529. 90 b. Wrestling 35 40
530. 1 d. Gymnastics 40 45
531. 1 d. 25 Swimming (horiz.) 50 55
532. 2 d. Diving 80 85

See also Nos. 555/8.

134. Goofy.

1984. Easter. Multicoloured.

534. 1 b. Type **134** 10 10
535. 2 b. Mickey Mouse .. 10 10
536. 3 b. Huey, Dewey and Louie 10 10
537. 4 b. Goofy (different) .. 10 10
538. 5 b. Donald Duck 10 10
539. 10 b. Chip 'n' Dale .. 10 10
540. 60 b. Pluto 35 35
541. 90 b. Scrooge McDuck .. 50 50
542. 5 d. Morty and Ferdie .. 2·25 2·40

Nos. 534/42 show Walt Disney cartoon characters painting eggs.

135. Young Crocodiles hatching.

1984. The Nile Crocodiles. Multicoloured.

544. 4 b. Type **135** 10 10
545. 6 b. Adult carrying young 10 10
546. 90 b. Adult .. .. .. 1·00 1·25
547. 1 d. 50 Crocodile at riverbank .. .. .. 1·90 2·50

136. Port Banjul.

1984. 250th Anniv. of "Lloyd's List" (newspaper). Multicoloured.

549. 60 b. Type **136** 60 30
550. 85 b. Bulk carrier 75 60
551. 90 b. Sinking of the "Dagomba" 75 70
552. 1 d. 25 19th century frigate 1·25 1·25

1984. Universal Postal Union Congress Hamburg. Nos. 507/8 optd. **19th UPU CONGRESS HAMBURG.**

553. 2 d. 50 Banjul (car ferry) .. 1·25 1·10
554. 5 d. Bintang Bolong (ferry) 2·25 2·25

138. Sprinting.

1984. Olympic Games, Los Angeles (2nd issue). Multicoloured.

555.	60 b. Type **138**	25	30
556.	85 b. Long jumping ..	35	40
557.	90 b. Long-distance running	35	40
558.	1 d. 25 Triple jumping ..	50	55

139. "Graf Zeppelin".

1984. 50th Anniversary of Gambia-South America Trans-Atlantic Flights. Mult.

559.	60 b. Type **139**	1·10	1·00
560.	85 b. Dornier "Wal" on S.S. "Westfalen" ..	1·60	1·60
561.	90 b. Dornier "DO 18" ..	1·75	2·00
562.	1 d.25 Dornier "Wal" ..	1·75	2·25

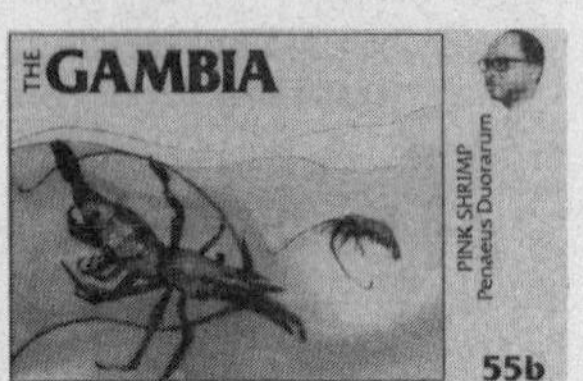

140. Pink Shrimp.

1984. Marine Life. Multicoloured.

563.	55 b. Type **140**	25	25
564.	75 b. Atlantic Loggerhead Turtle	40	35
565.	1 d. 50 Portuguese Man-of-War	70	70
566.	2 d. 35 Fiddler Crab ..	95	1·25

141. "Antanartia hippomene".

1984. Butterflies. Multicoloured.

568.	10 b. Type **141**	20	20
569.	85 b. "Pseudacraea eurytus"	70	70
570.	90 b. "Charaxes lactitinctus"	70	70
571.	3 d. "Graphium pylades"	1·75	2·75

142. Oral Re-hydration Therapy.

1985. Campaign for Child Survival.

573.	**142.** 10 b. blk., bl. and brn.	10	10
574.	– 85 b. multicoloured	35	40
575.	– 1 d. 10 multicoloured	45	50
576.	– 1 d. 50 multicoloured	60	65

DESIGNS: 85 b. Growth monitoring. 1 d. 10, Health care worker with women and babies ("Promotion of breast feeding"). 1 d. 50, Universal immunisation.

143. Women at Market.

1985. Women and Development. Mult.

577.	60 b. Type **143**	25	30
578.	85 b. Type **143**	35	40
579.	1 d. Woman office worker	40	45
580.	1 d. 25 As 1 d.	50	55

144. Turkey Vulture.

1985. Birth Bicentenary of John J. Audubon (ornithologist). Designs showing original paintings. Multicoloured.

581.	60 b. Type **144**	1·40	75
582.	85 b. American Anhinga ..	1·60	1·50
583.	1 d. 50 Green Heron ..	2·00	2·25
584.	5 d. Wood Duck	3·25	3·75

145. The Queen Mother.

1985. Life and Times of Queen Elizabeth the Queen Mother. Multicoloured.

586.	85 b. The Queen Mother and King George VI reviewing Home Guard	25	30
587.	3 d. Type **145**	80	85
588.	5 d. The Queen Mother with posy	1·40	1·50

1985. 150th Birth Anniversary of Mark Twain (author). Designs as T **118** of Anguilla showing Walt Disney cartoon characters in scenes from "Life on the Mississippi". Multicoloured.

590.	1 d. 50 Mickey Mouse steering the "Calamity Jane"	55	55
591.	2 d. Mickey and Minnie Mouse at antebellum mansion	70	70
592.	2 d. 50 Donald Duck and Goofy heaving the lead	85	85
593.	3 d. Poker game aboard the "Gold Dust" ..	1·00	1·00

1985. Birth Bicentenaries of Grimm Brothers (folklorists). As T **119** of Anguilla, but vert, showing Walt Disney cartoon characters in scenes from "Faithful John". Multicoloured.

595.	60 b. The King (Mickey Mouse) and portrait of the Princess (Minnie Mouse)	40	40
596.	85 b. The King showing the Princess his treasures ..	50	50
597.	2 d. 35, Faithful John (Goofy) playing trumpet	1·10	1·10
598.	5 d. Faithful John turned to stone	2·00	2·00

MINIMUM PRICE

The minimum price quoted is 10p which represents a handling charge rather than a basis for valuing common stamps. For further notes about prices see introductory pages.

1985. Olympic Gold Medal Winners, Los Angeles. Nos. 527/32 optd.

600.	60 b. Type **133** (optd. **GOLD MEDALLIST CLAUDIA LOCH WEST GERMANY**)	35	35
601.	85 b. High jumping (optd. **GOLD MEDALLIST ULRIKE MEYFARTH WEST GERMANY**) ..	45	45
602.	90 b. Wrestling (optd. **GOLD MEDALLIST PASQUALE PASSARELLI WEST GERMANY**)	45	45
603.	1 d. Gymnastics (optd. **GOLD MEDALLIST LI NING CHINA**)	50	50
604.	1 d. 25, Swimming (optd. **GOLD MEDALLIST MICHAEL GROSS WEST GERMANY**)	60	60
605.	2 d. Diving (optd. **GOLD MEDALLIST SYLVIE BERNIER CANADA**) ..	90	90

147. Inspecting Maize.

1985. United Nations Anniversaries. Mult.

607.	60 b. Type **147**	40	35
608.	85 b. Football match, Independence Stadium, Banjul	50	40
609.	1 d. 10 Rice fields	60	50
610.	2 d. Central Bank of The Gambia	85	75
611.	3 d. Cow and calf	1·50	1·40
612.	4 d. Banjul harbour ..	2·00	2·00
613.	5 d. Gambian fruits ..	2·25	2·25
614.	6 d. Oyster Creek Bridge ..	2·50	2·75

Nos. 607, 609, 611 and 613 commemorate the 40th anniversary of the Food and Agriculture Organization and Nos. 608, 610, 612 and 614 the 40th anniversary of the United Nations Organization.

148. Fishermen in Fotoba, Guinea.

1985. 50th Anniv. of Diocese of The Gambia and Guinea. Multicoloured.

615.	60 b. Type **148**	30	30
616.	85 b. St. Mary's Primary School, Banjul	30	40
617.	1 d. 10 St. Mary's Cathedral Banjul ..	35	65
618.	1 d. 50 Mobile dispensary at Christy Kunda ..	50	85

149. "Virgin and Child" (Dieric Bouts).

1985. Christmas. Religious Paintings. Mult.

619.	60 b. Type **149**	20	25
620.	85 b. "The Annunciation" (Robert Campin) ..	25	30
621.	1 d. 50 "Adoration of the Shepherds" (Gerard David)	45	50
622.	5 d. "The Nativity" (Gerard David)	1·60	1·75

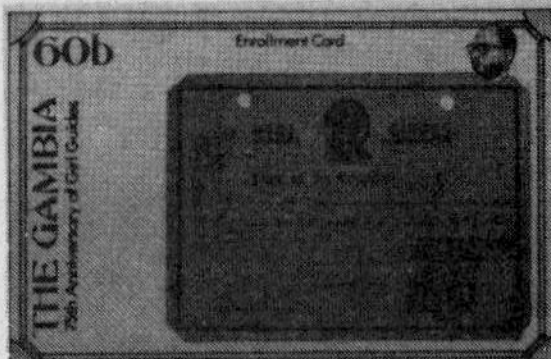

150. Enrolment Card.

1985. 75th Anniv. of Girl Guide Movement. Multicoloured.

624.	60 b. Type **150**	40	30
625.	85 b. 2nd Bathurst Company centre ..	50	35
626.	1 d. 50 Lady Baden-Powell (vert.)	70	80
627.	5 d. Miss Rosamond Fowlis (Gambian Guide Association leader) (vert.) ..	2·00	3·00

151. Girl and Village Scene.

1985. International Youth Year. Mult.

629.	60 b. Type **151**	25	30
630.	85 b. Youth and wrestling bout	30	35
631.	1 d. 10 Girl and Griot storyteller	40	65
632.	1 d. 50 Youth and crocodile pool	50	80

1986. Appearance of Halley's Comet. As T **123** of Anguilla. Multicoloured.

634.	10 b. Maria Mitchell (astronomer) and Kitt Peak National Observatory, Arizona	30	20
635.	20 b. Neil Armstrong, first man on Moon, 1969 ..	45	25
636.	75 b. "Skylab 4" and Comet Kohoutek, 1973 ..	75	65
637.	1 d. N.A.S.A.'s infra-red astronomical satellite and Halley's Comet ..	90	80
638.	2 d. Comet of 1577 from Turkish painting ..	1·40	1·40
639.	10 d. N.A.S.A's International Cometary Explorer	4·00	4·50

1986. 60th Birthday of Queen Elizabeth II. As T **125** of Anguilla.

641.	1 d. black and yellow ..	25	30
642.	2 d. 50 multicoloured ..	65	70
643.	10 d. multicoloured ..	2·50	2·75

DESIGNS: No. 641, Duke of York and family, Royal Tournament, 1936. 642, Queen attending christening, 1983. 643, In West Germany, 1978.

152. Two Players competing for Ball.

1986. World Cup Football Championship, Mexico. Multicoloured.

645.	75 b. Type **152**	60	60
646.	1 d. Player kicking ball ..	85	85
647.	2 d. 50 Player kicking ball (different)	1·75	1·75
648.	10 d. Player heading ball	4·50	5·00

153. Mercedes "500" (1986).

1986. "Ameripex" International Stamp Exhibition, Chicago. Centenary (1985) of First Benz Motor Car. Multicoloured.

650. 25 b. Type **153** 15 10
651. 75 b. Cord "810" (1935) .. 40 40
652. 1 d. Borgward "Isabella Coupe" (1957) 60 60
653. 1 d. 25 Lamborghini "Countach" (1985/6) .. 70 70
654. 2 d. Ford "Thunderbird" (1955) .. .. .. 1·25 1·25
655. 2 d. 25 Citroen "DS19" (1956) .. .. .. 1·40 1·40
656. 5 d. Bugatti "Atlante" (1936) .. .. .. 2·50 2·50
657. 10 d. Horch "853" (1936) .. 4·50 4·50

The 25 b. value is inscribed "MECEDES" and the 10 d. "LARL BENZ".

1986. Centenary of Statue of Liberty (1st issue). Multicoloured. As T **211** of Dominica, showing Statue of Liberty and immigrants to the U.S.A..

659. 20 b. John Jacob Astor (financier) 10 10
660. 1 d. Jacob Riis (journalist) 40 50
661. 1 d. 25 Igor Sikorsky (aeronautics engineer) .. 60 60
662. 5 d. Charles Boyer (actor) 2·50 2·50

See also Nos. 705/9.

1986. Royal Wedding. As T **213** of Antigua. Multicoloured.

664. 1 d. Prince Andrew and Miss Sarah Ferguson .. 40 45
665. 2 d. 50 Prince Andrew .. 1·00 1·40
666. 4 d. Prince Andrew as helicopter pilot .. .. 1·60 2·00

1986. World Cup Football Championship Winners, Mexico. Nos. 645/8 optd. **WINNERS Argentine 3 W. Germany 2.**

668. 75 b. Type **152** 30 40
669. 1 d. Player kicking ball .. 40 55
670. 2 d. 50 Player kicking ball (different) .. .. 1·00 1·25
671. 10 d. Player heading ball 4·25 4·75

154. Minnie Mouse (Great Britain).

1986. Christmas. Designs showing Walt Disney cartoon characters posting letters in various countries. Multicoloured.

673. 1 d. Type **154** 75 50
674. 1 d. 25 Huey (U.S.A.) .. 80 60
675. 2 d. Huey, Dewey and Louie (France) .. 1·25 85
676. 2 d. 35 Kanga and Roo (Australia) .. .. 1·40 90
677. 5 d. Goofy (Germany) .. 2·25 2·00

Nos. 673/7 also show the emblem of "Stockholmia '86" International Stamp Exhibition.

1986. Appearance of Halley's Comet (2nd issue). Nos. 634/9 optd as T **218** of Antigua.

679. 10 b. Maria Mitchell (astronomer) and Kitt Peak National Observatory, Arizona 30 15
680. 20 b. Neil Armstrong, first man on Moon, 1969 .. 50 20
681. 75 b. "Skylab 4" and Comet Kohoutek, 1973 .. 75 40
682. 1 d. N.A.S.A.'s infra-red astronomical satellite and Halley's Comet .. 85 45
683. 2 d. Comet of 1577 from Turkish painting .. 1·40 1·25
684. 10 d. N.A.S.A.'s International Cometary Explorer .. .. .. 3·75 4·00

155. Bugarab and Tabala.

1987. Manding Musical Instruments. Mult.

686. 75 b. Type **155** 15 20
687. 1 d. Balaphong and fiddle 15 25
688. 1 d. 25 Bolongbato and konting (vert.) 20 30
689. 10 d. Antique and modern koras (vert.) .. .. 1·60 2·00

156. "Snowing".

1987. Birth Centenary of Marc Chagall (artist). Multicoloured.

691. 75 b. Type **156** 25 25
692. 85 b. "The Boat" 30 30
693. 1 d. "Maternity" 35 35
694. 1 d. 25 "The Flute Player" 40 40
695. 2 d. 35 "Lovers and the Beast" 70 70
696. 4 d. "Fishes at Saint Jean" 1·00 1·00
697. 5 d. "Entering the Ring" 1·25 1·25
698. 10 d. "Three Acrobats" .. 2·00 2·00

157. "America", 1851.

1987. America's Cup Yachting Championship. Multicoloured.

700. 20 b. Type **157** 20 15
701. 1 d. "Courageous", 1974 .. 35 30
702. 2 d. 50 "Volunteer", 1887 75 75
703. 10 d. "Intrepid", 1967 .. 2·25 2·50

158. Arm of Statue of Liberty. **159.** "Lantana camara".

1987. Centenary of Statue of Liberty (1986) (2nd issue). Multicoloured.

705 1 b. Type **158** 10 10
706 2 b. Launch passing Statue (horiz) 10 10
707 3 b. Schooner passing Statue (horiz) 10 10
708 5 b. U.S.S. "John F. Kennedy" (aircraft carrier) and "Queen Elizabeth 2" (liner) (horiz) 10 10
709 50 b. Checking Statue for damage 25 25
710 75 b. Cleaning in progress 30 30
711 1 d. Working on Statue .. 40 40
712 1 d. 25 Statue and fireworks 45 45
713 10 d. Statue illuminated 2·25 2·25
714 12 d. Statue and fireworks (different) .. .. 2·50 2·50

1987. Flowers of Abuko Nature Reserve. Multicoloured.

715. 75 b. Type **159** 15 15
716. 1 d. "Clerodendrum thomsoniae" 15 20
717. 1 d. 50 "Haemanthus multiflorus" 25 30
718. 1 d. 70 "Gloriosa simplex" 25 30
719. 1 d. 75 "Combretum microphyllum" 30 35
720. 2 d. 25 "Eulophia quineensis" 35 40
721. 5 d. "Erythrina senegalensis" 80 85
722. 15 d. "Dichrostachys glomerata" .. .. 2·40 2·50

160. Front of Mail Bus. **161.** Basketball.

1987. "Capex '87" International Stamp Exhibition, Toronto and 10th Anniv. of Gambia Public Transport Corporation. Mail Buses. Multicoloured.

724. 20 b. Type **160** 15 10
725. 75 b. Bus in Banjul (horiz.) 25 25
726. 1 d. Passengers queueing for bus (horiz.) 25 25
727. 10 d. Two buses on rural road .. .. .. 2·00 2·75

1987. Olympic Games, Seoul (1988) (1st issue). Multicoloured.

729. 50 b. Type **161** 35 20
730. 1 d. Volleyball 50 35
731. 3 d. Hockey (horiz.) .. 1·10 85
732. 10 d. Handball (horiz.) .. 2·50 2·25

See also Nos. 779/82.

162. "A Partridge in a Pear Tree".

1987. Christmas. Multicoloured. Designs showing a Victorian couple in scenes from carol "The Twelve Days of Christmas".

734. 20 b. Type **162** 20 25
735. 40 b. "Two turtle doves" 20 25
736. 60 b. "Three French hens" 20 25
737. 75 b. "Four calling birds" 30 35
738. 1 d. "Five golden rings" .. 30 35
739. 1 d. 25 "Six geese a-laying" 40 45
740. 1 d. 50 "Seven swans a-swimming" 40 45
741. 2 d. "Eight maids a-milking" 50 55
742. 3 d. "Nine ladies dancing" 70 75
743. 5 d. "Ten lords a-leaping" 1·00 1·10
744. 10 d. "Eleven pipers piping" .. .. .. 1·60 1·75
745. 12 d. "Twelve drummers drumming" .. .. 1·90 2·00

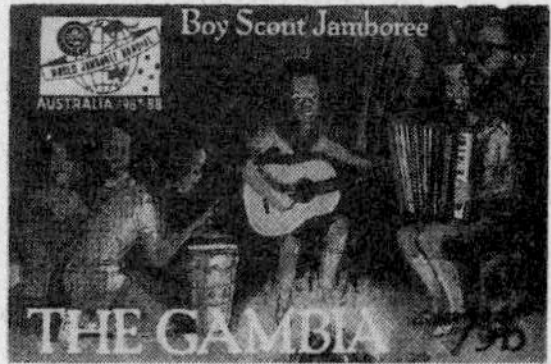

163. Campfire Singsong.

1987. World Scout Jamboree, Australia. Multicoloured.

747. 75 b. Type **163** 25 15
748. 1 d. Scouts examining African katydid .. 30 25
749. 1 d. 25 Scouts watching Red-tailed tropic bird .. 45 30
750. 12 d. Scouts helping bus passenger .. .. 2·50 3·00

1987. 60th Anniv of Mickey Mouse (Walt Disney cartoon character) (1st issue). As T **220** of Dominica. Multicoloured.

752. 60 b. Morty and Ferdie examining Trevithick's locomotive, 1804 .. 15 15
753. 75 b. Clarabelle Cow in "Empire State Express", 1893 .. .. 20 20
754. 1 d. Donald Duck inspecting Stephenson's "Rocket", 1829 .. .. 25 25
755. 1 d. 25 Piglet and Winnie the Pooh with Santa Fe Railway locomotive, 1920 .. .. .. 30 30
756. 2 d. Donald and Daisy Duck with Class "GG-1", Pennsylvannia Railway, 1933 .. .. .. 45 45
757. 5 d. Mickey Mouse in "Stourbridge Lion", 1829
758. 10 d. Goofy in "Best Friend of Charleston", 1830 .. .. .. 1·00 1·00 / 1·90 1·90
759. 12 d. Brer Bear and Brer Rabbit with Union Pacific No M10001, 1934 2·25 2·25

See also Nos. 849/57.

164 Common Duiker and Acacia

1988. Flora and Fauna. Multicoloured.

761 50 b. Type **164** 15 10
762 75 b. Red-billed hornbill and casuarina (vert) .. 20 15
763 90 b. West African dwarf crocodile and rice .. 20 20
764 1 d. Leopard and papyrus (vert) 20 20
765 1 d. 25 Crowned crane and millet 30 25
766 2 d. Waterbuck and baobab tree (vert) .. 35 35
767 3 d. Oribi and Senegal palm 50 55
768 5 d. Hippopotamus and papaya (vert) 80 85

165 Wedding Portrait, 1947

1988. Royal Ruby Wedding.

770 **165** 75 b. brn, blk & orge 30 15
771 – 1 d. brown, black & bl 40 20
772 – 3 d. multicoloured .. 90 80
773 – 10 d. multicoloured .. 2·25 2·75

DESIGNS: 1 d. Engagement photograph; 3 d. Wedding portrait, 1947 (different); 10 d. Queen Elizabeth II and Prince Philip (photo by Karsh), 1986.

1988. Stamp Exhibitions. Nos. 689, 703, 722 and 726 optd.

775 1 d. Passengers queuing for bus (optd **Independence 40**, Israel) .. 15 20
776 10 d. Antique and modern koras (optd **FINLANDIA 88**, Helsinki) .. .. 1·60 1·75
777 10 d. "Intrepid" (yacht), 1967 (optd **Praga '88**, Prague) .. .. 1·60 1·75
778 15 d. "Dichrostachys glomerata" (optd **OLYMPHILEX '88**, Seoul) .. .. .. 2·40 2·50

1988. Olympic Games, Seoul (2nd issue). As T **161**. Multicoloured.

779 1 d. Archery 15 20
780 1 d. 25 Boxing 20 25
781 5 d. Gymnastics 80 85
782 10 d. Start of 100 metre race (horiz) .. .. 1·60 1·75

166 Red Cross Flag

1988. Anniversaries and Events. Mult.

784 50 b. Type **166** (125th anniv) 40 40
785 75 b. "Friendship 7" spacecraft (25th anniv of first American manned Earth orbit) 50 50
786 1 d. British Airways "Concorde" (10th anniv of "Concorde" London –New York service) 75 75
787 1 d.25 "Spirit of St. Louis" (60th anniv of first solo transatlantic flight) 80 80
788 2 d. "X-15" (20th anniv of fastest aircraft flight) 1·10 1·10
789 3 d. Bell "X-1" rocket plane (40th anniv of first supersonic flight) 1·25 1·25
790 10 d. English and Spanish galleons (400th anniv of Spanish Armada) 3·00 3·00
791 12 d. "Titanic" (75th anniv of sinking) 3·50 3·50

1988. 500th Birth Anniv of Titian (artist). As T **238** of Antigua. Multicoloured.

793 25 b. "Emperor Charles V" 10 10
794 50 b. "St. Margaret and the Dragon" 15 15
795 60 b. "Ranuccio Farnese" 15 15
796 75 b. "Tarquin and Lucretia" 20 20
797 1 d. "The Knight of Malta" 25 25
798 5 d. "Spain succouring Faith" 1·00 1·00
799 10 d. "Doge Francesco Venier" 1·90 1·90
800 12 d. "Doge Grimani before the Faith" (detail) 2·25 2·25

167 John Kennedy sailing

1988. 25th Death Anniv of President John F. Kennedy. Multicoloured.

802 75 b. Type **167** 15 15
803 1 d. Kennedy signing Peace Corps legislation, 1962 15 20
804 1 d.25 Speaking at U.N., New York (vert) 20 25
805 12 d. Grave and eternal flame, Arlington National Cemetery (vert) 1·90 2·00

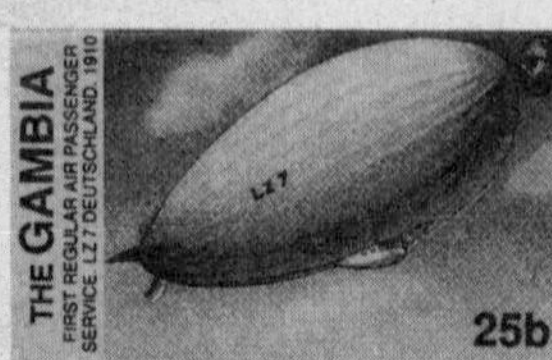

168 "LZ 7" "Deutschland" (first regular air passenger service), 1910

1988. Milestones of Transportation. Mult.

807 25 b. Type **168** 20 20
808 50 b. Stephenson's "Locomotion" (first permanent public railway), 1825 30 30
809 75 b. G.M. "Sun Racer" (first world solar challenge), 1987 40 40
810 1 d. Sprague's "Premiere" (first operational electric tramway), 1888 45 45
811 1 d.25 "Gold Rush" Bicycle (holder of man-powered land speed record), 1986 55 55
812 2 d.50 Robert Goddard and rocket launcher (first liquid fuel rocket), 1925 85 85
813 10 d. "Orukter Amphibolos" (first steam traction engine), 1805 2·50 2·50
814 12 d. "Sovereign of the Seas" (largest cruise liner), 1988 2·75 2·75

169 Emmett Kelley **170** Prince Henry the Navigator and Caravel

1988. Entertainers. Multicoloured.

816 20 b. Type **169** 10 10
817 1 d. Gambia National Ensemble 25 25
818 1 d.25 Jackie Gleason 30 30
819 1 d.50 Laurel and Hardy 40 40
820 2 d.50 Yul Brynner 65 65
821 3 d. Cary Grant 80 80
822 10 d. Danny Kaye 2·25 2·50
823 20 d. Charlie Chaplin 4·00 4·50

1988. Exploration of West Africa. Mult.

825 50 b. Type **170** 50 50
826 75 b. Jesse Ramsden's sextant, 1785 60 60
827 1 d. 15th-century hourglass 70 70
828 1 d.25 Prince Henry the Navigator and Vasco da Gama 80 80
829 2 d.50 Vasco da Gama and ship 1·25 1·25
830 5 d. Mungo Park and map of Gambia River (horiz) 2·25 2·25
831 10 d. Map of West Africa, 1563 (horiz) 2·75 2·75
832 12 d. Portuguese caravel (horiz) 3·25 3·25

171 Projected Space Plane and Ernst Mach (physicist)

1988. 350th Anniv of Publication of Galileo's "Discourses". Space Achievements. Mult.

834 50 b. Type **171** 15 10
835 75 b. OAO III astronomical satellite and Niels Bohr (physicist) 20 15
836 1 d. Space shuttle, projected space station and Robert Goddard (physicist) (horiz) 25 20
837 1 d.25 Jupiter probe, 1979, and Edward Barnard (astronomer) (horiz) 30 25
838 2 d. Hubble Space Telescope and George Hale (astronomer) 45 35
839 3 d. Earth-to-Moon laser measurement and Albert Michaelson (physicist) (horiz) 65 55
840 10 d. HEAO-2 "Einstein" orbital satellite and Albert Einstein (physicist) 1·75 2·00
841 20 d. "Voyager" (first non-stop round-the-world flight), 1987, and Wright Brothers (aviation pioneers) (horiz) 3·50 3·75

HAVE YOU READ THE NOTES AT THE BEGINNING OF THIS CATALOGUE?
These often provide answers to the enquiries we receive.

172 Passing Out Parade

1989. Army Day. Multicoloured.

843 75 b. Type **172** 15 15
844 1 d. Standards of The Gambia Regiment 15 15
845 1 d.25 Side drummer in ceremonial uniform (vert) 20 20
846 10 d. Marksman with Atlantic Shooting Cup (vert) 1·50 1·75
847 15 d. Soldiers on assault course (vert) 2·00 2·25
848 20 d. Gunner with 105 mm field gun 2·50 2·75

173 Mickey Mouse, 1928

1989. 60th Birthday of Mickey Mouse (2nd issue). Multicoloured.

849 2 d. Type **173** 40 40
850 2 d. Mickey Mouse, 1931 40 40
851 2 d. Mickey Mouse, 1936 40 40
852 2 d. Mickey Mouse, 1955 40 40
853 2 d. Mickey Mouse, 1947 40 40
854 2 d. Mickey Mouse as magician, 1940 40 40
855 2 d. Mickey Mouse with palette, 1960 40 40
856 2 d. Mickey Mouse as Uncle Sam, 1976 40 40
857 2 d. Mickey Mouse, 1988 40 40

Nos. 849/57 were printed together, se-tenant, forming a composite design.

174 "Le Coup de Lance" (detail)

1989. Easter. Religious Paintings by Rubens. Multicoloured.

859 50 b. Type **174** 15 15
860 75 b. "Flagellation of Christ" 15 15
861 1 d. "Lamentation for Christ" 15 15
862 1 d. 25, "Descent from the Cross" 20 20
863 2 d. "Holy Trinity" 30 30
864 5 d. "Doubting Thomas" 75 75
865 10 d. "Lamentation over Christ" 1·50 1·75
866 12 d. "Lamentation with Virgin and St. John" 1·75 2·00

175 African Emerald Cuckoo

1989. West African Birds. Multicoloured.

868 20 b. Type **175** 20 20
869 60 b. Grey-headed bush shrike 35 35
870 75 b. South African crowned crane 35 35
871 1 d. Secretary bird 40 40
872 2 d. Red-billed hornbill 60 60
873 5 d. Superb sunbird 1·40 1·40
874 10 d. Pearl-spotted owlet ("Little owl") 2·50 2·50
875 12 d. Bateleur 2·50 2·50

176 "Druryia antimachus"

1989. Butterflies of Gambia. Multicoloured.

877 50 b. Type **176** 20 20
878 75 b. "Euphaedra neophron" 30 30
879 1 d. "Aterica rabena" 30 30
880 1 d. 25 "Salamis parhassus" 40 40
881 5 d. "Precis rhadama" 1·40 1·40
882 10 d. "Papilio demodocus" 2·00 2·00
883 12 d. "Charaxes etesipe" 2·25 2·25
884 15 d. " Danaus formosa" 2·25 2·25

177 Nigerian Steam Locomotive, 1959

1989. African Steam Locomotives. Mult.

886 50 b. Type **177** 20 20
887 75 b. Garratt Class "14A" 25 25
888 1 d. British-built locomotive, Sudan 30 30
889 1 d. 25 American built locomotive, 1925 40 40
890 5 d. Scottish-built locomotive, 1955 1·40 1·40
891 7 d. Scottish-built locomotive, 1926 1·60 1·60
892 10 d. East African Railways British-built tank locomotive 2·00 2·00
893 12 d. American-built locomotive, Ghana 2·00 2·00

1989. "Philexfrance '89" International Stamp Exhibition, Paris. Nos. 686/9 optd **PHILEXFRANCE '89**.

895 75 b. Type **155** 10 10
896 1 d. Balaphong and fiddle 15 20
897 1 d. 25, Bolongbato and konting (vert) 20 25
898 10 d. Antique and modern koras (vert) 1·50 2·00

1989. Japanese Art. As T **250** of Antigua. Multicoloured.

900 50 b. "Sparrow and Bamboo" (Hiroshige) (vert) 15 15
901 75 b. "Peonies and a Canary" (Hokusai) (vert) 15 15
902 1 d. "Crane and Marsh Grasses" (Hiroshige) (vert) 20 20
903 1 d. 25, "Crossbill and Thistle" (Hokusai) (vert) 30 30
904 2 d. "Cuckoo and Azalea" (Hokusai) (vert) 45 45
905 5 d. "Parrot on a Pine Branch" (Hiroshige) (vert) 95 95
906 10 d. "Mandarin Ducks in a Stream" (Hiroshige) (vert) 1·75 2·00
907 12 d. "Bullfinch and Drooping Cherry" (Hokusai) (vert) 1·75 2·00

179 Rialto Bridge, Venice

1989. World Cup Football Championship, Italy (1990) (1st issue). Designs showing landmarks and players. Multicoloured.

909 75 b. Type **179** 25 25
910 1 d. 25 The Baptistery, Pisa 35 35
911 7 d. Casino, San Remo .. 1·60 1·60
912 12 d. Colosseum, Rome .. 2·25 2·25

See also Nos. 1064/7.

180 "Vitex doniana"

1989. Medicinal Plants. Multicoloured.

914 20 b. Type **180** 15 15
915 50 b. "Ricinus communis" 20 20
916 75 b. "Palisota hirsuta" .. 25 25
917 1 d. "Smilax kraussiana" 30 30
918 1 d. 25 "Aspilia africana" 40 40
919 5 d. "Newbouldia laevis" 1·25 1·25
920 8 d. "Monodora tenuifolia" 1·60 1·60
921 10 d. "Gossypium arboreum" .. .. 1·75 1·75

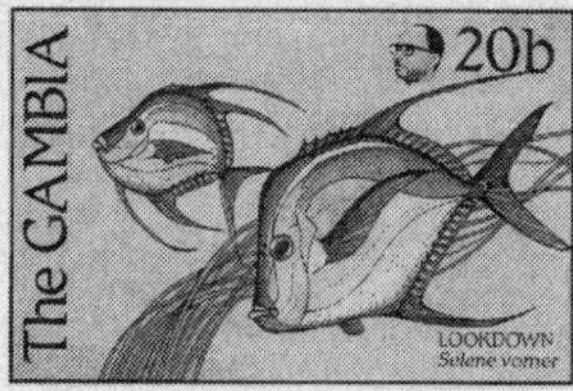

181 Lookdown Fish

1989. Fishes. Multicoloured.

923 20 b. Type **181** 15 15
924 75 b. Boarfish 35 35
925 1 d. Grey triggerfish .. 40 40
926 1 d. 25 Skipjack tuna .. 45 45
927 2 d. Bermuda chub .. 65 65
928 4 d. Atlantic manta .. 1·10 1·10
929 5 d. Striped mullet .. 1·25 1·25
930 10 d. Ladyfish .. .. 2·25 2·25

1989. "World Stamp Expo '89" International Stamp Exhibition, Washington. As T **256** of Antigua, but showing Walt Disney cartoon characters and American carousel horses. Multicoloured.

932 20 b. Little Hiawatha on Daniel Muller Indian pony 10 10
933 50 b. Morty on Herschell-Spillman stander .. 15 15
934 75 b. Goofy on Gustav Dentzel stander .. 20 20
935 1 d. Mickey Mouse on Daniel Muller armoured stander 25 25
936 1 d. 25, Minnie Mouse on jumper from Smithsonian Collection .. 30 30
937 2 d. Webby on Illion "American Beauty" .. 55 55
938 8 d. Donald Duck on Zalar jumper .. .. .. 1·75 1·75
939 10 d. Mickey Mouse on Parker bucking horse 1·90 1·90

183 Mickey and Minnie Mouse in Pierce-Arrow, 1922

1989. Christmas. Designs showing Walt Disney cartoon characters with cars. Mult.

942 20 b. Type **183** 10 10
943 50 b. Goofy in Spyker, 1919 15 15
944 75 b. Donald and Grandma Duck with Packard, 1929 20 20
945 1 d. Mickey Mouse driving Daimler, 1920 .. .. 25 25
946 1 d. 25, Mickey Mouse in Hispano "Suiza", 1924 30 30
947 2 d. Mickey and Minnie Mouse in Opel "Laubfrosch", 1924 .. .. 45 45
948 10 d. Donald Duck driving Vauxhall "30/98", 1927 2·00 2·00
949 12 d. Goofy with Peerless, 1923 .. .. .. 2·25 2·25

184 Charles Nicolle (typhus transmission) and Vaccination

1989. Great Medical Discoveries. Mult.

951 20 b. Type **184** 15 15
952 50 b. Paul Ehrlich (immunization pioneer) and medical examination 20 20
953 75 b. Selman Waksman (discoverer of streptomycin) and T.B. clinic 25 25
954 1 d. Edward Jenner (smallpox vaccination), and Jenner conducting experiment, 1796 .. 30 30
955 1 d. 25 Robert Koch (developer of tuberculin test) and Gambian using vaccination gun .. 40 40
956 5 d. Sir Alexander Fleming (discoverer of penicillin) and doctor giving injection .. .. .. 1·25 1·25
957 8 d. Max Theiler (developer of yellow fever vaccine) and child clinic .. 1·75 1·75
958 10 d. Louis Pasteur (bacteriologist) and health survey .. .. 1·90 1·90

185 "Bulbophyllum lepidum"

1989. Orchids. Multicoloured.

960 20 b. Type **185** 15 15
961 75 b. "Tridactyle tridactylites" 30 30
962 1 d. "Vanilla imperialis" .. 35 35
963 1 d. 25 "Oeceoclades maculata" 40 40
964 2 d. "Polystachya affinis" 65 65
965 4 d. "Ancistrochilus rothschildianus" .. 1·25 1·25
966 5 d. "Angraecum distichum" .. .. 1·50 1·50
967 10 d. "Liparis guineensis" 2·50 2·50

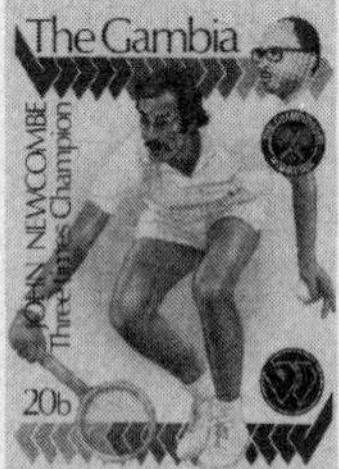

186 John Newcombe

1990. Wimbledon Tennis Champions. Mult.

969 20 b. Type **186** 10 10
970 20 b. Mrs. G. W. Hillyard 10 10
971 50 b. Roy Emerson .. 15 15
972 50 b. Dorothy Chambers .. 15 15
973 75 b. Donald Budge .. 20 20
974 75 b. Suzanne Lenglen .. 20 20
975 1 d. Laurence Doherty .. 25 25
976 1 d. Helen Wills Moody .. 25 25
977 1 d. 25 Bjorn Borg .. 30 30
978 1 d. 25 Maureen Connolly 30 30
979 4 d. Jean Borotra .. 80 80
980 4 d. Maria Bueno .. 80 80
981 5 d. Anthony Wilding .. 90 90
982 5 d. Louise Brough .. 90 90
983 7 d. Fred Perry .. 1·25 1·25
984 7 d. Margaret Court .. 1·25 1·25
985 10 d. Bill Tilden .. 1·75 1·75
986 10 d. Billie Jean King .. 1·75 1·75
987 12 d. Rod Laver .. 2·00 2·00
988 12 d. Martina Navratilova 2·00 2·00

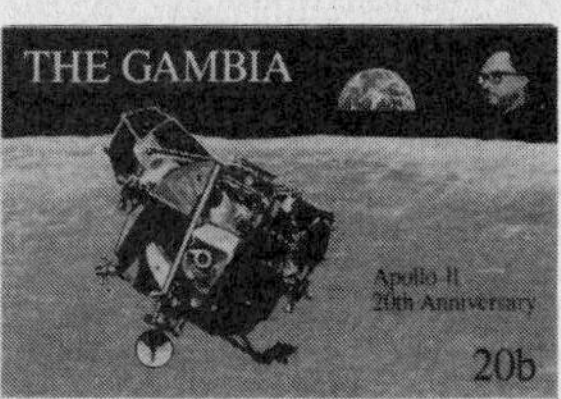

187 Lunar Module "Eagle"

1990. 20th Anniv (1989) of First Manned Landing on Moon. Multicoloured.

990 20 b. Type **187** 10 10
991 50 b. Lift-off of "Apollo 11" (vert) 10 10
992 75 b. Neil Armstrong stepping on to Moon .. 10 10
993 1 d. Buzz Aldrin and American flag 15 20
994 1 d. 25 "Apollo 11" emblem (vert) 20 25
995 1 d. 75 Crew of "Apollo 11" 25 30
996 8 d. Lunar Module "Eagle" on Moon .. .. 1·10 1·25
997 12 d. Recovery of "Apollo 11" after splashdown .. 1·60 1·75

188 Bristol Blenheim Mk I

1990. R.A.F. Aircraft of Second World War. Multicoloured.

999 10 b. Type **188** 10 10
1000 20 b. Fairey Battle .. 10 10
1001 50 b. Bristol Blenheim Mk IV 10 10
1002 60 b. Vickers-Armstrong Wellington Mk 1C .. 10 10
1003 75 b. Armstrong-Whitworth Whitley Mk V 10 10
1004 1 d. Handley-Page Hampden Mk 1 .. 15 20
1005 1 d. 25, Supermarine Spitfire Mk 1A and Hawker Hurricane Mk I 20 25
1006 2 d. Avro Manchester .. 30 35
1007 3 d. Short Stirling Mk I 45 50
1008 5 d. Handley-Page Halifax Mk I 70 75
1009 10 d. Avro Lancaster Mk III .. .. 1·50 1·60
1010 12 d. De Havilland Mosquito Mk IV .. 1·60 1·75

189 White-faced Scops Owl

1990. African Birds. Multicoloured.

1012 1 d. 25 Type **189** .. 20 25
1013 1 d. 25 Village weaver .. 20 25
1014 1 d. 25 Red-throated bee eater 20 25
1015 1 d. 25 Brown harrier eagle 20 25
1016 1 d. 25 Red bishop .. 20 25
1017 1 d. 25 Scarlet-chested sunbird 20 25
1018 1 d. 25 Red-billed hornbill 20 25
1019 1 d. 25 Mosque swallow .. 20 25
1020 1 d. 25 White-faced whistling duck .. 20 25
1021 1 d. 25 African fish eagle 20 25
1022 1 d. 25 Eastern white pelican 20 25
1023 1 d. 25 Carmine bee eater 20 25
1024 1 d. 25 Hadada ibis .. 20 25
1025 1 d. 25 Egyptian plover .. 20 25
1026 1 d. 25 Variable sunbird 20 25
1027 1 d. 25 African skimmer 20 25
1028 1 d. 25 Woodland kingfisher 20 25
1029 1 d. 25 African jacana .. 20 25
1030 1 d. 25 African pygmy goose 20 25
1031 1 d. 25 Hammerkop .. 20 25

Nos. 1012/31 were printed together, se-tenant, forming a composite design of birds at a lake.

190 Penny Black

1990. 150th Anniv of the Penny Black.

1032 **190** 1 d. 25 black and blue 20 25
1033 12 d. black and red .. 1·60 1·75

191 Flag and National Assembly Building

1990. 25th Anniv of Independence. Mult.

1035 1 d. Type **191** 15 20
1036 3 d. Pres. Sir Dawda Jawara 45 50
1037 12 d. Map of Yundum airport and Air Gambia airliner .. .. 1·60 1·75

192 Baobab Tree

1990. Gambian Life. Multicoloured.

1039 5 b. Type **192** 10 10
1040 10 b. Woodcarving, Albert Market, Banjul .. 10 10
1041 20 b. President Jawara planting seedling (vert) 10 10
1042 50 b. Sailing canoe and map 10 10
1043 75 b. Batik fabric .. 10 10

1044 1 d. Hibiscus and Bakau beach 15 20
1045 1 d. 25 Bougainvillea and Tendaba Camp .. 20 25
1046 2 d. Shrimp fishing and sorting 30 35
1047 5 d. Groundnut oil mill, Denton Bridge .. 70 75
1048 10 d. Handicraft pot and kora (musical instrument) .. .. .. 1·50 1·60
1049 15 d. "Ansellia africana" (orchid) (vert) .. 2·10 2·25
1050 30 d. "Euriphene gambiae" (butterfly) and ancient stone ring near Georgetown .. 4·25 4·50

193 Daisy Duck at 10 Downing Street

1990. "Stamp World London 90" International Stamp Exhibition. Walt Disney cartoon characters in England. Mult.
1051 20 b. Type **193** 10 10
1052 50 b. Goofy in Trafalgar Square 10 10
1053 75 b. Mickey Mouse on White Cliffs of Dover (horiz) 10 10
1054 1 d. Mickey Mouse at Tower of London .. 15 20
1055 5 d. Mickey Mouse and Goofy at Hampton Court Palace (horiz) .. 70 75
1056 8 d. Mickey Mouse by Magdalen Tower, Oxford .. .. 1·10 1·25
1057 10 d. Mickey Mouse on Old London Bridge (horiz) .. .. 1·50 1·60
1058 12 d. Scrooge McDuck and Rosetta Stone, British Museum (horiz) .. 1·60 1·75

194 Lady Elizabeth Bowes-Lyon in High Chair

1990. 90th Birthday of Queen Elizabeth the Queen Mother.
1060 **194** 6 d. black, mve & yell 85 90
1061 – 6 d. black, mve & yell 85 90
1062 – 6 d. black, mve & yell 85 90
DESIGNS: No. 1061, Lady Elizabeth Bowes-Lyon as a young girl; 1062, Lady Elizabeth Bowes-Lyon with wild flowers.

195 Vialli, Italy

1990. World Cup Football Championship, Italy (2nd issue). Multicoloured.
1064 1 d. Type **195** 15 20
1065 1 d. 25 Cannegia, Argentina 20 25
1066 3 d. Marchena, Costa Rica 45 50
1067 5 d. Shaiba, United Arab Emirates 70 75

1990. Olympic Games, Barcelona (1st issue). As T **268** of Antigua. Multicoloured.
1069 20 b. Men's discus .. 10 10
1070 50 b. Men's 100 metres .. 10 10
1071 75 b. Women's 400 metres 10 10
1072 1 d. Men's 200 metres .. 15 20
1073 1 d. 25 Women's rhythmic gymnastics 20 25
1074 3 d. Football 45 50
1075 10 d. Men's marathon .. 1·50 1·60
1076 12 d. "Tornado" class yachting .. .. 1·60 1·75
See also Nos. 1308/15 and 1351/62.

1990. Christmas. Paintings by Renaissance Masters. As T **272** of Antigua. Multicoloured.
1078 20 b. "The Annunciation, with St. Emidius" (detail) (Crivelli) (vert) 10 10
1079 50 b. "The Annunciation" (detail) (Campin) (vert) 10 10
1080 75 b. "The Solly Madonna" (detail) (Raphael) (vert) .. 10 15
1081 1 d. 25 "The Tempi Madonna" (Raphael) (vert) 20 25
1082 2 d. "Madonna of the Linen Window" (detail) (Raphael) (vert) .. 30 35
1083 7 d. "The Annunciation, with St. Emidius" (different detail) (Crivelli) (vert) .. 1·00 1·10
1084 10 d. "The Orleans Madonna" (Raphael) (vert) .. .. .. 1·50 1·60
1085 15 d. "Madonna and Child" (detail) (Crivelli) (vert) .. .. .. 2·10 2·25

1990. 350th Death Anniv of Rubens. As T **273** of Antigua. Multicoloured.
1087 20 b. "The Lion Hunt" (sketch) 10 10
1088 75 b. "The Lion Hunt" (detail) 10 15
1089 1 d. "The Tiger Hunt" (detail) 15 20
1090 1 d. 25 "The Tiger Hunt" (different detail) .. 20 25
1091 3 d. "The Tiger Hunt" (different detail) .. 45 50
1092 5 d. "The Boar Hunt" (detail) 70 75
1093 10 d. "The Lion Hunt" (different detail) .. 1·50 1·60
1094 15 d. "The Tiger Hunt" (different detail) .. 2·10 2·25

196 Summit Logo

1991. World Summit for Children, New York.
1096 **196** 1 d. multicoloured .. 15 20

1991. International Literacy Year (1990). As T **269** of Antigua, but scenes from Disney cartoon film "The Sword in the Stone". Multicoloured.
1097 3 d. Sir Kay and Wart searching for lost arrow (horiz) 45 50
1098 3 d. Merlin the Magician (horiz) 45 50
1099 3 d. Merlin teaching Wart (horiz) 45 50
1100 3 d. Wart writing on blackboard (horiz) .. 45 50
1101 3 d. Wart transformed into bird and Madame Mim (horiz) 45 50
1102 3 d. Merlin and Madame Mim (horiz) 45 50
1103 3 d. Madame Mim transformed into dragon (horiz) 45 50
1104 3 d. Wart pulling sword from stone (horiz) .. 45 50
1105 3 d. King Arthur on throne (horiz) 45 50

197 "Bebearia senegalensis"

1991. Wildlife. Multicoloured.
1107 1 d. Type **197** 15 20
1108 1 d. "Graphium ridleyanus" (butterfly) .. 15 20
1109 1 d. "Precis antilope" (butterfly) 15 20
1110 1 d. "Charaxes ameliae" (butterfly) 15 20
1111 1 d. Addax 15 20
1112 1 d. Sassaby 15 20
1113 1 d. Civet 15 20
1114 1 d. Green monkey .. 15 20
1115 1 d. Spur-winged goose .. 15 20
1116 1 d. Red-billed hornbill .. 15 20
1117 1 d. Osprey 15 20
1118 1 d. Glossy ibis 15 20
1119 1 d. Egyptian plover .. 15 20
1120 1 d. Golden-tailed woodpecker 15 20
1121 1 d. Green wood hoopoe .. 15 20
1122 1 d. Gaboon viper .. 15 20
1123 1 d. 50 Red-billed fire finch 25 30
1124 1 d. 50 Leaflove 25 30
1125 1 d. 50 Placplac 25 30
1126 1 d. 50 African emerald cuckoo 25 30
1127 1 d. 50 Red colobus monkey 25 30
1128 1 d. 50 African elephant 25 30
1129 1 d. 50 Duiker 25 30
1130 1 d. 50 Giant eland .. 25 30
1131 1 d. 50 Oribi 25 30
1132 1 d. 50 Western African dwarf crocodile .. 25 30
1133 1 d. 50 Crowned crane .. 25 30
1134 1 d. 50 Jackal 25 30
1135 1 d. 50 Yellow-throated longclaw 25 30
1136 1 d. 50 Abyssinian ground hornbill 25 30
1137 1 d. 50 "Papilio hesperus" 25 30
1138 1 d. 50 "Papilio antimachus" 25 30
1139 5 d. Martial eagle .. 75 80
1140 5 d. Red-cheeked cordon-bleu 75 80
1141 5 d. Red bishop 75 80
1142 5 d. Great white pelican 75 80
1143 5 d. Patas monkey .. 75 80
1144 5 d. Vervet monkey .. 75 80
1145 5 d. Roan antelope .. 75 80
1146 5 d. Western hartebeest 75 80
1147 5 d. Waterbuck 75 80
1148 5 d. Warthog 75 80
1149 5 d. Spotted hyena .. 75 80
1150 5 d. Olive baboon .. 75 80
1151 5 d. "Palla decius" .. 75 80
1152 5 d. "Acraea pharsalus" 75 80
1153 5 d. "Neptidopsis ophione" 75 80
1154 5 d. "Acraea caecilia" .. 75 80
Nos. 1107/22, 1123/38 and 1139/54 respectively were issued together, se-tenant, forming composite designs.

198 "Papilio dardanus"

1991. Butterflies. Multicoloured.
1156 20 b. Type **198** 10 10
1157 50 b. "Bematistes poggei" 10 10
1158 1 d. "Vanessa cardui" .. 15 20
1159 1 d. 50 "Amphicallia tigris" 25 30
1160 3 d. "Hypolimnas dexithea" 45 50
1161 8 d. "Acraea egina" .. 1·10 1·25
1162 10 d. "Salamis temora" .. 1·50 1·75
1163 15 d. "Precis octavia" .. 2·25 2·40

1991. 65th Birthday of Queen Elizabeth II. As T **280** of Antigua. Multicoloured.
1165 50 b. The Queen and Prince Charles at Windsor polo match .. 10 10
1166 1 d. The Queen and Princess Anne at the Derby, 1988 .. .. 15 20
1167 1 d. 25 The Queen at the Royal London Hospital, 1970 .. 20 25
1168 12 d. The Queen and Prince Philip at Balmoral, 1976 .. 1·60 1·75

1991. 10th Wedding Anniv of Prince and Princess of Wales. As T **280** of Antigua. Multicoloured.
1170 20 b. Prince and Princess with sons in June, 1989 10 10
1171 75 b. Separate photographs of Prince, Princess and sons .. 10 10
1172 1 d. 50 Prince Henry on first day of school, 1987, and Prince William at polo match 25 30
1173 15 d. Separate photographs of Prince and Princess of Wales .. 2·10 2·25

1991. "Phila Nippon '91" International Stamp Exhibition, Tokyo. As T **279** of Antigua showing Walt Disney cartoon characters playing Japanese sports and games. Multicoloured.
1175 50 b. Donald Duck and Mickey Mouse playing "go" (horiz) 10 10
1176 75 b. Morty, Ferdie and Pete as Sumo wrestlers (horiz) 10 10
1177 1 d. Minnie Mouse, Clarabelle Cow and Daisy Duck playing battledore and shuttlecock (horiz) 15 20
1178 1 d. 25 Goofy and Mickey at Okinawa bullfight .. 20 25
1179 5 d. Mickey flying hawk 70 75
1180 7 d. Mickey, Minnie and Donald playing "jan-ken-pon" .. 1·00 1·10
1181 10 d. Goofy as archer (horiz) .. .. 1·50 1·60
1182 15 d. Morty and Ferdie flying kites .. .. 2·10 2·25

1991. International Literacy Year (1990). As T **269** of Antigua showing Walt Disney cartoon characters in Kipling's "Just So" stories. Multicoloured.
1184 50 b. "How the Whale got his Throat" (horiz) .. 10 10
1185 75 b. "How the Camel got his Hump" (horiz) .. 10 10
1186 1 d. "How the Leopard got his Spots" (horiz) 15 20
1187 1 d. 25 "The Elephant's Child" (horiz) 20 25
1188 1 d. 50 "The Singsong of Old Man Kangaroo" (horiz) 25 30
1189 7 d. "The Crab that played with the Sea" (horiz) .. .. 1·00 1·10
1190 10 d. "The Cat that walked by Himself" (horiz) .. .. 1·50 1·60
1191 15 d. "The Butterfly that Stamped" (horiz) .. 2·10 2·25

199 Canadian Pacific Railway Brake-van

1991. Railway Brake-vans. Multicoloured.
1193 1 d. Type **199** 15 20
1194 1 d. Cumberland and Pennsylvania 15 20
1195 1 d. Ferrocarril Interoceanico, Mexico .. 15 20
1196 1 d. Northern Pacific all-steel cupola van .. 15 20
1197 1 d. Morristown and Erie 15 20
1198 1 d. Burlington Northern streamlined cupola van 15 20
1199 1 d. McCloud River brake-coach 15 20
1200 1 d. Santa Fe wide vision van 15 20

1201 1 d. Frisco 15 20
1202 1 d. 50 Colorado and Southern 25 30
1203 1 d. 50 Santa Fe transfer caboose 25 30
1204 1 d. 50 Canadian National 25 30
1205 1 d. 50 Union Pacific transfer steel van 25 30
1206 1 d. 50 Virginia and Truckee 25 30
1207 1 d. 50 British Rail standard van with end windows 25 30
1208 1 d. 50 International Railways, Central America 25 30
1209 1 d. 50 Northern Pacific steel cupola van 25 30
1210 1 d. 50 Burlington Northern wooden van 25 30
1211 2 d. Oahu Railway, Hawaii 30 35
1212 2 d. British Rail standard van 30 35
1213 2 d. Union Pacific wide view steel van 30 35
1214 2 d. Chicago Belt 30 35
1215 2 d. McCloud River four-wheel caboose 30 35
1216 2 d. Angelina County Lumber Co. 30 35
1217 2 d. Coahuila and Zacatecas, Mexico 30 35
1218 2 d. United Yucatan Railways 30 35
1219 2 d. Rio Grande 30 35

200 Tiger Shark

1991. Fishes. Multicoloured.
1221 20 b. Type **200** 10 10
1222 25 b. Common jewel fish 10 10
1223 50 b. Five spot fish 10 10
1224 75 b. Smalltooth sawfish 10 10
1225 1 d. Five spot tilapia 15 20
1226 1 d. 25 Dwarf jewel fish 20 25
1227 1 d. 50 Five spot jewel fish 25 30
1228 3 d. Bumphead 45 50
1229 10 d. Egyptian mouth-brooder 1·50 1·60
1230 15 d. Burton's mouth-brooder 2·10 2·25

1991. Hummel Figurines. As T **302** of Antigua. Multicoloured.
1232 20 b. Children waving 10 10
1233 75 b. Children under umbrella 10 10
1234 1 d. Girl kissing friend 15 20
1235 1 d. 50 Children at window 25 30
1236 2 d. 50 Two girls in aprons 35 40
1237 5 d. Two boys in bow ties 70 75
1238 10 d. Two girls sitting on fence with birds 1·50 1·60
1239 15 d. Boy and girl in Swiss costume 2·10 2·25

1991. Death Centenary of Vincent van Gogh (artist). As T **278** of Antigua. Mult.
1241 20 b. "The Old Cemetery Tower at Nuenen in the Snow" (horiz) 10 10
1242 25 b. "Head of Peasant Woman with White Cap" 10 10
1243 50 b. "The Green Parrot" 10 10
1244 75 b. "Vase with Carnations" 10 10
1245 1 d. "Vase with Red Gladioli" 15 20
1246 1 d. 25 "Beach at Scheveningen in Calm Weather" (horiz) 20 25
1247 1 d. 50 "Boy cutting Grass with Sickle" (horiz) 25 30
1248 2 d. "Coleus Plant in a Flowerpot" (detail) 30 35
1249 3 d. "Self-portrait, 1887" 45 50
1250 4 d. "Self-portrait" (different) 55 60
1251 5 d. "Self-portrait" (different) 70 75
1252 6 d. "Self-portrait, 1887" (different) 85 90
1253 8 d. "Still Life with Bottle, Two Glasses, Cheese and Bread" (detail) 1·10 1·25
1254 10 d. "Still Life with Cabbage, Clogs and Potatoes" (horiz) 1·50 1·60
1255 12 d. "Montmartre: The Street Lamps" 1·60 1·75
1256 15 d. "Head of a Peasant Woman with Brownish Cap" 2·10 2·25

1991. Christmas. Religious Paintings by Fra Angelico. As T **287** of Antigua. Multicoloured.
1258 20 b. "The Madonna of Humility" 10 10
1259 50 b. "Madonna and Child with Angels" 10 10
1260 75 b. "Virgin and Child with Angels" 10 10
1261 1 d. "The Annunciation" 15 20
1262 1 d. 25 "Presentation in the Temple" 20 25
1263 5 d. "The Annunciation" (different) 70 75
1264 10 d. "Madonna della Stella" 1·50 1·60
1265 15 d. "Naming of St. John the Baptist" 2·10 2·25

201 Son House

1992. Famous Blues Singers. Multicoloured.
1267 20 b. Type **201** 10 10
1268 25 b. W.C. Handy 10 10
1269 50 b. Muddy Waters 10 10
1270 75 b. Lightnin Hopkins 10 10
1271 1 d. Ma Rainey 15 20
1272 1 d. 25 Mance Lipscomb 20 25
1273 1 d. 50 Mahalia Jackson 25 30
1274 2 d. Ella Fitzgerald 30 35
1275 3 d. Howlin Wolf 45 50
1276 5 d. Bessie Smith 70 75
1277 7 d. Leadbelly 1·00 1·10
1278 10 d. Joe Willie Wilkins 1·50 1·60

202 Pope John Paul II

1992. Papal Visit. Multicoloured.
1280 1 d. Type **202** 15 20
1281 1 d. 25 Pope John Paul II and Pres. Sir Dawda Jawara 20 25
1282 20 d. Gambian and Papal flags 3·00 3·25

1992. 40th Anniv of Queen Elizabeth II's Accession. As T **288** of Antigua. Mult.
1284 20 b. Pottery market 10 10
1285 50 b. Ruins of early fort 10 10
1286 1 d. Fishing boat 15 20
1287 15 d. Canoes on beach 2·10 2·25

203 Mickey Mouse as Christopher Columbus

1992. International Stamp Exhibitions. Walt Disney cartoon characters. Mult.
(a) "Granada '92", Spain. Voyage of Columbus
1289 20 b. Type **203** 10 10
1290 75 b. Mickey's plans derided 10 10
1291 1 d. 50 Mickey lands in America 25 30
1292 15 d. Mickey presents treasure to Minnie 2·10 2·25

(b) World Columbian Stamp "Expo '92". Chicago Landmarks
1294 50 b. Navy Pier 10 10
1295 1 d. Wrigley Building 15 20
1296 1 d. 25 University of Chicago 20 25
1297 12 d. Alder Planetarium 1·60 1·75

1992. Easter. Religious Paintings. As T **291** of Antigua but vert. Multicoloured.
1299 20 b. "Christ presented to the People" (Rembrandt) 10 10
1300 50 b. "Christ carrying the Cross" (Grunewald) 10 10
1301 75 b. "The Crucifixion" (Grunewald) 10 10
1302 1 d. "The Crucifixion" (Rubens) 15 20
1303 1 d. 25 "The Road to Calvary" (detail) (Tintoretto) 20 25
1304 1 d. 50 "The Road to Calvary" (Tintoretto) (different) 25 30
1305 15 d. "The Crucifixion" (Masaccio) 2·10 2·25
1306 20 d. "The Descent from the Cross" (detail) (Rembrandt) 3·00 3·25

204 Nadia Comaneci (Rumania) (combined gymnastics events) and Map of Barcelona

1992. Olympic Games, Barcelona (2nd series). Past Medal Winners. Multicoloured.
1308 20 b. Type **204** 10 10
1309 50 b. D. Moorcroft (G.B.) (5000 metres) and map 10 10
1310 75 b. M. Nemeth (Hungary) (javelin) and decorative tiles 10 10
1311 1 d. J. Pedraza (Mexico) (20k walk) and decorative plate 15 20
1312 1 d. 25 "Soling" class yachting (Brazil), state arms and flag 20 25
1313 1 d. 50 Women's hockey (G.D.R.) and Barcelona building 25 30
1314 12 d. M. Jordan (U.S.A.) (basketball) and map 1·60 1·75
1315 15 d. V. Borzov (U.S.S.R.) (100 metres) and galleon 2·10 2·25

205 "Hibiscus rosa-sinensis"

1992. Flowers. Multicoloured.
1317 20 b. Type **205** 10 10
1318 50 b. "Monodora myristica" 10 10
1319 75 b. "Bombax costatum" 10 10
1320 1 d. "Oncoba spinosa" 15 20
1321 1 d. 25 "Combretum grandiflorum" 20 25
1322 1 d. 50 "Rothmannia longiflora" 25 30
1323 2 d. "Clerodendrum splendens" 30 35
1324 5 d. "Mussaenda erythrophylla" 70 75
1325 10 d. "Nauclea latifolia" 1·50 1·60
1326 12 d. "Clerodendrum capitatum" 1·60 1·75
1327 15 d. "Costus spectabilis" 2·10 2·25
1328 18 d. "Strophanthus preussii" 2·50 2·60

206 "Joven Antonia" (River Gambia)

1992. River Boats of the World. Mult.
1330 20 b. Type **206** 10 10
1331 50 b. "Dresden" (River Elbe) 10 10
1332 75 b. "Medway Queen" (River Medway) 10 10
1333 1 d. "Lady Wright" (River Gambia) 15 20
1334 1 d. 25 "Devin" (River Vltava) 20 25
1335 1 d. 50 "Lady Chilel Jawara" (River Gambia) 25 30
1336 5 d. "Robert Fulton" (River Hudson) 70 75
1337 10 d. "Coonawarra" (River Murray) 1·50 1·60
1338 12 d. "Nakusp" (River Columbia) 1·60 1·75
1339 15 d. "Lucy Ashton" (Firth of Clyde) 2·10 2·25

1992. 50th Anniv of Japanese Attack on Pearl Harbor. As T **286** of Antigua. Mult.
1341 2 d. U.S.S. "Pennsylvania" (battleship) 30 35
1342 2 d. Japanese torpedo bombers over Pearl Harbor 30 35
1343 2 d. U.S.S. "Ward" (destroyer) sinking midget submarine 30 35
1344 2 d. Ford Naval Station under attack 30 35
1345 2 d. Agency report of Japanese attack 30 35
1346 2 d. Newspaper headline 30 35
1347 2 d. Japanese troops on Guam 30 35
1348 2 d. U.S. forces regaining Wake Island 30 35
1349 2 d. Doolittle bomber raid on Japan 30 35
1350 2 d. American aircraft attacking Japanese carrier, Midway 30 35

207 Women's Double Sculls

1992. Winter Olympic Games, Albertville, and Olympic Games, Barcelona (3rd issue). Multicoloured.
1351 20 b. Type **207** 10 10
1352 50 b. Men's kayak (vert) 10 10
1353 75 b. Women's rapid precision pistol shooting 10 10
1354 1 d. Judo (vert) 15 20
1355 1 d. 25 Men's javelin (vert) 20 25
1356 1 d. 50 Men's vaulting horse (vert) 25 30
1357 2 d. Men's downhill skiing (vert) 30 35
1358 3 d. Windsurfing (vert) 45 50
1359 5 d. Men's high jump 70 75
1360 10 d. Four-man bobsled (vert) 1·50 1·60
1361 12 d. 90 metre ski-jump (vert) 1·60 1·75
1362 15 d. Men's slalom skiing 2·10 2·25

1992. "Genova '92" International Thematic Stamp Exhibition. Dinosaurs. As T **290** of Antigua. Multicoloured.
1364 20 b. Dryosaurus 10 10
1365 25 b. Saurolophus 10 10
1366 50 b. Allosaurus 10 10
1367 75 b. Fabrosaurus 10 10
1368 1 d. Deinonychus 15 20
1369 1 d. 25 Cetiosaurus 20 25
1370 1 d. 50 Camptosaurus 20 25
1371 2 d. Ornithosuchus 30 35
1372 3 d. Spinosaurus 45 50
1373 5 d. Ornithomimus 70 75
1374 10 d. Kentrosaurus 1·50 1·60
1375 12 d. Schlermochus 1·60 1·75

1992. Christmas. Religous Paintings. As T **300** of Antigua. Multicoloured.

1378 50 b. "The Holy Family" (Raphael) 10 10
1379 75 b. "The Little Holy Family" (Raphael) .. 10 10
1380 1 d. "The Little Holy Family" (detail) (Raphael) 15 20
1381 1 d. 25 "Escape to Egypt" (Melchior Broederlam) 20 25
1382 1 d. 50 "Flight into Egypt" (Adriaen Isenbrant) 20 25
1383 2 d. "The Holy Family" (El Greco) 30 35
1384 2 d. "Flight into Egypt" (detail) (Cosimo Tura) 30 35
1385 2 d. "Flight into Egypt" (detail) (Master of Hoogstraelen) .. 30 35
1386 4 d. "The Holy Family" (Bernard van Orley) .. 55 60
1387 5 d. "Holy Family with Infant Jesus Sleeping" (detail) (Charles Le Brun) 70 75
1388 10 d. "Rest on The Flight to Egypt" (Orazio Gentileschi) .. .. 1·50 1·60
1389 12 d. "Rest on The Flight to Egypt" (detail) (Orazio Gentileschi) .. 1·60 1·75

1992. 60th Anniv of Goofy (Disney cartoon character). As T **258** of Dominica. Mult.

1391 50 b. Goofy in "Orphan's Benefit", 1934 .. 10 10
1392 75 b. Goofy and Donald Duck in "Moose Hunters", 1937 .. 10 10
1393 1 d. Goofy in "Mickey's Amateurs", 1937 .. 15 20
1394 1 d. 25 Goofy, Donald and Mickey Mouse in "Lonesome Ghosts", 1937 .. .. .. 20 25
1395 5 d. Goofy, Donald and Mickey in "Boat Builders", 1938 .. 70 75
1396 7 d. Goofy, Donald and Mickey in "The Whalers", 1938 .. 1·00 1·10
1397 10 d. Goofy and Wilbur the grasshopper in "Goofy and Wilbur", 1939 .. .. .. 1·50 1·60
1398 15 d. Goofy in "Saludos Amigos", 1941 .. 2·10 2·25

208 Pres. Jawara playing Golf and Map of Australia

1992. Open Golf Championships. Mult.

1400 20 b. Type **208** 10 10
1401 1 d. Pres. Jawara and Gambia Open trophy .. 15 20
1402 1 d. 50 Pres. Jawara (winner of Gambia Open, 1985) 20 25
1403 2 d. Pres. Jawara and map of Japan .. 30 35
1404 3 d. Pres. Jawara and map of U.S.A. .. 45 50
1405 5 d. Gambia Open trophy 70 75
1406 10 d. Pres. Jawara and map of Scotland .. 1·50 1·60
1407 12 d. Pres. Jawara and map of Italy .. .. 1·60 1·75

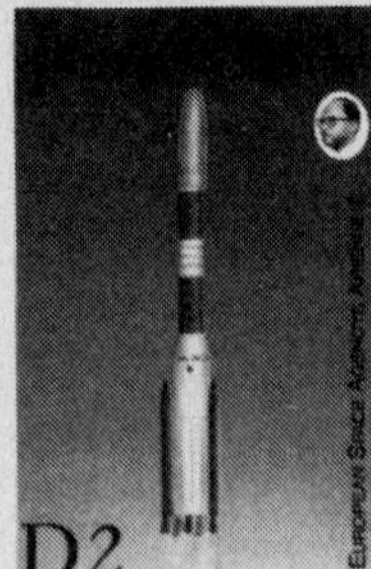

209 Launch of European "Ariane 4"

1993. Anniversaries and Events.

1409 2 d. Type **209** 30 35
1410 2 d. Konrad Adenauer and Berlin Airlift (horiz) 30 35
1411 2 d. "LZ 127 Graf Zeppelin", 1928 (horiz) 30 35
1412 5 d. "Santa Maria" (horiz) 70 75
1413 6 d. Jentink's duiker (horiz) 90 95
1414 7 d. World map and emblem (horiz) .. 1·00 1·00
1415 9 d. Wolfgang Amadeus Mozart .. .. 1·25 1·40
1416 10 d. Lions Club emblem 1·50 1·60
1417 10 d. "Enterprise" (yacht), 1930 .. .. 1·50 1·60
1418 10 d. Imperial amazon ("Sisserou Parrot") .. 1·50 1·60
1419 12 d. American space shuttle .. .. 1·60 1·75
1420 12 d. Fleet of Columbus (horiz) .. .. 1·60 1·75
1421 15 d. Adenauer and returning Prisoners of War (horiz) .. 2·10 2·25
1422 18 d. Airship "LZ1", 1900 (horiz) .. .. 2·50 2·75

ANNIVERSARIES AND EVENTS: Nos. 1409, 1419, International Space Year; 1410, 1421, 25th death anniv of Konrad Adenauer (German statesman); Nos. 1411, 1422, 75th death anniv of Count Ferdinand von Zeppelin; 1412, 1420, 500th death anniv of discovery of America by Columbus; 1413, 1418, Earth Summit '92, Rio; 1414, International Nutrition Conference, Rome; 1415, Death bicentenary of Mozart; 1416, 75th anniv of International Association of Lions Clubs; 1417, Americas Cup Yachting Championship.

1993. 15th Death Anniv (1992) of Elvis Presley (singer). As Nos. 1666/8 of Dominica. Multicoloured.

1424 3 d. Elvis Presley .. 45 50
1425 3 d. Elvis with guitar .. 45 50
1426 3 d. Elvis with microphone 45 50

1993. Bicentenary of the Louvre, Paris. Paintings. As T **305** of Antigua. Mult.

1427 3 d. "St John the Baptist" (Da Vinci) .. 45 50
1428 3 d. "Virgin of the Rocks" (Da Vinci) 45 50
1429 3 d. "Bacchus" (Da Vinci) 45 50
1430 3 d. "Lady of the Court, Milan" (Da Vinci) .. 45 50
1431 3 d. "Virgin of the Rocks" (detail) (Da Vinci) .. 45 50
1432 3 d. "Mona Lisa" (Da Vinci) 45 50
1433 3 d. "Mona Lisa" (detail) (Da Vinci) 45 50
1434 3 d. Sketches for "Two Horsemen" (Da Vinci) 45 50
1435 3 d. "The Oath of Horatii" (left detail) (David) 45 50
1436 3 d. "The Oath of Horatii" (right detail) (David) 45 50
1437 3 d. "The Love of Paris and Helen" (detail) (David) 45 50
1438 3 d. "The Sabine Women" (detail) (David) .. 45 50
1439 3 d. "Leonidas at Thermopylae" (detail) (David) 45 50
1440 3 d. "The Coronation of Napoleon" (left detail) (David) 45 50
1441 3 d. "The Coronation of Napoleon" (centre detail) (David) .. 45 50
1442 3 d. "The Coronation of Napoleon" (right detail) (David) 45 50
1443 3 d. "Peasant Family at Home" (detail) (L. le Nain) 45 50
1444 3 d. "Smoking Room" (left detail) (L. le Nain) 45 50
1445 3 d. "Smoking Room" (right detail) (L. le Nain) 45 50
1446 3 d. "The Cart" (detail) (L. le Nain) 45 50
1447 3 d. "Peasants' Repast" (detail) (L. le Nain) .. 45 50
1448 3 d. "Portrait in an Interior" (detail) (L. le Nain) 45 50
1449 3 d. "Portrait in an Interior" (different detail) (L. le Nain) .. 45 50
1450 3 d. "The Forge" (L. le Nain) 45 50

Nos. 1432/3 are incorrectly inscribed "Monna Lisa".

210 Peace Corps and Gambian Flags

1993. 25th Anniv of U.S. Peace Corps.

1452 **210** 2 d. multicoloured .. 30 35

211 Jackie Robinson and Ruby Dee ("The Jackie Robinson Story")

1993. Baseball Films. Multicoloured.

1453 3 d. Type **211** 45 50
1454 3 d. Robert DeNiro ("Bang the Drum Slowly") 45 50
1455 3 d. James Earl Jones and Billy Dee Williams ("The Bingo Long Travelling All-Stars and Motor Kings") .. 45 50
1456 3 d. Kevin Costner and Susan Sarandon ("Bull Durham") 45 50
1457 3 d. Cast photograph ("Eight Men Out") .. 45 50
1458 3 d. Ray Liotta ("Field of Dreams") 45 50
1459 3 d. Charlie Sheen ("Major League") 45 50
1460 3 d. Tom Selleck ("Mr. Baseball") 45 50
1461 3 d. Wallace Beery, 1927, and Elliott Gould, 1986 ("Casey at the Bat") .. 45 50
1462 3 d. Anna Nilsson and Babe Ruth ("Babe comes Home") .. 45 50
1463 3 d. Joe Brown ("Elmer the Great") 45 50
1464 3 d. Bud Abbott and Lou Costello ("The Naughty Nineties") 45 50
1465 3 d. Frank Sinatra, Gene Kelly and Esther Williams ("Take Me Out to the Ball Game") 45 50
1466 3 d. Tab Hunter and Gwen Verdon ("Damn Yankees") 45 50
1467 3 d. Dan Dailey ("The Pride of St. Louis") .. 45 50
1468 3 d. John Candy and Richard Pryor ("Brewster's Millions") 45 50

212 Giraffe

1993. Animals of West Africa. Multicoloured.

1470 2 d. Type **212** 30 35
1471 2 d. Baboon 30 35
1472 2 d. Caracal .. 30 35
1473 2 d. Large-spotted genet 30 35
1474 2 d. Bushbuck 30 35
1475 2 d. Red-fronted gazelle 30 35
1476 2 d. Red-flanked duiker 30 35
1477 2 d. Cape buffalo .. 30 35
1478 2 d. African civet .. 30 35
1479 2 d. Side-striped jackal .. 30 35
1480 2 d. Ratel 30 35
1481 2 d. Striped polecat .. 30 35
1482 5 d. Vervet 70 75
1483 5 d. Blackish-green guenon 70 75
1484 5 d. Long-tailed pangolin 70 75
1485 5 d. Leopard 70 75
1486 5 d. Elephant 70 75
1487 5 d. Hunting dog .. 70 75
1488 5 d. Spotted hyena .. 70 75
1489 5 d. Lion 70 75
1490 5 d. Hippopotamus .. 70 75
1491 5 d. Nile crocodile .. 70 75
1492 5 d. Aardvark .. 70 75
1493 5 d. Warthog 70 75

Nos. 1470/81 and 1482/93 were each printed together, se-tenant, with the backgrounds forming composite designs.

213 Long-tailed Pangolin hanging by Tail

1993. Endangered Species. Long-tailed Pangolin. Multicoloured.

1495 1 d. 25 Type **213** .. 20 25
1496 1 d. 50 Sitting on branch 20 25
1497 2 d. Climbing up branch 30 35
1498 5 d. Climbing down branch 70 75

214 Osprey

1993. Birds of Prey. Multicoloured.

1500 1 d. 25 Type **214** .. 20 25
1501 1 d. 50 Egyptian vulture (horiz) 20 25
1502 2 d. Martial eagle .. 30 35
1503 3 d. Ruppell's griffon (horiz) 45 50
1504 5 d. Augur buzzard .. 70 75
1505 8 d. Greater kestrel .. 1·10 1·25
1506 10 d. Secretary bird .. 1·50 1·60
1507 15 d. Bateleur (horiz) .. 2·10 2·25

215 Rose-ringed Parakeet

1993. African Birds. Multicoloured.

1509 2 d. Type **215** 30 35
1510 2 d. Variable sunbird 30 35
1511 2 d. Red-billed hornbill .. 30 35
1512 2 d. Red-billed fire finch 30 35
1513 2 d. Go-away bird .. 30 35
1514 2 d. Crimson-breasted shrike 30 35
1515 2 d. Grey-headed Bush shrike 30 35
1516 2 d. Western nicator .. 30 35
1517 2 d. Egyptian plover .. 30 35
1518 2 d. Congo peafowl .. 30 35
1519 2 d. Painted snipe .. 30 35
1520 2 d. Crowned crane .. 30 35

1993. 40th Anniv of Coronation. As T **307** of Antigua.

1521 2 d. multicoloured .. 30 35
1522 5 d. multicoloured .. 70 75
1523 8 d. brown and black .. 1·10 1·25
1524 10 d. multicoloured .. 1·50 1·75

DESIGNS—38 × 47 mm: 2 d. Queen Elizabeth II at Coronation (photograph by Cecil Beaton); 5 d. Orb and sceptre; 8 d. Sir Winston Churchill; 10 d. Queen Elizabeth II at Trooping the Colour.

216 Hugo Eckener and Zeppelin "Luftschiffe 3"

1993. Aviation Anniversaries. Multicoloured.

1526 2 d. Type **216** 30 35
1527 2 d. Guyot's balloon, 1785 (vert) 30 35
1528 5 d. Zeppelin "Luftschiffe 3" and crowd 70 75
1529 5 d. Sopwith Snipe (fighter) 70 75
1530 8 d. Eckener and "Graf Zeppelin" .. .. 1·10 1·25
1531 10 d. "Comte D'Artois" (hot air balloon), 1785 (vert) .. .. .. 1·50 1·60
1532 15 d. S.E.5 (fighter) .. 2·10 2·25

ANNIVERSARIES: Nos. 1526, 1528, 1530, Birth anniv of Hugo Eckener (airship pioneer); Nos. 1527, 1531, Bicentenary of first airmail flight; Nos. 1529, 1532, 75th Anniv of Royal Air Force.

217 Henry Ford and "Model T", 1910

1993. Centenaries of Henry Ford's First Petrol Engine (Nos. 1534/45) and Karl Benz's First Four-wheeled Car (Nos. 1546/57). Mult.

1534 2 d. Type **217** 30 35
1535 2 d. Car of 1896 .. .. 30 35
1536 2 d. Henry Ford with Barney Oldfield and "999", 1902 .. .. 30 35
1537 2 d. Henry Ford, 1893, and car of 1896 .. 30 35
1538 2 d. "Model A", 1903 .. 30 35
1539 2 d. "Model T" with roof lowered, 1908 .. .. 30 35
1540 2 d. "Model T" with roof raised, 1908 .. .. 30 35
1541 2 d. "Model K", 1906 .. 30 35
1542 2 d. "Model A", 1931 .. 30 35
1543 2 d. "Model A", 1906 .. 30 35
1544 2 d. "Model N", 1906 .. 30 35
1545 2 d. "Model F", 1905 .. 30 35
1546 2 d. Benz "Velo", 1894 .. 30 35
1547 2 d. Car of 1894 .. 30 35
1548 2 d. Three-wheeled car of 1885 from side .. 30 35
1549 2 d. "Mannheim", 1905 .. 30 35
1550 2 d. Car of 1892 .. .. 30 35
1551 2 d. Car of 1900 from front 30 35
1552 2 d. Racing car of 1911 from side 30 35
1553 2 d. "Velo", 1893 .. 30 35
1554 2 d. Black car of 1900 from side 30 35
1555 2 d. Red car of 1900 from side 30 35
1556 2 d. Racing car of 1911 from front 30 35
1557 2 d. Three-wheeled car of 1885 from back .. 30 35

Nos. 1534/45 and 1546/57 were each printed together, se-tenant, with the backgrounds forming composite designs.

218 Marilyn Monroe

1993. Musical Entertainers.

1559/93 3 d. × 35 multicoloured 14·00 16·00

Nos. 1559/93 were issued as four sheetlets, three of nine different designs (Nos. 1559/85) and one of eight (Nos. 1586/93), depicting Marilyn Monroe (Nos. 1559/67), Elvis Presley (Nos. 1568/76), Madonna (Nos. 1577/85) and Buddy Holly, Otis Redding, Bill Haley, Dinah Washington, musical instruments, Ritchie Valens, Clyde McPhatter, Elvis Presley (Nos. 1586/93).

219 Siamese

1993. Oriental Cats. Multicoloured.

1594 2 d. Type **219** 30 35
1595 2 d. Colourpoint longhair sitting 30 35
1596 2 d. Burmese 30 35
1597 2 d. Birman 30 35
1598 2 d. Snowshoe 30 35
1559 2 d. Tonkinese 30 35
1600 2 d. Foreign shorthair stretching 30 35
1601 2 d. Balinese 30 35
1602 2 d. Oriental shorthair .. 30 35
1603 2 d. Foreign shorthair lying 30 35
1604 2 d. Colourpoint longhair with black face standing 30 35
1605 2 d. Colourpoint longhair with white face standing 30 35

Nos. 1594/1605 were printed together, se-tenant, with the background forming a composite design.

1993. Royal Dogs. As T **214**. Multicoloured.

1607 2 d. Shih tzu (Emperor of China) 30 35
1608 2 d. Skye terrier (Queen Victoria) 30 35
1609 2 d. Berner laufhund (King Louis XVI, France) 30 35
1610 2 d. Boxer (King Francis I, France) 30 35
1611 2 d. Welsh corgi (Queen Elizabeth II) 30 35
1612 2 d. Dumfrieshire (Princess Anne) 30 35
1613 2 d. Lurcher (King George VI) 30 35
1614 2 d. Welsh corgi (Princess Anne) 30 35
1615 2 d. Pekinese (Empress Ts'Eu-Hi, China) .. 30 35
1616 2 d. Papillon (King Louis XIII, France) .. 30 35
1617 2 d. Otterhound (King John) 30 35
1618 2 d. Pug (Napoleon I, France) 30 35

Nos. 1607/18 were printed together, se-tenant, with the background forming a composite design.

1993. Asian International Stamp Exhibitions. As T **268** of Dominica. Multicoloured. (a) "Indopex '93", Surabaya, Indonesia

1620 20 b. National Monument and statue, Jakarta .. 10 10
1621 20 b. Pura Taman Ayun Temple, Bali 10 10
1622 2 d. Guardian statue, Singosari Palace, Java 30 35
1623 2 d. Candi Jawi, Java .. 30 35
1624 5 d. Telek Luh mask .. 70 75
1625 5 d. Jero Gde mask .. 70 75
1626 5 d. Barong Macan mask 70 75
1627 5 d. Monkey mask .. 70 75
1628 5 d. Mata Gde mask .. 70 75
1629 5 d. Jauk Kras mask .. 70 75
1630 5 d. "Tree Mask" (Soedibio) 70 75
1631 5 d. "Dry Lizard" (Hendra Gunawan) .. 70 75
1632 5 d. "The Corn Eater" (Sudjana Kerton) .. 70 75
1633 5 d. "Night Watchman" (Djoko Pekik) .. 70 75
1634 5 d. "Hunger" (Kerton) 70 75
1635 5 d. "Arje Player" (Soedjojono) 70 75
1636 5 d. Central Temple, Lara Djonggrang 70 75
1637 5 d. Irian Jaya Monument, Jakarta .. 70 75
1638 15 d. Brahma and Siva Temples, Java .. 2·10 2·25
1639 15 d. Date of the Year Temple, Java .. .. 2·10 2·25

(b) "Taipei '93", Taiwan

1641 20 b. Fawang Si Pagoda, Henan 10 10
1642 20 b. Wanshoubao Pagoda, Shashi .. 10 10
1643 2 d. Red Pavilion, Shibaozhai 30 35
1644 2 d. Songyue Si Pagoda, Henan 30 35
1645 5 d. Pottery camel (walking) 70 75
1646 5 d. Pottery horse and rider 70 75
1647 5 d. Pottery camel (standing with mouth closed) 70 75
1648 5 d. Yellow-glazed pottery horse 70 75
1649 5 d. Pottery camel (standing with mouth open) 70 75
1650 5 d. Pottery saddled horse 70 75
1651 5 d. Qianlong vase .. 70 75
1652 5 d. Small wine cup .. 70 75
1653 5 d. Mei-ping vase .. 70 75
1654 5 d. Urn vase 70 75
1655 5 d. Tureen 70 75
1656 5 d. Lidded potiche .. 70 75
1657 5 d. Tianning Si Pagoda, Beijing 70 75
1658 5 d. Bond Centre, Hong Kong 70 75
1659 15 d. Forbidden City pavilion, Beijing .. 2·10 2·25
1660 15 d. Xuanzhuang Pagoda, Shenxi .. 2·10 2·25

(c) "Bangkok '93", Thailand

1662 20 b. Sanctuary of Prasat Phanom Wan 10 10
1663 20 b. Lai Kham Vihan, Chiang Mai 10 10
1664 2 d. Upmarket spirit shrine, Bangkok .. 30 35
1665 2 d. Walking Buddha statue, Wat Phra Si Ratana Mahathat .. 30 35
1666 5 d. "Early Fruit Stand" 70 75
1667 5 d. "Scene Rendered in Chinese Style" .. 70 75
1668 5 d. "Buddha descends from Tauatimsa" .. 70 75
1669 5 d. "Sang Thong Tales" (detail) 70 75
1670 5 d. "The Damned in Hell" 70 75
1671 5 d. "King Sanjaya travels on Elephant" .. 70 75
1672 5 d. U Thong C Buddha (bronze) 70 75
1673 5 d. Seated Buddha (bronze) 70 75
1674 5 d. Phra Chai Buddha (ivory and gold) .. 70 75
1675 5 d. Buddha (bronze) .. 70 75
1676 5 d. U Thong A Buddha (bronze) 70 75
1677 5 d. Crowned Buddha (bronze) 70 75
1678 5 d. Statue of Buddha, Wat Mahathat .. 70 75
1679 5 d. The Gopura of Prasat Phanom Rung .. 70 75
1680 15 d. Slender Chedis, Mongkon .. .. 2·10 2·25
1681 15 d. The Prang of Prasat Hin Phimai .. .. 2·10 2·25

220 "Woman with a Comb" (Picasso)

1993. Anniversaries and Events. Mult.

1683 2 d. Type **220** 30 35
1684 2 d. "Pont-Neuf in Paris" (Hanna Rudzka-Cybisowa) (horiz) .. 30 35
1685 5 d. "The Mirror" (Picasso) 70 75
1686 5 d. Early astronomical instrument 70 75
1687 7 d. "Woman on a Pillow" (Picasso) .. 1·00 1·10
1688 10 d. Niedzica Castle (horiz) .. .. 1·50 1·60
1689 10 d. "Honegger's Liturgical Symphony" (Marian Bogusz) (horiz) 1·50 1·60
1690 10 d. Modern telescope .. 1·50 1·60

ANNIVERSARIES AND EVENTS: Nos. 1683, 1685, 1687, 20th death anniv of Picasso (artist); Nos. 1684, 1688/9, "Polska '93" International Stamp Exhibition, Poznan; Nos. 1686, 1690, 450th death anniv of Copernicus (astronomer).

221 Mudville Player at the Plate

1993. "Casey at the Bat". Scenes from Walt Disney's cartoon film. Multicoloured.

1692 2 d. Type **221** 30 35
1693 2 d. Mudville player out 30 35
1694 2 d. Umpire and player arguing 30 35
1695 2 d. Fans applauding .. 30 35
1696 2 d. Casey reading newspaper at plate .. 30 35
1697 2 d. Casey letting second pitch go by 30 35
1698 2 d. Over-confident Casey 30 35
1699 2 d. Casey's striking out 30 35
1700 2 d. Casey striking out at night 30 35

1993. World Cup Football Championship 1994, U.S.A. As T **310** of Antigua. Multicoloured.

1702 1 d. 25 Hannich (Hungary) and Stopyra (France) 20 25
1703 1 d. 50 Labd (Morocco) and Gary Lineker (England) 25 30
1704 2 d. Segota (Canada) and Morozov (Russia) .. 30 35
1705 3 d. Roger Milla (Cameroun) 45 50
1706 5 d. Rodax (Austria) and Weiss (Czechoslovakia) 70 75
1707 10 d. Claesen (Belgium), Bossis and Amoros (France) .. .. 1·50 1·60
1708 12 d. Candida (Brazil) and Ramirez (Costa Rica) 1·60 1·75
1709 15 d. Silva (Brazil) and Michel Platini (France) 2·10 2·25

GHANA

Formerly the Br. Colony of Gold Coast. Attained Dominion status on 6 March 1957, and became a republic within the Br. Commonwealth in 1960.

1957. 12 pence = 1 shilling.
20 shillings = 1 pound.
1965. 100 pesewas = 1 cedi.
1967. 100 new pesewas = 1 new cedi.
1972. 100 pesewas = 1 cedi = 0·8 (old) new cedi.

NOTE. CANCELLED REMAINDERS

In 1961 remainders of some issues of 1957 to 1960 were put on the market concelled-to-order in such a way as to be indistinguishable from genuine postally used copies. Our used quotations which are indicated by an asterisk are, therefore, for cancelled-to-order copies.

29. Dr. Kwame Nkrumah, Palm-nut Vulture and Map of Africa.

1957. Independence Commem.

No.	Description		
166. **29.**	2d. red	10	10*
167.	2½d. green	10	10*
168.	4d. brown	10	10*
169.	1s. 3d. blue	15	10*

1957. Queen Elizabeth stamps of 1952 of Gold Coast optd. **GHANA INDEPENDENCE 6TH MARCH 1957.**

No.	Description		
170.	½d. brown and red	10	10*
171.	1d. blue	10	10*
172.	1½d. green	10	10*
173.	2d. brown	30	30
174.	2½d. red	1·00	1·25
175.	3d. mauve	20	10*
176.	4d. blue	3·00	4·00
177.	6d. black and orange	10	10*
178.	1s. black and red	10	10*
179.	2s. olive and red	60	10*
180.	5s. purple and black	60	10*
181.	10s. black and olive	60	40*

31. Viking Ship.

1957. Inaug. of Black Star Shipping Line.

No.	Description		
182. **31.**	2½d. green	70	20
183. –	1s. 3d. blue	1·00	1·25
184. –	5s. purple	1·50	3·00

DESIGNS—HORIZ. 1s. 3d., Galleon. 5s. M.V. "Volta River".

DESIGNS—HORIZ. 2½d. State Opening of Parliament. 1s. 3d., National Monument. VERT. 2s. Ghana Coat of Arms.

34. Ambassador Hotel, Accra.

1958. 1st Anniv. of Independence. Flag and Coat of Arms in national colours.

No.	Description		
185. **34.**	½d. black and red	10	10
186. –	2½d. black, red & yellow	10	10
187. –	1s. 3d. black and blue	25	10
188. –	2s. yellow and black	35	35

38. Map showing the Independent African States.

1958. 1st Conference of Independent African States, Accra. Star in black and yellow.

No.	Description		
189. **38.**	2½d. red and yellow	10	10
190.	3d. green and brown	10	10
191. –	1s. blue, yellow & orge.	15	10
192. –	2s. 6d. pur., yell. & orge.	30	35

DESIGN—VERT. 1s., 2s. 6d. Map of Africa and flaming torch.

40. Palm-nut Vulture over Globe.

DESIGNS—HORIZ. As Type **42**: 1s 3d., "Britannia" airliner. As Type **40**: 2s 6d., Palm-nut vulture and jet aircraft.

42. "Stratocruiser" and Yellow-nosed Albatross.

1958. Inaug. of Ghana Airways. Inscr. as in T **40/42.**

No.	Description		
193. **40.**	2½d. black, bistre and red	45	10
194. –	1s 3d. multicoloured (air)	90	20
195. **42.**	2s. multicoloured	1·00	40
196. –	2s. 6d. black and bistre	1·00	80

1958. Prime Minister's Visit to United States and Canada. Optd. **PRIME MINISTER'S VISIT. U.S.A. AND CANADA.**

No.	Description		
197. **29.**	2d. red	10	10
198.	2½d. green	10	10
199.	4d. brown	10	10
200.	1s. 3d. blue	15	20

45. 46. Dr. Nkrumah and Lincoln Statue, Washington.

1958. United Nations Day.

No.	Description		
201. **45.**	2½d. brn., grn. and blk.	10	10
202.	1s. 3d. brn., blue & blk.	20	10
203.	2s. 6d. brn., violet & blk.	25	35

1959. 150th Birth Anniv. of Abraham Lincoln.

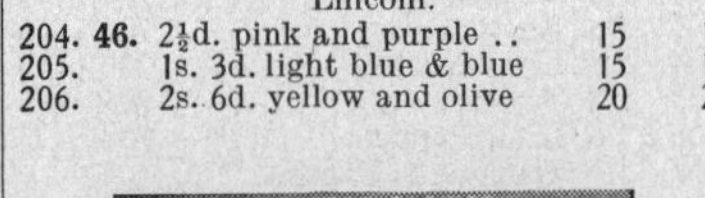

No.	Description		
204. **46.**	2½d. pink and purple	15	10
205.	1s. 3d. light blue & blue	15	10
206.	2s. 6d. yellow and olive	20	20

49. Talking Drums and Elephant-horn Blower.

1959. Independence. Inscr. "SECOND ANNIVERSARY OF INDEPENDENCE".

No.	Description		
207. –	½d. multicoloured	10	10
208. **49.**	2½d. multicoloured	10	10
209. –	1s. 3d. multicoloured	15	10
210. –	2s. multicoloured	30	60

DESIGNS—HORIZ. ½d. Kente cloth and traditional symbols. 2s. Map of Africa, Ghana flag and palms. VERT. 1s. 3d., "Symbol of Greeting".

52. Globe and Flags.

1959. Africa Freedom Day.

No.	Description		
211. **52.**	2½d. multicoloured	15	10
212.	8½d. multicoloured	15	20

54. Nkrumah Statue, Accra. 55. Ghana Timber.

65a. Red-fronted Gazelle.

1959. Multicoloured.

No.	Description		
213	½d. "God's Omnipotence" (postage)	10	10
213a	½d. "Gye Nyame"	30	10
214	1d. Type **54**	10	10
215	1½d. Type **55**	10	10
216	2d. Volta river	10	10
217	2½d. Cocoa bean	10	10
218	3d. "God's Omnipotence"	10	10
218a	3d. "Gye Nyame"	30	10
219	4d. Diamond and mine	3·50	40
220	6d. Red-crowned bishop (bird)	50	10
221	11d. Golden spider lily	25	10
222	1s. Shell ginger	25	10
223	2s. 6d. Giant blue turaco	2·25	15
224	5s. Tiger orchid	5·00	50
225	10s. Tropical African cichlid	2·75	70
225a	£1 Type **65a**	11·00	4·75
226	1s. 3d. Pennant-winged nightjar (air)	2·00	10
227	2s. Crowned cranes	1·75	10

SIZES—HORIZ. As Type **54**: ½d. As Type **55**: 2d., 2½d., 3d., 4d., 6d., 1s. 3d., 2s. 6d. As Type **65a**: 10s. VERT. As Type **55**: 11d., 1s., 2s., 5s. The 3d. is a different symbolic design from the ½d.

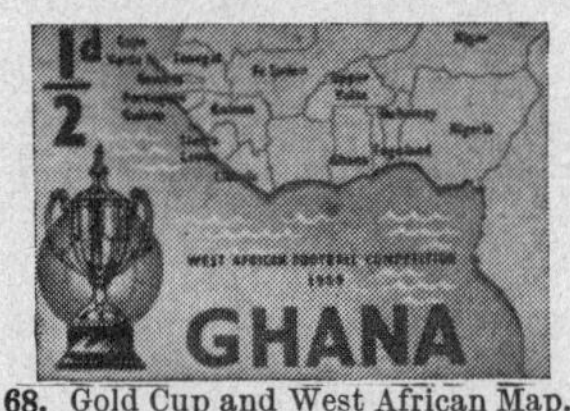

68. Gold Cup and West African Map.

1959. West African Football Competition, 1959. Multicoloured.

No.	Description		
228.	½d. Type **68**	10	10*
229.	1d. Footballers	10	10*
230.	3d. Goalkeeper saving ball	15	10*
231.	8d. Forward attacking goal	70	15*
232.	2s. 6d. "Kwame Nkrumah" Gold Cup	1·00	15*

Nos. 229 and 232 are vert. and the rest horiz.

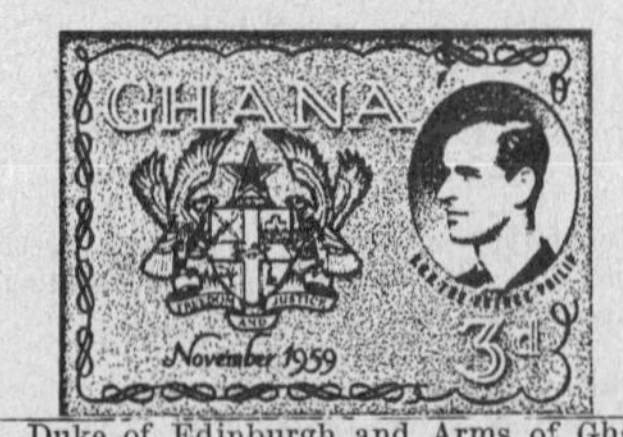

73. Duke of Edinburgh and Arms of Ghana.

1959. Visit of the Duke of Edinburgh

No.	Description		
233. **73.**	3d. black and mauve	30	10*

74. Ghana Flag and Talking Drums.

1959. U.N. Trusteeship Council. Multicoloured.

No.	Description		
234.	3d. Type **74**	10	10*
235.	6d. Ghana flag and U.N. emblem	10	10*
236.	1s. 3d. As 6d. but emblem above flag	30	15*
237.	2s. 6d. "Totem pole"	40	15*

Nos. 235/7 are vert.

78. Eagles in Flight.

1960. 3rd Anniv. of Independence. Mult.

No.	Description		
238.	½d. Type **78**	10	10*
239.	3d. Fireworks	10	10*
240.	1s. 3d. "Third Anniversary"	30	10*
241.	2s. "Ship of State"	30	15*

82. Flags and Map forming letter "A".

1960. African Freedom Day. Mult.

No.	Description		
242.	3d. Type **82**	10	10*
243.	6d. Letter "f"	20	10*
244.	1s. Letter "d"	20	10*

85. Dr. Nkrumah.

1960. Republic Day. Inscr. "REPUBLIC DAY 1st JULY 1960". Multicoloured.

No.	Description		
245.	3d. Type **85**	10	10
246.	1s. 3d. Ghana Flag	20	10
247.	2s. Torch of Freedom	30	20
248.	10s. Ghana Arms	80	1·00

The 10s. is horiz. and the rest vert.

90. Athlete.

1960. Olympic Games.

No.	Description		
249. –	3d. multicoloured	10	10
250. –	6d. multicoloured	15	10
251. **90.**	1s. 3d. multicoloured	25	10
252.	2s. 6d. multicoloured	35	20

DESIGN—VERT. 3d., 6d. Olympic torch.

91. Pres. Nkrumah.

1960 Founder's Day. Inscr. as in T **91**.
253. **91.** 3d. multicoloured .. 10 10
254. – 6d. multicoloured .. 10 10
255. – 1s. 3d. multicoloured .. 20 20
DESIGNS—VERT. 6d. Pres. Nkrumah within star. 1s. 3d. Map of Africa and column.

94. U.N. Emblem and Ghana Flag.

1960. Human Rights Day.
256. **94.** 3d. multicoloured .. 10 10
257. – 6d. yellow, black & blue 20 10
258. – 1s. 3d. multicoloured .. 40 20
DESIGNS U.N. Emblem with torch (6d.) or within laurel (1s. 3d.).

97. Talking Drums.

1961. Africa Freedom Day. Inscr. "15th APRIL 1961".
259. **97.** 3d. multicoloured .. 10 10
260. – 6d. red, black and green 20 10
261. – 2s. multicoloured .. 50 45
DESIGNS—VERT. 6d. Map of Africa. HORIZ. 2s. Flags and map.

100. Eagle on Column.

1961. 1st Anniv of Republic. Multicoloured.
262. 3d. Type **100** 10 10
263. 1s. 3d. "Flower" .. 10 10
264. 2s. Ghana flags. .. 20 40

103. Dove with Olive Branch.

DESIGNS—HORIZ 1s. 3d. World map, chain and olive branch. 5s. Rostrum, Conference room.

1961. Belgrade Conf.
265. **103.** 3d. green 10 10
266. – 1s. 3d. blue 25 10
267. – 5s. purple 75 50

106. Pres. Nkrumah and Globe.

1961. Founder's Day Multicoloured.
268. 3d. Type **106** 10 10
269. 1s. 3d. Pres. in Kente cloth 30 10
270. 5s. Pres. in national costume 1·25 1·75
Nos. 269/70 are vert.

109. Queen Elizabeth II and African Map.

1961. Royal Visit.
271. **109.** 3d. multicoloured .. 15 10
272. 1s. 3d. multicoloured .. 75 20
273. 5s. multicoloured .. 2·50 2·75

110. Ships in Tema Harbour.

1962. Opening of Tema Harbour.
274. **110.** 3d. multicoloured (post.) 15 10
275. – 1s. 3d. multicoloured (air) 60 15
276. – 2s. 6d. multicoloured .. 90 70
DESIGN 1s. 3d., 2s. 6d. Aircraft and ships at Tema.

112. Africa and Peace Dove.

1962. 1st Anniv. of Casablanca Conf.
277. **112.** 3d. multicoloured (post.) 10 10
278. 1s. 3d. multicoloured (air) 30 10
279. 2s. 6d. multicoloured .. 40 40

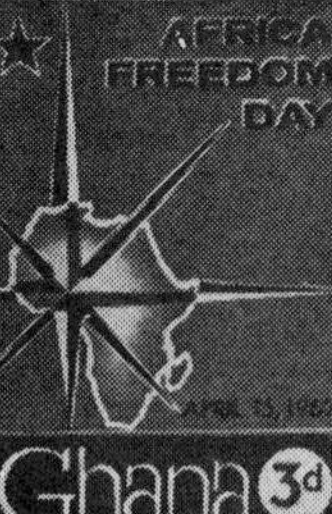

113. Compass over Africa. **115.** Atomic Bomb-burst Skull.

1962. Africa Freedom Day.
280. **113.** 3d. sepia, turq. & purple 10 10
281. 6d. sepia, turq. & brown 10 10
282. 1s. 3d. sepia, turq. & red 15 10

1962. The Accra Assembly.
283. – 3d. black and lake .. 10 10
284. **115.** 6d. black and red .. 25 15
285. – 1s. 3d. turquoise .. 30 15
DESIGNS: 3d. Ghana Star over "five continents". 1s. 3d., Dove of Peace.

117. Patrice Lumumba.

1962. 1st Death Anniv. of Lumumba.
286. **117.** 3d. black and yellow .. 10 10
287. 6d. black, green & lake 10 10
288. 1s. 3d. blk., pink & grn. 15 15

118. Star over Two Columns.

1962. 2nd. Anniv. of Republic. Inscribed "1st JULY 1962". Multicoloured.
289. 3d. Type **118** 10 10
290. 6d. Flaming torch .. 20 20
291. 1s. 3d. Eagle trailing flag .. 40 40
The 1s. 3d. is horiz.

121. President Nkrumah.

DESIGNS: 3d. Nkrumah Medallion. 1s. 3d., President and Ghana Star. 2s. Laying "Ghana" brick.

1962. Founder's Day.
292. **121.** 1d. multicoloured .. 10 10
293. – 3d. multicoloured .. 10 10
294. – 1s. 3d. black and blue .. 30 10
295. – 2s. multicoloured .. 30 20

125. Campaign Emblem. **126.** Campaign Emblem.

1962. Malaria Eradication.
296. **125.** 1d. red 10 10
297. 4d. green 40 50
298. 6d. bistre 40 15
299. 1s. 3d. violet 50 50

1963. Freedom from Hunger.
300. **126.** 1d. multicoloured .. 15 10
301. – 4d. sepia, yellow & orge. 75 45
302. – 1s. 3d. ochre, blk. & grn. 1·60 80
DESIGNS—HORIZ. 4d. Emblem in hands. 1s. 3d. World map and emblem.

129. Map of Africa. **133.** Red Cross.

1963. Africa Freedom Day.
303. **129.** 1d. gold and red .. 10 10
304. – 4d. red, black & yellow 10 10
305. – 1s. 3d. multicoloured .. 25 10
306. – 2s. 6d. multicoloured .. 45 75
DESIGNS—HORIZ. 4d. Carved stool. VERT. 1s. 3d., Map and bowl of fire. 2s. 6d., Topi and flag.

1963. Centenary of Red Cross. Multicoloured.
307. 1d. Type **133** .. 40 15
308. 1½d. Centenary emblem .. 55 60
309. 4d. Nurses and child .. 1·75 15
310. 1s. 3d. Emblem, Globe and laurel .. .. 3·25 1·60
The 1½d. and 4d. are horiz.

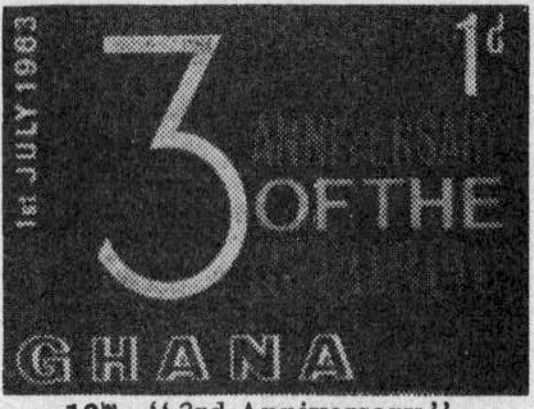

137. "3rd Anniversary".

1963. 3rd Anniv. of Republic. Multicoloured.
311. 1d. Type **137** 10 10
312. 4d. Three Ghanian flags .. 10 10
313. 1s. 3d. Map, flag and star (vert.) 35 30
314. 2s. 6d. Flag and torch (vert.) 55 75

141. Pres. Nkrumah and Ghana Flag. **145.** Rameses II, Abu Simbel.

1963. Founder's Day.
315. **141.** 1d. multicoloured .. 10 10
316. – 4d. multicoloured .. 15 10
317. – 1s. 3d. multicoloured .. 30 10
318. – 5s. yellow and mauve .. 65 75
DESIGNS—VERT. 4d. As Type **141** but with larger flag behind Pres. Nkrumah. HORIZ. 1s. 3d. Pres. Nkrumah and fireworks. 5s. Native symbol of wisdom.

1963. Preservation of Nubian Monuments. Multicoloured.
319. 1d. Type **145** 10 10
320. 1½d. Rock paintings .. 15 50
321. 2d. Queen Nefertari .. 15 10
322. 4d. Sphinx, Sebua .. 25 15
323. 1s. 3d. Rock Temple, Abu Simbel 70 85
The 1d. and 4d. are vert., the rest horiz.

150. Steam and Diesel Locomotives.

1963. 60th Anniv. of Ghana Railway.
324. **150.** 1d. multicoloured .. 10 10
325. 6d. multicoloured .. 60 10
326. 1s. 3d. multicoloured .. 1·25 60
327. 2s. 6d. multicoloured .. 2·25 2·25

151. Eleanor Roosevelt and "Flame of Freedom".

1963. 5th Anniv. of Declaration of Human Rights. Multicoloured.
328. 1d. Type **151** 10 10
329. 4d. Type **151** 10 10
330. 6d. Eleanor Roosevelt .. 10 10
331. 1s. 3d. Eleanor Roosevelt and emblems (horiz.) .. 15 15

154. Sun and Globe Emblem.

1964. Int. Quiet Sun Years.
332. **154.** 3d. multicoloured .. 15 10
333. 6d. multicoloured .. 25 10
334. 1s. 3d. multicoloured .. 25 15

155. Harvesting Corn on State Farm.

1964. 4th Anniv. of Republic.

335. 155. 3d. olive, brown & yell. 10 10
336. – 6d. grn., brn & turquoise 10 10
337. – 1s. 3d. red, brn. & salmon 10 10
338. – 5s. multicoloured. 40 60

DESIGNS: 6d. Oil refinery, Tema. 1s. 3d., "Communal Labour". 5s. Procession headed by flag.

159. Globe and Dove.

1964. 1st Anniv. of African Unity Charter.

339. 159. 3d. multicoloured 10 10
340. – 6d. green and red .. 10 10
341. – 1s. 3d. multicoloured .. 15 10
342. – 5s. multicoloured .. 45 60

DESIGNS—VERT. 6d. Map of Africa and quill pen. 5s. Planting flower. HORIZ. 1s. 3d., Hitched rope on map of Africa.

163. Pres Nkrumah and Hibiscus Flowers.

1964. Founder's Day.

343. 163. 3d. multicoloured .. 10 10
344. 6d. multicoloured .. 15 10
345. 1s. 3d. multicoloured .. 35 10
346. 2s. 6d. multicoloured .. 50 35

164. Hurdling.

1964. Olympic Games, Tokyo. Multicoloured.

347. 1d. Type **164** 10 10
348. 2½d. Running 10 50
349. 3d. Boxing 10 10
350. 4d. Long-jumping 10 10
351. 6d. Football 15 10
352. 1s. 3d. Athlete holding Olympic Torch .. 20 10
353. 5s. Olympic "Rings" and Flags .. .. 85 2·50

Nos. 249/52 are vert.

171. G. Washington Carver (botanist) and Plant.

1964. UNESCO Week.

354. 171. 6d. blue and green .. 15 10
355. – 1s. 3d. purple and blue 45 10
356. 171. 5s. sepia and red .. 1·90 3·00

DESIGN: 1s. 3d., Albert Einstein (scientist) and Atomic symbol.

173. African Elephant.

1964. Multicoloured.

357. 1d. Type **173** .. 50 20
358. 1½d. Secretary bird (horiz.) 75 1·25
359. 2½d. Purple wreath (flower) 60 1·25
360. 3d. Grey parrot .. 1·00 40
361. 4d. Blue-naped mousebird (horiz.) .. .. .. 1·25 60
362. 6d. African tulip tree (horiz.) 60 30
363. 1s 3d. Violet starling (horiz.) .. .. .. 1·75 1·25
364. 2s 6d. Hippopotamus (horiz.) .. .. .. 1·75 4·25

181. I.C.Y. Emblem.

1965. Int. Co-operation Year.

365. 181. 1d. multicoloured .. 35 20
366. 4d. multicoloured .. 1·25 45
367. 6d. multicoloured .. 1·50 20
368. 1s. 3d. multicoloured .. 1·75 1·90

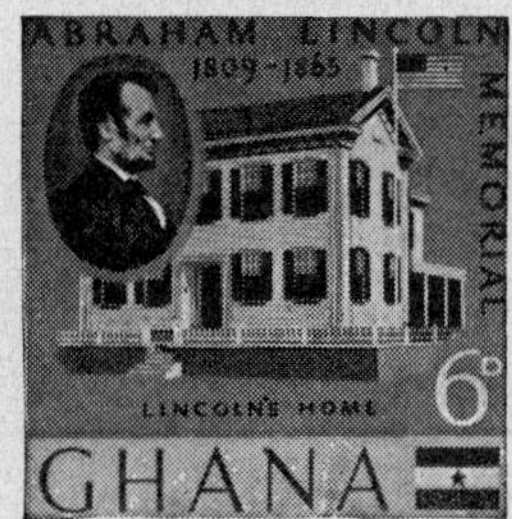

182. I.T.U. Emblem and Symbols.

1965. Centenary of I.T.U.

369. 182. 1d. multicoloured .. 15 15
370. 6d. multicoloured .. 45 15
371. 1s. 3d. multicoloured .. 85 25
372. 5s. multicoloured .. 2·25 2·75

183. Lincoln's Home.

1965. Death Cent. of Abraham Lincoln.

373. 183. 6d. multicoloured .. 15 10
374. – 1s. 3d. black, red & blue 30 15
375. – 2s. black, brn. & yellow 40 30
376. – 3s. black and red .. 85 1·50

DESIGNS: 1s. 3d., Lincoln's Inaugural Address. 2s. Abraham Lincoln. 5s. Adaption of U.S. 90 c. Lincoln stamp of 1869.

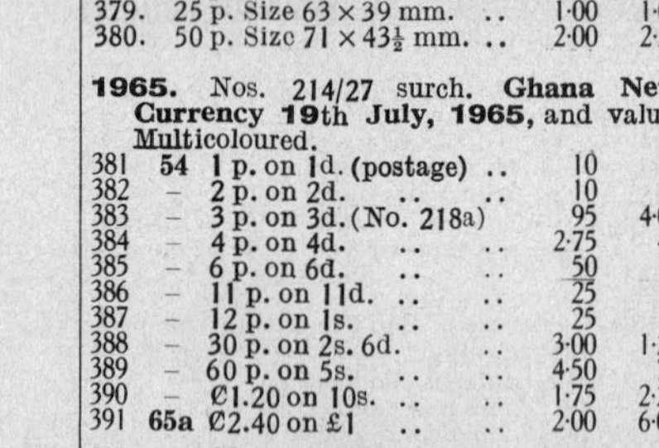

187. Obverse (Pres. Nkrumah) and Reverse of 5 p. Coin.

1965. Introduction of Decimal Currency. Multicoloured designs showing coins expressed in the same denominations as on the stamps.

377. 5 p. Type **187** 25 10
378. 10 p. As Type **187** .. 30 10
379. 25 p. Size 63 × 39 mm. .. 1·00 1·00
380. 50 p. Size 71 × 43½ mm. .. 2·00 2·25

1965. Nos. 214/27 surch. **Ghana New Currency 19th July, 1965,** and value. Multicoloured.

381 **54** 1 p. on 1d. (postage) .. 10 10
382 – 2 p. on 2d. 10 10
383 – 3 p. on 3d. (No. 218a) 95 4·00
384 – 4 p. on 4d. .. .. 2·75 45
385 – 6 p. on 6d. 50 10
386 – 11 p. on 11d. 25 10
387 – 12 p. on 1s. 25 10
388 – 30 p. on 2s. 6d. .. 3·00 1·25
389 – 60 p. on 5s. .. .. 4·50 70
390 – ₵1.20 on 10s. .. .. 1·75 2·25
391 **65a** ₵2.40 on £1 .. .. 2·00 6·00
392 – 15 p. on 1s. 3d. (air) .. 2·00 45
393 – 24 p. on 2s. .. .. 2·50 30

189. "OAU" and Flag (reduced size illustration. Actual size 60 × 30 mm.).

1965. O.A.U. Summit Conf., Accra. Mult.

394. 1 p. Type **189** 10 10
395. 2 p. "OAU", Heads & Flag 10 10
396. 5 p. O.A.U. Emblem & Flag 10 10
397. 6 p. African Map and Flag 10 10
398. 15 p. "Sunburst" and Flag 20 30
399. 24 p. "OAU" on Map, and Flag 35 60

Nos. 397/9 are horiz., 37½ × 27½ mm.

195. Goalkeeper saving Ball.

1965. African Soccer Cup Competition. Mult.

400. 6 p. Type **195** 10 10
401. 15 p. Player with ball (vert.) 20 25
402. 24 p. Player, ball and Soccer Cup 35 50

198. Pres. Kennedy and Grave Memorial.

1965. 2nd Death Anniv. of Pres. Kennedy.

403. 198. 6 p. multicoloured .. 15 10
404. – 15 p. violet, red & green 40 35
405. – 24 p. black and purple .. 50 60
406. – 30 p. dull purple & black 60 75

DESIGNS: 15 p. Pres. Kennedy and Eternal Flame. 24 p. Pres. Kennedy and Memorial Inscription. 30 p. Pres. Kennedy.

202. Section of Dam and Generators.

1966. Volta River Project.

408. 202. 6 p. multicoloured .. 15 10
409. – 15 p. multicoloured .. 20 15
410. – 24 p. multicoloured .. 25 20
411. – 30 p. black and blue .. 35 50

DESIGNS: 15 p. Dam and Lake Volta. 24 p. Word "GHANA" as Dam. 30 p. "Fertility".

1966. "Black Stars" Victory in African Soccer Cup Competition. Optd. **Black Stars Retain Africa Cup 21st Nov. 1965.**

412. 195. 6 p. multicoloured .. 10 10
413. – 15 p. multicoloured .. 20 20
414. – 24 p. multicoloured .. 35 35

207. W.H.O. Building and Ghana Flag.

1966. Inauguration of W.H.O. Headquarters, Geneva. Multicoloured.

415. 6 p. Type **207** 40 10
416. 15 p. Type **207** 90 50
417. 24 p. W.H.O. Building and Emblem .. .. 1·25 1·00
418. 30 p. W.H.O. Building and Emblem .. .. 1·40 1·75

209. Herring.

1966. Freedom from Hunger. Multicoloured.

420. 6 p. Type **209** 15 10
421. 15 p. Flat Fish 35 15
422. 24 p. Spade Fish 65 35
423. 30 p. Red Snapper 80 75
424. 60 p. Tuna .. .. 2·00 2·50

214. African "Links" and Ghana Flag.

1966. 3rd Anniv. of African Charter. Mult.

426. 6 p. Type **214** 15 10
427. 15 p. Flags as "Quill" and Diamond (horiz.) .. 35 20
428. 24 p. Ship's Wheel, Map and Cocoa Bean (horiz.) .. 40 25

217. Player Heading Ball, and Jules Rimet Cup.

1966. World Cup Football Championships. Multicoloured.

429. 5 p. Type **217** 15 10
430. 15 p. Goalkeeper clearing ball 40 20
431. 24 p. Player and Jules Rimet Cup (Replica) 55 35
432. 30 p. Players and Jules Rimet Cup (Replica) .. 75 90
433. 60 p. Players with ball .. 1·50 2·50

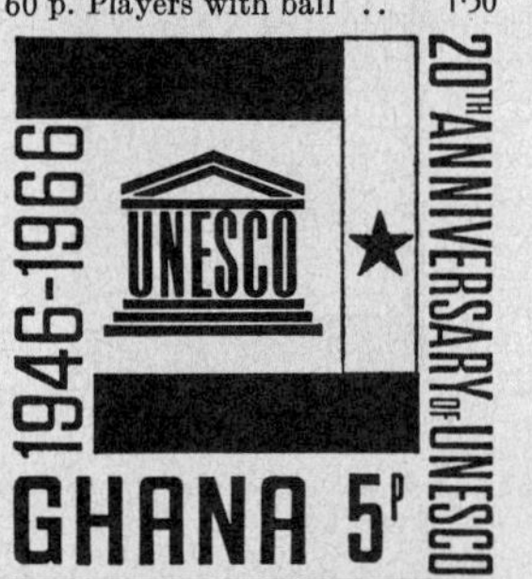

222. U.N.E.S.C.O. Emblem.

1966. 20th Anniv. of U.N.E.S.C.O.

435. 222. 5 p. multicoloured .. 25 15
436. 15 p. multicoloured .. 60 40
437. 24 p. multicoloured .. 90 85
438. 30 p. multicoloured .. 1·25 2·00
439. 60 p. multicoloured .. 2·25 3·75

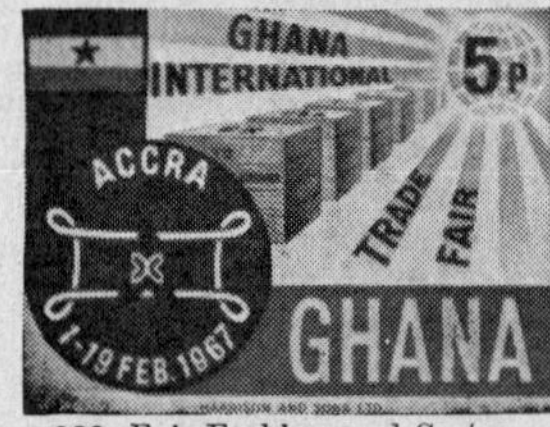

223. Fair Emblem and Crates.

1967. Ghana Trade Fair, Accra. Multicoloured.

441. 5 p. Type **223** 10 10
442. 15 p. Fair Emblem and World Map 15 15
443. 24 p. Shipping and flags .. 25 30
444. 36 p. Fair Emblem and hand-held hoist 40 80

1967. New Currency. Nos. 216/26 and 393 surch. with new value.

445. 1½ n.p. on 2d. (postage) .. 5·50 3·25
446. 3½ n.p. on 4d. .. .. 1·50 30
447. 5 n.p. on 6d. 60 15
448. 9 n.p. on 11d. 30 15
449. 10 n.p. on 1s. 30 15
450. 25 n.p. on 2s. 6d. .. .. 3·25 2·50
451. 1 n.c. on 10s. .. .. 6·50 12·00
452. 2 n.c. on £1 .. .. 12·00 23·00
453. 12½ n.p. on 1s. 3d. (air) .. 3·00 1·00
454. 20 n.p. on 24 p. on 2s. .. 3·00 2·00

229. Ghana Eagle and Flag.

1967. 1st Anniv. of 24 February Revolution.
455. **229.** 1 n.p. multicoloured .. 10 15
456. 4 n.p. multicoloured .. 10 10
457. 12½ n.p. multicoloured 40 55
458. 25 n.p. multicoloured .. 85 2·00

230. Maize.

232. The Ghana Mace.

1967. Multicoloured.
460. 1 n.p. Type **230** 10 10
461. 1½ n.p. Forest Kingfisher 90 45
462. 2 n.p. Type **232** 10 10
463. 2½ n.p. Commelina .. 35 10
464. 3 n.p. Mud-fish 20 40
465. 4 n.p. Rufous-crowned Roller .. .. .. 1·50 10
466. 6 n.p. Akosombo Dam .. 15 10
467. 8 n.p. Adomi Bridge .. 15 10
468. 9 n.p. Chameleon 45 10
469. 10 n.p. Tema Harbour .. 15 10
470. 20 n.p. Bush hare (blue) .. 20 10
471. 50 n.p. Black-winged Stilt 4·00 65
472. 1 n.c. Wooden Stool .. 2·25 75
473. 2 n.c. Frangipani .. .. 2·00 3·50
474. 2 n.c. 50 Seat of State .. 3·50 5·00

SIZES—(As Type **230**)—VERT. 4 n.p. HORIZ. 8 n.p. (As Type **232**). VERT. 1½ n.p., 2½ n.p., 20 n.p., 2 n.c. and 2 n.c. 50. HORIZ. 3 n.p., 6 n.p., 9 n.p., 10 n.p., 50 n.p. and 1 n.c.

245. Kumasi Fort.

1967. Castles and Forts.
475. **245.** 4 n.p. multicoloured .. 25 10
476. – 12½ n.p. multicoloured 1·00 1·00
477. – 20 n.p. multicoloured .. 1·40 2·00
478. – 25 n.p. multicoloured .. 1·75 2·50

DESIGNS: 12½ n.p. Christiansborg Castle and British Galleon. 20 n.p. Elimina Castle and Portuguese Galleon. 25 n.p. Cape Coast, Castle and Spanish Galleon.

249. "Luna 10".

1967. "Peaceful Use of Outer Space". Mult.
479. 4 n.p. Type **249** 10 10
480. 10 n.p. "Orbiter 1" .. 10 15
481. 12½ n.p. Man in Space .. 20 30

252. Scouts and Camp-fire.

1967. 50th Anniv. of Ghanaian Scout Movement. Multicoloured.
483. 4 n.p. Type **252** 20 10
484. 10 n.p. Scout on march .. 50 20
485. 12½ n.p. Lord Baden-Powell 70 70

255. U.N. Headquarters Building.

1967. U.N. Day (24 October).
487. **255.** 4 n.p. multicoloured .. 15 10
488. – 10 n.p. multicoloured 20 15
489. – 50 n.p. multicoloured .. 40 70
490. – 2 n.c. 50 multicoloured 1·50 4·00

DESIGN: 50 n.p., 2 n.c. 50, General View of U.N. H.Q., Manhattan.

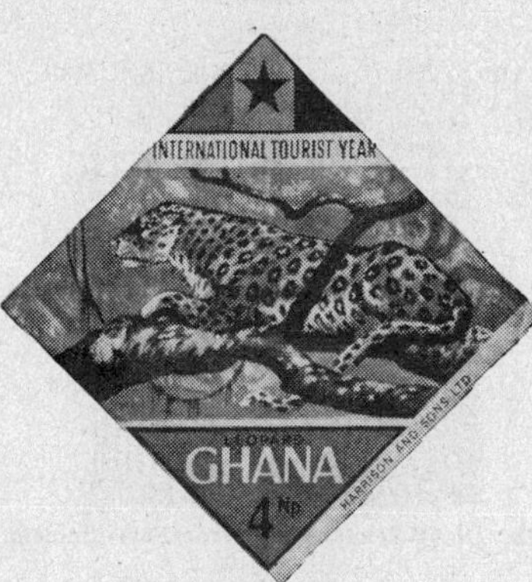

257. Leopard.

1967. International Tourist Year. Mult.
492 4 n.p. Type **257** 50 10
493 12½ n.p. "Papilio demodocus" (butterfly) .. 1·00 1·25
494 20 n.p. Carmine bee eater 2·00 3·00
495 50 n.p. Waterbuck .. 3·00 5·00

261. Revolutionaries entering Accra.

1968. 2nd Anniv. of February Revolution. Multicoloured.
497. 4 n.p. Type **261** 10 10
498. 12½ n.p. Marching Troops 20 20
499. 20 n.p. Cheering People .. 30 40
500. 40 n.p. Victory Celebrations 50 1·25

265. Microscope and Cocoa Beans.

1968. Cocoa Research.
501. **265.** 2½ n.p. multicoloured .. 10 10
502. – 4 n.p. multicoloured .. 10 10
503. **265.** 10 n.p. multicoloured .. 15 15
504. – 25 n.p. multicoloured .. 60 80

DESIGNS: 4 n.p. and 25 n.p. Microscope and Cocoa Tree, Beans and Pods.

267. Kotoka and Flowers.

1968. 1st Death Anniv. of Lt.-Gen. E. K. Kotoka. Multicoloured.
506. 4 n.p. Type **267** 10 10
507. 12½ n.p. Kotoka & Wreath 20 20
508. 20 n.p. Kotoka in Civilian Clothes 35 65
509. 40 n.p. Lt.-Gen. Kotoka .. 50 1·00

271. Tobacco.

1968. Multicoloured.
510. 4 n.p. Type **271** 15 10
511. 5 n.p. North African crested porcupine .. 15 15
512. 12½ n.p. Rubber 50 75
513. 20 n.p. "Cymothoe sangaris" (butterfly) .. 1·25 2·00
514. 40 n.p. "Charaxes ameliae" (butterfly) .. .. 1·75 3·75

276. Surgeons, Flag and W.H.O. Emblem.

1968. 20th Anniv. of W.H.O.
516. **276.** 4 n.p. multicoloured .. 25 10
517. 12½ n.p. multicoloured 60 35
518. 20 n.p. multicoloured .. 95 70
519. 40 n.p. multicoloured .. 1·50 1·50

277. Hurdling.

1969. Olympic Games, Mexico (1968). **Mult.**
521. 4 n.p. Type **277** 10 10
522. 12½ n.p. Boxing 20 30
523. 20 n.p. Torch, Olympic Rings and Flags .. 40 70
524. 40 n.p. Football .. .. 70 1·50

281. U.N. Building.

1969. U.N. Day. Multicoloured.
526. 4 n.p. Type **281** 10 10
527. 12½ n.p. Native school staff and U.N. Emblem 15 20
528. 20 n.p. U.N. Building and Emblem over Ghanaian Flag.. .. 25 35
529. 40 n.p. U.N. Emblem encircled by flags .. 60 90

285. Dr. J. B. Danquah.

1969. Human Rights Year. Multicoloured.
531. 4 n.p. Type **285** 10 10
532. 12½ n.p. Dr. Martin Luther King 30 30
533. 20 n.p. As 12½ n.p. .. 45 60
534. 40 n.p. Type **285** .. .. 70 1·10

287. Constituent Assembly Building.

1969. 3rd Anniv. of Revolution. Mult.
536. 4 n.p. Type **287** 10 10
537. 12½ n.p. Arms of Ghana .. 10 10
538. 20 n.p. As Type **287** .. 15 15
539. 40 n.p. As 12½ n.p. .. 20 35

1969. New Constitution. Nos. 460/74 optd. **NEW CONSTITUTION 1969.**
541. **230.** 1 n.p. multicoloured .. 10 50
542. – 1½ n.p. multicoloured .. 85 1·00
543. **232.** 2 n.p. multicoloured .. 10 65
544. – 2½ n.p. multicoloured .. 10 65
545. – 3 n.p. multicoloured .. 60 90
546. – 4 n.p. multicoloured .. 2·00 30
547. – 6 n.p. multicoloured .. 15 70
548. – 8 n.p. multicoloured .. 15 50
549. – 9 n.p. multicoloured .. 15 75
550. – 10 n.p. multicoloured .. 20 40
551. – 20 n.p. multicoloured .. 35 70
552. – 50 n.p. multicoloured .. 5·00 5·00
553. – 1 n.c. multicoloured .. 2·25 5·50
554. – 2 n.c. multicoloured .. 3·50 8·00
555. – 2 n.c. 50 multicoloured 3·50 9·00

On Nos. 541, 545, 547/50 and 552/3 the overprint is horiz. The rest are vert.

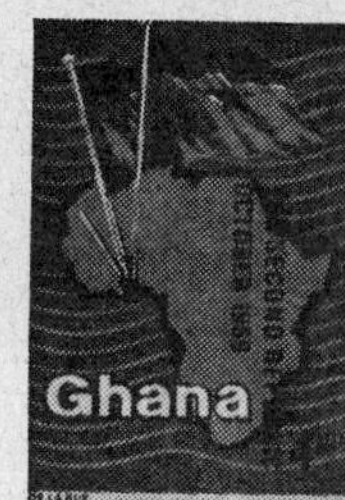

290. Map of Africa and Flags.

1969. Inaug. of 2nd Republic. Multicoloured.
556. 4 n.p. Type **290** 10 10
557. 12½ n.p. Figure "2", Branch and Ghanaian Colours .. 30 10
558. 20 n.p. Hands receiving egg 45 30
559. 40 n.p. Type **290** 85 70

293. I.L.O. Emblem and Cog-wheels.

1970. 50th Anniv. of I.L.O.
560. **293.** 4 np. multicoloured .. 10 10
561. 12½ n.p. multicoloured 20 25
562. 20 n.p. multicoloured .. 30 45

294. Red Cross and Globe.

1970. 50th Anniv. of League of Red Cross Societies. Multicoloured.

564. 4 n.p. Type **294** 30 10
565. 12½ n.p. Henri Dunant and Red Cross emblem 65 20
566. 20 n.p. Patient receiving medicine 80 55
567. 40 n.p. Patient having arm bandaged .. .. 1·10 1·40
Nos. 565/7 are horiz.

298. General Kotoka, "VC-10" and Airport.

1970. Inaug. of Kotoka Airport. Mult.

569. 4 n.p. Type **298** 10 10
570. 12½ n.p. Control Tower and tail of "VC-10" 20 15
571. 20 n.p. Aerial view of airport 30 30
572. 40 n.p. Airport and flags .. 60 80

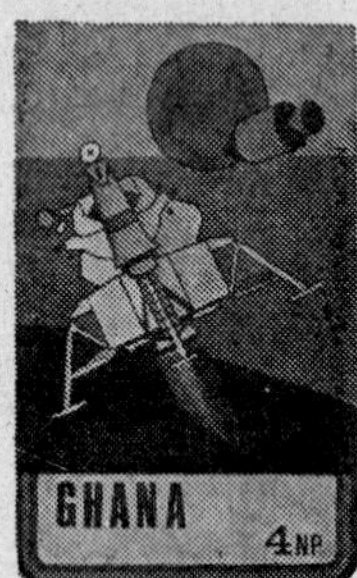

302. Lunar Module landing on Moon.

1970. Moon Landing. Multicoloured.

573. 4 n.p. Type **302** 30 10
574. 12½ n.p. Astronaut's first step onto the Moon .. 85 60
575. 20 n.p. Astronaut with equipment on Moon .. 1·40 1·40
576. 40 n.p. Astronauts .. 3·00 3·00
Nos. 575/6 are horiz.

306. Adult Education.

1970. Int. Education Year. Multicoloured.

578. 4 n.p. Type **306** 10 10
579. 12½ n.p. International education 20 20
580. 20 n.p. "Ntesie" and I.E.Y. symbols .. 35 30
581. 40 n.p. Nursery School .. 60 85

310. Saluting March-Past.

1970. 1st Anniv. of Second Republic. Mult.

582. 4 n.p. Type **310** 10 10
583. 12½ n.p. Busia Declaration 15 15
584. 20 n.p. Doves Symbol .. 25 30
585. 40 n.p. Opening of Parliament 50 65

314. "Crinum ornatum".

1970. Flora and Fauna. Multicoloured.

586. 4 n.p. Type **314** .. .. 1·25 10
587. 12½ n.p. Lioness .. .. 1·25 45
588. 20 n.p. "Ansellia africana" (flower) .. .. 1·40 90
589. 40 n.p. African elephant .. 4·25 3·00

315. Kuduo Brass Casket.

1970. Monuments and Archaeological Sites in Ghana. Multicoloured.

590. 4 n.p. Type **315** 15 10
591. 12½ n.p. Akan Traditional House 40 20
592. 20 n.p. Larabanga Mosque 70 50
593. 40 n.p. Funerary Clay Head .. .. 1·00 1·10

316. Trade Fair Building.

1971. Int. Trade Fair, Accra. Multicoloured.

595. 4 n.p. Type **316** 10 10
596. 12½ n.p. Cosmetics and pharmaceutical goods .. 50 20
597. 20 n.p. Vehicles 55 25
598. 40 n.p. Construction equipment 90 95
599. 50 n.p. Transport and packing case .. .. 1·00 1·10
The 50 n.p. is vert.

317. Christ on the Cross.

1971. Easter. Multicoloured.

600. 4 n.p. Type **317** .. 15 10
601. 12½ n.p. Christ & Disciples 35 35
602. 20 n.p. Christ blessing Disciples 55 75

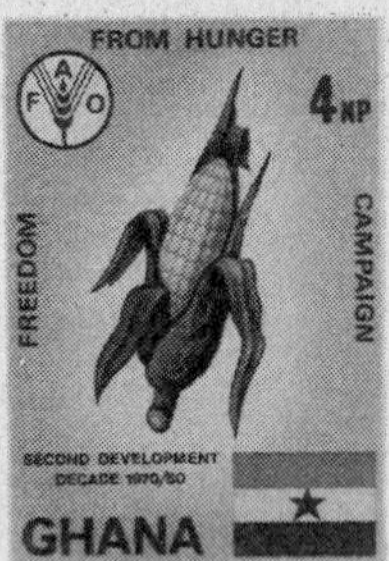

318. Corn Cob.

1971. Freedom From Hunger Campaign.

603. **318.** 4 n.p. multicoloured .. 10 10
604. 12½ n.p. multicoloured 35 60
605. 20 n.p. multicoloured 65 1·10

Remainder stocks of the above stamps were overprinted on the occasion of the death of Lord Boyd Orr and further surcharged 12½, 20 and 60 n.p.

It is understood that 8070 sets from the agency were overprinted locally and returned to New York. Limited remainders of these stamps (only 330 of 60 n.p.) were sold at the G.P.O. We do not list these as they were not freely on sale in Ghana.

319. Guides Emblem and Ghana Flag.

1971. Golden Jubilee of Ghana Girl Guides. Each design includes Guides emblem. Mult.

606. 4 n.p. Type **319** 20 10
607. 12½ n.p. Mrs. E. Ofuatey-Kodjoe (founder) and guides with flags .. 60 50
608. 20 n.p. Guides laying stones 90 90
609. 40 n.p. Camp-fire and tent 1·50 1·75
610. 50 n.p. Signallers .. 1·75 2·00

320. Child-care Centre.

1971. Y.W.C.A. World Council Meeting Accra. Multicoloured.

612. 4 n.p. Type **320** 10 10
613. 12½ n.p. Council Meeting 10 15
614. 20 n.p. School typing class 15 30
615. 40 n.p. Building Fund Day 30 60

321. Firework Display. **322.** Weighing Baby.

1971. Christmas. Multicoloured.

617. 1 n.p. Type **321** 10 20
618. 3 n.p. African Nativity 15 30
619. 6 n.p. The Flight into Egypt 15 30

1971. 25th Anniv. of U.N.I.C.E.F. Mult.

620. 5 n.p. Type **322** 10 10
621. 15 n.p. Mother and child (horiz.) 30 70
622. 30 n.p. Nurse .. .. 40 1·75
623. 50 n.p. Young boy (horiz.) 60 2·50

323. Unity Symbol and Trade Fair Emblem.

1972. All African Trade Fair. Multicoloured.

625. 5 np. Type **323** 10 10
626. 15 np. Horn of Plenty .. 20 30
627. 30 np. Fireworks on map of Africa 35 70
628. 60 np. "Participating Nations" .. .. 50 1·50
629. 1 nc. As No. 628 .. 80 2·25

On 24 June, 1972, on the occasion of the Belgian International Philatelic Exhibition, Nos. 625/9 were issued overprinted **"BELGICA 72"**. Only very limited supplies were sent to Ghana (we understand not more than 900 sets), and for this reason we do not list them.

324. Books for the Blind.

1972. Int. Book Year. Multicoloured.

630. 5 p. Type **324** 20 10
631. 15 p. Children's books .. 55 50
632. 30 p. Books for recreation 90 85
633. 50 p. Books for students .. 1·60 2·00
634. 1 c. Book and flame of knowledge (vert.) .. 2·25 2·75

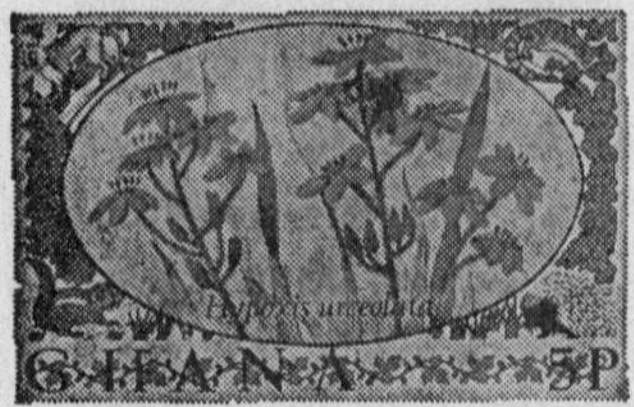

325. "Hypoxis urceolata".

1972. Flora and Fauna. Multicoloured.

636. 5 p. Type **325** 30 10
637. 15 p. Mona monkey .. 65 65
638. 30 p. "Crinum ornatum" .. 4·00 3·00
639. 1 c. De Winton's Tree squirrel .. .. .. 5·00 6·50

326. Football.

1972. Olympic Games, Munich. Mult.

640. 5 p. Type **326** 10 10
641. 15 p. Running 20 20
642. 30 p. Boxing 40 60
643. 50 p. Long-jumping .. .. 70 1·40
644. 1 c. High-jumping .. 1·25 2·25

327. Senior Scout and Cub.

1972. 65th Anniv. of Boy Scouts. Mult.

646. 5 p. Type **327** 30 10
647. 15 p. Scout and tent .. 65 45
648. 30 p. Sea scouts .. 1·25 1·00
649. 50 p. Leader with cubs .. 1·60 1·75
650. 1 c. Training school .. 3·00 3·25

328. "The Holy Night" (Correggio).

1972. Christmas. Multicoloured.

652 1 p. Type **328** 10 10
653 3 p. "Adoration of the Kings" (Holbein the Elder) 10 10
654 15 p. "Madonna of the Passion" (School of Ricco) 30 30
655 30 p. "King Melchior" .. 55 55
656 60 p. "King Gaspar, Mary and Jesus" .. .. 1·00 1·25
657 1 c. "King Balthasar" .. 1·75 2·25

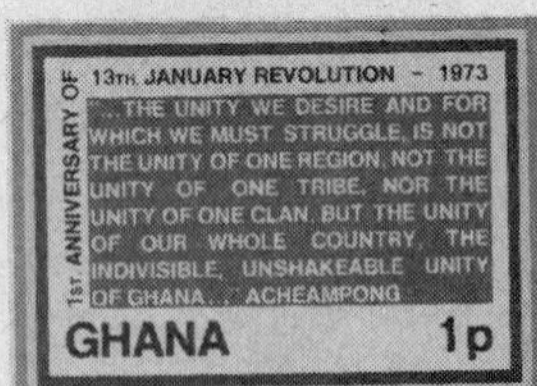

329. Extract from Speech.

1973. 1st Anniv. of 13 January Revolution. Multicoloured.

659. 1 p. Type **329** 10 10
660. 3 p. Market scene .. 10 10
661. 5 p. Selling bananas (vert.) 10 10
662. 15 p. Farmer with hoe and produce (vert.) .. 20 25
663. 30 p. Market traders .. 30 40
664. 1 c. Farmer cutting palm-nuts .. .. .. 70 1·40

330. Under 5's Clinic.

1973. 25th Anniv. of W.H.O. Multicoloured.

666. 5 p. Type **330** 10 10
667. 15 p. Radiography .. 25 30
668. 30 p. Immunisation .. 35 50
669. 50 p. Starving child .. 50 1·25
670. 1 c. W.H.O. H.Q., Geneva 1·00 2·25

1973. World Scouting Conference. Nairobi/ Addis Ababa. Nos. 646/50 optd. **1st WORLD SCOUTING CONFERENCE IN AFRICA.**

671. **327.** 5 p. multicoloured .. 10 15
672. – 15 p. multicoloured .. 35 60
673. – 30 p. multicoloured .. 60 1·25
674. – 50 p. multicoloured .. 80 1·75
675. – 1 c. multicoloured .. 1·50 2·75

332. Poultry Farming.

1973. 10th Anniv. of World Food Programme. Multicoloured.

677. 5 p. Type **332** 10 10
678. 15 p. Mechanisation .. 15 15
679. 50 p. Cocoa harvest .. 40 90
680. 1 c. F.A.O. H.Q., Rome .. 60 1·90

333. "Green Alert".

1973. 50th Anniv. of Interpol. Multicoloured.

682. 5 p. Type **333** 15 10
683. 30 p. "Red Alert" .. 75 80
684. 50 p. "Blue Alert" .. 1·50 1·75
685. 1 c. "Black Alert" .. 3·00 4·00

334. Handshake.

1973. 10th Anniv. of O.A.U. Multicoloured.

686. 5 p. Type **334** 10 10
687. 30 p. Africa Hall Addis Ababa 15 30
688. 50 p. O.A.U. emblem .. 30 80
689. 1 c. "X" in colours of Ghana flag .. .. 45 1·25

335. Weather Balloon.

1973. Cent. of I.M.O./W.M.O. Multicoloured.

690. 5 p. Type **335** 10 10
691. 15 p. Satellite "Tiros" .. 20 20
692. 30 p. Computer weather map 40 65
693. 1 c. Radar screen .. 80 2·25

336. Epiphany Scene.

1973. Christmas. Multicoloured.

695. 1 p. Type **336** 10 10
696. 3 p. Madonna and Child .. 10 10
697. 30 p. "Madonna and Child" (Murillo) .. 30 75
698. 50 p. "Adoration of the Magi" (Tiepolo) .. 45 1·00

337. "Christ carrying the Cross" (Thomas de Kolozsvar).

1974. Easter.

700. **337.** 5 p. multicoloured .. 10 10
701. – 30 p. bl., silver & brn. 20 35
702. – 50 p. red, silver & brn. 30 60
703. – 1 c. green, silver & brn. 50 1·25

DESIGNS (from 15th-century English carved alabaster)—30 p. "The Betrayal". 50 p. "The Deposition". 1 c. "The Risen Christ and Mary Magdalene".

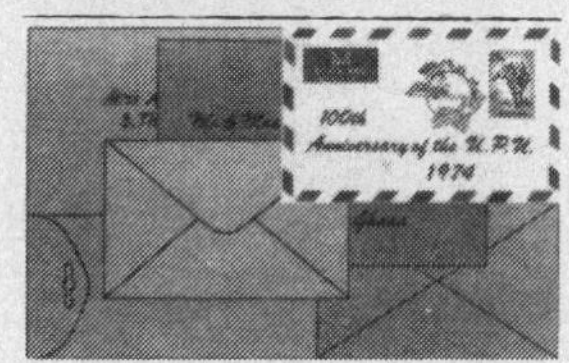

338. Letters.

1974. Centenary of U.P.U. Multicoloured.

705. 5 p. Type **338** 10 10
706. 9 p. U.P.U. Monument and H.Q. 15 15
707. 50 p. Airmail letter .. 50 1·00
708. 1 c. U.P.U. Monument and Ghana stamp .. .. 80 1·75

1974. "Internaba 1974" Stamp Exn. As Nos. 705/8 additionally inscr. "INTERNABA 1974".

710. 5 p. multicoloured .. 10 10
711. 9 p. multicoloured .. 15 15
712. 50 p. multicoloured .. 40 1·00
713. 1 c. multicoloured .. 60 1·75

339. Footballers.

1974. World Cup Football Championships.

715. **339.** 5 p. multicoloured .. 10 10
716. – 30 p. multicoloured .. 25 50
717. – 50 p. multicoloured .. 35 75
718. – 1 c. multicoloured .. 50 1·50

DESIGNS: As Type **339** showing footballers in action.

340. Roundabout.

1974. Change to Driving on the Right.

720. **340.** 5 p. grn., red & blk. .. 10 10
721. – 15 p. pur., red & blk. 25 35
722. – 30 p. multicoloured .. 45 60
723. – 50 p. multicoloured .. 70 1·10
724. – 1 c. multicoloured .. 1·40 2·00

DESIGNS—HORIZ. 15 p. Warning triangle sign. VERT. 30 p. Highway arrow and slogan. 50 p. Warning hands. 1 c. Car on symbolic hands.

1974. West Germany's Victory in World Cup. Nos. 715/18 optd. **WEST GERMANY WINNERS.**

725. 5 p. multicoloured .. 10 10
726. 30 p. multicoloured .. 35 40
727. 50 p. multicoloured .. 50 55
728. 1 c. multicoloured .. 90 1·25

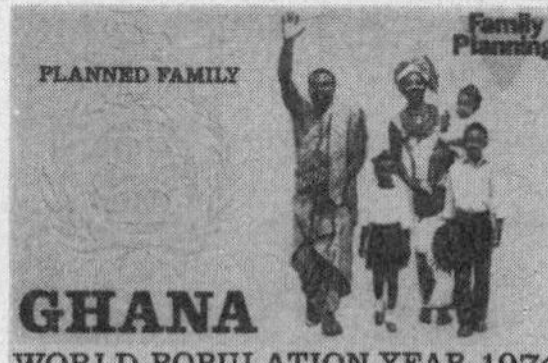

342. "Planned Family".

1974. World Population Year. Multicoloured.

730. 5 p. Type **342** 10 10
731. 30 p. Family planning clinic 25 35
732. 50 p. Immunization .. 35 60
733. 1 c. Population census enumeration .. .. 60 1·40

343. Angel.

1974. Christmas. Multicoloured.

734. 5 p. Type **343** 10 10
735. 7 p. The Magi (diamond 47 × 47 mm.) 10 10
736. 9 p. The Nativity .. 10 10
737. 1 c. The Annunciation .. 60 1·40

1975. "Apollo-Soyuz" Space Link. Nos. 715/18 optd. with **Apollo Soyuz July 15, 1975.**

739. **339.** 5 p. multicoloured .. 10 10
740. – 30 p. multicoloured .. 25 25
741. – 50 p. multicoloured .. 45 55
742. – 1 c. multicoloured .. 70 80

345. Tractor Driver.

1975. International Women's Year. Mult.

744. 7 p. Type **345** 15 10
745. 30 p. Motor mechanic .. 35 35
746. 60 p. Factory workers .. 60 80
747. 1 c. Cocoa research .. 90 1·40

346. Angel.

1975. Christmas.

749. **346.** 2 p. multicoloured .. 10 10
750. – 5 p. yellow and green 10 10
751. – 7 p. yellow and green 10 10
752. – 30 p. yellow and green 20 20
753. – 1 c. yellow and green 50 1·00

DESIGNS: 5 p. Angel with harp. 7 p. Angel with lute. 30 p. Angel with viol. 1 c. Angel with trumpet.

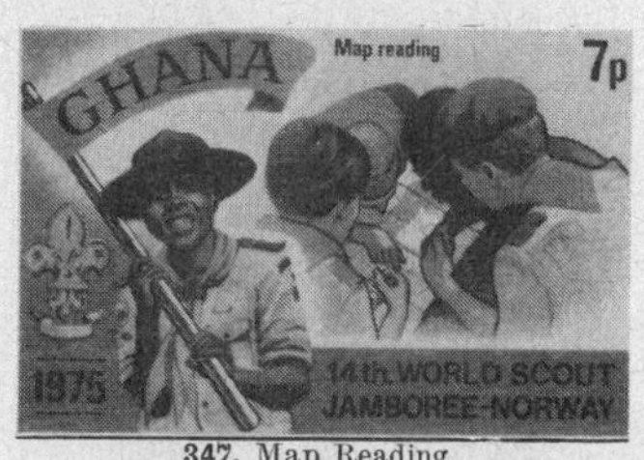

347. Map Reading.

1976. 14th World Scout Jamboree, Norway. Multicoloured.

755. 7 p. Type **347** 30 10
756. 30 p. Sailing 85 75
757. 60 p. Hiking .. .. 1·50 1·75
758. 1 c. Life-saving .. .. 2·00 2·50

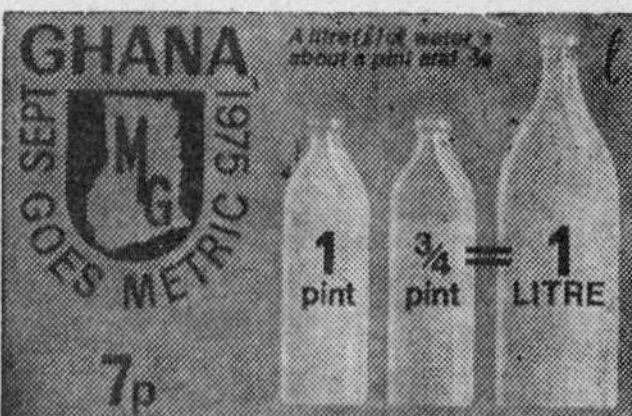

348. Bottles (litre).

1976. Metrication Publicity. Mult.

760. 7 p. Type **348** 15 10
761. 30 p. Scales (kilogramme) 40 40
762. 60 p. Tape measure and bale of cloth (metre) .. 80 1·00
763. 1 c. Ice, thermometer and kettle (temperature) .. 1·25 1·75

349. Fair Site.

1976. Int. Trade Fair, Accra.

764. **349.** 7 p. multicoloured .. 10 10
765. – 30 p. multicoloured .. 20 20
766. – 60 p. multicoloured .. 50 60
767. – 1 c. multicoloured .. 70 1·00

DESIGNS: As Type **349**, showing different views of the Fair.

1976. Interphil Stamp Exn. Nos. 755/8 optd. "**INTERPHIL" 76 BICENTENNIAL EXHIBITION.**

768. **347.** 7 p. multicoloured .. 15 15
769. – 30 p. multicoloured .. 35 50
770. – 60 p. multicoloured .. 55 75
771. – 1 c. multicoloured .. 80 1·25

351. Shot-put.

1976. Olympic Games, Montreal. Mult.

773. 7 p. Type **351** 10 10
774. 30 p. Football 20 25
775. 60 p. Women's 1500 metres 35 50
776. 1 c. Boxing 60 80

352. Supreme Court.

1976. Centenary of Supreme Court.

778. **352.** 8 p. multicoloured .. 10 10
779. – 30 p. multicoloured .. 20 25
780. – 60 p. multicoloured .. 35 50
781. – 1 c. multicoloured .. 60 1·00

DESIGNS: As Type **352** showing different views of the Court Buildings.

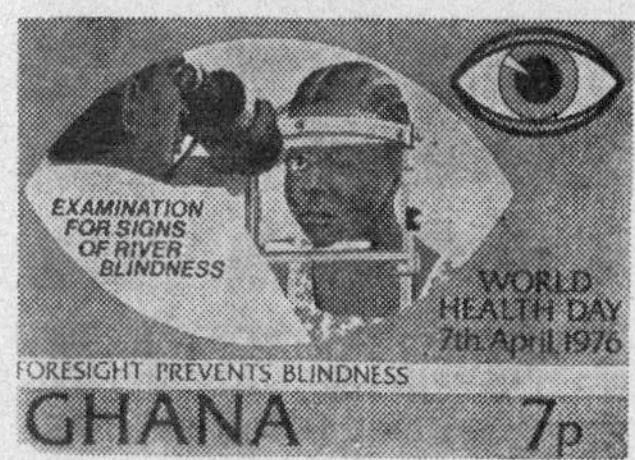

353. Examination for River Blindness.

1976. Prevention of Blindness. Mult.

782. 7 p. Type **353** 55 10
783. 30 p. Entomologist .. 1·50 1·10
784. 60 p. Checking effects of insecticide .. .. 2·50 2·50
785. 1 c. Normal eye's view .. 3·75 4·00

354. Fireworks Party, Christmas Eve.

1976. Christmas. Multicoloured.

786.	6 p. Type **354**	15	10
787.	8 p. Children and gifts ..	20	15
788.	30 p. Christmas feast ..	60	50
789.	1 c. As 8 p.	1·50	2·00

355. " Gallows Frame " Telephone and Alexander Graham Bell.

1976. Cent. of Telephone. Multicoloured.

791.	8 p. Type **355**	20	15
792.	30 p. Bell and 1895 telephone	45	45
793.	60 p. Bell and 1929 telephone	90	90
794.	1 c. Bell and 1976 telephone	1·40	1·40

1977. Olympic Winners. Nos. 773/6 optd. **WINNERS** and country name.

796.	**351.** 7 p. multicoloured ..	15	15
797.	– 30 p. multicoloured ..	40	40
798.	– 60 p. multicoloured ..	60	85
799.	– 1 c. multicoloured ..	80	1·50

OPTD. 7 p., 30 p. **EAST GERMANY.** 60 p. **USSR.** 1 c. **USA.**

357. Dipo Dancers and Drum Ensemble.

1977. Second World Black and African Festival of Arts and Culture, Nigeria. Multicoloured.

801.	8 p. Type **357**	25	15
802.	30 p. Arts and Crafts ..	70	70
803.	60 p. Acon music and dancing priests ..	1·40	1·40
804.	1 c. African Huts	2·00	2·25

1977. Prince Charles's Visit to Ghana. Nos. 791/94 optd. **PRINCE CHARLES VISITS GHANA 17th TO 25th MARCH, 1977.**

806.	8 p. Type **355**	50	55
807.	30 p. 1895 telephone ..	1·60	1·25
808.	60 p. 1929 telephone ..	2·50	2·25
809.	1 c. 1976 telephone ..	3·25	2·75

359. Olive Colobus Monkey.

1977. Wildlife. Multicoloured.

811.	8 p. Type **359**	45	15
812.	20 p. Temminck's Giant Squirrel	1·25	80
813.	30 p. Hunting Dog ..	1·75	1·25
814.	60 p. African Manatee (sea cow)	3·00	2·25

360. " Le Chapeau de Paille " (Rubens—400th Birth Anniv.).

1977. Painters' Anniversaries. Multicoloured.

816.	8 p. Type **360**	15	10
817.	30 p. " Isabella of Portugal " (Titian–500th Birth Anniv.)	40	40
818.	60 p. " Duke and Duchess of Cumberland " (Gainsborough–250th Birth Anniv.)	50	65
819.	1 c. " Rubens and Isabella Brandt "	85	1·25

361. The Magi, Madonna and Child.

1977. Christmas. Multicoloured.

821.	1 p. Type **361**	10	10
822.	2 p. Choir, St. Andrew's Anglican Church, Abossey Okai	10	10
823.	6 p. Methodist Church, Wesley, Accra	10	10
824.	8 p. Madonna and Child ..	15	10
825.	30 p. Holy Spirit Cathedral, Accra	50	50
826.	1 c. Ebenezer Presbyterian Church, Osu, Accra ..	1·60	1·60

1978. Referendum. Nos. 821/26 optd. **REFERENDUM 1978 VOTE EARLY.**

828.	1 p. Type **361**	10	10
829.	2 p. Choir, St. Andrew's Anglican Church, Abossey Okai	10	10
830.	6 p. Methodist Church, Wesley, Accra	10	10
831.	8 p. Madonna and Child ..	15	10
832.	30 p. Holy Spirit Cathedral, Accra	50	50
833.	1 c. Ebenezer Presbyterian Church, Accra ..	1·50	1·50

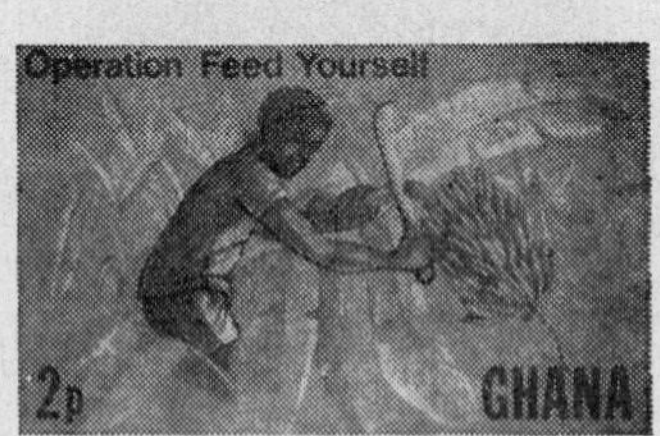

363. Cutting Bananas.

1978. Operation " Feed Yourself ". Mult.

835.	2 p. Type **363**	10	10
836.	8 p. Home produce ..	10	10
837.	30 p. Market	35	35
838.	60 p. Fishing	65	60
839.	1 c. Mechanisation ..	1·00	1·25

364. Wright Biplane.

1978. 75th Anniv. of Powered Flight.

840.	**364.** 8 p. black, brn. & ochre	20	10
841.	– 30 p. black, brn. & grn.	40	30
842.	– 60 p. black, brn. & red	60	60
843.	– 1 c. black, brn. & blue	1·75	1·10

DESIGNS: 30 p. " Heracles ". 60 p. D. H. " Comet ". 1 c. " Concorde ".

1978. " CAPEX 1978 " International Stamp Exhibition, Toronto. Nos. 840/3 optd. **" CAPEX 78 JUNE 9–18 1978 ".**

845.	**364.** 8 p. black, brn. & ochre	15	15
846.	– 30 p. blk., brn. & grn.	25	25
847.	– 60 p. blk., brown & red	50	50
848.	– 1 c. blk., brown & blue	1·10	80

366. Players and African Cup Emblem.

1978. Football Championships. Multicoloured.

850.	8 p. Type **366**	20	15
851.	30 p. Players and African Cup Emblem (different)	30	30
852.	60 p. Players and World Cup Emblem	60	60
853.	1 c. Goalkeeper and World Cup Emblem	1·00	1·00

367. " The Betrayal ".

1978. Easter. Drawings by Durer.

855.	**367.** 11 p. black and mauve	10	10
856.	– 39 p. black and flesh ..	25	30
857.	– 60 p. black and yellow	40	45
858.	– 1 c. black and green ..	60	65

DESIGNS: 39 p. " The Cruxifixion ". 60 p. " The Deposition ". 1 c. " The Resurrection ".

1978. Football Victories of Ghana and Argentina. Nos. 850/3 optd. **" GHANA WINNERS "** (8, 30 p.) or **ARGENTINA WINS** (others).

859.	**366.** 8 p. multicoloured ..	15	15
860.	– 30 p. multicoloured ..	30	30
861.	– 60 p. multicoloured ..	45	45
862.	– 1 c. multicoloured ..	75	75

369. " Bauhinia purpurea ".

1978. Flowers. Multicoloured.

864.	11 p. Type **369**	20	10
865.	39 p. " Cassia fistula " ..	65	55
866.	60 p. " Plumeria acutifolia "	85	70
867.	1 c. " Jacaranda mimosifolia	1·25	1·00

370. Mail Van.

1978. 75th Anniv. of Ghana Railways. Multicoloured.

868.	11 p. Type **370**	30	10
869.	39 p. Pay and bank car ..	70	65
870.	60 p. Steam locomotive, 1922	1·00	1·00
871.	1 c. Diesel locomotive, 1960	1·50	1·40

371. " Orbiter " Spacecraft.

1979. " Pioneer " Venus Space Project Multicoloured.

872.	11 p. Type **371**	15	10
873.	39 p. " Multiprobe " space craft	35	30
874.	60 p. "Orbiter" and "Multiprobe " spacecraft in Venus orbit	45	45
875.	3 c. Radar chart of Venus	1·40	1·60

372. " O Come All Ye Faithful ".

1979. Christmas. Lines and Scenes from Christmas Carols. Multicoloured.

877.	8 p. Type **372**	10	10
878.	10 p. " O Little Town of Bethlehem "	10	10
879.	15 p. " We Three Kings of Orient Are "	10	10
880.	20 p. " I Saw Three Ships come Sailing By " ..	10	15
881.	2 c. " Away in a Manger "	65	80
882.	4 c. " Ding Dong Merrily on High "	1·00	1·40

373. Dr. J. B. Danquah (lawyer and nationalist).

1980. Famous Ghanaians. Multicoloured.

884.	20 p. Type **373**	15	10
885.	65 p. John Mensah Sarbah (nationalist)	30	30
886.	80 p. Dr. J. E. K. Aggrey (educationalist) ..	40	40
887.	2 c. Dr. Kwame Nkrumah (nationalist)	65	65
888.	4 c. G. E. (Paa) Grant (lawyer)	1·40	1·60

374. Tribesman ringing Clack Bells.

1980. Death centenary of Sir Rowland Hill. (1979). Multicoloured.

889.	20 p. Type **374**	15	15
893.	25 p. Type **374**	20	20
894.	50 p. Chieftain with Golden Elephant Staff	45	50
890.	65 p. As 50 p.	45	50
895.	1 c. Signalling with drums	80	1·00
891.	2 c. As 1 c.	1·25	1·40
892.	4 c. Chieftain with ivory and gold staff	2·50	2·75
896.	5 c. As 4 c.	3·75	5·25

375. Children in Classroom.

1980. International Year of the Child (1979). Multicoloured.

898. 20 p. Type **375** 15 15
899. 65 p. Playing football .. 35 45
900. 2 c. Playing in a boat .. 75 1·00
901. 4 c. Mother and child .. 1·40 1·75

1980. "London 1980" International Stamp Exhibition. Nos. 889/96 optd. **"LONDON 1980" 6th - 14th May 1980.**

903. **374.** 20 p. multicoloured .. 15 15
907. – 25 p. multicoloured .. 30 40
908. – 50 p. multicoloured .. 55 75
904. – 65 p. multicoloured .. 45 60
909. – 1 c. multicoloured .. 95 1·60
905. – 2 c. multicoloured .. 1·10 1·60
906. – 4 c. multicoloured .. 2·00 3·00
910. – 5 c. multicoloured .. 3·00 4·00

1980. Papal Visit. Nos. 898/901 optd. **"PAPAL VISIT" 8th - 9th May 1980.**

912. **375.** 20 p. multicoloured .. 30 35
913. – 65 p. multicoloured .. 70 60
914. – 2 c. multicoloured .. 1·25 1·40
915. – 4 c. multicoloured .. 2·25 2·50

378. Parliament House.

1980. 3rd Republic Commemoration. Mult.

917. 20 p. Type **378** 10 10
918. 65 p. Supreme Court .. 20 25
919. 2 c. The Castle 40 70

379. Airliner and Map of West Africa.

1980. 5th Anniv. of Economic Community of West African States. Multicoloured.

921. 20 p. Type **379** 10 10
922. 65 p. Antenna and map .. 15 20
923. 80 p. Cog-wheels and map 20 25
924. 2 c. Corn and map .. 35 50

380. "OAU".

1980. First Organization of African Unity Summit Conference, Nigeria.

925. **380.** 20 p. multicoloured .. 10 10
926. – 65 p. multicoloured .. 15 20
927. – 80 p. deep red, red and black 15 25
928. – 2 c. multicoloured .. 20 65

DESIGNS: 65 p. Maps of Africa and Ghana and banner. 80 p. Map of Africa. 2 c. Map of Africa, banner and Ghanaian flag.

381. "The Adoration of the Magi".

1980. Christmas. Paintings by Fra Angelico. Multicoloured.

929. 15 p. Type **381** 10 10
930. 20 p. "The Virgin and Child Enthroned with Four Angels" 10 10
931. 2 c. "The Virgin and Child Enthroned with Eight Angels" 35 80
932. 4 c. "The Annunciation" 60 1·60

382. "Health".

1980. 75th Anniv. of Rotary International. Multicoloured.

934. 20 p. Type **382** 10 10
935. 65 p. World map 15 30
936. 2 c. Hands 35 85
937. 4 c. Pouring food .. .. 60 1·50

383. Narina Trogon.

1981. Birds. Multicoloured.

939. 20 p. Type **383** 80 15
940. 65 p. White-crowned robin chat .. .. .. 1·75 50
941. 2 c. Swallow-tailed bee eater .. .. .. 2·50 1·25
942. 4 c. Rose-ringed parakeet 4·00 3·25

384. Pope John Paul II, Archbishop of Canterbury and President Limann during Papal Visit.

1981. 1st Anniv. of Papal Visit.

944. **384.** 20 p. multicoloured .. 35 15
945. 65 p. multicoloured .. 60 55
946. 80 p. multicoloured .. 80 70
947. 2 c. multicoloured .. 1·50 2·00

385. Royal Yacht "Britannia".

1981. Royal Wedding. Multicoloured.

948. 20 p. Prince Charles and Lady Diana Spencer .. 10 10
952. 65 p. As 20 p. 15 25
949. 80 p. Prince Charles on visit to Ghana 15 20
953. 1 c. As 80 p. 25 35
955. 2 c. Type **385** .. .. 1·25 1·50
954. 3 c. Type **385** .. .. 70 1·10
950. 4 c. Type **385** 50 80
956. 5 c. As 20 p. .. .. 2·50 2·75

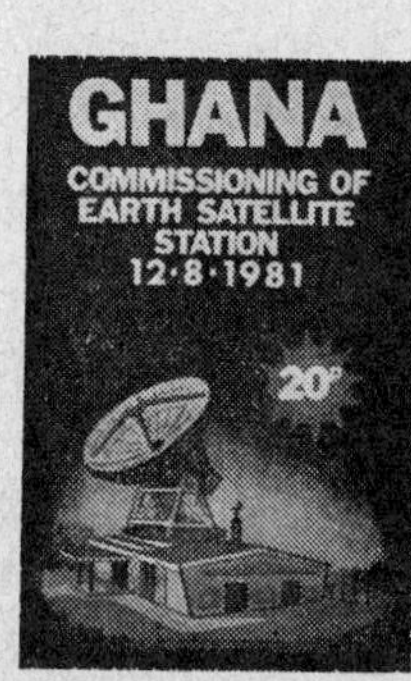

386. Earth Satellite Station.

1981. Commissioning of Earth Satellite Station. Multicoloured.

957. 20 p. Type **386** 10 10
958. 65 p. Satellites beaming signals to Earth .. 15 15
959. 80 p. Satellite 15 20
960. 4 c. Satellite orbiting Earth 1·00 1·50

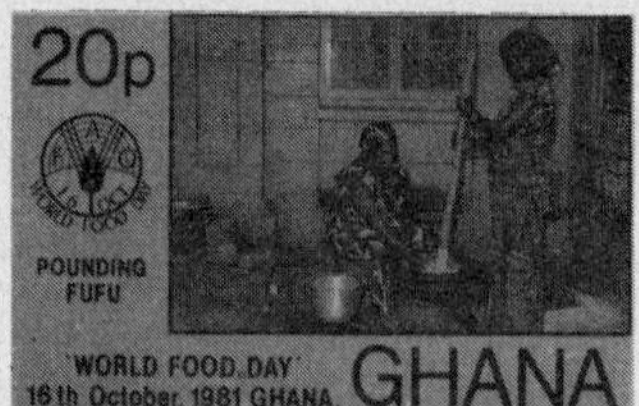

387. Pounding Fufu.

1981. World Food Day. Multicoloured.

962. 20 p. Type **387** 10 10
963. 65 p. Plucking Cocoa .. 25 35
964. 80 p. Preparing Banku .. 35 40
965. 2 c. Garri processing .. 1·00 2·00

388. "The Betrothal of St. Catherine of Alexandria" (Lucas Cranach).

1981. Christmas. Details from Paintings. Multicoloured.

967. 15 p. Type **388** 20 10
968. 20 p. "Angelic Musicians play for Mary and Child" (Aachener Altares) .. 20 10
969. 65 p. "Child Jesus embracing his Mother" (Gabriel Metsu) 45 25
970. 80 p. "Madonna and Child" (Fra Filippo Lippi) .. 55 30
971. 2 c. "The Madonna with Infant Jesus" (Barnaba da Modena) .. .. 1·25 80
972. 4 c. "The Immaculate Conception" (Murillo) 1·75 1·40

389. Blind Person.

1982. International Year of Disabled People. Multicoloured.

974. 20 p. Type **389** 10 10
975. 65 p. Disabled person with crutches 35 35
976. 80 p. Blind child reading braille 45 45
977. 4 c. Disabled people helping one another .. 2·25 2·25

390. African Clawless Otter.

1982. Flora and Fauna. Multicoloured.

979. 20 p. Type **390** 20 15
980. 65 p. Bushbuck 50 40
981. 80 p. Aardvark 60 50
982. 1 c. Scarlet Bell Tree .. 75 60
983. 2 c. Glory lilies .. .. 1·40 1·25
984. 4 c. Blue-Pea .. .. 2·50 2·25

HAVE YOU READ THE NOTES AT THE BEGINNING OF THIS CATALOGUE?
These often provide answers to the enquiries we receive.

391. "Precis westermanni".

1982. Butterflies. Multicoloured.

986 20 p. Type **391** 60 15
987 65 p. "Papilio menestheus" 1·25 85
988 2 c. "Antanartia delius" .. 2·25 3·00
989 4 c. "Charaxes castor" .. 3·50 4·25

392. Scouts planting Tree.

1982. 75th Anniv. of Boy Scout Movement. Multicoloured.

991. 20 p. Type **392** 35 15
992. 65 p. Scouts cooking on campfire 90 55
993. 80 p. Sea Scouts sailing .. 1·25 70
994. 3 c. Scouts observing African elephant .. 2·50 3·00

393. Initial Stages of Construction.

1982. Kpong Hydro-Electric Project. Multicoloured.

996. 20 p. Type **393** 45 10
997. 65 p. Truck removing rubble .. .. .. 1·00 45
998. 80 p. Hydro-Electric turbines .. .. 1·25 65
999. 2 c. Aerial view of completed plant .. 2·50 1·60

394. Footballers.

1982. World Cup Football Championship, Spain.

1000. **394.** 20 p. multicoloured 10 10
1005. 30 p. multicoloured .. 20 20
1001. – 65 p. multicoloured .. 35 35
1002. – 80 p. multicoloured (Heading) .. 45 45
1006. – 80 p. multicoloured (Three Footballers) 45 45
1007. – 1 c. multicoloured .. 55 55
1008. – 3 c. multicoloured .. 1·60 1·60
1003. – 4 c. multicoloured .. 2·00 2·00

DESIGNS: 65 p. to 4 c. Scenes showing footballers.

395. The fight against Tuberculosis.

1982. Centenary of Robert Koch's Discovery of Tubercle Bacillus. Multicoloured.

1009. 20 p. Type **395** 60 15
1010. 65 p. Robert Koch .. 1·40 1·00
1011. 80 p. Robert Koch in Africa .. .. .. 1·75 1·60
1012. 1 c. Centenary of discovery of Tuberculosis .. 2·00 2·50
1013. 2 c. Robert Koch and Nobel Prize, 1905 .. 2·75 3·50

396. The Three Kings Worship Jesus.

1982. Christmas. Multicoloured.

1014.	15 p. Type **396**	10	10
1015.	20 p. Mary, Joseph and baby Jesus	10	10
1016.	65 p. The Three Kings sight star	30	30
1017.	4 c. Winged Angel	1·40	1·75

397. Ghana and Commonwealth Flags with Coat of Arms.

1983. Commonwealth Day. Multicoloured.

1019.	20 p. Type **397**	25	15
1020.	55 p. Satellite view of Ghana	45	55
1021.	80 p. Minerals of Ghana	1·00	1·00
1022.	3 c. African fish eagle	2·75	3·50

1983. Italy's Victory in World Cup Football Championship (1982). Nos. 1000/8 optd **WINNER ITALY 3–1**.

1023.	20 p. multicoloured	10	10
1028.	30 p. multicoloured	15	15
1024.	65 p. multicoloured	15	15
1025.	80 p. multicoloured	15	20
1029.	80 p. multicoloured	50	50
1030.	1 c. multicoloured	60	60
1031.	3 c. multicoloured	1·50	1·75
1026.	4 c. multicoloured	1·25	1·75

1983. No. 470 surch **C1**.

1031a	1 c. on 20 n.p. Bush hare (blue)	30	20

399. Short Fin Pilot Whale.

1983. Coastal Marine Mammals. Mult.

1032.	1 c. Type **399**	85	85
1033.	1 c. 40 Risso's Dolphin	90	90
1034.	2 c. 30 False Killer Whale	1·10	1·10
1035.	3 c. Spinner Dolphin	1·40	1·40
1036.	5 c. Atlantic Humpbacked Dolphin	1·75	1·75

400. "Hemichramis fasciatus"

401. Communication Devices.

1983.

1038.	**400.** 5 p. multicoloured	10	10
1039.	– 10 p. multicoloured	15	10
1040.	– 20 p. multicoloured	30	10
1041.	– 50 p. grn., orge. and bl	30	20
1042.	– 1 c. orge., bl. and blk.	40	20
1043.	– 2 c. multicoloured	30	30
1044.	– 3 c. multicoloured	30	30
1045.	– 4 c. multicoloured	30	30
1046.	– 5 c. multicoloured	35	30
1047.	– 10 c. multicoloured	40	40

DESIGNS—HORIZ. 10 p. "Hemichramis fasciatus" (different). 2 c. Jet airliner. VERT. 20 p. "Haemanthus rupestris". 50 p. Mounted warrior. 1 c. Scorpion. 3 c. White-collared mangabey. 4 c. Demidoff's galago. 5 c. "Kaemferia nigerica". 10 c. Grey-backed camaroptera.

1983. World Communications Year. Mult.

1048.	1 c. Type **401**	20	20
1049.	1 c. 40 Satellite dish aerial	25	25
1050.	2 c. 30 Cable and cable-laying ship	45	45
1051.	3 c. Switchboard operators	50	50
1052.	5 c. Aircraft cockpit and air traffic controllers	70	70

402. Children receiving Presents.

1983. Christmas. Multicoloured.

1054.	70 p. Type **402**	20	10
1055.	1 c. Nativity and Star of Bethlehem (vert.)	20	10
1056.	1 c. 40 Children celebrating (vert.)	35	30
1057.	2 c. 30 Family praying together (vert.)	45	50
1058.	3 c. Dancing to Bongo drum	55	65

403. Soldiers with Rifles.

1983. Namibia Day.

1060.	**403.** 50 p. green and black	10	10
1061.	– 1 c. multicoloured	10	10
1062.	– 1 c. 40 blue, bright blue and black	15	15
1063.	– 2 c. 30 multicoloured	20	25
1064.	– 3 c. multicoloured	25	30

DESIGNS: 1 c. Soldiers supported by tank. 1 c. 40, Machete cutting chains. 2 c. 30, Peasant woman. 3 c. Soldiers and artillery support.

1984. (a) Nos. 948/50, 952 and 954 surch.

1065.	1 c. on 20 p. Prince Charles and Lady Diana Spencer	3·00	3·00
1066.	9 c. on 65 p. Prince Charles and Lady Diana Spencer	4·00	4·00
1067.	9 c. on 80 p. Prince Charles on visit to Ghana	4·00	4·00
1068.	20 c. on 3 c. Type **385**	5·00	6·00
1069.	20 c. on 4 c. Type **385**	5·00	6·00

(b) Nos. 991/2 and 994 surch.

1071.	10 c. on 20 p. Type **392**	40	45
1072.	19 c. on 65 p. Scouts cooking on campfire	80	85
1073.	30 c. on 3 c. Scouts observing African elephant	1·25	1·40

(c) Nos. 1000/3, 1005/6 and 1008 surch.

1075.	**394.** 1 c. on 20 p. mult.	10	10
1076.	– 9 c. on 65 p. mult.	40	45
1077.	– 9 c. on 3 c. mult.	40	45
1078.	**394.** 10 c. on 30 p. mult.	40	45
1079.	– 10 c. on 80 p. mult.	40	45
1080.	– 20 c. on 80 p. mult.	85	90
1081.	– 20 c. on 4 c. mult.	85	90

(d) Nos. 1019–22 surch.

1083.	1 c. on 20 p. Type **397**	10	10
1084.	9 c. on 55 p. Satellite view of Ghana	40	45
1085.	30 c. on 80 p. Minerals of Ghana	1·25	1·40
1086.	50 c. on 3 c. African Fish Eagle	2·10	2·25

(e) Nos. 1023/6, 1028/9 and 1031 surch.

1087.	**394.** 1 c. on 20 p. mult.	10	10
1088.	– 9 c. on 65 p. mult.	40	45
1089.	– 9 c. on 3 c. mult.	40	45
1090.	**394.** 10 c. on 30 p. mult.	40	45
1091.	– 10 c. on 80 p. mult.	40	45
1092.	– 20 c. on 80 p. mult.	80	85
1093.	– 20 c. on 4 c. mult.	80	85

1984. Universal Postal Union Congress, Hamburg. Nos. 1035/6 optd. **19th U.P.U. CONGRESS–HAMBURG** and surch.

1095.	10 c. on 3 c. Spinner Dolphin	40	45
1096.	50 c. on 5 c. Atlantic Humpbacked Dolphin	2·10	2·25

407. Cross and Crown of Thorns.

1984. Easter. Multicoloured.

1098.	1 c. Type **407**	10	10
1099.	1 c. 40 Christ praying	10	10
1100.	2 c. 30 The Resurrection	10	10
1101.	3 c. Palm Sunday	10	15
1102.	50 c. Christ on the road to Emmaus	1·90	2·25

408. Women's 400 Metre Race.

1984. Olympic Games, Los Angeles. Multicoloured.

1104.	1 c. Type **408**	10	10
1105.	1 c. 40 Boxing	10	10
1106.	2 c. 30 Field hockey	15	15
1107.	3 c. Men's 400 metre hurdles race	15	15
1108.	50 c. Rhythmic gymnastics	2·40	3·50

409. "Amorphophallus johnsonii".

1984. Flowers. Multicoloured.

1110.	1 c. Type **409**	10	10
1111.	1 c. 40 "Pancratium trianthum"	10	10
1112.	2 c. 30 "Eulophia cucullata"	15	15
1113.	3 c. "Amorphophallus abyssinicus"	15	15
1114.	50 c. "Chorophytum togoense"	3·50	5·00

410. Young Bongo.

1984. Endangered Antelopes. Multicoloured.

1116.	1 c. Type **410**	30	20
1117.	2 c. 30 Bongo bucks fighting	55	55
1118.	3 c. Bongo family	70	70
1119.	20 c. Bongo herd in high grass	2·50	3·50

411. Dipo Girl.

1984. Ghanaian Culture. Multicoloured.

1121.	1 c. Type **411**	10	10
1122.	1 c. 40 Adowa dancer	10	10
1123.	2 c. 30 Agbadza dancer	10	15
1124.	3 c. Damba dancer	10	15
1125.	50 c. Dipo dancer	1·75	3·00

412. The Three Wise Men bringing Gifts.

414. The Queen Mother attending Church Service.

1984. Christmas. Multicoloured.

1127.	70 p. Type **412**	10	10
1128.	1 c. Choir of angels	10	10
1129.	1 c. 40 Mary and shepherds at manger	10	10
1130.	2 c. 30 The flight into Egypt	10	10
1131.	3 c. Simeon blessing Jesus	10	15
1132.	50 c. Holy Family and angels	1·75	3·00

1984. Olympic Winners. Nos. 1104/8 optd.

1134.	1 c. Type **408** (optd. **VALERIE BRISCO-HOOKS (U.S.A.)**)	10	10
1135.	1 c. 40 Boxing (optd. **U.S. WINNERS**)	10	10
1136.	2 c. 30 Field hockey (optd. **PAKISTAN FIELD HOCKEY**)	10	10
1137.	3 c. Men's 400 metre hurdles race (optd. **EDWIN MOSES U.S.A.**)	10	10
1138.	50 c. Rhythmic gymnastics (optd. **FRANCE**)	1·50	1·60

1985. Life and Times of Queen Elizabeth the Queen Mother. Multicoloured.

1140.	5 c. Type **414**	10	15
1141.	12 c. At Ascot Races	25	30
1142.	100 c. At Clarence House on her 84th birthday	2·00	2·50

Stamps as Nos. 1140/2 but with face values of 8 c., 20 c. and 70 c. exist from additional sheetlets with changed background colours.

415. Moslems going to Mosque.

1985. Islamic Festival of Id-el-Fitr. Multicoloured.

1144. 5 c. Type **415** 20 20
1145. 8 c. Moslems at prayer .. 30 30
1146. 12 c. Pilgrims visiting the Dome of the Rock .. 45 45
1147. 18 c. Preaching the Koran 60 60
1148. 50 c. Banda Nkwanta Mosque, Accra, and map of Ghana .. 1·60 1·60

416. Youths clearing Refuse ("Make Ghana Clean").

1985. International Youth Year. Mult.

1149. 5 c. Type **416** 10 10
1150. 8 c. Planting sapling ("Make Ghana Green") 15 15
1151. 12 c. Youth carrying bananas ("Feed Ghana") 20 25
1152. 100 c. Open-air class ("Educate Ghana") .. 1·60 2·25

417. Honda "Interceptor", 1984.

1985. Centenary of the Motorcycle. Mult.

1154. 5 c. Type **417** 55 55
1155. 8 c. DKW 1938 .. .. 65 65
1156. 12 c. BMW "R 32" 1923 1·00 1·00
1157. 100 c. NSU, 1900 .. 5·50 6·50

418. Fork-tailed Flycatcher.

1985. Birth Bicentenary of John J. Audubon (ornithologist). Designs showing original paintings. Multicoloured.

1159. 5 c. Type **418** 75 30
1160. 8 c. Barred Owl .. .. 1·75 1·25
1161. 12 c. Black-throated Mango .. .. .. 1·75 1·50
1162. 100 c. White-crowned Pigeon .. .. .. 4·50 6·50

No. 1159 is inscribed "York-tailed Fly Catcher" in error.

419. United Nations Building, New York.

1985. 40th Anniv. of United Nations Organization. Multicoloured.

1164. 5 c. Type **419** 10 10
1165. 8 c. Flags of member nations and U.N. Building 15 15
1166. 12 c. Dove with olive branch 20 25
1167. 18 c. General Assembly 30 35
1168. 100 c. Flags of Ghana and United Nations .. 1·60 1·75

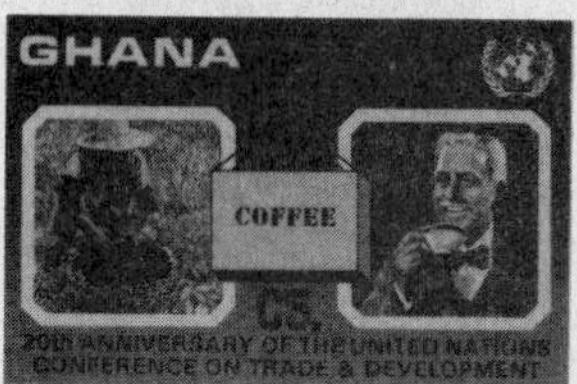

420. Coffee.

1985. 20th Anniv. of United Nations Conference on Trade and Development. Designs showing export products. Multicoloured.

1170. 5 c. Type **420** 10 10
1171. 8 c. Cocoa 15 15
1172. 12 c. Timber 25 25
1173. 18 c. Bauxite .. .. 1·25 90
1174. 100 c. Gold .. .. 6·50 7·50

421. Growth Monitoring.

1985. U.N.I.C.E.F. Child Survival Campaign. Multicoloured.

1176. 5 c. Type **421** 30 10
1177. 8 c. Oral rehydration therapy 50 30
1178. 12 c. Breast feeding .. 70 40
1179. 100 c. Immunization .. 3·00 4·00

422. Airline Stewardess and Boys with Stamp Album.

1986. "Ameripex" International Stamp Exhibition, Chicago. Multicoloured.

1181. 5 c. Type **422** 10 10
1182. 25 c. Globe and Ghana Airways aircraft .. 45 45
1183. 100 c. Ghana Airways stewardess (vert.) .. 1·75 2·75

423. Kejetia Roundabout, Kumasi.

1986. "Inter-Tourism '86" Conference. Multicoloured.

1185. 5 c. Type **423** 10 10
1186. 15 c. Fort St. Jago, Elmina 30 30
1187. 25 c. Tribal warriors .. 45 45
1188. 100 c. Chief holding audience .. .. 1·75 3·00

MINIMUM PRICE

The minimum price quoted is 10p which represents a handling charge rather than a basis for valuing common stamps. For further notes about prices see introductory pages.

424. Tackling.

1987. World Cup Football Championship, Mexico (1986). Multicoloured.

1190. 5 c. Type **424** 15 10
1191. 15 c. Player taking control of ball .. 20 15
1192. 25 c. Player kicking ball 30 25
1193. 100 c. Player with ball .. 1·10 1·25

425. Fertility Doll.

1987. Ghanaian Fertility Dolls. Designs showing different dolls.

1195. **425.** 5 c. multicoloured .. 10 10
1196. – 15 c. multicoloured .. 15 15
1197. – 25 c. multicoloured .. 30 25
1198. – 100 c. multicoloured 1·00 1·25

426. Children of Different Races, Peace Doves and Sun.

1987. International Peace Year (1986). Multicoloured.

1200. 5 c. Type **426** 10 10
1201. 25 c. Plough, peace dove and rising sun .. 45 25
1202. 100 c. Peace dove, olive branch and globe (vert.) .. .. .. 2·00 2·25

427. Lumber and House under Construction.

1987. "Gifex '87" International Forestry Exposition, Accra. Multicoloured.

1204. 5 c. Type **427** 10 10
1205. 15 c. Planks and furniture 15 15
1206. 25 c. Felled trees .. 30 25
1207. 200 c. Logs and wood carvings .. .. 1·90 2·25

1987. Appearance of Halley's Comet (1986). As T **123** of Anguilla. Multicoloured.

1208. 5 c. Mikhail Lomonosov (scientist) and Chamber of Curiosities, St. Petersburg 20 10
1209. 25 c. Lunar probe "Surveyor III", 1966 .. 70 30
1210. 200 c. Wedgwood plaques for Isaac Newton, 1790, and "Apollo 11" Moon landing, 1968 .. .. 3·25 2·25

428. Demonstrator and Arms breaking Shackles.

1987. Solidarity with the People of Southern Africa. Multicoloured.

1212. 5 c. Type **428** 10 1
1213. 15 c. Miner and gold bars 15 1
1214. 25 c. Xhosa warriors .. 30 2
1215. 100 c. Nelson Mandela and shackles .. .. 1·00 1·5

429. Aerophones.

1987. Musical Instruments. Multicoloured.

1217. 5 c. Type **429** 10 10
1218. 15 c. Xylophone .. 15 15
1219. 25 c. Chordophones .. 30 25
1220. 100 c. Membranophones 1·00 1·25

430. Woman filling Water Pot at Pump.

1987. International Year of Shelter for the Homeless. Multicoloured.

1222. 5 c. Type **430** 10 10
1223. 15 c. Building house from breeze blocks 15 15
1224. 25 c. Modern village with stream 25 25
1225. 100 c. Modern houses with verandahs .. 1·00 1·25

431. Ga Women preparing Kpokpoi for Homowo Festival.

1988. Ghana Festivals. Multicoloured.

1226. 5 c. Type **431** 10 10
1227. 15 c. Efute hunters with deer, Aboakyir festival 15 15
1228. 25 c. Fanti chief dancing at Odwira festival .. 25 25
1229. 100 c. Chief in palanquin, Yam festival .. .. 85 1·25

432. Port Installation.

1988. 5th Anniv. (1987) of 31 December Revolution. Multicoloured.

1230. 5 c. Type **432** 30 15
1231. 15 c. Repairing railway line 60 40
1232. 25 c. Planting cocoa .. 50 30
1233. 100 c. Miners with ore truck .. .. .. 2·25 2·50

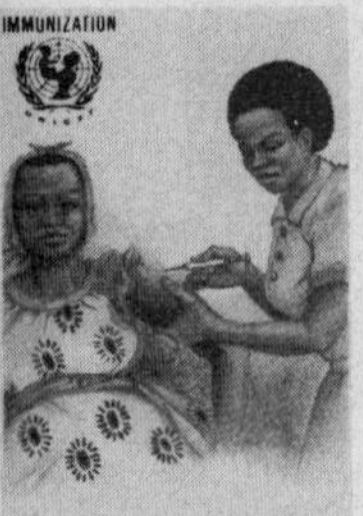
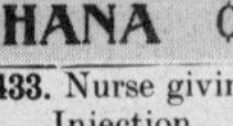

433. Nurse giving Injection.

435 Akwadjan Men

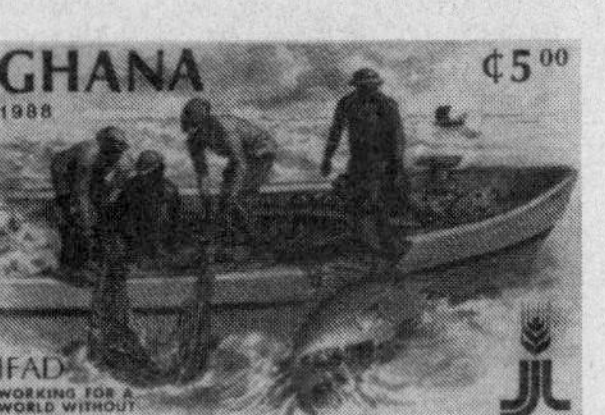

434 Fishing

1988. U.N.I.C.E.F. Global Immunization Campaign. Multicoloured.

1234. 5 c. Type **433** 20 10
1235. 15 c. Girl receiving injection 25 20
1236. 25 c. Schoolgirl crippled by polio 50 50
1237. 100 c. Nurse giving oral vaccine to baby .. 1·60 2·00

1988. 10th Anniv of International Fund for Agricultural Development. Multicoloured.

1238 5 c. Type **434** 15 10
1239 15 c. Women harvesting crops 20 15
1240 25 c. Cattle 40 30
1241 100 c. Village granaries .. 1·40 1·75

1988. Tribal Costumes. Multicoloured.

1242 5 c. Type **435** 15 10
1243 25 c. Banaa man 35 20
1244 250 c. Agwasen woman .. 2·00 1·75

1988. Nos. 460, 464/6, 469/70, 1031a, 1038/42, 1044 and 1046 surch.

1245 – 20 c. on 50 p. green, orange and black (No. 1041) .. 20 15
1246 – 20 c. on 1 c. orge, bl & black (No. 1042) 20 15
1247 – 50 c. on 10 n.p. mult (No. 469) .. 25 25
1248 – 50 c. on 20 n.p. deep blue and blue (No. 470) (surch **C50**) 75 35
1249 – 50 c. on 20 n.p. deep blue and blue (No. 470) (surch **C50.00**) 75 35
1250 – 50 c. on 10 p. mult (No. 1039) .. 20 15
1251 – 50 c. on 1 c. on 20 n.p. deep blue and blue (No. 1031a) (surch **C50**) 75 35
1252 – 50 c. on 1 c. on 20 n.p. dp blue & blue (No. 1031a) (surch **C50.00**) .. 75 35
1254 – 50 c. on 1 c. orange, bl & blk (No. 1042) 75 35
1255a **230** 60 c. on 1 n.p. mult 70 35
1256 – 60 c. on 4 n.p. mult (No. 465) 30 30
1257 – 60 c. on 3 c. mult (No. 1044) .. 30 30
1258 **400** 80 c. on 5 p. mult .. 35 35
1259 – 80 c. on 5 c. mult (No. 1046) .. 1·10 1·10
1260 – 100 c. on 3 n.p. mult (No. 464) .. 1·75 1·75
1261 – 100 c. on 20 n.p. deep blue & bl (No. 470) 40 40
1262 – 100 c. on 20 p. mult (No. 1040) .. 40 40
1263 – 100 c. on 3 c. mult (No. 1044) .. 40 40
1264 – 200 c. on 6 n.p. mult (No. 466) .. 1·25 1·10

440 Boxing

1988. Olympic Games, Seoul. Multicoloured.

1265 20 c. Type **440** 15 15
1266 60 c. Athletics 45 45
1267 80 c. Discus-throwing .. 60 60
1268 100 c. Javelin-throwing .. 80 80
1269 350 c. Weightlifting .. 2·00 2·50

441 Nutrition Lecture

1988. 125th Anniv of Int. Red Cross. Mult.

1271 20 c. Type **441** 40 15
1272 50 c. Red Cross volunteer with blind woman .. 90 90
1273 60 c. Distributing flood relief supplies .. 1·00 1·00
1274 200 c. Giving first aid .. 2·50 2·75

442 Tropical Forest

1988. Christmas. Multicoloured.

1275 20 c. Type **442** 15 10
1276 60 c. Christ Child (vert) .. 35 35
1277 80 c. Virgin and Child with Star (vert) .. 50 50
1278 100 c. Three Wise Men following Star .. 60 70
1279 350 c. Symbolic Crucifixion (vert) .. 2·00 2·50

443 "African Solidarity"

1989. 25th Anniv (1988) of Organization of African Unity. Multicoloured.

1281 20 c. Type **443** 10 10
1282 50 c. O.A.U. Headquarters, Addis Ababa 15 20
1283 60 c. Emperor Haile Selassie and Ethiopian flag (horiz) 20 25
1284 200 c. Kwame Nkrumah (former Ghanaian President) and flag (horiz) 60 65

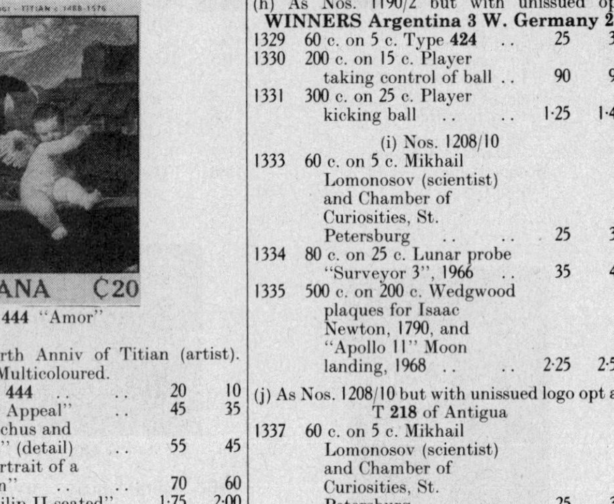

444 "Amor"

1989. 500th Birth Anniv of Titian (artist). Multicoloured.

1285 20 c. Type **444** 20 10
1286 60 c. "The Appeal" .. 45 35
1287 80 c. "Bacchus and Ariadne" (detail) .. 55 45
1288 100 c. "Portrait of a Musician" 70 60
1289 350 c. "Philip II seated" 1·75 2·00

1989. Olympic Medal Winners, Seoul. Nos. 1251/5 optd.

1291 20 c. Type **436** (optd **A. ZUELOW DDR 60 KG**) 10 10
1292 20 c. Athletics (optd **G. BORDIN ITALY MARATHON**) .. 20 25
1293 80 c. Discus-throwing (optd **J. SCHULT DDR**) 25 30
1294 10 c. Javelin-throwing (optd **T. KORJUS FINLAND**) 30 35
1295 350 c. Weightlifting (optd **B. GUIDIKOV BULGARIA 75 KG**) 1·00 1·10

1989. Various stamps surch (a) Nos. 949/50 and 952/4.

1297 80 c. on 65 p. Prince Charles and Lady Diana Spencer .. 35 40
1298 100 c. on 80 p. Prince Charles on visit to Ghana 45 50
1299 100 c. on 1 c. Prince Charles on visit to Ghana 45 50
1300 300 c. on 3 c. Type **385** .. 1·25 1·40
1301 500 c. on 4 c. Type **385** .. 2·25 2·50

(b) Nos. 1048/51

1302 60 c. on 1 c. Type **401** .. 25 30
1303 80 c. on 1 c. 40 Satellite dish aerial 35 40
1304 200 c. on 2 c. 30 Cable and cable-laying ship .. 90 95
1305 300 c. on 3 c. Switchboard operators .. .. 1·25 1·40

(c) Nos. 1104/7

1307 60 c. on 1 c. Type **408** .. 25 30
1308 80 c. on 1 c. 40 Boxing .. 35 40
1309 200 c. on 2 c. 30 Hockey .. 90 95
1310 300 c. on 3 c. Men's 400 metre hurdles race .. 1·25 1·40

(d) Nos. 1134/7

1312 60 c. on 1 c. Type **408** (optd **VALERIE BRISCO-HOOKS (U.S.A.)**) 25 30
1313 80 c. on 1 c. 40 Boxing (optd **U.S. WINNERS**) 35 40
1314 200 c. on 2 c. 30 Field hockey (optd **PAKISTAN (FIELD HOCKEY)**) 90 95
1315 300 c. on 3 c. Men's 400 metre hurdles race (optd **EDWIN MOSES U.S.A.**) .. 1·25 1·40

(e) Nos. 1140/2

1317 80 c. on 5 c. Type **414** .. 35 40
1318 250 c. on 12 c. At Ascot Races .. .. .. 1·10 1·25
1319 300 c. on 100 c. At Clarence House on her 84th birthday .. .. 1·25 1·40

(f) Nos. 1159/61

1321 80 c. on 5 c. Type **418** .. 35 40
1322 100 c. on 8 c. Barred owl 45 50
1323 300 c. on 12 c. Black-throated mango .. 1·25 1·40

(g) Nos. 1190/2

1325 60 c. on 5 c. Type **424** .. 35 35
1326 200 c. on 15 c. Player taking control of ball .. 1·25 1·25
1327 300 c. on 25 c. Player kicking ball .. .. 1·75 1·75

(h) As Nos. 1190/2 but with unissued opt **WINNERS Argentina 3 W. Germany 2**

1329 60 c. on 5 c. Type **424** .. 25 30
1330 200 c. on 15 c. Player taking control of ball .. 90 95
1331 300 c. on 25 c. Player kicking ball .. .. 1·25 1·40

(i) Nos. 1208/10

1333 60 c. on 5 c. Mikhail Lomonosov (scientist) and Chamber of Curiosities, St. Petersburg 25 30
1334 80 c. on 25 c. Lunar probe "Surveyor 3", 1966 .. 35 40
1335 500 c. on 200 c. Wedgwood plaques for Isaac Newton, 1790, and "Apollo 11" Moon landing, 1968 .. .. 2·25 2·50

(j) As Nos. 1208/10 but with unissued logo opt as T **218** of Antigua

1337 60 c. on 5 c. Mikhail Lomonosov (scientist) and Chamber of Curiosities, St. Petersburg 25 30
1338 80 c. on 25 c. Lunar probe "Surveyor 3", 1966 .. 35 40
1339 500 c. on 200 c. Wedgwood plaques for Isaac Newton, 1790, and "Apollo 11" Moon landing, 1968 .. .. 2·25 2·50

448 French Royal Standard and Field Gun

1989. "Philexfrance 89" International Stamp Exhibition, Paris. Multicoloured.

1341 20 c. Type **448** 35 20
1342 60 c. Regimental standard, 1789, and French infantryman .. 70 55
1343 80 c. Revolutionary standard, 1789, and pistol 85 75
1344 350 c. Tricolour, 1794, and musket .. .. 2·75 3·25

1989. Japanese Art. Portraits. As T **250** of Antigua. Multicoloured.

1346 20 c. "Minamoto- no-Yoritomo" (Fujiwara-no-Takanobu) (vert) .. 10 10
1347 50 c. "Takami Senseki" (Watanabe Kazan) (vert) 15 20
1348 60 c. "Ikkyu Sojun" (study) (Bokusai) (vert) 20 25
1349 75 c. "Nakamura Kuranosuka" (Ogata Korin) (vert) 20 25
1350 125 c. "Portrait of a Lady" (Kyoto branch, Kano school) (vert) .. 35 40
1351 150 c. "Portrait of Zemmui" (anon, 12th-century) (vert) .. 45 50
1352 200 c. "Ono no Komachi the Poetess" (Hokusai) (vert) 60 65
1353 500 c. "Kobo Daisi as a Child" (anon) (vert) .. 1·50 1·60

449 Storming the Bastille

1989. Bicentenary of the French Revolution. Multicoloured.

No.	Description	Unused	Used
1355	20 c. Type **449**	15	10
1356	60 c. Declaration of Human Rights ..	30	30
1357	80 c. Storming the Bastille (horiz)	35	35
1358	200 c. Revolution monument (horiz) ..	90	1·00
1359	350 c. Tree of Liberty (horiz)	1·40	1·60

450 Spindle Shank

1989. Fungi (1st series). Multicoloured.

No.	Description	Unused	Used
1360	20 c. Type **450**	20	20
1361	50 c. Shaggy ink cap ..	30	30
1362	60 c. "Xerocomus subtomentosus" ..	35	35
1363	80 c. Purple blewit ..	50	50
1364	150 c. "Suillus placidus"	85	85
1365	200 c. "Lepista nuda" ..	1·10	1·10
1366	300 c. Fairy ring champignon	1·60	1·60
1367	500 c. Field mushroom ..	2·75	2·75

See also Nos. 1489/96.

"The course of true love never did run smooth. 1:i"

451 "The Course of True Love ...."

1989. 425th Birth Anniv of Shakespeare. Verses and scenes from "A Midsummer Night's Dream". Multicoloured.

No.	Description	Unused	Used
1369	40 c. Type **451** ..	15	15
1370	40 c. "Love looks not with the eye but with the mind"	15	15
1371	40 c. "Nature here shows art"	15	15
1372	40 c. "Things growing are not ripe till their season"	15	15
1373	40 c. "He is defiled that draws a sword on thee"	15	15
1374	40 c. "It is not enough to speak, but to speak true"	15	15
1375	40 c. "Thou art as wise as thou art beautiful" ..	15	15
1376	40 c. Wildcat in wood (face value at left) ..	15	15
1377	40 c. Man ..	15	15
1378	40 c. Woman with flower	15	15
1379	40 c. King and queen ..	15	15
1380	40 c. Bottom ..	15	15
1381	40 c. Wildcat in wood (face value at right) ..	15	15
1382	40 c. Woman ..	15	15
1383	40 c. Leopard ..	15	15
1384	40 c. Tree trunk and man	15	15
1385	40 c. Meadow flowers	15	15
1386	40 c. Mauve flowers ..	15	15
1387	40 c. Plants ..	15	15
1388	40 c. Lion ..	15	15
1389	40 c. Fern and flowers ..	15	15

Nos. 1369/89 were printed together, forming a composite design.

1989. Birds. As T **244** of Dominica. Mult.

No.	Description	Unused	Used
1390	20 c. Bronze mannikin (horiz)	20	10
1391	50 c. African pied wagtail (horiz)	35	30
1392	60 c. African pygmy kingfisher (inscr "Halcyon malimbicus") (horiz) ..	1·00	1·00
1392a	60 c. African pygmy kingfisher (inscr "Ispidina picta") ..	50	50
1393	80 c. Blue-breasted kingfisher (inscr "Ispidina picta") (horiz) ..	1·50	1·50
1393a	80 c. Blue-breasted kingfisher (inscr "Halcyon Malimbicus") ..	75	75
1394	150 c. Striped kingfisher	85	85
1395	200 c. Shrika	1·10	1·10
1396	300 c. Grey parrot ..	1·40	1·40
1397	500 c. Black kite ..	2·50	2·50

452 Command Module "Columbia" orbiting Moon

1989. 20th Anniv of First Manned Landing on Moon. Multicoloured.

No.	Description	Unused	Used
1399	20 c. Type **452**	15	15
1400	80 c. Neil Armtrong's footprint on Moon ..	30	40
1401	200 c. Edwin Aldrin on Moon	75	85
1402	300 c. "Apollo 11" capsule on parachutes ..	1·10	1·25

453 Desertification of Pasture

1989. World Environment Day. Mult.

No.	Description	Unused	Used
1404	20 c. Type **453** ..	30	15
1405	60 c. Wildlife fleeing bush fire	50	45
1406	400 c. Industrial pollution	2·25	2·25
1407	500 c. Erosion	2·50	2·50

454 "Bebearia arcadius"

1990. Butterflies. Multicoloured.

No.	Description	Unused	Used
1408	20 c. Type **454**	10	10
1409	60 c. "Charaxes laodice"	10	10
1410	80 c. "Euryphura porphyrion"	15	20
1411	100 c. "Neptis nicomedes"	20	25
1412	150 c. "Citrinophila erastus"	30	35
1413	200 c. "Aethiopana honorius"	35	40
1414	300 c. "Precis westermanni"	55	60
1415	500 c. "Cymothoe hypatha"	90	95

455 "Cymbium costatum Linne"

1990. Seashells. Multicoloured.

No.	Description	Unused	Used
1417	20 c. Type 455	20	20
1418	60 c. "Cardium glans" Gmelin	30	30
1419	80 c. "Conus genuanus" Linne	35	35
1420	200 c. "Ancilla tankervillei" Swainson ..	80	80
1421	350 c. "Tectarius coronatus" Valenciennes	1·25	1·25

456 Nehru welcoming President Nkrumah of Ghana

1990. Birth Centenary of Jawaharlal Nehru (Indian statesman). Multicoloured.

No.	Description	Unused	Used
1422	20 c. Type **456**	10	10
1423	60 c. Nehru addressing Bandung Conference, 1955	10	10
1424	80 c. Nehru with garland and flowers (vert) ..	15	20
1425	200 c. Nehru releasing pigeon (vert)	35	40
1426	350 c. Nehru (vert) ..	65	70

457 Wyon Medal, 1838

1990. 150th Anniv of the Penny Black.

No.	Type	Description	Unused	Used
1427	**457**	20 c. black and violet	10	10
1428	–	60 c. black and green	10	10
1429	–	80 c. black and violet	15	20
1430	–	200 c. black and green	35	40
1431	–	350 c. black and green	65	70
1432	–	400 c. black and red	70	75

DESIGNS: 60 c. Bath mail coach, 1840; 80 c. Leeds mail coach, 1840; 200 c. Proof of Queen's head engraved by Heath, 1840; 350 c. Master die, 1840; 400 c. London mail coach, 1840.

458 Anniversary Emblem

1990. 10th Anniv (1989) of 4 June Revolution. Multicoloured.

No.	Description	Unused	Used
1434	20 c. Type **458**	10	10
1435	60 c. Foodstuffs	10	10
1436	80 c. Cocoa	15	20
1437	200 c. Mining	35	40
1438	350 c. Scales of Justice and sword	65	70

459 Map of Africa and Satellite Network

1990. 25th Anniv of Intelsat Satellite System. Multicoloured.

No.	Description	Unused	Used
1439	20 c. Type **459**	10	10
1440	60 c. Map of Americas ..	10	10
1441	80 c. Map of Asia and Pacific	15	20
1442	200 c. Map of South America and Africa ..	35	40
1443	350 c. Map of Indian Ocean and Pacific ..	65	70

460 Housewife using Telephone

1990. 2nd Anniv of Introduction of International Direct Dialling Service. Mult.

No.	Description	Unused	Used
1444	20 c. Type **460**	10	10
1445	60 c. Businessman using telephone	10	10
1446	80 c. Man using phonecard telephone	15	20
1447	200 c. Public telephones for internal and IDD services	35	40
1448	350 c. Satellite station ..	65	70

461 Blue Flycatcher

1990. African Tropical Rain Forest. Mult.

No.	Description	Unused	Used
1449	40 c. Type **461**	20	20
1450	40 c. Boomslang (snake)	20	20
1451	40 c. Superb sunbird ..	20	20
1452	40 c. Bateleur	20	20
1453	40 c. Yellow-casqued hornbill	20	20
1454	40 c. "Salamis temora" (butterfly)	20	20
1455	40 c. Potto	20	20
1456	40 c. Leopard	20	20
1457	40 c. Bongo	20	20
1458	40 c. Grey parrot ..	20	20
1459	40 c. Okapi	20	20
1460	40 c. Gorilla	20	20
1461	40 c. Flap-necked chameleon	20	20
1462	40 c. West African dwarf crocodile	20	20
1463	40 c. Python	20	20
1464	40 c. Giant ground pangolin	20	20
1465	40 c. "Pseudacraea boisduvali" (butterfly)	20	20
1466	40 c. North African crested porcupine ..	20	20
1467	40 c. "Rosy-columned aerangis" (orchid) ..	20	20
1468	40 c. "Cymothoe sangaris" (butterfly)	20	20

Nos. 1449/68 were printed together, se-tenant, forming a composite design.

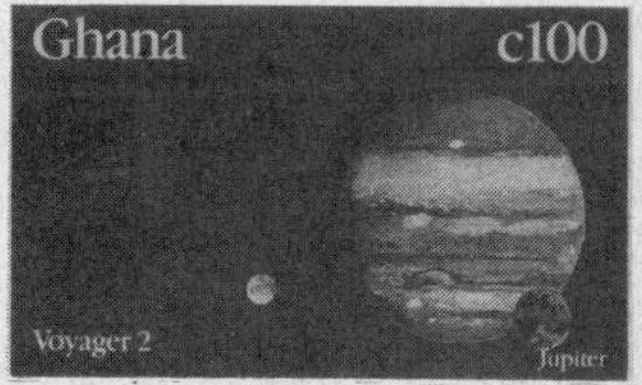

462 Jupiter

1990. Space Flight of "Voyager 2". Mult.

No.	Description	Unused	Used
1470	100 c. Type **462**	20	25
1471	100 c. Neptune and Triton	20	25
1472	100 c. Ariel, moon of Uranus	20	25
1473	100 c. Saturn from "Mimas"	20	25
1474	100 c. Saturn	20	25
1475	100 c. Rings of Saturn ..	20	25
1476	100 c. Neptune	20	25
1477	100 c. Uranus from "Miranda"	20	25
1478	100 c. Volcano on Io ..	20	25

463 "Eulophia guineensis"

1990. Orchids. Multicoloured.

No.	Description	Unused	Used
1480	20 c. Type **463**	10	10
1481	40 c. "Eurychone rothschildiana"	10	15
1482	60 c. "Bulbophyllum barbigerum"	10	15

1483 80 c. "Polystachya galeata" 15 20
1484 200 c. "Diaphananthe kamerunensis" .. 35 40
1485 300 c. "Podangis dactyloceras" 55 60
1486 400 c. "Ancistrochilus rothschildianus" .. 70 75
1487 500 c. "Rangaeris muscicola" 90 95

464 "Coprinus atramentarius"

1990. Fungi (2nd series). Multicoloured.

1489 20 c. Type **464** 10 10
1490 50 c. "Marasmius oreades" 10 10
1491 60 c. "Oudemansiella radicata" 10 10
1492 80 c. "Boletus edulis" (cep) 15 20
1493 150 c. "Hebeloma crustuliniforme" 30 35
1494 200 c. "Coprinus micaceus" 35 40
1495 300 c. "Lepiota procera" 55 60
1496 500 c. "Amanita phalloides" 90 95

465 Italian and Swedish Players chasing Ball

1990. World Cup Football Championship, Italy. Multicoloured.

1498 20 c. Type **465** 10 10
1499 50 c. Egyptian player penetrating Irish defence 10 10
1500 60 c. Cameroon players celebrating 10 10
1501 80 c. Rumanian player beating challenge .. 15 20
1502 100 c. Russian goalkeeper Dassayev 20 25
1503 150 c. Roger Milla of Cameroon (vert) .. 30 35
1504 400 c. South Korean player challenging opponent 70 75
1505 600 c. Klinsman of West Germany celebrating .. 1·10 1·25

1990. 350th Death Anniv of Rubens. As T **273** of Antigua, but vert. Multicoloured.

1507 20 c. "Duke of Mantua" 10 10
1508 50 c. "Jan Brant" .. 10 10
1509 60 c. "Portrait of a Young Man" 10 10
1510 80 c. "Michel Ophovius" 15 20
1511 100 c. "Caspar Gevaerts" 20 25
1512 200 c. "Head of Warrior" (detail) 35 40
1513 300 c. "Study of a Bearded Man" .. 55 60
1514 400 c. "Paracelsus" .. 70 75

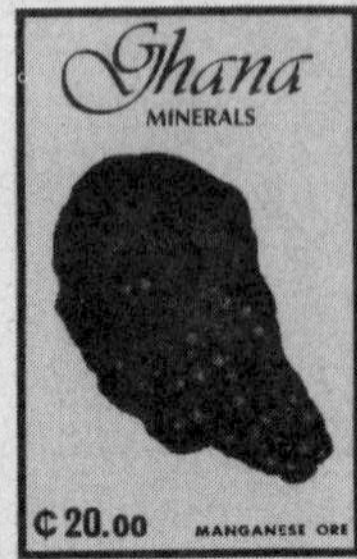

466 Manganese Ore

1991. Minerals. Multicoloured.

1516 20 c. Type **466** 10 10
1517 60 c. Iron ore 10 10
1518 80 c. Bauxite ore 15 20
1519 200 c. Gold ore 35 40
1520 350 c. Diamond 65 70

467 Dance Drums

1991. Tribal Drums. Multicoloured.

1522 20 c. Type **467** 10 10
1523 60 c. Message drums .. 10 10
1524 80 c. War drums .. 15 20
1525 200 c. Dance drums (different) 35 40
1526 350 c. Ceremonial drums 65 70

468 "Amorphophallus dracontioides"

1991. Flowers (1st series). Multicolorued.

1528 20 c. Type **468** 10 10
1529 60 c. "Anchomanes difformis" 10 10
1530 80 c. "Kaemferia nigerica" 15 20
1531 200 c. "Aframomum sceptrum" 35 40
1532 350 c. "Amorphophallus flavovirens" 65 70

1991. Flowers (2nd series). As T **468** but inscr "GHANA". Multicoloured.

1534 20 c. "Urginea indica" .. 10 10
1535 60 c. "Hymenocallis littoralis" 10 10
1536 80 c. "Crinum jagus" .. 15 20
1537 200 c. "Dipcadi tacazzeanum" 35 40
1538 350 c. "Haremanthus rupestris" 65 70

469 Transport and Telecommunication Symbols

1991. 40th Anniv of United Nations Development Programme. Multicoloured.

1540 20 c. Type **469** 10 10
1541 60 c. Agricultural research 10 10
1542 80 c. Literacy 15 20
1543 200 c. Advances in agricultural crop growth .. 35 40
1544 350 c. Industrial symbols 65 70

470 Drawing of Scout from First Handbook

1991. 50th Death Anniv of Lord Baden-Powell.

1545 **470** 20 c. black and buff .. 10 10
1546 – 50 c. grey, blue & blk 10 10
1547 – 60 c. multicoloured .. 10 10
1548 – 80 c. black and buff .. 15 20
1549 – 100 c. multicoloured 20 25
1550 – 200 c. multicoloured 35 40
1551 – 500 c. multicoloured 90 95
1552 – 600 c. multicoloured 1·10 1·25

DESIGNS—VERT. 50 c. Lord Baden-Powell; 80 c. Handbook illustration by Norman Rockwell; 500 c. Scout at prayer. HORIZ. 60 c. Hands holding Boy Scout emblem; 100 c. Mafeking Siege 1d. Goodyear stamp and African runner; 200 c. Scouts with Blitz victim, London, 1944; 600 c. Mafeking Siege 1d. Goodyear stamp.

471 Women sorting Fish

1991. Chorkor Smoker (fish smoking process). Multicoloured.

1554 20 c. Type **471** 10 10
1555 60 c. Cleaning the ovens 10 10
1556 80 c. Washing fish .. 15 20
1557 200 c. Laying fish on pallets 35 40
1558 350 c. Stacking pallets over ovens 65 70

472 "Cephalopholis taeniops"

1991. Fishes. Multicoloured.

1559 20 c. Type **472** 10 10
1560 50 c. "Synodontis sorex" 10 10
1561 80 c. "Balistes forcipatus" 15 20
1562 100 c. "Petrocephalus bane" 20 25
1563 200 c. "Syngnathus rastellatus" 35 40
1564 300 c. "Gymnarchus niloticus" 55 60
1565 400 c. "Hemichromis bimaculatus" 70 75
1566 500 c. "Sphyrna zygaena" 90 95

1991. Death Centenary (1990) of Vincent van Gogh (artist). As T **278** of Antigua. Mult.

1568 20 c. "Reaper with Sickle" 10 10
1569 50 c. "The Thresher" .. 10 10
1570 60 c. "The Sheaf-Binder" 10 10
1571 80 c. "The Sheep-Shearers" 15 20
1572 100 c. "Peasant Woman cutting Straw" .. 20 25
1573 200 c. "The Sower" .. 35 40
1574 500 c. "The Plough and the Harrow" (horiz) .. 90 95
1575 600 c. "The Woodcutter" 1·10 1·25

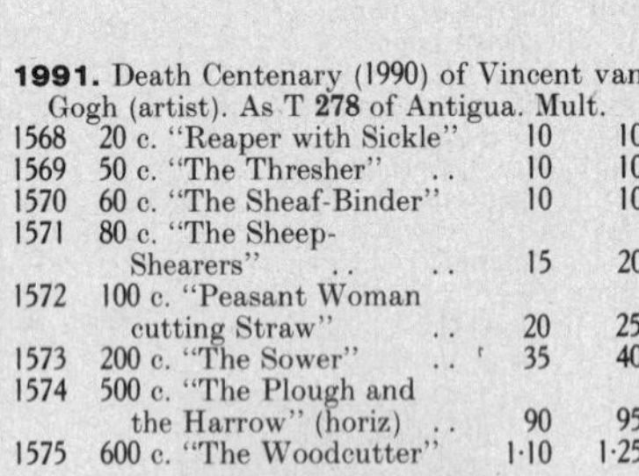

473 Gamal Nasser (Egypt) and Conference Hall

1991. 10th Non-Aligned Ministers' Conference, Accra. Statesmen. Multicoloured.

1577 20 c. Type **473** 10 10
1578 60 c. Josip Tito (Yugoslavia) 10 10
1579 80 c. Pandit Nehru (India) 15 20
1580 200 c. Kwame Nkrumah (Ghana) 35 40
1581 350 c. Achmad Sukarno (Indonesia) 65 70

474 Green-winged Pytilia

1991. Birds. Multicoloured.

1582/1629 80 c. × 16, 100 c. × 32 Set of 48 8·00 10·00

Nos. 1582/1629 were issued together, se-tenant, as three sheetlets of 16 forming composite designs. The 80 c. values show Green-winged pytilia, Orange-cheeked waxbill, African paradise flycatcher, Great blue turaco ("Blue plantain-eater"), Red bishop, Splendid glossy starling, Red-faced lovebird, African palm swift, Narina trogon, Tawny eagle, Bateleur, Hoopoe, Secretary bird, African white-backed vulture, Bare-headed rockfowl, Abyssinian ground hornbill, and the 100 c. African open-bill stork, African spoonbill, Pink-backed pelican, Little bittern, Purple swamphen ("King reed-hen"), Saddle-bill stork, Glossy ibis, White-faced whistling duck, Black-headed heron, Hammerkop, African darter, Woolly-necked stork, Yellow-billed stork, Black-winged stilt, Goliath heron, Lily trotter, Shikra, Abyssinian roller, Carmine bee eater, Pin-tailed whydah, Purple glossy starling, Yellow-mantled whydah, Pel's fishing owl, Crested touraco, Red-cheeked cordon-bleu, Olive-bellied sunbird, Red-billed hornbill, Red-billed quelea, Crowned crane, Blue quail, Egyptian vulture and Helmet guineafowl.

475 "Nularda" (beetle)

1991. Insects. Multicoloured.

1631 20 c. Type **475** 10 10
1632 50 c. "Zonocrus" (grass-hopper) 10 10
1633 60 c. "Gryllotalpa africana" (mole cricket) 10 10
1634 80 c. Weevil 15 20
1635 100 c. "Coenagrion" (dragonfly) 20 25
1636 150 c. "Sahlbergella" (fly) 30 35
1637 200 c. "Anthia" (ant) .. 35 40
1638 350 c. "Megacephala" (beetle) 65 70

476 Boti Falls

1991. Multicoloured.

1639a 20 c. Oil palm fruit .. 10 10
1640 50 c. Type **476** 10 10
1641 60 c. Larabanga Mosque (horiz) 10 10
1642 80 c. Fort Sebastian, Shama (horiz) .. 15 20
1643 100 c. Cape Coast Castle (horiz) 20 25
1644 200 c. "Leucodon cowrie" (shell) (horiz) 35 40
1645 400 c. "Achatina achatina" (shell) (horiz) 70 75

1991. Christmas. Religious Paintings. As T **287** of Antigua. Multicoloured.

1646 20 c. "Adoration of the Magi" (Bosch) .. 10 10
1647 50 c. "The Annunciation" (Campin) 10 10
1648 60 c. "Virgin and Child" (detail) (Bouts) .. 10 10
1649 80 c. "Presentation in the Temple" (Memling) .. 15 20
1650 100 c. "Virgin and Child enthroned with Angel and Donor" (Memling) 20 25

1651 200 c. "Virgin and Child with Saints and Donor" (Van Eyck) 35 40

1652 400 c. "St. Luke painting the Virgin" (Van der Weyden) 70 75

1653 700 c. "Virgin and Child" (Bouts) .. .. 1·25 1·40

477 Women collecting Water from Bore Hole

1992. Decade of Revolutionary Progress. Multicoloured.

1655 20 c. Type **477** 10 10

1656 50 c. Miners 10 10

1657 60 c. Wood carver .. 10 10

1658 80 c. Forestry 15 20

1659 200 c. Cacao tree .. 35 40

1660 350 c. Village electrification .. 65 70

478 Mount Fuji and Flying Fish

1992. "Phila Nippon '91" International Stamp Exhibition, Tokyo. Multicoloured.

1661 20 c. Type **478** 10 10

1662 60 c. Itsukushima Jingu Shrine 10 10

1663 80 c. Geisha 15 20

1664 100 c. Samurai house .. 20 25

1665 200 c. Bonsai tree .. 35 40

1666 400 c. Olympic Sports Hall 70 75

1667 500 c. Great Buddha (statue) 90 95

1668 600 c. Nagoya Castle .. 1·10 1·25

479 East and West Germans celebrating

1992. Reunification of Germany. Mult.

1670 20 c. Type **479** 10 10

1671 60 c. Signing Reunification Treaty 10 10

1672 80 c. Chariot on Brandenburg Gate and fireworks 15 20

1673 1000 c. Germans with unified currency .. 1·75 2·00

480 Steam Locomotive, 1903

1992. Ghanaian Railways. Multicoloured.

1675 20 c. Type **480** 10 10

1676 50 c. A1A-A1A diesel passenger locomotive .. 10 10

1677 60 c. First class coach, 1931 .. .. .. 10 10

1678 80 c. Company inspection coach 15 20

1679 100 c. Steam locomotive No. 401 on Kumasi turntable 20 25

1680 200 c. Cocoa wagon, 1921 35 40

1681 500 c. Steam locomotive No. 223 "Prince of Wales" 90 95

1682 600 c. Cattle wagon .. 1·10 1·25

1992. Olympic Games, Albertville and Barcelona. Past Medal Winners. As T **204** of Gambia. Multicoloured.

1684 20 c. E. Blay (Ghana) (boxing) and windmill 10 10

1685 60 c. M. Ahey (Ghana) (athletics) and Catalan coat of arms 10 10

1686 80 c. T. Wilson (U.S.A.) (70 metres ski jump) and grapes 15 20

1687 100 c. Four-man bobsled (East Germany) and passport 20 25

1688 200 c. G. Louganis (U.S.A.) (platform diving) and decorative vase 35 40

1689 300 c. L. Visser (Netherlands) (5000 metres speed skating) and wine bottle cork .. 55 60

1690 350 c. J. Passler (Italy) (biathlon) and lily .. 65 70

1691 400 c. M. Retton (U.S.A.) (gymnastics) and silhouette of castle .. 70 75

1692 500 c. J. Hingsen (West Germany) (decathlon) and gold and silver coins 90 95

1693 600 c. R. Neubert (West Germany) (heptathlon) and leather work .. 1·10 1·25

481 "Angides lugubris"

1992. Reptiles. Multicoloured.

1695 20 c. Type **481** 10 10

1696 50 c. "Kinixys erosa" (tortoise) 10 10

1697 60 c. "Agama agama" (lizard) 10 10

1698 80 c. "Chameleo gracilis" (chameleon) 15 20

1699 100 c. "Naja melanleuca" (snake) 20 25

1700 200 c. "Crocodylus niloticus" (crocodile) .. 35 40

1701 400 c. "Chelonia mydas" (turtle) 70 75

1702 500 c. "Varanus exanthematicus" (lizard) 90 95

1992. Easter. Religious Paintings. As T **291** of Antigua but vert designs. Multicoloured.

1704 20 c. "The Four Apostles" (detail) (Durer) .. 10 10

1705 50 c. "The Last Judgement" (detail) (Rubens) 10 10

1706 60 c. "The Four Apostles" (different detail) (Durer) 10 10

1707 80 c. "The Last Judgement" (different detail) (Rubens) 15 20

1708 100 c. "Crucifixion" (Rubens) 20 25

1709 200 c. "The Last Judgement" (different detail) (Rubens) 30 35

1710 500 c. "Christum Videre" (Rubens) 90 95

1711 600 c. "The Last Judgement" (different detail) (Rubens) .. .. 1·10 1·25

1992. "Granada '92" International Stamp Exhibition, Spain. Spanish Paintings. As T **292** of Antigua. Multicoloured.

1713 20 c. "Two Men at Table" (Velazquez) (horiz) 10 10

1714 60 c. "Christ in the House of Mary and Martha" (detail) (Velazquez) (horiz) 10 10

1715 80 c. "The Supper at Emmaus" (Velazquez) (horiz) 15 20

1716 100 c. "Three Musicians" (Velazquez) (horiz) .. 20 25

1717 200 c. "Old Woman cooking Eggs" (Velazquez) 35 40

1718 400 c. "Old Woman cooking Eggs" (detail) (Velazquez) 70 75

1719 500 c. "The Surrender of Breda" (detail) (Velazquez) 90 95

1720 700 c. "The Surrender of Breda" (different detail) (Velazquez) .. 1·25 1·40

482 "Danaus chrysippus"

1992. "Genova '92" International Thematic Stamp Exhibition. Butterflies. Mult.

1722 20 c. Type **482** 10 10

1723 60 c. "Papilio dardanus" 10 10

1724 80 c. "Cynthia cardui" .. 15 20

1725 100 c. "Meneris tulbaghia" 20 25

1726 200 c. "Salamis temora" 35 40

1727 400 c. "Charaxes jasius" 70 75

1728 500 c. "Precis oenone" .. 90 95

1729 700 c. "Precis sophia" .. 1·25 1·40

1992. Prehistoric Animals. As T **290** of Antigua. Multicoloured.

1731 20 c. Iguanodon .. 10 10

1732 50 c. Anchisaurus .. 10 10

1733 60 c. Heterodontosaurus 10 10

1734 80 c. Ouranosaurus .. 15 20

1735 100 c. Anatosaurus .. 20 25

1736 200 c. Elaphrosaurus .. 35 40

1737 500 c. Coelophysis .. 90 1·00

1738 600 c. Rhamphorynchus 1·10 1·25

483 Martin Pinzon and "Pinta"

1992. World Columbian Stamp "Expo '92", Chicago. 500th Anniv of Discovery of America by Columbus. Multicoloured.

1740 200 c. Type **483** 35 40

1741 200 c. Vicente Pinzon and "Nina" 35 40

1742 200 c. Columbus and Father Marchena at La Rabida 35 40

1743 200 c. Columbus in his cabin 35 40

1744 200 c. Fleet sights land .. 35 40

1745 200 c. Columbus on Samana Cay 35 40

1746 200 c. Wreck of "Santa Maria" 35 40

1747 200 c. Amerindians at Spanish Court .. 35 40

484 "Olivancillaria hiatula"

1992. Shells. Multicoloured.

1749 20 c. Type **485** 10 10

1750 20 c. "Tympanotonus fuscatus" 10 10

1751 60 c. "Donax rugosus" .. 10 10

1752 60 c. "Murex cornutus" .. 10 10

1753 80 c. "Sigaretus concavus" 15 20

1754 80 c. "Tivela tripla" .. 15 20

1755 200 c. "Pila africana" .. 35 40

1756 200 c. "Cypraea stercoraria" 35 40

1757 350 c. "Thais hiatula" .. 65 70

1758 350 c. "Cassis tesselata" 65 70

485 "Presentation in the Temple" (Master of the Braunschweiti)

1992. Christmas. Religious Paintings. Mult.

1760 20 c. Type **485** 10 10

1761 50 c. "Presentation in the Temple" (detail) (Master of St. Severin) 10 10

1762 60 c. "The Visitation" (Sebastiano del Piombo) 10 10

1763 80 c. "The Visitation" (detail) (Giotto) .. 15 20

1764 100 c. "The Circumcision" (detail) (Studio of Bellini) 20 25

1765 200 c. "The Circumcision" (Studio of Garofalo) .. 35 40

1766 500 c. "The Visitation" (Studio of Van der Weyden) 90 95

1767 800 c. "The Visitation" (detail) (Studio of Van der Weyden) .. .. 1·40 1·50

486 "Calappa rubroguttata"

1993. Crabs. Multicoloured.

1769 20 c. Type **486** 10 10

1770 60 c. "Cardisoma amatum" 10 10

1771 80 c. "Maia squinado" .. 15 20

1772 400 c. "Ocypoda cursor" 70 75

1773 800 c. "Grapus grapus" 1·40 1·50

487 "Clerodendrum thomsoniae"

1993. Flowers. Multicoloured.

1775 20 c. Type **487** 10 10

1776 20 c. "Lagerstroemia flos-reginae" 10 10

1777 60 c. "Cassia fistula" .. 10 10

1778 60 c. "Spathodea campanulata" 10 10

1779 80 c. "Hildegardia barteri" 15 20

1780 80 c. "Mellitea ferrugenea" 15 20

1781 200 c. "Petrea volubilis" 35 40

1782 200 c. "Ipomoea asarifolia" 35 40

1783 350 c. "Bryphyllum pinnatum" 65 70

1784 350 c. "Ritchiea reflexa" 65 70

MINIMUM PRICE

The minimum price quoted is 10p which represents a handling charge rather than a basis for valuing common stamps. For further notes about prices see introductory pages.

488 Zeppelin "LZ-3" entering Floating Hangar, Lake Constance

1993. Anniversaries and Events. Mult.

1786 20 c. Type **488** 10 10
1787 100 c. Launch of European "Ariane 4" rocket (vert) 20 25
1788 200 c. Leopard 35 40
1789 300 c. Colosseum and fruit 55 60
1790 400 c. Mozart (vert) .. 70 75
1791 600 c. Launch of Japanese "H-1" rocket (vert) .. 1·10 1·25
1792 800 c. Zeppelin "LZ-10" "Schwaben" .. .. 1·40 1·50

ANNIVERSARIES AND EVENTS: Nos. 1786, 1792, Death anniv of Count Ferdinand von Zeppelin; Nos. 1787, 1791, International Space Year; No. 1788, Earth Summit '92, Rio; No. 1789, International Conference on Nutrition, Rome; No. 1790, Death bicentenary of Mozart.

1993. Bicentenary of the Louvre, Paris. As T **309** of Antigua. Multicoloured.

1794 200 c. "Carnival Minuet" (left detail) (Giovanni Domenico Tiepolo) .. 35 40
1795 200 c. "Carnival Minuet" (centre detail) (Giovanni Domenico Tiepolo) 35 40
1796 200 c. "Carnival Minuet" (right detail) (Giovanni Domenico Tiepolo) .. 35 40
1797 200 c. "The Tooth Puller" (left detail) (Giovanni Domenico Tiepolo) .. 35 40
1798 200 c. "The Tooth Puller" (right detail) (Giovanni Domenico Tiepolo) .. 35 40
1799 200 c. "Rebecca at the Well" (Giovanni Battista Tiepolo) .. 35 40
1800 200 c. "Presenting Christ to the People" (left detail) (Giovanni Battista Tiepolo) .. 35 40
1801 200 c. "Presenting Christ to the People" (right detail) (Giovanni Battista Tiepolo) .. 35 40

489 Energy Foods

1993. International Conference on Nutrition, Rome. Multicoloured.

1803 20 c. Type **489** .. 10 10
1804 60 c. Body-building foods 10 10
1805 80 c. Protective foods .. 15 20
1806 200 c. Disease prevention equipment 35 40
1807 400 c. Quality control and preservation of fish products 70 75

490 Kwame Nkrumah Mausoleum

1993. Proclamation of 4th Republic. Mult.

1808 50 c. Type **490** 10 10
1809 100 c. Kwame Nkrumah Conference Centre .. 20 25
1810 200 c. Book of Constitution (vert) .. 35 40
1811 350 c. Independence Square (vert) .. 65 70
1812 400 c. Christiansborg Castle (vert) .. 70 75

491 Resurrection Egg

1993. Easter. Faberge Eggs. Multicoloured.

1813 50 c. Type **491** 10 10
1814 80 c. Imperial Red Cross egg with Resurrection triptych 15 20
1815 100 c. Imperial Uspensky Cathedral egg 20 25
1816 150 c. Imperial Red Cross egg with portraits .. 30 35
1817 200 c. Orange Tree egg .. 35 40
1818 250 c. Rabbit egg .. 50 55
1819 400 c. Imperial Coronation egg 70 75
1820 900 c. Silver-gilt enamel Easter egg .. .. 1·60 1·75

1993. Centenaries of Henry Ford's First Petrol Engine (Nos. 1823/4) and Karl Benz's First Four-wheeled Car (others). As T **264** of Dominica. Multicoloured.

1822 150 c. Mercedes Benz "300 SLR", Mille Miglia, 1955 .. .. 30 35
1823 400 c. Ford "Depot Wagon", 1920 .. .. 70 75
1824 600 c. Ford "Mach I Mustang", 1970 .. 1·10 1·25
1825 800 c. Mercedes Benz racing car, Monaco Grand Prix, 1937 .. 1·40 1·50

1993. Aviation Anniversaries. As T **266** of Dominica. Multicoloured.

1827 50 c. "Graf Zeppelin" over Alps (vert) 10 10
1828 150 c. Zeppelin "LZ-7" "Deutschland" .. 30 35
1829 400 c. Vulcan bomber .. 70 75
1830 400 c. U.S. Mail Ford Tri-motor 70 75
1831 600 c. Nieuport 27 (vert) 1·10 1·25
1832 600 c. Loading mail on "Graf Zeppelin" (vert) 1·10 1·25
1833 800 c. Zeppelin "LZ-10" "Schwaben" .. 1·40 1·50

ANNIVERSARIES: Nos. 1827/28, 1833, 125th birth anniv of Hugo Eckener (airship commander); Nos. 1829, 1831, 75th anniv of Royal Air Force; Nos. 1830, 1832, Bicentenary of first airmail flight.

492 African Buffalo

1993. Wild Animals. Multicoloured.

1835 20 c. Type **492** .. 10 10
1836 50 c. Giant forest hog .. 10 10
1837 60 c. Potto 10 10
1838 80 c. Bay duiker .. 15 20
1839 100 c. Royal antelope .. 20 25
1840 200 c. Serval 35 40
1841 500 c. Golden cat .. 90 95
1842 800 c. "Megaloglossus woermanni" (bat) .. 1·40 1·50

1993. 40th Anniv of Coronation. Nos. 1549/52 optd **40TH ANNIVERSARY OF CORONATION H.M. ELIZABETH II**.

1844 100 c. multicoloured .. 20 25
1845 200 c. multicoloured .. 35 40
1846 500 c. multicoloured .. 90 95
1847 600 c. multicoloured .. 1·10 1·5

1993. 35th Anniv of Rotary International and 60th Anniv of Ghana Red Cross Society (1992). Nos. 1562 and 1564/6 optd **35 YEARS OF ROTARY INTERNATIONAL GHANA 1958** (Nos. 1849, 1852) or **GHANA RED CROSS SOCIETY FOUNDED 1932** and cross (others).

1849 100 c. "Petrocephalus bane" 20 25
1850 300 c. "Gymnarchus niloticus" 55 60
1851 400 c. "Hemichromis bimaculatus" 70 75
1852 500 c. "Sphyrna zygaena" 90 95

496 "Cantharellus cibarius"

1993. Mushrooms. Multicoloured.

1854 20 c. Type **496** 10 10
1855 50 c. "Russula cyanoxantha" .. 10 10
1856 60 c. "Clitocybe rivulosa" 10 10
1857 80 c. "Cortinarius elatior" 15 20
1858 80 c. "Mycena galericulata" 15 20
1859 200 c. "Tricholoma gambosum" 35 40
1860 200 c. "Boletus edulis" .. 35 40
1861 200 c. "Lepista saeva" .. 35 40
1862 250 c. "Gyroporus castaneus" 40 45
1863 300 c. "Boletus chrysenteron" .. 55 60
1864 350 c. "Nolanea sericea" 65 70
1865 350 c. "Hygrophorus puiceus" 65 70
1866 500 c. "Gomphidius glutinosus" .. .. 90 1·00
1867 600 c. "Russula olivacea" 1·10 1·25
1868 1000 c. "Russula aurata" 1·75 1·90

497 "The Actor" (Picasso)

1993. Anniversaries and Events. Mult.

1870 20 c. Type **497** 10 10
1871 80 c. "Portrait of Allan Stein" (Picasso) .. 15 20
1872 200 c. "Tatoo" (Lesek Sobocki) 35 40
1873 600 c. "Prison" (Sasza Blonder) .. .. 1·10 1·25
1874 800 c. "Seated Male Nude" (Picasso) .. 1·40 1·50

ANNIVERSARIES AND EVENTS: Nos. 1870/1, 1874, 20th death anniv of Picasso (artist); Nos. 1872/3, "Polska '93" International Stamp Exhibition, Poznan.

498 Abedi Pele (Ghana)

1993. World Cup Football Championship, U.S.A. Multicoloured.

1876 50 c. Type **498** 10 10
1877 80 c. Pedro Troglio (Argentina) 15 20
1878 100 c. Fernando Alvez (Uruguay) 20 25
1879 200 c. Franco Baresi (Italy) 35 40
1880 250 c. Gomez (Colombia) and Katanec (Yugoslavia) 45 50
1881 600 c. Diego Maradona (Argentina) .. .. 1·10 1·25
1882 800 c. Hasek (Czechoslovakia) and Wynalda (U.S.A.) .. 1·40 1·50
1883 1000 c. Lothar Matthaeus (Germany) .. .. 1·75 1·90

499 Common Turkey

1993. Domestic Animals. Multicoloured.

1885 50 c. Type **499** 10 10
1886 100 c. Goats 20 25
1887 150 c. Muscovy ducks .. 30 35
1888 200 c. Donkeys 35 40
1889 250 c. Red junglefowl cock 45 50
1890 300 c. Pigs 55 60
1891 400 c. Helmet gineafowl 70 75
1892 600 c. Dog .. .. 1·10 1·25
1893 800 c. Red junglefowl hen 1·40 1·50
1894 1000 c. Sheep .. .. 1·75 1·90

POSTAGE DUE STAMPS

1958. Postage Due stamps of Gold Coast optd. **GHANA** and bar.

D 9. D **1.** 1d. black 10 20
D 10. 2d. black 10 25
D 11. 3d. black 10 30
D 12. 6d. black 15 45
D 13. 1s. black .. .. 20 1·00

D **3.**

1958.

D 14. D **3.** 1d. red 10 30
D 15. 2d. green 10 30
D 16. 3d. orange 10 30
D 17. 6d. blue 10 50
D 18. 1s. violet .. .. 15 2·00

1965. Surch. **Ghana New Currency 19th July, 1965,** and value.

D 19. D **3.** 1 p. on 1d. 10 60
D 20. 2 p. on 2d. 10 60
D 21. 3 p. on 3d. 10 60
D 22. 6 p. on 6d. .. .. 10 1·25
D 23. 12 p. on 1s. .. 15 1·60

1968. Nos. D 20/2 additionally surch.

D 24. D **3.** $1\frac{1}{2}$ n.p. on 2 p. on 2d. 5·50 4·25
D 25. $2\frac{1}{2}$ n.p. on 3 p. on 3d. 1·00 4·00
D 26. 5 n.p. on 6 p. on 6d... 1·00

1970. Inscr. in new currency.

D 27. D **3.** 1 n.p. red .. .. 60 2·25
D 28. $1\frac{1}{2}$ n.p. green .. 60 2·50
D 29. $2\frac{1}{2}$ n.p. orange .. 80 2·75
D 30. 5 n.p. blue .. .. 1·40 3·25
D 31. 10 n.p. violet .. 2·00 3·75

1980. Currency described as "p".

D 32. D **3.** 2 p. orange .. .. 75 1·75
D 33. 3 p. brown .. .. 75 1·75

GIBRALTAR

A Br. colony at the W. entrance to the Mediterranean.

1886. 12 pence = 1 shilling;
20 shillings = 1 pound.
1971. 100 (new) pence = 1 pound.

1886. Stamps of Bermuda (Queen Victoria) optd. **GIBRALTAR.**

1. 9. ½d. green .. 7·00 6·00
2. 1d. red .. 32·00 4·00
3. 2d. purple .. 80·00 75·00
4. 2½d. blue .. £100 2·75
5. 4d. orange .. 95·00 85·00
6. 6d. lilac .. £200 £180
7. 1s. brown .. £400 £350

2.

7.

1886. Various frames.

39. 2. ½d. green .. 2·25 1·25
40. 1d. red .. 3·50 35
10. 2d. purple .. 29·00 17·00
42. 2½d. blue .. 15·00 40
12. 4d. brown .. 60·00 60·00
13. 6d. lilac .. 85·00 85·00
14. 1s. brown .. £180 £180

1889. Surch. with new value in **CENTIMOS.**

15. 2. 5 c. on ½d. green .. 8·00 13·00
16. 10 c. on 1d. red .. 7·00 6·50
17. 25 c. on 2d. purple .. 4·00 5·00
18. 25 c. on 2½d. blue .. 25·00 1·50
19. 40 c. on 4d. brown .. 60·00 75·00
20. 50 c. on 6d. lilac .. 60·00 65·00
21. 75 c. on 1s. brown .. 60·00 75·00

1889.

22 7 5c. green .. 2·75 45
23 10 c. red .. 2·00 45
24 20 c. green and brown .. 22·00 14·00
25 20 c. green .. 7·00 30·00
26 25 c. blue .. 12·00 70
27 40 c. brown .. 2·50 2·25
28 50 c. lilac .. 2·00 1·50
29 75 c. green .. 28·00 32·00
30 1 p. brown .. 70·00 20·00
31 1 p. brown and blue .. 3·50 3·25
32 2 p. black and red .. 7·00 24·00
33 5 p. grey .. 42·00 85·00

1898. As 1886.

41. 2. 2d. purple and blue .. 11·00 1·50
43. 4d. brown and green .. 10·00 8·00
44. 6d. violet and red .. 26·00 20·00
45. 1s. brown and red .. 26·00 16·00

8.

9.

1903.

66 8 ½d. green .. 2·25 80
57b 1d. purple on red .. 2·00 55
58a 2d. green and red .. 4·75 3·00
49 2½d. purple & blk. on blue 2·00 60
60a 6d. purple and violet .. 12·00 8·00
61 1s. black and red .. 26·00 10·00
62 9 2s. green and blue .. 60·00 65·00
53 4s. purple and green .. 70·00 £110
54 8s. purple & blk. on blue 95·00 £120
55 £1 purple & black on red .. £425 £475

1907.

67. 8. 1d. red .. 1·75 45
68. 2d. grey .. 6·50 9·00
69. 2½d. blue .. 3·50 1·25
70. 6d. purple .. £120 £350
71. 1s. black on green .. 21·00 18·00
72. 9. 2s. purple & blue on blue 38·00 42·00
73. 4s. black and red .. 75·00 95·00
74. 8s. purple and green .. £180 £180

1912. As T **8/9,** but portrait of King George V. (3d. A. Inscr. "3 PENCE". B. Inscr. "THREE PENCE".)

89 ½d. green .. 30 55
90 1d. red .. 1·00 50
91a 1½d. brown .. 75 30
93 2d. grey .. 1·25 85
79 2½d. blue .. 3·25 1·75
95a 3d. blue (A) .. 1·40 1·50
109 3d. blue (B) .. 6·50 2·00
97a 6d. purple .. 1·60 3·50
81 1s. black on green .. 5·50 4·50
102a 1s. olive and black .. 13·00 12·00
82 2s. purple & blue on blue 19·00 3·00
103 2s. brown and black .. 9·00 29·00
104 2s. 6d. green and black .. 8·00 17·00
83 4s. black and red .. 27·00 55·00
105 5s. red and black .. 12·00 45·00
84 8s. purple and green .. 60·00 70·00
106 10s. blue and black .. 32·00 55·00
85 £1 purple & black on red .. £150 £190
107 £1 orange and black .. £140 £180
108 £5 violet and black .. £1500 £2750

1918. Optd. **WAR TAX.**

86. ½d. green (No. 89) .. 30 80

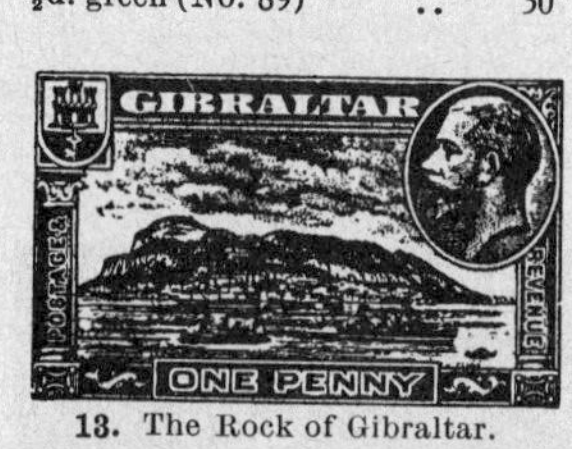

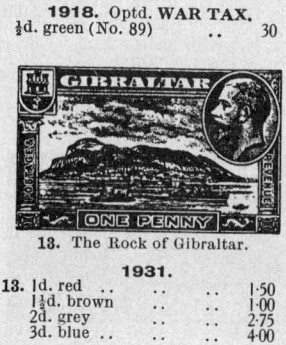

13. The Rock of Gibraltar.

1931.

110. 13. 1d. red .. 1·50 1·75
111. 1½d. brown .. 1·00 2·00
112. 2d. grey .. 2·75 1·00
113. 3d. blue .. 4·00 3·25

1935. Silver Jubilee. As T **13** of Antigua.

114. 2d. blue and black .. 1·60 2·50
115. 3d. brown and blue .. 3·25 3·50
116. 6d. green and blue .. 8·50 9·50
117. 1s. grey and purple .. 8·50 8·50

1937. Coronation. As T **2** of Aden.

118. ½d. green .. 25 10
119. 2d. grey .. 80 75
120. 3d. blue .. 2·00 1·25

14. King George VI.

DESIGNS—HORIZ. 2d. The Rock (North side). 3d., 5d. Europa Point. 6d. Moorish Castle. 1s. Southport Gate. 2s. Eliott Memorial. 5s. Govt. House. 10s. Catalan Bay.

15. Rock of Gibraltar.

1938. King George VI.

121. 14. ½d. green .. 10 20
122b. 15. 1d. brown .. 40 55
123. 1½d. red .. 35·00 75
123b. – 1½d. violet .. 30 85
124a. – 2d. grey .. 30 35
124c. – 2d. red .. 30 50
125b. – 3d. blue .. 30 30
125c. – 5d. orange .. 70 1·25
126b. – 6d. red and violet .. 2·00 1·25
127b. – 1s. black and green .. 3·00 3·75
128b. – 2s. black and brown .. 3·25 4·50
129b. – 5s. black and red .. 12·00 17·00
130a. – 10s. black and blue .. 35·00 25·00
131. 14. £1 orange .. 32·00 40·00

1946. Victory. As T **9** of Aden.

132. ½d. green .. 10 10
133. 3d. blue .. 20 20

1948. Silver Wedding. As T **10/11** of Aden.

134. ½d. green .. 70 40
135. £1 orange .. 60·00 50·00

1949. U.P.U. As T **20/23** of Antigua.

136. 2d. red .. 1·75 75
137. 3d. blue .. 2·00 85
138. 6d. purple .. 2·00 85
139. 1s. green .. 2·75 1·50

1950. Inaug. of Legislative Council. Optd. **NEW CONSTITUTION 1950.**

140. 2d. red (No. 124c) .. 30 1·00
141. 3d. blue (No. 125b) .. 30 1·00
142. 6d. red & vio. (No. 126b) .. 40 1·00
143. 1s. black & grn. (No. 127b) 40 1·40

1953. Coronation. As T **13** of Aden.

144. ½d. black and green .. 20 30

24. Cargo and Passenger Wharves.

1953.

145 24 ½d. blue and green .. 15 30
146a – 1d. green .. 1·40 30
147 – 1½d. black .. 90 90
148 – 2d. brown .. 1·00 40
149a – 2½d. red .. 2·25 50
150 – 3d. blue .. 2·25 10
151 – 4d. blue .. 2·25 1·50
152 – 5d. purple .. 35 60
153 – 6d. black and blue .. 30 30
154a – 1s. blue and brown .. 30 45
155a – 2s. orange and violet 17·00 2·50
156 – 5s. brown .. 24·00 12·00
157 – 10s. brown and blue .. 65·00 35·00
158 – £1 red and yellow .. 70·00 38·00

DESIGNS—HORIZ. 1d. South view from Straits. 1½d. Tunny fishing industry. 2d. Southport Gate. 2½d. Sailing in the Bay. 3d. Liner. 4d. Coaling wharf. 5d. Airport. 6d. Europa Point. 1s. Straits from Buena Vista. 2s. Rosia Bay and Straits. 5s. Main entrance, Govt. House. VERT. 10s. Tower of Homage, Moorish Castle. £1, Arms of Gibraltar.

1954. Royal Visit. As No. 150 but inscr. "ROYAL VISIT 1954".

159. 3d. blue .. 15 20

38. Gibraltar Candytuft.

DESIGNS—As Type **38**—HORIZ. 1d. Moorish Castle. 2d. St. George's Hall. 3d. The Rock by moonlight. 4d. Catalan Bay. 1s. Barbary ape, 2s. Barbary Partridge. 5s. Blue Rock Thrush. VERT. 2½d. The keys. 6d. Map of Gibraltar. 7d. Air Terminal. 9d. American War Memorial. 10s. Rock lily.

40. Rock and Badge of Gibraltar Regiment.

1960.

160 38 ½d. purple and green .. 15 30
161 – 1d. black and green .. 10 10
162 – 2d. blue and brown .. 15 15
163a – 2½d. black and blue .. 15 15
164 – 3d. blue and orange .. 30 10
199 – 4d. brown and turq .. 30 40
166 – 6d. brown and green .. 70 40
167 – 7d. blue and red .. 70 75
168 – 9d. blue and turquoise 50 50
169 – 1s. brown and green .. 90 30
170 – 2s. brown and blue .. 13·00 2·25
171 – 5s. blue and green .. 8·00 5·00
172 – 10s. yellow and blue .. 14·00 9·00
173 40 £1 black and brown .. 23·00 14·00

1963. Freedom from Hunger. As T **28** of Aden.

174. 9d. sepia .. 11·00 2·00

1963. Cent of Red Cross. As T **33** of Antigua.

175. 1d. red and black .. 1·00 1·00
176. 9d. red and blue .. 13·00 3·00

1964. 400th Birth Anniv of Shakespeare. As T **34** of Antigua.

177. 7d. bistre .. 40 20

1964. New Constitution. Nos. 164 and 166 optd. **NEW CONSTITUTION 1964.**

178. 3d. blue and orange .. 15 10
179. 6d. sepia and green .. 15 20

1965. Cent of I.T.U. As T **36** of Antigua.

180. 4d. green and yellow .. 5·00 50
181. 2s. green and blue .. 14·00 3·00

1965. I.C.Y. As T **37** of Antigua.

182. ½d. green and lavender .. 20 60
183. 4d. purple and turquoise .. 1·00 80

The value of the ½d. stamp is shown as "1/2".

1966. Churchill Commem. As T **38** of Antigua.

184. ½d. blue .. 20 50
185. 1d. green .. 30 10
186. 4d. brown .. 1·50 10
187. 9d. violet .. 1·75 1·50

1966. World Cup Football Championship. As T **40** of Antigua.

188. 2½d. multicoloured .. 75 30
189. 6d. multicoloured .. 1·00 50

53. Bream.

1966. European Sea Angling Championships. Gibraltar.

190. 53. 4d. red, blue and black 20 10
191. – 7d. red, green and black 30 20
192. – 1s. brown, green & black 30 20

DESIGNS: 7d. Scorpion Fish. 1s Stone Bass.

1966. Inauguration of W.H.O. Headquarters Geneva. As T **41** of Antigua.

193. 6d. black, green and blue 3·00 1·50
194. 9d. black, purple & ochre 4·00 1·50

56. "Our Lady of Europa".

1966. Centenary of Re-enthronement of "Our Lady of Europa".

195. 56. 2s. blue and black .. 30 50

1966. 20th Anniv. of U.N.E.S.C.O. As T **54/6** of Antigua.

196. 2d. multicoloured .. 25 10
197. 7d. yellow, violet & olive 60 10
198. 5s. black, purple & orange 2·50 1·75

57. H.M.S. "Victory".

1967. Multicoloured.

200 ½d. Type **57** .. 10 15
201 1d. "Arab" (early steamer) .. 10 10
202 2d. H.M.S. "Carmania" (merchant cruiser) .. 15 10
203 2½d. "Mons Calpe" (ferry) 30 30
204 3d. "Canberra" (liner) .. 20 10
205 4d. H.M.S. "Hood" (battle cruiser) .. 30 10
205a 5d. "Mirror" (cable ship) 3·25 55
206 6d. Xebec (sailing vessel) 30 30
207 7d. "Amerigo Vespucci" (Italian cadet ship) .. 30 35
208 9d. "Raffaello" (liner) .. 30 50
209 1s. "Royal Katherine" (galleon) .. 25 35
210 2s. H.M.S. "Ark Royal" (aircraft carrier, 1937) 2·25 1·50
211 5s. H.M.S. "Dreadnought" (nuclear submarine) .. 3·50 5·00
212 10s. "Neuralia" (liner) 14·00 16·00
213 £1 "Mary Celeste" (sailing vessel) .. 14·00 16·00

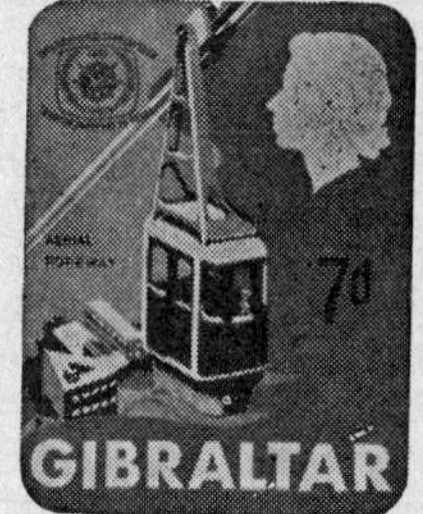

58. Aerial Ropeway.

1967. Int. Tourist Year. Multicoloured.

214. 7d. Type **58** .. 10 10
215. 9d. Shark fishing (horiz.) 10 10
216. 1s. Skin-diving (horiz.) .. 15 15

59. Mary, Joseph and Child Jesus.

1967. Christmas. Multicoloured.

217. 2d. Type **59** .. 10 10
218. 6d. Church window (vert.) 10 10

61. Gen. Eliott and Route Map.

967. 250th Birth Anniv. of General Eliott. Multicoloured.

19.	4d. Type **61**	10	10
20.	9d. Heathfield Tower and Monument, Sussex	10	10
21	1s. General Eliott (vert.)	10	10
22.	2s. Eliott directing Rescue Operations	30	15

No. 222 is 55×21 mm.

65. Lord Baden-Powell.

1968. 60th Anniv. of Gibraltar Scout Assn.

223. **65.**	4d. buff and violet ..	15	10
224. –	7d. ochre and green ..	15	10
225. –	9d. blue, orge. & black	20	15
226. –	1s. yellow and green ..	20	15

DESIGNS: 7d. Scout Flag over the Rock. 9d. Tent, Scouts and Salute. 1s. Scout Badges.

66. Nurse and W.H.O. Emblem.

1968. 20th Anniv. of World Health Organization. Multicoloured.

227.	2d. Type **66**	10	10
228.	4d. Doctor and W.H.O. Emblem	10	10

68. King John signing Magna Carta. **70.** Shepherd, Lamb and Star.

1968. Human Rights Year.

229. **68.**	1s. orange, brown & gold	15	10
230. –	2s. myrtle and gold ..	15	20

DESIGN: 2s. "Freedom" and Rock of Gibraltar.

1968. Christmas. Multicoloured.

231.	4d. Type **70**	10	10
232.	9d. Mary holding Holy Child	10	10

72. Parliament Houses.

1969. Commonwealth Parliamentary Assn., Conference.

233. **72.**	4d green and gold ..	10	10
234. –	9d. violet and gold ..	10	10
235. –	2s. red, gold and blue..	15	20

DESIGNS—HORIZ. 9d. Parliamentary Emblem and outline of "The Rock". VERT. 2s. Clock Tower, Westminster (Big Ben) and Arms of Gibraltar.

75. Silhouette of Rock, and Queen Elizabeth.

1969. New Constitution.

236. **75.**	½d. gold and orange ..	10	10
237.	5d. silver and green ..	10	10
238.	7d. silver and purple ..	10	10
239.	5s. silver and blue ..	35	70

77. Soldier and Cap Badge, Royal Anglian Regiment, 1969.

1969. Military Uniforms (1st series). Mult.

240.	1d. Royal Artillery Officer, 1758, and modern cap badge	20	10
241.	6d. Type **77**	45	20
242.	9d. Royal Engineers' Artificer, 1786, and modern cap badge	55	30
243.	2s. Private, Fox's Marines, 1704, and modern Royal Marines' cap badge ..	3·00	1·60

See also Nos. 248/51, 290/3, 300/303, 313/16, 331/4, 340/3 and 363/6.

80. "Madonna of the Chair" (detail, Raphael).

1969. Christmas. Multicoloured.

244.	5d. Type **80**	10	10
245.	7d. "Virgin and Child" (detail, Morales) ..	15	15
246.	1s. "The Virgin of the Rocks" (detail, Leonardo da Vinci)	15	20

83. Europa Point.

1970. Europa Point.

247. **83.**	2s. multicoloured ..	30	30

1970. Military Uniforms (2nd series). As T **77**. Multicoloured.

248.	2d. Royal Scots Officer (1839) and Cap Badge ..	30	10
249.	5d. South Wales Borderers Private (1763) and Cap Badge	60	10
250.	7d. Queen's Royal Regiment Private (1742) and Cap Badge	70	15
251.	2s. Royal Irish Rangers piper (1969) and Cap Badge	3·25	1·75

88. Stamp and Rock of Gibraltar.

1970. "Philympia 70" Stamp Exhibition, London.

252. **88.**	1s. red and green ..	10	10
253. –	2s. blue and mauve ..	20	25

DESIGN: 2s. Stamp and Moorish Castle. The stamps shown in the designs are well known varieties with values omitted.

90. "The Virgin Mary" (stained-glass window, Gabriel Loire).

1970. Christmas.

254. **90.**	2s. multicoloured ..	30	30

91. Saluting Battery, Rosia.

92. Saluting Battery, Rosia, Modern View.

1971. Decimal Currency. Each value printed se-tenant in two designs showing respectively old and new views.

255.	½p. Type **91**	15	20
256.	½p. Type **92**	15	20
257.	1p. } Prince George of	80	30
258.	1p. } Cambridge Quarters and Trinity Church	80	30
259.	1½p. } The Wellington Bust,	20	30
260.	1½p. } Almeda Gardens ..	20	30
317.	2p. } Gibraltar from the	75	1·25
318.	2p. } North Bastion	75	1·25
263.	2½p. } Catalan Bay ..	20	30
264.	2½p. }	20	30
265.	3p. } Covent Garden ..	20	20
266.	3p. }	20	20
319.	4p. } The Exchange and	1·00	1·25
320.	4p. } Spanish Chapel ..	1·00	1·25
269.	5p. } Commercial Square	30	20
270.	5p. } and Library ..	30	20
271.	7p. } South Barracks	65	65
272.	7p. } and Rosia Magazine	65	65
273.	8p. } Moorish Mosque	70	70
274.	8p. } and Castle	70	70
275.	9p. } Europa Pass Road..	70	70
276.	9p. }	70	70
277.	10p. } South Barracks	80	80
278.	10p. } from Rosia Bay ..	80	80
279.	12½p. } Southport Gates..	1·00	1·40
280.	12½p. }	1·00	1·40
281.	25p. } The Alameda,	1·40	1·40
282.	25p. } Trooping the Guards	1·40	1·40
283.	50p. } Europa Pass Gorge	1·40	2·50
284.	50p. } (vert.)	1·40	2·50
285.	£1 } Prince Edward's	2·75	4·00
286.	£1 } Gate (vert.) ..	2·75	4·00

93. **94.** Regimental Arms.

1971. Coil Stamps.

287. **93.**	½p. orange	15	30
288.	1p. blue..	15	30
289.	2p. green	65	1·10

1971. Military Uniforms (3rd series). As T **77**. Multicoloured.

290.	1p. The Black Watch (1845)	45	20
291.	2p. Royal Regt. of Fusiliers (1971)	85	30
292.	4p. King's Own Royal Border Regt. (1704) ..	1·75	70
293.	10p. Devonshire and Dorset Regt. (1801) ..	5·00	2·50

1971. Presentation of Colours to the Gibraltar Regiment.

294. **94.**	3p. black, gold and red	30	30

95. Nativity Scene.

1971. Christmas. Multicoloured.

295.	3p. Type **95**	45	45
296.	5p. Mary and Joseph going to Bethlehem	55	55

96. Soldier Artificer, 1773.

1972. Bicentenary of Royal Engineers in Gibraltar. Multicoloured.

297.	1p. Type **96**	40	20
298.	3p. Modern tunneller ..	60	50
299.	5p. Old and new uniforms and badge (horiz.) ..	75	65

1972. Military Uniforms (4th series). As T **77**. Multicoloured.

300.	1p. The Duke of Cornwall's Light Infantry, 1704 ..	60	20
301.	3p. King's Royal Rifle Corps, 1830	1·75	50
302.	7p. 37th North Hampshire, Officer, 1825	2·75	1·25
303.	10p. Royal Navy, 1972 ..	3·25	2·00

97. "Our Lady of Europa".

1972. Christmas.

304. **97.**	3p. multicoloured ..	10	10
305.	5p. multicoloured ..	10	20

1972. Royal Silver Wedding. As T **52** of Ascension, but with Keys of Gibraltar and "Narcissus niveus" in background.

306.	5p. red	20	20
307.	7p. green	20	20

99. Flags of Member Nations and E.E.C. Symbol.

1973. Britain's Entry into the E.E.C.

308. **99.**	5p. multicoloured ..	40	30
309.	10p. multicoloured ..	60	50

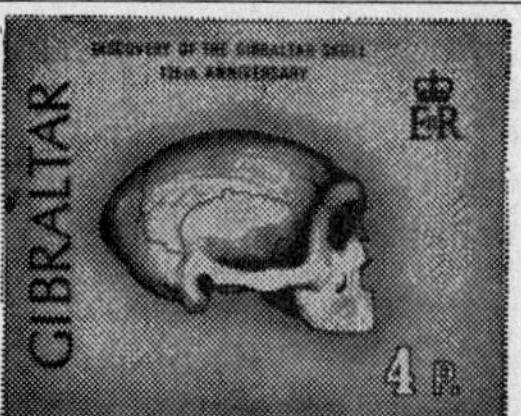

100. Skull.

1973. 125th Anniv. of Gibraltar Skull Discovery. Multicoloured.

310.	4p. Type **100**	1·00	50
311.	6p. Prehistoric man ..	1·00	70
312.	10p. Prehistoric family ..	1·50	1·25

No. 312 is size 40×26 mm.

1973. Military Uniforms (5th series). As T **77**. Multicoloured.

313.	1p. King's Own Scottish Borderers, 1770 ..	40	20
314.	4p. Royal Welch Fusiliers, 1800	1·25	1·40
315.	6p. Royal Northumberland Fusiliers, 1736	2·00	1·50
316.	10p. Grenadier Guards, 1898	3·00	2·50

101. " Nativity " (Danckerts).

1973. Christmas.

321.**101.**	4p. violet and red ..	25	15
322.	6p. mauve and blue ..	35	60

1973. Royal Wedding. As Type **43** of Anguilla. Background colours given. Multicoloured.

323.	6p. blue	10	10
324.	14p. green..	20	20

102. Victorian Pillar-box.

1974. Centenary of U.P.U. Multicoloured.

325.	2p. Type **102**	15	20
326.	6p. Pillar-box of George VI	25	30
327.	14p. Pillar-box of Elizabeth II	40	65

Nos. 325/7 also come self-adhesive from booklet panes.

1974. Military Uniforms (6th series). As T **77**. Multicoloured.

331.	4p. East Lancashire Regt., 1742	50	50
332.	6p. Somerset Light Infantry, 1833	70	70
333.	10p. Royal Sussex Regt., 1790	1·00	1·25
334.	16p. R.A.F. officer, 1974	2·25	2·50

103. " Madonna with the Green Cushion " (Solario).

1974. Christmas. Multicoloured.

335.	4p. Type **103**	40	30
336.	6p. "Madonna of the Meadow" (Bellini)	60	80

104. Churchill and Houses of Parliament.

1974. Birth Centenary of Sir Winston Churchill. Multicoloured.

337.**104.**	6p. black, purple and lavender	25	15
338. –	20p. black, brown and red	50	50

DESIGN: 20p. Churchill and "King George V" (battleship).

1975. Military Uniforms (7th series). As Type **77**. Multicoloured.

340.	4p. East Surrey Regt., 1846	30	30
341.	6p. Highland Light Infantry, 1777	50	50
342.	10p. Coldstream Guards, 1704	70	80
343.	20p. Gibraltar Regt., 1974	1·25	1·50

105. Girl Guides' Badge.

1975. 50th Anniv. of Gibraltar Girl Guides.

346.**105.**	5p. gold, blue & violet	30	40
347.	7p. gold and brown ..	40	50
348. –	15p. silver, blk. & brn.	65	85

No. 348 is as Type **105** but shows a different badge.

106. Child at Prayer.

1975. Christmas. Multicoloured.

349.	6p. Type **106**	40	45
350.	6p. Angel with lute ..	40	45
351.	6d. Child singing carols ..	40	45
352.	6p. Three children ..	40	45
353.	6p. Girl at prayer ..	40	45
354.	6p. Boy and lamb ..	40	45

107. Bruges Madonna.

1975. 500th Birth Anniv. of Michelangelo. Multicoloured.

355.	6p. Type **107**	15	25
356.	9p. Taddei Madonna ..	20	40
357.	15p. Pieta	30	75

Nos. 355/7 also come self-adhesive from booklet panes.

INDEX

Countries can be quickly located by referring to the index at the end of this volume.

108. Bicentennial Emblem and Arms of Gibraltar.

1976. Bicent. of American Revolution.

361. **108.**	25 p. multicoloured ..	50	50

1976. Military Uniforms (8th series). As T **24**. Mult.

363.	1p. Suffolk Regt., 1795 ..	15	15
364.	6p. Northamptonshire Regt. 1779	30	30
365.	12p. Lancashire Fusiliers, 1793	55	55
366.	25p. Ordnance Corps, 1896	1·10	1·10

109. The Holy Family.

1976. Christmas. Multicoloured.

367.	6p. Type **109**	25	15
368.	9p. Madonna and Child ..	30	25
369.	12p. St. Bernard	45	45
370.	20p. Archangel Michael ..	70	80

Nos. 367/70 show different stained-glass windows from St. Joseph's Church, Gibraltar.

110. Queen Elizabeth II, Royal Arms and Gibraltar Arms.

1977. Silver Jubilee. Multicoloured.

371. **110.**	6p. red	25	20
372.	£1 blue	1·75	2·25

111. Toothed Orchid.

1977. Birds, Flowers, Fish and Butterflies. Multicoloured.

374	½p. Type **111**	60	85
375	1p. Red mullet (horiz) ..	15	10
376	2p. "Maculinea arion" (butterfly) (horiz) ..	30	50
377	2½p. Sardinian warbler ..	40	55
378	3p. Giant squill ..	20	10
379	4p. Grey wrasse (horiz) ..	30	10
380	5p. "Vanessa atalanta" (butterfly) (horiz) ..	50	60
381	6p. Black kite	45	30
382	9p. Shrubby scorpion-vetch	90	70
383	10p. John dory (fish) (horiz)	40	20
384	12p. "Colias crocea" (butterfly) (horiz) ..	1·00	35
384b	15p. Winged asparagus pea	2·75	55
385	20p. Audouin's gull ..	1·25	1·75
386	25p. Barbary nut (iris) ..	1·25	2·00
387	50p. Swordfish (horiz) ..	2·00	95
388	£1 "Papilio machaon" (butterfly) (horiz) ..	4·75	4·50
389	£2 Hoopoe	7·50	10·00
389a	£5 Arms of Gibraltar ..	10·00	10·00

112. " Our Lady of Europa " Stamp.

1977. " Amphilex '77 " Stamp Exn., Amsterdam. Multicoloured.

390.	6p. Type **112**	10	20
391.	12p. " Europa Point " stamp	20	30
392.	25p. " E.E.C. Entry " stamp	30	50

113. " The Annunciation " (Rubens).

1977. Christmas and 400th Birth Anniv. of Rubens. Multicoloured.

393.	3p. Type **113**	10	10
394.	9p. " The Adoration of the Magi "	20	20
395.	12p. " The Adoration of the Magi " (horiz.)	25	30
396.	15p. " The Holy Family under the Apple Tree "	30	40

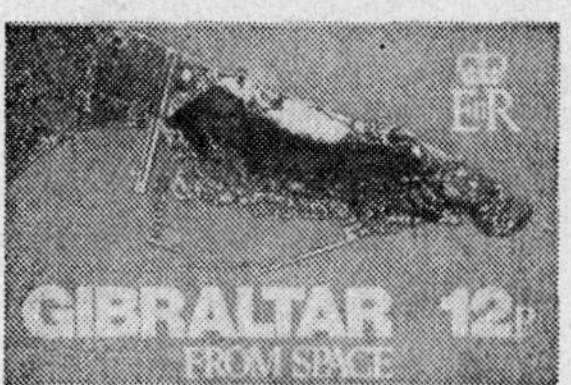

114. Aerial View of Gibraltar.

1978. Gibraltar from Space.

398. **114.**	12p. multicoloured ..	25	40

115. Holyroodhouse.

1978. 25th Anniv. of Coronation. Mult.

400.	6p. Type **115** ..	20	15
401.	9p. St. James' Palace ..	25	15
402.	12p. Sandringham ..	30	25
403.	18p. Balmoral	40	40
406.	25p. Windsor Castle ..	70	1·50

Nos. 402/3 also exist as self-adhesive stamps from booklet panes, No. 406 only coming in this form.

116. " Sunderland ", 1938–58.

1978. 60th Anniv. of Royal Air Force. Mult.
407. 3p. Type **116** 15 10
408. 9p. " Cauldron ", 1918 .. 35 35
409. 12p. " Shackleton ", 1953–66 .. .. 40 45
410. 16p. " Hunter ", 1954–77 45 60
411. 18p. " Nimrod ", 1969–78 50 70

117. " Madonna with Animals ".

1978. Christmas. Paintings by Durer. Multicoloured.
412. 5p. Type **117** 15 10
413. 9p. " The Nativity " .. 20 15
414. 12p. " Madonna of the Goldfinch " 25 30
415. 15p. " Adoration of the Magi " 35 40

118. Sir Rowland Hill and 1d. Stamp of 1886.

1979. Death Cent. of Sir Rowland Hill.
416. **118** 3p. multicoloured .. 10 10
417. – 9p. multicoloured .. 20 15
418. – 12p. multicoloured .. 25 20
419. – 25p. blk., purple & yell. 35 50
DESIGNS: 9p. 1971 1p. coil stamp. 12p. 1840 Post Office Regulations. 25p. " G " cancellation.

119. Posthorn, Dish Antenna and Early Telephone.

1979. Europa. Communications.
420. **119.** 3p. green and pale green 15 10
421. 9p. brown and ochre .. 40 65
422. 12p. blue and violet .. 55 80

120. African Child.

1979. Christmas. International Year of the Child. Multicoloured.
423. 12p. Type **120** 25 30
424. 12p. Asian child 25 30
425. 12p. Polynesian child .. 25 30
426. 12p. American Indian child 25 30
427. 12p. Nativity and children of different races .. 25 30
428. 12p. European child .. 25 30

121. Early Policeman.

1980. 150th Anniv. of Gibraltar Police Force. Multicoloured.
429. 3p. Type **121** 20 10
430. 6p. Policemen of 1895, early 1900's and 1980 .. 20 15
431. 12p. Police officer and police ambulance .. 25 20
432. 37p. Policewoman and police motor cyclist .. 55 80

122. Peter Amigo (Archbishop).

1980. Europa. Personalities. Multicoloured.
433. 12p. Type **122** 20 25
434. 12p. Gustavo Bacarisas (artist) 20 25
435. 12p. John Mackintosh (philanthropist) .. 20 25

123. Queen Elizabeth the Queen Mother.

1980. 80th Birthday of The Queen Mother.
436. **123.** 15 p. multicoloured .. 30 30

124. " Horatio Nelson " (J. F. Rigaud).

1980. 175th Death Anniv. of Nelson Paintings. Multicoloured.
437. 3p. Type **124.** 15 10
438. 9p. " H.M.S. Victory " (horiz.) 25 25
439. 15p. " Horatio Nelson " (Sir William Beechey) .. 35 35
440. 40p. " H.M.S. Victory " being towed into Gibraltar (Clarkson Stanfield)(horiz.) 80 1·00

125. Three Kings.

1980. Christmas.
442. **125.** 15p. brown and yellow 25 35
443. – 15p. brown and yellow 25 35
DESIGN: No. 443, Nativity scene.

126. Hercules creating the Mediterranean.

1981. Europa. Multicoloured.
444. 9p. Type **126** 20 15
445. 15p. Hercules and pillars 25 35

127. Dining-room.

1981. 450th Anniv. of The Convent. Mult.
446. 4p. Type **127.** 10 10
447. 14p. King's Chapel .. 20 20
448. 15p. The Convent .. 20 20
449. 55p. Cloister .. .. 85 1·10

128. Prince Charles and Lady Diana Spencer.

1981. Royal Wedding.
450. **128.** £1 multicoloured .. 1·50 1·75

129.

1981. Booklet Stamps.
451. **129.** 1p. black 10 10
452. 4p. blue 10 10
453. 15p. green 25 30

130. Paper Aeroplane.

1981. 50th Anniv. of Gibraltar Airmail Service. Multicoloured.
454. 14p. Type **130** 20 20
455. 15p. Airmail letters, post box and aircraft tail fin 20 20
456. 55p. Aircraft circling globe 80 90

131. Carol Singers.

1981. Christmas. Children's Drawings. Multicoloured.
457. 15p. Type **131.** 30 15
458. 55p. Postbox (vert.) .. 1·00 85

132. I.Y.D.P. Emblem and Stylised Faces.

1981. International Year for Disabled Persons.
459. **132.** 14p. multicoloured .. 30 30

133. Douglas " DC 3 ".

1982. Aircraft. Multicoloured.
460 1p. Type **133** 25 55
461 2p. Vickers "Viking" .. 30 70
462 3p. Airspeed "Ambassador" 30 70
463 4p. Vickers "Viscount" .. 40 20
464 5p. Boeing "727" 90 50
465 10p. Vickers "Vanguard" 1·00 40
466 14p. Short "Solent" .. 1·00 1·25
467 15p. Fokker "F.27 (Friendship)" .. .. .. 1·50 50
468 17p. Boeing "737" .. 1·00 55
469 20p. BAC "One-eleven" .. 1·00 50
470 25p. Lockheed "Constellation" .. .. .. 2·75 2·25
471 50p. De Havilland "Comet 4B" .. .. .. 4·00 2·25
472 £1 Saro "Windhover" .. 5·50 2·25
473 £2 Hawker Siddeley "Trident 2" .. .. 6·50 5·00
474 £5 D.H. "89A (Dragon Rapide)" .. .. 9·00 14·00

134. Crest, H.M.S. " Opossum ".

1982. Naval Crests (1st series). Multicoloured.
475. ½p. Type **134** 10 10
476. 15½p. H.M.S. " Norfolk " 45 50
477. 17p. H.M.S. " Fearless " 50 55
478. 60p. H.M.S. " Rooke " .. 1·25 1·60
See also Nos. 493/6, 510/13, 522/5, 541/4 565/8, 592/5, 616/9, 638/41 and 651/4.

135. "Spitfires" at Gibraltar.

1982. Europa. Operation Torch. Mult.
479. 14p. Type **135** 25 50
480. 17p. General Giraud, General Eisenhower and Gibraltar 35 60

136. Gibraltar Chamber of Commerce Centenary.

1982. Anniversaries. Multicoloured.
481. ½p. Type **136** 10 10
482. 15½p. British Forces Postal Service centenary .. 30 25
483. 60p. 75th anniv. of Gibraltar Scout Association .. .. .. 1·10 1·25

137. Printed Circuit forming Map of World.

1982. International Direct Dialling.
484. **137.** 17p. black, blue and orange 35 35

138. Gibraltar illuminated at Night and Holly.

1982. Christmas. Multicoloured.
485. 14p. Type **138** 45 30
486. 17p. Gibraltar illuminated at night and Mistletoe .. 50 35

139. Yacht Marina.

1983. Commonwealth Day. Multicoloured.
487. 4p. Type **139** 10 10
488. 14p. Scouts and Guides Commonwealth Day Parade 30 35
489. 17p. Flag of Gibraltar (vert.) 35 40
490. 60p. Queen Elizabeth II (from photo by Tim Graham) (vert.) .. .. 1·25 1·40

140. St. George's Hall Gallery.

1983. Europa.
491. **140.** 16p. black and brown 35 35
492. – 19p. black and blue .. 40 40
DESIGN: 19p. Water catchment slope.

1983. Naval Crests (2nd series). Multicoloured. As Type **134**.
493. 4p. H.M.S. "Faulknor" .. 25 10
494. 14p. H.M.S. "Renown" .. 60 35
495. 17p. H.M.S. "Ark Royal" 70 40
496. 60p. H.M.S. "Sheffield" .. 1·75 1·50

141. Landport Gate, 1729.

1983. Fortress Gibraltar in the 18th Century. Multicoloured.
497. 4p. Type **141** 20 10
498. 17p. Koehler Gun, 1782 .. 60 40
499. 77p. King's Bastion, 1779 2·00 1·75

142. "Adoration of the Magi" (Raphael).

1983. Christmas. 500th Birth Anniv. of Raphael. Multicoloured.
501. 4p. Type **142** 20 10
502. 17p. "Madonna of Foligno" (vert.) 70 35
503. 60p. "Sistine Madonna" (vert.) .. .. .. 1·75 1·40

143. 1932 2d. Stamp and Globe.

1984. Europa. Post and Telecommunications. Multicoloured.
504. 17p. Type **143** 35 40
505. 23p. Circuit board and globe 45 50

144. Hockey.

1984. Sports. Multicoloured.
506. 20p. Type **144** 40 50
507. 21p. Basketball 40 50
508. 26p. Rowing 55 70
509. 29p. Football 60 75

1984. Naval Crests (3rd series). As T **134**. Multicoloured.
510. 20p. H.M.S. "Active" .. 1·25 1·25
511. 21p. H.M.S. "Foxhound" 1·25 1·25
512. 26p. H.M.S. "Valiant" .. 1·50 1·50
513. 29p. H.M.S. "Hood" .. 1·60 1·60

145. Mississippi River Boat Float.

1984. Christmas. Epiphany Floats. Mult.
514. 20p. Type **145** 40 50
515. 80p. Roman Temple float 1·60 2·00

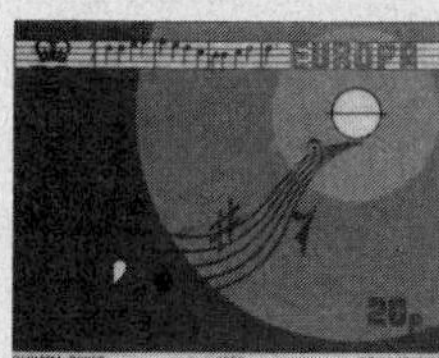

146. Musical Symbols, and Score from Beethoven's 9th (Choral) Symphony.

1985. Europa. European Music Year. Mult.
516. **146.** 20p. multicoloured .. 60 50
517. – 29p. multicoloured .. 90 1·25
DESIGN: The 29p. is as T **146**, but shows different symbols.

147. Globe and Stop Polio Campaign Logo.

1985. Stop Polio Campaign.
518. 26p. multicoloured (Type **147**) 60 60
519. 26p. multicoloured ("ST" visible) 60 60
520. 26p. multicoloured ("STO" visible) 60 60
521. 26p. multicoloured ("STOP" visible) .. 60 60

Each design differs in the position of the logo across the centre of the globe. On No. 518 only the letter "S" is fully visible, on No. 519 "ST", on No. 520 "STO" and on No. 521 "STOP". Other features of the design also differ, so that the word "Year" moves towards the top of the stamp and on No. 521 the upper logo is omitted.

1985. Naval Crests (4th series). As T **134**. Multicoloured.
522. 4p. H.M.S. "Duncan" .. 35 10
523. 9p. H.M.S. "Fury" .. 60 50
524. 21p. H.M.S. "Firedrake" .. 1·25 1·50
525. 80p. H.M.S. "Malaya" .. 3·25 4·25

148. I.Y.Y. Logo.

1985. International Youth Year. Mult.
526. 4p. Type **148** 25 10
527. 20p. Hands passing diamond .. .. .. 95 1·00
528. 80p. 75th anniv. logo of Girl Guide Movement .. 2·50 3·00

149. St. Joseph.

1985. Christmas. Centenary of St. Joseph's Parish Church. Multicoloured.
529. 4p. Type **149** 20 25
530. 4p. St. Joseph's Parish Church 20 25
531. 80p. Nativity crib .. .. 1·75 2·25

150. "Papilio machaon" (butterfly) and The Convent.

1986. Europa. Nature and the Environment. Multicoloured.
532. 22p. Type **150** .. .. 1·25 50
533. 29p. Herring gull and Europa Point .. .. 1·75 3·00

151. 1887 Queen Victoria 6d. Stamp.

1986. Centenary of First Gibraltar Postage Stamps. Designs showing stamps. Mult.
534. 4p. Type **151** 25 1
535. 22p. 1903 Edward VII 2½d. 85 85
536. 32p. 1912 George V 1d. .. 1·25 1·75
537. 36p. 1938 George VI £1 .. 1·40 2·00
538. 44p. 1953 Coronation ½d. (29 × 46 mm) .. .. 1·75 2·40

152. Queen Elizabeth II in Robes of Order of the Bath.

1986. 60th Birthday of Queen Elizabeth II.
540. **152.** £1 multicoloured .. 2·00 3·00

1986. Naval Crests (5th series). As T **134**. Multicoloured.
541. 22p. H.M.S. "Lightning" .. 1·25 75
542. 29p. H.M.S. "Hermione" .. 1·50 1·25
543. 32p. H.M.S. "Laforey" .. 1·75 2·25
544. 44p. H.M.S. "Nelson" .. 2·00 3·00

154. Three Kings and Cathedral of St. Mary the Crowned.

1986. Christmas. International Peace Year. Multicoloured.
546. 18p. Type **154** .. .. 1·00 40
547. 32p. St. Andrew's Church 1·50 2·00

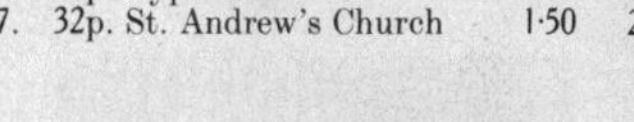

155. Neptune House.

1987. Europa. Architecture. Multicoloured.
563. 22p. Type **155** .. .. 1·25 50
564. 29p. Ocean Heights .. 2·00 1·40

1987. Naval Crests (6th series). As T **134**. Multicoloured.
565. 18p. H.M.S. "Wishart" (destroyer) .. .. 1·25 75
566. 22p. H.M.S. "Charybdis" (cruiser) .. .. .. 1·40 1·10
567. 32p. H.M.S. "Antelope" (destroyer) .. .. 1·90 2·75
568. 44p. H.M.S. "Eagle" (aircraft carrier) .. 2·50 3·75

156. 13-inch Mortar, 1783.

1987. Guns. Multicoloured.

69. 1p. Type **156** 10 10
70. 2p. 6-inch coastal gun, 1909 10 10
71. 3p. 8-inch howitzer, 1783 .. 15 10
72. 4p. Bofors "L40/70" AA gun, 1951 .. .. 15 10
73. 5p. 100 ton rifled muzzle-loader, 1882 .. .. 15 15
74. 10p. 5.25-inch heavy AA gun, 1953 .. .. 25 30
75. 18p. 25-pounder gun-how, 1943 .. .. .. 45 40
76. 19p. 64-pounder rifled muzzle-loader, 1873 .. 50 50
77. 22p. 12-pounder gun, 1758 55 50
78. 50p. 10-inch rifled muzzle-loader, 1870 .. .. 1·40 1·40
79. £1 Russian 24-pounder gun, 1854 .. .. 2·50 2·50
80. £3 9.2-inch "Mk.10" coastal gun, 1935 .. 7·50 8·50
81. £5 24-pounder gun, 1779 .. 11·00 13·00

157. Victoria Stadium.

1987. Bicentenary of Royal Engineers' Royal Warrant. Multicoloured.

582. 18p. Type **157** .. .. 1·25 65
583. 32p. Freedom of Gibraltar scroll and casket .. 1·75 2·25
584. 44p. Royal Engineers' badge .. .. .. 2·50 3·25

158. The Three Kings.

1987. Christmas. Multicoloured.

585. 4p. Type **158** 15 10
586. 22p. The Holy Family .. 90 1·00
587. 44p. The Shepherds .. 1·75 2·00

159. "Canberra" (liner) passing Gibraltar.

1988. Europa. Transport and Communications. Multicoloured.

588 22p. Type **159** .. .. 1·25 1·75
589 22p. "Gibline I" (ferry), dish aerial and aircraft 1·25 1·75
590 32p. Horse-drawn carriage and modern coach .. 1·75 2·25
591 32p. Car, telephone and Rock of Gibraltar .. 1·75 2·25

1988. Naval Crests (7th series). As T **134**.

592. 18p. multicoloured .. 1·00 65
593. 22p. black, brown and gold 1·25 1·00
594. 32p. multicoloured .. 1·75 2·25
595. 44p. multicoloured .. 2·50 3·25

DESIGNS: 18p. H.M.S. "Clyde". 22p. H.M.S. "Foresight". 32p. H.M.S. "Severn". 44p. H.M.S. "Rodney".

160 European Bee Eater

1988. Birds. Multicoloured.

596 4p. Type **160** 35 15
597 22p. Atlantic puffin .. 1·00 80
598 32p. Honey buzzard .. 1·25 1·50
599 44p. Blue rock thrush .. 1·50 2·25

161 "Zebu" (brigantine)

1988. Operation Raleigh. Multicoloured.

600 19p. Type **161** 55 60
601 22p. Miniature of Sir Walter Raleigh and logo 60 70
602 32p. "Sir Walter Raleigh" (expedition ship) and world map .. .. 85 1·25

162 "Snowman" (Rebecca Falero)

1988. Christmas. Children's Paintings. Mult.

604 4p. Type **162** 15 10
605 22p. "The Nativity" (Dennis Penalver) .. 55 60
606 44p. "Father Christmas" (Gavin Key) (23 × 31 mm) .. .. .. 1·00 1·25

163 Soft Toys and Toy Train

1989. Europa. Children's Toys. Multicoloured.

607 25p. Type **163** .. .. 1·00 75
608 32p. Soft toys, toy boat and doll's house .. 1·25 1·75

164 Port Sergeant with Keys

1989. 50th Anniv of Gibraltar Regiment. Mult.

609 4p. Type **164** 25 10
610 22p. Regimental badge and colours 80 90
611 32p. Drum major .. .. 1·25 1·75

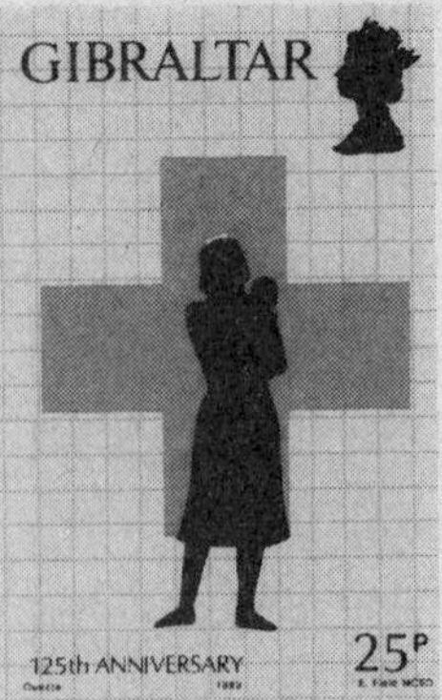

165 Nurse and Baby

1989. 125th Anniv of International Red Cross.

613 **165** 25p. black, red & brn 60 60
614 – 32p. black, red & brn 75 80
615 – 44p. black, red & brn 1·00 1·40

DESIGNS—32p. Famine victims; 44p. Accident victims.

1989. Naval Crests (8th series). As T **134**.

616 22p. multicoloured .. 1·00 65
617 25p. black and gold .. 1·00 1·25
618 32p. gold, black and red .. 1·40 1·75
619 44p. multicoloured .. 2·25 2·50

DESIGNS: 22p. H.M.S. "Blankney"; 25p. H.M.S. "Deptford"; 32p. H.M.S. "Exmoor"; 44p. H.M.S. "Stork".

167 Father Christmas in Sleigh

1989. Christmas. Multicoloured.

622 4p. Type **167** 15 10
623 22p. Shepherds and sheep 70 70
624 32p. The Nativity .. 1·10 1·50
625 44p. The Three Wise Men 1·75 2·25

168 General Post Office Entrance

1990. Europa. Post Office Buildings. Multicoloured.

626 22p. Type **168** 65 90
627 22p. Interior of General Post Office 65 90
628 32p. Interior of South District Post Office .. 1·00 1·50
629 32p. South District Post Office .. .. .. 1·00 1·50

169 19th-century Firemen

1990. 125th Anniv of Gibraltar Fire Service. Multicoloured.

630 4p. Type **169** 30 15
631 20p. Early fire engine (horiz) 80 80
632 42p. Modern fire engine (horiz) .. .. .. 1·40 2·00
633 44p. Modern fireman in breathing apparatus .. 1·60 2·00

170 Henry Corbould (artist) and Penny Black

1990. 150th Anniv of the Penny Black. Mult.

634 19p. Type **170** 60 60
635 22p. Bath Royal Mail coach 70 70
636 32p. Sir Rowland Hill and Penny Black .. .. 1·25 1·75

1990. Naval Crests (9th series). As T **134**. Mult.

638 22p. H.M.S. "Calpe" .. 85 60
639 25p. H.M.S. "Gallant" .. 95 1·00
640 32p. H.M.S. "Wrestler" .. 1·10 1·40
641 44p. H.M.S. "Greyhound" 1·75 2·40

171 Model of Europort Development

1990. Development Projects. Multicoloured.

642 22p. Type **171** 75 80
643 23p. Construction of building material factory .. 75 85
644 25p. Land reclamation .. 95 1·10

172 Candle and Holly

1990. Christmas. Multicoloured.

645 4p. Type **172** 15 10
646 22p. Father Christmas .. 65 65
647 42p. Christmas tree .. 1·25 1·60
648 44p. Nativity crib .. 1·25 1·60

173 Space Laboratory and Spaceplane (Columbus Development Programme)

1991. Europa. Europe in Space. Mult.

649 25p. Type **173** 75 60
650 32p. "ERS-1" earth resources remote sensing satellite .. .. 1·00 1·50

1991. Naval Crests (10th series). As T **134**.

651 4p. black, blue and gold .. 25 10
652 21p. multicoloured .. 1·00 1·00
653 22p. multicoloured .. 1·00 1·00
654 62p. multicoloured .. 2·75 3·25

DESIGNS: 4p. H.M.S. "Hesperus"; 21p. H.M.S. "Forester"; 22p. H.M.S. "Furious"; 62p. H.M.S. "Scylla".

174 Shag

1991. Endangered Species. Birds. Mult.
655 13p. Type **174** 50 55
656 13p. Barbary partridge .. 50 55
657 13p. Egyptian vulture .. 50 55
658 13p. Black stork 50 55

1991. No. 580 surch **£1.05**.
659 £1.05 on £3 9.2-inch "Mk.10" coastal gun, 1935 .. .. .. 2·75 2·25

176 "North View of Gibraltar" (Gustavo Bacarisas)

1991. Local Paintings. Multicoloured.
660 22p. Type **176** 60 50
661 26p. "Parson's Lodge" (Eleana Mifsud) .. 70 70
662 32p. "Governor's Parade" (Jacobo Azagury) .. 90 1·10
663 42p. "Waterport Wharf" (Rudesindo Mannia) (vert) .. .. .. 1·40 1·75

177 "Once in Royal David's City"

1991. Christmas. Carols. Multicoloured.
664 4p. Type **177** 15 10
665 24p. "Silent Night" .. 70 70
666 25p. "Angels We Have Heard on High" .. 70 75
667 49p. "O Come All Ye Faithful" .. .. 1·40 2·00

179 Columbus and "Santa Maria"

1992. Europa. 500th Anniv of Discovery of America by Columbus. Multicoloured.
669 24p. Type **179** .. .. 1·00 1·25
670 24p. Map of Old World and "Nina" .. .. 1·00 1·25
671 34p. Map of New World and "Pinta" .. .. 1·25 1·50
672 34p. Map of Old World and look-out .. .. 1·25 1·50

Nos. 669/70 and 671/2 were issued together, se-tenant, each pair forming a composite design.

1992. 40th Anniv of Queen Elizabeth II's Accession. As T **143** of Ascension. Mult.
673 4p. Gibraltar from north 15 10
674 20p. H.M.S. "Arrow" (frigate) and Gibraltar from south .. 60 60
675 24p. Southport Gates .. 75 75
676 44p. Three portraits of Queen Elizabeth .. 1·25 1·50
677 54p. Queen Elizabeth II 1·60 1·75

180 Compass Rose, Sail and Atlantic Map

1992. Round the World Yacht Rally. Multicoloured designs, each incorporating compass rose and sail.
678 21p. Type **180** 65 70
679 24p. Map of Indonesian Archipelago (horiz) .. 85 95
680 25p. Map of Indian Ocean (horiz) 85 95

181 Holy Trinity Cathedral

1992. 150th Anniv of Anglican Diocese of Gibraltar-in-Europe. Multicoloured.
682 4p. Type **181** 15 10
683 24p. Diocesan crest and map (horiz) 65 55
684 44p. Construction of Cathedral and Sir George Don (horiz) .. .. 1·25 1·50
685 54p. Bishop Tomlinson .. 1·50 2·00

182 Sacred Heart of Jesus Church

1992. Christmas. Churches. Multicoloured.
686 4p. Type **182** 15 10
687 24p. Cathedral of St. Mary the Crowned 65 55
688 34p. St. Andrew's Church of Scotland .. .. 1·00 1·10
689 49p. St. Joseph's Church .. 1·40 1·60

183 "Drama and Music"

1993. Europa. Contemporary Art. Mult.
690 24p. Type **183** 70 80
691 24p. "Sculpture, Art and Pottery" 70 80
692 34p. "Architecture" .. 90 1·00
693 34p. "Printing and Photography" .. .. 90 1·00

185 Landport Gate

1993. Architectural Heritage. Multicoloured.
695 1p. Type **185** 10 10
696 2p. St. Mary the Crowned Church (horiz) 10 10
697 3p. Parsons Lodge Battery (horiz) 10 10
698 4p. Moorish Castle (horiz) 10 10
699 5p. General Post Office .. 10 10
700 10p. South Barracks (horiz) 20 25
701 21p. American War Memorial 40 45
702 24p. Garrison Library (horiz) 50 55
703 25p. Southport Gates .. 50 55
704 26p. Casemates Gate (horiz) 50 55
705 50p. Central Police Station (horiz) .. .. .. 1·00 1·10
706 £1 Prince Edward's Gate 2·00 2·10
707 £3 Lighthouse, Europa Point .. .. .. 6·00 6·25

186 £sd and Decimal British Coins (25th anniv of decimal currency)

1993. Anniversaries. Multicoloured.
709 21p. Type **186** 40 45
710 24p. R.A.F. crest with biplane and modern fighter (75th anniv) .. 50 55
711 34p. Garrison Library badge and building (bicent) 70 75
712 49p. Sir Winston Churchill and air raid (50th anniv of visit) .. .. 95 1·00

187 Mice decorating Christmas Tree

1993. Christmas. Multicoloured.
713 5p. Type **187** 10 10
714 24p. Mice pulling cracker 50 55
715 44p. Mice singing carols .. 90 95
716 49p. Mice building snowman .. .. 1·00 1·10

188 Exploding Atom (Lord Penney)

1994. Europa. Scientific Discoveries. Mult.
717 24p. Type **188** 50 55
718 24p. Polonium and radium experiment (Marie Curie) 50 55
719 34p. First diesel engine (Rudolph Diesel) .. 70 75
720 34p. Early telescope (Galileo) 70 75

POSTAGE DUE STAMPS.

1956. As Type D **1** of Barbados.
D 1. 1d. green .. .. .. 2·00 2·75
D 2. 2d. brown .. .. .. 2·50 3·75
D 3. 4d. blue .. .. .. 3·00 5·50

1971. As Nos. D1/3, inscr. in decimal currency.
D 4. ½p. green 30 80
D 5. 1p. brown 30 70
D 6. 2p. blue 30 80

D **2.**

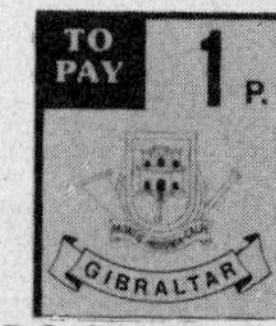

D **3.** Gibraltar Coat of Arms.

1976.
D 7. D **2.** 1p. orange 15 25
D 8. 3p. blue 15 40
D 9. 5p. red 20 50
D 10. 7p. violet 25 60
D 11. 10p. green 35 60
D 12. 20p. green 70 95

1984.
D 13. D **3.** 1p. black 10 10
D 14. 3p. red 10 10
D 15. 5p. blue 10 15
D 16. 10p. blue 20 25
D 17. 25p. mauve 50 55
D 18. 50p. orange .. .. 1·00 1·10
D 19. £1 green .. .. 2·00 2·10

GILBERT AND ELLICE ISLANDS

A Br. colony in the S. Pacific.
1911. 12 pence = 1 pound;
20 shillings = 1 pound.
1966. 100 cents = $1 Australian.

1911. Stamps of Fiji (King Edward VII) optd. **GILBERT & ELLICE PROTECTORATE.**

1. 23. ½d. green .. .. .. 4·50 28·00
2. 1d. red .. .. .. 45·00 27·00
3. 2d. grey .. .. .. 6·00 12·00
4. 2½d. blue .. .. .. 12·00 24·00
5. 5d. purple and green .. 32·00 55·00
6. 6d. purple .. .. .. 20·00 38·00
7. 1s. black on green .. .. 17·00 35·00

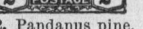

2. Pandanus pine. 3.

1911.

8. 2. ½d. green .. .. .. 4·25 9·00
9. 1d. red .. .. .. 2·00 5·50
10. 2d. grey .. .. .. 1·50 5·50
11. 2½d. blue .. .. .. 1·50 7·50

1912.

27. 3. ½d. green .. .. .. 80 1·25
13. 1d. red .. .. .. 75 2·75
28. 1d. violet .. .. .. 1·75 2·50
29. 1½d. red .. .. .. 1·25 1·00
30. 2d. grey .. .. .. 3·50 12·00
15. 2½d. blue .. .. .. 1·75 8·50
16. 3d. purple on yellow .. 90 6·50
17. 4d. black & red on yellow 60 4·00
18. 5d. purple and green .. 1·50 7·00
19. 6d. purple .. .. .. 1·25 7·50
20. 1s. black on green .. 1·25 5·50
21. 2s. purple & blue on blue .. 14·00 24·00
22. 2s. 6d. black & red on blue 10·00 23·00
23. 5s. green & red on yellow 24·00 48·00
35. 10s. green & red on green £180 £325
24. £1 purple and black on red £650 £1400

1918. Optd. **WAR TAX.**

26. 3. 1d. red .. .. .. 30 3·50

1935. Silver Jubilee. As T **13** of **Antigua.**

36. 1d. blue and black .. 2·25 5·00
37. 1½d. blue and red .. .. 1·75 2·75
38. 3d. brown and blue .. 5·00 8·50
39. 1s. grey and purple .. 32·00 24·00

1937. Coronation. As T **2** of Aden.

40. 1d. violet 35 45
41. 1½d. red 45 45
42. 3d. blue 60 50

6. Great Frigate Bird.

7. Pandanus Pine.

1939.

43. 6. ½d. blue and green .. 20 50
44. 7. 1d. green and purple .. 30 80
45. – 1½d. black and red .. 30 90
46. – 2d. brown and black .. 20 1·00
47. – 2½d. black and olive .. 30 70
48. – 3d. black and blue .. 45 1·00
49. – 5d. blue and brown .. 2·75 1·00
50. – 6d. olive and violet .. 40 50
51. – 1s. black and blue .. 2·50 1·25
52. – 2s. blue and orange .. 15·00 7·50
53. – 2s. 6d. blue and green .. 17·00 14·00
54. – 5s. red and blue .. .. 18·00 14·00

DESIGNS: 1½d. Canoe crossing reef. 2d. Canoe and boat-house. 2½d. Native House. 3d. Seascape. 5d. Ellice Is. canoe. 6d. Coconut palms. 1s. Jetty, Ocean Is. 2s. H.M.C.S. "Nimanoa". 2s. 6d. Gilbert Is. canoe. 5s. Coat of arms.

1946. Victory. As T **9** of Aden.

55. 1d. purple 15 15
56. 3d. blue 15 15

1949. Silver Wedding. As T **10/11** of **Aden.**

57. 1d. violet 40 50
58. £1 red .. .. .. 15·00 17·00

1949. U.P.U. As T **20/23** of Antigua.

59. 1d. purple 55 65
60. 2d. black .. .. .. 1·25 80
61. 3d. blue .. .. .. 1·50 1·10
62. 1s. blue .. .. .. 2·25 1·40

1953. Coronation. As T **13** of Aden.

63. 2d. black and grey .. 55 1·60

18. Great Frigate Bird

1956. As 1939 issue but with portrait of Queen Elizabeth II as in T **18** and colours **changed.**

64. 18. ½d. black and blue .. 35 70
65. 7. 1d. olive and violet .. 60 30
66. – 2d. green and purple .. 90 1·25
67. – 2½d. black and green .. 50 60
68. – 3d. black and red .. 50 45
69. – 5d. blue and orange .. 7·00 1·75
70. – 6d. brown and black .. 55 75
71. – 1s. black and olive .. 55 50
72. – 2s. blue and sepia .. 8·00 4·50
73. – 2s. 6d. red and blue .. 9·50 5·50
74. – 5s. blue and green .. 12·00 7·50
75. – 10s. blk. & turq. (as 1½d.) 22·00 15·00

19. Loading Phosphate from Cantilever.

1960. Diamond Jubilee of Phosphate Discovery at Ocean Is. Inscr. "1900 1960".

76. 19. 2d. green and red .. 80 50
77. – 2½d. black and olive .. 80 50
78. – 1s. black and turquoise .. 85 55

DESIGNS: 2½d. Phosphate rock. 1s. Phosphate-mining.

1963. Freedom from Hunger. As T **28** of Aden.

79. 10d. blue .. .. .. 3·00 30

1963. Red Cross Cent. As T **33** of Antigua.

80. 2d. red and black .. 1·50 30
81. 10d. red and blue .. 3·50 1·25

23. Eastern Reef Heron in Flight.

1964. First Air Service.

82. – 3d. blue, blk. & light blue 30 10
83. 23. 1s. light blue, blk. & dp. bl. 55 10
84. – 3s. 7d. green, black & emer. 80 35

DESIGNS—VERT. 3d. D. H. "Heron" aircraft and route map. 3s. 7d. D. H. "Heron" aircraft over Tarawa Lagoon.

1965. Cent of I.T.U. As T **36** of Antigua.

87. 3d. orange and green .. 20 10
88. 2s. 6d. turquoise and purple 80 20

26. Gilbertese Women's Dance.

1965. Multicoloured.

89. ½d. Maneaba and Gilbertese Man blowing Bu Shell .. 10 10
90. 1d. Ellice Islanders Reef-fishing by Flare .. 10 10
91. 2d. Gilbertese Girl weaving Head-garland 10 10
92. 3d. Gilbertese Woman performing Ruoia 10 10
93. 4d. Gilbertese Man performing Kamei 15 10
94. 5d. Gilbertese Girl drawing water 20 10
95. 6d. Ellice Islander performing a Fatele 20 10
96. 7d. Ellice Youths performing Spear dance .. 25 10
97. 1s. Gilbertese Girl tending Ikaroa Babai plant .. 40 10
98. 1s. 6d. Ellice Islanders dancing a Fatele .. 1·00 65
99. 2s. Ellice Islanders pounding Pulaka .. .. 1·00 1·25
100. 3s. 7d. Type **26** .. .. 2·25 65
101. 5s. Gilbertese Boys playing a Stick Game .. .. 2·25 80
102. 10s. Ellice Youths beating the Box for the Fatele .. 4·00 1·25
103. £1 Coat of Arms .. .. 4·50 2·50

Nos. 89/99 are vert

1965. I.C.Y. As T **37** of Antigua.

104. ½d. purple and turquoise .. 10 10
105. 3s. 7d. green and lavender 60 15

1966. Churchill Commem. As T **38** of Antigua.

106. ½d. blue 10 10
107. 3d. green 30 10
108. 3s. brown 65 35
109. 3s. 7d. violet 65 35

1966. Decimal Currency. Nos. 89/103 **surch.**

110. 1 c. on 1d. 10 10
111. 2 c. on 2d. 10 10
112. 3 c. on 3d. 10 10
113. 4 c. on ½d. 10 10
114. 5 c. on 6d. 15 10
115. 6 c. on 4d. 15 10
116. 8 c. on 5d. 15 10
117. 10 c. on 1s. 15 10
118. 15 c. on 7d. 80 30
119. 20 c. on 1s. 6d. 45 25
120. 25 c. on 2s. 45 20
121. 35 c. on 3s. 7d. .. .. 1·25 20
122. 50 c. on 5s. 75 35
123. $1 on 10s. 75 40
124. $2 on £1 .. .. .. 1·50 1·25

1966. World Cup Football Championship. As T **40** of Antigua.

125. 3 c. multicoloured .. 15 10
126. 35 c. multicoloured .. 45 20

1966. Inauguration of W.H.O. Headquarters, Geneva. As T **41** of Antigua.

127. 3 c. black, green and blue 30 10
128. 12 c. black, purple & ochre 60 40

1966. 20th Anniv. of U.N.E.S.C.O. As T **54/6** of Antigua.

129. 5 c. multicoloured .. 50 10
130. 10 c. yellow, violet & olive 70 10
131. 20 c. black, purple & orge. 1·25 45

41. H.M.S. "Royalist".

1967. 75th Anniv. of Protectorate.

132. 41. 3 c. red, blue and green .. 30 20
133. – 10 c. multicoloured .. 15 10
134. – 35 c. sepia, yellow & grn. 30 20

DESIGNS: 10 c. Trading post. 35 c. **Island** family.

1968. Decimal Currency. As Nos. 89/103, but with values inscr. in decimal **currency.**

135. – 1 c. mult. (as 1d.) .. 10 15
136. – 2 c. mult. (as 2d.) .. 15 10
137. – 3 c. mult. (as 3d.) .. 15 10
138. – 4 c. mult. (as ½d.) .. 15 10
139. – 5 c. mult. (as 6d.) .. 15 10
140. – 6 c. mult. (as 4d.) .. 20 10
141. – 8 c. mult. (as 5d.) .. 20 10
142. – 10 c. mult. (as 1s.) .. 20 10
143. – 15 c. mult. (as 7d.) .. 50 20
144. – 20 c. mult. (as 1s. 6d.) .. 65 15
145. – 25 c. mult. (as 2s.) .. 1·25 20
146. 26. 35 c. multicoloured .. 1·50 20
147. – 50 c. mult. (as 5s.) .. 1·50 1·25
148. – $1 mult. (as 10s.) .. 1·50 2·00
149. – $2 mult. (as £1) .. 4·00 2·00

45. Map of Tarawa Atoll.

1968. 25th Anniv. of Battle of Tarawa.

150. 3 c. Type **45** 20 10
151. 10 c. Marines landing .. 20 10
152. 15 c. Beach-head assault 30 15
153. 35 c. Raising U.S. and British Flags 40 20

46. Young Pupil against outline of Abemama Island.

1969. End of Inaugural Year of South Pacific University.

154. 46. 3 c. multicoloured .. 10 10
155. – 10 c. multicoloured .. 10 10
156. – 35 c. black, brown & grn. 15 20

DESIGNS: 10 c. Boy and girl students and Tarawa atoll. 35 c. University graduate and South Pacific Islands.

47. "Virgin and Child" in Pacific Setting.

1969. Christmas.

157. – 2 c. multicoloured .. 15 20
158. 47. 10 c. multicoloured .. 15 10

DESIGN: 2 c. as Type **12** but with grass foreground instead of sand.

48. "Kiss of Life".

1970. Centenary of British Red Cross.

159. 48. 10 c. multicoloured .. 20 10
160. – 15 c. multicoloured .. 30 20
161. – 35 c. multicoloured .. 60 35

Nos. 160/1 are as Type **48**, but arranged differently.

49. Foetus and Patients.

1970. 25th Anniv. of U.N.

162. 49. 5 c. multicoloured .. 15 10
163. – 10 c. black, grey & red 15 10
164. – 15 c. multicoloured .. 20 10
165. – 35 c. blue, grn. & black 30 15

DESIGNS: 10 c. Nurse and Surgical Instruments. 15 c. X-ray Plate and Technician. 35 c. U.N. Emblem and Map.

53. Map of Gilbert Islands.

1970. Centenary of Landing in Gilbert Islands by London Missionary Society.

166. 53. 2 c. multicoloured .. 15 30
167. – 10 c. black and green .. 20 10
168. – 25 c. brown and blue .. 20 15
169. – 35 c. blue, blk. & red 30 30

DESIGNS—VERT. 10 c. Sailing-Ship "John Williams III". 25 c. Rev. S. J. Whitmee. HORIZ. 35 c. M.V. "John Williams VII".

57. " Child with Halo " (T. Collis).

1970. Christmas Sketches. Multicoloured.

No.	Description	Unused	Used
170.	2 c. Type 57	10	15
171.	10 c. " Sanctuary, Tarawa Cathedral " (Mrs. A. Burroughs)	10	10
172.	35 c. " Three Ships inside Star " (Mrs. C. Barnett)	20	20

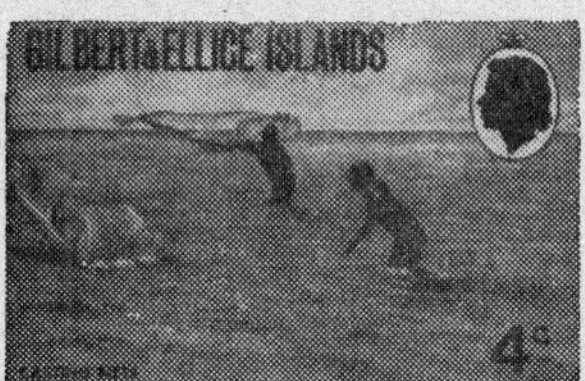

60. Casting Nets.

1971. Multicoloured.

No.	Description	Unused	Used
173.	1 c. Cutting toddy (vert.)	10	10
174.	2 c. Lagoon fishing ..	15	20
175.	3 c. Cleaning pandanus leaves	15	15
176.	4 c. Type 60	20	25
177.	5 c. Gilbertese canoe ..	35	15
178.	6 c. De-husking coconuts (vert.)	30	35
179.	8 c. Weaving pandanus fronds (vert.)	35	15
180.	10 c. Weaving a basket (vert.)	40	15
181.	15 c. Tiger shark and fisherman (vert.) ..	3·75	1·50
182.	20 c. Beating rolled pandanus leaf	2·00	90
183.	25 c. Loading copra ..	2·00	1·00
184.	35 c. Fishing at night ..	2·00	50
185.	50 c. Local handicrafts (vert.)	1·75	1·25
186.	$1 Weaving coconut screens (vert.)	2·50	2·25
187.	$2 Coat of Arms (vert.) ..	10·00	10·00

61. House of Representatives.

1971. New Constitution. Multicoloured.

No.	Description	Unused	Used
188.	3 c. Type 61	10	20
189.	10 c. Maneaba Betio (Assembly hut) ..	20	10

62. Pacific Nativity Scene.

1971. Christmas.

No.	Description	Unused	Used
190. 62.	3 c. blk., yell. & blue ..	10	10
191. –	10 c. black, gold & blue	10	10
192. –	35 c. black, gold & red ..	25	20

DESIGNS: 10 c. Star and palm leaves. 35 c. Outrigger canoe and star.

63. Emblem and Young Boys.

1971. 25th Anniv. of U.N.I.C.E.F. Mult.

No.	Description	Unused	Used
193.	3 c. Type 63	10	20
194.	10 c. Young boy	15	10
195.	35 c. Young boy's face ..	45	45

Nos. 193/5 include the Unicef Emblem within each design.

64. Flag and Map of South Pacific.

1972. 25th Anniv. of South Pacific Commission. Multicoloured.

No.	Description	Unused	Used
196.	3 c. Type 64	10	30
197.	10 c. Flag and native boats	15	10
198.	35 c. Flags of member nations	15	80

65. " Alveopora ".

1972. Coral. Multicoloured.

No.	Description	Unused	Used
199.	3 c. Type 65	25	20
200.	10 c. " Euphyllia " ..	35	10
201.	15 c. " Melithea " ..	55	20
202.	35 c. " Spongodes " ..	1·00	35

66. Star of Peace.

1972. Christmas. Multicoloured.

No.	Description	Unused	Used
208.	3 c. Type 66	10	10
209.	10 c. " The Nativity " ..	10	10
210.	35 c. Baby in " manger " (horiz.)	20	20

1972. Royal Silver Wedding. As T 52 of Ascension, but with Floral Head-dresses in background.

No.	Description	Unused	Used
211.	3 c. brown	10	15
212.	35 c. brown	25	15

68. Funafuti (" The Land of Bananas ").

1973. Legends of Island Names (1st series). Multicoloured.

No.	Description	Unused	Used
213.	3 c. Type 68	10	15
214.	10 c. Butaritari (" The Smell of the Sea ") ..	15	10
215.	25 c. Tarawa (" The Centre of the World ") ..	25	20
216.	35 c. Abemama (" The Land of the Moon ") ..	30	20

See also Nos. 252/5.

69. Dancer.

1973. Christmas. Multicoloured.

No.	Description	Unused	Used
217.	3 c. Type 69	10	10
218.	10 c. Canoe and lagoon ..	10	10
219.	35 c. Lagoon at evening ..	20	10
220.	50 c. Map of Christmas Island	30	55

1973. Royal Wedding. As Type 47 of Anguilla. Background colours given. Multicoloured.

No.	Description	Unused	Used
221.	3 c. green	10	15
222.	35 c. blue	20	15

70. Meteorological Observation.

1973. Cent. of I.M.O./W.M.O. Multicoloured.

No.	Description	Unused	Used
223.	3 c. Type 70	80	30
224.	10 c. Island observing-station	80	20
225.	35 c. Wind-finding radar ..		
226.	50 c. World weather watch stations	1·50	40
		2·00	1·50

71. Te Mataaua Crest.

1974. Canoe Crests. Multicoloured.

No.	Description	Unused	Used
227.	3 c. Type 71	10	10
228.	10 c. " Te-Nimta-wawa "	15	10
229.	35 c. " Tara-tara-venei-na "	25	10
230.	50 c. " Te Bou-uoua " ..	35	50

72. £1 Stamp of 1924 and Te Koroba (canoe).

1974. Centenary of U.P.U.

No.	Description	Unused	Used
232. 72.	4 c. multicoloured ..	10	10
233. –	10 c. multicoloured ..	10	10
234. –	25 c. multicoloured ..	15	15
235. –	35 c. multicoloured ..	20	20

DESIGNS: 10 c. 5 s. stamp of 1939 and sailing vessel "Kiakia". 25 c. $2 stamp of 1971 and B.A.C. "1–11". 35 c. U.P.U. Emblem.

73. Toy Canoe.

1974. Christmas. Multicoloured.

No.	Description	Unused	Used
236.	4 c. Type 73	10	10
237.	10 c. Toy windmill ..	10	10
238.	25 c. Coconut "ball" ..	15	15
239.	35 c. Canoes and constellation Pleiades	20	15

74. North Front Entrance, Blenheim Palace.

1974. Birth Cent. of Sir Winston Churchill.

No.	Description	Unused	Used
240.	4 c. Type 74	10	10
241.	10 c. Churchill painting ..	10	10
242.	35 c. Churchill's statue, London	25	15

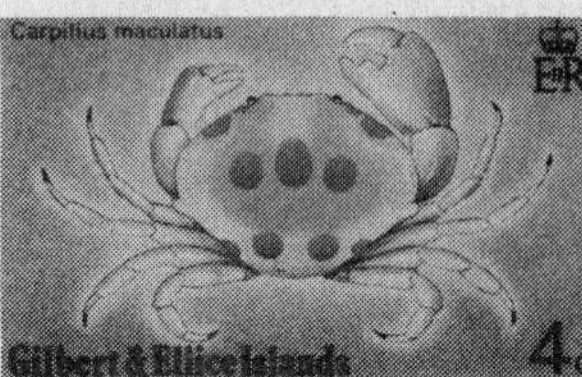

75. Barometer Crab.

No.	Description	Unused	Used
243.	4 c. Type 75	25	20
244.	10 c. "Ranina ranina" ..	35	10
245.	25 c. Pelagic Swimming Crab	70	30
246.	35 c. Ghost Crab	85	55

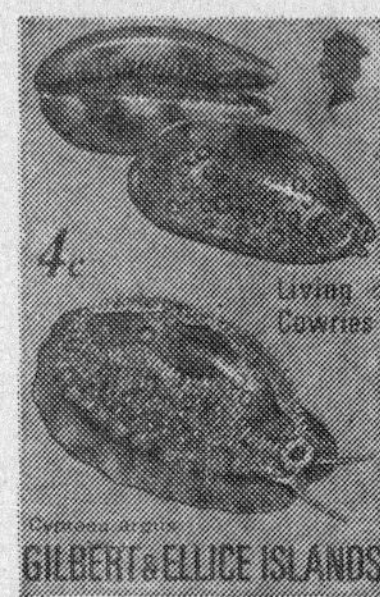

76. Eyed Cowrie.

1975. Cowrie Shells. Multicoloured.

No.	Description	Unused	Used
247.	4 c. Type 76	40	20
248.	10 c. Sieve Cowrie ..	70	10
249.	25 c. Mole Cowrie ..	1·50	60
250.	35 c. Map Cowrie ..	1·75	85

1975. Legends of Island Names (2nd series). As T 68. Multicoloured.

No.	Description	Unused	Used
252.	4 c. Beru (" The Bud ") ..	10	10
253.	10 c. Onotoa (" Six Giants ")	10	10
254.	25 c. Abaiang (" Land to the North ") ..	20	15
255.	35 c. Marakei (" Fish-trap floating on eaves ") ..	30	20

77. " Christ is Born ".

1975. Christmas. Multicoloured.

No.	Description	Unused	Used
256.	4 c. Type 77	10	10
257.	10 c. Protestant Chapel, Tarawa	10	10
258.	25 c. Catholic Church, Ocean Island	20	40
259.	35 c. Fishermen and star ..	25	55

POSTAGE DUE STAMPS

D 1.

1940.

D 1. D 1. 1d. green .. .. 7·50 14·00
D 2. 2d. red .. .. .. 8·50 14·00
D 3. 3d. brown .. .. 12·00 15·00
D 4. 4d. blue .. .. 14·00 23·00
D 5. 4d. olive .. .. 19·00 23·00
D 6. 6d. purple .. .. 19·00 23·00
D 7. 1s. violet .. .. 21·00 35·00
D 8. 1s. 6d. green .. .. 40·00 65·00

GILBERT ISLANDS

On 1st January, 1976 the Gilbert Islands and Tuvalu (Ellice) Islands became separate Crown Colonies. The Islands became independent on 12 July 1979, under the name of Kiribati.

100 cents = $1.

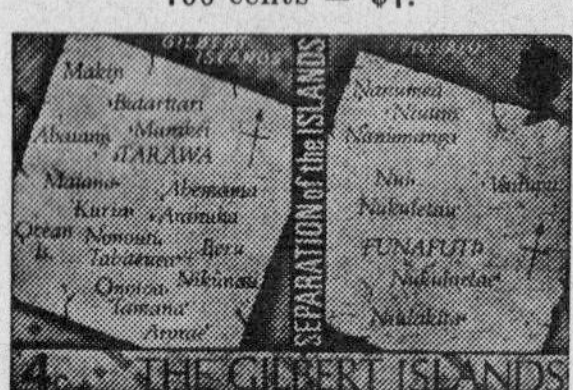

1. Charts of Gilbert Islands and Tuvalu (formerly Ellice) Islands.

1976. Separation of the Islands. Mult.
1. 4 c. Type 1 .. .. .. 50 75
2. 35 c. Maps of Tarawa and Funafuti .. .. .. 1·25 2·00

1976. Nos. 173/87 of Gilbert and Ellice Islands optd. **THE GILBERT ISLANDS.**
3 1 c. Cutting toddy 25 20
5 2 c. Lagoon fishing .. 50 30
12 3 c. Cleaning pandanus leaves 40 50
7 4 c. Type **60** 30 50
13 5 c. Gilbertese canoe .. 50 50
14 6 c. De-husking coconuts .. 50 60
15 8 c. Weaving pandanus fronds 50 60
16 10 c. Weaving a basket .. 50 60
17 15 c. Tiger Shark .. .. 1·50 1·25
18 20 c. Beating a pandanus leaf 1·50 90
19 25 c. Loading copra .. 2·00 1·25
20 35 c. Fishing at night .. 2·00 1·75
21 50 c. Local handicrafts .. 2·00 2·75
22 $1 Weaving coconut screens 6·00 9·00

3. "Teraaka" (training ship).

1976. Multicoloured.
23 1 c. Type **3** 20 15
24 3 c. "Tautunu" (inter-island freighter) 30 20
25 4 c. Moorish idol (fish) .. 30 20
26 5 c. Hibiscus 30 20
27 6 c. Eastern reef heron .. 35 30
28 7 c. Catholic Cathedral, Tarawa 30 30
29 8 c. Frangipani 30 30
30 10 c. Meneaba, Bikenibeu .. 30 30
31 12 c. Betio Harbour .. 45 45
32 15 c. Evening scene .. 55 45
33 20 c. Marakei Atoll .. 35 35
34 35 c. G.I.P.C. Chapel, Tangintebu 35 40
35 40 c. Flamboyant tree .. 40 45
36 50 c. "Hypolimnas bolina elliciana", (butterfly) .. 2·25 1·75
37 $1 "Tabakea" (Tarawa Lagoon ferry) .. .. 2·00 2·50
38 $2 National flag .. .. 2·25 2·75

4. Church.

1976. Christmas. Children's Drawings. Multicoloured.
39. 5 c. Type **4** 35 15
40. 15 c. Feasting (vert.) .. 50 15
41. 20 c. Maneaba (vert.) .. 55 30
42. 35 c. Dancing 70 45

5. Porcupine Fish Helmet.

1976. Artefacts. Multicoloured.
43. 5 c. Type **5** 35 15
44. 15 c. Shark's Teeth Dagger 50 35
45. 20 c. Fighting Gauntlet .. 55 40
46. 35 c. Coconut Body Armour 70 55

6. The Queen in Coronation Robes.

1977. Silver Jubilee. Multicoloured.
48. 8 c. Prince Charles' visit, 1970 .. .. .. 15 10
49. 20 c. Prince Philip's visit, 1959 .. .. .. 20 15
50. 40 c. Type **6** 30 35

7. Commodore Byron and H.M.S. "Dolphin".

1977. Explorers. Multicoloured.
51 5 c. Type **7** .. .. 1·00 1·50
52 15 c. Capt. Fanning and "Betsey" .. .. 1·50 2·75
53 20 c. Admiral Bellingshausen and "Vostok" .. 2·00 3·25
54 35 c. Capt. Wilkes and U.S.S. "Vincennes" .. 3·50 5·75

8. H.M.S. "Resolution" and H.M.S. "Discovery".

1977. Christmas and Bicent. of Capt. Cook's Discovery of Christmas Is. Mult.
55. 8 c. Type **8** 55 10
56. 15 c. Logbook entry (horiz.) 70 15
57. 20 c. Capt. Cook 85 20
58. 40 c. Landing party (horiz.) 1·75 60

9. Scout Emblem.

1977. 50th Anniv. of Scouting in the Gilbert Is. Multicoloured.
60. 8 c. Type **9** 20 10
61. 15 c. Patrol meeting (horiz.) 30 20
62. 20 c. Scout making mat (horiz.) 40 20
63. 40 c. Canoeing 50 55

10. Taurus. (The Bull).

1978. The Night Sky over the Gilbert Is.
64. 10. 10 c. black and blue .. 20 15
65. – 20 c. black and red .. 30 30
66. – 25 c. black and green .. 35 35
67. – 45 c. black and orange .. 50 60

DESIGNS: 20 c. Canis Major (the **Great Dog**). 25 c. Scorpio (the Scorpion). 45 c. Orion (the Giant Warrior).

11. Unicorn of Scotland.

1978. 25th Anniv. of Coronation.
68. 11. 45 c. green, violet & silver 30 40
69. – 45 c. multicoloured .. 30 40
70. – 45 c. green, violet & silver 30 40

DESIGNS: No. 69, Queen Elizabeth II. No. 70, Great Frigate Bird.

12. Birds in Flight to Tarawa.

1978. 25th Anniv. of Return of George V School to Tarawa. Multicoloured.
71. 10 c. Type **12** 10 10
72. 20 c. Tarawa, Abemama and school badge 20 20
73. 25 c. Rejoicing islanders .. 20 20
74. 45 c. King George V School Tarawa and Abemama .. 35 35

13. "Te Kaue ni Maie".

1978. Christmas. Kaue (traditional head decorations). Multicoloured.
75. 10 c. Type **13** 15 10
76. 20 c. "Te Itera" 20 15
77. 25 c. "Te Bau" 25 20
78. 45 c. "Te Tai" 35 30

14. H.M.S. "Endeavour".

1979. Bicentenary of Captain Cook's Voyages, 1768–79.
80. 14. 10 c. multicoloured .. 25 15
81. – 20 c. multicoloured .. 40 30
82. – 25 c. black, lilac & green 50 45
83. – 45 c. multicoloured .. 75 80

DESIGNS: 20 c. Green Turtle. 25 c. Quadrant. 45 c. Flaxman/Wedgwood medallion.

For later issues see KIRIBATI.

GOLD COAST

A Br. colony on the W. coast of Africa. For later issues after independence in 1957 see under Ghana.

12 pence = 1 shilling;
20 shillings = 1 pound.

1.

4.

1875.
4 1. ½d. yellow .. .. .. 32·00 22·00
11a ½d. green 75 30
5 1d. blue .. .. .. 13·00 6·50
12a 1d. red .. .. .. 1·00 40
6 2d. green .. .. .. 48·00 11·00
13b 2d. grey .. .. .. 1·40 50
14 2½d. blue and orange .. 1·75 35
15a 3d. olive .. .. .. 4·50 4·00
16 4d. mauve .. .. .. 2·25 80
17 6d. orange .. .. .. 3·75 3·00
18a 1s. mauve .. .. .. 3·50 1·00
19a 2s. brown .. .. .. 23·00 15·00

1889. Surch. **ONE PENNY** and bar.
20. 1. 1d. on 6d. orange .. £100 48·00

1889.
26. 4. ½d. mauve and green .. 75 25
27. 1d. mauve and red .. 40 25
27a. 2d. mauve and red .. 27·00 65·00
28. 2½d. mauve and blue .. 4·25 3·00
29. 3d. mauve and orange .. 4·50 1·00
30. 6d. mauve and violet .. 5·50 1·00
31. 1s. green and black .. 6·00 5·50
32. 2s. green and red .. .. 9·00 15·00
22. 5s. mauve and blue .. 48·00 12·00
33. 5s. green and mauve .. 42·00 21·00
23. 10s. mauve and red .. 65·00 15·00
34. 10s. green and brown .. £110 40·00
24. 20s. green and red .. £3250
25. 20s. mauve & black on red £150 35·00

1901. Surch. **ONE PENNY** and bar.
35. 4. 1d. on 2½d. mauve & blue 1·25 3·00
36. 1d. on 6d. mauve & violet 1·25 3·00

1902. As T **4**, but with portrait of King Edward VII.
38. ½d. purple and green .. 40 40
39. 1d. purple and red .. 75 15
51. 2d. purple and orange .. 3·50 50
41. 2½d. purple and blue .. 4·00 7·50
42. 3d. purple and orange .. 1·50 1·25
43. 6d. purple and violet .. 1·50 1·25
44. 1s. green and black .. 3·50 2·50
45. 2s. green and red .. .. 11·00 12·00
57. 2s. 6d. green and yellow .. 27·00 70·00
46. 5s. green and mauve .. 20·00 45·00
47. 10s. green and brown .. 45·00 90·00
48. 20s. purple & black on red £100 £140

1907. As last.
59. ½d. green .. .. .. 1·75 30
60. 1d. red .. .. .. 1·50 20
61. 2d. grey .. .. .. 2·00 30
62. 2½d. blue .. .. .. 3·50 1·75
63. 3d. purple on yellow .. 4·75 55
64a. 6d. purple .. .. 3·50 3·00
65. 1s. black and green .. 4·75 40
66. 2s. purple & blue on blue .. 4·00 13·00
67. 2s. 6d. black & red on blue 20·00 42·00
68. 5s. green and red on yellow 48·00 85·00

8.

13. King George V and Christiansborg Castle.

1908.
69. 8. 1d. red 50 10

1913. As T **3** and **8** (1d.) but portraits of King George V.
86 ½d. green 30 30
72 1d. red 30 10
87 1d. brown 30 10
88 1½d. red 30 10
89 2d. grey 30 30
76 2½d. blue 75 55
90 2½d. orange .. .. 30 6·50
77a 3d. purple on yellow .. 30 40
91 3d. blue 30 40
94 6d. purple .. .. 45 2·50
79b 1s. black on green .. 50 35
96 2s. purple & blue on blue 2·00 3·25
97 2s. 6d. blk. & red on blue 4·00 10·00
98 5s. green & red on yellow 7·00 28·00
83a 10s. green and red on grn. 17·00 55·00
100a 15s. purple and green .. £100 £225
84 20s. purple & black on red £100 80·00
102 £2 green and orange .. £350 £750

1918. Surch. **WAR TAX ONE PENNY.**
85. 1d. on 1d. red (No. 72) .. 20 30

1928.
103. 13. ½d. green 30 30
104. 1d. brown 30 10
105. 1½d. red .. .. .. 35 1·50
106. 2d. grey 30 10
107. 2½d. orange .. .. 1·10 3·50
108. 3d. blue 55 40
109. 6d. black and purple .. 55 30
110. 1s. black and orange .. 85 75
111. 2s. black and violet .. 10·00 2·50
112. 5s. red and olive .. 28·00 32·00

1935. Silver Jubilee. As T 13 of Antigua.
113. 1d. blue and black .. 60 30
114. 3d. brown and blue .. 2·75 5·50
115. 6d. green and blue .. 2·75 6·00
116. 1s. grey and purple .. 2·75 7·00

1937. Coronation. As T 2 of Aden.
117. 1d. brown .. .. .. 1·25 65
118. 2d. grey .. .. .. 1·40 2·00
119. 3d. blue .. .. .. 1·40 1·25

14.

15. King George VI and Christiansborg Castle, Accra.

1938.
120. 14. ½d. green 30 40
121. 1d. brown 30 10
122. 1½d. red 35 30
123. 2d. black 35 10
124. 3d. blue 35 10
125. 4d. mauve 50 80
126. 6d. purple 50 10
127. 9d. orange 60 40
128. 15. 1s. black and olive .. 70 20
129. 1s. 3d. brown and blue .. 1·75 20
130. 2s. blue and violet .. 3·25 3·75
131. 5s. olive and red .. 5·00 7·50
132. 10s. black and violet .. 6·50 14·00

1946. Victory. As T 9 of Aden.
133a. 2d. grey 10 10
134a. 4d. mauve .. .. .. 30 1·00

16. Northern Territories Mounted Constabulary.

DESIGNS—HORIZ. 1d. Christiansborg Castle. 1½d. Emblem of Joint Provincial Council. 2½d. Map showing position of Gold Coast. 3d. Manganese mine. 4d. Lake Bosumtwi. 1s. Breaking cocoa pods. 2s. Trooping the Colour. 5s. Surfboats. VERT. 2d. Talking drums. 6d. Cocoa farmer. 10s. Forest.

1948.
135. 16. ½d. green 20 30
136. – 1d. blue 15 15
137. – 1½d. red .. .. .. 1·25 70
138. – 2d. brown 55 10
139. – 2½d. brown and red .. 2·00 1·50
140. – 3d. blue .. .. .. 3·50 30
141. – 4d. mauve .. .. .. 3·00 1·25
142. – 6d. black and orange .. 30 15
143. – 1s. black and red .. 40 15
144. – 2s. olive and red .. 2·75 1·50
145. – 5s. purple and black .. 17·00 2·75
146. – 10s. black and olive .. 8·00 4·50

1948. Silver Wedding. As T 10/11 of Aden.
147. 1½d. red 30 15
148. 10s. olive .. .. .. 10·00 7·00

1949. U.P.U. As T 20/23 of Antigua.
149. 2d. brown 30 30
150. 2½d. orange .. .. 1·00 1·75
151. 3d. blue 75 70
152. 1s. green 75 50

1952. As 1948 but portrait of Queen Elizabeth II. Designs as for corresponding values except where stated.
153. ½d. brown & red (as 2½d.) 10 10
154. 1d. blue 10 10
155. 1½d. green 30 90
156. 2d. brown 30 10
157. 2½d. red (as ½d.) .. 35 35
158. 3d. mauve 50 10
159. 4d. blue 30 30
160. 6d. black and orange .. 30 15
161. 1s. black and red .. 30 15
162. 2s. olive and red .. 10·00 70
163. 5s. purple and black .. 16·00 2·75
164. 10s. black and olive .. 10·00 12·00

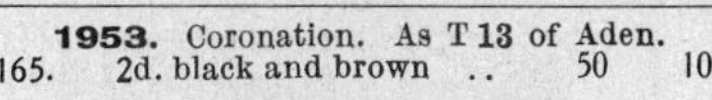

1953. Coronation. As T 13 of Aden.
165. 2d. black and brown .. 50 10

POSTAGE DUE STAMPS

D1.

1923.
D 1. D 1. ½d. black .. .. 14·00 80·00
D 2. 1d. black .. .. 75 1·00
D 5. 2d. black .. .. 2·00 11·00
D 6. 3d. black .. .. 1·50 10·00
D 7. 6d. black .. .. 2·00 10·00
D 8. 1s. black .. .. 2·25 35·00

For later issues see **GHANA**.

GREAT BRITAIN

Consisting of England, Wales Scotland and Northern Ireland, lying to the N.W. of the European continent.

1840. 12 pence = 1 shilling;
20 shillings = 1 pound sterling.
1971. 100 (new) pence = 1 pound sterling.

1.

3.

1840. Letters in lower corners. Imperf.
2. 1. 1d. black £3000 £150
5. 2d. blue £5500 £300

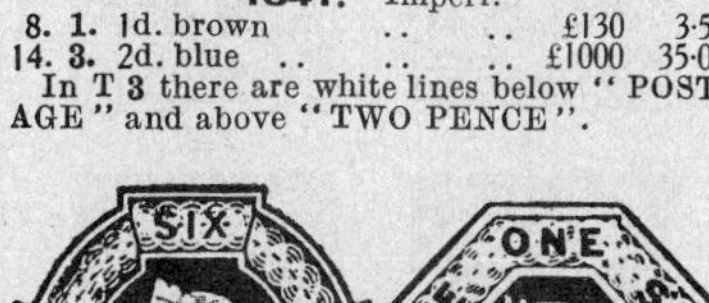

1841. Imperf.
8. 1. 1d. brown .. .. .. £130 3·50
14. 3. 2d. blue .. .. .. £1000 35·00

In T 3 there are white lines below "POSTAGE" and above "TWO PENCE".

12. 10.

1847. Imperf.
59. 12. 6d. purple £2500 £400
57. 10. 10d. brown £2250 £575
54. 1s. green £2750 £350

1854. Perf.
29. 1. 1d. brown .. .. .. £100 1·00
40. 1d. red .. .. .. 25·00 1·00
34. 3. 2d. blue .. .. .. £1000 25·00

14.

18.

19.

1855. No letters in corners.
66a. 14. 4d. red .. .. .. £600 40·00
70. 18. 6d. lilac .. .. .. £500 40·00
72. 19. 1s. green £650 £140

7.

5.

8.

6.

1858. Letters in four corners.
48. 7. ½d. red .. .. .. 45·00 6·00
43. 5. 1d. red .. .. .. 4·50 50
51. 8. 1½d. red .. .. .. £175 20·00
46. 6. 2d. blue .. .. .. £150 6·00

21.

22.

23.

24.

25.

1862. Small white letters in corners.
77 21. 3d. red £700 £100
80 22. 4d. red .. .. .. £500 35·00
84 23. 6d. lilac .. .. .. £650 30·00
87 24. 9d. bistre £1100 £130
90 25. 1s. green .. .. .. £700 65·00

30.

32.

1865. Designs as 1862 and T 30 and 32, but large white letters in coners.
103 21 3d. red .. .. £200 12·00
94 22 4d. red .. .. £225 15·00
97 23 6d. lilac (with hyphen) £350 28·00
109 6d. lilac (without hyphen) .. .. £275 25·00
110 24 9d. straw £600 £100
112 30 10d. brown £1000 £130
117 25 1s. green .. .. £350 10·00
118 32 2s. blue .. .. £950 60·00
121 2s. brown £6000 £1000

35.

38.

1867.
126. 35. 5s. red £2500 £275
128. – 10s. green £18000 £850
129. – £1 brown £22000 £1200
137. 38. £5 orange £4250 £1200

The 10s. and £1 are as Type 35, but have different frames.

34.

1872. Large white letters in corners.
123. 34. 6d. brown .. .. £350 18·00
125. 6d. grey .. .. .. £600 80·00

41.

46.

1873. Large coloured letters in corners.
141 41 2½d. mauve .. .. £225 14·00
157 2½d. blue .. .. £180 8·00
143 21 3d. red .. .. £200 12·00
152 22 4d. red £600 £140
153 4d. green .. .. £400 90·00
160 4d. brown .. .. £180 25·00
161 34 6d. grey .. .. £150 25·00
156 46 8d. orange £550 £110
150 25 1s. green .. .. £250 28·00
163 1s. brown .. .. £225 45·00

The 3d., 4d. and 1s. are as 1862, and the 6d. as Type 34, but all with large coloured letters.

52.

53.

1880. Various frames.
164. 52. ½d. green .. .. 15·00 3·00
187. ½d. blue .. .. 8·00 1·50
166. 53. 1d. brown .. .. 5·00 2·00
167. – 1½d. brown .. .. 80·00 14·00
168. – 2d. red .. .. 95·00 30·00
169. – 5d. blue .. .. £350 45·00

57.

58.

61.

1881.
173 57 1d. lilac .. .. 1·00 30

1883. Types, as 1873, surch. **3d.** or **6d.**
159. 21. 3d. on 3d. lilac .. .. £225 70·00
162. 34. 6d. on 6d. lilac .. .. £200 70·00

1883.
178. 58. 2s. 6d. lilac .. .. £200 65·00
180. – 5s. red .. .. £400 80·00
183. – 10s. blue £750 £225
185. 61. £1 brown £10000 £850
212. £1 green £2000 £350

The 5s. and 10s. are similar to Type 58, but have different frames.

62.

63.

1883. Various frames.
188. 62. 1½d. purple .. .. 55·00 18·00
189. 63. 2d. purple .. .. 70·00 30·00
190. 2½d. purple .. .. 40·00 5·00
191. 62. 3d. purple .. .. 90·00 40·00
192. 4d. green .. .. £225 95·00
193. 5d. green .. .. £225 95·00
194. 63. 6d. green £250 £100
195. 9d. green £475 £225
196. 62. 1s. green £350 £130

71. 72. 73. 74. 75. 76. 77. 78. 79. 80. 81. 82.

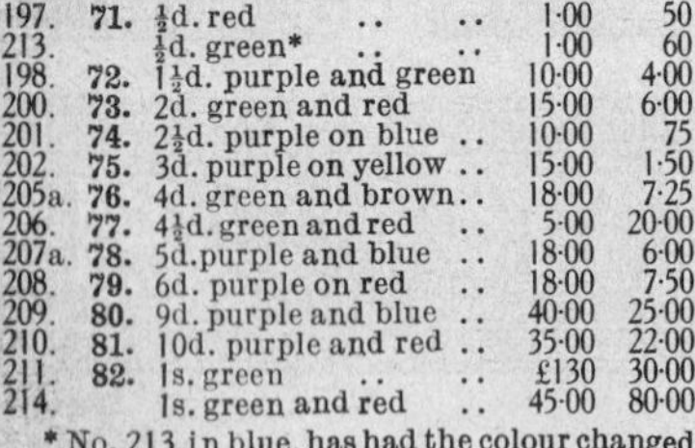

1887.

197.	**71.**	½d. red	1·00	50
213.		½d. green*	1·00	60
198.	**72.**	1½d. purple and green	10·00	4·00
200.	**73.**	2d. green and red	15·00	6·00
201.	**74.**	2½d. purple on blue ..	10·00	75
202.	**75.**	3d. purple on yellow ..	15·00	1·50
205a.	**76.**	4d. green and brown ..	18·00	7·25
206.	**77.**	4½d. green and red ..	5·00	20·00
207a.	**78.**	5d. purple and blue ..	18·00	6·00
208.	**79.**	6d. purple on red ..	18·00	7·50
209.	**80.**	9d. purple and blue ..	40·00	25·00
210.	**81.**	10d. purple and red ..	35·00	22·00
211.	**82.**	1s. green	£130	30·00
214.		1s. green and red ..	45·00	80·00

* No. 213, in blue, has had the colour changed after issue.

83.

90.

1902. Designs not shown are as 1887 (2s. 6d. to £1 as 1883) but with portrait of King Edward VII.

217	**83**	½d. green	40	30
219		1d. red	40	30
222	–	1½d. purple and green	10·00	4·75
291	–	2d. green and red ..	10·00	5·00
231	**83**	2½d. blue	4·00	2·50
232	–	3d. purple on yellow ..	15·00	2·50
236a	–	4d. green and brown ..	15·00	7·00
240	–	4d. orange	7·50	6·50
294	–	5d. purple and blue ..	10·00	4·75
246	**83**	6d. purple	12·00	4·00
249	**90**	7d. grey	3·00	6·00
307	–	9d. purple and blue ..	30·00	22·00
311	–	10d. purple and red ..	30·00	20·00
314	–	1s. green and red ..	25·00	8·00
260	–	2s. 6d. purple	£100	45·00
263	–	5s. red	£100	55·00
319	–	10s. blue	£300	£200
320	–	£1 green	£750	£300

98. (Hair heavy).

99. (Lion unshaded).

1911.

322	**98.**	½d. green	2·50	1·00
327	**99.**	1d. red	2·25	1·00

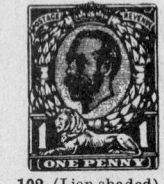

101. (Hair light). 102. (Lion shaded).

1912.

344	**101**	½d. green	2·50	70
341	**102**	1d. red	1·25	30

104.

105.

106.

107.

108.

109.

1912. Lined background.

418	**105**	½d. green	15	25
419	**104**	1d. red	15	25
420	**105**	1½d. brown	15	25
368	**106**	2d. orange	1·00	50
422	**104**	2½d. blue	3·00	1·25
375	**106**	3d. violet	2·00	75
379		4d. green	4·00	75
381	**107**	5d. brown	3·50	3·00
426a		6d. purple	1·50	50
387		7d. green	6·00	3·75
390		8d. black on yellow ..	15·00	6·50
392	**108**	9d. black	5·00	2·25
427		9d. green	5·00	2·25
394		10d. blue	9·00	12·00
429		1s. brown	10·00	1·00
450	**109**	2s. 6d. brown	40·00	15·00
451		5s. red	90·00	50·00
452		10s. blue	£225	50·00
403		£1 green	£950	£600

112.

1924. British Empire Exn. Dated "1924".

430.	**112.**	1d. red	5·00	6·00
431.		1½d. brown	7·50	11·00

1925. Dated "1925".

432.	**112.**	1d. red	8·00	17·00
433.		1½d. brown	25·00	50·00

113.

114.

115.

116. St. George and the Dragon.

1929. 9th U.P.U. Congress, London.

434.	**113.**	½d. green	1·50	1·50
435.	**114.**	1d. red	1·50	1·50
436.		1½d. brown	1·00	1·00
437.	**115.**	2½d. blue	7·50	9·00
438.	**116.**	£1 black	£550	£400

118.

119.

120.

121.

122.

1934. Solid background.

439.	**118.**	½d. green	10	25
440.	**119.**	1d. red	10	25
441.	**118.**	1½d. brown	10	25
442.	**120.**	2d. orange	25	25
443.	**119.**	2½d. blue	75	60
444.	**120.**	3d. violet	75	50
445.		4d. green	1·00	55
446.	**121.**	5d. brown	4·00	1·50
447.	**122.**	9d. olive	10·00	1·60
448.		10d. blue	12·00	8·00
449.		1s. brown	12·00	50

123.

1935. Silver Jubilee.

453.	**123.**	½d. green	25	20
454.		1d. red	1·00	1·00
455.		1½d. brown	25	20
456.		2½d. blue	4·00	5·50

Emblems at right differ.

124. King Edward VIII.

1936.

457.	**124.**	½d. green	20	15
458.		1d. red	50	20
459.		1½d. brown	25	15
460.		2½d. blue	25	60

126. King George VI and Queen Elizabeth.

1937. Coronation.

461.	**126.**	1½d. brown	40	25

128. 129.

130. 131. King George VI.

1937.

462	**128**	½d. green	10	15
503		½d. orange	10	15
463		1d. red	10	15
504		1d. blue	15	15
464		1½d. brown	20	15
505		1½d. green	25	30
488		2d. orange	50	40
506		2d. brown	25	20
489		2½d. blue	15	10
507		2½d. red	20	15
490		3d. violet	1·90	50
468	**129**	4d. green	35	40
508		4d. blue	1·90	1·10
469		5d. brown	2·75	35
470		6d. purple	1·50	40
471	**130**	7d. green	3·75	50
472		8d. red	4·50	50
473		9d. green	6·00	50
474		10d. blue	5·50	60
474a		11d. purple	2·50	1·50
475		1s. brown	6·25	40

1939.

476	**131**	2s. 6d. brown ..	40·00	7·00
476a		2s. 6d. green ..	9·00	1·00
477		5s. red	18·00	1·50
478a	–	10s. blue	40·00	4·50
478b	–	£1 brown	15·00	19·00

The 10s. and £1 values have the portrait in the centre in an ornamental frame.

134. Queen Victoria and King George VI.

1940. Cent. of First Adhesive Postage Stamps.

479.	**134.**	½d. green	30	20
480.		1d. red	90	40
481.		1½d. brown	30	30
482.		2d. orange	50	40
483.		2½d. blue	1·90	80
484.		3d. violet	4·00	3·50

135.

1946. Victory Commemoration.

491.	**135.**	2½d. blue	25	15
492.	–	3d. violet	25	15

DESIGN—HORIZ. 3d. Symbols of Peace and Reconstruction.

137.

138. King George VI and Queen Elizabeth.

1948. Royal Silver Wedding.

493. 137.	2½d. blue	.. ..	30	30
494. 138.	£1 blue	.. ..	32·00	32·00

139. Globe and Laurel Wreath.

140. "Speed".

1948. Olympic Games. Inscr. "OLYMPIC GAMES 1948".

495. 139.	2½d. blue	.. ..	10	10
496. 140.	3d. violet	.. ..	30	30
497. –	6d. purple	.. ..	60	30
498. –	1s. brown	.. ..	1·25	1·50

DESIGNS: 6d. Olympic symbol. 1s. Winged Victory.

143. Two Hemispheres.

144. U.P.U. Monument, Berne.

1949. 75th Anniv. of U.P.U. Inscr. as in T 143/4.

499. 143.	2½d. blue	.. ..	10	10
500. 144.	3d. violet	.. ..	30	40
501. –	6d. purple	.. ..	60	75
502. –	1s. brown	.. ..	1·25	1·50

DESIGNS: 6d. Goddess Concordia, globe and points of compass, 1s. Posthorn and globe.

147. H.M.S. "Victory".

1951.

509. 147.	2s. 6d. green	.. ..	8·00	75
510. –	5s. red	.. ..	30·00	1·50
511. –	10s. blue	.. ..	18·00	10·00
512. –	£1 brown	.. ..	40·00	14·00

DESIGNS; 5s. White Cliffs of Dover. 10s. St. George and dragon. £1, Royal Coat of Arms.

152. Festival Symbol.

1951. Festival of Britain.

513. –	2½d. red	.. ..	25	15
514. 152.	4d. blue	.. ..	50	45

DESIGN; 2½d. Britannia, cornucopia and Mercury.

154. 155.

157.

158.

159.

Queen Elizabeth II and National Emblems.

1952.

570 154.	½d. orange	.. ..	10	10
571	1d. blue	.. ..	10	10
517	1½d. green	.. ..	10	15
573	2d. brown	.. ..	10	10
574 155.	2½d. red	.. ..	10	10
575	3d. lilac	.. ..	10	10
576a	4d. blue	.. ..	15	10
577	4½d. brown	.. ..	10	15
578 157.	5d. brown	.. ..	25	20
579	6d. purple	.. ..	25	15
580	7d. green	.. ..	40	20
617b 158.	8d. mauve	.. ..	20	25
582	9d. olive	.. ..	40	15
583	10d. blue	.. ..	1·00	15
553	11d. plum	.. ..	40	1·00
584 159.	1s. bistre	.. ..	40	15
585	1s. 3d. green	.. ..	25	15
618a	1s. 6d. blue	.. ..	2·00	1·00

The 4d., 4½d. and 1s. 3d. values are printed with colour tones reversed.

Stamps with either one or two vertical black lines on the back were issued in 1957 in connection with the Post Office automatic facing machine experiment in the Southampton area. Later the lines were replaced by almost invisible phosphor bands on the face, in the above and later issues. They are listed in the Stanley Gibbons British Commonwealth Catalogue.

161.

163.

1953. Coronation. Portraits of Queen Elizabeth II.

532. 161.	2½d. red	.. ..	10	25
533. –	4d. blue	.. ..	40	1·50
534. 163.	1s. 3d. green	.. ..	3·50	2·50
535. –	1s. 6d. blue	.. ..	6·00	3·50

DESIGNS: 4d. Coronation and National Emblems. 1s. 6d. Crowns and Sceptres dated "2 JUNE 1953".

166. Carrickfergus Castle.

1955.

595a. 166.	2s. 6d. brown	.. ..	50	30
596a. –	5s. red	.. ..	1·00	60
597a. –	10s. blue	.. ..	2·50	3·00
762. –	£1 black	.. ..	4·00	4·00

CASTLES: 5s. Caernarvon. 10s. Edinburgh. £1, Windsor.

170. Scout Badge and "Rolling Hitch".

171. "Scouts coming to Britain".

1957. World Scout Jubilee Jamboree.

557. 170.	2½d. red	.. ..	15	10
558. 171.	4d. blue	.. ..	50	1·00
559. –	1s. 3d. green	.. ..	4·50	4·50

DESIGN: 1s. 3d. Globe within a compass.

1957. Inter-Parliamentary Union Confrence. As No. 576a but inscr "46th PARLIAMENTARY CONFERENCE".

560	4d. blue	.. .. ..	1·00	1·00

176. Welsh Dragon.

1958. 6th British Empire and Commonwealth Games, Cardiff. Inscr. as in T 176.

567. 176.	3d. lilac	.. ..	15	10
568. –	6d. mauve	.. ..	25	45
569. –	1s. 3d. green	.. ..	2·25	2·25

DESIGNS: 6d. Flag and Games Emblem. 1s. 3d. Welsh Dragon.

180. Postboy of 1660.

181. Posthorn of 1660.

1960. "General Letter Office" Tercent.

619. 180.	3d. lilac	.. ..	20	10
620. 181.	1s. 3d. green	.. ..	3·50	3·50

182. Conference Emblem.

1960. 1st Anniversary of European Postal and Telecommunications Conference.

621. 182.	6d. green and purple	40	60
622.	1s. 6d. brown and blue	5·00	4·50

184. "Growth of Savings".

1961. Cent. of Post Office Savings Bank. Inscr. "POST OFFICE SAVINGS BANK".

623. –	2½d. black and red	..	10	10
624. 184.	3d. brown and violet	..	10	10
625. –	1s. 6d. red and blue	..	2·25	2·00

DESIGNS—VERT. 2½d. Thrift plant. HORIZ. 1s. 6d. Thrift plant.

186. C.E.P.T. Emblem.

187. Doves and emblem.

1961. Europa.

626. 186.	2d. orge., pink & brn.	10	10
627. 187.	4d. buff, mauve & blue	20	10
628. –	10d. turq., green & blue	40	35

DESIGN: 10d. As 4d. but arranged differently.

189. Hammer Beam Roof, Westminster Hall.

1961. 7th Commonwealth Parliamentary Conference.

629. 189.	6d. purple and gold	..	25	25
630. –	1s. 3d. green and blue		2·50	2·00

DESIGN—VERT. 1s. 3d. Palace of Westminster.

191. "Units of Productivity".

1962. National Productivity Year.

631. 191.	2½d. green and red	..	20	10
632. –	3d. blue and violet	..	25	10
633. –	1s. 3d. red, blue & grn.		1·75	1·60

DESIGNS: 3d. Arrows over map. 1s. 3d. Arrows in formation.

194. Campaign Emblem and Family.

1963. Freedom from Hunger.

634. 194.	2½d. red and pink	..	10	10
635. –	1s. 3d. brown and yell.		2·00	1·75

DESIGN: 1s. 3d. Children of three races.

196. "Paris Conference".

1963. Centenary of Paris Postal Conf.

636. 196.	6d. green and mauve	..	50	40

197. Posy of Flowers.

1963. National Nature Week. Multicoloured.

637.	3d. Type 197	..	25	20
638.	4½d. Woodland life	..	40	40

199. Rescue at Sea.

1963. 9th Int. Lifeboat Conference, Edinburgh. Multicoloured.
639. 2½d. Type **199** 10 10
640. 4d. 19th-cent. Lifeboat .. 40 30
641. 1s. 6d. Lifeboatmen .. 2·50 2·50

202. Red Cross.

1963. Red Cross Centenary Congress.
642. **202.** 3d. red and lilac .. 10 10
643. – 1s. 3d. red, blue & grey 2·75 2·50
644. – 1s. 6d. red, bl. & bistre 2·50 2·50
DESIGNS: Nos. 643/4 are as Type **202** but differently arranged.

205. Commonwealth Cable.

1963. COMPAC (Trans-Pacific Telephone Cable). Opening.
645. **205.** 1s. 6d. blue and black 2·50 2·25

206. Puck and Bottom. ("A Midsummer Night's Dream").

210. Hamlet contemplating Yorick's skull ("Hamlet") and Queen Elizabeth II.

1964. Shakespeare Festival.
646. **206.** 3d. multicoloured .. 10 10
647. – 6d. multicoloured .. 20 30
648. – 1s. 3d. multicoloured .. 90 1·00
649. – 1s. 6d. multicoloured .. 1·25 1·00
650. **210.** 2s. 6d. slate-purple .. 2·00 2·00
DESIGNS—As Type **206**: 6d. Feste ("Twelfth Night"). 1s. 3d. Balcony Scene ("Romeo and Juliet"). 1s. 6d. "Eve of Agincourt" ("Henry V").

211. Flats near Richmond Park.

1964. 20th Int. Geographical Congress, London. Multicoloured.
651. 2½d. Type **211** 10 10
652. 4d. Shipbuilding yards, Belfast 25 25
653. 8d. Beddgelert Forest Park, Snowdonia 60 50
654. 1s. 6d. Nuclear reactor, Dounreay .. .. 3·25 3·25
The designs represent "Urban development", "Industrial activity", "Forestry" and "Technological development" respectively.

215. Spring Gentian.

1964. 10th Int. Botanical Congress, Edinburgh. Multicoloured.
655. 3d. Type **215** 10 10
656. 6d. Dog Rose 20 20
657. 9d. Honeysuckle .. .. 1·60 2·00
658. 1s. 3d. Fringed Water Lily 2·50 1·90

219. Forth Road Bridge.

1964. Opening of Forth Road Bridge.
659. **219.** 3d. black, blue & violet 15 10
660. – 6d. black, blue & red .. 45 40
DESIGN: 6d. Forth Road and Railway Bridges.

221. Sir Winston Churchill.

1965. Churchill Commem.
661. **221.** 4d. black and drab .. 15 10
662. – 1s. 3d. black and grey 45 30
The 1s. 3d. shows a closer view of Churchill's head.

222. Simon de Montfort's Seal.

1965. 700th Anniversary of Simon de Montfort's Parliament.
663. **222.** 6d. olive 10 10
664. – 2s. 6d. blk., grey & drab 1·25 1·25
DESIGN: (58½ × 21½ mm.): 2s. 6d. Parliament buildings (after engraving by Hollar, 1647).

224. Bandsmen and Banner.

1965. Cent. of Salvation Army. Mult.
665. 3d. Type **224** 10 10
666. 1s. 6d. Three Salvationists 1·00 1·00

226. Lister's Carbolic Spray.

1965. Centenary of Joseph Lister's Discovery of Antiseptic Surgery.
667. **226.** 4d. blue, brown & grey 10 10
668. – 1s. black, purple & blue 1·00 1·25
DESIGN: 1s. Lister and chemical symbols.

228. Trinidad Carnival Dancers.

1965. Commonwealth Arts Festival.
669. **228.** 6d. black and orange.. 10 10
670. – 1s. 6d. black and violet 1·25 1·50
DESIGN: 1s. 6d. Canadian folk-dancers.

230. Flight of Spitfires.

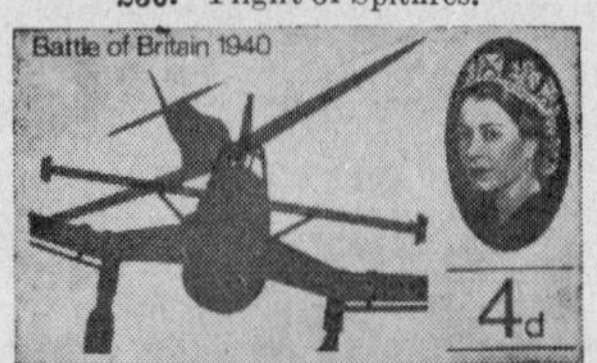

234. Spitfire attacking Stuka Dive-bomber.

1965. 25th Anniv. of Battle of Britain. Inscr. "Battle of Britain 1940".
671 **230.** 4d. olive and black .. 30 35
672 – 4d. olive and black .. 30 35
673 – 4d. multicoloured .. 30 35
674 – 4d. olive and black .. 30 35
675 **234.** 4d. olive and black .. 30 35
676 – 4d. multicoloured .. 30 35
677p – 9d. violet, orange and purple .. .. 1·25 80
678p – 1s. 3d. grey, blk. & blue 1·25 80
DESIGNS: No. 672, Pilot in Hurricane. No. 673, Wing-tips of Spitfire and Messerschmitt "ME-109". No. 674, Spitfires attacking Heinkel "HE-111" bomber. No. 676, Hurricanes over wreck of Dornier "DO-17z2" bomber. 9d. Anti-aircraft artillery in action. 1s. 3d. Air battle over St. Paul's Cathedral.

239. Tower and "Nash" Terrace, Regent's Park.

1965. Opening of Post Office Tower.
679 – 3d. yell., blue & green 10 10
680p **239.** 1s. 3d. green and blue 50 50
DESIGN—VERT. 3d. Tower and Georgian Buildings.

240. U.N. Emblem.

1965. 20th Anniv. of U.N.O. and Int. Co-operation Year.
681. **240.** 3d. black, orge. & blue 15 20
682. – 1s. 6d. blk., pur. & blue 1·10 90
DESIGN: 1s. 6d. I.C.Y. Emblem.

242. Telecommunications Network.

1965. Centenary of I.T.U. Multicoloured.
683. 9d. Type **242** 20 20
684. 1s. 6d. Radio waves and switchboard .. .. 1·40 1·10

244. Robert Burns (after Skirving chalk drawing).

1966. Burns Commem.
685. **244.** 4d. black, indigo & blue 15 15
686. – 1s. 3d. blk., bl. & orge. 70 70
DESIGN: 1s. 3d. Robert Burns (after Nasmyth portrait).

246. Westminster Abbey.

1966. 900th Anniv. of Westminster Abbey.
687. **246.** 3d. black, brown & blue 15 10
688. – 2s. 6d. black 85 90
DESIGN: 2s. 6d. Fan Vaulting, Henry VII Chapel.

248. View near Hassocks, Sussex.

1966. Landscapes.
689 **248.** 4d. blk., grn. & bl. .. 15 15
690 – 6d. blk., grn. & bl. .. 15 15
691 – 1s. 3d. black, yellow and blue 35 35
692 – 1s. 6d. black, orange & blue 50 50
VIEWS: 6d. Antrim, Northern Ireland. 1s. 3d. Harlech Castle, Wales. 1s. 6d. Cairngorm Mountains, Scotland.

253. Goalmouth Melee.

1966. World Cup Football Competition. Multicoloured.
693. 4d. Players with ball (vert.) 15 10
694. 6d. Type **253** 20 20
695. 1s. 3d. Goalkeeper saving goal 50 50

255. Black-headed Gull.

1966. British Birds. Multicoloured.
696. 4d. Type **255** 10 15
697. 4d. Blue tit 10 15
698. 4d. European robin .. 10 15
699. 4d. Blackbird 10 15

1966. England's World Cup Football Victory. As No. 693 but inscr. "ENGLAND WINNERS".
700. – 4d. multicoloured .. 20 20

260. Jodrell Bank Radio Telescope.

1966. British Technology.
701. **260.** 4d. black and lemon.. 15 15
702. – 6d. red, blue & orange 15 15
703. – 1s. 3d. multicoloured.. 30 40
704. – 1s. 6d. multicoloured.. 50 45
DESIGNS: 6d. British Motor-Cars. 1s. 3d. SRN 6 Hovercraft. 1s. 6d. Windscale Reactor.

264.

265.

1966. 900th Anniv. of Battle of Hastings. Multicoloured.
705. 4d. Type **264** 10 15
706. 4d. Type **265** 10 15
707. 4d. "Yellow" horse .. 10 15
708. 4d. "Blue" horse .. 10 15
709. 4d. "Purple" horse .. 10 15
710. 4d. "Grey" horse .. 10 15
711. 6d. Norman ship .. 10 10
712. 1s. 3d. Norman horsemen attacking Harold's Troops (59 × 22½ mm.) .. 20 20

272. King of the Orient.

1966. Christmas. Multicoloured.
713. 3d. Type **272** 10 10
714. 1s. 6d. Snowman .. 35 35

274. Sea Freight.

1967. European Free Trade Assn. (EFTA). Multicoloured

715.	9d. Type **274**	15	15
716.	1s. 6d. Air Freight ..	30	30

276. Hawthorn and Bramble.

1967. British Wild Flowers. Multicoloured.

717p	4d. Type **276**	10	10
718p	4d. Larger Bindweed and Viper's Buglos(s)	10	10
719p	4d. Ox-eye Daisy, Coltsfoot and Buttercup ..	10	10
720p	4d. Bluebell, Red Campion and Wood Anemone ..	10	10
721p	9d. Dog Violet	10	10
722	1s. 9d. Primroses	20	20

282.

1967.

723 **282.**	½d. brown	10	20
724	1d. olive	10	10
726	2d. brown	10	15
729	3d. violet	10	10
731	4d. sepia	10	10
733	4d. red..	10	10
735	5d. blue	10	10
736	6d. purple	20	20
737	7d. green	40	30
738	8d. red..	15	30
739	8d. turquoise	45	50
740	9d. green	50	30
741	10d. drab	45	50
742	1s. violet	40	30
743	1s. 6d. blue and indigo	50	30
744	1s. 9d. orange & black	40	30

For decimal issue, see Nos. X841 etc.

284. "Mares and Foals in a Landscape" (George Stubbs).

1967. British Paintings.

748. –	4d. multicoloured ..	10	10
749. **284.**	9d. multicoloured ..	20	20
750. –	1s. 6d. multicoloured	35	25

PAINTINGS—VERT. 4d. "Master Lambton" (Sir Thomas Lawrence). HORIZ. 1s. 6d. "Children Coming Out of School" L. S. Lowry).

286. Gipsy Moth IV.

1967. Sir Francis Chichester's World Voyage.

751. **286.**	1s. 9d. multicoloured..	25	25

287. Radar Screen.

1967. British Discovery and Invention. Mult.

752	4d. Type **287**	10	10
753	1s. "Penicillium notatum"	10	10
754	1s. 6d. "VC-10" jet engines	25	15
755	1s. 9d. Television equipment	30	20

292. "Madonna and Child" (Murillo).

1967. Christmas.

756. –	3d. multicoloured ..	10	10
757. **292.**	4d. multicoloured ..	10	10
758. –	1s. 6d. multicoloured..	35	35

PAINTINGS—VERT. 3d. "The Adoration of the Shepherds" (School of Seville). HORIZ. 1s. 6d. "The Adoration of the Shepherds" (Louis Le Nain).

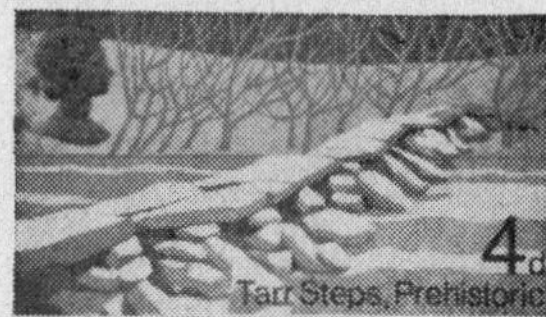

294. Tarr Steps, Exmoor.

1968. British Bridges. Multicoloured.

763.	4d. Type **294**	10	10
764.	9d. Aberfeldy Bridge ..	10	10
765.	1s. 6d. Menai Bridge ..	20	15
766.	1s. 9d. M4 Viaduct ..	25	30

298. "T U C" and Trades Unionists.

1968. British Annivs. Events described on stamps.

767. **298.**	4d. multicoloured ..	10	10
768. –	9d. violet, grey & black	10	10
769. –	1s. multicoloured ..	20	20
770. –	1s. 9d. ochre & brown	25	25

DESIGNS: 9d. Mrs. Emmeline Pankhurst (statue). 1s. Sopwith "Camel" and Lightning Fighters. 1s. 9d. Captain Cook's "Endeavour" and Signature.

302. "Queen Elizabeth I" (Unknown Artist).

1968. British Paintings.

771. **302.**	4d. multicoloured ..	10	10
772. –	1s. multicoloured ..	15	15
773. –	1s. 6d. multicoloured..	20	20
774. –	1s. 9d. multicoloured..	25	25

PAINTINGS—VERT. 1s. "Pinkie" (Lawrence). 1s. 6d., "Ruins of St. Mary Le Port" (Piper). HORIZ. 1s. 9d., "The Hay Wain" (Constable).

306. Boy and Girl with Rocking Horse.

1968. Christmas. Multicoloured.

775.	4d. Type **306**	10	10
776.	9d. Girl with Doll's House	15	15
777.	1s. 6d. Boy with Train Set	25	25

Nos. 776/7 are vert.

310. Elizabethan Galleon.

1969. British Ships. Multicoloured.

778.	5d. R.M.S. "Queen Elizabeth 2"	10	10
779.	9d. Type **310**	10	15
780.	9d. East Indiaman ..	10	15
781.	9d. "Cutty Sark" ..	10	15
782.	1s. S.S. "Great Britain"	25	25
783.	1s. R.M.S. "Mauretania"	25	25

Nos. 778 and 782/3 are 58 × 23 mm.

315. "Concorde" in Flight.

1969. 1st Flight of "Concorde".

784. **315.**	4d. multicoloured ..	10	10
785. –	9d. multicoloured ..	20	20
786. –	1s. 6d. indigo, grey and blue	30	30

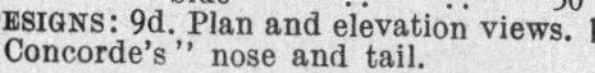
DESIGNS: 9d. Plan and elevation views. 1s. 6d. "Concorde's" nose and tail.

318. Queen Elizabeth II.

1969.

787. **318.**	2s. 6d. brown.. ..	50	30
788.	5s. lake	2·25	60
789.	10s. blue	7·00	7·50
790.	£1 black	3·00	1·60

For decimal issues see Nos. 829/31b.

No. 790 has an italic "£". For later version with roman "£" see No. 831b.

319. Page from "Daily Mail", and Vickers "Vimy" Aircraft.

1969. Annivs. Events described on stamps.

791. **319.**	5d. multicoloured ..	10	10
792. –	9d. multicoloured ..	20	20
793. –	1s. claret, red and blue	20	20
794. –	1s. 6d. multicoloured..	20	20
795. –	1s. 9d. turquoise, yellow and sepia ..	25	25

DESIGNS: 9d. Europa and C.E.P.T. Emblems. 1s. I.L.O. Emblem. 1s. 6d., Flags of N.A.T.O. countries. 1s. 9d., Vickers "Vimy" Aircraft and globe showing Flight.

324. Durham Cathedral.

1969. British Architecture (Cathedrals). Multicoloured.

796.	5d. Type **324**	10	10
797.	5d. York Minster	10	10
798.	5d. St. Giles' Cathedral, Edinburgh	10	10
799.	5d. Canterbury Cathedral	10	10
800.	9d. St. Paul's Cathedral ..	15	15
801.	1s. 6d. Liverpool Metropolitan Cathedral ..	15	15

332. Queen Eleanor's Gate, Caernarvon Castle.

1969. Investiture of H.R.H. The Prince of Wales.

802. –	5d. multicoloured ..	10	10
803. –	5d. multicoloured ..	10	10
804. **332.**	5d. multicoloured ..	10	10
805. –	9d. multicoloured ..	20	10
806. –	1s. black and gold ..	20	10

DESIGNS: No. 802, The King's Gate, Caernarvon Castle. No. 803, The Eagle Tower, Caernarvon Castle. No. 805, Celtic Cross, Margam Abbey. No. 806, H.R.H. The Prince of Wales.

335. Mahatma Gandhi.

1969. Gandhi Centenary Year.

807. **335.**	1s. 6d. multicoloured..	30	30

336. National Giro "G" Symbol.

1969. Post Office Technology Commem.

808. **336.**	5d. multicoloured ..	10	10
809. –	9d. green, blue & black	15	15
810. –	1s. green, lav. & black	15	15
811. –	1s. 6d. pur., blue & blk.	40	40

DESIGNS: 9d. International Subscriber dialling (Telecommunications). 1s. Pulse Code Modulations (Telecommunications). 1s. 6d. Automatic Sorting (Postal Mechanisation).

340. Herald Angel.

1969. Christmas. Multicoloured.

812.	4d. Type **340**	10	10
813.	5d. The Three Shepherds	10	10
814.	1s. 6d. The Three Kings ..	30	30

343. Fife Harling.

1970. British Rural Architecture. Mult.

815.	5d. Type **343**	10	10
816.	9d. Cotswold Limestone ..	20	20
817.	1s. Welsh Stucco ..	20	20
818.	1s. 6d. Ulster Thatch ..	35	35

The 1s. and 1s. 6d. are larger (38 × 27 mm.).

347. Signing the Declaration of Arbroath.

1970. Anniversaries. Events described on stamps. Multicoloured.

819.	5d. Type **347**	10	10
820.	9d. Florence Nightingale attending patients ..	15	15
821.	1s. Signing of International Co-operative Alliance ..	25	15
822.	1s. 6d. Pilgrims and "Mayflower"	30	30
823.	1s. 9d. Sir William and Sir John Herschel, Francis Baily and Telescope ..	30	30

352. Mr Pickwick and Sam ("Pickwick Papers").

357. Queen Elizabeth II.

1970. Literary Annivs. Death Cent. of Charles Dickens (novelist) (5d × 4). Birth Bicent. of William Wordsworth (poet) (1s. 6d.) Multicoloured.

824. 5d. Type **352** 10 10
825. 5d. Mr. and Mrs. Micawber ("David Copperfield") 10 10
826. 5d. David Copperfield and Betsy Trotwood ("David Copperfield") 10 10
827. 5d. "Oliver asking for more" ("Oliver Twist") .. 10 10
828. 1s. 6d. "Grasmere" (from engraving by J. Farrington, R.A.) 20 20

1970. Decimal Currency. Designs as T **318**, but inscr. in decimal currency as T **357**.

829. **357.** 10p. red .. .. 1·00 75
830. 20p. green 70 15
831. 50p. blue .. .. 1·50 40
831b. £1 black .. .. 3·50 75

On No. 831b. the "£" is in roman type.

360. Cyclists.

1970. 9th British Commonwealth Games. Multicoloured.

832. 5d. Runners 10 10
833. 1s. 6d. Swimmers 50 50
834. 1s. 9d. Type **360** 50 50

361. 1d. Black (1840).

1970. "Philympia 70" Stamp Exn. Mult.

835. 5d. Type **361** 10 10
836. 9d. 1s. green (1847) .. 35 35
837. 1s. 6d. 4d. red (1855) .. 40 40

364. Shepherds and Apparition of the Angel.

1970. Christmas. Multicoloured.

838. 4d. Type **364** 10 10
839. 5d. Mary, Joseph, and Christ in the Manger .. 10 10
840. 1s. 6d. The Wise Men bearing Gifts 35 35

367.

1971. Decimal currency. As Nos. 723, etc., but new colours and with decimal figures of value, as in T **367**.

X841	½p. blue	10	10
X844	1p. red	10	10
X848	1½p. black	20	15
X926	2p. green	10	10
X1001	2p. light green & green	40	40
X851	2½p. mauve	15	10
X929	2½p. red	20	20
X855	3p. blue	20	10
X930c	3p. mauve	10	10
X859	3½p. grey	30	15
X931	3½p. brown	45	45
X861	4p. brown	20	20
X933	4p. blue	10	10
X865	4½p. blue	20	25
X866	5p. violet	20	10
X935	5p. brown	10	10
X869	5½p. violet	20	20
X870	6p. green	30	15
X936	6p. yellow	10	15
X872	6½p. blue	30	15
X875	7p. brown	35	20
X937	7p. red	1·50	2·00
X877	7½p. brown	30	25
X879	8p. red	25	15
X881	8½p. green	35	20
X882	9p. yellow and black ..	60	30
X883	9p. violet	45	25
X884	9½p. purple	45	30
X885	10p. brown & lt brown	40	30
X939	10p. brown	30	20
X940	10p. orange	15	15
X890	10½p. yellow	40	30
X891	10½p. blue	60	45
X892	11p. red	60	25
X893	11½p. drab	45	30
X942	11½p. brown	50	45
X943	12p. green	45	40
X898	12½p. green	45	25
X900	13p. brown	45	35
X944	13p. grey	60	45
X945	13½p. brown	65	60
X903	14p. blue	60	40
X905	15p. blue	25	20
X948	15½p. violet	50	40
X949	16p. brown	60	30
X950	16½p. brown	85	75
X951	17p. green	70	40
X952	17p. blue	50	40
X953	17½p. brown	80	80
X954	18p. violet	70	75
X955	18p. grey	70	60
X913	18p. green	30	35
X956	19p. red	60	40
X957	19½p. grey	1·75	1·50
X958	20p. purple	80	20
X959	20p. green	30	35
X960	20p. black	50	40
X961	20½p. blue	1·00	85
X962	22p. blue	80	45
X963	22p. green	60	55
X964	22p. orange	60	50
X965	23p. red	1·10	60
X966	23p. green	70	40
X967	24p. violet	1·75	85
X968	24p. red	1·00	80
X1053	24p. brown	35	40
X970	25p. purple	90	90
X971	26p. red	90	30
X972	26p. brown	70	70
X973	27p. brown	1·00	85
X974	27p. violet	75	75
X975	28p. violet	90	90
X976	28p. ochre	75	75
X977	28p. grey	45	50
X978	29p. brown	2·00	1·25
X979	29p. mauve	1·50	75
Y1674	29p. grey	45	50
X980	30p. grey	45	50
X981	31p. purple	1·25	1·25
X982	31p. blue	90	90
X983	32p. blue	1·00	1·00
X1057	33p. green	50	55
X985	34p. brown	1·10	80
X986	34p. grey	55	60
X987	34p. mauve	75	60
X988	35p. brown	1·25	75
X989	35p. yellow	55	60
Y1677	36p. blue	55	60
X990	37p. red	1·25	85
Y1678	38p. red	60	65
X991	39p. mauve	60	65
Y1679	41p. drab	65	70
X992	50p. brown	75	80
X993	75p. black	1·10	1·25
X1024	75p. grey and black ..	8·00	5·00

368. "A Mountain Road" (T. P. Flanagan).

1971. "Ulster '71" Festival. Paintings. Multicoloured.

881. 3p. Type **368** 10 10
882. 7½p. "Deer's Meadow" (Tom Carr) 50 50
883. 9p. "Slieve na brock" (Colin Middleton) 50 50

371. John Keats (150th Death Anniv.).

1971. Literary Annivs.

884. **371.** 3p. black, gold & blue 10 10
885. – 5p. black, gold & grn. 50 50
886. – 7½p. black, gold & brn. 50 50

DESIGNS AND ANNIVERSARIES: 5p. Thomas Gray (Death Bicent.). 7½p. Sir Walter Scott (Birth Bicent.).

374. Servicemen and Nurse of 1921.

1971. British Annivs. Events described on stamps. Multicoloured.

887. 3p. Type **374** 10 10
888. 7½p. Roman Centurion .. 50 50
889. 9p. Rugby Football, 1871 50 50

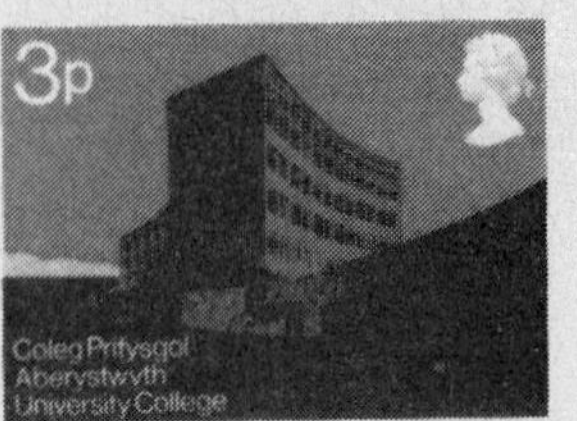

377. Physical Sciences Building, University College of Wales, Aberystwyth.

1971. British Architecture (Modern University Buildings).

890. **377.** 3p. multicoloured .. 10 10
891. – 5p. multicoloured .. 20 20
892. – 7½p. ochre, blk. & brn. 50 50
893. – 9p. multicoloured .. 90 90

DESIGNS: 5p. Faraday Building, Southampton University. 7½p. Engineering Department, Leicester University. 9p. Hexagon Restaurant, Essex University.

381. "Dream of the Wise Men".

1971. Christmas. Multicoloured.

894. 2½p. Type **381** 10 10
895. 3p. "Adoration of the Magi" 10 10
896. 7½p. "Ride of the Magi" 90 90

384. Sir James Clark Ross.

1972. British Polar Explorers. Multicoloured.

897. 3p. Type **384** 10 10
898. 5p. Sir Martin Frobisher 20 20
899. 7½p. Henry Hudson .. 50 50
900. 9p. Capt. Robert Scott .. 90 90

See also Nos. 923/7.

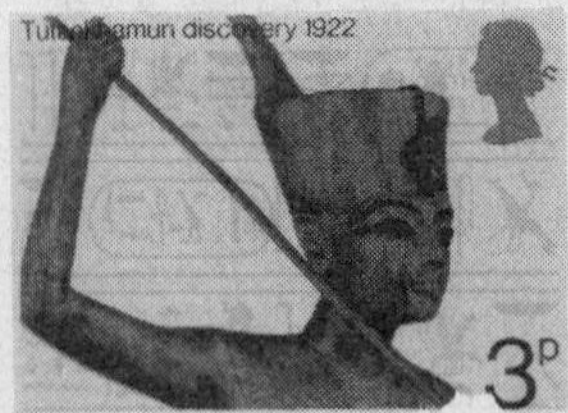

388. Statuette of Tutankhamun.

1972. General Anniversaries. Multicoloured.

901. 3p. Type **388** 10 10
902. 7½p. 19th-Century Coastguard 50 50
903. 9p. Ralph Vaughan Williams (composer) and Score 50 50

ANNIVERSARIES: 3p. Discovery of Tutankhamun's tomb. 50th Anniv. 7½p. Formation of H.M. Coastguard. 150th Anniv. 9p. Birth Cent.

391. St. Andrew's, Greensted-juxta-Ongar, Essex.

1972. British Architecture. Village Churches. Multicoloured.

904. 3p. Type **391** 10 10
905. 4p. All Saints, Earls Barton, Northants. 20 20
906. 5p. St. Andrew's, Letheringsett, Norfolk 20 25
907. 7½p. St. Andrew's, Helpringham, Lincs. 70 80
908. 9p. St. Mary the Virgin, Huish Episcopi, Somerset 75 90

396. Microphones, 1924-69.

1972. Broadcasting Annivs. Multicoloured.

909. 3p. Type **396** 10 10
910. 5p. Horn Loudspeaker .. 15 20
911. 7½p. T.V. Camera, 1972 60 60
912. 9p. Oscillator and Spark Transmitter, 1897 60 60

ANNIVERSARIES: Nos. 909/11, Daily Broadcasting by the B.B.C. 50th Anniv. No. 912, Marconi and Kemp's Radio Experiments. 75th Anniv.

400. Angel holding Trumpet.

1972. Christmas. Multicoloured.

913. 2½p. Type **400** 10 15
914. 3p. Angel playing Lute .. 10 15
915. 7½p. Angel playing Harp 90 80

403. Queen Elizabeth and Duke of Edinburgh.

1972. Royal Silver Wedding.

916. **403.** 3p. blk., blue & silver 20 20
917. 20p. blk., purple & silver 80 80

404. "Europe".

1973. Britain's Entry into European Communities.

919. **404.** 3p multicoloured .. 10 10
920. 5p. mult. (blue jig-saw) 25 35
921. 5p. mult. (green jig-saw) 25 35

405. Oak Tree.

1973. Tree Planting Year British Trees (1st issue).

922. **405.** 9 p. multicoloured .. 50 50
See also No. 949.

1973. British Explorers. As Type **384**. **Mult.**

923. 3p. David Livingstone .. 25 20
924. 3p. H. M. Stanley .. 25 20
925. 5p. Sir Francis Drake .. 20 30
926. 7½p. Sir Walter Raleigh .. 20 30
927. 9p. Charles Sturt 25 40

412. W. G. Grace.

1973. County Cricket 1873-1973. **Designs as T 412 showing caricatures of W. G. Grace by Harry Furniss.**

928. **412.** 3p. blk., brn. & gold.. 10 10
929. – 7½p. blk., grn. & gold.. 70 70
930. – 9p. blk., blue & gold 90 90

414. "Self-portrait" (Reynolds).

1973. British Paintings. 250th Birth Anniv. of Sir Joshua Reynolds, and 150th Death Anniv. of Sir Henry Raeburn. Multicoloured.

931. 3p. Type **414** 10 10
932. 5p. "Self-portrait" (Raeburn) .. 20 25
933. 7½p. "Nelly O' Brien" (Reynolds) .. 45 40
934. 9p. "Rev. R. Walker (The Skater)" (Raeburn) .. 50 50

418. Court Masque Costumes.

1973. 400th Birth. Anniv. of Inigo Jones (architect and designer). Multicoloured.

935. 3p. Type **418** .. 10 15
936. 3p. St. Paul's Church, Covent Garden 10 15
937. 5p. Prince's Lodging, Newmarket 40 45
938. 5p. Court Masque Stage Scene 40 45

422. Palace of Westminster, seen from Whitehall.

1973. 19th Commonwealth Parliamentary Conference.

939. **422.** 8p. stone, grey & black 50 60
940. – 10p. gold and black .. 50 40
DESIGN: 10p. Palace of Westminster, seen from Millbank.

424. Princess Anne and Capt. Mark Phillips.

1973. Royal Wedding.

941. **424.** 3½p. violet and silver .. 10 10
942. 20p. brown and silver 90 90

425. "Good King Wenceslas".

1973. Christmas. Designs as T **425** showing various scenes from the carol "Good King Wenceslas".

943. **425.** 3p. multicoloured .. 15 15
944. – 3p. multicoloured .. 15 15
945. – 3p. multicoloured .. 15 15
946. – 3p. multicoloured .. 15 15
947. – 3p. multicoloured .. 15 15
948. – 3½p. multicoloured .. 15 15

431. Horse Chestnut.

1974. British Trees (2nd issue).

949. **431.** 10p. multicoloured .. 50 50

432. First Motor Fire-engine, 1904.

1974. Bicentenary of Fire Prevention (Metropolis) Act. Multicoloured.

950. 3½p. Type **432** 10 10
951. 5½p. Prize-winning fire-engine, 1863 .. .. 25 25
952. 8p. First steam fire-engine, 1830 .. .. .. 35 35
953. 10p. Fire-engine, 1766 .. 40 40

436. P. & O. Packet, "Peninsular", 1888.

1974. Cent. of Universal Postal Union. Mult.

954. 3½p. Type **436** 10 10
955. 5½p. Farman Biplane, 1911 20 25
956. 8p. Airmail-blue van and postbox, 1930 .. .. 30 35
957. 10p. Imperial Airways "C" Class Flying-boat, 1937 50 40

440. Robert the Bruce.

1974. Medieval Warriors. Multicoloured.

958. 4½p. Type **440** 10 10
959. 5½p. Owain Glyndwr .. 20 20
960. 8p. Henry the Fifth .. 40 40
961. 10p. The Black Prince .. 40 40

444. Churchill in Royal Yacht Squadron Uniform.

1974. Birth Centenary of Sir Winston Churchill.

962. **444.** 4½p. silver, bl. & grn... 15 15
963. – 5½p. silver, brn. & grey 20 25
964. – 8p. silver, red & pink.. 50 50
965. – 10p. silver, brn. & stone 55 50
DESIGNS: 5½p. Prime Minister, 1940. 8p. Secretary for War and Air, 1919. 10p. War Correspondent, South Africa, 1899.

448. "Adoration of the Magi" (York Minster, c. 1355).

1974. Christmas. Church Roof Bosses. **Mult.**

966. 3½p. Type **448** 10 10
967. 4½p. "The Nativity" (St. Helen's Church, Norwich, c. 1480) 10 10
968. 8p. "Virgin and Child" (Ottery St. Mary Church, c. 1350) 45 45
969. 10p. "Virgin and Child" (Worcester Cathedral, c. 1224) 50 50

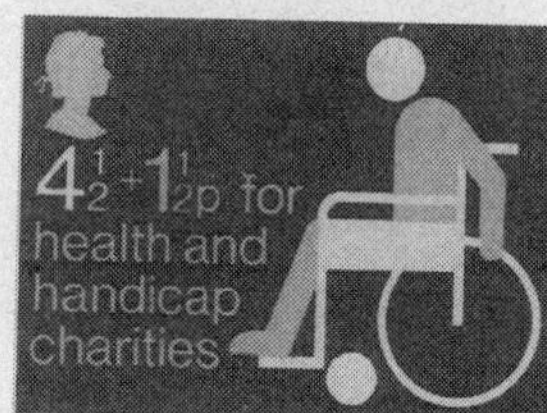

452. Invalid in Wheelchair.

1975. Health and Handicap Funds.

970. **452.** 4½p.+1½p. blue & azure 25 25

453. "Peace—Burial at Sea".

1975. Birth Bicentenary of J. M. W. Turner (painter).

971. 4½p. Type **453** 10 10
972. 5½p. "Snowstorm—Steamer off a Harbour's Mouth" 15 15
973. 8p. "The Arsenal, Venice" 40 40
974. 10p. "St. Laurent" .. 45 45

457. Charlotte Square, Edinburgh.

1975. European Architectural Heritage Year. Multicoloured.

975. 7p. Type **457** 30 30
976. 7p. The Rows, Chester .. 30 30
977. 8p. Royal Observatory, Greenwich .. 20 25
978. 10p. St. George's Chapel, Windsor 20 25
979. 12p. National Theatre, London 20 35

462. Sailing Dinghies.

1975. Sailing. Multicoloured.

980. 7p. Type **462** 20 20
981. 8p. Racing Keel Yachts .. 30 30
982. 10p. Cruising Yachts .. 30 30
983. 12p. Multihulls 35 35

466. Stephenson's "Locomotion", 1825.

1975. 150th Anniversary of Public Railways. Multicoloured.

984. 7p. Type **466** 20 20
985. 8p. "Abbotsford", 1876 25 25
986. 10p. "Caerphilly Castle", 1923 .. .. .. 30 30
987. 12p. High Speed Train, 1975 .. .. .. 35 35

470. Palace of Westminster.

1975. 62nd Inter-Parliamentary Union Conference.

988. **470.** 12p. multicoloured .. 50 50

471. Emma and Mr. Woodhouse ("Emma").

1975. Birth Bicentenary of Jane Austen (novelist). Multicoloured.

989. 8½p. Type **471** 20 20
990. 10p. Catherine Morland ("Northanger Abbey") 25 25
991. 11p. Mr. Darcy ("Pride and Prejudice") .. 30 30
992. 13p. Mary and Henry Crawford ("Mansfield Park") 35 35

475. Angels with Harp and Lute.

1975. Christmas. Multicoloured.

993. 6½p. Type **475** 20 15
994. 8½p. Angel with Mandolin 20 20
995. 11p. Angel with Horn 30 35
996. 13p. Angel with Trumpet 40 40

479. Housewife.

1976. Cent. of Telephone. Multicoloured.

997.	8½p. Type **479**	20	20
998.	10p. Policeman	25	25
999.	11p. District Nurse ..	30	30
1000.	13p. Industrialist ..	35	35

483. Hewing Coal (Thomas Hepburn).

1976. Industrial and Social Reformers. **Mult.**

1001.	8½p. Type **483**	20	20
1002.	10p. Machinery (Robert Owen)	25	25
1003.	11p. Chimney cleaning (Lord Shaftesbury) ..	30	30
1004.	13p. Hands clutching prison bars (Elizabeth Fry) ..	35	35

487. Benjamin Franklin (bust by Jean-Jacques Caffieri).

1976. Bicentenary of American Revolution.

1005. **487.**	11p. multicoloured ..	50	50

488. " Elizabeth of Glamis ".

1976. Centenary of Royal Nat. Rose Society. Multicoloured.

1006.	8½p. Type **488**	20	20
1007.	10p. " Grandpa Dickson "	30	30
1008.	11p. " Rosa Mundi " ..	45	50
1009.	13p. " Sweet Briar " ..	45	40

492. Archdruid.

1976. British Cultural Traditions. **Mult.**

1010.	8½p. Type **492**	20	20
1011.	10p. Morris dancing ..	25	25
1012.	11p. Scots piper	30	30
1013.	13p. Welsh harpist ..	35	35

The 8½p. and 13p. commemorate the 800th Anniv. of the Royal National Eisteddfod.

496. Woodcut from " The Canterbury Tales ".

1976. 500th Anniv. of British Printing. Multicoloured.

1014	8½p. Type **496**	20	20
1015	10p. Extract from "The Tretyse of Love" ..	25	25
1016	11p. Woodcut from "The Game and Playe of Chesse" by William Caxton	30	30
1017	13p. Early printing press	35	35

501. Angel with Crown.

1976. Christmas. English Medieval Embroidery. Mult.

1018.	6½p. Virgin and Child ..	15	15
1019.	8½p. Type **501** ..	20	20
1020.	11p. Angel appearing to Shepherds	35	35
1021.	13p. The Three Kings ..	40	40

504. Lawn Tennis.

1977. Racket Sports. Multicoloured.

1022.	8½p. Type **504**	20	20
1023.	10p. Table tennis ..	25	25
1024.	11p. Squash	30	30
1025.	13p. Badminton	35	35

508.

1977.

1026	**508**	£1 green and olive ..	3·00	20
1026b		£1·30 brown and blue	6·50	6·00
1026c		£1·33 mauve & black	6·50	6·00
1026d		£1·41 brown and blue	7·00	6·00
1026e		£1·50 olive and black	6·00	4·00
1026f		£1·60 brown and blue	6·00	6·00
1027		£2 green and brown	5·50	75
1028		£5 pink and blue ..	13·00	2·00

559. Steroids—Conformational Analysis.

1977. Centenary of Royal Institute of Chemistry. Multicoloured.

1029.	8½p. Type **509**	20	20
1030.	10p. Vitamin C molecular structure	30	30
1031.	11p. Starch chromatography graph	30	30
1032.	13p. Chemical model of salt crystal	30	30

513.

1977. Silver Jubilee. Multicoloured.

1033.	8½p. Type **513**	20	20
1034.	9p. Type **513**	25	25
1035.	10p. " Leaf " initials ..	25	25
1036.	11p. " Star " initials ..	30	30
1037.	13p. " Oak " initials ..	40	40

517. " Gathering of Nations ".

1977. Commonwealth Heads of Government Meeting, London.

1038. **517.**	13p. multicoloured ..	50	50

518. West European Hedgehog.

1977. British Wildlife. Multicoloured.

1039.	9p. Type **518**	25	20
1040.	9p. Brown Hare	25	20
1041.	9p. Eurasian Red Squirrel	25	20
1042.	9p. European Otter ..	25	20
1043.	9p. Eurasian Badger ..	25	20

523. " Three French Hens, Two Turtle Doves and a Partridge in a Pear Tree ".

1977. Christmas. " The Twelve Days of Christmas ". Multicoloured.

1044.	7p. Type **523**	15	15
1045.	7p. " Six Geese a-laying, Five Gold Rings, Four Colly Birds "	15	15
1046.	7p. " Eight Maids a-milking, Seven Swans a-Swimming "	15	15
1047.	7p. " Ten Pipers piping; Nine Drummers drumming "	15	15
1048.	7p. " Twelve Lords a-leaping, Eleven Ladies dancing "	15	15
1049.	9p. " A Partridge in a Pear Tree "	20	20

529. Oil—North Sea Production Platform.

1978. Energy Resources. Multicoloured.

1050.	9p. Type **529**	25	20
1051.	10½p. Coal—modern pithead	25	30
1052.	11p. Natural gas—flame rising from sea ..	30	30
1053.	13p. Electricity—nuclear power station and uranium atom	30	30

533. The Tower of London.

1978. British Architecture (Historic Buildings). Multicoloured.

1054.	9p. Type **533**	25	20
1055.	10½p. Holyroodhouse ..	25	30
1056.	11p. Caernarvon Castle ..	30	30
1057.	13p. Hampton Court Palace	30	30

537. State Coach.

1978. 25th Anniv. of Queen's Coronation.

1059. **537.**	9p. gold and blue ..	20	20
1060. –	10½p. gold and red ..	25	30
1061. –	11p. gold and green ..	30	30
1062. –	13p. gold and violet ..	35	30

DESIGNS: 10½p. St. Edward's Crown. **11p.** The Sovereign's Orb. 13p. Imperial State Crown.

541. Shire Horse.

1978. Horses. Multicoloured.

1063.	9p. Type **541**	20	20
1064.	10½p. Shetland Pony ..	25	25
1065.	11p. Welsh Pony ..	30	30
1066.	13p. Thoroughbred ..	35	35

545. " Penny-farthing " and 1884 Safety Bicycle.

1978. Centenaries of Cyclists' Touring Club and British Cycling Federation. Mult.

1067.	9p. Type **545**	20	20
1068.	10½p. 1920 Touring bicycles	25	25
1069.	11p. Modern small-wheeled bicycles ..	30	30
1070.	13p. 1978 Road-racers ..	35	35

549. Singing Carols round the Christmas Tree.

1978. Christmas. Carol-singing. **Mult.**

1071.	7p. Type **549**	20	20
1072.	9p. The Waits	25	25
1073.	11p. 18th-century carol singers	30	30
1074.	13p. " The Boar's Head Carol "	35	35

553. Old English Sheepdog.

1979. Dogs. Multicoloured.

1075.	9p. Type **553**	20	20
1076.	10½p. Welsh springer spaniel	30	30
1077.	11p. West Highland terrier	30	30
1078.	13p. Irish setter	30	30

557. Primrose.

1979. Spring Wild Flowers. Multicoloured.

1079. 9p. Type **557** 20 20
1080. 10½p. Daffodil 30 30
1081. 11p. Bluebell 30 30
1082. 13p. Snowdrop 30 30

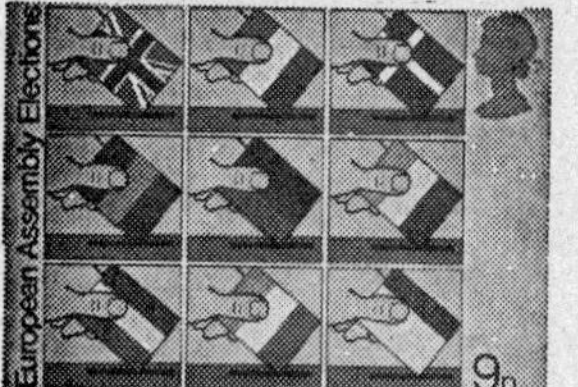

561. Hands placing National Flags into Ballot Boxes.

1979. First Direct Elections to European Assembly.

1083 **561.** 9p. multicoloured .. 20 20
1084 – 10½p. multicoloured 30 30
1085 – 11p. multicoloured .. 30 30
1086 – 13p. multicoloured .. 30 30

DESIGNS: Nos. 1084/6 differ from Type **561** in the position of the hands and flags.

565. "Saddling 'Mahmoud' for the Derby, 1936" (Sir Alfred Munnings).

1979. Horseracing paintings and Bicentenary of the Derby (9p). Multicoloured.

1087. 9p. Type **565** 25 25
1088. 10½p. "The Liverpool Great National Steeple Chase, 1839" (aquatint, F. C. Turner) 30 30
1089. 11p. "The First Spring Meeting, Newmarket, 1793" (J. N. Sartorius) 30 30
1090. 13p. "Racing at Dorsett Ferry, Windsor, 1684" (Francis Barlow) .. 30 30

569. "The Tale of Peter Rabbit" (Beatrix Potter).

1979. International Year of the Child. Multicoloured.

1091. 9p. Type **569** 35 20
1092. 10½p. "The Wind in the Willows" (Kenneth Grahame) .. 40 35
1093. 11p. "Winnie-the-Pooh" (A. A. Milne) .. 45 40
1094. 13p. "Alice's Adventures in Wonderland" (Lewis Carroll) .. 50 55

573. Sir Rowland Hill.

1979. Death Centenary of Sir Rowland Hill. Multicoloured.

1095. 10p. Type **573** 25 25
1096. 11½p. General Post, c. 1839 30 35
1097. 13p. London Post, c. 1839 35 40
1098. 15p. Uniform Postage, 1840 .. .. .. 50 40

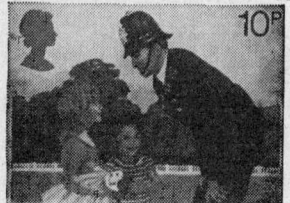

577. Policeman on the Beat.

1979. 150th Anniv. of Metropolitan Police. Multicoloured.

1100. 10p. Type **577** 25 25
1101. 11½p. Policeman directing Traffic 30 35
1102. 13p. Mounted Policewoman 35 40
1103. 15p. River Patrol Boat .. 50 40

581. The Three Kings.

1979. Christmas.

1104. 8p. Type **581** 20 20
1105. 10p. Angel appearing to the Shepherds .. 25 25
1106. 11½p. The Nativity .. 30 35
1107. 13p. Mary and Joseph travelling to Bethlehem 40 40
1108. 15p. The Annunciation .. 50 45

586. Common Kingfisher.

1980. Centenary of Wild Bird Protection Act. Multicoloured.

1109. 10p. Type **586** 25 25
1110. 11½p. Dipper 30 35
1111. 13p. Moorhen 40 40
1112. 15p. Yellow Wagtails .. 45 45

590. "Rocket" at Moorish Arch, Liverpool.

1980. 150th Anniv. of Liverpool and Manchester Railway. Multicoloured.

1113. 12p. Type **590** 25 25
1114. 12p. First and Second Class carriages at Olive Mount 25 25
1115. 12p. Third Class carriage and sheep truck passing Chat Moss 25 25
1116. 12p. Flat truck carrying horse-drawn carriage and horse-box near Bridgewater Canal 25 25
1117. 12p. Truck and Mailcoach at Manchester .. 25 25

595. Montage of London Buildings.

1980. "London 1980" International Stamp Exhibition.

1118. **595.** 50p. brown .. .. 1·50 1·50

596. Buckingham Palace.

1980. London Landmarks. Multicoloured.

1120. 10½p. Type **596** 25 25
1121. 12p. The Albert Memorial 30 30
1122. 13½p. Royal Opera House 35 35
1123. 15p. Hampton Court .. 40 40
1124. 17½p. Kensington Palace 40 40

601. Charlotte Bronte ("Jane Eyre").

1980. Women Novelists. Multicoloured.

1125. 12p. Type **601** 30 30
1126. 13½p. George Eliot ("The Mill on the Floss") .. 35 35
1127. 15p. Emily Bronte ("Wuthering Heights") 40 45
1128. 17½p. Elizabeth Gaskell ("North and South") 60 60

605. Queen Elizabeth the Queen Mother.

1980. 80th Birthday of The Queen Mother.

1129. **605.** 12p. multicoloured .. 50 50

606. Sir Henry Wood.

1980. British Conductors. Multicoloured.

1130. 12p. Type **606** 30 30
1131. 13½p. Sir Thomas Beecham 35 40
1132. 15p. Sir Malcolm Sargent 45 45
1133. 17½p. Sir John Barbirolli 55 50

610. Running.

1980. Sport Centenaries. Multicoloured.

1134. 12p. Type **610** 30 30
1135. 13½p. Rugby 35 40
1136. 15p. Boxing 40 40
1137. 17½p. Cricket 60 55

CENTENARIES: 12p. Amateur Athletics Association. 13½p. Welsh Rugby Union. 15p. Amateur Boxing Association. 17½p. England-Australia Test Match.

614. Christmas Tree.

1980. Christmas. Multicoloured.

1138. 10p. Type **614** 25 25
1139. 12p. Candles 30 35
1140. 13½p. Mistletoe and apples 35 40
1141. 15p. Crown, chains and bell 40 40
1142. 17½p. Holly wreath .. 40 40

619. St. Valentine's Day.

1981. Folklore. Multicoloured.

1143. 14p. Type **619** 35 35
1144. 18p. Morris Dancers .. 45 50
1145. 22p. Lammastide .. 60 60
1146. 25p. Medieval Mummers 75 70

623. Blind Man with Guide Dog.

1981. International Year of Disabled Persons. Multicoloured.

1147. 14p. Type **623** .. 35 35
1148. 18p. Hands spelling "Deaf" in sign language .. 45 50
1149. 22p. Disabled man in wheelchair 60 60
1150. 25p. Disabled artist painting with foot 75 70

627. "Aglais urticae".

1981. Butterflies. Multicoloured.

1151 14p. Type **627** 35 35
1152 18p. "Maculinea arion" 50 50
1153 22p. "Inachis io" .. 60 65
1154 25p. "Carterocephalus palaemon" 70 75

631. Glenfinnan. Scotland..

1981. 50th Anniv. of National Trust for Scotland. British Landscapes. Multicoloured.

1155.	14p. Type **631**	30	30
1156.	18p. Derwentwater, England	40	40
1157.	20p. Stackpole Head, Wales	50	50
1158.	22p. Giant's Causeway, N. Ireland	60	60
1159.	25p. St. Kilda, Scotland	70	70

636. Prince Charles and Lady Diana Spencer.

1981. Royal Wedding.

1160. **636.**	14p. multicoloured ..	25	25
1161.	25p. multicoloured ..	75	75

637. " Expeditions ".

1981. 25th Anniv. of Duke of Edinburgh Award Scheme. Multicoloured.

1162.	14p. Type **637**	35	35
1163.	18p. " Skills "	50	50
1164.	22p. " Service "	60	60
1165.	25p. " Recreation " ..	70	70

641. Cockle-dredging from "Linsey II"

1981. Fishing Industry. Multicoloured.

1166.	14p. Type **641**	35	35
1167.	18p. Hauling in Trawl Net	50	50
1168.	22p. Lobster Potting ..	60	60
1169.	25p. Hoisting Seine Net	70	65

645. Father Christmas.

1981. Christmas. Children's Pictures. Mult.

1170.	11½p. Type **645**	30	30
1171.	14p. Jesus Christ ..	40	40
1172.	18p. Flying Angel ..	50	50
1173.	22p. Joseph and Mary arriving at Bethlehem	60	60
1174.	25p. Three Kings approching Bethlehem ..	70	70

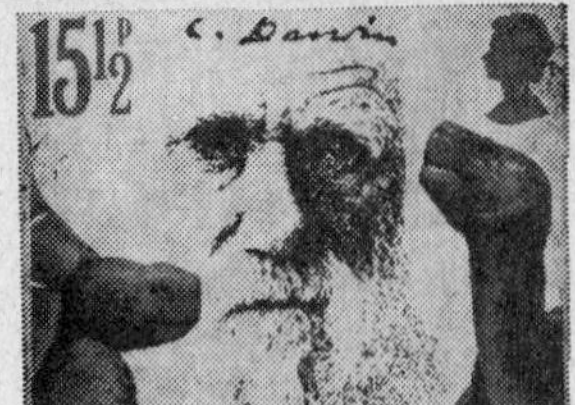

650. Charles Darwin and Giant Tortoises.

1982. Death Centenary of Charles Darwin. Multicoloured.

1175.	15½p. Type **650**	35	35
1176.	19½p. Darwin and Marine Iguanas	60	60
1177.	26p. Darwin and cactus ground finch and large ground finch	70	70
1178.	29p. Darwin and prehistoric skulls ..	75	75

654. Boys' Brigade.

1982. Youth Organizations. Multicoloured.

1179.	15½p. Type **654**	35	35
1180.	19½p. Girls' Brigade	60	50
1181.	26p. Boy Scout Movement	85	75
1182.	29p. Girl Guide Movement	1·00	90

658. Ballerina.

1982. Europa. British Theatre. Multicoloured.

1183	15½p. Type **658**	35	35
1184	19½p. Harlequin ..	60	50
1185	26p. Hamlet ..	90	75
1186	29p. Opera singer	1·25	90

662. Henry VIII and " Mary Rose ".

1982. Maritime Heritage. Multicoloured.

1187.	15½p. Type **662** ..	35	35
1188.	19½p. Admiral Blake and " Triumph " ..	60	60
1189.	24p. Lord Nelson and H.M.S. " Victory " ..	70	70
1190.	26p. Lord Fisher and H.M.S. " Dreadnought "	80	80
1191.	29p. Viscount Cunningham and H.M.S. " Warspite "	90	90

667. " Strawberry Thief " (William Morris).

1982. British Textiles. Multicoloured.

1192.	15½p. Type **667** ..	35	35
1193.	19½p. Untitled (Steiner and Co.) ..	55	55
1194.	26p. " Cherry Orchard " (Paul Nash)	70	70
1195.	29p. " Chevron " (Andrew Foster) ..	90	90

671. Development of Communications. (Illustration reduced: Actual size 70 × 20 mm.)

1982. Information Technology. Mult.

1196.	15½p. Type **671** ..	45	50
1197.	26p. Modern Technology Aids	80	85

673. Austin " Seven " and " Metro ".

1982. British Motor Industry. Mult.

1198.	15½p. Type **673**	50	50
1199.	19½p. Ford " Model T " and " Escort " ..	70	70
1200.	26p. Jaguar " SS1 " and " XJ6 " ..	85	90
1201.	29p. Rolls-Royce " Silver Ghost " and " Silver Spirit "	1·00	1·25

677. " While Shepherds Watched ".

1982. Christmas. Carols. Multicoloured.

1202.	12½p. Type **677**	30	30
1203.	15½p. " The Holly and the Ivy "	40	40
1204.	19½p. " I Saw Three Ships "	60	60
1205.	26p. " We Three Kings "	70	70
1206.	29p. " Good King Wenceslas "	80	80

682. Salmon.

1983. British River Fishes. Multicoloured.

1207.	15½p. Type **682**	35	35
1208.	19½p. Pike	55	55
1209.	26p. Trout	70	70
1210.	29p. Perch	90	90

686. Tropical Island.

1983. Commonwealth Day. Geographical Regions. Multicoloured.

1211.	15½p. Type **686** ..	35	35
1212.	19½p. Desert	55	55
1213.	26p. Temperate Farmland	70	70
1214.	29p. Mountain Range ..	90	90

690. Humber Bridge.

1983. Europa. Engineering Achievements. Multicoloured.

1215.	16p. Type **690**	45	45
1216.	20½p. Thames Flood Barrier	95	1·10
1217.	28p. " Iolair " (oilfield emergency support vessel)	1·10	1·25

693. Musketeer and Pikeman, The Royal Scots (1633).

1983. British Army Uniforms. Multicoloured.

1218.	16p. Type **693** ..	40	40
1219.	20½p. Fusilier and Ensign, The Royal Welsh Fusiliers (mid-18th century)	70	70
1220.	26p. Riflemen, 95th Rifles (The Royal Green Jackets) (1805)	85	85
1221.	28p. Sergeant (khaki service uniform) and Guardsman (full dress), The Irish Guards (1900) ..	85	85
1222.	31p. Paratroopers, The Parachute Regiment (1983)	1·10	1·10

698. 20th-century Garden, Sissinghurst.

1983. British Gardens. Multicoloured.

1223.	16p. Type **698**	40	40
1224.	20½p. 19th-century garden, Biddulph Grange ..	50	50
1225.	28p. 18th-century garden, Blenheim	70	90
1226.	31p. 17th-century garden, Pitmedden	90	1·00

702. Merry-go-round.

1983. British Fairs. Multicoloured.

1227.	16p. Type **702** ..	40	40
1228.	20½p. Big wheel, helter-skelter and performing animals ..	65	65
1229.	28p. Side shows	85	85
1230.	31p. Early produce fair ..	90	90

706. " Christmas Post " (pillar-box).

1983. Christmas. Multicoloured.

1231. 12½p. Type **706** 30 30
1232. 16p. "The Three Kings" (chimney pots) 35 35
1233. 20½p. "World at Peace" (Blackbird) 60 60
1234. 28p. "Light of Christmas" (street lamp) 70 80
1235. 31p. "Christmas Dove" (hedge sculpture) 85 1·00

711. Arms of College of Arms.

1984. 500th Anniv. of College Arms. Mult.

1236. 16p. Type **711** 40 40
1237. 20½p. Arms of King Richard III (founder) 60 60
1238. 28p. Arms of Earl Marshal of England 85 85
1239. 31p. Arms of City of London 95 95

715. Highland Cow.

1984. Cattle. Multicoloured.

1240. 16p. Type **715** 40 40
1241. 20½p. Chillingham Wild Bull 65 65
1242. 26p. Hereford Bull 70 70
1243. 28p. Welsh Black Bull 70 70
1244. 31p. Irish Moiled Cow 90 90

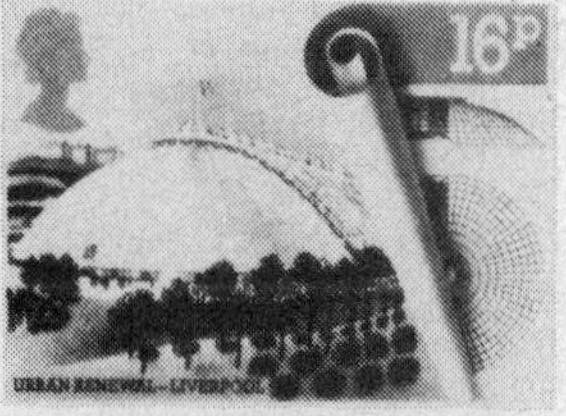

720. Garden Festival Hall, Liverpool.

1984. Urban Renewal. Multicoloured.

1245. 16p. Type **720** 40 40
1246. 20½p. Milburngate Centre, Durham 60 60
1247. 28p. Bush House, Bristol 90 90
1248. 31p. Commercial Street development, Perth 90 90

725. Abduction of Europa.

1984. 25th Anniv. of C.E.P.T. (Europa) (Nos. 1249, 1251), and Second Elections to European Parliament (others).

1249. – 16p. grey, bl. & gold 90 90
1250. **725.** 16p. grey, bl., blk. & gold 90 90
1251. – 20½p red, pur. & gold 1·50 1·50
1252. **725.** 20½p. red, pur., blk. & gold 1·50 1·50

DESIGN: Nos. 1249 and 1251, Bridge (C.E.P.T. 25th Anniversary logo).

MINIMUM PRICE

The minimum price quoted is 10p which represents a handling charge rather than a basis for valuing common stamps. For further notes about prices see introductory pages.

726. Lancaster House.

1984. London Economic Summit Conference.

1253. **726.** 31p. multicoloured 1·00 1·00

727. View of Earth from "Apollo 11".

1984. Centenary of Greenwich Meridian. Multicoloured.

1254. 16p. Type **727** 40 40
1255. 20½p. Navigational Chart of the English Channel 65 65
1256. 28p. Greenwich Observatory 85 90
1257. 31p. Sir George Airey's Transit Telescope 90 1·10

731. Bath Mail Coach leaving London, 1784.

1984. Bicentenary of First Mail Coach Run, Bath and Bristol to London. Multicoloured.

1258. 16p. Type **731** 60 60
1259. 16p. Attack on Exeter Mail, 1816 60 60
1260. 16p. Norwich Mail in Thunderstorm, 1827 60 60
1261. 16p. Holyhead and Liverpool Mails, 1828 60 60
1262. 16p. Edinburgh Mail snowbound, 1831 60 60

736. Nigerian Clinic.

1984. 50th Anniv. of British Council. Mult.

1263. 17p. Type **736** 50 50
1264. 22p. Violinist and Acropolis, Athens 65 65
1265. 31p. Building project, Sri Lanka 90 90
1266. 34p. British Council library, Middle East 1·00 1·00

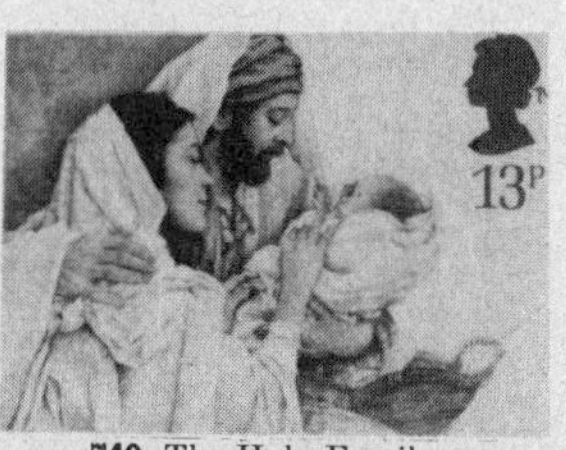

740. The Holy Family.

1984. Christmas. Multicoloured.

1267. 13p. Type **740** 30 30
1268. 17p. Arrival in Bethlehem 50 50
1269. 22p. Shepherd and Lamb 60 60
1270. 31p. Virgin and Child 95 95
1271. 34p. Offering of Frankincense 1·00 1·00

745. "The Flying Scotsman".

1985. Famous Trains. Multicoloured.

1272. 17p. Type **745** 50 50
1273. 22p. "The Golden Arrow" 70 70
1274. 29p. "The Cheltenham Flyer" 90 90
1275. 31p. "The Royal Scot" 1·00 1·00
1276. 34p. "The Cornish Riviera" 1·10 1·10

750. "Bombus terrestris" (bee).

1985. Insects. Multicoloured.

1277 17p. Type **750** 40 40
1278 22p. "Coccinella septempunctata" (ladybird) 60 60
1279 29p. "Decticus verrucivorus" (bush-cricket) 80 80
1280 31p. "Lucanus cervus" (stag beetle) 90 90
1281 34p. "Anax imperator" (dragonfly) 90 90

755. "Water Music" (George Frideric Handel).

1985. Europa. European Music Year. British Composers. 300th Birth Anniv. of Handel. Multicoloured.

1282. 17p. Type **755** 65 65
1283. 22p. "The Planets" Suite (Gustav Holst) 90 90
1284. 31p. "The First Cuckoo" (Frederick Delius) 1·40 1·40
1285. 34p. "Sea Pictures" (Edward Elgar) 1·50 1·50

759. R.N.L.I. Lifeboat and Signal Flags.

1985. Safety at Sea. Multicoloured.

1286. 17p. Type **759** 50 50
1287. 22p. Beachy Head Lighthouse and chart 65 65
1288. 31p. "Marecs A" communications satellite and dish aerials 1·10 1·10
1289. 34p. Buoys 1·10 1·10

763. Datapost Motorcyclist, City of London.

1985. 350 Years of Royal Mail Public Service. Multicoloured.

1290. 17p. Type **763** 50 50
1291. 22p. Rural postbus 65 65
1292. 31p. Parcel delivery in winter 1·10 1·10
1293. 34p. Town letter delivery 1·10 1·10

767. King Arthur and Merlin.

1985. Arthurian Legends. Multicoloured.

1294. 17p. Type **767** 50 50
1295. 22p. Lady of the Lake 65 75
1296. 31p. Queen Guinevere and Sir Lancelot 1·10 1·10
1297. 34p. Sir Galahad 1·10 1·25

771. Peter Sellers (from photo by Bill Brandt).

1985. British Film Year. Multicoloured.

1298. 17p. Type **771** 50 50
1299. 22p. David Niven (from photo by Cornell Lucas) 75 75
1300. 29p. Charlie Chaplin (from photo by Lord Snowdon) 1·10 1·10
1301. 31p. Vivien Leigh (from photo by Angus McBean) 1·25 1·25
1302. 34p. Alfred Hitchcock (from photo by Howard Carter) 1·40 1·40

776. Principal Boy.

1985. Christmas. Pantomime Characters. Multicoloured.

1303. 12p. Type **776** 35 30
1304. 17p. Genie 45 40
1305. 22p. Dame 70 80
1306. 31p. Good fairy 95 1·00
1307. 34p. Pantomime cat 1·00 1·10

781. Light Bulb and North Sea Oil Drilling Rig (Energy).

1986. Industry Year. Multicoloured.

1308.	17p. Type **781**	45	45
1309.	22p. Thermometer and pharmaceutical laboratory (Health)	60	60
1310.	31p. Garden hoe and steelworks (Steel) ..	90	90
1311.	34p. Loaf of bread and cornfield (Agriculture)	1·10	1·10

785. Dr Edmond Halley as Comet.

1986. Appearance of Halley's Comet. Multicoloured.

1312.	17p. Type **785**	45	45
1313.	22p. "Giotto" spacecraft approaching comet ..	70	70
1314.	31p. "Twice in a lifetime"	1·10	1·10
1315.	34p. Comet orbiting sun and planets	1·10	1·10

789. Queen Elizabeth II in 1928, 1942 and 1952.

1986. 60th Birthday of Queen Elizabeth II. Multicoloured.

1316.	17p. Type **789**	70	70
1317.	17p. Queen Elizabeth II in 1958, 1973 and 1982	70	70
1318.	34p. Type **789**	1·25	1·25
1319.	34p. As No. 1317 ..	1·25	1·25

791. Barn Owl.

1986. Europa. Nature Conservation. Endangered Species. Multicoloured.

1320.	17p. Type **791**	50	50
1321.	22p. Pine Marten ..	75	75
1322.	31p. Wild Cat	1·10	1·10
1323.	34p. Natterjack Toad ..	1·25	1·25

795. Peasants working in Fields.

1986. 900th Anniv. of Domesday Book. Multicoloured.

1324	17p. Type **795**	50	50
1325	22p. Freeman working at town trades	75	75
1326	31p. Knights and retainers	1·10	1·10
1327	34p. Lord at Banquet ..	1·25	1·25

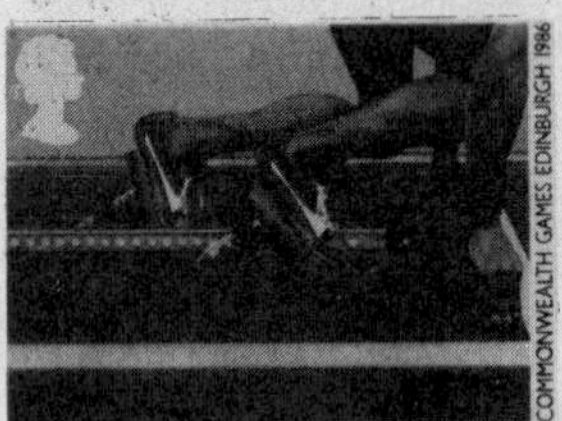

799. Athletics.

1986. 13th Commonwealth Games, Edinburgh, and World Hockey Cup for Men, London. Multicoloured.

1328.	17p. Type **799**	50	50
1329.	22p. Rowing	70	70
1330.	29p. Weightlifting ..	90	90
1331.	31p. Rifle shooting ..	1·10	1·10
1332.	34p. Hockey	1·25	1·25

No. 1332. also commemorates centenary of Hockey Association.

804. Prince Andrew and Miss Sarah Ferguson (from photo by Gene Nocon).

1986. Royal Wedding.

1333.	**804.** 12p. multicoloured ..	60	60
1334.	– 17p. multicoloured ..	90	90

DESIGN: 17p. As Type **804** but with naval motif.

806. Stylized Cross on Ballot Paper.

1986. 32nd Commonwealth Parliamentary Association Conference.

1335.	**806.** 34p. multicoloured ..	1·25	1·25

807. Lord Dowding and Hawker "Hurricane".

1986. History of Royal Air Force. Multicoloured.

1336.	17p. Type **807**	50	40
1337.	22p. Lord Tedder and Hawker "Typhoon" ..	70	85
1338.	29p. Lord Trenchard and De Havilland "DH9A"	90	1·00
1339.	31p. Sir Arthur Harris and Avro "Lancaster"	1·10	1·10
1340.	34p. Lord Portal and De Havilland "Mosquito"	1·25	1·25

Nos. 1336/40 were issued to celebrate 50th anniv. of first R.A.F. Commands.

812. The Glastonbury Thorn.

1986. Christmas. Folk Customs. Mult.

1341.	12p. Type **812**	50	50
1342.	13p. Type **812**	30	30
1343.	18p. The Tanad Valley Plygain	45	45
1344.	22p. The Hebrides Tribute	65	65
1345.	31p. The Dewsbury Church Knell	80	80
1346.	34p. The Hereford Boy Bishop	90	90

817. North American Blanket Flower.

1987. Flower Photographs by Alfred Lammer. Multicoloured.

1347.	18p. Type **817**	50	50
1348.	22p. Globe thistle ..	65	65
1349.	31p. "Echeveria" ..	1·10	1·10
1350.	34p. Autumn crocus ..	1·10	1·10

821. "Principia Mathematica".

1987. 300th Anniv. of "Principia Mathematica" by Sir Isaac Newton. Multicoloured.

1351.	18p. Type **821**	50	50
1352.	22p. "Motion of Bodies in Ellipses" ..	70	70
1353.	31p. "Optick Treatise" ..	1·10	1·10
1354.	34p. "The System of the World"	1·25	1·25

825. Willis Faber and Dumas Building, Ipswich.

1987. Europa. British Architects in Europe.

1355.	18p. Type **825**	50	50
1356.	22p. Pompidou Centre, Paris	70	70
1357.	31p. Staatsgalerie, Stuttgart	1·10	1·10
1358.	34p. European Investment Bank, Luxembourg	1·25	1·25

829. Brigade Members with Ashford Litter, 1887.

1987. Centenary of St. John Ambulance Brigade. Multicoloured.

1359.	18p. Type **829**	50	50
1360.	22p. Bandaging blitz victim, 1940	65	65
1361.	31p. Volunteer with fainting girl, 1965 ..	1·10	1·10
1362.	34p. Transport of transplant organ by "Air Wing", 1987 ..	1·10	1·10

833. Arms of the Lord Lyon King of Arms.

1987. 300th Anniv. of Revival of Order of the Thistle. Multicoloured.

1363.	18p. Type **833**	50	50
1364.	22p. Scottish Heraldic Banner of Prince Charles	65	65
1365.	31p. Arms of Royal Scottish Academy of Painting, Sculpture and Architecture ..	1·10	1·10
1366.	34p. Arms of Royal Society of Edinburgh	1·10	1·10

837. Crystal Palace, "Monarch of the Glen" (Landseer) and Grace Darling.

1987. 150th Anniv. of Queen Victoria's Accession. Multicoloured.

1367.	18p. Type **837**	50	50
1368.	22p. "Great Eastern", Beeton's "Book of Household Management" and Prince Albert	65	65
1369.	31p. Albert Memorial, ballot box and Disraeli	1·10	1·10
1370.	34p. Diamond Jubilee emblem, newspaper placard for Relief of Mafeking and morse key	1·10	1·10

841. Pot by Bernard Leach.

1987. Studio Pottery. Multicoloured.

1371.	18p. Type **841**	50	50
1372.	26p. Pot by Elizabeth Fritsch	70	70
1373.	31p. Pot by Lucie Rie ..	1·10	1·10
1374.	34p. Pot by Hans Coper	1·25	1·25

845. Decorating the Christmas Tree.

1987. Christmas. Multicoloured.

1375.	13p. Type **845** ..	30	30
1376.	18p. Waiting for Father Christmas	50	50
1377.	26p. Sleeping child and Father Christmas in sleigh	75	75
1378.	31p. Child reading ..	95	1·10
1379.	34p. Child playing recorder and snowman	1·10	1·25

850. "Bull-rout" (Jonathan Couch).

1988. Bicentenary of Linnean Society. Archive Illustrations. Multicoloured.

1380	18p. Type **850**	45	45
1381	26p. "Yellow Waterlily" (Major Joshua Swatkin)	70	70
1382	31p. "Whistling ('Bewick's') Swan" (Edward Lear) ..	1·10	1·10
1383	34p. "Morchella esculenta" (James Sowerby)	1·10	1·10

854. Revd. William Morgan (Bible translator, 1588).

1988. 400th Anniv. of Welsh Bible. Mult.

1384.	18p. Type **854**	45	45
1385.	26p. William Salesbury (New Testament translator, 1567) ..	70	70
1386.	31p. Bishop Richard Davies (New Testament translator, 1567)	1·10	1·10
1387.	34p. Bishop Richard Parry (editor of Revised Welsh Bible, 1620)	1·10	1·10

858. Gymnastics (Centenary of British Amateur Gymnastics Association).

1988. Sports Organizations. Multicoloured.

1388.	18p. Type **858**	45	45
1389.	26p. Downhill skiing (Ski Club of Great Britain)	70	70
1390.	31p. Tennis (centenary of Lawn Tennis Association)	1·10	1·10
1391.	34p. Football (centenary of Football League) ..	1·10	1·10

862. "Mallard" and Mailbags on Pick-up Arms.

1988. Europa. Transport and Mail Services in 1930s. Multicoloured.

1392	18p. Type **862**	50	50
1393	26p. Loading trans-atlantic mail on liner "Queen Elizabeth" ..	80	80
1394	31p. Glasgow tram No. 1173 and pillar box ..	1·10	1·10
1395	34p. Imperial Airways Handley Page "HP 42" and airmail van ..	1·25	1·25

866 Early Settler and Sailing Clipper

1988. Bicent of Australian Settlement. Mult.

1396	18p. Type **866**	60	60
1397	18p. Queen Elizabeth II with British and Australian Parliament Buildings	60	60
1398	34p. W. G. Grace (cricketer) and tennis racquet	1·10	1·10
1399	34p. Shakespeare, John Lennon (entertainer) and Sydney Opera House	1·10	1·10

Stamps in similar designs were also issued by Australia.

870 Spanish Galeasse off The Lizard

1988. 400th Anniv of Spanish Armada. Mult.

1400	18p. Type **870**	65	65
1401	18p. English Fleet leaving Plymouth	65	65
1402	18p. Engagement off Isle of Wight	65	65
1403	18p. Attack of English Fire-ships, Calais ..	65	65
1404	18p. Armada in storm, North Sea	65	65

Nos. 1400/4 were printed together, se-tenant, forming a composite design.

875 "The Owl and the Pussy-cat"

1988. Death Centenary of Edward Lear (artist and author).

1405	**875**	19p. blk, cream & red	50	50
1406	–	27p. blk, cream & yell	65	80
1407	–	32p. blk, cream & grn	1·10	1·10
1408	–	35p. black, cream & bl	1·10	1·25

DESIGNS: 27p. "Edward Lear as a Bird" (self-portrait); 32p. "Cat" (from alphabet book); 35p. "There was a Young Lady whose Bonnet..." (limerick).

879 Carrickfergus Castle

1988.

1410	**879**	£1 green	2·50	50
1411	–	£1.50 red	3·50	1·00
1412	–	£2 blue	5·00	1·50
1413	–	£5 brown	12·00	3·00

DESIGNS: £1.50, Caernarfon Castle; £2, Edinburgh Castle; £5, Windsor Castle.

For similar designs, but with silhouette Queen's head see Nos. 1611/14.

883 Journey to Bethlehem

1988. Christmas. Christmas Cards. Mult.

1414	14p. Type **883**	35	35
1415	19p. Shepherds and Star	40	45
1416	27p. Three Wise Men ..	70	70
1417	32p. Nativity	90	1·00
1418	35p. The Annunciation ..	1·00	1·10

888 Atlantic Puffin

1989. Centenary of Royal Society for the Protection of Birds. Multicoloured.

1419	19p. Type **888**	45	45
1420	27p. Avocet	1·10	1·10
1421	32p. Oystercatcher ..	1·10	1·10
1422	35p. Northern gannet ..	1·25	1·25

892 Rose

1989. Greetings Stamps. Multicoloured.

1423	19p. Type **892**	2·75	2·25
1424	19p. Cupid	2·75	2·25
1425	19p. Yachts	2·75	2·25
1426	19p. Fruit	2·75	2·25
1427	19p. Teddy bear ..	2·75	2·25

897 Fruit and Vegetables

1989. Food and Farming Year. Multicoloured.

1428	19p. Type **897**	50	50
1429	27p. Meat products ..	80	80
1430	32p. Dairy produce ..	1·10	1·10
1431	35p. Cereal products ..	1·25	1·25

901 Mortar Board

1989. Anniversaries. Multicoloured.

1432	19p. Type **901** (150th Anniv of Public Education in England)	70	70
1433	19p. Cross on Ballot Paper (3rd Direct Elections to European Parliament)	70	70
1434	35p. Posthorn (26th Postal, Telegraph and Telephone International Congress, Brighton) ..	1·25	1·25
1435	35p. Globe (Inter-Parliamentary Union Centenary Conference, London)	1·25	1·25

905 Toy Train and Airplane

1989. Europa. Games and Toys. Mult.

1436	19p. Type **905**	50	50
1437	27p. Building bricks ..	90	90
1438	32p. Dice and board games	1·25	1·25
1439	35p. Toy robot, boat and doll's house	1·40	1·40

909 Ironbridge, Shropshire **913**

1989. Industrial Archaeology. Multicoloured.

1440	19p. Type **909**	50	50
1441	27p. Tin Mine, St. Agnes Head, Cornwall	80	80
1442	32p. Cotton Mills, New Lanark, Strathclyde ..	1·00	1·00
1443	35p. Pontcysyllte Aqueduct, Clwyd ..	1·10	1·10

1989.

1449	**913**	(2nd) blue	30	35
1511	–	(2nd) deep blue ..	50	50
1447	–	(1st) black	1·00	50
1512	–	(1st) red	40	40

915 Snowflake (×10)

1989. 150th Anniv of Royal Microscopical Society. Multicoloured.

1453	19p. Type **915**	50	50
1454	27p. "Calliphora erythrocephala" (fly) (×5)	85	85
1455	32p. Blood cells (×500) ..	1·25	1·25
1456	35p. Microchip (×600) ..	1·40	1·40

919 Royal Mail Coach

1989. Lord Mayor's Show, London. Mult.

1457	20p. Type **919**	60	60
1458	20p. Escort of Blues and Royals	60	60
1459	20p. Lord Mayor's coach	60	60
1460	20p. Coach team passing St. Paul's	60	60
1461	20p. Blues and Royals drum horse	60	60

This issue commemorates the 800th anniversary of the installation of the first Lord Mayor of London.

924 14th-century Peasants from Stained-glass Window

1989. Christmas. 800th Anniv of Ely Cathedral.

1462	**924**	15p. gold, silver & bl	35	35
1463	–	15p.+1p. gold, silver and blue	50	40
1464	–	20p.+1p. gold, silver and red	60	50
1465	–	34p.+1p. gold, silver and green ..	1·25	1·40
1466	–	37p.+1p. gold, silver and green ..	1·25	1·40

DESIGNS: 15p.+1p. Arches and roundels, West Front; 20p.+1p. Octagon Tower; 34p.+1p. Arcade from West Transept; 37p.+1p. Triple arch from West Front.

929 Queen Victoria and Queen Elizabeth II

930 Kitten

1990. 150th Anniv of the Penny Black.

1467	**929**	15p. blue	50	50
1469		20p. black and cream	75	75
1471		29p. mauve	1·00	1·00
1473		34p. grey	1·25	1·25
1474		37p. red	1·40	1·40

1990. 150th Anniv of Royal Society for Prevention of Cruelty to Animals. Mult.

1479	20p. Type **930**	65	50
1480	29p. Rabbit	1·00	80
1481	34p. Duckling	1·40	1·10
1482	37p. Puppy	1·40	1·10

934 Teddy Bear

1990. Greetings Stamps. "Smiles". Multicoloured (except No. 1492).

1483	20p. Type **934**	1·60	1·25
1484	20p. Dennis the Menace ..	1·60	1·25
1485	20p. Punch	1·60	1·25
1486	20p. Cheshire Cat ..	1·60	1·25
1487	20p. The Man in the Moon	1·60	1·25
1488	20p. The Laughing Policeman	1·60	1·25
1489	20p. Clown	1·60	1·25
1490	20p. Mona Lisa	1·60	1·25
1491	20p. Queen of Hearts ..	1·60	1·25
1492	20p. Stan Laurel (comedian) (gold and black) ..	1·60	1·25

See also Nos. 1550/9.

944 Alexandra Palace ("Stamp World London 90" Exhibition)

1990. Europa (Nos. 1493 and 1495) and "Glasgow 1990 European City of Culture" (Nos. 1494 and 1496). Multicoloured.

1493	20p. Type **944**	50	50
1494	20p. Glasgow School of Art	50	50
1495	29p. British Philatelic Bureau, Edinburgh ..	1·10	1·10
1496	37p. Templeton Carpet Factory, Glasgow ..	1·25	1·25

948 Export Achievement Award

1990. 25th Anniv of Queen's Awards for Export and Technology. Multicoloured.

1497	20p. Type **948**	55	55
1498	20p. Technological Achievement Award ..	55	55
1499	37p. Type **948**	1·10	1·10
1500	37p. As No. 1498 ..	1·10	1·10

950 Cycad and Sir Joseph Banks Building

1990. 150th Anniv of Kew Gardens. Mult.

1502	20p. Type **950**	50	50
1503	29p. Stone Pine and Princess of Wales Conservatory	80	80
1504	34p. Willow Tree and Palm House ..	1·10	1·25
1505	37p. Cedar Tree and Pagoda	1·25	1·40

954 Thomas Hardy and Clyffe Clump, Dorset

1990. 150th Birth Anniv of Thomas Hardy (author).

1506	**954**	20p. multicoloured ..	60	70

955 Queen Elizabeth the Queen Mother

1990. 90th Birthday of Queen Elizabeth the Queen Mother. Multicoloured.

1507	20p. Type **955**	50	80
1508	29p. Queen Elizabeth ..	80	80
1509	34p. Elizabeth, Duchess of York	1·10	1·25
1510	37p. Lady Elizabeth Bowes-Lyon	1·25	1·40

959 Victoria Cross

1990. Gallantry Awards. Multicoloured.

1517	20p. Type **959**	65	65
1518	20p. George Cross ..	65	65
1519	20p. Distinguished Service Cross and Distinguished Service Medal (horiz) ..	65	65
1520	20p. Military Cross and Military Medal (horiz)	65	65
1521	20p. Distinguished Flying Cross and Distinguished Flying Medal (horiz) ..	65	65

964 Armagh Observatory, Jodrell Bank Radio Telescope and La Palma Telescope

1990. Astronomy. Multicoloured.

1522	22p. Type **964**	50	40
1523	26p. Newton's moon and tides diagram with early telescopes ..	80	90
1524	31p. Greenwich Old Observatory and early astronomical equipment	1·00	1·00
1525	37p. Stonehenge, gyroscope and navigating by stars	1·10	1·10

Nos. 1522/5 commemorate the Centenary of the British Astronomical Association and the Bicentenary of the Armagh Observatory.

968 Building a Snowman

1990. Christmas. Multicoloured.

1526	17p. Type **968**	45	35
1527	22p. Fetching the Christmas tree	55	65
1528	26p. Carol singing ..	80	80
1529	31p. Tobogganing ..	1·00	1·00
1530	37p. Ice skating ..	1·10	1·10

973 "King Charles Spaniel"

1991. Dogs. Paintings by George Stubbs. Multicoloured.

1531	22p. Type **973**	75	75
1532	26p. "A Pointer" ..	80	80
1533	31p. "Two Hounds in a Landscape"	85	85
1534	33p. "A Rough Dog" ..	95	95
1535	37p. "Fino and Tiny" ..	1·10	1·10

978 Thrush's Nest

1991. Greetings Stamps. "Good Luck". Mult.

1536	(1st) Type **978**	85	90
1537	(1st) Shooting star and rainbow	85	90
1538	(1st) Magpies and charm bracelet	85	90
1539	(1st) Black cat	85	90
1540	(1st) Common kingfisher with key	85	90
1541	(1st) Mallard and frog ..	85	90
1542	(1st) Four-leaf clover in boot and match box ..	85	90
1543	(1st) Pot of gold at end of rainbow	85	90
1544	(1st) Heart-shaped butterflies	85	90
1545	(1st) Wishing well and sixpence	85	90

Nos. 1536/45 were initially sold at 22p. each. It is intended that the price will be increased to reflect future alterations in postage rates. The backgrounds of the stamps form a composite design.

988 Michael Faraday (inventor of electric motor) (birth bicentenary)

1991. Scientific Achievements. Multicoloured.

1546	22p. Type **988**	65	65
1547	22p. Charles Babbage (computer science pioneer) (birth bicent)	65	65

1548 31p. Radar sweep of East Anglia (50th anniv of operational radar network) 95 95
1549 37p. Gloster E28/39 aircraft over East Anglia (50th anniv of first flight of Sir Frank Whittle's jet engine) .. 1·10 1·10

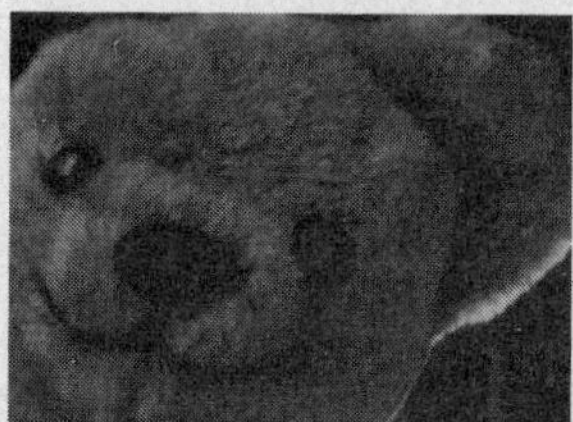

992 Teddy Bear

1991. Greetings Stamps. "Smiles". As Nos. 1483/92, but inscr "1st" as in T **992**. Multicoloured (except No. 1559).

1550 (1st) Type **992** 40 45
1551 (1st) Dennis the Menace 40 45
1552 (1st) Punch 40 45
1553 (1st) Cheshire Cat .. 40 45
1554 (1st) The Man in the Moon 40 45
1555 (1st) The Laughing Policeman 40 45
1556 (1st) Clown 40 45
1557 (1st) Mona Lisa 40 45
1558 (1st) Queen of Hearts .. 40 45
1559 (1st) Stan Laurel (comedian) (gold and black) 40 45

Nos. 1550/9 were initially sold at 22p. each but this was later increased to reflect new postage rates.

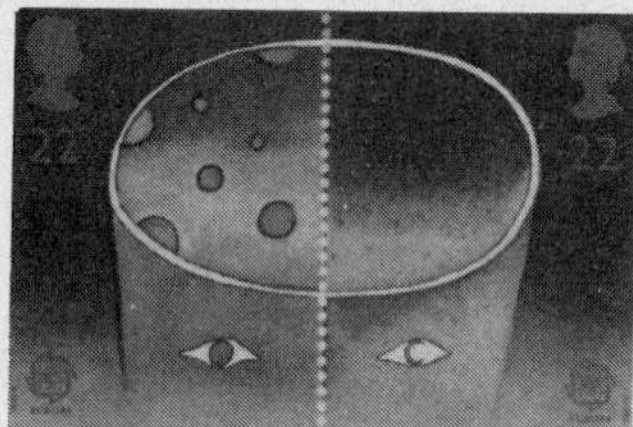

993 Man looking at Space **994**
(¾ size illustration)

1991. Europa. Europe in Space. Mult.

1560 22p. Type **993** 55 55
1561 22p. Type **994** 55 55
1562 37p. Space looking at Man (Queen's head on left) 1·10 1·10
1563 37p. Similar to No. 1562 (Queen's head on right) 1·10 1·10

Stamps of the same value were printed together in horizontal pairs, each pair forming a composite design.

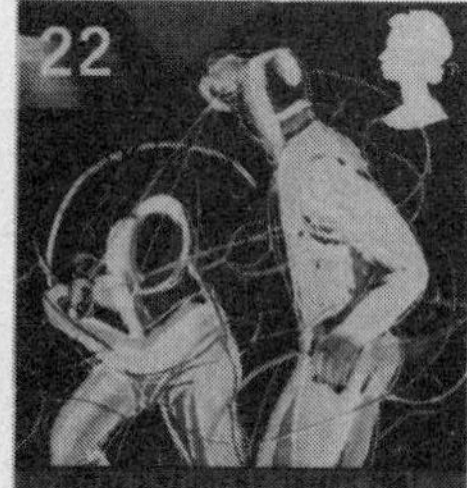

997 Fencing

1991. World Student Games, Sheffield (Nos. 1564/6) and World Cup Rugby Championship (No. 1567).

1564 22p. Type **997** 50 50
1565 26p. Hurdling 80 80
1566 31p. Diving 95 95
1567 37p. Rugby .. .. 1·10 1·10

1001 "Silver Jubilee"

1991. 9th World Congress of Roses, Belfast. Multicoloured.

1568 22p. Type **1001** 75 50
1569 26p. "Mme Alfred Carriere" 80 80
1570 31p. "Rosa moyesii" .. 85 85
1571 33p. "Harvest Fayre" .. 95 95
1572 37p. "Mutabilis" .. 1·10 1·25

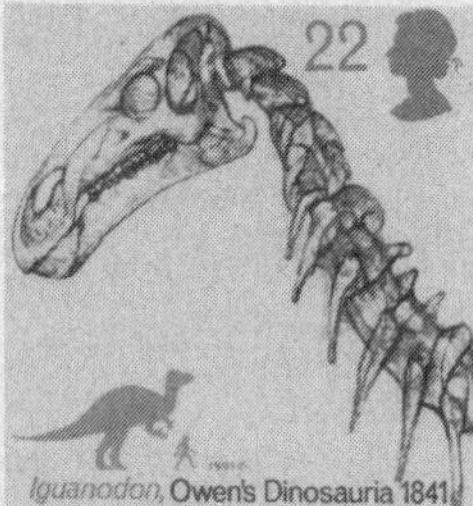

1006 Iguanodon

1991. 150th Anniv of Dinosaurs' Identification by Owen. Multicoloured.

1573 22p. Type **1006** 75 50
1574 26p. Stegosaurus .. 90 1·00
1575 31p. Tyrannosaurus .. 1·00 1·10
1576 33p. Protoceratops .. 1·10 1·10
1577 37p. Triceratops .. 1·25 1·25

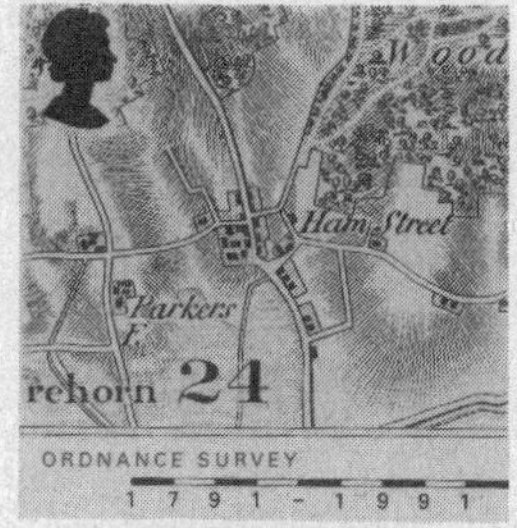

1011 Map of 1816

1991. Bicentenary of Ordnance Survey. Maps of Hamstreet, Kent.

1578 **1011** 24p. black, mauve and cream .. 50 50
1579 – 28p. multicoloured .. 80 85
1580 – 33p. multicoloured .. 95 1·00
1581 – 39p. multicoloured .. 1·10 1·25

DESIGNS: 28p. Map of 1906; 33p. Map of 1959; 39p. Map of 1991

1015 Adoration of the Magi

1991. Christmas. Illuminated Letters from "Acts of Mary and Jesus" Manuscript in Bodleian Library, Oxford. Multicoloured.

1582 18p. Type **1015** 70 40
1583 24p. Mary and Baby Jesus in the Stable 80 50
1584 28p. The Holy Family and Angel .. .. .. 85 1·00
1585 33p. The Annunciation .. 95 1·10
1586 39p. The Flight into Egypt .. .. .. 1·10 1·40

1020 Fallow Deer in Scottish Forest

1992. The Four Seasons. Wintertime. Mult.

1587 18p. Type **1020** 45 50
1588 24p. Hare on North Yorkshire Moors .. 60 65
1589 28p. Fox in the Fens .. 70 75
1590 33p. Redwing and Home Counties village .. 85 90
1591 39p. Welsh mountain sheep in Snowdonia .. 1·00 1·10

1025 Flower Spray

1992. Greetings Stamps. "Memories". Mult.

1592 (1st) Type **1025** 40 45
1593 (1st) Double locket .. 40 45
1594 (1st) Key 40 45
1595 (1st) Model car and cigarette cards .. 40 45
1596 (1st) Compass and map .. 40 45
1597 (1st) Pocket watch .. 40 45
1598 (1st) 1854 1d. Red stamp and pen 40 45
1599 (1st) Pearl necklace .. 40 45
1600 (1st) Marbles 40 45
1601 (1st) Bucket, spade and starfish 40 45

Nos. 1592/1601 were issued together, se-tenant, the backgrounds forming a composite design.

1035 Queen Elizabeth in Coronation Robes and Parliamentary Emblem

1992. 40th Anniv of Accession. Mult.

1602 24p. Type **1035** 90 75
1603 24p. Queen Elizabeth in Garter robes and archiepiscopal arms .. 90 75
1604 24p. Queen Elizabeth with baby Prince Andrew and Royal Arms .. 90 75
1605 24p. Queen Elizabeth at Trooping the Colour and service emblems 90 75
1606 24p. Queen Elizabeth and Commonwealth emblem 90 75

1040 Tennyson in 1888 and "The Beguiling of Merlin" (Sir Edward Burne-Jones)

1992. Death Centenary of Alfred, Lord Tennyson (poet). Multicoloured.

1607 24p. Type **1040** 50 50
1608 28p. Tennyson in 1864 and "I am Sick of the Shadows" (John Waterhouse) 65 65
1609 33p. Tennyson in 1856 and "April Love" (Arthur Hughes) .. .. 1·10 1·10
1610 39p. Tennyson as a young man and "Mariana" (Dante Gabriel Rossetti) .. .. 1·10 1·10

1044 Carrickfergus Castle

1992. Designs as Nos. 1410/13, but showing Queen's head in silhouette as T **1044**.

1611 **1044** £1 green and gold † 1·50 1·50
1612 – £1.50 purple & gold † 2·25 2·25
1613 – £2 blue and gold † .. 3·00 3·00
1614 – £5 brown and gold † 7·50 7·50

†The Queen's head on these stamps is printed in optically variable ink which changes colour from gold to green when viewed from different angles.

1045 British Olympic Association Logo (Olympic Games, Barcelona)

1992. Europa. International Events. Mult.

1615 24p. Type **1045** .. 65 65
1616 24p. British Paralympic Association symbol (Paralympics '92, Barcelona) 65 65
1617 24p. "Santa Maria" (500th anniv of discovery of America by Columbus) 65 65
1618 39p. "Kaisei" (Japanese cadet brigantine) (Grand Regatta Columbus, 1992) .. 1·10 1·10
1619 39p. British Pavilion, "EXPO '92", Seville .. 1·10 1·10

1050 Pikeman

1992. 350th Anniv of the Civil War. Mult.

1620 24p. Type **1050** 55 55
1621 28p. Drummer 70 70
1622 33p. Musketeer .. .. 1·00 1·00
1623 39p. Standard Bearer .. 1·10 1·10

1054 "The Yeoman of the Guard"

1992. 150th Birth Anniv of Sir Arthur Sullivan (composer). Gilbert and Sullivan Operas. Multicoloured.

1624 18p. Type **1054** 40 45
1625 24p. "The Gondoliers" .. 55 55
1626 28p. "The Mikado" .. 70 70
1627 33p. "The Pirates of Penzance" 90 90
1628 39p. "Iolanthe" .. .. 1·10 1·10

1059 "Acid Rain Kills"

1992. Protection of the Environment. Children's Paintings. Multicoloured.

1629	24p. Type **1059**	60	45
1630	28p. "Ozone Layer"	75	80
1631	33p. "Greenhouse Effect"	80	90
1632	39p. "Bird of Hope" ..	90	90

1063 European Star

1992. Single European Market.

1633 **1063**	24p. multicoloured ..	60	60

1064 "Angel Gabriel", St. James's, Pangbourne

1992. Christmas. Stained Glass Windows. Multicoloured.

1634	18p. Type **1064**	40	40
1635	24p. "Madonna and Child", St. Mary's, Bibury	65	65
1636	28p. "King with Gold", Our Lady and St. Peter, Leatherhead	80	80
1637	33p. "Shepherds", All Saints, Porthcawl ..	95	95
1638	39p. "Kings with Frankincense and Myrrh", Our Lady and St. Peter, Leatherhead	1·10	1·10

1069 Mute Swan Cob and St. Catherine's Chapel, Abbotsbury

1993. 600th Anniv of Abbotsbury Swannery. Multicoloured.

1639	18p. Type **1069**	40	40
1640	24p. Cygnet and decoy ..	55	55
1641	28p. Swans and cygnet ..	85	85
1642	33p. Eggs in nest and tithe barn, Abbotsbury	1·00	1·00
1643	39p. Young swan and the Fleet	1·10	1·10

1074 Long John Silver and Parrot ("Treasure Island")

1993. Greetings Stamps. "Gift Giving". Gold, cream and black (No. 1645) or multicoloured (others).

1644	(1st) Type **1074**	40	45
1645	(1st) Tweedledum and Tweedledee ("Alice Through the Looking-Glass")	40	45
1646	(1st) William ("William" books)	40	45
1647	(1st) Mole and Toad ("The Wind in the Willows")	40	45
1648	(1st) Teacher and Wilfred ("The Bash Street Kids")	40	45
1649	(1st) Peter Rabbit and Mrs. Rabbit ("The Tale of Peter Rabbit") ..	40	45
1650	(1st) Snowman and Father Christmas ("The Snowman")	40	45
1651	(1st) The Big Friendly Giant and Sophie ("The BFG")	40	45
1652	(1st) Bill Badger and Rupert Bear	40	45
1653	(1st) Aladdin and the Genie	40	45

1084 Decorated Enamel Dial

1993. 300th Birth Anniv of John Harrison (inventor of the marine chronometer). Details of "H4" Clock. Multicoloured.

1654	24p. Type **1084**	50	50
1655	28p. Escapement, remontoire and fusee ..	70	70
1656	33p. Balance, spring and temperature compensator	85	85
1657	39p. Back of movement ..	1·00	1·00

1088 "Britannia" (¾-size illustration)

1993.

1658 **1088**	£10 multicoloured ..	15·00	16·00

1089 "Dendrobium hellwigianum"

1993. 14th World Orchid Conference, Glasgow. Multicoloured.

1659	18p. Type **1089**	40	40
1660	24p. "Paphiopedilum" Maudiae "Magnificum"	50	50
1661	28p. "Cymbidium lowianum"	75	75
1662	33p. "Vanda" Rothschildiana ..	85	85
1663	39p. "Dendrobium vexillarius var albiviride"	1·10	1·10

1094 "Family Group" (bronze sculpture) (Henry Moore)

1993. Europa. Contemporary Art. Mult.

1767	24p. Type **1094**	40	45
1768	28p. "Kew Gardens" (lithograph) (Edward Bawden)	45	50
1769	33p. "St. Francis and the Birds" (Stanley Spencer)	50	55
1770	39p. "Still Life: Odyssey I" (Ben Nicholson) ..	60	65

1098 Emperor Claudius (from gold coin)

1993. Roman Britain. Multicoloured.

1771	24p. Type **1098**	40	45
1772	28p. Emperor Hadrian (bronze head)	45	50
1773	33p. Goddess Roma (from gemstone)	50	55
1774	39p. Christ (Hinton St. Mary mosaic)	60	65

1102 "Midland Maid" and other Narrow Boats, Grand Junction Canal

1993. Inland Waterways. Multicoloured.

1775	24p. Type **1102**	40	45
1776	28p. "Yorkshire Lass" and other Humber keels, Stainforth and Keadby Canal ..	45	50
1777	33p. "Valley Princess" and other horse-drawn barges, Brecknock and Abergavenny Canal ..	50	55
1778	39p. Steam barges, including "Pride of Scotland", and fishing boats, Crinan Canal ..	60	65

Nos. 1775/8 commemorate the bicentenary of the Acts of Parliament authorising the canals depicted.

1106 Horse Chestnut

1993. The Four Seasons. Autumn. Fruits and Leaves. Multicoloured.

1779	18p. Type **1106**	30	35
1780	24p. Blackberry	40	45
1781	28p. Hazel	45	50
1782	33p. Rowan	50	55
1783	39p. Pear	60	65

1111 "The Reigate Squire"

1993. Sherlock Holmes. Centenary of the Publication of "The Final Problem". Multicoloured.

1784	24p. Type **1111**	40	45
1785	24p. "The Hound of the Baskervilles"	40	45
1786	24p. "The Six Napoleons"	40	45
1787	24p. "The Greek Interpreter"	40	45
1788	24p. "The Final Problem"	40	45

1116

1993. Self-adhesive.

1789 **1116**	(1st) red	40	45

No. 1789 was initially sold at 24p., which was increased to 25p. on 1 November 1993.

1117 Bob Cratchit and Tiny Tim

1993. Christmas. 150th Anniv of Publication of "A Christmas Carol" by Charles Dickens. Multicoloured.

1790	19p. Type **1117**	30	35
1791	25p. Mr. and Mrs. Fezziwig	40	45
1792	30p. Scrooge	45	50
1793	35p. The prize turkey ..	55	60
1794	41p. Mr. Scrooge's nephew	65	70

1122 Class "5" No. 44957 and Class "B1" No. 61342 on West Highland Line

1994. The Age of Steam. Railway photographs by Colin Gifford.

1795 **1122**	19p. grn, grey & blk	30	35
1796 –	25p. lilac, grey & blk	40	45
1797 –	30p. brn, grey & blk	45	50
1798 –	35p. pur, grey & blk	55	60
1799 –	41p. blue, grey & blk	65	70

DESIGNS: 25p. Class "A1" No. 60149 "Amadis" at Kings Cross; 30p. Class "4" No. 43000 on turntable at Blyth North; 35p. Class "4" No. 42455 near Wigan Central; 41p. Class "Castle" No. 7002 "Devizes Castle" on bridge crossing Worcester and Birmingham Canal.

1127 Dan Dare and the Mekon

1994. Greetings Stamps. "Messages". Mult.

1800	(1st) Type **1127** ..	40	45
1801	(1st) The Three Bears ..	40	45
1802	(1st) Rupert Bear ..	40	45
1803	(1st) Alice ("Alice in Wonderland") ..	40	45
1804	(1st) Noggin and The Ice Dragon ..	40	45
1805	(1st) Peter Rabbit posting a letter ..	40	45
1806	(1st) Red Riding Hood and wolf	40	45
1807	(1st) Orlando the Marmalade Cat ..	40	45
1808	(1st) Biggles ..	40	45
1809	(1st) Paddington Bear on station	40	45

1137 Castell Y Waun (Chirk Castle), Clwyd, Wales

1994. 25th Anniv of Investiture of the Prince of Wales. Paintings by Prince Charles. Multicoloured.

1810	19p. Type **1137**	30	35
1811	25p. Ben Arkle, Sutherland, Scotland ..	40	45
1812	30p. Mourne Mountains, County Down, Northern Ireland ..	45	50
1813	35p. Dersingham, Norfolk, England	55	60
1814	41p. Dolwyddelan, Gwynedd, Wales ..	65	70

1142 Bather at Blackpool

1994. Centenary of Picture Postcards. Mult.

1815	19p. Type **1142**	30	35
1816	25p. "Where's my Little Lad?"	40	45
1817	30p. "Wish You were Here!"	45	50
1818	35p. Punch and Judy show	55	60
1819	41p. "The Tower Crane" machine	65	70

1147 British Lion and French Cockerel over Tunnel

1994. Opening of Channel Tunnel. Mult.

1820	25p. Type **1147**	40	45
1821	25p. Symbolic hands over train	40	45
1822	41p. Type **1147**	65	70
1823	41p. As No. 1821 ..	65	70

1149 Groundcrew replacing Smoke Canisters on Boston of 88 Sqn

1994. 50th Anniv of D-Day. Multicoloured.

1824	25p. Type **1149**	40	45
1825	25p. H.M.S. "Warspite" (battleship) shelling enemy positions ..	40	45
1826	25p. Commandos landing on Gold Beach ..	40	45
1827	25p. Infantry regrouping on Sword Beach ..	40	45
1828	25p. Tank and infantry advancing, Ouistreham	40	45

REGIONAL ISSUES

I. CHANNEL ISLANDS

Islands in the English Channel off N.W. coast of France. Occupied by German Forces from June, 1940 to May, 1945, when separate issues for both islands were made. "Regional" issues were introduced from 1958.

C1. Gathering Vraic (seaweed).

1948. 3rd Anniversary of Liberation.

C 1.	C **1.**	1d. red	20	20
C 2.	–	2½d. blue	30	30

DESIGN: 2½d. Islanders gathering vraic.

II. GUERNSEY.

2.

3.

1958.

6	**2.**	2½d. red	35	40
7p	**3.**	3d. lilac	20	20
9		4d. blue	10	25
10		4d. sepia	15	20
11		4d. red	15	30
12		5d. blue	15	30

For War Occupation issues and issues of independent postal administration from 1967 see GUERNSEY.

III. ISLE OF MAN.

1.

2.

1958.

1	**1.**	2½d. red	45	80
2	**2.**	3d. lilac	20	10
3p		4d. blue	20	15
5		4d. sepia	20	30
6		4d. red	45	60
7		5d. blue	45	60

3.

1971. Decimal Currency.

8.	**3.**	2½p. red	20	15
9.		3p. blue	20	15
10.		5p. violet	70	75
11.		7½p. brown	70	90

For issues of independent postal administration from 1973 see ISLE OF MAN.

IV. JERSEY.

8.

9.

1958.

9.	**8.**	2½d. red	35	50
10p.	**9.**	3d. lilac	20	20
11p.		4d. blue	20	25
12.		4d. sepia	20	25
13.		4d. red	20	30
14.		5d. blue	20	40

For War Occupation issues and issues of independent postal administration from 1969 see JERSEY.

V. NORTHERN IRELAND.

N 1.

N 2.

N 3.

N 4.

1958.

NI 1.	N **1.**	**3d. lilac**	20	10
NI 2.		**4d. blue**	20	15
NI 8.		**4d. sepia**	20	15
NI 9.		**4d. red**	20	20
NI 10.		**5d. blue**	20	20
NI 3.	N **2.**	**6d. purple**	20	20
NI 4.		**9d. green**	30	50
NI 5.	N **3.**	**1s. 3d. green** ..	30	50
NI 6.		**1s. 6d. blue**.. ..	30	50

1971.

NI 12	N 4	2½p. mauve ..	60	25
NI 14		3p. blue	20	15
NI 15		3½p. grey	20	20
NI 17		4½p. blue	25	25
NI 18		5p. violet	1·00	1·00
NI 19		5½p. violet ..	20	20
NI 21		6½p. turquoise ..	20	20
NI 22		7p. brown	35	25
NI 23		7½p. brown ..	2·00	2·00
NI 24		8p. red	30	30
NI 25		8½p. green ..	30	30
NI 26		9p. violet	30	30
NI 28		10p. brown ..	35	35
NI 29		10½p. blue ..	40	40
NI 30		11p. red	40	40
NI 34		11½p. drab ..	80	60
NI 31		12p. green ..	50	45
NI 36		12½p. green ..	50	40
NI 37		13p. brown ..	90	35
NI 32		13½p. brown ..	60	70
NI 39		14p. blue	55	35
NI 40		15p. blue	60	30
NI 41		15½p. violet ..	80	65
NI 42		16p. brown ..	90	1·00
NI 44		17p. blue	50	40
NI 45		18p. violet ..	80	80
NI 46		18p. grey	80	70
NI 47		18p. green ..	30	35
NI 49		19p. red	60	60
NI 69		19p. bistre ..	30	35
NI 50		19½p. grey ..	1·75	1·75
NI 51		20p. black ..	55	40
NI 52		20½p. blue ..	4·00	4·00
NI 53		22p. blue	90	1·10
NI 54		22p. green ..	85	1·00
NI 55		22p. red	85	40
NI 56		23p. green ..	80	1·10
NI 57		24p. red	70	1·10
NI 58		24p. brown ..	40	45
NI 70		25p. red	40	45
NI 60		26p. red	90	1·25
NI 61		26p. brown ..	70	60
NI 62a		28p. blue	80	80
NI 63		28p. grey	45	50
NI 71		30p. grey	45	50
NI 64		31p. purple ..	1·25	1·10
NI 65		32p. blue	1·10	1·10
NI 66		34p. grey	1·00	1·00
NI 67		37p. red	1·00	1·10
NI 68		39p. mauve ..	60	65
NI 72		41p. drab	65	70

VI. SCOTLAND.

S 1.

S 2.

S 3.

S 4.

1958.

S 7	S **1.**	**3d. lilac**	10	15
S 8		**4d. blue**	10	15
S 9		**4d. sepia**	10	10
S 10		**4d. red**	10	10
S 11		**5d. blue**	20	10
S 3	S **2.**	**6d. purple**	20	15
S 4		**9d. green**	30	30
S 5	S **3.**	**1s. 3d. green**	30	30
S 6		**1s. 6d. blue**	35	30

1971. Decimal Currency.

S 14	S 4	2½p. mauve	25	15
S 16		3p. blue	15	15
S 17		3½p. grey	20	20
S 19		4½p. blue	25	20
S 20		5p. violet	1·25	1·25
S 21		5½p. violet	20	20
S 23		6½p. blue	20	20
S 24		7p. brown	25	25
S 25		7½p. brown	1·50	1·50
S 26		8p. red	30	40
S 27		8½p. green	30	30
S 28		9p. violet	30	30
S 29		10p. brown	35	30
S 31		10½p. blue	45	35
S 32		11p. red	45	35
S 36		11½p. drab	85	60
S 33		12p. green	50	30
S 38		12½p. green	50	40
S 39		13p. brown	80	30
S 34		13½p. brown	60	65
S 54		14p. blue	40	30
S 56		15p. blue	50	30
S 41		15½p. violet	70	65
S 42		16p. brown	70	45
S 58		17p. blue	50	35
S 44		18p. violet	80	80
S 59		18p. grey	80	80
S 60		18p. green	30	35
S 62		19p. red	60	45
S 81		19p. bistre	30	35
S 45		19½p. grey	1·75	1·75
S 64		20p. black	60	30
S 46		20½p. blue	4·00	4·00
S 47		22p. blue	80	1·10
S 65		22p. green	1·00	1·10
S 66		22p. red	90	40
S 67		23p. green	90	1·10
S 69		24p. red	70	70
S 70		24p. brown	40	45
S 82		25p. red	40	45
S 49		26p. red	1·00	1·10
S 73		26p. brown	70	70
S 74		28p. blue	85	75
S 75		28p. grey	45	50
S 83		30p. grey	45	50
S 76		31p. purple	1·50	1·50
S 77		32p. blue	1·10	1·00
S 78		34p. grey	1·00	1·00
S 79		37p. red	1·00	1·00
S 80		39p. mauve	60	65
S 84		41p. drab	65	70

VII. WALES.

W 1.

W 2.

W 3.

W 4.

1958.

W 1	W **1.**	**3d. lilac**	20	10
W 8		**4d. blue**	20	10
W 9		**4d. sepia**	20	10
W 10		**4d. red**	20	20
W 11		**5d. blue**	20	10
W 3	W **2.**	**6d. purple**	40	20
W 4		**9d. green**	30	35
W 5	W **3.**	**1s. 3d. green** ..	30	30
W 6		**1s. 6d. blue**.. ..	35	30

1971. Decimal Currency.

W 13	W 4	2½p. mauve ..	20	15
W 15		3p. blue	20	20
W 16		3½p. grey	20	25
W 18		4½p. blue	25	20
W 19		5p. violet	1·00	1·00
W 20		5½p. violet ..	20	25
W 22		6½p. blue	20	20
W 23		7p. brown	25	25
W 24		7½p. brown ..	1·75	1·90
W 25		8p. red	30	30
W 26		8½p. green ..	30	30
W 27		9p. violet	30	30
W 29		10p. brown ..	35	30
W 30		10½p. blue ..	40	35
W 31		11p. red	40	45
W 35		11½p. drab ..	85	60

W 32	W 4	12p. green	50	45
W 37		12½p. green	70	60
W 38		13p. brown	50	35
W 33		13½p. brown	60	70
W 40		14p. blue	55	30
W 41		15p. blue	40	30
W 42		15½p. violet	80	65
W 43		16p. brown	1·50	1·25
W 45		17p. blue	50	35
W 46		18p. violet	80	75
W 47		18p. grey	1·00	45
W 48		18p. green	30	35
W 50		19p. red	60	45
W 70		19p. bistre	30	35
W 51		19½p. grey	1·75	1·75
W 52		20p. black	30	30
W 53		20½p. blue	4·00	4·00
W 54		22p. blue	1·10	1·00
W 55		22p. green	80	1·10
W 56		22p. red	60	50
W 57		23p. green	80	1·10
W 58		24p. red	70	1·10
W 59		24p. brown	40	45
W 71		25p. red	40	45
W 61		26p. red	90	1·10
W 62		26p. brown	70	70
W 63a		28p. blue	80	65
W 64		28p. grey	45	50
W 72		30p. grey	45	50
W 65		31p. purple	1·10	1·10
W 66		32p. blue	1·10	1·10
W 67		34p. grey	1·00	1·00
W 68		37p. red	1·00	1·00
W 69		39p. mauve	60	65
W 73		41p. drab	65	70

OFFICIAL STAMPS
(for Government Departments)

ADMIRALTY
Overprinted **ADMIRALTY OFFICIAL.**

1903. Stamps of King Edward VII.

O 107	**83.**	½d. turquoise	7·00	4·00
O 102	–	1d. red	5·00	2·50
O 103	–	1½d. purple and green	60·00	45·00
O 104	–	2d. green and red	£100	50·00
O 105	**83.**	2½d. blue	£120	40·00
O 106	–	3d. purple on yellow	£100	38·00

ARMY
Overprinted **ARMY OFFICIAL.**

1896. Stamps of Queen Victoria.

O 41.	**71.**	½d. red	1·50	75
O 42.		½d. green	1·75	4·00
O 43.	**57.**	1d. lilac	1·50	75
O 44.	**74.**	2½d. purple on blue	4·00	3·00
O 45.	**79.**	6d. purple on red	16·00	10·00

1902. Stamps of King Edward VII.

O 48.	**83.**	½d. turquoise	2·00	65
O 49.		1d. red	1·50	55
O 50.		6d. purple	60·00	32·00

BOARD OF EDUCATION
Overprinted **BOARD OF EDUCATION.**

1902. Stamps of Queen Victoria.

O 81.	**78.**	5d. purple and blue	£525	£100
O 82.	**82.**	1s. green and red	£950	£375

1902. Stamps of King Edward VII.

O 83.	**83.**	½d. turquoise	18·00	6·00
O 84.		1d. red	18·00	5·00
O 85.		2½d. blue	£500	50·00
O 86.	–	5d. purple and blue	£2000	£950
O 87.	–	1s. green and red	£35000	£25000

GOVERNMENT PARCELS
Overprinted **GOVT. PARCELS.**

1883. Stamps of Queen Victoria.

O 61	**62**	1½d. purple	£100	25·00
O 62	–	6d. green (No. 194)	£800	£275
O 63	–	9d. green (No. 195)	£650	£180
O 64	**25**	1s. brown (No. 163)	£425	70·00

1887. Stamps of Queen Victoria.

O 69	**57**	1d. lilac	28·00	8·00
O 65	**72**	1½d. purple and green	14·00	2·00
O 70	**73**	2d. green and red	45·00	7·00
O 71	**77**	4½d. green and red	£100	75·00
O 66	**79**	6d. purple on red	28·00	10·00
O 67	**80**	9d. purple and blue	55·00	15·00
O 68	**82**	1s. green	£120	70·00
O 72		1s. green and red	£160	50·00

1902. Stamps of King Edward VII.

O 74.	**83.**	1d. red	17·00	6·00
O 75.	–	2d. green and red	65·00	18·00
O 76.	**83.**	6d. purple	£100	18·00
O 77.	–	9d. purple and blue	£225	50·00
O 78.	–	1s. green and red	£350	85·00

INLAND REVENUE
Overprinted **I. R. OFFICIAL.**

Stamps of Queen Victoria.

1882.

O 1	**52.**	½d. green	12·00	3·00
O 5		½d. blue	25·00	15·00
O 3	**57.**	1d. lilac	1·50	65
O 6	–	2½d. purple (No. 190)	£110	35·00
O 4	**34.**	6d. grey (No. 161)	75·00	20·00
O 7	–	1s. green (No. 196)	£2500	£450
O 9	–	5s. red (No. 181)	£1300	£400
O 10	–	10s. blue (No. 183)	£2250	£475
O 11	**61.**	£1 brown	£18000	

1888.

O 13.	**71.**	½d. red	1·50	50
O 17.		½d. green	4·00	3·00
O 14.	**74.**	2½d. purple on blue	50·00	4·00
O 18.	**79.**	6d. purple on red	£100	22·00
O 15.	**82.**	1s. green	£200	20·00
O 19.		1s. green and red	£600	£100
O 16.	**61.**	£1 green	£3750	£450

1902. Stamps of King Edward VII.

O 20.	**83.**	½d. turquoise	17·00	1·50
O 21.		1d. red	10·00	70
O 22.		2½d. blue	£400	60·00
O 23.		6d. purple	£85000	£65000
O 24.	–	1s. green and red	£500	65·00
O 25.	–	5s. red	£4000	£1300
O 26.	–	10s. blue	£15000	£9500
O 27.	–	£1 green	£12000	£6000

OFFICE OF WORKS
Overprinted **O.W. OFFICIAL.**

1896. Stamps of Queen Victoria.

O 31.	**71.**	½d. red	90·00	40·00
O 32.		½d. green	£150	75·00
O 33.	**57.**	1d. lilac	£150	40·00
O 34.	**78.**	5d. purple and blue	£750	£150
O 35.	**81.**	10d. purple and red	£1300	£225

1902. Stamps of King Edward VII.

O 36.	**83.**	½d. turquoise	£350	80·00
O 37.	–	1d. red	£350	80·00
O 38.	–	2d. green and red	£600	75·00
O 39.	**83.**	2½d. blue	£700	£200
O 40.	–	10d. purple and red	£5000	£1500

ROYAL HOUSEHOLD
Overprinted **R.H. OFFICIAL.**

1902. Stamps of King Edward VII.

O 91.	**83.**	**½d. turquoise**	**£150**	**95·00**
O 92.		**1d. red**	**£130**	**85·00**

POSTAGE DUE STAMPS.

D 1. D 4.

1914.

D 10	D 1.	½d. green	50	30
D 56		½d. orange	10	45
D 11		1d. red	50	30
D 57		1d. blue	10	15
D 12		1½d. brown	35·00	15·00
D 58		1½d. green	90	2·00
D 69		2d. black	20	40
D 60		3d. violet	40	15
D 15		4d. green	10·00	2·00
D 61		4d. blue	40	20
D 62		5d. brown	45	45
D 63		6d. purple	60	30
D 76		8d. red	75	75
D 17		1s. blue	6·00	75
D 64		1s. brown	1·40	25
D 65		2s. 6d. purple on yell.	4·00	45
D 66		5s. red on yellow	7·50	80
D 67		10s. blue on yellow	9·00	4·00
D 68		£1 black on yellow	45·00	7·50

On the 2s. 6d. to £1 the inscription **reads** "TO PAY".

1970. Decimal Currency.

D 77.	–	½p. blue	10	20
D 78.	–	1p. purple	10	15
D 79.	–	2p. green	10	15
D 80.	–	3p. blue	15	15
D 81.	–	4p. brown	15	15
D 82.	–	5p. violet	20	20
D 83.	–	7p. brown	35	45
D 84.	D 4.	10p. red	30	20
D 85.		11p. green	50	60
D 86.		20p. brown	60	50
D 87.		50p. blue	1·50	40
D 88.		£1 black	2·75	60
D 89.		£5 yellow and black	30·00	2·00

DESIGN: ½p. to 7p. similar to Type **D 4**, but with "TO PAY" reading vertically upwards at the left.

D 5. D 7

1982.

D 90.	D 5.	1p. red	10	10
D 91.		2p. blue	10	10
D 92.		3p. mauve	10	15
D 93.		4p. blue	10	20
D 94.		5p. brown	10	20
D 95.	–	10p. brown	15	25
D 96.	–	20p. green	30	30
D 97.	–	25p. blue	40	70
D 98.	–	50p. black	75	50
D 99.	–	£1 red	1·50	50
D100.	–	£2 blue	3·00	50
D101.	–	£5 orange	7·50	50

DESIGN: 10p. to £5, As Type **D 5** but with "TO PAY" horizontal.

1994.

D102	D 7	1p. red, yellow & blk	10	10
D103		2p. mauve, pur & blk	10	10
D104		5p. yellow, brn & blk	10	10
D105		10p. yell, grn & blk	15	20
D106		20p. green, vio & blk	30	35
D107		25p. mve, red & blk	40	45
D108		£1 violet, mve & blk	1·50	1·60
D109		£1.20 blue, grn & blk	1·75	1·90
D110		£5 dp grn, grn & blk	7·50	7·75

GUERNSEY, ISLE OF MAN and JERSEY are now in Country alphabetical order.

GRENADA

One of the Windward Is., Br. W. Indies. Ministerial Government was introduced on 1 January 1960. Achieved Associated Statehood on 3 March 1967 and Independence during 1974.

1861. 12 pence = 1 shilling;
20 schillings = 1 pound.
1949. 100 cents = 1 West Indian dollar.

1.

5.

1861.

14.	**1.**	1d. green	55·00	5·00
6.		6d. red	£600	12·00

1875. Surch. **POSTAGE** and value in words.

21.	**5.**	½d. mauve	11·00	5·50
22.		2½d. lake	45·00	5·50
23.		4d. blue	90·00	8·00
13.		1s. mauve	£650	9·00

1883. Revenue stamp surch. crown and value (in green) optd. **POSTAGE.**

27.	**5.**	1d. orange	£225	45·00

1883. Revenue stamp as last but optd. **POSTAGE** twice diagonally.

29.	**5.**	Half of 1d. orange	£180	£110

13.

21.

1883.

30.	**13.**	½d. green	90	60
31.		1d. red	55·00	3·25
32.		2½d. blue	6·50	50
33.		4d. grey	4·50	1·75
34.		6d. mauve	3·50	3·75
35.		8d. brown	8·00	12·00
36.		1s. violet	95·00	55·00

1886. Revenue stamps as No. 27 but surch. **POSTAGE** and value in words or figures.

43.	**5.**	½d. on 2s. orange	12·00	17·00
37.		1d. on 1½d. orange	32·00	25·00
39.		1d. on 4d. orange	£120	80·00
38.		1d. on 1s. orange	32·00	30·00
41.		4d. on 2s. orange	28·00	16·00

1887. As Type 3, but inscr. "GRENADA POSTAGE & REVENUE" at top.

40.	**13.**	1d. red	50	20

1890. Revenue stamp as No. 27 but surch. **POSTAGE AND REVENUE 1d.**

45	5	1d. on 2s. orange	48·00	48·00

1891. Surch **POSTAGE AND REVENUE 1d.**

46.	**13.**	1d. on 8d. brown	9·00	11·00

1891. Surch. **2½d.**

47.	**13.**	2½d. on 8d. brown	8·00	11·00

1895.

48.	**21.**	½d. mauve and green	1·75	50
49.		1d. mauve and red	3·75	30
50.		2d. mauve and brown	30·00	32·00
51.		2½d. mauve and blue	5·00	70
52.		3d. mauve and orange	6·50	16·00
53.		6d. mauve and green	6·50	10·00
54.		8d. mauve and black	12·00	27·00
55.		1s. green and orange	16·00	24·00

23. Flagship of Columbus
(Columbus named Grenada
"La Concepcion").

1898. Discovery of Grenada by Columbus.

56.	**23.**	2½d. blue	12·00	5·00

1902. As T **21**, but portrait of King Edward VII.

57	½d. purple and green	2·00	30
58	1d. purple and red	2·00	20
59	2d. purple and brown	2·50	6·50
60	2½d. purple and blue	3·25	1·25
71	3d. purple and orange	2·25	4·50
72	6d. purple and green	2·75	4·00
63	1s. green and orange	3·25	15·00
64	2s. green and blue	15·00	40·00
65	5s. green and red	35·00	48·00
66	10s. green and purple	95·00	£170

26. Badge of the Colony. **28.**

1906.

No.	Type	Description	Unused	Used
77.	**26.**	½d. green	1·25	30
78.		1d. red	1·00	10
79.		2d. orange..	1·50	3·00
80.		2½d. blue	3·00	1·50
84.		3d. purple on yellow ..	1·75	1·75
85.		6d. purple..	16·00	23·00
86.		1s. black on green ..	3·00	3·75
87.		2s. blue & purple on blue	15·00	12·00
88.		5s. green & red on yellow	48·00	60·00
83.		10s. green & red on green	75·00	£140

1913.

No.	Type	Description	Unused	Used
112	28	½d. green	75	15
113		1d. red	50	20
114		1d. brown	1·00	15
115		1½d. red	1·25	80
116		2d. orange	1·00	15
117		2d. grey	2·25	1·75
117a		2½d. blue	1·50	85
118		2½d. grey	75	6·50
96		3d. purple on yellow ..	40	85
121		3d. blue	1·25	5·50
123		4d. black & red on yell	75	3·25
124		5d. purple and green ..	1·25	3·50
97		6d. purple	90	7·00
126		6d. black and red ..	2·00	2·50
127		9d. purple and black ..	2·25	6·00
98a		1s. black on green ..	80	4·50
129		1s. brown	3·00	12·00
99		2s. purple & blue on bl	3·25	10·00
131		2s. 6d. blk & red on bl	6·00	14·00
132		3s. green and violet ..	6·00	26·00
133		5s. green & red on yell	12·00	28·00
101		10s. green & red on grn	45·00	65·00

1916. Optd. **WAR TAX.**

No.	Type	Description	Unused	Used
111.	**28.**	1d. red	20	20

31. Grand Anse Beach.

DESIGNS—VERT. 1½d. Grand Etang. 2½d. St. George's.

32. Badge of the Colony.

1934.

No.	Type	Description	Unused	Used
135.	**31.**	½d. green	15	40
136a.	**32.**	1d. black and brown	65	35
137a.	–	1½d. black and red ..	1·25	55
138.	**32.**	2d. black and orange	90	40
139.	–	2½d. blue	40	30
140.	**32.**	3d. black and olive ..	45	1·00
141.		6d. black and purple	80	1·10
142.		1s. black and brown	80	2·50
143.		2s. 6d. black and blue	7·00	16·00
144.		5s. black and violet ..	32·00	38·00

1935. Silver Jubilee. As T **13** of Antigua.

No.	Description	Unused	Used
145.	½d. black and green ..	40	20
146.	1d. blue and grey ..	50	70
147.	1½d. blue and red ..	50	55
148.	1s. grey and purple ..	4·75	11·00

1937. Coronation. As T **2** of Aden.

No.	Description	Unused	Used
149.	1d. violet	40	20
150.	1½d. red..	40	20
151.	2½d. blue	80	30

35. King George VI. **40.** Badge of the Colony.

1937.

No.	Type	Description	Unused	Used
152b	**35**	¼d. brown	20	30

1938. As 1934, but with portrait of King George VI.

No.	Type	Description	Unused	Used
153b	**31**	½d. green	15	60
154	**32**	1d. black and brown	30	20
155	–	1½d. black and red ..	40	20
156	**32**	2d. black and orange	30	30
157	–	2½d. blue	30	30
158ab	**32**	3d. black and olive ..	30	80
159		6d. black and purple	60	30
160		1s. black and brown	60	30
161		2s. black and blue ..	10·00	1·25
162		5s. black and violet ..	2·75	1·50
163e		10s. blue and red ..	24·00	7·00

1946. Victory. As T **9** of Aden.

No.	Description	Unused	Used
164.	1½d. red	10	10
165.	3½d. blue	10	10

1948. Silver Wedding. As T **10/11** of Aden.

No.	Description	Unused	Used
166.	1½d. red	10	10
167.	10s. grey	6·50	15·00

1949. U.P.U. As T **20/23** of Antigua.

No.	Description	Unused	Used
168.	5 c. blue	20	10
169.	6 c. olive	35	40
170.	12 c. mauve	35	20
171.	24 c. brown	35	20

41. King George VI. **42.** Badge of the Colony.

1951.

No.	Type	Description	Unused	Used
172.	**41.**	½ c. black and brown ..	15	1·00
173.		1 c. black and green ..	15	25
174.		2 c. black and brown ..	15	30
175.		3 c. black and red ..	15	10
176.		4 c. black and orange ..	35	40
177.		5 c. black and violet ..	20	10
178.		6 c. black and olive ..	30	60
179.		7 c. black and blue ..	1·50	10
180.		12 c. black and purple	2·00	30
181.	**42.**	25 c. black and brown..	2·25	50
182.		50 c. black and blue ..	5·00	40
183.		$1·50 black and orange	7·50	3·50
184.		$2·50 slate and red ..	5·50	4·50

No. 184 is larger (24½ × 30½ mm.).

1951. Inauguration of B.W.I. University College. As T **24/25** of Antigua.

No.	Type	Description	Unused	Used
185.	**22.**	3 c. black and red ..	45	20
186.	**23.**	6 c. black and olive ..	45	20

1951. New Constitution. Optd. **NEW CONSTITUTION 1951.**

No.	Type	Description	Unused	Used
187.	**41.**	3 c. black and red ..	10	10
188.		4 c. black and orange..	10	10
189.		5 c. black and violet ..	10	10
190.		12 c. black and purple..	10	15

1953. Coronation. As T **13** of Aden.

No.	Description	Unused	Used
191.	3 c. black and red ..	15	10

1953. As T **41**, but with portrait of Queen Elizabeth II, and T **42**, but Royal Cypher changed.

No.	Type	Description	Unused	Used
192	**41.**	½ c. black and brown ..	10	10
193		1 c. black and green ..	10	10
214		2 c. black and brown ..	10	10
195		3 c. black and red ..	10	10
196		4 c. black and orange..	10	10
197		5 c. black and violet ..	10	10
198		6 c. black and olive ..	45	30
199		7 c. black and blue ..	1·25	10
200		12 c. black and purple..	30	10
201	**42.**	25 c. black and brown..	75	20
202		50 c. black and blue ..	5·00	40
203		$1.50 black and orange	9·50	8·50
204		$2.50 slate and red ..	13·00	5·00

No. 204 is larger (24½ × 30½ mm.).

1958. British Caribbean Federation. As T **28** of Antigua.

No.	Description	Unused	Used
205.	3 c. green	35	10
206.	6 c. blue	45	30
207.	12 c. red	55	10

48. Queen Victoria, Queen Elizabeth II, Mail Van and Post Office, St. George's.

1961. Grenada Stamp Centenary.

No.	Type	Description	Unused	Used
208.	**48.**	3 c. red and black ..	15	10
209.	–	8 c. blue and orange ..	40	20
210.	–	25 c. lake and blue ..	40	20

DESIGNS (incorporating Queen Victoria and Queen Elizabeth II): 8 c. Flagship of Columbus. 25 c. "Solent I" (paddle-steamer) and Dakota aircraft.

1963. Freedom from Hunger. As T **28** of Aden.

No.	Description	Unused	Used
211.	8 c. green	30	15

1963. Cent of Red Cross. As T **33** of Antigua.

No.	Description	Unused	Used
212.	3 c. red and black.. ..	10	15
213.	25 c. red and blue.. ..	20	15

1965. Cent of I.T.U. As T **36** of Antigua.

No.	Description	Unused	Used
221.	2 c. orange and olive ..	10	10
222.	50 c. yellow and red ..	25	20

1965. I.C.Y. As T **37** of Antigua.

No.	Description	Unused	Used
223.	1 c. purple and turquoise..	10	15
224.	25 c. green and lavender..	20	15

1966. Churchill Commem. As T **38** of Antigua.

No.	Description	Unused	Used
225.	1 c. blue	10	15
226.	3 c. green	10	15
227.	25 c. brown	15	10
228.	35 c. violet..	25	10

1966. Royal Visit. As T **39** of Antigua.

No.	Description	Unused	Used
229.	3 c. black and blue ..	15	15
230.	35 c. black and mauve ..	40	15

52. Hillsborough, Carriacou.

1966. Multicoloured.

No.	Description	Unused	Used
231.	1 c. Type **52**	10	10
232.	2 c. Bougainvillea ..	10	10
233.	3 c. Flamboyant Plant ..	10	10
234.	5 c. Levera Beach ..	10	10
235.	6 c. Careenage (inscr. "CARENAGE"), St. George's ..	20	10
236.	8 c. Annandale Falls ..	20	10
237.	10 c. Cocoa Pods ..	15	10
238.	12 c. Inner Harbour ..	10	10
239.	15 c. Nutmeg	15	10
240.	25 c. St. George's	20	10
241.	35 c. Grand Anse Beach ..	30	10
242.	50 c. Bananas	80	90
243.	$1 Badge of the Colony ..	3·50	1·25
244.	$2 Queen Elizabeth II ..	4·25	2·50
245.	$3 Map of Grenada ..	4·25	9·00

Nos. 243/5 are vert. and larger, 25 × 39 mm.

1966. World Cup Football Championship. As T **40** of Antigua.

No.	Description	Unused	Used
246.	5 c. multicoloured ..	10	10
247.	50 c. multicoloured ..	25	20

1966. Inauguration of W.H.O. Headquarters, Geneva. As T **41** of Antigua.

No.	Description	Unused	Used
248.	8 c. black, green and blue	10	10
249.	25 c. black, purple & ochre	25	20

1966. 20th Anniv. of U.N.E.S.C.O. As T **54/56** of Antigua.

No.	Description	Unused	Used
250.	2 c. multicoloured.. ..	10	10
251.	15 c. yellow, violet & orge.	15	10
252.	50 c. black, purple & orge.	30	35

1967. Statehood. Nos. 232/3, 236 and **240.** optd. **ASSOCIATED STATEHOOD 1967.**

No.	Description	Unused	Used
253	2 c. multicoloured ..	10	15
254	3 c. multicoloured ..	10	10
255	8 c. multicoloured ..	15	10
256	25 c. multicoloured ..	15	15

1967. World Fair, Montreal, Nos. 232, 237, 239 and 243/4 surch., or optd. **expo 67 MONTREAL · CANADA** and emblem only.

No.	Description	Unused	Used
257.	1 c. on 15 c. multicoloured	10	15
258.	2 c. multicoloured ..	10	15
259.	3 c. on 10 c. multicoloured	10	15
260.	$1 multicoloured	30	15
261.	$2 multicoloured ..	45	25

1967. Nos. 231/45 optd. **ASSOCIATED STATEHOOD.**

No.	Type	Description	Unused	Used
262.	**52.**	1 c. multicoloured ..	10	10
263.	–	2 c. multicoloured ..	10	10
264.	–	3 c. multicoloured ..	10	10
265.	–	5 c. multicoloured ..	10	10
266.	–	6 c. multicoloured ..	10	10
267.	–	8 c. multicoloured ..	10	10
268.	–	10 c. multicoloured ..	10	10
269.	–	12 c. multicoloured ..	10	10
270.	–	15 c. multicoloured ..	15	10
271.	–	25 c. multicoloured ..	20	10
272.	–	35 c. multicoloured ..	55	10
273.	–	50 c. multicoloured ..	70	20
274.	–	$1 multicoloured ..	70	60
275.	–	$2 multicoloured ..	1·25	2·50
276.	–	$3 multicoloured ..	2·25	2·50

70. Kennedy and Local Flower.

1968. 50th Birth Anniv. of Pres. Kennedy. Multicoloured.

No.	Description	Unused	Used
277.	1 c. Type **70**	10	15
278.	15 c. Type **70**	10	10
279.	25 c. Kennedy and Strelitzia	10	10
280.	35 c. Kennedy and Roses	10	10
281.	50 c. As 25 c.	15	15
282.	$1 As 35 c.	25	65

73. Scout Bugler.

1968. World Scout Jamboree, Idaho. Mult.

No.	Description	Unused	Used
283.	1 c. Type **73**	10	10
284.	2 c. Scouts camping ..	10	10
285.	3 c. Lord Baden-Powell..	10	10
286.	35 c. Type **73**	20	10
287.	50 c. As 2 c.	25	20
288.	$1 As 3 c...	40	40

76. "Near Antibes".

1968. Paintings by Sir Winston Churchill. Multicoloured.

No.	Description	Unused	Used
289.	10 c. Type **76**	10	10
290.	12 c. "The Mediterranean"	15	10
291.	15 c. "St. Jean, Cap Ferrat"	15	10
292.	25 c. Type **76**	20	10
293.	35 c. As No. 291	25	10
294.	50 c. Sir Winston painting	35	25

1968. No. 275 surch.

No.	Description	Unused	Used
295	$5 on $2 multicoloured ..	1·50	2·25

1968. "Children Need Milk". Surch. **CHILDREN NEED MILK** and value.

(a) Nos. 244/5.

No.	Description	Unused	Used
296.	2 c.+3 c. on $2 multicoloured	10	10
297.	3 c.+3 c. on $3 multicoloured	10	10

(b) Nos. 243/4.

No.	Description	Unused	Used
298.	1 c.+3 c. on $1 multicoloured	10	40
299.	2 c.+3 c. on $2 multicoloured	17·00	40·00

83. Edith McGuire (U.S.A.).

1968. Olympic Games, Mexico.

No.	Type	Description	Unused	Used
300.	**83.**	1 c. brn., blk. and blue..	10	10
301.	–	2 c. multicoloured ..	10	10
302.	–	3 c. scarlet, brn. & grn.	10	10
303.	**83.**	10 c. multicoloured ..	10	10
304.	–	50 c. multicoloured ..	30	40
305.	–	60 c. red, brn. and orge.	40	50

DESIGNS: 2 c., 50 c. Arthur Wint (Jamaica). 3 c., 60 c. Ferreira de Silva (Brazil).

86. Hibiscus.

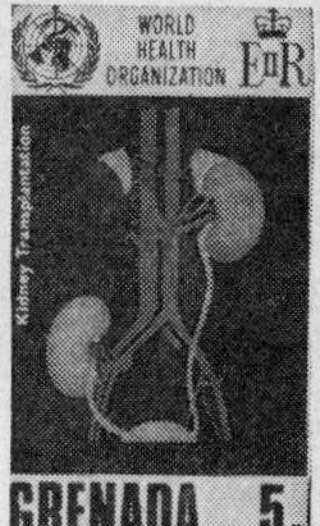

102. Kidney Transplant.

1968. Multicoloured.

No.	Description	Unused	Used
306	1 c. Type **86**	10	10
307	2 c. Strelitzia	10	10
308	3 c. Bougainvillea	10	10
309	5 c. Rock hind	10	10
310	6 c. Sailfish	10	10
311	8 c. Snapper	10	30
312	10 c. Marine toad	10	10
313	12 c. Turtle	15	10
314	15 c. Tree boa	90	60
314a	15 c. Thunbergia	4·75	2·50
315	25 c. Greater Trinidadian murine opossum	30	10
316	35 c. Nine-banded armadillo	35	10
317	50 c. Mona monkey	45	25
317a	75 c. Yacht in St. Georges Harbour	8·50	7·50
318	$1 Bananaquit	3·00	1·50
319	$2 Brown pelican	3·50	6·50
320	$3 Magnificent frigate bird	4·50	5·00
321	$5 Bare-eyed thrush	4·50	14·00

Nos. 309, 311/12, 314, 316 and 317a. are horiz. Nos. 318/21 are larger ($25\frac{1}{2} \times 48$ mm.).

1968. 20th Anniversary of World Health Organization. Multicoloured.

No.	Description	Unused	Used
322.	5 c. Type **102**	15	10
323.	25 c. Heart transplant	35	10
324.	35 c. Lung transplant	35	10
325.	50 c. Eye transplant	40	30

106. "The Adoration of the Kings" (Veronese).

1968. Christmas.

No.	Description	Unused	Used
326. **106.**	5 c. multicoloured	10	10
327. –	15 c. multicoloured	10	10
328. –	35 c. multicoloured	10	10
329. –	$1 multicoloured	30	40

DESIGNS: 15 c. "Madonna and Child with Saints John and Catherine" (Titian). 35 c. "The Adoration of the Kings" (Botticelli). $1, "A Warrior adoring" (Catena).

1969. Caribbean Free Trade Area Exhibition. Nos. 300/5 surch. **VISIT CARIFTA EXPO '69 APRIL 5-30** and value.

No.	Description	Unused	Used
330. **83.**	5 c. on 1 c.	10	10
331. –	8 c. on 2 c.	10	10
332. –	25 c. on 3 c.	10	10
333. **83.**	35 c. on 10 c.	10	10
334. –	$1 on 50 c.	20	25
335. –	$2 on 60 c.	35	40

111. Dame Hylda Bynoe (Governor) and Island Scene.

1969. Carifta Expo '69. Multicoloured.

No.	Description	Unused	Used
336.	5 c. Type **111**	10	10
337.	15 c. Premier E. M. Gairy and Island scene	10	10
338.	50 c. Type **111**	10	20
339.	60 c. Emblems of 1958 and 1967 World Fairs	10	25

114. Dame Hylda Bynoe.

1969. Human Rights Year. Multicoloured

No.	Description	Unused	Used
340.	5 c. Type **114**	10	10
341.	25 c. Dr. Martin Luther King	10	10
342.	35 c. As 5 c.	10	10
343.	$1 "Balshazzar's Feast" (Rembrandt) (horiz.)	20	25

117. Batsman and Wicket Keeper.

1969. Cricket.

No.	Description	Unused	Used
344. **117.**	3 c. yell., brn. and blue	25	50
345. –	10 c. multicoloured	30	15
346. –	25 c. brn., ochre & grn.	60	70
347. –	35 c. multicoloured	80	85

DESIGNS: 10 c. Batsman playing defensive stroke. 25 c. Batsman sweeping ball. 35 c. Batsman playing on-drive.

129. Astronaut handling Moon Rock.

1969. 1st Man on the Moon. Multicoloured.

No.	Description	Unused	Used
348.	½ c. Astronaut handling Moon Rock (different)	10	10
349.	1 c. Moon rocket en-route to the moon	10	10
350.	2 c. Space Module landing on moon	10	10
351.	3 c. Declaration left on the moon by astronauts	10	10
352.	8 c. Module separating from Space Ship	10	10
353.	25 c. Spacecraft after lift-off	15	10
354.	35 c. Spacecraft in orbit	15	10
355.	50 c. Final descent of Space Module	20	10
356.	$1 Type **129**	35	30

The ½ c. is larger (56 × 36 mm.), and has a different frame design than Type **129**. The 25, 35 and 50 c. are vert.

130. Gandhi. (Reduced size illustration—actual size $54 \times 30\frac{1}{2}$ mm.).

1969. Birth Cent. of Mahatma Gandhi. Mult.

No.	Description	Unused	Used
358.	6 c. Type **130**	15	10
359.	15 c. Gandhi (standing)	20	10
360.	25 c. Gandhi (walking)	30	10
361.	$1 Head of Gandhi	1·00	60

1969. Christmas. Nos. 326/9 optd. **1969** and surch. (No. 363).

No.	Description	Unused	Used
363. –	2 c. on 15 c. multicoloured	10	10
364. **106.**	5 c. multicoloured	10	10
365. –	35 c. multicoloured	15	10
366. –	$1 multicoloured	60	1·25

135. "Blackbeard" (Edward Teach).

1970. Pirates.

No.	Description	Unused	Used
367. **135.**	15 c. black	35	10
368. –	25 c. green	50	10
369. –	50 c. lilac	90	20
370. –	$1 carmine	1·50	75

DESIGNS: 25 c. Anne Bonney. 50 c. Jean Lafitte. $1, Mary Read.

1970. No. 348 surch.

No.	Description	Unused	Used
371	5 c. on ½ c. multicoloured	10	10

HAVE YOU READ THE NOTES AT THE BEGINNING OF THIS CATALOGUE?
These often provide answers to the enquiries we receive.

141/2. "The Last Supper" (detail, Del Sarto). (Illustration reduced. Actual size 64 × 45 mm.).

1970. Easter. Paintings.

No.	Description	Unused	Used
372. **141.**	5 c. multicoloured	10	10
373 **142.**	5 c. multicoloured	10	10
374. –	15 c. multicoloured	20	10
375. –	15 c. multicoloured	20	10
376. –	25 c. multicoloured	25	10
377. –	25 c. multicoloured	25	10
378. –	60 c. multicoloured	40	30
379. –	60 c. multicoloured	40	30

DESIGNS: 15 c. "Christ crowned with Thorns" (detail—Van Dyck). 25 c. "The Passion of Christ" (detail—Memling). 60 c. "Christ in the Tomb" (detail—Rubens).

Each value was issued in sheets containing the two stamps se-tenant. Each design is spread over two stamps as in Type **141/2**.

149. Girl with Kittens in Pram. (Illustration reduced. Actual size 59 × 34 mm.)

1970. Birth Bicentenary of Wordsworth. "Children and Pets". Multicoloured.

No.	Description	Unused	Used
381.	5 c. Type **149**	15	10
382.	15 c. Girl with puppy and kitten	20	10
383.	30 c. Boy with fishing-rod and cat	35	15
384.	60 c. Boys and girls with cats and dogs	55	30

153. Parliament of India.

1970. Commonwealth Parliamentary Assn. 7th Regional Conf. Stamps showing Parliaments country given. Multicoloured.

No.	Description	Unused	Used
386.	5 c. Type **153**	10	10
387.	25 c. Great Britain, Westminster	10	10
388.	50 c. Canada	15	15
389.	60 c. Grenada	15	15

157. Tower of the Sun.

1970. World Fair, Osaka. Multicoloured.

No.	Description	Unused	Used
391.	1 c. Type **157**	10	10
392.	2 c. Livelihood and Industry Pavilion	10	10
393.	3 c. Flower Painting (1634)	10	10
394.	10 c. "Adam and Eve" (Tintoretto)	10	10
395.	25 c. Organization For Economic Co-operation and Development (O.E.C.D.) Pavilion	25	10
396.	50 c. San Francisco Pavilion	55	20

164. Roosevelt and "Raising U.S. Flag on Iwo Jima". (Illustration reduced. Actual size 60 × 35 mm.).

1970. 25th Anniv. of Ending of World War Two. Multicoloured.

No.	Description	Unused	Used
398.	½ c. Type **164**	10	10
399.	5 c. Zhukov and "Fall of Berlin"	40	15
400.	15 c. Churchill and "Evacuation at Dunkirk"	75	25
401.	25 c. De Gaulle and "Liberation of Paris"	1·00	45
402.	50 c. Eisenhower and "D-Day Landing"	1·40	90
403.	60 c. Montgomery and "Battle of Alamein"	1·60	1·75

1970. "Philympia 1970" Stamp Exhibition, London. Nos. 353/6 optd. **PHILYMPIA LONDON 1970.**

No.	Description	Unused	Used
405. –	25 c. multicoloured	10	10
406. –	35 c. multicoloured	10	10
407. –	50 c. multicoloured	15	15
408. **129.**	$1 multicoloured	20	30

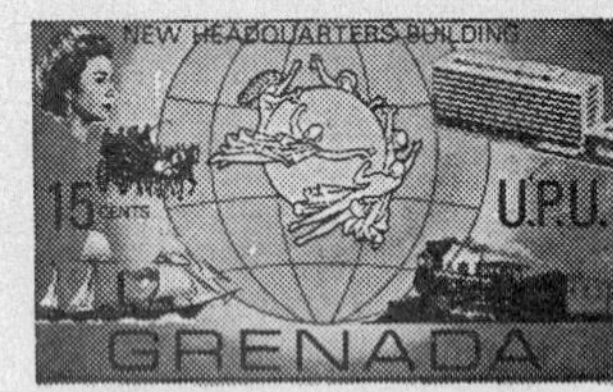

170. U.P.U. Emblem, Building and Transport.

1970. U.P.U. Headquarters Building. **Mult.**

No.	Description	Unused	Used
409.	15 c. Type **170**	25	10
410.	25 c. As Type **170**, but modern transport	25	10
411.	50 c. Sir Rowland Hill and U.P.U. Building	45	15
412.	$1 Abraham Lincoln and U.P.U. Building	70	50

The 50 c. and $1 are both vert.

171. "The Madonna of the Goldfinch" (Tiepolo).

1970. Christmas. Multicoloured.

No.	Description	Unused	Used
414.	½ c. Type **171**	10	10
415.	½ c. "The Virgin and Child with St. Peter and St. Paul" (Bouts)	10	10
416.	½ c. "The Virgin and the Child" (Bellini)	10	10
417.	2 c. "The Madonna of the Basket" (Correggio)	10	10
418.	3 c. Type **171**	10	10
419.	35 c. As No. 415	40	10
420.	50 c. As 2 c.	55	20
421.	$1 As No. 416	85	65

172. 19th-Century Nursing.

1970. Cent. of British Red Cross. Multicoloured.

No.	Description	Unused	Used
423.	5 c. Type **172**	20	10
424.	15 c. Military Ambulance, 1918	35	10
425.	25 c. First-Aid Post, 1941	55	10
426.	60 c. Red Cross Transport, 1970	1·00	80

173. John Dewey and Art Lesson.

1971. Int. Education Year. Multicoloured.

No.	Description		
428.	5 c. Type **173**	10	10
429.	10 c. Jean-Jacques Rousseau and "Alphabetisation"	15	10
430.	50 c. Maimonides and laboratory	50	15
431.	$1 Bertrand Russell and mathematics class	95	40

174. Jennifer Hosten and outline of Grenada.

1971. Winner of "Miss World" Competition (1970).

No.	Description		
433. 174.	5 c. multicoloured	10	10
434.	10 c. multicoloured	15	10
435.	15 c. multicoloured	15	10
436.	25 c. multicoloured	15	10
437.	35 c. multicoloured	20	10
438.	50 c. multicoloured	45	55

175. French and Canadian Scouts.

1971. 13th World Scout Jamboree, Asagiri, Japan. Multicoloured.

No.	Description		
440.	5 c. Type **175**	10	10
441.	35 c. German and American scouts	30	25
442.	50 c. Australian and Japanese scouts	50	50
443.	75 c. Grenada and British scouts	65	75

176. " Napoleon reviewing the Guard ". (E. Detaille).

1971. 150th Death Anniversary of Napoleon Bonaparte. Paintings. Multicoloured.

No.	Description		
445.	5 c. Type **176**	15	15
446.	15 c. " Napoleon before Madrid " (Vernet)	25	15
447.	35 c. " Napoleon crossing Mt. St. Bernard " (David)	30	15
448.	$2 " Napoleon in his study " (David)	1·25	1·75

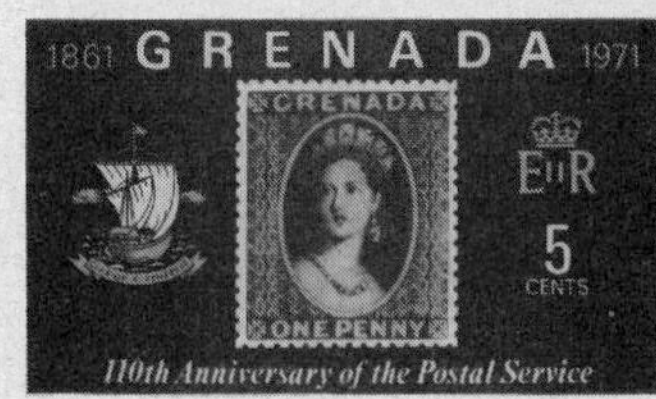

177. 1d. Stamp of 1861 and Badge of Grenada. (Illustration reduced. Actual size 59 × 34 mm.)

1971. 110th Anniv. of the Postal Service. Multicoloured.

No.	Description		
450.	5 c. Type **177**	10	20
451.	15 c. 6d. stamp of 1861 and Queen Elizabeth II	15	15
452.	35 c. 1d. and 6d. stamps of 1861 and badge of Grenada	30	20
453.	50 c. Scroll and 1d. stamp of 1861	45	1·10

178. Apollo splashdown. (Illustration reduced. Actual size 58 × 35 mm.)

1971. Apollo Moon Exploration Series. Multicoloured.

No.	Description		
455.	1 c. Type **178**	10	10
456.	2 c. Recovery of "Apollo 13"	10	10
457.	3 c. Separation of Lunar Module from "Apollo 14"	10	10
458.	10 c. Shepard and Mitchell taking samples of moon rock	25	10
459.	25 c. Moon Buggy	65	20
460.	$1 "Apollo 15" blast-off (vert.)	2·00	2·00

179. 67th Regt. of Foot, 1787.

1971. Military Uniforms. Multicoloured.

No.	Description		
462.	½ c. Type **179**	10	10
463.	1 c. 45th Regt. of Foot, 1792	10	10
464.	2 c. 29th Regt. of Foot, 1794	10	10
465.	10 c. 9th Regt. of Foot, 1801	45	20
466.	25 c. 2nd Regt. of Foot, 1815	85	35
467.	$1 70th Regt. of Foot, 1764	2·50	2·00

180. "The Adoration of the Kings" (Memling).

1972. Christmas (1971). Multicoloured.

No.	Description		
469.	15 c. Type **180**	15	10
470.	25 c. " Madonna and Child " (Michelangelo)	25	10
471.	35 c. " Madonna and Child " (Murillo)	35	10
472.	50 c. " The Virgin with the Apple " (Memling)	45	40

1972. Winter Olympic Games, Sapporo, Japan. Nos. 462/4 surch. **WINTER OLYMPICS FEB. 3-13, 1972 SAPPORO, JAPAN.** Olympic rings and premium. Nos. 476/7 additionally surch. **AIR MAIL.**

No.	Description		
474.	$2 on 2 c. multicoloured (postage)	60	90
476.	35 c. on ½ c. multicoloured (air)	20	25
477.	50 c. on 1 c. multicoloured	25	35

1972. General Election. Nos. 307/8, 310 and 315 optd. **VOTE FEB. 28 1972.**

No.	Description		
478.	2 c. multicoloured	10	10
479.	3 c. multicoloured	10	10
480.	6 c. multicoloured	10	15
481.	25 c. multicoloured	15	30

183. King Arthur.

1972. U.N.I.C.E.F. Multicoloured.

No.	Description		
482.	½ c. Type **183**	10	10
483.	1 c. Robin Hood	10	10
484.	2 c. Robinson Crusoe (vert.)	10	10
485.	25 c. Type **183**	10	10
486.	50 c. As 1 c.	25	35
487.	75 c. As 2 c.	30	60
488.	$1 Mary and her little lamb (vert.)	45	80

1972. "Interpex" Stamp Exhib., New York. Nos. 433/8 optd. **INTERPEX 1972.**

No.	Description		
490. 174.	5 c. multicoloured	10	10
491.	10 c. multicoloured	10	10
492.	15 c. multicoloured	10	10
493.	25 c. multicoloured	10	10
494.	35 c. multicoloured	15	15
495.	50 c. multicoloured	25	30

1972. Nos. 306/8 and 433 surch.

No.	Description		
497. –	12 c. on 1 c. multicoloured	35	50
498. –	12 c. on 2 c. multicoloured	35	50
499. –	12 c. on 3 c. multicoloured	35	50
500. 174.	12 c. on 5 c. multicoloured	35	50

1972. Air. Optd. **AIR MAIL** or surch. in addition.

No.	Description		
501. –	5 c. mult. (No. 309)	10	10
518. 175.	5 c. multicoloured	50	10
502. –	8 c. mult. (No. 311)	15	10
503. –	10 c. mult. (No. 312)	15	10
504. –	15 c. mult. (No. 314a)	30	20
505. –	25 c. mult. (No. 315)	35	20
506. –	30 c. on 1 c. mult. (No. 306)	40	25
507. –	35 c. mult. (No. 316)	45	25
519. –	35 c. mult. (No. 441)	1·50	30
508. –	40 c. on 2 c. mult. (No. 307)	50	25
509. –	45 c. on 3 c. mult. (No. 308)	55	35
510. –	50 c. mult. (No. 317)	55	35
520. –	50 c. mult. (No. 442)	1·75	45
511. –	60 c. on 5 c. mult. (No. 309)	60	40
512. –	70 c. on 6 c. mult. (No. 310)	70	50
521. –	75 c. mult. (No. 443)	2·25	1·00
513. –	$1 mult. (No. 318)	3·25	60
514. –	$1·35 on 8 c. mult. (No. 311)	3·25	1·25
515. –	$2 mult. (No. 319)	4·25	3·00
516. –	$3 mult. (No. 320)	5·00	3·50
517. –	$5 mult. (No. 321)	6·00	7·50

187. Yachting.

1972. Olympic Games, Munich. Multicoloured.

No.	Description		
522.	½ c. Type **187** (postage)	10	10
523.	1 c. Show-jumping	10	10
524.	2 c. Running (vert.	10	10
525.	35 c. As 2 c.	40	20
526.	50 c. As 1 c.	55	40
527.	25 c. Boxing (air)	30	15
528.	$1 as 25 c.	90	75

1972. Royal Silver Wedding. As T **52** of Ascension, but with Badge of Grenada and Nutmegs in background.

No.	Description		
530	8 c. brown	10	10
531.	$1 blue	45	55

INDEX

Countries can be quickly located by referring to the index at the end of this volume.

189. Boy Scout Saluting.

1972. 65th Anniv. of Boy Scouts. Mult.

No.	Description		
532.	½ c. Type **189** (postage)	10	10
533.	1 c. Scouts knotting ropes	10	10
534.	2 c. Scouts shaking hands	10	10
535.	3 c. Lord Baden Powell	10	10
536.	75 c. As 2 c.	1·40	2·00
537.	$1 As 3 c.	1·60	2·25
538.	25 c. Type **189** (air)	50	40
539.	25 c. As 1 c.	70	50

190. Madonna and Child.

1972. Christmas. Multicoloured.

No.	Description		
541.	1 c. Type **190**	10	10
542.	3 c. The Three Kings	10	10
543.	5 c. The Nativity	10	10
544.	25 c. Type **190**	15	15
545.	35 c. As 3 c.	20	20
546.	$1 As 5 c.	60	60

191. Greater Flamingoes.

1973. National Zoo. Multicoloured.

No.	Description		
548.	25 c. Type **191**	80	35
549.	35 c. Brazilian tapir	80	45
550.	60 c. Blue and yellow macaws	1·50	1·00
551.	70 c. Ocelot	1·50	1·25

192. Class II Racing Yacht.

1973. World Yachting Centre. Multicoloured.

No.	Description		
552.	25 c. Type **192**	35	15
553.	35 c. Harbour, St. George's	40	15
554.	60 c. Yacht " Bloodhound "	55	55
555.	70 c. St. George's	70	75

193. Helios (Greek god) and Earth orbiting the Sun.

1973. Centenary of I.M.O./W.M.O. Greek Gods. Multicoloured.

No.	Description		
556.	½ c. Type **193**	10	10
557.	1 c. Poseidon and " Normad "	10	10
558.	2 c. Zeus and radarscope	10	10
559.	3 c. Iris and weather balloon	10	10
560.	35 c. Hermes and " ATS-3 " satellite	45	10
561.	50 c. Zephyrus and diagram of pressure zones	65	25
562.	75 c. Demeter and space photo	85	50
563.	$1 Selene and rainfall diagram	90	80

194. Racing Class Yachts.

1973. Carriacou Regatta. Multicoloured.

No.	Description		
565.	½c. Type **194**	10	10
566.	1 c. Cruising Class Yacht	10	10
567.	2 c. Open-decked sloops ..	10	10
568.	35 c. "Mermaid" (sloop) ..	35	20
569.	50 c. St. George's Harbour	50	35
570.	75 c. Map of Carriacou ..	70	60
571.	$1 Boat-building	90	80

195. Ignatius Semmelweis (obstetrician).

1973. 25th Anniv. of W.H.O. Multicoloured.

No.	Description		
573.	½ c. Type **195**	10	10
574.	1 c. Louis Pasteur	10	10
575.	2 c. Edward Jenner	10	10
576.	3 c. Sigmund Freud	10	10
577.	25 c. Emil Von Behring (bacteriologist)	65	10
578.	35 c. Carl Jung	75	20
579.	50 c. Charles Calmette (bacteriologist)	1·10	50
580.	$1 William Harvey	1·40	1·25

196. Princess Anne and Capt. Mark Phillips.

1973. Royal Wedding.

No.	Description		
582. 196.	25 c. multicoloured ..	10	10
583.	$2 multicoloured ..	45	55

197. "Virgin and Child" (Maratti).

1973. Christmas. Multicoloured.

No.	Description		
585.	½ c. Type **197**	10	10
586.	1 c. "Madonna and Child" (Crivelli)	10	10
587.	2 c. "Virgin and Child with two Angels" (Verrocchio)	10	10
588.	3 c. "Adoration of the Shepherds" (Roberti) ..	10	10
589.	25 c. "The Holy Family with the Infant Baptist" (Baroccio)	15	10
590.	35 c. "The Holy Family" (Bronzino)	20	10
591.	77 c. "Mystic Nativity" (Botticelli)	30	20
592.	$1 "Adoration of the Kings" (Geertgen) ..	40	30

1974. Independence. Nos. 306/9, 311/13, 315/16 and 317*a*/21 optd. with **INDEPENDENCE 7TH FEB. 1974.**

No.	Description		
594. 86.	1 c. multicoloured ..	10	10
595. –	2 c. multicoloured ..	10	10
596. –	3 c. multicoloured ..	10	10
597. –	5 c. multicoloured ..	10	10
598. –	8 c. multicoloured ..	15	10
599. –	10 c. multicoloured ..	20	15
600. –	12 c. multicoloured ..	20	15
601. –	25 c. multicoloured ..	45	35
602. –	35 c. multicoloured ..	75	50
603. –	75 c. multicoloured ..	2·00	1·25
604. –	$1 multicoloured ..	3·75	1·50
605. –	$2 multicoloured ..	6·00	3·50
606. –	$3 multicoloured ..	8·00	5·00
607. –	$5 multicoloured ..	12·00	9·50

199. Creative Arts Theatre, Jamaica Campus.

1974. 25th Anniv. of University of West Indies. Multicoloured.

No.	Description		
608.	10 c. Type **199**	10	10
609.	25 c. Marryshow House ..	10	10
610.	50 c. Chapel, Jamaica Campus (vert.)	20	10
611.	$1 University arms (vert.)	30	30

200. Nutmeg Pods and Scarlet Mace.

1974. Independence. Multicoloured.

No.	Description		
613.	3 c. Type **200**	10	10
614.	8 c. Map of Grenada ..	10	10
615.	25 c. Prime Minister Eric Gairy	15	10
616.	35 c. Grand Anse beach and flag	15	10
617.	$1 Coat of arms	35	40

201. Footballers (West Germany v. Chile).

1974. World Cup Football Championships, West Germany. Multicoloured.

No.	Description		
619.	½ c. Type **201**	10	10
620.	1 c. East Germany v. Australia	10	10
621.	2 c. Yugoslavia v. Brazil ..	10	10
622.	10 c. Scotland v. Zaire ..	10	10
623.	25 c. Netherlands v. Uruguay	15	10
624.	50 c. Sweden v. Bulgaria ..	20	10
625.	75 c. Italy v. Haiti ..	35	15
626.	$1 Poland v. Argentina ..	50	25

202. Early U.S. Mail-trains and "Concorde".

1974. Centenary of U.P.U. Multicoloured.

No.	Description		
628	½ c. Type **202**	10	10
629	1 c. "Caesar" (snow) (1839) and helicopter	10	10
630	2 c. Airmail transport ..	10	10
631	8 c. Pigeon post (1480) and telephone dial	15	10
632	15 c. 18th-century bellman and tracking antenna ..	30	10
633	25 c. Messenger (1450) and satellite	35	15
634	35 c. French pillar-box (1850) and mail-boat ..	75	25
635	$1 18th-century German postman and mail train of the future	2·00	2·25

203. Sir Winston Churchill.

1974. Birth Centenary of Sir Winston Churchill.

No.	Description		
637. 203.	35 c. multicoloured ..	15	10
638.	$2 multicoloured ..	45	50

204. "Madonna and Child of the Eucharist" (Botticelli).

1974. Christmas. "Madonna and Child" paintings by named artists. Multicoloured.

No.	Description		
640.	½ c. Type **204**	10	10
641.	1 c. Niccolo di Pietro ..	10	10
642.	2 c. Van der Weyden ..	10	10
643.	3 c. Bastiani	10	10
644.	10 c. Giovanni	10	10
645.	25 c. Van der Weyden ..	20	10
646.	50 c. Botticelli	35	20
647.	$1 Mantegna	55	50

205. Yachts, Point Saline.

1975. Multicoloured.

No.	Description		
649.	½ c. Type **205**	10	10
650.	1 c. Yacht Club race, St. George's	10	10
651.	2 c. Carenage taxi ..	10	10
652.	3 c. Large working boats ..	10	10
653.	5 c. Deep-water dock, St. George's	10	10
654.	6 c. Cocoa beans in drying trays	10	10
655.	8 c. Nutmegs	30	10
656.	10 c. Rum distillery, River Antoine Estate, c. 1785	10	10
657.	12 c. Cocoa tree	30	10
658.	15 c. Fishermen at Fontenoy	10	10
659.	20 c. Parliament Building	15	15
660.	25 c. Fort George cannons	20	15
661.	35 c. Pearls Airport ..	20	15
662.	50 c. General Post Office ..	25	30
663.	75 c. Caribs Leap, Sauteurs Bay	45	50
664.	$1 Carenage, St. George's	65	70
665.	$2 St. George's harbour by night	1·00	1·50
666.	$3 Grand Anse beach ..	1·25	2·00
667.	$5 Canoe Bay & Black Bay	1·75	2·75
668.	$10 Sugar-loaf Island ..	4·50	6·50

Nos. 663/8 are size 45 × 28 mm.

206. Sail-fish.

1975. Big Game Fishing. Multicoloured.

No.	Description		
669.	½ c. Type **206**	10	10
670.	1 c. Blue Marlin	10	10
671.	2 c. White Marlin	10	10
672.	10 c. Yellowfin Tuna ..	10	10
673.	25 c. Wahoo	25	10
674.	50 c. Dolphin	40	15
675.	70 c. Grouper	60	20
676.	$1 Great Barracuda ..	80	35

207. Granadilla Barbadine.

1975. Flowers. Multicoloured.

No.	Description		
678.	½ c. Type **207**	10	10
679.	1 c. Bleeding Heart (Easter Lily)	10	10
680.	2 c. Poinsettia	10	10
681.	3 c. Cocoaflower	10	10
682.	10 c. Gladioli	10	10
683.	25 c. Redhead/Yellowhead	25	10
684.	50 c. Plumbago	45	15
685.	$1 Orange flower	70	25

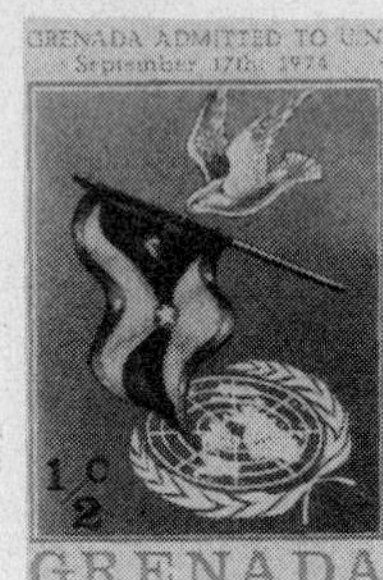

208. Dove, Grenada Flag and U.N. Emblem.

1975. Grenada's Admission to the U.N. (1974). Multicoloured.

No.	Description		
687.	½ c. Type **208**	10	10
588.	1 c. Grenada and U.N. flags	10	10
689.	2 c. Grenada coat of arms	10	10
690.	35 c. U.N. emblem over map of Grenada ..	15	10
691.	50 c. U.N. buildings and flags	20	15
692.	$2 U.N. emblem and scroll	45	45

CANCELLED REMAINDERS*. Some of the following issues have been remaindered, cancelled to order, at a fraction of their face-value. For all practical purposes these are undistinguishable from genuine postally used copies. Our used quotations which are indicated by an asterisk are the same for cancelled-to-order or postally used copies.

209. Paul Revere's Midnight Ride.

1975. Bicentenary of American Revolution. (1st issue). Multicoloured.

No.	Description		
694.	½ c. Type **209** (postage) ..	10	10*
695.	1 c. Crispus Attucks ..	10	10*
696.	2 c. Patrick Henry ..	10	10*
697.	3 c. Franklin visits Washington	10	10*
698.	5 c. Rebel troops	10	10*
699.	10 c. John Paul Jones ..	10	10*
700.	40 c. "John Hancock" (air) (Copley)	35	10*
701.	50 c. "Ben Franklin" (Roslin)	50	15*
702.	75 c. "John Adams" (Copley)	70	15*
703.	$1 "Lafayette" (Casanova)	80	20*

Nos. 700/3 are vert.

See also Nos. 785/91.

210. "Blood of the Redeemer" (G. Bellini).

1975. Easter. Multicoloured.

No.	Description	Unused	Used
705.	½ c. Type **210**	10	10*
706.	1 c. " Pieta " (Bellini) ..	10	10*
707.	2 c. " The Entombment " (Van der Weyden) ..	10	10*
708.	3 c. " Pieta " (Bellini) ..	10	10*
709.	35 c. "Pieta" (Bellini) ..	30	10*
710.	75 c. " The Dead Christ" (Bellini)	50	10*
711.	$1 "The Dead Christ supported by Angels" (Procaccini)	65	10*

211. Wildlife Study.

1975. 14th World Scout Jamboree, Norway. Multicoloured.

No.	Description	Unused	Used
713.	½ c. Type **211**	10	10*
714.	1 c. Sailing	10	10*
715.	2 c. Map-reading	10	10*
716.	35 c. First-aid	40	10*
717.	40 c. Physical training ..	45	10*
718.	75 c. Mountaineering ..	70	10*
719.	$2 Sing-song	1·60	20*

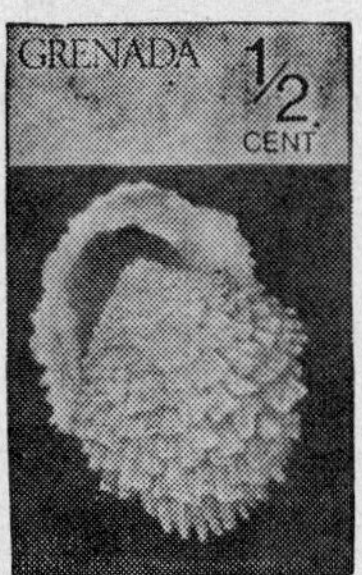

212. Leafy Jewel Box.

1975. Seashells. Multicoloured.

No.	Description	Unused	Used
721.	½ c. Type **212**	10	10*
722.	1 c. Emerald Nerite ..	10	10*
723.	2 c. Yellow Cockle ..	10	10*
724.	25 c. Purple Sea Snail ..	75	10*
725.	50 c. Turkey Wing ..	1·50	10*
726.	75 c. West Indian Fighting Conch	2·00	10*
727.	$1 Noble Wentletrap ..	2·25	15*

213. "Lycorea ceres".

1975. Butterflies. Multicoloured.

No.	Description	Unused	Used
729	½ c. Type **213**	10	10*
730	1 c. "Adelpha cytherea" ..	10	10*
731	2 c. "Atlides polybe" ..	10	10*
732	35 c. "Anteos maerula" ..	70	10*
733	45 c. "Parides neophilus"	75	10*
734	75 c. "Nymula orestes" ..	1·10	15*
735	$2 "Euptychia cephus" ..	1·75	20*

214. Rowing.

1975. Pan-American Games, Mexico City. Multicoloured.

No.	Description	Unused	Used
737.	½ c. Type **214**	10	10*
738.	1 c. Swimming	10	10*
739.	2 c. Show-jumping	10	10*
740.	35 c. Gymnastics.. ..	15	10*
741.	45 c. Football	15	10*
742.	75 c. Boxing	25	15*
743.	$2 Cycling	65	20*

215. " The Boy David " (Michelangelo).

1975. 500th Birth Anniv. of Michelangelo. Multicoloured.

No.	Description	Unused	Used
745.	½ c. Type **215**	10	10*
746.	1 c. " Young Man " (detail)	10	10*
747.	2 c. " Moses "	10	10*
748.	40 c. " Prophet Zachariah "	30	10*
749.	50 c. " St. John the Baptist "	30	10*
750.	75 c. " Judith and Holofernes "	50	15*
751.	$2 " Doni Madonna " (detail from " Holy Family ")	1·00	20*

216. " Madonna and Child " (Filippino Lippi).

1975. Christmas. " Virgin and Child " paintings by Artists named. Multicoloured.

No.	Description	Unused	Used
753.	½ c. Type **216**	10	10*
754.	1 c. Mantegna	10	10*
755.	2 c. Luis de Morales ..	10	10*
756.	35 c. G. M. Morandi ..	20	10*
757.	50 c. Antonello da Messina	25	10*
758.	75 c. Durer	35	10*
759.	$1 Velasquez	45	10*

217. Bananaquit.

1976. Flora and Fauna. Multicoloured.

No.	Description	Unused	Used
761.	½ c. Type **217** ..	10	10
762.	1 c. Brazilian Agouti ..	10	10
763.	2 c. Hawksbill Turtle (horiz.)	10	10
764.	5 c. Dwarf Poinciana ..	10	10
765.	35 c. Albacore ..	90	45
766.	40 c. Cardinal's Guard ..	95	50
767.	$2 Nine-banded Armadillo	3·00	2·25

218. Carnival Time.

1976. Tourism. Multicoloured.

No.	Description	Unused	Used
769	½ c. Type **218**	10	10
770	1 c. Scuba diving ..	10	10
771	2 c. Liner "Southward" at St. George's	10	10
772	35 c. Game fishing ..	65	20
773	50 c. St. George's Golf Course	2·25	1·00
774	75 c. Tennis	2·50	1·75
775	$1 Ancient rock carving at Mount Rich ..	2·75	2·75

219. " Pieta " (Master of Okolicsno).

1976. Easter. Paintings by Artists named. Multicoloured.

No.	Description	Unused	Used
777.	½ c. Type **219**	10	10
778.	1 c. Correggio	10	10
779.	2 c. Van der Weyden ..	10	10
780.	3 c. Durer..	10	10
781.	35 c. Master of the Holy Spirit	20	10
782.	75 c. Raphael	45	60
783.	$1 Raphael	50	75

220. Sharpshooters.

1976. Bicentenary of American Revolution. (2nd Issue). Multicoloured.

No.	Description	Unused	Used
785.	½ c. Type **220**	10	10
786.	1 c. Defending the Liberty Pole	10	10
787.	2 c. Loading muskets ..	10	10
788.	35 c. The fight for Liberty	40	15
789.	50 c. Peace Treaty, 1783..	60	50
790.	$1 Drummers	1·25	1·25
791.	$3 Gunboat	3·25	3·50

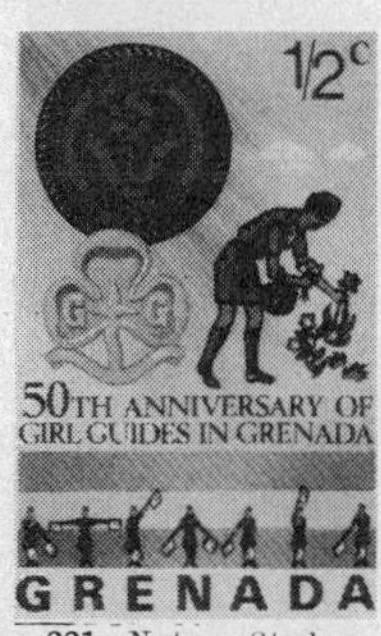

221. Nature Study.

1976. 50th Anniv. of Girl Guides in Grenada. Multicoloured.

No.	Description	Unused	Used
793.	½ c. Type **221**	10	10
794.	1 c. Campfire cooking ..	10	10
795.	2 c. First Aid	10	10
796.	50 c. Camping	65	55
797.	75 c. Home economics ..	1·00	1·00
798.	$2 First Aid	2·50	3·00

222. Volleyball.

1976. Olympic Games, Montreal. Mult.

No.	Description	Unused	Used
800.	½ c. Type **222**	10	10
801.	1 c. Cycling	10	10
802.	2 c. Rowing	10	10
803.	35 c. Judo	30	10
804.	45 c. Hockey	60	40
805.	75 c. Gymnastics.. ..	70	90
806.	$1 High jump	75	1·25

223. " Cha-U-Kao at the Moulin Rouge ".

1976. 75th Death Anniv. of Toulouse-Lautrec. Multicoloured.

No.	Description	Unused	Used
808.	½ c. Type **223**	10	10
809.	1 c. " Quadrille of the Moulin Rouge " ..	10	10
810.	2 c. " Profile of a Woman "	10	10
811.	3 c. " Salon in the Rue des Mountains " ..	10	10
812.	40 c. " The Laundryman "	60	35
813.	50 c. " Marcelle Lender dancing the Bolero " ..	70	45
814.	$2 " Signor Boileau at the Cafe "	1·75	2·50

1976. West Indian Victory in World Cricket Cup. Nos. 559/60 of Barbados.

No.	Description	Unused	Used
816.	35 c. Map of the Caribbean	1·75	35
817.	$1 The Prudential Cup..	3·25	3·75

224. Piper " Apache ".

1976. Aeroplanes. Multicoloured.

No.	Description	Unused	Used
818.	½ c. Type **224**	10	10
819.	1 c. Beech " Twin Bonanza "	10	10
820.	2 c. D.H. " Twin Otter "	10	20
821.	40 c. Britten Norman " Islander "	70	50
822.	50 c. D.H. " Heron " ..	75	60
823.	$2 H.S. " 748 "	2·50	3·50

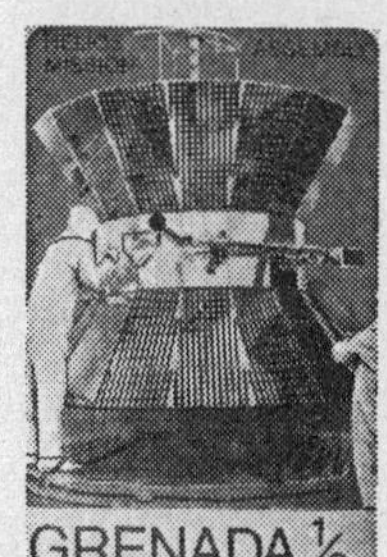

225. Satellite Assembly.

1976. Viking and Helios Space Missions. Multicoloured.

No.	Description	Unused	Used
825.	½ c. Type **225**	10	10
826.	1 c. Helios satellite ..	10	10
827.	2 c. Helios encapsulation	10	10
828.	15 c. Systems test ..	10	10
829.	45 c. Viking lander (horiz.)	20	20
830.	75 c. Lander on Mars ..	35	70
831.	$2 Viking encapsulation..	90	2·50

226. S.S. " Geestland ".

1976. Ships. Multicoloured.

No.	Description	Unused	Used
833.	½ c. Type **226**	10	10
834.	1 c. M.V. " Federal Palm "	10	10
835.	2 c. H.M.S. " Blake " ..	10	10
836.	25 c. M.V. " Vistafjord "	45	15
837.	75 c. S.S. " Canberra " ..	1·10	1·00
838.	$1 S.S. " Regina " ..	1·40	1·25
839.	$5 S.S. " Arandora Star "	4·75	6·00

227. San Barbara Altarpiece (Botticelli).

1976. Christmas. Multicoloured.

841. ½ c. Type **227** 10 10
842. 1 c. "Annunciation" (Botticelli) 10 10
843. 2 c. "Madonna of Chancellor Rolin" (Jan van Eyck) 10 10
844. 35 c. "Annunciation" (Fra Filippo Lippi) .. 20 10
845. 50 c. "Madonna of the Magnificat" (Botticelli) 30 20
846. 75 c. "Madonna of the Pomegranate" (Botticelli) 45 40
847. $3 "Madonna with St. Cosmas and other Saints" (Botticelli) .. .. 1·25 2·50

228. Alexander Graham Bell and Telephones.

1976. Centenary of First Telephone Transmission. Multicoloured.

849. ½ c. Type **228** 10 10
850. 1 c. Telephone users within globe 10 10
851. 2 c. Telephone satellite .. 10 10
852. 18 c. Telephone viewer and console 20 15
853. 40 c. Satellite and tracking stations 45 45
854. $1 Satellite transmitting to ships .. .. .. 80 1·25
855. $2 Dish aerial and modern telephone .. .. 1·40 2·25

229. Coronation Scene.

1977. Silver Jubilee. Multicoloured. (a) Perf.

857. ½ c. Type **229** 10 10
858. 1 c. Sceptre and orb .. 10 10
859. 35 c. The Queen on horseback 15 10
860. $2 Spoon and ampulla .. 35 35
861. $2.50 The Queen and Prince Philip 65 60

(b) Roul. Self-adhesive.

863. 35 c. As $2.50 .. .. 25 25
864. 50 c. As $2 .. .. 55 70
865. $1 As 1 c... .. .. 1·00 1·50
866. $3 As 35 c. .. .. 2·75 3·75

Nos. 863/6 come from booklets.

230. Water Skiing.

1977. Easter Water Parade. Multicoloured.

867. ½ c. Type **230** 10 10
868. 1 c. Speedboat race .. 10 10
869. 2 c. Row boat race .. 10 10
870. 22 c. Swimming 15 15
871. 35 c. Work Boat race .. 25 20
872. 75 c. Water polo 50 75
873. $2 Game fishing .. .. 1·40 2·50

231. Meeting Place, Grand Anse Beach.

1977. 7th Meeting of Organization of American States.

875. **231.** 35 c. multicoloured .. 10 10
876. $1 multicoloured .. 25 60
877. $2 multicoloured .. 40 1·25

232. Rafting.

1977. Caribbean Scout Jamboree, Jamaica. Multicoloured.

878. ½ c. Type **232** 10 10
879. 1 c. Tug-of-war 10 10
880. 2 c. Sea Scouts regatta .. 10 10
881. 18 c. Camp fire 25 15
882. 40 c. Field kitchen .. 50 30
883. $1 Scouts and sea scouts .. 1·25 1·50
884. $2 Hiking and map reading 1·75 3·00

233. Angel and Shepherd.

1977. Christmas. Ceiling Panels from Church of St. Martin, Zillis. Multicoloured.

886. ½ c. Type **233** 10 10
887. 1 c. St. Joseph 10 10
888. 2 c. Virgin and Child fleeing to Egypt 10 10
889. 22 c. Angel 10 10
890. 35 c. Magus on horseback 15 10
891. 75 c. Three horses .. 20 35
892. $2 Virgin and Child .. 50 1·40

1977. Royal Visit. Nos. 857/61 optd. **Royal Visit W.I. 1977.**

894. ½ c. Type **229** 10 10
895. 1 c. Sceptre and Orb .. 10 10
896. 35 c. Queen on horseback 15 10
897. $2 Spoon and ampulla .. 40 40
898. $2·50 The Queen and Prince Philip 45 45

235. Christjaan Eijkman (Medicine).

1978. Nobel Prize Winners. Multicoloured.

900. ½ c. Type **235** 10 10
901. 1 c. Sir Winston Churchill (Literature) 10 10
902. 2 c. Woodrow Wilson (Peace) 10 10
903. 35 c. Frederic Passy (Peace) 15 10
904. $1 Albert Einstein (Physics) 55 60
905. $3 Carl Bosch (Chemistry) 1·75 2·00

236. Count von Zeppelin and 1st Zeppelin Airship.

1978. 75th Anniv. of 1st Zeppelin Flight and 50th Anniv. of Lindbergh's Transatlantic Flight. Multicoloured.

907. ½ c. Type **236** 10 10
908. 1 c. Lindbergh with "Spirit of St. Louis" 10 10
909. 2 c. Airship "Deutschland" 10 10
910. 22 c. Lindbergh's arrival in France 25 10
911. 75 c. Lindbergh and "Spirit of St. Louis" in flight 60 30
912. $1 Zeppelin over Alps .. 70 40
913. $3 Zeppelin over White House .. .. .. 1·50 1·40

237. Rocket Launching.

1978. Space Shuttle. Multicoloured.

915. ½ c. Type **237** 10 10
916. 1 c. Booster jettison .. 10 10
917. 2 c. External tank jettison 10 10
918. 18 c. Space Shuttle in orbit 15 15
919. 75 c. Satellite placement .. 35 35
920. $2 Landing approach .. 1·00 1·00

238. Black-headed Gull.

1978. Wild Birds of Grenada. Multicoloured.

922. ½ c. Type **238** 10 10
923. 1 c. Wilson's petrel .. 10 10
924. 2 c. Killdeer 10 10
925. 50 c. White-necked jacobin 1·50 30
926. 75 c. Blue-faced booby .. 2·00 45
927. $1 Broad-winged hawk .. 3·00 75
928. $2 Red-necked pigeon .. 4·00 1·75

239. "The landing of Marie de Medici at Marseilles".

1978. 400th Birth Anniv. of Peter Paul Rubens. Multicoloured.

930. 5 c. Type **239** 10 10
931. 15 c. "Rubens and Isabella Brandt" 10 10
932. 18 c. "Marchesa Brigida Spindola-Doria" 10 10
933. 25 c. "Ludovicus Nonninus" 10 10
934. 45 c. "Helene Fourment and her Children" .. 15 15
935. 75 c. "Clara Serena Rubens" 25 25
936. $3 "Le Chapeau de Paille" 60 80

240. Ludwig van Beethoven.

1978. 150th Death Anniv. of Beethoven. Multicoloured.

938. 5 c. Type **240** 10 10
939. 15 c. Woman violinist (horiz.) 15 10
940. 18 c. Musical instruments (horiz.) 20 15
941. 22 c. Piano (horiz.) .. 20 15
942. 50 c. Violins 40 30
943. 75 c. Piano and sonata score 60 45
944. $3 Beethoven's portrait and home (horiz.) .. 2·25 1·75

241. King Edward's Chair.

1978. 25th Anniv. of Coronation. Mult. (a) Perf.

946. 35 c. Type **241** 15 10
947. $2 Queen with regalia .. 35 35
948. $2.50 St. Edward's Crown 40 40

(b) Roul. × imperf. Self-adhesive.

950. 25 c. Queen Elizabeth II taking salute, Trooping the Colour 15 15
951. 35 c. Queen at Maundy Thursday ceremony .. 15 25
952. $5 Queen and Prince Philip 2·00 2·75

243. Goalkeeper reaching for Ball.

1978. World Cup Football Championships, Argentina.

953. **243.** 40 c. multicoloured .. 10 10
954. – 60 c. multicoloured .. 15 20
955. – 90 c. multicoloured .. 25 30
956. – $2 multicoloured .. 60 60

DESIGNS: 60 c. to $2. Designs similar to Type **243** with goalkeeper reaching for ball.

244. Aerial Phenomena, Germany, 1561 and U.S.A., 1952.

1978. Unidentified Flying Objects Research. Multicoloured.

958. 5 c. Type **244** 15 10
959. 35 c. Various aerial phenomena, 1950 .. .. 35 25
960. $3 U.F.O.'s, 1965 .. 2·00 1·75

245. Wright Glider, 1902.

1978. 75th Anniv. of Powered Flight. Mult.

962. 5 c. Type **245** 10 10
963. 15 c. "Flyer I", 1903 .. 10 10
964. 18 c. "Flyer 3" 10 10
965. 22 c. "Flyer 3" from above 15 10
966. 50 c. Orville Wright and "Flyer" 25 20
967. 75 c. "Flyer 3", Pau, France, 1908 .. .. 35 25
968. $3 Wilbur Wright and glider .. .. .. 1·10 70

246. Cook and Hawaiian Feast.

1978. 250th Birth Anniv. of Captain James Cook and Bicentenary of Discovery of Hawaii. Multicoloured.

970. 18 c. Type **246** 60 15
971. 35 c. Cook and Hawaiian dance 80 25
972. 75 c. Cook and Honolulu harbour .. .. .. 1·75 1·25
973. $3 Cook's statue and H.M.S. "Resolution" .. .. 4·00 4·00

247. "Paumgartner Altarpiece" (detail).

1978. Christmas. Paintings by Durer. Multicoloured.

975. 40 c. Type **247** 25 15
976. 60 c. "The Adoration of the Magi" 30 20
977. 90 c. "Virgin and Child" 40 20
978. $2 "Virgin and Child with St. Anne" (detail) .. 75 55

248. National Convention and Cultural Centre (interior).

1979. 5th Anniv. of Independence. Mult.

980. 5 c. Type **248** 10 10
981. 18 c. National Convention and Cultural Centre (exterior) 10 10
982. 22 c. Easter Water Parade, 1978 .. .. 10 10
983. 35 c. Sir Eric M. Gairy (Prime Minister) .. 15 10
984. $3 The Cross, Fort Frederick 60 80

249. "Acalypha hispida".

1979. Flowers. Multicoloured.

985. 18 c. Type **249** 10 10
986. 50 c. "Hibiscus rosa sinensis" 30 15
987. $1 "Thunbergia grandiflora" 55 25
988. $3 "Nerium oleander" .. 1·60 1·10

250. Birds in Flight.

1979. 30th Anniv. of Declaration of Human Rights. Multicoloured.

990. 15 c. Type **250** 10 10
991. $2 Bird in Flight 55 65

251. Children playing Cricket.

1979. International Year of the Child. Multicoloured.

992. 18 c. Type **251** 40 15
993. 22 c. Children playing baseball 40 20
994. $5 Children playing in a tree .. .. .. 3·75 5·00

252. "Around the World in 80 Days".

1979. 150th Birth Anniv. of Jules Verne. Multicoloured.

996. 18 c. Type **252** 25 10
997. 35 c. "20,000 Leagues under the Sea" .. 35 15
998. 75 c. "From the Earth to the Moon" 50 25
999. $3 "Master of the World" 1·40 80

253. Mail Runner, Africa (early 19th-century).

1979. Death Centenary of Sir Rowland Hill. Multicoloured.

1001. 20 c. Type **253** 10 10
1002. 40 c. Pony Express, America (mid. 19th-century) .. 10 10
1003. $1 Pigeon post 20 25
1004. $3 Mail coach, Europe (18–19th-century) .. 50 80

254. "The Pistol of Peace" (vaccination gun), Map of Grenada and Children.

1979. International Year of the Child.

1006. **254.** 5 c. multicoloured .. 30 20
1007. $1 multicoloured .. 1·40 1·75

255. Reef Shark.

1979. Marine Wildlife. Multicoloured.

1008. 40 c. Type **255** 40 30
1009. 45 c. Spotted Eagle Ray 40 30
1010. 50 c. Manytooth Conger 45 40
1011. 60 c. Golden Olive 70 55
1012. 70 c. West Indian Murex 85 70
1013. 75 c. Giant Tun 90 70
1014. 90 c. Brown Booby .. 2·00 1·25
1015. $1 Magnificent Frigate Bird 2·00 1·25

256. The Flight into Egypt.

1979. Christmas. Tapestries. Multicoloured.

1017. 6 c. Type **256** 10 10
1018. 25 c. The Flight into Egypt (detail) 10 10
1019. 30 c. Angel (vert.) .. 15 10
1020. 40 c. Jesus (Doge Marino Grimani) (vert.) .. 15 15
1021. 90 c. The Annunciation to the Shepherds (vert.) 40 30
1022. $1 The Flight into Egypt (Rome) (vert.) .. 45 35
1023. $2 The Virgin in Glory (vert.) 75 60

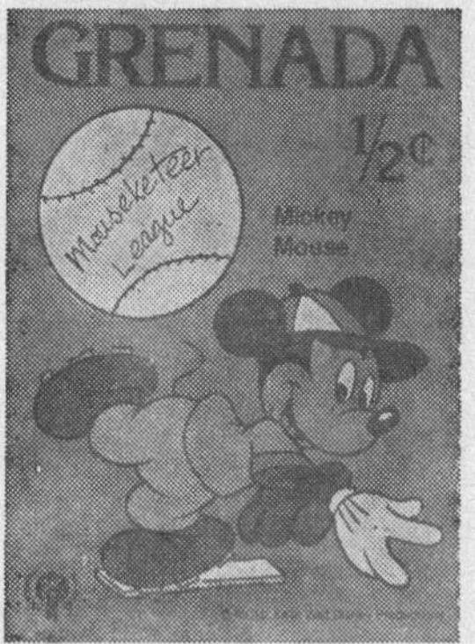

257. Mickey Mouse playing Baseball.

1979. International Year of the Child. Disney Characters. Multicoloured.

1025. ½ c. Type **257** 10 10
1026. 1 c. Donald Duck jumping on springs 10 10
1027. 2 c. Goofy in basketball net 10 10
1028. 3 c. Goofy running down hurdles 10 10
1029. 4 c. Donald Duck playing golf 10 10
1030. 5 c. Mickey Mouse playing cricket 10 10
1031. 10 c. Mickey Mouse playing football 10 10
1032. $2 Mickey Mouse playing tennis .. .. .. 2·75 2·00
1033. $2.50 Minnie Mouse riding horse .. .. .. 2·75 2·00

258. Paul Harris (founder).

1980. 75th Anniv. of Rotary International. Multicoloured.

1035. 6 c. Type **258** 10 10
1036. 30 c. "Health" 20 15
1037. 90 c. "Hunger" 40 30
1038. $2 "Humanity" 80 80

1980. 1st Anniv of Revolution (1st issue). Nos. 651/2, 654/7, 659/60 and 662/8 optd **PEOPLE'S REVOLUTION 13 MARCH 1979**.

1040. 2 c. Carenage taxi .. 10 10
1041. 3 c. Large working boats 10 10
1042. 6 c. Cocoa beans in drying trays 10 10
1043. 8 c. Nutmegs 10 10
1044. 10 c. Rum distillery, River Antoine Estate, c. 1785 10 10
1045. 12 c. Cocoa tree 10 10
1046. 20 c. Parliament Building 10 15
1047. 25 c. Fort George Cannons 30 30
1048. 50 c. General Post Office 30 30
1049. 75 c. Carib's Leap, Sauteurs Bay 50 40
1050. $1 Carenage, St. George's 60 60
1051. $2 St. George's Harbour by night .. .. 1·25 2·00
1052. $3 Grand Anse beach .. 2·00 3·25
1053. $5 Canoe Bay and Black Bay .. .. .. 3·25 5·00
1054. $10 Sugar-loaf Island .. 4·75 7·50

See also Nos. 1065/8.

260. Boxing.

1980. Olympic Games, Moscow. Multicoloured.

1055. 25 c. Type **260** 10 10
1056. 40 c. Cycling 15 15
1057. 90 c. Show-jumping .. 20 30
1058. $2 Running .. .. 40 1·00

261. Tropical Kingbird.

1980. Wild Birds. Multicoloured.

1060. 20 c. Type **261** 60 15
1061. 40 c. Rufous-breasted Hermit 75 25
1062. $1 Troupial .. .. 1·25 1·25
1063. $2 Ruddy Quail Dove .. 2·00 2·50

1980. "London 1980". International Stamp Exhibition. Nos. 1001/4 optd. "**LONDON 1980**".

1065. **253.** 20 c. Mail runner, Africa 20 20
1066. – 40 c. Pony Express, America 30 30
1067. – $1 Pigeon post .. 60 60
1068. – $3 Mail coach, Europe 1·75 1·75

263. Free Hot Lunch at Schools.

1980. 1st Anniv. of Revolution (2nd issue). Multicoloured.

1069. 10 c. Type **263** 10 10
1070. 40 c. Canning (agro-industry) 15 20
1071. $1 National Health care 40 45
1072. $2 New housing projects 75 90

264. Jamb Statues, West Portal, Chartres Cathedral.

1980. Famous Works of Art. Multicoloured.

1074. 8 c. Type **264** 10 10
1075. 10 c. "Les Demoiselles d'Avignon" (painting, Picasso) 10 10
1076. 40 c. Winged Victory of Samothrace (statue) .. 25 20
1077. 50 c. "The Night Watch" (painting, Rembrandt) 25 20
1078. $1 "Portrait of Edward VI as a Child" (painting, Holbein the Younger) 45 45
1079. $3 Portrait head of Queen Nefertiti (carving) .. 1·25 1·25

265. Carib Canoes.

1980. Shipping. Multicoloured.

1081 ½ c. Type **265** 10 10
1082 1 c. Boat building .. 10 10
1083 2 c. Small working boat 15 10
1084 4 c. Columbus's "Santa Maria" 40 10

1085 5 c. West Indiaman barque, c. 1840 .. 40 10
1086 6 c. "Orinoco" (paddle-steamer), c. 1851 .. 40 10
1087 10 c. Working schooner .. 40 10
1088 12 c. Trimaran at Grand Anse anchorage .. 45 10
1089 15 c. Spice Island cruising yacht "Petite Amie" .. 50 10
1090 20 c. Fishing pirogue .. 60 10
1091 25 c. Harbour Police launch 1·25 20
1092 30 c. Grand Anse speed-boat .. .. .. 1·00 20
1093 40 c. "Seimstrand" (freighter) .. .. 1·00 25
1094 50 c. "Ariadne" (cadet schooner) .. .. 1·00 35
1095 90 c. "Geestide" (freighter) .. .. 1·50 50
1096 $1 "Cunard Countess" (liner) .. .. .. 1·75 70
1097 $3 Rum-runner .. .. 3·75 3·00
1098 $5 "Statendam" (liner) off St. George's .. .. 6·50 6·00
1099 $10 Coastguard patrol boat 11·00 12·00

Nos. 1081/99 come with and without date imprint.

1980. Christmas. Scenes from Walt Disney's "Snow White and the Seven Dwarfs". As Type **257**. Multicoloured.

1100. ½ c. Snow White at well .. 10 10
1101. 1 c. The Wicked Queen 10 10
1102. 2 c. Snow White singing to animals 10 10
1103. 3 c. Snow White doing housework for Dwarfs 10 10
1104. 4 c. The Seven Dwarfs .. 10 10
1105. 5 c. Snow White with Dwarfs 10 10
1106. 10 c. Witch offering Snow White apple 10 10
1107. $2.50 Snow White with Prince and Dwarfs .. 2·75 1·25
1108. $3 Snow White and Prince .. .. .. 3·25 1·75

1981. 50th Anniv. of Walt Disney's Pluto (cartoon character). As T **257**. Mult.

1110. $2 Pluto with birthday cake .. .. .. 1·25 1·00

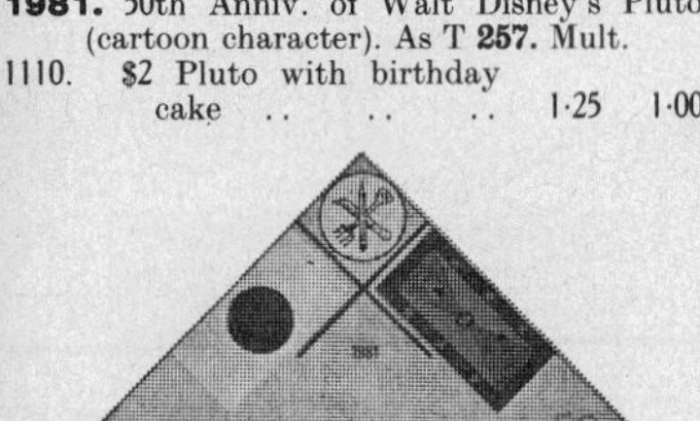

266. Revolution and Grenada Flags. (Illustration reduced. Actual size: 55 × 28 mm.)

1981. Festival of the Revolution. Mult.

1112. 5 c. Type **266** 10 10
1113. 10 c. Teacher, pupil, book and pencil ("education") 10 10
1114. 15 c. Food processing plant ("industry") .. 10 10
1115. 25 c. Selection of fruits and farm scene ("agriculture") .. 15 15
1116. 40 c. Crawfish and boat ("fishing") 20 20
1117. 90 c. "Cunard Countess" arriving at St. George's Harbour ("shipping") 50 50
1118. $1 Straw-work ("native handicrafts") 60 60
1119. $3 Map of Caribbean with expanded view of Grenada .. .. 1·75 1·75

1981. Easter. Walt Disney Cartoon Characters. As T **257**. Multicoloured.

1120. 35 c. Mickey Mouse and Goofy 25 25
1121. 40 c. Donald Duck, Chip and Daisy Duck .. 25 25
1122. $2 Minnie Mouse .. 1·40 1·25
1123. $2.50 Pluto and Mickey Mouse .. .. .. 1·60 1·40

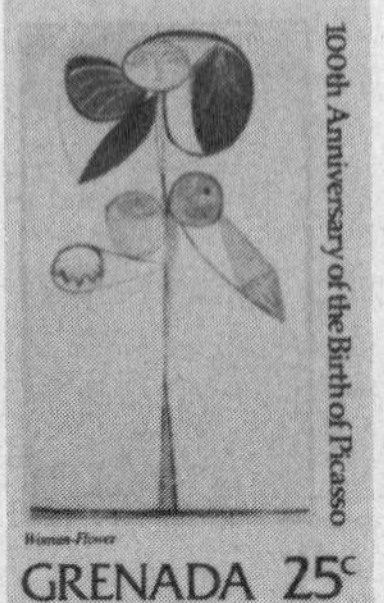

267. " Woman-Flower ".

1981. Birth Centenary of Picasso. Mult.

1125. 25 c. Type **267** 15 15
1126. 30 c. " Portrait of Madame " 20 15
1127. 90 c. " Cavalier with Pipe " 40 45
1128. $4 " Large Heads " .. 1·50 1·75

268. Prince Charles playing Polo.

1981. Royal Wedding. Multicoloured.

1134. 30 c. Prince Charles and Lady Diana Spencer .. 20 20
1135. 40 c. Holyrood House .. 30 30
1130. 50 c. As 30 c. 20 20
1131. $2 As 40 c. 60 75
1132. $4 Type **268** .. .. 1·00 1·40

269. Lady Diana Spencer.

1981. Royal Wedding. Booklet stamps. Multicoloured. Self-adhesive.

1136. $1 Type **269** 30 65
1137. $2 Prince Charles .. 30 45
1138. $5 Prince Charles and Lady Diana Spencer .. 1·00 1·75

270. " The Bath " (Mary Cassatt).

1981. " Decade for Women ". Paintings. Multicoloured.

1139. 15 c. Type **270** 10 10
1140. 40 c. " Mademoiselle Charlotte du Val d'Ognes " (Constance Marie Charpentier) 30 20
1141. 60 c. " Self-portrait " (Mary Beale) 50 30
1142. $3 " Woman in White Stockings " (Suzanne Valadon) .. .. 1·75 1·25

1981. Christmas. Horiz. designs as T **257** showing scenes from Walt Disney's cartoon film " Cinderella ".

1144. ½ c. multicoloured .. 10 10
1145. 1 c. multicoloured .. 10 10
1146. 2 c. multicoloured .. 10 10
1147. 3 c. multicoloured .. 10 10
1148. 4 c. multicoloured .. 10 10
1149. 5 c. multicoloured .. 10 10
1150. 10 c. multicoloured .. 10 10
1151. $2.50 multicoloured .. 3·25 1·50
1152. $3 multicoloured .. 3·25 1·75

271. Landing.

1981. Space Shuttle Project. Multicoloured.

1154. 30 c. Type **271** 20 15
1155. 60 c. Working in space .. 40 30
1156. 70 c. Lift off 45 35
1157. $3 Separation .. .. 1·40 1·25

272. West German Footballer and Flag.

1981. World Cup Football Championship, Spain (1982). Multicoloured.

1159. 25 c. + 10 c. Type **272** .. 55 30
1160. 40 c. + 20 c. Argentinian footballer and flag. .. 70 40
1161. 50 c. + 25 c. Brazilian footballer and flag .. 80 50
1162. $1 + 50 c. English footballer and flag .. 1·25 95

273. General Post Office, St. Georges.

1981. Centenary of U.P.U. Membership. Multicoloured.

1164. 25 c. Type **273** 20 15
1165. 30 c. 1861 1d. stamp .. 25 20
1166. 90 c. New U.P.U. Headquarters Building 25 c. commemoratives .. 75 50
1167. $4 1961 Stamp Centenary 25 c. commemorative 2·25 2·00

274. Artist without Hands.

1982. International Year for the Disabled (1981). Multicoloured.

1169. 30 c. Type **274** 55 15
1170. 40 c. Computer operator without hands .. 60 20
1171. 70 c. Blind schoolteacher teaching braille .. 85 35
1172. $3 Midget playing drums 2·40 1·40

275. Tending Vegetable Patch.

1982. 75th Anniv. of Boy Scout Movement and 125th Birth Anniv. of Lord Baden-Powell. Multicoloured.

1174. 70 c. Type **275** 50 45
1175. 90 c. Map reading .. 55 50
1176. $1 Bee keeping 65 60
1177. $4 Hospital reading .. 2·25 2·25

276. "Dryas julia".

1982. Butterflies. Multicoloured.

1179 10 c. Type **276** 75 20
1180 60 c. "Phoebis agarithe" 2·25 90
1181 $1 "Anartia amathea" .. 2·75 1·75
1182 $3 "Battis polydamas" .. 4·25 5·50

277. " Saying Grace "

1982. Norman Rockwell (painter) Commemoration. Multicoloured.

1184. 15 c. Type **277** 35 10
1185. 30 c. " Card Tricks " .. 60 15
1186. 60 c. " Pharmacist " .. 90 25
1187. 70 c. " Pals " 95 35

278. Kensington Palace.

1982. 21st Birthday of Princess of Wales. Multicoloured.

1188. 50 c. Type **278** 35 35
1189. 60 c. Type **278** 45 35
1190. $1 Prince and Princess of Wales 80 75
1191. $2 As $1 .. .. .. 1·25 1·00
1192. $3 Princess of Wales .. 1·75 2·00
1193. $4 As $3 .. .. .. 2·00 2·00

279. Mary McLeod Bethune appointed Director of Negro Affairs, 1942.

1982. Birth Centenary of Franklin D. Roosevelt. Multicoloured.

1195. 10 c. Type **279** 10 10
1196. 60 c. Huddie Ledbetter " Leadbelly " in concert (Works Progress administration) 35 30
1197. $1.10 Signing bill No. 8802, 1941 (Fair employment committee) 65 55
1198. $3 Farm Security administration .. .. 1·40 1·25

1982. Birth of Prince William of Wales Nos. 1188/93 optd. **ROYAL BABY 21.6.82.**

1200. 50 c. Type **278** 25 30
1201. 60 c. Type **278** 30 35
1202. $1 Prince and Princess of Wales 50 55
1203. $2 As $1 .. .. .. 95 1·00
1204. $3 Princess of Wales .. 1·60 1·75
1205. $4 As $3 .. .. .. 1·75 1·90

280. Apostle and Tormentor.

1982. Easter. Details from Painting " The Way to Calvary " (Raphael). Multicoloured.

1207. 40 c. Type **280** 50 20
1208. 70 c. Captain of the guards (vert.) 75 35
1209. $1.10 Christ and apostle (vert.) .. .. .. 1·00 45
1210. $4 Mourners (vert.) .. 2·75 1·75

HAVE YOU READ THE NOTES AT THE BEGINNING OF THIS CATALOGUE?

These often provide answers to the enquiries we receive.

281. "Orient Express".

1982. Famous Trains of the World. Mult.
1212. 30 c. Type **281** 60 20
1213. 60 c. "Trans-Siberian Express" 80 35
1214. 70 c. "Golden Arrow" .. 1·00 45
1215. 90 c. "Flying Scotsman" 1·25 55
1216. $1 German Federal Railways .. .. 1·50 1·00
1217. $3 German National Railways .. .. 3·00 3·50

282. Footballers.

1982. World Cup Football Championship Winners.
1219. **282.** 60 c. multicoloured .. 35 35
1220. $4 multicoloured .. 2·00 2·00

1982. Christmas. Scenes from Walt Disney's cartoon film "Robin Hood". As T **257**, but horiz.
1222. ½ c. multicoloured .. 10 10
1223. 1 c. multicoloured .. 10 10
1224. 2 c. multicoloured .. 10 10
1225. 3 c. multicoloured .. 10 10
1226. 4 c. multicoloured .. 10 10
1227. 5 c. multicoloured .. 10 10
1228. 10 c. multicoloured .. 10 10
1229. $2.50 multicoloured .. 1·50 1·25
1230. $3 multicoloured .. 1·75 1·50

283. Killer Whale.

1983. Save the Whales. Multicoloured.
1232. 15 c. Type **283** 85 30
1233. 40 c. Sperm Whale .. 1·75 70
1234. 70 c. Blue Whale .. .. 2·50 2·25
1235. $3 Common Dolphin .. 3·50 5·00

284. Construction of Ark.

1983. 500th Birth Anniv. of Raphael. Mult.
1237. 25 c. Type **284** 20 15
1238. 30 c. Jacob's vision .. 20 20
1239. 90 c. Joseph interprets the dreams of his brothers 50 45
1240. $4 Joseph interprets Pharaoh's dreams .. 1·90 2·00

285. Dentistry, Health Centre.

1983. Commonwealth Day. Multicoloured.
1242. 10 c. Type **285** 10 10
1243. 70 c. Airport runway construction 35 35
1244. $1.10 Tourism 55 55
1245. $3 Boat-building .. 1·40 1·40

286. Maritime Communications via Satellite.

1983. World Communications Year. Mult.
1246. 30 c. Type **286** 15 15
1247. 40 c. Rural telephone installation 20 20
1248. $2.50 Satellite weather map 1·25 1·25
1249. $3 Airport control room .. 1·40 1·40

287. Franklin Sport Sedan, 1928.

1983. 75th Anniv. of Model "T" Ford Car. Multicoloured.
1251. 6 c. Type **287** 10 10
1252. 10 c. Delage "D8", 1933 10 10
1253. 40 c. Alvis, 1938 .. .. 20 25
1254. 60 c. Invicta "S-type" tourer, 1931 .. .. 30 35
1255. 70 c. Alfa-Romeo "1750 Gran Sport", 1930 .. 35 40
1256. 90 c. Isotta Fraschini, 1930 40 45
1257. $1 Bugatti Royale Type "41" 45 50
1258. $2 B.M.W. "328", 1938 95 1·00
1259. $3 Marmon "V 16", 1931 1·40 1·50
1260. $4 Lincoln "K 8" saloon, 1932 .. .. .. 1·90 2·00

288. "Norge" (airship).

1983. Bicentenary of Manned Flight. Mult.
1262. 30 c. Type **288** 60 30
1263. 60 c. Gloster "VI" seaplane .. .. .. 1·00 75
1264. $1.10 Curtiss "NC-4" flying boat .. .. 1·60 1·60
1265. $4 Dornier "Do 18" flying boat .. .. .. 3·50 4·00

289. Morty.

1983. Christmas. Multicoloured.
1267. ½ c. Type **289** 10 10
1268. 1 c. Ludwig von Drake .. 10 10
1269. 2 c. Gyro Gearloose .. 10 10
1270. 3 c. Pluto and Figaro .. 10 10
1271. 4 c. Morty and Ferdie .. 10 10
1272. 5 c. Mickey Mouse and Goofy 10 10
1273. 10 c. Chip'n Dale .. 10 10
1274. $2.50 Mickey and Minnie Mouse .. .. 2·50 1·40
1275. $3 Donald and Grandma Duck .. .. .. 2·75 1·75

Nos. 1267/75 show Disney cartoon characters in scenes from "It's beginning to look a lot like Christmas" (song).

290. Daisy Duck on Pommel Horse.

1984. Olympic Games, Los Angeles. Mult.
A. Inscr "1984 LOS ANGELES"
B. Inscr "1984 OLYMPICS LOS ANGELES" and Olympic emblem

		A		B	
1277.	½ c. Type **290** ..	10	10	10	10
1278.	1 c. Mickey Mouse boxing	10	10	10	10
1279.	2 c. Daisy Duck in archery event ..	10	10	10	10
1280.	3 c. Clarabelle Cow on uneven bars	10	10	10	10
1281.	4 c. Mickey and Minnie Mouse in hurdles race ..	10	10	10	10
1282.	5 c. Donald Duck with Chip'n'Dale weightlifting ..	10	10	10	10
1283.	$1 Little Hiawatha in single kayak	1·50	90	1·50	90
1284.	$2 The Tortoise and the Hare in marathon ..	2·00	1·75	2·00	1·75
1285.	$3 Mickey Mouse polevaulting ..	2·50	2·25	2·50	2·25

291. William I.

1984. English Monarchs. Multicoloured.
1287 $4 Type **291** .. .. 2·50 2·75
1288 $4 William II .. .. 2·50 2·75
1289 $4 Henry I .. .. 2·50 2·75
1290 $4 Stephen .. .. 2·50 2·75
1291 $4 Henry II .. .. 2·50 2·75
1292 $4 Richard I .. .. 2·50 2·75
1293 $4 John .. .. .. 2·50 2·75
1294 $4 "Henry III" .. .. 2·50 2·75
1295 $4 Edward I .. .. 2·50 2·75
1296 $4 Edward II .. .. 2·50 2·75
1297 $4 Edward III .. .. 2·50 2·75
1298 $4 Richard II .. .. 2·50 2·75
1299 $4 Henry IV .. .. 2·50 2·75
1300 $4 Henry V .. .. 2·50 2·75
1301 $4 Henry VI .. .. 2·50 2·75
1302 $4 Edward IV .. .. 2·50 2·75
1303 $4 Edward V .. .. 2·50 2·75
1304 $4 Richard III .. .. 2·50 2·75
1305 $4 Henry VII .. .. 2·50 2·75
1306 $4 Henry VIII .. .. 2·50 2·75
1307 $4 Edward VI .. .. 2·50 2·75
1308 $4 Jane Grey .. .. 2·50 2·75
1309 $$ Mary I .. .. 2·50 2·75
1310 $4 Elizabeth I .. .. 2·50 2·75
1311 $4 James I .. .. 2·50 2·75
1312 $4 Charles I .. .. 2·50 2·75
1313 $4 Charles II .. .. 2·50 2·75
1314 $4 James II .. .. 2·50 2·75
1315 $4 William III .. .. 2·50 2·75
1316 $4 Mary II .. .. 2·50 2·75
1317 $4 Anne .. .. .. 2·50 2·75
1318 $4 George I .. .. 2·50 2·75
1319 $4 George II .. .. 2·50 2·75
1320 $4 George III .. .. 2·50 2·75
1321 $4 George IV .. .. 2·50 2·75
1322 $4 William IV .. .. 2·50 2·75
1323 $4 Victoria .. .. 2·50 2·75
1324 $4 Edward VII .. .. 2·50 2·75
1325 $4 George V .. .. 2·50 2·75
1326 $4 Edward VIII .. .. 2·50 2·75
1327 $4 George VI .. .. 2·50 2·75
1328 $4 Elizabeth II .. .. 2·50 2·75

Although inscribed "Henry III" the portrait on No. 1294 is actually of Edward II.

292. Lantana.

1984. Flowers. Multicoloured.
1329. 25 c. Type **292** 20 15
1330. 30 c. Plumbago 25 20
1331. 90 c. Spider Lily 70 60
1332. $4 Giant Alocasia .. 2·50 3·00

293. Blue Parrot Fish.

1984. Coral Reef Fish. Multicoloured.
1334. 10 c. Type **293** 85 3
1335. 30 c. Flame-back Cherub Fish .. .. .. 1·75 9
1336. 70 c. Painted Wrasse .. 3·00 3·0
1337. 90 c. Straight-tailed Razor Fish .. .. 3·25 3·2

1984. Universal Postal Union Congress Hamburg. Nos. 1331/2 optd. **19th U.P.U. CONGRESS-HAMBURG.**
1339. 90 c. Spider Lily .. 60 65
1340. $4 Giant Alocasia .. 2·50 3·00

295. Freighter.

1984. Ships. Multicoloured.
1342. 40 c. Type **295** .. .. 1·25 55
1343. 70 c. "Queen Elizabeth 2" .. .. .. 1·50 1·25
1344. 90 c. Sailing boats .. 1·90 1·75
1345. $4 "Amerikanis" .. 6·00 7·00

296. "The Night" (detail) (Correggio).

1984. 450th Death Anniv. of Correggio (painter). Multicoloured.
1347. 10 c. Type **296** 35 15
1348. 30 c. "The Virgin adoring the Child" 70 40
1349. 40 c. "The Mystical Marriage of St. Catherine and St. Sebastian" .. .. 1·75 1·25
1350. $4 "The Madonna and the Fruit Basket" .. 4·00 4·75

297. "L'Absinthe" (Degas).

1984. 150th Birth Anniv. of Edgar Degas (painter). Multicoloured.
1352. 25 c. Type **297** 65 30
1353. 70 c. "Pouting" (horiz.) 1·25 1·00
1354. $1.10 "The Millinery Shop" .. .. .. 1·75 1·75
1355. $3 "The Bellelli Family" (horiz.) .. .. 3·25 3·75

298. Train on "Puffing Billy" Line, Victoria.

1984. "Ausipex" International Stamp Exhibition, Melbourne. Multicoloured.
1357. $1.10 Type **298** .. .. 2·00 1·50
1358. $4 Yacht "Australia II" (winner of America's Cup) .. .. .. 4·50 5·00

299. "Locomotion" (1825).

1984. Railway Locomotives. Multicoloured.

No.	Description	Mint	Used
1360.	30 c. Type **299**	80	35
1361.	40 c. "Novelty" (1829)	95	40
1362.	60 c. "Washington Farmer" (1836)	1·10	55
1363.	70 c. French Crampton type (1859)	1·25	70
1364.	90 c. Dutch State Railways (1873)	1·50	1·00
1365.	$1.10 "Champion" (1882)	1·75	1·50
1366.	$2 Webb Compound type (1893)	2·25	2·50
1367.	$4 Berlin "No. 74" (1900)	3·75	4·50

1984. Opening of Port Saline International Airport (1st issue). Nos. 1247 and 1249 optd. **OPENING OF PORT SALINE INT'L AIRPORT.**

No.	Description	Mint	Used
1369.	40 c. Rural telephone installation	25	30
1370.	$3 Airport control room	1·75	1·90

See also Nos. 1393/5.

301. Donald Duck as Father Christmas looking into Mirror.

1984. Christmas. Walt Disney Cartoon Characters. Multicoloured.

No.	Description	Mint	Used
1372.	45 c. Type **301**	1·00	40
1373.	60 c. Donald Duck filling stocking with presents	1·25	45
1374.	90 c. As Father Christmas pulling a sleigh	1·50	75
1375.	$2 As Father Christmas decorating Christmas tree	2·50	2·25
1376.	$4 Donald Duck and nephews singing carols	3·50	3·75

1985. Birth Bicentenary of John J. Audubon (ornithologist) (1st issue). As T **198** of Antigua. Multicoloured.

No.	Description	Mint	Used
1378.	50 c. Clapper rail (vert.)	1·25	50
1379.	70 c. Hooded warbler (vert.)	1·50	75
1380.	90 c. Common flicker (vert.)	2·00	1·10
1381.	$4 Bohemian waxwing (vert.)	4·25	4·50

See also Nos. 1480/3.

302. Honda "XL500R".

1985. Centenary of the Motor Cycle. Multicoloured.

No.	Description	Mint	Used
1383.	25 c. Type **302**	80	50
1384.	50 c. Suzuki "GS1100ES"	1·25	1·00
1385.	90 c. Kawasaki "KZ700"	1·90	1·75
1386.	$4 BMW "K100"	5·00	5·50

303. "Explorer".

1985. 75th Anniv. of Girl Guide Movement. Designs showing work for Guide badges. Multicoloured.

No.	Description	Mint	Used
1388.	25 c. Type **303**	40	30
1389.	60 c. "Cook"	75	65
1390.	90 c. "Musician"	1·25	95
1391.	$3 "Home nurse"	2·75	2·50

304. Avro "748" on Inaugural Flight from Barbados.

1985. Opening of Point Saline International Airport (1984) (2nd issue). Multicoloured.

No.	Description	Mint	Used
1393.	70 c. Type **304**	2·00	65
1394.	$1 Pan Am "L1011" on inaugural flight from New York	2·50	1·25
1395.	$4 "Tri-Star" on inaugural flight to Miami	5·50	4·50

305. McDonnell Douglas "DC-8".

1985. 40th Anniv. of International Civil Aviation Organization. Multicoloured.

No.	Description	Mint	Used
1397.	10 c. Type **305**	30	20
1398.	50 c. "Super Constellation"	75	75
1399.	60 c. Vickers "Vanguard"	85	85
1400.	$4 De Havilland "Twin Otter"	4·00	4·50

306. Model Boat Racing.

1985. Water Sports. Multicoloured.

No.	Description	Mint	Used
1402.	10 c. Type **306**	20	10
1403.	50 c. Scuba diving, Carriacou	45	30
1404.	$1·10, Windsurfers on Grand Anse Beach	85	85
1405.	$4 Windsurfing	2·50	3·00

307. Bird of Paradise (flower).

1985. Native Flowers. Multicoloured.

No.	Description	Mint	Used
1407	½ c. Type **307**	10	20
1408	1 c. Passion Flower	10	20
1409	2 c. Oleander	10	20
1410	4 c. Bromeliad	10	20
1411	5 c. Anthurium	10	20
1412	6 c. Bougainvillea	15	20
1413	10 c. Hibiscus	20	20
1414	15 c. Ginger	30	30
1415	25 c. Poinsettia	30	30
1416	30 c. Mexican Creeper	30	30
1417	40 c. Angel's Trumpet	40	40
1418	50 c. Amaryllis	45	45
1419	60 c. Prickly Pear	60	60
1420	70 c. Chenille Plant	65	65
1420c	75 c. Cordia	1·00	1·25
1421	$1 Periwinkle	90	1·00
1422	$1·10, Ixora	1·00	1·25
1423	$3 Shrimp Plant	2·00	2·50
1424	$5 Plumbago	2·25	3·25
1425	$10 "Lantana camara"	4·00	6·50
1425c	$20 Peregrina	8·50	14·00

308. The Queen Mother at Royal Opera House, London.

1985. Life and Times of Queen Elizabeth the Queen Mother. Multicoloured.

No.	Description	Mint	Used
1426.	$1 Type **308**	55	60
1427.	$1·50, The Queen Mother playing snooker at London Press Club (horiz)	80	85
1428.	$2·50, At Epsom Races, 1960	1·40	1·50

Stamps as Nos. 1426/8 but with face values of 90 c., $1 and $3 exist from additional sheetlets with changed background colours.

309. Youth Gardening (Horticulture).

1985. International Youth Year. Mult.

No.	Description	Mint	Used
1430.	25 c. Type **309**	25	20
1431.	50 c. Young people on beach (Leisure)	45	30
1432.	$1·10, Girls in classroom (Education)	90	80
1433.	$3 Nurse and young patient (Health Care)	2·25	2·00

1985. 300th Birth Anniv. of Johann Sebastian Bach (composer). As T **206** of Antigua. Mult.

No.	Description	Mint	Used
1435.	25 c. Crumhorn	65	20
1436.	70 c. Oboe d'Amore	1·25	70
1437.	$1 Violin	1·75	1·25
1438.	$3 Harpsichord	3·00	3·00

310. Cub Scouts Camping.

1985. 4th Caribbean Cuboree. Multicoloured.

No.	Description	Mint	Used
1440.	10 c. Type **310**	30	15
1441.	50 c. Cub scouts swimming ("Physical Fitness")	65	40
1442.	$1 Stamp collecting	1·25	80
1443.	$4 Birdwatching	3·00	3·00

1985. Royal Visit. As T **207** of Antigua. Multicoloured.

No.	Description	Mint	Used
1445.	50 c. Flags of Great Britain and Grenada	60	35
1446.	$1 Queen Elizabeth II (vert.)	1·25	1·00
1447.	$4 Royal Yacht "Britannia"	3·50	4·25

1985. 150th Birth Anniv. of Mark Twain (author). As T **118** of Anguilla. Designs showing Walt Disney cartoon characters in scenes from "The Prince and the Pauper". Multicoloured.

No.	Description	Mint	Used
1449.	25 c. Mortie as Tom meeting the Prince (Ferdie)	30	20
1450.	50 c. Tom and the Prince exchanging clothes	45	35
1451.	$1·10, The Prince with John Cantry	1·00	75
1452.	$1·50, The Prince knights Mike Hendon (Goofy)	1·25	1·00
1453.	$2 Tom and the Whipping Boy	1·75	1·40

1985. Birth Bicentenaries of Grimm Brothers (folklorists). As T **119** of Anguilla, showing Walt Disney cartoon characters in scenes from "The Fisherman and his Wife". Multicoloured.

No.	Description	Mint	Used
1455.	30 c. The Fisherman (Goofy) catching enchanted fish	25	20
1456.	60 c. The Fisherman scolded by his Wife (Clarabelle)	50	50
1457.	70 c. The Fisherman's Wife with dream cottage	60	60
1458.	$1 The Fisherman's Wife as King	80	90
1459.	$3 The Fisherman and Wife in their original shack	2·00	2·75

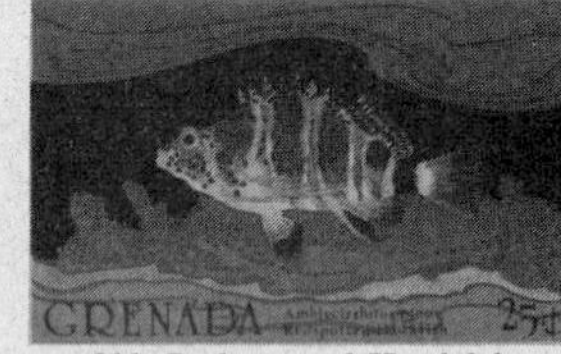

311. Red spotted Hawkfish.

1985. Marine Life. Multicoloured.

No.	Description	Mint	Used
1461.	25 c. Type **311**	80	35
1462.	50 c. Spotfin Butterflyfish	1·40	85
1463.	$1·10, Fire Coral and Orange Sponges	2·50	2·25
1464.	$3 Pillar Coral	4·75	5·50

1985. 40th Anniv. of U.N.O. Multicoloured. As T **208** of Antigua showing United Nations (New York) stamps.

No.	Description	Mint	Used
1466.	50 c. Mary McLeod Bethune (educationist) and 1975 International Women's Year 10 c.	50	30
1467.	$2 Maimonides (physician) and 1966 W.H.O. 5 c.	3·00	2·50
1468.	$2.50 Alexander Graham Bell (telephone inventor) and 1956 I.T.U. 3 c.	3·00	3·00

312. "Adoration of the Sheperds' (Mantegna).

1985. Christmas. Religious Paintings. Multicoloured.

No.	Description	Mint	Used
1470.	25 c. Type **312**	20	15
1471.	60 c. "Journey of the Magi" (Sassetta)	40	40
1472.	90 c. "Madonna and Child enthroned with Saints" (Raphael)	50	60
1473.	$4 "Nativity" (Monaco)	1·50	3·00

1986. Centenary of Statue of Liberty (1st issue). Multicoloured. As T **211** of Dominica.

No.	Description	Mint	Used
1475.	5 c. Columbus Monument, 1893 (vert.)	15	20
1476.	25 c. Columbus Monument, 1986 (vert.)	40	20
1477.	40 c. Mounted police, Central Park, 1895	1·75	90
1478.	$4 Mounted police, 1986	6·50	6·00

See also Nos. 1644/52.

1986. Birth Bicentenary of John J. Audubon (ornithologist) (2nd issue). Multicoloured. As T **198** of Antigua.

No.	Description	Mint	Used
1480.	50 c. Snowy egret	1·00	55
1481.	90 c. Greater flamingo	1·75	1·00
1482.	$1.10 Canada goose	2·00	1·25
1483.	$3 Smew	3·50	3·75

1986. Visit of President Reagan. Nos. 1418 and 1424 optd. **VISIT OF PRES REAGAN 20 FEB. 1986.**

No.	Description	Mint	Used
1485.	50 c. Amaryllis	40	40
1486.	$5 Plumbago	3·25	3·50

314. Methodist Church, St. Georges.

1986. Bicentenary of Methodist Church in Grenada.
1487. **314.** 60 c. multicoloured .. 70 80

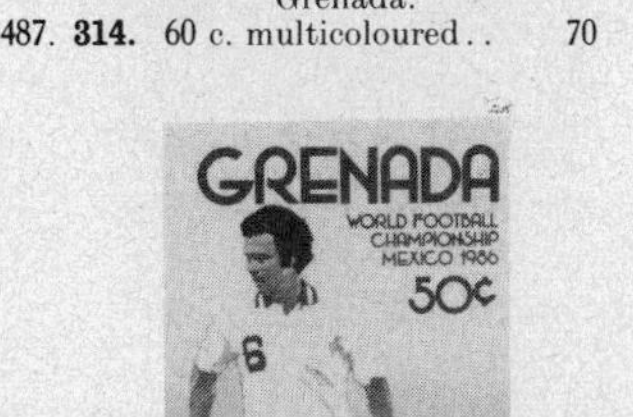

315. Player with Ball.

1986. World Cup Football Championship, Mexico. Multicoloured.
1489. 50 c. Type **315** 70 50
1490. 70 c. Player heading ball 90 70
1491. 90 c. Player controlling ball .. .. .. 1·25 1·00
1492. $4 Player controlling ball with right foot .. 5·00 5·50

1986. Appearance of Halley's Comet (1st issue). As T **123** of Anguilla. Multicoloured.
1494. 5 c. Clyde Tombaugh (astronomer) and Dudley Observatory, New York 25 20
1495. 20 c. N.A.S.A.—U.S.A.F. "X-24B" Space Shuttle prototype, 1973 .. .. 35 25
1496. 40 c. German comet medal, 1618 .. .. 50 45
1497. $4 Destruction of Sodom and Gomorrah, 1949 B.C. .. .. 3·00 3·50
See also Nos. 1533/6 and 1980/3.

1986. 60th Birthday of Queen Elizabeth II. As T **125** of Anguilla.
1499. 2 c. black and yellow .. 10 15
1500. $1.50 multicoloured .. 75 90
1501. $4 multicoloured .. 2·00 2·75
DESIGNS: 2 c. Princess Elizabeth in 1951. $1.50, Queen presenting trophy at polo match, Windsor, 1965. $4 at Epsom, Derby Day, 1977.

1986. "Ameripex" International Stamp Exhibition, Chicago. As T **212** of Dominica, showing Walt Disney cartoon characters playing baseball. Multicoloured.
1503. 1 c. Goofy as pitcher .. 10 10
1504. 2 c. Goofy as catcher .. 10 10
1505. 3 c. Mickey Mouse striking ball and Donald Duck as catcher .. 10 10
1506. 4 c. Huey forcing out Dewey 10 10
1507. 5 c. Chip n'Dale chasing flyball 10 10
1508. 6 c. Mickey Mouse, Donald Duck and Clarabelle in argument 10 10
1509. $2 Minnie Mouse and Donald Duck reading baseball rules .. .. 1·75 1·75
1510. $3 Ludwig von Drake as umpire with Goofy and Pete colliding .. 2·25 2·25

1986. Royal Wedding. As T **213** of Antigua. Multicoloured.
1512. 2 c. Prince Andrew and Miss Sarah Ferguson 10 15
1513. $1.10 Prince Andrew .. 70 70
1514. $4 Prince Andrew with H.M.S. "Brazen's" helicopter .. .. 2·50 3·00

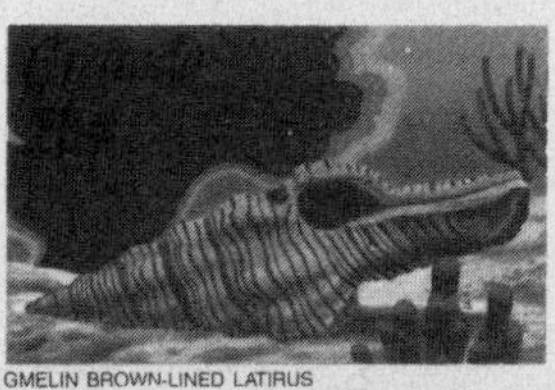

316. Brown-lined Latirus.

1986. Sea Shells. Multicoloured.
1516. 25 c. Type **316** 35 20
1517. 60 c. Lamellose wentletrap 65 55
1518. 70 c. Turkey wing .. 75 60
1519. $4 Rooster tail conch .. 2·75 3·50

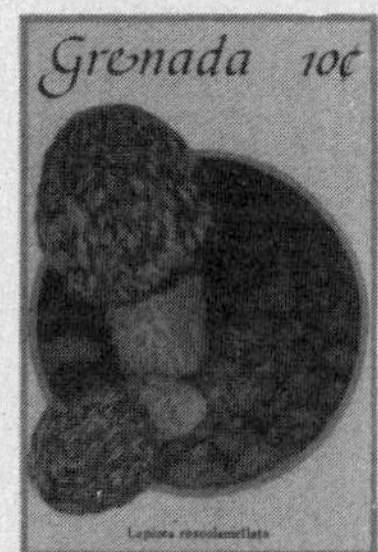

317. "Lepiota roseolamellata".

1986. Mushrooms. Multicoloured.
1521. 10 c. Type **317** 50 30
1522. 60 c. "Lentinus bertieri" 1·50 1·00
1523. $1 "Lentinus retinervis" 2·25 1·50
1524. $4 "Eccilia cystiophorus" .. .. 5·50 5·50

1986. World Cup Football Championship Winners. Mexico. Nos. 1489/92 optd. **WINNERS Argentina 3 W. Germany 2.**
1526. 50 c. Type **315** 50 50
1527. 70 c. Player heading ball 65 65
1528. 90 c. Player controlling ball 85 85
1529. $4 Player controlling ball with right foot .. 3·25 3·50

318. Dove on Rifles and Mahatma Gandhi (Disarmament Week).

1986. International Events. Multicoloured.
1531. 60 c. Type **318** 50 50
1532. $4 Hands passing olive branch and Martin Luther King (International Peace Year) (horiz.) .. .. 2·00 2·50

1986. Appearance of Halley's Comet (2nd issue). Nos. 1494/7 optd with T **218** of Antigua.
1533. 5 c. Clyde Tombaugh (astronomer) and Dudley Observatory, New York 50 50
1534. 20 c. N.A.S.A.—U.S.A.F. "X-24B" Space Shuttle prototype, 1973 .. .. 75 50
1535. 40 c. German comet medal, 1618 .. .. 1·00 65
1536. $4 Destruction of Sodom and Gomorrah, 1949 B.C. .. .. .. 4·50 5·00

1986. Christmas. Multicoloured. As T **220** of Antigua showing Walt Disney cartoon characters.
1538. 30 c. Mickey Mouse asleep in armchair (vert.) 25 20
1539. 45 c. Young Mickey Mouse with Father Christmas (vert.) .. 35 30
1540. 60 c. Donald Duck with toy telephone 50 30
1541. 70 c. Pluto with pushcart 55 45
1542. $1.10 Daisy Duck with doll 80 85
1543. $2 Goofy as Father Christmas (vert.) .. 1·50 1·60
1544. $2·50 Goofy singing carols at piano (vert.) 1·75 2·00
1545. $3 Mickey Mouse, Donald Duck and nephew riding toy train .. .. .. 2·25 2·50

319. Cockerel and Hen.

1986. Fauna and Flora. Multicoloured.
1547. 10 c. Type **319** 20 10
1548. 30 c. Fish-eating bat .. 35 20
1549. 60 c. Goat 55 35
1550. 70 c. Cow 60 40
1551. $1 Anthurium .. .. 1·50 1·25
1552. $1·10 Royal poinciana .. 1·50 1·25
1553. $2 Frangipani .. .. 2·50 2·75
1554. $4 Orchid .. .. 6·50 7·00

320. Maserati "Biturbo" (1984).

1986. Centenary of Motoring. Multicoloured.
1556. 10 c. Type **320** 20 20
1557. 30 c. AC "Cobra" (1960) 30 30
1558. 60 c. Corvette (1963) .. 50 50
1559. 70 c. Dusenberg "SJ7" (1932) 60 60
1560. 90 c. Porsche (1957) .. 75 75
1561. $1·10 Stoewer (1930) .. 85 85
1562. $2 Volkswagen "Beetle" (1957) .. .. .. 1·40 1·40
1563. $3 Mercedes "600 Limo" (1963) .. .. .. 1·90 2·00

321. Pole Vaulting.

1986. Olympic Games, Seoul, South Korea (1988). Multicoloured.
1565. 10 c. + 5 c. Type **321** .. 10 20
1566. 50 c. + 20 c. Gymnastics 35 45
1567. 70 c. + 30 c. Putting the shot 50 65
1568. $2 + $1 High jumping .. 1·50 2·00
The premiums on Nos. 1565/9 were to support the participation of the Grenada team.

1986. Birth Centenary of Marc Chagall (artist). Designs as T **225** of Antigua, showing various paintings.
1570/1609 $1 × 40 multicoloured Set of 40 .. .. 24·00 24·00

1987. America's Cup Yachting Championship. As T **222** of Antigua. Multicoloured.
1611. 10 c. "Columbia", 1958 .. 15 10
1612. 60 c. "Resolute", 1920 .. 40 40
1613. $1.10 "Endeavor", 1934 80 80
1614. $4 "Rainbow", 1934 .. 2·25 3·60

322. Virgin Mary and Outline Map of Grenada.

1987. 500th Anniv (1992) of Discovery of America by Christopher Columbus (1st issue). Multicoloured.
1616. 10 c. Type **322** 20 20
1617. 30 c. "Santa Maria", "Pinta" and "Nina" (horiz.) 35 35
1618. 50 c. Columbus and outline map of Grenada 45 45
1619. 60 c. Christopher Columbus 45 45
1620. 90 c. King Ferdinand and Queen Isabella of Spain (horiz.) 60 60
1621. $1.10 Map of Antilles by Columbus 75 75
1622. $2 Caribs with sailing raft (horiz.) .. .. 1·40 1·40
1623. $3 Columbus in the New World, 1493 (contemporary drawing) .. 1·75 1·75
See also Nos. 2051/4, 2091/8, 2222/9, 2389/94 and 2423/4.

1987. Milestones of Transportation. As T **226** of Antigua. Multicoloured.
1625 10 c. Cornu's first helicopter, 1907 .. 25 25
1626 15 c. Monitor and Merrimack (first battle between ironclad warships), 1862 .. 35 35
1627 30 c. "LZ1" (first Zeppelin), 1900 .. 50 50
1628 50 c. "Sirius" (first translantic paddle-steamer crossing), 1838 55 55
1629 60 c. Steam locomotive on Trans-Siberian Railway (longest line) 55 55
1630 70 c. U.S.S. "Enterprise" (largest aircraft carrier), 1960 .. .. .. 60 60
1631 90 c. Blanchard's balloon (first balloon across English Channel), 1785 80 80
1632 $1.50 U.S.S. "Holland I" (first steam-powered submarine), 1900 .. 1·40 1·40
1633 $2 S.S. "Oceanic I" (first luxury liner), 1871 .. 1·90 1·90
1634 $3 Lamborghini "Countach" (fastest commercial car), 1984 2·25 2·25

323. Black Grouper.

1987. "Capex '87" International Stamp Exhibition, Toronto. Game Fishes. Mult.
1635. 10 c. Type **323** 30 15
1636. 30 c. Blue marlin (horiz.) 40 15
1637. 60 c. White marlin .. 60 45
1638. 70 c. Big eye thresher shark (horiz.) 70 60
1639. $1 Bonefish (horiz.) .. 90 80
1640. $1.10 Wahoo (horiz.) .. 1·00 90
1641. $2 Sailfish (horiz.) .. 1·75 2·00
1642. $4 Albacore (horiz.) .. 2·75 3·00

1987. Centenary of Statue of Liberty (2nd issue). As T **227** of Antigua. Multicoloured.
1644. 10 c. Computer projections of statue and base (horiz.) .. 15 15
1645. 25 c. Statue and fireworks (horiz.) .. 20 15
1646. 50 c. Statue and fireworks (different) (horiz.) 35 35
1647. 60 c. Statue and boats .. 45 45
1648. 70 c. Computer projection of top of statue (horiz.) .. 50 50
1649. $1 Rear view of Statue and fireworks 80 80
1650. $1.10 Aerial view of statue 95 95
1651. $2 Statue and flotilla .. 1·75 1·75
1652. $4 "Queen Elizabeth 2" in New York Harbour 3·00 3·00

324. Alice and the Rabbit Hole.

1987. 50th Anniv. of First Full-Length Disney Cartoon Film. Scenes from various films.

1653/1706. 30 c. × 54 multicoloured Set of 54 .. .. 7·50 8·00

325. Isacc Newton holding Apple (Law of Gravity).

1987. Great Scientific Discoveries. Mult.

1708. 50 c. Type **325** 75 75
1709. $1.10 John Jacob Berzelius and symbols of chemical elements 1·50 1·50
1710. $2 Robert Boyle (law of Pressure and Volume) 2·25 2·25
1711. $3 James Watt and drawing of steam engine .. .. .. 3·25 3·25

No. 1711 is inscribed "RUDOLF DIESEL" in error.

1987. 60th Anniv. of International Social Security Association. Nos. 1413, 1418 and 1423 optd. **International Social Security Association** and Emblem.

1714. 10 c. Hibiscus 10 15
1715. 50 c. Amaryllis 25 30
1716. $3 Shrimp plant .. 1·40 2·00

1987. Bicentenary of U.S. Constitution. As T **232** of Antigua. Multicoloured.

1717. 15 c. Independence Hall, Philadelphia (vert.) .. 10 10
1718. 50 c. Benjamin Franklin (Pennsylvania delegate) (vert.) .. 25 30
1719. 60 c. State Seal, Massachusetts .. 25 30
1720. $4 Robert Morris (Pennsylvania delegate) (vert.) .. 1·75 2·40

328. Goofy in "The Shadow".

1987. "Hafnia '87" International Stamp Exhibition. Walt Disney cartoon characters in scenes from Hans Christian Andersen's fairy tales. Multicoloured.

1722. 25 c. Type **328** 20 20
1723. 30 c. Mother Stork and brood in "The Storks" 20 20
1724. 50 c. King Richard, Robin Hood and Little John (from Robin Hood) in "The Emperor's New Clothes" 35 35
1725. 60 c. Goofy and Pluto in "The Tinderbox" .. 35 35
1726. 70 c. Daisy and Donald Duck in "The Shepherdess and the Chimney Sweep" .. 40 40
1727. $1.50 Mickey and Minnie Mouse in "The Little Mermaid" 90 90
1728. $3 Clarabelle and Goofy in "The Princess and the Pea" .. .. 1·75 2·00
1729. $4 Minnie Mouse and Pegleg Pete in "The Marsh King's Daughter" .. .. 2·00 2·25

329. "The Annunciation" (Fra Angelico).

1987. Christmas. Religious Paintings. Multicoloured.

1731. 15 c. Type **329** 40 10
1732. 30 c. "The Annunciation" (attr. Hubert van Eyck) .. 65 30
1733. 60 c. "The Adoration of the Magi" (Januarius Zick) .. .. .. 1·25 75
1734. $4 "The Flight into Egypt" (Gerard David) .. .. .. 4·00 4·50

330. T. Albert Marryshow.

1988. Birth Centenary of T. Albert Marryshow (nationalist).

1736. **330.** 25 c. brown, light brown and red .. 30 30

1988. Royal Ruby Wedding. As T **234** of Antigua. Multicoloured.

1737. 15 c. brown, blk. & bl. .. 30 10
1738. 50 c. multicoloured .. 60 40
1739. $1 brown and black .. 1·00 75
1740. $4 multicoloured .. 3·00 3·25

DESIGNS: 15 c. Wedding photograph, 1947. 50 c. Queen Elizabeth II with Prince Charles and Princess Anne, c. 1955. $1, Queen with Princess Anne, c. 1957. $4, Queen Elizabeth (from photo by Tim Graham), 1980.

331 Goofy and Daisy Duck lighting Olympic Torch, Olympia

1988. Olympic Games, Seoul. Designs showing Walt Disney cartoon characters. Mult.

1742 1 c. Type **331** 10 10
1743 2 c. Donald and Daisy Duck carrying Olympic torch 10 10
1744 3 c. Donald Duck, Goofy and Mickey Mouse carrying flags of U.S., Korea and Spain .. 10 10
1745 4 c. Donald Duck releasing doves .. 10 10
1746 5 c. Mickey Mouse flying with rocket belt .. 10 10
1747 10 c. Morty and Ferdie carrying banner with Olympic motto .. 10 10
1748 $6 Donald Duck, Minnie Mouse and Hodori the Tiger (mascot of Seoul Games) .. .. 3·00 2·50
1749 $7 Pluto, Hodori and old post office, Seoul .. 3·50 4·00

1988. Stamp Exhibitions. Nos. 1631/4 optd.

1751 90 c. Blanchard's balloon, 1785 (optd **OLYMPHILEX' 88**, Seoul) .. 40 45
1752 $1.50 U.S.S. "Holland I" 1900 (optd **INDEPENDENCE 40**, Israel) .. 60 75
1753 $2 "Oceanic I", 1871 (optd **FINLANDIA 88**, Helsinki) .. .. 80 1·00
1754 $3 Lamborghini "Countach", 1984 (optd **Praga 88,** Prague) .. 1·25 1·60

332 Scout fishing from Boat

1988. World Scout Jamboree, Australia. Mult.

1755 20 c. Type **332** 20 15
1756 70 c. Scouts hiking through forest (horiz) 70 60
1757 90 c. Practising first aid (horiz) 90 80
1758 $3 Shooting rapids in inflatable canoe .. 2·25 2·50

333 "Santa Maria de Guia" (Columbus), 1498, and Map of Rotary District

1988. Rotary District 405 Conference, St. George's.

1760 **333** $2 multicoloured .. 80 1·00

334 Roseate Tern

1988. Birds. Multicoloured.

1762 10 c. Type **334** 25 20
1763 25 c. Laughing gull .. 35 25
1764 50 c. Osprey 60 45
1765 60 c. Rose-breasted grosbeak 60 45
1766 90 c. Purple gallinule .. 65 55
1767 $1.10 White-tailed tropic bird 70 75
1768 $3 Blue-faced booby .. 1·40 2·00
1769 $4 Common shoveler .. 1·75 2·50

335 Vauxhall Type "OE 30/98", 1925

1988. Cars. Multicoloured.

1771 $2 Type **335** 80 85
1772 $2 Wills "Sainte Claire", 1926 .. .. .. 80 85
1773 $2 Bucciali, 1928 .. 80 85
1774 $2 Irving Napier "Golden Arrow", 1929 .. .. 80 85
1775 $2 Studebaker "President", 1930 .. 80 85
1776 $2 Thomas "Flyer", 1907 80 85
1777 $2 Isotta-Fraschini "Tipo J", 1908 .. .. 80 85
1778 $2 Fiat 10/14HP, 1910 .. 80 85
1779 $2 Mercer "Type 35 Raceabout", 1911 .. 80 85
1780 $2 Marmon "Model 34 Cloverleaf", 1917 .. 80 85
1781 $2 Tatra "Type 77", 1934 80 85
1782 $2 Rolls-Royce "Phantom III", 1938 .. .. 80 85
1783 $2 Studebaker "Champion Starlight", 1947 .. 80 85
1784 $2 Porsche "Gmund", 1948 .. .. .. 80 85
1785 $2 Tucker, 1948 .. .. 80 85
1786 $2 Peerless "V-16", 1931 80 85
1787 $2 Minerva "AL", 1931 .. 80 85
1788 $2 Reo "Royale", 1933 .. 80 85
1789 $2 Pierce Arrow "Silver Arrow", 1933 .. .. 80 85
1790 $2 Hupmobile "Aerodynamic", 1934 .. 80 85
1791 $2 Peugeot "404", 1965 .. 80 85
1792 $2 Ford "Capri", 1969 .. 80 85
1793 $2 Ferrari "312T", 1975 .. 80 85
1794 $2 Lotus "T-79", 1978 .. 80 85
1795 $2 Williams-Cosworth "FW07", 1979 .. 80 85
1796 $2 H.R.G. "1500 Sports", 1948 .. .. 80 85
1797 $2 Crosley "Hotshot", 1949 .. .. .. 80 85
1798 $2 Volvo "PV444", 1955 80 85
1799 $2 Maserati "Tipo 61", 1960 .. .. .. 80 85
1800 $2 Saab "96", 1963 .. 80 85

1988. 500th Birth Anniv of Titian (artist). As T **238** of Antigua. Multicoloured.

1801 10 c. "Lavinia Vecellio" 10 10
1802 20 c. "Portrait of a Man" 10 10
1803 25 c. "Andrea de Franceschi" 10 15
1804 90 c. "Head of a Soldier" 40 45
1805 $1 "Man with a Flute" .. 45 50
1806 $2 "Lucrezia and Tarquinius" 80 85
1807 $3 "Duke of Mantua with Dog" .. .. .. 1·25 1·40
1808 $4 "La Bella di Tiziano" 1·60 1·75

336 "Graf Zeppelin" over Chicago World's Fair, 1933

1988. Airships. Multicoloured.

1810 10 c. Type **336** 10 10
1811 15 c. "LZ-1" over Lake Constance, 1901 (horiz) 15 15
1812 25 c. "Washington" (balloon) and "George Washington Curtis" (balloon barge), 1862 .. 20 20
1813 45 c. "Hindenburg" and Maybach "Zeppelin" car (horiz) 30 30

1814	50 c. Goodyear airship in Statue of Liberty Centenary Race, 1986	30	30
1815	60 c. "Hindenburg" over Statue of Liberty, 1937 (horiz)	35	35
1816	90 c. Aircraft docking experiment with "Hindenburg", 1936 (horiz)	60	60
1817	$2 "Hindenburg" over Olympic Stadium, Berlin, 1936	1·25	1·25
1818	$3 "Hindenburg" over Christ of the Andes Monument, 1937 ..	1·75	1·75
1819	$4 "Hindenburg" and "Bremen" (liner), 1936 (horiz)	2·00	2·00

337 Tasmanian Wolf, Mickey Mouse and Pluto

1988. "Sydpex '88" National Stamp Exhibition, Sydney and 60th Birthday of Mickey Mouse. Multicoloured.

1821	1 c. Type **337**	10	10
1822	2 c. Mickey Mouse feeding wallabies	10	10
1823	3 c. Mickey Mouse and Goofy with kangaroo ..	10	10
1824	4 c. Mickey and Minnie Mouse riding emus ..	10	10
1825	5 c. Mickey and Minnie Mouse with wombat ..	10	10
1826	10 c. Mickey Mouse and Donald Duck watching platypus	10	10
1827	$5 Mickey Mouse and Goofy photographing kookaburra	2·50	3·00
1828	$6 Mickey Mouse and Koala on map of Australia	2·75	3·25

338 Pineapple

1988. 10th Anniv of International Fund for Agricultural Development. Multicolured.

1830	25 c. Type **338**	15	15
1831	75 c. Bananas	40	40
1832	$3 Mace and nutmeg (horiz)	1·50	2·00

339 Lignum Vitae

1988. Flowering Trees and Shrubs. Mult.

1833	15 c. Type **339**	15	15
1834	25 c. Saman	20	15
1835	35 c. Red frangipani ..	25	20
1836	45 c. Flowering maple ..	30	25
1837	60 c. Yellow poui ..	40	30
1838	$1 Wild chestnut ..	60	60
1839	$3 Mountain immortelle	1·50	2·00
1840	$4 Queen of flowers ..	1·75	2·25

340 Mickey Mantle (New York Yankees)
(Illustration reduced, actual size 50 × 38mm)

1988. Major League Baseball Players (1st series). Designs showing portraits or league emblems.

1842/1922	30 c. × 81 mult Set of 81	8·75	9·00

1988. Christmas. "Mickey's Christmas Eve". As T **246** of Antigua showing Walt Disney cartoon characters. Multicoloured.

1923	$1 Donald Duck's nephew on mantelpiece ..	45	50
1924	$1 Goofy with string of popcorn	45	50
1925	$1 Chip n'Dale decorating Christmas tree ..	45	50
1926	$1 Father Christmas in sleigh	45	50
1927	$1 Donald's nephew with stocking	45	50
1928	$1 Donald's nephew unpacking decorations	45	50
1929	$1 Donald Duck with present	45	50
1930	$1 Mickey Mouse with present	45	50

341 Tina Turner

1988. Entertainers. Multicoloured.

1932	10 c. Type **341**	15	15
1933	25 c. Lionel Ritchie ..	20	20
1934	45 c. Whitney Houston ..	30	30
1935	60 c. Joan Armatrading	45	45
1936	75 c. Madonna	55	55
1937	$1 Elton John	70	75
1938	$3 Bruce Springsteen ..	1·90	2·25
1939	$4 Bob Marley	2·50	3·00

No. 1935 is incorrectly inscribed "JOAN AMMERTRADING".

342 Canada Atlantic Railway No. 2, 1889

1989. North American Railway Locomotives. Multicoloured.

1941	$2 Type **342**	95	1·00
1942	$2 Virginia & Truckee Railroad "J. W. Bowker" type, 1875 ..	95	1·00
1943	$2 Philadelphia & Reading Railway "Ariel", 1872 ..	95	1·00
1944	$2 Chicago & Rock Island Railroad "America" type, 1867 ..	95	1·00
1945	$2 Lehigh Valley Railroad Consolidation No. 63, 1866	95	1·00
1946	$2 Great Western Railway "Scotia", 1860 ..	95	1·00
1947	$2 Grand Trunk Railway "Birkenhead" Class, 1854	95	1·00
1948	$2 Camden & Amboy Railroad "Monster", 1837	95	1·00
1949	$2 Baltimore & Ohio Railroad "Grass-hopper" Class, 1834 ..	95	1·00
1950	$2 Baltimore & Ohio Railroad "Tom Thumb", 1829 ..	95	1·00
1951	$2 United Railways of Yucatan "Yucatan", 1925	95	1·00
1952	$2 Canadian National Railways Class "T2", 1924	95	1·00
1953	$2 St. Louis–San Francisco Railroad "Light Mikado" class, 1919	95	1·00
1954	$2 Atlantic Coast Line Railroad "Light Pacific" class, 1919 ..	95	1·00
1955	$2 Edaville Railroad No. 7, 1913	95	1·00
1956	$2 Denver & Rio Grande Western Railroad Class "K27", 1903 ..	95	1·00
1957	$2 Pennsylvania Railroad Class "E-2" No. 7002, 1902	95	1·00
1958	$2 Pennsylvania Railroad Class "H6", 1899 ..	95	1·00
1959	$2 Mohawk & Hudson Railroad "De Witt Clinton", 1893 ..	95	1·00
1960	$2 St. Clair Tunnel Company No. 598, 1891	95	1·00
1961	$2 Chesapeake & Ohio Railroad Class "M-1" No. 500 steam turbine electric, 1947 ..	95	1·00
1962	$2 Rutland Railroad No. 93, 1946	95	1·00
1963	$2 Pennsylvania Railroad Class "T1", 1942 ..	95	1·00
1964	$2 Chesapeake & Ohio Railroad Class "H-8", 1942	95	1·00
1965	$2 Atchison, Topeka & Santa Fe Railway Model "FT" diesel, 1941	95	1·00
1966	$2 Gulf, Mobile & Ohio Railroad Models "S-1" & "S-2", 1940 ..	95	1·00
1967	$2 New York, New Haven & Hartford Railroad Class "15", 1937 ..	95	1·00
1968	$2 Seaboard Air Line Railroad Class "R", 1936	95	1·00
1969	$2 Newfoundland Railway Class "R-2", 1930 ..	95	1·00
1970	$2 Canadian National Railway No. 9000, 1928	95	1·00

343 Women's Long Jump (Jackie Joyner-Kersee, U.S.A.)

1989. Olympic Gold Medal Winners, Seoul (1988). Multicoloured.

1971	10 c. Type **343**	10	10
1972	25 c. Women's Singles Tennis (Steffi Graf, West Germany) ..	10	15
1973	45 c. Men's 1500 metres (Peter Rono, Kenya) ..	20	25
1974	75 c. Men's 1000 metres single kayak (Greg Barton, U.S.A.) ..	30	35
1975	$1 Women's team foil (Italy)	40	45
1976	$2 Women's 100 metres freestyle swimming (Kristin Otto, East Germany)	85	90
1977	$3 Men's still rings gymnastics (Holger Behrendt, East Germany)	1·25	1·40
1978	$4 Synchronized swimming pair (Japan)	1·75	1·90

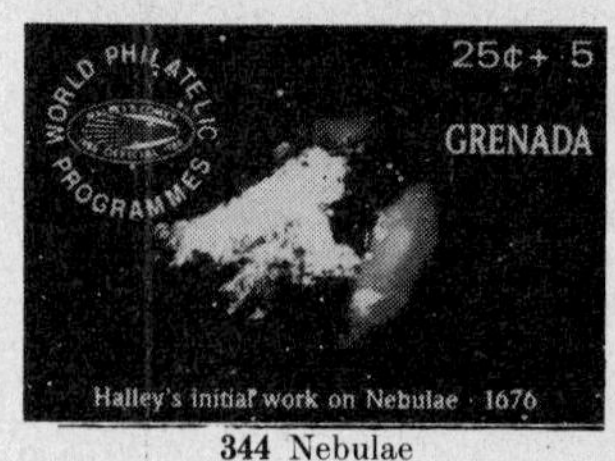

344 Nebulae

1989. Appearance of Halley's Comet (1986) (3rd issue).

1980	**344** 25 c. + 5 c. mult ..	15	20
1981	– 75 c. + 5 c. blk & grn	45	50
1982	– 90 c. + 5 c. mult ..	50	60
1983	– $2 + 5 c. multicoloured	1·00	1·40

DESIGNS: 75 c. + 5 c. Marine astronomical experiments; 90 c. + 5 c. Moon's surface; $2 + 5 c. Edmond Halley, Sir Isaac Newton and his book "Principia". (102 × 69 mm). $5 + 5 c. 17th-century warships and astrological signs.

1989. Japanese Art. Paintings by Hiroshige. As T **250** of Antigua. Multicoloured.

1985	10 c. "Shinagawa on Edo Bay"	15	15
1986	25 c. "Pine Trees on the Road to Totsuka" ..	20	20
1987	60 c. "Kanagawa on Edo Bay"	40	40
1988	75 c. "Crossing Banyu River to Hiratsuka" ..	45	45
1989	$1 "Windy Shore at Odawara" ..	60	60
1990	$2 "Snow-Covered Post Station of Mishima" ..	1·00	1·00
1991	$3 "Full Moon at Fuchu"	1·40	1·40
1992	$4 "Crossing the Stream at Okitsu" ..	1·90	1·90

345 Great Blue Heron

1989. Birds. Multicoloutred.

1994	5 c. Type **345** ..	10	10
1995	10 c. Green heron ..	10	10
1996	15 c. Turnstone ..	10	10
1997	25 c. Blue-winged teal ..	10	15
1998	35 c. Little ringed plover (vert)	15	20
1999	45 c. Green-throated carib ("Emerald-throated hummingbird") (vert)	20	25
2000	50 c. Rufous-breasted hermit (vert) ..	25	30
2001	60 c. Lesser Antillean bullfinch (vert) ..	30	35
2002	75 c. Brown pelican (vert) ..	35	40
2003	$1 Black-crowned night heron (vert) ..	50	55
2004	$3 American kestrel ("Sparrow Hawk") (vert)	1·40	1·50
2005	$5 Barn swallow (vert) ..	2·40	2·50
2006	$10 Red-billed tropic bird (vert)	5·00	5·25
2007	$20 Barn owl (vert) ..	9·50	9·75

1989. World Cup Football Championship, Italy (1990) (1st issue). As T **252** of Antigua. Multicoloured.

2008	10 c. Scotland player ..	20	20
2009	25 c. England and Brazil players	30	30
2010	60 c. Paolo Rossi (Italy)	55	55
2011	75 c. Jairzinho (Brazil) ..	60	60
2012	$1 Sweden striker ..	80	80
2013	$2 Pele (Brazil) ..	1·50	1·50
2014	$3 Mario Kempes (Argentina) ..	2·00	2·00
2015	$4 Pat Jennings (Northern Ireland) ..	2·25	2·25

See also Nos. 2174/7.

346 Xebec and Sugar Cane

1989. "Philexfrance '89" International Stamp Exhibition, Paris. Designs showing French sailing vessels and plantation crops. Mult.

2017	25 c. Type **346**	25	25
2018	75 c. Lugger and cotton	60	60
2019	$1 Full-rigged ship and cocoa	75	75
2020	$4 Ketch and coffee ..	2·50	3·00

347 Alan Shepard and "Freedom 7" Spacecraft, 1961 (first American in Space)

1989. 20th Anniv of First Manned Landing on Moon. Multicoloured.

2022	15 c. Type **347**	25	25
2023	35 c. "Friendship 7" spacecraft, 1962 (first manned earth orbit) ..	35	35
2024	45 c. "Apollo 8" orbiting Moon, 1968 (first manned lunar orbit) ..	40	40
2025	70 c. "Apollo 15" lunar rover, 1972	65	65
2026	$1 "Apollo 11" emblem and lunar module "Eagle" on Moon, 1969	75	75
2027	$2 "Gemini 8" and "Agena" rocket, 1966 (first space docking) ..	1·50	1·50
2028	$3 Edward White in space, 1965 (first U.S. space walk)	2·00	2·25
2029	$4 "Apollo 7" emblem ..	2·50	2·75

348 "Hygrocybe occidentalis"

1989. Fungi. Multicoloured.

2031	15 c. Type **348**	25	25
2032	40 c. "Marasmius haematocephalus" ..	35	35
2033	50 c. "Hygrocybe hypohaemacta" ..	45	45
2034	70 c. "Lepiota pseudoignicolor" ..	70	70
2035	90 c. "Cookeina tricholoma"	80	80
2036	$1.10 "Leucopaxillus gracillimus"	90	90
2037	$2.25 "Hygrocybe nigrescens"	1·75	1·75
2038	$4 "Clathrus crispus" ..	2·50	3·00

349 Y.W.C.A. Logo and Grenada Scenery

1989. Centenary of Young Women's Christian Association. Multicoloured.

2040	50 c. Type **349**	35	35
2041	75 c. Y.W.C.A. logo and town (horiz)	55	55

350 "Historis odius"

1989. Butterflies. Multicoloured.

2042	6 c. Type **350**	20	20
2043	30 c. "Marpesia petreus"	35	35
2044	40 c. "Danaus gilippus"	40	40
2045	60 c. "Dione juno" ..	60	60
2046	$1.10 "Agraulis vanillae"	90	90
2047	$1.25 "Danaus plexippus"	1·00	1·00
2048	$4 "Papilio androgeus"	2·50	2·75
2049	$5 "Dryas julia" ..	2·75	3·00

351 Amerindian Hieroglyph

1989. 500th Anniv (1992) of Discovery of America by Columbus (2nd issue). Designs showing different hieroglyphs.

2051	**351**	45 c. brown, blk & bl	40	40
2052	–	60 c. brown, blk & grn	50	50
2053	–	$1 black, black & vio	75	75
2054	–	$4 dp brn , blk & brn	2·50	3·00

352 Amos leaving Home

1989. "World Stamp Expo '89" International Stamp Exhibition, Washington. Designs showing Walt Disney cartoon characters in scenes from "Ben and Me". Multicoloured.

2056	1 c. Type **352**	10	10
2057	2 c. Meeting of Benjamin Franklin and Amos ..	10	10
2058	3 c. The Franklin stove ..	10	10
2059	4 c. Ben and Amos with bi-focals ..	10	10
2060	5 c. Amos on page of "Pennsylvania Gazette"	10	10
2061	6 c. Ben working printing press	10	10
2062	10 c. Conducting experiment with electricity ..	10	10
2063	$5 Ben disembarking in England	3·00	3·50
2064	$6 Ben with Document of Agreement	3·25	3·75

1990. Christmas. Paintings by Rubens. As T **259** of Antigua. Multicoloured.

2066	20 c. "Christ in the House of Mary and Martha"	20	20
2067	35 c. "The Circumcision"	35	35
2068	60 c. "Trinity adored by Duke of Mantua and Family"	50	50
2069	$2 "Holy Family with St. Francis"	1·75	1·75
2070	$3 "The Ildefonso Altarpiece"	2·00	2·00
2071	$4 "Madonna and Child with Garland and Putti"	2·50	2·50

353 Alexander Graham Bell and Early Telephone System (150th anniv of invention)

1990. Anniversaries. Multicoloured.

2073	10 c. Type **353**	10	10
2074	25 c. George Washington and Capitol (bicentenary of presidential inauguration)	10	15
2075	35 c. Shakespeare and birthplace, Stratford (425th birth anniv) ..	15	20
2076	75 c. Nehru and Gandhi (birth cent of Nehru) ..	35	40
2077	$1 Dr. Hugo Eckener, Ferdinand von Zeppelin and Zeppelin "Delag" (80th anniv of first passenger Zeppelin) ..	50	55
2078	$2 Charlie Chaplin (birth cent)	95	1·00
2079	$3 Container ship in Hamburg Harbour (800th anniv)	1·40	1·50
2080	$4 Friedrich Ebert (first President) and Heidelberg gate (70th anniv of German Republic) ..	2·00	2·10

No. 2080 is inscribed "40th Anniversary of German Republic" in error.

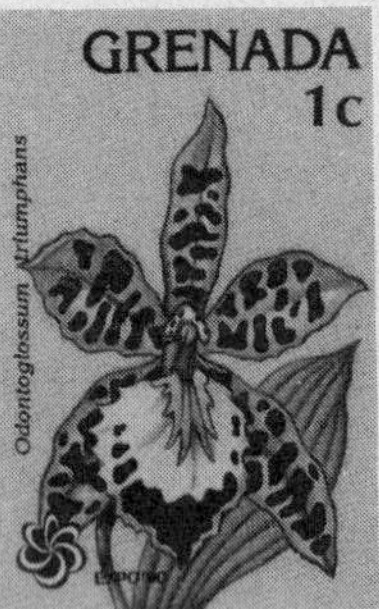

354 "Odontoglossum triumphans"

1990. "EXPO '90" International Garden and Greenery Exhibition, Osaka. Caribbean Orchids. Multicoloured.

2082	1 c. Type **354**	10	10
2083	25 c. "Oncidium splendidum"	10	15
2084	60 c. "Laelia anceps" ..	30	35
2085	75 c. "Cattleya trianaei"	35	40
2086	$1 "Odontoglossum rossii"	50	55
2087	$2 "Brassia gireoudiana"	95	1·00
2088	$3 "Cattleya dowiana"	1·40	1·50
2089	$4 "Sobralia macrantha"	2·00	2·10

1990. 500th Anniv (1992) of Discovery of America by Columbus (3rd issue). New World Natural History—Butterflies. As T **260** of Antigua. Multicoloured.

2091	15 c. "Marpesia petreus"	10	10
2092	25 c. "Junonia evarete"	10	15
2093	75 c. "Siproeta stelenes"	35	40
2094	90 c. "Historis odius" ..	45	50
2095	$1 "Mestra cana" ..	50	55
2096	$2 "Biblis hyperia" ..	95	1·00
2097	$3 "Dryas julia" ..	1·40	1·50
2098	$4 "Anartia amathea" ..	2·00	2·10

1990. Local Fauna. As T **254** of Antigua. Multicoloured.

2100	10 c. Caribbean monk seal	10	10
2101	15 c. Little brown bat ..	10	10
2102	45 c. Brown rat	20	25
2103	60 c. Common rabbit ..	30	35
2104	$1 Water opossum ..	50	55
2105	$2 White-nosed ichneumon	95	1·00
2106	$3 Little big-eared bat (vert)	1·40	1·50
2107	$4 Mouse opossum ..	2·00	2·10

1990. 50th Anniv of Second World War. As T **274** of Antigua. Multicoloured.

2109	25 c. British tanks during Operation Battleaxe, 1941	10	10
2110	35 c. Allied tank in southern France, 1944	15	20
2111	45 c. U.S. forces landing on Guadalcanal, 1942 ..	20	20
2112	50 c. U.S. attack in New Guinea, 1943	25	30
2113	60 c. Hoisting U.S. flag on Leyte, Phillippines, 1944	30	35
2114	75 c. U.S. tanks entering Cologne, 1945	35	40
2115	$1 Anzio offensive, 1944 ..	50	55
2116	$2 Battle of the Bismarck Sea, 1943	95	1·00
2117	$3 U.S. battle fleet, 1944	1·40	1·50
2118	$4 German fighter attacking Salerno landing, 1943	2·00	2·10

1990. "Stamp World London 90" International Stamp Exhibition (1st issue). As T **193** of Gambia, but horiz showing Walt Disney cartoon characters and British trains.

2120	5 c. Mickey Mouse driving "King Arthur" class locomotive, 1925 ..	10	10
2121	10 c. Mickey and Minnie Mouse with "Puffing Billy", 1813 ..	10	10
2122	20 c. Mickey Mouse with Pluto pulling Durham colliery wagon, 1765 ..	10	10
2123	45 c. Mickey Mouse timing locomotive No. 2509, "Silver Link", 1935 ..	20	25
2124	$1 Mickey Mouse and Donald Duck with locomotive No. 60149, "Amadis", 1948	50	55
2125	$2 Goofy and Mickey Mouse with Liverpool & Manchester Railway locomotive, 1830 ..	95	1·00
2126	$4 Goofy and Donald Duck with "Flying Scotsman", 1870 ..	2·00	2·10
2127	$5 Mickey Mouse and Gyro the Mechanic with Advance Passenger Train, 1972	2·40	2·50

355 U.S. Paratroop Drop over Grenada

1990. 50th Anniv of United States' Airborne Forces.

2129	**355**	75 c. multicoloured ..	35	40

1990. 90th birthday of Queen Elizabeth the Queen Mother. As T **194** of Gambia showing photographs from the 1960s. Multicoloured.

2131	$2 Queen Mother in coat and hat	95	1·00
2132	$2 Queen Mother in evening dress	95	1·00
2133	$2 Queen Mother in Garter robes	95	1·00

1990. Olympic Games, Barcelona (1992) (1st issue). As T **268** of Antigua. Mult.

2135	10 c. Men's steeplechase	15	15
2136	15 c. Dressage ..	15	15
2137	45 c. Men's 200 m. butterfly swimming	30	30
2138	50 c. Men's hockey ..	35	35
2139	65 c. Women's beam gymnastics	35	35
2140	75 c. "Flying Dutchman" class yachting ..	40	40
2141	$2 Freestyle wrestling ..	1·00	1·00
2142	$3 Men's springboard diving	1·50	1·75
2143	$4 Women's 1000 m. sprint cycling ..	2·00	2·25
2144	$5 Men's basketball ..	2·50	2·75

See also Nos. 2414/21.

357 Yellow Goatfish

1990. Coral Reef Fishes. Multicoloured.

2147	10 c. Type **357**	10	10
2148	25 c. Black margate ..	10	15
2149	65 c. Bluehead wrasse ..	30	35
2150	75 c. Pudding wife ..	35	40
2151	$1 Foureye butterflyfish	50	55
2152	$2 Honey damselfish ..	95	1·00
2153	$3 Queen angelfish ..	1·40	1·50
2154	$5 Cherubfish	2·40	2·50

358 Tropical Mockingbird

1990. Birds. Multicoloured.

2156 15 c. Type **358** 10 10
2157 25 c. Grey kingbird 10 15
2158 65 c. Bare-eyed thrush 30 35
2159 75 c. Antillean crested hummingbird 35 40
2160 $1 House wren 50 55
2161 $2 Purple martin 95 1·00
2162 $4 Hooded tanager 2·00 2·10
2163 $5 Scaly-breasted ground dove 2·40 2·50

359 Coral Crab

1990. Crustaceans. Multicoloured.

2165 5 c. Type **359** 10 10
2166 10 c. Smoothtail spiny lobster 10 10
2167 15 c. Flamestreaked box crab 10 10
2168 25 c. Spotted swimming crab 10 10
2169 75 c. Sally lightfoot rock crab 35 40
2170 $1 Spotted spiny lobster 50 55
2171 $3 Longarm spiny lobster 1·40 1·50
2172 $20 Caribbean spiny lobster 9·50 9·75

360 Cameroon Player

1990. World Cup Football Championship, Italy (2nd issue). Multicoloured.

2174 10 c. Type **360** 10 10
2175 25 c. Michel (Spain) 10 15
2176 $1 Brehme (West Germany) 50 55
2177 $5 Nevin (Scotland) 2·40 2·50

1990. Christmas. Paintings by Raphael. As T **272** of Antigua. Multicoloured.

2180 10 c. "The Ansidei Madonna" (vert) 10 10
2181 15 c. "The Sistine Madonna" (vert) 10 10
2182 $1 "The Madonna of the Baldacchino" (vert) 50 55
2183 $2 "The Large Holy Family" (detail) (vert) 95 1·00
2184 $5 "Madonna in the Meadow" (vert) 2·40 2·50

1991. 350th Death Anniv of Rubens. As T **273** of Antigua. Multicoloured.

2186 5 c. "The Brazen Serpent" (detail) 10 10
2187 10 c. "The Garden of Love" 10 10
2188 25 c. "Head of Cyrus" (detail) 10 10
2189 75 c. "Tournament in Front of a Castle" 35 40
2190 $1 "The Brazen Serpent" (different detail) 50 55
2191 $2 "Judgement of Paris" (detail) 95 1·00
2192 $4 "The Brazen Serpent" 2·00 2·10
2193 $5 "The Karmesse" (detail) 2·40 2·50

362 "The Sorcerer's Apprentice"

1991. 50th Anniv of "Fantasia" (cartoon film). Multicoloured.

2195 5 c. Type **362** 10 10
2196 10 c. Dancing mushrooms ("The Nutcracker Suite") 10 10
2197 20 c. Pterodactyls ("The Rite of Spring") 10 10
2198 45 c. Centaurs ("The Pastoral Symphony") 20 25
2199 $1 Bacchus and Jacchus ("The Pastoral Symphony") 50 55
2200 $2 Dancing ostrich ("Dance of the Hours") 95 1·00
2201 $4 Elephant ballet ("Dance of the Hours") 2·00 2·10
2202 $5 Diana ("The Pastoral Symphony") 2·40 2·50

363 "Adelpha iphicla"

1991. Butterflies. Multicoloured.

2205 5 c. Type **363** 10 10
2206 10 c. "Nymphalidae claudina" 10 10
2207 15 c. "Brassolidae polyxena" 10 10
2208 20 c. "Zebra Longwing" 10 10
2209 25 c. "Marpesia corinna" 10 10
2210 30 c. "Morpho hecuba" 15 20
2211 45 c. "Morpho rhetenor" 25 30
2212 50 c. "Dismorphia spio" 30 35
2213 60 c. "Prepona omphale" 30 35
2214 70 c. "Morpho anaxibia" 35 40
2215 75 c. "Marpesia iole" 50 55
2216 $1 "Amarynthis meneria" 95 1·00
2217 $2 "Morpho cisseis" 1·25 1·50
2218 $3 "Danaidae plexippus" 1·40 1·50
2219 $4 "Morpho achilleana" 2·00 2·10
2220 $5 "Calliona argenissa" 2·40 2·50

1991. 500th Anniv (1992) of Discovery of America by Columbus History of Exploration. As T **277** of Antigua. Mult.

2222 5 c. Vitus Bering in Bering Sea, 1728–9 10 10
2223 10 c. De Bougainville off Pacific island, 1766–69 10 10
2224 25 c. Polynesian canoe 10 10
2225 50 c. De Mendana off Solomon Islands, 1567–69 25 30
2226 $1 Darwin's H.M.S. "Beagle", 1831–35 50 55
2227 $2 Cook's H.M.S. "Endeavour", 1768–71 95 1·00
2228 $4 Willem Schouten in LeMaire Strait, 1615–17 2·00 2·10
2229 $5 Tasman off New Zealand, 1642–44 2·40 2·50

1991. "Phila Nippon '91" International Stamp Exhibition, Tokyo. As T **279** of Antigua showing Walt Disney cartoon characters at Japanese festivals. Mult.

2231 5 c. Minnie Mouse and Daisy Duck at Dolls festival 10 10
2232 10 c. Morty and Ferdie with Boys' Day display 10 10
2233 20 c. Mickey and Minnie Mouse at Star festival 10 10
2234 45 c. Minnie and Daisy folk-dancing 20 25
2235 $1 Huey, Dewey and Louie wearing Eboshi headdresses 50 55
2236 $2 Mickey and Goofy pulling decorated cart at Gion festival 95 1·00
2237 $4 Minnie and Daisy preparing rice broth, Seven Plants festival 2·00 2·10
2238 $5 Huey and Dewey with straw boat at Lanterns festival 2·40 2·50

1991. Death Centenary (1990) of Vincent van Gogh (artist). As T **278** of Antigua. Mult.

2240 20 c. "Blossoming Almond Branch in Glass" 10 10
2241 25 c. "La Mousme sitting" 10 10
2242 30 c. "Still Life with Red Cabbages and Onions" (horiz) 15 20
2243 40 c. "Japonaiserie: Flowering Plum Tree" 20 25
2244 45 c. "Japonaiserie: Bridge in Rain" 20 25
2245 60 c. "Still Life with Basket of Apples" (horiz) 30 35
2246 75 c. "Italian Woman" 35 40
2247 $1 "The Painter on his Way to Work" 50 55
2248 $2 "Portrait of Pere Tanguy" 95 1·00
2249 $3 "Still Life with Plaster Statuette, a Rose and Two Novels" 1·40 1·50
2250 $4 "Still Life: Bottle, Lemons and Oranges" (horiz) 2·00 2·10
2251 $5 "Orchard with Blossoming Apricot Trees" (horiz) 2·40 2·50

364 "Psilocybe cubensis"

1991. Fungi. Multicoloured.

2253 15 c. Type **364** 10 10
2254 25 c. "Leptonia caeruleo-capitata" 10 10
2255 65 c. "Cystolepiota eriophora" 30 35
2256 75 c. "Chlorophyllum molybdites" 35 40
2257 $1 "Xerocomus hypo-xanthus" 50 55
2258 $2 "Volvariella cubensis" 95 1·00
2259 $4 "Xerocomus cocco-lobae" 2·00 2·10
2260 $5 "Pluteus chryso-phlebius" 2·40 2·50

365 Johannes Kepler (astronomer)

1991. Exploration of Mars. Designs showing astronomers, spacecraft and Martian landscapes. Multicoloured.

2262/97 75 c. × 9, $1.25 × 9, $2 × 9, $7 × 9 Set of 36 45·00 48·00

1991. 65th Birthday of Queen Elizabeth II. As T **280** of Antigua. Multicoloured.

2299 15 c. Royal Family on balcony after Trooping the Colour, 1985 10 10
2300 40 c. Queen and Prince Philip at Peterborough, 1988 20 25
2301 $2 Queen and Queen Mother at Windsor, 1986 95 1·00
2302 $4 Queen and Prince Philip on visit to United Arab Emirates 2·00 2·10

1991. 10th Wedding Anniv of the Prince and Princess of Wales. As T **280** of Antigua. Multicoloured.

2304 10 c. Prince and Princess in July 1985 10 10
2305 50 c. Separate photographs of Prince, Princess and sons 25 30

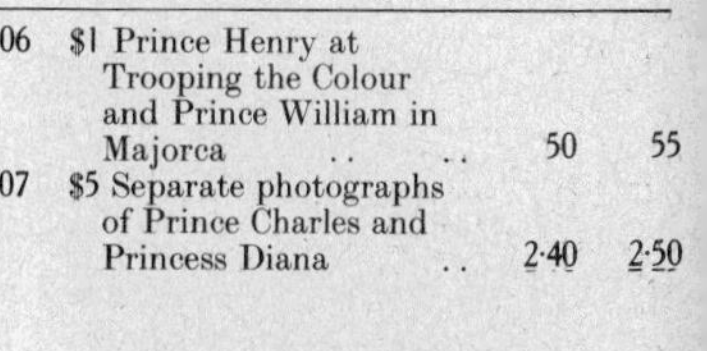

2306 $1 Prince Henry at Trooping the Colour and Prince William in Majorca 50 55
2307 $5 Separate photographs of Prince Charles and Princess Diana 2·40 2·50

366 Anglican High School Pupils

1991. 75th Anniv of Anglican High School (10, 25 c.) and 40th Anniv of University of the West Indies (45, 50 c.). Multicoloured.

2309 10 c. Type **366** 10 10
2310 25 c. Artist's impression of new Anglican High School 10 10
2311 45 c. Marryshow House, Grenada 20 25
2312 50 c. University Administrative Building, Barbados 25 30

367 Stephenson's Locomotive, 1814 (Great Britain)

1991. Great Railways of the World. Mult.

2313 75 c. Type **367** 35 40
2314 75 c. George Stephenson 35 40
2315 75 c. Killingworth locomotive, 1816 (Great Britain) 35 40
2316 75 c. "Locomotion", 1825 (Great Britain) 35 40
2317 75 c. "Locomotion" in Darlington, 1825 (Great Britain) 35 40
2318 75 c. Opening of Stockton & Darlington Railway, 1825 35 40
2319 75 c. "Royal George", 1827 (Great Britain) 35 40
2320 75 c. "Northumbrian Rocket", 1829 (Great Britain) 35 40
2321 75 c. "Planet", 1830 (Great Britain) 35 40
2322 $1 "Old Ironsides", 1832 (U.S.A.) 50 55
2323 $1 "Wilberforce", 1832 (Great Britain) 50 55
2324 $1 "Der Adler", 1835 (Germany) 50 55
2325 $1 "North Star", 1837 (Great Britain) 50 55
2326 $1 London & Birmingham Railway No.1, 1838 (Great Britain) 50 55
2327 $1 Stephenson's 2-2-2, 1838 (Austria) 50 55
2328 $1 "Mud Digger" locomotive, 1840 (U.S.A.) 50 55
2329 $1 Standard Norris, 1840 (U.S.A.) 50 55
2330 $1 "Centaur", 1840 (Great Britain) 50 55
2331 $2 "Lion", 1841 (Great Britain) 95 1·00
2332 $2 "Beuth", 1843 (Germany) 95 1·00
2333 $2 "Derwent", 1845 (Great Britain) 95 1·00
2334 $2 "Bets", 1846 (Hungary) 95 1·00
2335 $2 Opening of Budapest to Vac railway, 1846 (Hungary) 95 1·00
2336 $2 Carriages, Stockton & Darlington Railway, 1846 (Great Britain) 95 1·00
2337 $2 Stephenson's "Long Boiler" type, 1847 (France) 95 1·00
2338 $2 Baldwin locomotive, 1850 (U.S.A.) 95 1·00
2339 $2 German 2-4-0 type, 1850 95 1·00

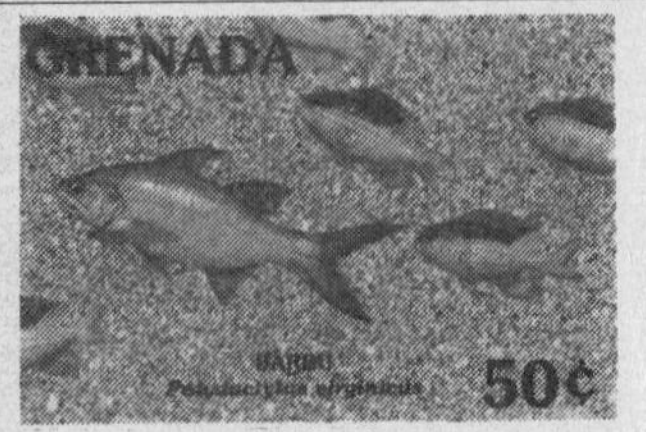

368 Barbu

1991. Marine Life of the Sandflats. Mult.

2341 50 c. Type **368** 25 30
2342 50 c. Beaugregory .. 25 30
2343 50 c. Porcupinefish .. 25 30
2344 50 c. Queen conch and conchfish 25 30
2345 50 c. Hermit crab .. 25 30
2346 50 c. Bluestripe lizardfish 25 30
2347 50 c. Spotfin mojarra .. 25 30
2348 50 c. Southern stingray .. 25 30
2349 50 c. Long-spined sea urchin and slippery dick 25 30
2350 50 c. Peacock flounder .. 25 30
2351 50 c. West Indian sea star 25 30
2352 50 c. Spotted goatfish .. 25 30
2353 50 c. Reticulated olive and West Indian sea egg 25 30
2354 50 c. Pearly razorfish .. 25 30
2355 50 c. Yellowhead jawfish and mottled jawfish .. 25 30

Nos. 2341/55 were printed together, se-tenant, forming a composite design.

1991. Christmas. Religious Paintings by Albrecht Durer. As T **287** of Antigua. Mult.

2357 10 c. "Adoration of the Magi" (detail) .. 10 10
2358 35 c. "Madonna with the Siskin" (detail) .. 15 20
2359 50 c. "Feast of the Rose Garlands" (detail) .. 25 30
2360 75 c. "Virgin with the Pear" (detail) 35 40
2361 $1 "Virgin in Half-length" (detail) 50 55
2362 $2 "Madonna and Child" (detail) .. .. 95 1·00
2363 $4 "Virgin and Child with St. Anne" (detail) .. 2·00 2·10
2364 $5 "Virgin and Child" (detail) .. .. 2·40 2·50

369 Goofy windsurfing

1992. Thrill Sports. Walt Disney cartoon characters. Multicoloured.

2366 5 c. Type **369** 10 10
2367 10 c. Mickey Mouse skateboarding .. 10 10
2368 20 c. Daisy Duck gliding 10 10
2369 45 c. Mickey's nephews stunt kite flying .. 20 25
2370 $1 Donald Duck mountain biking 50 55
2371 $2 Donald and Chipmunk parachuting .. .. 95 1·00
2372 $4 Mickey go-karting .. 2·00 2·10
2373 $5 Minnie water skiing .. 2·40 2·50

1992. 40th Anniv of Queen Elizabeth II's Accession. As T **288** of Antigua. Mult.

2375 10 c. Waterfall 10 10
2376 50 c. Street in St. George's 25 30
2377 $1 Colonial-style houses, St. George's 50 55
2378 $5 St. George's from the sea .. .. .. 2·40 2·50

1992. "Granada '92" International Stamp Exhibition, Spain. Spanish Paintings. As T **292** of Antigua. Multicoloured.

2380 10 c. "The Corpus Christi Procession in Seville" (Manuel Cabral y Aguado) (horiz) .. 10 10
2381 35 c. "The Mancorbo Channel" (Carlos de Haes) 15 20
2382 50 c. "Amalia de Llano y Dotres, Countess of Vilches" (Federico de Madrazo y Kuntz) .. 25 30
2383 75 c. "Conchita Serrano y Dominguez, Countess of Santovenia" (Eduardo Rosales Gallina) .. 35 40
2384 $1 "Queen Maria Isabel de Braganza" (Bernardo Lopez Piquer) 50 55
2385 $2 "The Presentation of Don John of Austria to Charles V" (detail) (Gallina) .. .. 95 1·00
2386 $4 "The Presentation of Don John of Austria to Charles V" (different detail) (Gallina) .. 2·00 2·10
2387 $5 "The Testament of Isabella the Catholic" (Gallina) (horiz) .. 2·40 2·50

370 Green-winged Macaw

1992. 500th Anniv of Discovery of America by Columbus (5th issue). World Columbian Stamp "Expo '92", Chicago. Multicoloured.

2389 10 c. Type **370** 10 10
2390 25 c. "Santa Maria" .. 10 10
2391 35 c. Christopher Columbus 15 20
2392 50 c. 15th-century sandglass 25 30
2393 75 c. Queen Isabella .. 35 40
2394 $4 Cantino map of 1502 (detail) .. .. 2·00 2·10

1992. "Genova '92" International Thematic Stamp Exhibition. Hummingbirds. As T **295** of Antigua, but vertical. Multicoloured.

2396 10 c. Ruby-throated hummingbird 10 10
2397 25 c. Vervain hummingbird 10 10
2398 35 c. Blue-headed hummingbird 15 20
2399 50 c. Cuban emerald .. 25 30
2400 75 c. Antillean mango .. 35 40
2401 $2 Purple-throated carib 95 1·00
2402 $4 Puerto Rican emerald 2·00 2·10
2403 $5 Green-throated carib 2·40 2·50

371 Gracie Fields

1992. 50th Anniv of United Service Organization (forces' entertainment programme). Multicoloured.

2405 15 c. Type **371** .. 10 10
2406 25 c. Jack Benny .. 10 10
2407 35 c. Jinx Falkenburg .. 15 20
2408 50 c. Francis Langford .. 25 30
2409 75 c. Joe E. Brown .. 35 40
2410 $1 Phil Silvers .. 50 55
2411 $2 Danny Kaye .. .. 95 1·00
2412 $5 Frank Sinatra .. 2·40 2·50

372 Badminton

1992. Olympic Games, Barcelona (2nd issue). Multicoloured.

2414 10 c. Type **372** 10 10
2415 25 c. Women's long jump 10 10
2416 35 c. Women's 100 metres 15 20
2417 50 c. 1000 metres cycling sprint 25 30
2418 75 c. Decathlon (horiz) .. 35 40
2419 $2 Judo (horiz) .. 95 1·00
2420 $4 Women's gymnastics—asymmetrical bars .. 2·00 2·10
2421 $5 Men's javelin .. 2·40 2·50

1992. 500th Anniv of Discovery of America by Columbus (6th issue). Organization of East Caribbean States. As Nos. 1670/1 of Antigua. Multicoloured.

2423 $1 Columbus meeting Amerindians 50 55
2424 $2 Ships approaching island .. .. .. 95 1·00

1992. Toy Trains from American Manufacturers. As T **257** of Dominica. Mult.

2425 10 c. "The Blue Comet" locomotive, Boucher (1933) 10 10
2426 35 c. No. 2220 switching locomotive, Voltamp (1906) 15 20
2427 40 c. No. 221 tunnel locomotive, Knapp (1905) 20 25
2428 75 c. "Grand Canyon" locomotive, American Flyer (1931) 35 40
2429 $1 "Streamliner" tin locomotive, Hafner (1930s) 50 55
2430 $2 No. 237 switching locomotive, Elektoy (1911) .. .. .. 95 1·00
2431 $4 Parlor car, Ives (1928) 2·00 2·10
2432 $5 "The Improved President's Special" locomotive, American Flyer (1927) .. .. 2·40 2·50

373 "Matador" (yacht), Newport News Regatta

1992. World Regattas. Multicoloured.

2435 15 c. Type **373** 10 10
2436 25 c. "Awesome", Antigua 10 10
2437 35 c. "Mistress Quickly", Bermuda 15 20
2438 50 c. "Emeraude", St. Tropez 25 30
2439 $1 "Diva G", German Admirals Cup 50 55
2440 $2 "Lady Be", French Admirals Cup .. .. 95 1·00
2441 $4 "Midnight Sun", Admirals Cup .. .. 2·00 2·10
2442 $5 "Carat", Sardinia Cup 2·40 2·50

1992. Christmas. Religious Paintings. As T **300** of Antigua. Multicoloured.

2444 10 c. "Adoration of the Magi" (detail) (Fra Filippo Lippi) .. 10 10
2445 15 c. "Madonna Adoring Child in a Wood" (Lippi) 10 10
2446 25 c. "Adoration of the Magi" (detail) (Botticelli) 10 10
2447 35 c. "The Epiphany—Adoration of the Magi" (detail) (Hieronymous Bosch) 15 20
2448 50 c. "Adoration of the Magi" (detail) (Giovanni de Paolo) .. 25 30
2449 75 c. "Adoration of the Magi" (Gentile da Fabriano) 35 40
2450 90 c. "Adoration of the Magi" (detail) (Juan Batista Maino) .. 45 50
2451 $1 "Adoration of the Child" (Master of Liesborn) 50 55
2452 $2 "Adoration of the Kings" (Master of Liesborn) .. .. 95 1·00
2453 $3 "Adoration of the Three Wise Men" (Pedro Berruguete) .. 1·40 1·50
2454 $4 "Adoration of the Child" (Lippi) .. 2·00 2·10
2455 $5 "Adoration of the Child" (Correggio) .. 2·40 2·50

374 Cher

1992. Gold Record Award Winners. Mult.

2457 90 c. Type **374** 45 50
2458 90 c. Michael Jackson .. 45 50
2459 90 c. Elvis Presley .. 45 50
2460 90 c. Dolly Parton .. 45 50
2461 90 c. Johnny Mathis .. 45 50
2462 90 c. Madonna .. 45 50
2463 90 c. Nat King Cole .. 45 50
2464 90 c. Janice Joplin .. 45 50

Nos. 2457/64 were printed together, se-tenant, with a composite background design.

375 Grenada Dove

1992. Anniversaries and Events. Mult.

2466 10 c. Type **375** 10 10
2467 25 c. "LZ1" on maiden flight, 1900 (horiz) .. 10 10
2468 50 c. ENDOSAT (robot plane) project (horiz) .. 25 30
2469 75 c. Konrad Adenauer (German statesman) and industrial skyline (horiz) 35 40
2470 $1.50 Golden lion tamarin (horiz) 75 80
2471 $2 Mountain gorilla (horiz) .. .. 95 1·00
2472 $2 Outline of man and heart (horiz) .. .. 95 1·00
2473 $3 Wolfgang Amadeus Mozart .. .. 1·40 1·50
2474 $4 "Voyager 2" and Neptune (horiz) .. 2·00 2·10
2475 $4 Adenauer with flag and map of West Germany (horiz) .. .. 2·00 2·10
2476 $5 Count von Zeppelin and "Graf Zeppelin" (horiz) .. .. 2·40 2·50
2477 $6 Admiral Richard Byrd (polar explorer) (horiz) 3·00 3·25

ANNIVERSARIES AND EVENTS: No. 2466, National bird; Nos. 2467, 2476, 75th death anniv of Count Ferdinand von Zeppelin; Nos. 2468, 2475, International Space Year; Nos. 2469, 2475, 25th death anniv of Konrad Adenauer; Nos. 2470/1, Earth Summit '92, Rio; No. 2472, United Nations World Health Organization Projects; No. 2473, Death bicentenary of Mozart; No. 2477, 75th anniv of International Association of Lions Clubs.

376 Care Bear on Beach

1992. Ecology.
2479 **376** 75 c. multicoloured .. 35 40

377 Samoyed and St. Basil's Cathedral, Moscow

1993. Dogs of the World. Multicoloured.
2481 10 c. Type **377** 10 10
2482 15 c. Chow and Ling Yin Monastery, China .. 10 10
2483 25 c. Boxer and Tower of London .. 10 10
2484 90 c. Basenji and Yamma Mosque, Niger .. 45 50
2485 $1 Golden labrador and Parliament Building, Ottawa 50 55
2486 $3 St. Bernard and Parsenn, Switzerland 1·40 1·50
2487 $4 Rhodesian ridgeback and Melrose House, South Africa .. .. 2·00 2·10
2488 $5 Afghan hound and Mazar-i-Sharif, Afghanistan .. .. 2·40 2·50

1993. Bicentenary of the Louvre, Paris. Paintings by Jean-Antoine Watteau. As T **305** of Antigua. Multicoloured.
2490 $1 "The Faux-pas" .. 50 55
2491 $1 "Portrait of a Gentleman" .. 50 55
2492 $1 "Young Lady with Archlute" 50 55
2493 $1 "Young Man Dancing" 50 55
2494 $1 "Autumn, Pamona and a Cherub" 50 55
2495 $1 "Judgement of Paris" 50 55
2496 $1 "Pierrot" (detail) .. 50 55
2497 $1 "Pierrot" (different detail) 50 55

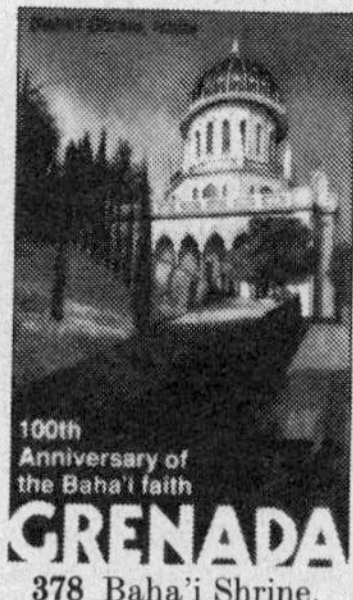

378 Baha'i Shrine, Haifa

1993. Centenary of Baha'i Faith.
2499 **378** 75 c. multicoloured .. 35 40

379 "Citheronia magnifica"

1993. Moths. Multicoloured.
2500 10 c. Type **379** 10 10
2501 35 c. "Automeris metali" 15 20
2502 45 c. "Thysania zenobia" 20 25
2503 75 c. "Agrius cingulatus" 35 40
2504 $1 "Composia fidelissima" 50 55
2505 $2 "Synchlora xysteraria" 95 1·00
2506 $4 "Eumorpha labruscae" 2·00 2·10
2507 $5 "Ascalapha odorata" 2·40 2·50

380 Heliconia

1993. Flowers. Multicoloured.
2509 10 c. Type **380** 10 10
2510 35 c. Pansy 15 20
2511 45 c. Water lily 20 25
2512 75 c. Bougainvillea .. 35 40
2513 $1 Calla lily 50 55
2514 $2 California poppy .. 95 1·00
2515 $4 Red ginger .. .. 2·00 2·10
2516 $5 Anthurium .. .. 2·40 2·50

1993. 40th Anniv of Coronation. As T **307** of Antigua.
2518 35 c. multicoloured .. 15 20
2519 70 c. multicoloured .. 30 35
2520 $1 brown and black .. 50 55
2521 $5 multicoloured .. 2·40 2·50
DESIGNS—38 × 47 mm: 35 c. Queen Elizabeth II at Coronation (photograph by Cecil Beaton); 70 c. Sceptres; $1 Queen Elizabeth receiving sceptre from Archbishop of Canterbury; $5 Queen and Prince Philip with their children, 1960s.

381 "Woman with Loaves" (Picasso)

1993. Anniversaries and Events. Each brown, deep brown and black (Nos. 2527, 2535) or multicoloured (others).
2523 25 c. Type **381** 10 10
2524 35 c. 16th-century telescope 15 20
2525 35 c. Public Library building 15 20
2526 35 c. Gaetan Boucher (speed skating, 1984) .. 15 20
2527 50 c. Willy Brandt with Senator Edward Kennedy (horiz) .. 25 30
2528 75 c. Carnival float (horiz) 35 40
2529 90 c. "Weeping Woman" (Picasso) 45 50
2530 $1 "Marii Prohaska" (Tyrus Czyzewski) .. 50 55
2531 $3 "Marysia et Burek a Geylan" (S. Wirkiewicz) 1·40 1·50
2532 $4 "Woman seated in Airchair" (Picasso) .. 2·00 2·10
2533 $4 Astronaut on Moon .. 2·00 2·10
2534 $5 Norbert Schramm (figure skating, 1984) 2·40 2·50
2535 $5 Willy Brandt and Kurt Waldheim (horiz) .. 2·40 2·50
ANNIVERSARIES AND EVENTS: Nos. 2523, 2529, 2532, 20th death anniv of Picasso (artist); Nos. 2524, 2533, 450th death anniv of Copernicus (astronomer); No. 2525, Centenary (1992) of Grenada Public Library; Nos. 2526, 2534, Winter Olympic Games '94, Lillehammer; Nos. 2527, 2535, 80th birth anniv (1992) of Willy Brandt (German politician); No. 2528, Grenada Carnival; Nos. 2530/1, "Polska '93" International Stamp Exhibition, Poznan.

382 Red-eyed Vireo

1993. Songbirds. Multicoloured.
2537 15 c. Type **382** 10 10
2538 25 c. Scissor-tailed flycatcher 10 10
2539 35 c. Palm chat 15 20
2540 35 c. Chaffinch 15 20
2541 45 c. Yellow wagtail .. 20 25
2542 45 c. Painted bunting .. 25 30
2543 50 c. Short-tailed pygmy tyrant ("Short-tailed pygmy flycatcher") .. 30 35
2544 65 c. Orange-breasted bunting ("Rainbow bunting") 30 35
2545 75 c. Red crossbill .. 35 40
2546 75 c. Kauai akialoa .. 35 40
2547 $1 Yellow-throated longclaw ("Yellow-throated wagtail") .. 50 55
2548 $4 Barn swallow .. 2·00 2·10
Nos. 2537/48 were printed together, se-tenant, with the backgrounds forming a composite design.

383 Atlantic Grey Cowrie and Atlantic Yellow Cowrie

1993. Seashells. Multicoloured.
2550 15 c. Type **383** 10 10
2551 15 c. Candy stick tellin and sunrise tellin .. 10 10
2552 25 c. Common Atlantic vase 10 10
2553 35 c. Lightning venus and royal comb venus .. 15 20
2554 35 c. Crown cone .. 15 20
2555 45 c. Reticulated cowrie-helmet 20 25
2556 50 c. Barbados mitre and variegated turret shell 25 30
2557 50 c. Common egg cockle and Atlantic strawberry cockle 25 30
2558 75 c. Measled cowrie .. 35 40
2559 75 c. Rooster tail conch .. 35 40
2560 $1 Lion's paw and Antillean scallop .. 50 55
2561 $4 Dog-head triton .. 2·00 2·10
Nos. 2550/61 were printed together, se-tenant, with the backgrounds forming a composite design.

1993. Asian International Stamp Exhibitions. As T **268** of Dominica. Multicoloured. (a) "Indopex '93", Surabaya, Indonesia.
2563 35 c. Megalithic Carving, Sumba Island .. 15 20
2564 45 c. Entrance to Gao Gajah, Bali 20 25
2565 $1.50 Statue of kris holder 75 80
2566 $1.50 Hanuman protecting Sita 75 80
2567 $1.50 Sendi of Visu mounted on Garuda .. 75 80
2568 $1.50 Wahana (votif figure) 75 80
2569 $1.50 Hanuman (different) 75 80
2570 $1.50 Singa (symbolic lion) 75 80
2571 $2 Loving-mother Bridge, Taroko Gorge National Park .. .. 95 1·00
2572 $4 Head of Kala over temple gateway, Northern Bali .. 2·00 2·10

(b) "Taipei '93", Taiwan
2574 35 c. Fire-breathing Dragon, New Year's Fair, Chongqing .. 15 20
2575 45 c. Stone elephant, Ming Tomb, Nanjing .. 20 25
2576 $1.50 "Ornamental Cock" (Han Meilin) 75 80
2577 $1.50 "He's even afraid of Cows" (Meilin) .. 75 80
2578 $1.50 "On a Moonlit Night" (Meilin) .. 75 80
2579 $1.50 "Eyes that see in the Dark" (Meilin) .. 75 80
2580 $1.50 "He's well behaved" (Meilin) 75 80
2581 $1.50 "He doesn't Bite" (Meilin) 75 80
2582 $2 Marble peifang, Ming 13 Tombs, Beijing .. 95 1·00
2583 $4 Stone pillar, Nanjing 2·00 2·10

(c) "Bangkok 1993", Thailand
2585 35 c. Nora Nair, Prasad Phra Thepidon, Wat Phra Kaew 15 20
2586 45 c. Stucco deities at Library of Wat Phra Singh 20 25
2587 $1.50 Wooden carved horses 75 80
2588 $1.50 Wheel of the law .. 75 80
2589 $1.50 Lanna bronze elephant 75 80
2590 $1.50 Kendi in the form of elephant 75 80
2591 $1.50 Bronze duck .. 75 80
2592 $1.50 Horseman 75 80
2593 $2 Naga snake, Chiang Mai's Temple .. .. 95 1·00
2594 $4 Stucco figures, Wat Chang Lom .. .. 2·00 2·10
No. 2590 is incorrectly inscribed "Kendi in the form of an Elphant".

1993. World Cup Football Championship, U.S.A (1994). As T **310** of Antigua. Mult.
2596 10 c. Nikolai Larionov (Russia) 10 10
2597 25 c. Andrea Carnevale (Italy) 10 10
2598 35 c. Enzo Schifo (Belgium) and Soon-Ho Choi (South Korea) .. 15 20
2599 45 c. Gary Lineker (England) 20 25
2600 $1 Diego Maradona (Argentina) 50 55
2601 $2 Lothar Mattaeus (Germany) .. .. 95 1·00
2602 $4 Jan Karas (Poland) and Julio Cesar Silva (Brazil) .. .. 2·00 2·10
2603 $5 Claudio Caniggia (Argentina) .. .. 2·40 2·50

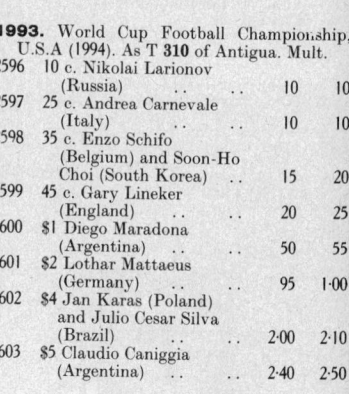

384 James K. Spensley

1993. Centenary of Italian Football. Past and present Genoa players. Each indigo, red and black.
2605 $3 Type **384** .. 1·40 1·50
2606 $3 Renzo de Vecchi .. 1·40 1·50
2607 $3 Giovanni de Pra' .. 1·40 1·50
2608 $3 Luigi Burlando .. 1·40 1·50
2609 $3 Felice Levratto .. 1·40 1·50
2610 $3 Guglielmo Stabile .. 1·40 1·50
2611 $3 Vittorio Sardelli .. 1·40 1·50
2612 $3 Juan Carlos Verdeal .. 1·40 1·50
2613 $3 Fosco Becattini .. 1·40 1·50
2614 $3 Julio Cesar Abadie .. 1·40 1·50
2615 $3 Luigi Meroni .. .. 1·40 1·50
2616 $3 Roberto Pruzzo .. 1·40 1·50

385 "The Band Concert", 1935

1993. 65th Anniv of Mickey Mouse. Scenes from Walt Disney cartoon films. Mult.
2618 25 c. Type **387** 10 10
2619 35 c. "Mickey's Circus", 1936 .. .. .. 15 20
2620 50 c. "Magician Mickey", 1937 .. .. .. 25 30
2621 75 c. "Moose Hunters", 1937 .. .. .. 35 40
2622 $1 "Mickey's Amateurs", 1937 .. .. .. 50 55
2623 $2 "Tugboat Mickey", 1940 .. .. .. 95 1·00
2624 $4 "Orphan's Benefit", 1941 .. .. .. 2·00 2·10
2625 $5 "Mickey's Christmas Carol", 1983 .. .. 2·40 2·50
No. 2624 is inscribed "Oprhan's Benefit" in error.

OFFICIAL STAMPS

1982. Optd. **P.R.G.** (a) Nos. 1085/97 and 1099.
O 1. 5 c. West Indiaman barque, c. 1840 .. .. .. 15 10
O 2. 6 c. R.M.S.P. " Orinoco ", c. 1851 .. .. .. 15 10
O 3. 10 c. Working Schooner .. 15 10
O 4. 12 c. Trimaran at Grand Anse anchorage .. 15 10
O 5. 15 c. Spice Island cruising yacht " Petite Amie " 20 15
O 6. 20 c. Fishing pirogue .. 25 15
O 7. 25 c. Harbour police launch 30 20
O 8. 30 c. Grand Anse speedboat 30 25
O 9. 40 c. M.V. " Seimstrand " 35 30
O10. 50 c. Three-masted schooner " Ariadne " 40 30
O11. 90 c. M.V. " Geestide " .. 70 70
O12. $1 M.V. "Cunard Countess" 70 70
O13. $3 Rum-runner .. .. 2·00 3·25
O14. $10 Coast-guard patrol boat .. .. 6·00 11·00

(b) Nos. 1130/2. and 113/4.
O 15. 30 c. Prince Charles and Lady Diana Spencer .. 1·75 2·25
O 16. 40 c. Holyrood House .. 2·25 2·75
O 17. 50 c. Prince Charles and Lady Diana Spencer .. 1·25 1·75
O 18. $2 Holyrood House .. 2·75 3·50
O 19. $4 Type **268** .. .. 6·50 8·00

POSTAGE DUE STAMPS

D 1.

1892.
D 8. D 1. 1d. black .. .. 2·00 5·00
D 9. 2d. black .. .. 7·00 1·75
D 10. 3d. black .. .. 10·00 5·50

1892. Surch. **SURCHARGE POSTAGE** and value.
D 4. 13. 1d. on 6d. mauve .. 50·00 1·25
D 5. 1d. on 8d. brown .. £350 3·25
D 6. 2d. on 6d. mauve .. 90·00 2·50
D 7. 2d. on 8d. brown .. £650 9·50

1921. As Type D 1 but inscr. "POSTAGE DUE" instead of "SURCHARGE POSTAGE".
D 11. D 1. 1d. black .. .. 90 1·00
D 12. 1½d. black .. .. 8·50 13·00
D 13. 2d. black .. .. 2·00 1·75
D 14. 3d. black .. .. 2·00 3·75

1952. As last but currency changed.
D 15. D 1. 2 c. black .. .. 30 3·75
D 16. 4 c. black .. .. 30 8·50
D 17. 6 c. black .. .. 45 10·00
D 18. 8 c. black .. .. 75 10·00

GRENADINES OF GRENADA

The southern part of the group, attached to Grenada. Main islands Petit Martinique and Carriacou.

100 cents = 1 dollar.

1973. Royal Wedding. Nos. 582/3 of Grenada optd. **GRENADINES.**
1. **196.** 25 c. multicoloured .. 20 10
2. $2 multicoloured .. 70 50

1974. Stamps of Grenada optd. **GRENADINES.**
4. 1 c. multicoloured (No. 306) 10 10
5. 2 c. multicoloured (No. 307) 10 10
6. 3 c. multicoloured (No. 308) 10 10
7. 5 c. multicoloured (No. 309) 10 10
8. 8 c. multicoloured (No. 311) 10 10
9. 10 c. multicoloured (No. 312) 10 10
10. 12 c. multicoloured (No. 313) 15 10
11. 25 c. multicoloured (No. 315) 25 10
12. $1 multicoloured (No. 318) .. 1·75 45
13. $2 multicoloured (No. 319) .. 2·50 1·00
14. $3 multicoloured (No. 320) .. 2·50 1·50
15. $5 multicoloured (No. 321) .. 3·50 1·75

1974. World Cup Football Championships. As Nos. 619/26 of Grenada inscr. "GRENADA GRENADINES".
16. ½ c. multicoloured 10 10
17. 1 c. multicoloured 10 10
18. 2 c. multicoloured 10 10
19. 10 c. multicoloured 10 10
20. 25 c. multicoloured 10 10
21. 50 c. multicoloured 15 15
22. 75 c. multicoloured 20 20
23. $1 multicoloured 25 25

1974. Cent. of U.P.A. As Nos. 628/30 and 633 of Grenada inscr. "GRENADA GRENADINES".
25. 8 c. multicoloured 10 10
26. 25 c. multicoloured 15 10
27. 35 c. multicoloured 15 10
28. $1 multicoloured 70 40

1974. Birth Cent. of Sir Winston Churchill. As Nos. 637/8 of Grenada inscr. "GRENADA GRENADINES".
30. 35 c. multicoloured 15 10
31. $2 multicoloured 40 45

1974. Christmas. As Nos. 640/7 of Grenada, but inscr. " GRENADA GRENADINES " and background colours changed.
33. **204.** ½ c. multicoloured .. 10 10
34. – 1 c. multicoloured .. 10 10
35. – 2 c. multicoloured .. 10 10
36. – 3 c. multicoloured .. 10 10
37. – 10 c. multicoloured .. 10 10
38. – 25 c. multicoloured .. 10 10
39. – 50 c. multicoloured .. 15 15
40. – $1 multicoloured .. 30 25

1975. Big Game Fishing. As Nos. 669/76 of Grenada inscr. " GRENADA GRENADINES " and background colours changed.
42. ½ c. multicoloured 10 10
43. 1 c. multicoloured 10 10
44. 2 c. multicoloured 10 10
45. 10 c. multicoloured 10 10
46. 25 c. multicoloured 15 10
47. 50 c. multicoloured 20 15
48. 70 c. multicoloured 25 20
49. $1 multicoloured 35 35

1975. Flowers. As Nos. 678/85 of Grenada inscr. " GRENADINES ".
51. ½ c. multicoloured 10 10
52. 1 c. multicoloured 10 10
53. 2 c. multicoloured 10 10
54. 3 c. multicoloured 10 10
55. 10 c. multicoloured 10 10
56. 25 c. multicoloured 10 10
57. 50 c. multicoloured 20 15
58. $1 multicoloured 30 20

CANCELLED REMAINDERS. Some of the following issues have been remaindered, cancelled-to-order, at a fraction of their face value. For all practical purposes these are indistinguishable from genuine postally used copies. Our used quotations which are indicated by an asterisk are the same for cancelled-to-order or postally used copies.

3. " Christ Crowned with Thorns " (Titian).

1975. Easter. Paintings showing Crucifixion and Deposition by artists listed. Multicoloured.
60. ½ c. Type **3** 10 10*
61. 1 c. Giotto 10 10*
62. 2 c. Tintoretto 10 10*
63. 3 c. Cranach 10 10*
64. 35 c. Caravaggio 15 10*
65. 75 c. Tiepolo 20 10*
66. $2 Velasquez 40 15*

4. " Dawn " (detail from Medici tomb).

1975. 500th Birth Anniv. of Michelangelo. Multicoloured.
68. ½ c. Type **4** 10 10*
69. 1 c. " Delphic Sibyl " .. 10 10*
70. 2 c. " Giuliano de Medici "
71. 40 c. " The Creation " (detail) 10 10*
30 10*
72. 50 c. " Lorenzo de Medici " 30 10*
73. 75 c. " Persian Sibyl " .. 35 10*
74. $2 " Head of Christ " .. 60 15*

1975. Butterflies. As T **213** of Grenada but inscr "GRENADINES". Multicoloured.
76 ½ c. "Morpho peleides" .. 10 10
77 1 c. "Danaus eresimus" ("Danaus gilippus") .. 10 10
78 2 c. "Dismorphia amphione" 10 10
79 35 c. "Hamadryas feronia" 35 15
80 45 c. "Philaethria dido" .. 45 15
81 75 c. "Phoebis argante" .. 70 25
82 $2 "Prepona laertes" .. 1·40 70

5. Progress " Standard " Badge.

1975. 14th World Scout Jamboree, Norway. Multicoloured.
84. ½ c. Type **5** 10 10*
85. 1 c. Boatman's badge .. 10 10*
86. 2 c. Coxswain's badge .. 10 10*
87. 35 c. Interpreter's badge .. 30 10*
88. 45 c. Ambulance badge .. 30 10*
89. 75 c. Chief Scout's award .. 40 10*
90. $2 Queen's Scout award .. 75 15*

6. The Surrender of Lord Cornwallis.

1975. Bicentenary of American Revolution (1976) (1st issue). Multicoloured.
92. ½ c. Type **6** 10 10*
93. 1 c. Minute-men 10 10*
94. 2 c. Paul Revere's ride .. 10 10*
95. 3 c. Battle of Bunker Hill 10 10*
96. 5 c. Fifer and drummer .. 10 10*
97. 45 c. Backwoodsman .. 50 10*
98. 75 c. Boston Tea Party .. 65 10*
99. $2 Naval engagement .. 1·50 10*
100. $2 George Washington .. 1·50 1·00
101. $2 White House and flags 1·50 1·00
Nos. 100/1 are larger, 35 × 60 mm.

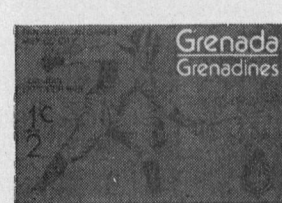

7. Fencing.

1975. Pan-American Games, Mexico City. Multicoloured.
103. ½ c. Type **7** 10 10*
104. 1 c. Hurdling 10 10*
105. 2 c. Pole-vaulting .. 10 10*
106. 35 c. Weightlifting .. 15 10*
107. 45 c. Throwing the javelin 15 10*
108. 75 c. Throwing the discus 15 10*
109. $2 Diving 35 15*

1975. Nos. 649/68 of Grenada additionally inscr. " GRENADINES ".
111. ½ c. Yachts, Port Saline .. 10 20
112. 1 c. Yacht Club race, St. George's 10 15
113. 2 c. Carenage taxi .. 10 15
114. 3 c. Large working boats .. 10 15
115. 5 c. Deep-water dock, St. George's 10 15
116. 6 c. Cocoa beans in drying trays 10 15
117. 8 c. Nutmegs 10 15
118. 10 c. Rum distillery, River Antoine Estate, c. 1785 10 15
119. 12 c. Cocoa tree 10 15
120. 15 c. Fishermen at Fontenoy 10 15
121. 20 c. Parliament Building 10 15
122. 25 c. Fort George cannons 10 15
123. 35 c. Pearls Airport .. 15 15
124. 50 c. General Post Office .. 20 40
125. 75 c. Caribs Leap, Sauteurs Bay 40 60
126. $1 Carenage, St. George's 60 85
127. $2 St. George's Harbour by night .. .. .. 1·25 2·00
128. $3 Grand Anse beach .. 1·75 2·50
129. $5 Canoe Bay and Black Bay .. .. .. 3·00 4·50
130. $10 Sugar-loaf Island .. 5·00 5·50

8. " Virgin and Child " (Durer).

1975. Christmas. " Virgin and Child " paintings by Artists named. Mult.
131. ½ c. Type **8** 10 10*
132. 1 c. Durer 10 10*
133. 2 c. Correggio 10 10*
134. 40 c. Botticelli 10 10*
135. 50 c. Niccolo da Cremona 10 10*
136. 75 c. Correggio 15 10*
137. $2 Correggio 30 15*

9. Bleeding Tooth.

1976. Shells. Multicoloured.
139. ½ c. Type **9** 10 10*
140. 1 c. Wedge Clam 10 10*
141. 2 c. Hawk Wing Conch .. 10 10*
142. 3 c. " Distorsio clathrata " 10 10*
143. 25 c. Scotch Bonnet .. 20 10*
144. 50 c. King Helmet .. 40 10*
145. 75 c. Queen Conch .. 65 15*

10. Cocoa Thrush.

1976. Flora and Fauna. Multicoloured.
147 ½ c. "Lignum vitae" .. 10 10
148 1 c. Type **10** 10 10
149 2 c. "Eurypelma sp." (spider) 10 10
150 35 c. Hooded tanager .. 1·00 40
151 50 c. "Nyctaginaceae" .. 1·00 80
152 75 c. Grenada dove .. 2·25 2·00
153 $1 Marine toad .. .. 2·25 2·25

11. Hooked Sailfish.

1976. Tourism. Multicoloured.
155. ½ c. Type **11** 10 15
156. 1 c. Careened schooner, Carriacou 10 15
157. 2 c. Carriacou Annual Regatta 10 15
158. 18 c. Boat building on Carriacou 25 20
159. 22 c. Workboat race, Carriacou Regatta .. 25 20
160. 75 c. Cruising off Petit Martinique 40 55
161. $1 Water skiing 55 75

12. Making a Camp Fire.

1976. 50th Anniv. of Girl Guides in Grenada. Multicoloured.

163.	½ c. Type **12**	10	10
164.	1 c. First Aid	10	10
165.	2 c. Nature Study ..	10	10
166.	50 c. Cookery ..	75	90
167.	$1 Sketching	1·25	1·75

13. " Christ Mocked " (Bosch).

1976. Easter. Multicoloured.

169.	½ c. Type **13**	10	10
170.	1 c. " Christ Crucified " (Antonello da Messina)	10	10
171.	2 c. " Adoration of the Trinity " (Durer) ..	10	10
172.	3 c. " Lamentation of Christ " (Durer) ..	10	10
173.	35 c. " The Entombment " (Van der Weyden)	20	10
174.	$3 " The Entombment " (Raphael)	75	1·50

14. "South Carolina" (frigate).

1976. Bicentenary of American Revolution (2nd issue). Multicoloured.

176	½ c. Type **14**	10	15
177	1 c. "Lee" (schooner) ..	10	15
178	2 c. H.M.S. "Roebuck" (frigate)	10	15
179	35 c. "Andrew Doria" (brig)	60	55
180	50 c. "Providence" (sloop)	80	1·25
181	$1 "Alfred" (frigate) ..	2·00	2·50
182	$2 "Confederacy" (frigate)	3·25	4·00

15. Piper " Apache ".

1976. Aeroplanes. Multicoloured.

184.	½ c. Type **15**	10	10
185.	1 c. Beech " Twin Bonanza "	10	10
186.	2 c. D.H. " Twin Otter "	10	10
187.	40 c. Britten Norman " Islander "	30	40
188.	50 c. D.H. " Heron " ..	40	45
189.	$2 H.S. " 748 "	1·25	2·00

16. Cycling.

1976. Olympic Games, Montreal. Mult.

191.	½ c. Type **16**	10	10
192.	1 c. Pommel horse ..	10	10
193.	2 c. Hurdling	10	10
194.	35 c. Shot putting ..	10	10
195.	45 c. Diving	15	15
196.	75 c. Sprinting	15	20
197.	$2 Rowing	35	80

17. " Virgin and Child " (Cima).

1976. Christmas. Multicoloured.

199.	½ c. Type **17**	10	10
200.	1 c. " The Nativity " (Romanino)	10	10
201.	2 c. " The Nativity " (Romanino) (different)	10	10
202.	35 c. " Adoration of the Kings " (Bruegel) ..	15	10
203.	50 c. " Madonna and Child " (Girolamo)	20	30
204.	75 c. " Adoration of the Magi " (Giorgione) (horiz.)	20	30
205.	$2 " Adoration of the Kings " (School of Fra Angelico) (horiz.)	40	80

18. Alexander Graham Bell and First Telephone.

1977. Centenary of First Telephone Transmission. T **18** and similar horiz. designs showing Alexander Graham Bell and telephone. Multicoloured.

207.	½ c. Type **18**	10	10
208.	1 c. 1895 telephone ..	10	10
209.	2 c. 1900 telephone ..	10	10
210.	35 c. 1915 telephone ..	15	10
211.	75 c. 1920 telephone ..	30	40
212.	$1 1929 telephone ..	50	75
213.	$2 1963 telephone ..	75	1·40

19. Coronation Coach.

1977. Silver Jubilee. Multicoloured. (a) Perf.

215.	35 c. Type **19**	10	10
216.	$2 Queen entering Abbey	30	20
217.	$4 Queen crowned ..	55	45

(b) Imperf. × roul. Self-adhesive.

219.	35 c. Royal visit	15	20
220.	50 c. Crown of St. Edward	40	80
221.	$2 The Queen and Prince Charles	1·50	1·60
222.	$5 Royal Standard ..	1·60	1·75

Nos. 219/22 come from booklets.

21. "Disrobing of Christ" (Fra Angelico).

1977. Easter. Paintings by artists named. Multicoloured.

223.	½ c. Type **21**	10	10
224.	1 c. Fra Angelico	10	10
225.	2 c. El Greco	10	10
226.	18 c. El Greco	10	10
227.	35 c. Fra Angelico ..	15	10
228.	50 c. Giottino	20	40
229.	$2 Antonello da Messina ..	50	1·10

22. "The Virgin adoring the Child" (Correggio).

1977. Christmas. Multicoloured.

231.	½ c. Type **22**	10	10
232.	1 c. " Virgin and Child " (Giorgione)	10	10
233.	2 c. " Virgin and Child " (Morales)	10	10
234.	18 c. " Madonna della Tenda " (Raphael) ..	10	10
235.	35 c. " Rest on the Flight into Egypt " (Van Dyck)	15	10
236.	50 c. " Madonna and Child " (Lippi)	20	40
237.	$2 " Virgin and Child " (Lippi) (different) ..	60	1·25

1977. Royal Visit. Nos. 215/17 optd. **Royal Visit W.I. 1977.**

239.	35 c. Type **19**	15	10
240.	$2 Queen entering Abbey	40	30
241.	$4 Queen crowned ..	70	50

24. Life-saving.

1977. Caribbean Scout Jamboree, Jamaica. Multicoloured.

243.	½ c. Type **24**	10	10
244.	1 c. Overnight hike ..	10	10
245.	2 c. Cubs tying knots ..	10	10
246.	22 c. Erecting a tent ..	15	10
247.	35 c. Gang show limbo dance	25	10
248.	75 c. Campfire cooking ..	50	65
249.	$3 Sea Scout's yacht race	1·75	3·50

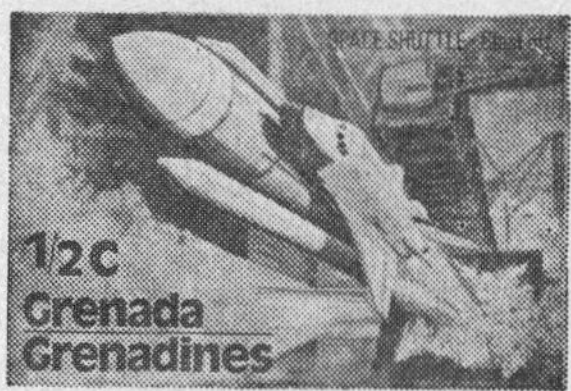

25. Blast-off.

1977. Space Shuttle. Multicoloured.

251.	½ c. Type **25**	10	10
252.	1 c. Booster jettison ..	10	10
253.	2 c. External tank jettison	10	10
254.	22 c. Working in orbit ..	20	15
255.	50 c. Shuttle re-entry ..	35	30
256.	$3 Shuttle landing ..	1·50	1·00

26. Alfred Nobel and Physiology/Medicine Medal.

1978. Nobel Prize Awards. Multicoloured.

258.	½ c. Type **26**	10	10
259.	1 c. Physics and Chemistry medal	10	10
260.	2 c. Peace medal (reverse)	10	10
261.	22 c. Nobel Institute, Oslo	25	15
262.	75 c. Peace Prize committee	65	70
263.	$3 Literature medal ..	1·75	2·00

27. German Zeppelin Stamp, 1930.

1978. 75th Anniv. of 1st Zeppelin Flight and 50th Anniv. of Lindbergh's Transatlantic Flight. Multicoloured.

265.	5 c. Type **27**	30	10
266.	15 c. French " Concorde " stamp, 1970	60	10
267.	25 c. Liechtenstein Zeppelin stamp, 1931 ..	40	10
268.	35 c. Panama Lindbergh stamp, 1928	40	10
269.	50 c. Russia Airship stamp, 1931	45	20
270.	$3 Spanish Lindbergh stamp, 1930	1·40	1·10

28. Coronation Ring.

1978. 25th Anniv. of Coronation. Mult.

(a) Horiz. designs. Perf.

272.	50 c. Type **28**	20	15
273.	$2 The Orb	50	40
274.	$2.50 Imperial State Crown	55	45

(b) Vert. designs. Roul. × imperf. Self-adhesive.

276.	18 c. Drummer, Royal Regiment of Fusiliers ..	25	35
277.	50 c. Drummer, Royal Anglian Regiment ..	25	45
278.	$5 Drum Major, Queen's Regiment	2·25	3·00

Nos. 276/8 come from booklets.

30. " Le Chapeau de Paille ".

1978. 400th Birth Anniv. of Rubens. Mult.

279.	5 c. Type **30**	10	10
280.	15 c. " Achilles slaying Hector "	15	10
281.	18 c. " Helene Fourment and her Children " ..	15	10
282.	22 c. " Rubens and Isabella Brandt "	20	10
283.	35 c. The Ildefonso Altar-piece	20	10
284.	$3 " Heads of negros " (detail)	1·10	1·00

31. Wright " Flyer I ".

1978. 75th Anniv. of Powered Flight.

286.	**31.**	5 c. black, blue & brown	10	10
287.	–	15 c. black, brown & red	10	10
288.	–	18 c. black, brown & red	10	10
289.	–	25 c. black, yell. & green	10	10
290.	–	35 c. black, pink & pur.	15	10
291.	–	75 c. black, lilac & yell.	25	25
292.	–	$3 blk., violet & mve.	75	75

DESIGNS—HORIZ. 25 c. Wright " Flyer ", 1905. 35 c. Wright glider. 75 c. " Flyer I " (different). $3, Wright glider (different). VERT. 15 c. Orville Wright. 18 c. Wilbur Wright.

32. Audubon's Shearwater.

1978. Birds. Multicoloured.

294.	5 c. Type **32**	40	10
295.	10 c. Semipalmated plover	60	10
296.	18 c. Purple-throated carib (horiz.)	85	15
297.	22 c. Red-billed whistling duck (horiz.)	1·00	20
298.	40 c. Caribbean martin (horiz.)	1·25	35
299.	$1 Yellow-tailed tropic-bird	2·25	1·10
300.	$2 Long-billed curlew	3·25	1·50

33. Players with Ball.

1978. World Cup Football Championship, Argentina. Multicoloured.

302.	15 c. Type **33**	10	10
303.	35 c. Running with ball	20	10
304.	50 c. Player with ball	25	20
305.	$3 Heading	80	80

34. Captain Cook and Kalaniopu (King of Hawaii), 1778.

1978. 250th Birth Anniv. of Captain James Cook. Multicoloured.

307.	18 c. Type **34**	45	10
308.	22 c. Cook and native of Hawaii	50	15
309.	50 c. Cook and death scene, 1779	85	30
310.	$3 Cook and offering ceremony	2·25	1·75

35. " Virgin at Prayer ".

1978. Christmas. Paintings by **Durer,** Multicoloured.

312.	40 c. Type **35**	20	10
313.	60 c. " The Dresden Altar-piece "	25	15
314.	90 c. " Madonna and Child with St. Anne "	30	15
315.	$2 " Madonna and Child with Pear "	60	50

36. " Strelitzia reginae ".

1979. Out Island Flowers. Multicoloured.

317.	22 c. Type **36**	15	10
318.	40 c. " Euphorbia pulcherrima "	25	15
319.	$1 " Heliconia humilis "	55	30
320.	$3 " Thunbergia alata "	1·25	80

37. Children with Pig.

1979. International Year of the Child. Multicoloured.

322.	18 c. Type **37**	10	10
323.	50 c. Children with donkey	20	25
324.	$1 Children with goats	25	30
325.	$3 Children fishing	65	80

38. " 20,000 Leagues under the Sea ".

1979. 150th Birth Anniv. of Jules Verne (author). Multicoloured.

327.	18 c. Type **38**	20	10
328.	38 c. " From the Earth to the Moon "	30	20
329.	75 c. " From the Earth to the Moon " (different)	55	35
330.	$3 " Five Weeks in a Balloon "	1·25	1·00

39. Sir Rowland Hill and Mail Van.

1979. Death Centenary of Sir Rowland Hill. Multicoloured.

332	15 c. Type **39**	10	10
333	$1 "Britanis" (cargo liner)	20	20
334	$2 Diesel mail train	30	30
335	$3 "Concorde"	90	70

40. " Virgin and Child " (11th-century Byzantine).

1979. Christmas. Sculptures. Multicoloured.

337.	6 c. Type **40**	10	10
338.	25 c. " Presentation in the Temple " (Andre Beauneveu)	10	10
339.	30 c. " Flight to Egypt " (Utrecht, c. 1510)	10	10
340.	40 c. " Madonna and Child " (Jacopo della Quercia)	10	10
341.	90 c. " Madonna della Mela " (Luca della Robbia)	15	15
342.	$1 " Madonna and Child " (Antonio Rossellino)	20	20
343.	$2 " Madonna and Child " (Antwerp, 1700)	35	35

41. Great Hammerhead Shark.

1979. Marine Wildlife. Multicoloured.

345.	40 c. Type **41**	40	30
346.	45 c. Banded Butterflyfish	45	30
347.	50 c. Permit (fish)	45	40
348.	60 c. Threaded Turban (shell)	65	55
349.	70 c. Milk Conch	75	70
350.	75 c. Great Blue Heron	85	85
351.	90 c. Coloured Atlantic Natica (shell)	95	95
352.	$1 Red Footed Booby	1·50	1·25

42. Doctor Goofy.

1979. International Year of the Child. Walt Disney Characters. Multicoloured.

354.	½ c. Type **42**	10	10
355.	1 c. Admiral Mickey Mouse	10	10
356.	2 c. Fireman Goofy	10	10
357.	3 c. Nurse Minnie Mouse	10	10
358.	4 c. Drum Major Mickey Mouse	10	10
359.	5 c. Policeman Donald Duck	10	10
360.	10 c. Pilot Donald Duck	10	10
361.	$2 Postman Goofy (horiz.)	2·25	1·50
362.	$2.50 Train driver Donald Duck (horiz.)	2·25	1·50

See also Nos. 434/7.

1980. 1st Anniv of Revolution. Nos. 116 and 119/29 optd **PEOPLE'S REVOLUTION 13 MARCH 1979.**

364.	6 c. Cocoa beans in drying trays	10	10
365.	12 c. Cocoa Tree	10	10
366.	15 c. Fishermen at Fontenoy	10	10
367.	20 c. Parliament Building, St. George	10	10
368.	25 c. Fort George cannons	15	10
369.	35 c. Pearls Airport	20	10
370.	50 c. General Post Office	35	15
371.	75 c. Caribs Leap, Sauteurs Bay	40	20
372.	$1 Carenage, St. George's	55	30
373.	$2 St. George's Harbour by night	85	70
374.	$3 Grand Anse Beach	1·60	1·60
375.	$5 Canoe Bay and Black Bay	2·25	2·50
376.	$10 Sugar-loaf Island	3·75	4·25

43. Classroom.

1980. 75th Anniv. of Rotary International. Multicoloured.

377.	6 c. Type **43**	10	10
378.	30 c. Different races encircling Rotary emblem	25	10
379.	60 c. Rotary executive presenting doctor with cheque	50	20
380.	$3 Nurses attending children	2·00	75

44. Yellow-bellied Seedeater.

1980. Wild Birds. Multicoloured.

382.	25 c. Type **44**	50	15
383.	40 c. Blue-hooded Euphonia	55	20
384.	90 c. Yellow Warbler	1·25	65
385.	$2 Tropical Mockingbird	1·75	1·25

45. Running.

1980. Olympic Games, Moscow. Multicoloured.

387.	30 c. Type **45**	15	15
388.	40 c. Football	15	20
389.	90 c. Boxing	30	35
390.	$2 Wrestling	60	75

1980. " London 1980 " International Stamp Exhibition. Nos. 332/5 optd. **LONDON 1980.**

392	15 c. Mail van	15	15
393	$1 "Britanis" (cargo liner)	75	50
394	$2 Diesel mail train	1·50	1·25
395	$3 "Concorde"	2·25	2·50

47. Longspine Squirrelfish.

1980. Fishes. Multicoloured.

396.	½ c. Type **47**	10	10
397.	1 c Blue Chromis	10	10
398.	2 c. Foureye Butterfly Fish	10	10
399.	4 c. Sergeant Major	10	10
400.	5 c. Yellowtail Snapper	10	10
401.	6 c. Mutton Snapper	10	10
402.	10 c. Cocoa Damselfish	10	10
403.	12 c. Royal Gramma	10	10
404.	15 c. Cherubfish	10	10
405.	20 c. Blackbar Soldierfish	15	10
406.	25 c. Comb Grouper	15	15
407.	30 c. Longsnout Butterfly fish	15	20
408.	40 c. Pudding Wife	20	25
409.	50 c. Midnight Parrotfish	25	35
410.	90 c. Redspotted Hawkfish	40	55
411.	$1 Hogfish	45	60
412.	$3 Beau Gregory	1·25	2·00
413.	$5 Rock Beauty	2·25	3·00
414.	$10 Barred Hamlet	4·75	7·00

1980. Christmas. Scenes from Walt Disney's " Bambi ". As Type **42.** Mult.

415.	½ c. Bambi with Mother	10	10
416.	1 c. Bambi with quails	10	10
417.	2 c. Bambi meets Thumper the rabbit	10	10
418.	3 c. Bambi meets Flower the skunk	10	10
419.	4 c. Bambi and Faline	10	10
420.	5 c. Bambi with his father	10	10
421.	10 c. Bambi on ice	10	10
422.	$2.50 Faline with foals	1·50	85
423.	$3 Bambi and Faline	1·50	1·00

48. " The Unicorn in Captivity " (15th century unknown artist).

1981. Art Masterpieces. Multicoloured.

425.	6 c. Type **48**	10	10
426.	10 c. " The Fighting " Temeraire " " (Turner) (horiz.)	10	10
427.	25 c. " Sunday Afternoon on the Ile de la Grande-Jatte " (Seurat) (horiz.)	15	15
428.	90 c. " Max Schmitt in a Single Scull " (Eakins) (horiz.)	45	45
429.	$2 " The Burial of the Count of Orgaz " (El Greco)	85	85
430.	$3 " Portrait of George Washington " (Stuart)	1·10	1·10

1981. Walt Disney's Pluto (cartoon character). 50th Anniv. As Type **42.**

432.	$2 Mickey Mouse serving birthday cake to Pluto	90	80

1981. Easter. Walt Disney Cartoon Characters. As T **42.** Multicoloured.

434.	35 c. Chip	25	25
435.	40 c. Dewey	25	25
436.	$2 Huey	80	80
437.	$2.50 Mickey Mouse	1·10	1·10

49. " Bust of a Woman ". 50. Balmoral Castle.

1981. Birth Centenary of Picasso. Mult.

439. 6 c. Type **49** 10 10
440. 40 c. Woman (study for " Les Demoiselles d'Avignon ") 25 15
441. 90 c. " Nude with raised Arms (The Dancer of Avignon) " 40 30
442. $4 " The Dryad " .. 1·25 1·25

1981. Royal Wedding. Multicoloured.

448 30 c. Prince Charles and Lady Diana Spencer .. 20 20
444 40 c. As 30 c. 20 20
449 40 c. Type **50** 20 20
445 $2 Type **50** 45 45
446 $4 Prince Charles as parachutist 70 70

51. Lady Diana Spencer.

1981. Royal Wedding. Booklet stamps. Multicoloured. Self-adhesive.

450. $1 Type **51** 20 35
451. $2 Prince Charles .. 30 50
452. $5 Prince Charles and Lady Diana Spencer (horiz.) 1·50 2·00

52. Amy Johnson (1st solo flight, Britain to Australia by Woman, May 1930).

1981. " Decade for Women ". Famous Female Aviators. Multicoloured.

453. 30 c. Type **52** 45 15
454. 70 c. Mme. La Baronne de Laroche (1st qualified woman pilot, March 1910) 70 30
455. $1.10 Ruth Nichols (solo Atlantic flight attempt, June 1931) .. .. 1·10 40
456. $3 Amelia Earhart (1st North Atlantic solo flight by woman, May 1932) .. 2·25 1·10

1981. Christmas. Designs as T **42** showing scenes from Walt Disney's cartoon film " Lady and the Tramp ".

458. ½ c. multicoloured .. 10 10
459. 1 c. multicoloured .. 10 10
460. 2 c. multicoloured .. 10 10
461. 3 c. multicoloured .. 10 10
462. 4 c. multicoloured .. 10 10
463. 5 c. multicoloured .. 10 10
464. 10 c. multicoloured .. 10 10
465. $2.50 multicoloured .. 1·50 1·00
466. $3 multicoloured .. .. 1·75 1·25

53. " 747 " Carrier.

1981. Space Shuttle Project. Multicoloured.

468. 10 c. Type **53** 30 10
469. 40 c. Re-entry 65 15
470. $1.10 External tank separation .. .. 1·50 45
471. $3 Touchdown .. .. 2·25 1·00

54. Footballer.

1981. World Cup Football Championship, Spain (1982).

473. **54.** 20 c. multicoloured .. 10 10
474. – 40 c. multicoloured .. 15 15
475. – $1 multicoloured .. 30 30
476. – $2 multicoloured .. 55 55

DESIGNS: 40 c. to $2 Various designs showing footballers.

55. Mail Van and Stage-coach.

1982. Centenary of U.P.U. Membership. Multicoloured.

478. 30 c. Type **55** 50 15
479. 40 c. U.P.U. emblem .. 50 20
480. $2.50 "Queen Elizabeth 2" (liner) and sailing ship .. 2·25 90
481. $4 Airliner and biplane .. 3·00 1·60

56. National Sports Meeting.

1982. 75th Anniv. of Boy Scout Movement and 125th Birth Anniv. of Lord Baden-Powell. Multicoloured.

483. 6 c. Type **56** 15 10
484. 90 c. Sea scouts sailing .. 65 30
485. $1.10 Handicraft 90 60
486. $3 Animal tending .. 1·90 1·40

57. "Anartia jatrophae".

1982. Butterflies. Multicoloured.

488 30 c. Type **57** 65 30
489 40 c. "Chioides vintra" .. 70 35
490 $1.10 "Cynthia cardui" .. 1·50 75
491 $3 "Historis odius" .. 2·50 1·60

58. Prince and Princess of Wales.

1982. 21st Birthday of Princess of Wales. Multicoloured.

493. 50 c. Blenheim Palace .. 50 30
494. 60 c. As 50 c. 60 35
495. $1 Type **58** 70 60
496. $2 Type **58** .. .. 1·50 1·25
497. $3 Princess of Wales .. 2·00 1·75
498. $4 As $3 .. .. .. 2·25 2·00

59. " New Deal "—Soil Conservation.

1982. Birth Centenary of Franklin D. Roosevelt. Multicoloured.

500. 30 c. Type **59** 30 15
501. 40 c. Roosevelt and George Washington Carver (scientist) 40 15
502. 70 c. Civilian conservation corps (reafforestation) .. 75 35
503. $3 Roosevelt with Pres. Barclay of Liberia, Casablanca Conference, 1943 .. .. .. 2·25 1·25

1982. Birth of Prince William of Wales. Nos. 493/8 optd. **ROYAL BABY 21.6.82.**

505. 50 c. Blenheim Palace .. 40 40
506. 60 c. As 50 c. 45 45
507. $1 Type **58** 60 60
508. $2 Type **58** .. .. 1·25 1·40
509. $3 Princess of Wales .. 1·75 1·90
510. $4 As $3 .. .. .. 2·00 2·25

60. " Presentation of Christ in the Temple ".

1982. Easter. Easter Paintings by Rembrandt. Multicoloured.

512. 30 c. Type **60** 40 15
513. 60 c. " Descent from the Cross " 55 20
514. $2 " Raising of the Cross " 1·75 1·00
515. $4 "Resurrection of Christ" 2·75 2·00

61. " Santa Fe ".

1982. Famous Trains of the World. Mult.

517. 10 c. Type **61** 50 15
518. 40 c. "Mistral" .. .. 1·00 20
519. 70 c. "Rheingold" .. .. 1·25 45
520. $1 "ET 403" .. .. 1·50 55
521. $1·10 Steam locomotive "Mallard" .. .. 1·75 70
522. $2 "Tokaido" .. .. 2·00 1·25

62. Footballers.

1982. World Cup Football Championship Winners.

524. **62.** 60 c. multicoloured .. 35 35
525. $4 multicoloured .. 1·75 1·75

1982. Christmas. Scenes from Walt Disney's cartoon film " The Rescuers " as T **42**, but horiz.

527. ½ c. multicoloured .. 10 10
528. 1 c. multicoloured .. 10 10
529. 2 c. multicoloured .. 10 10
530. 3 c. multicoloured .. 10 10
531. 4 c. multicoloured .. 10 10
532. 5 c. multicoloured .. 10 10
533. 10 c. multicoloured .. 10 10
534. $2.50 multicoloured .. 1·75 1·25
535. $3 multicoloured .. 1·75 1·25

63. Short-finned Pilot Whale.

1982. Save the Whale. Multicoloured.

537. 10 c. Type **63** 75 55
538. 60 c. Dall's Porpoise .. 2·00 1·60
539. $1.10 Humpback Whale .. 3·00 2·25
540. $3 Bowhead Whale .. 5·50 5·00

64. " David and Goliath ".

1983. 500th Birth Anniv. of Raphael. Mult.

542. 25 c. Type **64** 20 15
543. 30 c. " David sees Bathsheba " 20 20
544. 90 c. Triumph of David " 65 45
545. $4 " Anointing of Solomon " 1·75 1·75

65. Voice and Visual Communication.

1983. World Communications Year. Mult.

547 30 c. Type **65** 15 15
548 60 c. Ambulance 25 25
549 $1.10 Helicopters 45 45
550 $3 Satellite .. .. 1·25 1·25

66. Chrysler " Imperial Roadster ", 1931.

1983. 75th Anniv. of Model "T" Ford Car. Multicoloured.

552. 10 c. Type **66** 10 10
553. 30 c. Doble steam car, 1925 15 20
554. 40 c. Ford " Mustang " 1965 20 25
555. 60 c. Packard tourer, 1930 25 30
556. 70 c. Mercer " Raceabout " 1913 .. .. .. 25 30
557. 90 c. Corvette " Stingray ", 1963 .. .. .. 25 35
558. $1.10 Auburn " 851 Supercharger Speedster ", 1935 30 40
559. $2.50 Pierce-Arrow " Silver Arrow ", 1933 .. .. 70 85
560. $3 Dusenberg dual cowl phaeton, 1929 .. .. 85 1·10
561. $4 Mercedes-Benz " SSK ", 1928 .. .. .. 1·10 1·50

67. Short " Solent " Flying Boat.

1983. Bicentenary of Manned Flight. Mult.

563. 40 c. Type **67** 75 20
564. 70 c. Curtiss " R3C–2 " seaplane 90 35
565. 90 c. Hawker " Nimrod " biplane .. .. .. 1·10 40
566. $4 Montgolfier balloon .. 3·25 2·75

68. Goofy.

1983. Christmas. Multicoloured.

No.	Description	Mint	Used
568.	½ c. Type **68**	10	10
569.	1 c. Clarabelle Cow ..	10	10
570.	2 c. Donald Duck	10	10
571.	3 c. Pluto	10	10
572.	4 c. Morty and Ferdie ..	10	10
573.	5 c. Huey, Dewey and Louie	10	10
574.	10 c. Daisy and Chip'n Dale	10	10
575.	$2.50 Big Bad Wolf ..	3·75	3·25
576.	$5 Mickey Mouse	4·50	3·75

Nos. 568/76 show Disney cartoon characters in scenes from "Jingle Bells" (Christmas carol).

69. Weightlifting.

1984. Olympic Games, Los Angeles. Mult.

No.	Description	Mint	Used
578.	30 c. Type **69**	15	15
579.	60 c. Gymnastics	35	35
580.	70 c. Archery	40	40
581.	$4 Sailing	1·75	1·90

70. Frangipani.

1984. Flowers. Multicoloured.

No.	Description	Mint	Used
583.	15 c. Type **70**	15	10
584.	40 c. Dwarf Poinciana ..	30	25
585.	70 c. Walking Iris	55	45
586.	$4 Lady's Slipper	2·25	2·50

71. Goofy.

1984. Easter. Multicoloured.

No.	Description	Mint	Used
588.	½ c. Type **71**	10	10
589.	1 c. Chip and Dale ..	10	10
590.	2 c. Daisy Duck and Huey	10	10
591.	3 c. Daisy Duck	10	10
592.	4 c. Donald Duck	10	10
593.	5 c. Merlin and Madam Mim	10	10
594.	10 c. Flower	10	10
595.	$2 Minnie and Mickey Mouse	1·50	1·75
596.	$4 Minnie Mouse	2·25	2·50

72. Bobolink.

1984. Songbirds. Multicoloured.

No.	Description	Mint	Used
598.	40 c. Type **72**	1·60	1·25
599.	50 c. Eastern Kingbird ..	1·75	1·40
600.	60 c. Barn Swallow ..	1·90	1·50
601.	70 c. Yellow Warbler ..	1·90	1·60
602.	$1 Rose-breasted Grosbeak	2·25	1·90
603.	$1.10 Yellowthroat ..	2·50	2·25
604.	$2 Catbird	3·25	3·75

1984. Universal Postal Union Congress, Hamburg. Nos. 585/6 optd. **19th U.P.U. CONGRESS HAMBURG.**

No.	Description	Mint	Used
606.	70 c. Walking Iris	1·00	50
607.	$4 Lady's Slipper	4·00	3·50

74. "Geestar" (freighter).

1984. Ships. Multicoloured.

No.	Description	Mint	Used
609	30 c. Type **74**	1·00	50
610	60 c. "Daphne" (liner) ..	1·50	1·00
611	$1.10 "Southwind" (schooner)	2·00	1·75
612	$4 "Oceanic" (liner) ..	4·50	5·00

1984. 450th Death Anniv. of Correggio (painter). As T **296** of Grenada. Multicoloured.

No.	Description	Mint	Used
614.	10 c. "The Hunt—Blowing the Horn"	10	10
615.	30 c. "St. John the Evangelist" (horiz.) ..	15	15
616.	90 c. "The Hunt—The Deer's Head"	50	50
617.	$4 "The Virgin crowned by Christ" (horiz.)	2·00	2·00

1984. 150th Birth Anniv. of Edgar Degas (painter). As T **297** of Grenada. Multicoloured.

No.	Description	Mint	Used
619.	25 c. "The Song of the Dog"	40	15
620.	70 c. "Cafe-concert" ..	70	35
621.	$1.10 "The Orchestra of the Opera"	1·50	1·00
622.	$3 "The Dance Lesson" ..	2·75	2·25

1984. "Ausipex" International Stamp Exhibition, Melbourne. As T **298** of Grenada. Multicoloured.

No.	Description	Mint	Used
624.	$1.10 Queen Victoria Gardens, Melbourne ..	50	50
625.	$4 Ayers Rock	2·00	2·00

75. Col. Steven's Model (1825).

1984. Railway Locomotives. Multicoloured.

No.	Description	Mint	Used
627.	20 c. Type **75**	65	25
628.	50 c. "Royal George" (1827)	1·00	50
629.	60 c. "Stourbridge Lion" (1829)	1·10	65
630.	70 c. "Liverpool" (1830) ..	1·25	75
631.	90 c. "South Carolina" (1832)	1·50	1·00
632.	$1.10 "Monster" (1836) ..	1·75	1·25
633.	$2 "Lafayette" (1837) ..	2·50	2·00
634.	$4 "Lion" (1838)	4·00	3·50

1984. Opening of Point Saline International Airport. Nos. 547 and 549 optd **OPENING OF POINT SALINE INT'L AIRPORT.**

No.	Description	Mint	Used
636.	30 c. Type **65**	20	25
637.	$1.10 Helicopters	70	75

1984. Christmas. Walt Disney Cartoon Characters. As T **301** of Grenada. Mult.

No.	Description	Mint	Used
639.	45 c. Donald Duck, and nephews knitting Christmas stockings ..	50	30
640.	60 c. Donald Duck and nephews sitting on sofa	60	40
641.	90 c. Donald Duck getting out of bed	85	65
642.	$2 Donald Duck putting presents in wardrobe ..	1·75	1·75
643.	$4 Nephews singing carols outside Donald Duck's window	2·75	2·75

1985. Birth Bicentenary of John J. Audubon (ornithologist). As T **198** of Antigua. Mult.

No.	Description	Mint	Used
645.	50 c. Blue-winged teal ..	1·25	30
646.	90 c. White ibis	1·75	60
647.	$1.10 Swallow-tailed kite ..	2·50	1·25
648.	$3 Moorhen	3·25	2·50

See also Nos. 736/9.

76. Kawasaki "750" (1972).

1985. Centenary of the Motor Cycle. Mult.

No.	Description	Mint	Used
650.	30 c. Type **76**	45	30
651.	60 c. Honda "Goldwing GL1000" (1974) (horiz) ..	70	50
652.	70 c. Kawasaki "Z650" (1976) (horiz) ..	80	60
653.	$4 Honda "CBX" (1977) ..	3·25	3·00

77. Nursing Cadets folding Bandages (Health).

1985. International Youth Year. Mult.

No.	Description	Mint	Used
655.	50 c. Type **77**	50	35
656.	70 c. Scuba diver and turtle (Environment) ..	70	50
657.	$1.10, Yachting (Leisure)	1·25	90
658.	$3 Boys playing chess (Education)	4·25	3·25

1985. 40th Anniv. of International Civil Aviation Organization. As T **305** of Grenada. Multicoloured.

No.	Description	Mint	Used
660.	5 c. Lockheed "Lodestar"	20	10
661.	70 c. Avro "748" Turbo-prop	1·25	45
662.	$1.10, Boeing "727" ..	1·75	85
663.	$4 Boeing "707"	2·75	2·25

78. Lady Baden-Powell (founder) and Grenadian Guide Leaders.

1985. 75th Anniv. of Girl Guide Movement. Multicoloured.

No.	Description	Mint	Used
665.	30 c. Type **78**.	25	20
666.	50 c. Guide leader and guides on botany field trip	45	30
667.	70 c. Guide leader and guides camping (vert.) ..	70	45
668.	$4 Guides sailing (vert.) ..	2·50	2·25

79. "Chiomara asychis".

1985. Butterflies. Multicoloured.

No.	Description	Mint	Used
670	½ c. Type **79**	10	10
671	1 c. "Anartia amathea"	10	10
672	2 c. "Pseudolycaena marsyas"	10	10
673	4 c. "Urbanus proteus" ..	10	10
674	5 c. "Polygonus manueli"	10	10
675	6 c. "Battus polydamas"	10	10
676	10 c. "Eurema daira" ..	10	10
677	12 c. "Phoebis agarithe"	20	10
678	15 c. "Aphrissa statira"	20	10
679	20 c. "Strymon simaethis"	30	10
680	25 c. "Mestra cana" ..	30	20
681	30 c. "Agraulis vanillae"	30	20
682	40 c. "Junonia evarete"	40	30
683	60 c. "Dryas julia" ..	50	40
684	70 c. "Philaethria dido"	65	50
685	$1.10 "Hamadryas feronia"	1·00	90
686	$2.50 "Strymon rufofusca"	2·00	1·75
687	$5 "Appias drusilla" ..	3·00	2·75
688	$10 "Polites dictynna" ..	5·50	5·00
688c	$20 "Euptychia cephus"	9·00	11·00

80. The Queen Mother before Prince William's Christening.

81. Scuba Diving.

1985. Life and Times of Queen Elizabeth the Queen Mother. Multicoloured.

No.	Description	Mint	Used
689.	$1 Type **80**	55	60
690.	$1·50 In winner's enclosure at Ascot (horiz)	80	85
691.	$2·50 With Prince Charles at Garter ceremony, Windsor Castle	1·25	1·50

Stamps as Nos 689/91 but with face values of 70 c., $1·10 and $3 exist from additional sheetlets with changed background colours.

1985. Water Sports. Multicoloured.

No.	Description	Mint	Used
693.	15 c. Type **81**	30	10
694.	70 c. Boys playing in waterfall	70	45
695.	90 c. Water skiing	85	55
696.	$4 Swimming	2·50	2·25

82. Queen Conch.

1985. Marine Life. Multicoloured.

No.	Description	Mint	Used
698.	60 c. Type **82**	50	40
699.	90 c. Porcupine Fish and Fire Coral	65	55
700.	$1.10, Ghost Crab	80	70
701.	$4 West Indies Spiny Lobster	2·25	2·25

1985. 300th Birth Anniv. of Johann Sebastian Bach (composer). As T **206** of Antigua. Mult.

No.	Description	Mint	Used
703.	15 c. Natural trumpet ..	40	10
704.	60 c. Bass viol	75	40
705.	$1.10, Flute	1·25	70
706.	$3 Double flageolet ..	2·00	1·75

1985. Royal Visit. As T **207** of Antigua. Multicoloured.

No.	Description	Mint	Used
708.	10 c. Arms of Great Britain and Grenada	20	15
709.	$1 Queen Elizabeth II (vert.)	1·25	1·25
710.	$4 Royal Yacht "Britannia"	3·75	3·75

1985. 40th Anniv. of United Nations Organization. Designs as T **208** of Antigua showing United Nations (New York) stamps. Multicoloured.

712. $1 Neil Armstrong (first man on Moon) and 1982 Peaceful Uses of Outer Space 20 c. .. .. 1·00 75

713. $2 Gandhi and 1971 Racial Equality Year 13 c. .. 2·50 1·90

714. $2.50, Maimonides (physician) and 1956 World Health Organization 3 c. .. 3·75 2·75

1985. 150th Birth Anniv. of Mark Twain (author). As T **118** of Anguilla showing Walt Disney cartoon characters illustrating scenes from "Letters from Hawaii". Multicoloured.

716. 25 c. Minnie Mouse dancing the hula 35 25

717. 50 c. Donald Duck surfing 55 40

718. $1.50 Donald Duck roasting marshmallow in volcano .. .. .. 1·50 1·25

719. $3 Mickey Mouse and Chip'n'Dale canoeing .. 2·50 2·50

1985. Birth Bicentenaries of Grimm Brothers (folklorists). As T **119** of Anguilla, but vert, showing Walt Disney cartoon characters in scenes from "The Elves and the Shoemaker". Multicoloured.

721. 30 c. Mickey Mouse as the unsuccessful Shoemaker 45 35

722. 60 c. Two elves making shoes 75 60

723. 70 c. The Shoemaker discovering the new shoes 85 70

724. $4 The Shoemaker's wife (Minnie Mouse) making clothes for the elves .. 3·25 3·25

83. "Madonna and Child" (Titian).

1985. Christmas. Religious Paintings. Mult.

726. 50 c. Type **83** 45 35

727. 70 c. "Madonna and Child with St. Mary and John the Baptist" (Bugiardini) 55 45

728. $1.10 "Adoration of the Magi" (Di Fredi) .. 90 90

729. $3 "Madonna and Child with Young St. John the Baptist" (Bartolomeo) .. 2·25 2·75

1986. Centenary of Statue of Liberty (1st issue). As T **211** of Dominica. Multicoloured.

731. 5 c. Croton Reservoir, New York (1875) 10 10

732. 10 c. New York Public Library (1986) 10 10

733. 70 c. Old Boathouse, Central Park (1894) .. 25 35

734. $4 Boating in Central Park (1986) .. .. .. 1·40 1·90

See also Nos. 892/903.

1986. Birth Bicentenary of John J. Audubon (ornithologist) (2nd issue). As T **198** of Antigua. Multicoloured.

736. 50 c. Louisiana heron .. 1·50 1·00

737. 70 c. Black-crowned night heron .. .. .. 2·00 1·25

738. 90 c. American bittern .. 2·25 1·40

739. $4 Glossy ibis .. .. 4·25 4·50

1986. Visit of President Reagan of U.S.A. Nos. 684 and 687, optd. **VISIT OF PRES. REAGAN 20 FEBRUARY 1986.**

741 70 c. "Philaethria dido" .. 1·25 1·00

742 $5 "Appias drusilla" .. 5·50 6·50

85. Two Footballers.

1986. World Cup Football Championship, Mexico. Designs showing footballers.

743. **85.** 10 c. multicoloured .. 30 20

744. – 70 c. multicoloured .. 1·10 1·00

745. – $1 multicoloured .. 1·50 1·25

746. – $4 multicoloured .. 4·25 4·25

1986. Appearance of Halley's Comet (1st issue). As T **123** of Anguilla. Multicoloured.

748. 5 c. Nicholas Copernicus (astronomer) and Earl of Rosse's six foot reflector telescope 20 20

749. 20 c. "Sputnik I" (first satellite) orbiting Earth, 1957 .. .. .. 40 40

750. 40 c. Tycho Brahe's notes and sketch of 1577 Comet 60 60

751. $4 Edmond Halley and 1682 Comet .. .. 3·00 3·50

See also Nos 790/3.

The captions of Nos. 750/1 are transposed.

1986. 60th Birthday of Queen Elizabeth II. As T **125** of Anguilla.

753. 2 c. black and yellow .. 10 15

754. $1·50 multicoloured .. 1·00 1·00

755. $4 multicoloured .. .. 2·25 2·50

DESIGN: 2 c. Princesses Elizabeth and Margaret, Windsor Park, 1933. $1·50, Queen Elizabeth. $4, In Sydney, Australia, 1970.

1986. "Ameripex '86" International Stamp Exhibition, Chicago. As T **212** of Dominica. Multicoloured.

757. 30 c. Donald Duck riding mule in Grand Canyon 45 45

758. 60 c. Daisy Duck, Timothy Mouse and Dumbo on Golden Gate Bridge, San Francisco 70 70

759. $1 Mickey Mouse and Goofy in fire engine and Chicago Watertower .. 1·25 1·25

760. $3 Mickey Mouse as airmail pilot and White House 3·00 3·00

1986. Royal Wedding. As T **213** of Antigua. Multicoloured.

762. 60 c. Prince Andrew and Miss Sarah Ferguson .. 45 45

763. 70 c. Prince Andrew in car 55 55

764. $4 Prince Andrew with naval helicopter .. 2·50 2·50

86. "Hygrocybe firma".

1986. Mushrooms of the Lesser Antilles. Multicoloured.

766. 15 c. Type **86** 70 30

767. 50 c. "Xerocomus coccolobae" .. .. 1·60 80

768. $2 "Volvariella cubensis" 3·25 2·50

769. $3 "Lactarius putidus" .. 4·50 4·00

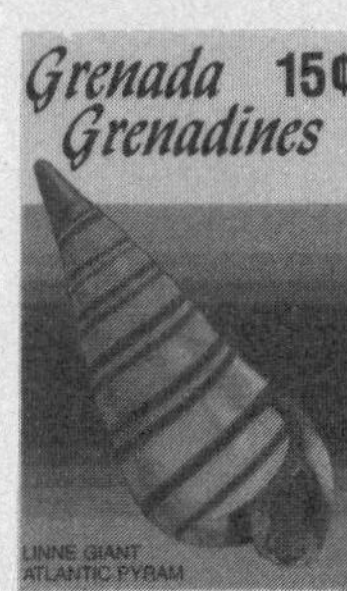

87. Giant Atlantic Pyram.

1986. Sea Shells. Multicoloured.

771. 15 c. Type **87** 60 20

772. 50 c. Beau's murex .. 1·40 60

773. $1.10 West Indian fighting conch .. .. .. 2·25 1·90

774. $4 Alphabet coral shell .. 4·50 4·50

1986. World Cup Football Championship Winners, Mexico. Nos. 743/6 optd. **WINNERS Argentina 3 W. Germany 2.**

776. **85.** 10 c. multicoloured .. 20 20

777. – 70 c. multicoloured .. 65 65

778. – $1 multicoloured .. 85 85

779. – $4 multicoloured .. 2·75 3·00

88. Common Opossum.

1986. Wildlife. Multicoloured.

781. 10 c. Type **88** 20 20

782. 30 c. Giant toad .. 40 40

783. 60 c. Land tortoise .. 80 80

784. 70 c. Murine opossum (vert.) 85 85

785. 90 c. Burmese mongoose (vert.) 90 90

786. $1.10 Nine-banded armadillo .. .. 1·00 1·00

787. $2 Agouti .. .. 1·75 2·00

788. $3 Humpback whale .. 3·50 3·75

1986. Appearance of Halley's Comet (2nd issue). Nos. 748/51 optd with T **218** of Antigua.

790. 5 c. Nicholas Copernicus (astronomer) and Earl of Rosse's six foot reflector telescope 30 25

791. 20 c. "Sputnik I" orbiting Earth, 1957 .. .. 50 35

792. 40 c. Tycho Brahe's notes and sketch of 1577 Comet 70 45

793. $4 Edmond Halley and 1682 Comet .. .. 4·00 4·50

1986. Christmas. As T **220** of Antigua showing Walt Disney cartoon characters. Mult.

795. 25 c. Chip n'Dale with hummingbird 15 15

796. 30 c. Robin delivering card to Mickey Mouse (vert.) 15 20

797. 50 c. Piglet, Pooh and Jose Carioca on beach .. 25 30

798. 60 c. Grandma Duck feeding birds (vert.) .. 30 35

799. 70 c. Cinderella and birds with mistletoe (vert.) .. 35 40

800. $1.50 Huey, Dewey and Louie windsurfing .. 75 80

801. $3 Mickey Mouse and Morty on beach with turtle .. .. .. 1·50 1·75

802. $4 Kittens playing on piano (vert.) .. .. 2·00 2·25

89. Cycling.

1986. Olympic Games, Seoul, South Korea (1988). Multicoloured.

804. 10 c. + 5 c. Type **89** .. 25 30

805. 50 c. + 20 c. Sailing .. 60 70

806. 70 c. + 30 c. Gymnastics .. 75 85

807. $2 + $1 Horse trials .. 2·25 2·50

90. Aston-Martin "Volanté" (1984).

1986. Centenary of Motoring. Multicoloured.

809. 10 c. Type **90** 20 20

810. 30 c. Jaguar "Mk V" (1948) 35 35

811. 60 c. Nash "Ambassador" (1956) 55 55

812. 70 c. Toyota "Supra" (1984) 60 60

813. 90 c. Ferrari "Testarrosa" (1985) 70 70

814. $1 BMW "501B" (1955) .. 75 75

815. $2 Mercedes-Benz "280 SL" (1968) .. .. .. 1·40 1·40

816. $3 Austro-Daimler "ADR8" (1932) .. .. 1·90 1·90

1986. Birth Centenary of Marc Chagall (artist). As T **225** of Antigua, showing various paintings.

818/57. $1.10 × 40 multicoloured Set of 40 .. .. 24·00 24·00

1987. America's Cup Yachting Championship. Multicoloured. As T **222** of Antigua.

859 25 c. "Defender", 1895 .. 50 35

860 45 c. "Galatea", 1886 .. 70 55

861 70 c. "Azzurra", 1981 .. 90 80

862 $4 "Australia II", 1983 .. 2·50 3·00

1987. 500th Anniv (1992) of Discovery of America by Christopher Columbus (1st issue). As T **322** of Grenada. Multicoloured.

864. 15 c. Christopher Columbus 25 25

865. 30 c. Queen Isabella of Castile 30 30

866. 50 c. "Santa Maria" .. 45 45

867. 60 c. Claiming the New World for Spain .. 50 50

868. 90 c. Early Spanish map of Lesser Antilles 65 65

869. $1 King Ferdinand of Aragon 70 70

870. $2 Fort La Navidad (drawing by Columbus) 1·40 1·40

871. $3 Galley and Caribs, Hispaniola (drawing by Columbus) .. .. 1·90 1·90

See also Nos. 1191/4, 1224/31, 1366/73, 1494/1500 and 1519/20.

1987. Milestones of Transportation. As T **226** of Antigua. Multicoloured.

873. 10 c. Saunders Roe "SR-N1" (first hovercraft), 1959 .. .. .. 20 20

874. 15 c. Bugatti "Royale" (largest car), 1931 .. 25 25

875. 30 c. Aleksei Leonov and "Voskhod II" (first spacewalk), 1965 .. 35 35

876. 50 c. C.S.S. "Hunley" (first submarine to sink enemy ship), 1864 .. .. 55 55

877. 60 c. Rolls Royce "Flying Bedstead" (first VTOL aircraft), 1954 .. 65 65

878. 70 c. "Jenny Lind" (first mass produced locomotive class), 1847 .. 70 70

879. 90 c. Duryea "Buggyaut" (first U.S. petrol-driven car), 1893 .. .. 80 80

880. $1.50 Steam locomotive, Metropolitan Railway, London (first underground line), 1863 1·40 1·40

881. $2 S.S. "Great Britain" (first transatlantic crossing by screw-steamship), 1843 .. 1·75 1·75

882. $3 "Budweiser Rocket" (fastest car), 1979 .. 2·25 2·25

1987. "Capex '87" International Stamp Exhibition, Toronto. Game Fishes. As T **323** of Grenada. Multicoloured.

883. 6 c. Yellow chub 15 15

884. 30 c. Kingfish 40 30

885. 50 c. Mako shark 55 45

886. 60 c. Dolphinfish 60 50

887. 90 c. Bonito 75 70

888. $1.10 Cobia .. .. 1·00 1·00

889. $3 Great tarpon .. .. 2·25 2·50

890. $4 Swordfish .. .. 2·50 3·00

1987. Centenary of Statue of Liberty (1986) (2nd issue). As T **227** of Antigua. Mult.

892. 10 c. Cleaning face of statue 15 15

893. 15 c. Commemorative lapel badges 25 25

894. 25 c. Band playing and statue 35 35

895. 30 c. Band on parade and statue 35 35

896. 45 c. Face of statue .. 40 40

897. 50 c. Cleaning head of statue (horiz.) 45 45

898. 60 c. Models of statue (horiz.) 50 50

899. 70 c. Small boat flotilla (horiz.) 65 65

900. $1 Unveiling ceremony .. 75 75

901. $1.10 Statue and Manhattan skyline .. 80 80

902. $2 Parade of warships .. 1·60 1·60

903. $3 Making commemorative flags .. .. .. 1·75 1·75

1987. Great Scientific Discoveries. As T **325** of Grenada. Multicoloured.

904. 60 c. Newton medal .. 65 50
905. $1 Louis Daguerre (inventor of daguerreotype) 95 80
906. $2 Antoine Lavoisier and apparatus .. .. 1·75 2·00
907. $3 Rudolf Diesel and diesel engine .. .. 3·50 3·75

No. 907 is inscribed "JAMES WATT" in error.

1987. Bicentenary of U.S. Constitution. As T **232** of Antigua. Multicoloured.

909. 10 c. Washington addressing delegates, Constitutional Convention 20 15
910. 50 c. Flag and State Seal, Georgia 75 65
911. 60 c. Capitol, Washington (vert.) 75 65
912. $4 Thomas Jefferson (statesman) (vert.) .. 3·50 4·00

1987. "Hafnia '87" International Stamp Exhibition, Copenhagen. Designs As T **328** of Grenada, but horiz., illustrating Hans Christian Andersen's fairy tales. Mult.

914. 25 c. Donald and Daisy Duck in "The Swineherd" 30 30
915. 30 c. Mickey Mouse, Donald and Daisy Duck in "What the Good Man Does in Always Right" 35 35
916. 50 c. Mickey and Minnie Mouse in "Little Tuk" 55 55
917. 60 c. Minnie Mouse and Ferdie in "The World's Fairest Rose" 55 55
918. 70 c. Mickey Mouse in "The Garden of Paradise" 60 60
919. $1.50 Goofy and Mickey Mouse in "The Naughty Boy" .. .. .. 1·40 1·40
920. $3 Goofy in "What the Moon Saw" .. .. 2·25 2·25
921. $4 Alice as "Thumbelina" 2·75 2·75

91. "The Virgin and Child with Saints Martin and Agnes".

1987. Christmas. Religious Paintings by El Greco. Multicoloured.

923. 10 c. Type **91** 30 15
924. 50 c. "St. Agnes" (detail from "The Virgin and Child with Saints Martin and Agnes") 90 70
925. 60 c. "The Annunciation" 90 70
926. $4 "The Holy Family with St. Anne" .. .. 4·00 4·50

1988. Royal Ruby Wedding. As T **234** of Antigua. Multicoloured.

928. 20 c. brown, blk. & grn. .. 30 15
929. 30 c. brown and black .. 35 20
930. $2 multicoloured .. .. 1·75 2·00
931. $3 multicoloured .. .. 2·25 2·75

DESIGNS: 20 c. Queen Elizabeth II with Princess Anne, c. 1957. 30 c. Wedding photograph, 1947. $2, Queen with Prince Charles and Princess Anne, c. 1955. $3, Queen Elizabeth (from photo by Tim Graham), 1980.

1988. Olympic Games, Seoul. Multicoloured. As T **331** of Grenada showing Walt Disney cartoon characters as Olympic competitors.

933 1 c. Minnie Mouse as rhythmic gymnast (horiz) 10 10
934 2 c. Pete and Goofy as pankration wrestlers (horiz) 10 10
935 3 c. Huey and Dewey as synchronized swimmers (horiz) 10 10
936 4 c. Huey, Dewey and Louey in hoplite race (horiz) 10 10
937 5 c. Clarabelle and Daisy Duck playing baseball (horiz) 10 10
938 10 c. Goofy and Donald Duck in horse race (horiz) 10 10
939 $6 Donald Duck and Uncle Scrooge McDuck wind-surfing (horiz) 3·00 3·25
940 $7 Mickey Mouse in chariot race (horiz) .. .. 3·50 3·75

92 Scout signalling with Semaphore Flags

1988. World Scout Jamboree, Australia. Mult.

942 50 c. Type **92** 30 35
943 70 c. Canoeing 35 40
944 $1 Cooking over campfire (horiz) 50 55
945 $3 Scouts around campfire (horiz) .. .. .. 1·60 2·00

1988. Birds. As T **334** of Grenada. Mult.

947 20 c. Yellow-crowned night heron 30 25
948 25 c. Brown pelican .. 30 25
949 45 c. Audubon's shearwater 40 35
950 60 c. Red-footed booby .. 50 40
951 70 c. Bridled tern .. 55 45
952 90 c. Red-billed tropic bird 70 60
953 $3 Blue-winged teal .. 1·75 2·00
954 $4 Sora .. .. .. 2·00 2·50

1988. 500th Birth Anniv of Titian (artist). As T **238** of Antigua. Multicoloured.

956 15 c. "Man with Blue Eyes" 10 10
957 30 c. "The Three Ages of Man" (detail) .. 15 15
958 60 c. "Don Diego Mendoza" 25 30
959 75 c. "Emperor Charles V seated" 35 40
960 $1 "A Young Man in a Fur" 45 50
961 $2 "Tobias and the Angel" 90 95
962 $3 "Pietro Bembo" .. 1·40 1·50
963 $4 "Pier Luigi Farnese" .. 1·75 1·90

1988. Airships. As T **336** of Grenada. Mult.

965 10 c. "Hindenburg" over Sugarloaf Mountain, Rio de Janeiro, 1937 (horiz) 10 10
966 20 c. "Hindenburg" over New York, 1937 (horiz) 10 10
967 30 c. U.S. Navy airships on Atlantic escort duty, 1944 (horiz) 15 15
968 40 c. "Hindenburg" approaching Lakehurst, 1937 .. .. .. 20 25
969 60 c. "Graf Zeppelin" and "Hindenburg" over Germany, 1936 .. .. 25 30
970 70 c. "Hindenburg" and "Los Angeles" moored at Lakehurst, 1936 (horiz) 30 35
971 $1 "Graf Zeppelin II" over Dover, 1939 .. .. 45 50
972 $2 "Deutschland" on scheduled passenger flight, 1912 (horiz) .. 80 1·00
973 $3 "Graf Zeppelin" over Dome of the Rock, Jerusalem, 1931 (horiz) 1·25 1·50
974 $4 "Hindenburg" over Olympic stadium, Berlin, 1936 (horiz) .. 1·60 1·75

93 Bambi and his Mother

1988. Disney Animal Cartoon Films.

976/1029 30 c. × 54 multicoloured Set of 54 .. .. 8·00 8·50

DESIGNS: Scenes from Bambi, Dumbo, Lady and The Tramp, The Aristocats, The Fox and the Hound and 101 Dalmatians.

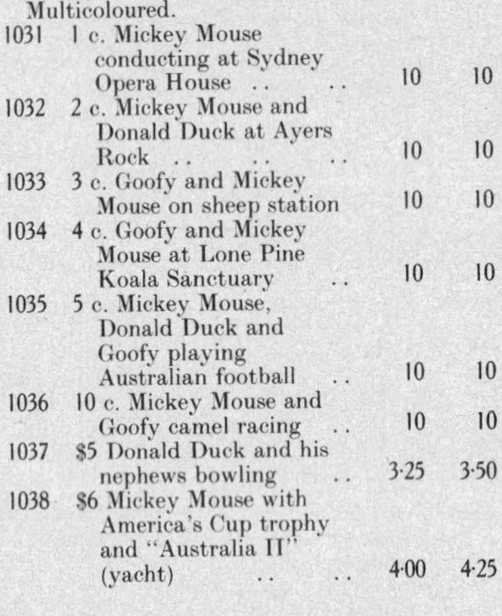

1988. "Sydpex '88" National Stamp Exhibition, Sydney and 60th Birthday of Mickey Mouse. As T **337** of Grenada. Multicoloured.

1031 1 c. Mickey Mouse conducting at Sydney Opera House 10 10
1032 2 c. Mickey Mouse and Donald Duck at Ayers Rock 10 10
1033 3 c. Goofy and Mickey Mouse on sheep station 10 10
1034 4 c. Goofy and Mickey Mouse at Lone Pine Koala Sanctuary .. 10 10
1035 5 c. Mickey Mouse, Donald Duck and Goofy playing Australian football .. 10 10
1036 10 c. Mickey Mouse and Goofy camel racing .. 10 10
1037 $5 Donald Duck and his nephews bowling .. 3·25 3·50
1038 $6 Mickey Mouse with America's Cup trophy and "Australia II" (yacht) .. .. 4·00 4·25

1988. Flowering Trees and Shrubs. As T **339** of Grenada. Multicoloured.

1040 10 c. Potato tree (vert) .. 15 15
1041 20 c. Wild cotton .. 15 15
1042 30 c. Shower of gold (vert) 20 20
1043 60 c. Napoleon's button (vert) 35 30
1044 90 c. Geiger tree 60 55
1045 $1 Fern tree 70 65
1046 $2 French cashew .. 1·25 1·50
1047 $4 Amherstia (vert) .. 2·00 2·50

1988. Cars. As T **335** of Grenada. Mult.

1049 $2 Doble "Series E", 1925 1·00 1·00
1050 $2 Alvis "12/50", 1926 .. 1·00 1·00
1051 $2 Sunbeam 3-litre, 1927 1·00 1·00
1052 $2 Franklin "Airman", 1928 .. .. .. 1·00 1·00
1053 $2 Delage "D8S", 1929 .. 1·00 1·00
1054 $2 Mors, 1897 .. .. 1·00 1·00
1055 $2 Peerless "Green Dragon", 1904 .. 1·00 1·00
1056 $2 Pope-Hartford, 1909 .. 1·00 1·00
1057 $2 Daniels "Submarine Speedster", 1920 .. 1·00 1·00
1058 $2 McFarlan 9.3 litre, 1922 1·00 1·00
1059 $2 Frazer Nash "Lemans" replica, 1949 .. .. 1·00 1·00
1060 $2 Pegaso "Z102", 1953 .. 1·00 1·00
1061 $2 Siata "Spyder V-8", 1953 .. .. .. 1·00 1·00
1062 $2 Kurtis-Offenhauser, 1953 .. .. .. 1·00 1·00
1063 $2 Kaiser-Darrin, 1954 .. 1·00 1·00
1064 $2 Tracta, 1930 .. .. 1·00 1·00
1065 $2 Maybach "Zeppelin", 1932 .. .. .. 1·00 1·00
1066 $2 Railton "Light Sports", 1934 .. .. 1·00 1·00
1067 $2 Hotchkiss, 1936 .. 1·00 1·00
1068 $2 Mercedes-Benz "W163", 1939 .. .. 1·00 1·00
1069 $2 Aston Martin "Vantage V8", 1982 .. .. 1·00 1·00
1070 $2 Porsche "956", 1982 .. 1·00 1·00
1071 $2 Lotus "Esprit Turbo", 1983 .. .. .. 1·00 1·00
1072 $2 McLaren "MP4/2", 1984 .. .. .. 1·00 1·00
1073 $2 Mercedes-Benz "190E 2.3-16", 1985 .. .. 1·00 1·00
1074 $2 Ferrari "250 GT Lusso", 1963 .. .. 1·00 1·00
1075 $2 Porsche "904", 1964 .. 1·00 1·00
1076 $2 Volvo "P1800", 1967 .. 1·00 1·00
1077 $2 McLaren-Chevrolet "M8D", 1970 .. .. 1·00 1·00
1078 $2 Jaguar "XJ6", 1981 .. 1·00 1·00

1988. "Mickey's Christmas Parade". As T **246** of Antigua showing Walt Disney cartoon characters. Multicoloured.

1079 $1 Dumbo 45 50
1080 $1 Goofy as Father Christmas 45 50
1081 $1 Minnie Mouse waving from window 45 50
1082 $1 Clarabelle, Mordie and Ferdie watching parade 45 50
1083 $1 Donald Duck's nephews 45 50
1084 $1 Donald Duck as drummer 45 50
1085 $1 Toy soldiers 45 50
1086 $1 Mickey Mouse on wooden horse 45 50

94 Middleweight Boxing (Gold, Henry Maske, East Germany)

1989. Olympic Medal Winners, Seoul (1988). Multicoloured.

1088 15 c. Type **94** 10 10
1089 50 c. Freestyle wrestling (130 kg) (Bronze, Andreas Schroeder, East Germany) .. 20 25
1090 60 c. Women's team gymnastics (Bronze, East Germany) .. 25 30
1091 75 c. Platform diving (Gold, Greg Louganis, USA) 30 35
1092 $1 Freestyle wrestling (52 kg) (Gold, Mitsuru Sato, Japan) 40 45
1093 $2 Men's freestyle 4 × 200 metres relay swimming (Bronze, West Germany) 85 90
1094 $3 Men's 5000 metres (Silver, Dieter Baumann, West Germany) .. .. 1·25 1·40
1095 $4 Women's heptathlon (Gold, Jackie Joyner-Kersee, U.S.A.) .. 1·75 1·90

1989. Japanese Art. Paintings by Hiroshige. As T **250** of Antigua. Multicoloured.

1097 15 c. "Crossing the Oi at Shimada by Ferry" .. 10 10
1098 20 c. "Daimyo and Entourage at Arai" .. 10 10
1099 45 c. "Cargo Portage through Goyu" .. 20 25
1100 75 c. "Snowfall at Fujigawa" 30 35
1101 $1 "Horses for the Emperor at Chirifu" .. 40 45
1102 $2 "Rainfall at Tsuchiyama" 85 90
1103 $3 "An Inn at Ishibe" .. 1·25 1·40
1104 $4 "On the Shore of Lake Biwa at Otsu" .. 1·75 1·90

1989. World Cup Football Championship, Italy (1990) (1st issue). As T **252** of Antigua. Multicoloured.

1106 15 c. World Cup trophy .. 10 10
1107 20 c. Flags of Argentina (winners 1986) and International Federation of Football Associations (FIFA) (horiz) 10 10
1108 45 c. Franz Beckenbauer (West Germany) with World Cup, 1974 .. 20 25
1109 75 c. Flags of Italy (winners 1982) and FIFA (horiz) 30 35
1110 $1 Pele (Brazil) with Jules Rimet trophy 40 45
1111 $2 Flags of West Germany (winners 1974) and FIFA (horiz) .. 85 90
1112 $3 Flags of Brazil (winners 1970) and FIFA (horiz) .. .. 1·25 1·40
1113 $4 Jules Rimet trophy and Brazil players .. 1·75 1·90

See also Nos. 1285/8.

1989. North American Railway Locomotives. As T **342** of Grenada. Multicoloured.

1115 $2 Morris & Essex Railroad "Dover", 1841 .. 1·25 1·25
1116 $2 Baltimore & Ohio Railroad "Memmon" No. 57, 1848 .. .. 1·25 1·25

1117 $2 Camden & Amboy Railroad "John Stevens", 1849 .. 1·25 1·25
1118 $2 Lawrence Machine Shop "Lawrence", 1853 1·25 1·25
1119 $2 South Carolina Railroad "James S. Corry", 1859 .. .. .. 1·25 1·25
1120 $2 Mine Hill & Schuylkill Haven Railroad Flexible Beam No. 3 type, 1860 .. .. 1·25 1·25
1121 $2 Delaware, Lackawanna & Western Railroad "Montrose", 1861 .. 1·25 1·25
1122 $2 Central Pacific Railroad "Pequop" No. 68, 1868 .. .. 1·25 1·25
1123 $2 Boston & Providence Railroad "Daniel Nason", 1863 .. .. 1·25 1·25
1124 $2 Morris & Essex Railroad "Joe Scranton", 1870 .. .. .. 1·25 1·25
1125 $2 Central Railroad of New Jersey No. 124, 1871 1·25 1·25
1126 $2 Baldwin tramway steam locomotive, 1876 1·25 1·25
1127 $2 Lackawanna & Bloomsburg Railroad "Luzerne", 1878 .. 1·25 1·25
1128 $2 Central Mexicano Railroad No. 150, 1892 .. 1·25 1·25
1129 $2 Denver, South Park & Pacific Railroad "Breckenridge" No. 15, 1879 .. .. .. 1·25 1·25
1130 $2 Miles Planting & Manufacturing Company plantation locomotive "Daisy", 1894 1·25 1·25
1131 $2 Central of Georgia Railroad Baldwin "854" No. 1136, 1895 .. .. 1·25 1·25
1132 $2 Savannah, Florida & Western Railroad No. 111, 1900 .. .. 1·25 1·25
1133 $2 Douglas, Gilmore & Company contractors locomotive No. 3, 1902 1·25 1·25
1134 $2 Lehigh Valley Coal Company compressed air locomotive No. 900, 1903 .. .. .. 1·25 1·25
1135 $2 Morgan's Louisiana & Texas Railroad McKeen diesel locomotive, 1908 1·25 1·25
1136 $2 Clear Lake Lumber Company Type "B Climax" locomotive No. 6, 1910 .. .. 1·25 1·25
1137 $2 Blue Jay Lumber Company Heisler locomotive No. 10, 1912 1·25 1·25
1138 $2 Stewartstown Railroad gasoline locomotive No. 6, 1920s .. .. 1·25 1·25
1139 $2 Bangor & Aroostock Railroad Class "G" No. 186, 1921 .. .. 1·25 1·25
1140 $2 Hammond Lumber Company No. 6, 1923 .. 1·25 1·25
1141 $2 Central Railroad of New Jersey diesel locomotive No. 1000, 1925 .. .. .. 1·25 1·25
1142 $2 Atchison, Topeka & Santa Fe Railroad "Super Chief" diesel express, 1935 .. .. 1·25 1·25
1143 $2 Norfolk & Western Railroad Class "Y-6", 1948 .. .. .. 1·25 1·25
1144 $2 Boston & Maine Railroad Budd diesel railcar, 1949 .. .. 1·25 1·25

1989. "Philexfrance '89" International Stamp Exhibition, Paris. As T **251** of Antigua showing Walt Disney cartoon characters in Paris. Multicoloured.

1145 1 c. Mickey Mouse and Donald Duck at Ecole Militaire inflating balloon 10 10
1146 2 c. Mickey and Minnie Mouse on river boat passing Conciergerie .. 10 10
1147 3 c. Mickey Mouse at Hotel de Ville (vert) .. 10 10
1148 4 c. Mickey Mouse at Genie of the Bastille monument (vert) .. 10 10
1149 5 c. Mickey and Minnie Mouse arriving at Opera House 10 10
1150 10 c. Mickey and Minnie Mouse on tandem in Luxembourg Gardens 10 10
1151 $5 Mickey Mouse in aeroplane over L'Arch de la Defense (vert) .. 2·75 3·00
1152 $6 Mickey Mouse at Place Vendome (vert) .. 3·25 3·50

95 Launch of "Apollo 11"

1989. 20th Anniv of First Manned Landing on Moon. Multicoloured.

1154 25 c. Type **95** 20 20
1155 50 c. Splashdown (horiz) 35 35
1156 60 c. Modules in space .. 40 40
1157 75 c. Aldrin setting up experiment (horiz) .. 50 50
1158 $1 "Apollo 11" leaving Earth orbit (horiz) .. 60 60
1159 $2 Moving "Apollo 11" to launch site .. .. 1·25 1·25
1160 $3 Lunar module "Eagle" leaving Moon (horiz) .. 1·75 1·75
1161 $4 "Eagle" landing on Moon .. .. .. 2·00 2·00

1989. Fungi. As T **348** of Grenada. Mult.

1163 6 c. "Collybia aurea" .. 15 15
1164 10 c. "Podaxis pistillaris" 15 15
1165 20 c. "Hygrocybe firma" 20 20
1166 30 c. "Agaricus rufoaurantiacus" .. 30 30
1167 75 c. "Leptonia howellii" 60 60
1168 $2 "Marasmiellus purpureus" .. .. 1·40 1·40
1169 $3 "Marasmius trinitatis" 2·00 2·00
1170 $4 "Hygrocybe martinicensis" .. .. 2·50 2·50

1989. Butterflies. As T **350** of Grenada. Mult.

1172 25 c. "Battus polydamas" (inscr "Papilio androgeus") 20 20
1173 35 c. "Phoebis sennae" .. 25 25
1174 45 c. "Hamadryas feronia" 35 35
1175 50 c. "Cynthia cardui" .. 35 35
1176 75 c. "Ascia monuste" .. 55 55
1177 90 c. "Eurema lisa" .. 65 65
1178 $2 "Aphrissa statira" .. 1·40 1·40
1179 $3 "Hypolimnas misippus" .. .. .. 1·90 1·90

96 Ethel Barrymore

1989. 425th Birth Anniv of Shakespeare. Shakespearean Actors. Multicoloured.

1181 15 c. Type **96** 15 10
1182 $1.10 Richard Burton .. 75 75
1183 $2 John Barrymore .. 1·40 1·40
1184 $3 Paul Robeson .. 1·90 1·90

97 Buddy Holly

1989. Musicians. Multicoloured.

1186 10 c. Type **97** 25 15
1187 25 c. Jimmy Hendrix .. 35 30
1188 75 c. Mighty Sparrow .. 55 55
1189 $4 Katsutoji Kineya .. 2·50 2·75

1989. 500th Anniv (1992) of Discovery of America by Columbus (2nd issue). Pre-Columbian Arawak Society. As T **247** of Antigua. Multicoloured.

1191 15 c. Arawaks canoeing .. 15 15
1192 75 c. Family and campfire 55 55
1193 90 c. Using stone tools .. 70 70
1194 $3 Eating and drinking .. 2·00 2·50

1989. "World Stamp Expo '89" International Stamp Exhibition, Washington. Designs showing Walt Disney cartoon characters illustrating proverbs from "Poor Richard's Almanack". As T **352** of Grenada. Mult.

1196 1 c. Uncle Scrooge McDuck with gold coins in sinking boat .. 10 10
1197 2 c. Robin Hood shooting apple off Friar Tuck .. 10 10
1198 3 c. Winnie the Pooh with honey 10 10
1199 4 c. Goofy, Minnie Mouse and Donald Duck exercising 10 10
1200 5 c. Pinnochio holding Jimminy Cricket .. 10 10
1201 6 c. Huey and Dewey putting up wallpaper .. 10 10
1202 8 c. Mickey Mouse asleep in storm 10 10
1203 10 c. Mickey Mouse as Benjamin Franklin selling "Pennsylvania Gazette" 10 10
1204 $5 Mickey Mouse with chicken, recipe book and egg .. .. 2·75 3·00
1205 $6 Mickey Mouse missing carriage .. .. 3·00 3·25

1990. Christmas. Paintings by Rubens. As T **259** of Antigua. Multicoloured.

1207 10 c. "The Annunciation" 10 10
1208 15 c. "The Flight of the Holy Family into Egypt" 10 10
1209 25 c. "The Presentation in the Temple" .. 15 15
1210 45 c. "The Holy Family under the Apple Tree" 20 25
1211 $2 "Madonna and Child with Saints" .. 95 1·00
1212 $4 "The Virgin and Child enthroned with Saints" 2·00 2·25
1213 $5 "The Holy Family" .. 2·40 2·50

1990. "EXPO '90" International Garden and Greenery Exhibition, Osaka. Caribbean Orchids. As T **354** of Grenada. Multicoloured.

1215 15 c. "Brassocattleya" Thalie 15 10
1216 20 c. "Odontocidium" Tigersun 15 15
1217 50 c. "Odontioda" Hambuhren 25 30
1218 75 c. "Paphiopedilum" Delrosi 35 40
1219 $1 "Vuylstekeara" Yokara 50 55
1220 $2 "Paphiopedilum" Geelong .. .. .. 95 1·00
1221 $3 "Wilsonara" Tigerwood .. .. .. 1·40 1·50
1222 $4 "Cymbidium" Ormoulu 2·00 2·00

1990. 500th Anniv (1992) of Discovery of America by Columbus (3rd issue). New World Natural History—Insects. As T **260** of Antigua. Multicoloured.

1224 35 c. "Dynastes hercules" (beetle) 15 20
1225 40 c. "Chalcolepidius porcatus" (beetle) .. 20 25
1226 50 c. "Acrocinus longimanus" (beetle) .. 25 30
1227 60 c. "Battus polydamas" (butterfly) .. 30 35
1228 $1 "Orthemis ferruginea" (skimmer) 50 55
1229 $2 "Psiloptera variolosa" (beetle) .. .. 95 1·00
1230 $3 "Hypolimas misippus" (butterfly) .. .. 1·40 1·50
1231 $4 Scarab beetle .. .. 2·00 2·10

1990. Wildlife. As T **254** of Antigua. Mult.

1233 5 c. West Indies giant rice rat 10 10
1234 25 c. Agouti 10 15
1235 30 c. Humpback whale .. 15 20
1236 40 c. Pilot whale .. 20 25
1237 $1 Spotted dolphin .. 50 55
1238 $2 Egyptian mongoose .. 95 1·00
1239 $3 Brazilian tree porcupine .. .. .. 1·40 1·50
1240 $4 American manatee .. 2·00 2·10

1990. 50th Anniv of Second World War. As T **274** of Antigua. Multicoloured.

1242 6 c. British tanks in France, 1939 .. .. 10 10
1243 10 c. Operation "Crusader", North Africa, 1941 10 10
1244 20 c. Retreat of the Afrika Corps, 1942 .. .. 10 10
1245 45 c. American landing on Aleutian Islands, 1943 20 25
1246 50 c. U.S. marines landing on Tarawa, 1943 .. 25 30
1247 60 c. U.S. army entering Rome, 1944 .. .. 30 35
1248 75 c. U.S. tanks crossing River Seine, 1944 .. 35 40
1249 $1 Battle of the Bulge, 1944 .. .. .. 50 55
1250 $5 American infantry in Italy, 1945 .. .. 2·40 2·50
1251 $6 "Enola Gay" dropping atomic bomb on Hiroshima, 1945 .. 3·00 3·25

1990. "Stamp World London 90" International Stamp Exhibition. As T **193** of Gambia showing Walt Disney cartoon characters at Shakespeare sites. Mult.

1253 15 c. Daisy Duck at Ann Hathaway's Cottage (horiz) 10 10
1254 30 c. Minnie and Bill Mouse at Shakespeare's birthplace, Stratford .. 15 20
1255 50 c. Minnie Mouse in front of Mary Arden's house, Wilmcote .. 25 30
1256 60 c. Mickey Mouse leaning on hedge in New Place gardens, Stratford (horiz) 30 35
1257 $1 Mickey Mouse walking in New Place gardens, Stratford (horiz) .. 50 55
1258 $2 Mickey Mouse carrying books in Scholars Lane, Stratford .. .. 95 1·00
1259 $4 Mickey Mouse and Royal Shakespeare Theatre, Stratford .. 2·00 2·10
1260 $5 Ludwig von Drake teaching Mickey Mouse at the Stratford Grammar School (horiz) 2·40 2·50

1990. 90th Birthday of Queen Elizabeth the Queen Mother. As T **194** of Gambia, showing photographs 1970–79.

1262 $2 Queen Mother wearing pink hat and coat .. 95 1·00
1263 $2 Prince Charles and Queen Mother at Garter ceremony .. .. 95 1·00
1264 $2 Queen Mother in blue floral outfit .. .. 95 1·00

1990. Birds. As T **358** of Grenada, but vert. Multicoloured.

1267 25 c. Yellow-bellied seed-eater 10 15
1268 45 c. Carib grackle .. 20 25
1269 50 c. Black-whiskered vireo 25 30
1270 75 c. Bananaquit .. 35 40
1271 $1 White-collared swift .. 50 55
1272 $2 Yellow-bellied elaenia 95 1·00
1273 $3 Blue-hooded euphonia 1·40 1·50
1274 $5 Eared dove .. .. 2·40 2·50

1990. Crustaceans. As T **359** of Grenada. Mult.

1276 10 c. Slipper lobster .. 10 10
1277 25 c. Green reef crab .. 10 15
1278 65 c. Caribbean lobsterette 30 35
1279 75 c. Blind deep sea lobster 35 40
1280 $1 Flattened crab .. 50 55
1281 $2 Ridged slipper lobster 95 1·00
1282 $3 Land crab .. .. 1·40 1·50
1283 $4 Mountain crab .. 2·00 2·10

98 Lineker, England

1990. World Cup Football Championship, Italy (2nd issue). Multicoloured.

1285 15 c. Type **98** 10 10
1286 45 c. Burruchaga, Argentina 20 25
1287 $2 Hysen, Sweden .. 95 1·00
1288 $4 Sang Ho, South Korea 2·00 2·10

1990. Olympic Games, Barcelona (1992). As T **268** of Antigua. Multicoloured.

1290 10 c. Boxing 10 10
1291 25 c. Olympic flame .. 10 15
1292 50 c. Football 25 30
1293 75 c. Discus throwing .. 35 40
1294 $1 Pole vaulting .. 50 55
1295 $2 Show jumping .. 95 1·00
1296 $4 Women's basketball .. 2·00 2·10
1297 $5 Men's gymnastics .. 2·40 2·50

1991. 350th Death Anniv of Rubens. As T **273** of Antigua. Multicoloured.

1299 5 c. "Adam and Eve" (Eve detail) (vert) .. 10 10
1300 15 c. "Esther before Ahasuerus" (detail) .. 10 10
1301 25 c. "Adam and Eve" (Adam detail) (vert) .. 15 10
1302 50 c. "Expulsion from Eden" 30 30
1303 $1 "Cain slaying Abel" (detail) (vert) 60 60
1304 $2 "Lot's Flight" .. 1·25 1·25
1305 $4 "Samson and Delilah" (detail) .. .. 2·25 2·25
1306 $5 "Abraham and Melchizedek" .. .. 2·50 2·50

1991. Coral Reef Fishes. As T **357** of Grenada. Multicoloured.

1308 15 c. Barred hamlet .. 10 10
1309 35 c. Squirrelfish .. 15 20
1310 45 c. Redspotted hawkfish 20 25
1311 75 c. Bigeye 35 40
1312 $1 Spiny puffer 50 55
1313 $2 Smallmouth Grunt .. 95 1·00
1314 £3 Harlequin bass .. 1·40 1·50
1315 $4 Creole fish .. .. 2·00 2·10

99 Angel with Star and Lantern

1991. Christmas (1990). Hummel Figurines. Multicoloured.

1317 10 c. Type **99** 10 10
1318 15 c. Christ Child and Angel playing mandolin 10 10
1319 25 c. Shepherd 10 15
1320 50 c. Angel with trumpet and lantern 25 30
1321 $1 Nativity scene .. 50 55
1322 $2 Christ Child and Angel holding candle .. 95 1·00
1323 $4 Angel with baskets .. 2·00 2·10
1324 $5 Angels singing .. 2·40 2·50

100 "Brassia maculata"

1991. Orchids. Multicoloured.

1326 5 c. Type **100** 10 10
1327 10 c. "Oncidium lanceanum" 10 10
1328 15 c. "Broughtonia sanguinea" 10 10
1329 25 c. "Diacrium bicornutum" 10 15
1330 35 c. "Cattleya labiata" 15 20
1331 45 c. "Epidendrum fragrans" 20 25
1332 50 c. "Oncidium papilio" 25 30
1333 75 c. "Neocogniauxia monophylla" .. 35 40
1334 $1 "Epidendrum polybulbon" 50 55
1335 $2 "Spiranthes speciosa" 95 1·00
1336 $4 "Epidendrum ciliare" 2·00 2·10
1337 $5 "Phais tankervilliae" 2·40 2·50
1338 $10 "Brassia caudata" .. 5·00 5·25
1339 $20 "Brassavola cordata" 9·50 10·00

1991. Butterflies. As T **363** of Grenada. Mult.

1340 5 c. Crimson-patched longwing 10 10
1341 10 c. "Morpho helena" .. 10 10
1342 15 c. "Morpho sulkowskyi" 10 10
1343 20 c. "Dynastor napoleon" 10 10
1344 25 c. "Pieridae callinira" 10 10
1345 30 c. "Anartia amathea" 15 20
1346 35 c. "Heliconiidae dido" 15 20
1347 45 c. "Papilionidae columbus" 20 25
1348 50 c. "Nymphalidae praeneste" 25 30
1349 60 c. "Panacea prola" .. 30 35
1350 75 c. "Dryas julia" .. 35 40
1351 $1 "Papilionidae orthosilaus" 50 55
1352 $2 "Pyrrhopyge cometes" 95 1·00
1353 $3 "Papilionidae paeon" 1·40 1·50
1354 $4 "Morpho cypris" .. 2·00 2·10
1355 $5 Choringa .. .. 2·40 2·50

101 Donald and Daisy Duck with Solar-powered Car

1991. Ecology Conservation. Walt Disney cartoon characters. Multicoloured.

1357 10 c. Type **101** 10 10
1358 15 c. Goofy saving water 10 10
1359 25 c. Donald and Daisy on nature hike 10 10
1360 45 c. Donald Duck returning chick to nest 20 25
1361 $1 Donald Duck and balloons 50 55
1362 $2 Minnie Mouse and Daisy Duck on hot day 95 1·00
1363 $4 Mickey's nephews cleaning beach .. 2·00 2·10
1364 $5 Donald Duck on pedal generator .. .. 2·40 2·50

1991. 500th Anniv (1992) of Discovery of America by Columbus (4th issue). History of Exploration. As T **277** of Antigua. Mult.

1366 15 c. Magellan's "Vitoria" rounding Cape Horn, 1519–21 .. .. 10 10
1367 20 c. Drake's Golden Hind, 1577–80 .. .. 10 10
1368 50 c. Cook's H.M.S. "Resolution", 1768–71 25 30
1369 60 c. Douglas World Cruiser seaplane, 1924 30 35
1370 $1 "Sputnik 1" satellite, 1957 .. .. 50 55
1371 $2 Gagarin's space flight, 1961 .. .. 95 1·00
1372 $4 Glenn's space flight, 1962 .. .. 2·00 2·10
1373 $5 Space shuttle, 1981 .. 2·40 2·50

1991. "Phila Nippon '91" International Stamp Exhibition, Tokyo. As T **279** of Antigua but horiz, showing Walt Disney cartoon characters in Japanese scenes. Multicoloured.

1375 15 c. Minnie Mouse with silkworms 10 10
1376 30 c. Mickey, Minnie, Morty and Ferdie at Torii Gate 15 20
1377 50 c. Donald Duck and Mickey Mouse trying origami 25 30
1378 60 c. Mickey and Minnie diving for pearls .. 30 35
1379 $1 Minnie Mouse in kimono 50 55
1380 $2 Mickey making masks 95 1·00
1381 $4 Donald and Mickey making paper .. .. 2·00 2·10
1382 $5 Minnie and Pluto making pottery .. 2·40 2·50

1991. Fungi. As T **364** of Grenada. Mult.

1384 5 c. "Pyrrhoglossum pyrrhum" 10 10
1385 45 c. "Agaricus purpurellus" 20 25
1386 50 c. "Amanita craseoderma" 25 30
1387 90 c. "Hygrocybe acutoconica" 45 50
1388 $1 "Limacella guttata" .. 50 55
1389 $2 "Lactarius hygrophoroides" .. .. 95 1·00
1390 $4 "Boletellus cubensis" 2·00 2·10
1391 $5 "Psilocybe caerulescens" .. .. 2·40 2·50

1991. 65th Birthday of Queen Elizabeth II. As T **280** of Antigua. Multicoloured.

1393 20 c. Queen, Prince Philip, Prince Charles and Prince William at Trooping the Colour, 1990 .. .. 10 10
1394 25 c. Queen and Prince Charles at polo match, 1985 .. .. .. 10 10
1395 $2 Queen and Prince Philip at Maundy service, 1989 .. .. 95 1·00
1396 $4 Queen with Queen Mother on her 87th birthday, 1987 .. 2·00 2·10

1991. 10th Wedding Anniv of Prince and Princess of Wales. As T **280** of Antigua. Multicoloured.

1398 5 c. Prince and Princess of Wales kissing, 1987 .. 10 10
1399 60 c. Portraits of Prince, Princess and sons .. 30 35
1400 $1 Prince Henry in 1988 and Prince William in 1987 .. .. .. 50 55
1401 $5 Princess Diana in 1990 and Prince Charles in 1988 .. .. .. 2·40 2·50

1991. Death Centenary (1990) of Vincent van Gogh (artist). As T **278** of Antigua. Mult.

1403 5 c. "Two Thistles" .. 10 10
1404 10 c. "Baby Marcelle Roulin" 10 10
1405 15 c. "Still Life: Basket with Six Oranges" (horiz) 10 10
1406 25 c. "Orchard in Blossom" 10 10
1407 45 c. "Armand Roulin" .. 20 25
1408 50 c. "Wood Gatherers in Snow" (detail) (horiz) 25 30
1409 60 c. "Almond Tree in Blossom" 30 35
1410 $1 "An Old Man" .. 50 55
1411 $2 "The Seine Bridge at Asnieres" (horiz) .. 95 1·00
1412 $3 "Vase with Lilacs, Daises and Anemones" 1·40 1·50
1413 $4 "Self Portrait" .. 2·00 2·10
1414 $5 "Patience Escalier" .. 2·40 2·50

102 Sargassum Triggerfish

1991. Reef Fishes. Multicoloured.

1416 50 c. Type **102** 25 30
1417 50 c. Tobaccofish .. 25 30
1418 50 c. Longsnout butterflyfish 25 30
1419 50 c. Cherubfish 25 30
1420 50 c. Black jack 25 30
1421 50 c. Masked goby and black jack 25 30
1422 50 c. Spotfin hogfish .. 25 30
1423 50 c. Fairy basslet .. 25 30
1424 50 c. Orangeback bass .. 25 30
1425 50 c. Candy basslet .. 25 30
1426 50 c. Blackcap basslet .. 25 30
1427 50 c. Longspine squirrelfish 25 30
1428 50 c. Jack-knife fish .. 25 30
1429 50 c. Bigeye 25 30
1430 50 c. Short bigeye .. 25 30

Nos. 1416/30 were printed together, se-tenant, forming a composite design.

1991. Christmas. Religious Paintings by Martin Schongauer. As T **287** of Antigua.

1432 10 c. black and brown .. 10 10
1433 35 c. multicoloured .. 15 20
1434 50 c. multicoloured .. 25 30
1435 75 c. multicoloured .. 35 40
1436 $1 multicoloured .. 50 55
1437 $2 multicoloured .. 95 1·00
1438 $4 black and brown .. 2·00 2·10
1439 $5 black, grey and red .. 2·40 2·50

DESIGNS: 10 c. "Angel of the Annunciation"; 35 c. "Madonna of the Rose Hedge" (detail); 50 c. "Madonna of the Rose Hedge" (different detail); 75 c. "Nativity" (detail); $1 "Adoration of the Shepherds" (detail); $2 "The Nativity"; $4 "Nativity" (different); $5 "Symbol of St. Matthew".

1992. Great Railways of the World. As T **367** of Grenada. Multicoloured.

1441 75 c. Class "Medoc", 1857 (Switzerland) 35 40
1442 75 c. Sterling type, 1870 (Great Britain) .. 35 40
1443 75 c. Locomotive No. 90, 1877 (France) 35 40
1444 75 c. Standard type, 1880 (U.S.A.) 35 40
1445 75 c. "Vittorio Emanuel II", 1884 (Italy) .. 35 40
1446 75 c. Johnson "Single" type, 1887 (Great Britain) 35 40
1447 75 c. Locomotive No. 999, 1893 (U.S.A.) 35 40
1448 75 c. Class "Q1", 1896 (Great Britain) .. 35 40
1449 75 c. "Claud Hamilton", 1900 (Great Britain) .. 35 40
1450 $1 Class "P8", 1906 (Germany) 50 55
1451 $1 Class "P", 1910 (Denmark) 50 55
1452 $1 Class "Ps", 1926 (U.S.A.) 50 55
1453 $1 "Kestrel", 1932 (Ireland) 50 55
1454 $1 Class "GS", 1937 (U.S.A.) 50 55
1455 $1 Class "12", 1938 (Belgium) 50 55
1456 $1 Class "J4-84", 1941 (U.S.A.) 50 55
1457 $1 PA Series "AIA-AIA", 1946 (U.S.A.) 50 55
1458 $1 Class "4E", 1954 (South Africa) 50 55
1459 $2 Trans Europe Express train, 1957 .. .. 95 1·00
1460 $2 FL9 "B.-AIA", 1960 (U.S.A.) .. .. 95 1·00
1461 $2 Shin-kansen train, 1964 (Japan) .. .. 95 1·00
1462 $2 Class "103.1", 1970 (Germany) .. .. 95 1·00
1463 $2 RTG Trainset, 1972 (France) .. .. 95 1·00
1464 $2 ETR "401" Pendolino train, 1976 (Italy) .. 95 1·00
1465 $2 Class "APT-P 370", 1981 (Great Britain) .. 95 1·00
1466 $2 LRC "B.-B", 1982 (Canada) .. .. 95 1·00
1467 $2 MAV BZMOT "601 1B1", 1983 (Hungary) 95 1·00

1992. 40th Anniv of Queen Elizabeth II's Accession. As T **288** of Antigua. Mult.

1469 60 c. Swimming jetty on beach 30 35
1470 75 c. View of Grenadines 35 40
1471 $2 Surf on beach .. 95 1·00
1472 $4 Secluded bay .. 2·00 2·10

1992. Olympic Games, Barcelona. As T **268** of Antigua. Multicoloured.

1474 10 c. Women's backstroke swimming 10 10
1475 15 c. Women's handball 10 10
1476 25 c. Men's 4 × 100 m relay 10 10
1477 35 c. Men's hammer throw 15 20
1478 50 c. Men's 110 m hurdles 25 30
1479 75 c. Men's pole vault .. 35 40
1480 $1 Men's volleyball .. 50 55
1481 $2 Men's weightlifting .. 95 1·00
1482 $5 Men's gymnastics .. 2·40 2·50
1483 $6 Football .. .. 3·00 3·25

1992. "Granada '92" International Stamp Exhibition, Spain. Spanish Paintings. As T **292** of Antigua. Multicoloured.

1485 10 c. "The Surrender of Seville" (Zurbaran) .. 10 10
1486 35 c. "The Liberation of St. Peter by an Angel" (Antonio de Pereda) .. 15 20
1487 50 c. "Joseph Explains the Dreams of the Pharaoh" (Antonio del Castillo Saavedra) (horiz) 25 30
1488 75 c. "The Flower Vase" (Juan de Arellano) .. 35 40
1489 $1 "The Duke of Pastrana" (Juan Carreno de Miranda) .. 50 55
1490 $2 "The Annunciation" (detail) (Francisco Rizi) 95 1·00
1491 $4 "The Annunciation" (different detail) (Rizi) 2·00 2·10
1492 $5 "Old Women Seated" (attr Antonio Puga) .. 2·40 2·50

103 Don Isaac Abarbanel, Minister of Finance

1992. 500th Anniv of Discovery of America by Columbus (5th issue). World Columbian Stamp "Expo '92", Chicago. Multicoloured.

1494 10 c. Type **103** 10 10
1495 25 c. Columbus on voyage 10 10
1496 35 c. Look out sighting land 15 20

1497 50 c. King Ferdinand and Queen Isabella of Spain .. 25 30
1498 60 c. Columbus showing map to Queen Isabella .. 30 35
1499 $5 "Santa Maria" and bird .. .. .. 2·40 2·50

1992. "Genova '92" International Thematic Stamp Exhibition. Hummingbirds. As T **295** of Antigua, but vertical. Multicoloured.
1501 5 c. Male blue-headed hummingbird 10 10
1502 10 c. Female rufous-breasted hermit .. 10 10
1503 20 c. Female blue-headed hummingbird 10 10
1504 45 c. Male green-throated carib 20 25
1505 90 c. Male Antillean crested hummingbird .. 45 50
1506 $2 Male purple-throated carib .. .. .. 95 1·00
1507 $4 Female purple-throated carib .. 2·00 2·10
1508 $5 Female Antillean crested hummingbird .. 2·40 2·50

1992. 50th Anniv of United Service Organization (forces' entertainment programme). As T **371** of Grenada. Mult.
1510 10 c. James Cagney .. 10 10
1511 15 c. Anne Sheridan .. 10 10
1512 35 c. Jerry Colonna .. 15 20
1513 50 c. Spike Jones .. 25 30
1514 75 c. Edgar Bergen .. 35 40
1515 $1 The Andrews Sisters .. 50 55
1516 $2 Dinah Shore .. .. 95 1·00
1517 $5 Bing Crosby .. .. 2·40 2·50
No. 1515 is incorrectly inscribed "THE ANDREW SISTERS".

1992. 500th Anniv of Discovery of America by Columbus (6th issue). Organization of East Caribbean States. As Nos. 1670/1 of Antigua.
1519 $1 Columbus meeting Amerindians 50 55
1520 $2 Ships approaching island .. .. .. 95 1·00

1992. Toy Trains from American Manufacturers. As T **257** of Dominica. Mult.
1521 10 c. No. 2220 switcher locomotive, Voltamp (1910) 10 10
1522 25 c. Clockwork locomotive of Bridge Port Line, American Miniature Railroad (1907) .. 10 10
1523 50 c. First electric toy locomotive, Ives (1910) 25 30
1524 75 c. "J.C. Penney Special" locomotive, American Flyer (1920s) 35 40
1525 $1 Clockwork cast-metal locomotive, Hafner (1916) 50 55
1526 $2 Pull toy copper-plated locomotive, probably Hubley (1900) .. .. 95 1·00
1527 $4 "Mayflower" locomotive, American Flyer (1928) .. .. .. 2·00 2·10
1528 $5 "Olympian" locomotive, Ives (1929) .. 2·40 2·50

1992. Christmas. Religious Paintings. As T **300** of Antigua. "The Annunciation" by various artists. Multicoloured.
1531 5 c. Robert Campin .. 10 10
1532 15 c. Melchior Broederlam 10 10
1533 25 c. Fra Filippo Lippi (two-panel diptych) .. 10 10
1534 35 c. Simone Martini .. 15 20
1535 50 c. Lippi (detail from left panel) 25 30
1536 75 c. Lippi (detail from right panel) 35 40
1537 90 c. Albert Bouts .. 45 50
1538 $1 D. Di Michelino .. 50 55
1539 $2 Rogier van der Weyden .. .. 95 1·00
1540 $3 Sandro Botticelli (detail of angel) .. 1·40 1·50
1541 $4 Botticelli (detail of Virgin Mary) .. 2·00 2·10
1542 $5 Bernardo Daddi (horiz) 2·40 2·50

1992. Gold Record Award Winners. As T **374** of Grenada. Multicoloured.
1544 90 c. Leonard Bernstein 45 50
1545 90 c. Ray Charles .. 45 50
1546 90 c. Bob Dylan 45 50
1547 90 c. Barbara Streisand .. 45 50
1548 90 c. Frank Sinatra .. 45 50
1549 90 c. Harry Belafonte .. 45 50
1550 90 c. Aretha Franklin .. 45 50
1551 90 c. Garth Brooks .. 45 50
Nos. 1544/51 were printed together, se-tenant, with a composite background design.

1992. 60th Anniv of Goofy (Disney cartoon character). Scenes from various cartoon films. As T **258** of Dominica. Multicoloured.
1553 5 c. "Father's Day Off", 1953 .. .. .. 10 10
1554 10 c. "Cold War", 1951 .. 10 10
1555 15 c. "Home Made Home", 1951 .. .. 10 10
1556 25 c. "Get Rich Quick", 1951 .. .. .. 10 10
1557 50 c. "Man's Best Friend", 1952 .. .. 25 30
1558 75 c. "Aquamania", 1961 35 40
1559 90 c. "Tomorrow We Diet", 1951 .. .. 45 50
1560 $1 "Teachers Are People", 1952 .. .. .. 50 55
1561 $2 "The Goofy Success Story", 1955 .. .. 95 1·00
1562 $3 "Double Dribble," 1946 1·40 1·50
1563 $4 "Hello Aloha", 1952 2·00 2·10
1564 $5 "Father's Lion", 1952 2·40 2·50

1992. Anniversaries and Events. As T **375** of Grenada. Multicoloured, except No. 1571.
1566 25 c. Zeppelin "Viktoria Luise" over Kiel Harbour (horiz) .. 10 10
1567 50 c. Space shuttle "Columbia" landing (horiz) 25 30
1568 75 c. German Federal Republic flag and arms (horiz) 35 40
1569 $1.50 Giant anteater (horiz) 75 80
1570 $2 Scarlet macaw .. 95 1·00
1571 $2 W.H.O. emblem (black and blue) (horiz) .. 95 1·00
1572 $3 Wolfgang Amadeus Mozart .. .. 1·40 1·50
1573 $4 The Berlin airlift (horiz) .. .. 2·00 2·10
1574 $4 Repairing "Intelsat VI" satellite in space (horiz) .. .. 2·00 2·10
1575 $5 Zeppelin "Hindenburg" on fire (horiz) 2·40 2·50
1576 $5 Admiral Richard Byrd's aircraft (horiz) 2·40 2·50
ANNIVERSARIES AND EVENTS: Nos. 1566, 1575, 75th death anniv of Count Ferdinand von Zeppelin; Nos. 1567, 1574, International Space Year; Nos. 1568, 1573, 25th death anniv of Konrad Adenauer (German statesman); Nos. 1569/70, Earth Summit '92, Rio; No. 1571, United Nations World Health Organization Projects; No. 1572, Death bicentenary of Mozart; No. 1576, 75th anniv of International Association of Lions Clubs.

104 "Atalanta" and "Mischief" (yachts), 1881

1992. History of The Americas Cup Challenge Trophy. Multicoloured.
1578 15 c. Type **104** 10 10
1579 25 c. "Valkyrie III" and "Defender", 1895 .. 10 10
1580 35 c. "Shamrock IV" and "Resolute", 1920 .. 25 30
1581 75 c. "Endeavour II" and "Ranger", 1937 .. 35 40
1582 $1 "Sceptre and "Columbia", 1958 .. 50 55
1583 $2 "Australia II" and "Liberty", 1983 .. 95 1·00
1584 $4 "Stars & Stripes" and "Kookaburra III", 1987 2·00 2·10
1585 $5 "New Zealand" and "Stars & Stripes", 1988 2·40 2·50

1993. Dogs of the World. As T **377** of Grenada, but vertical. Multicoloured.
1587 35 c. Irish setter and Glendalough, Ireland .. 15 20
1588 50 c. Boston terrier and Boston State House, U.S.A. 25 30
1589 75 c. Beagle and Temple to Athena, Greece .. 35 40
1590 $1 Weimaraner and Nesselwang, Germany 50 55
1591 $3 Norwegian elkhound and Urnes Stave Church, Norway .. 1·40 1·50
1592 $4 Mastiff and Sphinx, Egypt .. .. .. 2·00 2·10
1593 $5 Akita and Torii Temple, Kyoto, Japan 2·40 2·50
1594 $5 Saluki and Rub'al Khali, Saudi Arabia 2·40 2·50

1993. Bicentenary of the Louvre, Paris. As T **305** of Antigua. Multicoloured (except No. 1599).
1596 $1 "Madonna and Child with the young John the Baptist" (Botticelli) 50 55
1597 $1 "The Buffet" (Chardin) 50 55
1598 $1 "Return from Market" (Chardin) 50 55
1599 $1 "Erasmus" (Durer) (black and grey) .. 50 55
1600 $1 "Self-portrait with Eryngium" (Durer) .. 50 55
1601 $1 "Jeanne of Aragon" (Raphael) 50 55
1602 $1 "La Belle Jardiniere" (detail) (Raphael) .. 50 55
1603 $1 "La Belle Jardiniere" (different detail) (Raphael) 50 55

105 "Battus polydamus"

1993. Butterflies. Multicoloured.
1605 15 c. Type **105** 10 10
1606 35 c. "Astraptes talus" .. 15 20
1607 45 c. "Pseudolycaena marsyas" 20 25
1608 75 c. "Siproeta stelenes" 35 40
1609 $1 "Phoebis sennae" .. 50 55
1610 $2 "Dione juno" .. 95 1·00
1611 $4 "Chlorostrymon simaethis" .. .. 2·00 2·10
1612 $5 "Urbanus proteus" .. 2·40 2·50

1993. Flowers. As T **380** of Grenada. Mult.
1614 35 c. Hibiscus 15 20
1615 35 c. Columbine 15 20
1616 45 c. Red ginger 20 25
1617 75 c. Bougainvillea .. 35 40
1618 $1 Crown imperial .. 50 55
1619 $2 Fairy orchid .. 95 1·00
1620 $4 Heliconia .. .. 2·00 2·10
1621 $5 Tulip .. .. 2·40 2·50

1993. 40th Anniv of Coronation. As T **307** of Antigua.
1623 35 c. multicoloured .. 15 20
1624 50 c. multicoloured .. 25 30
1625 $2 green and black .. 95 1·00
1626 $4 multicoloured .. 2·00 2·10
DESIGNS—38×47 mm: 35 c. Queen Elizabeth II at Coronation (photograph by Cecil Beaton); 50 c. Ampulla and spoon; $2 Queen Elizabeth II leaving for Coronation; $4 Prince Henry's christening.

1993. Anniversaries and Events. As T **381** of Grenada. Multicoloured.
1628 15 c. "Painter and Model" (Picasso) (horiz) .. 10 10
1629 35 c. Keith Tkachuk and Dmitri Mironov (ice hockey, 1992) (horiz) .. 15 20
1630 50 c. Early telescope .. 25 30
1631 75 c. "Gra w Gudziki" (Ludomir Slerdinski) (horiz) 35 40
1632 75 c. Willy Brandt and Lyndon Johnson, 1961 (horiz) 35 40
1633 $1 "Artist and his Model" (Picasso) (horiz) .. 50 55
1634 $2 "Pocalunek Mongolskiego Ksiecia" (S. Wirkiewicz) (horiz) 95 1·00
1635 $4 "The Drawing Lesson" (Picasso) (horiz) .. 2·00 2·10
1636 $4 Radio telescope .. 2·00 2·10
1637 $5 Alberto Tomba (Giant Slalom, 1984) (horiz) 2·40 2·50
1638 $5 Willy Brandt and Eleanor Hulles, 1957 (horiz) .. .. 2·40 2·50
ANNIVERSARIES AND EVENTS: Nos. 1628, 1633, 1635, 20th death anniv of Picasso (artist); Nos. 1629, 1637, Winter Olympic Games '94, Lillehammer; Nos. 1630, 1636, 450th death anniv of Copernicus (astronomer); Nos. 1631, 1634, "Polska '93" International Stamp Exhibition, Poznan; Nos. 1632, 1638, 80th birth anniv of Willy Brandt (German politician).

1993. Songbirds. As T **382** of Grenada. Multicoloured.
1640 15 c. Painted bunting .. 10 10
1641 15 c. White-throated sparrow 10 10
1642 25 c. Common grackle .. 10 10
1643 25 c. Amazonian royal flycatcher 10 10
1644 35 c. Swallow tanager .. 15 20
1645 35 c. Vermilion flycatcher 15 20
1646 45 c. Black-headed bunting 20 25
1647 50 c. Rose-breasted grosbeak 25 30
1648 75 c. Corn bunting .. 35 40
1649 75 c. Rose-breasted thrush tanager 35 40
1650 $1 Buff-throated saltator 50 55
1651 $4 Plush-capped finch .. 2·00 2·10
Nos. 1640/51 were printed together, se-tenant, with the backgrounds forming a composite design.
Nos. 1645/6 show the scientific inscriptions transposed between the designs.

1993. Shells. As T **383** of Grenada. Mult.
1653 15 c. Hawkwing conch .. 10 10
1654 15 c. Music volute .. 10 10
1655 25 c. Globe vase and deltoid rock shell .. 10 10
1656 35 c. Spiny vase 15 20
1657 35 c. Common sundial and common purple snail .. 15 20
1658 45 c. Caribbean donax and gaudy asaphis .. 20 25
1659 45 c. Mouse cone .. 20 25
1660 50 c. Gold-mouthed triton 25 30
1661 75 c. Tulip mussel and trigonal tivela .. 35 40
1662 75 c. Common dove shell and chestnut latirus .. 35 40
1663 $1 Wide-mouthed purpura 50 55
1664 $4 Atlantic thorny oyster and Atlantic wing oyster .. .. .. 2·00 2·10
Nos. 1653/64 were printed together, se-tenant, with the backgrounds forming a composite design.

1993 Asian International Stamp Exhibitions. As T **268** of Dominica. Multicoloured. (a) "Indopex '93", Surabaya, Indonesia
1666 35 c. National Museum, Central Jakarta (horiz) 15 20
1667 45 c. Sacred wheel and deer (horiz) 20 25
1668 $1 Ramayana relief, Panataran Temple (horiz) 50 55
1669 $1.50 "Bullock Carts" (Batara Lubis) (horiz) 75 80
1670 $1.50 "Surat Irsa II" (A. D. Pirous) (horiz) .. 75 80
1671 $1.50 "Self-portrait with Goat" (Kartika) (horiz) 75 80
1672 $1.50 "The Cow-est Cow" (Ivan Sagito) (horiz) .. 75 80
1673 $1.50 "Rain Storm" (Sudjana Kerton) (horiz) 75 80
1674 $1.50 "Story of Pucuk Flower" (Effendi) (horiz) 75 80
1675 $5 Candi Tikus, Trawulan, East Java (horiz) .. 2·40 2·50

(b) "Taipei '93", Taiwan
1677 35 c. Macau Palace Casino, Hong Kong (horiz) 15 20
1678 45 c. Stone lion, Ming Tomb, Nanjing (horiz) 20 25
1679 $1 Stone camels, Ming Tomb, Nanjing (horiz) 50 55
1680 $1.50 Nesting quail incense burner (horiz) 75 80
1681 $1.50 Standing quail incense burner (horiz) 75 80
1682 $1.50 Seated qilin incense burner (horiz) .. 75 80
1683 $1.50 Pottery horse, Han period (horiz) .. 75 80
1684 $1.50 Seated caparisoned elephant (horiz) .. 75 80
1685 $1.50 Cow in imitation of Delft faience (horiz) .. 75 80
1686 $5 Stone lion and elephant, Ming Tomb, Nanjing (horiz) .. 2·40 2·50

(c) "Bangkok 1993", Thailand
1688 35 c. Three Naga snakes, Chiang Mai's Temple (horiz) 15 20
1689 45 c. Sri Mariamman Temple, Singapore (horiz) 20 25
1690 $1 Topiary, Hua Hin Resort (horiz) .. 50 55
1691 $1.50 "Buddha's Victory over Mara" (horiz) .. 75 80
1692 $1.50 "Mythological Elephant" (horiz) .. 75 80
1693 $1.50 "Battle with Mara" (Thon Buri) (horiz) .. 75 80

1694 $1.50 "Untitled" (Panya Wijinthanasarn) (horiz) 75 80
1695 $1.50 "Temple Mural" (horiz) 75 80
1696 $1.50 "Elephants in Pahcekha Buddha's Heaven" (horiz) .. 75 80
1697 $5 Pak Tai Temple, Cheung Chau Island (horiz) 75 80

1993. World Cup Football Championship, U.S.A. (1994). As T **310** of Antigua. Mult.
1699 15 c. McCall (Scotland) and Verri (Brazil) (horiz) 10 10
1700 25 c. Verri (Brazil) and Maradona (Argentina) (horiz) 10 10
1701 35 c. Schillaci (Italy) and Saldana (Uruguay) (horiz) 15 20
1702 45 c. Gullit (Holland) and Wright (England) (horiz) 20 25
1703 $1 Verri (Brazil) and Maradona (Argentina) (different) (horiz) .. 50 55
1704 $2 Zubizarreta and Fernandez (Spain) with Albert (Belgium) (horiz) 95 1·00
1705 $4 Hagi (Rumania) and McGrath (Ireland) (horiz) .. .. 2·00 2·10
1706 $5 Gorriz (Spain) and Scifo (Belgium) (horiz) 2·40 2·50

1993. 65th Anniv of Mickey Mouse. Scenes from Walt Disney cartoon films. As T **385** of Grenada.
1708 15 c. "Mickey's Rival", 1936 .. .. .. 10 10
1709 35 c. "The Worm Turns", 1937 .. .. .. 15 20
1710 50 c. "The Pointer", 1939 25 30
1711 75 c. "Society Dog Show", 1939 .. .. .. 35 40
1712 $1 "A Gentleman's Gentleman", 1941 .. 50 55
1713 $2 "The Little Whirlwind", 1941 .. 95 1·00
1714 $4 "Mickey Down Under", 1948 .. .. 2·00 2·10
1715 $5 "R'coon Dawg", 1951 2·40 2·50

OFFICIAL STAMPS

1982. Optd. **P.R.G.** (a) Nos. 400/12 and 414.
O 1. 5 c. Yellowtail Snapper .. 10 15
O 2. 6 c. Mutton Snapper .. 10 15
O 3. 10 c. Cocoa Damselfish .. 10 15
O 4. 12 c. Royal Gramma .. 10 15
O 5. 15 c. Cherubfish 10 15
O 6. 20 c. Blackbar Soldierfish 10 20
O 7. 25 c. Comb Grouper .. 10 20
O 8. 30 c. Longsnout Butterfly-fish 15 20
O 9. 40 c. Pudding Wife .. 15 25
O10. 50 c. Midnight Parrotfish 20 30
O11. 90 c. Redspotted Hawkfish 40 55
O12. $1 Hogfish 40 60
O13. $3 Beau Gregory.. .. 1·25 2·25
O14. $10 Barred Hamlet .. 4·25 6·00

(b) Nos. 444/6 and 448/9.
O 15. 30 c. Prince Charles and Lady Diana Spencer .. 2·00 2·00
O 16. 40 c. Prince Charles and Lady Diana Spencer .. 1·60 1·60
O 17. 40 c. Type **50** .. .. 2·00 2·75
O 18. $2 Type **50** .. .. 2·50 3·50
O 19. $4 Prince Charles as para-chutist .. .. .. 6·50 8·50

(c) Nos. 473/6.
O20. **54.** 20 c. multicoloured .. 10 20
O21. – 40 c. multicoloured .. 15 25
O22. – $1 multicoloured .. 35 70
O23. – $2 multicoloured .. 70 1·40

GRENADINES OF ST. VINCENT

Part of a group of islands south of St. Vincent which include Bequia, Mustique, Canouan and Union.

100 cents = 1 dollar.

1973. Royal Wedding. As T **47** of Anguilla. Multicoloured. Background colours given
1. 25 c. green 10 10
2. $1 brown 25 15

1974. Nos. 286/300 of St. Vincent optd. **GRENADINES OF.** Multicoloured.
3. 1 c. Green Heron 10 10
4. 2 c. Lesser Antillean bull-finches 15 15
25. 3 c. St. Vincent amazon .. 40 30
6. 4 c. Rufous-throated solitaire (vert.) 15 10
7. 5 c. Red-necked pigeon (vert.) 15 10
8. 6 c. Bananaquits 15 10
9. 8 c. Purple-throated carib.. 15 10
10. 10 c. Mangrove cuckoo (vert.) 15 10
11. 12 c. Common black hawk (vert.) 20 15
12. 20 c. Bare-eyed thrush .. 35 20
13. 25 c. Hooded tanager .. 40 20
14. 50 c. Blue hooded euphonia 70 40
15. $1 Barn owl (vert.).. .. 1·50 75
16. $2.50 Yellow-bellied elaenia (vert.) .. .. .. 2·00 1·25
17. $5 Ruddy quail dove .. 3·50 2·25

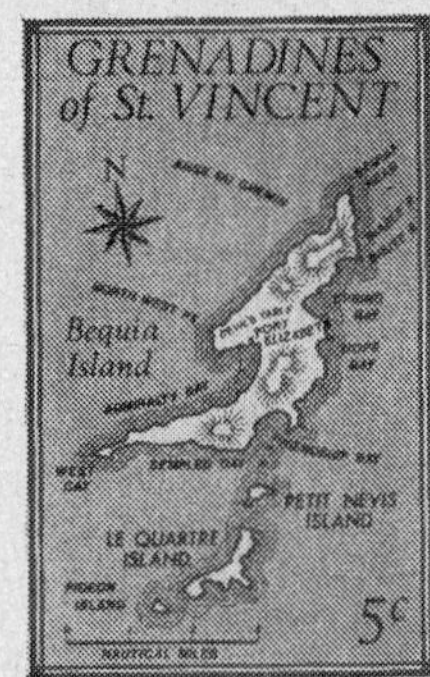

2. Map of Bequia.

1974. Maps (1st series).
18. **2.** 5 c. black, grn. & deep grn. 10 10
19. – 15 c. multicoloured .. 10 10
20. – 20 c. multicoloured .. 10 10
21. – 30 c. black, pink & red .. 10 10
22. – 40 c. blk., violet & purple 10 10
23. – $1 black, ultram. & blue 25 20

MAPS: 15 c. Prune Island. 20 c. Mayreau Island and Tobago Cays. 30 c. Mustique Island. 40 c. Union Island. $1, Canouan Island.
See also Nos. 85/8.

1974. Centenary of U.P.U. As Nos. 392/5 of St. Vincent.
26. 2 c. multicoloured 10 10
27. 15 c. multicoloured 10 10
28. 40 c. multicoloured 10 10
29. $1 multicoloured 25 15

4. Boat-building.

1974. Bequia Island (1st series). Multicoloured.
34. 5 c. Type **4** 15 15
31. 30 c. Careening at Port Elizabeth 10 15
32. 35 c. Admiralty Bay .. 10 15
33. $1 Fishing-boat race .. 20 25
See also Nos. 185/88.

5. Music Volute.

1974. Shells and molluscs. Multicoloured.
35. 1 c. Atlantic Thorny Oyster 10 10
36. 2 c. Zigzag Scallop 10 10
37. 3 c. Reticulated Helmet .. 10 10
38. 4 c. Type **5** 10 10
39. 5 c. Amber Pen Shell .. 10 10
40. 6 c. Angular Triton.. .. 10 10
41. 8 c. Flame Helmet 10 10
42. 10 c. Caribbean Olive .. 10 10
43. 12 c. Common Sundial .. 10 10
44. 15 c. Glory of the Atlantic Cone 25 20
45. 20 c. Flame Auger 30 35
46. 25 c. King Venus 50 20
47. 35 c. Long-spined Star-shell 35 25
48. 45 c. Speckled Tellin .. 35 30
49. 50 c. Rooster Tail Conch .. 40 25
50. $1 Green Star Shell.. .. 1·00 75
51. $2.50 Incomparable Cone .. 2·25 1·25
52. $5 Rough File Clam .. 4·00 2·75
52a. $10 Measled Cowrie .. 10·00 4·00
Nos. 38/42, 45, 47 and 49/50 come with and without an imprint below the design.

1974. Birth Centenary of Sir Winston Churchill. As Nos. 403/6 of St. Vincent, but inscr. "GRENADINES OF ST. VINCENT", and values (Nos. 53/5) and colours changed.
53. **75.** 5 c. multicoloured .. 10 10
54. – 40 c. multicoloured .. 10 10
55. – 50 c. multicoloured .. 15 10
56. – $1 multicoloured .. 25 20

6. Cotton House, Mustique.

1975. Mustique Island. Multicoloured.
57. 5 c. Type **6** 10 10
58. 35 c. "Blue Waters" Endeavour Bay.. .. 10 10
59. 45 c. Endeavour Bay .. 10 10
60. $1 "Les Jolies Eaux", Gelliceaux Bay 25 20

7. Danaus plexippus".

1975. Butterflies. Multicoloured.
61 3 c. Type **7** 20 10
62 5 c. "Agraulis vanillae" .. 25 10
63 35 c. "Battus polydamas" 80 10
64 45 c. "Evenus dindymus" and "Junonia evarete" .. 1·00 10
65 $1 "Anartia jatrophae" .. 1·75 45

8. Resort Pavilion.

1975. Petit St. Vincent. Multicoloured.
66. 5 c. Type **8** 10 10
67. 35 c. The Harbour .. 10 10
68. 45 c. The Jetty 15 10
69. $1 Sailing in coral lagoon.. 50 30

9. Ecumenical Church, Mustique.

1975. Christmas. Multicoloured.
70. 5 c. Type **9** 10 10
71. 25 c. Catholic Church, Union Island 10 10
72. 50 c. Catholic Church, Bequia 10 10
73. $1 Anglican Church, Bequia 25 15

10. Sunset Scene.

1976. Union Island (1st series). Multicoloured.
74. 5 c. Type **10** 10 10
75. 35 c. Customs and Post Office, Clifton 10 10
76. 45 c. Anglican Church, Ashton 10 10
77. $1 Mail schooner, Clifton Harbour 25 20
See also Nos. 242/5.

11. Staghorn Coral.

1976. Corals. Multicoloured.
78. 5 c. Type **11** 10 10
79. 35 c. Elkhorn coral .. 25 10
80. 45 c. Pillar coral 30 10
81. $1 Brain coral 80 20

12. 25 c. Bicentennial Coin.

1976. Bicent. of American Revolution.
82. **12.** 25 c. silver, black and blue 10 10
83. – 50 c. silver, black and red 20 10
84. – $1 silver, black & mauve 25 20

DESIGNS: 50 c. Half-dollar coin. $1, One dollar coin.

1976. Maps (2nd series). As T **2.**
85. 5 c. blk., deep grn. and grn. 10 10
86. 10 c. black, green and blue 10 10
87. 35 c. black, brown and red 20 20
88. 45 c. black, red and orange 25 25

Nos. 85/8 exist in 7 different designs to each value as follows: A, Bequia, B, Canouan, C, Mayreau, D, Mustique, E, Petit St. Vincent, F, Prune, G, Union. To indicate any particular design use the appropriate catalogue No. together with the prefix for the island concerned.

13. Station Hill School and Post Office.

1977. Mayreau Island. Multicoloured.
89. 5 c. Type **13** 10 10
90. 35 c. Church at Old Wall.. 10 10
91. 45 c. La Sourciere Anchorage 10 10
92. $1 Saline Bay 25 15

14. Coronation Crown Coin.

1977. Silver Jubilee. Multicoloured.
93. 25 c. Type **14** 15 10
94. 50 c. Silver Wedding Crown 15 10
95. $1 Silver Jubilee Crown .. 20 15

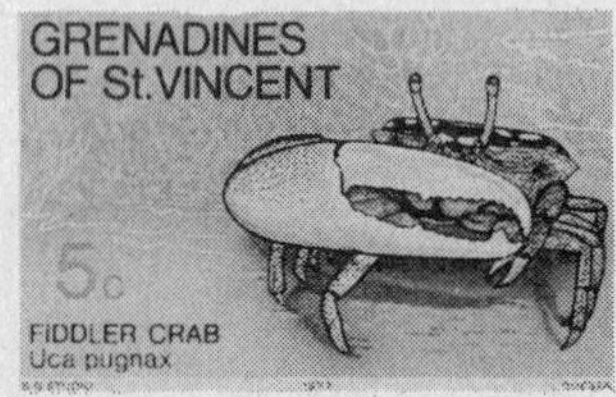

15. Fiddler Crab.

1977. Crustaceans. Multicoloured.
96. 5 c. Type **15** 10 10
97. 35 c. Ghost crab 20 10
98. 50 c. Blue crab 25 10
99. $1.25 Spiny lobster .. 55 40

16. Snorkel Diving.

1977. Prune Island. Multicoloured.

No.	Description		
100.	5 c. Type **16**	10	10
101.	35 c. Palm Is. Resort ..	10	10
102.	45 c. Casuarina Beach ..	10	15
103.	$1 Palm Is. Beach Club ..	30	50

17. Mustique Island.

1977. Royal Visit. Surch. as in T **17**.

No.	Description		
104. **17.**	40 c. turquoise and green	20	10
105.	$2 ochre and brown ..	65	25

18. The Clinic, Charlestown.

1977. Canouan Island Views (1st series). Multicoloured.

No.	Description		
106.	5 c. Type **18**	10	10
107.	35 c. Town Jetty, Charlestown	10	10
108.	45 c. Mail schooner arriving at Charlestown	10	10
109.	$1 Grand Bay	30	45

See also Nos. 307/10.

19. Tropical Mockingbird.

1978. Birds and Birds' Eggs. Multicoloured.

No.	Description		
110.	1 c. Type **19**	10	15
111.	2 c. Mangrove cuckoo ..	15	15
112.	3 c. Osprey	20	15
113.	4 c. Smooth billed ani ..	20	15
114.	5 c. House wren	20	20
115.	6 c. Bananaquit	20	20
116.	8 c. Carib grackle	20	30
117.	10 c. Yellow-bellied elaenia	20	30
118.	12 c. Collared plover ..	30	30
119.	15 c. Cattle egret	30	30
120.	20 c. Red-footed booby ..	30	30
121.	25 c. Red-billed tropic bird	30	30
122.	40 c. Royal tern	45	30
123.	50 c. Grenada flycatcher ..	45	40
124.	80 c. Purple gallinuk ..	70	55
125.	$1 Broad-winged hawk ..	75	75
126.	$2 Scaly-breasted ground dove	90	1·40
127.	$3 Laughing gull	1·25	1·60
128.	$5 Common noddy ..	2·25	2·00
129.	$10 Grey kingbird	5·00	3·00

1978. 25th Anniv. of Coronation. British Cathedrals. Designs as Nos. 422/5 of Monserrat. Multicoloured.

No.	Description		
130.	5 c. Worcester Cathedral	10	10
131.	40 c. Coventry Cathedral	10	10
132.	$1 Winchester Cathedral	15	10
133.	$3 Chester Cathedral ..	25	35

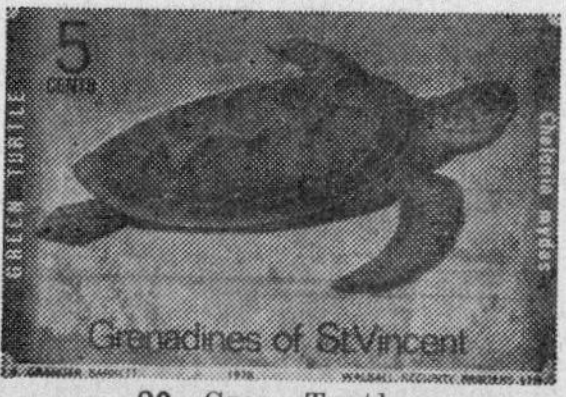

20. Green Turtle.

1978. Turtles. Multicoloured.

No.	Description		
135.	5 c. Type **20**	10	10
136.	40 c. Hawksbill Turtle ..	15	10
137.	50 c. Leatherback Turtle	15	10
138.	$1.25 Loggerhead Turtle	40	40

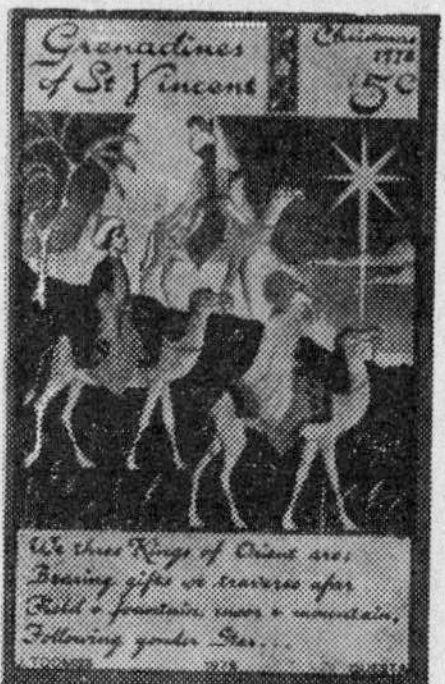

21. Three Kings following Star.

1978. Christmas. Scenes and Verses from the Carol " We Three Kings ". Multicoloured.

No.	Description		
139.	5 c. Type **21**	10	10
140.	10 c. King presenting gold	10	10
141.	25 c. King presenting frankincense	10	10
142.	50 c. King presenting myrrh	10	10
143.	$2 Kings paying homage to infant Jesus	30	20

22. Sailing Yachts.

1979. National Regatta.

No.	Description		
145. **22.**	5 c. multicoloured ..	10	10
146. –	40 c. multicoloured ..	20	10
147. –	50 c. multicoloured ..	25	10
148. –	$2 multicoloured ..	75	60

DESIGNS: 40 c. to $2, Various sailing yachts.

1979. Wildlife. As T **114** of St. Vincent. Multicoloured.

No.	Description		
149.	20 c. Green Iguana ..	10	10
150.	40 c. Common Opossum ..	15	10
151.	$2 Red-legged Tortoise ..	60	65

1979. Death Centenary of Sir Rowland Hill. As T **103** of St. Vincent. Multicoloured.

No.	Description		
152.	80 c. Sir Rowland Hill ..	20	15
153.	$1 Great Britain 1d. and 4d. stamps of 1858 with "A10" (Kingstown, St. Vincent) postmark ..	25	25
154.	$2 St. Vincent ½d. and 1d. stamps of 1894 with Bequia postmark ..	35	40

1979. International Year of the Child. Designs as Nos. 570/3 of St. Vincent.

No.	Description		
156.	6 c. black, silver and blue	10	10
157.	40 c. black, silver & salmon	10	10
158.	$1 black, silver and buff ..	20	10
159.	$3 black, silver and lilac	45	30

1979. Independence. As T **106** of St. Vincent. Multicoloured.

No.	Description		
160.	5 c. National flag and " Ixora salicifolia " (flower)	10	10
161.	40 c. House of Assembly and " Ixora odorata " (flower)	10	10
162.	$1 Prime Minister R. Milton Cato and " Ixora javanica " (flower)	20	20

23. False Killer Whale.

1980. Whales and Dolphins. Multicoloured.

No.	Description		
163.	10 c. Type **23**	20	10
164.	50 c. Spinner Dolphin ..	45	35
165.	90 c. Bottle-nosed Dolphin	65	70
166.	$2 Short-finned Pilot Whale ("Blackfish") ..	1·25	1·10

1980. " London 1980 " International Stamp Exhibition. As T **110** of St. Vincent. Multicoloured.

No.	Description		
167.	40 c. Queen Elizabeth II ..	15	10
168.	50 c. St. Vincent 2 c. stamp of 1965	15	10
169.	$3 First Grenadines stamps	60	1·00

1980. Sport. As T **112** of St. Vincent. **Mult.**

No.	Description		
171.	25 c. Running	10	10
172.	50 c. Sailing	10	10
173.	$1 Long-jumping	20	20
174.	$2 Swimming	30	30

1980. Hurricane Relief. Nos. 171/4 optd. **HURRICANE RELIEF 50 c.**

No.	Description		
175. **22.**	25 c. + 50 c. multicoloured	10	20
176. –	50 c. + 50 c. multicoloured	20	30
177. –	$1 + 50 c. multicoloured	25	40
178. –	$2 + 50 c. multicoloured	40	60

24. Scene and verse from the Carol " De Borning Day ".

1980. Christmas. Multicoloured.

No.	Description		
179.	5 c. Type **24**	10	10
180.	50 c. " Mary and de Baby lonely "	10	10
181.	60 c. " Mary and de Baby weary "	10	10
182.	$1 " Mary and de Baby rest easy " ..	15	15
183.	$2 " Star above shine in de sky "	25	25

25. Post Office, Port Elizabeth.

1981. Bequia Island (2nd series). Mult.

No.	Description		
185.	50 c. Type **25**	15	15
186.	60 c. Moonhole	20	20
187.	$1.50 Fishing boats, Admiralty Bay	40	40
188.	$2 "The Friendship Rose" (yacht) at jetty	55	55

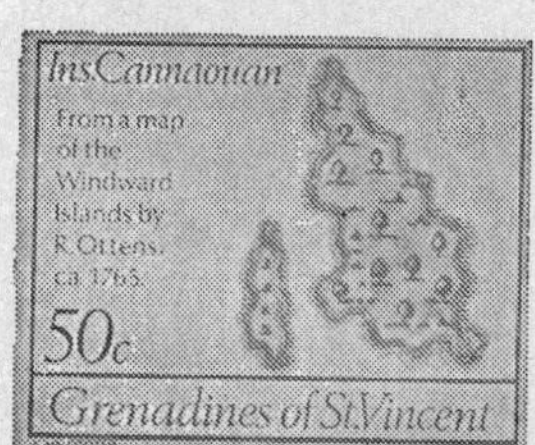

26. Ins. Cannaouan (from map of Windward Islands by R. Ottens, c. 1765).

1981. Details from Early Maps. Mult.

No.	Description		
189	50 c. Type **26**	40	30
190	50 c. Cannouan Is. (from chart by J. Parsons, 1861)	40	30
191	60 c. Ins. Moustiques (from map of Windward Islands by R. Ottens, c. 1765)	45	35
192	60 c. Mustique Is, (from chart by J. Parsons, 1861)	45	35
193	$2 Ins. Bequia (from map of Windward Islands by R. Ottens, c. 1765) ..	80	75
194	$2 Bequia Is. (from map surveyed in 1763 by T. Jefferys)	80	75

1981. Royal Wedding. Royal Yachts. As T **26** of Kiribati. Multicoloured.

No.	Description		
195.	50 c. " Mary "	15	15
196.	50 c. Prince Charles and Lady Diana Spencer ..	40	40
197.	$3 " Alexandra "	30	30
198.	$3 As No. 196	90	90
199.	$3.50 " Britannia " ..	35	35
200.	$3.50 As No. 196	90	90

27. Bar Jack.

1981. Game Fish. Multicoloured.

No.	Description		
204.	10 c. Type **27**	15	10
205.	50 c. Tarpon	30	10
206.	60 c. Cobia	35	10
207.	$2 Blue Marlin	1·00	70

28. H.M.S. "Experiment" (frigate).

1982. Ships. Multicoloured.

No.	Description		
208	1 c. Type **28**	10	10
209	3 c. "Lady Nelson" (cargo liner)	10	10
210	5 c. "Daisy" (brig) ..	10	10
211	6 c. Carib canoe	10	10
212	10 c. "Hairoun Star" (freighter)	20	10
213	15 c. "Jupiter" (liner) ..	20	10
214	20 c. "Christina" (steam yacht)	25	10
215	25 c. "Orinoco" (mail paddle-steamer) ..	30	15
216	30 c. H.M.S. "Lively" (frigate)	30	15
217	50 c. "Alabama" (Confederate warship) ..	45	25
218	60 c. "Denmark" (freighter)	55	30
219	75 c. "Santa Maria" ..	70	50
220	$1 "Baffin" (research vessel)	75	55
221	$2 "Queen Elizabeth 2" (liner)	1·25	1·25
222	$3 R.Y. "Britannia" ..	1·75	1·75
223	$5 "Geeststar" (freighter)	2·40	2·50
224	$10 "Grenadines Star" (ferry)	4·50	5·00

29. Fruit of Prickly Pear.

1982. Prickly Pear Cactus. Multicoloured.

No.	Description		
225.	10 c. Type **29**	15	15
226.	50 c. Prickly Pear flower buds	35	35
227.	$1 Flower of Prickly Pear Cactus	60	60
228.	$2 Prickly Pear Cactus ..	1·25	1·25

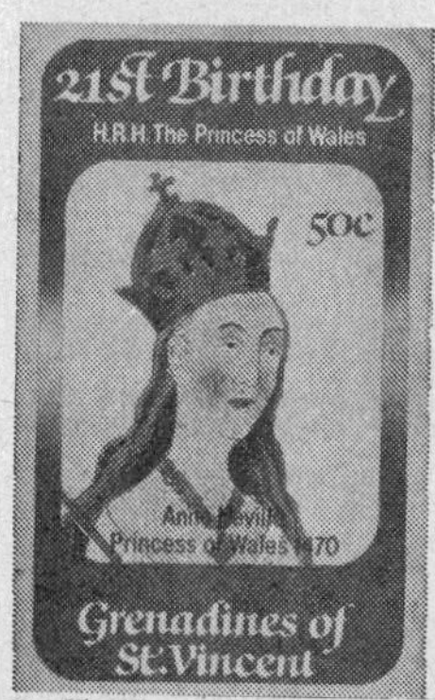

30. Anne Neville. Princess of Wales, 1470.

1982. 21st Birthday of Princess of Wales. Multicoloured.

No.	Description		
229.	50 c. Type **30**	15	15
230.	60 c. Coat of arms of Anne Neville	15	15
231.	$6 Diana, Princess of Wales	70	80

31. Old and New Uniforms.

1982. 75th Anniv. of Boy Scout Movement. Multicoloured.

232.	$1.50 Type **31**	60	60
233.	$2.50 Lord Baden-Powell	90	90

1982. Birth of Prince William of Wales. Nos. 224/6 optd. **ROYAL BABY** and island name.

234.	50 c. Type **30**	15	15
235.	60 c. Coat of arms of Anne Neville	15	15
236.	$6 Diana, Princess of Wales	70	80

Nos. 229/31 exist overprinted with 5 different island names as follows: A. Bequia, B. Canouan, C. Mayreau, D. Mustique, E. Union Island. To indicate any particular overprint use the appropriate catalogue No. together with the prefix for the island concerned.

33. Silhouette Figures of Mary and Joseph.

1982. Christmas. Silhouette of figures. Multicoloured.

237.	10 c. Type **33**	10	10
238.	$1. 50 Animals in stable ..	45	45
239.	$2. 50 Mary and Joseph with baby Jesus	60	60

1983. No. 123 surch.

241.	45 c. on 50 c. Grenada flycatcher	20	25

35. Power Station, Clifton.

1983. Union Island (2nd series). Multicoloured.

242.	50 c. Type **35**	15	15
243.	60 c. Sunrise, Clifton harbour	15	15
244.	$1.50 Junior Secondary School, Ashton ..	40	40
245.	$2 Frigate Rock and Conch Shell Beach	55	55

36. British Man-of-war.

1983. Bicent. of Treaty of Versailles. Mult.

246.	45 c. Type **36**	15	15
247.	60 c. American man-of-war	15	15
248.	$1.50 Soldiers carrying U.S. flags	45	45
249.	$2 British troops in battle	55	55

37. Montgolfier Balloon, 1783.

1983. Bicentenary of Manned Flight. Mult.

250.	45 c. Type **37**	15	15
251.	60 c. Ayres " Turbo-thrush Commander " (horiz.) ..	15	15
252.	$1.50 Lebaudy " 1 " dirigible (horiz.)	45	45
253.	$2 Space shuttle " Columbia "	55	55

38. Coat of Arms of James I

1983. Leaders of the World. British Monarchs. Multicoloured.

255.	60 c. Type **38**	25	25
256.	60 c. Henry VIII	25	25
257.	60 c. Coat of Arms of James I	25	25
258.	60 c. James I	25	25
259.	75 c. Henry VIII at Hampton Court	25	25
260.	75 c. Hampton Court ..	25	25
261.	75 c. James I at Edinburgh Castle	25	25
262.	75 c. Edinburgh Castle ..	25	25
263.	$2.50 The " Mary Rose " ..	35	25
264.	$2.50 Vignette of Henry VIII and Portsmouth harbour	35	25
265.	$2.50 James I and the Gunpowder plot	35	25
266.	$2.50 Vignette of James I and Gunpowder plot ..	35	25

39. Quarter Dollar and Half Dollar, 1797.

1983. Old Coinage. Multicoloured.

267.	20 c. Type **39**	10	10
268.	45 c. Nine Bitts, 1811–14	15	15
269.	75 c. Twelve Bitts and six Bitts, 1811–14 ..	25	25
270.	$3 Sixty six Shillings, 1798	80	80

40. Class "D 13".

1984. Leaders of the World. Railway Locomotives (1st series). The first design in each pair shows technical drawings and the second the locomotive at work.

271.	5 c. multicoloured	10	10
272.	5 c. multicoloured	10	10
273.	10 c. multicoloured ..	10	10
274.	10 c. multicoloured ..	10	10
275.	15 c. multicoloured ..	15	15
276.	15 c. multicoloured ..	15	15
277.	35 c. multicoloured ..	20	20
278.	35 c. multicoloured ..	20	20
279.	45 c. multicoloured ..	20	20
280.	45 c. multicoloured ..	20	20
281.	60 c. multicoloured ..	25	25
282.	60 c. multicoloured ..	25	25
283.	$1 multicoloured	35	35
284.	$1 multicoloured	35	35
285.	$2.50 multicoloured ..	50	50
286.	$2.50 multicoloured ..	50	50

DESIGNS: Nos. 271/2, Class "D 13", U.S.A. 1892. (Type **40**). 273/4, High Speed Train "125", Great Britain (1980) 275/6, Class "T9", Great Britain (1899). 277/8, "Claud Hamilton", Great Britain (1900). 279/80, Class "J", U.S.A. (1941). 281/2, Class "D 16", U.S.A. (1895), 283/4. "Lode Star", Great Britain (1907). 285/6, "Blue Peter", Great Britain (1948).

See also Nos. 311/26, 351/8, 390/7, 412/9, 443/58, 504/19 and 520/35.

41. Spotted Eagle Ray.

1984. Reef Fishes. Multicoloured.

287.	45 c. Type **41**	15	15
288.	60 c. Queen Trigger Fish ..	20	20
289.	$1.50 White Spotted File Fish	45	65
290.	$2 Schoolmaster	55	80

42. R. A. Woolmer.

1984. Leaders of the World. Cricketers (1st series). The first design in each pair shows a head portrait and the second the cricketer in action.

291.	1 c. multicoloured	10	10
292.	1 c. multicoloured	10	10
293.	3 c. multicoloured	10	10
294.	3 c. multicoloured	10	10
295.	5 c. multicoloured	10	10
296.	5 c. multicoloured	10	10
297.	30 c. multicoloured ..	20	20
298.	30 c. multicoloured ..	20	20
299.	60 c. multicoloured ..	40	40
300.	60 c. multicoloured ..	40	40
301.	$1 multicoloured	50	50
302.	$1 multicoloured	50	50
303.	$2 multicoloured	80	80
304.	$2 multicoloured	80	80
305.	$3 multicoloured	1·10	1·10
306.	$3 multicoloured	1·10	1·10

DESIGNS: Nos. 291/2, R. A. Woolmer (Type **42**). 293/4, K. S. Ranjitsinhji. 295/6, W. R. Hammond. 297/8, D. L. Underwood. 299/300, W. G. Grace. 301/2, E. A. E. Baptiste. 303/4, A. P. E. Knott. 305/6, L. E. G. Ames.

See also Nos. 331/8 and 364/9.

43. Junior Secondary School.

1984. Canouan Island (2nd series). Multicoloured.

307.	35 c. Type **43**	20	20
308.	45 c. Police Station ..	25	25
309.	$1 Post Office	50	50
310.	$3 Anglican Church ..	1·25	1·50

INDEX

Countries can be quickly located by referring to the index at the end of this volume.

1984. Leaders of the World. Railway Locomotives (2nd series). As T **40**. The first design in each pair shows technical drawings and the second the locomotive at work.

311.	1 c. multicoloured	10	10
312.	1 c. multicoloured	10	10
313.	5 c. multicoloured	10	10
314.	5 c. multicoloured	10	10
315.	20 c. multicoloured ..	15	15
316.	20 c. multicoloured ..	15	15
317.	35 c. multicoloured ..	15	15
318.	35 c. multicoloured ..	15	15
319.	60 c. multicoloured ..	20	20
320.	60 c. multicoloured ..	20	20
321.	$1 multicoloured	25	25
322.	$1 multicoloured	25	25
323.	$1.50 multicoloured ..	30	30
324.	$1.50 multicoloured ..	30	30
325.	$3 multicoloured	55	55
326.	$3 multicoloured	55	55

DESIGNS: Nos. 311/12, Class "C62", Japan (1948). 313/14, Class "V", Great Britain (1903). 315/16, "Catch-Me-Who-Can", Great Britain (1808). 317/18, Class "E10", Japan (1948). 319/20, "J. B. Earle", Great Britain (1904). 321/2, "Lyn", Great Britain (1898). 323/4, "Talyllyn", Great Britain (1865). 325/6, "Cardean", Great Britain (1906).

44. Lady of the Night.

1984. Night-blooming Flowers. Mult.

327.	35 c. Type **44**	35	30
328.	45 c. Four o'clock	45	35
329.	75 c. Mother-in-Law's Tongue	60	50
330.	$3 Queen of the night ..	2·00	2·25

1984. Leaders of the World. Cricketers (2nd series). As T **42**. The first in each pair listed shows a head portrait and the second the cricketer in action.

331.	5 c. multicoloured	10	10
332.	5 c. multicoloured	10	10
333.	30 c. multicoloured ..	20	15
334.	30 c. multicoloured ..	20	15
335.	$1 multicoloured	40	30
336.	$1 multicoloured	40	30
337.	$2.50 multicoloured ..	80	70
338.	$2.50 multicoloured ..	80	70

DESIGNS: Nos. 331/2, S. F. Barnes. 333/4, R. Peel. 335/6, H. Larwood. 337/8, Sir John Hobbs.

45. Facel "Vega HK500".

1984. Leaders of the World. Automobiles (1st series). The first design in each pair shows technical drawings and the second paintings.

339.	5 c. black, blue and green	10	10
330.	5 c. multicoloured	10	10
341.	25 c. black, lilac and pink	10	10
342.	25 c. multicoloured ..	10	10
343.	50 c. black, blue and orange	15	15
344.	50 c. multicoloured ..	15	15
345.	$3 black, stone and brown	45	45
346.	$3 multicoloured	45	45

DESIGNS: Nos. 339/40, Facel "Vega HK500" (Type **45**). 341/2, B.M.W. "328". 343/4, Frazer-Nash "TT Replica 1.5L". 345/6, Buick "Roadmaster Riviera".

See also Nos. 378/85 and 431/42.

46. Three Wise Men and Star.

1984. Christmas. Multicoloured.

347. 20 c. Type **46** 10 10
348. 45 c. Journeying to Bethlehem 20 25
349. $3 Presenting gifts .. 1·00 1·40

1985. Leaders of the World. Railway Locomotives (3rd series). As T **40**. The first in each pair shows technical drawings and the second the locomotive at work.

351. 1 c. multicoloured 10 10
352. 1 c. multicoloured 10 10
353. 15 c. multicoloured .. 10 10
354. 15 c. multicoloured .. 10 10
355. 75 c. multicoloured .. 25 25
356. 75 c. multicoloured .. 25 25
357. $3 multicoloured 70 70
358. $3 multicoloured 70 70

Designs: Nos. 351/2, P.L.M. "Grosse C", France (1898). 353/4, Class "C12", Japan (1932). 355/6, Class "D50", Japan (1923), 357/8, "Fire Fly", Great Britain (1840).

47. Caribbean King Crab.

1985. Shell Fish. Multicoloured.

360. 25 c. Type **47** 25 15
361. 60 c. Queen Conch .. 35 35
362. $1 White Sea Urchin .. 45 50
363. $3 West Indian Top Shell 1·00 1·50

1985. Leaders of the World. Cricketers (3rd series). As T **42** (55 c., 60 c.), the first in each pair showing a head portrait and the second the cricketer in action, or horiz. designs showing teams ($2).

364. 55 c. multicoloured .. 30 35
365. 55 c. multicoloured .. 30 35
366. 60 c. multicoloured .. 35 40
367. 60 c. multicoloured .. 35 40
368. $2 multicoloured 80 85
369. $2 multicoloured 80 85

Designs—vert. (As T **42**). Nos. 364/5, M. D. Moxon. 366/7, L. Potter. horiz. (59 × 42 mm.). No. 368, Kent team. 369, Yorkshire team.

48. "Cypripedium calceolus".

1985. Leaders of the World. Flowers. Multicoloured.

370. 5 c. Type **48** 10 10
371. 5 c. "Gentiana asclepiadea" 10 10
372. 55 c. "Clianthus formosus" 20 20
373. 55 c. "Celmisia coriacea" .. 20 20
374. 60 c. "Erythronium americanum" 20 20
375. 60 c. "Laelia anceps" .. 20 20
376. $2 "Leucadendron discolor" 50 50
377. $2 "Meconopsis horridula" 50 50

1985. Leaders of the World. Automobiles (2nd series). As T **45**. The first in each pair shows technical drawings and the second paintings.

378. 5 c. black, yellow and blue 10 10
379. 5 c. multicoloured 10 10
380. 60 c. black, yellow and orange 15 15
381. 60 c. multicoloured .. 15 15
382. $1 black, green and blue .. 20 20
383. $1 multicoloured 20 20
384. $1.50 black, blue and green 25 25
385. $1.50 multicoloured .. 25 25

Designs: Nos. 378/9, Winton (1903). 380/1, Invicta 4½ litre (1931). 382/3, Daimler "SP250 Dart" (1959). 384/5, Brabham "Repco BT 19" (1966).

49. Windsurfing.

1985. Tourism. Watersports. Multicoloured.

386. 35 c. Type **49** 15 15
387. 45 c. Water-skiing 15 15
388. 75 c. Scuba-diving .. 20 25
389. $3 Deep-sea game fishing 80 1·40

1985. Leaders of the World. Railway Locomotives (4th series). As T **40**. The first design in each pair shows technical drawings and the second the locomotive at work.

390. 10 c. multicoloured .. 10 10
391. 10 c. multicoloured .. 10 10
392. 40 c. multicoloured .. 20 20
393. 40 c. multicoloured .. 20 20
394. 50 c. multicoloured .. 20 20
395. 50 c. multicoloured .. 20 20
396. $2.50 multicoloured .. 80 80
397. $2.50 multicoloured .. 80 80

Designs: Nos. 390/1, Class "581" 12-car train, Japan (1968). 392/3, Class "231-132BT", Ageria (1936). 394/5, "Class "S." "Slieve Gullion", Great Britain (1913). 396/7, Class "Beattie" Well Tank, Great Britain (1874).

50. Passion Fruits and Blossom.

1985. Fruits and Blossoms. Multicoloured.

398. 30 c. Type **50** 15 20
399. 75 c. Guava 35 40
400. $1 Sapodilla 50 55
401. $2 Mango .. .. .. 1·00 1·10

51. Queen Elizabeth the Queen Mother.

1985. Leaders of the World. Life and Times of Queen Elizabeth the Queen Mother. Various vertical portraits.

403. **51.** 40 c. multicoloured .. 15 20
404. – 40 c. multicoloured .. 15 20
405. – 75 c. multicoloured .. 15 20
406. – 75 c. multicoloured .. 15 20
407. – $1.10 multicoloured .. 20 25
408. – $1.10 multicoloured .. 20 25
409. – $1.75 multicoloured .. 30 40
410. – $1.75 multicoloured .. 30 40

Each value issued in pairs showing a floral pattern across the bottom of the portraits which stops short of the left-hand edge on the first stamp and of the right-hand edge on the second.

1985. Leaders of the World. Railway Locomotives (5th series). As T **40**. The first design in each pair shows technical drawings and the second the locomotive at work.

412. 35 c. multicoloured .. 15 20
413. 35 c. multicoloured .. 15 20
414. 70 c. multicoloured .. 25 30
415. 70 c. multicoloured .. 25 30
416. $1.20 multicoloured .. 35 40
417. $1.20 multicoloured .. 35 40
418. $2 multicoloured 60 65
419. $2 multicoloured 60 65

Designs: Nos. 412/13, "Coronation" Class, Great Britain (1937). 414/15, Class "E18", Germany (1935). 416/7, "Hayes", type, U.S.A. (1854), 418/19, Class "2120", Japan (1890).

1985. Royal Visit. Nos. 199/200, 222, 287, 398 and 407/8 optd. **CARIBBEAN ROYAL VISIT—1985** or surch. also.

420. **50.** 30 c. multicoloured .. 2·50 2·00
421. **41.** 45 c. multicoloured .. 3·00 2·50
422. – $1.10 multicoloured (No. 407) .. .. 4·50 4·00
423. – $1.10 multicoloured (No. 408) .. .. 4·50 4·00
424. – $1.50 on $3.50 multicoloured (No. 199) .. 3·00 3·00
425. – $1.50 on $3.50 multicoloured (No. 200) .. 9·00 9·00
426. – $3 multicoloured (No. 222) .. .. .. 5·50 5·00

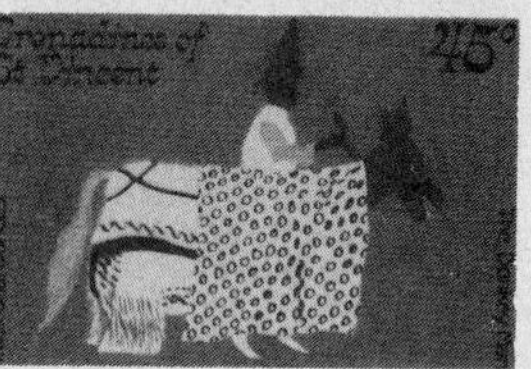

52. Donkey Man.

1985. Traditional Dances. Multicoloured.

427. 45 c. Type **52** 25 30
428. 75 c. Cake Dance (vert.) .. 35 40
429. $1 Bois-Bois Man (vert.) .. 50 55
430. $2 Maypole Dance .. 1·00 1·10

1986. Leaders of the World. Automobiles (3rd series). As T **45**. The first in each pair shows technical drawings and the second paintings.

431. 15 c. blk., lilac & mve. .. 10 10
432. 15 c. multicoloured .. 10 10
433. 45 c. blk., yell. & brn. .. 15 20
434. 45 c. multicoloured .. 15 20
435. 60 c. black, green and blue 20 25
436. 60 c. multicoloured .. 20 25
437. $1 black, brown and green 25 30
438. $1 multicoloured 25 30
439. $1.75 blk., yell. & orge. .. 35 45
440. $1.75 multicoloured .. 35 45
441. $3 multicoloured 55 65
442. $3 multiciloured 55 65

Designs: Nos. 431/2, Mercedes-Benz 4.5 litre (1914). 433/4, Rolls Royce "Silver Wraith" (1954) 435/6, Lamborghini "Countach" (1974). 437/8, Marmon "V-16" (1932). 439/40, Lotus-Ford "49 B" (1968). 441/2, Delage 1.5 litre (1927).

1986. Leaders of the World. Railway Locomotives (6th series). As T **40**. The first in each pair shows technical drawings and the second the locomotive at work.

443. 15 c. multicoloured .. 10 10
444. 15 c. multicoloured .. 10 10
445. 45 c. multicoloured .. 15 20
446. 45 c. multicoloured .. 15 20
447. 60 c. multicoloured .. 20 30
448. 60 c. multicoloured .. 20 30
449. 75 c. multicoloured .. 25 35
450. 75 c. multicoloured .. 25 35
451. $1 multicoloured 30 40
452. $1 multicoloured 30 40
453. $1.50 multicoloured .. 35 50
454. $1.50 multicoloured .. 35 50
455. $2 multicoloured 50 65
456. $2 multicoloured 50 65
457. $3 multicoloured 65 80
458. $3 multicoloured 65 80

Designs: Nos. 443/4, Class "T15", Germany (1897). 445/6, Class "13", Great Britain (1900). 447/8, "Halesworth", Great Britain (1879). 449/50, Class "Problem", Great Britain (1859). 451/2, Class "Western" diesel, Great Britain (1961). 453/4, Drummond's "Bug", Great Britain (1899). 455/6, Class "Clan", Great Britain (1951). 457/8, Class "1800", Japan (1884).

1986. 60th Birthday of Queen Elizabeth II. Multicoloured. As T **167** of British Virgin Islands.

459. 5 c. Queen Elizabeth II .. 10 10
460. $1 At Princess Anne's christening, 1950 .. 30 35
461. $4 Princess Elizabeth .. 90 1·10
462. $6 In Canberra, 1982 (vert.) 1·40 1·90

53. Handmade Dolls.

1986. Handicrafts. Multicoloured.

464 10 c. Type **53** 10 10
465 60 c. Basketwork 20 20
466 $1 Scrimshaw work .. 30 30
467 $3 Model sailing dinghy .. 80 1·25

54. Uruguayan Team.
(Illustration reduced, actual size 67 × 37 mm.).

1986. World Cup Football Championship, Mexico. Multicoloured.

468. 1 c. Type **54** 10 10
469. 10 c. Polish team 10 10
470. 45 c. Bulgarian player (28 × 42 mm.) 25 30
471. 75 c. Iraqi player (28 × 42 mm.) 35 40
472. $1·50 South Korean player (28 × 42 mm.) 75 80
473. $2 Northern Irish player (28 × 42 mm.) .. .. 1·00 1·10
474. $4 Portuguese team .. 2·00 2·10
475. $5 Canadian team .. .. 2·50 2·75

55. "Marasmius pallescens".

1986. Fungi. Multicoloured.

477. 45 c. Type **55** .. .. 1·25 65
478. 60 c. "Leucocoprinus fragilissimus" .. .. 1·50 80
479. 75 c. "Hygrocybe occidentalis" .. .. 2·00 1·00
480. $3 "Xerocomus hypoxanthus" .. .. 6·00 4·00

1986. Royal Wedding (1st issue). Multicoloured. As T **168** of British Virgin Islands.

481. 60 c. Miss Sarah Ferguson and Princess Diana applauding 20 25
482. 60 c. Prince Andrew at shooting match 20 25
483. $2 Prince Andrew and Miss Sarah Ferguson (horiz.) 75 80
484. $2 Prince Charles with Prince Andrew, Princess Anne and Princess Margaret on balcony (horiz.) 75 80

1986. Royal Wedding (2nd issue). Nos. 481/4 optd. **Congratulations to T.R.H. The Duke and Duchess of York.**

486. 60 c. Miss Sarah Ferguson and Princess Diana applauding 30 35
487. 60 c. Prince Andrew at shooting match 30 35
488. $2 Prince Andrew and Miss Sarah Ferguson (horiz.) 1·00 1·10
489. $2 Prince Charles, Prince Andrew, Princess Anne and Princess Margaret on balcony (horiz.) .. 1·00 1·10

56. "Brachymesia furcata".

1986. Dragonflies. Multicoloured.

490. 45 c. Type **56** 20 20
491. 60 c. "Lepthemis vesiculosa" 25 25
492. 75 c. "Perithemis domitta" 30 30
493. $2.50 "Tramea abdominalis" (vert.) .. 85 1·10

57. American Kestrel.

1986. Birds of Prey. Multicoloured.

495.	10 c. Type **57**	30	15
496.	45 c. Common black hawk	90	50
497.	60 c. Peregrine falcon ..	1·10	60
498.	$4 Osprey	3·75	4·25

58. Santa playing Steel Band Drums.

1986. Christmas. Multicoloured.

499.	45 c. Type **58**	25	30
500.	60 c. Santa windsurfing ..	30	35
501.	$1.25 Santa skiing	60	65
502.	$2 Santa limbo dancing ..	1·00	1·10

1987. Railway Locomotives (7th series). As T **40**. The first in each pair shows technical drawings and the second the locomotive at work.

504.	10 c. multicoloured ..	10	10
505.	10 c. multicoloured ..	10	10
506.	40 c. multicoloured ..	20	25
507.	40 c. multicoloured ..	20	25
508.	50 c. multicoloured ..	25	30
509.	50 c. multicoloured ..	25	30
510.	60 c. multicoloured ..	25	30
511.	60 c. multicoloured ..	25	30
512.	75 c. multicoloured ..	35	40
513.	75 c. multicoloured ..	35	40
514.	$1 multicoloured	45	50
515.	$1 multicoloured	45	50
516.	$1.25 multicoloured ..	55	60
517.	$1.25 multicoloured ..	55	60
518.	$1.50 multicoloured ..	70	75
519.	$1.50 multicoloured ..	70	75

DESIGNS: Nos. 504/5, Class "1001", No. 1275, Great Britain (1874). 506/7, Class "4P Garratt", Great Britain (1927). 508/9, "Papyrus", Great Britain (1929). 510/11, Class "V1", Great Britain (1930). 512/13, Class "40" diesel, No. D200, Great Britain (1958). 514/15, Class "42 Warship" diesel, Great Britain (1958). 516/17, Class "P-69" U.S.A. (1902). 518/19, class "60-3 Shay", No. 15, U.S.A. (1913).

1987. Railway Locomotives (8th series). As T **40**. The first in each pair shows technical drawings and the second the locomotive at work.

520.	10 c. multicoloured ..	10	10
521.	10 c. multicoloured ..	10	10
522.	40 c. multicoloured ..	20	25
523.	40 c. multicoloured ..	20	25
524.	50 c. multicoloured ..	25	30
525.	50 c. multicoloured ..	25	30
526.	60 c. multicoloured ..	25	30
527.	60 c. multicoloured ..	25	30
528.	75 c. multicoloured ..	35	40
529.	75 c. multicoloured ..	35	40
530.	$1 multicoloured	45	50
531.	$1 multicoloured	45	50
532.	$1.50 multicoloured ..	70	75
533.	$1.50 multicoloured ..	70	75
534.	$2 multicoloured	90	95
535.	$2 multicoloured	90	95

DESIGNS: Nos. 520/1, Class "142", East Germany (1977). 522/3, Class "120", West Germany (1979). 524/5, Class "X", Australia (1954). 526/7, Class "59", Great Britain (1986). 528/9, New York Elevated Railroad Spuyten Duyvel, U.S.A. (1875). 530/1, Camden & Amboy Railroad Stevens (later John Bull), U.S.A. (1831). 532/3, "Royal Hudson" Class "H1-d", No. 2850, Canada (1938). 534/5, "Pioneer Zephyr" 3-car set, U.S.A. (1934).

59. Queen Elizabeth with Prince Andrew.

1987. Royal Ruby Wedding and 150th Anniv. of Queen Victoria's Accession.

536.	**59.**	15 c. multicoloured ..	15	15
537.	–	45 c. brown, black and yellow	30	30
538.	–	$1.50 multicoloured ..	90	90
539.	–	$3 multicoloured ..	1·75	1·75
540.	–	$4 multicoloured ..	2·00	2·00

DESIGNS: 45 c. Queen Victoria and Prince Albert, c 1855. $1.50, Queen and Prince Philip after Trooping the Colour, 1977. $3 Queen and Duke of Edinburgh, 1953. $4 Queen in her study, c 1980.

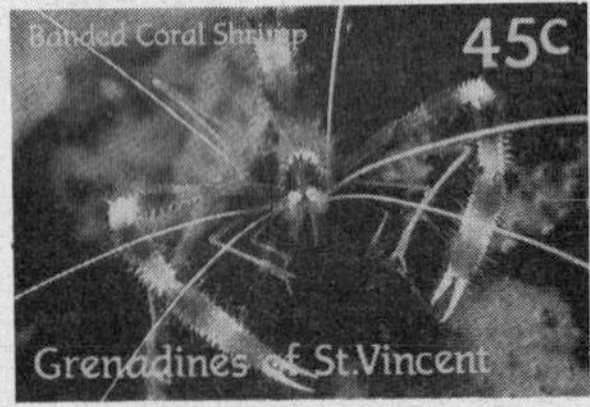

60. Banded Coral Shrimp.

1987. Marine Life. Multicoloured.

542.	45 c. Type **60**	45	45
543.	50 c. Arrow crab and flamingo tongue ..	50	50
544.	65 c. Cardinal fish	70	70
545.	$5 Moray eel	4·00	4·00

61 "Australia IV"

1988. Ocean Racing Yachts. Multicoloured.

547	50 c. Type **61**	50	50
548	65 c. "Crusader II" ..	60	60
549	75 c. "New Zealand K27"	75	75
550	$2 "Italia"	1·50	1·50
551	$4 "White Crusader" ..	2·50	2·50
552	$5 "Stars and Stripes" ..	3·00	3·00

62 Seine-fishing Boats racing

1988. Bequia Regatta. Multicoloured.

554	5 c. Type **62**	10	10
555	50 c. "Friendship Rose" (cruising yacht) ..	20	25
556	75 c. Fishing boats racing	30	35
557	$3.50 Yachts racing ..	1·50	1·60

63 "Twin-Otter" making Night Approach (Illustration reduced, actual size 50 × 38mm)

1988. Mustique Airways. Multicoloured.

559	15 c. Type **63**	10	10
560	65 c. Beech "Baron" aircraft in flight ..	20	25
561	75 c. "Twin-Otter" over forest	20	25
562	$5 Beech "Baron" on airstrip	1·25	1·75

64 "Sv. Pyotr" in Arctic (Bering)

1988. Explorers. Multicoloured.

564	15 c. Type **64**	10	10
565	75 c. Bering's ships in pack ice	25	30
566	$1 Livingstone's steam launch "Ma-Robert" on Zambesi	35	40
567	$2 Meeting of Livingstone and H. M. Stanley at Ujiji	60	75
568	$3 Speke and Burton at Tabori	90	1·25
569	$3.50 Speke and Burton in canoe on Lake Victoria	1·00	1·40
570	$4 Sighting the New World, 1492	1·10	1·50
571	$4.50 Columbus trading with Indians	1·40	1·75

65 Asif Iqbal Razvi

1988. Cricketers of 1988 International Season. Multicoloured.

573	20 c. Type **65** ..	30	30
574	45 c. R. J. Hadlee ..	50	50
575	75 c. M. D. Crowe ..	70	70
576	$1.25 C. H. Lloyd ..	1·00	1·00
577	$1.50 A. R. Boarder ..	1·25	1·25
578	$2 M. D. Marshall ..	1·75	1·75
579	$2.50 G. A. Hick	2·00	2·00
580	$3.50 C. G. Greenidge (horiz)	2·50	2·50

66 Pam Shriver

1988. International Tennis Players. Mult.

582	15 c. Type **66**	10	10
583	50 c. Kevin Curran (vert)	15	20
584	75 c. Wendy Turnbull (vert)	20	25
585	$1 Evonne Cawley (vert)	35	40
586	$1.50 Ilie Nastase ..	45	55
587	$2 Billie Jean King (vert)	65	75
588	$3 Bjorn Borg (vert) ..	1·00	1·25
589	$3.50 Virginia Wade with Wimbledon trophy (vert)	1·25	1·50

No. 584 is inscribed "WENDY TURN-BALL" in error.

67 Mickey and Minnie Mouse visiting Fatehpur Sikri

1989. "India–89" International Stamp Exhibition. Multicoloured. Designs showing Walt Disney cartoon characters in India.

591	1 c. Type **67**	10	10
592	2 c. Mickey and Minnie Mouse aboard "Palace on Wheels" train	10	10
593	3 c. Mickey and Minnie Mouse passing Old Fort, Delhi ..	10	10
594	5 c. Mickey and Minnie Mouse on camel, Pinjore Gardens, Haryana	10	10
595	10 c. Mickey and Minnie Mouse at Taj Mahal, Agra ..	10	10
596	25 c. Mickey and Minnie Mouse in Chandni Chowk, Old Delhi	10	10
597	$4 Goofy on elephant with Mickey and Minnie Mouse at Agra Fort, Jaipur	1·75	1·75
598	$5 Goofy, Mickey and Minnie Mouse at Gandhi Memorial, Cape Comorin ..	2·25	2·25

1989. Japanese Art. As T **250** of Antigua. Multicoloured.

600	5 c. "The View at Yotsuya" (Hokusai) ..	10	10
601	30 c. "Landscape at Ochanomizu" (Hokuju)	15	15
602	45 c. "Itabashi" (Eisen) ..	25	25
603	65 c. "Early Summer Rain" (Kunisada) ..	30	30
604	75 c. "High Noon at Kasumigaseki" (Kuniyoshi)	35	35
605	$1 "The Yoshiwara Embankment by Moon-light" (Kuniyoshi) ..	45	45
606	$4 "The Bridge of Boats at Sano" (Hokusai) ..	1·90	1·90
607	$5 "Lingering Snow on Mount Hira" (Kunitora)	2·25	2·25

68 Player with Ball and Mt Vesuvius

1989. World Cup Football Championship, Italy (1st issue). Designs showing players and Italian landmarks. Multicoloured.

609	$1.50 Type **68**	80	70
610	$1.50 Fallen player, opponent kicking ball and Coliseum ..	80	70

611 $1.50, Player blocking ball and Venice 80 70
612 $1.50 Player tackling and Forum, Rome 80 70
613 $1.50 Two players competing for ball and Leaning Tower, Pisa .. 80 70
614 $1.50 Goalkeeper and Florence 80 70
615 $1.50 Two players competing for ball and St. Peter's, Vatican .. 80 70
616 $1.50 Player kicking ball and Pantheon 80 70

Nos. 609/16 were printed together, se-tenant, forming a composite foreground design.

See also Nos. 680/3.

1989. 500th Anniv (1992) of Discovery of America by Columbus (1st issue). Pre-Columbian Arawak Society. As T **247** of Antigua. Multicoloured.

617 25 c. Arawak smoking Tobacco 10 15
618 75 c. Arawak rolling cigar 30 35
619 $1 Applying body paint .. 40 45
620 $1.50 Making fire .. 65 70
621 $1.50 Cassava production 65 70
622 $1.50 Woman baking bread 65 70
623 $1.50 Using stone implement 65 70
624 $4 Arawak priest .. 1·75 1·90

Nos. 620/4 were printed together, se-tenant, forming a composite design.

See also Nos. 818/23 and 864/5.

70 Command Module "Columbia"

1989. 10th Anniv of First Manned Landing on Moon. Multicoloured.

626 5 c. Type **70** 10 10
627 40 c. Astronaut Neil Armstrong saluting U.S. flag 30 30
628 55 c. "Columbia" above lunar surface 40 40
629 65 c. Lunar module "Eagle" leaving Moon .. 40 40
630 70 c. "Eagle" on Moon .. 45 45
631 $1 "Columbia" re-entering Earth's atmosphere .. 55 55
632 $3 "Apollo 11" emblem .. 1·60 1·60
633 $5 Armstrong and Aldrin on Moon .. .. 2·50 2·50

71 "Marpesia petreus"

1989. Butterflies. Multicoloured.

635 5 c. Type **71** 15 15
636 30 c. "Papilio androgues" 25 20
637 45 c. "Chiorostrymon maesites" 40 30
638 65 c. "Junonia coenia" .. 50 40
639 75 c. "Eurema gratiosa" .. 55 45
640 $1 "Hypolimnas misippus" 70 60
641 $4 "Urbanus proteus" .. 2·50 2·50
642 $5 "Junonia evarete" .. 2·75 3·00

72 "Solanum urens"

1989. Flowers from St. Vincent Botanical Gardens. Multicoloured.

644 80 c. Type **72** 50 50
645 $1.25 "Passiflora andersonii" 70 70
646 $1.65 "Miconia andersonii" 85 85
647 $1.85 "Pitcairnia sulphurea" .. .. 1·00 1·00

1989. Christmas. As T **183** of Gambia. Mult.

648 5 c. Goofy and Mickey Mouse in Rolls-Royce "Silver Ghost", 1907 .. 10 10
649 10 c. Daisy Duck driving first Stanley Steamer, 1897 .. .. .. 10 10
650 15 c. Horace Horsecollar and Clarabelle Cow in Darracq "Genevieve", 1904 .. .. .. 10 10
651 45 c. Donald Duck driving Detroit electric coupe, 1914 .. .. .. 25 25
652 55 c. Mickey and Minnie Mouse in first Ford, 1896 30 25
653 $2 Mickey Mouse driving Reo "Runabout", 1904 90 90
654 $3 Goofy driving Winton mail truck, 1899 .. 1·40 1·40
655 $5 Mickey and Minnie Mouse in Duryea car, 1893 .. .. .. 2·25 2·25

1990. 50th Anniv of Second World War. As T **98** of Grenada Grenadines. Multicoloured.

657 10 c. Destroyer in action, First Battle of Narvik, 1940 .. .. .. 10 10
658 15 c. Allied tank at Anzio, 1944 .. .. .. 10 10
659 20 c. U.S. carrier under attack, Battle of Midway, 1942 .. .. 10 10
660 45 c. U.S. bombers over Gustav Line, 1944 .. 20 25
661 55 c. Map showing Allied zones of Berlin, 1945 30 35
662 65 c. German U-boat pursuing convoy, Battle of the Atlantic, 1943 .. 30 35
663 90 c. Allied tank, North Africa, 1943 .. .. 45 50
664 $3 U.S. forces landing on Guam, 1944 .. 1·40 1·50
665 $5 Crossing the Rhine, 1945 2·40 2·50
666 $6 Japanese battleships under attack, Leyte Gulf, 1944 .. .. 3·00 3·25

1990. "Stamp World London 90" International Stamp Exhibition (1st issue). Mickey's Shakespeare Company. As T **193** of Gambia showing Walt Disney cartoon characters. Multicoloured.

668 20 c. Goofy as Mark Anthony ("Julius Caesar") 10 10
669 30 c. Clarabelle Cow as the Nurse ("Romeo and Juliet") 15 20
670 45 c. Pete as Falstaff ("Henry IV") 20 25
671 50 c. Minnie Mouse as Portia ("The Merchant of Venice") 25 30
672 $1 Donald Duck as Hamlet ("Hamlet") 50 55
673 $2 Daisy Duck as Ophelia ("Hamlet") .. .. 95 1·00
674 $4 Donald and Daisy Duck as Benedick and Beatrice ("Much Ado About Nothing") .. 2·00 2·10
675 $5 Minnie Mouse and Donald Duck as Katherine and Petruchio ("The Taming of the Shrew") .. .. 2·40 2·50

74 Exhibition Emblem

1990. "Stamp World London 90" International Stamp Exhibition (2nd issue). 150th Anniv of the Penny Black.

677 **74** $1 black, pink & mauve 50 55
678 – $5 black, lilac and blue 2·40 2·50

DESIGN: $5 Negative image of Penny Black.

1990. World Cup Football Championship, Italy (2nd issue). As T **210** of St. Vincent. Multicoloured.

680 25 c. McCleish, Scotland .. 10 15
681 50 c. Rasul, Egypt .. 25 30
682 $2 Lindenberger, Austria 95 1·00
683 $4 Murray, U.S.A. .. 2·00 2·10

1990. "EXPO 90" International Garden and Greenery Exposition, Osaka. Orchids. As T **213** of St. Vincent. Multicoloured.

685 5 c. "Paphiopedilum" .. 10 10
686 25 c. "Dendrobium phalaenopsis" and "Cymbidium" hybrid .. 10 15
687 30 c. "Miltonia candida" hybrid 15 20
688 50 c. "Epidendrum ibaguense" and "Cymbidium" Elliot Rogers 25 30
689 $1 "Rossioglossum grande" 50 55
690 $2 "Phalaenopsis" Elisa Chamg Lou and "Masdevallia coccinea" .. 95 1·00
691 $4 "Cypripedium acaule" and "Cypripedium calceolus" .. .. 2·00 2·10
692 $5 "Orchis spectabilis" .. 2·40 2·50

75 Scaly-breasted Ground Dove

1990. Birds of the Caribbean. Multicoloured.

694 5 c. Type **75** 10 10
695 25 c. Purple martin .. 10 15
696 45 c. Painted bunting .. 20 25
697 55 c. Blue-hooded euphonia 30 35
698 75 c. Blue-grey tanager .. 35 40
699 $1 Red-eyed vireo .. 50 55
700 $2 Palm chat .. .. 95 1·00
701 $3 Northern jacana .. 1·40 1·50
702 $4 Green-throated carib 2·00 2·10
703 $5 St. Vincent amazon .. 2·40 2·50

1991. 90th Birthday of Queen Elizabeth the Queen Mother. As T **194** of Gambia.

705 $2 multicoloured .. .. 95 1·00
706 $2 multicoloured .. .. 95 1·00
707 $2 multicoloured .. .. 95 1·00
708 $2 multicoloured .. .. 95 1·00
709 $2 multicoloured .. .. 95 1·00
710 $2 multicoloured .. .. 95 1·00
711 $2 multicoloured .. .. 95 1·00
712 $2 multicoloured .. .. 95 1·00
713 $2 multicoloured .. .. 95 1·00
714 $2 multicoloured .. .. 95 1·00
715 $2 multicoloured .. .. 95 1·00
716 $2 multicoloured .. .. 95 1·00
717 $2 black and lilac .. 95 1·00
718 $2 black and lilac .. 95 1·00
719 $2 black, green and lilac .. 95 1·00
720 $2 multicoloured .. .. 95 1·00
721 $2 black and lilac .. 95 1·00
722 $2 multicoloured .. .. 95 1·00
723 $2 multicoloured .. .. 95 1·00
724 $2 multicoloured .. .. 95 1·00
725 $2 multicoloured .. .. 95 1·00
726 $2 multicoloured .. .. 95 1·00
727 $2 multicoloured .. .. 95 1·00
728 $2 multicoloured .. .. 95 1·00
729 $2 multicoloured .. .. 95 1·00
730 $2 multicoloured .. .. 95 1·00
731 $2 multicoloured .. .. 95 1·00

DESIGNS: No. 705, Lady Elizabeth Bowes-Lyon with sister; 706, Young Lady Elizabeth in long dress; 707, Young Lady Elizabeth wearing a hat; 708, Lady Elizabeth leaning on wall; 709, Lady Elizabeth on pony; 710, Studio portrait; 711, Lady Elizabeth in evening dress; 712, Duchess of York in fur-lined cloak; 713, Duchess of York holding rose; 714, Coronation, 1937; 715, King and Queen with Princess Elizabeth at Royal Lodge, Windsor; 716, Queen Elizabeth in blue hat; 717, King George VI and Queen Elizabeth; 718, Queen Elizabeth with Princess Elizabeth; 719, Queen Elizabeth watching sporting fixture; 720, Queen Elizabeth in white evening dress; 721, Princess Anne's christening, 1950; 722, Queen Mother with yellow bouquet; 723, Queen Mother and policewoman; 724, Queen Mother at ceremonial function; 725, Queen Mother in pink coat; 726, Queen Mother in academic robes; 727, Queen Mother in carriage with Princess Margaret; 728, Queen Mother in blue coat and hat; 729, Queen Mother with bouquet; 730, Queen Mother outside Clarence House on her birthday; 731, Queen Mother in turquoise coat and hat.

1991. Death Centenary (1990) of Vincent van Gogh (artist). As T **195** of British Virgin Islands. Multicoloured.

733 5 c. "View of Arles with Irises" 10 10
734 10 c. "Saintes-Maries" (vert) 10 10
735 15 c. "Old Woman of Arles" (vert) 10 10
736 20 c. "Orchard in Blossom, bordered by Cypresses" 10 10
737 25 c. "Three White Cottages in Saintes-Maries" 10 10
738 35 c. "Boats at Saintes-Maries" 15 20
739 40 c. "Interior of a Restaurant in Arles" .. 20 25
740 45 c. "Peasant Women" (vert) 20 25
741 55 c. "Self-portrait" (vert) 30 35
742 60 c. "Pork Butcher's Shop from a Window" (vert) 30 35
743 75 c. "The Night Cafe in Arles" 35 40
744 $1 "2nd Lieut. Millet of the Zouaves" 50 55
745 $2 "The Cafe Terrace, Place du Forum, Arles at Night" (vert) .. 95 1·00
746 $3 "The Zouave" (vert) .. 1·40 1·50
747 $4 "The Two Lovers" (detail) (vert) .. .. 2·00 2·10
748 $5 "Still Life" .. .. 2·40 2·50

1991. 65th Birthday of Queen Elizabeth II. As T **280** of Antigua. Multicoloured.

750 15 c. Inspecting the Yeomen of the Guard .. 10 10
751 40 c. Queen Elizabeth II with the Queen Mother at the Derby, 1988 .. 20 25
752 $2 The Queen and Prince Philip leaving Euston, 1986 .. .. .. 95 1·00
753 $4 The Queen at the Commonwealth Institute, 1987 .. .. 2·00 2·10

1991. 10th Wedding Anniv of Prince and Princess of Wales. As T **280** of Antigua. Multicoloured.

755 10 c. Prince and Princess at polo match, 1987 .. 10 10
756 50 c. Separate family portraits 25 30
757 $1 Prince William and Prince Henry at Kensington Palace, 1991 50 55
758 $5 Portraits of Prince Charles and Princess Diana .. .. .. 2·40 2·50

76 First Japanese Steam Locomotive and Map

1991 "Phila Nippon '91" International Stamp Exhibition, Toyko. Japanese Railway Locomotives. Each in black, red and green.

760 10 c. Type **76** 10 10
761 25 c. First imported American steam locomotive 10 15
762 35 c. Class "8620" steam locomotive 15 20
763 50 c. Class "C53" steam locomotive 25 30
764 $1 Class "DD-51" diesel locomotive 50 55
765 $2 Class "KTR001 Tango Explorer" electric rail car (inscr "RG 22327") 95 1·00
766 $4 Class "EF55" electric locomotive .. .. 2·00 2·10
767 $5 Class "EF58" electric locomotive .. .. 2·40 2·50

77 President Gorbachev and Brandenburg Gate

1991. Anniversaries and Events. Mult.

769 45 c. Type **77** 20 25
770 60 c. General de Gaulle in Djibouti, 1959 .. .. 30 35
771 65 c. "DIE MAUER MUSS WEG!" slogan 30 35
772 80 c. East German border guard escaping to West 40 45
773 $1 "Abduction from the Seraglio" 50 55
774 $1.50 Lilienthal and glider 75 80
775 $1.75 Trans-Siberian logo 85 90
776 $1.75 Trans-Siberian steam locomotive (vert) .. 85 90
777 $2 Czechoslovakia 1918 20 h. stamp and scout delivering mail .. 95 1·00
778 $2 Zurich couple maypole dancing .. .. 95 1·00
779 $2 Man and woman in Vaud traditional costumes .. .. 95 1·00
780 $2 Georg Laves (architect) and Hoftheater .. 95 1·00
781 $3 Dresden, 1749 .. .. 1·40 1·50
782 $4 Scouts and cog train on Snowdon (vert) .. 2·00 2·10

ANNIVERSARIES AND EVENTS: Nos. 769, 771/2, Bicentenary of Brandenburg Gate; 770, Birth centenary of Charles de Gaulle (French statesman); 773, 781, Death bicentenary of Mozart; 774, Centenary of Otto Lilienthal's gliding experiments; 775/6, Centenary of Trans-Siberian Railway; 777, 782, 50th death anniv of Lord Baden-Powell and World Scout Jamboree, Korea; 778/9, 700th anniv of Swiss Confederation; 780, 750th anniv of Hanover.

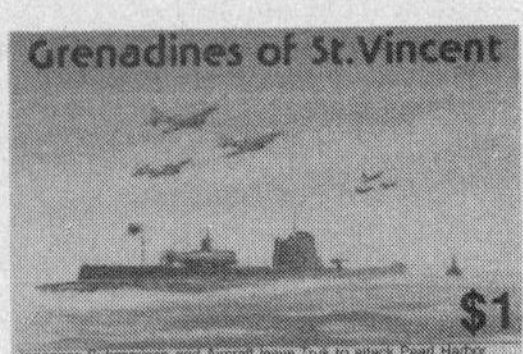

78 Japanese Aircraft and Submarines leaving Truk

1991. 50th Anniv of Japanese Attack on Pearl Harbor. Multicoloured.

784 $1 Type **78** 50 55
785 $1 "Akagi" (Japanese aircraft carrier) .. 50 55
786 $1 Nakajima B5 N2 "Kate" aircraft .. 50 55
787 $1 Torpedo bombers attacking Battleship Row 50 55
788 $1 Burning aircraft, Ford Island airfield 50 55
789 $1 Doris Miller winning Navy Cross 50 55
790 $1 U.S.S. "West Virginia" and "Tennessee" (battle-ships) ablaze 50 55
791 $1 U.S.S. "Arizona" (battleship) sinking .. 50 55
792 $1 U.S.S. "New Orleans" (cruiser) 50 55
793 $1 President Roosevelt declaring war 50 55

1991. Christmas. Walt Disney Company Christmas Cards. As T **228** of St. Vincent. Multicoloured.

794 10 c. Pluto pulling Mickey Mouse in sledge, 1974 (horiz) 10 10
795 55 c. Mickey, Pluto and Donald Duck watching toy band, 1961 (horiz) .. 30 75
796 65 c. "The Same Old Wish", 1942 (horiz) .. 30 35
797 75 c. Mickey, Peter Pan, Donald and Nephews with Merlin the magician, 1963 (horiz) .. 35 40
798 $1.50 Mickey and Donald with leprechauns, 1958 (horiz) 75 80
799 $2 Mickey and friends with book "Old Yeller", 1957 (horiz) .. .. .. 95 1·00
800 $4 Mickey controlling Pinnochio, 1953 (horiz) 2·00 2·10
801 $5 Cinderella and Prince dancing, 1987 (horiz) .. 2·40 2·50

1992. 40th Anniv of Queen Elizabeth II's Accession. As T **288** of Antigua. Mult.

803 15 c. View across bay .. 10 10
804 45 c. Schooner at anchor, Mayreau 20 25
805 $2 Hotel on hillside .. 95 1·00
806 $4 Tourist craft at anchor 2·00 2·10

1992. International Stamp Exhibitions. As T **215** of Lesotho. Walt Disney cartoon characters. Multicoloured.

(a) "Granada '92", Spain. Spanish Explorers

808 15 c. Big Pete as Hernando Cortes in Mexico (horiz) 10 10
809 40 c. Mickey Mouse as Hernando de Soto at Mississippi River (horiz) 20 25
810 $2 Goofy as Vasco Nunez de Balboa sights Pacific (horiz) .. .. .. 95 1·00
811 $4 Donald Duck as Francisco Coronado on Rio Grande (horiz) .. 2·00 2·10

(b) "World Columbian Stamp Expo '92", Chicago. Local Personalities

813 10 c. Mickey Mouse and Pluto outside Walt Disney's birthplace (horiz) 10 10
814 50 c. Donald Duck and nephews in George Pullman's railway sleeping car (horiz) .. 25 30
815 $1 Daisy Duck as Jane Addams (social reformer) and Hull House (horiz) 50 55
816 $5 Mickey as Carl Sandburg (novelist, poet and historian) (horiz) .. 2·40 2·50

79 King Ferdinand and Queen Isabella of Spain

1992. 500th Anniv of Discovery of America by Columbus (2nd issue). Multicoloured.

818 10 c. Type **79** 10 10
819 45 c. "Santa Maria" and "Nina" in Acul Bay, Haiti 20 25
820 55 c. "Santa Maria" (vert) 30 35
821 $2 Ships of Columbus (vert) .. .. .. 95 1·00
822 $4 Wreck of "Santa Maria" 2·00 2·10
823 $5 "Pinta" and "Nina" .. 2·40 2·50

1992. "Genova '92" International Thematic Stamp Exhibition (1st issue). Butterflies. As T **235** of St. Vincent. Multicoloured.

825 15 c. "Paulogramma sp" (horiz) 10 10
826 20 c. "Heliconius cydno" (horiz) 10 10
827 30 c. "Eutresis hypereia" (horiz) 15 20
828 45 c. "Eurytides columbus" 20 25
829 55 c. "Papilio ascolius" (horiz) 30 35
830 75 c. "Anaea pasibula" (horiz) 35 40
831 80 c. "Heliconius doris" (horiz) 40 45
832 $1 "Perisama pitheas" (horiz) 50 55
833 $2 "Batesia hypochlora" (horiz) .. .. .. 95 1·00
834 $3 "Heliconius erato" (horiz) .. .. .. 1·40 1·50
835 $4 "Elzunia cassandrina" (horiz) .. .. .. 2·00 2·10
836 $5 "Sais ivcidice" (horiz) 2·40 2·50

See also Nos. 851/62.

1992. Fungi. As T **236** of St. Vincent. Mult.

838 10 c. "Entoloma bakeri" .. 10 10
839 15 c. "Hydropus paraensis" 10 10
840 20 c. "Leucopaxillus gracillimus" 10 10
841 45 c. "Hygrotrama dennisianum" 15 20
842 50 c. "Leucoagaricus hortensis" 25 30
843 65 c. "Pyrrhoglosssum pyrrhum" 30 35
844 75 c. "Amanita craeoderma" 35 40
845 $1 "Lentinus bertieri" .. 50 55
846 $2 "Dennisiomyces griseus" .. .. 95 1·00
847 $3 "Xerulina asprata" .. 1·40 1·50
848 $4 "Hygrocybe acutoconica" .. .. 2·00 2·10
849 $5 "Lepiota spiculata" .. 2·40 2·50

1992. "Genova '92" International Thematic Stamp Exhibition (2nd issue). Hummingbirds. As T **237** of St. Vincent. Multicoloured.

851 5 c. Antillean crested hummingbird (female) (horiz) 10 10
852 10 c. Blue-tailed emerald (female) 10 10
853 35 c. Antillean mango (male) (horiz) 10 10
854 45 c. Antillean mango (female) (horiz) .. 20 25
855 55 c. Green-throated carib (horiz) 25 30
856 65 c. Green violetear (male) 30 35
857 75 c. Blue-tailed emerald (male) (horiz) 35 40
858 $1 Purple-thoated carib .. 50 55
859 $2 Copper-rumped hummingbird (horiz) .. 95 1·00
860 $3 Rufous-breasted hermit 1·40 1·50
861 $4 Antillean crested hummingbird (male) .. 2·00 2·10
862 $5 Green-breasted mango (male) .. .. .. 2·40 2·50

1992. 500th Anniv of Discovery of America by Columbus (3rd issue). Organization of East Caribbean States. As Nos. 911/12 of Montserrat. Multicoloured.

864 $1 Columbus meeting Amerindians 50 55
865 $2 Ships approaching island .. .. .. 95 1·00

1992. Olympic Games, Albertville and Barcelona. As T **216** of Lesotho. Mult.

866 10 c. Men's volleyball .. 10 10
867 15 c. Men's gymnastics (horiz) 10 10
868 25 c. Men's cross-country skiing 10 10
869 30 c. Men's 110 metres hurdles (horiz) 15 20
870 45 c. Men's 120 metre ski jumping (horiz) .. 25 30
871 55 c. Women's 4 × 100 metre relay 25 30
872 75 c. Men's triple jump .. 35 40
873 80 c. Men's mogul skiing 40 45
874 $1 Men's 110 metre butterfly swimming (horiz) 50 55
875 $2 "Tornado" Class yachting (horiz) .. 95 1·00
876 $3 Men's decathlon (horiz) 1·40 1·50
877 $5 Show jumping (horiz) .. 2·40 2·50

1992. Christmas. Religious Paintings. As T **218** of Lesotho. Multicoloured.

879 10 c. "Our Lady with St. Roch and St. Anthony of Padua" (Giorgione) .. 10 10
880 40 c. "Anthony of Padua" (Master of the Embroidered Leaf) .. 20 25
881 45 c. "Madonna and Child" (detail) (Orazio Gentileschi) 20 25
882 50 c. "Madonna and Child with St. Anne" (detail) (Da Vinci) 25 30
883 55 c. "The Holy Family" (Crespi) 25 30
884 65 c. "Madonna and Child" (Del Sarto) 30 35
885 75 c. "Madonna and Child with Sts. Lawrence and Julian" (Gentile da Fabriano) 35 40
886 $1 "Virgin and Child" (detail) (School of Parma) 50 55
887 $2 "Madonna with the Iris" (detail) (style of Durer) .. .. .. 95 1·00
888 $3 "Virgin and Child with St. Jerome and St. Dominic" (Lippi) .. 1·40 1·50
889 $4 "Rapolano Madonna" (Ambrogio Lorenzetti) 2·00 2·10
890 $5 "The Virgin and Child with Angels in a Garden with a Rose Hedge" (Stefano da Verona) .. 2·40 2·50

80 "Nina" in Baracoa Harbour

1992. Anniversaries and Events. Mult.

892 10 c. Type **80** 10 10
893 75 c. Zeppelin "LZ-3" .. 35 40
894 75 c. Blind man with guide dog (vert) 35 40
895 75 c. Training guide dog .. 35 40
896 $1 Ships of Columbus .. 50 55
897 $1 Adenauer, state arms and German flag .. 50 55
898 $1 "America III" and "Il Moro" (yachts) with trophy 50 55
899 $1 Hands breaking bread and emblem (vert) .. 50 55
900 $2 "Voyager 2" and planet 95 1·00
901 $3 Adenauer and children watching Berlin Airlift 1·40 1·50
902 $4 "LZ-37" in flames .. 2·00 2·10
903 $4 Adenauer and ruins in Cologne .. .. 2·00 2·10
904 $4 Mozart with his wife Constanze (vert) .. 2·00 2·10
905 $5 Adenauer and modern office blocks .. .. 2·40 2·50

ANNIVERSARIES AND EVENTS: Nos. 892, 896, 500th anniv of discovery of America by Columbus; Nos. 893, 902, 75th death anniv of Count Ferdinand von Zeppelin (airship pioneer); Nos. 894/5, 75th anniv of International Association of Lions Clubs; Nos. 897, 901, 903, 905, 25th death anniv of Konrad Adenauer (German statesman); No. 898, Americas Cup yachting championship; No. 899, International Conference on Nutrition, Rome; No. 900, International Space Year; No. 904, Death bicentenary of Mozart.

81 Olivia and Flaversham

1992. Walt Disney Cartoon Films.

907/50 60 c. × 44 mult Set of 44 .. 12·00 14·00

Nos. 907/50 were printed as five se-tenant sheetlets, each of nine different designs except for that for "Darkwing Duck" which contains eight vertical designs (Nos. 943/50). The other four sheetlets depict scenes from "The Great Mouse Detective", "Oliver and Company", "The Legend of Sleepy Hollow" and "Ducktales the Movie".

1992. 15th Death Anniv of Elvis Presley (singer). As T **260** of Dominica. Mult.

952 $1 Elvis Presley 50 55
953 $1 Elvis with guitar .. 50 55
954 $1 Elvis with microphone 50 55

82 Prince Mickey searching for Bride

1992. "Tales of Uncle Scrooge" (fairy stories). Walt Disney cartoon characters.

955/1008 60 c. × 54 mult Set of 54 .. 14·50 17·00

Nos. 955/1008 (issued as six sheetlets each of nine different designs) depict scenes from "The Princess and the Pea", "Little Red Riding Hood", "Goldilocks and the Three Bears", "The Pied Piper of Hamelin", "Hop O'-My-Thumb" and "Puss in Boots".

OFFICIAL STAMPS.

1982. Nos. 195/200 optd. **OFFICIAL.**

No.	Description	Unused	Used
O 1.	50 c. " Mary "	15	20
O 2.	50 c. Prince Charles and Lady Diana Spencer ..	35	35
O 3.	$3 " Alexandra ".. ..	35	35
O 4.	$3 Prince Charles and Lady Diana Spencer ..	80	80
O 5.	$3.50 " Britannia " ..	50	50
O 6.	$3.50 Prince Charles and Lady Diana Spencer ..	1·00	1·00

APPENDIX

The following stamps have either been issued in excess of postal needs, or have not been made available to the public in reasonable quantities at face value.

BEQUIA

1984.

Leaders of the World. Railway Locomotives (1st series). Two designs for each value, the first showing technical drawings and the second the locomotive at work. 1, 5, 10, 25, 35, 45 c., $1.50 $2, each ×2.

Grenadines of St. Vincent 1982 Ships definitives (Nos. 208/24) optd. **"BEQUIA".** 1, 3, 5, 6, 10, 15, 20, 25, 30, 50, 60, 75 c., $1, $2, $3, $5, $10.

Leaders of the World. Automobiles (1st series). Two designs for each value, the first showing technical drawings and the second the car in action. 5, 40 c., $1, $1.50, each ×2.

Leaders of the World, Olympic Games, Los Angeles. 1, 10, 60 c., $3, each ×2.

Leaders of the World. Railway Locomotives (2nd series). Two designs for each value, the first showing technical drawings and the second the locomotive at work. 1, 10, 20, 25, 75 c., $1, $2.50, $3, each ×2.

Leaders of the World. Automobiles (2nd series). Two designs for each value, the first showing technical drawings and the second the car in action. 5, 10, 20, 25, 75 c., $1.50, $3, each ×2.

1985.

Leaders of the World. Railway Locomotives (3rd series). Two designs for each value, the first showing technical drawings and the second the locomotive at work. 25, 55, 60 c, $2, each ×2.

Leaders of the World. Dogs. 25, 35, 55 c., $2, each ×2.

Leaders of the World. Warships of the Second World War. Two designs for each value, the first showing technical drawings and the second the ship at sea. 15, 50 c., $1, $1.50, each ×2.

Leaders of the World. Flowers. 10, 20, 70 c., $2.50, each ×2.

Leaders of the World. Automobiles (3rd series). Two designs for each value, the first showing technical drawings and the second the car in action. 5, 25, 50 c., $1, $1.25, $2, each ×2.

Leaders of the World. Railway Locomotives (4th series). Two designs for each value, the first showing technical drawings and the second the locomotive at work. 25, 55, 60, 75 c., $1, $2.50, each ×2.

Leaders of the World. Life and Times of Queen Elizabeth the Queen Mother. Two designs for each value, showing different portraits. 20, 65 c., $1.35, $1.80, each ×2.

Leaders of the World. Automobiles (4th series). Two designs for each value, the first showing technical drawings and the second the car in action. 10, 35, 75 c., $1.15, $1.50, $2, each ×2.

1986

Leaders of the World. Automobiles (5th sereis). Two designs for each value, the first showing technical drawings and the second the car in action. 25, 50, 65, 75 c., $1, $3, each ×2.

60th Birthday of Queen Elizabeth II. 5, 75 c., $2, $8.

World Cup Football Championship, Mexico. 1, 2, 5, 10, 45, 60, 75 c., $1.50, $1.50, $2, $3.50, $6.

Royal Wedding (1st issue). 60 c., $2, each ×2.

Railway Engineers and Locomotives. $1, $2.50, $3, $4.

Royal Wedding (2nd issue) Previous issue optd. "Congratulation T.R.H. The Duke & Duchess of York" 60 c., $2, each ×2.

Automobiles (6th series). Two designs for each value, the first showing technical drawings and the second the car in action. 20, 60, 75, 90 c., $1, $3, each ×2.

1987.

Automobiles (7th series). Two designs for each value, the first showing technical drawings and the second the car in action. 5, 20, 35, 60, 75, 80 c., $1.25, $1.75, each ×2.

Royal Ruby Wedding 15, 75 c., $1, $2.50, $5.

Railway Locomotives (5th series). Two designs for each value, the first showing technical drawings and the second the locomotive at work. 15, 25, 40, 50, 60, 75 c., $1, $2, each ×2.

1988.

Explorers. 15, 50 c., $1.75, $2, $2.50, $3, $3.50, $4.

International Lawn Tennis Players. 15, 45, 80 c., $1.25, $1.75, $2, $2.50, $3.

1989.

"Philexfrance 89" International Stamp Exhibition, Paris. Walt Disney Cartoon Characters. 1, 2, 3, 4, 5, 10 c., $5, $6.

UNION ISLAND

1984.

Leaders of the World. British Monarchs. Two designs for each value, forming a composite picture. 1, 5, 10, 20, 60 c., $3, each ×2.

Leaders of the World. Railway Locomotives (1st series). Two designs for each value, the first showing technical drawings and the second the locomotive at work. 5, 60 c., $1, $2.

Grenadines of St. Vincent 1982 Ships definitives (Nos. 208/24) optd. **"UNION ISLAND".** 1, 3, 5, 6, 10, 15, 20, 25, 30, 50, 60, 75 c., $1, $2, $3, $5, $10.

Leaders of the World. Cricketers. Two designs for each value, the first showing a portrait and the second the cricketer in action. 1, 10, 15, 55, 60, 75 c., $1.50, $3, each ×2.

Leaders of the World. Railway Locomotives (2nd series). Two designs for each value, the first showing technical drawings and the second the locomotive at work. 5, 10, 20, 25, 75 c., $1, $2.50, $3, each ×2.

1985.

Leaders of the World. Automobiles (1st series). Two designs for each value, the first showing technical drawings and the second the car in action 1, 50, 75 c., $2.50, each ×2.

Leaders of the World. Birth Bicentenary of John J. Audubon (ornithologist). Birds. 15, 50 c., $1, $1.50, each ×2.

Leaders of the World. Railway Locomotives (3rd series). Two designs for each value, the first showing technical drawings and the second the locomotive at work. 5, 50, 60 c., $2, each ×2.

Leaders of the World. Butterflies. 15, 25, 75 c., $2, each ×2.

Leaders of the World. Automobiles (2nd series). Two designs for each value, the first showing technical drawings and the second the car in action. 5, 60 c., $1, $1.50, each ×2.

Leaders of the World. Automobiles (3rd series). Two designs for each value, the first showing technical drawings and the second the car in action. 10, 55, 60, 75, 90 c., $1, $1.50, $2, each ×2.

Leaders of the World. Life and Times of Queen Elizabeth the Queen Mother. Two designs for each value, showing different portraits. 55, 70 c., $1.05, $1.70, each ×2.

1986.

Leaders of the World. Railway Locomotives (4th series). Two designs for each value, the first showing technical drawings and the second the locomotive at work. 15, 30, 45, 60, 75 c., $1.50, $2.50, $3, each ×2.

60th Birthday of Queen Elizabeth II. 10, 60 c., $2, $8.

World Cup Football Championship, Mexico. 1, 10, 30, 75 c., $1, $2.50, $3, $6.

Royal Wedding (1st issue). 60 c., $2, each ×2.

Automobiles (4th series). Two designs for each value, the first showing technical drawings and the second the car in action. 10, 60, 75 c., $1, $1.50, $3, each ×2.

Royal Wedding (2nd issue) Previous issue optd. as Bequia. 60 c., $2, each ×2.

Railway Locomotive (5th series). Two designs for each value, the first showing technical drawings and the second the locomotive at work. 15, 45, 60, 75 c., $1, $2, $3, each ×2.

1987.

Railway Locomotives (6th series). Two designs for each value, the first showing technical drawings and the second the locomotive at work. 15, 25, 40, 50, 60, 75 c., $1, $2, each ×2.

Royal Ruby Wedding. 15, 45 c., $1.50, $3, $4.

Railway Locomotives (7th series). Two designs for each value, the first showing technical drawings the second the locomotive at work. 15, 20, 30, 45, 50, 75 c., $1, $1.50, each ×2.

1989.

"Philexfrance 89" International Stamp Exhibition, Paris. Walt Disney Cartoon Characters. 1, 2, 3, 4, 5, 10 c., $5, $6.

GRIQUALAND WEST

A Br. colony, later annexed to the Cape of Good Hope and now part of South Africa, whose stamps it uses.

12 pence = 1 shilling.
20 shillings = 1 pound.

1874. Stamp of Cape of Good Hope (" Hope " seated) with pen-and-ink surch.

No.	Type	Description	Unused	Used
1.	4.	1d. on 4d. blue	£650	£1100

1877. Stamps of Cape of Good Hope (" Hope " seated) optd. **G.W.**

No.	Type	Description	Unused	Used
2.	6.	1d. red	£400	70·00
3.		4d. blue	£300	60·00

1877. Stamps of Cape of Good Hope (" Hope " seated) optd. **G** in various types.

No.	Type	Description	Unused	Used
14	6	½d. grey	4·50	6·00
25		1d. red	7·00	3·50
6a	4	4d. blue	£110	18·00
26	6	4d. blue	12·00	3·50
8a	4	6d. violet	60·00	17·00
9a		1s. green	75·00	13·00
29	6	5s. orange	£225	6·00

GUERNSEY

An island in the English Channel off N.W. coast of France. Occupied by German Forces from June, 1940, to May, 1945. "Regional" issues were introduced from 1958 (see after GREAT BRITAIN); the island's Postal Service was organised as a separate Postal Administration in 1969.

(a) War Occupation Issues.

1.

1941.

No.	Type	Description	Unused	Used
1f	1	½d. green	2·50	2·75
2		1d. red	2·50	1·25
3a		2½d. blue	5·50	4·50

(b) Independent Postal Administration.

4. Castle Cornet and Edward the Confessor.

5. View of Sark.

1969.

No.	Type	Description	Unused	Used
13.	4.	½d. mauve and black ..	10	10
14.	–	1d. blue and black* ..	10	10
14b.	–	1d. blue and black* ..	50	60
15.	–	1½d. brown and black ..	10	10
16.	–	2d. multicoloured ..	10	10
17.	–	3d. multicoloured ..	15	15
18.	–	4d. multicoloured ..	25	25
19.	–	5d. multicoloured ..	25	15
20.	–	6d. multicoloured ..	30	35
21.	–	9d. multicoloured ..	70	60
22.	–	1s. multicoloured	55	45
23.	–	1s. 6d. green and black *	40	50
23b.	–	1s. 6d. green & black * ..	6·00	1·90
24.	–	1s. 9d. multicoloured ..	2·50	3·00
25.	–	2s. 6d. violet and black ..	10·00	4·50
26.	5.	5s. multicoloured	4·00	6·00
27.	–	10s. multicoloured ..	27·00	28·00
28a.	–	£1 multicoloured	2·00	2·00

DESIGNS—As Type **4:** 1d. Map and William I. 1½d. Martello Tower and Henry II. 2d. Arms of Sark and King John. 3d. Arms of Alderney and Edward III. 4 d. Guernsey Lily and Henry V. 5d. Arms of Guernsey and Elizabeth I. 6d. Arms of Alderney and Charles II. 9d. Arms of Sark and George III. 1s. Arms of Guernsey and Queen Victoria. 1s. 6d., as 1d. 1s. 9d., Guernsey Lily and Elizabeth I. 2s. 6d., Martello Tower and King John. As Type **5:** 10s. View of Alderney. 20s. View of Guernsey.

*On Nos. 14 and 23 the degree of latitude is inscr. (incorrectly) as 40° 30′ N. On Nos. 14b and 23b it has been corrected to 49° 30′.

19. Isaac Brock as Colonel.

1969. Birth Bicentenary of Sir Isaac Brock. Multicoloured.

No.	Description	Unused	Used
29.	4d. Type **19**	30	30
30.	5d. Sir Isaac Brock as Major-General	30	30
31.	1s. 9d. Isaac Brock as Ensign	2·00	2·00
32.	2s. 6d. Arms and flags ..	2·00	2·00

The 2s. 6d., is horiz.

23. H.M.S. "L103" (landing craft) entering St. Peter's Harbour.

1970. 25th Anniversary of Liberation.

No.	Type	Description	Unused	Used
33.	23.	4d. blue	35	50
34.	–	5d. brown, lake and grey	35	50
35.	–	1s. 6d. brn. & buff	3·75	2·25

DESIGNS—HORIZ. 5d. British ships entering St. Peter Port. VERT. 1s. 6d., Brigadier Snow reading Proclamation.

26. Guernsey " Toms ".

1970. Agriculture and Horticulture. Mult.

No.	Description	Unused	Used
36.	4d. Type **26**	80	30
37.	5d. Guernsey cow	90	30
38.	9d. Guernsey bull	11·00	3·25
39.	1s. 6d. Freesias	11·50	3·75

32. St. Peter's Church, Sark.

1970. Christmas. Churches (1st series). Mult.

No.	Description	Unused	Used
40.	4d. St. Anne's Church, Alderney (horiz.)	35	20
41.	5d. St. Peter's Church (horiz.)	45	25
42.	9d. Type **32**	2·00	1·50
43.	1s. 6d. St. Tugual Chapel, Herm	2·75	1·50

See also Nos. 63/6.

34. Martello Tower and King John.

1971. Decimal currency. Nos. 13, etc., but with new colours and decimal values as T **34.**

No.	Description	Unused	Used
44.	½p. mve. & blk. (as No. 13)	10	15
45.	1p. blue & blk (as No. 14b)	10	10
46.	1½p. brn. & blk. (as No. 15)	15	15
47.	2p. mult. (as No. 18) ..	15	15
48.	2½p. mult. (as No. 19) ..	15	10
49.	3p. mult. (as No. 17) ..	20	20
50.	3½p. mult. (as No. 24) ..	25	25
51.	4p. mult. (as No. 16) ..	35	25
52.	5p. grn. & blk. (as No. 14b)	30	25
53.	6p. mult. (as No. 20) ..	30	35
54.	7½p. mult. (as No. 22) ..	40	45
55.	9p. mult. (as No. 21) ..	1·00	1·25
56a.	10p. violet & blk. (as No. 25)	1·00	1·50
57a.	20p. mult. (as No. 26) ..	80	75
58.	50p. mult. (as No. 27) ..	2·00	3·25

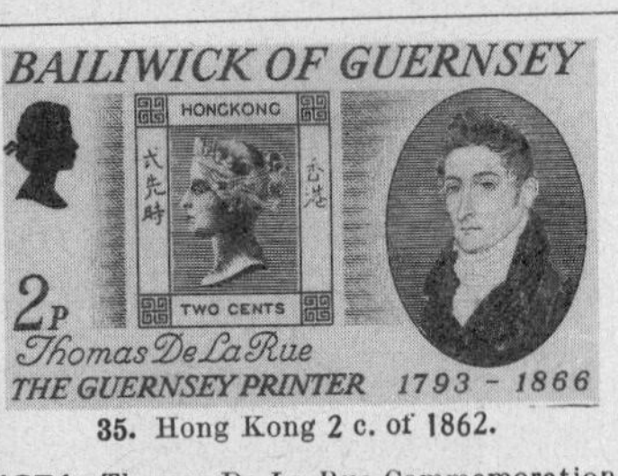

35. Hong Kong 2 c. of 1862.

1971. Thomas De La Rue Commemoration.

No.	Type	Description	Unused	Used
59.	35.	2p. purple	50	30
60.	–	2½p. red	50	30
61.	–	4p. green	3·50	2·50
62.	–	7½p. blue	3·50	2·50

DESIGNS (Each showing portraits of Queen Elizabeth and Thomas De La Rue): 2½p. Great Britain 4d. of 1855–7. 4p. Italy. 5c. of 1862. 7½p. Confederate States 5c. of 1862.

1971. Christmas. Churches (2nd series). As T 32. Multicoloured.

No.	Description	Unused	Used
63.	2p. Ebenezer Church, St. Peter Port (horiz.)	25	25
64.	2½p. Church of St. Pierre du Bois (horiz.)	25	25
65.	5p. St. Joseph's Church, St. Peter Port	2·50	2·50
66.	7½p. Church of St. Philippe de Torteval	2·50	2·50

37. "Earl of Chesterfield" (1794).

1972. Mail Packet Ships (1st series). Mult.

No.	Description	Unused	Used
67.	2p. Type **37**	25	15
68.	2½p. "Dasher" (1827)	25	20
69.	7½p. "Ibex" (1891)	75	75
70.	9p. "Alberta" (1900)	1·00	85

See also Nos. 80/3.

1972. World Conf. of Guernsey Breeders, Guernsey. As No. 38 but size 48×29 mm, and additional inscription with face value changed.

No.	Description	Unused	Used
71.	5p. multicoloured	1·00	1·00

39. Bermuda Buttercup.

1972. Wild Flowers. Multicoloured.

No.	Description	Unused	Used
72.	2p. Type **39**	15	20
73.	2½p. Heath Spotted Orchid (vert.)	15	20
74.	7½p. Kaffir Fig	80	80
75.	9p. Scarlet Pimpernel (vert.)	1·10	1·10

40. Angels adoring Christ.

1972. Royal Silver Wedding and Christmas. Stained-glass windows from Guernsey Churches. Multicoloured.

No.	Description	Unused	Used
76.	2p. Type **40**	10	10
77.	2½p. The Epiphany	15	15
78.	7½p. The Virgin Mary	75	75
79.	9p. Christ	80	80

See also Nos. 89/92.

1973. Mail Packet Boats (2nd series). As T 37. Multicoloured.

No.	Description	Unused	Used
80.	2½p. "St. Julien" (1925)	10	10
81.	3p. "Isle of Guernsey" (1930)	20	20
82.	7½p. "St. Patrick" (1947)	65	60
83.	9p. "Sarnia" (1961)	85	75

41. Supermarine "Sea Eagle".

1973. 50th Anniv. of Air Service. Mult.

No.	Description	Unused	Used
84.	2½p. Type **41**	10	10
85.	3p. Westland "Wessex"	15	15
86.	5p. De Havilland "Rapide"	25	25
87.	7½p. Douglas "Dakota"	55	50
88.	9p. Vickers "Viscount"	60	55

42. "The Good Shepherd".

1973. Christmas. Stained-glass windows from Guernsey Churches. Multicoloured.

No.	Description	Unused	Used
89.	2½p. Type **42**	10	10
90.	3p. Christ at the well of Samaria	10	10
91.	7½p. St. Dominic	30	30
92.	20p. Mary and the Child Jesus	60	60

43. Princess Anne and Capt. Mark Phillips.

1973. Royal Wedding.

No.	Type	Description	Unused	Used
93.	43.	25p. multicoloured	85	80

44. "John Lockett", 1875.

1974. 150th Anniv. of Royal National Life-boat Institution. Multicoloured.

No.	Description	Unused	Used
94.	2½p. Type **44**	10	10
95.	3p. "Arthur Lionel", 1912	10	10
96.	8p "Euphrosyne Kendal", 1954	45	45
97.	10p. "Arun", 1972	45	45

45. Private, East Regt., 1815. **46.** Driver, Field Battery Royal Guernsey Artillery, 1848.

1974. Guernsey Militia. Multicoloured.

(a) As Type **45**.

No.	Description	Unused	Used
98.	½p. Type **45**	10	10
99.	1p. Officer, 2nd North Regt., 1825	10	10
100.	1½p. Gunner, Guernsey Artillery, 1787	10	10
101.	2p. Gunner, Guernsey Artillery, 1815	10	10
102.	2½p. Corporal, Royal Guernsey Artillery, 1868	10	10
103.	3p. Field Officer, Royal Guernsey Artillery, 1895	10	10
104.	3½p. Sergeant, 3rd Regt., 1867	10	10
105.	4p. Officer, East Regt., 1822	15	15
105a.	5p. Field Officer, Royal Guernsey Artillery	15	15
106.	5½p. Colour-Sergeant of Grenadiers, East Regt., 1833	20	25
107.	6p. Officer, North Regt., 1832	20	25
107a.	7p. Officer, East Regt., 1822	25	25
108.	8p. Field Officer, Rifle Company, 1868	25	30
109.	9p. Private, 4th West Regt., 1785	30	35
110.	10p. Field Officer, 4th West Regt., 1824	30	35

(b) As Type **46**.

No.	Description	Unused	Used
111.	20p. Type **46**	55	55
112.	50p. Officer, Field Battery, Royal Guernsey Artillery, 1868	1·50	1·40
113.	£1 Cavalry Trooper, Light Dragoons, 1814 (horiz.)	3·00	2·75

47. Badge of Guernsey and U.P.U. Emblem.

1974. Centenary of U.P.U. Multicoloured.

No.	Description	Unused	Used
114.	2½p. Type **47**	10	10
115.	3p. Map of Guernsey	10	10
116.	8p. U.P.U. Building, Berne, and Guernsey flag	45	45
117.	10p. "Salle des Etats"	45	45

48. "Cradle Rock".

1974. Renoir Paintings. Multicoloured.

No.	Description	Unused	Used
118.	3p. Type **48**	10	10
119.	5½p. "Moulin Huet Bay"	15	15
120.	8p. "Au Bord de la Mer" (vert.)	40	40
121.	10p. Self-portrait (vert.)	45	45

49. Guernsey Spleenwort.

1975. Guernsey Ferns. Multicoloured.

No.	Description	Unused	Used
122.	3½p. Type **49**	10	10
123.	4p. Sand Quillwort	10	10
124.	8p. Guernsey Quillwort	40	40
125.	10p. Least Adder's Tongue	45	45

50. Victor Hugo House.

1975. Victor Hugo's Exile in Guernsey. Mult.

No.	Description	Unused	Used
126.	3½p. Type **50**	10	10
127.	4p. Candie Gardens (vert.)	10	10
128.	8p. United Europe Oak, Hauteville (vert.)	40	40
129.	10p. Tapestry Room, Hauteville	50	50

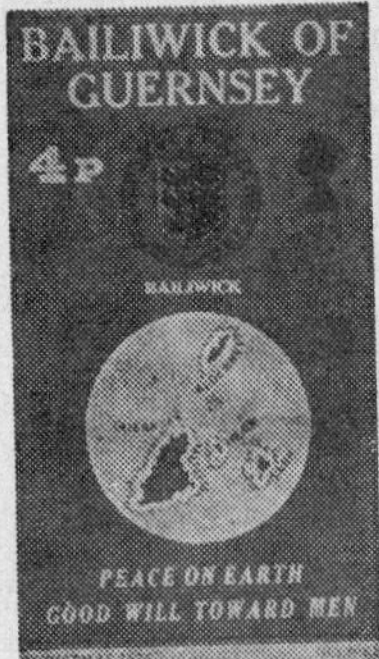

51. Globe and Seal of Bailiwick.

1975. Christmas. Multicoloured.

No.	Description	Unused	Used
131.	4p. Type **51**	10	10
132.	6p. Guernsey flag	15	15
133.	10p. Guernsey flag and Alderney shield (horiz.)	35	35
134.	12p. Guernsey flag and Sark shield (horiz.)	50	50

52. Les Hanois.

1976. Bailiwick Lighthouses. Mult.

No.	Description	Unused	Used
135.	4p. Type **52**	10	10
136.	6p. Les Casquets	15	15
137.	11p. Quesnard	40	35
138.	13p. Point Robert	45	50

53. Milk Can.

1976. Europa.

No.	Type	Description	Unused	Used
139.	53.	10p. brown and green	30	30
140.	–	25p. grey and blue	70	70

DESIGN: 25p. Christening Cup.

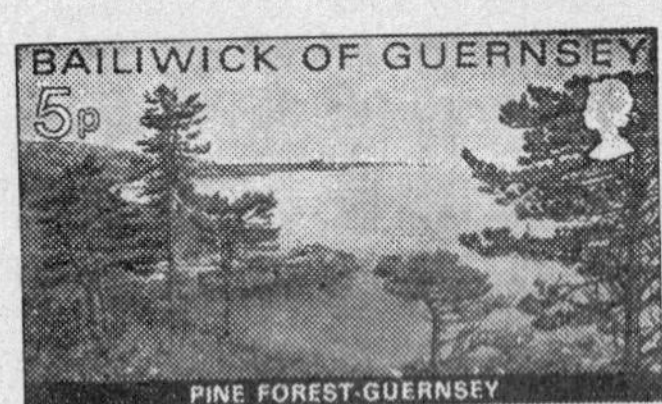

54. Pine Forest, Guernsey.

1976. Bailiwick Views. Multicoloured.

No.	Description	Unused	Used
141.	5p. Type **54**	15	10
142.	7p. Herm and Jethou	15	15
143.	11p. Grand Greve Bay, Sark (vert.)	40	35
144.	13p. Trois Vaux Bay, Alderney (vert.)	40	50

55. Royal Court House, Guernsey.

1976. Christmas. Buildings. Multicoloured.

No.	Description	Unused	Used
145.	5p. Type **55**	15	10
146.	7p. Elizabeth College, Guernsey	15	15
147.	11p. La Seigneurie, Sark	40	35
148.	13p. Island Hall, Alderney	40	50

56. Queen Elizabeth II.

1977. Silver Jubilee. Multicoloured.
149. 7p. Type 56 .. .. 20 20
150. 35p. Queen Elizabeth (half-length portrait) .. 80 80

57. Woodland, Talbots Valley.

1977. Europa. Multicoloured.
151. 7p. Type 57 .. .. 25 25
152. 25p. Pastureland, Talbots Valley 75 75

58. Statue-menhir, Castel.

1977. Prehistoric Monuments. Multicoloured.
153. 5p. Type 58 .. .. 10 10
154. 7p. Megalithic tomb, St. Saviour (horiz.) .. 15 15
155. 11p. Cist, Tourgis (horiz.) .. 40 35
156. 13p. Statue-menhir, St. Martin 50 50

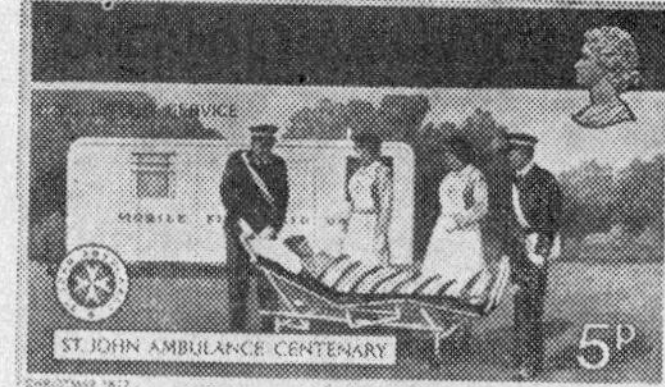

59. Mobile First Aid Unit.

1977. Christmas and St. John Ambulance Centenary. Multicoloured.
157. 5p. Type 59 .. .. 10 10
158. 7p. Mobile radar unit .. 15 15
159. 11p. Marine ambulance "Flying Christine II" (vert.) .. 40 35
160. 13p. Cliff rescue (vert.) .. 50 50

60. View from Clifton, c. 1830.

1978. Old Guernsey Prints (1st series).
161. 60. 5p. black and green .. 10 10
162. – 7p. black and stone .. 15 15
163. – 11p. black and pink .. 40 35
164. – 13p. black and blue .. 50 50
DESIGNS: 7p. Market Square, St. Peter Port, c. 1838. 11p. Petit-Bo Bay, c. 1839. 13p. The Quay, St. Peter Port, c. 1830.
See also Nos. 249/52.

61. " Prosperity " Memorial.

1978. Europa. Multicoloured.
165. 5p. Type 61 .. .. 35 35
166. 7p. Victoria Monument (vert.) 40 40

62. Queen Elizabeth II.

1978. 25th Anniversary of Coronation.
167. 62. 20p. black, grey & blue 60 60

1978. Royal Visit. As T 62, but inscr. "VISIT OF H.M. THE QUEEN AND H.R.H. THE DUKE OF EDINBURGH JUNE 28–29, 1978 TO THE BAILIWICK OF GUERNSEY".
168. 7p. black, grey and green 25 25

63. Northern Gannet.

1978. Birds. Multicoloured.
169. 5p. Type 63 .. .. 15 15
170. 7p. Firecrest 25 25
171. 11p. Dartford warbler .. 35 35
172. 13p. Spotted redshank .. 40 40

64. Solanum.

1978. Christmas. Multicoloured.
173. 5p. Type 64 .. .. 10 10
174. 7p. Christmas Rose .. 20 20
175. 11p. Holly (vert.) .. 40 30
176. 13p. Mistletoe (vert.) .. 50 50

65. One Double Coin, 1830.

67. Pillar-box and Postmark, 1853, and Mail Van and Postmark, 1979.

1979. Coins.
177. 65. ½p. multicoloured .. 10 10
178. – 1p. multicoloured .. 10 10
179. – 2p. multicoloured .. 10 10
180. – 4p. multicoloured .. 10 10
181. – 5p. blk., silver and brn. 15 10
182. – 6p. black, silver and red 15 15
183. – 7p. blk., silver & green 15 20
184. – 8p. blk., silver & brown 20 20
185. – 9p. multicoloured .. 25 20
186. – 10p. multicoloured (green background) 50 50
187. – 10p. multicoloured (orge. background) 35 30
188. – 11p. multicoloured .. 25 30
189. – 11½p. multicoloured .. 25 30
190. – 12p. multicoloured .. 30 30
191. – 13p. multicoloured .. 30 30
192. – 14p. black, silver & blue 30 30
193. – 15p. blk., silver & brn. 35 35
194. – 20p. blk., silver & brn. 50 45
195. – 50p. black, silver & red 1·25 1·25
196. – £1 black, silver & green 2·40 2·40
197. – £2 black, silver and blue 4·75 4·75
198. – £5 multicoloured .. 10·00 10·50
DESIGNS:—VERT. (as Type 65). 1p. Two doubles, 1899. 2p. Four doubles, 1902. 4p. Eight doubles, 1959. 5p. Three pence, 1956. 6p. Five new pence, 1968. 7p. Fifty new pence, 1969. 8p. Ten new pence, 1970. 9p. Half new penny, 1971. 10p. (both) One new penny, 1971. 11p. Two new pence, 1971. 11½p. Half penny, 1979. 12p. One penny, 1977. 13p. Two pence, 1977. 14p. Five pence, 1977. 15p. Ten pence, 1977. 20p. Twenty-five pence, 1972. (26×45 mm.) 50p. William I commemorative 10s., 1966. £5, Seal of the Bailiwick. HORIZ. (45×26 mm.) £1, Silver Jubilee crown. 1977. £2, Royal Silver Wedding crown. 1972.

1979. Europa. Communications. Multicoloured.
201. 6p. Type 67 .. .. 30 30
202. 8p. Telephone, 1897, and telex machine, 1979 .. 30 30

68. Steam Tram, 1879.

1979. History of Public Transport. Mult.
203. 6p. Type 68 .. .. 15 15
204. 8p. Electric tram, 1896 .. 20 20
205. 11p. Motor bus, 1911 .. 40 35
206. 13p. Motor bus, 1979 .. 50 45

69. Bureau and Postal Headquarters.

1979. 10th Anniv. of Guernsey Postal Administration. Multicoloured.
207. 6p. Type 69 .. .. 15 15
208. 8p. "Mails and telegrams" 25 15
209. 13p. "Parcels" 30 35
210. 15p. "Philately" .. 40 45

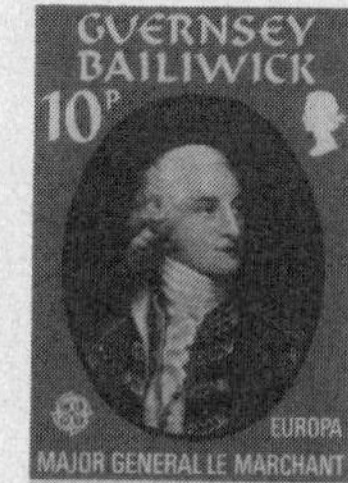

70. Major-General Le Marchant.

1980. Europa Personalities. Multicoloured.
212. 10p. Type 70 .. .. 35 35
213. 13½p. Admiral Lord de Saumarez 45 45

71. Policewoman with Lost Child.

1980. 60th Anniv. Guernsey Police Force. Multicoloured.
214. 7p. Type 71 .. .. 15 15
215. 15p. Motorcycle escort .. 60 45
216. 17½p. Dog-handler .. 65 50

72. Golden Guernsey Goat.

1980. Golden Guernsey Goats. Multicoloured.
217. 7p. Type 72 .. .. 20 20
218. 10p. Head of goat .. 40 35
219. 15p. Goat 60 45
220. 17½p. Goat and kids .. 75 60

73. " Sark Cottage ".

1980. Peter Le Lievre Paintings. Multicoloured.
221. 7p. Type 73 .... .. 30 20
222. 10p. " Moulin Huet " .. 35 25
223. 13½p. " Boats at Sea " .. 40 30
224. 15p. " Cow Lane " (vert.) 50 40
225. 17½p. " Peter Le Lievre " (vert.) 55 50

74. "Polyommatus icarus".

1981. Butterflies. Multicoloured.
226 8p. Type 74 .. .. 25 25
227 12p. "Vanessa atalanta" .. 40 40
228 22p. "Aglais urticae" .. 75 70
229 25p. "Lasionmmata megera" 85 90

75. Sailors paying respect to " Le Petit Bonhomme Andriou " (rock resembling head of a man).

76. Prince Charles.

1981. Europa. Folklore.
230. 75. 12p. gold, brown and light brown 45 45
231. – 18p. gold, blue and light blue 55 55
DESIGN: 18p. Fairies and Guernsey Lily.

1981. Royal Wedding. Multicoloured.
232. 8p. Type 76 .. .. 20 20
233. 8p. Prince Charles and Lady Diana Spencer .. 20 20
234. 8p. Lady Diana 20 20
235. 12p. Type 76 .. .. 30 30
236. 12p. As No. 233 .. .. 30 30
237. 12p. As No. 234 .. .. 30 30
238. 25p. Royal Family (49×32 mm.) 75 75

77. Sark Launch.

1981. Inter-island Transport. Multicoloured.
240. 8p. Type 77 .. .. 20 20
241. 12p. "Trislander" aero-plane 40 40
242. 18p. Hydrofoil 60 60
243. 22p. Herm catamaran .. 75 75
244. 25p. "Sea Trent" (coaster) 85 85

78. Rifle Shooting.

1981. International Year for Disabled Persons. Multicoloured.
245. 8p. Type **78** 20 20
246. 12p. Riding 50 40
247. 22p. Swimming 75 65
248. 25p. " Work " 80 70

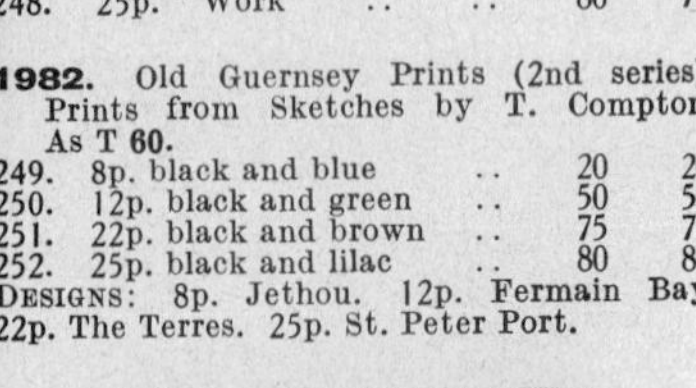

1982. Old Guernsey Prints (2nd series). Prints from Sketches by T. Compton. As T **60**.
249. 8p. black and blue .. 20 20
250. 12p. black and green .. 50 50
251. 22p. black and brown .. 75 75
252. 25p. black and lilac .. 80 80
DESIGNS: 8p. Jethou. 12p. Fermain Bay. 22p. The Terres. 25p. St. Peter Port.

79. Sir Edgar MacCulloch (founder-president) and Guille-Alles Library, St. Peter Port.

1982. Centenary of La Societe Guernesiaise. Multicoloured.
253 8p. Type **79** 20 20
254 13p. French invasion fleet crossing English Channel, 1066 ("history") 45 45
255 20p. H.M.S. "Crescent", 1793 ("history") .. 55 55
256 24p. "Aeshna sp." ("entomology") 70 70
257 26p. Common snipe caught for ringing ("ornithology") 75 75
258 29p. Samian Bowl, 160–200 A.D. ("archacology") .. 80 80
The 13p. and 20p. designs also include the Europa C.E.P.T. emblem.

80. " Sea Scouts ".

1982. 75th Anniversary of Boy Scout Movement. Multicoloured.
259. 8p. Type **80** 20 25
260. 13p. " Scouts " 50 50
261. 26p. " Cub Scouts " .. 80 80
262. 29p. " Air Scouts " .. 1·00 1·00

81. Midnight Mass.

1982. Christmas. Multicoloured.
263. 8p. Type **81** 20 20
264. 13p. Exchanging gifts .. 40 40
265. 24p. Christmas meal .. 90 90
266. 26p. Exchanging cards .. 90 90
267. 29p. Queen's Christmas message 95 95

82. Flute Player and Boats.

1982. Centenary of Boys' Brigade. Mult.
268. 8p. Type **82** 25 25
269. 13p. Cymbal player and tug 'o' war 45 45
270. 24p. Trumpet player and bible class 75 75
271. 26p. Drummer and cadets marching 85 85
272. 29p. Boy's Brigade band .. 95 95

83. Building Albert Pier Extension, 1850s.

1983. Europa. Development of St. Peter Port Harbour. Multicoloured.
273. 13p. Type **83** 35 35
274. 13p. St. Peter Port harbour, 1983 .. .. .. 35 35
275. 20p. St. Peter Port, 1680 .. 75 75
276. 20p. Artist's impression of future development scheme 75 75

84. " View at Guernsey " (Renoir).

1983. Centenary of Renoir's Visit to Guernsey. Multicoloured.
277. 9p. Type **84** 25 25
278. 13p. " Children on the Seashore " (25 × 39 mm) .. 45 45
279. 26p. " Marine, Guernsey " 80 80
280. 28p. " La Baie du Moulin Huet a travers les Arbres " 1·00 1·00
281. 31p. " Brouillard a Guernsey " 1·10 1·10

85. Launching " Star of the West ", 1869, and Capt. J. Lenfestey.

1983. Guernsey Shipping (1st series). Mult.
282. 9p. Type **85** 25 25
283. 13p. Leaving St. Peter Port 40 40
284. 26p. Off Rio Grande Bar .. 80 80
285. 28p. Off St. Lucia .. .. 1·00 1·00
286. 31p. Map of 1879-80 voyage 1·10 1·10
See also Nos. 415/19.

86. Dame of Sark as young Woman.

1984. Birth Centenary of Sibyl Hathaway, Dame of Sark. Multicoloured.
287. 9p. Type **86** 25 25
288. 13p. German occupation, 1940–45 .. .. .. 40 45
289. 26p. Royal visit, 1957 .. 90 90
290. 28p. Chief Pleas 95 95
291. 31p. The Dame of Sark rose 1·10 1·10

87. C.E.P.T. 25th Anniversary logo.

1984. Europa.
292. **87.** 13p. light bl., bl. & blk. 50 50
293. 20½p. green, deep green and black 75 75

88. The Royal Court and St. George's Flag.

1984. Links with the Commonwealth. Mult.
294. 9p. Type **88** 30 30
295. 31p. Castle Cornet and Union flag .. .. 1·10 1·10

89. St. Apolline Chapel.

1984. Views. Multicoloured.
296 1p. Little Chapel .. 10 10
297 2p. Fort Grey (horiz) .. 10 10
298 3p. Type **89** 10 10
299 4p. Petit Port (horiz) .. 10 10
300 5p. Little Russel (horiz) .. 10 10
301 6p. The Harbour, Herm (horiz) 10 15
302 7p. Saints (horiz) .. 15 20
303 8p. St. Saviour 20 20
304 9p. New Jetty (inscr "Cambridge Berth") (horiz) 20 25
305 10p. Belvoir, Herm (horiz) 25 25
306 11p. La Seigneurie, Sark (horiz) 25 25
306b 12p. Petit Bot 25 30
307 13p. St. Saviours reservoir (horiz) 30 30
308 14p. St. Peter Port .. 30 35
309 15p. Havelet 30 35
309c 16p. Hostel of St. John (horiz) 30 35
309d 18p. Le Variouf 35 40
310 20p. La Coupee, Sark (horiz) 40 45
310b 21p. King's Mills (horiz) 40 45
310c 26p. Town Church .. 50 55
311 30p. Grandes Rocques (horiz) 60 65
312 40p. Torteval Church .. 80 85
313 50p. Bordeaux (horiz) .. 1·00 1·10
314 £1 Albecq (horiz) .. 2·00 2·10
315 £2 L'Ancresse (horiz) .. 4·00 4·25
See also Nos. 398/9a.

90. "A Partridge in a Pear Tree".

91. Sir John Doyle and Coat of Arms.

1984. Christmas. "The Twelve Days of Christmas". Multicoloured.
316. 5p. Type **90** 20 20
317. 5p. "Two turtle doves" .. 20 20
318. 5p. "Three French hens" 20 20
319. 5p. "Four colly birds" .. 20 20
320. 5p "Five gold rings" .. 20 20
321. 5p. "Six geese a-laying" .. 20 20
322. 5p. "Seven swans a-swimming" 20 20
323. 5p. "Eight maids a-milking" 20 20
324. 5p. "Nine drummers drumming" 20 20
325. 5p. "Ten pipers piping" .. 20 20
326. 5p. "Eleven ladies dancing" 20 20
327. 5p. "Twelve lords a-leaping" 20 20

1984. 150th Death Anniv. of Lieut-General Sir John Doyle. Multicoloured.
328. 13p. Type **91** 40 40
329. 29p. Battle of Germantown, 1777 (horiz.) .. 1·00 1·00
330. 31p. Reclamation of Braye du Valle, 1806 (horiz.) .. 1·10 1·10
331. 34p. Mail for Alderney, 1812 (horiz.) .. .. 1·10 1·10

92. Cuckoo Wrasse.

1985. Fishes. Multicoloured.
332. 9p. Type **92** 40 40
333. 13p. Red Gurnard 60 60
334. 29p. Red Mullet .. .. 1·50 1·10
335. 31p. Mackerel .. .. 1·50 1·10
336. 34p. Sunfish .. .. 1·60 1·25

93. Dove.

1985. 40th Anniv. of Peace in Europe.
337. **93.** 22p. multicoloured .. 1·00 1·00

94. I.Y.Y. Emblem and Young People of Different Races.

1985. International Youth Year. Mult.
338. 9p. Type **94** 40 40
339. 31p. Girl Guides cooking over campfire .. .. 1·00 1·00

95. Stave of Music enclosing Flags.

1985. Europa. European Music Year. Multicoloured.
340. 14p. Type **95** 45 40
341. 22p. Stave of music and musical instruments .. 95 1·00

96. Guide Leader, Girl Guide and Brownie.

1985. 75th Anniv. of Girl Guide Movement.
342 **96** 34 p. multicoloured .. 1·25 1·25

97. Santa Claus.

1985. Christmas. Gift-bearers. Mult.

343. 5p. Type **97** 25 25
344. 5p. Lussibruden (Sweden) 25 25
345. 5p. King Balthazar .. 25 25
346. 5p. Saint Nicholas (Netherlands) 25 25
347. 5p. La Befana (Italy) .. 25 25
348. 5p. Julenisse (Denmark) .. 25 25
349. 5p. Christkind (Germany) 25 25
350. 5p. King Wenceslas (Czechoslovakia) .. 25 25
351. 5p. Shepherd of Les Baux (France) 25 25
352. 5p. King Caspar 25 25
353. 5p. Baboushka (Russia) .. 25 25
354. 5p. King Melchior 25 25

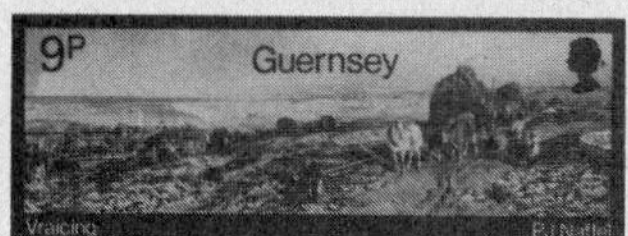

98. "Vraicing" (Illustration reduced, actual size 58 × 22 mm.)

1985. Paintings by Paul Jacob Naftel. Multicoloured.

355. 9p. Type **98** 30 30
356. 14p. "Castle Cornet" .. 40 40
357. 22p. "Rocquaine Bay" .. 90 90
358. 31p. "Little Russel" .. 1·40 1·40
359. 34p. "Seaweed gatherers" 1·50 1·50

99. Squadron off Nargue Island, 1809.

1986. 150th Death Anniv. of Admiral Lord De Saumarez. Multicoloured.

360. 9p. Type **99** 40 40
361. 14p. Battle of the Nile, 1798 50 50
362. 29p. Battle of St. Vincent, 1797 .. .. .. 1·25 1·25
363. 31p. H.M.S. "Crescent" off Cherbourg, 1793 .. .. 1·40 1·40
364. 34p. Battle of the Saints, 1782 .. .. .. 1·40 1·40

100. Profile of Queen Elizabeth II (after R. Maklouf).

1986. 60th Birthday of Queen Elizabeth II.

365. **100.** 60p. multicoloured .. 2·25 2·25

101. Northern Gannet and Nylon Net ("Operation Gannet").

1986. Europa. Nature and Environmental Protection. Multicoloured.

366. 10p. Type **101** 45 45
367. 14p. Loose-flowered orchid 65 65
368. 22p. Guernsey elm .. 85 85

102. Prince Andrew and Miss Sarah Ferguson.

1986. Royal Wedding. Multicoloured.

369. 14p. Type **102** 60 60
370. 34p. Prince Andrew and Miss Sarah Ferguson (different) (47 × 30 mm.) 1·40 1·40

103. Bowls.

1986. Sport in Guernsey. Multicoloured.

371. 10p. Type **103** 30 30
372. 14p. Cricket 50 50
373. 22p. Squash 75 75
374. 29p. Hockey .. .. 1·10 1·10
375. 31p. Swimming (horiz.) .. 1·25 1·25
376. 34p. Rifle-shooting (horiz.) 1·40 1·40

104. Guernsey Museum and Art Gallery, Candie Gardens.

1986. Centenary of Guernsey Museums. Multicoloured.

377. 14p. Type **104** 60 60
378. 29p. Fort Grey Maritime Museum .. .. .. 1·10 1·10
379. 31p. Castle Cornet .. 1·10 1·10
380. 34p. National Trust of Guernsey Folk Museum 1·40 1·40

105. "While Shepherds Watched their Flocks by Night".

107. Post Office Headquarters.

1986. Christmas. Carols. Multicoloured.

381. 6p. Type **105** 25 25
382. 6p. "In The Bleak Mid-Winter" 25 25
383. 6p. "O Little Town of Bethlehem" 25 25
384. 6p. "The Holly and the Ivy" 25 25
385. 6p. "O Little Christmas Tree" 25 25
386. 6p. "Away in a Manger" 25 25
387. 6p. "Good King Wenceslas" 25 25
388. 6p. "We Three Kings of Orient Are" 25 25
389. 6p. "Hark the Herald Angels Sing" 25 25
390. 6p. "I Saw Three Ships" 25 25
391. 6p. "Little Donkey" .. 25 25
392. 6p. "Jingle Bells" .. 25 25

1987. Europa. Modern Architecture. Mult.

394. 15p. Type **107** 55 55
395. 15p. Architect's elevation of Post Office Headquarters 55 55
396. 22p. Guernsey Grammar School 80 80
397. 22p. Architect's elevation of Grammar School .. 80 80

1987. Designs as Nos. 306, 306b, 309 and 309a but smaller.

398. 11p. La Seigneurie, Sark (22 × 18 mm.) 30 30
398a. 12p. Petit Bot (18 × 22 mm.) 25 25
399. 15p. Havelet (18 × 22 mm.) 45 45
399a. 16p. Hostel of St. John (22 × 18 mm.) 35 35

108. Sir Edmund Andros and La Plaiderie, Guernsey.

1987. 350th Birth Anniv. of Sir Edmund Andros (colonial administrator). Mult.

400. 15p. Type **108** 45 45
401. 29p. Governor's Palace, Virginia .. .. .. 1·00 1·00
402. 31p. Governor Andros in Boston .. .. .. 1·10 1·10
403. 34p. Map of New Amsterdam (New York), 1661 .. .. 1·40 1·40

109. The Jester's Warning to Young William.

1987. 900th Death Anniv. of William the Conqueror. Multicoloured.

404. 11p. Type **109** 45 35
405. 15p. Hastings battlefield .. 50 50
406. 15p. Norman soldier with pennant 50 50
407. 22p. William the Conqueror 80 75
408. 22p. Queen Matilda and Abbaye aux Dames, Caen 80 80
409. 34p. William's coronation regalia and Halley's comet .. .. .. 1·25 1·25

110. John Wesley preaching on the Quay, Alderney.

1987. Bicentenary of John Wesley's Visit to Guernsey. Multicoloured.

410. 7p. Type **110** 30 30
411. 15p. Wesley preaching at Mon Plaisir, St. Peter Port 45 45
412. 29p. Preaching at Assembly Rooms .. 1·25 1·25
413. 31p. Wesley and La Ville Baudu (early Methodist meeting place) .. 1·25 1·25
414. 34p. Wesley and first Methodist Chapel, St. Peter Port .. .. 1·25 1·25

111. "Golden Spur" off St. Sampson Harbour.

1988. Guernsey Shipping (2nd series). "Golden Spur". Multicoloured.

415. 11p. Type **111** 35 35
416. 15p. "Golden Spur" entering Hong Kong harbour 50 50
417. 29p. Anchored off Macao .. 1·25 1·25
418. 31p. In China Tea Race .. 1·25 1·25
419. 34p. "Golden Spur" and map showing voyage of 1872–74 .. .. .. 1·25 1·25

112 Rowing Boat and Bedford "Rascal" Mail Van

1988. Europa. Transport and Communications. Multicoloured.

420 16p. Type **112** 60 60
421 16p. Rowing boat and "Viscount" mail plane 60 60
422 22p. Postman on bicycle and horse-drawn carriages, Sark .. 95 95
423 22p. Postmen on bicycles and carriage 95 95

Nos. 420/1 and 422/3 were each printed together, se-tenant, the two stamps of each value forming a composite design.

113 Frederick Corbin Lukis and Lukis House, St. Peter Port

1988. Birth Bicentenary of Frederick Corbin Lukis (archaeologist). Multicoloured.

424 12p. Type **113** 40 40
425 16p. Natural history books and reconstructed pot .. 50 50
426 29p. Lukis directing excavation of Le Creux es Faies and prehistoric beaker .. .. .. 1·10 1·10
427 31p. Lukis House Observatory and garden 1·10 1·10
428 34p. Prehistoric artifacts 1·10 1·10

114 Powerboats and Rescue Helicopter off Jethou

1988. World Offshore Powerboat Championships. Multicoloured.

429 16p. Type **114** 60 60
430 30p. Powerboats in Gouliot Passage .. .. 1·10 1·10
431 32p. Start of race at St. Peter Port (vert) .. 1·10 1·10
432 35p. Admiralty chart showing course (vert) .. 1·40 1·40

115 Joshua Gosselin and Herbarium

1988. Bicentenary of Joshua Gosselin's "Flora Sarniensis". Multicoloured.

No.	Description	Unused	Used
433	12p. Type **115**	40	40
434	16p. Hares-tail grass ..	55	55
435	16p. Dried hares-tail grass	55	55
436	23p. Variegated catchfly ..	80	75
437	23p. Dried variegated catchfly	80	75
438	35p. Rock sea lavender ..	1·40	1·25

116 Coutances Cathedral, France

118 Outline Map of Guernsey

117 Le Cat (Tip Cat)

1988. Christmas. Ecclesiastical Links. Mult.

No.	Description	Unused	Used
439	8p. Type **116**	25	25
440	8p. Interior of Notre Dame du Rosaire Church, Guernsey	25	25
441	8p. Stained glass, St. Sampson's Church, Guernsey ..	25	25
442	8p. Dol-de-Bretagne Cathedral, France ..	25	25
443	8p. Bishop's throne, Town Church, Guernsey ..	25	25
444	8p. Winchester Cathedral	25	25
445	8p. St. John's Cathedral, Portsmouth	25	25
446	8p. High altar, St. Joseph's Church, Guernsey ..	25	25
447	8p. Mont Saint-Michel, France	25	25
448	8p. Chancel, Vale Church, Guernsey	25	25
449	8p. Lychgate, Forest Church, Guernsey ..	25	25
450	8p. Marmoutier Abbey, France	25	25

1989. Europa. Children's Toys and Games. Multicoloured.

No.	Description	Unused	Used
451	12p. Type **117**	40	40
452	16p. Girl with Cobo Alice doll	60	60
453	23p. Le Colimachaon (hopscotch)	1·25	1·25

1989. Coil Stamp. No value expressed.

No.	Description	Unused	Used
454	**118** (–) blue	30	35
455	(–) green	50	55

No. 454 is inscribed "MINIMUM BAILIWICK POSTAGE PAID" and No. 455 "MINIMUM FIRST CLASS POSTAGE TO UK PAID". They were initially sold at 14p. and 18p. but it is intented this will change in line with future postage rate rises.

119 Guernsey Airways DH86 "Express" and Mail Van

1989. 50th Annivs of Guernsey Airport (Nos. 456, 458, and 460) and 201 Squadron's Affiliation with Guernsey (Nos. 457, 459 and 461). Multicoloured.

No.	Description	Unused	Used
456	12p. Type **119**	50	40
457	12p. Supermarine "Southampton" flying boat at mooring ..	50	40
458	18p. B.E.A. DH89 "Rapide"	65	55
459	18p. Sunderland "Mk V" flying boat taking off ..	65	55
460	35p. Air U.K. BAe "146"	1·10	1·00
461	35p. Shackleton "Mk 3" ..	1·10	1·00

120 "Queen Elizabeth II" (June Mendoza)

1989. Royal Visit.

No.	Description	Unused	Used
462	**120** 30p. multicoloured ..	1·00	1·00

121 "Ibex" at G.W.R. Terminal, St. Peter Port

1989. Centenary of Great Western Railway Steamer Service to Channel Islands. Mult.

No.	Description	Unused	Used
463	12p. Type **121**	30	30
464	18p. "Great Western" (paddle-steamer) in Little Russel	65	65
465	29p. "St. Julien" passing Casquets Light ..	90	90
466	34p. "Roebuck" off Portland	1·25	1·10
467	37p. "Antelope" and boat train at Weymouth quay	1·40	1·25

122 Two-toed Sloth

1989. 10th Anniv of Guernsey Zoological Trust. Animals of the Rainforest. Mult.

No.	Description	Unused	Used
469	18p. Type **122**	1·00	90
470	29p. Capuchin monkey ..	1·00	90
471	32p. White-lipped tamarin	1·00	90
472	34p. Common squirrel-monkey	1·00	90
473	37p. Common gibbon ..	1·00	90

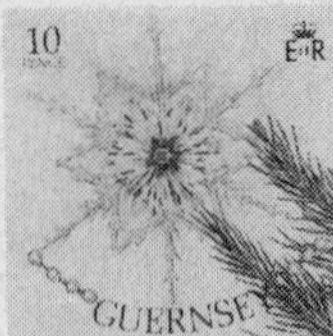

123 Star

1989. Christmas. Christmas Tree Decorations. Multicoloured.

No.	Description	Unused	Used
474	10p. Type **123**	30	30
475	10p. Fairy	30	30
476	10p. Candles	30	30
477	10p. Bird	30	30
478	10p. Present	30	30
479	10p. Carol-singer	30	30
480	10p. Christmas cracker ..	30	30
481	10p. Bauble	30	30
482	10p. Christmas stocking	30	30
483	10p. Bell	30	30
484	10p. Fawn	30	30
485	10p. Church	30	30

124 Sark Post Office, c. 1890

1990. Europa. Post Office Buildings.

No.	Description	Unused	Used
486	**124** 20p. deep brown, sepia and light brown ..	60	60
487	– 20p. multicoloured ..	60	60
488	– 24p. deep brown, sepia and light brown ..	75	75
489	– 24p. multicoloured ..	75	75

DESIGNS: No. 487, Sark Post Office, 1990; 488, Arcade Post Office counter, St. Peter Port, c. 1840; 489, Arcade Post Office counter, St. Peter Port, 1990.

125 Penny Black and Mail Steamer off St. Peter Port, 1840

1990. 150th Anniv of the Penny Black. Mult.

No.	Description	Unused	Used
490	14p. Type **125**	45	45
491	20p. Penny Red, 1841, and pillar box of 1853 ..	60	60
492	32p. Bisected 2d., 1940, and German Army band ..	1·00	90
493	34p. Regional 3d., 1958, and Guernsey emblems	1·10	95
494	37p. Independent postal administration 1½d., 1969, and queue outside Main Post Office ..	1·10	1·00

126 Lt. Philip Saumarez writing Log Book

1990. 250th Anniv of Anson's Circumnavigation. Multicoloured.

No.	Description	Unused	Used
496	14p. Type **126**	45	45
497	20p. Anson's squadron leaving Portsmouth, 1740	60	60
498	29p. Ships at St. Catherine's Island, Brazil	1·00	90
499	34p. H.M.S. "Tryal" (sloop) dismasted, Cape Horn, 1741 ..	1·10	95
500	37p. Crew of H.M.S. "Centurion" on Juan Fernandez	1·10	1·00

127 Grey Seal and Pup

1990. Marine Life. Multicoloured

No.	Description	Unused	Used
501	20p. Type **127**	60	60
502	26p. Bottle-nosed dolphin	1·00	80
503	31p. Basking shark ..	1·00	85
504	37p. Common porpoise ..	1·25	1·10

128 Blue Tit and Great Tit

1990. Christmas. Winter Birds. Multicoloured.

No.	Description	Unused	Used
505	10p. Type **128**	25	25
506	10p. Snow bunting ..	25	25
507	10p. Common kestrel ..	25	25
508	10p. Common starling ..	25	25
509	10p. Greenfinch	25	25
510	10p. European robin ..	25	25
511	10p. Winter wren ..	25	25
512	10p. Barn owl	25	25
513	10p. Mistle thrush ..	25	25
514	10p. Grey heron	25	25
515	10p. Chaffinch	25	25
516	10p. Common kingfisher ..	25	25

129 Air Raid and 1941 ½d. Stamp

1991. 50th Anniv of First Guernsey Stamps. Multicoloured.

No.	Description	Unused	Used
517	37p. Type **129**	1·10	80
518	53p. 1941 1d. stamp ..	1·50	1·50
519	57p. 1941 2½d. stamp ..	1·50	1·50

130 Visit of Queen Victoria to Guernsey, and Discovery of Neptune, 1846

1991. Europa. Europe in Space. Mult.

No.	Description	Unused	Used
520	21p. Type **130**	65	65
521	21p. Visit of Queen Elizabeth II and Prince Phillip to Sark, and "Sputnik" (first artificial satellite), 1957	65	65
522	26p. Maiden voyage of "Sarnia" (ferry), and "Vostok 1" (first manned space flight), 1961	90	75
523	26p. Cancelling Guernsey stamps, and first manned landing on Moon, 1969	90	75

131 Children in Guernsey Sailing Trust "GP14" Dinghy

1991. Cent of Guernsey Yacht Club. Mult.

524	15p. Type **131**	50	50
525	21p. Guernsey Regatta . .	80	70
526	26p. Lombard Channel Islands' Challenge race	90	90
527	31p. Rolex Swan Regatta	1·00	1·00
528	37p. Old Gaffers' Association gaff-rigged yacht	1·25	1·10

132 Pair of Oystercatchers

1991. Nature Conservation. L'Eree Shingle Bank Reserve. Mutlicoloured.

530	15p. Type **132**	40	40
531	15p. Three turnstones . .	40	40
532	15p. Dunlins and turnstones	40	40
533	15p. Curlew and turnstones	40	40
534	15p. Ringed plover with chicks	40	40
535	21p. Gull and wild flowers	50	50
536	21p. Yellow horned poppy	50	50
537	21p. Pair of stone chats and wild flowers . .	50	50
538	21p. Wild flowers on shingle	50	50
539	21p. Sea Kale on shore . .	50	50

Nos. 530/4 and 535/9 were each printed together, se-tenant, with the backgrounds forming composite designs.

133 "Rudolph the Red-nosed Reindeer" (Melanie Sharpe)

1991. Christmas. Children's Paintings. Mult.

540	12p. Type **133**	35	35
541	12p. "Christmas Pudding" (James Quinn)	35	35
542	12p. "Snowman" (Lisa Guille)	35	35
543	12p. "Snowman in Top Hat" (Jessica Ede-Golightly)	35	35
544	12p. "Robins and Christmas Tree" (Sharon Le Page)	35	35
545	12p. "Shepherds and Angels" (Anna Coquelin)	35	35
546	12p. "Nativity" (Claudine Lihou)	35	35
547	12p. "Three Wise Men" (Jonathan Le Noury) . .	35	35
548	12p. "Star of Bethlehem and Angels" (Marcia Mahy)	35	35
549	12p. "Christmas Tree" (Laurel Garfield) . .	35	35
550	12p. "Santa Claus" (Rebecca Driscoll) . .	35	35
551	12p. "Snowman and Star" (Ian Lowe)	35	35

134 Queen Elizabeth II in 1952

1992. 40th Anniv of Accession. Multicoloured.

552	23p. Type **134**	70	50
553	28p. Queen Elizabeth in 1977	75	75
554	33p. Queen Elizabeth in 1986	85	85
555	39p. Queen Elizabeth in 1991	1·10	1·00

135 Christopher Columbus

1992. 500th Anniv of Discovery of America by Columbus. Multicoloured.

556	23p. Type **135**	55	50
557	23p. Examples of Columbus's signature . .	70	50
558	28p. "Santa Maria" . .	85	90
559	28p. Map of first voyage	1·00	90

137 Stock

1992. Horticultural Exports. Multicoloured.

562	1p. "Stephanotis floribunda"	10	10
563	2p. Potted hydrangea . .	10	10
564	3p. Type **137**	10	10
565	4p. Anemones	10	10
566	5p. Gladiolus	10	15
567	6p. "Asparagus plumosus" and "Gypsophila paniculata"	10	15
568	7p. Guernsey lily	15	20
569	8p. Enchantment lily . .	15	20
570	9p. Clematis "Freckles" . .	20	25
571	10p. Alstroemeria . .	20	25
572	16p. Standard carnation (horiz)	30	35
573	20p. Spray rose	40	45
574	23p. Mixed freesia (horiz)	45	50
575	24p. Standard rose (horiz)	50	55
576	25p. Iris "Idea" (horiz) . .	50	55
577	28p. Lisianthus (horiz) . .	55	60
578	30p. Spray chrysanthemum (horiz)	60	65
579	40p. Spray carnation . .	80	85
580	50p. Single freesia (horiz)	1·00	1·10
581	£1 Floral arrangement (35 × 26½ mm)	2·00	2·10
582	£2 Chelsea Flower Show exhibit (35 × 26½ mm) . .	4·00	4·25

138 Building the Ship

1992. "Operation Asterix" (excavation of Roman ship). Multicoloured.

583	16p. Type **138**	40	35
584	23p. Loading the cargo . .	55	55
585	28p. Ship at sea	65	70
586	33p. Ship under attack . .	80	80
587	39p. Crew swimming ashore	95	95

139 Tram No. 10 decorated for Battle of Flowers

1992. Guernsey Trams. Multicoloured.

588	16p. Type **139**	40	35
589	23p. Tram No. 10 passing Hougue a la Perre . .	55	55
590	28p. Tram No. 1 at St. Sampsons	65	70
591	33p. First steam tram at St. Peter Port, 1879 . .	80	80
592	39p. Last electric tram, 1934	95	95

140 Man in Party Hat

1992. Christmas. Seasonal Fayre. Mult.

593	13p. Type **140**	25	30
594	13p. Girl and Christmas tree	25	30
595	13p. Woman and balloons	25	30
596	13p. Mince pies and champagne	25	30
597	13p. Roast turkey	25	30
598	13p. Christmas pudding . .	25	30
599	13p. Christmas cake . .	25	30
600	13p. Fancy cakes	25	30
601	13p. Cheese	25	30
602	13p. Nuts	25	30
603	13p. Ham	25	30
604	13p. Chocolate log . .	25	30

Nos. 593/604 were printed together, se-tenant, forming a composite design.

141 Rupert Bear, Bingo and Dog

1993. Rupert Bear and Friends (cartoon characters created by Mary and Herbert Tourtel).

605	**141** 24p. multicoloured . .	50	55

142 Tapestry by Kelly Fletcher

1993. Europa. Contemporary Art. Mult.

607	24p. Type **142**	50	55
608	24p. "Le Marchi a Paissaon" (etching and aquatint, Sally Reed) (48 × 33½ mm) . .	50	55
609	28p. "Red Abstract" (painting, Molly Harris)	55	60
610	28p. "Dress Shop, King's Road" (painting, Damon Bell) (48 × 33½ mm) . .	55	60

143 Arrest of Guernsey Parliamentarians, Fermain Bay

(Illustration reduced, actual size 58 × 21 mm)

1993. 350th Anniv of Siege of Castle Cornet. Multicoloured.

611	16p. Type **143**	30	35
612	24p. Parliamentary ships attacking Castle Cornet	50	55
613	28p. Parliamentary captives escaping . .	55	60
614	33p. Castle cannon firing at St. Peter Port	65	70
615	39p. Surrender of Castle Cornet, 19 December, 1651	80	85

144 Playing Cards

1993. Birth Bicentenary of Thomas de la Rue (printer).

617	**144** 16p. multicoloured . .	30	35
618	– 24p. multicoloured . .	50	55
619	– 28p. multicoloured . .	55	60
620	– 33p. red	65	70
621	– 39p. green	80	85

DESIGNS: 24p. Fountain pens; 28p. Envelope folding machine; 33p. Great Britain 1855 4d. stamp; 39p. Thomas de la Rue and Mauritius £1 banknote.

145 "The Twelve Pearls"

1993. Christmas. Stained Glass Windows by Mary-Eily de Putron from the Chapel of Christ the Healer. Multicoloured.

622	13p. Type **145**	25	30
623	13p. "Healing rays" . .	25	30
624	13p. "Hand of God over the Holy City" . .	25	30
625	13p. "Wing and Seabirds" (facing left) . .	25	30
626	13p. "Christ the Healer" . .	25	30
627	13p. "Wing and Seabirds" (facing right) . .	25	30
628	13p. "The Young Jesus in the Temple" . .	25	30
629	13p. "The Raising of Jairus's Daughter" . .	25	30
630	13p. "Suffer little Children to come unto Me" . .	25	30
631	13p. "Pilgrim's Progress"	25	30
632	13p. "The Light of the World"	25	30
633	13p. "Raphael, the Archangel of Healing, with Tobias"	25	30

146 Les Fouaillages (ancient burial ground)

1994. Europa. Archeological Discoveries. Multicoloured.

634	24p. Type **146**	50	55
635	24p. Mounted Celtic warrior	50	55
636	30p. Jars, arrow heads and stone axe from Les Fouaillages	60	65
637	30p. Sword, spear head and torque from King's Road burial	60	65

POSTAGE DUE STAMPS

D 1. Castle Cornet.

1969. Face values in black.

D 1. D 1. 1d. plum .. .. 2·00 1·25
D 2. 2d. green .. .. 2·00 1·25
D 3. 3d. red .. .. .. 3·50 4·00
D 4. 4d. blue .. .. 4·50 5·00
D 5. 5d. ochre .. .. 5·50 6·00
D 6. 6d. turquoise .. .. 8·00 8·50
D 7. 1s. brown .. .. 19·00 20·00

1971. Decimal Currency. Face values in black.

D 8. D 1. ½p. plum 10 10
D 9. 1p. green 10 10
D 10. 2p. red 10 10
D 11. 3p. blue 10 15
D 12. 4p. ochre 15 15
D 13. 5p. blue 15 15
D 14. 6p. violet 20 20
D 15. 8p. orange 25 20
D 16. 10p. brown 30 30
D 17. 15p. grey 40 40

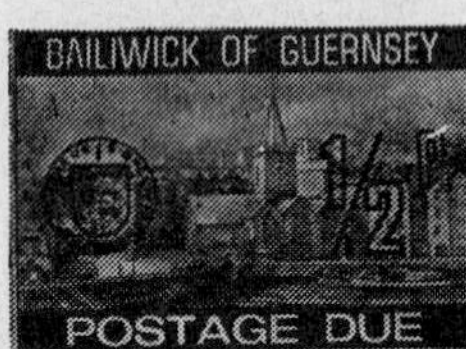

D 2. St. Peter Port.

1977. Face values in black.

D 18. D 2. ½p. brown 10 10
D 19. 1p. purple 10 10
D 20. 2p. orange 10 10
D 21. 3p. red 10 10
D 22. 4p. blue 10 10
D 23. 5p. green 15 15
D 24. 6p. green 20 20
D 25. 8p. brown 25 25
D 26. 10p. blue 30 30
D 27. 14p. green 35 35
D 28. 15p. violet 35 35
D 29. 16p. red 45 45

D 3. Milking Cow.

1982. Guernsey Scenes, c. 1900.

D 30. D 3. 1p. blue and green .. 10 10
D 31. – 2p. brn., lt. brn. & blue 10 10
D 32. – 3p. green and lilac .. 10 10
D 33. – 4p. green & orange .. 10 10
D 34. – 5p. blue and green .. 10 10
D 35. – 16p. blue & lt. blue .. 30 35
D 36. – 18p. blue and green .. 35 40
D 37. – 20p. green and blue .. 40 45
D 38. – 25p. blue and pink .. 50 55
D 39. – 30p. green & yellow .. 60 65
D 40. – 50p. brn. and blue .. 1·00 1·10
D 41. – £1 lt. brn. & brn. .. 2·00 2·10

DESIGNS: 2p. Vale Mill. 3p. Sark cottage. 4p. Quay-side, St. Peter Port. 5p. Well, Water Lane, Moulin Huet. 16p. Seaweed gathering. 18p. Upper Walk, White Rock. 20p. Cobo Bay. 25p. Saint's Bay. 30p. La Coupee, Sark. 50p. Old Harbour, St. Peter Port. £1, Greenhouses, Doyle Road, St. Peter Port.

C. ALDERNEY

The following issues are provided by the Guernsey Post Office for use on Alderney. They are also valid for postal purposes throughout the rest of the Bailiwick of Guernsey.

A 1. Island Map.

1983. Island Scenes. Multicoloured.

A 1 1p. Type A 1 .. .. 10 10
A 2 4p. Hanging Rock .. 10 10
A 3 9p. States' Building, St. Anne 20 25
A 4 10p. St. Anne's Church 20 25
A 5 11p. Yachts in Braye Bay 20 25
A 6 12p. Victoria St., St. Anne 25 30
A 7 13p. Map of Channel .. 25 25
A 8 14p. Fort Clonque .. 30 35
A 9 15p. Corblets Bay and Fort 30 35
A10 16p. Old Tower, St. Anne 30 35
A11 17p. Golf course and Essex Castle 35 40
A12 18p. Old Harbour .. 35 40
A12a 20p. Quesnard Lighthouse 40 45
A12b 21p. Braye Harbour .. 45 45
A12c 23p. Island Hall .. 45 50
A12d 24p. "J. T. Daly" (steam locomotive) 45 50
A12e 28p. "Louis Marchesi of the Round Table" (lifeboat) 55 60

Nos. A12a/e are larger, 38 × 27 mm.

A 2. Oystercatcher.

1984. Birds. Multicoloured.

A 13. 9p. Type A 2 .. .. 2·00 1·25
A 14. 13p. Turnstone .. .. 2·00 1·60
A 15. 26p. Ringed Plover .. 6·00 3·25
A 16. 28p. Dunlin .. .. 6·50 3·50
A 17. 31p. Curlew .. .. 8·00 3·75

A. 3. Wessex Helicopter of the Queen's Flight.

1985. 50th Anniversary of Alderney Airport. Multicoloured.

A 18. 9p. Type A 3 .. .. 3·50 1·90
A 19. 13p. Britten-Norman "Trislander" .. .. 4·00 2·50
A 20. 29p. De Havilland "Heron" 8·00 3·50
A 21. 31p. De Havilland "Dragon Rapide" .. .. 8·50 4·25
A 22. 34p. Saro "Windhover" .. 9·50 4·50

A 4. Royal Engineers, 1890.

1985. Regiments of the Alderney Garrison. Multicoloured.

A 23. 9p. Type A 4 .. .. 90 75
A 24. 14p. Duke of Albany's Own Highlanders, 1856 1·60 1·60
A 25. 29p. Royal Artillery, 1855 1·75 1·75
A 26. 31p. South Hampshire Regiment, 1810 .. 2·25 2·25
A 27. 34p. Royal Irish Regiment, 1782 .. 2·50 2·50

A. 5 Fort Grosnez.

1986. Alderney Forts. Multicoloured.

A 28. 10p. Type A 5 .. .. 1·50 1·10
A 29. 14p. Fort Tourgis .. 2·25 1·75
A 30. 31p. Fort Clonque .. 5·25 4·00
A 31. 34p. Fort Albert .. .. 5·50 4·25

A 6. "Liverpool" (full-rigged ship), 1902.

1987. Alderney Shipwrecks. Multicoloured.

A 32. 11p. Type A 6 .. .. 2·00 1·25
A 33. 15p. "Petit Raymond" (schooner), 1906 .. .. 3·00 1·60
A 34. 29p. "Maina" (yacht), 1910 6·50 4·50
A 35. 31p. "Burton" (steamer), 1911 .. .. .. 7·25 5·00
A 36. 34p. "Point Law" (oil tanker), 1975 .. .. 8·00 5·50

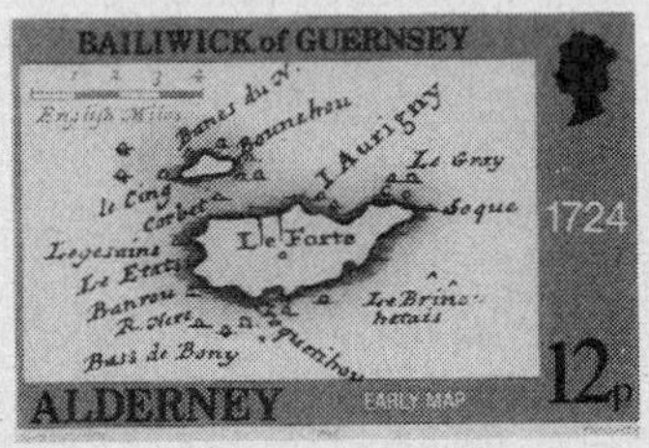

A 7 Moll's Map of 1724

1989. 250th Anniv of Bastide's Survey of Alderney.

A37 A 7 12p. multicoloured .. 40 40
A38 – 18p. black, blue & brn 60 60
A39 – 27p. black, blue & grn 1·10 1·10
A40 – 32p. black, blue & red 1·25 1·25
A41 – 35p. multicoloured .. 1·40 1·40

DESIGNS: 18p. Bastide's survey of 1739; 27p. Goodwin's map of 1831; 32p. General Staff map of 1943; 35p. Ordnance Survey map, 1988.

A 8 H.M.S. "Alderney" (bomb ketch), 1738

1990. Royal Navy Ships named after Alderney.

A42 A 8 14p. black and bistre 45 45
A43 – 20p. black and brown 60 60
A44 – 29p. black and brown 1·10 1·10
A45 – 34p. black and blue 1·10 1·10
A46 – 37p. black and blue .. 1·25 1·25

DESIGNS: 20p. H.M.S. "Alderney" (sixth rate), 1742; 29p. H.M.S. "Alderney" (sloop), 1755; 34p. H.M.S. "Alderney" (submarine), 1945; 37p. H.M.S. "Alderney" (frigate patrol vessel), 1979.

A 9 Wreck of H.M.S. "Victory", 1744

1991. Automation of The Casquets Lighthouse. Multicoloured.

A47 21p. Type A 9 .. .. 50 50
A48 26p. Lighthouse keeper's daughter rowing back to the Casquets 60 60
A49 31p. Helicopter leaving pad on St. Thomas Tower .. 70 70
A50 37p. Migrating birds over lighthouse .. .. 1·00 1·00
A51 50p. Trinity House vessel "Patricia" and arms .. 1·40 1·40

A 10 Two French Warships on Fire

1992. 300th Anniv of the Battle of La Hogue. Multicoloured.

A52 23p. Type A 10 .. .. 60 60
A53 28p. Crews leaving burning ships 70 70
A54 33p. French warship sinking 80 80
A55 50p. "The Battle of La Hogue" (47 × 32 mm) .. 1·25 1·25

Nos. A52/4 show details of the painting on the 50p. value.

A 11 Spiny Lobster

1993. Endangered Species. Marine Life. Mult.

A56 24p. Type A 11 .. .. 50 55
A57 28p. Plumose anemone .. 55 60
A58 33p. Starfish 65 70
A59 39p. Sea urchin 80 85

Nos. A56/9 were printed together, se-tenant, the backgrounds forming a composite design.

A 12 Blue-tailed Damselfly, Dark Hair Water Crowfoot and Branched Bur-reed

1994. Flora and Fauna. Multicoloured.

A60 1p. Type A 12 .. .. 10 10
A61 2p. White-toothed shrew and flax-leaved St. John's wort 10 10
A62 3p. Fulmar and kaffir fig 10 10
A63 4p. Clouded yellow (butterfly) and red clover 10 10
A64 5p. Bumble bee, prostrate broom and giant broom-rape 10 10
A65 6p. Dartford warbler and lesser dodder 15 20
A66 7p. Peacock (butterfly) and stemless thistle .. 15 20
A67 8p. Mole and bluebell .. 15 20
A68 9p. Great green grasshopper and common gorse 20 25
A69 10p. Six-spot burnet (moth) and viper's bugloss 20 25
A70 16p. Common blue (butterfly) and pyramidal orchid .. 30 35
A71 20p. Common rabbit and creeping buttercup .. 40 45
A72 24p. Great black-backed gull and sand crocus .. 50 55
A73 30p. Puffin and English stonecrop 60 65
A74 40p. Emperor (moth) and bramble 80 85
A75 50p. Pale-spined hedgehog and pink oxalis .. 1·00 1·10
A76 £1 Common tern and bermuda grass (horiz) 2·00 2·10

GUYANA

Formerly British Guiana, attained independence on 26th May, 1966, and changed its name to Guyana.

100 cents = 1 dollar.

CANCELLED REMAINDERS. In 1969 remainders of some issues were put on the market cancelled-to-order in such a way as to be indistinguishable from genuine postally used copies for all practical purposes. Our quotations which are indicated by an asterisk are the same for cancelled-to-order or postally used copies.

1966. Nos. 331, etc., optd. **GUYANA INDEPENDENCE, 1966.**

393	**55.**	1 c. black	10	10
379	–	2 c. myrtle	10	10
395	–	3 c. olive and brown	10	10
396	–	4 c. violet	10	10
397	–	5 c. red and black	10	10
398	–	6 c. green	10	10
384	–	8 c. blue	10	10
400	–	12 c. black and brown	10	10
435	–	24 c. black and orange	2·00	10
436	–	36 c. red and black	40	10
403	–	48 c. blue and brown	30	30
404	–	72 c. red and green	30	50
405	–	$1 multicoloured	45	35
406	–	$2 mauve	1·50	75
407	–	$5 blue and black	1·00	1·75

74. Flag and Map.

1966. Independence. Multicoloured.

408.	5 c. Type **74**	10	10
409.	15 c. Type **74**	10	10
410.	25 c. Arms of Guyana	10	10
411.	$1 Arms of Guyana	30	40

76. Bank Building.

1966. Opening of Bank of Guyana.

412. **76.**	5 c. multicoloured	10	10
413.	25 c. multicoloured	10	10

77. British Guiana One Cent Stamp of 1856. (¾-size illus.).

1967. World's Rarest Stamp Commem.

414. **77.**	5 c. multicoloured	10	10*
415.	25 c. multicoloured	10	10*

78. Chateau Margot.

1967. 1st Anniv. of Independence. Mult.

416.	6 c. Type **78**	10	10*
417.	15 c. Independence Arch	10	10*
418.	25 c. Fort Island	10	10*
419.	$1 National Assembly	20	15

Nos. 418/9 are horiz.

83. "Millie" (Blue and Yellow Macaw).

84. Wicket-keeping.

1967. Christmas.

441. **83.**	5 c. yell., bl., blk. & green	10	10*
443.	5 c. yell., blue, black & red	10	10*
442.	25 c. yell., blue, blk. & vio.	15	10*
444.	25 c. yell., blue, blk. & grn.	15	10*

1968. M.C.C.'s West Indies Tour. Mult.

445.	5 c. Type **84**	10	10*
446.	6 c. Batting	10	10*
447.	25 c. Bowling	30	10*

87. Sunfish.

1968. Multicoloured.

448	1 c. Type **87**	10	10
449	2 c. Pirai	10	10
450	3 c. Lukunani	10	10
451	5 c. Hassar	10	10
452	6 c. Patua	40	10
490	10 c. Spix's guan	25	20
491	15 c. Harpy eagle	30	10
492	20 c. Hoatzin	30	30
493	25 c. Guianan cock of the rock	30	10
457	40 c. Great kiskadee	60	20
495	50 c. Brazilian agouti	35	15
459	60 c. White-lipped peccary	80	10
460	$1 Paca	1·00	10
461	$2 Nine-banded armadillo	1·50	2·00
462	$5 Ocelot	2·00	3·00

Nos. 453/7 are vert.

102. "Christ of St. John of the Cross" (Salvador Dali).

1968. Easter.

463. **102.**	5 c. multicoloured	10	10*
464.	25 c. multicoloured	20	10*

103. "Efficiency Year".

1968. "Savings Bonds and Efficiency". Multicoloured.

465.	6 c. Type **103**	10	10*
466.	25 c. Type **103**	10	10*
467.	30 c. "Savings Bonds"	10	10*
468.	40 c. "Savings Bonds"	10	10*

105. Open Book, Star and Crescent.

1968. 1400th Anniv. of Holy Quran.

469. **105.**	6 c. black, gold & flesh	10	10*
470.	25 c. black, gold & lilac	10	10*
471.	30 c. black, gold & green	10	10*
472.	40 c. black, gold & blue	10	10*

107. Broadcasting Greetings.

1968. Christmas.

473. **107.**	6 c. brown, black & grn.	10	10*
474.	25 c. brown, violet & grn.	10	10*
475. –	30 c. green & turquoise	10	10*
476. –	40 c. red and turquoise	10	10*

DESIGNS: 30 c. and 40 c. Map showing Radio Link, Guyana – Trinidad.

109. Festival Ceremony.

1969. Hindu Festival of Phagwah. Mult.

477.	6 c. Type **109**	10	10
478.	25 c. Ladies spraying Scent	10	10
479.	30 c. Type **109**	10	10
480.	40 c. As No. 478	10	10

111. "Sacrament of the Last Supper" (Dali).

1969. Easter Commemoration.

481. **111.**	6 c. multicoloured	10	10
482.	25 c. multicoloured	10	10
483.	30 c. multicoloured	10	10
484.	40 c. multicoloured	10	10

112. Map showing "CARIFTA" Countries.

114. Building "Independence" (first aluminium ship).

1969. 1st Anniv. of "CARIFTA".

500. **112.**	6 c. red, blue & turquoise	10	10
501. –	25 c. lemon, brn. & red	10	10

DESIGN—HORIZ. 25 c. "Strength in Unity".

1969. 50th Anniv. of I.L.O.

502. **114.**	30 c. blue, black & silver	30	15
503. –	40 c. multicoloured	30	15

DESIGN—HORIZ. 40 c. Bauxite Processing plant.

116. Scouts raising Flag.

1969. 3rd Caribbean Scout Jamboree and Diamond Jubilee of Scouting in Guyana. Multicoloured.

504.	6 c. Type **116**	10	10
505.	8 c. Camp Fire cooking	10	10
506.	25 c. As Type **116**	10	10
507.	30 c. As 8 c.	10	10
508.	50 c. As Type **116**	15	15

118. Gandhi and Spinning Wheel.

1969. Birth Cent. of Mahatma Gandhi.

509.	**118.**	6 c. black, brn. & olive	20	30
510.		15 c. blk., brn. & lilac	25	35

119. "Mother Sally" Dance Troupe.

121. Forbes Burnham and Map.

1969. Christmas. Unissued stamps optd. as in T **119**. Multicoloured.

511.	5 c. Type **119**	10	10
512.	6 c. City Hall, Georgetown (horiz.)	10	10
513.	25 c. As Type **119**	10	10
514.	60 c. As 6 c.	20	25

1970. Republic Day.

515. **121.**	5 c. sepia, ochre and blue	10	10
516. –	6 c. multicoloured	10	10
517. –	15 c. multicoloured	10	10
518. –	25 c. multicoloured	15	10

DESIGNS—VERT. 6 c. Rural self-help. HORIZ. 15 c. University of Guyana. 25 c. Guyana House.

125. "The Descent from the Cross".

1970. Easter. Paintings by Rubens. Mult.

519.	5 c. Type **125**	10	10
520.	6 c. "Christ on the Cross"	10	10
521.	15 c. Type **125**	10	10
522.	25 c. As 6 c.	15	10

127. "Peace" and U.N. Emblem.

1970. 25th Anniv. of United Nations. Mult.

523.	5 c. Type **127**	10	10
524.	6 c. U.N. Emblem, Gold-panning and Drilling	10	10
525.	15 c. Type **127**	10	10
526.	25 c. As 6 c.	10	10

128. "Mother and Child" (Philip Moore).

1970. Christmas.

527.128.	5 c. multicoloured ..	10	10
528.	6 c. multicoloured ..	10	10
529.	15 c. multicoloured ..	10	15
530.	25 c. multicoloured ..	10	15

129. National Co-operative Bank.

1971. Republic Day.

531.129.	6 c. multicoloured ..	10	10
532.	15 c. multicoloured ..	10	10
533.	25 c. multicoloured ..	10	10

130. Racial Equality Symbol.

1971. Racial Equality Year.

534.130.	5 c. multicoloured ..	10	10
535.	6 c. multicoloured ..	10	10
536.	15 c. multicoloured ..	10	15
537.	25 c. multicoloured ..	10	15

131. Young Volunteer felling Tree (from painting by J. Criswick).

1971. 1st Anniv. of Self-help Road Project.

538.131.	5 c. multicoloured ..	10	10
539.	20 c. multicoloured ..	20	10
540.	25 c. multicoloured ..	25	10
541.	50 c. multicoloured ..	35	80

132. Yellow Allamanda.

1971. Flowering Plants. Multicoloured.

542	1 c. Pitcher Plant of Mt. Roraima	10	10
543	2 c. Type **132**	10	10
544	3 c. Hanging Heliconia ..	10	10
545	5 c. Annatto tree ..	10	10
546	6 c. Cannon-ball tree ..	10	10
547	10 c. Cattleya	2·75	10
548a	15 c. Christmas Orchid ..	65	10
549	20 c. "Paphinia cristata"	2·25	20
550	25 c. Marabunta ..	90	3·00
550ab	25 c. Marabunta ..	45	10
551	40 c. Tiger Beard ..	2·75	10
552	50 c. "Guzmania lingulata"	40	75
553	60 c. Soldier's Cap ..	40	75
554	$1 "Chelonanthus uliginoides"	40	45
555	$2 "Norantea guianensis"	60	1·50
556	$5 "Odontadenia grandiflora"	1·00	1·50

No. 550 shows the flowers facing upwards and has the value in the centre. No. 550a has the flowers facing downwards with the value to the right.

133. Child praying at Bedside.

1971. Christmas. Multicoloured.

557.	5 c. Type **133**	10	10
558.	20 c. Type **133**	10	10
559.	25 c. Carnival Masquerader (vert.)	10	10
560.	50 c. as 25 c.	20	30

134. Obverse and Reverse of Guyana $1 Coin.

1972. Republic Day.

561.134.	5 c. silver, black and red	10	10
562. –	20 c. silver, black and red	15	10
563.134.	25 c. silver, black & blue	15	15
564. –	50 c. silver, blk. & grn.	25	30

DESIGN: 20 c., 50 c. Reverse and obverse of Guyana $1 coin.

135. Hands and Irrigation Canal.

1972. Youman Nabi (Mohammed's Birthday).

565.135.	5 c. multicoloured ..	10	10
566.	25 c. multicoloured ..	10	10
567.	30 c. multicoloured ..	10	10
568.	60 c. multicoloured ..	20	20

136. Map and Emblem.

1972. Conf. of Foreign Ministers of Non-aligned Countries.

569.136.	8 c. multicoloured ..	10	10
570.	25 c. multicoloured ..	10	10
571.	40 c. multicoloured ..	15	15
572.	50 c. multicoloured ..	20	20

137. Hand reaching for Sun.

1972. 1st Caribbean Festival of Arts.

573.137.	8 c. multicoloured ..	10	10
574.	25 c. multicoloured ..	10	10
575.	40 c. multicoloured ..	15	20
576.	50 c. multicoloured ..	20	25

138. Joseph, Mary and the Infant Jesus.

1972. Christmas.

577.138.	8 c. multicoloured ..	10	10
578.	25 c. multicoloured ..	10	10
579.	40 c. multicoloured ..	15	25
580.	50 c. multicoloured ..	15	25

139. Umana Yana (Meeting-house).

1973. Republic Day. Multicoloured.

581.	8 c. Type **139**	10	10
582.	25 c. Bethel Chapel ..	10	10
583.	40 c. As 25 c.	20	20
584.	50 c. Type **139**	25	20

140. Pomegranate.

1973. Easter. Multicoloured.

585.	8 c. Type **140**	10	10
586.	25 c. Cross and map (34 × 17 mm.)	10	10
587.	40 c. As 25 c.	10	10
588.	50 c. Type **140**	15	15

141. Stylized Blood Cell.

1973. 25th Anniv. of Guyana Red Cross.

589.141.	8 c. red and black ..	10	10
590.	25 c. red and purple ..	20	15
591.	40 c. red and blue ..	30	45
592.	50 c. red and green ..	40	70

142. Steel-Band Players.

1973. Christmas. Multicoloured.

593.	8 c. Type **142**	10	10
594.	25 c. Type **142**	20	10
595.	40 c. Virgin and Child stained-glass window ..	50	65
596.	50 c. As 40 c.	55	65

143. Symbol of Progress.

1974. Republic Day. Multicoloured.

597.	8 c. Type **143**	10	10
598.	25 c. Wai-Wai Indian ..	10	10
599.	40 c. Type **143**	15	25
600.	50 c. As 25 c.	15	30

1974. No. 546 surch.

601.	8 c. on 6 c. multicoloured ..	10	10

145. Kite with Crucifixion Motif.

1974. Easter.

602.145.	8 c. multicoloured ..	10	10
603. –	25 c. black and green ..	10	10
604. –	40 c. black and mauve ..	10	15
605.145.	50 c. multicoloured ..	15	25

DESIGN: Nos. 603/4, "Crucifixion" in pre-Columbian style.

146. British Guiana 24 c. Stamp of 1874.

1974. Cent. of Universal Postal Union.

606.146.	8 c. multicoloured ..	20	10
607. –	25 c. lt. grn., grn. & blk.	30	10
608.146.	40 c. multicoloured ..	30	20
609. –	50 c. grn., brn. and blk.	35	25

DESIGNS—VERT. (42 × 25 mm.). 25 c., 50 c. U.P.U. emblem and Guyana postman.

147. Guides with Banner.

1974. Golden Jubilee of Girl Guides. Mult.

610.	8 c. Type **147**	20	10
611.	25 c. Guides in camp ..	40	15
612.	40 c. As 25 c.	60	40
613.	50 c. Type **147**	60	45

148. Buck Toyeau.

1974. Christmas. Multicoloured.

615. 8 c. Type **148** 10 10
616. 35 c. Five-fingers and awaras 10 10
617. 50 c. Pawpaw and tangerine 15 10
618. $1 Pineapple and sapodilla 30 60

1975. No. 544 surch.

620. 8 c. on 3 c. multicoloured 10 10

149. Golden Arrow of Courage. **150.** Old Sluice Gate.

1975. Republic Day. Guyana Orders and Decorations. Multicoloured.

621. 10 c. Type **149** 10 10
622. 35 c. Cacique's Crown of Honour 10 15
623. 50 c. Cacique's Crown of Valour 15 20
624. $1 Order of Excellence .. 35 60

1975. Silver Jubilee of International Commission on Irrigation and Drainage. Mult.

625. 10 c. Type **150** 10 10
626. 35 c. Modern sluice gate (horiz.) 10 15
627. 50 c. Type **150** 15 30
628. $1 As 35 c. 35 60

151. I.W.Y. Emblem and Rock Drawing.

1975. International Women's Year. Designs showing different rock drawings.

630. **151.** 10 c. green and yellow .. 10 10
631. – 35 c. violet and blue .. 20 10
632. – 50 c. blue and orange .. 25 15
633. – $1 brown and blue .. 45 45

152. Freedom Monument.

1975. Namibia Day. Multicoloured.

635. 10 c. Type **152** 10 10
636. 35 c. Unveiling of Monument 15 10
637. 50 c. Type **152** 25 10
638. $1 As 35 c. 35 35

MINIMUM PRICE

The minimum price quoted is 10p which represents a handling charge rather than a basis for valuing common stamps. For further notes about prices see introductory pages.

153. G.N.S. Emblem.

1975. 1st Anniv. of National Service.

639. **153.** 10 c. yell., grn. & violet 10 10
640. – 35 c. orge., grn. & violet 10 10
641. – 50 c. blue, grn. & brown 15 15
642. – $1 mve., grn. & light grn. 40 40

Nos. 640/2 are as Type **153** but have different symbols within the circle.

154. Court Building, 1875, and Forester's Badge.

1975. Centenary of Guyanese Ancient Order of Foresters. Multicoloured.

644. 10 c. Type **154** 10 10
645. 35 c. Rock drawing of hunter and quarry .. 10 10
646. 50 c. Crossed axes and bugle-horn 15 10
647. $1 Bow and arrow .. 40 40

1976. No. 553 surch.

649. 35 c. on 60 c. Soldier's Cap 20 25

156. Shoulder Flash.

1976. 50th Anniv. of St. John Ambulance in Guyana.

650. **156.** 8 c. silver, blk. & mauve 10 10
651. – 15 c. silver, blk. & orge. 10 10
652. – 35 c. silver, blk. & grn. 20 20
653. – 40 c. silver, blk. & blue 25 25

Nos. 651/3 areas Type **156** but show different shoulder flashes.

157. Triumphal Arch.

1976. 10th Anniv. of Independence. Mult.

654. 8 c. Type **157** 10 10
655. 15 c. Stylised Victoria Regia lily 10 10
656. 35 c. "Onward to Socialism" 15 15
657. 40 c. Worker pointing the way 15 15

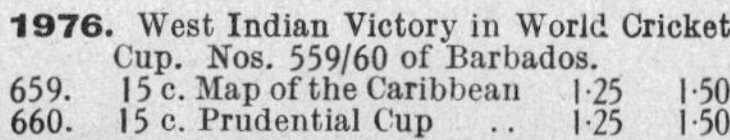
1976. West Indian Victory in World Cricket Cup. Nos. 559/60 of Barbados.

659. 15 c. Map of the Caribbean 1·25 1·50
660. 15 c. Prudential Cup .. 1·25 1·50

158. Flame in Archway.

1976. Deepavali Festival. Multicoloured.

661. 8 c. Type **158** 10 10
662. 15 c. Flame in hand .. 10 10
663. 35 c. Flame in bowl .. 15 20
664. 40 c. Goddess Latchmi .. 15 25

159. "Festival Emblem and Musical instrument".

1977. Second World Black and African Festival of Arts and Culture, Nigeria.

666. **159.** 10 c. red, black and gold 10 10
667. 25 c. blue, black & gold 20 10
668. 50 c. blue, black & gold 25 25
669. $1 green, black & gold 60 75

160. 1 c. and 5 c. Coins.

1977. New Coinage.

671. **160.** 8 c. multicoloured .. 20 10
672. – 15 c. brown, grey & black 25 10
673. – 35 c. green, grey & black 45 30
674. – 40 c. red, grey and black 50 35
675. – $1 multicoloured .. 1·00 1·10
676. – $2 multicoloured .. 1·60 2·25

DESIGNS: 15 c. 10 and 25 c. coins. **35 c.**, **50 c.** and **$1** coins. 40 c. $5 and $10 coins. **$1**, **$50** and **$100** coins. $2, Reverse of **$1** coin.

161. Hand Pump, circa 1850.

1977. Nat. Fire Prevention Week. Mult.

677. 8 c. Type **161** 25 10
678. 15 c. Steam engine, circa 1860 .. .. .. 50 10
679. 35 c. Fire engine, circa 1930 .. .. .. 80 60
680. 40 c. Fire engine, 1977 .. 1·00 85

162. Cuffy Monument.

1977. Cuffy Monument. Multicoloured.

681. 8 c. Type **162** 10 10
682. 15 c. Cuffy Monument (different view) 10 10
683. 35 c. Type **162** 15 20
684. 40 c. As 15 c. 15 30

163. American Manatee.

1978. Wildlife Conservation. Multicoloured.

685. 8 c. Type **163** 55 10
686. 15 c. Giant sea turtle .. 75 20
687. 35 c. Harpy Eagle (vert.) .. 2·50 1·50
688. 40 c. Iguana (vert.) .. 2·50 1·50

164. L.F.S. Burnham (Prime Minister) and Parliament Buildings, Georgetown.

1978. 25th Anniv. of Prime Minister's Entry into Parliament.

689. **164.** 8 c. black, violet & grey 10 10
690. – 15 c. black, blue & grey 10 10
691. – 35 c. black, red and grey 15 20
692. – 40 c. black, orge. & grey 15 20

DESIGNS: 15 c. Burnham, graduate and children ("Free Education"). 35 c. Burnham and industrial works (Nationalization of Bauxite industry). 40 c. Burnham and village scene ("The Co-operative Village").

165. Dr. George Giglioli (scientist & physician). **166.** "Prepona pheridamus".

1978. National Science Research Council. Multicoloured.

694. 10 c. Type **165** 10 10
695. 30 c. Institute of Applied Science and Technology 15 15
696. 50 c. Emblem of National Science Research Council 25 25
697. 60 c. Emblem of Commonwealth Science Council (commemorating the 10th meeting) (horiz.) .. 25 25

1978. Butterflies. Multicoloured.

698 5 c. Type **166** 70 10
699 10 c. "Archonias bellona" 70 10
700 15 c. "Eryphanis polyxena" 80 10
701 20 c. "Helicopis cupido" 80 10
702 25 c. "Nessaea batesi" .. 90 10
702a 30 c. "Nymphidium mantus" .. .. 1·25 1·00
703 35 c. "Anaea galanthis" 90 10
704 40 c. "Morpho rhetenor" (male) 90 10
705 50 c. "Hamadryas amphinome" 90 20
705a 60 c. "Papilio androgeus" 1·25 1·00
706 $1 "Agrias claudina" .. 2·50 20
707 $2 "Morpho rhetenor" (female) .. .. 4·00 35
708 $5 "Morpho deidamia" .. 6·00 90
708a $10 "Elbella patrobas" .. 7·50 4·00

Nos. 706/8 are vertical, 25 × 39 mm.

168. Amerindian Stone-chip Grater in Preparation.

1978. National/International Heritage Year. Multicoloured.
709. 10 c. Type **168** 10 10
710. 30 c. Cassiri jar and decorated Amerindian jar .. 15 10
711. 50 c. Old Dutch fort, Kyk-over-al 20 15
712. 60 c. Fort Island 20 20

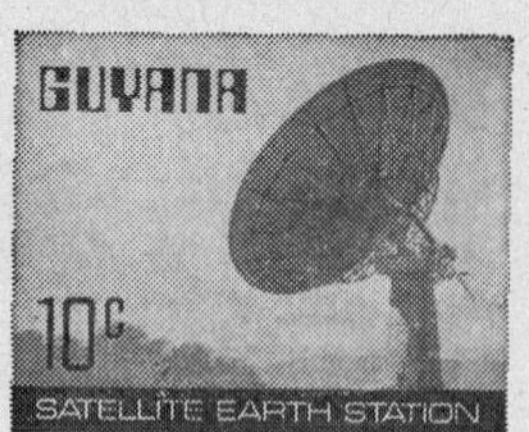

169. Dish Aerial by Night.

1979. Satellite Earth Station. Multicoloured.
713. 10 c. Type **169** 10 10
714. 30 c. Dish aerial by day .. 20 15
715. 50 c. Satellite with solar veins 30 15
716. $3 Cylinder satellite .. 1·50 90

170. Sir Rowland Hill and British Guiana 1850 12 c. "Cottonreel" Stamp.

1979. Death Centenary of Sir Rowland Hill. Multicoloured.
717. 10 c. Type **170** 15 10
718. 30 c. British Guiana 1856 1 c. black on magenta stamp (vert.) 30 15
719. 50 c. British Guiana 1898 1 c. Mount Roraima stamp 45 25
720. $3 Printing press used for early British Guiana stamps (vert.) .. .. 1·10 1·50

171. "Me and my Sister".

1979. International Year of the Child. Children's Paintings. Multicoloured.
721. 10 c. Type **171** 10 10
722. 30 c. "Fun with the Fowls" (horiz.) .. 15 15
723. 50 c. "Two boys catching Ducks" (horiz.) .. 20 20
724. $3 "Mango Season" (horiz.) .. .. .. 65 1·25

172. "An 8 Hour Day".

1979. 60th Anniv of Guyana Labour Union. Multicoloured.
725 10 c. Type **172** 10 10
726 30 c. "Abolition of Night Baking" (horiz) .. 10 10
727 50 c. "Introduction of the Workmen's Compensation Ordinance" .. 15 15
728 $3 H. N. Critchlow (founder) 55 90

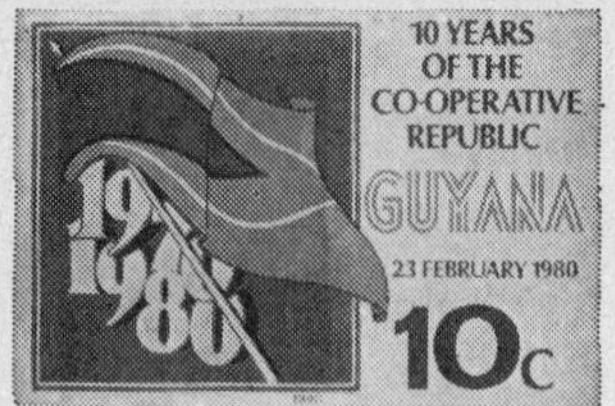

173. Guyana Flag.

1980. 10th Anniv. of Republic.
729. **173.** 10 c. multicoloured .. 10 10
730. – 35 c. black and orange .. 30 10
731. – 60 c. multicoloured .. 50 20
732. – $3 multicoloured .. 80 90
DESIGNS: 35 c. Demerara River Bridge. 60 c. Kaieteur Falls. $3, "Makanaima, the Great Ancestral Spirit of the Amerindians".

174. Snoek.

1980. "London 1980" International Stamp Exhibition. Fishes. Multicoloured.
733. 35 c. Type **174** 35 25
734. 35 c. Haimara 35 25
735. 35 c. Electric Eel 35 25
736. 35 c. Golden Rivulus .. 35 25
737. 35 c. Pencil Fish 35 25
738. 35 c. Four-eyed Fish .. 35 25
739. 35 c. Pirai or Carib Fish 35 25
740. 35 c. Smoking Hassar .. 35 25
741. 35 c. Devil Ray 35 25
742. 35 c. Flying Patwa .. 35 25
743. 35 c. Arapaima Pirariucii 35 25
744. 35 c. Lukanani 35 25

175. Children's Convalescent Home (Community Service).

1980. 75th Anniv. of Rotary International. Multicoloured.
745. 10 c. Type **175** 10 10
746. 30 c. Georgetown Rotary Club and Rotary International emblems .. 10 10
747. 50 c. District 404 emblem (vert.) 20 20
748. $3 Rotary anniversary emblem (vert.) 80 80

176. "C" encircling Globe, Caduceus Emblem and Sea.

1980. 25th Anniv. of Commonwealth Caribbean Medical Research Council. Mult.
749. 10 c. Type **176** 10 10
750. 60 c. Researcher with microscope, Caduceus emblem, stethoscope and beach scene 40 20
751. $3 Caduceus emblem, "C" encircling researcher and island silhouettes .. 1·10 1·00

177. "Virola surinamensis".

1980. Christmas. Trees and leaves. Mult.
752. 10 c. Type **177** 10 10
753. 30 c. "Hymenaea courbaril" 20 10
754. 50 c. "Mora excelsa" .. 30 15
755. $3 "Peltogyne venosa" 1·25 1·10

178. Brazilian Tree Porcupine.

1981. Wildlife. Multicoloured.
756 30 c. Type **178** 60 50
757 30 c. Red howler 60 50
758 30 c. Common squirrel-monkey 60 50
759 30 c. Two-toed sloth .. 60 50
760 30 c. Brazilian tapir .. 60 50
761 30 c. Collared peccary .. 60 50
852 30 c. Six-banded armadillo 60 50
763 30 c. Tamandua 60 50
764 30 c. Giant anteater .. 60 50
765 30 c. Murine opossum .. 60 50
766 30 c. Brown four-eyed opossum 60 50
767 30 c. Brazilian agouti .. 60 50

1981. Liberation of Southern Africa Conference. No. 635 surch. **1981 CONFERENCE. $1.05.**
768. $1·05 on 10 c. Type **152** .. 40 50

1981. Royal Wedding (1st issue). Nos. 554 and 556 surch. **ROYAL WEDDING 1981.**
769. $3·60 on $5 "Odontadenia grandiflora .. .. 1·00 1·00
770. $7·20 in $1 "Chelonanthus uliginoides .. .. 1·25 1·75
See also Nos. 841/3 and 930/6.

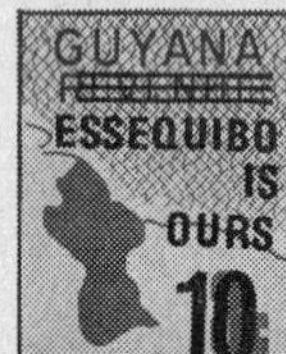

181. Map of Guyana.

1981.
771 **181** 10 c. on 3 c. black, blue and red 40 10
943 30 c. on 2 c. black, blue and grey 40 15
773 50 c. on 2 c. black, blue and grey 55 25
774 60 c. on 2 c. black, blue and grey 70 30
775 75 c. on 3 c. black, blue and red 70 45
See also Nos. 940/76.

1981. No. 544 surch.
775c. 720 c. on 3 c. mult. .. 50·00 15·00

1981. Various stamps optd. **1981.**
776 **105** 25 c. black, gold & lilac 10 10
777 – 30 c. black, gold & grn 15 15
778 – 35 c. mult (No. 645) .. 15 15
865 – $1 mult (No. 554) .. 40 35
See also Nos. 791/3 and 809 etc.

1981. Nos. 545 and 555 surch.
780. 75 c. on 5 c. Annatto Tree 50 30
781. 210 c. on $5 "Odontadenia grandiflora" 80 70
781a. 220 c. on 5 c. Annatto Tree .. .. .. 60·00 8·00

1981. Nos. D8/11 surch. **ESSEQUIBO IS OURS.**
782. D2. 10 c. on 2 c. black .. 25 10
783. 15 c. on 12 c. red .. 25 15
784. 20 c. on 1 c. green .. 20 20
785. 45 c. on 2 c. black .. 75 25
786. 55 c. on 4 c. blue .. 30 30
787. 60 c. on 4 c. blue .. 50 25
788. 65 c. on 2 c. black .. 40 40
789. 70 c. on 4 c. blue .. 1·00 1·25
790. 80 c. on 4 c. blue .. 35 40

1981. Nos. 454, 457 and 555 optd. **1981.**
791 15 c. Harpy eagle .. 4·00 10
792 40 c. Great kiskadee .. 4·00 40
866 $2 "Norantea guianensis" 90 95

1981. Nos. 545, 554, 556, 716, 843, F7 and F9 surch.
794. 50 c. on 5 c. Annatto tree (postage) 30 20
795. 120 c. on $1 "Chelonanthus uliginoides 75 50
796. 140 c. on $1 "Chelonanthus uliginoides" 70 50
797. 150 c. on $2 "Norantea guianensis" (F9) .. 75 50
798. 360 c. on $2 "Norantea guianensis" (F9) .. 3·00 1·50
799. 720 c. on 60 c. Soldier's Cap (F7) .. .. .. 3·00 2·75
800. 220 c. on $3 Cylinder satellite .. .. 1·75 75
801. 250 c. on $5 "Odontadenia grandiflora .. .. 1·25 80
802. 280 c. on $5 "Odontadenia grandiflora .. .. 1·50 1·25
803. 375 c. on $5 "Odontadenia grandiflora" .. .. 1·75 1·40
804. $1·10 on $2 "Norantea guianensis" (843) (air) .. 12·00 12·00
No. 804 has the Royal Wedding optd. cancelled by three bars.

1981. No. 448. surch.
805. 15 c. on 1 c. Type **87** (postage) 30 30
806. 100 c. on 1 c. Type **87** (air) 55 55
807. 110 c. on 1 c. Type **87** .. 60 60

1981. No. 700 optd. **ESSEQUIBO IS OURS.**
808. 15 c. "Eryphanis polyxena 50 10

1981. Various stamps optd. **1981.**
864 – 15 c. mult (No. 548a) 3·50 10
810 – 15 c. mult (No. 659) 4·00 20
811 – 15 c. mult (No. 660) 3·50 20
811c – 40 c. mult (No. F5) .. — £200
812 – 50 c. mult (No. 623) 60 20
813 **150** 50 c. multicoloured .. 1·00 25
814 – 50 c. blue and orange (No. 632) .. .. 17·00 1·00
815 – 50 c. mult (No. 646) 2·25 25
816 **159** 50 c. blue, blk & gold 9·50 1·00
817 – 50 c. mult (No. F6) .. 3·00 30
818 – 60 c. mult (No. 731) 60 25
819 – 60 c. mult (No. 750) 60 25
820 – $1 mult (No. 624) 6·00 1·00
821 **159** $1 green, black & gold 5·00 50
823 – $3 mult (No. 732) .. 2·50 95
824 – $5 mult (No. 556) .. 3·25 2·25

1981. Various stamps surch.
825 **116** 55 c. on 6 c. mult .. 3·25 80
826 **111** 70 c. on 6 c. mult .. 70 30
827 100 c. on 6 c. mult .. 1·00 35
828 – 100 c. on 8 c. multicolured (No. 505) .. 4·25 40
829 – 100 c. on $1.05 on 10 c. multi (No. 768) .. 23·00 3·50
830 **116** 110 c. on 6 c. mult .. 4·00 40
831 **149** 110 c. on 10 c. mult .. 2·00 40
832 **151** 110 c. on 10 c. green and yellow .. 3·75 70
834 – 125 c. on $2 multicoloured (No. 555) 10·00 1·00
835 **116** 180 c. on 6 c. mult .. 4·50 65
840 – 240 c. on $3 multicoloured (No. 728) 9·50 1·50
836 **116** 400 c. on 6 c. mult .. 5·00 1·75
837a 440 c. on 6 c. mult .. 3·00 1·75
838 – 550 c. on $10 multicoloured (No. O21) 4·50 2·00
839 – 625 c. on 40 c. multicoloured (No. F5) 9·50 3·00

1981. Royal Wedding (2nd issue). Nos. 544 and 555/6 surch **Royal Wedding 1981** (No. 843 **Air Mail** also).
841 60 c. on 3 c. Hanging heliconia (postage) .. 70 80
842 75 c. on $5 "Odontadenia grandiflora" 80 90
843 $1.10 on $2 "Norantea guianensis" (air) .. 1·00 1·10

1981. World Cup Football Championship, Spain (1982) (1st issue). No. 781a surch **Espana 82.**
844. 220 c. on 5 c. Annatto tree 1·25 90
See also Nos. 937/9.

1981. 150th Birth Anniv. of Heinrich von Stephan (founder of U.P.U.) No. 720 surch. **1831—1981 Von Stephan. 330.**
845. 330 c. on $3 Printing press used for early British Guiana stamps .. .. 1·50 1·25

1981. No. 452 surch.
847 12 c. on 12 c. on 6 c. Patua 20 25
848 15 c. on 10 c. on 6 c. Patua 15 10
849 15 c. on 30 c. on 6 c. Patua 15 10
850 15 c. on 50 c. on 6 c. Patua 15 10
851 15 c. on 60 c. on 6 c. Patua 15 10
Nos. 847/51 are further surcharges on previously unissued stamps.

214. Coromantyn Free Negro Armed Ranger, c. 1772. and Cuffy Monument.

1981. 16th Anniv. of Guyana Defence Force. Multicoloured.

853. 15 c. on 10 c. Type **214** .. 40 10
854. 50 c. Private, 27th Foot Regiment, c. 1825 .. 70 50
855. $1 on 30 c. Private, Col. Fourgeoud's Marines c. 1775 .. .. .. 1·00 75
856. $1.10 on $3 W.O. and N.C.O., Guyana Defence Force 1966 .. .. .. 1·60 1·10

The 15 c., $1 and $1.10 values are surcharged on previously unissued stamps.

215. Louis Braille.

1981. International Year for Disabled Persons. Famous Disabled People. Multicoloured.

857. 15 c. on 10 c. Type **215** .. 30 10
858. 50 c. Helen Keller and Rajkumari Singh .. 75 55
859. $1 on 60 c. Beethoven and Sonny Thomas.. .. 80 60
860. $1.10 on $3 Renoir .. 90 70

The 15 c., $1 and $1.10 values are surcharged on previously unissued stamps.

1981. No. 452 surch (Nos. 862/3 optd **AIR** also).

861. 12 c. on 6 c. Patua (postage) 15 10
862. 50 c. on 6 c. Patua (air) .. 20 15
863. $1 on 6 c. Patua.. .. 50 30

1981. Nos. 601, 620, 644, O 13, 717, 720, 728, 749, 751 and 755 surch.

867 110 c. on 10 c. Type **154** 2·75 45
868 110 c. on 110 c. on 8 c. on 3 c. Hanging heliconia 2·75 60
869 110 c. on 110 c. on 8 c. on 6 c. Cannon-ball tree .. 2·75 75
869a 110 c. on 10 c. on 25 c. Marabunta .. .. 2·25 75
870 110 c. on 10 c. Type **170** 2·00 40
871 110 c. on 10 c. Type **176** 7·00 90
872 110 c. on $3 Printing press used for early British Guiana stamps .. 1·75 45
873 110 c. on $3 H. N. Critchlow .. .. 6·00 70
874 110 c. on $3 Caduceus emblem, "C" encircling researcher, and island silhouettes .. .. 2·00 45
875 110 c. on $3 "Peltogyne venosa" .. .. 4·00 80

1981. No. 698 surch. **Nov. 81 50 c.**

876. 50 c. on 5 c. Type **166** .. 2·75 20

222. Yellow Allamanda ("Allamanda cathartica").

1981. Flowers. Coil stamps.

877. **222.** 15 c. on 2 c. lilac, blue and green 15 15
878. – 15 c. on 8 c. lilac, blue and mauve 15 15

DESIGN: 15 c. on 8 c. Mazaruni Pride ("Sipanea prolensis").

Nos. 877/8 are surcharges on previously unissued stamps.

1981. Air. Human Rights Day. No. 748 surch. **HUMAN RIGHTS DAY 1981 110 AIR.**

879. 110 c. on $3 Rotary anniversary emblem 1·75 1·50

1981. 35th Anniv. of U.N.I.C.E.F. No. 724 surch. **U.N.I.C.E.F. 1946-1981 125.**

880. 125 c. on $2 "Mango Season" .. .. .. 1·00 60

1981. "Cancun 81" International Conference. No. 698 surch **Cancun 81 50 c.**

880a. 50 c. on 5 c. Type **166**. .. 2·00 75

225. Tape Measure and Guyana Metrication Board Van.

1982. Metrication. Multicoloured.

881. 15 c. Type **225** 15 15
882. 15 c. "Metric man" .. 15 15
883. 15 c. "Postal service goes metric" 15 15
884. 15 c. Weighing child on metric scales 15 15
885. 15 c. Canje Bridge .. 15 15
886. 15 c. Tap filling litre bucket 15 15

1982. Various stamps optd. **1982.**

887. – 20 c. multicoloured (No. 549) .. .. 2·00 20
888. **105.** 25 c. black, gold and lilac.. .. .. 60 25
889. – 25 c. mult. (No. 550a) 2·50 35

See also Nos. 914/7, 919/21, 923/4, 977/8, 992/8, 1001, 1004, 1006/8, 1015, 1017, 1059, 1117 and OP 3/4.

1982. No. 506 optd **POSTAGE** and Nos. 546 and 601 surch.

890 20 c. on 6 c. Cannon-ball tree 35 20
892 25 c. Type **116** .. .. 1·00 10
893 125 c. on 8 c. on 6 c. Cannon-ball tree .. 35 35

230. Guyana Soldier and Flag.

1982. Savings Campaign.

894. **230.** $1 multicoloured .. 30 30

No. 894 is a fiscal stamp overprinted for postal use.

1982. 125th Birth Anniv. of Lord Baden-Powell and 75th Anniv. of Boy Scout Movement. Nos. 543, 545 and 601 surch. as given in brackets.

895. 15 c. on 2 c. Type 132 **(BADEN-POWELL 1857-1982)** 10 10
896. 15 c. on 2 c. Type 132 **(Scout Movement 1907-1982)** 10 10
897. 15 c. on 2 c. Type 132 **(1907-1982)** 15 15
898. 15 c. on 2 c. Type 132 **(1857-1982)** 15 15
899. 15 c. on 2 c. Type 132 **(1982)** 10 10
900. 110 c. on 5 c. Annatto tree **(BADEN-POWELL 1857-1982)** .. .. 1·00 40
901. 110 c. on 5 c. Annatto tree **(Scout Movement 1907-1982)** 60 40
902. 110 c. on 5 c. Annatto tree **(1907-1982)** .. .. 1·25 80
903. 110 c. on 5 c. Annatto tree **(1857-1982)** .. .. 1·25 80
904. 110 c. on 5 c. Annatto tree **(1982)** 60 40
905. 125 c. on 8 c. on 6 c. Cannon-ball tree **(BADEN-POWELL 1857-1982)** .. .. 1·00 50
906. 125 c. on 8 c. on 6 c. Cannon-ball tree **(Scout Movement 1907-1982)** .. .. 1·00 50
907. 125 c. on 8 c. on 6 c. Cannon-ball tree **(1907-1982)** .. .. 1·50 90
908. 125 c. on 8 c. on 6 c. Cannon-ball tree **(1857-1982)** .. .. 1·50 90
909. 125 c. on 8 c. on 6 c. Cannon-ball tree **(1982)** 75 50

1982. 250th Birth. Anniv. of George Washington. Nos. 708, 718 and 720 optd. **GEORGE WASHINGTON 1732-1982** or surch. also.

910. 100 c. on $3 Printing press used for early British Guiana stamps 45 50
911. 400 c. on 30 c. British Guiana 1856 1 c. black on purple .. .. 1·60 1·90
912. $5 "Morpho deidamia" .. 6·50 5·00

1982. Savings Campaign. As T **230**. Mult.

913. 110 c. on $5 Guyana male and female soldiers with flag 50 35

No. 913 is a fiscal stamp surcharged for postal use.

See also No. 990.

1982. Easter. Optd. **1982** or surch. also.

914. **111.** 25 c. multicoloured .. 35 20
915. 30 c. multicoloured .. 30 15
916. 45 c. on 6 c. mult. .. 45 35
917. 75 c. on 40 c. mult. .. 75 35

1982. No. 703 surch.

918 20 c. on 35 c. "Anaea galanthis" .. .. 1·25 10

1982. No. F5 optd. **1982** and surch. in addition.

919. 180 c. on 40 c. Tiger Beard 3·25 60

1982. Nos. 555/6 optd. **1982.**

920. $2 "Norantea guianensis" 80 70
921. $5 "Odontadenia grandiflora" .. .. .. 1·40 1·60

1982. No. 542 surch.

922. 220 c. on 1 c. Pitcher Plant of Mt. Roraima.. .. 1·25 60

1982. Nos. 472 and 684 optd. **1982.**

923. **105.** 40 c. blk., gold & blue 35 20
924. – 40 c. multicoloured .. 50 40

1982. Nos. 469, 751 and 842/3 surch.

925. **105.** 80 c. on 6 c. black, gold and flesh 30 35
926. 85 c. on 6 c. black, gold and flesh 50 35
927. – 160 c. on $1.10 on $2 mult. (No. 843) .. 1·00 55
928. – 210 c. on $3 mult. (No. 751) .. 2·50 70

1982. Royal Wedding (3rd issue). Nos. 841/3 surch.

930 85 c. on 60 c. on 3 c. Hanging heliconia .. 2·00 35
931 130 c. on 60 c. on 3 c. Hanging heliconia .. 2·00 55
933 170 c. on $1.10 on $2 "Norantea guianensis" 10·00 4·50
934 210 c. on 75 c. on $5 "Odontadenia grandiflora" (B) .. .. 2·00 90
935 235 c. on 75 c. on $5 "Odontadenia grandiflora" .. .. .. 2·50 1·50
936 300 c. on $1.10 on $2 "Norantea guianensis" 2·75 1·00

1982. World Cup Football Championship, Spain (2nd issue). Nos. 544, 546 and 554 optd. **ESPANA 1982.** or surch. also.

937. $1 "Chelonanthus uliginoides" 75 60
938. 110 c. on 3 c. Hanging Heliconia (B.) 75 40
939. 250 c. on 6 c. Cannon-ball tree (B.).. .. .. 1·00 90

See also No. 1218.

1982.

940 **181** 15 c. on 2 c. black, blue and grey .. 50 15
941 20 c. on 2 c. black, blue and grey .. 2·50 30
1029 25 c. on 2 c. black, blue and grey .. 50 10
989 40 c. on 2 c. black, blue and grey .. 75 15
945 45 c. on 2 c. black, blue and grey .. 1·75 45
948 75 c. on 2 c. black, blue and grey .. 3·00 25
949 80 c. on 2 c. black, blue and grey .. 2·25 20
950 85 c. on 2 c. black, blue and grey .. 75 25
951 100 c. on 3 c. black, blue and red .. 1·00 35
952 110 c. on 3 c. black, blue and red .. 80 30
953 120 c. on 3 c. black, blue and red .. 5·50 35
954 125 c. on 3 c. black, blue and red .. 1·50 35
955 130 c. on 3 c. black, blue and red .. 1·00 35
956 150 c. on 3 c. black, blue and red .. 5·00 40
957 160 c. on 3 c. black, blue and red .. 2·00 40
958 170 c. on 3 c. black, blue and red .. 1·40 45
959 175 c. on 3 c. black, blue and red .. 5·00 45
960 180 c. on 3 c. black, blue and red .. 2·00 50
961 200 c. on 3 c. black, blue and red .. 2·25 45
962 210 c. on 3 c. black, blue and red .. 6·00 50
963 220 c. on 3 c. black, blue and red .. 7·50 60
964 235 c. on 3 c. black, blue and red .. 7·00 60
965 240 c. on 3 c. black, blue and red .. 6·00 60
966 250 c. on 3 c. black, blue and red .. 2·25 60
967 300 c. on 3 c. black, blue and red .. 8·50 75
968 330 c. on 3 c. black, blue and red .. 2·75 90
969 375 c. on 3 c. black, blue and red .. 6·00 1·00
970 400 c. on 3 c. black, blue and red .. 8·50 1·10
971 440 c. on 3 c. black, blue and red .. 4·00 1·10
972 500 c. on 3 c. black, blue and red .. 3·50 1·40
973 550 c. on 3 c. black, blue and red .. 4·00 1·75
974 625 c. on 3 c. black, blue and red .. 2·75 2·00
975 1500 c. on 3 c. mult... 10·00 4·00
976 2000 c. on 3 c. mult... 11·00 5·50

1982. No. 548a optd. **1982.**

977. 15 c. Christmas Orchid .. 4·25 10

1982. No. O 26 optd. **POSTAGE.**

978. 110 c. on 6 c. Type **116** .. 3·75 35

1982. Air. 21st Birthday of Princess of Wales. Nos. 542, 545 and 555 surch.

979. 110 c. on 5 c. Annatto tree 60 50
980. 220 c. on 1 c. Pitcher Plant of Mt. Roraima.. .. 1·25 80
981. 330 c. on $2 "Norantea guianensis" .. .. 1·50 1·50

1982. Birth of Prince William of Wales. Surch. (a) On stamps of British Guiana.

982. 50 c. on 2 c. myrtle (No. 332) 40 45
983. $1·10 on 3 c. olive and brown (No. 333) .. 1·00 80

(b) On stamps of Guyana previously optd. **"GUYANA INDEPENDENCE 1966."**

984. 50 c. on 2 c. myrtle (No. 379) .. .. .. 5·50 2·50
985. $1·10 on 3 c. olive and brown (No. 395) .. 8·00 2·50
986. $1.25 on 6 c. green (No. 383) 70 80
987. $2.20 on 24 c. black and orange (No. 401) .. 1·50 1·50

1982. Savings Campaign. As No. 913 but showing inverted comma before "OURS" in opt.

990. 110 c. on $5 Guyana male and female soldiers with flag .. .. .. 5·50 75

1982. Italy's Victory in World Cup Football Championship. No. F7 surch. **ESPANA 1982. ITALY $2.35.**

991. $2.35 on 180 c. on 60 c. Soldier's Cap .. .. 2·50 75

1982. Wildlife Protection. Nos. 687 and 733/8 optd. **1982.**

992. 35 c. Harpy Eagle .. 2·00 40
993. 35 c. Type **174** .. 2·00 40
994. 35 c. Haimara .. .. 2·00 40
995. 35 c. Electric Eel .. .. 2·00 40
996. 35 c. Golden Rivulus .. 2·00 40
997. 35 c. Pencil Fish .. .. 2·00 40
998. 35 c. Four-eyed Fish .. 2·00 40

1982. Central American and Caribbean Games, Havana. Nos. 542/3 surch. **C.A. & CARIB GAMES 1982.**

999. 50 c. on 2 c. Type **132** .. 1·00 45
1000. 60 c. on 1 c. Pitcher Plant of Mt. Roraima .. 1·25 30

1982. No. 730 optd. **1982.**

1001. 35 c. black and orange .. 30 20

1982. Nos. 841 and 979 further surch.

1002. 130 c. on 60 c. on 3 c. Hanging Heliconia .. 60 50
1003. 170 c. on 110 c. on 5 c. Annatto tree .. 1·50 75

1982. No. 841 optd. **1982** and surch.

1004. 440 c. on 60 c. on 3 c. Hanging Heliconia .. 2·25 1·50

1982. Commonwealth Games, Brisbane, Australia. No. 546 surch. **Commonwealth GAMES AUSTRALIA 1982.**

1005. $1.25 on 6 c. Cannon-ball tree .. .. .. 1·50 40

1982. Nos. 552, 641 and 719 optd. **1982.**
1006. 50 c. multicoloured (No. 552) 2·00 25
1007. 50 c. blue, green & brown brown (No. 641) .. 1·50 25
1008. 50 c. mult. (No. 719) .. 60 25

1982. Various Official stamps additionally optd. **POSTAGE** for postal purposes.
1009. 15 c. Christmas Orchid (No. O 23) .. .. 6·50 30
1010. 50 c. "Guzamania lingulata" (No. O 14) 1·25 25
1011. 100 c. on $3 Cylinder satellite (No. O 19) .. 1·75 50

1982. International Food Day. No. 617 optd. **INT FOOD DAY 1982.**
1012. 50 c. Pawpaw and tangerine .. .. .. 15·00 1·25

1982. International Year of the Elderly. No. 747 optd. **INT YEAR OF THE ELDERLY.**
1013. 50 c. District 404 emblem 5·50 50

1982. Centenary of Robert Koch's Discovery of Tubercle Bacillus. No. 750 optd. **DR. R. KOCH CENTENARY TBC BACILLUS DISCOVERY**
1014. 60 c. Researcher with microscope, Caduceus emblem, stethoscope and beach scene .. 2·50 30

1982. International Decade for Women. No. 633 optd. **1982.**
1015. $1 brown and blue .. 3·25 80

1982. Birth Centenary of F. D. Roosevelt (American statesman). No. 706 optd. **F. D. ROOSEVELT 1882-1982.**
1016. $1 "Agrias claudina .. 1·75 60

1982. 1st Anniv. of G.A.C. Inaugural Flight Georgetown to Boa Vista, Brazil. No. 842 optd. with **1982** and surch. **GAC Inaug. Flight Georgetown-Boa Vista, Brasil.**
1017. 200 c. on 75 c. on $5 "Odontadenia grandiflora .. .. .. 15·00 3·00

1982. CARICOM Heads of Government Conference, Kingston, Jamaica. Nos. 881/6 surch. **CARICOM Heads of Gov't Conference July 1982.**
1018. 50 c. on 15 c. Type **225** .. 1·00 30
1019. 50 c. on 15 c. "Metric man" .. .. .. 1·00 30
1020. 50 c. on 15 c. "Postal service goes metric" .. 1·00 30
1021. 50 c. on 15 c. Weighing child on metric scales .. 1·00 30
1022. 50 c. on 15 c. Canje Bridge 1·00 30
1023. 50 c. on 15 c. Tap filling litre bucket .. .. 1·00 30

1982. Christmas. Nos. 895/9 optd. **CHRISTMAS 1982.**
1024. 15 c. on 2 c. Type **132** (surch. BADEN POWELL 1857–1982) .. 20 15
1025. 15 c. on 2 c. Type **132** (surch. "Scout Movement 1907–1982") .. 20 15
1026. 15 c. on 2 c. Type **132** (surch. "1907–1982") 30 25
1027. 15 c. on 2 c. Type **132** (surch. "1857–1982") 30 25
1028. 15 c. on 2 c. Type **132** (surch "1982") .. 2·50 2·50

1982. Nos. 543 and 546 surch. in figures (no "c" after face value).
1034 15 c. on 2 c. Type **132** .. 10 10
1035 20 c. on 6 c. Cannon-ball tree 10 10
See also No. 1086.

1982. No. 452 surch.
1032. 50 c. on 6 c. Patua .. 20 25
1033. 100 c. on 6 c. Patua .. 40 45

1983. Optd. **1983.**
1036. – 15 c. mult. (No. 655) 4·50 2·00
1037. – 15 c. brown, grey and black (No. 672) .. 50 10
1038. – 15 c. mult. (No. 682) 40 10
1039. **214.** 15 c. on 10 c. mult... 35 10
1040. **215.** 15 c. on 10 c. mult... 15 10
1041. – 50 c. mult. (No. 646) 4·00 25
1042. – 50 c. mult. (No. 696) 4·00 25
1043. – 50 c. mult. (No. 719) 1·50 25
See also Nos. 1060/1, 1069/70, 1072/9c, 1096, 1101 and 1110/16.

1983. No. O 17 optd. **POSTAGE.**
1044. 15 c. Harpy Eagle .. 6·50 10

1983. National Heritage. Nos. 710/12 and 778 surch.
1045. 90 c. on 30 c. Cassiri and decorated Amerindian jars .. .. .. 2·00 1·00
1046. 90 c. on 35 c. Rock drawing of hunter and quarry 35 50
1047. 90 c. on 50 c. Fort Kyk-over-al .. .. 2·00 1·00
1048. 90 c. on 60 c. Fort Island 3·00 50

258. Guyana Flag (inscr. "60th BIRTHDAY ANNIVERSARY").

1983. 60th Birthday of President Burnham and 30 Years in Parliament. Mult.
1049. 25 c. Type **258** 15 20
1050. 25 c. As T **258**, but position of flag reversed and inscr. "30th ANNIVERSARY IN PARLIAMENT" .. 15 20
1051. $1.30 Youth display (41 × 25 mm.) 75 65
1052. $6 Presidential standard (43½ × 25 mm.) .. 2·50 2·75

1983. Surch. in words.
1053. **170.** 50 c. on 10 c. mult. (No. 717) .. .. 1·00 30
1054. – 50 c. on 100 c. on $3 mult. (No. 910) .. 1·50 30
1055. **152.** $1 on 10 c. mult. (No. 635) .. .. 6·00 45
1056. $1 on $1.05 on 10 c. mult. (No. 768) .. 3·50 45
1056a. – $1 on $1.10 on $2 mult. (No. 843) .. 3·00 3·00
1057. – $1 on 220 c. on 5 c. mult. (No. 844) .. 7·00 1·00
1058. – $1 on 330 c. on $2 mult. (No. 981) .. 1·00 45
1059. – $1 on $12 on $1.10 on $2 mult. (No. P3) .. 18·00 5·00
No. 1056a is surcharged on an **unissued** Royal Wedding surcharge, similar to **No. 843.** See also Nos. 1080/4.

1983. No. 859 optd. **1983.**
1060. $1 on 60 c. Beethoven and Sonny Thomas .. 4·00 45

1983. Conference of Foreign Ministers of Non-aligned Countries, New Delhi. No. 569 surch. and No. 570 optd. **1983.**
1061. **136.** 25 c. multicoloured .. 2·00 25
1062. 50 c. on 8 c. mult. .. 3·00 25

1983. No. 771 further surch.
1064. **181.** 20 c. on 10 c. on 3 c. black, blue & red .. 55 10

1983. Commonwealth Day. Nos. 383 and 401. surch. **Commonwealth Day 14 March 1983.**
1065. **60.** 25 c. on 6 c. green .. 1·00 20
1066. $1.20 on 6 c. green .. 50 50
1067. **63.** $1.30 on 24 c. black and orange 60 55
1068. $2.40 on 24 c. black and orange .. .. 1·25 1·25

1983. Easter. Nos. 482/3 optd. **1983.**
1069. **111.** 25 c. multicoloured .. 15 10
1070. 30 c. multicoloured .. 30 15

262.

1983. 25th Anniv. of International Maritime Organization. British Guiana fiscal stamp optd.
1071. **262.** $4.80 blue and green 4·50 5·50

1983. Optd. **1983.**
1072. **152.** 50 c. mult. (No. 637) 1·50 25
1073. **159.** 50 c. blue, black and yellow (No. 668) 5·00 25
1073a. – 50 c. mult. (No. 723)
1074. – 50 c. mult. (No. 854) 60 25
1075. – 50 c. mult. (No. 858) 30 25
1076. – $1 mult. (No. 628) .. 7·50 45
1077. – $1 mult. (No. 638) .. 7·50 45
1078. – $1 mult. (No. 675) .. 4·00 45
1079. – $1 on 30 c. mult. No. 855) .. .. 1·25 45
1079a. – $3 mult. (No. 720) .. 10·00 90
1079b. – $3 mult. (No. 724) ..
1079c. – $3 mult. (No. 748) ..

1983. Surch. **FIFTY CENTS.**
1080. **148.** 50 c. on 8 c. mult. (No. 615) .. .. 1·75 25
1081. **162.** 50 c. on 8 c. mult. (No. 681) .. .. 6·00 25
1082. **171.** 50 c. on 10 c. mult. (No. 721) .. .. 3·00 25
1083. – 50 c. on 10 c. on 25 c. mult. (No. O 13) .. 4·00 25
1084. – 50 c. on 330 c. on $3 mult. (No. 845) .. 3·50 25

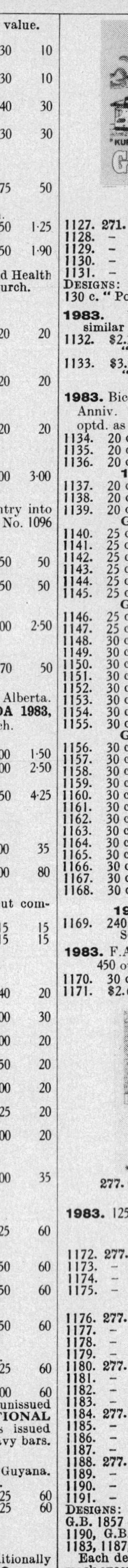

1983. Surch, with **c** after new face value.
1085 **105** 15 c. on 6 c. blk, gold & pink (No. 469) .. 30 10
1086 – 20 c. on 6 c. multicoloured (No. 546) 30 10
1087 **111** 50 c. on 6 c. multicoloured (No. 481) 40 30
1099 – 50 c. on 6 c. multicoloured (No. 489) 30 30

1983. No. 639 surch.
1089. **153.** 110 c. on 10 c. yell., green and violet .. 1·75 50

1983. Nos. 551 and 556 surch.
1090. 250 c. on 40 c. Tiger Beard 6·50 1·25
1091. 400 c. on $5 "Odontadenia grandiflora" .. .. 6·50 1·90

1983. World Telecommunications and Health Day. Nos. 842 and 980 further surch.
1092. 25 c. on 220 c. on 1 c. Pitcher Plant of Mt. Roraima (surch **ITU 1983 25**) .. 20 20
1093. 25 c. on 220 c. on 1 c. Pitcher Plant of Mt. Roraima (surch **WHO 1983 25**) .. 20 20
1094. 25 c. on 220 c. on 1 c. Pitcher Plant of Mt. Roraima (surch **17 MAY '83 ITU/WHO 25** .. 20 20
1095. $4.50 on 75 c. on $5 "Odontadenia grandiflora" (surch **ITU/WHO 17 MAY 1983**) .. 11·00 3·00

1983. 30th Anniv. of President's Entry into Parliament, Nos. 690 and 692 surch, No. 1096 additionally optd **1983.**
1096. $1 on 15 c. black, blue and grey .. .. 4·50 50
1097. $1 on 40 c. black, orange and grey .. .. 6·50 50

1983. No. 611 optd **1983.**
1101. 25 c. Guides in camp .. 42·00 2·50

1983. No. 452 surch **$1.**
1102 $1 on 6 c. Patua 70 50

1983. 15th World Scout Jamboree, Alberta. Nos. 835/6 and O 25 optd. **CANADA 1983,** Nos. 1103 and 1105 additionally surch.
1103. – $1.30 on 100 c. on 8 c. multicoloured .. 3·00 1·50
1104. **116.** 180 c. on 6 c. mult... 3·00 2·50
1105. $3.90 on 400 c. on 6 c. multicoloured .. 3·50 4·25

1983. Nos. 659/60 surch.
1106. 60 c. on 15 c. Map of the Caribbean .. .. 7·00 35
1107. $1.50 on 15 c. Prudential Cup .. .. .. 8·00 80

1983. As Nos. 1049/50, but without commemorative inscr above flag.
1108. 25 c. As Type **258** .. 15 15
1109. 25 c. As No. 1050 .. 15 15

1983. Optd **1983.**
1110. **105.** 30 c. black, gold and green (No. 471) .. 40 20
1111. – 30 c. multicoloured (No. 695) .. .. 9·00 30
1112. – 30 c. multicoloured (No. 718) .. .. 4·00 20
1113. – 30 c. multicoloured (No. 722) .. .. 7·50 20
1114. – 30 c. multicoloured (No. 746) .. .. 4·00 20
1115. – 60 c. multicoloured (No. 697) .. .. 4·25 20
1116. – 60 c. multicoloured (No. 731) .. .. 5·00 20

1983. No. 553 optd **1982.**
1117. 60 c. Soldier's Cap .. 4·00 35

1983. Surch.
1118. **157.** 120 c. on 8 c. mult. (No. 654) .. .. 3·25 60
1119. **159.** 120 c. on 10 c. red, black and gold (No. 666) .. .. 3·50 60
1120. – 120 c. on 35 c. mult. (No. 622) .. .. 3·50 60
1121. – 120 c. on 35 c. orange, green and violet (No. 640) .. .. 3·50 60

1983. Nos. 716 and 729 surch.
1122. 120 c. on 10 c. Type **173** .. 3·25 60
1123. 120 c. on 375 c. on $3 Cylinder satellite .. 3·00 60
No. 1123 also carries an otherwise unissued surcharge in red, reading **INTERNATIONAL SCIENCE YEAR 1982 375.** As issued much of this is obliterated by two heavy bars.

1983. British Guiana No. D1a and Guyana. No. D8 surch **120 GUYANA.**
1124. **D 1.** 120 c. on 1 c. green .. 3·25 60
1125. **D 2.** 120 c. on 1 c. olive .. 3·25 60
See also Nos. 1399 and 1402.

1983. CARICOM Day. No. 823 additionally surch **CARICOM DAY 1983 60.**
1126. 60 c. on $3 "Makanaima the Great Ancestral Spirit of the Amerindians" 1·75 35

271. "Kurupukari".

1983. Riverboats.
1127. **271.** 30 c. black and red .. 20 20
1128. – 60 c. black and violet 40 35
1129. – 120 c. black and yell. 1·00 60
1130. – 130 c. black .. .. 1·00 65
1131. – 150 c. black and green 1·10 80
DESIGNS: 60 c. "Makouria". 120 c. "Powis". 130 c. "Pomeroon". 150 c. "Lukanani".

1983. Unissued Royal Wedding surch. similar to No. 843, additionally surch.
1132. $2.30 on $1.10 on $2 "Norantea guianensis" 3·00 1·50
1133. $3.20 on $1.10 on $2 "Norantea guianensis" 3·50 1·75

1983. Bicentenary of Manned Flight and 20th Anniv. of Guyana Airways. Nos. 701/2a optd. as indicated in brackets.
1134. 20 c. multicoloured (**BW**) 10 10
1135. 20 c. multicoloured (**LM**) 10 10
1136. 20 c. multicoloured (**GY 1963 1983**) .. 10 10
1137. 20 c. multicoloured (**JW**) 10 10
1138. 20 c. multicoloured (**CU**) 10 10
1139. 20 c. multicoloured (**Mont Golfier 1783–1983**) 10 10
1140. 25 c. multicoloured (**BGI**) 50 25
1141. 25 c. multicoloured (**GEO**) 15 10
1142. 25 c. multicoloured (**MIA**) 50 25
1143. 25 c. multicoloured (**BVB**) 50 25
1144. 25 c. multicoloured (**PBM**) 50 25
1145. 25 c. multicoloured (**Mont Golfier 1783–1983**) 20 15
1146. 25 c. multicoloured (**POS**) 50 25
1147. 25 c. multicoloured (**JFK**) 50 25
1148. 30 c. multicoloured (**AHL**) 25 15
1149. 30 c. multicoloured (**BCG**) 25 15
1150. 30 c. multicoloured (**BMJ**) 25 15
1151. 30 c. multicoloured (**EKE**) 25 15
1152. 30 c. multicoloured (**GEO**) 25 15
1153. 30 c. multicoloured (**GFO**) 25 15
1154. 30 c. multicoloured (**IBM**) 25 15
1155. 30 c. multicoloured (**Mont Golfier 1783–1983**) 25 15
1156. 30 c. multicoloured (**KAI**) 25 15
1157. 30 c. multicoloured (**KAR**) 25 15
1158. 30 c. multicoloured (**KPG**) 25 15
1159. 30 c. multicoloured (**KRG**) 25 15
1160. 30 c. multicoloured (**KTO**) 25 15
1161. 30 c. multicoloured (**LTM**) 25 15
1162. 30 c. multicoloured (**MHA**) 25 15
1163. 30 c. multicoloured (**MWJ**) 25 15
1164. 30 c. multicoloured (**MYM**) 25 15
1165. 30 c. multicoloured (**NAI**) 25 15
1166. 30 c. multicoloured (**ORJ**) 25 15
1167. 30 c. multicoloured (**USI**) 25 15
1168. 30 c. multicoloured (**VEG**) 25 15

1983. No. 649 further surch.
1169. 240 c. on 35 c. on 60 c. Soldier's Cap .. .. 1·25 1·00

1983. F.A.O. Fisheries Project. Nos. 448 and 450 optd. **FAO 1983** and surch also.
1170. 30 c. on 1 c. Type **87** .. 15 15
1171. $2.60 on 3 c. Lukunani .. 1·50 1·75

277. G.B. 1857 1d. with Georgetown "AO3" Postmark.

1983. 125th Anniv. of Use of Great Britain Stamps in Guyana.
(a) Inscriptions in black.
1172. **277.** 25 c. brown and blk. 15 10
1173. – 30 c. red and black .. 15 15
1174. – 60 c. violet and blk. 35 30
1175. – 120 c. green and blk. 70 55
(b) Inscriptions in blue.
1176. **277.** 25 c. brown & black .. 15 10
1177. – 25 c. red and black .. 15 10
1178. – 25 c. violet & black .. 15 10
1179. – 25 c. green & black .. 15 10
1180. **277.** 30 c. brown & black .. 15 15
1181. – 30 c. red and black .. 15 15
1182. – 30 c. violet & black .. 15 15
1183. – 30 c. green & black .. 15 15
1184. **277.** 45 c. brown & black .. 30 25
1185. – 45 c. red and black .. 30 25
1186. – 45 c. violet & black .. 30 25
1187. – 45 c. green & black .. 30 25
1188. **277.** 120 c. brown & black 70 55
1189. – 130 c. red and black 75 60
1190. – 150 c. violet & black 80 70
1191. – 200 c. green and black 90 95
DESIGNS: Nos. 1173, 1177, 1181, 1185, 1189, G.B. 1857 4 d. red. Nos. 1174, 1178, 1182, 1186, 1190, G.B. 1856 6 d. lilac. Nos. 1175, 1179, 1183, 1187, 1191, G.B. 1856 1 s. green.
Each design incorporates the "AO3" postmark except Nos. 1189/91 which show mythical postmarks of the Crowned-circle type inscribed "DEMERARA", "BERBICE" or "ESSEQUIBO".

1983. International Communications Year. No. 716 surch. **INT. COMMUNICATIONS YEAR 50.**
1192. 50 c. on 375 c. on $3 Cylinder satellite .. 4·00 30
No. 1192 also carries an otherwise unissued "375" surcharge. As issued much of this surcharge is obliterated by two groups of six thin horizontal lines.

1983. St. John's Ambulance Commemoration. Nos. 650 and 653 surch.
1193. **156.** 75 c. on 8 c. silver, black and mauve 3·75 30
1194. – $1.20 on 40 c. silver, black and blue .. 5·50 50

1983. International Food Day. No. 616 surch. **$1.20 Int. Food Day 1983.**
1195. $1.20 on 35 c. Five-fingers and awaras .. 1·00 50

1983. 65th Anniv. of I.L.O. and 25th Death Anniv. of H. N. Critchlow (founder of Guyana Labour Union). No. 840 further optd. **1918–1983 I.L.O.**
1196. 240 c. on $3 H. N. Critchlow .. .. 1·50 1·50

1983. Deepavali Festival. Nos. 661 and 663/4 surch. **25 c.**
1197. 25 c. on 8 c. Type **158** .. 20 10
1198. $1.50 on 35 c. Flame in bowl .. .. .. 1·25 60
1199. $1.50 on 40 c. Goddess Latchmi 80 60

1983. No. 732 optd. **1982** and No. 798 further optd. **1983.**
1200. $3 "Makanaima the Great Ancestral Spirit of the Amerindians" .. 1·50 1·00
1201. 360 c. on $2 "Norantea guianensis" .. .. 1·75 1·40

1983. Wildlife Protection. Nos. 686 and 688 surch. and No. 762 optd. **1983.**
1202. 30 c. Six-banded Armadillo 40 15
1203. 60 c. on 15 c. Giant sea turtle 60 30
1204. $1.20 on 40 c. Iguana .. 95 50

1983. Human Rights Day. No. 1079c optd. **Human Rights Day.**
1205. $3 Rotary anniversary emblem .. .. 1·75 1·25

1983. Olympic Games, Los Angeles (1984). Nos. 733/44 surch. **LOS ANGELES 1984.**
1206. 55 c. on 125 c. on 35 c. Type **174** 25 25
1207. 55 c. on 125 c. on 35 c. Haimara 25 25
1208. 55 c. on 125 c. on 35 c. Electric Eel 25 25
1209. 55 c. on 125 c. on 35 c. Golden Rivulus .. 25 25
1210. 55 c. on 125 c. on 35 c. Pencil Fish 25 25
1211. 55 c. on 125 c. on 35 c. Four-eyed Fish .. 25 25
1212. 55 c. on 125 c. on 35 c. Pirai or Carib Fish .. 25 25
1213. 55 c. on 125 c. on 35 c. Smoking Hassar .. 25 25
1214. 55 c. on 125 c. on 35 c. Devil Ray 25 25
1215. 55 c. on 125 c. on 35 c. Flying Patwa 25 25
1216. 55 c. on 125 c. on 35 c. Arapaima Pirariucii .. 25 25
1217. 55 c. on 125 c. on 35 c. Lukanani 25 25
1217a. 125 c. on 35 c. Type **174** 1·50
1217b. 125 c. on 35 c. Haimara 1·50
1217c. 125 c. on 35 c. Electric Eel 1·50
1217d. 125 c. on 35 c. Golden Rivulus 1·50
1217e. 125 c. on 35 c. Pencil Fish 1·50
1217f. 125 c. on 35 c. Four-eyed Fish 1·50
1217g. 125 c. on 35 c. Pirai or Carib Fish 1·50
1217h. 125 c. on 35 c. Smoking Hassar 1·50
1217i. 125 c. on 35 c. Devil Ray 1·50
1217j. 125 c. on 35 c. Flying Patwa 1·50
1217k. 125 c. on 35 c. Arapaima Pirariucii 1·50
1217l. 125 c. on 35 c. Lukanani 1·50

1983. No. F7 with unissued (**"ESPANA 1982"**) surch. further optd. **1983.**
1218. 180 c. on 60 c. Soldier's Cap .. .. .. 1·50 65

1983. Commonwealth Heads of Government Meeting, New Delhi. No. 542 surch. **COMMONWEALTH HEADS OF GOV'T MEETING—INDIA 1983 150.**
1219. 150 c. on 1 c. Pitcher Plant of Mt. Roraima 1·00 60

1983. Christmas. No. 861 further surch. **CHRISTMAS 1983 20c.**
1220. 20 c. on 12 c. on 6 c. Patua 50 10

1984. Nos. 838 and F9 optd. **POSTAGE.**
1221. $2 "Norantea guianensis" .. .. 2·50 70
1221a. 550 c. on $10 "Elbella patrobas" .. .. 5·50 5·50

1984. Flowers. Unissued stamps as T **222** surch.
1222. 17 c. on 2 c. lilac, blue and green 35 35
1223. 17 c. on 8 c. lilac, blue and mauve 35 35

1984. Republic Day. No. 703 and 705a variously optd., 703 surch. also.
1224. 25 c. on 35 c. mult. (surch **ALL OUR HERITAGE 25**) 10 10
1225. 25 c. on 35 c. mult. (surch. **1984 25**) .. 10 10
1226. 25 c. on 35 c. mult. (surch. **REPUBLIC DAY 25**) 10 10
1227. 25 c. on 35 c. mult. (surch. **25**) 10 10
1228. 25 c. on 35 c. mult. (surch. **BERBICE 25**) 20 15
1229. 25 c. on 35 c. mult. (surch. **DEMERARA 25**) 20 15
1230. 25 c. on 35 c. mult. (surch. **ESSEQUIBO 25**) 20 15
1231. 25 c. on 35 c. mult. (surch. **1984 25**) .. 40 35
1232. 60 c. mult. (optd. **ALL OUR HERITAGE**) .. 25 30
1233. 60 c. mult. (optd. **REPUBLIC DAY**) .. 25 30
1234. 60 c. mult. (optd. **1984**) 25 30

1984. Guyana Olympic Committee Appeal. Nos. 841/3 handstamped **OLYMPIC GAMES 84 25 c. POSTAGE (+2.25 SURTAX)** and rings.
1235 25 c.+2.25 c. on 60 c. on 3 c. Hanging Heliconia 4·00 4·50
1236 25 c.+2.25 c. on 75 c. on $5 "Odontadenia grandiflora" .. .. 4·00 4·50
1237 25 c.+2.25 on $1.10 on $2 "Norantea guianensis" 4·00 4·50

1984. Nature Protection. Various stamps optd. **Protecting our Heritage** and some additionally surch.
1238. 20 c. on 15 c. mult. (No. 454) .. .. .. 4·00 10
1239. 20 c. on 15 c. mult. (No. 791) .. .. .. 4·00 10
1240a. 20 c. on 15 c. mult. (No. 1044) .. .. .. 9·00 1·00
1241. 25 c. mult. (No. 550a) .. 7·00 10
1242. 30 c. on 15 c. mult. (No. 548a) .. .. .. 9·00 30
1243. 40 c. mult. (No. 457) .. 5·50 20
1244. 50 c. mult. (No. 552) .. 75 25
1245. 50 c. mult. (No. F6) .. 75 25
1246. 60 c. mult. (No. 496) .. 7·00 30
1247. 90 c. on 40 c. mult. (No. 551) .. .. .. 7·50 40
1248. 180 c. on 40 c. mult. (No. 919) .. .. .. 7·50 70
1249. $2 mult. (No. 461) .. 38·00 1·25
1250. 225 c. on 10 c. mult. (No. 453) .. .. .. 13·00 90
1251. 260 c. on $1 mult. (No. 497) .. .. .. 7·00 1·00
1252. 320 c. on 40 c. mult. (No. 551) .. .. .. 6·00 1·50
1253. 350 c. on 40 c. mult. (No. 551) .. .. .. 10·00 1·75
1254. 380 c. on 50 c. mult. (No. 458) .. .. .. 3·75 1·75
1255. 450 c. on $5 mult. (No. 462) .. .. .. 4·00 1·90

1984. Easter. Nos. 483 and 916/17 optd. **1984** and No. 481 surch.
1256. **111.** 30 c. multicoloured .. 20 20
1257. 45 c. on 6 c. mult. .. 25 25
1258. 75 c. on 40 c. mult. .. 35 35
1259. 130 c. on 6 c. mult. .. 65 60

1984. Nos. 937/9 and 991 surch.
1260. 75 c. on $1 "Chelonanthus uliginoides" .. 7·50 35
1261. 75 c. on 110 c. on 3 c. Hanging Heliconia .. 8·50 35
1262. 225 c. on 250 c. on 6 c. Cannon-ball tree .. 2·25 1·25
1263. 230 c. on $2.35 on 180 c. on 60 c. Soldier's Cap 2·50 2·00

1984. Nos. 899/901, 904/6 and 909 surch.
1264. 20 c. on 15 c. on 2 c. Type **132** (No. 899) .. 1·25 30
1265. 75 c. on 110 c. on 5 c. Annatto tree (No. 904) 8·00 70
1266. 90 c. on 110 c. on 5 c. Annatto tree (No. 900) 5·00 85
1267. 90 c. on 110 c. on 5 c. Annatto tree (No. 901) 6·00 85
1268. 120 c. on 125 c. on 8 c. on 6 c. Cannon-ball tree (No. 905) .. .. 6·00 1·00
1269. 120 c. on 125 c. on 8 c. on 6 c. Cannon-ball tree (No. 906) .. .. 6·00 1·00
1270. 120 c. on 125 c. on 8 c. on 6 c. Cannon-ball tree (No. 909) .. .. 2·50 1·00

1984. World Telecommunications and Health Day. Nos. 802 and 980 surch.
1271. 25 c. on 220 c. on 1 c. Pitcher Plant of Mt. Roraima (surch. **ITU DAY 1984**) 20 20
1272. 25 c. on 220 c. on 1 c. Pitcher Plant of Mt. Roraima (surch. **WHO DAY 1984**) 20 20
1273. 25 c. on 220 c. on 1 c. Pitcher Plant of Mt. Roraima (surch. **ITU/WHO DAY 1984**) 20 20
1274. $4.50 on 280 c. on $5 "Odontadenia grandiflora" (surch. **ITU/WHO DAY 1984**) .. .. .. 1·75 1·75

1984. No. 1005 surch.
1275. 120 c. on $1.25 on 6 c. Cannon-ball tree .. 6·00 55

1984. World Forestry Conference. Nos. 752/5 surch or optd. **1984** ($3) and No. 875 surch.
1276. 55 c. on 30 c. "Hymenaea courbaril" .. .. 2·25 30
1277. 75 c. on 110 c. on $3 "Peltogyne venosa" .. 40 35
1278. 160 c. on 50 c. "Mora excelsa" 75 70
1279. 260 c. on 10 c. Type **177** 1·25 1·25
1280. $3 "Peltogyne venosa" .. 1·40 1·40

1984. No. 625 surch.
1281. 55 c. on 110 c. on 10 c. Type **150** 30 30
1282. 90 c. on 110 c. on 10 c. Type **150** 40 45
Nos. 1281/2 also carry an otherwise unissued 110 c. surch.

1984. U.P.U. Congress, Hamburg. Nos. 1188/91 optd **UPU Congress 1984 Hamburg.**
1283. 120 c. brown and black 50 55
1284. 130 c. red and black .. 55 60
1285. 150 c. violet and black .. 60 65
1286. 200 c. green and black .. 80 85

1984. Nos. 982/3 and 986/7 surch.
1287 45 c. on 50 c. on 2 c. green 20 25
1288 60 c. on $1.10 on 3 c. olive and brown 75 30
1289 120 c. on $1.25 on 6 c. grn 50 55
1290 200 c. on $2.20 on 24 c. black and orange .. 80 85

1984. Nos. 979/80 and 1003 surch. and No. 981 optd. **1984.**
1291. 75 c. on 110 c. on 5 c. Annatto tree 30 35
1292. 120 c. on 170 c. on 110 c. on 5 c. Annatto tree .. 50 55
1293. 200 c. on 220 c. on 1 c. Pitcher Plant of Mt. Roraima .. .. 6·00 85
1294. 330 c. on $2 "Norantea guianensis" .. .. 1·40 1·75

1984. CARICOM Day. No. 1200 additionally surch. **CARICOM DAY 1984 60.**
1295. 60 c. on $3 "Hakanaima the Great Ancestral Spirit of the Amerindians" 30 30

1984. No. 544 surch.
1296. 150 c. on 3 c. Hanging Heliconia 75 65

1984. CARICOM Heads of Government Conference. No. 544 surch. **60 CARICOM HEADS OF GOV'T CONFERENCE JULY 1984.**
1297. 60 c. on 3 c. Hanging Heliconia 30 30

301. Children and Thatched School.

1984. Centenary of Guyana Teachers' Association. Multicoloured.
1298. 25 c. Type **301** 10 15
1299. 25 c. Torch and graduates 10 15
1300. 25 c. Torch and target emblem 10 15
1301. 25 c. Teachers of 1884 and 1984 in front of school 10 15

1984. 60th Anniv of International Chess Federation. No. 1048 optd or surch also.
1302. 25 c. on 90 c. on 60 c. Fort Island (surch. **INT. CHESS FED. 1924–1984**) 30 15
1303. 25 c. on 90 c. on 60 c. Fort Island (surch. **1984**) 70 15
1304. 75 c. on 90 c. on 60 c. Fort Island (surch. **INT. CHESS FED. 1924–1984**) .. 70 35
1305. 75 c. on 90 c. on 60 c. Fort Island (surch. **1984**) .. .. 1·00 35
1306. 90 c. on 60 c. Fort Island (optd. **INT. CHESS FED. 1924–1984**) .. 75 45
1307. 90 c. on 60 c. Fort Island (optd. **1984**) .. .. 1·40 45

1984. Olympic Games, Los Angeles. No. 1051 surch.
1308. 25 c. on $1.30 mult. (surch. **TRACK AND FIELD**) 20 25
1309. 25 c. on $1.30 mult. (surch. **BOXING**) .. 20 25
1310. 25 c. on $1.30 mult. (surch. **OLYMPIC GAMES 1984 LOS ANGELES**) 20 25
1311. 25 c. on $1.30 mult. (surch. **CYCLING**) .. 40 25
1312. 25 c. on $1.30 mult. (surch. **OLYMPIC GAMES 1984**) .. 2·50 50
1313. $1.20 on $1.30 mult. (surch. **TRACK AND FIELD**) .. .. 1·00 1·10
1314. $1.20 on $1.30 mult. (surch. **BOXING**) .. 1·00 1·10
1315. $1.20 on $1.30 mult. (surch. **OLYMPIC GAMES 1984 LOS ANGELES**) .. .. 1·00 1·10
1316. $1·20 on $1·30 mult. (surch. **CYCLING**) .. 1·50 1·10
1317. $1.20 on $1.30 mult. (surch. **OLYMPIC GAMES 1984**) .. 3·00 1·50

1984. 60th Anniv. of Girl Guide Movement in Guyana. Nos. 900/9 surch. **25 GIRL GUIDES 1924–1984.**
1318. 25 c. on 110 c. on 5 c. Annatto tree (No. 900) 10 15
1319. 25 c. on 110 c. on 5 c. Annatto tree (No. 901) 10 15
1320. 25 c. on 110 c. on 5 c. Annatto tree (No. 902) 20 15
1321. 25 c. on 110 c. on 5 c. Annatto tree (No. 903) 20 15
1322. 25 c. on 110 c. on 5 c. Annatto tree (No. 904) 1·00 40
1323. 25 c. on 125 c. on 8 c. on 6 c. Cannon-ball tree (No. 905) 10 15
1324. 25 c. on 125 c. on 8 c. on 6 c. Cannon-ball tree (No. 906) 10 15
1325. 25 c. on 125 c. on 8 c. on 6 c. Cannon-ball tree (No. 907) 20 15
1326. 25 c. on 125 c. on 8 c. on 6 c. Cannon-ball tree (No. 908) 20 15
1327. 25 c. on 125 c. on 8 c. on 6 c. Cannon-ball tree (No. 909) .. .. 1·00 40

1984. Various stamps surch.
1328 20 c. on 15 c. on 2 c. Type **132** (No. 1034) .. 30 10
1341 25 c. on 10 c. Cattleya (No. 547) .. .. 15·00 2·00
1343 25 c. on 15 c. Christmas orchid (No. 548a) .. 90·00
1342 25 c. on 15 c. Christmas orchid (No. 864) .. 4·00 15
1346 25 c. on 15 c. Christmas orchid (No. 977) .. 4·00 10
1347 25 c. on 15 c. Christmas orchid (No. 1009) .. 4·00 10
1348 25 c. on 15 c. Christmas orchid (No. O23) .. 4·00 10
1342a 25 c. on 35 c. on 60 c. Soldier's cap (No. 649) 75·00
1331 60 c. on 110 c. on 8 c. on 3 c. Hanging heliconia (No. 868) .. 27·00
1332 120 c. on 125 c. on 8 c. on 6 c. Cannon-ball tree (No. 893) .. .. 3·50 50

1333 120 c. on 125 c. on $2 "Norantea guianensis" (No. 834) .. .. 27·00
1334 120 c. on 125 c. on $2 "Norantea guianensis" (No. O 20) .. 1·25 50
1335 120 c. on 140 c. on $1 "Chelonanthus uliginoides" (No. 796) .. 4·50 50
1349 130 c. on 110 c. on $2 "Norantea guianensis" (No. 804) .. .. 70·00
1350 130 c. on 110 c. on $2 "Norantea guianensis" (No. O 22) .. .. 8·50 2·50
1336 200 c. on 220 c. on 1 c. Pitcher plant of Mt. Roraima (No. 922) .. 3·00 85
1337 320 c. on $1.10 on $2 "Norantea guianensis" (No. 804) .. .. 4·25 1·50
1338 350 c. on 375 c. on $5 "Odontadenia grandiflora" (No. 803) .. 3·25 1·60
1339 390 c. on 400 c. on $5 "Odontadenia grandiflora" (No. 1091) .. 4·00 2·00
1340 450 c. on $5 "Odontadenia grandiflora" (No. O 16) 4·25 2·50
1351a 600 c. on $7.20 on $1 "Chelonanthus uliginoides" (No. 770) .. 2·25 1·25

1984. Various stamps optd. **1984.**

1352. 20 c. "Paphinia cristata" (No. 549) .. .. 8·50 10
1358. 25 c. Marabunta (No. 550) .. .. .. 65·00
1359. 25 c. Marabunta (No. F4) 3·25 50
1359a. 25 c. Marabunta (No. F4a) .. .. 1·75 10
1354. 50 c. on 8 c. Type **136** (No. 1062) .. .. 7·50 25
1355. 60 c. on 1 c. Pitcher Plant of Mt. Roraima (No. 1000) 55 25
1356. $2 "Norantea "guianensis" (No. O 33) 1·75 1·00
1360. $3.60 on $5 "Odontadenia grandiflora" (No. 769) 2·25 1·50

1984. 40th Anniv. of International Civil Aviation Organization. Nos. 981, 1017 and 1148/68 optd. **ICAO.**

1361. 30 c. mult. (No. 1148) .. 10 15
1362. 30 c. mult. (No. 1149) .. 10 15
1363. 30 c. mult. (No. 1150) .. 10 15
1364. 30 c. mult. (No. 1151) .. 10 15
1365. 30 c. mult. (No. 1152) .. 10 15
1366. 30 c. mult. (No. 1153) .. 10 15
1367. 30 c. multicoloured (No. 1154) (optd. 'IMB/ICAO'') 10 15
1368. 30 c. multicoloured (No. 1155) optd. "KCV/ICAO") 10 15
1369. 30 c. multicoloured (No. 1156) (optd "KAI/ICAO") 10 15
1370. 30 c. mult. (No. 1157) .. 10 15
1371. 30 c. mult. (No. 1158) .. 10 15
1372. 30 c. mult. (No. 1155) (optd. "1984") 10 15
1373. 30 c. multicoloured (No. 1155) (optd. "KPM/ICAO") 10 15
1374. 30 c. mult. (No. 1159) .. 10 15
1375. 30 c. mult. (No. 1160) .. 10 15
1376. 30 c. mult. (No. 1161) .. 10 15
1377. 30 c. multicoloured (No. 1155) (optd. "PMT/ICAO") 10 15
1378. 30 c. mult. (No. 1162) .. 10 15
1379. 30 c. mult. (No. 1163) .. 10 15
1380. 30 c. mult. (No. 1164) .. 10 15
1381. 30 c. mult. (No. 1165) .. 10 15
1382. 30 c. mult. (No. 1166) .. 10 15
1383. 30 c. mult. (No. 1167) .. 10 15
1384. 30 c. mult. (No. 1168) .. 10 15
1385. 200 c. on 330 c. on $2 mult. (No. 981) 65 70
1386. 200 c. on 75 c. on $5 mult. (No. 1017) .. .. 2·50 1·50

No. 1385 also carries an otherwise unissued surcharge **G.A.C. Inaug. Flight Georgetown—Toronto 200.**

1984. Wildlife Protection. Nos. 756/67 optd **1984.**

1387. 30 c. Type **178** 25 25
1388. 30 c. Red Howler .. 25 25
1389. 30 c. Common Squirrel-monkey 25 25
1390. 30 c. Two-toed Sloth .. 25 25
1391. 30 c. Brazilian Tapir .. 25 25
1392. 30 c. Collared Peccary .. 25 25
1393. 30 c. Six-banded Armadillo 25 25
1394. 30 c. Tamandua ("Ant Eater") 25 25
1395. 30 c. Giant Anteater .. 25 25
1396. 30 c. Brown Murine Opossum 25 25
1397. 30 c. Brown Four-eyed Opossum 25 25
1398. 30 c. Brazilian Agouti .. 25 25

1984. Nos. D10/11 surch. **120 GUYANA.**

1399. **D2.** 120 c. on 4 c. blue .. 4·50 45
1402. 120 c. on 12 c. red .. 4·50 45

1984. 175th Birth Anniv of Louis Braille (inventor of alphabet for the blind). No. 1040 surch. **$1.50.**

1403. $1.50 on 15 c. on 10 c. Type **215** .. .. 5·50 55

1984. International Food Day. No. 1012 surch.

1404. 150 c. on 50 c. Pawpaw and tangerine 50 55

The surcharge places a "1" alongside the original face value and obliterates the "1982" date on the previous overprint.

1984. Birth Centenary of H. N. Critchlow (founder of Guyana Labour Union). No. 873 surch. and No. 1196, both optd. **1984.**

1405. 240 c. on 110 c. on $3 H. N. Critchlow (No. 873) 1·00 85
1406. 240 c. on $3 H. N. Critchlow (No. 1196) .. 6·00 85

1984. Nos. 910/12 and 1184/7 surch.

1407. **277.** 25 c. on 45 c. brown and black 15 15
1408. – 25 c. on 45 c. red and black (No. 1185) .. 15 15
1409. – 25 c. on 45 c. violet and black (No. 1186) 15 15
1410. – 25 c. on 45 c. green and black (No. 1187) 15 15
1411. – 120 c. on 100 c. on $3 mult. (No. 910) .. 5·00 45
1412. – 120 c. on 400 c. on 30 c. mult. (No. 911) 65 45
1413. – 320 c. on $5 multicoloured (No. 912) 6·00 1·25

1984. Deepavali Festival. Nos. 544/5 surch. **MAHA SABHA 1934–1984** and new value.

1414. 25 c. on 5 c. Annatto tree 10 10
1415. $1.50 on 3 c. Hanging Heliconia 50 55

1984. A.S.D.A. Philatelic Exhibition, New York. Nos. 1188/91 optd. **Philatelic Exhibition New York 1984.**

1416. **277.** 120 c. brn. and black 40 45
1417. – 130 c. red and black 45 50
1418. – 150 c. violet & black 50 55
1419. – 200 c. green & black 70 75

1984. Olympic Games, Los Angeles (2nd issue). Design as No. 1051, but with Olympic rings and inscr **"OLYMPIC GAMES 1984. LOS ANGELES".**

1420. $1.20, Youth display (41 × 25 mm) .. .. 1·50 45

1984. Nos. 847, 861 and 1032/3 surch.

1421. 20 c. on 12 c. on 12 c. on 6 c. mult. (No. 847) .. 35 10
1422. 20 c. on 12 c. on 6 c. mult. (No. 861) .. .. 60·00
1423. 25 c. on 50 c. on 6 c. mult. (No. 1032) 10 10
1424. 60 c. on $1 on 6 c. mult. (No. 1033) 20 25

318. Pair of Swallow-tailed Kites on Tree.

1984. Christmas. Swallow-tailed Kites. Mult.

1425. 60 c. Type **318** .. .. 1·50 1·25
1426. 60 c. Swallow-tailed Kite on branch .. .. 1·50 1·25
1427. 60 c. Kite in flight with wings raised .. .. 1·50 1·25
1428. 60 c. Kite in flight with wings lowered .. 1·50 1·25
1429. 60 c. Kite gliding .. 1·50 1·25

Nos. 1425/9 were printed together se-tenant with the backgrounds forming a composite design. Each stamp is inscribed "CHRISTMAS 1982".

319. St. George's Cathedral, Georgetown.

1985. Georgetown Buildings. Each black and stone.

1430. 25 c. Type **319** 10 10
1431. 60 c. Demerara Mutual Life Assurance Building 20 25
1432. 120 c. As No. 1431 .. 40 45
1433. 120 c. Town Hall .. 40 45
1434. 120 c. Victoria Law Courts 40 45
1435. 200 c. As No. 1433 .. 70 75
1436. 300 c. As No. 1434 .. 1·00 1·10

Nos. 1432/4 were printed together, se-tenant forming a composite design.

1985. International Youth Year. No. 1420 optd. **International Youth Year 1985.**

1437. $1.20, Youth display .. 1·75 45

Examples of No. 1420 used for this overprint all show the second line of the original inscription as "LOS ANGELLES".

1985. Republic Day. Nos. 1049/50 and 1052 optd. or surch. **Republic Day 1970–1985.**

1438. 25 c. Type **238** 10 10
1439. 25 c. Flag (inscr. "30th ANNIVERSARY IN PARLIAMENT") .. 10 10
1440. 120 c. on $6 Presidential standard 40 45
1441. 130 c. on $6 Presidential standard 45 50

322. Young Ocelot on Branch.

1985. Wildlife Protection. Multicoloured.

1442. 25 c. Type **322** olive background .. 1·50 10
1443. 60 c. Young ocelot (different) (brown background) 30 25
1444. 120 c. As No. 1443 .. 15 20
1445. 120 c. Type **322** .. 15 20
1446. 120 c. Young ocelot different) (brown background) .. 15 20
1447. 130 c. As No. 1446 .. 45 50
1448. 320 c. Scarlet macaw (28 × 46 mm.) .. 3·50 1·25
1449. 330 c. Young ocelot reaching for branch (28 × 46 mm.) .. .. 1·50 1·25

1985. No. 940, Revenue stamp as T **181**, Nos. 912, 1016 and unissued Official value (No. O 24 optd. **OPS**) surch.

1450. 30 c. on 50 c. mult. (as No. 719) 20 10
1451. 55 c. on 2 c. black, blue and grey 30 20
1452. 55 c. on 15 c. on 2 c. black, blue and grey 30 20
1453. 90 c. on $1 mult. (No. 1016) 1·25 30
1454. 225 c. on $5 mult. (No. 912) 1·75 70
1455. 230 c. on $5 mult. (No. 912) 1·50 75
1456. 260 c. on $5 mult. (No. 912) 1·50 80

1985. International Youth Year Save the Children Fund Campaign. Nos. 880, 1073a, 1079b and 1082 optd. **International Youth Year 1985** or surch. also.

1457. 50 c. "Two Boys catching Ducks" (No. 1073a) 1·50 20
1458. 50 c. on 10 c. Type **171** (No. 1082) .. .. 3·25 20
1459. 120 c. on 125 c. on $3 "Mango Season" (No. 880) .. .. 1·50 45
1460. $3 "Mango Season" (No. 1079b) .. .. 1·50 1·10

1985. 125th Anniv. of British Guiana Post Office (1st issue). No. 699 surch. with names of post offices and postal agencies open in 1860.

1461. 25 c. on 10 c. mult. (**Airy Hall**) 15 10
1462. 25 c. on 10 c. mult. (**Belfield Arab Coast**) .. 15 10
1463. 25 c. on 10 c. mult. (**Belfield E. C. Dem.**) .. 15 10
1464. 25 c. on 10 c. mult. (**Belladrum**) 15 10
1465. 25 c. on 10 c. mult. (**Beterver-wagting**) .. 15 10
1466. 25 c. on 10 c. mult. (**Blairmont Ferry**) .. 15 10
1467. 25 c. on 10 c. mult. (**Boeraserie**) 15 10
1468. 25 c. on 10 c. mult. (**Brahm**) 15 10
1469. 25 c. on 10 c. mult. (**Bushlot**) 15 10
1470. 25 c. on 10 c. mult. (**De Kinderen**) 15 10
1471. 25 c. on 10 c. mult. (**Fort Wellington**) 15 10
1472. 25 c. on 10 c. mult. (**Georgetown**) .. 15 10
1473. 25 c. on 10 c. mult. (**Hague**) 15 10
1474. 25 c. on 10 c. mult. (**Leguan**) 15 10
1475. 25 c. on 10 c. mult. (**Mahaica**) 15 10
1476. 25 c. on 10 c. mult. (**Mahaicony**) 15 10
1477. 25 c. on 10 c. mult. (**New Amsterdam**) .. 15 10
1478. 25 c. on 10 c. mult. (**Plaisance**) 15 10
1479. 25 c. on 10 c. mult. (**No. 6 Police Station**) .. 15 10
1480. 25 c. on 10 c. mult. (**Queenstown**) .. 15 10
1481. 25 c. on 10 c. mult. (**Vergenoegen**) .. 15 10
1482. 25 c. on 10 c. mult. (**Vigilance**) 15 10
1483. 25 c. on 10 c. mult. (**Vreed-en-Hoop**) .. 15 10
1484. 25 c. on 10 c. mult. (**Wakenaam**) .. 15 10
1485. 25 c. on 10 c. mult. (**Windsor Castle**) .. 15 10

See also Nos. 1694/1717, 2140/64 and 2278/2301.

1985. I.T.U./W.H.O. Day. Nos. 1148/68 optd. **1985** or with single capital letter.

1486. 30 c. mult. (1148) .. 15 15
1487. 30 c. mult. (1149) .. 15 15
1488. 30 c. mult. (1150) .. 15 15
1489. 30 c. mult. (1151) .. 15 15
1490. 30 c. mult. (1152) .. 15 15
1491. 30 c. mult. (1153) .. 15 15
1492. 30 c. mult. (1154) (**I**) .. 15 15
1493. 30 c. mult. (1155) (**T**) .. 15 15
1494. 30 c. mult. (1156) (**U**) .. 15 15
1495. 30 c. mult. (1157) .. 15 15
1496. 30 c. mult. (1158) .. 15 15
1497. 30 c. mult. (1155) (**W**) .. 15 15
1498. 30 c. mult. (1155) (**H**) .. 15 15
1499. 30 c. mult. (1155) (**O**) .. 15 15
1500. 30 c. mult. (1159) .. 15 15
1501. 30 c. mult. (1160) .. 15 15
1502. 30 c. mult. (1161) (**D**) .. 15 15
1503. 30 c. mult. (1155) (**A**) .. 15 15
1504. 30 c. mult. (1162) (**Y**) .. 15 15
1505. 30 c. mult. (1163) .. 15 15
1506. 30 c. mult. (1164) .. 15 15
1507. 30 c. mult. (1165) .. 15 15
1508. 30 c. mult. (1166) .. 15 15
1509. 30 c. mult. (1167) .. 15 15
1510. 30 c. mult. (1168) .. 15 15

1985. No. 861 surch.

1511. 20 c. on 12 c. on 6 c. Patua 10 10

1985. 10th Anniv. of Caribbean Agricultural Research Development Institute. No. 544 surch. **CARDI 1975-85 60.**

1512. 60 c. on 3 c. Hanging Heliconia 30 25

1985. No. 839 surch.

1513. 600 c. on 625 c. on 40 c. Tiger Beard .. .. 8·50 2·50

1985. 80th Anniv. of Rotary International. Nos. 707 and 879 surch. **ROTARY INTERNATIONAL 1905-1985.**

1514. 120 c. on 110 c. on $3 Rotary anniversary emblem .. .. 6·00 45
1515. 300 c. on $2 "Morpho rhetenor" .. .. 2·00 1·10

1985. CARICOM Day. No. 1200 surch. **CARICOM DAY 1985 60.**

1516. 60 c. on $3 "Makanaima the Great Ancestral Spirit of the Amerindians" .. 30 30

1985. 135th Anniv. of First British Guiana Stamps. No. 870 surch. **135th Anniversary Cotton Reel 1980-1985 120.**

1517. 120 c. on 110 c. on 10 c. Type **170** 65 55

"REICHENBACHIA" ISSUES. Due to the proliferation of these designs the catalogue uses the book plate numbers as description for each design. The following index gives the species on each plate.

Series 1

Plate No. 1 (Series 1) "Odontoglossum crispum"
Plate No. 2 (Series 1) "Cattleya percivaliana"
Plate No. 3 (Series 1) "Cypripedium sanderianum"
Plate No. 4 (Series 1) "Odontoglossum rossi"
Plate No. 5 (Series 1) "Cattleya dowiana aurea"
Plate No. 6 (Series 1) "Coelogyne cristata maxima"
Plate No. 7 (Series 1) "Odontoglossum insleayi splendens"
Plate No. 8 (Series 1) "Laelia euspatha"
Plate No. 9 (Series 1) "Dendrobium wardianum"
Plate No. 10 (Series 1) "Laelia autumnalis xanthotropis"
Plate No. 11 (Series 1) "Phalaenopsis grandiflora aurea"
Plate No. 12 (Series 1) "Cattleya lawrenceana"
Plate No. 13 (Series 1) "Masdevallia shuttleworthii" and "M. xanthocorys"
Plate No. 14 (Series 1) "Aeranthus sesquipedalis"
Plate No. 15 (Series 1) "Cattleya mendelii Duke of Marlborough"
Plate No. 16 (Series 1) "Zygopetalum intermedium"
Plate No. 17 (Series 1) "Phaius humblotii"
Plate No. 18 (Series 1) "Chysis bractescens"
Plate No. 19 (Series 1) "Masdevallia backhousiana"
Plate No. 20 (Series 1) "Cattleya citrina"
Plate No. 21 (Series 1) "Oncidium jonesianum" and "Oncidium jonesianum phaeanthum"
Plate No. 22 (Series 1) "Saccolabium giganteum"
Plate No. 23 (Series 1) "Cypripedium io"
Plate No. 24 (Series 1) "Odontoglossum blandum"
Plate No. 25 (Series 1) "Maxillaria sanderiana"
Plate No. 26 (Series 1) "Odontoglossum Edward II"
Plate No. 27 (Series 1) "Vanda teres"
Plate No. 28 (Series 1) "Odontoglossum hallii xanthoglossum"
Plate No. 29 (Series 1) "Odontoglossum crispum hrubyanum"
Plate No. 30 (Series 1) "Oncidium concolor"
Plate No. 31 (Series 1) "Trichopilia suavis alba"
Plate No. 32 (Series 1) "Cattleya superba splendens"
Plate No. 33 (Series 1) "Odontoglossum luteo-purpureum"
Plate No. 34 (Series 1) "Cypripedium niveum"
Plate No. 35 (Series 1) "Stanhopea shuttleworthii"
Plate No. 36 (Series 1) "Laelia anceps percivaliana"
Plate No. 37 (Series 1) "Odontoglossum hebraicum"
Plate No. 38 (Series 1) "Cypripedium oenanthum superbum"
Plate No. 39 (Series 1) "Dendrobium superbiens"
Plate No. 40 (Series 1) "Laelia harpophylla"
Plate No. 41 (Series 1) "Lycaste skinneri" and "alba"
Plate No. 42 (Series 1) "Phalaenopsis stuartiana"
Plate No. 43 (Series 1) "Cattleya trianaei ernesti"
Plate No. 44 (Series 1) "Sobralia xantholeuca"
Plate No. 45 (Series 1) "Odontoglossum crispum kinlesideanum"
Plate No. 46 (Series 1) "Cattleya trianaei schroederiana"
Plate No. 47 (Series 1) "Epidendrum vitellinum"
Plate No. 48 (Series 1) "Laelia anceps stella" and "barkeriana"
Plate No. 49 (Series 1) "Odontoglossum harryanum"
Plate No. 50 (Series 1) "Dendrobium leechianum"
Plate No. 51 (Series 1) "Phalaenopsis speciosa"
Plate No. 52 (Series 1) "Laelia elegans schilleriana"
Plate No. 53 (Series 1) "Zygopetalum wendlandi"
Plate No. 54 (Series 1) "Cypripedium selligerum majus"
Plate No. 55 (Series 1) "Angraecum articulatum"
Plate No. 56 (Series 1) "Laelia anceps sanderiana"
Plate No. 57 (Series 1) "Vanda coerulea"
Plate No. 58 (Series 1) "Dendrobium nobile sanderianum"
Plate No. 59 (Series 1) "Laelia gouldiana"
Plate No. 60 (Series 1) "Odontoglossum grande"
Plate No. 61 (Series 1) "Cypripedium rothschildianum"
Plate No. 62 (Series 1) "Vanda sanderiana"
Plate No. 63 (Series 1) "Dendrobium aureum"
Plate No. 64 (Series 1) "Oncidium macranthum"
Plate No. 65 (Series 1) "Cypripedium tautzianum"
Plate No. 66 (Series 1) "Cymbidium mastersi"
Plate No. 67 (Series 1) "Angraecum caudatum"
Plate No. 68 (Series 1) "Laelia albida"
Plate No. 69 (Series 1) "Odontoglossum roezlii"
Plate No. 70 (Series 1) "Oncidium ampliatum majus"
Plate No. 71 (Series 1) "Renanthera lowii"
Plate No. 72 (Series 1) "Cattleya warscewiczii"
Plate No. 73 (Series 1) "Oncidium lanceanum"
Plate No. 74 (Series 1) "Vanda hookeriana"
Plate No. 75 (Series 1) "Cattleya labiata gaskelliana"
Plate No. 76 (Series 1) "Epidendrum prismatocarpum"
Plate No. 77 (Series 1) "Cattleya guttata leopoldi"
Plate No. 78 (Series 1) "Oncidium splendidum"
Plate No. 79 (Series 1) "Odontoglossum hebraicum aspersum"
Plate No. 80 (Series 1) "Cattleya dowiana var chrysotoxa"
Plate No. 81 (Series 1) "Cattleya trianae alba"
Plate No. 82 (Series 1) "Odontoglossum humeanum"
Plate No. 83 (Series 1) "Cypripedium argus"
Plate No. 84 (Series 1) "Odontoglossum luteopurpureum prionopetalum"
Plate No. 85 (Series 1) "Cattleya rochellensis"
Plate No. 86 (Series 1) "Odontoglossum triumphans" (inscr "ONTOGLOSSUM" in error)
Plate No. 87 (Series 1) "Phalaenopsis casta"
Plate No. 88 (Series 1) "Oncidium tigrinum"
Plate No. 89 (Series 1) "Cypripedium lemoinierianum"
Plate No. 90 (Series 1) "Catasetum bungerothii"
Plate No. 91 (Series 1) "Cattleya ballantiniana"
Plate No. 92 (Series 1) "Dendrobium brymerianum"
Plate No. 93 (Series 1) "Cattleya eldorado crocata"
Plate No. 94 (Series 1) "Odontoglossum sanderianum"
Plate No. 95 (Series 1) "Cattleya labiata warneri"
Plate No. 96 (Series 1) "Odontoglossum schroder-ianum"

Series 2

Plate No. 1 (Series 2) "Cypripedium morganiae burfordiense"
Plate No. 2 (Series 2) "Cattleya bowringiana"
Plate No. 3 (Series 2) "Dendrobium formosum"
Plate No. 4 (Series 2) "Phaius tuberculosus"
Plate No. 5 (Series 2) "Odontoglossum crispum mundyanum"
Plate No. 6 (Series 2) "Laelia praestans"
Plate No. 7 (Series 2) "Dendrobium phalaenopsis var statterianum"
Plate No. 8 (Series 2) "Cypripedium boxalli atratum"
Plate No. 9 (Series 2) "Odontoglossum wattianum"
Plate No. 10 (Series 2) "Cypripedium lathamianum inversum"
Plate No. 11 (Series 2) "Paphinia rugosa" and "Zygopetalum xanthinum"
Plate No. 12 (Series 2) "Dendrobium melanodiscus"
Plate No. 13 (Series 2) "Laelia anceps schroderiana"
Plate No. 14 (Series 2) "Phaius hybridus cooksonii"
Plate No. 15 (Series 2) "Disa grandiflora"
Plate No. 16 (Series 2) "Selenipedium hybridum grande"
Plate No. 17 (Series 2) "Cattleya schroederae alba"
Plate No. 18 (Series 2) "Lycaste skinnerii armeniaca"
Plate No. 19 (Series 2) "Odontoglossum excellens"
Plate No. 20 (Series 2) "Laelio-cattleya elegans var blenheimensis"
Plate No. 21 (Series 2) "Odontoglossum coradinei"
Plate No. 22 (Series 2) "Odontoglossum wilckeanum var rothschildianum"
Plate No. 23 (Series 2) "Cypripedium lawrenceanum hyeanum"
Plate No. 24 (Series 2) "Cattleya intermedia punctatissima"
Plate No. 25 (Series 2) "Laelia purpurata"
Plate No. 26 (Series 2) "Masdevallia harryana splendens"
Plate No. 27 (Series 2) "Selenipedium hybridum nitidissimum"
Plate No. 28 (Series 2) "Cattleya mendelii var measuresiana"
Plate No. 29 (Series 2) "Odontoglossum vexill-arium" ("miltonia vexillaria")
Plate No. 30 (Series 2) "Saccolabium coeleste"
Plate No. 31 (Series 2) "Cypripedium hybridum youngianum"
Plate No. 32 (Series 2) "Miltonia (hybrida) bleuana"
Plate No. 33 (Series 2) "Laelia grandis"
Plate No. 34 (Series 2) "Cattleya labiata var lueddemanniana"
Plate No. 35 (Series 2) "Odontoglossum coronarium"
Plate No. 36 (Series 2) "Cattleya granulosa var. schofieldiana"
Plate No. 37 (Series 2) "Odontoglossum (hybridum) leroyanum"
Plate No. 38 (Series 2) "Cypripedium (hybridum) laucheanum" and "eyermanianum"
Plate No. 39 (Series 2) "Cychnoches chlorochilon"
Plate No. 40 (Series 2) "Cattleya O'Brieniana"
Plate No. 41 (Series 2) "Odontoglossum ramosissimum"
Plate No. 42 (Series 2) "Dendrobium phalaenopsis var"
Plate No. 43 (Series 2) "Cypripedium (hybridum) pollettianum" and "maynardii"
Plate No. 44 (Series 2) "Odontoglossum naevium"
Plate No. 45 (Series 2) "Cypripedium (hybridium) castleanum"
Plate No. 47 (Series 2) "Cattleya amethystoglossa"
Plate No. 48 (Series 2) "Cattleya (hybrida) arnoldiana"
Plate No. 49 (Series 2) "Cattleya labiata"
Plate No. 50 (Series 2) "Dendrobium (hybridum) venus" and "cassiope"
Plate No. 51 (Series 2) "Selenipedium (hybridum) weidlichianum"
Plate No. 52 (Series 2) "Cattleya mossiae var. reineckiana"
Plate No. 53 (Series 2) "Cymbidium lowianum"
Plate No. 54 (Series 2) "Oncidium loxense"
Plate No. 56 (Series 2) "Coelogyne sanderae"
Plate No. 58 (Series 2) "Coelogyne pandurata"
Plate No. 59 (Series 2) "Schomburgkia sanderiana"
Plate No. 60 (Series 2) "Oncidium superbiens"
Plate No. 61 (Series 2) "Dendrobium johnsoniae"
Plate No. 62 (Series 2) "Laelia hybrida behrensiana"
Plate No. 63 (Series 2) Hybrid "Calanthes Victoria Regina", "Bella" and "Burfordiense"
Plate No. 64 (Series 2) "Cattleya mendelii Quorndon House var"
Plate No. 65 (Series 2) "Arachnanthe clarkei"
Plate No. 66 (Series 2) "Zygopetalum burtii"
Plate No. 67 (Series 2) "Cattleya (hybrida) parthenia"
Plate No. 68 (Series 2) "Phalaenopsis sanderiana" and "intermedia portei"
Plate No. 69 (Series 2) "Phaius blumei var. assamicus"
Plate No. 70 (Series 2) "Angraecum humblotii"
Plate No. 71 (Series 2) "Odontoglossum pescatorei"
Plate No. 72 (Series 2) "Cattleya rex"
Plate No. 73 (Series 2) "Zygopetalum crinitum"
Plate No. 74 (Series 2) "Cattleya lueddemanniana alba"
Plate No. 75 (Series 2) "Cymbidium (hybridum) winnianum"
Plate No. 76 (Series 2) Hybrid "Masdevallias courtauldiana", "geleniana" and "measuresiana"
Plate No. 77 (Series 2) "Cypripedium" (hybridum) calypso
Plate No. 78 (Series 2) "Masdevallia chimaera var. mooreana"
Plate No. 79 (Series 2) "Miltonia phalaenopsis"
Plate No. 80 (Series 2) "Lissochilus giganteus"
Plate No. 82 (Series 2) "Thunia brymeriana"
Plate No. 83 (Series 2) "Miltonia moreliana"
Plate No. 84 (Series 2) "Oncidium krameranium"
Plate No. 85 (Series 2) "Cattleya Victoria Regina"
Plate No. 86 (Series 2) "Zygopetalum klabochorum"
Plate No. 87 (Series 2) "Laelia autumnalis alba"
Plate No. 88 (Series 2) "Spathoglottis kimballiana"
Plate No. 89 (Series 2) "Laelio-cattleya" ("The Hon. Mrs. Astor")
Plate No. 90 (Series 2) "Phaius hybridus amabilis" and "marthiae"
Plate No. 91 (Series 2) "Zygopetalum rostratum"
Plate No. 92 (Series 2) "Coelogyne swaniana"
Plate No. 93 (Series 2) "Laelio-cattleya" (hybrida) "phoebe"
Plate No. 94 (Series 2) "Epidendrum atro-purpureum var randianum"
Plate No. 95 (Series 2) "Dendrobium imperatrix"
Plate No. 96 (Series 2) "Vanda parishii var marriottiana"

331. "Cattleya lawrenceana" Plate No. 12 (Series 1).

1985. Centenary of Publication of Sanders's "Reichenbachia" (1st issue). Orchids. Mult.

1518 25 c. Type **331** 40 30
1519 60 c. Plate No. 2 (Series 1) 50 35
1520 60 c. Plate No. 7 (Series 1) 50 35
1521 60 c. Plate No. 10 (Series 1) 50 35
1522 60 c. Plate No. 19 (Series 1) 50 35
1523 60 c. Plate No. 31 (Series 1) 50 35
1524 120 c. Plate No. 27 (Series 1) 75 55
1525 130 c. Plate No. 3 (Series 1) 75 55
1759 130 c. Plate No. 6 (Series 1) 35 20
1760 130 c. Plate No. 13 (Series 1) 35 20
1528 130 c. Plate No. 18 (Series 1) .. .. 1·50 55
1761 130 c. Plate No. 20 (Series 1) 35 20
1762 130 c. Plate No. 25 (Series 1) 35 20
1531 130 c. Plate No. 29 (Series 1) .. .. 1·25 55
1532 130 c. Plate No. 30 (Series 1) .. .. 1·25 55
1533 200 c. Plate No. 4 (Series 1) .. .. 1·25 85

See also Nos. 1551/66, 1571/1806, 1597, 1620/1863, 1663/73, 1679/83, 1731/8, 1747/54, 1809/19, 1822, 1868/9, 1872/81, 1884/7, 1907, 1912/15, 1916/24, 1925/9, 2066/73, 2171/8, 2180/2, 2190/3, 2216/16, 2219/20, 2225/7, 2235/42, 2314/18, 2322/5, 2328, 2314/18, 2322/5, 2329/31, 2468/71 2498/2511 and 2605/8.

GUYANA
c 25 c

332. Arms of Guyana.

1985.

1534. **332.** 25 c. multicoloured .. 15 15

1985. 85th Birthday of Queen Elizabeth the Queen Mother (1st issue). Nos. 1528 and 1531/2 optd. **QUEEN MOTHER 1900-1985.**

1536. 130 c. Plate No. 18 (Series 1) 45 50
1537. 130 c. Plate No. 29 (Series 1) 45 50
1538. 130 c. Plate No. 30 (Series 1) 45 50

1985. International Youth Year. Nos. 900/4 surch. **International Youth Year 1985 25.**

1540. 25 c. on 110 c. on 5 c. multicoloured (900) .. 10 10
1541. 25 c. on 110 c. on 5 c. multicoloured (901) .. 10 10
1542. 25 c. on 110 c. on 5 c. multicoloured (902) .. 25 10
1543. 25 c. on 110 c. on 5 c. multicoloured (903) .. 25 10
1544. 25 c. on 100 c. on 5 c. multicoloured (904) .. 80 15

1985. 75th Anniv. of Girl Guide Movement. No. 612 surch. **1910-1985 225.**

1545. 225 c. on 350 c. on 225 c. on 40 c. Guide in camp 7·00 90

No. 1545 also carries two otherwise unissued surcharges at top right.

1985. Birth Bicentenary of John J. Audubon (ornithologist). No. 992 surch. **J. J. Audubon 1785-1985 240.**

1546. 240 c. on 35 c. Harpy Eagle .. .. .. 8·00 1·75

337. Leaders of the 1763 Rebellion.

1985. 150th Anniv (1984) of Abolition of Slavery (1st issue).

1547. **337.** 25 c. black and grey .. 50 10
1548. – 60 c. black & mauve .. 30 25
1549. – 130 c. black and blue .. 50 50
1550. – 150 c. black and lilac .. 80 55

Designs: 60 c. Damon and Parliament Buildings, Georgetown. 130 c. Quamina and Demerara, 1823. 150 c. "Den Arendt" (slave ship), 1627.

For these designs in changed colours see Nos. 2552/5.

1985. Centenary of Publication of Sanders' "Reichenbachia" (2nd issue). As T **331** showing orchids. Multicoloured.

1551 25 c. Plate No. 52 (Series 1) 40 25
1763 55 c. Plate No. 9 (Series 1) 25 10
1764 55 c. Plate No. 22 (Series 1) 25 10
1765 55 c. Plate No. 49 (Series 1) 25 10
1766 55 c. Plate No. 64. (Series 1) 25 10
1556 60 c. Plate No. 44 (Series 1) 50 35
1557 60 c. Plate No. 47 (Series 1) 50 35
1558 120 c. Plate No. 36 (Series 1) 75 55
1559 130 c. Plate No. 16 (Series 1) 75 55
1560 130 c. Plate No. 38 (Series 1) 75 55
1561 150 c. Plate No. 32 (Series 1) 75 55
1562 150 c. Plate No. 34 (Series 1) 75 55
1563 150 c. Plate No. 35 (Series 1) 75 55
1564 150 c. Plate No. 41 (Series 1) 75 55
1565 150 c. Plate No. 48 (Series 1) 75 55
1566 150 c. Plate No. 62 (Series 1) 75 55

1985. Signing of Guyana—Libya Friendship Treaty. No. 621 surch. **Guyana/Libya Friendship 1985.**

1567. **149.** 150 c. on 10 c. mult. .. 7·50 2·75

1985. Namibia Day. No. 636 surch. with Fleur-de-lis and new value.

1568. 150 c. on 35 c. Unveiling of Monument .. .. 2·00 55

1985. World Cup Football Championship, Mexico (1986) (1st issue). No. F 2 surch. **Mexico 1986.**

1569. 275 c. on 3 c. Hanging Heliconia .. .. 2·25 95

See also No. 1727.

1985. Centenary of Publication of Sanders' "Reichenbachia" (3rd issue). As T **331** showing orchids. Multicoloured.

1571 25 c. Plate No. 8 (Series 1) 30 30
1572 25 c. Plate No. 23 (Series 1) 30 30
1573 25 c. Plate No. 51 (Series 1) 30 30
1574 25 c. Plate No. 61 (Series 1) 30 30
1575 25 c. Plate No. 63 (Series 1) 30 30
1576 25 c. Plate No. 70 (Series 1) 30 30
1577 25 c. Plate No. 72 (Series 1) 30 30
1578 120 c. Plate No. 1 (Series 1) (horiz.) .. 75 55
1579 120 c. Plate No. 11 (Series 1) (horiz.) .. 75 55
1580 120 c. Plate No. 28 (Series 1) (horiz.) .. 75 55
1767 150 c. Plate No. 40 (Series 1) (horiz.) .. 35 20
1768 150 c. Plate No. 42 (Series 1) (horiz.) .. 35 20
1769 150 c. Plate No. 45 (Series 1) (horiz.) .. 35 20
1584 200 c. Plate No. 14 (Series 1) .. .. 1·00 80
1585 200 c. Plate No. 21 (Series 1) (horiz.) .. 1·00 80
1770 200 c. Plate No. 43 (Series 1) (horiz.) .. 45 30

1985. 30th Anniv. of Commonwealth Caribbean Medical Research Council. Nos. 819, 871, 874, 928 and 1014 optd. **1955–1985** or surch. also.

1587. – 60 c. mult. (No. 819) .. 20 25
1588. – 60 c. multicoloured (No. 1014) 20 25
1589. **176.** 120 c. on 110 c. on 10 c. multicoloured (No. 871) 40 45
1590. – 120 c. on 110 c. on $3 mult. (No. 874) .. 40 45
1592. – 120 c. on 210 c. on $3 mult. (No. 928) .. 40 45

1985. 20th Anniv. of Guyana Defence Force. No. 856 surch. **1965–1985.**

1593. 25 c. on $1.10 on $3 W.O. and N.C.O., Guyana Defence Force, 1966 .. 50 10
1594. 225 c. on $1.10 on $3 W.O. and N.C.O., Guyana Defence Force, 1966 .. .. 1·75 1·00

1985. Fire Prevention. Nos. 678 and 680 optd. **1985** and surch.

1595. 25 c. on 40 c. Fire engine, 1977 .. .. .. 5·00 20
1596. 320 c. on 15 c. Steam engine, circa 1860 .. 10·00 3·00

1985. Centenary of Publication of Sanders' "Reichenbachia" (4th issue). As T **331.** Multicoloured.

1597. 60 c. Plate No. 55 (Series 1) 60 30

1985. Columbus Day. Unissued value as T **331** surch. **CRISTOBAL COLON 1492–1992.** Multicoloured.

1598. 350 c. on 120 c. Plate No. 65 (Series 1) .. .. 3·00 1·75

1985. 20th Death Anniv. of Sir Winston Churchill. No. 707 optd. **SIR WINSTON CHURCHILL 1965–1985.**

1599. $2 "Morpho rhetenor" (female) .. .. 2·50 1·00

1985. 35th Anniv. of International Commission on Irrigation and Drainage. No. 625 with unissued surcharge further surch. **1950–1985.**

1600. **150.** 25 c. on 110 c. on 10 c. multicoloured 10 10
1601. 200 c. on 110 c. on 10 c. multicoloured 65 70

1985. 40th Anniv. of U.N.O. Nos. 714/16, 800 and O 19 optd. **United Nations 1945–1985.**

1602. 30 c. mult. (No. 714) .. 1·00 10
1603. 50 c. mult. (No. 715) .. 1·00 20
1604. 100 c. on $3 mult. (No. O 19) .. .. .. 1·00 40
1605. 225 c. on 220 c. on $3 mult. (No. 800) .. 4·00 75
1606. $3 mult. (No. 716) .. 2·00 1·10

1985. Nos. 551/3, O 14/15, O 18, O 21, O P1/2 and F 7 optd. **POSTAGE.**

1607. 30 c. on $2 "Norantea guianensis" (No. O 18) 20 10
1608. 40 c. Tiger Beard (No. 551) .. .. .. 22·00 20
1609. 50 c. "Guzmania lingulata" (No. 552) .. 35 20
1610. 50 c. "Guzmania lingulata" (No. O 14) 30 20
1611. 60 c. Soldier's Cap (No. 553) .. .. .. 2·00 25
1612. 60 c. Soldier's Cap (No. O 15) .. .. .. 1·50 25
1613. 60 c. Soldier's Cap (No. F 7) 50 25
1614. $10 "Elbella patrobas" (No. O 21) .. .. 7·00 5·50
1615. $15 on $1 "Chelonanthus uliginoides" (No. O P1) 8·00 8·00
1616. $20 on $1 "Chelonanthus uliginoides" (No. O P2) 9·00 9·50

1985. Deepavali Festival. Nos. 542/3 surch. **Deepavali 1985.**

1617. 25 c. on 2 c. Type **132** .. 10 10
1618. 150 c. on 1 c. Pitcher plant of Mt. Roraima 50 55

1985. Centenary of Publication of Sanders' "Reichenbachia" (5th issue). As T **331** showing orchids. Multicoloured.

1620 25 c. Plate No. 59 (Series 1) 30 20
1771 30 c. Plate No. 53 (Series 1) 10 10
1622 60 c. Plate No. 57 (Series 1) (horiz.) .. 50 35
1623 60 c. Plate No. 73 (Series 1) (horiz.) .. 50 35
1624 60 c. Plate No. 75 (Series 1) (horiz.) .. 50 35
1772 75 c. Plate No. 55 (Series 1) 20 15
1773 100 c. Plate No. 65 (Series 1) 25 15
1627 120 c. Plate No. 37 (Series 1) 75 55
1628 120 c. Plate No. 46 (Series 1) 75 55
1629 120 c. Plate No. 56 (Series 1) 75 55
1630 120 c. Plate No. 58 (Series 1) 75 55
1631 120 c. Plate No. 67 (Series 1) 75 55
1632 130 c. Plate No. 66 (Series 1) 80 65
1633 150 c. Plate No. 26 (Series 1) 90 75
1634 200 c. Plate No. 33 (Series 1) (horiz.) .. 1·00 85
1774 225 c. Plate No. 24 (Series 1) 35 35

351. Clive Lloyd (cricketer).

1985. Clive Lloyd's Testimonial Year. Multicoloured.

1636. 25 c. Type **351** 50 40
1637. 25 c. Clive Lloyd, bat and wicket 50 40
1638. 25 c. Cricket equipment 50 40
1639. 60 c. As No. 1638 (25 × 33 mm.) 60 40
1640. $1.30 As No. 1637 (25 × 33 mm.) 70 75
1641. $2.25 Type **351** (25 × 33 mm.) 80 90
1642. $3.50 Clive Lloyd with the Prudential Cup .. 90 1·25

1985. Wildlife Protection. Nos. 756/67 optd. **1985.**

1643. 30 c. Type **178** 40 40
1644. 30 c. Red howler 40 40
1645. 30 c. Common squirrel-monkey 40 40
1646. 30 c. Two-toed sloth .. 40 40
1647. 30 c. Brazilian tapir .. 40 40
1648. 30 c. Collared peccary .. 40 40
1649. 30 c. Six-banded armadillo 40 40
1650. 30 c. Tamandua 40 40
1651. 30 c. Giant anteater .. 40 40
1652. 30 c. Murine opossum .. 40 40
1653. 30 c. Brown four-eyed opossum 40 40
1654. 30 c. Brazilian agouti .. 40 40

1985. No. 847 surch.

1655. 20 c. on 12 c. on 12 c. on 6 c. Patua (No. 847) .. 45 15

1986. Centenary of the Appearance of "Reichenbachia". Volume I. Nos. 1802 and 1806 optd. **REICHENBACHIA 1886–1986.**

1657. 150 c. Plate No. 42 (Series 1) 60 60
1658. 200 c. Plate No. 43 (Series 1) 75 75

1986. Republic Day. Nos. 1108/9 and 1052 optd. **Republic Day 1986.** or surch. also.

1659. 25 c. As Type **258** .. 10 10
1660. 25 c. As No. 1050 .. 10 10
1661. 120 c. on $6 Presidential standard 40 45
1662. 225 c. on $6 Presidential standard 70 75

1986. Centenary of Publication of Sanders'. "Reichenbachia" (6th issue). As T **331.** Multicoloured.

1663. 40 c. Plate No. 77 (Series 1) 35 20
1664. 45 c. Plate No. 54 (Series 1) 35 25
1665. 50 c. Plate No. 92 (Series 1) 35 25
1666. 60 c. Plate No. 95 (Series 1) 40 30
1667. 75 c. Plate No. 5 (Series 1) 45 35
1668. 90 c. Plate No. 84 (Series 1) 55 40
1669. 150 c. Plate No. 78 (Series 1) 75 60
1670. 200 c. Plate No. 79 (Series 1) 90 80
1671. 300 c. Plate No. 83 (Series 1) .. .. 1·50 1·25
1672. 320 c. Plate No. 50 (Series 1) .. .. 1·60 1·40
1673. 360 c. Plate No. 85 (Series 1) .. .. 1·75 1·50

1986. Easter. No. 481 optd. **1986** and surch. also.

1674. **111.** 25 c. on 6 c. mult. .. 25 10
1675. 50 c. on 6 c. mult. .. 40 20
1676. 100 c. on 6 c. mult. .. 65 40
1677. 200 c. on 6 c. mult. .. 1·25 70

1986. 60th Anniv. of St. John's Ambulance in Guyana. No. 652 surch. **1926 1986.**

1678. 150 c. on 35 c. silver, black and green .. 2·50 55

1986. Centenary of Publication of Sanders' "Reichenbachia" (7th issue). As T **331.** Multicoloured.

1679. 25 c. Plate No. 71 (Series 1) (horiz.) .. 40 20
1680. 120 c. Plate No. 69 (Series 1) (horiz.) .. 1·00 55
1681. 150 c. Plate No. 87 (Series 1) (horiz.) .. 1·25 65
1682. 225 c. Plate No. 60 (Series 1) .. .. 1·50 90
1683. 350 c Plate No. 94 (Series 1) (horiz.) .. 2·00 1·50

1986. 60th Birthday of Queen Elizabeth II. No. 1768 optd. **1926 1986 QUEEN ELIZABETH.**

1684. 130 c. Plate No. 13 (Series 1) 60 50

1986. Wildlife Protection. Nos. 685, 739/44 and 993/8 surch. **Protect the 60.**

1686. 60 c. on 35 c. Type **174** .. 35 35
1687. 60 c. on 35 c. Haimara .. 35 35
1688. 60 c. on 35 c. Electric eel 35 35
1689. 60 c. on 35 c. Golden rivulus 35 35
1690. 60 c. on 35 c. Pencil fish 35 35
1691. 60 c. on 35 c. Four-eyed fish 35 35
1691a. 60 c. on 35 c. Pirai or Carib fish 35 35
1691b. 60 c. on 35 c. Smoking Hassar 35 35
1691c. 60 c. on 35 c. Devil Ray 35 35
1691d. 60 c. on 35 c. Flying Patwa 35 35
1691e. 60 c. on 35 c. Arapaima Pirariucii 35 35
1691f. 60 c. on 35 c. Lukanani 35 35
1692. $6 on 8 c. Type **163** .. 2·25 2·25

1986. No. 799 surch.

1693. 600 c. on 720 c. on 60 c. Soldier's cap .. .. 4·50 75

1986. 125th Anniv. of British Guiana Post Office (2nd issue). No. 702a surch. with names of postal agencies opened between 1860 and 1880.

1694. 25 c. on 30 c. mult. (surch. **Abary**) .. 15 15
1695. 25 c. on 30 c. mult. (surch. **Anna Regina**) 15 15
1696. 25 c. on 30 c. mult. (surch. **Aurora**) .. 15 15
1697. 25 c. on 30 c. mult. (surch. **Bartica Grove**) 15 15
1698. 25 c. on 30 c. mult. (surch. **Bel Air**) .. 15 15
1699. 25 c. on 30 c. mult. (surch. **Belle Plaine**) .. 15 15
1700. 25 c. on 30 c. mult. (surch. **Clonbrook**) .. 15 15
1701. 25 c. on 30 c. mult. (surch. **T.P.O. Dem. Railway**) .. 15 15
1702. 25 c. on 30 c. mult. (surch. **Enmore**) .. 15 15
1703. 25 c. on 30 c. mult. (surch. **Fredericksburg**) 15 15
1704. 25 c. on 30 c. mult. (surch. **Good Success**) 15 15
1705. 25 c. on 30 c. mult. (surch. **1986**) .. 15 15
1706. 25 c. on 30 c. mult. (surch. **Mariabba**) .. 15 15
1707. 25 c. on 30 c. mult. (surch. **Massaruni**) .. 15 15
1708. 25 c. on 30 c. mult. (surch. **Nigg**) 15 15
1709. 25 c. on 30 c. mult. (surch. **No. 50**) .. 15 15
1710. 25 c. on 30 c. mult. (surch. **No. 63 Benab**) 15 15
1711. 25 c. on 30 c. mult. (surch. **Philadelphia**) .. 15 15
1712. 25 c. on 30 c. mult. (surch. **Sisters**) .. 15 15
1713. 25 c. on 30 c. mult. (surch. **Skeldon**) .. 15 15
1714. 25 c. on 30 c. mult. (surch. **Suddie**) .. 15 15
1715. 25 c. on 30 c. mult. (surch. **Taymouth Manor**) 15 15
1716. 25 c. on 30 c. mult. surch. **Wales**) .. 15 15
1717. 25 c. on 30 c. mult. (surch. **Whim**) .. 15 15

1986. 20th Anniv. of Independence. (a) No. 332 of British Guiana surch **GUYANA INDEPENDENCE 1966–1986,** Nos. 398 and 491 surch. **1986** and No. 656 surch. with Fleur-de-lis and value.

1718. 25 c. on 2 c. green (No. 332) 15 10
1719. 25 c. on 35 c. mult. (No. 656) 15 10
1720. 60 c. on 2 c. green (No. 332) 20 10
1721. 120 c. on 6 c. green (No. 398) 35 20
1722. 130 c. on 24 c. black and orange (No. 401) .. 75 30

(b) Nos. 1188/91 surch. **INDEPENDENCE 1966–1986.**

1723. **277.** 25 c. on 120 c. brown, black and blue (No. 1188) 25 20
1724. – 25 c. on 130 c. red, black and blue (No. 1189) 25 20
1725. – 25 c. on 150 c. violet and blue (No. 1190) 25 20
1726. – 225 c. on 200 c. green, black and blue (No. 1191) 65 60

1986. World Cup Football Championship, Mexico (2nd issue). No. 544 surch. **MEXICO 1986 225.**

1727. 225 c. on 3 c. Hanging heliconia .. .. 2·50 60

1986. CARICOM Day. No. 705a optd. **CARICOM DAY 1986.**

1728. 60 c. "Papilio androgeus" 60 15

1986. CARICOM Heads of Government Conference, Georgetown. Nos. 544 and 601 surch. **CARICOM HEADS OF GOV'T CONFERENCE JULY 1986** and value.

1729. 25 c. on 8 c. on 6 c. Cannon-ball Tree .. 20 10
1730. 60 c. on 3 c. Hanging Heliconia 40 25

1986. Centenary of Publication of Sanders' "Reichenbachia" (8th issue). As T **331.** Multicoloured.

1731. 30 c. Plate No. 86 (Series 1) 25 15
1732. 55 c. Plate No. 17 (Series 1) 40 20
1733. 60 c. Plate No. 93 (Series 1) 40 20
1734. 100 c. Plate No. 68 (Series 1) 55 20
1735. 130 c. Plate No. 91 (Series 1) 60 30
1736. 250 c. Plate No. 74 (Series 1) 90 60
1737. 260 c. Plate No. 39 (Series 1) 90 60
1738. 375 c. Plate No. 90 (Series 1) .. .. 1·25 85

1986. International Peace Year. Nos. 542 and 546 surch. **INT. YEAR OF PEACE** and value.

1739. 25 c. on 1 c. Pitcher Plant of Mt. Roraima 10 10
1740. 60 c. on 6 c. Cannon-ball tree 10 10
1741. 120 c. on 6 c. Cannon-ball tree 15 20
1742. 130 c. on 6 c. Cannon-ball tree 15 20
1743. 150 c. on 6 c. Cannon-ball tree 20 25

363. Halley's Comet and British Guiana 1907 2 c. Stamp.

1986. Appearance of Halley's Comet.

1744. **363.** 320 c. red, black and lilac 40 50
1745. – 320 c. multicoloured 40 50

DESIGN: No. 1745, Guyana 1985 320 c. Scarlet macaw stamp.

1986. Centenary of Publication of Sanders' "Reichenbachia" (9th issue). As T **331.** Multicoloured.

1747. 40 c. Plate No. 96 (Series 1) 25 15
1748. 45 c. Plate No. 81 (Series 1) 25 15
1749. 90 c. Plate No. 89 (Series 1) 45 20
1750. 100 c. Plate No. 88 (Series 1) 45 20
1751. 150 c. Plate No. 76 (Series 1) 60 35
1752. 180 c. Plate No. 15 (Series 1) 70 40
1753. 320 c. Plate No. 82 (Series 1) 85 55
1754. 330 c. Plate No. 80 (Series 1) .. .. 1·00 70

1986. No. 489 surch. **20.**

1755. 20 c. on 6 c. Patua .. 40 15

1986. 50th Anniv. of Guyana United Sadr Islamic Association. Nos. 469/70 optd. **GUSIA 1936–1986,** No. 1757 surch. also.

1756. **105.** 25 c. black, gold and lilac 20 10
1757. $1.50 on 6 c. black, gold and flesh .. 65 40

1986. Regional Pharmacy Conference. No. 545 surch. **REGIONAL PHARMACY CONFERENCE 1986 130.**

1758. 130 c. on 5 c. Annatto tree .. .. .. 1·50 30

1986. Centenary of Publication of Sanders' "Reichenbachia" (10th issue) Multicoloured. As T **331.**

1809. 30 c. Plate No. 30 (Series 2) 25 15
1810. 45 c. Plate No. 21 (Series 2) (horiz.) .. 30 15
1811. 75 c. Plate No. 8 (Series 2) 55 15
1812. 80 c. Plate No. 42 (Series 2) (horiz.) .. 55 15
1813. 90 c. Plate No. 4 (Series 2) 65 25
1814. 130 c. Plate No. 38 (Series 2) 70 35
1815. 160 c. Plate No. 5 (Series 2) (horiz.) .. 85 40
1816. 200 c. Plate No. 9 (Series 2) .. .. 1·00 50
1817. 320 c. Plate No. 12 (Series 2) .. .. 1·75 70
1818. 350 c. Plate No. 29 (Series 2) (horiz.) .. 2·00 70
1819. 360 c. Plate No. 34 (Series 2) .. .. 2·00 70

1986. 20th Anniv. of Independence (2nd issue). As T **332** but additionally inscr. "1966–1986" at foot.

1820. 25 c. multicoloured .. 15 15

1986. Centenary of Publication of Sanders' "Reichenbachia" (11th issue). Design as No. 1735, but with different face value. Multicoloured.

1822. 40 c. Plate No. 91 (Series 1) 60 15

1986. Nos. 1361/84 surch.

1823. 120 c. on 30 c. mult. (No. 1361) 40 40
1824. 120 c. on 30 c. mult. (No. 1362) 40 40
1825. 120 c. on 30 c. mult. (No. 1363) 40 40
1826. 120 c. on 30 c. mult. (No. 1364) 40 40
1827. 120 c. on 30 c. mult. (No. 1365) 40 40
1828. 120 c. on 30 c. mult. (No. 1366) 40 40
1829. 120 c. on 30 c. mult. (No. 1367) 40 40
1830. 120 c. on 30 c. mult. (No. 1368) 40 40
1831. 120 c. on 30 c. mult. (No. 1369) 40 40
1832. 120 c. on 30 c. mult. (No. 1370) 40 40
1833. 120 c. on 30 c. mult. (No. 1371) 40 40
1834. 120 c. on 30 c. mult. (No. 1372) 40 40
1835. 120 c. on 30 c. mult. (No. 1373) 40 40
1836. 120 c. on 30 c. mult. (No. 1374) 40 40
1837. 120 c. on 30 c. mult. (No. 1375) 40 40
1838. 120 c. on 30 c. mult. (No. 1376) 40 40
1839. 120 c. on 30 c. mult. (No. 1377) 40 40
1840. 120 c. on 30 c. mult. (No. 1378) 40 40
1841. 120 c. on 30 c. mult. (No. 1379) 40 40
1842. 120 c. on 30 c. mult. (No. 1380) 40 40
1843. 120 c. on 30 c. mult. (No. 1381) 40 40
1844. 120 c. on 30 c. mult. (No. 1382) 40 40
1845. 120 c. on 30 c. mult. (No. 1383) 40 40
1846. 120 c. on 30 c. mult. (No. 1384) 40 40

1986. 12th World Orchid Conference, Tokyo. (1st issue). Unissued design as No. 1731, but with different face value, surch. **12th World Orchid Conference TOKYO JAPAN MARCH 1987 650.**

1847. 650 c. on 40 c. Plate No. 86 (Series 1) .. .. 4·00 2·75

No. 1847 is inscribed "ONTOGLOSSUM TRIUMPHANS" in error.

See also No. 2138.

1986. Columbus Day. Unissued design as No. 1863, but with different face value, surch. **1492–1992 CHRISTOPHER COLUMBUS 320.**

1864. 320 c. on 150 c. Plate No. 24 (Series 1) .. .. 1·25 75

1986. International Food Day. Nos. 1170/1 further surch. **1986** and value.

1866. 50 c. on 30 c. on 1 c. Type **87** 20 15
1867. 225 c. on $2.60 on 3 c. Lukunani 60 45

1986. Centenary of Publication of Sanders' "Reichenbachia" (12th issue). As T **331**, one as No. 1731 with different face value. Multicoloured.

1868. 40 c. Plate No. 86 (Series 1) 40 15
1869. 90 c. Plate No. 10 (Series 2) 60 30

1986. Air. 40th Annivs. of U.N.I.C.E.F. and U.N.E.S.C.O. No. 706 surch.

1870. 120 c. on $1 "Agrias claudina" (surch. **UNICEF 1946–1986 AIR 120**) 35 35
1871. 120 c. on $1 "Agrias claudina" (surch. **UNESCO 1946–1986 AIR 120**) 35 35

1986. Centenary of Publication of Sanders' "Reichenbachia" (13th issue). As T **331.** Multicoloured.

1872. 45 c. Plate No. 17 (Series 2) 30 15
1873. 50 c. Plate No. 33 (Series 2) 30 15
1874. 60 c. Plate No. 27 (Series 2) 45 15
1875. 75 c. Plate No. 56 (Series 2) 55 20
1876. 85 c. Plate No. 45 (Series 2) 55 20
1877. 90 c. Plate No. 13 (Series 2) 70 20
1878. 200 c. Plate No. 44 (Series 2) .. .. 1·00 45
1879. 300 c. Plate No. 50 (Series 2) .. .. 1·60 60
1880. 320 c. Plate No. 10 (Series 2) .. .. 1·75 70
1881. 390 c. Plate No. 6 (Series 2) .. .. 2·00 95

1986. Deepavali Festival. Nos. 543 and 601 surch. **Deepavali 1986** and values

1882. 25 c. on 2 c. Type **132** .. 15 10
1883. 200 c. on 8 c. on 6 c. Cannon-ball tree .. 55 40

1986. Centenary of Publication of Sanders' "Reichenbachia" (14th issue). As T **331**, two as Nos. 1732 and 1734 with different face values. Multicoloured.

1884. 40 c. Plate No. 68 (Series 1) 40 15
1885. 80 c. Plate No. 17 (Series 1) 70 25
1886. 200 c. Plate No. 2 (Series 2) .. .. 1·40 60
1887. 225 c. Plate No. 24 (Series 2) .. .. 1·75 70

1986. Christmas. No. 452 surch **CHRISTMAS 1986 20.**

1888 20 c. on 6 c. Patua .. 10 10

1986. Wildlife Protection. Nos. 756/67 optd. **1986.**

1894. 30 c. Type **178** 35 35
1895. 30 c. Red howler .. 35 35
1896. 30 c. Common squirrel-monkey 35 35
1897. 30 c. Two-toed sloth .. 35 35
1898. 30 c. Brazilian tapir .. 35 35
1899. 30 c. Collared peccary .. 35 35
1900. 30 c. Six-banded armadillo 35 35
1901. 30 c. Tamandua 35 35
1902. 30 c. Giant anteater .. 35 35
1903. 30 c. Murine opossum .. 35 35
1904. 30 c. Brown four-eyed opossum 35 35
1905. 30 c. Brazilian agouti .. 35 35

1986. No. 1642 surch. **$15.**

1906. $15 on $3.50 Clive Lloyd with Prudential Cup .. 10·00 8·50

1986. Centenary of Publication of Sanders' "Reichenbachia" (15th issue). Design as No. 1877, but with different face value. Multicoloured.

1907. 50 c. Plate No. 13 (Series 2) 65 15

375. Memorial.

1986. President Burnham Commemoration. Multicoloured.

1908. 25 c. Type **375** 10 10
1909. 120 c. Map of Guyana and flags 35 20
1910. 130 c. Parliament Buildings and mace .. 35 20
1911. $6 L.F. Burnham and Georgetown mayoral chain (vert.) .. .. 1·25 1·25

1986. Centenary of Publication of Sanders' "Reichenbachia" (16th issue). As Nos. 1554/5, 1874 and 1887 but with different face values. Multicoloured.

1912. 50 c. Plate No. 49 (Series 1) (22.12) .. 30 15
1913. 50 c. Plate No. 64 (Series 1) 30 15
1914. 85 c. Plate No. 24 (Series 2) 55 25
1915. 90 c. Plate No. 27 (Series 2) 55 25

1986. Centenary of Publication of Sanders' "Reichenbachia" (17th issue). As T **331.** Multicoloured.

1916. 25 c. Plate No. 20 (Series 2) 25 15
1917. 40 c. Plate No. 7 (Series 2) 25 15
1918. 85 c. Plate No. 15 (Series 2) 40 20
1919. 90 c. Plate No. 3 (Series 2) 40 20
1920. 120 c. Plate No. 14 (Series 2) 55 30
1921. 130 c. Plate No. 32 (Series 2) 55 30
1922. 150 c. Plate No. 22 (Series 2) 70 35
1923. 320 c. Plate No. 18 (Series 2) .. .. 1·00 55
1924. 330 c. Plate No. 28 (Series 2) .. .. 1·00 70

1987. Centenary of Publication of Sanders' "Reichenbachia" (18th issue). As Nos. 1853, 1876, 1886, 1918 and 1923 but with different face values Multicoloured.

1925 35 c. Plate No. 45 (Series 2) 30 15
1926 50 c. Plate No. 15 (Series 2) 30 15
1927 50 c. Plate No. 55 (Series 1) 30 15
1928 85 c. Plate No. 18 (Series 2) 55 25
1929 90 c. Plate No. 2 (Series 2) 55 25

1987. 10th Anniv. of Guyana Post Office Corporation (1st issue). Unissued designs as Nos. 1849 and 1863, but with different face values, surch or optd. **G P O C 1977–1987.**

1930 $2.25 Plate No. 53 (Series 1) 75 35
1931 $10 on 150 c. Plate No. 24 (Series 1) .. .. 2·25 2·50

1987. Various "Reichenbachia" issues surch.

2375 120 c. on 40 c. Plate No. 91 (Series 1) (No. 1822) 15 15
2380 120 c. on 40 c. Plate No. 90 (Series 1) 15 15
2387 120 c. on 50 c. Plate No. 9 (Series 1) 15 15
1994 120 c. on 50 c. Plate No. 49 (Series 1) (No. 1912) 30 30
1995 120 c. on 50 c. Plate No. 64 (Series 1) (No. 1913) 30 30
2388 120 c. on 50 c. Plate No. 22 (Series 1) 15 15
2389 120 c. on 50 c. Plate No. 3 (Series 2) 15 15
2390 120 c. on 50 c. Plate No. 6 (Series 2) 15 15
2391 120 c. on 50 c. Plate No. 20 (Series 2) 15 15
2392 120 c. on 50 c. Plate No. 32 (Series 2) 15 15
2019 120 c. on 50 c. Plate No. 24 (Series 1) 30 30
2020 120 c. on 50 c. Plate No. 53 (Series 1) 30 30
2021 120 c. on 50 c. Plate No. 65 (Series 1) 30 30
1980 120 c. on 55 c. Plate No. 9 (Series 1) (No. 1763) 30 30
2003 120 c. on 55 c. Plate No. 49 (Series 1) (No. 1765) 30 30
1981 120 c. on 55 c. Plate No. 64 (Series 1) (No. 1766) 30 30
2006 120 c. on 55 c. Plate No. 22 (Series 1) (No. 1764) 30 30
2009 120 c. on 55 c. Plate No. 15 (Series 1) 30 30
2010 120 c. on 55 c. Plate No. 81 (Series 1) 30 30
2011 120 c. on 55 c. Plate No. 82 (Series 1) 30 30
2012 120 c. on 55 c. Plate No. 89 (Series 1) 30 30
2394 120 c. on 60 c. Plate No. 2 (Series 1) (No. 1519) 15 15
2027 120 c. on 60 c. Plate No. 10 (Series 1) (No. 1521) 30 30
2028 120 c. on 60 c. Plate No. 19 (Series 1) (No. 1522) 30 30
2029 120 c. on 60 c. Plate No. 31 (Series 1) (No. 1523) 30 30
2030 120 c. on 60 c. Plate No. 5 (Series 1) 30 30
2403 120 c. on 60 c. Plate No. 50 (Series 1) 15 15
2404 120 c. on 60 c. Plate No. 54 (Series 1) 15 15
2405 120 c. on 60 c. Plate No. 69 (Series 1) 15 15
2034 120 c. on 60 c. Plate No. 71 (Series 1) 30 30
2406 120 c. on 60 c. Plate No. 79 (Series 1) 15 15
2036 120 c. on 60 c. Plate No. 87 (Series 1) 30 30
2407 120 c. on 60 c. Plate No. 94 (Series 1) 15 15
2038 120 c. on 75 c. Plate No. 60 (Series 1) 30 30
2039 120 c. on 75 c. Plate No. 83 (Series 1) 30 30
2040 120 c. on 75 c. Plate No. 92 (Series 1) 30 30
2041 120 c. on 75 c. Plate No. 95 (Series 1) 30 30
1933 200 c. on 25 c. Plate No. 8 (Series 1) (No. 1571) 40 40
1934 200 c. on 25 c. Plate No. 51 (Series 1) (No. 1573) 40 40
1949 200 c. on 25 c. Plate No. 52 (Series 1) (No. 1551) 40 40
1951 200 c. on 25 c. Plate No. 72 (Series 1) (No. 1577) 40 40
1952 200 c. on 25 c. Plate No. 71 (Series 1) (No. 1679) 40 40
1953 200 c. on 30 c. Plate No. 86 (Series 1) (No. 1731) 40 40
1954 200 c. on 30 c. Plate No. 53 (Series 1) (No. 1770) 40 40
1932 200 c. on 40 c. Plate No. 90 (Series 1) 40 40
1937 200 c. on 40 c. Plate No. 68 (Series 1) (No. 1884) 40 40
1955 200 c. on 40 c. Plate No. 77 (Series 1) (No. 1663) 40 40
1956 200 c. on 40 c. Plate No. 86 (Series 1) (No. 1868) 40 40
1957 200 c. on 45 c. Plate No. 81 (Series 1) (No. 1748) 40 40
1958 200 c. on 45 c. Plate No. 77 (Series 1) 40 40
1959 200 c. on 45 c. Plate No. 78 (Series 1) 40 40
1960 200 c. on 45 c. Plate No. 85 (Series 1) 40 40
2044 200 c. on 45 c. Plate No. 84 (Series 1) 30 30
1939 200 c. on 50 c. Plate No. 92 (Series 1) (No. 1665) 40 40
1940 200 c. on 50 c. Plate No. 22 (Series 1) 40 40
1961 200 c. on 50 c. Plate No. 24 (Series 1) 40 40
1962 200 c. on 50 c. Plate No. 53 (Series 1) 40 40
1963 200 c. on 50 c. Plate No. 65 (Series 1) 40 40
2046 200 c. on 50 c. Plate No. 55 (Series 1) (No. 1927) 40 40
1941 200 c. on 55 c. Plate No. 22 (Series 1) (No. 1764) 40 40
1964 200 c. on 55 c. Plate No. 49 (Series 1) (No. 1765) 40 40
1965 200 c. on 55 c. Plate No. 17 (Series 1) (No. 1732) 40 40
2050 200 c. on 55 c. Plate No. 15 (Series 1) 40 40
2051 200 c. on 55 c. Plate No. 81 (Series 1) 40 40
2052 200 c. on 55 c. Plate No. 82 (Series 1) 40 40
2053 200 c. on 55 c. Plate No. 89 (Series 1) 40 40
1942 200 c. on 60 c. Plate No. 5 (Series 1) 40 40
1967 200 c. on 60 c. Plate No. 7 (Series 1) (No. 1520) 40 40
1968 200 c. on 60 c. Plate No. 10 (Series 1) (No. 1521) 40 40
1969 200 c. on 60 c. Plate No. 19 (Series 1) (No. 1522) 40 40
1970 200 c. on 60 c. Plate No. 31 (Series 1) (No. 1523) 40 40
1971 200 c. on 60 c. Plate No. 44 (Series 1) (No. 1556) 40 40
1972 200 c. on 60 c. Plate No. 47 (Series 1) (No. 1557) 40 40
1973 200 c. on 60 c. Plate No. 57 (Series 1) (No. 1622) 40 40
1974 200 c. on 60 c. Plate No. 73 (Series 1) (No. 1623) 40 40
1975 200 c. on 60 c. Plate No. 75 (Series 1) (No. 1624) 40 40
1976 200 c. on 60 c. Plate No. 71 (Series 1) 40 40
1977 200 c. on 60 c. Plate No. 87 (Series 1) 40 40
1943 200 c. on 75 c. Plate No. 5 (Series 1) (No. 1667) 40 40
1944 200 c. on 75 c. Plate No. 60 (Series 1) 40 40
1945 200 c. on 75 c. Plate No. 92 (Series 1) 40 40
1946 200 c. on 85 c. Plate No. 18 (Series 2) (No. 1928) 40 40
1947 200 c. on 375 c. Plate No. 90 (Series 1) (No. 1738) 40 40
1987 225 c. on 40 c. Plate No. 91 (Series 1) (No. 1822) 50 50
1988 225 c. on 40 c. Plate No. 90 (Series 1) 50 50
2055 225 c. on 40 c. Plate No. 86 (Series 1) 50 50
2056 225 c. on 40 c. Plate No. 68 (Series 1) (No. 1884) 50 50
1988a 225 c. on 50 c. Plate No. 92 (Series 1) (No. 1665) 1·00 1·00
1989 225 c. on 50 c. Plate No. 22 (Series 1) 50 50
1990 225 c. on 60 c. Plate No. 55 (Series 1) (No. 1597) 50 50
1990a 225 c. on 60 c. Plate No. 95 (Series 1) (No. 1666) 1·00 1·00
1991 225 c. on 60 c. Plate No. 93 (Series 1) (No. 1733) 50 50
2058 225 c. on 65 c. Plate No. 76 (Series 1) 50 50
2059 225 c. on 65 c. Plate No. 80 (Series 1) 50 50
2060 225 c. on 65 c. Plate No. 88 (Series 1) 50 50
2061 225 c. on 65 c. Plate No. 96 (Series 1) 50 50
1992 225 c. on 80 c. Plate No. 93 (Series 1) 50 50
1978 225 c. on 90 c. Plate No. 89 (Series 1) (No. 1749) 40 40
1993 225 c. on 150 c. Plate No. 42 (Series 1) (No. 1657) 50 50
2062 600 c. on 80 c. Plate No. 17 (Series 1) (No. 1885) 1·25 1·25
2063 600 c. on 80 c. Plate No. 39 (Series 1) 1·25 1·25
2064 600 c. on 80 c. Plate No. 74 (Series 1) 1·25 1·25
2065 600 c. on 80 c. Plate No. 93 (Series 1) 1·25 1·25

1987. Nos. 1518 and 1572 surch **TWO DOLLARS**.

1935 $2 on 25 c. Plate No. 12 (Series 1) (No. 1518) 40 40
1936 $2 on 25 c. Plate No. 23 (Series 1) (No. 1572) 40 40

1987. Various "Reichenbachia" issues surch **1987**.

1983 $10 on 25 c. Plate No. 53 (Series 1) 1·75 1·75
1984 $12 on 80 c. Plate No. 74 (Series 1) 2·00 2·00
1985 $15 on 80 c. Plate No. 39 (Series 1) 2·50 2·50
1986 $25 on 25 c. Plate No. 53 (Series 1) 4·00 4·00

1987. Centenary of Publication of Sanders' "Reichenbachia" (19th issue). Multicoloured.

2066 180 c. Plate 41 (Series 2) 75 40
2067 230 c. Plate 25 (Series 2) 85 50
2068 300 c. Plate 85 (Series 2) 1·10 65
2069 330 c. Plate 82 (Series 2) 1·25 70
2070 425 c. Plate 87 (Series 2) 1·50 85
2071 440 c. Plate 88 (Series 2) 1·50 85
2072 590 c. Plate 52 (Series 2) 1·75 1·25
2073 650 c. Plate 65 (Series 2) 2·25 1·50

1987. 10th Anniv of Guyana Post Office Corporation (2nd issue). Nos. 543, 545, 548a and 601 surch **Post Office Corp. 1977-1987**.

2074 25 c. on 2 c. Type **132** 15 10
2075 25 c. on 5 c. Annatto tree 15 10
2076 25 c. on 8 c on 6 c. Cannon-ball tree 15 10
2077 25 c. on 15 c. Christmas orchid 15 10
2078 60 c. on 15 c. Christmas orchid 35 10
2079 $1.20 on 2 c. Type **132** 50 40
2080 $1.30 on 15 c. Christmas orchid 50 40

1987. No. 1534 surch **1987 200**.

2081 **332** 200 c. on 25 c. mult 50 40

1987. Various "Reichenbachia" issues optd **1987**.

2112 120 c. Plate No. 1 (Series 1) (No. 1578) 30 30
2113 120 c. Plate No. 11 (Series 1) (No. 1579) 30 30
2114 120 c. Plate No. 28 (Series 1) (No. 1580) 30 30
2115 120 c. Plate No. 37 (Series 1) (No. 1627) 30 30
2116 120 c. Plate No. 46 (Series 1) (No. 1628) 30 30
2117 120 c. Plate No. 56 (Series 1) (No. 1629) 30 30
2118 120 c. Plate No. 58 (Series 1) (No. 1630) 30 30
2132 120 c. Plate No. 67 (Series 1) (No. 1631) 30 30
2084 130 c. Plate No. 3 (Series 1) (No. 1525) 30 30
2093 130 c. Plate No. 6 (Series 1) (No. 1767) 30 30
2094 130 c. Plate No. 20 (Series 1) (No. 1770) 30 30
2087 130 c. Plate No. 18 (Series 1) (No. 1536) 30 30
2088 130 c. Plate No. 29 (Series 1) (No. 1537) 30 30
2089 130 c. Plate No. 30 (Series 1) (No. 1538) 30 30
2090 130 c. Plate No. 16 (Series 1) (No. 1559) 30 30
2091 130 c. Plate No. 66 (Series 1) (No. 1632) 30 30
2092 130 c. Plate No. 13 (Series 1) (No. 1684) 30 30
2109 130 c. Plate No. 91 (Series 1) (No. 1735) 30 30
2111 130 c. Plate No. 25 (Series 1) (No. 1771) 30 30
2123 150 c. Plate No. 40 (Series 1) (No. 1801) 40 40
2124 150 c. Plate No. 45 (Series 1) (No. 1803) 40 40
2125 150 c. Plate No. 42 (Series 1) (No. 1657) 40 40
2137 150 c. Plate No. 26 (Series 1) (No. 1633) 40 40
2095 200 c. Plate No. 4 (Series 1) (No. 1533) 40 40
2096 200 c. Plate No. 14 (Series 1) (No. 1584) 40 40
2097 200 c. Plate No. 21 (Series 1) (No. 1585) 40 40
2098 200 c. Plate No. 33 (Series 1) (No. 1634) 40 40
2099 200 c. Plate No. 43 (Series 1) (No. 1658) 40 40
2100 200 c. Plate No. 79 (Series 1) (No. 1670) 40 40
2101 200 c. Plate No. 9 (Series 2) (No. 1816) 40 40
2102 200 c. Plate No. 2 (Series 2) (No. 1886) 40 40
2103 250 c. Plate No. 74 (Series 1) (No. 1736) 50 50
2104 260 c. Plate No. 39 (Series 1) (No. 1737) 50 50

1987. 12th World Orchid Conference, Tokyo (2nd issue). Nos. 1776 surch **12th World Orchid Conference. 650**.

2138 650 c. on 55 c. Plate No. 9 (Series 1) 3·00 2·00

1987. 125th Anniv of British Guiana Post Office (3rd issue). No. 699 surch with names of postal agencies opened by 1885.

2140 25 c. on 10 c. multi (surch **AGRICOLA**) 15 15
2141 25 c. on 10 c. mult (surch **BAGOTVILLE**) 15 15
2142 25 c. on 10 c. mult (surch **BOURDA**) 15 15
2143 25 c. on 10 c. mult (surch **BUXTON**) 15 15
2144 25 c. on 10 c. mult (surch **CABACABURI**) 15 15
2145 25 c. on 10 c. mult (surch **CARMICHAEL STREET**) 15 15
2146 25 c. on 10 c. mult (surch **COTTON TREE**) 15 15
2147 25 c. on 10 c. mult (surch **DUNOON**) 15 15
2148 25 c. on 10 c. mult (surch **FELLOWSHIP**) 15 15
2149 25 c. on 10 c. mult (surch **GROVE**) 15 15
2150 25 c. on 10 c. mult (surch **HACKNEY**) 15 15
2151 25 c. on 10 c. mult (surch **LEONORA**) 15 15
2152 25 c. on 10 c. multd (surch **1987**) 15 15
2153 25 c. on 10 c. mult (surch **MALLALI**) 15 15
2154 25 c. on 10 c. mult (surch **PROVIDENCE**) 15 15
2155 25 c. on 10 c. mult (surch **RELIANCE**) 15 15
2156 25 c. on 10 c. mult (surch **SPARTA**) 15 15
2157 25 c. on 10 c. mult (surch **STEWARTVILLE**) 15 15
2158 25 c. on 10 c. mult (surch **TARLOGY**) 15 15
2159 25 c. on 10 c. mult (surch **T.P.O. BERBICE RIV.**) 15 15
2160 25 c. on 10 c. mult (surch **T.P.O. DEM. RIV.**) 15 15
2161 25 c. on 10 c. mult (surch **T.P.O. ESSEO. RIV.**) 15 15
2162 25 c. on 10 c. mult (surch **T.P.O. MASSA-RUNI RIV.**) 15 15
2163 25 c. on 10 c. mult (surch **TUSCHEN (De VRIENDEN)**) 15 15
2164 25 c. on 10 c. multd (surch **ZORG**) 15 15

1987. 50th Anniv of First Georgetown–Port-of-Spain Flight by P.A.A. No. 708a optd **28 MARCH 1927 PAA GEO- POS**.

2165 $10 "Elbella patrobas" 2·00 2·50

1987. No. 704 surch with figures only.

2166 25 c. on 40 c. "Morpho rhetenor" (male) 70 10

1987. Easter. Nos. 481/2 and 484 optd **1987** or surch also.

2167 **111** 25 c. multicoloured 15 10
2168 120 c. on 6 c. mult 20 20
2169 320 c. on 6 c. mult 50 45
2170 500 c. on 40 c. mult 75 70

1987. Centenary of Publication of Sanders' "Reichenbachia" (20th issue). As T **331**. Mult.

2171 240 c. Plate No. 47 (Series 2) 80 45
2172 260 c. Plate No. 39 (Series 2) 90 55
2173 275 c. Plate No. 58 (Series 2) (horiz) 90 55
2174 390 c. Plate No. 37 (Series 2) (horiz) 1·10 70
2175 450 c. Plate No. 19 (Series 2) (horiz) 1·50 90
2176 460 c. Plate No. 54 (Series 2) (horiz) 1·50 90
2177 500 c. Plate No. 51 (Series 2) 1·75 1·10
2178 560 c. Plate No. 1 (Series 2) 2·00 1·50

1987. No. 706 optd **1987**.

2179 167 $1 multicoloured 1·00 15

1987. Centenary of Publication of Sanders' "Reichenbachia" (21st issue). As T **331**. Mult.

2180 500 c. Plate No. 86 (Series 2) 1·75 1·10
2181 520 c. Plate No. 89 (Series 2) 1·90 1·25
2182 $20 Plate No. 83 (Series 2) 6·00 6·50

1987. As T **332**, but within frame.

2183 25 c. multicoloured 15 15

1987. "Capex '87" International Stamp Exhibition, Toronto. Nos. 1744/5 optd **CAPEX '87**.

2185 **363** 320 c. red, blk & lilac 50 55
2186 320 c. multicoloured 50 55

1987. Commonwealth Heads of Government Meeting, Vancouver. Nos. 1066/8 further optd **1987**.

2187 $1.20 on 6 c. green 15 20
2188 $1.30 on 24 c. black & orge 30 20
2189 $2.40 on 24 c. black & orge 50 35

1987. Centenary of Publication of Sanders' "Reichenbachia" (22nd issue). As T **331**. Mult.

2190 400 c. Plate No. 80 (Series 2) 1·25 80
2191 480 c. Plate No. 77 (Series 2) 1·50 1·00
2192 600 c. Plate No. 94 (Series 2) 2·00 1·50
2193 $25 Plate No. 72 (Series 2) 6·50 7·00

396 Steam Locomotive "Alexandra"

1987. Guyana Railways.

2194 **396** $1.20 green 25 25
2195 – $1.20 green 25 25
2196 – $1.20 green 25 25
2197 – $1.20 green 25 25
2198 **396** $1.20 purple .. 25 25
2199 – $1.20 purple .. 25 25
2200 – $1.20 purple .. 25 25
2201 – $1.20 purple .. 25 25
2202 **396** $3.20 blue 60 60
2203 – $3.20 blue 60 60
2204 – $3.20 blue 60 60
2205 – $3.20 blue 60 60
2206 – $3.20 blue 60 60
2207 – $3.30 black 60 60
2208 **396** $3.30 black 60 60
2209 – $3.30 black 60 60
2210 – $3.30 black 60 60
2211 – $3.30 black 60 60
2212 – $10 multicoloured .. 1·50 1·50
2213 – $12 multicoloured .. 1·75 1·75

DESIGNS: As T **396** —Nos. 2195, 2199, 2203, 2207, Front view of diesel locomotive; Nos. 2196, 2200, 2204, 2210, Steam locomotive with searchlight; Nos. 2197, 2201, 2205, 2209, Side view of diesel locomotive. 82 × 55 mm—No. 2206, Molasses warehouses and early locomotive; No. 2211, Diesel locomotive and passenger train. 88 × 39 mm—No. 2212, Cattle train; No. 2213, Molasses train.

1987. 50th Anniv of First Flights from Georgetown to Massaruni and Mabaruma. No. 706 optd.

2214 $1 multicoloured (optd **FAIREY NICHOLL 8 AUG 1927 GEO-MAZ**) 15 15
2215 $1 multicoloured (optd **FAIREY NICHOLL 15 AUG 1927 GEO-MAB**) .. 15 15

1987. Centenary of Publication of Sanders' "Reichenbachia" (23rd issue). As T **331**. Mult.

2216 200 c. Plate No. 43 (Series 2) 75 45
2217 200 c. Plate No. 48 (Series 2) 75 45
2218 200 c. Plate No. 92 (Series 2) 75 45

1987. Centenary of Publication of Sanders' "Reichenbachia" (24th issue). No.2219 surch **600**. Multicoloured.

2219 600 c. on 900 c. Plate No. 74 (Series 2) .. .. 2·00 2·00
2220 900 c. Plate No. 74 (Series 2) .. .. .. 4·00 4·00

1987. Columbus Day.

2221 225 c. on 350 c. on 120 c. Plate No. 65 (Series 1) (No. 1598 further surch **225**) 30 35
2222 950 c. on 900 c. Plate No. 74 (Series 2) (No. 2220 surch **950 CRIST-OVAO COLOMBO 1492 – 1992**) .. .. 1·40 1·40
2223 950 c. on 900 c. Plate No. 74 (Series 2) (No. 2220 surch **950 CHRISTOPHE COLOMB 1492 – 1992**) 1·40 1·40

1987. Centenary of Publication of Sanders' "Reichenbachia" (25th issue). As T **331**. Multicoloured.

2225 325 c. Plate No. 68 (Series 2) (horiz) .. .. 1·25 70
2226 420 c. Plate No. 95 (Series 2) (horiz) .. .. 1·50 90
2227 575 c. Plate No. 60 (Series 2) .. .. .. 1·75 1·25

1987. Deepavali Festival. Nos. 544/5 surch **DEEPAVALI 1987 25** and new value.

2228 25 c. on 3 c. Hanging heliconia 10 10
2229 $3 on 5 c. Annatto tree .. 40 45

1987. Christmas. No. 489 surch **CHRISTMAS 1987 20**.

2230 20 c. on 6 c. Patua .. 10 10

1987. Royal Ruby Wedding. No. 1684 optd **1987**.

2233 130 c. Plate No. 13 (Series 1) 15 20

1987. Centenary of Publication of Sanders' "Reichenbachia" (26th issue). As T **331**. Multicoloured.

2235 255 c. Plate No. 61 (Series 2) .. .. .. 1·75 1·00
2236 290 c. Plate No. 53 (Series 2) .. .. .. 2·00 1·25
2237 375 c. Plate No. 96 (Series 2) .. .. .. 2·50 1·40
2238 680 c. Plate No. 64 (Series 2) .. .. .. 3·50 2·25
2239 720 c. Plate No. 49 (Series 2) .. .. .. 4·00 3·50
2240 750 c. Plate No. 66 (Series 2) .. .. .. 4·00 3·50
2241 800 c. Plate No. 79 (Series 2) .. .. .. 4·50 4·00
2242 850 c. Plate No. 76 (Series 2) .. .. .. 4·50 4·00

1987. Air. No. 1620 surch **AIR 75**.

2243 75 c. on 25 c. Plate No. 59 (Series 1) 30 15

1987. Wildlife Protection. Nos. 756/67 optd **1987**, Nos. 1432/4 surch **320** and Nos. 1631/3, 1752/3 and 1847 optd **PROTECT OUR HERITAGE '87**.

2244 30 c. Type **178** 15 15
2245 30 c. Red howler .. 15 15
2246 30 c. Common squirrel-monkey .. 15 15
2247 30 c. Two-toed sloth .. 15 15
2248 30 c. Brazilian tapir .. 15 15
2249 30 c. Collared peccary .. 15 15
2250 30 c. Six-banded armadillo 15 15
2251 30 c. Tamandua 15 15
2252 30 c. Giant anteater .. 15 15
2253 30 c. Murine opossum .. 15 15
2254 30 c. Brown four-eyed opossum 15 15
2255 30 c. Brazilian agouti .. 15 15
2256 120 c. Plate No. 67 (Series 1) 30 30
2257 130 c. Plate No. 66 (Series 1) 30 30
2258 150 c. Plate No. 26 (Series 1) 35 35
2259 180 c. Plate No. 15 (Series 1) 40 40
2260 320 c. Plate No. 82 (Series 1) 60 60
2261 320 c. on 120 c. Demerara Mutual Life Assurance Building 60 60
2262 320 c. on 120 c. Town Hall 60 60
2263 320 c. on 120 c. Victoria Law Courts 60 60
2264 650 c. on 40 c. Plate No. 86 (Series 1) .. .. 1·75 1·75

1987. Air. Various "Reichenbachia" issues optd **AIR**.

2265 60 c. Plate No. 55 (Series 1) (No. 1597) 30 30
2463 75 c. Plate No. 55 (Series 1 (No. 1853) 15 15
2464 75 c. Plate No. 5 (Series 1) (No. 1667) 15 15
2466 75 c. Plate No. 83 (Series 1) 15 15
2467 75 c. Plate No. 95) (Series 1) 15 15

1988. World Scout Jamboree, Australia. Nos. 830, 837 and 1104 optd **AUSTRALIA 1987 Jamboree 1988** or surch also.

2266 **116** 440 c. on 6 c. mult (No. 837) 35 30
2267 $10 on 110 c. on 6 c. mult (No. 830) .. 80 60
2268 $10 on 180 c. on 6 c. mult (No. 1104) .. 80 60
2269 $10 on 440 c. on 6 c. mult (No. 837) .. 80 60

1988. 10th Anniv of International Fund for Agricultural Development. Nos. 448 and 450 surch **IFAD For a World Without Hunger**.

2270 25 c. on 1 c. Type **87** .. 10 10
2271 $5 on 3 c. Lukunani .. 20 25

1988. Republic Day. Nos. 545, 548a and 555 surch **Republic Day 1988**.

2272 25 c. on 5 c. Annatto tree 10 10
2273 120 c. on 15 c. Christmas orchid 15 10
2274 $10 on $2 "Noranthea guianensis" 55 50

1988. Centenary of Publication of Sanders' "Reichenbachia" (28th series). As T **331**. Multicoloured.

2276 $10 Plate No. 40 (Series 2) 1·75 1·75
2277 $12 Plate No. 91 (Series 2) 1·75 1·75

1988. 125th Anniv of British Guiana Post Office (4th issue). No. 702a surch with names of postal agencies opened between 1886 and 1900.

2278 25 c. on 30 c. mult (surch **Albouystown**) .. 15 15
2279 25 c. on 30 c. mult (surch **Anns Grove**) .. 15 15
2280 25 c. on 30 c. mult (surch **Amacura**) 15 15
2281 25 c. on 30 c. mult (surch **Arakaka**) 15 15
2282 25 c. on 30 c. mult (surch **Baramanni**) 15 15
2283 25 c. on 30 c. mult (surch **Cuyuni**) 15 15
2284 25 c. on 30 c. mult (surch Hope Placer) 15 15
2285 25 c. on 30 c. mult (surch **H M P S**) 15 15
2286 25 c. on 30 c. mult (surch **Kitty**) 15 15
2287 25 c. on 30 c. mult (surch **M'M'Zorg**) 15 15
2288 25 c. on 30 c. mult (surch **Maccaseema**) .. 15 15
2289 25 c. on 30 c. mult (surch **1988**) 15 15
2290 25 c. on 30 c. mult (surch **Morawhanna**) .. 15 15
2291 25 c. on 30 c. mult (surch **Naamryck**) 15 15
2292 25 c. on 30 c. mult (surch **Purini**) 15 15
2293 25 c. on 30 c. mult (surch **Potaro Landing**) .. 15 15
2294 25 c. on 30 c. mult (surch **Rockstone**) 15 15
2295 25 c. on 30 c. mult (surch **Rosignol**) 15 15
2296 25 c. on 30 c. mult (surch **Stanleytown**) .. 15 15
2297 25 c. on 30 c. mult (surch **Santa Rosa**) .. 15 15
2298 25 c. on 30 c. mult (surch **Tumatumari**) .. 15 15
2299 25 c. on 30 c. mult (surch **Weldaad**) 15 15
2300 25 c. on 30 c. mult (surch **Wismar**) 15 15
2301 25 c. on 30 c. mult (surch **TPO Berbice Railway**) 15 15

1988. Olympic Games, Seoul. Nos. 1206/17 further surch **120 Olympic Games 1988**.

2302 120 c. on 55 c. on 125 c. on 35 c. Type **174** .. 15 15
2303 120 c. on 55 c. on 125 c. on 35 c. Haimara .. 15 15
2304 120 c. on 55 c. on 125 c. on 35 c. Electric eel .. 15 15
2305 120 c. on 55 c. on 125 c. on 35 c. Golden rivulus .. 15 15
2306 120 c. on 55 c. on 125 c. on 35 c. Pencil fish .. 15 15
2307 120 c. on 55 c. on 125 c. on 35 c. Four-eyed fish .. 15 15
2308 120 c. on 55 c. on 125 c. on 35 c. Pirai or Carib fish 15 15
2309 120 c. on 55 c. on 125 c. on 35 c. Smoking hassar .. 15 15
2310 120 c. on 55 c. on 125 c. on 35 c. Devil ray .. 15 15
2311 120 c. on 55 c. on 125 c. on 35 c. Flying patwa .. 15 15
2312 120 c. on 55 c. on 125 c. on 35 c. Arapaima pirariucii .. 15 15
2313 120 c. on 55 c. on 125 c. on 35 c. Lukanani .. 15 15

1988. Centenary of Publication of Sanders' "Reichenbachia" (29th issue). As T **331**. Multicoloured.

2314 320 c. Plate No. 16 (Series 2) 55 40
2315 475 c. Plate No. 73 (Series 2) 80 50
2316 525 c. Plate No. 36 (Series 2) .. .. .. 1·00 65
2317 530 c. Plate No. 69 (Series 2) .. .. .. 1·00 65
2318 $15 Plate No. 67 (Series 2) 2·75 2·25

1988. CARICOM Day. Nos. 545/6 and 555 surch **Caricom Day 1988** and new value.

2319 25 c. on 5 c. Annatto tree 10 10
2320 $1.20 on 6 c. Cannon-ball tree 10 10
2321 $10 on $2 "Norantea guianensis" 45 50

1988. Centenary of Publication of Sanders' "Reichenbachia" (30th issue). As T **331**. Multicoloured.

2322 700 c. Plate No. 62 (Series 2) .. .. .. 1·00 65
2323 775 c. Plate No. 59 (Series 2) .. .. .. 1·25 70
2324 875 c. Plate No. 31 (Series 2) .. .. .. 1·50 85
2325 950 c. Plate No. 78 (Series 2) .. .. .. 1·75 90

1988. 40th Anniv of World Health Day. No. 705a optd.

2326 60 c. "Papilio androgeus" (optd **WHO 1948–1988**) 3·50 4·50
2327 60 c. "Papilio androgeus" (optd **1988**) 15 10

1988. Centenary of Publication of Sanders' "Reichenbachia" (31st issue). As T **331**. Multicoloured.

2328 350 c. Plate No. 74 (Series 2) 35 30

1988. Centenary of Publication of Sanders "Reichenbachia" (32nd issue). As T **331**, but additionally inscr "1985–1988". Mult.

2329 130 c. Plate No. 73 (Series 2) 40 25
2330 200 c. Plate No. 96 (Series 2) 50 30
2331 260 c. Plate No. 16 (Series 2) 70 35

1988. Conservation of Resources.

(a) Nos. 1444/6 optd

2333 120 c. Young Ocelot (No. 1444) (optd **CONSERVE TREES**) 10 10
2334 120 c. Young Ocelot (No. 1444) (optd **CON-SERVE ELECTRI-CITY**) 10 10
2335 120 c. Young Ocelot (No. 1444) (optd **CON-SERVE WATER**) .. 10 10
2336 120 c. Type **322** (optd **CONSERVE ELECTRICITY**) .. 10 10
2337 120 c. Type **322** (optd **CONSERVE WATER**) 10 10
2338 120 c. Type **322** (optd **CONSERVE TREES**) 10 10
2339 120 c. Young Ocelot (No. 1446) (optd **CON-SERVE WATER**) .. 10 10
2340 120 c. Young Ocelot (No. 1446) (optd **CON-SERVE TREES**) .. 10 10
2341 120 c. Young Ocelot (No. 1446) (optd **CONSERVE ELECTRICITY**) .. 10 10

(b) Nos. 1634, 1670, 1683 and 1863 optd **CONSERVE WATER** (optd)

2342 200 c. Plate No. 33 (Series 1) 10 10
2343 200 c. Plate No. 79 (Series 1) 10 10
2344 225 c. Plate No. 24 (Series 1) 10 10
2345 350 c. Plate No. 94 (Series 1) 15 20

1988. Road Safety Campaign. Nos. 2194/2201 optd.

2346 **396** $1.20 green (optd **BEWARE OF ANIMALS**) .. 40 40
2347 – $1.20 green (No. 2195) (optd **BEWARE OF CHILDREN**) 40 40
2348 – $1.20 green (No. 2196) (optd **DRIVE SAFELY**) .. 40 40
2349 – $1.20 green (No. 2197) (optd **DO NOT DRINK AND DRIVE**) 40 40
2350 **396** $1.20 purple (optd **BEWARE OF ANIMALS**) .. 40 40
2351 – $1.20 purple (No. 2199) (optd **BEWARE OF CHILDREN**) .. 40 40
2352 – $1.20 purple (No. 2200) (optd **DRIVE SAFELY**) .. 40 40
2353 – $1.20 purple (No. 2201) (optd **DO NOT DRINK AND DRIVE**) .. 40 40

1988. No. 706 optd **1988** or surch **120**.

2354 $1 "Agrias claudina" .. 30 15
2355 120 c. on $1 "Agrias claudina" 30 15

1988. Various "Reichenbachia" issues surch.

2356 120 c. on 25 c. Plate No. 61 (Series 1) (No. 1574) 15 15
2357 120 c. on 25 c. Plate No. 63 (Series 1) (No. 1575) 15 15
2358 120 c. on 25 c. Plate No. 70 (Series 1) (No. 1576) 15 15
2359 120 c. on 25 c. Plate No. 59 (Series 1) (No. 1620) 15 15

2360 120 c. on 25 c. Plate No. 71 (Series 1) (No. 1679) 15 15
2429 120 c. on 25 c. Plate No. 72 (Seires 1) (No. 1577) 15 15
2361 120 c. on 30 c. Plate No. 53 (Series 1) (No. 1621) 15 15
2362 120 c. on 30 c. Plate No. 86 (Series 1) (No. 1731) 15 15
2363 120 c. on 30 c. Plate No. 30 (Series 2) (No. 1809) 15 15
2365 120 c. on 30 c. Plate No. 7 (Series 2) 15 15
2366 120 c. on 30 c. Plate No. 14 (Series 2) 15 15
2368 120 c. on 30 c. Plate No. 22 (Series 2) 15 15
2369 120 c. on 30 c. Plate No. 28 (Series 2) 15 15
2371 120 c. on 35 c. Plate No. 45 (Series 2) (No. 1925) 15 15
2372 120 c. on 40 c. Plate No. 77 (Series 1) (No. 1663) 15 15
2374 120 c. on 40 c. Plate No. 96 (Series 1) (No. 1747) 15 15
2377 120 c. on 40 c. Plate No. 86 (Series 1) (No. 1868) 15 15
2378 120 c. on 40 c. Plate No. 68 (Series 1) (No. 1884) 15 15
2381 120 c. on 45 c. Plate No. 54 (Series 1) (No. 1664) 15 15
2382 120 c. on 45 c. Plate No. 81 (Series 1) (No. 1748) 15 15
2383 120 c. on 45 c. Plate No. 21 (Series 2) (No. 1810) 15 15
2384 120 c. on 50 c. Plate No. 92 (Series 1) (No. 1665) 15 15
2385 120 c. on 50 c. Plate No. 13 (Series 2) (No. 1907) 15 15
2386 120 c. on 50 c. Plate No. 15 (Series 2) (No. 1926) 15 15
2393 120 c. on 55 c. Plate No. 17 (Series 1) (No. 1732) 15 15
2395 120 c. on 60 c. Plate No. 57 (Series 1) (No. 1622) 15 15
2397 120 c. on 60 c. Plate No. 73 (Series 1) (No. 1623) 15 15
2398 120 c. on 60 c. Plate No. 75 (Series 1) (No. 1624) 15 15
2400 120 c. on 60 c. Plate No. 95 (Series 1) (No. 1666) 15 15
2401 120 c. on 60 c. Plate No. 93 (Series 1) (No. 1733) 15 15
2402 120 c. on 60 c. Plate No. 27 (seies 2) (No. 1874) 15 15
2408 120 c. on 70 c. Plate No. 8 (Series 2) 15 15
2409 120 c. on 70 c. Plate No. 9 (Series 2) 15 15
2411 120 c. on 70 c. Plate No. 12 (Series 2) 15 15
2413 120 c. on 70 c. Plate No. 17 (Series 2) 15 15
2414 120 c. on 80 c. Plate No. 39 (Series 1) 15 15
2415 120 c. on 80 c. Plate No. 74 (Series 1) 15 15
2416 120 c. on 80 c. Plate No. 93 (Series 1) 15 15
2417 120 c. on 85 c. Plate No. 45 (Series 2) (No. 1876) 15 15
2418 120 c. on 85 c. Plate No. 24 (Series 2) (No. 1914) 15 15
2419 120 c. on 85 c. Plate No. 15 (Series 2) (No. 1918) 15 15
2420 120 c. on 85 c. Plate No. 18 (Series 2) (No. 1928) 15 15
2421 120 c. on 90 c. Plate No. 84 (Series 1) (No. 1668) 15 15
2422 120 c. on 90 c. Plate No. 89 (Series 1) (No. 1749) 15 15
2423 120 c. on 90 c. Plate No. 10 (Series 2) (No. 1869) 15 15
2424 120 c. on 90 c. Plate No. 13 (Series 2) (No. 1877) 15 15
2425 120 c. on 90 c. Plate No. 27 (Series 2) (No. 1915) 15 15
2426 120 c. on 90 c. Plate No. 2 (Series 2) (No. 1929) 15 15
2427 200 c. on 80 c. Plate No. 42 (Series 2) (No. 1812) 15 15
2428 200 c. on 90 c. Plate No. 4 (Series 2) (No. 1813) 15 15
2430 240 c. on 140 c. Plate No. 30 (Series 2) 15 15
2431 240 c. on 140 c. Plate No. 34 (Series 2) 15 15
2432 240 c. on 425 c. Plate No. 87 (Series 2) (No. 2070) 15 15
2433 260 c. on 375 c. Plate No. 90 (Series 1) (No. 1378) 15 15

1988. Conservation of Resources. Various "Reichenbachia" issues optd **CONSERVE OUR RESOURCES**.

2434 100 c. Plate No. 65 (Series 1) (No. 1854) 15 15
2435 100 c. Plate No. 68 (Series 1) (No. 1734) 15 15
2436 100 c. Plate No. 88 (Series 1) (No. 1750) 15 15
2437 100 c. Plate No. 65 (Series 1) (No. 1854) 15 15
2438 120 c. Plate No. 27 (Series 1) (No. 1524) 15 15
2439 120 c. Plate No. 36 (Series 1) (No. 1558) 15 15
2440 120 c. Plate No. 37 (Series 1) (No. 1627) 15 15
2441 120 c. Plate No. 56 (Series 1) (No. 1629) 15 15
2442 120 c. Plate No. 58 (Series 1) (No. 1630) 15 15
2443 120 c. Plate No. 67 (Series 1) (No. 1631) 15 15
2444 120 c. Plate No. 69 (Series 1) (No. 1680) 15 15
2445 130 c. Plate No. 38 (Series 1) (No. 1560) 15 15
2446 130 c. Plate No. 66 (Series 1) (No. 1632) 15 15
2447 130 c. Plate No. 91 (Series 1) (No. 1735) 15 15
2448 130 c. Plate No. 13 (Series 1) (No. 1684) 15 15
2449 130 c. Plate No. 20 (Series 1) (No. 1770) 15 15
2450 150 c. Plate No. 26 (Series 1) (No. 1633) 15 15
2451 150 c. Plate No. 78 (Series 1) (No. 1669) 15 15
2452 150 c. Plate No. 87 (Series 1) (No. 1681) 15 15
2453 150 c. Plate No. 76 (Series 1) (No. 1751) 15 15
2454 250 c. Plate No. 74 (Series 1) (No. 1736) 15 15

1988. 125th Anniv of International Red Cross. Nos. 2202/5 and 2207/10 optd with cross.

2455 **396** $3.20 blue 20 20
2456 – $3.20 blue (No. 2203) 20 20
2457 – $3.20 blue (No. 2204) 20 20
2458 – $3.20 blue (No. 2205) 20 20
2459 – $3.30 black (No. 2207) 20 20
2460 **396** $3.30 black 20 20
2461 – $3.30 black (No. 2209) 20 20
2462 – $3.30 black (No. 2210) 20 20

1988. Centenary of Publication of Sanders' "Reichenbachia" (33rd issue). As T **331**. Multicoloured.

2468 270 c. Plate No. 90 (Series 2) 70 60
2469 360 c. Plate No. 84 (Series 2) 1·00 75
2470 550 c. Plate No. 70 (Series 2) (horiz) 1·75 1·10
2471 670 c. Plate No. 71 (Series 2) (horiz) 2·25 1·40

1988. 60th Anniv of Cricket in Guyana. Nos. 1584, 1670, 1681 and 1815 optd **1928–1988 CRICKET JUBILEE** or surch also.

2472 200 c. Plate No. 14 (Series 1) 40 40
2473 200 c. Plate No. 79 (Series 1) 40 40
2474 800 c. on 150 c. Plate No. 87 (Series 1) 1·75 1·75
2475 800 c. on 160 c. Plate No. 5 (Series 2) 1·75 1·75

1988. Olympic Games, Seoul. (a) Nos. 1628, 1634, 1671, 1681, 1683, 1814, 1818/19, 1880 and 2069 optd **OLYMPIC GAMES 1988** or surch also.

2476 120 c. Plate No. 46 (Series 1) 10 10
2477 130 c. Plate No. 38 (Series 2) 10 10
2478 150 c. Plate No. 87 (Series 1) 10 10
2479 200 c. Plate No. 33 (Series 1) 10 10
2480 300 c. Plate No. 83 (Series 1) 15 20
2481 300 c. on 360 c. Plate No. 34 (Series 2) 15 20
2482 320 c. Plate No. 10 (Series 2) 15 20
2483 330 c. Plate No. 82 (Series 2) 15 20
2484 350 c. Plate No. 94 (Series 1) 15 20
2485 350 c. Plate No. 29 (Series 2) 15 20

(b) Design as No. 1420, but incorrectly inscr "LOS ANGELLES" optd or surch **"OLYMPICS 1988"** (A) or **"KOREA 1988"** (B).

2486 $1.20 multicoloured (A) 10 10
2487 $1.20 multicoloured (B) 10 10
2488 130 c. on $1.20 mult (A) 10 10
2489 130 c. on $1.20 mult (B) 10 10
2490 150 c. on $1.20 mult (A) 10 10
2491 150 c. on $1.20 mult (B) 10 10
2492 200 c. on $1.20 mult (A) 10 10
2493 200 c. on $1.20 mult (B) 10 10
2494 350 c. on $1.20 mult (A) 15 20
2495 350 c. on $1.20 mult (B) 15 20

1988. Columbus Day. Nos. 1672/3 optd or surch **V CENTENARY OF THE LANDING OF CHRISTOPHER COLUMBUS IN THE AMERICAS**.

2496 320 c. Plate No. 50 (Series 1) 15 20
2497 $15 on 360 c. Plate No. 85 (Series 1) 65 70

1988. Centenary of Publication of Sanders' "Reichenbachia" (34th issue). As T **331**. Multicoloured.

2498 100 c. Plate No. 44 (Series 2) 70 55
2499 130 c. Plate No. 42 (Series 2) (horiz) 70 55
2500 140 c. Plate No. 4 (Series 2) 90 65
2501 160 c. Plate No. 50 (Series 2) 90 65
2502 175 c. Plate No. 51 (Series 2) 1·10 75
2503 200 c. Plate No. 11 (Series 2) 1·10 75
2504 200 c. Plate No. 23 (Series 2) 1·10 75
2505 200 c. Plate No. 26 (Series 2) 1·10 75
2506 200 c. Plate No. 75 (Series 2) 1·10 75
2507 200 c. Plate No. 93 (Series 2) 1·10 75
2508 250 c. Plate No. 79 (Series 2) 1·40 90
2509 280 c. Plate No. 62 (Series 2) 1·50 1·00
2510 285 c. Plate No. 63 (Series 2) 1·50 1·00
2511 380 c. Plate No. 35 (Series 2) 1·75 1·25

1988. Christmas (1st issue). Various "Reichenbachia" issues optd or surch.

(a) Optd or surch **SEASON'S GREETINGS**.

2519 120 c. on 100 c. Plate No. 6 (Series 1) 15 20
2520 120 c. on 100 c. Plate No. 13 (Series 1) 15 20
2521 120 c. on 100 c. Plate No. 20 (Series 1) 15 20
2522 120 c. on 100 c. Plate No. 25 (Series 1) 15 20
2523 120 c. on 100 c. Plate No. 40 (Series 1) (horiz) 15 20
2524 120 c. on 100 c. Plate No. 42 (Series 1) (horiz) 15 20
2525 120 c. on 100 c. Plate No. 43 (Series 1) (horiz) 15 20
2526 120 c. on 100 c. Plate No. 45 (Series 1) (horiz) 15 20
2512 150 c. Plate No. 32 (Series 1) (No. 1561) 20 25
2513 150 c. Plate No. 62 (Series 1) (No. 1566) 20 25
2514 225 c. Plate No. 60 (Series 1) (No. 1682) 30 35
2532 240 c. on 180 c. Plate No. 15 (Series 1) (No. 1752) 30 35
2515 260 c. Plate No. 39 (Series 1) (No. 1737) 35 40
2516 320 c. Plate No. 82 (Series 1) (No. 1753) 40 45
2517 330 c. Plate No. 80 (Series 1) (No. 1754) 45 50
2518 360 c. Plate No. 85 (Series 1) (No. 1673) 45 50

(b) Optd **SEASON'S GREETINGS 1988**.

2527 225 c. Plate No. 24 (Series 1) (No. 1863) 30 35
2528 225 c. Plate No. 60 (Series 1) (No. 1682) 30 35
2530 225 c. on 350 c. on 120 c. Plate No. 65 (Series 1) (No. 2221) 30 35

1988. Christmas (2nd issue). Nos. 489, 1188/91 and 1449 surch or optd **CHRISTMAS 1988**.

2533 – 20 c. on 6 c. mult (No. 452) 10 10
2534 **277** 120 c. brown, blk & bl 15 20
2535 – 120 c. on 130 c. red, black and blue (No. 1189) 15 20
2536 – 120 c. on 150 c. violet, black and blue (No. 1190) 15 20
2537 – 120 c. on 200 c. green, black and blue (No. 1191) 15 20
2538 – 500 c. on 330 c. mult (No. 1449) 60 70

1988. AIDS Information Campaign. Nos. 707/8a optd or surch with various slogans.

2539 120 c. on $5 "Morpho deidamia" (A) 50 50
2540 120 c. on $5 "Morpho deidamia" (B) 50 50
2541 120 c. on $5 "Morpho deidamia" (C) 50 50
2542 120 c. on $5 "Morpho deidamia" (D) 50 50
2543 120 c. on $5 "Morpho deidamia" (E) 50 50
2544 120 c. on $10 "Elbella patrobas" (A) 50 50
2545 120 c. on $10 "Elbella patrobas" (B) 50 50
2546 120 c. on $10 "Elbella patrobas" (C) 50 50
2547 120 c. on $10 "Elbella patrobas" (D) 50 50
2548 120 c. on $10 "Elbella patrobas" (E) 50 50
2549 $2 "Morpho rhetenor" (female) (E) 75 75
2550 $5 "Morpho deidamia" (E) 1·60 1·60
2551 $10 "Elbella patrobas" (E) 2·50 2·50

OVERPRINTS: (A) **Be compassionate towards AIDS victims.**; (B) **Get information on AIDS. it may save your life.**; (C) **Get the facts. Education helps to prevent AIDS.**; (D) **Say no to Drugs and limit the spread of AIDS.**; (E) **Protect yourself from AIDS. Better safe than sorry.**.

1988. 150th Anniv of Abolition of Slavery (1984) (2nd issue). Designs as Nos. 1547/50, but colours changed.

2552 **337** 25 c. black and brown 10 10
2553 – 60 c. black and lilac 10 10
2554 – 130 c. black and green 15 20
2555 – 150 c. black and blue 20 25

1989. Olympic Medal Winners, Seoul. Nos. 1672, 1923 and 2178 surch **SALUTING WINNERS OLYMPIC GAMES 1988**.

2556 550 c. on 560 c. Plate No. 1 (Series 2) 70 75
2557 900 c. on 320 c. Plate No. 18 (Series 2) 1·10 1·25
2558 1050 c. on 320 c. Plate No. 50 (Series 1) 1·40 1·50

1989. Republic Day. Nos. 2194/2201 and 2212 optd **REPUBLIC DAY 1989**.

2559 **396** $1.20 green 15 20
2560 – $1.20 green (No. 2195) 15 20
2561 – $1.20 green (No. 2196) 15 20
2562 – $1.20 green (No. 2197) 15 20
2563 **396** $1.20 purple 15 20
2564 – $1.20 purple (No. 2199) 15 20
2565 – $1.20 purple (No. 2200) 15 20
2566 – $1.20 purple (No. 2201) 15 20
2567 – $10 multicoloured 1·25 1·40

1989. Nos. 2202/5 and 2207/10 surch.

2568 **396** $5 on $3.20 blue 65 70
2569 – $5 on $3.20 blue (No. 2203) 65 70
2570 – $5 on $3.20 blue (No. 2204) 65 70
2571 – $5 on $3.20 blue (No. 2205) 65 70
2572 – $5 on $3.30 black (No. 2207) 65 70
2573 **396** $5 on $3.30 black 65 70
2574 – $5 on $3.30 black (No. 2209) 65 70
2575 – $5 on $3.30 black (No. 2210) 65 70

1989. Various "Reichenbachia" issues surch.

2576 120 c. on 140 c. Plate No. 25 (Series 2) 15 20
2577 120 c. on 140 c. Plate No. 52 (Series 2) 15 20
2578 120 c. on 140 c. Plate No. 65 (Series 2) 15 20
2580 120 c. on 140 c. Plate No. 38 (Series 2) 15 20
2581 120 c. on 140 c. Plate No. 41 (Series 2) 15 20
2579 120 c. on 175 c. Plate No. 54 (Series 2) 15 20
2582 170 c. on 175 c. Plate No. 58 (Series 2) 20 25
2583 250 c. on 280 c. Plate No. 66 (Series 2) 30 35
2584 250 c. on 280 c. Plate No. 67 (Series 2) 30 35
2585 300 c. on 290 c. Plate No. 53 (Series 2) (No. 2236) 40 45

1989. Nos. 1744/5 and 2185/6 surch **TEN DOLLARS $10.00** (Nos. 2586, 2588) or **TEN DOLLARS** (Nos. 2587, 2589).

2586 **363** $10 on 320 c. red, blk & lilac (No. 1744) 1·25 1·40
2587 – $10 on 320 c. mult (No. 1745) 1·25 1·40
2588 **363** $10 on 320 c. red, blk & lilac (No. 2185) 1·25 1·40
2589 – $10 on 320 c. mult 1·25 1·40

1989. Nos. O54/7, O59/63 and O65/9 optd **POSTAGE** or surch also.

2591 125 c. on 130 c. Plate No. 92 (Series 2) 10 10
2592 125 c. on 140 c. Plate No. 36 (Series 2) 10 10
2593 150 c. Plate No. 43 (Series 2) 10 10
2594 150 c. on 175 c. Plate No. 31 (Series 2) 10 10
2595 250 c. Plate No. 59 (Series 2) 10 10
2596 250 c. on 225 c. Plate No. 26 (Series 2) 10 10
2597 250 c. on 230 c. Plate No. 68 (Series 2) 10 10
2598 250 c. on 260 c. Plate No. 69 (Series 2) 10 10

2599 300 c. on 275 c. Plate No. 90 (Series 2) 10 15
2600 350 c. Plate No. 95 (Series 2) 15 20
2601 350 c. on 330 c. Plate No. 23 (Series 2) 15 20
2602 600 c. Plate No. 70 (Series 2) 25 30
2603 $12 Plate No. 71 (Series 2) 50 55
2604 $15 Plate No. 84 (Series 2) 60 65

1989. Centenary of Publication of Sanders' "Reichenbachia" (35th issue). As T **331**. Mult.
2605 200 c. Plate No. 49 (Series 2) 15 15
2606 200 c. Plate No. 53 (Series 2) 15 15
2607 200 c. Plate No. 60 (Series 2) 15 15
2608 200 c. Plate No. 64 (Series 2) 15 15

1989. No. 1442 surch **250**.
2609 **322** 250 c. on 25 c. mult .. 20 10

1989. 40th Anniv of Guyana Red Cross. No. 1872 surch **RED CROSS 1948 1988** and new value.
2610 375 c. on 45 c. Plate No. 17 (Series 2) 40 30
2611 425 c. on 45 c. Plate No. 17 (Series 2) 40 30

1989. World Health Day. Nos. 1875 and 2239 surch.
2612 250 c. on 75 c. Plate No. 56 (Series 2) surch **HEALTH FOR ALL** 15 15
2613 250 c. on 75 c. Plate No. 56 (Series 2) surch **ALL FOR HEALTH** .. 15 15
2614 675 c. on 720 c. Plate No. 49 (Series 2) surch **ALL FOR HEALTH** .. 40 40
2615 675 c. on 720 c. Plate No. 49 (Series 2) surch **HEALTH FOR ALL** 40 40

1989. Scouting Anniversaries. Nos. 1873, 1879, 2322, 2509 and unissued value as No. 1873 optd or surch also.
2616 250 c. on 50 c. Plate No. 33 (Series 2) (surch **BOY SCOUTS 1909 1989**) 15 15
2617 250 c. on 50 c. Plate No. 33 (Series 2) (surch **GIRL GUIDES 1924 1989**) 15 15
2618 250 c. on 100 c. Plate No. 33 (Series 2) (surch **BOY SCOUTS 1909 1989**) 15 15
2619 250 c. on 100 c. Plate No. 33 (Series 2) (surch **GIRL GUIDES 1924 1989**) 15 15
2620 300 c. Plate No. 50 (Series 2) (optd **BOY SCOUTS 1909 1989**) .. 20 20
2621 300 c. Plate No. 50 (Series 2) (optd **GIRL GUIDES 1924 1989**) .. 20 20
2622 $25 on 280 c. Plate No. 62 (Series 2) (surch **LADY BADEN POWELL 1889 - 1989**) .. .. 1·40 1·40
2623 $25 on 700 c. Plate No. 62 (Series 2) (surch **LADY BADEN POWELL 1889 - 1989**) .. .. 1·40 1·40

The events commemorated are the 80th anniversary of Boy Scout Movement in Guyana, 65th anniversary of Girl Guide Movement in Guyana and birth centenary of Lady Baden-Powell.

1989. 150 Years of Photography. No. 1881 surch **PHOTOGRAPHY 1839 - 1989** and new value.
2624 550 c. on 390 c. Plate No. 6 (Series 2) 40 40
2625 650 c. on 390 c. Plate No. 6 (Series 2) 40 40

1989. 70th Anniv of International Labour Organization. No. 1875 surch **I.L.O. 1919–1989 300**.
2627 300 c. on 75 c. Plate No. 56 (Series 2) 20 20

1989. Various stamps surch.
(a) With obliterating devices over original value
2628 80 c. on 6 c. Patua (No. 452) 10 10
2629 $1 on 2 c. Type **132** .. 10 10
2630 $2.05 on 3 c. Hanging heliconia (No. 544) .. 10 10
2631 $2.55 on 5 c. Annatto tree (No. 545) 10 15
2632 $3.25 on 6 c. Cannon-ball tree (No. 546) 10 10
2633 $5 on 6 c. Type **111** .. 10 10
2634 $6.40 on 10 c. "Archonias bellona" (699) 10 10
2648 $6.40 on $3.30 black (No. 2207) 10 10
2649 $6.40 on $3.30 black (T **396**) 10 10
2650 $6.40 on $3.30 black (No. 2209) 10 10
2651 $6.40 on $3.30 black (No. 2210) 10 10
2646 640 c. on 675 c. on 720 c. Plate No. 49 (Series 2) (No. 2614) 10 10
2647 640 c. on 675 c. on 720 c. Plate No. 49 (Series 2) (No. 2615) 10 10
2652 $7.65 on $3.20 blue (T **396**) 10 10
2653 $7.65 on $3.20 blue (No. 2203) 10 10
2654 $7.65 on $3.20 blue (No. 2204) 10 10
2655 $7.65 on $3.20 blue (No. 2205) 10 10
2635 $8.90 on 60 c. "Papilio androgeus" (No. 705a) 10 10
2643 $50 on $2 "Morpho rhetenor" (female) (No. 707) 50 55
2644 $100 on $2 "Morpho rhetenor" (female) (No. 707) .. .. .. 1·10 1·25
(b) Without obliterating devices
2636 80 c. on 6 c. Patua (No. 452) 10 10
2637 $6.40 on 10 c. "Archonias bellona" (No. 699) .. 10 10
2638 $7.65 on 40 c. "Morpho rhetenor" (male) (No. 704) 10 10
2639 $8.90 on 60 c. "Papilio androgeus" (No. 705a) 10 10

1989. CARICOM Day. No. 1878 surch **CARICOM DAY**.
2656 125 c. on 200 c. Plate No. 44 (Series 2) 10 10

454 "Stalachtis calliope"

1989. Butterflies. Multicoloured.
2657 80 c. Type **454** 10 10
2658 $2.25 "Morpho rhetenor" 10 10
2659 $5 "Agrias claudia" .. 10 10
2660 $6.40 "Marpesia marcella" 10 10
2661 $7.65 "Papilio zagreus" 10 10
2662 $8.90 "Chorinea faunus" 10 10
2663 $25 "Cepheuptychia cephus" 25 30
2664 $100 "Nessaea regina" .. 1·10 1·25

455 Kathryn Sullivan (first U.S woman to walk in space)

1989. 25 Years of Women in Space. Mult.
2665 $6.40 Type **455** 10 10
2666 $12.80 Svetlana Savitskaya (first Soviet woman to walk in space) 15 20
2667 $15.30 Judy Resnik and Christa McAuliffe and "Challenger" logo .. 15 20
2668 $100 Sally Ride (first U.S woman astronaut) .. 1·10 1·25

1989. Centenary of Ahmadiyya (Moslem organization). Nos. 543/5 surch **AHMADIYYA CENTENARY 1899-1989**.
2669 80 c. on 2 c. Type **132** .. 10 10
2670 $6.40 on 3 c. Hanging heliconia 25 30
2671 $8.90 on 5 c. Annatto tree 35 40

457 Head of Harpy Eagle

1990. Endangered Species. Harpy Eagle. Multicoloured.
2672 $2.25 Type **457** 10 10
2673 $5 Harpy eagle with monkey prey 10 10
2674 $8.90 Eagle on branch (facing right) 10 10
2675 $30 Eagle on branch (facing left) 30 35

458 Channel-billed Toucan

1990. Birds of Guyana. Multicoloured.
2676 $15 Type **458** 15 20
2677 $25 Blue and yellow macaw 25 30
2678 $50 Wattled jacana (horiz) 50 55
2679 $60 Hoatzin (horiz) .. 65 70

1990. 85th Anniv of Rotary International. Optd **Rotary International 1905–1990** and emblem. (a) On Nos. 2657/64.
2681 80 c. Type **454** 10 10
2682 $2.25 "Morpho rhetenor" 10 10
2683 $5 "Agrias claudia" .. 10 10
2684 $6.40 "Marpesia marcella" 10 10
2685 $7.65 "Papilio zagreus" .. 10 10
2686 $8.90 "Chorinea faunus" 10 10
2687 $25 "Euptychia cephus" 25 30
2688 $100 "Nessaea regina" .. 1·00 1·10
(b) On Nos. 2665/8
2689 $6.40 Type **455** 10 10
2690 $12.80 Svetlana Savitskaya (first Soviet woman to walk in space) 15 20
2691 $15.30 Judy Resnik and Christa McAuliffe with "Challenger" logo .. 15 20
2692 $100 Sally Ride (first U.S. woman astronaut) .. 1·00 1·10

460 Indian Post Runner, 1837

1990. 150th Anniv of the Penny Black and 500th Anniv of Thurn and Taxis Postal Service. Multicoloured.
2693/2746 $15.30 × 27, $17.80 × 9, $20 × 18
Set of 54 7·50 10·50
Nos. 2693/2746 depict various forms of mail transport.

EXPRESS LETTER STAMPS

1986. Various stamps surch. **EXPRESS** and new values.
E1. $12 on 350 c. on 120 c. multicoloured (No. 1598) 3·00 3·00
E2. $15 on 40 c. multicoloured (No. 1868) .. .. 4·00 4·00
E3. $20 on $6.40 multicoloured 4·50 4·50
E4. $25 on 25 c. multicoloured (as No. 1621, but value changed) .. .. .. 5·00 5·00

No. E3 was previously a miniature sheet for Halley's Comet containing two 320 c. stamps. As surcharged the original values on both designs have been cancelled and replaced by a single $20 face value.

1987. No. E3 additionally optd with small Maltese cross above surch.
E5 $20 on $6.40 mult .. 4·00 4·00

1987. Centenary of Publication of Sanders' "Reichenbachia". As T **331** additionally inscr "EXPRESS". Multicoloured.
E6 $15 Plate No. 11 (Series 2) 2·25 2·25
E7 $20 Plate No. 93 (Series 2) 2·50 2·75
E8 $25 Plate No. 63 (Series 2) 3·00 3·50
E9 $45 Plate No. 35 (Series 2) 6·00 6·50

1987. Nos. 1744/5 imperf between surch **EXPRESS FORTY DOLLARS** and star.
E10 $40 on $6.40 multicoloured 8·00 8·50

1987. No. E 2 additionally optd **1987**.
E11 $15 on 40 c. multicoloured 3·25 3·50

1988. Nos. 2206 and 2211 surch **SPECIAL DELIVERY** and new value.
E12 $40 on $3.20 blue .. .. 5·50 6·50
E13 $45 on $3.30 black .. 6·00 7·00

1989. Imperf between pairs of Nos. 1744/5 and 2185/6 surch **EXPRESS FORTY DOLLARS** (without stars).
E14 $40 on $6.40 multicoloured (Nos. 1744/5) .. .. 1·60 1·75
E15 $40 on $6.40 multicoloured (Nos. 2185/6) .. .. 1·60 1·75

1989. Nos. 2206 and 2211 surch **SPECIAL DELIVERY**.
E16 $190 on $3.30 black .. 7·50 8·00
E17 $225 on $3.20 blue .. 8·50 9·00

OFFICIAL STAMPS

1981. Nos. 556, F4 and F6/7 optd. **OPS** or surch also.
O 13. 10 c. on 25 c. Marabunta .. 1·50 1·75
O 14. 50 c. "Guzmania lingulata" 1·60 50
O 15. 60 c. Soldier's Cap .. 1·25 30
O 16. $5 Odonadenia grandiflora" .. .. .. 4·50 2·50

1981. Nos. 454, 708a, 716, 804, 834 and F9 optd. **OPS.** or surch. also.
O17 15 c. Harpy eagle (post) .. 5·00 45
O18 30 c. on $2 "Norantea guianensis" (F9) .. 45 45
O19 100 c. on $3 Cylinder satellite .. .. 3·00 75
O20 125 c. on $2 "Norantea guianensis" .. .. 3·00 80
O21 $10 "Elbella patrobas" 6·50 7·50
O22 $1.10 on $2 "Norantea guianensis" (804) (air) 2·50 3·50

1981. Nos. 548a, 719, 828 and 830 optd. **OPS** or surch. also.
O 23. 15 c. Christmas Orchid .. 5·00 1·50
O 24. 50 c. British Guiana 1898 1 c. stamp .. .. 1·25 45
O 25. 100 c. on 8 c. Camp-fire cooking .. .. .. 3·75 70
O 26. 110 c. on 6 c. Type **116** .. 4·50 90

1982. Various stamps optd. **OPS.**
O 27. – 20 c. multicoloured (No. 701) .. .. 1·25 30
O 28. **136.** 40 c. multicoloured .. 75 25
O 29. – 40 c. red, grey and blk. (No. 674) .. .. 1·00 25
O 30. – $2 multicoloured (No. 676) .. .. 6·00 1·00

1982. Nos. 911 and 980. optd. or surch. **OPS.**
O 31. 250 c. on 400 c. on 30 c. multicoloured (post.) 80 80
O 32. 220 c. on 1 c. multicoloured (air) .. .. 2·50 80

1982. No. F9 optd. **OPS.**
O 33. $2 "Norantea guianensis .. 9·00 2·00

1982. No. 979. optd. **OPS.**
O 34. 110 c. on 5 c. Annatto tree .. .. 2·25 80

1984. No. 912 surch. **OPS.**

No.	Description	Unused	Used
O 35.	150 c. on $5 mult.	1·00	1·00
O 36.	200 c. on $5 mult.	1·10	1·10
O 37.	225 c. on $5 mult.	1·25	1·25
O 38.	230 c. on $5 mult.	1·25	1·25
O 39.	260 c. on $5 mult.	1·50	1·50
O 40.	320 c. on $5 mult.	1·75	1·75
O 41.	350 c. on $5 mult.	1·90	1·90
O 42.	600 c. on $5 mult.	2·75	2·75

1984. Nos. O 34 and O 34 surch. and No. 981 optd. **OPS.**

No.	Description	Unused	Used
O 43.	25 c. on 110 c. on 5 c. Annatto tree	20	20
O 44.	30 c. on 110 c. on 5 c. Annatto tree	25	25
O 45.	45 c. on 220 c. on 1 c. Pitcher Plant of Mt. Roraima	25	25
O 46.	55 c. on 110 c. on 5 c. Annatto tree	30	30
O 47.	60 c. on 220 c. on 2 c. Pitcher Plant of Mt. Roraima	30	30
O 48.	75 c. on 220 c. on 1 c. Pitcher Plant of Mt. Roraima	40	40
O 49.	90 c. on 220 c. on 1 c. Pitcher Plant of Mt. Roraima	50	50
O 50.	120 c. on 220 c. on 1 c. Pitcher Plant of Mt. Roraima	65	65
O 51.	130 c. on 220 c. on 1 c. Pitcher Plant of Mt. Roraima	70	70
O 52.	330 c. on $2 "Norantea guianensis"	1·75	1·75

1987. Centenary of Publication of Sanders' "Reichenbachia". As T **331** additionally inscr "OFFICIAL". Multicoloured.

No.	Description	Unused	Used
O53	120 c. Plate No. 48 (Series 2)	25	25
O54	130 c. Plate No. 92 (Series 2)	25	25
O55	140 c. Plate No. 36 (Series 2)	25	25
O56	150 c. Plate No. 43 (Series 2)	25	25
O57	175 c. Plate No. 31 (Series 2)	30	30
O58	200 c. Plate No. 61 (Series 2)	35	35
O59	225 c. Plate No. 26 (Series 2)	35	35
O60	230 c. Plate No. 68 (Series 2) (horiz)	35	35
O61	250 c. Plate No. 59 (Series 2)	40	40
O62	260 c. Plate No. 69 (Series 2)	40	40
O63	275 c. Plate No. 90 (Series 2)	40	40
O64	320 c. Plate No. 75 (Series 2)	50	50
O65	330 c. Plate No. 23 (Series 2)	60	60
O66	350 c. Plate No. 95 (Series 2) (horiz)	60	60
O67	600 c. Plate No. 70 (Series 2) (horiz)	95	95
O68	$12 Plate No. 71 (Series 2) (horiz)	1·75	1·75
O69	$15 Plate No. 84 (Series 2)	2·00	2·00

OFFICIAL PARCEL POST STAMPS.

1981. Nos. P1/2 optd. **OPS.**

No.	Description	Unused	Used
OP 1.	$15 on $1 "Chelonanthus uliginoides"	8·00	3·00
OP 2.	$20 on $1 "Chelonanthus uliginoides"	10·00	3·75

1983. No. 843 surch **OPS Parcel Post $12.00** and additionally optd **1982**.

No.	Description	Unused	Used
OP 3.	$12 on $1.10 on $2 "Norantea guianensis"	55·00	17·00

1983. No. OP3 with additional **ŌPS** opt.

No.	Description	Unused	Used
OP 4.	$12 on $1.10 on $2 "Norantea guianensis"	24·00	6·50

1983. No. P4 optd **OPS**.

No.	Description	Unused	Used
OP5	$12 on $1.10 on $2 "Norantea guianensis"	11·00	5·00

PARCEL POST STAMPS

1981. No. 554 surch. **PARCEL POST** and new value.

No.	Description	Unused	Used
P1.	$15 in $1 "Chelonanthus uliginoides"	10·00	5·50
P2.	$20 on $1 "Chelonanthus uliginoides"	12·00	8·50

1983. No. 843 surch **PARCEL POST.**

No.	Description	Unused	Used
P3	$12 on $1.10 on $2 "Norantea guianensis"	10·00	4·00

1983. Unissued Royal Wedding surch. similar to No. 843, further surch **Parcel Post $12.00**

No.	Description	Unused	Used
P4.	$12 on $1.10 on $2 "Norantea guianensis"	1·75	2·00

1985. No. 673 surch. **TWENTY FIVE DOLLARS PARCEL POST 25.00.**

No.	Description	Unused	Used
P5.	$25 on 35 c. green, grey and black	16·00	16·00

POSTAGE DUE STAMPS

D 2.

1967.

No.	Type	Description	Unused	Used
D 8.	D2.	1 c. green	20	2·00
D 9.		2 c. black	20	2·00
D 10.		4 c. blue	20	2·00
D 11.		12 c. red	30	2·00

POSTAL FISCAL STAMPS.

1975. Nos. 543/5 and 550a/6 optd. **REVENUE ONLY.**

No.	Description	Unused	Used
F 1.	2 c. Type **132**	30	40
F 2.	3 c. Hanging Heliconia	30	40
F 3.	5 c. Annatto tree	30	30
F 4.	25 c. Marabunta	70	30
F 4a.	25 c. Marabunta (No. 550)	15·00	13·00
F 5.	40 c. Tiger Beard	60	30
F 6.	50 c. "Guzmania lingulata"	60	40
F 7.	60 c. Soldier's Cap	70	50
F 8.	$1 "Chelonanthus uliginoides"	1·00	1·25
F 9.	$2 "Norantea guianensis"	2·00	2·50
F10.	$5 "Odontadenis grandiflora"	5·50	8·00

Although intended for fiscal use Nos. F1/10 were allowed, by the postal authorities as "an act of grace", to do duty as postage stamps until 30 June 1976.

GWALIOR

A "convention" state of Central India.

12 pies = 1 anna; 16 annas = 1 rupee.

1885. Queen Victoria stamps of India optd. **GWALIOR** at foot and native opt. at top.

No.	Type	Description	Unused	Used
1.	23.	½ a. turquoise	60·00	11·00
2.	–	1 a. purple	48·00	18·00
6.	–	1½ a. brown	42·00	—
3.	–	2 a. blue	38·00	11·00
8.	–	4 a. green (No. 69)	45·00	—
9.	–	6 a. brown (No. 80)	48·00	—
10.	–	8 a. mauve	42·00	—
11.	–	1 r. grey (No. 101)	42·00	—

Stamps of India overprinted **GWALIOR** above native overprint unless otherwise stated.

1885. Queen Victoria.

No.	Type	Description	Unused	Used
16	23.	½ a. turquoise	20	10
17	–	9 p. red	26·00	45·00
18	–	1 a. purple	30	15
20	–	1½ a. brown	35	40
21	–	2 a. blue	40	10
23	–	2½ a. green	3·00	8·50
25	–	3 a. orange	35	15
14	–	4 a. green (No. 69)	13·00	9·00
27	–	4 a. green (No. 96)	85	35
29	–	6 a. brown (No. 80)	75	3·25
30	–	8 a. mauve	70	60
32	–	12 a. purple on red	1·50	55
33	–	1 r. grey (No. 101)	70	75
34	37.	1 r. green and red	2·25	2·75
35	38.	2 r. red and orange	5·00	3·00
36		3 r. brown and green	7·00	3·50
37		5 r. blue and violet	12·00	6·50

1899. Queen Victoria.

No.	Type	Description	Unused	Used
38.	40.	3 p. red	10	20
39.		3 p. grey	5·50	50·00
40.	23.	½ a. green	15	60
41.	–	1 a. red	20	35
42.	–	2 a. lilac	40	2·00
43.	–	2½ a. blue	70	1·90

1903. King Edward VII.

No.	Type	Description	Unused	Used
46	41.	3 p. grey	30	15
48	–	½ a. green (No. 122)	10	10
49	–	1 a. red (No. 123)	10	10
50f	–	2 a. lilac	50	15
52	–	2½ a. blue	45	4·50
53	–	3 a. orange	50	20
54	–	4 a. olive	1·10	40
56	–	6 a. bistre	2·50	80
57	–	8 a. mauve	1·90	1·25
59	–	12 a. purple on red	2·00	3·25
60	–	1 r. green and red	2·00	1·10
61	52.	2 r. red and orange	7·50	10·00
62		3 r. brown and green	22·00	32·00
63		5 r. blue and violet	16·00	23·00

1907. King Edward VII inscr. "INDIA POSTAGE AND REVENUE".

No.	Description	Unused	Used
64	½ a. green (No. 149)	10	40
66	1 a. red (No. 150)	40	10

1912. King George V.

No.	Type	Description	Unused	Used
67	55.	3 p. grey	10	10
68	56.	½ a. green	20	10
102	79.	½ a. green	20	10
88	80.	9 p. green	1·25	20
69	57.	1 a. red	20	10
80		1 a. brown	20	10
103	81.	1 a. brown	10	10
90	82.	1½ a. mauve	30	10
81	58.	1½ a. brown (No. 165)	60	50
82		1½ a. red	15	20
70	59.	2 a. lilac	30	10
91	70.	2 a. lilac	25	15
104	59.	2 a. red	30	1·00
83	61.	2½ a. blue	85	1·50
84		2½ a. orange	20	30
71	62.	3 a. orange	40	15
92		3 a. blue	50	40
72	63.	4 a. olive	45	50
93	71.	4 a. green	80	80
73	64.	6 a. bistre	65	75
74	65.	8 a. mauve	65	30
75	66.	12 a. red	90	1·60
76	67.	1 r. brown and green	1·25	40
77		2 r. red and orange	4·50	3·00
78		5 r. blue and violet	17·00	6·50

1922. No. 192 (King George V) optd **GWALIOR** only.

No.	Type	Description	Unused	Used
79.	57.	9 p. on 1 a. red	10	35

1928. King George V. Opt. in larger type (19 mm. long).

No.	Type	Description	Unused	Used
96.	67.	1 r. brown and green	1·10	1·50
97.		2 r. red and orange	2·50	2·50
98.		5 r. blue and violet	12·00	18·00
99.		10 r. green and red	32·00	30·00
100.		15 r. blue and olive	55·00	48·00
101.		25 r. orange and blue	90·00	90·00

1938. King George VI.

No.	Type	Description	Unused	Used
105.	91.	3 p. slate	3·00	10
106.		½ a. brown	2·25	10
107.		9 p. green	30·00	2·50
108.		1 a. red	3·25	15
109.	–	3 a. green (No. 253)	3·50	2·50
110.	–	4 a. brown (No. 255)	30·00	1·25
111.	–	6 a. green (No. 256)	2·50	4·50
112.	93.	1 r. slate and brown	3·50	1·50
113.		2 r. purple and brown	12·00	6·00
114.		5 r. green and blue	40·00	25·00
115.		10 r. purple and red	38·00	35·00
116.		15 r. brown and green	£120	£140
117.		25 r. slate and purple	£110	£120

1942. King George VI.

No.	Type	Description	Unused	Used
118	100a.	3 p. slate	45	10
119.		½ a. mauve	45	10
120.		9 p. green	45	10
121.		1 a. red	40	10
122.	101.	1½ a. violet	3·00	20
123.		2 a. red	55	20
124.		3 a. violet	2·25	30
125.	102.	4 a. brown	75	20
126.		6 a. green	20·00	13·00
127.		8 a. violet	2·75	2·75
128.		12 a. purple	5·50	12·00

OFFICIAL STAMPS

Stamps of India overprinted with native inscription at top and bottom, unless otherwise stated.

1895. Queen Victoria.

No.	Type	Description	Unused	Used
O 1	23.	½ a. turquoise	10	10
O 3	–	1 a. purple	65	10
O 4	–	2 a. blue	80	20
O 7	–	4 a. green (No. 96)	1·10	55
O 9	–	8 a. mauve	1·00	70
O 10	37.	1 r. green and red	3·00	3·00

1901. Queen Victoria.

No.	Type	Description	Unused	Used
O 23	40.	3 p. red	30	30
O 24		3 p. grey	75	1·25
O 26	23.	½ a. green	20	10
O 27	–	1 a. red	2·00	10
O 28	–	2 a. lilac	55	1·50

1903. King Edward VII.

No.	Type	Description	Unused	Used
O 29a.	41.	3 p. grey	30	10
O 31.	–	½ a. green (No. 122)	1·10	10
O 32.	–	1 a. red (No. 123)	40	10
O 33a.	–	2 a. lilac	70	15
O 44.	–	4 a. olive	2·50	70
O 36.	–	8 a. mauve	3·00	70
O 38.	–	1 r. green and red	2·25	1·10

1907. King Edward VII inscr. "POSTAGE & REVENUE".

No.	Type	Description	Unused	Used
O 49.	–	½ a. green (No. 149)	65	10
O 48.	–	1 a. red (No. 150)	2·50	10

1913. King George V.

No.	Type	Description	Unused	Used
O61	55	3 p. grey	10	10
O62	56	½ a. green	10	15
O73	79	½ a. green	15	15
O63	80	9 p. green	10	15
O53a	57	1 a. red	20	10
O64		1 a. brown	10	10
O74	81	1 a. brown	15	15
O65	82	1½ a. mauve	50	15
O55	59	2 a. lilac	40	20
O66	70	2 a. lilac	20	15
O75	59	2 a. red	20	30
O77	63	4 a. olive	35	40
O67	71	4 a. green	50	30
O68	65	8 a. mauve	50	35
O58	67	1 r. brown and green	8·00	9·50

1922. No. O 97 (King George V. Official) optd. **GWALIOR** only.

No.	Type	Description	Unused	Used
O 59.	57.	9 p. on 1 a. red	10	20

1927. King George V. Optd. in larger type (21 mm. long).

No.	Type	Description	Unused	Used
O 69.	67.	1 r. brown and green	70	90
O 70.		2 r. red and orange	3·50	4·50
O 71.		5 r. blue and violet	10·00	75·00
O 72.		10 r. green and red	55·00	£130

1938. King George VI.

No.	Type	Description	Unused	Used
O 78.	91.	½ a. brown	7·50	25
O 79.		1 a. red	1·10	15
O 91.	93.	1 r. slate and brown	9·00	7·50
O 92.		2 r. purple and brown	19·00	40·00
O 93.		5 r. green and blue	48·00	£200
O 94.		10 r. purple and red	£130	£450

1940. King George VI. Optd at bottom only.

No.	Type	Description	Unused	Used
O 80	O 20.	3 p. slate	50	10
O 81		½ a. brown	4·00	25
O 82		½ a. purple	50	10
O 83		9 p. green	70	45
O 84		1 a. red	3·25	10
O 85		1 a. 3 p. yell.-brn.	18·00	1·60
O 86		1 a. 6 p. violet	80	30
O 87		2 a. orange	80	30
O 88		4 a. brown	90	1·00
O 89		8 a. violet	2·25	4·25

1942. No. O65 surch **1 A 1 A** and bar.

No.	Type	Description	Unused	Used
O90	82	1 a. on 1¼ a. mauve	14·00	2·25

HELIGOLAND

An island off the N. coast of Germany, ceded to that country by Great Britain in 1890.

1867. 16 schillings = 1 mark.
1875. 100 pfennig = 1 mark.

Many of the Heligoland stamps found in old collections, and the majority of those offered at a small fraction of catalogue prices to-day, are reprints which have very little value.

1.

1867. Perf. (½, 1, 2 and 6 sch. also roul.).

No.	Type	Description	Unused	Used
5	1	½ sch. green and red	21·00	£1500
6b		½ sch. green and red	90·00	£150
7		½ sch. red and green	24·00	£1100
8a		1 sch. red and green	£110	£180
9		1½ sch. green and red	55·00	£250
3		2 sch. red and green	8·00	50·00
4		6 sch. green and red	10·00	£250

2.

3.

4.

5.

1875.

10	2	1 pf. (¼d.) green and red..	8·00	£500
11		2 pf. (½d.) red and green..	8·00	£600
12a	3	3 pf. (⅝d.) grn., red & yell.	£160	£850
13	2	5 pf. (¾d.) green and red..	8·00	18·00
14a		10 pf. (1½d.) red and green	7·50	20·00
15b	3	20 pf. (2½d.) green, red and yellow	11·00	28·00
16	2	25 pf. (3d.) green and red	10·00	26·00
17		50 pf. (6d.) red and green	16·00	32·00
18	4	1 m. (1s.) grn., red & blk.	£140	£200
19	5	5 m. (5s.) grn., red & blk.	£110	£950

HONG KONG

A Br. colony at the mouth of the Canton R., consisting of the island of Hong Kong and peninsula of Kowloon. Under Japanese Occupation from 25th December 1941, until liberated by British forces on 16th September, 1945.

100 cents = 1 Hong Kong dollar.

1.

1862.

8a	1	2 c. brown	65·00	4·00
34		4 c. grey	5·00	45
10		6 c. lilac	£190	5·00
11a		8 c. yellow	£190	5·00
12a		12 c. blue	12·00	3·00
22		16 c. yellow	£650	50·00
4		18 c. lilac	£300	28·00
14		24 c. green	£225	5·00
15a		30 c. red	£325	9·00
16		30 c. mauve	£100	2·25
17a		48 c. red	£450	12·00
18		96 c. olive	£1600	£450
19		96 c. grey	£500	24·00

1877. Surch. in figures and words, thus **5 cents.**

23.	1.	5 c. on 8 c. yellow.. ..	£350	65·00
24.		5 c. on 18 c. lilac.. ..	£300	40·00
25.		10 c. on 12 c. blue ..	£400	48·00
26.		10 c. on 16 c. yellow ..	£1600	£110
27.		10 c. on 24 c. green ..	£500	65·00
20.		16 c. on 18 c. lilac ..	£1300	£130
21.		28 c. on 30 c. mauve ..	£550	40·00

1880.

33	1	2 c. red	13·00	45
56		2 c. green	12·00	45
57		4 c. red	5·50	45
35		5 c. blue	11·00	40
58		5 c. yellow	7·50	2·75
30		10 c. mauve	£180	7·50
37		10 c. green	80·00	60
38		10 c. purple on red ..	9·00	45
59		10 c. blue	18·00	80
39a		30 c. green	22·00	9·50
61		30 c. brown	10·00	14·00
31		48 c. brown	£400	55·00

1885. Surch. in figures and words, thus **20 CENTS.**

54	1	10 c. on 30 c. green ..	£275	£450
40		20 c. on 30 c. red.. ..	48·00	2·25
45a		20 c. on 30 c. green ..	55·00	65·00
41		50 c. on 48 c. brown ..	£170	11·00
46		50 c. on 48 c. purple ..	£200	£160
42		$1 on 96 c. olive	£275	27·00
47		$1 on 96 c. purple on red	£375	£180
53a		$1 on 96 c. black.. ..	£500	£1200

1891. Surch in figures and words, thus **7 cents**.

43	1	7 c. on 10 c. green ..	45·00	5·50
44		14 c. on 30 c. mauve ..	80·00	45·00

式 (**13.**) (20 c.) 五十 (**14.**) (50 c.) 壹員 (**15.**) ($1)

1891. T 1 surch. with figures and words and with Chinese surcharge also.

55	–	10 c. on 30 c. green ..	18·00	42·00
48a	13	20 c. on 30 c. green ..	13·00	1·50
49	14	50 c. on 48 c. purple ..	38·00	2·50
50	15	$1 on 96 c. purple on red	£200	11·00
52		$1 on 96 c. black ..	55·00	15·00

The Chinese surch on No. 55 is larger than Type **13**.

1891. 50th Anniv. of Colony. Optd. **1841 HONG KONG JUBILEE 1891.**

51	1	2 c. red	£180	70·00

20. 24.

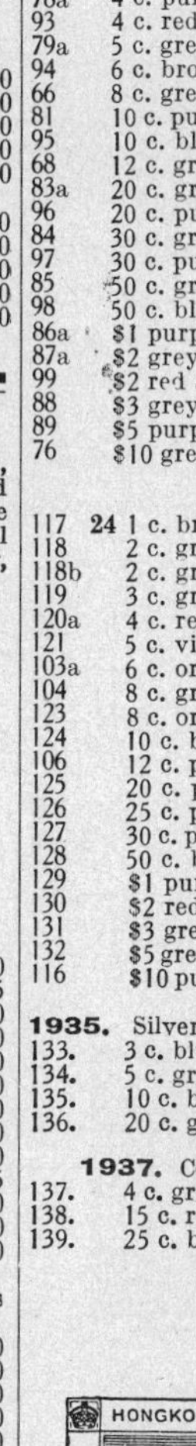

1903.

62	20	1 c. purple and brown ..	70	15
91		1 c. brown	1·75	75
77		2 c. green	2·00	65
78a		4 c. purple on red ..	2·00	10
93		4 c. red	2·75	30
79a		5 c. green and orange ..	4·00	3·25
94		6 c. brown and purple ..	8·50	2·50
66		8 c. grey and violet ..	3·50	70
81		10 c. purple & blue on blue	6·50	40
95		10 c. blue	9·00	30
68		12 c. green & pur. on yell.	4·75	2·25
83a		20 c. grey and brown ..	10·00	1·25
96		20 c. purple and green ..	28·00	28·00
84		30 c. green and black ..	12·00	6·00
97		30 c. purple and yellow ..	38·00	13·00
85		50 c. green and purple ..	25·00	3·75
98		50 c. black on green ..	20·00	8·00
86a		$1 purple and olive ..	55·00	9·50
87a		$2 grey and red	80·00	60·00
99		$2 red and black.. ..	£130	£110
88		$3 grey and blue.. ..	85·00	£110
89		$5 purple and green ..	£160	£180
76		$10 grey & orange on blue	£475	£325

1912.

117	24	1 c. brown	30	25
118		2 c. green	1·00	20
118b		2 c. grey	9·00	4·50
119		3 c. grey	2·50	50
120a		4 c. red	75	15
121		5 c. violet	2·25	15
103a		6 c. orange	2·00	90
104		8 c. grey	15·00	3·25
123		8 c. orange	1·00	70
124		10 c. blue	1·50	10
106		12 c. purple on yellow ..	1·25	3·25
125		20 c. purple and olive ..	2·00	10
126		25 c. purple	1·50	30
127		30 c. purple and orange..	6·50	1·25
128		50 c. black on green ..	3·75	10
129		$1 purple & blue on blue	11·00	50
130		$2 red and black ..	45·00	3·50
131		$3 green and purple ..	90·00	27·00
132		$5 green and red on green	£170	30·00
116		$10 purple & black on red	£200	50·00

1935. Silver Jubilee. As T **13** of Antigua.

133.		3 c. blue and black ..	2·00	2·25
134.		5 c. green and blue ..	6·00	2·25
135.		10 c. brown and blue ..	6·00	1·00
136.		20 c. grey and purple ..	19·00	4·50

1937. Coronation. As T **2** of Aden.

137.		4 c. green	2·50	1·75
138.		15 c. red	5·50	2·50
139.		25 c. blue	6·50	1·75

29. King George VI. **30.** Street Scene.

1938.

140	29	1 c. brown	60	60
141		2 c. grey	80	15
142		4 c. orange	1·25	1·00
143		5 c. green	55	10
144		8 c. brown	1·00	2·00
145b		10 c. violet	3·25	40
146		15 c. red	60	20
147		20 c. black	40	15
148		20 c. red	3·00	20
149		25 c. blue	14·00	60
150		25 c. olive	1·75	1·25
151a		30 c. olive	8·00	7·00
152		30 c. blue	2·50	10
153b		50 c. lilac	3·00	10
154		80 c. red	1·75	60
155		$1 purple and blue ..	7·00	2·00
156		$1 orange and green ..	4·00	10
157		$2 orange and green ..	55·00	13·00
158		$2 violet and red ..	6·00	60
159		$5 purple and red ..	45·00	45·00
160		$5 green and violet ..	35·00	4·25
161		$10 green and violet ..	£350	60·00
162		$10 violet and blue ..	70·00	18·00

1941. Cent. of British Occupation. Dated "1841 1941".

163.	30.	2 c. orange and brown ..	2·25	1·25
164.	–	4 c. purple and mauve ..	2·50	1·25
165.	–	5 c. black and green ..	1·00	40
166.	–	15 c. black and red ..	4·00	60
167.	–	25 c. brown and blue ..	6·50	1·25
168.	–	$1 blue and orange ..	15·00	4·25

DESIGNS—HORIZ: 4 c. "Empress of Japan" (liner) and junk. 5 c. University. 15 c. Harbour. $1, "Falcon" (clipper) and seaplane. VERT: 25 c. Hong Kong Bank.

For Japanese issues see "Japanese Occupation of Hong Kong".

36.

1946. Victory.

169.	36.	30 c. blue and red ..	1·25	40
170.		$1 brown and red ..	1·25	40

1948. Silver Wedding. As T **10/11** of Aden.

171.		10 c. violet	75	50
172.		$10 red	95·00	38·00

1949. U.P.U. As T **20/23** of Antigua.

173.		10 c. violet	2·50	30
174.		20 c. red	7·50	1·00
175.		30 c. blue	7·50	1·00
176.		80 c. mauve	10·00	2·75

1953. Coronation. As T **13** of Aden.

177.		10 c. black and purple ..	2·00	15

1954. As T **29** but portrait of Queen Elizabeth, facing left.

178		5 c. orange..	75	10
179		10 c. lilac	1·75	10
180a		15 c. green..	2·50	30
181		20 c. brown	3·00	30
182a		25 c. red	2·00	20
183		30 c. grey	3·00	10
184		40 c. blue	2·50	10
185		50 c. purple	3·00	10
186		65 c. grey	16·00	7·00
187		$1 orange and green ..	4·50	10
188		$1.30 blue and red ..	20·00	90
189		$2 violet and red	8·00	40
190		$5 green and purple ..	38·00	1·50
191		$10 violet and blue ..	38·00	5·50

38. University Arms.

1961. Golden Jubilee of Hong Kong University.

192.	38.	$1 multicoloured ..	3·25	1·25

39. Statue of Queen Victoria.

1962. Stamp Centenary.

193.	39.	10 c. black and mauve..	30	10
194.		20 c. black and blue ..	90	70
195.		50 c. black and bistre..	1·00	20

40. Queen Elizabeth II (after Annigoni).

1962.

196	40.	5 c. orange	20	30
223		10 c. violet	30	20
224		15 c. green	35	60
199		20 c. brown	80	30
226		25 c. mauve	50	1·50
201		30 c. blue	1·75	10
202		40 c. turquoise.. ..	1·00	15
203		50 c. red	60	10
230a		65 c. blue	2·00	4·00
231		$1 sepia	6·00	1·00
206	–	$1.30 multicoloured ..	2·75	10
207	–	$2 multicoloured ..	3·50	15
208	–	$5 multicoloured ..	8·00	75
209	–	$10 multicoloured ..	18·00	1·75
210	–	$20 multicoloured ..	55·00	15·00

Nos. 206/10 are as T **40** but larger (26 × 40½ mm).

1963. Freedom from Hunger. As T **28** of Aden.

211		$1.30 green	22·00	4·25

1963. Cent of Red Cross. As T **33** of Antigua.

212.		10 c. red and black ..	3·00	30
213.		$1·30 red and blue ..	11·00	3·25

1965. Cent of I.T.U. As T **36** of Antigua.

214.		10 c. purple and yellow ..	3·00	25
215.		$1·30 olive and green ..	12·00	2·25

1965. I.C.Y. As T **37** of Antigua.

216.		10 c. purple and turquoise	2·00	20
217.		$1·30 green and lavender	8·00	2·00

1966. Churchill Commem. As T **38** of Antigua.

218.		10 c. blue	2·50	15
219.		50 c. green..	2·50	20
220.		$1·30 brown	8·00	1·50
221.		$2 violet	11·00	6·00

1966. Inauguration of W.H.O. Headquarters, Geneva. As T **41** of Antigua.

237.		10 c. black, green and blue	2·00	30
238.		50 c. black, purple & ochre	3·50	1·40

1966. 20th Anniv. of U.N.E.S.C.O. As T **54/6** of Antigua.

239.		10 c. multicoloured ..	2·50	10
240.		50 c. yellow, violet & olive	6·50	60
241.		$2 black, purple & orange	21·00	10·00

42. Ram's Heads on Chinese Lanterns.

1967. Chinese New Year.

242.	42.	10 c. red, olive & yellow	2·00	25
243.	–	$1·30 green, red & yellow	11·00	5·50

DESIGN: $1·30, Three rams ("Year of the Ram").

44. Cable Route Map.

1967. Completion of Malaysia–Hong Kong Link of SEACOM Telephone Cable.

244.	44.	$1·30 blue and red ..	6·00	2·00

45. Rhesus Macaques in Tree ("Year of the Monkey").

1968. Chinese New Year ("Year of the Monkey").

245.	45.	10 c. gold, black & red	3·00	25
246.	–	$1·30 gold, black & red	8·00	5·00

DESIGN: $1·30, Family of rhesus macaques.

47. "Iberia" (liner) at Ocean Terminal.

1968. Sea Craft.

247.	47.	10 c. multicoloured ..	1·25	10
248.	–	20 c. blue, black & brown	1·75	55
249.	–	40 c. orge., blk. & mauve	4·75	4·50
250.	–	50 c. red, black & green	5·00	65
251.	–	$1 yellow, black and red	7·00	2·75
252.	–	$1.30 blue, black & pink	14·00	2·00

DESIGNS: 20 c. Pleasure Launch. 40 c. Car Ferry. 50 c. Passenger Ferry. $1, Sampan. $1.30, Junk.

53. "Bauhinia blakeana".

1968. Multicoloured.
253. 65 c. Type **53** .. .. 3·75 30
254. $1 Arms of Hong Kong .. 2·00 1·50

55. "Aladdin's Lamp" and Human Rights Emblem.

1968. Human Rights Year.
255. **55.** 10 c. orge, blk. & green 1·00 50
256. 50 c. yell., blk. & purple 1·75 1·50

56. Cockerel.

1969. Chinese New Year ("Year of the Cock"). Multicoloured.
257. 10 c. Type **56** .. .. 3·00 20
258. $1·30 Cockerel (different) (vert.) .. .. 26·00 6·50

58. Arms of Chinese University.

1969. Establishment of Chinese University of Hong Kong.
259. **58.** 40 c. violet, gold & blue 1·75 1·25

59. Earth Station and Satellite.

1969. Opening of Communications Satellite Tracking Station.
260. **59.** $1 multicoloured .. 3·75 2·00

60. Chow's Head.

62. "Expo 70" Emblem.

1970. Chinese New Year ("Year of the Dog"). Multicoloured.
261. 10 c. Type **60** .. .. 4·00 50
262. $1.30 Chow standing (horiz.) .. .. .. 26·00 8·00

1970. Expo 70. Multicoloured.
263. 15 c. Type **62** 30 50
264. 25 c. Expo 70 emblem and junks (horiz.) 30 60

64. Plaque in Tung Wah Hospital.

1970. Cent. of "Tung Wah Hospital".
265. **64.** 10 c. multicoloured .. 50 10
266. 50 c. multicoloured .. 1·00 60

65. Symbol.

1970. Asian Productivity Year.
267. **65.** 10 c. multicoloured .. 40 30

66. Pig.

1971. Chinese New Year ("Year of the Pig").
268. **66.** 10 c. multicoloured .. 3·00 30
269. $1·30 multicoloured .. 13·00 5·50

67. "60" and Scout Badge.

1971. Diamond Jubilee of Scouting in Hong Kong.
270. **67.** 10 c. blk., red & yellow 30 10
271. 50 c. blk., green & blue 1·75 55
272. $2 blk., mauve & viloet 5·00 6·50

68. Festival Emblem.

1971. Hong Kong Festival.
273. **68.** 10 c. orange & purple .. 1·25 20
274. – 50 c. multicoloured .. 1·50 90
275. – $1 multicoloured .. 2·75 4·00
DESIGNS—HORIZ. (39×23 mm.) 50 c. Coloured streamers. VERT. (23×39 mm.) $1, "Orchid".

69. Stylised Rats.

1972. Chinese New Year. ("Year of the Rat").
276. **69.** 10 c. red, black & gold .. 2·00 35
277. $1.30 red, blk. & gold 11·00 5·50

70. Tunnel Entrance.

1972. Opening of Cross Harbour Tunnel.
278. **70.** $1 multicoloured .. 2·50 1·75

1972. Royal Silver Wedding. As T **52** of Ascension, but with Phoenix and Dragon in background.
279. 10 c. multicoloured .. 15 10
280. 50 c. multicoloured .. 70 1·10

72. Ox.

73. Queen Elizabeth II.

1973. Chinese New Year ("Year of the Ox").
281. **72.** 10 c. orge., brn. & black 1·00 20
282. – $1.30 yell., orge. & blk. 4·00 4·50
DESIGN—HORIZ. $1.30, Ox.

1973.
311 **73.** 10 c. orange 55 30
284 15 c. green .. .. 5·00 3·75
313 20 c. violet 30 10
286 25 c. brown .. .. 5·00 4·00
315 30 c. blue 50 30
316 40 c. blue 60 80
289 50 c. red .. .. 1·25 40
318 60 c. lavender .. .. 1·25 1·25
290 65 c. brown .. .. 7·00 8·00
320 70 c. yellow .. .. 1·25 30
321 80 c. red .. .. 1·50 1·25
321b 90 c. brown .. .. 5·00 1·00
322a $1 green .. .. 2·00 50
323 – $1·30 yellow and violet 1·75 30
324 – $2 green and brown .. 2·00 1·25
324b – $5 pink and blue .. 2·25 1·25
324c – $10 pink and green .. 2·25 3·00
324d – $20 pink and black .. 4·50 6·00
Values of $1.30 and above are size 27 × 32 mm.

1973. Royal Wedding. As Type **47** of Anguilla. Multicoloured. Background colours given.
297. 50 c. brown 30 15
298. $2 mauve .. .. 1·00 80

75. Festival Symbols forming Chinese Character.

1973. Hong Kong Festival.
299. **75.** 10 c. red and green .. 20 10
300. 50 c. mauve & orange 75 35
301. – $1 green and mauve .. 1·25 2·00
DESIGNS—Festival symbols arranged to form a Chinese character: 10 c. "Hong". 50 c. "Kong". $1, "Festival".

76. Tiger.

1974. Chinese New Year ("Year of the Tiger").
302. **76.** 10 c. multicoloured .. 2·00 30
303. – $1·30 multicoloured .. 8·00 9·00
DESIGN—VERT. $1·30, similar to Type **76.**

77. Chinese Mask.

1974. Arts Festival.
304. **77.** 10 c. multicoloured .. 50 10
305. – $1 multicoloured .. 2·00 2·75
306. – $2 multicoloured .. 2·25 3·75
DESIGNS: $1, $2, Chinese masks similar to Type **77.**

78. Pigeons with Letters.

1974. Centenary of U.P.U.
308. **78.** 10 c. bl., grn. & blk. .. 30 10
309. – 50 c. mauve, orge., blk. 75 30
310. – $2 multicoloured .. 1·25 2·50
DESIGNS: 50 c. Globe within letters. **$2, Hands** holding letters.

79. Stylised Rabbit.

1975. Chinese New Year ("Year of the Rabbit").
325. **79.** 10 c. silver and red .. 75 50
326. – $1·30 gold and green .. 4·25 5·50
DESIGN: $1·30, Pair of rabbits.

80. Queen Elizabeth II, the Duke of Edinburgh and Hong Kong Arms.

1975. Royal Visit.
329. **80.** $1·30 multicoloured .. 1·50 1·75
330. $2 multicoloured .. 1·50 3·00

81. Mid-Autumn Festival.

1975. Hong Kong Festivals of 1975. **Mult.**
331. 50 c. Type **81** 75 30
332. $1 Dragon-boat Festival 2·00 2·00
333. $2 Tin Hau Festival .. 3·25 3·75

82. Hwamei.

1975. Birds. Multicoloured.
335. 50 c. Type **82** .. .. 1·50 30
336. $1·30 Chinese Bulbul .. 3·75 4·25
337. $2 Black-capped Kingfisher .. .. .. 4·25 6·00

83. Dragon.

1976. Chinese New Year (" Year of the Dragon ").
338. 83. 20 c. mauve, pur. & gold .. 40 10
339. – $1·30 green, red & gold .. 2·00 2·50
DESIGN: $1·30, As Type 83 but dragon reversed.

84. " 60 " and Girl Guides Badge.

1976. Diamond Jubilee of Girl Guides. Mult.
354. 20 c. Type 84 .. .. 30 10
355. $1·30 Badge, stylised diamond and " 60 " .. 2·00 2·50

85. " Postal Services " in Chinese Characters.

1976. Opening of New G.P.O.
356. 85. 20 c. green, grey & black 20 10
357. – $1·30 orge., grey & blk. 1·00 1·25
358. – $2 yellow, grey & black 1·25 2·25
DESIGNS: $1·30, Old G.P.O. $2, New G.P.O.

86. Tree Snake on Branch.

1977. Chinese New Year (" Year of the Snake "). Multicoloured.
359. 20 c. Type 86 .. .. 35 15
360. $1.30 Snake facing left .. 2·50 4·00

87. Presentation of the Orb.

1977. Silver Jubilee. Multicoloured.
361. 20 c. Type 87 .. .. 20 10
362. $1.30 The Queen's Visit, 1975 .. .. .. 70 1·10
363. $2 The Orb (vert.) .. 80 1·10

88. Tram Cars.

1977. Tourism. Multicoloured.
364. 20 c. Type 88 .. .. 40 10
365. 60 c. Star ferryboat .. 1·00 1·75
366. $1.30 The Peak railway .. 1·25 1·75
367. $2 Junk and sampan .. 1·25 2·50

89. Buttercup Orchid.

1977. Orchids. Multicoloured.
368. 20 c. Type 89 .. .. 75 15
369. $1.30 Lady's Slipper Orchid 1·75 1·75
370. $2 Susan Orchid .. .. 2·25 3·25

90. Horse.

1978. Chinese New Year (" Year of the Horse ").
371. 90. 20 c. mauve, olive and bistre 35 10
372. $1.30 orange, brown and light brown .. .. 1·40 2·40

91. Queen Elizabeth II.

1978. 25th Anniversary of Coronation.
373. 91. 20 c. mauve and blue 30 10
374. $1.30 blue and mauve 1·00 1·25

92. Girl and Boy holding Hands.

1978. Centenary of Po Leung Kuk (children's charity). Multicoloured.
375. 20 c. Type 92 .. .. 15 10
376. $1.30 Ring of children .. 70 1·25

93. Electronics Industry.

1979. Hong Kong Industries.
377. 93. 20 c. yell., olive & orge. 10 10
378. – $1.30 multicoloured .. 75 90
379. – $2 multicoloured .. 75 1·40
DESIGNS: $1.30, Toy industry. $2, Garment industry.

94. "Precis orithya".

1979. Butterflies. Multicoloured.
380 20 c. Type 94 .. .. 40 10
381 $1 "Graphium sarpedon" 80 70
382 $1.30 "Heliophorus epicles" 95 1·10
383 $2 "Danaus genutia" .. 1·25 2·50

95. Diagrammatic View of Railway Station.

1979. Mass Transit Railway. Multicoloured.
384. 20 c. Type 95 .. .. 30 10
385. $1.30 Diagrammatic view of car 70 50
386. $2 Plan showing route of railway 80 85

96. Tsui Shing Lau Pagoda.

1980. Rural Architecture.
387. 96. 20 c. blk., mauve & yell. 10 10
388. – $1.30 multicoloured .. 70 85
389. – $2 multicoloured .. 80 1·60
DESIGNS—HORIZ. $1.30, Village House, Sai O. $2, Ching Chung Koon Temple.

97. Queen Elizabeth the Queen Mother.

1980. 80th Birthday of The Queen Mother.
390. 97. $1.30 multicoloured .. 55 1·00

98. Botanical Gardens.

1980. Parks. Multicoloured.
391. 20 c. Type 98 .. .. 10 10
392. $1 Ocean Park 30 45
393. $1.30 Kowloon Park .. 40 75
394. $2 Country Parks .. 55 1·50

99. " Epinephelus akaara ".

1981. Fishes. Multicoloured.
395. 20 c. Type 99 .. .. 15 10
396. $1 " Nemipterus virgatus " 45 45
397. $1.30 " Choerodon azurio " 55 60
398. $2 " Scarus ghobban " .. 65 1·40

100. Wedding Bouquet from Hong Kong.

1981. Royal Wedding. Multicoloured.
399. 20 c. Type 100 .. .. 10 10
400. $1.30 Prince Charles in Hong Kong 35 35
401. $5 Prince Charles and Lady Diana Spencer .. .. 1·25 1·50

101. Surburban Development.

1981. Public Housing.
402. 101. 20 c. multicoloured .. 10 10
403. – $1 multicoloured .. 30 30
404. – $1.30 multicoloured .. 40 40
405. – $2 multicoloured .. 60 60
DESIGNS: $1 to $2, Various suburban developments.

102. " Victoria from the Harbour, c. 1855 ".

1982. Hong Kong Port, Past and Present. Multicoloured.
407. 20 c. Type 102 .. .. 20 10
408. $1 " West Point, Hong Kong, 1847 " 55 55
409. $1.30 Fleet of junks .. 75 75
410. $2 Liner " Queen Elizabeth 2 " at Hong Kong .. 1·00 1·50

103. Large Indian Civet.

1982. Wild Animals.

411. 103. 20 c. blk., pink & brn. 20 10
412. – $1 multicoloured .. 70 70
413. – $1.30 blk., grn. & orge. 80 90
414. – $5 black, brn.& yell. 1·40 2·75

DESIGNS: $1, Chinese pangolin. $1.30, Chinese porcupine. $5, Indian muntjac.

104. Queen Elizabeth II.

1982.

415 104. 10 c. bright red, red and yellow 50 40
416 20 c. blue, violet and lavender 60 40
417 30 c. light violet, violet and pink .. 70 20
474 40 c. red and blue .. 70 20
419 50 c. chestnut, brown and green 70 20
476 60 c. purple and grey 1·00 80
477 70 c. green, myrtle and yellow .. .. 1·00 40
478 80 c. bistre, brown & green .. .. 1·25 90
479 90 c. bottle green, green and turquoise 1·25 50
480 $1 deep orange, orange and red .. 1·25 40
481 $1.30 blue and mauve 1·75 45
482 $1.70 deep blue, blue and green .. .. 1·50 1·00
483 $2 blue and pink .. 2·25 1·50
484 – $5 red, pur. & yell. .. 2·75 3·25
485 – $10 brn. and light brn. 2·75 4·00
486 – $20 red and blue .. 3·00 6·50
487 – $50 red and grey .. 10·00 22·00

Nos. 484/7 are as Type **104** but larger, 26 × 30 mm.

106. Table Tennis.

1982. Sport for the Disabled. Multicoloured.

431. 30 c. Type **106** 30 10
432. $1 Racing.. .. 50 60
433. $1.30 Basketball .. .. 1·00 90
434. $5 Archery .. .. 2·00 3·00

107. Dancing.

1983. Performing Arts.

435. 107. 30 c. light blue & blue 30 10
436. $1.30 red and purple.. 1·00 90
437. $5 green & deep green 2·25 3·50

INDEX

Countries can be quickly located by referring to the index at the end of this volume.

108. Aerial View of Hong Kong.

1983. Commonwealth Day. Multicoloured.

438. 30 c. Type **108** 30 10
439. $1 "Liverpool Bay" (container ship) .. .. 80 1·10
440. $1.30 Hong Kong flag .. 80 1·10
441. $5 Queen Elizabeth II and Hong Kong .. .. 1·40 3·00

109. Victoria Harbour.

1983. Hong Kong by Night. Multicoloured.

442. 30 c. Type **109** 45 10
443. $1 Space Museum, Tsim Sha Tsui Cultural Centre 1·25 1·40
444. $1.30 Fireworks display .. 1·25 1·40
445. $5 "Jumbo", floating restaurant .. .. .. 3·25 4·75

110. Old and new Observatory Buildings.

1983. Centenary of Hong Kong Observatory.

446. 110. 40 c. orange, brown & black 45 10
447. – $1 mauve, deep mauve and black .. .. 1·25 1·40
448. – $1.30 blue, deep blue and black .. .. 1·25 1·40
449. – $5 yellow, green & black 3·50 5·00

DESIGNS: $1 Wind measuring equipment. $1.30 Thermometer. $5 Ancient and modern seismometers.

111. "DH 86" Dorado (Hong Kong–Penang Service, 1936).

1984. Aviation in Hong Kong. Multicoloured.

450. 40 c. Type **111** 40 10
451. $1 Sikorsky "S–42B" (San Francisco–Hong Kong Service, 1937) .. 1·00 1·40
452. $1.30 Cathy-Pacific "Jumbo" jet leaving Kai Tak Airport .. .. .. 1·00 1·40
453. $5 Baldwin brothers' balloon, 1891 (vert.) .. 2·50 4·75

112. Map by Capt. E. Belcher.

1984. Maps of Hong Kong.

454. 40 c. Type **112** 40 15
455. $1 Bartholomew map of 1929 .. .. .. 65 1·25
456. $1.30 Early map of Hong Kong Waters .. .. 75 1·25
457. $5 Chinese style map of 1819 .. .. .. 1·75 4·50

113. Cockerel.

1984. Chinese Animal Lanterns. Mult.

458. 40 c. Type **113** 30 15
459. $1 Dog 50 70
460. $1.30 Butterfly 55 80
461. $5 Fish .. .. .. 1·60 3·50

114. Jockey on Horse and Nurse with Baby ("Health Care").

1984. Centenary of Royal Hong Kong Jockey Club. Designs showing aspects of Club's charity work. Multicoloured.

462. 40 c. Type **114** 40 15
463. $1 Disabled man playing handball ("Support for disabled") .. .. 75 1·25
464. $1.30 Ballerina ("The Arts") .. .. .. 80 1·25
465. $5 Humboldt penguins ("Ocean Park") .. .. 2·50 4·50

115. Hung Sing Temple.

1985. Historic Buildings. Multicoloured.

467. 40 c. Type **115** 35 20
468. $1 St. John's Cathedral .. 1·00 1·25
469. $1.30 The Old Supreme Court Building .. .. 1·10 1·25
470. $5 Wan Chai Post Office .. 2·75 4·50

116. Prow of Dragon Boat.

1985. 10th International Dragon Boat Festival. Designs showing different parts of dragon boat. Multicoloured.

488. 40 c. Type **116** 30 15
489. $1 Drummer and rowers .. 50 60
490. $1.30 Rowers 55 70
491. $5 Stern of boat .. .. 1·75 3·00

117. The Queen Mother with Prince Charles and Prince William, 1984.

1985. Life and Times of Queen Elizabeth the Queen Mother. Multicoloured.

493 40 c. At Glamis Castle, aged 7 .. .. .. 35 10
494 $1 Type **117** 85 90
495 $1.30 The Queen Mother 1970 (from photo by Cecil Beaton) 85 90
496 $5 With Prince Henry at his Christening (from photo by Lord Snowdon) 1·60 3·00

118. "Melastoma candidum".

1985. Native Flowers. Multicoloured.

497. 40 c. Type **118** 60 15
498. 50 c. Chinese Lily 60 40
499. 60 c. Grantham's Camellia 60 55
500. $1.30 "Narcissus tazetta" 1·10 85
501. $1.70 "Bauhinia blakeana" 1·40 1·25
502. $5 Chinese New Year Flower .. .. .. 3·00 5·50

119. Hong Kong Academy for Performing Arts.

1985. New Buildings. Multicoloured.

503. 50 c. Type **119** 40 15
504. $1.30 Exchange Square (vert.) 85 70
505. $1.70 Hong Kong Bank Headquarters (vert.) .. 1·10 90
506. $5 Hong Kong Coliseum .. 2·25 2·75

120. Halley's Comet in the Solar System.

1986. Appearance of Halley's Comet. Mult.

507. 50 c. Type **120** 25 15
508. $1.30 Edmond Halley and Comet 40 50
509. $1.70 Comet over Hong Kong 50 80
510. $5 Comet passing the Earth 1·50 3·00

1986. 60th Birthday of Queen Elizabeth II. As T **110** of Ascension. Multicoloured.

512. 50 c. At wedding of Miss Celia Bowes-Lyon, 1931 30 10
513. $1 Queen in Garter procession, Windsor Castle 1977 .. .. 50 40
514. $1.30 In Hong Kong, 1975 55 50
515. $1.70 At Royal Lodge, Windsor, 1980 (from photo by Norman Parkinson) 60 60
516. $5 At Crown Agents Head Office, London, 1983 .. 1·25 2·50

121. Train, Airliner and Map of World.

1986. "Expo '86" World Fair, Vancouver. Multicoloured.

517. 50 c. Type **121** 30 15
518. $1.30 Hong Kong Bank Headquarters and map of world 60 65
519. $1.70 Container ship and map of world 80 85
520. $5 Dish aerial and map of world .. .. .. 2·00 3·25

MORE DETAILED LISTS

are given in the Stanley Gibbons Catalogues referred to in the country headings. For lists of current volumes see Introduction.

122. Hand-liner Sampan.

1986. Fishing Vessels. Designs showing fishing boat and outline of fish. Multicoloured.

No.	Description		Unused	Used
521.	50 c. Type **122**	.. ..	30	15
522.	$1.30 Stern trawler	..	60	60
523.	$1.70 Long liner junk	..	75	90
524.	$5 Junk trawler	.. ..	1·75	3·25

123. "The Second Puan Khequa" (attr Spoilum).

1986. 19th-century Hong Kong Portraits. Multicoloured.

No.	Description		Unused	Used
525.	50 c. Type **123**	.. ..	25	15
526.	$1.30 "Chinese Lady" (19th-century copy)	..	60	50
527.	$1.70 "Lamqua" (self-portrait)	.. .. ..	70	70
528.	$5 "Wife of Wo Hing Qua" (attr G. Chinnery)	..	1·75	2·50

124. Rabbit.

1987. Chinese New Year ("Year of the Rabbit"). Designs showing stylized rabbits.

No.	Type	Description	Unused	Used
529.	**124.**	50 c. multicoloured ..	30	10
530.	–	$1.30 multicoloured ..	50	50
531.	–	$1.70 multicoloured ..	60	60
532.	–	$5 multicoloured ..	1·40	2·10

Nos. 530/1 have the "0" omitted from their face values.

125. "Village Square, Hong Kong Island, 1838" (Auguste Borget).

1987. 19th-century Hong Kong Scenes. Multicoloured.

No.	Description		Unused	Used
534.	50 c. Type **125**	.. ..	30	10
535.	$1.30 "Boat Dwellers, Kowloon Bay, 1838" (August Borget)	..	60	50
536.	$1.70 "Flagstaff House, 1846" (Murdoch Bruce)		70	65
537.	$5 "Wellington Street late 19th-century" (C. Andrasi)	.. .. ..	1·25	2·00

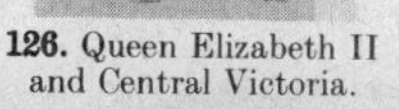

126. Queen Elizabeth II and Central Victoria.

127. Hong Kong Flag.

1987.

No.	Type	Description		Unused	Used
600	**126**	10 c. multicoloured	..	20	30
601		40 c. multicoloured	..	30	40
602		50 c. multicoloured	..	30	30
603		60 c. multicoloured	..	40	30
604		70 c. multicoloured	..	40	30
605		80 c. multicoloured	..	40	40
606		90 c. multicoloured	..	40	40
607		$1 multicoloured	..	40	30
607a		$1.20 multicoloured	..	1·00	75
608		$1.30 multicoloured	..	50	50
609		$1.40 multicoloured	..	50	50
609a		$1.70 multicoloured	..	1·25	1·25
610		$1.80 multicoloured	..	60	50
611		$2 multicoloured	..	70	50
611a		$2.30 multicoloured	..	1·40	1·25
612	–	$5 multicoloured	..	1·50	1·25
613	–	$10 multicoloured	..	2·00	2·25
614	–	$20 multicoloured	..	3·50	3·75
615	–	$50 multicoloured	..	8·00	9·00

DESIGNS: 25 × 31 mm. Queen Elizabeth II and $5 Kowloon. $10 Victoria Harbour. $20 Legislative Council Building. $50 Government House.

With the exception of Nos. 607a and 611a which are undated, all the above exist with or without a date in the design.

1987.

No.	Type	Description		Unused	Used
553	**127**	10 c. multicoloured	..	10	10
554	–	50 c. brown, red & blk		10	10
554c	–	80 c. mve, grn & blk		15	20
554d	–	90 c. blue, brn & blk		15	20
554e	–	$1.30 green, bl & blk		30	35
554f	–	$2.30 brn, violet & blk		40	45

DESIGN: 50 c. to $2.30, Map of Hong Kong.

128. Alice Ho Miu Ling Nethersole Hospital, 1887.

1987. Hong Kong Medical Centenaries. Multicoloured.

No.	Description		Unused	Used
555.	50 c. Type **128**		45	10
556.	$1.30 Matron and nurses, Nethersole Hospital, 1891	.. .. ..	1·00	80
557.	$1.70 Scanning equipment, Faculty of Medicine	..	1·10	85
558.	$5 Nurse and patient Faculty of Medicine	..	2·75	3·25

129. Casual Dress with Fringed Hem, 220–589.

1987. Historical Chinese Costumes. Mult.

No.	Description		Unused	Used
559.	50 c. Type **129**	.. ..	35	10
560.	$1.30 Two-piece dress and wrap, 581–960	..	90	75
561.	$1.70 Formal dress, Song Dynasty, 960–1279	..	1·10	80
562.	$5 Manchu empress costume, 1644–1911	..	2·50	3·00

130. Dragon.

1988. Chinese New Year ("Year of the Dragon"). Designs showing dragons.

No.	Type	Description	Unused	Used
563.	**130.**	50 c. multicoloured ..	40	15
564.	–	$1.30 multicoloured ..	90	75
565.	–	$1.70 multicoloured ..	1·10	80
566.	–	$5 multicoloured ..	2·50	3·25

131. White-breasted Kingfisher.

1988. Hong Kong Birds. Multicoloured.

No.	Description		Unused	Used
568	50 c. Type **131**	.. ..	50	15
569	$1.30 Fukien niltava	..	1·25	80
570	$1.70 Black kite	.. ..	1·50	90
571	$5 Lesser pied kingfisher		2·75	3·50

132 Chinese Banyan

1988. Trees of Hong Kong. Multicoloured.

No.	Description		Unused	Used
572	50 c. Type **132**	.. ..	25	10
573	$1.30 Hong Kong orchid tree	.. .. ..	50	40
574	$1.70 Cotton tree	..	55	45
575	$5 Schima	.. ..	1·50	1·75

133 Lower Terminal, Peak Tramway

1988. Centenary of The Peak Tramway. Mult.

No.	Description		Unused	Used
577	50 c. Type **133**	..	35	10
578	$1.30 Tram on incline	..	70	50
579	$1.70 Peak Tower Upper Terminal	.. ..	75	50
580	$5 Tram	.. ..	1·75	1·75

134 Hong Kong Catholic Cathedral

1988. Centenary of Hong Kong Catholic Cathedral.

No.	Type	Description		Unused	Used
582	**134**	60 c. multicoloured	..	70	40

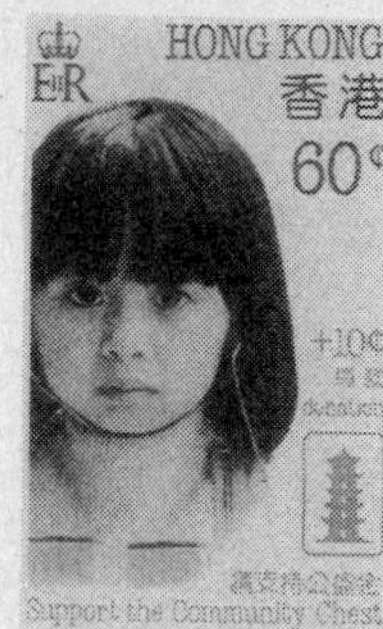

135 Deaf Girl

1988. Community Chest Charity.

No.	Type	Description	Unused	Used
583	**135**	60 c. + 10 c. black, red and blue ..	30	40
584	–	$1.40 + 20 c. black, red and green ..	50	60
585	–	$1.80 + 30 c. black, red and orange ..	55	65
586	–	$5 + $1 blk, red & brn	1·40	1·60

DESIGNS: $1.40, Elderly woman; $1.80, Blind boy using braille typewriter; $5 Mother and baby.

136 Snake

1989. Chinese New Year ("Year of the Snake"). Multicoloured.

No.	Description		Unused	Used
587	60 c. Type **136**	..	15	15
588	$1.40 Snake and fish	..	45	40
589	$1.80 Snake on branch	..	50	45
590	$5 Coiled snake	.. ..	1·50	1·60

137 Girl and Doll

1989. Cheung Chau Bun Festival. Mult.

No.	Description		Unused	Used
592	60 c. Type **137**	.. ..	20	15
593	$1.40 Girl in festival costume	.. ..	40	40
594	$1.80 Paper effigy of god Taai Si Wong	..	55	55
595	$5 Floral gateway	..	1·25	1·75

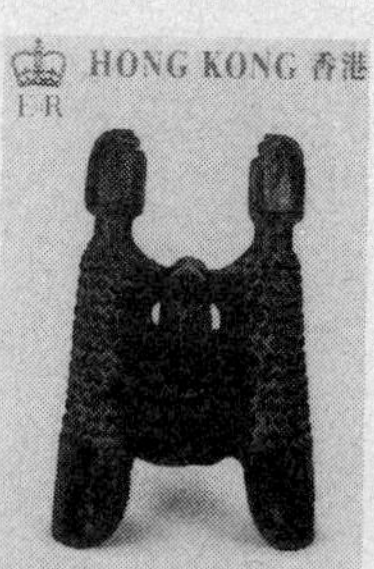

138 "Twins" (wood carving, Cheung Yee)

1989. Modern Art. Multicoloured.

No.	Description		Unused	Used
596	60 c. Type **138**	.. ..	20	15
597	$1.40 "Figures" (acrylic on paper, Chan Luis)	..	40	40
598	$1.80 "Lotus" (copper sculpture, Van Lau)	..	55	55
599	$5 "Zen Painting" (ink and colour on paper, Lui Shou-kwan)	.. ..	1·25	1·75

139 Lunar New Year Festivities

1989. Hong Kong People. Multicoloured.

616	60 c. Type **139**	20	10
617	$1.40 Shadow boxing and horse racing	40	30
618	$1.80 Foreign-exchange dealer and traditional builder	55	40
619	$5 Multi-racial society ..	1·25	1·50

140 University of Science and Technology

1989. Building for the Future.

620	**140**	60 c. black, yell & brn	20	10
621	–	70 c. black, pale pink and pink	20	15
622	–	$1.30 blk, lt grn & grn	35	30
623	–	$1.40 black, lt bl & bl	40	30
624	–	$1.80 black, turq & bl	55	40
625	–	$5 brown, orge & red	1·40	1·50

DESIGNS: 70 c. Cultural Centre; $1.30, Eastern Harbour motorway interchange; $1.40, New Bank of China Building; $1.80, Convention and Exhibition Centre; $5 Light Rail Transit train.

141 Prince and Princess of Wales and Hong Kong Skyline

1989. Royal Visit. Multicoloured.

626	60 c. Type **141**	20	10
627	$1.40 Princess of Wales ..	45	30
628	$1.80 Prince of Wales ..	55	40
629	$5 Prince and Princess of Wales in evening dress	1·50	1·75

143 Horse

1990. Chinese New Year ("Year of the Horse").

631	**143**	60 c. multicoloured ..	20	15
632	–	$1.40 multicoloured ..	45	35
633	–	$1.80 multicoloured ..	55	45
634	–	$5 multicoloured ..	1·40	1·50

DESIGNS: $1.40 to $5, Different horse designs.

144 Chinese Lobster Dish

1990. International Cuisine. Designs showing various dishes. Multicoloured.

636	60 c. Type **144**	20	15
637	70 c. Indian	25	15
638	$1.30 Chinese vegetables ..	40	35
639	$1.40 Thai	40	35
640	$1.80 Japanese	50	45
641	$5 French	1·40	1·50

145 Air Pollution and Clean Air

1990. U.N. World Environment Day. Mult.

642	60 c. Type **145**	20	15
643	$1.40 Noise pollution and music	45	30
644	$1.80 Polluted and clean water	50	40
645	$5 Litter on ground and in bin	1·40	1·50

146 Street Lamp and Des Voeux Road, 1890

1990. Centenary of Electricity Supply.

647	**146**	60 c. blk, bisstre & brn	30	10
648	–	$1.40 multicoloured ..	75	45
649	–	$1.80 black, bistre & bl	80	50
650	–	$5 multicoloured ..	2·00	2·25

DESIGNS: $1.40, Street lamp and "Jumbo" (floating restaurant), 1940; $1.80, Street lamp and pylon, 1960; $5 Street lamp and Hong Kong from harbour, 1980.

147 Christmas Tree and Skyscrapers

1990. Christmas. Multicoloured.

652	50 c. Type **147**	20	10
653	60 c. Dove with holly ..	20	15
654	$1.40 Firework display ..	40	30
655	$1.80 Father Christmas hat on skyscraper	45	40
656	$2 Children with Father Christmas	50	50
657	$5 Candy stick with bow and Hong Kong skyline	1·40	2·00

148 Ram

1991. Chinese New Year ("Year of the Ram").

658	**148**	60 c. multicoloured ..	20	10
659	–	$1.40 multicoloured ..	45	35
660	–	$1.80 multicoloured ..	55	50
661	–	$5 multicoloured ..	1·40	2·00

DESIGNS: $1.40 to $5, Different ram designs.

149 Letter "A", Clock, Teddy Bear and Building Bricks (Kindergarten)

1991. Education. Multicoloured.

663	80 c. Type **149**	30	15
664	$1.80 Globe, laboratory flask and mathematical symbols (Primary and Secondary)	60	40
665	$2.30 Machinery (Vocational)	75	65
666	$5 Mortar board, computer and books (Tertiary) ..	1·75	2·50

150 Rickshaw

1991. 100 Years of Public Transport. Mult.

667	80 c. Type **150**	20	15
668	90 c. Double-decker bus ..	20	20
669	$1.70 Harbour ferry ..	50	55
670	$1.80 Tram	50	55
671	$2.30 Mass Transit Railway train	75	85
672	$5 Jetfoil	1·50	2·00

151 Victorian Pillar Box and Cover of 1888

1991. 150th Anniv of Hong Kong Post Office. Multicoloured.

673	80 c. Type **151**	20	15
674	$1.70 Edwardian pillar box and cover	50	50
675	$1.80 King George V pillar box and cover of 1935 ..	50	50
676	$2.30 King George VI pillar box and cover of 1938 ..	65	75
677	$5 Queen Elizabeth II pillar box and cover of 1989	1·40	1·75

152 Bronze Buddha, Lantau Island

1991. Landmarks.

679	**152**	80 c. red and black ..	30	15
680	–	$1.70 green and black	70	60
681	–	$1.80 violet and black	70	60
682	–	$2.30 blue and black ..	85	85
683	–	$5 orange and black ..	1·50	2·00

DESIGNS: $1.70, Peak Pavilion; $1.80, Clock Tower; $2.30, Catholic Cathedral; $5 Wong Tai Sin Temple.

153 Monkey

1992. Chinese New Year ("Year of the Monkey").

686	**153**	80 c. multicoloured ..	20	15
687	–	$1.80 multicoloured ..	45	40
688	–	$2.30 multicoloured ..	60	60
689	–	$5 multicoloured ..	1·50	2·00

DESIGNS: $1.40 to $5, Different monkey designs.

1992. 40th Anniv of Queen Elizabeth II's Accession. As T **143** of Ascension. Mult.

691	80 c. Royal barge in Hong Kong harbour	20	15
692	$1.70 Queen watching dancing display ..	45	35
693	$1.80 Fireworks display ..	45	35
694	$2.30 Three portraits of Queen Elizabeth ..	60	60
695	$5 Queen Elizabeth II ..	1·50	1·75

154 Running

1992. Olympic Games, Barcelona. Mult.

696	80 c. Type **154**	25	20
697	$1.80 Swimming and javelin	55	55
698	$2.30 Cycling	75	85
699	$5 High jump	1·25	1·50

155 Queen Elizabeth II

157 Principal Male Character

156 Stamps and Perforation Gauge

1992.

702	155	10 c. mauve, black and cerise ..	10	10
702a		20 c. blk, indigo & bl	10	10
703		50 c. red, black & yell	10	10
704		60 c. blue, blk & lt bl	10	10
705		70 c. mve, blk & lilac	10	10
706		80 c. mauve, blk & red	15	20
707		90 c. green, blk & grey	15	20
708		$1 brown, blk & yell	15	20
709		$1.20 vio, blk & lilac	20	25
709a		$1.30 blue, blk & orge	20	25
710		$1.70 blue, blk & lt bl	30	35
711		$1.80 mve, blk & grey	30	35
711a		$1.90 grn, blk & stone	30	35
712		$2 blue, black & green	35	40
713		$2.30 brn, blk & pink	40	45
713a		$2.40 blue, blk & grey	40	45
714		$5 green, blk & lt grn	85	90
715		$10 brn, blk & lt brn	1·75	1·90
716		$20 red, black & orge	3·50	3·75
717		$50 deep grey, black and grey	8·50	8·75

Nos. 715/17 are larger, 26 × 30 mm.

1992. Stamp Collecting. Multicoloured.

718	80 c. Type **156**	30	20
719	$1.80 Handstamp of 1841, 1891 Jubilee overprint and tweezers	60	55
720	$2.30 Stamps of 1946 and 1949 under magnifying glass	75	70
721	$5 2 c. of 1862 and watermark detector ..	1·50	1·75

1992. Chinese Opera. Multicoloured.

724	80 c. Type **157**	25	20
725	$1.80 Martial character ..	50	45
726	$2.30 Principal female character	70	60
727	$5 Comic character ..	1·50	1·75

158 Hearts

1992. Greetings Stamps. Multicoloured.

728	80 c. Type **158**	25	20
729	$1.80 Stars	45	40
730	$2.30 Presents	65	65
731	$5 Balloons	1·40	1·50

159 Cockerel

1993. Chinese New Year ("Year of the Cock").

732	159	80 c. multicoloured ..	25	20
733	–	$1.80 multicoloured ..	55	45
734	–	$2.30 multicoloured ..	75	70
735	–	$5 multicoloured ..	1·75	2·00

DESIGNS: $1.80 to $5, Different cock designs.

160 Pipa

1993. Chinese String Musical Instruments. Multicoloured.

737	80 c. Type **160**	25	20
738	$1.80 Erhu	45	45
739	$2.30 Ruan	60	60
740	$5 Gehu	1·40	1·60

161 Hong Kong in 1954

1993. 40th Anniv of Coronation. Mult.

741	80 c. Type **161**	25	20
742	$1.80 Hong Kong in 1963	40	40
743	$2.30 Hong Kong in 1975	55	60
744	$5 Hong Kong in 1992 ..	1·25	1·60

162 University of Science and Technology Building and Student

1993. Hong Kong's Contribution to Science and Technology. Multicoloured.

747	80 c. Type **162**	25	20
748	$1.80 Science Museum building and energy machine exhibit ..	40	40
749	$2.30 Governor's award and circuit board ..	55	60
750	$5 Dish aerials and world map	1·25	1·60

163 Red Calico Egg-fish

1993. Goldfish. Multicoloured.

752	$1 Type **163**	25	20
753	$1.90 Red cap oranda ..	45	45
754	$2.40 Red and white fringetail	60	60
755	$5 Black and gold dragon-eye	1·40	1·60

164 Dog

1994. Chinese New Year ("Year of the Dog").

766	164	$1 multicoloured ..	15	20
767	–	$1.90 multicoloured ..	30	35
768	–	$2.40 multicoloured ..	40	45
769	–	$5 multicoloured ..	85	90

DESIGNS: $1.90 to $5, Different dog designs.

165 Modern Police Constables on Traffic Duty

1994. 150th Anniv of Royal Hong Kong Police Force. Multicoloured.

772	$1 Type **165**	15	20
773	$1.20 Marine policeman with binoculars ..	20	25
774	$1.90 Police uniforms of 1950	30	35
775	$2 Tactical firearms unit officer with sub-machine gun	35	40
776	$2.40 Early 20th-century police uniforms ..	40	45
777	$5 Sikh and Chinese constables of 1900 ..	85	90

POSTAGE DUE STAMPS

D 1. Post Office Scales.

1923.

D 1b	D 1.	1 c. brown	15	70
D 2a		2 c. green	9·00	4·75
D 6a		2 c. grey	70	9·50
D 3		4 c. red	22·00	6·00
D 7a		4 c. orange	2·00	8·00
D 18		5 c. red (21 × 18 mm.)	1·25	4·50
D 4		6 c. yellow	23·00	13·00
D 8		6 c. red	8·00	6·50
D 9		8 c. brown	4·50	28·00
D 5		10 c. blue	19·00	7·50
D 15		10 c. violet	1·50	3·25
D 16		20 c. black	2·75	3·25
D 22		50 c. blue	3·00	9·50

1976. As Type **D 1** but smaller design (21 × 17 mm) with redrawn value.

D 25a.	D 1.	10 c. violet	20	1·25
D 26a.		20 c. grey	25	1·50
D 27a.		50 c. blue	50	2·00
D 28a.		$1 yellow	40	2·50

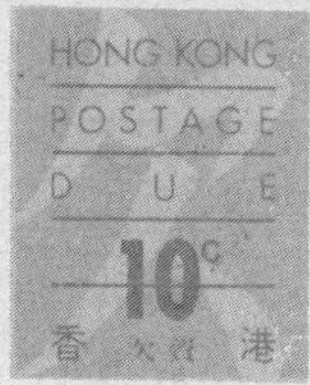

D 2.

1987.

D 31.	D 2.	10 c. green	10	10
D 32.		20 c. brown	10	10
D 33.		50 c. violet	10	10
D 34.		$1 orange	15	20
D 35.		$5 blue	80	85
D 36.		$10 red	1·60	1·75

JAPANESE OCCUPATION OF HONG KONG

100 sen = 1 yen.

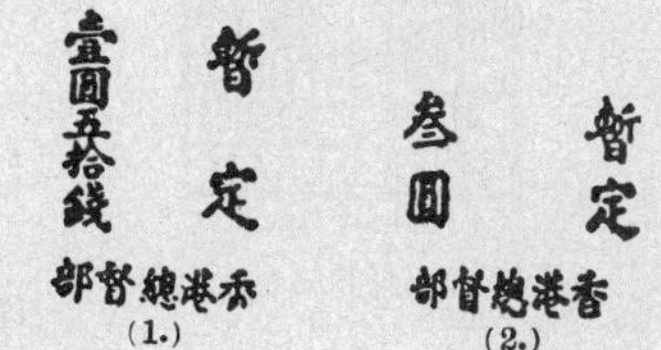

暫定 壹圓五拾錢 香港總督部 (1.)

暫定 叁圓 香港總督部 (2.)

1945. Stamps of Japan surch as T **1** (No. J1) or T **2**.

J1	126	1.50 yen on 1 s. brown	20·00	18·00
J2	84	3 yen on 2 s. red ..	12·00	15·00
J3	–	5 yen on 5 s. red (No. 396)	£425	90·00

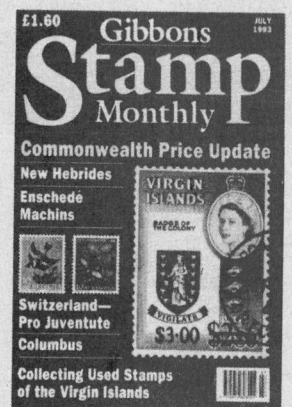

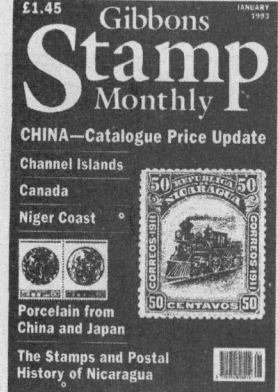

HYDERABAD

A state in India. Now uses Indian stamps.

12 pies = 1 anna; 16 annas = 1 rupee.

1.

1869.

1.	1.	1 a. green	9·00	6·00

2.

3.

1870.

2.	2.	½ a. brown	4·00	4·00
3.		2 a. green	38·00	35·00

1871.

13	3	½a. brown	40	10
13b		½a. red	40	10
14		1 a. purple	2·25	2·75
14b		1 a. brown	30	10
14c		1 a. black	40	10
15		2 a. green	85	10
16b		3 a. brown	45	60
17b		4 a. grey	1·50	1·00
17c		4 a. green	1·75	85
18		8 a. brown	1·25	1·40
19		12 a. blue	2·50	2·75
19a		12 a. green	2·00	2·50

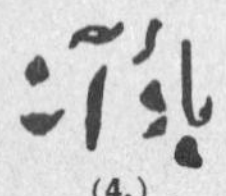

(4.)

1898. Surch. with T **4.**

20.	3.	¼ a. on ½ a. brown	50	75

5.

6.

1900.

21.	5.	¼ a. blue	3·00	1·90

1905.

22.	6.	¼ a. blue	1·25	30
32.		¼ a. grey	30	10
33.		¼ a. purple	30	10
23b.		½ a. red	1·50	25
34.		½ a. green	40	10
26.		1 a. red	1·00	10
27.		2 a. lilac	75	10
28.		3 a. orange	85	40
29.		4 a. green	90	25
30.		8 a. purple	1·10	30
31.		12 a. green	3·00	90

8. Symbol. 9.

1915.

35.	8.	½ a. green	60	10
58.		½ a. red	60	50
36.		1 a. red	75	10
37.	9.	1 r. yellow	9·00	11·00

(10.)

1930. Surch as T **10.**

38.	6.	4 p. on ¼ a. grey	40·00	13·00
39.		4 p. on ¼ a. purple	15	10
40.	8.	8 p. on ½ a. green	15	10

12. Symbols.

13. The Char Minar.

1931.

60.	12.	2 p. brown	1·00	1·10
41.		4 p. black	20	10
59.		6 p. red	3·50	2·75
42.		8 p. green	30	10
43.	13.	1 a. brown	20	10
44.	–	2 a. violet	1·25	10
45.	–	4 a. blue	1·00	15
46.	–	8 a. orange	2·25	1·25
47.	–	12 a. red	3·25	6·00
48.	–	1 r. yellow	3·00	2·50

In No. 59 "POSTAGE" is at foot.

DESIGNS—(Approx. 32½ × 21) HORIZ. 2 a. High Court of Justice. 4 a. Osman Sagar Reservoir. 12 a. Bidar College. VERT. 8 a. Entrance to Ajanta Caves. 1 r. Victory Tower, Daulatabad.

15. Unani General Hospital.

1937. Inscr. "H.E.H. THE NIZAM'S SILVER JUBILEE".

49.	15.	4 p. slate and violet	20	30
50.	–	8 p. slate and brown	25	45
51.	–	1 a. slate and yellow	40	30
52.	–	2 a. slate and green	60	1·40

DESIGNS: 8 p. Osmania General Hospital. 1 a. Osmania University. 2 a. Osmania Jubilee Hall.

16. Family Reunion.

1945. Victory Commemoration.

53.	16.	1 a. blue	10	10

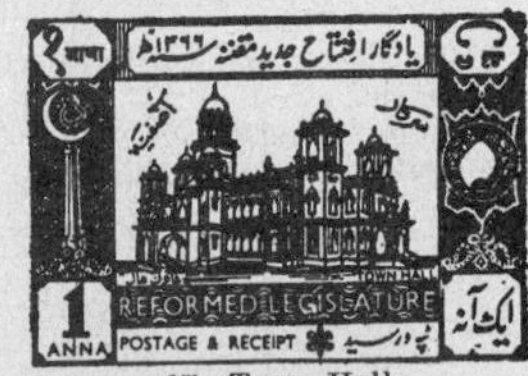

17. Town Hall.

1947. Reformed Legislature.

54.	17.	1 a. black	40	40

18. Power House, Hyderabad.

1947. Inscr. as in T 18.

55.	18.	1 a. 4 p. green	45	70
56.	–	3 a. blue	50	1·00
57.	–	6 a. brown	3·00	6·50

DESIGNS—HORIZ. 3 a. Kaktyai Arch, Warangal Fort. 6 a. Golkunda Fort.

OFFICIAL STAMPS

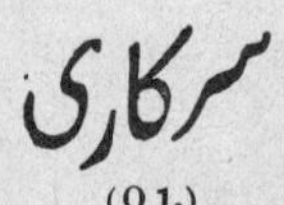

(O 1.)

1873. Optd. with Type O **1.**

O 2.	2.	½ a. brown	—	£160
O 1.	1.	1 a. green	38·00	17·00
O 3.	2.	2 a. olive	—	95·00

1873. Optd. with Type O **1.**

O 9	3	½a. brown	2·75	1·25
O11		1 a. brown	35·00	25·00
O12		1 a. drab	1·25	1·00
O19		1 a. black	35·00	10
O13		2 a. green	2·25	2·75
O20d		3 a. brown	2·00	70
O15		4 a. grey	5·50	5·50
O20e		4 a. green	—	3·25
O16		8 a. brown	18·00	13·00
O17		12 a. blue	21·00	35·00
O20g		12 a. green	—	48·00

1909. Optd. as Type O **1**, or similar smaller opt.

O30	6	¼ a. grey	45	20
O31		¼ a. lilac	70	10
O21a		½ a. red	55·00	15
O33		½ a. green	70	10
O40	8	½ a. green	90	10
O54		½ a. red	8·00	4·25
O34	6	1 a. red	75	10
O41e	8	1 a. red	60	10
O35	6	2 a. lilac	85	15
O36		3 a. orange	6·00	1·25
O37		4 a. green	1·50	10
O38		8 a. purple	2·50	20
O39		12 a. green	5·00	30

1930. Official stamps surch as T **10**.

O 42.	6.	4 p. on ¼ a. grey	£120	17·00
O 43.		4 p. on ¼ a. lilac	60	10
O 45.		8 p. on ½ a. green	35·00	45·00
O 44.	8.	8 p. on ½ a. green	55	10

1934. Optd as Type O **1** but smaller.

O 55.	12.	2 p. brown	6·50	4·75
O 46.		4 p. black	70	10
O 56.		6 p. red	7·50	12·00
O 47.		8 p. green	35	10
O 48.	13.	1 a. brown	45	10
O 49.	–	2 a. violet (No. 44)	2·50	10
O 50.	–	4 a. blue (No. 45)	1·25	15
O 51.	–	8 a. orange (No. 46)	6·50	50
O 52.	–	12 a. red (No. 47)	4·75	1·25
O 53.	–	1 r. yellow (No. 48)	8·00	2·00

IDAR

A State in Western India. Now uses Indian stamps.

12 pies = 1 anna; 16 annas = 1 rupee.

1. Maharaja Shri Himatsinhji. 2.

1939.

1b	1.	½ a. green	6·50	13·00

1944.

3.	2.	½ a. green	1·00	30·00
4.		1 a. violet	1·00	30·00
5.		2 a .blue	1·25	42·00
6.		4 a. red	2·50	48·00

INDIA

A peninsula in the S. of Asia. Formerly consisted of British India and numerous Native States, some of which issued stamps of their own. Divided in 1947 into the Dominion of India and the Dominion of Pakistan. Now a republic within the British Commonwealth.

1852. 12 pies = 1 anna; 16 annas = 1 rupee.
1957. 100 naye paise = 1 rupee.
1964. 100 paisa = 1 rupee.

1.

1852. "Scinde Dawk". Imperf.

S 1.	1.	½ a. white	£4250	£800
S 2.		½ a. blue	£10000	£3250
S 3.		½ a. red	—	£7000

3.

10.

9.

11.

1854. Imperf.

1.	3.	½ a. red	£800	
2.		½ a. blue	45·00	12·00
14.		1 a. red	40·00	35·00
31.	10.	2 a. green	85·00	22·00
23.	9.	4 a. blue and red	£1900	£225

1855. Perf.

75	11	½ a. blue	2·00	30
59		1 a. brown	2·50	30
41		2 a. pink	£250	14·00
63		2 a. orange	18·00	2·75
46		4 a. black	90·00	4·75
64		4 a. green	£225	18·00
73		8 a. red	17·00	4·00

12.

1860. Inscr. "EAST INDIA POSTAGE". Various Frames.

57	12.	8 p. mauve	6·00	7·00
77	–	9 p. lilac	7·50	7·50
71	–	4 a. green	11·00	70
81	–	6 a. brown	5·00	1·50
72	–	6 a. 8 p. grey	24·00	18·00
82	–	12 a. brown	6·00	14·00
79	–	1 r. grey	26·00	14·00

14.

23.

1866. Optd. **POSTAGE.**

66.	14.	6 a. purple	£500	£110

1882. Inscr. "INDIA POSTAGE". Various frames.

84.	23.	½ a. turquoise	2·25	10
86.	–	9 p. red	50	1·50
88.	–	1 a. purple	2·25	10
90.	–	1 a. 6 brown	50	70
91.	–	2 a. blue	2·75	20
94.	–	3 a. orange	5·00	45
96.	–	4 a. green	8·50	30
97.	–	4 a. 6 p. green	11·00	5·00
98.	–	8 a. mauve	14·00	2·00
100.	–	12 a. purple on red	5·50	2·00
101.	–	1 r. grey	12·00	5·00

1891. No. 97 surch. **2½ As.**

102.		2½ a. on 4½ a. green	1·60	60

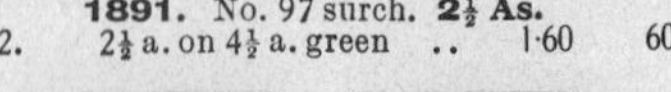

40.

37.

38.

1892. As 1882 and some new designs.

111	**40.**	3 p. red	10	10
112		3 p. grey	20	55
113	**23.**	½a. green	60	35
115	–	1 a. red	60	15
116	–	2 a. lilac	3·25	50
103	–	2½ a. green	1·00	40
118	–	2½ a. blue	3·25	3·75
106	**37.**	1 r. green and red ..	6·50	2·00
107	**38.**	2 r. red and orange ..	35·00	11·00
108		3 r. brown and green ..	25·00	10·00
109		5 r. blue and violet ..	32·00	22·00

1898. Surch. ¼.

110.	**23.**	"¼" on ½ a. turquoise	10	30

41.

52.

1902. As 1882 and 1892, but portrait of King Edward VII (inscribed "INDIA POSTAGE").

120	**41**	3 p. grey	60	10
121	–	½ a. green	40	10
123	–	1 a. red	50	10
125	–	2 a. lilac	1·50	10
126	–	2½ a. blue	3·25	20
127	–	3 a. orange	3·25	20
128	–	4 a. green	3·00	30
132	–	6 a. bistre	10·00	4·25
133	–	8 a. purple	7·50	1·00
135	–	12 a. purple on red ..	7·50	2·00
136	–	1 r. green and red ..	6·50	70
139	**52**	2 r. red and orange ..	27·00	3·25
140		3 r. brown and green ..	21·00	19·00
142		5 r. blue and violet ..	50·00	35·00
144		10 r. green and red ..	80·00	20·00
146		15 r. blue and brown ..	£130	42·00
147		25 r. orange and blue ..	£750	£800

1905. No. 122 surch. ¼.

148.		"¼" on ½ a. green ..	40	10

1906. As Nos. 122 and 123, but inscr. "INDIA POSTAGE & REVENUE".

149.	½ a. green	1·50	10
150.	1 a. red	90	10

55.

56.

57.

58.

59.

70.

60.

61.

62.

63.

71.

64.

65.

66.

67.

1911.

* Two types of 1½ a. brown. Type A as illustrated. Type B inscr. "1½ As. ONE AND A HALF ANNAS".

152	**55.**	3 p. grey	30	15
155	**56.**	½ a. green	35	10
161	**57.**	1 a. red	1·25	10
197		1 a. brown	35	10
163	**58.**	1½ a. brown (A)* ..	1·60	30
165		1½ a. brown (B)* ..	1·75	2·50
198		1½ a. red (B)*	90	30
166	**59.**	2 a. lilac	1·25	15
206	**70.**	2 a. lilac	90	10
170	**60.**	2½ a. blue	1·75	2·25
171	**61.**	2½ a. blue	1·10	20
207		2½ a. orange	90	10
173	**62.**	3 a. orange	2·50	20
209		3 a. blue	4·50	10
210	**63.**	4 a. olive	1·50	10
211	**71.**	4 a. green	5·50	10
176	**64.**	6 a. bistre	3·75	90
212	**65.**	8 a. mauve	4·00	10
213	**66.**	12 a. red	5·00	20
214	**67.**	1 r. brown and green ..	5·00	30
215		2 r. red and orange ..	8·00	45
216		5 r. blue and violet ..	20·00	1·25
217		10 r. green and red ..	35·00	2·25
218		15 r. blue and olive ..	24·00	24·00
219		25 r. orange and blue ..	90·00	24·00

See also Nos. 232, etc.

1921. Surch. **NINE PIES** and bar.

192.	**57.**	9 p. on 1 a. red	40	20

1922. Surch. ¼.

195.	**56.**	"¼" on ½ a. green ..	30	30

72. D.H. "Hercules".

1929. Air.

220.	**72.**	2 a. green	1·50	50
221.		3 a. blue	1·00	1·25
222.		4 a. olive	2·25	65
223.		6 a. bistre	2·25	90
224.		8 a. purple	2·50	1·00
225.		12 a. red	7·50	4·00

73. Purana Qila.

1931. Inscr. as in T **73.**

226.	**73.**	¼ a. green and orange ..	1·10	1·40
227.	–	½ a. violet and green ..	1·00	40
228.	–	1 a. mauve and brown	1·00	20
229.	–	2 a. green and blue ..	1·50	1·00
230.	–	3 a. brown and red ..	2·50	2·50
231.	–	1 r. violet and green ..	5·50	15·00

DESIGNS: ½ a. War Memorial Arch. 1 a. Council House. 2 a. Viceroy's House. 3 a. Secretariat. 1 r. Dominion Columns and Secretariat.

79.

80.

81.

82.

83.

1932.

232	**79**	½ a. green	35	10
233	**80**	9 p. green	30	10
234	**81**	1 a. brown	1·50	10
235	**82**	1¼ a. mauve	30	10
236	**70**	2 a. red	8·00	3·50
236a	**59**	2 a. red	3·75	50
237	**62**	3 a. red	1·25	10
238	**83**	3½ a. blue	1·25	10

84. Gateway of India, Bombay.

1935. Silver Jubilee.

240.	**84.**	½ a. black and green ..	45	10
241.	–	9 p. black and green ..	45	10
242.	–	1 a. black and brown ..	45	10
243.	–	1¼ a. black and violet ..	45	10
244.	–	2½ a. black and orange ..	75	65
245.	–	3½ a. black and blue ..	2·50	1·75
246.	–	8 a. black and purple ..	2·50	2·25

DESIGNS: 9 p. Victoria Memorial, Calcutta. 1 a. Rameswaram Temple, Madras. 1¼ a. Jain Temple, Calcutta. 2½ a. Taj Mahal, Agra. 3½ a. Golden Temple, Amritsar. 8 a. Pagoda in Mandalay.

91. King George VI.

DESIGNS—As Type **92.** 2½ a. Bullock cart. 3 a. Tonga. 3½ a. Camel. 4 a. Mail train. 6 a. Mail steamer. 8 a. Mail lorry. 12 a. Mail 'plane.

92. Dak Runner.

93. King George VI.

1937.

247.	**91.**	3 p. slate	40	10
248.		½ a. brown	40	10
249.		9 p. green	3·25	20
250.		1 a. red	15	10
251.	**92.**	2 a. red	1·75	20
252.	–	2½ a. violet	60	10
253.	–	3 a. green	3·75	20
254.	–	3½ a. blue	2·25	50
255.	–	4 a. brown	12·00	10
256.	–	6 a. blue	11·00	50
257.	–	8 a. violet	6·50	30
258.	–	12 a. red	18·00	70
259.	**93.**	1 r. slate and brown ..	1·00	15
260.		2 r. purple and brown	3·75	20
261.		5 r. green and blue ..	15·00	40
262.		10 r. purple and red ..	15·00	60
263.		15 r. brown and green	60·00	55·00
264.		25 r. slate and purple	70·00	14·00

100a. King George VI. 101.

102. King George VI.

1940.

265.	**100a.**	3 p. slate	25	10
266.		½ a. mauve	40	10
267.		9 p. green	40	10
268.		1 a. red	40	10
269.	**101.**	1 a. 3 p. yell.-brn. ..	75	10
269a.		1½ a. violet	40	10
270.		2 a. red	45	10
271.		3 a. violet	70	10
272.		3½ a. blue	70	10
273.	**102.**	4 a. brown	45	10
274.		6 a. green	80	10
275.		8 a. violet	1·50	30
276.		12 a. purple ..	2·50	40
277.		14 a. purple ..	14·00	65

No. 277 is as No. 258, but with large head.

105. "Victory" and King George VI.

1946. Victory Commem.

278.	**105.**	9 p. green	25	10
279.		1½ a. purple	25	10
280.		3½ a. blue	75	60
281.		12 a. red	1·50	55

1946. Surch. **3 PIES** and bars.

282.	**101.**	3 p. on 1 a. 3 p. yellow-brown ..	10	10

DOMINION OF INDIA

303. Douglas DC 4.

1947. Independence. Inscr. "Long Live India" and "15TH AUG 1947".

301.	–	1½ a. green	15	10
302.	–	3½ a. red, blue & green	30	35
303.	**303.**	12 a. blue	1·25	1·50

DESIGNS—VERT. 1½ a. Asokan Capital. HORIZ. 3½ a. Indian National Flag.

1948. Air. Inauguration of India–Britain Service. As T **303,** but showing Lockheed Constellation flying in opposite direction and inscr. "AIR INDIA INTERNATIONAL FIRST FLIGHT 8TH JUNE 1948".

304.	**303.**	12 a. black and blue	1·00	1·25

305. Mahatma Gandhi.

The 10 r. depicts a profile portrait of Mahatma Gandhi and is larger (22½ × 37 mm.).

1948. 1st Anniv. of Indian Independence.

305.	**305.**	1½ a. brown	1·75	30
306.	–	3½ a. violet	4·00	1·25
307.	–	12 a. green	5·50	60
308.	–	10 r. brown & red ..	55·00	40·00

307. Ajanta Panel.

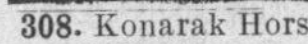

308. Konarak Horse.

314. Bhuvanesvara.

315. Gol Gumbad, Bijapur.

319. Red Fort, Delhi.

322. Satrunjaya Temple, Palitana.

1949.

309.	**307.**	3 p. violet	15	10
310.	**308.**	6 p. brown	25	10
311.	–	9 p. green	40	10
312.	–	1 a. blue (A)	60	10
333.	–	1 a. blue (B)	2·50	10
313.	–	2 a. red	80	10
333a.	–	2½ a. lake	2·25	1·50
314.	–	3 a. salmon	1·50	10
315.	–	3½ a. blue	3·00	2·50
316.	**314.**	4 a. lake	5·00	10
333b.		4 a. blue	5·25	10
317.	**315.**	6 a. violet	2·00	10
318.	–	8 a. green	2·00	10
319.	–	12 a. blue	1·75	10
320.	–	1 r. violet and green ..	9·00	10
321.	**319.**	2 r. red and violet ..	9·50	15
322.	–	5 r. green and brown ..	26·00	70
323.	–	10 r. brown and blue ..	35·00	3·75
324.	**322.**	15 r. brown and red ..	13·00	15·00

1 anna: (A) Left arm of statue outstretched (B) Reversed—right arm outstretched.

DESIGNS—As Type **307**: 9 p. Trimurti. 1 a. Bodhisattva. 2 a. Nataraja. As Type **314**: 2½ a., 3½ a. Bodh Gaya Temple. 3 a. Sanchi Stupa, East Gate. As Type **315**: 8 a. Kandarya Mahadeva Temple. 12 a. Golden Temple, Amritsar. As Type **319**—VERT. 1 r. Victory Tower, Chittorgarh. 10 r. Qutb Minar, Delhi. HORIZ. 5 r. Taj Mahal, Agra.

323. Globe and Asokan Capital.

1949. 75th Anniv. of U.P.U.

325.	**323.**	9 p. green	1·00	75
326.		2 a. red	1·25	1·25
327.		3½ a. blue	2·00	2·25
328.		12 a. red	3·50	2·50

REPUBLIC OF INDIA

324. Rejoicing Crowds.

1950. Inauguration of Republic.

329.	**324.**	2 a. red	1·00	15
330.	–	3½ a. blue	1·75	2·75
331.	–	4 a. violet	1·75	40
332.	–	12 a. purple	3·75	2·25

DESIGNS—VERT. 3½ a. Quill, ink-well and verse. HORIZ. 4. a Ear of corn and plough. 12 a. Spinning-wheel and cloth.

329. " Stegodon Ganesa ".

1951. Centenary of Geological Survey.

334.	**329.**	2 a. black and red ..	1·50	15

330. Torch. 331. Kabir.

1951. 1st Asian Games, New Delhi.

335.	**330.**	2 a. purple and orange	1·00	30
336.	–	12 a. brown and blue	5·00	90

1952. Indian Saints and Poets.

337.	**331.**	9 p. green	30	20
338.	–	1 a. red (Tulsidas) ..	30	10
339.	–	2 a. orange (Meera) ..	60	10
340.	–	4 a. blue (Surdas) ..	1·25	30
341.	–	4½ a. mauve (Ghalib)	30	30
342.	–	12 a. brown (Tagore)	1·50	60

332. Locomotives in 1853 and 1953.

1953. Centenary of Indian Railways.

343.	**332.**	2 a. black	60	10

333. Mount Everest.

1953. Conquest of Mount Everest.

344.	**333.**	2 a. violet	50	10
345.		14 a. brown	3·00	25

334. Telegraph Poles of 1851 and 1951.

1953. Centenary of Indian Telegraphs.

346.	**334.**	2 a. green	30	10
347.		12 a. blue	3·00	40

335. Postal Transport, 1854.

1954. Indian Stamp Centenary.

348.	**335.**	1 a. purple	30	20
349.	–	2 a. mauve	30	10
350.	–	4 a. brown	2·50	30
351.	–	14 a. blue	1·50	40

DESIGNS: 2 a., 14 a. Dove and Aeroplane. 4 a., Ship, cyclist, aeroplane and train.

338. U.N. Emblem and Lotus.

1954. U.N. Day.

352.	**338.**	2 a. turquoise ..	40	20

339. Forest Research Institute.

1954. 4th World Forestry Congress, Dehra Dun.

353.	**339.**	2 a. blue	20	10

340. Tractor. 344. Woman Spinning.

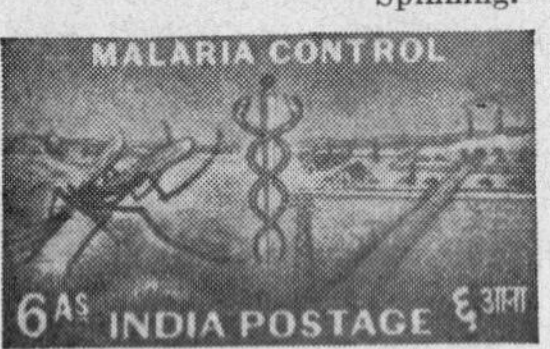

347. "Malaria Control" (Mosquito and Staff of Aesculapius).

1955. India's Five Year Plan.

354	**340.**	3 p. mauve	30	10
355	–	6 p. violet	30	10
356	–	9 p. brown	40	10
357	–	1 a. green	45	10
358	**344.**	2 a. blue	30	10
359	–	3 a. green	50	10
360	–	4 a. red	50	10
361	**347.**	6 a. brown	1·50	10
362	–	8 a. blue	5·00	10
363	–	10 a. turquoise ..	80	70
364	–	12 a. blue	50	10
365	–	14 a. green	1·50	20
413	–	1 r. myrtle	3·50	10
367	–	1 r. 2 a. grey	1·75	2·75
368	–	1 r. 8 a. purple ..	7·00	3·50
369	–	2 r. mauve	4·25	10
415	–	5 r. brown	9·00	30
371	–	10 r. orange	14·00	3·00

DESIGNS—As Type **340**: 6 p. Power loom. 9 p. Bullock-driven well. 1 a. Damodar Valley Dam. 4 a. Bullocks. 8 a. Chittarajan Locomotive Works. 12 a. Hindustan Aircraft Factory, Bangalore. 1 r. Telephone engineer. 2 r. Rare Earth Factory, Alwaye. 5 r. Sindri Fertiliser Factory. 10 r. Steel plant. As Type **344**: 3 a. Woman hand-weaving. As Type **347**: 10 a. Aeroplane over Marine Drive, Bombay. 14 a. Aeroplane over Kashmir landscape. 1 r. 2 a. Aeroplane over Cape Comorin. 1 r. 8 a. Aeroplane over Mt. Kangchenjunga.

358. Bodhi Tree.

1956. Buddha Jayanti.

372.	**358.**	2 a. sepia	50	10
373.	–	14 a. red	3·25	3·00

DESIGN—HORIZ. 14 a. Round parasol and Bodhi tree.

360. Lokmanya Bal Gangadhar Tilak. 361. Map of India.

1956. Birth Cent. of Tilak (journalist).

374.	**360.**	2 a. brown	10	10

1957. Value in naye paise.

375	**361.**	1 n.p. green	10	10
376		2 n.p. brown	10	10
377		3 n.p. brown	10	10
402		5 n.p. green	10	10
379		6 n.p. grey	10	10
404		8 n.p. turquoise ..	60	10
405		10 n.p. myrtle ..	15	10
381		13 n.p. red	30	10
407		15 n.p. violet	60	10
408		20 n.p. blue	30	10
409		25 n.p. blue	30	10
410		50 n.p. orange ..	30	10
411		75 n.p. purple	40	10
385a		90 n.p. purple	80	75

362. The Rani of Jhansi.

363. Shrine.

1957. Centenary of Indian Mutiny.

386.	**362.**	15 n.p. brown ..	15	10
387.	**363.**	90 n.p. purple ..	1·50	40

364. Henri Dunant and Conference Emblem.

1957. 19th Int. Red Cross Conf., New Delhi.

388.	**364.**	15 n.p. grey and red ..	10	10

365. " Nutrition ".

DESIGNS—HORIZ. 15 n.p. " Education ". VERT. 90 n.p. " Recreation ".

1957. Children's Day.

389.	**365.**	8 n.p. purple	10	15
390.	–	15 n.p. turquoise ..	10	10
391.	–	90 n.p. brown ..	25	15

369. Calcutta University.

DESIGNS—VERT. No. 392, Bombay University. As Type **369**.—HORIZ. No. 394, Madras University.

1957. Centenary of Indian Universities.

392.	–	10 n.p. violet (21½ × 38 mm.)	15	15
393.	**369.**	10 n.p. grey	15	15
394.	–	10 n.p. brown	20	15

371. J. N. Tata (founder) and Steel Plant.

1958. 50th Anniv. of Steel Industry.
395. **371.** 15 n.p. red 10 10

372. Dr. D. K. Karve.

1958. Birth Cent. of Karve (educationist).
396. **372.** 15 n.p. brown .. 10 10

373. "Wapiti" and "Hunter" Aircraft.

1958. Silver Jubilee of Indian Air Force.
397. **373.** 15 n.p. blue 75 10
398. 90 n.p. blue .. .. 1·00 1·25

375. Bilpin Chandra Pal.

376. Nurse with Child Patient.

1958. Birth Centenary of Pal (patriot).
418. **375.** 15 n.p. green 10 10

1958. Children's Day.
419. **376.** 15 n.p. violet 10 10

377. Jagadish Chandra Bose.

1958. Birth Cent. of Bose (botanist).
420. **377.** 15 n.p. turquoise .. 10 10

378. Exhibition Gate.

1958. India 1958 Exn., New Delhi.
421. **378.** 15 n.p. purple .. 10 10

379. Sir Jamsetjee Jejeebhoy.

381. Boys awaiting admission to Children's Home.

380. "The Triumph of Labour" (after Chowdhury).

1959. Death Centenary of Sir Jamsetjee Jejeebhoy (philanthropist).
422. **379.** 15 n.p. brown .. 10 10

1959. 40th Anniv. of I.L.O.
423. **380.** 5 n.p. green 10 10

1959. Children's Day.
424. **381.** 15 n.p. green 10 10

382. "Agriculture".

1959. 1st World Agriculture Fair, New Delhi.
425. **382.** 15 n.p. grey 10 10

383. Thiruvalluvar (philosopher).

1960. Thiruvalluvar Commem.
426. **383.** 15 n.p. purple .. 10 10

384. Yaksha pleading with the Cloud (from the "Meghaduta").

385. Shakuntala writing a letter to Dushyanta (from the "Shakuntala").

1960. Kalidasa (poet) Commem.
427. **384.** 15 n.p. grey 30 10
428. **385.** 1 r. 3 n.p. yell. & brn. 1·10 40

386. S. Bharati (poet).

387. Dr. M. Visvesvaraya.

1960. Subramania Bahrati Commem.
429. **386.** 15 n.p. blue 10 10

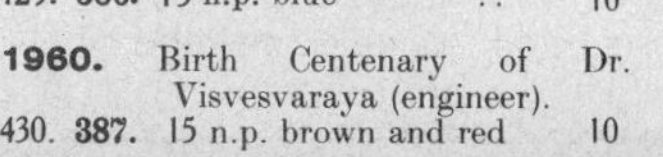

1960. Birth Centenary of Dr. M. Visvesvaraya (engineer).
430. **387.** 15 n.p. brown and red 10 10

388. "Children's Health".

1960. Children's Day.
431. **388.** 15 n.p. green 10 10

389. Children greeting U.N. Emblem.

1960. U.N.I.C.E.F. Day.
432. **389.** 15 n.p. brown & drab 10 10

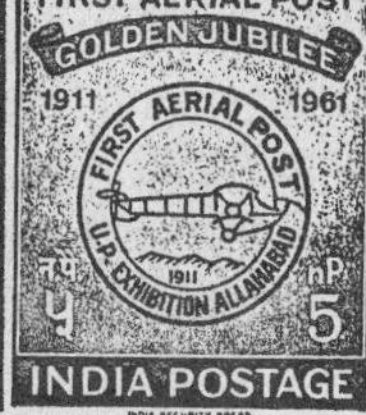

390. Tyagaraja.

391. "First Aerial Post" Cancellation.

392. "Air India" Boeing 707 Jetliner and Humber-Sommer 'Plane.

1961. 114th Death Anniv of Tyagaraja (musician).
433. **390.** 15 n.p. blue 10 10

1961. 50th Anniv. of 1st Official Airmail Flight, Allahabad-Naini.
434. **391.** 5 n.p. olive .. .. 1·10 30
435. **392.** 15 n.p. green and grey 1·10 30
436. – 1 r. purple and grey.. 3·75 1·25

Design—As Type **392**: 1 r. H. Pecquet flying Humber-Sommer 'plane, and "Aerial Post" cancellation.

394. Shivaji on Horseback.

1961. Chatrapati Shivaji (Maratha ruler) Commemoration.
437 **394** 15 n.p. brown and green 50 30

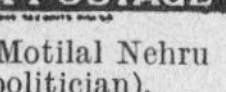

15 नये पै. nP
1861-1941
7 MAY 1961
INDIA POSTAGE

395. Motilal Nehru (politician).

396. Tagore (poet).

1961. Birth Cent. of Pandit Motilal Nehru.
438. **395.** 15 n.p. brn. & orge. .. 10 10

1961. Birth Cent. of Rabindranath Tagore.
439. **396.** 15 n.p. orge. and turq. 40 30

397. All India Radio Emblem and Transmitting Aerials.

1961. Silver Jubilee of All India Radio Broadcasting Service.
440. **397.** 15 n.p. blue 10 10

398. Ray.

399. Bhatkande.

1961. Birth Centenary of Prafulla Chandra Ray (social reformer).
441. **398.** 15 n.p. grey 10 20

1961. Birth Centenary (1960) of V. N. Bhatkande (composer).
442. **399.** 15 n.p. drab 10 10

400. Child at Lathe.

401. Fair Emblem and Main Gate.

1961. Children's Day.
443. **400.** 15 n.p. brown .. 10 20

1961. Indian Industries Fair, New Delhi.
444. **401.** 15 n.p. blue and red .. 10 10

402. Indian Forest.

403. Pitalkhora: Yaksha.

1961. Centenary of Scientific Forestry.
445. **402.** 15 n.p. green & brn... 20 20

1961. Cent. of Indian Archaeological Survey.
446. **403.** 15 n.p. brown .. 15 10
447. – 90 n.p. olive & brown 30 20

Design—horiz. 90 n.p. Kalibangan seal.

405. M. M. Malaviya.

406. Gauhati Refinery.

1961. Birth Centenary of Malaviya (educationist).
448. **405.** 15 n.p. slate 10 20

1962. Inaug. of Gauhati Oil Refinery.
449. **406.** 15 n.p. blue 20 20

PANCHAYATI RAJ

15 nP

INDIA POSTAGE

407. Bhikaiji Cama.

408. Village Panchayati at work and Parliament Building.

1962. Birth Centenary of Bhikaiji Cama (patriot).
450. **407.** 15 n.p. purple .. 10 10

1962. Inauguration of Panchayati System of Local Government.
451. **408.** 15 n.p. mauve .. 10 10

409. D. Saraswati (religious reformer).

410. G. S. Vidhyarthi (journalist).

1962. Dayanard Saraswati Commem.
452. **409.** 15 n.p. brown 10 10

1962. Ganesh Shankar Vidhyarthi Commem.
453. **410.** 15 n.p. brown .. 10 10

न.पै.15 nP
Dr. RAJENDRA PRASAD
PRESIDENT OF INDIA
1950-1962
INDIA POSTAGE

411. Malaria Eradication Emblem.

412. Dr. R. Prasad.

1962. Malaria Eradication.
454. **411.** 15 n.p. yellow and lake 10 10

1962. Retirement of President Dr. Rajendra Prasad.
455. **412.** 15 n.p. purple 15 10

413. Calcutta High Court.

1962. Centenary of Indian High Courts.
456. **413.** 15 n.p. green 20 20
457. – 15 n.p. brown (Madras) 20 20
458. – 15 n.p. slate (Bombay) 20 20

416. Ramabai Ranade.

1962. Birth Centenary of Ramabai Ranade (social reformer).
459. **416.** 15 n.p. orange .. 10 20

417. Indian Rhinoceros.

1962. Wild Life Week.
460. **417.** 15 n.p. brown and turq. 40 15
See also Nos. 472/6.

418. "Passing the Flag to Youth".

1962. Children's Day.
461. **418.** 15 n.p. red and green .. 15 20

419. Human Eye within Lotus Blossom.

1962. 19th Int. Ophthalmology Congress, New Delhi.
462. **419.** 15 n.p. brown 15 10

420. S. Ramanujan.

1962. 75th Birth Anniv of Srinivasa Ramanujan (mathematician).
463. **420.** 15 n.p. brown .. 40 30

421. S. Vivekananda.

423. Hands reaching for F.A.O. Emblem.

1963. Birth Cent. of Vivekananda (philosopher).
464. **421.** 15 n.p. brown and olive 15 20

1963. Surch.
465. **385.** 1 r. on 1 r. 3 n.p. yellow and brown .. 30 10

1963. Freedom from Hunger.
466. **423.** 15 n.p. blue .. .. 1·00 30

424. Henri Dunant (founder) and Centenary Emblem.

427. D. Naoroji (parliamentarian).

425. Artillery and Helicopter.

1963. Centenary of Red Cross.
467. **424.** 15 n.p. red and grey .. 2·00 30

1963. Defence Campaign.
468. **425.** 15 n.p. green 40 10
469. – 1 r. brown 70 65
DESIGN: 1 r. Sentry and parachutists.

1963. Dadabhoy Naoroji Commem.
470. **427.** 15 n.p. grey 10 10

428. Annie Besant (patriot and theosophist).

1963. Annie Besant Commem.
471 **428** 15 n.p. green 15 10
No. 471 is incorrectly dated "1837". Mrs Besant was born in 1847.

1963. Wild Life Preservation. **Animal** designs as T **417.**
472. 10 n.p. black and orange .. 75 1·50
473. 15 n.p. brown and green .. 1·50 60
474. 30 n.p. slate and ochre .. 3·75 1·50
475. 50 n.p. orange and green .. 3·00 80
476. 1 r. brown and blue .. 2·50 50
ANIMALS. As Type **417:** 10 n.p. Gaur. LARGER ($25\frac{1}{2} \times 35\frac{1}{2}$ mm.). 15 n.p. Lesser panda. 30 n.p. Indian elephant. ($35\frac{1}{2} \times 25\frac{1}{2}$ mm.): 50 n.p. Tiger 1 r. Lion.

434. "School Meals".

1963. Children's Day.
477. **434.** 15 n.p. bistre 10 10

435. Eleanor Roosevelt at Spinning-wheel.

1963. 15th Anniv. of Declaration of Human Rights.
478. **435.** 15 n.p. purple .. 10 15

436. Dipalakshmi (bronze).

1964. 26th Int. Orientalists Congress, New Delhi.
479. **436.** 15 n.p. blue 10 15

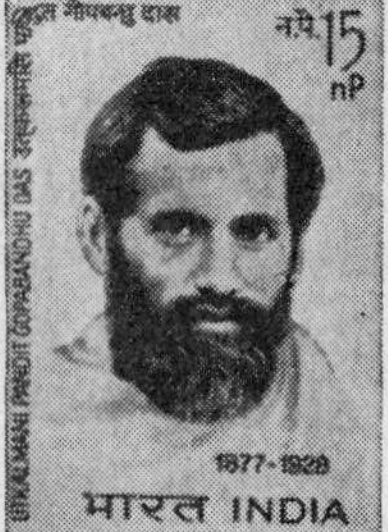

437. Gopabandhu Das (social reformer).

1964. Gopabandhu Das Commem.
480. **437.** 15 n.p. purple .. 10 10

438. Purandaradasa.

1964. 400th Death Anniv of Purandaradasa (composer).
481. **438.** 15 n.p. brown .. 15 10

439. S. C. Bose and I.N.A. Badge.

1964. 67th Birth Anniv. of Subhas Chandra Bose (nationalist). Inscr. "INA" on badge.
482. **439.** 15 n.p. olive 40 20
483. – 55 n.p. blk., orge & red 40 45
DESIGN: 55 n.p. Bose and Indian National Army.

15 KASTURBA GANDHI 1869-1944 भारत INDIA

441. Sarojini Naidu.

442. Kasturba Ghandi.

1964. 95th Birth Anniv of Sarojini Naidu (poetess).
484. **441.** 15 n.p. green & purple 10 10

1964. 20th Death Anniv. of Kasturba Ghandi.
485. **442.** 15 n.p. brown 10 10

443. Dr. W. M. Haffkine (immunologist).

1964. Haffkine Commem.
486. **443.** 15 n.p. brown on buff 10 10

444. Jawaharlal Nehru (statesman).

1964. Nehru Mourning Issue.
487. **444.** 15 p. slate 10 10

445. Sir Asutosh Mookerjee.

1964. Birth Centenary of Sir Asutosh Mookerjee (education reformer).
488. **445.** 15 p. brown and olive 10 10

446. Sri Aurobindo.

1964. 92nd Birth Anniv of Sri Aurobindo (religious teacher).
489. **446.** 15 p. purple 15 10

447. Raja R. Roy (social reformer).

1964. Raja Rammohun Roy Commem.
490. **447.** 15 n.p. brown.. .. 10 10

448. I.S.O. Emblem and Globe.

1964. 6th Int. Organization for Standardisation General Assembly, Bombay.
491. **448.** 15 p. red 15 20

449 Jawaharlal Nehru (from 1 r. commemorative coin)

450. St. Thomas (after statue, Ortona Cathedral, Italy).

1964. Children's Day.
492. **449.** 15 p. slate 10 10

1964. St. Thomas Commem.
493. **450.** 15 p. purple 10 30
No. 493 was issued on the occasion of Pope Paul's visit to India.

MINIMUM PRICE

The minimum price quoted is 10p which represents a handling charge rather than a basis for valuing common stamps. For further notes about prices see introductory pages.

451. Globe.

1964. 22nd Int. Geological Congress.
494. **451.** 15 p. green 20 30

452. J. Tata (industrialist).

1965. Jamsetji Tata Commem.
495. **452.** 15 p. dull purple & orge. 15 20

453. Lala Lajpat Rai.

1965. Birth Centenary of Lala Lajpat Rai (social reformer).
496. **453.** 15 p. brown 10 10

454. Globe and Congress Emblem.

1965. 20th Int. Chamber of Commerce Congress, New Delhi.
497. **454.** 15 p. green and red .. 15 15

455. Freighter "Jalausha" and Visakhapatnam.

1965. National Maritime Day.
498. **455.** 15 p. blue 30 30

456. Abraham Lincoln.

1965. Death Centenary of Lincoln.
499. **456.** 15 p. brown and ochre 15 10

457. I.T.U. Emblem and Symbols.

1965. Centenary of I.T.U.
500. **457.** 15 p. purple .. 90 30

458. "Everlasting Flame".

1965. 1st Death Anniv. of Nehru.
501. **458.** 15 p. red and blue .. 15 10

459. I.C.Y. Emblem.

1965. Int. Co-operation Year.
502. **459.** 15 p. green and brown 90 50

460. Climbers on Summit. **467.** Plucking Tea.

477. Atomic Reactor, Trombay.

1965. Indian Mount Everest Expedition.
503. **460.** 15 p. purple 20 10

1965.

504.	–	2 p. brown	10	40
505.	–	3 p. olive	10	1·25
505a.	–	4 p. brown	10	1·75
506.	–	5 p. red	10	10
507.	–	6 p. black	10	1·75
508.	–	8 p. brown	30	3·00
509.	–	10 p. blue	40	10
510.	**467.**	15 p. green	80	10
511.	–	20 p. purple	1·60	10
512.	–	30 p. sepia	15	10
513.	–	40 p. purple	15	10
514.	–	50 p. green	20	10
515.	–	60 p. grey	35	10
516.	–	70 p. blue	60	10
517.	–	1 r. brown and plum ..	60	10
518.	–	2 r. blue and violet ..	2·00	10
519.	–	5 r. violet and brown ..	2·50	40
520.	**477.**	10 r. black and green ..	12·00	80

DESIGNS—As Type **467**—VERT. 2 p. Bidri Vase. 3 p. Brass Lamp. 5 p. "Family Planning". 6 p. Konarak Elephant. 8 p. Spotted deer. 30 p. Indian Dolls. 50 p. Mangoes. 60 p. Somnath Temple. HORIZ. 4 p. Coffee Berries. 10 p. Electric Locomotive. 15 p. Plucking Tea. 20 p. Folland "Gnat" Fighter. 40 p. Calcutta G.P.O. 70 p. Hampi Chariot (sculpture). As Type **477**—VERT. 1 r. Medieval Sculpture. HORIZ. 2 r. Dal Lake, Kashmir. 5. r Bhakra Dam, Punjab.

479. G. B. Pant (statesman).

480. V. Patel.

1965. Govind Ballabh Pant Commem.
522. **479.** 15 p. brown and green 10 20

1965. 90th Birth Anniv. of Vallabhbhai Patel (statesman).
523. **480.** 15 p. brown 10 30

481. C. Das.

482. Vidyapati (poet).

1965. 95th Birth Anniv. of Chittaranjan Das (lawyer and patriot).
524. **481.** 15 p. brown 10 10

1965. Vidyapati Commem.
525. **482.** 15 p. brown 10 10

483. Sikandra, Agra.

1966. Pacific Area Travel Assn., Conf., New Delhi.
526. **483.** 15 p. slate 10 10

484. Soldier, Fighters and Warship.

1966. Indian Armed Forces.
527. **484.** 15 p. violet 50 30

485. Lal Bahadur Shastri (statesman).

486. Kambar (poet).

1966. Shastri Mourning Issue.
528. **485.** 15 p. black 10 10

1966. Kambar Commem.
529. **486.** 15 p. green 10 10

487. B. R. Ambedkar. **488.** Kunwar Singh (patriot).

1966. 75th Birth Anniv of Dr. Bhim Rao Ambedkar (lawyer).
530. **487.** 15 p. purple 10 10

1966. Kunwar Singh Commem.
531. **488.** 15 p. brown 10 10

489. G. K. Gokhale.

1966. Birth Centenary of Gopal Krishna Gokhale (patriot).
532. **489.** 15 p. purple and yellow 10 10

490. Acharya Dvivedi (poet).

1966. Dvivedi Commem.
533. **490.** 15 p. drab 10 10

491. Maharaja Ranjit Singh (warrior).

1966. Maharaja Ranjit Singh Commem.
534. **491.** 15 p. purple 15 15

492. Homi Bhabha (scientist) and Nuclear Reactor.

1966. Dr. Homi Bhabha Commem.
535. **492.** 15 p. purple 15 30

493. A. K. Azad (scholar).

1966. Abul Kalam Azad Commem.
536. **493.** 15 p. blue 15 15

494. Swami Tirtha.

1966. 60th Death Anniv. of Swami Rama Tirtha (social reformer).
537. **494.** 15 p. blue 15 30

495. Infant and Dove Emblem.

1966. Children's Day.
538. **495.** 15 p. purple .. 30 20

496. Allahabad High Court.

1966. Cent. of Allahabad High Court.
539. **496.** 15 p. purple .. 20 30

497. Indian Family.

1966. Family Planning.
540. **497.** 15 p. brown 15 15

498. Hockey Game.

1966. India's Hockey Victory in 5th Asian Games.
541. **498.** 15 p. blue 90 50

499. " Jai Kisan ".

1967. 1st Death Anniv. of Shastri.
542. **499.** 15 p. green 15 30

500. Voter and Polling Booth. **501.** Gurudwara Shrine, Patna.

1967. Indian General Election.
543. **500.** 15 p. brown 15 15

1967. 300th Birth Anniv (1966) of Guru Gobind Singh (Sikh religious leader).
544. **501.** 15 p. violet 15 15

502. Taj Mahal, Agra.

1967. Int. Tourist Year.
545. **502.** 15 p. brown and orange 15 15

503. Nandalal Bose and " Garuda ".

1967. 1st Death Anniv. of Nandalal Bose (painter).
546. **503.** 15 p. brown 15 15

504. Survey Emblem and Activities.

1967. Bicentenary of Survey of India.
547. **504.** 15 p. lilac 20 30

505. Basaveswara.

1967. 800th Anniv. of Basaveswara (reformer and statesman).
548. **505.** 15 p. red 15 15

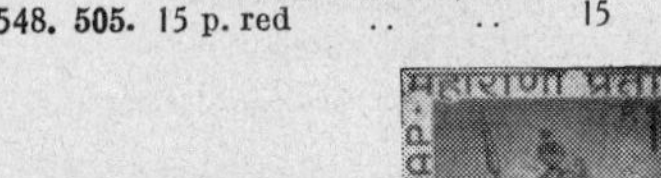

506. Narsinha Mehta (poet). **507.** Maharana Pratap.

1967. Narsinha Mehta Commem.
549. **506.** 15 p. sepia 15 15

1967. Maharana Pratap (Rajput leader) Commemoration.
550. **507.** 15 p. brown 15 15

508. Narayana Guru. **509.** Pres. Radhakrishnan.

1967. Narayana Guru (philosopher) Commem.
551 **508** 15 p. brown 15 20

1967. 75th Birth Anniv of Sarvepalli Radhakrishnan (former President).
552 **509** 15 p. red 30 15

510. Martyrs' Memorial, Patna.

1967. 25th Anniv. of "Quit India" Movement.
553. **510.** 15 p. lake 15 15

511. Route Map.

1967. Centenary of Indo-European Telegraph Service.
554. **511.** 15 p. black and blue 15 20

512. Wrestling.

1967. World Wrestling Championships, New Delhi.
555. **512.** 15 p. purple & brown 30 20

513. Nehru leading Naga Tribesmen. **514.** Rashbehari Basu (nationalist).

1967. 4th Anniv of Nagaland as a State of India.
556. **513.** 15 p. blue 15 15

1967. Rashbehari Basu Commem.
557. **514.** 15 p. purple 15 20

515. Bugle, Badge and Scout Salute.

1967. 60th Anniv of Scout Movement in India.
558 **515** 15 p. brown 60 30

516. Men Embracing Universe.

1968. Human Rights Year.
559. **516.** 15 p. green 30 30

517. Globe and Book of Tamil.

1968. Int. Conf.—Seminar of Tamil Studies, Madras.
560. **517.** 15 p. lilac 30 15

518. U.N. Emblem and Transport.

1968. United Nations Conference on Trade and Development, New Delhi.
561 **518** 15 p. blue 30 15

519. Quill and Bow Symbol.

1968. Centenary of Amrita Bazar Patrika (newspaper).
562. **519.** 15 p. sepia and yellow 15 15

520. Maxim Gorky. **521.** Emblem and Medal.

1968. Birth Cent. of Maxim Gorky.
563. 520. 15 p. plum 15 20

1968. 1st Triennale Art Exhibition, New Delhi.
564 521 15 p. orange, bl & lt bl 30 20

522. Letter-box and "100,000".

1968 Opening of 100,000th Indian Post Office.
565. 522. 20 p. red, blue & black 20 15

523. Stalks of Wheat, Agricultural Institute and Production Graph.

1968. Wheat Revolution.
566. 523. 20 p. green and brown 30 15

524. "Self-Portrait".

1968. 30th Death Anniv. of Gaganendranath Tagore.
567. 524. 20 p. purple and ochre 30 15

525. Lakshminath Bezbaruah.

1968. Birth Centenary of Lakshminath Bezbaruah (writer).
568 525 20 p. brown 15 15

526. Athlete's Legs and Olympic Rings.

1968. Olympic Games, Mexico.
569. 526. 20 p. brown and grey .. 15 15
570. 1 r. sepia and olive .. 30 15

527. Bhagat Singh and Followers.

1968. 61st Birth Anniv of Bhagat Singh (patriot).
571 527 20 p. brown 20 20

INDEX

Countries can be quickly located by referring to the index at the end of this volume.

528. Azad Hind Flag, Swords and Chandra Bose (founder).
529. Sister Nivedita.

1968. 25th Anniv. of Azad Hind Government.
572. 528. 20 p. blue 20 15

1968. Birth Cent of Sister Nivedita (social reformer).
573 529 20 p. green 30 30

530. Marie Curie and Radium Treatment.

1968. Birth Centenary of Marie Curie.
574. 530. 20 p. lilac .. .. 1·25 50

531. Map of the World.

1968. 21st Int. Geographical Congress, New Delhi.
575. 531. 20 p. blue 15 15

532. Cochin Synagogue.

1968. 400th Anniv. of Cochin Synagogue.
576. 532. 20 p. blue and red .. 40 30

533. I.N.S. "Nilgiri".

1968. Navy Day.
577. 533. 20 p. blue 80 40

534. Red-billed Blue Magpie.

1968. Birds.
578. 534. 20 p. multicoloured .. 55 40
579. – 50 p. red, black & grn. 1·10 75
580. – 1 r. blue and brown .. 1·75 1·00
581. – 2 r. multicoloured .. 1·75 1·40

DESIGNS—HORIZ. 50 p. Brown-fronted pied woodpecker. 2 r. Yellow-backed sunbird. VERT. 1 r. Slaty-headed scimitar babbler.

538. Bankim Chandra Chatterjee.
539. Dr. Bhagavan Das.

1969. 130th Birth Anniv. of Chatterjee (writer).
582. 538. 20 p. blue 15 20

1969. Birth Cent of Das (philosopher).
583. 539. 20 p. brown 15 15

540. Dr. Martin Luther King.

1969. Martin Luther King Commem.
584. 540. 20 p. brown 30 20

541. Mirza Ghalib and Letter Seal.

1969. Death Cent. of Mirza Ghalib (poet).
585. 541. 20 p. sepia, red & flesh 15 15

542. Osmania University.

1969. 50th Anniv. of Osmania University.
586. 542. 20 p. green 15 20

543. Rafi Ahmed Kidwai and Mail Plane.

1969. 20th Anniv. of Rafi Ahmed Kidwai (Author of "All-up" Airmail Scheme).
587. 543. 20 p. blue 50 30

544. I.L.O. Badge and Emblem.

1969. 50th Anniv. of Int. Labour Organization.
588. 544. 20 p. brown 15 20

545. Memorial, and Hands dropping Flowers.

1969. 50th Anniv of Jallianwala Bagh Massacre, Amritsar.
589. 545. 20 p. red 15 20

546. K. Nageswara Rao Pantulu (journalist).

1969. Kasinadhuni Nageswara Rao Pantulu Commem.
590. 546. 20 p. brown 15 20

547. Ardaseer Cursetjee Wadia, and Ships.

1969. Ardaseer Cursetjee Wadia (ship-builder) Commemoration.
591. 547. 20 p. turquoise .. 40 30

548. Serampore College.

1969. 150th Anniv. of Serampore College.
592. 548. 20 p. plum 15 20

549. Dr. Zakir Husain.

1969. Dr. Zakir Husain Commem.
593. 549. 20 p. sepia 15 20

550. Laxmanrao Kirloskar.

1969. Birth Centenary of Laxmanrao Kirloskar (agriculturist).
594. 550. 20 p. black .. 15 15

551. Gandhi and his wife.

1969. Birth Cent. of Mahatma Gandhi.
595. 551. 20 p. brown 40 20
596. – 75 p. flesh and drab .. 1·00 80
597. – 1 r. blue .. .. 1·00 65
598. – 5 r. brown and orange . 4·25 5·50

DESIGNS AND SIZES—VERT. 75 p. Gandhi's head and shoulders (28 × 38 mm.). 1 r. Gandhi walking (woodcut) (20 × 38 mm.). HORIZ. 5 r. Gandhi with charkha (36 × 26 mm.).

555. "Ayanta" (bulk carrier) and I.M.C.O. Emblem.

1969. 10th Anniv. of Inter-Government Maritime Consulative Organization.
599. 555. 20 p. blue 80 40

556. Outline of Parliament Building and Globe.

1969. Inter-Parliamentary Conf., New Delhi.
600. **556.** 20 p. blue 15 20

557. Astronaut walking beside Space Module on Moon.

GURU NANAK DEV

558. Gurudwara Nankana Sahib (birthplace).

1969. 1st Man on the Moon.
601. **557.** 20 p. brown 15 20

1969. 500th Birth Anniv of Guru Nanak Dev (Sikh religious leader).
602. **558.** 20 p. violet 15 20

559. Tiger's Head and Hands holding Globe.

1969. Int. Union for the Conservation of Nature and Natural Resources Conf., New Delhi.
603. **559.** 20 p. brown and green 30 30

560. Sadhu Vaswani.

भारत INDIA 20
THAKKAR BAPA

561. Thakkar Bapa.

1969. 90th Birth Anniv. of Sadhu Vaswani (educationist).
604. **560.** 20 p. grey 15 15

1969. Birth Centenary of Thakkar Bapa (humanitarian).
605 **561** 20 p. brown 15 20

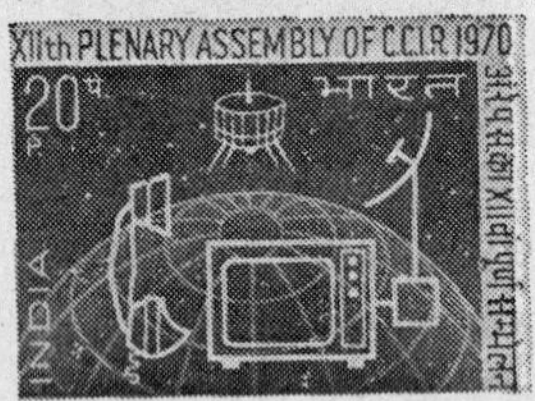

562. Satellite, Television, Telephone and Globe.

1970. 12th Plenary Assembly of Int. Radio Consultative Committee.
606. **562.** 20 p. blue 20 20

563 C. N. Annadurai.

564. M. N. Kishore and Printing Press.

1970. 1st Death Anniv of Conjeevaram Natrajan Annadurai (statesman).
607. **563.** 20 p. purple and blue 15 15

1970. 75th Death Anniv of Munshi Newal Kishore (publisher).
608. **564.** 20 p. lake 15 20

565. Nalanda College.

1970. Centenary of Nalanda College.
609. **565.** 20 p. brown 40 40

566. Swami Shraddhanand (social reformer).

1970. Swami Shraddhanand Commem.
610. **566.** 20 p. brown 40 40

567. Lenin.

1970. Birth Centenary of Lenin.
611. **567.** 20 p. brown and sepia 20 20

568. New U.P.U. H.Q. Building.

1970. New U.P.U. Headquarters Building, Berne.
612. **568.** 20 p. green, grey & black 15 20

569. Sher Shah Suri (15th Century ruler).

1970. Sher Shah Suri Commem.
613. **569.** 20 p. green 15 20

570. V. D. Savarkar (patriot) and Cellular Jail, Andaman Islands.

1970. Vinayak Damodar Savarkar Commem.
614. **570.** 20 p. brown 15 20

571. "UN" and Globe.

1970. 25th Anniv. of United Nations
615. **571.** 20 p. blue 30 20

572. Symbol and Workers.

1970. Asian Productivity Year.
616. **572.** 20 p. violet 20 20

573. Dr. Montessori and I.E.Y. Emblem.

1970. Birth Centenary of Dr. Maria Montessori (educationist).
617. **573.** 20 p. purple 30 30

574. J. N. Mukherjee (revolutionary) and Horse.

1970. Jatindra Nath Mukherjee Commem.
618. **574.** 20 p. brown 65 30

575. V.S. Srinivasa Sastri.

1970. Srinivasa Sastri (educationist) Commemoration.
619 **575** 20 p. yellow and purple 30 30

576. I. C. Vidyasagar.

1970. 150th Birth Anniv of Iswar Chandra Vidyasagar (educationist).
620 **576** 20 p. brown and purple 30 30

577. Maharishi Valmiki.

1970. Maharishi Valmiki (ancient author) Commemoration.
621 **577** 20 p. purple 15 30

578. Calcutta Port.

1970. Cent. of Calcutta Port Trust.
622. **578.** 20 p. blue 50 40

579. University Building.

1970. 50th Anniv. of Jamia Millia Islamia University.
623. **579.** 20 p. green 40 40

580. Jamnalal Bajaj.

1970. Jamnalal Bajaj (industrialist) Commemoration.
624. **580.** 20 p. grey 15 30

581. Nurse and Patient.

1970. 50th Anniv. of Indian Red Cross.
625. **581.** 20 p. red and blue .. 40 40

582. Sant Namdeo.

1970. 700th Birth Anniv of Sant Namdeo (mystic).
626. **582.** 20 p. orange 15 30

583. Beethoven.

1970. Birth Bicentenary of Beethoven.
627. **583.** 20 p. orange and black 1·25 50

584. Children examining Stamps.

1970. Indian National Philatelic Exhibition, New Dehli.
628. **584.** 20 p. orange and green 30 10
629. – 1 r. brown and ochre.. 1·50 80

DESIGN: 1 r. Gandhi commemorative through magnifier.

MINIMUM PRICE

The minimum price quoted is 10p which represents a handling charge rather than a basis for valuing common stamps. For further notes about prices see introductory pages.

585. Girl Guide.

1970. Diamond Jubilee of Girl Guide Movement in India.
630 **585** 20 p. purple 50 30

586. Hands and Lamp (emblem).

1971. Centenary of Indian Life Insurance.
631. **586.** 20 p. brown and red .. 20 30

587. Vidyapith Building.

1971. 50th Anniv of Kashi Vidyapith University.
632. **587.** 20 p. brown 20 30

588. Sant Ravidas.

1971. Sant Ravidas (15th-cent mystic) Commemoration.
633 **588** 20 p. red 30 30

589. C. F. Andrews.

1971. Birth Centenary of Charles Freer Andrews (missionary).
634 **589** 20 p. brown 35 30

590. Acharya Narendra Deo (scholar).

1971. 15th Death Anniv. of Acharya Narendra Deo.
635. **590.** 20 p. green 15 30

591. Crowd and "100".

1971. Centenary of Decennial Census.
636. **591.** 20 p. brown and blue 30 30

592. Sri Ramana Maharshi (mystic).

1971. 21st Death Anniv. of Ramana Maharshi.
637. **592.** 20 p. orange and brown 20 30

593. Raja Ravi Varma and "Damayanti and the Swan".

1971. 65th Death Anniv. of Ravi Varma (artist).
638. **593.** 20 p. green 30 40

594. Dadasaheb Phalke and Camera (cinematographer).

1971. Birth Centenary of Dadasaheb Phalke (cinematographer).
639 **594** 20 p. purple 70 40

595. "Abhisarika" (Tagore). **596.** Swami Virjanand (Vedic scholar).

1971. Birth Centenary of Abanindranath Tagore (painter).
640 **595** 20 p. grey, yell & brn .. 30 30

1971. Swami Virjanand Commemoration.
641. **596.** 20 p. brown 30 40

597. Cyrus the Great and Procession.

1971. 2500th Anniv. of Charter of Cyrus the Great.
642. **597.** 20 p. brown 45 45

598. Globe and Money Box.

1971. World Thrift Day.
643. **598.** 20 p. grey 20 30

599. Ajanta Caves Paintings. **600** "Women at Work" (Geeta Gupta).

1971. 25th Anniv. of UNESCO.
644. **599.** 20 p. brown .. .. 1·00 40

1971. Children's Day.
645 **600** 20 p. red 20 40

607. Refugees.

1971. Obligatory Tax. Refugee Relief.

(a) Optd. **REFUGEE RELIEF** in Hindi and English.
646. – 5 p. red (No. 506 10 10

(b) Optd. **Refugee Relief.**
647. – 5 p. red (No. 506) 1·50 55

(c) Optd. **REFUGEE RELIEF.**
649. – 5 p. red (No. 506) .. 2·25 70

(d) Optd **Refugee relief**.
650c. – 5 p. red (No. 506) .. 6·50 1·75

(e) Optd. **Refugee Relief** in Hindi and English.
650d. – 5 p. red (No. 506) ..

(f) Type **607.**
651. **607.** 5 p. red 10 10

From 15 November 1971 until 31 March 1973 the Indian Government levied a 5 p. surcharge on all mail, except postcards and newspapers, for the relief of refugees from the former East Pakistan.

608. C. V. Raman (scientist) and Light Graph.

1971. 1st Death Anniv of Chandrasekhara Venkata Raman.
652 **608** 20 p. orange and brown 30 30

609. Visva Bharati Building and Rabindranath Tagore (founder).

1971. 50th Anniv of Visva Bharati University.
653 **609** 20 p. sepia and brown 20 30

610. Cricketers.

1971. Indian Cricket Victories.
654. **610.** 20 p. green, myrtle & sage 1·75 65

611. Map and Satellite.

1972. 1st Anniv of Arvi Satellite Earth Station.
655 **611** 20 p. purple 15 30

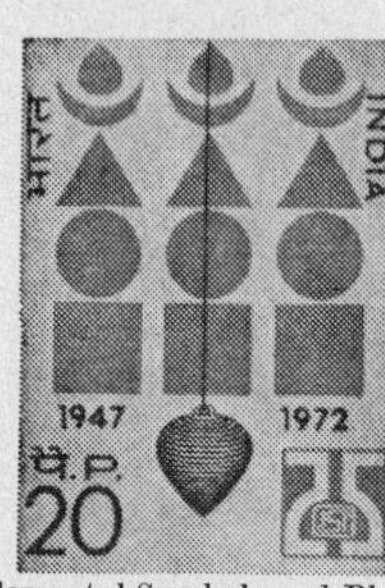

612. Elemental Symbols and Plumb-line.

1972. 25th Anniv of Indian Standards Institution.
656 **612** 20 p. grey and black .. 15 40

613. Signal-box Panel.

1972. 50th Anniv. of Int. Railways Union.
657. **613.** 20 p. multicoloured .. 40 40

614. Hockey-player.

1972. Olympic Games, Munich.
658. **614.** 20 p. violet 75 25
659. – 1 r. 45 green and lake 1·50 2·00
DESIGN: 1 r. 45, Various sports.

615. Symbol of Sri Aurobindo.

1972. Birth Centenary of Sri Aurobindo (religious teacher).
660. **615.** 20 p. yellow and blue 20 30

616. Celebrating Independence Day in front of Parliament.

1972. 25th Anniv. of Independence. (1st issue).
661. **616.** 20 p. multicoloured .. 15 30
See also Nos. 673/4.

617. Inter-Services Crest.

1972. Defence Services Commem.
662. **617.** 20 p. multicoloured .. 30 40

618. V. O. Chidambaran Pillai (trade union leader) and Ship.

1972. Birth Cent. of V. O. Chidambaram Pillai.
663. **618.** 20 p. blue and brown 40 40

619. Bhai Vir Singh.

1972. Birth Cent of Bhai Vir Singh (poet).
664 **619** 20 p. purple 30 40

620. T. Prakasam.

1972. Birth Centenary of Tanguturi Prakasam (lawyer).
665. **620.** 20 p. brown 20 40

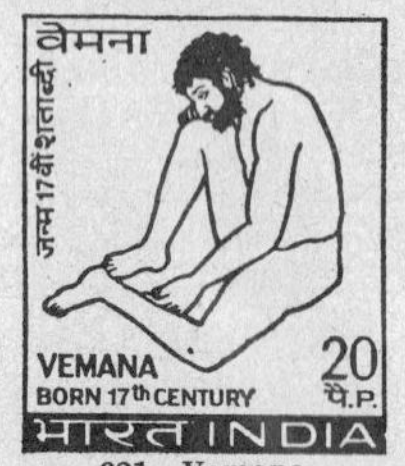

621. Vemana.

1972. 300th Birth Anniv. of Vemana (poet).
666. **621.** 20 p. black 20 40

622. Bertrand Russell.

1972. Birth Centenary of Bertrand Russell (philosopher).
667. **622.** 1 r. 45 black .. .. 2·50 2·75

623. Symbol of " Asia '72".

1972. "Asia '72" (Third Asian International Trade Fair), New Delhi.
668. **623.** 20 p. black & orange.. 10 20
669. – 1 r. 45 orange and blk. 60 1·75
DESIGN: 1 r. 45, Hand of Buddha.

624. V. A. Sarabhai and Rocket.

1972. 1st Death Anniv. of Dr. Vikram A. Sarabhai (scientist).
670. **624.** 20 p. brown and green 20 40

625. Flag of U.S.S.R. and Kremlin Tower.

1972. 50th Anniv. of U.S.S.R.
671. **625.** 20 p. red and yellow 20 40

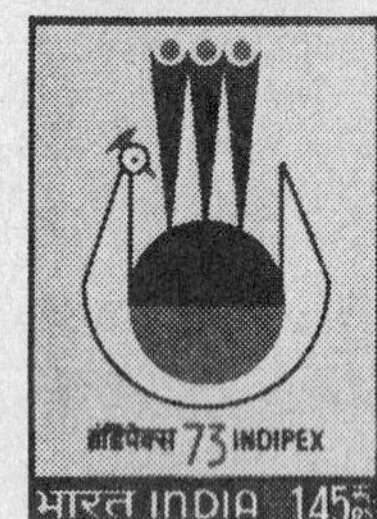

626. Exhibition Symbol.

1973. "Indipex '73" Stamp Exhibition (1st issue).
672. **626.** 1 r. 45 mve., gold & blk 45 1·25

627. " Democracy".

1973. 25th Anniv. of Independence. (2nd issue.) Multicoloured.
673. 20 p. Type **627** 15 15
674. 1 r. 45 " Gnat " fighters over India Gate .. .. 85 1·60
SIZE-HORIZ. 1 r. 45, 38 × 20 mm.

628. Sri Ramakrishna Paramahamsa (religious leader).

1973. Sri Ramakrishna Paramahamsa Commemoration.
675. **628.** 20 p. brown 20 40

629. Postal Corps Emblem.

1973. 1st Anniv. of Army Postal Corps.
676. **629.** 20 p. blue and red .. 40 50

630. Flag and Map of Bangladesh.

1973. "Jai Bangla (Inauguration of 1st Bangladesh Parliament).
677. **630.** 20 p. multicoloured .. 15 40

631. Kumaran Asan.

1973. Birth Centenary of Kumaran Asan (writer and poet).
678. **631.** 20 p. brown 20 45

632. Flag and Flames.

1973. Homage to Martyrs for Independence.
679. **632.** 20 p. multicoloured .. 15 40

633. Dr. Bhim Rao Ambedkar (laywer).

1973. Ambedkar Commemoration.
680. **633.** 20 p. green and purple 20 75

634. " Radha-Kishangarh " (Nihal Chand).

1973. Indian Miniature Paintings. Mult.
681. 20 p. Type **634** 30 35
682. 50 p. " Dance Duet " (Aurangzeb's period) .. 60 1·50
683. 1 r. " Lovers on a Camel " (Nasir-ud-din) .. .. 1·50 2·75
684. 2 r. " Chained Elephant " (Zain-al-Abidin) .. 2·00 3·25

635. Mount Everest.

1973. 15th Anniv. of Indian Mountaineering Foundation.
685. **635.** 20 p. blue 40 50

336. Tail of Boeing " 747 ".

1973. 25th Anniv. of Air-India's International Services.
686. **636.** 1 r. 45 blue and red .. 4·00 4·00

637. Cross, Church of St. Thomas' Mount, Madras.

1973. 19th Death Cent. of St. Thomas.
687. **637.** 20 p. grey and brown 20 50

638. Michael Madhusudan Dutt (poet—Death Centenary).

1973. Centenaries.
688. **638.** 20 p. green and brown 80 50
689. – 30 p. brown .. .. 80 2·00
690. – 50 p. brown .. .. 1·00 2·00
691. – 1 r. violet and red .. 1·00 1·50
DESIGNS—HORIZ. 30 p. Vishnu Digambar Paluskar (musician, birth centenary). 50 p. Dr. G. A. Hansen (centenary of discovery of leprosy bacillus). 1 r. Nicolaus Copernicus (astronomer, 5th birth centenary).

639. A. O. Hume.

1973. Allan Octavian Hume (founder of Indian National Congress) Commemoration.
692 **639** 20 p. grey 20 40

640. Gandhi and Nehru.

1973. Gandhi and Nehru Commemoration.
693. **640.** 20 p. multicoloured .. 20 40

641. R. C. Dutt.

1973. Romesh Chandra Dutt (writer) Commemoration.
694 **641** 20 p. brown 20 40

642. K. S. Ranjitsinhji.

1973. K. S. Ranjitsinhji (cricketer) Commemoration.
695 **642** 30 p. green .. .. 3·50 2·75

643. Vithalbhai Patel.

1973. Vithalbhai Patel (lawyer) Commem.
696 **643** 50 p. brown 20 65

644. Sowar of President's Bodyguard.

1973. Bicent. of President's Bodyguard.
697. **644.** 20 p. multicoloured .. 35 40

645. Interpol Emblem.

1973. 50th Anniv. of Interpol.
698. **645.** 20 p. brown 30 40

646. Syed Ahmad Khan (social reformer).

1973. Syed Ahmad Khan Commemoration.
699. **646.** 20 p. brown 20 50

647. "Children at Play" (Bela Raval).

1973. Children's Day.
700. **647.** 20 p. multicoloured .. 20 30

648. Indipex Emblem.
(Illustration reduced. Actual size 54 × 36 mm.)

1973. "Indipex '73" Philatelic Exhibition, New Delhi. (2nd issue). Multicoloured.
701. 20 p. Type **648** 20 30
702. 1 r. Ceremonial elephant and $1\frac{1}{2}$ a. stamp of 1947 (vert.) .. .. 1·00 1·75
703. 2 r. Common Peafowl (vert.) 1·50 2·25

649. Emblem of National Cadet Corps.

1973. 25th Anniv of National Cadet Corps.
705 **649** 20 p. multicoloured .. 20 30

650. Rajagopalachari (statesman).

1973. Chakravanti Rajagopalachari Commemoration.
706 **650** 20 p. brown 20 50

651. "Sun" Mask.

1974. Indian Masks. Multicoloured.
707. 20 p. Type **651** 15 15
708. 50 p. "Moon" mask .. 30 55
709. 1 r. "Narasimha" .. 80 1·25
710. 2 r. "Ravana" (horiz.) .. 1·25 2·00

652. Chhatrapati.

1974. 300th Anniv. of Coronation of Chhatrapati Shri Shivaji Maharaj (patriot and ruler).
712. **652.** 25 p. multicoloured .. 30 30

653. Maithili Sharan Gupta (poet).

1974. Indian Personalities (1st series).
713. **653.** 25 p. brown 15 40
714. – 25 p. deep brown .. 15 40
715. – 25 p. brown 15 40
PORTRAITS: No. 714, Jainarain Vyas (politician and journalist). No. 715, Utkal Gourab Madhusudan Das (social reformer).

654. Kandukuri Veeresalingam (social reformer).

1974. Indian Personalities (2nd series).
716. **654.** 25 p. brown 25 50
717. – 50 p. purple .. .. 55 1·75
718. – 1 r. brown .. .. 70 1·75
PORTRAITS: 50 p. Tipu Sultan. 1 r. Max Mueller (Sanskrit scholar).

655. Kamala Nehru.

1974. Kamala Nehru Commemoration.
719. **655.** 25 p. multicoloured .. 50 50

656. W.P.Y. Emblem.

1974. World Population Year.
720. **656.** 25 p. purple and brown 20 30

657. Spotted Deer.

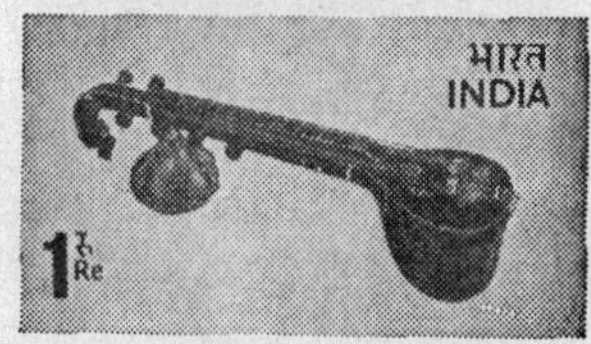

657a. Sitar.

1974.
(a) Values expressed with "p" or "Re"
721. – 15 p. brown .. .. 2·50 50
722. **657.** 25 p. brown 75 60
723. **657a.** 1 r. brown and black 2·50 30

(b) Values expressed as numerals only.
724 – 2 p. brown .. .. 50 1·25
725 – 5 p. red 30 10
729 – 10 p. blue 30 15
730 – 15 p. brown .. .. 1·50 10
731 – 20 p. green 15 10
732 – 25 p. brown .. .. 3·00 90
732b – 30 p. brown .. .. 1·50 45
733 – 50 p. violet .. .. 2·00 70
734 – 60 p. grey 50 80
735 **657a.** 1 r. brown and black .. 3·25 10
736 – 2 r. violet and brown .. 9·50 40
737 – 5 r. violet and brown .. 1·25 1·00
738c – 10 r. grey and green .. 1·10 1·10
DESIGNS—As Type **657**. VERT. 2 p. Bidri vase. 5 p. "Family Planning". 15 p. Tiger. 25 p. Gandhi. 30 p. Indian dolls. 60 p. Somnath Temple. HORIZ. 10 p. Electric Locomotive. 20 p. Handicrafts toy. 50 p. Demoiselle Crane in flight. As Type **657a**. 2 r. Himalayas. 5 r. Bhakra Dam, Punjab. 10 r. Atomic Reactor, Trombay.

For 30 p., 35 p., 50 p., 60 p., and 1 r. values as No. 732 see Nos. 968, 979, 1073, 1320 and 1436.

658. President V. Giri.

1974. Retirement of President Giri.
739. **658.** 25 p. multicoloured .. 15 30

659. U.P.U. Emblem.

1974. Centenary of U.P.U.
740. **659.** 25 p. vio., bl. & blk. .. 40 10
741. – 1 r. multicoloured .. 2·00 1·75
742. – 2 r. multicoloured .. 2·25 2·50
DESIGNS:—1 r. Birds and nest, "Madhubani" style. VERT. 2 r. Arrows around globe.

660. Lady Flute-player (sculpture).

1974. Centenary of Mathura Museum.
744. **660.** 25 p. chestnut & brown 50 30
745. – 25 p. chestnut & brown 50 30
DESIGN: No. 745, Vidyadhara with garland.

661. Nicholas Roerich (medallion by H. Dropsy).

1974. Birth Centenary of Professor Roerich (humanitarian).

46. **661.** 1 r. green & yellow .. 50 55

Bhagwan Mahavira 2500th Nirvana Anniversary

662. Pavapuri Temple.

1974. 2,500th Anniv. of Bhagwan Mahavira's Attainment of Nirvana.

747. **662.** 25 p. black 40 20

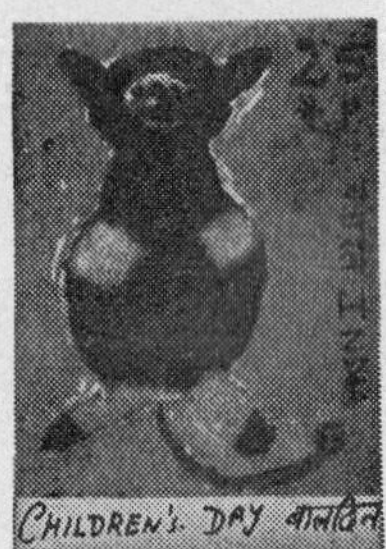

663. " Cat " (Rajesh Bhatia).

1974. Children's Day.

748. **663.** 25 p. multicoloured .. 40 40

664. "Indian Dancers" (Amita Shah).

1974. U.N.I.C.E.F. in India.

749. **664.** 25 p. multicoloured .. 35 40

665. Territorial Army Badge.

1974. 25th Anniv. of Indian Territorial Army.

750. **665.** 25 p. blk., yell. & green 50 40

666. Krishna as Gopai Bai with Cows (Rajasthan painting on cloth).

1974. 19th International Dairy Congress, New Delhi.

751. **666.** 25 p. purple and brown 40 30

भारत INDIA 25 Help the retardates

667. Symbol and Child's Face.

1974. Help for Retarded Children.

752. **667.** 25 p. red and black .. 30 40

668. Marconi.

1974. Birth Centenary of Gugielmo Marconi (radio pioneer).

753. **668.** 2 r. blue .. .. 1·50 1·25

669. St. Francis Xavier's Shrine.

1974. St. Francis Xavier Celebration.

754. **669.** 25 p. multicoloured .. 15 30

670. Saraswati (Deity of Language and Learning).

1975. World Hindi Convention, Nagpur.

755. **670.** 25 p. grey and red .. 30 30

671. Parliament House, New Delhi.

1975. 25th Anniv. of Republic.

756. **671.** 25 p. blk., silver & blue 30 30

672. Table-tennis Bat.

1975. World Table-Tennis Championships, Calcutta.

757. **672.** 25 p. blk., red & green 55 30

673. " Equality, Development and Peace ".

1975. International Women's Year.

758. **673.** 25 p. multicoloured .. 1·25 45

674. Stylised Cannon.

1975. Bicent. of Indian Army Ordnance Corps.

759. **674.** 25 p. multicoloured .. 55 45

675. Arya Samaj Emblem.

1975. Cent. of Arya Samaj Movement.

760. **675.** 25 p. red and brown.. 30 30

676. Saraswati.

1975. World Telugu Language Conf., Hyderabad.

761. **676.** 25 p. black & green .. 45 30

677. Satellite " Aryabhata ".

1975. Launch of First Indian Satellite.

762. **677.** 25 p. light bl., bl. & pur. 40 40

678. Blue-winged Pitta.

1975. Indian Birds. Multicoloured.

763. 25 p. Type **678** 45 15
764. 50 p. Asian Black-headed Oriole .. .. 90 1·25
765. 1 r. Western Tragopan (vert.) .. .. 2·00 2·75
766. 2 r. Himalayan Monal Pheasant (vert.) .. .. 2·50 4·25

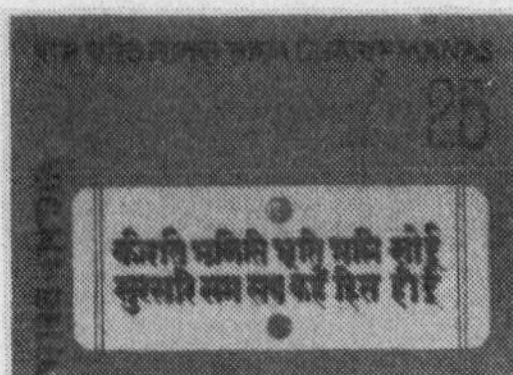

679. Page from "Ramcharitmanas" (manuscript).

1975. 4th Centenary of "Ramcharitmanas" (epic poem by Goswami Tulsidas).

767. **679.** 25 p. blk., yell. and red 40 20

680. Young Women within Y.W.C.A. Badge.

MICHELANGELO INDIA 50

681. " The Creation ".

1975. Centenary of Indian Y.W.C.A.

768. **680.** 25 p. multicoloured .. 20 30

1975. 500th Birth Anniversary of Michelangelo. "Creation" Frescoes from Sistine Chapel.

769. **681.** 50 p. multicoloured .. 60 60
770. – 50 p. multicoloured .. 60 60
771. – 50 p. multicoloured .. 60 60
772. – 50 p. multicoloured .. 60 60

Nos. 770 and 772 are size 49 × 34 mm.
Nos. 769/70 and 771/2 form composite designs.

682. Commission Emblem.

1975. 25th Anniv. of Int. Commission of Irrigation and Drainage.

773. **682.** 25 p. multicoloured .. 40 20

683. Stylised Ground Antenna.

1975. Inauguration of Satellite Instructional Television Experiment.

774 **683** 25 p. multicoloured .. 40 20

684. St. Arunagirinathar.

1975. 600th Birth Anniv. of St. Arunagirinathar.

775. **684.** 50 p. purple and black 1·00 1·00

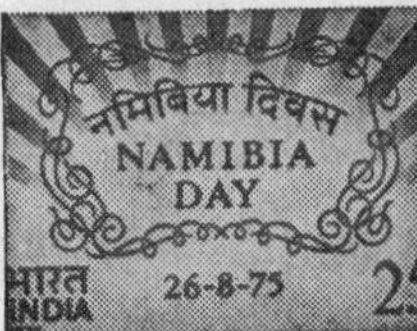

685. Commemorative Text.

1975. Namibia Day.

776. **685.** 25 p. black and red .. 40 40

686. Mir Anees (poet). 687. Memorial Temple to Ahilyabai Holkar (ruler).

1975. Indian Celebrities.

777. **686.** 25 p. green 25 50
778. **687.** 25 p. brown 25 50

688. Bharata Natyam.

1975. Indian Dances. Multicoloured.

779. 25 p. Type **688** 55 20
780. 50 p. Orissi .. .. 85 1·00
781. 75 p. Kathak .. .. 1·00 25
782. 1 r. Kathakali .. .. 1·25 1·25
783. 1 r. 50 Kuchipudi .. 2·00 2·75
784. 2 r. Manipuri .. .. 2·25 3·50

689. Ameer Khusrau.

1975. 650th Death Anniv. of Ameer Khusrau (poet).

785. **689.** 50 p. brown and bistre 80 1·50

690. V. K. Krishna Menon.

1975. 1st Death Anniv. of V. K. Krishna Menon (statesman).

786. **690.** 25 p. green 40 60

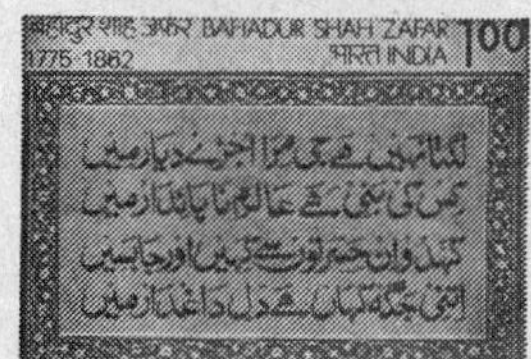

691. Text of Poem.

1975. Birth Bicentenary of Emperor Bahadur Shah Zafar.

787. **691.** 1 r. black, buff & brn. 65 90

692. Sansadiya Soudha, New Delhi.

1975. 21st Commonwealth Parliamentary Conference, New Delhi.

788. **692.** 2 r. green .. .. 1·75 2·50

693. V. Patel.

1975. Birth Centenary of Vallabhbhai Patel (statesman).

789. **693.** 25 p. green 15 30

694. N. C. Bardoloi.

1975. Birth Centenary of Nabin Chandra Bardoloi (politician).

790. **694.** 25 p. brown 30 50

695. "Cow" (Sanjay Nathubhai Patel).

1975. Children's Day.

791. **695.** 25 p. multicoloured .. 60 60

696. Original Printing Works, Nasik Road.

1975. 50th Anniv. of India Security Press.

792. **696.** 25 p. multicoloured .. 40 40

697. Gurdwara Sisganj (site of martyrdom).

1975. Tercentenary of the Martyrdom of Guru Tegh Bahadur (Sikh leader).

793 **697** 25 p. multicoloured .. 30 30

698. Theosophical Society Emblem.

1975. Centenary of Theosophical Society.

794. **698.** 25 p. multicoloured .. 40 40

699. Weather Cock.

1975. Centenary of Indian Meteorological Department.

795. **699.** 25 p. multicoloured .. 50 50

700. Early Mail Cart.

1975. "Inpex 75" Nat. Philatelic Exn., Calcutta.

796. **700.** 25 p. black and brown 50 30
797. – 2 r. brn., pur. and blk. 2·25 3·00

DESIGN: 2 r. Indian Bishop Mark, 1775.

701. L. N. Mishra.

1976. 1st Death Anniv of Lalit Narayan Mishra (politician).

798 **701** 25 p. brown 40 40

702. Tiger.

1976. Birth Cent. of Jim Corbett (naturalist).

799. **702.** 25 p. multicoloured .. 80 60

703. Painted Storks.

1976. Keoladeo Ghana Bird Sanctuary, Bharatpur.

800. **703.** 25 p. multicoloured .. 70 40

704. Vijayanta Tank.

1976. 200th Anniv. of 16th Light Cavalry Regiment.

801. **704.** 25 p. green and brown 90 30

705. Alexander Graham Bell.

1976. Alexander Graham Bell. Commem.

802. **705.** 25 p. brown and black 70 40

706. Muthuswami Dikshitar.

1976. Birth Bicentenary of Muthuswami Dikshitar (composer).

803. **706.** 25 p. violet 60 40

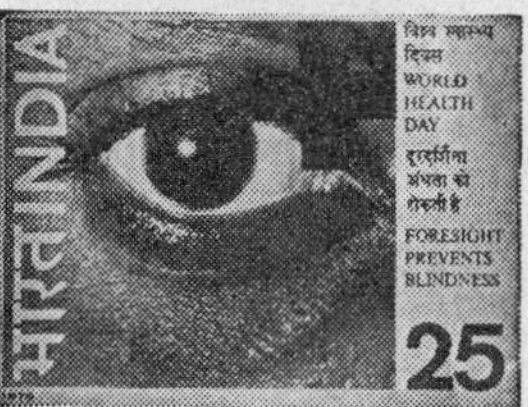

707. Eye and Red Cross.

1976. World Health Day. Prevention of Blindness.

804. **707.** 25 p. brown and red .. 60 40

708. "Industries".

1976. Industrial Development.

805. **708.** 25 p. multicoloured .. 30 30

709. Diesel Locomotive, 1963.

1976. Locomotives. Multicoloured.

806. 25 p. Type **709** 55 10
807. 50 p. Steam locomotive, 1895 .. .. .. 1·50 55
808. 1 r. Steam locomotive, 1963 .. .. .. 2·50 1·25
809. 2 r. Steam locomotive, 1853 .. .. .. 3·25 2·50

710. Nehru.

1976.

810. 710. 25 p. violet .. .. 5·00 70
811. – 25 p. brown .. .. 1·00 30

DESIGN: No. 811, Gandhi.
For these designs in a smaller format see Nos. 732, 968/9, 979/80, 1073/4 and 1320.

713. "Spirit of 76" (Willard).

1976. Bicent. of American Revolution.
812. 713. 2 r. 80 multicoloured .. 1·25 1·25

714. K. Kamaraj (politician).

1976. Kumaraswumy Kamaraj Commem.
813 714 25 p. brown 15 15

715. "Shooting".

1976. Olympic Games, Montreal.
814. 715. 25 p. violet and red .. 30 10
815. – 1 r. multicoloured .. 1·00 90
816. – 1 r. 50 mauve & black 1·50 2·50
817. – 2 r. 80 multicoloured .. 1·60 2·75

DESIGNS: 1 r. Shot-put. 1 r. 50, Hockey. 2 r. 80, Sprinting.

716. Subhadra Kumari Chauhan (poetess).

1976. S. K. Chauhan Commemoration.
818. 716. 25 p. blue 15 40

717. Param Vir Chakra Medal.

1976. Param Vir Chakra Commemoration.
819. 717. 25 p. multicoloured .. 15 40

718. University Building, Bombay.

1976. 60th Anniv. of Shreemati Nathibai Damodar Thackersey Women's University.
820 718 25 p. violet 30 30

719. Bharatendu Harischandra (writer).

1976. Harishchandra Commemoration.
821. 719. 25 p. brown 15 30

720. S. C. Chatterji. 721. Planned Family.

1976. Birth Centenary of Sarat Churdra Chatterji (writer).
822 720 25 p. black 15 30

1976. Family Planning.
823. 721. 25 p. multicoloured .. 15 30

722. Maharaja Agrasen and Coins.

1976. Maharaja Agrasen Commemoration.
824. 722. 25 p. brown 10 30

723. Swamp Deer.

1976. Indian Wildlife. Multicoloured.
825. 25 p. Type 723 .. .. 45 50
826. 50 p. Lion .. .. 1·25 2·25
827. 1 r. Leopard (horiz.) .. 1·75 2·25
828. 2 r. Caracal (horiz.) .. 2·00 3·50

HAVE YOU READ THE NOTES AT THE BEGINNING OF THIS CATALOGUE?
These often provide answers to the enquiries we receive.

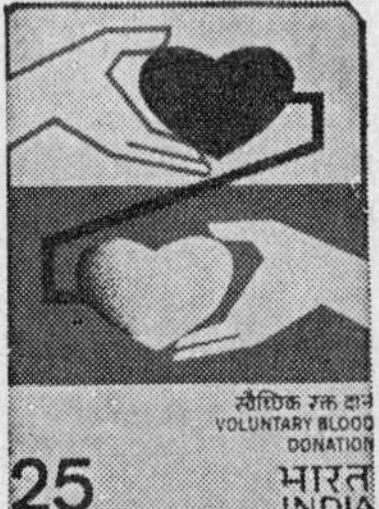

724. Hands holding Hearts.

1976. Voluntary Blood Donation.
829. 724. 25 p. yell., red & blk. 30 40

725. Suryakant Tripathi ("Nirala").

1976. 80th Birth Anniv. of "Nirala" (poet and novelist).
830. 725. 25 p. violet 15 30

726. "Loyal Mongoose" (H. D. Bhatia).

1976. Children's Day.
831. 726. 25 p. multicoloured .. 40 40

727. Hiralal Shastri (social reformer).

1976. Shastri Commemoration.
832 727 25 p. brown 20 30

728. Dr. Hari Singh Gour.

1976. Dr. Hari Singh Gour (lawyer).
833. 728. 25 p. purple 20 30

729. A300 B2 Airbus.

1976. Inauguration of Indian Airlines' Airbus Service.
834 729 2 r. multicoloured .. 2·25 2·25

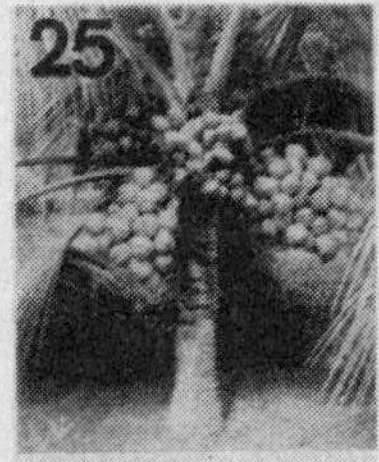

730. Hybrid Coconut Palm.

1976. Diamond Jubilee of Coconut Research.
835. 730. 25 p. multicoloured .. 20 30

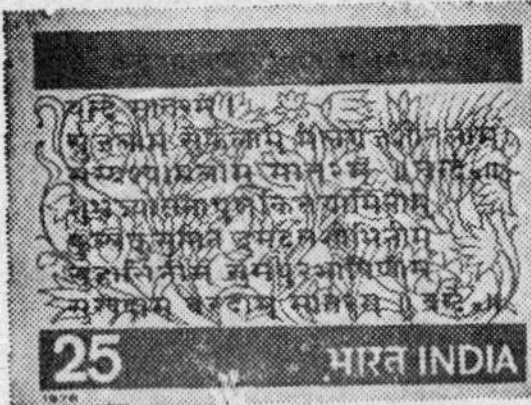

731. First Stanza of "Vande Mataram".

1976. Centenary of "Vande Mataram" (patriotic song by B. C. Chatterjee).
836 731 25 p. multicoloured .. 20 30

732. Globe and Film Strip.

1977. Sixth International Film Festival of India, New Delhi.
837. 732. 2 r. multicoloured .. 1·50 2·25

733. Seismograph and Crack in Earth's Crust.

1977. Sixth World Conference on Earthquake Engineering, New Delhi.
838. 733. 2 r. lilac .. .. 1·40 2·25

734. Tarun Ram Phookun.

1977. Tarun Ram Phookun (politican).
839. 734. 25 p. grey 15 30

735. Paramansa Yogananda.

1977. Paramansa Yogananda (religious leader).
840. **735.** 25 p. orange 30 30

736. Asian Regional Red Cross Emblem.

1977. 1st Asian Regional Red Cross Conference, New Delhi.
841. **736.** 2 r. red, pink and blue 2·00 2·50

737. Fakhruddin Ali Ahmed.

1977. Death of President Ahmed.
842. **737.** 25 p. multicoloured .. 35 35

738. Emblem of Asian–Oceanic Postal Union.

1977. 15th Anniv. of Asian–Oceanic Postal Union.
843. **738.** 2 r. multicoloured .. 1·50 2·00

739. Narottam Morarjee and "Loyalty" (liner).

1977. Birth Cent of Morarjee (ship owner).
844 **739** 25 p. blue 75 50

740. Makhanlal Chaturvedi (writer and poet).

1977. Chaturvedi Commemoration.
845. **740.** 25 p. brown 15 30

741. Mahaprabhu Vallabhacharya (philosopher).

1977. Vallabhacharya Commemoration.
846. **741.** 1 r. brown 30 40

742. Federation Emblem.

1977. 50th Anniv. of Federation of Indian Chambers of Commerce and Industry.
847. **742.** 25 p. purple, brown and yellow 15 40

744. " Environment Protection ".

1977. World Environment Day.
848. **744.** 2 r. multicoloured .. 60 1·25

745. Rajya Sabha Chamber.

1977. 25th Anniv. of Rajya Sabha (Upper House of Parliament).
849. **745.** 25 p. multicoloured .. 15 30

746. Lotus.

1977. Indian Flowers. Multicoloured.

850.	25 p. Type **746** ..	25	15
851.	50 p. Rhododendron (vert.)	45	70
852.	1 r. Kadamba (vert.) ..	75	1·00
853.	2 r. Gloriosa Lily	1·00	2·00

747. Berliner Gramophone.

1977. Centenary of Sound Recording.
854. **747.** 2 r. brown and black 1·00 2·00

748. Coomaraswamy and Siva.

1977. Birth Centenary of Ananda Kentish Coomaraswamy (art historian).
855. **748.** 25 p. multicoloured .. 40 40

749. Ganga Ram and Hospital.

1977. 50th Death Anniv of Sir Ganga Ram (social reformer).
856 **749** 25 p. purple 30 30

750. Dr. Samuel Hahnemumann (founder of homeopathy).

1977. 32nd Int. Homeopathic Congress, New Delhi.
857. **750.** 2 r. black and green .. 2·75 2·75

751. Ram Manohar Lohia (politician).

1977. Ram Manohar Lohia Commemoration.
858. **751.** 25 p. brown 30 30

752. Early Punjabi Postman.

1977. " Inpex '77 " Nat. Philatelic Exn., Bangalore.
859. **752.** 25 p. multicoloured .. 50 30
860. – 2 r. grey and red .. 2·00 2·75
DESIGN: 2 r. Unissued " Lion and Palm " stamp of 1853.

753. Scarlet " Scinde Dawks " of 1852.

1977. " Asiana '77 " Int. Philatelic Exn., Bangalore.
861. **753.** 1 r. multicoloured .. 1·25 1·0
862. – 3 r. blue, orge. & black 2·25 2·7
DESIGN: 3 r. Foreign mail arriving at Ballar Pier, Bombay, 1927.

754. " Mother and Child " (Khajuraho sculpture).

1977. 15th Int. Congress on Pediatrics.
863. **754.** 2 r. blue and brown .. 2·25 2·7

755. Statue of Kittur Rani Channamma, Belgaum.

1977. Kittur Rani Channamma, (ruler) Commemoration.
864 **755** 25 p. green 80 40

756. Symbolic Sun.

1977. Union Public Service Commission.
865. **756.** 25 p. multicoloured .. 35 30

757. Ear of Corn.

1977. "Agriexpo '77" Agricultural Exhibition, New Delhi.
866 **757** 25 p. green 40 40

758. "Cats" (Nikur Dilpbhai Mody).

1977. Children's Day. Multicoloured.
867. 25 p. Type **758** 50 30
868. 1 r. " Friends " (Bhavsar Ashish Ramanlal) .. 2·75 3·00

759. Jotirao Phooley (social reformer).

1977. Indian Personalities.

869. **759.** 25 p. olive 30 40
870. – 25 p. brown 30 40
DESIGN: No. 870, Senapti Bapat (patriot).

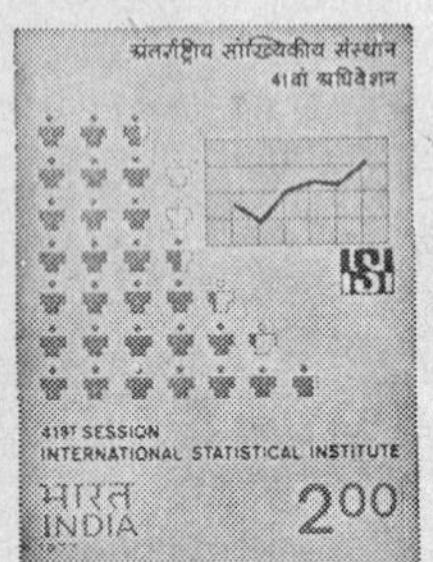

760. Diagram of Population Growth.

1977. 41st Session of International Statistical Institute, New Dehli.

871. **760.** 2 r. turquoise and red 85 1·40

761. Kamta Prasad Guru and Vyakarna (Hindi Grammar).

1977. Kamta Prasad Guru (writer) Commem.

872 **761** 25 p. brown 20 30

762. Kremlin Tower and Soviet Flag.

1977. 60th Anniv. of Russian Revolution.

873. **762.** 1 r. multicoloured .. 45 75

763. Climber crossing a Crevasse.

1978. Conquest of Kanchenjunga (1977). Multicoloured.

874. 25 p. Type **763** 10 10
875. 1 r. Indian flag near summit (horiz.) 45 80

764. "Shikara" on Lake Dal, Kashmir.

1978. 27th Pacific Area Travel Association Conf., New Delhi.

876. **764.** 1 r. multicoloured .. 2·00 1·50

765. Children in Library.

1978. 3rd World Book Fair, New Delhi.

877. **765.** 1 r. brown and slate .. 45 80

766. The Mother-Pondicherry.

1978. Birth Centenary of Mother-Pondicherry (philosopher).

878 **766** 25 p. brown and grey .. 20 30

767. Wheat and Globe.

1978. 5th International Wheat Genetics Symposium, New Delhi.

879. **767.** 25 p. yellow and turq. 20 30

768. Nanalal Dalpatram Kavi (poet).

1978. Nanalal Dalpatram Kavi Commem.

880. **768.** 25 p. brown 20 30

769. Surjya Sen (revolutionary).

1978. Surjya Sen Commemoration.

881. **769.** 25 p. bistre and red .. 20 30

770. "Two Vaishnavas" (Jamini Roy).

1978. Modern Indian Paintings. Mult.

882. 25 p. Type **770** 20 30
883. 50 p. "The Mosque" (Sailoz Mookherjea) .. 40 1·25
884. 1 r. "Head" (Rabindranath Tagore) .. .. .. 70 1·50
885. 2 r. "Hill Women" (Amrita Sher Gil) .. .. 90 2·00

771. "Self Portrait" (Rubens).

1978. 400th Birth Anniv. of Peter Paul Rubens.

886. **771.** 2 r. multicoloured .. 2·00 3·00

772. Charlie Chaplin.

1978. Charlie Chaplin Commemoration.

887. **772.** 25 p. blue and gold .. 90 45

773. Deendayal Upadhyaya (politician).

1978. Deendayal Upadhyaya Commem.

888. **773.** 25 p. brown & orange 20 40

774. Syama Prasad Mookerjee.

1978. Syama Prasad Mookerjee (politician) Commemoration.

889 **774** 25 p. brown 30 50

775. Airavat (mythological elephant). Jain Temple, Gujerat (Kachchh Museum).

1978. Treasures for Indian Museums. Mult.

890. 25 p. Type **775** 30 30
891. 50 p. Kalpadruma (magical tree), Besnagar (Indian Museum) .. .. 65 1·00
892. 1 r. Obverse and reverse of Kushan gold coin (National Museum) .. .. 1·25 1·50
893. 2 r. Dagger and knife of Emperor Jehangir, Mughal (Salar Jung Museum) .. 2·75 2·00

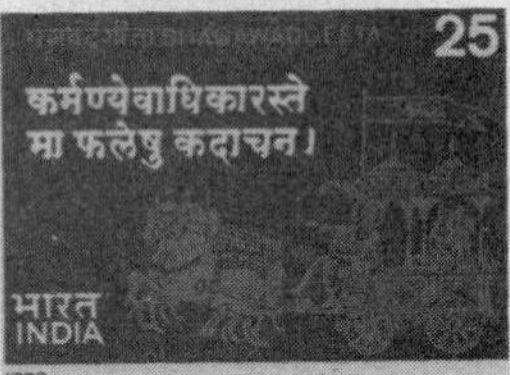

776. Krishna and Arjuna in Battle Chariot.

1978. Bhagawadgeeta (Divine Song of India) Commemoration.

894 **776** 25 p. gold and red .. 20 30

777. Bethune College.

1978. Centenary of Bethune College, Calcutta.

895. **777.** 25 p. brown and green 20 30

778. E. V. Ramasami.

1978. E. V. Ramasami (social reformer) Commemoration.

896 **778** 25 p. black 20 20

779. Uday Shankar.

1978. Uday Shankar (dancer) Commem.

897. **779.** 25 p. brown 20 30

780. Leo Tolstoy.

1978. 150th Birth Anniv. of Leo Tolstoy (writer).
898. **780.** 1 r. multicoloured .. 30 30

781. Vallathol Narayana Menon.

1978. Birth Centenary of Vallathol Narayana Menon (poet).
899. **781.** 25 p. purple and brown 15 40

782. " Two Friends " (Dinesh Sharma).

1978. Children's Day.
900. **782.** 25 p. multicoloured .. 20 40

783. Machine Operator.

1978. National Small Industries Fair, New Delhi.
901 **783** 25 p. green 20 30

784. Sowars of Skinner's Horse.

1978. 175th Anniv. of Skinner's Horse (cavalry regiment).
902. **784.** 25 p. multicoloured .. 60 60

785. Mohammad Ali Jauhar.

1978. Birth Centenary of Mohammad Ali Jauhar (patriot).
903. **785.** 25 p. olive 20 30

786. Chakravarti Rajagopalachari.

1978. Birth Centenary of Chakravarti Rajagopalachari (first post-independence Governor-General).
904. **786.** 25 p. brown 20 30

787. Wright Brothers and " Flyer ".

1978. 75th Anniv. of First Powered Flight.
905. **787.** 1 r. violet and yellow 55 30

788. Ravenshaw College.

1978. Cent of Ravenshaw College, Cuttack.
906 **788** 25 p. red and green .. 20 30

789. Schubert.

1978. 150th Death Anniv. of Franz Schubert (composer).
907. **789.** 1 r. multicoloured .. 50 55

790. Uniforms of 1799, 1901 and 1979 with Badge.

1979. 4th Reunion of Punjab Regiment.
908 **790** 25 p. multicoloured 90 70

791. Bhai Parmanand.

1979. Bhai Parmanand (scholar) Commem.
909 **791** 25 p. violet 20 30

792. Gandhi with Young Boy.

1979. International Year of the Child.
910. **792.** 25 p. brown and red .. 40 30
911. – 1 r. brown and orge. 85 1·50
DESIGN: 1 r. India I.Y.C. emblem.

793. Albert Einstein.

1979. Birth Centenary of Albert Einstein (physicist).
912. **793.** 1 r. blue 30 50

794. Rajarshi Shahu Chhatrapati.

1979. Rajarshi Shahu Chhatrapati (ruler of Kolhapur State, and precursor of social reform in India) Commemoration.
913. **794.** 25 p. purple 20 30

795. Exhibition Logo.

1979. " India 80 " International Stamp Exhibition (1st issue).
914. **795.** 30 p. green and orange 20 30
See also Nos. 942/5 and 955/8.

796. Postcards under Magnifying Glass.

1979. Centenary of Indian Postcards.
915. **796.** 50 p. multicoloured .. 20 40

797. Raja Mahendra Pratap.

1979. Raja Mahendra Pratap (patriot) Commemoration.
916 **797** 30 p. green 20 40

798. Flounder, Herring and Prawn.

1979.

920	–	2 p. violet	10	10
921	798	5 p. blue	10	10
922a	–	10 p. green	10	10
923a	–	15 p. green	10	10
924a	–	20 p. red	10	10
925a	–	25 p. brown ..	30	10
925ba	–	25 p. green	10	10
926ab	–	30 p. green	10	10
927ab	–	35 p. red	30	10
928ba	–	50 p. violet ..	10	10
929b	–	1 r. brown	10	10
932a	–	2 r. lilac ..	10	15
933b	–	2 r.25 red and green	10	10
934	–	2 r.80 red and green	15	20
934b	–	3 r.25 orange & green	15	20
935b	–	5 r. red and green ..	60	40
936	–	10 r. red and green	40	45

DESIGNS—HORIZ. 2 p. Adult Education class. 10 p. Irrigation canal. 25 p. (925) Chick hatching from egg. 25 p. (925b) Village, wheat and tractor. 30 p. Harvesting maize. 50 p. Woman dairy farmer, cows and milk bottles. (36 × 19 mm.) 10 r. Forest on hillside. VERT. (17 × 20 mm.) 15 p. Farmer and agricultural symbols. 20 p. Mother feeding child. 35 p. "Family". (17 × 28 mm.) 1 r. Cotton plant. 2 r. Weaving. (20 × 38 mm.) 2 r. 25, Cashew. 2 r. 80, Apples. 3 r. 25, Oranges. 5 r. Rubber tapping.

For 75 p. in same design as No. 927 see No. 1214.

800. Jatindra Nath Das.

1979. 50th Death Anniv. of Jatindra Nath Das (revolutionary).
941. **800.** 30 p. brown 20 30

801. De Havilland " Puss Moth " Aeroplane.

1979. " Air India 80 " International Stamp Exhibition (2nd issue). Mail-carrying Aircraft. Multicoloured.
942. 30 p. Type **801** 25 25
943. 50 p. Indian Air Force " Chetak " helicopter .. 40 45
944. 1 r. Indian Airlines Boeing " 737 " airliner.. .. 55 75
945. 2 r. Air India Boeing " 747 " airliner 75 95

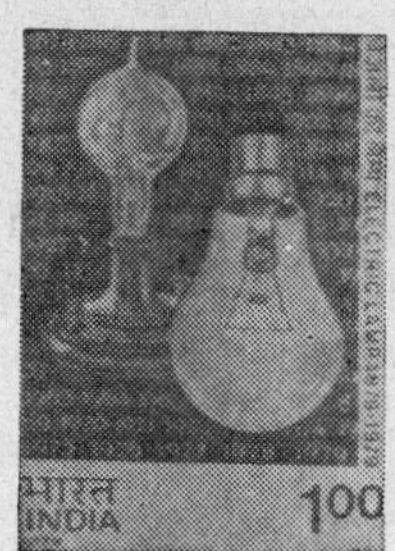

802. Early and Modern Lightbulbs.

1979. Centenary of Electric Lightbulb.
946. **802.** 1 r. purple 20 30

803. Gilgit Record.

1979. International Archives Week.
947 **803** 30 p. yellow and brown 20 40

804. Hirakud Dam, Orissa.

1979. 50th Anniv. and 13th Congress of International Commission on Large Dams.
948. **804.** 30 p. brown and turq. 20 30

805. Fair Emblem.

1979. India International Trade Fair.
949. 805. 1 r. black and red .. 20 30

806. Child learning to Read.

1979. International Children's Book Fair, New Delhi.
950. 806. 30 p. multicoloured .. 20 30

807. Dove with Olive Branch and I.A.E.A. Emblem.

1979. 23rd International Atomic Energy Agency Conference, New Delhi.
951. 807. 1 r. multicoloured .. 20 45

808. "Hindustan Pushpak" Aircraft and "Rohini – 1" Glider.

1979. Flying and Gliding.
952. 808. 30 p. blk., brn. & blue 80 60

809. Gurdwara Baoli Sahib Temple, Goindwal, Amritsar District.

1979. 500th Birth Anniv of Guru Amar Das (Sikh leader).
953 809 30 p. multicoloured .. 20 30

810. Ring of People encircling U.N. Emblem and Cog-wheel.

1980. Third United Nations Industrial Development Organization General Conference, New Delhi.
954. 810. 1 r. multicoloured .. 20 30

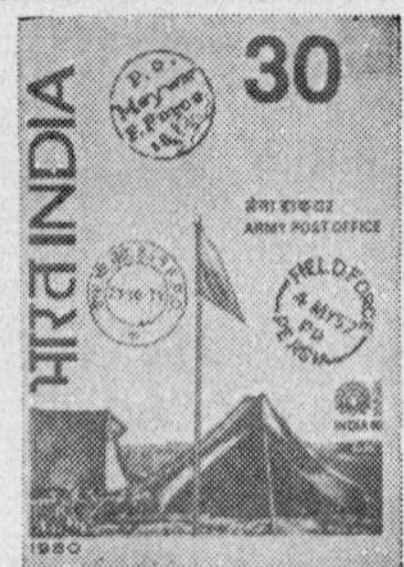

811. Army Post Office and Postmarks.

1980. "India 80" International Stamp Exhibition (3rd issue).
955. 811. 30 p. green 40 30
956. – 50 p. brn. and deep brn. 70 1·00
957. – 1 r. red .. .. 80 1·00
958. – 2 r. brown .. .. 80 1·75

DESIGNS: 50 p. Money order transfer document, 1879. 1 r. Copper prepayment tickets, 1774. 2 r. Sir Rowland Hill and birthplace at Kidderminster.

812. Energy Symbols.

1980. Institution of Engineers Commem.
959. 812. 30 p. gold and blue .. 20 30

813. Uniforms of 1780 and 1980, Crest and Ribbon.

1980. Bicentenary of Madras Sappers.
960. 813. 30 p. multicoloured .. 60 50

814. Books.

1980. Fourth World Book Fair, New Delhi.
961. 814. 30 p. blue 30 30

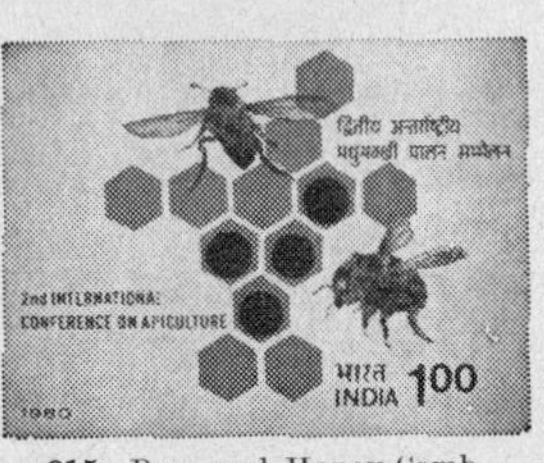

815. Bees and Honey-Comb.

1980. Second International Conference on Apiculture.
962. 815. 1 r. bistre and brown 30 45

816. Welthy Fisher and Saksharta Nicketan (Literacy House), Lucknow.

1980. Welthy Fisher Commemoration.
963. 816. 30 p. blue 30 30

817. Darul-Uloom, Deoband.

1980. Darul-Uloom Commemoration.
964. 817. 30 p. green 20 30

818. Keshub Chunder Sen.

1980. Keshub Chunder Sen (religious and social reformer). Commemoration.
965. 818. 30 p. brown 20 30

819. Chhatrapati Shivaji Maharaj.

1980. 300th Death Anniv. of Chhatrapati Shivaji Maharaj (Warrior).
966. 819. 30 p. multicoloured .. 20 30

820. Table Tennis.

1980. Fifth Asian Table Tennis Championships, Calcutta.
967. 820. 30 p. purple .. 30 30

1980. As Nos. 732 and 810. Size 17 × 20 mm.
968. 30 p. brown (Gandhi) .. 1·75 50
969. 30 p. violet (Nehru) .. 30 30

821. N. M. Joshi.

1980. Narayan Malhar Joshi (trade unionist) Commemoration.
970 821 30 p. mauve 60 40

822. Ulloor S. Parameswara Iyer.

1980. Ulloor S. Parameswara Iyer (poet). Commemoration.
971 822 30 p. purple 60 40

823. S. M. Zamin Ali.

1980. Syed Mohammed Zamin Ali (educationlist and poet) Commemoration.
972 823 30 p. green 20 40

824. Helen Keller.

1980. Birth Centenary of Helen Keller. (campaigner for the handicapped).
973. 824. 30 p. black and orange 50 40

825. High-jumping.

1980. Olympic Games, Moscow. Multicoloured.
974. 1 r. Type 825 .. 40 40
975. 2 r. 80 Horse-riding .. 1·10 1·75

826. Prem Chand.

1980. Birth Cent of Prem Chand (novelist).
976 826 30 p. brown 20 30

827. Mother Teresa and Nobel Peace Prize Medallion.

1980. Award of 1979 Nobel Peace Prize to Mother Teresa.
977 827 30 p. violet 30 30

828. Lord Mountbatten.

1980. Lord Mountbatten Commemoration.
978. 828. 2 r. 80 multicoloured 1·75 2·50

1980. As Nos. 968/9, but new face value.
979. 35 p. brown 50 30
980. 35 p. violet 30 20
DESIGNS: No. 979, Gandhi. No. 980, Nehru.

829. Scottish Church College, Calcutta.

1980. 150th Anniv. of Scottish Church College, Calcutta.
981. 829. 35 p. lilac 20 30

830. Rajah Annamalai Chettiar. 831. Gandhi marching to Dandi.

1980. Rajah Annamalai Chettiar (banker and educationist) Commemoration.
982 830 35 p. lilac 20 30

1980. 50th Anniv of "Dandi March" (Gandhi's defiance of Salt Tax Law) Commemoration.
983. 831. 35 p. blk., blue & gold 15 45
984. – 35 p. blk., mauve & gold 15 45
DESIGN: No. 984, Gandhi picking up handful of salt at Dandi.

832. Jayaprakash Narayan.

1980. Jayaprakash Narayan (socialist) Commemoration.
985 832 35 p. brown 40 40

833. Great Indian Bustard.

1980. International Symposium on Bustards.
986. 833. 2 r. 30 multicoloured .. 1·00 2·00

834. Arabic Commemorative Inscription.

1980. Moslem Year 1400 A.H. Commem.
987. 834. 35 p. multicoloured .. 15 30

835. "Girls Dancing" (Pampa Paul).

1980. Children's Day.
988. 835. 35 p. multicoloured .. 40 40

836. Dhyan Chand.

1980. Dhyan Chand (hockey player). Commemoration.
989. 836. 35 p. brown 80 75

837. Gold Mining.

1980. Cent of Kolar Gold Fields, Karnataka.
990 837 1 r. multicoloured .. 60 30

838. M. A. Ansari.

1980. Mukhtayar Ahmad Ansari (medical practitioner and politician) Commemoration.
991 838 35 p. green 40 40

839. India Government Mint, Bombay.

1980. 150th Anniv. of India Government Mint, Bombay.
992. 839. 35 p. blk., blue & silver 20 30

840. Bride from Tamil Nadu.

1980. Indian Bridal Costumes. Multicoloured.
993. 1 r. Type 840 .. .. 50 65
994. 1 r. Rajasthan 50 65
995. 1 r. Kashmir 50 65
996. 1 r. Bengal 50 65

841. Mazharul Haque.

1981. Mazharul Haque (journalist) Commem.
997 841 35 p. blue 20 40

842. St. Stephen's College.

1981. Centenary of St. Stephen's College, Delhi.
998. 842. 35 p. red 20 40

843. Gommateshwara 844. G. V. Mavalankar.

1981. Gommateshwara Statue at Shravanabelgola. Millennium.
999. 843. 1 r. multicoloured .. 20 30

1981. 25th Death Anniv of Ganesh Vasudeo Mavalankar (parliamentarian).
1000 844 35 p. red 20 40

845. Flame of Martyrdom.

1981. "Homage to Martyrs".
1001. 845. 35 p. multicoloured .. 20 30

846. Heinrich von Stephan and U.P.U. Emblem.

1981. 150th Birth Anniv. of Heinrich von Stephan (founder of U.P.U.).
1002. 846. 1 r. brown 20 50

847. Disabled Child being helped by Able-bodied Child.

1981. International Year for Disabled Persons.
1003. 847. 1 r. black and blue .. 20 30

848. Bhil. 849. Stylised Trees.

1981. Tribes of India. Multicoloured.
1004. 1 r. Type 848 .. .. 25 25
1005. 1 r. Dandami Maria .. 25 25
1006. 1 r. Toda 25 25
1007. 1 r. Khlamngam Naga .. 25 25

1981. Forests Conservation.
1008. 849. 1 r. multicoloured .. 20 30

850. Nilmoni Phukan.

1981. Nilmoni Phukan (poet) Commemoration.
1009. 850. 35 p. brown 20 40

851. Sanjay Gandhi.

1981. 1st Death Anniv. of Sanjay Gandhi (politician).
1010. 851. 35 p. multicoloured .. 20 40

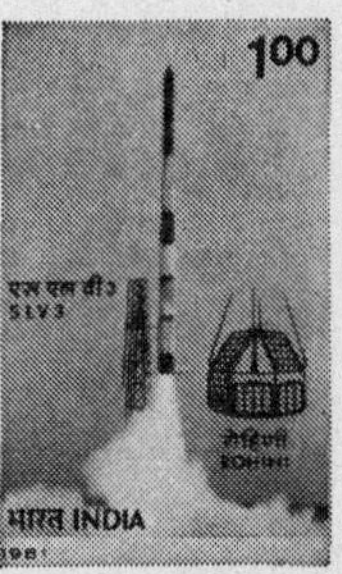
852. Launch of "SLV 3" and Diagram of "Rohini".

1981. Launch of "SLV 3" Rocket with "Rohini" Satellite.
1011. 852. 1 r. black, pink & blue 30 30

853. Games Logo.

1981. Asian Games, New Delhi (1st issue). Multicoloured.

1012. 1 r. Type **853** .. .. 1·00 50
1013. 1 r. Games emblem and stylised hockey players 1·00 50

See also Nos. 1026, 1033, 1057, 1059 and 1061/6.

854. Flame of the Forest.

1981. Flowering Trees. Multicoloured.

1014. 35 p. Type **854** 30 15
1015. 50 p. Crateva 45 40
1016. 1 r. Golden Shower .. 55 40
1017. 2 r. Bauhinia .. .. 70 1·00

855. W.F.D. Emblem and Wheat.

1981. World Food Day.

1018. **855.** 1 r. yellow and blue.. 20 20

856. "Stichopthalma camadeva".

1981. Butterflies. Multicoloured.

1019. 35 p. Type **856** 60 15
1020. 50 p. "Cethosia biblis" 1·25 50
1021. 1 r. "Cyrestis achates" 1·50 50
1022. 2 r. "Teinopalpus imperialis" (vert.) .. 1·60 2·00

857. Bellary Raghava.

1981. Bellary Raghava (actor) Commem.

1023. **857.** 35 p. green 40 30

858. Regimental Flag.

1981. 40th Anniv. of Mahar Regiment.

1024. **858.** 35 p. multicoloured.. 60 30

859. "Toyseller" (Kumari Ruchita Sharma).

1981. Children's Day. Child's Painting.

1025. **859.** 35 p. multicoloured.. 40 30

860. Rajghat Stadium.

1981. Asian Games, New Delhi (2nd issue).

1026. **860.** 1 r. multicoloured .. 75 30

861. Kashi Prasad Jayasawal and Yaudheya Coin.

1981. Birth Centenary of Kashi Prasad Jayasawal (lawyer and historian).

1027. **861.** 35 p. blue 30 30

862. Indian and P.L.O. Flags, and People.

1981. Palestinian Solidarity.

1028. **862.** 1 r. multicoloured .. 1·50 40

863. I.N.S. "Taragiri" (frigate).

1981. Indian Navy Day.

1029. **863.** 35 p. multicoloured.. 1·50 85

864. Henry Heras and Indus Valley Seal.

1981. Henry Heras (historian) Commem.

1030. **864.** 35 p. lilac 45 30

865. Map of South-East Asia showing Cable Route.

1981. Inauguration of I.O.C.O.M. (Indian Ocean Commonwealth Cable) Submarine Telephone Cable.

1031 **865** 1 r. multicoloured .. 1·25 35

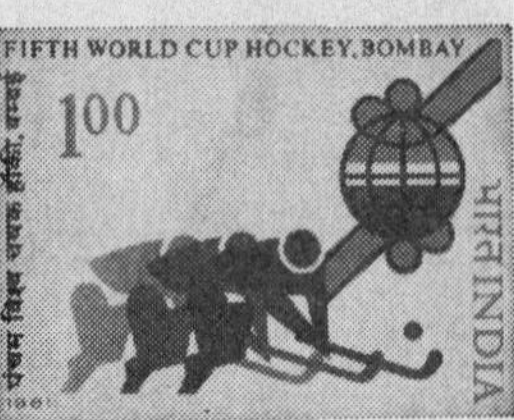
866. Stylised Hockey-player and Championship Emblem.

1981. World Cup Hockey Championship, Bombay.

1032. **866.** 1 r. multicoloured .. 75 30

867. Jawaharlal Nehru Stadium.

1981. Asian Games, New Delhi (3rd issue).

1033. **867.** 1 r. multicoloured .. 30 20

868. Early and Modern Telephones.

1982. Centenary of Telephone Services.

1034. **868.** 2 r. black, blue & grey 30 30

869. Map of World.

1982. International Soil Science Congress, New Delhi.

1035. **869.** 1 r. multicoloured .. 30 20

870. Sir J. J. School of Art.

1982. 125th Anniv. of Sir J. J. School of Art, Bombay.

1036. **870.** 35 p. multicoloured.. 20 20

871. "Three Musicians".

1982. Birth Centenary (1981) of Picasso.

1037. **871.** 2 r. 85 multicoloured 50 50

872. Deer (stone carving), 5th-century **A.D.**

1982. Festival of India. Ancient Sculpture. Multicoloured.

1038. 2 r. Type **872** 20 40
1039. 3 r. 05 Kaliya Mardana (bronze statue), 9th-century A.D... .. 35 60

873. Radio Telescope, Ooty.

1982. Festival of India. Science and Technology.

1040. **873.** 3 r. 05 multicoloured 35 40

874. Robert Koch and Symbol of Disease.

1982. Centenary of Robert Koch's Discovery of Tubercle Bacillus.

1041. **874.** 35 p. lilac 75 40

875. Durgabai Deshmukh.

1982. 1st Death Anniv. of Durgabai Deshmukh (social reformer).

1042. **875.** 35 p. blue 30 40

876. Blue Poppy.

1982. Himalayan Flowers. Multicoloured.

1043 35 p. Type **876** 40 20
1044 1 r. Showy inula .. 85 30
1045 2 r. Cobra lily .. 1·40 1·75
1046 2 r. 85 Brahma kamal .. 1·60 2·25

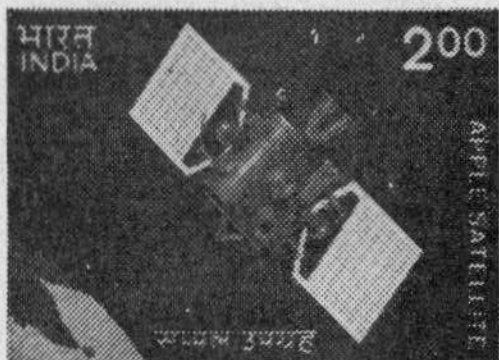
877. "Apple" Satellite.

1982. 1st Anniv. of "Apple" Satellite Launch.

1047. **877.** 2 r. multicoloured .. 40 80

878. Bidhan Chandra Roy.

1982. Birth Centenary of Bidhan Chandra Roy (doctor and politician).
1048. **878.** 50 p. brown 50 70

879. " Sagar Samrat " Oil Rig.

1982. 25th Anniv. of Oil and Natural Gas Commission.
1049. **879.** 1 r. multicoloured .. 40 40

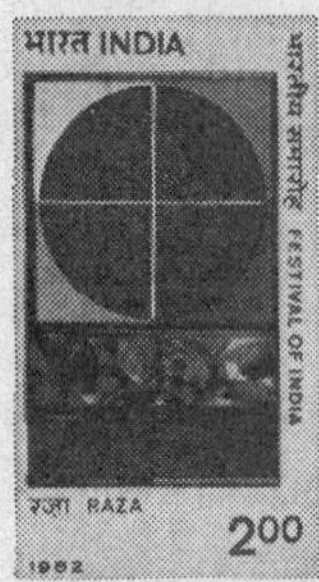

880. "Bindu" (S. H. Raza).

1982. Festival of India. Contemporary Paintings. Multicoloured.
1050 2 r. Type **880** 30 50
1051 3 r. 05 "Between the Spider and the Lamp" (M. F. Hussain) .. 45 1·25

881. Red Deer.

1982. Wildlife Conservation.
1052. **881.** 2 r. 85 multicoloured 1·00 1·25

882. " Wapiti " and " Mig-25 " Aircraft.

1982. 50th Anniv. of Indian Air Force.
1053. **882.** 1 r. multicoloured .. 2·00 60

883. J. Tata with " Puss Moth ".

1982. 50th Anniv. of Civil Aviation in India.
1054. **883.** 3 r. 25 multicoloured 2·75 1·25

884. Police Patrol.

1982. Police Commemoration Day.
1055. **884.** 50 p. green 50 30

885. Coins and Economic Symbols.

1982. Centenary of Post Office Savings Bank.
1056. **885.** 50 p. brown and light brown 20 20

886. Wrestling Bout.

1982. Asian Games, New Delhi (4th issue).
1057. **886.** 1 r. multicoloured .. 30 30

887. Troposcatter Communication Link.

1982. 1st Anniv. of Troposcatter Communication Link between India and U.S.S.R.
1058. **887.** 3 r. 05 multicoloured 30 40

888. Krishna shooting Arrow at Fish.

1982. Asian Games, New Delhi (5th issue).
1059. **888.** 1 r. multicoloured .. 1·25 30

889. "Mother and Child" (Deepak Sharma)

1982. Children's Day.
1060. **889.** 50 p. multicoloured .. 30 30

890. Stylised Cyclists.

1982. Asian Games, New Delhi (6th issue). Multicoloured.
1061. 50 p. Type **890** 10 10
1062. 2 r. Javelin-throwing .. 25 30
1063. 2 r. 85 Discus-throwing 30 45
1064. 3 r. 25 Football 40 55

891. Yachting.

1982. Asian Games, New Delhi (7th issue). Multicoloured.
1065. 2 r. Type **891** 25 30
1066. 2 r. 25 Rowing 30 40

892. Chetwode Building.

1982. 50th Anniv of Indian Military Academy, Dehradun.
1067 **892** 50 p. multicoloured .. 30 40

893. Purushottamdas Tandon.

1982. Birth Cent of Purushottamdas Tandon (politician).
1068 **893** 50 p. brown 30 50

894. Darjeeling Himalayan Railway.

1982. Cent. of Darjeeling Himalayan Railway.
1069. **894.** 2 r. 85 multicoloured 2·50 2·75

895. Vintage Rail Coach and Silhouette of Steam Engine.

1982. " Impex 82 " Stamp Exhibition. Multicoloured.
1070. 50 p. Type **895** 40 50
1071. 2 r. 1854 ½ anna blue stamp and 1947 3½ anna Independence Commem. (33 × 44 mm.) .. 1·10 1·50

INDEX

Countries can be quickly located by referring to the index at the end of this volume.

896. Antarctic Camp.

1983. 1st Indian Antarctic Expedition.
1072. **896.** 1 r. multicoloured .. 2·00 1·75

1983. As Nos. 968/9, but with new face value.
1073a 50 p. brown (Gandhi) .. 2·00 80
1074a 50 p. blue (Nehru) .. 75 30

897. Roosevelt with Stamp Collection.

1983. Birth Centenary of Franklin D. Roosevelt (American statesman).
1075. **897.** 3 r. 25 brown .. 45 1·00

898. "Great White Cranes at Bharatpur" (Diane Pierce).

1983. International Crane Workshop, Bharatpur.
1076. **898.** 2 r. 85 mult .. .. 1·50 2·00

899. Jat Regiment Uniforms Past and Present.

1983. Presentation of Colours to Battalions of the Jat Regiment.
1077. **899.** 50 p. mult. 80 80

900. Non-aligned Summit Logo.

1983. 7th Non-aligned Summit Conference. New Delhi.
1078. **900.** 1 r. lt. brown, brown and black 20 30
1079. – 2 r. multicoloured .. 30 95
DESIGN: 2 r. Nehru.

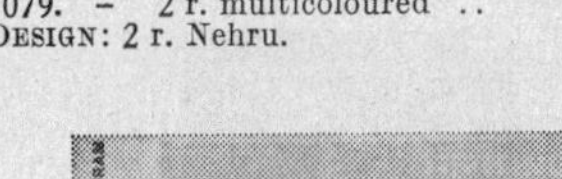

901. Shore Temple, Mahabalipuram.

1983. Commonwealth Day. Multicoloured.
1080. 1 r. Type **901** 15 30
1081. 2 r. Gomukh, Gangtotri Glacier 30 95

902. Acropolis and Olympic Emblems.

1983. International Olympic Committee Session, New Delhi.
1082. **902.** 1 r. multicoloured .. 20 40

903. " St. Francis and Brother Falcon" (statue by Giovanni Collina).

1983. 800th Birth Anniv. of St. Francis of Assisi.
1083. **903.** 1 r. brown 20 30

904. Karl Marx and " Das Kapital ".

1983. Death Centenary of Karl Marx.
1084. **904.** 1 r. brown 20 30

905. Darwin and Map of Voyage.

1983. Death Centenary of Charles Darwin.
1085. **905.** 2 r. multicoloured .. 1·25 2·00

906. Swamp Deer.

1983. 50th Anniv. of Kanha National Park.
1086. **906.** 1 r. multicoloured .. 40 50

907. Globe and Satellite.

1983. World Communications Year.
1087. **907.** 1 r. multicoloured .. 30 40

908. Simon Bolivar.

1983. Birth Bicentenary of Simon Bolivar (South American statesman).
1088. **908.** 2 r. multicoloured .. 75 1·50

909. Meera Behn.

1983. India's Struggle for Freedom (1st series).
1089. 50 p. red and green .. 50 1·00
1090. 50 p. brown, green & red 50 1·00
1091. 50 p. multicoloured .. 50 75
1092. 50 p. brown, green & red 15 30
1093. 50 p. brn., grn. & orge... 15 30
1094. 50 p. grn., yell. & orge. 15 30

Designs—vert. No. 1089, Type **909**. 1090, Mahadev Desai 1092, Hemu Kalani (revolutionary). 1093, Acharya Vinoba Bhave (social reformer). 1094, Surendranath Banerjee (political reformer). horiz. (43 × 31 mm.). No. 1091, Quit India Resolution.

See also Nos. 1119/24, 1144/9, 1191/4, 1230/5, 1287/96 and 1345/9.

910. Ram Nath Chopra.

1983. Ram Nath Chopra (pharmacologist). Commemoration.
1095. **910.** 50 p. red 30 60

911. Nanda Devi Mountain.

1983. 25th Anniv. of Indian Mountaineering Federation.
1096. **911.** 2 r. multicoloured .. 60 80

912. Great Indian Hornbill.

1983. Centenary of Natural History Society, Bombay.
1097. **912.** 1 r. multicoloured .. 75 35

913. View of Garden.

1983. Rock Garden, Chandigarh.
1098. **913.** 1 r. multicoloured .. 60 60

914. Golden Langur.

1983. Indian Wildlife. Monkeys. Mult.
1099. 1 r. Type **914** 40 30
1100. 2 r. Lion-tailed Macaque 85 1·25

915. Ghats of Varanasi.

1983. Fifth General Assembly of World Tourism Organization.
1101. **915.** 2 r. multicoloured .. 40 40

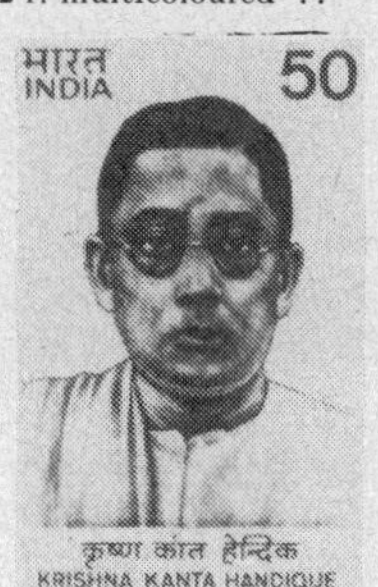

916. Krishna Kanta Handique.

1983. Krishna Kanta Handique (scholar).
1102. **916.** 50 p. blue 30 50

918. Woman and Child (From "Festival" by Kashyap Premsawala).

1983. Children's Day.
1103. **918.** 50 p. multicoloured .. 30 50

920. "Udan Khatola", First Indian Hot Air Balloon.

1983. Bicentenary of Manned Flight.
1104. 1 r. Type **920** 30 20
1105. 2 r. Montgolfier balloon .. 50 60

921. Tiger.

1983. Ten Years of Project Tiger.
1106. **921.** 2 r. multicoloured .. 1·25 1·50

922. Commonwealth Logo.

1983. Commonwealth Heads of Government Meeting, New Delhi. Multicoloured.
1107. 1 r. Type **922** 10 15
1108. 2 r. Goanese couple, early 19th century 25 30

923. "Pratiksha".

1983. Birth Centenary of Nanda Lal Bose (artist).
1109. **923.** 1 r. multicoloured .. 30 30

925. Lancer.

1984. Bicentenary of 7th Light Calvary.
1110. **925.** 1 r. multicoloured .. 2·00 90

926. Troopers in Ceremonial Uniform and Tank.

1984. The Deccan Horse Calvary Regiment (1790–1984).
1111. **926.** 1 r. multicoloured .. 2·00 90

927. Society Building and Sir William Jones (founder).

1984. Bicentenary of Asiatic Society.
1112. **927.** 1 r. green and purple 30 50

928. Insurance Logo.

1984. Centenary of Postal Life Insurance.
1113. **928.** 1 r. multicoloured .. 30 30

929. " Sea Harrier " Aircraft.

1984. President's Review of the Fleet. Mult.
1114 1 r. Type **929** 50 60
1115 1 r. "Vikrant" (aircraft carrier) 50 60
1116 1 r. "Vela" (submarine) .. 50 60
1117 1 r. "Kashin" (destroyer) 50 60
Nos. 1114/17 were printed together, se-tenant, forming a composite design.

930. I.L.A. Logo and Hemispheres.

1984. 12th International Leprosy Congress.
1118. **930.** 1 r. multicoloured .. 30 30

1984. India's Struggle for Freedom (2nd series). As T **909**.
1119. 50 p. grn., lt. grn. & orge. 15 25
1120. 50 p. brn., grn. & orge... 15 25
1121. 50 p. multicoloured .. 15 25
1122. 50 p. multicoloured .. 15 25
1123. 50 p. multicoloured .. 15 25
1124. 50 p. multicoloured .. 15 25
DESIGNS: No. 1119, Vasudeo Balvant Phadke (revolutionary). 1120, Baba Kanshi Ram (revolutionary). 1121, Tatya Tope. 1122, Nana Sahib. 1123, Begum Hazarat Mahal. 1124, Mangal Pandey.

932. "Salyut 7".

1984. Indo-Soviet Manned Space Flight.
1125. **932.** 3 r. multicoloured .. 55 55

935. G. D. Birla.

1984. 90th Birth Anniv. of G. D. Birla (industrialist).
1126. **935.** 50 p. brown 30 60

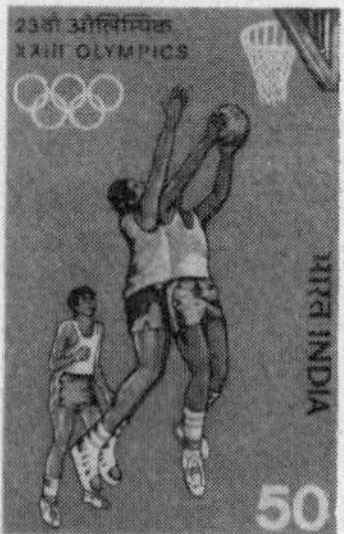

936. Basketball.

1984. Olympic Games, Los Angeles. Multicoloured.
1127. 50 p. Type **936** 30 20
1128. 1 r. High jumping .. 35 20
1129. 2 r. Gymnastics (horiz.) 60 85
1130. 2 r. 50 Weightlifting (horiz.) .. .. 1·00 1·50

937. Gwalior.

1984. Forts. Multicoloured.
1131. 50 p. Type **937** 50 30
1132. 1 r. Vellore (vert.) 75 30
1133. 1 r. 50 Simhagad (vert.) 1·00 1·40
1134. 2 r. Jodhpur .. .. 1·25 1·75

938. B. V. Paradkar and Newspaper.

1984. B. V. Paradkar (journalist) Commemoration.
1135. **938.** 50 p. brown 30 50

939. Dr. D. N. Wadia and Institute of Himalayan Geology, Dehradun.

1984. Birth Centenary (1983) of Dr. D. N. Wadia (geologist).
1136. **939.** 1 r. multicoloured .. 50 30

940. "Herdsman and Cattle in Forest".

1984. Children's Day.
1137. **940.** 50 p. multicoloured 40 60

941. Indira Gandhi (Illustration reduced, actual size 51×51 mm.).

1984. Indira Gandhi (Prime Minister) Commemoration (1st issue).
1138. **941.** 50 p. black, violet and orange .. 80 70
See also Nos. 1151, 1167 and 1170.

942. Congress and Emblem.

1984. 12th World Mining Congress, New Delhi.
1139. **942.** 1 r. black and yellow 40 30

943. Dr. Rajendra Prasad at Desk.

1984. Birth Centenary of Dr. Rajendra Prasad (former President).
1140. **943.** 50 p. multicoloured 55 55

944. Mrinalini (rose).

1984. Roses. Multicoloured.
1141. 1 r. 50, Type **944** .. 1·25 1·25
1142. 2 r. Sugandha .. .. 1·50 1·50

945. "Fergusson College" (Gopal Deuskar).

1985. Centenary of Fergusson College, Pune.
1143. **945.** 1 r. multicoloured .. 30 30

1985. India's Struggle for Freedom (3rd series). As T **909**.
1144. 50 p. brn., grn. & orge... 30 30
1145. 50 p. brn., grn. & orge... 30 30
1146. 50 p. brn., grn. & orge... 30 30
1147. 50 p. brn., grn. & orge... 30 30
1148. 50 p. bl., grn. & orge. .. 30 30
1149. 50 p. blk., grn. & orge... 30 30
DESIGNS:—VERT. No. 1144, Narhar Vishnu Gadgil (politician). 1145, Jairamdas Doulatram (journalist). 1147, Kakasaheb Kalelkar (author). 1148, Master Tara Singh (politician). 1149, Ravishankar Maharaj (politician). HORIZ. No. 1146, Jatindra and Nellie Sengupta (politicians).

947. Gunner and Howitzer from Mountain Battery.

1985. 50th Anniv. of Regiment of Artillery.
1150. **947.** 1 r. multicoloured .. 2·50 1·25

948. Indira Gandhi making Speech.

1985. Indira Gandhi Commemoration (2nd issue).
1151. **948.** 2 r. multicoloured .. 1·75 1·75

949. Minicoy Lighthouse.

1985. Centenary of Minicoy Lighthouse.
1152. **949.** 1 r. multicoloured .. 2·25 75

950. Medical College Hospital.

1985. 150th Anniv. of Medical College, Calcutta.

1153. **950.** 1 r. yellow, brown and purple .. 1·25 45

951. Medical College, Madras.

1985. 150th Anniv. of Medical College, Madras.

1154. **951.** 1 r. light brown and brown .. .. 1·25 45

952. Riflemen of 1835 and 1985, and Map of North-East India.

1985. 150th Anniv. of Assam Rifles.

1155. **952.** 1 r. multicoloured .. 2·00 1·00

953. Potato Plant.

1985. 50th Anniv. of Potato Research in India.

1156. **953.** 50 p. deep brown and brown 80 70

954. Baba Jassa Singh Ahluwalia.

1985. Death Bicentenary (1983) of Baba Jassa Singh Ahluwalia (Sikh leader).

1157. **954.** 50 p. purple 70 70

955. St. Xavier's College.

1985. 125th Anniv. of St. Xavier's College, Calcutta.

1158. **955.** 1 r. multicoloured .. 50 50

956. White-winged Wood Duck.

1985. Wildlife Conservation. White-winged Wood Duck.

1159. **956.** 2 r. multicoloured .. 3·25 3·25

957. "Mahara".

1985. Bougainvillea. Multicoloured.

1160. 50 p. Type **957** 75 75

1161. 1 r. "H. B. Singh" .. 1·25 1·25

958. Yaudheya Copper Coin, *c* 200 B.C.

1985. Festival of India (1st issue).

1162. **958.** 2 r. multicoloured .. 1·50 1·50

959. Statue of Didarganj Yakshi (deity).

1985. Festival of India (2nd issue).

1163. **959.** 1 r. multicoloured .. 40 30

962. Swami Haridas.

1985. Swami Haridas (philosopher) Commemoration.

1164. **962.** 1 r. multicoloured .. 1·00 1·00

HAVE YOU READ THE NOTES AT THE BEGINNING OF THIS CATALOGUE?

These often provide answers to the enquiries we receive.

963. Stylised Mountain Road.

1985. 25th Anniv. of Border Roads Organization.

1165. **963.** 2 r. red, violet and black .. .. 1·25 1·25

964. Nehru addressing General Assembly.

1985. 40th Anniv. of United Nations Organization.

1166. **964.** 2 r. multicoloured .. 50 50

965. Indira Gandhi with Crowd.

1985. Indira Gandhi Commemoration (3rd issue).

1167. **965.** 2 r. brown-black and black .. .. 1·25 1·50

966. Girl using Home Computer.

1985. Children's Day.

1168. **966.** 50 p. multicoloured 50 60

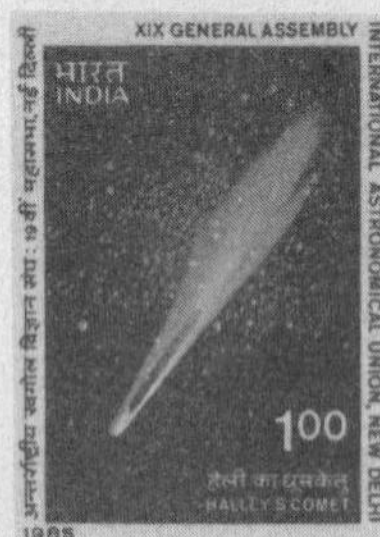

967. Halley's Comet.

1985. 19th General Assembly of International Astronomical Union, New Delhi.

1169. **967.** 1 r. multicoloured .. 80 80

968. Indira Gandhi.

1985. Indira Gandhi Commemoration (4th issue).

1170. **968.** 3 r. multicoloured .. 1·75 1·75

969. St. Stephen's Hospital.

1985. Centenary of St. Stephen's Hospital, Delhi.

1171. **969.** 1 r. black and brown 50 40

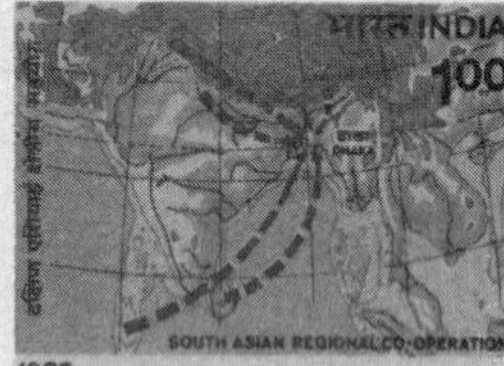

971. Map showing Member States.

1985. 1st Summit Meeting of South Asian Association for Regional Co-operation, Dhaka, Bangladesh. Multicoloured.

1172. 1 r. Type **971** 75 25

1173. 3 r. Flags of member nations (44 × 32 mm.) .. 1·75 2·25

972. Shyama Shastri.

1985. Shyama Shastri (composer) Commemoration.

1174. **972.** 1 r. multicoloured .. 1·50 80

975. Young Runners and Emblem.

1985. International Youth Year.

1175. **975.** 2 r. multicoloured .. 60 60

976. Handel and Bach. (Illustration reduced, actual size 55 × 35 mm.).

1985. 300th Birth Annivs. of George Frederick Handel and Johann Sebastian Bach (composers).

1176. **976.** 5 r. multicoloured .. 2·25 2·25

977. A. O. Hume (founder) and Early Congress Presidents.

1985. Centenary of Indian National Congress. Designs showing miniature portraits of Congress Presidents.

1177. **977.** 1 r. black, orange, green and grey .. 75 75
1178. – 1 r. black, orange and green 75 75
1179. – 1 r. black, orange and green 75 75
1180. – 1 r. black, orange, green and grey .. 75 75

Nos. 1178/80 each show sixteen miniature portraits. The individual stamps can be distinguished by the position of the face value and inscription which are at the top on Nos. 1177/8 and at the foot on Nos. 1179/80. No. 1180 shows a portrait of Prime Minister Rajiv Gandhi in a grey frame at bottom right.

978. Bombay and Duncan Dry Docks, Bombay.

1986. 250th Anniv. of Naval Dockyard, Bombay.

1181. **978.** 2 r. 50 multicoloured 2·25 2·25

979. Hawa Mahal and Jaipur 1904 2 a. Stamp.

1986. "INPEX 86" Philatelic Exhibition, Jaipur. Multicoloured.

1182. 50 p. Type **979** 75 40
1183. 2 r. Mobile camel post office, Thar Desert .. 1·50 2·00

980. I.N.S. "Vikrant" (aircraft carrier).

1986. Completion of 25 Years Service by I.N.S. "Vikrant".

1184. **980.** 2 r. multicoloured .. 2·75 2·75

981. Humber-Sommer Biplane and Later Mail Planes.

1986. 75th Anniversary of First Official Airmail Flight, Allahabad—Naini. Mult.

1185. 50 p. Type **981** .. .. 1·50 75
1186. 3 r. Modern Air India mail plane and Humber-Sommer biplane (37 × 24 mm) .. 3·75 4·25

982. Triennale Emblem.

1986. 6th Triennale Art Exhibition, New Delhi.

1187. **982.** 1 r. pur., yell. & blk. 1·00 70

983. Chaitanya Mahaprabhu.

1986. 500th Birth Anniv. of Chaitanya Mahaprabhu (religious leader).

1188. **983.** 2 r. multicoloured .. 2·00 2·25

984. Main Building, Mayo College.

1986. Mayo College (public school), Ajmer, Commemoration.

1189. **984.** 1 r. multicoloured .. 1·00 75

985. Two Footballers.

1986. World Cup Football Championship, Mexico.

1190. **985.** 5 r. multicoloured .. 3·00 3·00

1986. India's Struggle for Freedom (4th series). As T **909**.

1191. 50 p. brown, grn. & red 70 80
1192. 50 p. brown, grn. & red 70 80
1193. 50 p. black, grn. & orge. 70 80
1194. 50 p. brown, grn. & red 70 80

Designs: No. 1191, Bhim Sen Sachar. 1192, Alluri Seetarama Raju. 1193, Sagarmal Gopa. 1194, Veer Surendra Sai.

987. Swami Sivananda.

1986. Swami Sivananda (spiritual leader) Birth Centenary.

1195. **987.** 2 r. multicoloured .. 2·00 2·00

988. Volleyball.

1986. Asian Games, Seoul, South Korea. Multicoloured.

1196. 1 r. 50 Type **988** .. .. 1·50 1·50
1197. 3 r. Hurdling .. .. 2·25 2·75

989. Madras G.P.O.

1986. Bicentenary of Madras G.P.O.

1198. **989.** 5 r. black and red .. 3·50 3·50

990. Parachutist.

1986. 225th Anniv. of 8th Battalion of Coast Sepoys (now 1st Battalion Parachute Regiment).

1199. **990.** 3 r. multicoloured .. 3·75 4·00

991. Early and Modern Policemen.

1986. 125th Anniv. of Indian Police. Designs showing early and modern police.

1200. **991.** 1 r. 50 multicoloured 2·25 2·50
1201. – 2 r. multicoloured .. 2·25 2·50

Nos. 1200/1 were printed together, se-tenant, forming a composite design.

992. Hand holding Flower and World Map.

1986. International Peace Year.

1202. **992.** 5 r. multicoloured .. 1·50 85

993. "Girl Rock Climber" (Sujasha Dasgupta).

1986. Children's Day.

1203. **993.** 50 p. multicoloured 1·50 1·25

994. Windmill.

1986. Science and Technology.

1211 – 35 p. red 10 10
1212 – 40 p. red 10 10
1213 – 60 p. green and red .. 10 10
1214 – 75 p. orange 10 10
1217 – 5 r. brown and orange 20 25
1218 – 20 r. brown and blue 80 85
1219 **994** 50 r. black, blue & red 2·00 2·10

Designs—horiz. (20 × 17 mm). 35 p. Family planning. (37 × 20 mm). 60 p. Indian family (as T **994**) 20 r. Bio gas. vert. (17 × 20 mm). 40 p. Television set, dish aerial and transmitter (as T **994**). 75 p. "Family" (as No. 927). 5 r. Solar energy.

995. Growth Monitoring.

1986. 40th Anniv. of U.N.I.C.E.F. Mult.

1221. 50 p. Type **995** .. .. 1·00 75
1222. 5 r. Immunization .. 3·25 4·00

996. Tansen.

1986. Tansen (musician and composer) Commemoration.

1223. **996.** 1 r. multicoloured .. 1·75 45

997. Indian Elephant.

1986. 50th Anniv. of Corbett National Park. Multicoloured.

1224. 1 r. Type **997** .. .. 2·50 1·00
1225. 2 r. Gharial .. .. 3·00 4·00

998. St. Martha's Hospital.

1986. Centenary of St. Martha's Hospital, Bangalore.
1226. **998.** 1 r. bl., orge. & blk. 1·50 1·00

999. Yacht "Trishna" and Route Map.

1987. Indian Army Round the World Yacht Voyage, 1985–7.
1227. **999.** 6 r. 50 multicoloured 3·25 2·75

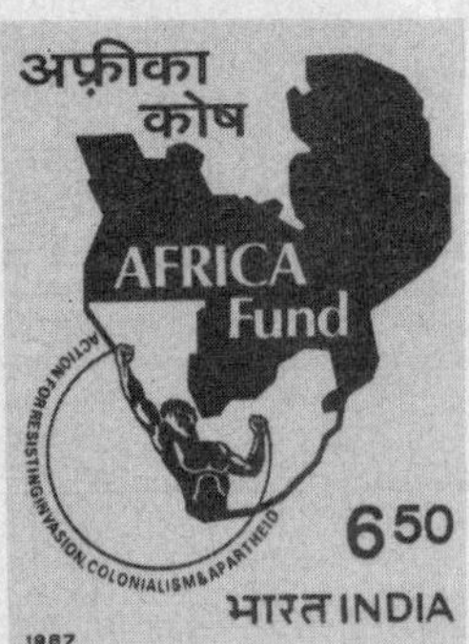

1000. Map of Southern Africa and Logo.

1987. Inauguration of AFRICA Fund.
1228. **1000.** 6 r. 50 black .. 3·25 3·00

1001. Emblem.

1987. 29th Congress of International Chamber of Commerce, New Delhi.
1229. **1001.** 5 r. violet, bl. & red 2·75 1·50

1987. India's Struggle for Freedom (5th series). As T **909**.
1230. 60 p. brown, grn. & orge. 70 30
1231. 60 p. violet, grn. & red 30 30
1232. 60 p. brown, grn. & red 30 30
1233. 60 p. blue, grn. & orge. 30 30
1234. 60 p. brown, grn. & red 30 30
1235. 60 p. brown, grn. & red 30 30
1236. 60 p. red, green & orge. 30 30
DESIGNS: No. 1230, Hakim Aimal Khan. No. 1231, Lala Har Dayal. No. 1232, M.N. Roy. No. 1233, Tripuraneni Ramaswamy Chowdary. No. 1234, Dr. Kailas Math Katyu. No. 1235, S. Satyamarti. No. 1236, Pandit Hriday Nath Kunzru.

MINIMUM PRICE

The minimum price quoted is 10p which represents a handling charge rather than a basis for valuing common stamps. For further notes about prices see introductory pages.

1002. Blast Furnace.

1987. Centenary of South Eastern Railway. Multicoloured.
1237. 1 r. Type **1002**. 40 15
1238. 1 r. 50 Metre-gauge tank locomotive, No. 691, 1887 (horiz.) 45 35
1239. 2 r. Electric train on viaduct, 1987 .. .. 55 50
1240. 4 r. Steam locomotive, c. 1900 (horiz.) .. 80 1·00

1003. Kalia Bhomora Bridge, Tezpur, Assam.

1987. Inauguration of Brahmaputra Bridge.
1241. **1003.** 2 r. multicoloured .. 30 30

1004. Madras Christian College.

1987. 150th Anniv. of Madras Christian College.
1242. **1004.** 1 r. 50 black and red 20 20

1005. Shree Shree Ma Anandamayee.

1987. Shree Shree Ma Anandamayee (Hindu spiritual leader) Commemoration.
1243. **1005.** 1 r. brown 20 20

1006. "Rabindranath Tagore" (self-portrait).

1987. Rabindranath Tagore (poet) Commem.
1244. **1006.** 2 r. multicoloured .. 30 30

1007. Garwhal Rifles Uniforms of 1887.

1987. Centenary of Garwhal Rifles Regiment.
1245. **1007.** 1 r. multicoloured .. 40 20

1008. J. Krishnamurti.

1987. J. Krishnamurti (philosopher) Commemoration.
1246. **1008.** 60 p. brown .. 40 60

1009. Regimental Uniforms of 1887.

1987. Centenary of 37th Dogra Regt (now 7th Battalion (1 Dogra), Mechanised Infantry Regt.
1247. **1009.** 1 r. multicoloured .. 40 20

1010. Hall of Nations, Pragati Maidan, New Delhi.

1987. "India-89" International Stamp Exhibition, New Delhi (1st issue). Multicoloured.
1248. 50 p. Exhibition logo .. 10 15
1249. 5 r. Type **1010** 45 50
See also Nos. 1264/7, 1333/4, 1341/2 and 1358/61.

1011. "Sadyah-Snata" Sculpture, Sanghol.

1987. Festival of India, U.S.S.R.
1251. **1011.** 6 r. 50 multicoloured 1·00 75

1012. Flag and Stylized Birds with "40" in English and Hindi. (Illustration reduced. Actual size 54 × 35 mm).

1987. 40th Anniv. of Independence.
1252. **1012.** 60 p. orge, grn. & bl. 20 20

1013. Sant Harchand Singh Longowal.

1987. Sant Harchand Singh Longowal (Sikh leader). Commemoration.
1253. **1013.** 1 r. multicoloured .. 30 20

1014. Guru Ghasidas.

1987. Guru Ghasidas (Hindu leader) Commemoration.
1254. **1014.** 60 p. red 20 20

1015. Thakur Anukul Chandra.

1987. Thakur Anukul Chandra (spiritual leader) Commemoration.
1255. **1015.** 1 r. multicoloured .. 40 20

1016. University of Allahabad.

1987. Centenary of Allahabad University.
1256. **1016.** 2 r. multicoloured .. 30 40

INDEX

Countries can be quickly located by referring to the index at the end of this volume.

1017. Pankha Offering.

1987. Phoolwalon Ki Sair Festival, Delhi.
1257. **1017.** 2 r. multicoloured .. 30 40

1018. Chhatrasal on Horseback.

1987. Chhatrasal (Bundela ruler) Commemoration.
1258. **1018.** 60 p. brown .. 30 20

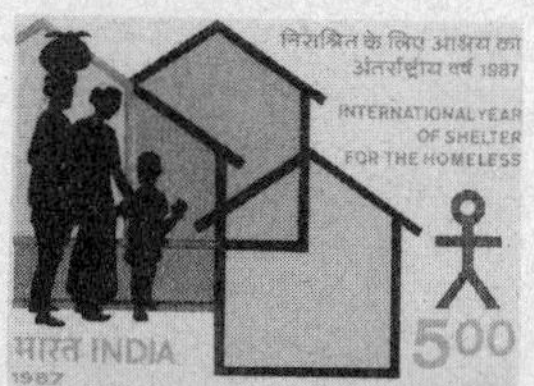

1019. Family and Stylised Houses.

1987. International Year of Shelter for the Homeless.
1259. **1019.** 5 r. multicoloured .. 45 60

1020. Map of Asia and Logo.

1987. Asia Regional Conference of Rotary International.
1260. **1020.** 60 p. brn. & grn. .. 15 15
1261. – 6 r. 50 multicoloured 60 80
DESIGN: 6 r. 50, Oral polio vaccination.

1021. Blind Boy, Braille Books and Computer.

1987. Centenary of Service to Blind.
1262. **1021.** 1 r. multicoloured .. 15 15
1263. – 2 r. dp. bl. & bl. .. 35 30
DESIGN: 2 r. Eye donation.

1022. Iron Pillar, Delhi.

1987. "India-89" International Stamp Exhibition, New Delhi (2nd issue). Delhi Landmarks. Multicoloured.
1264 60 p. Type **1022** 10 15
1265 1 r. 50 India Gate .. 15 20
1266 5 r. Dewan-e-Khas, Red Fort 45 50
1267 6 r. 50 Old Fort 60 65

1023. Tyagmurti Goswami Ganeshdutt.

1987. Tyagmurti Goswami Ganeshdutt (spiritual leader and social reformer). Commemoration.
1269. **1023.** 60 p. red 20 20

1024. "My Home" (Siddharth Deshprabha).

1987. Children's Day.
1270. **1024.** 60 p. multicoloured 30 20

1025. Chinar.

1987. Indian Trees. Multicoloured.
1271. **1025.** 60 p. multicoloured 15 15
1272. – 1 r. 50 multicoloured 20 20
1273. – 5 r. black, green and brown 55 65
1274. – 6 r. 50 brown, red and green .. 80 80
DESIGNS:—HORIZ. 1 r. 50, Pipal. 6 r. 50, Banyan. VERT. 5 r. Sal.

1026. Logo (from sculpture "The Worker and the Woman Peasant" by V. Mukhina).

1987. Festival of U.S.S.R., India.
1275 **1026** 5 r. multicoloured .. 50 50

1027. White Tiger.

1987. Wildlife. Multicoloured.
1276. 1 r. type **1027** 40 15
1277. 5 r. Snow leopard (horiz.) 85 85

1028. Execution of Veer Narayan Singh.

1987. Veer Narayan Singh (patriot) Commemoration.
1278. **1028.** 60 p. brown .. 20 20

1029. Rameshwari Nehru.

1987. Rameshwari Nehru (women's rights campaigner) Commemoration.
1279. **1029.** 60 p. brown .. 20 20

1030. Father Kuriakose Elias Chavara.

1987. Father Kuriakose Elias Chavara (founder of Carmelites of Mary Immaculate) Commemoration.
1280. **1030.** 60 p. brown .. 20 20

1031. Dr. Rajah Sir Muthiah Chettiar.

1987. Dr Rajah Sir Muthiah Chettiar (politician) Commemoration.
1281. **1031.** 60 p. grey 20 20

1032. Golden Temple, Amritsar.

1987. 400th Anniv. of Golden Temple, Amritsar.
1282. **1032.** 60 p. multicoloured 30 20

1033. Rukmini Devi and Dancer.

1987. Rukmini Devi (Bharatanatyam dance pioneer). Commemoration.
1283. **1033.** 60 p. red 30 20

1034. Dr. Hiralal.

1987. Dr. Hiralal (historian) Commemoration.
1284. **1034.** 60 p. blue 20 20

1035 Light Frequency Experiment and Bodhi Tree

1988. 75th Session of Indian Science Congress Association.
1285 **1035** 4 r. multicoloured .. 50 60

1036 Rural Patient

1988. 13th Asian Pacific Dental Congress.
1286 **1036** 4 r. multicoloured .. 50 50

1988. India's Struggle for Freedom (6th series). As T **909**.
1287 60 p. black, green & orge 20 20
1288 60 p. brown, green & orge 20 20
1289 60 p. red, green and orge 20 20
1290 60 p. purple, green & orge 20 20
1291 60 p. purple, green & red 20 20
1292 60 p. black, green & orge 20 20
1293 60 p. lilac, green and red 20 20
1294 60 p. dp green, grn & red 20 20
1295 60 p. brown, green & grn 20 20
1296 60 p mauve, green & orge 20 20

DESIGNS: No. 1287, Mohan Lal Sukhadia; No. 1288, Dr. S. K. Sinha; No. 1289, Chandra Shekhar Azad; No. 1290, G. B. Pant; No. 1291, Dr. Anugrah Narain Singh; No. 1292, Kuladhor Chaliha; No. 1293, Shivprasad Gupta; No. 1294, Sarat Chandra Bose; No. 1295, Baba Kharak Singh; 1296, Sheikh Mohammad Abdullah;

1037 U Tirot Singh

1988. U Tirot Singh (Khasis leader) Commem.
1297 **1037** 60 p. brown 20 20

1038 Early and Modern Regimental Uniforms

1988. Bicentenary of 4th Battalion of the Kumaon Regiment.
1298 **1038** 1 r. multicoloured .. 30 20

1039 Balgandharva

1988. Birth Cent of Balgandharva (actor).
1299 **1039** 60 p. brown 20 20

1040 Soldiers and Infantry Combat Vehicle

1988. Presentation of Colours to Mechanised Infantry Regiment.
1300 **1040** 1 r. multicoloured .. 35 20

1041 B. N. Rau

1988. B. N. Rau (constitutional lawyer) Commemoration.
1301 **1041** 60 p. black 20 20

1042 Mohindra Government College

1988. Mohindra Government College, Patiala.
1302 **1042** 1 r. mauve 20 20

1043 Dr. D. V. Gundappa

1988. Dr. D. V. Gundappa (scholar) Commem.
1303 **1043** 60 p. grey 20 20

1044 Rani Avantibai

1988. Rani Avantibai of Ramgarh Commem.
1304 **1044** 60 p. mauve .. 20 20

1045 "Malayala Manorama" Office, Kottayam

1988. Centenary of "Malayala Manorama" (newspaper).
1305 **1045** 1 r. black and blue .. 20 20

1046 Maharshi Dadhichi

1988. Maharshi Dadhichi (Hindu saint) Commemoraton.
1306 **1046** 60 p. red 20 20

1047 Mohammad Iqbal

1988. 50th Death Anniv of Mohammad Iqbal (poet)
1307 **1047** 60 p. gold and red .. 20 20

1048 Samarth Ramdas

1988. Samarth Ramdas (Hindu spiritual leader) Commemoration.
1308 **1048** 60 p. green .. 20 20

1049 Swati Tirunal Rama Varma

1988. 175th Birth Anniv of Swati Tirunal Rama Varma (composer).
1309 **1049** 60 p. mauve .. 20 20

1050 Bhaurao Patil and Class

1988. Bhaurao Patil (educationist) Commem.
1310 **1050** 60 p. brown 20 20

1051 "Rani Lakshmi Bai" (M. F. Husain)
(Illustration reduced, actual size 54 × 39 mm)

1988. Martyrs from 1st War of Independence.
1311 **1051** 60 p. multicoloured .. 20 20

1052 Broad Peak

1988. Himalayan Peaks.

1312	**1052**	1 r.50 lilac, violet and blue ..	30	30
1313	–	4 r. multicoloured	60	60
1314	–	5 r. multicoloured	70	70
1315	–	6 r.50 multicoloured	85	85

DESIGNS: 4 r. K 2 (Godwin Austen); 5 r. Kanchenjunga; 6 r.50, Nanda Devi.

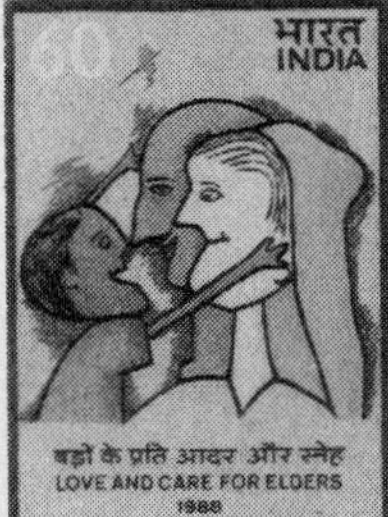

1053 Child with Grandparents

1988. "Love and Care for Elders".
1316 **1053** 60 p. multicoloured .. 20 20

1054 Victoria Terminus, Bombay

1988. Centenary of Victoria Terminus Station, Bombay.
1317 **1054** 1 r. multicoloured .. 30 20

1055 Lawrence School, Lovedale

1988. 130th Anniv of Lawrence School, Lovedale.
1318 **1055** 1 r. brown and green 20 20

1056 Khejri Tree

1988. World Environment Day.
1319 **1056** 60 p. multicoloured .. 20 15

1988. As No. 732, but new face value.
1320 60 p. black (Gandhi) .. 10 10

1057 Rani Durgawati

1938. Rani Durgawati (Gondwana ruler) Commemoration.
1322 **1057** 60 p. red 20 20

1058 Acharya Shanti Dev

1988. Acharya Shanti Dev (Buddhist scholar) Commemoration.
1323 **1058** 60 p. brown .. 20 20

1059 Y. S. Parmar

1988. Dr. Yashwant Singh Parmar (former Chief Minister of Himachal Pradesh) Commemoration.
1324 **1059** 60 p. violet .. 20 20

1060 Arm pointing at Proclamation in Marathi
(Illustration reduced, actual size 53 × 38mm)

1988. 40th Anniv of Independence. Bal Gangadhar Tilak (patriot) Commem. Mult.
1325 60 p. Type **1060** 20 20
1326 60 p. Battle scene .. 20 20
Nos. 1325/6 were printed together, se-tenant, forming a composite design showing a painting by M. F. Husain.

1061 Durgadas Rathore

1988. 150th Birth Anniv of Durgadas Rathore (Regent of Marwar).
1327 **1061** 60 p. brown 20 20

1062 Gopinath Kaviraj

1988. Gopinath Kaviraj (scholar) Commem.
1328 **1062** 60 p. brown 20 20

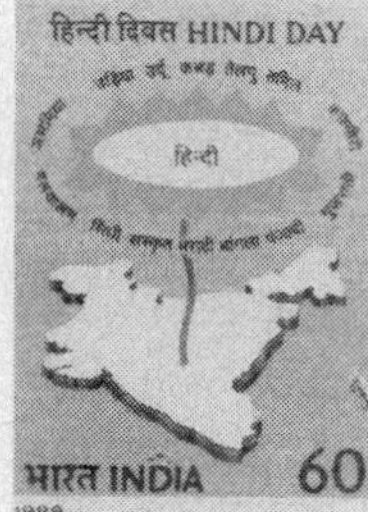

1063 Lotus and Outline Map of India

1988. Hindi Day.
1329 **1063** 60 p. red, green & brn 20 20

1064 Indian Olympic Association Logo

1988. "Sports-1988" and Olympic Games, Seoul.
1330 **1064** 60 p. purple .. 20 15
1331 – 5 r. multicoloured 70 45
DESIGN—HORIZ. 5 r. Various sports.

1065 Jerdon's Courser

1988. Wildlife Conservation. Jerdon's Courser.
1332 **1065** 1 r. multicoloured .. 65 20

1988. "India-89" International Stamp Exhibition, New Delhi (3rd issue). General Post Offices. As T **1022**. Multicoloured.
1333 4 r. Bangalore G.P.O. .. 40 35
1334 5 r. Bombay G.P.O. .. 50 45

1066 "Times of India" Front Page

1988. 150th Anniv of "The Times of India".
1335 **1066** 1 r.50 blk, gold & yell 20 20

1067 "Maulana Abul Kalam Azad" (K. Hebbar)

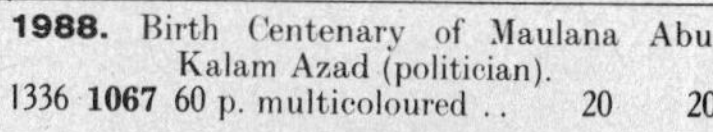
1988. Birth Centenary of Maulana Abul Kalam Azad (politician).
1336 **1067** 60 p. multicoloured .. 20 20

1068 Nehru
(Illustration reduced, actual size (54 × 39mm)

1988. Centenary (1989) of Jawaharlal Nehru (1st issue).
1337 **1068** 60 p. black, orange and green 20 15
1338 – 1 r. multicoloured 25 15
DESIGN—VERT. 1 r. "Jawaharlal Nehru" (Svetoslav Roerich).
See also NO. 1393.

1069 Birsa Munda

1988. Birsa Munda (Munda leader). Commem.
1339 **1069** 60 p. brown 20 20

1070 Bhakra Dam

1988. 25th Anniv of Dedication of Bhakra Dam.
1340 **1070** 60 p. red 35 50

1071 Dead Letter Office Cancellations of 1886

1988. "India-89" International Stamp Exhibition, New Delhi (4th issue). Postal Cancellations.
1341 **1071** 60 p. brn, blk & red 25 15
1342 – 6 r.50 brown & blk 1·00 1·00
DESIGN: 6 r.50, Travelling post office handstamp of 1864.

1072 K. M. Munshi

1988. Birth Centenary (1987) of K. M. Munshi (author and politician).
1343 **1072** 60 p. green .. 15 15

HAVE YOU READ THE NOTES AT THE BEGINNING OF THIS CATALOGUE?
These often provide answers to the enquiries we receive.

1073 Mannathu Padmanabhan

1989. Mannathu Padmanabhan (social reformer) Commemoration.
1344 **1073** 60 p. brown .. 15 15

1989. India's Struggle for Freedom (7th series). As T **909**.
1345 60 p. black, green & orge 20 20
1346 60 p. orange, green & lilac 20 20
1347 60 p. black, green & orge 20 20
1348 60 p. brown, green & orge 20 20
1349 60 p. brown, green & orge 20 20
DESIGNS:—No. 1345, Hare Krishna Mahtab; 1346, Balasaheb Gangadhar Kher; 1347, Raj Kumari Amrit Kaur; 1348, Saifuddin Kitchlew; 1349, Asaf Ali.

1074 Lok Sabha Secretariat

1989. 60th Anniv of Lok Sabha Secretariat (formerly Legislative Assembly Department).
1355 **1074** 60 p. green 15 15

1075 Goddess Durga seated on Lion (5th-cent terracotta plaque)

1989. 125th Anniv of Lucknow Museum.
1356 **1075** 60 p. deep blue & blue 15 15

1076 Baldev Ramji Mirdha

1989. Birth Centenary of Baldev Ramji Mirdha (nationalist).
1357 **1076** 60 p. green 15 15

1077 Girl with Stamp Collection

1989. "India-89" International Stamp Exhibition, New Delhi (5th issue). Philately.
1358 **1077** 60 p. yell, red & bl 15 10
1359 – 1 r.50 grey, yellow and black .. 20 15
1360 – 5 r. red and blue .. 60 50
1361 – 6 r.50 blk, brn & bl 70 60
DESIGNS: 1 r.50, Dawk gharry, c. 1842; 5 r. Travancore 1888 2 ch. conch shell stamp; 6 r.50, Early Indian philatelic magazines.

1078 St. John Bosco and Boy

1989. St. John Bosco (founder of Salesian Brothers) Commemoration.
1362 **1078** 60 p. red 15 15

1079 Modern Tank and 19th-century Sowar

1989. 3rd Cavalry Regiment.
1363 **1079** 60 p. multicoloured . . 30 15

1080 Dargah Sharif, Ajmer

1989. Dargah Sharif (Sufi shrine), Ajmer.
1364 **1080** 1 r. multicoloured . . 20 20

1081 Task Force and Indian Naval Ensign

1989. President's Review of the Fleet.
1365 **1081** 6 r.50 multicoloured 1·25 1·00

1082 Shaheed Laxman Nayak and Barbed Wire Fence

1989. Shaheed Laxman Nayak Commem.
1366 **1082** 60 p. brn, grn & orge 15 15

1083 Rao Gopal Singh

1989. Rao Gopal Singh Commemoration.
1367 **1083** 60 p. brown 15 15

1084 Sydenham College

1989. 75th Anniv (1988) of Sydenham College, Bombay.
1368 **1084** 60 p. black 30 15

1085 Bishnu Ram Medhi

1989. Birth Centenary (1988) of Bishnu Ram Medhi (politician).
1369 **1085** 60 p. green, deep green and red . . 30 15

1086 Dr. N. S. Hardikar

1989. Birth Centenary of Dr. Narayana Subbarao Hardikar (nationalist).
1370 **1086** 60 p. brown . . 15 15

1087 "Advaita" in Devanagari Script

1989. Sankaracharya (philosopher) Commem.
1371 **1087** 60 p. multicoloured . . 20 20

1088 Gandhi Bhavan, Punjab University

1989. Punjab University, Chandigarh.
1372 **1088** 1 r. brown and blue 15 15

INDEX

Countries can be quickly located by referring to the index at the end of this volume.

1089 Scene from Film "Raja Harischandra"

1989. 75 Years of Indian Cinema.
1373 **1089** 60 p. black & yellow 20 15

1090 Cactus and Cogwheels

1989. Centenary of Kirloskar Brothers Ltd (engineering group).
1374 **1090** 1 r. multicoloured . . 15 15

1091 Early Class and Modern University Students

1989. Centenary of First D.A.V. College.
1375 **1091** 1 r. multicoloured . . 15 15

1092 Post Office, Dakshin Gangotri Base, Antarctica

1989. Opening of Post Office, Dakshin Gangotri Research Station, Antarctica.
1376 **1092** 1 r. multicoloured . . 40 15

1093 First Allahabad Bank Building

1989. 125th Anniv (1990) of Allahabad Bank.
1377 **1093** 60 p. purple and blue 15 15

1094 Nehru inspecting Central Reserve Police, Neemuch, 1954

1989. 50th Anniv of Central Reserve Police Force (formerly Crown Representative's Police).
1378 **1094** 60 p. brown 20 20

1095 Dairy Cow

1989. Centenary of Military Farms.
1379 **1095** 1 r. multicoloured . . 20 15

1096 Mustafa Kemal Ataturk

1989. 50th Death Anniv (1988) of Mustafa Kemal Ataturk (Turkish statesman).
1380 **1096** 5 r. multicoloured . . 70 45

1097 Dr. S. Radhakrishnan

1989. Birth Centenary (1988) of Dr. Sarvepalli Radhakrishnan (former President).
1381 **1097** 60 p. black . . 15 15

1098 Football Match

1989. Cent of Mohun Bagan Athletic Club.
1382 **1098** 1 r. multicoloured . . 20 15

1099 Dr. P. Subbarayan

1989. Birth Centenary of Dr. P. Subbarayan (politician).
1383 **1099** 60 p. brown . . 15 15

1100 Shyamji Krishna Varma

1989. Shyamji Krishna Varma (nationalist) Commemoration.
1384 **1100** 60 p. brn, grn & red 15 15

1101 Sayajirao Gaekwad III

1989. 50th Death Anniv of Maharaja Sayajirao Gaekwad III of Baroda.
1385 **1101** 60 p. grey 15 15

1102 Symbolic Bird with Letter

1989. "Use Pincode" Campaign.
1386 **1102** 60 p. multicoloured . . 15 15

1103 Namakkal Kavignar

1989. Namakkal Kavignar (writer) Commem.
1387 **1103** 60 p. black 15 15

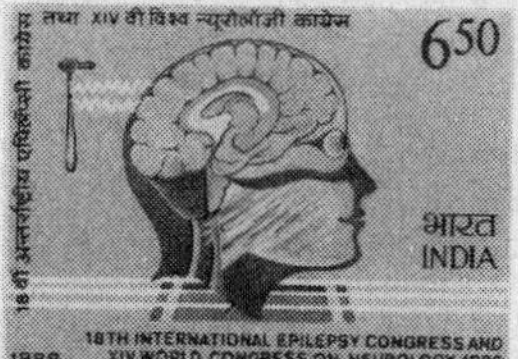

1104 Diagram of Human Brain

1989. 18th Int. Epilepsy Congress and 14th World Congress on Neurology, New Delhi.
1388 **1104** 6 r. 50 multicoloured 1·00 65

1105 Pandita Ramabai and Original Sharada Sadan Building

1989. Pandita Ramabai (women's education pioneer) Commemoration.
1389 **1105** 60 p. brown . . 15 15

1106 Releasing Homing Pigeons

1989. Orissa Police Pigeon Post.
1390 **1106** 1 r. red 20 15

1107 Acharya Narendra Deo

1989. Birth Centenary of Acharya Narendra Deo (scholar).
1391 **1107** 60 p. brn, grn & orge 15 15

1108 Acharya Kripalani

1989. Acharya Kripalani (politician) Commemoration.
1392 **1108** 60 p. black, grn & red 15 15

1109 Nehru
(illustration reduced to ¾ size)

1989. Birth Centenary of Jawaharlal Nehru (2nd issue).
1393 **1109** 1 r. brown, deep brown and buff . . 30 15

1110 Meeting Logo

1989. 8th Asian Track and Field Meeting, New Delhi.
1394 **1110** 1 r. black, orge & grn 15 15

1111 Sir Gurunath Bewoor

1989. Sir Gurunath Bewoor (former Director-General, Posts and Telegraphs) Commem.
1395 **1111** 60 p. brown 15 15

1112 Balkrishna Sharma Navin

1989. Balkrishna Sharma Navin (politician and poet) Commemoration.
1396 **1112** 60 p. black 15 15

1113 Abstract Painting of Houses

1989. Cent of Bombay Art Society (1988).
1397 **1113** 1 r. multicoloured . . 15 15

1114 Lesser Florican

1989. Wildlife Conservation. Lesser Florican.
1398 **1114** 2 r. multicoloured . . 35 30

1115 Centenary Logo

1989. Centenary of Indian Oil Production.
1399 **1115** 60 p. brown 20 15

1116 Dr. M. G. Ramachandran

1990. Dr. M. G. Ramachandran (former Chief Minister of Tamil Nadu) Commemoration.
1400 **1116** 60 p. brown 15 15

1117 Volunteers working at Sukhna Lake, Chandigarh

1990. Save Sukhna Lake Campaign.
1401 **1117** 1 r. multicoloured . . 15 15

1118 Gallantry Medals

1990. Presentation of New Colours to Bombay Sappers.
1402 **1118** 60 p. multicoloured . . 40 20

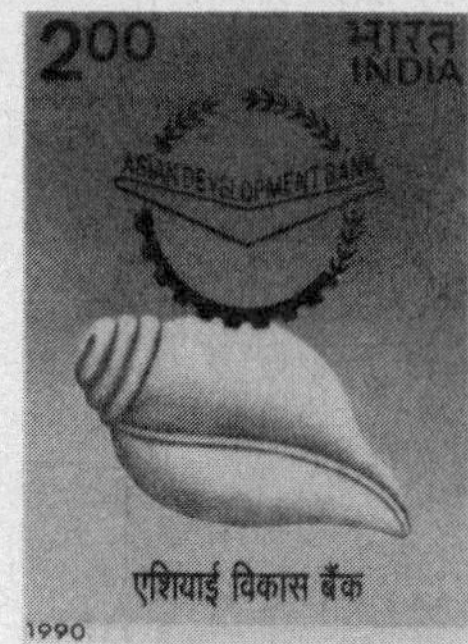

1119 Conch Shell and Logo

1990. 23rd Annual General Meeting of Asian Development Bank, New Delhi.
1403 **1119** 2 r. black, orge & yell 20 15

1120 Penny Black and Envelope

1990. 150th Anniv of the Penny Black.
1404 **1120** 6r. multicoloured . . 75 40

1121 Ho Chi-Minh and Vietnamese House

1990. Birth Centenary of Ho Chi-Minh (Vietnamese leader).
1405 **1121** 2 r. brown and green 20 15

1122 Chaudhary Charan Singh

1990. 3rd Death Anniv of Chaudhary Charan Singh (former Prime Minister).
1406 **1122** 1 r. brown . . 15 10

1123 Armed Forces' Badge and Map of Sri Lanka

1124 Wheat

1990. Indian Peace-keeping Operations in Sri Lanka.
1407 **1123** 2 r. multicoloured .. 20 15

1990. 60th. Anniv of Indian Council of Agricultural Research (1989).
1408 **1124** 2 r. blk, grn & dp grn 20 15

1125 Khudiram Bose

1990. Khudiram Bose (patriot) Commemoration.
1409 **1125** 1 r. orange, grn & red 20 10

1126 "Life in India" (Tanya Vorontsova)

1990. Indo–Soviet Friendship. Children's Paintings. Multicoloured.
1410 1 r. Type **1126** 30 40
1411 6 r. 50 "St. Basil's Cathedral and Kremlin, Moscow" (Sanjay Adhikari) .. .. 95 1·00

Stamps in similar designs were also issued by U.S.S.R.

1127 K. Kelappan

1990. K. Kelappan (social reformer) Commemoration.
1412 **1127** 1 r. brown 20 10

1128 Girl in Garden

1990. Year of the Girl Child.
1413 **1128** 1 r. multicoloured .. 20 10

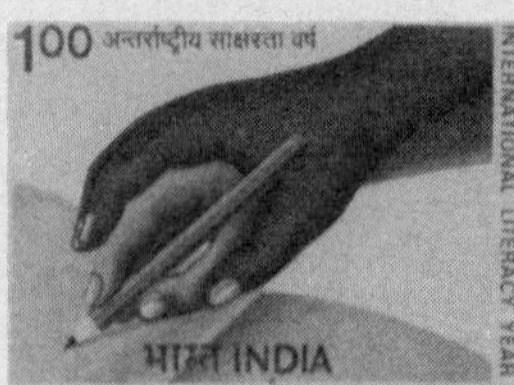

1129 Hand guiding Child's Writing

1990. International Literacy Year.
1414 **1129** 1 r. multicoloured .. 10 10

1130 Woman using Water Pump

1990. Safe Drinking Water Campaign.
1415 **1130** 4 r. black, red & grn 60 60

1131 Sunder Lal Sharma

1990. 50th Death Anniv of Sunder Lal Sharma (patriot).
1416 **1131** 60 p. red .. 10 10

1132 Kabbadi

1990. 11th Asian Games, Peking. Mult.
1417 1 r. Type **1132** 25 15
1418 4 r. Athletics 60 70
1419 4 r. Cycling 60 70
1420 6 r. 50 Archery .. .. 1·00 1·25

1133 A. K. Gopalan

1990. Ayillyath Kuttiari Gopalan (social reformer) Commemoration.
1421 **1133** 1 r. brown .. 10 10

1134 Gurkha Soldier

1990. 50th Anniv of 3rd and 5th Battalions, 5th Gurkha Rifles.
1422 **1134** 2 r. black and brown 60 50

1135 Suryamall Mishran

1990. 75th Birth Anniv of Suryamall Mishran (poet).
1423 **1135** 2 r. brown and orange 10 10

1136 "Doll and Cat" (Subhash Kumar Nagarajan)

1990. Children's Day.
1424 **1136** 1 r. multicoloured .. 20 10

1137 Security Post and Border Guard on Camel

1990. 25th Anniv of Border Security Force.
1425 **1137** 5 r. blue, brown & blk 55 55

1138 Hearts and Flowers

1990. Greetings Stamps. Multicoloured.
1426 1 r. Type **1138** 15 10
1427 4 r. Ceremonial elephants (horiz) 35 40

1139 Bikaner

1990. Cities of India. Multicoloured.
1428 4 r. Type **1139** 35 35
1429 5 r. Hyderabad .. 45 45
1430 6 r. 50 Cuttack 60 60

1140 Bhakta Kanakadas and Udipi Temple

1141 Shaheed Minar Monument

1990. Bhakta Kanakadas (mystic and poet) Commemoration.
1431 **1140** 1 r. red 15 15

1990. 300th Anniv of Calcutta.
1432 **1141** 1 r. multicoloured .. 10 10
1433 – 6 r. black, brn & red 45 50

DESIGNS—HORIZ (44×36 mm). 6 r. 18th-century shipping on the Ganges.

1142 Dnyaneshwar (poet) and Manuscript

1990. 700th Anniv of Dnyaneshwari (spiritual epic).
1434 **1142** 2 r. multicoloured .. 10 15

1143 Madan Mohan Malaviya (founder) and University

1991. 75th Anniv of Banaras Hindu University.
1435 **1143** 1 r. red 10 10

1991. As No. 732 but new face value.
1436 1 r. brown (Gandhi) .. 10 10

1144 Road Users

1991. International Traffic Safety Conference, New Delhi.
1437 **1144** 6 r. 50 black, bl & red 40 45

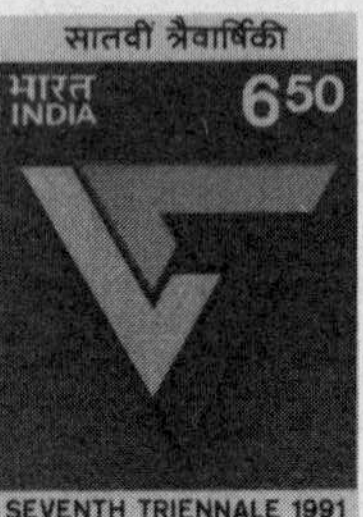

1145 Exhibition Emblem

1991. 7th Triennale Art Exhibition, New Delhi.
1438 **1145** 6 r. 50 multicoloured 40 45

1146 Jagannath Sunkersett and Central Railways Headquarters

1991. 98th Birth Anniv of Jagannath Sunkersett (educationist and railway pioneer).
1439 **1146** 2 r. blue and red .. 10 15

1147 Tata Memorial Centre

1991. 50th Anniv of Tata Memorial Medical Centre.
1440 **1147** 2 r. brown and stone 10 15

1148 River Dolphin

1991. Endangered Marine Mammals.
1441 **1148** 4 r. brown, bl & grn 60 60
1442 – 6 r. 50 multicoloured 90 90
DESIGN: 6 r. 50, Sea Cow.

1149 Drugs

1991. International Conference on Drug Abuse, Calcutta.
1443 **1149** 5 r. violet and red .. 90 90

1150 Hand, Bomb Explosion and Dove

1991. World Peace.
1444 **1150** 6 r. 50 black, light brown and brown 65 75

1151 Remote Sensing Satellite "IA"

1991. Launch of Indian Remote Sensing Satellite "IA".
1445 **1151** 6 r. 50 brown & blue 50 60

1152 Babu Jagjivan Ram

1991. Babu Jagjivan Ram (politician) Commemoration.
1446 **1152** 1 r. brown 10 10

1153 Dr. B. R. Ambedkar and Demonstration

1991. Birth Centenary of Dr. Bhimrao Ramji Ambedkar (social reformer).
1447 **1153** 1 r. brown and blue 10 10

1154 Valar Dance

1991. Tribal Dances. Multicoloured.
1448 2 r. 50 Type **1154** .. 20 15
1449 4 r. Kayang 30 30
1450 5 r. Hozagiri 35 35
1451 6 r. 50 Velakali 50 65

1155 Ariyakudi Ramanuja Iyengar and Temples

1991. Ariyakudi Ramanuja Iyengar (singer and composer) Commemoration.
1452 **1155** 2 r. brown and green 15 15

1156 Karpoori Thakur

1991. Jan Nayak Karpoori Thakur (politician and social reformer) Commemoration.
1453 **1156** 1 r. brown 10 10

1157 Emperor Penguins

1991. 30th Anniv of Antarctic Treaty. Mult.
1454 5 r. Type **1157** 65 70
1455 6 r. 50 Antarctic map and pair of gentoo penguins 65 70
Nos. 1454/5 were printed together, se-tenant, forming a composite design.

1158 Rashtrapati Bhavan Building, New Delhi

1991. 60th Anniv of New Delhi. Multicoloured.
1456 5 r. Type **1158** 30 30
1457 6 r. 50 New Delhi monuments 35 35
Nos. 1456/7 were printed together, se-tenant, forming a composite design.

1159 Sri Ram Sharma Acharya

1991. Sri Ram Sharma Acharya (social refomer) Commemoration.
1458 **1159** 1 r. green and red .. 10 10

1160 "Shankar awarded Padma Vibhushan" (cartoon)

1991. Keshav Shankar Pillai (cartoonist) Commemoration.
1459 **1160** 4 r. brown 25 30
1460 – 6 r. 50 lilac 30 40
DESIGN—VERT. 6 r. 50, "The Big Show".

1161 Sriprakash and Kashi Vidyapith University

1991. 20th Death Anniv of Sriprakash (politician).
1461 **1161** 2 r. brown & lt brown 15 15

1162 Gopinath Bardoloi

1991. Birth Centenary (1990) of Gopinath Bardoloi (Assamese politician).
1462 **1162** 1 r. lilac 10 10

1163 Rajiv Gandhi

1991. Rajiv Gandhi (Congress Party leader) Commemoration.
1463 **1163** 1 r. multicoloured .. 20 20

1164 Muni Mishrimalji and Memorial

1991. Birth Centenary of Muni Mishrimalji (Jain religious leader).
1464 **1164** 1 r. brown 10 10

1165 Mahadevi Verma (poetess) and "Varsha"

1991. Hindu Writers.
1465 **1165** 2 r. black and blue .. 15 15
1466 – 2 r. black and blue .. 15 15
DESIGN: No. 1466, Jayshankar Prasad (poet and dramatist) and scene from "Kamayani".

1166 Parliament House and C.P.A. Emblem

1991. 37th Commonwealth Parliamentary Association Conference, New Delhi.
1467 **1166** 6 r. 50 blue & brown 30 40

1167 Frog

1991. Greetings Stamps.
1468 **1167** 1 r. green and red .. 15 20
1469 – 6 r. 50 red and green 30 40
DESIGN: 6 r. 50, Symbolic bird carrying flower.

1168 "Cymbidium aloifolium"

1991. Orchids. Multicoloured.
1470 1 r. Type **1168** 20 15
1471 2 r. 50 "Paphiopedilum venustum" 25 25
1472 3 r. "Aerides crispum" .. 25 25
1473 4 r. "Cymbidium bicolour" 30 30
1474 5 r. "Vanda spathulata" 35 40
1475 6 r. 50 "Cymbidium devonianum" 45 60

1169 Gurkha Soldier in Battle Dress

1991. 90th Anniv of 2nd Battalion, Third Gurkha Rifles.
1476 **1169** 4 r. multicoloured .. 50 50

1170 Couple on Horse (embroidery)

1991. 3rd Death Anniv of Kamaladevi Chattopadhyaya (founder of All India Handicrafts Board).
1477 **1170** 1 r. lake, red & yell 15 10
1478 – 6 r. 50 multicoloured 40 50
DESIGN: 6 r. 50, Traditional puppet.

1171 Chithira Tirunal and Temple Sculpture

1991. Chithira Tirunal Bala Rama Varma (former Maharaja of Travancore) Commem.
1479 **1171** 2 r. violet 40 40

1172 "Children in Traditional Costume" (Arpi Snehalbhai Shah)

1991. Children's Day.
1480 **1172** 1 r. multicoloured .. 20 15

1173 Mounted Sowar and Tanks

1991. 70th Anniv (1992) of the 18th Cavalry Regiment.
1481 **1173** 6 r. 50 multicoloured 70 70

1174 Kites

1991. India Tourism Year.
1482 **1174** 6 r. 50 multicoloured 50 50

1175 Sports on Bricks

1991. International Conference on Youth Tourism, New Delhi.
1483 **1175** 6 r. 50 multicoloured 50 50

1176 "Mozart at Piano" (unfinished painting, J. Lange)

1991. Death Bicentenary of Mozart.
1484 **1176** 6 r. 50 multicoloured 60 65

1177 Homeless Family

1991. South Asian Association for Regional Co-operation Year of Shelter.
1485 **1177** 4 r. brown and ochre 40 40

1178 People running on Heart

1991. "Run for Your Heart" Marathon, New Delhi.
1486 **1178** 1 r. black, grey & red 15 15

1179 "Sidhartha with an Injured Bird" (Asit Kumar Haldar)

1991. Birth Centenary (1990) of Asit Kumar Haldar (artist).
1487 **1179** 2 r. yellow, red & blk 30 30

1180 Bhujangasana

1991. Yoga Exercises. Multicoloured.
1488 2 r. Type **1180** 20 20
1489 5 r. Dhanurasana .. 40 45
1490 6 r. 50 Ustrasana .. 50 55
1491 10 r. Utthita trikonasana 85 95

1181 Y.M.C.A. Logo

1992. Centenary (1991) of National Council of Young Men's Christian Association.
1492 **1181** 1 r. red and blue .. 10 10

1182 Madurai Temple Tower and Hooghly River Bridge

1992. 14th Congress of International Association for Bridge and Structural Engineering, New Delhi.
1493 **1182** 2 r. brown, red & bl 15 15
1494 – 2 r. brown, red & bl 15 15
DESIGN: No. 1494, Gate, Sanchi Stupa and Hall of Nations, New Delhi.

1183 Goat Seal from Harappa Culture, 2500 to 1500 B.C.

1992. 5th International Goat Conference, New Delhi.
1495 **1183** 6 r. blue and brown 35 35

1184 Early 19th-Century Letter with Mail Pouch and National Archives Building, New Delhi

1992. Centenary (1991) of National Archives.
1496 **1184** 6 r. multicoloured .. 35 35

1185 Krushna Chandra Gajapathi

1992. Krushna Chandra Gajapathi (former Chief Minister of Orissa) Commemoration.
1497 **1185** 1 r. lilac 10 10

1186 Vijay Singh Pathik

1992. Vijay Singh Pathik (writer) Commem.
1498 **1186** 1 r. brown 10 10

1187 Hang-gliding

1992. Adventure Sports. Multicoloured.
1499 2 r. Type **1187** 15 15
1500 4 r. Windsurfing .. 30 30
1501 5 r. River rafting .. 35 35
1502 11 r. Skiing 80 90

HAVE YOU READ THE NOTES AT THE BEGINNING OF THIS CATALOGUE?
These often provide answers to the enquiries we receive.

1188 Henry Gidney and Anglo-Indians

1992. 50th Death Anniv of Sir Henry Gidney (ophthalmologist).
1503 **1188** 1 r. black and blue .. 15 10

1189 Telecommunications Training Centre, Jabalpur

1992. 50th Anniv of Telecommunications Training Centre, Jabalpur.
1504 **1189** 1 r. bistre 15 10

1190 Sardar Udham Singh

1992. Sardar Udham Singh (patriot) Commemoration.
1505 **1190** 1 r. black and brown 15 10

1191 Men's Discus

1992. Olympic Games, Barcelona. Mult.
1506 1 r. Type **1191** .. 15 10
1507 6 r. Women's gymnastics 40 40
1508 8 r. Men's hockey .. 60 60
1509 11 r. Boxing 85 95

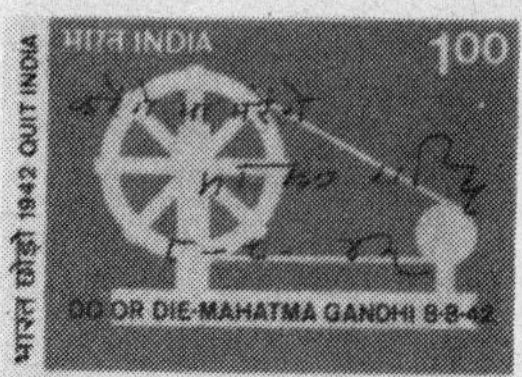
1192 Spinning Wheel Emblem

1992. 50th Anniv of "Quit India" Movement.
1510 **1192** 1 r. black and pink 15 10
1511 – 2 r. black, brn & grey 20 20
DESIGN: 2 r. Mahatma Gandhi and mantra.

1193 Treating Casualty

1992. 50th Anniv of 60th Parachute Field Ambulance.
1512 **1193** 1 r. multicoloured .. 20 15

1194 Dr. S. R. Ranganathan and Madras University

1992. Birth Centenary of Shiyali Ramamrita Ranganathan (librarian).
1513 **1194** 1 r. blue 10 10

1195 "Dev Narayan"

1992. Phad Scroll Paintings from Rajasthan.
1514 **1195** 5 r. multicoloured .. 35 40

1196 Hamuman Prasad Poddar

1992. Hanuman Prasad Poddar (editor) Commemoration.
1515 **1196** 1 r. green 10 10

1197 MIG 29 Fighter and IL76 Transport

1992. 60th Anniv of Indian Air Force. Mult.
1516 1 r. Type **1197** 15 15
1517 10 r. MIG 27 fighter and Westland Wapiti biplane 75 75

1198 Lighting Candle

1992. 150th Anniv of Sisters of Jesus and Mary's Arrival in India.
1518 **1198** 1 r. blue and grey .. 15 15

MINIMUM PRICE

The minimum price quoted is 10p which represents a handling charge rather than a basis for valuing common stamps. For further notes about prices see introductory pages.

1199 "Sun" (Harshit Prashant Patel)

1992. Children's Day.
1519 **1199** 1 r. multicoloured .. 10 10

1200 Yogiji Maharaj

1992. Birth Centenary of Yogiji Maharaj (Hindu reformer).
1520 **1200** 1 r. blue 10 10

1201 Army Service Corps Transport

1992. Army Service Corps Commemoration.
1521 **1201** 1 r. multicoloured .. 10 10

1202 Stephen Smith and Early Rocket Post Covers

1992. Birth Centenary (1991) of Stephen Smith (rocket mail pioneer).
1522 **1202** 11 r. multicoloured .. 70 70

1203 Electricity Pylons, Farmers and Crops

1992. 25th Anniv of Haryana State.
1523 **1203** 2 r. red, dp grn & grn 10 10

1204 Madanlal Dhingra

1992. Madanlal Dhingra (revolutionary) Commemoration.
1524 **1204** 1 r. brown, red & grn 10 10

1205 Osprey

1992. Birds of Prey. Multicoloured.
1525 2 r. Type **1205** 15 15
1526 6 r. Peregrine falcon .. 45 45
1527 8 r. Lammergeier .. 60 60
1528 11 r. Golden eagle .. 90 90

1206 Pandit Ravishankar Shukla

1992. Pandit Ravishankar Shukla (social reformer) Commemoration.
1529 **1206** 1 r. purple .. 10 10

1207 William Carey

1993. Bicent of William Carey's Appointment as Baptist Missionary to India.
1530 **1207** 6 r. multicoloured .. 35 40

1208 Fakirmohan Senapati

1993. Fakirmohan Senapati Commemoration.
1531 **1208** 1 r. red 10 10

1209 Workers and C.S.I.R Emblem

1993. 50th Anniv of Council of Scientific and Industrial Research.
1532 **1209** 1 r. purple 10 10

1210 Parachute Drop and Field Gun

1993. 50th Anniv of 9th Parachute Field Artillery Regiment.
1533 **1210** 1 r. multicoloured .. 10 10

1211 Westland Wapiti Biplane

1993. 60th Anniv of No. 1 Squadron, Indian Air Force.
1534 **1211** 1 r. multicoloured .. 10 10

1212 Rahul Sankrityayan

1993. Birth Centenary of Rahul Sankrityayan (politician).
1535 **1212** 1 r. black, cinnamon and brown .. 10 10

1213 Parliament Building and Emblem

1993. 89th Inter-Parliamentary Union Conference, New Dehli.
1536 **1213** 1 r. black 10 10

1214 Neral Metheran Locomotive, 1905

1993. Mountain Locomotives. Multicoloured.
1537 1 r. Type **1214** .. 15 10
1538 6 r. Darjeeling, 1889 .. 35 35
1539 8 r. Nilgiri, 1914 .. 50 50
1540 11 r. Kalka-Simla, 1934 .. 70 80

1215 Students and College Building

1993. Centenary of Meerut College.
1541 **1215** 1 r. black and brown 10 10

1216 Mahalanobis and Office Block

1993. Prasanta Chandra Mahalanobis Commemoration.
1542 **1216** 1 r. brown 10 10

1217 Bombay Town Hall

1993. Centenary of Bombay Municipal Corporation.
1543 **1217** 2 r. multicoloured .. 10 10

1218 Abdul Ghaffar Khan and Mountainside

1993. Abdul Ghaffar Khan Commemoration.
1544 **1218** 1 r. multicoloured .. 10 10

1219 National Integration Emblem

1993. National Integration Campaign.
1545 **1219** 1 r. orange and green 10 10

1220 Dadabhai Naoroji and Houses of Parliament, London

1993. Centenary of Dadabhai Naoroji's Election to the House of Commons.
1546 **1220** 6 r. multicoloured .. 25 30

1221 Swami Vivekananda and Art Institute, Chicago

1993. Centenary of Swami Vivekananda's Chicago Address.
1547 **1221** 2 r. orange and grey 10 10

1222 "Lagerstroemia speciosa"

1993. Flowering Trees.
1548 **1222** 1 r. red, green & brn 10 10
1549 – 6 r. multicoloured .. 25 30
1550 – 8 r. multicoloured .. 35 40
1551 – 11 r. multicoloured 45 50
DESIGNS: 6 r. "Cochlospermum religiosum"; 8 r. "Erythrina variegata"; 11 r. "Thespesia populnea".

1223 College Building and Emblem

1993. 50th Anniv of College of Military Engineering, Pune.
1552 **1223** 2 r. multicoloured .. 10 10

1224 Dr. Dwaram Venkataswamy Naidu playing Violin

1993. Birth Centenary of Dwaram Venkataswamy Naidu (violinist).
1553 **1224** 1 r. red 10 10

1225 Children on Elephant

1993. Children's Day.
1554 **1225** 1 r. multicoloured .. 10 10

1226 People with Stress

1993. Heart Care Festival.
1555 **1226** 6 r. 50 multicoloured 30 35

1227 Dr. Kotnis performing Operation

1993. Dr. Dwarkanath Kotnis (surgeon) Commemoration.
1556 **1227** 1 r. black 10 10

1228 Tea Symbol

1993. Indian Tea Production.
1557 **1228** 6 r. green and red .. 25 30

1229 Papal Seminary Arms and Building

1993. Centenary of Papal Seminary, Pune.
1558 **1229** 6 r. multicoloured .. 25 30

1230 Meghnad Saha and Eclipse of the Sun

1993. Meghnad Saha (astronomer) Commem.
1559 **1230** 1 r. blue 10 10

1231 Speedpost Letter and Arrows circling Globe

1993. "Inpex '93" National Stamp Exn, Calcutta. Multicoloured.
1560 1 r. Type **1231** 10 10
1561 2 r. "Custom-house Wharf, Calcutta" (Sir Charles D'Oyly) .. 10 10

1232 Dinanath Mangeshkar

1993. Dinanath Mangeshkar Commem.
1562 **1232** 1 r. red 10 10

1233 Nargis Dutt

1993. Nargis Dutt Commemoration.

1563	1233	1 r. red	10	10

1234 S. C. Bose inspecting Troops

1993. 50th Anniv of Indian National Army.

1564	1234	1 r. grn, dp grn & red	10	10

1235 Satyendra Nath Bose and Equation

1994. Birth Centenary of Satyendra Nath Bose (scientist).

1565	1235	1 r. brown	10	10

1236 Dr. Sampurnanand

1994. Dr. Sampurnanand (politician) Commemoration.

1566	1236	1 r. brown, grn & red	10	10

OFFICIAL STAMPS

1866. Optd. **Service.**

O 20	**11.**	½ a. blue	17·00	40
O 8	**12.**	8 p. mauve	17·00	35·00
O 23	**11.**	1 a. brown	18·00	45
O 27		2 a. orange	4·50	2·25
O 13		4 a. green	£120	50·00
O 29	–	4 a. green (No. 69) ..	3·00	1·50
O 30	**11.**	8 a. red	3·25	1·50

1866. Fiscal stamp with head of Queen Victoria, surch. **SERVICE TWO ANNAS.**

O 15.		2 a. purple	£325	£225

1866. Fiscal stamps optd. **SERVICE POSTAGE.**

O 19.		½ a. mauve on lilac ..	£350	80·00
O 16.		2 a. purple	£750	£375
O 17.		4 a. purple	£2250	£900
O 18.		8 a. purple	£3750	£2250

1874. Optd. **On H.M.S. (Queen Victoria).**

O 31.	**11.**	½ a. blue	5·00	20
O 32.		1 a. brown	7·50	20
O 33a.		2 a. orange	22·00	5·50
O 34.	–	4 a. green (No. 69) ..	6·50	2·50
O 35.	**11.**	8 a. red	3·50	1·75

1883. Queen Victoria stamps of 1882 and 1892 optd. **On H.M.S.**

O 37a	**40.**	3 p. red	20	10
O 39	**23.**	½ a. turquoise ..	25	10
O 49		½ a. green	90	45
O 41	–	1 a. purple	30	10
O 50	–	1 a. red	1·40	10
O 42	–	2 a. blue	2·50	30
O 51	–	2 a. lilac	18·00	45
O 44a	–	4 a. green	4·50	30
O 46	–	8 a. mauve	5·00	50
O 48	**37.**	1 r. green and red ..	3·50	40

1902. King Edward VII stamps optd. **On H.M.S.**

O 54	**41.**	3 p. grey	70	30
O 56	–	½ a. green (No. 122) ..	1·00	40
O 57	–	1 a. red (No. 123) ..	70	10
O 59	–	2 a. lilac	2·25	10
O 60	–	4 a. olive	4·25	20
O 62	–	6 a. bistre	1·50	15
O 63	–	8 a. mauve	6·00	85
O 65	–	1 r. green and red ..	4·00	45
O 68a	**52.**	2 r. red and orange ..	7·00	80
O 69		5 r. blue and violet ..	14·00	1·50
O 70		10 r. green and red ..	17·00	8·50
O 71		15 r. blue and olive ..	60·00	30·00
O 72		25 r. orange and blue ..	£140	60·00

1906. Nos. 149/50 optd. **On H.M.S.**

O 66.		½ a. green	30	10
O 67.		1 a. red	90	10

1912. King George V stamps optd. **SERVICE.**

O 73	**55.**	3 p. grey	20	10
O 76	**56.**	½ a. green	20	10
O 81	**57.**	1 a. red	60	10
O 111		1 a. brown	15	10
O 83	**59.**	2 a. lilac	45	10
O 112	**70.**	2 a. lilac	20	10
O 129		2 a. red	85	85
O 132	**63.**	4 a. olive	85	10
O 113	**71.**	4 a. green	30	10
O 87	**64.**	6 a. bistre	1·50	2·00
O 115	**65.**	8 a. mauve	60	10
O 116	**66.**	12 a. red	60	65
O 117	**67.**	1 r. brown and green ..	1·25	65
O 92		2 r. red and orange ..	3·00	2·00
O 93		5 r. blue and violet ..	11·00	11·00
O 94		10 r. green and red ..	28·00	28·00
O 95		15 r. blue and olive ..	75·00	95·00
O 96		25 r. orange and blue ..	£180	£130

1921. No. O81 surch **NINE PIES.**

O97	**57**	9 p. on 1 a. red ..	50	40

1925. Nos. O 70/2 surch. in words.

O 99.	**52.**	1 r. on 15 r. blue & olive	4·25	2·75
O 100.		1 r. on 25 r. orge. & bl.	18·00	48·00
O 101.		2 r. on 10 r. grn. & red	3·75	3·00

1925. Nos. O 94/6 surch in words.

O 102	**67**	1 r. on 15 r. bl & olive	18·00	55·00
O 103		1 r. on 25 r. orge & bl	5·00	8·00
O 104		2 r. on 10 r. grn & red	£700	

1926. No. O 62 surch. in words.

O 105.		1 a. on 6 a. bistre ..	30	30

1926. Surch. **SERVICE ONE ANNA** and two bars.

O 106.	**58.**	1 a. on 1½ a. brown (A)	20	10
O 107.		1 a. on 1½ a. brown (B)	60	1·40
O 108.	**61.**	1 a. on 2½ a. blue ..	60	1·00

1932. Optd. **SERVICE.**

O 126.	**79.**	½ a. green	60	10
O 127.	**80.**	9 p. green	20	10
O 127a.	**81.**	1 a. brown	1·25	10
O 128.	**82.**	1¼ a. mauve	30	10
O 130a.	**59.**	2 a. red	1·00	10
O 131.	**61.**	2½ a. orange	20	10

1937. King George VI stamps optd. **SERVICE.**

O 135.	**91.**	½ a. brown	10·00	15
O 136.		9 p. green	10·00	10
O 137.		1 a. red	1·00	10
O 138.	**93.**	1 r. slate and brown ..	50	40
O 139.		2 r. purple and brown	1·50	2·50
O 140.		5 r. green and blue ..	2·50	3·50
O 141.		10 r. purple and red ..	13·00	4·75

1939. King George V stamp surch. **SERVICE 1A.**

O 142.	**82.**	1 a. on 1¼ a. mauve ..	7·00	20

O 20. King George VI. **O 21.** Asokan Capital.

1939.

O 143.	**O 20.**	3 p. slate	20	10
O 144.		½ a. brown ..	1·75	10
O 144a.		½ a. purple ..	20	10
O 145.		9 p. green ..	30	10
O 146.		1 a. red	30	10
O 146a.		1 a. 3 p. brown ..	2·75	40
O 146b.		1½ a. violet ..	65	10
O 147.		2 a. orange ..	60	10
O 148.		2½ a. violet ..	60	15
O 149.		4 a. brown ..	60	10
O 150.		8 a. violet ..	90	20

1948. 1st Anniv of Independence. Optd **SERVICE.**

O 150a.	**305.**	1½ a. brown ..	42·00	30·00
O 150b.		3½ a. violet ..	£600	£400
O 150c.		12 a. green ..	£1500	£1400
O 150d.	–	10 r. brown and red (No. 308) ..	£9000	

1950.

O 151	**O 21.**	3 p. violet	10	10
O 152		6 p. brown	10	10
O 153		9 p. green	20	10
O 154		1 a. blue	55	10
O 155		2 a. red	90	10
O 156		3 a. red	3·50	90
O 157		4 a. purple	9·00	10
O 158		4 a. blue	40	10
O 159		6 a. violet	2·75	40
O 160		8 a. brown	1·75	10
O 186	–	1 r. violet	15	10
O 187	–	2 r. red	25	10
O 188	–	5 r. green	50	60
O 189	–	10 r. brown	1·25	80

The rupee values are larger and with a different frame.

1957. Value in naye paise.

O 165	**O 21.**	1 n.p. slate	10	10
O 166		2 n.p. violet ..	10	10
O 167		3 n.p. brown ..	10	10
O 168		5 n.p. green ..	10	10
O 169		6 n.p. turquoise ..	10	10
O 180		10 n.p. green ..	50	50
O 170		13 n.p. red	10	10
O 182		15 n.p. violet ..	10	10
O 172		20 n.p. red	15	30
O 184		25 n.p. blue ..	10	10
O 185		50 n.p. brown ..	15	10

O 23. O 25.

1967.

O 200	**O 23.**	2 p. violet	10	50
O 201		3 p. brown	10	60
O 202		5 p. green	10	10
O 203		6 p. blue	55	45
O 204		10 p. green	10	30
O 205		15 p. plum	10	30
O 206		20 p. red	10	30
O 207		25 p. red	5·00	3·50
O 208		30 p. blue	10	40
O 209		50 p. brown	10	40
O 197		1 r. purple	30	10

1971. Obligatory Tax. Refugee Relief. Nos. O 205/6 are optd. **REFUGEE RELIEF** in England and Hindi (No. O 205) or in English only (No. O 206).

O 210.	**O 23.**	5 p. green	30	30
O 211.		5 p. green	1·00	40
O 213.	**O 25.**	5 p. green	15	15

See note below Nos. 646/51.

O 26.

1977. Various Designs redrawn, showing face-value in figures only and smaller Capital with Hindi motto beneath as Type **O 26.**

O 214	**O 26.**	2 p. violet	20	60
O 254		5 p. green	10	10
O 255		10 p. green ..	10	10
O 256		15 p. purple ..	10	10
O 257		20 p. red	10	10
O 258		25 p. red	10	10
O 259		30 p. blue	10	10
O 260		35 p. violet ..	10	10
O 261		40 p. violet ..	10	10
O 262		50 p. brown ..	10	10
O 263		60 p. brown ..	10	10
O 264		1 r. brown	10	10
O 225a		2 r. red	40	1·00
O 226a		5 r. green	60	1·50
O 227		10 r. red	1·25	2·75

The 2, 5 and 10 r. values are larger.

O 27. O 28.

1981. Redrawn with face value figures in bottom corners.

O 265.	**O 27.**	2 r. red	10	15
O 266.		5 r. green	20	25
O 267.		10 r. brown ..	40	45

1982. As 1977 and 1981 issue but with simulated perforations. Imperf.

O 231	**O 28**	5 p. green	50	50
O 232		10 p. green ..	55	55
O 233		15 p. purple ..	55	55
O 234		20 p. red	60	60
O 235		25 p. red	1·25	1·00
O 236		35 p. violet ..	70	35
O 237		50 p. brown ..	1·25	85
O 238		1 r. brown ..	1·50	85
O 239		2 r. red	1·75	2·25
O 240		5 r. green	2·00	2·75
O 241		10 r. brown ..	2·50	4·00

INDIAN CUSTODIAN FORCES IN KOREA

Stamps used by the Indian Forces on custodian duties in Korea in 1953.

12 pies = 1 anna; 16 annas = 1 rupee.

भारतीय
संरक्षा कटक
कोरिया

(1.)

1953. Stamps of India (archaeological series), optd. with **T 1.**

K 1.	**307.**	3 p. violet	1·00	3·25
K 2.	**308.**	6 p. brown	1·00	3·25
K 3.	–	9 p. green	1·25	3·25
K 4.	–	1 a. blue (B)	1·00	3·25
K 5.	–	2 a. red	1·00	3·25
K 6.	–	2½ a. lake	1·00	4·00
K 7.	–	3 a. salmon	1·25	4·00
K 8.	**314.**	4 a. blue	1·75	4·50
K 9.	**315.**	6 a. violet	7·50	8·50
K 10.	–	8 a. green	3·25	8·50
K 11.	–	12 a. blue	4·50	17·00
K 12.	–	1 r. violet and green ..	6·00	17·00

INDIAN EXPEDITIONARY FORCES

Stamps used by Indian Forces during, and after, the War of 1914–18.

12 pies = 1 anna; 16 annas = 1 rupee.

1914. Stamps of India (King George V) optd. **I.E.F.**

E 1.	**55.**	3 p. grey	15	25
E 2.	**56.**	½ a. green	20	20
E 3.	**57.**	1 a. red	40	20
E 5.	**59.**	2 a. lilac	60	30
E 6.	**61.**	2½ a. blue	80	1·25
E 7.	**62.**	3 a. orange	80	60
E 8.	**63.**	4 a. olive	70	60
E 9.	**65.**	8 a. mauve	1·00	1·00
E 12.	**66.**	12 a. red	2·25	5·00
E 13.	**67.**	1 r. brown and green ..	2·50	4·00

INDIAN FORCES IN INDO-CHINA

Stamps used by Indian Forces engaged in the International Commission in Indo-China.

1954. 12 pies = 1 anna; 16 annas = 1 rupee.
1957. 100 nay paise = 1 rupee.
1964. 100 paisa = 1 rupee.

अन्तर्राष्ट्रीय आयोग कम्बोज	अन्तर्राष्ट्रीय आयोग लाओस	अन्तर्राष्ट्रीय आयोग वियत नाम
(N 1)	(N 2)	(N 3.)

1954. Stamps of India (archaeological series) overprinted.

(a) Optd. with T N 1, for use in Cambodia.

N 1. 307. 3 p. violet .. .. 60 4·00
N 2. – 1 a. blue (B) 90 75
N 3. – 2 a. red 90 80
N 4. – 8 a. green .. .. 2·00 3·50
N 5. – 12 a. blue .. .. 2·25 4·00

(b) Optd. with T N 2, for use in Laos.

N 6. 307. 3 p. violet .. .. 60 4·00
N 7. – 1 a. blue (B) 90 75
N 8. – 2 a. red 90 80
N 9. – 8 a. green .. .. 2·00 3·50
N 10. – 12 a. blue .. .. 2·25 4·00

(c) Optd. with T N 3, for use in Viet-Nam.

N 11. 307. 3 p. violet .. .. 60 4·00
N 12. – 1 a. blue (B) 90 75
N 13. – 2 a. red 90 80
N 14. – 8 a. green .. .. 2·00 3·50
N 15. – 12 a. blue .. .. 2·25 4·00

1957. Map type of India overprinted.

(a) Optd. with T N 1, for use in Cambodia.

N 16. 361. 2 n.p. brown 60 30
N 17. 6 n.p. grey 45 30
N 18. 13 n.p. red 55 40
N 19. 50 n.p. orange .. 2·00 1·25
N 20. 75 n.p. purple .. 2·00 1·25

(b) Optd. with T N 2, for use in Laos.

N 21 361. 2 n.p. brown 60 30
N 39 3 n.p. brown 10 20
N 40 5 n.p. green 10 15
N 22 6 n.p. grey 45 30
N 23 13 n.p. red 55 40
N 24 50 n.p. orange .. 2·00 1·25
N 25 75 n.p. purple .. 2·00 1·25

(c) Optd. with T N 3, for use in Vietnam.

N 43 361. 1 n.p. turquoise .. 10 20
N 26 2 n.p. brown 60 30
N 45 3 n.p. brown 10 20
N 46 5 n.p. green 10 15
N 27 6 n.p. grey 45 30
N 28 13 n.p. red 55 40
N 29 50 n.p. orange .. 2·00 1·25
N 30 75 n.p. purple .. 2·00 1·25

1965. Children's Day stamp of India optd. ICC for use in Laos and Vietnam.

N 49. 469. 15 p. slate .. .. 30 2·75

1968. Nos. 504/6, 509/10, 515 and 517/18, of India optd. **ICC** in English and Indian, for use in Laos and Vietnam.

N 50. – 2 p. brown .. .. 10 1·25
N 51. – 3 p. olive .. .. 10 1·25
N 52. – 5 p. red 10 40
N 53. – 10 p. blue .. .. 1·50 1·00
N 54. 467. 15 p. green .. .. 60 1·00
N 55. – 60 p. grey .. .. 35 1·00
N 56. – 1 r. brown and plum 50 1·50
N 57. – 2 r. blue and violet .. 1·00 5·50

INDIAN U.N. FORCE IN CONGO

Stamps used by Indian Forces attached to the United Nations Force in Congo.

100 naye paise = 1 rupee.

1962. Map type of India optd. **U.N. FORCE (INDIA) CONGO.**

U 1. 361. 1 n.p. turquoise .. 70 1·50
U 2. 2 n.p. brown 70 80
U 3. 5 n.p. green 70 55
U 4. 8 n.p. turquoise .. 70 30
U 5. 13 n.p. red 70 40
U 6. 50 n.p. orange .. 70 70

INDIAN U.N. FORCE IN GAZA (PALESTINE)

Stamps used by Indian Forces attached to the United Nations Force in Gaza.

100 paise = 1 rupee.

1965. Children's Day stamp of India optd. **UNEF.**

G 1. 449. 15 p. slate .. .. 60 2·75

INDORE (HOLKAR STATE)

A state in C. India. Now uses Indian stamps.

12 pies = 1 anna; 16 annas = 1 rupee.

1. Maharaja Tukoji Rao II Holkar XI.

1886.

2. 1. ½ a. mauve .. .. .. 1·25 1·10

2.

1889. No gum. Imperf.

4. 2. ½ a. black on pink .. .. 1·60 1·90

3. Maharaja Shivaji Rao Holkar XII. 5. Maharaja Tukoji Rao III Holkar XIII.

1889.

5. 3. ¼ a. orange 50 30
6a. ½ a. purple 45 15
7. 1 a. green 65 50
8. 2 a. red .. .. 1·75 1·00

1904.

9. 5. ¼ a. orange 30 10
10. ½ a. red .. .. 7·50 10
11. 1 a. green .. .. 6·50 10
12. 2 a. brown .. .. 1·60 10
13. 3 a. violet .. .. 5·00 30
14a. 4 a. blue .. .. 8·00 2·50
The ½ a. is inscr. "HOLKAR" 5·00 1·10

पाव आना.

(6.)

1905. No. 6a surch. as T 6.

15. 3. ¼ a. on ½ a. purple .. 1·50 11·00

7. Maharaja Yeshwant Rao II Holkar XIV. 9.

1928.

16. 7. ¼ a. orange 30 10
17. ½ a. purple 30 10
18. 1 a. green 50 10
19. 1¼ a. green 60 15
20. 2 a. brown .. .. 2·50 80
21. 2 a. green .. .. 6·50 60
22. 3 a. violet .. .. 1·50 6·50
23. 3 a. blue .. .. 12·00
24. 3½ a. violet .. .. 4·00 8·50
25. 4 a. blue .. .. 3·25 2·25
26. 4 a. yellow .. .. 18·00 1·50
27. 8 a. grey .. .. 5·50 5·00
28. 8 a. orange .. .. 12·00 14·00
29. 12 a. red .. .. 5·00 10·00
30. – 1 r. black and blue .. 8·00 14·00
31. – 2 r. black and red .. 30·00 35·00
32. – 5 r. black and brown .. 48·00 50·00
The rupee values are larger (23 × 28 mm.).

1940. Surch. diagonally in words.

33. – ¼ a. on 5 r. (No. 32) .. 3·00 35
34. – ½ a. on 2 r. (No. 31) .. 5·50 1·00
35. 7. 1 a. on 1¼ a. green (No. 19) 6·00 35

1941.

36. 9. ¼ a. orange .. .. 1·50 10
37. ½ a. red .. .. 1·00 10
38. 1 a. green .. .. 5·00 10
39. 1¼ a. green .. .. 9·50 30
40. 2 a. blue .. .. 9·00 1·00
41. 4 a. yellow .. .. 9·00 7·50
42. – 2 r. black and red .. 9·00 80·00
43. – 5 r. black and orange .. 10·00 £100
The rupee values are larger (23 × 28 mm.).

OFFICIAL STAMPS

1904. Optd. **SERVICE.**

S 1. 5. ¼ a. orange 10 35
S 2. ½ a. red 10 10
S 3. 1 a. green 10 15
S 4. 2 a. brown 30 20
S 5. 3 a. violet .. .. 1·75 1·25
S 6. 4 a. blue .. .. 2·25 1·40

IONIAN ISLANDS

A group of islands off the W. coast of Greece, placed under the protection of Gt. Britain in 1815 and ceded to Greece in 1864. Under Italian occupation in 1941 and occupied by Germany in 1943.

12 pence = 1 shilling.
20 shillings = 1 pound.

1.

1859. Imperf.

1. 1. (½d.) orange .. .. 70·00 £500
2. (1d.) blue .. .. 20·00 £180
3. (2d.) red .. .. 15·00 £180

IRELAND

The Republic of Ireland (Eire) is an independent state comprising Ireland, except the six counties of N. Ireland. It was formerly part of the United Kingdom of Great Britain and Ireland.

1922. 12 pence = 1 shilling;
20 shillings = 1 pound.
1971. 100 (new) pence = 1 pound (Punt).

Rialtaṗ Sealadaċ na hÉireann 1922 — Rialtaṗ Sealadaċ na hÉireann 1922.

(1.) "Provisional Govern- (2.) ment of Ireland, 1922".

1922. Optd with T 1 (date in thin figures and no full point).

1 105 ½d. green 40 40
2 104 1d. red 45 35
4a 2½d. blue .. .. 85 3·00
5 106 3d. violet .. .. 3·25 3·75
6 4d. green .. .. 2·50 7·00
7 107 5d. brown .. .. 3·50 8·50
8 108 9d. brown .. .. 9·00 17·00
9 10d. blue .. .. 7·00 20·00
17 109 2s. 6d. brown .. .. 32·00 65·00
19 5s. red .. .. 60·00 £110
21 10s. blue £120 £225
On Nos. 17, 19 and 21 the overprint is in four lines instead of five.

1922. Optd with T 2 (date in thick figures followed by full point).

30. 105. ½d. green .. .. 1·60 80
31. 104. 1d. red 50 50
10. 105. 1½d. brown .. .. 1·75 85
12. 106. 2d. orange .. .. 1·75 60
35. 104. 2½d. blue .. .. 7·00 18·00
36. 106. 3d. violet .. .. 2·25 3·00
37. 4d. green .. .. 2·25 4·00
38. 107. 5d. brown .. .. 3·50 7·50
39. 6d. purple .. .. 7·00 2·50
40. 108. 9d. black .. .. 11·00 14·00
41. 9d. green .. .. 4·50 22·00
42. 10d. blue .. .. 25·00 48·00
43. 1s. brown .. .. 7·50 8·50

Saorstát Éireann 1922

(5. "Irish Free State, 1922").

1922. Optd. with T 5.

52 105. ½d. green 30 30
53 104. 1d. red 30 35
54 105. 1½d. brown .. .. 2·50 8·50
55 106. 2d. orange .. .. 1·00 2·00
56 104. 2½d. blue .. .. 4·00 6·50
57 106. 3d. violet .. .. 3·50 13·00
58 4d. green .. .. 2·50 4·50
59 107. 5d. brown .. .. 3·00 4·75
60 6d. purple .. .. 2·00 1·75
61 108. 9d. green .. .. 3·00 5·50
62 10d. blue .. .. 15·00 38·00
63 1s. brown .. .. 9·00 9·50
86 109. 2s. 6d. brown .. 38·00 40·00
87 5s. red .. .. 60·00 80·00
88 10s. blue £140 £150

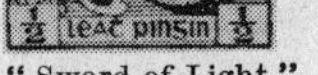

6. "Sword of Light". 7. Map of Ireland.

8. Arms of Ireland. 9. Celtic Cross.

1922.

71 6 ½d. green 55 45
112 7 1d. red 30 10
73 1½d. purple .. .. 1·25 1·75
114 2d. green 30 10
75 8 2½d. brown .. .. 3·25 3·25
116 9 3d. blue (18¾ × 22½ mm.) 40 10
227 3d. blue (17 × 21 mm.) .. 60 15
117 8 4d. blue 40 10
118 6 5d. violet (18¾ × 22½ mm.) 65 10
228 5d. violet (17 × 21 mm.) 30 15
119aa 6d. purple .. .. 1·25 20
119a 8d. red 80 50
120 8 9d. violet .. .. 1·50 50
121 9 10d. brown 60 45
121a 11d. red .. .. 1·25 1·75
82 6 1s. blue .. .. 28·00 4·50

12. Daniel O'Connell.

1929. Cent. of Catholic Emancipation.

89. 12. 2d. green 40 35
90. 3d. blue .. .. .. 4·00 8·50
91. 9d. violet .. .. .. 4·00 4·00

13. Shannon Barrage.

1930. Completion of Shannon Hydro-Electric Scheme.

92. 13. 2d. deep brown 60 40

14. Reaper. 15. The Cross of Cong.

1931. Bicent. of Royal Dublin Society.

93. 14. 2d. blue 45 20

1932. Int. Eucharistic Congress.

94. 15. 2d. green 50 30
95. 3d. blue .. .. .. 2·25 5·00

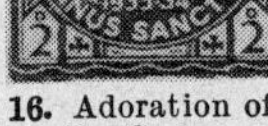

16. Adoration of the Cross. 17. Hurler.

1933. "Holy Year".

96. 16. 2d. green 60 15
97. 3d. blue .. .. .. 2·50 2·00

1934. 50th Anniv. of Gaelic Athletic Assn.

98. 17. 2d. green 60 30

18. St. Patrick.

1937.

123a	18	2s. 6d. green	1·50	2·00
124ba		5s. purple	4·50	4·50
125ab		10s. blue	12·00	12·00

19. Ireland and New Constitution.

1937. Constitution Day.

105.	**19.**	2d. red	1·00	20
106.		3d. blue	4·00	3·25

For similar stamps see No. 176/7.

20. Father Mathew.

1938. Centenary of Temperance Crusade.

107.	**20.**	2d. black	1·50	60
108.		3d. blue	10·00	6·00

21. George Washington, American Eagle and Irish Harp.

1939. 150th Anniv. of U.S. Constitution and Installation of First U.S. President.

109.	**21.**	2d. red	2·00	60
110.		3d. blue	4·50	4·00

24. Volunteer and G.P.O., Dublin.

1941. 25th Anniv. of Easter Rising (1916).
(a) Provisional issue. Optd. with two lines of Irish characters between the dates "1941" and "1916".

126.	**7.**	2d. orange	2·00	50
127.	**9.**	3d. blue	38·00	9·50

(b) Definitive Issue.

128.	**24.**	2½d. blue	70	40

25. Dr. Douglas Hyde.

26. Sir William Rowan Hamilton.

1943. 50th Anniv. of Gaelic League.

129.	**25.**	½d. green	40	30
130.		2½d. purple	1·25	10

1943. Centenary of Announcement of Discovery of Quaternions.

131.	**26.**	½d. green	40	40
132.		2½d. brown	1·50	10

27. Bro. Michael O'Clery.

28. Edmund Ignatius Rice.

1944. Death Tercentenary of O'Clery (Franciscan historian). (commemorating the "Annals of the Four Masters").

133.	**27.**	½d. green	10	10
134.		1s. brown	70	10

1944. Death Centenary of Edmund Rice (founder of Irish Christian Brothers).

135.	**28.**	2½d. slate	60	30

29. "Youth sowing Seeds of Freedom."

1945. Death Centenary of Thomas Davis (Founder of Young Ireland Movement).

136.	**29.**	2½d. blue	1·00	25
137.		6d. purple	7·00	3·75

30. "Country and Homestead".

1946. Birth Centenary of Michael Davitt and Charles Parnell.

138.	**30.**	2½d. red	1·50	15
139.		3d. blue	3·00	2·75

31. Angel Victor over Rock of Cashel.

1948. Air. Inscr." VOX HIBERNIÆ ".

140.	**31.**	1d. brown	2·25	3·25
141.	–	3d. blue	4·50	2·25
142.	–	6d. purple	1·00	1·00
142a.	–	8d. lake	5·50	4·50
143.	–	1s. green	1·75	1·00
143a.	**31.**	1s 3d. orange ..	5·50	1·25
143b.		1s. 5d. blue ..	3·50	1·00

DESIGNS: 3d., 8d. Angel Victor over Lough Derg. 6d. Over Croagh Patrick. 1s. Over Glendalough.

35. Theobald Wolfe Tone.

1948. 150th Anniv. of Insurrection.

144.	**35.**	2½d. purple	1·25	10
145.		3d. violet	3·75	3·25

For later issues see Volume 1.

POSTAGE DUE STAMPS

D 1.

1925.

D 1	**D 1.**	½d. green	12·00	16·00
D 6		1d. red	1·00	60
D 7		1½d. red	1·75	6·50
D 8		2d. green	2·25	60
D 9		3d. blue	2·00	1·50
D 10		5d. violet	3·50	3·00
D 11a		6d. plum	70	85
D 12		8d. orange	8·00	7·50
D 13		10d. purple	8·50	7·50
D 14		1s. green	7·50	8·50

ISLE OF MAN

An island in the Irish Sea to the north-west of England. Man became a possession of the English Crown during the Middle Ages, but retains its own Assembly.

Regional issues from 1958–71 are listed at end of GREAT BRITAIN.

Isle of Man had an independent postal administration from 1973.

100 pence = 1 pound.

4. Castletown.

5. Manx Cat.

1973. Multicoloured.

12.	½p. Type **4**	10	10
13.	1p. Port Erin	10	10
14.	1½p. Snaefell	10	10
15.	2p. Laxey	10	10
16.	2½p. Tynwald Hill	10	10
17.	3p. Douglas Promenade ..	10	10
18.	3½p. Port St. Mary ..	15	15
19.	4p. Fairy Bridge	15	15
20.	4½p. As 2½p.	20	20
21.	5p. Peel	20	20
22.	5½p. As 3p.	25	25
23.	6p. Cregneish	25	25
24.	7p. As 2p.	30	30
25.	7½p. Ramsey Bay	25	25
26.	8p. As 7½p.	35	35
27.	9p. Douglas Bay	30	35
28.	10p. Type **5**	30	35
29.	11p. Monk's Bridge, Ballasalla	45	50
30.	13p. Derbyhaven	55	50
31.	20p. Manx Loaghtyn Ram	65	65
32.	50p. Manx Shearwater ..	1·60	1·60
33.	£1 Viking Longship ..	3·25	3·25

SIZES: Nos. 13/27 and 29/30 as Type **4**. Nos. 31/3 as Type **5**.

6. Viking landing on Man, A.D. 938.

1973. Inaug. of Postal Independence.

34.	**6.**	15p. multicoloured ..	80	80

7. " Sutherland ".

1973. Cent. of Steam Railway. Multicoloured.

35.	2½p. Type **7**	20	20
36.	3p. " Caledonia "	20	20
37.	7½p. " Kissack "	60	90
38.	9p. " Pender "	70	90

8. Leonard Randles, First Winner, 1923.

1973. Golden Jubilee of Manx Grand Prix Multicoloured.

39.	3p. Type **8**	30	20
40.	3½p. Alan Holmes, Double Winner, 1957	30	20

9. Princess Anne and Capt. Mark Phillips.

1973. Royal Wedding.

41.	**9.**	25p. multicoloured ..	1·00	90

10. Badge, Citation and Sir William Hillary (Founder).

1974. 150th Anniv. of Royal National Lifeboat Institution. Multicoloured.

42.	3p. Type **10**	10	10
43.	3½p. Wreck of " St. George ", 1830	15	15
44.	8p. R.N.L.B. " Manchester and Salford ", 1868-87 ..	60	65
45.	10p. R.N.L.B. " Osman Gabriel "	60	65

11. Stanley Woods, 1935.

1974. Tourist Trophy Motor-cycle Races (1st issue). Multicoloured.

46.	3p. Type **11**	10	10
47.	3½p. Freddy Frith, 1937 ..	10	10
48.	8p. Max Deubel and Emil Horner, 1961	45	45
49.	10p. Mike Hailwood, 1961	50	45

See also Nos 63/6.

12. Rushen Abbey and Arms.

1974. Historical Anniversaries. Multicoloured.

50.	3½p. Type **12**	10	10
51.	4½p. Magnus Haraldson rows King Edgar on the Dee ..	10	10
52.	8p. King Magnus and Norse fleet	40	40
53.	10p. Bridge at Avignon and bishop's mitre	50	50

COMMEMORATIONS: Nos. 50 and 53, William Russell, Bishop of Sodor and Man. 600th Death Anniv Nos. 51/2, Rule of King Magnus Haraldson. 1000th Anniv.

13. Churchill, and Bugler Dunne at Colenso, 1899.

1974. Birth Centenary of Sir Winston Churchill. Multicoloured.

54.	3½p. Type **13**	10	10
55.	4½p. Churchill and Government Buildings, Douglas	10	10
56.	8p. Churchill and Manx ack-ack crew	25	35
57.	20p. Churchill as Freeman of Douglas	65	55

14. Cabin School and Names of Pioneers.

1975. Manx Pioneers in Cleveland, Ohio. Multicoloured.

59.	4½p. Type **14**	10	10
60.	5½p. Terminal Tower Building, J. Gill and R. Carran	15	10
61.	8p. Clague House Museum, & Robert & Margaret Clague	35	40
62.	10p. "S.S. William T. Graves" and Thomas Quayle ..	50	50

15. Tom Sheard, 1923.

1975. Tourist Trophy Motor-cycle Races (2nd issue). Multicoloured.

63.	5½p. Type **15**	10	15
64.	7p. Walter Handley, 1925	20	20
65.	10p. Geoff. Duke, 1955 ..	40	30
66.	12p. Peter Williams, 1973	40	45

16. Sir George Goldie and Birthplace.

1975. 50th Death Anniv. of Sir George Goldie. Multicoloured.

67.	5½p. Type **16** ..	10	15
68.	7p. Goldie and map of Africa (vert.)	20	20
69.	10p. Goldie as President of Geographical Society (vert.)	40	30
70.	12p. River scene on the Niger	40	45

17. Title Page of Manx Bible.

1975. Christmas and Bicentenary of Manx Bible. Multicoloured.

71.	5½p. Type **17**	15	15
72.	7p. Rev. Philip Moore and Ballaugh Old Church ..	20	20
73.	11p. Bishop Hildesley and Bishops Court	40	35
74.	13p. John Kelly saving Bible manuscript	45	40

18. William Christian listening to Patrick Henry.

1976. American Independence. Commemorating Col. William Christian. Mult.

75.	5½p. Type **18**	15	15
76.	7p. Conveying the Fincastle Resolutions	20	20
77.	13p. Patrick Henry and William Christian ..	35	35
78.	20p. Christian as an Indian fighter	50	50

19. First Horse Tram, 1876.

1976. Centenary of Douglas Horse-Trams. Multicoloured.

80.	5½p. Type **19**	10	15
81.	7p. "Toast-rack" tram, 1890	15	15
82.	11p. Horse-bus, 1895 ..	45	35
83.	13p. Royal tram, 1972 ..	50	45

20. Barrose Beaker. 21. Diocesan Banner.

1976. Europa. Ceramic Art. Multicoloured.

84.	5p. Type **20**	20	25
85.	5p. Souvenir teapot ..	20	25
86.	5p. Laxey jug	20	25
87.	10p. Cronk Aust food vessel (horiz.)	40	45
88.	10p. Sansbury bowl (horiz.)	40	45
89.	10p. Knox urn (horiz.) ..	40	45

1976. Christmas and Centenary of Mothers' Union. Multicoloured.

90.	6p. Type **21**	15	15
91.	7p. Onchan banner ..	15	15
92.	11p. Castletown banner ..	40	35
93.	13p. Ramsey banner ..	40	45

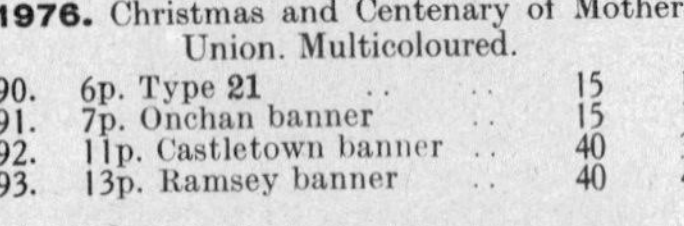

22. Queen Elizabeth II.

1977. Silver Jubilee. Multicoloured.

94.	6p. Type **22**	20	20
95.	7p. Queen Elizabeth and Prince Philip (vert.) ..	20	20
96.	25p. Queen Elizabeth (different)	80	70

23. Carrick Bay from "Tom-the-Dipper".
(Illustration reduced. Actual size 58 × 22 mm.)

1977. Europa. Multicoloured.

97.	6p. Type **23**	20	20
98.	10p. View from Ramsey	30	30

24. F. A. Applebee, 1912.

1977. Linked Anniversaries. Multicoloured.

99.	6p. Type **24**	15	15
100.	7p. St. John's Ambulance Brigade at Governor's Bridge, 1938	15	20
101.	11p. Scouts operating the scoreboard	40	40
102.	13p. John Williams, 1976	40	40

ANNIVERSARIES: TT Races. 70th Anniv. Scouts Movement. 70th Anniv. St. John's Ambulance Brigade. Cent.

25. Old Summer House, Mount Morrison, Peel.

1977. Bicent. of First Visit of John Wesley. Multicoloured.

103.	6p. Type **25**	15	15
104.	7p. Wesley preaching in Castletown Square ..	20	20
105.	11p. Wesley preaching outside Bradden Church ..	35	35
106.	13p. New Methodist Church, Douglas	40	40

Nos. 104/5 are larger, 38 × 26 mm.

26. Short Type 184 Seaplane and H.M.S. "Ben-My-Chree", 1915.

1978. 60th Anniv. of Royal Air Force.

107.	6p. Type **26**	15	15
108.	7p. Bristol Scout and H.M.S. "Vindex", 1915	20	20
109.	11p. Boulton Paul "Defiant" over Douglas Bay, 1941	40	35
110.	13p. "Jaguar" over Ramsey, 1977	45	40

27. Watch Tower, Langness.

1978. Multicoloured.

111.	½p. Type **27**	20	10
112.	1p. Jurby Church (horiz.)	20	10
113.	6p. Government Buildings	30	25
114.	7p. Tynwald Hill (horiz.)	35	30
115.	8p. Milner's Tower ..	35	30
116.	9p. Laxey Wheel	35	35
117.	10p. Castle Rushen (horiz.)	35	35
118.	11p. St. Ninian's Church ..	40	40
119.	12p. Tower of Refuge (horiz.)	40	30
120.	13p. St. German's Cathedral (horiz.)	40	30
121.	14p. Point of Ayre Lighthouse (horiz.)	50	40
122.	15p. Corrin's Tower (horiz.)	50	30
123.	16p. Douglas Head Lighthouse (horiz.)	75	65
124.	20p. Fuchsia	60	50
125.	25p. Manx cat	75	65
126.	50p. Chough	1·25	1·25
127.	£1 Viking warrior ..	2·50	2·50
128.	£2 Queen Elizabeth II ..	4·75	3·75

Nos. 124/7 are larger, 25 × 31 mm. and No. 128, 38 × 48 mm.

28. Queen Elizabeth in Coronation Regalia.

1978. 25th Anniversary of Coronation.

132.	**28.** 25p. multicoloured ..	75	75

29. Wheel-headed Cross-slab.

1978. Europa. Celtic and Norse Crosses. Multicoloured.

133.	6p. Type **29**	15	15
134.	6p. Celtic wheel-cross ..	15	15
135.	6p. Keeil Chiggyrt Stone	15	15
136.	11p. Olaf Liotulfson Cross	30	30
137.	11p. Odd's and Thorleif's Crosses	30	30
138.	11p. Thor Cross	30	30

30. J. K. Ward and Ward Library, Peel.

1978. Anniversaries and Events. Mult.

139.	6p. Type **30**	15	15
140.	7p. Swimmer, cyclist and walker	20	20
141.	11p. American Bald Eagle, Manx arms and maple leaf (42 × 26 mm.) ..	35	35
142.	13p. Lumber camp, Three Rivers, Quebec ..	40	40

ANNIVERSARIES AND EVENTS: 6, 13p. James Kewley Ward (Manx pioneer in Canada) commemoration. 7p. Commonwealth Games, Edmonton. 11p. North American Manx Association. 50th Anniv.

31. Hunt the Wren.

1978. Christmas.

143.	**31.** 5p. multicoloured ..	30	25

32. P.M.C. Kermode and "Nassa kermodei".

1979. Centenary of Natural History and Antiquarian Society. Multicoloured.

144	6p. Type **32**	15	15
145	7p. Peregrine falcon ..	20	20
146	11p. Fulmar	35	35
147	13p. "Epitriptus cowini" (fly)	40	40

33. Postman, 1859.

1979. Europa. Communications. Multicoloured.

148. 6p. Type **33** 20 20
149. 11p. Postman, 1979 .. 30 30

34. Viking Longship Emblem. **35.** Viking Raid at Garwick.

1979. Millennium of Tynwald. Multicoloured.

150b 3p. Type **34** 10 10
151 4p. " Three Legs of Man " emblem 15 15
152 6p. Type **35** 15 15
153 7p. 10th-century meeting of Tynwald .. 20 20
154 11p. Tynwald Hill and St. John's Church .. 30 30
155 13p. Procession to Tynwald Hill 45 35

The 4p. value is as Type **34** and the remainder as Type **35**.

36. Queen and Court on Tynwald Hill.

1979. Royal Visit. Multicoloured.

156. 7p. Type **36** 30 20
157. 13p. Queen and Procession from St. John's Church to Tynwald Hill .. 40 40

37. " Odin's Raven".

1979. Voyage of " Odin's Raven ".

158. **37.** 15p. multicoloured .. 50 50

38. John Quilliam seized by the Press Gang.

1979. 150th Death Anniv. of Captain John Quilliam. Multicoloured.

159. 6p. Type **38** .. 15 15
160. 8p. Steering H.M.S. "Victory", Battle of Trafalgar .. 20 20
161. 13p. Captain John Quilliam and H.M.S. " Spencer " 50 40
162. 15p. Captain John Quilliam (member of the House of Keys) 55 45

39. Young Girl with Teddybear and Cat.

1979. Christmas. International Year of the Child. Multicoloured.

163. 5p. Type **39** .. 25 25
164. 7p. Father Christmas with young Children .. 35 35

40. Conglomerate Arch, Langness.

1980. 150th Anniversary of Royal Geographical Society. Multicoloured.

165. 7p. Type **40** 20 20
166. 8p. Braaid Circle 20 20
167. 12p. Cashtal-yn-Ard .. 30 30
168. 13p. Volcanic rocks at Scarlett 45 40
169. 15p. Sugar-loaf Rock .. 55 45

41. " Mona's Isle I ".

1980. 150th Anniv. of Isle of Man Steam Packet Company. Multicoloured.

170. 7p. Type **41** 20 20
171. 8p. "Douglas I" 20 20
172. $11\frac{1}{2}$p. H.M.S. "Mona's Queen II" sinking U-Boat 30 30
173. 12p. H.M.S. "King Orry III" at surrender of German fleet, 1918 .. 30 30
174. 13p. "Ben-My-Chree IV".. 35 35
175. 15p. "Lady of Mann II".. 55 40

42. Stained Glass Window, T. E. Brown Room, Manx Museum.

1980. Europa. Personalities. Thomas Edward Brown (poet and scholar) Commemoration. Multicoloured.

177. 7p. Type **42** 20 20
178. $13\frac{1}{2}$p. Clifton College, Bristol 40 40

43. King Olav V and "Norge" (Norwegian royal yacht).

1980. Visit of King Olav of Norway, August 1979.

179. **43.** 12p. multicoloured .. 50 50

44. Winter Wren and View of Calf of Man.

1980. Christmas and Wildlife Conservation Year. Multicoloured.

181. 6p. Type **44** 30 30
182. 8p. European Robin and view of Port Erin Marine Biological Station .. 45 45

45. William Kermode and Brig " Robert Quayle ", 1819.

1980. Kermode Family in Tasmania Commemoration. Multicoloured.

183. 7p. Type **45** 20 20
184. 9p. " Mona Vale ", Van Diemen's Land, 1834.. 25 25
185. $13\frac{1}{2}$p. Ross Bridge, Tasmania 40 35
186. 15p. " Mona Vale ", Tasmania 45 40
187. $17\frac{1}{2}$p. Robert Quayle Kermode and Parliament Buildings, Tasmania 50 45

46. Peregrine Falcon.

1980. Multicoloured.

188. 1p. Type **46** 25 25
189. 5p. Loaghtyn ram .. 40 40

47. Luggers passing Red Pier, Douglas.

1981. Centenary of Royal National Mission to Deepsea Fishermen. Multicoloured.

190. 8p. Type **47** 25 25
191. 9p. Peel Lugger " Wanderer " rescuing survivors from " Lusitania " 30 30
192. 18p. Nickeys leaving Port St. Mary 55 45
193. 20p. Nobby entering Ramsey Harbour 55 50
194. 22p. Nickeys " Sunbeam " and " Zebra " at Port Erin 60 50

48. " Crosh Cuirn " Superstition.

1981. Europa. Folklore. Multicoloured.

195. 8p. Type **48** 25 25
196. 18p. " Bollan Cross " superstition 55 55

49. Lt. Mark Wilks (Royal Manx Fencibles) and Peel Castle.

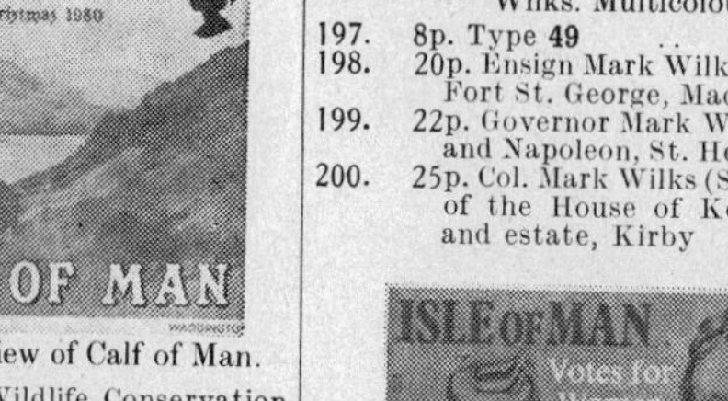

1981. 150th Death Anniv. of Colonel Mark Wilks. Multicoloured.

197. 8p. Type **49** 25 25
198. 20p. Ensign Mark Wilks and Fort St. George, Madras 50 50
199. 22p. Governor Mark Wilks and Napoleon, St. Helena 70 55
200. 25p. Col. Mark Wilks (Speaker of the House of Keys) and estate, Kirby .. 80 80

50. Miss Emmeline Goulden (Mrs. Pankhurst) and Mrs. Sophia Jane Goulden.

1981. Centenary of Manx Women's Suffrage.

201. **50.** 9p. black, grey and stone 35 30

51. Prince Charles and Lady Diana Spencer.

1981. Royal Wedding.

202. **51.** 9p. black, blue and pale blue 25 25
203. 25p. black, blue & pink 75 75

52. Douglas War Memorial, Poppies and Commemorative Inscription.

1981. 60th Anniv. of The Royal British Legion. Multicoloured.

205. 8p. Type **52** 25 25
206. 10p. Major Robert Cain (war hero) 30 35
207. 18p. Festival of Remembrance, Royal Albert Hall 55 45
208. 20p. T.S.S. " Tynwald " at Dunkirk, May 1940 .. 60 50

53. Nativity Scene (stained glass window, St. George's Church).

1981. Christmas. Multicoloured.

209. 7p. Type **53** 25 25
210. 9p. Children from Special School performing nativity play (48 × 30 mm.) .. 35 35

54. Joseph and William Cunningham (founders of Isle of Man Boy Scout Movement) and Cunningham House Headquarters.

1982. 75th Anniv. of Boy Scout Movement and 125th Birth Anniv. of Lord Baden-Powell. Multicoloured.

211. 9p. Type **54** 30 30
212. 10p. Baden-Powell visiting Isle of Man, 1911 .. 30 30
213. $19\frac{1}{2}$p. Baden-Powell and Scout emblem (40 × 31 mm.) 55 55
214. 24p. Scouts and Baden-Powell's last message .. 75 75
215. 29p. Scout salute, handshake, emblem and globe 95 95

55. "The Principals and Duties of Christianity" (Bishop T. Wilson) (first book printed in Manx, 1707). Illustration reduced: Actual size 49×32 mm.)

982. Europa. Historic Events. Mult.
16. 9p. Type **55** 25 25
17. 19½p. Landing at Derbyhaven (visit of Thomas, 2nd Earl of Derby, 1507) 50 50

56. Charlie Collier (first TT race (single cylinder) winner) and Tourist Trophy Race, 1907.

982. 75th Anniv. of Tourist Trophy Motorcycle Racing. Multicoloured.
218. 9p. Type **56** 20 20
219. 10p. Freddie Dixon (Sidecar and Junior TT winner) and Junior TT race, 1927 25 25
220. 24p. Jimmie Simpson (TT winner and first to lap at 60, 70 and 80 mph) and Senior TT, 1932 .. 70 70
221. 26p. Mike Hailwood (winner of fourteen TT's) and Senior TT, 1961 90 90
222. 29p. Jock Taylor (Sidecar TT winner, 1978, 1980 and 1981) and Sidecar TT (with Benga Johansson), 1980 .. .. .. 1·00 1·00

57. "Mona I".

1982. 150th Anniv. of Isle of Man Steam Packet Company Mail Contract. Mult.
223. 12p. Type **57** 40 40
224. 19½p. "Manx Maid II" .. 60 60

58. Three Wise Men bearing Gifts.

1982. Christmas. Multicoloured.
225. 8p. Type **58** 40 40
226. 11p. Christmas snow scene (vert.) 45 45

60. Opening of Salvation Army Citadel, and T. H. Carnell, J.P.

1983. Centenary of Salvation Army in Isle of Man. Multicoloured.
228. 10p. Type **60** 30 30
229. 12p. Early meeting place and Gen. William Booth 40 40
230. 19½p. Salvation Army band 60 60
231. 26p. Treating lepers and Lt.-Col. Thomas Bridson 90 90

61. Atlantic Puffins.

61a. "Queen Elizabeth II" (Ricardo Macarron).

1983. Sea Birds. Multicoloured.
232. 1p. Type **61** 15 15
233. 2p. Northern Gannets .. 15 15
234. 5p. Lesser Black-headed Gulls 30 30
235. 8p. Common Cormorants .. 30 30
236. 10p. Kittiwakes 35 35
237. 11p. Shags 35 35
238. 12p. Grey Herons 40 40
239. 13p. Herring-gulls 40 40
240. 14p. Razorbills 40 40
241. 15p. Great Black-backed Gulls 50 50
242. 16p. Common Shelducks .. 50 50
243. 18p. Oystercatchers .. 60 60
244. 20p. Arctic Terns 75 75
245. 25p. Common Guillemots 1·00 1·00
246. 50p. Redshanks .. .. 1·75 1·75
247. £1 Mute Swans .. .. 3·00 3·00
248. £5 Type **61a** .. .. 10·00 10·50

62. Design Drawings by Roger Casement for the Great Laxey Wheel. (Illustration reduced. Actual size 85×28 mm.)

1983. Europa. The Great Laxey Wheel.
249. **62.** 10p. blk., blue and buff 40 35
250. – 20½p. multicoloured .. 70 70
DESIGN: 20½p. Roger Casement and the Great Laxey Wheel.

63. Nick Keig (international yachtsman) and Trimaran "Three Legs of Man III".

1983. 150th Anniv. of King William's College. Multicoloured.
251. 10p. Type **63** 30 30
252. 12p. King William's College, Castletown 40 40
253. 28p. Sir William Bragg (winner of Nobel Prize for Physics) and spectrometer 90 90
254. 31p. General Sir George White, V.C., and action at Charasiah .. .. 1·10 1·10

64. New Post Office Headquarters, Douglas.

1983. World Communications Year and 10th Anniv. of Isle of Man Post Office Authority. Multicoloured.
255. 10p. Type **64** 40 30
256. 15p. As Type **64** but inscr. "POST OFFICE DECENNIUM 1983" .. 60 50

65. Shepherds.

1983. Christmas. Multicoloured.
257. 9p. Type **65** 50 50
258. 12p. Three Kings 50 50

66. "Manx King" (full-rigged ship).

1984. The Karren Fleet. Multicoloured.
259. 10p. Type **66** 35 35
260. 13p. "Hope" (barque) .. 45 45
261. 20½p. "Rio Grande" (brig) 70 70
262. 28p. "Lady Elizabeth" (barque) 85 85
263. 31p. "Sumatra" (barque) 95 95

67. C.E.P.T. 25th Anniversary Logo

1984. Europa.
265. **67.** 10p. orange, brown and pale orange 35 35
266. 20½p. blue, deep blue and pale blue .. 70 70

68. Railway Air Service "D.H.84"

1984. 50th Anniv. of First Official Airmail to the Isle of Man. 40th Anniv. of International Civil Aviation Organization. Multicoloured.
267. 11p. Type **68** .. 35 35
268. 13p. West Coast Air Services "D.H.86" 40 40
269. 26p. B.E.A. "DC-3" .. 85 85
270. 28p. B.E.A. Vickers "Viscount" 95 95
271. 31p. Telair "Islander" .. 1·10 1·10

69. Window from Glencrutchery House, Douglas.

1984. Christmas. Stained-glass Windows. Multicoloured.
272. 10p. Type **69** 50 50
273. 13p. Window from Lonan Old Church 50 50

70. William Cain's Birthplace, Ballasalla.

1984. William Cain (civic leader, Victoria) Commemoration. Multicoloured.
274. 11p. Type **70** 30 30
275. 22p. The "Anna" leaving Liverpool, 1852 .. .. 65 65
276. 28p. Early Australian railway 90 90
277. 30p. William Cain as Mayor of Melbourne, and Town Hall .. .. 1·00 1·00
278. 33p. Royal Exhibition Building, Melbourne .. 1·10 1·10

71. Queen Elizabeth II and Commonwealth Parliamentary Association Badge.

1984. Links with the Commonwealth. 30th Commonwealth Parliamentary Association Conference. Multicoloured.
279. 14p. Type **71** 45 45
280. 33p. Queen Elizabeth II and Manx emblem .. 1·00 1·00

72. Cunningham House Headquarters, and Mrs. Willie Cunningham and Mrs. Joseph Cunningham (former Commissioners).

1985. 75th Anniv. of Girl Guide Movement. Multicoloured.
281. 11p. Type **72** 45 45
282. 14p. Princess Margaret, Isle of Man standard and guides 70 70
283. 29p. Lady Olave Baden-Powell opening Guide Headquarters, 1955 .. 1·10 1·10
284. 31p. Guide uniforms from 1910 to 1985 .. .. 1·25 1·25
285. 34p. Guide handclasp, salute and early badge 1·50 1·50

73. Score of Manx National Anthem.

1985. Europa. European Music Year.
286. **73.** 12p. black, light brown and brown 45 45
287. – 12p. black, light brown and brown 45 45
288. – 22p. black, light blue and blue 95 95
289. – 22p. black, light blue and blue 95 95
DESIGNS: No. 287, William H. Gill (lyricist). 288, Score of hymn "Crofton". 289, Dr. John Clague (composer).

HAVE YOU READ THE NOTES AT THE BEGINNING OF THIS CATALOGUE?
These often provide answers to the enquiries we receive.

74. Charles Rolls in 20 h.p. Rolls-Royce (1906 Tourist Trophy Race).

1985. Century of Motoring. Multicoloured.

290. 12p. Type **74** 40 40
291. 12p. W. Bentley in 3 litre Bentley (1922 Tourist Trophy Race) 40 40
292. 14p. F. Gerrard in E.R.A. (1950 British Empire Trophy Race) 55 55
293. 14p. Brian Lewis in Alfa Romeo (1934 Mannin Moar Race) 55 55
294. 31p. Jaguar "XJ-SC" ("Roads Open" car, 1984 Motor Cycle T.T. Races) 1·25 1·25
295. 31p. Tony Pond and Mike Nicholson in Vauxhall "Chevette" (1981 Rothmans International Rally) .. .. .. 1·25 1·25

75. Queen Alexandra and Victorian Sergeant with Wife.

1985. Centenary of Soldiers', Sailors' and Airmen's Families Association. Designs showing Association Presidents. Mult.

296. 12p. Type **75** 55 55
297. 15p. Queen Mary and Royal Air Force family 70 70
298. 29p. Earl Mountbatten and Royal Navy family .. 1·25 1·25
299. 34p. Prince Michael of Kent and Royal Marine with parents, 1982 .. 1·40 1·40

76. Kirk Maughold (birthplace).

1985. Birth Bicentenary of Lieutenant-General Sir Mark Cubbon (Indian administrator). Multicoloured.

300. 12p. Type **76** 45 45
301. 22p. Lieutenant-General Sir Mark Cubbon (vert.) 85 85
302. 45p. Memorial statue, Bangalore, India (vert.) 1·75 1·75

77. St. Peter's Church, Onchan.

1985. Christmas. Manx Churches. Mult.

303. 11p. Type **77** 45 45
304. 14p. Royal Chapel of St. John, Tynwald 55 55
305. 31p. Bride Parish Church 1·25 1·25

78. Swimming.

1986. Commonwealth Games, Edinburgh. Multicoloured.

306. 12p. Type **78** 50 50
307. 15p. Race walking .. 60 60
308. 31p. Rifle-shooting .. 1·40 1·40
309. 34p. Cycling .. .. 1·40 1·40

No. 309 also commemorates the 50th anniversary of Manx International Cycling Week.

79. Viking Necklace and Peel Castle.

1986. Centenary of Manx Museum. Mult.

310. 12p. Type **79** 45 45
311. 15p. Meayll Circle, Rushen 55 55
312. 22p. Skeleton of Great Deer and Manx Museum (vert.) 85 85
313. 26p. Viking longship model (vert.) 95 95
314. 29p. Open Air Museum, Cregneash .. .. 1·10 1·10

80. Viking Longship.

1986. Manx Heritage Year.

315. **80.** 2p. multicoloured .. 25 25
316. – 10p. black, green and grey 75 75

DESIGN: 10p. Celtic cross logo.

81. "Usnea articulata" (lichen) and "Neotinea intacta" (orchid), The Ayres.

1986. Europa. Protection of Nature and the Environment. Multicoloured.

317. 12p. Type **81** 55 55
318. 12p. Hen harrier, Calf of Man 55 55
319. 22p. Manx stoat, Eary Cushlin 90 90
320. 22p. "Stenobothus stigmaticus" (grasshopper), St. Michael's Isle .. 90 90

82. Ellanbane (home of Myles Standish).

1986. "Ameripex '86" International Stamp Exhibition, Chicago. Captain Myles Standish of the "Mayflower". Multicoloured.

321. 12p. Type **82** 35 35
322. 15p. "Mayflower" crossing the Atlantic, 1620 .. 55 55
323. 31p. Pilgrim Fathers landing at Plymouth, 1620 .. 1·10 1·10
324. 34p. Captain Myles Standish .. .. .. 1·40 1·40

83. Prince Andrew in Naval Uniform and Miss Sarah Ferguson.

1986. Royal Wedding. Multicoloured.

326. 15 p. Type **83** 60 60
327. 40p. Engagement photograph .. .. .. 1·40 1·40

84. Prince Philip (from photo by Karsh).

1986. Royal Birthdays. Multicoloured.

328. 15p. Type **84** 60 60
329. 15p. Queen Elizabeth II (from photo by Karsh) 60 60
330. 34p. Queen Elizabeth and Prince Philip (from photo by Karsh) (48 × 35 mm.) .. .. 1·50 1·50

Nos. 328/30 also commemorate "Stockholmia '86" International Stamp Exhibition, Sweden and the 350th anniversary of the Swedish Post Office.

85. European Robins on Globe and "Peace and Goodwill" in Braille.

1986. Christmas and International Peace Year. Multicoloured.

331. 11p. Type **85** 50 50
332. 14p. Hands releasing peace dove 55 55
333. 31p. Clasped hands and "Peace" in sign language 1·25 1·25

86. North Quay.

1987. Victorian Douglas. Multicoloured.

334. 2p. Type **86** 10 10
335. 3p. Old Fishmarket .. 10 10
336. 10p. The Breakwater .. 35 35
337. 15p. Jubilee Clock 50 50
338. 31p. Loch Promenade .. 1·40 1·40
339. 34p. Beach .. .. .. 1·60 1·60

87. "Douglas Quay, 1899".

1987. Paintings by John Miller Nicholson. Multicoloured.

340. 12p. Type **87** 35 35
341. 26p. "Fishing Boats, Douglas, 1900" 90 90
342. 29p. "Peel Harbour, 1905" 1·25 1·25
343. 34p. "Fishing Boats and Castle, Peel, 1909" .. 1·50 1·50

88. Sea Terminal, Douglas.

1987. Europa. Architecture. Multicoloured.

344. 12p. Type **88** 60 60
345. 12p. Tower of Refuge, Douglas 60 60
346. 22p. Gaiety Theatre, Douglas .. .. .. 1·10 1·10
347. 22p. Villa Marina, Douglas 1·10 1·10

89. Supercharged "BMW" 500cc Motor Cycle, 1939.

1987. 80th Anniv. of Tourist Trophy Motor Cycle Races. Multicoloured.

348. 12p. Type **89** 40 40
349. 15p. Manx "Kneeler" Norton 350cc, 1953 .. 60 60
350. 29p. MV Agusta 500cc 4, 1956 .. .. .. 1·00 1·00
351. 31p. Guzzi 500cc V8, 1957 1·10 1·10
352. 34p. Honda 250cc 6, 1967 .. 1·40 1·40

Nos. 348/52 also commemorate the Centenary of the St. John Ambulance Brigade.

90. Fuchsia and Wild Roses.

1987. Wild Flowers. Multicoloured.

354. 16p. Type **90** 60 60
355. 29p. Field scabious and ragwort .. .. .. 1·10 1·10
356. 31p. Wood anemone and celandine .. .. 1·25 1·25
357. 34p. Violets and primroses 1·50 1·50

91. Stirring the Christmas Pudding.

1987. Christmas. Victorian Scenes. Mult.

358.	12p. Type **91**	50	50
359.	15p. Bringing home the Christmas tree	75	75
360.	31p. Decorating the Christmas tree	1·25	1·25

92. Russell Brookes in Vauxhall "Opel" (Manx Rally winner, 1985). (Illustration reduced. Actual size 60 × 24 mm.).

1988. Motor Sport. Multicoloured.

361.	13p. Type **92**	70	70
362.	26p. Ari Vatanen in Ford "Escort" (Manx Rally winner, 1976)	1·10	1·10
363.	31p. Terry Smith in Repco "March 761" (Hill Climb winner, 1980)	1·25	1·25
364.	34p. Nigel Mansell in Williams/Honda (British Grand Prix winner, 1986 and 1987)	1·40	1·40

93. Horse Tram Terminus, Douglas Bay Tramway.

93a Queen Elizabeth II taking Salute at Trooping the Colour

1988. Manx Railways and Tramways. Mult.

365	1p. Type **93**	10	10
366	2p. Snaefell Mountain Railway	10	10
367	3p. Marine Drive Tramway	10	10
367c	4p. Douglas Cable Tramway	10	10
368	5p. Douglas Head Incline Railway	10	10
369	10p. Manx Electric Railway train at Maughold Head ..	20	25
370	13p. As 4p.	25	30
371	14p. Manx Northern Railway No. 4, "Caledonia", at Gob-y-Deigan	30	35
372	15p. Laxey Mine Railway Lewin locomotive "Ant"	30	35
373	16p. Port Erin Breakwater Tramway locomotive "Henry B. Loch" ..	30	35
374	17p. Ramsey Harbour Tramway	35	40
375	18p. Locomotive No. 7, "Tynwald", on Foxdale line	35	40
375a	18p. T.P.O. Special leaving Douglas, 3 July 1991	35	40
376	19p. Baldwin Reservoir Tramway steam locomotive "Injebreck" ..	40	45
377	20p. I.M.R. No. 13, "Kissack", near St. Johns	40	45
377a	21p. As 14p.	40	45
377b	23p. Double-decker horse tram, Douglas	45	50
378	25p. I.M.R. No. 12, "Hutchinson", leaving Douglas	50	55
379	50p. Groudle Glen Railway locomotive "Polar Bear"	1·00	1·10
380	£1 I.M.R. No. 11, "Maitland", pulling Royal Train, 1963	2·00	2·10
380a	£2 Type **93a**	4·00	4·25

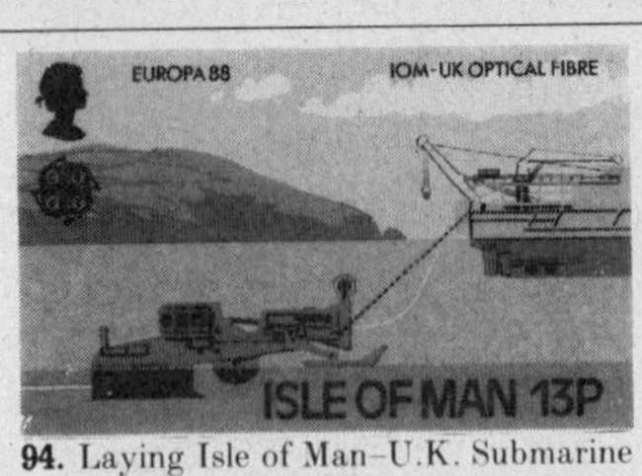

94. Laying Isle of Man–U.K. Submarine Cable.

1988. Europa. Transport and Communications. Multicoloured.

381.	13p. Type **94**	50	50
382.	13p. Cable ship	50	50
383.	22p. Earth station, Braddan	75	75
384.	22p. "INTELSAT 5" satellite	75	75

Nos. 381/2 and 383/4 were each printed together, se-tenant. Nos. 381/2 forming a composite design.

95 "Euterpe" (full-rigged ship) off Ramsey, 1863

1988. Manx Sailing Ships. Multicoloured.

385	16p. Type **95**	50	50
386	29p. "Vixen" (topsail schooner) leaving Peel for Australia, 1853 ..	85	85
387	31p. "Ramsey" (full-rigged ship) off Brisbane, 1870	1·00	1·00
388	34p. "Star of India" (formerly "Euterpe") (barque) off San Diego, 1976	1·25	1·25

Nos. 386/7 also commemorate the Bicent of Australian Settlement.

96 "Magellanica"

1988. 50th Anniv of British Fuchsia Society. Multicoloured.

390	13p. Type **96**	40	40
391	16p. "Pink Cloud" ..	50	50
392	22p. "Leonora"	70	70
393	29p. "Satellite"	1·00	1·00
394	31p. "Preston Guild" ..	1·10	1·10
395	34p. "Thalia"	1·25	1·25

97 Long-eared Owl

1988. Christmas. Manx Birds. Multicoloured.

396	12p. Type **97**	50	50
397	15p. European robin ..	75	75
398	31p. Grey partridge ..	1·25	1·25

98 Ginger Cat

1989. Manx Cats. Multicoloured.

399	16p. Type **98**	50	50
400	27p. Black and white cat	90	90
401	30p. Tortoiseshell and white cat	1·10	1·10
402	40p. Tortoiseshell cat ..	1·40	1·40

99 Tudric Pewter Clock, c. 1903

1989. 125th Birth Anniv of Archibald Knox (artist and designer). Multicoloured.

403	13p. Type **99**	35	35
404	16p. "Celtic Cross" watercolour	45	45
405	23p. Silver cup and cover, 1902–03	75	75
406	32p. Gold and silver brooches from Liberty's Cymric range (horiz) ..	1·10	1·10
407	35p. Silver jewel box, 1900 (horiz)	1·25	1·25

100 William Bligh and Old Church, Onchan

1989. Bicentenary of the Mutiny on the "Bounty". Multicoloured.

408	13p. Type **100**	25	30
409	16p. Bligh and loyal crew cast adrift	30	35
410	23p. Pitcairn Islands 1989 Settlement Bicentenary 90 c., No. 345	80	85
411	27p. Norfolk Island 1989 Bicentenary 39 c., No. 461	90	95
412	30p. Midshipman Peter Heywood and Tahiti ..	70	70
413	32p. H.M.S. "Bounty" anchored off Pitcairn Island	75	75
414	35p. Fletcher Christian and Pitcairn Island ..	80	80

101 Skipping and Hopscotch

1989. Europa. Children's Games. Mult.

416	13p. Type **101**	55	55
417	13p. Wheelbarrow, leapfrog and piggyback	55	55
418	23p. Building model house and blowing bubbles ..	90	90
419	23p. Girl with doll and doll's house	90	90

Nos. 416/17 and 418/19 were printed together, se-tenant, forming composite designs.

102 Atlantic Puffin

104 Mother with Baby, Jane Cookall Maternity Home

103 Red Cross Cadets learning Resuscitation

1989. Sea Birds. Multicoloured.

420	13p. Type **102**	60	60
421	13p. Black guillemot ..	60	60
422	13p. Common cormorant	60	60
423	13p. Kittiwake	60	60

1989. 125th Anniv of International Red Cross and Centenary of Noble's Hospital, Isle of Man.

424	**103**	14p. multicoloured ..	40	40
425	–	17p. grey and red ..	65	65
426	–	23p. multicoloured ..	90	90
427	–	30p. multicoloured ..	1·10	1·10
428	–	35p. multicoloured ..	1·40	1·40

DESIGNS: 17p. Anniversary logo; 23p. Signing Geneva Convention, 1864; 30p. Red Cross ambulance; 35p. Henri Dunant (founder).

1989. Christmas. 50th Anniv of Jane Crookall Maternity Home and 75th Anniv of St. Ninian's Church, Douglas. Multicoloured.

429	13p. Type **104**	45	45
430	16p. Mother with child ..	55	55
431	34p. Madonna and Child ..	1·10	1·10
432	37p. Baptism, St. Ninian's Church	1·25	1·25

105 "The Isle of Man Express going up a Gradient"

1990. Isle of Man Edwardian Postcards. Mult.

433	15p. Type **105**	30	30
434	19p. "A way we have in the Isle of Man" ..	55	55
435	32p. "Douglas–waiting for the male boat" ..	1·00	1·00
436	34p. "The last toast rack home, Douglas Parade"	1·10	1·10
437	37p. "The last Isle of Man boat"	1·25	1·25

106 Modern Postman

107 Penny Black

1990. Europa. Post Office Buildings. Mult.

438	15p. Type **106**	50	50
439	15p. Ramsey Post Office, 1990 (40 × 26 mm) ..	50	50
440	24p. Postman, 1890 ..	75	75
441	24p. Douglas Post Office, 1890 (40 × 26 mm) ..	75	75

1990. 150th Anniv of the Penny Black.

442 **107** 1p. black, buff & gold 10 10
443 – 19p. gold, black & buff 65 65
444 – 32p. multicoloured .. 1·10 1·10
445 – 34p. multicoloured .. 1·10 1·10
446 – 37p. multicoloured .. 1·25 1·25

DESIGNS: 19p. Wyon Medal, 1837; 32p. Wyon's stamp essay; 34p. Perkins Bacon engine-turned essay, 1839; 37p. Twopence Blue, 1840.

108 Queen Elizabeth the Queen Mother

1990. 90th Birthday of Queen Elizabeth the Queen Mother.

448 **108** 90p. multicoloured .. 2·75 2·75

109 Hurricane, Blenheim and Home Defence

1990. 50th Anniv of Battle of Britain. Mult.

449 15p. Type **109** 40 40
450 15p. Spitfire with rescue aircraft and launch .. 40 40
451 24p. Rearming fighters .. 90 90
452 24p. Ops room and scramble 90 90
453 29p. Civil Defence personnel 95 95
454 29p. Anti-aircraft battery 95 95

110 Churchill with Freedom of Douglas Casket

1990. 25th Death Anniv of Sir Winston Churchill. Multicoloured.

455 19p. Type **110** 60 60
456 32p. Churchill and London blitz .. .. .. 1·10 1·10
457 34p. Churchill and search-lights over Westminster 1·25 1·25
458 37p. Churchill with R.A.F. fighters .. .. 1·25 1·25

111 Boy on Toboggan and Girl posting Letter

1990. Christmas. Multicoloured.

459 14p. Type **111** 40 40
460 18p. Girl on toboggan and skaters 60 60
461 34p. Boy with snowman .. 1·10 1·10
462 37p. Children throwing snowballs .. .. 1·25 1·25

112 Henry Bloom Noble and Orphans (Marshall Wane)

1991. Manx Photography.

464 **112** 17p. brown, grey & blk 45 45
465 – 21p. brown and ochre 60 60
466 – 26p. brn, stone & blk 90 90
467 – 31p. brn, lt brn & blk 1·10 1·10
468 – 40p. multicoloured .. 1·40 1·40

DESIGNS: 21p. Douglas (Frederick Frith); 26p. Studio portrait of three children (Hilda Newby); 31p. Cashtal yn Ard (Christopher Killip); 40p. Peel Castle (Colleen Corlett).

113 Lifeboat "Sir William Hillary", Douglas

1991. Manx Lifeboats. Multicoloured.

469 17p. Type **113** 45 45
470 21p. "Osman Gabriel", Port Erin 60 60
471 26p. "Ann and James Ritchie", Ramsey .. 90 90
472 31p. "The Gough Ritchie", Port St. Mary .. .. 1·10 1·10
473 37p. "John Batstone", Peel 1·40 1·40

No. 469 is inscribed "HILARY" and No. 471 "James & Ann Ritchie", both in error.

114 "Intelsat" Communications Satellite

1991. Europa. Europe in Space. Mult.

474 17p. Type **114** 55 55
475 17p. "Ariane" rocket launch and fishing boats in Douglas harbour .. 55 55
476 26p. Weather satellite and space station 90 90
477 26p. Ronaldsway Airport, Manx Radio transmitter and Space shuttle launch 90 90

Nos. 474/5 and 476/7 were each printed together, se-tenant, each pair forming a composite design.

115 Oliver Godfrey with Indian 500cc at Start, 1911

1991. 80th Anniv of Tourist Trophy Mountain Course. Multicoloured.

478 17p. Type **115** 40 40
479 21p. Freddie Dixon on Douglas "banking" sidecar, 1923 .. .. 60 60
480 26p. Bill Ivy on Yamaha 125cc, 1968 .. .. 85 85
481 31p. Giacomo Agostini on MV Agusta 500cc, 1972 1·10 1·10
482 37p. Joey Dunlop on RVF Honda 750cc, 1985 .. 1·25 1·25

116 Laxey Hand-cart, 1920

1991. Fire Engines. Multicoloured.

485 17p. Type **116** 40 40
486 21p. Horse-drawn steamer, Douglas, 1909 .. .. 60 60
487 30p. Merryweather "Hat-field" pump, 1936 .. 85 85
488 33p. Dennis "F8" pumping appliance, Peel, 1953 .. 1·10 1·10
489 37p. Volvo turntable ladder, Douglas, 1989 .. 1·25 1·25

117 Mute Swans, Douglas Harbour

1991. Swans. Multicoloured.

490 17p. Type **117** 50 50
491 17p. Black swans, Curraghs Wildlife Park 50 50
492 26p. Whooper swans, Bishop's Dub, Ballaugh 90 90
493 26p. Whistling ("Bewick's") swans, Eairy Dam, Foxdale .. 90 90
494 37p. Coscaroba swans, Curraghs Wildlife Park 1·10 1·10
495 37p. Whooper ("Trumpeter") swans, Curraghs Wildlife Park 1·10 1·10

The two designs of each value were printed together, se-tenant, forming a composite design.

118 The Three Kings

1991. Christmas. Paper Sculptures. Mult.

496 16p. Type **118** 50 40
497 20p. Mary with manger .. 65 70
498 26p. Shepherds with sheep 80 85
499 37p. Choir of angels .. 1·10 1·10

119 North African and Italian Campaigns, 1942–43

1992. 50th Anniv of Parachute Regiment. Multicoloured.

502 23p. Type **119** 55 55
503 23p. D-Day, 1944 .. .. 55 55
504 28p. Arnhem, 1944 .. 60 60
505 28p. Rhine crossing, 1945 60 60
506 39p. Operations in Near, Middle and Far East, 1945–68 .. .. .. 95 95
507 39p. Liberation of Falkland Islands, 1982 .. .. 95 95

120 Queen Elizabeth II at Coronation, 1953

1992. 40th Anniv of Accession. Multicoloured.

508 18p. Type **120** 50 50
509 23p. Queen visiting Isle of Man, 1979 .. .. 60 60
510 28p. Queen in evening dress 70 70
511 33p. Queen visiting Isle of Man, 1989 .. .. 85 85
512 39p. Queen arriving for film premiere, 1990 .. 95 95

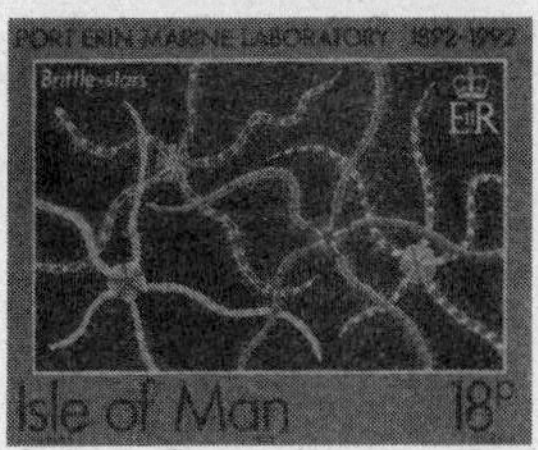

121 Brittle-stars

1992. Centenary of Port Erin Marine Laboratory. Multicoloured.

513 18p. Type **121** 50 50
514 23p. Phytoplankton .. 60 60
515 28p. Herring 70 70
516 33p. Great scallop .. 85 85
517 39p. Dahlia anemone and delesseria 95 95

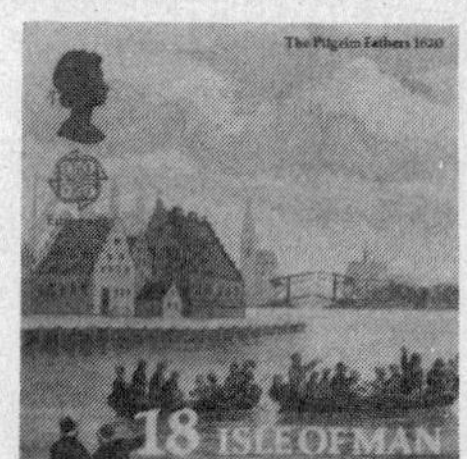

122 The Pilgrim Fathers embarking at Delfshaven

1992. Europa. 500th Anniv of Discovery of America by Columbus. Multicoloured.

518 18p. Type **122** 55 55
519 18p. "Speedwell" leaving Delfshaven 55 55
520 28p. "Mayflower" setting sail for America .. 90 90
521 28p. "Speedwell" anchored at Dartmouth 90 90

The two designs for each value were printed together, se-tenant in horizontal pairs forming composite design.

123 Central Pacific Locomotive "Jupiter", 1869

1992. Construction of the Union Pacific Railroad, 1866–69. Multicoloured.

522 33p. Type **123** 90 90
523 33p. Union Pacific loco-motive No. 119, 1869 .. 90 90
524 39p. Union Pacific loco-motive No. 844, 1992 .. 1·00 1·00
525 39p. Union Pacific loco-motive No. 3985, 1992 .. 1·00 1·00

124 "King Orry V" in Douglas Harbour (¾-size illustration)

1992. Manx Harbours. Multicoloured.

27 18p. Type **124** 50 50
28 23p. Castletown 60 60
29 37p. Port St. Mary .. 95 95
30 40p. Ramsey .. .. 1·00 1·00

126 Stained Glass Window, St. German's Cathedral, Peel

1992. Christmas. Manx Churches. Mult.

532 17p. Type **126** 50 50
533 22p. Reredos, St. Matthew the Apostle Church, Douglas 70 70
534 28p. Stained glass window, St. George's Church, Douglas 85 85
535 37p. Reredos, St. Mary of the Isle Catholic Church, Douglas .. .. 1·00 1·00
536 40p. Stained glass window, Trinity Methodist Church, Douglas .. 1·10 1·10

127 Mansell on Lap of Honour, British Grand Prix, 1992

1992. Nigel Mansell's Victory in Formula 1 World Motor Racing Championship. Mult.

537 20p. Type **127** 50 50
538 24p. Mansell in French Grand Prix, 1992 .. 60 60

128 H.M.S. "Amazon" (frigate)

128a Queen Elizabeth II (hologram)

1993. Ships. Multicoloured.

539 1p. Type **128** 10 10
540 2p. "Fingal" (lighthouse tender) 10 10
541 4p. "Sir Winston Churchill" (cadet schooner) .. 10 10
542 5p. "Dar Mlodziezy" (full-rigged cadet ship) 10 10
543 20p. "Tynwald I" (paddle-steamer) .. 40 45
544 21p. "Ben Veg" (freighter) 40 45
545 22p. "Waverley" (paddle-steamer) 45 50
546 23p. Royal Yacht "Britannia" 45 50
547 24p. "Francis Drake" (ketch) 50 55
548 25p. "Royal Viking Sky" (liner) 50 55
549 26p. "Lord Nelson" (cadet barque) 55 60
550 27p. "Europa" (liner) .. 55 60
551 30p. "Snaefell V" (ferry) leaving Ardrossan .. 60 65
552 40p. "Lady of Mann I" (ferry) off Ramsey .. 80 85
553 50p. "Mona's Queen II" (paddle ferry) leaving Fleetwood .. .. 1·00 1·10
554 £1 "Queen Elizabeth 2" (liner) and "Mona's Queen V" (ferry) off Liverpool .. .. 2·00 2·10
555 £2 Manx Red Ensign .. 4·00 4·25
556 £5 Type **128a** .. .. 10·00 10·50

129 No. 1 Motor Car and No. 13 Trailer at Groudle Glen Hotel (¾-size illustration)

1993. Cent of Manx Electric Railway. Mult.

559 20p. Type **129** 40 45
560 24p. No. 9 Tunnel Car and No. 19 Trailer at Douglas Bay Hotel .. 50 55
561 28p. No. 19 Motor Car and No. 59 Royal Trailer Special at Douglas Bay 55 60
562 39p. No. 33 Motor Car, No. 45 Trailer and No. 13 Van at Derby Castle .. 80 85

130 "Sir Hall Caine" (statue) (Bryan Kneale)

1993. Europa. Contemporary Art. Works by Bryan Kneale. Multicoloured.

563 20p. Type **130** 40 45
564 20p. "The Brass Bedstead" (painting) 40 45
565 28p. Abstract bronze sculpture 55 60
566 28p. "Polar Bear Skeleton" (drawing) 55 60

131 Graham Oates and Bill Marshall (1933 International Six Day Trial) on Ariel Square Four

1993. Manx Motor Cycling Events. Mult.

567 20p. Type **131** 40 45
568 24p. Sergeant Geoff Duke (1947 Royal Signals Display Team) on Triumph 3T Twin .. 50 55
569 28p. Denis Parkinson (1953 Senior Manx Grand Prix) on Manx Norton 55 60
570 33p. Richard Swallow (1991 Junior Classic MGP) on Aermacchi 65 70
571 39p. Steve Colley (1992 Scottish Six Day Trial) on Beta Zero 80 85

132 "Inachis io" (Peacock)

1993. Butterflies. Multicoloured.

573 24p. Type **132** 50 55
574 24p. "Argynnis aglaja" (Dark green fritillary) .. 50 55
575 24p. "Cynthia cardui" (Painted lady) 50 55
576 24p. "Celastrina argiolus" (Holly blue) 50 55
577 24p. "Vanessa atalanta" (Red admiral) 50 55

133 Children decorating Christmas Tree

1993. Christmas. Multicoloured.

578 19p. Type **133** 40 45
579 23p. Girl with snowman .. 45 50
580 28p. Boy opening presents 55 60
581 39p. Girl with teddy bear 80 85
582 40p. Children with toboggan 80 85

134 White-throated Robin

1994. Calf of Man Bird Observatory. Mult.

583 20p. Type **134** 40 45
584 20p. Black-eared wheatear 40 45
585 24p. Goldcrest 50 55
586 24p. Northern oriole .. 50 55
587 30p. Kingfisher 60 65
588 30p. Hoopoe 60 65

135 Gaiety Theatre, Douglas

1994. Manx Tourism Centenary. Mult.

590 24p. Type **135** 50 55
591 24p. Sports 50 55
592 24p. Artist at work and yachts racing 50 55
593 24p. TT Races and Red Arrows display .. 50 55
594 24p. Musical instruments 50 55
595 24p. Laxey Wheel and Manx cat 50 55
596 24p. Tower of Refuge, Douglas, with bucket and spade 50 55
597 24p. Cyclist 50 55
598 24p. Tynwald Day and classic car 50 55
599 24p. Santa Mince Pie train, Groudle Glen 50 55

136 "Eubranchus tricolor" (sea slug)

1994. Europa. Discoveries of Edward Forbes (marine biologist). Multicoloured.

600 20p. Type **136** 40 45
601 20p. "Loligo forbesii" (squid) 40 45
602 20p. Edward Forbes and signature 40 45
603 30p. "Solaster moretonis" (fossil starfish) 60 65
604 30p. "Adamsia carciniopados" (anenome) on hermit crab 60 65
605 30p. "Solaster endeca" (starfish) 60 65

POSTAGE DUE STAMPS

D 1.

D 2.

1973.

D 1. D 1. ½p. red, black and yell. 2·25 1·40
D 2. 1p. red, black and brn. 75 55
D 3. 2p. red, black and green 15 20
D 4. 3p. red, black and grey 25 25
D 5. 4p. red, black and pink 35 30
D 6. 5p. red, black and blue 40 35
D 7. 10p. red, blk. & violet 50 45
D 8. 20p. red, black and grn. 90 70

1975.

D 9. D 2. ½p. yellow, black & red 10 10
D 10. 1p. brown, black & red 10 10
D 11. 4p. lilac, black & red 10 10
D 12. 7p. blue, black & red 20 20
D 13. 9p. grey, black & red 25 25
D 14. 10p. mauve, blk. & red 30 30
D 15. 50p. orge., blk. & red 1·40 1·40
D 16. £1 grn., blk. & red .. 2·00 2·00

D 3.

1982.

D 17. D 3. 1p. multicoloured .. 10 10
D 18. 2p. multicoloured .. 10 10
D 19. 5p. multicoloured .. 10 10
D 20. 10p. multicoloured .. 20 25
D 21. 20p. multicoloured .. 40 45
D 22. 50p. multicoloured .. 1·00 1·10
D 23. £1 multicoloured .. 2·00 2·10
D 24. £2 multicoloured .. 4·00 4·25

D 4

1992.

D25 D 4 £5 multicoloured .. 10·00 10·50

JAIPUR

A state of Rajasthan, India (q.v.). Now uses Indian stamps.

12 pies = 1 anna; 16 annas = 1 rupee.

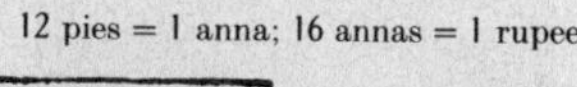

1. Chariot of the Sun God, Surya. **3.**

1904.

No.	Type	Description	Unused	Used
3	1	½ a. blue	2·75	3·75
4		1 a. red	3·00	8·00
5		2 a. green	2·50	9·50

1904.

No.	Type	Description	Unused	Used
9	3	¼ a. olive	30	30
25		½ a. blue	35	30
28		1 a. red	45	90
29		2 a. green	1·25	1·50
30		4 a. brown	1·50	3·25
14		8 a. violet	3·00	2·75
15a		1 r. yellow	9·00	11·00

This set was issued engraved in 1904 and surface-printed in 1913.

4. Chariot of the Sun God, Surya.

(5.)

1911. No gum.

No.	Type	Description	Unused	Used
17.	4.	¼ a. olive	30	40
18.		½ a. blue	30	40
20.		1 a. red	30	50
21.		2 a. green	2·00	5·50

1926. Surch. with T **5.**

No.	Type	Description	Unused	Used
32.	3.	3 a. on 8 a. violet	90	1·40
33.		3 a. on 1 r. yellow	1·10	2·25

6. Chariot of the Sun God, Surya.

7. Maharaja Sawai Man Singh II.

1931. Investiture of H.H. the Maharaja. Centres in black.

No.	Type	Description	Unused	Used
40.	6.	¼ a. purple	50	60
58.	7.	¼ a. red	30	10
41.		½ a. violet	20	10
59.		¾ a. red	3·00	1·50
42.	–	1 a. blue	3·50	4·25
60.	7.	1 a. blue	3·50	1·00
43.	–	2 a. orange	3·25	4·25
61.	7.	2 a. orange	3·50	1·40
44.	–	2½ a. red	25·00	32·00
62.	7.	2½ a. red	70	60
45.	–	3 a. green	10·00	26·00
63.	7.	3 a. green	70	40
46.	–	4 a. green	11·00	28·00
64.	7.	4 a. green	9·00	45·00
47.	–	6 a. blue	6·00	28·00
65.	7.	6 a. blue	1·40	11·00
48.	–	8 a. brown	9·00	45·00
66.	7.	8 a. brown	8·50	45·00
49.	–	1 r. olive	22·00	90·00
67.	7.	1 r. bistre	16·00	65·00
50.	–	2 r. green	15·00	£100
51.	–	5 r. purple	28·00	£110

DESIGNS—VERT. 1 a. (No. 42), Elephant and banner. 2 a. (No. 43), Sowar in armour. 2½ a. (No. 44) Common Peafowl. 8 a. (No. 48), Sireh-Deorhi Gate. HORIZ. 3 a. (No. 45), Bullock carriage. 4 a. (No. 46), Elephant carriage. 6 a. (No. 47), Albert Museum. 1 r. (No. 49), Chandra Mahal. 2 r. Amber Palace. 5 r. Maharajas Sawai Jai Singh and Sir Man Singh.

1932. As T **7**, but inscr. "POSTAGE & REVENUE". Portrait in black.

No.	Type	Description	Unused	Used
52.		1 a. blue	30	20
53.		2 a. brown	50	45
54.		4 a. green	2·25	2·75
55.		8 a. brown	3·00	4·50
56.		1 r. bistre	12·00	50·00
57.		2 r. green	55·00	£180

1936. Nos. 57 and 51 surch. **One Rupee.**

No.	Type	Description	Unused	Used
68.		1 r. on 2 r. green	2·75	35·00
69.		1 r. on 5 r. purple	2·75	27·00

1938. No. 41 surch. in native characters.

No.	Type	Description	Unused	Used
70.	7.	¼ a. on ½ a. violet	4·00	8·00

13. Maharaja and Amber Palace.

1947. Silver Jubilee of Reign of H.H. the Maharaja of Jaipur. Inscr. as in T **13.**

No.	Type	Description	Unused	Used
71.	–	¼ a. brown and green	35	1·25
72.	13.	½ a. green and violet	15	1·10
73.	–	¾ a. black and red	35	1·60
74.	–	1 a. brown and blue	30	1·25
75.	–	2 a. violet and red	20	1·25
76.	–	3 a. green and black	55	2·25
77.	–	4 a. blue and brown	45	1·25
78.	–	8 a. red and brown	60	2·00
79.	–	1 r. purple and green	1·10	8·50

DESIGNS: ¼ a. Palace Gate. ¾ a. Map of Jaipur. 1 a. Observatory. 2 a. Wind Palace. 3 a. Coat of Arms. 4 a. Amber Fort Gate. 8 a. Chariot of the Sun. 1 r. Maharaja's portrait between State flags.

1947. No. 41 surch. **3 PIES** and bars.

No.	Type	Description	Unused	Used
80.	7.	3 p. on ½ a. violet	9·00	16·00

OFFICIAL STAMPS

1929. Optd. **SERVICE.** No gum (except for No. O6).

No.	Type	Description	Unused	Used
O1a	3	¼ a. bistre	55	45
O2		½ a. blue	45	15
O3c		1 a. red	50	20
O5		2 a. green	45	40
O6a		4 a. brown (with gum)	2·00	1·75
O7		8 a. violet	16·00	45·00
O8		1 r. orange	32·00	£130

1931. Stamps of 1931–32 optd. **SERVICE.**

No.	Type	Description	Unused	Used
O 23	7	¼ a. red	30	10
O 13		½ a. violet	20	10
O 24		¾ a. orange	1·10	30
O 25		1 a. blue	5·50	30
O 14	–	1 a. blue (No. 42)	£180	1·50
O 18	–	1 a. blue (No. 52)	60	10
O 15	–	2 a. orange (No. 43)	2·00	2·75
O 19	–	2 a. brown (No. 53)	60	10
O 26	7	2 a. orange	4·75	70
O 27		2½ a. red	7·50	35·00
O 16	–	4 a. green (No. 46)	15·00	15·00
O 20	–	4 a. green (No. 54)	£170	3·50
O 28	7	4 a. green	4·25	1·90
O 21	–	8 a. brown (No. 55)	2·50	1·10
O 29	7	8 a. brown	4·00	3·00
O 22	–	1 r. bistre (No. 56)	9·00	9·50
O 30	7	1 r. bistre	£180	

1932. No. O 5 surch.

No.	Type	Description	Unused	Used
O 17.	3.	½ a. on 2 a. green	£100	40

1947. Official stamps surch.

No.	Type	Description	Unused	Used
O 33.	7.	3 p. on ½ a. violet	1·75	6·00
O 32.		9 p. on 1 a. blue	1·10	1·25

1949. No. O 14 surch. in native characters.

No.	Type	Description	Unused	Used
O 34.	7.	¼ a. on ½ a. violet	8·00	8·50

For later issues see **RAJASTHAN.**

JAMAICA

An island in the W. Indies. Part of the Br. Caribbean Federation from 3rd Jan. 1958, until 6th Aug. 1962 when Jamaica became an independent state within the Commonwealth.

1860. 12 pence = 1 shilling.
20 shillings = 1 pound.
1969. 100 cents = 1 dollar.

8.

11.

1860. Portrait as T **8.** Various frames.

No.	Type	Description	Unused	Used
7	8	½d. red	12·00	3·50
16a		½d. green	80	10
8		1d. blue	48·00	75
18a		1d. red	24·00	50
9		2d. red	50·00	70
20a		2d. grey	42·00	50
21a		3d. green	2·50	1·00
22a		4d. orange	2·00	35
52a		6d. lilac	7·00	11·00
23a		6d. yellow	4·00	3·50
24		1s. brown	5·00	4·50
25		2s. red	27·00	17·00
26		5s. lilac	48·00	48·00

See also Nos. 47a etc.

1889.

No.	Type	Description	Unused	Used
27.	11.	1d. purple and mauve	2·25	10
28a.		2d. green	4·50	6·00
29.		2½d. purple and blue	4·75	40

1890. No. 22a surch. **TWO PENCE HALF-PENNY.**

No.	Type	Description	Unused	Used
30.	8.	2½d. on 4d. orange	27·00	8·50

13. Llandovery Falls, Jamaica.

1900.

No.	Type	Description	Unused	Used
31.	13.	1d. red	1·00	10
32.		1d. black and red	1·75	10

14. Arms of Jamaica **16.**

1903.

No.	Type	Description	Unused	Used
33.	14.	½d. grey and green	1·50	10
34.		1d. grey and red	1·50	10
35.		2½d. grey and blue	2·25	30
42.		2½d. blue	2·50	1·25
36.		5d. grey and yellow	14·00	23·00
44.		6d. purple	12·00	12·00
45.		5s. grey and violet	40·00	30·00

1906.

No.	Type	Description	Unused	Used
38a.	16.	½d. green	3·75	20
40.		1d. red	1·25	10

1908. Queen Victoria portraits as 1860.

No.	Type	Description	Unused	Used
47a.		3d. purple on yellow	2·00	1·40
48.		4d. brown	70·00	38·00
49.		4d. black on yellow	7·00	26·00
50.		4d. red on yellow	1·50	5·00
54.		1s. black on green	3·75	8·50
56.		2s. purple on blue	6·00	3·50

17.

1911.

No.	Type	Description	Unused	Used
57.	17.	2d. grey	2·00	13·00

1912. As T **17**, but King George V.

No.	Type	Description	Unused	Used
89a		½d. green	30	10
58a		1d. red	40	30
59		1½d. orange	1·00	30
60		2d. grey	90	1·75
61		2½d. blue	75	15
62		3d. purple on yellow	40	45
63		4d. black and red on yellow	50	2·00
64a		6d. purple and mauve	70	1·00
65a		1s. black on green	70	3·50
66		2s. purple and blue on blue	10·00	18·00
67		5s. green and red on yellow	35·00	55·00

1916. Optd **WAR STAMP** in one line.

No.	Type	Description	Unused	Used
76	16.	½d. green	10	15
77a	–	3d. purple on yellow (62)	1·00	1·25

1916. Optd **WAR STAMP** in two lines.

No.	Type	Description	Unused	Used
73	16.	½d. green	10	
74	–	1½d. orange (No. 59)	10	
75	–	3d. purple on yellow (62)	15	

23. Jamaica Exhibition, 1891. **24.** Arawak Woma[n] preparing Cassava

2½d JAMAICA 2½d
RETURN OF A CONTINGENT 1919
POSTAGE REVENUE

27. Return of War Contingent.

34.

1919.

No.	Type	Description	Unused	Used
91a	23.	½d. green and olive	25	
79	24.	1d. red and orange (A)*	1·75	1·
92		1d. red and orange (B)*	1·50	
93	–	1½d. green	30	
94	–	2d. blue and green	3·50	
82a	27.	2½d. blue	90	9
96a	–	3d. green and blue	40	
97a	–	4d. brown and green	50	
98a	–	6d. black and blue	6·50	
99a	–	1s. orange	1·00	
100	–	2s. blue and brown	2·50	
101	–	3s. violet and orange	7·00	9·5
102c	–	5s. blue & bistre	22·00	22·0
103	34.	10s. green	48·00	60·0

* Two types of the 1d. (A) Without an[d] (B) with "POSTAGE & REVENUE" at foot.
DESIGNS—41½ × 26 mm.: 1½d. War Contingen[t] embarking. 6d. Port Royal, 1853. 27 × 22 mm. 3d. Landing of Columbus. 22 × 29 mm. 2d. King's House, Spanish Town. 22 × 28 mm. 4d. Cathedral, Spanish Town. 25 × 30 mm. 1s. Statue of Queen Victoria. 3s. Sir Charle[s] Metcalfe Monument. 25 × 31 mm.: 2s Admira[l] Rodney Memorial. 5s. Jamaican scenery.

37.

1923. Child Welfare. Designs as T **37.**

No.	Type	Description	Unused	Used
104.	37.	½d. + ½d. black and green	60	3·0
105.	–	1d. + ½d. black and red	1·50	10·0
106.	–	2½d. + ½d. black and blue	7·00	18·0

41.

43. Coco palms at Don Christopher's Cove.

1929. Various frames.

41		1d. red..	60	10
		1½d. brown	60	15
		9d. red..	2·75	1·00

1932.

.	43.	2d. black and green	4·75	1·75
.	–	2½d. green and blue	80	80
.	–	6d. grey and purple	4·50	1·25

SIGNS—VERT. 2½d. Wag Water River, St. lrew. HORIZ. 6d. Priestman's River. Port-d.

35. Silver Jubilee. As T **13** of Antigua.

.	1d. blue and red	20	15
.	1½d. blue and black	40	55
.	6d. green and blue	3·50	6·00
.	1s. grey and purple	3·50	6·00

1937. Coronation. As T **2** of Aden.

.	1d. red	30	15
.	1½d. grey	50	30
.	2½d. blue	1·25	70

. King George VI. **49.** Coco Palms at Don Christopher's Cove.

50. Bananas.

45. Priestman's River, Portland.

54. Bamboo Walk.

1938.

21	48	½d. green	40	10
21b		½d. orange	20	30
22		1d. red	40	10
22a		1d. green	30	10
23		1½d. brown	40	10
24	49	2d. black and green	30	50
25	–	2½d. green and blue	2·25	90
26	50	3d. blue and green	50	60
26a		3d. green and blue	1·75	1·00
26b		3d. green and red	1·25	20
27	–	4d. brown and green	30	10
28a	45	45 6d. black & purple	1·00	10
29	–	9d. red	30	30
30	–	1s. green and brown	2·25	20
31	54	2s. blue and brown	11·00	80
32ba	–	5s. blue and brown	6·00	2·75
33aa	–	10s. green	9·00	5·00
33a	–	£1 brown and violet	27·00	26·00

DESIGNS—As Type **49**: 2½d. Wag Water River, St. Andrew. As Type **50**: 4d. Citrus grove. 9d. Kingston Harbour. 1s. Suger industry. £1, Tobacco growing and cigar making. As No. 02c, but with King's portrait added, 5s. As Type **34**: 10s. King George VI.

57. Courthouse, Falmouth.

59. Institute of Jamaica.

1945. New Constitution. Inscr. "NEW CONSTITUTION 1944".

134	57	1½d. brown	20	20
135a	–	2d. green	20	30
136	59	3d. blue..	20	20
137	–	4½d. black	20	25
138	–	2s. brown	30	40
139	–	5s. blue	85	70
140	59	10s. green	85	1·50

DESIGNS—As Type **57**—VERT. 2s. "Labour and Learning". HORIZ. 2d. Kings Charles II and George VI. As Type **59**—HORIZ. 4½d. House of Assembly. 5s. Scroll, flag and King George VI.

1946. Victory. As T **9** of Aden.

141a	1½d. brown	30	40
142	3d. blue	90	90

1948. Silver Wedding. As T **10/11** of Aden.

143.	1½d. brown..	30	10
144.	£1 red	24·00	42·00

1949. U.P.U. As T **20/23** of Antigua.

145.	1½d. brown	30	15
146.	2d. green	55	1·25
147.	3d. blue	55	80
148.	6d. purple	65	1·75

1951. Inauguration of B.W.I. University College. As T **24/25** of Antigua.

149.	2d. black and brown	30	30
150.	6d. black and purple	35	30

69. Scout Badge and Map of Caribbean.

70. Scout Badge and Map of Jamaica.

1952. 1st Caribbean Scout Jamboree.

151	69	2d. blue, green & black	15	10
152	70	6d. green, red and black	15	30

1953. Coronation. As T **13** of Aden.

153.	2d. black and green	20	10

1953. Royal Visit. As T **49** but with portrait of Queen Elizabeth II and inscr "ROYAL VISIT 1953".

154.	2d. black and green	20	10

73. Man-o'-War at Port Royal.

1955. Tercentenary Issue.

155.	73	2d. black and green	20	10
156.	–	2½d. black and blue	15	35
157.	–	3d. black and claret	15	30
158.	–	6d. black and red	20	20

DESIGNS: 2½d. Old Montego Bay. 3d. Old Kingston. 6d. Proclamation of Abolition of Slavery, 1838.

74. Palms.

75. Mahoe.

76. Blue Mountain Peak.

77. Arms of Jamaica.

1956.

159	74	½d. black and red	10	10
160	–	1d. black and green	10	10
161	–	2d. black and red	10	10
162	–	2½d. black and blue	20	40
163	75	3d. green and brown	20	10
164	–	4d. green and blue	20	10
165	–	5d. red and green	20	1·00
166	–	6d. black and red	1·25	10
167	76	8d. blue and orange	15	10
168	–	1s. green and blue	40	10
169	–	1s. 6d. blue and purple	40	10
170	–	2s. blue and green	2·25	1·00
171	77	3s. black and blue	60	90
172	–	5s. black and red	1·00	1·75
173	–	10s. black and green	14·00	7·50
174	–	£1 black and purple	18·00	7·50

DESIGNS—As Type **74**: 1d. Sugar cane. 2d. Pineapples. 2½d. Bananas. As Type **75**: 4d. Breadfruit. 5d. Ackee. 6d. Streamertail. As Type **76**: 1s. Royal Botanic Gardens, Hope. 1s. 6d. Rafting on the Rio Grande. 2s. Fort Charles. As Type **77** but vert. 10s., £1, Arms without portrait.

1958. British Caribbean Federation. As T **28** of Antigua.

175.	2d. green	55	10
176.	5d. blue	95	1·75
177.	6d. red	95	40

81. "Britannia" flying over 1860 Packet-steamer.

83. 1s. Stamps of 1860 and 1956.

1960. Centenary of Jamaica Postage Stamps.

178.	81.	2d. blue and purple	45	10
179.	–	6d. red and olive	45	20
180.	83.	1s. brown, green & blue	45	25

DESIGN—As Type **81**: 6d. Postal mule-cart and motor-van.

1962. Independence. (a) Nos. 159/74 optd **INDEPENDENCE** and **1962.** (3d. to 2s.) or **1962 1962** (others).

205	74	½d. black and red	10	15
182	–	1d. black and green	10	10
183	–	2½d. black and blue	10	85
184	75	3d. green and brown	10	10
185	–	5d. red and olive	15	60
186	–	6d. black and red	75	10
187	76	8d. blue and orange	15	10
188	–	1s. green and blue	15	10
189	–	2s. blue and olive	80	1·10
190	77	3s. black and blue	90	1·50
191	–	10 s. black and green	2·00	4·00
192	–	£1 black and purple	2·75	5·50

86. Military Bugler and Map.

(b) As T **86** inscr. "INDEPENDENCE".

193.	86.	2d. multicoloured	30	10
194.		4d. multicoloured	30	10
195.	–	1s. 6d. black and red	75	85
196.	–	5s. multicoloured	1·50	2·25

DESIGNS: 1s. 6d. Gordon House and banner. 5s. Map, factories and fruit.

89. Kingston Seal, Weightlifting, Boxing, Football and Cycling.

1962. 9th Central American and Caribbean Games, Kingston.

197.	89.	1d. sepia and red	10	10
198.	–	6d. sepia and blue	10	10
199.	–	8d. sepia and bistre	10	10
200.	–	2s. multicoloured	25	40

DESIGNS: 6d. Diver, sailing, swimming and water polo. 8d. Javelin, discus, pole-vault, hurdles and relay-racing. 2s. Kingston Coat of Arms and athlete.

93. Farmer and Crops.

1963. Freedom from Hunger.

201.	93.	1d. multicoloured	15	10
202.		8d. multicoloured	50	30

1963. Cent of Red Cross. As T **33** of Antigua.

203.	2d. red and black	15	10
204.	1s. 6d. red and blue	40	65

95. Carole Joan Crawford ("Miss World 1963").

1964. "Miss World 1963" Commem.

214	95	3d. multicoloured	10	10
215		1s. multicoloured	15	10
216		1s. 6d. multicoloured	20	20

96. Lignum Vitae.

103. Gypsum Industry.

1964.
217 **96** 1d. blue, green & brown 10 10
218 – 1½d. multicoloured .. 15 10
219 – 2d. red, yell. and green 15 10
220 – 2½d. multicoloured .. 70 60
221 – 3d. yellow, black & grn. 15 10
222 – 4d. ochre and violet .. 35 10
223 – 6d. multicoloured .. 2·25 10
224 – 8d. multicoloured .. 1·25 75
225 **103** 9d. blue and bistre .. 45 10
226 – 1s. black and brown .. 20 10
227 – 1s. 6d. black, blue & buff 1·00 15
228 – 2s. brown, black & blue 1·50 15
229a – 3s. blue and green .. 35 65
230 – 5s. black, ochre & blue 1·25 70
231 – 10s. multicoloured .. 1·25 1·00
232 – £1 multicoloured .. 1·50 1·00

DESIGNS—As Type **96**—HORIZ. 1½d. Ackee (fruit). 2½d. Land shells. 3d. National flag over Jamaica. 4d. "Murex antillarum" (sea shell). 6d. "Papilio homerus" (butterfly). 8d. Streamertail. VERT. 2d. Blue Mahoe (tree). As Type **103**—HORIZ. 1s. National Stadium. 1s. 6d. Palisadoes International Airport 2s. Bauxite mining. 3s. Blue marlin (sport fishing). 5s. Exploration of Sunken City, Port Royal. £1 Queen Elizabeth II and National Flag. VERT. 10s. Arms of Jamaica.

114. Scout Badge and Alligator (reduced size Illustration. Actual size 61½ × 30½ mm.)

1964. 6th Inter-American Scout Conf., Kingston.
233. – 3d. red, black and pink 10 10
234. – 8d. blue, olive and black 10 20
235. **114.** 1s. gold, blue & lt. blue 15 20
DESIGNS—VERT (25½ × 30 mm.): 3d. Scout belt. 8d. Globe, scout hat and scarf.

115. Gordon House, Kingston.

1964. 10th Commonwealth Parliamentary Conf. Kingston.
236. **115.** 3d. black and green .. 10 10
237. – 6d. black and red .. 10 10
238. – 1s. 6d. black and blue .. 15 20
DESIGNS: 6d. Headquarters House, Kingston. 1s. 6d. House of Assembly, Spanish Town.

118. Eleanor Roosevelt.

1964. 16th Anniversary of Declaration of Human Rights.
239. **118.** 1s. blk., red & grn. .. 10 10

119. Guides' Emblem on Map.

1965. Golden Jubilee of Jamaica Girl Guides' Assn. Inscr. "1915-1965".
240. **119.** 3d. yellow, green & black 10 10
241. – 1s. yellow, black & grn. 20 20
DESIGN — TRIANGULAR (61½ × 30½ mm.): 1s. Guide emblems.

121. Uniform Cap.

1965. Cent. of Salvation Army. Mult.
242. 3d. Type **121** 15 10
243. 1s. 6d. Flag-bearer and drummer 35 25

123. Paul Bogle, William Gordon and Morant Bay Court House.

1965. Cent. of Morant Bay Rebellion.
244. **123.** 3d. brown, blue & black 10 10
245. 1s. 6d. brn., grn. & blk. 10 10
246. 3s. brown, red & black 20 40

124. Abeng-blower "Telstar", Morse Key and I.T.U. Emblem.

1965. Centenary of I.T.U.
247. **124.** 1s. blk, slate & red .. 40 15

1966. Royal Visit. Nos. 221, 223, 226/7 optd. **ROYAL VISIT MARCH 1966.**
248. 3d. yellow, black & green 15 10
249. 6d. multicoloured .. 90 10
250. 1s. black and brown .. 55 10
251. 1s. 6d. black, blue & buff 70 60

126. Sir Winston Churchill.

1966. Churchill Commem.
252. **126.** 6d. black and green .. 35 20
253. 1s. brown and blue .. 65 70

127. Statue of Athlete and Flags.

1966. 8th British Empire and Commonwealth Games.
254. **127.** 3d. multicoloured .. 10 10
255. – 6d. multicoloured .. 10 10
256. – 1s. multicoloured .. 10 10
257. – 3s. gold and blue .. 20 35
DESIGNS: 6d. Racing cyclists. 1s. National Stadium, Kingston. 3s. Games Emblem.

131. Bolivar's Statue and Flags of Jamaica and Venezuela.

1966. 150th Anniv. "Jamaica Letter".
259. **131.** 8d. multicoloured .. 10 10

INDEX

Countries can be quickly located by referring to the index at the end of this volume.

132. Jamaican Pavilion.

1967. World Fair, Montreal.
260 **132.** 6d. multicoloured .. 10 10
261. 1s. multicoloured .. 10 10

133. Sir Donald Sangster (Prime Minister).

1967. Sangster Memorial Issue.
262. **133.** 3d. multicoloured .. 10 10
263. 1s. 6d. multicoloured .. 10 10

134. Traffic Duty.

1967. Centenary of Constabulary Force.
264. **134.** 3d. multicoloured .. 10 10
265. – 1s. multicoloured .. 15 10
266. – 1s. 6d. multicoloured .. 20 30
DESIGNS: 1s. 6d. Badge and Constables of 1867 and 1967. (56½ × 20½ mm.): 1s. Personnel of the Force.

1968. M.C.C.'s West Indies Tour. As Nos. 445/7 of Guyana.
267. 6d. multicoloured 20 30
268. 6d. multicoloured 20 30
269. 6d. multicoloured 20 30

137. Sir Alexander and Lady Bustamante.

1968. Labour Day.
270. **137.** 3d. red and black .. 10 10
271. 1s. olive and black .. 10 10

138. Human Rights Emblem over Map of Jamaica.

1968. Human Rights Year. Multicoloured.
272. 3d. Type **138** 10 10
273. 1s. Hands cupping Human Rights Emblem .. 10 10
274. 3s. Jamaican holding "Human Rights" .. 20 40

141. I.L.O. Emblem.

1969. 50th Anniversary of Labour Organization.
275. **141.** 6d. yellow and brown .. 10 10
276. 3s. green and brown .. 20 30

142. Nurse and Children being weighed an measured.

1969. 20th Anniv. of W.H.O. Multicoloured
277. 6d. Type **142** 10
278. 1s. Malaria Eradication (horiz.) 10
279. 3s. Trainee nurse 20

1969. Decimal Currency. Nos. 217, 2 221/3 and 225/32 surch. **C-DAY 8t September 1969** in three lines, a value.
280. **95.** 1 c. on 1d. bl., grn. & brn. 10
281. – 2 c. on 2d. red, yell. & grn. 10
282. – 3 c. on 3d. yell., blk and green 10
283. – 4 c. on 4d. ochre & violet 55
284. – 5 c. on 6d. multicoloured 1·00
285. **103.** 8 c. on 9d. blue & bistre 10
286. – 10 c. on 1s. blk., & brn. 10
287. – 15 c. on 1s. 6d. black, blue and buff .. 30
288. – 20 c. on 2s. brn., blk. & bl. 1·50
289. – 30 c. on 3s. blue & green 1·50 2·
290. – 50 c. on 5s. black, ochre and blue .. .. 1·25 2·
291. – $1 on 10s. multicoloured 1·50 3·
292. – $2 on £1 multicoloured 1·50 6·

146. "The Adoration of the Kings" (detail, Foppa).

1969. Christmas. Paintings. Multicoloured
293. 2 c. Type **146** 10 1
294. 5 c. "Madonna, Child and St. John" (Raphael) .. 10 1
295. 8 c. "The Adoration of the Kings" (detail, Dosso Dossi) 15 1

149. Half Penny, 1869.

1969. Centenary of 1st Jamaican Coins.
296b. **149.** 3 c. silver, blk. and mve. 20 20
297. – 15 c. silver, blk. & grn. 10 10
DESIGN: 15 c. One Penny, 1869.

151. George William Gordon.

156. "Christ Appearing to St. Peter" (Carracci).

1970. National Heroes. Multicoloured; background colours given.
298. **151.** 1 c. mauve 10 10
299. – 3 c. blue 10 10
300. – 5 c. grey 10 10
301. – 10 c. red 15 10
302. – 15 c. green 20 15
PORTRAITS: 3 c. Sir Alexander Bustamante. 5 c. Norman Manley. 10 c. Marcus Garvey. 15 c. Paul Bogle.

70. Easter. Centres multicoloured; frame colours given.

.156. 3 c. red 10 10
. – 10 c. green 10 10
. – 20 c. grey 20 35

SIGNS: 10 c. "Christ Crucified" (Antonello). c. Easter Lily.

1970. No. 219 surch.

. 2 c. on 2d. red, yell. & grn. 15 20

160. Lignum Vitae.

70. Decimal currency. Designs as Nos. 217, 219, 221/23, 225/32, but with values inscr as T **160** in new currency.

 160 1 c. blue, green & brn 40 60
 – 2 c. red, yellow and green (as 2d.) .. 15 10
 – 3 c. yellow, black and green (as 3d.) .. 15 10
 – 4 c. ochre and violet (as 4d.) 80 10
 – 5 c. mult (as 6d.) .. 2·25 10
 103 8 c. blue and yellow .. 40 10
 – 10 c. blk & brn (as 1s.) 20 10
 – 15 c. black, blue and buff (as 1s. 6d.) .. 80 90
 – 20 c. brown, black and blue (as 2s.) .. 1·00 1·25
 – 30 c. blue & grn (as 3s.) 1·50 1·75
 – 50 c. black, ochre and blue (as 5s.) .. 1·25 2·75
 – $1 mult (as 10s.) .. 1·25 2·75
 – $2 mult (as £1) .. 1·50 2·75

161. Cable Ship "Dacia".

1970. Centenary of Telegraph Service.

0. **161.** 3 c. yell., blk. and red 15 10
1. – 10 c. black and green .. 20 10
2. – 50 c. multicoloured .. 50 1·00

ESIGNS: 10 c. Bright's Cable Gear aboard Dacia". 50 c. Morse key and chart.

164. Bananas, Citrus, Sugar-Cane and Tobacco.

970. 75th Anniversary of Jamaican Agricultural Society.

3. **164.** 2 c. multicoloured .. 10 30
4. 10 c. multicoloured .. 20 20

165. "The Projector" (1845).

1970. 125th Anniv. of Jamaican Railways.

25. 3 c. Type **165** 25 10
26. 15 c. Steam locomotive No. 54 (1944) 70 30
27. 50 c. Steam locomotive No. 102 (1967) .. .. 1·75 2·00

168. Church of St. Jago de la Vega.

1971. Centenary of Disestablishment of Church of England in Jamaica.

328. **168.** 3 c. multicoloured .. 10 10
329. 10 c. multicoloured .. 10 10
330. 20 c. multicoloured .. 20 25
331. – 30 c. multicoloured .. 25 45

DESIGNS: 30 c. Emblem of Church of England in Jamaica.

169. Henry Morgan and Ships.

1971. Pirates and Buccaneers. Multicoloured.

332. 3 c. Type **169** 35 10
333. 15 c. Mary Read, Anne Bonny and trial pamphlet 65 15
334. 30 c. Pirate schooner attacking merchantman 1·25 1·25

170. 1s. Stamp of 1919 with Frame Inverted.

1971. Tercentenary of Post Office.

335. – 3 c. black and brown .. 10 10
336. – 5 c. black and green .. 10 10
337. – 8 c. black and violet .. 15 10
338. – 10 c. brn., black and blue 15 10
339. – 20 c. multicoloured .. 35 35
340. **170.** 50 c. brn., black and grey 55 80

DESIGNS—HORIZ. 3 c. Dummer packet letter, 1705. 5 c. Pre-stamp inland letter, 1793. 8 c. Harbour St. P.O., Kingston, 1820. 10 c. Modern stamp and cancellation. 20 c. British stamps used in Jamaica, 1859.

171. Satellite and Dish Aerial.

1972. Opening of Jamaican Earth Satellite Station.

341. **171.** 3 c. multicoloured .. 15 10
342. 15 c. multicoloured .. 20 15
343. 50 c. multicoloured .. 65 1·25

172. Causeway, Kingston Harbour.

1972. Multicoloured.

344. 1 c. Pimento 10 10
345. 2 c. Red Ginger 10 10
346. 3 c. Bauxite Industry .. 10 10
347. 4 c. Type **172** 10 10
348. 5 c. Oil Refinery 10 10
349. 6 c. Senate Building, University of the West Indies 10 10
350. 8 c. National Stadium .. 10 10
351. 9 c. Devon House .. 10 10
352. 10 c. Air Jamaica Hostess and aircraft 10 10
353. 15 c. Old Iron Bridge, Spanish Town 65 10
354. 20 c. College of Arts, Science and Technology .. 30 15
355. 30 c. Dunn's River Falls .. 35 15
356. 50 c. River rafting .. 60 40
357. $1 Jamaica House .. 75 75
358. $2 Kings House .. .. 1·00 1·50

The 1, 2, 15 and 30 c. are vert. designs, size 35 × 27 mm., and the remainder are horiz. as Type **172**.

1972. 10th Anniv. of Independence Nos. 346, 352 and 356 optd. **TENTH ANNIVERSARY INDEPENDENCE 1962-1972.**

359. 3 c. multicoloured 10 10
360. 10 c. multicoloured .. 10 10
361. 50 c. multicoloured .. 60 1·40

175. Arms of Kingston.

1972. Centenary of Kingston as Capital.

362. **175.** 5 c. multicoloured .. 10 10
363. 30 c. multicoloured .. 20 25
364. – 50 c. multicoloured .. 40 75

DESIGN—HORIZ. 50 c. design similar to Type **175**.

176. Mongoose on Map.

1973. Centenary of Introduction of the Small Indian Mongoose.

365. **176.** 8 c. green, yell. & black 10 10
366. – 40 c. dp. blue, blue & blk. 25 50
367. – 60 c. pink, salmon & blk. 50 1·00

DESIGNS: 40 c. Mongoose and rat. 60 c. Mongoose and chicken.

177. "Euphorbia punicea".

1973. Flora. Multicoloured.

369. 1 c. Type **177** 10 10
370. 6 c. "Hylocereus triangularis" 15 10
371. 9 c. "Columnea argentea" 15 10
372. 15 c. "Portlandia grandiflora" 25 15
373. 30 c. "Samyda pubescens" 50 60
374. 50 c. "Cordia sebestena" 80 1·25

178. "Broughtonia sanguinea".

1973. Orchids. Multicoloured.

375. 5 c. Type **178** 40 10
376. 10 c. "Arpophyllum jamaicense" (vert.) .. 50 10
377. 20 c. "Oncidium pulchellum" (vert.) .. 1·25 25
378. $1 "Brassia maculata" .. 2·75 2·75

179. "Mary", 1808-15.

1974. Mail Packet Boats. Multicoloured.

380 5 c. Type **179** 20 10
381 10 c. "Queensbury", 1814-27 .. .. .. 25 10
382 15 c. "Sheldrake", 1829-34 45 40
383 50 c. "Thames I", 1842 .. 1·75 2·25

180. "Journeys".

1974. National Dance Theatre Company. Mult.

385. 5 c. Type **180**. 10 10
386. 10 c. "Jamaican Promenade" 10 10
387. 30 c. "Jamaican Promenade" (diff.) 25 30
388. 50 c. "Misa Criolla" .. 45 80

181. U.P.U. Emblem and Globe.

1974. Centenary of U.P.U.

390. **181.** 5 c. multicoloured .. 10 10
391. 9 c. multicoloured .. 10 10
392. 50 c. multicoloured .. 35 80

182. Senate Building and Sir Hugh Wooding.

1975. 25th Anniversary. of University of West Indies. Multicoloured.

393. 5 c. Type **182** 10 10
394. 10 c. University Chapel and Princess Alice 10 10
395. 30 c. Type **182** 20 25
396. 50 c. As 10 c. 35 60

183. Commonwealth Symbol.

1975. Heads of Commonwealth Conf. Mult.

397. 5 c. Type **183** 10 10
398. 10 c. Jamaican coat of arms 10 10
399. 30 c. Dove of Peace .. 15 30
400. 50 c. Jamaican flag .. 30 80

184. "Eurytides marcellinus".

1975. Butterflies (1st series), showing the family "Papilionidae". Multicoloured.

401 10 c. Type **184** 55 20
402 20 c. "Papilo thoas" .. 1·10 1·10
403 25 c. "Papilo thersites" .. 1·25 1·60
404 30 c. "Papilo homerus" .. 1·40 2·00

See also Nos. 429/32 and 443/6.

185. Koo Koo or Actor Boy.

1975. Christmas. Belisario prints of " John Canoe " Festival (1st series). Multicoloured.

406. 8 c. Type **185** 10 10
407. 10 c. Red Set-girls 10 10
408. 20 c. French Set-girls .. 20 15
409. 50 c. Jaw-bone or House John Canoe 40 70

See also Nos. 421/3.

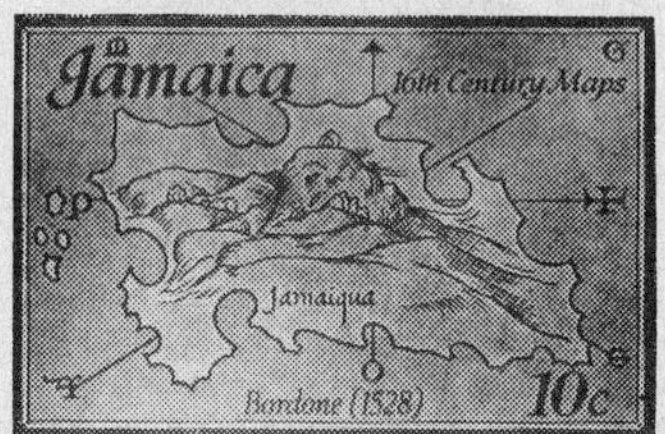

186. Bordone Map. 1528.

1976. 16th Century Maps of Jamaica.

411. **186.** 10 c. brn., light brn. & red .. 20 10
412. – 20 c. multicoloured .. 35 25
413. – 30 c. multicoloured .. 60 75
414. – 50 c. multicoloured .. 85 1·25

DESIGNS: 20 c. Porcacchi map, 1576. 30 c. De Bry map. 1594. 50 c. Langenes map, 1598.
See also Nos. 425/8.

187. Olympic Rings.

1976. Olympic Games, Montreal.

415. **187.** 10 c. multicoloured .. 10 10
416. 20 c. multicoloured .. 15 15
417. 25 c. multicoloured .. 15 20
418. 50 c. multicoloured .. 30 90

1976. West Indian Victory in World Cricket Cup. As Nos. 559/60 of Barbados.

419. 10 c. Map of the Caribbean 40 40
420. 25 c. Prudential Cup .. 85 1·25

1976. Christmas. Belisario Prints (2nd series). As T **185.** Multicoloured.

421. 10 c. Queen of the set-girls 10 10
422. 20 c. Band of the Jaw-bone John-Canoe 20 10
423. 50 c. Koo Koo (actor-boy) 35 60

1977. 17th Cent. Maps of Jamaica. As T **186.**

425. 9 c. multicoloured .. 30 10
426. 10 c. red, brown and buff 30 10
427. 25 c. blk., blue & pale blue 70 60
428. 40 c. black, blue & green .. 80 85

DESIGNS: 9 c. Hickeringill map, 1661. 10 c. Ogilby map, 1671. 25 c. Visscher map, 1680. 40 c. Thornton map, 1689.

1977. Butterflies (2nd series), showing the families "Nymphalidae" and "Pieridae". As T **184.** Multicoloured.

429 10 c. "Eurema elathea" .. 35 10
430 20 c. "Dynamine egaea" .. 75 55
431 25 c. "Chlosyne pantoni" 1·00 1·25
432 40 c. "Hypolimnas missippus" .. .. .. 1·50 2·00

188. Map, Scout Emblem and Streamertail.

1977. Sixth Caribbean Scout Jamboree, Jamaica.

434. **188.** 10 c. multicoloured .. 20 10
435. 20 c. multicoloured .. 40 15
436. 25 c. multicoloured .. 45 20
437. 50 c. multicoloured .. 75 1·10

189. Trumpeter.

1977. 50th Anniversary of Jamaica Military Band. Multicoloured

438. 9 c. Type **189** 15 10
439. 10 c. Clarinet players .. 15 10
440. 20 c. Two kettle drummers (vert.) 40 35
441. 25 c. Cellist and trumpeter (vert.) 55 65

1978. Butterflies (3rd series). As T **184.** Multicoloured.

443 10 c. "Callophrys crethona" 25 10
444 20 c. "Siproeta stelenes" .. 50 20
445 25 c. "Urbanus proteus" .. 65 35
446 50 c. "Anaea troglodyta" 1·40 1·60

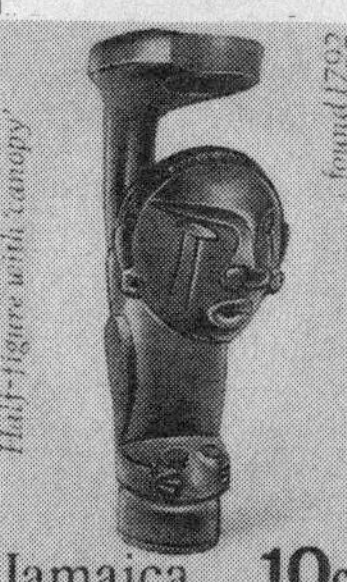

190. Half-figure with Canopy. 191. Norman Manley (statue).

1978. Arawak Artefacts (1st series).

448. **190.** 10 c. brn., yell. & blk. 10 10
449. – 20 c. brn., mve. & blk. 10 10
450. – 50 c. brn., grn. & blk. 30 35

DESIGNS: 20 c. Standing figure. 50 c. Birdman.
See also Nos. 479/83.

1978. 24th Commonwealth Parliamentary Conference. Multicoloured.

452. 10 c. Type **191** 10 10
453. 20 c. Sir Alexander Bustamante (statue) .. 10 10
454. 25 c. City of Kingston Crest 20 15
455. 40 c. Gordon House Chamber, House of Representatives 30 45

192. Band and Banner.

1978. Christmas. Centenary of Salvation Army. Multicoloured.

456. 10 c. Type **192** 20 10
457. 20 c. Trumpeter 25 10
458. 25 c. Banner 25 10
459. 50 c. William Booth (founder) 40 1·25

193. " Negro Aroused " (sculpture by Edna Manley).

1978. International Anti-Apartheid Year.

460. **193.** 10 c. multicoloured .. 20 10

194. Tennis, Montego Bay.

1979. Multicoloured.

461. 1 c. Type **194** 30 40
462. 2 c. Golf, Tryall Hanover 70 70
463. 4 c. Horse riding, Negril Beach 15 40
464. 5 c. Old waterwheel, Tryall Hanover 15 10
465. 6 c. Fern Gully, Ocho Rios 20 20
466. 7 c. Dunn's River Falls, Ocho Rios 15 15
467. 8 c. Jamaican Tody .. 40 30
468. 10 c. Jamaican Mango .. 40 10
469. 12 c. Yellow Billed Amazon 40 50
470. 15 c. Streamertail 55 20
471. 35 c. White-chinned Thrush 55 20
472. 50 c. Jamaican Woodpecker 70 20
473. 65 c. Rafting, Martha Brae Trelawny 40 40
474. 75 c. Blue Marlin fleet, Port Antonio 40 30
475. $1 Scuba diving, Ocho Rios 40 50
476. $2 Sailing boats, Montego Bay 50 35
477. $5 Arms and map of Jamaica (37 × 27 mm.) .. 1·00 1·60

1979. 10th Anniversary of Air Jamaica. No. 352 optd. **10th ANNIVERSARY AIR JAMAICA, 1st APRIL 1979.**

478. 10 c. multicoloured .. 15 30

197. Grinding Stone, circa 400 B.C.

1979. Arawak Artefacts (2nd series). Multicoloured.

479. 5 c. Type **197** 10 10
480. 10 c. Stone implements, c. 500 B.C. (horiz.) .. 10 10
481. 20 c. Cooking pot, c. 300 A.D. (horiz.) 10 15
482. 25 c. Serving boat, c. 300 A.D. (horiz.) 10 20
483. 50 c. Storage jar fragment, c. 300 A.D. 25 35

198. 1962 1s. 6d. Independence Commemorative Stamp.

1979. Death Centenary of Sir Rowland Hill.

484. **198.** 10 c. blk., brn. and red 10 10
485. – 20 c. yellow and brown 15 15
486. – 25 c. mauve and blue .. 20 20
487. – 50 c. multicoloured .. 30 40

DESIGNS: 20 c. 1920 1s. with frame inverted. 25 c. 1860 6d. stamp. 50 c. 1968 3d. Human Rights Year commemorative.

199. Group of Children.

1979. Christmas. International Year of the Child. Multicoloured.

489. 10 c. Type **199** 10 10
490. 20 c. Doll (vert.) 10 10
491. 25 c. " The Family " (painting by child) .. 15 1
492. 50 c. " House on the Hill " (painting by child) .. 25 4

200. Date Tree Hall, 1886 (original home of Institute).

1980. Centenary of Institute of Jamaica. Multicoloured.

493. 5 c. Type **200** 10 10
494. 15 c. Institute building 1980 15 10
495. 35 c. Microfilm reader (vert.) 20 20
496. 50 c. Hawksbill Turtle and Green Turtle 35 40
497. 75 c. Jamaican Owl (vert.) 1·25 1·25

201. Don Quarrie (200 Metres, 1976).

1980. Olympic Games, Moscow. Jamaican Olympic Gold Medal Winners. Mult.

498. 15 c. Type **201** 15 10
499. 35 c. Arthur Wint (4 × 400 Metres Relay, 1952) .. 25 30
500. 35 c. Leslie Laing (4 × 400 Metres Relay, 1952) .. 25 30
501. 35 c. Herbert McKenley (4 × 400 Metres Relay, 1952) 25 30
502. 35 c. George Rhoden (4 × 400 Metres Relay, 1952) .. 25 30

202. Parish Church.

1980. Christmas. Kingston Churches (1st series). Multicoloured.

503. 15 c. Type **202** 10 10
504. 20 c. Coke Memorial Church 10 10
505. 25 c. Church of the Redeemer 15 10
506. $5 Holy Trinity Cathedral 1·00 2·00

See also Nos. 537/9 and 570/2.

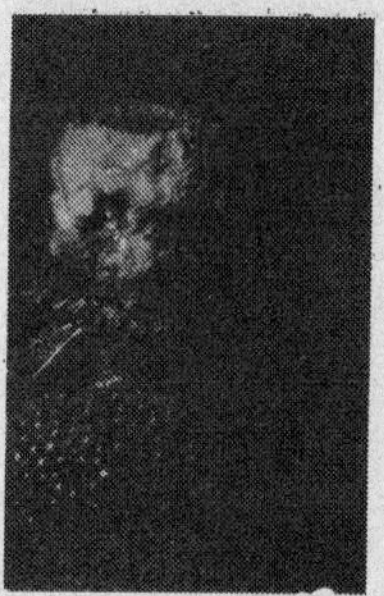
203. Blood Cup Sponge.

1981. Marine Line (1st series). Multicoloured.

508. 20 c. Type **203** 15 10
509. 45 c. Tube Sponge (horiz.) 25 35
510. 60 c. Black Coral 35 45
511. 75 c. Tyre Reef (horiz.) .. 40 75

See also Nos. 541/5.

204. Brown's Hutia (or Indian Coney).

1981. Brown's Hutia (or Indian Coney). Multicoloured.

512. 20 c. Hutia facing right .. 15 20
513. 20 c. Type **204** 15 20
514. 20 c. Hutia facing left and eating 15 20
515. 20 c. Hutia family .. 15 20

205. White Orchid.

1981. Royal Wedding. Multicoloured.

16.	20 c. Type **205**	15	10
17.	45 c. Royal Coach	25	10
18.	60 c. Prince Charles and Lady Diana Spencer . .	30	20
19.	$5 St. James' Palace . .	70	1·10

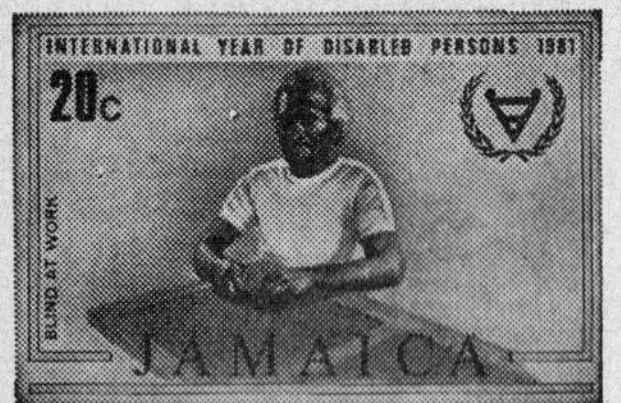

206. Blind Man at work.

981. International Year for Disabled Persons. Multicoloured.

21.	20 c. Type **206**	15	15
22.	45 c. Painting with the mouth	40	40
23.	60 c. Deaf student communicating with sign language	50	50
24.	$1.50 Basketball players . .	1·25	1·25

07. W.F.D. Emblem on 1964 1½d. Definitive.

1981. World Food Day. Stamps on Stamps.

25.	**207.**	20 c. multicoloured . .	30	15
26.	–	45 c. blk., red and orge.	60	40
27.	–	$2 black, blue and grn.	1·75	1·40
28.	–	$4 blk, green and brn.	3·00	2·50

DESIGNS—VERT. (as T **207**) 45 c. 1922 1d. value. HORIZ. (40 × 26 mm.) $2 As 1938 3d. but with W.F.D. emblem replacing King's head. $4 As 1938 1s. but with W.F.D. emblem replacing King's head.

208. " Survival " (song title).

1981. Bob Marley (musician) Commemoration. Song Titles. Multicoloured.

529.	1 c. Type **208**	10	10
530.	2 c. " Exodus "	10	10
531.	3 c. " Is this Love " . .	10	10
532.	15 c. " Coming in from the Cold "	50	15
533.	20 c. " Positive Vibration "	60	20
534.	60 c. " War "	1·40	1·40
535.	$3 " Could you be Loved "	7·00	6·50

No. 533 is incorrectly inscribed " OSITIVE VIBRATION ".

209. Webb Memorial Baptist Church.

1981. Christmas. Churches (2nd series). Multicoloured.

537.	10 c. Type **209**	10	10
538.	45 c. Church of God in Jamaica	30	15
539.	$5 Bryce United Church . .	2·25	2·50

210. Gorgonian Coral.

1982. Marine Life (2nd series. Multicoloured.

541.	20 c. Type **210**	25	10
542.	45 c. Hard Sponge and diver (horiz.)	45	25
543.	60 c. American Manatee (horiz.)	60	40
544.	75 c. Plume Worm (horiz.)	70	50
545.	$3 Coral Banded Shrimp (horiz.)	2·00	1·60

211. Cub Scout.

1982. 75th Anniversary of Boy Scout Movement. Multicoloured.

546.	20 c. Type **211**	40	15
547.	45 c. Scout camp	75	40
548.	60 c. " Out of Many, One People"	95	50
549.	$2 Lord Baden-Powell . .	1·75	1·75

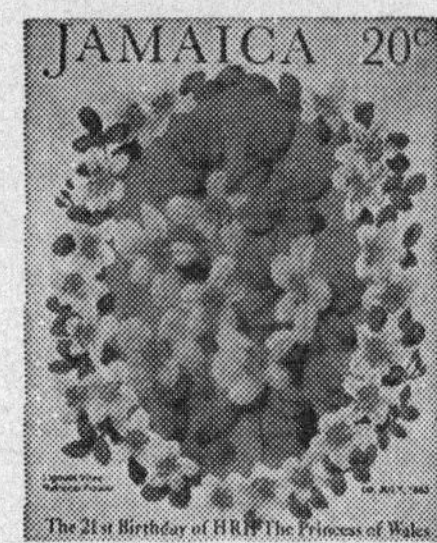

212. " Lignum vitae " (national flower).

1982. 21st Birthday of Princess of Wales.

551.	20 c. Type **212**	20	20
552.	45 c. Carriage ride	35	35
553.	60 c. Wedding	50	50
554.	75 c. " Saxifraga longifolia "	70	70
555.	$2 Princess of Wales . .	1·00	1·50
556.	$3 " Viola gracilis major "	1·25	2·00

1982. Birth of Prince William of Wales. Nos. 551/6 optd. **ROYAL BABY 26.6.82.**

558.	20 c. Type **212**	20	20
559.	45 c. Carriage ride	35	35
560.	60 c. Wedding	50	50
561.	75 c. "Saxifraga longifolia"	70	70
562.	$2 Princess of Wales . .	1·00	1·50
563.	$3 " Viola gracilis major "	1·25	2·00

213. Prey Captured.

1982. Jamaican Birds (1st series). Jamaican Lizard Cuckoo. Multicoloured.

565.	$1 Type **213**	80	80
566.	$1 Searching for prey . .	80	80
567.	$1 Calling prior to prey search	80	80
568.	$1 Adult landing	80	80
569.	$1 Adult flying in . .	80	80

See also Nos. 642/5 and 707/10.

1982. Christmas. Churches (3rd series). As T **209**. Multicoloured.

570.	20 c. United Pentecostal Church	20	10
571.	45 c. Disciples of Christ Church	35	25
572.	75 c. Open Bible Church . .	65	90

214. Queen Elizabeth II.

1983. Royal Visit. Multicoloured.

573.	$2 Type **214**	2·75	2·50
574.	$3 Coat of arms	3·75	3·50

215. Folk Dancing.

1983. Commonwealth Day. Multicoloured.

575.	20 c. Type **215**	15	15
576.	45 c. Bauxite mining . .	35	35
577.	75 c. World map showing position of Jamaica . .	45	45
578.	$2 Coat of arms and family	1·25	1·40

216. General Cargo Ship at Wharf.

1983. 25th Anniversary of International Maritime Organization. Multicoloured.

579.	15 c. Type **216**	75	20
580.	20 c. "Veendam" (cruise liner) at Kingston . .	1·00	30
581.	45 c. Container ship entering port	1·75	85
582.	$1 Tanker passing International Seabed Headquarters Building . .	2·75	3·25

217. Norman Manley and Sir Alexander Bustamante.

1983. 21st Anniversary of Independence.

583.	**217.**	15 c. multicoloured . .	15	15
584.		20 c. multicoloured . .	15	20
585.		45 c. multicoloured . .	30	40

218. Ship-to-Shore Radio.

1983. World Communications Year. Mult.

586.	20 c. Type **218**	15	15
587.	45 c. Postal services . .	35	40
588.	75 c. Telephone communications	55	1·00
589.	$1 T.V. via satellite . .	75	1·50

219. " Racing at Caymanas " (Sidney McLaren).

1983. Christmas. Paintings. Multicoloured.

590.	15 c. Type **219**	10	10
591.	20 c. " Seated Figures " (Karl Parboosingh) . .	10	10
592.	75 c. " The Petitioner " (Henry Daley) (vert.) . .	30	30
593.	$2 " Banana Plantation " (John Dunkley) (vert.) . .	70	1·25

220. Sir Alexander Bustamante.

1984. Birth Centenary of Sir Alexander Bustamante. Multicoloured.

594.	20 c. Type **220**	40	65
595.	20 c. Blenheim Birthplace	40	65

221. "D.H. 60G Gipsy Moth" Seaplane.

1984. Seaplanes and Flying Boats. Multicoloured.

596.	25 c. Type **221**	75	15
597.	55 c. Consolidated "Commodore" flying boat . .	1·25	65
598.	$1.50 Sikorsky "S-38" flying boat	2·00	2·50
599.	$3 Sikorsky "S-40" flying boat	2·75	3·25

222. Cycling.

1984. Olympic Games, Los Angeles. Multicoloured.

600.	25 c. Type **222**	10	10
601.	55 c. Relay running . .	20	25
602.	$1.50 Start of race . .	60	1·00
603.	$3 Finish of race	1·10	1·75

1984. Nos. 465 and 469 surch.

605.	5 c. on 6 c. Fern Gully, Ocho Rios	15	30
606.	10 c. on 12 c. Yellow-billed Amazon	60	50

224. Head of Jamaican Boa Snake.

1984. Jamaican Boa Snake. Multicoloured.

607.	25 c. Type **224**	45	15
608.	55 c. Boa snake on branch over tree	75	55
609.	70 c. Snake with young . .	90	1·00
610.	$1 Snake on log	1·10	1·40

225. "Enterprise" (1845).

1984. Railway Locomotives (1st series). Multicoloured.

612. 25 c. Type **225** 60 15
613. 55 c. Tank locomotive (1880) 85 60
614. $1.50 Kitson-Meyer tank locomotive (1904) .. 1·25 1·50
615. $3 Super-heated locomotive (1916) .. .. 2·00 2·50

See also Nos. 634/7.

226. "Accompong Madonna" (Namba Roy).

1984. Christmas. Sculptures. Multicoloured.

616. 20 c. Type **226** 20 10
617. 25 c. "Head" (Alvin Marriott) 25 10
618. 55 c. "Moon" (Edna Manley) 50 50
619. $1.50 "All Women are Five Women" (Mallica Reynolds (Kapo)) .. 1·00 1·75

227. Brown Pelicans flying.

1985. Birth Bicentenary of John J. Audubon (ornithologist). Brown Pelican. Mult.

620. 20 c. Type **227** 55 15
621. 55 c. Diving for fish .. 70 30
622. $2 Young pelican taking food from adult .. .. 1·25 1·50
623. $5 "Brown Pelican" (John J. Audubon) .. .. 1·75 2·50

228. The Queen Mother at Belfast University.

1985. Life and Times of Queen Elizabeth the Queen Mother. Multicoloured.

625. 25 c. With photograph album, 1963 .. .. 10 10
626. 55 c. With Prince Charles at Garter Ceremony, Windsor Castle, 1983 .. 15 15
627. $1.50 Type **228** 35 45
628. $3 With Prince Henry at his christening (from photo by Lord Snowdon) 65 90

229. Maps and Emblems.

1985. International Youth Year and 5th Pan-American Scout Jamboree.

630. **229.** 25 c. multicoloured .. 20 10
631. 55 c. multicoloured .. 30 20
632. 70 c. multicoloured .. 40 30
633. $4 multicoloured .. 1·25 2·00

1985. Railway Locomotives (2nd series). As T **225**. Multicoloured.

634 25 c. Baldwin locomotive No. 16 .. .. .. 45 10
635 55 c. Rogers locomotive .. 70 15
636 $1.50 Locomotive "The Projector" .. .. 1·00 75
637 $4 Diesel locomotive No. 102 .. .. .. 2·00 1·75

230. "The Old Settlement" (Ralph Campbell).

1985. Christmas. Jamaican Paintings. Mult.

638. 20 c. Type **230** 10 10
639. 55 c. "The Vendor" (Albert Huie) (vert.) 15 15
640. 75 c. "Road Menders" (Gaston Tabois) .. 20 25
641. $4 "Woman, must I not be about my Father's business?" (Carl Abrahams) (vert.) .. 1·10 1·40

1986. Jamaican Birds (2nd series). As T **213**. Multicoloured.

642. 25 c. Chestnut-bellied Cuckoo 40 10
643. 55 c. Jamaican Becard .. 55 30
644. $1.50 White-eyed Thrush .. 70 1·00
645. $5 Rufous-tailed Flycatcher .. .. 1·60 3·00

1986. 60th Birthday of Queen Elizabeth II. As T **110** of Ascension. Multicoloured.

646. 20 c. Princess Elizabeth and Princess Margaret, 1939 .. .. .. 10 10
647. 25 c. With Prince Charles and Prince Andrew, 1962 10 10
648. 70 c. Queen visiting War Memorial, Montego Bay, 1983 .. .. .. 15 25
649. $3 On state visit to Luxembourg, 1976 .. 65 90
650. $5 At Crown Agents Head Office, London, 1983 .. 1·25 1·75

231. Bustamante Children's Hospital.

1986. "Ameripex '86" International Stamp Exhibition, Chicago. Multicoloured.

651. 25 c. Type **231** 30 10
652. 55 c. Air Jamaica jet airliner and map of holiday resorts 35 15
653. $3 Norman Manley Law School .. .. .. 1·00 1·40
654. $5 Bauxite and agricultural exports .. .. 4·00 4·00

1986. Royal Wedding. As T **112** of Ascension. Multicoloured.

656. 20 c. Prince Andrew and Miss Sarah Ferguson, Ascot, 1985 .. .. 15 10
657. $5 Prince Andrew making speech, Fredericton, Canada, 1985 .. .. 1·40 1·90

232. Richard "Shrimpy" Clarke.

1986. Jamaican Boxing Champions. Multicoloured.

658. 45 c. Type **232** 20 15
659. 70 c. Michael McCallum .. 30 20
660. $2 Trevor Berbick .. 70 55
661. $4 Richard "Shrimpy" Clarke, Michael McCallum and Trevor Berbick .. .. .. 1·25 1·25

1986. Nos. 472/3 surch.

662. 5 c. on 50 c. Jamaican woodpecker 65 70
663. 10 c. on 65 c. Rafting, Martha Brae Trelawny 65 70

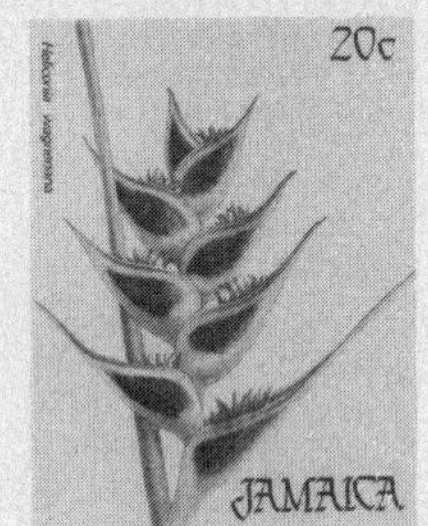

234. "Heliconia wagneriana".

1986. Christmas. Flowers (1st series). Mult.

664. 20 c. Type **234** 10 10
665. 25 c. "Heliconia psittacorum" (horiz.) 10 10
666. 55 c. "Heliconia rostrata" 20 30
667. $5 "Strelitzia reginae" (horiz.) .. .. .. 1·60 2·75

See also Nos. 703/6 and 739/42.

235. Crown Cone.

1987. Sea Shells. Multicoloured.

668. 35 c. Type **235** 20 10
669. 75 c. Measled cowrie .. 30 20
670. $1 Trumpet triton .. 40 50
671. $5 Rooster tail conch .. 1·40 2·00

236. Norman Manley.

237. Arms of Jamaica.

1987. Portraits.

672 **236** 1 c. red and pink .. 10 10
673 2 c. red and pink .. 10 10
674 3 c. green and stone 10 10
675 4 c. green & lt green 10 10
676 5 c. blue and grey .. 10 10
677 6 c. blue and grey .. 10 10
678 7 c. violet and mauve 10 10
679 8 c. mauve and pink 10 10
680 9 c. brown & lt brown 10 10
681 – 10 c. red and pink .. 10 10
682 – 20 c. orange and flesh 10 10
683 – 30 c. green & lt green 10 10
684 – 40 c. dp green & green 10 10
685 – 50 c. green and grey 10 10
686 – 60 c. blue & lt blue .. 10 10
687 – 70 c. violet & lt violet 10 10
688 – 80 c. violet and lilac 10 10
689 – 90 c. brown & lt brn 10 10
690 **237** $1 brown and cream 10 10
691 $2 orange and cream 10 10
692 $5 green and stone .. 25 30
693 $10 turquoise & blue 50 55
693c $25 violet & lavender 1·25 1·40
693d $50 mauve and lilac 2·50 2·75

DESIGN: 10 c. to 90 c. Sir Alexander Bustamante.

The 5, 20, 40, 50, 90 c. and $1 exist with or without imprint date at foot.

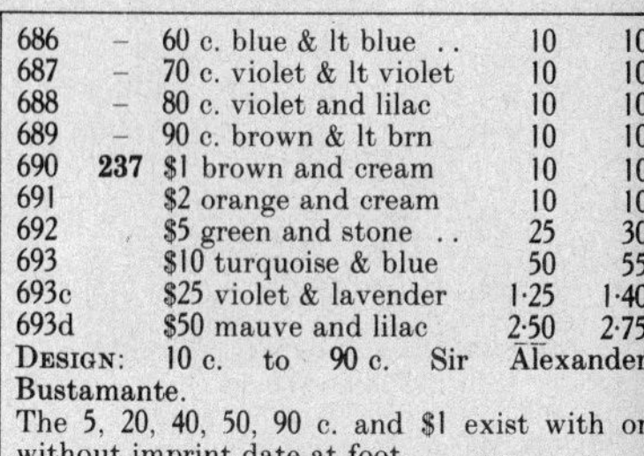

238. Jamaican Flag and Coast at Sunset.

1987. 25th Anniv. of Independence. Mult.

694. 55 c. Type **238** 60 50
695. 70 c. Jamaican flag and inscription (horiz.) .. 80 1·00

239. Marcus Garvey.

1987. Birth Centenary of Marcus Garvey (founder of Universal Negro Improvement Association). Each black, green and yellow.

696. 25 c. Type **239** 40 65
697. 25 c. Statue of Marcus Garvey 40 65

240. Salvation Army School for the Blind.

1987. Centenary of Salvation Army in Jamaica. Multicoloured.

698. 25 c. Type **240** 40 10
699. 55 c. Col. Mary Booth and Bramwell Booth Memorial Hall 65 30
700. $3 Welfare Service lorry, 1929 .. .. .. 1·75 2·00
701. $5 Col. Abram Davey and S.S. "Alene", 1887 .. 2·50 3·00

1987. Christmas. Flowers (2nd series). As T **234**. Multicoloured.

703. 20 c. Hibiscus hybrid .. 10 10
704. 25 c. "Hibiscus elatus" .. 10 10
705. $4 "Hibiscus cannabinus" 90 95
706. $5 "Hibiscus rosa-sinensis" 1·25 1·40

1988. Jamaican Birds (3rd series). As T **213**. Multicoloured.

707 45 c. Chestnut-bellied cuckoo, black-billed amazon and Jamaican euphonia 50 75
708 45 c. Jamaican white-eyed vireo, rufous-throated solitaire and yellow elaenia 50 75
709 $5 Snowy plover, little blue heron and great blue heron (white phase) .. 2·25 2·50
710 $5 Black-necked stilt, snowy egret and black-crowned night heron .. 2·25 2·50

The two designs of each value were printed together, se-tenant, each pair forming a composite design.

243 Blue Whales

1988. Marine Mammals. Multicoloured.
'11 20 c. Type **243** 60 20
'12 25 c. Gervais's whales .. 60 20
'13 55 c. Killer whales .. 90 35
'14 $5 Common dolphins .. 3·00 4·00

1988. West Indian Cricket. As T **186** of Barbados, each showing portrait, cricket equipment and early belt buckle. Mult.
'15 25 c. Jackie Hendriks .. 40 10
'16 55 c. George Headley .. 75 20
'17 $2 Michael Holding .. 1·50 1·00
'18 $3 R. K. Nunes .. .. 1·75 1·50
'19 $4 Allan Rae .. .. 2·00 1·75

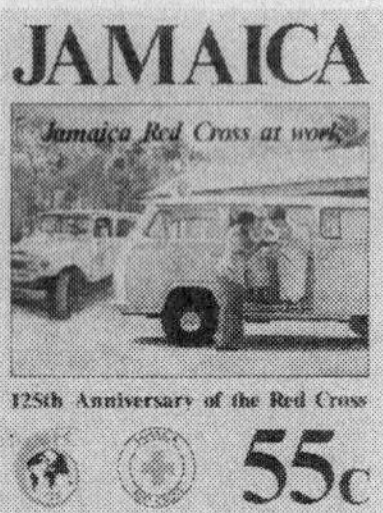

244 Jamaican Red Cross Workers with Ambulance

1988. 125th Anniv of International Red Cross. Multicoloured.
'20 55 c. Type **244** 50 20
'21 $5 Henri Dunant (founder) in field hospital .. 2·00 2·40

245 Boxing

1988. Olympic Games, Seoul. Multicoloured.
722 25 c. Type **245** 10 10
723 45 c. Cycling 10 10
724 $4 Athletics .. .. 1·00 1·10
725 $5 Hurdling .. .. 1·00 1·25

246 Bobsled Team Members and Logo

1988. Jamaican Olympic Bobsled Team. Mult.
727 25 c. Type **246** 10 30
728 25 c. Two-man bobsled .. 10 30
729 $5 Bobsled team members (different) and logo .. 1·00 1·50
730 $5 Four-man bobsled .. 1·00 1·50

1988. Hurricane Gilbert Relief Fund. Nos. 722/5 surch + **25 c HURRICANE GILBERT RELIEF FUND**.
731 25 c.+25 c. Type **245** .. 10 15
732 45 c.+45 c. Cycling .. 20 25
733 $4+$4 Athletics .. 1·75 1·90
734 $5+$5 Hurdling .. .. 2·10 2·25

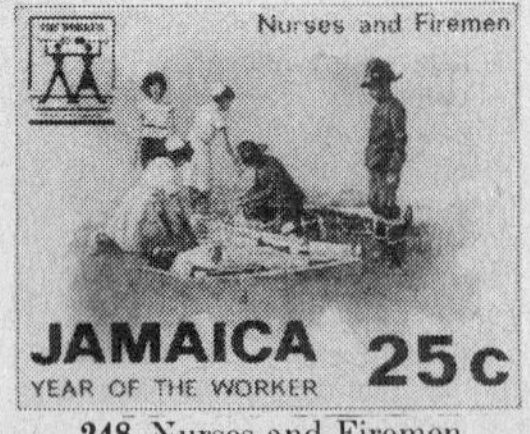

248 Nurses and Firemen

1988. Year of the Worker. Multicoloured.
735 25 c. Type **248** 30 10
736 55 c. Woodcarver .. 35 20
737 $3 Textile workers .. 1·10 1·75
738 $5 Workers on fish farm .. 1·60 2·25

1988. Christmas Flowers (3rd series). As T **234**. Multicoloured.
739 25 c. "Euphorbia pulcherrima" 15 10
740 55 c. "Spathodea campanulata" (horiz) 20 15
741 $3 "Hylocereus triangularis" 80 80
742 $4 "Broughtonia sanguinea" (horiz) .. 90 90

249 Old York Castle School

1989. Bicent of Methodist Church in Jamaica.
743 **249** 25 c. black and blue .. 10 10
744 – 45 c. black and red .. 15 10
745 – $5 black and green .. 1·25 1·50
DESIGNS: 45 c. Revd. Thomas Coke and Parade Chapel, Kingston; $5 Father Hugh Sherlock and St. John's Church.

250 "Syntomidopsis variegata"

1989. Jamaican Moths (1st series). Mult.
746 25 c. Type **250** 45 10
747 55 c. "Himantoides perkinsae" 70 30
748 $3 "Arctia nigriplaga" .. 1·40 1·75
749 $5 "Sthenognatha toddi" .. 1·75 2·25
See also Nos. 758/61 and 790/3.

251 Arawak Fisherman with Catch

1989. 500th Anniv (1992) of Discovery of America by Columbus (1st issue). Mult.
750 25 c. Type **251** 20 10
751 70 c. Arawak man smoking 40 30
752 $5 King Ferdinand and Queen Isabella inspecting caravels .. 1·75 2·00
753 $10 Columbus with chart 3·25 3·50
See also Nos. 774/7 and 802/7.

252 Girl Guide

1990. 75th Anniv of Girl Guide Movement in Jamaica. Multicoloured.
755 45 c. Type **252** 45 15
756 55 c. Guide leader .. 45 15
757 $5 Brownie, guide and ranger .. .. .. 2·50 3·25

1990. Jamaican Moths (2nd series). As T **250**. Multicoloured.
758 25 c. "Eunomia rubripunctata" 30 10
759 55 c. "Perigonia jamaicensis" 50 25
760 $4 "Uraga haemorrhoa" .. 1·25 1·75
761 $5 "Empyreuma pugione" 1·40 1·75

1990. "EXPO 90" International Garden and Greenery Exhibition, Osaka. Nos. 758/61 optd **EXPO '90** and logo.
762 25 c. "Eunomia rubripunctata" 30 10
763 55 c. "Perigonia jamaicensis" 50 25
764 $4 "Uraga haemorrhoa" .. 1·25 1·75
765 $5 "Empyreuma pugione" 1·40 1·75

254 Teaching English

1990. International Literacy Year. Mult.
766 55 c. Type **254** 30 15
767 $5 Teaching maths .. 2·00 2·50

255 "To the Market"

1990. Christmas. Children's Paintings. Mult.
768 20 c. Type **255** 15 10
769 25 c. "House and Garden" 15 10
770 55 c. "Jack and Jill" .. 20 15
771 70 c. "Market" 20 20
772 $1.50 "Lonely" 60 80
773 $5 "Market Woman" (vert) 1·50 2·25

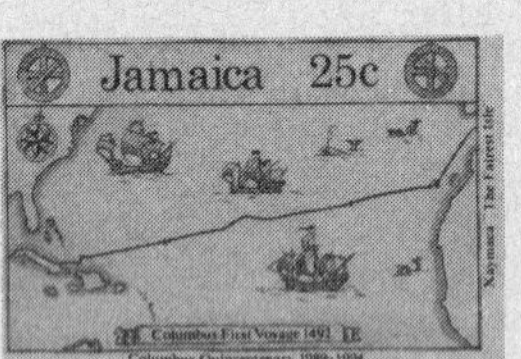

256 Map of First Voyage, 1492

1990. 500th Anniv (1992) of Discovery of America by Columbus (2nd issue). Mult.
774 25 c. Type **256** 10 10
775 45 c. Map of second voyage, 1493 .. .. 15 10
776 $5 Map of third voyage, 1498 .. .. .. 1·10 1·40
777 $10 Map of fourth voyage, 1502 .. .. .. 2·00 2·40

257 Weather Balloon, Dish Aerial and Map of Jamaica

1991. 11th World Meteorological Congress, Kingston.
780 **257** 50 c. multicoloured .. 25 15
781 $10 multicoloured .. 1·75 2·00

258 Bust of Mary Seacole

1991. International Council of Nurses Meeting of National Representatives. Multicoloured.
782 50 c. Type **258** 25 15
783 $1.10 Mary Seacole House 50 60

259 Jamaican Iguana

1991. 50th Anniv of Natural History Society of Jamaica. Jamaican Iguana. Mult.
785 $1.10 Type **259** 30 40
786 $1.10 Head of iguana looking right 30 40
787 $1.10 Iguana climbing .. 30 40
788 $1.10 Iguana on rock looking left 30 40
789 $1.10 Close-up of iguana's head 30 40

1991. Jamaican Moths (3rd series). As T **250**. Multicoloured.
790 50 c. "Urania sloanus" .. 25 10
791 $1.10 "Phoenicoprocta jamaicensis" 45 20
792 $1.40 "Horama grotei" .. 50 30
793 $8 "Amplypterus gannascus" .. .. 1·75 2·00

1991. "Phila Nippon '91" International Stamp Exhibition, Tokyo. Nos. 790/3 optd **PHILA NIPPON 91** and emblem.
794 50 c. "Urania sloanus" .. 25 10
795 $1.10 "Phoenicoprocta jamaicensis" 45 20
796 $1.40 "Horama grotei" .. 50 30
797 $8 "Amplypterus gannascus" .. .. 1·75 2·00

261 "Doctor Bird"

1991. Christmas. Children's Paintings. Mult.
798 50 c. Type **261** 20 10
799 $1.10 "Road scene" .. 35 20
800 $5 "Children and house" 75 80
801 $10 "Cows grazing" .. 1·40 2·00

262 Indians threatening Ships

1991. 500th Anniv (1992) of Discovery of America by Columbus (3rd issue). Mult.
802 50 c. Type **262** 15 10
803 $1.10 Spaniards setting dog on Indians 20 15
804 $1.40 Indian with gift of pineapple 20 15
805 $25 Columbus describes Jamaica with crumpled paper .. .. .. 2·50 3·25

263 Compasses and Square Symbol

1992 250th Anniv of First Provisional Grand Master of English Freemasonry in Jamaica. Multicoloured.

808		50 c. Type **263**	15	10
809		$1.10 Symbol in stained glass window	20	20
810		$1.40 Compasses and square on book ..	20	20
811		$25 Eye in triangle symbol	2·50	3·00

264 Ship in Flooded Street

1992. 300th Anniv of Destruction of Port Royal. Multicoloured.

813		50 c. Type **264**	10	10
814		$1.10 Church tower falling	20	15
815		$1.40 Houses collapsing ..	20	15
816		$25 Inhabitants falling into fissure	2·25	2·50

265 Credit Union Symbol

1992. 50th Anniv of Credit Union Movement.

818	**265**	50 c. blue, emer & grn	20	15
819	–	$1.40 multicoloured ..	35	35

DDESIGNS: $1.40, O'Hare Hall.

266 Jamaican Flag and Beach Scene

1992. 30th Anniv of Independence.

820	**266**	50 c. multicoloured ..	10	10
821		$1.10 multicoloured ..	15	15
822		$25 multicoloured ..	2·00	2·00

267 "Rainbow" (Cecil Baugh)

1993. Art Ceramics and Pottery. Mult.

823		50 c. Type **267**	10	10
824		$1.10 "Yabba Pot" (Louisa Jones)	15	15
825		$1.40 "Sculptured Vase" (Gene Pearson) ..	15	15
826		$25 "Lidded Form" (Norma Harrack) ..	2·00	2·00

268 Girls' Brigade Parade

1993. Centenary of Girls' Brigade. Mult.

827		50 c. Type **268**	10	10
828		$1.10 Brigade members ..	20	20

269 Cadet, Armoured Car and Emblem

1993. 50th Anniv of Jamaica Combined Cadet Force. Multicoloured.

829		50 c. Type **269**	10	10
830		$1.10 Cadet and light aircraft (horiz)	10	10
831		$1.40 Cadet and patrol boats	15	15
832		$3 Cadet and emblem (horiz)	30	30

270 Constant Spring Golf Course

1993. Golf Courses. Multicoloured.

833		50 c. Type **270**	10	10
834		$1.10 Type **270**	10	10
835		$1.40 Half Moon	10	10
836		$2 As $1.40	10	10
837		$3 Jamaica Jamaica ..	15	20
838		$10 As $3	50	55

271 Norman Manley

1994. Birth Centenary of Norman Manley.

840	**271**	$25 multicoloured ..	1·25	1·40
841		$50 multicoloured ..	2·50	2·75

273 Flags of Great Britain and Jamaica

1994. Royal Visit. Multicoloured.

843		$1.10 Type **273**	10	10
844		$1.40 Royal Yacht "Britannia"	10	10
845		$25 Queen Elizabeth II ..	1·25	1·40
846		$50 Queen Elizabeth and Prince Philip	2·50	2·75

274 Douglas DC-9

1994. 25th Anniv of Air Jamaica. Mult.

847		50 c. Type **274**	10	10
848		$1.10 Douglas DC-8 ..	10	10
849		$5 Boeing 727	25	30
850		$50 Airbus A300	2·50	2·75

OFFICIAL STAMPS

1890. Optd. OFFICIAL

O 3.	**8.**	½d. green..	4·00	20
O 4.	**11.**	1d. red	4·00	45
O 5.		2d. grey	4·50	1·00

JAMMU AND KASHMIR

A state in the extreme N. of India.

12 pies = 1 anna; 16 annas = 1 rupee.

1.

Gum. The stamps of Jammu and Kashmir were issued without gum.

1866. Imperf.

41	**1**	½a. black	18·00	38·00
26		½a. red	23·00	35·00
44		½a. blue	22·00	
20		½a. green	65·00	£180
48		½a. yellow	95·00	
15		1 a. black	£200	
27		1 a. red	25·00	£150
5		1 a. blue	£275	70·00
20		1 a. green	65·00	£180
24		1 a. yellow	£425	
16		4 a. black	£200	
10		4 a. red	45·00	70·00
19		4 a. blue	£110	
22		4 a. green	£110	£250
25		4 a. yellow	£350	

Prices for the circular stamps (Nos. 5/48) are for cut-square examples. Cut-to-shape examples are worth from 10% to 20% of these prices, according to condition.

½ a. ½ a.

1 a. **4.** ½ a.

1867.

69a	**4.**	½ a. black	95·00	£130
58		½ a. blue	95·00	65·00
60		½ a. red	3·25	2·50
64		½ a. orange	85·00	90·00
68		½ a. green	£1300	£800
69b		1 a. black	£850	£750
55		1 a. blue	£350	£200
61		1 a. red	6·00	6·50
65		1 a. orange	£950	£650
69		1 a. green	£1800	£1300

The characters denoting the value are in the upper part of the inner circle.

8. (¼a.)

12. (¼a.)

1867. Imperf.

90.	**8.**	¼ a. black	1·10	1·10
91.		½ a. blue	1·10	70
93.		1 a. blue	£2500	£1100
95.		1 a. orange	7·00	6·00
97.		2 a. yellow	7·50	8·00
99.		4 a. green	18·00	17·00
101.		8 a. red	20·00	17·00

1878. Imperf. or perf.

39	**12.**	⅛ a. yellow	30	50
25		¼ a. red	1·50	1·75
31		¼ a. orange	7·50	6·50
30a		¼ a. blue	£700	£450
42		¼ a. brown	30	20
05		½ a. violet	13·00	12·00
47		½ a. red	60	30
32		½ a. orange	18·00	12·00
43		½ a. blue	4·00	
27		1 a. red	1·25	1·60
06		1 a. mauve	18·00	19·00
33		1 a. orange	13·00	7·00
48		1 a. grey	40	40
50		1 a. green	40	40
08		2 a. violet	19·00	19·00
10		2 a. blue	30·00	30·00
28		2 a. red	2·00	2·75
34		2 a. orange	14·00	7·00
52		2 a. red on yellow ..	65	55
53		2 a. red on green ..	1·00	1·25
29		4 a. red	4·75	5·00
35		4 a. orange	22·00	35·00
55		4 a. green	1·75	2·75
30		8 a. red	5·00	5·50
36		8 a. orange	38·00	50·00
59		8 a. blue	4·00	5·50
61a		8 a. lilac	10·00	14·00

OFFICIAL STAMPS

1878. Imperf. or perf.

O 6.	**12.**	¼ a. black	35	35
O 7.		½ a. black	15	20
O 8.		1 a. black	20	20
O 9.		2 a. black	30	30
O 10.		4 a. black	35	50
O 11.		8 a. black	60	70

JASDAN

A State of India. Now uses **Indian stamps.**

12 pie = 1 anna; 16 annas = 1 rupee.

1. Sun.

1942.

1	1	1 a. green	7·00	60·00

JERSEY

Island in the English Channel off N.W. coast off France. Occupied by German forces from June 1940 to May 1945 with separate stamp issues.

The general issue of 1948 for Channel Islands and the regional issues of 1958 are listed at end of GREAT BRITAIN.

Jersey had its own postal administration from 1969.

1941. 12 pence = 1 shilling.
20 shillings = 1 pound.
1971. 100 (new) pence = 1 pound sterling.

(a) War Occupation Issues.

1. 2. Old Jersey Farm.

1941.

1.	**1.**	½d. green	3·75	2·50
2.		1d. red	4·00	2·75

1943.

3.	**2.**	½d. green	7·00	5·50
4.	–	1d. red	1·50	50
5.	–	1½d. brown	2·50	3·00
6.	–	2d. yellow	4·00	2·25
7a.	–	2½d. blue	75	1·50
8.	–	3d. violet	1·00	2·75

DESIGNS: 1d. Portelet Bay. 1½d., Corbiere Lighthouse. 2d. Elizabeth Castle. 2½d., Mont Orgueil Castle. 3d. Gathering vraic (seaweed).

(b) Independent Postal Administration.

10. Elizabeth Castle.

1969. Multicoloured.

15.	½d. Type **10**	10	60
16.	1d. La Hougue Bie (Prehistoric Tomb)	15	20
17.	2d. Portelet Bay	10	15
18.	3d. Corbiere Lighthouse ..	20	15
19.	4d. Mont Orgueil Castle by night	15	10
20.	5d. Arms and Royal Mace ..	15	10
21.	6d. Jersey Cow	30	40
22.	9d. Chart of the English Channel	55	90
23.	1s. Mont Orgueil Castle by day	90	90
24.	1s. 6d. Chart of the English Channel	1·75	1·75
25.	1s. 9d. Queen Elizabeth II (after Cecil Beaton) ..	1·75	1·75
26.	2s. 6d. Jersey Airport ..	3·75	2·50
27.	5s. Legislative Chamber ..	15·00	7·50
28.	10s. The Royal Court ..	30·00	22·00
29.	£1 Queen Elizabeth II (after Cecil Beaton)	2·00	1·50

The 1s. 9d. and £1 are vert.

24. First Day Cover.

1969. Inauguration of Post Office.

30.	**24.**	4d. multicoloured ..	25	30
31.		5d. multicoloured ..	30	50
32.		1s. 6d. multicoloured ..	1·40	2·75
33.		1s. 9d. multicoloured ..	1·40	2·75

25. Lord Coutanche, former Bailiff of Jersey.

1970. 25th Anniv. of Liberation. Mult.

34.	4d. Type **25**	25	25
35.	5d. Sir Winston Churchill ..	35	25
36.	1s. 6d. " Liberation " (Edmund Blampied) ..	2·50	2·00
37.	1s. 9d. S.S. " Vega " ..	2·50	2·00

Nos. 36/7 are horiz.

29. " A Tribute to Enid Blyton ".

1970. " Battle of Flowers " Parade. Mult.

38.	4d. Type **29**	25	35
39.	5d. " Rags to riches " (Cinderella and pumpkin)	40	45
40.	1s. 6d. " Gourmet's delight " (lobster and cornucopia)	11·00	3·50
41.	1s. 9d. " We're the greatest " (ostriches)	11·00	3·50

33. Jersey Airport.

1970. Decimal currency. Nos. 15, etc., but with new colours, new design (6p.) and decimal values, as T **33.**

42.	½p. mult. (as No. 15) ..	10	10
43.	1p. mult. (as No. 18) ..	10	10
44.	1½p. mult. (as No. 21) ..	10	10
45.	2p. mult. (as No. 19) ..	10	10
46.	2½p. mult. (as No. 20) ..	10	10
47.	3p. mult. (as No. 16) ..	10	10
48.	3½p. mult. (as No. 17) ..	15	15
49.	4p. mult. (as No. 22) ..	15	15
49a.	4½p. mult. (as No. 20) ..	20	20
50.	5p. mult. (as No. 23) ..	10	15
50a.	5½p. mult. (as No. 21) ..	40	25
51.	6p. multicoloured (Martello Tower, Archirondel, 23 × 22 mm.)	25	30
52.	7½p. mult (as No. 24) ..	30	40
52a.	8p. mult. (as No. 19) ..	25	25
53.	9p. mult. (as No. 25) ..	30	30
54.	10p. mult. (as No. 26) ..	30	55
55.	20p. mult. (as No. 27) ..	60	75
56.	50p. mult. (as No. 28) ..	1·25	1·25

34. White Eared-Pheasant.

1971. Wildlife Preservation Trust (1st series). Multicoloured.

57.	2p. Type **24**	75	25
58.	2½p. Thick-billed Parrot (vert.)	75	25
59.	7½p. Western Black-and-White Colobus (vert.) ..	10·00	4·25
60.	9p. Ring-tailed Lemur ..	10·00	4·25

See also Nos. 73/6, 217/21, 324/9 and 447/51.

35. Poppy Emblem and Field.

1971. 50th Anniversary of Royal British Legion. Multicoloured.

61.	2p. Royal British Legion Badge	40	35
62.	2½p. Type **35**	40	35
63.	7½p. Jack Counter and Victoria Cross	2·50	2·75
64.	9p. Crossed Tricolour and Union Jack	2·50	2·75

36. " Tante Elizabeth " (E. Blampied).

1971. Paintings (1st series). Multicoloured.

65.	2p. Type **36**	15	15
66.	2½p. " English Fleet in the Channel " (P. Monamy) (horiz.)	20	20
67.	7½p. " The Boyhood of Raleigh " (Millais) (horiz.)	4·00	3·25
68.	9p. " The Blind Beggar " (W. W. Ouless)	4·00	3·25

See also Nos. 115/118.

37. Jersey Fern. 38. Artillery Shako.

1972. Wild Flowers of Jersey. Multicoloured.

69.	3p. Type **37**	25	15
70.	5p. Jersey Thrift	60	50
71.	7½p. Jersey Orchid ..	2·50	3·00
72.	9p. Jersey Viper's Bugloss	2·75	3·00

1972. Wildlife Preservation Trust (2nd series). As T **34.** Multicoloured.

73.	2½p. Cheetah	55	20
74.	3p. Rothschild's Mynah (vert.)	30	35
75.	7½p. Spectacled Bear ..	1·60	2·00
76.	9p. Tuatara	2·00	2·00

1972. Royal Jersey Militia. Multicoloured.

77.	2½p. Type **38**	15	20
78.	3p. Shako (2nd North Regt.)	20	20
79.	7½p. Shako (5th South-West Regt.)	90	1·00
80.	9p. Helmet (3rd Jersey Light Infantry)	1·00	1·00

39. Princess Anne.

1972. Royal Silver Wedding. Multicoloured.

81.	2½p. Type **39**	10	10
82.	3p. Queen Elizabeth and Prince Philip (horiz.) ..	10	10
83.	7½p. Prince Charles ..	40	40
84.	20p. The Royal Family (horiz.)	50	50

40. Armorican Bronze Coins.

1973. Centenary of La Societe Jersiaise. Multicoloured.

85.	2½p. Silver cups	10	10
86.	3p. Gold torque (vert.) ..	10	10
87.	7½p. Royal Seal of Charles II (vert.)	50	40
88.	9p. Type **40**	50	50

41. Balloon and Letter.

1973. Jersey Aviation History (1st series). Multicoloured.

89.	3p. Type **41**	10	10
90.	5p. Seaplane " Astra " ..	15	15
91.	7½p. Supermarine " Sea Eagle "	50	60
92.	9p. De Havilland " Express "	50	60

See also Nos. 340/3.

42. " North Western ".

1973. Centenary of Jersey Eastern Railway. Early Locomotives. Multicoloured.

93.	2½p. Type **42**	10	10
94.	3p. " Calvados "	10	10
95.	7½p. " Carteret "	50	40
96.	9p. " Caesarea "	50	50

43. Princess Anne and Capt. Mark Phillips.

1973. Royal Wedding.

97.	**43.**	3p. multicoloured ..	10	10
98.		20p. multicoloured ..	90	90

44. Spider Crab.

1973. Marine Life. Multicoloured.

99. 2½p. Type **44** 10 10
100. 3p. Conger-eel 10 10
101. 7½p. Lobster 35 35
102. 20p. Ormer 55 55

45. Freesias.

1974. Spring Flowers. Multicoloured.

103. 3p. Type **45** 10 10
104. 5½p. Anemones 10 10
105. 8p. Carnations and Gladioli 40 40
106. 10p. Daffodils and Iris .. 50 50

46. First Letter Box and Contemporary Cover.

1974. Centenary of U.P.U. Multicoloured.

107. 2½p. Type **46** 10 10
108. 3p. Postmen, 1862 and 1969 10 10
109. 5½p. Letter-box and letter, 1974 .. .. .. 25 30
110. 20p. R.M.S. "Aquila" (1874) and aeroplane (1974) 70 60

47. John Wesley.

1974. Anniversaries.

111. **47.** 3p. black and brown .. 10 10
112. – 3½p. violet and blue .. 10 10
113. – 8p. black and lilac .. 30 35
114. – 20p. black and stone .. 70 65

PORTRAITS AND EVENTS: 3p. (Methodism in Jersey.) Bicent. 3½p. Sir William Hillary, founder (R.N.L.I.) 150th anniv. 8p. Canon Wace (poet and historian), 800th death anniv. 20p. Sir Winston Churchill. (Birth Cent.).

48. "Catherine" and "Mary" (Royal yachts).

1974. Marine Paintings by Peter Monamy (2nd series). Multicoloured.

115. 3½p. Type **48** 10 10
116. 5½p. French two-decker .. 15 15
117. 8p. Dutch vessel (horiz.) .. 25 30
118. 25p. Battle of Cap La Hague, 1692 (55 × 27 mm.) 65 60

49. Potato Digger.

1975. 19th Century Farming. Multicoloured.

119. 3p. Type **49** 10 10
120. 3½p. Cider Crusher .. 10 15
121. 8p. Six-horse plough .. 35 35
122. 10p. Hay cart 55 50

50. H.M. Queen Elizabeth, the Queen Mother (photograph by Cecil Beaton).

1975. Royal Visit.

123 **50** 20p. multicoloured .. 75 75

51. Shell.

1975. Jersey Tourism. Multicoloured.

124. 5p. Type **51** 10 10
125. 8p. Parasol 15 15
126. 10p. Deckchair 35 35
127. 12p. Sandcastle with flags of Jersey and the U.K. 50 50

52. Common Tern.

1975. Sea Birds. Multicoloured.

129. 4p. Type **52** 15 15
130. 5p. British storm petrel .. 15 15
131. 8p. Brent geese 30 35
132. 25p. Shag 60 55

53. Siskin "3–A".

1975. 50th Anniv. of Royal Air Force Association, Jersey Branch. Multicoloured.

133. 4p. Type **53** 10 10
134. 5p. "Southampton" flying-boat 15 15
135. 10p. Mk. 1 "Spitfire" .. 30 30
136. 25p. Folland "Gnat" .. 60 60

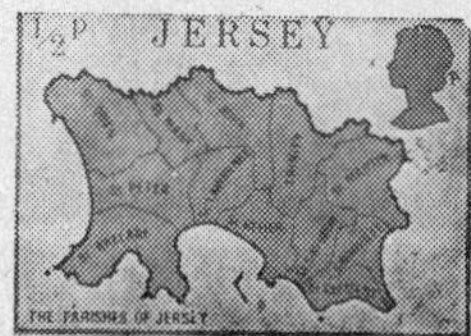

54. Map of Jersey Parishes.

55. Parish Arms and Island Scene.

1976. Multicoloured.
(a) Parish Arms and Views.

137. ½p. Type **54** 10 10
138. 1p. Zoological Park .. 10 10
139. 5p. St. Mary's Church .. 15 15
140. 6p. Seymour Tower .. 15 15
141. 7p. La Corbiere Lighthouse 20 20
142. 8p. St. Saviour's Church 20 20
143. 9p. Elizabeth Castle .. 25 25
144. 10p. Gorey Harbour .. 25 25
145. 11p. Jersey Airport .. 30 25
146. 12p. Grosnez Castle .. 30 30
147. 13p. Bonne Nuit Harbour 35 35
148. 14p. Le Hocq Tower .. 35 40
149. 15p. Morel Farm 40 45

(b) Emblems.

150. 20p. Type **55** 50 50
151. 30p. Flag and map .. 75 75
152. 40p. Postal H.Q. and badge 1·00 1·00
153. 50p. Parliament, Royal Court and arms .. 1·25 1·25
154. £1 Lieutenant-Governor's flag and Government House 2·50 2·50
155. £2 Queen Elizabeth II (vert.) .. .. .. 4·00 4·25

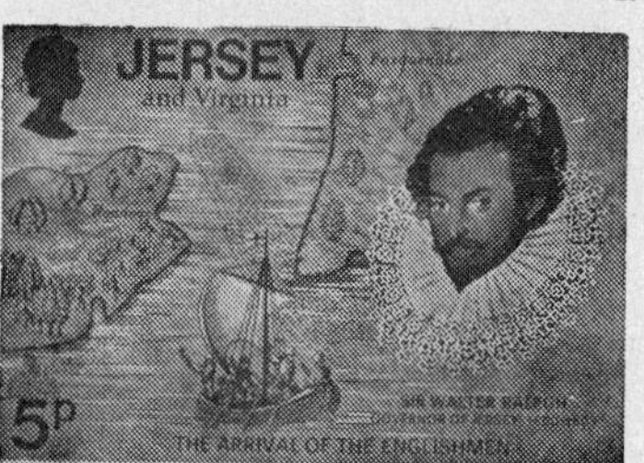

56. Sir Walter Raleigh and map of Virginia.

1976. Bicentenary of American Independence. Multicoloured.

160. 5p. Type **56** 10 10
161. 7p. Sir George Carteret and map of New Jersey .. 15 15
162. 11p. Philippe Dauvergne and Long Island Landing 40 35
163. 13p. John Copley and sketch 45 50

57. Dr. Grandin and Map of China.

1976. Birth Centenary of Dr. Lilian Grandin (medical missionary).

164. **57.** 5p. multicoloured .. 10 10
165. – 7p. yell., brn. and blk. 15 15
166. – 11p. multicoloured .. 50 35
167. – 13p. multicoloured .. 50 50

DESIGNS: 7p. Sampan on the Yangtze. 11p. Overland trek. 13p. Dr. Grandin at work.

58. Coronation, 1953 (photographed by Cecil Beaton).

1977. Silver Jubilee. Multicoloured.

168. 5p. Type **58** 15 15
169. 7p. Visit to Jersey, 1957 .. 30 20
170. 25p. Queen Elizabeth II (photo by Peter Grugeon) 80 80

59. Coins of 1871 and 1877.

1977. Centenary of Currency Reform. Mult.

171. 5p. Type **59** 10 10
172. 7p. Obverse and reverse of 1949 Liberation penny 15 15
173. 11p. Obverse and reverse of 1966 crown .. 40 35
174. 13p. Obverse and reverse of 1972 Silver Wedding £2 45 50

60. Sir William Weston and "Santa Anna", 1530.

1977. Centenary of St. John Ambulance. Multicoloured.

175. 5p. Type **60** 10 10
176. 7p. Sir William Drogo and ambulance, 1877 15 15
177. 11p. Duke of Connaught and ambulance, 1917 40 35
178. 13p. Duke of Gloucester and stretcher-team, 1977 45 50

61. Arrival of Queen Victoria, 1846.

1977. 125th Anniv. of Victoria College. Mult.

179. 7p. Type **61** 20 20
180. 10½p. Victoria College, 1852 25 20
181. 11p. Sir Galahad Statue, 1924 (vert.) 30 35
182. 13p. College Hall (vert.) .. 35 35

62. Harry Vardon Statuette and Map of Course.

1978. Cent. Royal Jersey Golf Club. Mult.

183. 6p. Type **62** 15 15
184. 8p. Vardon grip and swing 20 20
185. 11p. Vardon putt 35 35
186. 13p. "The Complete Golfer" and British and U.S.A. Open Golf Trophies 40 40

63. Mont Orgueil Castle.

1978. Europa. Castles from Paintings by Thomas Phillips. Multicoloured.

187. 6p. Type **63** 20 20
188. 8p. St. Aubin's Fort .. 40 40
189. 10½p. Elizabeth Castle .. 50 50

64. "Gaspe Basin" (P. J. Ouless).

1978. Links with Canada. Multicoloured.

90. 6p. Type **64** 15 15
91. 8p. Map of Gaspe Peninsula 20 20
92. 10½p. "Century" (brigantine) 25 25
93. 11p. Early map of Jersey 40 30
94. 13 p. St. Aubin's Bay town and harbour 45 35

65. Queen Elizabeth and Prince Philip.

1978. 25th Anniversary of Coronation.

195. **65.** 8p. silver, black and red 30 30
196. – 25p. silver, black & blue 70 70

DESIGN: 25p. Hallmarks of 1953 and 1977.

66. Mail Cutter, 1778–1827.

1978. Bicent. of England–Jersey Government Mail Packet Service.

197. **66.** 6p. black, brown & yell. 15 15
198. – 8p. black, grn. & yell. 20 20
199. – 10½p. blk., ultram. & bl. 30 30
200. – 11p. black, purple & lilac 45 35
201. – 13p. black, red and pink 55 45

DESIGNS—SHIPS. 8p. "Flamer", 1831–7. 10½p. "Diana", 1877–90. 11p. "Ibex", 1891–1925. 13p. "Caesarea", 1960–75.

67. Jersey Calf.

1979. 9th International Conference of World Jersey Cattle Bureau. Multicoloured.

202. 6p. Type **67** 20 20
203. 25p. "Ansom Designette" (calf presented to the Queen, 1978) (45 × 30 mm.). 80 80

68. Jersey Pillar Box, c. 1860.

1979. Europa. Multicoloured.

204. 8p. Type **68** 20 25
205. 8p. Clearing modern post box 20 25
206. 10½p. Telephone switchboard, c. 1900 .. .. 25 30
207. 10½p. Modern SPC. telephone system 25 30

69. Percival "Mew Gull".

1979. 25th International Air Rally. Mult.

208. 6p. Type **69** 15 15
209. 8p. De Havilland "Chipmunk" 20 20
210. 10½p. Druine "Turbulent" 30 30
211. 11p. De Havilland "Tiger Moth" 45 35
212. 13p. North American "Harvard" Mk. 4 .. 50 40

70. "My First Sermon".

1979. International Year of the Child, and 150th Birth Anniversary of Sir John Millais (painter). Paintings. Multicoloured.

213. 8p. Type **70** 25 25
214. 10½p. "Orphans" 30 30
215. 11p. "The Princes in the Tower" 40 30
216. 25p. "Christ in the House of his Parents" (50 × 32 mm.) 65 55

1979. Wildlife Preservation Trust (3rd series). As T **34**. Multicoloured.

217. 6p. Pink pigeon (vert.) .. 15 15
218. 8p. Orang-utan (vert.) .. 20 20
219. 11½p. Waldrapp ibis .. 40 35
220. 13p. Gorilla (vert.) .. 45 35
221. 15p. Rodriguez flying fox (vert.) 60 35

71. Plan of Mont Orgueil.

1980. Jersey Fortresses. Drawings by Thomas Phillips. Multicoloured.

222. 8p. Type **71** 25 25
223. 11½p. Plan of La Tour de St. Aubin 30 30
224. 13p. Plan of Elizabeth Castle 45 45
225. 25p. Map of Jersey (38 × 27 mm.) 80 80

72. Sir Walter Raleigh and Paul Ivy (engineer) discussing Elizabeth Castle.

1980. Europa. Links with Britain. Multicoloured.

226. 9p. } Type **72** 20 20
227. 9p. } .. 20 20
228. 13½p. Charles II presenting deeds of Smith's island, Virginia to Sir George Carteret 40 35
229. 13½p. Lady Carteret, maid and Jean Chevalier .. 40 35

Nos. 226/7 and Nos. 228/9 were issued together, se-tenant, forming composite designs.

73. Planting.

1980. Centenary of Jersey Royal Potato. Multicoloured.

230. 7p. Type **73** 15 15
231. 15p. Digging 45 35
232. 17½p. Weighbridge .. 65 60

74. Three Lap Event.

1980. 60th Anniv. of Jersey Motor Cycle and Light Car Club. Multicoloured.

233. 7p. Type **74** 25 25
234. 9p. Jersey International Road Race 25 25
235. 13½p. Scrambling 40 40
236. 15p. Sand racing (saloon cars) 45 45
237. 17½p. National Hill Climb 50 50

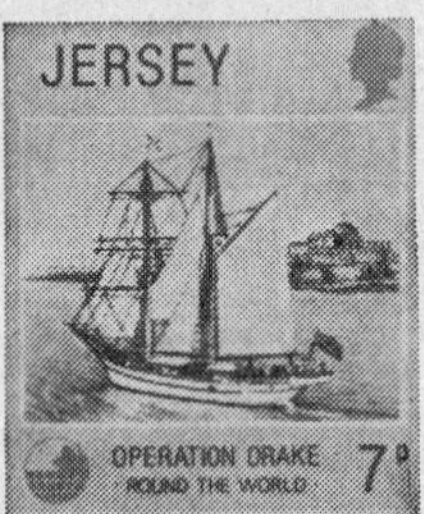

75. "Eye of the Wind".

1980. "Operation Drake" and 150th Anniv. of Royal Geographical Society. (14p.). Multicoloured.

238. 7p. Type **75** 20 20
239. 9p. Inflatable raft .. 25 25
240. 13½p. Shooting rapids .. 35 35
241. 14p. "Discovery" .. 45 35
242. 15p. Aerial walkway .. 45 35
243. 17½p. Goodyear airship "Europa" 55 45

76. Detail of "The Death of Major Peirson".

1981. Bicentenary of Battle of Jersey. Details of J. S. Copley's painting.

244. **76.** 7p. multicoloured .. 25 25
245. – 10p. multicoloured .. 30 30
246. – 15p. multicoloured .. 50 50
247. – 17½p. multicoloured .. 65 65

77. De Bagot. **78a.** "Queen Elizabeth II" (Norman Hepple).

1981. Crests of Jersey Families.

249 **77** ½p. blk, silver & grn 10 10
250 – 1p. multicoloured .. 10 10
251 – 2p. multicoloured .. 10 10
252 – 3p. multicoloured .. 10 10
253a – 4p. silver, blk & mve 10 10
254 – 5p. multicoloured .. 15 15
255 – 6p. multicoloured .. 20 20
256 – 7p. multicoloured .. 20 20
257 – 8p. multicoloured .. 25 25
258 – 9p. multicoloured .. 30 30
259b – 10p. multicoloured .. 20 25
260 – 11p. multicoloured .. 35 35
261a – 12p. multicoloured .. 20 25
262a – 13p. multicoloured .. 25 30
263a – 14p. multicoloured .. 25 30
264a – 15p. multicoloured .. 25 30
265 – 16p. multicoloured .. 30 35
266 – 17p. multicoloured .. 50 50
266a – 18p. multicoloured .. 55 55
266b – 19p. multicoloured .. 60 60
267 – 20p. blk, silver & yell 60 60
268 – 25p. black and blue 45 50
268a **77** 26p. blk, silver & red 45 50
269a – 30p. multicoloured .. 50 55
270a – 40p. multicoloured .. 1·00 1·00
271a – 50p. multicoloured .. 1·25 1·25
272 – 75p. multicoloured .. 2·00 1·75
273 – £1 multicoloured .. 3·00 3·00
274 **78a** £5 multicoloured .. 10·00 10·50

DESIGNS—VERT. (as T **77**). 1p. De Carteret. 2p. La Cloche. 3p. Dumaresq. 4p. Payn. 5p. Jancrin. 6p. Poingdestre. 7p. Pipon. 8p. Marett. 9p. Le Breton. 10p. Le Maistre. 11p. Bisson. 12p. Robin. 13p. Herault. 14p. Messervy. 15p. Fiott. 16p. Malet. 17p. Mabon. 18p. De St. Martin. 19p. Hamptonne. 20p. Badier. 25p. L'Arbalestier. 30p. Journeaux. 40p. Lempriere. 50p. D'Auvergne. 75p. Remon. HORIZ. (38 × 22 mm.). £1, Jersey crest and map of The Channel.

79. Knight of Hambye slaying Dragon.

1981. Europa. Folklore. Multicoloured.

275. 10p. Type **79** 25 25
276. 10p. Servant slaying Knight of Hambye and awaiting execution .. 25 25
277. 18p. St. Brelade celebrating Easter on island 50 50
278. 18p. Island revealing itself as a Blue Whale. 50 50

LEGENDS: 10p. (both) Slaying of the Dragon of Lawrence by the Knight of Hambye. 18p. (both) Voyages of St. Brelade.

80. The Harbour by Gaslight.

1981. 150th Anniv. of Gas in Jersey. Mult.

279. 7p. Type **80** 25 25
280. 10p. The Quay 30 30
281. 18p. Royal Square .. 55 45
282. 22p. Market Place .. 65 55
283. 25p. Central Market .. 75 65

81. Prince Charles and Lady Diana Spencer.

1981. Royal Wedding.

284. **81.** 10p. multicoloured .. 55 25
285. 25p. multicoloured .. 1·25 1·25

82. Christmas Tree in Royal Square.

1981. Christmas. Multicoloured.

286.	7p. Type **82**	25	25
287.	10p. East Window, Parish Church, St. Helier ..	40	40
288.	18p. Boxing Day meet of Jersey Drag Hunt ..	60	60

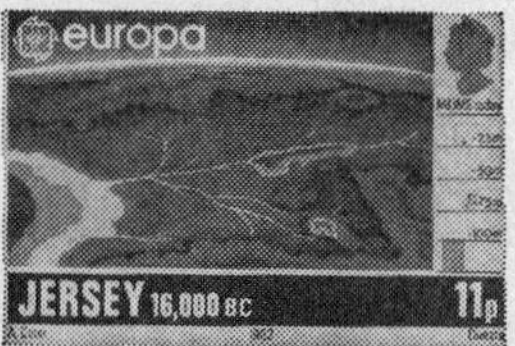

83. Jersey, 16,000 B.C.

1982. Europa. Formation of Jersey. Mult.

289.	11p. Type **83**	30	30
290.	11p. In 10,000 B.C. (vert.)	30	30
291.	19½p. In 7,000 B.C. (vert.)	60	60
292.	19½p. In 4,000 B.C. ..	60	60

84. Rollo, Duke of Normandy, William the Conqueror and " Clameur de Haro " (traditional procedure for obtaining justice).

1982. Links with France. Multicoloured.

293.	8p. Type **84**	25	25
294.	8p. John of England and Philippe Auguste of France, and Siege of Rouen	25	25
295.	11p. Jean Martell (brandy merchant), early still and view of Cognac	35	35
296.	11p. Victor Hugo, " Le Rocher des Proscrits " (rock where he used to meditate) and Marine Terrace	35	35
297.	19½p. Pierre Teilhard de Chardin (philosopher) and " Maison Saint Louis " (science institute) ..	60	60
298.	19½p. Père Charles Rey (scientist), anemotachymeter and The Observatory, St. Louis ..	60	60

85. Sir William Smith, Founder of Boys' Brigade.

1982. Youth Organizations. Mult.

299.	8p. Type **85**	25	25
300.	11p. Boy's Brigade "Old Boys" band, Liberation Parade, 1945 (vert.) ..	35	35
301.	24p. William Smith and Lord Baden-Powell at Royal Albert Hall, 1903	75	75
302.	26p. Lord and Lady Baden-Powell, St. Helier, 1924 (vert.) ..	90	90
303.	29p. Scouts at "Westward Ho" campsite, St. Ouen's Bay	1·10	1·10

Nos. 299/301 commemorate the centenary of the Boys' Brigade and Nos. 302/3 the 75th anniversary of the Boy Scout Movement.

86. H.M.S. "Tamar" and H.M.S. "Dolphin" at Port Egmont.

1983. Jersey Adventurers (1st series). Mult.

304.	8p. Type **86**	25	25
305.	11p. H.M.S. "Dolphin" and H.M.S. "Swallow" off Magellan Strait	35	35
306.	19½p. Discovering Pitcairn Island	60	60
307.	24p. Carteret taking possession of English Cove, New Ireland ..	85	85
308.	26p. H.M.S. "Swallow" sinking a pirate, Macassar Strait	90	90
309.	29p. H.M.S. "Endymion" leading convoy from West Indies	1·00	1·00

See also Nos. 417/21 and 573/8.

87. 1969 5s. Legislative Chamber Definitive.

1983. Europa. Multicoloured.

310.	11 p. Type **87**	50	50
311.	11 p. Royal Mace (23 × 32 mm)	50	50
312.	19½p. 1969 10s. Royal Court definitive showing green border error ..	85	85
313.	19½p. Bailiff's Seal (23 × 32 mm)	85	85

88. Charles Le Geyt and Battle of Minden (1759).

1983. World Communications Year and 250th Birth Anniv. of Charles Le Geyt (1st Jersey postmaster). Multicoloured.

314.	8p. Type **88**	25	25
315.	11p. London to Weymouth mail coach	35	35
316.	24p. P.O. Mail Packet " Chesterfield " attacked by French privateer ..	75	75
317.	26p. Mary Godfray and the Hue Street Post Office ..	90	90
318.	29p. Mail steamer leaving St. Helier harbour ..	1·10	1·10

89. Assembly Emblem.

1983. 13th General Assembly of the A.I.P.L.F. (Association Internationale des Parlementaires de Langue Francaise) Jersey.

319. **89.**	19½p. multicoloured ..	90	90

90. " Cardinal Newman ".

1983. 50th Death Anniv. of Walter Ouless (artist). Multicoloured.

320.	8p. Type **90**	25	25
321.	11p. " Incident in the French Revolution "	45	45
322.	20½p. " Thomas Hardy " ..	85	85
323.	31p. " David with the head of Goliath " (38 × 32 mm)	1·25	1·25

91. Golden Lion Tamarin.

1984. Wildlife Preservation Trust (4th series). Multicoloured.

324.	9p. Type **91**	30	30
325.	12p. Snow leopard ..	40	40
326.	20½p. Jamaican boa ..	65	65
327.	26p. Round island gecko ..	80	80
328.	28p. Coscoroba swan ..	90	90
329.	31p. St. Lucia amazon ..	1·00	1·00

92. C.E.P.T. 25th Anniversary Logo.

1984. Europa.

330. **92.**	9p. light bl., bl. & black	30	30
331.	12p. light grn., grn. & blk.	40	40
332.	20½p. lilac, pur. & black	70	70

94. "Sarah Bloomshoft" at Demie de Pas Light, 1906.

1984. Centenary of Jersey R.N.L.I. Lifeboat Station. Multicoloured.

334.	9p. Type **94**	40	40
335.	9p. "Hearts of Oak" and "Maurice Georges", 1949	40	40
336.	12p. "Elizabeth Rippon" and "Hanna", 1949 ..	50	50
337.	12p. "Elizabeth Rippon" and "Santa Maria", 1951	50	50
338.	20½p. "Elizabeth Rippon" and "Bacchus", 1973 ..	75	75
339.	20½p. "Thomas James King" and "Cythara", 1983	75	75

95. Bristol "Type 170" Freighter.

1984. Jersey Aviation History (2nd series). Multicoloured.

340.	9p. Type **95**	30	30
341.	12p. Airspeed "A.S.57 Ambassador 2"	40	40
342.	26p. De Havilland "D.H.114 Heron 1B" ..	90	90
343.	31p. De Havilland "D.H.89A Dragon Rapide"	1·10	1·10

96. "Robinson Crusoe leaves the Wreck".

1984. Links with Australia. Paintings by John Alexander Gilfillan. Multicoloured.

344.	9p. Type **96**	30	30
345.	12p. "Edinburgh Castle" ..	40	40
346.	20½p. "Maori Village" ..	75	75
347.	26p. "Australian Landscape"	90	90
348.	28p. "Waterhouse's Corner, Adelaide"	1·00	1·00
349.	31p. "Captain Cook at Botany Bay"	1·10	1·10

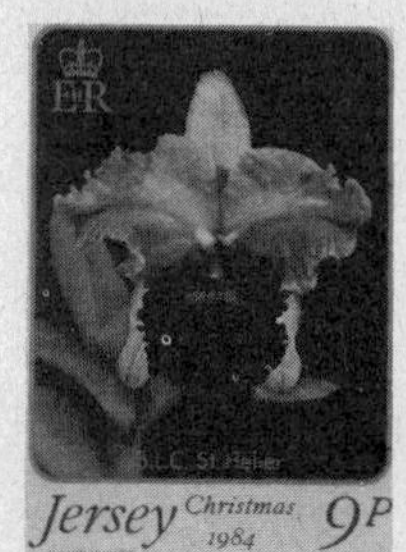

97. "B.L.C. St. Helier" Orchid.

1984. Christmas. Jersey Orchids (1st series). Multicoloured.

350.	9p. Type **97**	45	45
351.	12p. "Oda Mt Bingham" ..	75	75

See also Nos. 433/7 and 613/17.

98. "Hebe off Corbiere, 1874".

1984. Death Centenary of Philip John Ouless (artist). Multicoloured.

352.	9p Type **98**	30	30
353.	12p. "The Gaspe engaging the Diomede"	40	40
354.	22p. "The Paddle-steamer London entering Naples, 1856"	80	80
355.	31p. "The Rambler entering Cape Town, 1840" ..	1·25	1·25
356.	34p. "St. Aubin's Bay from Mount Bingham, 1871"	1·40	1·40

99. John Ireland (composer) and Faldouet Dolmen.

1985. Europa. European Music Year. Mult.

357.	10p. Type **99**	40	45
358.	13p. Ivy St. Helier (actress) and His Majesty's Theatre, London ..	55	60
359.	22p. Claude Debussy (composer) and Elizabeth Castle	90	95

100. Girls Brigade.

1985. International Youth Year. Mult.
60. 10p. Type **100** 30 30
61. 13p. Girl Guides (75th anniversary) 50 50
62. 29p. Prince Charles and Jersey Youth Service Activities Base .. .. 1·00 1·00
63. 31p. Sea Cadet Corps .. 1·00 1·00
64. 34p. Air Training Corps .. 1·10 1·10

101. "Duke of Normandy" at Cheapside.

1985. The Jersey Western Railway. Mult.
65. 10p. Type **101** 50 50
66. 13p. Saddletank at First Tower 60 60
67. 22p. "La Moye" at Millbrook .. .. 1·00 1·00
68. 29p. "St. Heliers" at St. Aubin .. .. .. 1·10 1·10
69. 34p. "St. Aubyns" at Corbiere .. .. .. 1·25 1·25

102. Memorial Window to Revd. James Hemery (former Dean) and St. Helier Parish Church.

1985. 300th Anniversary of Huguenot Immigration. Multicoloured.
70. 10p. Type **102** 30 30
371. 10p. Judge Francis Jeune, Baron St. Helier, and Houses of Parliament .. 30 30
372. 13p. Silverware by Pierre Amiraux 45 45
373. 13p. Francis Voisin (merchant) and Russian port 45 45
374. 22p. Robert Brohier, Schweppes carbonation plant and bottles .. 75 75
375. 22p. George Ingouville, V.C., R.N., and attack on Viborg 75 75

103. Howard Davis Hall, Victoria College.

1985. Thomas Benjamin Davis (philanthropist) Commemoration. Mult.
376. 10p. Type **103** 40 40
377. 13p. Racing schooner "Westward" 60 60
378. 31p. Howard Davis Park, St. Helier .. .. 1·10 1·10
379. 34p. Howard Davis Experimental Farm, Trinity .. 1·25 1·25

104. "Amaryllis belladonna" (Pandora Sellars).

1986. Jersey Lilies. Multicoloured.
380. 13p. Type **104** 50 50
381. 34p. "A Jersey Lily" (Lily Langtry) (Sir John Millais) (30 × 48 mm) .. 1·25 1·25

105. King Harold, William of Normandy and Halley's Comet, 1066 (from Bayeux Tapestry).

1986. Appearance of Halley's Comet. Multicoloured.
383. 10 p. Type **105** 40 40
384. 22p. Lady Carteret, Edmond Halley, map and Comet 85 85
385. 31p. Aspects of communications in 1910 and 1986 on TV screen .. .. 1·25 1·25

106. Dwarf Pansy.

1986. Europa. Environmental Conservation. Multicoloured.
386. 10p. Type **106** 35 35
387. 14p. Sea Stock 65 65
388. 22p. Sand Crocus 95 95

107. Queen Elizabeth II (from photo by Karsh).

1986. 60th Birthday of Queen Elizabeth II.
389. **107.** £1 multicoloured .. 3·00 3·00

108. Le Rat Cottage.

1986. 50th Anniv. of National Trust for Jersey. Multicoloured.
390. 10p. Type **108** 30 30
391. 14p. The Elms (Trust headquarters) 45 45
392. 22p. Morel Farm 80 80
393. 29p. Quetivel Mill .. .. 1·00 1·10
394. 31p. La Vallette .. .. 1·10 1·25

109. Prince Andrew and Miss Sarah Ferguson.

1986. Royal Wedding.
395. **109.** 14p. multicoloured .. 50 50
396. 40p. multicoloured .. 1·50 1·50

110. "Gathering Vraic".

1986. Birth Centenary of Edmund Blampied (artist).
397. **110.** 10p. multicoloured .. 30 30
398. – 14p. blk., bl. & grey .. 50 50
399. – 29p. multicoloured .. 1·00 1·00
400. – 31p. blk., orge. & grey 1·25 1·25
401. – 34p. multicoloured .. 1·40 1·40

DESIGNS: 14p. "Driving Home in the Rain". 29p. "The Miller". 31p. "The Joy Ride". 34p. "Tante Elizabeth".

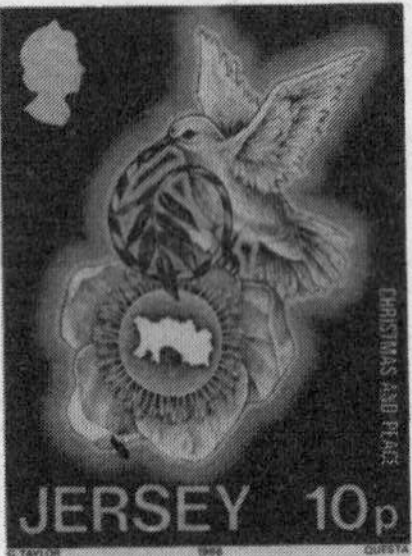

111. Island Map on Jersey Lily, and Dove holding Olive Branch.

1986. Christmas International Peace Year. Multicoloured.
402 10p. Type **111** 40 40
403 14p. Mistletoe wreath encircling European robin and dove .. 60 60
404 34p. Christmas cracker releasing dove .. .. 1·25 1·25

112. "Westward" under Full Sail.

1987. Racing Schooner "Westward". Mult.
405. 10p. Type **112** 40 40
406. 14p. T. B. Davis at the helm 60 60
407. 31p. "Westward" overhauling "Britannia" .. 1·10 1·10
408. 34p. "Westward" fitting-out at St. Helier .. 1·25 1·25

113. De Havilland "DH86" "Belcroute Bay".

1987. 50th Anniv. of Jersey Airport. Multicoloured.
409. 10p. Type **113** 30 30
410. 14p. Boeing "757" and Douglas "DC 9" .. 40 40
411. 22p. Britten Norman "Trislander" and "2A Islander" 70 70
412. 29p. Short "SD330" and Vickers "Viscount 800" 1·00 1·10
413. 31p. BAC "1–11" and HPR 7 "Dart Herald" .. 1·25 1·40

114. St. Mary and St. Peter's Roman Catholic Church.

1987. Europa. Modern Architecture. Mult.
414. 11p. Type **114** 35 35
415. 15p. Villa Devereux, St. Brelade 65 65
416. 22p. Fort Regent Leisure Centre, St. Helier (57 × 29 mm.) 90 90

115. H.M.S. "Racehorse" and H.M.S. "Carcass" (bomb ketches) trapped in Arctic.

1987. Jersey Adventurers (2nd series). Philippe D'Auvergne. Multicoloured.
417. 11p. Type **115** 40 40
418. 15p. H.M.S. "Alarm" on fire, Rhode Island .. 50 50
419. 29p. H.M.S. "Arethusa" wrecked off Ushant .. 90 90
420. 31p. H.M.S. "Rattlesnake" stranded on Isle de Trinidad .. .. 1·10 1·10
421. 34p. Mont Orgueil Castle and fishing boats .. 1·25 1·25

See also Nos. 501/6 and 539/44.

116. Grant of Lands to Normandy, 911 and 933.

1987. 900th Death Anniv. of William the Conqueror. Multicoloured.
422. 11p. Type **116** 40 40
423. 15p. Edward the Confessor and Duke Robert I of Normandy landing on Jersey, 1030 .. .. 45 45
424. 22p. King William's coronation, 1066, and fatal fall, 1087 .. .. 70 70
425. 29p. Death of William Rufus, 1100, and Battle of Tinchebrai, 1106 .. 85 85
426. 31p. Civil war between Matilda and Stephen, 1135–41 .. .. 95 95
427. 34p. Henry inherits Normandy, 1151; John asserts ducal rights in Jersey, 1213 .. .. 1·10 1·10

117. "Grosnez Castle".

1987. Christmas. Paintings by John Le Capelain. Multicoloured.

428. 11p. Type **117** 40 40
429. 15p. "St. Aubin's Bay" .. 60 60
430. 22p. "Mont Orgueil Castle" 80 80
431. 31p. "Town Fort and Harbour, St. Helier" .. 1·10 1·10
432. 34p. "The Hermitage" .. 1·25 1·25

118. "Cymbidium pontac".

1988. Jersey Orchids (2nd series). Mult.

433. 11p. Type **118** 40 40
434. 15p. "Odontioda" "Eric Young" (vert.) 50 50
435. 29p. "Lycaste auburn" "Seaford" and "Ditchling" 90 90
436. 31p. "Odontoglossum" "St. Brelade" (vert.) .. 1·10 1·10
437. 34p. "Cymbidium mavourneen" "Jester" .. .. 1·25 1·25

119. Labrador Retriever.

1988. Centenary of Jersey Dog Club. Mult.

438. 11p. Type **119** 40 40
439. 15p. Wire-haired dachshund 60 60
440. 22p. Pekingese 80 80
441. 31p. Cavalier King Charles spaniel .. .. .. 1·10 1·10
442. 34p. Dalmatian .. .. 1·25 1·25

120. D.H. "Dash 7" Aircraft, London Landmarks and Jersey Control Tower.

1988. Europa. Transport and Communications. Multicoloured.

443. 16p. Type **120** 50 50
444. 16p. Weather radar and Jersey airport landing system (vert.) 50 50
445. 22p. Hydrofoil, St. Malo and Elizabeth Castle, St. Helier 90 90
446. 22p. Port control tower and Jersey Radio maritime communication centre, La Moye (vert.) 90 90

121 Rodriguez Fody

1988. Wildlife Preservation Trust (5th series). Multicoloured.

447 12p. Type **121** 50 50
448 16p. Volcano rabbit (horiz) 60 60
449 29p. White-faced marmoset 1·00 1·00
450 31p. Ploughshare tortoise (horiz) .. .. .. 1·10 1·10
451 34p. Mauritius kestrel .. 1·25 1·25

122 Rain Forest Leaf Frog, Costa Rica

1988. Operation Raleigh. Multicoloured.

452 12p. Type **122** 45 45
453 16p. Archaelogical survey, Peru 55 55
454 22p. Climbing glacier, Chile 70 70
455 29p. Red Cross Centre, Solomon Islands .. 90 80
456 31p. Underwater exploration, Australia .. 1·10 85
457 34p. "Zebu" (brigantine) returning to St. Helier 1·40 1·10

123 St. Clement Parish Church

1988. Christmas. Jersey Parish Churches (1st series). Multicoloured.

458 12p. Type **123** 35 35
459 16p. St. Ouen 60 60
460 31p. St. Brelade .. .. 1·00 1·00
461 34p. St. Lawrence .. .. 1·10 1·10

See also Nos. 535/8 and 597/600.

124 Talbot "Type 4 CT Tourer", 1912

1989. Vintage Cars (1st series). Multicoloured.

462 12p. Type **124** 40 40
463 16p. De Dion "Bouton Type 1-D", 1920 .. 50 50
464 23p. Austin 7 "Chummy", 1926 .. .. .. 65 65
465 30p. Ford "Model T", 1926 90 90
466 32p. Bentley 8 litre, 1930 .. 1·10 1·10
467 35p. Cadillac "452A-V16 Fleetwood Sports Phaeton", 1931 .. 1·40 1·40

See also Nos. 591/6.

125 Belcroute Bay

1989. Jersey Scenes. As T **125** and Queen's portrait as T **107**. Multicoloured.

468 1p. Type **125** 10 10
469 2p. High Street, St. Aubin 10 10
470 4p. Royal Jersey Golf Course 10 10
471 5p. Portelet Bay 10 10
472 10p. Les Charrieres D'Anneport 20 25
473 13p. St. Helier Marina .. 25 30
474 14p. Sand yacht racing, St. Ouen's Bay 30 35
475 15p. Rozel Harbour .. 30 35
476 16p. St. Aubin's Harbour 30 35
477 17p. Jersey Airport .. 35 40
478 18p. Corbiere Lighthouse 35 40
479 19p. Val de la Mare .. 40 45
480 20p. Elizabeth Castle .. 40 45
481 21p. Greve de Lecq .. 40 45
482 22p. Samares Manor .. 45 50
483 23p. Bonne Nuit Harbour 45 50
484 24p. Grosnez Castle .. 50 55
485 25p. Augres Manor .. 50 55
486 26p. Central Market .. 50 55
487 27p. St. Brelade's Bay .. 55 60
488 30p. St. Ouen's Manor .. 60 65
489 40p. La Hougue Bie .. 80 85
490 50p. Mont Orgueil Castle 1·00 1·10
491 75p. Royal Square, St. Helier .. .. .. 1·50 1·60
491b £2 Type **107** .. .. 4·00 4·25

126 Agile Frog

1989. Endangered Jersey Fauna. Mult.

492 13p. Type **126** 40 40
493 13p. "Heteropterus morpheus" (butterfly) (vert) 40 40
494 17p. Barn owl (vert) .. 65 65
495 17p. Green lizard 65 65

127 Toddlers' Toys

1989. Europa. Children's Toys and Games. Designs showing clay plaques. Mult.

496 17p. Type **127** 50 50
497 17p. Playground games .. 50 50
498 23p. Party games .. 90 90
499 23p. Teenage sports .. 90 90

128 Queen Elizabeth II and Royal Yacht "Britannia" in Elizabeth Harbour

1989. Royal Visit.

500 **128** £1 multicoloured .. 2·00 2·10

129 Philippe D' Auvergne presented to Louis XVI, 1786

1989. Bicentenary of the French Revolution. Philippe D' Auvergne. Multicoloured.

501 13p. Type **129** 35 35
502 17p. Storming the Bastille, 1789 .. .. .. 55 45
503 23p. Marie de Bouillon and revolutionaries,1790 .. 65 55
504 30p. Auvergne's headquarters at Mont Orgueil, 1795 .. .. 1·10 1·00
505 32p. Landing arms for Chouan rebels, 1796 .. 1·10 1·00
506 35p. The last Chouan revolt, 1799 .. .. 1·25 1·10

See also Nos. 539/44.

130 "St. Helier" off Elizabeth Castle

1989. Centenary of Great Western Railway Steamer Service to Channel Islands. Mult.

507 13p. Type **130** 50 50
508 17p. "Caesarea II" off Corbiere Lighthouse .. 60 60
509 27p. "Reindeer" in St. Helier harbour .. .. 1·00 1·00
510 32p. "Ibex" racing "Frederica" off Portelet 1·10 1·10
511 35p. "Lynx" off Noirmont 1·25 1·25

131 "Gorey Harbour"

1989. 150th Birth Anniv of Sarah Louisa Kilpack (artist). Multicoloured.

512 13p. Type **131** 50 50
513 17p. "La Corbiere" .. 60 60
514 23p. "Greve de Lecq" .. 1·00 1·00
515 32p. "Bouley Bay" .. 1·10 1·10
516 35p. "Mont Orgueil" .. 1·25 1·25

132 Head Post Office, Broad Street, 1969

1990. Europa. Post Office Buildings. Mult.

517 18p. Type **132** 50 50
518 18p. Postal Headquarters, Mont Millais, 1990 .. 50 50
519 24p. Hue Street Post Office, 1815 (horiz) .. 85 85
520 24p. Head Post Office, Halkett Place, 1890 (horiz) 85 85

133 "Battle of Flowers" Parade

1990. Festival of Tourism. Multicoloured.

521 18p. Type **133** 60 60
522 24p. Sports 75 75
523 29p. Mont Orgueil Castle and German Underground Hospital Museum 95 95
524 32p. Salon Culinaire .. 1·00 1·00

134 Early Printing Press and Jersey Newspaper Mastheads

1990. International Literacy Year. Jersey News Media. Multicoloured.

526 14p. Type **134** 55 55
527 18p. Modern press, and offices of "Jersey Evening Post" in 1890 and 1990 .. .. 60 60
528 34p. Radio Jersey broadcaster .. .. .. 1·10 1·10
529 37p. Channel Television studio cameraman .. 1·10 1·10

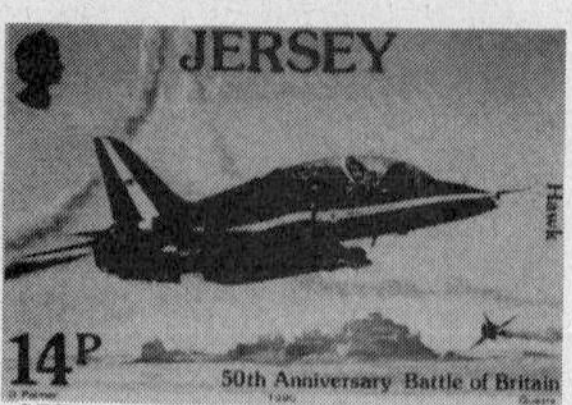

135 BAe Hawk

1990. 50th Anniv of Battle of Britain. Mult.

530 14p. Type **135** 45 45
531 18p. Supermarine Spitfire 50 50
532 24p. Hawker Hurricane .. 75 75
533 34p. Vickers Wellington .. 1·25 1·25
534 37p. Avro Lancaster .. 1·25 1·25

1990. Christmas. Jersey Parish Churches (2nd series). As T **123**. Multicoloured.

535 14p. St. Helier 40 40
536 18p. Grouville 60 60
537 34p. St. Saviour .. .. 1·10 1·10
538 37p. St. John .. .. 1·25 1·25

1991. 175th Death Anniv of Philippe d'Auvergne. As T **129**. Multicoloured.

539 15p. Prince's Tower, La Hougue Bie 50 50
540 20p. Auvergne's arrest in Paris 65 65
541 26p. Auvergne plotting against Napoleon .. 80 85
542 31p. Execution of George Cadoudal .. .. 1·00 1·00
543 37p. H.M.S. "Surly" (cutter) attacking French convoy .. 1·25 1·25
544 44p. Auvergne's last days in London .. .. 1·40 1·40

136 "Landsat 5" and Thematic Mapper Image over Jersey

1991. Europa. Europe in Space. Mult.

545 20p. Type **136** 55 55
546 20p. "ERS-1" earth resources remote sensing satellite 55 55
547 26p. "Meteosat" weather satellite 85 85
548 26p. "Olympus" direct broadcasting satellite .. 85 85

137 1941 1d. Stamp (50th anniv of first Jersey postage stamp)

1991. Anniversaries. Multicoloured.

549 15p. Type **137** 40 40
550 20p. Steam train (centenary of Jersey Eastern Railway extension to Gorey Pier) 50 50
551 26p. Jersey cow and Herd Book (125th anniv of Jersey Herd Book) .. 70 70
552 31p. Stone-laying ceremony (from painting by P. J. Ouless) (150th anniv of Victoria Harbour) .. 80 80
553 53p. Marie Bartlett and hospital (250th anniv of Marie Bartlett's hospital bequest) .. .. 1·50 1·50

138 "Melitaea cinxia"

1991. Butterflies and Moths. Multicoloured.

554 15p. Type **138** 50 40
555 20p. "Euplagia quadripunctaria" 70 80
556 37p. "Deilephilia porcellus" 1·25 1·25
557 57p. "Inachis io" .. 1·75 1·75

139 Drilling for Water, Ethiopia

1991. Overseas Aid. Multicoloured.

558 15p. Type **139** 50 40
559 20p. Building construction, Rwanda 65 65
560 26p. Village polytechnic, Kenya 80 85
561 31p. Treating leprosy, Tanzania .. .. 1·00 1·00
562 37p. Ploughing, Zambia .. 1·25 1·25
563 44p. Immunisation clinic, Lesotho .. .. 1·40 1·40

140 "This is the Place for Me"

1991. Christmas. Illustrations by Edmund Blampied for J.M. Barrie's "Peter Pan". Multicoloured.

564 15p. Type **140** 40 40
565 20p. "The Island Come True" 65 65
566 37p. "The Never Bird" .. 1·25 1·25
567 53p. "The Great White Father" .. .. 1·60 1·60

141 Pied Wagtail

1992. Winter Birds. Multicoloured.

568 16p. Type **141** 45 45
569 22p. Firecrest 60 60
570 28p. Common snipe .. 70 70
571 39p. Lapwing .. .. 1·00 1·00
572 57p. Fieldfare .. .. 1·50 1·50

See also Nos. 635/9.

142 Shipping at Shanghai, 1860

1992. Jersey Adventurers (3rd series). 150th Birth Anniv of William Mesny. Mult.

573 16p. Type **142** 50 50
574 16p. Mesny's junk running Taiping blockade, 1862 50 50
575 22p. General Mesny outside river gate, 1874 .. 75 75
576 22p. Mesny in Burma, 1877 75 75
577 33p. Mesny and Governor Chang, 1882 .. .. 1·00 1·00
578 33 p. Mesny in mandarin's sedan chair, 1886 .. 1·00 1·00

143 "Tickler" (brigantine)

1992. Jersey Shipbuilding. Multicoloured.

579 16p. Type **143** 50 50
580 22p. "Hebe" (brig) .. 70 70
581 50p. "Gemini" (barque) .. 1·50 1·50
582 57p. "Percy Douglas" (full-rigged ship) .. .. 1·75 1·75

144 John Bertram (ship owner) and Columbus

1992. Europa. 500th Anniv of Discovery of America by Columbus. Multicoloured.

584 22p. Type **144** 70 70
585 28p. Sir George Carteret (founder of New Jersey) 85 85
586 39p. Sir Walter Ralegh (founder of Virginia) .. 1·25 1·25

145 "Snow Leopards" (Allison Griffiths)

1992. Batik Designs. Multicoloured.

587 16p. Type **145** 50 50
588 22p. "Three Elements" (Nataly Miorin) .. 70 70
589 39p. "Three Men in a Tub" (Amanda Crocker) .. 1·25 1·25
590 57p. "Cockatoos" (Michelle Millard) .. .. 1·75 1·75

1992. Vintage Cars (2nd series). As T **124**. Multicoloured.

591 16p. Morris Cowley "Bullnose", 1925 .. 35 35
592 22p. Rolls Royce "20/25", 1932 .. .. .. 50 50
593 28p. Chenard and Walcker "T5", 1924 .. .. 70 70
594 33p. Packard 900 series "Light Eight", 1932 .. 80 80
595 39p. Lanchester "21", 1927 90 90
596 50p. Buick "30 Roadster", 1913 .. .. .. 1·25 1·25

1992. Christmas. Jersey Parish Churches (3rd series). As T **123**. Multicoloured.

597 16p. Trinity 40 35
598 22p. St. Mary 55 60
599 39p. St. Martin .. .. 1·00 1·00
600 57p. St. Peter .. .. 1·40 1·40

146 Farmhouse

1993. Multicoloured.

601 (–) Type **146** 35 40
602 (–) Trinity Church .. 35 40
603 (–) Daffodils and cows .. 35 40
604 (–) Jersey cows 35 40
605 (–) Sunbathing 50 55
606 (–) Windsurfing 50 55
607 (–) Crab (Queen's head at left) 50 55
608 (–) Crab (Queen's head at right) 50 55
609 (–) "Singin' in the Rain" float 60 65
610 (–) "Dragon Dance" float 60 65
611 (–) "Bali, Morning of the World" float 60 65
612 (–) "Zulu Fantasy" float 60 65

The above do not show face values, but are inscribed "BAILIWICK POSTAGE PAID" (Nos. 601/4), "U.K. MINIMUM POSTAGE PAID" (Nos. 605/8) or "EUROPE POSTAGE PAID" (Nos. 609/12). They were initially sold at 17p., 23p. or 28p., but it is intended that these face values will be increased to reflect postage rate changes in the future.

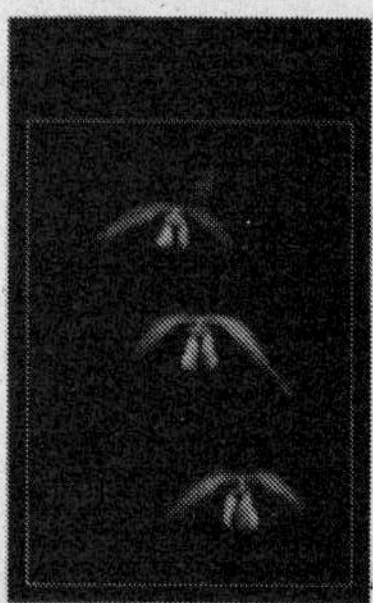

147 "Phragmipedium Eric Young" "Jersey"

1993. Jersey Orchids (3rd series). Mult.

613 17p. Type **147** 35 40
614 23p. "Odontoglossum Augres" "Trinity" .. 45 50
615 28p. "Miltonia Saint Helier" "Colomberie" .. 55 60
616 39p. "Phragmipedium pearcei" 80 85
617 57p. "Calanthe Grouville" "Grey" .. .. 1·10 1·25

148 Douglas Dakota

1993. 75th Anniv of Royal Air Force. Mult.

618 17p. Type **148** 35 40
619 23p. Wight Seaplane .. 45 50
620 28p. Avro Shackleton AEW2 .. .. .. 55 60
621 33p. Gloster Meteor and D.H. Vampire 65 70
622 39p. BAe Harrier GR1A .. 80 85
623 57p. Panavia Tornado F3 1·10 1·25

Nos. 618/23 also commemorate the 50th anniv of the Royal Air Force Association and the 40th anniv of the first air display on Jersey.

149 "Jersey's Opera House" (Ian Rolls)

1993. Europa. Contemporary Art. Mult.

625 23p. Type **149** 45 50
626 28p. "The Ham and Tomato Bap" (Jonathan Hubbard) 55 60
627 39p. "Vase of Flowers" (Neil MacKenzie) .. 80 85

150 1943 ½d. Occupation Stamp

1993. 50th Anniv of Edmund Blampied's Occupation Stamps. Designs showing stamps from the 1943 issue.

628 **150** 17p. green, lt grn & blk 35 40
629 – 23p. red, pink & black 45 50
630 – 28p. brown, cinnamon and black .. 55 60
631 – 33p. orge, salmon & blk 65 70
632 – 39p. blue, cobalt & blk 80 85
633 – 50p mve, lt mve & blk 1·00 1·10

DESIGNS: 23p. 1d. value; 28p. 1½d. value; 33p. 2d. value; 39p. 2½d. value; 50p. 3d. value.

151 Queen Elizabeth II (from painting by Marca McGregor)

1993. 40th Anniv of Coronation.

634 **151** £1 multicoloured .. 2·00 2·10

152 Short-toed Treecreeper

1993. Summer Birds. Multicoloured.

635 17p. Type **152** 35 40
636 23p. Dartford warbler .. 45 50
637 28p. Common wheatear .. 55 60
638 39p. Cirl bunting 80 85
639 57p. Jay .. .. .. 1·10 1·25

INDEX
Countries can be quickly located by referring to the index at the end of this volume.

153 Two Angels holding "Hark the Herald Angels Sing" Banner

1993. Christmas. Stained Glass Windows by Henry Bosdet from St. Aubin on the Hill Church. Multicoloured.

640 17p. Type **153** 35 40
641 23p. Two angels playing harps 45 50
642 39p. Two angels playing violins 80 85
643 57p. Two angels holding "Once in Royal David's City" banner .. .. 1·10 1·25

154 "Coprinus comatus"

1994. Fungi. Multicoloured.

644 18p. Type **154** 35 40
645 23p. "Amanita muscaria" 45 50
646 30p. "Cantharellus cibarius" 60 65
647 41p. "Macrolepiota procera" 80 85
648 60p. "Clathrus ruber" .. 1·25 1·40

156 Maine Coon

1994. 21st Anniv of Jersey Cat Club. Mult.

650 18p. Type **156** 35 40
651 23p. British shorthair (horiz) 45 50
652 35p. Persian 70 75
653 41p. Siamese (horiz) .. 80 85
654 60p. Non-pedigree .. 1·25 1·40

157 Mammoth Hunt, La Cotte de St. Brelade

1994. Europa. Archaeological Discoveries. Multicoloured.

655 23p. Type **157** 45 50
656 23p. Stone Age hunters pulling mammoth into cave 45 50
657 30p. Chambered passage, La Hougue Bie .. 60 65
658 30p. Transporting stones 60 65

POSTAGE DUE STAMPS

D 1.

D **3.** Arms of St. Clement and Dovecote at Samares.

1969.

D 1. D **1.** 1d. violet .. .. 2·50 1·90
D 2. 2d. sepia .. .. 3·50 2·00
D 3. 3d. mauve .. .. 5·00 3·25
D 4. – 1s. green .. .. 13·00 8·50
D 5. – 2s. 6d. grey .. .. 25·00 22·00
D 6. – 5s. red .. .. .. 35·00 40·00

DESIGNS: 1s., 2s. 6d. and 5s. Map.

1971. Decimal Currency. Design as Nos. D 4/6, but values in new currency.

D 7. ½p. black 10 10
D 8. 1p. blue 10 10
D 9. 2p. brown 10 10
D 10. 3p. purple 10 10
D 11. 4p. red 10 10
D 12. 5p. green 15 15
D 13. 6p. orange 15 15
D 14. 7p. yellow 15 15
D 15. 8p. blue 25 25
D 16. 10p. green 35 35
D 17. 11p. brown 35 40
D 18. 14p. violet 40 45
D 19. 25p. green 80 90
D 20. 50p. purple .. .. 1·40 1·50

1978. Parish Arms and Views.

D 21. D **3.** 1p. black and green .. 10 10
D 22. – 2p. black and yellow 10 10
D 23. – 3p. black and brown 10 10
D 24. – 4p. black and red .. 15 15
D 25. – 5p. black and blue .. 15 20
D 26. – 10p. black and olive .. 25 30
D 27. – 12p. black and blue .. 30 35
D 28. – 14p. black and orange 30 40
D 29. – 15p. black and mauve 35 40
D 30. – 20p. black and green 45 50
D 31. – 50p. black and brown 1·25 1·40
D 32. – £1 black and blue .. 2·50 2·50

DESIGNS: 2p. Arms of St. Lawrence and Handois Reservoir. 3p. Arms of St. John and Sorel Point. 4p. Arms of St. Ouen and Pinnacle Rock. 5p. Arms of St. Peter and Quetivel Mill. 10p. Arms of St. Martin and St. Catherine's Breakwater. 12p. Arms of St. Helier and Harbour. 14p. Arms of St. Saviour and Highlands College. 15p. Arms of St. Brelade and Beauport Bay. 20p. Arms of Grouville and La Hougue Bie. 50p. Arms of St. Mary and Perry Farm. £1, Arms of Trinity and Bouley Bay.

D **4.** St. Brelade.

1982. Jersey Harbours.

D 33. D **4.** 1p. green 10 10
D 34. – 2p. yellow 10 10
D 35. – 3p. brown 10 10
D 36. – 4p. red 10 10
D 37. – 5p. blue 10 10
D 38. – 6p. green 10 15
D 39. – 7p. mauve 15 20
D 40. – 8p. red 15 20
D 41. – 9p. green 20 45
D 42. – 10p. blue 20 25
D 43. – 20p. green 40 45
D 44. – 30p. purple 60 65
D 45. – 40p. orange 80 85
D 46. – £1 violet .. .. 2·00 2·10

DESIGNS: 2p. St. Aubin. 3p. Rozel. 4p. Greve de Lecq. 5p. Bouley Bay. 6p. St. Catherine. 7p. Gorey. 8p. Bonne Nuit. 9p. La Roque. 10p. St. Helier. 20p. Ronez. 30p. La Collette. 40p. Elizabeth Castle. £1, Upper Harbour Marina.

JHALAWAR

A State of Rajasthan, India. Now uses Indian stamps.

4 paisa = 1 anna.

1. Apsara (dancing nymph of Hindu Paradise).

1886. Imperf.

1 **1** 1 p. green .. .. .. 1·50 5·50
2 – ¼ a. green .. .. 60 1·25

The ¼ a. is larger and has a different frame.

JIND

A "convention" state of the Punjab, India, which now uses Indian stamps.

12 pies = 1 anna; 16 annas = 1 rupee.

J **1.** (½ a.)

J **6.** (¼ a.)

1874. Imperf.

J 8 J **1.** ½ a. blue .. .. 30 2·00
J 9 1 a. purple .. .. 1·25 4·50
J 3 2 a. bistre .. .. 1·00 2·50
J 11 4 a. green .. .. 1·00 6·00
J 12 8 a. purple .. .. 7·00 10·00

1882. Various designs and sizes. Imperf or perf.

J15 J **6** ¼ a. brown .. .. 30 1·25
J17 ½ a. bistre 60 70
J20 1 a. brown .. .. 1·50 3·00
J22 2 a. blue .. .. 1·00 1·00
J23 4 a. green 80 90
J25 8 a. red .. .. 3·25 3·75

Stamps of India (Queen Victoria) overprinted.

1885. Optd. **JHIND STATE** vert. (curved).

1 **23** ½ a. turquoise .. .. 65 1·40
2 – 1 a. purple .. .. 12·00 17·00
3 – 2 a. blue .. .. 4·25 7·50
4 – 4 a. green (No. 71) .. 28·00 40·00
5 – 8 a. mauve £275
6 – 1 r. grey (No.101) .. £200

1885. Optd. **JEEND STATE.**

7 **23** ½ a. turquiose .. .. 48·00
8 – 1 a. purple .. .. 48·00
9 – 23 a. blue .. .. 65·00
10 – 4 a. green (No. 71) .. 80·00
11 – 8 a. mauve .. .. 85·00
12 – 1 r. grey (No. 101) .. 95·00

1886. Optd. **JHIND STATE** horiz.

17 **23** ½ a. turquiose 10 10
18 – 1 a. purple 20 15
20 – 1½ a. brown .. .. 50 1·40
21 – 2 a. blue 50 40
23 – 3 a. orange 45 45
15 – 4 a. green (No. 71) .. 26·00
24 – 4 a. green (No. 96) .. 1·10 1·00
27 – 6 a. brown .. .. 50 3·25
28 – 8 a. mauve .. .. 1·60 6·50
30 – 12 a. purple on red .. 1·75 8·50
31 – 1 r. grey (No. 101) .. 6·00 25·00
32 **37** 1 r. green and red .. 5·00 25·00
33 **38** 2 r. red and orange .. £170 £400
34 3 r. brown and green .. £275 £450
35 5 r. blue and violet .. £325 £500

1900. Optd. **JHIND STATE** horiz.

36. **40.** 3 p. red 35 95
37. 3 p. grey .. .. .. 10 1·25
38. **23.** ½ a. green .. .. 1·25 2·25
40. – 1 a. red .. .. .. 15 2·75

Stamps of India optd. **JHIND STATE.**

1903. King Edward VII.

41 **41.** 3 p. grey 10 10
43 – ½ a. green (No. 122) .. 15 70
44 – 1 a. red (No. 123) .. 75 75
46 – 2 a. lilac 45 55
47 – 2½ a. blue .. .. 30 3·50
48 – 3 a. orange 35 35
50 – 4 a. olive .. .. .. 2·00 3·75
51 – 6 a. bistre .. .. 2·50 7·50
52 – 8 a. mauve .. .. 1·60 7·50
54 – 12 a. purple on red .. 1·50 6·00
55 – 1 r. green and red .. 1·75 6·50

1907. King Edward VII (inscr. "INDIA POSTAGE and REVENUE").

56. ½ a. green (No. 149) .. 10 20
57. 1 a. red (No. 150) .. 15 50

1913. King George V.

58. **55.** 3 p. grey .. .. .. 10 1·25
59. **56.** ½ a. green 10 60
60. **57.** 1 a. red 10 35
61. **59.** 2 a. lilac .. .. .. 15 2·25
62. **62.** 3 a. orange .. .. 1·50 6·50
63. **64.** 6 a. bistre .. .. 3·25 14·00

1914. Stamps of India (King George V) optd. **JIND STATE** in two lines.
64. **55.** 3 p. grey .. 20 20
65. **56.** ½ a. green 50 15
66. **57.** 1 a. red 25 15
80. 1 a. brown 1·00 50
67. **58.** 1½ a. brown (A. No. 163) 45 1·75
68. 1½ a. brown (B. No. 165) 35 1·50
81. 1½ a. red (B.) 20 1·50
69. **59.** 2 a. lilac .. 40 45
70. **61.** 2½ a. blue 35 2·75
82. 2½ a. orange 30 3·75
71. **62.** 3 a. orange 35 1·50
83. 3 a. blue .. 50 3·25
72. **63.** 4 a. olive .. 45 2·10
73. **64.** 6 a. brown 60 4·50
74. **65.** 8 a. mauve 1·00 2·75
75. **66.** 12 a. red .. 75 4·50
76. **67.** 1 r. brown and green .. 3·00 6·00
77. 2 r. red and orange .. 4·00 38·00
78. 5 r. blue and violet .. 25·00 £110

1922. No. 192 of India optd. **JIND.**
79. **57.** 9 p. on 1 a. red .. 1·50 10·00

Stamps of India optd. **JIND STATE** in one line.

1927. King George V.
84. **55.** 3 p. grey 10 10
85. **56.** ½ a. green 10 30
86. **80.** 9 p. green 20 40
87. **57.** 1 a. brown 10 10
88. **82.** 1¼ a. mauve 20 30
89. **58.** 1½ a. red 30 1·00
90. **70.** 2 a. lilac 30 30
91. **61.** 2½ a. orange 35 3·75
92. **62.** 3 a. blue 50 3·50
93. **83.** 3½ a. blue 40 6·00
94. **71.** 4 a. green 45 80
95. **64.** 6 a. bistre 45 7·00
96. **65.** 8 a. mauve 65 1·90
97. **66.** 12 a. red 1·10 7·50
98. **67.** 1 r. brown and green .. 90 2·00
99. 2 r. red and orange .. 8·00 45·00
100. 5 r. blue and violet .. 8·00 19·00
101. 10 r. green and red .. 10·00 18·00
102. 15 r. blue and olive .. 50·00 £200
103. 25 r. orange and blue .. 80·00 £300

1934. King George V.
104. **79.** ½ a. green 15 15
105. **81.** 1 a. brown 20 15
106. **59.** 2 a. orange 35 45
107. **62.** 3 a. red .. 40 40
108. **63.** 4 a. olive 50 70

1937. King George VI.
109. **91.** 3 p. slate 2·50 75
110. ½ a. brown 50 1·60
111. 9 p. green 50 1·50
112. 1 a. red .. 40 35
113. **92.** 2 a. red .. 1·40 7·50
114. – 2½ a. violet 80 8·00
115. – 3 a. green 2·50 7·00
116. – 3½ a. blue 95 8·00
117. – 4 a. brown 3·25 8·00
118. – 6 a. green 1·10 9·50
119. – 8 a. violet 2·00 11·00
120. – 12 a. red 1·75 11·00
121. **93.** 1 r. slate and brown .. 11·00 16·00
122. 2 r. purple and brown .. 15·00 45·00
123. 5 r. green and blue .. 30·00 40·00
124. 10 r. purple and red .. 55·00 55·00
125. 15 r. brown and green .. £180 £475
126. 25 r. slate and purple .. £300 £500

1941. Stamps of India (King George VI) optd. **JIND**

(a) On issue of 1937.
127. **91.** 3 p. slate 6·50 8·00
128. ½ a. brown 1·00 30
129. 9 p. green 6·00 8·00
130. 1 a. red 1·00 2·00
131. **93.** 1 r. slate and brown 7·50 13·00
132. 2 r. purple and brown 13·00 15·00
133. 5 r. green and blue .. 35·00 45·00
134. 10 r. purple and red .. 50·00 50·00
135. 15 r. brown and green £140 £110
136. 25 r. slate and purple £160 £325

(b) On issue of 1940.
137. **100a.** 3 p. slate .. 40 50
138. ½ a. mauve .. 40 60
139. 9 p. green .. 40 1·25
140. 1 a. red .. 55 45
141. **101.** 1 a. 3 yellow-brown 85 2·00
142. 1½ a. violet .. 3·75 2·50
143. 2 a. red .. 1·25 1·50
144. 3 a. violet .. 6·00 1·75
145. 3½ a. blue .. 2·50 3·25
146. **102.** 4 a. brown .. 2·50 1·75
147. 6 a. green .. 3·25 5·00
148. 8 a. violet .. 2·25 5·50
149. 12 a. purple 7·50 6·50

OFFICIAL STAMPS
Postage stamps of Jind optd. **SERVICE.**

1885. Nos. 1/3 (Queen Victoria).
O 1. **23.** ½ a. green 30 30
O 2. – 1 a. purple 30 10
O 3. – 2 a. blue 22·00 27·00

1886. Nos. 17/32 and No. 38 (Q.V.).
O 12. **23.** ½ a. turquoise .. 40 10
O 22. – ½ a. green (No. 38) 40 20
O 14. – 1 a. purple 4·00 15
O 16. – 2 a. blue 45 30
O 17. – 4 a. green (No. 24) 50 35
O 19. – 8 a. mauve 1·60 2·00
O 21. **37.** 1 r. green and red 6·00 20·00

1903. Nos. 42/55 (King Edward VII).
O 24. **41.** 3 p. grey 10 10
O 25. – ½ a. green (No. 43) 1·40 10
O 26. – 1 a. red (No. 44) 60 10
O 28. – 2 a. lilac 20 10
O 29. – 4 a. olive 40 45
O 31. – 8 a. mauve 2·25 1·50
O 32. – 1 r. green and red .. 2·50 2·25

1907. Nos. 56/7 (King Edward VII).
O 33. ½ a. green 15 10
O 34. 1 a. red 25 10

1914. Official stamps of India, Nos. O 75/96 (King George V), optd. **JIND STATE.**
O 35. **55.** 3 p. grey 10 10
O 36. **56.** ½ a. green 10 10
O 37. **57.** 1 a. red 10 10
O 46. 1 a. brown 30 10
O 39. **59.** 2 a. lilac 15 15
O 40. **63.** 4 a. olive 30 15
O 41. **64.** 6 a. bistre 40 2·25
O 42. **65.** 8 a. mauve 30 1·00
O 43. **67.** 1 r. brown and green .. 90 1·50
O 44. 2 r. red and orange .. 6·00 35·00
O 45. 5 r. blue and violet .. 16·00 75·00

Stamps of India optd. **JIND STATE SERVICE.**

1927. King George V.
O 47. **55.** 3 p. grey 10 15
O 48. **56.** ½ a. green 10 60
O 49. **80.** 9 p. green 35 15
O 50. **57.** 1 a. brown 10 10
O 51. **82.** 1¼ a. mauve 15 15
O 52. **70.** 2 a. lilac 15 15
O 64. **59.** 2 a. orange 15 15
O 53. **61.** 2½ a. orange 30 7·00
O 54. **71.** 4 a. green 25 20
O 55. **64.** 6 a. bistre 40 6·50
O 56. **65.** 8 a. mauve 35 1·25
O 57. **66.** 12 a. red 60 5·50
O 58. **67.** 1 r. brown and green .. 1·25 2·50
O 59. 2 r. red and orange .. 13·00 13·00
O 60. 5 r. blue and purple .. 10·00 85·00
O 61. 10 r. green and red .. 20·00 45·00

1934. King George V.
O 62. **79.** ½ a. green 15 10
O 63. **81.** 1 a. brown 15 10
O 65. **63.** 4 a. olive 1·90 30

1937. King George VI.
O 66. **91.** ½ a. brown 45·00 30
O 67. 9 p. green 70 2·75
O 68. 1 a. red 45 30
O 69. **93.** 1 r. slate and brown .. 20·00 30·00
O 70. 2 r. purple and brown 35·00 £120
O 71. 5 r. green and blue .. 80·00 £200
O 72. 10 r. purple and red .. £140 £450

1939. Official stamps of India optd. **JIND.**
O 73. **O20.** 3 p. slate 45 20
O 74. ½ a. brown 2·00 50
O 75. ½ a. purple 50 30
O 76. 9 p. green 2·00 3·75
O 77. 1 a. red 2·25 15
O 78. 1½ a. violet 3·75 50
O 79. 2 a. orange 80 30
O 80. 2½ a. violet 80 3·50
O 81. 4 a. brown 1·40 75
O 82. 8 a. violet 1·75 1·90

1943. Stamps of India (King George VI) optd. **JIND SERVICE.**
O 83. **93.** 1 r. slate and brown .. 18·00 30·00
O 84. 2 r. purple and brown 35·00 80·00
O 85. 5 r. green and blue .. 80·00 £180
O 86. 10 r. purple and red .. £140 £275

JOHORE

A State of the Federation of Malaya incorporated in Malaysia in 1963.

100 cents=1 dollar (Straits or Malayan).

Queen Victoria stamps of Straits Settlements overprinted.

1876. Optd. with Crescent and star.
1. **1.** 2 cents brown .. £6500 £3000

1882. Optd. **JOHORE.**
8 1 2 c. red .. 42·00 55·00

1884. Optd. **JOHOR.**
10 1 2 c. red .. 4·50 4·50

1891. Surch. **JOHOR Two CENTS.**
17 1 2 c. on 24 c. green .. 22·00 35·00

21. Sultan Aboubakar. 24. Sultan Ibrahim

1891.
21 21 1 c. purple 30 50
22 2 c. purple and yellow .. 50 1·50
23 3 c. purple and red 55 50
24 4 c. purple and black .. 2·75 6·50
25 5 c. purple and green .. 7·00 20·00
26 6 c. purple and blue .. 8·00 20·00
27 $1 green and red .. 45·00 95·00

1892. Surch. **3 CENTS** and bar.
28 21 3 c. on 4 c. purple & black 75 50
29 3 c. on 5 c. purple & green 80 2·00
30 3 c. on 6 c. purple & blue .. 1·00 2·00
31 3 c. on $1 green and red .. 9·50 32·00

1896. Sultan's Coronation. Optd. **KEMAHKOTAAN**
32 21 1 c. purple 45 85
33 2 c. purple and yellow .. 45 1·00
34 3 c. purple and red .. 55 1·00
35 4 c. purple and black .. 80 2·25
36 5 c. purple and green .. 5·50 7·50
37 6 c. purple and blue .. 3·25 6·00
38 $1 green and red .. 35·00 65·00

1896.
39 24 1 c. green 70 45
40 2 c. green and blue .. 40 30
41a 3 c. green and purple .. 1·25 50
42 4 c. green and red .. 50 35
43 4 c. yellow and red .. 75 50
44 5 c. green and brown .. 75 1·25
45 6 c. green and yellow .. 80 1·60
46 10 c. green and black .. 7·00 38·00
47 25 c. green and mauve .. 9·00 32·00
48 50 c. green and red .. 12·00 35·00
49 $1 purple and green .. 22·00 55·00
50 $2 purple and red .. 22·00 55·00
51 $3 purple and blue .. 28·00 80·00
52 $4 purple and brown .. 28·00 65·00
53 $5 purple and yellow .. 60·00 90·00

1903. Surch. in figures and words.
54 24 3 c. on 4 c. yellow and red 50 1·10
55 10 c. on 4 c. grn & red (A) 2·50 4·50
59 10 c. on 4 c. grn & red (B) 9·00 30·00
58 10 c. on 4 c. yell & red (B) 22·00 35·00
56 50 c. on $3 purple & blue 20·00 60·00
60 50 c. on $5 purple & yell 50·00 £110
57 $1 on $2 purple and red 48·00 85·00

10 c. on 4 c. Type A, "cents" in small letters. Type B, "CENTS" in capitals.

33. Sultan Sir Ibrahim.

1904.
78 33 1 c. purple and green .. 20 15
89 2 c. purple and orange .. 40 80
63 3 c. purple and black .. 1·00 40
91 4 c. purple and red 55 30
109 5 c. purple and green .. 30 30
66 8 c. purple and blue 2·50 5·00
84 10 c. purple and black 20·00 2·50
116 25 c. purple and green 1·40 1·00
119 50 c. purple and red 2·50 1·40
120 $1 green and mauve 2·00 85
121 $2 green and red 4·75 3·50
122 $3 green and blue 28·00 60·00
73 $4 green and brown 24·00 85·00
124 $5 green and orange 32·00 48·00
125 $10 green and black 48·00 £120
75 $50 green and blue £130 £190
77 $100 green and red £250 £400
128 $500 blue and red £16000

1912. Surch. **3 CENTS** and bars.
88 33 3 c. on 8 c. purple & blue 1·75 3·50

1918.
103 **28.** 1 c. purple and black .. 30 20
89 2 c. purple and green .. 40 80
104 2 c. purple and sepia .. 75 1·60
105 2 c. green 30 30
106 3 c. green 1·50 3·50
107 3 c. purple and sepia 95 1·50
110 6 c. purple and red 40 45
93 10 c. purple and blue 1·50 1·40
112 10 c. purple and yellow 30 25
113 12 c. purple and blue 1·00 1·25
114 12 c. blue 24·00 7·50
115 21 c. purple and orange 2·50 3·00
117 30 c. purple and orange .. 3·25 3·25
118 40 c. purple and brown .. 3·25 4·00

37. Sultan Sir Ibrahim and Sultana. 38. Sultan Sir Ibrahim.

1935.
129 37 8 c. violet and grey .. 1·25 40

1940.
130 38 8 c. black and blue .. 10·00 20

1948. Silver Wedding. As T **10/11** of Aden.
131. 10 c. violet 20 15
132. $5 green 24·00 30·00

39. Sultan Sir Ibrahim.

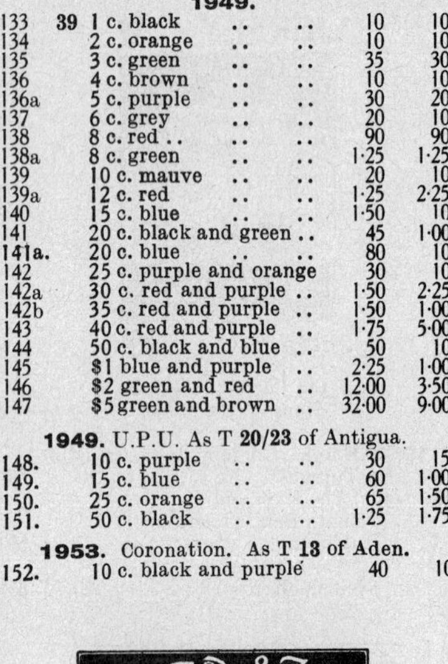

1949.
133 39 1 c. black 10 10
134 2 c. orange 10 10
135 3 c. green 35 30
136 4 c. brown 10 10
136a 5 c. purple 30 20
137 6 c. grey 20 10
138 8 c. red .. 90 90
138a 8 c. green 1·25 1·25
139 10 c. mauve 20 10
139a 12 c. red 1·25 2·25
140 15 c. blue 1·50 10
141 20 c. black and green .. 45 1·00
141a. 20 c. blue 80 10
142 25 c. purple and orange 30 10
142a 30 c. red and purple .. 1·50 2·25
142b 35 c. red and purple .. 1·50 1·00
143 40 c. red and purple .. 1·75 5·00
144 50 c. black and blue 50 10
145 $1 blue and purple 2·25 1·00
146 $2 green and red 12·00 3·50
147 $5 green and brown 32·00 9·00

1949. U.P.U. As T **20/23** of Antigua.
148. 10 c. purple 30 15
149. 15 c. blue 60 1·00
150. 25 c. orange 65 1·50
151. 50 c. black 1·25 1·75

1953. Coronation. As T **13** of Aden.
152. 10 c. black and purple 40 10

40. Sultan Sir Ibrahim.

1955. Diamond Jubilee of Sultan.
153 40 10 c. red 10 10

41. Sultan Sir Ismail and Johore Coat of Arms.

1960. Coronation of Sultan.
154 41 10 c. multicoloured .. 20 20

1960. As Nos. 92/102 of Kedah but with inset portrait of Sultan Sir Ismail.
155. 1 c. black 10 20
156. 2 c. red 10 20
157. 4 c. sepia 10 10
158. 5 c. lake 10 10
159. 8 c. green 1·50 2·00
160. 10 c. purple 20 10
161. 20 c. blue 20 10
162. 50 c. black and blue 20 10
163. $1 blue and purple 1·25 1·50
164. $2 green and red 4·25 6·00
165. $5 brown and green 18·00 19·00

42. "Vanda hookeriana".

1965. Inset portrait of Sultan Ismail. Multicoloured.
166 1 c. Type **42** 10 30
167 2 c. "Arundina graminifolia" 10 35
168 5 c. "Paphiopedilum niveum" 10 10
169 6 c. "Spathoglottis plicata" 30 15
170 10 c. "Arachnis flosaeris" 30 10
171 15 c. "Rhyncostylis retusa" 1·00 10
172 20 c. "Phalaenopsis violacea" 1·50 40

The higher values used in Johore were Nos. 20/7 of Malaysia (National Issues).

44. "Delias ninus".

1971. Butterflies. Inset portrait of Sultan Ismail. Multicoloured.

175	1 c. Type **44**	15	50
176	2 c. "Danaus melanippus"	45	50
177	5 c. "Parthenos sylvia"	65	10
178	6 c. "Papilio demoleus"	65	65
179	10 c. "Hebomoia glaucippe"	65	10
180	15 c. "Precis orithya"	65	10
181	20 c. "Valeria valeria"	80	30

The higher values in use with this issue were Nos. 64/71 of Malaysia (National Issues).

45. "Rafflesia hasseltii" (inset portrait of Sultan Ismail).

1979. Flowers. Multicoloured.

188.	1 c. Type **45**	10	10
189.	2 c. "Pterocarpus indicus"	10	10
190.	5 c. "Lagerstroemia speciosa"	10	10
191.	10 c. "Durio zibethinus"	15	10
192.	15 c. "Hibiscus rosa-sinensis"	15	10
193.	20 c. "Rhododendron scortechinii"	20	10
194.	25 c. "Phaeomeria speciosa"	25	10

46. Coconuts. (Inset portrait of Sultan Mahmood).

1986. Agricultural Products of Malaysia. Multicoloured.

202.	1 c. Coffee	10	10
203.	2 c. Type **46**	10	10
204.	5 c. Cocoa	10	10
205.	10 c. Black pepper	10	10
206.	15 c. Rubber	10	10
207.	20 c. Oil palm	10	10
208.	30 c. Rice	15	20

POSTAGE DUE STAMPS

D 1.

1938.

D 1. D **1.**	1 c. red	9·00	27·00
D 2.	4 c. green	29·00	38·00
D 3.	8 c. orange	38·00	£130
D 4.	10 c. brown	38·00	45·00
D 5.	12 c. purple	45·00	£110

KEDAH

A state of the Federation of Malaya, incorporated in Malaysia in 1963.

100 cents = 1 dollar (Straits or Malayan).

1. Sheaf of Rice. **2.** Malay ploughing.

1912.

1	1	1 c. black and green	30	25
26		1 c. brown	40	20
52		1 c. black	30	10
27		2 c. green	30	20
2		3 c. black and red	2·25	30
19		3 c. purple	65	70
53		3 c. green	1·50	65
3		4 c. red and grey	9·00	25
20		4 c. red	1·50	20
54		4 c. violet	90	10
4		5 c. green and brown	2·00	3·00
55		5 c. yellow	1·50	10
56		6 c. red	70	65
5		8 c. black and blue	1·00	2·00
57		8 c. black	8·50	10
30	2	10 c. blue and sepia	1·25	75
58		12 c. black and blue	2·25	4·00
31		20 c. black and green	2·00	2·00
32		21 c. purple	2·00	11·00
33		25 c. blue and purple	2·25	5·50
34		30 c. black and red	2·75	4·25
59		35 c. purple	5·00	25·00
9		40 c. black and purple	3·50	14·00
36		50 c. brown and blue	1·75	6·50
37	–	$1 black & red on yellow	6·50	7·50
12	–	$2 green and brown	12·00	60·00
39	–	$3 black and blue on blue	30·00	55·00
40	–	$5 black and red	45·00	95·00

DESIGN—As Type **2**: $1 to $5, Council Chamber.

1919. Surch. in words.

24.	50 c. on $2 green and brown	40·00	50·00
25.	$1 on $3 blk. & blue on blue	20·00	75·00

1922. Optd. **MALAYA-BORNEO EXHIBITION.**

45.	**1.**	1 c. brown	2·25	13·00
41.		2 c. green	3·50	16·00
46.		3 c. purple	3·00	28·00
47.		4 c. red	3·00	25·00
48.	**2.**	10 c. blue and sepia	4·50	32·00
42.		21 c. purple	19·00	70·00
43.		25 c. blue and purple	20·00	70·00
44.		50 c. brown and blue	20·00	85·00

6. Sultan Abdul Hamid Halimshah.

1937.

60.	**6.**	10 c. blue and brown	2·00	50
61.		12 c. black and violet	17·00	12·00
62.		25 c. blue and purple	6·50	4·50
63.		30 c. green and red	8·00	9·50
64.		40 c. black and purple	2·50	13·00
65.		50 c. brown and blue	3·75	4·50
66.		$1 black and green	2·75	9·00
67.		$2 green and brown	90·00	75·00
68.		$5 black and red	32·00	75·00

1948. Silver Wedding. As T **10/11** of Aden.

70.	10 c. violet	20	20
71.	$5 red	24·00	32·00

1949. U.P.U. As T **20/23** of Antigua.

72.	10 c. purple	25	20
73.	15 c. blue	50	1·25
74.	25 c. orange	65	1·25
75.	50 c. black	1·25	2·25

7. Sheaf of Rice. **8.** Sultan Tunku Badlishah.

1950.

76	7	1 c. black	10	30
77		2 c. orange	10	15
78		3 c. green	30	1·00
79		4 c. brown	20	10
79ab		5 c. purple	35	30
80		6 c. grey	20	15
81		8 c. red	30	1·75
81a		8 c. green	75	1·75
82		10 c. mauve	20	10
82a		12 c. red	85	2·50
83		15 c. blue	40	35
84		20 c. black and green	40	2·50
84a		20 c. blue	85	10
85	8	25 c. purple and orange	30	30
85a		30 c. red and purple	1·25	1·25
85b		35 c. red and purple	85	1·50
86		40 c. red and purple	1·00	6·00
87		50 c. black and blue	50	10
88		$1 blue and purple	2·50	1·75
89		$2 green and red	18·00	22·00
90		$5 green and brown	38·00	32·00

1953. Coronation. As T **13** of Aden.

91	10 c. black and purple	40	10

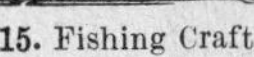

15. Fishing Craft. **20.** Sultan Abdul Halim Mu' Adzam Shah.

1957. Inset portrait of Sultan Tunku Badlishah.

92.	–	1 c. black	10	35
93.	–	2 c. red	10	40
94.	–	4 c. sepia	10	10
95.	–	5 c. lake	10	20
96.	–	8 c. green	2·00	4·00
97.	–	10 c. sepia	20	10
98.	**15.**	20 c. blue	45	45
99.	–	50 c. black and blue	75	1·50
100.	–	$1 blue and purple	2·75	5·50
101.	–	$2 green and red	14·00	13·00
102.	–	$5 brown and green	24·00	24·00

DESIGNS—HORIZ. 1 c. Copra. 2 c. Pineapples. 4 c. Ricefield. 5 c. Masjid Alwi Mosque, Kangar. 8 c. East Coast Railway. $1, Govt. Offices. $2, Bersilat (form of wrestling). $5, Weaving. VERT. 10 c. Tiger. 50 c. Aborigines with blowpipe.

1959. Installation of Sultan.

103.	**20.**	10 c. yellow, brown & blue	10	10

21. Sultan Abdul Halim Mu' Adzam Shah.

1959. As Nos. 92/102 but with inset portrait of Sultan Tuanku Abdul as in T **21.**

104.	1 c. black	10	30
105.	2 c. red	10	30
106.	4 c. sepia	10	10
107.	5 c. lake	10	10
108.	8 c. green	3·50	1·25
109.	10 c. sepia	50	10
109a.	10 c. purple	2·50	10
110.	20 c. blue	20	10
111a.	50 c. black and blue	30	10
112.	$1 blue and purple	1·50	2·25
113.	$2 green and red	7·50	8·50
114a.	$5 brown and green	12·00	11·00

22. "Vanda hookeriana".

1965. Flowers. Multicoloured.

115.	1 c. Type **22**	10	30
116.	2 c. "Arundina graminifolia"	10	30
117.	5 c. "Paphiopedilum niveum"	10	10
118.	6 c. "Spethoglottis plicata"	15	30
119.	10 c. "Arachnis flos-aeris"	30	10
120.	15 c. "Rhyncostylis retusa"	1·00	10
121.	20 c. "Phalaenopsis violacea"	1·40	50

The higher values used in Kedah were Nos. 20/7 of Malaysia.

23. "Danaus melanippus".

1971. Butterflies. Multicoloured.

124	1 c. "Delias ninus"	15	55
125	2 c. Type **23**	35	55
126	5 c. "Parthenos sylvia"	45	10
127	6 c. "Papilio demoleus"	60	70
128	10 c. "Hebomia glaucippe"	45	10
129	15 c. "Precis orithya"	60	10
130	20 c. "Valeria valeria"	1·10	45

The higher values in use with this issue were Nos. 64/71 of Malaysia.

24. "Pterocarpus indicus".

1979. Flowers. Multicoloured.

135	1 c. "Rafflesia hasseltii"	10	10
136	2 c. Type **24**	10	10
137	5 c. "Lagerstroemia speciosa"	10	10
138	10 c. "Durio zibethinus"	15	10
139	15 c. "Hibiscus rosa-sinensis"	15	10
140	20 c. "Rhododendron scortechinii"	20	10
141	25 c. "Etlingera elatior" (inscr "Phaeomeria speciosa")	25	10

25. Sultan Abdul Halim Mu'Adzam Shah.

1983. Silver Jubilee of Sultan's Installation Multicoloured.

142.	20 c. Type **25**	55	30
143.	40 c. Paddy fields (horiz.)	75	60
144.	60 c. Paddy fields and Mount Jerai (horiz.)	1·00	2·00

26. Cocoa.

1986. Agro-based products of Malaysia. Multicoloured.

152.	1 c. Coffee	10	10
153.	2 c. Coconuts	10	10
154.	5 c. Type **26**	10	10
155.	10 c. Black pepper	10	10
156.	15 c. Rubber	10	10
157.	20 c. Oil palm	10	10
158.	30 c. Rice	15	20

KELANTAN

A state in the Federation of Malaya, incorporated in Malaysia in 1963.

100 cents = 1 dollar (Straits or Malayan).

1.

3. Sultan Ismail.

1911.

No.	Type	Description	Mint	Used
1a	1	1 c. green	1·50	30
15		1 c. black	50	50
16		2 c. brown	3·75	3·50
16a		2 c. green	90	40
2		3 c. red	1·75	15
16b		3 c. brown	2·50	1·50
17		4 c. black and red	60	10
18		5 c. green & red on yell	60	10
19		6 c. purple	2·50	2·00
19a		6 c. red	4·00	5·50
5		8 c. blue	5·00	1·00
20		10 c. black and mauve	2·00	10
21		30 c. purple and red	4·00	5·50
8		50 c. black and orange	5·50	2·50
9		$1 green	45·00	48·00
9a		$1 green and brown	27·00	2·00
10		$2 green and red	1·00	4·00
11		$5 green and blue	4·00	7·50
12		$25 green and orange	38·00	75·00

1922. Optd. **MALAYA BORNEO EXHIBITION.**

No.	Type	Description	Mint	Used
37	1	1 c. green	2·50	30·00
30		4 c. black and red	2·75	35·00
31		5 c. green & red on yellow	4·50	35·00
38		10 c. black and mauve	4·75	48·00
32		30 c. purple and red	4·50	55·00
33		50 c. black and orange	7·50	60·00
34		$1 green and brown	20·00	80·00
35		$2 green and red	45·00	£150
36		$5 green and blue	£130	£300

1928.

No.	Type	Description	Mint	Used
40.	3.	1 c. olive and yellow	30	45
41.		2 c. green	2·00	10
42.		4 c. red	4·50	55
43.		5 c. brown	4·50	10
44.		6 c. red	8·50	2·25
45.		8 c. olive	4·50	10
46.		10 c. purple	18·00	2·75
47.		12 c. blue	2·25	3·00
48.		25 c. red and purple	4·50	3·50
49.		30 c. violet and red	35·00	16·00
50.		40 c. orange and green	7·50	19·00
51.		50 c. olive and orange	50·00	7·50
39.		$1 blue	7·50	60·00
52.		$1 violet and green	38·00	12·00
53.		$2 red	£150	£180
54.		$5 red	£250	£425

All except No. 39 are larger than T **3.**

1948. Silver Wedding. As T **10/11** of Aden.

No.	Description	Mint	Used
55.	10 c. violet	60	1·25
56.	$5 red	23·00	48·00

1949. U.P.U. As T **20/23** of Antigua.

No.	Description	Mint	Used
57.	10 c. purple	25	30
58.	15 c. blue	50	90
59.	25 c. orange	60	2·25
60.	50 c. black	1·25	2·25

5. Sultan Tenkgu Ibrahim.

1951.

No.	Type	Description	Mint	Used
61	5.	1 c. black	10	30
62b		2 c. orange	30	30
63		3 c. green	2·25	1·25
64		4 c. brown	15	15
65a		5 c. purple	45	40
66		6 c. grey	20	20
67		8 c. red	45	3·00
68		8 c. green	75	1·75
69		10 c. mauve	20	10
70		12 c. red	75	2·25
71		15 c. blue	1·75	60
72		20 c. black and green	45	5·00
73		20 c. blue	80	25
74		25 c. purple and orange	55	55
75		30 c. red and purple	1·25	1·75
76		35 c. red and purple	90	1·50
77		40 c. red and purple	2·50	8·50
78		50 c. black and blue	70	40
79		$1 blue and purple	4·00	3·50
80		$2 green and red	15·00	20·00
81		$5 green and brown	45·00	40·00

1953. Coronation. As T **13** of Aden.

No.	Description	Mint	Used
82	10 c. black and purple	40	30

1957. As Nos. 92/102 of Kedah but inset portrait of Sultan Tengku Ibrahim.

No.	Description	Mint	Used
83	1 c. black	10	30
84	2 c. red	50	40
85	4 c. sepia	10	10
86	5 c. lake	10	10
87	8 c. green	80	2·00
88	10 c. sepia	40	10
89	10 c. purple	4·00	4·00
90	20 c. blue	40	30
91	50 c. black and blue	45	35
92	$1 blue and purple	2·50	1·50
93	$2 green and red	6·00	6·00
94	$5 brown and green	12·00	12·00

6. Sultan Yahya Petra and Crest of Kelantan.

1961. Coronation of the Sultan.

No.	Type	Description	Mint	Used
95.	6.	10 c. multicoloured	40	30

7. Sultan Yahya Petra.

1961. As Nos. 83, etc., but with inset portrait of Sultan Yahya Petra as in T **7.**

No.	Description	Mint	Used
96.	1 c. black	10	55
97.	2 c. red	10	55
98.	4 c. sepia	10	10
99.	5 c. lake	10	10
100.	8 c. green	3·75	4·00
101.	10 c. purple	40	10
102.	20 c. blue	1·00	30

8. Vanda hookeriana".

1965. As Nos. 115/21 of Kedah but with inset portrait of Sultan Yahya Petra as in T **8.**

No.	Type	Description	Mint	Used
103.	8.	1 c. multicoloured	10	30
104.	–	2 c. multicoloured	10	30
105.	–	5 c. multicoloured	15	10
106.	–	6 c. multicoloured	70	70
107.	–	10 c. multicoloured	30	10
108.	–	15 c. multicoloured	1·50	20
109.	–	20 c. multicoloured	1·50	1·25

The higher values used in Kelantan were Nos. 20/7 of Malaysia (National Issues).

9. "Parthenos sylvia".

1971. Butterflies. As Nos. 124/30 of Kedah, but with portrait of Sultan Yahya Petra as in T **9.**

No.	Type	Description	Mint	Used
112.	–	1 c. multicoloured	15	75
113.	–	2 c. multicoloured	35	75
114.	9.	5 c. multicoloured	60	20
115.	–	6 c. multicoloured	60	80
116.	–	10 c. multicoloured	60	10
117.	–	15 c. multicoloured	85	10
118.	–	20 c. multicoloured	1·00	75

The higher values in use with this series were Nos. 64/71 of Malaysia (National Issues).

10. " Lagerstroemia speciosa ".

1979. Flowers. As Nos. 135/41 of Kedah but with portrait of Sutan Yahya Petra as in T **10.**

No.	Description	Mint	Used
123	1 c. "Rafflesia hasseltii"	10	30
124	2 c. "Pterocarpus indicus"	10	30
125	5 c. Type **10**	10	10
126	10 c. "Durio zibethinus"	15	10
127	15 c. "Hibiscus rosa-sinensis"	15	10
128	20 c. "Rhododendron scortechinii"	20	10
129	25 c. "Etlingera elatior" (inscr "Phaeomeria speciosa")	25	30

11. Sultan Tengku Ismail Petra.

1980. Coronation of Sultan Tengku Ismail Petra.

No.	Type	Description	Mint	Used
130.	11.	10 c. multicoloured	30	40
131.		15 c. multicoloured	30	15
132.		50 c. multicoloured	80	1·75

12. Black Pepper.

1986. Agro-based products of Malaysia. Multicoloured.

No.	Description	Mint	Used
140.	1 c. Coffee	10	10
141.	2 c. Coconuts	10	10
142.	5 c. Cocoa	10	10
143.	10 c. Type **12**	10	10
144.	15 c. Rubber	10	10
145.	20 c. Oil palm	10	10
146.	30 c. Rice	15	20

KENYA

Formerly part of Kenya, Uganda and Tanganyika (q.v.). Became Independent in 1963 and a Republic in 1964.

100 cents = 1 shilling.

1. Cattle Ranching.

3. National Assembly.

1963. Independence.

No.	Type	Description	Mint	Used
1.	1.	5 c. multicoloured	10	45
2.	–	10 c. brown	10	10
3.	–	15 c. mauve	75	10
4.	–	20 c. black and green	15	10
5.	–	30 c. black and yellow	15	10
6.	–	40 c. brown and blue	15	20
7.	–	50 c. red, black & green	15	10
8.	–	65 c. turquoise & yellow	55	65
9.	3.	1 s. multicoloured	20	10
10.	–	1 s. 30 brn., blk. and grn.	3·00	10
11.	–	2 s. multicoloured	75	40
12.	–	5 s. brown, blue & green	1·25	40
13.	–	10 s. brown and blue	7·00	2·25
14.	–	20 s. black and red	5·50	5·50

Designs—As Type **1:** 10 c. Wood-carving. 15 c. Heavy industry. 20 c. Timber industry. 30 c. Jomo Kenyatta facing Mt. Kenya. 40 c. Fishing industry. 50 c. Kenya flag. 65 c. Pyrethrum industry. As Type **3**: 1 s. 30, Tourism (Treetops hotel). 2 s. Coffee industry. 5 s. Tea industry. 10 s. Mombasa Port. 20 s. Royal College, Nairobi.

4. Cockerel.

1964. Inaug. of Republic. Multicoloured.

No.	Description	Mint	Used
15.	15 c. Type **4**	20	15
16.	30 c. Pres. Kenyatta	25	10
17.	50 c. African Lion	35	10
18.	1 s. 30 Hartlaub's Turaco	3·00	50
19.	2 s. 50 Nandi Flame	1·50	3·75

5. Thomson's Gazelle.

7. Greater Kudu.

1966.

No.	Type	Description	Mint	Used
20.	5.	5 c. orange, black & sepia	20	20
21.	–	10 c. black and green	10	10
22.	–	15 c. black and orange	10	10
23.	–	20 c. ochre, blk. & blue	10	15
24.	–	30 c. indigo, blue & blk.	20	10
25	–	40 c. black and brown	60	30
26.	–	50 c. black and orange	60	10
27.	–	65 c. black and green	1·25	2·00
28.	–	70 c. black and red	2·50	1·25
29.	7.	1 s. brown, black & blue	30	10
30.	–	1 s. 30 blue, grn. & blk.	3·50	20
31.	–	1 s. 50 blk., brn. and grn.	2·00	2·00
32.	–	2 s. 50 yell., blk. & brn.	3·00	1·25
33.	–	5 s. yell., blk. and green	1·00	70
34.	–	10 s. ochre, blk. and brn.	2·50	2·00
35.	–	20 s. multicoloured	8·00	10·00

Designs—As Type **5**: 10 c. Sable antelope. 15 c. Aardvark ("Ant Bear"). 20 c. Lesser bushbaby. 30 c. Warthog. 40 c. Common Zebra. 50 c. African buffalo. 65 c. Black rhinoceros. 70 c. Ostrich. As Type **7**: 1 s. 30, African elephant. 1 s. 50, Bat-eared fox. 2 s. 50, Cheetah. 5 s. Savanna monkey ("Vervet Monkey") 10 s. Giant ground pangolin. 20 s. Lion.

8. Rose Dawn.

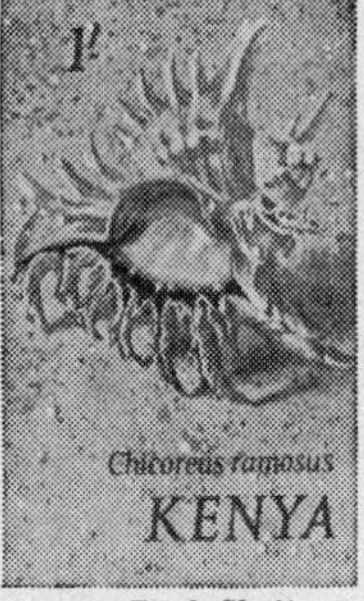

9. Rock Shell.

1971. Seashells. Multicoloured.

36 5 c. Type **8** 10 30
37 10 c. Bishop's Cap 10 10
38 15 c. Strawberry Shell .. 15 10
39 20 c. Black Prince 15 10
40 30 c. Mermaid's Ear .. 20 10
41 40 c. Top Shell 20 10
42 50 c. Violet Shell 30 10
43 50 c. Violet Shell .. .. 8·50 1·75
44 60 c. Cameo 30 55
45 70 c. Pearly Nautilus .. 45 1·50
46 70 c. Pearly Nautilus .. 8·50 4·50
47a 1 s. Type **9** 20 10
48 1 s. 50 Triton 90 10
49 2 s. 50 Neptune's Trumpet 1·00 10
50a 5 s. Turban Shell .. .. 1·00 10
51 10 s. Cloth of Gold .. 3·75 15
52a 20 s. Spider Shell .. .. 3·75 35

INSCRIPTIONS: No.42, "Janthina globosa". No.43, "Janthina janthina". No.45, "Nautilus pompileus". No.46, "Nautilus pompilius".
Nos.47/52 are larger, as Type **9**.

1975. Nos. 48/9 and 52 surch.

53. 2 s. on 1 s. 50 Triton .. 4·50 3·50
54. 3 s. on 2 s. 50 Neptune's Trumpet .. .. .. 9·50 17·00
55. 40 s. on 20 s. Spider Shell .. 6·00 12·00

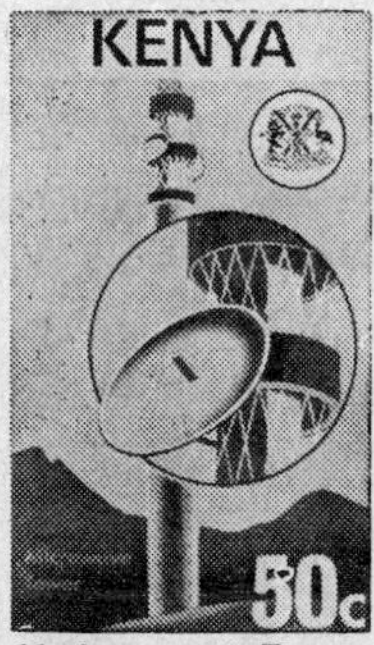

11. Microwave Tower.

1976. Telecommunications Development. Multicoloured.

56. 50 c. Type **11** 10 10
57. 1 s. Cordless switchboard (horiz.) 10 10
58. 2 s. Telephones 20 30
59. 3 s. Message Switching Centre (horiz.) 25 45

12. Akii Bua, Ugandan Hurdler.

1976. Olympic Games, Montreal. Mult.

61. 50 c. Type **12** 10 10
62. 1 s. Filbert Bayi, Tanzanian runner 15 10
63. 2 s. Steve Muchoki, Kenyan boxer 45 35
64. 3s. Olympic flame and East African flags 60 50

13. Diesel Train Tanzania-Zambia Railway.

1976. Railway Transport. Multicoloured.

66. 50 c. Type **13** 35 10
67. 1 s. Nile Bridge, Uganda .. 60 15
68. 2 s. Nakuru Station, Kenya 2·25 1·25
69. 3 s. Class "A" steam locomotive, 1896 .. 2·50 1·75

14. Nile Perch.

1977. Game Fish of East Africa. Mult.

71. 50 c. Type **14** 25 10
72. 1 s. Tilapia 35 10
73. 3 s. Sailfish .. .. 1·75 90
74. 5 s. Black Marlin .. .. 2·25 1·25

15. Maasai Manyatta (Village), Kenya.

1977. Second World Black and African Festival of Arts and Culture, Nigeria. Multicoloured.

76. 50 c. Type **15** 15 10
77. 1 s. "Heatbeat of Africa" (Ugandan dancers) .. 25 10
78. 2 s. Makonde sculpture, Tanzania .. .. 1·25 1·50
79. 3 s. "Early man and technology" (skinning hippopotamus) .. .. .. 1·75 2·00

16. Rally car and Villagers.

1977. 25th Anniv of Safari Rally. Mult.

81. 50 c. Type **16** 20 10
82. 1s. Pres. Kenyatta starting rally 30 10
83. 2s. Car fording river .. 70 1·00
84. 5 s. Car and elephants .. 1·25 1·75

17. Canon Kivebulaya.

1977. Centenary of Ugandan Church. Multicoloured.

86. 50 c. Type **17** 10 10
87. 1 s. Modern Namirembe Cathedral 10 10
88. 2 s. The first Cathedral .. 30 45
89. 5 s. Early congregation, Kigezi 50 85

18. Sagana Royal Lodge, Nyeri, 1952.

1977. Silver Jubilee. Multicoloured.

91. 2 s. Type **18** 20 20
92. 5 s. Treetops Hotel (vert.) 30 45
93. 10 s. Queen Elizabeth and Pres. Kenyatta 50 75
94. 15 s. Royal visit, 1972 .. 70 1·10

19. Pancake Tortoise.

1977. Endangered Species. Multicoloured.

96. 50 c. Type **19** 30 10
97. 1 s. Nile Crocodile .. 40 10
98. 2 s. Hunter's Hartebeest .. 1·40 75
99. 3 s. Red Colobus monkey 1·75 1·00
100. 5 s. Dugong .. .. 2·00 1·50

20. Kenya-Ethiopia Border Point.

1977. Nairobi–Addis Ababa Highway. Mult.

102. 50 c. Type **20** 15 10
103. 1 s. Archer's Post .. 20 10
104. 2 s. Thika Flyover .. 75 60
105. 5 s. Marsabit Game Lodge 1·75 1·50

21. Gypsum.

20. Amethyst.

1977. Multicoloured.

107. 10 c. Type **21** 90 20
108. 20 c. Trona .. .. 1·25 20
109. 30 c. Kyanite .. .. 1·40 20
110. 40 c. Amazonite .. .. 1·40 10
111. 50 c. Galena .. .. 1·40 10
112. 70 c. Silicified wood .. 1·75 30
113. 80 c. Fluorite .. .. 1·75 30
114. 1 s. Type **22** .. .. 1·75 10
115. 1 s. 50 Agate .. .. 1·75 20
116. 2 s. Tourmaline .. .. 1·75 20
117. 3 s. Aquamarine .. .. 1·75 45
118. 5 s. Rhodolite garnet .. 1·75 80
119. 10 s. Sapphire .. .. 2·00 1·75
120. 20 s. Ruby .. .. 5·00 2·75
121. 40 s. Green grossular garnet 13·00 13·00

23. Joe Kadenge (Kenya) and Forwards.

1978. World Cup Football championship, Argentina. Multicoloured.

122. 50 c. Type **23** 10 10
123. 1 s. Mohamed Chuma (Tanzania) and cup presentation 10 10
124. 2 s. Omari Kidevu (Zanzibar) and goalmouth scene 30 60
125. 3 s. Polly Ouma (Uganda) and three forwards .. 40 85

24. Boxing.

1978. Commonwealth Games, Edmonton. Multicoloured.

127. 50 c. Type **24** 15 10
128. 1 s. Welcoming the Olympic Games Team, 1968 .. 20 10
129. 3 c. Javelin throwing .. 60 80
130. 5 s. Pres. Kenyatta admiring boxer's trophy .. 75 1·25

25. " Overloading is Dangerous ".

1978. Road Safety. Multicoloured.

131. 50 c. Type **25** 35 10
132. 1 s. " Speed does not pay " 50 20
133. 1 s. 50 " Ignoring Traffic Signs may cause death " 65 40
134. 2 s. " Slow down at School Crossing " 90 80
135. 3 s. " Never cross a continuous line " .. .. 1·10 1·25
136. 5 s. " Approach Railway Level Crossing with extreme caution " .. 1·75 2·25

26. Pres. Kenyatta at Mass Rally, 1963.

1978. Kenyatta Day. Multicoloured.

137. 50 c. " Harambee Water Project ". 15 10
138. 1 s. Handing over of Independence Instruments, 1963 .. .. .. 25 10
139. 2 s. Type **26** 45 30
140. 3 s. " Harambee, 15 Great Years " 70 55
141. 5 s. " Struggle for Independence, 1952 " 90 80

27. Freedom Fighters, Namibia.

1978. International Anti-Apartheid Year.

142. **27.** 50 c. multicoloured .. 20 10
143. – 1 s. black and blue .. 25 10
144. – 2 s. multicoloured .. 60 30
145. – 3 s. multicoloured .. 80 55
146. – 5 s. multicoloured .. 90 80

DESIGNS: 1 s. International seminar on Apartheid. 2 s. Steve Biko's tombstone. 3 s. Nelson Mandela. 5 s. Bishop Lamont.

28. Children Playing.

1979. International Year of the Child. Multicoloured.

147. 50 c. Type **28** 15 10
148. 2 s. Boy fishing 50 40
149. 3 s. Children singing and dancing 70 60
150. 5 s. Children with camels .. 90 85

29. " The Lion and the Jewel ".

1979. Kenya National Theatre. Multicoloured.

151.	50 c. Type **29**	15	10
152.	1 s. " Utisi "	20	10
153.	2 s. Theatre programmes	35	30
154.	3 s. Kenya National Theatre	50	45
155.	5 s. " Genesis "	90	75

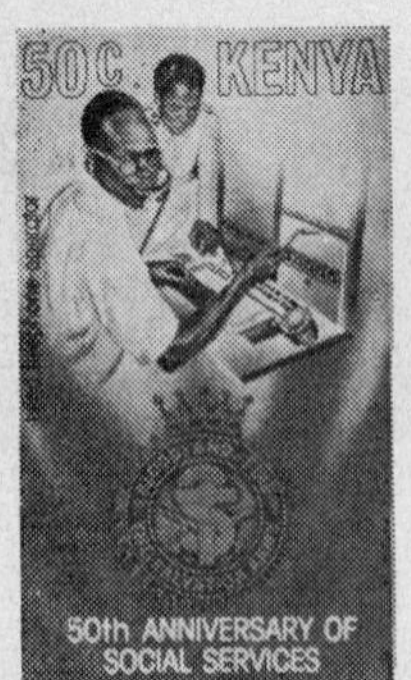

30. Blind Telephone Operator.

1979. 50th Anniv. of Salvation Army Social Services.

156.	50 c. Type **30**	30	10
157.	1 s. Care for the aged	30	10
158.	3 s. Village polytechnic (horiz.)	1·00	90
159.	5 s. Vocational training (horiz.)	1·25	1·40

31. " Father of the Nation " (Kenyatta's funeral procession).

1979. 1st Death Anniv. of President Kenyatta. Multicoloured.

160.	50 c. Type **31**	10	10
162.	1 s. " First president of Kenya " (Kenyatta receiving independence)	15	10
163.	3 s. " Kenyatta the politician " (speaking at rally)	35	45
164.	5 s. " A true son of Kenya " (Kenyatta as a boy carpenter)	60	85

32. British East Africa Company 1890 1a. Stamp.

1979. Death Centenary of Sir Rowland Hill.

164.	**32.**	50 c. multicoloured	15	10
165.	–	1 s. multicoloured	15	10
166.	–	2 s. black, red & brown	30	40
167.	–	5 s. multicoloured	60	1·00

DESIGNS: 1 s. Kenya, Uganda and Tanganyika 1935 1 s. Stamp. 2 s. Penny Black. 5 s. 1964 2 s. 50, Inauguration of Republic commemorative.

33. Roads, Globe and Conference emblem.

1980. I.R.F. African Highway Conference, Nairobi. Multicoloured.

168.	50 c. Type **33**	10	10
169.	1 s. New weighbridge, Athi River	15	10
170.	3 s. New Nyali Bridge, Mombasa	40	75
171.	5 s. Highway to Jomo Kenyatta Int. Airport	70	1·50

34. Mobile Unit in action in Masailand.

1980. Flying Doctor Service. Multicoloured.

172.	50 c. Type **34**	10	10
173.	1 s. Donkey transport to Turkana airstrip (vert.)	15	10
174.	3 s. Surgical team in action at outstation (vert.)	50	90
175.	5 s. Emergency airlift from North Eastern Province	80	1·40

35. Statue of Sir Rowland Hill.

1980. " London 1980 " International Stamp Exhibition.

177.	**35.**	25 s. multicoloured	1·50	2·50

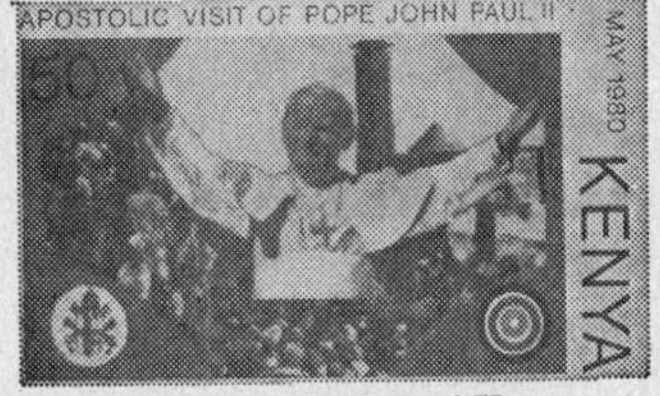

36. Pope John Paul II.

1980. Papal Visit. Multicoloured.

179.	50 c. Type **36**	30	10
180.	1 s. Pope, arms and cathedral (vert.)	40	10
181.	5 s. Pope, flags and dove (vert.)	85	70
182.	10 s. Pope, President Moi and map of Africa	1·40	1·40

37. " Taeniura lymma ".

1980. Marine Life. Multicoloured.

183.	50 c. Type **37**	25	10
184.	2 s. " Amphiprion allardi "	75	60
185.	3 s. " Chromodoris quadricolor "	90	1·00
186.	5 s. " Eretmochelys imbricata "	1·40	2·00

38. National Archives.

1980. Historic Buildings. Multicoloured.

187.	50 c. Type **38**	10	10
188.	1 s. Provincial Commissioner's Office, Nairobi	15	10
189.	1 s. 50 Nairobi House	20	20
190.	2 s. Norfolk Hotel	25	50
191.	3 s. McMillan Library	35	75
192.	5 s. Kipande House	55	1·25

39. " Disabled enjoys Affection ".

1981. International Year for Disabled Persons Multicoloured.

193.	50 c. Type **39**	15	10
194.	1 s. President Moi presenting flag to Disabled Olympic Games team captain	20	10
195.	3 s. Blind people climbing Mount Kenya, 1975	55	55
196.	5 s. Disabled artist at work	85	1·00

40. Longonot Complex.

1981. Satellite Communications. Multicoloured.

197.	50 c. Type **40**	15	10
198.	2 s. " Intelsat V "	50	35
199.	3 s. " Longonot I "	60	55
200.	5 s. " Longonot II "	85	85

41. Kenyatta Conference Centre.

1981. O.A.U. (Organization of African Unity) Summit Conference, Nairobi.

201.	**41.**	50 c. multicoloured	15	10
202.	–	1 s. black, yellow & blue	20	10
203.	–	3 s. multicoloured	40	40
204.	–	5 s. multicoloured	65	65
205.	–	10 s. multicoloured	1·00	1·00

DESIGNS: 1 s. " Panaftel " earth stations. 3 s. Parliament Building. 5 s. Jomo Kenyatta International Airport. 10 s. O.A.U. flag.

42. St. Paul's Cathedral.

1981. Royal Wedding. Multicoloured.

207.	50 c. Prince Charles and President Daniel Arap Moi	10	10
208.	3 s. Type **42**	15	20
209.	5 s. Royal Yacht "Britannia"	25	30
210.	10 s. Prince Charles on safari in Kenya	40	55

MINIMUM PRICE

The minimum price quoted is 10p which represents a handling charge rather than a basis for valuing common stamps. For further notes about prices see introductory pages.

43. Giraffe.

1981. Rare Animals. Multicoloured.

212.	50 c. Type **43**	15	10
213.	2 s. Bongo	35	20
214.	5 s. Roan Antelope	70	55
215.	10 s. Agile Mangabey	1·25	1·75

44. " Technical Development ".

1981. World Food Day. Multicoloured.

216.	50 c. Type **44**	10	10
217.	1 s. " Mwea rice projects "	15	10
218.	2 s. " Irrigation schemes "	30	25
219.	5 s. " Breeding livestock "	60	70

45. Kamba.

1981. Ceremonial Costumes (1st series). Multicoloured.

220.	50 c. Type **45**	30	10
221.	1 s. Turkana	35	10
222.	2 s. Giriama	75	45
223.	3 s. Masai	1·00	75
224.	5 s. Luo	1·40	1·25

See also Nos. 329/33, 413/17 and 515/19.

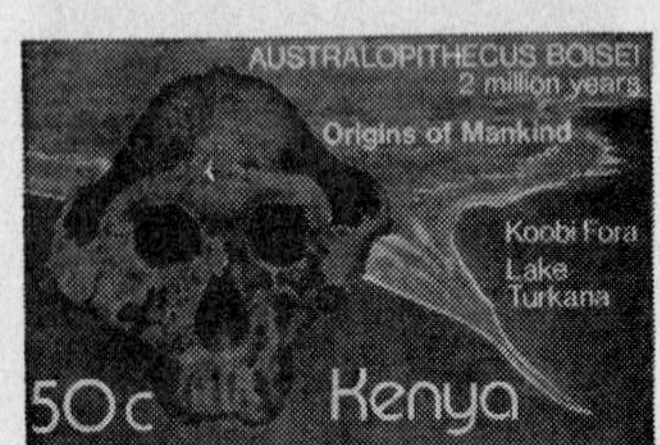

46. " Australopithecus boisei ".

1982. " Origins of Mankind ". Skulls. Multicoloured.

225.	50 c. Type **46**	75	10
226.	2 s. " Homo erectus "	1·75	65
227.	3 s. " Homo habilis "	2·25	1·40
228.	5 s. " Proconsul africanus "	3·00	2·75

47. Tree-planting.

1982. 75th Anniv. of Boy Scout Movement (Nos. 229, 231, 233 and 235) and 60th Anniv. of Girl Guide Movement (Nos. 230, 232, 234 and 236). Multicoloured.

No.	Description	Unused	Used
229	70 c. Type **47**	50	30
230	70 c. Paying homage ..	50	30
231	3 s. 50 "Be Prepared" ..	1·00	1·00
232	3 s. 50 "International Friendship"	1·00	1·00
233	5 s. Helping disabled ..	1·40	1·50
234	5 s. Community service ..	1·40	1·50
235	6 s. Paxtu Cottage (Lord Baden-Powell's home) ..	1·75	2·00
236	6 s. 50 Lady Baden-Powell	1·75	2·00

48. Footballer displaying Shooting Skill.

1982. World Cup Football Championship, Spain. Footballers silhouetted against Map of World. Multicoloured.

No.	Description	Unused	Used
238.	70 c. Type **48**	1·00	40
239.	3 s. 50 Heading	2·00	1·60
240.	5 s. Goalkeeping	2·50	2·50
241.	10 s. Dribbling	4·00	4·50

49. Cattle Judging.

1982. 80th Anniv. of Agricultural Society of Kenya. Multicoloured.

No.	Description	Unused	Used
243.	70 c. Type **49**	65	10
244.	2 s. 50 Farm machinery ..	1·50	1·25
245.	3 s. 50 Musical ride ..	1·75	2·00
246.	6 s. 50 Agricultural Society emblem	2·25	2·75

50. Micro-wave Radio System.

1982. I.T.U. Plenipotentiary Conference, Nairobi. Multicoloured.

No.	Description	Unused	Used
247.	70 c. Type **50**	60	10
248.	3 s. 50 Sea-to-shore service link	1·50	1·50
249.	5 s. Rural telecommunications system ..	2·00	2·50
250.	6 s. 50 I.T.U. emblem ..	2·50	3·00

1982. No. 113 surch.

No.	Description	Unused	Used
251.	70 c. on 80 c. Fluorite ..	70	70

52. Container Cranes.

1983. 5th Anniv. of Kenya Ports Authority. Multicoloured.

No.	Description	Unused	Used
252.	70 c. Type **52**	75	10
253.	2 s. Port by night ..	1·60	1·50
254.	3 s. 50 Container Cranes (different)	2·25	2·50
255.	5 s. Map of Mombasa Port	2·75	3·25

53. Shada Zambarau. **54.** Waridi Kikuba.

1983. Flowers. Multicoloured.

No.	Description	Unused	Used
257	10 c. Type **53**	30	20
258	20 c. Kilua Kingulima ..	45	20
259	30 c. Mwalika Mwiya ..	45	20
260	40 c. Ziyungi Buluu ..	45	20
261	50 c. Kilua Habashia ..	45	20
262	70 c. Chanuo Kato ..	50	20
262a	80 c. As 40 c.	2·75	60
262b	1s. Waridi Kikuba ..	2·75	60
263	1 s. Type **54**	45	20
264	1 s. 50 Mshormoro Mtambazi	1·00	50
265	2 s. Papatuo Boti	1·00	50
266	2 s. 50 Tumba Mboni ..	1·25	50
266a	3 s. Mkuku Mrembo ..	3·50	2·25
267	3 s. 50 Mtongo Mbeja ..	1·50	1·00
267b	4 s. Mnukia Muuma ..	3·50	3·75
268	5 s. Nyungu Chepuo ..	1·50	1·00
268a	7 s. Mlua Miba	4·50	5·00
269	10 s. Muafunili	1·50	2·00
270	20 s. Mbake Nyanza ..	2·25	3·00
271	40 s. Njuga Pagwa ..	4·00	7·00

The 1 s. 50 to 40 s. are in the same format as T **54**.

55. Coffee Plucking.

1983. Commonwealth Day. Multicoloured.

No.	Description	Unused	Used
272.	70 c. Type **55**	10	10
273.	2 s. President Daniel Arap Moi	15	20
274.	5 s. Satellite View of Earth (horiz.)	45	45
275.	10 s. Masai dance (horiz.)	90	1·00

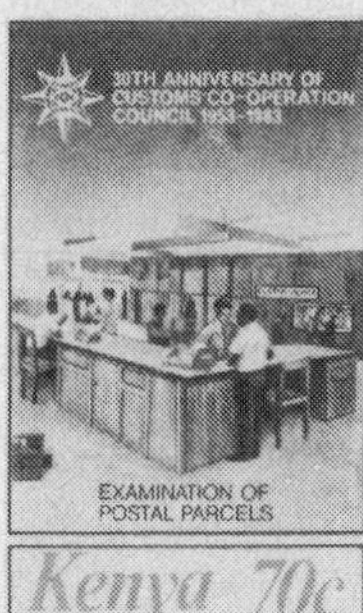

56. Examining Parcels.

1983. 30th Anniv. of Customs Co-operation Council. Multicoloured.

No.	Description	Unused	Used
276.	70 c. Type **56**	25	10
277.	2 s. 50 Customs Headquarters, Mombasa ..	55	30
278.	3 s. 50 Customs Council Headquarters, Brussels	65	40
279.	10 s. Customs patrol boat ..	2·00	2·25

57. Communications via Satellite.

1983. World Communications Year. Multicoloured.

No.	Description	Unused	Used
280.	70 c. Type **57**	60	10
281.	2 s. 50 "Telephone and Postal service"	1·25	1·25
282.	3 s. 50 Communications by sea and air (horiz.) ..	1·60	2·00
283.	5 s. Road and rail communications (horiz.)	2·00	2·75

58. Ships in Kilindini Harbour.

1983. 25th Anniv. of Intergovernmental Maritime Organization. Multicoloured.

No.	Description	Unused	Used
284.	70 c. Type **58**	85	10
285.	2 s. 50 Life-saving devices	1·75	1·25
286.	3 s. 50 Mombasa container terminal	2·25	1·75
287.	10 s. Marine park ..	3·25	4·25

59. President Moi signing Visitors' Book.

1983. 29th Commonwealth Parliamentary Conference. Multicoloured.

No.	Description	Unused	Used
288.	70 c. Type **59**	25	10
289.	2 s. 50 Parliament building, Nairobi (vert.) ..	70	45
290.	5 s. State opening of Parliament (vert.) ..	1·25	80

60. Kenyan and British Flags.

1983. Royal Visit. Multicoloured.

No.	Description	Unused	Used
292.	70 c. Type **60**	50	10
293.	3 s. 50 Sagana State Lodge	1·50	70
294.	5 s. Treetops Hotel ..	2·00	1·25
295.	10 s. Queen Elizabeth II & President Moi	3·00	3·50

61. President Moi.

1983. 20th Anniv. of Independence. Mult.

No.	Description	Unused	Used
297.	70 c. Type **61**	10	10
298.	2 s. President Moi planting tree	20	20
299.	3 s. 50 Kenyan flag & emblem	35	35
300.	5 s. School milk scheme ..	50	50
301.	10 s. People of Kenya ..	1·00	1·10

62. White-backed Night Heron.

1984. Rare Birds of Kenya. Multicoloured.

No.	Description	Unused	Used
303.	70 c. Type **62**	1·00	20
304.	2 s. 50 Quail plover ..	1·75	1·75
305.	3 s. 50 Taita olive thrush	2·00	2·00
306.	5 s. Mufumbiri shrike ..	2·25	2·25
307.	10 s. White-winged apalis	3·00	3·75

63. Radar Tower.

1984. 40th Anniv. of International Civil Aviation Organization. Multicoloured.

No.	Description	Unused	Used
308.	70 c. Type **63**	10	10
309.	2 s. 50 Kenya School of Aviation (horiz.) ..	30	30
310.	3 s. 50 Aircraft taking off from Moi airport (horiz.)	40	45
311.	5 s. Air traffic control centre	55	60

64. Running.

1984. Olympic Games, Los Angeles.

No.	Description	Unused	Used
312.	**64.** 70 c. black, green & deep green ..	30	10
313.	– 2 s. 50 blk., pur. & vio.	55	30
314.	– 5 s. black bl. & dp. bl.	1·40	1·25
315.	– 10 s. blk., yell. & brn.	2·75	3·00

DESIGNS: 2 s. 50 Hurdling. 5 s. Boxing. 10 s. Hockey.

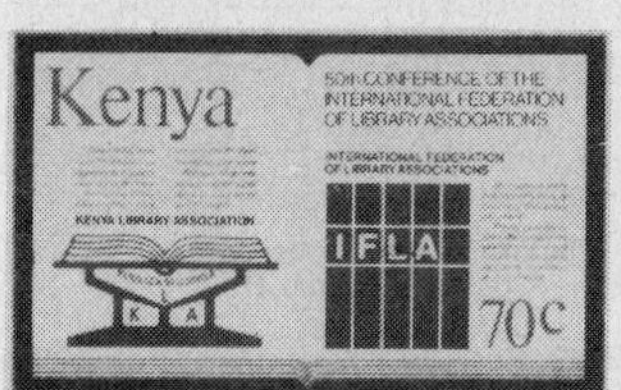

65. Conference and Kenya Library Association Logos.

1984. 50th Conference of the International Federation of Library Associations. Mult.

No.	Description	Unused	Used
317.	70 c. Type **65**	10	10
318.	3 s. 50 Mobile library ..	40	50
319.	5 s. Adult library	55	70
320.	10 s. Children's library ..	1·00	1·50

66. Doves and Cross.

1984. 4th World Conference on Religion and Peace. As T **66**, each design showing a different central symbol. Multicoloured.

321 70 c. Type **66** 30 10
322 2 s. 50 Arabic inscription .. 1·00 1·25
323 3 s. 50 Peace emblem .. 1·40 1·60
324 6 s. 50 Star and Crescent .. 1·75 2·25

67. Export Year Logo.

1984. Kenya Export Year. Multicoloured.

325. 70 c. Type **67** 30 10
326. 3 s. 50 Forklift truck with air cargo (horiz.) .. 1·50 1·50
327. 5 s. Loading ship's cargo .. 2·25 2·25
328. 10 s. Kenyan products (horiz.) .. .. .. 3·25 4·00

1984. Ceremonial Costumes (2nd series). As T **45**. Multicoloured.

329. 70 c. Luhya 55 15
330. 2 s. Kikuyu .. .. 1·25 1·25
331. 3 s. 50 Pokomo .. .. 1·75 1·75
332. 5 s. Nandi .. .. .. 2·00 2·00
333. 10 s. Rendile .. .. 3·00 3·75

68. Staunton Knight and Nyayo National Stadium.

1984. 60th Anniv of International Chess Federation. Multicoloured.

334 70 c. Type **68** .. .. 1·00 20
335 2 s. 50 Staunton rook and Fort Jesus .. .. 1·75 1·25
336 3 s. 50 Staunton bishop and National Monument 2·25 1·75
337 5 s. Staunton queen and Parliament Building .. 2·50 2·25
338 10 s. Staunton king and Nyayo Fountain .. 3·50 4·00

69. Cooking with Wood-burning Stove and Charcoal Fire.

1985. Energy Conservation. Multicoloured.

339. 70 c. Type **69** 20 10
340. 2 s. Solar energy panel on roof 50 60
341. 3 s. 50 Production of gas from cow dung 70 90
342. 10 s. Ploughing with oxen 2·00 3·00

70. Crippled Girl Guide making Table-mat.

1985. 75th Anniv. of Girl Guide Movement. Multicoloured.

344. 1 s. Type **70** 55 15
345. 3 s. Girl Guides doing community service .. 1·25 1·00
346. 5 s. Lady Olave Baden-Powell (founder) .. 2·00 2·00
347. 7 s. Girl Guides gardening 2·75 3·50

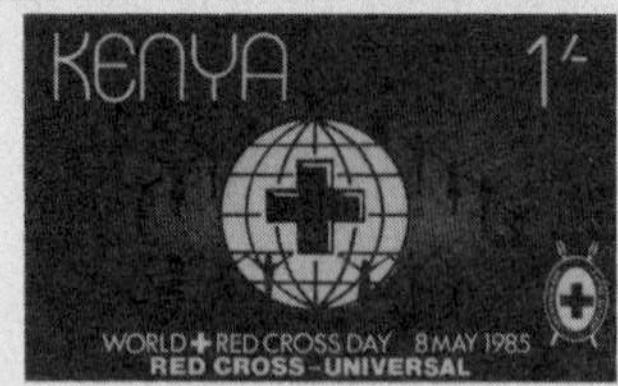

71. Stylised Figures and Globe.

1985. World Red Cross Day.

348. **71.** 1 s. black and red .. 60 15
349. – 4 s. multicoloured .. 2·00 2·00
350. – 5 s. multicoloured .. 2·25 2·25
351. – 7 s. multicoloured .. 2·75 3·25

DESIGNS: 4 s. First Aid team. 5 s. Hearts containing crosses ("Blood Donation"). 7 s. Cornucopia ("Famine Relief").

72. Man with Malaria.

1985. 7th International Congress of Protozoology, Nairobi. Multicoloured.

352 1 s. Type **72** 55 15
353 3 s. Child with Leishmaniasis .. .. 1·90 1·60
354 5 s. Cow with Trypanosomiasis .. 2·50 2·00
355 7 s. Dog with Babesiosis 3·25 3·50

73. Repairing Water Pipes.

1985. United Nations Women's Decade Conference. Multicoloured.

356. 1 s. Type **73** 15 10
357. 3 s. Traditional food preparation 50 50
358. 5 s. Basket-weaving .. 80 70
359. 7 s. Dressmaking .. .. 1·00 90

74. The Last Supper.

1985. 43rd International Eucharistic Congress, Nairobi. Multicoloured.

360. 1 s. Type **74** 45 10
361. 3 s. Village family ("The Eucharist and the Christian Family") .. 1·25 90
362. 5 s. Congress altar, Uhuru Park .. .. 1·50 1·25
363. 7 s. St. Peter Claver's Church, Nairobi .. 2·00 2·25

75. Black Rhinoceros.

1985. Endangered Animals. Multicoloured.

365. 1 s. Type **75** 80 20
366. 3 s. Cheetah .. .. 2·00 1·50
367. 5 s. De Brazza's Monkey .. 2·50 2·25
368. 10 s. Grevy's Zebra .. 3·75 4·00

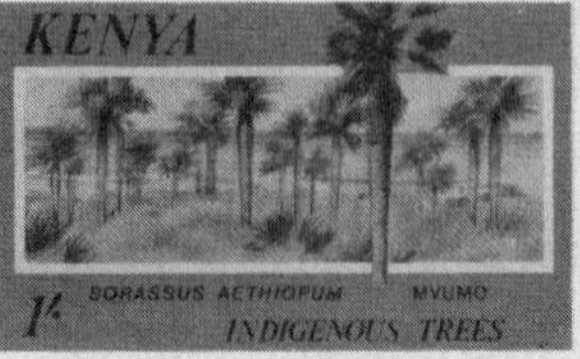

76. "Borassus aethiopum".

1986. Indigenous Trees. Multicoloured.

370 1 s. Type **76** 50 15
371 3 s. "Acacia xanthophloea" 1·60 1·60
372 5 s. "Ficus natalensis" .. 2·50 2·50
373 7 s. "Spathodea nilotica" 3·25 3·50

77. Dove and U.N. Logo (from poster).

1986. International Peace Year. Mult.

375. 1 s. Type **77** 20 10
376. 3 s. U.N. General Assembly (horiz.) .. 55 50
377. 7 s. Nuclear explosion .. 1·25 1·10
378. 10 s. Quotation from Wall of Isaiah, U.N. Building, New York (horiz.) .. 1·75 1·75

78. Dribbling the Ball.

1986. World Cup Football Championship, Mexico. Multicoloured.

379. 1 s. Type **78** 55 15
380. 3 s. Scoring from a penalty 1·25 85
381. 5 s. Tackling .. .. 2·00 1·50
382. 7 s. Cup winners .. .. 2·75 2·50
383. 10 s. Heading the ball .. 3·25 3·25

79. Rural Post Office and Telephone.

1986. "Expo '86" World Fair, Vancouver. Multicoloured.

385. 1 s. Type **79** 50 15
386. 3 s. Container depot, Embakasi .. .. 1·50 1·10
387. 5 s. Aircraft landing at game park airstrip .. 2·00 1·50
388. 7 s. Container ship .. 2·75 2·75
389. 10 s. Transporting produce to market .. .. 3·25 3·50

80. Telephone, Computer and Dish Aerial.

1986. African Telecommunications. Mult.

390. 1 s. Type **80** 30 10
391. 3 s. Telephones of 1876, 1936 and 1986 .. .. 80 60
392. 5 s. Dish aerial, satellite, telephones and map of Africa .. .. 1·00 1·00
393. 7 s. Kenyan manufacture of telecommunications equipment .. .. 1·50 1·75

81. Mashua.

1986. Dhows of Kenya. Multicoloured.

394. 1 s. Type **81** 55 20
395. 3 s. Mtepe .. .. .. 1·50 1·25
396. 5 s. Dau La Mwao .. 2·00 2·00
397. 10 s. Jahazi .. .. 3·25 3·75

82. Nativity.

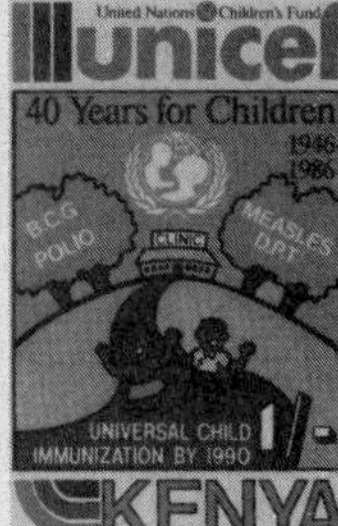

83. Immunization.

1986. Christmas. Multicoloured.

399. 1 s. Type **82** 20 10
400. 3 s. Shepherd and sheep .. 60 45
401. 5 s. Angel and slogan "LOVE PEACE UNITY" (horiz.) .. 1·00 75
402. 7 s. The Magi riding camels (horiz.) .. .. .. 1·25 1·40

1987. 40th Anniv. of U.N.I.C.E.F. Multicoloured.

403. 1 s. Type **83** 20 10
404. 3 s. Food and nutrition .. 60 35
405. 4 s. Oral rehydration therapy 80 45
406. 5 s. Family planning .. 95 60
407. 10 s. Female literacy .. 1·50 1·25

84. Akamba Woodcarvers.

1987. Tourism. Multicoloured.

408. 1 s. Type **84** 30 10
409. 3 s. Tourists on beach .. 1·10 1·00
410. 5 s. Tourist and guide at view point .. .. 1·75 2·00
411. 7 s. Pride of lions .. .. 2·50 3·00

1987. Ceremonial Costumes (3rd series). As T **45**. Multicoloured.

413. 1 s. Embu 15 10
414. 3 s. Kisii 45 45
415. 5 s. Samburu 65 80
416. 7 s. Taita .. .. .. 1·00 1·25
417. 10 s. Boran .. .. .. 1·40 1·75

85. Telecommunications by Satellite.

1987. 10th Anniv. of Kenya Posts and Telecommunications Corporation. Mult.

No.	Description	Unused	Used
418.	1 s. Type **85**	20	15
419.	3 s. Rural post office, Kajiado	40	50
420.	4 s. Awarding trophy, Welfare Sports	50	65
421.	5 s. Village and telephone box	60	75
422.	7 s. Speedpost labels and outline map of Kenya ..	80	1·10

86. Volleyball.

1987. 4th All-Africa Games, Nairobi. Mult.

No.	Description	Unused	Used
424.	1 s. Type **86**	10	10
425.	3 s. Cycling	20	30
426.	4 s. Boxing..	30	40
427.	5 s. Swimming	35	45
428.	7 s. Steeplechasing ..	50	75

87. "Aloe volkensii".

1987. Medicinal Herbs. Multicoloured.

No.	Description	Unused	Used
430.	1 s. Type **87**	20	10
431.	3 s. "Cassia didymobotrya"	65	65
432.	5 s. "Erythrina abyssinica"	1·00	1·00
433.	7 s. "Adenium obesum" ..	1·40	1·50
434.	10 s. Herbalist's clinic ..	1·75	2·00

88. "Epamera sidus". **89.** "Papilio rex".

1988. Butterflies. Multicoloured.

No.	Description	Unused	Used
434a	10 c. "Cyrestis camillus"	10	10
435	20 c. Type **88**	10	10
436	40 c. "Vanessa cardui" ..	15	10
437	50 c. "Colotis evippe" ..	15	10
438	70 c. "Precis western manni"	20	10
439	80 c. "Colias electo" ..	20	10
440	1 s. "Eronia leda" ..	20	10
440a	1 s. 50 "Papilio dardanus"	25	10
441	2 s. Type **89**	25	10
442	2 s. 50 "Colotis phisadia"	25	20
443	3 s. "Papilio desmondi"	30	20
444	3 s. 50 "Papilio demodocus	30	30
445	4 s. "Papilio phorcas" ..	30	30
446	5 s. "Charaxes druceanus"	40	40
447	7 s. "Cymothoe teita" ..	50	50
448	10 s. "Charaxes zoolina"	70	80
449	20 s. "Papilio dardanus"	1·40	1·60
450	40 s. "Charaxes cithaeron"	2·75	3·00

The 10 c. to 1 s. 50 are in the same format as T **88**.

90 Samburu Lodge and Crocodiles

1988. Kenyan Game Lodges. Multicoloured.

No.	Description	Unused	Used
451	1 s. Type **90**	25	10
452	3 s. Naro Moru River Lodge and rock climbing	65	55
453	4 s. Mara Serena Lodge and zebra with foal ..	75	65
454	5 s. Voi Safari Lodge and buffalo	85	80
455	7 s. Kilimanjaro Buffalo Lodge and giraffes ..	1·10	1·25
456	10 s. Meru Mulika Lodge and rhinoceroses ..	1·50	1·75

91 Athletes and Stadium, Commonwealth Games, Brisbane, 1982

1988. "Expo '88" World Fair, Brisbane, and Bicent of Australian Settlement. Mult.

No.	Description	Unused	Used
457	1 s. Type **91**	15	10
458	3 s. Flying Doctor Service aircraft	50	45
459	4 s. H.M.S. "Sirius" (frigate), 1788	55	55
460	5 s. Ostrich and emu ..	70	80
461	7 s. Queen Elizabeth II, Pres. Arap Moi of Kenya and Prime Minister Hawke of Australia ..	90	1·25

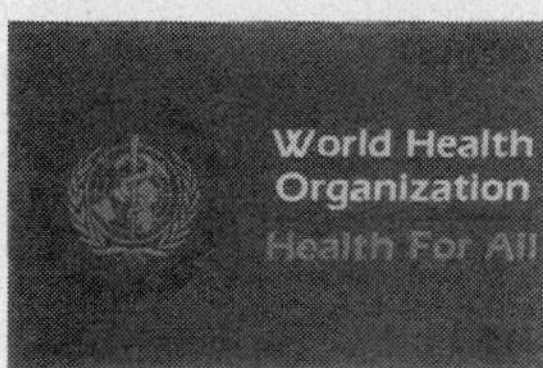

92 W.H.O. Logo and Slogan

1988. 40th Anniv of W.H.O.

No.	Type	Description	Unused	Used
463	**92**	1 s. blue, gold & dp blue	20	10
464	–	3 s. multicoloured ..	70	60
465	–	5 s. multicoloured ..	90	90
466	–	7 s. multicoloured ..	1·40	1·60

DESIGNS: 3 s. Mother with young son and nutritious food; 5 s. Giving oral vaccine to baby; 7 s. Village women drawing clean water from pump.

93 Handball

1988. Olympic Games, Seoul. Multicoloured.

No.	Description	Unused	Used
467	1 s. Type **93**	15	10
468	3 s. Judo	30	30
469	5 s. Weightlifting ..	40	45
470	7 s. Javelin	55	70
471	10 s. Relay racing ..	65	90

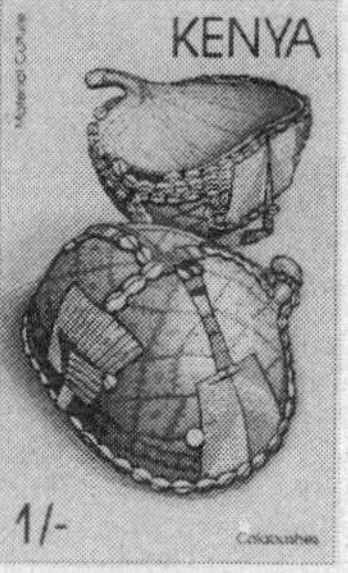

94 Calabashes

1988. Kenyan Material Culture. Mult.

No.	Description	Unused	Used
473	1 s. Type **94**	15	10
474	3 s. Milk gourds	40	40
475	5 s. Cooking pots (horiz) ..	55	55
476	7 s. Winnowing trays (horiz)	75	75
477	10 s. Reed baskets (horiz)	1·00	1·10

95 Pres. Arap Moi taking Oath, 1978

1988. 10th Anniv of "Nyayo" Era. Mult.

No.	Description	Unused	Used
479	1 s. Type **95**	20	10
480	3 s. Building soil conservation barrier ..	70	60
481	3 s. 50 Passengers boarding bus	70	60
482	4 s. Metalwork shop ..	80	80
483	5 s. Moi University, Eldoret	90	90
484	7 s. Aerial view of hospital	1·40	1·60
485	10 s. Pres. Arap Moi and Mrs. Thatcher at Kapsabet Telephone Exchange	2·25	2·50

96 Kenya Flag

1988. 25th Anniv of Independence. Mult.

No.	Description	Unused	Used
486	1 s. Type **96**	15	10
487	3 s. Coffee picking ..	40	40
488	5 s. Proposed Kenya Posts and Telecommunications Headquarters building	70	70
489	7 s. Kenya Airways "Harambee Star" "A310-300" Airbus ..	1·40	1·50
490	10 s. New diesel locomotive No. 9401	2·50	2·75

97 Gedi Ruins, Malindi

1989. Historic Monuments. Multicoloured.

No.	Description	Unused	Used
491	1 s. 20 Type **97**	20	10
492	3 s. 40 Vasco Da Gama Pillar, Malindi (vert) ..	45	45
493	4 s. 40 Ishiakani Monument, Kiunga ..	55	55
494	5 s. 50 Fort Jesus, Mombasa	70	80
495	7 s. 50 She Burnan Omwe, Lamu (vert) ..	95	1·25

98 125th Anniversary and Kenya Red Cross Logos

1989. 125th Anniv of International Red Cross. Multicoloured.

No.	Description	Unused	Used
496	1 s. 20 Type **98**	20	10
497	3 s. 40 Red Cross workers with car crash victim ..	50	50
498	4 s. 40 Disaster relief team distributing blankets ..	60	60
499	5 s. 50 Henri Dunant (founder)	75	85
500	7 s. 70 Blood donor ..	1·00	1·25

99 Female Giraffe and Calf

1989. Reticulated Giraffe. Multicoloured.

No.	Description	Unused	Used
501	1 s. 20 Type **99**	50	15
502	3 s. 40 Giraffe drinking ..	1·25	1·25
503	4 s. 40 Two giraffes ..	1·40	1·40
504	5 s. 50 Giraffe feeding ..	1·50	1·75

100 "Pleurotus sajor-ceju"

1989. Mushrooms. Multicoloured.

No.	Description	Unused	Used
506	1 s. 20 Type **100**	45	15
507	3 s. 40 "Agaricus bisporus"	80	60
508	4 s. 40 "Agaricus bisporus" (different)	95	85
509	5 s. 50 "Termitomyces schimperi"	1·40	1·40
510	7 s. 70 "Lentinus edodes"	2·25	2·50

101 Independence Monuments

1989. Birth Centenary of Jawaharlal Nehru (Indian statesman). Multicoloured.

No.	Description	Unused	Used
511	1 s. 20 Type **101**	40	15
512	3 s. 40 Nehru with graduates and open book	80	65
513	5 s. 50 Jawaharlal Nehru	1·25	1·25
514	7 s. 70 Industrial complex and cogwheels	1·90	2·25

1989. Ceremonial Costumes (4th series). As T **45**. Multicoloured.

No.	Description	Unused	Used
515	1 s. 20 Kipsigis	30	15
516	3 s. 40 Rabai	70	60
517	5 s. 50 Duruma	95	95
518	7 s. 70 Kuria	1·40	1·50
519	10 s. Bajuni	1·75	2·00

102 EMS Speedpost Letters and Parcel

1990. 10th Anniv of Pan African Postal Union. Multicoloured.

520 1 s. 20 Type **102** 15 10
521 3 s. 40 Mail runner 35 35
522 5 s. 50 Mandera Post Office 55 60
523 7 s. 70 EMS Speedpost letters and globe (vert) 80 1·00
524 10 s. P.A.P.U. logo (vert) 90 1·40

103 "Stamp King" with Tweezers and Magnifying Glass

1990. "Stamp World London 90" International Stamp Exhibition.

525 **103** 1 s. 50 multicoloured 15 10
526 – 4 s. 50 multicoloured 50 40
527 – 6 s. 50 black, red & bl 55 70
528 – 9 s. multicoloured 75 1·25

DESIGNS: 4 s. 50, Penny Black and Kenya Stamp Bureau postmark; 6 s. 50, Early British cancellations; 9 s. Ronald Ngala Street Post Office, Nairobi.

104 Moi Golden Cup

1990. World Cup Football Championship, Italy. Trophies. Multicoloured.

530 1 s. 50 Type **104** 30 10
531 4 s. 50 East and Central Africa Challenge Cup 80 80
532 6 s. 50 East and Central Africa Club Championship Cup 1·00 1·00
533 9 s. World Cup 1·60 1·75

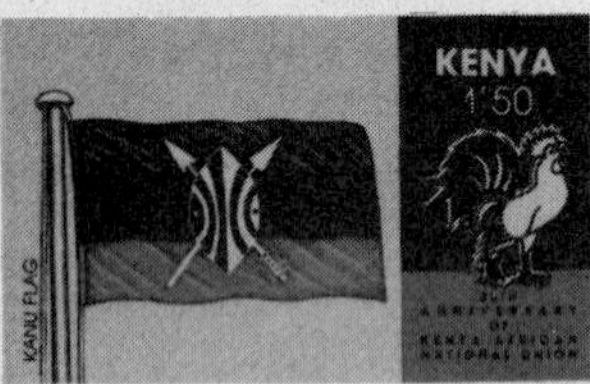

105 K.A.N.U. Flag

1990. 50th Anniv of Kenya African National Union. Multicoloured.

534 1 s. 50 Type **105** 15 10
535 2 s. 50 Nyayo Monument 15 15
536 4 s. 50 Party Headquarters 35 35
537 5 s. Jomo Kenyatta (Party founder) 40 40
538 6 s. 50 President Arap Moi 50 60
539 9 s. President Moi addressing rally 70 90
540 10 s. Queue of voters 80 1·10

106 Desktop Computer

1990. 125th Anniv of I. T. U. Multicoloured.

541 1 s. 50 Type **106** 15 10
542 4 s. 50 Telephone switchboard assembly, Gilgil 35 35
543 6 s. 50 "125 YEARS" 45 65
544 9 s. Urban and rural telecommunications 70 1·00

1990. 90th Birthday of Queen Elizabeth the Queen Mother. As T **134** of Ascension.

545 10 s. multicoloured 80 1·00
546 40 s. black and green 2·75 3·25

DESIGNS—21 × 36 mm. 10 s. Queen Mother at British Museum, 1988. 29 × 37 mm. 40 s. Queen Elizabeth at hospital garden party, 1947.

109 Kenya 1988 2 s. Definitive

1990. Cent of Postage Stamps in Kenya. Mult.

547 1 s. 50 Type **109** 25 10
548 4 s. 50 East Africa and Uganda 1903 1 a. 55 55
549 6 s. 50 British East Africa Co 1890 ½a. optd on G.B. 1d. 80 80
550 9 s. Kenya and Uganda 1922 20 c. 1·25 1·40
551 20 s. Kenya, Uganda, Tanzania 1971 2 s. 50 railway commemorative 2·00 2·50

110 Adult Literacy Class

1990. International Literacy Year. Mult.

552 1 s. 50 Type **110** 20 10
553 4 s. 50 Teaching by radio 55 55
554 6 s. 50 Technical training 75 85
555 9 s. International Literacy Year logo 1·25 1·50

111 National Flag

1991. Olympic Games, Barcelona (1992) (1st issue). Multicoloured.

556 2 s. Type **111** 20 10
557 6 s. Basketball 50 50
558 7 s. Hockey 60 60
559 8 s. 50 Table tennis 80 90
560 11 s. Boxing 85 1·00

See also Nos. 580/4.

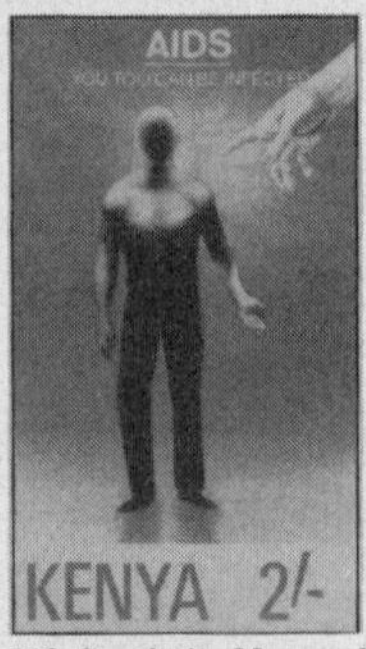

112 Symbolic Man and Pointing Finger

1992. AIDS Day. Multicoloured.

561 2 s. Type **112** 20 15
562 6 s. Victim and drugs 40 35
563 8 s. 50 Male and female symbols 60 60
564 11 s. Symbolic figure and hypodermic syringe 90 1·10

1992. 40th Anniv of Queen Elizabeth II's Accession. As T **143** of Ascension. Mult.

565 3 s. Queen and Prince Philip with Pres. Moi 15 10
566 8 s. Storks in tree 40 35
567 11 s. Treetops Hotel 55 55
568 14 s. Three portraits of Queen Elizabeth 75 80
569 40 s. Queen Elizabeth II 2·00 2·50

114 Leopard

1992. Kenya Wildlife. Multicoloured.

570 3 s. Type **114** 25 15
571 8 s. Lion 70 70
572 10 s. Elephant 85 85
573 11 s. Buffalo 85 85
574 14 s. Black rhinoceros 1·10 1·25

115 International Harvester Safari Truck, 1926

1992. Vintage Cars. Multicoloured.

575 3 s. Type **115** 20 10
576 8 s. Fiat "509", 1924 60 60
577 10 s. Hupmobile, 1923 70 70
578 11 s. Chevrolet "Box Body", 1928 70 70
579 14 s. Bentley/Parkward, 1934 80 80

116 Kenyan Athlete winning Race

1992. Olympic Games, Barcelona (2nd issue). Multicoloured.

580 3 s. Type **116** 20 10
581 8 s. Men's judo 55 55
582 10 s. Kenyan women's volleyball players 65 65
583 11 s. Kenyan men's 4 × 100 metres relay runners 65 65
584 14 s. Men's 10,000 metres 75 80

117 Holy Child, Joseph and Animals

1992. Christmas. Multicoloured.

585 3 s. Type **117** 15 10
586 8 s. Mary with Holy Child 45 45
587 11 s. Christmas tree 55 55
588 14 s. Adoration of the Magi 75 75

118 Asembo Bay Lighthouse, Lake Victoria

1993. Lighthouses. Multicoloured.

589 3 s. Type **118** 15 10
590 8 s. Old Ras Serani lighthouse, Mombasa 45 45
591 11 s. New Ras Serani lighthouse, Mombasa 55 55
592 14 s. Gingira, Lake Victoria 75 75

119 Superb Starling

120 Yellow-billed Hornbill

1993. Birds. Multicoloured. (a) As T **119**.

593 50 c. Type **119** 10 10
594 1 s. Red and yellow barbet 10 10
595 3 s. Black-throated honeyguide ("Greater honeyguide") 10 10
596 7 s. Malachite kingfisher 15 20
597 8 s. Speckled pigeon 15 20
598 10 s. Cinnamon-chested bee eater 20 25
599 11 s. Scarlet-chested sunbird 20 25
600 14 s. Bagalafecht weaver ("Reichenow's weaver") 20 25

(b) As T **120**

601 50 s. Type **120** 1·00 1·10
602 80 s. Lesser flamingo 1·60 1·75
603 100 s. Hadada ibis 2·00 2·10

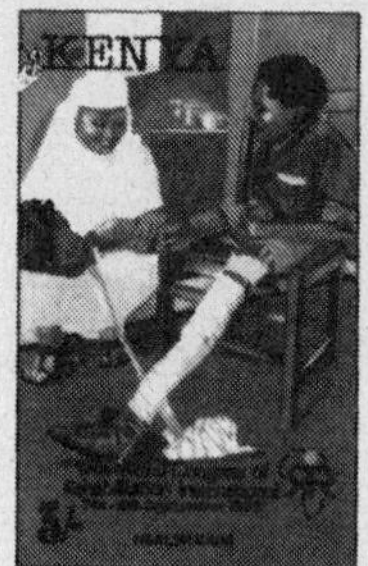

121 Nurse bandaging Boy's Legs

1993. 17th World Congress of Rehabilitation International.

611	**121**	3 s. multicoloured ..	15	10
612	–	8 s. multicoloured ..	25	25
613	–	10 s. multicoloured ..	25	25
614	–	11 s. multicoloured ..	25	25
615	–	14 s. black, blue & orge	35	35

DESIGNS—HORIZ. 8 s. Singing group on crutches; 10 s. Vocational training; 11 s. Wheelchair race. VERT. 14 s. Congress emblem.

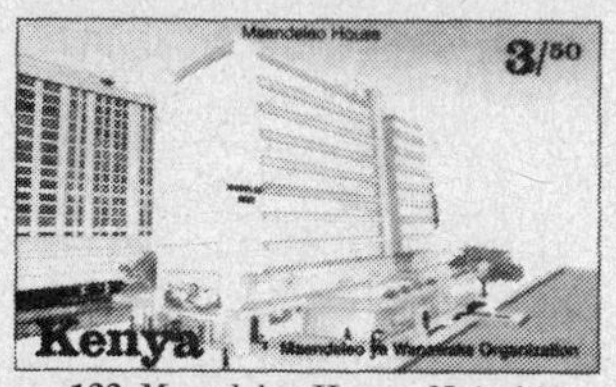

122 Maendeleo House, Nairobi

1994. 40th Anniv of Maendeleo Ya Wanawake Organization. Multicoloured.

616	3 s. 50 Type **122**	10	10
617	9 s. Planting saplings ..	15	20
618	11 s. Rural family planning clinic (vert)	20	25
619	12 s. 50 Women carrying water	30	35
620	15 s. 50 Improved wood-burning cooking stove (vert)	35	40

POSTAGE DUE STAMPS

D 3.

1967.

D 13	**D 3.**	5 c. red	15	2·00
D 41		10 c. green ..	10	10
D 42		20 c. blue ..	10	10
D 44		30 c. brown	10	10
D 45		40 c. purple	10	10
D 46		80 c. red ..	10	10
D 47		1 s. orange	10	10
D 48		2 s. violet ..	10	10

OFFICIAL STAMPS

Intended for use on official correspondence of the Kenya Government only, but there is no evidence that they were so used.

1964. Stamps of 1963 optd. **OFFICIAL.**

O 21.	**46.**	5 c. multicoloured ..	10
O 22.	–	10 c. brown ..	10
O 23.	–	15 c. mauve ..	65
O 24.	–	20 c. black and green ..	20
O 25.	–	30 c. black and yellow	30
O 26.	–	50 c. red, black & green	2·25

KENYA, UGANDA AND TANGANYIKA

Kenya, a Br. Crown colony and Protectorate including British East Africa. From 1935 it had a common postal service with Tanganyika and Uganda. Tanganyika became independent and had its own stamps in 1961, Uganda in 1962 and Kenya in December 1963, when the stamps of Kenya, Tanganyika and Uganda (except for the Postage Due Stamps) were withdrawn. For earlier issues see under Br. East Africa, Tanganyika and Uganda.

1903–19. 16 annas = 100 cents = 1 rupee.
1922. 100 cents = 1s sterling.

1. 2.

1903.

17a	**1**	½ a. green	3·25	1·60
2		1 a. grey and red	1·75	30
19a		2 a. purple	2·50	1·00
21		2½ a. blue	7·50	17·00
22a		3 a. purple and green ..	3·75	19·00
23		4 a. green and black ..	7·50	13·00
24		5 a. grey and brown ..	7·50	14·00
25		8 a. grey and blue ..	7·00	8·00
9	**2**	1 r. green	13·00	42·00
27		2 r. purple	30·00	48·00
28		3 r. green and black ..	45·00	85·00
29		4 r. grey and green ..	48·00	£110
30		5 r. grey and red ..	55·00	85·00
31		10 r. grey and blue ..	£120	£150
15		20 r. grey and stone ..	£400	£600
16		50 r. grey and brown ..	£1000	£1400

1907.

34.	**1.**	1 c. brown	40	15
35.		3 c. green	3·50	25
36.		6 c. red	2·75	10
37.		10 c. lilac and olive ..	9·00	8·50
38.		12 c. purple	5·00	2·75
39.		15 c. blue	9·50	8·50
40.		25 c. green and black ..	4·00	6·50
41.		50 c. green and brown ..	7·00	12·00
42.		75 c. grey and blue ..	4·50	23·00

1912. As T **1/2**, but portraits of King George V.

44	1 c. black	30	75
45	3 c. green	2·00	30
46	6 c. red	50	20
47	10 c. orange	2·00	20
48	12 c. grey	2·75	50
49	15 c. blue	2·75	55
50	25 c. black & red on yellow	45	90
51	50 c. black and lilac ..	1·50	80
52a	75 c. black and green ..	90	11·00
53	1 r. black and green ..	1·75	3·25
54	2 r. red and black on blue	20·00	28·00
55	3 r. violet and green ..	20·00	48·00
56	4 r. red & green on yellow	45·00	85·00
57	5 r. blue and purple ..	45·00	95·00
58	10 r. red & green on green	75·00	£120
59	20 r. black & purple on red	£250	£250
60	20 r. purple & blue on blue	£225	£225
61	50 r. red and green ..	£500	£600
62	100 r. purple & blk on red	£2750	£1800
63	500 r. green & red on green	£12000	

1919. No. 46 surch **4 cents.**

64.	4 c. on 6 c. red	40	15

6. 7.

1922.

76.	**6.**	1 c. brown	70	1·00
77.		5 c. violet	2·50	30
78.		5 c. green	2·00	10
79.		10 c. green	1·50	10
80.		10 c. black	2·00	10
81a.		12 c. black	2·25	23·00
82.		15 c. red	1·25	10
83.		20 c. orange	2·50	10
84.		30 c. blue	1·50	20
85.		50 c. grey	2·00	10
86.		75 c. olive	2·50	7·50
87.	**7.**	1 s. green	2·75	2·00
88.		2 s. purple	7·50	7·00
89.		2 s. 50 brown ..	18·00	60·00
90.		3 s. grey	15·00	6·00
91.		4 s. grey	18·00	70·00
92.		5 s. red	22·00	18·00
93.		7 s. 50 orange ..	60·00	£130
94.		10 s. blue	48·00	48·00
95.		£1 black and orange ..	£140	£190
96.		£2 green and purple ..	£600	
97.		£3 purple and yellow ..	£750	
98.		£4 black and mauve ..	£1200	
99.		£5 black and blue ..	£1500	
100.		£10 black and green ..	£7500	
101.		£20 red and green ..	£12000	
102.		£25 black and red ..	£13000	
103.		£50 black and brown ..	£17000	
104.		£75 purple and grey ..	£35000	
105.		£100 red and black ..	£40000	

8. South African Crowned Cranes.

DESIGNS—VERT. 10 c. £1, Lion. 30 c. 5 s. Jinja Railway Bridge, Ripon Falls. HORIZ. 15 c. 2 s. Kilimanjaro. 65 c. Mt. Kenya. 1 s., 3 s. Lake Naivasha.

9. Dhow on Lake Victoria.

1935. King George V.

110.	**8.**	1 c. black and brown ..	15	70
111.	**9.**	5 c. black and green ..	40	20
112.	–	10 c. black and yellow	2·25	20
113.	–	15 c. black and red ..	75	10
114.	**8.**	20 c. black and orange	85	10
115.	–	30 c. black and blue ..	80	90
116.	**9.**	50 c. purple and black	75	10
117.	–	65 c. black and brown	90	2·00
118.	–	1 s. black and green ..	75	35
119.	–	2 s. red and purple ..	4·25	3·50
120.	–	3 s. blue and black ..	5·00	13·00
121.	–	5 s. black and red ..	15·00	23·00
122.	**8.**	10 s. purple and blue ..	40·00	50·00
123.	–	£1 black and red ..	£120	£130

1935. Silver Jubilee. As T **13** of Antigua.

124.	20 c. blue and olive ..	50	10
125.	30 c. brown and blue ..	2·25	2·00
126.	65 c. green and blue ..	1·75	2·50
127.	1 s. grey and purple ..	2·00	1·40

1937. Coronation. As T **2** of Aden.

128.	5 c. green	25	10
129.	20 c. orange	55	15
130.	30 c. blue	85	95

15. Dhow on Lake Victoria.

1938. As 1935 (except 10 c.), but with portrait of King George VI as in T **15.**

131a	**8.**	1 c. black and brown	15	40
132	**15.**	5 c. black and green	70	10
133		5 c. brown and orange	35	1·75
134	–	10 c. brn. & orge. ..	75	10
135	–	10 c. black and green	30	20
136	–	10 c. brown and grey	45	40
137a	–	15 c. black and red ..	1·50	2·75
138	–	15 c. black and green	80	2·00
139b	**8.**	20 c. black and orange	3·00	10
140	**15.**	25 c. black and red ..	1·25	90
141b	–	30 c. black and blue ..	75	10
142	–	30 c. pur. & brn. ..	55	10
143	**8.**	40 c. black and blue ..	1·50	1·75
144e	**15.**	50 c. purple and black	3·50	30
145ba	–	1 s. black and brown	3·00	50
146b	–	2 s. red and purple ..	7·00	20
147b	–	3 s. blue and black ..	16·00	90
148b	–	5 s. black and red ..	16·00	40
149b	**8.**	10 s. purple and blue	23·00	2·75
150ab	–	£1 black and red ..	12·00	14·00

DESIGN—HORIZ. 10 c. Lake Naivasha.

1941. Stamps of South Africa surch **KENYA TANGANYIKA UGANDA** and value. Alternate stamps inscr in English or Afrikaans.

151.	**7.**	5 c. on 1d. blk. and red	60	1·25
152.	**22a.**	10 c. on 3d. blue ..	1·00	3·75
153.	**8.**	20 c. on 6d. grn. & red	60	2·25
154.	–	70 c. on 1s. (No. 120) ..	5·50	4·50

Prices for Nos. 151/4 are for unused or used pairs.

1946. Victory. As T **9** of Aden.

155.	20 c. orange	10	10
156.	30 c. blue	10	10

1948. Silver Wedding. As T **10/11** of Aden.

157.	20 c. orange	15	10
158.	£1 red	35·00	38·00

1949. U.P.U. As T **20/23** of Antigua.

159.	20 c. orange	20
160.	30 c. blue	50
161.	50 c. grey	50
162.	1 s. brown	75

1952. Visit of Queen Elizabeth II (a Princess) and Duke of Edinburgh. As Nos 135 and 145 but inscr. "ROYAL VISI 1952".

163.	10 c. black and green ..	10	
164.	1 s. black and brown ..	20	1·[illegible]

1953. Coronation. As T **13** of Aden.

165	20 c. black and orange ..	15

1954. Royal Visit. As No. 171 but insc "ROYAL VISIT 1954".

166.	**18.**	30 c. black and blue ..	10

18. Owen Falls Dam. 21. Queen Elizabeth II

20. Royal Lodge, Sagana.

DESIGNS (Size as Type **18**)—VERT 10 c., 50 c. Giraffe. 20 c., 40 c. 1 s Lion. HORIZ. 1 c., 1 s. 30, 5 s. Elephants 65 c., 2 s. Kilimanjaro.

1954.

167	**18**	5 c. black and brown	10	[illegible]
168	–	10 c. red	60	[illegible]
169a	–	15 c. black and blue ..	55	[illegible]
170	–	20 c. black and orange	40	[illegible]
171	**18**	30 c. black and blue ..	55	[illegible]
172	–	40 c. brown	2·75	[illegible]
173	–	50 c. purple	50	[illegible]
174	–	65 c. green and purple	2·75	[illegible]
175	–	1 s. black and purple	30	[illegible]
176	–	1 s. 30 lilac and orange	5·50	[illegible]
177	–	2 s. black and green ..	1·75	[illegible]
178	–	5 s. black and orange	5·50	[illegible]
179	**20**	10 s. black and blue ..	13·00	1·5[illegible]
180	**21**	£1 red and black ..	16·00	9·5[illegible]

25. Map of E. Africa showing Lakes.

1958. Cent. of Discovery of Lakes Tanganyika and Victoria by Burton and Speke.

181.	**25.**	40 c. blue and green ..	20	20
182.		1 s. 30c. green & purple	30	80

26. Sisal.

29. Queen Elizabeth II.

28. Mt. Kenya and Giant Plants.

1960.

33. 26. 5 c. blue 10 15
34. – 10 c. green 10 10
35. – 15 c. purple 20 10
36. – 20 c. mauve 10 10
37. – 25 c. green .. .. 2·75 1·00
38. – 30 c. red 10 10
39. – 40 c. blue 15 10
90. – 50 c. violet 15 10
91. – 65 c. olive 30 55
92. 28. 1 s. violet and purple 65 10
93. – 1 s. 30 brown and red 1·50 15
94. – 2 s. indigo and blue .. 1·50 20
95. – 2 s. 50 olive & turq. .. 2·75 1·75
96. – 5 s. red and purple .. 3·50 80
97. – 10 s. myrtle and green 5·50 4·50
98. 29. 20 s. blue and lake .. 13·00 11·00

Designs—As Type **26**: 10 c. Cotton. 15 c. Coffee. 20 c. Blue Wildebeest. 25 c. Ostrich. 0 c. Thomson's Gazelle. 40 c. Manta Ray. 0 c. Common Zebra. 65 c. Cheetah. As Type 8: 1 s. 30, Murchison Falls and Hippopotamus. 2 s. Mt. Kilimanjaro and Giraffe. s. 50, Candelabra tree and Black Rhinoceros. s. Crater Lake and Mountains of the Moon. 0 s. Ngorongoro Crater and African Buffalo.

30. Land Tillage.

1963. Freedom from Hunger.

99. 30. 15 c. blue and olive .. 10 10
200. – 30 c. brown and yellow 20 10
201. 30. 50 c. blue and orange 30 10
202. – 1 s. 30 brown and blue 55 1·40

Design: 30 c., 1 s. 30, African with corncob.

31. Scholars and Open Book.

1963. Founding of East African University.

203. 31. 30 c. multicoloured .. 10 10
204. 1 s. 30 multicoloured .. 20 20

32. Red Cross Emblem.

1963. Centenary of Red Cross.

205. 32. 30 c. red and blue .. 75 10
206. 50 c. red and brown .. 1·00 35

35. East African " Flags ".

1964. Olympic Games, Tokyo.

207. – 30 c. yellow and purple 10 10
208. – 50 c. purple & yellow 15 10
209. 35. 1 s. 30 yell., grn. & blue 20 10
210. 2 s. 50 mve., vio. & bl. 25 75

Designs—vert. 30 c., 50 c. Chrysanthemum Emblem.

36. Rally Badge.

Design. Nos. 213/14, Cars en route.

1965. 13th East African Safari Rally.

211. 36. 30 c. blk., yell. & turq. 10 10
212. 50 c. blk., yell. & brn. 10 10
213. – 1 s. 30 green, ochre & blue 20 10
214. – 2 s. 50 grn., red & blue 30 75

38. I.T.U. Emblem and Symbols.

1965. Centenary of I.T.U. "I.T.U." and symbols in gold.

215. 38. 30 c. brown & mauve 15 10
216. 50 c. brown & grey .. 15 10
217. 1 s. 30 brown & blue .. 35 10
218. 2 s. 50 brown & turq. 70 80

39. I.C.Y. Emblem.

1965. Int. Co-operation Year.

219. 39. 30 c. green and gold .. 10 10
220. 50 c. black and gold .. 15 10
221. 1 s. 30 blue and gold .. 30 10
222. 2 s. 50 red and gold .. 75 1·75

40. Game Park Lodge, Tanzania.

1966. Tourism. Multicoloured.

223. 30 c. Type **40** 15 10
224. 50 c. Murchison Falls, Uganda 50 10
225. 1 s. 30 Lesser Flamingoes, Lake Nakuru, Kenya .. 1·90 25
226. 2 s. 50 Deep Sea Fishing, Tanzania .. .. 1·90 2·00

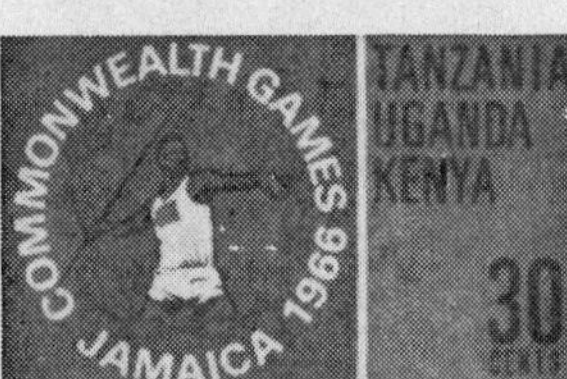

41. Games Emblem.

1966. 8th British Empire and Commonwealth Games, Jamaica.

227. 41. 30 c. multicoloured .. 10 10
228. 50 c. multicoloured .. 15 10
229. 1 s. 30 multicoloured .. 20 10
230. 2 s. 50 multicoloured .. 35 65

42. U.N.E.S.C.O. Emblem.

1966. 20th Anniv. of U.N.E.S.C.O.

231. 42. 30 c. blk., grn. & red .. 25 10
232. 50 c. blk., grn. & brn... 35 10
233. 1 s. 30 blk., grn. & grey 85 15
234. 2 s. 50 blk., grn. & yell. 1·50 1·75

43. D. H. " Dragon Rapide ".

1967. 21st Anniv. of East African Airways. Multicoloured.

235. 30 c. Type **43** .. 30 10
236. 50 c. " Super VC-10 " .. 40 10
237. 1 s. 30 " Comet 4 " .. 85 15
238. 2 s. 50 " F-27 Friendship " 1·25 1·75

44. Pillar Tomb.

1967. Archaeological Relics.

239. 44. 30 c. ochre, blk. & pur. 15 10
240. – 50 c. red, blk. & brn. .. 50 10
241. – 1 s. 30 blk., yell. & grn. 75 10
242. – 2 s. 50 blk., ochre & red 1·40 1·50

Designs: 50 c. Rock painting. 1 s. 30, Clay head. 2 s. 50, Proconsul skull.

48. Unified Symbols of Kenya, Tanzania, and Uganda. (Illustration reduced. Actual size 58×21 mm.)

1967. Foundation of East African Community.

243. 48. 5 s. gold, blk. & grey .. 40 1·00

49. Mountaineering.

1968. Mountains of East Africa. Mult.

244. 30 c. Type **49** 15 10
245. 50 c. Mount Kenya .. 20 10
246. 1 s. 30 Mount Kilimanjaro 40 10
247. 2 s. 50 Ruwenzori Mountains 65 1·25

50. Family and Rural Hospital.

1968. World Health Organization.

248. 50. 30 c. grn., lilac & brn. 10 10
249. – 50 c. slate, lilac & black 10 10
250. – 1 s. 30 brown, lilac and light brown 15 10
251. – 2 s. 50 grey, black & lilac 25 60

Designs: 50 c. Family and Nurse. 1 s. 30, Family and Microscope. 2 s. 50, Family and Hypodermic Syringe.

51. Olympic Stadium, Mexico City.

1968. Olympic Games, Mexico.

252. 51. 30 c. green and black 10 10
253. – 50 c. green and black 10 10
254. – 1 s. 30 red, black & grey 20 10
255. – 2 s. 50 sepia and brown 30 60

Designs—horiz. 50 c. High-diving Boards. 1 s. 30, Running Tracks. vert. 2 s. 50, Boxing Ring.

52. " M.V. Umoja ".

1969. Water Transport.

256. 52. 30 c. blue and grey .. 15 10
257. – 50 c. multicoloured .. 20 10
258. – 1 s. 30 green and blue 45 15
259. – 2 s. 50 orange and blue 1·00 1·75

Designs: 50 c. "S.S. Harambee". 1 s. 30, "M.V. Victoria". 2 s. 50, "St. Michael".

53. I.L.O. Emblem and Agriculture.

1969. 50th Anniv. of Int. Labour Organization.

260. 53. 30 c. blk., grn. & yell. 10 10
261. – 50 c. multicoloured .. 10 10
262. – 1 s. 30 black, brown and orange .. 10 10
263. – 2 s. 50 blk., bl. & turq. 20 40

Designs—I.L.O. Emblem and 50 c. Building-work. 1 s. 30, Factory-workers, 2 s. 50, Shipping.

54. Pope Paul VI and Ruwenzori Mountains.

55. Euphorbia Tree shaped as Africa, and Emblem.

1969. Visit of Pope Paul VI to Uganda.

264. 54. 30 c. black, gold & blue 15 10
265. 70 c. black, gold & red 25 10
266. 1 s. 50 blk., gold & bl. 40 70
267. 2 s. 50 black, gold & violet 55 75

1969. 5th Anniv. of African Development Bank.

268. 55. 30 c. green and gold .. 10 10
269. 70 c. grn., gold & vio. 15 10
270. 1 s. 50 grn., gold & bl. 25 10
271. 2 s. 50 green, gold & brown 30 45

56. Marimba.

1970. Musical Instruments.

272. 56. 30 c. buff and brown .. 15 10
273. – 70 c. green, brn. & yell. 25 10
274. – 1 s. 50 brown & yellow 50 10
275. – 2 s. 50 orange, yellow and brown 75 80

Design: 70 c. Amadinda, 1 s. 50, Nzomari. 2 s. 50, Adeudeu.

57. Satellite Earth Station.

1970. Inaug. of Satellite Earth Station.

276. **57.** 30 c. multicoloured .. 10 10
277. – 70 c. multicoloured .. 15 10
278. – 1 s. 50 blk., vio. & orge. 25 10
279. – 2 s. 50 multicoloured .. 55 90

Designs: 70 c. Transmitter—Daytime. 1 s. 50, Transmitter—Night. 2 s. 50, Earth and satellite.

58. Athlete.

1970. 9th Commonwealth Games.

280. **58.** 30 c. brown and black 10 10
281. 70 c. green, brown and black 10 10
282. 1 s. 50 lilac, brown and black 15 10
283. 2 s. 50 blue, brown and black 20 60

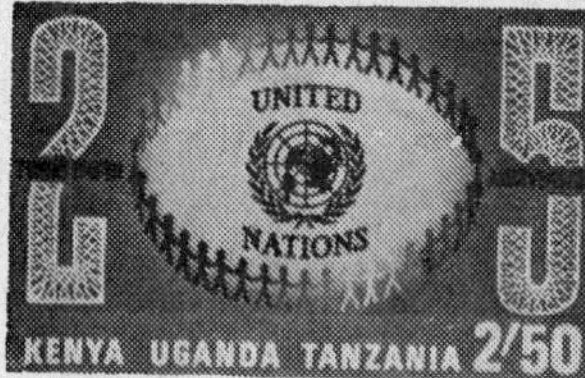

59. " 25 " and U.N. Emblem.

1970. 25th Anniv. of United Nations.

284. **59.** 30 c. multicoloured .. 10 10
285. 70 c. multicoloured .. 10 10
286. 1 s. 50 multicoloured .. 20 10
287. 2 s. 50 multicoloured .. 45 1·25

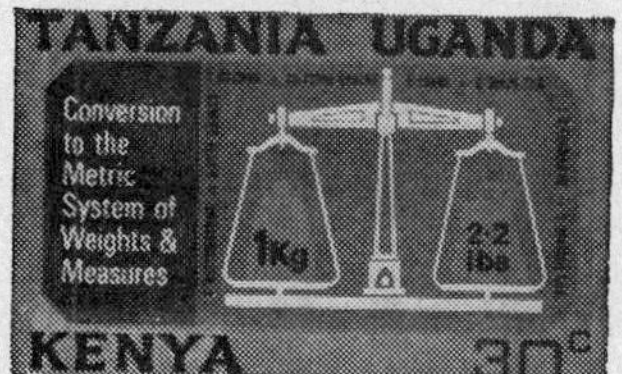

60. Balance and Weight Equivalents.

1970. Conversion to Metric System. Mult.

288. 30 c. Type **60** 10 10
289. 70 c. Fahrenheit and Centigrade Thermometers .. 10 10
290. 1 s. 50 Petrol Pump and Liquid Capacities .. 15 10
291. 2 s. 50 Surveyors and Land Measures .. .. 35 1·00

61. Class "11" Locomotive.

1971. Railway Transport. Multicoloured.

292. 30 c. Type **61** 35 10
293. 70 c. Class "90" Locomotive 55 10
294. 1 s. 50 Class "59" Locomotive .. .. .. 1·25 50
295. 2 s. 50 Class "30" Locomotive .. .. .. 2·25 2·75

62. Syringe and Cow.

1971. O.A.U. Rinderpest Campaign.

297. **62.** 30 c. blk., brn. and grn. 10 10
298. – 70 c. blk., blue & brn. 10 10
299. **62.** 1 s. 50 blk., pur. & brn. 15 10
300. – 2 s. 50 blk., red & brn. 25 50

Design: 70 c., 2 s. 50, As Type **62** but with bull facing right.

63. Livingstone meets Stanley.

1971. Centenary of Livingstone and Stanley meeting at Ujiji.

301. **63.** 5 s. multicoloured .. 30 75

64. Pres. Nyerere and Supporters.

1971. 10th Anniv. of Tanzanian Independence. Multicoloured.

302. 30 c. Type **64** .. 10 10
303. 70 c. Ujama village .. 10 10
304. 1 s. 50 Dar-es-Salaam University 20 20
305. 2 s. 50 Kilimanjaro airport 75 2·00

65. Flags and Trade Fair Emblem.

1972. All-Africa Trade Fair.

306. **65.** 30 c. multicoloured .. 10 10
307. 70 c. multicoloured .. 10 10
308. 1 s. 50 multicoloured .. 10 10
309. 2 s. 50 multicoloured .. 25 55

66. Child with Cup.

1972. 25th Anniv. of U.N.I.C.E.F. Mult.

310. 30 c. Type **66** 10 10
311. 70 c. Children with ball .. 10 10
312. 1 s. 50 Child at blackboard 10 10
313. 2 s. 50 Child and tractor .. 25 60

67. Hurdling.

1972. Olympic Games, Munich. Mult.

314. 40 c. Type **67** 10 10
315. 70 c. Running 10 10
316. 1 s. 50 Boxing 20 10
317. 2 s. 50 Hockey .. .. 30 1·00

68. Ugandan Kobs.

1972. 10th Anniv. of Ugandan Independence. Multicoloured.

319. 40 c. Type **68** 25 10
320. 70 c. Conference Centre .. 25 10
321. 1 s. 50 Makerere University 55 25
322. 2 s. 50 Coat of Arms .. 1·00 2·00

69. Community Flag.

1972. 5th Anniv. of East African Community.

324. **69.** 5 s. multicoloured .. 75 1·25

70. Run-of-the-wind Anemometer.

1972. Cent. of IMO/WMO. Multicoloured.

325. 40 c. Type **70** 10 10
326. 70 c. Weather balloon (vert.) 15 10
327. 1 s. 50 Meterological rocket 25 15
328. 2 s. 50 Satellite Receiving aerial .. .. .. 55 1·75

71. " Learning by Serving ".

1973. 24th World Scouting Conference, Nairobi.

329. **71.** 40 c. multicoloured .. 15 10
330. – 70 c. red, violet & blk. 20 10
331. – 1 s. 50 blue, vio. & blk. 45 30
332. – 2 s. 50 multicoloured .. 1·00 2·00

Designs: 70 c. Baden-Powell's grave, Nyeri. 1 s. 50, World Scout emblem. 2 s. 50, Lord Baden-Powell.

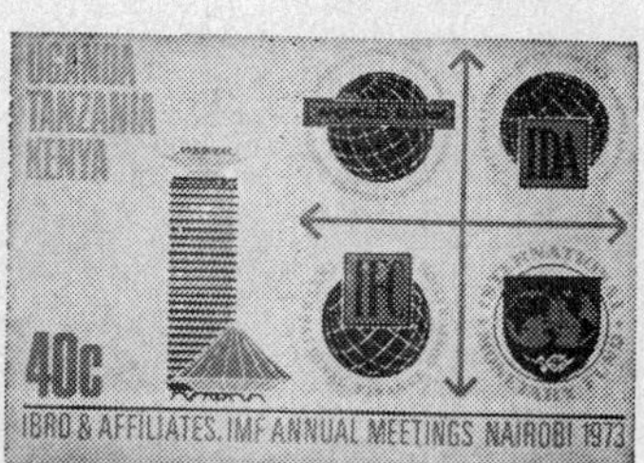

72. Kenyatta Conference Centre.

1973. I.M.F./World Bank Conference.

333. **72.** 40 c. grn., grey & blk. 10 10
334. – 70 c. brn., grey & black 10 10
335. – 1 s. 50 multicoloured .. 25 35
336. – 2 s. 50 orange, grey & black .. .. 35 1·50

Designs: Nos. 334/6 show different arrangements of Bank emblems and the Conference Centre, the 1 s. 50 being vertical.

73. Police Dog-handler.

1973. 50th Anniversary of Interpol.

338. **73.** 40 c. yell., blue & black 55 15
339. – 70 c. grn., yell. & blk. 90 15
340. – 1 s. 50 vio., yell. & blk. 1·50 90
341. – 2 s. 50 grn., orge. & blk. 3·75 5·00
342. – 2 s. 50 grn., orge. & blk. 3·75 5·00

Designs: 70 c. East African policemen. 1 s. 50, Interpol emblem. 2 s. 50 (2), Interpol H.Q. No. 341 is inscribed "St. Clans" and No. 342 "St. Cloud".

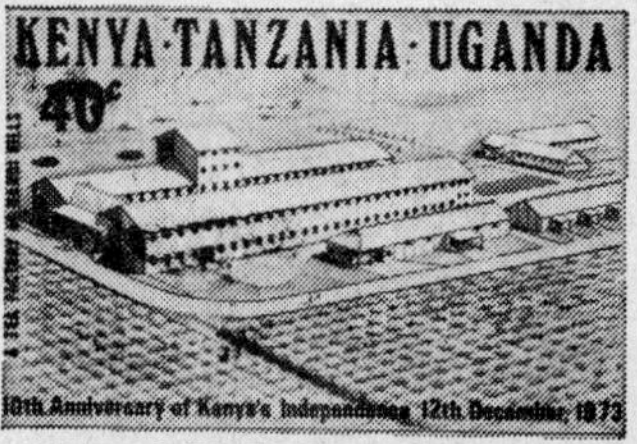

74. Tea Factory.

1973. 10th Anniv. of Kenya's Independence. Multicoloured.

343. 40 c. Type **74** 10 10
344. 70 c. Kenyatta Hospital .. 10 10
345. 1 s. 50 Nairobi Airport .. 30 20
346. 2 s. 50 Kindaruma hydro-electric scheme .. .. 65 1·50

75. Party H.Q.

1973. 10th Anniv. of Zanzibar's Revolution. Multicoloured.

347. 40 c. Type **75** 10 10
348. 70 c. Housing scheme .. 10 10
349. 1 s. 50 Colour T.V. .. 30 25
350. 2 s. 50 Amaan Stadium .. 65 1·75

76. " Symbol of Union ".

1974. 10th Anniv. of Tanganyika-Zanzibar Union. Multicoloured.

351. 40 c. Type **76** 10 10
352. 70 c. Handclasp and map 20 10
353. 1 s. 50 "Communications" 55 25
354. 2 s. 50 Flags of Tanu, Tanzania & Afro-Shirazi Party .. .. .. 1·10 1·50

77. East African Family (" Stability of the Home ").

1974. 17th Social Welfare Conf., Nairobi.

355. **77.** 40 c. yell., brn. & blk. 10 10
356. – 70 c. multicoloured .. 10 10
357. – 1 s. 50 yell., grn. & blk. 20 30
358. – 2 s. 50 red, vio. & blk. 45 1·50

Designs: 70 c. Dawn and Drummer (U.N. Second Development Plan). 1 s. 50, Agricultural scene (Rural Development Plan). 2 s. 50, Transport and Telephone ("Communications").

78. New Postal H.Q., Kampala.

1974. Centenary of U.P.U. Multicoloured.

No.	Description	Unused	Used
359.	40 c. Type **78**	10	10
360.	70 c. Mail-train and post-van	15	10
361.	1 s. 50 U.P.U. Building, Berne	15	20
362.	2 s. 50 Loading mail into "VC-10"	30	1·00

79. Family-planning Clinic.

1974. World Population Year.

No.	Type	Description	Unused	Used
363.	79.	40 c. multicoloured	10	10
364.	–	70 c. mauve and red	10	10
365.	–	1 s. 50 multicoloured	15	20
366.	–	2 s. 50 blue, emerald and green	30	1·40

DESIGNS: 70 c. "Tug of War". 1 s. 50, Population "scales". 2 s. 50, W.P.Y. emblem.

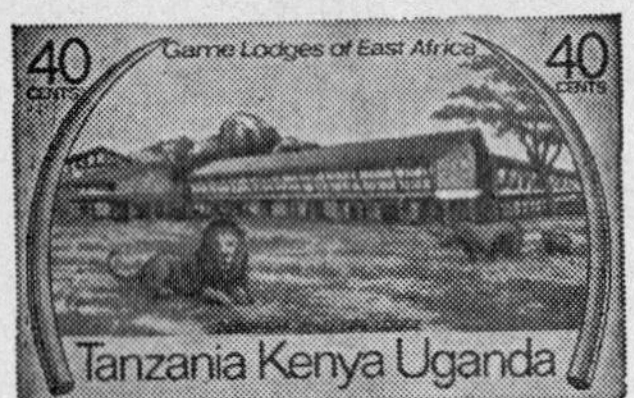

80. Seronera Wild-life Lodge, Tanzania.

1975. East African Game Lodges. Mult.

No.	Description	Unused	Used
367.	40 c. Type **80**	15	10
368.	70 c. Mweya Safari Lodge, Uganda	20	10
369.	1 s. 50 "Ark"—Aberdare Forest Lodge, Kenya	35	30
370.	2 s. 50 Paraa Safari Lodge, Uganda	80	2·00

81. Kitana (wooden comb), Bajun of Kenya.

1975. African Arts. Multicoloured.

No.	Description	Unused	Used
371.	50 c. Type **81**	10	10
372.	1 s. Earring, Chaga of Tanzania	15	10
373.	2 s. Okoco (armlet), Acholi of Uganda	45	45
374.	3 s. Kitete, Kamba gourd, Kenya	85	1·10

82. International Airport, Entebbe.

1975. O.A.U. Summit Conference, Kampala, Multicoloured.

No.	Description	Unused	Used
375.	50 c. Type **82**	10	10
376.	1 s. Map of Africa and flag (vert.)	10	10
377.	2 s. Nile Hotel, Kampala	30	65
378.	3 s. Martyrs' Shrine Namugongo (vert.)	40	1·25

83. Ahmed (" Presidential " Elephant).

1975. Rare Animals. Multicoloured.

No.	Description	Unused	Used
379.	50 c. Type **83**	50	10
380.	1 s. Albino buffalo	50	10
381.	2 s. Ahmed in grounds of National Museum	1·50	1·50
382.	3 s. Abbott's Duiker	1·50	2·50

84. Maasai Manyatta Village, Kenya.

1975. 2nd World Black and African Festival of Arts and Culture, Nigeria (1977). Mult.

No.	Description	Unused	Used
383.	50 c. Type **84**	15	10
384.	1 s. "Heartbeat of Africa" (Ugandan Dancers)	20	10
385.	2 s. Makonde sculpture, Tanzania	65	75
386.	3 s. "Early Man and Technology" (Skinning animal)	95	1·25

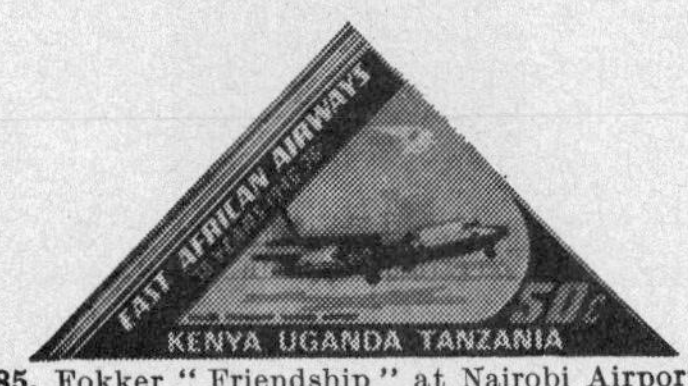

85. Fokker " Friendship " at Nairobi Airport.

1975. 30th Anniv. of East African Airways. Multicoloured.

No.	Description	Unused	Used
387.	50 c. Type **85**	75	25
388.	1 s. "DC9" at Kilimanjaro Airport	85	25
389.	2 s. Super "VC 10" at Entebbe Airport	2·50	2·50
390.	3 s. East African Airways Crest	3·00	3·00

Further commemorative sets were released during 1976–78 using common designs, but each inscribed for one republic only. See Kenya, Tanzania and Uganda.

Co-operation between the postal services of the three member countries virtually ceased after 30 June 1977. The postal services of Kenya, Tanzania and Uganda then operated independently.

OFFICIAL STAMPS

For use on official correspondence of the Tanganyika Government only.

1959. Stamps of 1954 optd. **OFFICIAL.**

No.	Type	Description	Unused	Used
O 1.	18.	5 c. black and brown	10	10
O 2.	–	10 c. red	15	10
O 3.	–	15 c. black and blue	20	10
O 4.	–	20 c. blk. & orge.	20	10
O 5.	18.	30 c. black and blue	15	10
O 6.	–	50 c. purple	20	10
O 7.	–	1 s. black and red	20	10
O 8.	–	1 s. 30 orge. & lilac	1·00	45
O 9.	–	2 s. black and green	1·10	70
O 10.	–	5 s. black and orange	2·50	1·25
O 11.	20.	10 s. black and blue	2·00	2·50
O 12.	21.	£1 red and black	6·00	10·00

1960. Stamps of 1960 optd. **OFFICIAL.**

No.	Type	Description	Unused	Used
O 13.	26.	5 c. blue	10	20
O 14.	–	10 c. green	10	10
O 15.	–	15 c. purple	10	20
O 16.	–	20 c. mauve	10	10
O 17.	–	30 c. red	10	10
O 18.	–	50 c. violet	30	20
O 19.	28.	1 s. violet and purple	30	10
O 20.	–	5 s. red and purple	5·00	65

POSTAGE DUE STAMPS

D 1. D 2.

1923.

No.	Type	Description	Unused	Used
D1.	D1.	5 c. violet	1·50	25
D2.		10 c. red	1·50	15
D3.		20 c. green	1·50	2·50
D4.		30 c. brown	9·50	9·50
D5.		40 c. blue	4·75	12·00
D6.		1 s. green	32·00	65·00

1935.

No.	Type	Description	Unused	Used
D 7.	D2.	5 c. violet	1·50	40
D 8.		10 c. red	30	10
D 9.		20 c. green	40	15
D10.		30 c. brown	60	50
D11.		40 c. blue	1·50	3·00
D12.		1 s. grey	12·00	19·00

KING EDWARD VII LAND

Stamps issued in connection with the Shackleton Antarctic Expedition in 1908. The expedition landed at Cape Royds in Victoria Land, instead of King Edward VII Land the intended destination.

1908. Stamp of New Zealand optd. **KING EDWARD VII LAND.**

No.	Type	Description	Unused	Used
A1	40	1d. red	£400	35·00

KIRIBATI

The group of islands in the Pacific, formerly known as the Gilbert Islands achieved independence on 12th July, 1979, and was renamed Kiribati.

100 cents = $1 (Australian).

15. National Flag.

1979. Independence. Multicoloured.

No.	Description	Unused	Used
84.	10 c. Type **15**	10	20
85.	45 c. Houses of Parliament and Maneaba ni Maungatabu (Houses of Assembly)	20	50

16. "Teraaka" (training ship).

1979. Multicoloured.

No.	Description	Unused	Used
86	1 c. Type **16**	10	10
87	3 c. "Tautunu" (inter-island freighter)	10	10
88	5 c. Hibiscus	10	10
89	7 c. Catholic Cathedral, Tarawa	10	10
90	10 c. Maneaba, Bikenibeu	10	10
91	12 c. Betio Harbour	15	15
92	15 c. Eastern reef heron	35	20
93	20 c. Flamboyant tree	20	20
129	25 c. Moorish idol (fish)	25	30
95	30 c. Frangipani	25	25
96	35 c. G.I.P.C. Chapel, Tangintebu	25	25
97	50 c. "Hypolimnas bolina" (butterfly)	75	55
98	$1 "Tabakea" (Tarawa Lagoon ferry)	70	75
99	$2 Evening scene	80	1·00
135	$5 National flag	3·00	5·50

17. Gilbert and Ellice Islands 1911 ½d. Stamp.

1979. Death Centenary of Sir Rowland Hill. Multicoloured.

No.	Description	Unused	Used
100.	10 c. Type **17**	10	10
101.	20 c. Gilbert & Ellice Islands 1956 2s. 6d. definitive	15	20
102.	25 c. G.B. Edward VII 2s. 6d.	15	20
103.	45 c. Gilbert and Ellice Islands 1924 10s.	25	35

18. Boy with Clam Shell.

1979. Int. Year of the Child. **Multicoloured.**

No.	Description	Unused	Used
105.	10 c. Type **18**	10	10
106.	20 c. Child climbing coconut palm (horiz.)	10	10
107.	45 c. Girl reading	15	20
108.	$1 Child in traditional costume	30	50

19. Downrange Station, Christmas Island.

1980. Satellite Tracking. Multicoloured.

No.	Description	Unused	Used
109.	25 c. Type **19**	10	10
110.	45 c. Map showing satellite trajectory	15	15
111.	$1 Rocket launch, Tanegashima, Japan (vert.)	30	35

20. T.S. " Teraaka ".

1980. " London 1980 " International Stamp Exhibition. Multicoloured.

No.	Description	Unused	Used
112.	12 c. Type **20**	10	10
113.	25 c. Loading Air Tungaru aeroplane, Bonriki Airport	10	10
114.	30 c. Radio operator	10	10
115.	$1 Bairiki Post Office	20	35

21. " Achaea janata ".

1980. Moths. Multicoloured.

No.	Description	Unused	Used
117.	12 c. Type **21**	10	10
118.	25 c. " Ethmia nigroapicella "	15	15
119.	30 c. " Utetheisa pulchelloides "	15	15
120.	50 c. " Anua coronata "	25	25

22. Captain Cook Hotel.

1980. Development. Multicoloured.

No.	Description	Unused	Used
136.	10 c. Type **22**	10	10
137.	20 c. Sports stadium	10	10
138.	25 c. International Airport, Bonriki	10	10
139.	35 c. National Library and Archives	15	10
140.	$1 Otintai Hotel	20	40

23. " Acalypha godseffiana ".

1981. Flowers. Multicoloured.

141.	12 c. Type **23**	10	10
142.	30 c. " Hibiscus schizopetalus "	15	15
143.	35 c. " Calotropis gigantea "	15	15
144.	50 c. " Euphorbia pulcherrima "	20	20

25. Maps of Abaiang and Marakei, and String Figures.

1981. Islands (1st series). Multicoloured.

145.	12 c. Type **25**	15	10
146.	30 c. Maps of Little Makin and Butaritari, and village house	25	10
147.	35 c. Map of Maiana, and Coral Road	30	15
148.	$1 Map of Christmas Island, and Captain Cook's H.M.S. "Resolution"	90	75

See also Nos. 201/4, 215/18, 237/40, 256/60 and 270/3.

26. " Katherine ".

27. Prince Charles and Lady Diana Spencer. (Illustration reduced. Actual size 80 × 25 mm).

1981. Royal Wedding. Royal Yachts. Multicoloured.

149	12 c. Type **26**	15	15
150	12 c. Type **27**	30	30
151	50 c. " Osborne " ..	35	40
152	50 c. Type **27**	65	75
153	$2 " Britannia "	50	80
154	$2 Type **27**	1·75	2·50

28. Tuna Bait Breeding Centre, Bonriki Fish Farm.

1981. Tuna Fishing Industry. Multicoloured.

158.	12 c. Type **28**	15	10
159.	30 c. Tuna fishing ..	25	20
160.	35 c. Cold storage, Betio ..	25	25
161.	50 c. Government Tuna Fishing Vessel " Nei Manganibuka " ..	50	50

HAVE YOU READ THE NOTES AT THE BEGINNING OF THIS CATALOGUE?
These often provide answers to the enquiries we receive.

29. Pomarine Skua.

1982. Birds. Multicoloured.

163	1 c. Type **29**	15	15
164	2 c. Mallard	15	15
165	4 c. Collared petrel ..	20	20
166	5 c. Blue-faced booby ..	20	20
167	7 c. Friendly quail dove	20	20
168	8 c. Common shoveller ..	20	20
169	12 c. Polynesian reed warbler	20	20
170	15 c. American golden plover	25	25
171	20 c. Eastern reef heron	30	30
171a	25 c. Brown noddy ..	2·00	1·50
172	30 c. Brown booby ..	30	30
173	35 c. Audubon's shearwater	30	35
174	40 c. White-throated storm petrel (vert) ..	35	40
175	50 c. Bristle-thighed curlew (vert)	40	45
175a	55 c. White tern (vert) ..	6·00	7·00
176	$1 Kuhl's lory (vert) ..	85	90
177	$2 Long-tailed koel (vert)	1·60	1·75
178	$5 Great frigate bird (vert)	4·25	4·50

30. De Havilland " DH114 (Heron) ".

1982. Air. Inauguration of Tungaru Airline. Multicoloured.

179.	12 c. Type **30**	10	10
180.	30 c. Britten-Norman " Trislander "	15	20
181.	35 c. Casa " 212 (Aviocar) "	15	25
182.	50 c. Boeing " 727 " ..	25	35

31. Mary of Teck, Princess of Wales, 1893.

1982. 21st Birthday of Princess of Wales. Multicoloured.

183.	12 c. Type **31**	10	10
184.	50 c. Coat of arms of Mary of Teck	20	20
185.	$1 Diana, Princess of Wales	30	35

1982. Birth of Prince William of Wales. Nos. 183/5 optd. **ROYAL BABY.**

186.	12 c. Type **31** ..	10	10
187.	50 c. Coat of arms of Mary of Teck	25	25
188.	$1 Diana, Princess of Wales	40	45

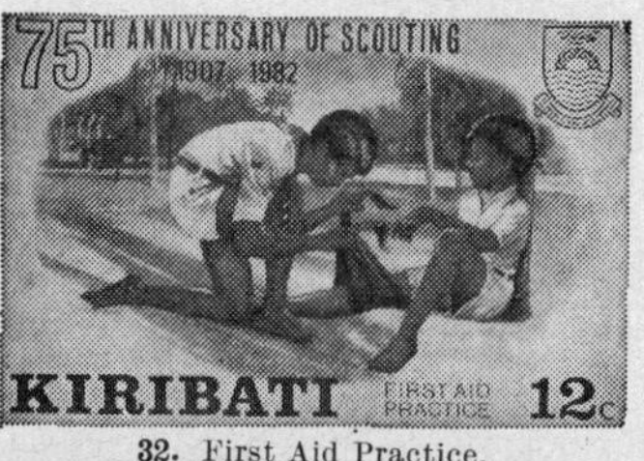

32. First Aid Practice.

1982. 75th Anniv. of Boy Scout Movement. Multicoloured.

189.	12 c. Type **32**	15	15
190.	25 c. Boat Repairs ..	20	30
191.	30 c. On parade	25	35
192.	40 c. Gilbert Islands 1977 8 c. Scouting stamp and " 75 "	35	60

33. Queen and Duke of Edinburgh with Local Dancer.

1982. Royal Visit. Multicoloured.

193.	12 c. Type **33**	15	15
194.	25 c. Queen, Duke of Edinburgh and outrigger canoe	20	20
195.	35 c. New Philatelic Bureau building	30	30

34. "Obaia, The Feathered" (Kiribati legend).

1983. Commonwealth Day. Multicoloured.

197.	12 c. Type **34**	10	10
198.	30 c. Robert Louis Stevenson Hotel, Abemama ..	15	20
199.	50 c. Container ship off Betio	20	25
200.	$1 Map of Kiribati ..	30	50

1983. Island Maps (2nd series). As T **25**. Multicoloured.

201.	12 c. Beru, Nikunau & canoe	15	15
202.	25 c. Abemama, Aranuka, Kuria and fish	20	20
203.	35 c. Nonouti & reef fishing (vert.)	30	35
204.	50 c. Tarawa and House of Assembly (vert.) ..	35	50

35. Collecting Coconuts.

1983. Copra Industry. Multicoloured.

205.	12 c. Type **35**	25	20
206.	25 c. Selecting coconuts for copra	45	35
207.	30 c. Removing husks ..	50	40
208.	35 c. Drying copra ..	55	45
209.	50 c. Loading copra at Betio	65	55

36. War Memorials.

1983. 40th Anniv. of Battle of Tarawa. Multicoloured.

210.	12 c. Type **36**	15	15
211.	30 c. Maps of Tarawa and Pacific Ocean	25	30
212.	35 c. Gun emplacement ..	30	35
213.	50 c. Modern and war-time landscapes	40	55
214.	$1 Aircraft carrier U.S.S. " Tarawa "	50	75

1983. Island Maps (3rd series). As T **25**. Multicoloured.

215.	12 c. Teraina and Captain Fenning's ship " Betsey " 1798	20	15
216.	30 c. Nikumaroro & Hawksbill Turtle	35	35
217.	35 c. Kanton & local postmark	35	40
218.	50 c. Banaba & Flying Fish	60	55

37. Tug " Riki ".

1984. Kiribati Shipping Corporation. Mult.

219.	12 c. Type **37**	30	15
220.	35 c. Ferry " Nei Nimanoa "	55	35
221.	50 c. Ferry " Nei Tebaa "	85	60
222.	$1 Cargo ship " Nei Momi "	1·40	1·10

38. Water and Sewage Schemes.

1984. "Ausipex" International Stamp Exhibition, Melbourne. Multicoloured.

224.	12 c. Type **38**	15	15
225.	30 c. "Nouamake", (game fishing boat)	25	30
226.	35 c. Overseas training schemes	30	40
227.	50 c. International communications link ..	40	55

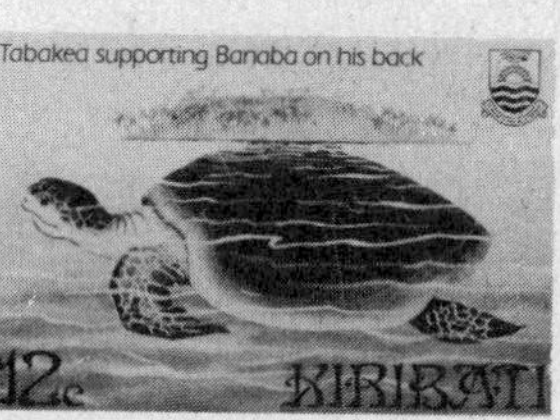

39. "Tabakea supporting Banaba".

1984. Kiribati Legends (1st series). Mult.

228.	12 c. Type **39**	15	20
229.	30 c. "Nakaa, Judge of the Dead"	25	35
230.	35 c. "Naareau and Dragonfly"	30	45
231.	50 c. "Whistling Ghosts"	35	55

See also Nos. 245/8.

40. Tang.

1985. Reef Fishes. Multicoloured.

232.	12 c. Type **40**	60	25
233.	25 c. White-barred Triggerfish	1·00	55
234.	35 c. Surgeon Fish ..	1·25	70
235.	80 c. Squirrel Fish ..	2·00	1·75

1985. Island Maps (4th series). As T **25**. Multicoloured.

237.	12 c. Tabuaeran and Great frigate bird ..	55	15
238.	35 c. Rawaki and germinating coconuts ..	85	40
239.	50 c. Arorae and xanthid crab	1·10	55
240.	$1 Tamana and fish hook	1·75	1·00

41. Youths playing Football on Beach.

1985. International Youth Year. Mult.
241. 15 c. Type **41** 60 45
242. 35 c. Logos of I.Y.Y. and Kiribati Youth Year 1·00 1·00
243. 40 c. Girl preparing food (vert.) 1·10 1·25
244. 55 c. Map illustrating Kiribati's youth exchange links 1·40 1·75

1985. Kiribati Legends (2nd series). As T **39**. Multicoloured.
245. 15 c. "Nang Kineia and the Tickling Ghosts" 50 30
246. 35 c. "Auriaria and Tituabine" 85 75
247. 40 c. "The first coming of Babai at Arorae" 1·00 1·00
248. 55 c. "Riiki and the Milky Way" 1·25 1·50

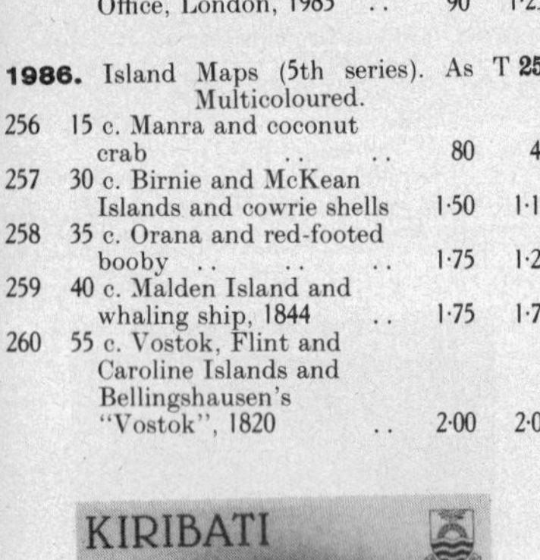

42. Map showing Telecommunications Satellite Link.

1985. Transport and Telecommunications Decade (1st issue). Multicoloured.
249. 15 c. Type **42** 1·00 75
250. 40 c. M.V. "Moanaraoi" (Tarawa–Suva service) 2·00 2·50
See also Nos. 268/9, 293/4 and 314/15.

1986. 60th Birthday of Queen Elizabeth II. As T **110** of Ascension. Multicoloured.
251. 15 c. Princess Elizabeth in Girl Guide uniform, Windsor Castle, 1938 15 15
252. 35 c. At Trooping the Colour, 1980 30 35
253. 40 c. With Duke of Edinburgh in Kiribati, 1982 35 40
254. 55 c. At banquet, Austrian Embassy, London, 1966 50 60
255. $1 At Crown Agents Head Office, London, 1983 90 1·25

1986. Island Maps (5th series). As T **25**. Multicoloured.
256 15 c. Manra and coconut crab 80 45
257 30 c. Birnie and McKean Islands and cowrie shells 1·50 1·10
258 35 c. Orana and red-footed booby 1·75 1·25
259 40 c. Malden Island and whaling ship, 1844 1·75 1·75
260 55 c. Vostok, Flint and Caroline Islands and Bellingshausen's "Vostok", 1820 2·00 2·00

43. "Lepidodactylus lugubris".

1986. Geckos. Multicoloured.
261. 15 c. Type **43** 45 45
262. 35 c. "Gehyra mutilata" 75 1·00
263. 40 c. "Hemidactylus frenatus" 90 1·25
264. 55 c. "Gehyra oceanica" 1·00 1·50
See also Nos. 274/7.

44. Maps of Australia and Kiribati.

1986. America's Cup Yachting Championship. Multicoloured.
265. 15 c. Type **44** 20 30
266. 55 c. America's Cup and map of course 50 75
267. $1·50 "Australia II" (1983 winner) 1·25 1·50

45. Freighter "Moamoa".

1987. Transport and Telecommunications Decade (2nd issue). Multicoloured.
268. 30 c. Type **45** 1·50 1·50
269. 55 c. Telephone switch-board and automatic exchange 2·50 3·00

1987. Island Maps (6th series). As T **25**. Multicoloured.
270. 15 c. Starbuck and red-tailed tropic bird 25 25
271. 30 c. Enderbury and white tern 40 50
272. 55 c. Tabiteuea and pandanus tree 50 70
273. $1 Onotoa and okai (house) 60 1·25

1987. Skinks. As T **43**. Multicoloured.
274. 15 c. "Emoia nigra" 15 20
275. 35 c. "Cryptoblepharus sp." 30 45
276. 40 c. "Emoia cyanura" 35 50
277. $1 "Lipinia noctua" 60 1·25

1987. Royal Ruby Wedding. Nos. 251/5 optd. **40TH WEDDING ANNIVERSARY.**
279. 15 c. Princess Elizabeth in Girl Guide uniform, Windsor Castle, 1938 15 15
280. 35 c. At Trooping the Colour, 1980 30 35
281. 40 c. With Duke of Edinburgh in Kiribati, 1982 35 45
282. 55 c. At banquet, Austrian Embassy, London, 1966 50 60
283. $1 At Crown Agents Head Office, London, 1983 90 1·25

46 Henri Dunant (founder)

1988. 125th Anniv of International Red Cross. Multicoloured.
284 15 c. Type **46** 35 30
285 35 c. Red Cross workers in Independence parade, 1979 60 60
286 40 c. Red Cross workers with patient 70 70
287 55 c. Gilbert & Ellice Islands 1970 British Red Cross Cent 10 c. stamp 90 1·00

47 Causeway built by Australia

1988. Bicentenary of Australian Settlement and "Sydpex '88" National Stamp Exhibition, Sydney. Multicoloured.
288 15 c. Type **47** 25 20
289 35 c. Capt. Cook and Pacific map 60 50
290 $1 Obverse of Australian $10 Bicent banknote 1·25 1·25
291 $1 Reverse of $10 Bicentenary banknote 1·25 1·25

48 Manual Telephone Exchange and Map of Kiritimati

1988. Transport and Communications Decade (3rd issue). Multicoloured.
293 35 c. Type **48** 50 50
294 45 c. Betio–Bairiki Causeway 60 60

49 "Hound" (brigantine), 1835

1989. Nautical History (1st series). Mult.
295 15 c. Type **49** 65 40
296 30 c. "Phantom" (brig), 1854 90 70
297 40 c. H.M.S."Alacrity" (schooner), 1873 1·00 90
298 $1 "Charles W. Morgan" (whaling ship), 1851 2·25 2·50
See also Nos. 343/7.

50 Eastern Reef Heron

1989. Birds with Young. Multicoloured.
299 15 c. Type **50** 35 35
300 15 c. Eastern reef heron chicks in nest 35 35
301 $1 White-tailed tropic bird 1·50 1·75
302 $1 Young white-tailed tropic bird 1·50 1·75
Nos. 299/300 and 301/2 were each printed together, se-tenant, each pair forming a composite design.

51 House of Assembly

1989. 10th Anniv of Independence. Mult.
303 15 c. Type **51** 25 25
304 $1 Constitution 1·25 1·25

1989. 20th Anniv of First Manned Landing on Moon. As T **126** of Ascension. Multicoloured.
305 20 c. "Apollo 10" on launch gantry 30 30
306 50 c. Crew of "Apollo 10" (30 × 30 mm) 70 70
307 60 c. "Apollo 10" emblem (30 × 30 mm) 80 80
308 75 c. "Apollo 10" splashdown, Hawaii 95 95

1989. "Philexfrance 89" International Stamp Exhibition, Paris, and "World Stamp Expo '89", Washington. As T **127** of Ascension showing Statue of Liberty. Multicoloured.
311 35 c. Examining fragment of Statue 70 85
312 35 c. Workman drilling Statue 70 85
313 35 c. Surveyor with drawing 70 85

52 Telecommunications Centre

1989. Transport and Communications Decade (4th issue). Multicoloured.
314 30 c. Type **52** 1·00 1·00
315 75 c. "Mataburo" (inter-island freighter) 2·00 2·25

1989. "Melbourne Stampshow '89". Nos. 301/2 optd with Exhibition emblem showing tram.
316 $1 White-tailed tropic bird 1·75 2·00
317 $1 Young white-tailed tropic bird 1·75 2·00

54 Virgin and Child (detail, "The Adoration of the Holy Child" (Denys Calvert))

1989. Christmas. Paintings. Multicoloured.
318 10 c. Type **54** 30 20
319 15 c. "The Adoration of the Holy Child" (Denys Calvert) 45 30
320 55 c. "The Holy Family and St. Elizabeth" (Rubens) 1·25 85
321 $1 "Madonna with Child and Maria Magdalena" (School of Correggio) 2·25 2·75

55 Gilbert and Ellice Islands 1912 1d. and G.B. Twopence Blue Stamps.

1990. 150th Anniv of the Penny Black and "Stamp World London 90" International Stamp Exhibition. Multicoloured.
322 15 c. Type **55** 40 30
323 50 c. Gilbert and Ellice Islands 1911 ½d. and G.B. Penny Black 90 80
324 60 c. Kiribati 1982 1 c. bird and G.B. 1870 ½d. 1·00 1·00
325 $1 Gilbert Islands 1976 1 c. ship and G.B. 1841 1d. brown 1·75 2·00

56 Blue-barred Orange Parrotfish

1990. Fishes. Mulricoloured.
326 1 c. Type **56** 10 10
327 5 c. Honycomb rock cod 10 10
328 10 c. Blue-fin jack 10 15
329 15 c. Paddle tail snapper 15 20
330 20 c. Variegated emperor 20 25
356 23 c. Bennett's pufferfish 25 30
331 25 c. Rainbow runner 25 30
332 30 c. Black-saddled coral trout 30 35
333 35 c. Great barracuda 35 40
334 40 c. Convict surgeonfish 40 45
335 50 c. Violet squirrelfish 45 50

336 60 c. Freckled hawkfish .. 60 65
337 75 c. Pennant coralfish .. 70 75
338 $1 Yellow and blue sea perch .. .. .. 95 1·00
339 $2 Pacific sailfish .. 2·00 2·10
340 $5 Whitetip reef shark .. 4·75 5·00

1990. 90th Birthday of Queen Elizabeth the Queen Mother. As T **134** of Ascension.
341 75 c. multicoloured .. 1·25 1·00
342 $2 black and green .. 2·75 3·00
DESIGNS—21 × 36 mm. 75 c. Queen Elizabeth the Queen Mother. 29 × 37 mm. $2 King George VI and Queen Elizabeth with air raid victim, London, 1940.

1990. Nautical History (2nd series). As T **49**. Multicoloured.
343 15 c. "Herald" (whaling ship), 1851 .. .. 30 20
344 50 c. "Belle" (barque), 1849 65 60
345 60 c. "Supply" (schooner), 1851 .. .. .. 75 80
346 75 c. "Triton" (whaling ship), 1848 .. .. 90 1·00

57 Manta Ray

1991. Endangered Fishes. Multicoloured.
348 15 c. Type **57** 40 30
349 20 c. Manta ray (different) 45 35
350 30 c. Whale shark .. 75 75
351 35 c. Whale shark (different) 80 85

1991. 65th Birthday of Queen Elizabeth II and 70th Birthday of Prince Philip. As T **139** of Ascension. Multicoloured.
366 65 c. Queen Elizabeth II .. 1·00 1·00
367 70 c. Prince Philip in R.A.F. uniform .. 1·00 1·00

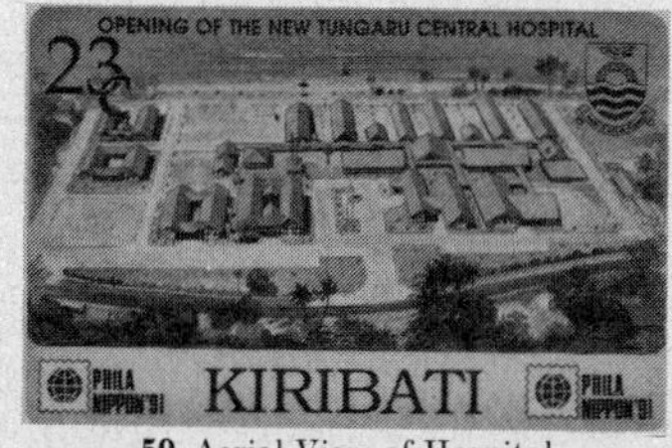
59 Aerial View of Hospital

1991. "Philanippon '91" International Stamp Exhibition, Tokyo, and Opening of Tungaru Central Hospital. Multicoloured.
368 23 c. Type **59** 30 30
369 50 c. Traditional dancers 60 60
370 60 c. Hospital entrance .. 70 70
371 75 c. Foundation stone and plaques 95 95

60 Mother and Child

1991. Christmas. Multicoloured.
373 23 c. Type **60** 30 30
374 50 c. The Holy Family in Pacific setting 65 65
375 60 c. The Holy Family in traditional setting .. 75 75
376 75 c. Adoration of the Shepherds .. .. 1·00 1·00

1992. 40th Anniv of Quenn Elizabeth II's Accession. As T **143** of Ascension. Mult.
377 23 c. Kiribati village .. 30 30
378 30 c. Lagoon at sunset .. 40 45
379 50 c. Tarawa waterfront .. 60 65
380 60 c. Three portraits of Queen Elizabeth .. 70 80
381 75 c. Queen Elizabeth II .. 90 1·00

1992. "EXPO '92" Worlds Fair, Seville. Nos. 356, 336/7 and 339 optd **EXPO '92 SEVILLA**.
382 23 c. Bennett's pufferfish 35 35
383 60 c. Freckled hawkfish .. 80 80
384 75 c. Pennant coralfish .. 95 95
385 $2 Pacific sailfish .. 2·25 2·25

62 Marine Training Centre Sign

1992. 25th Anniv of Marine Training Centre. Multicoloured.
386 23 c. Type **62** 45 35
387 50 c. Cadets on parade .. 80 80
388 60 c. Fire school 80 80
389 75 c. Lifeboat training .. 1·10 1·25

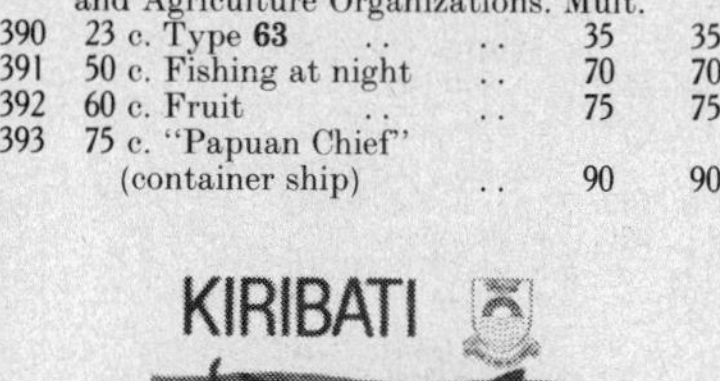
63 Healthy Children

1992. United Nations World Health and Food and Agriculture Organizations. Mult.
390 23 c. Type **63** 35 35
391 50 c. Fishing at night .. 70 70
392 60 c. Fruit 75 75
393 75 c. "Papuan Chief" (container ship) .. 90 90

64 Phoenix Petrel

1993. Birds. Multicoloured.
394 23 c. Type **64** 30 30
395 23 c. Cook's petrel .. 30 30
396 60 c. Northern pintail .. 75 75
397 60 c. Eurasian wigeon .. 75 75
398 75 c. Spectacled tern .. 90 90
399 75 c. Black-naped tern .. 90 90
400 $1 New Zealand stilt .. 1·25 1·25
401 $1 Wandering tattler .. 1·25 1·25

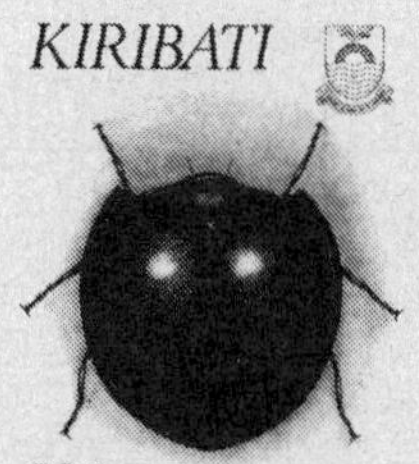
65 "Chilocorus nigritus"

1993. Insects. Multicoloured.
402 23 c. Type **65** 30 30
403 60 c. "Rodolia pumila" (ladybird) 70 70
404 75 c. "Rodolia cardinalis" (ladybird) 85 85
405 $1 "Cryptolaemus montrouzieri" .. .. 1·25 1·25

66 U.S. Air Reconnaissance Aircraft

1993. 50th Anniv of Battle of Tarawa. Mult.
406 23 c. Type **66** 20 25
407 23 c. U.S.S. "Nautilus" (submarine) 20 25
408 23 c. U.S.S. "Indianapolis" (cruiser) 20 25
409 23 c. U.S.S. "Pursuit" (destroyer) 20 25
410 23 c. Kingfisher spotter sea plane 20 25
411 23 c. U.S.S. "Ringgold" and "Dashiell" (destroyers) 20 25
412 23 c. Sherman tank on seabed 20 25
413 23 c. Fighter aircraft in lagoon 20 25
414 23 c. Naval wreck on seabed 20 25
415 23 c. First U.S. aircraft to land on Betio 20 25
416 75 c. Landing craft leaving transports 70 75
417 75 c. Marines landing on Betio 70 75
418 75 c. Landing craft approaching beach .. 70 75
419 75 c. Marines pinned down in surf 70 75
420 75 c. U.S.S. "Maryland" (battleship) 70 75
421 75 c. Aerial view of Betio Island 70 75
422 75 c. U.S. Navy memorial 70 75
423 75 c. Memorial to expatriates 70 75
424 75 c. Japanese memorial .. 70 75
425 75 c. Plan of Betio Island 70 75

67 Shepherds and Angels

1993. Christmas. Pacific Nativity scenes. Multicoloured.
426 23 c. Type **67** 20 25
427 40 c. Three Kings .. 40 45
428 60 c. Holy Family .. 60 65
429 75 c. Virgin and Child .. 70 75

69 Bryde's Whale and Calf

1994. Whales. Multicoloured.
432 23 c. Type **69** 20 25
433 23 c. Bryde's whale with two calves 20 25
434 40 c. Blue whale and calf (face value at left) .. 40 45
435 40 c. Blue whales and calf (face value at right) .. 40 45
436 60 c. Humpback whale and calf (face value at left) 60 65
437 60 c. Humpback whale and calf (face value at right) 60 65
438 75 c. Killer whale and calf 70 75
439 75 c. Killer whale and two calves 70 75

OFFICIAL STAMPS

1981. Nos. 86/135 optd **O.K.G.S.**
O 1 1 c. Type **16** 10 10
O 2 3 c. M.V. "Tautunu" (inter-island frighter) .. 10 10
O 3 5 c. Hibiscus 10 10
O 4 7 c. Catholic Cathedral, Tarawa 10 10
O 5 10 c. Maneaba, Bikenbeu 10 10
O 6 12 c. Betio Harbour .. 15 15
O 7 15 c. Eastern reef heron .. 15 20
O 8 20 c. Flamboyant tree .. 20 25
O 9 25 c. Moorish idol (fish) .. 25 30
O10 30 c. Frangipani 30 35
O11 35 c. G.I.P.C. Chapel, Tangintebu 35 40
O12 50 c. "Hypolimnas bolina" (butterfly) 50 55
O13 $1 "Tabakea" (Tarawa Lagoon ferry) .. .. 1·00 1·00
O14 $2 Evening scene .. 2·00 2·25
O15 $5 National flag .. .. 3·75 3·75

1983. Nos. 169, 172/3, 175 and 177 optd. **O.K.G.S.**
O 25. 12 c. Polynesian reed warbler 40 30
O 26. 30 c. Brown booby .. 70 50
O 27. 35 c. Audubon's shear-water 80 60
O 28. 50 c. Bristle-thighed curlew 1·00 80
O 29. $2 Long-tailed koel .. 3·00 2·75

POSTAGE DUE STAMPS

D 1. Kiribati Coat of Arms.

1981.
D 1. D 1. 1 c. black and mauve.. 10 10
D 2. 2 c. black and blue .. 10 10
D 3. 5 c. black and green.. 10 10
D 4. 10 c. black and brown 10 15
D 5. 20 c. black and blue.. 20 25
D 6. 30 c. black and brown 30 35
D 7. 40 c. black and purple 40 45
D 8. 50 c. black and green.. 45 50
D 9. $1 black and red .. 95 1·00

KISHANGARH

A state of Rajasthan, India. Now uses Indian stamps.

12 pies = 1 anna. 16 annas = 1 rupee.

1.

1899. Imperf. or perf.

No.	Description	Unused	Used
1. 1.	1 a. green	18·00	45·00
3.	1 a. blue	£375	

2. (¼a.)

5. (2 a.) Maharaja Sardul Singh.

1899. Various arms designs. Perf. or imperf.

No.	Type	Description	Unused	Used
21	2	¼ a. green	£170	£275
22a		¼ a. red	25	40
25		½ a. green	13·00	16·00
8		½ a. red	£1100	£750
26a		½ a. blue	40	40
7		½ a. lilac	70·00	£110
27	2	1 a. grey	3·25	1·90
29		1 a. mauve	75	60
12b		1 a. pink	50·00	£130
15	5	2 a. orange	4·00	4·50
31	2	4 a. brown	2·00	4·00
32		1 r. green	10·00	15·00
17		1 r. lilac	20·00	25·00
33		1 r. yellow	£450	£275
34		2 r. red	38·00	45·00
35		5 r. mauve	32·00	45·00

11. (½ a.)

12. Maharaja Sardul Singh.

1903. Imperf. or perf.

No.	Description	Unused	Used
39. 11.	½ a. pink	5·00	3·00
40. 12.	2 a. orange	3·00	4·00
41. 2.	8 a. grey	5·00	7·50

13. Maharaja Madan Singh.

14. Maharaja Madan Singh.

1904.

No.	Description	Unused	Used
42a. 13.	¼ a. red	45	35
43a.	½ a. brown	35	30
44a.	1 a. blue	50	75
45.	2 a. orange	8·00	7·00
46a.	4 a. brown	8·00	9·00
47.	8 a. violet	6·00	11·00
48.	1 r. green	14·00	17·00
49.	2 r. yellow	16·00	55·00
50.	5 r. brown	21·00	75·00

1912.

No.	Description	Unused	Used
63 14.	¼ a. blue	20	45
64	½ a. green	20	70
65	1 a. red	1·00	2·00
54	2 a. purple	2·50	5·00
67	4 a. blue	6·00	8·00
68	8 a. brown	7·00	32·00
69	1 r. mauve	14·00	75·00
70	2 r. green	50·00	£130
71	5 r. brown	£100	£250

INDEX

Countries can be quickly located by referring to the index at the end of this volume.

15.

16. Maharaja Yagyanarayan Singh.

1913.

No.	Description	Unused	Used
59.15.	¼ a. blue	20	35
60.	2 a. purple	7·00	17·00

1928.

No.	Description	Unused	Used
72.16.	¼ a. blue	40	1·75
73.	½ a. green	1·10	65
74. –	1 a. red	60	1·25
75. –	2 a. purple	3·00	7·00
76.16.	4a. brown	1·25	1·75
77.	8 a. violet	3·50	17·00
78.	1 r. green	8·50	35·00
79.	2 r yellow	25·00	80·00
80.	5 r. red	27·00	£100

Nos. 74/5 are larger.

OFFICIAL STAMPS

1918. Optd. **ON K S D.**

No.	Type	Description	Unused	Used
O 5	2.	¼ a. green	—	£100
O 6		½ a. pink	2·00	60
O 7		½ a. blue	£100	32·00
O 9		1 a. mauve	17·00	1·50
O10	5.	2 a. orange	—	£110
O11	2.	4 a. brown	28·00	16·00
O16		8 a. grey	38·00	22·00
O12		1 r. green	95·00	85·00
O13		2 r. brown	—	£700
O14		5 r. mauve	—	£950

1918. Optd. **ON K S D.**

No.	Description	Unused	Used
O 15.12.	2 a. orange	35·00	6·00

1918. Optd. **ON K S D.**

No.	Description	Unused	Used
O 17. 13.	¼ a. red	—	£140
O 18.	½ a. brown	70	35
O 19.	1 a. blue	7·00	4·00
O 20.	2 a. orange	—	£550
O 21.	4 a. brown	30·00	18·00
O 22.	8 a. violet	£170	£130
O 23.	1 r. green	£325	£300
O 24.	5 r. brown		

1918. Optd. **ON K S D.**

No.	Description	Unused	Used
O 28. 14.	¼ a. blue	50	50
O 29.	½ a. green	75	75
O 30a.	1 a. red	1·00	1·00
O 31.	2 a. purple	5·50	4·00
O 32.	4 a. blue	20·00	15·00
O 33.	8 a. brown	75·00	40·00
O 34.	1 r. mauve	£225	£225
O 35.	2 r. green		
O 36.	5 r. brown	£950	

1918. Optd. **ON K S D.**

No.	Description	Unused	Used
O 25.15.	¼ a. blue	6·00	
O 27.	2 a. purple	£190	£200

For later issues see **RAJASTHAN.**

KUWAIT

An independent Arab Shaikhdom on the N.W. coast of the Persian Gulf with Indian and later British postal administration. On 1st February, 1959, the Kuwait Government assumed responsibility for running its own postal service. In special treaty relations with Great Britain until 19 June 1961 when Kuwait became completely independent.

1923. 12 pies = 1 anna; 16 annas = 1 rupee.
1957. 100 naye paise = 1 rupee.

Stamps of India optd. **KUWAIT.**

1923. King George V.

No.	Type	Description	Unused	Used
16	56	½ a. green	1·00	1·25
16a	79	½ a. green	4·50	70
2	57	1 a. brown	1·50	1·25
17a	81	1 a. brown	4·50	50
3	58	1½ a. brown (No. 163)	1·25	4·00
4	59	2 a. lilac	1·75	70
19b		2 a. red	3·50	1·60
18	70	2 a. lilac	1·75	60
19		2 a. red	23·00	60·00
5	61	2½ a. blue	2·00	7·50
6	62	3 a. orange	4·00	16·00
20		3 a. blue	2·75	1·50
21		3 a. red	5·50	4·00
22a	63	4 a. green	5·00	8·50
22	71	4 a. green	25·00	60·00
9	64	6 a. bistre	8·50	13·00
23	65	8 a. mauve	9·00	13·00
11	66	12 a. red	14·00	27·00
12	67	1 r. brown and green	14·00	14·00
26		2 r. red and orange	10·00	50·00
27		5 r. blue and violet	70·00	£180
28		10 r. green and red	£160	£350
29		15 r. blue and olive	£450	£700

1933. Air.

No.	Description	Unused	Used
31. 72.	2 a. green	11·00	20·00
32.	3 a. blue	1·25	2·00
33.	4 a. olive	85·00	£170
34.	6 a. bistre	1·50	4·00

1939. King George VI.

No.	Description	Unused	Used
36. 91.	½ a. brown	8·00	1·25
38.	1 a. red	8·00	1·00
39. 92.	2 a. red	8·00	2·00
41. –	3 a. green	8·00	1·75
43. –	4 a. brown	30·00	10·00
44. –	6 a. green	25·00	6·50
45. –	8 a. violet	28·00	28·00
46. –	12 a. red	23·00	30·00
47. 93.	1 r. slate and brown	4·50	2·25
48.	2 r. purple and brown	3·75	8·50
49.	5 r. green and blue	12·00	15·00
50.	10 r. purple and red	60·00	60·00
51.	15 r. brown and green	85·00	£140

1942. King George VI stamps of 1940.

No.	Description	Unused	Used
52.100a.	3 p. slate	1·00	1·50
53.	½ a. purple	1·00	1·50
54.	9 p. green	1·25	5·50
55.	1 a. red	1·00	1·00
56. 101.	1½ a. violet	1·50	4·25
57.	2 a. red	1·50	1·50
58.	3 a. violet	1·50	2·25
59.	3½ a. blue	3·25	3·75
60. 102.	4 a. brown	1·25	1·50
60a.	6 a. green	14·00	8·50
61.	8 a. violet	4·50	1·75
62.	12 a. purple	5·50	2·00
63. –	14 a. purple (No. 277)	8·50	12·00

From 1948 onwards, for stamps with similar surcharges, but without name of country, see British Postal Agencies in Eastern Arabia.

Stamps of Great Britain surch. **KUWAIT** and new values in Indian currency.

1948. King George VI.

No.	Description	Unused	Used
64. 128.	½ a. on ½d. pale green	40	60
84.	½ a. on ½d. orange	50	1·50
65.	1 a. on 1d. pale red	40	50
85.	1 a. on 1d. blue	50	60
66.	1½ a. on 1½d. pale brown	40	50
86.	1½ a. on 1½d. green	50	2·25
67.	2 a. on 2d. pale orange	40	60
87.	2 a. on 2d. brown	50	50
68.	2½ a. on 2½d. light blue	30	50
88.	2½ a. on 2½d. red	50	1·25
69.	3 a. on 3d. pale violet	40	20
89. 129.	4 a. on 4d. blue	50	45
70.	6 a. on 6d. purple	40	20
71. 130.	1 r. on 1s. brown	50	60
72. 131.	2 r. on 2s. 6d. green	1·50	3·00
73.	5 r. on 5s. red	2·50	4·25
73a. –	10 r. on 10s. bright blue (No. 478a)	38·00	6·00

1948. Silver Wedding.

No.	Description	Unused	Used
74. 137.	2½ a. on 2½d. blue	50	30
75. 138.	15 r. on £1 blue	30·00	28·00

1948. Olympic Games.

No.	Description	Unused	Used
76. 139.	2½ a. on 2½d. blue	1·00	1·25
77. 140.	3 a. on 3d. violet	1·00	1·25
78.	6 a. on 5d. purple	1·25	1·25
79. –	1 r. on 1s. brown	1·25	1·25

1949. U.P.U.

No.	Description	Unused	Used
80. 143.	2½ a. on 2½d. blue	75	85
81. 144.	3 a. on 3d. violet	1·00	1·25
82. –	6 a. on 6d. purple	1·40	1·25
83. –	1 r. on 1s. brown	1·60	1·00

1951. Pictorial high values.

No.	Description	Unused	Used
90. 147.	2 r. on 2s. 6d. green	13·00	4·25
91. –	5 r. on 5s. red (No. 510)	16·00	5·00
92. –	10 r. on 10s. blue No. 511)	27·00	6·00

1952. Queen Elizabeth II.

No.	Description	Unused	Used
110 154.	½ a. on ½d. orange	30	40
94	1 a. on 1d. blue	20	10
95	1½ a. on 1½d. green	15	10
113	2 a. on 2d. brown	30	40
97 155.	2½ a. on 2½d. red	15	10
98	3 a. on 3d. lilac	40	10
99	4 a. on 4d. blue	1·25	65
100 157.	6 a. on 6d. purple	1·00	10
101 160.	12 a. on 1s. 3d. green	5·00	2·25
119	1 r. on 1s. 6d. blue	3·00	30

1953. Coronation.

No.	Description	Unused	Used
103. 161.	2½ a. on 2½d. red	2·75	75
104.	4 a. on 4d. blue	3·00	80
105. 163.	12 a. on 1s. 3d. green	4·50	2·00
106. –	1 r. on 1s. 6d. blue	4·00	80

1955. Pictorials.

No.	Description	Unused	Used
107. 166.	2 r. on 2s. 6d. brown	6·00	1·50
108. –	5 r. on 5s. red	7·00	3·50
109. –	10 r. on 10s. blue	8·00	4·00

1957. Queen Elizabeth II.

No.	Description	Unused	Used
120. 157.	1 n.p. on 5d. brown	10	60
121. 154.	3 n.p. on ½d. orange	50	1·00
122.	6 n.p. on 1d. blue	50	1·00
123.	9 n.p. on 1½d. green	50	90
124.	12 n.p. on 2d. pale brn.	50	90
125. 155.	15 n.p. on 2½d. red	50	20
126.	20 n.p. on 3d. lilac	50	20
127.	25 n.p. on 4d. blue	2·00	3·00
128. 157.	40 n.p. on 6d. purple	90	20
129. 158.	50 n.p. on 9d. olive	5·50	3·50
130. 160.	75 n.p. on 1s. 3d. green	5·50	4·00

For stamps issued by Kuwait government see volume 2.

OFFICIAL STAMPS

1923. Stamps of India (King George V) optd. **KUWAIT SERVICE.**

No.	Type	Description	Unused	Used
O 1	56	½ a. green	50	14·00
O 2	57	1 a. brown	70	8·00
O 3	58	1½ a. brown (No. 163)	1·50	20·00
O 4	59	2 a. lilac	3·25	17·00
O 17	70	2 a. lilac	50·00	£110
O 5	61	2½ a. blue	2·75	32·00
O 6	62	3 a. orange	3·25	45·00
O 19		3 a. blue	2·25	28·00
O 8	63	4 a. green	3·00	42·00
O 20	71	4 a. green	4·25	60·00
O 9	65	8 a. mauve	4·50	45·00
O 22	66	12 a. red	18·00	£100
O 10	67	1 r. brown and green	10·00	85·00
O 11		2 r. red and orange	16·00	£120
O 12		5 r. blue and violet	48·00	£250
O 13		10 r. green and red	95·00	£350
O 14		15 r. blue and olive	£160	£475

LABUAN

An island off the N. coast of Borneo, ceded to Great Britain in 1846, and a Crown Colony from 1902. Incorporated with Straits Settlements in 1906, it used Straits stamps till it became part of N. Borneo in 1946.

100 cents = 1 dollar.

1.

6 Cents (10.)

Two Cents (11.)

1879.

No.	Type	Description	Unused	Used
5	1	2 c. green	11·00	15·00
39		2 c. red	1·40	3·50
6		6 c. orange	70·00	80·00
40		6 c. green	5·00	4·50
7		8 c. red	65·00	75·00
41		8 c. violet	2·25	4·50
43		10 c. brown	4·00	7·00
9		12 c. red	£170	£200
45		12 c. blue	3·25	6·00
4		16 c. blue	40·00	75·00
46		16 c. grey	3·25	6·00
21		40 c. orange	8·50	35·00

1880. Surch. in figures.

No.	Description	Unused	Used
12 1.	6 on 16 c. blue	£1100	£550
11	8 on 12 c. red	£600	£475

1881. Surch. **EIGHT CENTS.**

No.	Description	Unused	Used
14. 1.	8 c. on 12 c. red	£160	£200

1881. Surch. **Eight Cents.**

No.	Description	Unused	Used
15. 1.	8 c. on 12 c. red	75·00	85·00

1883. Manuscript surch. **one Dollar A.S.H.**

No.	Description	Unused	Used
22. 1.	$1 on 16 c. blue	£1900	

1885. Surch. **2 CENTS** horiz.

No.	Description	Unused	Used
23. 1.	2 c. on 8 c. red	£100	
24.	2 c. on 16 c. blue	£700	£700

1885. Surch. **2 Cents** horiz.

No.	Description	Unused	Used
25. 1.	2 c. on 16 c. blue	85·00	£140

1885. Surch. with large **2 Cents** diag.

No.	Description	Unused	Used
26. 1.	2 c. on 8 c. red	42·00	75·00

1891. Surch. as **T 10.**

No.	Description	Unused	Used
35. 1.	6 c. on 8 c. violet	4·50	4·50
37.	6 c. on 16 c. blue	£1300	£1200
38.	6 c. on 40 c. orange	£4250	£2500

1892. Surch. as **T 11.**

No.	Description	Unused	Used
49. 1.	2 c. on 40 c. orange	£120	80·00
50.	6 c. on 16 c. grey	£200	£120

Most issues from 1894 exist cancelled-to-order with black bars. Our prices are for stamps postally used, cancelled-to-order examples being worth considerably less.

1894. Types of North Borneo (different colours) optd. **LABUAN.**

No.	Type	Description	Unused	Used
62	24	1 c. black and mauve	1·50	3·75
63	25	2 c. black and blue	2·50	4·50
64	26	3 c. black and yellow	3·75	7·50
65a	27	5 c. black and green	18·00	8·50
67	28	6 c. black and red	2·50	6·50
68	29	8 c. black and pink	9·00	16·00
70	30	12 c. black and orange	17·00	35·00
71	31	18 c. black and olive	22·00	38·00
73a	32	24 c. blue and mauve	13·00	30·00
80	10	25 c. green	15·00	16·00
81	–	50 c. mauve (as No. 82)	15·00	17·00
82	–	$1 blue (as No. 83)	32·00	25·00

1895. No. 83 of North Borneo surch. **LABUAN** and value in cents.

No.	Description	Unused	Used
75.	4 c. on $1 red	1·00	1·25
76.	10 c. on $1 red	1·25	1·40
77.	20 c. on $1 red	13·00	6·00
78.	30 c. on $1 red	15·00	20·00
79.	40 c. on $1 red	12·00	12·00

1896. Jubilee of Cession of Labuan to Gt. Britain. Nos. 62 to 68 optd. **1846 JUBILEE 1896.**

No.	Type	Description	Unused	Used
83f	24	1 c. black and mauve	17·00	13·00
84	25	2 c. black and blue	19·00	12·00
85	26	3 c. black and yellow	20·00	20·00
86b	27	5 c. black and green	32·00	16·00
87	28	6 c. black and red	16·00	17·00
88b	29	8 c. black and pink	21·00	11·00

1897. Stamps of North Borneo. Nos. 92 to 106 (different colours) optd. **LABUAN.**

Opt. at top of stamp.

No.	Description	Unused	Used
89	1 c. black and brown	2·25	4·00
90	2 c. black and blue	6·00	3·50
91b	3 c. black and yellow	7·50	5·00
92a	5 c. black and green	21·00	25·00
93b	6 c. black and red	3·50	16·00
94a	8 c. black and pink	13·00	10·00
95a	12 c. black and orange	21·00	32·00

Overprint at foot of stamp.

No.	Description	Unused	Used
98a. –	12 c. black and orange (as No. 106)	30·00	35·00

Opt. at foot. Inscr. "POSTAL REVENUE".

No.	Description	Unused	Used
96b –	18 c. black and olive (as No. 108)	15·00	27·00

Opt. at foot. Inscr. "POSTAGE AND REVENUE".

No.	Description	Unused	Used
99a. –	18 c. black and olive (as No. 110)	60·00	60·00

Opt. at top. Inscr. "POSTAGE AND REVENUE".

No.	Description	Unused	Used
101b. –	18 c. black and olive (as No. 110)	24·00	38·00

Opt. at top. "POSTAGE AND REVENUE" omitted.
97a – 24 c. blue and lilac (as No. 109) .. .. 10·00 30·00
Opt. at top. Inscr. "POSTAGE AND REVENUE".
100. – 24 c. blue and mauve (No. 111) .. .. 15·00 40·00

1899. Stamps of Labuan surch **4 CENTS.**
102 4 c. on 5 c. blk & grn (92a) 19·00 26·00
103 4 c. on 6 c. blk & red (93b) 15·00 19·00
104a 4 c. on 8 c. black and pink (94a) .. .. .. 15·00 30·00
105 4 c. on 12 c. black and orange (98a) .. .. 25·00 29·00
106 4 c. on 18 c. black and olive (101b) .. .. 16·00 17·00
107 4 c. on 24 c. blue and mauve (100) .. .. 16·00 22·00
108 4 c. on 25 c. green (80) .. 5·50 7·50
109 4 c. on 50 c. purple (81) .. 5·50 7·50
110 4 c. on $1 blue (82) .. 5·50 7·50

1900. Stamps of North Borneo, as Nos. 95 to 107, optd **LABUAN.**
111 2 c. black and green .. 3·50 2·50
112 4 c. black and brown .. 4·25 17·00
113 4 c. black and red .. 10·00 2·75
114 5 c. black and blue .. 20·00 18·00
115 10 c. brown and grey .. 35·00 50·00
116 16 c. green and brown .. 45·00 55·00

18.

1902.
117 18 1 c. black and purple 2·75 4·00
118 2 c. black and green 2·75 3·00
119 3 c. black and brown 2·75 4·00
120 4 c. black and red 2·75 2·75
121 8 c. black and orange 2·75 5·50
122 10 c. brown and blue 3·00 5·50
123 12 c. black and yellow 3·25 7·00
124 16 c. green and brown 3·00 8·50
125 18 c. black and brown 3·00 8·00
126 25 c. green and blue 3·25 10·00
127 50 c. purple and lilac 10·00 23·00
128 $1 red and orange 5·50 24·00

1904. Surch **4 cents.**
129 – 4 c. on 5 c. black and green (92a) .. .. 18·00 28·00
130 – 4 c. on 6 c. black and red (93b) .. .. 12·00 27·00
131 – 4 c. on 8 c. black and pink (94a) .. .. 16·00 30·00
132 – 4 c. on 12 c. black and orange (98a) .. .. 19·00 30·00
133 – 4 c. on 18 c. black and olive (101b) .. .. 17·00 32·00
134 – 4 c. on 24 c. blue and mauve (100) .. .. 15·00 32·00
135 10 4 c. on 25 c. green (80) .. 8·50 18·00
136 4 c. on 50 c. purple (81) 8·50 18·00
137 4 c. on $1 blue (82) .. 8·50 18·00

POSTAGE DUE STAMPS
1901. Optd. **POSTAGE DUE.**
D 1. 2 c. black and green (111) 9·00 16·00
D 2. 3 c. black & yellow (91) .. 14·00 60·00
D 3. 4 c. black and red (113) .. 17·00 60·00
D 4. 5 c. black and blue (114) .. 24·00 65·00
D 5. 6 c. black and red (93b) .. 12·00 60·00
D 6. 8 c. black and pink (94a) 30·00 65·00
D 7. 12 c. black & orange (98a) 48·00 65·00
D 8. 18 c. black & olive (101b) 13·00 60·00
D 9. 24 c. blue & mauve (100) 24·00 60·00

LAGOS

A British colony on the southern coast of Nigeria. United with Southern Nigeria in 1906 to form the Colony and Protectorate of Southern Nigeria.

12 pence = 1 shilling.
20 shillings = 1 pound.

1.

3.

1874.
21 1. ½d. green .. .. .. 1·00 20
17 1d. mauve .. .. .. 15·00 10·00
22 1d. red .. .. .. 1·25 30
11 2d. blue .. .. .. 35·00 12·00
23 2d. grey .. .. .. 40·00 5·00
19 3d. brown .. .. .. 11·00 5·00
5 4d. red .. .. .. 60·00 40·00
24 4d. lilac .. .. .. 75·00 8·50
25 6d. green .. .. .. 5·00 23·00
26 1s. orange .. .. .. 5·00 13·00
27 2s. 6d. black £275 £250
28 5s. blue £450 £400
29 10s. brown £1200 £800

1887.
30. 1. 2d. mauve and blue .. 1·50 1·00
31. 2½d. blue .. .. .. 1·50 1·75
32. 3d. mauve and brown .. 2·50 3·25
33. 4d. mauve and black .. 2·00 1·75
34. 5d. mauve and green .. 2·00 11·00
35. 6d. mauve .. .. 4·50 3·00
35a. 6d. mauve and red .. 4·50 12·00
36. 7½d. mauve and red .. 2·00 23·00
37. 10d. mauve and yellow .. 2·75 13·00
38. 1s. green and black .. 3·00 15·00
39. 2s. 6d. green and red .. 22·00 60·00
40. 5s. green and blue .. 32·00 £110
41. 10s. green and brown .. 60·00 £150

1893. Surch. **HALF PENNY** and bars.
42. 1. ½d. on 4d. mauve & black 3·00 2·50

1904.
54a 3 ½d. green .. .. 5·00 1·75
55a 1d. purple & black on red 1·00 10
56 2d. purple and blue .. 2·00 75
47 2½d. purple & blue on bl 1·00 1·50
58 3d. purple and brown .. 3·00 90
59 6d. purple and mauve .. 4·50 1·40
60 1s. green and black .. 4·25 6·00
61 2s. 6d. green and red .. 10·00 25·00
62 5s. green and blue .. 19·00 70·00
63 10s. green and brown .. 48·00 £130

LAS BELA

A state of Baluchistan. Now part of Pakistan.

12 pies = 1 anna. 16 annas = 1 rupee.

1.

The 1 a. has the English inscriptions in a circle with the native inscription across the centre.

1897.
1. 1. ½ a. black on white .. 13·00 7·50
2 ½ a. black on blue .. 8·00 5·00
3. ½ a. black on grey .. 7·50 4·50
12. ½ a. black on green .. 7·00 6·00
8. – 1 a. black on orange .. 12·00 13·00

LEEWARD ISLANDS

A group of islands in the Br. W. Indies, including Antigua, Barbuda, British Virgin Islands, Dominica (till end of 1939), Montserrat, Nevis, and St. Christopher (St. Kitts). Stamps of Leeward Islands were used concurrent with the issues for the respective islands until they were withdrawn on the 1st July, 1956.

1890. 12 pence = 1 shilling;
20 shillings = 1 pound.
1951. 100 cents = 1 West Indian dollar.

1.

(3.)

1890.
1. 1. ½d. mauve and green .. 1·25 45
2. 1d. mauve and red .. 1·50 10
3. 2½d. mauve and blue .. 2·75 15
4. 4d. mauve and orange .. 2·75 7·00
5. 6d. mauve and brown .. 6·00 7·50
6. 7d. mauve and grey .. 1·75 9·00
7. 1s. green and red .. 11·00 28·00
8. 5s. green and blue .. £130 £225

1897. Diamond Jubilee. Optd. with T **3.**
9. 1. ½d. mauve and green .. 2·50 8·00
10. 1d. mauve and red .. 3·25 8·50
11. 2½d. mauve and blue .. 3·50 8·50
12. 4d. mauve and orange .. 24·00 55·00
13. 6d. mauve and brown .. 40·00 80·00
14. 7d. mauve and grey .. 45·00 80·00
15. 1s. green and red .. £120 £190
16. 5s. green and blue .. £600 £900

1902. Surch. in words.
17. 1. 1d. on 4d. mauve & orange 80 3·75
18. 1d. on 6d. mauve & brown 1·00 5·50
19. 1d. on 7d. mauve and grey 90 3·25

1902. As T **1**, but portrait of King Edward VII.
20. ½d. purple and green .. 1·75 40
21. 1d. purple and red .. 3·00 10
22. 2d. purple and brown .. 2·25 4·00
23. 2½d. purple and blue .. 1·50 1·25
24. 3d. purple and black .. 1·00 5·50
25. 6d. purple and brown .. 1·00 6·50
26. 1s. green and red .. 1·75 14·00
27. 2s. 6d. green and black .. 20·00 48·00
28. 5s. green and blue .. 40·00 55·00

1907. As last. Colours changed.
36. ¼d. brown 60 75
37. ½d. green .. .. .. 1·25 65
38. 1d. red .. .. .. 2·50 50
39. 2d. grey .. .. .. 1·00 7·50
40. 2½d. blue .. .. .. 1·60 2·50
41. 3d. purple and yellow .. 1·25 4·25
42. 6d. purple .. .. .. 3·00 5·50
43. 1s. black on green .. 2·75 15·00
44. 2s. 6d. black & red on blue 29·00 45·00
45. 5s. green and red on yellow 30·00 48·00

10. King George V.

14. King George VI.

1912.
46 10. ¼d. brown 70 20
59 ½d. green 40 30
60 1d. red 40 15
61 1d. violet 40 50
63 1½d. red .. .. .. 1·00 75
64 1½d. brown 40 10
65 2d. grey 65 30
67 2½d. blue 75 30
66 2½d. yellow .. .. 3·75 32·00
69 3d. purple on yellow .. 40 4·00
68 3d. blue .. .. .. 2·00 16·00
70 4d. black & red on yellow 1·25 13·00
71 5d. purple and green .. 75 4·25
53 6d. purple .. .. .. 1·00 6·00
54 1s. black on green .. 1·00 5·00
55 2s. purple & blue on blue 3·75 26·00
75 2s. 6d. black & red on blue 6·50 22·00
76 3s. green and violet .. 8·50 22·00
77 4s. black and red .. .. 8·50 32·00
57b 5s. green & red on yellow 10·00 42·00
Larger type, as T **15** of Malta.
79. 10s. green and red on green 48·00 70·00
80. £1 purple and black on red £225 £250

1935. Silver Jubilee. As T **13** of Antigua.
88. 1d. blue and red .. 90 55
89. 1½d. blue and grey .. 1·50 70
90. 2½d. brown and blue .. 1·50 2·50
91. 1s. grey and purple .. 5·50 9·00

1937. Coronation. As T **2** of Aden.
92. 1d. red 30 15
93. 1½d. brown 40 35
94. 2½d. blue 40 45

1938.
95a 14 ¼d. brown 10 30
96 ½d. green 30 30
97 ½d. grey 30 40
99 1d. red .. .. .. 1·00 80
100 1d. green 55 15
101 1½d. brown 60 40
102 1½d. orange and black .. 50 15
103 2d. grey 70 45
104 2d. red .. .. .. 1·40 40
105a 2½d. blue 60 60
106 2½d. black and purple .. 55 15
107a 3d. orange 40 60
108 3d. blue 65 15
109a 6d. purple .. .. 3·75 2·00
110b 1s. black on green .. 3·50 80
111ab 2s. purple & blue on blue 8·50 1·25
112a 5s. green & red on yellow 26·00 14·00
113b 10s. green & red on green £110 50·00
114b £1 purple and black on red 32·00 24·00
Nos. 113b/4b are as Type **15** of Bermuda but with portrait of King George VI.

1946. Victory. As T **9** of Aden.
115. 1½d. brown 15 10
116. 3d. orange 15 20

1949. Silver Wedding. As **10/11** of Aden.
117. 2½d. blue 10 10
118. 5s. green .. .. .. 3·75 2·75

1949. U.P.U. As T **20/23** of Antigua.
119. 2½d. black 15 10
120. 3d. blue 40 50
121. 6d. mauve 40 40
122. 1s. turquoise 45 40

1951. Inauguration of B.W.I. University College. As T **24/25** of Antigua.
123. 3 c. orange and black .. 30 30
124. 12 c. red and violet .. 60 30

1953. Coronation. As T **13** of Aden.
125. 3 c. black and green .. 20 55

1954. As T **14** but portrait of Queen Elizabeth II facing left.
126. ½ c. brown 10 20
127. 1 c. grey 10 20
128. 2 c. green 10 10
129. 3 c. yellow and black .. 20 30
130. 4 c. red 20 10
131. 5 c. black and purple .. 50 30
132. 6 c. yellow 50 20
133. 8 c. blue 80 10
134. 12 c. purple 80 10
135. 24 c. black and green .. 80 10
136. 48 c. purple and blue .. 6·00 2·75
137. 60 c. brown and green .. 6·00 2·25
138. $1.20 green and red .. 5·00 2·75

Larger type as T **15** of Malta.
139. $2.40 green and red .. 5·50 5·00
140. $4.80 purple and black 5·50 6·50

LESOTHO

Formerly Basutoland, attained independence on 4th October, 1966, and changed its name to Lesotho.

100 cents = 1 rand.

33. Moshoeshoe I and Moshoeshoe II.

1966. Independence.
106 33 2½ c. brown, black & red 10 10
107 5 c. brown, black & blue 10 10
108 10 c. brown, black & grn. 15 10
109 20 c. brown, black & pur. 20 15

1966. Nos. 69 etc. of Basutoland optd. **LESOTHO.**
110. 8. ½ c. black and sepia .. 10 10
111. – 1 c. black and green .. 10 10
112. – 2 c. blue and orange .. 60 10
113. 26. 2½ c. sage and red .. 20 10
114. – 3½ c. indigo and blue .. 30 10
115. – 5 c. brown and green .. 20 10
116. – 10 c. bronze and purple .. 20 10
117. – 12½ c. brown & turquoise 30 20
118. – 25 c. blue and red .. 40 20
119. – 50 c. black and red .. 80 50
120. 9. 1 r. black and purple .. 1·00 75

35. "Education, Culture and Science".

1966. 20th Anniv. of U.N.E.S.C.O.
121 35 2½ c. yellow and green .. 10 10
122 5 c. green and olive .. 15 10
123 12½ c. blue and red .. 35 10
124 25 c. orange and blue .. 60 25

36. Maize.

1967.
125 36 ½ c. green and violet .. 10 10
126 – 1 c. sepia and red .. 10 10
127 – 2 c. yellow and green .. 10 10
128 – 2½ c. black and ochre .. 10 10
151 – 3 c. choc., green & brown 15 15
129 – 3½ c. blue and yellow .. 10 10
130 – 5 c. bistre and blue .. 10 10
131 – 10 c. brown and grey .. 10 10
132 – 12½ c. black and orange .. 20 10
133 – 25 c. black and blue .. 75 20
134 – 50 c. black, blue & turq. 4·50 45
135 – 1 r. multicoloured .. 1·25 75
136 – 2 r. black, gold & purple 1·50 1·75
DESIGNS—HORIZ. 1 c. Cattle. 2 c. Aloes. 2½ c. Basotho Hat. 3 c. Sorghum. 3½ c. Merino Sheep ("Wool"). 5 c. Basotho Pony. 10 c. Wheat. 12½ c. Angora Goat ("Mohair"). 25 c. Maletsunyane Falls. 50 c. Diamonds. 1 r. Arms of Lesotho. VERT. 2 r. Moshoeshoe II.
See also Nos. 191/203.

46. Students and University.

1967. 1st Conferment of University Degrees.
137. 46. 1 c. sepia, blue & orange 10 10
138. 2½ c. sepia, ultram. & blue 10 10
139. 12½ c. sepia, blue and red 10 10
140. 25 c. sepia, blue & violet 15 10

47. Statue of Moshoeshoe I.

1967. 1st Anniv. of Independence.
41. **47.** 2½ c. black and green .. 10 10
42. – 12½ c. multicoloured .. 25 10
43. – 25 c. black, green & ochre 35 15
DESIGNS: 12½ c. National Flag. 25 c. Crocodile (national emblem).

50. Lord Baden-Powell and Scout Saluting.

1967. 60th Anniv. of Scout Movement.
144. **50.** 15 c. multicoloured .. 20 10

51. W.H.O. Emblem and World Map.

1968. 20th Anniv. of World Health Organization.
145. **51.** 2½ c. blue, gold and red .. 15 10
146. – 25 c. multicoloured .. 45 10
DESIGN: 25 c. Nurse and Child.

55. Running Hunters.

1968. Rock Paintings.
160. **55.** 3 c. brn., turq. and grn. 25 10
161. – 3½ c. yellow, olive & sepia 30 10
162. – 5 c. red, ochre & brown 35 10
163. – 10 c. yellow, red & purple 45 10
164. – 15 c. buff, yellow & brown 75 30
165. – 20 c. green, yell. & brown 90 55
166. – 25 c. yell., brown & black 1·00 75
DESIGNS—HORIZ. 3½ c. Baboons. 10 c. Archers. 20 c. Eland. 25 c. Hunting Scene. VERT. 5 c. Javelin thrower. 15 c. Blue Cranes.

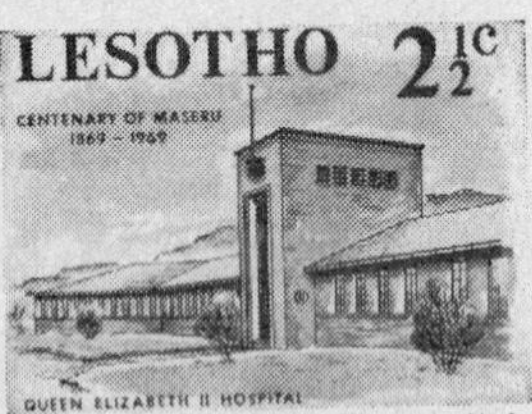

62. Queen Elizabeth II Hospital.

1969. Cent. of Maseru (capital). Mult.
167. 2½ c. Type **62** 10 10
168. 10 c. Lesotho Radio Station 10 10
169. 12½ c. Leabua Jonathan Airport 15 10
170. 25 c. Royal Palace .. 20 15

66. Rally Car passing Basuto Tribesman.

1969. "Roof of Africa" Car Rally.
171. **66.** 2½ c. yell., mve. & plum 10 10
172. – 12½ c. blue, yell. & grey 15 10
173. – 15 c. blue, blk. & mauve 15 10
174. – 20 c. blk., red & yellow 15 10
DESIGNS: 12½ c. Rally car on mountain road. 15 c. Chequered flags and "Roof of Africa" Plateau. 20 c. Map of rally route and Independence Trophy.

71. Gryponyx and Footprints.

1970. Prehistoric Footprints (1st series).
175. – 3 c. brown and sepia .. 35 20
176. **71.** 5 c. pur., pink & sepia 45 30
177. – 10 c. yell., blk. & sepia 60 35
178. – 15 c. yell., blk. & sepia 1·10 1·00
179. – 25 c. blue and black .. 1·90 2·00
DESIGNS: 3 c. Dinosaur footprints at Moyeni. 10 c. Plateosauravus and footprints. 15 c. Tritylodon and footprints. 25 c. Massospondylus and footprints.
No. 175 is larger, 60 × 23 mm.
See also Nos. 596/8.

75. Moshoeshoe I, as a Young Man.

1970. Death Cent. of Chief Moshoeshoe I.
180. **75.** 2½ c. green and mauve 10 10
181. – 25 c. blue and brown .. 20 20
DESIGN: 25 c. Moshoeshoe I as an old man.

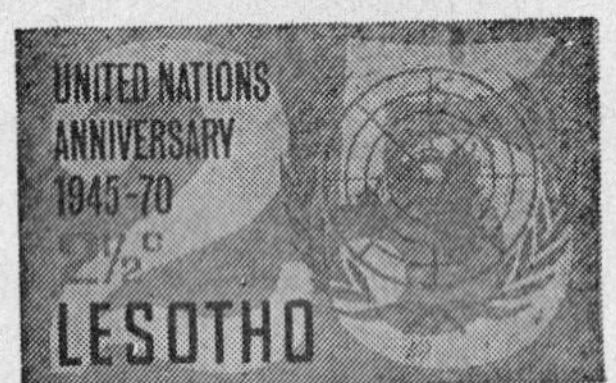

77. U.N. Emblem and "25".

1970. 25th Anniv. of U.N.
182. **77.** 2½ c. pink, blue & purple 10 10
183. – 10 c. multicoloured .. 10 10
184. – 12½ c. red, blue and drab 10 10
185. – 25 c. multicoloured .. 15 15
DESIGNS: 10 c. U.N. Building. 12½ c. "People of the World". 25 c. Symbolic Dove.

78. Gift Shop, Maseru.

1970. Tourism. Multicoloured.
186. 2½ c. Type **78** 10 10
187. 5 c. Trout Fishing .. 25 10
188. 10 c. Pony Trekking .. 35 10
189. 12½ c. Skiing, Maluti Mountains 60 10
190. 20 c. Holiday Inn, Maseru 60 50

79. Maize.

1971. As Nos. 147/58 but in new format omitting portrait, as in T **79**. New designs for 4 c., 2 r.
191. **79.** ½ c. green and violet .. 10 10
192. – 1 c. brown and red .. 10 10
193. – 2 c. yellow and green .. 10 10
194. – 2½ c. blk., grn. & yell. 10 10
195. – 3 c. brn., grn. & yellow 10 10
196. – 3½ c. blue and yellow .. 10 10
196a. – 4 c. multicoloured .. 20 10
197. – 5 c. brown and blue .. 15 10
198. – 10 c. brown and grey .. 15 10
199. – 12½ c. brown and orange 25 30
200. – 25 c. slate and blue .. 60 40
201. – 50 c. black, blue & green 6·00 3·50
202. – 1 r. multicoloured .. 2·75 2·25
203. – 2 r. brown and blue .. 2·75 3·00
DESIGNS—HORIZ. 4 c. National flag. VERT. 2 r. Statue of Moshoeshoe I.

80. Lammergeier.

1971. Birds. Multicoloured.
204. 2½ c. Type **80** .. .. 1·25 10
205. 5 c. Bald Ibis .. .. 2·00 1·10
206. 10 c. Rufous rockjumper .. 2·75 1·25
207. 12½ c. Blue bustard .. 3·25 1·60
208. 15 c. Painted snipe .. 4·00 2·75
209. 20 c. Golden-breasted bunting .. .. .. 4·00 2·75
210. 25 c. Ground woodpecker 4·25 3·00

81. Lionel Collett Dam.

1971. Soil Conservation. Multicoloured.
211. 4 c. Type **81** 10 10
212. 10 c. Contour ridges .. 10 10
213. 15 c. Earth dams .. 25 10
214. 25 c. Beaver dams .. 35 35

82. Diamond Mining.

1971. Development. Multicoloured.
215. 4 c. Type **82** 75 20
216. 10 c. Pottery 30 10
217. 15 c. Weaving 45 40
218. 20 c. Construction .. 55 65

83. Mail Cart.

1972. Centenary of Post Office.
219. **83.** 5 c. brown and pink .. 15 10
220. – 10 c. multicoloured .. 15 10
221. – 15 c. blue, black and brown 30 15
222. – 20 c. multicoloured .. 45 70
DESIGNS—HORIZ. 10 c. Postal Bus. 20 c. Maseru Post Office. VERT. 15 c., 4d. Cape of Good Hope stamp of 1876.

84. Sprinting.

1972. Olympic Games, Munich. Mult.
223. 4 c. Type **84** 10 10
224. 10 c. Shot putting .. 15 10
225. 15 c. Hurdling 20 10
226. 25 c. Long-jumping .. 30 20

85. "Adoration of the Shepherds" (Matthias Stomer).

1972. Christmas.
227. **85.** 4 c. multicoloured .. 10 10
228. 10 c. multicoloured .. 10 10
229. 25 c. multicoloured .. 15 20

86. W.H.O. Emblem.

1973. 25th Anniv. of W.H.O.
230. **86.** 20 c. yellow and blue .. 30 20

1973. O.A.U. 10th Anniv. Nos. 194 and 196a/8 optd. **O.A.U. 10th Anniversary Freedom in Unity.**
231. 2½ c. black, green & brown 10 10
232. 4 c. multicoloured .. 10 10
233. 5 c. brown and blue .. 10 10
234. 10 c. brown and blue .. 15 15

88. Basotho Hat and W.F.P. Emblem.

1973. 10th Anniv. of World Food Programme. Multicoloured.
235. 4 c. Type **88** 10 10
236. 15 c. School feeding .. 20 15
237. 20 c. Infant feeding .. 20 20
238. 25 c. "Food for work" .. 25 25

89. "Aeropetes tulbaghia".

1973. Butterflies. Multicoloured.
239 4 c. Type **89** 40 10
240 5 c. "Papilio demodocus" 50 25
241 10 c. "Vanessa cardui" .. 90 50
242 15 c. "Precis hierta" .. 1·40 1·00
243 20 c. "Precis oenone" .. 1·40 1·00
244 25 c. "Danaus chrysippus" 1·75 1·75
245 30 c. "Colotis evenina" .. 2·00 2·00

90. Kimberlite Volcano.

1973. Int. Kimberlite Conference. Mult.
246. 10 c. Map of diamond-mines (horiz.) .. .. .. 1·50 50
247. 15 c. Kimberlite-diamond rock (horiz.) .. .. 1·75 1·00
248. 20 c. Type **90** .. .. 2·00 1·50
249. 30 c. Diamond prospecting 3·00 3·00

91. " Health ".

1974. Youth and Development. Mult.
250. 4 c. Type **91** 10 10
251. 10 c. " Education " .. 10 10
252. 20 c. " Agriculture " .. 20 10
253. 25 c. " Industry " 35 20
254. 30 c. " Service " 35 25

92. Open Book and Wreath.

1974. 10th Anniv. of U.B.L.S. Multicoloured
255. 10 c. Type **92** 10 10
256. 15 c. Flags, mortar-board and scroll 15 10
257. 20 c. Map of Africa .. 20 10
258. 25 c. King Moshoeshoe II capping a graduate .. 20 15

93. Senqunyane River Bridge, Marakabei.

1974. Rivers and Bridges. Multicoloured.
259. 4 c. Type **93** 10 10
260. 5 c. Tsoelike River and bridge 10 10
261. 10 c. Makhaleng River Bridge 20 10
262. 15 c. Seaka Bridge, Orange/ Senqu River 35 35
263. 20 c. Masianokeng Bridge, Phuthiatsana River .. 40 40
264. 25 c. Mahobong Bridge, Hlotse River 45 45

94. U.P.U. Emblem

1974. Centenary of U.P.U.
265. **94.** 4 c. green and black .. 10 10
266. – 10 c. orge., yell. & blk. 15 10
267. – 15 c. multicoloured .. 20 15
268. – 20 c. multicoloured .. 30 20
DESIGNS: 10 c. Map of air-mail routes. 15 c. Post Office H.Q., Maseru. 20 c. Horseman taking rural mail.

95. Siege of Thaba-Bosiu.

1974. 150th Anniv of Siege of Thaba-Bosiu. Multicoloured.
269 4 c. Type **95** 10 10
270 5 c. The wreath-laying .. 10 10
271 10 c. Moshoeshoe I (vert) 25 10
272 20 c. Makoanyane, the warrior (vert) 65 30

96. Mamokhorong.

1974. Basotho Musical Instruments. Mult.
273. 4 c. Type **96** 10 10
274. 10 c. Lesiba 10 10
275. 15 c. Setolotolo 15 20
276. 20 c. Meropa 15 20

97. Horseman in Rock Archway.

1975. Sehlabathebe National Park. Mult.
278. 4 c. Type **97** 15 10
279. 5 c. Mountain view through arch 15 10
280. 15 c. Antelope by stream .. 35 30
281. 20 c. Mountains and lake .. 40 35
282. 25 c. Tourists by waterfall 50 50

98. Morena Moshoeshoe I.

1975. Leaders of Lesotho.
283. **98.** 3 c. black and blue .. 10 10
284. – 4 c. black and mauve .. 10 10
285. – 5 c. black and pink .. 10 10
286. – 6 c. black and brown .. 10 10
287. – 10 c. black and red .. 10 10
288. – 15 c. black and red .. 20 20
289. – 20 c. black and green .. 25 30
290. – 25 c. black and blue .. 25 40
DESIGNS: 4 c. King Moshoeshoe II. 5 c. Morena Letsie I. 6 c. Morena Lerotholi. 10 c. Morena Letsie II. 15 c. Morena Griffith. 20 c. Morena Seeiso Griffith Lerotholi. 25 c. Mofumahali Mantsebo Seeiso, O.B.E.
The 25 c. also commemorates International Women's Year.

99. Mokhibo Dance.

1975. Traditional Dances. Multicoloured.
291. 4 c. Type **99** 10 10
292. 10 c. Ndlamo 10 10
293. 15 c. Baleseli 25 40
294. 20 c. Mohobelo 30 45

100. Enrolment.

1976. 25th Anniv. of Lesotho Red Cross. Multicoloured.
296. 4 c. Type **100** 40 10
297. 10 c. Medical aid 60 10
298. 15 c. Rural service .. 1·00 55
299. 25 c. Relief supplies .. 1·40 70

101. Tapestry.

1976. Multicoloured.
300. 2 c. Type **101** 10 10
301. 3 c. Mosotho horseman .. 20 10
302. 4 c. Map of Lesotho .. 35 10
303. 5 c. Lesotho brown diamond 55 10
304. 10 c. Lesotho Bank .. 30 10
305. 15 c. Lesotho and O.A.U. flags 65 20
306. 25 c. Sehlabathebe National Park 80 35
307. 40 c. Pottery 80 50
308. 50 c. Pre-historic rock art 1·50 90
309. 1 r. King Moshoeshoe II (vert.) .. .. .. 1·40 1·75

102. Football.

1976. Olympic Games, Montreal. Mult.
310. 4 c. Type **102** 10 10
311. 10 c. Weightlifting .. 10 10
312. 15 c. Boxing 20 10
313. 25 c. Throwing the discus 35 25

103. " Rising Sun ".

1976. 10th Anniv. of Independence. Mult.
314. 4 c. Type **103** 10 10
315. 10 c. Open gates 10 10
316. 15 c. Broken chains .. 40 20
317. 25 c. Aeroplane over hotel 50 35

104. Telephones, 1876 and 1976.

1976. Centenary of Telephone. Multicoloured.
318. 4 c. Type **104** 10 10
319. 10 c. Early handset and telephone-user, 1976 .. 10 10
320. 15 c. Wall telephone and telephone exchange .. 20 15
321. 25 c. Stick telephone and Alexander Graham Bell 35 40

105. " Aloe striatula ".

1977. Aloes and Succulents. Multicoloured.
322. 3 c. Type **105** 20 10
323. 4 c. " Aloe aristata " .. 25 10
324. 5 c. " Kniphofia caulescens " 30 10
325. 10 c. " Euphorbia pulvinata " 45 10
326. 15 c. " Aloe saponaria " .. 80 40
327. 20 c. " Caralluma lutea " 1·10 65
328. 25 c. " Aloe polyphylla " 1·60 90
See also Nos. 347/54.

106. Large-toothed Rock Hyrax.

1977. Animals. Multicoloured.
329. 4 c. Type **106** 30 10
330. 5 c. Cape porcupine .. 30 10
331. 10 c. Zorilla (polecat) .. 40 10
332. 15 c. Klipspringer .. .. 1·25 70
333. 25 c. Chacma baboon .. 1·75 1·10

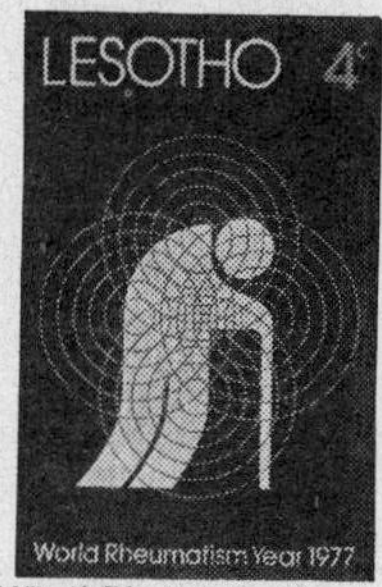

107. " Rheumatic Man ".

1977. World Rheumatism Year.
334. **107.** 4 c. yellow and red .. 10 10
335. – 10 c. blue and dark blue 10 10
336. – 15 c. yellow and blue .. 25 10
337. – 25 c. red and black .. 40 45
DESIGNS: Each show the " Rheumatic Man " as Type **107**. 10 c. Surrounded by " pain ". 15 c. Surrounded by " chain ". 25 c. Supporting globe.

108. " Barbus holubi ".

1977. Fish. Multicoloured.
338. 4 c. Type **108** 15 10
339. 10 c. " Labeo capensis " .. 30 10
340. 15 c. " Salmo gairdneri " 60 35
341. 25 c. " Oreodaimon quathlambae " 85 60

1977. No. 198 surch.
342. 3 c. on 10 c. brown & blue 1·25 90

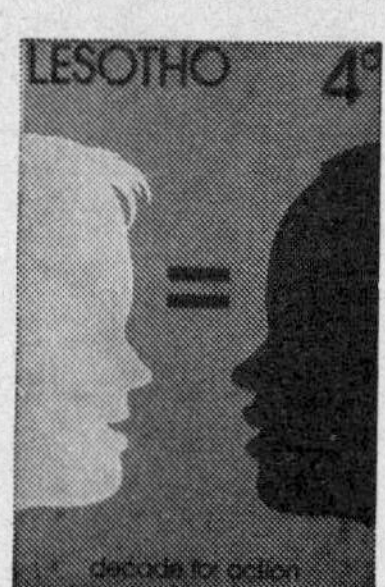

110. Black and White Heads.

1977. Decade for Action to Combat Racism.
343. **110.** 4 c. black and mauve .. 10 10
344. – 10 c. black and blue .. 10 10
345. – 15 c. black and orange .. 15 15
346. – 25 c. black and green .. 25 25
DESIGNS: 10 c. Jigsaw pieces. 15 c. Cogwheels. 25 c. Handshake.

1978. Flowers. As T **105**. Multicoloured.
347. 2 c. " Papaver aculeatum " 10 20
348. 3 c. " Diascia integerrima " 10 20
349. 4 c. " Helichrysum trilineatum " 10 10
350. 5 c. " Zaluzianskya maritima " 10 10
351. 10 c. " Gladiolus natalensis " 20 20
352. 15 c. " Chironia krebsii " 30 40
353. 25 c. " Wahlenbergia undulata " .. .. 50 1·00
354. 40 c. " Brunsvigia radulosa " .. .. .. 85 1·75

111. Edward Jenner vaccinating Child.

1978. Global Eradication of Smallpox. Mult.

355. 5 c. Type **111** 10 10
356. 25 c. Head of child and W.H.O. emblem .. 30 25

112. Tsoloane Falls.

1978. Waterfalls. Multicoloured.

357. 4 c. Type **112** 15 10
358. 10 c. Qiloane Falls .. 25 10
359. 15 c. Tsoelikana Falls .. 45 30
360. 25 c. Maletsunyane Falls .. 75 75

113. Wright " Flyer ", 1903.

1978. 75th Anniv. of First Powered Flight. Multicoloured.

361. 5 c. Type **113** .. 10 10
362. 25 c. Wilbur and Orville Wright and " Flyer " .. 30 20

114. " Orthetrum farinosum ". 115. Oudehout Branch in Flower.

1978. Insects. Multicoloured.

363 4 c. Type **114** 10 10
364 10 c. "Phymateus viripides" 20 10
365 15 c. "Belonogaster lateritis" 30 30
366 25 c. "Sphodromantis gastrica" 50 65

1979. Trees. Multicoloured.

367. 4 c. Type **115** 15 10
368. 10 c. Wild Olive 20 10
369. 15 c. Blinkblaar 35 70
370. 25 c. Cape Holly .. .. 70 1·40

116. Mampharoane.

1979. Reptiles. Multicoloured.

371. 4 s. Type **116** 10 10
372. 10 s. Qoaane 20 10
373. 15 s. Leupa 30 35
374. 25 s. Masumu 60 65

117. Basutoland 1933 1d. Stamp.

1979. Death Centenary of Sir Rowland Hill.

375. **117.** 4 s. multicoloured .. 10 10
376. – 15 s. multicoloured .. 30 20
377. – 25 s. black, orge. & bistre 40 30

DESIGNS: 15 s. Basutoland 1962 ½ c. new currency definitive. 25 s. Penny Black.

118. Detail of painting " Children's Games " by Brueghel.

1979. International Year of the Child.

379. **118.** 4 s. multicoloured .. 10 10
380. – 10 s. multicoloured .. 10 10
381. – 15 s. multicoloured .. 15 15

DESIGNS: 10, 15 s. Different details taken from Brueghel's " Children's Games ".

119. Beer Strainer, Broom and Mat.

1980. Grasswork. Multicoloured.

383. 4 s. Type **119** 10 10
384. 10 s. Winnowing Basket .. 10 10
385. 15 s. Basotho Hat .. 20 15
386. 25 s. Grain storage .. 35 25

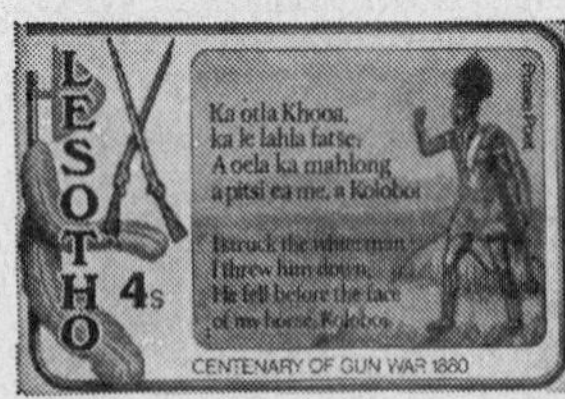

120. Praise Poet.

1980. Centenary of Gun War. Multicoloured.

387. 4 s. Type **120** .. 15 10
388. 5 s. Lerotholi, Commander of Basotho Army .. 15 10
389. 10 s. Ambush at Qalabane 20 10
390. 15 s. Snider and Martini-Henry rifles .. 40 35
391. 25 s. Map showing main areas of action .. 50 45

121. Olympic Flame, Flags and Kremlin.

1980. Olympic Games, Moscow. Mult.

392. 25 s. Type **121** 25 25
393. 25 s. Doves, flame and flags 25 25
394. 25 s. Football 25 25
395. 25 s. Running 25 25
396. 25 s. Opening ceremony .. 25 25

1980. Nos. 203 and 300/9 surch.

402 2 s. on 2 c. Type **101** .. 10 10
403 3 s. on 3 c. Mosotho horseman 10 10
410 5 s. on 5 c. Lesotho brown diamond 10 10
404 6 s. on 4 c. Map of Lesotho 10 10
411 10 s. on 10 c. Lesotho Bank 10 10
412 25 s. on 25 c. Sehlabathebe National Park 25 30
406 40 s. on 40 c. Pottery .. 45 50
407 50 s. on 50 c. Pre-historic rock art 50 55
408 75 s. on 15 c. Lesotho and O.A.U. flags 70 75
409 1 m. on 1 r. King Moshoeshoe II .. .. .. 80 1·00
417 2 m. on 2 r. Statue of King Moshoeshoe I .. .. 1·90 2·00

123. Beer Mug.

1980. Pottery. Multicoloured.

418. 4 s. Type **123** 10 10
419. 10 s. Beer brewing pot .. 10 10
420. 15 s. Water pot 15 15
421. 25 s. Pot shapes 25 30

124. Queen Elizabeth, the Queen Mother with Prince Charles.

1980. 80th Birthday of The Queen Mother. Multicoloured.

423. 5 s. Type **124** 25 25
424. 10 s. The Queen Mother .. 30 30
425. 1 m. 1947 Basutoland Royal Visit stamp (54 × 43 mm.) 1·25 1·25

125. Lesotho Evangical Church, Morija.

1980. Christmas. Multicoloured.

426. 4 s. Type **125** 10 10
427. 15 s. St. Agnes' Anglican Church, Teyateyaneng .. 10 10
428. 25 s. Our Lady's Victory Cathedral, Maseru .. 15 10
429. 75 s. University Chapel, Roma 45 50

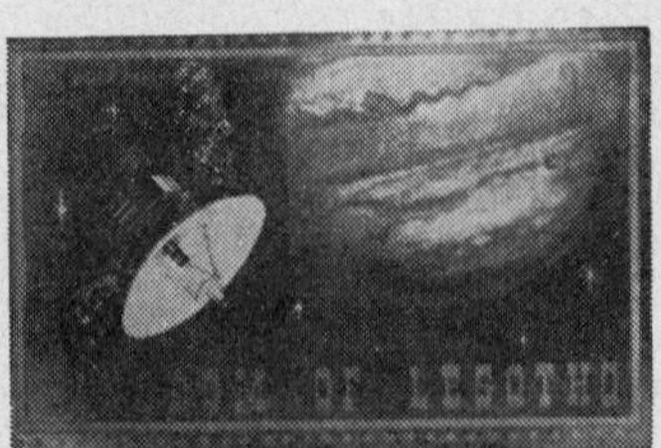

126. " Voyager " Satellite and Jupiter.

1981. Space Exploration. Multicoloured.

431. 25 c. Type **126** 40 30
432. 25 c. " Voyager " and Saturn 40 30
433. 25 c. " Voyager " passing Saturn 40 30
434. 25 c. " Space Shuttle " releasing satellite 40 30
435. 25 c. " Space Shuttle " launching into space .. 40 30

127. Greater Kestrel.

1981. Birds. Multicoloured.

437 1 s. Type **127** 15 10
438 2 s. Speckled Pigeon (horiz.) 15 10
439 3 s. South African Crowned Crane 15 10
503 5 s. Bokmakierie Shrike .. 10 10
504 6 s. Cape Robin Chat .. 10 10
505 7 s. Yellow Canary .. 10 10
506 10 s. Red-billed Pintail (horiz.) 15 10
507 25 s. Malachite Kingfisher 35 30
508 40 s. Yellow-tufted Malachite Sunbird (horiz.) .. 55 35
509 60 s. Cape Longclaw (horiz.) 80 70
510 75 s. Hoopoe (horiz.) .. 1·25 85
448 1 m. Red Bishop (horiz.) .. 2·50 1·00
449 2 m. Egyptian Goose (horiz.) 3·50 3·00
450 5 m. Lilac-breasted Roller (horiz.) .. .. .. 6·00 7·00

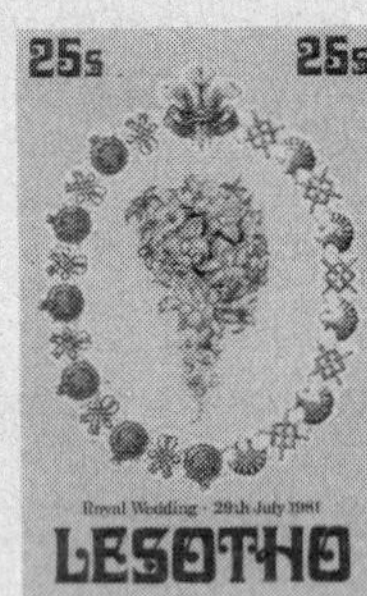

128. Wedding Bouquet from Lesotho.

1981. Royal Wedding. Multicoloured.

451. 25 s. Type **128** 30 40
452. 50 s. Prince Charles riding 55 75
453. 75 s. Prince Charles and Lady Diana Spencer .. 75 1·00

130. " Santa planning his Annual Visit ".

1981. Christmas. Paintings by Norman Rockwell.

455. 6 s. Type **130** 20 10
456. 10 s. " Santa reading his Mail " 30 10
457. 15 s. " The Little Spooners " 35 15
458. 20 s. " Raleigh Rockwell Travels " 45 20
459. 25 s. " Ride 'em Cowboy " 55 25
460. 60 s. " The Discovery " 1·00 75

131. Duke of Edinburgh, Award Scheme Emblem and Flags.

1981. 25th Anniv. of Duke of Edinburgh Award Scheme. Multicoloured.

462. 6 s. Type **131** 10 10
463. 7 s. Tree planting 10 10
464. 25 s. Gardening 30 30
465. 40 s. Mountain climbing .. 50 50
466. 75 s. Award Scheme emblem 85 85

132. African Wild Cat.

1981. Wildlife. Multicoloured.

468.	6 s. Type **132**	15	10
469.	20 s. Chacma Baboon (44×31 mm.)	30	30
470.	25 s. Cape Eland	35	35
471.	40 s. Porcupine	60	60
472.	50 s. Oribi (44×31 mm.) ..	75	75

133. Scout Bugler.

1982. 75th Anniv. of Boy Scout Movement. Multicoloured.

474.	6 s. Type **133** ..	45	25
475.	30 s. Scouts hiking ..	70	50
476.	40 s. Scout sketching ..	75	60
477.	50 s. Scout with flag ..	80	65
478.	75 s. Scouts saluting ..	90	80

134. Jules Rimet Trophy with Footballers and Flags of 1930 Finalists (Argentina and Uruguay).

1982. World Cup Football Championship, Spain. Each showing Trophy with Players and Flags from Past Finals. Multicoloured.

480.	15 s. Type **134**	20	20
481.	15 s. Czechoslovakia and Italy, 1934 ..	20	20
482.	15 s. Hungary and Italy, 1938	20	20
483.	15 s. Brazil and Uruguay, 1950	20	20
484.	15 s. Hungary and W. Germany, 1954 ..	20	20
485.	15 s. Sweden and Brazil, 1958	20	20
486.	15 s. Czechoslovakia and Brazil, 1962 ..	20	20
487.	15 s. W. Germany and England, 1966 ..	20	20
488.	15 s. Italy and Brazil, 1970	20	20
489.	15 s. Holland and W. Germany, 1974 ..	20	20
490.	15 s. Holland and Argentina, 1978 ..	20	20
491.	15 s. Map of World on footballs ..	20	20

Nos. 480/8 show the Jules Rimet Trophy and Nos. 489/91 the World Cup Trophy.

135. Portrait of George Washington.

1982. 250th Anniv. of George Washington. Multicoloured.

493.	6 s. Type **135**	10	10
494.	7 s. Washington with step-children and dog ..	10	10
495.	10 s. Washington with Indian chief	15	10
496.	25 s. Washington with troops	35	35
497.	40 s. Washington arriving in New York	50	50
498.	1 m. Washington on parade	1·25	1·25

136. Lady Diana Spencer in Tetbury, May 1981.

1982. 21st Birthday of Princess of Wales. Multicoloured.

514.	30 s. Lesotho coat of arms	30	30
515.	50 s. Type **136**	45	50
516.	75 s. Wedding picture at Buckingham Palace ..	70	70
517.	1 m. Formal portrait ..	1·00	1·25

137. Mosotho reading Sesotho Bible.

1982. Centenary of Sesotho Bible. Mult.

518.	6 s. Type **137**	10	10
519.	15 s. Sesotho bible and Virgin Mary holding infant Jesus	20	20
520.	1 m. Sesotho bible and Cathedral (horiz.) (62×42 mm.)	45	65

138. Birthday Greetings.

1982. Birth of Prince William of Wales. Multicoloured.

521.	6 s. Type **138** ..	60	60
522.	60 s. Princess Diana and Prince William ..	80	80

139. "A Partridge in a Pear Tree".

1982. Christmas. "The Twelve Days of Christmas". Walt Disney cartoon Characters. Multicoloured.

523.	2 s. Type **139**	10	10
524.	2 s. "Two turtle doves" ..	10	10
525.	3 s. "Three French hens"	10	10
526.	3 s. "Four calling birds" ..	10	10
527.	4 s. "Five golden rings" ..	10	10
528.	4 s. "Six geese a-laying" ..	10	10
529.	75 s. "Seven swans a-swimming"	1·25	1·25
530.	75 s. "Eight maids a-milking"	1·25	1·25

140. "Lepista caffrorum".

1983. Fungi. Multicoloured.

532.	10 s. Type **140**	15	10
533.	30 s. "Broomeia congregata"	30	40
534.	50 s. "Afroboletus luteolus"	60	75
535.	75 s. "Lentinus tuberregium"	90	1·25

141. Ba-Leseli Dance.

1983. Commonwealth Day. Multicoloured.

536.	5 s. Type **141**	10	10
537.	30 s. Tapestry weaving ..	25	30
538.	60 s. Queen Elizabeth II (vert.)	50	65
539.	75 s. King Moshoeshoe II (vert.)	65	80

142. "Dancers in a Trance" (rock painting from Ntloana Tsoana).

1983. Rock Paintings. Multicoloured.

540.	6 s. Type **142**	15	10
541.	25 s. "Baboons", Sehong-hong	40	35
542.	60 s. "Hunters attacking Mountain Reedbuck", Makhetha ..	90	1·10
543.	75 s. "Eland", Lehaha la Likhomo	1·25	1·60

143. Montgolfier Balloon, 1783.

1983. Bicentenary of Manned Flight. Mult.

545.	7 s. Type **143**	15	10
546.	30 s. Wright brothers and "Flyer"	40	40
547.	60 s. First airmail flight ..	75	75
548.	1 m. "Concorde" ..	1·50	1·50

144. Rev. Eugene Casalis.

1983. 150th Anniv. of Arrival of the French Missionaries. Multicoloured.

550.	6 s. Type **144**	10	10
551.	25 s. The founding of Morija	30	40
552.	40 s. Baptism of Libe ..	50	70
553.	75 s. Map of Lesotho ..	90	1·25

145. Mickey Mouse and Pluto greeted by Friends.

1983. Christmas. Walt Disney Characters in scenes from "Old Christmas" (Washington Irving's sketchbook). Multicoloured.

554.	1 s. Type **145**	10	1
555.	2 s. Donald Duck and Pluto	10	1
556.	3 s. Donald Duck with Huey, Dewey and Louie	10	10
557.	4 s. Goofy, Donald Duck and Mickey Mouse ..	10	10
558.	5 s. Goofy holding turkey, Donald Duck and Mickey Mouse	10	10
559.	6 s. Goofy and Mickey Mouse	10	10
560.	7 s. Donald and Daisy Duck	1·75	1·00
561.	1 m. Goofy and Clarabell ..	2·25	1·50

146. "Danaus chrysippus".

1984. Butterflies. Multicoloured.

563	1 s. Type **146**	15	10
564	2 s. "Aeropetes tulbaghia"	15	10
565	3 s. "Colotis evenina" ..	20	10
566	4 s. "Precis oenone" ..	20	10
567	5 s. "Precis hierta" ..	20	10
568	6 s. "Catopsilia florella" ..	20	10
569	7 s. "Phalanta phalantha"	20	10
570	10 s. "Acraea stenobea" ..	30	10
571	15 s. "Cynthia cardui" ..	50	10
572	20 s. "Colotis subfasciatus"	60	10
573	30 s. "Charaxes jasius" ..	65	20
574	50 s. "Eurema brigitta" ..	85	30
575	60 s. "Pieris helice" ..	95	35
576	75 s. "Colotis regina" ..	1·25	40
577	1 m. "Hypolimnas misippus"	1·50	70
578	5 m. "Papilio demodocus"	4·50	4·00

147. "Thou shalt not have Strange Gods before Me".

1984. Easter. The Ten Commandments. Multicoloured.

579.	20 s. Type **147**	25	25
580.	20 s. "Thou shalt not take the name of the Lord thy God in vain"	25	25
581.	20 s. "Remember thou keep holy the Lord's Day"	25	25
582.	20 s. "Honour thy father and mother" ..	25	25
583.	20 s. "Thou shalt not kill"	25	25
584.	20 s. "Thou shalt not commit adultery" ..	25	25
585.	20 s. "Thou shalt not steal"	25	25
586.	20 s. "Thou shalt not bear false witness against thy neighbour" ..	25	25
587.	20 s. "Thou shalt not covet thy neighbour's wife" ..	25	25
588.	20 s. "Thou shalt not covet thy neighbour's goods"	25	25

148. Torch Bearer.

1984. Olympic Games, Los Angeles. Mult.

590.	10 s. Type **148**	10	10
591.	30 s. Horse-riding	30	35
592.	50 s. Swimming	50	55
593.	75 s. Basketball	70	75
594.	1 m. Running	95	1·10

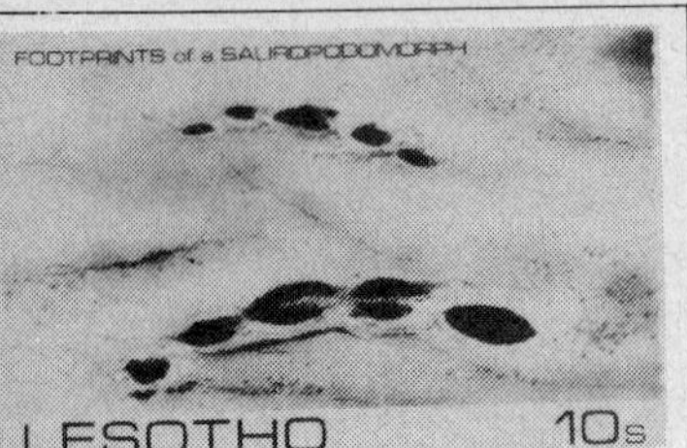

149. Sauropodomorph Footprints.

984. Prehistoric Footprints (2nd series). Multicoloured.

96. 10 s. Type **149** 55 20
97. 30 s. Lesothosaurus footprints .. .. .. 1·50 1·25
98. 50 s. Footprint of carnivorous dinosaur .. 1·75 1·50

150. Wells Fargo Coach, 1852.

1984. "Ausipex" International Stamp Exhibition, Melbourne. Bicentenary of First Mail Coach Run. Multicoloured.

599. 6 s. Type **150** 10 10
600. 7 s. Basotho mail cart, circa 1900 .. .. 10 10
601. 10 s. Bath mail coach, 1784 10 10
602. 30 s. Cobb coach, 1853 .. 30 35
603. 50 s. Exhibition logo and Royal Exhibition buildings, Melbourne (82 × 25 mm.) 50 55

151. "The Orient Express" (1900). (Illustration reduced, actual size 46 mm × 28 mm.).

1984. Railways of the World. Multicoloured.

605. 6 s. Type **151** 40 10
606. 15 s. German State Railways Class "05" No. 05001 (1935) 45 20
607. 30 s. Caledonian Railway "Cardean" (1906) .. 70 45
608. 60 s. Santa Fe "Super Chief" (1940) .. .. 1·25 90
609. 1 m. L.N.E.R. "Flying Scotsman" (1934) .. 1·75 1·25

152. Eland Calf.

1984. Baby Animals. Multicoloured.

611. 15 s. Type **152** 35 20
612. 20 s. Young Chacma Baboons 40 25
613. 30 s. Oribi calf 55 30
614. 75 s. Young Natal Red Hares .. .. .. 1·25 75
615. 1 m. Black-backed Jackal pups (46 × 27 mm.) .. 1·50 1·25

153. Crown of Lesotho.

1985. Silver Jubilee of King Moshoeshoe II. Multicoloured.

616. 6 s. Type **153** 10 10
617. 30 s. King Moshoeshoe in 1960 .. .. .. 20 30
618. 75 s. King Moshoeshoe in traditional dress, 1985 .. 50 65
619. 1 m. King Moshoeshoe in uniform, 1985 .. .. 70 90

154. Christ condemned to Death.

1985. Easter. The Stations of the Cross. Multicoloured.

620. 20 s. Type **154** 15 15
621. 20 s. Christ carrying the Cross 15 15
622. 20 s. Falling for the first time 15 15
623. 20 s. Christ meets Mary .. 15 15
624. 20 s. Simon of Cyrene helping to carry the Cross 15 15
625. 20 s. Veronica wiping the face of Christ 15 15
626. 20 s. Christ falling a second time 15 15
627. 20 s. Consoling the women of Jerusalem 15 15
628. 20 s. Falling for the third time 15 15
629. 20 s. Christ being stripped 15 15
630. 20 s. Christ nailed to the Cross 15 15
631. 20 s. Dying on the Cross .. 15 15
632. 20 s. Christ taken down from the Cross 15 15
633. 20 s. Christ being laid in the sepulchre 15 15

155. Duchess of York with Princess Elizabeth, 1931.

1985. Life and Times of Queen Elizabeth the Queen Mother. Multicoloured.

635. 10 s. Type **155** 15 10
636. 30 s. The Queen Mother in 1975 .. .. .. 50 50
637. 60 s. Queen Mother with Queen Elizabeth and Princess Margaret, 1980 80 80
638. 2 m. Four generations of Royal Family at Prince Henry's christening, 1984 2·25 2·25

CENTENARY OF THE MOTOR CAR
1885
1985
BMW
LESOTHO
6s

156. B.M.W. "732i".

1985. Century of Motoring. Multicoloured.

640. 6 s. Type **156** 25 15
641. 10 s. Ford "Crown Victoria" 35 15
642. 30 s. Mercedes-Benz "500SE" 75 50
643. 90 s. Cadillac "Eldorado Biarritz .. .. .. 2·00 2·00
644. 2 m. Rolls-Royce "Silver Spirit" .. .. .. 3·00 3·25

157. American Cliff Swallow.

1985. Birth Bicentenary of John J. Audubon (ornithologist). Designs showing original paintings. Multicoloured.

646. 5 s. Type **157** 30 15
647. 6 s. Great crested grebe (horiz.) 30 15
648. 10 s. Vesper sparrow (horiz.) 45 15
649. 30 s. Greenshank (horiz.) .. 1·00 55
650. 60 s. Stilt sandpiper (horiz.) .. .. .. 1·75 1·75
651. 2 m. Glossy ibis (horiz.) .. 3·25 3·50

158. Two Youths Rock-climbing.

1985. International Youth Year and 75th Anniv. of Girl Guide Movement. Mult.

652. 10 s. Type **158** 20 10
653. 30 s. Young technician in hospital laboratory .. 50 40
654. 75 s. Three guides on parade .. .. .. 1·00 1·00
655. 2 m. Guide saluting .. 2·40 2·75

159. U.N. (New York) 1951 1 c. Definitive and U.N. Flag.

1985. 40th Anniv. of U.N.O.

657. **159.** 10 s. multicoloured .. 25 10
658. – 30 s. multicoloured .. 60 35
659. – 50 s. multicoloured .. 95 65
660. – 2 m. black and green 5·00 3·25

DESIGNS—VERT. 30 s. Ha Sofonia Earth Satellite Station. 2 m. Maimonides (physician, philosopher and scholar). HORIZ. 50 s. Lesotho Airways aircraft at Maseru Airport.

160. Cosmos.

1985. Wild Flowers. Multicoloured.

661. 6 s. Type **160** 40 15
662. 10 s. Small agapanthus .. 55 15
663. 30 s. Pink witchweed .. 1·10 50
664. 60 s. Small iris .. .. 1·75 1·25
665. 90 s. Wild geranium or Cranesbill .. .. 2·40 2·00
666. 1 m. Large spotted orchid 3·75 3·75

1985. 150th Birth Anniv. of Mark Twain. Walt Disney cartoon characters illustrating various Mark Twain quotations. As T **118** of Anguilla. Multicoloured.

667. 6 s. Mrs Jumbo and baby Dumbo 40 15
668. 50 s. Uncle Scrooge and Goofy reading newspaper .. .. 1·25 80
669. 90 s. Winnie the Pooh, Tigger, Piglet and Owl 1·75 1·40
670. 1 m. 50 Goofy at ship's wheel .. .. .. 2·75 2·25

1985. Birth Bicentenaries of Grimm Brothers (folklorists). Walt Disney cartoon characters in scenes from "The Wishing Table". As T **119** of Anguilla. Multicoloured.

672. 10 s. The tailor (Donald Duck) 35 15
673. 60 s. The second son (Dewey) with magic donkey and gold coins .. 1·25 75
674. 75 s. The eldest son (Huey) with wishing table laden with food .. .. 1·50 90
675. 1 m. The innkeeper stealing the third son's (Louie) magic cudgel .. 2·00 1·50

161. Male Lammergeier on Watch.

1986. Flora and Fauna of Lesotho. Multicoloured.

677. 7 s. Type **161** 60 15
678. 9 s. Prickly pear 60 15
679. 12 s. Stapelia 60 15
680. 15 s. Pair of lammergeiers 1·50 35
681. 35 s. Pig's ears .. .. 1·10 50
682. 50 s. Male lammergeier in flight .. .. .. 2·50 1·60
683. 1 m. Adult and juvenile lammergeiers .. .. 3·50 3·50
684. 2 m. Columnar cereus .. 3·75 4·00

162. Two Players chasing Ball.

1986. World Cup Football Championship, Mexico. Multicoloured.

686. 35 s. Type **162** .. .. 1·00 50
687. 50 s. Goalkeeper saving goal .. .. .. 1·50 1·25
688. 1 m. Three players chasing ball .. .. .. 2·75 2·50
689. 2 m. Two players competing for ball .. .. 4·50 4·50

1986. Appearance of Halley's Comet. As T **123** of Anguilla. Multicoloured.

691. 9 s. Galileo and 200 inch Hale telescope, Mount Palomar Observatory, California 50 15
692. 15 s. Halley's Comet and "Pioneer Venus 2" spacecraft 75 20
693. 70 s. Halley's Comet of 684 A.D. (from "Nuremberg Chronicle", 1493) .. 1·60 1·25
694. 3 m. Comet and landing of William the Conqueror, 1066 .. .. .. 4·00 4·50

163. International Year of the Child Gold Coin.

1986. First Anniv. of New Currency (1980). Multicoloured.

696.	30 s. Type **163**	6·50	5·50
697.	30 s. Five maloti banknote	6·50	5·50
698.	30 s. Fifty lisente coin ..	6·50	5·50
699.	30 s. Ten maloti banknote	6·50	5·50
700.	30 s. One sente coin ..	6·50	5·50

These stamps were prepared in 1980, but were not issued at that time.

1986. 60th Birthday of Queen Elizabeth II. As T **125** of Anguilla.

701.	90 s. black & yellow ..	60	60
702.	1 m. multicoloured ..	65	65
703.	2 m. multicoloured ..	1·40	1·40

DESIGNS. 90 s. Princess Elizabeth in Pantomime. 1 m. Queen at Windsor Horse Show, 1971. 2 m. At Royal Festival Hall, 1971.

1986. Centenary of Statue of Liberty. Immigrants to the U.S.A. As T **211** of Dominica. Multicoloured.

705.	15 s. Bela Bartok (composer)	75	20
706.	35 s. Felix Adler (philosopher)	75	30
707.	1 m. Victor Herbert (composer)	2·50	1·50
708.	3 m. David Niven (actor)	3·50	3·50

1986. "Ameripex" International Stamp Exhibition, Chicago. Walt Disney cartoon characters delivering mail. As T **212** of Dominica. Multicoloured.

710.	15 s. Mickey Mouse and Goofy as Japanese mail runners	40	20
711.	35 s. Mickey Mouse and Pluto with mail sledge ..	70	30
712.	1 m. Goofy as postman riding Harley-Davidson motorcycle	1·50	1·25
713.	2 m. Donald Duck operating railway mailbag apparatus	2·25	2·00

1986. Various stamps surch.

(a)

715	9 s. on 10 s. Red-billed pintail (horiz) (506) ..	1·25	1·25
722	9 s. on 30 s. "Charaxes jasius" (573)	15	10
723	9 s. on 60 s. "Pontia helice" (575)	4·00	4·00
716	15 s. on 1 s. Type **127** ..	4·00	3·00
724	15 s. on 1 s. Type **146** ..	2·75	2·75
717	15 s. on 2s. Speckled pigeon (horiz) (438)	4·00	4·50
725	15 s. on 2 s. "Aeropetes tulbaghia" (564) ..	20	20
726	15 s. on 3 s. "Colotis evenina" (565)	20	20
718	15 s. on 5 s. "Precis hierta" (567)	20	20
719	15 s. on 60 s. Cape longclaw (horiz) (509)	20	10
721	35 s. on 75 s. Hoopoe (510)	16·00	16·00
728	35 s. on 75 s. "Colotis regina" (576)	35	35

(b) On Nos. 503, 507, 566 and 569

729	9 s. on 5 s. Bokmakierie shrike	15	20
731	35 s. on 25 s. Malachite kingfisher	60	60
732	20 s. on 4 s. "Precis oenone"	10	10
733	40 s. on 7 s. "Phalanta phalantha"	15	20

(c) No. 722 further surch

734	3 s. on 9 s. on 30 s. "Charaxes jasius" ..	15	15
735	7 s. on 9 s. on 30 s. "Charaxes jasius" ..	25	25

1986. Royal Wedding. As T **213** of Antigua. Multicoloured.

736.	50 s. Prince Andrew and Miss Sarah Ferguson ..	40	40
737.	1 m. Prince Andrew ..	70	70
738.	3 m. Prince Andrew piloting helicopter ..	2·00	2·00

171. Basotho Pony and Rider.

1986. 20th Anniv. of Independence. Mult.

740.	9 s. Type **171**	30	10
741.	15 s. Basotho woman spinning mohair ..	40	15
742.	35 s. Crossing river rowing boat	55	30
743.	3 m. Thaba Tseka Post Office	2·75	3·00

1986. Christmas. Walt Disney cartoon characters. As T **220** of Antigua. Mult.

745.	15 s. Chip'n' Dale pulling Christmas cracker ..	30	15
746.	35 s. Mickey and Minnie Mouse	55	30
747.	1 m. Pluto pulling Christmas taffy	1·25	1·25
748.	2 m. Aunt Matilda baking	2·00	2·00

172. Rally Car. **173.** Lawn Tennis.

1987. Roof of Africa Motor Rally. Mult.

750.	9 s. Type **172**	20	10
751.	15 s. Motorcyclist	25	15
752.	35 s. Motorcyclist (different)	45	30
753.	4 m. Rally car (different)	3·00	3·00

1987. Olympic Games, Seoul (1988) (1st issue). Multicoloured.

754.	9 s. Type **173**	20	10
755.	15 s. Judo	20	15
756.	20 s. Athletics	25	20
757.	35 s. Boxing	40	30
758.	1 m. Diving	1·10	1·25
759.	3 m. Ten-pin bowling ..	2·50	3·00

See also Nos. 838/41.

174. Isaac Newton and Reflecting Telescope.

1987. Great Scientific Discoveries. Mult.

761.	5 s. Type **174**	15	10
762.	9 s. Alexander Graham Bell and first telephone	15	15
763.	75 s. Robert Goddard and liquid fuel rocket ..	55	60
764.	4 m. Chuck Yeager and "X-1" rocket plane ..	2·50	3·00

175. Grey Rhebuck.

1987. Flora and Fauna. Multicoloured.

766.	5 s. Type **175**	30	15
767.	9 s. Cape clawless otter ..	30	15
768.	15 s. Cape grey mongoose	40	20
769.	20 s. Free State daisy (vert.)	45	20
770.	35 s. River bells (vert.) ..	60	30
771.	1 m. Turkey flower (vert.)	1·50	1·50
772.	2 m Sweet briar (vert.) ..	2·25	2·50
773.	3 m. Mountain reedbuck ..	2·75	3·00

176. Scouts hiking.

1987. World Scout Jamboree, Australia. Multicoloured.

775.	9 s. Type **176**	40	20
776.	15 s. Scouts playing football	45	20
777.	Kangaroos	60	30
778.	75 s. Scout saluting ..	1·25	75
779.	4 m. Australian scout windsurfing	3·50	3·75

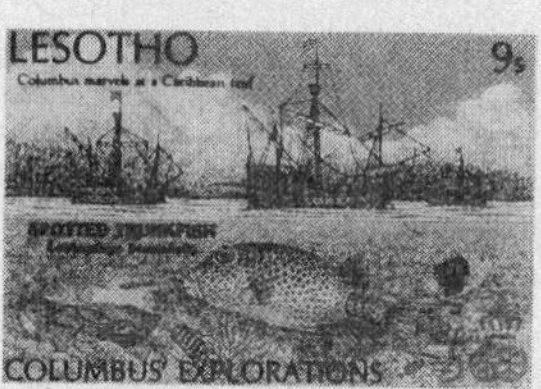

177. Spotted Trunkfish and Columbus's Fleet.

1987. 500th Anniv. (1992) of Discovery of America by Columbus. Multicoloured.

781.	9 s. Type **177**	20	15
782.	15 s. Green turtle and ships	25	15
783.	Columbus watching common dolphins from ship ..	40	30
784.	5 m. White-tailed tropic bird and fleet at sea ..	3·50	4·00

No. 782 is inscribed "Caribbean" in error.

178. "Madonna and Child" (detail).

1987. Christmas. Paintings by Raphael. Multicoloured.

786.	9 s. Type **178**	25	10
787.	15 s, "Marriage of the Virgin"	35	15
788.	35 s. "Coronation of the Virgin" (detail) ..	70	35
789.	90 s. "Madonna of the Chair"	1·75	1·75

179. Lesser Pied Kingfisher.

1988. Birds. Multicoloured.

791.	2 s. Type **179**	10	10
792.	3 s. Three-banded plover ..	10	10
793.	5 s. Spur-winged goose ..	10	10
794.	10 s. Clapper lark	10	10
795.	12 s. Red-eyed bulbul ..	10	10
796.	16 s. Cape weaver	10	10
797.	20 s. Paradise sparrow ("Red-headed Finch") ..	10	10
798.	30 s. Mountain chat ..	15	20
799.	40 s. Stonechat	15	20
800.	55 s. Pied barbet	20	25
801.	60 s. Cape glossy starling	25	30
802.	75 s. Cape sparrow ..	30	35
803.	1 m. Cattle egret	40	45
804.	3 m. Giant kingfisher ..	1·25	1·40
805.	10 m. Helmet guineafowl ..	4·00	4·25

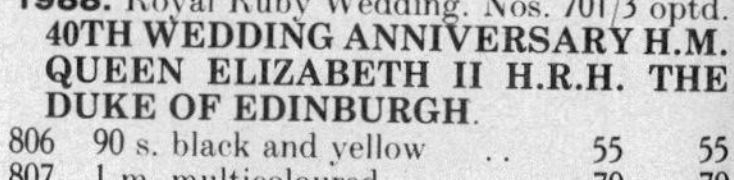
1988. Royal Ruby Wedding. Nos. 701/3 optd. **40TH WEDDING ANNIVERSARY H.M. QUEEN ELIZABETH II H.R.H. THE DUKE OF EDINBURGH.**

806	90 s. black and yellow ..	55	55
807	1 m. multicoloured ..	70	70
808	2 m. multicoloured ..	1·25	1·25

181 Mickey Mouse and Goofy outside Presidential Palace, Helsinki

1988. "Finlandia '88" International Stamp Exhibition, Helsinki. Designs showing Walt Disney cartoon characters in Finland. Mult.

810	1 s. Type **181**	10	10
811	2 s. Goofy and Mickey Mouse in sauna ..	10	10
812	3 s. Goofy and Mickey Mouse fishing in lake ..	10	10
813	4 s. Mickey and Minnie Mouse and Finlandia Hall, Helsinki	10	10
814	5 s. Mickey Mouse photographing Goofy at Sibelius Monument, Helsinki	10	10
815	10 s. Mickey Mouse and Goofy pony trekking ..	10	10
816	3 m. Goofy, Mickey and Minnie Mouse at Helsinki Olympic Stadium	1·75	1·75
817	5 m. Mickey Mouse and Goofy meeting Santa at Arctic Circle	2·50	2·50

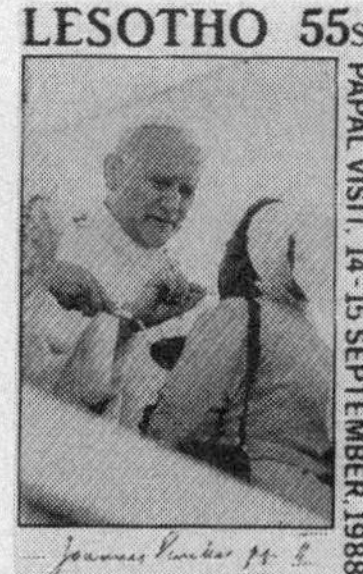

182 Pope John Paul II giving Communion

1988. Visit of Pope John Paul II. Mult.

819	55 s. Type **182**	30	25
820	2 m. Pope leading procession	1·00	1·00
821	3 m. Pope at airport ..	1·50	1·50
822	4 m. Pope John Paul II ..	2·00	2·00

183 Large-toothed Rock Hyrax

1988. Small Mammals of Lesotho. Mult.

824	16 s. Type **183**	15	10
825	40 s. Ratel and black-throated honey guide (bird)	25	25
826	75 s. Small-spotted genet	45	45
827	3 m. Yellow mongoose ..	1·75	2·00

184 "Birth of Venus" (detail) (Botticelli)

1988. Famous Paintings. Multicoloured.

829 15 s. Type **184** 15 15
830 25 s. "View of Toledo" (El Greco) 20 20
831 40 s. "Maids of Honour" (detail) (Velasquez) .. 25 25
832 50 s. "The Fifer" (Manet) 30 30
833 55 s. "Starry Night" (detail) (Van Gogh) .. 30 30
834 75 s. "Prima Ballerina" (Degas) 45 45
835 2 m. "Bridge over Water Lilies" (Monet) .. 1·00 1·00
836 3 m. "Guernica" (detail) (Picasso) .. .. 1·50 1·50

185 Wrestling

1988. Olympic Games, Seoul (2nd series). Multicoloured.

838 12 s. Type **185** 10 10
839 16 s. Show jumping (vert) 10 10
840 55 s. Shooting 20 30
841 3 m. 50 As 16 s. (vert) .. 1·40 1·75

186 Yannick Noah and Eiffel Tower, Paris

1988. 75th Anniv of International Tennis Federation. Multicoloured.

843 12 s. Type **186** 20 15
844 20 s. Rod Laver and Sydney Harbour Bridge and Opera House .. 25 20
845 30 s. Ivan Lendl and Prague 30 25
846 65 s. Jimmy Connors and Tokyo (vert) 45 40
847 1 m. Arthur Ashe and Barcelona (vert) .. 70 60
848 1 m. 55 Althea Gibson and New York (vert) .. 90 80
849 2 m. Chris Evert and Vienna (vert) .. .. 1·25 1·00
850 2 m. 40 Boris Becker and Houses of Parliament, London (vert) .. .. 1·60 1·40
851 3 m. Martina Navratilova and Golden Gate Bridge, San Francisco .. .. 1·75 1·60

No. 844 is inscribed "SIDNEY" in error.

1988. Christmas. 500th Birth Anniv of Titian (artist). As T **238** of Antigua, but inscr "CHRISTMAS 1988". Multicoloured.

853 12 s. "The Averoldi Polyptych" (detail) .. 15 10
854 20 s. "Christ and the Adulteress" (detail) .. 15 10
855 35 s. "Christ and the Adulteress" (different detail) 20 20
856 45 s. "Angel of the Annunciation" .. 30 30
857 65 s. "Saint Dominic" .. 40 40
858 1 m. "The Vendramin Family" (detail) .. 60 60
859 2 m. "Mary Magdalen" .. 1·00 1·00
860 3 m. "The Tribute Money" 1·50 1·75

187 Pilatus "PC-6 Turbo Porter"

1989. 125th Anniv of International Red Cross. Aircraft. Multicoloured.

862 12 s. Type **187** 15 10
863 20 s. Unloading medical supplies from Cessna "Caravan" 20 15
864 55 s. De Havilland "DHC-6 Otter" 40 40
865 3 m. Douglas "DC-3" .. 2·00 2·25

1989. Japanese Art. Paintings by Hiroshige. As T **250** of Antigua. Multicoloured.

867 12 s. "Dawn Mist at Mishima" 10 10
868 16 s. "Night Snow at Kambara" 10 10
869 20 s. "Wayside Inn at Mariko Station" .. 10 10
870 35 s. "Shower at Shono" .. 20 10
871 55 s. "Snowfall on the Kisokaido near Oi" .. 25 25
872 1 m. "Autumn Moon at Seba" 45 45
873 3 m. 20 "Evening Moon at Ryogoku Bridge" .. 1·40 1·40
874 5 m. "Cherry Blossoms at Arashiyama" .. .. 2·10 2·10

188 Mickey Mouse as General

1989. "Philexfrance 89" International Stamp Exhibition, Paris. Designs showing Walt Disney cartoon characters in French military uniforms of the Revolutionary period. Mult.

876 1 s. Type **188** 10 10
877 2 s. Ludwig von Drake as infantryman 10 10
878 3 s. Goofy as grenadier .. 10 10
879 4 s. Horace Horsecollar as cavalryman 10 10
880 5 s. Pete as hussar .. 10 10
881 10 s. Donald Duck as marine 10 10
882 3 m. Gyro Gearloose as National Guard .. 2·00 2·00
883 5 m. Scrooge McDuck as admiral .. .. 2·75 2·75

189 "Paxillus involutus"

1989. Fungi. Multicoloured.

900 12 s. Type **189** 15 10
901 16 s. "Ganoderma applanatum" 15 15
902 55 s. "Suillus granulatus" 35 35
903 5 m. "Stereum hirsutum" 3·00 3·50

INDEX

Countries can be quickly located by referring to the index at the end of this volume.

190 Sesotho Huts

1989. Maloti Mountains. Multicoloured.

905 1 m. Type **190** 70 70
906 1 m. American aloe and mountains 70 70
907 1 m. River valley with waterfall 70 70
908 1 m. Sesotho tribesman on ledge 70 70

Nos. 890/3 were printed together, se-tenant, forming a composite design.

191 Marsh Sandpiper

1989. Migrant Birds. Multicoloured.

910 12 s. Type **191** 20 10
911 65 s. Little stint 50 40
912 1 m. Ringed plover .. 70 60
913 4 m. Curlew sandpiper .. 2·50 3·25

192 Launch of "Apollo 11"

1989. 20th Anniv of First Manned Landing on Moon. Multicoloured.

915 12 s. Type **192** 15 10
916 16 s. Lunar module "Eagle" landing on Moon (horiz) 15 15
917 40 s. Neil Armstrong leaving "Eagle" .. 25 25
918 55 s. Edwin Aldrin on Moon (horiz) 30 30
919 1 m. Aldrin performing scientific experiment (horiz) 60 60
920 2 m. "Eagle" leaving Moon (horiz) .. .. 1·00 1·00
921 3 m. Command module "Columbia" in Moon orbit (horiz) .. 1·50 1·50
922 4 m. Command module on parachutes .. .. 1·90 1·90

193 English Penny Post Paid Mark, 1680

1989. 'World Stamp Expo '89' International Stamp Exhibition, Washington. Stamps and Postmarks.

924 **193** 75 s. red, black & stone 40 40
925 – 75 s. black, grey & red 40 40
926 – 75 s. violet, blk & brn 40 40
927 – 75 s. brown, black and light brown .. 40 40
928 – 75 s. black and yellow 40 40
929 – 75 s. multicoloured .. 40 40
930 – 75 s. black and lilac .. 40 40
931 – 75 s. black, red & brn 40 40
932 – 75 s. red, black & yell 40 40

DESIGNS: No. 925, German postal seal and feather, 1807; 926, British Post Offices in Crete 1898 20 pa. stamp; 927, Bermuda 1848 Perot 1d. provisional; 928, U.S.A. Pony Express cancellation, 1860; 929, Finland 1856 5 k. stamp; 930, Fiji 1870 "Fiji Times" 1d. stamp, 1870; 931, Sweden newspaper wrapper handstamp, 1823; 932, Bhor 1879 ½a. stamp.

1989. Christmas. Paintings by Velasquez. As T **259** of Antigua. Multicoloured.

934 12 s. "The Immaculate Conception" 10 10
935 20 s. "St. Anthony Abbot and St. Paul the Hermit" 15 10
936 35 s. "St. Thomas the Apostle" 25 25
937 55 s. "Christ in the House of Martha and Mary" .. 35 35
938 1 m. "St. John writing The Apocalypse on Patmos" 60 60
939 3 m. "The Virgin presenting the Chasuble to St. Ildephonsus" .. .. 1·60 1·75
940 4 m. "The Adoration of the Magi" .. .. .. 2·00 2·25

194 Scene from 1966 World Cup Final, England

1989. World Cup Football Championship, Italy. Scenes from past finals. Multicoloured.

942 12 s. Type **194** 15 10
943 16 s. 1970 final, Mexico .. 15 15
944 55 s. 1974 final, West Germany 50 40
945 5 m. 1982 final, Spain .. 3·00 3·50

1990. No. 795 and 798/9 surch.

947 16 s. on 12 s. Red-eyed bulbul 55 40
948e 16 s. on 30 s. Mountain chat 10 10
948f 16 s. on 40 s. Stonechat .. 10 10

197 "Byblia anvatara"

1990. Butterflies. Multicoloured.

949 12 s. Type **197** 10 10
950 16 s. "Cynthia cardui" .. 10 10
951 55 s. "Precis oenone" .. 20 25
952 65 s. "Pseudacraea boisduvali" 25 30
953 1 m. "Precis orithya" .. 40 45
954 2 m. "Precis sohpia" .. 80 85
955 3 m. "Danaus chrysippus" 1·25 1·40
956 4 m. "Druryia antimachus" 1·60 1·75

198 "Satyrium princeps"

1990. 'EXPO 90" International Garden and Greenery Exhibition, Osaka. Local Orchids. Multicoloured.

958 12 s. Type **198** 10 10
959 16 s. "Huttonaea pulchra" 10 10
960 55 s. "Herschelia graminifolia" 20 25
961 1 m. "Ansellia gigantea" 40 45

962 1 m. 55 "Polystachya pubescens" 60 65
963 2 m. 40 "Penthea filicornis" .. .. 95 1·00
964 3 m. "Disperis capensis" 1·25 1·40
965 4 m. "Disa uniflora" .. 1·60 1·75

1990. 90th Birthday of Queen Elizabeth the Queen Mother. As T **99** of Grenada Grenadines.
967 1 m. 50 black and mauve 60 65
968 1 m. 50 black and mauve 60 65
969 1 m. 50 black and mauve 60 65
DESIGNS: No. 967, Lady Elizabeth Bowes-Lyon and brother in fancy dress; 968, Lady Elizabeth Bowes-Lyon in evening dress; 969, Lady Elizabeth Bowes-Lyon wearing hat.

199 King Moshoeshoe II and Prince Mohato wearing Seana-Marena Blankets

1990. Traditional Blankets. Multicoloured.
971 12 s. Type **199** 10 10
972 16 s. Prince Mohato wearing Seana-Marena blanket 10 10
973 1 m. Pope John Paul II wearing Seana-Marena blanket 40 45
974 3 m. Basotho horsemen wearing Matlama blankets .. .. 1·25 1·40

200 Filling Truck at No. 1 Quarry

1990. Lesotho Highlands Water Project. Multicoloured.
976 16 s. Type **200** 10 10
977 20 s. Tanker lorry on Pitseng–Malibamatso road 10 10
978 55 s. Piers for Malibamatso Bridge 20 25
979 2 m. Excavating Mphosong section of Pitseng–Malibamatso road .. 80 85

201 Mother breastfeeding Baby

1990. U.N.I.C.E.F. Child Survival Campaign. Multicoloured.
981 12 s. Type **201** 10 10
982 55 s. Baby receiving oral rehydration therapy .. 20 25
983 1 m. Weight monitoring .. 40 45

1990. Olympic Games, Barcelona (1992). As T **268** of Antigua. Multicoloured.
984 16 s. Men's triple jump .. 10 10
985 55 s. Men's 200 metres race 20 25
986 1 m. Men's 5000 metres race 40 45
987 4 m. Show jumping .. 1·60 1·75

202 "Virgin and Child" (detail, Rubens)

1990. Christmas. Paintings by Rubens. Mult.
989 12 s. Type **202** 10 10
990 16 s. "Adoration of the Magi" (detail) 10 10
991 55 s. "Head of One of the Three Kings" 20 25
992 80 s. "Adoration of the Magi" (different detail) 30 35
993 1 m. "Virgin and Child" (different detail) .. 40 45
994 2 m. "Adoration of the Magi" (different detail) 80 85
995 3 m. "Virgin and Child" (different detail) .. 1·25 1·40
996 4 m. "Adoration of the Magi" (different detail) 1·60 1·75

204 Mickey Mouse at Nagasaki Peace Park

1991. "Phila Nippon '91" International Stamp Exhibition, Tokyo. Walt Disney cartoon characters in Japan. Multicoloured.
998 20 s. Type **204** 10 10
999 30 s. Mickey Mouse on Kamakura Beach .. 15 20
1000 40 s. Mickey and Donald Duck with Bunraku puppet .. 15 20
1001 50 s. Mickey and Donald eating soba .. 20 25
1002 75 s. Mickey and Minnie Mouse at tea house .. 30 35
1003 1 m. Mickey running after bullet train .. 40 45
1004 3 m. Mickey Mouse with deer at Todaiji Temple, Nara .. .. 1·25 1·40
1005 4 m. Mickey and Minnie outside Imperial Palace 1·60 1·75

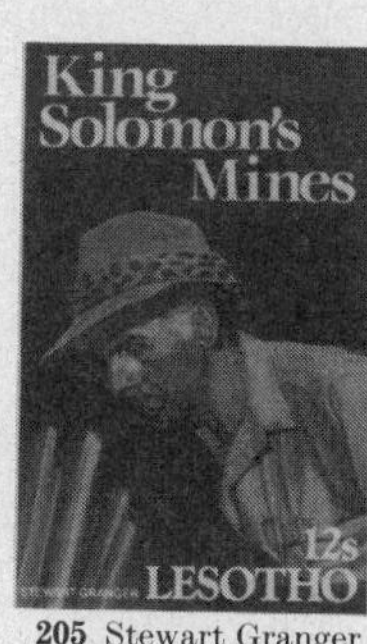

205 Stewart Granger ("King Solomon's Mines")

1991. Famous Films with African Themes. Multicoloured.
1007 12 s. Type **205** 10 10
1008 16 s. Johnny Weissmuller ("Tarzan the Ape Man") 10 10
1009 30 s. Clark Gable and Grace Kelly ("Mogambo") 15 20
1010 55 s. Sigourney Weaver and gorilla ("Gorillas in the Mist") 20 25
1011 70 s. Humphrey Bogart and Katharine Hepburn ("The African Queen") 30 35
1012 1 m. John Wayne and capture of rhinoceros ("Hatari!") 40 45
1013 2 m. Meryl Streep and aircraft ("Out of Africa") 80 85
1014 4 m. Arsenio Hall and Eddie Murphy ("Coming to America") 1·60 1·75

206 "Satyrus aello"

1991. Butterflies. Multicoloured.
1016 2 s. Type **206** 10 10
1017 3 s. "Erebia medusa" .. 10 10
1018 5 s. "Melanargia galathea" 10 10
1019 10 s. "Erebia aethiops" .. 10 10
1020 20 s. "Coenonympha pamphilus" 10 10
1021 25 s. "Pyrameis atalanta" 10 10
1022 30 s. "Charaxes jasius" .. 15 20
1023 40 s. "Colias palaeno" .. 15 20
1024 50 s. "Colias cliopatra" .. 20 25
1025 60 s. "Colias philodice" 25 30
1026 70 s. "Rhumni gonepterix" 30 35
1027 1 m. "Colias caesonia" .. 40 45
1028 2 m. "Pyrameis cardui" 80 85
1029 3 m. "Danaus chrysippus" 1·25 1·50
1030 10 m. "Apatura iris" .. 4·00 4·25

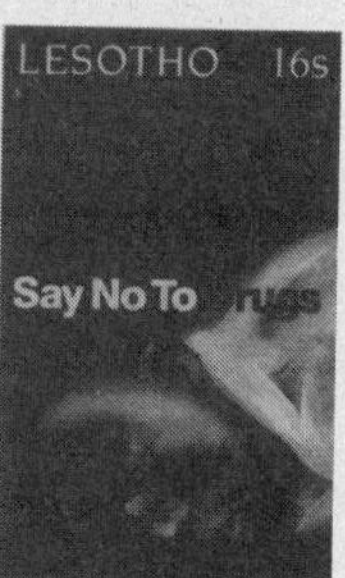

207 Victim of Drug Abuse

1991. "No To Drugs" Campaign.
1031 **207** 16 s. multicoloured .. 10 10

208 Wattled Cranes

1991. Southern Africa Development Co-ordination Conference Tourism Promotion. Multicoloured.
1032 12 s. Type **208** 10 10
1033 16 s. Butterfly on flowers 10 10
1034 25 s. Zebra and tourist bus at Mukurub (rock formation), Namibia .. 10 10

209 De Gaulle in 1939

1991. Birth Centenary of Charles de Gaulle (French statesman).
1036 **209** 20 s. black and brown 10 10
1037 – 40 s. black and purple 15 20
1038 – 50 s. black and green 20 25
1039 – 60 s. black and blue .. 25 30
1040 – 4 m. black and red .. 1·60 1·75
DESIGNS: 40 s. General De Gaulle as Free French leader; 50 s. De Gaulle as provisional President of France 1944–46; 60 s. Charles de Gaulle in 1958; 4 m. Pres. De Gaulle.

1991. 10th Wedding Anniv of Prince and Princess of Wales. As T **280** of Antigua. Multicoloured.
1041 50 s. Prince and Princess of Wales 20 25
1042 70 s. Prince Charles at polo and Princess Diana holding Prince Henry 30 35
1043 1 m. Prince Charles with Prince Henry and Princess Diana in evening dress 40 45
1044 3 m. Prince William and Prince Henry in school uniform .. .. 1·25 1·50

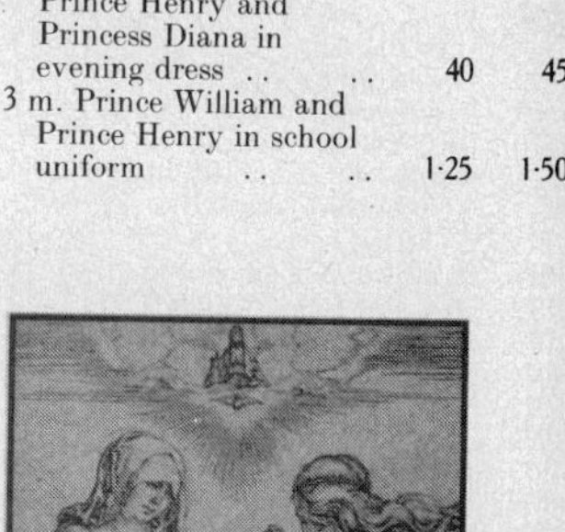

211 "St. Anne with Mary and the Child Jesus"

1991. Christmas. Drawings by Albrecht Durer.
1046 **211** 20 s. black and mauve 10 10
1047 – 30 s. black and blue .. 15 20
1048 – 50 s. black and green 20 25
1049 – 60 s. black and red .. 25 30
1050 – 70 s. black and yellow 30 35
1051 – 1 m. black and orange 40 45
1052 – 2 m. black and purple 80 85
1053 – 4 m. black and blue .. 1·60 1·75
DESIGNS: 30 s. "Mary on Grass Bench"; 50 s. "Mary with Crown of Stars"; 60 s. "Mary with Child beside Tree"; 70 s. "Mary with Child beside Wall"; 1 m. "Mary in Halo on Crescent Moon"; 2 m. "Mary breastfeeding Child"; 4 m. "Mary with Infant in Swaddling Clothes".

212 Mickey Mouse and Pluto pinning the Tail on the Donkey

1991. Children's Games. Walt Disney cartoon characters. Multicoloured.
1055 20 s. Type **212** 10 10
1056 30 s. Mickey playing mancala 15 20
1057 40 s. Mickey rolling hoop 15 20
1058 50 s. Minnie Mouse hula-hooping 20 25
1059 70 s. Mickey and Pluto throwing a frisbee .. 30 35
1060 1 m. Donald Duck with a diabolo 40 45
1061 2 m. Donald's nephews playing marbles 80 85
1062 3 m. Donald with Rubik's cube .. .. .. 1·25 1·50

213 Lanner Falcon

1992. Birds. Multicoloured.

1064 30 s. Type **213** 15 20
1065 30 s. Bateleur 15 20
1066 30 s. Paradise sparrow (inscr "Red-headed finch") 15 20
1067 30 s. Lesser striped swallow 15 20
1068 30 s. Alpine swift .. 15 20
1069 30 s. Didric cuckoo .. 15 20
1070 30 s. Yellow-tufted malachite sunbird (inscr "Crimson-breasted shirke") 15 20
1071 30 s. Burchell's gonolek .. 15 20
1072 30 s. Pin-tailed whydah .. 15 20
1073 30 s. Lilac-breasted roller 15 20
1074 30 s. Black korhaan .. 15 20
1075 30 s. Black-collared barbet 15 20
1076 30 s. Secretary bird .. 15 20
1077 30 s. Red-billed quelea .. 15 20
1078 30 s. Red bishop .. 15 20
1079 30 s. Ring-necked dove .. 15 20
1080 30 s. Yellow canary .. 15 20
1081 30 s. Cape longclaw .. 15 20
1082 30 s. Cordon-bleu (inscr "Blue waxbill") .. 15 20
1083 30 s. Golden bishop .. 15 20

Nos. 1064/83 were printed together, se-tenant, forming a composite design.

1992. 40th Anniv of Queen Elizabeth II's Accession. As T **288** of Antigua. Mult.

1084 20 s. Huts on mountain .. 10 10
1085 30 s. View from mountains 15 20
1086 1 m. Cacti and mountain 40 45
1087 4 m. Thaba-Bosiu .. 1·60 1·75

215 Minnie Mouse as Spanish Lady, 1540–1660

1992. International Stamp Exhibitions. Walt Disney cartoon characters. Mult.

(a) "Granada 92", Spain. Traditional Spanish Costumes.

1089 20 s. Type **215** 10 10
1090 50 s. Mickey Mouse as Don Juan at Lepanto, 1571 .. .. .. 20 25
1091 70 s. Donald in Galician costume, 1880 .. .. 30 35
1092 2 m. Daisy Duck in Aragonese costume, 1880 .. .. .. 80 85

(b) "World Columbian Stamp Expo '92". Red Indian Life.

1094 30 s. Donald Duck making arrowheads 15 20
1095 40 s. Goofy playing lacrosse 15 20
1096 1 m. Mickey Mouse and Donald Duck planting corn 40 45
1097 3 m. Minnie Mouse doing bead work .. .. 1·25 1·40

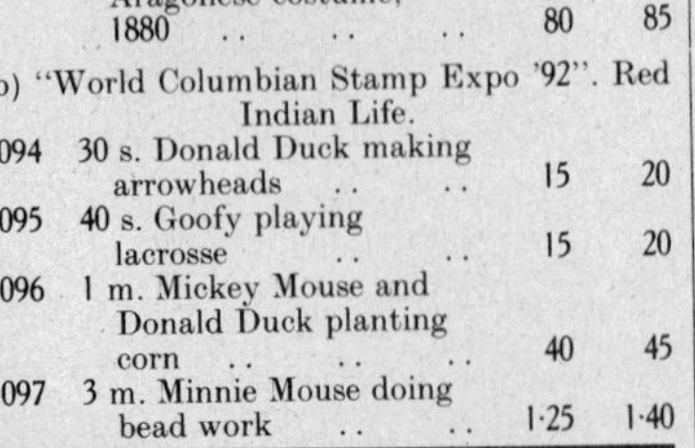

HAVE YOU READ THE NOTES AT THE BEGINNING OF THIS CATALOGUE?
These often provide answers to the enquiries we receive.

216 Men's Discus

1992. Olympic Games, Albertville and Barcelona. Multicoloured.

1099 20 s. Type **216** 10 10
1100 30 s. Men's long jump .. 15 20
1101 40 s. Women's 4 × 100 metres relay 15 20
1102 70 s. Women's 100 metres 30 35
1103 1 m. Men's parallel bars 40 45
1104 2 m. Men's double luge (horiz) 80 85
1105 3 m. Women's 30k cross-country skiing (horiz) 1·25 1·40
1106 4 m. Men's biathlon .. 1·60 1·75

217 Stegosaurus

1992. Prehistoric Animals. Multicoloured.

1108 20 s. Type **217** 10 10
1109 30 s. Ceratosaurus .. 15 20
1110 40 s. Procompsognathus 15 20
1111 50 s. Lesothosaurus .. 20 25
1112 70 s. Plateosaurus .. 30 35
1113 1 m. Gasosaurus .. 40 45
1114 2 m. Massospondylus .. 80 85
1115 3 m. Archaeopteryx .. 1·25 1·40

218 "Virgin and Child" (Sassetta)

1992. Christmas. Religious Paintings. Mult.

1117 20 s. Type **218** 10 10
1118 30 s. "Coronation of the Virgin" (Master of Bonastre) 15 20
1119 40 s. "Virgin and Child" (Master of SS. Cosmas and Damian) .. 15 20
1120 70 s. "The Virgin of Great Panagia" (detail) (12th-century Russian school) 30 35
1121 1 m. "Madonna and Child" (Vincenzo Foppa) 40 45
1122 2 m. "Madonna and Child" (School of Lippo Memmi) 80 85
1123 3 m. "Virgin and Child" (Barnaba da Modena) 1·25 1·40
1124 4 m. "Virgin and Child with Saints" (triptych) (Simone dei Crocifissi) 1·60 1·75

220 Baby Harp Seal (Earth Summit '92, Rio)

1993. Anniversaries and Events. Mult.

1127 20 s. Type **220** 10 10
1128 30 s. Giant panda (Earth Summit '92, Rio) .. 15 20
1129 40 s. Zeppelin over globe (75th death anniv of Count Ferdinand von Zeppelin) 15 20
1130 70 s. Woman grinding maize (International Conference on Nutrition, Rome) .. 30 35
1131 4 m. Lt. Robinson's BE2c shooting down Zeppelin (75th death anniv of Count Ferdinand von Zeppelin) .. .. 1·60 1·75
1132 5 m. Valentina Tereshkova and "Vostok 6" (30th anniv of first woman in space) .. 2·00 2·10

221 "Orpheus and Eurydice" (detail)

1993. Bicentenary of the Louvre, Paris. Paintings by Poussin. Multicoloured.

1134 70 s. Type **221** 30 35
1135 70 s. "Rape of the Sabine Women" (left detail) .. 30 35
1136 70 s. "Rape of the Sabine Women" (right detail) 30 35
1137 70 s. "The Death of Sapphira" (left detail) 30 35
1138 70 s. "The Death of Sapphira" (right detail) 30 35
1139 70 s. "Echo and Narcissus" (left detail) 30 35
1140 70 s. "Echo and Narcissus" (right detail) 30 35
1141 70 s. "Self-portrait" .. 30 35

222 Aloe

1993. Flowers. Multicoloured.

1143 20 s. Type **222** 10 10
1144 30 s. Calla lily 15 20
1145 40 s. Bird of paradise plant 15 20
1146 70 s. Amaryllis 30 35
1147 1 m. Agapanthus 40 45
1148 2 m. Crinum 80 85
1149 4 m. Watsonia .. .. 1·60 1·75
1150 5 m. Gazania .. .. 2·00 2·10

223 "Precis westermanni"

1993. Butterflies. Multicoloured.

1152 20 s. Type **223** 10 10
1153 40 s. "Precis sophia" .. 15 20
1154 70 s. "Precis terea" .. 30 35
1155 1 m. "Byblia acheloia" .. 40 45
1156 2 m. "Papilio antimachus" 80 85
1157 5 m. "Pseudacraea boisduvali" .. .. 2·00 2·10

No. 1157 is inscribed "Pesudacraea boisduvali" in error.

1993. 40th Anniv of Coronation. As T **307** of Antigua.

1159 20 s. multicoloured .. 10 10
1160 40 s. multicoloured .. 15 20
1161 1 m. black and green .. 40 45
1162 5 m. multicoloured .. 2·00 2·10

DESIGNS: 20 s. Queen Elizabeth II at Coronation (photograph by Cecil Beaton); 40 s. St. Edward's Crown and Sceptre; 1 m. Queen Elizabeth the Queen Mother; 5 m. Queen Elizabeth II and family.

225 "Vulcan" Type Locomotive, East African Railways, 1929

1993. African Railways. Multicoloured.

1164 20 s. Type **225** 10 10
1165 30 s. Class "15A" steam locomotive, Zimbabwe Railways, 1952 .. 15 20
1166 40 s. Class "25" steam locomotive, South African Railways, 1953 15 20
1167 70 s. Class "A 58" Garratt steam locomotive, East African Railways .. 30 35
1168 1 m. Class "9E" electric locomotives, South African Railways .. 40 45
1169 2 m. Class "87" diesel locomotive, East African Railways, 1971 80 85
1170 3 m. Class "92" diesel locomotive, East African Railways, 1971 1·25 1·40
1171 5 m. Class "26" steam locomotive, South African Railways, 1982 2·00 2·10

226 Court-house

1993. Traditional Houses. Multicoloured.

1173 20 s. Type **226** 10 10
1174 30 s. House with reed fence 15 20
1175 70 s. Unmarried girls' house 30 35
1176 4 m. Hut made from branches .. .. 1·60 1·75

227 Black and White Shorthair

1993. Domestic Cats. Multicoloured.

1178 20 s. Type **227** 10 10
1179 30 s. Shorthair tabby lying down 15 20
1180 70 s. Head of shorthair tabby 30 35
1181 5 m. Black and white shorthair with shorthair tabby .. .. .. 2·00 2·10

228 Pluto in Chung Cheng Park, Keelung

1993. "Taipei '93" Asian International Stamp Exhibition, Taiwan. Walt Disney cartoon characters in Taiwan. Multicoloured.

1183	20 s. Type **228**	10	10
1184	30 s. Donald Duck at Chiao-Tienkung Temple Festival	15	20
1185	40 s. Goofy with lantern figures	15	20
1186	70 s. Minnie Mouse shopping at temple festival	30	35
1187	1 m. Daisy Duck at Queen's Head Rock, Yehliu (vert)	40	45
1188	1 m. 20 Mickey and Minnie at National Concert Hall (vert) ..	45	50
1189	2 m. Donald at Chiang Kai-shek Memorial Hall (vert)	80	85
1190	2 m. 50 Donald and Daisy at the Grand Hotel, Taipei	1·00	1·10

229 Tseliso "Frisco" Khomari (Lesotho)

1994. World Cup Football Championship '94, U.S.A.

1192	20 s. Type **229**	10	10
1193	30 s. Thato "American Spoon" Mohale (Lesotho)	15	20
1194	40 s. Jozic Davor (Yugoslavia) and Freddy Rincorn (Colombia)	15	20
1195	50 s. Lefika "Mzee" Lekhotla (Lesotho) ..	20	25
1196	70 s. Litsisio "House-on-fire" Khali (Lesotho) ..	30	35
1197	1 m. Roger Milla (Cameroun)	40	45
1198	1 m. 20, David Platt (England)	45	50
1199	2 m. Karl Heinz Rummenigge (Germany) and Soren Lerby (Denmark) ..	80	85

POSTAGE DUE STAMPS

1966. Nos. D 9/10 of Basutoland optd. **LESOTHO.**

D 11. D 2.	1 c. red	30	60
D 12.	5 c. violet	30	90

D 1.

D 2.

1967.

D 13. D 1.	1 c. blue	15	2·25
D 14.	2 c. red	15	2·75
D 15.	5 c. green	20	2·75

1986.

D 19 D 2	2 s. green	10	10
D 20	5 s. blue	10	10
D 21	35 s. violet	10	10

APPENDIX

The following stamps have either been issued in excess of postal needs, or have not been available to the public in reasonable quantities at face value.

1981–83.

15th Anniv. of Independence. Classic Stamps of the World. 10 m. × 40, each embossed on gold foil.

MAFEKING

A town in Bechuanaland. Special stamps issued by British garrison during Boer War.

12 pence = 1 shilling.
20 shillings = 1 pound.

1900. Stamps of Cape of Good Hope surch. **MAFEKING BESIEGED** and value.

1. **6.**	1d. on ½d. green	£150	48·00
2. **17.**	1d. on ½d. green	£190	55·00
3.	3d. on 1d. red	£160	48·00
4. **6.**	6d. on 3d. mauve	£9500	£250
5.	1s. on 4d. olive	£4000	£325

1900. Stamps of Bechuanaland Prot. (Queen Victoria) surch. **MAFEKING BESIEGED** and value.

6. **71.**	1d. on ½d. red (No. 59) ..	£160	48·00
7. **57.**	3d. on 1d. lilac (No. 61)	£850	65·00
8. **73.**	6d. on 2d. green and red (No. 62) ..	£1100	65·00
9. **75.**	6d. on 3d. purple on yell. (No. 63)	£3500	£250
14. **79.**	1s. on 6d. purple on red (No. 65)	£3250	80·00

1900. Stamps of Br. Bechuanaland surch. **MAFEKING BESIEGED** and value.

10. **3.**	6d. on 3d. lilac and black (No. 12)	£350	60·00
11. **76.**	1s. on 4d. green & brown (No. 35)	£1200	65·00
15. **79.**	1s. on 6d. purple on red (No. 36)	£9500	£600
16. **82.**	2s. on 1s. green (No. 37)	£6500	£300

3. Cadet Sgt.-Major Goodyear.

4. General Baden-Powell.

1900.

17. **3.**	1d. blue on blue ..	£800	£275
19. **4.**	3d. blue on blue ..	£1200	£400

MALACCA

A British Settlement on the Malay Peninsula which became a state of the Federation of Malaya, incorporated in Malaysia in 1963.

100 cents = 1 dollar (Malayan).

1948. Silver Wedding. As T **10/11** of Aden.

1.	10 c. violet	30	40
2.	$5 brown	25·00	35·00

1949. As T **58** of Straits Settlements.

3.	1 c. black	10	70
4.	2 c. orange	30	45
5.	3 c. green	30	1·50
6.	4 c. brown	15	10
6a.	5 c. purple	45	1·00
7.	6 c. grey	30	75
8.	8 c. red	30	3·50
8a.	8 c. green	85	3·50
9.	10 c. mauve	15	10
9a.	12 c. red	95	2·25
10.	15 c. blue	30	60
11.	20 c. black and green ..	30	4·00
11a.	20 c. blue	1·25	1·75
12.	25 c. purple and orange ..	30	70
12a.	35 c. red and purple ..	1·00	2·00
13.	40 c. red and purple ..	1·25	8·50
14.	50 c. black and blue ..	50	1·00
15.	$1 blue and purple ..	4·00	11·00
16.	$2 green and red	14·00	17·00
17.	$5 green and brown ..	35·00	35·00

1949. U.P.U. As T **20/23** of Antigua.

18.	10 c. purple	20	45
19.	15 c. blue	45	1·75
20.	25 c. orange	45	3·00
21.	50 c. black	1·00	3·75

1953. Coronation. As T **13** of Aden.

22	10 c. black and purple ..	30	20

1. Queen Elizabeth II.

1954.

23. **1.**	1 c. black	10	50
24.	2 c. orange	30	60
25.	4 c. brown	30	10
26.	5 c. mauve	30	70
27.	6 c. grey	10	15
28.	8 c. green	30	50
29.	10 c. purple	30	10
30.	12 c. red	20	1·25
31.	20 c. blue	20	40
32.	25 c. purple and orange ..	20	40
33.	30 c. red and purple ..	20	30
34.	35 c. red and purple ..	20	40
35.	50 c. black and blue ..	30	60
36.	$1 blue and purple ..	2·25	5·00
37.	$2 green and red ..	17·00	22·00
38.	$5 green and brown ..	18·00	24·00

1957. As Nos. 92/102 of Kedah but inset portrait of Queen Elizabeth II.

39.	1 c. black	10	40
40.	2 c. red	10	40
41.	4 c. sepia	10	10
42.	5 c. lake	10	10
43.	8 c. green	1·25	2·25
44.	10 c. sepia	20	10
45.	20 c. blue	30	40
46.	50 c. black and blue ..	30	50
47.	$1 blue and purple ..	2·00	2·50
48.	$2 green and red	8·50	14·00
49.	$5 brown and green ..	12·00	15·00

2. Copra.

1960. As Nos. 39/49 but with inset picture of Melaka tree and Pelandok (mouse-deer) as in T **2**.

50	1 c. black	10	30
51	2 c. red	10	30
52	4 c. sepia	10	10
53	5 c. lake	10	10
54	8 c. green	2·00	1·75
55	10 c. purple	20	10
56	20 c. blue	20	30
57	50 c. black and blue ..	30	30
58	$1 blue and purple	1·50	2·50
59	$2 green and red	4·50	5·00
60	$5 brown and green ..	8·50	7·00

3. "Vanda hookeriana".

1965. As Nos. 115/21 of Kedah but with Arms of Malacca inset and inscr. "MELAKA" as in T **3**.

61. **3.**	1 c. multicoloured ..	10	50
62. –	2 c. multicoloured ..	10	50
63. –	5 c. multicoloured ..	10	10
64. –	6 c. multicoloured ..	30	45
65. –	10 c. multicoloured ..	20	10
66. –	15 c. multicoloured ..	1·75	40
67. –	20 c. multicoloured ..	2·25	90

The higher values used in Malacca were Nos. 20/7 of Malaysia.

4. "Papilio demoleus".

1971. Butterflies. As Nos. 124/30 of Kedah but with Arms of Malacca as in T **4**. Inscr. "melaka".

70. –	1 c. multicoloured ..	15	60
71. –	2 c. multicoloured ..	40	60
72. –	5 c. multicoloured ..	55	10
73. **4.**	6 c. multicoloured ..	55	80
74. –	10 c. multicoloured ..	55	10
75. –	15 c. multicoloured ..	90	10
76. –	20 c. multicoloured ..	1·00	1·00

The higher values in use with this issue were Malaysia Nos. 64/71.

5. "Durio zibethinus".

1979. Flowers. As Nos. 135/41 of Kedah but with Arms of Malacca and inscr. "melaka" as in T **5**.

82	1 c. "Rafflesia hasseltii" ..	10	30
83	2 c. "Peterocarpus indicus"	10	30
84	5 c. "Lagerstroemia speciosa"	10	10
85	10 c. Type **5**	15	10
86	15 c. "Hibiscus rosa-sinesis"	15	10
87	20 c. "Rhododendron scortechinii"	20	10
88	25 c. "Etlingera elatior" (inscr "Phaeomeria speciosa"	25	30

6. Rubber.

1986. As Nos. 152/8 of Kedah but with Arm[s] of Malacca and inscr. "MELAKA" as in T 6[.]

96.	1 c. Coffee	10	
97.	2 c. Coconuts	10	
98.	5 c. Cocoa	10	
99.	10 c. Black pepper ..	10	
100.	15 c. Type **6**	10	
101.	20 c. Oil palm	10	
102.	30 c. Rice	15	2

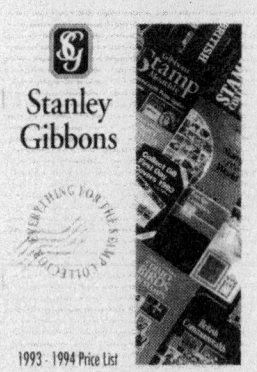

MALAWI

Formerly Nyasaland, became an independent epublic within the Commonwealth on the h July, 1966.

1964. 12 pence = 1 shilling;
20 shillings = 1 pound
1970. 100 tambalas = 1 kwacha.

44. Dr. H. Banda (Prime Minister) and Independence Monument.

1964. Independence.

1.	44.	3d. olive and sepia ..	10	10
2.	–	6d. multicoloured ..	10	10
3.	–	1s. 3d. multicoloured ..	20	10
4.	–	2s. 6d. multicoloured ..	30	35

ESIGNS (each with Dr. Hastings Banda): . Rising Sun. 1s. 3d. National Flag. 2s. 6d. oat of arms.

48. Tung Tree.

964. As Nos. 199/210 of Nyasaland but inscr. "MALAWI" as in T **48.** The 9d., 1s. 6d. and £2 are new values and designs.

52	½d. violet	10	10
6	1d. black and green ..	10	10
7	2d. brown	10	10
8	3d. brown, green & bistre	15	10
9	4d. blue and yellow ..	25	15
56	6d. purple, green and blue	25	10
57	9d. brown, green & yellow	35	10
58	1s. brown, blue & yellow ..	25	10
23	1s. 3d. bronze and brown ..	50	60
59	1s. 6d. brown and green ..	30	10
24	2s. 6d. brown and blue ..	1·10	1·00
25	5s. multicoloured (I) ..	65	2·00
25a	5s. multicoloured (II) ..	4·00	90
26	10s. green, salmon & black	1·50	2·00
27	£1 brown and yellow ..	6·00	5·50
62	£2 multicoloured	25·00	24·00

ESIGNS (New): 1s. 6d. Burley tobacco. £2, Cyrestis camillus" (butterfly).

Two types of 5s. I, inscr "LAKE NYASA". I, inscr "LAKE MALAWI".

49. Christmas Star and Globe.

1964. Christmas.

28.	49.	3d. green and gold ..	10	10
29.		6d. mauve and gold ..	10	10
30.		1s. 3d. violet and gold ..	10	10
31.		2s. 6d. blue and gold ..	20	25

50. Coins.

964. Malawi's 1st Coinage. Coins in black and silver.

32.	50.	3d. green	10	10
33.		9d. mauve	15	10
34.		1s. 6d. purple	20	10
35.		3s. blue	30	40

1965. Nos. 223/4 surch.

36.	1s. 6d. on 1s. 3d. bronze & brown	10	10
37.	3s. on 2s. 6d. brown & blue	20	20

52. Chilembwe leading Rebels.

1965. 50th Anniversary of 1915 Rising.

238.	52.	3d. violet and green ..	10	10
239.		9d. olive and orange ..	10	10
240.		1s. 6d. brown and blue ..	10	10
241.		3s. turquoise and blue ..	20	25

53. " Learning and Scholarship ".

1965. Opening of Malawi University.

242.	53.	3d. black and green ..	10	10
243.		9d. black and mauve ..	10	10
244.		1s. 6d. black and violet ..	10	10
245.		3s. black and blue ..	15	40

54. "Papilio ophidicephalus".

1966. Malawi Butterfiles. Multicoloured.

247	4d. Type **54**	60	10
248	9d. "Papilio desmondi" (magdae)	85	10
249	1s. 6d. "Epamera handmani"	1·25	30
250	3s. "Amauris crawshayi"	2·50	4·00

58. British Central Africa 6d. Stamp of 1891.

1966. 75th Anniv. of Postal Services.

263.	58.	4d. blue and green ..	10	10
264.		9d. blue and red ..	10	10
265.		1s. 6d. blue and lilac ..	15	10
266.		3s. grey and blue ..	25	30

59. President Banda.

1966. Republic Day.

268.	59.	4d. brown, silver & green	10	10
269.		9d. brown, silver & mauve	10	10
270.		1s. 6d. brown, silver & vio.	10	10
271.		3s. brown, silver and blue	20	10

60. Bethlehem.

1966. Christmas.

273.	60.	4d. green and gold ..	10	10
274.		9d. purple and gold ..	10	10
275.		1s. 6d. red and gold ..	15	10
276.		3s. blue and gold ..	40	50

61. "Ilala I".

1967. Lake Malawi Steamers.

277.	61.	4d. black, yellow & grn.	30	10
278.	–	9d. black, yellow & mve.	35	10
279.	–	1s. 6d. black, red & violet	55	15
280.	–	3s. black, red and blue ..	1·25	1·25

DESIGNS: 9d. "Dove". 1s. 6d. "Chauncy Maples I" (wrongly inscr. "Chauncey"). 3s. "Gwendolen".

62. " Turquoise-gold Chichlid ".

1967. Lake Malawi Chichlids. Multicoloured.

281.	4d. Type **62**	15	10
282.	9d. " Red Finned Chichlid "	20	10
283.	1s. 6d. " Zebra Chichlid "	30	10
284.	3s. " Golden Chichlid " ..	1·00	1·00

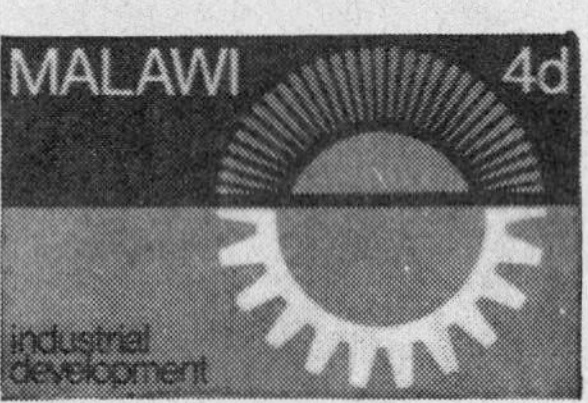

63. Rising Sun and Gearwheel.

1967. Industrial Development.

285.	63.	4d. black and green ..	10	10
286.		9d. black and red ..	10	10
287.		1s. 6d. black and violet	10	10
288.		3s. black and blue ..	15	15

64. Mary and Joseph beside Crib.

1967. Christmas.

290.	64.	4d. blue and green ..	10	10
291.		9d. blue and red ..	10	10
292.		1s. 6d. blue and yellow	10	10
293.		3s. deep blue and blue	15	15

65. "Calotropis procera".

1968. Wild Flowers. Multicoloured.

295.	4d. Type **65**	15	10
296.	9d. "Borreria dibrachiata"	15	10
297.	1s. 6d. " Hibiscus rhodanthus"	15	10
298.	3s. " Bidens pinnatipartita"	20	20

66. Saddleback Steam Locomotive, "Thistle" No. 1.

1968. Malawi Locomotives.

300.	66.	4d. green, blue and red	30	10
301.	–	9d. red, blue and green	40	10
302.	–	1s. 6d. multicoloured ..	65	20
303.	–	3s. multicoloured	1·25	1·75

DESIGNS: 9d. Class "G" steam locomotive. 1s. 6d. Diesel locomotive "Zambesi". 3s. Diesel railcar.

67. " The Nativity " (Piero della Francesca).

1968. Christmas. Multicoloured.

305.	4d. Type **67**	10	10
306.	9d. " The Adoration of the Shepherds " (Murillo) ..	10	10
307.	1s. 6d. " The Adoration of the Shepherds " (Reni) ..	10	10
308.	3s. " Nativity, with God the Father and Holy Ghost " (Pittoni) ..	15	10

69. Nyassa Lovebird.

70. Carmine Bee Eater.

1968. Birds (1st series). Multicoloured.

310.	1d. Scarlet-chested Sunbird (horiz.)	15	10
311.	2d. Violet Starling (horiz.)	15	10
312.	3d. White-browed Robin Chat (horiz.)	20	10
313.	4d. Red-billed Fire Finch (horiz.)	35	40
314.	6d. Type **69**	45	15
315.	9d. Yellow-rumped Bishop	50	60
316.	1s. Type **70**	60	15
317.	1s. 6d. Grey-headed Bush Shrike	5·00	6·00
318.	2s. Paradise Whydah ..	5·00	7·00
319.	3 s. African Paradise Flycatcher (vert.)	4·50	3·75
320.	5s. Bateleur (vert.) ..	6·50	4·00
321.	10s. Saddle-bill Stork (vert.)	5·50	7·50
322.	£1 Purple Heron (vert.) ..	12·00	17·00
323.	£2 Knysna Turaco ..	35·00	48·00

SIZES: 1d. to 9d. as Type **69**, 1s. 6d. to £2 as Type **70**.

See also Nos. 473/85.

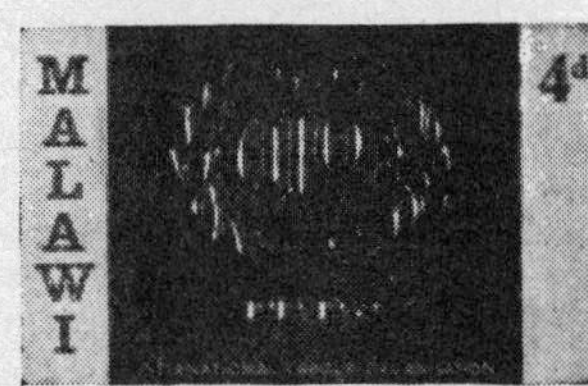

71. I.L.O. Emblem.

1969. 50th Anniv. of Int. Labour Organization.

324.	71.	4d. gold and green ..	10	10
325.		9d. gold and brown ..	10	10
326.		1s. 6d. gold and brown	10	10
327.		3s. gold and blue ..	15	15

72. White-fringed Ground Orchid.

1969. Orchids of Malawi. Multicoloured.

329.	4d. Type **72**	15	10
330.	9d. Red Ground Orchid ..	20	10
331.	1s. 6d. Leopard Tree Orchid	30	10
332.	3s. Blue Ground Orchid ..	60	1·75

73. African Development Bank Emblem.

1969. 5th Anniv. of African Development Bank.

334. **73.** 4d. yellow, brn. & ochre .. 10 10
335. 9d. yellow, ochre & green 10 10
336. 1s. 6d. yell., ochre & brn. 10 10
337. 3s. yellow, ochre & blue 15 15

74. Dove over Bethlehem.

1969. Christmas.

339. **74.** 2d. black and yellow .. 10 10
340. 4d. black and turquoise 10 10
341. 9d. black and red .. 10 10
342. 1s. 6d. black and violet 10 10
343. 3s. black and blue .. 15 15

75. "Zonocerus elegans" (grasshopper).

1970. Insects of Malawi. Multicoloured.

345 4d. Type **75** 15 10
346 9d. "Mylabris dicincta" (beetle) 15 10
347 1s. 6d. "Henosepilachna elaterii" (ladybird) .. 20 10
348 3s. "Sphodromantis speculaburenda" (mantid) .. 35 45

1970. Rand Easter Show. No. 317 optd. **Rand Easter Show 1970.**

350. 1s. 6d. multicoloured .. 20 90

77. Runner.

1970. 9th Commonwealth Games, Edinburgh

351. **77.** 4d. blue and green .. 10 10
352. 9d. blue and red .. 10 10
353. 1s. 6d. blue and yellow 10 10
354. 3s. deep blue and blue .. 15 15

1970. Decimal Currency. Nos. 316 and 318 surch.

356. 10 t. on 1 s. multicoloured 80 25
357. 20 t. on 2s. multicoloured 1·60 1·25

79. "Aegocera trimeni".

1970. Moths. Multicoloured.

358 4d. Type **79** 20 10
359 9d. "Faidherbia bauhiniae" 30 10
360 1s. 6d. "Parasa karschi" .. 50 10
361 3s. "Teracotona euprepia" 1·25 2·00

80. Mother and Child.

1970. Christmas.

363 **80.** 2d. black and yellow .. 10 10
364. 4d. black and green .. 10 10
365. 9d. black and red .. 10 10
366. 1s. 6d. black and purple 10 10
367. 3s. black and blue .. 15 15

1971. No. 319 surch. **30 t Special United Kingdom Delivery Service.**

369. 30 t. on 3s. multicoloured 20 1·75

No. 369 was issued for use on letters carried by an emergency airmail service from Malawi to Great Britain during the British postal strike. The fee of 30 t. was to cover the charge for delivery by a private service, and ordinary stamps to pay the normal airmail postage had to be affixed as well. These stamps were in use from 8th Feb. to 8th March.

82. Decimal Coinage and Cockerel.

1971. Decimal Coinage.

370. **82.** 3 t. multicoloured .. 10 10
371. 8 t. multicoloured .. 15 10
372. 15 t. multicoloured .. 20 10
373. 30 t. multicoloured .. 35 45

83. Greater Kudu. 85. Christ on the Cross.

1971. Decimal Currency. Antelopes. Mult.

375. 1 t. Type **83** 10 10
376. 2 t. Nyala 15 10
377. 3 t. Mountain Reedbuck .. 20 20
378. 5 t. Puku 40 20
379. 8 t. Impala 45 20
380. 10 t. Eland 60 10
381. 15 t. Klipspringer .. .. 1·00 20
382. 20 t. Suni .. .. 1·50 50
383. 30 t. Roan Antelope .. 5·00 70
384. 50 t. Waterbuck 90 65
385. 1 k. Bushbuck .. .. 2·00 85
386. 2 k. Red Forest Duiker .. 3·50 1·50
387. 4 k. Common Duiker .. 20·00 17·00

Nos. 380/7 are larger, size 25 × 42 mm.
No. 387 is incorrectly inscr. "Gray Duiker".

1971. Easter. Multicoloured.

388. **85.** 3 t. black and green .. 10 10
389. – 3 t. black and green .. 10 10
390. **85.** 8 t. black and red .. 10 10
391. – 8 t. black and red .. 10 10
392. **85.** 15 t. black and violet .. 15 15
393. – 15 t. black and violet .. 15 15
394. **85.** 30 t. black and blue .. 25 25
395. – 30 t. black and blue .. 25 25

DESIGN: Nos. 389, 391, 393, 395, The Resurrection.
Both designs from "The Small Passion" (Durer).

87. "Holarrhena febrifuga".

1971. Flowering Shrubs and Trees. Mult.

397. 3 t. Type **87** 10 10
398. 8 t. "Brachystegia spiciformis" 15 10
399. 15 t. "Securidaca longepedunculata" .. 25 10
400. 30 t. "Pterocarpus rotundifolius" 40 50

88. Drum Major. 89. "Madonna and Child" (William Dyce).

1971. 50th Anniv. of Malawi Police Force.

402. **88.** 30 t. multicoloured .. 65 1·00

1971. Christmas. Multicoloured.

403. 3 t. Type **89** 10 10
404. 8 t. "The Holy Family" (M. Schongauer) .. 15 10
405. 15 t. "The Holy Family with St. John" (Raphael) 30 20
406. 30 t. "The Holy Family" (Bronzino) 65 80

90. Vickers "Viscount".

1972. Air. Malawi Aircraft. Multicoloured.

408. 3 t. Type **90** 25 10
409. 8 t. Hawker Siddeley "748" 40 10
410. 15 t. Britten-Norman "Islander" 65 30
411. 30 t. B.A.C. "One-Eleven" 1·10 1·75

91. Figures (Chencherere Hill).

1972. Rock Paintings.

413. **91.** 3 t. green and black .. 35 10
414. – 8 t. red, grey and black 45 10
415. – 15 t. multicoloured .. 70 30
416. – 30 t. multicoloured .. 1·00 1·00

DESIGNS: 8 t. Lizard and Cat (Chencherere Hill). 15 t. Schematics (Diwa Hill). 30 t. Sun Through Rain (Mikolongwe Hill).

92. Boxing.

1972. Olympic Games, Munich.

418. **92.** 3 t. multicoloured .. 10 10
419. 8 t. multicoloured .. 10 10
420. 15 t. multicoloured .. 15 10
421. 30 t. multicoloured .. 35 45

93. Arms of Malawi.

1972. Commonwealth Parliamentary Conf

423. **93.** 15 t. multicoloured .. 30 3

94. "Adoration of the Kings" (Orcagna).

1972. Christmas. Multicoloured.

424. 3 t. Type **94** 10 10
425. 8 t. "Madonna and Child Enthroned" (Florentine School) 10 10
426. 15 t. "Virgin and Child" (Crivelli) .. 20 10
427. 30 t. "Virgin and Child with St. Anne" (Flemish School) 45 70

95. "Charaxes bohemani".

1973. Butterflies. Multicoloured.

429 3 t. Type **95** 20 10
430 8 t. "Uranothauma crawshayi" .. 45 10
431 15 t. "Charaxes acuminatus" .. 65 30
432 30 t. "Amauris ansorgei" (inscr in error "EUPHAEDRA ZADDACHI") .. 3·00 7·00
433 30 t. "Amauris ansorgei" (inscr corrected) .. 3·00 7·00

96. Livingstone and Map.

1973. Death Centenary of David Livingstone. (1st issue).

435. **96.** 3 t. multicoloured .. 10 10
436. 8 t. multicoloured .. 15 10
437. 15 t. multicoloured .. 30 10
438. 30 t. multicoloured .. 45 60

See also No. 450.

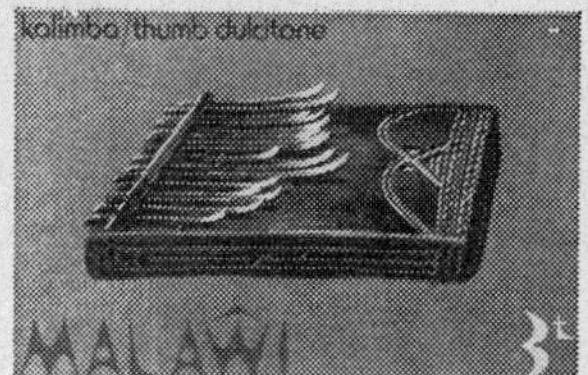

97. Thumb Dulcitone.

1973. Musical Instruments. Multicoloured.

440. 3 t. Type **97** 10 10
441. 8 t. Hand zither (vert.) .. 15 10
442. 15 t. Hand drum (vert.) .. 20 10
443. 30 t. One-stringed fiddle .. 40 60

98. The Magi.

1973. Christmas.

445. 98. 3 t. blue, lilac & ultram. 10 10
446. 8 t. red, lilac and brown 10 10
447. 15 t. mve., blue & deep mve. 15 10
448. 30 t. yell., lilac & brown 30 55

99. Stained-glass Window, Livingstonia Mission.

1973. Death Centenary of David Livingstone. (2nd issue).

450. 99. 50 t. multicoloured .. 45 1·00

100. Largemouth Black Bass.

1973. 35th Anniv. of Malawi Angling Society. Multicoloured.

452. 3 t. Type **100** 20 10
453. 8 t. Rainbow trout .. 25 10
454. 15 t. Lake salmon .. 45 20
455. 30 t. Tiger fish 75 75

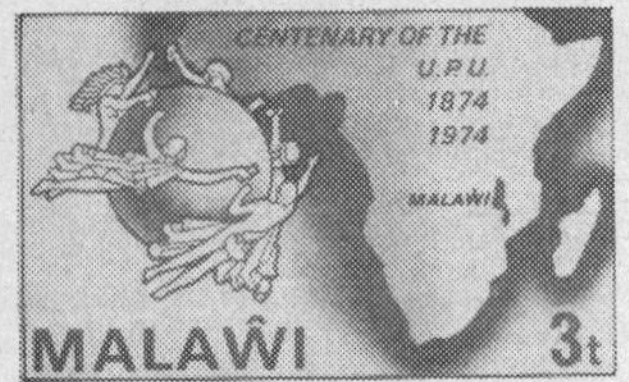

101. U.P.U. Monument and Map of Africa.

1974. Centenary of U.P.U.

457. 101. 3 t. green and brown .. 10 10
458. 8 t. red and brown .. 10 10
459. 15 t. violet and brown .. 15 10
460. 30 t. blue and brown .. 30 70

102. Capital Hill, Lilongwe.

1974. 10th Anniv. of Independence.

462. 102. 3 t. multicoloured .. 10 10
463. 8 t. multicoloured .. 10 10
464. 15 t. multicoloured .. 10 10
465. 30 t. multicoloured .. 25 35

103. " Madonna of the Meadow " (Bellini).

1974. Christmas. Multicoloured.

467. 3 t. Type **103** .. 10 10
468. 8 t. " The Holy Family with Sts. John and Elizabeth " (Jordaens) .. 10 10
469. 15 t. " The Nativity " (Pieter de Grebber) .. 15 10
470. 30 t. " Adoration of the Shepherds " (Lorenzo di Credi) 30 50

104. Arms of Malawi. 105. African Snipe.

106. Spur-winged Goose.

1975.

472 104 1 t. blue 10 30
472a 5 t. red 30 30

1975. Birds (2nd series). Multicoloured.

(a) As Type **105**

473 1 t. Type **105** .. .. 30 1·00
474 2 t. Double-handed sand grouse (horiz) .. .. 50 1·00
475 3 t. Blue quail (horiz) .. 1·50 70
476 5 t. Bare-throated francolin 3·00 70
477 8 t. Harlequin quail (horiz) 4·25 70

(b) As Type **106**

502 10 t. Type **106** .. .. 2·00 1·25
503 15 t. Barrow's bustard .. 2·00 1·75
480 20 t. Comb duck .. .. 1·00 1·75
481 30 t. Helmet guineafowl .. 1·25 70
482 50 t. African pygmy goose (horiz) .. .. .. 2·00 1·60
483 1 k. Garganey .. .. 3·00 5·00
504 2 k. White-faced whistling duck .. .. .. 9·50 9·50
485 4 k. African green pigeon 13·00 16·00

107. M.V. "Mpasa".

1975. Ships of Lake Malawi. Multicoloured.

486. 3 t. Type **107** 15 10
487. 8 t. M.V. "Ilala II" .. 25 10
488. 15 t. M.V. "Chauncy Maples II" 40 20
489. 30 t. M.V. "Nkwazi" .. 65 1·10

108. " Habenaria splendens ".

1975. Malawi Orchids. Multicoloured.

491. 3 t. Type **108** 15 10
492. 10 t. " Eulophia cucullata " 25 10
493. 20 t. " Disa welwitschii " 40 20
494. 40 t. " Angraecum conchiferum " 70 85

109. Thick-tailed Bushbaby.

1975. Malawi Animals. Multicoloured.

496. 3 t. Type **109** 10 10
497. 10 t. Leopard 35 10
498. 20 t. Roan Antelope .. 55 30
499. 40 t. Common Zebra .. 1·00 2·00

1975. 10th African, Caribbean and Pacific Ministerial Conference. No. 482 optd. **10th ACP Ministerial Conference 1975.**

514. 50 t. African Pygmy Goose 75 1·10

111. " A Castle with the Adoration of the Magi ".

1975. Christmas. Religious Medallions. Multicoloured.

515. 3 t. Type **111** 10 10
516. 10 t. " The Nativity " .. 15 10
517. 20 t. " Adoration of the Magi (different) 20 10
518. 40 t. " Angel appearing to Shepherds " .. .. 50 1·00

112. Alexander Graham Bell.

1976. Centenary of Telephone.

520. 112. 3 t. green and black .. 10 10
521. 10 t. purple and black 10 10
522. 20 t. violet and black .. 20 10
523. 40 t. blue and black .. 50 70

113. President Banda.

1976. 10th Anniv. of Republic. Mult.

525. 113. 3 t. green 10 10
526. 10 t. purple 10 10
527. 20 t. blue 20 10
528. 40 t. blue 50 70

114. Bagnall Diesel Shunter.

1976. Malawi Locomotives. Multicoloured.

530. 3 t. Type **114** 20 10
531. 10 t. "Shire" Class diesel locomotive 50 10
532. 20 t. Nippon Sharyo diesel locomotive 90 45
533. 40 t. Hunslet diesel locomotive .. .. 1·90 2·75

1976. Centenary of Blantyre Mission. Nos. 479 and 481 optd. **Blantyre Mission Centenary 1876–1976.**

535. 15 t. Barrow's bustard .. 55 70
536. 30 t. Helmet guineafowl .. 85 1·40

116. Child on Bed of Straw.

1976. Christmas.

537. 116. 3 t. multicoloured .. 10 10
538. 10 t. multicoloured .. 10 10
539. 20 t. multicoloured .. 20 10
540. 40 t. multicoloured .. 40 60

117. Man and Woman.

1977. Handicrafts showing wood-carvings. Multicoloured.

542. 4 t. Type **117** 10 10
543. 10 t. Elephant (horiz.) .. 15 10
544. 20 t. Rhinoceros (horiz.) .. 20 10
545. 40 t. Antelope 50 70

118. Chileka Airport.

1977. Transport. Multicoloured.

547. 4 t. Type **118** 20 10
548. 10 t. Blantyre-Lilongwe Road 30 10
549. 20 t. M.V. "Ilala II" .. 90 30
550. 40 t. Blantyre-Nacala rail line .. .. .. 1·60 1·40

119. " Pseudotropheus johanni ".

1977. Fish of Lake Malawi. Multicoloured.

552. 4 t. Type **119** 15 10
553. 10 t. " Pseudotropheus livingstoni " 25 10
554. 20 t. " Pseudotropheus zebra " 85 25
555. 40 t. " Genyochromis mento " 95 95

120. " Madonna and Child with St. Catherine and the Blessed Stefano Maconi " (Bergognone).

1977. Christmas.

557. 120. 4 t. multicoloured .. 10 10
558. – 10 t. multicoloured .. 10 10
559. – 20 t. multicoloured .. 20 10
560. – 40 t. multicoloured .. 50 70

DESIGNS: 10 t. " Madonna and Child with the Eternal Father and Angels " (Bergognone). 20 t. Bottigella altarpiece (detail, Foppa). 40 t. " Madonna of the Fountain " (van Eyck).

121. " Entry of Christ into Jerusalem " (Giotto).

1978. Easter. Paintings by Giotto. Mult.

562.	4 t. Type **121**	10	10
563.	10 t. " The Crucifixion " ..	10	10
564.	20 t. " Descent from the Cross "	25	10
565.	40 t. " Jesus appears before Mary "	50	55

122. Nyala.

1978. Wildlife. Multicoloured.

567.	4 t. Type **122**	25	10
568.	10 t. Lion (horiz.)	60	15
569.	20 t. Common Zebra (horiz.)	85	60
570.	40 t. Mountain Reedbuck	1·40	2·00

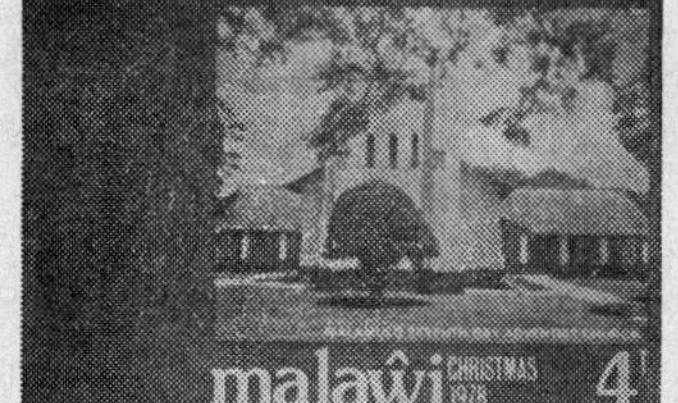

123. Malamulo Seventh Day Adventist Church.

1978. Christmas. Multicoloured.

572.	4 t. Type **123**	10	10
573.	10 t. Likoma Cathedral ..	10	10
574.	20 t. St. Michael's and All Angels' Blantyre ..	20	10
575.	40 t. Zomba Catholic Cathedral ..	40	60

124. " Vanilla polylepis ".

1979. Orchids. Multicoloured.

577.	1 t. Type **124**	30	10
578.	2 t. " Cirrhopetalum umbellatum "	30	10
579.	5 t. " Calanthe natalensis "	30	10
580.	7 t. " Ansellia gigantea " ..	30	10
581.	8 t. " Tridactyle bicaudata "	30	10
582.	10 t. " Acampe pachyglossa "	30	10
583.	15 t. " Eulophia quartiniana "	40	15
584.	20 t. " Cyrtorchis arcuata "	45	30
585.	30 t. " Eulophia tricristata "	65	30
586.	50 t. " Disa hamatopetala "	80	50
587.	75 t. " Cynorchis glandulosa "	1·00	1·25
588.	1 k. " Aerangis kotschyana "	1·40	80
589.	1 k. 50 " Polystachya dendrobiiflora " ..	1·50	1·75
590.	2 k. " Disa ornithantha "	1·75	1·75
591.	4 k. " Cyrtorchis praetermissa "	3·00	3·50

125. Tsamba.

1979. National Tree Planting Day. Mult.

592.	5 t. Type **125**	15	10
593.	10 t. Mulanje Cedar ..	20	10
594.	20 t. Mlombwa	30	20
595.	40 t. Mbawa	60	75

126. Train crossing Viaduct.

1979. Opening of Salima-Lilongwe Railway Line. Multicoloured.

597.	5 t. Type **126**	25	10
598.	10 t. Diesel railcar at station	40	10
599.	20 t. Train rounding bend	60	30
600.	40 t. Diesel train in cutting	85	1·25

127. Young Child.

1979. International Year of the Child. Designs showing young children. Multicoloured; background colours given.

602.	**127.** 5 t. green	10	10
603.	– 10 t. red	10	10
604.	– 20 t. mauve	25	10
605.	– 40 t. blue	45	60

128. 1964 3d. Independence Commemorative Stamp.

1979. Death Centenary of Sir Rowland Hill. Designs showing Independence 1964 Commemorative Stamps. Multicoloured.

606.	5 t. Type **128**	10	10
607.	10 t. 6d. value	10	10
608.	20 t. 1s. 3d. value ..	20	10
609.	40 t. 2s. 6d. value ..	35	60

129. River Landscape.

1979. Christmas. Multicoloured.

611.	5 t. Type **129**	10	10
612.	10 t. Sunset	10	10
613.	20 t. Forest and hill ..	25	10
614.	40 t. Plain and mountains	50	50

130. Limbe Rotary Club Emblem.

1980. 75th Anniv. of Rotary International.

615.	**130.** 5 t. multicoloured ..	10	10
616.	– 10 t. multicoloured ..	10	10
617.	– 20 t. blue, gold and red	30	15
618.	– 40 t. gold and blue ..	75	1·60

DESIGNS: 10 t. Blantyre Rotary Club Pennant. 20 t. Lilongwe Rotary Club Pennant. 40 t. Rotary International emblem.

131. Mangochi District Post Office.

1980. " London 1980 " International Stamp Exhibition.

620.	**131.** 5 t. black and green ..	10	10
621.	– 10 t. black and red ..	10	10
622.	– 20 t. black and violet ..	15	10
623.	– 1 k. black and blue ..	65	1·00

DESIGNS: 10 t. New Blantyre Sorting Office. 20 t. Mail transfer hut, Walala. 1 k. First Nyasaland Post Office, Chiromo.

132. Agate Nodule.

1980. Gemstones. Multicoloured.

625.	5 t. Type **132**	60	10
626.	10 t. Sunstone	80	10
627.	20 t. Smoky Quartz ..	1·40	30
628.	1 k. Kyanite crystal ..	3·50	5·00

133. Elephants.

1980. Christmas. Children's Paintings. Multicoloured.

629.	5 t. Type **133**	25	10
630.	10 t. Flowers	25	10
631.	20 t. "Shire" Class diesel train	45	15
632.	1 k. Malachite Kingfisher	1·25	1·75

134. Suni.

1981. Wildlife. Multicoloured.

633.	7 t. Type **134**	15	10
634.	10 t. Blue Duiker	20	10
635.	20 t. African Buffalo ..	30	15
636.	1 k. Lichtenstein's Hartebeest	1·25	1·60

135. " Kanjedza II " Standard " A " Earth Station.

1981. International Communications. Mult.

637.	7 t. Type **135**	10	10
638.	10 t. Blantyre International Gateway Exchange ..	15	10
639.	20 t. " Kanjedza I " standard " B " earth station	25	15
640.	1 k. " Satellite communications "	1·50	1·50

136. Maize.

1981. World Food Day. Agricultural Produce. Multicoloured.

642.	7 t. Type **136**	15	10
643.	10 t. Rice	20	10
644.	20 t. Finger-millet ..	30	20
645.	1 k. Wheat	1·00	1·40

137. " The Adoration of the Shepherds " (Murillo).

1981. Christmas. Paintings. Multicoloured.

646.	7 t. Type **137**	15	10
647.	10 t. " The Holy Family " (Lippi) (horiz.) ..	20	10
648.	20 t. " The Adoration of the Shepherds " (Louis le Nain) (horiz.) ..	35	15
649.	1 k. " The Virgin and Child " St. John the Baptist and an Angel " (Paolo Morando)	90	1·25

138. Impala Herd.

1982. National Parks. Wildlife. Mult.

650.	7 t. Type **138**	20	10
651.	10 t. Lions	35	10
652.	20 t. Greater Kudu ..	50	20
653.	1 k. Greater Flamingoes ..	2·25	3·00

139. Kamuzu Academy.

1982. Kamuzu Academy.

654.	**139.** 7 t. multicoloured ..	10	10
655.	– 20 t. multicoloured ..	20	10
656.	– 30 t. multicoloured ..	30	40
657.	– 1 k. multicoloured ..	75	1·75

DESIGNS: 20 t. to 1 k.. Various views of the Academy.

140. Attacker challenging Goalkeeper.

1982. World Cup Football Championship, Spain. Multicoloured.

658.	7 t. Type **140**	40	10
659.	20 t. FIFA World Cup trophy	80	50
660.	30 t. Football stadium ..	1·25	2·00

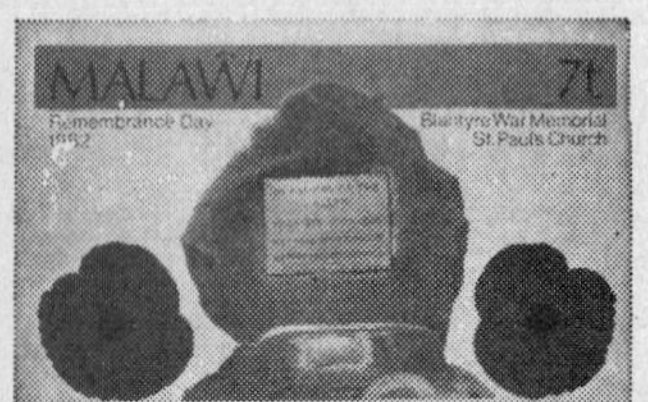

141. Blantyre War Memorial, St. Paul's Church.

1982. Remembrance Day. Multicoloured.

662.	7 t. Type **141**	10	10
663.	20 t. Zomba war memorial	15	10
664.	30 t. Chichiri war memorial	20	30
665.	1 k. Lilongwe war memorial	65	2·25

142. Kwacha International Conference Centre.

1983. Commonwealth Day. Multicoloured.

666.	7 t. Type **142**	10	10
667.	20 t. Tea-picking, Mulanje	20	10
668.	30 t. World map showing position of Malawi ..	30	30
669.	1 k. Pres. Dr. H. Kamuzu Banda	80	1·50

143. "Christ and St. Peter".

1983. 500th Birth Anniv. of Raphael. Details from the cartoon for "The Miraculous Draught of Fishes" Tapestry. Mult.

670.	7 t. Type **143**	25	10
671.	20 t. "Hauling in the Catch"	60	30
672.	30 t. "Fishing Village" (horiz.)	90	1·40

144. Pair by Lake.

1983. African Fish Eagle. Multicoloured.

674.	30 t. Type **144**	80	1·00
675.	30 t. Making gull-like call	80	1·00
676.	30 t. Diving on prey ..	80	1·00
677.	30 t. Carrying fish ..	80	1·00
678.	30 t. Feeding on catch ..	80	1·00

145. Kamuzu International Airport.

1983. Bicentenary of Manned Flight. Mult.

679.	7 t. Type **145**	10	10
680.	20 t. Kamuzu International Airport (different)	25	15
681.	30 t. BAC "One Eleven" ..	40	45
682.	1 k. Flying boat at Cape Maclear	1·10	2·25

146. "Clerodendrum myriciodes".

1983. Christmas. Flowers. Multicoloured.

684.	7 t. Type **146**	40	10
685.	20 t. "Gloriosa superba"	90	15
686.	30 t. "Gladiolus laxiflorus"	1·25	40
687.	1 k. "Aframomum angustifolium"	2·50	3·25

147. "Melanochromis auratus".

1984. Fishes. Multicoloured.

688.	1 t. Type **147**	10	20
689.	2 t. "Haplochromis compressiceps"	15	20
690.	5 t. "Labeotropheus fuelleborni"	20	20
691.	7 t. "Pseudotropheus lombardoi"	20	10
692.	8 t. Gold "Pseudotropheus" Zebra	20	10
693.	10 t. "Trematocranus jacobfreibergi"	20	10
694.	15 t. "Melanochromis crabro"	30	10
695.	20 t. Marbled "Pseudotropheus" Zebra ..	30	10
696.	30 t. "Labidochromis caeruleus"	40	10
697.	40 t. "Haplochromis venustus"	60	30
698.	50 t. "Aulonacara" of Thumbi	70	50
699.	75 t. "Melanochromis vermivorus"	90	1·00
700.	1 k. "Pseudotropheus" Zebra	1·25	1·50
701.	2 k. "Trematocranus spp."	2·00	2·75
702.	4 k. "Aulonacara" of Mbenje	2·75	5·00

Nos. 688 and 691/7 exist with different imprint dates at foot.

148. Smith's Red Hare.

1984. Small Mammals. Multicoloured.

703.	7 t. Type **148**	30	10
704.	20 t. Gambian Sun Squirrel	80	20
705.	30 t. South African Hedgehog	1·25	75
706.	1 k. Large-spotted Genet	2·25	4·00

149. Running.

1984. Olympic Games, Los Angeles. Mult.

707.	7 t. Type **149**	10	10
708.	20 t. Boxing	25	15
709.	30 t. Cycling	35	30
710.	1 k. Long jumping ..	1·00	1·75

150. "Euphaedra neophron".

1984. Butterflies.

712.	**150.** 7 t. multicoloured ..	75	10
713.	– 20 t. yellow, brown and red	1·50	30
714.	– 30 t. multicoloured ..	1·75	90
715.	– 1 k. multicoloured ..	3·25	4·00

Designs: 20 t. "Papilio dardanus". 30 t. "Antanartia schaeneia". 1 k. "Spindasis nyassae".

151. "Virgin and Child" (Duccio).

1984. Christmas. Religious Paintings. Multicoloured.

716.	7 t. Type **151**	40	10
717.	20 t. "Madonna and Child" (Raphael) ..	90	20
718.	30 t. "Virgin and Child" (ascr. to Lippi) ..	1·40	55
719.	1 k. "The Wilton Diptych"	2·75	3·75

152. "Leucopaxillus gracillimus".

1985. Fungi. Multicoloured.

720.	7 t. Type **152**	75	10
721.	20 t. "Limacella guttata"	1·75	30
722.	30 t. "Termitomyces eurrhizus"	2·00	90
723.	1 k. "Xerulina asprata" ..	3·25	4·00

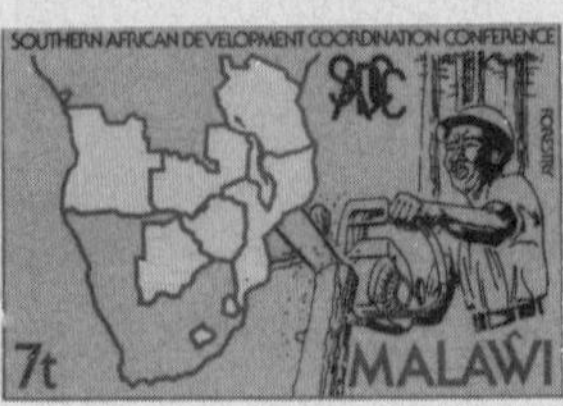

153. Map showing Member States, and Lumberjack (Forestry).

1985. 5th Anniv. of Southern African Development Co-ordination Conference. Designs showing map and aspects of development.

724.	**153.** 7 t. black, green and light green	50	10
725.	– 15 t. black, red and pink	80	20
726.	– 20 t. black, violet and mauve	2·00	75
727.	– 1 k. black, blue and light blue	3·00	3·75

Designs: 15 t. Radio mast (Communications). 20 t. Diesel locomotive (Transport). 1 k. Trawler and net (Fishing).

154. M.V. "Ufulu".

1985. Ships of Lake Malawi (2nd series). Multicoloured.

728.	7 t. Type **154**	70	10
729.	15 t. M.V. "Chauncy Maples II"	1·25	20
730.	20 t. M.V. "Mtendere" ..	1·75	50
731.	1 k. M.V. "Ilala II" ..	3·50	4·50

155. Stierling's Woodpecker. **156.** "The Virgin of Humility" (Jaime Serra).

1985. Birth Bicentenary of John J. Audubon (ornithologist). Multicoloured.

733.	7 t. Type **155**	65	10
734.	15 t. Lesser seedcracker ..	1·25	20
735.	20 t. East coast akelat ..	1·50	40
736.	1 k. Boehm's beeater ..	3·00	4·00

1985. Christmas. Nativity Paintings. Mult.

738.	7 t. Type **156**	30	10
739.	15 t. "The Adoration of the Magi" (Stefano da Zevio)	60	15
740.	20 t. "Madonna and Child" (Gerard van Honthorst)	65	20
741.	1 k. "Virgin of Zbraslav" (Master of Vissy Brod)	2·00	2·00

157. Halley's Comet and Path of "Giotto" Spacecraft.

1986. Appearance of Halley's Comet. Mult.

742.	8 t. Type **157**	20	10
743.	15 t. Halley's Comet above Earth	30	15
744.	20 t. Comet and dish aerial, Malawi	40	20
745.	1 k. "Giotto" spacecraft ..	1·60	1·60

158. Two Players competing for Ball.

1986. World Cup Football Championship, Mexico. Multicoloured.

746.	8 t. Type **158**	40	10
747.	15 t. Goalkeeper saving goal	65	15
748.	20 t. Two players competing for ball (different)	75	25
749.	1 k. Player kicking ball ..	2·75	2·00

159. President Banda. **160.** "Virgin and Child" (Botticelli).

1986. 20th Anniv. of Republic. Mult.

751.	8 t. Type **159**	40	60
752.	15 t. National flag ..	50	15
753.	20 t. Malawi coat of arms	55	25
754.	1 k. Kamuzu Airport and emblem of national airline	2·00	2·00

1986. Christmas. Multicoloured.

755.	8 t. Type **160**	35	10
756.	15 t. "Adoration of the Shepherds" (Guido Reni)	60	15
757.	20 t. "Madonna of the Veil" (Carlo Dolci) ..	80	30
758.	1 k. "Adoration of the Magi" (Jean Bourdichon)	3·25	3·00

161. Wattled Crane.

1987. Wattled Crane. Multicoloured.

763	8 t. Type **161**	60	10
764	15 t. Two cranes	1·00	20
765	20 t. Cranes at nest ..	1·25	30
766	75 t. Crane in lake ..	2·75	3·50

162. "Shamrock" No. 2 Locomotive, 1902.

1987. Steam Locomotives. Multicoloured.

767	10 t. Type **162**	65	10
768	25 t. "D" class, No. 8, 1914	1·10	20
769	30 t. "Thistle" No. 1, 1902	1·25	40
770	1 k. "Kitson" class, No. 6, 1903	3·00	2·25

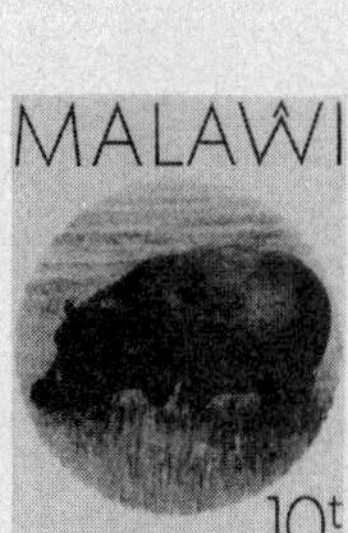

163. Hippopotamus grazing. **164.** "Stathmostelma spectabile".

1987. Hippopotamus. Multicoloured.

771	10 t. Type **163**	50	10
772	25 t. Hippopotami in water	1·25	20
773	30 t. Female and calf in water	1·25	50
774	1 k. Hippopotami and cattle egret	2·50	3·00

1987. Christmas. Wild Flowers. Mult.

776	10 t. Type **164**	50	10
777	25 t. "Pentanisia schweinfurthii"	90	20
778	30 t. "Chironia krebsii" ..	1·00	40
779	1 k. "Ochna macrocalyx"	2·25	2·50

165. Malawi and Staunton Knights.

1988. Chess. Local and Staunton chess pieces. Multicoloured.

780	15 t. Type **165**	70	15
781	35 t. Bishops	1·25	50
782	50 t. Rooks	1·50	1·25
783	2 k. Queens	4·75	5·50

166 High Jumping

1988. Olympic Games, Seoul. Multicoloured.

784	15 t. Type **166**	30	10
785	35 t. Javelin throwing ..	50	20
786	50 t. Tennis	75	40
787	2 k. Shot-putting ..	1·60	1·75

167 Eastern Forest Scrub Warbler 168 "Madonna in the Church" (Jan van Eyck)

1988. Birds. Multicoloured.

789	1 t. Type **167**	10	10
790	2 t. Yellow-throated woodland warbler ..	10	10
791	5 t. Moustached green tinkerbird	10	10
792	7 t. Waller's red-winged starling	10	10
793	8 t. Oriole-finch	10	10
794	10 t. Starred robin ..	10	10
795	15 t. Bar-tailed trogon ..	10	10
796	20 t. Green-backed twin-spot	10	10
797	30 t. African grey cuckoo shrike	10	10
798	40 t. Black-fronted bush shrike	10	10
799	50 t. White-tailed crested flycatcher ..	15	20
800	75 t. Green barbet ..	20	25
801	1 k. Lemon dove ("Cinnamon Dove") ..	30	35
802	2 k. Silvery-cheeked hornbill	60	65
803	4 k. Crowned eagle ..	1·25	1·40
804	10 k. Anchieta's sunbird	3·00	3·25

1988. 300th Anniv of Lloyd's of London. As T **123** of Ascension. Multicoloured.

805	15 t. Rebuilt Royal Exchange, 1844 ..	30	10
806	35 t. Opening ceremony, Nkula Falls Hydro-electric Power Station	60	20
807	50 t. Air Malawi "1-11" airliner (horiz)	85	40
808	2 k. "Seawise University" (formerly "Queen Elizabeth") on fire, Hong Kong, 1972 ..	2·75	2·25

1988. Christmas. Multicoloured.

809	15 t. Type **168**	20	10
810	35 t. "Virgin, Infant Jesus and St. Anna" (da Vinci)	35	20
811	50 t. "Virgin and Angels" (Cimabue)	45	50
812	2 k. "Virgin and Child" (Baldovinetti Apenio) ..	1·75	2·00

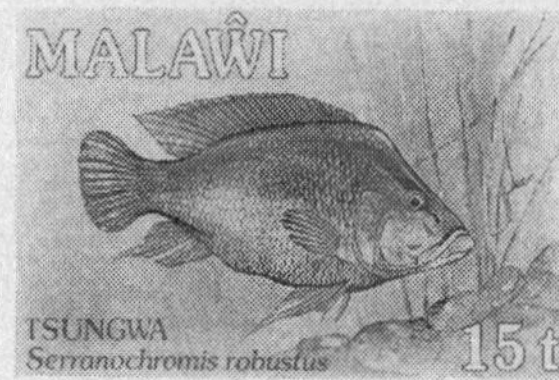

169 "Serranochromis robustus"

1989. 50th Anniv of Malawi Angling Society. Multicoloured.

813	15 t. Type **169**	50	10
814	35 t. Lake salmon ..	95	30
815	50 t. Yellow fish ..	1·40	1·00
816	2 k. Tiger fish	3·75	4·50

170 Independence Arch, Blantyre

1989. 25th Anniv of Independence. Mult.

817	15 t. Type **170**	30	10
818	35 t. Grain silos	55	30
819	50 t. Capital Hill, Lilongwe	75	80
820	2 k. Reserve Bank Headquarters	2·25	3·00

171 Blantyre Digital Telex Exchange

1989. 25th Anniv of African Development Bank. Multicoloured.

821	15 t. Type **171**	30	10
822	40 t. Dzalanyama steer ..	55	30
823	50 t. Mikolongwe heifer ..	75	80
824	2 k. Zebu bull	2·25	3·00

172 Rural House with Verandah

1989. 25th Anniv of Malawi–United Nations Co-operation. Multicoloured.

825	15 t. Type **172**	30	10
826	40 t. Rural house ..	55	30
827	50 t. Traditional hut and modern houses ..	75	80
828	2 k. Tea plantation ..	2·25	3·00

173 St. Michael and All Angels Church

1989. Christmas. Churches of Malawi. Mult.

829	15 t. Type **173**	30	10
830	40 t. Catholic Cathedral, Limbe	55	30
831	50 t. C.C.A.P. Church, Nkhoma	75	80
832	2 k. Cathedral, Likoma Island	2·25	3·00

174 Ford "Sedan", 1915

1990. Vintage Vehicles. Multicoloured.

833	15 t. Type **174**	30	10
834	40 t. Two-seater Ford, 1915	55	30
835	50 t. Ford pick-up, 1915 ..	75	80
836	1 k. Chevrolet bus, 1930 ..	2·25	3·00

175 Player heading Ball into Net

1990. World Cup Football Championship, Italy. Multicoloured.

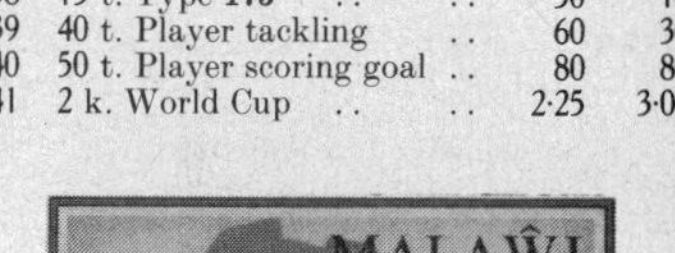

838	15 t. Type **175**	30	10
839	40 t. Player tackling ..	60	30
840	50 t. Player scoring goal ..	80	80
841	2 k. World Cup	2·25	3·00

176 Anniversary Emblem on Map

1990. 10th Anniv of Southern Africa Development Co-ordination Conference. Mult.

843	15 t. Type **176**	20	10
844	40 t. Chambo fish ..	40	40
845	50 t. Cedar plantation ..	45	50
846	2 k. Male nyala (antelope)	2·25	2·75

177 "Aerangis kotschyana"

1990. Orchids. Multicoloured.

848	15 t. Type **177**	40	10
849	40 t. "Angraecum eburneum"	70	45
850	50 t. "Aerangis luteo-alba rhodostica"	90	80
851	2 k. "Cyrtorchis arcuata whytei"	2·50	3·00

178 "The Virgin and the Child Jesus" (Raphael)

1990. Christmas. Paintings by Raphael. Mult.
853 15 t. Type **178** 25 10
854 40 t. "Transfiguration" (detail) 50 30
855 50 t. "St. Catherine of Alexandrie" (detail) .. 60 60
856 2 k. "Transfiguration" .. 2·00 3·00

179 Buffalo

1991. Wildlife. Multicoloured.
858 20 t. Type **179** 25 10
859 60 t. Cheetah 75 65
860 75 t. Greater kudu .. 75 75
861 2 k. Black rhinoceros .. 2·50 3·00

180 Chiromo Post Office, 1891

1991. Centenary of Postal Services. Mult.
863 20 t. Type **180** 25 10
864 60 t. Re-constructed mail exchange hut at Walala 60 55
865 75 t. Mangochi post office 75 75
866 2 k. Satellite Earth station 2·00 2·75

181 Red Locust

1991. Insects. Multicoloured.
868 20 t. Type **181** 25 10
869 60 t. Weevil 60 55
870 75 t. Cotton stainer bug .. 75 75
871 2 k. Pollen beetle .. 2·25 2·75

182 Child in a Manger

1991. Christmas. Multicoloured.
872 20 t. Type **182** 20 10
873 60 t. Adoration of the Kings and Shepherds .. 50 40
874 75 t. Nativity 60 60
875 2 k. Virgin and Child .. 1·60 2·00

183 Red Bishop

1992. Birds. Multicoloured.
876 75 t. Type **183** 45 50
877 75 t. Lesser striped swallow 45 50
878 75 t. Long-crested eagle .. 45 50
879 75 t. Lilac-breasted roller 45 50
880 75 t. African paradise flycatcher 45 50
881 75 t. White-fronted bee eater 45 50
882 75 t. White-winged black tern 45 50
883 75 t. African fire finch .. 45 50
884 75 t. White-browed robin chat 45 50
885 75 t. African fish eagle .. 45 50
886 75 t. Malachite kingfisher 45 50
887 75 t. Lesser masked weaver 45 50
888 75 t. Barn owl 45 50
889 75 t. Variable sunbird .. 45 50
890 75 t. Lesser flamingo .. 45 50
891 75 t. Crowned crane .. 45 50
892 75 t. African pitta .. 45 50
893 75 t. African darter .. 45 50
894 75 t. White-faced whistling duck 45 50
895 75 t. African pied wagtail 45 50

184 Long Jumping

1992. Olympic Games, Barcelona. Mult.
896 20 t. Type **184** 20 10
897 60 t. High jumping .. 40 30
898 75 t. Javelin 50 45
899 2 k. Running .. .. 1·25 1·50

185 "The Angel Gabriel" (detail, "The Annunciation") (Philippe de Champaigne)

1992. Christmas. Religious Paintings. Mult.
901 20 t. Type **185** 20 10
902 75 t. "Virgin and Child" (Bernandino Luini) .. 50 40
903 95 t. "Virgin and Child" (Sassoferrato) .. 65 60
904 2 k. "Virgin Mary" (detail, "The Annunciation") (De Champaigne) .. 1·25 1·50

186 "Voyager 2" passing Saturn

1992. International Space Year. Mult.
905 20 t. Type **186** 20 10
906 75 t. Centre of galaxy .. 50 40
907 95 t. Kanjedza II Standard A Earth Station .. 60 55
908 2 k. Communications satellite .. .. 1·40 1·60

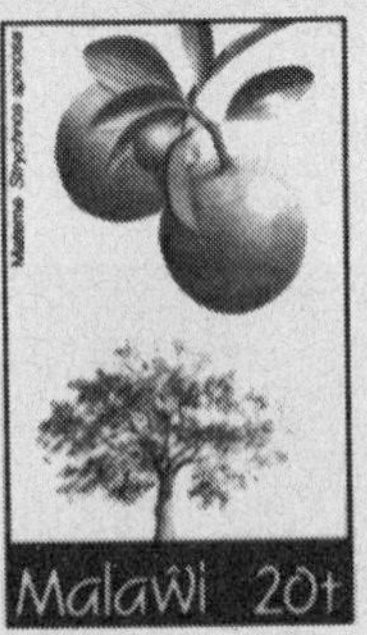

187 "Strychnos spinosa"

1993. Indigenous Fruits. Multicoloured.
909 20 t. Type **187** 15 10
910 75 t. "Adansonia digitata" 45 35
911 95 t. "Ximenia caffra" .. 55 45
912 2 k. "Uapaca kirkiana" .. 1·00 1·40

188 "Apaturopsis cleocharis"

1993. Butterflies. Multicoloured.
913 20 t. Type **188** 15 10
914 75 t. "Euryphura achlys" 35 30
915 95 t. "Cooksonia aliciae" 45 40
916 2 k. "Charaxes protoclea azota" .. .. .. 1·00 1·25

190 Kentrosaurus

1993. Prehistoric Animals. Multicoloured.
921 20 t. Type **190** 10 10
922 75 t. Stegosaurus 20 25
923 95 t. Sauropod 25 30

POSTAGE DUE STAMPS

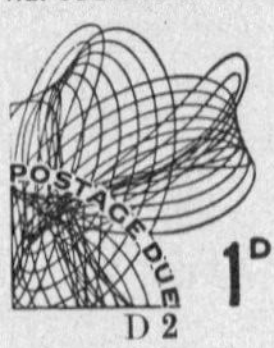

D 2

1967.
D 6 D **2** 1d. red .. .. 15 2·25
D 7 2d. brown .. .. 20 2·25
D 8 4d. violet .. .. 25 2·50
D 9 6d. blue .. .. 25 2·75
D10 8d. green .. .. 35 3·00
D11 1s. black .. .. 45 3·25

1971. Values in tambalas. No accent over "W" of "MALAWI".
D12 D **2** 2 t. brown .. .. 30 2·00
D13 4 t. mauve .. .. 60 2·00
D14 6 t. blue .. .. 45 2·25
D15 8 t. green .. .. 50 2·25
D16 10 t. brown .. .. 75 2·25

1975. With circumflex over "W" of "MALAWI".
D27 D **2** 2 t. brown 10 10
D28 4 t. purple 10 10
D29 6 t. blue 10 10
D21 8 t. green 20 30
D31 10 t. black 10 10

MALAYA (BRITISH MILITARY ADMINISTRATION)

The following stamps were for use throughout Malayan States and in Singapore during the period of the British Military Administration and were gradually replaced by individual issues for each state.

100 cents = 1 dollar.

1945. Straits Settlements stamps optd **BMA MALAYA**.
1a **58** 1 c. black 10 10
2a 2 c. orange 20 10
4 3 c. green 20 15
5 5 c. brown 55 10
6a 6 c. grey 20 10
7 8 c. red 20 10
8a 10 c. purple 40 10
10 12 c. blue .. .. 1·75 3·00
12a 15 c. blue 55 20
13a 25 c. purple and red .. 1·40 20
14a 50 c. black on green .. 60 10
15 $1 black and red .. 1·75 10
16 $2 green and red .. 2·25 65
17 $5 green and red on green 55·00 60·00
18 $5 purple and orange .. 3·25 2·00

For stamps inscribed "MALAYA" at top and with Arabic characters at foot see under Kelantan, Negri Sembilan, Pahang, Perak, Selangor or Trengganu.

MALAYA (JAPANESE OCCUPATION OF)

Japanese forces invaded Malaya on 8 December 1941 and the conquest of the Malay penisula was completed by the capture of Singapore on 15 February.

The following stamps were used in Malaya until the defeat of Japan in 1945.

100 cents = 1 dollar.

(a) **JOHORE**

POSTAGE DUE STAMPS

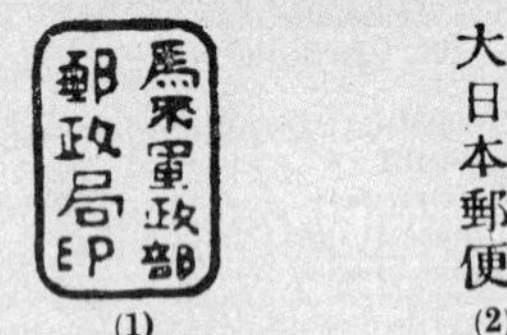

(**1**) (**2**)

1942. Nos. D1/5 of Johore optd with T **1**.
JD1 D **1** 1 c. red .. .. 45·00 75·00
JD2 4 c. green .. .. 55·00 75·00
JD3 8 c. orange .. .. 65·00 85·00
JD4 10 c. brown .. 15·00 45·00
JD5 12 c. purple .. .. 25·00 45·00

1943. Postage Due stamps of Johore opt with T **2**.
JD 6 D **1** 1 c. red .. .. 2·25 11·00
JD 7 4 c. green .. .. 2·50 11·00
JD 8 8 c. orange .. 4·00 13·00
JD 9 10 c. brown .. 3·50 17·00
JD10 12 c. purple .. 4·50 22·00

(b) **KEDAH**

1942. Stamps of Kedah optd **DAI NIPPON 2602**.
J 1 **1** 1 c. black .. .. 2·25 3·50
J 2 2 c. green .. .. 23·00 30·00
J 3 4 c. violet .. .. 3·25 4·00
J 4 5 c. yellow .. .. 1·90 3·25
J 5 6 c. red .. .. 1·75 4·75
J 6 8 c. black .. .. 2·50 1·75
J 7 **6** 10 c. blue and brown .. 6·00 6·50
J 8 12 c. black and violet .. 13·00 17·00
J 9 25 c. blue and purple .. 4·50 8·50
J10 30 c. green and red .. 65·00 75·00
J11 40 c. black and purple 17·00 27·00
J12 50 c. brown and blue .. 19·00 30·00
J13 $1 black and green .. £130 £150
J14 $2 green and brown .. £140 £150
J15 $5 black and red .. 55·00 60·00

(c) **KELANTAN**

(**5**) Sunagawa Seal

(**6**) Handa Seal

1942. Stamps of Kelantan optd.

(a) With T **5**

J32 **4** 1 c. on 50 c. green & orge 90·00 80·00
J33 2 c. on 40 c. orange & grn 85·00 85·00
J18 4 c. on 30 c. violet & red £850 £900
J34 5 c. on 12 c. blue .. 75·00 75·00
J20 6 c. on 25 c. orange & vio £160 £180
J35 8 c. on 5 c. brown .. 85·00 65·00
J36 10 c. on 6 c. red .. 70·00 85·00
J23 12 c. on 8 c. green .. 45·00 £100
J24 25 c. on 10 c. purple .. £850 £950
J38 30 c. on 4 c. red .. £950 £1000
J26 40 c. on 2 c. green .. 48·00 80·00
J40 50 c. on 1 c. green & yell £500 £550
J28 $1 on 4 c. black and red 48·00 70·00
J29 $2 on 5 c. grn & red on yellow .. .. 48·00 70·00
J30 $5 on 6 c. red .. .. 50·00 70·00

(b) With T **6**

J41 **4** 1 c. on 50 c. green & orge 80·00 £100
J42 2 c. on 40 c. orge & grn 70·00 £110
J43 8 c. on 5 c. brown .. 60·00 £100
J44 10 c. on 6 c. red .. 80·00 £110
J31 12 c. on 8 c. green .. £100 £140

(d) **PENANG**

(11) Okugawa Seal

(12) Ochiburi Seal

1942. Straits Settlements stamps optd.

(a) As T **11**

J56 **58** 1 c. black .. .. 8·50 10·00
J57 2 c. orange .. .. 22·00 20·00
J58 3 c. green .. .. 18·00 20·00
J59 5 c. brown .. .. 22·00 22·00
J60 8 c. grey .. .. 24·00 24·00
J61 10 c. purple .. .. 38·00 38·00
J62 12 c. blue .. .. 22·00 26·00
J63 15 c. blue .. .. 24·00 30·00
J64 40 c. red and purple .. 80·00 85·00
J65 50 c. black/green .. £130 £140
J66 $1 black & red on blue £160 £170
J67 $2 green and red .. £350 £375
J68 $5 green & red on green £950 £1100

(b) With T **12**

J69 **58** 1 c. black .. .. 50·00 60·00
J70 2 c. orange .. .. 55·00 65·00
J71 3 c. green .. .. 55·00 65·00
J72 5 c. brown £550 £550
J73 8 c. grey .. .. 40·00 45·00
J74 10 c. purple .. .. 40·00 50·00
J75 12 c. blue .. .. 40·00 50·00
J76 15 c. blue .. .. 40·00 50·00

1942. Stamps of Straits Settlements optd **DAI NIPPON 2602 PENANG**.

J77 **58** 1 c. black .. .. 1·00 1·00
J78 2 c. orange .. .. 3·50 2·75
J79 3 c. green .. .. 1·40 1·75
J80 5 c. brown .. .. 1·00 2·50
J81 8 c. grey .. .. 2·25 1·40
J82 10 c. purple .. .. 1·50 2·00
J83 12 c. blue .. .. 2·00 5·50
J84 15 c. blue .. .. 1·75 2·00
J85 40 c. red and purple .. 2·50 6·50
J86 50 c. black and green .. 3·50 12·00
J87 $1 black & red on blue 6·00 18·00
J88 $2 green and red .. 25·00 55·00
J89 $5 green & red on green £325 £425

(e) **SELANGOR**

1942. Agri-horticultural Exhibition. Stamps of Straits optd **SELANGOR EXHIBITION DAI NIPPON 2602 MALAYA**.

J90 **58** 2 c. orange .. .. 12·00 22·00
J91 8 c. grey .. .. 13·00 22·00

(f) **SINGAPORE**

(15) Seal of Post Office of Malayan Military Dept

1942. Stamps of Straits Settlements optd with T **15**.

J92 **58** 1 c. black .. .. 10·00 15·00
J93 2 c. orange .. .. 10·00 13·00
J94 3 c. green .. .. 48·00 70·00
J95 8 c. grey .. .. 22·00 18·00
J96 15 c. blue .. .. 14·00 15·00

(g) **TRENGGANU**

1942. Stamps of Trengganu optd with T **1**.

J 97 **4** 1 c. black .. .. 95·00 85·00
J 98 2 c. green £140 £140
J 99a 2 c. on 5 c. purple on yellow (No. 59) .. 45·00 65·00
J100 3 c. brown .. .. 80·00 80·00
J101 4 c. red £140 £140
J102 5 c. purple on yellow 10·00 14·00
J103 6 c. orange .. .. 7·50 20·00
J104 8 c. grey .. .. 9·00 13·00
J105 8 c. on 10 c. blue (No. 60) .. .. 13·00 24·00
J106 10 c. blue .. .. 9·50 20·00
J107 12 c. blue .. .. 8·00 19·00
J108 20 c. purple & orange 8·50 19·00
J109 25 c. green & purple 7·50 20·00
J110 30 c. purple & black 7·00 19·00
J111 35 c. red on yellow .. 12·00 21·00
J112 50 c. green and red 60·00 70·00
J113 $1 purple and blue on blue £1300 £1300
J114 $3 green and red on green .. .. 45·00 70·00
J115 – $5 green and red on yellow (No. 31) .. £120 £170
J116 – $25 purple and blue (No. 40) .. £750
J117 $50 green and yellow (No. 41) £4750
J118 $100 green and red (No. 42) £850

1942. Stamps of Trengganu optd **DAI NIPPON 2602 MALAYA**.

J119 **4** 1 c. black .. .. 8·00 9·00
J120 2 c. green £150 £180
J121 2 c. on 5 c. purple on yellow (No. 59) .. 6·00 8·00
J122 3 c. brown .. .. 9·00 14·00
J123 4 c. red .. .. 7·50 11·00
J124 5 c. purple on yellow .. 5·00 8·50
J125 6 c. orange .. .. 5·00 11·00
J126 8 c. grey .. .. 65·00 20·00
J127 8 c. on 10 c. blue (No. 60) .. .. 5·50 10·00
J128 12 c. blue .. .. 5·00 11·00
J129 20 c. purple and orange 7·00 13·00
J130 25 c. green and purple 7·00 20·00
J131 30 c. purple and black 7·00 17·00
J132 $3 green & red on green 50·00 £100

1942. Stamps of Trengganu optd with T **2**.

J133 **4** 1 c. black .. .. 6·50 16·00
J134 2 c. green .. .. 6·50 20·00
J135 2 c. on 5 c. purple on yellow (No. 59) .. 5·50 18·00
J136 5 c. purple on yellow .. 5·50 19·00
J137 6 c. orange .. .. 7·50 22·00
J138 8 c. grey .. .. 48·00 60·00
J139 8 c. on 10 c. bl (No. 60) 15·00 35·00
J140 10 c. blue .. .. 75·00 £140
J141 12 c. blue .. .. 9·50 28·00
J142 20 c. purple and orange 10·00 28·00
J143 25 c. green and purple 9·50 32·00
J144 30 c. purple and black 10·00 32·00
J145 35 c. red on yellow .. 10·00 35·00

1942. Postage Due stamps of Trengganu optd T **2**.

JD17 **D 1** 1 c. red .. .. 50·00 80·00
JD18a 4 c. green .. .. 50·00 85·00
JD19 8 c. yellow .. 14·00 50·00
JD20 10 c. brown .. 14·00 50·00

GENERAL ISSUES

1942. Stamps of various states optd with T **1**.

(a) Straits Settlements

J146 **58** 1 c. black .. .. 3·25 3·25
J147 2 c. green £1100 £1100
J148 2 c. orange .. .. 2·75 2·25
J149 3 c. green .. .. 2·75 2·25
J150 5 c. brown .. .. 22·00 26·00
J151 8 c. grey .. .. 3·00 2·25
J152 10 c. purple .. .. 32·00 38·00
J153 12 c. blue .. .. 70·00 90·00
J154 15 c. blue .. .. 3·50 3·00
J155 30 c. purple & orange £950 £1000
J156 40 c. red and purple .. 75·00 90·00
J157 50 c. black and green 42·00 45·00
J158 $1 black & red on blue 70·00 75·00
J159 $2 green and red .. £120 £130
J160 $5 green & red on grn £170 £180

There also exists a similar overprint with double-lined frame.

(b) Negri Sembilan

J161b **6** 1 c. black .. .. 15·00 14·00
J162 2 c. orange .. .. 13·00 13·00
J163 3 c. green .. .. 17·00 18·00
J164b 5 c. brown .. .. 14·00 11·00
J165 6 c. grey £120 £120
J166 8 c. red .. .. 35·00 38·00
J167a 10 c. purple .. .. 65·00 65·00
J168 12 c. blue £700 £700
J169 15 c. blue .. .. 16·00 8·00
J170 25 c. purple and red 28·00 35·00
J171 **6** 30 c. purple & orange £120 £130
J172 40 c. red and purple £550 £550
J173 50 c. black on green .. £190 £190
J174 $1 black & red on blue £100 £120
J175 $5 green & red on grn £375 £400

(c) Pahang

J176 **15** 1 c. black .. .. 25·00 30·00
J177 3 c. green .. .. 85·00 90·00
J178 5 c. brown .. .. 11·00 6·50
J179 8 c. grey £150 £150
J180 8 c. red .. .. 20·00 10·00
J181 10 c. purple .. .. 48·00 48·00
J182 12 c. blue £1000 £1100
J183 15 c. blue .. .. 70·00 70·00
J184 25 c. purple and red .. 18·00 29·00
J185 30 c. purple & orange 12·00 26·00
J186 40 c. red and purple .. 15·00 28·00
J187 50 c. black on green .. £225 £250
J188 $1 black & red on blue 85·00 95·00
J189 $5 green & red on grn £550 £650

(d) Perak

J190 **51** 1 c. black .. .. 35·00 30·00
J191 2 c. orange .. .. 20·00 18·00
J192 3 c. green .. .. 22·00 25·00
J193 5 c. brown .. .. 6·50 5·50
J194 8 c. grey .. .. 32·00 32·00
J195 8 c. red .. .. 14·00 32·00
J196 10 c. purple .. .. 13·00 21·00
J197 12 c. blue £120 £130
J198 15 c. blue .. .. 16·00 24·00
J199 25 c. purple and red .. 14·00 22·00
J200 30 c. purple & orange 17·00 32·00
J201 40 c. red and purple .. £160 £170
J202 50 c. black on green .. 30·00 40·00
J203 $1 black & red on blue £250 £250
J204 $2 green and red .. £1300 £1300
J205 $5 green & red on grn £450

(e) Selangor

J206 **46** 1 c. black .. .. 11·00 17·00
J207 2 c. green £500 £500
J208 2 c. orange .. .. 40·00 42·00
J210 3 c. green .. .. 17·00 14·00
J211 5 c. brown .. .. 5·00 5·50
J212 6 c. red £170 £170
J213 8 c. grey .. .. 16·00 17·00
J214 10 c. purple .. .. 12·00 21·00
J215 12 c. blue .. .. 40·00 40·00
J216 15 c. blue .. .. 15·00 19·00
J217a 25 c. purple and red 55·00 75·00
J218 30 c. purple & orange 11·00 23·00
J219 40 c. red and purple 70·00 75·00
J220 50 c. black on green 42·00 42·00
J221 48 $1 blk & red on bl 30·00 42·00
J222 $2 green and red .. 35·00 60·00
J223 $5 green & red on grn 55·00 75·00

1942. Various stamps optd **DAI NIPPON 2602 MALAYA**.

(a) Stamps of Straits Settlements

J224 **58** 2 c. orange 50 50
J225 3 c. green .. .. 45·00 55·00
J226 8 c. grey .. .. 2·25 1·75
J227 15 c. blue .. .. 6·50 5·00

(b) Stamps of Negri Sembilan

J228 **6** 1 c. black 90 60
J229 2 c. orange .. .. 2·00 50
J230 3 c. green .. .. 1·25 45
J231 5 c. brown 45 55
J232 6 c. grey .. .. 1·40 1·00
J233 8 c. red .. .. 2·00 1·25
J234 10 c. purple .. .. 3·00 3·00
J235 15 c. blue .. .. 6·00 3·00
J236 25 c. purple and red 2·00 4·75
J237 30 c. purple and orange 3·50 3·00
J238 $1 black & red on blue £100 £110

(c) Stamps of Pahang

J239 **15** 1 c. black 90 85
J240 5 c. brown 75 70
J241 8 c. red .. .. 22·00 2·50
J242 10 c. purple .. .. 8·50 5·00
J243 12 c. blue .. .. 1·00 3·50
J244 25 c. purple and red .. 3·75 7·50
J245 30 c. purple and orange 80 4·00

(d) Stamps of Perak

J246 **51** 2 c. orange .. .. 1·00 70
J247 3 c. green 60 60
J248 8 c. red 60 40
J249 10 c. purple .. .. 5·00 5·00
J250 15 c. blue .. .. 3·25 2·00
J251 50 c. black on green .. 1·75 2·75
J252 $1 black & red on blue £275 £325
J253 $5 green & red on grn 28·00 45·00

(e) Stamps of Selangor

J254 **46** 3 c. green 40 70
J255 12 c. blue .. .. 1·10 4·75
J256 15 c. blue .. .. 2·75 2·00
J257 40 c. red and purple . 2·00 2·50
J258 **48** $2 green and red .. 10·00 21·00

1942. No. 108 of Perak surch **DAI NIPPON 2602 MALAYA 2 Cents**.

J259 **88** 2 c. on 5 c. brown .. 1·25 1·00

1942. Stamps of Perak optd **DAI NIPPON YUBIN** ("Japanese Postal Service") or surch also in figures and words.

J260 **51** 1 c. black .. .. 2·00 4·00
J261 2 c. on 5 c. brown .. 2·00 5·50
J262 8 c. red .. .. 2·75 1·25

1943. Various stamps optd vert or horiz with T **2** or surch in figures and words.

(a) Stamps of Straits Settlements

J263 **58** 8 c. grey .. .. 1·10 50
J264 12 c. blue .. .. 55 4·00
J265 40 c. red and purple .. 65 1·75

(b) Stamps of Negri Sembilan

J266 **6** 1 c. black 30 40
J267 2 c. on 5 c. brown .. 40 45
J268 6 c. on 5 c. brown .. 40 75
J269 25 c. purple and red .. 1·10 6·50

(c) Stamp of Pahang

J270 **7** 6 c. on 5 c brown .. 50 75

(d) Stamps of Perak

J272 **51** 1 c. black 80 60
J274 2 c. on 5 c. brown .. 45 45
J275 5 c. brown 45 40
J276 8 c. red 55 50
J277 10 c. purple 60 50
J278 30 c. purple & orange 1·25 2·50
J279 50 c. black on green .. 3·00 8·50
J280 $5 green & red on grn 40·00 60·00

(e) Stamps of Selangor

J288 **46** 1 c. black 35 50
J289 2 c. on 5 c. brown .. 30 50
J282 3 c. green 40 45
J290 3 c. on 5 c. brown .. 20 1·75
J291 5 c. brown .. .. 30 1·75
J293 6 c. on 5 c. brown .. 15 60
J283 12 c. blue .. .. 45 1·40
J284 15 c. blue .. .. 2·75 3·00
J285 **48** $1 black & red on blue 3·00 11·00
J295 **46** $1 on 10 c. purple .. 30 1·00
J296 $1.50 on 30 c. purple and orange .. 30 1·00
J286 **48** $2 green and red .. 10·00 26·00
J287 $5 green & red on grn 22·00 55·00

25 Tapping Rubber

27 Japanese Shrine, Singapore

1943.

J297 **25** 1 c. green 15 35
J298 – 2 c. green 15 15
J299 **25** 3 c. grey 15 15
J300 – 4 c. red 15 15
J301 – 8 c. blue 15 15
J302 – 10 c. purple 15 15
J303 **27** 15 c. violet .. .. 35 1·00
J304 – 30 c. olive 35 35
J305 – 50 c. blue 75 85
J306 – 70 c. blue .. .. 14·00 10·00

DESIGNS—VERT. 2 c. Fruit. 4 c. Tin dredger. 8 c. War Memorial. 10 c. Huts. 30 c. Sago palms. 50 c. Straits of Johore. HORIZ. 70 c. Malay Mosque, Kuala Lumpur.

28 Ploughman

29 Rice-planting

1943. Savings Campaign.

J307 **28** 8 c. violet .. .. 7·00 2·75
J308 15 c. red .. .. 6·00 2·75

1944. "Re-birth of Malaya".

J309 **29** 8 c. red .. .. 8·00 2·75
J310 15 c. mauve .. .. 4·00 3·00

大日本
マライ郵便
50 セント

(30)

1944. Stamps intended for use on Red Cross letters. Surch with T **30**.

(a) On Straits Settlements

J311 **58** 50 c. on 50 c. black/grn 9·00 19·00
J312 $1 on $1 black & red/bl 14·00 26·00
J313 $1.50 on $2 grn on red 23·00 60·00

(b) On Johore

J314 **24** 50 c. on 50 c. pur & red 7·00 16·00
J315 $1.50 on $2 green & red 5·50 11·00

(c) On Selangor

J316 **48** $1 on $2 black & red bl 4·00 11·00
J317 $1.50 on $2 green & red 6·00 15·00

POSTAGE DUE STAMPS

1942. Postage Due stamps of Malayan Postal Union optd with T **2**.

JD21	D 1	1 c. violet	12·00	16·00
JD22		3 c. green	24·00	26·00
JD23		4 c. green	20·00	20·00
JD24		8 c. red	30·00	35·00
JD25		10 c. orange ..	18·00	22·00
JD26		12 c. blue	19·00	27·00
JD27		50 c. black	45·00	55·00

1942. Postage Due stamps of Malayan Postal Union optd **DAI NIPPON 2620 MALAYA.**

JD28	D 1	1 c. violet	1·10	4·00
JD29		3 c. green	6·00	9·00
JD30		4 c. green	5·50	8·50
JD31		8 c. red	6·50	9·50
JD32		10 c. orange ..	1·60	6·50
JD33		12 c. blue	1·60	11·00

1943. Postage Due stamps of Malayan Postal Union optd with T **2**.

JD34	D 1	1 c. violet	40	1·75
JD35		3 c. green	40	1·90
JD36		4 c. green	26·00	28·00
JD37		5 c. red	50	2·50
JD38		9 c. orange ..	60	3·25
JD39		10 c. orange ..	60	3·25
JD40		12 c. blue	60	4·75
JD41		15 c. blue	60	4·25

MALAYA (THAI OCCUPATION OF)

Stamps issued for use in the four Malay states of Kedah, Kelantan, Perlis and Trengganu, ceded by Japan to Thailand on 19 October 1943 and restored to British rule on the defeat of the Japanese.

100 cents = 1 dollar.

TM 1. War Memorial.

1943.

TM 1.	TM 1.	1 c. yellow ..	25·00	30·00
TM 2.		2 c. brown ..	10·00	18·00
TM 3.		3 c. green	18·00	35·00
TM 4.		4 c. purple ..	12·00	26·00
TM 5.		8 c. red	20·00	18·00
TM 6.		15 c. blue	26·00	45·00

MALAYAN FEDERATION

An independent country within the British Commonwealth, comprising all the Malay States (except Singapore) and the Settlements of Malacca and Penang. The component units retained their individual stamps. In 1963 the Federation became part of Malaysia (q.v.).

100 cents (sen) = 1 Malayan dollar.

1. Tapping Rubber.

1957.

1	1	6 c. blue, red and yellow	40	10
2	–	12 c. multicoloured ..	60	10
3	–	25 c. multicoloured ..	75	10
4ab	–	30 c. red and lake ..	50	10

DESIGNS—HORIZ. 12 c. Federation coat of arms. 25 c. Tin dredge. VERT. 30 c. Map of the Federation.

5. Prime Minister Tunku Abdul Rahman and Populace greeting Independence.

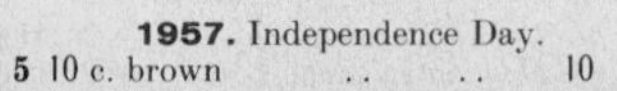

1957. Independence Day.

5	5	10 c. brown	10	10

6. United Nations Emblem.

DESIGN: 30 c. as Type **6** but vert.

1958. U.N. Economic Commission for Asia and Far East Conference, Kuala Lumpur.

6.	6.	12 c. red	30	40
7.	–	30 c. purple	40	20

8. Merdeka Stadium, Kuala Lumpur.

DESIGN—VERT. 30 c. Portrait of the Yan di-Pertuan Agong (Tuanku Abdul Rahman).

1958. 1st Anniv. of Independence.

8.	8.	10 c. multicoloured ..	15	10
9.	–	30 c. multicoloured ..	40	10

11. Malayan with "Torch of Freedom".

DESIGN—VERT. 10 c. "Human Rights".

1958. 10th Anniv. of Declaration of Human Rights.

10.	–	10 c. multicoloured ..	10	10
11.	11.	30 c. green	30	30

12. Mace and Malayan Peoples.

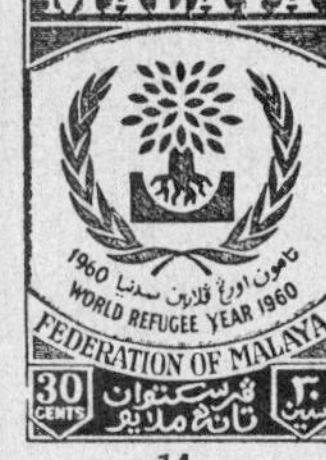

14.

1959. Inauguration of Parliament.

12.	12.	4 c. red	10	10
13.		10 c. violet	10	10
14.		25 c. green	35	20

1960. World Refugee Year

15.	–	12 c. purple	10	30
16.	14.	30 c. green	10	10

DESIGN: 12 c. As Type **14** but horiz.

15. Seedling Rubber Tree and Map.

16. The Yang di-Pertuan Agong (Tuanku Syed Putra).

1960. Natural Rubber Research Conf. and 15th Int. Rubber Study Group Meeting, Kuala Lumpur.

17.	15.	6 c. multicoloured ..	20	30
18.		30 c. multicoloured ..	50	15

No. 18 is inscr. "INTERNATIONAL RUBBER STUDY GROUP 15TH MEETING KUALA LUMPUR" at foot.

1961. Installation of Yang di-Pertuan Agong, Tuanku Syed Putra.

19.	16.	10 c. black and blue ..	10	10

17. Colombo Plan Emblem.

18. Malaria Eradication Emblem.

1961. Colombo Plan Conf., Kuala Lumpur.

20.	17.	12 c. black and mauve ..	35	1·75
21.		25 c. black and green ..	80	1·50
22.		30 c. black and blue ..	70	30

1962. Malaria Eradication.

23.	18.	25 c. brown	20	35
24.		30 c. lilac	20	15
25.		50 c. blue	40	30

19. Palmyra Palm Leaf.

1962. National Language Month.

26.	19.	10 c. brown and violet ..	15	10
27.		20 c. brown and green ..	25	30
28.		50 c. brown and mauve	45	70

20. "Shadows of the Future".

1962. Introduction of Free Primary Education.

29.	20.	10 c. purple	10	10
30.		25 c. ochre	30	40
31.		30 c. green	80	10

21. Harvester and Fisherman.

1963. Freedom from Hunger.

32.	21.	25 c. pink and green ..	85	1·25
33.		30 c. pink and lake ..	1·50	50
34.		50 c. pink and blue ..	1·50	1·25

22. Dam and Pylon.

1963. Cameron Highlands Hydro-Electric Scheme.

35.	22.	20 c. green and violet ..	35	10
36.		30 c. turquoise and blue	45	60

MALAYAN POSTAL UNION

In 1936 postage due stamps were issued in Type D 1 for use in Negri Sembilan, Pahang, Perak, Selangor and Straits Settlements but later their use was extended to the whole of the Federation and in Singapore, and from 1963 throughout Malaysia.

POSTAGE DUE STAMPS

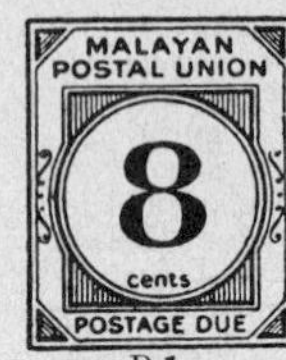

D 1.

1936.

D 1	D 1.	1 c. purple	3·50	70
D 14		1 c. violet	30	60
D 15		2 c. slate	30	75
D 8		3 c. green	9·00	11·00
D 2		4 c. green	7·00	1·00
D 17		4 c. sepia	45	3·25
D 9		5 c. red	12·00	7·50
D 3		8 c. red	2·75	3·50
D 19		8 c. orange	1·75	3·50
D 11		9 c. orange	60·00	48·00
D 4		10 c. orange	2·50	30
D 5		12 c. blue	5·00	8·00
D 20		12 c. mauve	1·00	3·75
D 12		15 c. blue	95·00	35·00
D 21		20 c. blue	4·00	6·00
D 6		50 c. black	20·00	5·00

1965. Surch. **10 cents.**

D 29.	D 1.	10 c. on 8 c. orange ..	30	1·75

MALAYSIA

General issues for use throughout the new Federation comprising the old Malayan Federation (Johore ("JOHOR"), Kedah, Kelantan, Malacca ("MELAKA"), Negri Sembilan ("NEGERI SEMBILAN"), Pahang, Penang ("PULAU PINANG"), Perak, Perlis, Selangor and Trengganu), Sabah (North Borneo), Sarawak and Singapore, until the latter became an independent state on 9th August, 1965.

Stamps inscr. "MALAYSIA" and state name are listed under the various states, as above.

100 cents (sen) = 1 Malaysian dollar.

A. NATIONAL SERIES

General issues for use throughout the Federation.

1. Federation Map.

1963. Inauguration of Federation.

1.	1.	10 c. yellow and violet ..	30	10
2.		12 c. yellow and green ..	70	60
3.		50 c. yellow and brown ..	1·00	10

2. Bouquet of Orchids.

1963. 4th World Orchid Congress, Singapore.

4.	2.	6 c. multicoloured ..	1·00	1·00
5.		25 c. multicoloured ..	1·25	25

4. Parliament House, Kuala Lumpur.

1963. 9th Commonwealth Parliamentary Conference, Kuala Lumpur.

7.	4.	20 c. mauve and gold ..	30	40
8.		30 c. green and gold ..	30	15

5. "Flame of Freedom" and Emblems of Goodwill, Health and Charity.

1964. Eleanor Roosevelt Commem.

9. 5. 25 c. blk., red & turquoise 15 10
10. 30 c. black, red and lilac 15 15
11. 50 c. black, red & yellow 15 10

6. Microwave Tower and I.T.U. Emblem.

1965. Centenary of I.T.U.

12. 6. 2 c. multicoloured .. 15 80
13. 25 c. multicoloured .. 60 50
14. 50 c. multicoloured .. 1·25 10

7. National Mosque.

1965. Opening of National Mosque, Kuala Lumpur.

15. 7. 6 c. red 10 10
16. 15 c. brown 10 10
17. 20 c. green 15 15

8. Air Terminal.

1965. Opening of Int. Airport, Kuala Lumpur.

18. 8. 15 c. black, green and blue 15 10
19. 30 c. black, green & mauve 30 20

9. Crested Wood Partridge. 17. Sepak Raga (ball-game) and Football.

1965. Birds. Multicoloured.

20. 25 c. Type 9 .. .. 50 10
21. 30 c. Blue-backed Fairy Bluebird 60 10
22. 50 c. Black-naped Oriole .. 70 10
23. 75 c. Rhinoceros Hornbill .. 1·25 10
24. $1 Zebra Dove .. .. 1·75 10
25. $2 Great Argus Pheasant .. 4·00 30
26. $5 Asiatic Paradise Flycatcher .. .. 13·00 1·50
27. $10 Blue-tailed Pitta .. 45·00 7·50

For the lower values see the individual sets listed under each of the states which form Malaysia.

1965. 3rd South East Asian Peninsular Games.

28. 17. 25 c. black and green .. 40 90
29. – 30 c. black and purple .. 40 20
30. – 50 c. black and blue .. 70 30

DESIGNS: 30 c. Running. 50 c. Diving.

20. National Monument.

1966. National Monument, Kuala Lumpur.

31. 20. 10 c. multicoloured .. 15 10
32. 20 c. multicoloured .. 25 20

21. The Yang di-Pertuan Agong (Tuanku Ismail Nasiruddin Shah).

1966. Installation of Yang di-Pertuan Agong, Tuanku Ismail Nasiruddin Shah.

33. 21. 15 c. black and yellow .. 10 10
34. 50 c. black and blue .. 20 20

22. School Building.

1966. 150th Anniv. of Penang Free School.

35. 22. 20 c. multicoloured .. 30 10
36. 50 c. multicoloured .. 60 10

23. "Agriculture".

1966. 1st Malaysia Plan. Multicoloured

37. 15 c. Type 23 .. .. 20 10
38. 15 c. "Rural Health" .. 20 10
39. 15 c. "Communications" .. 75 15
40. 15 c. "Education" .. 20 10
41. 15 c. "Irrigation" 20 10

28. Cable Route Maps. (Reduced size illustration. Actual size 68 × 22 mm.).

1967. Completion of Malaysia-Hong Kong Link of SEACOM Telephone Cable.

42. 28. 30 c. multicoloured .. 80 30
43. 75 c. multicoloured .. 2·50 2·50

29. Hibiscus and Paramount Rulers.

1967. 10th Anniv. of Independence.

44. 29. 15 c. multicoloured .. 20 10
45. 50 c. multicoloured .. 50 40

30. Mace and Shield.

1967. Centenary of Sarawak Council.

46. 30. 15 c. multicoloured .. 10 10
47. 50 c. multicoloured .. 30 40

31. Straits Settlements 1867 8 c. Stamp and Malaysian 1965 25 c. Stamp.

1967. Stamp Cent.

48. 31. 25 c. multicoloured .. 1·25 1·75
49. – 30 c. multicoloured .. 1·25 1·00
50. – 50 c. multicoloured .. 1·75 1·50

DESIGN: 30 c. Straits Settlements 1867. 24 c. Stamp and Malaysian 1965 30 c. Stamp. 50 c. Straits Settlements 1867. 32 c. Stamp and Malaysian 1965 50 c. Stamp.

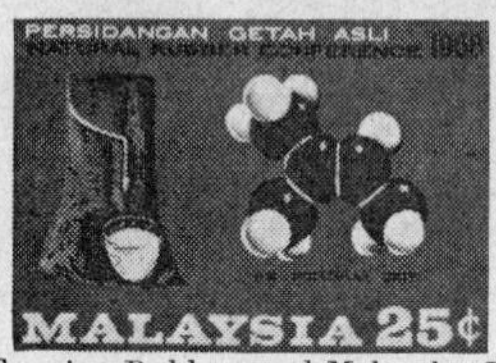

34. Tapping Rubber, and Molecular Unit.

1968. Natural Rubber Conf., Kuala Lumpur. Multicoloured.

51. 25 c. Type 34 .. .. 25 10
52. 30 c. Tapping Rubber, and Export Consignment .. 40 20
53. 50 c. Tapping Rubber, and Aircraft Tyres 40 10

37. Mexican Sombrero and Blanket with Olympic Rings. 39. Tunku Abdul Rahman against background of Pandanus Weave.

1968. Olympic Games, Mexico. Mult.

54. 30 c. Type 37 .. .. 20 10
55. 75 c. Olympic Rings and Mexican Embroidery .. 40 20

1969. Solidarity Week.

56. 39. 15 c. multicoloured .. 15 10
57. – 20 c. multicoloured .. 20 60
58. – 50 c. multicoloured .. 20 20

DESIGNS—VERT. 20 c. As Type 39 (different). HORIZ. 50 c. Tunku Abdul Rahman with pandanus pattern.

42. Peasant Girl with sheaves of Paddy.

1969. National Rice Year.

59. 42. 15 c. multicoloured .. 15 10
60. 75 c. multicoloured .. 55 75

43. Satellite tracking Aerial.

1970. Satellite Earth Station.

61. 43. 15 c. drab, black and blue 75 15
62. – 30 c. multicoloured .. 75 1·40
63. – 30 c. multicoloured .. 75 1·40

DESIGN—HORIZ. (40 × 27 mm): Nos. 62/3, "Intelsat III" in Orbit.

No. 62 has inscription and value in white and No. 63 has them in gold.

45. "Euploea leucostictus". 46. Emblem.

1970. Butterflies. Multicoloured.

64 25 c. Type 45 .. .. 1·00 10
65 30 c. "Zeuxidia amethystus" .. .. 1·50 10
66 50 c. "Polyura athamas" .. 1·75 10
67 75 c. "Papilio memnon" .. 2·00 10
68 $1 "Appias nero" .. 2·00 10
69 $2 "Trogonoptera brookiana" .. .. 3·50 10
70 $5 "Narathlura centaurus" 5·00 1·50
71 $10 "Terinos terpander" .. 12·00 5·00

Lower values were issued for use in the individual States.

1970. 50th Anniv. of Int. Labour Organisation.

72. 46. 30 c. grey and blue .. 10 20
73. 75 c. pink and blue .. 20 30

47. U.N. Emblem encircled by Doves.

1970. 25th Anniv. of United Nations.

74. 47. 25 c. gold, black & brown 45 40
75. – 30 c. multicoloured .. 45 35
76. – 50 c. black and green .. 85 75

DESIGNS: 30 c. Line of Doves and U.N. Emblem. 50 c. Doves looping U.N. Emblem.

50. The Yang di-Pertuan Agong (Tuanku Abdul Halim Shah).

1971. Installation of Yang di-Pertuan Agong. (Paramount Ruler of Malaysia).

77. 50. 10 c. blk., gold & yellow 20 30
78. 15 c. blk., gold & mauve 20 30
79. 50 c. blk., gold and blue 60 1·60

51. Bank Negara Complex.

1971. Opening of Bank Negara Building.

80. 51. 25 c. black and silver .. 70 90
81. 50 c. black and gold .. 70 1·10

52. Aerial view of Parliament Buildings. (Illustration reduced. Actual size 59 × 33 mm.)

1971. 17th Commonwealth Parliamentary Association Conference, Kuala Lumpur. Multicoloured.

82. 25 c. Type 52 .. .. 1·00 50
83. 75 c. Ground view of Parliament Buildings (horiz. 73 × 23½ mm) .. .. 1·75 1·75

53. 54. 55.
Malaysian Carnival.
(Illustration reduced. Actual size 63½ × 32 mm.)

1971. Visit ASEAN Year.

84. **53.** 30 c. multicoloured .. 1·25 45
85. **54.** 30 c. multicoloured .. 1·25 45
86. **55.** 30 c. multicoloured .. 1·25 45

ASEAN = Association of South East Asian Nations.
Nos. 84/6 form a composite design of a Malaysian Carnival, as Types **53/5**.

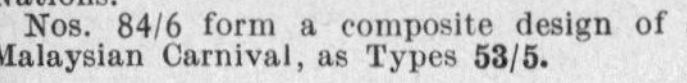

56. Trees, Elephant and Tiger.

1971. 25th Anniv. of U.N.I.C.E.F. Mult.

87. 15 c. Type **56** .. .. 1·40 45
88. 15 c. Cat and kittens .. 1·40 45
89. 15 c. Sun, flower and bird (vert. 22 × 29 mm.) .. 1·40 45
90. 15 c. Monkey, elephant and lion in jungle .. .. 1·40 45
91. 15 c. Spider and butterflies 1·40 45

57. Athletics.

1971. 6th S.E.A.P. Games, Kuala Lumpur. Multicoloured.

92. 25 c. Type **57** 45 40
93. 30 c. Sepak Raga players 60 50
94. 50 c. Hockey 90 95

S.E.A.P. = South East Asian Peninsular.

58. 59. 60.
Map and Tourist Attractions.
(Illustration reduced. Actual size 66 × 37 mm.).

1971. Pacific Area Tourist Association Conference.

95. **58.** 30 c. multicoloured .. 1·75 60
96. **59.** 30 c. multicoloured .. 1·75 60
97. **60.** 30 c. multicoloured .. 1·75 60

Nos. 95/7 form a composite design of a map showing tourist attractions, as Types **58/60**.

61. Kuala Lumpur City Hall.
(Illustration reduced. Actual size 54 × 33 mm.).

1972. City Status for Kuala Lumpur. Mult.

98. 25 c. Type **61** .. .. 1·00 1·25
99. 50 c. City Hall in Floodlights 2·00 1·25

62. SOCSO Emblem. **64.** Fireworks, National Flag and Flower.

63. W.H.O. Emblem.

1973. Social Security Organization.

100. **62.** 10 c. multicoloured .. 15 15
101. 15 c. multicoloured .. 25 10
102. 50 c. multicoloured .. 60 1·40

1973. 25th Anniv. of W.H.O.

103. **63.** 30 c. multicoloured .. 45 25
104. – 75 c. multicoloured .. 1·25 1·75

The 75 c. is similar to Type **63**, but vertical.

1973. 10th Anniv. of Malaysia.

105. **64.** 10 c. multicoloured .. 30 25
106. 15 c. multicoloured .. 40 15
107. 50 c. multicoloured .. 1·25 1·60

65. Emblems of Interpol and Royal Malaysian Police.

1973. 50th Anniv. of Interpol. Mult.

108. 25 c. Type **65** .. .. 1·00 50
109. 75 c. Emblems within "50" 1·75 2·00

66. Aeroplane and M.A.S. Emblem.

1973. Malaysian Airline System. Foundation.

110. **66.** 15 c. multicoloured .. 25 10
111. 30 c. multicoloured .. 45 60
112. 50 c. multicoloured .. 75 1·60

67. Kuala Lumpur.

1974. Establishment of Kuala Lumpur as Federal Territory.

113. **67.** 25 c. multicoloured .. 50 85
114. 50 c. multicoloured .. 1·00 1·75

68. Development Projects.

1974. 7th Annual Meeting of Asian Development Bank's Board of Governors, Kuala Lumpur.

115. **68.** 30 c. multicoloured .. 25 50
116. 75 c. multicoloured .. 80 1·75

69. Scout Badge and Map.

1974. Malaysian Scout Jamboree. Mult.

117. 10 c. Type **69** 30 20
118. 15 c. Scouts saluting and flags (46 × 24 mm.) .. 35 30
119. 50 c. Scout Badge .. .. 1·25 2·25

70. Coat of arms and Power Installations.

1974. 25th Anniv. of National Electricity Board. Multicoloured.

120. 30 c. Type **70** 30 50
121. 75 c. National Electricity Board Building (37 × 27 mm.) 1·00 2·00

71. U.P.U. and Post Office Emblems within "100".

1974. Centenary of U.P.U.

122. **71.** 25 c. green, yell. & red 20 35
123. 30 c. blue, yell. and red 25 35
124. 75 c. orange, yell. & red 65 1·75

72. Gravel Pump in Tin Mine.

1974. Fourth World Tin Conf. Kuala Lumpur. Multicoloured.

125. 15 c. Type **72** .. .. 1·25 15
126. 20 c. Open-cast mine .. 1·50 70
127. 50 c. Dredger within "ingot" .. .. .. 3·25 3·25

73. Hockey-players. World Cup and Federation Emblem.

1975. Third World Cup Hockey Championships.

128. **73.** 30 c. multicoloured .. 90 60
129. 75 c. multicoloured .. 2·10 2·25

74. Congress Emblem.

1975. 25th Anniv. of Malaysian Trade Union Congress.

130. **74.** 20 c. multicoloured .. 20 25
131. 25 c. multicoloured .. 30 30
132. 30 c. multicoloured .. 45 60

75. Emblem of M.K.P.W. (Malayan Women's Organization).

1975. International Women's Year.

133. **75.** 10 c. multicoloured .. 15 25
134. 15 c. multicoloured .. 30 25
135. 50 c. multicoloured .. 1·25 2·25

76. Ubudiah Mosque, Kuala Kangsar.

1975. Koran Reading Competition. Multicoloured.

136. 15 c. Type **76** .. .. 1·25 30
137. 15 c. Zahir Mosque, Alor Star .. .. .. 1·25 30
138. 15 c. National Mosque, Kuala Lumpur .. 1·25 30
139. 15 c. Sultan Abu Bakar Mosque, Johore Bahru 1·25 30
140. 15 c. Kuching State Mosque, Sarawak .. 1·25 30

77. Plantation and Emblem.

1975. 50th Anniv. of Malaysian Rubber Research Institute. Multicoloured.

141. 10 c. Type **77** 40 15
142. 30 c. Latex cup and emblem 1·10 70
143. 75 c. Natural rubber in test-tubes .. .. 1·90 2·25

77a. "Hebomoia glaucippe".

1976. Multicoloured.

144 10 c. Type **77a** .. .. 75 3·50
145 15 c. "Precis orithya" .. 80 3·50

78. Scrub Typhus. **79.** The Yang di Pertuan Agong (Tuanku Yahya Petra).

1976. 75th Anniv. of Institute of Medical Research. Multicoloured.

146. 20 c. Type **78** 25 15
147. 25 c. Malaria diagnosis .. 40 20
148. $1 Beri-beri .. .. 1·60 2·50

1976. Installation of Yang di-Pertuan Agong.

149. **79.** 10 c. blk., brn. & yell. 25 10
150. 15 c. blk., brn. & mauve 40 10
151. 50 c. blk., brn. & blue 2·25 2·50

80. State Council Complex.

1976. Opening of State Council Complex and Administrative Building, Sarawak.

152. **80.** 15 c. green and yellow .. 35 10
153. 20 c. green and mauve .. 45 40
154. 50 c. green and blue .. 1·00 1·40

81. E.P.F. Building.

1976. 25th Anniv. of Employees' Provident Fund. Multicoloured.

155. 10 c. Type **81** 15 10
156. 25 c. E.P.F. emblems (27×27 mm.) 25 35
157. 50 c. E.P.F. Building at night .. .. .. 60 1·00

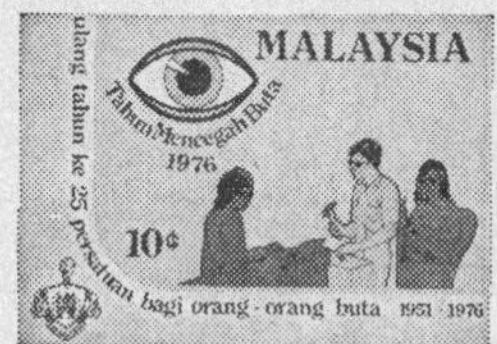

82. Blind People at Work.

1976. 25th Anniv. of Malayan Assn. for the Blind. Multicoloured.

158. 10 c. Type **82** 15 15
159. 75 c. Blind man and shadow 1·25 2·10

83. Independence Celebrations, 1957.

1977. 1st Death Anniv. of Tun Abdul Razak (Prime Minister).

160. 15 c. Type **83** .. .. 1·00 40
161. 15 c. " Education " .. 1·00 40
162. 15 c. Tun Razak and map (" Development ") .. 1·00 40
163. 15 c. " Rukunegara " (National Philosophy) .. 1·00 40
164. 15 c. ASEAN meeting .. 1·00 40

84. F.E.L.D.A. Village Scheme.

1977. 21st Anniv. of Federal Land Development Authority (F.E.L.D.A.). Multicoloured.

165. 15 c. Type **84** 25 10
166. 30 c. Oil Palm settlement 60 80

85. Figure " 10 ".

1977. 10th Anniv. of Association of South East Asian Nations (A.S.E.A.N.) Mult.

167. 10 c. Type **85** 10 10
168. 75 c. Flags of members .. 60 65

MORE DETAILED LISTS

are given in the Stanley Gibbons Catalogues referred to in the country headings.
For lists of current volumes see Introduction.

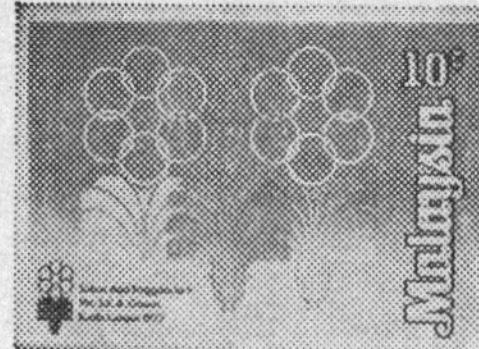

86. Games Logos.

1977. Ninth South East Asia Games, Kuala Lumpur. Multicoloured.

169. 10 c. Type **86** 15 15
170. 20 c. " Ball " 20 15
171. 75 c. Symbolic athletes .. 75 1·50

87. Islamic Development Bank Emblem.

1978. Islamic Development Bank Board of Governors' Meeting, Kuala Lumpur.

172. **87.** 30 c. multicoloured .. 20 15
173. 75 c. multicoloured .. 60 55

88. Mobile Post Office.

1978. Fourth Commonwealth Conference of Postal Administrations, Kuala Lumpur. Multicoloured.

174. 10 c. Type **88** 30 10
175. 25 c. G.P.O., Kuala Lumpur 75 85
176. 50 c. Rural delivery by motorcycle .. .. 1·10 1·50

89. Boy Scout Emblem.

1978. Fourth Malaysian Scout Jamboree, Sarawak. Multicoloured.

177. 15 c. Type **89** 40 10
178. $1 Bees and honeycomb .. 2·00 1·25

90. Dome of the Rock, Jerusalem.

1978. Palestinian Welfare.

179. **90.** 15 c. multicoloured .. 35 10
180. 30 c. multicoloured .. 60 60

91. Globe and Emblems.

1978. Global Eradication of Smallpox.

181. **91.** 15 c. black, red & blue 15 20
182. 30 c. black, red & green 20 10
183. 50 c. black, red & pink 35 45

92. " Seratus Tahun Getah Asli " and Tapping Knives Symbol.

1978. Centenary of Rubber Industry.

184. **92.** 10 c. gold and green .. 10 10
185. – 20 c. blue, brn. & green 10 10
186. – 75 c. gold and green .. 45 65

DESIGNS: 20 c. Rubber tree seedling and part of " maxi stump ". 75 c. Graphic design of rubber tree, latex cup and globe arranged to form " 100 ".

93. Sultan of Selangor's New Palace.

1978. Inaug. Shah Alam New Town, as State Capital of Selangor. Multicoloured.

187. 10 c. Type **93** 10 10
188. 30 c. Aerial view of Shah Alam 15 10
189. 75 c. Shah Alam 45 90

94. Tiger.

1979. Animals. Multicoloured.

190. 30 c. Type **94** 70 10
191. 40 c. Malayan Flying lemur 70 10
192. 50 c. Lesser Malay Chevrotain 80 10
193. 75 c. Leathery Pangolin .. 90 10
194. $1 Malayan Turtle .. 1·50 10
195. $2 Malayan Tapir .. .. 1·50 10
196. $5 Gaur .. .. 4·25 1·00
197. $10 Orang-utang (vert.) .. 7·00 3·25

96. View of Central Bank of Malaysia.

1979. 20th Anniv. of Central Bank of Malaysia. Multicoloured.

198. 10 c. Type **96** .. 10 10
199. 75 c. Central Bank (vert.) 40 45

97. I.Y.C. Emblem.

1979. International Year of the Child.

200. **97.** 10 c. gold, blue and salmon 30 10
201. – 15 c. multicoloured .. 40 10
202. – $1 multicoloured .. 1·75 2·25

DESIGNS: 15 c. Children holding hands in front of globe. $1, Children playing.

98. Dam and Power Station.

1979. Opening of Hydro-Electric Pow Station, Temengor.

203. **98.** 15 c. multicoloured .. 15
204. – 25 c. multicoloured .. 25
205. – 50 c. multicoloured .. 45

DESIGNS: 25 c., 50 c. Different views of Dan

99. Exhibition Emblem.

1979. 3rd World Telecommunications Exhibi tion, Geneva.

206. **99.** 10 c. orge., blue & silver 10 2
207. – 15 c. multicoloured .. 15 1
208. – 50 c. multicoloured .. 40 1·5

DESIGNS—(34×24 mm.). 15 c. Telephon receiver joining the one half of World to th other. (39×28 mm.). 50 c. Communication equipment.

100. Tuanku Haji Ahmad Shah.

1980. Installation of Tuanku Haji Ahmad Shah as Yang di-Pertuan Agong.

209. **100.** 10 c. blk., gold & yell... 10 2
210. 15 c. blk., gold & purple 15 1
211. 50 c. blk., gold and blue 40 1·1

101. Pahang and Sarawak Maps within Telephone Dials.

1980. Kuantan–Kuching Submarine Cable Project. Multicoloured.

212. 10 c. Type **101** 10 20
213. 15 c. Kuantan and Kuching views within telephone dials 15 10
214. 50 c. Pahang and Sarawak Maps within telephone receiver 35 90

102. Bangi Campus.

1980. 10th Anniv. of National University of Malaysia. Multicoloured.

215. 10 c. Type **102** 15 15
216. 15 c. Jalan Pantai Baru campus 20 10
217. 75 c. Great Hall .. .. 65 1·75

103. Mecca.

1980. Moslem Year 1400 A.H. Commemoration.

218. **103.** 15 c. multicoloured .. 10 10
219. 50 c. multicoloured .. 30 90

No. 219 is inscribed in Roman lettering.

INDEX

Countries can be quickly located by referring to the index at the end of this volume.

104. Disabled Child learning to Walk.

981. International Year of Disabled Persons. Multicoloured.

0. 10 c. Type **104** 30 25
1. 15 c. Girl sewing 55 10
2. 75 c. Disabled athlete .. 1·50 2·25

105. Industrial Scene.

981. Expo "81" Industrial Training Exposition, Kuala Lumpur and Seminar, Genting Highlands. Multicoloured.

3. 10 c. Type **105** 10 10
4. 15 c. Worker and bulldozer 15 10
5. 30 c. Workers at ship-building plant 25 35
6. 75 c. Agriculture and fishing produce, workers and machinery .. .. 65 1·50

106. "25".

981. 25th Anniv. of Malaysian National Committee for World Energy Conferences. Multicoloured.

27. 10 c. Type **106** 15 15
28. 15 c. Drawings showing importance of energy sources in industry .. 20 10
29. 75 c. Symbols of various energy sources .. .. 1·00 2·00

.07. Drawing showing development of Sabah from Village to Urbanised Area.

1981. Centenary of Sabah. Multicoloured.

230. 15 c. Type **107** 50 15
231. 80 c. Drawing showing traditional and modern methods of agriculture 2·00 3·25

108. "Samanea saman".

1981. Trees. Multicoloured.

232. 15 c. Type **108** 55 10
233. 50 c. "Dyera costulata" (vert.) .. .. .. 1·50 1·25
234. 80 c. "Dryobalanops aromatica" (vert.) .. 1·75 2·75

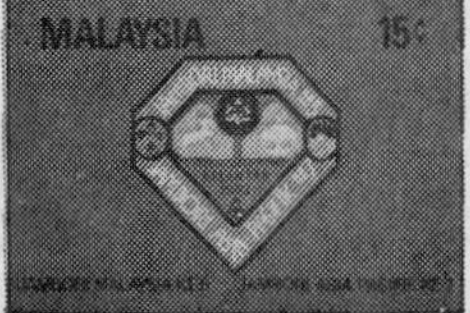

109. Jamboree Emblem.

1982. 5th Malaysian/7th Asia-Pacific Boy Scout Jamboree. Multicoloured.

235. 15 c. Type **109** 30 10
236. 50 c. Malaysian flag and scout emblem 70 80
237. 80 c. Malaysian and Asia-Pacific scout emblem .. 1·10 2·75

110. A.S.E.A.N. Building Emblem.

1982. 15th Anniv. of A.S.E.A.N. (Association of South East Asian Nations). Ministerial Meeting. Multicoloured.

238. 15 c. Type **110** 15 10
239. $1 Flags of members .. 60 1·50

111. Dome of the Rock, Jerusalem.

1982. "Freedom for Palestine".

240. **111.** 15 c. gold, green and blk. 75 15
241. $1 silver, green and blk. 2·75 2·75

112. Views of Kuala Lumpur in 1957 and 1982.

1982. 25th Anniv. of Independence. Mult.

242. 10 c. Type **112** 10 10
243. 15 c. Malaysian industries 15 15
244. 50 c. Soldiers on parade .. 40 55
245. 80 c. Independence ceremony 70 1·75

113. Shadow Play.

1982. Traditional Games. Multicoloured.

247. 10 c. Type **113** 30 30
248. 15 c. Cross Top 40 15
249. 75 c. Kite flying .. .. 1·50 2·50

114. Sabah Hats.

1982. Malaysian Handicrafts. Multicoloured.

250. 10 c. Type **114** 15 30
251. 15 c. Gold-threaded cloth 15 20
252. 75 c. Sarawak pottery .. 85 2·00

115. Gas Exploration Logo.

1983. Export of Liquefied Natural Gas from Bintulu Field, Sarawak. Multicoloured.

253. 15 c. Type **115** 65 15
254. 20 c. "Tenaga Satu" (liquid gas tanker) .. .. 1·00 50
255. $1 Gas drilling equipment 2·75 3·50

116. Flag of Malaysia.

1983. Commonwealth Day. Multicoloured.

256. 15 c. Type **116** 10 10
257. 20 c. The King of Malaysia 15 15
258. 40 c. Oil palm tree and refinery 25 30
259. $1 Satellite view of earth 60 1·50

117. "Tilapia nilotica".

1983. Freshwater Fishes. Multicoloured.

260. 20 c. Type **117** 40 55
261. 20 c. "Cyprinus carpio" .. 40 55
262. 40 c. "Puntius gonionotus" 70 1·00
263. 40 c. "Ctenopharyngodon idellus" .. .. .. 70 1·00

118. Lower Pergau River Bridge.

1983. Opening of the East-West Highway. Multicoloured.

264. 15 c. Type **118** 60 15
265. 20 c. Perak river reservoir bridge 70 45
266. $1 Map showing East-west highway .. .. .. 2·25 3·25

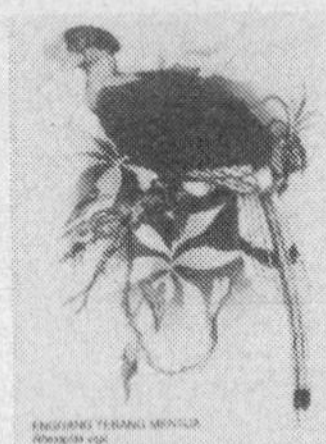

119. Northrop "RF-5E" Fighter.

1983. 50th Anniv. of Malaysian Armed Forces. Multicoloured.

267. 15 c. Type **119** 45 15
268. 20 c. Missile boat 75 45
269. 40 c. Battle of Pasir Panjang .. .. 1·25 1·25
270. 80 c. Trooping the Colour 1·75 2·50

120. Helmeted Hornbill.

1983. Hornbills of Malaysia. Multicoloured.

280. 15 c. Type **120** 40 10
281. 20 c. Wrinkled hornbill .. 55 40
282. 50 c. Long-crested hornbill 85 1·00
283. $1 Rhinoceros hornbill .. 1·60 3·00

121. Bank Building, Ipoh.

1984. 25th Anniv. of Bank Negara. Mult.

284. 20 c. Type **121** 40 30
285. $1 Bank building, Alor Setar 1·40 2·50

122. Sky-scraper and Mosque, Kuala Lumpur.

1984. 10th Anniv. of Federal Territory. Multicoloured.

286. 20 c. Type **122** 50 20
287. 40 c. Aerial view .. .. 1·00 1·00
288. 80 c. Gardens and clock-tower (horiz.) .. .. 1·75 2·75

123. Map showing Industries.

124. Semananjung Keris.

1984. Formation of Labuan Federal Territory. Multicoloured.

289. 20 c. Type **123** 50 25
290. $1 Flag and map of Labuan 2·00 2·75

1984. Traditional Malay Weapons. Mult.

291. 40 c. Type **124** 70 90
292. 40 c. Pekakak keris .. 70 90
293. 40 c. Jawa keris 70 90
294. 40 c. Lada tumbuk .. 70 90

125. Map of World and Transmitter.

1984. 20th Anniv. of Asia-Pacific Broadcasting Union. Multicoloured.

295. 20 c. Type **125** 40 25
296. $1 Clasped hands within "20" .. .. .. 2·00 3·00

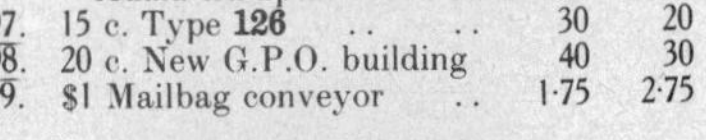

126. Facsimile service.

1984. Opening of New General Post Office, Kuala Lumpur. Multicoloured.

297. 15 c. Type **126** 30 20
298. 20 c. New G.P.O. building 40 30
299. $1 Mailbag conveyor .. 1·75 2·75

127. Yang di Pertuan Agong (Tuanku Mahmood).

1984. Installation of Yang di Pertuan Agong (Tuanku Mahmood).

300. **127.** 15 c. multicoloured .. 40 20
301. 20 c. multicoloured .. 40 20
302. – 40 c. multicoloured .. 75 1·00
303. – 80 c. multicoloured .. 1·40 2·25

DESIGN—HORIZ. 40 c., 80 c. Yang di Pertuan Agong and Federal Crest.

128. White Hibiscus.

1984. Hibiscus. Multicoloured.

304.	10 c. Type **128**	35	15
305.	20 c. Red Hibiscus ..	70	20
306.	40 c. Pink Hibiscus ..	1·25	1·00
307.	$1 Orange Hibiscus ..	2·25	3·25

129. Parliament Building.

1985. 25th Anniv. of Federal Parliament. Multicoloured.

308.	20 c. Type **129**	30	15
309.	$1 Parliament Building (different) (horiz.) ..	1·75	1·50

130. Banded Lingsang.

1985. Protected Animals of Malaysia. (1st series). Multicoloured.

310.	10 c. Type **130**	30	10
311.	40 c. Slow Loris (vert.) ..	80	80
312.	$1 Spotted Giant Flying Squirrel (vert.)	1·75	2·75

See also Nos. 383/6.

131. Stylised Figures.

1985. International Youth Year. Mult.

313.	20 c. Type **131**	30	15
314.	$1 Young workers ..	1·75	2·75

132. F.M.S.R. "No. 1" Steam Locomotive, 1885.

1985. Centenary of Malayan Railways.

315.	**132.**	15 c. black, red and orange	60	15
316.	–	20 c. multicoloured ..	70	30
317.	–	$1 multicoloured ..	1·75	2·50

Designs: 20 c. Class "20" diesel locomotive, 1957. $1 Class "23" diesel locomotive, 1983.

133. Blue Proton "Saga 1.3s" Car.

1985. Production of Proton "Saga" (Malaysian national car). Multicoloured.

319.	20 c. Type **133** ..	30	15
320.	40 c. White Proton "Saga 1.3s"	45	60
321.	$1 Red Proton "Saga 1.5s"	80	2·00

134. Penang Bridge.

1985. Opening of Penang Bridge. Mult.

322.	20 c. Type **134**	40	15
323	40 c. Penang Bridge and location map	65	50
324.	$1 Symbolic bridge linking Penang to mainland (40 × 24 mm)	1·50	1·50

135. Offshore Oil Rig.

1985. Malaysian Petroleum Production. Multicoloured.

325.	15 c. Type **135**	20	10
326.	20 c. Malaysia's first oil refinery (horiz.)	30	30
327.	$1 Map of Malaysian offshore oil and gas fields (horiz.)	1·25	1·75

136. Sultan Azlan Shah and Perak Royal Crest.

1985. Installation of the Sultan of Perak.

328.	**136.**	15 c. multicoloured ..	15	10
329.		20 c. multicoloured ..	25	25
330.		$1 multicoloured ..	1·25	2·25

137. Crested Fireback Pheasant. **139.** Two Indonesian Dancers.

1986. Protected Birds of Malaysia (1st series). Multicoloured.

331.	20 c. Type **137**	80	1·00
332.	20 c. Malay peacock-pheasant	80	1·00
333.	40 c. Bulwer's pheasant (horiz.)	1·25	1·50
334.	40 c. Great argus pheasant (horiz.)	1·25	1·50

See also Nos. 394/7.

1986. Pacific Area Travel Association Conference, Malaysia. Multicoloured.

335.	20 c. Type **139**	30	40
336.	20 c. Dyak dancer and longhouse, Malaysia ..	30	40
337.	20 c. Dancers and church, Philippines	30	40
338.	40 c. Thai dancer and temple	50	70
339.	40 c. Chinese dancer, Singapore	50	70
340.	40 c. Indian dancer and Hindu temple stairway	50	70

140. Stylized Competitors.

1986. Malaysia Games. Multicoloured.

341.	20 c. Type **140**	75	20
342.	40 c. Games emblems (vert.)	1·40	1·40
343.	$1 National and state flags (vert.)	3·00	3·50

141. Rambutan. **143.** MAS Logo and Map showing Routes.

142. Skull and Slogan "Drugs Can Kill".

1986. Fruits of Malaysia. Multicoloured.

344	40 c. Type **141**	20	25
345	50 c. Pineapple	25	30
346	80 c. Durian	40	45
347	$1 Mangosteen	50	55
348	$2 Starfruit	1·00	1·10
349	$5 Banana	2·50	2·75
350	$10 Mango	5·25	5·50
351	$20 Papaya	10·50	11·00

1986. 10th Anniv. of National Association for Prevention of Drug Addiction. Multicoloured.

352.	20 c. Type **142**	35	20
353.	40 c. Bird and slogan "Stay Free From Drugs"	55	55
354.	$1 Addict and slogan "Drugs Can Destroy" (vert.)	1·10	2·00

1986. Inaugural Flight of Malaysian Airlines Kuala Lumpur–Los Angeles Service. Multicoloured.

355.	20 c. Type **143**	35	15
356.	40 c. Logo, stylized aircraft and route diagram ..	60	60
357.	$1 Logo and stylized aircraft	1·10	1·75

144. Building Construction.

1986. 20th Anniv. of National Productivity Council and 25th Anniv. of Asian Productivity Organization. (40 c., $1). Multicoloured.

358.	20 c. Type **144**	60	25
359.	40 c. Planning and design (horiz.)	1·00	85
360.	$1 Computer-controlled car assembly line (horiz.) ..	2·00	2·50

145. Old Seri Menanti Palace, Negri Sembilan.

1986. Historic Buildings of Malaysia (1st series). Multicoloured.

361.	15 c. Type **145**	15	1
362.	20 c. Old Kenangan Palace, Perak	20	1
363.	40 c. Old Town Hall, Malacca	35	4
364.	$1 Astana, Kuching, Sarawak	75	1·4

See also Nos. 465/8.

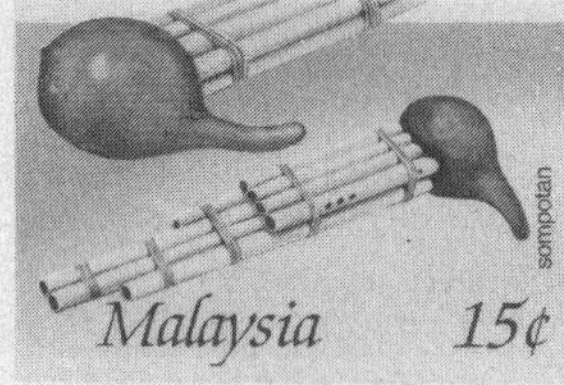

146. Sompotan (bamboo pipes).

1987. Malaysian Musical Instruments. Multicoloured.

365.	15 c. Type **146**	15	10
366.	20 c. Sapih (four-stringed chordophone)	20	15
367.	50 c. Serunai (pipes) (vert.)	45	30
368.	80 c. Rebab (three-stringed fiddle) (vert.)	70	45

147. Modern Housing Estate.

1987. International Year of Shelter for the Homeless. Multicoloured.

369.	20 c. Type **147**	20	15
370.	$1 Stylised families and houses	80	65

148. Drug Addict and Family.

1987. International Conference on Drug Abuse, Vienna. Multicoloured.

371.	20 c. Type **148**	45	40
372.	20 c. Hands holding drugs and damaged internal organs	45	40
373.	40 c. Healthy boy and broken drug capsule ..	75	65
374.	40 c. Drugs and healthy internal organs	75	65

Nos. 371/2 and 373/4 were printed together, se-tenant, forming composite designs.

149. Spillway and Power Station.

1987. Opening of Sultan Mahmud Hydro-electric Scheme, Kenyir, Trengganu. Mult.

375.	20 c. Type **149**	35	10
376.	$1 Dam, spillway and reservoir	1·40	1·00

150. Crossed Maces and Parliament Building, Kuala Lumpur.

987. 33rd Commonwealth Parliamentary Conference. Multicoloured.

77.	20 c. Type **150**	15	10
78.	$1 Parliament building and crossed mace emblem ..	60	75

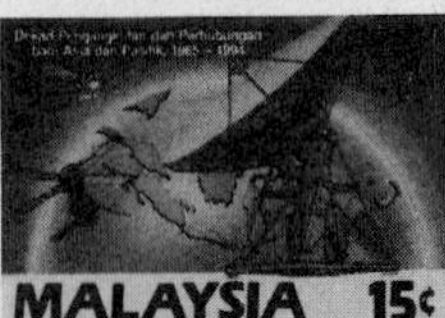

151. Dish Aerial, Satellite and Globe.

1987. Asia/Pacific Transport and Communications Decade. Multicoloured.

79.	15 c. Type **151**	25	10
80.	20 c. Diesel train and car	40	20
81.	40 c. Container ships and lorry	60	55
82.	$1 Malaysian Airlines jumbo jet, Kuala Lumpur Airport ..	1·00	1·40

152. Temminck's Golden Cat.

1987. Protected Animals of Malaysia (2nd series). Multicoloured.

383.	15 c. Type **152**	50	20
384.	20 c. Flatheaded cat ..	50	20
385.	40 c. Marbled cat	90	80
386.	$1 Clouded leopard ..	1·75	2·50

153. Flags of Member Nations and "20".

1987. 20th Anniv. of Association of South East Asian Nations. Multicoloured.

387.	20 c. Type **153**.	15	10
388.	$1 Flags of member nations and globe ..	65	1·00

154. Mosque and Portico.

1988. Opening of Sultan Salahuddin Abdul Aziz Shah Mosque. Multicoloured.

389.	15 c. Type **154**	10	10
390.	20 c. Dome, minarets and Sultan of Selangor ..	15	15
391.	$1 Interior and dome (vert.)	60	1·00

155. Aerial View.

1988. Sultan Ismail Hydro-electric Power Station, Paka, Trengganu. Multicoloured.

392.	20 c. Type **155**	15	10
393.	$1 Power station and pylons	65	70

156 Black-naped Blue Monarch

1988. Protected Birds of Malaysia (2nd series). Multicoloured.

394	20 c. Type **156**	35	35
395	20 c. Scarlet-backed flowerpecker	35	35
396	50 c. Yellow-backed sunbird	70	70
397	50 c. Black and red broadbill	70	70

157 Outline Map and Products of Sabah

1988. 25th Anniv of Sabah and Sarawak as States of Malaysia. Multicoloured.

398	20 c. Type **157**	20	20
399	20 c. Outline map and products of Sarawak ..	20	20
400	$1 Flags of Malaysia, Sabah and Sarawak (30 × 40 mm)	70	70

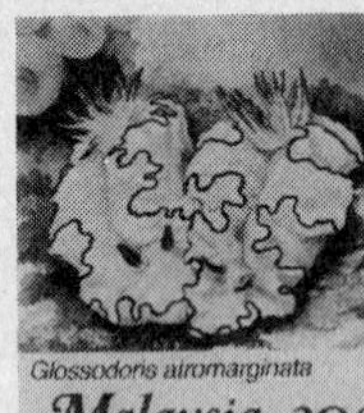

158 "Glossodoris atromarginata"

1988. Marine Life (1st series). Multicoloured.

401	20 c. Type **158**	25	25
402	20 c. "Phyllidia ocellata" ..	25	25
403	20 c. "Chromodoris annae"	25	25
404	20 c. "Flabellina macassarana"	25	25
405	20 c. "Fryeria ruppelli" ..	25	25

Nos. 401/5 were printed together, se-tenant, forming a composite background design.

See also Nos. 410/13, 450/3 and 492/6.

159 Sultan's Palace, Malacca

1989. Declaration of Malacca as Historic City. Multicoloured

407	20 c. Type **159**	15	15
408	20 c. Independence Memorial Building ..	15	15
409	$1 Porta De Santiago Fortress (vert)	75	1·40

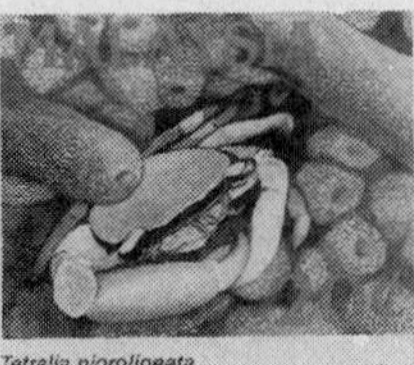

160 "Tetralia nigrolineata"

1989. Marine Life (2nd series). Crustaceans. Multicoloured.

410	20 c. Type **160**	20	30
411	20 c. "Neopetrolisthes maculatus" (crab) ..	20	30
412	40 c. "Periclimenes holthuisi" (shrimp) ..	30	50
413	40 c. "Synalpheus neomeris" (shrimp) ..	30	50

161 Map of Malaysia and Scout Badge

1989. 7th National Scout Jamboree. Mult.

414	10 c. Type **161**	20	10
415	20 c. Saluting national flag	30	25
416	80 c. Scouts around camp fire (horiz)	1·10	1·60

162 Cycling

1989. 15th South East Asian Games, Kuala Lumpur. Multicoloured.

417	10 c. Type **162**	15	15
418	20 c. Athletics	25	20
419	50 c. Swimming (vert) ..	50	60
420	$1 Torch bearer (vert) ..	85	1·40

163 Sultan Azlan Shah

1989. Installation of Sultan Azlan Shah as Yang di Pertuan Agong.

421	**163** 20 c. multicoloured ..	15	15
422	40 c. multicoloured ..	25	35
423	$1 multicoloured ..	60	1·00

164 Putra World Trade Centre and Pan-Pacific Hotel

1989. Commonwealth Heads of Government Meeting, Kuala Lumpur. Multicoloured.

424	20 c. Type **164**	15	10
425	50 c. Traditional dancers (vert)	35	55
426	$1 National flag and map showing Commonwealth countries	60	1·25

165 Clock Tower, Kuala Lumpur City Hall and Big Ben

1989. Inaugural Malaysia Airlines "747" Non-stop Flight to London. Each showing Malaysia Airlines Boeing "747-400". Mult.

427	20 c. Type **165**	20	35
428	20 c. Parliament Buildings, Kuala Lumpur, and Palace of Westminster	20	35
429	$1 World map showing route	80	1·25

166 Sloth and Map of Park

1989. 50th Anniv of National Park. Mult.

430	20 c. Type **166**	25	15
431	$1 Pair of Malay ocellated pheasants	1·00	1·50

167 Outline Map of South-east Asia and Logo

1990. "Visit Malaysia Year". Multicoloured.

432	20 c. Type **167**	15	15
433	50 c. Traditional drums ..	35	55
434	$1 Scuba diving, windsurfing and yachting ..	65	1·25

168 "Dillenia suffruticosa"

1990. Wildflowers (1st series). Multicoloured.

435	15 c. Type **168**	15	15
436	20 c. "Mimosa pudica" ..	20	20
437	50 c. "Ipmoea carnea" ..	40	60
438	$1 "Nymphaea pubescens"	65	1·25

See also Nos. 505/8.

169 Monument and Rainbow

1990. Kuala Lumpur, Garden City of Lights. Multicoloured.

439 20 c. Type **169** 15 20
440 40 c. Mosque and sky-scrapers at night (horiz) 25 40
441 $1 Kuala Lumpur skyline (horiz) .. .. .. 60 1·25

170 Seri Negara Building

1990. 1st Summit Meeting of South–South Consultation and Co-operation Group, Kuala Lumpur. Multicoloured.

442 20 c. Type **170** 15 15
443 80 c. Summit logo .. 60 1·10

171 Alor Setar

1990. 250th Anniv of Alor Setar. Mult.

444 20 c. Type **171** 15 20
445 40 c. Musicians and monument (vert) .. 25 35
446 $1 Zahir Mosque (vert) .. 70 1·25

172 Sign Language Letters

1990. International Literacy Year. Mult.

447 20 c. Type **172** 10 10
448 40 c. People reading .. 25 35
449 $1 Symbolic person reading (vert) .. .. .. 65 1·25

173 Leatherback Turtle

1990. Marine Life (3rd series). Sea Turtles. Multicoloured.

450 15 c. Type **173** 20 10
451 20 c. Common green turtle 20 15
452 40 c. Olive Ridley turtle .. 35 40
453 $1 Hawksbill turtle .. 75 1·00

174 Safety Helmet, Dividers and Industrial Skyline

1991. 25th Anniv of MARA (Council of the Indigenous People). Multicoloured.

454 20 c. Type **174** 15 10
455 40 c. Documents and graph 25 30
456 $1 25th Anniversary logo 65 90

175 "Eustenogaster calyptodoma"

1991. Insects. Wasps. Multicoloured.

457 15 c. Type **175** 20 30
458 20 c. "Vespa affinis indonensis" 20 20
459 50 c. "Sceliphorn javanum" 50 50
460 $1 "Ampulex compressa" 90 1·00

176 Tunku Abdul Rahman Putra and Independence Rally

1991. Former Prime Ministers of Malaysia. Multicoloured.

462 $1 Type **176** 70 85
463 $1 Tun Abdul Razak Hussein and jungle village 70 85
464 $1 Tun Hussein Onn and standard-bearers .. 70 85

177 Maziah Palace, Trengganu

1991. Historic Buildings of Malaysia (2nd series). Multicoloured.

465 15 c. Type **177** 20 10
466 20 c. Grand Palace, Johore 20 15
467 40 c. Town Palace, Kuala Langat, Selangor .. 35 40
468 $1 Jahar Palace, Kelantan 65 75

178 Museum Building, Brass Lamp and Fabric

1991. Centenary of Sarawak Museum. Mult.

469 30 c. Type **178** 20 15
470 $1 Museum building in 1991, vase and fabric .. 65 75

179 Rural Postman on Cycle

1992. Inauguration of Post Office Corporation. Multicoloured.

471 30 c. Type **179** 25 30
472 30 c. Urban postman on motorcycle 25 30
473 30 c. Inner city post van .. 25 30
474 30 c. Industrial post van .. 25 30
475 30 c. Malaysian Airlines Boeing 747 and globe .. 25 30

180 Hill Forest and Jelutong Tree

1992. Tropical Forests. Multicoloured.

476 20 c. Type **180** 15 10
477 50 c. Mangrove swamp and Bakau Minyak tree .. 35 40
478 $1 Lowland forest and Chengal tree 75 85

181 Tuanku Ja'afar and Coat of Arms

1992. 25th Anniv of Installation of Tuanku Ja'afar as Yang di-Pertuan Besar of Negri Sembilan. Multicoloured.

479 30 c. Type **181** 20 20
480 $1 Palace, Negri Sembilan 80 1·00

182 Badminton Players

1992. Malaysian Victory in Thomas Cup Badminton Championship. Multicoloured.

481 $1 Type **182** 55 75
482 $1 Thomas Cup and Malaysian flag 55 75

183 Women in National Costumes

1992. 25th Anniv of A.S.E.A.N. (Association of South East Asian Nations). Multicoloured.

484 30 c. Type **183** 25 30
485 50 c. Regional flowers .. 45 40
486 $1 Traditional architecture 90 1·25

MALAYSIA 30¢

184 Straits Settlements 1867 3½ c. and Malaysian Federation 1957 10 c. Stamps

1992. 125th Anniv of Postage Stamps and "Kuala Lumpur '92" Int Stamp Exn. Mult.

487 30 c. Type **184** 25 30
488 30 c. Straits Settlements 1867 2 c. and Malaysia 1963 Federation Inauguration 12 c. .. 25 30
489 50 c. Straits Settlements 1868 4 c. and Malaysia 1990 Kuala Lumpur 40 c. 40 50
490 50 c. Straits Settlements 1867 12 c. and Malaysia "Kuala Lumpur '92" $2 40 50

Malaysia 30¢

185 "Acropora"

1992. Marine Life (4th series). Corals. Multicoloured.

492 30 c. Type **185** 25 30
493 30 c. "Dendronephthya" .. 25 30
494 30 c. "Dendrophyllia" .. 25 30
495 30 c. "Sinularia" .. 25 30
496 30 c. "Melithaea" .. 25 30

186 Girls smiling

1993. 16th Asian–Pacific Dental Congress. Multicoloured.

498 30 c. Type **186** 25 30
499 30 c. Girls smiling with koala bear 25 30
500 50 c. Dentists with Japanese, Malaysian and South Korean flags .. 40 50
501 $1 Dentists with Australian, Thai, Chinese and Indonesian flags .. 40 50

MALAYSIA 30¢

187 View of Golf Course

1993. Cent of Royal Selangor Golf Club. Mult.

502 30 c. Type **187** 25 20
503 50 c. Old and new club houses 40 40
504 $1 Bunker on course (horiz) 75 80

MINIMUM PRICE

The minimum price quoted is 10p which represents a handling charge rather than a basis for valuing common stamps. For further notes about prices see introductory pages.

188 "Alpinia rafflesiana"

1993. Wildflowers (2nd series). Multicoloured.

505	20 c. Type 188	15	10
506	30 c. "Achasma megalocheilos"	20	20
507	50 c. "Zingiber spectabile"	35	35
508	$1 "Costus speciosus"	65	70

189 Forest under Magnifying Glass

1993. 14th Commonwealth Forestry Conf. Multicoloured.

509	30 c. Type 189	20	20
510	50 c. Hand holding forest	35	35
511	$1 Forest in glass dome (vert)	65	65

190 White-breasted Kingfisher

1993. Kingfishers. Multicoloured.

512	30 c. Type 190	20	25
513	30 c. Pair of blue-eared kingfishers	20	25
514	50 c. Chestnut-collared kingfisher	35	40
515	50 c. Pair of three-toed kingfishers	35	40

191 SME MD 3-160m Aircraft

1993. Langkawi International Maritime and Aerospace Exhibition '93. Multicoloured.

516	30 c. Type 191	15	20
517	50 c. Eagle X-TS (aircraft)	25	30
518	$1 "Kasturi" (frigate)	50	55

192 Jeriau Waterfalls

1994. Visit Malaysia. Multicoloured.

520	20 c. Type 192	10	10
521	30 c. Flowers	15	20
522	50 c. Turtle and fishes	25	30
523	$1 Orang-utan and other wildlife	50	55

193 Planetarium and Planets

1994. National Planetarium, Kuala Lumpur. Multicoloured.

524	30 c. Type 193	15	20
525	50 c. Static displays	25	30
526	$1 Planetarium auditorium	50	55

B. FEDERAL TERRITORY ISSUES.

For use in the Federal Territory of Kuala Lumpur.

K 1. "Rafflesia hasseltii".

1979. Flowers. Multicoloured.

K1	1 c. Type K 1	10	20
K2	2 c. "Pterocarpus indicus"	10	20
K3	5 c. "Lagerstroemia speciosa"	10	10
K4	10 c. "Durio zibethinus"	10	10
K5	15 c. "Hibiscus rosa-sinensis"	15	10
K6	20 c. "Rhododendron scortechinii"	15	10
K7	25 c. "Etlingera elatior" (inscr "Phaeomeria speciosa")	15	10

K 2. Coffee.

1986. Agricultural Products of Malaysia. Multicoloured.

K 15.	1 c. Type K 2	10	10
K 16.	2 c. Coconuts	10	10
K 17.	5 c. Cocoa	10	10
K 18.	10 c. Black pepper	10	10
K 19.	15 c. Rubber	10	10
K 20.	20 c. Oil palm	10	10
K 21.	30 c. Rice	15	20

POSTAGE DUE STAMPS

Until 15th August, 1966, the postage due stamps of Malayan Postal Union were in use throughout Malaysia.

D 1.

D 2.

1966.

D 1	D 1.	1 c. red	20	1·25
D 17		2 c. blue	20	1·25
D 3		4 c. green	85	2·25
D 18		8 c. green	30	1·50
D 19		10 c. blue	40	1·75
D 6		12 c. violet	60	2·50
D 20		20 c. brown	50	2·00
D 21		50 c. bistre	90	3·00

1986.

D22	D 2	5 c. mauve and lilac	10	10
D23		10 c. black and grey	10	10
D24		20 c. red and brown	10	10
D25		50 c. green and blue	25	30
D26		$1 blue and cobalt	50	55

MALDIVE ISLANDS

A group of islands W. of Ceylon. A republic from 1 Jan., 1953, but reverted to a sultanate in 1954. Became independent on 26 July, 1965, and left the British Commonwealth until re-admitted as an Associate Commonwealth Member on 9 July 1982.

1906. 100 cents = 1 rupee.
1951. 100 larees = 1 rupee.

1906. Nos. 268, 277/9 and 283/4 of Ceylon optd MALDIVES.

1	44	2 c. brown	11·00	26·00
2	48	3 c. green	15·00	26·00
3		4 c. orange and blue	32·00	65·00
4	–	5 c. purple	4·50	6·50
5	48	15 c. blue	50·00	£100
6		25 c. brown	60·00	£110

2. Minaret, Juma Mosque, Male.

5. Palm Tree and Boat.

1909.

7.	2.	2 c. brown	2·25	90
11.		2 c. grey	2·00	2·00
8.		3 c. green	40	70
12.		3 c. brown	70	1·75
9.		5 c. purple	40	35
15.		6 c. red	1·25	3·00
10.		10 c. red	3·50	80
16.		10 c. green	55	55
17.		15 c. black	5·50	6·50
18.		25 c. brown	5·50	6·50
19.		50 c. purple	5·50	5·50
20.		1 r. blue	7·00	2·75

1950.

21.	5.	2 l. olive	90	40
22.		3 l. blue	3·50	40
23.		5 l. green	3·75	50
24.		6 l. brown	50	30
25.		10 l. red	60	30
26.		15 l. orange	60	30
27.		25 l. purple	45	30
28.		50 l. violet	50	30
29.		1 r. brown	8·00	24·00

8. Native Products.

1952.

30.	–	3 l. blue (Fish)	60	30
31.	8.	5 l. green	50	50

9. Male Harbour.

10. Fort and Building.

1956.

32.	9.	2 l. purple	10	10
33.		3 l. slate	10	10
34.		5 l. brown	10	10
35.		6 l. violet	10	10
36.		10 l. green	10	10
37.		15 l. brown	10	10
38.		25 l. red	10	10
39.		50 l. orange	10	10
40.	10.	1 r. green	15	10
41.		5 r. blue	60	20
42.		10 r. mauve	85	40

13. Tomb of Sultan.

1960.

51.	13.	2 l. purple	10	10
52.	–	3 l. green	10	10
53.	–	5 l. brown	1·75	1·25
54.	–	6 l. blue	10	10
55.	–	10 l. red	10	10
56.	–	15 l. sepia	10	10
57.	–	25 l. violet	10	10
58.	–	50 l. grey	10	10
59.	–	1 r. orange	15	10
60.	–	5 r. blue	1·75	60
61.	–	10 r. green	5·00	1·25

DESIGNS: 3 l. Custom House. 5 l. Cowrie shells. 6 l. Old Royal Palace. 10 l. Road to Juma Mosque, Male. 15 l. Council House. 25 l. New Government Secretariat. 50 l. Prime Minister's Office. 1 r. Old Ruler's Tomb. 5 r. Old Ruler's Tomb (distant view). 10 r. Maldivian Port.

Higher values were also issued, intended mainly for fiscal use.

24. "Care of Refugees".

1960. World Refugee Year.

62.	24.	2 l. violet, orange & green	10	10
63.		3 l. brown, green and red	10	10
64.		5 l. green, sepia and red	10	10
65.		10 l. green, violet and red	10	10
66.		15 l. violet, green and red	10	10
67.		25 l. bl., brown and green	10	10
68.		50 l. olive, red and blue	10	10
69.		1 r. red, slate and violet	15	35

25. Coconuts.

26. Map of Male.

1961.

70.	25.	2 l. brown and green	10	10
71.		3 l. brown and blue	10	10
72.		5 l. brown and mauve	10	10
73.		10 l. brown and orange	10	10
74.		15 l. brown and black	10	10
75.	26.	25 l. multicoloured	10	10
76.		50 l. multicoloured	10	10
77.		1 r. multicoloured	20	30

11. Cycling.

1960. Olympic Games.

43.	11.	2 l. purple and green	10	10
44.		3 l. slate and purple	10	10
45.		5 l. brown and blue	10	10
46.		10 l. green and brown	10	10
47.		15 l. sepia and blue	10	10
48.	–	25 l. red and olive	10	10
49.	–	50 l. orange and violet	10	10
50.	–	1 r. green and purple	20	55

DESIGN—VERT. 25 l. to 1 r. Basketball.

27. 5 c. Stamp of 1906.

1961. 55th Anniv. of 1st Maldivian Stamp.

78.	27.	2 l. purple, blue & green	10	10
79.		3 l. purple, blue & green	10	10
80.		5 l. purple, blue & green	10	10
81.		6 l. purple, blue & green	10	10
82.	–	10 l. green, red & purple	10	10
83.	–	15 l. green, red & purple	10	10
84.	–	20 l. green, red & purple	10	10
85.	–	25 l. red, green & black	10	10
86.	–	50 l. red, green & black	20	50
87.	–	1 r. red, green & black	35	90

DESIGNS: 10 l. to 20 l. Post horn and 5 c. stamp of 1906. 25 l. to 1 r. Olive sprig and 2 c. stamp of 1906.

30. Malaria Eradication Emblem.

1962. Malaria Eradication.

No.	Type	Description	Unused	Used
88.	**30.**	2 l. brown	10	10
89.		3 l. green	10	10
90.		5 l. turquoise	10	10
91.		10 l. red	10	10
92.	–	15 l. sepia	10	10
93.	–	25 l. blue	15	10
94.	–	50 l. myrtle	20	10
95.	–	1 r. purple	45	25

Nos. 92/5 are as Type **30**, but have English inscriptions at the side.

31. Children of Europe and America.

1962. 15th Anniv. of U.N.I.C.E.F.

No.	Type	Description	Unused	Used
96.	**31.**	2 l. multicoloured ..	10	10
97.		6 l. multicoloured ..	10	10
98.		10 l. multicoloured ..	10	10
99.		15 l. multicoloured ..	10	10
100.	–	25 l. multicoloured ..	10	10
101.	–	50 l. multicoloured ..	10	10
102.	–	1 r. multicoloured ..	10	20
103.	–	5 r. multicoloured ..	45	2·00

DESIGN: Nos. 100/3, Children of Middle East and Far East.

33. Sultan Mohamed Farid Didi.

1962. 9th Anniv. of Enthronement of Sultan.

No.	Type	Description	Unused	Used
104.	**33.**	3 l. brown and green ..	10	10
105.		5 l. brown and blue ..	10	10
106.		10 l. brown and blue ..	10	10
107.		20 l. brown and olive ..	10	10
108.		50 l. brown and mauve	10	10
109.		1 r. brown and violet ..	15	25

34. Angel Fish.

1963. Tropical Fish. Multicoloured.

No.	Description	Unused	Used
110	2 l. Type **34**	10	10
111	3 l. Type **34**	10	10
112	5 l. Type **34**	10	10
113	10 l. Moorish idol (fish) ..	10	10
114	25 l. As 10 l.	10	10
115	50 l. Soldier fish	10	10
116	1 r. Surgeon fish ..	30	30
117	5 r. Butterfly fish ..	3·00	5·00

39. Fishes in Net.

1963. Freedom from Hunger.

No.	Type	Description	Unused	Used
118.	**39.**	2 l. brown and green ..	30	60
119.	–	5 l. brown and red ..	50	50
120.	**39.**	7 l. brown & turquoise ..	70	50
121.	–	10 l. brown and blue ..	85	50
122.	**39.**	25 l. brown & red ..	3·00	2·75
123.	–	50 l. brown and violet ..	4·75	5·50
124.	**39.**	1 r. brown and mauve ..	7·50	9·50

DESIGNS—VERT. 5 l., 10 l., 50 l. Handful of grain.

41. Centenary Emblem.

1963. Centenary of Red Cross.

No.	Type	Description	Unused	Used
125.	**41.**	2 l. red and purple ..	30	90
126.		15 l. red and green ..	50	80
127.		50 l. red and brown ..	1·25	1·75
128.		1 r. red and blue ..	2·00	2·00
129.		4 r. red and olive ..	6·50	19·00

42. Maldivian Scout Badge.

1964. World Scout Jamboree, Marathon (1963).

No.	Type	Description	Unused	Used
130.	**42.**	2 l. green and violet ..	10	10
131.		3 l. green and brown ..	10	10
132.		25 l. green and blue ..	15	10
133.		1 r. green and red ..	55	1·10

43. Mosque, Male.

1964. "Maldives Embrace Islam".

No.	Type	Description	Unused	Used
134.	**43.**	2 l. purple	10	10
135.		3 l. green	10	10
136.		10 l. red	10	10
137.		40 l. dull purple ..	20	15
138.		60 l. blue	40	15
139.		85 l. brown	40	20

44. Putting the Shot.

1964. Olympic Games, Tokyo.

No.	Type	Description	Unused	Used
140.	**44.**	2 l. purple and blue ..	10	10
141.		3 l. red and brown ..	10	10
142.		5 l. bronze and green ..	15	10
143.		10 l. violet and purple	20	10
144.	–	15 l. sepia and brown ..	20	10
145.	–	25 l. indigo and blue ..	30	10
146.	–	50 l. bronze and olive ..	55	20
147.	–	1 r. purple and grey ..	95	40

DESIGNS: 15 l. to 1 r. Running.

46. Telecommunications Satellite.

1965. Int. Quiet Sun Years.

No.	Type	Description	Unused	Used
148.	**46.**	5 l. blue	10	10
149.		10 l. brown	15	10
150.		25 l. green	30	10
151.		1 r. mauve	60	45

INDEPENDENT

47. Isis (wall carving, Abu Simbel).

1965. Nubian Monuments Preservation.

No.	Type	Description	Unused	Used
152.	**47.**	2 l. green and purple ..	10	10
153.	–	3 l. lake and green ..	10	10
154.	**47.**	5 l. green and purple ..	10	10
155.	–	10 l. blue and orange ..	10	10
156.	**47.**	15 l. brown and violet	15	10
157.	–	25 l. purple and blue ..	20	10
158.	**47.**	50 l. green and sepia ..	30	15
159.	–	1 r. ochre and green ..	60	30

DESIGNS: 3, 10, 25 l., 1 r. Rameses II on throne (wall carving, Abu Simbel).

48. Pres. Kennedy and Doves.

1965. 2nd Death Anniv. of Pres. Kennedy.

No.	Type	Description	Unused	Used
160.	**48.**	2 l. black and mauve ..	10	10
161.		5 l. brown and mauve ..	10	10
162.		25 l. blue and mauve ..	10	10
163.	–	1 r. pur., yellow & green	25	25
164.	–	2 r. bronze, yellow & grn.	40	40

DESIGN: 1 r., 2 r. Pres. Kennedy and hands holding olive-branch.

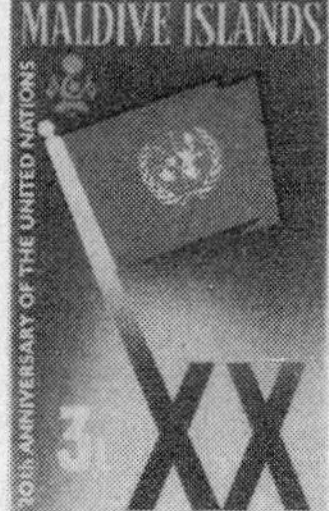

49. "XX" and U.N. Flag.

1965. 20th Anniv. of U.N.

No.	Type	Description	Unused	Used
165.	**49.**	3 l. blue and brown ..	10	10
166.		10 l. blue and violet ..	10	10
167		1 r. blue and green ..	35	35

50. I.C.Y. Emblem.

1965. Int. Co-operation Year.

No.	Type	Description	Unused	Used
168.	**50.**	5 l. brown and bistre ..	15	10
169.		15 l. brown and lilac ..	20	10
170.		50 l. brown and olive ..	45	30
171.		1 r. brown and red ..	1·25	1·50
172.		2 r. brown and blue ..	1·75	3·00

51. Seashells.

1966. Multicoloured.

No.	Description	Unused	Used
174.	2 l. Type **51**	20	40
175.	3 l. Yellow flowers ..	20	40
176.	5 l. Seashells (different) ..	30	15
177.	7 l. Camellias	30	15
178.	10 l. Type **51**	50	15
179.	15 l. Crab Plover and seagull	1·75	30
180.	20 l. Yellow flowers ..	80	30
181.	30 l. Type **51**	1·50	35
182.	50 l. Crab Plover and seagull	3·50	55
183.	1 r. Type **51**	2·50	55
184.	1 r. Camellias	2·50	55
185.	1 r. 50 Yellow flowers ..	3·25	1·75
186.	2 r. Camellias	4·50	2·25
187.	5 r. Crab Plover and seagull	14·00	8·50
188.	10 r. Seashells (different) ..	15·00	12·00

The 3 l., 7 l., 20 l., 1 r. (No. 181), 1 r. 50, and 2 r. are DIAMOND (43½ × 43½ mm.).

52. Maldivian Flag.

1966. 1st Anniv. of Independence.

No.	Type	Description	Unused	Used
189.	**52.**	10 l. green, red & turq.	15	10
190.		1 r. multicoloured ..	60	40

53. "Luna 9" on Moon.

1966. Space Rendezvous and Moon Landing.

No.	Type	Description	Unused	Used
191.	**53.**	10 l. brown, indigo & bl.	15	10
192.	–	25 l. green and red ..	20	10
193.	**53.**	50 l. brown and green ..	25	15
194.	–	1 r. turquoise & brown	55	35
195.	–	2 r. green and violet ..	85	65
196.	–	5 r. pink and turquoise	1·75	1·60

DESIGNS: 25 l., 1 r., 5 r. "Gemini 6" and "7" rendezvous in space. 2 r. "Gemini" spaceship as seen from the other spaceship.

54. U.N.E.S.C.O. Emblem and Owl on Book.

1966. 20th Anniv. of U.N.E.S.C.O. Mult.

No.	Description	Unused	Used
198.	2 l. Type **54**	10	40
199.	3 l. U.N.E.S.C.O. emblem and globe and microscope	10	40
200.	5 l. U.N.E.S.C.O. emblem and mask, violin and palette	15	15
201.	50 l. Type **54**	1·00	45
202.	1 r. Design as 3 l.	1·75	75
203.	5 r. Design as 5 l.	6·50	9·00

55. Sir Winston Churchill and Cortege.

1966. Churchill Commem. Flag in red and blue.

No.	Type	Description	Unused	Used
204.	**55.**	2 l. brown	15	40
205.	–	10 l. turquoise ..	60	10
206.	**55.**	15 l. green	85	10
207.	–	25 l. violet	1·40	15
208.	–	1 r. brown	3·50	75
209.	**55.**	2 r. 50 red	8·00	9·50

DESIGN: 10 l., 25 l., 1 r. Churchill and catafalque.

56. Footballers and Jules Rimet Cup.

1967. England's Victory in World Cup Football Championship. Multicoloured.

210 2 l. Type **56** 10 40
211 3 l. Player in red shirt kicking ball 10 40
212 5 l. Scoring goal 10 10
213 25 l. As 3 l. 30 10
214 50 l. Making a tackle .. 55 20
215 1 r. Type **56** .. .. 1·40 55
216 2 r. Emblem on Union Jack .. .. .. 2·50 3·00

57. Clown Butterfly Fish.

1967. Tropical Fishes. Multicoloured.

218. 2 l. Type **57** 10 30
219. 3 l. Striped Puffer .. 10 30
220. 5 l. Blue Spotted Boxfish 15 10
221. 6 l. Picasso Fish 15 20
222. 50 l. Blue Angelfish .. 2·00 30
223. 1 r. Blue Spotted Boxfish 3·50 75
224. 2 r. Blue Angelfish .. 6·00 6·00

58. Hawker Siddeley "HS748" over Airport Building.

1967. Inauguration of Hulule Airport.

225. **58.** 2 l. violet and olive .. 10 40
226. – 5 l. green and lavender 10 10
227. **58.** 10 l. violet and green .. 15 10
228. – 15 l. green and ochre .. 20 10
229. **58.** 30 l. ultramarine & blue 50 10
230. – 50 l. brown and mauve 75 20
231. **58.** 5 r. blue & orange .. 3·25 4·00
232. – 10 r. brown and blue .. 5·50 6·50

DESIGN: 5 l., 15 l., 50 l. and 10 r. Airport building and aircraft.

59. "Man and Music" Pavilion.

1967. World Fair, Montreal. Multicoloured.

233. 2 l. Type **59** 10 10
234. 5 l. "Man and His Community" Pavilion .. 10 10
235. 10 l. Type **59** 10 10
236. 50 l. As 5 l... .. .. 25 20
237. 1 r. Type **59** 55 40
238. 2 r. As 5 l. .. .. .. 1·00 90

1968. Int. Tourist Year (1967). Nos. 225/32 optd. **International Tourist Year 1967.**

240. **58.** 2 l. violet and olive .. 10 30
241. – 5 l. green and lavender 10 15
242. **58.** 10 l. violet and green .. 15 15
243. – 15 l. green and ochre .. 15 15
244. **58.** 30 l. ultramarine & blue 20 20
245. – 50 l. brown and mauve 30 30
246. **58.** 5 r. blue and orange .. 2·50 3·25
247. – 10 r. brown and blue .. 3·75 5·00

MINIMUM PRICE

The minimum price quoted is 10p which represents a handling charge rather than a basis for valuing common stamps. For further notes about prices see introductory pages.

61. Cub signalling and Lord Baden-Powell.

1968. Maldivian Scouts and Cubs.

248 **61** 2 l. brown, green & yell 10 30
249 – 3 l. red, blue and lt blue 10 30
250 **61** 25 l. violet, lake & red 1·50 30
251 – 1 r. green, brown and light green .. .. 3·50 1·60

DESIGN: 3 l. and 1 r. Scouts and Lord Baden-Powell.

62. French Satellite "A 1".

1968. Space Martyrs.

252. **62.** 2 l. mauve and blue .. 10 30
253. – 3 l. violet and brown .. 10 30
254. – 7 l. brown and lake .. 15 30
255. – 10 l. blue, drab and black 15 15
256. – 25 l. green and violet .. 40 15
257. **62.** 50 l. blue and brown .. 75 30
258. – 1 r. purple and green .. 1·10 50
259. – 2 r. brown, blue & black 1·75 1·75
260. – 5 r. mauve, drab & blk. 2·75 3·00

DESIGNS: 3 l., 25 l. "Luna 10". 7 l., 1 r. "Orbiter" and "Mariner". 10 l., 2 r. Astronauts White, Grissom and Chaffee. 5 r. Cosmonaut V. M. Komarov.

63. Putting the Shot.

1968. Olympic Games, Mexico. Mult.

262. 2 l. Type **63** 10 15
263. 6 l. Throwing the discus .. 10 15
264. 10 l. Type **63** 10 10
265. 25 l. As 6 l. 10 10
266. 1 r. Type **63** 35 35
267. 2 r. 50 As 6 l. 65 85

64. "Adriatic Seascape" (Bonington).

1968. Paintings. Multicoloured.

268. 50 l. Type **64** 50 30
269. 1 r. "Ulysses deriding Polyphemus" (Turner) 80 45
270. 2 r. "Sailing Boat at Argenteuil" (Monet) .. .. 1·40 1·40
271. 5 r. "Fishing Boat at Les Saintes-Maries" (Van Gogh) .. .. .. 3·25 3·75

65. "Graf Zeppelin" and Montgolfier's Balloon.

1968. Development of Civil Aviation.

272 **65** 2 l. brown, green & blue 15 40
273 – 3 l. blue, violet & brown 15 40
274 – 5 l. green, red and blue 15 15
275 – 7 l. blue, purple & orge 90 55
276 **65** 10 l. brown, blue & pur 35 15
277 – 50 l. red, green & olive 1·50 20
278 – 1 r. green, blue & red .. 2·25 50
279 – 2 r. purple, bistre & blue 14·00 10·00

DESIGNS: 3 l., 1 r. Boeing "707" and Douglas "DC-3". 5 l., 50 l. Wright Brothers' aircraft and Lilienthal's glider. 7 l., 2 r. Projected Boeing Supersonic "733" and "Concorde".

66. W.H.O. Building, Geneva.

1968. 20th Anniv. of World Health Organization.

280. **66.** 10 l. violet, turq. & blue 50 10
281. 25 l. green, brn. & yellow 90 15
282. 1 r. brown, emer. & grn. 2·50 90
283. 2 r. violet, pur. & mve. 4·25 5·00

1968. 1st Anniv. of Scout Jamboree, Idaho. Nos. 248/51 optd. **International Boy Scout Jamboree, Farragut Park, Idaho, U.S.A. August 1–9, 1967.**

284 **61** 2 l. brown, green & yell 10 40
285 – 3 l. red, blue and lt blue 10 40
286 **61** 25 l. violet, lake and red 1·25 40
287 – 1 r. green, brown and light green .. .. 4·25 2·10

68. Curlew and Redshank.

1968. Multicoloured.

288. 2 l. Type **68** 40 60
289. 10 l. Conches .. .. 1·00 20
290. 25 l. Shells .. .. 1·50 25
291. 50 l. Type **68** .. .. 4·50 90
292. 1 r. Conches .. .. 4·50 95
293. 2 r. Shells .. .. .. 4·75 4·50

69. Throwing the Discus.

1968. Olympic Games, Mexico. Multicoloured.

294. 10 l. Type **69** 10 10
295. 50 l. Running 10 10
296. 1 r. Cycling 45 35
297. 2 r. Basketball .. .. 1·25 1·00

70. Fishing Dhow.

1968. Republic Day.

298. **70.** 10 l. brown, blue & grn. 75 20
299. – 1 r. green, red and blue 2·25 80

DESIGN: 1 r. National flag, crest and map.

71. "The Thinker" (Rodin).

1969. U.N.E.S.C.O. "Human Rights". Designs showing sculptures by Rodin. Multicoloured.

300. 6 l. Type **71** 30 15
301. 10 l. "Hands" 30 15
302. 1 r. 50 "Eve" .. .. 2·00 2·00
303. 2 r. 50 "Adam" .. .. 2·50 2·75

72. Module nearing Moon's Surface.

1969. 1st Man on the Moon. Multicoloured.

305. 6 l. Type **72** 15 15
306. 10 l. Astronaut with hatchet 15 15
307. 1 r. 50 Astronaut and module 1·10 1·10
308. 2 r. 50 Astronaut using camera .. .. .. 1·75 1·75

1969. Gold Medal Winner, Olympic Games, Mexico (1968). Nos. 295/6 optd **Gold Medal Winner Mohamed Gammoudi 5000 m. run Tunisa REPUBLIC OF MALDIVES** or similar opt.

310. 50 l. multicoloured .. 40 40
311. 1 r. multicoloured .. 60 60

The inscription on No. 310 honours P. Trentin (cycling, France).

74. Red-striped Butterfly Fish.

1970. Tropical Fishes. Multicoloured.

312. 2 l. Type **74** 40 60
313. 5 l. Spotted Triggerfish .. 65 30
314. 25 l. Scorpion Fish .. 1·50 35
315. 50 l. Forceps Fish.. .. 2·25 85
316. 1 r. Imperial Angelfish .. 3·50 1·00
317. 2 r. Regal Angelfish .. 5·00 5·00

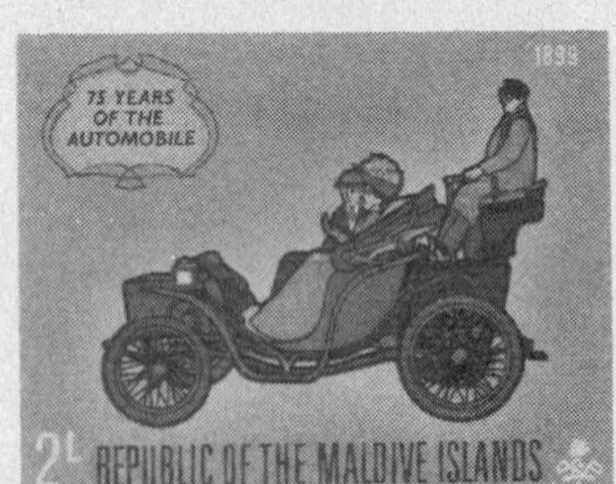

75. Columbia Dauman Victoria, 1899.

1970. "75 Years of the Automobile". Multicoloured.

318. 2 l. Type **75** 15 30
319. 5 l. Duryea phaeton, 1902 20 30
320. 7 l. Packard S-24, 1906 .. 25 30
321. 10 l. Autocar Runabout, 1907 .. .. .. 30 30
322. 25 l. Type **75** 75 30
323. 50 l. As 5 l. .. .. 1·75 55
324. 1 r. As 7 l... .. .. 2·75 90
325. 2 r. As 10 l. .. .. 4·00 4·50

76. U.N. Headquarters, New York.

1970. 25th Anniv. of United Nations. Mult.

327.	2 l. Type **76**	10	50
328.	10 l. Surgical operation (W.H.O.)	55	15
329.	25 l. Student, actress and musician (U.N.E.S.C.O.)	1·25	30
330.	50 l. Children at work and play (U.N.I.C.E.F.) ..	1·50	60
331.	1 r. Fish, corn and farm animals (F.A.O.) ..	1·75	90
332.	2 r. Miner hewing coal (I.L.O.)	3·50	4·00

77. Ship and Light Buoy.

1970. 10th Anniv. of I.M.C.O. Multicoloured.

333.	50 l. Type **77**	45	40
334.	1 r. Ship and lighthouse ..	1·40	85

78. "Guitar-player and Masqueraders" (A. Watteau).

1970. Famous Paintings showing the Guitar. Multicoloured.

335.	3 l. Type **78**	10	30
336.	7 l. "Spanish Guitarist" (Manet)	10	30
337.	50 l. "Costumed Player" (Watteau)	50	35
338.	1 r. "Mandoline-player" (Roberti)	85	55
339.	2 r. 50 "Guitar-player and Lady" (Watteau) ..	2·25	2·50
340.	5 r. "Mandoline-player" (Frans Hals)	4·00	4·25

79. Australian Pavilion.

1970. "EXPO 70" World Fair, Osaka, Japan. Multicoloured.

342.	2 l. Type **79**	10	40
343.	3 l. West German Pavilion	10	40
344.	10 l. U.S. Pavilion ..	15	10
345.	25 l. British Pavilion ..	30	15
346.	50 l. Soviet Pavilion ..	50	35
347.	1 r. Japanese Pavilion ..	90	65

80. Learning the Alphabet.

1970. Int. Education Year. Multicolour

348.	5 l. Type **80**	15	15
349.	10 l. Training teachers ..	20	10
350.	25 l. Geography lesson ..	50	15
351.	50 l. School inspector ..	70	45
352.	1 r. Education by television	1·00	75

1970. "Philympia 1970" Stamp Exn., London. Nos. 306/8 optd. **Philympia London 1970.**

353.	10 l. multicoloured ..	10	10
354.	1 r. 50 multicoloured ..	65	65
355.	2 r. 50 multicoloured ..	1·00	1·25

82. Footballers.

1970. World Cup Football Championships, Mexico.

357. **82.**	3 l. multicoloured ..	10	40
358. –	6 l. multicoloured ..	10	40
359. –	7 l. multicoloured ..	10	30
360. –	25 l. multicoloured ..	60	20
361. –	1 r. multicoloured ..	2·25	90

DESIGNS: 6 l. to 1 r. Different designs showing footballers in action.

83. Little Boy and U.N.I.C.E.F. Flag.

1970. 25th Anniv. of U.N.I.C.E.F. Mult.

362.	5 l. Type **83**	10	15
363.	10 l. Little girl with U.N.I.C.E.F. "balloon"	10	15
364.	1 r. Type **83**	1·00	65
365.	2 r. As 10 l.	2·00	2·25

84. Astronauts Lovell, Haise and Swigert.

1971. Safe Return of "Apollo 13". Multicoloured.

366.	5 l. Type **84**	15	15
367.	20 l. "Explosion in Space"	15	15
368.	1 r. Splashdown ..	50	50

85. "Multiracial Flower".

1971. Racial Equality Year.

369. **85.**	10 l. multicoloured ..	10	15
370.	25 l. multicoloured ..	20	15

86. "Mme. Charpentier and her Children" (Renoir).

1971. Famous Paintings showing "Mother and Child". Multicoloured.

371.	5 l. Type **86**	10	10
372.	7 l. "Susanna van Collen and her Daughter" (Rembrandt)	15	10
373.	10 l. "Madonna nursing the Child" (Titian)	20	10
374.	20 l. "Baroness Belleli and her Children" (Degas) ..	40	15
375.	25 l. "The Cradle" (Morisot)	45	15
376.	1 r. "Helena Fourment and her Children" (Reubens)	1·50	75
377.	3 r. "On the Terrace" (Renoir)	3·50	3·75

87. Alan Shepard.

1971. Moon Flight of "Apollo 14". Mult.

378	6 l. Type **87**	30	10
379	10 l. Staurt Roosa ..	35	10
380	1 r. 50 Edgar Mitchell ..	2·75	2·00
381	5 r. Mission insignia ..	6·50	5·50

88. "Ballerina" (Degas).

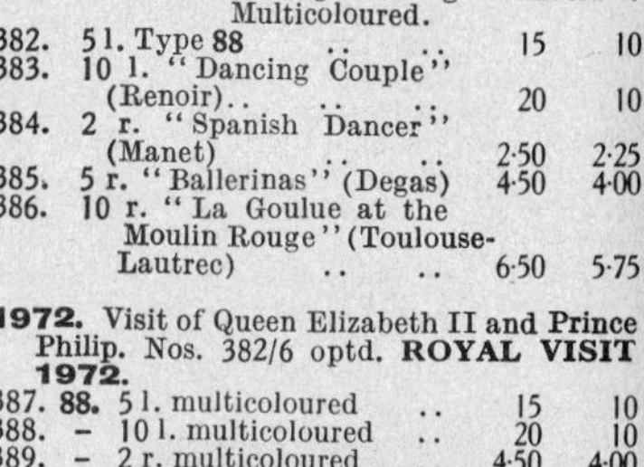

1971. Famous Paintings showing "Dancers". Multicoloured.

382.	5 l. Type **88**	15	10
383.	10 l. "Dancing Couple" (Renoir)	20	10
384.	2 r. "Spanish Dancer" (Manet)	2·50	2·25
385.	5 r. "Ballerinas" (Degas)	4·50	4·00
386.	10 r. "La Goulue at the Moulin Rouge" (Toulouse-Lautrec)	6·50	5·75

1972. Visit of Queen Elizabeth II and Prince Philip. Nos. 382/6 optd. **ROYAL VISIT 1972.**

387. **88.**	5 l. multicoloured ..	15	10
388. –	10 l. multicoloured ..	20	10
389. –	2 r. multicoloured ..	4·50	4·00
390. –	5 r. multicoloured ..	8·00	7·00
391. –	10 r. multicoloured ..	9·50	9·00

90. Book Year Emblem.

1972. Int. Book Year.

392. **90.**	25 l. multicoloured ..	15	10
393.	5 r. multicoloured ..	1·60	2·00

91. Scottish Costume.

1972. National Costumes of the World. Mult.

394.	10 l. Type **91**	30	10
395.	15 l. Netherlands	30	15
396.	25 l. Norway	55	15
397.	50 l. Hungary	90	55
398.	1 r. Austria	1·50	80
399.	2 r. Spain	3·00	2·50

92. Stegosaurus.

1972. Prehistoric Animals. Multicoloured.

400	2 l. Type **92**	40	40
401	7 l. Dimetrodon (inscr "Edaphosaurus") ..	75	30
402	25 l. Diplodocus ..	1·50	40
403	50 l. Triceratops ..	1·75	75
404	2 r. Pteranodon ..	4·50	4·50
405	5 r. Tyrannosaurus ..	9·00	9·00

93. Cross-country Skiing.

1972. Winter Olympic Games, Sapporo, Japan. Multicoloured.

406	3 l. Type **93**	10	30
407	6 l. Bobsleighing	10	30
408	15 l. Speed skating	20	20
409	50 l. Ski jumping	1·00	45
410	1 r. Figure skating (pairs)	1·75	70
411	2 r. 50 Ice hockey	5·50	3·25

94. Scout Saluting.

1972. 13th Boy Scout Jamboree Asagiri, Japan (1971). Multicoloured.

412.	10 l. Type **94**	65	20
413.	15 l. Scout signalling	85	20
414.	50 l. Scout blowing bugle	3·00	1·25
415.	1 r. Scout playing drum	4·50	2·25

95. Cycling.

1972. Olympic Games, Munich. Mult.

416.	5 l. Type **95**	10	10
417.	10 l. Running	10	10
418.	25 l. Wrestling	15	10
419.	50 l. Hurdling	30	25
420.	2 r. Boxing	1·00	1·25
421.	5 r. Volleyball	2·10	2·50

96. Globe and Conterence Emblem.

1972. U.N. Environmental Conservation Conf., Stockholm.

423. **96.**	2 l. multicoloured	10	30
424.	3 l. multicoloured	10	30
425.	15 l. multicoloured	30	15
426.	50 l. multicoloured	75	40
427.	2 r. 50 multicoloured	3·25	3·75

97. "Flowers" (Van Gogh).

1973. Floral Paintings. Multicoloured.

428.	1 l. Type **97**	10	20
429.	2 l. "Flowers in Jug" (Renoir)	10	20
430.	3 l. "Chrysanthemums" (Renoir)	10	20
431.	50 l. "Mixed Bouquet" (Bosschaert)	40	15
432.	1 r. As 3 l.	65	40
433.	5 r. As 2 l.	3·00	3·25

1973. Gold-Medal Winners, Munich Olympic Games. Nos. 420/1 optd. as listed below.

435.	2 r. multicoloured	2·25	1·75
436.	5 r. multicoloured	3·25	2·75

OVERPRINTS: 2 r. **LEMECHEV MIDDLE-WEIGHT GOLD MEDALLIST.** 5 r. **JAPAN GOLD MEDAL WINNER.**

99. Animal Care.

1973. International Scouting Congress, Nairobi and Addis Ababa. Multicoloured.

438	1 l. Type **99**	10	20
439	2 l. Lifesaving	10	20
440	3 l. Agricultural training	10	20
441	4 l. Carpentry	10	20
442	5 l. Playing leapfrog	10	20
443	1 r. As 2 l.	2·75	75
444	2 r. As 4 l.	5·00	3·25
445	3 r. Type **99**	6·50	4·50

100. "Makaira herscheli".

1973. Fishes. Multicoloured.

447.	1 l. Type **100**	10	20
448.	2 l. "Katsuwonus pelamys"	10	20
449.	3 l. "Thunnus thynnus"	10	20
450.	5 l. "Coryphaena hippurus"	10	20
451.	60 l. "Lutjanus gibbus"	40	30
452.	75 l. "Lutjanus gibbus"	50	30
453.	1 r. 50 "Variola louti"	1·10	1·10
454.	2 r. 50 "Coryphaena hippurus"	1·60	1·75
455.	3 r. "Plectropoma maculatum"	1·75	2·25
456.	10 r. "Scomberomorus commerson"	4·75	6·50

Nos. 451/2 are smaller, size 29×22 mm.

101. Golden-fronted Leafbird.

1973. Fauna. Multicoloured.

458.	1 l. Type **101**	10	15
459.	2 l. Indian Flying Fox	10	15
460.	3 l. Land tortoise	10	15
461.	4 l. Butterfly ("Kallima inachus")	15	15
462.	50 l. As 3 l.	40	25
463.	2 r. Type **101**	3·00	2·75
464.	3 r. As 2 l.	3·00	2·75

102. "Lantana camara".

1973. Flowers of the Maldive Islands. Mult.

466.	1 l. Type **102**	10	10
467.	2 l. "Nerium oleander"	10	10
468.	3 l. "Rosa polyantha"	10	10
469.	4 l. "Hibiscus manihot"	10	10
470.	5 l. "Bougainvillea glabra"	10	10
471.	10 l. "Plumera alba"	10	10
472.	50 l. "Poinsettia pulcherrima"	55	20
473.	5 r. "Ononis natrix"	3·75	3·50

103. "Tiros" Weather Satellite.

1974. World Meteorological Organization. Multicoloured.

475.	1 l. Type **103**	10	10
476.	2 l. "Nimbus" satellite	10	10
477.	3 l. "Nomad" (weather ship)	10	10
478.	4 l. Scanner, A.P.T. Instant Weather Picture equipment	10	10
479.	5 l. Richard's wind-speed recorder	10	10
480.	2 r. Type **103**	2·00	1·50
481.	3 r. As 3 l.	2·25	1·75

104. "Apollo" Spacecraft and Pres. Kennedy.

1974. American and Russian Space Exploration Projects. Multicoloured.

483.	1 l. Type **104**	10	15
484.	2 l. "Mercury" capsule and John Glenn	10	15
485.	3 l. "Vostok 1" and Yuri Gargarin	10	15
486.	4 l. "Vostok 6" and Valentina Tereshkova	10	15
487.	5 l. "Soyuz 11" and "Salyut" space-station	10	15
488.	2 r. "Skylab" space laboratory	3·00	2·25
489.	3 r. As 2 l.	3·50	2·75

105. Copernicus and "Skylab" Space Laboratory.

1974. 500th Birth Anniv. of Nicholas Copernicus (astronomer). Multicoloured.

491.	1 l. Type **105**	10	15
492.	2 l. Orbital space-station of the future	10	15
493.	3 l. Proposed "Space-shuttle" craft	10	15
494.	4 l. "Mariner 2" Venus probe	10	15
495.	5 l. "Mariner 4" Mars probe	10	15
496.	25 l. Type **105**	70	15
497.	1 r. 50 As 2 l.	3·00	2·25
498.	5 r. As 3 l.	7·50	7·00

106. "Maternity" (Picasso).

1974. Paintings by Picasso. Multicoloured.

500.	1 l. Type **106**	10	10
501.	2 l. "Harlequin and Friend"	10	10
502.	3 l. "Pierrot Sitting"	10	10
503.	20 l. "Three Musicians"	25	15
504.	75 l. "L'Aficionado"	55	30
505.	5 r. "Still Life"	3·50	3·00

107. U.P.U. Emblem, Steam and Diesel Locomotives.

1974. Cent. of Universal Postal Union. Multicoloured.

507.	1 l. Type **107.**	10	10
508.	2 l. Paddle-steamer and modern mailboat	10	10
509.	3 l. Airship and Boeing "747" airliner	10	10
510.	1 r. 50 Mailcoach and motor van	85	85
511.	2 r. 50 As 2 l.	1·60	1·60
512.	5 r. Type **107.**	3·50	3·50

108. Footballers.

1974 World Cup Football Championships, West Germany.

514. **108.**	1 l. multicoloured	15	10
515. –	2 l. multicoloured	15	10
516. –	3 l. multicoloured	15	10
517. –	4 l. multicoloured	15	10
518. –	75 l. multicoloured	1·25	50
519. –	4 r. multicoloured	3·50	2·50
520. –	5 r. multicoloured	3·75	2·50

DESIGNS: Nos. 515/20, show football scenes similar to Type **108**.

109. "Capricorn".

1974. Signs of the Zodiac. Multicoloured.

522.	1 l. Type **109**	10	15
523.	2 l. "Aquarius"	10	15
524.	3 l. "Pisces"	10	15
525.	4 l. "Aries"	10	15
526.	5 l. "Taurus"	10	15
527.	6 l. "Gemini"	10	15
528.	7 l. "Cancer"	10	15
529.	10 l. "Leo"	15	15
530.	15 l. "Virgo"	20	15
531.	20 l. "Libra"	20	15
532.	25 l. "Scorpio"	20	15
533.	5 r. "Sagittarius"	10·00	7·50

110. Churchill and Bomber Aircraft.

1974. Birth Cent. of Sir Winston Churchill. Multicoloured.

535	1 l. Type **110**	10	30
536	2 l. Churchill as pilot	10	30
537	3 l. Churchill as First Lord of the Admiralty	15	30
538	4 l. Churchill and H.M.S. "Indomitable" (aircraft carrier)	15	30
539	5 l. Churchill and fighter aircraft	15	30
540	60 l. Churchill and anti-aircraft battery	2·50	1·50
541	75 l. Churchill and tank in desert	2·75	1·50
542	5 r. Churchill and flying-boat	11·00	9·00

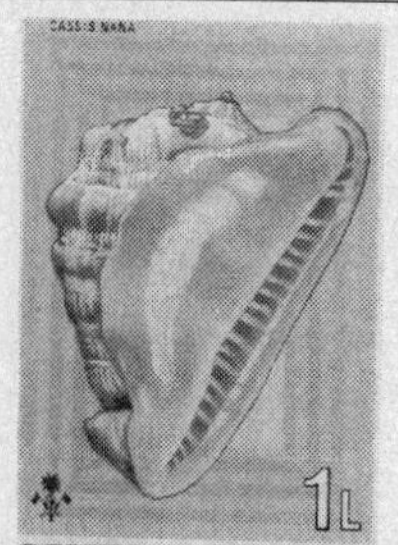

111. " Cassia nana ".

1975. Seashells and Cowries. Multicoloured.
544. 1 l. Type **111** 10 15
545. 2 l. " Murex triremus " .. 10 15
546. 3 l. " Harpa major " .. 10 15
547. 4 l. " Lambis chiragra " .. 10 15
548. 5 l. " Conus pennaceus " .. 10 15
549. 60 l. " Cypraea diliculum " (22 × 30 mm.) 2·00 1·00
550. 75 l. "Clanculus pharaonis" (22 × 30 mm.) .. 2·50 1·10
551. 5 r. " Chicoreus ramosus " 8·00 7·00

112. Royal Throne.

1975. Historical Relics and Monuments. Multicoloured.
553. 1 l. Type **112** 10 10
554. 10 l. " Dullisa " (candlesticks) 10 10
555. 25 l. Lamp-tree 15 10
556. 60 l. Royal umbrellas .. 30 20
557. 75 l. Eid-Miskith Mosque (horiz.) 35 25
558. 3 r. Tomb of Al-Hafiz Abu-al Barakath-al Barubari (horiz.) .. .. .. 1·60 2·00

113. Guavas.

1975. Exotic Fruits. Multicoloured.
559. 2 l. Type **113** 10 15
560. 4 l. Maldive mulberry .. 15 15
561. 5 l. Mountain apples .. 15 15
562. 10 l. Bananas 20 15
563. 20 l. Mangoes 40 15
564. 50 l. Papaya .. .. 1·00 30
565. 1 r. Pomegranates .. 1·75 45
566. 5 r. Coconut .. .. 8·50 8·50

114. " Phyllangia ".

1975. Marine Life. Corals, Urchins and Sea Stars. Multicoloured.
568 1 l. Type **114** 10 10
569 2 l. "Madrepora oculata" 10 10
570 3 l. "Acropora gravida" .. 10 10
571 4 l. "Stylotella" 10 10
572 5 l. "Acrophora cervicornis" 10 10
573 60 l. "Strongylocentrotus purpuratus" 75 55
574 75 l. "Pisaster ochraceus" 85 65
575 5 r. "Marthasterias glacialis" .. .. 5·00 5·50

115. Clock Tower and Customs Building within " 10 ".

1975. 10th Anniv. of Independence. Mult.
577. 4 l. Type **115** 10 10
578. 5 l. Government offices .. 10 10
579. 7 l. N.E. Waterfront, Male 10 10
580. 15 l. Mosque and Minaret 10 10
581. 10 r. Sultan Park and Museum .. .. 4·00 6·00

1975. " Nordjamb 75 " World Scout Jamboree, Norway. Nos. 443/5 optd. **14th Boy Scout Jamboree July 29—August 7,1975.**
582. – 1 r. multicoloured .. 30 30
583. – 2 r. multicoloured .. 50 50
584. **99.** 3 r. multicoloured .. 1·00 1·00

117. Madura Prau.

1975. Maldive Ships. Multicoloured.
586. 1 l. Type **117** 10 10
587. 2 l. Ganges patela 10 10
588. 3 l. Indian palla (vert.) .. 10 10
589. 4 l. "Odhi" (dhow) (vert.) 10 10
590. 5 l. Maldivian schooner .. 10 10
591. 25 l. "Cutty Sark" (British tea clipper) .. 35 20
592. 1 r. Maldivian baggala (vert.) 85 70
593. 5 r. "Maldive Courage" (freighter) .. .. 3·75 4·25

118. "Brahmophthalma wallichi" (moth).

1975. Butterflies and Moth. Multicoloured.
595 1 l. Type **118** 10 10
596 2 l. "Teinopalpus imperialis" 10 10
597 3 l. "Cethosia biblis" .. 10 10
598 4 l. "Idea jasonia" .. 10 10
599 5 l. "Apatura ilia" .. 10 10
600 25 l. "Kallima horsfieldi" 55 35
601 1 r. 50 "Hebomoia leucippe" .. .. 2·50 2·50
602 5 r. "Papilio memnon" .. 7·00 6·00

119. " The Dying Captive ".

1975. 500th Birth Anniv of Michelangelo. Multicoloured.
604 1 l. Type **119** 10 10
605 2 l. Detail of "The Last Judgement" 10 10
606 3 l. "Apollo" 10 10
607 4 l. Detail of Sistine Chapel ceiling 10 10
608 5 l. "Bacchus" 10 10
609 1 r. Detail of "The Last Judgement" (different) 1·00 30
610 2 r. "David" .. .. 2·00 1·25
611 5 r. "Cumaean Sibyl" .. 4·00 3·50

120. Beaker and Vase.

1975. Maldivian Lacquerware. Multicoloured.
613. 2 l. Type **120** 10 10
614. 4 l. Boxes 10 10
615. 50 l. Jar with lid .. 40 20
616. 75 l. Bowls with covers .. 50 30
617. 1 r. Craftsman at work .. 65 40

121. Map of Maldives.

1975. Tourism. Multicoloured.
618. 4 l. Type **121** 10 10
619. 5 l. Motor launch and small craft 10 10
620. 7 l. Sailing-boats 10 10
621. 15 l. Underwater diving .. 10 10
622. 3 r. Hulule Airport .. 1·40 1·60
623. 10 r. Motor cruisers .. 4·00 5·00

122. Cross-country Skiing.

1976. Winter Olympic Games, Innsbruck. Multicoloured.
624. 1 l. Type **122** 10 10
625. 2 l. Speed-skating (pairs) .. 10 10
626. 3 l. Figure-skating (pairs) 10 10
627. 4 l. Four-man bobsleighing 10 10
628. 5 l. Ski-jumping 10 10
629. 25 l. Figure-skating (women's) 15 10
630. 1 r. 15 Skiing (slalom) .. 65 75
631. 4 r. Ice-hockey .. .. 2·25 2·50

123. " General Burgoyne " (Reynolds).

1976. Bicent. of American Revolution. Mult.
633. 1 l. Type **123** 10 10
634. 2 l. " John Hancock " (Copley) 10 10
635. 3 l. " Death of Gen. Montgomery " (Trumbull) (horiz.) 10 10
636. 4 l. " Paul Revere " (Copley) 10 10
637. 5 l. " Battle of Bunker Hill " (Trumbull) (horiz.) .. 10 10
638. 2 r. " The Crossing of the Delaware " (Sully)(horiz.) 1·75 1·50
639. 3 r. " Samuel Adams " (Copley) .. .. 2·25 2·00
640. 5 r. " Surrender of Cornwallis " (Trumbull)(horiz.) 2·75 2·50

124. Thomas Edison.

1976. Centenary of Telephone. Multicoloured.
642 1 l. Type **124** 10 10
643 2 l. Alexander Graham Bell 10 10
644 3 l. Telephone of 1919, 1937 and 1972 .. .. 10 10
645 10 l. Cable entrance into station 10 10
646 20 l. Equaliser circuit assembly 15 10
647 1 r. "Salernum" (cable ship) 70 55
648 10 r. "Intelsat IV-A" and Earth Station .. .. 4·25 5·50

1976. " Interphil 76 " International Stamp Exhibition, Philadelphia. Nos. 638/40, optd. " **INTERPHIL** " and dates.
650. 2 r. multicoloured .. 1·25 1·50
651. 3 r. multicoloured .. 1·75 2·00
652. 5 r. multicoloured .. 2·25 2·50

126. Wrestling.

1976. Olympic Games, Montreal. Mult.
654 1 l. Type **126** 10 10
655 2 l. Putting the shot .. 10 10
656 3 l. Hurdling 10 10
657 4 l. Hockey 10 10
658 5 l. Running 10 10
659 6 l. Javelin-throwing .. 10 10
660 1 r. 50 Discus-throwing .. 1·25 1·50
661 5 r. Volleyball .. .. 3·50 4·00

127. " Dolichos lablab ".

1976. Vegetables. Multicoloured.
663. 2 l. Type **127** 10 10
664. 4 l. " Moringa pterygosperma " 10 10
665. 10 l. " Solanum melongena " 10 10
666. 20 l. " Moringa pterygosperma " 75 75
667. 50 l. " Cucumis sativus " .. 80 65
668. 75 l. " Trichosanthes anguina " 85 75
669. 1 r. " Momordica charantia " 95 85
670. 2 r. " Trichosanthes anguina " .. .. 3·00 3·50

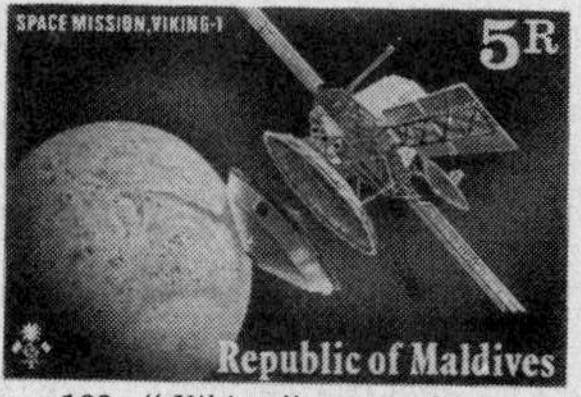

128. " Viking " approaching Mars.

1977. " Viking " Space Mission.
671. **128.** 5 r. multicoloured .. 2·50 2·75

129. Coronation Ceremony.

1977. Silver Jubilee of Queen Elizabeth II. Multicoloured.

673 1 l. Type **129** 10 10
674 2 l. Queen and Prince Philip 10 10
675 3 l. Royal Couple with Princes Andrew and Edward 10 10
676 1 r. 15 Queen with Archbishops 25 35
677 3 r. State coach in procession 65 55
678 4 r. Royal couple with Prince Charles and Princess Anne 75 90

130. Beethoven and Organ.

1977. 150th Death Anniv. of Ludwig van Beethoven. Multicoloured.

680. 1 l. Type **130** 10 10
681. 2 l. Portrait and manuscript of " Moonlight Sonata " 10 10
682. 3 l. With Goethe at Teplitz 10 10
683. 4 l. Beethoven and string instruments 10 10
684. 5 l. Beethoven's home, Heiligenstadt 10 10
685. 25 l. Hands and gold medals 40 15
686. 2 r. Portrait and " Missa Solemnis " .. .. 2·50 1·75
687. 5 r. Composer's hearing-aids 4·00 3·25

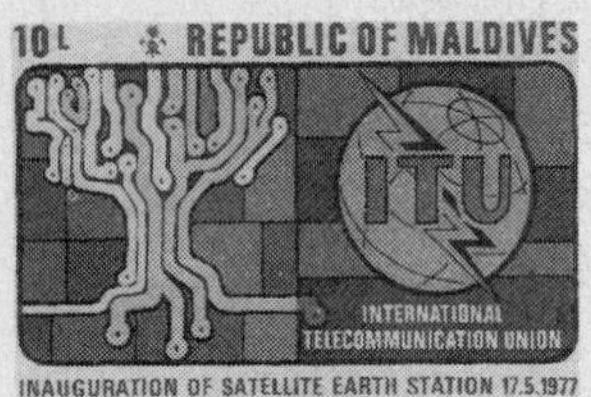

131. Printed Circuit and I.T.U. Emblem.

1977. Inauguration of Satellite Earth Station. Multicoloured.

689. 10 l. Type **131** 10 10
690. 90 l. Central Telegraph Office 45 45
691. 10 r. Satellite Earth Station 5·00 6·50

132. " Miss Anne Ford " (Gainsborough).

1977. Artists' Birth Anniversaries. Mult.

693 1 l. Type **132** (250th anniv) 10 10
694 2 l. Group painting by Rubens (400th anniv) .. 10 10
695 3 l. "Girl with Dog" (Titian) (500th anniv) .. 10 10
696 4 l. "Mrs Thomas Graham" (Gainsborough) .. 10 10
697 5 l. "Artist with Isabella Brant" (Rubens) .. 10 10
698 95 l. Portrait by Titian .. 55 40
699 1 r. Portrait by Gainsborough 55 40
700 10 r. "Isabella Brant" (Rubens) .. .. 4·00 6·00

133. Lesser Frigate Birds.

1977. Birds of the Maldive Islands. Mult.

702. 1 l. Type **133** 10 10
703. 2 l. Crab Plover 10 10
704. 3 l. White-tailed Tropic Bird 10 10
705. 4 l. Wedge-tailed Shearwater 10 10
706. 5 l. Grey Heron 10 10
707. 20 l. White Tern 30 20
708. 95 l. Cattle Egret .. .. 1·25 95
709. 1 r. 25 Black-naped Tern 1·75 1·40
710. 5 r. Pheasant Coucal .. 6·50 6·50

134. Charles Lindbergh.

1977. 50th Anniv of Lindbergh's Transatlantic Flight and 75th Anniv of First Navigable Airships. Multicoloured.

712 1 l. Type **134** 10 10
713 2 l. Lindbergh and "Spirit of St. Louis" 10 10
714 3 l. "Mohawk" aircraft (horiz) 10 10
715 4 l. Julliot's airship "Lebaudy I" (horiz) .. 10 10
716 5 l. Airship "Graf Zeppelin" and portrait of Zeppelin 10 10
717 1 r. Airship "Los Angeles" (horiz) 60 30
718 3 r. Lindbergh and Henry Ford .. .. .. 1·40 1·50
719 10 r. Vickers rigid airship 3·50 4·50

135. Boat Building.

1977. Occupations. Multicoloured.

721. 6 l. Type **135** 30 15
722. 15 l. Fishing 35 15
723. 20 l. Cadjan weaving .. 40 15
724. 90 l. Mat-weaving .. .. 1·00 70
725. 2 r. Lace-making (vert.) .. 2·25 2·50

136. Rheumatic Heart.

1977. World Rheumatism Year. Multicoloured.

726. 1 l. Type **136** 10 10
727. 50 l. Rheumatic shoulder 20 15
728. 2 r. Rheumatic hands .. 85 1·00
729. 3 r. Rheumatic knees .. 1·10 1·25

137. Lilienthal's Glider.

1978. 75th Anniv. of First Powered Aircraft. Multicoloured.

730. 1 l. Type **137** 10 15
731. 2 l. Chanute's glider .. 10 15
732. 3 l. Wright Brothers' glider, 1900 .. .. 10 15
733. 4 l. A. V. Roe's triplane .. 10 15
734. 5 l. Wilbur Wright demonstrating aircraft for King Alfonso of Spain .. 10 15
735. 10 l. A. V. Roe's second biplane 15 15
736. 20 l. Wright Brothers and A. G. Bell at Washington 30 15
737. 95 l. Hadley's triplane .. 1·50 1·25
738. 5 r. " B.E.2s " at Upavon, Wiltshire, 1914 .. .. 5·50 5·50

138. Newgate Prison.

1978. World Eradication of Smallpox. Mult.

740. 15 l. Foundling Hospital, London (horiz.) 55 30
741. 50 l. Type **138** .. .. 1·25 50
742. 2 r. Edward Jenner (discoverer of smallpox vaccine) .. .. .. 3·25 2·50

139. Television Set.

1978. Inauguration of Television in Maldive Islands. Multicoloured.

743 15 l. Type **139** 40 30
744 25 l. Television aerials .. 55 30
745 1 r. 50 Control desk (horiz) 2·25 2·25

140. Mas Odi.

1978. Maldive Ships. Multicoloured.

746. 1 l. Type **140** 10 10
747. 2 l. Battela 10 10
748. 3 l. Bandu Odi (vert.) .. 10 10
749. 5 l. "Maldive Trader" (freighter) 10 10
750. 1 r. "Fath-hul Baaree" (brigantine) (vert.) .. 35 30
751. 1 r. 25 Mas Dhoni 65 55
752. 3 r. Baggala .. .. 1·50 1·25
753. 4 r. As 1 r. 25 .. .. 1·75 1·60

141. Ampulla.

1978. 25th Anniv. of Coronation. Mult.

755. 1 l. Type **141** 10 10
756. 2 l. Sceptre with Dove .. 10 10
757. 3 l. Golden Orb 10 10
758. 1 r. 15 St. Edward's Crown 15 15
759. 2 r. Sceptre with Cross .. 20 25
760. 5 r. Queen Elizabeth II .. 55 70

142. Capt. Cook.

1978. 250th Birth Anniv. of Capt. James Cook and Bicentenary of Discovery of Hawaiian Islands. Multicoloured.

762. 1 l. Type **142** 10 15
763. 2 l. Kamehameha I .. 10 15
764. 3 l. H.M.S. "Endeavour" 10 15
765. 25 l. Route of third voyage 45 45
766. 75 l. H.M.S. "Discovery" H.M.S. "Resolution" and map of Hawaiian Islands (horiz.) .. .. .. 1·25 1·25
767. 1 r. 50 Cook meeting Hawaiian islanders (horiz.) 2·00 2·25
768. 10 r. Death of Capt. Cook (horiz.) .. .. .. 7·50 9·00

143. " Schizophrys aspera ".

1978. Crustaceans. Multicoloured.

770 1 l. Type **143** 10 10
771 2 l. "Atergatis floridus" .. 10 10
772 3 l. "Perenon planissimum" 10 10
773 90 l. "Portunus granulatus" 50 40
774 1 r. "Carpilius maculatus" 50 40
775 2 r. "Huenia proteus" .. 1·00 1·25
776 25 r. "Etisus laevimanus" 9·00 12·00

144. " Four Apostles ".

1978. 450th Death Anniv. of Albrecht Durer (artist).

778. **144.** 10 l. multicoloured .. 10 10
779. – 20 l. multicoloured .. 10 10
780. – 55 l. multicoloured .. 15 20
781. – 1 r. black, brown & buff 20 30
782. – 1 r. 80 multicoloured 35 60
783. – 3 r. multicoloured .. 70 1·25

DESIGNS—VERT. 20 l. " Self-portrait at 27 ". 55 l. " Madonna with Child with a Pear ". 1 r. 80, " Hare ". 3 r. " Great Piece of Turf ". HORIZ. 1 r. " Rinhoceros ".

145. T.V. Tower and Building.

1978. 10th Anniv. of Republic. Mult.

785. 1 l. Fishing boat 10 10
786. 5 l. Montessori School .. 10 10
787. 10 l. Type **145** 10 10
788. 25 l. Islet 15 15
789. 50 l. Boeing "737" aircraft 20 15
790. 95 l. Beach scene 30 30
791. 1 r. 25 Dhow at night .. 50 45
792. 3 r. President's residence .. 75 90
793. 5 r. Masjidh Afeefuddin Mosque .. .. .. 1·75 2·00

The 1, 5, 25 to 95, l., 1 r. 25 and 3, 5 r. are horiz. designs.

146. Human Rights Emblem.

1978. 30th Anniv. of Declaration of Human Rights.

795. **146.** 30 l. pink, lilac and green 15 15
796. 90 l. yellow, brown and green 40 50
797. 1 r. 80 pale blue, deep blue and green .. 70 85

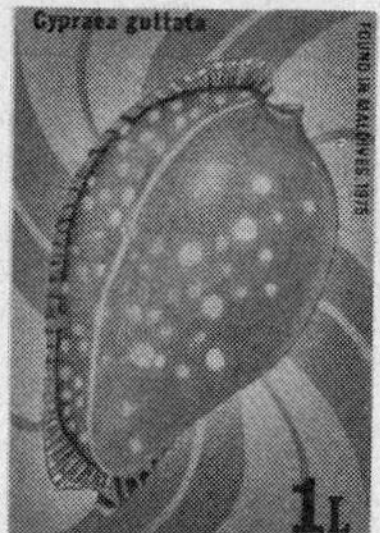

147. "Cypraea guttata".

1979. Shells. Multicoloured.

798. 1 l. Type **147** 10 10
799. 2 l. "Conus imperialis" .. 10 10
800. 3 l. "Turbo marmoratus" .. 10 10
801. 10 l. "Lambis truncata" 20 10
802. 1 r. "Cypraea leucodon" 1·00 40
803. 1 r. 80 "Conus figulinus" 1·75 1·25
804. 3 r. "Conus Gloria-maris" 2·50 2·00

148. Delivery by Bellman.

1979. Death Centenary of Sir Rowland Hill. Multicoloured.

806. 1 l. Type **148** 10 10
807. 2 l. Mail coach, 1840 (horiz.) 10 10
808. 3 l. First London letter box, 1855 .. .. .. 10 10
809. 1 r. 55 Penny Black .. 35 50
810. 5 r. First Maldive Islands stamp .. .. .. 90 1·25

149. Girl with Teddy Bear.

1979. International Year of the Child (1st issue). Multicoloured.

812 5 l. Type **149** 10 10
813 1 r. 25 Boy with sailing boat 40 50
814 2 r. Boy with toy rocket .. 45 55
815 3 r. Boy with toy airship 60 75

See also Nos. 838/46.

150. "White Feathers".

1979. 25th Death Anniv. of Henri Matisse (artist). Multicoloured.

817. 20 l. Type **150** 15 15
818. 25 l. "Joy of Life" .. 15 15
819. 30 l. "Eggplants" .. 15 15
820. 1 r. 50 "Harmony in Red" 55 55
821. 5 r. "Still-life" .. .. 1·75 2·00

151. Sari with Overdress.

1979. National Costumes. Multicoloured.

823. 50 l. Type **151** 15 15
824. 75 l. Sashed apron dress .. 20 20
825. 90 l. Serape 25 25
826. 95 l. Ankle-length dress .. 30 30

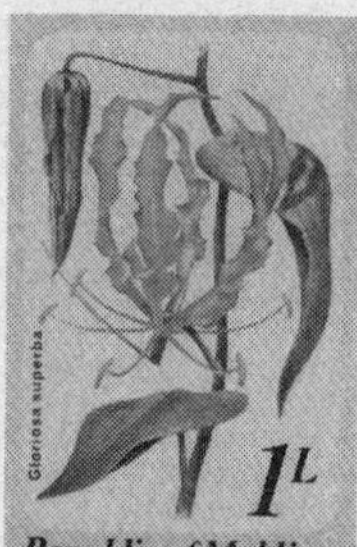

152. "Gloriosa superba".

1979. Flowers. Multicoloured.

827. 1 l. Type **152** 10 10
828. 3 l. "Hibiscus tiliaceus" 10 10
829. 50 l. "Barringtonia asiatica" 20 20
830. 1 r. "Abutilon indicum" 40 40
831. 5 r. "Guettarda speciosa" 1·75 2·00

153. Weaving.

1979. Handicraft Exhibition. Multicoloured.

833. 5 l. Type **153** 10 10
834. 10 l. Lacquerwork .. 10 10
835. 1 r. 30 Tortoiseshell jewellery 45 50
836. 2 r. Carved woodwork .. 70 80

154. Mickey Mouse attacked by Bird.

1979. International Year of the Child (2nd issue). Disney Characters. Multicoloured.

838 1 l. Goofy delivering parcel on motor-scooter (vert) 10 10
839 2 l. Type **154** 10 10
840 3 l. Goofy half-covered with letters 10 10
841 4 l. Pluto licking Minnie Mouse's envelopes .. 10 10
842 5 l. Mickey Mouse delivering letter letters on roller skates (vert) 10 10
843 10 l. Donald Duck placing letter in mail-box .. 10 10
844 15 l. Chip and Dale carrying letter .. 10 10
845 1 r. 50 Donald Duck on monocycle (vert) .. 75 75
846 5 r. Donald Duck with ostrich in crate (vert) .. 2·25 2·50

155. Post-Ramadan Dancing.

1980. National Day. Multicoloured.

848. 5 l. Type **155** 10 10
849. 15 l. Musicians and dancer, Eeduu Festival 10 10
850. 95 l. Sultan's Ceremonial Band 30 30
851. 2 r. Dancer and drummers, Circumcision Festival .. 55 70

156. Leatherback Turtle.

1980. Turtle Conservation Campaign. Mult.

853. 1 l. Type **156** 10 10
854. 2 l. Flatback Turtle .. 10 10
855. 5 l. Hawksbill Turtle .. 10 10
856. 10 l. Loggerhead Turtle .. 10 10
857. 75 l. Olive Ridley 30 30
858. 10 r. Atlantic Ridley .. 3·25 3·50

157. Paul Harris (founder).

1980. 75th Anniv. of Rotary International. Multicoloured.

860. 75 l. Type **157** 25 10
861. 90 l. Humanity 30 20
862. 1 r. Hunger 30 25
863. 10 r. Health .. .. 3·00 3·75

1980. "London 1980" International Stamp Exhibition. Nos. 809/10 optd. **LONDON 1980.**

865. 1 r. 55 Penny Black .. 1·25 75
866. 5 r. First Maldives Stamp 2·50 2·00

159. Swimming.

1980. Olympic Games, Moscow. Mult.

868 10 l. Type **159** 10 10
869 50 l. Running 20 15
870 3 r. Putting the shot .. 90 1·00
871 4 r. High jumping .. 1·10 1·25

160. White-tailed Tropic Bird.

1980. Birds. Multicoloured.

873. 75 l. Type **160** 25 15
874. 95 l. Sooty Tern 35 30
875. 1 r. Common Noddy .. 35 30
876. 1 r. 55 Curlew 50 40
877. 2 r. Wilson's Petrel .. 60 50
878. 4 r. Caspian Tern .. 1·10 1·00

161. Seal of Ibrahim II.

1980. Seals of the Sultans.

880. **161.** 1 l. rose and black .. 10 10
881. – 2 l. rose and black .. 10 10
882. – 5 l. rose and black .. 10 10
883. – 1 r. rose and black .. 30 30
884. – 2 r. rose and black .. 50 60

DESIGNS: 2 l. Mohammed Imadudeen II. 5 l. Bin Haji Ali. 1 r. Kuda Mohammed Rasgefaanu. 2 r. Ibrahim Iskander I.

162. Queen Elizabeth the Queen Mother.

1980. 80th Birthday of The Queen Mother.

886. **162.** 4 r. multicoloured .. 1·00 1·25

163. Munnaru.

1980. 1400th Anniv. of Hegira. Mult.

888. 5 l. Type **163** 10 10
889. 10 l. Hukuru Miskiiy mosque 10 10
890. 30 l. Medhuziyaaraiy .. 25 15
891. 55 l. Liyaa Filaa (wooden tablets) 30 25
892. 90 l. Ugenun (teaching the Koran) 50 45

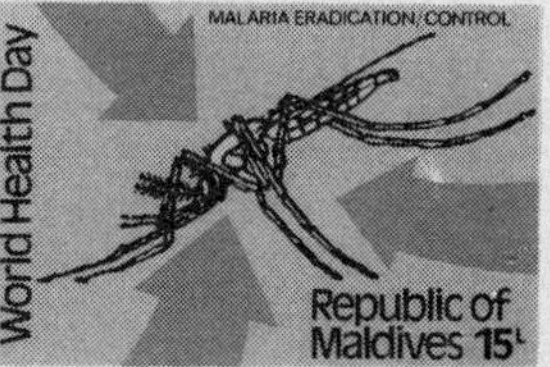

164. Malaria Eradication.

1980. World Health Day. Multicoloured.

894. 15 l. Type **164** 10 10
895. 25 l. Nutrition 15 10
896. 1 r. 50 Dental health .. 1·00 70
897. 5 r. Clinics .. .. 2·25 2·25

165. White Rabbit.

1980. Walt Disney's " Alice in Wonderland ". Multicoloured.

899. 1 l. Type **165** 10 10
900. 2 l. Alice falling down rabbit hole 10 10
901. 3 l. Alice and talking door-knob 10 10
902. 4 l. Alice with Tweedledum and Tweedledee .. 10 10
903. 5 l. Alice and caterpillar .. 10 10
904. 10 l. The Cheshire cat .. 10 10
905. 15 l. Alice helping the Queen's gardeners .. 10 10
906. 2 r. 50 Alice and the Queen of Hearts .. .. 1·50 1·25
907. 4 r. Alice on trial .. .. 2·00 1·75

166. Indian Ocean Ridley Turtle.

1980. Marine Animals. Multicoloured.

909. 90 l. Type **166** .. .. 1·25 50
910. 1 r. 25 Angel Flake Fish .. 1·50 85
911. 2 r. Spiny Lobster .. 2·25 1·40

167. Pendant Lamp.

1981. National Day. Multicoloured.

913. 10 l. Tomb of Ghaazee Muhammad Thakurufaan (horiz.) 10 10
914. 20 l. Type **167** 10 10
915. 30 l. Chair used by Muhammad Thakurufaan 15 10
916. 95 l. Muhammad Thakurufaan's palace (horiz.) .. 35 40
917. 10 r. Cushioned divan .. 2·75 3·50

168. Prince Charles and Lady Diana Spencer.

1981. British Royal Wedding. Multicoloured.

918. 1 r. Type **168** 15 15
919. 2 r. Buckingham Palace .. 25 25
920. 5 r. Prince Charles—polo player 40 50

169. First Majlis Chamber.

1981. 50th Anniv. of Citizens Majlis (grievance rights). Multicoloured.

922. 95 l. Type **169** 30 50
923. 1 r. Sultan Muhammed Shamsuddin III .. 35 35

170. " Self-portrait with a Palette ".

1981. Birth Centenary of Pablo Picasso. Multicoloured.

925. 5 l. Type **170** 10 10
926. 10 l. " Woman in Blue " .. 15 10
927. 25 l. " Boy with Pipe " .. 25 10
928. 30 l. " Card Player " .. 25 10
929. 90 l. " Sailor " 60 40
930. 3 r. " Self-portrait " .. 1·50 1·00
931. 5 r. " Harlequin " .. 2·00 1·40

171. Airmail Envelope.

1981. 75th Anniv. of Postal Service.

933. 171. 25 l. multicoloured .. 10 10
934. 75 l. multicoloured .. 20 25
935. 5 r. multicoloured .. 70 95

172. Aircraft taking-off.

1981. Male International Airport. Mult.

936. 5 l. Type **172** 10 10
937. 20 l. Passengers leaving aircraft 20 15
938. 1 r. 80 Refuelling .. 75 75
939. 4 r. Plan of airport .. 1·40 1·40

173. Homer.

1981. International Year of Disabled People. Multicoloured.

941. 2 l. Type **173** 10 10
942. 5 l. Miguel Cervantes 10 10
943. 1 r. Beethoven .. .. 2·25 75
944. 5 r. Van Gogh .. .. 3·75 2·75

174. Preparation of Maldive Fish.

1981. Decade for Women. Multicoloured.

946. 20 l. Type **174** 10 10
947. 90 l. 16th century Maldive women 25 25
948. 1 r. Farming 30 30
949. 2 r. Coir rope-making .. 55 55

175. Collecting Bait.

1982. Fishermen's Day. Multicoloured.

950. 5 l. Type **175** 30 15
951. 15 l. Fishing boats .. 45 25
952. 90 l. Fisherman with catch 90 50
953. 1 r. 30 Sorting fish .. 1·25 65

176. Bread Fruit.

1981. World Food Day. Multicoloured.

955. 10 l. Type **176** 15 10
956. 25 l. Hen with chicks .. 40 15
957. 30 l. Maize 40 20
958. 75 l. Skipjack Tuna .. 85 40
959. 1 r. Pumpkin .. .. 1·00 50
960. 2 r. Coconuts .. .. 1·50 1·75

177. Pluto and Cat.

1982. 50th Anniversary of Pluto (Walt Disney Cartoon Character).

962. 177. 4 r. multicoloured .. 2·50 2·00

178. Balmoral.

1982. 21st Birthday of Princess of Wales. Multicoloured.

964. 95 l. Type **178** 20 20
965. 3 r. Prince and Princess of Wales 55 55
966. 5 r. Princess on aircraft steps 85 85

179. Scout saluting and Camp-site.

1983. 75th Anniv. of Boy Scout Movement. Multicoloured.

968. 1 r. 30, Type **179** .. 40 40
969. 1 r. 80, Lighting a fire .. 50 50
970. 4 r. Life-saving .. .. 1·10 1·10
971. 5 r. Map-reading .. .. 1·40 1·40

180. Footballer.

1982. World Cup Football Championship, Spain.

973. 180. 90 l. multicoloured .. 1·00 50
974. – 1 r. 50 multicoloured .. 1·60 70
975. – 3 r. multicoloured .. 2·25 1·25
976. – 5 r. multicoloured .. 2·75 2·00

DESIGNS: 1 r. 50 to 5 r. Various footballers.

1982. Birth of Prince William of Wales. Nos. 964/6 optd. **ROYAL BABY 21.6.82.**

978. 95 l. Type **178** 20 20
979. 3 r. Prince and Princess of Wales 55 55
980. 5 r. Princess on aircraft steps 85 85

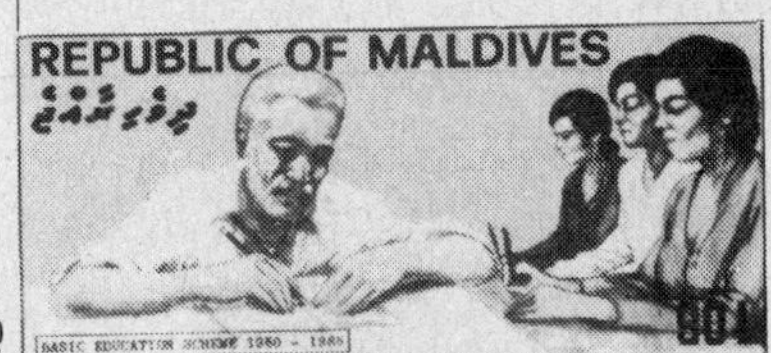

181. Basic Education Scheme.

1983. National Education. Multicoloured.

982. 90 l. Type **181** 15 20
983. 95 l. Primary education .. 15 20
984. 1 r. 30 Teacher training .. 20 25
985. 2 r. 50 Printing educational material 40 45

182. Koch isolates the Bacillus.

1983. Centenary of Robert Koch's Discovery of Tubercle Bacillus. Multicoloured.

987. 5 l. Type **182** 10 10
988. 15 l. Micro-organism and microscope 15 10
989. 95 l. Dr. Robert Koch in 1905 .. .. .. 35 35
990. 3 r. Dr. Koch and plates from publication .. 85 1·00

183. Blohm and Voss " Ha 139 " Seaplane.

1983. Bicentenary of Manned Flight. Mult.

992. 90 l. Type **183** .. .. 1·50 50
993. 1 r. 45 Macchi-castoldi " MC.72 " .. .. 2·00 1·25
994. 4 r. Boeing " F4B-3 " .. 3·50 2·50
995. 5 r. " La France " airship 3·75 2·75

184. "Curved Dash" Oldsmobile, 1902.

1983. Classic Motor Cars. Multicoloured.

997. 5 l. Type **184** 10 15
998 30 l. Aston Martin "Tourer" 1932 .. .. 30 15
999. 40 l. Lamborghini "Muira", 1966 .. .. 30 20
1000. 1 r. Mercedes-Benz "300SL" 1945 .. .. 60 40
1001. 1 r. 40 Stutz "Bearcat", 1913 .. .. 75 90
1002. 5 r. Lotus "Elite", 1913 2·25 3·00

185. Rough-toothed Dolphin.

1983. Marine Mammals. Multicoloured.

1004. 30 l. Type **185** .. 1·25 50
1005. 40 l. Indo-Pacific Hump-backed Dolphin .. 1·40 55
1006. 4 r. Finless Porpoise .. 4·75 2·75
1007. 6 r. Pygmy Sperm Whale 7·00 4·50

186. Dish Aerial.

1983. World Communications Year. Mult.

1009. 50 l. Type **186** 20 10
1010. 1 r. Land, sea and air communications .. 45 45
1011. 2 r. Ship-to-shore communications 70 70
1012. 10 r. Air traffic controller 2·50 3·00

187. "La Donna Gravida".

1983. 500th Birth Anniv of Raphael. Mult.

1014 90 l. Type **187** 25 25
1015 3 r. "Giovanna d'Aragona" (detail) .. 75 75
1016 4 r. "Woman with Unicorn" .. .. .. 1·00 1·00
1017 6 r. "La Muta" .. .. 1·50 1·50

188. Refugee Camp.

1983. Solidarity with the Palestinian People. Multicoloured.

1019. 4 r. Type **188** .. .. 1·50 1·50
1020. 5 r. Refugee holding dead child .. .. .. 1·60 1·60
1021. 6 r. Child carrying food .. 1·90 1·90

189. Education Facilities.

1983. National Development Programme. Multicoloured.

1022. 7 l. Type **189** 10 10
1023. 10 l. Health service and education 10 10
1024. 5 r. Growing more food .. 1·25 1·25
1025. 6 r. Fisheries development 1·50 1·50

190. Baseball.

1984. Olympic Games, Los Angeles. Mult.

1027. 50 l. Type **190** 15 15
1028. 1 r. 55 Backstroke .. 40 40
1029. 3 r. Judo 80 90
1030. 4 r. Shot putting .. 1·25 1·40

1984. U.P.U. Congress, Hamburg. Nos. 994/5 optd **19th UPU CONGRESS HAMBURG**.

1032. 4 r. Boeing "F4B-3" .. 1·40 1·40
1033. 5 r. "La France" airship 1·60 1·60

1984. Surch.

(a) Nos. 964/6

1035. 1 r. 45 on 95 l. Type **178** 4·00 2·25
1036. 1 r. 45 on 3 r. Prince and Princess of Wales .. 4·00 2·25
1037. 1 r. 45 on 5 r. Princess on aircraft steps .. .. 4·00 2·25

(b) Nos. 978/80

1039. 1 r 45 on 95 l. Type **178** 4·00 2·25
1040. 1 r. 45 on 3 r. Prince and Princess of Wales .. 4·00 2·25
1041. 1 r 45. on 5 r. Princess on aircraft steps .. .. 4·00 2·25

193. Hands breaking Manacles.

1984. Namibia Day. Multicoloured.

1043. 6 r. Type **193** .. .. 1·50 1·60
1044. 8 r. Namibian family .. 2·00 2·10

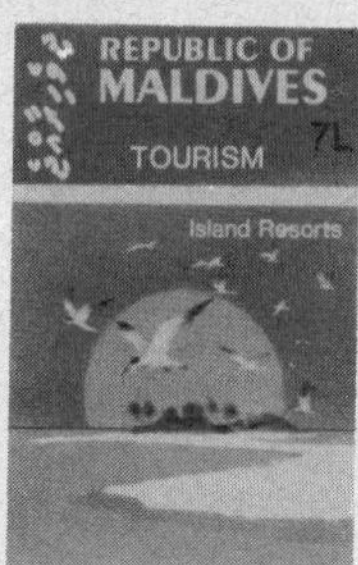

194. Island Resort and Common Terns.

1984. Tourism. Multicoloured.

1046. 7 l. Type **194** 10 10
1047. 15 l. Dhow 10 10
1048. 20 l. Snorkelling 10 10
1049. 2 r. Wind-surfing .. 50 40
1050. 4 r. Aqualung diving .. 85 75
1051. 6 r. Night fishing .. 1·50 1·25
1052. 8 r. Game fishing .. 1·75 1·50
1053. 10 r Turtle on beach .. 2·00 1·75

195. Frangipani.

1984. "Ausipex" International Stamp Exhibition, Melbourne. Multicoloured.

1054. 5 r. Type **195** .. .. 2·25 1·75
1055. 10 r. Cooktown Orchid .. 4·25 3·75

196. Facade of Male Mosque.

1984. Opening of Islamic Centre. Multicoloured.

1057. 2 r. Type **196** 45 50
1058. 5 r. Male Mosque and minaret (vert.) .. 1·10 1·25

197. Air Maldives Boeing "737".

1984. 40th Anniv of I.C.A.O. Mult.

1059 7 l. Type **197** 15 15
1060 4 r. Airlanka Lockheed "L-1011 Tristar" .. 1·50 1·25
1061 6 r. Air Alitalia McDonnell Douglas "DC-30" .. .. 1·90 1·60
1062 8 r. L.T.U. Lockheed "L-1011 Tristar" .. 2·50 2·25

198. Daisy Duck.

1984. 50th Birthday of Donald Duck. Walt Disney Cartoon Characters. Multicoloured.

1064. 3 l. Type **198** 10 10
1065. 4 l. Huey, Dewey and Louie 10 10
1066. 5 l. Ludwig von Drake .. 10 10
1067. 10 l. Gyro Gearloose .. 10 10
1068. 15 l. Uncle Scrooge painting self-portrait 10 10
1069. 25 l. Donald Duck with camera 10 10
1070. 5 r. Donald Duck and Gus Goose .. .. 1·25 1·00
1071. 8 r. Gladstone Gander .. 1·75 1·00
1072. 10 r. Grandma Duck .. 2·25 2·00

199. "The Day" (detail).

200. "Edmond Iduranty" (Degas).

1984. 450th Death Anniversary of Correggio (artist). Multicoloured.

1075. 5 r. Type **199** .. .. 1·25 1·25
1076. 10 r. "The Night" (detail) .. .. 1·75 2·00

1984. 150th Birth Anniv. of Edgar Degas (artist). Multicoloured.

1078. 75 l. Type **200** 20 20
1079. 2 r. "James Tissot" .. 50 50
1080. 5 r. "Achille de Gas in Uniform" .. .. 1·25 1·25
1081. 10 r. "Lady with Chrysanthemums" .. .. 2·50 2·75

201. Pale-footed Shearwater.

1985. Birth Bicentenary of John J. Audubon (ornithologist) (1st issue). Designs showing original paintings. Multicoloured.

1083. 3 r. Type **201** .. .. 1·50 80
1084. 3 r. 50 Little grebe (horiz.) .. .. 1·75 90
1085. 4 r. Common cormorant 1·90 1·00
1086. 4 r. 50 White-faced storm petrel (horiz.) .. .. 2·00 1·10

See also Nos. 1192/9.

202. Squad Drilling.

1985. National Security Service. Mult.

1088. 15 l. Type **202** 20 10
1089. 20 l. Combat patrol .. 20 10
1090. 1 r. Fire fighting .. 70 25
1091. 2 r. Coastguard cutter .. 1·40 55
1092. 10 r. Independence Day Parade (vert.) .. 2·50 2·50

1985. Olympic Games Gold Medal Winners, Los Angeles. Nos. 1027/30 optd.

1094. 50 l. Type **190** (optd. **JAPAN**) 10 10
1095. 1 r. 55, Backstroke swimming (optd. **GOLD MEDALIST THERESA ANDREWS USA**) .. 30 35
1096. 3 r. Judo (optd. **GOLD MEDALIST FRANK WIENEKE USA**) .. 55 60
1097. 4 r. Shot-putting (optd. **GOLD MEDALIST CLAUDIA LOCH WEST GERMANY**) .. 80 85

204. Queen Elizabeth the Queen Mother, 1981.

1985. Life and Times of Queen Elizabeth the Queen Mother. Multicoloured.

1099. 3 r. Type **204** 55 60
1100. 5 r. Visiting the Middlesex Hospital (horiz.) .. 95 1·00
1101. 7 r. The Queen Mother .. 1·40 1·50

Stamps as Nos. 1099/1101, but with face values of 1 r., 4 r. and 10 r., exist from additional sheetlets with changed background colours.

1985. 300th Birth Anniversary of Johann Sebastian Bach (composer). As T **206** of Antigua. Multicoloured.

1103.	15 l. Lira da Braccio	10	10
1104.	2 r. Tenor oboe	50	45
1105.	4 r. Serpent	90	85
1106.	10 r. Table organ ..	1·90	2·25

205. Masodi (fishing boat).

1985. Maldives Ships and Boats. Mult.

1108	3 l. Type **205**	10	10
1109	5 l. Battela (dhow) ..	10	10
1110	10 l. Addu odi (dhow) ..	10	10
1111	2 r. 60 Modern dhoni (fishing boat)	40	35
1112	2 r. 70 Mas Dhoni (fishing boat)	40	35
1113	3 r. Baththeli dohni ..	45	40
1114	5 r. "Inter 1" (inter-island vessel)	75	80
1115	10 r. Dhoni-style yacht ..	1·40	1·75

206. Windsurfing.

1985. 10th Anniversary of World Tourism Organization. Multicoloured.

1116.	6 r. Type **206**	1·10	1·40
1117.	8 r. Scuba diving ..	1·50	1·75

207. United Nations Building, New York.

1985. 40th Anniversary of United Nations Organization and International Peace Year. Multicoloured.

1119.	15 l. Type **207**	10	10
1120.	2 r. Hands releasing peace dove	40	45
1121.	4 r. U.N. Security Council meeting (horiz.)	80	85
1122.	10 r. Lion and lamb ..	1·90	2·25

208. Maldivian Delegate voting in U.N. General Assembly.

1985. 20th Anniv. of United Nations Membership. Multicoloured.

1124.	20 l. Type **208**	10	10
1125.	15 r. U.N. and Maldivian flags, and U.N. Building, New York ..	2·75	3·25

209. Youths playing Drums.

1985. International Youth Year. Mult.

1126.	90 l. Type **209**	15	20
1127.	6 r. Tug-of-war	1·10	1·40
1128.	10 r. Community service (vert.)	1·90	2·25

210. Quotation and Flags of Member Nations.

1985. 1st Summit Meeting of South Asian Association for Regional Co-operation, Dhaka, Bangladesh.

1130.	**210.** 3 r. multicoloured ..	1·50	1·25

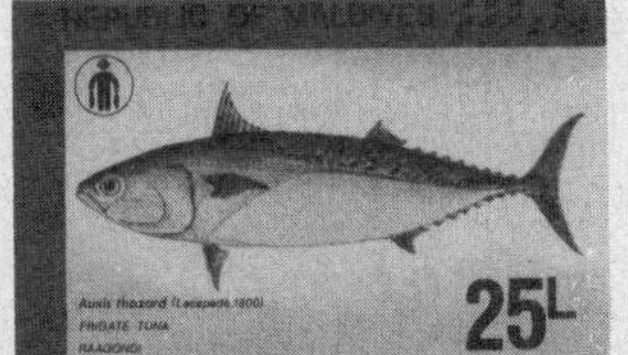

211. Frigate Tuna.

1985. Fishermen's Day. Species of Tuna. Multicoloured.

1131.	25 l. Type **211**	10	10
1132.	75 l. Little Tuna ..	20	15
1133.	3 r. Dogtooth Tuna ..	75	60
1134.	5 r. Yellowfin Tuna ..	1·25	1·00

1985. 150th Birth Anniv. of Mark Twain. Designs as T **118** of Anguilla, showing Walt Disney cartoon characters illustrating various Mark Twain quotations. Multicoloured.

1136.	2 l. Winnie the Pooh ..	10	10
1137.	3 l. Gepetto and Figaro the cat	10	10
1138.	4 l. Goofy and basket of broken eggs	10	10
1139.	20 l. Goofy as doctor scolding Donald Duck	15	10
1140.	4 r. Mowgli and King Louis	90	80
1141.	13 r. The wicked Queen and mirror	3·25	3·00

1985. Birth Bicentenaries of Grimm Brothers (folklorists). Designs as T **119** of Anguilla, showing Walt Disney cartoon characters in scenes from "Dr. Knowall". Multicoloured.

1143	1 l. Donald Duck as Crabb driving oxcart ..	10	10
1144	5 l. Donald Duck as Dr. Knowall	10	10
1145	10 l. Dr. Knowall in surgery	10	10
1146	15 l. Dr. Knowall with Uncle Scrooge as a lord	10	10
1147	3 r. Dr. and Mrs. Knowall in pony and trap ..	55	65
1148	15 r. Dr. Knowall and thief	2·75	3·25

1986. Appearance of Halley's Comet (1st issue). As T **123** of Anguilla. Multicoloured.

1150.	20 l. N.A.S.A. space telescope and Comet ..	50	25
1151.	1 r. 50 E.S.A. "Giotto" spacecraft and Comet	1·25	1·10
1152.	2 r. Japanese "Planet A" spacecraft and Comet	1·50	1·40
1153.	4 r. Edmond Halley and Stonehenge	2·75	2·75
1154.	5 r. Russian "Vega" spacecraft and Comet	3·00	3·00

See also Nos. 1206/10.

1986. Centenary of Statue of Liberty. Multicoloured. As T **211** of Dominica, showing the Statue of Liberty and immigrants to the U.S.A.

1156.	50 l. Walter Gropius (architect)	40	20
1157.	70 l. John Lennon (musician)	1·50	80
1158.	1 r. George Balanchine (choreographer) ..	1·50	80
1159.	10 r. Franz Werfel (writer)	3·75	4·00

1986. "Ameripex" International Stamp Exhibition, Chicago. As T **212** of Dominica, showing Walt Disney cartoon characters and U.S.A. stamps. Multicoloured.

1161.	3 l. Johnny Appleseed and 1966 Johnny Appleseed stamp ..	10	10
1162.	4 l. Paul Bunyan and 1958 Forest Conservation stamp	10	10
1163.	5 l. Casey and 1969 Professional Baseball Centenary stamp ..	10	10
1164.	10 l. Ichabod Crane and 1974 "Legend of Sleepy Hollow" stamp ..	10	10
1165.	15 l. John Henry and 1944 75th anniv. of completion of First Transcontinental Railroad stamp ..	10	10
1166.	20 l. Windwagon Smith and 1954 Kansas Territory Centenary stamp	10	10
1167.	13 r. Mike Fink and 1970 Great Northwest stamp	3·50	3·25
1168.	14 r. Casey Jones and 1950 Railroad Engineers stamp ..	3·75	3·50

1986. 60th Birthday of Queen Elizabeth II. As T **125** of Anguilla.

1170.	1 r. black and yellow ..	35	25
1171.	2 r. multicoloured ..	55	55
1172.	12 r. multicoloured ..	2·75	2·75

DESIGNS: 1 r. Royal Family at Girl Guides Rally, 1938; 2 r. Queen in Canada; 12 r. At Sandringham, 1970.

212. Player running with Ball.

1986. World Cup Football Championship, Mexico. Multicoloured.

1174.	15 l. Type **212**	30	20
1175.	2 r. Player gaining control of ball ..	1·50	1·00
1176.	4 r. Two players competing for ball ..	2·75	2·00
1177.	10 r. Player bouncing ball on knee ..	5·50	4·50

1986. Royal Wedding. As T **213** of Antigua. Multicoloured.

1179.	10 l. Prince Andrew and Miss Sarah Ferguson	10	10
1180.	2 r. Prince Andrew ..	60	60
1181.	12 r. Prince Andrew in naval uniform ..	2·75	3·00

213. Moorish Idol and Sea Fan.

1986. Marine Wildlife. Multicoloured.

1183.	50 l. Type **213**	60	30
1184.	90 l. Regal angelfish ..	80	45
1185.	1 r. Anemone fish ..	85	45
1186.	2 r. Tiger cowrie and stinging coral	1·40	1·00
1187.	3 r. Emperor angelfish and staghorn coral ..	1·75	1·25
1188.	4 r. Black-naped tern ..	2·75	2·00
1189.	5 r. Fiddler crab and staghorn coral ..	2·75	2·00
1190.	10 r. Hawksbill turtle ..	3·50	3·25

1986. Birth Bicentenary (1985) of John J. Audubon (ornithologist) (2nd issue). As T **201** showing original paintings. Multicoloured.

1192.	3 l. Little blue heron (horiz.)	10	10
1193.	4 l. White-tailed kite ..	10	10
1194.	5 l. Greater shearwater (horiz.)	10	10
1195.	10 l. Magnificent frigate bird	15	10
1196.	15 l. Black-necked grebe	25	20
1197.	20 l. Goosander	30	20
1198.	13 r. Peregrine falcon (horiz.)	4·50	4·50
1199.	14 r. Prairie chicken (horiz.)	4·50	4·50

1986. World Cup Football Championship Winners, Mexico. Nos. 1174/7 optd. **WINNERS Argentina 3 W. Germany 2.**

1201.	15 l. Type **212**	20	15
1202.	2 r. Player gaining control of ball ..	85	65
1203.	4 r. Two players competing for ball ..	1·50	1·25
1204.	10 r. Player bouncing ball on knee ..	2·75	2·50

1986. Appearance of Halley's Comet (2nd issue). Nos. 1150/4 optd. as **218** of Antigua.

1206.	20 l. N.A.S.A. space telescope and Comet	20	15
1207.	1 r. 50 E.S.A. "Giotto" spacecraft and Comet	50	45
1208.	2 r. Japanese "Planet A" spacecraft and Comet	75	65
1209.	4 r. Edmond Halley and Stonehenge	1·25	1·00
1210.	5 r. Russian "Vega" spacecraft and Comet	1·40	1·25

214. Servicing Aircraft.

1986. 40th Anniv. of U.N.E.S.C.O. Mult.

1212.	1 r. Type **214.**	20	25
1213.	2 r. Boat building ..	40	45
1214.	3 r. Children in classroom	55	60
1215.	5 r. Student in laboratory	95	1·00

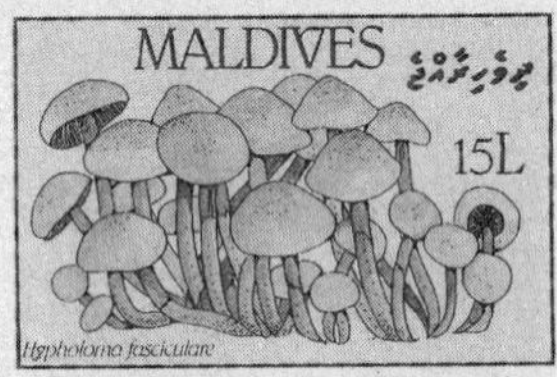

215. "Hypholoma fasciculare".

1986. Fungi of the Maldives. Multicoloured.

1217.	15 l. Type **215**	50	15
1218.	50 l. "Kuehneromyces mutabilis" (vert.) ..	80	30
1219.	1 r. "Amanita muscaria" (vert.)	1·25	50
1220.	2 r. "Agaricus campestris"	1·75	1·00
1221.	3 r. "Amanita pantherina" (vert.) ..	2·00	1·25
1222.	4 r. "Coprinus comatus" (vert.)	2·25	1·75
1223.	5 r. "Pholiota spectabilis"	2·40	2·25
1224.	10 r. "Pluteus cervinus"	3·50	3·50

216. Ixora.

1987. Flowers. Multicoloured.

1226.	10 l. Type **216**	10	10
1227.	20 l. Frangipani	10	10
1228.	50 l. Crinum	25	15
1229.	2 r. Pink rose	50	50
1230.	4 r. Flamboyant flower	80	80
1231.	10 r. Ground orchid ..	2·75	3·00

217. Guides studying Wild Flowers.

1987. 75th Anniv (1985) of Girl Guide Movement. Multicoloured.

1233 15 l. Type **217** 10 10
1234 2 r. Guides with pet rabbits 40 40
1235 4 r. Guide observing white spoonbill 80 90
1236 12 r. Lady Baden-Powell and Guide flag .. 2·50 3·00

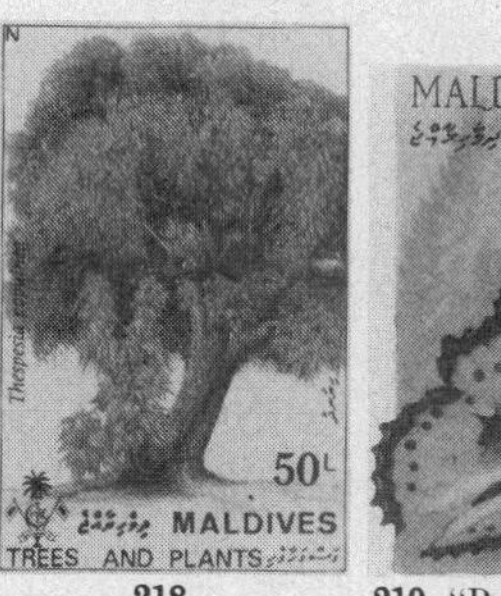

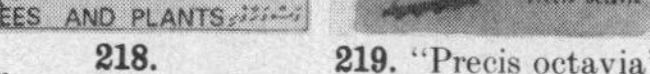

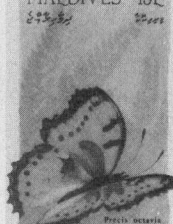

218. "Thespesia populnea". 219. "Precis octavia".

1987. Trees and Plants. Multicoloured.

1238 50 l. Type **218** 10 10
1239 1 r. "Cocos nucifera" .. 15 20
1240 2 r. "Calophyllum mophyllum" 30 35
1241 3 r. "Xanthosoma indica" (horiz) 45 50
1242 5 r. "Ipomoea batatas" (horiz) 80 85
1243 7 r. "Artocarpus altilis" 1·10 1·25

No. 1241 is inscr "Xyanthosoma indica" in error.

1987. America's Cup Yachting Championship. As T **222** of Antigua. Multicoloured.

1245. 15 l. "Intrepid", 1970 .. 10 10
1246. 1 r. "France II", 1974 .. 20 20
1247. 2 r. "Gretel", 1962 .. 40 50
1248. 12 r. "Volunteer", 1887 .. 2·00 2·50

1987. Butterflies. Multicoloured.

1250 15 l. Type **219** 45 30
1251 20 l. "Atrophaneura hector" 45 30
1252 50 l. "Teinopalpus imperialis" 75 40
1253 1 r. "Kallima horsfieldi" 1·00 45
1254 2 r. "Cethosia biblis" .. 1·60 1·00
1255 4 r. "Idea jasonia" .. 2·50 1·60
1256 7 r. "Papilio memnon" .. 3·50 3·00
1257 10 r. "Aeropetes tulbaghia" .. .. 4·00 4·00

220. Isaac Newton experimenting with Spectrum.

1988. Great Scientific Discoveries. Mult.

1259 1 r. 50 Type **220** 90 70
1260 3 r. Euclid composing "Principles of Geometry" (vert) .. 1·40 1·10
1261 4 r. Mendel formulating theory of Genetic Evolution (vert) .. 1·60 1·40
1262 5 r. Galileo and moons of Jupiter .. .. 2·00 1·75

221. Donald Duck and Weather Satellite. (Illustration reduced. Actual size 50 × 38 mm.).

1988. Space Exploration. Walt Disney cartoon characters. Multicoloured.

1264. 3 l. Type **221** 10 10
1265. 4 l. Minnie Mouse and navigation satellite .. 10 10
1266. 5 l. Mickey Mouse's nephews talking via communication satellite 10 10
1267. 10 l. Goofy in lunar rover (vert.) 10 10
1268. 20 l. Minnie Mouse delivering pizza to flying saucer (vert.) 10 10
1269. 13 r. Mickey Mouse directing spacecraft docking (vert.) .. 2·00 2·00
1270. 14 r. Mickey Mouse and "Voyager 2" .. .. 2·00 2·00

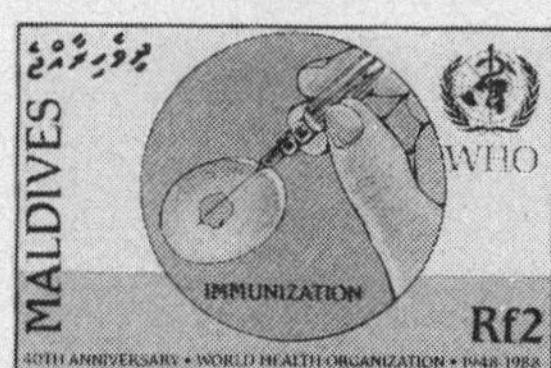

222 Syringe and Bacterium ("Immunization")

1988. 40th Anniv of W.H.O. Multicoloured.

1272 2 r. Type **222** 25 30
1273 4 r. Tap ("Clean Water") 50 55

223 Water Droplet and Atoll

1988. World Environment Day (1987). Mult.

1274 15 l. Type **223** 10 10
1275 75 l. Coral reef 15 15
1276 2 r. Audubon's shearwaters in flight .. 30 45

224 Globe, Carrier Pigeon and Letter

1988. Transport and Telecommunications Decade. Each showing central globe. Mult.

1278 2 r. Type **224** 60 60
1279 3 r. Dish aerial and girl using telephone .. 70 70
1280 5 r. Satellite, television, telephone and antenna tower .. .. 1·25 1·25
1281 10 r. Car, ship and airliner 2·25 2·50

1988. Royal Ruby Wedding. Nos. 1170/2 optd. **40TH WEDDING ANNIVERSARY H.M. QUEEN ELIZABETH II H.R.H. THE DUKE OF EDINBURGH.**

1282 1 r. black and yellow .. 35 20
1283 2 r. multicoloured .. 50 40
1284 12 r. multicoloured .. 2·50 3·00

226 Discus-throwing

1988. Olympic Games, Seoul. Multicoloured.

1286 15 l. Type **226** 10 10
1287 2 r. 100 metres race .. 40 35
1288 4 r. Gymnastics (horiz) .. 70 70
1289 12 r. Three-day equestrian event (horiz) .. .. 2·25 2·75

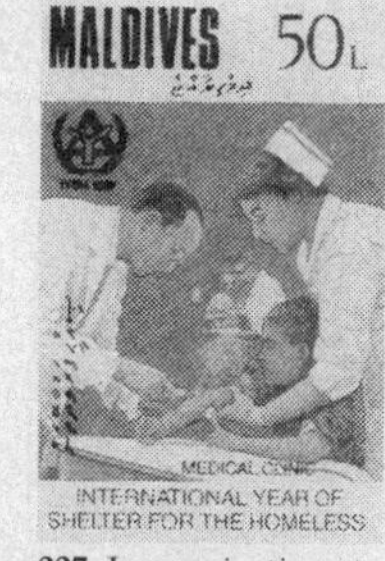

227 Immunization at Clinic

1988. International Year of Shelter for the Homeless. Multicoloured.

1291 50 l. Type **227** 30 30
1292 3 r. Prefab housing estate 1·10 1·10

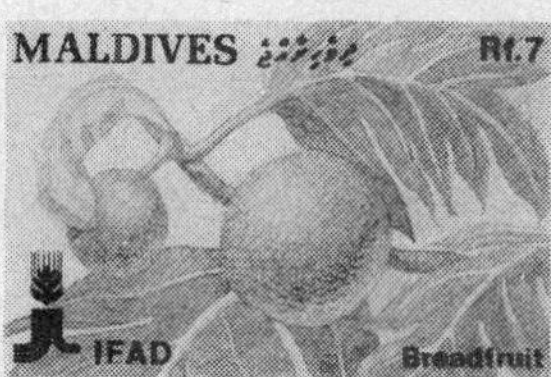

228 Breadfruit

1988. 10th Anniv of International Fund for Agricultural Development. Multicoloured.

1294 7 r. Type **228** .. .. 1·00 1·10
1295 10 r. Mangos (vert) .. 1·50 1·75

1988. World Aids Day. Nos. 1272/3 optd **WORLD AIDS DAY** and emblem.

1297 2 r. Type **222** 35 35
1298 4 r. Tap ("Clean Water") 65 65

230 Pres. Kennedy and Launch of "Apollo" Spacecraft

1989. 25th Death Anniv (1988) of John F. Kennedy (American statesman). U.S. Space Achievements. Multicoloured.

1299 5 r. Type **230** 85 85
1300 5 r. Lunar module and astronaut on Moon .. 85 85
1301 5 r. Astronaut and buggy on Moon 85 85
1302 5 r. President Kennedy and spacecraft .. 85 85

1989. Olympic Medal Winners, Seoul. Nos. 1286/9 optd.

1304 15 l. Type **226** (optd **J. Schult DDR**) .. 10 10
1305 2 r. Athletics 100 metres (optd **C. LEWIS USA**) 25 25
1306 4 r. Gymnastics (horiz) (optd **MEN'S ALL AROUND V. ARTEMOV USSR**) .. 50 60
1307 12 r. Three-day equestrain event (horiz) (optd **TEAM SHOW JUMPING W. GERMANY**) .. 1·40 1·60

1989. 500th Birth Anniv of Titian (artist). As T **238** of Antigua showing paintings. Mult.

1309 15 l. "Benedetto Varchi" 10 10
1310 1 r. "Portrait of a Young Man" 15 15
1311 2 r. "King Francis I of France" 25 25
1312 5 r. "Pietro Aretino" .. 65 65
1313 15 r. "The Bravo" .. 2·00 2·00
1314 20 r. "The Concert" (detail) .. .. 2·50 2·50

1989. 10th Anniv of Asia–Pacific Telecommunity. Nos. 1279/80 optd **ASIA-PACIFIC TELECOMMUNITY 10 YEARS** and emblem. Multicoloured.

1316 3 r. Dish aerial and girl using telephone .. 35 40
1317 5 r. Satellite, television, telephone and antenna tower 55 60

1989. Japanese Art. Paintings by Hokusai. As T **250** of Antigua. Multicoloured.

1318 15 l. "Fuji from Hodogaya" 10 10
1319 50 l. "Fuji from Lake Kawaguchi" 10 10
1320 1 r. "Fuji from Owari" .. 15 15
1321 2 r. "Fuji from Tsukudajima in Edo" 25 25
1322 4 r. "Fuji from a Teahouse at Yoshida" 55 55
1323 6 r. "Fuji from Tagonoura" 75 75
1324 10 r. "Fuji from Mishima-goe" .. .. 1·40 1·40
1325 12 r. "Fuji from the Sumida River in Edo" 1·60 1·60

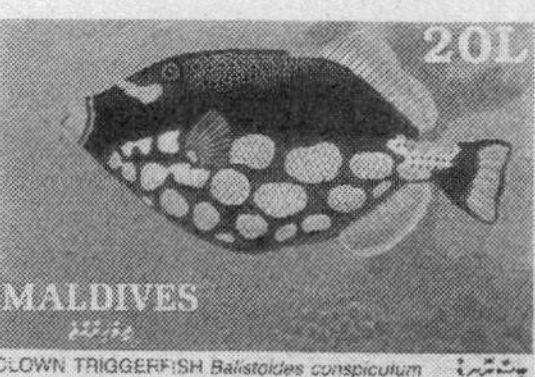

233 Clown Triggerfish

1989. Tropical Fishes. Multicoloured.

1327 20 l. Type **233** 15 15
1328 50 l. Bluestripe snapper .. 20 20
1329 1 r. Blue surgeonfish .. 30 30
1330 2 r. Oriental sweetlips .. 50 50
1331 3 r. Wrasse 70 70
1332 8 r. Threadfin butterflyfish .. .. .. 1·75 1·75
1333 10 r. Bicolour parrotfish 2·25 2·25
1334 12 r. Sabre squirrelfish .. 2·40 2·40

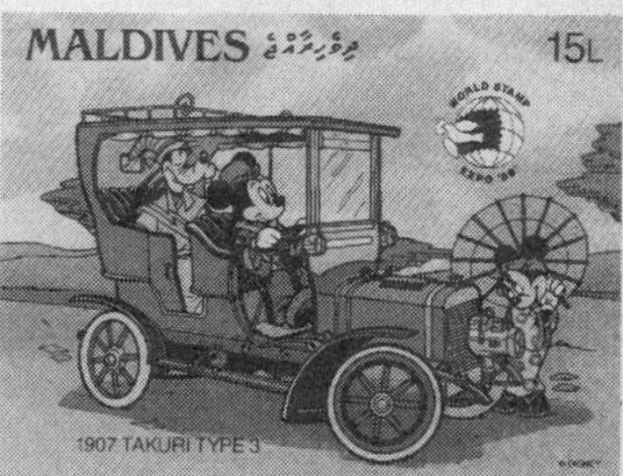

234 Goofy, Mickey and Minnie Mouse with Takuri "Type 3", 1907

1989. "World Stamp Expo '89" International Stamp Exhibition, Washington (1st issue). Designs showing Walt Disney cartoon characters with Japanese cars. Mult.

1336 15 l. Type **234** 10 10
1337 50 l. Donald and Daisy Duck in Mitsubishi "Model A", 1917 .. 15 15
1338 1 r. Goofy in Datsun "Roadstar", 1935 .. 25 25
1339 2 r. Donald and Daisy Duck with Mazda, 1940 40 40
1340 4 r. Donald Duck with Nissan "Bluebird 310", 1959 .. .. 70 70
1341 6 r. Donald and Daisy Duck with Subaru "360", 1958 .. 1·00 1·00
1342 10 r. Mickey Mouse and Pluto in Honda "5800", 1966 .. .. 1·75 1·75
1343 12 r. Mickey Mouse and Goofy in Daihatsu "Fellow", 1966 .. 1·90 1·90

235 Lunar Module "Eagle"

1989. 20th Anniv of First Manned Landing on Moon. Multicoloured.

1346 1 r. Type **235** 20 15
1347 2 r. Astronaut Aldrin collecting dust samples 35 35
1348 6 r. Aldrin setting up seismometer 90 90
1349 10 r. Pres. Nixon congratulating "Apollo 11" astronauts .. 1·40 1·60

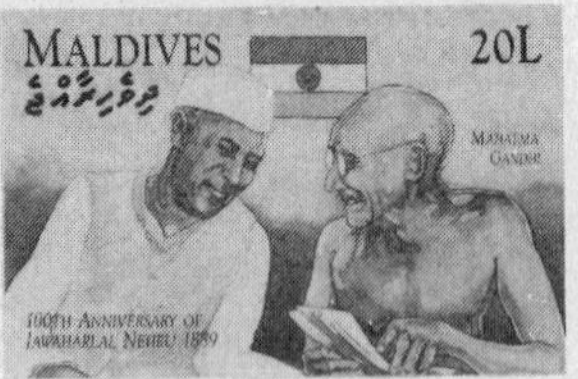

236 Jawaharlal Nehru with Mahatma Gandhi

1989. Anniversaries and Events. Mult.

1351 20 l. Type **236** (birth cent) 20 20
1352 50 l. Opium poppies and logo (anti-drugs campaign) (vert) .. 25 25
1353 1 r. William Shakespeare (425th birth anniv) .. 25 25
1354 2 r. Storming the Bastille (bicent of French Revolution) (vert) .. 35 35
1355 3 r. "Concorde" (20th anniv of first flight) .. 70 70
1356 8 r. George Washington (bicent of inauguration) 1·60 1·60
1357 10 r. William Bligh (bicent of mutiny on the "Bounty" .. .. 1·75 1·75
1358 12 r. Hamburg harbour (800th anniv) (vert) .. 2·00 2·00

237 Sir William van Horne, Locomotive and Map of Canadian Pacific Railway, 1894

1989. Railway Pioneers. Multicoloured.

1360 10 l. Type **237** 10 10
1361 25 l. Matthew Murray and Middleton Colliery rack locomotive, 1811 .. 10 10
1362 50 l. Louis Favre and locomotive entering tunnel, 1856 .. .. 10 10
1363 2 r. George Stephenson and "Locomotion", 1825 20 25
1364 6 r. Richard Trevithick and "Pen-y-darran" locomotive, 1804 .. 65 70
1365 8 r. George Nagelmackers and "Orient Express" dining car, 1869 .. 90 95
1366 10 r. William Jessop and horse-drawn line, 1770 1·10 1·25
1367 12 r. Isambard Brunel and G.W.R. train, 1833 .. 1·40 1·50

238 Bodu Thakurufaanu Memorial Centre, Utheemu

1990. 25th Anniv of Independence. Mult.

1369 20 l. Type **238** 10 10
1370 25 l. Islamic Centre, Male 10 10
1371 50 l. National flag and logos of international organizations 10 10
1372 2 r. Presidential Palace, Male 20 25
1373 5 r. National Security Service 55 60

239 "Louis XVI in Coronation Robes" (Duplesis)

1990. Bicentenary of French Revolution and "Philexfrance '89" International Stamp Exhibition, Paris French. Paintings. Mult.

1375 15 l. Type **239** 10 10
1376 50 l. "Monsieur Lavoisier and his Wife" (David) 10 10
1377 1 r. "Madame Pastoret" (David) 10 15
1378 2 r. "Oath of Lafayette, 14 July 1790" (anon) .. 20 25
1379 4 r. "Madame Trudaine" (David) 45 50
1380 6 r. "Chenard celebrating the Liberation of Savoy" (Boilly) .. 65 70
1381 10 r. "An Officer swears Allegiance to the Constitution" (anon) 1·10 1·25
1382 12 r. "Self Portrait" (David) .. .. 1·40 1·50

1990. "Stamp World London 90" International Stamp Exhibition. As T **193** of Gambia, showing Walt Disney cartoon characters playing British sports. Multicoloured.

1384 15 l. Donald Duck, Mickey Mouse and Goofy playing rugby .. 10 10
1385 50 l. Donald Duck and Chip-n-Dale curling .. 10 10
1386 1 r. Goofy playing polo .. 10 15
1387 2 r. Mickey Mouse and nephews playing soccer 20 25
1388 4 r. Mickey Mouse playing cricket 45 50
1389 6 r. Minnie and Mickey Mouse at Ascot races .. 65 70
1390 10 r. Mickey Mouse and Goofy playing tennis 1·10 1·25
1391 12 r. Donald Duck and Mickey Mouse playing bowls .. .. .. 1·40 1·50

240 Silhouettes of Queen Elizabeth II and Queen Victoria

1990. 150th Anniv of the Penny Black.

1393 **240** 8 r. black and green 90 95
1394 – 12 r. black and blue .. 1·40 1·50

DESIGN: 12 r. As Type **240**, but with position of silhouettes reversed.

1990. 90th Birthday of Queen Elizabeth the Queen Mother. As T **103** of Grenada Grenadines.

1396 6 r. black, mauve & blue 65 70
1397 6 r. black, mauve & blue 65 70
1398 6 r. black, mauve & blue 65 70

DESIGNS: No. 1396, Lady Elizabeth Bowes-Lyon; 1397, Lady Elizabeth Bowes-Lyon wearing headband; 1398, Lady Elizabeth Bowes-Lyon leaving for her wedding.

241 Sultan's Tomb

1990. Islamic Heritage Year. Each black and blue.

1400 1 r. Type **242** 10 15
1401 1 r. Thakurufaan's Palace 10 15
1402 1 r. Male Mosque .. 10 15
1403 2 r. Veranda of Friday Mosque 20 25
1404 2 r. Interior of Friday Mosque 20 25
1405 2 r. Friday Mosque and Monument 20 25

1990. 50th Anniv of Second World War. As T **101** of Grenada Grenadines. Multicoloured.

1406 15 l. Defence of Wake Island, 1941 .. .. 10 10
1407 25 l. Stilwell's army in Burma, 1944 .. .. 10 10
1408 50 l. Normandy offensive, 1944 .. .. .. 10 10
1409 1 r. Capture of Saipan, 1944 .. .. .. 10 15
1410 2 r. 50 D-Day landings, 1944 .. .. .. 30 35
1411 3 r. 50 Allied landings in Norway, 1940 .. .. 40 45
1412 4 r. Lord Mountbatten, Head of Combined Operations, 1943 .. 45 50
1413 6 r. Japanese surrender, Tokyo Bay, 1945 .. 65 70
1414 10 r. Potsdam Conference, 1945 .. .. .. 1·10 1·25
1415 12 r. Allied invasion of Sicily, 1943 .. .. 1·40 1·50

243 Great Crested Tern

1990. Birds. Multicoloured.

1417 25 l. Type **243** 10 10
1418 50 l. Koel 10 10
1419 1 r. White tern 10 15
1420 3 r. 5C Cinnamon bittern 40 45
1421 6 r. Sooty tern 65 70
1422 8 r. Audubon's shearwater 90 95
1423 12 r. Common noddy .. 1·40 1·50
1424 15 r. Lesser frigate bird 1·60 1·75

244 Emblem, Dish Aerial and Sailboards

1990. 5th South Asian Association for Regional Co-operation Summit.

1426 **244** 75 l. black and orange 10 10
1427 – 3 r. 50 multicoloured 40 45

DESIGN: 3 r. 50, Flags of member nations.

245 "Spathoglottis plicata"

1990. "EXPO '90" International Garden and Greenery Exhibition, Osaka. Flowers. Multicoloured.

1429 20 l. Type **245** 10 10
1430 75 l. "Hippeastrum puniceum" 10 10
1431 2 r. "Tecoma stans" (horiz) 20 25
1432 3 r. 50 "Catharanthus roseus" (horiz) .. 40 45
1433 10 r. "Ixora coccinea" (horiz) .. .. 1·10 1·25
1434 12 r. "Clitorea ternatea" (horiz) .. .. 1·40 1·50
1435 15 r. "Caesalpinia pulcherrima" .. .. .. 1·60 1·75

1990. International Literacy Year. As T **269** of Antigua, showing Walt Disney cartoon characters illustrating fables by Aesop. Multicoloured.

1437 15 l. "The Hare and the Tortoise" (horiz) .. 10 10
1438 50 l. "The Town Mouse and the Country Mouse" (horiz) .. 10 10
1439 1 r. "The Fox and the Crow" (horiz) 10 15
1440 3 r. 50 "The Travellers and the Bear" (horiz) 40 45
1441 4 r. "The Fox and the Lion" (horiz) 45 50
1442 6 r. "The Mice Meeting" (horiz) 65 70
1443 10 r. "The Fox and the Goat" (horiz) .. .. 1·10 1·25
1444 12 r. "The Dog in the Manger" (horiz) .. 1·40 1·50

247 East African Class "31" Locomotive

1990. Steam Railway Locomotives. Mult.

1446 20 l. Type **247** 10 10
1447 50 l. Sudan Railways Class "Mikado" .. 10 10
1448 1 r. South African Beyer-Garratt Class "GM" .. 10 15
1449 3 r. Rhodesia Railways Class "7" 35 40
1450 5 r. U.S.A. Central Pacific Class "229" 55 60
1451 8 r. U.S.A. Reading Class "415" 90 95
1452 10 r. Canada Porter narrow gauge .. .. 1·10 1·25
1453 12 r. U.S.A. Great Northern Class "515" .. 1·40 1·50

248 Ruud Gullit of Holland

1990. World Cup Football Championship, Italy. Multicoloured.

1455 1 r. Type **248** 10 15
1456 2 r. 50 Paul Gascoigne of England 30 35
1457 3 r. 50 Brazilian challenging Argentine player .. 40 45
1458 5 r. Brazilian taking control of ball .. 55 60
1459 7 r. Italian and Austrian jumping for header .. 80 85
1460 10 r. Russian being chased by Turkish player .. 1·10 1·25
1461 15 r. Andres Brehme of West Germany .. 1·60 1·75

249 Winged Euonymus

1991. Bonsai Trees and Shrubs. Mult.

1463	20 l. Type **249**	10	10
1464	50 l. Japanese black pine	10	10
1465	1 r. Japanese five needle pine	10	15
1466	3 r. 50 Flowering quince	40	45
1467	5 r. Chinese elm	55	60
1468	8 r. Japanese persimmon	90	95
1469	10 r. Japanese wisteria	1·10	1·25
1470	12 r. Satsuki azalea	1·40	1·50

250 "Summer" (Rubens)

1991. 350th Death Anniv of Rubens. Mult.

1472	20 l. Type **250**	10	10
1473	50 l. "Landscape with Rainbow" (detail)	10	10
1474	1 r. "Wreck of Aeneas"	10	15
1475	2 r. 50 "Chateau de Steen" (detail)	30	35
1476	3 r. 50 "Landscape with Herd of Cows"	40	45
1477	7 r. "Ruins on the Palantine"	80	85
1478	10 r. "Landscape with Peasants and Cows"	1·10	1·25
1479	12 r. "Wagon fording Stream"	1·40	1·50

251 Greek Messenger from Marathon, 490 BC (2480th Anniv)

1991. Anniversaries and Events (1990). Mult.

1481	50 l. Type **251**	10	10
1482	1 r. Anthony Fokker in early aircraft (birth centenary)	10	15
1483	3 r. 50 "Early Bird" satellite (25th anniv)	40	45
1484	7 r. Signing Reunification of Germany agreement (horiz)	80	85
1485	8 r. King John signing Magna Carta (775th anniv)	90	95
1486	10 r. Dwight D. Eisenhower (birth centenary)	1·10	1·25
1487	12 r. Sir Winston Churchill (25th death anniv)	1·40	1·50
1488	15 r. Pres. Reagan at Berlin Wall (German reunification) (horiz)	1·60	1·75

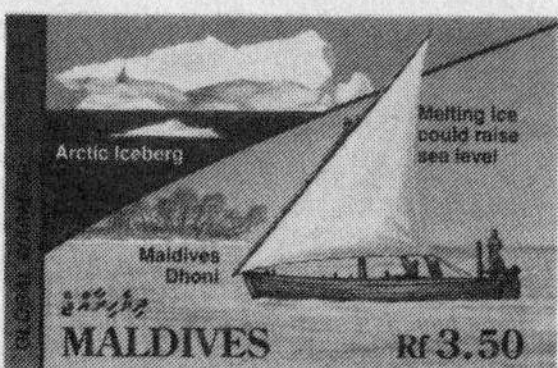

252 Arctic Iceberg and Maldives Dhoni

1991. Global Warming. Multicoloured.

1490	3 r. 50 Type **252**	40	45
1491	7 r. Antarctic iceberg and "Maldive Trader" (freighter)	80	85

253 S.A.A.R.C. Emblem and Medal

1991. Year of the Girl Child.

1492	**253** 7 r. multicoloured	80	85

254 Children on Beach

1991. Year of the Maldivian Child. Children's Paintings. Multicoloured.

1493	3 r. 50 Type **254**	40	45
1494	5 r. Children in a park	55	60
1495	10 r. Hungry child dreaming of food	1·10	1·25
1496	25 r. Scuba diver	2·75	3·00

1991. Death Centenary (1990) of Vincent van Gogh (artist). As T **278** of Antigua. Mult.

1497	15 l. "Still Life: Japanese Vase with Roses and Anemones"	10	10
1498	20 l. "Still Life: Red Poppies and Daisies"	10	10
1499	2 r. "Vincent's Bedroom in Arles" (horiz)	20	25
1500	3 r. 50 "The Mulberry Tree" (horiz)	40	45
1501	7 r. "Blossoming Chestnut Branches" (horiz)	80	85
1502	10 r. "Peasant Couple going to Work" (horiz)	1·10	1·25
1503	12 r. "Still Life: Pink Roses" (horiz)	1·40	1·50
1504	15 r. "Child with Orange"	1·60	1·75

1991. 65th Birthday of Queen Elizabeth II. As T **280** of Antigua. Multicoloured.

1506	2 r. Queen at Trooping the Colour, 1990	20	25
1507	5 r. Queen with Queen Mother and Princess Margaret, 1973	55	60
1508	8 r. Queen and Prince Philip in open carriage, 1986	90	95
1509	12 r. Queen at Royal Estates Ball	1·40	1·50

1991. 10th Wedding Anniv of Prince and Princess of Wales. As T **280** of Antigua. Multicoloured.

1511	1 r. Prince and Princess skiing, 1986	10	10
1512	3 r. 50 Separate photographs of Prince, Princess and sons	40	45
1513	7 r. Prince Henry in Christmas play and Prince William watching polo	80	85
1514	15 r. Princess Diana at Ipswich, 1990, and Prince Charles playing polo	1·60	1·75

256 Boy Painting

1991. Hummel Figurines. Multicoloured.

1516	10 l. Type **256**	10	10
1517	25 l. Boy reading at table	10	10
1518	50 l. Boy with school satchel	10	10
1519	2 r. Girl with basket	20	25
1520	3 r. 50 Boy reading	40	45
1521	8 r. Girl and young child reading	90	95
1522	10 r. School girls	1·10	1·25
1523	25 r. School boys	3·00	3·25

257 Class "C 57" Steam Locomotive

1991. "Phila Nippon '91" International Stamp Exhibition, Tokyo. Japanese Steam Locomotives. Multicoloured.

1525	15 l. Type **257**	10	10
1526	25 l. Class "6250" locomotive (horiz)	10	10
1527	1 r. Class "D 51" locomotive	10	10
1528	3 r. 50 Class "8620" locomotive (horiz)	40	45
1529	5 r. Class "10" locomotive (horiz)	55	60
1530	7 r. Class "C 61" locomotive	80	85
1531	10 r. Class "9600" locomotive (horiz)	1·10	1·25
1532	12 r. Class "D 52" locomotive (horiz)	1·40	1·50

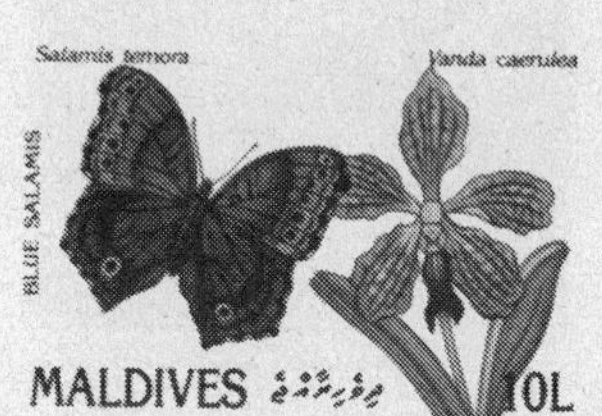

258 "Salamis temora" and "Vanda caerulea"

1991. Butterflies and Flowers. Multicoloured.

1534	10 l. Type **258**	10	10
1535	25 l. "Meneris tulbaghia" and "Incarvillea younghusbandii"	10	10
1536	50 l. "Polyommatus icarus" and "Campsis grandiflora"	10	10
1537	2 r. "Danaus plexippus" and "Thunbergia grandiflora"	20	25
1538	3 r. 50 "Colias interior" and "Medinilla magnifica"	40	45
1539	5 r. "Ascalapha ordorata" and "Meconopsis horridula"	55	60
1540	8 r. "Papilio memnon" and "Dillenia obovata"	90	95
1541	10 r. "Precis octavia" and "Thespesia populnea"	1·10	1·25

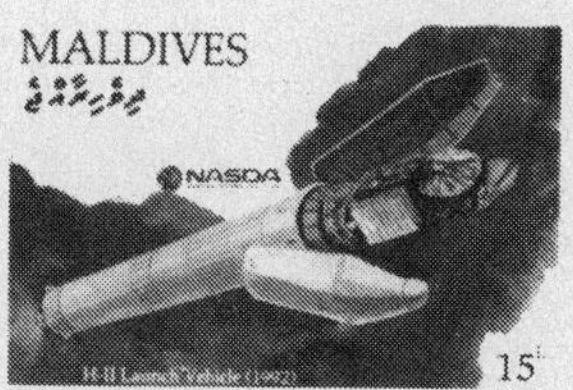

259 "H-II" Rocket

1991. Japanese Space Programme. Mult.

1543	15 l. Type **259**	10	10
1544	20 l. Projected "H-II" orbiting plane	10	10
1545	2 r. Satellite "GMS-5"	20	25
1546	3 r. 50 Satellite "MOMO-1"	40	45
1547	7 r. Satellite "CS-3"	80	85
1548	10 r. Satellite "BS-2a, 2b"	1·10	1·25
1549	12 r. "H-I" Rocket (vert)	1·40	1·50
1550	15 r. Space Flier unit and U.S. Space shuttle	1·60	1·75

260 Williams "FW-07"

1991. Formula 1 Racing Cars. Multicoloured.

1552	20 l. Type **260**	10	10
1553	50 l. Brabham/BMW "BT50" turbo	10	10
1554	1 r. Williams/Honda "FW-11"	10	10
1555	3 r. 50 Ferrari "312 T3"	40	45
1556	5 r. Lotus/Honda "99T"	55	60
1557	7 r. Benetton/Ford "B188"	80	85
1558	10 r. Tyrrell "P34" six-wheeler	1·10	1·25
1559	21 r. Renault "RE-30B" turbo	2·40	2·50

261 "Testa Rossa", 1957

1991. Ferrari Cars. Multicoloured.

1561	5 r. Type **261**	55	60
1562	5 r. "275GTB", 1966	55	60
1563	5 r. "Aspirarta", 1951	55	60
1564	5 r. "Testarossa"	55	60
1565	5 r. Enzo Ferrari	55	60
1566	5 r. "Dino 246", 1958	55	60
1567	5 r. "Type 375", 1952	55	60
1568	5 r. Nigel Mansell's Formula 1 racing car	55	60
1569	5 r. "312T", 1975	55	60

262 Franklin D. Roosevelt

1991. 50th Anniv of Japanese Attack on Pearl Harbor. American War Leaders. Mult.

1570	3 r. 50 Type **262**	35	40
1571	3 r. 50 Douglas MacArthur and map of Philippines	35	40
1572	3 r. 50 Chester Nimitz and Pacific island	35	40
1573	3 r. 50 Jonathan Wainwright and barbed wire	35	40
1574	3 r. 50 Ernest King and aircraft carrier	35	40
1575	3 r. 50 Claire Chennault and "Flying Tiger" plane	35	40
1576	3 r. 50 William Halsey and aircraft carrier	35	40
1577	3 r. 50 Marc Mitscher and aircraft carrier	35	40
1578	3 r. 50 James Doolittle and "B-25" bomber	35	40
1579	3 r. 50 Raymond Spruance and dive bomber	35	40

1992. Anniversaries and Events. As T **285** of Antigua. Multicoloured.

1580	20 l. Brandenburg Gate and postcard commemorating Berlin Wall	10	10
1581	50 l. Schwarzenburg Palace	10	10
1582	1 r. Spa at Baden	10	10
1583	1 r. 75 Berlin Wall and man holding child	20	25
1584	2 r. Royal Palace, Berlin	20	25
1585	4 r. Demonstrator and border guards	45	50
1586	5 r. Viennese masonic seal	55	60
1587	6 r. De Gaulle and Normandy landings, 1944 (vert)	65	70
1588	6 r. Lilienthal's signature and "Flugzeug Nr. 16"	65	70
1589	7 r. St. Marx	80	85
1590	7 r. Modern Trans-Siberian electric locomotive (vert)	80	85
1591	8 r. Kurt Schwitters (artist) and Landesmuseum	90	95

1592 9 r. Map of Switzerland and man in Uri traditional costume .. 1·00 1·10
1593 10 r. De Gaulle in Madagascar, 1958 .. 1·10 1·25
1594 10 r. Scouts exploring coral reef .. .. 1·10 1·25
1595 11 r. Scout salute and badge (vert) .. .. 1·25 1·40
1596 12 r. Steam locomotive .. 1·40 1·50
1597 15 r. Imperial German badges .. .. 1·60 1·75
1598 20 r. Josepsplatz, Vienna 2·25 2·40

ANNIVERSARIES AND EVENTS: Nos. 1580, 1583, 1585, 1597, Bicentenary of Brandenburg Gate, Berlin; Nos. 1581/2, 1584, 1586, 1589, 1598, Death bicentenary of Mozart (1991); Nos. 1587, 1593, Birth centenary of Charles de Gaulle (French statesman) (1990); No. 1588, Centenary of Otto Lilienthal's first gliding experiments; Nos. 1590, 1596, Centenary of Trans-Siberian Railway; No. 1591, 750th anniv of Hannover; No. 1592, 700th anniv of Swiss Confederation; Nos. 1594/5, 17th World Scout Jamboree, Korea.

264 Mickey Mouse on Flying Carpet, Arabia

1992. Mickey's World Tour. Designs showing Walt Disney cartoon characters in different countries. Multicoloured.
1600 25 l. Type **264** 10 10
1601 50 l. Goofy and Big Ben, Great Britain 10 10
1602 1 r. Mickey wearing clogs, Netherlands 10 10
1603 2 r. Pluto eating pasta, Italy 20 25
1604 3 r. Mickey and Donald doing Mexican hat dance 35 40
1605 3 r. 50 Mickey, Goofy and Donald as tiki, New Zealand 40 45
1606 5 r. Goofy skiing in Austrian Alps .. 55 60
1607 7 r. Mickey and city gate, Germany 80 85
1608 10 r. Donald as samurai, Japan .. .. .. 1·10 1·25
1609 12 r. Mickey as heroic statue, Russia .. 1·40 1·50
1610 15 r. Mickey, Donald, Goofy and Pluto as German band .. .. 1·75 1·90

265 Whimbrel

1992. Birds. Multicoloured.
1612 10 l. Type **265** 10 10
1613 25 l. Great egret .. 10 10
1614 50 l. Grey heron .. 10 10
1615 2 r. Shag 20 25
1616 3 r. 50 Roseate tern .. 40 45
1617 5 r. Greenshank 55 60
1618 8 r. Hoopoe 90 95
1619 10 r. Black-shouldered kite .. .. .. 1·10 1·25
1620 25 r. Scarlet ibis .. .. 2·75 3·00
1621 50 r. Grey plover .. 5·50 6·00

1992. 40th Anniv of Queen Elizabeth II's Accession. As T **288** of Antigua. Mult.
1622 1 r. Palm trees on beach 10 10
1623 3 r. 50 Path leading to jetty 35 40
1624 7 r. Tropical plant .. 80 85
1625 10 r. Palm trees on beach (different) .. .. 1·10 1·25

266 Blue Surgeonfish

1992. Fishes. Multicoloured.
1627 7 l. Type **266** 10 10
1628 20 l. Bigeye 10 10
1629 50 l. Yellowfin tuna .. 10 10
1630 1 r. Two-spot red snapper 10 10
1631 3 r. 50 Sabre squirrelfish 40 45
1632 5 r. Picasso triggerfish .. 55 60
1633 8 r. Bennet's butterfly fish 90 95
1634 10 r. Parrotfish .. .. 1·10 1·25
1635 12 r. Grouper .. .. 1·40 1·50
1636 15 r. Skipjack tuna .. 1·60 1·75

1992. International Stamp Exhibitions. As T **215** of Lesotho showing Walt Disney cartoon characters. Multicoloured.
(a) "Granada '92", Spain. The Alhambra
1638 2 r. Minnie Mouse in Court of the Lions .. 25 30
1639 5 r. Goofy in Lions Fountain 55 60
1640 8 r. Mickey Mouse at the Gate of Justice .. 90 95
1641 12 r. Donald Duck serenading Daisy at the Vermilion Towers .. 1·40 1·50

(b) "World Columbian Stamp Expo '92". Chicago Landmarks
1643 1 r. Mickey meeting Jean Baptiste du Sable (founder) 10 10
1644 3 r. 50 Donald Duck at Old Chicago Post Office 35 40
1645 7 r. Donald at Old Fort Dearborn 80 85
1646 15 r. Goofy in Museum of Science and Industry .. 1·60 1·75

267 Coastguard Patrol Boats

1992. Centenary of National Security Service. Multicoloured.
1648 3 r. 50 Type **267** 40 45
1649 5 r. Infantry in training 55 60
1650 10 r. Aakoatey fort .. 1·10 1·25
1651 15 r. Fire Service .. 1·60 1·75

268 Flowers of the United States of America

1992. National Flowers. Multicoloured.
1653 25 l. Type **268** 10 10
1654 50 l. Australia 10 10
1655 2 r. England 20 25
1656 3 r. 50 Brazil 40 45
1657 5 r. Holland 55 60
1658 8 r. France 90 95
1659 10 r. Japan .. .. 1·10 1·25
1660 15 r. Africa .. .. 1·60 1·75

269 "Laetiporus sulphureus"

1992. Fungi. Multicoloured.
1662 10 l. Type **269** 10 10
1663 25 l. "Coprinus atramentarius" .. 10 10
1664 50 l. "Ganoderma lucidum" 10 10
1665 3 r. 50 "Russula aurata" 35 40
1666 5 r. "Polyporus umbellatus" 55 60
1667 8 r. "Suillus grevillei" .. 90 95
1668 10 r. "Clavaria zollingeri" 1·10 1·25
1669 25 r. "Boletus edulis" .. 2·75 3·00

1992. Olympic Games, Albertville and Barcelona (1st issue). As T **216** of Lesotho. Multicoloured.
1671 10 l. Pole vault 10 10
1672 25 l. Men's pommel horse (horiz) 10 10
1673 50 l. Men's shot put .. 10 10
1674 1 r. Men's horizontal bar (horiz) 10 10
1675 2 r. Men's triple jump (horiz) 20 25
1676 3 r. 50 Table tennis .. 40 45
1677 5 r. Two man bobsled .. 55 60
1678 7 r. Freestyle wrestling (horiz) 80 85
1679 8 r. Freestyle ski-jump .. 90 95
1680 9 r. Baseball .. .. 1·00 1·10
1681 10 r. Women's cross-country Nordic skiing 1·10 1·25
1682 12 r. Men's 200 metres backstroke (horiz) .. 1·40 1·50

See also Nos. 1684/91.

270 Hurdling

1684 10 l. Type **270** 10 10
1685 1 r. Boxing 10 10
1686 3 r. 50 Women's sprinting 40 45
1687 5 r. Discus 55 60
1688 7 r. Basketball 80 85
1689 10 r. Long-distance running .. .. 1·10 1·25
1690 12 r. Aerobic gymnastics 1·40 1·50
1691 20 r. Fencing .. .. 2·25 2·40

271 Deinonychus

1992. "Genova '92" International Thematic Stamp Exhibition. Prehistoric Animals. Multicoloured.
1693 5 l. Type **271** 10 10
1694 10 l. Styracosaurus .. 10 10
1695 25 l. Mamenchisaurus .. 10 10
1696 50 l. Stenonychosaurus .. 10 10
1697 1 r. Parasaurolophus .. 10 10
1698 1 r. 25 Scelidosaurus .. 10 10
1699 1 r. 75 Tyrannosaurus .. 15 20
1700 2 r. Stegosaurus 20 25
1701 3 r. 50 Iguanodon .. 40 45
1702 4 r. Anatosaurus .. 45 50
1703 5 r. Monoclonius .. 55 60
1704 7 r. Tenontosaurus .. 80 85
1705 8 r. Brachiosaurus .. 90 1·00
1706 10 r. Euoplocephalus .. 1·10 1·25
1707 25 r. Triceratops .. 2·75 3·00
1708 50 r. Apatosaurus .. 5·50 5·75

1992. 60th Anniv of Goofy (Disney cartoon character). Goofy in various cartoon films. As T **258** of Dominica. Multicoloured.
1714 10 l. "Father's Weekend", 1953 .. .. .. 10 10
1715 50 l. "Symphony Hour", 1942 .. .. .. 10 10
1716 75 l. "Frank Duck Brings 'Em Back Alive", 1946 10 10
1717 1 r. "Crazy with the Heat", 1947 .. .. 10 10
1718 2 r. "The Big Wash", 1948 20 25
1719 3 r. 50 "How to Ride a Horse", 1950 .. .. 40 45
1720 5 r. "Two Gun Goofy", 1952 .. .. .. 55 60
1721 8 r. "Saludos Amigos", 1943 (vert) 90 95
1722 10 r. "How to be a Detective", 1952 .. 1·10 1·25
1723 12 r. "For Whom the Bulls Toil", 1953 .. 1·40 1·50
1724 15 r. "Double Dribble", 1946 (vert) .. .. 1·60 1·75

276 Minnie Mouse in "Le Missioner" (Toulouse-Lautrec)

1992. Opening of Euro Disney Resort, France. Disney cartoon characters superimposed on Impressionist paintings. Multicoloured.
1726 5 r. Type **276** 55 60
1727 5 r. Goofy in "The Card Players" (Cezanne) .. 55 60
1728 5 r. Mickey and Minnie Mouse in "The Cafe Terrace, Place du Forum" (Van Gogh) .. 55 60
1729 5 r. Mickey in "The Bridge at Langlois" (Van Gogh) 55 60
1730 5 r. Goofy in "Chocolate Dancing" (Toulouse-Lautrec) 55 60
1731 5 r. Mickey and Minnie in "The Seine at Asnieres" (Renoir) 55 60
1732 5 r. Minnie in "Ball at the Moulin Rouge" (Toulouse-Lautrec) .. 55 60
1733 5 r. Mickey in "Wheat-field with Cypresses" (Van Gogh) 55 60
1734 5 r. Minnie in "When will you Marry?" (Gauguin) 55 60

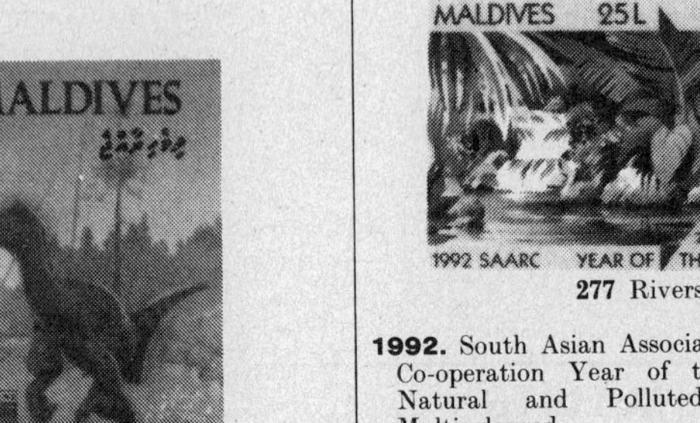

277 Rivers

1992. South Asian Association for Regional Co-operation Year of the Environment. Natural and Polluted Environments. Multicoloured.
1736 25 l. Type **277** 10 10
1737 50 l. Beaches 10 10
1738 5 r. Oceans 55 60
1739 10 r. Weather .. .. 1·10 1·25

278 Jurgen Klinsmann (Germany)

1993. World Cup Football Championship, U.S.A (1994). German Players and Officials. Multicoloured.

1740	10 l. Type **278**	10	10
1741	25 l. Pierre Littbarski ..	10	10
1742	50 l. Lothar Matthaus ..	10	10
1743	1 r. Rudi Voller	10	10
1744	2 r. Thomas Hassler ..	20	25
1745	3 r. 50 Thomas Berthold	40	45
1746	4 r. Jurgen Kohler ..	45	50
1747	5 r. Berti Vogts	55	60
1748	6 r. Bodo Illgner ..	65	70
1749	7 r. Klaus Augenthaler ..	80	85
1750	8 r. Franz Beckenbauer ..	90	95
1751	10 r. Andreas Brehme ..	1·10	1·25
1752	12 r. Guido Buchwald ..	1·40	1·50

279 Zeppelin bombing London, 1914–18

1993. Anniversaries and Events. Mult.

1754	1 r. Type **279**	10	10
1755	3 r. 50 Radio telescope ..	40	45
1756	3 r. 50 Chancellor Adenauer and Pres. de Gaulle	40	45
1757	6 r. Indian rhinoceros ..	65	70
1758	6 r. Columbus and globe	65	70
1759	7 r. Conference emblems	80	85
1760	8 r. Green seaturtle ..	90	95
1761	10 r. "America" (yacht), 1851	1·10	1·25
1762	10 r. Melvin Jones (founder) and emblem	1·10	1·25
1763	12 r. Columbus landing on San Salvador	1·40	1·50
1764	15 r. "Voyager I" approaching Saturn ..	1·60	1·75
1765	15 r. Adenauer, N.A.T.O. flag and fighter aircraft	1·60	1·75
1766	20 r. "Graf Zeppelin" over New York, 1929 ..	2·25	2·40

ANNIVERSARIES AND EVENTS: Nos. 1754, 1766, 75th death anniv of Count Ferdinand von Zeppelin; Nos. 1755, 1764, International Space Year; Nos. 1756, 1765, 25th death anniv of Konrad Adenauer; Nos. 1757, 1760, Earth Summit '92, Rio; Nos. 1758, 1763, 500th anniv of discovery of America by Columbus; No. 1759, International Conference on Nutrition, Rome; No. 1761, Americas Cup Yachting Championship; No.1762, 75th anniv of International Association of Lions Clubs.

1993. 15th Death Anniv of Elvis Presley (singer). As T **260** of Dominica. Mult.

1768	3 r. 50 Elvis Presley ..	40	45
1769	3 r. 50 Elvis with guitar	40	45
1770	3 r. 50 Elvis with microphone	40	45

1993. Bicentenary of the Louvre, Paris. As T **305** of Antigua. Multicoloured.

1771	8 r. "The Study" (Fragonard)	90	95
1772	8 r. "Denis Diderot" (Fragonard)	90	95
1773	8 r. "Marie-Madelaine Guimard" (Fragonard)	90	95
1774	8 r. "Inspiration" (Fragonard)	90	95
1775	8 r. "Waterfalls, Tivoli" (Fragonard)	90	95
1776	8 r. "The Music Lesson" (Fragonard)	90	95
1777	8 r. "The Bolt" (Fragonard)	90	95
1778	8 r. "Blind-man's Buff" (Fragonard)	90	95
1779	8 r. "Self-portrait" (Corot)	90	95
1780	8 r. "Woman in Blue" (Corot)	90	95
1781	8 r. "Woman with a Pearl" (Corot) ..	90	95
1782	8 r. "Young Girl at her Toilet" (Corot) ..	90	95
1783	8 r. "Haydee" (Corot) ..	90	95
1784	8 r. "Chartres Cathedral" (Corot)	90	95
1785	8 r. "The Belfry of Douai" (Corot) ..	90	95
1786	8 r. "The Bridge of Mantes" (Corot) ..	90	95
1787	8 r. "Madame Seriziat" (David)	90	95
1788	8 r. "Pierre Seriziat" (David)	90	95
1789	8 r. "Madame De Verninac" (David) ..	90	95
1790	8 r. "Madame Recamier" (David)	90	95
1791	8 r. "Self-portrait" (David)	90	95
1792	8 r. "General Bonaparte" (David)	90	95
1793	8 r. "The Lictors bringing Brutus his Son's Body" (David) (left detail) ..	90	95
1794	8 r. "The Lictors bringing Brutus his Son's Body" (David) (right detail) ..	90	95

281 James Stewart and Marlene Dietrich ("Destry Rides Again")

1993. Famous Western Films. Multicoloured.

1796	5 r. Type **281**	55	60
1797	5 r. Gary Cooper ("The Westerner")	55	60
1798	5 r. Henry Fonda ("My Darling Clementine")	55	60
1799	5 r. Alan Ladd ("Shane")	55	60
1800	5 r. Kirk Douglas and Burt Lancaster ("Gunfight at the O.K. Corral") ..	55	60
1801	5 r. Steve McQueen ("The Magnificent Seven") ..	55	60
1802	5 r. Robert Redford and Paul Newman ("Butch Cassidy and The Sundance Kid") ..	55	60
1803	5 r. Jack Nicholson and Randy Quaid ("The Missouri Breaks") ..	55	60

1993. 40th Anniv of Coronation. As T **307** of Antigua.

1805	3 r. 50 multicoloured ..	40	45
1806	5 r. multicoloured ..	55	60
1807	10 r. blue and black ..	1·10	1·25
1808	10 r. blue and black ..	1·10	1·25

DESIGNS: No. 1805, Queen Elizabeth II at Coronation (photograph by Cecil Beaton); No. 1806, St. Edward's Crown; No. 1807, Guests in the Abbey; No. 1808, Queen Elizabeth II and Prince Philip.

282 Yellow Goatfish

1993. Fishes. Multicoloured.

1809	3 r. 50 Type **282** ..	40	45
1810	3 r. 50 Emperor angelfish	40	45
1811	3 r. 50 Madagascar butterflyfish ..	40	45
1812	3 r. 50 Empress angelfish	40	45
1813	3 r. 50 Longnose butterflyfish ..	40	45
1814	3 r. 50 Racoon butterfly-fish	40	45
1815	3 r. 50 Harlequin filefish	40	45
1816	3 r. 50 Wedgetailed triggerfish ..	40	45
1817	3 r. 50 Clark's anemone-fish	40	45
1818	3 r. 50 Clown triggerfish	40	45
1819	3 r. 50 Zebra lionfish ..	40	45
1820	3 r. 50 Maldive clownfish	40	45
1821	3 r. 50 Black pyramid butterflyfish ..	40	45
1822	3 r. 50 Bird wrasse ..	40	45
1823	3 r. 50 Checkerboard wrasse	40	45
1824	3 r. 50 Blue face angelfish	40	45
1825	3 r. 50 Bannerfish ..	40	45
1826	3 r. 50 Threadfin butterflyfish ..	40	45
1827	3 r. 50 Picasso triggerfish	40	45
1828	3 r. 50 Pennantfish ..	40	45
1829	3 r. 50 Grouper ..	40	45
1830	3 r. 50 Black back butterflyfish ..	40	45
1831	3 r. 50 Redfin triggerfish	40	45
1832	3 r. 50 Redfin butterfly-fish	40	45

Nos. 1809/20 and 1821/32 were printed together, se-tenant, with the backgrounds forming composite designs.

283 Gull-billed Tern

1993. Birds. Multicoloured.

1834	3 r. 50 Type **283** ..	40	45
1835	3 r. 50 White-tailed tropicbird	40	45
1836	3 r. 50 Great frigate bird	40	45
1837	3 r. 50 Wilson's petrel ..	40	45
1838	3 r. 50 White tern ..	40	45
1839	3 r. 50 Brown booby ..	40	45
1840	3 r. 50 Marsh harrier ..	40	45
1841	3 r. 50 Common noddy ..	40	45
1842	3 r. 50 Green heron ("Little heron") ..	40	45
1843	3 r. 50 Turnstone ..	40	45
1844	3 r. 50 Curlew ..	40	45
1845	3 r. 50 Crab plover ..	40	45
1846	3 r. 50 Pallid harrier (vert)	40	45
1847	3 r. 50 Cattle egret (vert)	40	45
1848	3 r. 50 Koel (vert) ..	40	45
1849	3 r. 50 Tree pipit (vert) ..	40	45
1850	3 r. 50 Short-eared owl (vert)	40	45
1851	3 r. 50 Common kestrel ("European kestrel") (vert)	40	45
1852	3 r. 50 Yellow wagtail (vert)	40	45
1853	3 r. 50 Grey heron ("Common heron") (vert)	40	45
1854	3 r. 50 Black bittern (vert)	40	45
1855	3 r. 50 Common snipe (vert)	40	45
1856	3 r. 50 Little egret (vert)	40	45
1857	3 r. 50 Little stint (vert)	40	45

Nos. 1834/45 and 1846/57 were printed together, se-tenant, with the backgrounds forming composite designs.

284 "Epitonium scalare"

1993. Shells. Multicoloured.

1859	7 l. Type **284**	10	10
1860	15 l. "Janthina janthina"	10	10
1861	50 l. "Mauritia arabica"	10	10
1862	3 r. 50 "Harpa major" ..	40	45
1863	4 r. "Hydatina amplustre"	45	50
1864	5 r. "Cribrarula cribaria"	55	60
1865	6 r. "Mitra mitra" ..	65	70
1866	7 r. "Lioconcha castrensis"	80	85
1867	8 r. "Terebra guttata" ..	90	95
1868	10 r. "Erronea onyx" ..	1·10	1·25
1869	12 r. "Mauritia mappa"	1·40	1·50
1870	20 r. "Murex tribulus" ..	2·25	2·40

285 Sifaka Lemur

1993. Endangered Species. Multicoloured.

1872	7 l. Type **285**	10	10
1873	10 l. Snow leopard ..	10	10
1874	15 l. Numbat	10	10
1875	25 l. Gorilla	10	10
1876	2 r. Koala	20	25
1877	3 r. 50 Cheetah	40	45
1878	5 r. Yellow-footed rock wallaby	55	60
1879	7 r. Orang-utan	80	85
1880	8 r. Black lemur ..	90	95
1881	10 r. Black rhinoceros ..	1·10	1·25
1882	15 r. Humpback whale ..	1·60	1·75
1883	20 r. Mauritius parakeet	2·25	2·40

286 Symbolic Heads and Arrows

1993. Productivity Year. Multicoloured.

1885	7 r. Type **286**	80	85
1886	10 r. Abstract	1·10	1·25

287 Early Astronomical Equipment

1993. Anniversaries and Events. Mult.

1887	3 r. 50 Type **287**	40	45
1888	3 r. 50 "Still Life with Pitcher and Apples" (Picasso)	40	45
1889	3 r. 50 "Zolte Roze" (Menasze Seidenbeurel)	40	45
1890	3 r. 50 Prince Naruhito and engagement photographs (horiz) ..	40	45
1891	5 r. "Bowls and Jug" (Picasso) ..	55	60
1892	5 r. Krysztofory Palace, Cracow	55	60
1893	8 r. "Jabtka i Kotara" (Waclaw Borowski) ..	90	95
1894	8 r. Marina Kiehl (Germany) (women's downhill skiing) ..	90	95
1895	10 r. "Bowls of Fruit and Loaves on a Table" (Picasso)	1·10	1·25
1896	10 r. Masako Owada and engagement photographs (horiz) ..	1·10	1·25
1897	15 r. American astronaut in space ..	1·60	1·75
1898	15 r. Vegard Ulvang (Norway) (30km cross-country skiing) ..	1·60	1·75

ANNIVERSARIES AND EVENTS: Nos. 1887, 1897, 450th death anniv of Copernicus (astronomer); Nos. 1888, 1891, 1895, 20th death anniv of Picasso (artist); Nos. 1889, 1892/3, "Polska '93" International Stamp Exhibition, Poznan; Nos. 1890, 1896, Marriage of Crown Prince Naruhito of Japan; Nos. 1894, 1898, Winter Olympic Games '94, Lillehammer.

288 "Limenitis procris" and "Mussaenda"

1993. Butterflies and Flowers. Multicoloured.

1900		7 l. Type **288**	10	10
1901		20 l. "Danaus limniace" and "Thevetia neriifolia"	10	10
1902		25 l. "Amblypodia centaurus" and "Clitoria ternatea" ..	10	10
1903		50 l. "Papilio crino" and "Crossandra infundibuliformis" ..	10	10
1904		5 r. "Mycalesis patnia" and "Thespesia populnia"	55	60
1905		6 r. 50 + 50 l. "Idea jasonia" and "Cassia glauca"	80	85
1906		7 r. "Catopsilia pomona" and "Calotropis" ..	80	85
1907		10 r. "Precis orithyia" and "Thunbergia grandiflora"	1·10	1·25
1908		12 r. "Vanessa cardui" and "Caesalpinia pulcherrima"	1·40	1·50
1909		15 r. "Papilio polymnestor" and "Nerium oleander" ..	1·60	1·75
1910		18 r. "Cirrochroa thais" and "Vinca rosea" ..	2·00	2·10
1911		20 r. "Pachliopta hector" and "Ixora coccinea"	2·25	2·40

289 Zeppelin in Searchlights

1993. Aviation Anniversaries. Multicoloured.

1913		3 r. 50 Type **289**	40	45
1914		5 r. Homing pigeon and message from Santa Catalina mail service, 1894	50	55
1915		10 r. Eckener and airship	1·10	1·25
1916		15 r. Pilot's badge and loading Philadelphia–Washington mail, 1918	1·60	1·75
1917		20 r. U.S.S. "Macon" (airship) and mooring mast, 1933	2·25	2·40

ANNIVERSARIES: Nos. 1913, 1915, 1917, 125th birth anniv of Hugo Eckener (airship pioneer); Nos. 1914, 1916, Bicent of first airmail flight.

290 Ford Model "T"

1993. Centenaries of Henry Ford's First Petrol Engine (Nos. 1919/30) and Karl Benz's First Four-wheeled Car (others).

1919	**290**	3 r. 50 multicoloured	40	45
1920	–	3 r. 50 multicoloured	40	45
1921	–	3 r. 50 black & violet	40	45
1922	–	3 r. 50 multicoloured	40	45
1923	–	3 r. 50 multicoloured	40	45
1924	–	3 r. 50 multicoloured	40	45
1925	–	3 r. 50 multicoloured	40	45
1926	–	3 r. 50 multicoloured	40	45
1927	–	3 r. 50 multicoloured	40	45
1928	–	3 r. 50 multicoloured	40	45
1929	–	3 r. 50 multicoloured	40	45
1930	–	3 r. 50 black, brown and violet ..	40	45
1931	–	3 r. 50 multicoloured	40	45
1932	–	3 r. 50 multicoloured	40	45
1933	–	3 r. 50 green, black and violet ..	40	45
1934	–	3 r. 50 multicoloured	40	45
1935	–	3 r. 50 multicoloured	40	45
1936	–	3 r. 50 multicoloured	40	45
1937	–	3 r. 50 multicoloured	40	45
1938	–	3 r. 50 multicoloured	40	45
1939	–	3 r. 50 multicoloured	40	45
1940	–	3 r. 50 multicoloured	40	45
1941	–	3 r. 50 multicoloured	40	45
1942	–	3 r. 50 black, brown and violet ..	40	45

DESIGNS: No. 1920, Henry Ford; No. 1921, Plans of first petrol engine; No. 1922, Ford "Probe GT", 1993; No. 1923, Front of Ford "Sportsman", 1947; No. 1924, Back of Ford "Sportsman"; No. 1925, Advertisement of 1915; No. 1926, Ford "Thunderbird", 1955; No. 1927, Ford logo; No. 1928, Ford "Edsel Citation", 1958; No. 1929, Ford half-ton pickup, 1941; No. 1930, Silhouette of early Ford car; No. 1931, Daimler-Benz "Straight 8", 1937; No. 1932, Karl Benz; No. 1933, Mercedes-Benz poster; No. 1934, Mercedes "38-250SS", 1929; No. 1935, Benz "Viktoria", 1893; No. 1936, Benz logo; No. 1937, Plan of Mercedes engine; No. 1938, Mercedes-Benz "300SL Gullwing", 1952; No. 1939, Mercedes-Benz "SL", 1993; No. 1940, Front of Benz 4-cylinder car, 1906; No. 1941, Back of Benz 4-cylinder car and advertisement; No. 1942, Silhouette of early Benz car.

Nos. 1919/30 and 1931/42 were printed together, se-tenant, forming a composite design.

291 Ivan, Sonia, Sasha and Peter in the Snow

1993. "Peter and the Wolf". Scenes from Walt Disney's cartoon film. Multicoloured.

1944	7 l. Type **291**	10	10
1945	15 l. Grandpa and Peter	10	10
1946	20 l. Peter on bridge ..	10	10
1947	25 l. Yascha, Vladimir and Mischa	10	10
1948	50 l. Sasha on lookout ..	10	10
1949	1 r. The Wolf	10	10
1950	3 r. 50 Peter dreaming ..	40	45
1951	3 r. 50 Peter taking gun	40	45
1952	3 r. 50 Peter with gun in snow	40	45
1953	3 r. 50 Sasha and Peter ..	40	45
1954	3 r. 50 Sonia and Peter ..	40	45
1955	3 r. 50 Peter with Ivan and Sasha	40	45
1956	3 r. 50 Ivan warning Peter of the wolf	40	45
1957	3 r. 50 Ivan, Peter and Sasha in tree	40	45
1958	3 r. 50 Wolf below tree ..	40	45
1959	3 r. 50 Wolf and Sonia ..	40	45
1960	3 r. 50 Sasha attacking the wolf	40	45
1961	3 r. 50 Sasha walking into wolf's mouth	40	45
1962	3 r. 50 Peter firing pop gun at wolf	40	45
1963	3 r. 50 Wolf chasing Sonia	40	45
1964	3 r. 50 Ivan tying rope to wolf's tail	40	45
1965	3 r. 50 Peter and Ivan hoisting wolf	40	45
1966	3 r. 50 Sasha and the hunters	40	45
1967	3 r. 50 Ivan and Peter on wolf hanging from tree	40	45

MALTA

An island in the Mediterranean Sea, S. of Italy. After a period of self-government under various Constitutions, independence was attained on 21 September 1964. The island became a republic on 13 December 1974.

1860. 12 pence = 1 shilling;
20 shillings = 1 pound.
1972. 10 mils = 1 cent;
100 cents = M£1.

1.

5.

1860. Various frames

18.	1.	½d. yellow	22·00	35·00
20.		½d. green	1·25	40
22.	–	1d. red	1·75	35
23.	–	2d. grey	3·75	1·25
26.	–	2½d. blue	30·00	90
27.	–	4d. brown	8·50	3·00
28.	–	1s. violet	30·00	9·00
30.	5.	5s. red	£110	80·00

6. Harbour of Valletta.

7. Gozo Fishing Boat.

8. Ancient Maltese Galley.

9. Emblematic figure of Malta.

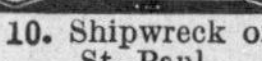

10. Shipwreck of St. Paul.

12.

1899.

45a	6.	¼d. brown	85	10
79		4d. black	10·00	2·50
32	7.	4½d. brown	11·00	8·50
58		4½d. orange	3·50	3·25
59	8.	5d. red	20·00	3·75
60		5d. green	3·00	3·25
34	9.	2s. 6d. olive	38·00	12·00
35	10.	10s. black	75·00	60·00

1902. No. 26 surch. **ONE PENNY.**

36.		1d. on 2½d. blue ..	40	65

1903.

47a.	12.	½d. green	1·50	10
48.		1d. black and red ..	5·50	10
49.		1d. red	1·00	10
50.		2d. purple and grey ..	5·00	45
51.		2d. grey	1·50	3·25
52.		2½d. purple and blue ..	11·00	40
53.		2½d. blue	4·00	1·25
42.		3d. grey and purple ..	80	50
54.		4d. black and brown ..	8·00	5·00
55.		4d. black & red on yellow	3·50	3·00
44.		1s. grey and violet ..	13·00	6·00
62.		1s. black on green ..	6·00	2·00
63.		5s. green & red on yellow	60·00	65·00

13.

15.

17.

18.

1914.

69	13	¼d. brown	30	10
71a		½d. green	60	15
73		1d. red	60	10
75		2d. grey	4·50	2·50
77		2½d. blue	80	20
78		3d. purple on yellow ..	2·50	5·00
80		6d. purple	7·00	11·00
81a		1s. black on green ..	10·00	13·00
86	15	2s. purple & blue on blue	50·00	28·00
88		5s. green & red on yellow	70·00	85·00
104	17	10s. black	£300	£475

1918. Optd. **WAR TAX.**

92.	13.	½d. green	30	15
93.	12.	3d. grey and purple ..	1·75	6·50

1921.

100.	18.	2d. grey	2·50	80

1922. Optd. **SELF-GOVERNMENT.**

114.	13.	¼d. brown	10	20
106.		½d. green	20	55
116.		1d. red	30	15
117.	18.	2d. grey	80	45
118.	13.	2½d. blue	30	45
108.		3d. purple on yellow ..	1·25	9·50
109.		6d. purple	1·25	9·50
110.		1s. black on green ..	2·50	8·50
120.	15.	2s. purple & blue on blue	35·00	70·00
112.	9.	2s. 6d. olive	17·00	27·00
113.	15.	5s. green & red on yellow	50·00	75·00
105.	10.	10s. black	£170	£275
121.	17.	10s. black	£100	£150

1922. Surch. in words.

122.	18.	¼d. on 2d. grey ..	20	25

22.

23.

1922.

123a	22.	¼d. brown	40	15
124		½d. green	75	10
125		1d. orange and purple ..	1·25	15
126		1d. violet	1·25	35
127		1½d. red	1·00	10
128		2d. brown and blue ..	1·25	30
129		2½d. blue	1·00	4·50
130		3d. blue	1·75	50
131		3d. black on yellow ..	1·00	6·50
132		4d. yellow and blue ..	1·25	1·60
133		6d. green and violet ..	2·00	1·25
134	23.	1s. blue and brown ..	3·75	2·50
135		2s. brown and blue ..	5·50	8·50
136		2s. 6d. purple and black	7·50	9·00
137		5s. orange and blue ..	15·00	27·00
138		10s. grey and brown ..	48·00	90·00
140	22.	£1 black and red ..	£100	£200

1925. Surch. in words.

141.	22.	2½d. on 3d. blue ..	30	1·00

1926. Optd. **POSTAGE.**

143.	22.	¼d brown	15	80
144.		½d. green	20	15
145.		1d. violet	40	25
146.		1½d. red	45	25
147.		2d. brown and blue ..	40	20
148.		2½d. blue	55	40
149.		3d. black on yellow ..	30	50
150.		4d. yellow and blue ..	3·00	8·00
151.		6d. green and violet ..	1·50	1·40
152.	23.	1s. blue and brown ..	4·50	7·00
153.		2s. brown and blue ..	38·00	95·00
154.		2s. 6d. purple and black	9·00	24·00
155.		5s. orange and blue ..	8·00	26·00
156.		10s. grey and brown ..	6·00	14·00

26.

27. Valetta Harbour.

28. St. Publius.

DESIGNS—As Type **27:** 2s. Mdina (Notabile). 5s. Neolithic temple, Mnajdra. As Type **28:** 2s. 6d. Gozo boat. 3 s. Neptune. 10s. St. Paul.

1926. Inscr. "POSTAGE".

157. **26.** ¼d. brown 40 15
158. ½d. green 40 15
159. 1d. red 65 50
160. 1½d. brown 75 10
161. 2d. grey .. .. 2·50 5·50
162. 2½d. blue .. .. 2·75 20
162a. 3d. violet .. .. 3·25 1·50
163. 4d. black and red .. 2·75 7·00
164. 4½d. violet and yellow .. 2·75 2·50
165. 6d. violet and red .. 3·00 2·00
166. **27.** 1s. black .. 4·50 2·25
167. **28.** 1s. 6d. black and green 5·50 9·00
168. – 2s. black and purple .. 5·50 13·00
169. – 2s. 6d. black and red .. 11·00 30·00
170. – 3s. black and blue .. 14·00 27·00
171. – 5s. black and green .. 20·00 45·00
172. – 10s. black and red .. 55·00 95·00

1928. Air. Optd. **AIR MAIL.**

173. **26.** 6d. violet and red .. 1·75 1·25

1928. Optd. **POSTAGE AND REVENUE.**

174. **26.** ¼d. brown 55 10
175. ½d. green 55 10
176. 1d. red .. .. 1·50 1·50
177. 1d. brown .. .. 2·50 10
178. 1½d. brown .. .. 1·50 30
179. 1½d. red .. .. 3·25 10
180. 2d. grey .. .. 3·25 8·00
181. 2½d. blue .. .. 1·25 10
182. 3d. violet .. .. 1·25 30
183. 4d. black and red .. 1·25 1·00
184. 4½d. violet and yellow .. 2·25 1·50
185. 6d. violet and red .. 2·25 1·00
186. **27.** 1s. black .. 2·25 2·00
187. **28.** 1s. 6d. black and green 5·00 9·00
188. – 2s. black and purple .. 18·00 35·00
189. – 2s. 6d. black and red .. 13·00 23·00
190. – 3s. black and blue .. 18·00 30·00
191. – 5s. black and green .. 26·00 60·00
192. – 10s. black and red .. 55·00 85·00

1930. As Nos. 157/72, but inscr. "POSTAGE & REVENUE".

193. ¼d. brown 50 10
194. ½d. green 50 10
195. 1d. brown 50 10
196. 1½d. red 70 10
197. 2d. grey .. .. 1·00 20
198. 2½d. blue .. .. 2·00 10
199. 3d. violet .. .. 1·50 20
200. 4d. black and red .. 1·25 2·25
201. 4½d. violet and yellow .. 2·25 1·50
202. 6d. violet and red .. 1·75 75
203. 1s. black .. .. 5·00 8·50
204. 1s. 6d. black and green 5·50 13·00
205. 2s. black and purple .. 7·50 15·00
206. 2s. 6d. black and red .. 13·00 40·00
207. 3s. black and blue .. 22·00 50·00
208. 5s. black and green .. 27·00 55·00
209. 10s. black and red .. 65·00 £100

1935. Silver Jubilee. As T **13** of Antigua.

210. ½d. black and green .. 40 50
211. 2½d. brown and blue .. 2·50 2·75
212. 6d. blue and olive .. 5·50 3·25
213. 1s. grey and purple .. 8·50 11·00

1937. Coronation. As T **2** of Aden.

214. ½d. green 10 10
215. 1½d. red 50 15
216. 2½d. blue 50 35

37. Grand Harbour, Valletta. **38.** H.M.S. "St. Angelo".

39. Verdala Palace.

1938. Various designs with medallion King George VI.

217. **37.** ¼d. brown 10 10
218. **38.** ½d. green 60 10
218a. ½d. brown 40 10
219. **39.** 1d. brown .. .. 4·25 30
219a. 1d. green 40 10
220. – 1½d. red 50 15
220b. – 1½d. black 30 15
221. – 2d. black 30 80
221a. – 2d. red 40 30
222. – 2½d. blue 30 30
222a. – 2½d. violet 60 10
223. – 3d. violet 30 70
223a. – 3d. blue 30 10
224. – 4½d. olive and brown .. 50 10
225. – 6d. olive and red .. 75 15
226. – 1s. black 75 30
227. – 1s. 6d. black and olive 6·50 3·50
228. – 2s. green and blue .. 3·25 2·75
229. – 2s. 6d. black and red .. 7·00 4·50
230. – 5s. black and green .. 7·00 5·50
231. – 10s. black and red .. 14·00 14·00

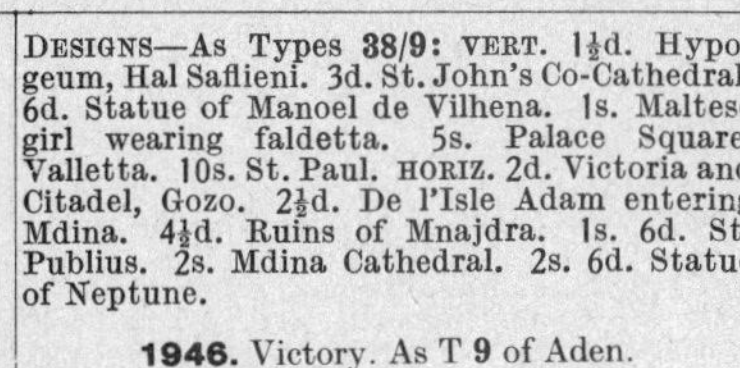

Designs—As Types **38/9**: Vert. 1½d. Hypogeum, Hal Saflieni. 3d. St. John's Co-Cathedral. 6d. Statue of Manoel de Vilhena. 1s. Maltese girl wearing faldetta. 5s. Palace Square, Valletta. 10s. St. Paul. Horiz. 2d. Victoria and Citadel, Gozo. 2½d. De l'Isle Adam entering Mdina. 4½d. Ruins of Mnajdra. 1s. 6d. St. Publius. 2s. Mdina Cathedral. 2s. 6d. Statue of Neptune.

1946. Victory. As T **9** of Aden.

232. 1d. green 10 10
233. 3d. blue 10 10

1948. Self-Government. As 1938 issue optd. **SELF-GOVERNMENT 1947.**

234 ¼d. brown 10 20
235 ½d. brown 15 10
236 1d. green 15 10
236a 1d. grey 10 10
237 1½d. black 50 10
237b 1½d. green 15 10
238 2d. red 50 10
238a 2d. yellow 15 10
239 2½d. violet 85 10
239a 2½d. red 30 65
240 3d. blue 30 15
240a 3d. violet 35 15
241 4½d. olive and brown .. 1·75 1·50
241a 4½d. olive and blue .. 50 90
242 6d. olive and red .. 80 15
243 1s. black .. .. 1·75 40
244 1s. 6d. black and olive 2·50 45
245 2s. green and blue .. 4·50 1·50
246 2s. 6d. black and red .. 12·00 2·50
247 5s. black and green .. 18·00 5·50
248 10s. black and red .. 19·00 16·00

1949. Silver Wedding. As T **10/11** of Aden.

249. 1d. green 45 10
250. £1 blue .. .. 40·00 35·00

1949. U.P.U. As T **20/23** of Antigua.

251. 2½d. violet 30 10
252. 3d. blue .. .. 1·75 50
253. 6d. red .. .. 1·75 50
254. 1s. black .. .. 1·75 1·75

53. Queen Elizabeth II when Princess. **54.** "Our Lady of Mount Carmel" (attrib. Palladino).

1950. Visits of Princess Elizabeth.

255. **53.** 1d. green 10 10
256. 3d. blue 20 10
257. 1s. black 55 45

1951. 7th Cent. of the Scapular.

258. **54.** 1d. green 10 10
259. 3d. violet 15 10
260. 1s. black 55 40

1953. Coronation. As T **13** of Aden.

261 1½d. black and green .. 30 10

55. St. John's Co-Cathedral. **56.** "Immaculate Conception" (Caruana) (altar-piece, Cospicua).

1954. Royal Visit.

262. **55.** 3d. violet 30 10

1954. Centenary of Dogma of the Immaculate Conception.

263. **56.** 1½d. green 10 10
264. 3d. blue 10 10
265. 1s. grey 20 20

57. Monument of the Great Siege, 1565. **74.** "Defence of Malta".

1956.

266 **57** ¼d. violet 10 10
267 – ½d. orange 40 10
314 – 1d. black 50 30
269 – 1½d. green 30 10
270 – 2d. sepia .. .. 1·00 10
271 – 2½d. brown 30 30
272 – 3d. red 55 10
273 – 4½d. blue 75 20
274 – 6d. blue 30 10
275 – 8d. ochre .. .. 1·00 1·00
276 – 1s. violet 35 10
277 – 1s. 6d. turquoise .. 4·50 20
278 – 2s. olive .. .. 5·50 80
279 – 2s. 6d. brown .. 5·50 2·25
280 – 5s. green .. .. 9·00 2·75
281 – 10s. red .. .. 35·00 8·00
282 – £1 brown .. .. 35·00 20·00

Designs—Vert. ½d. Wignacourt Aqueduct Horsetrough. 1d. Victory Church. 1½d. War Memorial. 2d. Mosta Dome. 3d. The King's Scroll. 4½d. Roosevelt's Scroll. 8d. Vedette. 1s. Mdina Gate. 1s. 6d. "Les Gavroches" (Statue). 2s. Monument of Christ the King. 2s. 6d. Monument of Grand Master Cottoner. 5s. Grand Master Perellos's Monument. 10s. St. Paul (statue). £1, Baptism of Christ (statue). Horiz. 2½d. Auberge de Castile. 6d. Neolithic Temples at Tarxien.

1957. George Cross Commem. Cross in Silver.

283. **74.** 1½d. green 15 10
284. – 3d. red 15 10
285. – 1s. brown 15 10

Designs—Horiz. 3d. Searchlights over Malta. Vert. 1s. Bombed buildings.

77. Design.

1958. Technical Education in Malta. Inscr. "TECHNICAL EDUCATION".

286. **77.** 1½d. black and green .. 10 10
287. – 3d. black, red and grey 10 10
288. – 1s. grey, purple & black 15 10

Designs—Vert. 3d. "Construction". Horiz. 1s. Technical School, Paola.

81. Sea Raid on Grand Harbour, Valletta.

1958. George Cross Commem. Cross in first colour outlined in silver.

289. – 1½d. green and black .. 15 10
290. **81.** 3d. red and black .. 15 10
291. – 1s. mauve and black .. 15 10

Designs—Horiz. 1½d. Bombed-out family. 1s. Searchlight crew.

83. Air Raid Casualties. **86.** Shipwreck of St. Paul (after Palombi).

87. Statue of St. Paul, Rabat, Malta.

1959. George Cross Commem.

292. **83.** 1½d. grn., black & gold 20 10
293. – 3d. mauve, black & gold 20 10
294. – 1s. grey, black and gold 70 55

Designs—Horiz. 3d. "For Gallantry". Vert. 1s. Maltese under bombardment.

1960. Shipwreck of St. Paul (19th Cent.). Inscr. as in T **86/7**.

295. **86.** 1½d. blue, gold & brown 15 10
296. – 3d. purple, gold and blue 15 10
297. – 6d. red, gold and grey .. 25 10
298. **87.** 8d. black and gold .. 30 40
299. – 1s. purple and gold .. 25 10
300. – 2s. 6d. blue, green & gold 1·00 1·50

Designs—As Type **86**: 3d. Consecration of St. Publius, First Bishop of Malta. 6d. Departure of St. Paul (after Palombi). As Type **87**: 1s. Angel with the "Acts of the Apostles". 2s. 6d. St. Paul with the "Second Epistle to the Corinthians".

92. Stamp of 1860.

1960. Centenary of Malta Stamp. Stamp in buff and blue.

301. **92.** 1½d. green 25 10
302. 3d. red 30 10
303. 6d. blue 40 25

93. George Cross.

1961. George Cross Commem.

304. **93.** 1½d. black, cream & bis. 15 10
305. – 3d. brown and blue .. 30 10
306. – 1s. green, lilac & violet 60 85

Designs: 3d. and 1s. show George Cross as Type **93** over backgrounds with different patterns.

96. "Madonna Damascena". **100.** Bruce, Zammit and Microscope.

1962. Great Siege Commem.

307. **96.** 2d. blue 10 10
308. – 3d. red 10 10
309. – 6d. bronze 10 10
310. – 1s. purple 15 20

Designs: 3d. Great Siege Monument. 6d. Grand Master La Valette. 1s. Assault on Fort St. Elmo.

1963. Freedom from Hunger. As T **28** of Aden.

311. 1s. 6d. sepia .. .. 3·75 2·75

1963. Cent of Red Cross. As T **33** of Antigua.

312. 2d. red on black 25 15
313. 1s. 6d. red and blue .. 3·00 3·75

1964. Anti-Brucellosis Congress.

316. **100.** 2d. brown, black & green 10 10
317. – 1s. 6d. black and purple 55 20

Design: 1s. 6d. Goat and laboratory equipment.

102. "Nicola Cotoner tending sick man" (M. Preti).

1964. 1st European Catholic Doctors' Congress, Valletta. Multicoloured

318. 2d. Type **102** 20 10
319. 6d. St. Luke and hospital .. 45 15
320. 1s. 6d. Sacra Infermeria, Valletta 85 85

106. Dove and British Crown. **110.** Neolithic Era.

109. "The Nativity".

1964. Independence.

321. **106.** 2d. olive, red and gold . . 30 10
322. – 3d. brown, red and gold 30 10
323. – 6d. slate, red and gold 90 15
324. **106.** 1s. blue, red and gold . . 90 15
325. – 1s. 6d. blue, red & gold 2·50 1·50
326. – 2s. 6d. blue, red & gold 2·50 2·75

DESIGNS: 1d., 3d., 1s 6d. Dove and Pope's Tiara. 6d., 2s 6d. Dove and U.N. Emblem.

1964. Christmas.

327. **109.** 2d. purple and gold . . 10 10
328. 4d. blue and gold . . 20 15
329. 8d. green and gold . . 45 45

1965. Multicoloured.

330. ½d. Type **110.** 10 10
331. 1d. Punic Era 10 10
332. 1½d. Roman Era 20 10
333. 2d. Proto Christian Era . . 10 10
334. 2½d. Saracenic Era . . 40 10
335. 3d. Siculo Norman Era . . 10 10
336. 4d. Knights of Malta . . 30 10
337. 4½d. Maltese Navy . . 40 40
337b. 5d. Fortifications 30 20
338. 6d. French Occupation . . 20 10
339. 8d. British Rule . . 20 10
339c. 10d. Naval Arsenal . . 45 1·25
340. 1s. Maltese Corps of the British Army 30 10
341. 1s. 3d. International Eucharistic Congress, 1913 . . 2·00 1·40
342. 1s. 6d. Self-Government, 1921 . . . . 60 10
343. 2s. Gozo Civic Council . . 70 10
344. 2s. 6d. State of Malta . . 70 50
345. 3s. Independence 1964 . . 1·25 75
346. 5s. HAFMED (Allied Forces, Mediterranean) . . . . 5·00 1·00
347. 10s. The Maltese Islands (map) . . . . 3·50 3·00
348. £1 Patron Saints . . 3·75 5·00

Nos. 339/48 are larger, 41 × 29 mm. from perf. to perf. and include portrait of Queen Elizabeth II.

129. "Dante" (Raphael). **131.** Turkish Fleet.

1965. 700th Birth Anniv. of Dante.

349. **129.** 2d. blue 10 10
350. 6d. green 15 10
351. 2s. brown 65 70

1965. 400th Anniv. of Great Siege. Mult.

352. 2d. Turkish camp 25 10
353. 3d. Battle scene 25 10
354. 6d. Type **131** 50 10
355. 8d. Arrival of relief Force 85 75
356. 1s. Grand Master J. de La Valette's Arms 55 10
357. 1s. 6d. "Allegory of Victory" (from mural by M. Preti) 1·25 30
358. 2s. 6d. Victory Medal . . 2·00 2·00

SIZES—As Type **131**: 1s. SQUARE (32½ × 32½ mm.): others.

137. "The Three Kings".

1965. Christmas.

359. **137.** 1d. purple and red . . 10 10
360. 4d. purple and blue . . 30 25
361. 1s. 3d. slate and purple 30 30

138. Sir Winston Churchill.

1966. Churchill Commem.

362. **138.** 2d. black, red and gold 15 10
363. – 3d. green, olive and gold 15 10
364. – 1s. purple, red and gold 20 10
365. – 1s. 6d. bl., ultram. & gold 35 40

DESIGN: 3d., 1s. 6d. Sir Winston Churchill and George Cross.

140. Grand Master La Valette.

1966. 400th Anniv. of Valletta. Mult.

366. 2d. Type **140.** 10 10
367. 3d. Pope Pius V 10 10
368. 6d. Map of Valletta . . 10 10
369. 1s. F. Laparelli (architect) 10 10
370. 2s. 6d. G. Cassar (architect) 20 30

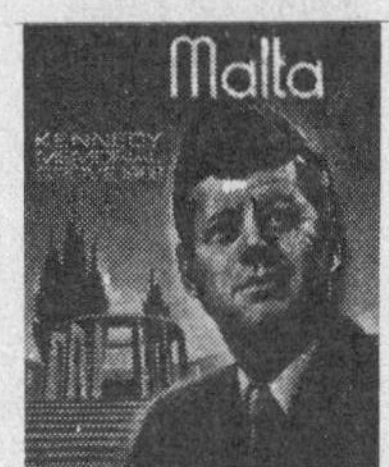

145. Pres. Kennedy and Memorial.

1966. Pres. Kennedy Commem.

371. **145.** 3d. olive, gold and black 10 10
372. 1s. 6d. blue, gold & blk. 10 10

146. "Trade".

1966. 10th Malta Trade Fair.

373. **146.** 2d. multicoloured . . 10 10
374. 8d. multicoloured . . 20 25
375. 2s. 6d. multicoloured 20 25

147. "The Child in the Manger". **148.** George Cross.

1966. Christmas.

376. **147.** 1d. multicoloured . . 10 10
377. 4d. multicoloured . . 10 10
378. 1s. 3d. multicoloured . . 10 10

1967. 25th Anniv. of George Cross Award to Malta.

379. **148.** 2d. multicoloured . . 10 10
380. 4d. multicoloured . . 10 10
381. 3s. multicoloured . . 15 15

149. Crucifixion of St. Peter.

1967. 1,900th Anniv. of Martyrdom of Saints Peter and Paul.

382. **149.** 2d. brown, orge. and black 10 10
383. – 8d. olive, gold and black 10 10
384. – 3s. blue and black . . 15 10

DESIGNS—As Type **149** 3s. Beheading of St. Paul. HORIZ. (47 × 25 mm.): 8d. Open Bible and Episcopal Emblems.

152. "St. Catherine of Siena".

1967. 300th Death Anniv. of Melchior Gafa (sculptor). Multicoloured.

385. 2d. Type **152** 10 10
386. 4d. "St. Thomas of Villanova" 10 10
387. 1s. 6d. "Baptism of Christ" (detail) 10 10
388. 2s. 6d. "St. John the Baptist" (from "Baptism of Christ") 10 10

156. Temple Ruins, Tarxien. **160.** "Angels".

1967. 15th Int. Historical Architecture Congress, Valletta. Multicoloured.

389. 2d. Type **156** 10 10
390. 6d. Facade of Palazzo Falzon, Notabile 10 10
391. 1s. Parish Church, Birkirkara 10 10
392. 3s. Portal, Auberge de Castille 15 15

1967. Christmas. Multicoloured.

393. 1d. Type **160** 10 10
394. 8d. "Crib" 10 10
395. 1s. 4d. "Angels" . . 10 10

163. Queen Elizabeth II and Arms of Malta.

1967. Royal Visit.

396. **163.** 2d. multicoloured . . 10 10
397. – 4d. black, purple & gold 10 10
398. – 3s. multicoloured . . 15 15

DESIGNS—VERT. 4d. Queen in Robes of Order of St. Michael and St. George. HORIZ. 3s. Queen and outline of Malta.

166. Human Rights Emblem and People.

1968. Human Rights Year. Multicoloured.

399. 2d. Type **166** 10 10
400 6d. Human Rights Emblem and People (different) . . 10 10
401. 2s. Type **166** (reversed) . . 10 10

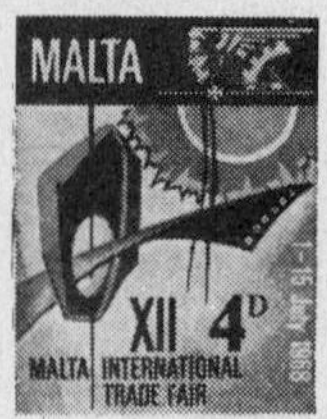

169. Fair "Products".

1968. Malta Int. Trade Fair.

402. **169.** 4d. multicoloured . . 10 10
403. 8d. multicoloured . . 10 10
404. 3s. multicoloured . . 15 10

170. Arms of the Order of St. John and La Valette.

1968. 4th Death Cent. of Grand Master La Valette. Multicoloured.

405. 1d. Type **170** 10 10
406. 8d. "La Valette" (A. de Favray) 10 10
407. 1s. 6d. La Valette's Tomb (28 × 23 mm.) . . 10 10
408. 2s. 6d. Angels and Scroll bearing Date of Death 15 20

The 8d., 2s. 6d. are vert.

174. Star of Bethlehem and Angel waking Shepherds.

1968. Christmas. Multicoloured.

409. 1d. Type **174.** 10 10
410. 8d. Mary and Joseph with Shepherd watching over Cradle 10 10
411. 1s. 4d. Three Wise Men and Star of Bethlehem . . 10 10

177. "Agriculture". **180.** Mahatma Gandhi.

1968. 6th Food and Agricultural Organization Regional Conf. for Europe. Multicoloured.

412. 4d. Type **177** 10 10
413. 1s. F.A.O. Emblem and Coin 10 10
414. 2s. 6d. "Agriculture" sowing Seeds 10 15

1969. Birth Cent. of Mahatma Gandhi.

415. **180.** 1s 6d. brown, blk. & gold 15 10

181. ILO Emblem.

1969. 50th Anniv. of Int. Labour Organization.

416. **181.** 2d. blue, gold and turq. 10 10
417. 6d. sepia, gold & brown 10 10

182. Robert Samut.

1969. Birth Centenary of Robert Samut (composer of Maltese National Anthem).
418. **182.** 2d. multicoloured .. 10 10

183. Dove of Peace, U.N. Emblem, and Sea-Bed.

1969. United Nations Resolution on Oceanic Resources.
419. **183.** 5d. multicoloured .. 10 10

184. "Swallows" returning to Malta.

1969. Maltese Migrant's Convention.
420. **184.** 10d. black, gold & olive 10 10

185. University Arms and Grand Master de Fonseca (founder).

1969. Bicent of University of Malta.
421. **185.** 2s. multicoloured .. 10 20

187. Flag of Malta and Birds.

1969. 5th Anniv. of Independence.
422. – 2d. multicoloured .. 10 10
423. **187.** 5d. black, red and gold 10 10
424. – 10d. black, blue & gold 10 10
425. – 1s. 6d. multicoloured.. 10 20
426. – 2s. 6d. blk., brn. & gold 15 25
DESIGN—SQUARE (31 × 31 mm.). 2d. 1919 War Monument. VERT. 10d. "Tourism". 1s. 6d. U.N. and Council of Europe Emblems. 2s. 6d. "Trade and Industry".

191. Peasants playing Tambourine and Bagpipes.

1969. Christmas. Children's Welfare Fund. Multicoloured.
427. 1d.+1d. Type **191.** .. 10 15
428. 5d.+1d. Angels playing trumpet and harp .. 15 15
429. 1s. 6d.+3d. Choir boys singing 15 30

194. "The Beheading of St. John" (Caravaggio).

1970. 13th Council of Europe Art Exhibition. Multicoloured.
430. 1d. Type **194.** 10 10
431. 2d. "St. John the Baptist" (M. Preti) .. 10 10
432. 5d. Interior of St. John's Co-Cathedral, Valletta 10 10
433. 6d. "Allegory of the Order" (Neapolitan school) .. 10 10
434. 8d. "St. Jerome" (Caravaggio) 10 20
435. 10d. Articles from the Order of St. John in Malta .. 10 10
436. 1s. 6d. "The Blessed Gerard receiving Godfrey de Bouillon" (A. de Favray) 15 25
437. 2s. Cape and Stolone (16th-cent.) 20 35
SIZES—HORIZ. 1d., 8d. 56×30 mm. 2d., 6d. 45×32 mm. 10d., 2s. 63×21 mm. 1s. 6d. 45×34 mm. SQUARE. 5d. 39×39 mm.

202. Artist's Impression of Fujiyama.

1970. World Fair, Osaka.
438. **202.** 2d. multicoloured .. 10 10
439. 5d. multicoloured .. 10 10
440. 3s. multicoloured .. 15 15

203. "Peace and Justice". **204.** Carol-Singers, Church and Star.

1970. 25th Anniv. of United Nations.
441. **203.** 2d. multicoloured .. 10 10
442. 5d. multicoloured .. 10 10
443. 2s. 6d. multicoloured.. 15 15

1970. Christmas. Multicoloured.
444. 1d.+½d. Type **204** .. 10 10
445. 10d.+2d. Church, Star and Angels with Infant .. 10 15
446 1s. 6d.+3d. Church, Star and Nativity Scene .. 15 25

207. Books and Quill.

1971. Literary Anniversaries. Multicoloured.
447. 1s. 6d. Type **207** (De Soldanis (historian) Death Bicent.) 10 10
448. 2s. Dun Karm (poet), books, pens and lamp (Birth Cent.) 10 15

209. Europa "Chain". **211.** "Centaurea spathulata".

210. "St. Joseph, Patron of the Universal Church" (G. Cali).

1971. Europa.
449. **209.** 2d. orge., black & olive 10 10
450. 5d. orge., black and red 10 10
451. 1s. 6d. orge., blk. & slate 20 75

1971. Cent. of Proclamation of St. Joseph as Patron Saint of Catholic Church, and 50th Anniv. of Coronation of the Statue of "Our Lady of Victories". Multicoloured.
452. 2d. Type **210** 10 10
453. 5d. Statue of "Our Lady of Victories" and Galley.. 10 10
454. 10d. Type **210** 10 10
455. 1s. 6d. As 5d. 20 40

1971. National Plant and Bird of Malta. Multicoloured.
456. 2s. Type **211** 10 10
457. 5d. Blue rock thrush (horiz.) 10 10
458. 10d. As 5d. 25 15
459. 1s. 6d. Type **211** .. .. 25 1·00

212. Angel.

1971. Christmas. Multicoloured.
460. 1d.+½d. Type **212** .. 10 10
461. 10d.+2d. Mary and the Child Jesus 15 20
462. 1s. 6d.+3d. Joseph lying awake 20 30

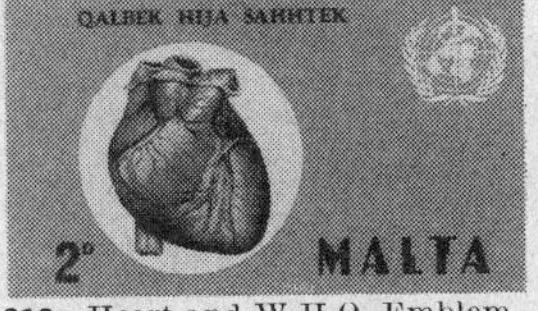

213. Heart and W.H.O. Emblem.

1972. World Health Day.
464. **213.** 2d. multicoloured .. 10 10
465. 10d. multicoloured .. 15 10
466. 2s. 6d. multicoloured .. 40 80

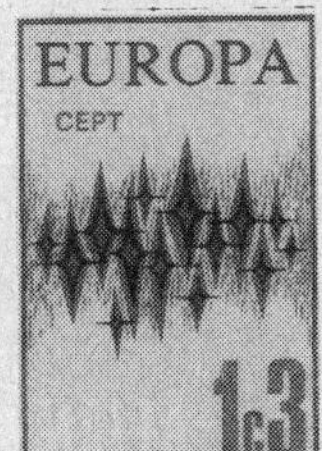

214. Maltese Cross. **216.** "Communications".

1972. Decimal Currency. Coins. Mult
467. 2 m. Type **214** 10 10
468. 3 m. Bee on Honeycomb.. 10 10
469. 5 m. Earthen lampstand.. 10 10
470. 1 c. George Cross 10 10
471. 2 c. Classical head.. .. 10 10
472. 5 c. Ritual altar 10 10
473. 10 c. Grandmaster's galley 20 10
474. 50 c. Great Siege Monument 1·00 1·25
SIZES: 3 m., 2 c. As Type **214.** 5 m., 1 c., 5 c. 25×30 mm. 10 c., 50 c. 31×38 mm.

1972. Nos. 337a, 339 and 341 surch.
475. 1 c. 3 m. on 5 d. mult. .. 10 10
476. 3 c. on 8 d. multicoloured.. 15 10
477. 5 c. on 1 s. 3 d. multicoloured 15 20

1972. Europa.
478. **216.** 1 c. 3 m. multicoloured 10 10
479. 3 c. multicoloured .. 10 10
480. 5 c. multicoloured .. 15 35
481. 7 c. 5 m. multicoloured 20 75

217. Angel.

1972. Christmas.
482. **217.** 8 m.+2 m. brn., grey and gold 10 10
483. – 3 c.+1 c. purple, violet and gold 15 35
484. – 7 c. 5 m.+1 c. 5 m. indigo, blue & gold .. 20 45
DESIGNS: No. 483, Angel with tambourine. No. 484, Singing angel.
See also Nos. 507/9.

MINIMUM PRICE

The minimum price quoted is 10p which represents a handling charge rather than a basis for valuing common stamps. For further notes about prices see introductory pages.

218. Archaeology. **220.** Emblem, and Woman holding Corn.

219. Europa "Posthorn".

1973. Multicoloured.
486 2 m. Type **218** 10 10
487 4 m. History 10 10
488 5 m. Folklore 10 10
489 8 m. Industry 10 10
490 1 c. Fishing Industry .. 10 10
491 1 c. 3 Pottery 10 10
492 2 c. Agriculture 10 10
493 3 c. Sport 10 10
494 4 c. Yacht marina.. .. 15 10
495 5 c. Fiesta 15 10
496 7 c. 5 Regatta 25 10
497 10 c. Voluntary service .. 25 10
498 50 c. Education .. .. 75 1·00
499 £1 Religion .. .. 2·00 2·75
500 £2 Coat-of-arms (32 × 27 mm.) .. .. .. 15·00 16·00
500b £2 National Emblem (32 × 27 mm.) .. .. 9·00 12·00

1973. Europa.
501. **219.** 3 c. multicoloured .. 15 10
502. 5 c. multicoloured .. 15 35
503. 7 c. 5 m. multicoloured 25 60

1973. Anniversaries.
504. **220.** 1 c. 3 m. multicoloured 10 10
505. – 7 c. 5 m. multicoloured 25 40
506. – 10 c. multicoloured 30 50
ANNIVERSARIES: 1 c. 3 m., World Food Programme. 10th anniv. 7 c. 5 m., W.H.O. 25th anniv. 10 c. Universal Declaration of Human Rights. 25th Anniv.

1973. Christmas. As T **217.** Multicoloured.
507. 8 m.+2 m. Angels and organ pipes 15 10
508. 3 c.+1 c. Madonna and Child 25 40
509. 7 c. 5 m.+1 c. 5 m. Buildings and Star.. .. .. 45 65

221. Girolamo Cassar (architect).

1973. Prominent Maltese.
511 **221** 1 c. 3 deep green, green and gold 10 10
512 – 3 c. green, blue & gold 10 10
513 – 5 c. brown, grn & gold 15 15
514 – 7 c. 5 bl, lt bl & gold 20 30
515 – 10 c. deep purple, purple and gold .. 20 40
DESIGNS: 3 c. Guiseppe Barth (ophthalmologist). 5 c. Nicolo' Isouard (composer). 7 c. 5, John Borg (botanist). 10 c. Antonio Sciortino (sculptor).

222. "Air Malta" Emblem.

1974. Air. Multicoloured.
516. 3 c. Type **222** 10 10
517. 4 c. Boeing "707" .. 15 10
518. 5 c. Type **222** 15 10
519. 7 c. 5 As 4 c 20 10
520. 20 c. Type **222** 55 60
521. 25 c. As 4 c. 55 60
522. 35 c. Type **222** .. .. 1·00 1·40

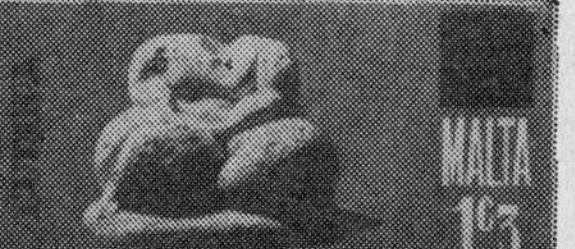

223. Prehistoric Sculpture.

1974. Europa.
523 223 1 c. 3 blue, blk & gold 15 10
524 – 3 c. brown, blk & gold 20 15
525 – 5 c. purple, blk & gold 25 45
526 – 7 c. 5 green, blk & gold 35 80
DESIGNS—VERT. 3 c. Old Cathedral Door, Mdina. 7 c. 5 "Vetlina" (sculpture by A. Sciortino). HORIZ. 5 c. Silver monstrance.

224. Heinrich von Stephan (founder) and Land Transport.

1974. Centenary of U.P.U.
527. **224.** 1 c. 3 grn., bl. & orge. 30 10
528. – 5 c. brn., red & green 30 10
529. – 7 c. 5 blue, vio. & grn. 35 20
530. – 50 c. pur., red & orge. 1·00 1·25
DESIGNS: (each containing portrait as Type **224**). 5 c. "Washington" (paddle-steamer) and "Royal Viking Star" (liner). 7 c. 5 Balloon and Boeing "747". 50 c. U.P.U. Buildings, 1874 and 1974.

225. Decorative Star and Nativity Scene.

1974. Christmas. Multicoloured.
532. 8 m. + 2 m. Type **225** .. 10 10
533. 3 c + 1 c. "Shepherds" 15 20
534. 5 c. + 1 c. "Shepherds with gifts" .. 20 35
535. 7 c. 5 + 1 c. 5 "The Magi" 30 40

226. Swearing-in of Prime Minister.

1975. Inauguration of Republic.
536. **226.** 1 c. 3 multicoloured .. 10 10
537. – 5 c. red and black .. 20 10
538. – 25 c. multicoloured .. 60 1·00
DESIGNS: 5 c. National flag. 25 c. Minister of Justice, President and Prime Minister.

227. Mother and Child ("Family Life").

1975. International Women's Year.
539. **227.** 1 c. 3 violet and gold .. 15 10
540. – 3 c. blue and gold .. 20 10
541. **227.** 5 c. brown and gold .. 50 20
542. – 20 c. brown and gold .. 2·25 3·00
DESIGN: 3 c., 20 c. Office Secretary ("Public Life").

228. "Allegory of Malta" (Francesco de Mura).

1975. Europa. Multicoloured.
543. 5 c. Type **228** .. 30 10
544. 15 c. "Judith and Holofernes" (Valentin de Boulogne) .. 50 75
The 15 c. is smaller: 47 × 23 mm.

229. Plan of Ggantija Temple.

1975. European Architectural Heritage Year.
545. **229.** 1 c. 3 black and red .. 10 10
546. – 3 c. purple, red & brn. 20 10
547. – 5 c. brown and red .. 40 35
548. – 25 c. grn., red & black 1·75 3·25
DESIGNS: 3 c. Mdina skyline. 5 c. View of Victoria, Gozo. 25 c. Silhouette of Fort St. Angelo.

230. Farm Animals. **231.** "The Right to Work".

1975. Christmas. Multicoloured.
549. 8 m. + 2 m. Type **230** .. 30 25
550. 3 c. + 1 c. Nativity scene (50 × 23 mm.) .. 60 75
551. 7 c. 5 + 1 c. 5 Approach of the Magi .. 1·50 1·75

1975. 1st Anniv of Republic.
552 **231** 1 c. 3 multicoloured .. 10 15
553 – 5 c. multicoloured .. 20 10
554 – 25 c. red, blue & black 70 1·10
DESIGNS: 5 c. "Safeguarding the Environment". 25 c. National Flag.

232. "Festa Tar-Rahal".

1976. Maltese Folklore. Multicoloured.
555. 1 c. 3 Type **232** .. 10 10
556. 5 c. "L-Imnarja" (horiz.) 15 10
557. 7 c. 5 "Il-Karnival" (horiz.) 45 70
558. 10 c. "Il-Gimgha L-Kbira" 70 1·40

233. Waterpolo.

1976. Olympic Games, Montreal. Mult.
559. 1 c. 7 Type **233** .. 10 10
560. 5 c. Sailing .. 20 10
561. 30 c. Athletics .. 65 1·50

234. Lace-making.

1976. Europa. Multicoloured.
562. 7 c. Type **234** .. 20 30
563. 15 c. Stone carving .. 25 40

235. Nicola Cotoner.

1976. 300th Anniv. of School of Anatomy and Surgery. Multicoloured.
564. 2 c. Type **235** .. 10 10
565. 5 c. Arm .. 10 10
566. 7 c. Giuseppe Zammit .. 15 10
567. 11 c. Sacra Infermeria .. 25 65

236. St. John the Baptist and St. Michael. **237.** Jean de la Valette's Armour.

1976. Christmas. Multicoloured.
568. 1 c.+5 m. Type **236** .. 15 20
569. 5 c.+1 c. Madonna and Child .. 50 70
570. 7 c.+1 c. 5 St. Christopher and St. Nicholas .. 65 1·00
571. 10 c.+2 c. Complete painting (32×27 mm.) .. 75 1·40
Nos. 568/71 show portions of "Madonna and Saints" by Domenico di Michelino.

1977. Suits of Armour. Multicoloured.
572. 2 c. Type **237** .. 10 10
573. 7 c. Aloph de Wignacourt's armour .. 20 10
574. 11 c. Jean Jacques de Verdelin's armour .. 25 50

1977. No. 336 surch.
575. 1 c. 7 on 4d. multicoloured 25 25

239. "Annunciation".

1977. 4th Birth Cent. of Rubens. Flemish Tapestries. Multicoloured.
576. 2 c. Type **239** .. 10 10
577. 7 c. "Four Evangelists" 25 10
578. 11 c. "Nativity" .. 45 45
579. 20 c. "Adoration of the Magi" .. 80 1·00
See also Nos. 592/5, 615/18 and 638/9.

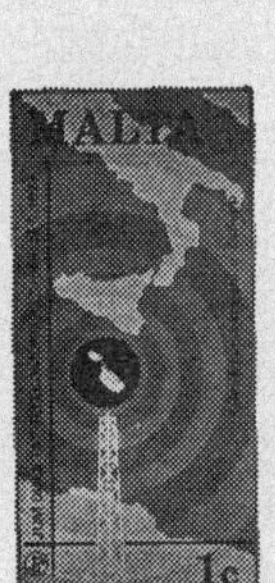

240. Map and Radio Aerial. **242.** "Aid to Handicapped Workers" (detail from Workers' Monument).

241. Ta' L-Isperanza.

1977. World Telecommunications Day.
580. **240.** 1 c. black, grn. and red 10 10
581. – 6 c. black, blue and red 15 10
582. – 8 c. black, brn. and red 15 10
583. – 17 c. blk., mauve & red 30 40
DESIGN—HORIZ. 8 and 17 c. Map, aerial and aeroplane tail-fin.

1977. Europa. Multicoloured.
584. 7 c. Type **241** .. 30 15
585. 20 c. Is-Salini .. 35 80

1977. Maltese Worker Commemoration.
586. **242.** 2 c. orange and brown 10 10
587. – 7 c. light brown & brown 15 10
588. – 20 c. multicoloured .. 40 60
DESIGNS—VERT. 7 c. "Stoneworker, modern industry and ship-building" (monument detail). HORIZ. 20 c. "Mother with Dead Son" and Service Medal.

243. The Shepherds.

1977. Christmas. Multicoloured.
589. 1 c.+5 m. Type **243** .. 10 20
590. 7 c.+1 c. The Nativity .. 15 30
591. 11 c.+1 c. 5 The Flight into Egypt .. 20 45

1978. Flemish Tapestries. (2nd series). As T **239**. Multicoloured.
592. 2 c. "The Entry into Jerusalem" .. 10 10
593. 7 c. "The Last Supper" (after Poussin) .. 20 10
594. 11 c. "The Raising of the Cross" (after Rubens) 25 25
595. 25 c. "The Resurrection" (after Rubens) .. 60 80

244. "Young Lady on Horseback and Trooper".

1978. 450th Death Anniv of Albrecht Durer.
596 **244** 1 c. 7 black, red & blue 10 10
597 – 8 c. black, red and grey 15 10
598 – 17 c. black, red & grey 40 45
DESIGNS: 8 c. "The Bagpiper". 17 c. "The Virgin and Child with a Monkey".

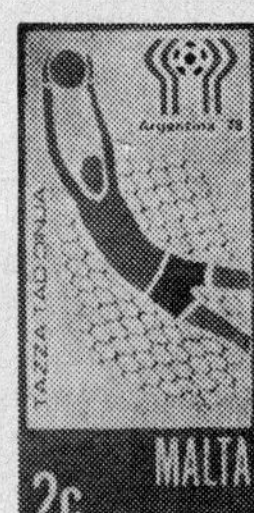

245. Monument to Grand Master Nicola Cotoner (Foggini). **246.** Goalkeeper.

1978. Europa. Monuments. Multicoloured.
599. 7 c. Type **245** .. 15 10
600. 25 c. Monument to Grand Master Ramon Perellos (Mazzuoli) .. 35 70

1978. World Cup Football Championship, Argentina. Multicoloured.
601. 2 c. Type **246** .. 10 10
602. 11 c. Players heading ball 15 10
603. 15 c. Tackling .. 25 35

247. Airliner over Megalithic Temple.

1978. Air. Multicoloured.
605. 5 c. Type **247** .. 15 10
606. 7 c. Air Malta Boeing "720B" .. 15 10
607. 11 c. Boeing "747" taking off from Luqa Airport .. 25 10
608. 17 c. Type **247** .. 35 30
609. 20 c. As 7 c. .. 50 40
610. 75 c. As 11 c. .. 1·50 2·25

248. Folk Musicians and Village Church.

1978. Christmas. Multicoloured.
611. 1 c.+5 m. Type **248** .. 10 10
612. 5 c.+1 c. Choir of Angels 10 15
613. 7 c.+1 c. 5 Carol Singers 15 20
614. 11 c.+3 c. Folk musicians, church, angels and carol singers (58×22 mm.) .. 20 30

1979. Flemish Tapestries (3rd series) showing paintings by Rubens. As T **239**. Multicoloured.
615. 2 c. "The Triumph of the Catholic Church" .. 10 10
616. 7 c. "The Triumph of Charity" .. 15 10
617. 11 c. "The Triumph of Faith" .. 25 20
618. 25 c. "The Triumph of Truth" .. 70 55

249. Fishing Boat and Aircraft Carrier.

1979. End of Military Facilities Agreement. Multicoloured.

No.	Description	Unused	Used
619.	2 c. Type **249**	10	10
620.	5 c. Raising the flag ceremony	10	10
621.	7 c. Departing soldier and olive sprig	15	10
622.	8 c. Type **249**	30	40
623.	17 c. As 5 c.	50	60
624.	20 c. As 7 c.	50	60

250. Speronara (fishing boat) and Tail of Air Malta Airliner. **251.** Children on Globe.

1979. Europa. Communications. Mult.

No.	Description	Unused	Used
625.	7 c. Type **250**	15	10
626.	25 c. Coastal watch tower and radio link towers ..	35	50

1979. International Year of the Child. Multicoloured.

No.	Description	Unused	Used
627.	2 c. Type **251**	10	10
628.	7 c. Children flying kites (27×33 mm.)	15	10
629.	11 c. Children in circle (27×33 mm.)	20	35

252. Shells (" Gibbula nivosa ").

1979. Marine Life. Multicoloured.

No.	Description	Unused	Used
630	2 c. Type **252**	10	10
631	5 c. Loggerhead turtle ("Garetta garetta") ..	20	10
632	7 c. Dolphin fish ("Coryphaena hippurus")	25	10
633	25 c. Noble pen shell ("Pinna nobilis") ..	90	1·25

253. " The Nativity " (detail).

1979. Christmas. Paintings by Giuseppe Cali. Multicoloured.

No.	Description	Unused	Used
634.	1 c.+5 m. Type **253** ..	10	10
635.	5 c.+1 c. " The Flight into Egypt " (detail) ..	10	15
636.	7 c.+1 c. 5 m. " The Nativity "	15	20
637.	11 c.+3 c. " The Flight into Egypt "	25	50

1980. Flemish Tapestries (4th series). As T **239**. Multicoloured.

No.	Description	Unused	Used
638.	2 c. " The Institution of Corpus Domini " (Rubens)	10	10
639.	8 c. " The Destruction of Idolatry " (Rubens) ..	20	20

254. Hal Saflieni Hypogeum, Paola. **255.** Dun Gorg Preca.

1980. Restoration of Monuments. Multicoloured.

No.	Description	Unused	Used
641.	2 c. 5 Type **254**	10	15
642.	6 c. Vilhena Palace, Mdina	25	20
643	8 c. Citadel of Victoria, Gozo (horiz.)	30	40
644.	12 c. Fort St. Elmo, Valletta (horiz.)	40	60

1980. Birth Centenary of Dun Gorg Preca (founder of Society of Christian Doctrine).

No.	Description	Unused	Used
645.	**255.** 2 c. 5 grey and black	10	10

256. Ruzar Briffa (poet).

1980. Europa.

No.	Description	Unused	Used
646.	**256.** 8 c. yell., brn. & grn...	20	10
647.	– 30 c. grn., brn. & lake	55	70

DESIGN: 30 c. Nikiol Anton Vassalu (scholar and patriot).

257. " Annunciation ".

1980. Christmas. Paintings by A. Inglott. Multicoloured.

No.	Description	Unused	Used
648.	2 c.+5 m. Type **257** ..	10	10
649.	6 c.+1 c. " Conception " ..	15	10
650.	8 c.+1 c. 5 " Nativity " ..	20	25
651.	12 c.+3 c. " Annunciation ", " Conception " and " Nativity " (47×38 mm.) ..	25	30

258. Rook and Pawn.

1980. 24th Chess Olympiad and International Chess Federation Congress. Multicoloured.

No.	Description	Unused	Used
652	2 c. 5 Type **258**	20	10
653	8 c. Bishop and pawn ..	50	15
654	30 c. King, queen and pawn (vert)	1·00	80

259. Barn Owl.

1981. Birds. Multicoloured.

No.	Description	Unused	Used
655.	3 c. Type **259**	30	15
656.	8 c. Sardinian Warbler ..	50	20
657.	12 c. Woodchat Shrike ..	60	60
658.	23 c. British Storm Petrel	1·10	1·25

260. Traditional Horse Race.

1981. Europa. Folklore. Multicoloured.

No.	Description	Unused	Used
659.	8 c. Type **260**	20	10
660.	30 c. Attempting to retrieve flag from end of " gostra " (greasy pole)	40	65

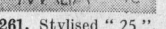

261. Stylised " 25 ". **262.** Disabled Artist at Work.

1981. 25th Maltese International Trade Fair.

No.	Description	Unused	Used
661.	**261.** 4 c. multicoloured ..	15	15
662.	25 c. multicoloured ..	50	60

1981. International Year for Disabled Persons. Multicoloured.

No.	Description	Unused	Used
663.	3 c. Type **262**	15	10
664.	35 c. Disabled child playing football	55	75

263. Wheat Ear in Conical Flask.

1981. World Food Day.

No.	Description	Unused	Used
665.	**263.** 8 c. multicoloured ..	15	15
666.	23 c. multicoloured ..	60	50

264. Megalithic Building.

1981. History of Maltese Industry. Mult.

No.	Description	Unused	Used
667.	5 m. Type **264**	10	10
668.	1 c. Cotton production ..	10	10
669.	2 c. Early ship-building ..	15	10
670.	3 c. Currency minting ..	20	10
671.	5 c. " Art "	30	25
672.	6 c. Fishing	40	25
673.	7 c. Agriculture	30	30
674.	8 c. Stone quarrying ..	30	35
675.	10 c. Grape pressing ..	35	40
676.	12 c. Modern ship-building	60	45
677.	15 c. Energy	70	55
678.	20 c. Telecommunications	70	75
679.	25 c. " Industry "	90	1·25
680.	50 c. Drilling for Water ..	1·75	1·90
681.	£1 Sea transport	5·00	5·00
682.	£3 Air transport	11·00	15·00

265. Children and Nativity Scene. **266.** Shipbuilding.

1981. Christmas. Multicoloured.

No.	Description	Unused	Used
683.	2 c.+1 c. Type **265** ..	15	10
684.	8 c.+2 c. Christmas eve procession (horiz.) ..	25	20
685.	20 c.+3 c. Preaching midnight sermon	50	60

1982. Shipbuilding Industry.

No.	Description	Unused	Used
686.	**266.** 3 c. multicoloured ..	15	10
687.	– 8 c. multicoloured ..	30	30
688.	– 13 c. multicoloured ..	55	55
689.	– 27 c. multicoloured ..	1·25	1·25

DESIGNS: 8 c. to 27 c. Differing shipyard scenes.

267. Elderly Man and Has-Serh (home for elderly).

1982. Care for Elderly. Multicoloured.

No.	Description	Unused	Used
690.	8 c. Type **267**	40	20
691.	30 c. Elderly woman and Has-Zmien (hospital for elderly)	1·40	1·40

268. Redemption of Islands by Maltese, 1428.

1982. Europa. Historical Events. Mult.

No.	Description	Unused	Used
692.	8 c. Type **268**	40	20
693.	30 c. Declaration of rights by Maltese, 1802 ..	1·00	1·40

269. Stylised Footballer.

1982. World Cup Football Championship, Spain.

No.	Description	Unused	Used
694.	**269.** 3 c. multicoloured ..	20	10
695.	– 12 c. multicoloured ..	60	55
696.	– 15 c. multicoloured ..	70	65

DESIGNS: 12 c., 15 c. Various stylised footballers.

270. Angel appearing to Shepherds.

1982. Christmas. Multicoloured.

No.	Description	Unused	Used
698.	2 c.+1 c. Type **270** ..	15	10
699.	8 c.+2 c. Nativity and Three Wise Men bearing gifts	40	40
700,	20 c.+3 c. Nativity scene (45×37 mm.)	85	85

271. "Ta Salvo Serafino" (oared brigantine), 1531.

1982. Maltese Ships (1st series). Mult.

No.	Description	Unused	Used
701	3 c. Type **271**	40	10
702	8 c. "La Madonna del Rosario" (tartane), 1740	80	30
703	12 c. "San Paulo" (xebec), 1743	1·25	55
704	20 c. "Ta Pietro Sablia" (xprunara), 1798 ..	1·60	90

See also Nos. 725/8, 772/5, 792/5 and 809/12.

272. "Manning Wardle", 1883.

1983. Centenary of Malta Railway. Mult.
705. 3 c. Type **272** 45 10
706. 13 c. "Black Hawthorn", 1884 .. .. .. 1·00 75
707. 27 c. "Beyer Peacock", 1895 .. .. .. 2·00 2·25

273. Peace Doves leaving Malta.

1983. Commonwealth Day. Multicoloured.
708. 8 c. Type **273** 30 30
709. 12 c. Tourist landmarks .. 40 50
710. 15 c. Holiday beach (vert.) 50 65
711. 23 c. Ship-building (vert.) 70 90

274. Ggantija Megalithic Temples, Gozo.

1983. Europa. Multicoloured.
712. 8 c. Type **274** 65 40
713. 30 c. Fort St. Angelo .. 1·75 2·10

275. Dish Aerials (World Communications Year).

1983. Anniversaries and Events. Mult.
714. 3 c. Type **275** 35 15
715. 7 c. Ships' prows and badge (25th anniv. of I.M.O. Convention) 60 40
716. 13 c. Container lorries and badge (30th anniv. of Customs Co-operation Council) 80 60
717. 20 c. Stadium and emblem (9th Mediterranean Games) 1·00 1·00

276. Monsignor Giuseppe de Piro. **277.** Annunciation.

1983. 50th Death Anniv. of Monsignor Giuseppe de Piro.
718. **276.** 3 c. multicoloured .. 15 15

1983. Christmas. Multicoloured.
719. 2 c.+1 c. Type **277** .. 30 15
720. 8 c.+2 c. The Nativity .. 75 50
721. 20 c.+3 c. Adoration of the Magi .. .. 1·40 1·10

278. Workers at Meeting.

1983. 40th Anniv. of General Workers' Union. Multicoloured.
722. 3 c. Type **278** 25 10
723. 8 c. Worker with family .. 50 40
724. 27 c. Union H.Q. Building 1·50 1·75

1983. Ships (2nd series). As T **271.** Mult.
725. 2 c. "Strangier" (full-rigged ship), 1813 .. 30 20
726. 12 c. "Tigre" (topsail schooner), 1839 .. .. 1·25 85
727. 13 c. "La Speranza" (brig), 1844 .. .. .. 1·25 1·00
728. 20 c. "Wignacourt" (barque), 1844 .. .. 1·75 2·00

279. Boeing "737".

1984. Air. Multicoloured.
729. 7 c. Type **279** 25 30
730. 8 c. Boeing "720B" .. 30 35
731. 16 c. Vickers "Vanguard" 60 65
732. 23 c. Vickers "Viscount" 85 90
733. 27 c. Douglas "DC.3 Dakota" 95 1·00
734. 38 c. A.W. "Atlanta" .. 1·40 1·75
735. 75 c. Dornier "Wal" .. 2·75 3·25

280. Bridge.

1984. Europa. 25th Anniv. of C.E.P.T.
736. **280.** 8 c. grn., blk. & yell. 35 35
737. 30 c. red, blk. & yell. 1·25 1·25

281. Early Policeman. **282.** Running.

1984. 170th Anniv. of Malta Police Force. Multicoloured.
738. 3 c. Type **281** 65 15
739. 8 c. Mounted police .. 1·50 55
740. 11 c. Motorcycle policeman 1·75 1·25
741. 25 c. Policeman and firemen 2·75 2·50

1984. Olympic Games, Los Angeles. Multicoloured.
742. 7 c. Type **282** 25 30
743. 12 c. Gymnastics 50 70
744. 23 c. Swimming .. .. 85 1·25

283. "The Visitation" (Pietru Caruana).

1984. Christmas. Paintings from Church of Our Lady of Porto Salvo, Valletta. Mult.
745. 2 c.+1 c. Type **283** .. 45 45
746. 8 c.+2 c. "The Epiphany" (Rafel Caruana) (horiz.) 85 1·00
747. 20 c.+3 c. "Jesus among the Doctors" (Rafel Caruana) (horiz.) .. 1·75 3·00

284. Dove on Map.

1984. 10th Anniv. of Republic. Mult.
748. 3 c. Type **284** 40 20
749. 8 c. Fort St. Angelo .. 75 60
750. 30 c. Hands .. .. 2·50 4·00

285. 1885 ½d. Green Stamp.

1985. Centenary of Malta Post Office. Mult.
751. 3 c. Type **285** 35 15
752. 8 c. 1885 1d. rose 55 40
753. 12 c. 1885 2½d. blue .. 75 1·10
754. 20 c. 1885 4d. brown .. 1·25 2·25

286. Boy, and Hands planting Vine.

1985. International Youth Year. Mult.
756 2 c. Type **286** 10 15
757 13 c. Young people and flowres (vert) 55 60
758 27 c. Girl holding flame in hand .. .. .. 1·25 1·40

287. Nicolo Baldacchino (tenor).

1985. Europa. European Music Year. Mult.
759. 8 c. Type **287** .. .. 1·50 50
760. 30 c. Francesco Azopardi (composer) .. .. 2·50 2·25

288. Guzeppi Bajada and Manwel Attard (victims).

1985. 66th Anniversary of 7 June 1919 Demonstrations. Multicoloured.
761. 3 c. Type **288** 35 15
762. 7 c. Karmnu Abela and Wenzu Dyer (victims) .. 75 35
763. 35 c. Model of projected Demonstration monument by Anton Agius (vert.) .. .. .. 2·25 1·75

289. Stylized Birds.

1985. 40th Anniversary of United Nations Organization. Multicoloured.
764. 4 c. Type **289** 20 15
765. 11 c. Arrow-headed ribbons 75 1·00
766. 31 c. Stylized figures .. 1·75 3·00

290. Giorgio Mitrovich (nationalist) (Death centenary).

1985. Celebrities' Anniversaries. Mult.
767. 8 c. Type **290** 70 35
768. 12 c. Pietru Caxaru (poet and administrator) (400th death anniv.) .. 1·40 1·25

291. The Three Wise Men.

1985. Christmas. Designs showing details of terracotta relief by Ganni Bonnici. Multicoloured.
769. 2 c.+1 c. Type **291** .. 55 75
770. 8 c.+2 c. Virgin and Child 1·25 1·75
771. 20 c.+3 c. Angels .. .. 2·25 3·00

1985. Maltese Ships (3rd series). Steamships. As T **271.** Multicoloured.
772. 3 c. "Scotia" (paddle-steamer), 1844 .. .. 65 20
773. 7 c. "Tagliaferro (screw steamer), 1822 .. .. 1·25 80
774. 15 c. "Gleneagles" (screw steamer), 1885 .. .. 1·75 2·25
775. 23 c. "L'Isle Adam" (screw steamer), 1886 .. .. 2·50 3·25

292. John XXIII Peace Laboratory and Statue of St. Francis of Assisi.

1986. International Peace Year. Mult.

776. 8 c. Type **292** .. .. 1·00 50
777. 11 c. Dove and hands holding olive branch (40×19 mm.). .. .. 1·50 2·00
778. 27 c. Map of Africa, dove and two heads .. .. 3·00 4·00

293. Symbolic Plant and "Cynthia cardui", "Vanessa atalanta" and "Polyommatus icarus".

1986. Europa. Environmental Conservation. Multicoloured.

779. 8 c. Type **293** .. .. 1·75 50
780. 35 c. Island, Neolithic frieze, sea and sun .. 3·25 5·00

294. Heading the Ball.

1986. World Cup Football Championship, Mexico. Multicoloured.

781. 3 c. Type **294** 60 20
782. 7 c. Saving a goal .. .. 1·25 80
783. 23 c. Controlling the ball .. 4·00 5·50

295. Father Diegu.

1986. Maltese Philanthropists. Multicoloured.

785. 2 c. Type **295** 40 30
786. 3 c. Adelaide Cini 50 30
787. 8 c. Alfonso Maria Galea .. 1·25 60
788. 27 c. Vincenzo Bugeja .. 3·25 5·50

296. "Nativity".

1986. Christmas. Multicoloured. Paintings by Giuseppe D'Arena.

789. 2 c.+1 c. Type **296** .. 50 60
790. 8 c.+2 c. "Nativity" (detail) (vert.) .. .. 1·50 2·00
791. 20 c+3 c. "Epiphany" .. 2·75 4·00

1986. Maltese Ships (4th series). As T **271.** Multicoloured.

792 7 c. "San Paul" (freighter), 1921 .. .. .. 1·25 50
793 10 c. "Knight of Malta" (mail steamer), 1930 .. 1·50 1·50
794 12 c. "Valetta City" (freighter), 1948 .. .. 1·75 2·25
795 20 c. "Saver" (freighter), 1959 .. .. .. 3·00 4·00

297. European Robin.

1987. 25th Anniv. of Malta Ornithological Society. Multicoloured.

796. 3 c. Type **297** 60 50
797. 8 c. Peregrine falcon (vert.) 1·50 90
798. 13 c. Hoopoe (vert.) .. 2·25 2·75
799. 23 c. Cory's shearwater .. 2·75 4·00

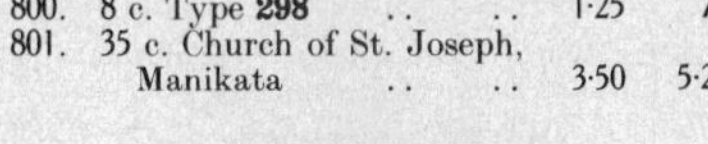

298. Aquasun Lido.

1987. Europa. Modern Architecture. Mult.

800. 8 c. Type **298** .. .. 1·25 75
801. 35 c. Church of St. Joseph, Manikata .. .. 3·50 5·25

299. 16th-century Pikeman.

1987. Maltese Uniforms (1st series). Mult.

802. 3 c. Type **299** 55 40
803. 7 c. 16th-century officer .. 1·00 80
804. 10 c. 18th-century standard bearer .. .. 1·50 1·75
805. 27 c. 18th-century General of the Galleys .. 3·25 4·00

See also Nos. 832/5, 851/4, 880/3 and 893/6.

300. Maltese Scenes, Wheat Ears and Sun.

1987. Anniversaries and Events. Mult.

806. 5 c. Type **300** (European Environment Year) .. 1·00 50
807. 8 c. Esperanto star as comet (Centenary of Esperanto) .. .. 1·25 60
808. 23 c. Family at house door (International Year of Shelter for the Homeless) .. .. 3·00 2·75

1987. Maltese Ships (5th series). As T **271.** Multicoloured.

809 2 c. "Medina" (freighter), 1969 .. .. .. 50 50
810 11 c. "Rabat" (container ship), 1974 .. .. 1·75 2·00
811 13 c. "Ghawdex" (passenger ferry), 1979 1·90 2·25
812 20 c. "Pinto" (car ferry), 1987 .. .. .. 2·50 3·00

301. "The Visitation".

1987. Christmas. Illuminated illustrations, score and text from 16th-century choral manuscript. Multicoloured.

813. 2 c.+1 c. Type **301** .. 40 40
814. 8 c.+2 c. "The Nativity" 1·25 2·00
815. 20 c.+3 c. "The Adoration of the Magi" .. .. 2·50 3·25

302. Dr. Arvid Pardo (U.N. representative).

1987. 20th Anniv. of United Nations Resolution on Peaceful Use of the Seabed. Multicoloured.

816. 8 c. Type **302** .. .. 1·00 75
817. 12 c. U.N. emblem and sea 1·75 2·50

303. Ven. Nazju Falzon (Catholic catechist).

1988. Maltese Personalities. Multicoloured.

819. 2 c. Type **303** 25 30
820. 3 c. Mgr. Sidor Formosa (philanthropist) 25 30
821. 4 c. Sir Luigi Preziosi (ophthalmologist) .. 30 30
822. 10 c. Fr. Anastasju Cuschieri (poet) 70 75
823. 25 c. Mgr. Pietru Pawl Saydon (Bible translator) .. .. .. 2·00 3·00

304. "St. John Bosco with Youth" (statue).

1988. Religious Anniversaries. Multicoloured.

824. 10 c. Type **304** (death centenary) 80 80
825. 12 c. "Assumption of Our Lady" (altarpiece by Perugino, Ta' Pinu, Gozo) (Marian Year) .. 1·00 1·25
826. 14 c. "Christ the King" (statue by Sciortino) (75th anniv. of International Eucharistic Congress, Valletta) .. 1·50 2·25

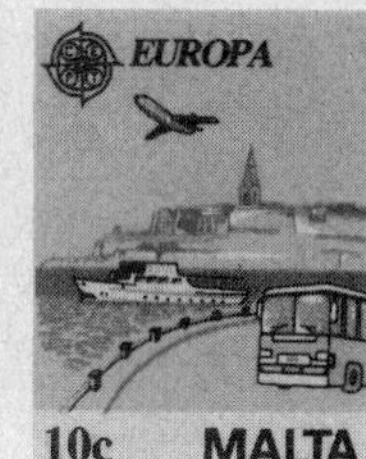

305. Bus, Ferry and Aircraft.

1988. Europa. Transport and Communications. Multicoloured.

827. 10 c. Type **305** .. .. 1·00 75
828. 35 c. Control panel, dish aerial and pylons .. 2·75 3·75

306 Globe and Red Cross Emblems

1988. Anniversaries and Events. Mult.

829 4 c. Type **306** (125th anniv of Int. Red Cross) .. 40 40
830 18 c. Divided globe (Campaign for North–South Interdependence and Solidarity) .. 1·75 2·25
831 19 c. Globe and symbol (40th anniv of W.H.O.) 1·75 2·25

1988. Maltese Uniforms (2nd series). As T **299.** Multicoloured.

832 3 c. Private, Maltese Light Infantry, 1800 .. .. 30 30
833 4 c. Gunner, Malta Coast Artillery, 1802 .. .. 35 35
834 10 c. Field Officer, 1st Maltese Provincial Battalion, 1805 .. 85 95
835 25 c. Subaltern, Royal Malta Regiment, 1809 .. 2·25 3·00

307 Athletics

309 Commonwealth Emblem

308 Shepherd with Flock

1988. Olympic Games, Seoul. Multicoloured.

836 4 c. Type **307** 30 30
837 10 c. Diving 70 80
838 35 c. Basketball .. .. 2·00 3·00

1988. Christmas. Multicoloured.

839 3 c.+1 c. Type **308** .. 25 30
840 10 c.+2 c. The Nativity .. 60 85
841 25 c.+3 c. Three Wise Men 1·50 2·25

1989. 25th Anniv of Independence. Mult.

842 2 c. Type **309** 25 25
843 3 c. Council of Europe flag 25 25
844 4 c. U.N. flag 30 30
845 10 c. Workers, hands gripping ring and national flag 75 85
846 12 c. Scales and allegorical figure of Justice .. 90 1·25
847 25 c. Prime Minister Borg Olivier with Independence constitution (42×28 mm) .. .. 1·90 3·00

310 New State Arms

1989.

848 **310** £1 multicoloured .. 4·00 4·25

311 Two Boys flying Kite

1989. Europa. Children's Games. Mult.

849 10 c. Type **311** .. .. 1·25 75
850 35 c. Two girls with dolls 3·25 4·25

1989. Maltese Uniforms (3rd series). As T **299**. Multicoloured.

851 3 c. Officer, Maltese Veterans, 1815 .. .. 35 35
852 4 c. Subaltern, Royal Malta Fencibles, 1839 .. 40 40
853 10 c. Private, Malta Militia, 1856 .. .. .. 1·00 1·25
854 25 c. Colonel, Royal Malta Fencible Artillery, 1875 2·25 3·25

312 Human Figures and Buildings

1989. Anniversaries and Commemorations. Designs showing logo and stylized human figures. Multicoloured.

855 3 c. Type **312** (20th anniv of U.N. Declaration on Social Progress and Development) 30 30
856 4 c. Workers and figure in wheelchair (Malta's Ratification of European Social Charter) .. 35 35
857 10 c. Family (40th anniv of Council of Europe) .. 80 90
858 14 c. Teacher and children (70th anniv of Malta Union of Teachers) .. 1·00 1·60
859 25 c. Symbolic knights (Knights of the Sovereign Military Order of Malta Assembly) .. 2·25 3·00

313 Angel and Cherub

1989. Christmas. Vault paintings by Mattia Preti from St. John's Co-Cathedral, Valletta.

860 3 c.+1 c. Type **313** .. 40 40
861 10 c.+2 c. Two angels .. 90 1·25
862 20 c.+3 c. Angel blowing trumpet .. .. 1·60 2·25

314 Presidents Bush and Gorbachev

1989. U.S.A.–U.S.S.R. Summit Meeting, Malta.

863 **314** 10 c. multicoloured .. 1·00 1·25

315 General Post Office, Auberge d'Italie, Valletta

1990. Europa. Post Office Buildings. Mult.

864 10 c. Type **315** 75 50
865 35 c. Branch Post Office, Zebbug (horiz) .. .. 2·25 3·25

316 Open Book and Letters from Different Alphabets (International Literacy Year)

1990. Anniversaries and Events. Mult.

866 3 c. Type **316** 25 25
867 4 c. Count Roger of Sicily and Norman soldiers (900th anniv of Sicilian rule) (horiz) 30 30
868 19 c. Communications satellite (25th anniv of I.T.U.) (horiz) .. .. 1·50 2·25
869 20 c. Football and map of Malta (Union of European Football Associations 20th Ordinary Congress, Malta) .. .. .. 1·50 2·25

317 Samuel Taylor Coleridge (poet) and Government House

1990. British Authors. Multicoloured.

870 4 c. Type **317** 25 30
871 10 c. Lord Byron (poet) and map of Valletta .. 50 70
872 12 c. Sir Walter Scott (novelist) and Great Siege 60 95
873 25 c. William Makepeace Thackeray (novelist) and Naval Arsenal .. .. 1·25 2·25

318 St. Paul

1990. Visit of Pope John Paul II. Bronze Bas-reliefs.

874 **318** 4 c. black, flesh & red 50 1·10
875 – 25 c. black, flesh & red 2·00 2·75

DESIGN: 25 c. Pope John Paul II.

319 Flags and Football

1990. World Cup Football Championship, Italy. Multicoloured.

876 5 c. Type **319** 35 30
877 10 c. Football in net .. 65 90
878 14 c. Scoreboard and football .. .. .. 1·00 1·60

1990. Maltese Uniforms (4th series). As T **299**. Multicoloured.

880 3 c. Captain, Royal Malta Militia, 1889 .. .. 30 30
881 4 c. Field officer, Royal Malta Artillery, 1905 .. 35 40
882 10 c. Labourer, Malta Labour Corps, 1915 .. 65 85
883 25 c. Lieutenant, King's Own Malta Regiment of Militia, 1918 .. .. 1·50 2·00

320 Innkeeper

1990. Christmas. Figures from Crib by Austin Galea, Marco Bartolo and Rosario Zammit. Multicoloured.

884 3 c.+1 c. Type **320** .. 30 40
885 10 c.+2 c. Nativity (41 × 28 mm) .. .. 70 1·10
886 25 c.+3 c. Shepherd with sheep .. .. .. 1·60 2·25

321 1899 10s. Stamp under Magnifying Glass

1991. 25th Anniv of Philatelic Society of Malta.

887 **321** 10 c. multicoloured .. 60 70

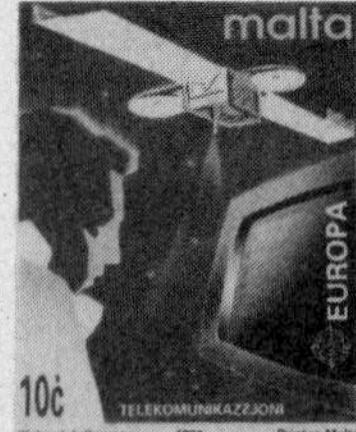

322 "Eurostar" Satellite and V.D.U. Screen

1991. Europa. Europe in Space. Mult.

888 10 c. Type **322** .. .. 1·00 70
889 35 c. "Ariane 4" rocket and projected HOTOL aerospaceplane .. .. 2·00 2·10

323 St. Ignatius Loyola (founder of Jesuits) (500th birth anniv)

1991. Religious Commemorations. Mult.

890 3 c. Type **323** 30 20
891 4 c. Abbess Venerable Maria Adeodata Pisani (185th birth anniv) (vert) 35 25
892 30 c. St. John of the Cross (400th death anniv) .. 2·00 2·25

1991. Maltese Uniforms (5th series). As T **299**. Multicoloured.

893 3 c. Officer with colour, Royal Malta Fencibles, 1860 .. .. .. 30 25
894 10 c. Officer with colour, Royal Malta Regiment of Militia, 1903 .. .. 70 60
895 19 c. Officer with Queen's colour, King's Own Malta Regiment, 1968 .. 1·40 1·40
896 25 c. Officer with colour, Malta Armed Forces, 1991 .. .. .. 1·75 1·75

324 Interlocking Arrows

1991. 25th Anniv of Union Haddiema Maghqudin (public services union).

897 **324** 4 c. multicoloured .. 30 30

325 Honey Buzzard

1991. Endangered Species. Birds. Mult.

898 4 c. Type **325** 45 50
899 4 c. Marsh harrier .. 45 50
900 10 c. Eleonora's falcon .. 80 90
901 10 c. Lesser kestrel .. 80 90

326 Three Wise Men

1991. Christmas. Multicoloured.

902	3 c.+1 c. Type **326** ..	25	25
903	10 c.+2 c. Holy Family ..	65	70
904	25 c.+3 c. Two shepherds	1·25	1·50

327 Ta' Hagrat Neolithic Temple

1991. National Heritage of the Maltese Islands. Multicoloured.

905	1 c. Type **327**	10	10
906	2 c. Cottoner Gate ..	10	10
907	3 c. St. Michael's Bastion, Valletta	10	15
908	4 c. Spinola Palace, St. Julian's	15	20
909	5 c. Birkirkara Church ..	15	20
910	10 c. Mellieha Bay ..	35	40
911	12 c. Wied iz-Zurrieq ..	40	45
912	14 c. Mgarr harbour, Gozo	50	55
913	20 c. Yacht marina ..	70	75
914	50 c. Gozo Channel ..	1·75	1·90
915	£1 "Arab Horses" (sculpture by Antonio Sciortino)	3·50	3·75
916	£2 Independence Monument (Ganni Bonnici) (vert)	7·00	7·25

328 Aircraft Tailfins and Terminal

1992. Opening of International Air Terminal. Multicoloured.

917	4 c. Type **328**	30	30
918	10 c. National flags and terminal	55	65

329 Ships of Columbus

1992. Europa. 500th Anniv of Discovery of America by Columbus. Multicoloured.

919	10 c. Type **329**	55	55
920	35 c. Columbus and map of Americas	2·00	2·25

330 George Cross and Anti-aircraft Gun Crew

1992. 50th Anniv of Award of George Cross to Malta. Multicoloured.

921	4 c. Type **330**	30	25
922	10 c. George Cross and memorial bell	75	55
923	50 c. Tanker "Ohio" entering Grand Harbour	3·50	3·75

331 Running

1992. Olympic Games, Barcelona. Mult.

924	3 c. Type **331**	20	20
925	10 c. High jumping ..	55	55
926	30 c. Swimming	2·00	2·00

332 Church of the Flight into Egypt

1992. Rehabilitation of Historical Buildings.

927	**332** 3 c. black, stone & grey	15	15
928	– 4 c. black, stone & pink	20	20
929	– 19 c. black, stone & lil	1·40	1·50
930	– 25 c. black, stone & grn	1·60	1·75

DESIGNS—HORIZ. 4 c. St. John's Co-Cathedral; 25 c. Auberge de Provence. VERT. 19 c. Church of Madonna del Pillar.

333 "The Nativity" (Giuseppe Cali)

1991. Christmas. Religious Paintings by Giuseppe Cali from Mosta Church. Mult.

931	3 c.+1 c. Type **333** ..	25	25
932	10 c.+2 c. "Adoration of the Magi"	65	65
933	25 c.+3 c. "Christ with the Elders in the Temple"	1·60	1·75

334 Malta College Building, Valletta

1992. 400th Anniv of University of Malta. Multicoloured.

934	4 c. Type **334**	30	25
935	30 c. Modern University complex, Tal-Qroqq (horiz)	1·60	1·75

335 Lions Club Emblem

1993. 75th Anniv of International Association of Lions Club. Multicoloured.

936	4 c. Type **335**	30	20
937	50 c. Eye (Sight First Campaign)	2·25	2·50

336 Untitled Painting by Pawl Carbonaro

1993. Europa. Contemporary Art. Mult.

938	10 c. Type **336**	50	40
939	35 c. Untitled painting by Alfred Chircop (horiz) ..	1·75	2·00

337 Mascot holding Flame

1993. 5th Small States of Europe Games. Multicoloured.

940	3 c. Type **337**	15	15
941	4 c. Cycling	20	20
942	10 c. Tennis	55	50
943	35 c. Yachting	1·75	2·00

338 Learning First Aid

1993. 50th Anniv of Award of Bronze Cross to Maltese Scouts and Guides. Multicoloured.

945	3 c. Type **338**	15	15
946	4 c. Bronze Cross ..	20	20
947	10 c. Scout building camp fire	55	50
948	35 c. Governor Lord Gort presenting Bronze Cross, 1943	1·75	2·00

339 "Papilio machaon"

1993. European Year of the Elderly. Butterflies. Multicoloured.

949	5 c. Type **339**	30	20
950	35 c. "Vanessa atalanta"	1·75	2·00

340 G.W.U. Badge and Interlocking "50"

1993. 50th Anniv of General Workers Union.

951	**340** 4 c. multicoloured ..	20	20

341 Child Jesus and Star

1993. Christmas. Multicoloured.

952	3 c.+1 c. Type **341** ..	20	20
953	10 c.+2 c. Christmas tree	50	50
954	25 c.+3 c. Star in traditional window ..	1·10	1·25

343 Symbolic Tooth and Probe

1994. 50th Anniv of Maltese Dental Association. Multicoloured.

956	5 c. Type **343**	15	20
957	44 c. Symbolic mouth and dental mirror	1·50	1·60

344 Sir Temi Zammit (discoverer of Brucella microbe)

1994. Europa. Discoveries. Multicoloured.

958	14 c. Type **344**		50	55
959	30 c. Bi-lingually inscribed candelabrum of 2nd century B.C. (deciphering of ancient Phoenician language) ..		1·00	1·10

POSTAGE DUE STAMPS

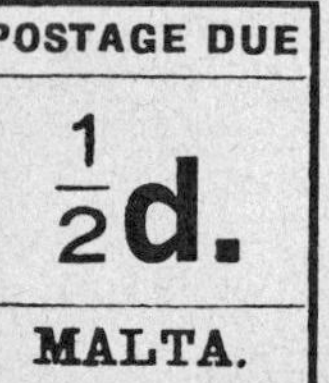

D 1.

D 2.

1925. Imperf.

D 1.	D 1.	$\frac{1}{2}$d. black	1·25	3·75
D 2.		1d. black	2·75	2·50
D 3.		1$\frac{1}{2}$d. black	2·75	3·50
D 4.		2d. black	4·00	7·00
D 5.		2$\frac{1}{2}$d. black	2·75	2·75
D 6.		3d. black on grey ..	8·50	11·00
D 7.		4d. black on yellow ..	4·75	9·00
D 8.		6d. black on yellow ..	4·75	11·00
D 9.		1s. black on yellow ..	7·50	15·00
D 10.		1s. 6d. black on yellow	13·00	40·00

1925. Perf.

D 32	D 2	$\frac{1}{2}$d. green	35	1·00
D 33		1d. violet	30	65
D 34		1$\frac{1}{2}$d. brown	35	1·75
D 14		2d. grey	11·00	1·50
D 35		2d. brown	85	70
D 36		2$\frac{1}{2}$d. orange ..	60	70
D 37		3d. blue	60	60
D 38		4d. green	1·00	80
D 39		6d. purple	75	1·00
D 40		1s. black	95	1·50
D 41		1s. 6d. red	2·25	4·50

D 3. Maltese Lace.

1973.

D 42.	D 3.	2 m. brown and red ..	10	10
D 43.		3 m. orange and red ..	10	10
D 44.		5 m. pink and red ..	10	10
D 45.		1 c. blue and green ..	15	15
D 46.		2 c. grey and black ..	15	15
D 47.		3 c. light brn. and brn.	15	15
D 48.		5 c. dull blue and blue	40	40
D 49.		10 c. lilac and plum ..	60	60

D 4

1993.

D50	D 4	1 c. magenta & mauve	10	10
D51		2 c. blue and lt blue	10	10
D52		5 c. green & turquoise	15	20
D53		10 c. orange & yellow	35	40

MAURITIUS

An island in the Indian Ocean, E. of Madagascar. Attained Self-Government on 1 September 1967, and became independent on 12 March 1968.

1847. 12 pence = 1 shilling.
20 shillings = 1 pound.
1878. 100 cents = 1 rupee.

1. (" POST OFFICE ").

2. (" POST PAID ").

1847. Imperf.

1.	1.	1d. red	£800000	£400000
2.		2d. blue	£800000	£500000

1848. Imperf.

23.	2.	1d. red	£1200	£350
25.		2d. blue	£1600	£450

3. 5.

1854. Surch. **FOUR-PENCE.** Imperf.

26	3	4d. green	£700	£375

1858. No value on stamps. Imperf.

27	3	(4d.) green	£400	£200
28		(6d.) red	19·00	26·00
29		(9d.) purple	£500	£200

1859. Imperf.

32	5	6d. blue	£475	28·00
33		6d. black	15·00	22·00
34		1s. red	£2000	45·00
35		1s. green	£300	70·00

6.

8.

1859. Imperf.

39	6	2d. blue	£1000	£400

1859. Imperf.

42	8	1d. red	£2500	£700
44		2d. blue	£1400	£325

9.

10.

1860.

56	9	1d. purple	35·00	6·50
57		1d. brown	48·00	5·00
60		2d. blue	55·00	5·00
61a		3d. red	35·00	8·50
62		4d. red	65·00	1·75
65		6d. green	75·00	3·75
50		6d. grey	£130	70·00
63		6d. violet	£100	23·00
51		9d. purple	70·00	30·00
66		9d. green	£100	£120
67	10	10d. red	£120	22·00
70	9	1s. yellow	£100	12·00
53		1s. green	£500	£130
69		1s. blue	£120	18·00
71		5s. mauve	£120	35·00

1862. Perf.

54	5	6d. black	14·00	26·00
55		1s. green	£1600	£300

HALF PENNY (11.)

HALF PENNY (13.)

1876. Surcharged with T **11**.

76.	9.	$\frac{1}{2}$d. on 9d. purple	3·00	6·50
77.	10.	$\frac{1}{2}$d. on 10d. red	80	9·50

1877. Surch. with T **13**.

79.	10.	$\frac{1}{2}$d. on 10d. red	2·25	24·00

One Penny (14.)

2 CENTS (16.)

1877. Surch. as T **14**.

80.	9.	1d. on 4d. red	7·50	12·00
81.		1s. on 5s. mauve	£180	85·00

1878. Surch. as T **16**.

83.	10.	2 c. red	5·50	4·50
84.	9.	4 c. on 1d. brown ..	7·50	3·75
85.		8 c. on 2d. blue ..	65·00	75
86.		13 c. on 3d. red	7·00	19·00
87.		17 c. on 4d. red	95·00	1·50
88.		25 c. on 6d. blue ..	£130	4·75
89.		38 c. on 9d. purple ..	18·00	38·00
90.		50 c. on 1s. green ..	85·00	2·50
91.		2 r. 50 on 5s. mauve ..	12·00	9·00

18.

19.

1879. Various frames.

101	18	1 c. violet	50	45
102		2 c. red	22·00	4·75
103		2 c. green	1·25	40
104	19	4 c. orange	55·00	2·50
105		4 c. red	1·50	30
106	–	8 c. blue	1·00	80
95	–	13 c. grey	£120	£130
107	–	15 c. brown	2·00	70
108	–	15 c. blue	5·50	40
109	–	16 c. brown	2·50	55
96	–	17 c. red	40·00	4·00
110	–	25 c. olive	3·75	1·50
98	–	38 c. purple	£140	£160
99	–	50 c. green	2·75	1·75
111	–	50 c. orange	26·00	8·00
100	–	2 r. 50 purple	25·00	45·00

1883. No. 96 surch **16 CENTS**.

112		16 c. on 17 c. red	90·00	42·00

1883. No. 96 surch **SIXTEEN CENTS**.

115		16 c. on 17 c. red	40·00	80

1885. No. 98 surch **2 CENTS** with bar.

116		2 c. on 38 c. purple ..	70·00	32·00

1887. No. 95 surch as above without bar.

117		2 c. on 13 c. grey	27·00	48·00

1891. Surch in words with or without bar.

123	18	1 c. on 2 c. violet ..	55	50
124	–	1 c. on 16 c. brown (No. 109)	55	1·25
118	19	2 c. on 4 c. red ..	35	30
119	–	2 c. on 17 c. red (No. 96)	65·00	65·00
120	9	2 c. on 38 c. on 9 d. (89)	1·00	3·50
121	–	2 c. on 38 c. pur (No. 98)	2·00	3·00

36.

1895.

127	36	1 c. purple and blue ..	60	60
128		2 c. purple and orange	2·00	20
129		3 c. purple	60	30
130		4 c. purple and green	3·50	30
131		6 c. green and red ..	3·00	2·50
132		18 c. green and blue ..	6·50	5·00

37.

1898. Diamond Jubilee.

133.	37.	36 c. orange and blue ..	9·00	13·00

1899. Surch in figures and words.

137	–	4 c. on 16 c. brown (No. 109)	1·25	3·75
134	36	6 c. on 18 c. (No. 132) ..	60	70
156		12 c. on 18 c. (No. 132)	90	5·00
163	37	12 c. on 36 c. (No. 133)	1·25	1·00
135		15 c. on 36 c. (No. 133)	1·00	90

40. Admiral Mahe de Labourdonnais, Governor of Mauritius 1735–46.

42.

1899. Birth Bicentenary of Labourdonnais.

136.	40.	15 c. blue	10·00	1·75

1900.

138	36	1 c. grey and black ..	50	10
139		2 c. purple	40	10
140		3 c. green & red on yell.	1·75	40
141		4 c. purple & red on yell.	1·25	10
142		4 c. green and violet ..	60	85
167a		4 c. black & red on blue	1·00	10
144		5 c. purple on buff ..	3·25	42·00
145		5 c. pur. & blk. on buff	1·60	1·75
168a		6 c. purple & red on red	1·50	10
147		8 c. grn. & blk. on buff	1·00	3·50
148		12 c. black and red ..	1·50	95
149		15 c. green and orange ..	6·00	6·00
171		15 c. blk. & blue on blue	4·00	35
151a		25 c. grn. & red on grn.	2·50	8·00
174		50 c. green on yellow ..	1·50	2·25
175	42	1 r. grey and red ..	19·00	32·00
154		2 r. 50 grn. & blk. on bl.	12·00	50·00
155		5 r. purple & red on red	48·00	75·00

1902. Optd **Postage & Revenue**.

157	36	4 c. purple & red on yell	30	20
158		6 c. green and red ..	35	2·50
159		15 c. green and orange	75	30
160	–	25 c. olive (No. 110) ..	85	2·25
161	–	50 c. green (No. 99) ..	3·75	1·00
162	–	2 r. 50 purple (No. 100)	55·00	65·00

46.

47.

1910.

181	46	1 c. black	85	20
206		2 c. brown	60	10
207		2 c. purple on yellow ..	60	20
183		3 c. green	1·25	10
184		4 c. green and red ..	1·25	10
210		4 c. green	1·00	10
211		4 c. brown	1·50	80
186		6 c. red	90	10
213		6 c. mauve	1·25	10
187		8 c. orange	1·50	1·25
215		10 c. grey	2·00	3·25
216		10 c. red	2·50	90
217		12 c. red	1·25	40
218		12 c. grey	1·00	1·50
219a		15 c. blue	75	25
220		20 c. blue	2·00	50
221		20 c. purple	6·50	10·00

1910.

185.	47.	5 c. grey and red ..	1·00	2·00
188.		12 c. grey	75	75
190.		25 c. blk. & red on yell.	1·75	8·50
191.		50 c. purple and black ..	1·75	12·00
192.		1 r. black on green ..	3·75	7·00
193.		2 r. 50 blk. & red on blue	7·50	42·00
194.		5 r. green & red on yell.	25·00	65·00
195.		10 r. green & red on grn.	80·00	£140

48.

1913.

223	48	1 c. black	55	40
224		2 c. brown	55	10
225		3 c. green	60	30
226		4 c. green and red ..	45	30
226b		4 c. green	2·50	45
227		5 c. grey and red ..	80	10
228		6 c. brown	60	60
229		8 c. orange	60	6·50
230		10 c. red	75	20
232b		12 c. grey	1·50	20
232		12 c. red	30	2·50
233		15 c. blue	70	20
234		20 c. purple	45	40
235		20 c. blue	9·50	80
236		25 c. blk. & red on yellow	30	15
237		50 c. purple and black ..	7·50	3·50
238		1 r. black on green ..	1·25	40
239		2 r. 50 blk. & red on bl.	15·00	6·00
240		5 r. grn. & red on yellow	20·00	55·00
204d		10 r. green & red on grn.	25·00	70·00

1924. As T **42** but Arms similar to T **46**.

222		50 r. purple and green ..	£700	£1300

1925. Surch. with figures, words and bar.

242	46	3 c. on 4 c. green ..	2·50	3·75
243		10 c. on 12 c. red ..	30	10
244		15 c. on 20 c. blue ..	55	15

1935. Silver Jubilee. As T **13** of Antigua.

245		5 c. blue and grey ..	30	10
246		12 c. green and blue ..	2·50	10
247		20 c. brown and blue ..	3·50	20
248		1 r. grey and purple ..	27·00	30·00

1937. Coronation. As T **2** of Aden.

249		5 c. violet	55	10
250		12 c. red	55	80
251		20 c. blue	55	10

51.

1938.

252 51 2 c. grey 30 10
253a 3 c. purple and red .. 1·25 1·25
254a 4 c. green .. .. 1·00 80
255a 5 c. violet .. .. 1·75 20
256b 10 c. red .. .. 2·00 10
257 12 c. orange .. .. 1·00 20
258 20 c. blue .. .. 1·00 10
259b 25 c. purple .. .. 2·50 10
260b 1 r. brown .. .. 7·50 70
261a 2 r. 50 violet .. .. 19·00 7·00
262a 5 r. olive .. .. 27·00 20·00
263a 10 r. purple .. .. 9·00 17·00

1946. Victory. As T **9** of Aden.

264 5 c. violet 10 10
265 20 c. blue 10 10

52. 1d. "Post Office" Mauritius and King George VI.

1948. Cent. of First British Colonial Stamp.

266. **52.** 5 c. orange and mauve 10 30
267. 12 c. orange and green 10 10
268. – 20 c. blue 10 10
269. – 1 r. blue and brown .. 15 30

Design: 20 c., 1 r. As Type **52**, but showing 2d. "Post Office" Mauritius.

1948. Silver Wedding. As T **10/11** of Aden.

270 5 c. violet 10 10
271 10 r. mauve .. .. 9·00 15·00

1949. U.P.U. As Nos. **20/23** of Antigua.

272 12 c. red 60 65
273 20 c. blue 60 80
274 35 c. purple 60 60
275 1 r. brown 60 20

55. Aloe Plant.

60. Legend of Paul and Virginie.

67. Arms of Mauritius.

1950.

276. – 1 c. purple 10 50
277. – 2 c. red 15 10
278. **55.** 3 c. green .. .. 60 2·00
279. – 4 c. green 20 65
280. – 5 c. blue 15 10
281. – 10 c. red 30 75
282. – 12 c. green .. .. 1·25 55
283. **60.** 20 c. blue 50 15
284. – 25 c. red 95 40
285. – 35 c. violet 30 10
286. – 50 c. green .. .. 1·75 50
287. – 1 r. brown .. .. 3·75 10
288. – 2 r. 50 orange .. .. 12·00 5·50
289. – 5 r. brown .. .. 13·00 12·00
290. **67.** 10 r. blue .. .. 14·00 15·00

Designs—Horiz. 1 c. Labourdonnais sugar factory. 2 c. Grand Port. 5 c. Rempart Mountain. 10 c. Transporting cane. 12 c. Mauritius dodo and map. 35 c. Government House, Reduit. 1 r. Timor deer. 2 r. 50, Port Louis; 5 r. Beach scene. Vert. 4 c. Tamarind Falls. 25 c. Labourdonnais statue. 50 c. Pieter Both Mountain.

1953. Coronation. As T **13** of Aden.

291 10 c. black and green .. 55 15

69. Historical Museum, Mahebourg.

1953. As 1950 but portrait of Queen Elizabeth II. Designs as for corresponding values except where stated.

293 – 2 c. red 10 10
294 – 3 c. green 30 40
295 – 4 c. purple (as 1 c.) .. 10 60
296 – 5 c. blue 10 10
297 – 10 c. green (as 4 c.) .. 10 10
298 **69.** 15 c. red 10 10
299 – 20 c. red (as 25 c.) .. 15 20
300a – 25 c. blue (as 20 c.) .. 55 10
301 – 35 c. violet 20 10
302 – 50 c. green 45 45
315 – 60 c. green (as 12 c.) .. 1·75 10
303 – 1 r. sepia 30 10
316 – 2 r. 50 orange .. .. 2·75 6·00
305 – 5 r. brown .. .. 8·00 4·50
306 – 10 r. blue .. .. 11·00 60

70. Queen Elizabeth II and King George III (after Lawrence).

1961. 100th Anniv. of British Post Office in Mauritius.

307. **70.** 10 c. black and red .. 10 10
308. 20 c. ultramarine & blue 20 25
309. 35 c. black and yellow .. 25 25
310. 1 r. purple and green .. 25 25

1963. Freedom from Hunger. As T **28** of Aden.

311 60 c. violet 40 10

1963. Cent of Red Cross. As T **33** of Antigua.

312 10 c. red and black .. 15 10
313 60 c. red and blue .. 60 20

71. Bourbon White Eye.

1965. Birds. Multicoloured.

317 2 c. Type **71** (yellow background) 10 15
318 3 c. Rodriguez fody (brown background) 30 15
319 4 c. Mauritius olive white eye 10 15
340 5 c. Mascarene paradise flycatcher 10 15
321 10 c. Mauritius fody .. 30 10
322 15 c. Mauritius parkeet (grey background) .. 1·00 30
323 20 c. Mauritius greybird (yellow background) .. 1·00 10
324 25 c. Mauritius kestrel .. 1·50 10
341 35 c. Pink pigeon .. 20 15
326 50 c. Reunion bulbul .. 50 35
327 60 c. Mauritius blue pigeon (extinct) (yellow background) 40 10
328 1 r. Mauritius dodo (extinct) (olive background) .. .. 1·50 10
329 2 r. 50 Rodriguez solitaire (extinct) .. .. 4·50 6·00
330 5 r. Mauritius red rail (extinct) .. .. 13·00 6·00
331 10 r. Broad-billed parrot (extinct) .. .. 22·00 9·50

For some values with background colours changed see Nos. 370/5.

1965. Centenary of I.T.U. As T **36** of Antigua.

332 10 c. orange and green .. 15 10
333 60 c. yellow and violet .. 40 20

1965. I.C.Y. As T **37** of Antigua.

334 10 c. purple and turquoise 15 10
335 60 c. green and violet .. 30 20

1966. Churchill Commem. As T **38** of Antigua.

336 2 c. blue 10 80
337 10 c. green 25 10
338 60 c. brown .. .. 1·10 15
339 1 r. violet .. .. 1·25 15

1966. 20th Anniv of U.N.E.S.C.O. As T **54/6** of Antigua.

342 5 c. multicoloured .. 15 20
343 10 c. yellow, violet & green 25 10
344 60 c. black, purple & orge 70 15

86. Red-tailed Tropic Bird.

1967. Self Government. Multicoloured.

345. 2 c. Type **86** 10 35
346. 10 c. Rodriguez brush warbler 20 10
347. 60 c. Rose-ringed parakeet (extinct) 30 10
348. 1 r. Grey-rumped swiftlet 35 10

1967. Self Government. Nos. 317/31 optd. **SELF GOVERNMENT 1967.**

349. **71.** 2 c. multicoloured .. 10 50
350. – 3 c. multicoloured .. 10 50
351. – 4 c. multicoloured .. 10 50
352. – 5 c. multicoloured .. 10 10
353. – 10 c. multicoloured .. 10 10
354. – 15 c. multicoloured .. 10 30
355. – 20 c. multicoloured .. 15 10
356. – 25 c. multicoloured .. 15 10
357. – 35 c. multicoloured .. 20 10
358. – 50 c. multicoloured .. 30 15
359. – 60 c. multicoloured .. 30 10
360. – 1 r. multicoloured .. 35 10
361. – 2 r. 50 multicoloured .. 1·00 2·00
362. – 5 r. multicoloured .. 3·00 3·25
363. – 10 r. multicoloured .. 5·50 8·50

91. Flag of Mauritius.

1968. Independence. Multicoloured.

364. 2 c. Type **91** 10 55
365. 3 c. Arms and Mauritius dodo emblem 10 55
366. 15 c. Type **91** 10 10
367. 20 c. As 3 c. 10 10
368. 60 c. Type **91** 30 10
369. 1 r. As 3 c. 40 10

1968. As Nos. 317/8, 322/3 and 327/8 but background colours changed as below.

370 **71** 2 c. olive .. .. 20 1·00
371 – 3 c. blue .. .. 1·50 2·00
372 – 15 c. brown 55 20
373 – 20 c. buff .. .. 3·00 1·25
374 – 60 c. red 90 15
375 – 1 r. purple .. .. 1·75 1·00

93. Dominique rescues Paul and Virginie.

1968. Bicentenary of Bernardin de St. Pierre's Visit to Mauritius. Multicoloured.

376. 2 c. Type **93** 10 50
377. 15 c. Paul and Virginie Crossing the River .. 20 10
378. 50 c. Visit of Labourdonnais to Madame de la Tour .. 30 10
379. 60 c. Meeting of Paul and Virginie in Confidence .. 30 10
380. 1 r. Departure of Virginie for Europe 40 20
381. 2 r. 50 Bernardin de St. Pierre 1·10 2·75

Nos. 377, 379 and 381 are vert.

99. Batarde.

1969. Multicoloured.

382 2 c. Type **99** 10 50
383 3 c. Red Reef Crab .. 10 1·00
384 4 c. Episcopal Mitre .. 90 1·50
440 5 c. Bourse 30 10
386 10 c. black, red and flesh (Starfish) .. .. 1·00 10
387 15 c. ochre, black & cobalt (Sea Urchin) 30 10
480 20 c. Fiddler Crab .. 30 30
389 25 c. red, black and green (Spiny Shrimp) 30 75
390 30 c. Single Harp Shells, and Double Harp Shell .. 1·50 1·25
483 35 c. Argonaute 75 15
484 40 c. Nudibranch 75 60
448 50 c. Violet and Orange Spider Shells 45 10
449 60 c. black, red and blue (Blue Marlin) 65 10
487 75 c. "Conus clytospira" .. 1·25 60
396 1 r. Dolphin 60 10
452 2 r. 50 Spiny Lobster .. 2·00 3·75
453 5 r. Sacre Chien Rouge .. 3·00 2·00
399 10 r. Croissant Queue Jaune 2·50 4·00

117. Gandhi as Law Student.

1969. Birth Centenary of Mahatma Gandhi. Multicoloured.

400. 2 c. Type **117** 10 10
401. 15 c. Gandhi as Stretcher-bearer during Zulu revolt 25 10
402. 50 c. Gandhi as Satyagrahi in South Africa .. 30 20
403. 60 c. Gandhi at No. 10 Downing Street, London 30 10
404. 1 r. Gandhi in Mauritius, 1901 .. .. 40 10
405. 2 r. 50 Gandhi, the "Apostle of Truth and Non Violence" .. .. 90 1·00

124. Frangourinier Cane-crusher (18th cent.).

1969. 150th Anniv. of Telfair's Improvements to the Sugar Industry. Multicoloured.

407. 2 c. Three-roller Vertical Mill 10 20
408. 15 c. Type **124** 10 10
409. 60 c. Beau Rivage Factory, 1867 .. .. 10 10
410. 1 r. Mon Desert-Alma Factory, 1969 .. .. 10 10
411. 2 r. 50 Dr. Charles Telfair (vert.) 25 50

1970. Expo 70. Nos. 394 and 396 optd. **EXPO '70' OSAKA.**

413. 60 c. black, red and blue .. 10 10
414. 1 r. multicoloured .. 10 10

129. Morne Plage, Mountain and Lufthansa Airliner.

1970. Inauguration of Lufthansa Flight, Mauritius-Frankfurt. Multicoloured.

415.	25 c. Type **129**	10	10
416.	50 c. Airliner and Map (vert.)	10	10

131. Lenin as a Student.

1970. Birth Centenary of Lenin.

417. **131.**	15 c. green and silver..	10	10
418. –	75 c. brown	20	20

DESIGN: 75 c. Lenin as founder of U.S.S.R.

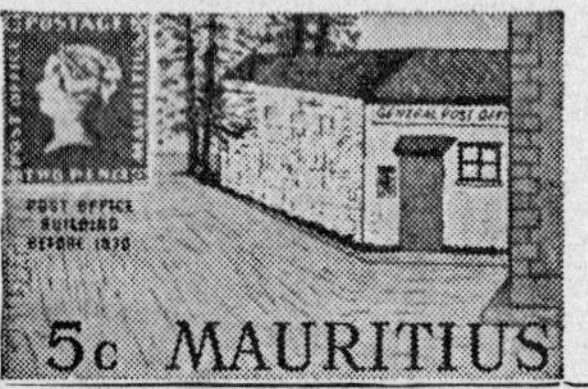

133. 2d. "Post Office" Mauritius and original Post Office.

1970. Port Louis, Old and New. Mult.

419.	5 c. Type **133**	10	10
420.	15 c. G.P.O. Building (built 1870)	10	10
421.	50 c. Mail Coach (c. 1870)	30	10
422.	75 c. Port Louis Harbour (1970)	40	10
423.	2 r. 50 Arrival of Pierre A. de Suffren (1783) ..	60	70

138. U.N. Emblem and Symbols.

1970. 25th Anniv. of U.N.

425. **138.**	10 c. multicoloured ..	10	10
426.	60 c. multicoloured ..	40	10

139. Rainbow over Waterfall.

1971. Tourism. Multicoloured.

427.	10 c. Type **139**	25	10
428.	15 c. Trois Mamelles Mountains	25	10
429.	60 c. Beach scene	45	10
430.	2 r. 50 Marine life	1·50	1·50

Nos. 427/30 have inscriptions on the reverse.

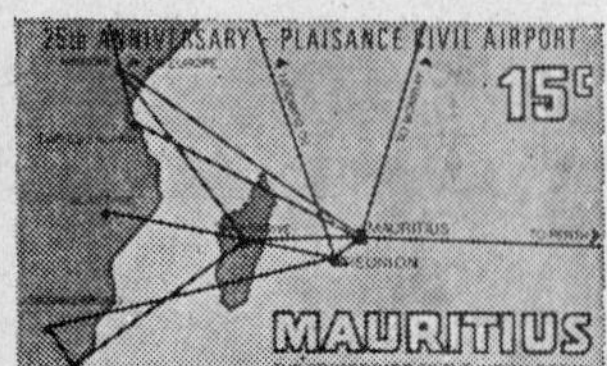

140. "Crossroads" of Indian Ocean.

1971. 25th Anniv. of Plaisance Airport. Multicoloured.

431.	15 c. Type **140**	15	10
432.	60 c. "Boeing 707" and Terminal Buildings ..	30	10
433.	1 r. Air Hostesses on gangway	35	10
434.	2 r. 50 "Roland Garros" (plane), Choisy Airfield, 1937	1·75	2·75

141. Princess Margaret Orthopaedic Centre.

1971. 3rd Commonwealth Medical Conference. Multicoloured.

435.	10 c. Type **141**	10	10
436.	75 c. Operating Theatre in National Hospital ..	20	20

142. Queen Elizabeth II and Prince Philip.

1972. Royal Visit. Multicoloured.

455.	15 c. Type **142**	15	10
456.	2 r. 50 Queen Elizabeth II (vert.)	2·50	2·50

143. Theatre Facade.

1972. 150th Anniv. of Port Louis Theatre. Multicoloured.

457.	10 c. Type **143**	10	10
458.	1 r. Theatre auditorium ..	40	20

144. Pirate Dhow.

1972. Pirates and Privateers. Multicoloured.

459.	15 c. Type **144**	65	15
460.	60 c. Treasure chest (vert.)	1·00	20
461.	1 r. Lememe and "L'Hirondelle" (vert.)	1·25	20
462.	2 r. 50 Robert Surcouf ..	4·50	7·50

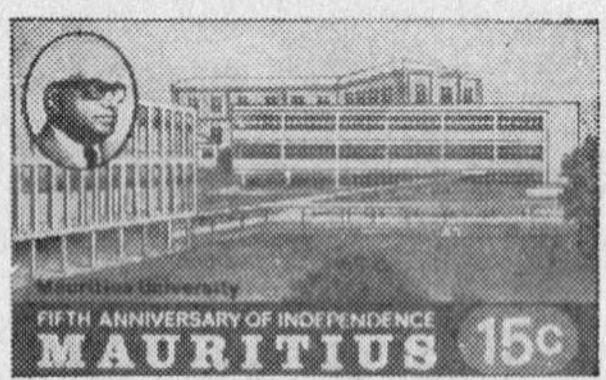

145. Mauritius University.

1973. 5th Anniv. of Independence. Mult.

463.	15 c. Type **145**	10	10
464.	60 c. Tea Development ..	15	15
465.	1 r. Bank of Mauritius ..	15	15

146. Map and Hands.

1973. O.C.A.M. Conf. Multicoloured.

466.	10 c. O.C.A.M. emblem (horiz.)	10	10
467.	2 r. 50 Type **146**	40	45

O.C.A.M. = Organization Commune Africaine Malgache et Mauricienne.

147. W.H.O. Emblem.

1973. 25th Anniv. of W.H.O.

468. **147.**	1 r. multicoloured ..	10	10

148. Meteorological Station, Vacoas.

1973. Centenary of I.M.O./W.M.O.

469. **148.**	75 c. multicoloured ..	30	50

149. Capture of the "Kent" 1800.

1973. Birth Bicentenary of Robert Surcouf (privateer).

470. **149.**	60 c. multicoloured ..	50	70

150. P. Commerson.

1974. Death Bicentenary (1973) of Philibert Commerson (naturalist).

471. **150.**	2 r. 50 multicoloured	30	40

151. Cow being Milked.

1974. Eighth Regional Conf. for Africa, Mauritius.

472. **151.**	60 c. multicoloured ..	20	20

152. Mail Train.

1974. Centenary of U.P.U. Multicoloured.

473.	15 c. Type **152**	40	15
474.	1 r. New G.P.O., Port Louis	40	20

153. "Cottage Life" (F. Leroy).

1975. Aspects of Mauritian Life. Paintings. Multicoloured.

493.	15 c. Type **153**	10	10
494.	60 c. "Milk Seller" (A. Richard) (vert.) ..	35	10
495.	1 r. "Entrance of Port Louis Market" (Thuillier)	35	10
496.	2 r. 50 "Washerwomen" (Max Boulle) (vert.) ..	95	80

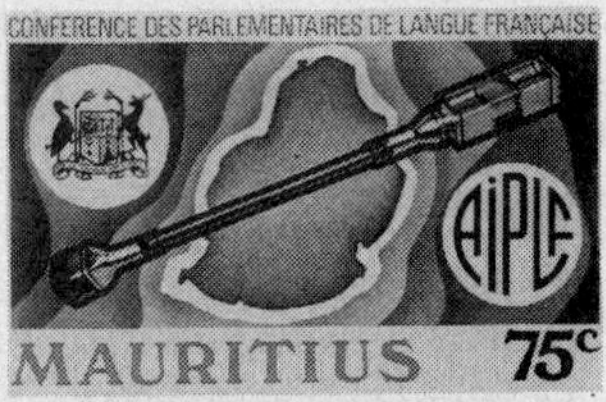

154. Mace across Map.

1975. French-speaking Parliamentary Assemblies Conf., Port Louis.

497. **154.**	75 c. multicoloured ..	30	60

155. Woman with Lamp ("The Light of the World").

1976. International Women's Year.

498. **155.**	2 r. 50 multicoloured ..	35	1·00

156. Parched Landscape.

1976. Drought in Africa. Multicoloured.

499.	50 c. Type **156**	15	15
500.	60 c. Map of Africa and carcass (vert.)	15	15

157. "Pierre Loti", 1953–70.

1976. Mail Carriers to Mauritius. Mult.

501.	10 c. Type **157**	25	10
502.	15 c. "Secunder", 1907 ..	30	10
503.	50 c. "Hindoostan", 1842	65	15
504.	60 c. "St. Geran", 1740 ..	70	15
505.	2 r. 50 "Maen", 1638 ..	2·50	5·00

158. "The Flame of Hindi carried across the Seas".

1976. Second World Hindi Convention. Multicoloured.

507.	10 c. Type **158**	10	10
508.	75 c. Type **158**	10	15
509.	1 r. 20 Hindi script ..	20	40

159. Conference Logo and Map of Mauritius.

1976. 22nd Commonwealth Parliamentary Conf. Multicoloured.

510.	1 r. Type **159**	40	10
511.	2 r. Conference logo ..	1·00	80

160. King Priest and Breastplate.

1976. Moenjodaro Excavations, Pakistan. Multicoloured.

512.	60 c. Type **160**	30	10
513.	1 r. House with well and goblet	50	10
514.	2 r. 50 Terracotta figurine and necklace	1·25	65

161. Sega Scene.

1977. 2nd World Black and African Festival of Arts and Culture, Nigeria.

515. **161.**	1 r. multicoloured ..	30	15

162. The Queen with Sceptre and Rod.

1977. Silver Jubilee. Multicoloured.

516.	50 c. The Queen at Mauritius Legislative Assembly 1972	20	10
517.	75 c. Type **162**	25	10
518.	5 r. Presentation of Sceptre and Rod	75	75

163. "Hugonia tomentosa".

1977. Indigenous Flowers. Multicoloured.

519.	20 c. Type **163**	10	10
520.	1 r. "Ochna mauritiana" (vert.)	20	10
521.	1 r. 50 "Dombeya acutangula"	30	20
522.	5 r. "Trochetia blackburniana" (vert.) ..	1·00	1·25

164. "Twin Otter".

1977. Air. Mauritius Inaugural Int. Flight. Multicoloured.

524.	25 c. Type **164**	40	10
525.	50 c. "Twin Otter" and Air Mauritius emblem	60	10
526.	75 c. Piper "Navajo" and Boeing "747"	75	10
527.	5 r. Boeing "707"	3·00	1·50

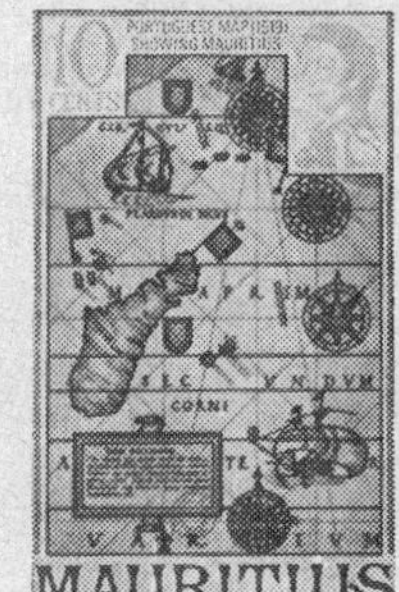

165. Portuguese Map of Mauritius, 1519.

1978.

529	**165.**	10 c. multicoloured ..	30	40
530	–	15 c. multicoloured ..	50	50
740	–	20 c. multicoloured ..	40	40
532	–	25 c. multicoloured ..	50	30
533	–	35 c. multicoloured ..	30	40
534	–	50 c. multicoloured ..	30	30
535	–	60 c. multicoloured ..	50	50
536	–	70 c. multicoloured ..	60	60
537	–	75 c. multicoloured ..	70	20
538	–	90 c. multicoloured ..	75	75
539	–	1 r. multicoloured ..	50	20
540	–	1 r. 20 multicoloured ..	75	75
541	–	1 r. 25 multicoloured ..	80	20
542	–	1 r. 50 multicoloured ..	75	40
543	–	2 r. multicoloured ..	60	30
544	–	3 r. multicoloured ..	60	30
545	–	5 r. multicoloured ..	60	50
546	–	10 r. multicoloured ..	90	90
547	–	15 r. multicoloured ..	1·25	1·25
548	–	25 r. grn., blk. & brn...	2·00	2·25

DESIGNS—HORIZ. 15 c. Scene of Dutch Occupation. 20 c. Map by Van Keulen, c. 1700. 50 c. Construction of Port Louis, c. 1736. 70 c. Map by Belin, 1763. 90 c. Battle of Grand Port, 1810. 1 r. Landing of the British, 1810. 1 r. 20, Government House c. 1840. 1 r. 50, Indian immigration to Mauritius, 1835. 2 r. Race Course (Champ de Mars), c. 1870. 3 r. Place d'Armes, c. 1880. 5 r. Royal Visit postcard, 1901. 10 r. Royal College of Curepipe, 1914. 25 r. First Mauritian Governor-General and First Prime Minister of Mauritius. VERT. 25 c. First settlement on Rodrigues, 1691. 35 c. Arrival of French settlers in Mauritius, 1715. 60 c. Pierre Poivre and the nutmeg tree. 75 c. First coin minted in Mauritius. 1 r. 25, Invitation and ball of Lady Gomm, 1847. 15 r. Unfurling of Mauritian flag.

166. Mauritius Dodo.

1978. 25th Anniv. of Coronation.

549. –	3 r. grey, black and blue	25	45
550. –	3 r. multicoloured ..	25	45
551. **166.**	3 r. grey, black and blue	25	45

DESIGNS: No. 549, Antelope of Bohun. No. 550, Queen Elizabeth II.

167. Problem of Infection, World War I.

1978. 50th Anniv. of Discovery of Penicillin.

552. **167.**	20 c. multicoloured ..	40	10
553. –	1 r. multicoloured ..	80	10
554. –	1 r. 50 black, brown and green	1·25	45
555. –	5 r. multicoloured ..	2·00	3·25

DESIGNS: 1 r. Microscope and first mould growth, 1928. 1 r. 50, Mould "penicillium notatum". 5 r. Sir Alexander Fleming and nurse administering injection.

168. "Papilio manlius" (butterfly).

1978. World Wildlife. Multicoloured.

557.	20 c. Type **168**	45	10
558.	1 r. Geckos	45	10
559.	1 r. 50, Greater Mascarene flying fox	50	30
560.	5 r. Mauritius kestrel ..	3·50	3·50

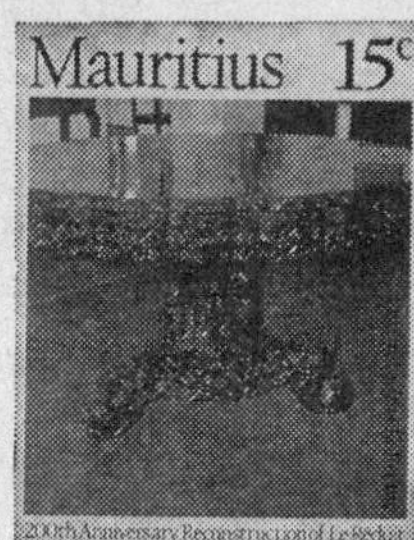

169. Ornate Table.

1978. Bicentenary of Reconstruction of Chateau Le Reduit. Multicoloured.

562.	15 c. Type **169**	10	10
563.	75 c. Chateau Le Reduit..	10	10
564.	3 r. Le Reduit gardens ..	30	45

170. Whitcomb Diesel Locomotive, "65 H.P." 1949.

1979. Railway Locomotives. Multicoloured.

565.	20 c. Type **170**	15	10
566.	1 r. "Sir William" 1922 ..	30	10
567.	1 r. 50 Kitson type 1930 ..	50	45
568.	2 r. Garratt type, 1927 ..	70	85

171. Father Laval and Crucifix.

1979. Beatification of Father Laval. Mult.

570.	20 c. Type **171**	10	10
571.	1 r. 50 Father Laval ..	10	10
572.	5 r. Father Laval's Tomb (horiz.)	35	50

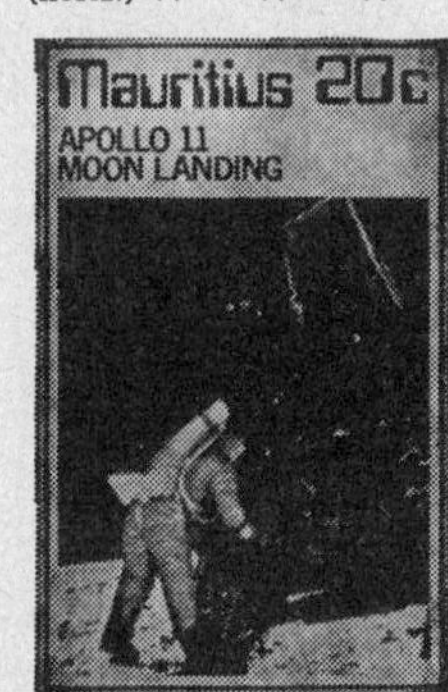

172. Astronaut descending from Lunar Module.

1979. 10th Anniv. of Moon Landing. Multi-coloured. Self-adhesive.

574.	20 c. Type **172**	15	15
575.	3 r. Astronaut performing experiment on moon ..	70	90
576.	5 r. Astronaut on Moon ..	2·00	3·25

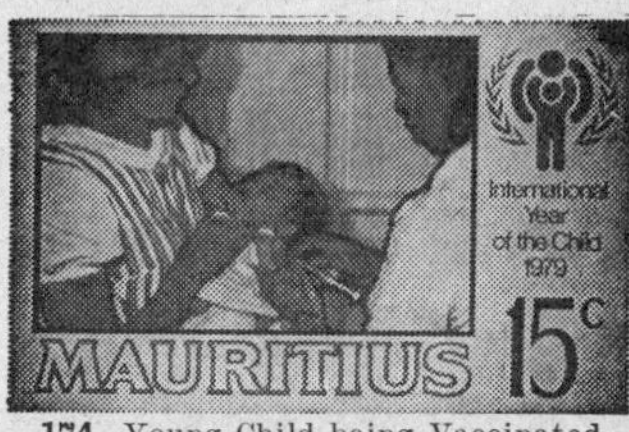

173. Great Britain 1855 4d. Stamp and Sir Rowland Hill.

1979. Death Centenary of Sir Rowland Hill. Multicoloured.

577.	25 c. Type **173**	10	10
578.	2 r. 1954 60 c. definitive ..	45	50
579.	5 r. 1847 1d. "POST OFFICE"	90	1·25

174. Young Child being Vaccinated.

1979. International Year of the Child.

581. **174.**	15 c. multicoloured ..	10	10
582. –	25 c. multicoloured ..	10	10
583. –	1 r. black, blue and bright blue	15	10
584. –	1 r. 50 multicoloured ..	30	20
585. –	3 r. multicoloured ..	50	50

DESIGNS—HORIZ. 25 c. Children playing. 1 r. 50, Girls in Chemistry laboratory. 3 r. Boy operating lathe. VERT. 1 r. I.Y.C. emblem.

175. The Lienard Obelisk.

1980. Pamplemousses Botanical Gardens. Multicoloured.

586.	20 c. Type **175**	10	10
587.	25 c. Poivre Avenue ..	10	10
588.	1 r. Varieties of Vacoas ..	20	10
589.	2 r. Giant water lilies ..	35	45
590.	5 r. Mon Plaisir (mansion)	60	1·25

176. "Emirne" (French steam packet).

1980. "London 1980" International Stamp Exhibition. Mail-carrying Ships. Mult.

592	25 c. Type **176**	15	10
593	1 r. "Boissevain" (cargo liner)	25	10
594	2 r. "La Boudeuse" (Bougainville's ship) ..	45	20
595	5 r. "Sea Breeze" (English clipper)	65	80

177. Blind Person Basket-making.

1980. Birth Centenary of Helen Keller (campaigner for the handicapped). Mult.

596 25 c. Type **177** 15 10
597. 1 r. Deaf child under instruction 35 10
598. 2 r. 50 Helen reading braille 55 35
599. 5 r. Helen at graduation, 1904 .. .. .. 1·00 90

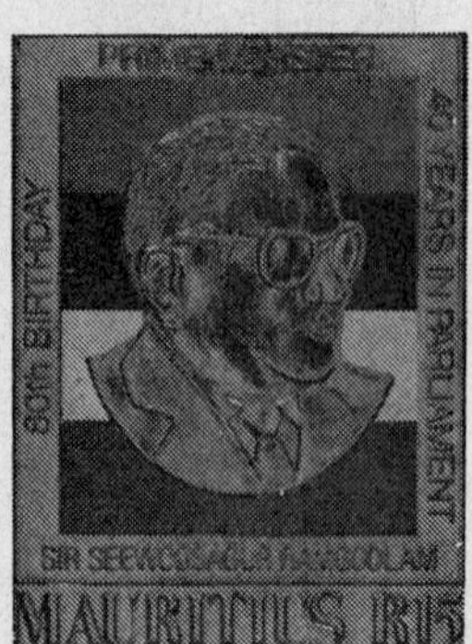

178. Prime Minister Sir Seewoosagur Ramgoolam.

1980. 80th Birthday and 40th Year in Parliament of Prime Minister Sir Seewoosagur Ramgoolam.

600. **178.** 15 r. multicoloured .. 1·25 1·40

179. Headquarters, Mauritius Institute.

1980. Centenary of Mauritius Institute. Multicoloured.

601. 25 c. Type **179** 15 10
602. 2 r. Rare copy of Veda .. 30 15
603. 2 r. 50 Rare cone 35 20
604. 5 r. "Le Torrent" (painting, Harpignies) 55 60

180. "Hibiscus liliiflorus".

1981. Flowers. Multicoloured.

605. 25 c. Type **180** 15 10
606. 2 r. "Erythrospermum monticolum" 40 45
607. 2 r. 50 "Chasalia boryana" 50 55
608. 5 r. "Hibiscus columnaris" 95 1·50

181. Beau-Bassin/Rose Hill.

1981. Mauritius. Coats of Arms. Mult.

609. 25 c. Type **181** 10 10
610. 1 r. 50 Curepipe 30 20
611. 2 r. Quatre-Bornes 35 25
612. 2 r. 50 Vacoas/Phoenix .. 40 30
613. 5 r. Port Louis 75 75

182. Prince Charles as Colonel-in-Chief, Royal Regiment of Wales.

1981. Royal Wedding. Multicoloured.

615. 25 c. Wedding bouquet from Mauritius .. 10 10
616. 2 r. 50 Type **182** 55 15
617. 10 r. Prince Charles and Lady Diana Spencer .. 1·40 90

183. Emmanuel Anquetil and Guy Rozemont.

1981. Famous Politicians and Physician.

618. **183.** 20 c. black and red .. 10 10
619. – 25 c. black and yellow .. 10 10
620. – 1 r. 25 black and green 30 25
621. – 1 r. 50 black and red .. 35 15
622. – 2 r black and blue .. 45 20
623. – 2 r. 50 black and brown 50 30
624. – 5 r. black and blue .. 1·25 90

DESIGNS: 25 c. Remy Ollier and Sookdes Bissoondoyal. 1 r. 25, Maurice Cure and Barthelemy Ohsan. 1 r. 50, Sir Guy Forget and Renganaden Seeneevassen. 2 r. Sir Abdul Razak Mohamed and Jules Koeing. 2 r. 50, Abdoollatiff Mahomed Osman and Dazzi Rama (Pandit Sahadeo). 5 r. Sir Thomas Lewis (physician) and electrocardiogram.

184. Drummer and Piper.

1981. Religion and Culture. Multicoloured.

625. 20 c. Type **184** 10 10
626. 2 r. Swami Sivananda (vert.) 65 65
627. 5 r. Chinese Pagoda .. 1·00 2·25

The 20 c. value commemorates the World Tamil Culture Conference (1980).

185. "Skills".

1981. 25th Anniv. of Duke of Edinburgh Award Scheme. Multicoloured.

628. 25 c. Type **185** 10 10
629. 1 r. 25 "Service" 10 10
630. 5 r. "Expeditions" 25 30
631. 10 r. Duke of Edinburgh .. 50 70

186. Kaaba (sacred shrine, Great Mosque of Mecca.)

1981. Moslem Year 1400 A.H. Commemoration. Multicoloured.

632. 25 c. Type **186** 10 10
633. 2 r. Mecca.. .. .. 50 60
634. 5 r. Mecca and Kaaba .. 1·00 1·75

187. Scout Emblem.

1982. 75th Anniv. of Boy Scout Movement and 70th Anniv. of Scouting in Mauritius.

635. **187.** 25 c. lilac and green .. 10 10
636. – 2 r. brown and ochre .. 30 30
637. – 5 r. green and olive .. 70 1·00
638. – 10 r. green and blue .. 1·25 2·00

DESIGNS: 2 r. Lord Baden-Powell and Baden-Powell House. 5 r. Grand Howl. 10 r. Ascent of Pieter Both.

188. Charles Darwin.

1982. 150th Anniv. of Charles Darwin's Voyage. Multicoloured.

639. 25 c. Type **188** 10 10
640. 2 r. Darwin's telescope .. 30 45
641. 2 r. 50 Darwin's elephant ride 35 55
642. 10 r. H.M.S. "Beagle" beached for repairs .. 1·40 2·50

189. Bride and Groom at Buckingham Palace.

1982. 21st Birthday of Princess of Wales. Multicoloured.

643. 25 c. Mauritius coat of arms 10 10
644. 2 r. 50 Princess Diana in Chesterfield, November, 1981 .. .. 45 35
645. 5 r. Type **189** 75 80
646. 10 r. Formal portrait .. 1·25 1·75

190. Prince and Princess of Wales with Prince William.

1982. Birth of Prince William of Wales.

647. **190.** 2 r. 50 multicoloured .. 65 30

191. Bois Fandamane Plant.

1982. Centenary of Robert Koch's Discovery of Tubercle Bacillus. Multicoloured.

648. 25 c. Type **191** 10 10
649. 1 r. 25 Central market, Port Louis 40 35
650. 2 r. Bois Banane plant .. 65 65
651. 5 r. Platte de Lezard plant 1·40 1·75
652. 10 r. Dr. Robert Koch .. 2·25 3·00

192. Arms and Flag of Mauritius.

1983. Commonwealth Day. Multicoloured.

653. 25 c. Type **192** 10 10
654. 2 r. 50 Satellite view of Mauritius 15 30
655. 5 r. Harvesting sugar cane 30 75
656. 10 r. Port Louis harbour .. 70 1·50

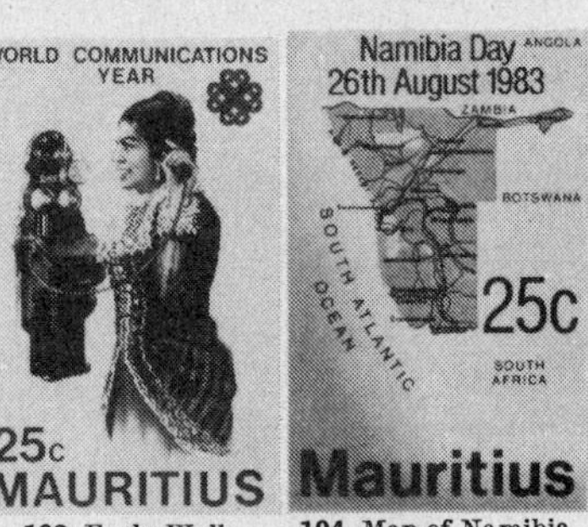

193. Early Wall-mounted Telephone. **194.** Map of Namibia.

1983. World Communications Year. Mult.

657. 25 c. Type **193** 10 10
658. 1 r. 25 Early telegraph apparatus (horiz.) .. 50 20
659. 2 r. Earth satellite station 90 50
660. 10 r. First hot air balloon in Mauritius, 1784 (horiz.) 2·25 2·75

1983. Namibia Day. Multicoloured.

661. 25 c. Type **194** 40 10
662. 2 r. 50 Hand breaking chains .. .. .. 1·25 65
663. 5 r. Family and settlement 1·75 2·00
664. 10 r. Diamond mining .. 2·75 3·25

195. Fish Trap. **196.** Swami Dayananda.

1983. Fishery Resources. Multicoloured.

665. 25 c. Type **195** 15 10
666. 1 r. Fishing boat (horiz.) .. 55 15
667. 5 r. Game fishing .. .. 1·50 1·75
668. 10 r. Octopus drying (horiz.) 2·00 3·00

1983. Death Centenary of Swami Dayananda. Multicoloured.

669. 25 c. Type **196** 10 10
670. 35 c. Last meeting with father 10 10
671. 2 r. Receiving religious instruction 40 45
672. 5 r. Swami demonstrating strength .. .. 80 1·40
673. 10 r. At a religious gathering .. .. .. 1·25 2·75

197. Adolf von Plevitz, 1837–93.

1983. 125th Anniv. of Adolf von Plevitz (reformer). Multicoloured.

674. 25 c. Type **197** 10 10
675. 1 r. 25 La Laura, Government school 30 30
676. 5 r. Von Plevitz addressing Commission of Enquiry, 1872 .. .. .. 90 1·25
677. 10 r. Von Plevitz with Indian farm workers .. 1·50 2·25

198. Courtship Chase.

1984. The Mauritius Kestrel. Multicoloured.
678. 25 c. Type **198** 45 10
679. 2 r. Kestrel in tree (vert.) .. 1·00 65
680. 2 r. 50 Young Kestrel .. 1·25 90
681. 10 r. Head (vert.) .. .. 2·75 4·00

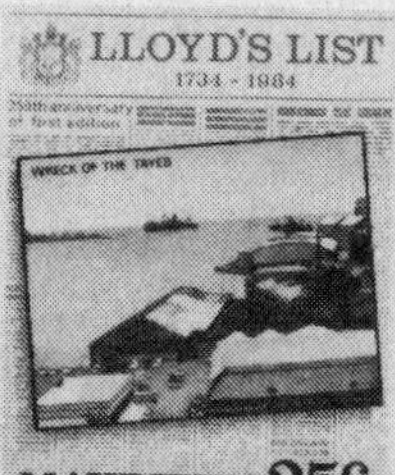

199. Wreck of S.S. "Tayeb".

1984. 250th Anniv. of "Lloyd's List" (newspaper). Multicoloured.
682. 25 c. Type **199** 25 10
683. 1 r. S.S. "Taher" 75 15
684. 5 r. East Indiaman "Triton" 2·00 2·50
685. 10 r. M.S. "Astor" .. 2·50 4·00

200. Blue Latan Palm.

1984. Palm Trees. Multicoloured.
686. 25 c. Type **200** 10 10
687. 50 c. "Hyophorbe vaughanii" 20 15
688. 2 r. 50 "Tectiphiala ferox" 1·25 65
689. 5 r. Round Island Bottle-palm .. .. 2·00 2·25
690. 10 r. "Hyophorbe amaricaulis" .. .. 3·25 3·75

201. Slave Girl.

1984. 150th Anniv. of Abolition of Slavery and Introduction of Indian Immigrants.
691. **201.** 25 c. purple, lilac and brown 15 10
692. – 1 r. purple, lilac and brown 60 10
693. – 2 r. purple and lilac .. 1·00 70
694. – 10 r. purple and lilac 3·00 3·50

DESIGNS—VERT. 1 r. Slave market. HORIZ. 2 r. Indian immigrant family. 10 r. Arrival of Indian immigrants.

HAVE YOU READ THE NOTES AT THE BEGINNING OF THIS CATALOGUE?
These often provide answers to the enquiries we receive.

202. 75th Anniversary Production of "Faust" and Leoville L'Homme.

1984. Centenary of Alliance Francaise (cultural organization). Multicoloured.
695. 25 c. Type **202** 20 10
696. 1 r. 25 Prize-giving ceremony and Aunauth Beejadbur 60 40
697. 5 r. First headquarters and Hector Clarenc .. .. 1·75 2·25
698. 10 r. Lion Mountain and Labourdonnais .. .. 2·25 3·25

203. The Queen Mother on Clarence House Balcony, 1980.

1985. Life and Times of Queen Elizabeth the Queen Mother. Multicoloured.
699. 25 c. The Queen Mother in 1926 .. .. .. 10 10
700. 2 r. With Princess Margaret at Trooping the Colour 30 30
701. 5 r. Type **203** .. .. 60 1·00
702. 10 r. With Prince Henry at his christening (from photo by Lord Snowdon) 1·10 1·75

204. High Jumping.

1985. 2nd Indian Ocean Islands Games. Multicoloured.
704. 25 c. Type **204** 20 10
705. 50 c. Javelin-throwing .. 35 20
706. 1 r. 25, Cycling 80 60
707. 10 r. Wind surfing .. .. 3·25 4·50

205. Adult and Fledgling Pink Pigeons.

1985. Pink Pigeon. Multicoloured.
708. 25 c. Type **205** 75 15
709. 2 r. Pink Pigeon displaying at nest .. .. .. 1·75 1·25
710. 2 r. 50, On nest .. .. 2·00 1·75
711. 5 r. Pair preening .. .. 3·25 3·50

206. Caverne Patates, Rodrigues.

1985. 10th Anniv. of World Tourism Organization. Multicoloured.
712. 25 c. Type **206** 30 10
713. 35 c. Coloured soils, Chamarel 30 10
714. 5 r. Serpent Island .. 2·25 2·50
715. 10 r. Coin de Mire Island .. 3·75 4·00

207. Old Town Hall, Port Louis.

1985. 250th Anniv. of Port Louis. Mult.
716. 25 c. Type **207** 10 10
717. 1 r. Al-Aqsa Mosque (180th anniv.) 45 10
718. 2 r. 50, Vase and trees (250th anniv. of settlement of Tamil-speaking Indians) 80 60
719. 10 r. Port Louis Harbour 2·50 3·00

208. Edmond Halley and Diagram.

1986. Appearance of Halley's Comet. Mult.
720. 25 c. Type **208** 10 10
721. 1 r. 25 Halley's Comet (1682) and Newton's Reflector 35 20
722. 3 r. Halley's Comet passing Earth 70 50
723. 10 r. "Giotto" spacecraft .. 2·25 2·50

1986. 60th Birthday of Queen Elizabeth II. As T **110** of Ascension. Multicoloured.
724. 25 c. Princess Elizabeth wearing Badge of Grenadier Guards, 1942. 10 10
725. 75 c. Investiture of Prince of Wales, 1969 .. .. 10 10
726. 2 r. With Prime Minister of Mauritius, 1972 .. .. 20 25
727. 3 r. In Germany, 1978 .. 30 35
728. 15 r. At Crown Agents Head Office, London, 1983 .. .. .. 1·50 1·75

209. Maize (World Food Day).

1986. International Events. Multicoloured.
729. 25 c. Type **209** 10 10
730. 1 r. African Regional Industrial Property Organization emblem (10th anniv.) 35 10
731. 1 r. 25 International Peace Year emblem 45 25
732. 10 r. Footballer and Mauritius Football Association emblem (World Cup Football Championship, Mexico) 2·75 2·75

210. "Cryptopus elatus".

1986. Orchids. Multicoloured.
733. 25 c. Type **210** 30 10
734. 2 r. "Jumellea recta" .. 90 40
735. 2 r. 50 "Angraecum mauritianum" .. .. 1·10 50
736. 10 r. "Bulbophyllum longiflorum" .. .. .. 2·25 2·50

211. Hesketh Bell Bridge.

1987. Mauritius Bridges. Multicoloured.
758. 25 c. Type **211** 25 10
759. 50 c. Sir Colville Deverell Bridge 35 10
760. 2 r. 50 Cavendish Bridge .. 1·10 55
761. 5 r. Tamarin Bridge .. 1·75 1·50
762. 10 r. Grand River North West Bridge .. .. 2·50 2·50

212. Supreme Court, Port Louis.

1987. Bicentenary of the Mauritius Bar. Multicoloured.
763. 25 c. Type **212** 10 10
764. 1 r. District Court, Flacq 30 10
765. 1 r. 25 Statue of Justice .. 45 20
766. 10 r. Barristers of 1787 and 1987 .. .. .. 1·60 1·50

213. Mauritius Dodo Mascot.

1987. International Festival of the Sea. Multicoloured.
767. 25 c. Type **213** 20 10
768. 1 r. 50 Yacht regatta (horiz.) 70 50
769. 3 r. Water skiing (horiz.) .. 1·50 1·10
770. 5 r. "Svanen" (barquentine) .. .. 2·00 2·50

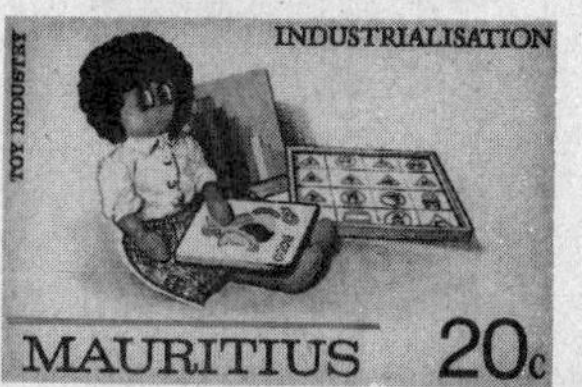

214. Toys.

1987. Industrialization. Multicoloured.
771. 20 c. Type **214** 10 10
772. 35 c. Spinning factory .. 10 10
773. 50 c. Rattan furniture .. 10 10
774. 2 r. 50 Spectacle factory .. 85 65
775. 10 r. Stone carving .. 2·25 2·25

215. Maison Ouvriere (Int. Year of Shelter for the Homeless).

1987. Art and Architecture.

776. **215.** 25 c. multicoloured .. 10 10
777. – 1 r. black and grey .. 20 10
778. – 1 r. 25 multicoloured 25 20
779. – 2 r. multicoloured .. 40 40
780. – 5 r. multicoloured .. 95 1·00

DESIGNS: 1 r. "Paul and Virginie" (lithograph). 1 r. 25, Chateau de Rosnay; 2 r. "Vielle Ferme" (Boulle). 5 r. "Trois Mamelles".

216. University of Mauritius.

1988. 20th Anniv. of Independence. Mult.

781. 25 c. Type **216** 10 10
782. 75 c. Anniversary gymnastic display 15 10
783. 2 r. 50 Hurdlers and aerial view of Sir Maurice Rault Stadium 55 45
784. 5 r. Air. Mauritius aircraft at Sir Seewoosagur Ramgoolam International Airport .. 1·10 1·00
785. 10 r. Governor-General Sir Veerasamy Ringadoo and Prime Minister Anerood Jugnauth .. 2·00 2·00

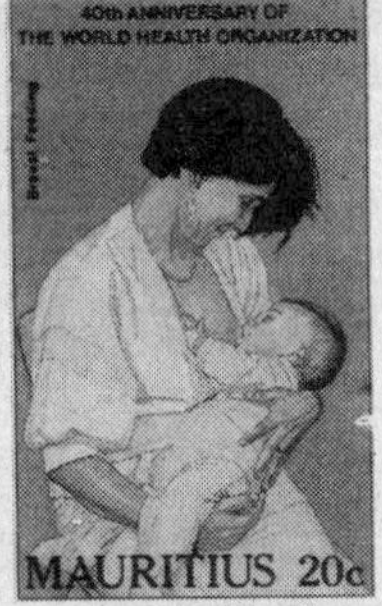

217 Breast Feeding

1988. 40th Anniv of W.H.O. Multicoloured.

786 20 c. Type **217** 10 10
787 2 r. Baby under vaccination umbrella and germ droplets 80 50
788 3 r. Nutritious food .. 95 80
789 10 r. W.H.O. logo .. 2·25 2·50

218 Modern Bank Building

1988. 150th Anniv of Mauritius Commercial Bank Ltd.

790 **218** 25 c. black, green & bl 10 10
791 – 1 r. black and red .. 15 10
792 – 1 r.25 multicoloured .. 30 30
793 – 25 r. multicoloured .. 5·00 5·00

DESIGNS: HORIZ—1 r. Mauritius Commercial Bank, 1897; 25 r. Fifteen dollar bank note of 1838. VERT—1 r.25, Bank arms.

219 Olympic Rings and Athlete

1988. Olympic Games, Seoul. Multicoloured.

794 25 c. Type **219** 10 10
795 35 c. Wrestling 10 10
796 1 r.50 Long distance running 50 40
797 10 r. Swimming .. .. 2·00 2·50

220 Nature Park

1989. Protection of the Environment. Mult.

799 15 c. Underwater view .. 10 10
806 30 c. Greenshank .. 10 10
800 40 c. Type **220** .. 10 10
808 50 c. Round Island (vert) 10 10
809 75 c. Bassin Blanc .. 10 10
810 1 r. Mangrove (vert) .. 10 10
801 1 r. 50 Whimbrel 10 15
811 2 r. Le Morne 15 20
802 3 r. Marine life 20 25
803 4 r. Fern tree (vert) .. 30 35
812 5 r. Riviere du Poste estuary 35 40
804 6 r. Ecological scenery (vert) 45 50
813 10 r. "Phelsuma ornata" (gecko) on plant (vert) 75 80
814 15 r. Benares waves .. 1·10 1·25
805 25 r. Migratory birds and map (vert) .. .. 1·75 1·90

221 La Tour Sumeire, Port Louis

1989. Bicentenary of the French Revolution.

818 **221** 30 c. black, grn & yell 10 10
819 – 1 r. black, brown and light brown .. 20 10
820 – 8 r. multicoloured .. 1·25 1·25
821 – 15 r. multicoloured .. 2·00 2·00

DESIGNS: 1 r. Salle de Spectacle du Jardin; 8 r. Portrait of Comte de Malartic; 15 r. Bicentenary logo.

222 Cardinal Jean Margeot

1989. Visit of Pope John Paul II. Mult.

822 30 c. Type **222** 20 10
823 40 c. Pope John Paul II and Prime Minister Jugnauth, Vatican, 1988 30 15
824 3 r. Marie Magdeleine de la Croix and Chapelle des Filles de Marie, Port Louis, 1864 .. .. 75 55
825 6 r. St. Francis of Assisi Church, Pamplemousses, 1756 .. .. 1·40 1·40
826 10 r. Pope John Paul II .. 2·50 2·75

223 Nehru

1989. Birth Centenary of Jawaharlal Nehru (Indian statesman). Multicoloured.

827 40 c. Type **223** 20 10
828 1 r. 50 Nehru with daughter, Indira, and grandsons 40 30
829 3 r. Nehru and Gandhi .. 1·00 90
830 4 r. Nehru with Presidents Nasser and Tito .. 1·25 1·25
831 10 r. Nehru with children 2·75 3·00

224 Cane Cutting

1990. 350th Anniv of Introduction of Sugar Cane to Mauritius. Multicolored.

832 30 c. Type **224** 10 10
833 40 c. Sugar factory, 1867 .. 10 10
834 1 r. Mechanical loading of cane 15 10
835 25 r. Modern sugar factory 3·50 4·00

225 Industrial Estate

1990. 60th Birthday of Prime Minister Sir Anerood Jugnauth. Multicoloured.

836 35 c. Type **225** 10 10
837 40 c. Sir Anerood Jugnauth at desk 10 10
838 1 r. 50 Mauritius Stock Exchange symbol .. 20 20
839 4 r. Jugnauth with Sir Seewoosagur Ramgoolam (former Governor-General) .. 1·00 1·00
840 10 r. Jugnauth greeting Pope John Paul II .. 2·00 2·50

226 Desjardins (naturalist) (150th death anniv)

1990. Anniversaries. Multicoloured.

841 30 c. Type **226** 10 10
842 35 c. Logo on TV screen (25th anniv of Mauritius Broadcasting Corporation) (horiz) .. 10 10
843 6 r. Line Barracks (now Police Headquarters) (250th anniv) .. .. 1·25 1·50
844 8 r. Town Hall, Curepipe (centenary of municipality) (horiz) .. .. 1·75 2·00

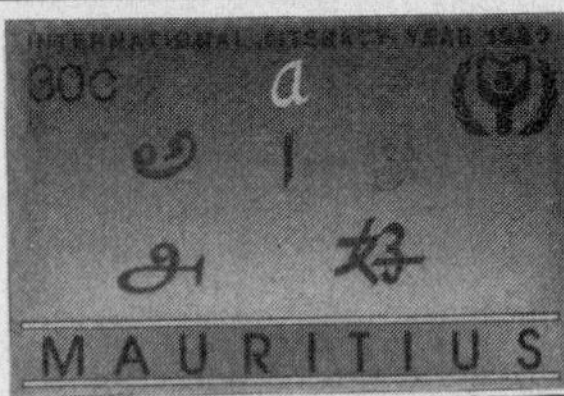

227 Letters from Alphabets

1990. International Literacy Year. Mult.

845 30 c. Type **227** 10 10
846 1 r. Blind child reading Braille 25 10
847 3 r. Open book and globe 75 75
848 10 r. Book showing world map with quill pen .. 2·75 2·50

1991. 65th Birthday of Queen Elizabeth II and 70th Birthday of Prince Philip. As T **139** of Ascension. Multicoloured.

849 8 r. Queen Elizabeth II .. 1·00 1·25
850 8 r. Prince Philip in Grenadier Guards ceremonial uniform .. 1·00 1·25

228 City Hall, Port Louis (25th anniv of City status)

1991. Anniversaries and Events. Mult.

851 40 c. Type **228** 10 10
852 4 r. Colonel Draper (race course founder) (150th death anniv) (vert) .. 75 75
853 6 r. Joseph Barnard (engraver) and "POST PAID" 2d. stamp (175th birth anniv) (vert) .. 1·00 1·00
854 10 r. Spitfire "Mauritius II" (50th anniv of Second World War) .. 2·25 2·50

229 "Euploea euphon"

1991. "Phila Nippon '91" International Stamp Exn, Tokyo. Butterflies. Mult.

855 40 c. Type **229** 20 10
856 3 r. "Hypolimnas misippus" (female) 50 40
857 8 r. "Papilio manlius" .. 1·25 1·25
858 10 r. "Hypolimnas misippus" (male) .. .. 1·40 1·60

230 Green Turtle, Tromelin

1991. Indian Ocean Islands. Multicoloured.

859 40 c. Type **230** 15 10
860 1 r. Glossy ibis, Agalega .. 30 10
861 2 r. Takamaka flowers, Chagos Archipelago .. 40 35
862 15 r. "Lambis violacea" sea shell, St. Brandon .. 2·25 2·50

231 Pres. Veerasamy Ringadoo and President's Residence

1992. Proclamation of Republic. Mult.

863 40 c. Type **231** 10 10
864 4 r. Prime Minister Anerood Jugnauth and Government House .. 60 70
865 8 r. Children and rainbow 1·25 1·40
866 10 r. Presidential flag .. 1·50 1·75

232 Ticolo (mascot)

1992. 8th African Athletics Championships, Port Louis. Multicoloured.

867 40 c. Type **232** 10 10
868 4 r. Sir Anerood Jugnauth Stadium (horiz) .. 55 60
869 5 r. High jumping (horiz) 65 70
870 6 r. Championships emblem 80 95

233 Bouquet (25th anniv of Fleurir Maurice)

1992. Local Events and Anniversaries. Mult.

871 40 c. Type **233** 10 10
872 1 r. Swami Krishnanandji Maharaj (25th anniv of arrival) 15 10
873 2 r. Boy with dog (humane education) (horiz) .. 25 25
874 3 r. Commission Headquarters (10th anniv of Indian Ocean Commission) (horiz) 35 35
875 15 r. Radio telescope antenna, Bras d'Eau (project inauguration) (horiz) .. .. .. 1·60 1·90

234 Bank of Mauritius Headquarters

1992. 25th Anniv of Bank of Mauritius. Mult.

876 40 c. Type **234** 10 10
877 4 r. Dodo gold coin (horiz) 45 45
878 8 r. First bank note issue (horiz) 85 90
879 15 r. Graph of foreign exchange reserves, 1967–92 (horiz) .. .. 1·75 2·00

235 Housing Development

1993. 25th Anniv of National Day. Mult.

880 30 c. Type **235** 10 10
881 40 c. Gross domestic product graph on computer screen .. 10 10
882 3 r. National colours on map of Mauritius .. 40 40
883 4 r. Ballot box 45 45
884 15 r. Grand Commander's insignia for Order of Star and Key of the Indian Ocean .. .. 1·75 2·00

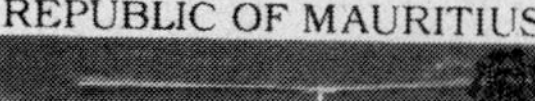

236 Bell 206 B Jet Ranger II Helicopter

1993. 25th Anniv of Air Mauritius Ltd. Mult.

885 40 c. Type **236** 15 10
886 3 r. Boeing 747 SP .. 35 35
887 4 r. ATR 42 .. .. 45 45
888 10 r. Boeing 767-200 ER .. 95 1·00

1993. No. 809 surch **40cs**.

890 40 c. on 75 c. Bassin Blanc 10 10

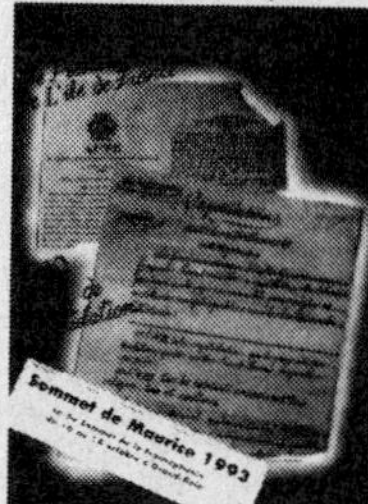

238 French Royal Charter, 1715, and Act of Capitulation, 1810

1993. 5th Summit of French-speaking Nations. Multicoloured.

891 1 r. Type **238** 15 10
892 5 r. Road signs 45 45
893 6 r. Code Napoleon .. 55 55
894 7 r. Early Mauritius newspapers 65 65

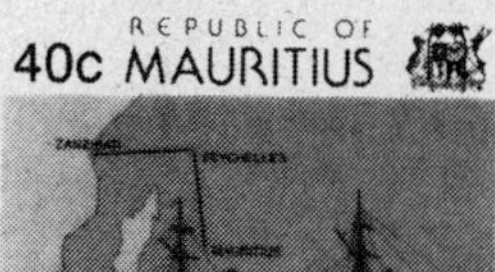

239 "Scotia" (cable ship) and Map of Cable Route

1993. Cent of Telecommunications. Mult.

895 40 c. Type **239** 15 10
896 3 r. Morse key and code .. 30 30
897 4 r. Signal Mountain Earth station 40 40
898 8 r. Communications satellite 65 65

240 Indian Mongoose

1994. Mammals. Multicoloured.

899 40 c. Type **240** 10 10
900 2 r. Indian black-naped hare 15 20
901 8 r. Pair of crab-eating macaque 60 65
902 10 r. Adult and infant common tenrec .. 75 80

EXPRESS DELIVERY STAMPS

1903. No. 136 surch. **EXPRESS DELIVERY 15 c.**

E 1. **40.** 15 c. on 15 c. blue .. 4·25 15·00

1903. No. 136 surch. **EXPRESS DELIVERY (INLAND) 15 c.**

E 3. **40.** 15 c. on 15 c. blue .. 4·25 1·00

1904. T **18** without value in label. (a) Surch. **(FOREIGN) EXPRESS DELIVERY 18 CENTS.**

E5 **42** 18 c. green .. .. 1·50 13·00

(b) Surch. **EXPRESS DELIVERY. (INLAND) 15 c.**

E6 **42** 15 c. green .. .. 1·50 1·50

POSTAGE DUE STAMPS

D 1.

1933.

D 1 **D 1.** 2 c. black 35 50
D 2 4 c. violet 40 65
D 3 6 c. red 40 80
D 4 10 c. green 40 70
D 5 20 c. blue 50 90
D 6 50 c. purple .. .. 55 8·00
D 7 1 r. orange .. .. 70 10·00

1982. Nos. 530/1, 535, 540, 542 and 547 surch. **POSTAGE DUE** and value.

D 14. 10 c. on 15 c. Dutch Occupation, 1638–1710 .. 10 10
D 15. 20 c. on 20 c. Van Keulen's map, c. 1700 .. 10 10
D 16. 50 c. on 60 c. Pierre Poivre, c. 1767 (vert.) .. 10 10
D 17. 1 r. on 1 r. 20 Government House, c. 1840 .. 10 10
D 18. 1 r. 50 on 1 r. 50 Indian immigration, 1835 .. 15 20
D 19. 5 r. on 15 r. Unfurling Mauritian flag, 1968 .. 50 65

MONTSERRAT

One of the Leeward Is., Br. W. Indies. Used general issues for Leeward Is. concurrently with Montserrat stamps until 1 July 1956, when Leeward Is. stamps were withdrawn.

1876. 12 pence = 1 shilling;
20 shillings = 1 pound.
1951. 100 cents = 1 West Indian dollar.

1876. Stamps of Antigua as T 1 optd **MONTSERRAT**.

1 1d. red .. .. .. 19·00 15·00
2 6d. green .. .. .. 55·00 40·00

3.

1880.

6. **3.** ½d. green .. .. .. 1·00 5·50
9. 2½d. brown .. .. £225 65·00
10. 2½d. blue .. .. .. 14·00 16·00
5. 4d. blue .. .. .. £140 40·00
12. 4d. mauve .. .. .. 3·25 3·00

4. Device of the Colony. 5.

1903.

24 **4** ½d. green 80 80
15 1d. grey and red 75 40
26a 2d. grey and brown .. 1·00 1·00
17 2½d. grey and blue .. 1·50 1·75
28a 3d. orange and purple .. 3·25 2·50
29a 6d. purple and olive .. 3·00 5·00
30 1s. green and purple .. 8·50 6·00
21 2s. green and brown .. 23·00 16·00
22 2s. 6d. green and black .. 15·00 30·00
33 **5** 5s. black and red .. .. 65·00 £100

1908.

36. **4.** 1d. red .. .. .. 1·40 30
38. 2d. grey .. .. .. 1·75 8·50
39. 2½d. blue .. .. .. 2·25 3·50
40. 3d. purple on yellow .. 1·00 12·00
43. 6d. purple .. .. 6·50 32·00
44. 1s. black on green .. 3·50 16·00
45. 2s. purple & blue on blue 24·00 38·00
46. 2s. 6d. blk. & red on blue 30·00 48·00
47. **5.** 5s. red & green on yellow 48·00 60·00

1914. As T **5**, but portrait of King George V.

48. 5s. red & green on yellow 48·00 75·00

8.

1916.

63. **8.** ¼d. brown .. .. 15 3·50
64. ½d. green 20 30
50. 1d. red 35 75
65. 1d. violet 30 40
67. 1½d. yellow .. .. 1·75 9·50
68. 1½d. red .. .. 30 1·75
69. 1½d. brown 70 50
70. 2d. grey .. .. .. 45 1·00
71a. 2½d. blue 60 90
72. 2½d. yellow .. .. 1·25 18·00
53. 3d. purple on yellow .. 75 5·50
73. 3d. blue .. .. .. 50 11·00
75. 4d. black & red on yellow 60 5·50
76. 5d. purple and olive .. 2·50 10·00
77. 6d. purple .. .. 1·25 6·00
78. 1s. black on green .. 3·00 7·00
79. 2s. pur. and blue on blue 4·25 11·00
80. 2s. 6d. blk. & red on blue 11·00 32·00
81. 3s. green and violet .. 12·00 17·00
82. 4s. black and red .. .. 14·00 23·00
83. 5s. green and red on yellow 19·00 28·00

1917. Optd. **WAR STAMP.**

60. **8.** ½d. green .. .. .. 10 1·00
62. 1½d. black and orange .. 10 30

10. Plymouth.

1932. Tercentenary issue.
84. 10. ½d. green .. .. .. 75 3·50
85. 1d. red .. .. .. 75 3·00
86. 1½d. brown .. .. .. 1·25 2·00
87. 2d. grey .. .. .. 1·25 11·00
88. 2½d. blue .. .. .. 1·25 9·50
89. 3d. orange .. .. .. 1·50 9·00
90. 6d. violet .. .. .. 2·25 19·00
91. 1s. olive .. .. .. 8·50 25·00
92. 2s. 6d. purple .. .. 48·00 60·00
93. 5s. brown £100 £130

1935. Silver Jubilee. As T **13** of Antigua.
94. 1d. blue and red .. .. 85 2·00
95. 1½d. blue and grey .. 75 2·50
96. 2½d. brown and blue .. 2·25 1·50
97. 1s. grey and purple .. 3·00 7·50

1937. Coronation. As T **2** of Aden.
98. 1d. red 30 40
99. 1½d. brown 40 25
100. 2½d. blue 40 60

DESIGNS: 1d., 1½d., 2½d. Sea Island cotton. 2d. 6d., 2s. 6d., 10s. Botanic Station.

11. Carr's Bay.

1938. King George VI.
101a. **11.** ½d. green 10 20
102a. – 1d. red 30 30
103a. – 1½d. purple 30 50
104a. – 2d. orange 40 70
105a. – 2½d. blue 40 30
106a. **11.** 3d. brown 55 40
107a. – 6d. violet .. .. 1·00 50
108a. **11.** 1s. red 75 30
109. – 2s. 6d. blue .. .. 13·00 80
110a. **11.** 5s. red .. .. 17·00 3·00
111. – 10s. blue .. .. 13·00 17·00
112. **11.** £1 black .. .. 13·00 23·00

1946. Victory. As T **9** of Aden.
113. 1½d. purple 10 10
114. 3d. brown 10 10

1949. Silver Wedding. As T **10/11** of Aden.
115. 2½d. blue 10 10
116. 5s. red .. .. .. 4·50 3·00

1949. U.P.U. As T **20/23** of Antigua.
117. 2½d. blue 15 30
118. 3d. brown 30 30
119. 6d. purple 30 30
120. 1s. purple 35 30

1951. Inauguration of B.W.I. University College. As T **24/25** of Antigua.
121. 3 c. black and purple .. 20 15
122. 12 c. black and violet .. 20 20

14. Government House.

1951.
123. **14.** 1 c. black 10 60
124. – 2 c. green 15 50
125. – 3 c. brown 30 60
126. – 4 c. red 30 30
127. – 5 c. violet 30 50
128. – 6 c. brown 30 20
129. – 8 c. blue 35 20
130. – 12 c. blue and brown .. 35 30
131. – 24 c. red and green .. 75 30
132. – 60 c. black and red .. 3·25 2·00
133. – $1·20 green and blue .. 5·50 3·00
134. – $2·40 black and green .. 4·50 12·00
135. – $4.80 black and purple .. 16·00 16·00

DESIGNS: 2 c., $1.20, Sea Island cotton; cultivation. 3 c. Map. 4 c., 24 c. Picking tomatoes. 5 c., 12 c. St. Anthony's Church. 6 c., $4.80, Badge. 8 c., 60 c. Sea Island cotton: ginning. $2.40, Government House (portrait on right).

1953. Coronation. As T **13** of Aden.
136. 2 c. black and green .. 15 10

1953. As 1951 but portrait of Queen Elizabeth II.
136a. ½ c. violet (As 3 c.) (I) .. 30 10
136b. ½ c. violet (II) 30 10
137. 1 c. black 10 10
138. 2 c. green 15 10
139. 3 c. brown (I) 30 10
139a. 3 c. brown (II) 35 20
140. 4 c. red 30 15
141. 5 c. violet 30 30
142. 6 c. brown (I) 30 10
142a. 6 c. brown (II) 40 15
143. 8 c. blue 40 10
144. 12 c. blue & brown .. 75 10
145. 24 c. red and green .. 1·00 10
145a. 48 c. olive & pur. (As 2 c.) 10·00 2·25
146. 60 c. black and red .. 4·50 1·50
147. $1·20 green and blue .. 11·00 4·00
148. $2.40 black and green .. 6·00 9·50
149. $4.80 black & purple (I) .. 6·00 10·00
149a. $4.80 black & purple (II) 6·00 7·50

I. Inscr. "Presidency" II. Inscr. "Colony".

1958. British Caribbean Federation. As T **28** of Antigua.
150. 3 c. green 55 20
151. 6 c. blue 75 35
152. 12 c. red 90 15

1963. Freedom from Hunger. As T **28** of Aden.
153. 12 c. violet 30 15

1963. Cent of Red Cross. As T **33** of Antigua.
154. 4 c. red and black .. 10 10
155. 12 c. red and blue .. 25 25

1964. 400th Birth Anniv of Shakespeare. As T **34** of Antigua.
156. 12 c. blue 10 10

1965. Cent of I.T.U. As T **36** of Antigua.
158. 4 c. red and violet .. 15 10
159. 48 c. green and red .. 30 20

21. Pineapple.

1965. Multicoloured.
160 1 c. Type **21** 10 10
161 2 c. Avocado 10 10
162 3 c. Soursop 10 10
163 4 c. Pepper 10 10
164 5 c. Mango 10 10
165 6 c. Tomato 10 10
166 8 c. Guava 10 10
167 10 c. Ochro 10 10
168 12 c. Lime 15 10
169 20 c. Orange 20 10
170 24 c. Banana 20 10
171 42 c. Onion 75 60
172 48 c. Cabbage .. .. 1·25 75
173 60 c. Pawpaw .. .. 2·00 90
174 $1.20 Pumpkin .. .. 2·00 1·75
175 $2.40 Sweet potato .. 5·50 2·75
176 $4.80 Egg plant .. .. 5·50 6·50

1965. I.C.Y. As T **37** of Antigua.
177. 2 c. purple and turquoise .. 10 20
178. 12 c. green and lavender .. 25 10

1966. Churchill Commem. As T **38** of Antigua.
179. 1 c. blue 10 10
180. 2 c. green 10 10
181. 24 c. brown 15 10
182. 42 c. violet 20 15

1966. Royal Visit. As T **39** of Antigua.
183. 14 c. black and blue .. 40 15
184. 24 c. black and mauve .. 60 15

1966. Inauguration of W.H.O. Headquarters, Geneva. As T **41** of Antigua.
185. 12 c. black, green and blue 10 10
186. 60 c. black, purple & ochre 25 20

1966. 20th Anniv of U.N.E.S.C.O. As T **54/6** of Antigua.
187. 4 c. multicoloured .. 10 10
188. 60 c. yellow, violet & olive 20 10
189. $1.80 black, purple & orge. 70 70

25. Yachting.

1967. Int. Tourist Year. Multicoloured.
190. 5 c. Type **25** 10 10
191. 15 c. Waterfall near Chance Mountain 15 10
192. 16 c. "Fishing, skin diving and swimming" .. 15 15
193. 24 c. Playing golf .. 65 25
No. 191 is vert.

1968. Nos. 168, 170, 172, 174/6 surch.
194. 15 c. on 12 c. Lime .. 20 15
195. 25 c. on 24 c. Banana .. 25 15
196. 50 c. on 48 c. Cabbage .. 45 15
197. $1 on $1.20 Pumpkin .. 1·50 40
198. $2.50 on $2.40 Sweet Potato .. .. 2·00 3·00
199. $5 on $4.80 Egg plant .. 2·50 3·75

27. Sprinting.

1968. Olympic Games, Mexico.
200. **27.** 15 c. mauve, grn. & gold 10 10
201. – 25 c. blue, orge. & gold 10 10
202. – 50 c. green, red & gold 10 10
203. – $1 multicoloured .. 20 20

DESIGNS—HORIZ. 25 c. Weightlifting. 50 c. Gymnastics. VERT. $1, Sprinting and Aztec Pillars.

31. Alexander Hamilton.

1968. Human Rights Year. Multicoloured.
204. 5 c. Type **31** 10 10
205. 15 c. Albert T. Marryshow 10 10
206. 25 c. William Wilberforce 10 10
207. 50 c. Dag Hammarskjold 10 10
208. $1 Dr. Martin Luther King 25 30

32. "The Two Trinities" (Murillo).

34. Map showing "CARIFTA" Countries.

1968. Christmas.
209. **32.** 5 c. multicoloured .. 10 10
210. – 15 c. multicoloured .. 10 10
211. **32.** 25 c. multicoloured .. 10 10
212. – 50 c. multicoloured .. 25 20

DESIGN: 15 c., 50 c. "The Adoration of the Kings" (detail, Botticelli).

1969. 1st Anniv. of "CARIFTA". Mult.
223. 15 c. Type **34** 10 10
224. 20 c. Type **34** 10 10
225. 35 c. "Strength in Unity" 10 10
226. 50 c. As 35 c. 15 15
Nos. 225/6 are horiz.

36. Telephone Receiver and Map of Montserrat.

1969. Development Projects. Multicoloured.
227. 15 c. Type **36** 10 10
228. 25 c. School symbols and map 10 10
229. 50 c. "HS 748" Aircraft and map 15 10
230. $1 Electricity pylon and map 25 20

40. Dolphin.

1969. Game Fish. Multicoloured.
231. 5 c. Type **40** 30 10
232. 15 c. Atlantic sailfish .. 45 10
233. 25 c. Blackfin tuna .. 50 10
234. 40 c. Spanish mackerel .. 70 45

41. King Caspar before the Virgin and Child (detail) (Norman 16th-cent. stained glass window).

1969. Christmas. Paintings multicoloured; frame colours given.
235. **41.** 15 c. black, gold & violet 10 10
236. 25 c. black and red .. 10 10
237. – 50 c. blk., blue & orge. 15 15

DESIGN—HORIZ. 50 c. "Nativity" (Leonard Limosin).

43. "Red Cross Sale".

1970. Cent. of British Red Cross. Mult.
238. 3 c. Type **43** 10 10
239. 4 c. School for deaf children 10 10
240. 15 c. Transport services for disabled 10 10
241. 20 c. Workshop 10 30

44. Red-Footed Booby.

1970. Bird. Multicoloured.
242 1 c. Type **44** 10 10
243 2 c. American kestrel .. 15 15
244 3 c. Magnificent frigate bird 15 15
245 4 c. Great egret 60 15
246 5 c. Brown pelican .. 1·25 10
247 10 c. Bananaquit 30 10
248 15 c. Smooth-billed ani .. 30 15
249 20 c. Red-billed tropic bird 35 15
250 25 c. Montserrat oriole .. 50 50
251 50 c. Green-throated carib 4·00 1·00
252 $1 Antillean crested hummingbird .. .. 4·00 1·00
253 $2.50 Little blue heron .. 4·00 4·50
254 $5 Purple-throated carib 7·50 9·00
254a $10 Forest thrush .. 15·00 15·00
The 2, 3, 4, 5, 10, 50 c. and $2.50 are vert.

45. "Madonna and Child with Animals" (Brueghel the Elder, after Durer).

1970. Christmas. Multicoloured.
255. 5 c. Type **45** 10 10
256. 15 c. "The Adoration of the Shepherds" (Domenichino) 10 10
257. 20 c. Type **45** 10 10
258. $1 As 15 c. 35 70

46. War Memorial.

1970. Tourism. Multicoloured.

259. 5 c. Type **46** 10 10
260. 15 c. Plymouth from Fort St. George 10 10
261. 25 c. Carr's Bay 15 10
262. 50 c. Golf Fairway .. 55 30

47. Girl Guide and Badge.

1970. Diamond Jubilee of Montserrat Girl Guides. Multicoloured.

264. 10 c. Type **47** 10 10
265. 15 c. Brownie and Badge .. 10 10
266. 25 c. As 15 c 15 10
267. 40 c. Type **47** 20 20

48. "Descent from the Cross" (Van Hemessen).

1971. Easter. Multicoloured.

268. 5 c. Type **48** 10 10
269. 15 c. "Noli me tangere" (Orcagna) 10 10
270. 20 c. Type **48** 10 10
271. 40 c. As 15 c. 15 15

49. D.F.C. and D.F.M. in Searchlights.

1971. Golden Jubilee of Commonwealth Ex-Services League. Multicoloured.

272. 10 c. Type **49** 10 10
273. 20 c. M.C., M.M. and jungle patrol 15 10
274. 40 c. D.S.C., D.S.M. and submarine action .. 20 15
275. $1 V.C. and soldier attacking bunker 50 70

50. "The Nativity with Saints" (Romanino).

1971. Christmas. Multicoloured.

276. 5 c. Type **50** 10 10
277. 15 c. "Choir of Angels" (Simon Marmion) .. 10 10
278. 20 c. Type **50** 10 10
279. $1 As 15 c. 35 40

51. Piper "Apache".

1971. 14th Anniv of Inauguration of L.I.A.T. (Leeward Islands Air Transport). Mult.

280. 5 c. Type **51** 10 10
281. 10 c. Beech "Twin Bonanza" 15 15
282. 15 c. De Havilland "Heron" 30 15
283. 20 c. Britten Norman "Islander" .. 35 15
284. 40 c. De Havilland "Twin Otter" 65 45
285. 75 c. Hawker Siddeley "748" .. .. 2·00 2·25

52. "Chapel of Christ in Gethsemane", Coventry Cathedral.

1972. Easter. Multicoloured.

287. 5 c. Type **52** 10 10
288. 10 c. "The Agony in the Garden" (Bellini) .. 10 10
289. 20 c. Type **52** 10 10
290. 75 c. As 10 c. 35 50

53. Lizard.

1972. Reptiles. Multicoloured.

291. 15 c. Type **53** 15 10
292. 20 c. Mountain Chicken (frog) 20 10
293. 40 c. Iguana (horiz.) .. 35 20
294. $1 Tortoise (horiz.) .. 2·00 2·00

54. "Madonna of the Chair" (Raphael).

1972. Christmas. Multicoloured.

303. 10 c. Type **54** 10 10
304. 35 c. "Virgin and Child with Cherub" (Fungai) 15 10
305. 50 c. "Madonna of the Magnificat" (Botticelli) 25 30
306. $1 "Virgin and Child with St. John and an Angel" (Botticelli) 40 65

1972. Royal Silver Wedding. As T **52** of Ascension, but with Lime, Tomatoes and Pawpaw in background.

307. 35 c. pink 10 10
308. $1 blue 20 20

56. "Passiflora herbertiana".

1973. Easter. Passion-flowers. Multicoloured.

309. 20 c. Type **56** 25 10
310. 35 c. "P. vitifolia" .. 35 10
311. 75 c. "P. amabilis" .. 1·40 1·40
312. $1 "P. alata-cuerulea" .. 1·75 1·75

57. Montserrat Monastery, Spain.

1973. 480th Anniv. of Columbus's Discovery of Montserrat. Multicoloured.

313. 10 c. Type **57** 15 10
314. 35 c. Columbus sighting Montserrat 30 15
315. 60 c. Columbus's ship off Montserrat .. .. 1·50 1·50
316. $1 Island badge and map of voyage .. .. 1·75 1·75

58. "Virgin and Child" (School of Gerard David).

1973. Christmas. Multicoloured.

318. 20 c. Type **58** 25 10
319. 35 c. "The Holy Family with St. John" (Jordaens) 30 10
320. 50 c. "Virgin and Child" (Bellini) 60 50
321. 90 c. "Virgin and Child with flowers" (Dolci) .. 85 1·00

1973. Royal Wedding. As T **47** of Anguilla. Multicoloured background colours given.

322. 35 c. green 10 10
323. $1 blue 20 20

59. Steel Band.

1974. 25th Anniv. of University of West Indies. Multicoloured.

324. 20 c. Type **59** 15 10
325. 35 c. Masqueraders (vert.) 20 10
326. 60 c. Student weaving (vert.) 1·00 1·00
327. $1 University Centre, Montserrat .. .. 1·10 1·25

60. Hands with Letters.

1974. Centenary of U.P.U.

329. **60.** 1 c. multicoloured .. 10 10
330. – 2 c. red, orange & black 10 10
331. **60.** 3 c. multicoloured .. 10 10
332. – 5 c. orge., red & blk. .. 10 10
333. **60.** 50 c. multicoloured .. 20 20
334. – $1 blue, grn. & blk. .. 40 65

DESIGN: 2 c., 5 c., $1 Figures from U.P.U. Monument.

1974. Various stamps surch.

335. 2 c. on $1 (No. 252) .. 30 75
336. 5 c. on 50 c. (No. 333) .. 40 60
337. 10 c. on 60 c. (No. 326) .. 1·75 2·25
338. 20 c. on $1 mult. (No. 252) 30 55
339. 35 c. on $1 (No. 334) .. 75 1·25

62. Churchill and Houses of Parliament.

1974. Birth Centenary of Sir Winston Churchill. Multicoloured.

340. 35 c. Type **62** 15 10
341. 70 c. Churchill and Blenheim Palace 20 20

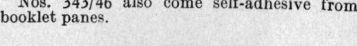

63. Carib "Carbet".

1975. Carib Artefacts.

343. **63.** 5 c. brn., yell. & black .. 10 10
344. – 20 c. blk., brn. & yell. .. 10 10
345. – 35 c. blk., yell. & brn. .. 15 10
346. – 70 c. yell., brn. & blk. .. 35 40

DESIGNS: 20 c. "Caracoli". 35 c. Club or mace. 70 c. Canoe.

Nos. 343/46 also come self-adhesive from booklet panes.

64. One-Bitt Coin.

1975. Local Coinage, 1785-1801.

351. **64.** 5 c. black, blue & silver 10 10
352. – 10 c. black, pink & silver 15 10
353. – 35 c. black, grn. & silver 20 15
354. – $2 black, red & silver .. 1·25 1·50

DESIGNS: 10 c. Eighth dollar. 35 c. Quarter dollar. $2, One dollar.

65. 1d. and 6d. Stamps of 1876.

1976. Centenary of 1st Montserrat Postage Stamp.

No.	Type	Description	Unused	Used
356.	65.	5 c. red, green & black ..	10	10
357.	–	10 c. yellow, red & black	15	10
358.	–	40 c. multicoloured ..	40	40
359.	–	55 c. mauve, grn. & blk.	50	50
360.	–	70 c. multicoloured ..	70	70
361.	–	$1.10 green, blue & black	1·00	1·00

DESIGNS: 10 c. G.P.O. and bisected 1d. stamp. 40 c. Bisects on cover. 55 c. G.B. 6d. used in Montserrat and local 6d. of 1876. 70 c. Stamps for 2½d. rate, 1876. $1.10, Packet boat "Antelope" and 6d. stamp.

66. "The Trinity".

1976. Easter. Paintings by Orcagna. Multicoloured.

No.	Description	Unused	Used
363.	15 c. Type **66**	10	10
364.	40 c. "The Resurrection"	15	15
365.	55 c. "The Ascension" ..	15	15
366.	$1.10 "Pentecost" ..	30	40

1976. Nos. 244, 246 and 247 surch.

No.	Description	Unused	Used
368.	2 c. on 5 c. multicoloured	10	15
369.	30 c. on 10 c. multicoloured	30	20
370.	45 c. on 3 c. multicoloured	40	25

68. White Frangipani.

1976. Flowering Trees. Multicoloured.

No.	Description	Unused	Used
371.	1 c. Type **68**	10	10
372.	2 c. Cannon-ball tree ..	10	10
373.	3 c. Lignum vitae ..	10	10
374.	5 c. Malay apple	15	10
375.	10 c. Jacaranda	20	10
376.	15 c. Orchid Tree ..	25	10
377.	20 c. Manjak	25	10
378.	25 c. Tamarind	25	10
379.	40 c. Flame of the Forest	35	20
380.	55 c. Pink Cassia ..	40	25
381.	70 c. Long John	50	30
382.	$1 Saman	65	40
383.	$2.50 Immortelle	1·25	1·50
384.	$5 Yellow Poui	2·00	2·25
385.	$10 Flamboyant	3·00	4·25

69. Mary and Joseph.

1976. Christmas. Multicoloured.

No.	Description	Unused	Used
386.	15 c. Type **69**	10	10
387.	20 c. The Shepherds ..	10	10
388.	55 c. Mary and Jesus ..	15	15
389.	$1.10 The Magi	30	50

70. Hudson River Review, 1976.

1976. Bicentenary of American Revolution. Multicoloured.

No.	Description	Unused	Used
391.	15 c. Type **70**	30	15
392.	40 c. } "Raleigh" attacking H.M.S. "Druid" 1777	60	40
393.	75 c. }	60	40
394.	$1.25 Hudson River Review	1·10	60

Nos. 391 and 394 and 392/3 were issued in se-tenant pairs, each pair forming a composite design.

71. The Crowning.

1977. Silver Jubilee. Multicoloured.

No.	Description	Unused	Used
396.	30 c. Royal Visit, 1966 ..	15	15
397.	45 c. Cannons firing a salute	20	20
398.	$1 Type **71**	35	60

72. "Ipomoea Alba".

1977. Flowers of the Night. Multicoloured.

No.	Description	Unused	Used
399.	15 c. Type **72** ..	20	10
400.	40 c. "Epiphyllum hookeri" (horiz.)	55	30
401.	55 c. "Cereus hexagonus" (horiz.)	55	45
402.	$1.50 "Cestrum nocturnum"	1·75	1·25

73. Princess Anne laying Foundation Stone of Glendon Hospital.

1977. Development. Multicoloured.

No.	Description	Unused	Used
404.	20 c. Type **73**	15	10
405.	40 c. "Statesman" (freighter) in Plymouth Port	25	15
406.	55 c. Glendon Hospital ..	30	20
407.	$1.50 Jetty at Plymouth Port	80	1·00

1977. Royal Visit. Nos. 380/1 and 383 surch. **SILVER JUBILEE 1977 ROYAL VISIT TO THE CARIBBEAN** and new value.

No.	Description	Unused	Used
409.	$1 on 55 c. Pink Cassia ..	30	45
410.	$1 on 70 c. Long John ..	30	45
411.	$1 on $2.50 Immortelle ..	30	45

75. The Stable at Bethlehem.

1977. Christmas. Multicoloured.

No.	Description	Unused	Used
412.	5 c. Type **75**	10	10
413.	40 c. The Three Kings ..	15	10
414.	55 c. Three Ships ..	20	10
415.	$2 Three Angels ..	55	75

76. Four-eye Butterflyfish.

1978. Fish. Multicoloured.

No.	Description	Unused	Used
417.	30 c. Type **76**	20	10
418.	40 c. French Angelfish ..	25	15
419.	55 c. Blue Tang	35	15
420.	$1.50 Queen Triggerfish ..	80	90

77. St. Paul's Cathedral.

1978. 25th Anniv. of Coronation. Mult.

No.	Description	Unused	Used
422.	40 c. Type **77**	10	10
423.	55 c. Chichester Cathedral	10	10
424.	$1 Lincoln Cathedral ..	20	25
425.	$2.50 Llandaff Cathedral	30	50

78. "Alpinia speciosa".

1978. Flowers. Multicoloured.

No.	Description	Unused	Used
427.	40 c. Type **78**	20	10
428.	55 c. "Allamanda cathartica"	25	15
429.	$1 "Petrea volubilis" ..	45	45
430.	$2 "Hippeastrum puniceum"	70	80

79. Private, 21st (Royal North British Fusiliers), 1786.

1978. Military Uniforms (1st series). British Infantry Regiments. Multicoloured.

No.	Description	Unused	Used
431.	30 c. Type **79**	15	15
432.	40 c. Corporal, 86th (Royal County Down), 1831 ..	20	15
433.	55 c. Sergeant, 14th (Buckinghamshire), 1837 ..	30	20
434.	$1.50 Officer, 55th (Westmorland), 1784	75	80

See also Nos. 441/4.

80. Cub Scouts.

1979. 50th Anniv. of Boy Scout Movement on Montserrat. Multicoloured.

No.	Description	Unused	Used
436.	40 c. Type **80**	25	10
437.	55 c. Scouts with signalling equipment	35	20
438.	$1.25 Camp fire (vert.) ..	60	55
439.	$2 Oath ceremony (vert.)	1·00	1·00

1979. Military Uniforms (2nd series). As T **79**. Multicoloured.

No.	Description	Unused	Used
441.	30 c. Private, 60th (Royal American), 1783 ..	15	15
442.	40 c. Private, 1st West India, 1819	20	15
443.	55 c. Officer, 5th (Northumberland), 1819 ..	30	25
444.	$2.50 Officer, 93rd (Sutherland Highlanders), 1830	1·00	1·10

81. Child reaching out to Adult.

1979. International Year of the Child.

No.	Type	Description	Unused	Used
446.	81.	$2 black, brown & flesh	50	55

82. Sir Rowland Hill with Penny Black and Montserrat 1876 1d. Stamp.

1979. Death Cent. of Sir Rowland Hill and Cent. of U.P.U. Membership. Multicoloured.

No.	Description	Unused	Used
448.	40 c. Type **82**	20	10
449.	55 c. U.P.U. emblem and notice announcing Leeward Islands entry into Union	25	15
450.	$1 1883 letter following U.P.U. membership ..	35	50
451.	$2 Great Britain Post Office Regulations Notice and Sir Rowland Hill ..	60	80

83. Plume Worm.

1979. Marine Life. Multicoloured.

No.	Description	Unused	Used
453.	40 c. Type **83**	30	15
454.	55 c. Sea Fans	40	20
455.	$2 Sponge and coral ..	1·00	1·00

84. Tree Frog.

1980. Reptiles and Amphibians. Mult.

No.	Description	Unused	Used
456.	40 c. Type **84**	20	15
457.	55 c. Tree Lizard	25	25
458.	$1 Crapaud	45	50
459.	$2 Wood Slave	80	90

85. "The Marquess of Salisbury" and 1838 Handstamps.

1980. "London 1980" International Stamp Exhibition. Multicoloured.

No.	Description	Unused	Used
460.	40 c. Type **85**	20	15
461.	55 c. "H.S. 748" aircraft and 1976 55 c. definitive	25	25
462.	$1.20 "La Plata" (liner) and 1903 5s. stamp ..	45	45
463.	$1.20 "Lady Hawkins" (packet steamer) and 1932 Tercentenary 5s. commemorative ..	45	45

464. $1.20 "Avon" (paddle-steamer) and Penny Red stamp with "A 08" postmark 45 45
465. $1.20 "Aeronca" aero-plane and 1953 $1.20 definitive 45 45

1980. 75th Anniv. of Rotary International. No. 383 optd. **75th Anniversary of Rotary International.**
467. $2.50 Immortelle 70 85

87. Greek, French and U.S.A. Flags.

1980. Olympic Games, Moscow. Multicoloured.
468. 40 c. Type **87** 15 15
469. 55 c. Union, Swedish and Belgian flags .. 15 15
470. 70 c. French, Dutch and U.S.A. flags .. 20 20
471. $1 German, Union and Finnish flags 25 25
472. $1.50 Australian, Italian and Japanese flags .. 30 40
473. $2 Mexican, West German and Canadian flags .. 35 55
474. $2.50 "The Discus Thrower" (sculpture, Miron) .. 40 75

1980. Nos. 371, 373, 376 and 379 surch.
476. 5 c. on 3 c. Lignum vitae .. 10 10
477. 35 c. on 1 c. Type **68** .. 20 15
478. 35 c. on 3 c. Lignum vitae 20 15
479. 35 c. on 15 c. Orchid Tree 20 15
480. 55 c. on 40 c. Flame of the Forest 25 15
481. $5 on 40 c. Flame of the Forest .. .. .. 1·25 2·00

89. "Lady Nelson", 1928.

1980. Mail Packet Boats (1st series). Mult.
482 40 c. Type **89** 20 15
483 55 c. "Chignecto", 1913 .. 30 25
484 $1 "Solent II", 1878 .. 50 50
485 $2 "Dee", 1841 .. .. 75 85
See also Nos. 615/19.

90. "Heliconius charithonia".

1981. Butterflies. Multicoloured.
486. 50 c. Type **90** .. 60 40
487. 65 c. "Pyrgus oileus" .. 70 45
488. $1.50 "Poebis agarithe" 90 85
489. $2.50 "Danaus plexippus" 1·25 1·10

91. Spadefish.

1981. Fishes. Multicoloured.
555 5 c. Type **91** 20 10
556 10 c. Hogfish 25 10
492 15 c. Creole Wrasse .. 65 10
493 20 c. Yellow Damselfish 70 10
559 25 c. Sergeant Major .. 35 20
560 35 c. Clown Wrasse .. 45 30
496 45 c. Schoolmaster .. 60 25
497 55 c. Striped Parrotfish .. 95 30
498 65 c. Bigeye 60 30
499 75 c. French Grunt .. 60 40
500 $1 Rock Beauty 75 55
501 $2 Blue Chromis .. 1·75 1·10
502 $3 Fairy Basslet and Blue-heads .. .. 1·90 1·75
503 $5 Cherubfish .. .. 2·75 2·75
504 $7. 50 Longspine Squirrel-fish .. .. .. 5·50 4·75
570 $10 Longsnout Butterfly-fish .. .. .. 5·50 6·00

92. Fort St. George.

1981. Montserrat National Trust. Mult.
506. 50 c. Type **92** .. 30 20
507. 65 c. Bird sanctuary, Fox's Bay 45 35
508. $1. 50 Museum 85 75
509. $2. 50 Bransby Point Battery, c. 1780 .. 1·40 1·40

1981. Royal Wedding, Royal Yachts. As T **26/27** of Kiribati. Multicoloured.
510 90 c. "Charlotte" .. 25 25
511 90 c. Prince Charles and Lady Diana Spencer .. 85 85
512 $3 "Portsmouth" .. 60 60
518 $3 As No. 511 .. .. 1·50 1·50
514 $4 "Britannia" 75 75
515 $4 As No. 511 .. .. 1·75 1·75

93. H.M.S. "Dorsetshire" and Seaplane.

1981. 50th Anniv. of Montserrat Airmail Service. Multicoloured.
519. 50 c. Type **93** 50 30
520. 65 c. Beechcraft "Twin Bonanza" aeroplane .. 65 30
521. $1. 50 De Haviland "Dragon Rapide" R.M. "Lord Shaftesbury" aeroplane 1·10 1·50
522. $2. 50 Hawker Siddeley Avro "748" aeroplane and Maps of Montserrat and Antigua .. .. 1·40 2·25

94. Methodist Church, Bethel.

1981. Christmas. Churches. Multicoloured.
523. 50 c. Type **94** 20 15
524. 65 c. St. George's Anglican Church, Harris .. 25 15
525. $1. 50 St. Peter's Anglican Church, St. Peter's .. 60 60
526. $2. 50 St. Patrick's R.C. Church, Plymouth .. 75 1·00

95. Rubiaceae ("Rondeletia buxifolia").

1981. Plant Life. Multicoloured.
528. 50 c. Type **95** 30 30
529. 65 c. Boraginaceae ("Heliotropium ternatum") (horiz.) 40 40
530. $1. 50 Simarubaceae ("Picramnia pentandra") 85 85
531. $2. 50 Ebenaceae ("Diospyrus revoluta") (horiz.) 1·25 1·25

96. Plymouth.

1982. 350th Anniv. of Settlement of Montserrat by Sir Thomas Warner.
532. **96.** 40 c. green 30 30
533. 55 c. red 35 35
534. 65 c. brown 40 40
535. 75 c. grey 45 50
536. 85 c. blue 50 60
537. 95 c. orange 55 65
538. $1 violet 60 70
539. $1.50 olive .. .. 80 1·00
540. $2 claret .. .. 1·10 1·25
541. $2.50 brown .. .. 1·40 1·60
The design of Nos. 532/41 is based on the 1932 Tercentenary set.

97. Catherine of Aragon, Princess of Wales, 1501.

1982. 21st Birthday of Princess of Wales. Multicoloured.
542. 75 c. Type **97** 15 15
543. $1 Coat of Arms of Catherine of Aragon .. 30 15
544. $5 Diana, Princess of Wales 1·25 1·50

98. Local Scout.

1982. 75th Anniv. of Boy Scout Movement. Multicoloured.
545. $1.50 Type **98** .. 85 70
546. $2.20 Lord Baden-Powell 1·25 1·10

99. Annunciation.

1982. Christmas. Multicoloured.
547. 35 c. Type **99** .. 20 15
548. 75 c. Shepherds' Vision .. 40 35
549. $1.50 The Stable .. 85 85
550. $2.50 Flight into Egypt 1·00 1·10

100. "Lepthemis Vesiculosa".

1983. Dragonflies. Multicoloured.
551. 50 c. Type **100** .. 25 20
552. 65 c. "Orthemis ferruginea" 30 25
553. $1.50 "Triacathagyna trifida" 70 75
554. $2.50 "Erythrodiplax umbrata" .. .. 1·25 1·25

101. Blue-headed Hummingbird.

1983. Hummingbirds. Multicoloured.
571. 35 c. Type **101** .. .. 1·25 35
572. 75 c. Green-throated Carib 1·50 55
573. $2 Antillean Crested Hummingbird .. .. 2·50 1·40
574. $3 Purple-throated Carib 3·00 1·75

102. Montserrat Emblem.

1983.
575. **102.** $12 blue and red .. 4·25 5·00
576. $30 red and blue .. 11·00 12·00

1983. Various stamps surch.
(a) Nos. 491, 494, 498/9, 501.
577. 40 c. on 25 c. Sergeant Major (No. 494) .. 30 30
578. 70 c. on 10 c. Hogfish (No. 491) 45 45
579. 90 c. on 65 c. Bigeye (No. 498) 55 60
580. $1.15 on 75 c. French Grunt (No. 499) .. 65 70
581. $1.50 on $2 Blue Chromis (No. 501) 85 90
(b) Nos. 512/15.
582. 70 c. on $3 "Portsmouth" 65 75
583. 70 c. on $3 Prince Charles and Lady Diana Spencer 90 1·00
584. $1.15 on $4 "Britannia" 1·10 1·25
585. $1.15 on $4, As No. 583 .. 1·50 1·60

INDEX
Countries can be quickly located by referring to the index at the end of this volume.

104. Montgolfier Balloon, 1783.

1983. Bicentenary of Manned Flight. Mult.
586. 35 c. Type **104** 15 15
587. 75 c. De Havilland "Twin Otter" (horiz.) 30 30
588. $1.50 Lockheed "Vega" (horiz.) 60 75
589. $2 "R 34" airship (horiz.) 85 1·25
Nos. 586/9 were re-issued optd. **"INAUGURAL FLIGHT Montserrat-Nevis-St. Kitts".**

105. Boys dressed as Clowns.

1983. Christmas. Carnival. Multicoloured.
591. 55 c. Type **105** 10 10
592. 90 c. Girls dressed as silver star bursts 20 20
593. $1.15 Flower girls .. 25 35
594. $2 Masqueraders 55 80

106. Statue of Discus Thrower.

1984. Olympic Games, Los Angeles. Mult.
595. 90 c. Type **106** 35 35
596. $1 Olympic torch 40 45
597. $1.15 Los Angeles Olympic stadium 45 50
598. $2.50 Olympic and American flags .. .. .. 80 1·00

107. Cattle Egret.

1984. Birds of Montserrat. Multicoloured.
600. 5 c. Type **107** 15 20
601. 10 c. Carib grackle .. 15 20
602. 15 c. Moorhen 15 20
603. 20 c. Brown booby .. 20 20
604. 25 c. Black-whiskeredvireo 20 20
605. 40 c. Scaly-breasted thrasher 35 25
606. 55 c. Laughing gull .. 50 30
607. 70 c. Glossy ibis .. 60 45
608. 90 c. Green heron 75 50
609. $1 Belted kingfisher (vert.) 90 65
610. $1.15 Bananaquit (vert.) .. 1·10 1·40
611. $3 American kestrel (vert.) 2·25 3·50
612. $5 Forest thrush (vert.) .. 3·50 6·00
613. $7.50 Black-crowned night heron (vert.) .. .. 5·50 9·50
614. $10 Bridled quail dove (vert.) .. .. .. 7·00 12·00

1984. Mail Packet Boats (2nd series). As T **89**. Multicoloured.
615 55 c. "Tagus II", 1907 .. 30 40
616 90 c. "Cobequid", 1913 .. 40 50
617 $1.15 "Lady Drake", 1942 55 70
618 $2 "Factor", 1948 .. 80 1·25

108. Hermit Crab and Top Shell.

1984. Marine Life. Multicoloured.
620. 90 c. Type **108** .. .. 1·00 75
621. $1.15 Rough File Shell .. 1·25 95
622. $1.50 True Tulip Snail .. 1·75 1·40
623. $2.50 West Indian Fighting Conch .. .. .. 2·50 2·50

109. "Bull Man".

1984. Christmas. Carnival Costumes. Mult.
624. 55 c. Type **109** 40 25
625. $1.15 Masquerader Captain 1·25 90
626. $1.50 "Fantasy" Carnival Queen .. .. .. 1·50 1·25
627. $2.30 "Ebony and Ivory" Carnival Queen .. .. 2·25 2·25

110. Mango.

1985. National Emblems. Multicoloured.
628. $1.15 Type **110** 40 55
629. $1.50 Lobster Claw .. 65 85
630. $3 Montserrat Oriole .. 90 1·40

111. "Oncidium urophyllum".

1985. Orchids of Montserrat. Multicoloured.
631. 90 c. Type **111** 45 55
632. $1.15 "Epidendrum difforme" 55 70
633. $1.50 "Epidendrum ciliare" 60 85
634. $2.50 "Brassavola cucullata" .. .. 1·00 1·40

112. Queen Elizabeth the Queen Mother.

1985. Life and Times of Queen Elizabeth the Queen Mother. Various vertical portraits.
636. **112.** 55 c. multicoloured .. 30 35
637. – 55 c. multicoloured .. 30 35
638. – 90 c. multicoloured .. 35 55
639. – 90 c. multicoloured .. 35 55
640. – $1.15 multicoloured .. 40 65
641. – $1.15 multicoloured .. 40 65
642. – $1.50 multicoloured .. 50 70
643. – $1.50 multicoloured .. 50 70
Each value was issued in pairs showing a floral pattern across the bottom of the portraits which stops short of the left-hand edge on the first stamp and of the right-hand edge on the second.

113. Cotton Plants.

1985. Montserrat Sea Island Cotton Industry. Multicoloured.
645. 90 c. Type **113** 35 45
646. $1 Operator at carding machine 35 50
647. $1.15 Threading loom .. 45 65
648. $2.50 Weaving with hand loom .. .. .. 1·00 1·60

1985. Royal Visit. Nos. 514/15, 543, 587/8 and 640/1 optd. **CARIBBEAN ROYAL VISIT—1985** or surch. also.
650. 75 c. mult. (No. 587) .. 2·50 2·50
651. $1 multicoloured (No. 543) 4·00 3·00
652. $1.15 mult. (No. 640) .. 4·00 3·00
653. $1.15 mult. (No. 641) .. 4·00 3·50
654. $1.50 mult. (No. 588) .. 5·50 5·00
655. $1.60 on $4 multicoloured (No. 514) .. .. .. 3·50 3·50
656. $1.60 on $4 multicoloured (No. 515) .. .. .. 10·00 10·00
No. 656 shows a new face value only, "Caribbean Royal Visit—1985" being omitted from the surcharge.

115. Black-throated Blue Warbler.

1985. Leaders of the World. Birth Bicentenary of John J. Audubon (ornithologist). Designs showing original paintings. Multicoloured.
657. 15 c. Type **115** 15 15
658. 15 c. Palm Warbler .. 15 15
659. 30 c. Bobolink 20 20
660. 30 c. Lark Sparrow .. 20 20
661. 55 c. Chipping Sparrow .. 30 30
662. 55 c. Northern Oriole .. 30 30
663. $2.50 American Goldfinch 1·00 1·00
664. $2.50 Blue Grosbeak .. 1·00 1·00

116. Herald Angel appearing to Goatherds.

1985. Christmas. Designs showing Caribbean Nativity. Multicoloured.
665. 70 c. Type **116** 15 15
666. $1.15 Three Wise Men following Star 25 35
667. $1.50 Carol singing around War Memorial, Plymouth 35 50
668. $2.30 Praying to "Our Lady of Montserrat", Church of Our Lady, St. Patrick's Village .. 60 1·00

117. Lord Baden-Powell.

1986. 50th Anniv. of Montserrat Girl Guide Movement. Multicoloured.
669. 20 c. Type **117** 15 20
670. 20 c. Girl Guide saluting .. 15 20
671. 75 c. Lady Baden-Powell 30 45
672. 75 c. Guide assisting in old people's home 30 45
673. 90 c. Lord and Lady Baden-Powell 40 55
674. 90 c. Guides serving meal in old people's home .. 40 55
675. $1.15 Girl Guides of 1936 .. 55 75
676. $1.15 Two guides saluting 55 75

1986. 60th Birthday of Queen Elizabeth II. As T **167** of British Virgin Islands. Multicoloured.
677. 10 c. Queen Elizabeth II 10 10
678. $1.50 Princess Elizabeth in 1928 .. .. .. 40 50
679. $3 In Antigua, 1977 .. 75 85
680. $6 In Canberra, 1982 (vert.) 1·50 1·75

118. King Harold and Halley's Comet, 1066 (from Bayeux Tapestry).

1986. Appearance of Halley's Comet. Multicoloured.
682. 35 c. Type **118** 20 20
683. 50 c. Comet of 1301 (from Giotto's "Adoration of the Magi") 25 25
684. 70 c. Edmond Halley and comet of 1531 .. .. 35 35
685. $1 Comets of 1066 and 1910 40 40
686. $1.15 Comet of 1910 .. 45 50
687. $1.50 E.S.A. "Giotto" spacecraft and comet .. 60 75
688. $2.30 U.S. space telescope and comet .. .. 90 1·25
689. $4 Computer reconstruction of 1910 comet .. 1·60 2·00

1986. Royal Wedding (1st issue). As T **168** of British Virgin Islands. Multicoloured.
691. 70 c. Prince Andrew .. 35 40
692. 70 c. Miss Sarah Ferguson 30 35
693. $2 Prince Andrew wearing stetson (horiz.) .. 30 35
694. $2 Miss Sarah Ferguson on skiing holiday (horiz.) .. 75 90
See also Nos. 705/8. 75 90

119. "Antelope" being attacked by "L'Atalante".

1986. Mail Packet Sailing Ships. Mult.
696 90 c. Type **119** .. .. 1·50 1·25
697 $1.15 "Montagu" (1810) .. 1·75 1·50
698 $1.50 "Little Catherine" being pursued by "L' Etoile" (1813) .. 2·25 2·25
699 $2.30 "Hinchingbrook I" (1813) .. .. 2·75 3·00

120. Radio Montserrat Building, Dagenham.

1986. Communications. Multicoloured.

701. 70 c. Type **120** .. .. 1·00 70
702. $1.15 Radio Gem dish aerial, Plymouth .. 1·00 1·25
703. $1.50 Radio Antilles studio, O'Garro's .. .. 1·75 1·75
704. $2.30 Cable and Wireless building, Plymouth .. 2·25 3·00

1986. Royal Wedding (2nd issue). Nos. 691/4 optd. **Congratulations to T.R.H. The Duke and Duchess of York.**

705. 70 c. Prince Andrew .. 50 50
706. 70 c. Miss Sarah Ferguson 50 50
707. $2 Prince Andrew wearing stetson (horiz.) .. .. 1·25 1·25
708. $2 Miss Sarah Ferguson on skiing holiday (horiz.) .. 1·25 1·25

122. Sailing and Windsurfing.

1986. Tourism. Multicoloured.

710. 70 c. Type **122** 50 70
711. $1.15 Golf .. .. .. 1·25 1·50
712. $1.50 Plymouth market .. 1·25 1·75
713. $2.30 Air Recording Studios .. .. .. 1·50 2·50

123. Christmas Rose.

1986. Christmas. Flowering Shrubs. Mult.

714. 70 c. Type **123** 60 40
715. $1.15 Candle flower .. 85 70
716. $1.50 Christmas tree Kalanchoe .. .. 1·25 1·00
717. $2.30 Snow on the mountain .. .. 1·75 2·00

124. Tiger Shark.

1987. Sharks. Multicoloured.

719. 40 c. Type **124** .. .. 1·00 55
720. 90 c. Lemon shark .. 1·75 1·10
721. $1.15 White shark .. .. 2·00 1·75
722. $3.50 Whale shark .. 4·00 4·25

1987. Nos. 601, 603, 607/8 and 611 surch.

724. 5 c. on 70 c. Glossy ibis .. 20 15
725. $1 on 20 c. Brown booby .. 1·00 80
726. $1.15 on 10 c. Carib grackle 1·10 90
727. $1.50 on 90 c. Green heron 1·40 1·40
728. $2.30 on $3 American kestrel (vert.) .. .. 2·25 2·75

127. "Phoebis trite".

1987. Butterflies. Multicoloured.

730 90 c. Type **127** .. .. 1·50 80
731 $1.15 "Biblis hyperia" .. 2·00 1·25
732 $1.50 "Polygorus leo" .. 2·50 2·00
733 $2.50 "Hypolimnas misippus" .. .. .. 4·00 4·25

128. "Oncidium variegatum".

1987. Christmas. Orchids. Multicoloured.

734. 90 c. Type **128** 60 45
735. $1.15 "Vanilla planifolia" (horiz.) 85 55
736. $1.50 "Gongora quinquenervis" .. .. .. 1·10 75
737. $3.50 "Brassavola nodosa" (horiz.) .. .. .. 2·00 1·75

1987. Royal Ruby Wedding. Nos. 601, 604/5 and 608 surch. **40th Wedding Anniversary HM Queen Elizabeth II HRH Duke of Edinburgh. November 1987** and value.

739. 5 c. on 90 c. Green heron .. 15 15
740. $1.15 on 10 c. Carib grackle 65 65
741. $2.30 on 25 c. Black-whiskered vireo .. .. 1·40 1·40
742. $5 on 40 c. Scaly-breasted thrasher .. .. .. 2·75 3·00

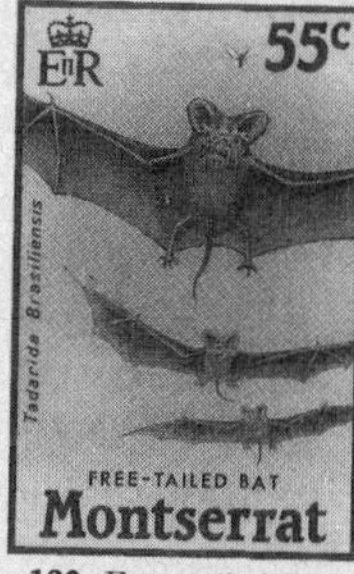

130. Free-tailed Bat.

1988. Bats. Multicoloured.

743. 55 c. Type **130** 50 35
744. 90 c. "Chiroderma improvisum" (fruit bat) .. 80 65
745. $1.15 Fisherman Bat .. 1·10 1·10
746. $2.30 "Brachyphylla cavernarum" (fruit bat) .. 2·25 2·50

131. Magnificent Frigate Bird.

1988. Easter. Birds. Multicoloured.

748. 90 c. Type **131** 60 45
749. $1.15 Caribbean elaenia .. 80 65
750. $1.50 Glossy ibis .. .. 1·00 1·00
751. $3.50 Purple-throated carib 2·00 2·25

132 Discus throwing

1988. Olympic Games, Seoul. Multicoloured.

753 90 c. Type **132** 40 45
754 $1.15 High jumping .. 50 55
755 $3.50 Athletics .. 1·60 1·75

133 Golden Tulip

1988. Sea Shells. Multicoloured.

757 5 c. Type **133** .. 10 10
758 10 c. Little knobby scallop 15 15
759 15 c. Sozoni's cone .. 15 15
760 20 c. Globular coral shell 20 20
761 25 c. Sundial 20 20
762 40 c. King helmet .. 30 30
763 55 c. Channelled turban .. 40 40
764 70 c. True tulip shell .. 55 55
765 90 c. Music volute .. 65 65
766 $1 Flame auger 70 70
767 $1.15 Rooster tail conch 80 80
768 $1.50 Queen conch .. 95 95
769 $3 Teramachi's slit shell 1·75 2·00
770 $5 Florida crown conch 3·25 3·50
771 $7.50 Beau's murex .. 5·00 5·50
772 $10 Triton's trumpet .. 7·00 7·50

134 University Crest

1988. 40th Anniv of University of West Indies.

773 **134** $5 multicoloured .. 2·40 2·50

1988. Princess Alexandra's Visit. Nos. 763, 766 and 769/70 surch **HRH PRINCESS ALEXANDRA'S VISIT NOVEMBER 1988** and new value.

774 40 c. on 55 c. Channelled turban 35 35
775 90 c. on $1 Flame auger .. 55 55
776 $1.15 on $3 Teramachi's slit shell 70 70
777 $1.50 on $5 Florida crown conch 85 85

136 Spotted Sandpiper

1988. Christmas. Sea Birds. Multicoloured.

778 90 c. Type **136** 70 55
779 $1.15 Turnstone .. 85 70
780 $3.50 Red-footed booby .. 2·00 2·50

137 Handicapped Children in Classroom

1988. 125th Anniv of International Red Cross.

782 **137** $3.50 multicoloured .. 1·50 1·60

138 Drum Major in Ceremonial Uniform

1989. 75th Anniv (1988) of Montserrat Defence Force. Uniforms. Multicoloured.

783 90 c. Type **138** 70 55
784 $1.15 Field training uniform 85 75
785 $1.50 Cadet in ceremonial uniform .. .. 1·25 1·50
786 $3.50 Gazetted Police Officer in ceremonial uniform .. .. 2·50 3·00

139 Amazon Lily

1989. Easter. Lilies. Multicoloured.

788 90 c. Type **139** 50 50
789 $1.15 Salmon blood lily (vert) 70 70
790 $1.50 Amaryllis (vert) .. 85 1·00
791 $3.50 Amaryllis (vert) .. 1·90 2·25

140 "Morning Prince" (schooner), 1942

1989. Shipbuilding in Montserrat. Mult.

793 90 c. Type **140** 40 45
794 $1.15 "Western Sun" (inter-island freighter) 55 60
795 $1.50 "Kim G" (inter-island freighter) under construction 70 75
796 $3.50 "Romaris" (inter-island ferry), c. 1942 .. 1·60 2·00

141 The Scarecrow

1989. 50th Anniv of "The Wizard of Oz" (film). Multicoloured.

797 90 c. Type **141** 40 45
798 $1.15 The Lion 55 60
799 $1.50 The Tin Man .. 70 75
800 $3.50 Dorothy .. .. 1·60 2·00

1989. Hurricane Hugo Relief Fund. Nos. 795/6 surch **Hurricane Hugo Relief Surcharge $2.50.**

802 $1.50 + $2.50 "Kim G" (inter-island freighter under construction) .. 1·90 2·00
803 $3.50 + $2.50 "Romaris" (inter-island ferry), c. 1942 .. .. 2·75 3·25

143 "Apollo 11" above Lunar Surface

1989. 20th Anniv of First Manned Landing on Moon. Multicoloured

804 90 c. Type **143** 35 40
805 $1.15 Astronaut alighting from lunar module "Eagle" 45 50
806 $1.50 "Eagle" and astronaut conducting experiment 60 65
807 $3.50 Opening "Apollo 11" hatch after splashdown 1·40 1·75

144 "Yamato" (Japanese battleship)

1990. World War II Capital Ships. Mult.

809 70 c. Type **144** 60 50
810 $1.15 U.S.S. "Arizona" at Pearl Harbour 80 70
811 $1.50 "Bismarck" (German battleship) in action .. 1·25 1·25
812 $3.50 H.M.S. "Hood" (battle cruiser) .. 2·00 2·50

145 The Empty Tomb

1990. Easter. Stained glass windows from St. Michael's Parish Church, Bray, Berkshire. Multicoloured.

814 $1.15 Type **145** 65 75
815 $1.50 The Ascension 85 95
816 $3.50 The Risen Christ with Disciples .. .. 1·60 1·75

1990. "Stamp World London 90" International Stamp Exhibition. Nos. 460/4 surch **Stamp World London 90** and value.

818 70 c. on 40 c. Type **85** .. 40 40
819 90 c. on 55 c. "H.S. 748" aircraft and 1976 55 c. definitive 55 55
820 $1 on $1.20 "La Plata" (liner) and 1903 5s. stamp 65 75
821 $1.15 on $1.20 "Lady Hawkins" (packet steamer) and 1932 Tercentenary 5s. commemorative .. 75 85
822 $1.50 on $1.20 "Avon" (paddle-steamer) and Penny Red stamp with "A 08" postmark .. 1·00 1·25

HAVE YOU READ THE NOTES AT THE BEGINNING OF THIS CATALOGUE?
These often provide answers to the enquiries we receive.

147 General Office, Montserrat, and 1884 ½d. Stamp

1990. 150th Anniv of the Penny Black. Mult.

823 90 c. Type **147** 55 55
824 $1.15 Sorting letters and Montserrat 1d. stamp of 1876 (vert) 75 75
825 $1.50 Posting letters and Penny Black (vert) .. 1·00 1·00
826 $3.50 Postman delivering letters and 1840 Two-pence Blue .. .. 2·50 3·00

148 Montserrat v. Antigua Match

1990. World Cup Football Championship, Italy. Multicoloured.

828 90 c. Type **148** 55 55
829 $1.15 U.S.A v. Trinidad match 75 75
830 $1.50 Montserrat team .. 1·00 1·25
831 $3.50 West Germany v. Wales match .. .. 2·00 2·25

149 Spinner Dolphin

1990. Dolphins. Multicoloured.

833 90 c. Type **149** 65 65
834 $1.15 Common dolphin .. 85 85
835 $1.50 Striped dolphin .. 1·25 1·25
836 $3.50 Atlantic spotted dolphin .. .. 2·25 2·50

150 Spotted Goatfish

1991. Tropical Fishes. Multicoloured.

838 90 c. Type **150** 65 65
839 $1.15 Cushion star 85 85
840 $1.50 Rock beauty .. .. 1·25 1·25
841 $3.50 French grunt .. .. 2·25 2·50

1991. Nos. 760/1, 768 and 771 surch.

843 5 c. on 20 c. Globular coral shell 20 20
844 5 c. on 25 c. Sundial .. 20 20
845 $1.15 on $1.50 Queen conch 1·40 1·60
846 $1.15 on $7.50 Beau's murex .. .. .. 1·40 1·60

152 Duck

1991. Domestic Birds. Multicoloured.

847 90 c. Type **152** 60 60
848 $1.15 Hen and chicks .. 80 80
849 $1.50 Rooster .. .. 1·10 1·40
850 $3.50 Helmet guineafowl .. 2·40 2·75

153 "Panaeolus antillarum"

1991. Fungi.

851 **153** 90 c. grey 70 70
852 – $1.15 red 90 90
853 – $1.50 brown .. .. 1·25 1·40
854 – $2 purple .. .. 1·75 2·00
855 – $3.50 blue .. .. 2·75 3·25

DESIGNS: $1.15, "Cantharellus cinnabarinus"; $1.50, "Gymnopilus chrysopellus"; $2, "Psilocybe cubensis"; $3.50, "Leptonia caeruleocapitata".

154 Red Water Lily

1991. Lilies. Multicoloured.

856 90 c. Type **154** 65 65
857 $1.15 Shell ginger .. 75 75
858 $1.50 Early day lily .. 1·00 1·25
859 $3.50 Anthurium .. .. 2·50 3·00

155 Tree Frog

1991. Frogs and Toad. Multicoloured.

860 $1.15 Type **155** .. .. 1·00 1·00
861 $2 Crapaud toad .. .. 1·60 1·60
862 $3.50 Mountain chicken (frog) .. .. .. 2·75 2·75

156 Black British Shorthair Cat

1991. Cats. Multicoloured.

864 90 c. Type **156** 70 70
865 $1.15 Seal point Siamese .. 90 90
866 $1.50 Silver tabby Persian 1·25 1·25
867 $2.50 Birman temple cat 1·75 1·75
868 $3.50 Egyptian mau .. 2·25 2·25

157 Navigational Instruments

1992. 500th Anniv of Discovery of America by Columbus. Multicoloured.

869 $1.50 Type **157** 80 90
870 $1.50 Columbus and coat of arms 80 90
871 $1.50 Landfall on the Bahamas 80 90
872 $1.50 Petitioning Queen Isabella 80 90
873 $1.50 Tropical birds .. 80 90
874 $1.50 Tropical fruits .. 80 90
875 $3 Ships of Columbus (81 × 26 mm) .. .. 1·50 1·75

See also Nos. 915/21.

158 Runner with Olympic Flame

1992. Olympic Games, Barcelona. Mult.

876 $1 Type **158** 60 60
877 $1.15 Monserrat, Olympic and Spanish flags .. 75 85
878 $2.30 Olympic flame on map of Montserrat .. 1·25 1·50
879 $3.60 Olympic events .. 1·75 2·00

159 Tyrannosaurus

1992. Death Centenary of Sir Richard Owen (zoologist). Multicoloured.

880 $1 Type **159** 80 80
881 $1.15 Diplodocus 90 90
882 $1.50 Apatosaurus .. .. 1·25 1·25
883 $3.45 Dimetrodon .. .. 2·50 2·75

160 Male Montserrat Oriole

1992. Montserrat Oriole. Multicoloured.

885 $1 Type **160** 70 70
886 $1.15 Male and female orioles 85 85
887 $1.50 Female oriole with chicks .. .. .. 1·25 1·25
888 $3.60 Map of Montserrat and male oriole .. 2·25 2·50

161 "Psophus stridulus" (grasshopper)

1992. Insects. Multicoloured.

889 5 c. Type **161** 10 10
890 10 c. "Gryllus campestris" (field cricket) 10 10
891 15 c. "Lepthemis vesiculosa" (dragonfly) .. 10 10
892 20 c. "Orthemis ferruginea" (red skimmer) .. 10 10
893 25 c. "Gerris lacustris" (pond skater) .. 10 10
894 40 c. "Byctiscus betulae" (leaf weevil) 20 25
895 55 c. "Atta texana" (leaf-cutter ants) 25 30
896 70 c. "Polistes fuscatus" (paper wasp) 30 35

897 90 c. "Sparmopolius fulvus" (bee fly) 45 50
898 $1 "Chrysopa carnea" (lace wing) 50 55
899 $1.15 "Phoebis philea" (butterfly) 60 65
900 $1.50 "Cynthia cardui" (butterfly) 75 80
901 $3 "Utetheisa bella" (moth) .. .. .. 1·40 1·50
902 $5 "Alucita pentadactyla" (moth) .. .. .. 2·40 2·50
903 $7.50 "Anartia jatropha" (butterfly) .. .. 3·75 4·00
904 $10 "Heliconius melpomene" (butterfly) 5·00 5·25

162 Adoration of the Magi (¾ size illustration)

1992. Christmas. Multicoloured.
905 $1.15 Type **162** 50 55
906 $4.60 Appearance of angel to shepherds .. .. 2·00 2·25

163 $1 Coin and $20 Banknote

1993. East Caribbean Currency. Mult.
907 $1 Type **163** 50 55
908 $1.15 10 c. and 25 c. coins with $10 banknote .. 55 60
909 $1.50 5 c. coin and $5 banknote 75 80
910 $3.60 1 c. and 2 c. coins with $1 banknote .. 1·75 1·90

164 Columbus meeting Amerindians

1993. Organization of East Caribbean States. 500th Anniv of Discovery of America by Columbus. Multicoloured.
911 $1 Type **164** 50 55
912 $2 Ships approaching island .. .. .. 95 1·00

165 Queen Elizabeth II on Montserrat with Chief Minister W. H. Bramble, 1966

1993. 40th Anniv of Coronation. Mult.
913 $1.15 Type **165** 55 60
914 $4.60 Queen Elizabeth II in State Coach, 1953 2·25 2·40

1993. 500th Anniv of Discovery of Montserrat. As Nos. 869/75, some with new values, each showing "500th ANNIVERSARY DISCOVERY OF MONTSERRAT" at foot and with additional historical inscr across the centre.
915 $1.15 multicoloured (As Type **157**) 55 60
916 $1.15 multicoloured (As No. 870) 55 60
917 $1.15 multicoloured (As No. 871) 55 60
918 $1.50 multicoloured (As No. 872) 75 80
919 $1.50 multicoloured (As No. 873) 75 80
920 $1.50 multicoloured (As No. 874) 75 80
921 $3.45 multicoloured (As No. 875) .. .. 1·60 1·75

Additional inscriptions: No. 915, "PRE-COLUMBUS CARIB NAME OF ISLAND ALLIOUGANA"; No. 916, "COLUMBUS NAMED ISLAND SANTA MARIA DE MONTSERRATE"; No. 917, "COLUMBUS SAILED ALONG COASTLINE 11th NOV. 1493"; No. 918, "ISLAND OCCUPIED BY FRENCH BRIEFLY IN 1667"; No. 919, "ISLAND DECLARED ENGLISH BY TREATY OF BREDA 1667"; No. 920, "AFRICAN SLAVES BROUGHT IN DURING 1600's"; No. 921, "IRISH CATHOLICS FROM ST. KITTS AND VIRGINIA SETTLED ON ISLAND BETWEEN 1628–1634".

166 Boeing Sentry, 1993

1993. 75th Anniv of Royal Air Force. Mult.
922 15 c. Type **166** 10 10
923 55 c. Vickers Valiant, 1962 25 30
924 $1.15 Handley Page Hastings, 1958 .. .. 55 60
925 $3 Lockheed Ventura, 1943 1·40 1·50

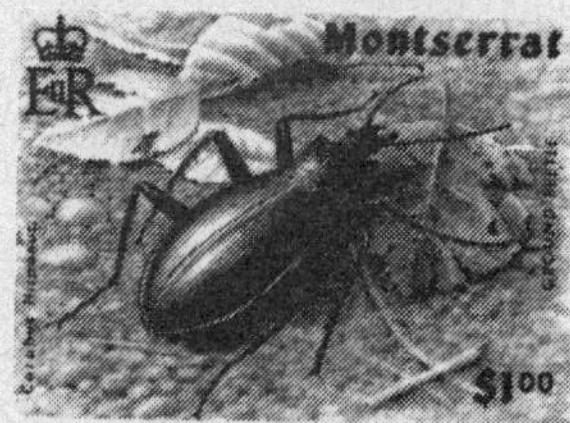

167 Ground Beetle

1994. Beetles. Multicoloured.
927 $1 Type **167** 50 55
928 $1.15 Click beetle 55 60
929 $1.50 Harlequin beetle .. 75 80
930 $3.45 Leaf beetle .. .. 1·60 1·75

168 "Gossypium barbadense"

1994. Flowers. Multicoloured.
932 90 c. Type **168** 45 50
933 $1.15 "Hibiscus sabdariffa" 55 60
934 $1.50 "Hibiscus esculentus" 75 80
935 $3.50 "Hibiscus rosa-sinensis" .. 1·60 1·75

OFFICIAL STAMPS

1976. Various stamps, some already surch. optd. **O.H.M.S.**
O 1. 5 c. multicoloured (No. 246) † 65
O 2. 10 c. multicoloured (No. 247) .. .. † 75
O 3. 30 c. on 10 c. multicoloured (No. 369) .. .. † 1·50
O 4. 45 c. on 3 c. multicoloured (No. 370) .. .. † 2·00
O 5. $5 multicoloured (No. 254) † £100
O 6. $10 multicoloured (No. 254a) .. .. † £550

These stamps were issued for use on mail from the Montserrat Philatelic Bureau. They were not sold to the public, either unused or used.

1976. Nos. 372, 374/82, 384/5 and 476 optd. **O.H.M.S.** or surch. also.
O 17 5 c. Malay Apple .. † 10
O 28 5 c. on 3 c. Lignum vitae † 10
O 18 10 c. Jacaranda .. † 10
O 19 15 c. Orchid Tree .. † 10
O 20 20 c. Manjak .. .. † 10
O 21 25 c. Tamarind .. † 15
O 33 30 c. on 15 c. Orchid Tree † 20
O 34 35 c. on 2 c. Cannon-ball Tree .. .. † 20
O 35 40 c. Flame of the Forest † 25
O 22 55 c. Pink Cassia .. † 35
O 23 70 c. Long John .. † 45
O 24 $1 Saman .. .. † 60
O 39 $2·50 on 40 c. Flame of the Forest .. .. † 2·00
O 25 $5 Yellow Poui .. .. † 2·75
O 16 $10 Flamboyant .. † 5·00

1981. Nos. 490/4, 496, 498, 500, 502/3 and 505 optd. **O.H.M.S.**
O 42. 5 c. Type **91** 10 10
O 43. 10 c. Hogfish 10 10
O 44. 15 c. Creole Wrasse .. 10 10
O 45. 20 c. Yellow Damselfish 15 15
O 46. 25 c. Sergeant Major .. 15 15
O 47. 45 c. Schoolmaster .. 25 20
O 48. 65 c. Bigeye 35 30
O 49. $1 Rock Beauty .. 65 65
O 50. $3 Fairy Basslet and Blueheads .. .. 1·75 1·75
O 51. $5 Cherubfish .. .. 3·00 3·00
O 52. $10 Longsnout Butterfly-fish .. .. .. 5·50 3·50

1983. Nos. 510/15 surch. and optd. **O.H.M.S.**
O 53. 45 c. on 90 c. "Charlotte" 25 30
O 54. 45 c. on 90 c. Prince Charles and Lady Diana Spencer 30 30
O 55. 75 c. on $3 "Portsmouth" 35 35
O 56. 75 c. on $3 Prince Charles and Lady Diana Spencer 45 45
O 57. $1 on $4 "Britannia" .. 50 50
O 58. $1 on $4 Prince Charles and Lady Diana Spencer 60 60

1983. Nos. 542/4 surch. and optd. **O.H.M.S.**
O 59. 70 c. on 75 c. Type **97** .. 60 40
O 60 $1 Coat of Arms of Catherine of Aragon 70 50
O 61. $1.50 on $5 Diana, Princess of Wales .. .. 1·00 80

1985. (12 Apr). Nos. 600/12 and 614 optd. **OHMS.**
O 62. 5 c. Type **107** 20 20
O 63. 10 c. Carib grackle .. 20 20
O 64. 15 c. Moorhen 20 20
O 65. 20 c. Brown booby .. 20 20
O 66. 25 c. Black-whiskered vireo 25 25
O 67. 40 c. Scaly-breasted thrasher 35 30
O 68. 55 c. Laughing gull .. 45 30
O 69. 70 c. Glossy ibis 60 40
O 70. 90 c. Green heron .. 75 40
O 71. $1 Belted kingfisher .. 90 45
O 72. $1.15 Bananaquit .. 1·25 70
O 73. $3 American kestrel 2·25 2·25
O 74. $5 Forest thrush .. 3·25 3·50
O 75. $10 Bridled quail dove .. 5·50 3·75

1989. Nos. 757/70 and 772 optd **O H M S**.
O 76 5 c. Type **133** .. 20 20
O 77 10 c. Little knobby scallop 20 20
O 78 15 c. Sozoni's cone .. 20 20
O 79 20 c. Globular coral shell 20 20
O 80 25 c. Sundial 25 25
O 81 40 c. King helmet .. 30 30
O 82 55 c. Channelled turban 40 40
O 83 70 c. True tulip shell .. 50 50
O 84 90 c. Music volute .. 65 65
O 85 $1 Flame auger .. 70 70
O 86 $1.15 Rooster tail conch 80 80
O 87 $1.50 Queen conch .. 95 95
O 88 $3 Teramachi's slit shell 1·75 1·75
O 89 $5 Florida crown counch .. .. .. 3·00 3·00
O 90 $10 Triton's trumpet 5·50 5·50

1989. Nos. 578 and 580/1 optd **OHMS.**
O91 70 c. on 10 c. Hogfish 50 50
O92 $1.15 on 75 c. French grunt 80 80
O93 $1.50 on $2 Blue chromis 1·10 1·10

1992. Nos. 838/41, 847/50, 856/9 surch or optd **OHMS.**
O 94 70 c. on 90 c. Type **150** .. 40 45
O 95 70 c. on 90 c. Type **152** .. 40 45
O 96 70 c. on 90 c. Type **154** .. 40 45
O 97 70 c. on $3.50 French grunt 40 45
O 98 $1 on $3.50 Helmeted guineafowl 60 65
O 99 $1 on $3.50 Anthurium .. 60 65
O100 $1.15 Cushion star .. 65 70
O101 $1.15 Hen and chicks .. 65 70
O102 $1.15 Shell ginger .. 65 70
O103 $1.50 Rock beauty .. 75 85
O104 $1.50 Rooster .. 75 85
O105 $1.50 Early day lily .. 75 85

1993. Nos. 889/902 and 904 optd **OHMS.**
O106 5 c. Type **161** 10 10
O107 10 c. "Gryllus campestris" (field cricket) .. 10 10
O108 15 c. "Lepthemis vesiculosa" (dragonfly) 10 10
O109 20 c. "Orthemis ferruginea" (red skimmer) .. 10 10
O110 25 c. "Gerris lacustris" (pond skater) .. 10 10
O111 40 c. "Byctiscus betulae" (leaf weevil) .. 20 25
O112 55 c. "Atta texana" (leaf-cutter ants) .. 25 30
O113 70 c. "Polistes fuscatus" (paper wasp) .. 30 35
O114 90 c. "Sparmopolius fulvus" (bee fly) .. 45 50
O115 $1 "Chrysopa carnea" (lace wing) .. 50 55
O116 $1.15 "Phoebis philea" (butterfly) .. 55 60
O117 $1.50 "Cynthia cardui" (butterfly) .. 75 80
O118 $3 "Utetheisa bella" (moth) .. 1·40 1·50
O119 $5 "Alucita pentadactyla" (moth) .. 2·40 2·50
O120 $10 "Heliconius melpomene" (butterfly) 5·00 5·25

MOROCCO AGENCIES

Stamps used at British postal agencies in Morocco, N. Africa, the last of which were closed on 30th April, 1957.

I. GIBRALTAR ISSUES OVERPRINTED.

For use at all British Post Offices in Morocco.
All British P.O.s in Morocco were under the control of the Gibraltar P.O. until 1907 when control was assumed by H.M. Postmaster-General.

1898. Stamps of Gibraltar (Queen) optd. **Morocco Agencies.**

9	**7.**	5 c. green ..	30	15
10		10 c. red	35	15
11		20 c. olive	1·75	70
3d		20 c. olive and brown	1·50	1·25
4		25 c. blue ..	1·50	60
5		40 c. brown	2·50	3·25
14		50 c. lilac	5·50	3·50
7		1 p. brown and blue	8·00	20·00
8		2 p. black and red	5·00	20·00

1903. Stamps of Gibraltar (King Edward VII) optd. **Morocco Agencies.**

24.	**8.**	5 c. green ..	1·50	1·25
25.		10 c. purple and red	2·25	50
26.		20 c. green and red	1·75	22·00
20.		25 c. purple & blk. on bl.	1·50	15
28.		50 c. purple and violet ..	6·00	22·00
29.		1 p. black and red	22·00	70·00
30.		2 p. black and blue	15·00	32·00

II. BRITISH CURRENCY.

On sale at British P.Os throughout Morocco, including Tangier, until 1937.
PRICES. Our prices for used stamps with these overprints are for examples used in Morocco. These stamps could also be used in the United Kingdom, with official sanction, from the summer of 1950 onwards, and with U.K. postmarks are worth about 50 per cent less.

Stamps of Great Britain optd. **MOROCCO AGENCIES.**

1907. King Edward VII.

31	83	½d. green..	85	6·00
32		1d. red ..	2·75	3·00
33	–	2d. green and red	2·75	4·50
34	–	4d. green and brown	3·75	3·25
35a	–	4d. orange	3·75	3·75
36	–	6d. purple	5·50	8·00
37	–	1s. green and red	14·00	16·00
38	–	2s. 6d. purple ..	48·00	75·00

1914. King George V.

42	**105.**	½d. green..	45	45
43	**104.**	1d. red ..	50	10
44	**105.**	1½d. brown	1·00	11·00
45	**106.**	2d. orange	1·00	35
58	**104.**	2½d. blue..	2·00	5·00
46	**106.**	3d. violet	1·00	35
47		4d. green	1·00	70
60	**107.**	6d. purple	40	60
49	**108.**	1s. brown	5·00	75
53	**109.**	2s. 6d. brown	28·00	25·00
74		5s. red ..	23·00	65·00

1935. Silver Jubilee.

62.	**123.**	½d. green	1·25	2·25
63.		1d. red ..	1·25	3·75
64.		1½d. brown	1·50	7·00
65.		2½d. blue	1·50	2·50

1935. King George V.

66.	**119.**	1d. red	3·00	3·00
67.	**118.**	1½d. brown	2·00	10·00
68.	**120.**	2d. orange	40	1·00
69.	**119.**	2½d. blue	1·75	4·25
70.	**120.**	3d. violet	40	15
71.		4d. green	40	15
72.	**122.**	1s. brown	80	1·00

1936. King Edward VIII.

75.	**124.**	1d. red ..	10	30
76.		2½d. blue	10	15

In 1937 unoverprinted Great Britain stamps replaced overprinted **MOROCCO AGENCIES** issues as stocks became exhausted. In 1949 overprinted issues reappeared and were in use at Tetuan (Spanish Zone), the only remaining British P.O. apart from that at Tangier.

1949. King George VI.

77.	**128.**	½d. green	1·50	2·00
94.		½d. orange	1·25	30
78.		1d. red	2·25	4·50
95.		1d. blue	1·25	30
79.		1½d. brown	2·50	3·75
96.		1½d. green	1·25	65
80.		2d. orange	2·50	4·50
97.		2d. brown	1·25	1·25
81.		2½d. blue	2·75	4·50
98.		2½d. red	1·25	80
82.		3d. violet	1·00	55
83.	**129.**	4d. green	45	50
84.		5d. brown	2·50	8·00
85.		6d. purple	80	1·00
86.	**130.**	7d. green	40	10·00
87.		8d. red	2·25	4·50
88.		9d. olive	40	8·00
89.		10d. blue	40	4·25
90.		11d. plum	70	4·00
91.		1s. brown	2·25	4·00
92.	**131.**	2s. 6d. green ..	9·50	21·00
93.		5s. red	28·00	38·00

1951. Pictorials.

99.	**147.**	2s. 6d. green ..	9·00	15·00
100.	–	5s. red (No. 510)	11·00	17·00

1952. Queen Elizabeth II.

101.	**154.**	½d. orange	10	10
102.		1d. blue	15	60
103.		1½d. green	15	10
104.		2d. brown	20	70
105.	**155.**	2½d. red	25	20
106.		4d. blue	60	2·00
107.	**156.**	5d. brown	65	60
108.		6d. purple	50	2·00
109.	**158.**	8d. mauve	1·25	1·00
110.	**159.**	1s. bistre	70	60

III. SPANISH CURRENCY.

Stamps surcharged in Spanish currency were sold at British P.Os throughout Morocco until the establishment of the French Zone and the Tangier International Zone, when their use was confined to the Spanish Zone.

Stamps of Great Britain optd. **MOROCCO AGENCIES** or surch. also in Spanish currency.

1907. King Edward VII.

112	83	5 c. on ½d. green ..	70	15
113		10 c. on 1d. red ..	1·75	10
114	–	15 c. on 1½d. purple and green	80	15
115	–	20 c. on 2d. green & red	70	15
116	83	25 c. on 2½d. blue ..	85	15
117	–	40 c. on 4d. grn. & brn.	90	1·75
118a	–	40 c. on 4d. orange ..	45	60
119a	–	50 c. on 5d. pur. & blue	1·25	80
120	–	1 p. on 10d. pur. & red	7·00	5·50
121	–	3 p. on 2s. 6d. purple..	17·00	23·00
122	–	6 p. on 5s. red ..	35·00	45·00
123	–	12 p. on 10s. blue ..	75·00	75·00

1912. King George V.

126	**101**	5 c. on ½d. green ..	90	10
127	**102**	10 c. on 1d. red ..	50	10

1914. King George V.

128	**105**	3 c. on ½d. green ..	20	2·50
129	**105**	5 c. on ½d. green ..	30	10
130	**104**	10 c. on 1d. red ..	30	10
131	**105**	15 c. on 1½d. brown ..	30	10
132	**106**	20 c. on 2d. orange ..	25	25
133	**104**	25 c. on 2½d. blue ..	60	25
148	**106**	40 c. on 4d. green ..	65	50
135	**108**	1 p. on 10d. blue ..	1·25	3·00
142	**109**	3 p. on 2s. 6d. brown	23·00	50·00
136		6 p. on 5s. red ..	27·00	48·00
138		12 p. on 10s. blue ..	£100	£150

1935. Silver Jubilee.

149.	**123.**	5 c. on ½d. green ..	1·00	45
150.		10 c. on 1d. red ..	2·75	2·25
151.		15 c. on 1½d. brown ..	1·90	8·50
152.		25 c. on 2½d. blue ..	5·50	2·25

1935. King George V.

153.	**118.**	5 c. on ½d. green ..	75	6·50
154.	**119.**	10 c. on 1d. red ..	2·50	2·75
155.	**118.**	15 c. on 1½d. brown ..	2·50	3·25
156.	**120.**	20 c. on 2d. orange ..	40	25
157.	**119.**	25 c. on 2½d. blue ..	1·25	3·75
158.	**120.**	40 c. on 4d. green ..	45	3·00
159.	**122.**	1 p. on 10d. blue ..	1·00	30

1936. King Edward VIII.

160.	**124.**	5 c. on ½d. green ..	10	10
161.		10 c. on 1d. red ..	50	60
162.		15 c. on 1½d. brown ..	10	10
163.		25 c. on 2½d. blue ..	10	10

1937. Coronation.

164.	**126.**	15 c. on 1½d. brown ..	40	20

1937. King George VI.

165.	**128.**	5 c. on ½d. green ..	45	15
182.		5 c. on ½d. orange ..	1·75	1·25
166.		10 c. on 1d. red ..	40	10
183.		10 c. on 1d. blue ..	2·75	1·50
167.		15 c. on 1½d. brown ..	45	25
184.		15 c. on 1½d. green ..	1·75	6·00
168.		25 c. on 2½d. blue ..	50	50
185.		25 c. on 2½d. red ..	1·75	2·00
169.	**129.**	40 c. on 4d. green ..	11·00	7·00
186.		40 c. on 4d. blue ..	60	8·50
170.	**130.**	70 c. on 7d. green ..	50	5·00
171.		1 p. on 10d. blue ..	30	3·50

1940. Stamp Cent.

172.	**134.**	5 c. on ½d. green ..	30	1·25
173.		10 c. on 1d. red ..	1·75	1·75
174.		15 c. on 1½d. brown ..	30	1·50
175.		25 c. on 2½d. blue ..	30	50

1948. Silver Wedding.

176.	**137.**	25 c. on 2½d. blue ..	30	15
177.	**138.**	45 p. on £1 blue ..	16·00	22·00

1948. Olympic Games.

178.	**139.**	25 c. on 2½d. blue ..	40	50
179.	**140.**	30 c. on 3d. violet ..	40	50
180.	–	60 c. on 6d. purple ..	40	50
181.	–	1 p. 20 c. on 1s. brown	55	50

1954. Queen Elizabeth II.

189	**154**	5 c. on ½d. orange ..	15	30
188		10 c. on 1d. blue ..	30	50
190	**155**	40 c. on 4d. blue ..	70	1·75

IV. FRENCH CURRENCY.

Stamps surch. in French currency were sold at British P.Os in the French Zone.

Stamps of Great Britain surch. **MOROCCO AGENCIES** and value in French currency.

1917. King George V.

191	**105.**	3 c. on ½d. green ..	30	2·50
192		5 c. on ½d. green ..	15	10
203	**104.**	10 c. on 1d. red ..	30	30
194	**105.**	15 c. on 1½d. brown ..	80	15
195	**104.**	25 c. on 2½d. blue ..	40	15
196	**106.**	40 c. on 4d. green ..	1·00	30
207	**107.**	50 c. on 5d. brown ..	50	10
198	**108.**	75 c. on 9d. green ..	50	75
209		90 c. on 9d. green ..	3·50	3·00
210		1 f. on 10d. blue ..	70	10
211		1 f. 50 c. on 1s. brown	4·50	2·25
200	**109.**	3 f. on 2s. 6d. brown ..	7·50	2·00
226		6 f. on 5s. red ..	6·00	20·00

1935. Silver Jubilee.

212.	**123.**	5 c. on ½d. green ..	15	15
213.		10 c. on 1d. red ..	85	50
214.		15 c. on 1½d. brown ..	15	50
215.		25 c. on 2½d. blue ..	20	15

1935. King George V.

216.	**118.**	5 c. on ½d. green ..	45	1·75
217.	**119.**	10 c. on 1d. red ..	35	30
218.	**118.**	15 c. on 1½d. brown ..	1·75	1·50
219.	**119.**	25 c. on 2½d. blue ..	30	15
220.	**120.**	40 c. on 4d. green ..	30	15
221.	**121.**	50 c. on 5d. brown ..	30	15
222.	**122.**	90 c. on 9d. olive ..	35	65
223.		1 f. on 10d. blue ..	30	30
224.		1 f. 50 c. on 1s. brown	30	65

1936. King Edward VIII.

227.	**124.**	5 c. on ½d. green ..	10	15
228.		15 c. on 1½d. brown ..	10	15

1937. Coronation.

229.	**126.**	15 c. on 1½d. brown ..	30	20

1937. King George VI.

230.	**128.**	5 c. on ½d. green ..	40	95

V. TANGIER INTERNATIONAL ZONE.

This Zone was established in 1924 and the first specially overprinted stamps issued in 1927.
PRICES. Our note re U.K. usage (at beginning of Section II) also applies to **TANGIER** optd. stamps.

Stamps of Great Britain optd. **TANGIER.**

1927. King George V.

231.	**105.**	½d. green	50	10
232.	**104.**	1d. red	40	10
233.	**105.**	1½d. brown	2·25	2·00
234.	**106.**	2d. orange	3·25	10

1934. King George V.

235.	**118.**	½d. green	1·00	1·40
236.	**119.**	1d. red	80	70
237.	**118.**	1½d. brown	15	10

1935. Silver Jubilee.

238.	**123.**	½d. green	1·00	85
239.		1d. red	7·00	4·25
240.		1½d. brown	1·25	15

1936. King Edward VIII.

241.	**124.**	½d. green	10	15
242.		1d. red	10	10
243.		1½d. brown	15	10

1937. Coronation.

244.	**126.**	1½d. brown	40	15

1937. King George VI.

245.	**128.**	½d. green	40	20
280.		½d. orange	30	30
246.		1d. red	1·25	30
281.		1d. blue	50	1·00
247.		1½d. brown	60	10
282.		1½d. green	50	6·00
261.		2d. orange	3·00	2·25
283.		2d. brown	50	90
262.		2½d. blue	35	1·00
284.		2½d. red	55	55
263.		3d. violet	35	20
264.	**129.**	4d. green	3·00	5·50
285.		4d. blue	55	2·25
265.		5d. brown	1·25	6·50
266.		6d. purple	35	30
267.	**130.**	7d. green	80	5·50
268.		8d. red	1·25	5·00
269.		9d. olive	50	8·00
270.		10d. blue	50	8·50
271.		11d. plum	50	6·50
272.		1s. brown	60	85
273.	**131.**	2s. 6d. green ..	4·00	7·50
274.		5s. red	9·00	28·00
275.	–	10s. blue (No. 478a)	35·00	75·00

1940. Stamp Cent.

248.	**134.**	½d. green	30	2·00
249.		1d. red	45	30
250.		1½d. brown	1·50	1·00

1946. Victory.

253.	**135.**	2½d. blue	30	20
254.	–	3d. violet	30	20

1948. Silver Wedding.

255.	**137.**	2½d. blue	30	15
256.	**138.**	£1 blue	24·00	28·00

1948. Olympic Games.

257.	**139.**	2½d. blue	65	70
258.	**140.**	3d. violet	65	50
259.	–	6d. purple	65	70
260.	–	1s. brown	65	30

1949. U.P.U.

276	143	2½d. blue	50	70
277	144	3d. violet	50	60
278	–	6d. purple	50	60
279	–	1s. brown	50	1·40

1951. Pictorial stamps.

286.	**147.**	2s. 6d. green ..	4·25	3·00
287.	–	5s. red (No. 510)	9·50	12·00
288.	–	10s. blue (No. 511)	15·00	13·00

1952. Queen Elizabeth II.

313	**154**	½d. orange	10	10
290		1d. blue	15	20
291		1½d. green	10	20
292		2d. brown	20	20
293	**155**	2½d. red	10	20
294		3d. lilac	20	20
295		4d. blue	45	1·00
296	**157**	5d. brown	60	90
297		6d. purple	45	15
298		7d. green	80	1·60
299	**158**	8d. mauve	80	1·50
300		9d. olive	1·25	75
301		10d. blue	1·40	2·75
302		11d. plum	1·40	3·25
303	**159**	1s. bistre	50	30
304		1s. 3d. green ..	65	55
305		1s. 6d. blue ..	80	1·75

1953. Coronation.

306.	**161.**	2½d. red	50	30
307.	–	4d. blue	1·00	30
308.	**163.**	1s. 3d. green ..	1·25	1·25
309.	–	1s. 6d. blue ..	1·25	60

1955. Pictorials.

310.	**166.**	2s. 6d. brown ..	3·25	4·50
311.	–	5s. red ..	5·50	8·50
312.	–	10s. blue	19·00	20·00

1957. British Post Office in Tangier. Cent. Queen Elizabeth II stamps optd. **1857-1957 TANGIER.**

323.	**154.**	½d. orange	10	10
324.		1d. blue	10	10
325.		1½d. green	10	10
326.		2d. brown	10	10
327.	**155.**	2½d. red	15	20
328.		3d. lilac	15	10
329.		4d. blue	30	20
330.	**157.**	5d. brown	30	35
331.		6d. purple	30	15
332.		7d. green	30	30
333.	**158.**	8d. mauve	30	50
334.		9d. olive	30	30
335.		10d. blue	30	30
336.		11d. plum	30	30
337.	**159.**	1s. bistre	30	30
338.		1s. 3d. green ..	45	50
339.		1s. 6d. blue ..	50	55
340.	**166.**	2s. 6d. brown ..	2·00	2·25
341.	–	5s. red ..	2·75	2·25
342.	–	10s. blue	4·75	3·50

MORVI

A state of India, Bombay district. Now uses Indian stamps.

12 pies = 1 anna.

1. Maharaja Sir Lakhdirji Waghji. 3.

1931.

8	**1.**	3 p. red ..	1·00	3·25
9b		6 p. green	80	4·00
5		½ a. blue	1·75	6·00
6		1 a. brown	3·00	12·00
10		1 a. blue ..	1·25	6·50
7		2 a. brown	4·00	16·00
11		2 a. violet	10·00	21·00

1934.

16.	**3.**	3 p. red ..	50	1·50
17.		6 p. green	65	2·00
14.		1 a. brown	1·00	5·00
15.		2 a. violet	2·25	10·00

MUSCAT

Independent Sultanate in Eastern Arabia with Indian and, subsequently, British postal administration.

12 pies = 1 anna. 16 annas = 1 rupee.

١٣٦٣ آل بوسعيد

(2.)

1944. Bicentenary of Al-Busaid Dynasty. Stamps of India (King George VI) optd. as T **2**.

1. **100a.** 3 p. slate .. .. 30 3·00
2. ½ a. mauve .. .. 30 3·00
3. 9 p. green .. .. 30 3·00
4. 1 a. red .. .. 30 3·00
5. **101.** 1½ a. plum .. .. 30 3·00
6. 2 a. red .. .. 30 3·00
7. 3 a. violet .. .. 40 3·00
8. 3½ a. blue .. .. 40 3·00
9. **102.** 4 a. brown .. .. 40 3·00
10. 6 a. green .. .. 55 3·00
11. 8 a. violet .. .. 55 3·25
12. 12 a. red .. .. 70 4·00
13. – 14 a. purple (No. 277) 60 5·00
14. **93.** 1 r. slate and brown .. 50 7·00
15. 2 r. purple and brown 60 12·00

OFFICIAL STAMPS

1944. Bicentenary of Al-Busaid Dynasty. Official stamps of India optd. as T **2**.

O 1. **O 20.** 3 p. slate .. .. 50 5·50
O 2. ½ a. purple .. .. 50 5·50
O 3. 9 p. green .. .. 50 5·50
O 4. 1 a. red .. .. 50 5·50
O 5. 1½ a. violet .. .. 50 5·50
O 6. 2 a. orange .. .. 50 5·50
O 7. 2½ a. violet .. .. 70 5·50
O 8. 4 a. brown .. .. 70 6·00
O 9. 8 a. violet .. .. 70 6·50
O 10. **93.** 1 r. slate and brown (No. O 138) .. 2·25 15·00

For later issues see **BRITISH POSTAL AGENCIES IN EASTERN ARABIA.**

NABHA

A "Convention" state in the Punjab, India. Stamps of India optd. NABHA STATE.

12 pies = 1 anna; 16 annas = 1 rupee.

1885. Queen Victoria. Vert. optd.

1. **23.** ½ a. turquoise .. .. 75 2·00
2. – 1 a. purple .. .. 19·00 55·00
3. – 2 a. blue .. .. 7·00 19·00
4. – 4 a. green (No. 96) .. 42·00 £100
5. – 8 a. mauve £275
6. – 1 r. grey (No. 79) .. £190

1885. Queen Victoria. Horiz. optd.

36 **40.** 3 p. red 10 15
14 **23.** ½ a. turquoise 10 10
15 – 9 p. red .. .. 35 1·60
17 – 1 a. purple 40 30
18 – 1½ a. brown .. .. 40 1·10
20 – 2 a. blue 50 50
22 – 3 a. orange .. .. 1·00 50
12 – 4 a. green (No. 69) .. 21·00 80·00
24 – 4 a. green (No. 96) .. 1·40 85
26 – 6 a. brown (No. 80) .. 80 1·75
27 – 8 a. mauve .. .. 70 1·40
28 – 12 a. purple on red .. 1·40 2·50
29 – 1 r. grey (No. 101) .. 5·50 22·00
30 **37.** 1 r. green and red .. 4·50 3·75
31 **38.** 2 r. red and orange .. 80·00 £140
32 3 r. brown and green .. 80·00 £140
33 5 r. blue and violet .. 85·00 £190

1903. King Edward VII.

37. 3 p. grey 10 15
38. ½ a. green (No. 122) .. 20 30
39. 1 a. red (No. 123) .. 30 50
40a. 2 a. lilac 75 20
40b. 2½ a. blue .. .. 17·00 60·00
41. 3 a. orange 35 30
42. 4 a. olive .. .. 75 1·75
43. 6 a. bistre .. .. 75 5·50
44. 8 a. mauve .. .. 2·50 6·50
45. 12 a. purple on red .. 1·40 8·50
46. 1 r. green and red .. 3·50 4·75

1907. As last, but inscr. "INDIA POSTAGE & REVENUE".

47. ½ a. green (No. 149) .. 40 80
48. 1 a. red (No. 150) .. 35 70

1913. King George V. Optd. in two lines.

49. **55.** 3 p. grey 15 15
50. **56.** ½ a. green 15 10
51. **57.** 1 a. red 30 10
59. 1 a. brown .. .. 1·25 90
52. **59.** 2 a. lilac 30 30
53. **62.** 3 a. orange 40 35
54. **63.** 4 a. olive 45 65
55. **64.** 6 a. bistre .. .. 50 2·25
56. **65.** 8 a. mauve .. .. 90 2·00
57. **66.** 12 a. red .. .. 80 7·00
58. **67.** 1 r. brown and green .. 3·00 2·75

1928. King George V. Optd. in one line.

60. **55.** 3 p. grey 25 15
61. **56.** ½ a. green 20 20
73. **79.** ½ a. green 20 30
61a. **80.** 9 p. green .. .. 60 1·10
62. **57.** 1 a. brown 25 15
74. **81.** 1 a. brown 20 30
63. **82.** 1¼ a. mauve .. .. 30 1·75
64. **70.** 2 a. lilac 65 35
65. **61.** 2½ a. orange .. .. 30 3·25
66. **62.** 3 a. blue .. .. 50 1·00
75. **57.** 3 a. red .. .. 1·40 4·00
76. **63.** 4 a. olive .. .. 1·00 1·40
67. **71.** 4 a. green .. .. 1·25 1·00
71. **67.** 2 r. red and orange .. 14·00 42·00
72. 5 r. blue and purple .. 48·00 £120

1938. King George VI. Nos. 247/63.

77. **91.** 3 p. slate .. .. 4·50 30
78. ½ a. brown .. .. 1·75 30
79. 9 p. green .. .. 14·00 2·50
80. 1 a. red .. .. 1·00 30
81. **92.** 2 a. red .. .. 85 2·50
82. – 2½ a. violet .. .. 85 4·00
83. – 3 a. green .. .. 1·00 2·75
84. – 3½ a. blue .. .. 1·00 8·50
85. – 4 a. brown .. .. 2·25 3·75
86. – 6 a. green .. .. 1·50 8·50
87. – 8 a. violet .. .. 1·75 8·50
88. – 12 a. red .. .. 2·25 10·00
89. **93.** 1 r. slate and brown .. 9·50 15·00
90. 2 r. purple and brown .. 18·00 50·00
91. 5 r. green and blue .. 48·00 £110
92. 10 r. purple and red .. 80·00 £250
93. 15 r. brown and green .. £200 £450
94. 25 r. slate and purple .. £200 £475

1942. King George VI. Optd. **NABHA** only.

95. **91.** 3 p. slate .. .. 25·00 1·50
105. **100a.** 3 p. slate 60 40
96. **91.** ½ a. brown .. .. 65·00 2·50
106. **100a.** ½ a. mauve .. .. 2·50 40
97. **91.** 9 p. green .. .. 10·00 8·00
107. **100a.** 9 p. green .. .. 1·75 40
98. **91.** 1 a. red .. .. 12·00 2·00
108. **100a.** 1 a. red .. .. 70 1·75
109. **101.** 1 a. 3 p. brown .. 70 80
110. 1½ a. violet 80 50
111. 2 a. red .. .. 70 1·50
112. 3 a. violet .. .. 1·50 2·25
113. 3½ a. blue .. .. 6·00 17·00
114. **102.** 4 a. brown .. .. 1·50 60
115. 6 a. green .. .. 4·75 20·00
116. 8 a. violet .. .. 4·50 15·00
117. 12 a. purple .. .. 4·25 20·00

OFFICIAL STAMPS

Stamps of Nabha optd. **SERVICE.**

1885. Nos. 1 to 3 (Queen Victoria).

O 1. ½ a. turquoise 70 30
O 2. 1 a. purple 20 15
O 3. 2 a. blue .. .. 35·00 65·00

1885. Nos. 14 to 30 (Queen Victoria).

O 6 ½ a. turquoise 10 10
O 7 1 a. purple 30 15
O 9 2 a. blue 55 30
O 12 3 a. orange .. .. 10·00 25·00
O 13 4 a. green (No. 4) .. 60 35
O 15 6 a. brown .. .. 9·00 9·00
O 17 8 a. mauve 70 70
O 18 12 a. purple on red .. 4·00 8·50
O 19 1 r. grey .. .. 22·00 £110
O 20 1 r. green and red .. 18·00 38·00

1903. Nos. 37 to 46 (King Edward VII).

O 25. 3 p. grey .. .. 65 4·25
O 26. ½ a. green 30 10
O 27. 1 a. red 15 10
O 28. 2 a. lilac 55 40
O 30. 4 a. olive .. .. 1·10 45
O 32. 8 a. mauve .. .. 1·00 90
O 34. 1 r. green and red .. 1·50 2·00

1907. Nos. 47/8 (King Edward VII inscr. "INDIA POSTAGE & REVENUE").

O 35. ½ a. green 15 20
O 36. 1 a. red 20 20

1913. Nos. 54 and 58, (King George V).

O 37. **63.** 4 a. olive .. .. 10·00 30·00
O 38. **67.** 1 r. brown and green .. 50·00

1913. Official stamps of India (King George V), optd. **NABHA STATE.**

O 39. **55.** 3 p. grey .. .. 20 3·50
O 40. **56.** ½ a. green 15 10
O 41. **57.** 1 a. red 15 10
O 42. **59.** 2 a. lilac 30 15
O 43. **63.** 4 a. olive 35 30
O 44. **65.** 8 a. mauve 60 60
O 46. **67.** 1 r. brown and green .. 1·75 1·90

1932. Stamps of India (King George V) optd. **NABHA STATE SERVICE.**

O47 **55.** 3 p. grey 10 15
O48 **81.** 1 a. brown 10 15
O49 **63.** 4 a. olive .. .. 14·00 2·00
O50 **65.** 8 a. mauve .. .. 1·00 1·75

1938. Stamps of India (King George VI) optd. **NABHA STATE SERVICE.**

O53 **91.** 9 p. green .. .. 1·25 1·75
O54 1 a. red .. .. 4·50 30

1943. Stamps of India (King George VI) optd. **NABHA.**

O55 **O 20.** 3 p. slate 45 40
O56 ½ a. brown 60 30
O57 ½ a. purple 90 30
O58 9 p. green .. .. 1·10 20
O59 1 a. red 40 20
O61 1½ a. violet 50 40
O62 2 a. orange 60 45
O64 4 a. brown .. .. 2·25 1·75
O65 8 a. violet .. .. 3·00 7·50

1943. Stamps of India (King George VI) optd. **NABHA SERVICE.**

O 66. **93.** 1 r. slate and brown .. 8·50 22·00
O 67. 2 r. purple and brown 23·00 90·00
O 68. 5 r. green and blue .. £200 £300

NAMIBIA

Formerly South West Africa which became independent on 21st March 1990.

1990. 100 cents = 1 rand.
1993. 100 cents = 1 Namibia dollar.

141 Pres. Sam Nujoma, Map of Namibia and National Flag

1990. Independence. Multicoloured.

538 18 c. Type **141** 30 15
539 45 c. Hands releasing dove and map of Namibia (vert) 70 70
540 60 c. National flag and map of Africa .. .. 1·00 1·25

142 Fish River Canyon

1990. Namibia Landscapes. Multicoloured.

541 18 c. Type **142** 25 20
542 35 c. Quiver-tree forest, Keetmanshoop .. 45 35
543 45 c. Tsaris Mountains .. 50 40
544 60 c. Dolerite boulders, Keetmanshoop .. 60 50

143 Stores on Kaiser Street, c. 1899

1990. Centenary of Windhoek. Multicoloured.

545 18 c. Type **143** 15 15
546 35 c. Kaiser Street, 1990 .. 25 25
547 45 c. City Hall, 1914 .. 30 30
548 60 c. City Hall, 1990 .. 40 40

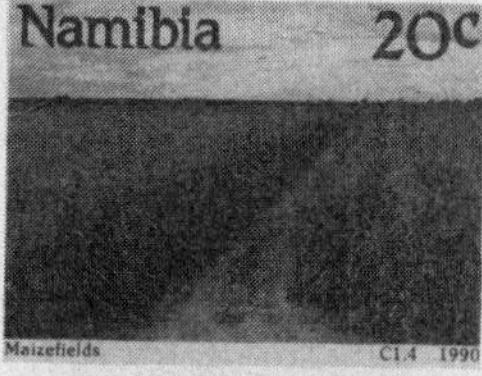

144 Maizefields

1990. Farming. Multicoloured.

549 20 c. Type **144** 15 15
550 35 c. Sanga bull 25 25
551 50 c. Damara ram 35 35
552 65 c. Irrigation in Okavango 45 45

145 Gypsum

1991. Minerals. As Nos. 519/21 and 523/33 of South West Africa, some with values changed, and new design (5 r.) inscr "Namibia" as T **145**. Multicoloured.

553 1 c. Type **145** 10 10
554 2 c. Fluorite 10 10
555 5 c. Mimetite 10 10
556 10 c. Azurite 15 10
557 20 c. Dioptase 20 10
558 25 c. Type **139** 20 15
559 30 c. Tsumeb lead and copper complex .. 25 20
560 35 c. Rosh Pinah zinc mine 25 20
561 40 c. Diamonds 40 25
562 50 c. Uis tin mine .. 40 25
563 65 c. Boltwoodite .. 40 35
564 1 r. Rossing uranium mine 55 50
565 1 r. 50 Wulfenite 80 70
566 2 r. Gold .. .. 1·10 90
567 5 r. Willemite (vert as T 145) .. .. 2·50 2·40

146 Radiosonde Weather Balloon

1991. Centenary of Weather Service. Mult.

568 20 c. Type **146** 20 20
569 35 c. Sunshine recorder .. 30 30
570 50 c. Measuring equipment 40 40
571 65 c. Meteorological station, Gobabeb .. 50 50

147 Herd of Zebras

1991. Endangered Species. Mountain Zebra. Multicoloured.

572 20 c. Type **147** 40 40
573 25 c. Mare and foal .. 45 45
574 45 c. Zebras and foal .. 75 75
575 60 c. Two zebras .. .. 1·00 1·00

148 Karas Mountains

1991. Mountains of Namibia. Multicoloured.

576 20 c. Type **148** 30 20
577 25 c. Gamsberg Mountains 35 30
578 45 c. Mount Brukkaros .. 60 55
579 60 c. Erongo Mountains .. 75 65

149 Bernabe de la Bat Camp

1991. Tourist Camps. Multicoloured.

580	20 c. Type **149**	30	30
581	25 c. Von Bach Dam Recreation Resort ..	35	35
582	45 c. Gross Barmen Hot Springs	55	55
583	60 c. Namutoni Rest Camp	70	70

150 Artist's Pallet

1992. 21st Anniv of Windhoek Conservatoire. Multicoloured.

584	20 c. Type **150**	15	15
585	25 c. French horn and cello	15	15
586	45 c. Theatrical masks ..	30	30
587	60 c. Ballet dancers ..	45	45

151 Blue Kurper

1992. Freshwater Angling. Multicoloured.

588	20 c. Type **151**	20	20
589	25 c. Largemouthed yellow fish	20	20
590	45 c. Carp	40	40
591	60 c. Sharptoothed catfish	60	60

152 Old Jetty

1992. Centenary of Swakopmund. Mult.

592	20 c. Type **152**	20	20
593	25 c. Recreation centre ..	20	20
594	45 c. State House and lighthouse	40	40
595	60 c. Sea front	55	55

153 Running

1992. Olympic Games, Barcelona. Mult.

597	20 c. Type **153**	20	20
598	25 c. Map of Namibia, Namibian flag and Olympic rings	20	20
599	45 c. Swimming	40	40
600	60 c. Olympic Stadium, Barcelona	55	55

154 Wrapping English Cucumbers

1992. Integration of the Disabled. Mult.

602	20 c. Type **154**	15	15
603	25 c. Weaving mats ..	15	15
604	45 c. Spinning thread ..	30	30
605	60 c. Preparing potplants	40	50

155 Elephants in Desert

1993. Namibia Nature Foundation. Rare and Endangered Species. Multicoloured.

606	20 c. Type **155**	20	20
607	25 c. Sitatunga in swamp	20	20
608	45 c. Black rhinoceros ..	35	40
609	60 c. Hunting dogs ..	45	50

156 Herd of Simmentaler Cattle

1993. Centenary of Simmentaler Cattle in Namibia. Multicoloured.

611	20 c. Type **156**	15	10
612	25 c. Cow and calf ..	15	10
613	45 c. Bull	30	35
614	60 c. Cattle on barge ..	50	55

157 Sand Dunes, Sossusvlei

1993. Namib Desert Scenery. Multicoloured.

615	30 c. Type **157**	25	20
616	40 c. Blutkuppe	25	20
617	65 c. River Kuiseb, Homeb	40	45
618	85 c. Desert landscape ..	60	65

158 Smiling Child

1993. S.O.S. Child Care in Namibia. Mult.

619	30 c. Type **158**	25	20
620	40 c. Family	25	20
621	65 c. Modern house ..	40	45
622	85 c. Young artist with mural	60	65

159 "Charaxes jasius"

1993. Butterflies. Multicoloured.

623	5 c. Type **159**	10	10
624	10 c. "Acraea anemosa"	10	10
625	20 c. "Papilio nireus" ..	10	10
626	30 c. "Junonia octavia" ..	15	20
627	40 c. "Hypolimnus misippus"	15	20
628	50 c. "Physcaeneura panda"	20	25
629	65 c. "Charaxes candiope"	25	30
630	85 c. "Junonia hierta" ..	35	40
631	90 c. "Colotis cellmene" ..	35	40
632	$1 "Cacyreus dicksoni" ..	40	45
633	$2 "Charaxes bohemani"	80	85
634	$2.50 "Stugeta bowkeri"	1·00	1·10
635	$5 "Byblia anvatara" ..	2·00	2·10

See also No. 648.

160 "Diplodus sargus" (fish)

1994. Coastal Angling. Multicoloured.

636	30 c. Type **160**	15	20
637	40 c. "Argyrosomus hololepidotus"	15	20
638	65 c. "Lithognathus aureti"	25	30
639	85 c. "Coracinus capensis"	35	40

161 Container Ship at Wharf

1994. Incorporation of Walvis Bay Territory into Namibia. Multicoloured.

641	30 c. Type **161**	15	20
642	65 c. Aerial view of Walvis Bay	25	30
643	85 c. Map of Namibia ..	35	40

162 "Adenolobus pechuelii"

1994. Flowers. Multicoloured.

644	35 c. Type **162**	15	20
645	40 c. "Hibiscus elliottiae"	15	20
646	65 c. "Pelargonium cortusifolium"	25	30
647	85 c. "Hoodia macrantha"	35	40

1994. Butterflies. As T **159**, but inscr "STANDARDISED MAIL". Multicoloured.

648	(–) "Graphium antheus" ..	15	20

No. 648 was initially sold at 35 c., but it is intended that this will be increased to reflect future postage rates.

NANDGAON (RAJNANDGAON)

A state of C. India. Now uses Indian stamps.

12 pies = 1 anna; 16 annas = 1 rupee.

1. 3 (2a.)

1891. Imperf.

1	1	½ a. blue	2·25	80·00
2		2 a. pink	12·00	£170

1893. Imperf.

5	3	½ a. green	15·00	30·00
6		1 a. red	27·00	60·00
4		2 a. red	4·25	38·00

OFFICIAL STAMPS

1893. Optd **M.B.D.** in oval.

O1	1	½ a. blue	£180	
O3	3	½ a. green	3·25	6·00
O4		1 a. red	6·00	17·00
O5		2 a. red	5·50	15·00

NATAL

On the E. coast of S. Africa. Formerly a British Colony, later a province of the Union of S. Africa.

12 pence = 1 shilling.
20 shillings = 1 pound.

1.

1857. Embossed stamps. Various designs.

1.	1.	1d. red	—	£1700
2.		1d. buff	—	£1000
3.		1d. blue	—	£1100
4.		3d. red	—	£400
5.	–	6d. green	—	£1100
6.	–	9d. blue	—	£7000
7.	–	1s. buff	—	£5500

The 3d., 6d., 9d. and 1s. are larger. Beware of reprints.

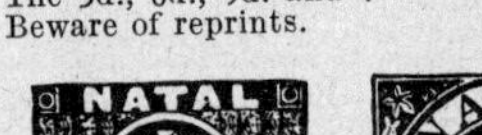

6. 7.

1859.

19.	6.	1d. red	80·00	23·00
12.		3d. blue	90·00	32·00
13.		6d. grey	£140	48·00
24.		6d. violet	38·00	25·00

1867.

25.	7.	1s. green	£120	26·00

1869. Variously optd. **POSTAGE** or **Postage.**

50.	6.	1d. red	70·00	26·00
82.		1d. yellow	70·00	65·00
53.		3d. blue	£110	40·00
83.		6d. violet	50·00	5·50
84.	7.	1s. green	80·00	4·50

1870. Optd. **POSTAGE in a curve.**

59.	7.	1s. green	50·00	10·00
108.		1s. orange	3·50	85

1870. Optd. **POSTAGE** twice, reading up and down.

60.	6.	1d. red	60·00	13·00
61.		3d. blue	60·00	13·00
62.		6d violet	£120	25·00

1873. Optd. **POSTAGE** once, reading up.

63.	7.	1s. brown	£110	18·00

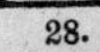

23. 28.

16.

1874. Queen Victoria. Various frames.

No.	Type	Description	Unused	Used
97a.	23.	½d. green..	75	30
99.	–	1d. red ..	1·00	10
107.	–	2d. olive ..	2·00	95
113.	28.	2½d. blue..	3·50	50
68.	–	3d. blue ..	75·00	14·00
101.	–	3d. grey	1·75	95
102.	–	4d. brown	2·75	65
103.	–	6d. lilac ..	3·25	70
73.	16.	5s. red ..	60·00	26·00

1877. No. 99 surch. ½ **HALF.**

No.	Description	Unused	Used
85.	½d. on 1d. red ..	20·00	65·00

POSTAGE — POSTAGE.

Half-penny — Half-Penny

(21.) (29.)

1877. Surch. as T **21.**

No.	Type	Description	Unused	Used
91.	6.	½d. on 1d. yellow..	8·00	11·00
92.		1d. on 6d. violet ..	45·00	8·50
93.		1d. on 6d. red ..	65·00	30·00

1885. Surch. in words.

No.	Description	Unused	Used
104.	½d. on 1d. red (No. 99) ..	16·00	11·00
105.	2d. on 3d. grey (No. 101)..	18·00	5·50
109.	2½d. on 4d. brown (No. 102)	11·00	8·50

1895. No. 23 surch. with T **29.**

No.	Type	Description	Unused	Used
114.	6.	½d. on 6d. violet ..	1·00	2·75

1895. No. 99 surch. **HALF.**

No.	Description	Unused	Used
125.	HALF on 1d. red..	70	75

31. 32.

1902.

No.	Type	Description	Unused	Used
127	31.	½d. green..	65	15
128		1d. red ..	1·00	15
129		1½d. green and black ..	1·25	1·00
130		2d. red and olive ..	80	25
131		2½d. blue..	1·00	3·00
132		3d. purple and grey ..	80	30
152		4d. red and brown ..	2·25	1·00
134		5d. black and orange ..	1·25	2·75
135		6d. green and purple ..	1·25	1·10
136		1s. red and blue..	3·50	1·10
137		2s. green and violet ..	48·00	9·00
138		2s. 6d. purple ..	35·00	12·00
139		4s. red and yellow ..	55·00	48·00
140	32.	5s. blue and red ..	18·00	8·00
141		10s. red and purple ..	48·00	24·00
142		£1 black and blue ..	£110	42·00
143		£1 10s. green and violet..	£225	65·00
162		£1 10s. orange & purple..	£1000	
144		£5 mauve and black ..	£1400	£325
145		£10 green and orange ..	£6000	£2250
145a		£20 red and green ..	£12000	

1908. As T **31/2** but inscr. " POSTAGE POSTAGE ".

No.	Type	Description	Unused	Used
165.	31.	6d. purple ..	4·50	2·00
166.		1s. black on green ..	6·00	2·00
167.		2s. purple & blue on blue	15·00	3·00
168.		2s. 6d. blk. & red on blue	25·00	3·00
169.	32.	5s. grn., & red on yellow	18·00	18·00
170.		10s. green & red on green	50·00	50·00
171.		£1 purple & black on red	£225	£170

OFFICIAL STAMPS

1904. Optd. **OFFICIAL.**

No.	Type	Description	Unused	Used
O 1.	31.	½d. green..	3·00	35
O 2.		1d. red ..	1·50	60
O 3.		2d. red and olive ..	12·00	7·50
O 4.		3d. purple and grey ..	7·50	4·00
O 5.		6d. green and purple ..	25·00	28·00
O 6.		1s. red and blue..	75·00	£120

HAVE YOU READ THE NOTES AT THE BEGINNING OF THIS CATALOGUE?

These often provide answers to the enquiries we receive.

NAURU

An island in the W. Pacific Ocean, formerly a German possession and then administered by Australia under trusteeship. Became a Republic on the 31 January 1968.

1916. 12 pence = 1 shilling;
20 shillings = 1 pound.
1966. 100 cents = 1 Australian dollar.

1916. Stamps of Gt. Britain (King George V) optd. **NAURU.**

No.	Type	Description	Unused	Used
1.	105.	½d. green	30	4·00
2.	104.	1d. red ..	1·00	3·00
15.	105.	1½d. brown	32·00	55·00
4.	106.	2d. orange	1·75	8·50
6.	104.	2½d. blue	2·75	5·50
7.	106.	3d. violet	2·00	3·50
8.		4d. green	2·00	8·00
9.	107.	5d. brown	2·25	8·50
10.		6d. purple	3·25	10·00
11.	108.	9d. black	8·50	19·00
12.		1s. brown	7·00	19·00
25.	109.	2s. 6d. brown	60·00	85·00
22.		5s. red ..	£100	£140
23.		10s. blue	£250	£325

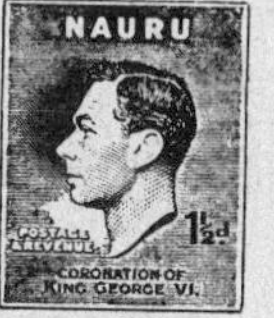

4. 6.

1924.

No.	Type	Description	Unused	Used
26.	4.	½d. brown	60	2·75
27.		1d. green..	1·50	2·75
28.		1½d. red ..	90	1·50
29.		2d. orange	2·25	7·00
30b.		2½d. blue..	1·25	3·50
31a.		3d. blue ..	1·50	7·50
32.		4d. green..	3·75	7·00
33.		5d. brown	3·25	3·75
34.		6d. violet	3·00	3·50
35.		9d. brown	5·50	17·00
36.		1s. red ..	5·00	2·75
37.		2s. 6d. green	24·00	28·00
38.		5s. red ..	35·00	48·00
39.		10s. yellow	85·00	85·00

1935. Silver Jubilee. Optd. **HIS MAJESTY'S JUBILEE, 1910-1935.**

No.	Type	Description	Unused	Used
40.	4.	1½d. red ..	60	80
41.		2d. orange..	1·00	4·00
42.		2½d. blue ..	1·50	1·50
43.		1s. red ..	4·00	3·50

1937. Coronation.

No.	Type	Description	Unused	Used
44.	6.	1½d. red ..	45	50
45.		2d. orange..	45	90
46.		2½d. blue ..	45	30
47.		1s. purple..	85	75

8. Anibare Bay. 18. "Iyo" ("calophyllum").

21. White Tern.

1954.

No.	Type	Description	Unused	Used
48	–	½d. violet ..	20	30
49a	8.	1d. green ..	20	30
50	–	3½d. red ..	1·50	50
51	–	4d. blue ..	1·50	1·00
52	–	6d. orange..	70	20
53	–	9d. red ..	60	20
54	–	1s. purple..	30	20
55	–	2s. 6d. green	2·75	60
56	–	5s. mauve..	8·00	2·00

DESIGNS—HORIZ. ½d. Nauruan netting fish. 3½d., Loading phosphate from cantilever. 4d. Great frigate bird. 6d. Canoe. 9d. "Domaneab" (Meeting House). 2s. 6d., Buada Lagoon. VERT. 1s. Palm trees. 5s. Map of Nauru.

1963.

No.	Type	Description	Unused	Used
57.	–	2d. multicoloured ..	1·00	2·00
58.	–	3d. multicoloured ..	75	35
59.	18.	5d. multicoloured ..	75	75
60.	–	8d. black and green ..	2·50	80
61.	–	10d. black..	50	30
62.	21.	1s. 3d. blue, black & green	4·00	2·50
63.	–	2s. 3d. blue ..	3·50	55
64.	–	3s. 3d. multicoloured ..	4·50	2·50

DESIGNS—As Type **21**—VERT. 2d. Micronesian pigeon. As Type **18**—HORIZ. 3d. Poison nut (flower) 8d. Black lizard. 3s. 3d., Finsch's reed warbler. (26 × 29 mm.): 10d. Capparis (flower). (26 × 21 mm.): 2s. 3d., Coral pinnacles.

1965. 50th Anniv. of Gallipoli Landing. As T **184** of Australia, but slightly larger (22 × 34½ mm.).

No.	Description	Unused	Used
65.	5d. sepia, black and green	15	10

24. Anibare Bay.

1966. Decimal currency. As earlier issues but with values in cents and dollars as in T **24.** Some colours changed.

No.	Type	Description	Unused	Used
66.	24.	1 c. blue ..	15	10
67.	–	2 c. purple (As No. 48) ..	15	40
68.	–	3 c. green (As No. 50) ..	30	50
69.	–	4 c. multicoloured (As T **18**)	25	10
70.	–	5 c. blue (As No. 54) ..	25	50
71.	–	7 c. black and brown (As No. 60) ..	30	10
72.	–	8 c. green (As No. 61) ..	30	10
73.	–	10 c. red (As No. 51) ..	40	10
74.	–	15 c. blue, black and green (As T **21**) ..	80	1·50
75.	–	25 c. brown (As No. 63) ..	45	40
76.	–	30 c. mult. (As No. 58) ..	70	30
77.	–	35 c. mult. (As No. 64) ..	1·25	35
78.	–	50 c. mult. (As No. 57) ..	2·50	80
79.	–	$1 mauve (As No. 56) ..	2·00	1·00

The 25 c. is as No. 63 but larger, 27½ × 25 mm.

1968. Nos. 66/79 optd. **REPUBLIC OF NAURU.**

No.	Type	Description	Unused	Used
80.	24.	1 c. blue ..	10	30
81.	–	2 c. purple ..	10	10
82.	–	3 c. green ..	15	10
83.	–	4 c. multicoloured ..	15	10
84.	–	5 c. blue ..	15	10
85.	–	7 c. black and brown ..	25	10
86.	–	8 c. green ..	25	10
87.	–	10 c. red ..	30	15
88.	–	15 c. blue, black and green	2·75	2·50
89.	–	25 c. brown ..	30	15
90.	–	30 c. multicoloured ..	55	15
91.	–	35 c. multicoloured ..	1·25	30
92.	–	50 c. multicoloured ..	2·00	50
93.	–	$1 purple ..	1·25	75

27. " Towards the Sunrise ".

1968. Independence.

No.	Type	Description	Unused	Used
94.	27.	5 c. multicoloured ..	10	10
95.	–	10 c. black, green & blue	10	10

DESIGN: 10 c. Planting Seedling, and Map.

29. Flag of Independent Nauru.

1969.

No.	Type	Description	Unused	Used
96.	29.	15 c. yellow, orange & blue	15	15

30. Island, " C " and Stars.

1972. 25th Anniv. of South Pacific Commission.

No.	Type	Description	Unused	Used
97.	30.	25 c. multicoloured ..	30	25

1973. 5th Anniv. of Independence. No. 96 optd. **Independence 1968-1973.**

No.	Type	Description	Unused	Used
98.	29.	15 c. yellow, orge. & blue	20	30

INDEX

Countries can be quickly located by referring to the index at the end of this volume.

32. Denea. 33. Artefacts and Map.

1973. Multicoloured.

No.	Description	Unused	Used
99.	1 c. Ekwenababae ..	50	20
100.	2 c. Kauwe ind ..	65	20
101.	3 c. Rimone ..	65	20
102.	4 c. Type **32** ..	65	30
103.	5 c. Erekogo ..	65	30
104.	7 c. Ikimago (fish) ..	30	20
105.	8 c. Catching flying-fish	30	20
106.	10 c. Itsibweb (ball game)	30	20
107.	15 c. Nauruan wrestling	35	20
108.	20 c. Great frigate birds	50	30
109.	25 c. Nauruan girl ..	50	30
110.	30 c. Catching common noddy birds ..	85	40
111.	50 c. Great frigate birds	2·00	75
112.	$1 Type **33** ..	2·25	75

Nos. 104/106 and 110/111 are horiz. designs.

34. Co-op Store.

1973. 50th Anniv. of Nauru Co-operative Society. Multicoloured.

No.	Description	Unused	Used
113.	5 c. Type **34** ..	20	30
114.	25 c. T. Detudamo (founder)	20	15
115.	50 c. N.C.S. trademark (vert.)	45	55

35. Phosphate Mining.

1974. 175th Anniv. of First Contact with the Outside World. Multicoloured.

No.	Description	Unused	Used
116.	7 c. M.V. "Eigamoiya" (bulk carrier) ..	1·25	90
117.	10 c. Type **35** ..	1·00	25
118.	15 c. Fokker Friendship "Nauru Chief" ..	1·00	30
119.	25 c. Nauruan chief in early times ..	1·25	35
120.	35 c. Capt. Fearn and H.M.S. "Hunter" ..	5·50	2·50
121.	50 c. H.M.S. "Hunter" off Nauru ..	2·50	1·40

36. Map of Nauru. 37. Rev. P. A. Delaporte.

1974. Centenary of U.P.U. Multicoloured.

No.	Description	Unused	Used
122.	5 c. Type **36** ..	20	20
123.	8 c. Nauru Post Office ..	20	20
124.	20 c. Nauruan postman ..	20	10
125.	$1 U.P.U. Building and Nauruan flag ..	50	60

1974. Christmas and 75th Anniv. of Rev. Delaporte's Arrival.

No.	Type	Description	Unused	Used
127.	37.	15 c. multicoloured ..	20	20
128.		20 c. multicoloured ..	30	30

38. Map of Nauru, Lump of Phosphate Rock and Albert Ellis.

1975. Phosphate Mining Anniversaries. Mult.
129. 5 c. Type **38** 30 30
130. 7 c. Coolies and mine .. 40 35
131. 15 c. Electric railway, barges and ship .. 1·25 1·25
132. 25 c. Modern ore extraction 1·50 1·40

ANNIVERSARIES. 5 c. 75th Anniversary of discovery. 7 c. 70th Anniversary of Mining Agreement. 15 c. 55th Anniversary of British Phosphate Commissioners. 25 c. 5th Anniversary of Nauru Phosphate Corporation.

39. Micronesian Outrigger.

1975. South Pacific Commission Conf., Nauru (1st issue). Multicoloured.
133. 20 c. Type **39** 75 40
134. 20 c. Polynesian double-hull 75 40
135. 20 c. Melanesian outrigger 75 40
136. 20 c. Polynesian outrigger 75 40

40. New Civic Centre.

1975. South Pacific Commission Conf., Nauru (2nd issue). Multicoloured.
137. 30 c. Type **40** 15 15
138. 50 c. Domaneab (meeting-house) .. 30 30

41. " Our Lady " (Yaren Church).

1975. Christmas. Stained-glass Windows. Multicoloured.
139. 5 c. Type **41** 15 10
140. 7 c. " Suffer little children ..." (Orro Church) .. 15 10
141. 15 c. As 7 c. 30 20
142. 25 c. Type **41** 45 35

42. Flowers floating towards Nauru.

1976. 30th Anniv. of Islanders' Return from Truk. Multicoloured.
143. 10 c. Type **42** 10 10
144. 14 c. Nauru encircled by garland 15 10
145. 25 c. Finsch's reed warbler and maps 35 25
146. 40 c. Arrival of islanders .. 45 35

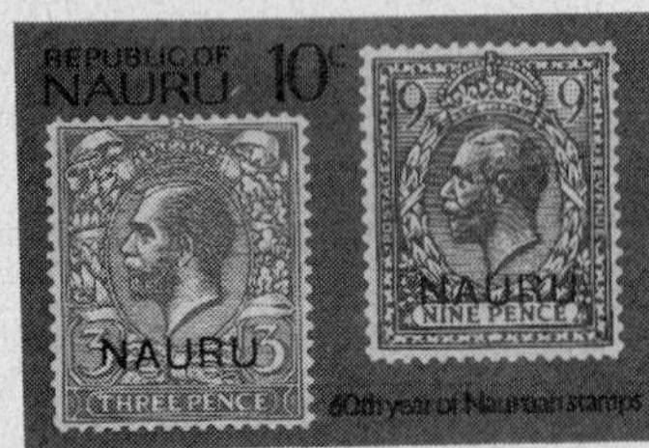

43. 3d. and 9d. Stamps of 1916.

1976. 60th Anniv. of Nauruan Stamps. Mult.
147. 10 c. Type **43** 15 15
148. 15 c. 6d. and 1s. stamps .. 20 15
149. 25 c. 2s.6d. stamp .. 30 25
150. 50 c. 5s. " Specimen " stamp 40 35

44. "Pandanus mei" and "Enna G" (cargo liner).

1976. South Pacific Forum, Nauru. Mult.
151. 10 c. Type **44** 15 10
152. 20 c. " Tournefortia argentea " and Nauruan aircraft .. 20 15
153. 30 c. " Thespesia populnea " and Nauru Tracking Station 25 15
154. 40 c. " Cordia Subcordata " and produce 35 25

45. Nauruan Choir.

1976. Christmas. Multicoloured.
155. 15 c. Type **45** 10 10
156. 15 c. Nauruan choir .. 10 10
157. 20 c. Angel in white dress 15 15
158. 20 c. Angel in red dress .. 15 15

46. Nauru House and Coral Pinnacles.

1977. Opening of Nauru House, Melbourne. Multicoloured.
159. 15 c. Type **46** 15 15
160. 30 c. Nauru House and Melbourne skyline .. 25 25

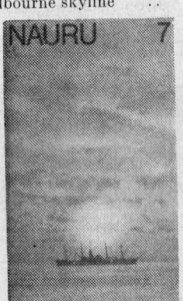

47. Cable Ship "Anglia".

1977. 75th Anniv. of First Trans-Pacific Cable and 20th Anniv. of First Artificial Earth Satellite.
161. **47.** 7 c. multicoloured .. 25 10
162. – 15 c. blue, grey & black 35 15
163. – 20 c. blue, grey & black 35 20
164. – 25 c. multicoloured .. 35 20

DESIGNS: 15 c. Tracking station, Nauru. 20 c. Stern of " Anglia ". 25 c. Dish aerial.

48. Father Kayser and First Catholic Church.

1977. Christmas. Multicoloured.
165. 15 c. Type **48** 10 10
166. 25 c. Congregational Church, Orro 15 15
167. 30 c. Catholic Church, Arubo 15 15

49. Arms of Nauru.

1978. 10th Anniv. of Independence.
168. **49.** 15 c. multicoloured .. 20 15
169. 60 c. multicoloured .. 35 30

1978. Nos. 159/60 surch.
170. **46.** 4 c. on 15 c. mult. .. 1·40 2·50
171. 5 c. on 15 c. mult. .. 1·40 2·50
172. – 8 c. on 30 c. mult. .. 1·40 2·75
173. – 10 c. on 30 c. mult. .. 1·40 2·75

51. Collecting Shellfish.

1978.
174. **51.** 1 c. multicoloured .. 40 20
175. – 2 c. Coral outcrop .. 40 20
176. – 3 c. White-capped Noddy 40 20
177. – 4 c. Girl with fish .. 45 20
178. – 5 c. Eastern Reef Heron 1·00 30
179. – 7 c. multicoloured .. 30 10
180. – 10 c. multicoloured .. 30 15
181. – 15 c. multicoloured .. 30 30
182. – 20 c. grey, black & blue 30 25
183. – 25 c. multicoloured .. 30 30
184. – 30 c. multicoloured .. 1·25 45
185. – 32 c. multicoloured .. 85 35
186. – 40 c. multicoloured .. 1·50 55
187. – 50 c. multicoloured .. 85 45
188. – $1 multicoloured .. 70 55
189. – $2 multicoloured .. 95 1·00
190. – $5 grey, black and blue 1·75 2·25

DESIGNS: 7 c. Catching fish, Buada Lagoon. 10 c. Ijuw Lagoon. 15 c. Girl framed by coral. 20 c. Pinnacles, Anibare Bay reef. 25 c. Pinnacle at Meneng. 30 c. Head of Great Frigate-bird. 32 c. White-capped Noddy birds in coconut palm. 40 c. Wandering Tattler 50 c. Great Frigate Birds on perch. $1, Old coral pinnacles at Topside. $2, New pinnacles at Topside. $5, Blackened pinnacles at Topside.

52. A.P.U. Emblem.

1978. 14th General Assembly of Asian Parliamentarians' Union, Nauru.
191. **52.** 15 c. multicoloured .. 20 25
192. – 20 c. black, blue & gold 20 25

DESIGN: 20 c. As Type **52**, but with different background.

53. Virgin and Child.

1978. Christmas. Multicoloured.
193. 7 c. Type **53** 10 10
194. 15 c. Angel in sun-rise scene (horiz.) 10 10
195. 20 c. As 15 c. 15 15
196. 30 c. Type **53** 20 20

54. Baden-Powell and Cub Scout.

1978. 70th Anniv. of First Scout Troop. Multicoloured.
197. 20 c. Type **54** 20 15
198. 30 c. Scout 25 20
199. 50 c. Rover Scout .. 35 30

55. Wright " Flyer " over Nauru.

1979. Flight Anniversaries. Multicoloured.
200. 10 c. Type **55** 15 10
201. 15 c. " Southern Cross " Boeing " 727 " (nose) .. 25 15
202. 15. c. " Southern Cross" and Boeing "727" (front view) 25 15
203. 30 c. " Flyer " over Nauru airfield 35 20

ANNIVERSARIES: Nos. 200, 203, 75th anniv. of powered flight. Nos. 201/2, 50th anniv. of Kingsford Smith's Pacific flight.

56. Sir Rowland Hill and Marshall Islands 10 pf. stamp of 1901.

1979. Death Centenary of Sir Rowland Hill. Multicoloured.
204. 5 c. Type **56** 15 10
205. 15 c. Sir Rowland Hill and " Nauru " opt. on G.B. 10 s. " Seahorse " stamp 1916–23 .. .. 25 20
206. 60 c. Sir Rowland Hill and Nauru 60 c. 10th Anniv. of Independence stamp, 1978 .. .. .. 55 40

57. Dish Antenna, Transmitting Station and Radio Mast.

1979. 50th Anniv. of International Consultative Radio Committee. Multicoloured.
208. 7 c. Type **57** 15 10
209. 32 c. Telex operator .. 35 25
210. 40 c. Radio operator .. 40 25

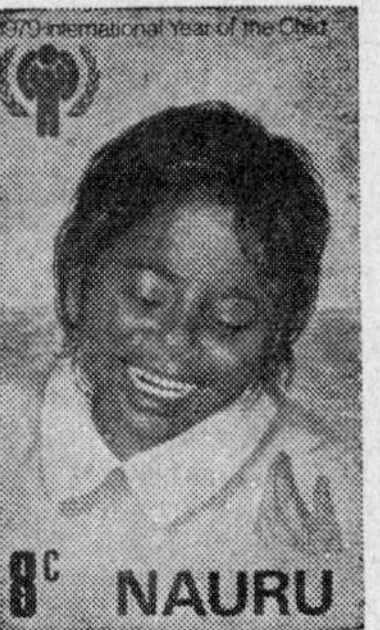

58. Smiling Child.

1979. International Year of the Child.
211. **58.** 8 c. multicoloured .. 10 10
212. – 15 c. multicoloured .. 15 15
213. – 25 c. multicoloured .. 20 20
214. – 32 c. multicoloured .. 20 20
215. – 50 c. multicoloured .. 25 25

DESIGNS: 15 c. to 50 c. Smiling Children.

59. Ekwenababae (flower), Scroll inscribed " Peace on Earth " and Star.

1979. Christmas. Multicoloured.

216. 7 c. Type **59** 10 10
217. 15 c. " Thespia populnea " (flower), Scroll inscribed " Goodwill toward Men " and star 10 10
218. 20 c. Denea (flower), scroll inscribed " Peace on Earth " and star .. 10 10
219. 30 c. Erekogo (flower), inscribed " Goodwill toward Men " and star 20 20

60. Dassault " Falcon " over Melbourne.

1980. 10th Anniv. of "Air Nauru". Mult.

220. 15 c. Type **60** 50 15
221. 20 c. Fokker "F28 Fellowship" over Tarawa .. 55 15
222. 25 c. Boeing " 727 " over Hong Kong 55 15
223. 30 c. Boeing " 737 " over Auckland.. .. .. 55 15

61. Steam Locomotive.

1980. 10th Anniv. of Nauru Phosphate Corporate. Multicoloured.

224. 8 c. Type **61** 10 10
225. 32 c. Electric locomotive .. 20 20
226. 60 c. Diesel locomotive .. 35 35

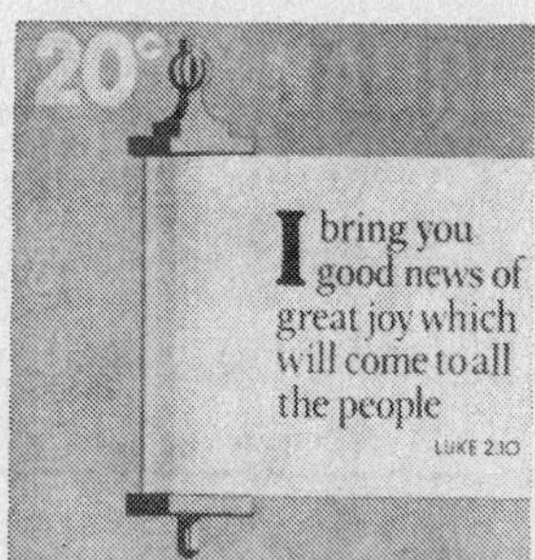

62. Verse 10 from Luke, Chapter 2 in English.

1980. Christmas. Verses from Luke, Chapter 2. Multicoloured.

228. 20 c. Type **62** 10 10
229. 20 c. Verse 10 in Nauruan 10 10
230. 30 c. Verse 14 in English.. 15 15
231. 30 c. Verse 14 in Nauruan 15 15

See also Nos. 248/51.

63. Nauruan, Australian, Union and New Zealand Flags on Aerial View of Nauru

1980. 20th Anniv. of U.N. Declaration on the Granting of Independence to Colonial Countries and Peoples. Multicoloured.

232. 25 c. Type **63** 15 15
233. 30 c. U.N. Trusteeship Council (72×23 mm.) .. 15 15
234. 50 c. Nauru independence ceremony, 1968.. .. 25 25

64. Timothy Detudamo.

1981. 30th Anniv. of Nauru Local Government Council, Head Chiefs. Multicoloured.

235. 20 c. Type **64** 15 15
236. 30 c. Raymond Gadabu .. 15 15
237. 50 c. Hammer DeRoburt 25 25

65. Casting Net by Hand.

1981. Fishing. Multicoloured.

238. 8 c. Type **65** 10 10
239. 20 c. Outrigger canoe .. 20 15
240. 32 c. Outboard motor boat 25 20
241. 40 c. Trawler 30 25

66. Bank of Nauru Emblem and Building.

1981. 5th Anniv. of Bank of Nauru.

243. **66.** $1 multicoloured .. 60 60

67. Inaugural Speech.

1981. U.N. Day. E.S.C.A.P. (United Nations Economic and Social Commission for Asia and the Pacific) Events. Multicoloured.

244. 15 c. Type **67** 15 15
245. 20 c. Presenting credentials 15 15
246. 25 c. Unveiling plaque .. 20 20
247. 30 c. Raising U.N. flag .. 25 25

1981. Christmas. Bible Verses. Designs as T **62.** Multicoloured.

248. 20 c. Matthew 1, 23 in English 15 15
249. 20 c. Matthew 1, 23 in Nauruan 15 15
250. 30 c. Luke 2, 11 in English 20 20
251. 30 c. Luke 2, 11 in Nauruan 20 20

68. Earth Satellite Station.

1981. 10th Anniv. of South Pacific Forum. Multicoloured.

252. 10 c. Type **68** 30 20
253. 20 c. "Enna G" (cargo liner) 35 25
254. 30 c. Airliner 35 30
255. 40 c. Local produce .. 45 40

MINIMUM PRICE

The minimum price quoted is 10p which represents a handling charge rather than a basis for valuing common stamps. For further notes about prices see introductory pages.

69. Nauru Scouts leaving for 1935 Frankston Scout Jamboree.

1982. 75th Anniv. of Boy Scout Movement. Multicoloured.

256 7 c. Type **69** 15 15
257 8 c. Two Nauru scouts on "Nauru Chief", 1935 (vert) 15 15
258 15 c. Nauru scouts making pottery, 1935 (vert) .. 20 20
259 20 c. Lord Huntingfield addressing Nauru scouts, Frankston Jamboree, 1935 .. .. .. 25 25
260 25 c. Nauru cub and scout, 1982 .. .. .. 30 30
261 40 c. Nauru cubs, scouts and scouters, 1982 .. 45 45

70. 100 kW Electricity Generating Plant under Construction (left side).

1982. Ocean Thermal Energy Conversion Multicoloured.

263. 25 c. Type **70** 50 30
264. 25 c. 100 kW Electricity Generating Plant under construction (right side) 50 30
265. 40 c. Completed plant (left) 70 40
266. 40 c. Completed plant (right) 70 40

Nos. 263/4 and 265/6 were each issued as horizontal se-tenant pairs, forming composite designs.

71. S.S. " Fido ".

1982. 75th Anniv. of Phosphate Shipments. Multicoloured.

267. 5 c. Type **71** 50 10
268. 10 c. Steam locomotive "Nellie" 85 20
269. 30 c. Modern "Clyde" class diesel locomotive .. 1·25 50
270. 60 c. M.V. "Eigamoiya" (bulk carrier) .. .. 1·50 80

72. Queen Elizabeth II on Horseback.

1982. Royal Visit. Multicoloured.

272. 20 c. Type **72** 40 30
273. 50 c. Prince Philip, Duke of Edinburgh 75 60
274. $1 Queen Elizabeth II and Prince Philip (horiz.) .. 1·40 1·25

73. Father Bernard Lahn.

1982. Christmas. Multicoloured.

275 10 c. Type **73** 35 30
276 30 c. Reverend Itubwa Amram 40 45
277 40 c. Pastor James Aingimen 45 60
278 50 c. Bishop Paul Mea .. 50 90

74. Speaker of the Nauruan Parliament.

1983. 15th Anniv. of Independence. Mult.

279. 15 c. Type **74** 15 15
280. 20 c. Family Court in session 20 20
281. 30 c. Law Courts building (horiz.) 25 25
282. 50 c. Parliamentary chamber (horiz.) .. 40 40

75. Nauru Satellite Earth Station.

1983. World Communications Year. Mult

283. 5 c. Type **75** 10 10
284. 10 c. Omni-directional range installation 15 15
285. 20 c. Emergency short-wave radio 20 25
286. 25 c. Radio Nauru control room 30 30
287. 40 c. Unloading air mail .. 45 45

76. Return of Exiles from Truk on M.V. " Trienza ", 1946.

1983. Angam Day. Multicoloured.

288. 15 c. Type **76** 20 25
289. 20 c. Mrs. Elsie Agio (exiled community leader) .. 20 25
290. 30 c. Child on scales .. 35 40
291. 40 c. Nauruan children .. 45 50

77. " The Holy Virgin, Holy Child and St. John " (School of Raphael).

1983. Christmas. Multicoloured.

292. 5 c. Type **77** 10 10
293. 15 c. "Madonna on the Throne, surrounded by Angels" (School of Sevilla) (horiz.) 15 15
294. 50 c. "The Mystical Betrothal of St. Catherine with Jesus" (School of Veronese) 40 40

78. S.S. " Ocean Queen ".

1984. 250th Anniv. of "Lloyd's List" (newspaper). Multicoloured.

295. 20 c. Type **78** 45 30
296. 25 c. M.V. "Enna G" .. 50 35
297. 30 c. M.V. "Baron Minto" .. 55 40
298. 40 c. Sinking of M.V. "Triadic", 1940 .. .. 75 55

79. 1974 U.P.U. $1 Stamp.

1984. Universal Postal Union Congress, Hamburg.

299. **79.** $1 multicoloured .. 1·10 1·25

80. "Hypolimnas bolina" (female).

1984. Butterflies. Multicoloured

300 25 c. Type **80** 50 40
301 30 c. "Hypolimnas bolina" (male) 55 55
302 50 c. "Danaus plexippus" 70 85

81. Coastal Scene.

1984. Life in Nauru. Multicoloured.

303. 1 c. Type **81** 10 20
304. 3 c. Nauruan woman (vert.) 15 20
305. 5 c. Modern trawler .. 20 20
306. 10 c. Golfer on the links .. 50 30
307. 15 c. Excavating phosphate (vert.) 55 40
308. 20 c. Surveyor (vert.) .. 40 40
309. 25 c. Air Nauru airliner .. 45 35
310. 30 c. Elderly Nauruan (vert.) 45 35
311. 40 c. Loading hospital patient on to aircraft .. 50 40
312. 50 c. Skin-diver with fish (vert.) 70 55
313. $1 Tennis player (vert.) .. 1·75 1·75
314. $2 Anabar Lagoon .. 2·00 2·25

82. Buada Chapel.

1984. Christmas. Multicoloured.

315. 30 c. Type **82** 60 50
316. 40 c. Detudamo Memorial Church 80 65
317. 50 c. Candle-light service, Kayser College (horiz.) 90 70

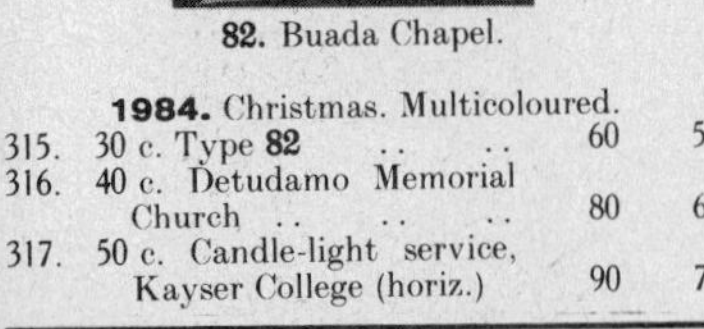

83. Air Nauru Jet on Tarmac.

1985. 15th Anniv. of Air Nauru. Mult.

318. 20 c. Type **83** 55 35
319. 30 c. Stewardesses on aircraft steps (vert.) .. 70 60
320. 40 c. Fokker "F28" over Nauru 85 75
321. 50 c. Freight being loaded onto Boeing "727" (vert.) .. .. .. 1·00 85

84. Open Cut Mining.

1985. 15th Anniv. of Nauru Phosphate Corporation. Multicoloured.

322. 20 c. Type **84** 70 60
323. 25 c. Diesel locomotive hauling crushed ore .. 1·25 1·00
324. 30 c. Phosphate drying plant .. .. .. 1·25 1·00
325. 50 c. Early steam locomotive .. .. 2·00 1·75

85. Mother and Baby on Beach.

1985. Christmas. Multicoloured.

326. 50 c. Beach scene .. .. 1·25 1·50
327. 50 c. Type **85** .. .. 1·25 1·50

Nos. 326/7 were printed se-tenant forming a composite design.

86. Adult Common Noddy with Juvenile.

1985. Birth Bicentenary of John J. Audubon (ornithologist). Brown Noddy. Multicoloured.

328. 10 c. Type **86** 35 35
329. 20 c. Adult and immature birds in flight 50 70
330. 30 c. Adults in flight .. 65 85
331. 50 c. Common noddy (John J. Audubon) .. 80 1·10

87. Douglas Motor Cycle.

1986. Early Transport on Nauru. Mult.

332. 15 c. Type **87** 70 70
333. 20 c. Primitive lorry .. 85 95
334. 30 c. German 2 ft gauge locomotive (1910) .. 1·25 1·50
335. 40 c. "Baby" Austin car .. 1·50 1·75

88. Island and Bank of Nauru.

1986. 10th Anniv. of Bank of Nauru. Children's Paintings. Multicoloured.

336. 20 c. Type **88** 30 30
337. 25 c. Borrower with notes and coins 35 35
338. 30 c. Savers 40 40
339. 40 c. Customers at bank counter 55 55

89. "Plumeria rubra".

1986. Flowers. Multicoloured.

340. 20 c. Type **89** 55 70
341. 25 c. "Tristellateia australia" 65 85
342. 30 c. "Bougainvillea cultivar" .. .. 75 1·00
343. 40 c. "Delonix regia" .. 1·00 1·25

90. Carol Singers.

1986. Christmas. Multicoloured.

344. 20 c. Type **90** 45 30
345. $1 Carol singers and hospital patient .. 2·00 2·25

91. Young Girls Dancing.

1987. Nauruan Dancers. Multicoloured.

346. 20 c. Type **91** 70 70
347. 30 c. Stick dance .. .. 90 1·00
348. 50 c. Boy doing war dance (vert.) .. .. .. 1·50 2·00

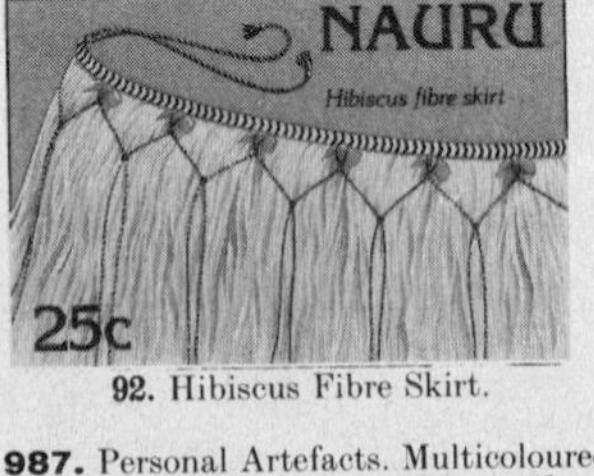

92. Hibiscus Fibre Skirt.

1987. Personal Artefacts. Multicoloured.

349. 25 c. Type **92** 75 75
350. 30 c. Headband and necklets 85 85
351. 45 c. Decorative necklets .. 1·10 1·10
352. 60 c. Pandanus leaf fan .. 1·60 1·60

93. U.P.U. Emblem and Air Mail Label.

1987. World Post Day.

353. **93.** 40 c. multicoloured .. 65 65

94. Open Bible.

1987. Centenary of Nauru Congregational Church.

355. **94.** 40 c. multicoloured .. 65 80

95. Nauruan Children's Party.

1987. Christmas. Multicoloured.

356. 20 c. Type **95** 75 35
357. $1 Nauruan Christmas dinner .. .. .. 2·75 2·75

96. Loading Phosphate on Ship.

1988. 20th Anniv of Independence. Mult.

358 25 c. Type **96** 80 80
359 40 c. Tomano flower (vert) 1·50 1·50
360 55 c. Great frigate bird (vert) .. .. .. 2·00 2·00
361 $1 Arms of Republic (35 × 35 mm) .. 2·25 2·50

97 Map of German Marshall Is. and 1901 5 m. Yacht Definitive

1988. 80th Anniv of Nauru Post Office. Mult.

362 30 c. Type **97** 35 40
363 50 c. Letter and post office of 1908 .. .. 60 70
364 70 c. Nauru Post Office and airmail letter .. 75 90

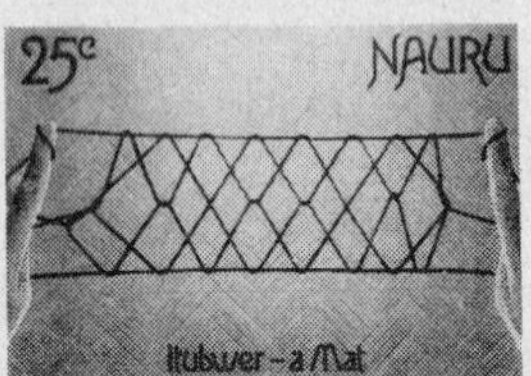

98 "Itubwer" (mat)

1988. String Figures. Multicoloured.

365 25 c. Type **98** 25 30
366 40 c. "Etegerer–the Pursuer" 40 45
367 55 c. "Holding up the Sky" 50 55
368 80 c. "Manujie's Sword" .. 75 80

99 U.P.U. Emblem and National Flag

1988. Cent of Nauru's Membership of U.P.U.
369 **99** $1 multicoloured .. 95 1·00

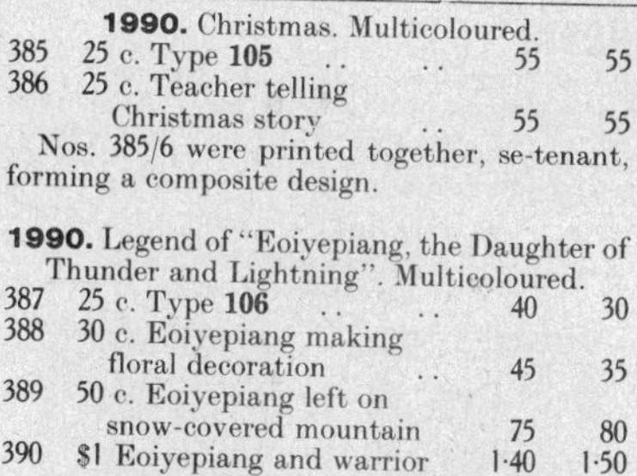

100 "Hark the Herald Angels"

1988. Christmas. Designs showing words and music from "Hark the Herald Angels Sing".
370 **100** 20 c. black, red & yell 20 25
371 – 60 c. blk, red & mauve 55 60
372 – $1 black, red and green 95 1·00

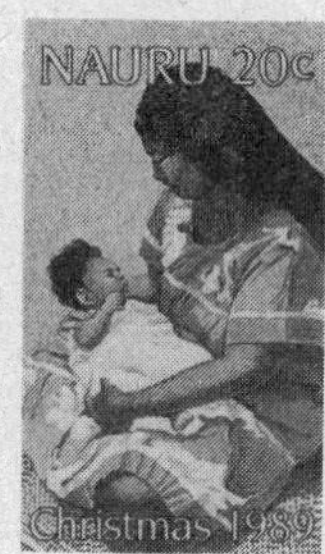

101 Logo (150th anniv of Nauru Insurance Corporation) **102** Mother and Baby

1989. Aniversaries and Events. Mult.
373 15 c. Type **101** 15 30
374 50 c. Logos (World Telecommunications Day and 10th anniv of Asian-Pacific Telecommunity) 50 75
375 $1 Photograph of island scene (150 years of photography) .. 95 1·40
376 $2 Capitol and U.P.U. emblem (20th U.P.U. Congress, Washington) 1·90 2·50

1989. Christmas. Multicoloured.
377 20 c. Type **102** 40 30
378 $1 Children opening presents .. .. 1·75 2·00

103 Eigigu working while Sisters play **104** Early Mining by Hand

1989. 20th Anniv of First Manned Landing on Moon. Legend of "Eigigu, the Girl in the Moon". Multicoloured.
379 25 c. Type **103** 90 90
380 30 c. Eigigu climbing tree 1·00 1·00
381 50 c. Eigigu stealing toddy from blind woman .. 1·75 1·75
382 $1 Eigigu on Moon .. 3·00 3·00

1990. 20th Anniv of Nauru Phosphate Corporation. Multicoloured.
383 50 c. Type **104** 65 65
384 $1 Modern mining by excavator .. .. 1·25 1·25

105 Sunday School Class **106** Eoiyepiang laying Baby on Mat

1990. Christmas. Multicoloured.
385 25 c. Type **105** 55 55
386 25 c. Teacher telling Christmas story .. 55 55
Nos. 385/6 were printed together, se-tenant, forming a composite design.

1990. Legend of "Eoiyepiang, the Daughter of Thunder and Lightning". Multicoloured.
387 25 c. Type **106** 40 30
388 30 c. Eoiyepiang making floral decoration .. 45 35
389 50 c. Eoiyepiang left on snow-covered mountain 75 80
390 $1 Eoiyepiang and warrior 1·40 1·50

107 Oleander

1991. Flowers. Multicoloured.
391 15 c. Type **107** 15 20
392 20 c. Lily 20 25
393 25 c. Passion flower .. 25 30
394 30 c. Lily (different) .. 30 35
395 35 c. Caesalpinia .. 35 40
396 40 c. Clerodendron .. 40 45
397 45 c. "Baubina pinnata" .. 40 45
398 50 c. Hibiscus (vert) .. 45 50
399 75 c. Apocymaceae .. 70 75
400 $1 Bindweed (vert) .. 95 1·00
401 $2 Tristellateia (vert) .. 2·00 2·10
402 $3 Impala lily (vert) .. 3·00 3·25

109 Star and Symbol of Asian Development Bank

1992. 25th Annual Meeting of Asian Development Bank.
404 **109** $1.50 multicoloured .. 1·75 1·75

110 Gifts under Christmas Tree

1992. Christmas. Children's Paintings. Mult.
405 45 c. Type **110** 55 55
406 60 c. Father Christmas in sleigh 70 70

111 Hammer DeRoburt

1993. 25th Anniv of Independence and Hammer DeRoburt (former President) Commemoration.
407 **111** $1 multicoloured .. 1·25 1·40

112 Running, Constitution Day Sports

1993. 15th Anniv of Constitution Day. Mult.
408 70 c. Type **112** 80 85
409 80 c. Part of Independence Proclamation .. .. 95 1·10

113 Seabirds, Flying Fish and Island

1993. 24th South Pacific Forum Meeting, Nauru. Multicoloured.
410 60 c. Type **113** 55 60
411 60 c. Seabirds, dolphin and island 55 60
412 60 c. Ikimago (fish), coral and sea urchins .. 55 60
413 60 c. Three different types of fish with corals .. 55 60
Nos. 410/13 were printed together, se-tenant, forming a composite design.

114 "Peace on Earth, Goodwill to Men" and Star

1993. Christmas. Multicoloured.
415 55 c. Type **114** 50 55
416 65 c. "Hark the Herald Angels Sing" and star .. 60 65

115 Girls with Dogs

1994. "Hong Kong '94" International Stamp Exhibition. Chinese New Year ("Year of the Dog"). Multicoloured.
417 $1 Type **115** .. .. 95 1·00
418 $1 Boys with dogs .. 95 1·00

NAWANAGAR

A state of India, Bombay District. Now uses Indian stamps.

6 docra = 1 anna.

1. (1 docra). **2.** (2 docra).

1877. Imperf. or perf.
1. **1.** 1 doc. blue.. .. .. 40 18·00

1880. Imperf.
3a. **2.** 1 doc. lilac .. .. 1·10 2·75
5. 2 doc. green .. .. 1·75 5·00
6a. 3 doc. yellow .. .. 3·00 7·00

4. (1 docra).

1893. Imperf. or perf.
11 **4.** 1 doc. black .. .. 60 2·50
12 2 doc. green .. .. 50 2·50
13b 3 doc. yellow .. .. 70 4·25

NEGRI SEMBILAN

A state of the Federation of Malaya, incorporated in Malaysia in 1963.

100 cents = 1 dollar (Straits or Malayan).

1891. Stamp of Straits Settlements optd. **Negri Sembilan.**
1. **5.** 2 c. red .. .. .. 2·50 4·25

2. Tiger. **3.**

1891.
2. **2.** 1 c. green .. .. .. 2·50 1·00
3. 2 c. red .. .. .. 3·25 4·50
4. 5 c. blue .. .. .. 24·00 28·00

1896.
5. **3.** 1 c. purple and green .. 5·00 2·50
6. 2 c. purple and brown .. 25·00 80·00
7. 3 c. purple and red .. 3·00 75
8. 5 c. purple and yellow .. 5·50 5·50
9. 8 c. purple and blue .. 25·00 13·00
10. 10 c. purple and orange .. 27·00 12·00
11. 15 c. green and violet .. 30·00 60·00
12. 20 c. green and olive .. 35·00 35·00
13. 25 c. green and red .. 65·00 80·00
14. 50 c. green and black .. 48·00 55·00

1898. Surch. in words and bar.
15. **3.** 1 c. on 15 c. grn. & violet 75·00 £150
16. **2.** 4 c. on 1 c. green .. 1·25 11·00
17. **3.** 4 c. on 3 c. purple and red 3·00 12·00
18. **2.** 4 c. on 5 c. blue .. .. 1·25 10·00

1898. Surch. in words only.
19. **3.** 4 c. on 8 c. purple and blue 2·25 3·75

6. Arms of Negri Sembilan. **7.**

1935.
21. **6.** 1 c. black 60 10
22. 2 c. green 80 20
23. 2 c. orange .. .. 1·00 32·00
24. 3 c. green .. .. .. 2·00 5·00
25. 4 c. orange 40 10
26. 5 c. brown 50 10
27. 6 c. red .. .. .. 6·50 1·75
28. 6 c. grey .. .. .. 2·25 55·00
29. 8 c. grey .. .. .. 1·75 10
30. 10 c. purple 40 10
31. 12 c. blue .. .. .. 1·25 30
32. 15 c. blue .. .. .. 3·75 38·00
33. 25 c. purple and red .. 75 70
34. 30 c. purple and orange .. 4·50 2·00
35. 40 c. red and purple .. 85 2·00
36. 50 c. black on green .. 3·75 1·25
37. $1 black and red on blue 2·25 2·25
38. $2 green and red .. 20·00 15·00
39. $5 green and red on green 13·00 38·00

1948. Silver Wedding. As T **10/11** of Aden.
40. 10 c. violet 15 40
41. $5 green .. .. .. 18·00 28·00

1949.
42 **7.** 1 c. black 10 10
43 2 c. orange 10 10
44 3 c. green 10 30
45 4 c. brown 10 10
46a 5 c. purple 30 30
47 6 c. grey 15 10
48 8 c. red 20 75
49 8 c. green .. .. .. 1·50 1·40
50 10 c. mauve 15 10
51 12 c. red .. .. .. 1·50 1·75
52 15 c. blue .. .. .. 1·40 10
53 20 c. black and green .. 25 75
54 20 c. blue 80 10
55 25 c. purple and orange .. 25 10
56 30 c. red and purple .. 1·25 2·25
57 35 c. red and purple .. 70 1·00
58 40 c. red and purple .. 80 3·00
59 50 c. black and blue .. 55 10
60 $1 blue and purple .. 2·50 1·25
61 $2 green and red .. .. 10·00 8·00
62 $5 green and brown .. 45·00 32·00

1949. U.P.U. As T **20/23** of Antigua.
63. 10 c. purple 20 10
64. 15 c. blue 50 70
65. 25 c. orange .. .. 50 1·50
66. 50 c. black .. .. 1·00 2·50

1953. Coronation. As T **13** of Aden.
67. 10 c. black and purple .. 40 30

1957. As Nos. 92/102 of Kedah but inset Arms of Negri Sembilan.
68 1 c. black 10 10
69 2 c. red 10 10
70 4 c. sepia 10 10
71 5 c. lake 10 10
72 8 c. green .. .. .. 85 1·25
73 10 c. sepia 30 10
74 10 c. purple .. .. 1·50 10
75 20 c. blue 30 10
76a 50 c. black and blue .. 20 10
77 $1 blue and purple .. 1·50 85
78 $2 green and red .. 4·25 7·50
79 $5 brown and green .. 10·00 13·00

8. Tuanku Munawir.

1961. Installation of Tuanku Munawir as Yang di- Pertuan Besar of Negri Sembilan.
80. **8.** 10 c. multicoloured .. 20 20

9. " Vanda hookeriana ".

1965. As Nos. 115/21 of Kedah but with Arms of Negri Sembilan inset and inscr. "NEGERI SEMBILAN" as in T **6**.
81. **9.** 1 c. multicoloured .. 10 40
82. – 2 c. multicoloured .. 10 40
83. – 5 c. multicoloured .. 20 10
84. – 6 c. multicoloured .. 20 40
85. – 10 c. multicoloured .. 20 10
86. – 15 c. multicoloured .. 80 10
87. – 20 c. multicoloured .. 1·25 75
The higher values used in Negri Sembilan were Nos. 20/7 of Malaysia (National Issues).

10. Negri Sembilan Crest and Tuanku Ja'afar.

1968. Installation of Tuanku Ja'afar as Yang di-Pertuan Besar of Negri Sembilan.
88. **10.** 15 c. multicoloured .. 15 40
89. 50 c. multicoloured .. 30 1·10

11. "Hebomoia glaucippe".

1971. Butterflies. As Nos. 124/30 of Kedah but with Arms of Negri Sembilan inset as T **11** and inscr. "negeri sembilan".
91. – 1 c. multicoloured .. 15 50
92. – 2 c. multicoloured .. 40 50
93. – 5 c. multicoloured .. 50 10
94. – 6 c. multicoloured .. 50 70
95. **11.** 10 c. multicoloured .. 50 10
96. – 15 c. multicoloured .. 70 10
97. – 20 c. multicoloured .. 80 20
The higher values in use with this issue were Nos. 64/71 of Malaysia (National Issues).

12. " Hibiscus rosa-sinensis ".

1979. Flowers. As Nos. 135/41 of Kedah but with Arms of Negri Sembilan and inscr. "negeri sembilan" as in T **12**.
103 1 c. "Rafflesia hasseltii" .. 10 30
104 2 c. "Pterocarpus indicus" 10 30
105 5 c. "Lagerstroemia speciosa" 10 10
106 10 c. "Durio zibethinus" .. 15 10
107 15 c. Type **12** 15 10
108 20 c. "Rhododendron scortechionii" 20 10
109 25 c. "Etlingera elatior" (inscr "Phaeomeria speciosa") 25 10

13. Oil Palm.

1986. As Nos. 152/8 of Kedah but with Arms of Negri Sembilan and inscr. "NEGERI SEMBILAN" as in T **13**
117. 1 c. Coffee 10 10
118. 2 c. Coconuts 10 10
119. 5 c. Cocoa 10 10
120. 10 c. Black pepper .. 10 10
121. 15 c. Rubber 10 10
122. 20 c. Type **13** 10 10
123. 30 c. Rice 15 20

NEVIS

One of the Leeward Islands, Br. W. Indies. Used stamps of St. Kitts–Nevis from 1903 until June 1980 when Nevis, although remaining part of St. Kitts–Nevis, had a separate postal administration.

1861. 12 pence = 1 shilling.
20 shillings = 1 pound.
1980. 100 cents = 1 dollar.

1.

2.

(The design on the stamps refers to a medicinal spring on the island.)

1861. Various frames.
15 **1** 1d. red .. .. .. 15·00 13·00
6 **2** 4d. red .. .. .. 75·00 55·00
12 4d. orange .. .. 95·00 19·00
7 – 6d. grey .. .. .. 70·00 40·00
20 – 1s. green .. .. 55·00 80·00

5.

1879.
25 **5** ½d. green .. .. .. 2·75 6·00
23 1d. mauve .. .. 38·00 26·00
27a 1d. red .. .. .. 3·50 3·25
28 2½d. brown .. .. 90·00 45·00
29 2½d. blue .. .. .. 11·00 6·50
30 4d. blue .. .. .. £275 45·00
31 4d. grey .. .. .. 4·00 2·50
32 6d. green £350 £350
33 6d. brown .. .. 17·00 42·00
34 1s. violet .. .. .. 85·00 £150

1883. Half of No. 23 surch **NEVIS ½d.**
35 **5** ½d. on half 1d. mauve .. £400 27·00

1980. Nos. 394/406 of St. Christopher, Nevis and Anguilla with " St. Christopher " and " Anguilla " obliterated.
37. 5 c. Radio and T.V. station 10 10
38. 10 c. Technical college .. 10 10
39. 12 c. T.V. assembly plant .. 30 30
40. 15 c. Sugar cane being harvested 10 10
41. 25 c. Crafthouse (craft centre) 10 10
42. 30 c. Cruise ship 20 15
43. 40 c. Lobster and sea crab .. 40 40
44. 45 c. Royal St. Kitts Hotel and golf course 70 70
45. 50 c. Pinney's Beach, Nevis 30 30
46. 55 c. New runway at Golden Rock 15 15
47. $1 Picking cotton 35 40
48. $5 The Brewery 50 60
49. $10 Pineapples and peanuts 70 85

1980. 80th Birthday of Queen Elizabeth the Queen Mother. As T **10** of St. Kitts.
50. $2 multicoloured 40 40

8. Nevis Lighter.

1980. Boats. Multicoloured.
51. 5 c. Type **8** 10 10
52. 30 c. Local fishing boat .. 15 10
53. 55 c. "Caona" (catamaran) 20 10
54. $3 "Polynesia" (cruise schooner) (39 × 53 mm.) .. 40 40

9. Virgin and Child.

1980. Christmas. Multicoloured.
55. 5 c. Type **9** 10 10
56. 30 c. Angel 10 10
57. $2·50 The Wise Men .. 30 30

10. Charlestown Pier.

11. New River Mill.

1981. Multicoloured.
58. 5 c. Type **10** 10 10
59. 10 c. The Court House and Library 10 10
60. 15 c. Type **11** 10 10
61. 20 c. The Nelson Museum 10 10
62. 25 c. St. James' Parish Church 15 15
63. 30 c. Nevis Lane 15 15
64. 40 c. Zetland Plantation .. 20 20
65. 45 c. Nisbet Plantation .. 20 25
66. 50 c. Pinney's Beach .. 25 25
67. 55 c. Eva Wilkin's Studio .. 25 30
68. $1 Nevis at dawn 50 45
69. $2.50 Ruins of Fort Charles 90 1·10
70. $5 The Old Bath House .. 1·25 1·50
71. $10 Beach at Nisbet's .. 2·25 3·00

1981. Royal Wedding. Royal Yachts. As T **26/27** of Kiribati. Multicoloured.
72 55 c. " Royal Caroline " .. 15 15
73 55 c. Prince Charles and Lady Diana Spencer .. 40 40
74 $2 " Royal Sovereign " .. 30 30
75 $2 As No. 73 .. .. 80 80
76 $5 " Britannia " 60 60
77 $5 As No. 73 .. .. 1·25 1·50

12. "Heliconius charithonia".

1982. Butterflies (1st series). Multicoloured.
81 5 c. Type **12** 10 10
82 30 c. "Siproeta stelenes" .. 15 10
83 55 c. "Marpesia petreus" .. 20 15
84 $2 "Phoebis agarithe" .. 60 70
See also Nos. 105/8.

13. Caroline of Brunswick, Princess of Wales, 1793.

1982. 21st Birthday of Princess of Wales. Multicoloured.
85. 30 c. Type **13** 15 15
86. 55 c. Coat of arms of Caroline of Brunswick .. 20 20
87. $5 Diana, Princess of Wales 1·00 1·25

1982. Birth of Prince William of Wales. Nos. 85/7 optd. **ROYAL BABY.**
88. 30 c. As Type **13** 15 15
89. 55 c. Coat of arms of Caroline of Brunswick .. 20 20
90. $5 Diana, Princess of Wales 1·00 1·25

14. Cyclist.

1982. 75th Anniv. of Boy Scout Movement. Multicoloured.
91. 5 c. Type **14** 20 10
92. 30 c. Athlete 50 10
93. $2·50 Camp cook .. .. 1·00 80

15. Santa Claus.

1982. Christmas. Children's Paintings. **Mult.**

94.	15 c. Type **15**	10	10
95.	30 c. Carollers	10	10
96.	$1·50 Decorated house and local band (horiz.)	25	25
97.	$2·50 Adoration of the Shepherds (horiz.)	50	50

16. Tube Sponge.

1983. Corals (1st series). Multicoloured.

98.	15 c. Type **16**	10	10
99.	30 c. Stinging coral	15	10
100.	55 c. Flower coral	25	10
101.	$3 Sea Rod and Red Fire Sponge	70	80

See also Nos. 423/6.

17. H.M.S. "Boreas" off Nevis.

1983. Commonwealth Day. **Multicoloured.**

103.	55 c. Type **17**	20	10
104.	$2 Capt Horatio Nelson and H.M.S. "Boreas" at anchor	65	75

1983. Butterflies (2nd series). As Type **12**. Multicoloured.

105	30 c. "Pyrgus oileus"	20	15
106	55 c. "Junonia evarete" (vert)	25	20
107	$1.10 "Urbanus proteus" (vert)	50	55
108	$2 "Hypolimnas misippus"	95	1·00

1983. Nos. 58 and 60/71 optd. **INDEPENDENCE 1983.**

109	5 c. Type **10**	10	10
110	15 c. Type **11**	10	10
111	20 c. Nelson Museum	10	10
112	25 c. St. James's Parish Church	10	15
113	30 c. Nevis Lane	15	15
114	40 c. Zetland Plantation	15	20
115	45 c. Nisbet Plantation	20	25
116	50 c. Pinney's Beach	20	25
117	55 c. Eva Wilkin's Studio	25	30
118	$1 Nevis at down	40	45
119	$2·50 Ruins of Fort Charles	90	1·10
120	$5 Old Bath House	1·25	1·50
121	$10 Beach at Nisbet's	2·25	2·50

19. Montgolfier Balloon, 1783.

1983. Bicentenary of Manned Flight. Mult.

122.	10 c. Type **19**	10	10
123.	45 c. Sikorsky "S-38" flying boat (horiz.)	15	10
124.	50 c. Beechcraft "Twin Bonanza" (horiz.)	15	10
125.	$2·50 B. Ae. "Sea Harrier" (horiz.)	50	60

20. Mary Praying over Holy Child.

1983. Christmas. Multicoloured.

127.	5 c. Type **20**	10	10
128.	30 c. Shepherds with flock	10	10
129.	55 c. Three Angels	15	10
130.	$3 Boy with girls	55	60

21. "County of Oxford" (1945).

1983. Leaders of the World. Railway Locomotives (1st series).

132.	**21.**	55 c. multicoloured	15	20
133.	–	55 c.multicoloured	15	20
134.	–	$1 red, blue and black	20	25
135.	–	$1 multicoloured	20	25
136.	–	$1 purple, blue & blk.	20	25
137.	–	$1 multicoloured	20	25
138.	–	$1 red, black & yellow	20	25
139.	–	$1 multicoloured	20	25
140.	–	$1 multicoloured	20	25
141.	–	$1 multicoloured	20	25
142.	–	$1 yellow, black & blue	20	25
143.	–	$1 multicoloured	20	25
144.	–	$1 yellow, black & pur.	20	25
145.	–	$1 multicoloured	20	25
146.	–	$1 multicoloured	20	25
147.	–	$1 multicoloured	20	25

DESIGNS: (The first in each pair shows technical drawings and the second the locomotive at work). Nos. 132/3 "County of Oxford", Great Britain (1945). 134/5 "Evening Star", Great Britain (1960). 136/7 "Stanier Class 5", Great Britain (1934). 138/9 "Pendennis Castle", Great Britain (1924). 140/1 "Winston Churchill", Great Britain (1946). 142/3 "Mallard", Great Britain (1935). 144/5 "Britannia", Great Britain (1951). 146/7 "King George V", Great Britain.

See also Nos. 219/26, 277/84, 297/308, 352/9 and 427/42.

22. Boer War.

1984. Leaders of the World. British Monarchs (1st series). Multicoloured.

148.	5 c. Type **22**	10	10
149.	5 c. Queen Victoria	10	10
150.	50 c. Queen Victoria at Osborne House	30	30
151.	50 c. Osborne House	30	30
152.	60 c. Battle of Dettingen	30	30
153.	60 c. George II	30	30
154.	75 c. George II at the Bank of England	30	30
155.	75 c. Bank of England	30	30
156.	$1 Coat of Arms of George II	35	35
157.	$1 George II (different)	35	35
158.	$3 Coat of Arms of Queen Victoria	80	80
159.	$3 Queen Victoria (different)	80	80

See also Nos. 231/6.

23. Golden Rock Inn.

1984. Tourism (1st series). Multicoloured.

160.	55 c Type **23**	35	20
161.	55 c. Rest Haven Inn	35	20
162.	55 c. Cliffdwellers Hotel	35	20
163.	55 c. Pinney's Beach Hotel	35	20

See also Nos 245/8.

24. Early Seal of Colony.

1984.

164.	**24.**	$15 red	4·50	5·50

25. Cadillac.

1984. Leaders of the World Automobiles (1st series). As T **25**. The first design in each pair shows technical drawings and the second paintings.

165.	1 c. yellow, black and mauve	10	10
166.	1 c. multicoloured	10	10
167.	5 c. blue, mauve and black	10	10
168.	5 c. multicoloured	10	10
169.	15 c. multicoloured	15	15
170.	15 c. multicoloured	15	15
171.	35 c. mauve, yellow and black	25	25
172.	35 c. multicoloured	25	25
173.	45 c. blue, mauve and black	25	25
174.	45 c. multicoloured	25	25
175.	55 c. multicoloured	25	25
176.	55 c. multicoloured	25	25
177.	$2.50 mauve, black and yellow	60	60
178.	$2.50 multicoloured	60	60
179.	$3 blue, yellow and black	70	70
180.	$3 multicoloured	70	70

DESIGNS: No. 165/6, Cadillac "V16 Fleetwood Convertible" (1932). 167/8, Packard "Twin Six Touring Car" (1916). 169/70, Daimler "2 Cylinder" (1886). 171/2, Porsche "911 S Targa" (1970). 173/4, Benz "Three Wheeler" (1885). 175/6, M.G. "TC" (1947). 177/8, Cobra "Roadster 289" (1966). 179/80, Aston Martin "DB6 Hardtop" (1966).

See also Nos. 203/10, 249/64, 326/37, 360/371 and 411/22.

26. Carpentry.

1984. 10th Anniv. of Culturama Celebrations. Multicoloured.

181.	30 c. Type **26**	10	10
182.	55 c. Grass mat and basket making	15	10
183.	$1 Pottery firing	25	25
184.	$3 Culturama Queen and dancers	55	55

27. Yellow Bell.

1984. Flowers. Multicoloured.

185.	5 c. Type **27**	10	10
186.	10 c. Plumbago	10	10
187.	15 c. Flamboyant	10	10
188.	20 c. Eyelash Orchid	20	20
189.	30 c. Bougainvillea	10	15
190.	40 c. Hibiscus	30	30
191.	50 c. Night-blooming Cereus	15	20
192.	55 c. Yellow Mahoe	20	25
193.	60 c. Spider-lily	20	25
194.	75 c. Scarlet Cordia	25	30
195.	$1 Shell-ginger	35	40
196.	$3 Blue Petrea	1·00	1·10
197.	$5 Coral Hibiscus	1·75	2·00
198.	$10 Passion Flower	3·25	3·50

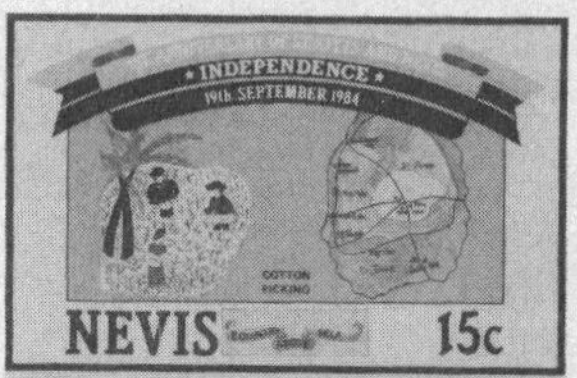

28. Cotton-picking and Map.

1984. 1st Anniv. of Independence of St. Kitts-Nevis. Multicoloured.

199.	15 c. Type **28**	15	10
200.	55 c. Alexander Hamilton's birthplace	20	10
201.	$1.10 Local agricultural produce	35	40
202.	$3 Nevis Peak and Pinneys Beach	75	1·00

1984. Leaders of the World. Automobiles (2nd series). As T **25**. The first in each pair shows technical drawings and the second paintings.

203.	5 c. black, blue and brown	10	10
204.	5 c. multicoloured	10	10
205.	30 c. black, turquoise and brown	15	15
206.	30 c. multicoloured	15	15
207.	50 c. black, drab & brown	15	15
208.	50 c. multicoloured	15	15
209.	$3 black, brown and green	45	45
210.	$3 multicoloured	45	45

DESIGNS: Nos. 203/4, Lagonda "Speed Model" touring car (1929). 205/6, Jaguar "E-Type" 4.2 litre (1967). 207/8, Volkswagen "Beetle" (1947). 209/10, Pierce Arrow "V12" (1932).

29. C. P. Mead.

1984. Leaders of the World. Cricketers (1st series). As T **29.** The first in each pair shows a head portrait and the second the cricketer in action. Multicoloured.

No.	Description	Unused	Used
211.	5 c. Type **29**	10	10
212.	5 c. C. P. Mead	10	10
213.	25 c. J. B. Statham ..	30	30
214.	25 c. J. B. Statham ..	30	30
215.	55 c. Sir Learie Constantine	40	40
216.	55 c. Sir Learie Constantine	40	40
217.	$2.50 Sir Leonard Hutton	1·25	1·25
218.	$2.50 Sir Leonard Hutton	1·25	1·25

See also Nos 237/4.

1984. Leaders of the World. Railway Locomotives (2nd series). As T **21.** The first in each pair shows technical drawings and the second the locomotive at work.

No.	Description	Unused	Used
219.	5 c. multicoloured	10	10
220.	5 c. multicoloured	10	10
221.	10 c. multicoloured ..	10	10
222.	10 c. multicoloured ..	10	10
223.	60 c. multicoloured ..	25	25
224.	60 c. multicoloured ..	25	25
225.	$2 multicoloured ..	70	70
226.	$2 multicoloured	70	70

DESIGNS: Nos. 219/20, Class "EF81", Japan (1968). 221/22, Class "5500", France (1927). 223/4, Class "240P", France (1940). 225/6, Shinkansen train, Japan (1964).

30. Fifer and Drummer from Honeybees Band.

1984. Christmas. Local Music. Multicoloured.

No.	Description	Unused	Used
227.	15 c. Type **30**	15	10
228.	40 c. Guitar and "barhow" players from Canary Birds Band	25	10
229.	60 c. Shell All Stars steel band	30	10
230.	$3 Organ and choir, St. John's Church, Fig Tree	1·25	1·00

1984. Leaders of the World. British Monarchs (2nd series). As T **22.** Multicoloured.

No.	Description	Unused	Used
231.	5 c. King John and Magna Carta	10	10
232.	5 c. Barons and King John	10	10
233.	55 c. King John	20	20
234.	55 c. Newark Castle ..	20	20
235.	$2 Coat of arms	55	55
236.	$2 King John (different) ..	55	55

1984. Leaders of the World. Cricketers (2nd series). As T **29.** The first in each pair listed shows a head portrait and the second the cricketer in action. Multicoloured.

No.	Description	Unused	Used
237.	5 c. J. D. Love	10	10
238.	5 c. J. D. Love	10	10
239.	15 c. S. J. Dennis	15	15
240.	15 c. S. J. Dennis	15	15
241.	55 c. B. W. Luckhurst ..	20	20
242.	55 c. B. W. Luckhurst ..	20	20
243.	$2.50 B. L. D'Oliveira ..	75	60
244.	$2.50 B. L. D'Oliveira ..	75	60

1984. Tourism (2nd series). As T **23.** Multicoloured.

No.	Description	Unused	Used
245.	$1.20 Croney's Old Manor Hotel	20	30
246.	$1.20 Montpelier Plantation Inn	20	30
247.	$1.20 Nisbet's Plantation Inn	20	30
248.	$1.20 Zetland Plantation Inn	20	30

1985. Leaders of the World. Automobiles (3rd series). As T **25.** The first in each pair shows technical drawings and the second paintings.

No.	Description	Unused	Used
249.	1 c. black, green and light green	10	10
250.	1 c. multicoloured	10	10
251.	5 c. black, blue and light blue	10	10
252.	5 c. multicoloured	10	10
253.	10 c. black, green and light green	10	10
254.	10 c. multicoloured ..	10	10
255.	50 c. black, green and brown	15	15
256.	50 c. multicoloured ..	15	15
257.	60 c. black, green and blue	15	15
258.	60 c. multicoloured ..	15	15
259.	75 c. black, red and orange	15	15
260.	75 c. multicoloured ..	15	15
261.	$2.50 black, green and blue	30	30
262.	$2.50 multicoloured ..	30	30
263.	$3 black, green and light green	30	30
264.	$3 multicoloured	30	30

DESIGNS: Nos. 249/50, Delahaye "Type 35 Cabriolet" (1935). 251/2, Ferrari "Testa Rossa" (1958). 253/4, Voisin "Aerodyne" (1934). 255/6, Buick "Riviera" (1963). 257/8, Cooper "Climax" (1960). 259/60, Ford "999" (1904). 261/2, MG "M-Type Midget" (1930). 263/4, Rolls Royce "Corniche" (1971).

31. Broad-winged Hawk.

1985. Local Hawks and Herons. Multicoloured.

No.	Description	Unused	Used
265.	20 c. Type **31**	75	20
266.	40 c. Red-tailed hawk ..	1·00	30
267.	60 c. Little blue heron ..	1·25	40
268.	$3 Great blue heron (white phase)	2·50	1·90

32. Eastern Bluebird.

1985. Leaders of the World. Birth Bicentenary of John J. Audubon (ornithologist) (1st issue). Multicoloured.

No.	Description	Unused	Used
269.	5 c. Type **32**	15	10
270.	5 c. Common cardinal ..	15	10
271.	55 c. Belted kingfisher ..	65	65
272.	55 c. Mangrove cuckoo ..	65	65
273.	60 c. Yellow warbler ..	65	65
274.	60 c. Cerulean warbler ..	65	65
275.	$2 Burrowing owl	1·75	1·75
276.	$2 Long-eared owl ..	1·75	1·75

See also Nos. 285/92.

1985. Leaders of the World. Railway Locomotives (3rd series). As T **21**, the first in pair showing technical drawings and the second the locomotive at work.

No.	Description	Unused	Used
277.	1 c. multicoloured	10	10
278.	1 c. multicoloured	10	10
279.	60 c. multicoloured ..	20	20
280.	60 c. multicoloured ..	20	20
281.	90 c. multicoloured ..	25	25
282.	90 c. multicoloured ..	25	25
283.	$2 multicoloured	60	60
284.	$2 multicoloured	60	60

DESIGNS: Nos. 277/8, Class "Wee Bogie", Great Britain (1882). 279/80, "Comet", Great Britain (1851). 281/2, Class "8H", Great Britain (1908). 283/4, Class "A", No. 23, Great Britain (1866).

1985. Leaders of the World. Birth Bicentenary of John J. Audubon (ornithologist) (2nd issue). As T **32.** Multicoloured.

No.	Description	Unused	Used
285.	1 c. Painted bunting ..	10	10
286.	1 c. Golden-crowned kinglet	10	10
287.	40 c. Common flicker ..	40	40
288.	40 c. Western tanager ..	40	40
289.	60 c. Varied thrush ..	45	45
290.	60 c. Evening grosbeak ..	45	45
291.	$2.50 Blackburnian warbler	1·00	1·00
292.	$2.50 Northern oriole ..	1·00	1·00

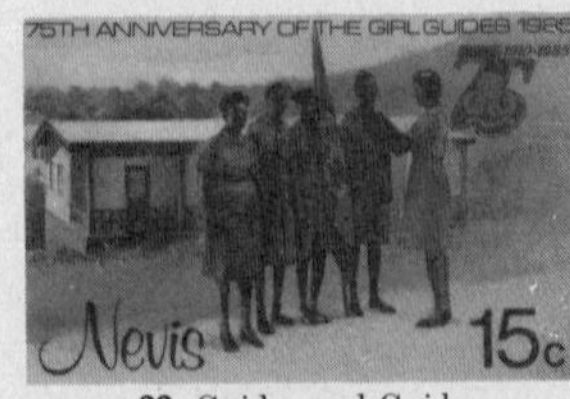

33. Guides and Guide Headquarters.

1985. 75th Anniv. of Girl Guide Movement. Multicoloured.

No.	Description	Unused	Used
293.	15 c. Type **33**	10	10
294.	60 c. Girl Guide uniforms of 1910 and 1985 (vert.)	20	25
295.	$1 Lord and Lady Baden-Powell (vert.)	35	40
296.	$3 Princess Margaret in Guide uniform (vert.) ..	90	1·25

1985. Leaders of the World. Railway Locomotives (4th series). As T **21.** The first in each pair shows technical drawings and the second the locomotive at work.

No.	Description	Unused	Used
297.	5 c. multicoloured	10	10
298.	5 c. multicoloured	10	10
299.	30 c. multicoloured ..	15	15
300.	30 c. multicoloured ..	15	15
301.	60 c. multicoloured ..	20	20
302.	60 c. multicoloured ..	20	20
303.	75 c. multicoloured ..	25	25
304.	75 c. multicoloured ..	25	25
305.	$1 multicoloured	25	25
306.	$1 multicoloured	25	25
307.	$2.50 multicoloured ..	60	60
308.	$2.50 multicoloured ..	60	60

DESIGNS: Nos. 297/8, "Snowdon Ranger" (1878). 299/300, Large Belpaire Passenger Locomotive (1904). 301/2, Great Western Railway "County Class" (1904). 303/4, "Nord L'Outrance" (1877). 305/6, Q.R. "Class PB-15" (1899). 307/8, D.R.G. "Class 64" (1928).

34. The Queen Mother at Garter Ceremony.

1985. Leaders of the World. Life and Times of Queen Elizabeth the Queen Mother. Various vertical portraits.

No.	Description	Unused	Used
309. **34.**	45 c. multicoloured ..	15	15
310. –	45 c. multicoloured ..	15	15
311. –	75 c. multicoloured ..	20	20
312. –	75 c. multicoloured ..	20	20
313. –	$1.20 multicoloured ..	35	35
314. –	$1.20 multicoloured ..	35	35
315. –	$1.50 multicoloured ..	40	40
316. –	$1.50 multicoloured ..	40	40

Each value was issued in pairs showing a floral pattern across the bottom of the portraits which stops short of the left-hand edge on the first stamp and of the right-hand edge on the second.

35. Isambard Kingdom Brunel.

1985. 150th Anniv. of Great Western Railway. Designs showing railway engineers and their achievements. Multicoloured.

No.	Description	Unused	Used
318.	25 c. Type **35**	35	35
319.	25 c. Royal Albert Bridge, 1859	35	35
320.	50 c. William Dean ..	45	45
321.	50 c. Locomotive "Lord of the Isles", 1895 ..	45	45
322.	$1 Locomotive "Lode Star", 1907	80	80
323.	$1 G. J. Churchward ..	80	80
324.	$2.50 Locomotive "Pendennis Castle", 1924	1·25	1·25
325.	$2.50 C. B. Collett	1·25	1·25

Nos. 318/19, 320/1, 322/3 and 324/5 were printed together se-tenant, each pair forming a composite design.

1985. Leaders of the World. Automobiles (4th series). As T **25.** The first in each pair shows technical drawings and the second paintings.

No.	Description	Unused	Used
326.	10 c. black, blue & red ..	10	10
327.	10 c. multicoloured ..	10	10
328.	35 c. black, turq, & blue ..	20	25
329.	35 c. multicoloured ..	20	25
330.	75 c. black, green & brown	35	40
331.	75 c. multicoloured ..	35	40
332.	$1.15 black, brown & green	50	60
333.	$1.15 multicoloured ..	50	60
334.	$1.50 black, blue & red ..	60	70
335.	$1.50 multicoloured ..	60	70
336.	$2 black, lilac and violet ..	75	1·00
337.	$2 multicoloured	75	1·00

DESIGNS: Nos. 326/7, Sunbeam "Coupe de L'Auto" (1912). 328/9, Cisitalia "Pininfarina Coupe" (1948). 330/1, Porsche "928 S" (1980). 332/3, MG "K3 Magnette" (1933). 334/5, Lincoln "Zephyr" (1937). 336/7, Pontiac 2 Door (1926).

1985. Royal Visit. Nos. 76/7, 83, 86, 92/3, 98/9 and 309/10 optd. **CARIBBEAN ROYAL VISIT—1985** or surch. also.

No.	Description	Unused	Used
338. **16.**	15 c. multicoloured ..	1·00	1·00
339. –	30 c. mult. (No. 92) ..	2·00	1·50
340. –	30 c. mult. (No. 99) ..	1·00	1·00
341. –	40 c. on 55 c. multicoloured (No. 86) ..	2·00	1·75
342. **34.**	45 c. multicoloured ..	2·25	2·00
343. –	45 c. mult. (No. 310) ..	2·25	2·00
344. –	55 c. mult. (No. 83) ..	1·25	1·25
345. –	$1.50 on $5 multicoloured (No. 76) ..	2·25	2·25
346. –	$1.50 on $5 multicoloured (No. 77) ..	4·50	4·50
347. –	$2.50 mult. (No. 93) ..	2·75	2·50

36. St. Pauls Anglican Church, Charlestown.

1985. Christmas. Churches of Nevis (1st series). Multicoloured.

No.	Description	Unused	Used
348.	10 c. Type **36**	15	10
349.	40 c. St. Theresa Catholic Church, Charlestown ..	30	30
350.	60 c. Methodist Church, Gingerland	45	50
351.	$3 St. Thomas Anglican Church, Lowland ..	2·00	2·25

See also Nos. 462/5.

1986. Leaders of the World. Railway Locomotives (5th series). As T **21.** The first in each pair shows technical drawings and the second the locomotive at work.

No.	Description	Unused	Used
352.	30 c. multicoloured ..	25	25
353.	30 c. multicoloured ..	25	25
354.	75 c. multicoloured ..	50	50
355.	75 c. multicoloured ..	50	50
356.	$1.50 multicoloured ..	80	80
357.	$1.50 multicoloured ..	80	80
358.	$2 multicoloured	1·10	1·10
359.	$2 multicoloured	1·10	1·10

DESIGNS: Nos. 352/3, "Stourbridge Lion", U.S.A. (1829). 354/5, "EP-2 Bi-Polar", U.S.A. (1919). 356/7, turbine U.P. "Box 4" gas (1953). 358/9, N.Y., N.H. and H.R. "FL9", U.S.A. (1955).

1986. Leaders of the World. Automobiles (5th series). As T **25**, the first in each pair showing technical drawings and the second paintings. P 12½.

No.	Description	Unused	Used
360.	10 c. black, brown and green	10	10
361.	10 c. multicoloured ..	10	10
362.	60 c. black, orange and red	20	25
363.	60 c. multicoloured ..	20	25
364.	75 c. black, light brown and brown	20	25
365.	75 c. multicoloured ..	20	25
366.	$1 black, light grey and grey	20	30
367.	$1 multicoloured ..	20	30
368.	$1.50 black, yellow and green	30	45
369.	$1.50 multicoloured ..	30	45
370.	$3 black, light blue and blue	60	80
371.	$3 multicoloured	60	80

DESIGNS: Nos. 360/1, Adler "Trumpf" (1936). 362/3, Maserati "Tipo 250F" (1957). 364/5, Oldsmobile "Limited" (1910). 366/7, Jaguar "C-Type" (1951). 368/9, ERA "1.5L B Type" (1937). 370/1 Chevrolet "Corvette" (1953).

37. "Spitfire" Prototype "K.5054", 1936. (Illustration reduced. Actual size 55 × 38 mm.)

1986. 50th Anniv. of "Spitfire" (fighter aircraft). Multicoloured.

372. $1 Type **37** 70 85
373. $2.50 Mark "IA" in Battle of Britain, 1940 .. .. 1·00 2·00
374. $3 Mark "XII" over convoy, 1944 .. .. 1·25 2·25
375. $4 Mark "XXIV", 1948 .. 1·50 2·75

38. Head of Amerindian.

1986. 500th Anniv (1992) of Discovery of America by Columbus (1st issue). Mult.

377. 75 c. Type **38** 55 55
378. 75 c. Exchanging gifts for food from Amerindians 55 55
379. $1.75 Columbus's coat of arms .. .. .. 1·40 1·40
380. $1.75 Breadfruit plant .. 1·40 1·40
381. $2.50 Columbus's fleet .. 1·75 1·75
382. $2.50 Christopher Columbus .. .. 1·75 1·75

The two designs of each value were printed together, se-tenant, each pair forming a composite design showing charts of Columbus's route in the background.

See also Nos. 546/53, 592/99, 678/83 and 685/6.

1986. 60th Birthday of Queen Elizabeth II. As T **167** of British Virgin Islands. Mult.

384. 5 c. Queen Elizabeth in 1976 .. .. .. 10 10
385. 75 c. Queen Elizabeth in 1953 .. .. .. 20 25
386. $2 In Australia 50 60
387. $8 In Canberra, 1982 (vert.) 2·00 2·50

39. Brazilian Player.

1986. World Cup Football Championship, Mexico. Multicoloured.

389. 1 c. Official World Cup mascot (horiz.) 10 10
390. 2 c. Type **39** 10 10
391. 5 c. Danish player .. 10 10
392. 10 c. Brazilian player (different) 10 10
393. 20 c. Denmark v Spain .. 20 20
394. 30 c. Paraquay v Chile .. 30 30
395. 60 c. Italy v West Germany 55 55
396. 75 c. Danish team (56 × 36 mm.) 65 65
397. $1 Paraguayan team (56 × 36 mm.) 80 80
398. $1.75 Brazilian team (56 × 36 mm.) .. .. 1·40 1·40
399. $3 Italy v England .. 2·00 2·00
400. $6 Italian team (56 × 36 mm.) .. .. 3·50 3·50

40. Clothing Machinist.

1986. Local Industries. Multicoloured.

402. 15 c. Type **40** 20 15
403. 40 c. Carpentry/joinery workshop 45 30
404. $1.20 Agricultural produce market .. .. 1·25 1·25
405. $3 Fishing boats landing catch .. .. .. 2·50 2·75

1986. Royal Wedding. Multicoloured. As T **168** of British Virgin Islands.

406. 60 c. Prince Andrew in midshipman's uniform .. 20 25
407. 60 c. Miss Sarah Ferguson 20 25
408. $2 Prince Andrew on safari in Africa (horiz.) .. 55 70
409. $2 Prince Andrew at the races (horiz.) 55 70

1986. Automobiles (6th series). As T **25**, the first in each pair showing technical drawings and the second paintings.

411. 15 c. multicoloured .. 10 10
412. 15 c. multicoloured .. 10 10
413. 45 c. black, light blue and blue 25 25
414. 45 c. multicoloured .. 25 25
415. 60 c. multicoloured .. 30 30
416. 60 c. multicoloured .. 30 30
417. $1 black, light green and green 40 40
418. $1 multicoloured 40 40
419. $1.75 black, lilac and deep lilac 60 60
420. $1.75 multicoloured .. 60 60
421. $3 multicoloured .. .. 1·10 1·10
422. $3 multicoloured .. .. 1·10 1·10

DESIGNS: Nos. 411/12, Riley "Brooklands Nine" (1930). 413/14, Alfa Romeo "GTA" (1966). 415/16, Pierce Arrow "Type 66" (1913). 417/18, Willy-Knight "66 A" (1928). 419/20, Studebaker "Starliner" (1953). 421/2, Cunningham "V-8" (1919).

41. Gorgonia.

1986 Corals (2nd series). Multicoloured.

423 15 c. Type **41** 35 15
424 60 c. Fire coral 80 55
425 $2 Elkhorn coral .. .. 1·50 2·00
426 $3 Vase sponge and feather star .. .. .. 1·75 2·50

1986. Railway Locomotives (6th series). As T **21**, the first in each pair showing technical drawings and the second the locomotive at work.

427. 15 c. multicoloured .. 10 10
428. 15 c. multicoloured .. 10 10
429. 45 c. multicoloured .. 25 25
430. 45 c. multicoloured .. 25 25
431. 60 c. multicoloured .. 30 30
432. 60 c. multicoloured .. 30 30
433. 75 c. multicoloured .. 40 40
434. 75 c. multicoloured .. 40 40
435. $1 multicoloured 45 50
436. $1 multicoloured 45 50
437. $1.50 multicoloured .. 60 70
438. $1.50 multicoloured .. 60 70
439. $2 multicoloured 70 80
440. $2 multicoloured 70 80
441. $3 multicoloured .. .. 90 1·10
442. $3 multicoloured .. .. 90 1·10

DESIGNS: Nos. 427/8, Connor Single Class, Great Britain (1859). 429/30, Class "P2" "Cock o' the North", Great Britain (1934). 431/2, Class "7000", Japan (1926). 433/4, Palatinate Railway Class "P3", Germany (1897). 435/6, "Dorchester", Canada (1836). 436/7, "Centennial" Class diesel, U.S.A. (1969). 439/40, "Lafayette", U.S.A. (1837). 441/2, Class "C–16", U.S.A. (1882).

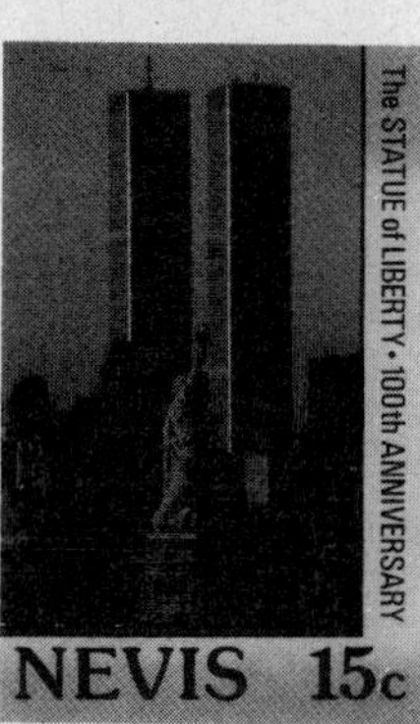

41a. Statue of Liberty and World Trade Centre, Manhattan.

1986. Centenary of Statue of Liberty. Multicoloured.

443. 15 c. Type **41a** 10 10
444. 25 c. Sailing ship passing statue 15 15
445. 40 c. Statue in scaffolding 20 20
446. 60 c. Statue (side view) and scaffolding 25 25
447. 75 c. Statue and regatta .. 30 30
448. $1 Tall Ships parade passing statue (horiz.) .. 35 35
449. $1.50 Head and arm of statue above scaffolding 50 50
450. $2 Ships with souvenir flags (horiz.) 70 70
451. $2.50 Statue and New York waterfront 80 80
452. $3 Restoring statue .. 1·10 1·10

1986. Royal Wedding (2nd issue). Nos. 406/9 optd. **Congratulations to T.R.H. The Duke & Duchess of York.**

454. 60 c. Prince Andrew in midshipman's uniform .. 35 35
455. 60 c. Miss Sarah Ferguson 35 35
456. $2 Prince Andrew on safari in Africa (horiz.) .. 1·10 1·10
457. $2 Prince Andrew at the races (horiz.) .. 1·10 1·10

42. Dinghy sailing.

1986. Sports. Multicoloured.

458. 10 c. Type **42** 10 10
459. 25 c. Netball 30 15
460. $2 Cricket .. .. .. 1·75 1·75
461. $3 Basketball .. .. 2·00 2·00

43. St. George's Anglican Church, Gingerland.

1986. Christmas. Churches of Nevis (2nd series). Multicoloured.

462. 10 c. Type **43** 10 10
463. 40 c. Trinity Methodist Church, Fountain .. 20 25
464. $1 Charlestown Methodist Church 45 55
465. $5 Wesleyan Holiness Church, Brown Hill .. 2·25 2·75

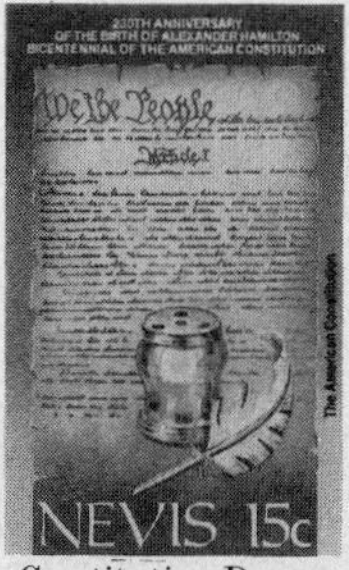

44. Constitution Document, Quill and Inkwell.

1987. Bicentenary of U.S. Constitution and 230th Birth Anniv. of Alexander Hamilton (U.S. statesman). Multicoloured.

466. 15 c. Type **44** 10 10
467. 40 c. Alexander Hamilton and Hamilton House .. 20 25
468. 60 c. Alexander Hamilton 25 35
469. $2 Washington and his Cabinet .. .. .. 90 1·25

1987. Victory of "Stars and Stripes" in America's Cup Yachting Championship. No. 54 optd. **America's Cup 1987 Winners 'Stars & Stripes'.**

471. $3 Windjammer S.V. "Polynesia" .. .. 1·40 1·75

46. Fig Tree Church.

1987. Bicentenary of Marriage of Horatio Nelson and Frances Nisbet. Multicoloured.

472 15 c. Type **46** 10 10
473 60 c. Frances Nisbet .. 30 30
474 $1 H.M.S. "Boreas" (frigate) 80 80
475 $3 Captain Horatio Nelson 2·25 2·50

47. Queen Angelfish. (Illustration reduced. Actual size 60 × 30 mm.).

1987. Coral Reef Fishes. Multicoloured.

477. 60 c. Type **47** 45 60
478. 60 c. Blue angelfish .. 45 60
479. $1 Stoplight parrotfish (male) 60 80
480. $1 Stoplight parrotfish (female) 60 80
481. $1.50 Red hind .. .. 90 1·25
482. $1.50 Rock hind .. .. 90 1·25
483. $2.50 Coney (bicoloured phase) .. .. .. 1·40 2·00
484. $2.50 Coney (red-brown phase) .. .. .. 1·40 2·00

Nos. 478, 480, 482 and 484 are inverted triangles.

48. "Panaeolus antillarum".

1987. Fungi (1st series). Multicoloured.

485. 15 c. Type **48** 30 20
486. 50 c. "Pycnoporus sanguineus" 75 50
487. $2 "Gymnopilus chrysopellus" .. .. 2·25 2·00
488. $3 "Cantharellus cinnabarinus" .. .. 2·75 2·75

See also Nos. 646/53.

49. Rag Doll.

1987. Christmas. Toys. Multicoloured.

489. 10 c. Type **49** 10 10
490. 40 c. Coconut boat .. 20 25
491. $1.20 Sandbox cart .. 55 60
492. $5 Two-wheeled cart .. 2·25 2·75

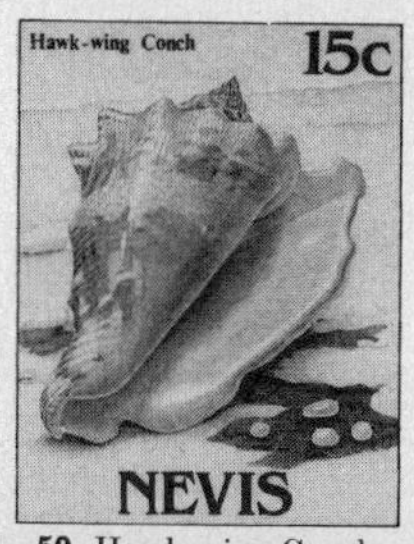

50. Hawk-wing Conch.

1988. Sea Shells and Pearls. Multicoloured.

493. 15 c. Type **50** 20 15
494. 40 c. Roostertail conch . . 30 20
495. 60 c. Emperor helmet . . 50 40
496. $2 Queen conch . . . . 1·60 1·75
497. $3 King helmet . . . . 1·75 1·90

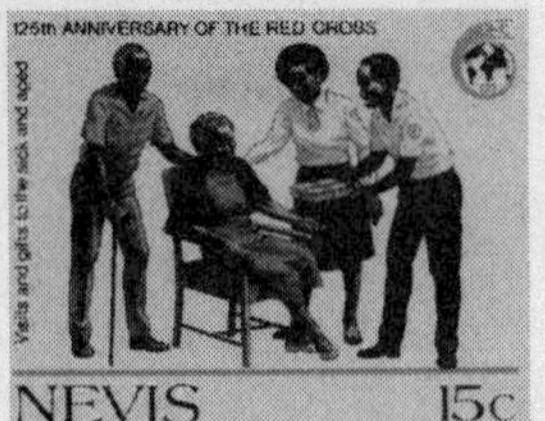

51 Visiting Pensioners at Christmas

1988. 125th Anniv of International Red Cross. Multicoloured.

498 15 c. Type **51** 10 10
499 40 c. Teaching children first aid 15 20
500 60 c. Providing wheelchairs for the disabled . . 25 30
501 $5 Helping cyclone victim 2·10 2·50

52 Athlete on Starting Blocks

1988. Olympic Games, Seoul. Multicoloured.

502 10 c. Type **52** 10 10
503 $1.20 At start 50 55
504 $2 During race 85 90
505 $3 At finish . . . . 1·25 1·40

Nos. 502/5 were printed together, se-tenant, each strip forming a composite design showing an athlete from start to finish of race.

53 Outline Map and Arms of St. Kitts–Nevis

1988. 5th Anniv of Independence.

507 **53** $5 multicoloured . . 2·10 2·25

1988. 300th Anniv of Lloyd's of London. As T **123** of Ascension. Multicoloured.

508 15 c. House of Commons passing Lloyd's Bill, 1871 20 10
509 60 c. "Cunard Countess" (liner) (horiz) 55 45
510 $2.50 Space shuttle deploying satellite (horiz) . . 1·90 2·00
511 $3 "Viking Princess" (cargo liner) on fire, 1966 1·90 2·00

54 Poinsettia

1988. Christmas. Flowers. Multicoloured.

512 15 c. Type **54** 10 10
513 40 c. Tiger claws 15 20
514 60 c. Sorrel flower . . 25 30
515 $1 Christmas candle . . 40 45
516 $5 Snow bush . . . . 2·10 2·25

55 British Fleet off St. Kitts

1989. "Philexfrance 89" International Stamp Exhibition, Paris. Battle of Frigate Bay, 1782. Multicoloured.

517 50 c. Type **55** 30 35
518 $1.20 Battle off Nevis . . 65 75
519 $2 British and French fleets exchanging broadsides . . . . 1·00 1·10
520 $3 French map of Nevis, 1764 . . . . 1·40 1·60

Nos. 517/19 were printed together, se-tenant, forming a composite design.

56 Cicada

1989. "Sounds of the Night". Multicoloured.

521 10 c. Type **56** 20 15
522 40 c. Grasshopper . . 40 35
523 60 c. Cricket 55 50
524 $5 Tree frog . . . . 3·75 4·00

1989. 20th Anniv of First Manned Landing on Moon. As T **126** of Ascension. Multicoloured.

526 15 c. Vehicle Assembly Building, Kennedy Space Centre 15 10
527 40 c. Crew of "Apollo 12" (30 × 30 mm) 20 20
528 $2 "Apollo 12" emblem (30 × 30 mm) . . . . 1·00 1·10
529 $3 "Apollo 12" astronaut on Moon . . . . 1·40 1·60

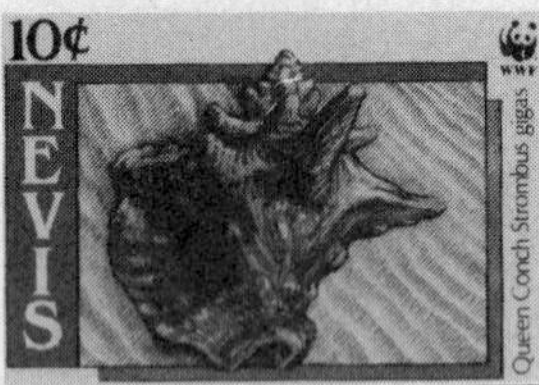

57 Queen Conch feeding

1990. Queen Conch. Multicoloured.

531 10 c. Type **57** 10 10
532 40 c. Queen Conch from front 20 25
533 60 c. Side view of shell . . 30 35
534 $1 Back and flare . . 50 55

58 Wyon Medal Portrait

1990. 150th Anniv of the Penny Black.

536 **58** 15 c. black and brown . . 10 10
537 – 40 c. black and green . . 20 25
538 – 60 c. black 30 35
539 – $4 black and blue . . 2·00 2·10

DESIGNS: 40 c. Engine-turned background; 60 c. Heath's engraving of portrait; $4 Essay with inscriptions.

59

1990. 500th Anniv of Regular European Postal Services.

541 **59** 15 c. brown 10 10
542 – 40 c. green 20 25
543 – 60 c. violet 30 35
544 – $4 blue . . . . 2·00 2·10

Nos. 541/4 commemorate the Thurn and Taxis postal service and the designs are loosely based on those of the initial 1852-58 series.

1990. 500th Anniv (1992) of Discovery of America by Columbus (2nd issue). New World Natural History—Crabs. As T **260** of Antigua. Multicoloured.

546 5 c. Sand fiddler . . 10 10
547 15 c. Great land crab . . 10 10
548 20 c. Blue crab . . 10 10
549 40 c. Stone crab 20 25
550 60 c. Mountain crab . . 30 35
551 $2 Sargassum crab . . 95 1·00
552 $3 Yellow box crab . . 1·40 1·50
553 $4 Spiny spider crab . . 2·00 2·10

1990. 90th Birthday of Queen Elizabeth the Queen Mother. As T **103** of Grenada Grenadines.

555 $2 black, mauve and buff 95 1·00
556 $2 black, mauve and buff 95 1·00
557 $2 black, mauve and buff 95 1·00

DESIGNS: No. 555, Duchess of York with corgi; 556, Queen Elizabeth in Coronation robes, 1937; 557, Duchess of York in garden.

61 MaKanaky, Cameroons

1990. World Cup Football Championship, Italy. Star Players. Multicoloured.

559 10 c. Type **61** 10 10
560 25 c. Chovanec, Czechoslovakia . . 10 15
561 $2.50 Robson, England . . 1·25 1·40
562 $5 Voller, West Germany 2·40 2·50

62 "Cattleya deckeri"

1990. Christmas. Native Orchids. Mult.

564 10 c. Type **62** 10 10
565 15 c. "Epidendrum ciliare" 10 10
566 20 c. "Epidendrum fragrans" 10 10
567 40 c. "Epidendrum ibaguense" 20 25
568 60 c. "Epidendrum latifolium" 30 35
569 $1.20 "Maxillaria conferta" 55 60
570 $2 "Epidendrum strobiliferum" . . . . 95 1·00
571 $3 "Brassavola cucullata" 1·40 1·50

1991. 350th Death Anniv of Rubens. As T **273** of Antigua, showing details from "The Feast of Achelous". Multicoloured.

573 10 c. Two jugs (vert) . . 10 10
574 40 c. Woman at table (vert) 20 25
575 60 c. Two servants with fruit (vert) 30 35
576 $4 Achelous (vert) . . 2·00 2·10

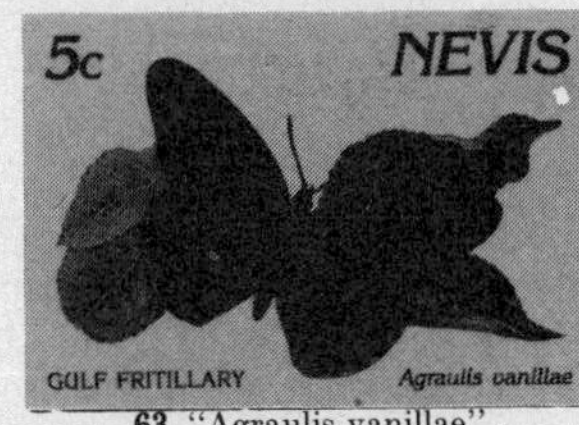

63 "Agraulis vanillae"

1991. Butterflies. Multicoloured.

578 5 c. Type **63** 10 10
579 10 c. "Historis odius" . . 10 10
580 15 c. "Marpesia corinna" 10 10
581 20 c. "Anartia amathea" 10 10
582 25 c. "Junonia evarete" 10 10
583 40 c. "Heliconius charithonia" 20 25
584 50 c. "Marpesia petreus" 25 30
585 60 c. "Dione juno" . . 30 35
586 75 c. "Heliconius doris" 35 40
586c 80 c. As 60 c. 40 45
587 $1 "Hypolimnas misippus" 50 55
588 $3 "Danaus plexippus" . . 1·40 1·50
589 $5 "Heliconius sara" . . 2·40 2·50
590 $10 "Tithorea harmonia" 5·00 5·25
591 $20 "Dryas julia" . . 9·50 9·75

64 "Viking Mars Lander", 1976

1991. 500th Anniv of Discovery of America by Columbus (1992) (3rd issue). History of Exploration. Multicoloured.

592 15 c. Type **64** 10 10
593 40 c. "Apollo 11", 1969 20 25
594 60 c. "Skylab", 1973 . . 30 35
595 75 c. "Salyut 6", 1977 . . 35 40
596 $1 "Voyager 1", 1977 . . 50 55
597 $2 "Venera 7", 1970 . . 95 1·00
598 $4 "Gemini 4", 1965 . . 2·00 2·10
599 $5 "Luna 3", 1959 . . 2·40 2·50

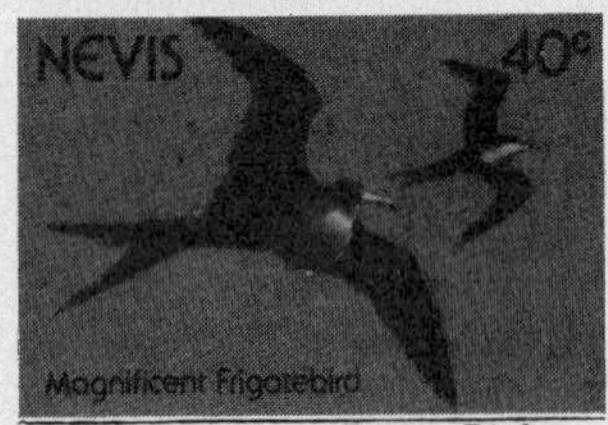

65 Magnificent Frigate Bird

1991. Island Birds. Multicoloured.

601 40 c. Type **65** 20 25
602 40 c. Roseate tern . . 20 25
603 40 c. Red-tailed hawk . . 20 25
604 40 c. Zenaida dove . . 20 25
605 40 c. Bananaquit 20 25
606 40 c. American kestrel . . 20 25
607 40 c. Grey kingbird . . 20 25
608 40 c. Prothonotary warbler 20 25
609 40 c. Blue-hooded euphonia 20 25
610 40 c. Antillean crested hummingbird 20 25
611 40 c. White-tailed tropic bird 20 25
612 40 c. Yellow-bellied sapsucker 20 25
613 40 c. Green-throated carib 20 25
614 40 c. Purple-throated carib 20 25
615 40 c. Red-billed whistling duck ("Black-bellied tree-duck") 20 25
616 40 c. Ringed kingfisher . . 20 25
617 40 c. Burrowing owl . . 20 25
618 40 c. Turnstone 20 25
619 40 c. Great blue heron . . 20 25
620 40 c. Yellow-crowned night-heron 20 25

Nos 601/20 were printed together, se-tenant, forming a composite design.

1991. 65th Birthday of Queen Elizabeth II. As T **280** of Antigua. Multicoloured.

No.	Description		
622	15 c. Queen Elizabeth at polo match with Prince Charles	10	10
623	40 c. Queen and Prince Philip on Buckingham Palace balcony ..	20	25
624	$2 In carriage at Ascot, 1986	95	1·00
625	$4 Queen Elizabeth II at Windsor polo match, 1989	2·00	2·10

1991. 10th Wedding Anniv of Prince and Princess of Wales. As T **280** of Antigua. Multicoloured.

No.	Description		
627	10 c. Prince Charles and Princess Diana ..	10	10
628	50 c. Prince of Wales and family	25	30
629	$1 Prince William and Prince Harry	50	55
630	$5 Prince and Princess of Wales	2·40	2·50

1991. "Phila Nippon '91" International Stamp Exhibition, Tokyo. Japanese Railway Locomotives. As T **257** of Maldives. Mult.

No.	Description		
632	10 c. Class "C62" steam locomotive	10	10
633	15 c. Class "C56" steam locomotive (horiz) ..	10	10
634	40 c. Class "C-55" streamlined steam locomotive (horiz)	20	25
635	60 c. Class "1400" steam locomotive (horiz) ..	30	35
636	$1 Class "485 Bonnet" diesel rail car	50	55
637	$2 Class "C61" steam locomotive	95	1·00
638	$3 Class "485" express train (horiz)	1·40	1·50
639	$4 Class "7000" electric train (horiz)	2·00	2·10

1991. Christmas. Drawings by Albrecht Durer. As T **211** of Lesotho.

No.	Description		
641	10 c. black and green ..	10	10
642	40 c. black and orange ..	20	25
643	60 c. black and blue ..	30	35
644	$3 black and mauve ..	1·40	1·50

DESIGNS: 10 c. "Mary being Crowned by an Angel"; 40 c. "Mary with the Pear"; 60 c. "Mary in a Halo"; $3 "Mary with Crown of Stars and Sceptre".

66 "Marasmius haemtocephalus"

1991. Fungi (2nd series). Multicoloured.

No.	Description		
646	15 c. Type **66**	15	20
647	40 c. "Psilocybe cubensis"	20	25
648	60 c. "Hygrocybe acutoconica"	30	35
649	75 c. "Hygrocybe occidentalis"	35	40
650	$1 "Boletellus cubensis" ..	50	55
651	$2 "Gymnopilus chrysopellus"	95	1·00
652	$4 "Cantharellus cinnabarinus"	2·00	2·10
653	$5 "Chlorophyllum molybdites"	2·40	2·50

1992. 40th Anniv of Queen Elizabeth II's Accession. As T **292** of Antigua. Mult.

No.	Description		
655	10 c. Charlestown from the sea	15	20
656	40 c. Charlestown square	20	25
657	$1 Mountain scenery ..	50	55
658	$5 Early cottage	2·40	2·50

67 Monique Knol (cycling), Netherlands

1992. Olympic Games, Barcelona. Gold Medal Winners of 1988. Multicoloured.

No.	Description		
660	20 c. Type **67**	15	20
661	25 c. Roger Kingdom (hurdles), U.S.A. ..	15	20
662	50 c. Yugoslavia (men's waterpolo)	25	35
663	80 c. Anja Fichtel (foil), West Germany ..	40	45
664	$1 Said Aouita, (mid-distance running), Morocco	50	55
665	$1.50 Yuri Sedykh (hammer throw), U.S.S.R.	70	75
666	$3 Shushunova (women's gymnastics), U.S.S.R.	1·40	1·50
667	$5 Valimir Artemov (men's gymnastics), U.S.S.R. ..	2·40	2·50

68 "Landscape" (Mariano Fortuny i Marsal)

1992. "Granada '92" International Stamp Exhibition, Spain. Spanish Paintings. Multicoloured.

No.	Description		
669	20 c. Type **68**	10	10
670	25 c. "Dona Juana la Loca" (Francisco Pradilla Ortiz) (horiz) ..	10	10
671	50 c. "Idyll" (Fortuny i Marsal)	25	30
672	80 c. "Old Man Naked in the Sun" (Fortuny i Marsal)	40	45
673	$1 "The Painter's Children in the Japanese Salon" (detail) (Fortuny i Marsal)	50	55
674	$2 "The Painter's Children in the Japanese Salon" (different detail) (Fortuny i Marsal) ..	95	1·00
675	$3 "Still Life: Sea Bream and Oranges" (Luis Eugenio Melendez (horiz)	1·40	1·50
676	$5 "Still Life: Box of Sweets, Pastry and Other Objects" (Melendez)	2·40	2·50

69 Early Compass and Ship

1992. 500th Anniv of Discovery of America by Columbus and "World Columbian Stamp Expo '92", Chicago. Multicoloured.

No.	Description		
678	20 c. Type **69**	15	20
679	50 c. Manatee and fleet ..	25	30
680	80 c. Green turtle and "Santa Maria" ..	40	45
681	$1.50 "Santa Maria" and arms	70	75
682	$3 Queen Isabella of Spain and commission ..	1·40	1·50
683	$5 Pineapple and colonists	2·40	1·50

1992. 500th Anniv of Discovery of America by Columbus (5th issue). Organization of East Caribbean States. As Nos. 911/12 of Montserrat. Multicoloured.

No.	Description		
685	$1 Columbus meeting Amerindians	50	55
686	$2 Ships approaching island	95	1·00

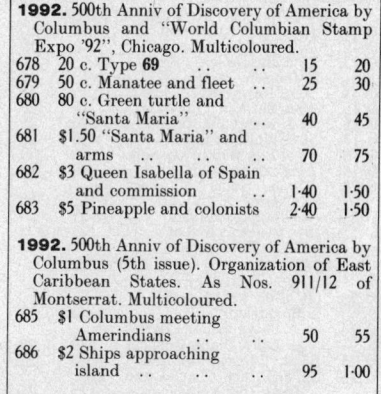

70 Minnie Mouse

1992. Mickey's Portrait Gallery. Mult.

No.	Description		
688	10 c. Type **70**	10	10
689	15 c. Mickey Mouse ..	10	10
690	40 c. Donald Duck ..	20	25
691	80 c. Mickey Mouse, 1930	40	45
692	$1 Daisy Duck	50	55
693	$2 Pluto	95	1·00
694	$4 Goofy	2·00	2·10
695	$5 Goofy, 1932	2·40	2·50

1993. Christmas. Religious Paintings. As T **218** of Lesotho. Multicoloured.

No.	Description		
697	20 c. "The Virgin and Child between Two Saints" (Giovanni Bellini) ..	10	10
698	40 c. "The Virgin and Child surrounded by Four Angels" (Master of the Castello Nativity) ..	20	25
699	50 c. "Virgin and Child surrounded by Angels with St. Frediano and St. Augustine" (detail) (Fillipo Lippi)	25	30
700	80 c. "The Virgin and Child between St. Peter and St. Sebastian" (Bellini)	40	45
701	$1 "The Virgin and Child with St. Julian and St. Nicholas of Myra" (Lorenzo di Credi) ..	50	55
702	$2 "St. Bernadino and a Female Saint presenting a Donor to Virgin and Child" (Francesco Bissolo)	95	1·00
703	$4 "Madonna and Child with Four Cherubs" (ascr Barthel Bruyn) ..	2·00	2·10
704	$5 "The Virgin and Child" (Quentin Metsys) ..	2·40	2·50

71 Care Bear and Butterfly

1993. Ecology.

No.	Description		
706 **71**	80 c. multicoloured ..	40	45

1993. Bicentenary of the Louvre, Paris. As T **305** of Antigua. Multicoloured.

No.	Description		
708	$1 "The Card Cheat" (left detail) (La Tour) ..	50	55
709	$1 "The Card Cheat" (centre detail) (La Tour)	50	55
710	$1 "The Card Cheat" (right detail) (La Tour) ..	50	55
711	$1 "St. Joseph, the Carpenter" (La Tour) ..	50	55
712	$1 "St. Thomas" (La Tour)	50	55
713	$1 "Adoration of the Shepherds" (left detail) (La Tour)	50	55
714	$1 "Adoration of the Shepherds" (right detail) (La Tour)	50	55
715	$1 "Mary Magdalene with a Candle" (La Tour) ..	50	55

1993. 15th Death Anniv of Elvis Presley (singer). As T **260** of Dominica. Mult.

No.	Description		
717	$1 Elvis Presley	50	55
718	$1 Elvis with guitar ..	50	55
719	$1 Elvis with microphone	50	55

72 Japanese Launch Vehicle H-11

1993. Anniversaries and Events. Mult.

No.	Description		
720	15 c. Type **72**	10	10
721	50 c. "Hindenburg" on fire, 1937 (horiz) ..	25	30
722	75 c. Konrad Adenauer and Charles de Gaulle (horiz)	35	40
723	80 c. Red Cross emblem and map of Nevis (horiz)	40	45
724	80 c. "Resolute", 1920 ..	40	45
725	80 c. Nelson Museum and map of Nevis (horiz) ..	40	45
726	80 c. St. Thomas's Church (horiz)	40	45
727	$1 Blue whale (horiz) ..	50	55
728	$3 Mozart	1·40	1·50
729	$3 Graph and U.N. emblems (horiz) ..	1·40	1·50
730	$3 Lions Club emblem ..	1·40	1·50
731	$5 Soviet "Energia" launch vehicle SL-17 ..	2·40	2·50
732	$5 Lebaudy's airship, 1903 (horiz)	2·40	2·50
733	$5 Adenauer and Pres. Kennedy (horiz) ..	2·40	2·50

ANNIVERSARIES AND EVENTS: Nos. 720, 731, International Space Year; Nos. 721, 732, 75th death anniv of Count Ferdinand von Zeppelin (airship pioneer); Nos. 722, 733, 25th death anniv of Konrad Adenauer (German statesman); No. 723, 50th anniv of St. Kitts-Nevis Red Cross; No. 724, Americas Cup Yachting Championship; No. 725, Opening of Nelson Museum; No. 726, 150th anniv of Anglican Diocese of North-eastern Caribbean and Aruba; No. 727, Earth Summit '92, Rio; No. 728, Death bicentenary of Mozart; No. 729, International Conference on Nutrition, Rome; No. 730, 75th anniv of International Association of Lions Clubs.

73 "Plumeria rubra"

1993. West Indian Flowers. Multioloured.

No.	Description		
735	10 c. Type **73**	10	10
736	25 c. "Bougainvillea" ..	10	10
737	50 c. "Allamanda cathartica"	25	30
738	80 c. "Anthurium andraeanum"	40	45
739	$1 "Ixora coccinea" ..	50	55
740	$2 "Hibiscus rosa-sinensis"	95	1·00
741	$4 "Justicia brandegeeana" ..	2·00	2·10
742	$5 "Antigonon leptopus"	2·40	2·50

74 Antillean Blue (male)

1993. Butterflies. Multicoloured.

744 10 c. Type **74** 10 10
745 25 c. Cuban crescentspot (female) 10 10
746 50 c. Ruddy daggerwing .. 25 30
747 80 c. Little yellow (male) 40 45
748 $1 Atala 50 55
749 $1.50 Orange-barred giant sulphur 75 80
750 $4 Tropic queen (male) .. 2·00 2·10
751 $5 Malachite .. .. 2·40 2·50

1993. 40th Anniv of Coronation. As T **307** of Antigua.

753 10 c. multicoloured .. 10 10
754 80 c. brown and black .. 40 45
755 $2 multicoloured .. .. 95 1·00
756 $4 multicoloured .. .. 2·00 2·10

DESIGNS—38 × 47 mm: 10 c. Queen Elizabeth II at Coronation (photograph by Cecil Beaton); 80 c. Queen wearing Imperial State Crown; $2 Crowning of Queen Elizabeth II; $4 Queen and Prince Charles at polo match.

75 Flag and National Anthem

1993. 10th Anniv of Independence of St. Kitts-Nevis. Multicoloured.

758 25 c. Type **75** 10 10
759 80 c. Pelican and map of St. Kitts-Nevis .. 40 45

1993. World Cup Football Championship 1994, U.S.A. As T **278** of Maldive Islands. Mult.

760 10 c. Imre Garaba (Hungary) and Michel Platini (France) (horiz) 10 10
761 25 c. Diego Maradona (Argentina) and Giuseppe Bergomi (Italy) (horiz) 10 10
762 50 c. Luis Fernandez (France) and Vasily Rats (Russia) (horiz) .. 25 30
763 80 c. Victor Munez (Spain) (horiz) 40 45
764 $1 Preben Elkjaer (Denmark) and Andoni Goicoechea (Spain) (horiz) 50 55
765 $2 Elzo Coelho (Brazil) and Jean Tigana (France) (horiz) .. .. .. 95 1·00
766 $3 Pedro Troglio (Argentina) and Sergei Alejnikov (Russia) (horiz) .. .. .. 1·40 1·50
767 $5 Jan Karas (Poland) and Antonio Luiz Costa (Brazil) (horiz) .. .. 2·40 2·50

OFFICIAL STAMPS

1980. Nos. 40/49 optd. **OFFICIAL.**

O 1. 15 c. Sugar cane being harvested 10 10
O 2. 25 c. Crafthouse (craft centre) 10 10
O 3. 30 c. Cruise ship 10 10
O 4. 40 c. Lobster and sea crab 15 15
O 5. 45 c. Royal St. Kitts Hotel and golf course .. 20 25
O 6. 50 c. Pinneys Beach, Nevis 20 25
O 7. 55 c. New runway at Golden Rock 20 25
O 8. $1 Picking cotton .. 30 35
O 9. $5 The Brewery .. .. 1·00 1·00
O 10. $10 Pineapples and peanuts 1·50 2·25

1981. Nos. 60/71 optd. **OFFICIAL.**

O 11. 15 c. New River Mill .. 10 10
O 12. 20 c. Nelson Museum .. 10 10
O 13. 25 c. St. James' Parish Church 10 15
O 14. 30 c. Nevis Lane .. 15 15
O 15. 40 c. Zetland Plantation 15 20
O 16. 45 c. Nisbit Plantation .. 20 25
O 17. 50 c. Pinney's Beach .. 20 25
O 18. 55 c. Eva Wilkin's Studio 25 30
O 19. $1 Nevis at dawn .. 40 45
O 20. $2·50 Ruins of Fort Charles 85 90
O 21. $5 Old Bath House .. 1·25 1·75
O 22. $10 Beach at Nisbet's .. 2·25 2·75

1983. Nos. 72/7 optd. **OFFICIAL** and surch.

O 23. 45 c. on $2 " Royal Sovereign " 20 25
O 24. 45 c. on $2 Prince Charles & Lady Diana Spencer 20 25
O 25. 55 c. " Royal Caroline " 20 25
O 26. 55 c. Prince Charles and Lady Diana Spencer .. 25 25
O 27. $1·10 on $5 " Britannia " 45 50
O 28. $1·10 on $5 Prince Charles & Lady Diana Spencer 55 60

1985. Nos. 187/98 optd. **OFFICIAL.**

O29. 15 c. Flamboyant .. 10 10
O30. 20 c. Eyelash Orchid .. 10 10
O31. 30 c. Bougainvillea .. 10 15
O32. 40 c. Hibiscus 15 20
O33. 50 c. Night-blooming Cereus 20 25
O34. 55 c. Yellow Mahoe .. 25 30
O35. 60 c. Spider-lily 25 30
O36. 75 c. Scarlet Cordia .. 30 35
O37. $1 Shell-ginger 40 45
O38. $3 Blue Petrea .. .. 1·25 1·40
O39. $5 Coral Hibiscus .. 2·10 2·25
O40. $10 Passion flower .. 4·25 4·50

1993. Nos. 578/91 optd **OFFICIAL**.

O41 5 c. Type **63** 10 10
O42 10 c. "Historis odius" .. 10 10
O43 15 c. "Marpesia corinna" 10 10
O44 20 c. "Anartia amathea" 10 10
O45 25 c. "Junonia evarete" .. 10 10
O46 40 c. "Heliconius charithonia" 20 25
O47 50 c. "Marpesia petreus" 25 30
O48 75 c. "Heliconius doris" .. 35 40
O49 80 c. "Dione juno" .. 40 45
O50 $1 "Hypolimnas misippus" 50 55
O51 $3 "Danaus plexippus" .. 1·40 1·50
O52 $5 "Heliconius sara" .. 2·40 2·50
O53 $10 "Tithorea harmonia" 5·00 5·25
O54 $20 "Dryas julia" .. 9·50 9·75

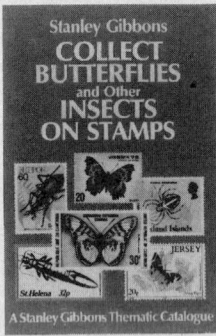

NEW BRUNSWICK

An eastern province of the Dominion of Canada, whose stamps are now used.

1851. 12 pence = 1 shilling.
20 shillings = 1 pound.
1860. 100 cents = 1 dollar.

1. Royal Crown and Heraldic Flowers of the United Kingdom.

1851.

1	1.	3d. red	£1600	£300
4		6d. yellow	£4500	£700
6		1s. mauve	£14000	£4500

2. Locomotive.

3. Queen Victoria.

1860.

9.	2.	1 c. purple	24·00	24·00
10.	3.	2 c. orange	12·00	14·00
13.	–	5 c. brown	£2750	
14.	–	5 c. green	12·00	12·00
17.	–	10 c. red	35·00	28·00
18.	–	12½ c. blue	50·00	40·00
19.	–	17 c. black	32·00	28·00

DESIGNS—VERT. 5 c. brown, Charles Connell. 5 c. green. 10 c. Queen Victoria. 17 c. King Edward VII when Prince of Wales. HORIZ. 12½ c. Steamship.

NEWFOUNDLAND

An island off the E. coast of Canada. A British Dominion merged since 1949 with Canada, whose stamps it now uses.

1857. 12 pence = 1 shilling.
20 shillings = 1 pound.
1866. 100 cents = 1 dollar.

1.

2.

3. Royal Crown and Heraldic flowers of the United Kingdom.

1857. Imperf.

1.	1.	1d. purple	75·00	£120
10.	2.	2d. red	£250	£300
11.	3.	3d. green	50·00	£120
12.	2.	4d. red	£1500	£600
13.	1.	5d. brown	65·00	£190
14.	2.	6d. red	£2500	£600
7.		6½d. red	£2250	£2500
8.		8d. red	£200	£250
9.		1s. red	£12000	£4000

The frame design of Type 2 differs from each value.

1861. Imperf.

21.	1.	1d. brown	£100	£180
22.	2.	2d. lake	£120	£350
23.		4d. lake	20·00	80·00
24a.	1.	5d. brown	32·00	£150
24b.	2.	6d. lake	17·00	£100
24c.		6½d. lake	65·00	£325
24d.		8d. lake	60·00	£350
24e.		1s. lake	27·00	£170

8. Prince Consort.

6. Codfish.

7. Common Seal on Ice-floe.

9. Queen Victoria.

10. Schooner.

11. Queen Victoria.

1866. Perf. (2 c. also roul.).

31	6	2 c. green	60·00	27·00
26	7	5 c. brown	£450	£170
32	8	10 c. black	£150	27·00
61	9	12 c. brown	35·00	42·00
29	10	13 c. orange	75·00	55·00
30	11	24 c. blue	32·00	32·00

12. King Edward VII, when Prince of Wales.

14. Queen Victoria

1868. Perf. or roul.

34	12.	1 c. purple	45·00	45·00
36		3 c. orange	£250	£100
42		3 c. blue	£250	3·00
38	7.	5 c. black	£200	£100
43		5 c. blue	£170	2·75
39	14.	6 c. red	5·50	16·00

19. Newfoundland Dog.

15. King Edward VII, when Prince of Wales.

16. Codfish.

17.

18. Common Seal on Ice-floe.

20. Atlantic brigantine.

21. Queen Victoria.

1880.

49	19	½ c. red	7·00	6·00
59		½ c. black	4·25	3·50
44a	15	1 c. brown	15·00	7·00
50a		1 c. green	5·50	1·25
46	16	2 c. green	42·00	20·00
51		2 c. orange	11·00	3·00
47a	17	3 c. blue	48·00	1·00
52		3 c. brown	38·00	70
59a	18	5 c. blue	48·00	1·50
54	20	10 c. black	45·00	48·00

1890.

55	21	3 c. grey	19·00	90

This stamp on pink paper was stained by sea-water.

22. Queen Victoria.

23. John Cabot.

24. Cape Bonavista.

25. Reindeer hunting.

1897. 400th Anniv. of Discovery of Newfoundland and 60th Year of Queen Victoria's Reign. Dated "1497 1897"

66.	22.	1 c. green	1·25	2·75
67.	23.	2 c. red	1·00	1·75
68.	24.	3 c. blue	1·25	30
69.	25.	4 c. olive	7·50	2·00
70.	–	5 c. violet	8·00	2·00
71.	–	6 c. brown	6·00	2·00
72.	–	8 c. orange	11·00	7·00
73.	–	10 c. brown	20·00	2·75
74.	–	12 c. blue	28·00	3·00
75.	–	15 c. red	12·00	12·00
76.	–	24 c. violet	17·00	17·00
77.	–	30 c. blue	35·00	45·00
78.	–	35 c. red	60·00	48·00
79.	–	60 c. black	12·00	7·00

DESIGNS—As Type 24: 5 c. Mining. 6 c. Logging. 8 c. Fishing. 10 c. Cabot's ship, the "Matthew". 15 c. Seals. 24 c. Salmon fishing. 35 c. Iceberg. As Type 23: 12 c. Willow/red grouse. 30 c. Seal of the Colony. 60 c. Henry VII.

36. Prince Edward, later Duke of Windsor.

37. Queen Victoria.

1897. Royal portraits.

83	36	½ c. olive	80	70
84	37	1 c. red	1·75	2·50
85	–	1 c. green	4·00	10
86	–	2 c. orange	1·00	1·40
87	–	2 c. red	6·00	15
88	–	3 c. orange	6·00	10
89	–	4 c. violet	22·00	3·00
90	–	5 c. blue	32·00	2·75

DESIGNS: 2 c. King Edward VII when Prince of Wales. 3 c. Queen Alexandra when Princess of Wales. 4 c. Queen Mary when Duchess of York. 5 c. King George V when Duke of York.

1897. Surch ONE CENT and bar.

91	21	1 c. on 3 c. grey	32·00	16·00

45. Map of Newfoundland.

46. King James I.

47. Arms of Colonisation Co.

49. "Endeavour" (immigrant ship), 1610.

1908.

94.	45.	2 c. lake	25·00	30

1910. Dated "1610 1910".

109	46	1 c. green	1·25	20
107	47	2 c. red	3·50	35
97	–	3 c. olive	2·50	11·00
98	49	4 c. violet	8·00	11·00
99	–	5 c. blue	10·00	4·25
111	–	6 c. purple	16·00	32·00
112	–	8 c. bistre	45·00	48·00
113	–	9 c. green	38·00	65·00
103	–	10 c. grey	50·00	90·00
115	–	12 c. brown	50·00	60·00
105	–	15 c. black	60·00	90·00

DESIGNS—HORIZ. 5 c. Cupids. 8 c. Mosquito. 9 c. Logging camp. 10 c. Paper mills. VERT. 3 c. John Guy. 6 c. Sir Francis Bacon. 12 c. King Edward VII. 15 c. King George V. (Cupids and Mosquito are places).

57. Queen Mary.

58. King George V.

67. Seal of Newfoundland.

1911. Coronation.

117a	57	1 c. green	2·25	20
118	58	2 c. red	2·25	20
119	–	3 c. brown	12·00	24·00
120	–	4 c. purple	14·00	23·00
121	–	5 c. blue	4·25	80
122	–	6 c. grey	10·00	23·00
123	–	8 c. blue	45·00	75·00
124	–	9 c. blue	11·00	32·00
125	–	10 c. green	20·00	30·00
126	–	12 c. plum	15·00	30·00
127	67	15 c. lake	15·00	40·00

PORTRAITS—VERT. As Types 57/8: 3 c. Duke of Windsor when Prince of Wales. 4 c. King George VI when Prince Albert. 5 c. Princess Mary, the Princess Royal. 6 c. Duke of Gloucester when Prince Henry. 8 c. Duke of Kent when Prince George. 9 c. Prince John. 10 c. Queen Alexandra. 12 c. Duke of Connaught.

68. Caribou.

Each inscr. with the name of a different action: 1 c. Suvla Bay. 3 c. Gueudecourt. 4 c. Beaumont Hamel. 6 c. Monchy. 10 c. Steenbeck. 15c. Langemarck. 24 c. Cambrai. 36 c. Combles. The 2 c., 5 c., 8 c. and 12 c. are inscribed "Royal Naval Reserve. Ubique".

1919. Newfoundland Contingent. 1914-18.

130	68.	1 c. green	1·10	20
131		2 c. red	1·10	50
132		3 c. brown	1·50	20
133		4 c. mauve	2·50	60
134		5 c. blue	2·00	60
135		6 c. grey	4·50	25·00
136		8 c. purple	5·50	35·00
137		10 c. green	4·25	2·00
138		12 c. orange	18·00	38·00
139		15 c. blue	17·00	45·00
140		24 c. brown	22·00	25·00
141		36 c. olive	8·50	20·00

1919. Air. Hawker Flight. No. 132a optd. **FIRST TRANS-ATLANTIC AIR POST April, 1919.**

142.	68.	3 c. brown	£14000	£8000

1919. Air. Alcock Flight. Surch. **Trans-Atlantic AIR POST 1919 ONE DOLLAR.**

143.	$1 on 15 c. red (No. 75)	£110	£110

1920. Surch. in words between bars.

144.	2 c. on 30 c. blue (No. 77)	3·50	10·00
146.	3 c. on 15 c. red (No. 75)	8·00	9·00
147.	3 c. on 35 c. red (No. 78)	4·75	7·50

1921. Air. Optd. **AIR MAIL to Halifax N.S. 1921.**

148a	35 c. red (No. 78)	80·00	80·00

73. Twin Hills, Tors Cove.

75. Statue of Fighting Newfoundlander, St. John's.

1923.

149. **73.** 1 c. green 60 10
150. – 2 c. red 60 10
151. **75.** 3 c. brown 55 10
152. – 4 c. purple 90 30
153. – 5 c. blue .. .. 1·50 90
154. – 6 c. grey .. .. 2·25 5·50
155. – 8 c. purple .. .. 2·25 3·25
156. – 9 c. green .. .. 17·00 27·00
157. – 10 c. violet .. .. 2·50 2·00
158. – 11 c. olive .. .. 2·25 12·00
159. – 12 c. lake .. .. 2·50 8·00
160. – 15 c. blue .. .. 2·50 11·00
161. – 20 c. brown .. .. 3·00 11·00
162. – 24 c. brown .. .. 42·00 75·00

DESIGNS—HORIZ. 2 c. South-west Arm, Trinity. 6 c. Upper Steadies, Humber River. 8 c. Quidi Vidi, near St. John's. 9 c. Reindeer crossing lake. 11 c. Shell Bird Island. 12 c. Mount Moriah, Bay of Islands. 20 c. Placentia. VERT. 4 c. Humber River. 5 c. Coast at Trinity. 10 c. Humber River Canon. 15 c. Humber River, near Little Rapids. 24 c. Topsail Falls.

1927. Air. Optd. **Air Mail DE PINEDO 1927.**

163. 60 c. black (No. 79) .. £19000 £6000

88. Newfoundland and Labrador.

89. S.S. "Caribou".

90. King George V and Queen Mary.

91. Duke of Windsor when Prince of Wales.

1928. "Publicity" issue.

164 **88** 1 c. green .. .. 1·00 80
180 **89** 2 c. red .. .. .. 1·50 20
181 **90** 3 c. brown .. .. 1·00 10
182 **91** 4 c. mauve .. .. 1·75 30
183 – 5 c. grey .. .. 5·00 1·75
184 – 6 c. blue .. .. 2·00 6·50
170 – 8 c. brown .. .. 1·75 14·00
171 – 9 c. green .. .. 1·75 8·00
185 – 10 c. violet .. .. 2·00 2·00
173 – 12 c. lake .. .. 1·75 13·00
174 – 14 c. purple .. .. 4·00 5·00
175 – 15 c. blue .. .. 2·75 22·00
176 – 20 c. black .. .. 2·50 6·50
177 – 28 c. green .. .. 24·00 45·00
178 – 30 c. brown .. .. 6·00 11·00

DESIGNS—HORIZ. 5 c. Express train. 6 c. Hotel, St. John's. 8 c. Heart's Content. 10 c. War Memorial, St. John's. 15 c. Trans-Atlantic flight. 20 c. Colonial Building, St. John's. VERT. 9 c., 14 c. Cabot Tower, St. John's. 12 c., 28 c. G.P.O., St. John's. 30 c. Grand Falls, Labrador.

1929. Surch. in words.

188. 3 c. on 6 c. (No. 154) .. 85 3·00

1930. Air. No. 141 surch. **Trans-Atlantic AIR MAIL By B.M. "Columbia" September 1930 Fifty Cents.**

191. **68.** 50 c. on 36 c. olive .. £4250 £4000

103. Aeroplane and Dog-team.

104. Vickers-Vimy Biplane and early Sailing Packet.

105. Routes of historic Trans-Atlantic Flights.

1931. Air.

192 **103** 15 c. brown .. .. 3·00 7·00
193 **104** 50 c. green .. .. 20·00 30·00
194 **105** $1 blue .. .. .. 40·00 75·00

107. Codfish. **108.** King George V.

110. Duke of Windsor when Prince of Wales. **111.** Reindeer.

112. Queen Elizabeth II when Princess. **121.** Paper Mills.

1932.

209 **107.** 1 c. green .. .. 1·25 15
222 1 c. grey 40 10
210 **108.** 2 c. red .. .. 1·50 10
223 2 c. green 40 10
211 – 3 c. brown .. .. 1·25 10
212 **110.** 4 c. lilac .. .. 2·75 80
224 4 c. red 75 15
213 **111.** 5 c. purple .. .. 2·25 55
225c 5 c. violet 60 20
214 **112.** 6 c. blue .. .. 4·00 9·00
226 – 7 c. lake .. .. 1·10 2·50
282 **121.** 8 c. red .. .. 1·00 1·75
215 – 10 c. brown 55 30
216 – 14 c. black .. .. 1·00 2·00
217 – 15 c. purple .. .. 1·25 1·75
218 – 20 c. green .. .. 1·00 50
228 – 24 c. blue .. .. 60 2·25
219 – 25 c. grey .. .. 1·50 1·75
220 – 30 c. blue .. .. 20·00 24·00
289 – 48 c. brown .. .. 3·00 5·00

DESIGNS—VERT. 3 c. Queen Mary. 7 c. Queen Mother when Duchess of York. HORIZ. 10 c. Salmon. 14 c. Newfoundland dog. 15 c. Seal. 20 c. Trans-Atlantic beacon. 24 c. Bell Island. 25 c. Sealing fleet. 30 c., 48 c. Fishing fleet.

1932. Air. Surch. **TRANS-ATLANTIC WEST TO EAST Per Dornier DO-X May, 1932. One Dollar and Fifty Cents.**

221. **105.** $1·50 c. on $1 blue .. £180 £225

1933. Optd. **L. & S. Post** ("Land and Sea") between bars.

229. **103.** 15 c. brown .. .. 2·00 6·00

INDEX

Countries can be quickly located by referring to the index at the end of this volume.

124. Put to flight.

1933. Air.

230. **124.** 5 c. brown .. .. 8·50 13·00
231. – 10 c. yellow .. .. 4·00 15·00
232. – 30 c. blue .. .. 24·00 32·00
233. – 60 c. green .. .. 40·00 65·00
234. – 75 c. brown .. .. 40·00 65·00

DESIGNS: 10 c. Land of Heart's Delight. 30 c. Spotting the herd. 60 c. News from home. 75 c. Labrador.

1933. Air. Balbo Trans-Atlantic Mass Formation Flight. No. 234 surch. **1933 GEN. BALBO FLIGHT, $4.50.**

235. $4.50 on 75 c. brown .. £275 £325

130. Sir Humphrey Gilbert.

131. Compton Castle, Devon.

1933. 350th Anniv. of Annexation. Dated "1583 1933"

236 **130** 1 c. black 50 60
237 **131** 2 c. green 85 35
238 – 3 c. brown .. .. 1·40 1·00
239 – 4 c. red 70 30
240 – 5 c. violet .. .. 1·75 70
241 – 7 c. blue .. .. 3·75 11·00
242 – 8 c. orange .. .. 5·50 8·50
243 – 9 c. blue .. .. 6·50 6·50
244 – 10 c. brown .. .. 4·00 5·00
245 – 14 c. black .. .. 10·00 28·00
246 – 15 c. red .. .. 7·50 14·00
247 – 20 c. green .. .. 10·00 12·00
248 – 24 c. purple .. .. 7·50 22·00
249 – 32 c. black .. .. 7·00 40·00

DESIGNS—VERT. 3 c. Gilbert Coat of Arms. 5 c. Anchor token. 14 c. Royal Arms. 15 c. Gilbert in the "Squirrel". 24 c. Queen Elizabeth I. 32 c. Gilbert's statue at Truro. HORIZ. 4 c. Eton College. 7 c. Gilbert commissioned by Elizabeth. 8 c. Fleet leaving Plymouth, 1583. 9 c. Arrival at St. John's. 10 c. Annexation, 5th August, 1583. 20 c. Map of Newfoundland.

1935. Silver Jubilee. As T **13** of Antigua.

250. 4 c. red 60 70
251. 5 c. violet .. .. 1·25 85
252. 7 c. blue .. .. 1·25 5·00
253. 24 c. olive .. .. 4·00 5·00

1937. Coronation. As T **2** of Aden.

254. 2 c. green .. .. 90 2·00
255. 4 c. red .. .. 1·60 1·00
256. 5 c. purple .. .. 2·25 2·50

144. Codfish.

1937. Coronation

257. **144.** 1 c. grey .. .. 1·25 20
258. – 3 c. brown .. .. 2·00 1·00
259. – 7 c. blue .. .. 1·75 75
260. – 8 c. red .. .. 1·50 1·75
261. – 10 c. black .. .. 3·25 4·00
262. – 14 c. black .. .. 1·40 2·00
263. – 15 c. red .. .. 7·50 4·00
264. – 20 c. green .. .. 2·25 4·25
265. – 24 c. blue .. .. 2·25 2·50
266. – 25 c. black .. .. 2·75 1·75
267. – 48 c. purple .. .. 8·00 4·50

DESIGNS: 3 c. Map of Newfoundland. 7 c. Reindeer. 8 c. Corner Brook Paper Mills. 10 c. Salmon. 14 c. Newfoundland Dog. 15 c. Harp Seal. 20 c. Cape Race. 24 c. Bell Island. 25 c. Sealing fleet. 48 c. The Banks Fishing Fleet.

155. King George VI.

DESIGNS: 3 c. Queen Mother. 4 c. Queen Elizabeth II, aged 12. 7 c. Queen Mary.

1938.

277. **155.** 2 c. green 20 10
278. – 3 c. red 30 10
279. – 4 c. blue .. .. 1·75 20
271. – 7 c. blue .. .. 75 3·00

159. King George VI and Queen Elizabeth.

1938. Royal Visit.

272. **159.** 5 c. blue 75 30

1939. Surch. in figures and **triangles.**

273. **159.** 2 c. on 5 c. blue .. 1·50 30
274. 4 c. on 5 c. blue .. 80 30

161. Grenfell on the "Strathcona" (after painting by Gribble).

1941. Sir Wilfred Grenfell's Labrador **Mission.**

275. **161.** 5 c. blue 20 35

162. Memorial University College.

1942.

290. **162.** 30 c. red .. .. 1·00 80

163. St. John's.

1943. Air.

291. **163.** 7 c. blue 30 30

1946. Surch. **TWO CENTS.**

292. **162.** 2 c. on 30 c. red .. 30 30

165. Queen Elizabeth II when Princess.

1947. 21st Birthday of Princess Elizabeth.

293. **165.** 4 c. blue 20 30

166. Cabot off Cape Bonavista.

1947. 450th Anniv. of Cabot's Discovery of Newfoundland.

294. **166.** 5 c. violet 15 45

POSTAGE DUE STAMPS

D 1.

1939.

D 1. **D 1.** 1 c. green .. .. 1·75 6·50
D 2. 2 c. red .. .. 5·00 5·50
D 3. 3 c. blue .. .. 4·00 18·00
D 4. 4 c. orange .. .. 5·50 12·00
D 5. 5 c. brown .. .. 5·50 22·00
D 6. 10 c. purple .. .. 6·00 15·00

NEW GUINEA

Formerly a German Colony, part of the island of New Guinea. Occupied by Australian forces during the 1914–18 war and now joined with Papua and administered by the Australian Commonwealth under trusteeship. After the Japanese defeat in 1945 Australian stamps were used until 1952 when the combined issue appeared for Papua and New Guinea (q.v.). The stamps overprinted "N.W. PACIFIC ISLANDS" were also used in Nauru and other ex-German islands.

12 pence = 1 shilling.
20 shillings = 1 pound

1914. "Yacht" key-types of German New Guinea surch. **G.R.I.** and value in English currency.

16 N 1d. on 3 pf. brown .. 40·00 50·00
17 1d. on 5 pf. green .. 14·00 23·00
18 2d. on 10 pf. red .. 18·00 27·00
19 2d. on 20 pf. blue .. 24·00 32·00
5 2½d. on 10 pf. red .. 65·00 £140
6 2½d. on 20 pf. blue .. 70·00 £140
22 3d. on 25 pf. black and red on yellow .. .. 85·00 £110
23 3d. on 30 pf. black and orange on buff .. 70·00 95·00
24 4d. on 40 pf. black & red 85·00 £110
25 5d. on 50 pf. black and purple on buff .. £130 £160
26 8d. on 80 pf. black and red on rose £325 £400
12 O 1s. on 1 m. red .. £1400 £1900
13 2s. on 2 m. blue £1500 £2250
14 3s. on 3 m. black .. £3000 £3750
15 5s. on 5 m. red and black £5000 £6000

Nos. 3/4, surch. 1.

31. N. "1" on 2d. on 10 pf. red .. £9500 £9500
32. "1" on 2 d. on 20 pf. blue £9000 £6000

R. G.R.I. Rabaul (Deutsch Neuguinea) I. № 570

4.

1914. Registration labels with names of various town surch. **G.R.I. 3d.**

33. 4. 3d. black and red .. £120 £160

1914. "Yacht" key-types of German Marshall Islands surch. **G.R.I.** and value in English currency.

50 N 1d. on 3 pf. brown .. 40·00 60·00
51 1d. on 5 pf. green .. 42·00 50·00
52 2d. on 10 pf. red .. 14·00 23·00
53 2d. on 20 pf. blue .. 15·00 26·00
64g 2½d. on 10 pf. red .. £5000
64h 2½d. on 20 pf. blue .. £8000
54 3d. on 25 pf. black and red on yellow .. £250 £350
55 3d. on 30 pf. black and orange on buff .. £275 £350
56 4d. on 40 pf. black & red 90·00 £120
57 5d. on 50 pf. black and purple on buff .. £130 £170
58 8d. on 80 pf. black and red on rose £375 £475
59 O 1s. on 1 m. red .. £1600 £2500
60 2s. on 2 m. blue .. £1100 £1700
61 3s. on 3 m. black .. £2750 £4000
62 5s. on 5 m. red & black £4750 £6500

1915. Nos. 52 and 53 surch. **1.**

63. N. "1" on 2d. on 10 pf. red .. £140 £170
64. "1" on 2d. on 20 pf. blue .. £3000 £2000

1915. Stamps of Australia optd. **N.W. PACIFIC ISLANDS.**

102 5a. ½d. green .. .. .. 50 3·25
103 1d. red .. .. .. 2·00 1·60
120 1d. violet .. .. .. 1·00 5·50
94 1. 2d. grey .. .. .. 5·00 11·00
121 5a. 2d. orange .. .. 2·75 4·50
122 2d. red .. .. .. 4·75 8·00
74 1. 2½d. blue .. .. 2·75 15·00
96 3d. olive .. .. .. 5·00 11·00
70 5a. 4d. orange .. .. 3·75 9·50
123 4d. violet .. .. .. 28·00 48·00
124 4d. blue .. .. .. 10·00 48·00
105 5d. brown .. .. 1·75 12·00
110 1. 6d. blue .. .. .. 4·50 14·00
89 9d. violet .. .. .. 13·00 15·00
90 1s. green .. .. .. 9·00 23·00
115 2s. brown .. .. .. 28·00 38·00
116 5s. grey and yellow .. 60·00 60·00
84 10s. grey and pink .. £110 £160
99 £1 brown and blue .. £300 £450

1918. Nos. 72 and 90 surch. **One Penny.**

100. 5a. 1d. on 5d. brown .. .. 90·00 80·00
101. 1. 1d. on 1s. green .. .. 90·00 80·00

12. Native Village.

1925.

125. 12. ½d. orange .. .. 2·00 4·00
126. 1d. green .. .. 2·00 4·00
126a. 1½d. red .. .. 2·25 2·25
127. 2d. red .. .. 2·00 4·50
128. 3d. blue .. .. 4·50 4·00
129. 4d. olive .. .. 12·00 15·00
130b. 6d. brown .. .. 4·50 45·00
131. 9d. purple .. .. 13·00 40·00
132. 1s. green .. .. 15·00 22·00
133. 2s. lake .. .. 30·00 40·00
134. 5s. brown .. .. 48·00 65·00
135. 10s. red £110 £160
136. £1 grey £200 £250

1931. Air. Optd. with aeroplane and **AIR MAIL.**

137. 12. ½d. orange .. .. .. 75 3·25
138. 1d. green .. .. .. 1·60 3·50
139. 1½d. red .. .. .. 1·00 4·50
140. 2d. red .. .. .. 1·00 7·00
141. 3d. blue .. .. .. 1·50 12·00
142. 4d. olive .. .. .. 1·25 7·50
143. 6d. brown .. .. .. 1·75 13·00
144. 9d. purple .. .. .. 3·00 16·00
145. 1s. green .. .. .. 3·00 16·00
146. 2s. lake .. .. .. 7·00 30·00
147. 5s. brown .. .. .. 20·00 55·00
148. 10 s. red .. .. .. 65·00 90·00
149. £1 grey £110 £150

14. Raggiana Bird of Paradise. (Dates either side of value).

1931. 10th Anniversary of Australian Administration. Dated "1921–1931".

150 14. 1d. green .. .. 1·75 40
151 1½d. red .. .. 4·00 8·50
152 2d. red .. .. 3·25 2·00
153 3d. blue .. .. 3·25 4·00
154 4d. olive .. .. 5·00 13·00
155 5d. green .. .. 3·50 14·00
156 6d. brown .. .. 3·50 14·00
157 9d. violet .. .. 6·00 14·00
158 1s. grey .. .. 5·00 15·00
159 2s. lake .. .. 7·00 25·00
160 5s. brown .. .. 35·00 48·00
161 10s. red .. .. 75·00 £120
162 £1 grey £140 £200

1931. Air. Optd. with aeroplane and **AIR MAIL.**

163. 14. ½d. orange .. .. .. 1·00 2·00
164. 1d. green .. .. .. 2·00 3·00
165. 1½d. red .. .. .. 1·60 7·00
166. 2d. red .. .. .. 1·00 2·75
167. 3d. blue .. .. .. 3·00 3·25
168. 4d. olive .. .. .. 3·00 5·00
169. 5d. green .. .. .. 3·50 7·00
170. 6d. brown .. .. .. 6·00 22·00
171. 9d. violet .. .. .. 7·50 15·00
172. 1s. grey .. .. .. 6·50 15·00
173. 2s. lake .. .. .. 11·00 45·00
174. 5s. brown .. .. .. 32·00 60·00
175. 10s. red .. .. .. 60·00 £100
176. £1 grey £100 £170

1932. As T 14, but without dates.

177. 1d. green 50 20
178. 1½d. red .. .. .. 60 8·00
179. 2d. red 55 20
179a. 2½d. green .. .. .. 4·00 10·00
180. 3d. blue 90 80
180a. 3½d. red .. .. .. 10·00 9·00
181. 4d. olive .. .. .. 75 3·00
182. 5d. green 75 70
183. 6d. brown .. .. .. 1·00 3·00
184. 9d. violet .. .. .. 7·50 17·00
185. 1s. grey .. .. .. 4·00 10·00
186. 2s. lake .. .. .. 4·00 17·00
187. 5s. brown .. .. .. 27·00 45·00
188. 10s. red .. .. .. 60·00 80·00
189. £1 grey .. .. .. 90·00 £100

1932. Air. T 14, but without dates, optd. with aeroplane and **AIR MAIL.**

190. ½d. orange .. .. .. 40 1·50
191. 1d. green .. .. .. 40 1·50
192. 1½d. mauve .. .. .. 60 4·50
193. 2d. red 60 30
193a. 2½d. green .. .. .. 3·50 2·25
194. 3d. blue .. .. .. 1·10 1·60
194a. 3½d. red .. .. .. 3·50 3·25
195. 4d. olive .. .. .. 2·50 7·00
196. 5d. green .. .. .. 4·50 7·50
197. 6d. brown .. .. .. 2·75 11·00
198. 9d. violet .. .. .. 5·50 9·00
199. 1s. grey .. .. .. 4·50 7·50
200. 2s. lake .. .. .. 5·50 32·00
201. 5s. brown .. .. .. 45·00 55·00
202. 10s. red .. .. .. 65·00 70·00
203. £1 grey .. .. .. 75·00 55·00

16. Bulolo Goldfields.

1935. Air.

204. 16. £2 violet £225 £130
205. £5 green £600 £450

1935. Silver Jubilee. Nos. 177 and 179 optd. **HIS MAJESTY'S JUBILEE 1910–1935.**

206. – 1d. green 45 35
207. – 2d. red 80 35

18. King George VI.

1937. Coronation.

208. 18. 2d. red 50 30
209. 3d. blue 80 45
210. 5d. green 50 45
211. 1s. purple .. .. .. 1·25 35

1939. Air. As T 16, but inscr. "AIR MAIL POSTAGE".

212. ½d. orange .. .. .. 1·00 4·00
213. 1d. green .. .. .. 3·00 3·00
214. 1½d. red .. .. .. 1·00 5·50
215. 2d. red .. .. .. 5·00 3·00
216. 3d. blue .. .. .. 6·50 12·00
217. 4d. olive .. .. .. 4·00 7·50
218. 5d. green .. .. .. 4·00 2·25
219. 6d. brown .. .. .. 9·00 11·00
220. 9d. violet .. .. .. 9·00 17·00
221. 1s. green .. .. .. 11·00 16·00
222. 2s. red .. .. .. 48·00 40·00
223. 5s. brown .. .. .. 95·00 85·00
224. 10s. pink £275 £190
225. £1 olive £100 £110

OFFICIAL STAMPS

1915. Nos. 16 and 17 optd. **O.S.**

O 1. N. 1d. on 3 pf. brown .. 25·00 70·00
O 2. 1d. on 5 pf. green .. 75·00 £130

1925. Optd. **O S.**

O 3 12. 1d. green .. .. 80 4·25
O 4 1½d. red .. .. 5·50 17·00
O 5 2d. red .. .. 1·60 3·75
O 6 3d. blue .. .. 2·00 5·50
O 7 4d. olive .. .. 3·00 8·50
O 8a 6d. brown .. .. 7·00 40·00
O 9 9d. purple .. .. 3·75 40·00
O 10 1s. green .. .. 5·00 40·00
O 11 2s. lake .. .. 27·00 75·00

1931. Optd. **O S.**

O 12. 14. 1d. green .. .. 1·75 12·00
O 13. 1½d. red .. .. 2·50 12·00
O 14. 2d. red .. .. 4·50 7·00
O 15. 3d. blue .. .. 2·50 6·00
O 16. 4d. olive .. .. 2·50 8·50
O 17. 5d. green .. .. 6·00 12·00
O 18. 6d. brown .. .. 9·00 17·00
O 19. 9d. violet .. .. 9·50 28·00
O 20. 1s. grey .. .. 12·00 28·00
O 21. 2s. lake .. .. 35·00 75·00
O 22. 5s. brown £100 £160

1932. T14, but without dates, optd. **O S.**

O 23. 1d. green .. .. 2·50 3·50
O 24. 1½d. red .. .. 3·00 12·00
O 25. 2d. red .. .. 3·00 2·75
O 26. 2½d. green .. .. 2·75 7·50
O 27. 3d. blue .. .. 6·00 16·00
O 28. 3½d. red .. .. 3·00 10·00
O 29. 4d. olive .. .. 5·00 14·00
O 30. 5d. green .. .. 5·00 14·00
O 31. 6d. brown .. .. 6·50 28·00
O 32. 9d. violet .. .. 10·00 40·00
O 33. 1s. grey .. .. 15·00 28·00
O 34. 2s. lake .. .. 35·00 85·00
O 35. 5s. brown £120 £170

For later issues see **PAPUA AND NEW GUINEA.**

NEW HEBRIDES

A group of islands in the Pacific Ocean, E. of Australia, under joint administration of Gt. Britain and France. The Condominium ended in 1980, when the New Hebrides became independent as the Republic of Vanuatu.

1908. 12 pence = 1 shilling;
20 shillings = 1 pound.
1938. 100 gold centimes = 1 gold franc.
1977. 100 centimes = 1 franc (New Hebrides).

BRITISH ADMINISTRATION

1908. Stamps of Fiji optd **NEW HEBRIDES CONDOMINIUM.**

1a 23 ½d. green .. .. 40 7·00
2 1d. red 45 40
5 2d. purple and orange 60 70
12 2d. grey .. .. 60 3·00
6 2½d. purple & blue on bl 60 70
13 2½d. blue .. .. 65 3·75
7 5d. purple and green 80 2·00
8 6d. purple and red 70 1·25
15 6d. purple .. .. 85 5·00
3 1s. green and red 16·00 8·00
16 1s. black on green 85 7·50

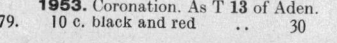

3. Weapons and Idols.

1911.

18. 3. ½d. green .. .. .. 85 1·60
19. 1d. red .. .. .. 2·75 2·00
20. 2d. grey .. .. .. 3·75 3·75
21. 2½d. blue .. .. .. 1·60 4·25
24. 5d. green .. .. .. 2·50 4·25
25. 6d. purple .. .. .. 2·00 4·75
26. 1s. black on green .. 1·50 8·50
27. 2s. purple on blue .. 14·00 19·00
28. 5s. green on yellow .. 27·00 48·00

1920. Surch. (a) On T 3.

40. 3. 1d. on ½d. green .. 2·75 18·00
30. 1d. on 5d. green .. 7·00 60·00
31. 1d. on 1s. black on green 1·00 11·00
32. 1d. on 2s. purple on blue 1·00 10·00
33. 1d. on 5s. green on yellow 1·00 10·00
41. 3d. on 1d. red .. .. 2·50 11·00
42. 5d. on 2½d. blue .. 4·75 18·00

(b) On No. F 16 French New Hebrides.

34. 3. 2d. on 40 c. red on yellow 1·00 13·00

5.

1925.

43. 5. ½d. (5 c.) black .. 1·00 6·00
44. 1d. (10c.) green .. 1·00 6·00
45. 2d. (20 c.) grey .. 1·75 2·25
46. 2½d. (25 c.) brown .. 1·00 6·00
47. 5d. (50 c.) blue .. 1·75 2·50
48. 6d. (60 c.) purple .. 3·00 8·00
49. 1s. (1 f. 25) black on green 3·00 14·00
50. 2s. (2 f. 50) purple on blue 6·00 19·00
51. 5s. (6 f. 25) green on yellow 6·00 22·00

6. Lopevi Islands and Outrigger Canoe.

1938.

52. 6. 5 c. green .. .. 2·50 2·25
53. 10 c. orange .. .. 1·25 50
54. 15 c. violet .. .. 2·50 2·00
55. 20 c. red .. .. 1·60 80
56. 25 c. brown .. .. 1·60 1·00
57. 30 c. blue .. .. 1·60 1·25
58. 40 c. olive .. .. 4·50 2·50
59. 50 c. purple .. .. 1·60 50
60. 1 f. red on green .. 4·00 6·50
61. 2 f. blue on green .. 30·00 16·00
62. 5 f. red on yellow .. 70·00 48·00
63. 10 f. violet on blue .. £190 70·00

1949. U.P.U. As T 20/23 of Antigua.

64. 10 c. orange 30 15
65. 15 c. violet 30 15
66. 30 c. blue 30 15
67. 50 c. purple 40 20

7. Outrigger Sailing Canoes.

1953.

68. 7. 5 c. green 50 10
69. 10 c. red 50 10
70. 15 c. yellow 50 10
71. 20 c. blue 50 10
72. – 25 c. olive 50 10
73. – 30 c. brown 50 10
74. – 40 c. sepia 50 10
75. – 50 c. violet .. .. 1·00 10
76. – 1 f. orange .. .. 6·50 70
77. – 2 f. purple .. .. 7·50 9·00
78. – 5 f. red .. .. 12·00 32·00

DESIGNS: 25 c. to 50 c. Native carving. 1 f. to 5 f. Two natives outside hut.

1953. Coronation. As T 13 of Aden.

79. 10 c. black and red .. 30 30

10. Quiros Galleon and Map.

956. 50th Anniv. of Condominium. Inscr. "1906 1956".

0. **10.** 5 c. green 15 10
1. 10 c. red 15 10
2. – 20 c. blue 10 10
3. – 50 c. lilac 15 15

ESIGN: 20 c., 50 c. "Marianne", "Talking rum" and "Britannia".

12. Port Vila: Iririki Islet.

1957.

84. **12.** 5 c. green 40 10
85. 10 c. red 30 10
86. 15 c. yellow 50 20
87. 20 c. blue 40 10
88. – 25 c. olive 45 10
89. – 30 c. brown 45 10
90. – 40 c. sepia 45 10
91. – 50 c. violet 45 10
92. – 1 f. orange .. .. 1·00 80
93. – 2 f. mauve .. .. 6·00 4·00
94. – 5 f. black .. .. .. 15·00 6·00

DESIGNS: 25 c. to 50 c. River scene and spear fisherman. 1 f. to 5 f. Woman drinking from coconut.

1963. Freedom from Hunger. As T **28** of Aden.

95. 60 c. green 50 15

1963. Cent of Red Cross. As T **33** of Antigua, but with British and French cyphers in place of Queen's portrait.

96. 15 c. red and black .. 35 10
97. 45 c. red and blue 45 20

18. Copra.

1963.

98. – 5 c. lake, brown and blue 50 30
99. – 10 c. brown, buff & green 15 10
100. **18.** 15 c. bistre, brown & violet 15 10
101. – 20 c. black, green and blue 45 10
102. – 25 c. violet, brown & red 50 70
103. – 30 c. brown, bistre & violet 75 10
104. – 40 c. red and blue .. 80 1·40
105. – 50 c. green, yellow and turquoise . .. 60 10
129. – 60 c. red and blue .. 40 15
106. – 1 f. red, black and green 2·50 3·25
107. – 2 f. black, brown & olive 2·50 1·75
108. – 3 f. multicoloured .. 13·00 8·00
109. – 5 f. blue, indigo and black 18·00 17·00

DESIGNS: 5 c. Exporting manganese, Forari. 10 c. Cocoa beans. 20 c. Fishing from Palikulo Point. 25 c. Picasso fish. 30 c. Nautilus shell. 40 c., 60 c. Sting-fish. 50 c. Blue lined surgeon. 1 f. Cardinal honey-eater (bird). 2 f. Buff-bellied flycatcher. 3 f. Thicket warbler. 5 f. White-collared kingfisher.

1965. Centenary of I.T.U. As T **36** of Antigua, but with British and French cyphers in place of the Queen's portrait.

110. 15 c. red and drab 20 10
111. 60 c. blue and red 35 20

1965. I.C.Y. As T **37** of Antigua, but with British and French cyphers in place of the Queen's portrait.

112. 5 c. purple and turquoise .. 15 10
113. 55 c. green and lavender .. 20 20

1966. Churchill Commemoration. As T **38** of Antigua, but with British and French cyphers in place of Queen's portrait.

114. 5 c. blue 20 10
115. 15 c. green 40 10
116. 25 c. brown 50 10
117. 30 c. violet 50 10

1966. World Cup Championship. As T **40** of Antigua, but with British and French cyphers in place of the Queen's portrait.

118. 20 c. multicoloured .. 20 15
119. 40 c. multicoloured .. 30 15

1966. Ingauguration of W.H.O. Headquarters, Geneva. As T **41** of Antigua, but with British and French cyphers in place of the Queen's portrait.

120. 25 c. black, green and blue 20 10
121. 60 c. black, purple and ochre 55 20

1966. 30th Anniv of U.N.E.S.C.O. As T **54/6** of Antigua, but with British and French cyphers in place of the Queen's portrait.

122. 15 c. multicoloured .. 20 10
123. 30 c. yellow, violet and olive 65 10
124. 45 c. black, purple & orge. 70 15

36. The Coast Watchers.

1967. 25th Anniv of Pacific War. Mult.

125 15 c. Type **36** 10 10
126 25 c. Map of War Zone, U.S. marine and Australian soldier .. 20 15
127 60 c. H.M.A.S. "Canberra" (cruiser) 30 15
128 1 f. "Flying Fortress" .. 35 15

40. Globe and Hemispheres.

1968. Bicent. of Bougainville's World Voyage.

130. **40.** 15 c. green, violet & red 15 10
131. – 25 c. olive, purple & blue 25 10
132. – 60 c. brown, purple & grn. 25 15

DESIGNS: 25 c. Ships "La Boudeuse" and "L'Etoile", and Map. 60 c. Bougainville, Ship's Figure-head and bougainvillea flowers.

43. "Concorde" and Vapour Trails.

1968. Anglo-French "Concorde" Project.

133. **43.** 25 c. blue, red and blue 50 20
134. – 60 c. red, black and blue 60 25

DESIGN: 60 c. "Concorde" in flight.

45. Kauri Pine.

1969. Timber Industry.

135. **45.** 20 c. multicoloured .. 10 10

46. Cyphers, Flags and Relay Runner receiving Baton.

1969. 3rd South Pacific Games, Port Moresby. Multicoloured.

136. 25 c. Type **46** 10 10
137. 1 f. Similar to No. 136 .. 20 20

NEW HEBRIDES

CONDOMINIUM

48. Diver on Platform.

1969. Pentecost Island Land Divers. Mult.

138. 15 c. Type **48** 10 10
139. 25 c. Diver Jumping .. 10 10
140. 1 f. Diver at end of Fall .. 20 20

51. U.P.U. Emblem and Headquarters Building.

1970. New U.P.U. Headquarters Building.

141. **51.** 1 f. 05 slate, orgc. & pur. 15 15

52. General Charles de Gaulle.

1970. 30th Anniv. of New Hebrides' Declaration for the Free French Government.

142. **52.** 65 c. multicoloured .. 35 25
143. 1 f. 10 multicoloured .. 45 25

1970. No. 101 surch.

144. 35 c. on 20 c. black, green and blue 30 30

54. "The Virgin and Child" (Bellini).

1970. Christmas. Multicoloured.

145. 15 c. Type **54** 10 10
146. 50 c. "The Virgin & Child" (Cima) 20 20

1971. Death of General Charles de Gaulle. Nos. 142/3 optd. **1890-1970 IN MEMORIAM 9-11-70.**

147. **52.** 65 c. multicoloured .. 15 10
148. 1 f. 10 multicoloured .. 15 20

NEW HEBRIDES CONDOMINIUM

gold 20 centimes postage

4th SOUTH PACIFIC GAMES - FOOTBALL

56. Football.

1971. 4th South Pacific Games, Papeete, French Polynesia.

149. 20 c. Type **56** 10 10
150. 65 c. Basketball (vert.) .. 30 20

65 GOLD CENTIMES

NEW HEBRIDES CONDOMINIUM

THE ROYAL SOCIETY EXPEDITION TO THE NEW HEBRIDES 1971

AGATHIS

57. Kauri Pine, Cone and Arms of Royal Society.

1971. Royal Society's Expedition to New Hebrides.

151. **57.** 65 c. multicoloured .. 20 15

58. "The Adoration of the Shepherds" (detail, Louis Le Nain).

1971. Christmas. Multicoloured.

152. 25 c. Type **58** 10 10
153. 50 c. "The Adoration of the Shepherds" (detail, Tintoretto) 30 30

59. "Drover" Mk. III.

1972. Aircraft. Multicoloured.

154. 20 c. Type **59** 35 15
155. 25 c. "Sandringham" flying-boat 45 15
156. 30 c. D.H. "Dragon Rapide" 45 15
157. 65 c. "Caravelle" .. 1·25 1·25

60. Ceremonial Headdress, South Malekula.

1972. Multicoloured.

158. 5 c. Type **60** 10 10
159. 10 c. Baker's Pigeon .. 25 10
160. 15 c. Gong and carving (North Ambrym) .. 15 15
161. 20 c. Red-headed Parrot Finch 40 25
162. 25 c. "Cribraria fischeri" (shell) 40 25
163. 30 c. "Oliva rubrolabiata" (shell) 50 30
164. 35 c. Chestnut-bellied Kingfisher 65 40
165. 65 c. "Strombus plicatus" (shell) 75 60
166. 1 f. Gong (North Malekula) and carving (North Ambrym) .. .. .. 1·25 1·00
167. 2 f. Palm Lorikeet .. 4·00 4·50
168. 3 f. Ceremonial headdress (South Malekula (different)) .. .. .. 3·75 6·00
169. 5 f. Green snail shell .. 7·50 14·00

61. "Adoration of the Kings" (Spranger).

1972. Christmas. Multicoloured.

170. 25 c. Type **61** 10 10
171. 70 c. "The Virgin and Child in a Landscape" (Provoost) 20 20

1972. Royal Silver Wedding. As T **52** of Ascension, but with Royal and French cyphers in background.

172. 35 c. deep violet 15 10
173. 65 c. green 20 10

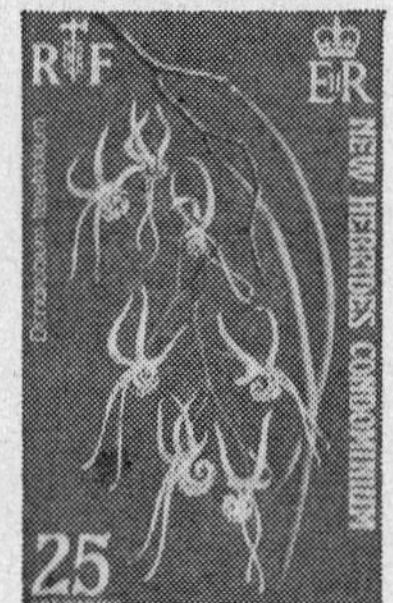

63. "Dendrobium teretifolium".

1973. Orchids. Multicoloured.

174. 25 c. Type **63** 25 10
175. 30 c. "Ephemerantha comata" 30 10
176. 35 c. "Spathoglottis petri" 35 10
177. 65 c. "Dendrobium mohlianum" 60 55

64. New Wharf at Vila.

1973. Opening of New Wharf at Vila. Multicoloured.

178. 25 c. Type **64** 20 10
179. 70 c. As T **64** but horiz. format 40 30

65. Wild Horses.

1973. Tanna Island. Multicoloured.

180. 35 c. Type **65** 30 15
181. 70 c. Yasur Volcano .. 35 20

66. Mother and Child.

1973. Christmas. Multicoloured.

182. 35 c. Type **66** 10 10
183. 70 c. Lagoon scene .. 20 20

67. Pacific Pigeon.

1974. Wild Life. Multicoloured.

184 25 c. Type **67** 95 25
185 35 c. "Lyssa curvata" (moth) .. .. .. 1·00 60
186 70 c. Green sea turtle .. 1·00 70
187 1 f. 15 Grey-headed flying fox .. .. .. 1·25 1·50

1974. Royal Visit. Nos. 164 and 167 optd. **ROYAL VISIT 1974.**

188. 35 c. multicoloured .. 15 10
189. 2 f. multicoloured .. 30 40

69. Old Post Office.

1974. Inaug. of New Post Office. Mult.

190. 35 c. Type **69** 15 50
191. 70 c. New Post Office .. 15 60

70. Capt. Cook and Map.

1974. Bicent. of Discovery. Multicoloured.

192. 35 c. Type **70** .. .. 2·00 2·00
193. 35 c. William Wales and beach landing .. .. 2·00 2·00
194. 35 c. William Hodges and island scene .. .. 2·00 2·00
195. 1 f. 15 Capt. Cook, map and H.M.S. "Resolution" (59 × 34 mm.) .. 4·00 4·50

71. U.P.U. Emblem and Letters.

1974. Centenary of U.P.U.

196. **71.** 70 c. multicoloured .. 30 70

72. "Adoration of the Magi" (Velazquez).

1974. Christmas. Multicoloured.

197. 35 c. Type **72** 10 10
198. 70 c. "The Nativity" (Gerard van Honthorst) 20 20

73. Charolais Bull.

1975.

199. **73.** 10 f. brown, grn. & blue 11·00 20·00

74. Canoeing.

1975. World Scout Jamboree, Norway. Mult.

200. 25 c. Type **74** 30 10
201. 35 c. Preparing meal .. 30 10
202. 1 f. Map-reading 70 15
203. 5 f. Fishing .. .. 2·00 2·50

75. "Pitti Madonna" (Michelangelo).

1975. Christmas. Michelangelo's Sculptures. Multicoloured.

204. 35 c. Type **75** 10 10
205. 70 c. "Bruges Madonna" .. 15 10
206. 2 f. 50 "Taddei Madonna" 70 50

76. "Concorde" in British Airways Livery.

1976. 1st Commercial Flight of "Concorde".

207. **76.** 5 f. multicoloured .. 12·00 6·00

77. Telephones of 1876 and 1976.

1976. Cent. of Telephone. Multicoloured.

208. 25 c. Type **77** 15 10
209. 70 c. Alexander Graham Bell 30 10
210. 1 f. 15 Satellite and Noumea Earth Station 50 50

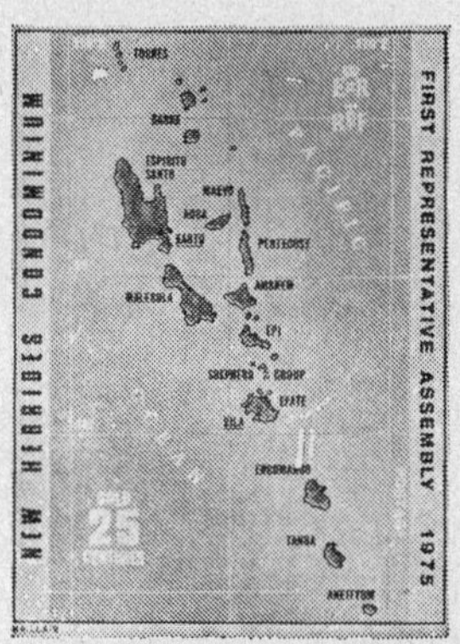

78. Map of the Islands.

1976. Constitutional Changes. Multicoloured.

211. 25 c. Type **78** 20 15
212. 1 f. View of Santo (horiz.) 45 60
213. 2 f. View of Vila (horiz.) .. 65 1·25

Nos. 212/13 are smaller, 36 × 26 mm.

79. "The Flight into Egypt" (Lusitano).

1976. Christmas. Multicoloured.

214. 35 c. Type **79** 10 10
215. 70 c. "Adoration of the Shepherds" 15 10
216. 2 f. 50 "Adoration of the Magi" 45 50

Nos. 215/16 show retables by the Master of Santos-o-Novo.

80. Royal Visit, 1974.

1977. Silver Jubilee. Multicoloured.

217. 35 c. Type **80** 15 10
218. 70 c. Imperial State Crown 20 10
219. 2 f. The Blessing 40 65

1977. Currency Change. Nos. 158/69 and 199 surch.

233	5 f. on 5 c. Type **60** ..	50	15
234	10 f. on 10 c. Baker's Pigeon ..	50	15
222	15 f. on 15 c. Gong and carving ..	60	60
223	20 f. on 20 c. Red-headed Parrot Finch ..	1·25	55
224	25 f. on 25 c. "Cribraria fischeri" (shell)	1·00	1·00
225	30 f. on 30 c. "Oliva rubrolabiata" (shell) ..	1·25	50
238	35 f. on 35 c. Chestnut-bellied Kingfisher ..	2·00	55
239	40 f. on 65 c. "Strombus plicatus" (shell)	1·50	55
228	50 f. on 1 f. Gong and carving ..	1·50	1·50
229	70 f. on 2 f. Palm Lorikeet	3·00	1·00
230	100 f. on 3 f. Ceremonial headdress	3·00	4·25
231	200 f. on 5 f. Green snail shell ..	7·00	14·00
241	500 f. on 10 f. Type **73** ..	19·00	17·00

89. Island of Erromango and Kauri Pine.

1977. Islands. Multicoloured.

242.	5 f. Type **89**	30	10
243.	10 f. Territory map and copra-making ..	40	30
244.	15 f. Espiritu Santo and cattle ..	30	30
245.	20 f. Efate and Vila P.O.	30	25
246.	25 f. Malekula and head-dresses ..	40	40
247.	30 f. Aobe, Maewo and pigs tusks ..	45	50
248.	35 f. Pentecost and land diver ..	50	65
249.	40 f. Tanna and volcano ..	70	60
250.	50 f. Shepherd Is. and canoe ..	70	40
251.	70 f. Banks Is. and dancers	1·75	2·25
252.	100 f. Ambrym and idols ..	1·75	90
253.	200 f. Aneityum and baskets ..	2·75	2·50
254.	500 f. Torres Is. and archer fishing ..	6·00	7·50

90. "Tempi Madonna" (Raphael).

1977. Christmas. Multicoloured.

255.	10 f. Type **90** ..	10	10
256.	15 f. "The Flight into Egypt" (Gerard David)	15	15
257.	30 f. "Virgin and Child" (Batoni) ..	20	40

91. "Concorde" over New York.

1978. "Concorde" Commemoration.

258.	10 f. Type **91** ..	65	65
259.	20 f. "Concorde" over London ..	85	85
260.	30 f. "Concorde" over Washington ..	1·10	1·10
261.	40 f. "Concorde" over Paris ..	1·40	1·40

92. White Horse of Hanover.

1978. 25th Anniv. of Coronation.

262. **92.**	40 f. brown, blue & silver	35	55
263. –	40 f. multicoloured ..	35	55
264. –	40 f. brown, blue & silver	35	55

DESIGNS: No. 263, Queen Elizabeth II. No. 264, Gallic Cock.

93. "Madonna and Child".

1978. Christmas. Paintings by Durer. Multicoloured.

265.	10 f. Type **93** ..	10	10
266.	15 f. "The Virgin and Child with St. Anne" ..	10	10
267.	30 f. "Madonna of the Siskin" ..	15	10
268.	40 f. "Madonna of the Pear"	20	15

1979. 1st Anniv. of Internal Self-Government. Surch. 11-1-79 **FIRST ANNIVERSARY INTERNAL SELF-GOVERNMENT** and new value.

269. **78.**	10 f. on 25 f. mult. (blue background) ..	10	10
270.	40 f. on 25 f. mult. (grn. background) ..	20	20

95. 1938 5 c. Stamp and Sir Rowland Hill.

1979. Death Centenary of Sir Rowland Hill. Multicoloured.

271.	10 f. Type **95** ..	10	10
272.	20 f. 1969 25 c. Pentecost Island Land Divers Commemorative ..	15	10
273.	40 f. 1925 2d. (20 c.) ..	20	20

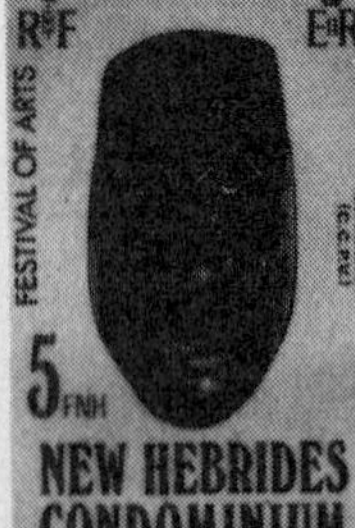

96. Chubwan Mask.

1979. Arts Festival. Multicoloured.

275.	5 f. Type **96** ..	10	10
276.	10 f. Nal-Nal clubs and spears ..	10	10
277.	20 f. Ritual puppet ..	15	10
278.	40 f. Neqatmalow head-dress ..	25	15

97. "Native Church" (Metas Masongo).

1979. Christmas and International Year of the Child. Children's Drawings. Mult.

279.	5 f. Type **97** ..	10	10
280.	10 f. "Priest and Candles" (Herve Rutu) ..	10	10
281.	20 f. "Cross and Bible" (Mark Deards) (vert.) ..	10	10
282.	40 f. "Green Candle and Santa Claus" (Dev Raj) (vert.)	15	15

98. White-bellied Honeyeater.

1980. Birds. Multicoloured.

283.	10 f. Type **98** ..	50	10
284.	20 f. Scarlet Robin	70	10
285.	30 f. Yellow-fronted White eye	90	45
286.	40 f. Fan-tailed Cuckoo ..	1·00	70

POSTAGE DUE STAMPS

1925. Optd. **POSTAGE DUE.**

D 1. **5.**	1d. (10 c.) green ..	38·00	1·00
D 2.	2d. (20 c.) grey ..	45·00	1·00
D 3.	3d. (30 c.) red ..	50·00	2·50
D 4.	5d. (50 c.) blue ..	55·00	4·50
D 5.	10d. (1 f.) red on blue ..	60·00	5·50

1938. Optd. **POSTAGE DUE.**

D 6. **6.**	5 c. green ..	17·00	25·00
D 7.	10 c. orange ..	17·00	25·00
D 8.	20 c. red ..	22·00	35·00
D 9.	40 c. olive ..	32·00	45·00
D 10.	1 f. red on green ..	45·00	55·00

1953. Nos 68/9, 71, 74 and 76 optd. **POSTAGE DUE.**

D 11. **7.**	5 c. green ..	5·00	7·50
D 12.	10 c. red ..	1·75	5·00
D 13.	20 c. blue ..	5·50	12·00
D 14. –	40 c. sepia (No. 74)	8·50	22·00
D 15. –	1 f. orange (No. 76)	6·00	22·00

1957. Optd. **POSTAGE DUE.**

D 16. **12.**	5 c. green ..	30	1·25
D 17.	10 c. red ..	30	1·25
D 18.	20 c. blue ..	1·25	1·75
D 19. –	40 c. sepia (No. 90)	2·50	3·50
D 20. –	1 f. orange (No. 92) ..	4·00	6·50

FRENCH ADMINISTRATION

1908. Stamps of New Caledonia optd. **NOUVELLES HEBRIDES.**

F 1. **15.**	5 c. green ..	2·75	2·75
F 2.	10 c. red ..	3·25	3·50
F 3. **16.**	25 c. blue on green ..	4·00	3·75
F 4.	50 c. red on green ..	5·50	5·25
F 5. **17.**	1 f. blue on green ..	11·50	11·50

1910. Stamps of New Caledonia optd. **NOUVELLES HEBRIDES CONDOMINIUM.**

F 6. **15.**	5 c. green ..	1·25	1·50
F 7.	10 c. red ..	1·25	60
F 8. **16.**	25 c. blue on green ..	2·00	3·25
F 9.	50 c. red on orange ..	4·75	6·00
F 10. **17.**	1 f. blue on green ..	13·00	14·00

The following issues are as stamps of British Administration but inscr. "NOUVELLES HEBRIDES" except where otherwise stated.

1911.

F 11 **3.**	5 c. green ..	1·00	1·75
F 12	10 c. red ..	45	60
F 13	20 c. grey ..	1·10	1·50
F 25	25 c. blue ..	90	3·00
F 26	30 c. brown on yellow ..	85	5·50
F 16	40 c. red on yellow ..	1·40	3·00
F 17	50 c. olive ..	2·00	2·75
F 18	75 c. orange ..	6·75	12·00
F 19	1 f. red on blue ..	2·25	2·50
F 20	2 f. violet ..	8·50	14·00
F 21	5 f. red on green ..	12·00	19·00

1920. Surch in fgures.

F 34	05 c. on 40 c. red on yellow (No. F 16) ..	26·00	55·00
F 32a	5 c. on 50 c. red on orange (No. F 4) ..	£400	£400
F 33	5 c. on 50 c. red on orange (No. F 9) ..	2·25	4·25
F 38	10 c. on 5 c. green (No. F 11)	1·60	2·25
F 33a	10 c. on 25 c. blue on green (No. F 8) ..	30	1·25
F 35	20 c. on 30 c. brown on yellow (No. F 26) ..	8·50	35·00
F 39	30 c. on 10 c. red (No. F 12)	1·25	1·50
F 41	50 c. on 25 c. blue (No. F 25)	2·75	15·00

1921. Stamp of New Hebrides (British) surch. in figures.

F 37.	10 c. on 5d. green (No. 24)	14·50	25·00

1925.

F 42. **5.**	5 c. (½d.) black ..	60	5·25
F 43.	10 c. (1d.) green ..	50	4·25
F 44.	20 c. (2d.) grey ..	50	1·75
F 45.	25 c. (2½d.) brown ..	50	3·00
F 46.	30 c. (3d.) red ..	55	3·00
F 47.	40 c. (4d.) red on yellow	80	2·75
F 48.	50 c. (5d.) blue ..	90	2·50
F 49.	75 c. (7½d.) brown ..	1·60	5·50
F 50.	1 f. (10d.) red on blue ..	2·00	3·00
F 51.	2 f. (1s. 8d.) violet ..	4·00	15·00
F 52.	5 f. (4d.) red on green ..	5·50	19·00

1938.

F 53. **6.**	5 c. green ..	1·60	1·50
F 54.	10 c. orange ..	1·60	85
F 55.	15 c. violet ..	1·25	1·40
F 56.	20 c. red ..	1·40	1·10
F 57.	25 c. brown ..	3·00	1·50
F 58.	30 c. blue ..	2·75	1·50
F 59.	40 c. olive ..	1·25	3·00
F 60.	50 c. purple ..	1·25	1·00
F 61.	1 f. red on green ..	1·60	2·50
F 62.	2 f. blue on green ..	17·00	16·00
F 63.	5 f. red on yellow ..	30·00	27·00
F 64.	10 f. violet on blue ..	75·00	60·00

1941. Free French Issue. As last optd. **France Libre.**

F 65. **6.**	5 c. green ..	3·25	12·00
F 66.	10 c. orange ..	3·75	9·25
F 67.	15 c. violet ..	4·75	15·00
F 68.	20 c. red ..	9·25	15·00
F 69.	25 c. brown ..	12·00	16·00
F 70.	30 c. blue ..	12·00	16·00
F 71.	40 c. olive ..	12·00	17·00
F 72.	50 c. purple ..	12·00	18·00
F 73.	1 f. red on green ..	12·00	16·00
F 74.	2 f. blue on green ..	12·00	18·00
F 75.	5 f. red on yellow ..	12·00	18·00
F 76.	10 f. violet on blue ..	14·00	19·00

1949. 75th Anniv. of U.P.U. As Br. Administration but with inscriptions in French.

F 77.	10 c. orange ..	2·25	2·75
F 78.	15 c. violet ..	4·50	4·25
F 79.	30 c. blue ..	5·75	7·00
F 80.	50 c. purple ..	6·75	7·50

1953.

F 81. **7.**	5 c. green ..	35	40
F 82.	10 c. red ..	55	40
F 83.	15 c. yellow ..	55	45
F 84.	20 c. blue ..	65	45
F 85. –	25 c. olive ..	55	45
F 86. –	30 c. brown ..	55	45
F 87. –	40 c. sepia ..	55	55
F 88. –	50 c. violet ..	55	45
F 89. –	1 f. orange ..	11·50	3·75
F 90. –	2 f. purple ..	16·00	24·00
F 91. –	5 f. red ..	27·00	50·00

1956. 50th Anniv. of Condominium.

F 92. **10.**	5 c. green ..	1·00	80
F 93.	10 c. red ..	1·00	80
F 94. –	20 c. blue ..	1·00	90
F 95. –	50 c. violet ..	1·40	1·75

1957.

F 96. **12.**	5 c. green ..	70	40
F 97.	10 c. red ..	70	40
F 98.	15 c. yellow ..	1·10	40
F 99.	20 c. blue ..	1·10	40
F 100. –	25 c. olive ..	1·10	40
F 101 –	30 c. brown ..	1·25	55
F 102. –	40 c. sepia ..	1·25	55
F 103. –	50 c. violet ..	1·25	45
F 104. –	1 f. orange ..	7·00	2·50
F 105. –	2 f. mauve ..	18·00	22·00
F 106. –	5 f. black ..	30·00	32·00

F 7. Emblem and Globe.

1963. Freedom from Hunger.

F 107. **F 7.**	60 c. green & brown	15·00	11·00

F 8. Centenary Emblem.

1963. Centenary of Red Cross.

F 108 **F 8**	15 c. red, grey & orge	9·00	6·00
F 109	45 c. red, grey and bistre	17·00	18·00

1963.

F 110. – 5 c. lake, brown & blue 40 30
F 111. – 10 c. brown, buff & grn.* 80 80
F 112. – 10 c. brown, buff & grn. 30 15
F 113. 18. 15 c. bistre, brn. & vio. 6·50 40
F 114. – 20 c. black, grn. & blue* 2·25 3·00
F 115. – 20 c. black, green & blue 60 25
F 116. – 25 c. violet, brn. & red 60 60
F 117. – 30 c. brn., bistre & vio. 7·50 60
F 118. – 40 c. red and blue .. 3·50 6·00
F 119. – 50 c. green, yellow and turquoise .. .. 7·50 60
F 120. – 60 c. red and blue .. 1·50 80
F 121. – 1 f. red, black & green 2·00 3·00
F 122. – 2 f. black, brown & olive 20·00 8·00
F 123. – 3 f. multicoloured* .. 11·00 20·00
F 124. – 3 f. multicoloured .. 5·50 10·00
F 125. – 5 f. blue, indigo & black 20·00 26·00

The stamps indicated by an asterisk have "RF" wrongly placed on the left.

F 9. "Syncom" Communications Satellite, Telegraph Poles and Morse Key.

1965. Centenary of I.T.U.

F 126 F 9 15 c. blue, grn & brn 8·00 6·00
F 127 60 c. red, grey & grn 20·00 22·00

1965. I.C.Y. As Nos. 112/13

F 128. 5 c. purple and turquoise 3·50 3·00
F 129. 55 c. green and lavender 9·50 9·00

1966. Churchill Commem. As Nos. 114/17.

F 130. 5 c. multicoloured .. 1·00 75
F 131. 15 c. multicoloured .. 3·25 1·00
F 132. 25 c. multicoloured .. 3·75 3·50
F 133. 30 c. multicoloured .. 4·50 4·50

1966. World Cup Football Championships. As Nos. 118/19.

F 134. 20 c. multicoloured .. 3·00 2·75
F 135. 40 c. multicoloured .. 4·50 4·25

1966. Inauguration of W.H.O. Headquarters, Geneva. As Nos. 120/1.

F 136. 25 c. black, green & blue 3·50 2·00
F 137. 60 c. black, mauve & ochre 5·50 5·00

1966. 20th Anniv. of U.N.E.S.C.O. As Nos. 122/4.

F 138. 15 c. multicoloured .. 1·75 1·00
F 139. 30 c. yellow, violet & olive 2·75 2·25
F 140. 45 c. black, purple & orge. 2·75 2·75

1967. 25th Anniv. of Pacific War. As Nos. 125/8.

F 141. 15 c. multicoloured .. 50 40
F 142. 25 c. multicoloured .. 75 50
F 143. 60 c. multicoloured .. 1·10 1·25
F 144. 1 f. multicoloured .. 1·75 2·00

1968. Bicentenary of Bougainville's World Voyage. As Nos. 130/2.

F 145. 15 c. green, violet & red 20 20
F 146. 25 c. olive, purple & blue 40 40
F 147. 60 c. brn., pur. and grn. 90 90

1968. Anglo-French "Concorde" Project. As Nos. 133/4.

F 148. 25 c. blue, red and violet 2·00 1·50
F 149. 60 c. red, black and blue 3·50 3·00

1969. Timber Industry. As No. 135.

F 150. 20 c. multicoloured .. 20 30

1969. 3rd South Pacific Games, Port Moresby, Papua New Guinea. As Nos. 136/7.

F 151. 25 c. multicoloured .. 30 30
F 152. 1 f. multicoloured .. 1·50 1·75

1969. Land Divers of Pentecost Island. As Nos. 138/40.

F 153. 15 c. multicoloured .. 30 30
F 154. 25 c. multicoloured .. 40 40
F 155. 1 f. multicoloured .. 1·40 1·40

1970. Inaug. of New U.P.U. Headquarters Building, Berne. As No. 141.

F 156. 1 f. 05 slate, orge. & purple 50 70

1970. New Hebrides' Declaration for the Free French Government. As Nos. 142/3.

F 157. 65 c. multicoloured .. 55 55
F 158. 1 f. 10 multicoloured .. 1·10 1·10

1970. No. F 115 surch.

F 159. 35 c. on 20 c. black, green and blue .. 60 50

1970. Christmas. As Nos. 145/6.

F 160. 15 c. multicoloured .. 15 15
F 161. 50 c. multicoloured .. 25 40

1971. Death of General Charles de Gaulle. Nos. F 157/8 optd. **1890-1970 IN MEMORIAM 9-11-70.**

F 162. 65 c. multicoloured .. 75 55
F 163. 1 f. 10 multicoloured .. 1·50 1·50

1971. 4th South Pacific Games, Papeete, French Polynesia. As Nos. 149/50

F 164. 20 c. multicoloured .. 35 20
F 165. 65 c. multicoloured .. 95 80

1971. Royal Society Expedition to New Hebrides. As No. 151.

F 166. 65 c. multicoloured .. 50 50

1971. Christmas. As Nos. 152/3.

F 167. 25 c. multicoloured .. 15 20
F 168. 50 c. multicoloured .. 30 35

1972. Aircraft. As Nos. 154/7.

F 169. 20 c. multicoloured .. 1·00 60
F 170. 25 c. multicoloured .. 1·00 70
F 171. 30 c. multicoloured .. 1·10 75
F 172. 65 c. multicoloured .. 3·00 4·00

1972. As Nos. 158/69.

F 173. 5 c. multicoloured .. 40 10
F 174. 10 c. multicoloured .. 1·75 50
F 175. 15 c. multicoloured .. 50 15
F 176. 20 c. multicoloured .. 2·25 30
F 177. 25 c. multicoloured .. 1·75 30
F 178. 30 c. multicoloured .. 1·75 30
F 179. 35 c. multicoloured .. 3·00 40
F 180. 65 c. multicoloured .. 2·50 60
F 181. 1 f. multicoloured .. 2·50 1·75
F 182. 2 f. multicoloured .. 15·00 10·00
F 183. 3 f. multicoloured .. 9·50 13·00
F 184. 5 f. multicoloured .. 17·00 22·00

1972. Christmas. As Nos. 170/1.

F 185. 25 c. multicoloured .. 25 20
F 186. 70 c. multicoloured .. 50 45

1972. Royal Silver Wedding. As Nos. 172/3.

F 187. 35 c. multicoloured .. 75 50
F 188. 65 c. multicoloured .. 1·25 1·50

1973. Orchids. As Nos. 174/7.

F 189. 25 c. multicoloured .. 1·00 40
F 190. 30 c. multicoloured .. 1·10 60
F 191. 35 c. multicoloured .. 1·25 75
F 192. 65 c. multicoloured .. 3·00 4·00

1973. Opening of New Wharf at Villa. As Nos. 178/9.

F 193. 25 c. multicoloured .. 75 50
F 194. 70 c. multicoloured .. 1·50 2·00

1973. Tanna Island. As Nos. 180/1.

F 195. 35 c. multicoloured .. 2·25 1·25
F 196. 70 c. multicoloured .. 3·25 3·25

1973. Christmas. As Nos. 182/3.

F 197. 35 c. multicoloured .. 45 35
F 198. 70 c. multicoloured .. 1·00 75

1974. Wild Life. As Nos. 184/7.

F 199. 25 c. multicoloured .. 3·75 1·50
F 200. 35 c. multicoloured .. 5·50 1·75
F 201. 70 c. multicoloured .. 5·50 3·75
F 202. 1 f. 15 multicoloured .. 6·00 8·50

1974. Royal Visit of Queen Elizabeth II. Nos. F 179 and F 182 optd. **VISITE ROYALE 1974.**

F 203. 35 c. Chestnut-bellied Kingfisher .. .. 2·00 50
F 204. 2 f. Green palm Lorikeet 5·00 6·00

1974. Inauguration of New Post Office, Villa. As Nos. 190/1.

F 205. 35 c. multicoloured .. 50 65
F 206. 70 c. multicoloured .. 60 85

1974. Bicent. of Rediscovery of New Hebrides by Captain Cook. As Nos. 192/5.

F 207. 35 c. multicoloured .. 4·50 4·00
F 208. 35 c. multicoloured .. 4·50 4·00
F 209. 35 c. multicoloured .. 4·50 4·00
F 210. 1 f. 15 multicoloured .. 10·00 8·50

1974. Centenary of Universal Postal Union. As No. 196.

F 210a. 70 c. blue, red & black 1·25 1·50

1974. Christmas. As Nos. 197/8.

F 211. 35 c. multicoloured .. 25 20
F 212. 70 f. multicoloured .. 55 45

1975. Charolais Bull. As No. 199.

F 213. 10 f. brn., grn. and blue 28·00 35·00

1975. World Scout Jamboree, Norway. As Nos. 200/3.

F 214. 25 c. multicoloured .. 55 20
F 215. 35 c. multicoloured .. 75 30
F 216. 1 f. multicoloured .. 1·90 1·10
F 217. 5 f. multicoloured .. 8·00 9·00

1975. Christmas. As Nos. 204/6.

F 218. 35 c. multicoloured .. 25 15
F 219. 70 c. multicoloured .. 40 25
F 220. 2 f. 50 multicoloured .. 2·25 2·75

1976. 1st Commercial Flight of "Concorde". As No. 207, but Concorde in Air France livery.

F 221. 5 f. multicoloured .. 18·00 14·00

1976. Centenary of Telephone. As Nos. 208/10.

F 222. 25 c. multicoloured .. 55 40
F 223. 70 c. multicoloured .. 1·40 1·50
F 224. 1 f. 15 multicoloured .. 1·75 2·25

1976. Constitutional Changes. As Nos. 211/13.

F 225. 25 c. multicoloured .. 50 30
F 226. 1 f. multicoloured .. 1·50 1·00
F 227. 2 f. multicoloured .. 2·50 1·90

1976. Christmas. Paintings. As Nos. 214/16.

F 228. 35 c. multicoloured .. 25 15
F 229. 70 c. multicoloured .. 40 25
F 230. 2 f. 50 multicoloured .. 2·25 2·75

1977. Silver Jubilee. As Nos. 217/9.

F 231. 35 c. multicoloured .. 50 20
F 232. 70 c. multicoloured .. 75 50
F 233. 2 f. multicoloured .. 1·00 1·25

1977. Currency Change. Nos. F 173/84 and F 213, surch.

F 234 5 f. on 5 c. mult .. 40 40
F 235 10 f. on 10 c. mult .. 85 40
F 236 15 f. on 15 c. mult .. 70 60
F 237 20 f. on 20 c. mult .. 1·50 85
F 238 25 f. on 25 c. mult .. 1·50 1·00
F 239 30 f. on 30 c. mult .. 1·75 1·50
F 240 35 f. on 35 c. mult .. 2·50 1·50
F 241 40 f. on 65 c. mult .. 2·50 2·00
F 242 50 f. on 1 f. mult .. 2·50 2·00
F 243 70 f. on 2 f. mult .. 4·25 2·75
F 244 100 f. on 3 f. mult .. 4·50 4·50
F 245 200 f. on 5 f. mult .. 14·00 19·00
F 246 500 f. on 10 f. mult .. 26·00 35·00

1977. Islands. As Nos. 242/54.

F 256. 5 f. multicoloured .. 40 20
F 257. 10 f. multicoloured .. 60 20
F 258. 15 f. multicoloured .. 60 20
F 259. 20 f. multicoloured .. 65 30
F 260. 25 f. multicoloured .. 70 40
F 261. 30 f. multicoloured .. 70 45
F 262. 35 f. multicoloured .. 1·25 60
F 263. 40 f. multicoloured .. 1·25 75
F 264. 50 f. multicoloured .. 2·00 75
F 265. 70 f. multicoloured .. 3·25 2·25
F 266. 100 f. multicoloured .. 3·00 2·50
F 267. 200 f. multicoloured .. 4·75 8·00
F 268. 500 f. multicoloured .. 10·00 13·00

1977. Christmas. As Nos. 255/7.

F 269. 10 f. multicoloured .. 20 20
F 270. 15 f. multicoloured .. 35 35
F 271. 30 f. multicoloured .. 85 85

1978. "Concorde". As Nos. 258/61.

F 272. 10 f. multicoloured .. 2·00 1·00
F 273. 20 f. multicoloured .. 2·25 1·50
F 274. 30 f. multicoloured .. 2·75 2·00
F 275. 40 f. multicoloured .. 3·50 3·25

1978. Coronation. As Nos. 262/4.

F 276. 40 f. brn., blue & silver 50 85
F 277. 40 f. multicoloured .. 50 85
F 278. 40 f. brn., blue & silver 50 85

1978. Christmas. As Nos. 265/8.

F 279. 10 f. multicoloured .. 20 20
F 280. 15 f. multicoloured .. 25 30
F 281. 30 f. multicoloured .. 40 60
F 282. 40 f. multicoloured .. 50 70

1979. Internal Self-Government. Design as T 37 surch. **PREMIER GOUVERNEMENT AUTONOME 11.1.78 - 11.1.79** and new value.

F 283. 10 f. on 25 f. mult. (blue background) 55 30
F 284. 40 f. on 25 f. mult. (green background) .. 1·25 1·50

1979. Death Centenary of Sir Rowland Hill. As Nos. 271/3.

F 285. 10 f. multicoloured .. 30 35
F 286. 20 f. multicoloured .. 45 55
F 287. 40 f. multicoloured .. 65 75

1979. Arts Festival. As Nos. 275/8

F 288. 5 f. multicoloured .. 20 10
F 289. 10 f. multicoloured .. 25 15
F 290. 20 f. multicoloured .. 45 40
F 291. 40 f. multicoloured .. 75 1·00

1979. Christmas and International Year of the Child. As Nos. 279/82.

F 292. 5 f. multicoloured .. 55 35
F 293. 10 f. multicoloured .. 75 35
F 294. 20 f. multicoloured .. 1·00 1·00
F 295. 40 f. multicoloured .. 1·90 2·00

1980. Birds. As Nos. 283/6.

F 296. 10 f. multicoloured .. 1·25 45
F 297. 20 f. multicoloured .. 1·50 1·00
F 298. 30 f. multicoloured .. 1·75 1·75
F 299. 40 f. multicoloured .. 2·00 2·25

POSTAGE DUE STAMPS

1925. Nos. F 32, etc., optd. **CHIFFRE TAXE.**

FD 53. 5. 10 c. (1d.) green .. 45·00 2·50
FD 54. 20 c. (2d.) grey .. 45·00 2·50
FD 55. 30 c. (3d.) red .. 45·00 2·50
FD 56. 50 c. (5d.) blue .. 45·00 2·50
FD 57. 1 f. (10d.) red on blue 45·00 2·50

1938. Optd. **CHIFFRE TAXE.**

FD 65. 6. 5 c. green .. .. 11·00 22·00
FD 66. 10 c. orange .. 14·00 22·00
FD 67. 20 c. red .. .. 18·00 28·00
FD 68. 40 c. olive .. 35·00 48·00
FD 69. 1 f. red on green .. 40·00 60·00

1941. Free French Issue. As last optd. **France Libre.**

FD 77. 6. 5 c green .. .. 8·75 20·00
FD 78. 10 c. orange .. 8·75 20·00
FD 79. 20 c. red .. .. 8·75 20·00
FD 80. 40 c. olive .. 8·75 20·00
FD 81. 1 f. red on green .. 13·00 20·00

1953. Optd. **TIMBRE-TAXE.**

FD 92. 7. 5 c green .. .. 3·50 8·00
FD 93. 10 c. red .. .. 3·50 8·00
FD 94. 20 c. blue .. .. 8·75 14·00
FD 95. – 40 c. sepia (No. F 87) 13·50 27·00
FD 96. – 1 f. orange (No. F 89) 20·00 32·00

1957. Optd. **TIMBRE-TAXE.**

FD 107. 12. 5 c. green .. .. 1·75 4·25
FD 108. 10 c. red .. .. 1·75 4·25
FD 109. 20 c. blue .. .. 4·25 6·50
FD 110. – 40 c. sepia (No. F 102) 9·00 13·00
FD 111. – 1 f. orange (No. F 104) 10·50 16·00

For later issues see **VANUATU.**

NEW REPUBLIC

A Boer republic originally part of Zululand. It was incorporated with the S. African Republic in 1888 and annexed to Natal in 1903.

12 pence = 1 shilling.
20 shillings = 1 pound.

NIEUWE REPUBLIEK 1d 8 NOV 86 ZUID-AFRIKA.

1.

1886. On yellow or blue paper.

1	1	1d. black	—	£2500
2		1d. violet	10·00	12·00
73		2d. violet	8·50	8·50
74		3d. violet	13·00	13·00
75		4d. violet	13·00	13·00
81		6d. violet	8·00	8·00
82		9d. violet	8·50	8·50
83		1s. violet	8·50	8·50
77		1s. 6d. violet ..	14·00	14·00
85		2s. violet	18·00	16·00
86		2s. 6d. violet ..	23·00	23·00
87		3s. violet	42·00	42·00
88		4s. violet	11·00	11·00
89		5s. violet	13·00	13·00
90		5s. 6d. violet ..	12·00	12·00
91		7s. 6d. violet ..	14·00	17·00
92		10s. violet	12·00	12·00
93		10s. 6d. violet ..	16·00	16·00
44		12s. violet	£300	
23		13s. violet	£400	
94		£1 violet	45·00	45·00
25		30s. violet	95·00	

Some stamps are found with Arms embossed in the paper, and others with the Arms and without a date above "ZUID-AFRIKA".

NEW SOUTH WALES

A S.E. state of the Australian Commonwealth, whose stamps it now uses.

12 pence = 1 shilling.
20 shillings = 1 pound.

1. Seal of the Colony. 8.

1850 Imperf.

11	1	1d. red	£2250	£275
25		2d. blue	£1800	£130
42		3d. green	£2500	£225

1851. Imperf.

47	8.	1d. red	£900	£100
83		1d. orange..	£170	16·00
86		2d. blue	£110	8·00
87		3d. green	£200	27·00
76		6d. brown	£1600	£250
79		8d. yellow..	£3500	£600

14. 15.

1854. Imperf.

104.	14.	1d. red	£130	22·00
107.		2d. blue	£130	8·00
111.		3d. green..	£800	80·00
113.	15.	5d. green..	£1000	£500
116.		6d. grey	£400	32·00
122.		6d. brown	£450	32·00
126.		8d. orange	£3500	£800
128.		1s. red	£750	65·00

For these stamps perforated, see No. 154, etc.

24.

1860. Perf.

173	14.	1d. red ..	32·00	13·00
134		2d. blue ..	90·00	10·00
226		3d. green ..	5·00	80
243	15.	5d. green ..	5·50	90
143		6d. brown	£275	45·00
165		6d. violet	55·00	4·50
218		8d. orange	90·00	17·00
168		1s. red	70·00	7·50
297c	24.	5s. purple	32·00	12·00

26.

28.

43.

1862. Queen Victoria. Various frames.

207	26	1d red ..	5·00	20
210	28	2d. blue	7·00	20
230c	–	4d. brown	25·00	1·00
234	–	6d. lilac	35·00	1·00
310	–	10d. lilac	12·00	2·75
237	–	1s black	65·00	2·00

1871. As No. 206, surch. **NINEPENCE.**

236d	9d. on 10d. brown	8·00	3·75

1885.

244b	43	5s. green and lilac	£325	80·00
251b		10s. red and violet	£140	40·00
246a		£1 red and lilac	£2250	£1000

45. View of Sydney.

46. Emu.

52. Capt. Arthur Phillip, 1st Governor, and Lord Carrington, Governor in 1888.

1888. Inscr. "ONE HUNDRED YEARS".

253	45.	1d. mauve	3·75	10
254	46.	2d. blue	3·25	10
335	–	4d brown	8·00	3·00
256	–	6d. red	20·00	2·50
297fa	–	6d. green	22·00	5·00
339	–	6d yellow	11·00	90
257	–	8d. purple	11·00	1·50
343	–	1s. brown	11·00	85
263	–	5s. violet	£120	27·00
346	52.	20s. blue	£140	60·00

DESIGNS—As Type **45.** 4d. Capt. Cook. 6d. Queen Victoria and Arms. 8d. Superb Lyrebird. 1s. Kangaroo. As Type **52.** 5s. Map of Australia.

55. Allegorical figure of Australia.

1890.

281.	55.	2½d. blue	2·25	40

1891. Types as 1862, but new value and colours, surch. in words.

282.	26.	½d. on 1d. grey ..	2·75	2·75
283.	–	7½d. on 6d. brown	5·00	2·50
284c.	–	12½d. on 1s. red ..	10·00	6·00

58.

59.

60.

61.

62. Superb Lyrebird.

63.

1892.

286	58	½d. grey	80	10
287a		½d. green	80	10
332	59	1d. red	1·00	10
315	60	2d. blue	1·50	10
296	61	2½d. violet	3·50	80
303		2½d blue	2·75	70
348	63	9d. brown and blue	6·00	90
345a	62	2s. 6d. green	27·00	12·00

58a. (Actual size 47 × 38 mm.)

1897. Diamond Jubilee and Hospital Charity.

287c.	58a.	1d. (1s.) green & brown	40·00	40·00
287d.	–	2½d. (2s. 6d.) gold & blue	£150	£150

DESIGN—VERT. 2½d. Two female figures.

OFFICIAL STAMPS

1879-92. Various issues optd. **O.S.**

A. Issues of 1854 to 1871.

O20b	26	1d. red	4·00	1·40
O21c	28	2d. blue	5·00	1·00
O25c	14	3d. green	5·00	3·50
O27a	–	4d. brown (No. 230c)	12·00	3·00
O28	15	5d. green	12·00	10·00
O31	–	6d. lilac (No. 234)	18·00	4·00
O32b	15	8d. orange	20·00	9·00
O11	–	9d. on 10d. (No. 309)	£350	£180
O18a	–	10d. lilac (No. 206)	£130	80·00
O33	–	1s. black (No. 237d)	25·00	5·00
O18	24	5s. purple	£170	80·00

B. Fiscal stamps of 1885.

O37	24	10s. red and violet	£1200	£600
O38		£1 red and violet	£4000	£3000

C. Issue of 1888 (Nos. 253/346b).

O 39.		1d. mauve	2·00	15
O 40.		2d. blue	2·00	15
O 41.		4d. brown	8·00	2·00
O 42.		6d. red	8·50	2·50
O 43.		8d. purple	14·00	6·50
O 44.		1s. brown	13·00	2·50
O 49.		5s. violet	£140	65·00
O 48.		20s. blue	£1100	£500

D. Issues of 1890 and 1892.

O 58.	58.	½d. grey	6·00	5·00
O 55.	26.	½d. on 1d. grey	50·00	40·00
O 54.	55.	2½d. blue	7·00	2·75
O 56.	–	7½d. on 6d. (No. 283)	38·00	27·00
O 57.	–	12½d. on 1s. (No. 284c)	60·00	50·00

POSTAGE DUE STAMPS

D 1.

1891.

D 1	D 1.	½d. green	2·50	2·00
D 2		1d. green	3·50	90
D 3		2d. green	5·50	80
D 4		3d. green	9·00	2·75
D 5		4d. green	7·50	80
D 6		6d. green	14·00	2·00
D 7		8d. green	60·00	9·00
D 8		5s. green	£120	30·00
D 9a		10s. green	£120	80·00
D 10b		20s. green	£180	£100

REGISTRATION STAMPS

13.

1856.

88.	13.	(6d.) red & bl. (Imp.) ..	£700	£150
92.		(6d.) orge & bl. (Imp.)	£700	£130
101.		(6d.) red & bl. (Perf.) ..	70·00	15·00
94.		(6d.) orge. & bl. (Perf.)	£325	40·00

NEW ZEALAND

A group of islands in the S. Pacific Ocean. A Commonwealth Dominion.

1855. 12 pence = 1 shilling;
20 shillings = 1 pound.
1967. 100 cents = dollar.

1.

3.

1855. Imperf.

35	1	1d. red	£350	£160
33		1d. orange ..	£400	£130
38		2d. blue	£225	70·00
40		3d. lilac	£300	£100
43		6d. brown ..	£500	70·00
45		1s. green	£700	£150

1862. Perf.

110	1	1d. orange	80·00	20·00
132		1d. brown	90·00	20·00
113		2d. blue	85·00	16·00
133		2d. orange	50·00	15·00
117		3d. lilac	65·00	18·00
119		4d. red	£1800	£250
120		4d. yellow	90·00	50·00
122		6d. brown	85·00	18·00
136		6d. blue	70·00	30·00
125		1s. green	£100	45·00

1873.

151.	3.	½d. red	5·00	50

5.

6.

7.

8.

9.

10.

11.

1874. Inscr. "POSTAGE".

180.	5.	1d. lilac ..	35·00	3·00
181.	6.	2d. red ..	35·00	1·40
154.	7.	3d. brown	95·00	55·00
182.	8.	4d. purple	£130	38·00
183.	9.	6d. blue ..	80·00	10·00
184.	10.	1s. green ..	£110	28·00
185.	11.	2s. red	£300	£275
186.		5s. grey ..	£325	£275

13.

16.

19.

F 4.

1882. Inscr. "POSTAGE & REVENUE".

236	13	½d. black	2·50	15
218	10	1d. red ..	3·50	10
238	9	2d. mauve	7·00	30
239	16	2½d. blue	38·00	3·50
221	10	3d. yellow	38·00	7·50
222	6	4d. green	45·00	2·50
200	19	5d. black	40·00	9·00
224b	8	6d. brown	45·00	5·50
202	9	8d. blue ..	65·00	45·00
245	7	1s. brown	70·00	5·50

1882.

F 90	F 4.	2s. blue	25·00	4·00
F 99		2s. 6d. brown	27·00	4·50
F 100		3s. mauve	70·00	5·50
F 102		5s. green	70·00	7·50
F 87		10s. brown	£130	12·00
F 89		£1 red	£170	45·00

The above are revenue stamps authorised for use as postage stamps as there were no other postage stamps available in these denominations. Other values in this and similar types were mainly used for revenue purposes.

23. Mount Cook or Aorangi.

24. Lake Taupo and Mount Ruapehu.

26. Lake Wakatipu and Mount Earnslaw.

25. Pembroke Peak, Milford Sound.

28. Huia Birds.

29. White Terrace, Rotomahana.

30. Otira Gorge and Mount Ruapehu.

31. Brown Kiwi.

32. Maori War Canoe.

33. Pink Terrace, Rotomahana.

34. Kaka and Kea.

35. Milford Sound.

1898.

246	**23.**	½d. deep purple ..	4·00	50
302		½d. green	3·50	15
247	**24.**	1d. blue and brown ..	2·75	20
248	**25.**	2d. lake	22·00	20
249	**26.**	2½d. blue (A)*	6·50	18·00
320		2½d. blue (B)*	7·00	1·75
309	**28.**	3d. brown	18·00	80
252	**29.**	4d. red	12·00	14·00
311a	**30.**	5d. brown	16·00	3·25
254	**31.**	6d. green	48·00	22·00
265		6d. red	35·00	2·75
325	**32.**	8d. blue	25·00	5·50
326	**33.**	9d. purple	25·00	6·00
268a	**34.**	1s. orange	48·00	3·00
328	**35.**	2s. green	65·00	20·00
329	–	5s. red	£170	£180

DESIGN—As Type **30:** 5s. Mount Cook.
*Type A of 2½d. is inscribed " WAKITIPU ", Type B " WAKATIPU ".

40. Commemorative of the New Zealand Contingent in the South African War.

1900.

274	**29.**	1d. red	12·00	10
275b	**40.**	1½d. brown	7·50	4·00
319	**25.**	2d. purple	5·50	70
322d	**24.**	4d. blue and brown ..	6·00	70

The 1d., 2d. and 4d. are smaller than the illustrations of their respective types.

INDEX
Countries can be quickly located by referring to the index at the end of this volume.

42.

1901.

303.	**42.**	1d. red	3·00	10

44. Maori Canoe "Te Arawa".

1906. Christchurch Exn. Inscr. "COMMEMORATIVE SERIES OF 1906".

370.	**44.**	½d. green	16·00	23·00
371.	–	1d. red	13·00	15·00
372.	–	3d. brown and blue ..	45·00	65·00
373.	–	6d. red and green ..	£140	£225

DESIGNS: 1d. Maori art. 3d. Landing of Cook. 6d. Annexation of New Zealand.

50.

1907.

386	**50**	1d. red	30·00	50
383	**28**	3d. brown	35·00	7·00
376	**31**	6d. red	40·00	6·00
385	**34**	1s. orange	£120	24·00

These are smaller in size than the 1898 and 1901 issues. Type **50** also differs from Type **42** in the corner ornaments.

51. King Edward VII.

53. Dominion.

1909.

387	**51**	½d. green	3·25	10
405	**53**	1d. red	1·25	10
388	**51**	2d. mauve	14·00	5·00
389		3d. brown	18·00	30
390a		4d. orange	7·00	2·50
391a		5d. brown	12·00	90
392		6d. red	30·00	40
393		8d. blue	10·00	65
394		1s. orange	48·00	1·75

1913. Optd. **AUCKLAND EXHIBITION. 1913.**

412	**51**	½d. green	11·00	25·00
413	**53**	1d. red	17·00	28·00
414	**51**	3d. brown	£100	£170
415		6d. red	£110	£200

62. King George V.

1915.

446	**62**	½d. green	40	10
416a		1½d. grey	2·00	60
438		1½d. brown	1·75	10
417		2d. violet	7·00	17·00
439		2d. yellow	1·00	10
419a		2½d. blue	3·25	1·50
440		3d. brown	6·00	40
421		4d. yellow	4·25	30·00
422a		4d. violet	5·00	30
423a		4½d. green	12·00	5·00
424a		5d. blue..	6·50	70
425a		6d. red	5·50	30
426a		7½d. brown	13·00	19·00
427a		8d. blue..	16·00	35·00
428		8d. brown	15·00	90
429a		9d. green	13·00	1·25
430		1s. orange	13·00	30

1915. No. 446 optd **WAR STAMP** and stars.

452	**62**	½d. green	1·60	20

64. "Peace" and Lion.

65. "Peace" and Lion.

69. New Zealand.

1920. Victory. Inscr. "VICTORY" or dated "1914 1919" (6d.).

453.	**64.**	½d. green	2·00	1·75
454.	**65.**	1d. red	4·00	30
455.	–	1½d. orange	3·50	20
456.	–	3d. brown	13·00	11·00
457.	–	6d. violet	13·00	14·00
458.	–	1s. orange	24·00	45·00

DESIGNS—HORIZ. (As Type **65**). 1½d. Maori Chief. (As Type **64**). 3d. Lion. 1s. King George V. VERT. (As Type **64**). 6d. "Peace" and "Progress".

1922. Surch.

459.	**64.**	2d. on ½d. green ..	2·00	85

1923. Restoration of Penny Postage.

460.	**69.**	1d. red	1·75	30

70. Exhibition Buildings.

1925. Dunedin Exn.

463.	**70.**	½d. green on green ..	2·50	11·00
464.		1d. red on rose.. ..	2·75	5·00
465.		4d. mauve on mauve ..	38·00	65·00

71.

73. Nurse.

1926.

468.	**71.**	1d. red	40	10
469.	–	2s. blue	45·00	16·00
470.	–	3s. mauve	70·00	85·00

The 2s. and 3s. are larger (21 × 25 mm.).

1929. Anti-T.B. Fund.

544.	**73.**	1d.+1d. red	11·00	14·00

1930. Inscr. "HELP PROMOTE HEALTH".

545.	**73.**	1d.+1d. red	18·00	24·00

74. Smiling Boy.

F 6. "Arms" Type.

75. New Zealand Lake Scenery.

1931. Health stamps.

546.	**74.**	1d.+1d. red	75·00	75·00
547.		2d.+1d. blue	75·00	65·00

1931. Air.

548.	**75.**	3d. brown	20·00	13·00
549.		4d. purple	22·00	13·00
550.		7d. orange	24·00	7·50

1931. Air. Surch **FIVE PENCE.**

551	**75**	5d on 3d. green ..	9·00	7·00

1931. Various frames.

F 191	**F 6**	1s. 3d. yellow ..	4·25	90
F 192		1s. 3d. yellow & blk	1·00	40
F 193		2s. 6d. brown ..	5·00	30
F 194		4s. red	11·00	50
F 195		5s. green	12·00	60
F 196		6s. red	25·00	2·50
F 197		7s. blue	27·00	4·25
F 198		7s. 6d. grey ..	60·00	48·00
F 199		8s. violet	35·00	17·00
F 200		9s. orange	20·00	29·00
F 201		10s. red	20·00	2·25
F 156		12s. 6d. purple ..	£140	£140
F 202		15s. green	38·00	17·00
F 203		£1 pink	24·00	3·50
F 159		25s. blue	£225	£325
F 205		30s. brown	£190	95·00
F 161		35s. yellow	£2000	£2250
F 206		£2 violet	70·00	18·00
F 163		£2 10s. red	£180	£225
F 208		£3 green	85·00	45·00
F 165		£3 10s. red	£1200	£950
F 210		£4 blue	£100	65·00
F 167		£4 10s. grey ..	£1100	£1000
F 211		£5 blue	£130	45·00

77. Hygeia, Goddess of Health.

78. The Path to Health.

1932. Health stamp.

552.	**77.**	1d.+1d. red	22·00	24·00

1933. Health stamp.

553.	**78.**	1d.+1d. red	8·00	13·00

1934. Air. Optd. **TRANS-TASMAN AIR MAIL. " FAITH IN AUSTRALIA ".**

554.	**75.**	7d. blue..	40·00	40·00

80. Crusader.

1934. Health stamp.

555.	**80.**	1d.+1d. red	6·50	7·00

81. Collared Grey Fantail.

83. Maori Woman.

85. Mt. Cook.

86. Maori Girl.

87. Mitre Peak.

89. Harvesting. **91.** Maori Panel.

93. Capt. Cook at Poverty Bay.

1935.

577	**81.**	½d. green	1·50	10
578	–	1d. red	70	10
579	**83.**	1½d. brown	6·50	3·00
580	–	2d. orange	30	10
581b	**85.**	2½d. brown and grey	50	1·75
561	**86.**	3d brown	8·00	90
583c	**87.**	4d. black and brown	80	10
584c	–	5d. blue	2·75	65
585b	**89.**	6d. red	75	10
586b	–	8d. brown	2·50	40
531	**91.**	9d red and black ..	2·25	1·75
588	–	1s. green	2·50	40
589d	**93.**	2s. olive	14·00	1·50
590b	–	3s. chocolate and brown	6·00	1·75

DESIGNS—VERT. (Small as Type **81**). 1d Kiwi. 2d. Maori carved house. 1s. Tui. (Larger as Type **87**). 8d Tuatara lizard. HORIZ. (As Type **85**). 5d. Swordfish. 3s Mt. Egmont.

95. Bell Block Aerodrome.

1935. Air.

570.	**95.**	1d. red	50	50
571.		3d. violet	3·00	3·00
572.		6d. blue..	6·00	1·75

96. King George V and Queen Mary.

1935. Silver Jubilee.

573.	**96.**	½d. green	1·00	70
574.		1d. red	1·40	50
575.		6d. orange	12·00	17·00

97. " The Key to Health ". **99.** N.Z. Soldier at Anzac Cove.

1935. Health stamp.

576.	**97.**	1d.+1d. red	1·50	2·25

1936. Charity. 21st Anniv. of Anzac Landing at Gallipoli.

591.	**99.**	½d+½d. green	40	1·40
592.		1d.+1d. red	40	90

100. Wool.

1936. Congress of British Empire Chambers of Commerce, Wellington, N.Z. Inscr. as in T **100**.

593.	**100.**	½d. green ..	30	30
594.	–	1d. red (Butter) ..	30	20
595.	–	2½d. blue (Sheep) ..	1·00	6·50
596.	–	4d. violet (Apples) ..	80	4·75
597.	–	6d. brown (Exports) ..	1·25	4·00

105. Health Camp.

1936. Health stamp.

598.	**105.**	1d.+1d. red	1·00	3·25

106. King George VI and Queen Elizabeth.

1937. Coronation.

599.	**106.**	1d. red	30	10
600.		2½d. blue	1·75	1·75
601.		6d. orange	2·40	1·40

107. Rock Climbing. **108.** King George VI.

1937. Health stamp.

602.	**107.**	1d.+1d. red	1·75	2·50

1938.

603.	**108.**	½d. green	6·50	10
604.		½d. orange	20	10
605.		1d. red	5·00	10
606.		1d. green	20	10
607.		1½d. brown	24·00	1·40
608.		1½d. red..	20	20
680.		2d. orange	15	10
609.		3d. blue..	20	10
681.		4d. purple	45	30
682.		5d. grey..	50	40
683.		6d. red	40	10
684.		8d. violet	65	30
685.		9d. brown	70	30
686a.	–	1s. brown and red ..	50	40
687.	–	1s. 3d. brown and blue	70	50
688.	–	2s. orange and green ..	1·50	1·00
689.	–	3s. brown and grey ..	1·75	2·00

The shilling values are larger (22 × 25½ mm.) and " NEW ZEALAND " appears at the top.

109. Children Playing. **110.** Beach Ball.

1938. Health stamp.

610.	**109.**	1d.+1d. red	3·50	1·60

1939. Health stamps. Surch.

611.	**110.**	1d. on ½d.+½d. green..	1·50	3·25
612.		2d. on 1d.+1d. red ..	2·75	3·25

1939. Surch in bold figures.

F 212.	**F 6.**	3/6 on 3s. 6d. green..	20·00	5·00
F 214.		5/6 on 5s. 6d. lilac ..	22·00	12·00
F 215.		11/– on 11s. yellow ..	60·00	42·00
F 216.		22/– on 22s. red ..	£180	£120
F 186.		35/– on 35s. orange..	£325	£200

112. ''Endeavour'', Chart of N.Z. and Captain Cook.

1940. Cent. of British Sovereignty. Inscr. "CENTENNIAL (OF NEW ZEALAND). 1840–1940 ".

613.	–	½d. green	30	10
614.	**112.**	1d. brown and red ..	2·75	10
615.	–	1½d. blue and mauve ..	30	20
616.	–	2d. green and brown ..	1·50	10
617.	–	2½d. green and blue ..	1·50	45
618.	–	3d. purple and red ..	2·75	30
619.	–	4d. brown and red ..	13·00	60
620.	–	5d. blue and brown ..	5·50	2·50
621.	–	6d. green and violet ..	13·00	60
622.	–	7d. black and red ..	1·50	3·75
623.	–	8d. black and red ..	12·00	1·50
624.	–	9d. olive and orange ..	7·50	75
625.	–	1s. green	15·00	3·00

DESIGNS—HORIZ. ½d. Arrival of the Maoris, 1350. 1½d. British Monarchs. 2d. Abel Tasman with "Heemskerk" and Chart. 3d. Landing of immigrants, 1840. 4d. Road, rail, ocean and air transport. 5d. H.M.S. "Britomart" at Akaroa, 1840. 6d. "Dunedin" and "frozen mutton" sea route to London. 7d., 8d. Maori Council. 9d, Gold mining methods, 1861 and 1940. VERT. 2½d. Treaty of Waitangi. 1s. Giant Kauri tree.

1940. Health stamps.

626.	**110.**	1d.+½d. green ..	7·00	9·00
627.		2d.+1d. orange ..	7·00	9·00

1941. Surch.

628.	**108.**	1d. on ½d. green ..	40	10
629.		2d. on 1½d. brown ..	40	10

1941. Health stamps. Optd. **1941**.

632.	**110.**	1d.+½d. green ..	25	1·50
633.		2d.+1d. orange ..	25	1·50

125. Boy and Girl on Swing.

1942. Health stamps.

634.	**125.**	1d.+½d. green ..	15	45
635.		2d.+1d. orange ..	15	40

126. Princess Margaret.

1943. Health stamps.

636.	**126.**	1d.+½d. green ..	10	50
637.	–	2d.+1d. brown ..	10	10

DESIGN: 2d. Queen Elizabeth II as Princess.

1944. Surch. **TENPENCE** between crosses.

662.	–	10d. on 1½d. blue and mauve (No. 615) ..	10	10

129. Queen Elizabeth II as Princess and Princess Margaret.

1944. Health stamps.

663.	**129.**	1d.+½d. green	10	15
664.		2d.+1d. blue	10	15

130. Peter Pan Statue, Kensington Gardens.

1945. Health stamps.

665.	**130.**	1d.+½d. green and buff	10	15
666.		2d.+1d. red and buff..	10	15

131. Lake Matheson.

132. King George VI and Parliament House, Wellington. **133.** St. Paul's Cathedral.

135. R.N.Z.A.F. Badge and Aeroplanes.

139. " St. George ", (Wellington College War memorial window). **141.** National Memorial Campanile.

1946. Peace Issue.

667.	**131.**	½d. green and brown ..	15	20
668.	**132.**	1d. green	10	10
669.	**133.**	1½d. red..	10	10
670.	–	2d. purple	15	10
671.	**135.**	3d. blue and grey ..	20	15
672.	–	4d. green and orange ..	20	20
673.	–	5d. green and blue ..	20	15
674.	–	6d. brown and red ..	15	10
675.	**139.**	8d. black and red ..	15	10
676.	–	9d. blue and black ..	15	10
677.	**141.**	1s. grey	15	15

DESIGNS—HORIZ. (As Type **132**). 2d. The Royal Family. (As Type **135**). 4d. Army (N.Z.) badge, tank and plough. 5d. Navy (anchor) badge, H.M.N.Z.S. "Achilles" (cruiser) and "Dominion Monarch" (liner). 6d. N.Z. Coat of Arms, foundry and farm. 9d. Southern Alps and Frans Josef Glacier, seen through chapel window.

142. Soldier helping Child over Stile.

1946. Health stamps.

678.	**142.**	1d.+½d. green & orange	10	10
679.		2d.+1d. brown & orge.	10	10

145. Statue of Eros.

1947. Health stamps.

690.	**145.**	1d.+½d. green.. ..	10	10
691.		2d.+1d. red	10	10

146. Port Chalmers, 1848.

1948. Centenary of Otago. Various designs inscr. "CENTENNIAL OF OTAGO".

692. **146.** 1d. blue and green .. 10 15
693. – 2d. green and brown .. 10 15
694. – 3d. purple 10 15
695. – 6d. black and red .. 10 15

DESIGNS—HORIZ. 2d. Cromwell, Otago. 6d. Otago University. VERT.: 3d. First church, Dunedin.

150. Boy Sunbathing and Children Playing.

1948. Health stamps.

696.**150.** 1d.+½d. blue and green 10 10
697. 2d.+1d. purple and red 10 10

151. Nurse and Child. 153. Queen Elizabeth II and Prince Charles.

1949. Health stamps.

698.**151.** 1d.+½d. green .. 10 10
699. 2d.+1d. blue 10 10

1950. As Type F 6, but without value, surch. **1½d. POSTAGE.**

700. 1½d. red 10 10

1950. Health stamps.

701. **153.** 1d.+½d. green .. 10 10
702. 2d.+1d. purple .. 10 10

155. Cairn on Lyttleton Hills.

1950. Cent. of Canterbury, N.Z.

703. – 1d. green and blue .. 15 15
704. **155.** 2d. red and orange .. 15 15
705. – 3d. blue 20 20
706. – 6d. brown and blue .. 20 25
707. – 1s. purple and blue .. 20 30

DESIGNS—VERT. 1d. Christchurch Cathedral. 3d. John Robert Godley. HORIZ. 6d. Canterbury University College. 1s. Aerial view of Timaru.

159. "Takapuna" class Yachts.

1951. Health stamps.

708. **159.** 1½d.+½d. red & yellow 10 30
709. 2d.+1d. green & yellow 10 10

160. Princess Anne. 161. Prince Charles.

1952. Health stamps.

710. **160.** 1½d.+½d. red 10 10
711. **161.** 2d.+1d. brown .. 10 10

1952. Surch. in figures.

712.**108.** 1d. on ½d. orange .. 20 40
713. 3d. on 1d. green .. 10 10

164. Queen Elizabeth II. 166. Westminster Abbey.

165. Coronation State Coach.

1953. Coronation.

714. – 2d. blue 30 20
715. **164.** 3d. brown 30 10
716. **165.** 4d. red .. .. 1·00 1·75
717. **166.** 8d. grey 80 80
718. – 1s. 6d. purple & blue 1·75 1·00

DESIGNS—As Type **165**: 2d. Queen Elizabeth II and Buckingham Palace. 1s. 6d. St. Edward's Crown and Royal Sceptre.

168. Girl Guides. 169. Boy Scouts.

1953. Health stamps.

719. **168.** 1½d.+½d. blue .. 10 10
720. **169.** 2d.+1d. green .. 10 20

170. Queen Elizabeth II.

171. Queen Elizabeth II and Duke of Edinburgh.

1953. Royal Visit.

721. **170.** 3d. purple 10 10
722. **171.** 4d. blue 10 25

172.

173. Queen Elizabeth II. 174.

1953. Small figures of value.

723. **172.** ½d. slate 15 30
724. 1d. orange 15 10
725. 1½d. brown 20 10
726. 2d. green 20 10
727. 3d. red 20 10
728. 4d. blue 40 40
729. 6d. purple .. .. 70 1·25
730. 8d. red 60 50

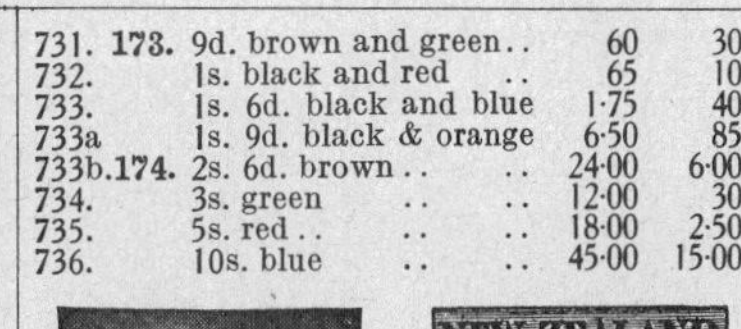

731. **173.** 9d. brown and green .. 60 30
732. 1s. black and red .. 65 10
733. 1s. 6d. black and blue 1·75 40
733a 1s. 9d. black & orange 6·50 85
733b.**174.** 2s. 6d. brown .. .. 24·00 6·00
734. 3s. green .. .. 12·00 30
735. 5s. red .. .. 18·00 2·50
736. 10s. blue .. .. 45·00 15·00

175. Young Climber and Mts. Aspiring and Everest. 176. Maori Mail-carrier.

177. Queen Elizabeth II. 179. Children's Health Camps Federation Emblem.

1954. Health stamps.

737. **175.** 1½d.+½d. brn. & violet 10 10
738. 2d.+1d. brn. and blue 10 10

1955. Centenary of New Zealand Stamp. Inscr. "1855–1955".

739. **176.** 2d. brown and green .. 10 10
740. **177.** 3d. red 10 10
741. – 4d. black and blue .. 15 25

DESIGN—HORIZ. (As Type **176**). 4d. Douglas DC 3 Airliner.

1955. Health stamps.

742. **179.** 1½d.+½d. brn. & chest. 10 25
743. 2d.+1d. red and green 10 15
744. 3d.+1d. brown and red 15 10

180. 183. Takahe.

181. "The Whalers of Foveaux Strait".

1955. As 1953 but larger figures of value and stars omitted from lower right corner.

745. **180.** 1d. orange 50 10
746. 1½d. brown 60 60
747. 2d. green 40 10
748. 3d. red .. .. 1·10 10
749. 4d. blue .. .. 1·75 45
750. 6d. purple .. .. 8·50 10
751. 8d. brown .. .. 6·00 5·00

1956. Southland Centennial.

752. **181.** 2d. green 10 10
753. – 3d. brown 10 10
754. **183.** 8d. slate and red .. 40 60

DESIGN—As Type **181**: 3d. Allegory of farming.

184. Children picking Apples.

187. Sir Truby King. 185. New Zealand Lamb and Map.

1956. Health stamps.

755. **184.** 1½d.+½d. brown .. 15 20
756. 2d.+1d. green .. 15 15
757. 3d.+1d. red 15 10

1957. 75th Anniv. of First Export of N.Z. Lamb.

758. **185.** 4d. blue 40 45
759. – 8d. red 60 65

DESIGN—HORIZ. 8d. Lamb sailing ship "Dunedin" and modern ship.

1957. 50th Anniv. of Plunket Society.

760. **187.** 3d. red 10 10

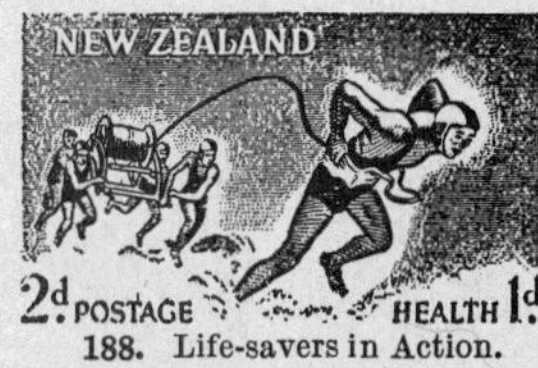

188. Life-savers in Action.

1957. Health stamps.

761. **188.** 2d.+1d. black & green 15 20
762. – 3d.+1d. blue and red 15 10

DESIGN: 3d. Children on seashore.

1958. Surch.

763 **180** 2d. on 1½d. brown .. 60 10
808 2½d. on 3d. red .. 15 15

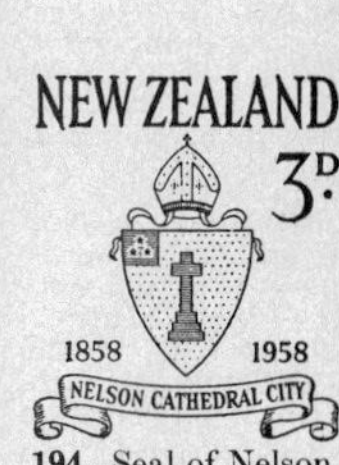

192. Boys Brigade Bugler. 194. Seal of Nelson.

1958. Health stamps.

764. – 2d.+1d. green .. 20 20
765. **192.** 3d.+1d. blue .. 20 20

DESIGN: 2d. Girls' Life Brigade cadet.

1958. 30th Anniv. of 1st Air Crossing of Tasman Sea. As T **120** of Australia.

766. 6d. blue 30 40

1958. Centenary of City of Nelson.

767 **194** 3d. red 10 10

195. "Pania" Statue, Napier. 197. 'Brown Kiwi' Jamboree Badge.

196. Australian Gannets on Cape Kidnappers.

1958. Centenary of Hawke's Bay Province.

768 **195** 2d. green 10 10
769 **196** 3d. blue 15 10
770 – 8d. brown 45 75

DESIGN—As Type **195**: 8d. Maori sheep-shearer.

1959. Pan-Pacific Scout Jamboree, Auckland.

771. **197.** 3d. brown and red .. 10 10

198. Careening H.M.S. "Endeavour" at Ship Cove.

1959. Centenary of Marlborough Province. Inscr. as in T **198**.

772. **198.** 2d. green 20 10
773. – 3d. blue 20 10
774. – 8d. brown 80 70

DESIGNS: 3d. Shipping wool, Wairau bar, 1857. 8d. Salt industry, Grassmere.

201. Red Cross Flag.

1959. Red Cross Commem.

775. **201.** 3d.+1d. red and blue 15 10

202. Grey Teal.

204. "The Explorer".

1959. Health stamps.

776. **202.** 2d.+1d. yellow, olive and red 15 25
777. – 3d.+1d. black, pink and blue 15 25
DESIGN: 3d. New Zealand Stilt.

1960. Centenary of Westland Province.

778. **204.** 2d. green 15 10
779. – 3d. salmon 15 10
780. – 8d. black .. .. 40 1·75
DESIGNS: 3d. "The Gold Digger". 8d. "The Pioneer Woman".

207. Manuka (Tea Tree).

215. Timber Industry.

219. Taniwha (Maori Rock Drawing).

225. Sacred Kingfisher.

1960.

781 **207.** ½d. green and red .. 10 10
782 – 1d. multicoloured .. 10 10
783 – 2d. multicoloured .. 10 10
784 – 2½d. multicoloured .. 70 10
785 – 3d. multicoloured .. 30 10
786 – 4d. multicoloured .. 40 10
787 – 5d. multicoloured .. 60 10
788 – 6d. lilac, grn. & turq. 50 10
788d – 7d. red, green & yellow 35 1·00
789 – 8d. multicoloured .. 40 10
790 – 9d. red and blue .. 30 10
791 **215.** 1s. brown and green .. 25 10
792b – 1s. 3d. red, sepia & blue 1·25 10
793 – 1s. 6d. olive and brown 70 10
794 – 1s. 9d. brown .. .. 22·00 15
795 – 1s. 9d. multicoloured .. 7·00 50
796 **219.** 2s. black and buff .. 3·25 10
797 – 2s. 6d. yell. and brown 1·75 65
798 – 3s. sepia .. .. 55·00 65
799 – 3s. bistre, blue & grn. 7·50 1·50
800 – 5s. myrtle .. .. 5·50 80
801 – 10s. blue .. .. 9·00 1·25
802 – £1 mauve .. .. 10·00 6·00

DESIGNS—As Type **207**: 1d. Karaka. 2d. Kowhai Ngutu-kaka (Kaka Beak). 2½d. Titoki (plant). 3d. Kowhai. 4d. Puarangi (Hibiscus). 5d. Matua tikumu (Mountain daisy). 6d. Pikiarero (Clematis). 7d. Koromiko. 8d. Rata. As Type **215**—HORIZ. 9d. National flag. 1s. 9d. Aerial top-dressing. VERT. 1s. 3d. Trout. 1s. 6d. Tiki. As Type **219**—HORIZ. 2s. 6d. Butter-making. 3s. Tongariro National Park and Chateau. 10s. Tasman Glacier. VERT. 5s. Sutherland Falls. £1, Pohutu Geyser.

1960. Health stamps.

803. **225.** 2d.+1d. sepia and blue 50 50
804. – 3d.+1d. purple & orge. 50 50
DESIGN: 3d. New Zealand Pigeon.

227. "The Adoration of the Shepherds" (Rembrandt).

228. Great Egret.

1960. Christmas.

805. **227.** 2d. red & brn. on cream 15 10

1961. Health stamps.

806. **228.** 2d.+1d. black & pur. 30 25
807. – 3d.+1d. sepia & green 30 25
DESIGN: 3d. New Zealand Falcon.

232. "Adoration of the Magi" (Durer).

1961. Christmas.

809. **232.** 2½d. multicoloured .. 10 10

233. Morse Key and Port Hills, Lyttleton.

1962. Telegraph Centenary.

810. **233.** 3d. sepia and green .. 10 10
811. – 8d. black and red .. 35 55
DESIGN: 8d. Modern teleprinter.

236. Saddleback.

DESIGN: 2½d. Red-fronted Parakeet.

1962. Health Stamps.

812. – 2½d.+1d. multicoloured 20 30
813. **236.** 3d.+1d. multicoloured 20 30

237. "Madonna in Prayer" (Sassoferrato).

238. Prince Andrew.

1962. Christmas.

814. **237.** 2½d. multicoloured .. 10 10

1963. Health stamps.

815. **238.** 2½d.+1d. blue .. 10 30
816. – 3d.+1d. red 10 10
DESIGN: 3d. Prince Andrew (different).

240. "The Holy Family" (Titian).

1963. Christmas.

817. **240.** 2½d. multicoloured .. 10 10

241. Steam Loco. "Pilgrim" and "DG" Diesel Electric Loco.

1963. Centenary of Railway. Inscr. as in T **241**. Multicoloured.

818. 3d. Type **241** 30 10
819. 1s. 9d. Diesel Express and Mt. Ruapehu .. .. 1·60 80

1963. Opening of COMPAC (Trans-Pacific Telephone Cable). As T **174** of Australia.

820. 8d. multicoloured .. 50 90

244. Road Map and Car Steering-wheel.

1964. Road Safety Campaign.

821 **244** 3d. black, yellow & blue 20 10

245. Silver Gulls.

1964. Health stamps. Multicoloured.

822 2½d.+1d. Type **245** .. 25 20
823 3d.+1d. Little penguin .. 25 20

246. Rev. S. Marsden taking first Christian service at Rangihoua Bay, 1814.

1964. Christmas.

824. **246.** 2½d. multicoloured .. 10 10

1964. Surch. **7D POSTAGE.**

825. F 6. 7d. on (—) red 40 90

248. Anzac Cove.

1965. 50th Anniv. of Gallipoli Landing.

826. **248.** 4d. brown 10 10
827. 5d. green and red .. 10 30
The 5d. also has a poppy in the design.

249. I.T.U. Emblem and Symbols.

1965. Centenary of I.T.U.

828 **249** 9d. blue and brown .. 40 35

1965. Churchill Commem. As T **186** of Australia.

829. 7d. black, grey and blue .. 15 50

251. Wellington Provincial Council Building.

1965. Cent. of Government in Wellington.

830. **251.** 4d. multicoloured .. 10 10

252. Kaka.

1965. Health stamps. Multicoloured.

831. 3d.+1d. Type **252** .. 30 15
832. 4d.+1d. Collared Grey Fantail 30 15

254. I.C.Y. Emblem.

1965. Int. Co-operation Year.

833. **254.** 4d. red and olive .. 15 10

255. "The Two Trinities", (Murillo).

1965. Christmas.

834. **255.** 3d. multicoloured .. 10 10

256. Arms of New Zealand.

1965. 11th Commonwealth Parliamentary Conf. Multicoloured.

835. 4d. Type **256** 25 20
836. 9d. Parliament House, Wellington, and Badge 45 90
837. 2s. Wellington from Mt. Victoria .. .. 1·25 3·00

259. "Progress" Arrowhead.

260. New Zealand Bell Bird.

1966. 4th National Scout Jamboree, Trentham.

838. **259.** 4d. gold, and green .. 10 10

1966. Health stamps. Multicoloured.
839. 3d.+1d. Type **260** .. 15 25
840. 4d.+1d. Weka Rail .. 15 25

262. "The Virgin with Child" (Maratta). **263.** Queen Victoria and Queen Elizabeth II.

1966. Christmas.
842. **262.** 3d. multicoloured .. 10 10

1967. Centenary of New Zealand Post Office Savings Bank.
843. **263.** 4d. black, gold & purple 10 10
844. – 9d. multicoloured .. 10 15
DESIGN: 9d. Half-sovereign of 1867 and Commemorative Dollar coin.

265. Manuka (Tea Tree). **268.** Running with Ball.

1967. Decimal Currency. Designs as earlier issues, but with values inscr in decimal currency as T **265**.

845	**265**	½ c. blue, green & red	10	10
846	–	1 c. mult (No. 782) ..	10	10
847	–	2 c. mult (No. 783) ..	10	10
848	–	2½ c. mult (No. 785)	10	10
849	–	3 c. mult (No. 786) ..	10	10
850	–	4 c. mult (No. 787) ..	30	10
851	–	5 c. lilac, olive & green (No. 788) ..	65	10
852	–	6 c. mult (No. 788c)	70	10
853	–	7 c. mult (No. 789) ..	85	20
854	–	8 c. red and blue (No. 790)	85	10
855	**215**	10 c. brown & green	1·00	10
856	–	15 c. green and brown (No. 793) ..	60	60
857	**219**	20 c. black and buff	2·50	10
858	–	25 c. yellow and brown (No. 797) ..	6·00	90
859	–	30 c. yellow, green and blue (No. 799)	5·00	25
860	–	50 c. green (No. 800)	5·00	75
861	–	$1 blue (No. 801) ..	20·00	1·25
862	–	$2 mauve (No. 802)	11·00	12·00
F 219	F 6	$4 violet	2·00	55
F 220		$6 green	3·00	1·50
F 221		$8 blue	4·00	3·50
F 222		$10 blue	5·00	3·50

For 15 c. in different colours, see No. 874.

1967. Health Stamps. Rugby Football.
867. 2½ c.+1 c. multicoloured .. 15 10
868. 3 c.+1 c. multicoloured .. 15 10
DESIGNS—VERT. 2½ c. Type **268**. HORIZ. 3 c. Positioning for Place-kick.

271. Brown Trout.

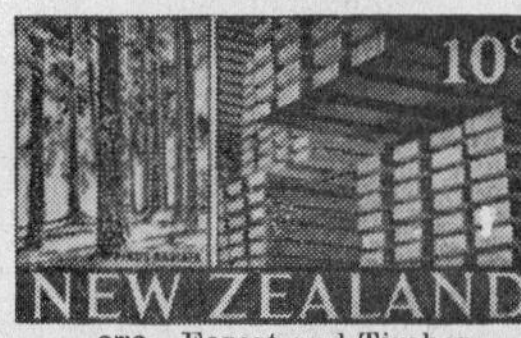

273. Forest and Timber.

1967.

870	–	7 c. multicoloured ..	1·50	90
871	**271.**	7½ c. multicoloured ..	30	70
872	–	8 c. multicoloured ..	75	70
873	**273.**	10c. multicoloured ..	50	10
874	–	15 c. grn., myrtle & red	1·00	60
875	–	18 c. multicoloured ..	1·40	55
876	–	20 c. multicoloured ..	1·40	20
877	–	25 c. multicoloured ..	6·00	2·00
878	–	28 c. multicoloured ..	60	10
879	–	$2 black, ochre & blue	35·00	19·00

DESIGNS: 7 c. "Kaiti" (trawler) and catch. 8 c. Apples and orchard. 15 c. as No. 793. 18 c. Sheep and the "Woolmark". 20 c. Consignments of beef and herd of cattle. 25 c. Dairy farm, Mt. Egmont and butter consignment. 28 c. Fox Glacier, Westland National Park. $2 as No. 802.

No. 871a was originally issued to commemorate the introduction of the brown trout into New Zealand.

No. 874 is slightly larger than No. 856, measuring 21 × 25 min. and the inscr. and numerals differ in size.

278. "The Adoration of the Shepherds" (Poussin). **279.** Mount Aspiring, Aurora Australis and Southern Cross.

1967. Christmas.
880. **278.** 2½ c. multicoloured .. 10 10

1967. Cent. of Royal Society of New Zealand.
881. **279.** 4 c. multicoloured .. 25 20
882. – 8 c. multicoloured .. 25 50
DESIGN: 8 c. Sir James Hector (founder).

281. Open Bible.

1968. Centenary of Maori Bible.
883. **281.** 3 c. multicoloured .. 10 10

282. Soldiers and Tank.

1968. New Zealand Armed Forces. Mult.
884. 4 c. Type **282** 30 15
885. 10 c. Airmen, Canberra and "Kittyhawk" Aircraft .. 50 25
886. 28 c. Sailors and H.M.N.Z.S. "Achilles", 1939 and H.M.N.Z.S. "Waikato", 1968 .. .. .. 70 1·40

285. Boy Breasting Tape and Olympic Rings.

1968. Health stamps. Multicoloured.
887. 2½ c.+1 c. Type **285** .. 10 10
888. 3 c.+1 c. Girl swimming and Olympic Rings .. 10 10

287. Placing Votes in Ballot Box. **288.** Human Rights Emblem.

1968. 75th Anniversary of Universal Suffrage in New Zealand.
890. **287.** 3 c. ochre, grn. & blue 10 10

1968. Human Rights Year.
891. **288.** 10 c. red, yellow & grn. 10 30

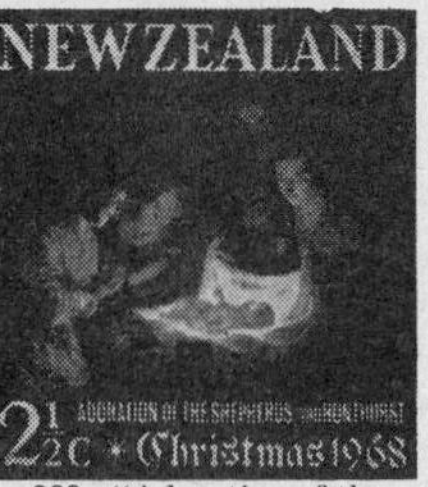

289. "Adoration of the Holy Child" (G. van Honthorst).

1968. Christmas.
892. **289.** 2½ c. multicoloured .. 10 10

290. ILO Emblem.

1969. 50th Anniv. of Int. Labour Organization.
893. **290.** 7 c. black and red .. 15 30

291. Supreme Court Building, Auckland.

1969. Cent. of New Zealand Law Society.
894. **291.** 3 c. multicoloured .. 10 10
895. – 10 c. multicoloured .. 35 45
896. – 18 c. multicoloured .. 45 70
DESIGNS—VERT. 10 c. Law Society's Coat of Arms. 18 c. "Justice" (from Memorial Window in University of Canterbury, Christchurch).

295. Student being conferred with degree.

1969. Cent. of Otago University. Mult.
897. 3 c. Otago University (vert.) 10 10
898. 10 c. Type **295** 20 25

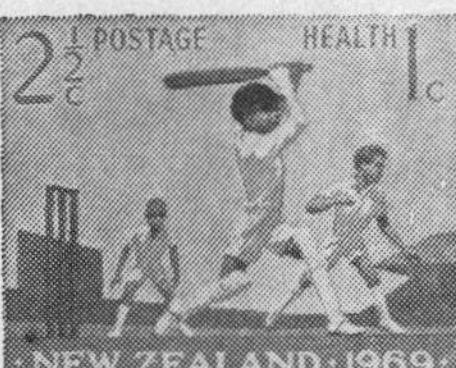

296. Boys playing Cricket.

1969. Health stamps.
899. **296.** 2½ c.+1 c. multicoloured 40 40
900. – 3 c.+1 c. multicoloured 40 40
901. – 4 c.+1 c. brown & ultram 40 1·40
DESIGNS—HORIZ. 3 c. Girls playing cricket. VERT. 4 c. Dr. Elizabeth Gunn (founder of 1st Children's Health Camp).

299. Oldest existing House in New Zealand, and Old Stone Mission Store. Kerikeri.

1969. Early European Settlement in New Zealand, and 150th Anniv. of Kerikeri. Multicoloured.
903. 4 c. Type **299** 20 25
904. 6 c. View of Bay of Islands 30 1·25

301. "The Nativity" (Federico Fiori (Barocci)).

1969. Christmas.
905. **301.** 2½ c. multicoloured .. 10 10

302. Captain Cook, Transit of Venus and "Octant".

1969. Bicentenary of Captain Cook's landing in New Zealand.
906. **302.** 4 c. black, red and blue 1·00 35
907. – 6 c. grn., brn. and blk. 1·25 2·75
908. – 18 c. brn., grn. & blk. 2·75 2·75
909. – 28 c. red, blk. and blue 4·50 4·75
DESIGNS: 6 c. Sir Joseph Banks (naturalist) and outline of H.M.S. "Endeavour". 18 c. Dr. Daniel Solander (botanist) and his plant. 28 c. Queen Elizabeth II and Cook's Chart, 1769.

306. Girl, Wheat Field and C.O.R.S.O. Emblem.

1969. 25th Anniversary of C.O.R.S.O. (Council of Organizations for Relief Services Overseas). Multicoloured.
911. 7 c. Type **306** 20 90
912. 8 c. Mother feeding her child, dairy herd and C.O.R.S.O. Emblem (horiz.) .. 20 90

308. "Cardigan Bay" (Champion trotter).

1970. Return of "Cardigan Bay" to New Zealand.
913. **308.** 10 c. multicoloured .. 20 25

309. "Vanessa gonerilla".

310. Queen Elizabeth II and New Zealand Coat of Arms.

1970.

914	–	½ c. multicoloured ..	10	20
915	**309**	1 c. multicoloured ..	10	10
916	–	2 c. multicoloured ..	10	10
917	–	2½c. multicoloured ..	40	20
918	–	3 c. multicoloured ..	15	10
919	–	4 c. multicoloured ..	15	10
920	–	5 c. multicoloured ..	45	10
921	–	6 c. black, green and red	45	20
922	–	7 c. multicoloured ..	55	40
923	–	7½ c. multicoloured ..	1·00	1·50
924	–	8 c. multicoloured ..	65	60

925 310 10 c. multicoloured .. 40 15
926 – 15 c. blk., flesh & brn. 1·50 50
927 – 18 c. grn., brn. & blk. 1·50 40
1020 – 20 c. black and brown 80 10
929 – 23 c. multicoloured .. 80 30
930b – 25 c. multicoloured .. 70 40
931 – 30 c. multicoloured .. 2·25 15
932 – 50 c. multicoloured .. 80 20
933 – $1 multicoloured .. 2·75 85
934 – $2 multicoloured .. 5·50 1·25

DESIGNS—As Type **309**. ½ c. "Lycaena salustius" (butterfly). 2 c. "Argyrophenga antipodum" (butterfly). 2½ c. "Nyctemera annulata" (moth). 3 c. "Detunda egregia" (moth). 4 c. "Charagia virescens" (moth). 5 c. Scarlet parrot fish. 6 c. Sea horses. 7 c. Leather jacket (fish). 7½ c. Garfish. 8 c. John Dory (fish). As Type **310**. HORIZ. 15 c. Maori fish hook. 20 c. Maori tattoo pattern. 23 c. Egmont National Park. 50 c. Abel Tasman National Park. $1 Geothermal power. $2 Agricultural technology. VERT. 18 c. Maori club. 25 c. Hauraki Gulf Maritime Park. 30 c. Mt. Cook National Park.

311. Geyser Restaurant.

1970. World Fair, Osaka. Multicoloured
935. 7 c. Type **311** 40 75
936. 8 c. New Zealand Pavilion 40 75
937. 18 c. Bush Walk 60 75

312. U.N. H.Q. Building.

314. "The Virgin adoring the Child" (Correggio).

313. Soccer.

1970. 25th Anniv. of United Nations.
938. **312.** 3 c. multicoloured .. 10 10
939. – 10 c. red and yellow .. 20 20
DESIGN: 10 c. Tractor on horizon.

1970. Health Stamps. Multicoloured.
940. 2½ c.+1 c. Netball (vert.) 10 20
941. 3 c.+1 c. Type **313** .. 10 20

1970. Christmas.
943. **314.** 2½ c. multicoloured .. 10 10
944. – 3 c. multicoloured .. 10 10
945. – 10 c. blk., orge. & silver 30 75
DESIGNS—VERT. 3 c. Stained Glass Window, Invercargill Presbyterian Church "The Holy Family". HORIZ. 10 c. Tower of Roman Catholic Church, Sockburn.

316. Chatham Islands Lily.

1970. Chatham Islands, Multicoloured.
946. 1 c. Type **316** 10 20
947. 2 c. Shy Albatross .. 30 30

317. Country Women's Institutes Emblem.

1971. 50th Anniv. of Country Women's Institutes and Rotary International in New Zealand. Multicoloured.
948. 4 c. Type **317** 10 10
949. 10 c. Rotary emblem and map of New Zealand .. 10 20

318. "Rainbow II" (yacht).

1971. One-Ton Cup Racing Trophy. Mult.
950. 5 c. Type **318** 15 20
951. 8 c. One-Ton Cup 25 65

319. Civic Arms of Palmerston North.

1971. City Centenaries. Multicoloured.
952. 3 c. Type **319** 10 10
953. 4 c. Arms of Auckland .. 10 10
954. 5 c. Arms of Invercargill .. 15 40

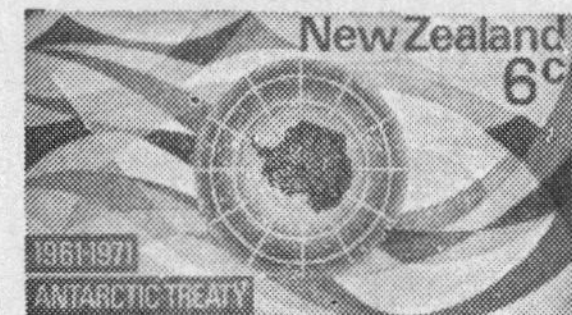

320. Antarctica on Globe.

1971. 10th Anniv. of Antarctic Treaty.
955. **320.** 6 c. multicoloured .. 1·50 1·50

321. Child on Swing.

1971. 25th Anniv. of U.N.I.C.E.F.
956. **321.** 7 c. multicoloured .. 50 70

1971. No. 917 surch.
957. 4 c. on 2½ c. multicoloured 15 10

323. Satellite-tracking Aerial.

1971. Opening of Satellite Earth Station.
958. **323.** 8 c. blk., grey and red 60 1·00
959. – 10 c. blk., green & violet 65 1·00
DESIGN: 10 c. Satellite.

324. Girls playing Hockey.

1971. Health Stamps. Multicoloured.
960. 3 c.+1 c. Type **324** .. 45 50
961. 4 c.+1 c. Boys playing Hockey 45 50
962. 5 c.+1 c. Dental Health .. 1·10 2·00

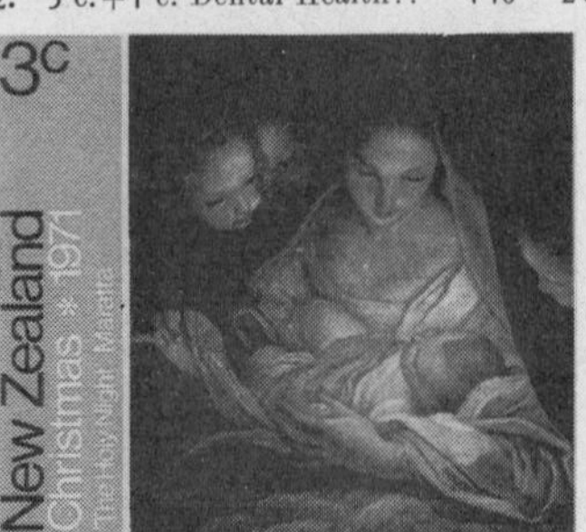

325. "Madonna bending over the Crib." (Maratta).

1971. Christmas. Multicoloured.
964. 3 c. Type **325** 10 10
965. 4 c. "The Annunication" (stained-glass window) 10 10
966. 10 c. "The Three Kings" 70 1·25
Nos. 965/6 are smaller, size 21½ × 38 mm.

326. "Tiffany" Rose.

1971. 1st World Rose Convention, Hamilton Roses. Multicoloured.
967. 2 c. Type **326** 15 30
968. 5 c. "Peace" 35 35
969. 8 c. "Chrysler Imperial" 60 1·10

327. Lord Rutherford and Alpha Particles.

1971. Birth Centenary of Lord Rutherford (scientist). Multicoloured.
970. 1 c. Type **327** 25 40
971. 7 c. Lord Rutherford and formula .. .. 85 1·40

328. Benz (1895).

1972. Int. Vintage Car Rally. Multicoloured.
972. 3 c. Type **328** 20 10
973. 4 c. Oldsmobile (1904) .. 25 10
974. 5 c. Ford "Model T" (1914) 35 10
975. 6 c. Cadillac Service car (1915) 55 45
976. 8 c. Chrysler (1924) .. 1·25 1·25
977. 10 c. Austin "7" (1923) .. 1·25 1·25

329. Coat of Arms of Wanganui.

330. Black Scree Cotula.

1972. Anniversaries.
978. **329.** 3 c. multicoloured .. 15 10
979. – 4 c. orge., brn. & blk. .. 15 10
980. – 5 c. multicoloured .. 25 10
981. – 8 c. multicoloured .. 1·50 1·60
982. – 10 c. multicoloured .. 1·50 1·60
DESIGNS AND EVENTS—VERT. 3 c. (Wanganui Council Govt. Cent.). 5 c. De Havilland DH 89 "Rapide Dominie" and Boeing "737" (National Airways Corp. 25th Anniv.). 8 c. French frigate and Maori palisade (landing by Marion du Fresne. Bicent.). HORIZ. 4 c. Postal Union symbol (Asian–Oceanic Postal Union. 10th Anniv.). 10 c. Stone cairn (New Zealand Methodist Church. 15th Anniv.).

1972. Alpine Plants. Multicoloured.
983. 4 c. Type **330** 30 10
984. 6 c. North Island Edelweiss 75 60
985. 8 c. Haast's Buttercup .. 1·25 1·25
986. 10 c. Brown Mountain Daisy 1·75 1·75

331. Boy playing Tennis.

332. "Madonna with Child" (Murillo).

1972. Health Stamps.
987. **331.** 3 c.+1 c. grey & brown 30 45
988. – 4 c.+1 c. brn., grey & yellow 30 45
DESIGN: No. 988, Girl playing tennis.

1972. Christmas. Multicoloured.
990. 3 c. Type **332** 10 10
991. 5 c. "The Last Supper" (stained-glass window, St. John's Church, Levin) 15 10
992. 10 c. Pohutukawa flower .. 55 1·00

333. Lake Waikaremoana.

1972. Lake Scenes. Multicoloured.
993. 6 c. Type **333** .. .. 1·00 1·25
994. 8 c. Lake Hayes .. .. 1·10 1·25
995. 18 c. Lake Wakatipu .. 2·00 2·25
996. 23 c. Lake Rotomahana .. 2·25 2·75

334. Old Pollen Street.

1973. Commemorations.
997. **334.** 3 c. multicoloured .. 15 10
998. – 4 c. multicoloured .. 15 10
999. – 5 c. multicoloured .. 15 15
1000. – 6 c. multicoloured .. 50 80
1001. – 8 c. grey, blue & gold 45 1·00
1002. – 10 c. multicoloured 50 1·60
DESIGNS AND EVENTS: 3 c. (Thames Borough. Cent.). 4 c. Coalmining and pasture (Westport Borough. Cent.). 5 c. Cloister (Canterbury University. Cent.) 6 c. Forest, birds and lake (Royal Forest and Bird Protection Society. 50th Anniv.) 8 c. Rowers (Success of N.Z. Rowers in 1972 Olympics). 10 c. Graph and people (E.C.A.F.E. 25th Anniv.).

335. Class "W" Locomotive.

1973. New Zealand Steam Locomotives. Multicoloured.
1003. 3 c. Type **335** 50 10
1004. 4 c. Class "X" 65 10
1005. 5 c. Class "Ab" 65 10
1006. 10 c. Class "Ja" .. .. 2·50 1·75

336. "Maori Woman and Child".

337. Prince Edward.

1973. Paintings by Frances Hodgkins. Multicoloured.

1027. 5 c. Type **336** 40 15
1028. 8 c. " Hilltop " 75 75
1029. 10 c. " Barn in Picardy " 1·00 1·25
1030. 18 c. " Self-portrait Still Life " .. .. .. 1·50 2·50

1973. Health Stamps.

1031. **337.** 3 c.+1 c. green & brn. 30 30
1032. 4 c.+1 c. red & brown 30 30

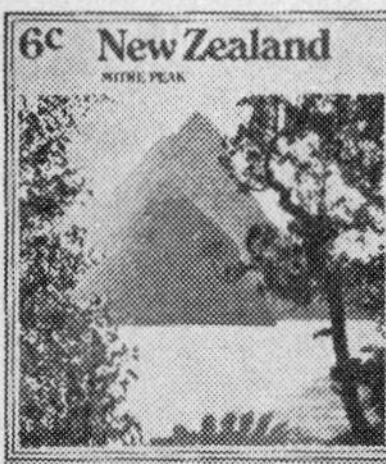

338. " Tempi Madonna " (Raphael). **339.** Mitre Peak.

1973. Christmas. Multicoloured.

1034. 3 c. Type **338** 10 10
1035. 5 c. " Three Kings " (Stained-glass window, St. Theresa's Church, Auckland) 10 10
1036. 10 c. Family entering church 25 50

1973. Mountain Scenery. Multicoloured.

1037. 6 c. Type **339** 80 90
1038. 8 c. Mt. Ngauruhoe .. 1·00 1·50
1039. 18 c. Mt. Sefton (horiz.).. 1·75 3·00
1040. 23 c. Burnett Range (horiz.) 2·00 3·00

340. Hurdling. **342.** "Spirit of Napier" Fountain.

1974. 10th British Commonwealth Games, Christchurch.

1041. **340.** 4 c. multicoloured .. 10 10
1042. – 5 c. black and violet.. 15 10
1043. – 10 c. multicoloured.. 20 15
1044. – 18 c. multicoloured.. 35 65
1045. – 23 c. multicoloured.. 50 85

DESIGNS: 5 c. Ball-player (4th Paraplegic Games, Dunedin). 10 c. Cycling. 18 c. Rifle-shooting. 23 c. Bowls.

1974. Cents. of Napier and U.P.U. Mult.

1047. 4 c. Type **342** 10 10
1048. 5 c. Clock Tower, Berne.. 10 15
1049. 8 c. U.P.U. Monument, Berne 35 90

343. Boeing Seaplane, 1919.

1974. History of New Zealand Airmail Transport. Multicoloured.

1050. 3 c. Type **343** 25 10
1051. 4 c. Lockheed "Electra", 1937 30 10
1052. 5 c. Bristol Freighter, 1958 35 10
1053. 23 c. Empire "S-30" Flying-boat, 1940 .. 1·50 1·50

344. Children, Cat and Dog.

1974. Health Stamps.

1054. **344.** 3 c.+1 c. multicoloured 20 30
1055. – 4 c.+1 c. multicoloured 25 30
1056. – 5 c.+1 c. multicoloured 1·00 1·25

Nos. 1055/56 are similar to Type **344** showing children with pets.

345. " The Adoration of the Magi " (Konrad Witz).

1974. Christmas. Multicoloured.

1058. 3 c. Type **345** 10 10
1059. 5 c. " The Angel window " (stained-glass window Old St. Pauls Church, Wellington) 10 10
1060. 10 c. Madonna Lily .. 30 50

346. Great Barrier Island.

1974. Off-shore Islands. Mult.

1061. 6 c. Type **346** 30 40
1062. 8 c. Stewart Island .. 40 80
1063. 18 c. White Island .. 70 1·50
1064. 23 c. The Brothers .. 1·00 2·00

347. Crippled Child.

1975. Anniversaries and Events. Mult.

1065. 3 c. Type **347** 10 10
1066. 5 c. Farming family .. 15 10
1067. 10 c. I.W.Y. symbols .. 20 55
1068. 18 c. Medical School Building, Otago University 35 80

COMMEMORATIONS: 3 c. New Zealand Crippled Children Society. 40th anniv. 5 c. Women's Division, Federated Farmers of New Zealand. 50th anniv. 10 c. International Women's Year. 18 c. Otago Medical School. Centenary.

348. Scow "Lake Erie".

1975. Historic Sailing Ships.

1069. **348.** 4 c. black and red .. 30 10
1070. – 5 c. black and blue.. 30 10
1071. – 8 c. black and yellow 45 35
1072. – 10 c. black and yellow 50 40
1073. – 18 c. black & brown.. 80 90
1074. – 23 c. black & lilac .. 95 1·25

SHIPS: 5 c. Schooner "Herald". 8 c. Brigantine "New Zealander". 10 c. Topsail schooner "Jessie Kelly". 18 c. Barque "Tory". 23 c. Full-rigged clipper "Ragitiki".

349. Lake Sumner Forest Park.

1975. Forest Park Scenes. Multicoloured.

1075. 6 c. Type **349** 50 70
1076. 8 c. North-west Nelson .. 60 1·00
1077. 18 c. Kaweka .. .. 1·25 1·75
1078. 23 c. Coromandel .. 1·50 2·00

350. Girl feeding Lamb.

1975. Health Stamps. Multicoloured.

1079. 3 c.+1 c. Type **350** .. 20 25
1080. 4 c.+1 c. Boy with hen chicks 20 25
1081. 5 c.+1 c. Boy with duck and duckling .. .. 60 1·10

351. " Virgin and Child " (Zanobi Machiavelli).

1975. Christmas. Multicoloured.

1083. 3 c. Type **351** 10 10
1084. 5 c. " Cross in Landscape " (stained-glass window, Greendale Church) .. 10 10
1085. 10 c. "I saw three ships . . ." (carol) 35 65

The 5 c. and 10 c. are horizontal.

352. " Sterling Silver ". **353.** Queen Elizabeth II (photograph by W. Harrison).

353a. Maripi (knife). **353b.** " Paua ".

1975.

(a) Garden Roses. Multicoloured.

1086 1 c. Type **352** 10 10
1087 2 c. " Lilli Marlene " .. 10 10
1088 3 c. " Queen Elizabeth " 60 10
1089 4 c. " Super Star " .. 10 10
1090 5 c. " Diamond Jubilee " 10 10
1091a 6 c. " Cresset " 40 40
1092a 7 c. " Michele Meilland " 40 10
1093a 8 c. " Josephine Bruce " 65 10
1094 9 c. " Iceberg " 15 20

(b) Type **353.**

1094ab. 10 c. multicoloured .. 30 10

(c) Maori Artefacts.

1095. **353a.** 11 c. brn., yell. & blk. 45 40
1096. – 12 c. brn., yell. & blk. 30 10
1097. – 13 c. brn., mve. & blk. 60 40
1098. – 14 c. brn., yell. & blk. 30 20

DESIGNS: 12 c. Putorino (flute). 13 c. Wahaika (club). 14 c. Kotiate (club).

(d) Seashells. Multicoloured.

1099. 20 c. Type **353b**.. .. 15 20
1100. 30 c. " Toheroa " .. 25 30
1101. 40 c. " Coarse Dosinia " 30 35
1102. 50 c. " Spiny Murex " .. 40 45
1103. $1 Scallop 70 85
1104. $2 Circular saw .. .. 1·00 1·75

(e) Building. Multicoloured.

1105. $5 " Beehive " (section of Parliamentary Buildings, Wellington) (22 × 26 mm.) .. .. 3·00 2·00

INDEX
Countries can be quickly located by referring to the index at the end of this volume.

354. Family and League of Mothers Badge.

1976. Anniversaries and Metrication. Mult.

1110. 6 c. Type **354** 10 10
1111. 7 c. Weight, temperature, linear measure and capacity 10 10
1112. 8 c. "William Bryon" (immigrant ship), mountain and New Plymouth 15 10
1113. 10 c. Two women shaking hands and Y.W.C.A. badge .. 15 40
1114. 25 c. Map of the world showing cable links .. 30 1·25

ANNIVERSARIES. 6 c. League of Mothers, 50th Anniversary. 7 c. Metrication. 8 c. Centenary of New Plymouth. 10 c. 50th Anniversary of New Zealand Y.W.C.A. 25 c. Link with International Telecommunications Network, Centenary.

355. Gig.

1976. Vintage Farm Transport. Multicoloured.

1115. 6 c. Type **355** 15 20
1116. 7 c. Thorneycroft lorry.. 20 10
1117. 8 c. Scandi wagon .. 50 20
1118. 9 c. Traction engine .. 30 40
1119. 10 c. Wool wagon .. 30 75
1120. 25 c. Cart .. .. 80 1·75

356. Purakaunui Falls.

1976. Waterfalls. Multicoloured.

1121. 10 c. Type **356** 40 10
1122. 14 c. Marakopa Falls .. 75 55
1123. 15 c. Bridal Veil Falls .. 80 60
1124. 16 c. Papakorito Falls .. 90 70

357. Boy and Pony.

1976. Health Stamps. Multicoloured.

1125. 7 c.+1 c. Type **357** .. 25 30
1126. 8 c.+1 c. Girl and calf .. 25 30
1127. 10 c.+1 c. Girls and bird 50 75

358. " Nativity " (Spanish carving).

1976. Christmas. Multicoloured.

1129. 7 c. Type **358** 15 10
1130. 11 c. " Resurrection " (stained-glass window, St. Joseph's Catholic Church, Grey Lynn) (horiz.) 25 30
1131. 18 c. Angels (horiz.) .. 40 60

359. Arms of Hamilton. **361.** Physical Education and Maori Culture.

1977. Anniversaries. Multicoloured.

1132. 8 c. Type **359** 15 10
1133. 8 c. Arms of Gisborne .. 15 10
1134. 8 c. Arms of Masterton .. 15 10
1135. 10 c. A.A. emblem .. 15 30
1136. 10 c. Arms of the Royal Australasian College of Surgeons 15 30

ANNIVERSARIES: No. 1132, Hamilton Cent. No. 1133, Gisborne Cent. No. 1134, Masterton Cent. No. 1135, Automobile Association in New Zealand. 75th Anniv. No. 1136, R.A.C.S. 50th Anniv.

1977. Education. Multicoloured.

1138. 8 c. Type **361** 30 60
1139. 8 c. Geography, science and woodwork .. 30 60
1140. 8 c. Teaching the deaf, kindergarten and wood-work 30 60
1141. 8 c. Tertiary and language classes 30 60
1142. 8 c. Home science, correspondence school and teacher training .. 30 60

1977. Nos. 918/19 surch.

1143 7 c. on 3 c. "Detunda egregia" (moth) .. 40 65
1144 8 c. on 4 c. "Charagia virescens" (moth) .. 40 65

363. Karitane Beach.

1977. Seascapes. Multicoloured.

1145. 10 c. Type **363** 20 10
1146. 16 c. Ocean Beach, Mount Maunganui 35 35
1147. 18 c. Piha Beach .. 40 40
1148. 30 c. Kaikoura Coast .. 50 50

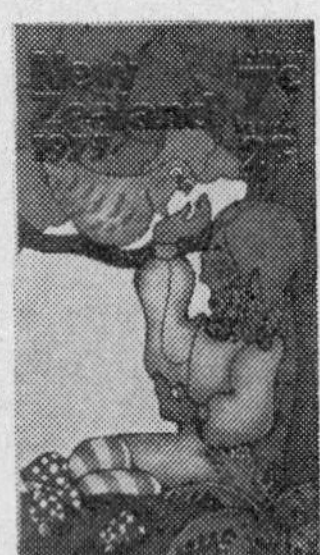

364. Girl with Pigeon.

1977. Health Stamps. Multicoloured.

1149. 7 c.+2 c. Type **364** .. 20 35
1150. 8 c.+2 c. Boy with frog 25 35
1151. 10 c.+2 c. Girl with Butterfly 45 70

365. "The Holy Family" (Correggio).

1977. Christmas. Multicoloured.

1153. 7 c. Type **365** 15 10
1154. 16 c. "Madonna and Child" (stained-glass window, St. Michael's and All Angels, Dunedin) .. 25 20
1155. 23 c. "Partridge in a Pear Tree" 40 45

The 16 c. and 23 c. are vertical.

366. Merryweather Manual Pump, 1860.

1977. Fire Fighting Appliances. Mult.

1156. 10 c. Type **366** 15 10
1157. 11 c. 2-wheel hose reel and ladder, 1880 .. 15 10
1158. 12 c. Shand Mason steam fire engine, 1873 .. 20 15
1159. 23 c. Chemical fire engine, 1888 .. .. .. 30 30

367. Town Clock and Coat of Arms, Ashburton. **368.** Students and Ivey Hall, Lincoln College.

1978. Centenaries.

1160. **367.** 10 c. multicoloured .. 15 10
1161. – 10 c. multicoloured .. 15 10
1162. – 12 c. red, yell. & blk. 15 15
1163. – 20 c. multicoloured .. 20 30

DESIGNS—VERT. No. 1161, Mount Egmont (Centenary of Stratford). No. 1162, Early telephone (Centenary of telephone in New Zealand). HORIZ. No. 1163, Aerial view of the Bay of Islands (Centenary of the Bay of Islands County).

1978. Centenary of Land Resources and Lincoln College of Agriculture. Multicoloured.

1164. 10 c. Type **368** 15 10
1165. 12 c. Sheep grazing .. 20 25
1166. 15 c. Fertiliser ground spreading 20 30
1167. 16 c. Agricultural Field Days 20 30
1168. 20 c. Harvesting grain .. 25 40
1169. 30 c. Dairy farming .. 40 70

369. **370.** Maui Gas Drilling Platform.

1978. Coil Stamps.

1170. **369.** 1 c. purple 10 30
1171. 2 c. orange 10 30
1172. 5 c. brown 10 35
1173. 10 c. blue 30 70

1978. Resources of the Sea. Multicoloured.

1174. 12 c. Type **370** 20 15
1175. 15 c. Trawler 30 25
1176. 20 c. Map of 200 mile fishing limit 40 35
1177. 23 c. Humpback Whale and Bottle-nosed Dolphins 50 40
1178. 35 c. Kingfish, snapper, grouper and squid .. 75 75

371. First Health Charity Stamp. **372.** "The Holy Family" (El Greco).

1978. Health Stamps.

1179. **371.** 10 c.+2 c. black, red and gold 25 35
1180. – 12 c.+2 c. mult. .. 25 40

DESIGN: 10 c. Type **371** (50th anniv. of Health Stamps). 12 c. Heart Operation (National Heart Foundation).

1978. Christmas. Multicoloured.

1182. 7 c. Type **372** 10 10
1183. 16 c. All Saints' Church, Howick (horiz.) .. 25 30
1184. 23 c. Beach scene (horiz.) 30 45

373. Sir Julius Vogel.

1979. Statesmen. Designs each brown and drab.

1185. 10 c. Type **373** 30 55
1186. 10 c. Sir George Grey .. 30 55
1187. 10 c. Richard John Seddon 30 55

374. Riverlands Cottage, Blenheim.

1979. Architecture (1st series).

1188. **374.** 10 c. black, bright blue and blue 10 10
1189. – 12 c. black, pale green and green 15 25
1190. – 15 c. black and grey .. 20 30
1191. – 20 c. black, yellow-brown and brown .. 25 30

DESIGNS: 12 c. The Mission House, Waimate North. 15 c. "The Elms", Tauranga. 20 c. Provincial Council Buildings, Christchurch.

See also Nos. 1217/20 and 1262/5.

375. Whangaroa Harbour.

1979. Small Harbours. Multicoloured.

1192. 15 c. Type **375** 20 10
1193. 20 c. Kawau Island .. 25 30
1194. 23 c. Akaroa Harbour (vert.) 30 35
1195. 35 c. Picton Harbour (vert.) 45 50

376. Children with Building Bricks.

1979. International Year of the Child.

1196. **376.** 10 c. multicoloured .. 15 10

377. Demoiselle.

1979. Health Stamps. Marine Life. Multicoloured.

1197. 10 c.+2 c. Type **377** .. 40 50
1198. 10 c.+2 c. Sea Urchin .. 40 50
1199. 12 c.+2 c. Fish and Underwater cameraman (vert.) 40 50

1979. Nos. 1091/3 and 1094a surch.

1201. 4 c. on 8 c. "Josephine Bruce" 10 20
1202. 14 c on 10 c. Type **353** .. 40 20
1203. 17 c. on 6 c. "Cresset" .. 40 70
1203a. 20 c. on 7 c. "Michele Meilland" 35 10

379. "Madonna and Child". (sculpture, Ghiberti).

1979. Christmas. Multicoloured.

1204. 10 c. Type **379** 15 10
1205. 25 c. Christ Church, Russell 30 40
1206. 35 c. Pohutukawa (tree) 40 55

380. Chamber, House of Representatives.

1979. 25th Commonwealth Parliamentary Conference, Wellington. Multicoloured.

1207. 14 c. Type **380** 15 10
1208. 20 c. Mace and Black Rod 20 20
1209. 30 c. "Beehive" wall hanging 30 45

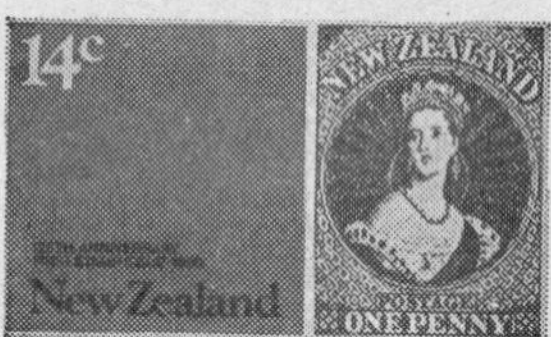

381. 1855 1d. Stamp.

1980. Anniversaries and Events.

1210. **381.** 14 c. blk, red & yellow 20 20
1211. – 14 c. blk, blue & yell. 20 20
1212. – 14 c. blk., grn. & yell. 20 20
1213. – 17 c. multicoloured 20 25
1214. – 25 c. multicoloured 25 30
1215. – 30 c. multicoloured 25 35

DESIGNS: No. 1211, 1855 2d. stamp. No. 1212, 1855 1s. stamp (New Zealand stamps, 125th anniv.). No. 1213, Geyser, wood-carving and building (Rotorua (town) cent.). No. 1214, "Earina autumnalis" and "Thelymitra venosa" (International Orchid Conference, Auckland). No. 1215, Ploughing and Golden Plough Trophy (World Ploughing Championships, Christchurch).

382. Ewelme Cottage, Parnell.

1980. Architecture (2nd series). Mult.

1217. 14 c. Type **382** 15 10
1218. 17 c. Broadgreen, Nelson 25 35
1219. 25 c. Courthouse, Oamaru 30 45
1220. 30 c. Government Buildings, Wellington .. 35 45

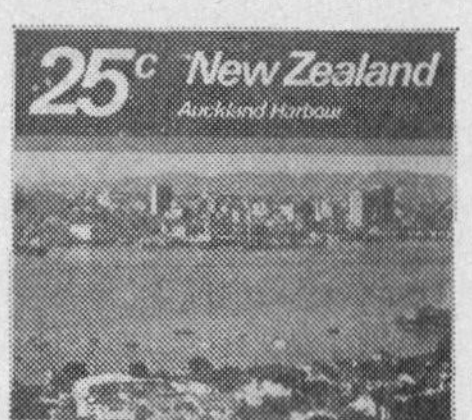

383. Auckland Harbour.

1980. Large Harbours. Multicoloured.

1221. 25 c. Type **383** 30 25
1222. 30 c. Wellington Harbour 35 30
1223. 35 c. Lyttelton Harbour 40 40
1224. 50 c. Port Chalmers .. 65 65

384. Surf-fishing.

1980. Health Stamps. Fishing. Mult.

No.	Description		
1225.	14 c. + 2 c. Type **384**	45	70
1226.	14 c. + 2 c. Wharf-fishing	45	70
1227.	17 c. + 2 c. Spear-fishing	45	55

385. " Madonna and Child with Cherubim " (sculpture, Andrea della Robbia).

1980. Christmas. Multicoloured.

No.	Description		
1229.	10 c. Type **385**	15	10
1230.	25 c. St. Mary's Church, New Plymouth	25	25
1231.	35 c. Picnic scene	40	55

386. Te Heu Heu (chief).

1980. Maori Personalities. Multicoloured.

No.	Description		
1232.	15 c. Type **386**	10	10
1233.	25 c. Te Hau (chief)	15	10
1234.	35 c. Te Puea (princess)	20	10
1235.	45 c. Ngata (politician)	30	15
1236.	60 c. Te Ata-O-Tu (warrior)	35	20

387. Lt. Col. the Hon. W. H. A. Feilding and Borough of Feilding Crest (cent.).

1981. Commemorations.

No.	Type	Description		
1237.	387.	20 c. multicoloured	20	20
1238.	—	25 c. orange and black	25	25

DESIGN and COMMEMORATION: 25 c. I.Y.D. emblem and cupped hands (International Year of Disabled).

388. The Family at Play.

1981. " Family Life ". Multicoloured.

No.	Description		
1239.	20 c. Type **388**	20	10
1240.	25 c. The family young and old	25	25
1241.	30 c. The family at home	30	35
1242.	35 c. The family at church	35	50

389. Kaiauai River.

1981. River Scenes. Multicoloured.

No.	Description		
1243.	30 c. Type **389**	30	30
1244.	35 c. Mangahao	40	40
1245.	40 c. Shotover (horiz.)	45	45
1246.	60 c. Cleddau (horiz.)	75	75

390. St. Paul's Cathedral.

1981. Royal Wedding. Multicoloured.

No.	Description		
1247.	20 c. Type **390**	20	30
1248.	20 c. Prince Charles and Lady Diana Spencer	20	30

391. Girl with Starfish. 392. " Madonna Suckling the Child " (painting, d'Oggiono).

1981. Health stamps. Children playing by the Sea. Multicoloured.

No.	Description		
1249.	20 c.+2 c. Type **391**	25	50
1250.	20 c.+2 c. Boy fishing	25	50
1251.	25 c.+2 c. Children exploring rock pool	25	35

Nos. 1249/50 were printed together, se-tenant, forming a composite design.

1981. Christmas. Multicoloured.

No.	Description		
1253.	14 c. Type **392**	15	10
1254.	30 c. St. John's Church, Wakefield	35	25
1255.	40 c. Golden Tainui (flower)	45	35

393. Tauranga Mission House. 394. Map of New Zealand.

1981. Commemorations. Multicoloured.

No.	Description		
1256.	20 c. Type **393**	25	10
1257.	20 c. Water tower, Hawera	25	10
1258.	25 c. Cat	35	35
1259.	30 c. "Dunedin" (refrigerated sailing ship)	35	40
1260.	35 c. Scientific research equipment	40	45

COMMEMORATIONS: No. 1256. Centenary of Tauranga (town). No. 1257. Centenary of Hawera (town). No. 1258. Centenary of S.P.C.A. (Society for the Prevention of Cruelty to Animals in New Zealand). No. 1259. Centenary of Frozen Meat Exports. No. 1260. International Year of Science.

1982.

No.	Type	Description		
1261	**394**	24 c. green and blue	30	10

395. Alberton, Auckland.

1982. Architecture (3rd series). Multicoloured.

No.	Description		
1262.	20 c. Type **395**	20	15
1263.	25 c. Caccia Birch, Palmerston North	25	25
1264.	30 c. Railway station, Dunedin	30	30
1265.	35 c. Post Office, Ophir	35	40

396. Kaiteriteri Beach, Nelson, (Summer).

1982. New Zealand Scenes. Multicoloured.

No.	Description		
1266.	35 c. Type **396**	40	40
1267.	40 c. St. Omer Park, Queenstown, (Autumn)	45	45
1268.	45 c. Mt. Ngauruhoe, Tongariro National Park, (Winter)	50	50
1269.	70 c. Wairarapa farm, (Spring)	75	75

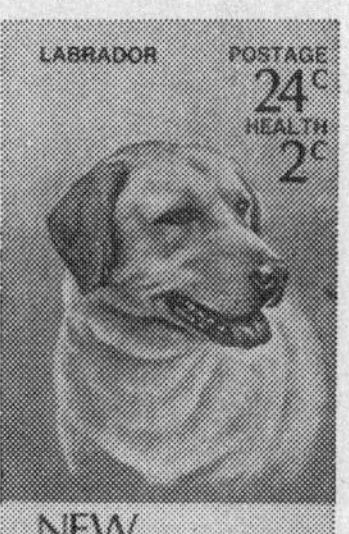

397. Labrador.

1982. Health Stamps. Dogs. Multicoloured.

No.	Description		
1270.	24 c.+2 c. Type **397**	75	80
1271.	24 c.+2 c. Border Collie	75	80
1272.	30 c.+2 c. Cocker Spaniel	75	80

398. " Madonna with Child and Two Angels " (painting by Piero di Cosimo).

1982. Christmas. Multicoloured.

No.	Description		
1274.	18 c. Type **398**	20	10
1275.	35 c. Rangiatea Maori Church, Otaki	35	30
1276.	45 c. Surf life-saving	50	40

399. Nephrite. 399a. Grapes.

399b. Kokako.

1982. (a) Minerals. Multicoloured.

No.	Description		
1277.	1 c. Type **399**	10	10
1278.	2 c. Agate	10	10
1279.	3 c. Iron Pyrites	10	10
1280.	4 c. Amethyst	10	10
1281.	5 c. Carnelian	10	10
1282.	9 c. Native Sulphur	20	10

(b) Fruits. Multicoloured.

No.	Description		
1283.	10 c. Type **399a**	75	10
1284.	20 c. Citrus Fruit	35	10
1285.	30 c. Nectarines	30	10
1286.	40 c. Apples	35	10
1287.	50 c. Kiwifruit	40	10

(c) Native Birds. Multicoloured.

No.	Description		
1288.	30 c. Kakapo	50	25
1289.	40 c. Mountain duck	60	35
1290.	45 c. New Zealand falcon	1·00	35
1291.	60 c. New Zealand teal	1·00	40
1292.	$1 Type **399b**	1·50	30
1293.	$2 Chatham Island robin	1·75	50
1294.	$3 Stitchbird	2·00	1·40
1295.	$4 Saddleback	2·75	3·00
1296.	$5 Takahe	3·25	3·50
1297.	$10 Little spotted Kiwi	6·50	6·75

400. Salvation Army Centenary Logo.

1983. Commemorations. Multicoloured.

No.	Description		
1303.	24 c. Type **400**	30	10
1304.	30 c. Old Arts building, University of Auckland	40	35
1305.	35 c. Stylised Kangaroo and Kiwi	45	35
1306.	40 c. Rainbow Trout	50	45
1307.	45 c. Satellite over Earth	55	50

COMMEMORATIONS: 24 c. Salvation Army Centenary. 30 c. Auckland University Centenary. 35 c. Closer Economic Relationship agreement with Australia. 40 c. Introduction of Rainbow Trout into New Zealand Centenary. 45 c. World Communications Year.

401. Queen Elizabeth II.

1983. Commonwealth Day. Multicoloured.

No.	Description		
1308.	24 c. Type **401**	20	10
1309.	35 c. Maori rock drawing	30	40
1310.	40 c. Woolmark and wool-scouring symbols	35	45
1311.	45 c. Coat of arms	40	55

402. " Boats, Island Bay " (Rita Angus).

1983. Paintings by Rita Angus. Mult.

No.	Description		
1312.	24 c. Type **402**	30	10
1313.	30 c. " Central Otago Landscape "	35	45
1314.	35 c. " Wanaka Landscape "	45	50
1315.	45 c. " Tree "	55	70

403. Mt. Egmont.

1983. Beautiful New Zealand. Mult.

No.	Description		
1316.	35 c. Type **403**	30	35
1317.	40 c. Cooks Bay	35	40
1318.	45 c. Lake Matheson (horiz.)	40	45
1319.	70 c. Lake Alexandrina (horiz.)	65	70

404. Tabby.

1983. Health Stamps. Cats. Mult.

1320. 24 c.+2 c. Type **404** .. 30 25

1321. 24 c.+2 c. Siamese .. 30 25

1322. 30 c.+2 c. Persian .. 50 30

405. " The Family of the Holy Oak Tree ".

1983. Christmas. Multicoloured.

1324. 18 c. Type **405** 10 10

1325. 35 c. St. Patrick's Church, Greymouth 30 35

1326. 45 c. " The Glory of Christmas " 40 45

406. Geology.

1984. Antarctic Research. Multicoloured.

1327. 24 c. Type **406** 25 10

1328. 40 c. Biology 35 40

1329. 58 c. Glaciology 50 55

1330. 70 c. Meteorology 60 70

407. " Mountaineer ".

1984. New Zealand Ferry Boats. Mult.

1332. 24 c. Type **407** 30 10

1333. 40 c. " Waikana " .. 40 40

1334. 58 c. " Britannia " .. 55 55

1335. 70 c. " Wakatere " .. 65 65

408. Mount Hutt.

1984. Ski-slope Scene. Multicoloured.

1336. 35 c. Type **408** 40 40

1337. 40 c. Coronet Park .. 45 45

1338. 45 c. Turoa 50 50

1339. 70 c. Whakapapa .. 75 75

409. Hamilton's Frog.

1984. Amphibians and Reptiles. Multicoloured.

1340. 24 c. Type **409** 30 30

1341. 24 c. Great Barrier Skink 30 30

1342. 30 c. Harlequin Gecko .. 35 35

1343. 58 c. Otago Skink .. 70 70

1344. 70 c. Gold-striped Gecko 75 75

410. Clydesdales ploughing.

1984. Health Stamps. Horses. Multicoloured.

1345. 24 c.+2 c. Type **410** .. 30 40

1346. 24 c.+2 c. Shetland ponies 30 40

1347. 30 c.+2 c. Thoroughbreds 45 40

411. "Adoration of the Shepherds."

1984. Christmas. Multicoloured.

1349 18 c. Type **411** 20 10

1350 35 c. "Old St. Paul's, Wellington" (vert) .. 40 40

1351 45 c. "The Joy of Christmas" (vert) .. 50 65

412. Mounted Riflemen, South Africa, 1901

1984. New Zealand Military History. Multicoloured.

1352. 24 c. Type **412** 30 10

1353. 40 c. Engineers, France, 1917 .. 45 45

1354. 58 c. Tanks of 2nd N.Z. Divisional Cavalry, North Africa, 1942 .. 60 60

1355. 70 c. Infantryman in jungle kit, and 25-pounder gun, Korea and South-East Asia, 1950–72 .. .. 70 75

413. St. John Ambulance Badge.

1985. Centenary of St. John Ambulance in New Zealand.

1357. **413.** 24 c. black, gold and red 25 10

1358. 30 c. blk. silver & bl. 35 30

1359. 40 c. black and grey 40 45

The colours of the badge depicted are those for Bailiffs and Dames Grand Cross (24 c.), Knights and Dames of Grace (30 c.) and Serving Brothers and Sisters (40 c.).

414. Nelson Horse-drawn Tram, 1862.

1985. Vintage Trams. Multicoloured.

1360. 24 c. Type **414** 35 10

1361. 30 c. Graham's Town steam tram, 1871 .. 45 50

1362. 35 c. Dunedin cable car, 1881 .. .. .. 45 60

1363. 40 c. Auckland electric tram, 1902 .. .. 45 60

1364. 45 c. Wellington electric tram, 1904 .. .. 55 80

1365. 58 c. Christchurch electric tram, 1905 .. .. 65 1·25

415. Shotover Bridge.

1985. Bridges of New Zealand. Mult.

1366. 35 c. Type **415** 40 50

1367. 40 c. Alexandra Bridge .. 45 60

1368. 45 c. South Rangitikei railway Bridge (vert.) 50 75

1369. 70 c. Twin Bridges (vert.) 70 1·10

416. Queen Elizabeth II (from photo by Camera Press).

1985. Mult., background colours given.

1370. **416.** 25 c. red 50 10

1371. 35 c. blue 90 10

417. Princess of Wales and Prince William.

1985. Health Stamps. Designs showing photographs by Lord Snowdon. Mult.

1372. 25 c.+2 c. Type **417** .. 35 55

1373. 25 c.+2 c. Princess of Wales and Prince Henry 35 55

1374. 35 c.+2 c. Prince and Princess of Wales with Princes William and Henry 35 55

418. The Holy Family in the Stable.

1985. Christmas. Multicoloured.

1376. 18 c. Type **418** 20 10

1377. 40 c. The shepherds .. 40 75

1378. 50 c. The angels 45 90

HAVE YOU READ THE NOTES AT THE BEGINNING OF THIS CATALOGUE?

These often provide answers to the enquiries we receive.

419. H.M.N.Z.S. "Philomel" (1914–47).

1985. New Zealand Naval History. Mult.

1379. 25 c. Type **419** 70 15

1380. 45 c. H.M.N.Z.S. "Achilles" (1936–46) .. 1·10 1·40

1381. 60 c. H.M.N.Z.S. "Rotoiti" (1949–65) .. 1·40 1·75

1382. 75 c. H.M.N.Z.S. "Canterbury" (from 1971) .. .. .. 1·75 2·00

420. Police Computer Operator.

1986. Centenary of New Zealand Police. Designs showing historical aspects above modern police activities. Multicoloured.

1384 25 c. Type **420** 35 50

1385 25 c. Detective and mobile control room 35 50

1386 25 c. Policewoman and badge 35 50

1387 25 c. Forensic scientist, patrol car and policeman with child .. 35 50

1388 25 c. Police College, Porirua, "Lady Elizabeth II" (patrol boat) and dog handler .. 35 50

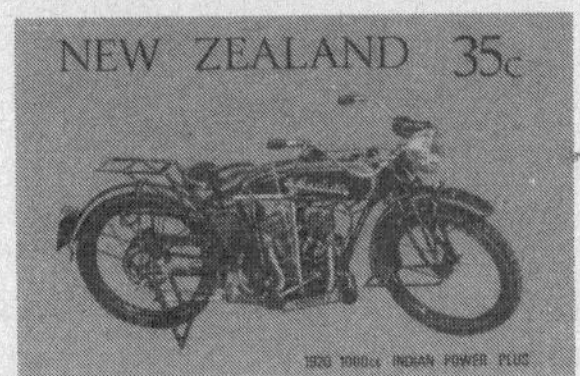

421. Indian "Power Plus" 1000 cc Motor Cycle (1920).

1986. Vintage Motor Cycles. Multicoloured.

1389. 35 c. Type **421** 40 30

1390. 45 c. Norton "CSI" 500 cc (1927) .. 50 45

1391. 60 c. B.S.A. "Sloper" 500 cc (1930) 65 65

1392. 75 c. Triumph "Model H" 550 cc (1915) .. 75 85

422. Tree of Life.

1986. International Peace Year. Mult.

1393. 25 c. Type **422** 30 30

1394. 25 c. Peace dove .. 30 30

423. Knights Point.

1986. Coastal Scenery. Multicoloured.

1395.	55 c. Type **423**	55	45
1396.	60 c. Becks Bay	55	45
1397.	65 c. Doubtless Bay ..	60	50
1398.	80 c. Wainui Bay ..	75	65

424. "Football" (Kylie Epapara).

1986. Health Stamps. Children's Paintings (1st series). Multicoloured.

1400.	30 c.+3 c. Type **424** ..	30	40
1401.	30 c.+3 c. "Children at Play" (Phillip Kata) ..	30	40
1402.	45 c.+3 c. "Children Skipping" (Mia Flannery) (horiz.)	40	50

See also Nos. 1433/5.

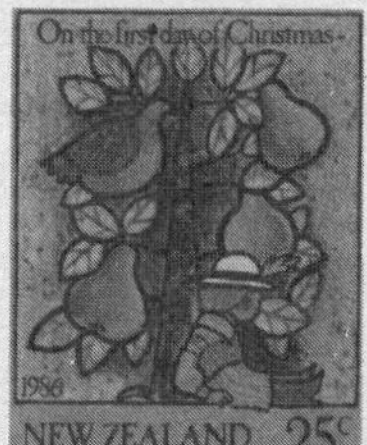

425. "A Partridge in a Pear Tree".

1986. Christmas. "The Twelve Days of Christmas" (carol). Multicoloured.

1404.	25 c. Type **425**	20	10
1405.	55 c. "Two turtle doves"	45	45
1406.	65 c. "Three French hens"	50	50

426. Conductor and Orchestra.

1986. Music in New Zealand.

1407.	**426**	30 c. multicoloured ..	25	10
1408.	–	60 c. blk, bl. & orge	45	50
1409.	–	80 c. multicoloured ..	70	75
1410.	–	$1 multicoloured	80	85

DESIGNS: 60 c. Cornet and brass band. 80 c. Piper and Highland pipe band. $1 Guitar and country music group.

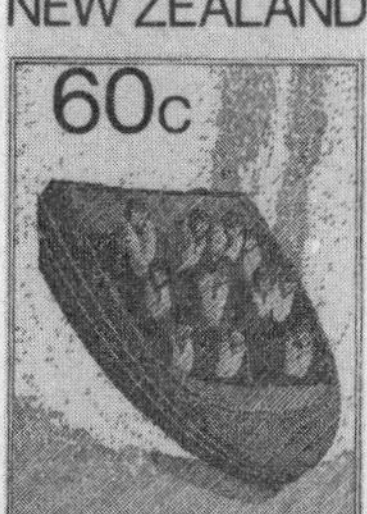

427. Jetboating.

1987. Tourism. Multicoloured.

1411.	60 c. Type **427**	50	50
1412.	70 c. Sightseeing flights	60	60
1413.	80 c. Camping	70	75
1414.	85 c. Windsurfing ..	70	75
1415.	$1.05 Mountaineering ..	90	1·00
1416.	$1.30 River rafting ..	1·10	1·25

428. Southern Cross Cup.

1987. Yachting Events. Designs showing yachts. Multicoloured.

1417.	40 c. Type **428**	35	15
1418.	80 c. Admiral's Cup ..	70	80
1419.	$1.05 Kenwood Cup ..	85	1·25
1420.	$1.30 America's Cup ..	1·10	1·40

429. Hand writing Letter and Postal Transport.

1987. New Zealand Post Ltd Vesting day. Multicoloured.

1421.	40 c. Type **429**	1·00	1·25
1422.	40 c. Posting letter, train and mailbox	1·00	1·25

430. Avro "626" and Wigram Airfield, 1937.

1987. 50th Anniv. of Royal New Zealand Air Force. Multicoloured.

1423.	40 c. Type **430**	35	15
1424.	70 c. "P-40 Kittyhawk" over World War II Pacific airstrip ..	55	60
1425.	80 c. Short "Sunderland" flying boat and Pacific lagoon	60	70
1426.	85 c. A-4 "Skyhawk" and Mt. Ruapehu	65	75

431. Urewera National Park and Fern Leaf.

1987. Centenary of National Parks Movement. Multicoloured.

1428.	70 c. Type **431**	70	55
1429.	80 c. Mt. Cook and buttercup	75	60
1430.	85 c. Fiordland and pine-apple shrub	80	65
1431.	$1.30 Tongariro and tussock	1·40	95

432. "Kite Flying" (Lauren Baldwin).

1987. Health Stamps. Children's Paintings (2nd series). Multicoloured.

1433.	40 c.+3 c. Type **432** ..	80	1·00
1434.	40 c.+3 c. "Swimming" (Ineke Schoneveld) ..	80	1·00
1435.	60 c.+3 c. "Horse Riding" (Aaron Tylee) (vert.)	1·25	1·40

433. "Hark the Herald Angels Sing".

1987. Christmas. Multicoloured.

1437	35 c. Type **433**	45	10
1438	70 c. "Away in a Manger"	90	55
1439	85 c. "We Three Kings of Orient Are"	1·10	65

434. Knot ("Pona").

1987. Maori Fibre-work. Multicoloured.

1440.	40 c. Type **434**	35	10
1441.	60 c. Binding ("Herehere")	45	45
1442.	80 c. Plait ("Whiri") ..	60	65
1443.	85 c. Cloak weaving ("Korowai") with flax fibre ("Whitau") ..	65	70

435. "Geothermal".

1988. Centenary of Electricity. Each shows radiating concentric circles representing energy generation.

1444.	**435.**	40 c. multicoloured ..	30	35
1445.	–	60 c. black, red and brown	40	45
1446.	–	70 c. multicoloured ..	50	55
1447.	–	80 c. multicoloured ..	55	60

DESIGNS: 60 c. "Thermal". 70 c. "Gas". 80 c. "Hydro".

436. Queen Elizabeth II and 1882 Queen Victoria 1d. Stamp.

1988. Centenary of Royal Philatelic Society of New Zealand. Multicoloured.

1448.	40 c. Type **436**	35	40
1449.	40 c. As Type **436**, but 1882 Queen Victoria 2d.	35	40

437. "Mangopare".

1988. Maori Rafter Paintings. Multicoloured.

1451.	40 c. Type **437**	40	40
1452.	40 c. "Koru"	40	40
1453.	40 c. "Raupunga" ..	40	40
1454.	60 c. "Koiri"	55	65

438 "Good Luck"

1988. Greetings Stamps. Multicoloured.

1455	40 c. Type **438**	40	50
1456	40 c. "Keeping in touch"	40	50
1457	40 c. "Happy birthday"	40	50
1458	40 c. "Congratulations" (41 × 27 mm)	40	50
1459	40 c. "Get well soon" (41 × 27 mm)	40	50

439 Paradise Shelduck

1988. Native Birds. Multicoloured.

1459a	5 c. Sooty crake ("Spotless crake") ..	10	10
1460	10 c. Double-banded plover ("Banded dotterel")	10	10
1461	20 c. Yellowhead ..	15	20
1462	30 c. Grey-backed white eye ("Silvereye") ..	20	25
1463	40 c. Brown kiwi ..	30	35
1589a	45 c. Rock wren ..	30	35
1464	50 c. Sacred kingfisher	35	40
1465	60 c. Spotted cormorant ("Spotted shag") ..	45	50
1466	70 c. Type **439**	50	55
1467	80 c. Fiordland crested penguin	60	65
1467a	80 c. New Zealand falcon	55	60
1468	90 c. New Zealand robin	65	70

The 40 and 45 c. also exist self-adhesive.

440 Milford Track

1988. Scenic Walking Trails. Multicoloured.

1469	70 c. Type **440**	50	60
1470	80 c. Heaphy Track ..	55	70
1471	85 c. Copland Track ..	60	75
1472	$1.30 Routeburn Track ..	90	1·10

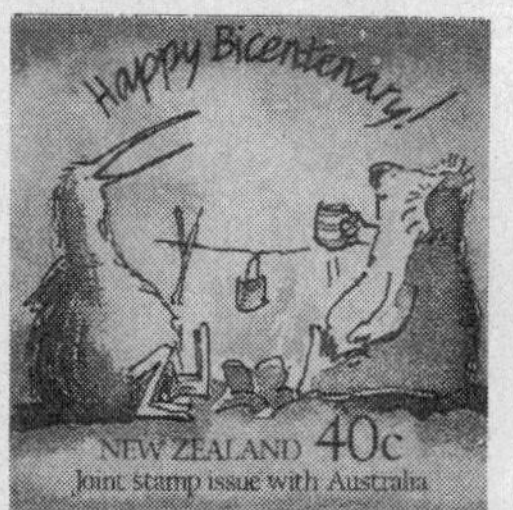

441 Kiwi and Koala at Campfire

1988. Bicent of Australian Settlement.
1474 **441** 40 c. multicoloured .. 60 35
A stamp in a similar design was also issued by Australia.

442 Swimming

1988. Health Stamps. Olympic Games, Seoul. Multicoloured.
1475 40 c.+3 c. Type **442** 35 45
1476 60 c.+3 c. Athletics 50 65
1477 70 c.+3 c. Canoeing 60 75
1478 80 c.+3 c. Show-jumping .. 70 85

443 "O Come All Ye Faithful"

1988. Christmas. Carols. Designs showing illuminated verses. Multicoloured.
1480 35 c. Type **443** 30 30
1481 70 c. "Hark the Herald Angels Sing" 55 65
1482 80 c. "Ding Dong Merrily on High" 60 70
1483 85 c. "The First Nowell" .. 65 80

444 "Lake Pukaki" (John Gully)

1988. New Zealand Heritage (1st issue). "The Land". Designs showing 19th-century paintings. Multicoloured.
1484 40 c. Type **444** 35 35
1485 60 c. "On the Grass Plain below Lake Arthur" (William Fox) .. 45 45
1486 70 c. "View of Auckland" (John Hoyte) 55 55
1487 80 c. "Mt. Egmont from the Southward" (Charles Heaphy) .. 60 60
1488 $1.05 "Anakiwa, Queen Charlotte Sound" (John Kinder) 80 80
1489 $1.30 "White Terraces, Lake Rotomahana", (Charles Barraud) .. 95 95
See also Nos. 1505/10, 1524/9, 1541/6, 1548/53 and 1562/7.

445 Brown Kiwi

1988.
1490 **445** $1 green .. .. 2·00 2·25
1490b $1 red 65 70
1490c $1 blue 70 75

446 Humpback Whale and Calf

1988. Whales. Multicoloured.
1491 60 c. Type **446** 75 65
1492 70 c. Killer whales 90 75
1493 80 c. Southern right whale 1·00 80
1494 85 c. blue whale .. .. 1·10 95
1495 $1.05 Southern bottlenose whale and calf .. 1·40 1·10
1496 $1.30 Sperm whale .. 1·50 1·40
Although inscribed "ROSS DEPENDENCY" Nos. 1491/6 were available from post offices throughout New Zealand.

447 Clover

1989. Wild Flowers. Multicoloured.
1497 40 c. Type **447** 40 35
1498 60 c. Lotus 50 55
1499 70 c. Montbretia .. 60 65
1500 80 c. Wild ginger .. 70 75

448 Katherine Mansfield

1989. New Zealand Authors. Multicoloured.
1501 40 c. Type **448** 30 35
1502 60 c. James K. Baxter .. 40 50
1503 70 c. Bruce Mason .. 50 60
1504 80 c. Ngaio Marsh .. 55 70

449 Moriori Man and Map of Chatham Islands

1989. New Zealand Heritage (2nd issue). The People. 45 35
1505 **449** 40 c. multicoloured ..
1506 – 60 c. brown, grey and deep brown .. 60 70
1507 – 70 c. green, grey and deep green .. 65 75
1508 – 80 c. blue, grey and deep blue .. 75 85
1509 – $1.05 grey, light grey and black .. 1·00 1·10
1510 – $1.30 red, grey, & brn 1·25 1·40
DESIGNS: 60 c. Gold prospector; 70 c. Settler ploughing; 80 c. Whaling; $1.05, Missionary preaching to Maoris; $1.30, Maori village.

450 White Pine (Kahikatea)

1989. Native Trees. Multicoloured.
1511 80 c. Type **450** 75 80
1512 85 c. Red pine (Rimu) .. 80 85
1513 $1.05 Totara .. .. 1·00 1·10
1514 $1.30 Kauri .. .. 1·25 1·40

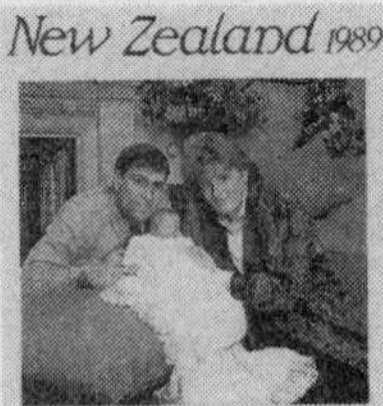

451 Duke and Duchess of York with Princess Beatrice

1989. Health Stamps. Multicoloured.
1516 40 c.+3 c. Type **451** .. 65 55
1517 40 c.+3 c. Duchess of York with Princess Beatrice 65 55
1518 80 c.+3 c. Princess Beatrice .. .. 1·25 90

452 One Tree Hill, Auckland, through Bedroom Window

1989. Christmas. Designs showing Star of Bethlehem. Multicoloured.
1520 35 c. Type **452** 35 30
1521 65 c. Shepherd and dog in mountain valley .. 65 70
1522 80 c. Star over harbour .. 85 90
1523 $1 Star over globe .. 1·25 1·40

453 Windsurfing

1989. New Zealand Heritage (3rd issue). The Sea. Multicoloured.
1524 40 c. Type **453** 40 35
1525 60 c. Fishes of many species 60 70
1526 65 c. Marlin and game fishing launch .. 65 75
1527 80 c. Rowing boat and yachts in harbour .. 80 85
1528 $1 Coastal scene .. 1·00 1·10
1529 $1.50 "Rotorua" (container ship) and tug 1·50 1·60

454 Games Logo

1989. 14th Commonwealth Games, Auckland. Multicoloured.
1530 40 c. Type **454** 40 35
1531 40 c. Goldie (games kiwi mascot) 40 35
1532 40 c. Gymnastics .. 40 35
1533 50 c. Weightlifting .. 50 55
1534 65 c. Swimming .. 65 70
1535 80 c. Cycling .. 80 90
1536 $1 Lawn bowling .. 1·00 1·25
1537 $1.80 Hurdling .. 1·75 1·90

MINIMUM PRICE

The minimum price quoted is 10p which represents a handling charge rather than a basis for valuing common stamps. For further notes about prices see introductory pages.

455 Short "S.30" Empire Flying Boat and Boeing "747"

1990. 50th Anniv of Air New Zealand.
1539 **455** 80 c. multicoloured .. 1·40 80

457 Maori Voyaging Canoe

1990. New Zealand Heritage (4th issue). The Ships. Multicoloured.
1541 40 c. Type **457** 60 35
1542 50 c. H.M.S. "Endeavour" (Cook), 1769 .. .. 75 50
1543 60 c. "Tory" (barque), 1839 .. .. .. 85 60
1544 80 c. "Crusader" (full-rigged immigrant ship), 1871 .. .. .. 1·25 85
1545 $1 "Edwin Fox" (full-rigged immigrant ship), 1873 .. .. .. 1·40 1·10
1546 $1.50 "Arawa" (steamer), 1884 .. .. .. 2·00 1·75

459 Grace Neill (social reformer) and Maternity Hospital, Wellington

1990. New Zealand Heritage (5th issue). Famous New Zealanders. Multicoloured.
1548 40 c. Type **459** 40 30
1549 50 c. Jean Batten (pilot) and Percival "Gull" aircraft 45 45
1550 60 c. Katherine Sheppard (suffragette) and 19th-century women .. 60 60
1551 80 c. Richard Pearse (inventor) and early flying machine .. 75 75
1552 $1 Lt.-Gen. Sir Bernard Freyberg and tank .. 95 95
1553 $1.50 Peter Buck (politician) and Maori pattern .. .. 1·25 1·40

460 Akaroa

1990. 150th Anniv of European Settlements. Multicoloured.
1554 80 c. Type **460** 75 75
1555 $1 Wanganui 95 95
1556 $1.50 Wellington .. 1·40 1·40
1557 $1.80 Takapuna Beach, Auckland .. .. 1·60 1·60

461 Jack Lovelock (athlete) and Race

1990. Health Stamps. Sportsmen (1st series). Multicoloured.

1559 40 c.+5 c. Type **461** .. 50 50

1560 80 c.+5 c. George Nepia (rugby player) and match 75 75

See also Nos. 1687/8.

462 Creation Legend of Rangi and Papa

1990. New Zealand Heritage (6th issue). The Maori. Multicoloured.

1562 40 c. Type **462** 40 30

1563 50 c. Pattern from Maori feather cloak 55 50

1564 60 c. Maori women's choir 60 60

1565 80 c. Maori facial tattoos 75 75

1566 $1 War canoe prow (detail) 90 95

1567 $1.50 Maori haka .. 1·40 1·50

464 Angel

1990. Christmas.

1569 **464** 40 c. purple, bl & brn 40 30

1570 – $1 purple, green & brn 80 80

1571 – $1.50 pur, red & brn 1·40 1·60

1572 – $1.80 pur, red & brn 1·60 1·75

DESIGNS: $1 to $1.80, Different angels.

465 Antarctic Petrel

1990. Antarctic Birds. Multicoloured.

1573 40 c. Type **465** 40 30

1574 50 c. Wilson's petrel .. 50 50

1575 60 c. Snow petrel .. 60 60

1576 80 c. Southern fulmar .. 75 75

1577 $1 Chinstrap penguin .. 85 85

1578 $1.50 Emperor penguin .. 1·40 1·50

Although inscribed "Ross Dependency" Nos. 1573/8 were available from post offices throughout New Zealand.

466 Coopworth Ewe and Lambs

1991. New Zealand Farming and Agriculture. Sheep Breeds. Multicoloured.

1579 40 c. Type **466** 40 30

1580 60 c. Perendale 55 55

1581 80 c. Corriedale 70 70

1582 $1 Drysdale 85 85

1583 $1.50 South Suffolk .. 1·25 1·25

1584 $1.80 Romney .. .. 1·50 1·60

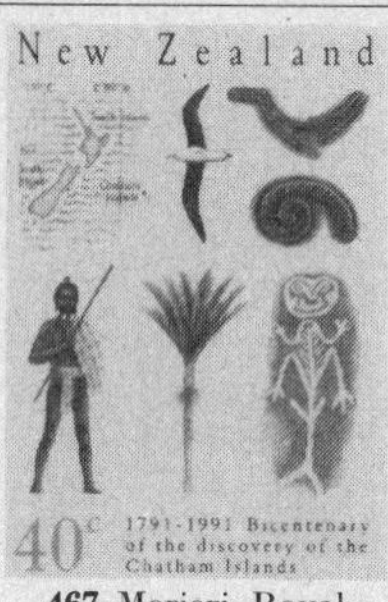

467 Moriori, Royal Albatross, Nikau Palm and Artefacts

1991. Bicentenary of Discovery of Chatham Islands. Multicoloured.

1585 40 c. Type **467** 40 40

1586 80 c. Carvings, H.M.S. "Chatham", Moriori house of 1870, and Tommy Solomon .. 70 70

468 Goal and Footballers

1991. Centenary of New Zealand Football Association. Multicoloured.

1587 80 c. Type **468** 75 75

1588 80 c. Five footballers and referee 75 75

Nos. 1587/8 were printed together, se-tenant, forming a composite design.

469 Tuatara on Rocks

1991. Endangered Species. The Tuatara. Multicoloured.

1590 40 c. Type **469** 40 45

1591 40 c. Tuatara in crevice .. 40 45

1592 40 c. Tuatara with foliage 40 45

1593 40 c. Tuatara in dead leaves 40 45

470 Clown

1991. "Happy Birthday". Multicoloured.

1594 40 c. Type **470** 35 45

1595 40 c. Balloons 35 45

1596 40 c. Party hat 35 45

1597 40 c. Birthday present (41 × 27 mm) 35 45

1598 40 c. Birthday cake (41 × 27 mm) 35 45

1599 45 c. Type **470** 30 35

1600 45 c. As No. 1595 .. 30 35

1601 45 c. As No. 1596 .. 30 35

1602 45 c. As No. 1597 .. 30 35

1603 45 c. As No. 1598 .. 30 35

471 Cat at Window

1991. "Thinking of You". Multicoloured.

1604 40 c. Type **471** 35 45

1605 40 c. Cat playing with slippers 35 45

1606 40 c. Cat with alarm clock 35 45

1607 40 c. Cat in window (41 × 27 mm) 35 45

1608 40 c. Cat at door (41 × 27 mm) 35 45

1609 45 c. As Type **471** .. 30 35

1610 45 c. As No. 1605 .. 30 35

1611 45 c. As No. 1606 .. 30 35

1612 45 c. As No. 1607 .. 30 35

1613 45 c. As No. 1608 .. 30 35

472 Punakaiki Rocks

1991. Scenic Landmarks. Multicoloured.

1614 40 c. Type **472** 35 30

1615 50 c. Moeraki Boulders .. 50 45

1616 80 c. Organ Pipes .. 75 75

1617 $1 Castle Hill 85 85

1618 $1.50 Te Kaukau Point 1·40 1·50

1619 $1.80 Ahuriri River Clay Cliffs .. .. .. 1·60 1·75

473 Dolphins Underwater

1991. Health Stamps. Hector's Dolphin. Multicoloured.

1620 45 c.+5 c. Type **473** .. 50 50

1621 80 c.+5 c. Dolphins leaping 90 90

474 Children's Rugby

1991. World Cup Rugby Championship. Multicoloured.

1623 80 c. Type **474** 75 75

1624 $1 Women's rugby .. 85 85

1625 $1.50 Senior rugby .. 1·40 1·40

1626 $1.80 "All Blacks" (national team) .. 1·60 1·60

475 "Three Shepherds"

1991. Christmas. Multicoloured.

1628 45 c. Type **475** 45 45

1629 45 c. Two Kings on camels 45 45

1630 45 c. Mary and Baby Jesus 45 45

1631 45 c. King with gift .. 45 45

1632 65 c. Star of Bethleham .. 60 60

1633 $1 Crown 85 85

1634 $1.50 Angel .. .. 1·40 1·40

476 "Dodonidia helmsii"

1991. Butterflies. Multicoloured.

1635 $1 Type **476** 65 70

1636 $2 "Zizina otis oxleyi" 1·25 1·40

1637 $3 "Bassaris itea" .. 2·00 2·10

479 Yacht "Kiwi Magic", 1987

1992. New Zealand Challenge for America's Cup. Multicoloured.

1655 45 c. Type **479** 40 35

1656 80 c. Yacht "New Zealand", 1988 .. .. 70 70

1657 $1 Yacht "America", 1851 85 85

1658 $1.50 "America's Cup" class yacht, 1992 .. 1·25 1·40

480 "Heemskerk"

1992. Great Voyages of Discovery. Mult.

1659 45 c. Type **480** 40 35

1660 80 c. "Zeehan" 70 70

1661 $1 "Santa Maria" .. 85 85

1662 $1.50 "Pinta" and "Nina" 1·25 1·40

Nos. 1659/60 commemorate the 350th anniv of Tasman's discovery of New Zealand and Nos. 1661/2 the 500th anniv of discovery of America by Columbus.

481 Sprinters

1992. Olympic Games, Barcelona (1st issue).

1663 **481** 45 c. multicoloured .. 40 40

See also Nos. 1670/3.

482 Weddell Seal and Pup

1992. Antarctic Seals. Multicoloured.

1664	45 c. Type **482**	40	35
1665	50 c. Crabeater seals swimming	45	45
1666	65 c. Leopard seal and penguins	60	60
1667	80 c. Ross seal	75	75
1668	$1 Southern elephant seal and harem	85	90
1669	$1.80 Hooker's sea lion and pup	1·50	1·60

Although inscribed "Ross Dependency" Nos. 1664/9 were available from post offices throughout New Zealand.

483 Cycling

1992. Olympic Games, Barcelona (2nd issue). Multicoloured.

1670	45 c. Type **483**	40	35
1671	80 c. Archery	70	70
1672	$1 Equestrian three-day eventing	85	85
1673	$1.50 Sailboarding . .	1·40	1·40

484 Ice Pinnacles, Franz Josef Glacier

1992. Glaciers. Multicoloured.

1675	45 c. Type **484**	40	35
1676	50 c. Tasman Glacier . .	50	45
1677	80 c. Snowball glacier, Marion Plateau . .	70	70
1678	$1 Brewster Glacier . .	85	85
1679	$1.50 Fox Glacier . .	1·40	1·40
1680	$1.80 Franz Josef Glacier	1·50	1·60

485 "Grand Finale" Camellia

1992. Camellias. Multicoloured.

1681	45 c. Type **485**	40	35
1682	50 c. "Showa-No-Sakae"	50	45
1683	80 c. "Sugar Dream" . .	70	70
1684	$1 "Night Rider" . .	85	85
1685	$1.50 "E.G. Waterhouse"	1·40	1·40
1686	$1.80 "Dr. Clifford Parks"	1·50	1·50

1992. Health Stamps. Sportsmen (2nd series). As T **461**. Multicoloured.

1687	45 c.+5 c. Anthony Wilding (tennis player) and match	55	60
1688	80 c.+5 c. Stewie Dempster (cricket) and batsman	70	80

486 Tree and Hills

1992. Landscapes. Multicoloured.

1690	45 c. Type **486**	30	35
1691	45 c. River and hills . .	30	35
1692	45 c. Hills and mountain	30	35
1693	45 c. Glacier	30	35
1694	45 c. Hills and waterfall	30	35
1695	45 c. Tree and beach . .	30	35
1696	45 c. Estuary and cliffs . .	30	35
1697	45 c. Fjord	30	35
1698	45 c. River delta . .	30	35
1699	45 c. Ferns and beach . .	30	35

487 Reindeer over Houses

1992. Christmas. Multicoloured.

1700	45 c. Type **487**	30	35
1701	45 c. Santa Claus on sleigh over houses	30	35
1702	45 c. Christmas tree in window	30	35
1703	45 c. Christmas wreath and children at window	30	35
1704	65 c. Candles and fireplace	45	50
1705	$1 Family going to church	65	70
1706	$1.50 Picnic under Pohutukawa tree . .	1·00	1·10

488 1920s Fashions

1992. New Zealand in the 1920s. Mult.

1707	45 c. Type **488**	30	35
1708	50 c. Dr. Robert Jack and early radio announcer	35	40
1709	80 c. "All Blacks" rugby player, 1924	55	60
1710	$1 Swaggie and dog . .	65	70
1711	$1.50 Ford "Model A" car and young couple . .	1·00	1·10
1712	$1.80 Amateur aviators and biplane	1·25	1·40

489 "Old Charley" Toby Jug

1993. Royal Doulton Ceramics Exhibition, New Zealand. Multicoloured.

1713	45 c. Type **489**	40	35
1714	50 c. "Bunnykins" nursery plate	45	40
1715	80 c. "Maori Art" tea set	65	70
1716	$1 "Ophelia" handpainted plate	80	90
1717	$1.50 "St. George" figurine	1·25	1·40
1718	$1.80 "Lambeth" salt-glazed stoneware vase	1·50	1·75

HAVE YOU READ THE NOTES AT THE BEGINNING OF THIS CATALOGUE?
These often provide answers to the enquiries we receive.

490 Women's Fashions of the 1930s

1993. New Zealand in the 1930s. Mult.

1720	45 c. Type **490**	40	35
1721	50 c. Unemployed protest march	45	40
1722	80 c. "Phar Lap" (racehorse)	65	70
1723	$1 State housing project	80	90
1724	$1.50 Boys drinking free school milk	1·25	1·40
1725	$1.80 Cinema queue . .	1·50	1·75

491 Women signing Petition

1993. Centenary of Women's Suffrage. Mult.

1726	45 c. Type **491**	40	35
1727	80 c. Aircraft propeller and woman on tractor	70	75
1728	$1 Housewife with children	85	95
1729	$1.50 Modern women . .	1·40	1·60

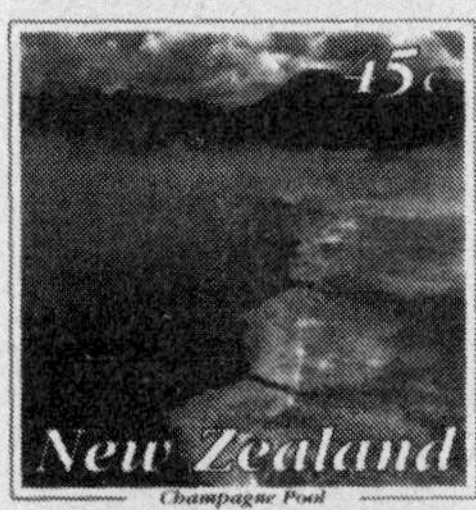

492 Champagne Pool

1993. Thermal Wonders, Rotorua. Mult.

1730	45 c. Type **492**	45	40
1731	50 c. Boiling mud . .	45	40
1732	80 c. Emerald pool . .	70	70
1733	$1 Hakereteke Falls . .	80	80
1734	$1.50 Warbrick Terrace	1·40	1·50
1735	$1.80 Pohutu Geyser . .	1·50	1·75

493 Yellow-eyed Penguin, Hector's Dolphin and New Zealand Fur Seal

1993. Endangered Species Conservation. Multicoloured.

1736	45 c. Type **493**	35	40
1737	45 c. Taiko (bird), Mount Cook lily and blue duck	35	40
1738	45 c. Giant snail, rock wren and Hamilton's frog	35	40
1739	45 c. Kaka (bird), Chatham Island pigeon and giant weta . .	35	40
1740	45 c. Tusked weta (23 × 28 mm)	35	40

494 Boy with Puppy

1993. Health Stamps. Children's Pets. Mult.

1741	45 c.+5 c. Type **494** . .	50	50
1742	80 c.+5 c. Girl with kitten	75	75

495 Christmas Decorations (value at left)

1993. Christmas. Multicoloured.

1746	45 c. Type **495**	45	45
1747	45 c. Christmas decorations (value at right)	45	45
1748	45 c. Sailboards, gifts and Christmas pudding (value at left)	45	45
1749	45 c. Sailboards, gifts and Christmas pudding (value at right) . .	45	45
1750	$1 Sailboards, baubles and Christmas cracker . .	90	90
1751	$1.50 Sailboards, present and wreath	1·40	1·40

496 Paua

1993. Marine Life. Multicoloured.

1752	45 c. Type **496**	35	40
1753	45 c. Greenshell mussels	35	40
1754	45 c. Terakihi	35	40
1755	45 c. Salmon	35	40
1756	45 c. Southern blue fin tuna, albacore tuna and kahawai	35	40
1757	45 c. Rock lobster . .	35	40
1758	45 c. Snapper	35	40
1759	45 c. Groper	35	40
1760	45 c. Orange roughy . .	35	40
1761	45 c. Squid, hoki and oreo dory	35	40

497 Sauropod

1993. Prehistoric Animals. Multicoloured.

1762	45 c. Type **497**	45	45
1763	45 c. Carnosaur and sauropod (30 × 25 mm)	45	45
1764	80 c. Pterosaur	75	75
1765	$1 Ankylosaur	85	85
1766	$1.20 Mauisaurus . .	1·25	1·25
1767	$1.50 Carnosaur	1·50	1·50

498 Soldiers, National Flag and Pyramids

499 Bungy Jumping

1993. New Zealand in the 1940s. Mult.

1771	45 c. Type **498**		40	40
1772	50 c. Aerial crop spraying		40	40
1773	80 c. Hydro-electric scheme		70	70
1774	$1 Marching majorettes ..		80	80
1775	$1.50 American troops ..		1·40	1·40
1776	$1.80 Crowd celebrating victory		1·50	1·50

1994. Tourism. Multicoloured.

1777	45 c. Type **499**		35	40
1778	45 c. White water rafting (25 × 25 mm)		35	40
1779	80 c. Trout fishing ..		60	65
1780	$1 Jet boating (horiz) ..		70	75
1781	$1.50 Tramping		1·10	1·25
1782	$1.80 Heli-skiing ..		1·25	1·40

500 "New Zealand Endeavour" (yacht)

1994. Round the World Yacht Race.

1783	**500**	$1 multicoloured ..	70	75

501 Mt. Cook and New Zealand Symbols (⅔-size illustration)

1994.

1784	**501**	$20 blue and gold ..	14·50	15·00

503 Rock and Roll Dancers

1994. New Zealand in the 1950s. Mult.

1787	45 c. Type **503**	35	40
1788	80 c. Sir Edmund Hillary on Mt. Everest	60	65
1789	$1 Aunt Daisy (radio personality)	70	75
1790	$1.20 Queen Elizabeth II during 1953 royal visit	90	95
1791	$1.50 Children playing with Opo the dolphin	1·10	1·25
1792	$1.80 Auckland Harbour Bridge	1·25	1·40

504 Mt. Cook and Mt. Cook Lily ("Winter")

1994. The Four Seasons. Multicoloured.

1793	45 c. Type **504**	35	40
1794	70 c. Lake Hawea and Kowhai ("Spring") ..	50	55
1795	$1.50 Opononi Beach and Pohutukawa ("Summer")	1·10	1·25
1796	$1.80 Lake Pukaki and Puriri ("Autumn") ..	1·25	1·40

505 Paua Shell

1994. New Zealand Life. Multicoloured.

1797	45 c. Type **505** (25 × 20 mm)	35	40
1798	45 c. Pavlova dessert (35 × 20 mm)	35	40
1799	45 c. Hokey pokey ice cream (25 × 20 mm) ..	35	40
1800	45 c. Fish and chips (35 × 20 mm)	35	40
1801	45 c. Jandals (30 × 20 mm)	35	40
1802	45 c. Bush shirt (25 × 30½ mm)	35	40
1803	45 c. Buzzy Bee (toy) (35 × 30½ mm)	35	40
1804	45 c. Gumboots and black singlet (25 × 30½ mm) ..	35	40
1805	45 c. Rugby boots and ball (35 × 30½ mm) ..	35	40
1806	45 c. Kiwifruit (30½ × 30½ mm)	35	40

506 Maui pulls up Te Ika

1994. Maori Myths. Multicoloured.

1807	45 c. Type **506**	35	40
1808	80 c. Rona snatched up by Marama	60	65
1809	$1 Maui attacking Tuna	70	75
1810	$1.20 Tane separating Rangi and Papa ..	90	95
1811	$1.50 Matakauri slaying the Giant of Wakatipu	1·10	1·25
1812	$1.80 Panenehu showing crayfish to Tangaroa ..	1·25	1·40

EXPRESS DELIVERY STAMPS

E 1.

1903.

E1	E 1	6d. red and violet ..	32·00	20·00

E 2. Express Mail Delivery Van.

1939.

E 6.	E 2.	6d. violet	1·50	1·75

LIFE INSURANCE DEPARTMENT

L. 1.

1891.

L 13	L 1.	½d. purple	55·00	2·75
L 14		1d. blue	55·00	75
L 15		2d. brown	70·00	3·50
L 4		3d. brown	£190	20·00
L 5		6d. green	£275	60·00
L 6		1s. pink	£650	£120

1905. Similar type but "V.R." omitted.

L 37	½d. green	3·25	4·50
L 22	1d. blue	£150	30·00
L 38	1d. red	1·50	1·50
L 26	1½d. black	40·00	6·50
L 27	1½d. brown	1·25	2·25
L 21	2d. brown	£1200	80·00
L 28	2d. purple	48·00	25·00
L 29	2d. yellow	3·50	2·00
L 30	3d. orange	45·00	23·00
L 40	3d. brown	13·00	16·00
L 41	6d. red	8·50	24·00

L 3. Castlepoint Lighthouse.

1947. Lighthouses.

L 42.	L 3.	½d. green and orange	90	60
L 43.	–	1d. olive and blue..	50	30
L 44.	–	2d. blue and black..	70	25
L 45.	–	2½d. black and blue..	9·50	13·00
L 46.	–	3d. mauve and blue..	2·25	35
L 47.	–	4d. brown and orange	2·00	50
L 48.	–	6d. brown and blue..	2·00	1·25
L 49.	–	1s. brown and blue ..	2·75	1·50

LIGHTHOUSES—HORIZ. 1d. Taiaroa. 2d. Cape Palliser. 6d. The Brothers Lighthouse. VERT. 2½d. Cape Campbell. 3d. Eddystone. 4d. Stephens Island. 1s. Cape Brett.

1967. Decimal currency. Stamps of 1947-65 surch.

L 50a.	1 c. on 1d. (No. L 43)	2·25	3·50
L 51.	2 c. on 2½d. (No. L 45)	8·00	10·00
L 52.	2½ c. on 3d. (N. L 46)	2·00	4·50
L 53.	3 c. on 4d. (No. L 47)	4·50	5·50
L 54.	5 c. on 6d. (No. L 48)	1·75	7·00
L 55a.	10 c. on 1s. (No. L 49)	1·25	4·00

L 13. Moeraki Point Lighthouse.

1969.

L 56	L 13.	½ c. yell., red & violet	2·00	2·00
L 57	–	2½ c. blue, grn. & buff	1·00	1·25
L 58	–	3 c. stone, yell. & brn.	75	75
L 59	–	4 c. grn., ochre & blue	1·00	1·00
L 60	–	8 c. multicoloured ..	45	2·50
L 61	–	10 c. multicoloured ..	45	2·50
L 62	–	15 c. multicoloured ..	60	1·75

DESIGNS—HORIZ. 2½ c. Puysegur Point Lighthouse. 4 c. Cape Egmont Lighthouse. VERT. 3 c. Baring Head Lighthouse. 8 c. East Cape. 10 c. Farewell Spit. 15 c. Dog Island Lighthouse.

1978. No. L57 surch.

L 63.	25 c. on 2½ c. blue, green and buff	75	1·75

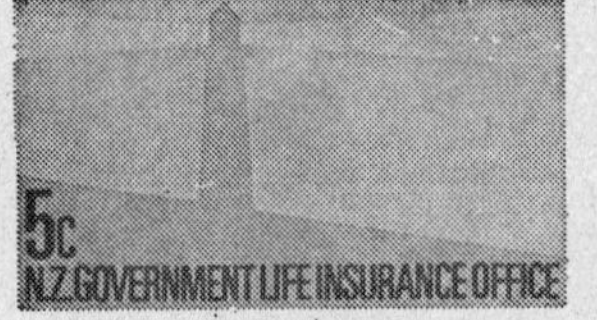

L 17.

1981.

L 64.	L 17.	5 c. multicoloured ..	10	10
L 65.		10 c. multicoloured ..	10	10
L 66.		20 c. multicoloured ..	15	15
L 67.		30 c. multicoloured ..	25	25
L 68.		40 c. multicoloured ..	35	30
L 69.		50 c. multicoloured ..	45	35

OFFICIAL STAMPS

Optd. **OFFICIAL.**

1907. Pictorials.

O 59.	**23.**	½d. green	7·50	50
O 61a.	**25.**	2d. purple	7·00	1·00
O 63.	**28.**	3d. brown	35·00	1·75
O 64.	**31.**	6d red..	£110	15·00
O 65.	**34.**	1s orange	85·00	15·00
O 66.	**35.**	2s. green	70·00	48·00
O 67.	–	5s red (No. 329) ..	£150	£170

1907. "Universal" type.

O 60c.	**42.**	1d. red	8·50	30

1908.

O 70	**50**	1d. red	60·00	2·00
O 72	**31**	6d. red (No. 254) ..	£110	35·00

1910. King Edward VII etc.

O 73	**51**	½d. green	3·75	30
O 78	**53**	1d. red..	3·00	10
O 74	**51**	3d. brown	14·00	80
O 75		6d. red..	19·00	3·75
O 76		8d. blue	14·00	18·00
O 77		1s. orange	45·00	12·00

1913. Queen Victoria.

O 82.	F 4.	2s. blue	42·00	30·00
O 83.		5s. green	70·00	80·00
O 84.		£1 red	£550	£450

1915. King George V.

O 96	**62**	½d. green	65	10
O 90		1½d. grey	3·75	40
O 91		1½d. brown ..	3·75	30
O 98		2d. yellow	1·50	30
O 100		3d. brown	3·00	70
O 101		4d. violet	12·00	2·25
O 102a		6d. red	3·75	60
O 103		8d. brown	70·00	85·00
O 104		9d. green	35·00	32·00
O 105		1s. orange	5·50	2·00

1927. King George V.

O 111.	**71.**	1d. red	1·50	10
O 112.		2s. blue	70·00	85·00

1933. "Arms".

O 113.	F 6.	5 s. green	£250	£275

Optd. **Official.**

1936. "Arms".

O 133.	F 6.	5s. green	27·00	5·00

1936. As 1935.

O120	**81.**	½d. green	4·75	3·75
O115	–	1d. red (No. 557) ..	1·50	50
O122	**83.**	1½d. brown ..	10·00	4·00
O123	–	2d. orange (No. 580)	1·50	10
O124a	**85.**	2½d. brown & grey	12·00	11·00
O125	**86.**	3d. brown	48·00	2·00
O126c	**87.**	4d. black & brown	3·25	40
O127b	**89.**	6d. red	5·50	30
O128a	–	8d. brn. (No. 586b)	5·50	11·00
O130	**91.**	9d. red and black	16·00	18·00
O131a	–	1s. green (No. 588)	19·00	85
O132d	**93.**	2s. olive	38·00	7·00

1938. King George VI.

O 134	**108.**	½d. green	10·00	1·40
O 135		½d. orange	1·25	1·75
O 136		1d. red	11·00	15
O 137		1d. green	2·00	10
O 138		1½d. brown	70·00	18·00
O 139		1½d. red	9·00	3·00
O 152		2d. orange	1·00	10
O 140		3d. blue	2·00	10
O 153		4d. purple	3·00	65
O 154		6d. red	8·00	40
O 155		8d. violet	8·00	6·00
O 156		9d. brown	9·00	6·50
O 157a	–	1s. brn. & red (No. 686b).. ..	8·00	4·50
O 158	–	2s. orange and green (No. 688)	19·00	16·00

1940. Centenary stamps.

O 141.	½d. green	1·00	35
O 142.	1d. brown and red..	3·50	10
O 143.	1½d. blue and mauve	1·75	2·00
O 144.	2d. green and brown..	3·50	10
O 145.	2½d. green and blue..	3·25	2·75
O 146.	3d. purple and red ..	7·00	80
O 147.	4d. brown and red ..	45·00	2·00
O 148.	6d. green and violet..	22·00	2·00
O 149.	8d. black and red ..	25·00	17·00
O 150.	9d. olive and red ..	8·50	7·00
O 151.	1s. green	42·00	4·00

O 6. Queen Elizabeth II.

1954.

No.	Type	Description	Unused	Used
O 159.	O 6.	1d. orange	50	20
O 160.		1½d. brown	1·00	2·50
O 161.		2d. green	30	15
O 162.		2½d. olive	4·25	1·50
O 163.		3d. red	40	10
O 164.		4d. blue	90	15
O 165.		9d. red	3·75	60
O 166.		1s. purple	60	10
O 167.		3s. slate	35·00	48·00

1959. Surch.

No.	Type	Description	Unused	Used
O 169.	O 6.	2½d. on 2d. green ..	40	1·00
O 168.		6d. on 1½d. brown ..	20	85

POSTAGE DUE STAMPS

D 1.

D 2.

1899.

No.	Type	Description	Unused	Used
D 9.	D 1.	½d. red and green ..	2·50	16·00
D 10.		1d. red and green ..	8·50	1·00
D 15.		2d. red and green ..	30·00	4·75
D 12.		3d. red and green ..	12·00	3·50
D 16.		4d. red and green ..	26·00	9·00
D 6.		5d. red and green ..	20·00	18·00
D 7.		6d. red and green ..	23·00	18·00
D 2.		8d. red and green ..	60·00	75·00
D 8.		10d. red and green ..	70·00	80·00
D 3.		1s. red and green ..	65·00	80·00
D 4.		2s. red and green ..	£110	£130

1902.

No.	Type	Description	Unused	Used
D18	D 2	½d. red and green ..	1·50	1·50
D30		1d. red and green ..	3·50	80
D22a		2d. red and green ..	5·00	1·50
D36		3d. red and green ..	15·00	42·00

D 3.

1939.

No.	Type	Description	Unused	Used
D 41.	D 3.	½d. green	3·75	4·50
D 42.		1d. red	1·75	30
D 46.		2d. blue	1·50	80
D 47.		3d. brown	4·75	5·00

NIGER COAST PROTECTORATE

A district on the west coast of Africa. In 1900 became part of Southern Nigeria.

12 pence = 1 shilling;
20 shillings = 1 pound.

1892. Stamps of Gt. Britain (Queen Victoria) optd. **BRITISH PROTECTORATE OIL RIVERS.**

No.	Type	Description	Unused	Used
1.	71.	½d. red	6·50	4·50
2.	57.	1d. lilac	5·50	4·50
3.	73.	2d. green and red	14·00	8·00
4.	74.	2½d. purple and blue ..	6·50	2·00
5.	78.	5d. purple and blue ..	7·50	7·50
6.	82.	1s. green	45·00	55·00

1893. Half of No. 2 surch. **½d.**

No.	Type	Description	Unused	Used
7.	57.	½d. on half of 1d. lilac ..	£150	£140

1893. Nos. 1 to 6 surch. in words or figs.

No.	Type	Description	Unused	Used
20	73.	½d. on 2d. green and red	£275	£225
21	74.	½d. on 2½d. pur. on blue	£200	£180
37	73.	1s. on 2d. green and red	£400	£350
40		5s. on 2d. green and red	£7000	£8000
41	78.	10s. on 5d. purple & blue	£6000	£8000
42	82.	20s. on 1s. green ..	£65000	

13.

14.

1893. Various frames with " OIL RIVERS " barred out and " NIGER COAST " above.

No.	Type	Description	Unused	Used
45.	13.	½d. red	4·00	3·75
46.		1d. blue	4·00	3·25
47.		2d. green	16·00	13·00
48.		2½d. red	4·25	3·50
49.		5d. lilac	12·00	9·00
50.		1s. black	14·00	12·00

1894. Various frames.

No.	Type	Description	Unused	Used
66.	14.	½d. green	2·00	1·00
67.		1d. red	2·50	1·00
68.		2d. red	1·75	1·00
69a.		2½d. blue	3·50	1·00
55.		5d. purple	5·50	5·50
71.		6d. brown	7·00	6·00
56a.		1s. black	14·00	7·00
73b.		2s. 6d. brown	22·00	60·00
74.		10s. violet	75·00	£140

1894. Surch with large figures.

No.	Description	Unused	Used
58	"½" on half 1d. (No. 46) ..	£550	£225
59	"1" on half 2d. (No. 3) ..	£550	£250

1894. No. 67 bisected and surch.

No.	Type	Description	Unused	Used
64.	14.	½d. on half of 1d. red ..	£1200	£250

1894. Surch. **ONE HALFPENNY** and bars.

No.	Type	Description	Unused	Used
65.	14.	½d. on 2½d. blue ..	£275	£200

NIGERIA

A former British colony on the west coast of Africa, comprising the territories of Northern and Southern Nigeria and Lagos. Now a Federation divided into the three self-governing Regions of Northern Nigeria, Western Nigeria and Eastern Nigeria and the Federal Territory of Lagos. Attained full independence within the British Commonwealth in 1960 and became a Federal Republic in 1963.

The Eastern Region (known as Biafra (q.v)) seceded in 1967, remaining independent until overrun by Federal Nigerian troops during January 1970.

1914. 12 pence = 1 shilling.
20 shillings = 1 pound.
1973. 100 kobo = 1 naira.

1.

1914.

No.	Type	Description	Unused	Used
15	1	½d. green	75	40
16		1d. red	85	30
26		1½d. orange	2·00	15
3		2d. grey	2·50	1·00
28		2d. brown	85	15
4		2½d. blue	1·75	1·00
5a		3d. purple on yellow ..	1·50	1·50
19		3d. violet	3·75	3·25
29		3d. blue	2·75	2·00
20		4d. black & red on yellow	65	55
7		6d. purple	3·50	3·50
22		1s. black on green ..	1·00	1·00
9		2s. 6d. blk. & red on blue	8·00	3·50
10		5s. green & red on yellow	7·50	24·00
11d		10s. green & red on green	29·00	75·00
12		£1 purple & black on red	£150	£180

1935. Silver Jubilee. As T **13** of Antigua.

No.	Description	Unused	Used
30.	1½d. blue and grey ..	60	40
31.	2d. green and blue ..	1·50	40
32.	3d. brown and blue ..	2·75	6·50
33.	1s. grey and purple ..	2·75	14·00

3. Apapa Wharf.

DESIGNS—VERT. 1d. Cocoa. 1½d. Tin dredger. 2d. Timber industry. 3d. Fishing village. 4d. Cotton ginnery. 6d. Habe Minaret. 1s. Fulani cattle. HORIZ. 5s. Oil palms. 10 s. Niger at Jebba. £1, Canoe pulling.

5. Victoria-Buea Road.

1936.

No.	Type	Description	Unused	Used
34	3	½d. green	85	95
35	–	1d. red	40	40
36	–	1½d. brown	40	40
37	–	2d. black	40	80
38	–	3d. blue	70	85
39	–	4d. brown	1·25	2·00
40	–	6d. violet	40	60
41	–	1 s. green	1·10	4·50
42	5	2s. 6d. black and blue ..	3·50	14·00
43	–	5s. black and green ..	6·00	19·00
44	–	10s. black and grey ..	45·00	60·00
45	–	£1 black and orange ..	75·00	£120

1937. Coronation. As T **2** of Aden.

No.	Description	Unused	Used
46.	1d. red	30	85
47.	1½d. brown	1·00	1·25
48.	3d. blue	1·40	1·75

15. King George VI.

DESIGNS: 2s. 6d., 5s As Nos. 42 and 44 but with portrait of King George VI.

1938.

No.	Type	Description	Unused	Used
49	15	½d. green	10	10
50a		1d. red	50	10
50b		1d. lilac	10	10
51a		1½d. brown	10	10
52		2d. black	10	50
52ab		2d. red	10	40
52a		2½d. orange	10	45
53		3d. blue	10	10
53b		3d. black	10	10
54		4d. orange	48·00	2·50
54a		4d. blue	15	1·25
55		6d. violet	30	10
56a		1s. olive	15	10
57		1s. 3d. blue	40	10
58c		2s. 6d. black and blue ..	1·75	1·75
59c		5s. black and orange ..	4·50	2·75

1946. Victory. As T **9** of Aden.

No.	Description	Unused	Used
60.	1½d. brown	15	10
61.	4d. blue	15	60

1948. Silver Wedding. As T **10/11** of Aden.

No.	Description	Unused	Used
62.	1d. mauve	35	10
63.	5s. orange	5·00	7·50

1949. U.P.U. As T **20/23** of Antigua.

No.	Description	Unused	Used
64.	1d. purple	20	10
65.	3d. blue	45	75
66.	6d. purple	60	1·40
67.	1s. olive	80	1·75

1953. Coronation. As T **13** of Aden.

No.	Description	Unused	Used
68	1½d. black and green ..	40	10

18. Old Manilla Currency.

26. Victoria Harbour.

29. New and Old Lagos.

1953.

No.	Type	Description	Unused	Used
69	18	½d. black and orange ..	15	30
70	–	1d. black and bronze ..	20	10
71	–	1½d. turquoise	35	40
72	–	2d. black and ochre ..	3·75	30
72cc	–	2d. slate	3·00	30
73	–	3d. black and purple ..	55	10
74	–	4d. black and blue ..	1·75	20
75	–	6d. brown and black ..	30	10
76	–	1s. black and purple ..	40	10
77	26	2s. 6d. black green ..	4·50	30
78	–	5s. black and red ..	3·25	75
79	–	10s. black and brown	7·50	1·75
80	29	£1 black and violet ..	13·00	5·50

DESIGNS—HORIZ. As Type **18**: 1d. Bornu horsemen. 1½d. "Groundnuts". 2d. "Tin". 3d. Jebba Bridge and R. Niger. 4d. "Cocoa". 1s. "Timber". As Type **26**: 5s. "Palm-oil". 10s. "Hides and skins". VERT. as Type **18**: 6d. Ife bronze.

1956. Royal Visit. No. 72 optd. **ROYAL VISIT 1956.**

No.	Description	Unused	Used
81.	2d. black and ochre	40	20

31. Victoria Harbour.

1958. Cent. of Victoria, S. Cameroons.

No.	Type	Description	Unused	Used
82.	31.	3d. black and purple ..	20	20

32. Lugard Hall.

1959. Attainment of Self-Government. Northern Region of Nigeria.

No.	Type	Description	Unused	Used
83.	32.	3d. black and purple ..	15	10
84.	–	1s. black and green ..	45	50

DESIGN: 1s. Kano Mosque.

35. Legislative Building.

1960. Independence Commem.

No.	Type	Description	Unused	Used
85.	35.	1d. black and red ..	10	10
86.	–	3d. black and blue ..	15	10
87.	–	6d. green and brown ..	20	15
88.	–	1s. 3d. blue and yellow ..	30	15

DESIGNS—As Type **35**: 3d. African paddling canoe. 6d. Federal Supreme Court. LARGER (40×24 mm.): 1s. 3d. Dove, torch and map.

39. Groundnuts.

48. Central Bank.

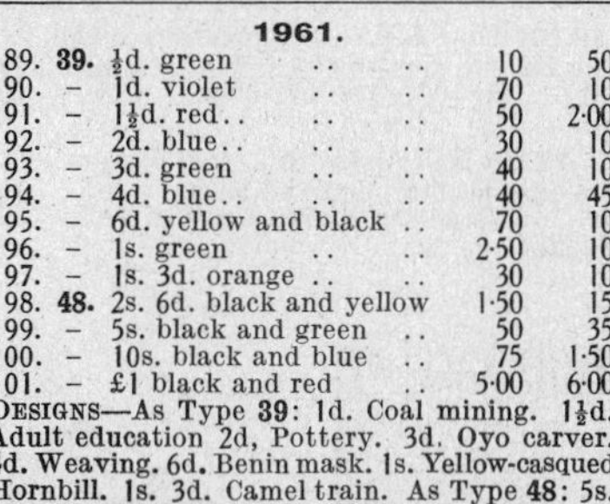

1961.

89. 39. ½d. green 10 50
90. – 1d. violet 70 10
91. – 1½d. red .. .. .. 50 2·00
92. – 2d. blue 30 10
93. – 3d. green 40 10
94. – 4d. blue 40 45
95. – 6d. yellow and black .. 70 10
96. – 1s. green .. .. 2·50 10
97. – 1s. 3d. orange 30 10
98. 48. 2s. 6d. black and yellow 1·50 15
99. – 5s. black and green .. 50 35
100. – 10s. black and blue .. 75 1·50
101. – £1 black and red .. 5·00 6·00

DESIGNS—As Type 39: 1d. Coal mining. 1½d. Adult education 2d, Pottery. 3d. Oyo carver. 4d. Weaving. 6d. Benin mask. 1s. Yellow-casqued Hornbill. 1s. 3d. Camel train. As Type 48: 5s. Nigeria Museum. 10s. Kano Airport. £1, Lagos Railway Station.

52. Globe and Diesel Locomotive.

1961. Admission into U.P.U. Inscr. as in T 52.

102. 52. 1d. orange and blue .. 10 10
103. – 3d. olive and black .. 10 10
104. – 1s. 3d. blue and red .. 20 10
105. – 2s. 6d. green and blue 30 45

DESIGNS: Globe and mail-van (3d.); aircraft (1s. 3d); liner (2s. 6d.).

56. Coat of Arms. 61. " Health ".

1961. 1st Anniv. of Independence.

106. 56. 3d. multicoloured .. 10 10
107. – 4d. green and orange .. 10 10
108. – 6d. green 20 10
109. – 1s. 3d. grey and blue .. 25 10
110. – 2s. 6d. green and blue .. 30 45

DESIGNS—HORIZ. 4d. Natural Resources Map. 6d. Nigerian Eagle. 1s. 3d. Eagles in flight. 2s. 6d. Nigerians and flag.

1962. Lagos Conf. of African and Malagasy States.

111. 61. 1d. bistre 10 10
112. – 3d. purple 10 10
113. – 6d. green 15 10
114. – 1s. brown 20 10
115. – 1s. 3d. blue 25 20

DESIGNS: Map and emblems symbolising Culture (3d.); Commerce (6d.); Communications (1s.); Co-operation (1s. 3d.).

66. Malaria Eradication Emblem and Parasites.

1962. Malaria Eradication.

116. 66. 3d. green and red .. 10 10
117. – 6d. blue and purple .. 15 10
118. – 1s. 3d. mauve & blue 20 10
119. – 2s. 6d. blue and brown 30 20

DESIGNS (embodying emblem): 6d. Insecticide-spraying. 1s. 3d. Aerial spraying. 2s. 6d. Mother, child and microscope.

70. National Monument.

1962. 2nd Anniv. of Independence.

120. 70. 3d. green and blue .. 10 10
121. – 5s. red, green and violet 1·00 45

DESIGN—VERT. 5s. Benin Bronze.

72. Fair Emblem. 76. " Arrival of Delegates ".

1962. Int. Trade Fair, Lagos.

122. 72. 1d. red and olive .. 10 10
123. – 6d. black and red .. 15 10
124. – 1s. black and brown .. 15 10
125. – 2s. 6d. yellow and blue 30 20

DESIGNS—HORIZ. 6d. "Cogwheels of Industry". 1s. "Cornucopia of Industry". 2s. 6d. Oilwells and tanker.

1962. 8th Commonwealth Parliamentary Conference, Lagos.

126. 76. 2½d. blue 15 15
127. – 4d. blue and rose .. 15 10
128. – 1s. 3d. sepia and yellow 20 20

DESIGNS—HORIZ. 4d. National Hall. VERT. 1s. 3d. Mace as Palm Tree.

80. Tractor and Maize.

81. Mercury Capsule and Kano Tracking Station.

1963. Freedom from Hunger.

129. – 3d. olive 75 20
130. 80. 6d. mauve .. .. 1·25 20

DESIGN—VERT. 3d. Herdsman.

1963. " Peaceful Use of Outer Space ".

131. 81. 6d. blue and green .. 25 10
132. – 1s. 3d. black & turquoise 35 20

DESIGN: 1s. 3d. Satellite and Lagos Harbour.

83. Scouts Shaking Hands.
(Illustration reduced. Actual size 60 × 30 mm.).

1963. 11th World Scout Jamboree. Marathon.

133. 83. 3d. red and bronze .. 25 15
134. – 1s. black and red .. 75 65

DESIGN: 1s. Campfire.

85. Emblem and First Aid Team.

1963. Centenary of Red Cross.

135. 85. 3d. red and blue .. 65 10
136. – 6d. red and green .. 95 10
137. – 1s. 3d. red and sepia .. 1·50 70

DESIGNS: 6d. Emblem and " Hospital Services ". 1s. 3d. Patient and emblem.

88. President Azikiwe and State House. 90. " Freedom of Worship ".

1963. Republic Day.

138. 88. 3d. olive and green .. 10 10
139. – 1s. 3d. brown and sepia 10 10
140. – 2s. 6d. turquoise & blue 15 15

The buildings on the 1s. 3d. and the 2s. 6d. are the Federal Supreme Court and the Parliament Building respectively.

1963. 15th Anniversary of Declaration of Human Rights.

141. – 3d. red 10 10
142. 90. 6d. green 10 10
143. – 1s. 3d. blue 20 10
144. – 2s. 6d. purple 35 30

DESIGNS—HORIZ. 3d. (Inscr. " 1948-1963"), Charter and broken whip. VERT. 1s. 3d. "Freedom from Want". 2s. 6d. " Freedom of Speech ".

93. Queen Nefertari. 98. President Azikiwe.

95. President Kennedy.

1964. Nubian Monuments Preservation.

145. 93. 6d. olive and green .. 50 10
146. – 2s. 6d. brn., olive & grn. 1·75 1·75

DESIGN: 2s. 6d. Rameses II.

1964. Pres. Kennedy Memorial Issue.

147. 95. 1s. 3d. lilac and black .. 50 15
148. – 2s. 6d. multicoloured .. 70 55
149. – 5s. multicoloured .. 1·00 1·60

DESIGNS: 2s. 6d. Kennedy and flags. 5s. Kennedy (U.S. Coin Head) and flags.

1964. 1st Anniv. of Republic.

150. 98. 3d. brown 10 10
151. – 1s. 3d. green 25 10
152. – 2s. 6d. green 50 40

DESIGNS (25 × 42 mm.): 1s. 3d. Herbert Macaulay. 2s. 6d. King Jaja of Opobo.

101. Boxing Gloves.

1964. Olympic Games, Tokyo.

153. 101. 3d. sepia and green .. 20 10
154. – 6d. green and blue .. 25 10
155. – 1s. 3d. sepia and olive .. 55 15
156. – 2s. 6d. sepia and brown 1·25 1·50

DESIGNS—HORIZ. 6d. High-jumping. VERT. 1s. 3d. Running. TRIANGULAR. 2s. 6d. Hurdling (size 60 × 30 mm.).

105. Scouts on Hill-top. 109. " Telstar ".

1965. 50th Anniv. of Nigerian Scout Movement.

157. 105. 1d. brown 10 10
158. – 3d. red, black and green 15 10
159. – 6d. red, sepia and green 25 20
160. – 1s. 3d. brown, yellow and deep green .. 40 70

DESIGN: 3d. Scout badge on shield. 6d. Scout badges. 1s. 3d. Chief Scout and Nigerian Scout.

1965. International Quiet Sun Years.

161. 109. 6d. violet and turquoise 15 15
162. – 1s. 3d. green and lilac .. 15 15

DESIGN: 1s. 3d. Solar Satellite.

111. Native Tom-tom and Modern Telephone.

1965. Centenary of I.T.U.

163. 111. 3d. black, red & brown 15 10
164. – 1s. 3d. blk., grn. & blue 1·25 1·00
165. – 5s. multicoloured .. 4·00 5·00

DESIGNS—VERT. 1s. 3d. Microwave Aerial. HORIZ. 5s. Telecommunications satellite and part of globe.

114. I.C.Y. Emblem and Diesel Locomotive.

1965. Int. Co-operation Year.

166. 114. 3d. green, red & orange 2·50 10
167. – 1s. black, blue & lemon 2·50 40
168. – 2s. 6d. grn., blue & yell. 8·50 4·50

DESIGNS: 1s. Students and Lagos Teaching Hospital. 2s. 6d. Kainji (Niger) Dam.

117. Carved Frieze.

1965. 2nd Anniv. of Republic.

169. 117. 3d. black, red & yellow 10 10
170. – 1s. 3d. brown, green & bl. 65 20
171. – 5s. brown, sepia & green 1·75 2·00

DESIGNS—VERT. 1s. 3d. Stone Images at Ikom. 5s. Tada Bronze.

121. African Elephants.

1965. Multicoloured.

172 ½d. Lion and cubs (vert.) 60 85
173 1d. Type 121 .. .. 40 15
174 1½d. Splendid Sunbird .. 4·25 4·50
222 2d. Village Weavers and Red-headed Malimbe .. 1·25 90
223 3d. Cheetah 65 65
177a 4d. Leopards 30 65
178 6d. Saddle-bill Stork (vert.) 1·25 30
179 9d. Grey Parrot .. .. 2·25 40
180 1s. Blue-breasted Kingfisher .. .. 1·50 40
181 1s. 3d. Crowned Crane .. 6·50 55
182 2s. 6d. Kobs 75 40
183 5s. Giraffes .. .. 1·50 1·50
184 10s. Hippopotamus (vert.) 6·00 3·00
185 £1 African Buffalo .. 13·00 8·50

Nos. 180/5 are larger, 46 × 26½ mm.

The 1d., 3d., 4d., 1s. 3d., 2s. 6d., 5s. and £1 exist optd. **F.G.N.** (Federal Government of Nigeria) twice in black. They were prepared in November 1968 as official stamps, but the scheme was abandoned. Some stamps held at a Head Post Office were sold in error and passed through the post. The Director of Posts then decided to put limited supplies on sale, but they had no postal validity.

1966. Commonwealth Prime Minister's Meeting, Lagos. Optd. **COMMONWEALTH P. M. MEETING 11. JAN. 1966.**

186. **48.** 2s. 6d. black & yellow 30 30

135. Y.W.C.A. Emblem and H.Q., Lagos.

1966. Diamond Jubilee of Nigerian Y.W.C.A.

187. **135.** 4d. multicoloured .. 15 10
188. 9d. multicoloured .. 15 40

137. Telephone Handset and Linesman.

1966. 3rd Anniv. of Republic.

189. – 4d. green 10 10
190. **137.** 1s. 6d. blk., brn. & violet 45 50
191. – 2s. 6d. multicoloured .. 1·25 2·00

DESIGNS—VERT. 4d. Dove and flag. HORIZ. 2s. 6d. Niger Bridge, Jebba.

139. "Education, Science and Culture".

1966. 20th Anniv. of U.N.E.S.C.O.

192. **139.** 4d. black, lake & orange 40 10
193. 1s. 6d. black, lake & turq. 1·75 2·50
194. 2s. 6d. black, lake & pink 2·75 5·00

140. Children Drinking.

1966. Nigerian Red Cross.

195. **140.** 4d. + 1d. blk., violet & red 30 25
196. – 1s. 6d. + 3d. multicoloured 1·00 3·50
197. – 2s. 6d. + 3d. multicoloured 1·25 4·00

DESIGNS—VERT. 1s. 6d. Tending patient. HORIZ. 2s. 6d. Tending casualties and Badge.

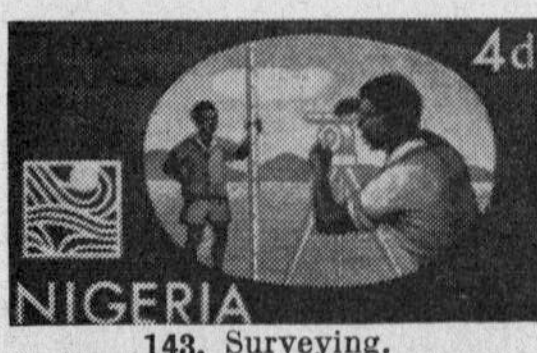

143. Surveying.

1967. Int. Hydrological Decade. Mult.

198. 4d. Type **143** 10 10
199. 2s. 6d. Water gauge on dam (vert.) 25 60

145. Globe and Weather Satellite.

1967. World Meteorological Day.

200. **145.** 4d. mauve and blue .. 15 10
201. – 1s. 6d. blk., yell. & blue 50 50

DESIGN: 1s. 6d. Passing storm and sun.

147. Eyo Masquerades.

1967. 4th Anniv. of Republic. Multicoloured.

202. 4d. Type **147** 20 10
203. 1s. 6d. Crowds watching acrobat .. .. .. 1·25 1·50
204. 2s. 6d. Stilt dancer (vert.) 1·50 2·50

150. Tending Sick Animal.

1967. Rinderpest Eradication Campaign.

205. **150.** 4d. multicoloured .. 15 10
206. 1s. 6d. multicoloured .. 55 75

151. Smallpox Vaccination.

1968. 20th Anniversary of World Health Organization.

207. **151.** 4d. mauve and black .. 15 10
208. – 1s. 6d. orge., lemon & blk. 55 40

DESIGN: 1s. 6d. African and Mosquito.

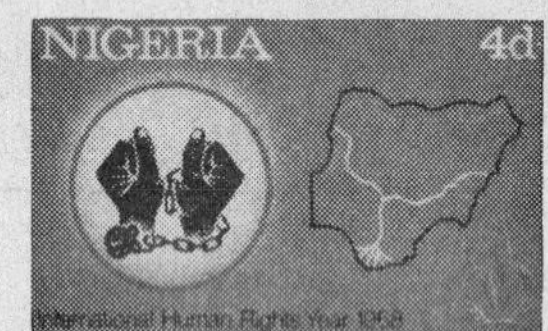

153. Chained Hands and Outline of Nigeria.

1968. Human Rights Year.

209. **153.** 4d. blue, black & yellow 10 10
210. – 1s. 6d. green, red & black 20 30

DESIGN—VERT. 1s. 6d. Nigerian Flag and Human Rights Emblem.

155. Hand grasping at Doves of Freedom.

1968. 5th Anniv. of Federal Republic.

211. **155.** 4d. multicoloured .. 10 10
212. 1s. 6d. multicoloured .. 20 20

156. Map of Nigeria and Olympic Rings.

1968. Olympic Games, Mexico.

213. **156.** 4d. black, green and red 10 10
214. – 1s. 6d. multicoloured .. 20 20

DESIGN: 1s. 6d. Nigerian Athletes, Flag and Olympic Rings.

158. G.P.O., Lagos.

1969. Inauguration of Philatelic Service.

215. **158.** 4d. black and green .. 10 10
216. 1s. 6d. black and blue .. 20 20

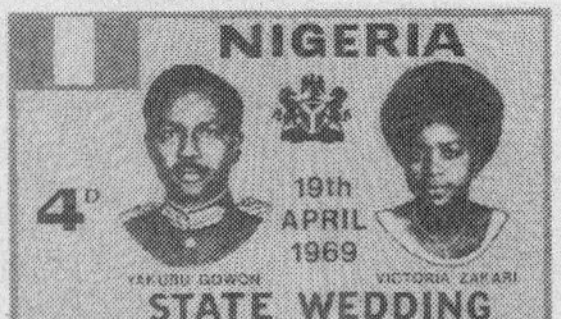

159. Yakubu Gowon and Victoria Zakari.

1969. Wedding of General Gowon.

217. **159.** 4d. brown and green .. 10 10
218. 1s. 6d. black and green 40 20

160. Bank Emblem and "5th Anniversary".

1969. 5th Anniv of African Development Bank.

233 **160** 4d. orange, black & bl 10 10
234 – 1s. 6d. yellow, black and purple 20 20

DESIGN: 1s. 6d. Bank emblem and rays.

162. I.L.O. Emblem.

1969. 50th Anniversary of I.L.O.

235. **162.** 4d. black and violet .. 10 10
236. – 1s. 6d. green and black 40 40

DESIGN: 1s. 6d. World map and I.L.O. Emblem.

164. Olumo Rock.

1969. Int. Year of African Tourism.

237. **164.** 4d. multicoloured .. 10 10
238. – 1s. black and green .. 20 10
239. – 1s. 6d. multicoloured .. 55 35

DESIGNS—VERT. 1s. Traditional musicians. 1s. 6d. Assob Falls.

167. Symbolic Tree.

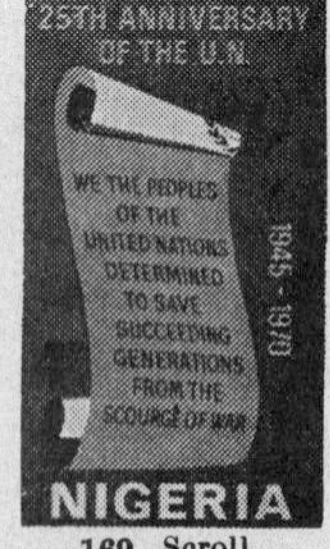

169. Scroll.

168. U.P.U. Headquarters Building.

1970. "Stamp of Destiny". End of Civil War.

240. **167.** 4d. gold, blue and black 10 10
241. – 1s. multicoloured .. 10 10
242. – 1s. 6d. green and black 15 10
243. – 2s. multicoloured .. 20 20

DESIGNS—VERT. 1s. Symbolic Wheel. 1s. 6d. United Nigerians supporting Map. HORIZ. 2s. Symbolic Torch.

1970. New U.P.U. Headquarters Building.

244. **168.** 4d. violet and yellow .. 10 10
245. 1s. 6d. blue and indigo 20 20

1970. 25th Anniv. of United Nations.

246. **169.** 4d. brn., buff and black 10 10
247. – 1s. 6d. blue, brown & gold 20 20

DESIGN: 1s. 6d. U.N. Building.

170. Oil Rig. **172.** Ibibio Face Mask.

171. Children and Globe.

1970. 10th Anniv. of Independence.

248. 2d. Type **170** 20 10
249. 4d. University Graduate 15 10
250. 6d. Durbar Horsemen .. 25 10
251. 9d. Servicemen raising Flag 30 10
252. 1s. Footballer 30 10
253. 1s. 6d. Parliament Building 30 30
254. 2s. Kainji Dam 60 80
255. 2s. 6d. Agricultural Produce 60 85

1971. Racial Equality Year. Multicoloured.

256. 4d. Type **171** 10 10
257. 1s. Black and white men uprooting "Racism" (vert.) 10 10
258. 1s. 6d. "The World in Black and White" (vert.) .. 15 50
259. 2s. Black and white men united 15 75

1971. Antiquities of Nigeria.

260. **172.** 4d. black and blue .. 10 10
261. – 1s. 3d. brn. and ochre .. 15 30
262. – 1s. 9d. grn., brn. & yell. 20 80

DESIGN: 1s. 3d. Benin bronze. 1s. 9d. Ife bronze.

173. Children and Symbol.

174. Mast and Dish Aerial.

1971. 25th Anniv. of U.N.I.C.E.F.

263. **173.** 4d. multicoloured .. 10 10
264. – 1s. 3d. orge., red & brn. 15 40
265. – 1s. 9d. pale turquoise & deep turquoise .. 15 85

DESIGNS: Each with U.N.I.C.E.F. symbol. 1s. 3d. Mother and child. 1s. 9d. Mother carrying child.

1971. Opening of Nigerian Earth Satellite Station.

266. **174.** 4d. multicoloured .. 15 10
267. – 1s. 3d. grn., blue & blk. 30 50
268. – 1s. 9d. brn., orge. & blk. 40 1·00
269. – 3s. mauve, blk. & pur. 85 2·00

DESIGNS: Nos. 267/9, as Type **174**, but showing different views of the Satellite Station.

175. Trade Fair Emblem. 177. Nok Style Terracotta Head.

176. Traffic.

1972. All-Africa Trade Fair.

270.	175.	4d. multicoloured	10	10
271.	–	1s. 3d. lilac, yell. & gold	15	35
272.	–	1s. 9d. yell., orge. & blk.	15	90

DESIGNS—HORIZ. 1s. 3d. Map of Africa with pointers to Nairobi. VERT. 1s. 9d. Africa on globe.

1972. Change to Driving on the Right.

273.	176.	4d. orge., brn. & black	20	10
274.	–	1s. 3d. multicoloured	80	70
275.	–	1s. 9d. multicoloured	90	1·25
276.	–	3s. multicoloured	2·00	3·00

DESIGNS: 1s. 3d. Roundabout. 1s. 9d. Highway. 3s. Road junction.

1972. All-Nigeria Arts Festival. Mult.

277.	4d. Type 177	10	10
278.	1s. 3d. Bronze pot from Igbo-Ukwu	25	60
279.	1s. 9d. Bone harpoon (horiz.)	30	1·25

178. Hides and Skins.

1973.

290	178	1 k. multicoloured	10	10
281	–	2 k. multicoloured	35	10
292	–	3 k. multicoloured	15	10
282a	–	5 k. multicoloured	50	10
294	–	7 k. multicoloured	30	80
295	–	8 k. multicoloured	40	10
344	–	10 k. multicoloured	1·00	20
297	–	12 k. blk., grn. & bl.	30	1·00
298	–	15 k. multicoloured	30	50
299	–	18 k. multicoloured	50	30
300	–	20 k. multicoloured	65	30
301	–	25 k. multicoloured	85	45
302	–	30 k. blk., yell. & bl.	40	1·00
303	–	35 k. multicoloured	4·00	3·00
288a	–	50 k. multicoloured	1·50	90
305	–	1 n. multicoloured	1·25	1·10
306	–	2 n. multicoloured	3·50	3·75

DESIGNS—HORIZ. 2 k. Natural gas tanks. 3 k. Cement works. 5 k. Cattle-ranching. 7 k. Timber mill. 8 k. Oil refinery. 10 k. Cheetahs. Yankari Game Reserve. 12 k. New Civic building. 15 k. Sugar-cane harvesting. 20 k. Vaccine production. 25 k. Modern wharf. 35 k. Textile machinery. 1 n. Eko Bridge. 2 n. Teaching Hospital, Lagos. VERT. 18 k. Palm oil production. 30 k. Argungu Fishing Festival. 50 k. Pottery.

179. Athlete.

1973. Second All-African Games, Lagos.

307.	179.	5 k. lilac, blue & blk.	15	10
308.	–	12 k. multicoloured	25	50
309.	–	18 k. multicoloured	60	1·00
310.	–	25 k. multicoloured	70	1·50

DESIGNS—HORIZ. 12 k. Football. 18 k. Table-tennis. VERT. 25 k. National stadium.

180. All-Africa House, Addis Ababa.

1973. 10th Anniv. of O.A.U. Multicoloured.

311.	5 k. Type 180	10	10
312.	18 k. O.A.U. flag (vert.)	30	40
313.	30 k. O.A.U. emblem and symbolic flight of ten stairs (vert.)	50	80

181. Dr. Hansen.

1973. Cent. of Discovery of Leprosy Bacillus.

314.	181.	5 k.+2 k. brown, pink and black	30	70

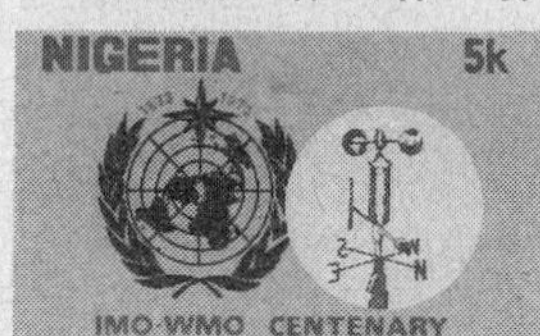

182. W.M.O. Emblem and Weather-vane.

1973. Centenary of I.M.O./W.M.O.

315.	182.	5 k. multicoloured	15	10
316.		30 k. multicoloured	1·25	2·00

183. University Complex.

1973. 25th Anniv. of Ibadan University. Multicoloured.

317.	5 k. Type 183	10	10
318.	12 k. Students' population growth (vert.)	25	30
319.	18 k. Tower and students	35	55
320.	30 k. Teaching Hospital	50	85

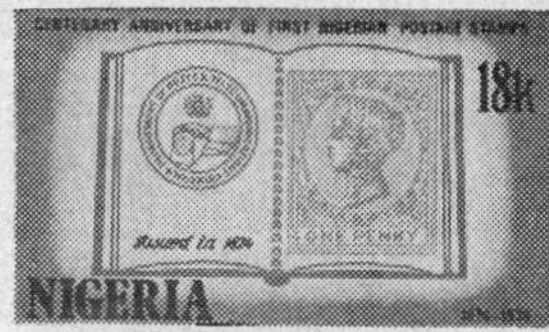

184. Lagos 1d. Stamp of 1874.

1974. Stamp Centenary.

321.	–	5 k. grn., orge. & blk.	20	10
322.	–	12 k. multicoloured	60	60
323.	184.	18 k. grn., mve. & blk.	80	1·00
324.	–	30 k. multicoloured	2·25	2·50

DESIGNS: 5 k. Graph of mail traffic growth. 12 k. Northern Nigeria £25 stamp of 1904. 30 k. Forms of mail transport.

185. U.P.U. Emblem on Globe.

1974. Centenary of U.P.U.

325.	185.	5 k. bl., orge. & blk.	15	10
326.	–	18 k. multicoloured	1·50	60
327.	–	30 k. brn., grn. & blk.	1·75	1·75

DESIGNS: 18 k. World transport map. 30 k. U.P.U. emblem and letters.

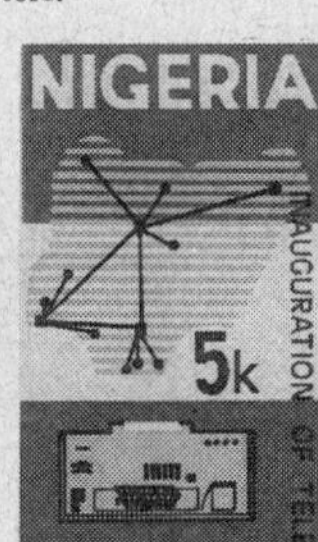

186. Starving and Well-fed Children. 187. Telex Network and Teleprinter.

1974. Freedom from Hunger Campaign. Mult.

328.	5 k. Type 186	10	10
329.	12 k. Poultry battery ("More Protein")	40	50
330.	30 k. Water-hoist ("Irrigation increases food production")	1·10	1·75

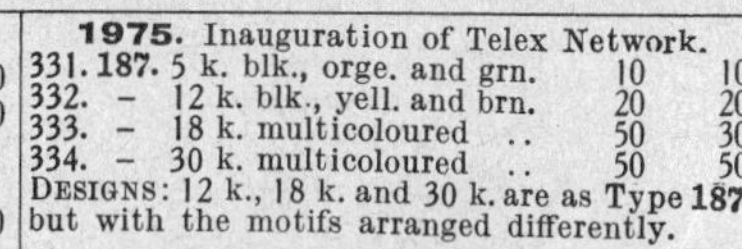

1975. Inauguration of Telex Network.

331.	187.	5 k. blk., orge. and grn.	10	10
332.	–	12 k. blk., yell. and brn.	20	20
333.	–	18 k. multicoloured	50	30
334.	–	30 k. multicoloured	50	50

DESIGNS: 12 k., 18 k. and 30 k. are as Type 187 but with the motifs arranged differently.

188. Queen Amina of Zaria. 190. Alexander Graham Bell.

1975. International Women's Year.

335.	188.	5 k. grn., yell. and blue	15	10
336.		18 k. pur., blue and mve.	50	65
337.		30 k. multicoloured	60	1·10

1976. Centenary of Telephone.

355.	190.	5 k. multicoloured	10	10
356.	–	18 k. multicoloured	40	55
357.	–	25 k. blue, light blue and brown	70	1·00

DESIGNS—HORIZ. 18 k. Gong and modern telephone system. VERT. 25 k. Telephones, 1876 and 1976.

191. Child Writing.

1976. Universal Primary Education. Launching.

358.	191.	5 k. yell., violet & mauve	10	10
359.	–	18 k. multicoloured	45	60
360.	–	25 k. multicoloured	70	85

DESIGNS—VERT. 18 k. Children entering school. 25 k. Children in class.

192. Festival Emblem.

1976. 2nd World Black and African Festival of Arts and Culture, Nigeria.

361.	192.	5 k. gold and brown	20	10
362.	–	10 k. brn., yell. & blk.	35	40
363.	–	12 k. multicoloured	50	55
364.	–	18 k. yell., brn. and blk.	70	80
365.	–	30 k. red and black	1·00	1·50

DESIGNS: 10 k. National Arts Theatre. 12 k. African hair-styles. 18 k. Musical instruments. 30 k. "Nigerian arts and crafts".

193. General Murtala Muhammed and Map of Nigeria.

1977. 1st Death Anniv. of General Muhammed (Head of State). Multicoloured.

366.	5 k. Type 193	10	10
367.	18 k. The General in dress uniform (vert.)	20	35
368.	30 k. The General in battle dress (vert.)	30	70

194. Scouts Saluting.

1977. 1st All-African Scout Jamboree, Jos, Nigeria. Multicoloured.

369.	5 k. Type 194	15	10
370.	18 k. Scouts cleaning street (horiz.)	70	70
371.	25 k. Scouts working on farm (horiz.)	85	95
372.	30 k. Jamboree emblem and map of Africa (horiz.)	1·10	1·40

195. Trade Fair Complex.

1977. First Lagos Int. Trade Fair.

373.	195.	5 k. black, blue & green	10	10
374.	–	18 k. blk., blue and pur.	20	25
375.	–	30 k. multicoloured	30	45

DESIGNS: 18 k. Globe and Trade Fair emblem. 30 k. Weaving and basketry.

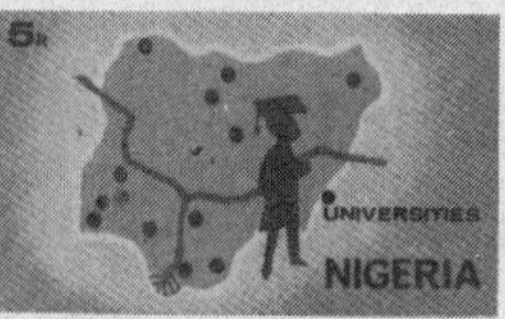

196. Map showing Nigerian Universities.

1978. Global Conference on Technical Co-operation between Developing Countries, Buenos Aires.

376.	196.	5 k. multicoloured	10	10
377.	–	12 k. multicoloured	15	15
378.	–	18 k. multicoloured	25	25
379.	–	30 k. yell., violet & black	45	60

DESIGNS: 12 k. Map of West African highways and telecommunications. 18 k. Technologists undergoing training. 30 k. World map.

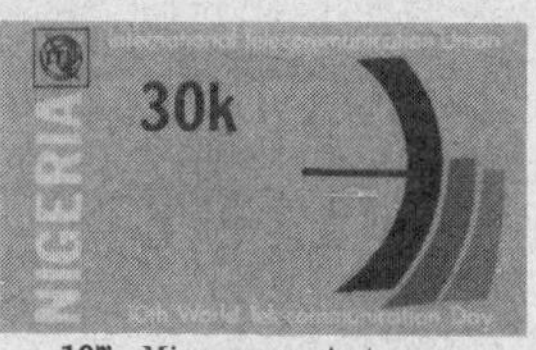

197. Microwave Antenna.

1978. 10th World Telecommunications Day.

380.	197.	30 k. multicoloured	50	60

198. Students on Operation "Feed the Nation".

1978. "Operation Feed the Nation" Campaign. Multicoloured.

381.	5 k. Type 198	10	10
382.	18 k. Family backyard farm	20	20
383.	30 k. Plantain farm (vert.)	35	60

199. Mother with Infected Child.

1978. Global Eradication of Smallpox.

384.	199.	5 k. black, brown & lilac	20	10
385.	–	12 k. multicoloured	35	20
386.	–	18 k. blk., brn. and yell.	60	40
387.	–	30 k. black, silver & pink	80	70

DESIGNS—HORIZ. 12 k. Doctor and infected child. 18 k. Group of children being vaccinated. VERT. 30 k. Syringe.

200. Nok Terracotta Human Figure, Bwari (900 B.C. – 200 A.D.). 201. Anti-Apartheid Emblem.

1978. Antiquities.

388.	200.	5 k. black, blue and red	10	10
389.	–	12 k. multicoloured	10	10
390.	–	18 k. black, blue and red	15	15
391.	–	30 k. multicoloured	20	20

DESIGNS—HORIZ. 12 k. Igbo-Ukwu bronze snail shell, Igbo Isaiah (9th-century A.D.). VERT. 18 k. Ife bronze statue of a king (12th – 15th century A.D.). 30 k. Benin bronze equestrian figure (about 1700 A.D.).

1978. International Anti-Apartheid Year.

392. 201. 18 k. black, yell. and red 15 15

202. Wright Brothers and " Flyer ".

1978. 75th Anniv. of Powered Flight.

393. 202.	5 k. multicoloured ..	20	10
394. –	18 k. black, blue and light blue	65	20

DESIGN: 18 k. Nigerian Air Force formation.

203. Murtala Muhammed Airport.

1979. Opening of Murtala Muhammed Airport.

395. 203. 5 k. black, grey and blue 30 30

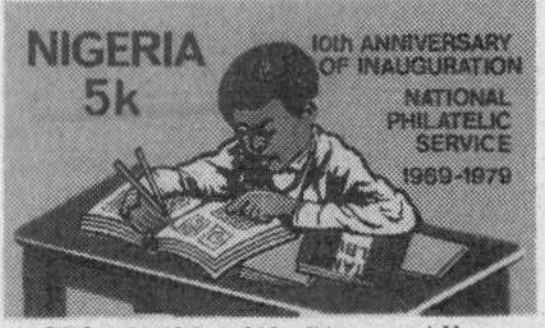

204. Child with Stamp Album.

1979. 10th Anniversary of National Philatelic Service.

396. 204. 5 k. multicoloured .. 10 10

205. Mother and Child.

1979. International Year of the Child.

397.	5 k. Type **205**	15	10
398.	18 k. Children studying ..	40	30
399.	25 k. Children playing (vert.)	50	50

206. Trainee Teacher making Audio Visual Aid Materials.

207. Necom House.

1979. 50th Anniversary of International Bureau of Education. Multicoloured.

400.	10 k. Type **206**	10	10
401.	30 k. Adult education class	25	30

1979. 50th Anniversary of Consultative Committee of International Radio.

402. 207. 10 k. multicoloured .. 15 20

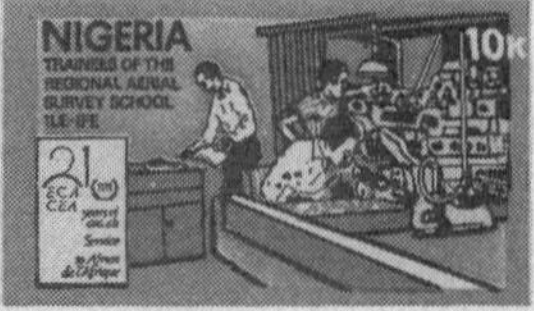

208. Trainees of the Regional Air Survey School, Ile-Ife.

1979. 21st Anniversary of Economic Commission for Africa.

403. 208. 10 k. multicoloured .. 20 20

209. Football, Cup and Map of Nigeria.

1980. African Cup of Nations Football Competition, Nigeria. Multicoloured.

404.	10 k. Type **209**	20	10
405.	30 k. Footballer (vert.) ..	60	50

210. Wrestling.

1980. Olympic Games, Moscow.

406. 210.	10 k. multicoloured ..	10	10
407. –	20 k. black and green	10	10
408. –	30 k. blk., orge. & blue	15	15
409. –	45 k. multicoloured ..	20	20

DESIGNS: VERT. 20 k. Long jump. 45 k. Netball. HORIZ. 30 k. Swimming.

211. Figures supporting O.P.E.C. Emblem.

1980. 20th Anniv. of O.P.E.C. (Organization of Petroleum Exporting Countries).

410. 211.	10 k. black, blue & yell.	20	10
411. –	45 k. black, blue & mve.	70	60

DESIGN—VERT. 45 k. O.P.E.C. emblem and globe.

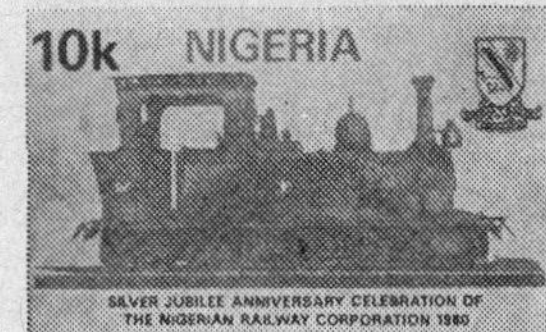

212. Steam Locomotive.

1980. Nigerian Railway Corporation. Multicoloured.

412.	10 k. Type **212**	75	10
413.	20 k. Loading goods train	1·50	85
414.	30 k. Diesel goods train ..	1·75	1·25

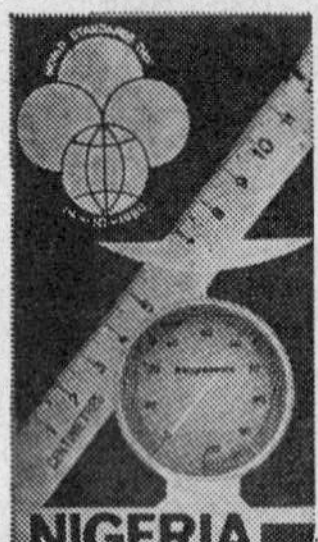

213. Metric Scales.

215. Disabled Woman Sweeping.

214. " Communication " Symbols and Map of West Africa.

1980. World Standards Day.

415. 213.	10 k. red and black ..	10	10
416. –	30 k. multicoloured ..	35	40

DESIGN—HORIZ. 30 k. Quality control.

1980. 5th Anniversary of Economic Community of West African States.

417. 214.	10 k. blk., orge. & olive	10	10
418. –	25 k. blk., green & red	10	10
419. –	30 k. blk., yell. & brn.	15	15
420. –	45 k. blk, turq. & blue	20	25

DESIGNS: 25 k. " Transport ". 30 k. " Agriculture ". 45 k. " Industry ".

1981. International Year for Disabled Persons.

421. 215.	10 k. multicoloured ..	20	10
422. –	30 k. blk., brn. & blue	65	65

DESIGN: 30 k. Disabled man filming.

216. President launching " Green Revolution " (food production campaign).

1981. World Food Day.

423. 216.	10 k. multicoloured ..	10	10
424. –	25 k. blk., yell. & green	20	50
425. –	30 k. multicoloured ..	25	55
426. –	45 k. blk., brn. & yell.	45	85

DESIGNS—VERT. 25 k. Food Crops. 30 k. Harvesting tomatoes. HORIZ. 45 k. Pig farming.

217. Rioting in Soweto.

1981. Anti-Apartheid Movement.

427. 217.	30 k. multicoloured ..	35	45
428. –	45 k. blk., red & green	50	80

DESIGN—VERT. 45 k. " Police brutality ".

218. " Preservation of Wildlife ".

1982. 75th Anniversary of Boy Scout Movement. Multicoloured.

429.	30 k. Type **218**	75	55
430.	45 k. Lord Baden-Powell taking salute	1·00	95

219. Early Inoculation.

1982. Centenary of Robert Koch's Discovery of Tubercle Bacillus.

431. 219.	10 k. multicoloured ..	25	15
432. –	30 k. black, brown and green	65	55
433. –	45 k. black, brown and green	1·10	1·10

DESIGNS:—HORIZ. 30 k. Technician and microscope. VERT. 45 k. Patient being X-Rayed.

220. " Keep Your Environment Clean ".

1982. 10th Anniversary of U.N. Conference on Human Environment.

434. 220.	10 k. multicoloured ..	15	10
435. –	20 k. orange, grey and black	40	40
436. –	30 k. multicoloured ..	55	60
437. –	45 k. multicoloured ..	80	85

DESIGNS: 20 k. " Check air pollution ". 30 k. " Preserve natural environment ". 45 k. " Reafforestation concerns all ".

221. " Salamis parhassus ".

1982. Nigerian Butterflies. Multicoloured.

438	10 k. Type **221**	15	10
439	20 k. "Iterus zalmoxis" ..	30	30
440	30 k. "Cymothoe beckeri"	40	40
441	45 k. "Papilio hesperus" ..	70	70

222. Carving of " Male and Female Twins ".

1982. 25th Anniv. of National Museum. Multicoloured.

442.	10 k. Type **222**	25	10
443.	20 k. Royal Bronze Leopard (horiz.)	50	55
444.	30 k. Soapstone seated figure	80	1·25
445.	45 k. Wooden Helmet mask	1·25	1·75

223. Three Generations.

1983. Family Day. Multicoloured.

446.	10 k. Type **223**	15	10
447.	30 k. Parents with three children (vert.)	50	65

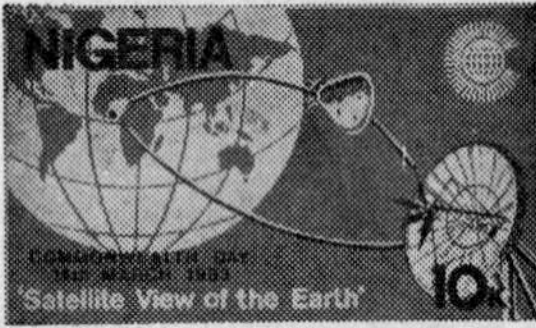

224. Satellite View of Globe.

1983. Commonwealth Day.

448. 224.	10 k. brown & black	10	10
449. –	25 k. multicoloured	30	30
450. –	30 k. blk., pur. & grey	35	35
451. –	45 k. multicoloured	45	45

DESIGNS—HORIZ. 25 k. National Assembly Buildings. VERT. 30 k. Drilling for oil. 45 k. Athletics.

225. Corps Members on Building Project.

1983. 10th Anniv. of National Youth Service Corps. Multicoloured.

452.	10 k. Type **225**	15	10
453.	25 k. On the assault-course (vert.)	30	30
454.	30 k. Corps members on parade	40	40

226. Postman on Bicycle.

1983. World Communications Year. Multicoloured.

455.	10 k. Type **226**	15	10
456.	25 k. Newspaper kiosk (horiz.)	30	40
457.	30 k. Town crier blowing elephant tusk (horiz.) ..	35	45
458.	45 k. T.V. newsreader (horiz.)	45	55

227. Pink Shrimp.

1983. World Fishery Resources.

459. 227.	10 k. red, blue & black	15	10
460. –	25 k. multicoloured ..	30	40
461. –	30 k. multicoloured ..	30	45
462. –	45 k. multicoloured ..	40	70

DESIGNS: 25 k. Long Necked Croaker. 30 k. Barracuda. 45 k. Fishing techniques.

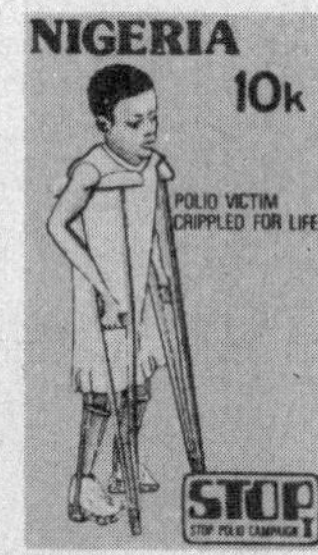

228. On Parade. **229.** Crippled Child.

1983. Centenary of Boys' Brigade, and 75th Anniv. of Founding in Nigeria. Mult.

463. 10 k. Type **228** 40 10
464. 30 k. Members working on Cassava plantation (horiz.) .. .. .. 1·50 1·50
465. 45 k. Skill training (horiz.) 2·25 2·50

1984. Stop Polio Campaign.

466. **229.** 10 k. blue, blk. & brn. 25 15
467. – 25 k. orge., blk. & yell. 55 70
468. – 30 k. red, black & brn. 70 90

DESIGNS—HORIZ. 25 k. Child receiving vaccine. VERT. 30 k. Healthy child.

230. Waterbuck. **232.** Boxing.

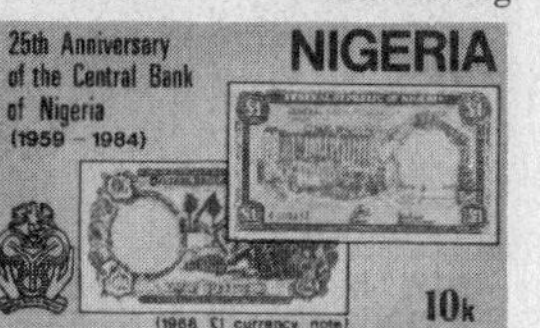

231. Obverse and Reverse of 1969 £1 Note.

1984. Nigerian Wildlife.

469. **230.** 10 k. green, brn. & blk. 20 10
470. – 25 k. multicoloured .. 50 50
471. – 30 k. brown, blk. & grn. 60 70
472. – 45 k. blue, orge. & blk. 80 95

DESIGNS—HORIZ. 25 k. Hartebeest. 30 k. African Buffalo. VERT. 45 k. Diademed Monkey.

1984. 25th Anniv. of Nigerian Central Bank.

473. **231.** 10 k. multicoloured .. 20 10
474. – 25 k. brown, black and green 45 50
475. – 30 k. red, black and green 55 60

DESIGNS: 25 k. Central Bank. 30 k. Obverse and reverse of 1959 £5 note.

1984. Olympic Games, Los Angeles. Mult.

476. 10 k. Type **232** 15 10
477. 25 k. Discus-throwing .. 35 50
478. 30 k. Weightlifting .. 40 60
479. 35 k. Cycling 60 90

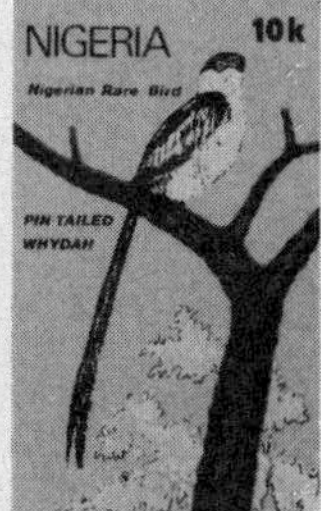

233. Irrigation Project, Lesotho. **234.** Pin-tailed Whydah.

1984. 20th Anniv. of African Development.

480. **233.** 10 k. multicoloured .. 20 10
481. – 25 k. multicoloured .. 50 50
482. – 30 k. blk, yell. & bl.. 60 60
483. – 45 k. blk., brn. & bl. 2·00 90

DESIGNS—HORIZ. 25 k. Bomi Hills Road, Liberia. 30 k. School building project, Seychelles. 45 k. Coal mining, Niger.

1984. Rare Birds. Multicoloured.

484. 10 k. Type **234** 75 10
485. 25 k. Spur-winged plover.. 1·50 60
486. 30 k. Red bishop .. .. 1·50 1·25
487. 45 k. Double-spurred francolin.. .. .. 1·75 2·00

235. Aircraft taking-off.

1984. 40th Anniversary of International Civil Aviation Organization. Multicoloured

488. 10 k. Type **235** 50 10
489. 45 k. Aircraft circling globe 2·00 1·75

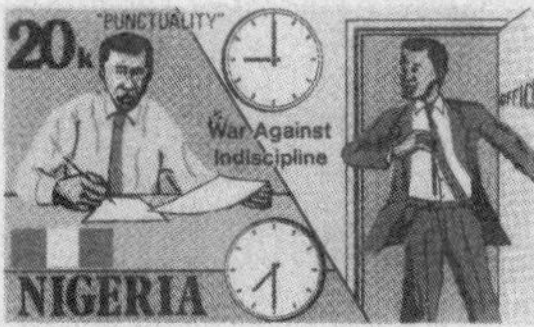

236. Office Workers and Clocks ("Punctuality").

1985. "War against Indiscipline". Mult.

490. 20 k. Type **236** 30 35
491. 50 k. Cross over hands passing banknotes ("Discourage Bribery") 70 75

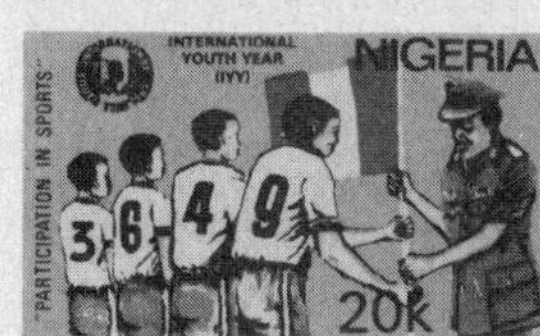

237. Footballers receiving Flag from Major-General Buhari.

1985. International Youth Year. Mult.

492. 20 k. Type **237** 30 35
493. 50 k. Girls of different tribes with flag (vert.) .. 70 75
494. 55 k. Members of youth organizations with flags (vert.) 75 80

238. Globe and O.P.E.C. Emblem.

1985. 25th Anniversary of Organization of Petroleum Exporting Countries.

495. **238.** 20 k. blue and red .. 1·00 35
496. – 50 k. black and blue 1·75 75

DESIGN—HORIZ. 50 k. World map and O.P.E.C. emblem.

239. Rolling Mill.

1985. 25th Anniv. of Independence. Mult.

497. 20 k. Type **239** 40 10
498. 50 k. Map of Nigeria .. 60 35
499. 55 k. Remembrance Arcade 60 40
500. 60 k. Eleme, first Nigerian oil refinery .. .. 1·25 50

240. Waterfall. **241.** Map of Nigeria and National Flag.

1985. World Tourism Day. Multicoloured.

502. 20 k. Type **240** 45 10
503. 50 k. Pottery, carved heads and map of Nigeria (horiz.) 55 40
504. 55 k. Calabash carvings and Nigerian flag .. 55 40
505. 60 k. Leather work .. 55 45

1985. 40th Anniv. of United Nations Organization and 25th Anniv. of Nigerian Membership.

506. **241.** 20 k. blk., grn. & bl. 15 10
507. – 50 k. black, bl. & red 30 30
508. – 55 k. black, bl. & red 30 30

DESIGNS—HORIZ. 50 k. United Nations Building, New York. 55 k. United Nations logo.

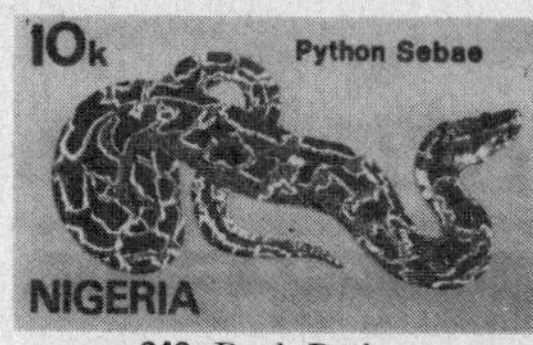

242. Rock Python.

1986. African Reptiles.

509. **242.** 10 k. multicoloured .. 35 10
510. – 20 k. blk., brn. & bl. 65 65
511. – 25 k. multicoloured .. 70 80
512. – 30 k. multicoloured .. 70 80

DESIGNS: 20 k. Long snouted crocodile. 25 k. Gopher tortoise. 30 k. Chameleon.

243. Social Worker with Children.

1986. Nigerian Life. Multicoloured.

513 1 k. Type **243** 10 10
514 2 k. Volkswagen motor assembly line (horiz) .. 10 10
515 5 k. Modern housing estate (horiz) 10 10
516 10 k. Harvesting oil palm fruit 10 10
517 15 k. Unloading freighter (horiz) 10 10
518 20 k. "Tecoma stans" (flower) 10 10
519 25 k. Hospital ward (horiz) 10 10
519a 30 k. Birom dancers .. 10 10
520 35 k. Telephonists operating switchboard (horiz) 10 10
521 40 k. Nkpokiti dancers .. 10 10
522 45 k. Hibiscus (horiz) .. 10 10
523 50 k. Post Office counter (horiz) 10 10
524 1 n. Stone quarry (horiz) 10 15
525 2 n. Students in laboratory (horiz) 10 10

244. Emblem and Globe.

1986. International Peace Year. Mult.

526. 10 k. Type **244** 10 10
527. 20 k. Hands of five races holding globe 20 20

245. "Goliathus goliathus" (beetle).

1986. Nigerian Insects. Multicoloured.

528 10 k. Type **245** 40 10
529 20 k. "Vespa vulgaris" (wasp) 55 40
530 25 k. "Acheta domestica" (cricket) 65 70
531 30 k. "Anthrenus verbasci" (beetle) .. .. 95 1·10

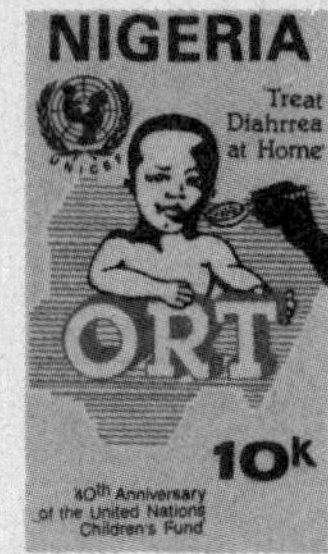

246. Oral Rehydration Therapy.

1986. 40th Anniv. of U.N.I.C.E.F.

533. **246.** 10 k. multicoloured .. 35 10
534. – 20 k. blk., brn. & yell. 60 45
535. – 25 k. multicoloured .. 70 60
536. – 30 k. multicoloured .. 90 90

DESIGNS: 20 k. Immunisation. 25 k. Breast feeding. 30 k. Mother and child.

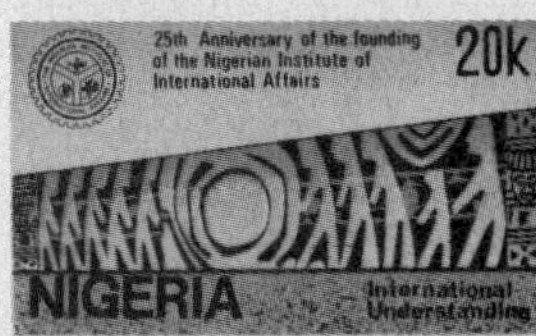

247. Stylized Figures on Wall ("International Understanding").

1986. 25th Anniv. of Nigerian Institute of International Affairs.

537. **247.** 20 k. blk., bl. & grn. 70 50
538. – 30 k. multicoloured .. 1·10 1·40

DESIGN—VERT. 30 k. "Knowledge" (bronze sculpture).

248. Freshwater Clam.

1987. Shells.

539 **248** 10 k. multicoloured .. 60 10
540 – 20 k. black, brn & pink 90 1·00
541 – 25 k. multicoloured .. 1·00 1·00
542 – 30 k. multicoloured .. 1·25 1·50

DESIGNS: 20 k. Periwinkle; 25 k. Bloody cockle (inscr. "BLODDY COCKLE"). 30 k. Mangrove oyster.

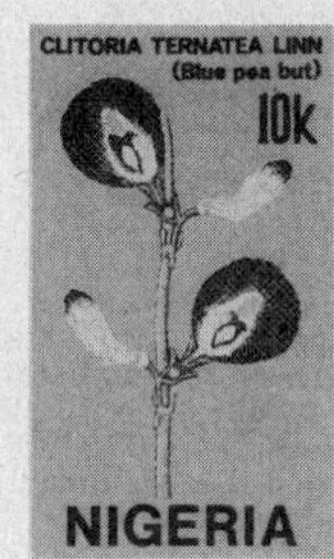

249. "Clitoria ternatea". **250.** Doka Hairstyle.

1987. Nigerian Flowers.

543. **249.** 10 k. multicoloured .. 10 10
544. – 20 k. brown, yellow and green 15 10
545. – 25 k. multicoloured .. 15 15
546. – 30 k. multicoloured .. 20 20

DESIGNS: 20 k. "Hibiscus tiliaceus". 25 k. "Acanthus montanus". 30 k. "Combretum racemosum".

1987. Women's Hairstyles.

547. **250.** 10 k. black, brown and grey 10 10
548. – 20 k. multicoloured .. 10 10
549. – 25 k. black, brown and red 15 10
550. – 30 k. multicoloured .. 15 10

DESIGNS: 20 k. Eting. 25 k. Agogo. 30 k. Goto.

251. Family sheltering under Tree. **252.** Red Cross Worker distributing Food.

1987. International Year of Shelter for the Homeless. Multicoloured.

551. 20 k. Type **251** 15 10
552. 30 k. Family and modern house 15 20

1988. 125th Anniv. of International Red Cross. Multicoloured.

553. 20 k. Type **252** 25 20
554. 30 k. Carrying patient to ambulance 25 50

253. Doctor vaccinating Baby.

1988. 40th Anniv. of W.H.O. Multicoloured.

555. 10 k. Type **253** 10 10
556. 20 k. W.H.O. logo and outline map of Nigeria .. 20 20
557. 30 k. Doctor and patients at mobile clinic 20 20

254 O.A.U. Logo

1988. 25th Anniv of Organization of African Unity.

558 **254** 10 k. brn, grn & orge 15 15
559 – 20 k. multicoloured .. 15 15

DESIGN: 20 k. Four Africans supporting map of Africa.

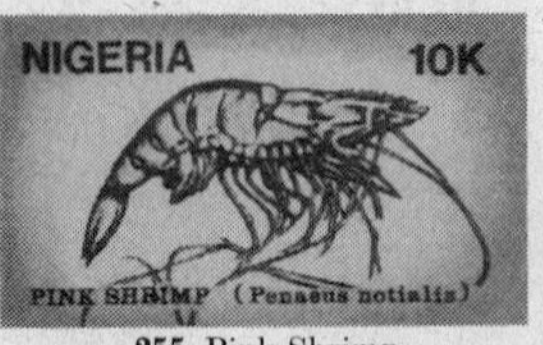

255 Pink Shrimp

1988. Shrimps.

560 **255** 10 k. multicoloured .. 20 10
561 – 20 k. black and green 30 10
562 – 25 k. black, red & brn 30 15
563 – 30 k. orange, brn & blk 35 20

DESIGNS: 20 k. Tiger shrimp; 25 k. Deepwater roseshrimp; 30 k. Estuarine prawn.

256 Weightlifting

1988. Olympic Games, Seoul. Multicoloured.

565 10 k. Type **256** 20 10
566 20 k. Boxing 25 15
567 30 k. Athletics (vert) .. 35 25

257 Banknote Production Line (Illustration reduced, actual size 74 x 22 mm)

1988. 25th Anniv of Nigerian Security Printing and Minting Co Ltd.

568 **257** 10 k. multicoloured .. 10 10
569 – 20 k. blk, silver & grn 10 10
570 – 25 k. multicoloured .. 15 15
571 – 30 k. multicoloured .. 25 25

DESIGNS: HORIZ (As T **257**)—20 k. Coin production line. VERT (37 × 44 mm)—25 k. Montage of products; 30 k. Anniversary logos.

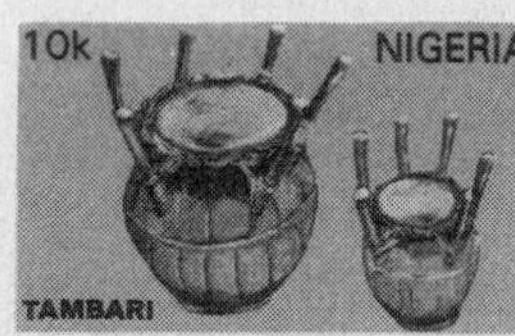

258 Tambari

1989. Nigerian Musical Instruments.

572 **258** 10 k. multicoloured .. 10 10
573 – 20 k. multicoloured .. 10 10
574 – 25 k. brown, grn & blk 15 15
575 – 30 k. brown and black 25 25

DESIGNS: 20 k. Kundung; 25 k. Ibid; 30 k. Dundun.

259 Construction of Water Towers, Mali

1989. 25th Anniv of African Development Bank. Multicoloured.

576 10 k. Type **259** 10 10
577 20 k. Paddy field, Gambia 10 10
578 25 k. Bank Headquarters, Abidjan, Ivory Coast .. 15 15
579 30 k. Anniversary logo (vert) 25 25

260 Lighting Camp Fire

1989. 70th Anniv of Nigerian Girl Guides Association. Multicoloured.

580 10 k. Type **260** 20 10
581 20 k. Guide on rope bridge (vert) 30 30

261 Etubom Costume **262** Dove with Letter and Map of Africa

1989. Traditional Costumes. Multicoloured.

582 10 k. Type **261** 15 10
583 20 k. Fulfulde 20 10
584 25 k. Aso-Ofi 25 15
585 30 k. Fuska Kura 30 25

1990. 10th Anniv of Pan African Postal Union. Multicoloured.

586 10 k. Type **262** 15 10
587 20 k. Parcel and map of Africa 25 30

263 Oil Lamps

1990. Nigerian Pottery.

588 **263** 10 k. black, brn & vio 10 10
589 – 20 k. black, brn & vio 10 10
590 – 25 k. brown and violet 15 15
591 – 30 k. multicoloured .. 20 20

DESIGNS: 20 k. Water pots; 25 k. Musical pots; 30 k. Water jugs.

264 Teacher and Class

1990. International Literacy Year.

593 **264** 20 k. multicoloured .. 15 10
594 – 30 k. brown, bl & yell 20 20

DESIGN: 30 k. Globe and book.

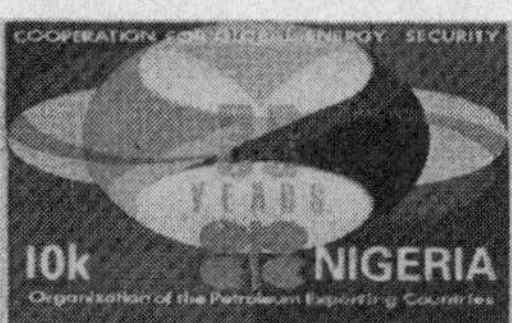

265 OPEC Logo

1990. 30th Anniv of the Organization of Petroleum Exporting Countries. Mult.

595 10 k. Type **265** 10 10
596 20 k. Logo and flags of member countries (vert) 10 10
597 25 k. World map and logo 15 15
598 30 k. Logo within inscription "Co-operation for Global Energy Security" (vert) 20 20

266 Grey Parrot **267** Eradication Treatment

1990. Wildlife. Multicoloured.

599 20 k. Type **266** 10 10
600 30 k. Roan antelope .. 10 10
601 1 n. 50 Grey-necked bald crow ("Rockfowl") .. 35 35
602 2 n. 50 Mountain gorilla .. 50 50

1991. National Guineaworm Eradication Day. Multicoloured.

604 10 k. Type **267** 10 10
605 20 k. Women collecting water from river (horiz) 15 15
606 30 k. Boiling pot of water 15 15

268 Hand Holding Torch (Progress)

1991. Organization of African Unity Heads of State and Governments Meeting, Abuja. Each showing outline map of Africa. Mult.

607 20 k. Type **268** 10 10
608 30 k. Cogwheel (Unity) .. 15 15
609 50 k. O.A.U flag (Freedom) 20 20

269 National Flags

1991. Economic Community of West African States Summit Meeting, Abuja. Multicoloured.

610 20 k. Type **269** 15 10
611 50 k. Map showing member states 30 30

270 Electric Catfish

1991. Nigerian Fishes. Multicoloured.

612 10 k. Type **270** 10 10
613 20 k. Niger perch .. 15 10
614 30 k. Talapia 20 15
615 50 k. African catfish .. 25 30

271 Telecom '91 Emblem

1991. "Telecom '91" 6th World Telecommunication Exhibition, Geneva.

617 **271** 20 k. black, green & vio 15 10
618 – 50 k. multicoloured .. 15 15

DESIGN—VERT. 50 k. Emblem and patchwork.

272 Boxing

1992. Olympic Games, Barcelona (1st issue). Multicoloured.

619 50 k. Type **272** 10 10
620 1 n. Nigerian athlete winning race 10 10
621 1 n. 50 Table tennis .. 15 15
622 2 n. Taekwondo 15 15

See also No. 624.

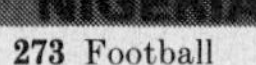

273 Football **274** Blood Pressure Gauge

1992. Olympic Games, Barcelona (2nd issue).

624 **273** 1 n. 50 multicoloured .. 20 20

1992. World Health Day. Multicoloured.

625 50 k. Type **274** 10 10
626 1 n. World Health Day '92 emblem 10 10
627 1 n. 50 Heart and lungs .. 15 15
628 2 n. Interior of heart .. 15 15

275 Map of World and Stamp on Globe

1992. "Olymphilex '92" Olympic Stamp Exhibition, Barcelona. Multicoloured.

630	50 k. Type **275**	15	10
631	1 n. 50 Examining stamps	20	20

276 Gathering Plantain Fruit

1992. 25th Anniv of International Institute of Tropical Agriculture.

633	**276**	50 k. multicoloured ..	10	10
634	–	1 n. multicoloured ..	10	10
635	–	1 n. 50 black, brn & grn	10	10
636	–	2 n. multicoloured ..	10	10

DESIGNS—VERT. 1 n. 50, Harvesting cassava tubers; 2 n. Stacking yams. HORIZ. 1 n. Tropical foods.

277 Centre Emblem

1992. Commissioning of Maryam Babangida Nat Centre for Women's Development.

638	**277**	50 k. gold, emerald and green ..	10	10
639	–	1 n. multicoloured ..	10	10
640	–	1 n. 50 multicoloured	15	15
641	–	2 n. multicoloured ..	15	15

DESIGNS—VERT. 1 n. Women working in fields; 2 n. Woman at Loom. HORIZ. 1 n. 50, Maryam Babangida National Centre.

All examples of No. 641 are without a "NIGERIA" inscription.

278 Healthy Food and Emblem

1992. International Conference on Nutrition, Rome. Multicoloured.

642	50 k. Type **278**	10	10
643	1 n. Child eating	10	10
644	1 n. 50 Fruit (vert) ..	15	15
645	2 n. Vegetables	15	15

279 Sabada Dance

1992. Traditional Dances. Multicoloured.

646	50 k. Type **279**	10	10
647	1 n. Sato	10	10
648	1 n. 50 Asian Ubo Ikpa ..	15	15
649	2 n. Dundun	15	15

280 Suburban Garden

1993. World Environment Day. Mult.

650	1 n. Type **280**	10	10
651	1 n. 50 Water pollution ..	10	10
652	5 n. Forest road	40	40
653	10 n. Rural house ..	75	75

281 Oni Figure

282 "Bulbophyllum distans"

1993. 50th Anniv of National Museums and Monuments Commission. Multicoloured.

654	1 n. Type **281**	10	10
655	1 n. 50 Bronze head of Queen Mother	10	10
656	5 n. Bronze pendant (horiz)	30	35
657	10 k. Nok head	70	75

1993. Orchids. Multicoloured.

658	1 n. Type **282**	10	10
659	1 n. 50 "Eulophia cristata"	10	10
660	5 n. "Eulophia horsfalli"	30	35
661	10 n. "Eulophia quartiniana"	60	65

283 Children in Classroom and Adults carrying Food

1994. Int Year of the Family. Mult.

663	1 n. 50 Type **283**	10	10
664	10 n. Market	60	65

POSTAGE DUE STAMPS

D 1.

1959.

D 1.	D 1.	1d. orange	10	55
D 2.		2d. orange	15	70
D 3.		3d. orange	20	1·00
D 4.		6d. orange	20	3·25
D 5.		1s. black	45	4·50

1961.

D 6.	D 1.	1d. red	10	25
D 7.		2d. blue	10	30
D 8.		3d. green	15	50
D 9.		6d. yellow	30	70
D 10.		1s. blue	45	1·75

1973. As Type D 1.

D 11.	2 k. red	10	10
D 12.	3 k. blue	10	10
D 13.	5 k. yellow	10	10
D 14.	10 k. green	10	10

MINIMUM PRICE

The minimum price quoted is 10p which represents a handling charge rather than a basis for valuing common stamps. For further notes about prices see introductory pages.

NIUAFO'OU

A remote island, part of the Kingdom of Tonga, with local autonomy.

100 seniti = 1 pa'anga.

1. Map of Niuafo'ou.

1983.

1.	**1.**	1 s. stone, black and red	10	10
2.		2 s. stone, black & green	10	10
3.		3 s. stone, black and blue	10	10
4.		3 s. stone, black & brown	10	10
5.		5 s. stone, black & purple	10	10
6.		6 s. stone, black and blue	10	10
7.		9 s. stone, black & green	15	15
8.		10 s. stone, black & blue	20	20
9.		13 s. stone, black & green	40	40
10.		15 s. stone, black & brn.	40	40
11.		20 s. stone, black & blue	45	45
12.		29 s. stone, black & pur.	60	60
13.		32 s. stone, black & grn.	70	70
14.		47 s. stone, black & red ..	90	1·00

1983. No. 820 of Tonga optd. **NIUAFO'OU KINGDOM OF TONGA,** or surch. also.

15.	1 p. on 2 p. green and black	2·00	2·50
16.	2 p. green	3·00	3·50

1983. Inauguration of Niuafo'ou Airport. As T **153** of Tonga.

17.	29 s. multicoloured	80	1·00
18.	1 p. multicoloured	2·50	3·25

1983. As T **1** but without value, surch.

19.	3 s. stone, black and blue ..	15	15
20.	5 s. stone, black and blue ..	15	15
21.	32 s. stone, black and blue	90	90
22.	2 p. stone, black and blue ..	5·50	6·00

4. Eruption of Niuafo'ou.

1983. 25th Anniv. of Re-settlement. Mult.

23.	5 s. Type **4**	40	30
24.	29 s. Lava flow	1·00	80
25.	32 s. Islanders move to safety	1·10	90
26.	1 p. 50 Evacuation by canoe	3·50	4·00

5. Purple Swamphen.

1983. Birds of Niuafo'ou.

27.	**5.**	1 s. black and mauve ..	20	20
28.	–	2 s. black and blue ..	20	20
29.	–	3 s. black and green ..	20	20
30.	–	5 s. black and yellow ..	20	20
31.	–	6 s. black and orange ..	20	20
32.	–	9 s. multicoloured ..	30	30
33.	–	10 s. multicoloured ..	35	35
34.	–	13 s. multicoloured ..	45	45
35.	–	15 s. multicoloured ..	45	45
36.	–	20 s. multicoloured ..	60	60
37.	–	29 s. multicoloured ..	1·00	1·00
38.	–	32 s. multicoloured ..	1·10	1·10
39.	–	47 s. multicoloured ..	1·75	1·75
40.	–	1 p. multicoloured ..	3·50	3·50
41.	–	2 p. multicoloured ..	5·00	5·00

DESIGNS—VERT. (22 × 29 mm.) 2 s. White-collared kingfisher. 3 s. Red-headed parrot finch. 5 s. Banded rail. 6 s. Polynesian scrub hen ("Niuafo'ou megapode"). 9 s. Green honeyeater. 10 s. Purple swamphen (different). (22 × 36 mm.) 29 s. Red-headed parrot finch (different). 32 s. White-collared kingfisher (different). (29 × 42 mm.) 1 p. As 10 s. HORIZ. (29 × 22 mm.) 13 s. Banded rail (different). 15 s. Polynesian scrub hen (different). (36 × 22 mm.) 20 s. As 13 s. 47 s. As 15 s. (42 × 29 mm.) 2 p. As 15 s.

6. Green Turtle.

1984. Wildlife and Nature Reserve. Mult.

42.	29 s. Type **6**	60	60
43.	32 s. Insular flying fox (vert.)	60	60
44.	47 s. Humpback whale ..	90	90
45.	1 p. 50 Polynesian scrub hen ("Niuafo'ou megapode") (vert.)	3·00	3·50

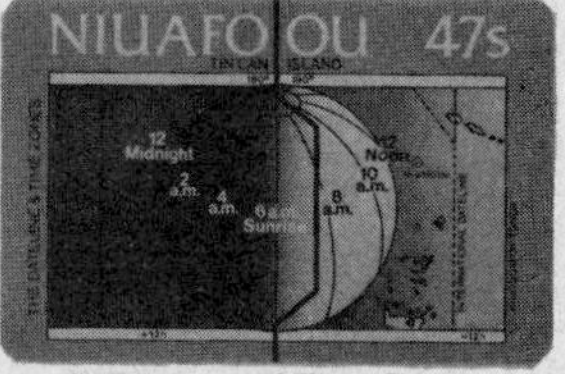

7. Diagram of Time Zones.

1984. Centenary of International Dateline. Multicoloured.

46.	47 s. Type **7**	60	50
47.	2 p. Location map showing Niuafo'ou	1·90	2·00

8. Australia 1913 £2 Kangaroo Definitive.

9. Dutch Brass Band entertaining Tongans.

1984. "Ausipex" International Stamp Exhibition, Melbourne. Multicoloured.

48.	32 s. Type **8**	75	50
49.	$1.50 Niuafo'ou 1983 10 s. map definitive	2·25	2·25

1985. 400th Birth Anniv. of Jacob Le Maire (discoverer of Niuafo'ou).

51.	**9.**	13 s. brown, yell. & orge.	25	25
52.	–	32 s. brown, yell. & bl.	55	55
53.	–	47 s. brown, yell. & grn.	75	80
54.	–	1 p. 50 brown, pale yellow and yellow ..	2·25	2·50

DESIGNS: No. 52, Tongans preparing kava. 53, Tongan canoes and outriggers. 54, "Eendracht" at anchor off Tafahi Island.

10. "Ysabel", 1902.

1985. Mail Ships. Multicoloured.

56.	9 s. Type **10**	20	20
57.	13 s. "Tofua I", 1908 ..	25	25
58.	47 s. "Mariposa", 1934 ..	65	65
59.	1 p. 50 "Matua", 1936 ..	1·90	1·90

11. Preparing to fire Rocket.

1985. Niuafo'ou Rocket Mails. Multicoloured.

60.	32 s. Type **11**	70	70
61.	42 s. Rocket in flight ..	90	90
62.	57 s. Ship's crew watching rocket's descent	1·25	1·25
63.	1 p. 50 Islanders reading mail	2·75	2·75

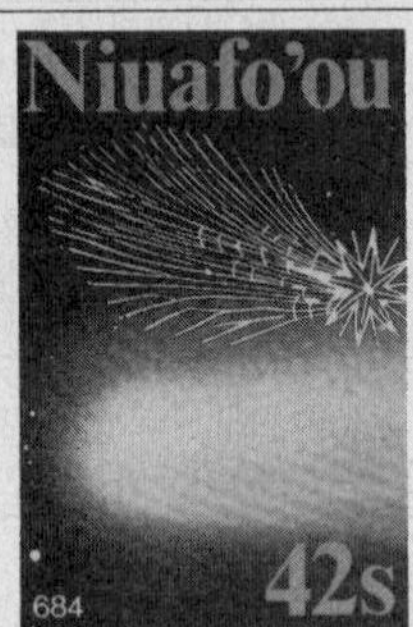

12. Halley's Comet, 684 A.D.

1986. Appearance of Halley's Comet. Multicoloured.

4.	42 s. Type **12**	2·75	2·00
5.	42 s. Halley's Comet, 1066, from Bayeux Tapestry ..	2·75	2·00
6.	42 s. Edmond Halley	2·75	2·00
7.	42 s. Halley's Comet, 1910 ..	2·75	2·00
8.	42 s. Halley's Comet, 1986 ..	2·75	2·00
9.	57 s. Type **12**	4·00	3·25
0	57 s. As No. 65	4·00	3·25
1.	57 s. As No. 66	4·00	3·25
2.	57 s. As No. 67	4·00	3·25
3.	57 s. As No. 68	4·00	3·25

Nos. 64/8 and 69/73 were printed together, e-tenant, forming composite designs.

1986. Nos. 32/9 surch.

4.	4 s. on 9 s. Green honey-eater	30	30
5.	4 s. on 10 s. Purple swamp-hen	30	30
6.	42 s. on 13 s. Banded rail ..	90	90
7.	42 s. on 15 s. Polynesian scrub hen	90	90
8.	57 s. on 29 s. Red-headed parrot finch	1·40	1·40
9.	57 s. on 32 s. White-collared kingfisher	1·40	1·40
30.	2 p. on 20 s. Banded rail ..	4·00	4·00
31.	2 p. 50 on 47 s. Polynesian scrub hen	4·00	4·00

1986. "Ameripex '86" International Stamp Exhibition, Chicago. 25th Anniv. of United States Peace Corps. As T **173** of Tonga. Multicoloured.

32.	57 s. Peace Corps surveyor and pipeline	1·25	1·25
33.	1 p. 50 Inspecting crops ..	2·25	2·25

14. Swimmers with Mail.

1986. Centenary of First Tonga Stamps. Designs showing Niuafo'ou mail transport. Multicoloured.

85.	42 s. Type **13**	90	90
86.	57 s. Collecting tin can mail	1·10	1·10
87.	1 p. Ship firing mail rocket	2·00	2·00
88.	2 p. 50 "Collecting the Mails" (detail) (C. Mayger)	3·50	3·50

15. Woman with Nourishing Foods ("Eat a balanced diet").

1987. Red Cross. Preventive Medicine. Mult.

90.	15 s. Type **15**	60	60
91.	42 s. Nurse with baby ("Give them post-natal care")	1·60	1·60
92.	1 p. Man with insecticide ("Insects spread disease")	2·50	2·50
93.	2 p. 50 Boxer ("Say no to alcohol, drugs, tobacco")	4·00	4·00

16. Hammerhead Shark.

1987. Sharks. Multicoloured.

94.	29 s. Type **16**	90	90
95.	32 s. Tiger shark	95	95
96.	47 s. Grey nurse shark ..	1·40	1·40
97.	1 p. Great white shark ..	2·50	2·50

17. Capt. E. C. Musick and Sikorsky "S-42" Flying Boat.

1987. Air. Pioneers of the South Pacific. Multicoloured.

99.	42 s. Type **17**	95	95
100.	57 s. Capt. J. W. Burgess and Shorts "S-30" flying boat	1·40	1·40
101.	1 p. 50. Sir Charles Kingsford Smith and Fokker "F.VIIb-3m" Southern Cross	2·25	2·25
102.	2 p. Amelia Earhart and Lockheed "Electra 10A"	2·75	2·75

18 Polynesian Scrub Hen and 1983 1 s. Map Definitive

1988. 5th Anniversaries of First Niuafo'ou Postage Stamp (42, 57 s.) or Niuafo'ou Airport Inauguration (1, 2 p.). Multicoloured.

103	42 s. Type **18**	75	75
104	57 s. As Type **18**, but with stamp at left	95	95
105	1 p. "Concorde" and 1983 Airport Inauguration 29 s. stamp	2·00	2·00
106	2 p. As 1 p., but with stamp at left	3·00	3·00

20 Audubon's Shearwaters and Blowholes, Houma, Tonga

1988. Islands of Polynesia. Multicoloured.

108	42 s. Type **20**	95	95
109	57 s. Kiwi at Akaroa Harbour, New Zealand	1·40	1·40
110	90 s. Red-tailed tropic birds at Rainmaker Mountain, Samoa ..	2·00	2·00
111	2 p.50 Laysan albatross at Kapoho Volcano, Hawaii	4·50	4·50

INDEX

Countries can be quickly located by referring to the index at the end of this volume.

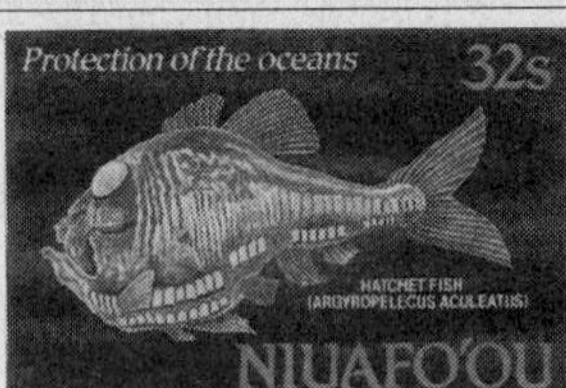

22 Hatchet Fish

1989. Fishes of the Deep. Multicoloured.

113	32 s. Type **22**	65	65
114	42 s. Snipe eel	80	80
115	57 s. Viper fish	1·00	1·00
116	1 p. 50 Football fish ..	2·25	2·75

23 Formation of Earth's Surface

1989. The Evolution of the Earth. Mult.

(a) Size 27 × 35½ mm

117	1 s. Type **23**	10	10
118	2 s. Cross-section of Earth's crust	10	10
119	5 s. Volcano	10	10
120	10 s. Cross-section of Earth during cooling ..	10	10
120a	13 s. Gem stones ..	15	20
121	15 s. Sea	15	20
122	20 s. Mountains	20	25
123	32 s. River gorge ..	30	35
124	42 s. Early plant life, Silurian	40	45
124a	45 s. Early marine life ..	40	45
125	50 s. Fossils and Cambrian lifeforms ..	45	50
126	57 s. Carboniferous forest and coal seams ..	55	60
126a	60 s. Dinosaurs feeding ..	55	60
126b	80 s. Tyrannosaurus and triceratops fighting ..	75	80

(b) Size 25½ × 40 mm

127	1 p. Dragonfly and amphibians, Carboniferous era ..	95	1·00
128	1 p. 50 Dinosaurs, Jurassic era	1·40	1·50
129	2 p. Archaeopteryx and mammals, Jurassic era	2·00	2·10
130	5 p. Human family and domesticated dog, Pleistocene era ..	4·75	5·00
130a	10 p. Mammoth and sabre-tooth tiger ..	9·50	10·00

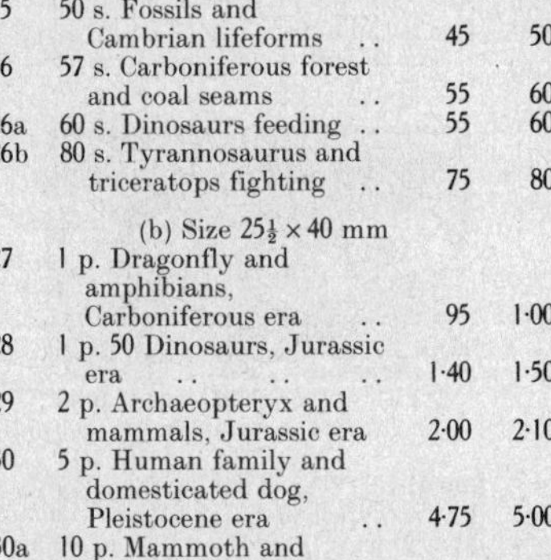

24 Astronaut on Moon and Newspaper Headline

1989. "World Stamp Expo '89" International Stamp Exhibition, Washington.

131 **24**	57 s. multicoloured ..	1·00	1·00

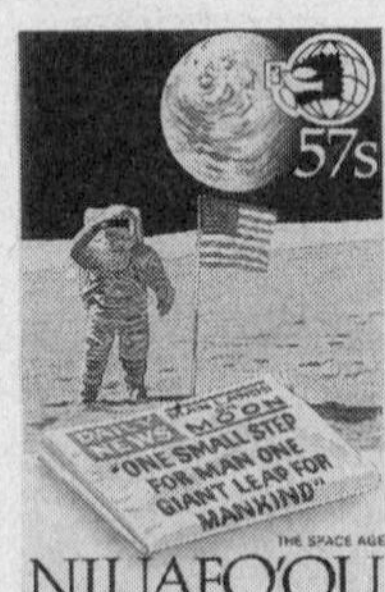

25 Lake Vai Lahi

1990. Niuafo'ou Crater Lake. Multicoloured.

133	42 s. Type **25**	70	70
134	42 s. Islands in centre of lake	70	70
135	42 s. South-west end of lake and islet ..	70	70
136	1 p. Type **25**	1·40	1·40
137	1 p. As No. 134	1·40	1·40
138	1 p. As No. 135	1·40	1·40

Nos. 133/8 were printed together in se-tenant strips of each value, forming a composite design.

26 Penny Black and Tin Can Mail Service

1990. 150th Anniv of the Penny Black. Mult.

139	42 s. Type **26**	80	80
140	57 s. U.S.A. 1847 10 c. stamp	1·10	1·10
141	75 s. Western Australia 1854 1d. stamp	1·25	1·25
142	2 p. 50 Mafeking Siege 1900 1d. stamp	4·00	4·00

27 Humpback Whale surfacing (illustration reduced, actual size 57 × 41 mm)

1990. Polynesian Whaling. Multicoloured.

143	15 s. Type **27**	55	55
144	42 s. Whale diving under canoe	1·00	1·00
145	57 s. Tail of Blue whale ..	1·25	1·25
146	2 p. Old man and pair of whales	3·25	3·25

1990. 40th Anniv of U.N. Development Programme. As T **203** of Tonga. Mult.

148	57 s. Agriculture and Fisheries	90	90
149	57 s. Education	90	90
150	2 p. 50 Healthcare ..	3·25	3·25
151	2 p. 50 Communications ..	3·25	3·25

28 H.M.S. "Bounty"

1991. Bicentenary of Charting of Niuafo'ou. Multicoloured.

152	32 s. Type **28**	75	75
153	42 s. Chart of "Pandora's" course	95	95
154	57 s. H.M.S. "Pandora" (frigate)	1·10	1·10

30 Longhorned Beetle Grub

1991. Longhorned Beetle. Multicoloured.
157 42 s. Type **30** 60 60
158 57 s. Adult beetle .. 80 80
159 1 p. 50 Grub burrowing .. 2·25 2·25
160 2 p. 50 Adult on tree trunk 3·25 3·25

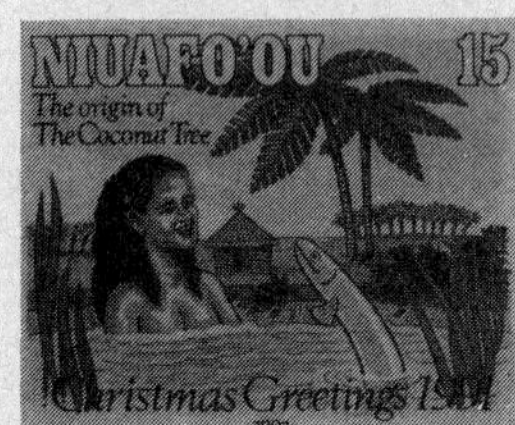

31 Heina meeting the Eel

1991. The Legend of the Coconut Tree. Mult.
161 15 s. Type **31** 35 35
162 42 s. Heina crying over the eel's grave 90 90

1992. 50th Anniv of War in the Pacific. As T **215** of Tonga, each showing contemporary newspaper headline. Multicoloured.
165 42 c. American battleship ablaze, Pearl Harbor .. 70 70
166 42 c. Destroyed American aircraft, Hawaii .. 70 70
167 42 c. Newspaper and Japanese A6M Zero fighter 70 70
168 42 c. Pres. Roosevelt signing Declaration of War 70 70
169 42 c. Japanese T 95 light tank and Gen. MacArthur 70 70
170 42 c. Douglas SBD Dauntless dive-bomber and Admiral Nimitz .. 70 70
171 42 c. Bren gun and Gen. Sir Thomas Blamey .. 70 70
172 42 c. Australian mortar crew, Kokoda 70 70
173 42 c. U.S.S. "Mississippi" in action and Maj. Gen. Julian C. Smith .. 70 70
174 42 c. U.S.S. "Enterprise" aircraft carrier 70 70
175 42 c. American marine and Maj. Gen. Curtis Lemay 70 70
176 42 c. B-29 bomber and Japanese surrender, Tokyo Bay 70 70

Nos. 165/76 were printed together, se-tenant, forming a composite design.

1992. 25th Anniv of the Coronation of King Tupou IV. As T **217** of Tonga.
177 45 s. multicoloured .. 65 65
178 80 s. multicoloured .. 1·25 1·25
179 80 s. black and brown .. 1·25 1·25
180 80 s. multicoloured .. 1·25 1·25
181 2 p. multicoloured .. 2·50 2·50

DESIGNS—(34×23 mm): No. 177, King Taufa'ahau Tupou IV and Queen Halaevalu during Coronation. (48×35 mm): No. 178, King Tupou IV and Tongan national anthem; 179, Extract from Investiture ceremony; 180, Tongan choir; 181, As 45 s.

32 Male and Female Scrub Hens searching for Food

1992. Endangered Species. Polynesian Scrub Hen. Multicoloured.
182 45 s. Type **32** 75 75
183 60 s. Female guarding egg 90 90
184 80 s. Chick .. .. 1·25 1·25
185 1 p. 50 Head of male .. 2·25 2·25

33 1983 2 s. Map Definitive and 1993 60 s. Dinosaur Definitive

1993. 10th Anniv of First Niuafo'ou Stamp. Multicoloured.
186 60 s. Type **33** 75 80
187 80 s. 1983 5 s. definitive and 1993 80 s. dinosaurs definitive .. .. 1·00 1·10

34 DeHavilland Twin Otter of South Pacific Island Airways

1993. 10th Anniv of First Flight to Niuafo'ou. Multicoloured.
188 1 p. Type **34** .. .. 1·25 1·40
189 2 p. 50 DeHavilland Twin Otter of Friendly Islands Airways .. .. 2·75 3·00

1993. 75th Birthday of King Taufa'ahau Tupou IV. As T **228** of Tonga. Mult.
190 45 s. King Tupou IV and "Pangai" (patrol boat) 40 45
191 80 s. King Tupou IV and musical instruments (38½×51 mm) 75 80
192 80 s. King Tupou IV and sporting events (38½×51 mm) 75 80
193 80 s. King Tupou IV with aircraft and telecommunications .. 75 80
194 2 p. As 45 s. but larger (38½×51 mm) .. .. 2·00 2·10

35 Blue-crowned Lorikeets

1993. Natural History of Lake Vai Lahi. Multicoloured.
195 60 s. Type **35** 70 70
196 60 s. Pacific reef heron 70 70
197 60 s. Black admiral (butterfly) and Niuafo'ou coconut beetle 70 70
198 60 s. Niuafo'ou dragonfly, Pacific black ducks and Niuafo'ou moths .. 70 70
199 60 s. Niuafo'ou megapode 70 70

Nos. 195/9 were printed together, se-tenant, forming a composite design.

1993. Children's Painting Competition Winners. As T **231** of Tonga.
200 10 s. multicoloured .. 10 10
201 10 s. black and grey .. 10 10
202 1 p. multicoloured .. 95 1·00
203 1 p. multicoloured .. 95 1·00

DESIGNS: Nos. 200 and 202, "Crater Lake Megapode and Volcano" (Paea Puletau); Nos. 201 and 203, "Ofato Beetle Grubs of Niuafo'ou" (Peni Finau).

36 "Scarabaeidea"

1994. Beetles. Multicoloured.
204 60 s. Type **36** 60 65
205 80 s. Coccinellidea" .. 75 80
206 1 p. 50 "Cerambycidea" .. 1·40 1·50
207 2 p. 50 "Pentatomidae" .. 2·40 2·50

NIUE

One of the Cook Is. group, in the S. Pacific. A dependency of New Zealand, the island achieved local self-government in 1974.

1902. 12 pence = 1 shilling.
20 shillings = 1 pound.
1967. 100 cents = 1 dollar.

1902. T **42** of New Zealand optd **NIUE** only.
1 **42** 1d. red £350 £350

Stamps of New Zealand surch **NIUE.** and value in native language.

1902. Pictorials of 1898, etc.
8. **23.** ½d. green 65 80
9. **42.** 1d. red 50 65
2. **27.** 2½d. blue (No. 382) .. 1·25 2·75
13. **28.** 3d. brown .. .. 6·00 5·00
14. **31.** 6d. red .. .. .. 7·00 10·00
16. **34.** 1s. orange .. .. 27·00 25·00

1911. King Edward VII **stamps.**
17 **51** ½d. green 45 40
18 6d. red .. .. .. 2·00 7·00
19 1s. orange .. .. 6·50 38·00

1917. Dominion and King George V stamps.
21 **53** 1d. red .. .. .. 5·50 5·50
22 **62** 3d. brown .. .. 48·00 75·00

1917. Stamps of New Zealand (King George V, etc.) optd. **NIUE** only.
23 **62** ½d. green .. .. 50 1·10
24 **53** 1d. red .. .. 3·00 4·00
25 **62** 1½d. grey .. .. 80 1·75
26 1½d. brown .. .. 70 2·50
28 2½d. blue .. .. 90 3·00
29 3d. brown .. .. 1·25 1·50
30 6d. red .. .. 4·75 16·00
31 1s. orange .. .. 4·75 16·00

1918. Stamps of New Zealand optd. **NIUE.**
33. **F 4.** 2s. blue .. .. .. 15·00 32·00
34. 2s. 6d. brown .. .. 18·00 42·00
35. 5s. green .. .. .. 20·00 48·00
36. 10s. red .. .. .. 70·00 90·00
37. £1 red £130 £150

1920. Pictorial types as Cook Islands (1920), but inscr. "NIUE".
38 **9** ½d. black and green .. 3·00 3·25
45 – 1d. black and red .. 75 75
40 – 1½d. black and red .. 2·50 4·00
46 – 2½d. black and blue .. 2·25 6·50
41 – 3d. black and blue .. 60 6·50
47 **7** 4d. black and violet .. 3·50 9·50
42 – 6d. brown and green .. 90 12·00
43 – 1s. black and brown .. 1·50 12·00

1927. Admiral type of New Zealand optd. **NIUE.**
49. **71.** 2s. blue .. .. 17·00 30·00

1931. No. 40 surch. **TWO PENCE.**
50. 2d. on 1½d. black and red 1·75 1·00

1931. Stamps of New Zealand (Arms types) optd. **NIUE.**
87 **F 6.** 2s. 6d. brown .. .. 4·50 7·00
84 5s. green .. .. 6·50 9·00
85 10s. red .. .. 50·00 75·00
86 £1 pink .. .. 40·00 48·00

1932. Pictorial stamps as Cook Islands (1932) but inscr. additionally "NIUE".
89 **20.** ½d. black and green .. 50 1·00
63 – 1d. black and red .. 50 30
64 **22.** 2d. black and brown .. 40 70
92 – 2½d. black and blue .. 60 95
93 – 4d. black and blue .. 1·25 90
67 – 6d. black and orange .. 70 65
61 – 1s. black and violet .. 2·00 5·00

1935. Silver Jubilee. Nos. 63, 65 and 94, colours changed optd. **SILVER JUBILEE OF KING GEORGE V. 1910-1935.**
69. 1d. red .. .. .. 60 1·50
70. 2½d. blue .. .. .. 3·25 3·00
71. 6d. green and orange .. 3·25 5·50

1937. Coronation. New Zealand stamps optd. **NIUE.**
72. **106.** 1d. red 30 10
73. 2½d. blue 40 30
74. 6d. orange 40 20

1938. As 1938 issue of Cook Islands, but inscr. "NIUE" "COOK ISLANDS".
95. **29.** 1s. black and violet .. 1·25 85
96. **30.** 2s. black and brown .. 7·50 2·75
97. – 3s. blue and green .. 11·00 7·00

1940. As T **32** of Cook islands, but inscr. "NIUE" "COOK ISLANDS".
78. **32.** 3d. on 1½d. black & purple 10 10

1946. Peace. New Zealand stamps optd. **NIUE.**
98. **132.** 1d. green 10 10
99. – 2d. purple (No. 670) .. 10 10
100. – 6d. brn. & red (No. 674) 10 10
101. **139.** 8d. black and red .. 10 10

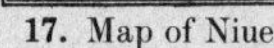

17. Map of Niue.

18. H.M.S. "Resolution".

1950.
113 **17** ½d. orange and blue .. 10 20
114 **18** 1d. brown and green .. 2·25 1·00
115 – 2d. black and red .. 20 20
116 – 3d. blue and violet .. 10 15
117 – 4d. olive and purple .. 10 15
118 – 6d. green and orange .. 60 30
119 – 9d. orange and brown .. 10 30
120 – 1s. purple and black .. 10 15
121 – 2s. brown and green .. 1·00 2·75
122 – 3s. blue and black .. 4·50 4·00

DESIGNS—HORIZ. 2d. Alofi Landing. 3d. Native hut. 4d. Arch of Hikutavake. 6d. Alofi Bay. 1s. Cave, Makefu. VERT. 9d. Spearing fish. 2s. Bananas. 3s. Matapa Chasm.

1953. Coronation. As types of New Zealand but inscr. "NIUE".
123. **164.** 3d. brown 65 30
124. **168.** 6d. grey 95 30

26.

27. "Pua".

1967. Decimal Currency. (a) Nos. 113/22 surch.
125 **17** ½ c. on ½d. 10 10
126 **18** 1 c. on 1d. 80 15
127 – 2 c. on 2d. 10 10
128 – 2½ c. on 3d. 10 10
129 – 3 c. on 4d. 10 10
130 – 5 c. on 6d. 10 10
131 – 8 c. on 9d. 10 10
132 – 10 c. on 1s. 10 10
133 – 20 c. on 2s. .. .. 60 1·25
134 – 30 c. on 3s. .. .. 1·50 1·75

(b) Arms type of New Zealand without value, surch. as in T **26.**
135. **26.** 25 c. brown 65 65
136. 50 c. green .. .. 1·00 1·00
137. $1 mauve .. .. 80 1·50
138. $2 pink .. .. 1·40 2·50

1967. Christmas. As T **278** of New Zealand but inscr. "NIUE".
139. 2½ c. multicoloured .. 10 10

1969. Christmas. As No. 905 of New Zealand but inscr. "NIUE".
140. 2½ c. multicoloured .. 10 10

1969. Flowers. Multicoloured; frame colours given.
141. **27.** ½ c. green 10 10
142. – 1 c. red 10 10
143. – 2 c. olive 10 10
144. – 2½ c. brown 10 10
145. – 3 c. blue 10 10
146. – 5 c. red 10 10
147. – 8 c. violet 10 10
148. – 10 c. yellow 10 10
149. – 20 c. blue .. .. 1·00 1·25
150. – 30 c. green .. .. 1·75 1·75

DESIGNS: 1 c. "Golden Shower". 2 c. Flamboyant. 2½c. Frangipani. 3 c. Niue Crocus. 5 c. Hibiscus. 8 c. "Passion Fruit". 10 c. "Kampui". 20 c. Queen Elizabeth II (after Anthony Buckley). 30 c. Tapeu Orchip.

37. Kalahimu.

1970. Indigenous Edible Crabs. Mult.
151. 3 c. Type **37** 10 10
152. 5 c. Kalavi 10 10
153. 30 c. Unga 30 25

1970. Christmas. As T **314** of New Zealand, but inscr. "**NIUE**".
154. 2½ c. multicoloured .. 10 10

38. Outrigger Canoe, and Aircraft over Jungle.

1970. Opening of Niue Airport. Multicoloured.
155 3 c. Type **38** 10 10
156 5 c. "Tofua II" (cargo liner) and aircraft over harbour 15 10
157 8 c. Aircraft over airport 15 20

39. Spotted Triller.

1971. Birds. Multicoloured.
158. 5 c. Type 39 .. .. 15 10
159. 10 c. Purple-capped Fruit Dove 70 15
160. 20 c. Blue Crowned Lory 80 20

1971. Christmas. As T 325 of New Zealand, but inscr. " Niue ".
161. 3 c. multicoloured 10 10

40. Niuean Boy. 41. Octopus Lure.

1971. Niuean Portraits. Multicoloured.
162. 4 c. Type 40 .. .. 10 10
163. 6 c. Girl with garland .. 10 10
164. 9 c. Man 10 10
165. 14 c. Woman with garland 15 20

1972. South Pacific Arts Festival, Fiji. Multicoloured.
166. 3 c. Type 41 .. .. 10 10
167. 5 c. War weapons 15 10
168. 10 c. Sika throwing (horiz.) 20 10
169. 25 c. Vivi dance (horiz.) .. 30 20

42. Alofi Wharf.

1972. 25th Anniversary of South Pacific Commission. Multicoloured.
170. 4 c. Type 42 .. .. 10 10
171. 5 c. Medical Services .. 15 10
172. 6 c. Schoolchildren .. 15 10
173. 18 c. Dairy cattle .. 25 20

1972. Christmas. As T 332 of New Zealand, but inscr. "NIUE".
174. 3 c. multicoloured 10 10

43. Kokio.

1973. Fishes. Multicoloured.
175. 8 c. Type 43 .. .. 25 25
176. 10 c. Loi 30 30
177. 15 c. Malau 40 40
178. 20 c. Palu 45 45

44. " Large Flower Piece " (Jan Brueghel). 46. King Fataaiki.

45. Capt. Cook and Bowsprit.

1973. Christmas. Flower studies by the artists listed. Multicoloured.
179. 4 c. Type 44 .. .. 10 10
180. 5 c. Bollongier 10 10
181. 10 c. Ruysch 20 20

1974. Bicent. of Capt. Cook's Visit. Mult.
182. 2 c. Type 45 .. .. 30 20
183. 3 c. Niue landing place .. 30 25
184. 8 c. Map of Niue 50 40
185. 20 c. Ensign of 1774 and Administration Building 70 80

1974. Self-Government. Multicoloured.
186. 4 c. Type 46 .. .. 10 10
187. 8 c. Annexation Ceremony, 1900 .. .. 10 10
188. 10 c. Legislative Assembly Chambers (horiz.) 10 10
189. 20 c. Village meeting (horiz.) 15 15

47. Decorated Bicycles.

1974. Christmas. Multicoloured
190. 3 c. Type 47 .. .. 10 10
191. 10 c. Decorated motorcycle 10 10
192. 20 c. Motor transport to church 20 20

48. Children going to Church.

1975. Christmas. Multicoloured.
193. 4 c. Type 48 .. .. 10 10
194. 5 c. Child with balloons on bicycle 10 10
195. 10 c. Balloons and gifts on tree 20 20

49. Hotel Buildings.

1975. Opening of Tourist Hotel. Mult.
196. 8 c. Type 49 .. .. 10 10
197. 20 c. Ground-plan and buildings 20 20

50. Preparing Ground for Taro.

1976. Food Gathering. Multicoloured.
198. 1 c. Type 50 .. .. 10 10
199. 2 c. Planting Taro .. 10 10
200. 3 c. Banana gathering .. 10 10
201. 4 c. Harvesting taro .. 10 10
202. 5 c. Gathering shell fish .. 30 10
203. 10 c. Reef fishing 20 10
204. 20 c. Luku gathering .. 20 15
205. 50 c. Canoe fishing .. 30 60
206. $1 Coconut husking .. 45 80
207. $2 Uga gathering .. 80 1·40

See also Nos. 249/58 and 264/73.

51. Water.

1976. Utilities. Multicoloured.
208 10 c. Type 51 .. .. 10 10
209 15 c. Telecommunications 15 15
210 20 c. Power 15 15

52. Christmas Tree, Alofi.

1976. Christmas. Multicoloured.
211. 9 c. Type 52 .. .. 15 15
212. 15 c. Church Service, Avatele 15 15

53. Queen Elizabeth II and Westminster Abbey.

1977. Silver Jubilee. Multicoloured.
213. $1 Type 53 .. .. 75 50
214. $2 Coronation regalia .. 1·00 75

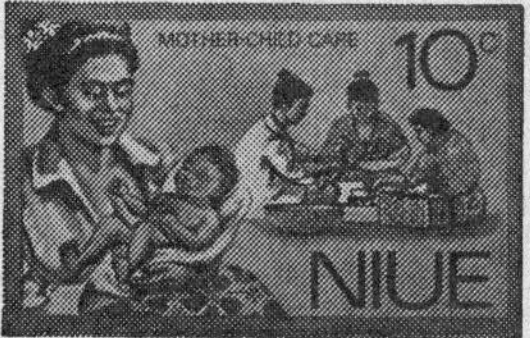

54. Child Care.

1977. Personal Services. Multicoloured.
216. 10 c. Type 54 .. .. 15 10
217. 15 c. School dental clinic 20 20
218. 20 c. Care of the aged .. 20 20

55. " The Annunciation ".

1977. Christmas. Paintings by Rubens. Multicoloured.
219. 10 c. Type 55 .. .. 20 10
220. 12 c. " Adoration of the Magi " 20 10
221. 20 c. " Virgin in a Garland " 35 20
222. 35 c. " The Holy Family " 55 35

1977. Nos. 198/207, 214, 216 and 218 surch.
224. 12 c. on 1 c. Type 50 .. 25 25
225. 16 c. on 2 c. Planting taro 30 30
226. 20 c. on 3 c. Banana gathering 40 40
227. 35 c. on 4 c. Harvesting taro 45 45
228. 40 c. on 5 c. Gathering shell fish 50 50
229. 60 c. on 20 c. Luku gathering 55 55
230. 70 c. on $1 Coconut husking 55 55
231. 85 c. on $2 Uga gathering 60 60
232. $1.10 on 10 c. Type 22 .. 70 70
233. $2.60 on 20 c. Care of the aged 90 90
234. $3.20 on $2 Coronation regalia .. .. .. 1·25 1·25

57. " An Island View, in Atooi ".

1978. Bicent. of Discovery of Hawaii. Paintings by John Webber. Multicoloured.
235. 12 c. Type 57 .. .. 85 30
236. 16 c. " A View of Karakaooa, in Owhyhee " 95 40
237. 20 c. " An Offering before Capt. Cook in the Sandwich Islands " .. .. 1·25 45
238. 30 c. " Tereoboo, King of Owhyhee, bringing presents to Capt. Cook " .. 1·40 50
239. 35 c. " A Canoe in the Sandwich Islands, the rowers masked " .. 1·50 55

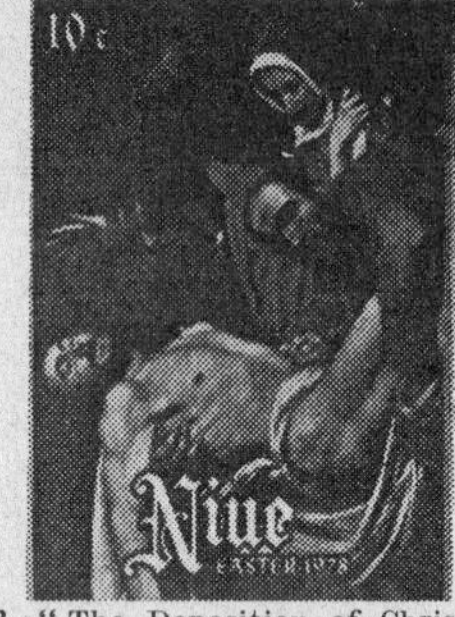

58. " The Deposition of Christ ". (Caravaggio).

1978. Easter. Paintings from the Vatican Galleries. Multicoloured.
241. 10 c. Type 58 .. .. 25 10
242. 20 c. " The Burial of Christ " (Bellini) .. 45 25

59. Flags of Niue and U.K.

1978. 25th Anniv. of Coronation. Mult.
245. $1.10 Type 59 .. .. 1·25 1·00
246. $1.10 Coronation portrait by Cecil Beaton .. 1·25 1·00
247. $1.10 Queen's personal flag for New Zealand .. 1·25 1·00

1978. Designs as Nos. 198/207 but margin colours changed and silver frame.
249. 12 c. Type 50 .. .. 20 20
250. 16 c. Planting taro .. 20 20
251. 30 c. Banana gathering .. 30 25
252. 35 c. Harvesting taro .. 30 30
253. 40 c. Gathering shell-fish 40 30
254. 60 c. Reef fishing 45 35
255. 75 c. Luku gathering .. 50 40
256. $1.10 Canoe fishing .. 75 80
257. $3.20 Coconut husking .. 1·00 1·25
258. $4.20 Uga gathering .. 1·25 1·40

60. " Festival of the Rosary ".

1978. Christmas. 450th Death Anniv. of Durer. Multicoloured.
259. 20 c. Type 60 .. .. 40 20
260. 30 c. " The Nativity " .. 50 30
261. 35 c. " Adoration of the Magi " 60 35

1979. Air. Designs as Nos. 249/58 but gold frames and additionally inscr. "AIRMAIL".
264. 15 c. Planting taro .. 20 15
265. 20 c. Banana gathering .. 25 15
266. 23 c. Harvesting taro .. 30 15
267. 50 c. Canoe fishing .. 70 20
268. 90 c. Reef fishing 85 35
269. $1.35 Type 50 .. .. 1·00 1·00
270. $2.10 Gathering shell fish 1·50 2·25
271. $2.60 Luku gathering .. 1·50 2·25
272. $5.10 Coconut husking .. 1·75 3·00
273. $6.35 Uga gathering .. 2·00 3·75

61. " Pieta " (Gregorio Fernandez).

1979. Easter. Paintings. Multicoloured.
274. 30 c. Type 61 .. .. 30 25
275. 35 c. " Burial of Christ " (Pedro Roldan) .. 35 25

62. " The Nurse and Child " (Franz Hals).

1979. International Year of the Child. Details of Paintings. Multicoloured.
278. 16 c. Type **62** 30 15
279. 20 c. " Child of the Duke of Osuna " (Goya) 35 20
280. 30 c. " Daughter of Robert Strozzi " (Titian) 55 35
281. 35 c. " Children eating Fruit " (Murillo) .. 60 40

63. Penny Black Stamp.

1979. Death Cent of Sir Rowland Hill. Mult.
284 20 c. Type **63** 20 15
285 20 c. Sir Rowland Hill and original Bath mail coach 20 15
286 30 c. Basel 1845 2½ r. stamp 30 20
287 30 c. Sir Rowland Hill and Alpine village coach .. 30 20
288 35 c. U.S.A. 1847 5 c. stamp 35 25
289 35 c. Sir Rowland Hill and "Washington" (first transatlantic U.S.A. mail vessel) 35 25
290 50 c. France 1849 20 c. stamp 50 35
291 50 c. Sir Rowland Hill and French Post Office railway van, 1849 50 35
292 60 c. Bavaria 1849 1 k. stamp 55 40
293 60 c. Sir Rowland Hill and Bavarian coach with mail 55 40

The two versions of each value were issued se-tenant within the sheet, forming composite designs.

64. Cook's Landing at Botany Bay.

1979. Death Bicentenary of Captain Cook. Multicoloured.
295. 20 c. Type **64** 55 30
296. 30 c. Cook's men during a landing on Erromanga.. 75 40
297. 35 c. H.M.S. "Resolution" and H.M.S. "Discovery" in Queen Charlotte's Sound 85 45
298. 75 c. Death of Captain Cook, Hawaii .. .. 1·50 70

65. Launch of " Apollo 11 ".

66. " Virgin of Tortosa " (P. Serra).

1979. 10th Anniv. of Moon Landing. Mult.
300. 30 c. Type **65** 30 20
301. 35 c. Lunar module on Moon 40 25
302. 60 c. Helicopter, recovery ship and command module after splashdown .. 50 40

1979. Christmas. Paintings. Multicoloured.
304. 20 c. Type **66** 10 10
305. 25 c. " Virgin with Milk " (R. de Mur) 15 15
306. 30 c. " Virgin and Child " (S. di G. Sassetta) .. 20 20
307. 50 c. " Virgin and Child " (J. Huguet) 25 25

1980. Hurricane Relief. Surch. **HURRICANE RELIEF Plus 2c.**
(a) On Nos. 284/93 **(HURRICANE RELIEF** spread over each se-tenant pair).
310. **63.** 20 c.+2 c. multicoloured 20 25
311. – 20 c.+2 c. multicoloured (No. 285) 20 25
312. – 30 c.+2 c. multicoloured (No. 286) 30 35
313. – 30 c.+2 c. multicoloured (No. 287) 30 35
314. – 35 c.+2 c. multicoloured (No. 288) 35 40
315. – 35 c.+2 c. multicoloured (No. 289) 35 40
316. – 50 c.+2 c. multicoloured (No. 290) 50 55
317. – 50 c.+2 c. multicoloured (No. 291) 50 55
318. – 60 c.+2 c. multicoloured (No. 292) 60 65
319. – 60 c.+2 c. multicoloured (No. 293) 60 65

(b) On Nos. 295/8.
320. **64.** 20 c.+2 c. multicoloured 20 25
321. – 30 c.+2 c. multicoloured 30 35
322. – 35 c.+2 c. multicoloured 35 40
323. – 75 c.+2 c. multicoloured 75 80

(c) On Nos. 300/2.
324. **65.** 30 c.+2 c. multicoloured 30 35
325. – 35 c.+2 c. multicoloured 35 40
326. – 60 c.+2 c. multicoloured 60 65

(d) On Nos. 304/7.
327. **66.** 20 c.+2 c. multicoloured 20 25
328. – 25 c.+2 c. multicoloured 25 30
329. – 30 c.+2 c. multicoloured 30 35
330. – 50 c.+2 c. multicoloured 50 55

68. " Pieta " (Bellini).

1980. Easter. " Pieta ". Paintings. Mult.
331. 25 c. Type **68** 30 15
332. 30 c. Botticelli 35 20
333. 35 c. A. Van Dyck .. 35 20

69. Ceremonial Stool, New Guinea.

1980. South Pacific Festival of Arts, New Guinea. Multicoloured.
336. 20 c. Type **69** 20 20
337. 20 c. Ku-Tagwa plaque, New Guinea 20 20
338. 20 c. Suspension Hook, New Guinea 20 20
339. 20 c. Ancestral Board, New Guinea 20 20
340. 25 c. Platform Post, New Hebrides 25 25
341. 25 c. Canoe ornament, New Ireland 25 25
342. 25 c. Carved figure, Admiral Islands 25 25
343. 25 c. Female with child, Admiralty Islands .. 25 25
344. 30 c. The God A'a, Rurutu (Austral Islands) .. 25 30
345. 30 c. Statue of Tangaroa, Cook Islands 25 30
346. 30 c. Ivory Pendant, Tonga 25 30
347. 30 c. Tapa (Hiapo) cloth, Niue 25 30
348. 35 c. Feather box (Waka), New Zealand 30 35
349. 35 c. Hei-Tiki Amulet, New Zealand 30 35
350. 35 c. House Post, New Zealand 30 35
351. 35 c. Feather image of God Ku, Hawaii 30 35

1980. " Zeapex ' 80 " International Stamp Exhibition, Auckland. Nos. 284/93 optd. (A) **ZEAPEX '80 AUCKLAND** or (B) **NEW ZEALAND STAMP EXHIBITION** and emblem.
353. **63.** 20 c. multicoloured (A) 20 20
354. – 20 c. multicoloured (B) 20 20
355. – 30 c. multicoloured (A) 30 25
356. – 30 c. multicoloured (B) 30 25
357. – 35 c. multicoloured (A) 35 25
358. – 35 c. multicoloured (B) 35 25
359. – 50 c. multicoloured (A) 45 30
360. – 50 c. multicoloured (B) 45 30
361. – 60 c. multicoloured (A) 55 35
362. – 60 c. multicoloured (B) 55 35

72. Queen Elizabeth the Queen Mother.

1980. 80th Birthday of The Queen Mother.
364. **72.** $1.10 multicoloured .. 1·25 1·50

73. 100 Metre Dash.

1980. Olympic Games, Moscow.
366. 20 c. Type **73** 15 15
367. 20 c. Allen Wells, Great Britain (winner, 100 meter dash) 15 15
368. 25 c. } 400 metre freestyle 15 20
369. 25 c. } (winner, Ines Diers, D.D.R.) .. 15 20
370. 30 c. } Soling Class (winner, 20 20
371. 30 c. } Denmark) .. 20 20
372. 35 c. } Football (winner, 20 25
373. 35 c. } Czechoslovakia) .. 20 25

Nos. 366/7, 368/9, 370/1, and 372/3 were printed se-tenant in pairs, each pair forming a composite design. On the 25 c. and 35 c. stamps the face value is at right on the first design and at left on the second in each pair. For the 30 c. No. 370 has a yacht with a green sail at left and No. 371 on yacht with a red sail.

74. " The Virgin and Child "

1980. Christmas. Various Virgin and Child paintings by Andrea del Sarto.
375. **74.** 20 c. multicoloured .. 15 15
376. – 25 c. multicoloured .. 15 15
377. – 30 c. multicoloured .. 20 20
378. – 35 c. multicoloured .. 20 20

75. " Phalaenopsis sp ".

1981. Flowers (1st series). Multicoloured.
381. 2 c. Type **75** 10 10
382. 2 c. Moth Orchid 10 10
383. 5 c. " Euphorbia pulcherrima " 10 10
384. 5 c. Poinsettia 10 10
385. 10 c. " Thunbergia alata " 10 10
386. 10 c. Black-eyed Susan .. 10 10
387. 15 c. " Cocholspermum hibiscoides " 15 15
388. 15 c. Buttercup Tree .. 15 15
389. 20 c. " Begonia sp ". .. 20 20
390. 20 c. Begonia 20 20
391. 25 c. " Plumeria sp " .. 25 25
392. 25 c. Frangipani 25 25
393. 30 c. " Strelitzia reginae " 30 30
394. 30 c. Bird of Paradise .. 30 30
395. 35 c. " Hibiscus syriacus " 30 30
396. 35 c. Rose of Sharon .. 30 30
397. 40 c. " Nymphaea sp ". .. 35 35
398. 40 c. Water Lily 35 35
399. 50 c. " Tibouchina sp ". .. 45 45
400. 50 c. Princess Flower .. 45 45
401. 60 c. " Nelumbo sp ". .. 55 55
402. 60 c. Lotus 55 55
403. 80 c. " Hybrid hibiscus " 75 75
404. 80 c. Yellow Hibiscus .. 75 75
405. $1 Golden Shower Tree (cassia fistula) .. .. 1·00 1·00
406. $2 " Orchid var ". .. 2·50 2·50
407. $3 " Orchid sp ". .. 3·50 3·50
408. $4 " Euphorbia pulcherrima poinsettia " .. .. 3·00 3·25
409. $6 " Hybrid hibiscus " .. 4·50 4·75
410. $10 Scarlet hibiscus (" hibiscus rosa-sinensis ") 7·50 7·75

Nos. 405/10 are larger, 47×33 mm.
See also Nos. 527/36.

76. " Jesus Defiled " (El Greco).

1981. Easter. Details of Paintings. Mult.
425. 35 c. Type **76** 30 30
426. 50 c. " Pieta " (Fernando Gallego) 50 50
427. 60 c. " The Supper at Emmaus " (Jacopo de Pontormo) 55 55

77. Prince Charles.

1981. Royal Wedding. Multicoloured.
430. 75 c. Type **77** 50 60
431. 95 c. Lady Diana Spencer 60 70
432. $1.20 Prince Charles and Lady Diana Spencer .. 70 80

78. Footballer Silhouettes.

1981. World Cup Football Championship, Spain (1982).
434. **78.** 30 c. grn., gold and blue 20 20
435. – 30 c. grn., gold and blue 20 20
436. – 30 c. grn., gold and blue 20 20
437. – 35 c. blue, gold and orge. 25 25
438. – 35 c. blue, gold and orge. 25 25
439. – 35 c. blue, gold and orge. 25 25
440. – 40 c. orge., gold and grn. 25 25
441. – 40 c. orge., gold and grn. 25 25
442. – 40 c. orge., gold and grn. 25 25

DESIGNS: Various footballer silhouettes. No. 435, gold figure 3rd from left. No. 436, gold figure 4th from left. No. 437, gold figure 3rd from left. No. 438, gold figure 4th from left. No. 439, gold figure 2nd from left. No. 440, gold figure 3rd from left. displaying close control. No. 441, gold figure 2nd from left. No. 442, gold figure 3rd from left, heading.

1982. International Year for Disabled Persons Nos. 430/2. surch +**5c.**
444. 75 c.+5 c. Type **77** .. 1·00 1·25
445. 95 c.+5 c. Lady Diana Spencer .. .. 1·25 1·50
446. $1.20+5 c. Prince Charles and Lady Diana .. 1·50 1·75

HAVE YOU READ THE NOTES AT THE BEGINNING OF THIS CATALOGUE?

These often provide answers to the enquiries we receive.

80. "The Holy Family with Angels" (detail).

1981. Christmas. 375th Birth Anniv. of Rembrandt. Multicoloured.
448. 20 c. Type **80** 45 30
449. 35 c. "Presentation in the Temple" 65 40
450. 50 c. "Virgin and Child in Temple" 75 60
451. 60 c. "The Holy Family" 90 75

81. Prince of Wales.

1982. 21st Birthday of Princess of Wales. Multicoloured.
454. 50 c. Type **81** 45 55
455. $1.25 Prince and Princess of Wales 75 90
456. $2.50 Princess of Wales .. 1·25 1·60

1982. Birth of Prince William of Wales (1st issue). Nos. 430/2 optd.
458. 75 c. Type **77** .. .. 2·25 1·75
459. 75 c. Type **77** .. .. 2·25 1·75
460. 95 c. Lady Diana Spencer 3·25 2·25
461. 95 c. Lady Diana Spencer 3·25 2·25
462. $1.20 Prince Charles and Lady Diana Spencer .. 4·25 2·75
463. $1.20 Prince Charles and Lady Diana Spencer .. 4·25 2·75
OVERPRINTS: Nos. 458, 460 and 462 **COMMEMORATING THE ROYAL BIRTH 21 JUNE 1982.** 459, 461 and 463 **BIRTH OF PRINCE WILLIAM OF WALES 21 JUNE 1982.**

1982. Birth of Prince William of Wales (2nd issue). As Nos. 454/6, but with changed inscriptions. Multicoloured.
465. 50 c. Type **81** 45 55
466. $1.25 Prince and Princess of Wales .. .. 85 1·00
467. $2.50 Princess of Wales .. 1·40 1·75

83. Infant.

1982. Christmas. Paintings of Infants by Bronzion, Murillo and Boucher.
469. **83.** 40 c. multicoloured .. 65 35
470. – 52 c. multicoloured .. 75 45
471. – 83 c. multicoloured .. 1·40 80
472. – $1.05 multicoloured .. 1·50 95

85. Prime Minister Robert Rex.

1983. Commonwealth Day. Multicoloured.
475. 70 c. Type **85** 65 70
476. 70 c. H.M.S. "Resolution" and H.M.S. "Adventure" off Niue, 1774 .. .. 65 70
477. 70 c. Passion flower .. 65 70
478. 70 c. Limes.. .. .. 65 70

86. Scouts signalling.

1983. 75th Anniv. of Boy Scout Movement and 125th Birth Anniv. of Lord Baden-Powell. Multicoloured.
479. 40 c. Type **86** 35 40
480. 50 c. Planting sapling .. 45 50
481. 83 c. Map-reading .. 85 90

1983. 15th World Scout Jamboree, Alberta, Canada. Nos. 479/81 optd with **XV WORLD JAMBOREE CANADA**.
483. 40 c. Type **86** .. 35 40
484. 50 c. Planting sapling .. 45 50
485. 83 c. Map-reading.. .. 85 90

88. Black Right Whale.

1983. Protect the Whales. Multicoloured.
487 12 c. Type **88** 75 65
488 25 c. Fin whale 95 80
489 35 c. Sei whale .. .. 1·50 1·25
490 40 c. Blue whale .. 1·75 1·50
491 58 c. Bowhead whale .. 1·90 1·60
492 70 c. Sperm whale .. 2·25 1·75
493 83 c. Humpback whale .. 2·50 2·25
494 $1.05 Minke whale .. 3·00 2·50
495 $2.50 Grey whale .. 4·25 4·00

89. Montgolfier Balloon, 1783.

1983. Bicentenary of Manned Flight. Mult.
496. 25 c. Type **89** 20 20
497. 40 c. Wright Brothers "Flyer", 1903 .. 35 35
498. 58 c. "Graf Zeppelin", 1928 50 50
499. 70 c. Boeing "247", 1933 .. 65 65
500. 83 c. "Apollo 8", 1968 .. 80 80
501. $1.05 Space shuttle "Columbia", 1982 .. 95 95

90. "The Garagh Madonna".

1983. Christmas. 500th Birth Anniv. of Raphael. Multicoloured.
503. 30 c. Type **90** 25 30
504. 40 c. "Madonna of the Granduca" 30 35
505. 58 c. "Madonna of the Goldfish" 45 50
506. 70 c. "The Holy Family of Francis I" 55 60
507. 83 c. "The Holy Family with Saints" 65 70

1983. Various stamps surch.
(a) Nos. 393/4, 399/404 and 407.
509. 52 c. on 30 c. "Strelitzia reginae" 40 45
510. 52 c. on 30 c. Bird of Paradise 40 45
511. 58 c. on 50 c. "Tibouchina sp." 50 55
512. 58 c. on 50 c. Princess Flower 50 55
513. 70 c. on 60 c. "Nelumbo sp." 55 60
514. 70 c. on 60 c. Lotus .. 55 60
515. 83 c. on 80 c. "Hybrid hibiscus" 70 75
516. 83 c. on 80 c. Yellow hibiscus 70 75
517. $3·70 on $3 "Orchid sp." 3·00 3·25
(b) Nos. 431/2 and 455/6.
518 $1.10 on 95 c. Lady Diana Spencer .. .. 3·00 2·25
519 $1.10 on $1.25 Prince and Princess of Wales .. 2·25 2·00
520 $2.60 on $1.20 Prince Charles and Lady Diana 5·50 3·50
521 $2.60 on $2.50 Princess of Wales .. .. .. 3·50 3·25

91. Morse Key Transmitter.

1984. World Communications Year. Multicoloured.
523. 40 c. Type **91** 30 35
524. 52 c. Wall mounted phone 40 45
525. 83 c. Communications satellite 60 65

92. "Phalaenopsis sp.".

1984. Flowers (2nd series). Multicoloured.
527. 12 c. Type **92** 15 15
528. 25 c. "Euphorbia pulcherrima" 20 20
529. 30 c. "Cochlospermum hibiscoides" .. 25 25
530. 35 c. "Begonia sp." .. 25 25
531. 40 c. "Plumeria sp." .. 35 30
532. 52 c. "Strelitzia reginae".. 45 40
533. 58 c. "Hibiscus syriacus" 50 45
534. 70 c. "Tibouchina sp." .. 85 50
535. 83 c. "Nelumbo sp." .. 75 60
536. $1.05 Hybrid hibiscus .. 90 75
537. $1.75 "Cassia fistula" .. 1·40 1·25
538. $2.30 "Orchid var" .. 1·75 1·60
539. $3.90 "Orchid sp." .. 3·25 3·00
540. $5 "Euphorbia pulcherrima poinsettia" .. .. 4·75 3·50
541. $6.60 "Hybrid hibiscus" .. 5·00 4·50
542. $8.30 "Hibiscus rosa-sinensis".. .. .. 6·50 5·75
Sizes: Nos. 537/542, 39 × 31 mm.

93. Discus Throwing.

1984. Olympic Games, Los Angeles. Multicoloured.
547. 30 c. Type **93** 25 30
548. 35 c. Sprinting (horiz.) .. 30 35
549. 40 c. Horse racing (horiz.) 35 40
550. 58 c. Boxing (horiz.) .. 50 55
551. 70 c. Javelin throwing .. 60 65

94. Koala.

1984. "Ausipex" International Stamp Exhibition, Melbourne.
a. Designs showing Koala Bears.
552. **94.** 25 c. mult. (postage) .. 50 30
553. – 35 c. multicoloured .. 55 35
554. – 40 c. multicoloured .. 60 40
555. – 58 c. multicoloured .. 80 55
556. – 70 c. multicoloured .. 95 65
b. Vert. designs showing Kangaroos.
557. – 83 c. multicoloured (air) 1·25 75
558. – $1.05 multicoloured .. 1·50 95
559. – $2.50 multicoloured .. 3·00 2·25

1984. Olympic Gold Medal Winners, Los Angeles. Nos. 547/51 optd.
561. 30 c. Type **93** 25 30
562. 35 c. Sprinting 30 35
563. 40 c. Horse racing.. .. 30 35
564. 58 c. Boxing 45 50
565. 70 c. Javelin throwing 55 60
OPTS: 30 c. **Discus Throw Rolf Denneberg Germany.** 35 c. **1,500 Meters Sebastian Coe Great Britain.** 40 c. **Equestrian Mark Todd New Zealand.** 58 c. **Boxing Tyrell Biggs United States.** 70 c. **Javelin Throw Arto Haerkoenen.**

96. Niue National Flag and Premier Sir Robert Rex.

1984. Self-Government. 10th Anniv. Multicoloured.
568. 40 c. Type **96** 30 35
569. 58 c. Map of Niue and Premier Rex 45 50
570. 70 c. Premier Rex receiving proclamation of self-government 55 60

1984. Birth of Prince Henry. Nos. 430 and 454 optd. **Prince Henry 15.9.84.**
573. $2 on 50 c. Type **81** .. 2·50 1·75
574. $2 on 75 c. Type **77** .. 2·50 1·75

98. "The Nativity" (A. Vaccaro).

1984. Christmas. Multicoloured.
575. 40 c. Type **98** 30 35
576. 58 c. "Virgin with Fly" (anon, 16th-century) .. 45 50
577. 70 c. "The Adoration of the Shepherds" (B. Murillo) 55 60
578. 80 c. "Flight into Egypt" (B. Murillo) 65 70

99. House Wren.

1985. John J. Audubon (ornithologist). Birth Bicentenary. Multicoloured.

581. 40 c. Type **99** .. .. 1·50 35
582. 70 c. Veery .. .. .. 1·75 60
583. 83 c. Grasshopper Sparrow 2·00 70
584. $1.50 Henslow's Sparrow .. 2·50 85
585. $2.50 Vesper Sparrow .. 3·25 2·00

100. The Queen Mother in Garter Robes.

1985. Life and Times of Queen Elizabeth the Queen Mother. Multicoloured.

587. 70 c. Type **100** 55 60
588. $1.15 In open carriage with the Queen 90 95
589. $1.50 With Prince Charles during 80th birthday celebrations .. .. 1·10 1·25

1985. South Pacific Mini Games, Rarotonga. Nos. 547/8 and 550/1 surch. **MINI SOUTH PACIFIC GAMES, RAROTONGA** and emblem.

591. 52 c. on 70 c. Javelin throwing 40 45
592. 83 c. on 58 c. Boxing .. 65 70
593. 95 c. on 35 c. Sprinting .. 75 80
594. $2 on 30 c. Type **93** .. 1·50 1·60

1985. Pacific Islands Conference, Rarotonga. Nos. 475/8 optd. **PACIFIC ISLANDS CONFERENCE, RAROTONGA** and emblem.

595. 70 c. Type **85** 55 60
596. 70 c. "Resolution" and "Adventure" off Niue, 1774 .. .. .. 55 60
597. 70 c. Passion flower .. 55 60
598. 70 c. Limes 55 60

No. 595 also shows an overprinted amendment to the caption which now reads **Premier Sir Robert Rex K.B.E.**

103. "R. Strozzi's Daughter" (Titian).

1985. International Youth Year. Mult.

599. 58 c. Type **103** 85 80
600. 70 c. "The Fifer" (E. Manet) .. .. .. 1·00 90
601. $1.15 "Portrait of a Young Girl" (Renoir) .. .. 1·60 1·50
602. $1.50 "Portrait of M. Berard" (Renoir) .. 2·00 2·25

104. "Virgin and Child".

1985. Christmas. Details of Paintings by Correggio. Multicoloured.

604. 58 c. Type **104** 80 50
605. 85 c. "Adoration of the Magi" .. .. .. 1·00 70
606. $1.05 "Virgin with Child and St. John" .. .. 1·40 85
607. $1.45 "Virgin and Child with St. Catherine" .. 1·90 1·25

105. "The Constellations" (detail).

1986. Appearance of Halley's Comet. Designs showing details from ceiling painting "The Constellations" by Giovanni De Vecchi. Nos. 611/13 show different spacecraft at top left. Multicoloured.

610. 60 c. Type **105** 50 50
611. 75 c. "Vega" spacecraft .. 65 65
612. $1.10 "Planet A" spacecraft 90 90
613. $1.50 "Giotto" spacecraft 1·25 1·25

106. Queen Elizabeth II and Prince Philip.

1986. 60th Birthday of Queen Elizabeth II. Multicoloured.

615. $1.10 Type **106** .. .. 1·00 1·00
616. $1.50 Queen and Prince Philip at Balmoral .. 1·25 1·25
617. $2 Queen at Buckingham Palace .. .. .. 1·75 1·75

107. U.S.A. 1847 Franklin 5 c. Stamp and Washington Sculpture, Mt. Rushmore, U.S.A.

1986. "Ameripex '86" International Stamp Exhibition, Chicago. Multicoloured.

620. $1 Type **107** .. .. 1·75 1·75
621. $1 Flags of Niue and U.S.A. and Mt. Rushmore sculptures .. .. 1·75 1·75

Nos. 620/1 were printed together, se-tenant, forming a composite design.

108. "Statue under Construction, Paris, 1883" (Victor Dargaud).

1986. Centenary of Statue of Liberty. Multicoloured.

622. $1 Type **108** .. .. 1·75 1·75
623. $2.50 "Unveiling of Statue of Liberty" (Edmund Morand) .. .. .. 2·50 2·50

109. Prince Andrew, Miss Sarah Ferguson and Westminster Abbey.
(Illustration reduced. Actual size 57 × 32 mm.).

1986. Royal Wedding.

625. **109.** $2.50 multicoloured .. 2·75 2·75

110. Great Egret.

1986. "Stampex '86" Stamp Exhibition, Adelaide. Australian Birds. Multicoloured.

628. 40 c. Type **110** .. .. 1·75 1·25
629. 60 c. Painted finch (horiz.) 2·00 1·50
630. 75 c. Australian king parrot .. .. .. 2·25 1·75
631. 80 c. Variegated wren (horiz.) .. .. .. 2·50 2·00
632. $1 Peregrine falcon .. 3·00 2·25
633. $1.65 Azure kingfisher (horiz.) .. .. .. 3·75 3·00
634. $2.20 Brilliant budgerigars 4·50 4·00
635. $4.25 Emu (horiz.) .. 6·50 6·00

111. "Virgin and Child" (Perugino).

1986. Christmas from Vatican Museum. Multicoloured.

636. 80 c. Type **111** .. .. 1·25 1·25
637. $1.15 "Virgin of St. N. dei Frari" (Titian) .. 1·50 1·50
638. $1.80 "Virgin with Milk" (Lorenzo di Credi) .. 2·40 2·40
639. $2.60 "Madonna of Foligno" (Rapheal) .. 3·25 3·25

1986. Visit of Pope John Paul II to South Pacific. Nos. 636/9 surch. **CHRISTMAS VISIT TO SOUTH PACIFIC OF POPE JOHN II, NOVEMBER 21–24 1986.**

642. 80 c. + 10 c. "Virgin and Child" (Perugino) .. 1·60 1·60
643. $1.15 + 10 c. "Virgin of St. N. dei Frari" (Titian) .. 1·90 1·90
644. $1.80 + 10 c. "Virgin with Milk" (Lorenzo di Credi) 3·00 3·00
645. $2.60 + 10 c. "Madonha of Foligno" (Raphael) .. 3·50 3·50

113. Boris Becker, Olympic Rings and Commemorative Coin.

1987. Olympic Games, Seoul (1988). Tennis (1st issue). Designs showing Boris Becker in play.

649. **113.** 80 c. multicoloured .. 1·50 1·50
650. $1.15 multicoloured .. 1·75 1·75
651. $1.40 multicoloured .. 2·00 2·00
652. $1.80 multicoloured .. 2·50 2·50

1987. Olympic Games, Seoul (1988). Tennis (2nd issue). As T **113**, but showing Steffi Graf.

653. 85 c. multicoloured .. 1·00 1·00
654. $1.05 multicoloured .. 1·25 1·25
655. $1.30 multicoloured .. 1·50 1·50
656. $1.75 multicoloured .. 1·75 1·75

1987. Royal Ruby Wedding. Nos. 616/17 surch. **40TH WEDDING ANNIV. 4.85.**

657. $4.85 on $1.50 Queen and Prince Philip at Balmoral .. .. 3·50 3·75
658. $4.85 on $2 Queen at Buckingham Palace .. 3·50 3·75

115. "The Nativity".

1987. Christmas. Religious Paintings by Durer. Multicoloured.

659. 80 c. Type **115** .. .. 1·00 1·00
660. $1.05 "Adoration of the Magi" .. .. .. 1·25 1·25
661. $2.80 "Celebration of the Rosary" .. .. .. 2·75 2·75

Nos. 659/61 each include detail of an angel with lute as in T **115.**

116 Franz Beckenbauer in Action

1988. European Cup Football Championship, West Germany. Multicoloured.

664 20 c. Type **116** 40 40
665 40 c. German "All Star" team in action 65 65
666 60 c. Bayern Munich team with European Cup, 1974 75 75
667 80 c. World Cup match, England, 1966 .. .. 95 95
668 $1.05 World Cup match, Mexico, 1970 .. .. 1·25 1·25
669 $1.30 Beckenbauer with pennant, 1974 .. .. 1·75 1·75
670 $1.80 Beckenbauer and European Cup, 1974 .. 2·00 2·00

1988. Steffi Graf's Tennis Victories. Nos. 653/6 optd.

671 85 c. mult (optd **Australia 24 Jan 88 French Open 4 June 88**) .. 60 65
672 $1.05 multicoloured (optd **Wimbledon 2 July 88 U S Open 10 Sept. 88**) 75 80
673 $1.30 multicoloured (optd **Women's Tennis Grand Slam: 10 September 88**) .. 90 95
674 $1.75 mult (optd **Seoul Olympic Games Gold Medal Winner**) .. 1·25 1·40

118 Angels

1988. Christmas. Details from "The Adoration of the Shepherds" by Rubens. Multicoloured.

675 60 c. Type **118** 85 85
676 80 c. Shepherds .. .. 1·25 1·25
677 $1.05 Virgin Mary .. 1·75 1·75
678 $1.30 Holy Child .. .. 2·00 2·00

119 Astronaut and "Apollo 11" Emblem

1989. 20th Anniv of First Manned Landing on Moon. Multicoloured.

680 $1.50 Type **119** . . . . 2·50 2·50
681 $1.50 Earth and Moon . . 2·50 2·50
682 $1.50 Astronaut and "Apollo 1" emblem . . 2·50 2·50

120 Priests

1989. Christmas. Details from "Presentation in the Temple" by Rembrandt. Mult.

684 70 c. Type **120** . . . . 1·00 1·00
685 80 c. Virgin and Christ Child in Simeon's arms 1·10 1·10
686 $1.05 Joseph . . . . 1·40 1·40
687 $1.30 Simeon and Christ Child . . . . . . 1·75 1·75

121 Fritz Walter

1990. World Cup Football Championship, Italy. German Footballers. Multicoloured.

689 80 c. Type **121** . . . . 1·75 1·75
690 $1.15 Franz Beckenbauer 2·00 2·00
691 $1.40 Uwe Seeler . . . . 2·25 2·25
692 $1.80 German team emblem and signatures of former captains . . 2·75 2·75

122 "Merchant Maarten Looten" (Rembrandt)

1990. 150th Anniv of the Penny Black. Rembrandt Paintings. Multicoloured.

693 80 c. Type **122** . . . . 1·25 1·25
694 $1.05 "Rembrandt's Son Titus with Pen in Hand" 1·50 1·50
695 $1.30 "The Shipbuilder and his Wife" . . . . 1·75 1·75
696 $1.80 "Bathsheba with King David's Letter" 2·25 2·25

123 Queen Elizabeth the Queen Mother

1990. 90th Birthday of Queen Elizabeth the Queen Mother.

698 **123** $1.25 multicoloured . . 2·50 2·50

124 "Adoration of the Magi" (Dirk Bouts)

1990. Christmas. Religious Paintings. Mult.

700 70 c. Type **124** 80 80
701 80 c. "Holy Family" (Fra. Bartolommeo) . . . . 1·00 1·00
702 $1.05 "Nativity" (Memling) 1·25 1·25
703 $1.30 "Adoration of the Kings" (Bruegel, the Elder) . . . . . . 1·50 1·50

1990. "Birdpex '90" Stamp Exhibition, Christchurch, New Zealand. No. 410 optd **Birdpex '90** and logo.

705 $10 Scarlet hibiscus . . 8·50 9·00

1991. 65th Birthday of Queen Elizabeth II. No. 409 optd **SIXTY FIFTH BIRTHDAY QUEEN ELIZABETH II**.

706 $6 "Hybrid hibiscus" . . 5·50 6·00

1991. 10th Wedding Anniv of Prince and Princess of Wales. Nos. 430/2 optd **TENTH ANNIVERSARY**.

707 75 c. Type **77** 80 80
708 95 c. Lady Diana Spencer 1·10 1·10
709 $1.20 Prince Charles and Lady Diana . . . . 1·40 1·40

129 "The Virgin and Child with Sts. Jerome and Dominic" (Lippi)

1991. Christmas. Religious Paintings. Mult.

710 20 c. Type **129** 20 20
711 50 c. "The Isenheim Altar-piece" (M. Grunewald) 50 50
712 $1 "The Nativity" (G. Pittoni) 90 90
713 $2 "Adoration of the Kings" (J. Brueghel the Elder) . . . . . . 1·75 1·75

MORE DETAILED LISTS

are given in the Stanley Gibbons Catalogues referred to in the country headings.
For lists of current volumes see Introduction.

130 Banded Rail

1992. Birds. Multicoloured.

718 20 c. Type **130** 15 20
719 50 c. Red-tailed tropic bird 35 40
720 70 c. Purple swamphen . . 50 55
721 $1 Pacific pigeon 70 75
722 $1.50 White-collared kingfisher . . . . 1·10 1·25
723 $2 Blue-crowned lory . . 1·50 1·60
724 $3 Purple-capped fruit dove . . . . . . 2·25 2·40
726 $5 Barn owl . . . . 3·75 4·00
727 $7 Longtailed koel ("Cockoo") (49 × 35 mm) 5·00 5·25
728 $10 Reef heron (49 × 35 mm) . . . . . . 7·25 7·50
729 $15 Spotted triller ("Polynesian Triller") (49 × 35 mm) . . . . 11·00 11·50

131 Columbus before King Ferdinand and Queen Isabella

1992. 500th Anniv of Discovery of America by Columbus. Multicoloured.

731 $2 Type **131** . . . . 1·75 1·75
732 $3 Fleet of Columbus . . 2·50 2·50
733 $5 Claiming the New World for Spain . . 4·50 4·50

132 Tennis and $10 Commemorative Coin

1992. Olympic Games, Barcelona. Mult.

734 $2.50 Type **132** . . . . 2·50 2·50
735 $2.50 Olympic flame and national flags . . . . 2·50 2·50
736 $2.50 Gymnastics and different $10 coin . . 2·50 2·50

1992. 6th Festival of Pacific Arts, Rarotonga. Nos. 336/51 surch **$1**.

738 $1 on 20 c. Type **69** . . 90 90
739 $1 on 20 c. Ku-Tagwa plaque, New Guinea . . 90 90
740 $1 on 20 c. Suspension hook, New Guinea . . 90 90
741 $1 on 20 c. Ancestral board, New Guinea . . 90 90
742 $1 on 25 c. Platform post, New Hebrides 90 90
743 $1 on 25 c. Canoe ornament, New Ireland 90 90
744 $1 on 25 c. Carved figure, Admiralty Islands . . 90 90
745 $1 on 25 c. Female with child, Admiralty Islands 90 90
746 $1 on 30 c. The God A'a, Rurutu (Austral Islands) 90 90
747 $1 on 30 c. Statue of Tangaroa, Cook Islands 90 90
748 $1 on 30 c. Ivory pendant, Tonga 90 90
749 $1 on 30 c. Tapa (Hiapo) cloth, Niue 90 90
750 $1 on 35 c. Feather box (Waka), New Zealand . . 90 90
751 $1 on 35 c. Hei-Tiki amulet, New Zealand . . 90 90
752 $1 on 35 c. House post, New Zealand 90 90
753 $1 on 35 c. Feather image of god Ku, Hawaii . . 90 90

134 "St. Catherine's Mystic Marriage" (detail) (Memling)

1992. Christmas.

754 **134** 20 c. multicoloured . . 15 15
755 – 50 c. multicoloured . . 50 50
756 – $1 multicoloured . . 90 90
757 – $2 multicoloured . . 1·75 1·75

DESIGNS: 50 c., $1, $2 Different details from "St. Catherine's Mystic Marriage" by Hans Memling.

135 Queen on Official Visit

1992. 40th Anniv of Queen Elizabeth II's Accession. Multicoloured.

759 70 c. Type **135** 65 65
760 $1 Queen in green evening dress 95 95
761 $1.50 Queen in white embroidered evening dress . . . . . . 1·25 1·25
762 $2 Queen with bouquet . . 1·90 1·90

136 Rough-toothed Dolphin

1993. Endangered Species. South Pacific Dolphins. Multicoloured.

763 20 c. Type **136** 25 25
764 50 c. Fraser's dolphin . . 75 75
765 75 c. Pantropical spotted dolphin . . . . 1·00 1·00
766 $1 Risso's dolphin . . 1·25 1·25

1993. Premier Sir Robert Rex Commemoration. Nos. 568/70 optd **1909 IN MEMORIAM 1992 SIR ROBERT R. REX K.B.E.** or surch also.

767 40 c. Type **96** 40 40
768 58 c. Map of Niue and Premier Rex 55 55
769 70 c. Premier Rex receiving proclamation of self-government 65 65
770 $1 on 40 c. Type **96** . . 95 95
771 $1 on 58 c. Map of Niue and Premier Rex . . 95 95
772 $1 on 70 c. Premier Rex receiving proclamation of self-government . . 95 95

138 Queen Elizabeth II in Coronation Robes and St. Edward's Crown

1993. 40th Anniv of Coronation.
773 **138** $5 multicoloured .. 4·25 4·50

139 "Virgin of the Rosary" (detail) (Guido Reni)

1993. Christmas.
774 **139** 20 c. multicoloured .. 25 25
775 – 70 c. multicoloured .. 70 70
776 – $1 multicoloured .. 95 95
777 – $1.50 multicoloured .. 1·40 1·40
778 – $3 multicoloured (32 × 47 mm) .. 2·75 2·75
DESIGNS: 70 c. to $3 Different details of "Virgin of the Rosary" (Reni).

OFFICIAL STAMPS

1985. Nos. 409/10 and 527/42 optd. **O.H.M.S.**
O 1. 12 c. "Phalaenopsis" sp. 10 10
O 2. 25 c. "Euphorbia pulcherrima" 20 25
O 3. 30 c. "Cochlospermum hibiscoides" 20 25
O 4. 35 c. "Begonia" sp. .. 25 30
O 5. 40 c. "Plumeria" sp. .. 30 35
O 6. 52 c. "Strelitzia reginae" 35 40
O 7. 58 c. "Hibiscus syriacus" 40 45
O 8. 70 c. "Tibouchina" sp. .. 50 55
O 9. 83 c. "Nelumbo" sp. .. 60 65
O 10. $1.05 Hybrid hibiscus .. 75 80
O 11. $1.75 "Cassia fistula" .. 1·25 1·40
O 12. $2.30 Orchid var. .. 1·60 1·75
O 13. $3.90 Orchid sp. .. 2·75 3·00
O 14. $4 "Euphorbia pulcherrima poinsettia .. 3·00 3·25
O 15. $5 "Euphorbia pulcherrima poinsettia" .. 3·75 4·00
O 16. $6 Hybrid hibiscus .. 4·50 5·00
O 17. $6.60 "Hybrid hibiscus" 5·00 5·25
O 18. $8.30 "Hibiscus rasasinensis" .. .. 6·00 6·25
O 19. $10 Scarlet hibiscus .. 7·25 7·50

1993. Nos. 718/23 optd **O.H.M.S.**
O20 20 c. Type **130** .. 15 20
O21 50 c. Red-tailed tropic bird 35 40
O22 70 c. Purple swamphen .. 50 55
O23 $1 Pacific pigeon .. 70 75
O24 $1.50 White-collared kingfisher .. .. 1·10 1·25
O25 $2 Blue-crowned lory .. 1·50 1·60
O26 $3 Crimson-crowned fruit dove .. .. .. 2·25 2·40
O28 $5 Barn owl .. .. 3·75 6·00

NORFOLK ISLAND

A small island East of New South Wales, administered by Australia until 1960 when local government was established.

1947. 12 pence = 1 shilling, 20 shillings = 1 pound.
1966. 100 cents = $1 Australian.

1. Ball Bay.

1947.
1. **1.** ½d. orange 35 60
2. 1d. violet 50 60
3. 1½d. green 50 70
4. 2d. violet 55 30
5. 2½d. red 80 30
6. 3d. brown 70 55
6a. 3d. green .. .. .. 15·00 3·75
7. 4d. red 70 40
8. 5½d. blue 70 40
9. 6d. brown 70 30
10. 9d. pink .. .. .. 1·25 40
11. 1s. green 70 40
12. 2s. brown .. .. .. 3·00 1·50
12a. 2s. blue .. .. .. 24·00 5·00

12. "Hibiscus insularis".

2. Warder's Tower.

4. First Governor's Residence.

17. Queen Elizabeth II (after Annigoni) and Cereus.

22. Red-tailed Tropic Bird.

1953.
24. **12.** 1d. green 15 10
25. – 2d. red and myrtle .. 20 10
26. – 3d. green 70 15
13. **2.** 3½d. lake .. .. .. 3·00 90
27. – 5d. purple 55 20
14 – 6½d. green .. .. .. 3·00 1·00
15. **4.** 7½d. blue .. .. .. 4·00 3·00
28. – 8d. red 80 50
16. – 8½d. brown .. .. 7·00 3·50
29. **17.** 9d. blue 80 45
17. – 10d. violet .. .. 5·00 75
30. – 10d. brown and violet .. 2·75 1·25
31. – 1s. 1d. red 80 35
32. – 2s. sepia .. .. .. 6·00 90
33. – 2s. 5d. violet .. .. 1·00 40
34. – 2s. 8d. brown & green .. 2·00 55
18. – 5s. brown .. .. .. 38·00 8·00
35. – 5s. sepia and green .. 6·00 75
36. **22.** 10s. green .. .. 60·00 26·00
DESIGNS—VERT. 2d. "Lagunaria patersonii". 5d. Lantana. 8d. Red hibiscus. 8½d. Barracks entrance. 10d. Salt House. 1s. 1d. Fringed hibiscus. 2s. Solander's Petrel. 2s. 5d. Passion-flower. 2s. 8d. Rose-apple. HORIZ. 3d. White Tern. 6½d. Airfield. 5s. Bloody Bridge.

8. Norfolk Is. Seal and Pitcairners Landing.

1956. Centenary of Landing of Pitcairners on Norfolk Is.
19. **8.** 3d. green .. .. .. 1·25 30
20. 2s. violet .. .. .. 1·75 50

1958. Surch.
21. **4.** 7d. on 7½d. blue .. .. 1·00 45
22. – 8d. on 8½d. brown (No. 16) 1·00 45

1959. 150th Anniv. of Australian P.O. No. 331 of Australia surch. **NORFOLK ISLAND 5D.** in red.
23. **143.** 5d. on 4d. slate .. 35 30

1960. As Nos. 13 and 14/15 but colours changed and surch.
37. **2.** 1s. 1d. on 3½d. blue .. 3·50 1·50
38. 2s. 5d. on 6½d. turquoise .. 3·50 1·25
39. **4.** 2s. 8d. on 7½d. sepia .. 8·50 2·75

36. Queen Elizabeth II and Map.

1960. Introduction of Local Government.
40 **36** 2s. 8d. purple .. .. 15·00 6·00

1960. Christmas. As No. 338 of Australia.
41. **150.** 5d. mauve 80 40

1961. Christmas. As No. 341 of Australia.
42. **153.** 5d. blue 30 40

27. Tweed Trousers ("Atypichthyslatus").

DESIGNS: 11d. "Trumpeter". 1s. "Po'ov". 1s. 3d. "Dreamfish". 1s. 6d. "Hapoeka" ("Promicrops lanceolatus"). 2s. 3d. "Ophie" ("carangidae").

1962.
43. **27.** 6d. sepia, yellow & green .. 1·00 25
44. – 11d. orange, brown & blue 2·50 80
45. – 1s. blue, pink and olive .. 1·00 25
46. – 1s. 3d. blue, brown & green 2·50 1·75
47. – 1s. 6d. sepia, violet & blue 3·00 80
48. – 2s. 3d. multicoloured .. 4·50 80

1962. Christmas. As No. 345 of Australia.
49. **157.** 5d. blue 35 30

1963. Christmas. As No. 361 of Australia.
50. **173.** 5d. red 30 20

33. Overlooking Kingston.

37. Norfolk Pine.

1964. Multicoloured.
51. 5d. Type **33** 75 20
52. 8d. Kingston .. .. 1·00 30
53. 9d. The Arches (Bumboras) 3·00 20
54. 10d. Slaughter Bay .. 3·00 30

1964. 50th Anniv. of Norfolk Island as Australian Territory.
55. **37.** 5d. black, red & orange 30 15
56. 8d. black, red and green 30 15

1964. Christmas. As No. 372 of Australia.
57. **183.** 5d. multicoloured .. 30 20

1965. 50th Anniv. of Gallipoli Landing. As T **184** of Australia, but slightly larger (22 × 34½ mm.).
58. 5d. brown, black and green 15 10

1965. Christmas. As No. 381 of Australia.
59. **190.** 5d. multicoloured .. 15 10

38. "Hibiscus insularis".

1966. Decimal Currency. As earlier issue but with values in cents and dollars. Surch. in black on silver tablets obliterating old value as in T **38**.
60. **38.** 1 c. on 1d. 20 10
61. – 2 c. on 2d. (No. 25) .. 20 10
62. – 3 c. on 3d. (No. 26) .. 50 10
63. – 4 c. on 5d. (No. 27) .. 25 10
64. – 5 c. on 8d. (No. 28) .. 30 10
65. – 10 c. on 10d. (No. 30) .. 40 15
66. – 15 c. on 1s. 1d. (No. 31) 45 15
67. – 20 c. on 2s (No. 32) .. 3·50 2·50
68. – 25 c. on 2s. 5d. (No. 33) 1·50 40
69. – 30 c. on 2s. 8d. (No. 34) 1·00 50
70. – 50 c. on 5s. (No. 35) .. 4·50 75
71. **22.** $1 on 10s. .. .. 3·50 1·75

39. Headstone Bridge.

1966. Multicoloured.
72. 7 c. Type **39** 40 15
73. 9 c. Cemetery Road .. 40 15

41. St. Barnabas' Chapel (interior).

1966. Cent. of Melanesian Mission. Mult.
74. 4 c. Type **41** 10 10
75. 25 c. St. Barnabas' Chapel (exterior) 20 10

43. Star over Philip Island.

1966. Christmas.
76. **43.** 4 c. multicoloured .. 10 10

44. H.M.S. "Resolution", 1774.

1967. Multicoloured.
77 1 c. Type **44** 10 10
78 2 c. "La Boussole" and "L'Astrolabe", 1788 .. 15 10
79 3 c. H.M.S. "Supply" (brig), 1788 .. .. .. 15 10
80 4 c. H.M.S. "Sirius" (frigate), 1790 .. .. 15 10
81 5 c. "Norfolk" (cutter), 1798 20 10
82 7 c. H.M.S. "Mermaid" (survey cutter), 1825 .. 20 10
83 9 c. "Lady Franklin" (full-rigged ship), 1853 .. 20 10
84 10 c. "Morayshire" (full-rigged transport), 1856 .. 20 20
85 15 c. "Southern Cross" (missionary ship), 1866 .. 45 30
86 20 c. "Pitcairn" (missionary schooner), 1891 .. .. 60 40
87 25 c. "Black Billy" (Norfolk Island whaleboat), 1895 1·00 75
88 30 c. "Iris" (cable ship), 1907 .. .. .. 2·00 1·75
89 50 c. "Resolution" (schooner), 1926 .. .. 3·00 2·25
90 $1 "Morinda" (freighter), 1931 .. .. .. 5·50 2·50

1967. 50th Anniv. of Lions Int. As T **205** of Australia.
91. 4 c. black, green and yellow 10 10

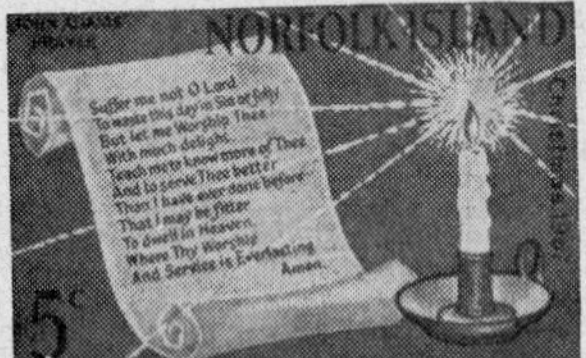

58. Prayer of John Adams and Candle.

1967. Christmas.

92. **58.** 5 c. black olive and red 10 10

1968. As T **191** of Australia, but inscr NORFOLK ISLAND.

93. 3 c. black, brown and red .. 10 10
94. 4 c. black, brown and green 10 10
95. 5 c. black, brown and violet 10 10
95a. 6 c. black, brown and lake 30 35

59. "Skymaster" and "Lancastrian" Aircraft.

1968. 21st Anniv. of QANTAS Air Service, Sydney-Norfolk Island.

96. **59.** 5 c. black, red and blue 10 10
97. 7 c. brown, red & turq. 10 10

60. Bethlehem Star and Flowers.

1968. Christmas.

98. **60.** 5 c. multicoloured .. 10 10

61. Captain Cook, Quadrant and Chart of Pacific Ocean.

1969. Captain Cook Bicentenary (1st issue). Observation of the transit of Venus across the Sun, Tahiti.

99. **61.** 10 c. multicoloured .. 10 10

See also Nos. 118/19, 129, 152/5, 200/2 and 213/14.

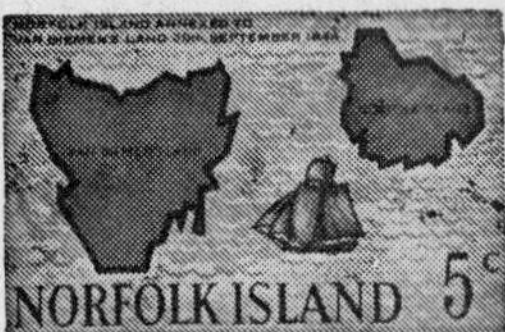

62. Van Diemen's Land, Norfolk Island and Sailing Cutter.

1969. 125th Anniv. of Annexation of Norfolk Island to Van Diemen's Land.

100. **62.** 5 c. multicoloured .. 10 10
101. 30 c. multicoloured .. 20 10

63. "The Nativity" (carved mother-of-pearl plaque).

1969. Christmas.

102. **63.** 5 c. multicoloured .. 10 10

64. New Zealand Grey Flyeater.

1970. Birds. Multicoloured.

103. 1 c. Scarlet robin 30 10
104. 2 c. Golden whistler .. 30 20
105. 3 c. Type **64** 30 10
106. 4 c. Long-tailed koel .. 60 10
107. 5 c. Red-fronted parakeet 1·50 45
108. 7 c. Long-tailed triller .. 45 10
109. 9 c. Island thrush 70 10
110. 10 c. Boobook owl .. 1·75 40
111. 15 c. Norfolk Island pigeon 1·50 65
112. 20 c. White-chested white-eye .. .. .. 4·50 3·25
113. 25 c. Norfolk Island parrots .. .. .. 2·50 40
114. 30 c. Collared grey fantail 4·50 1·75
115. 45 c. Norfolk Islands starling .. .. .. 3·50 80
116. 50 c. Crimson rosella .. 4·00 1·75
117. $1 Sacred kingfisher .. 9·00 9·00

Nos. 105/6, 109, 112, 114/5 and 117 are horiz; the remainder being vert.

65. Cook and Map of Australia.

1970. Captain Cook Bicentenary. (2nd issue). Discovery of Australia's East Coast. Mult.

118. 5 c. Type **65** 15 10
119. 20 c. H.M.S. "Endeavour" and Aborigine 40 10

66. First Christmas Service, 1788.

1970. Christmas.

120. **66.** 5 c. multicoloured .. 10 10

67. Bishop Patteson, and Martyrdom of St. Stephen.

1971. Death Cent. of Bishop Patteson. Multicoloured.

121. 6 c. Type **67** 10 10
122. 6 c. Bible, Martyrdom of St. Stephen and knotted palm-frond 10 10
123. 10 c. Bishop Patteson and stained glass 10 10
124. 10 c. Cross and Bishop's Arms 10 10

68. Rose Window, St. Barnabas Chapel, Kingston.

1971. Christmas.

125. **68.** 6 c. multicoloured .. 10 10

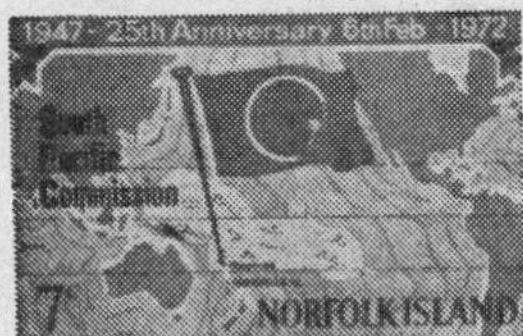

69. Map and Flag.

1972. 25th Anniv. of South Pacific Commission.

126. **69.** 7 c. multicoloured .. 15 20

70. "St. Mark" (Stained-glass Window) (All Saints, Norfolk Is.).

71. Cross and Pines (Stained-glass Window) All Saints Church).

1972. Christmas.

127. **70.** 7 c. multicoloured .. 10 10

1972. Cent. of First Pitcairner-built Church.

128. **71.** 12 c. multicoloured .. 10 10

72. H.M.S. "Resolution" in the Antarctic.

1973. Capt. Cook Bicentenary (3rd issue). Crossing of the Antarctic Circle.

129. **72.** 35 c. multicoloured .. 3·00 2·25

73. Child and Christmas Tree.

1973. Christmas. Multicoloured.

130. 7 c. Type **73** 20 10
131. 12 c. Type **73** 25 10
132. 35 c. Fir trees and star 70 80

74. Protestant Clergyman's Quarters.

1973. Historic Buildings. Multicoloured.

133. 1 c. Type **74** 10 10
134. 2 c. Royal Engineer's Office 10 10
135. 3 c. Double Quarters for Free Overseers 25 15
136. 4 c. Guard House 20 20
137. 5 c. Entrance to Pentagonal Gaol 25 15
138. 7 c. Pentagonal Gaol .. 35 35
139. 8 c. Prisoners' Barracks .. 1·25 45
140. 10 c. Officer's Quarters, New Military Barracks 50 55
141. 12 c. New Military Barracks 50 30
142. 14 c. Beach Stores .. 60 70
143. 15 c. The Magazine .. 1·75 50
144. 20 c. Entrance, Old Military Barracks 80 90
145. 25 c. Old Military Barracks 1·50 1·00
146. 30 c. Old Stores (Crankmill) 1·00 60
147. 50 c. Commissariat Stores 1·25 2·00
148. $1 Government House .. 2·25 4·00

75. Royal Couple and Map.

1974. Royal Visit.

149. **75.** 7 c. multicoloured .. 40 15
150. 25 c. multicoloured .. 1·25 75

76. Chichester's "Madame Elijah".

1974. 1st Aircraft Landing on Norfolk Island.

151. **76.** 14 c. multicoloured .. 1·00 70

77. "Captain Cook" (Engraving by J. Basire).

1974. Capt. Cook Bicentenary (4th issue). Discovery of Norfolk Is. Multicoloured.

152. 7 c. Type **77** .. .. 1·50 75
153. 10 c. H.M.S. "Resolution" (H. Roberts) .. .. 2·50 1·75
154. 14 c. Norfolk Island Pine 2·75 2·25
155. 25 c. "Norfolk Island flax" (G. Raper) .. .. 3·25 3·00

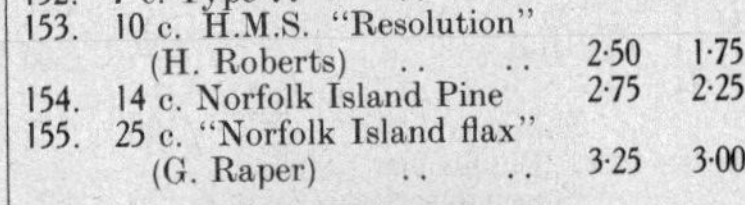

78. Nativity Scene (Pear-shell pew carving).

1974. Christmas.

156. **78.** 7 c. multicoloured .. 15 10
157. 30 c. multicoloured .. 60 75

79. Norfolk Pine.

1974. Centenary of Universal Postal Union. Multicoloured. Imperf. Self-adhesive.

158. 10 c. Type **79** 35 40
159. 15 c. Offshore islands .. 40 45
160. 35 c. Crimson Rosella and Sacred Kingfisher .. 70 75
161. 40 c. Pacific map 75 90

INDEX

Countries can be quickly located by referring to the index at the end of this volume.

80. H.M.S. "Mermaid" (survey cutter).

1975. 150th Anniv. of Second Settlement. Multicoloured.

163.	10 c. Type **80**	45	45
164.	35 c. Kingston, 1835 (from painting by T. Seller)	80	80

81. Star on Norfolk Island Pine. 82. Memorial Cross.

1975. Christmas.

165. **81.**	10 c. multicoloured ..	15	10
166.	15 c. multicoloured ..	20	10
167.	35 c. multicoloured ..	30	35

1975. Centenary of St. Barnabas Chapel. Multicoloured.

168.	30 c. Type **82**	20	15
169.	60 c. Laying foundation stone, and Chapel in 1975	40	40

83. Launching of "Resolution".

1975. 50th Anniv. of Launching of "Resolution" (schooner). Multicoloured.

170.	25 c. Type **83**	25	40
171.	45 c. "Resolution" at sea	40	70

84. Whaleship "Charles W. Morgan".

1976. Bicent. of American Revolution. Mult.

172.	18 c. Type **84**	30	15
173.	25 c. Thanksgiving Service	40	20
174.	40 c. "Flying Fortress" over Norfolk Island	75	45
175.	45 c. California Quail ..	1·00	55

85. Swallow-tailed Tern and Sun.

1976. Christmas.

176. **85.**	18 c. multicoloured ..	25	15
177.	25 c. multicoloured ..	40	20
178.	45 c. multicoloured ..	85	50

86. "Bassaris itea".

1977. Butterflies and Moths. Multicoloured.

179	1 c. Type **86**	10	40
180	2 c. "Utetheisa pulchelloides"	10	40
181	3 c. "Agathia asterias" ..	10	20
182	4 c. "Cynthia kershawi" ..	10	25
183	5 c. "Leucania loreyimima"	15	30
184	10 c. "Hypolimnas bolina"	30	35
185	15 c. "Pyrrhorachis pyrrhogona" ..	30	30
186	16 c. "Austrocarea iocephala" ..	30	30
187	17 c. "Pseudocoremia christiani"	35	30
188	18 c. "Cleora idiocrossa" ..	35	30
189	19 c. "Simplicia caeneusalis"	35	30
190	20 c. "Austrocidaria ralstonae"	40	30
191	30 c. "Hippotion scrofa" ..	50	40
192	40 c. "Papilio ilioneus" ..	55	40
193	50 c. "Tiracola plagiata"	70	60
194	$1 "Precis villida" ..	1·00	75
195	$2 "Cepora perimale" ..	1·75	1·40

87. Queen's View, Kingston.

1977. Silver Jubilee.

196. **87.**	25 c. multicoloured ..	35	30

88. Hibiscus Flowers and Oil Lamp. 89. Captain Cook (from a portrait by Nathaniel Dance).

1977. Christmas.

197. **88.**	18 c. multicoloured ..	15	10
198.	25 c. multicoloured ..	15	10
199.	45 c. multicoloured ..	30	35

1978. Capt. Cook Bicentenary (5th issue). Discovery of Hawaii. Multicoloured.

200.	18 c. Type **89** ..	30	20
201.	25 c. Discovery of northern Hawaiian islands ..	40	30
202.	80 c. British flag against island background ..	90	70

90. Guide Flag and Globe.

1978. 50th Anniv. of Girl Guides. Multicoloured. Imperf. Self-adhesive.

203.	18 c. Type **90**	30	15
204.	25 c. Trefoil and scarf badge	45	25
205.	35 c. Trefoil and Queen Elizabeth	60	35
206.	45 c. Trefoil and Lady Baden-Powell	75	45

91. St. Edward's Crown.

1978. 25th Anniv. of Coronation. Mult.

207.	25 c. Type **91**	15	15
208.	70 c. Coronation regalia ..	40	45

92. View of Duncombe Bay with Scout at Camp Fire.

1978. 50th Anniv. of Boy Scout Movement. Multicoloured. Imperf. Self-adhesive.

209.	20 c. Type **92**	35	30
210.	25 c. View from Kingston and emblem	55	40
211.	35 c. View of Anson Bay and Link Badge ..	85	75
212.	45 c. Sunset scene and Lord Baden-Powell	1·00	85

93. Chart showing Route of Arctic Voyage.

1978. Captain Cook Bicentenary (6th issue). Northern-most Voyage. Multicoloured.

213.	25 c. Type **93**	60	30
214.	90 c. "H.M.S. "Resolution" and H.M.S. "Discovery" in Pack Ice" (Webber)	1·50	80

94. Poinsettia and Bible.

1978. Christmas. Multicoloured.

215.	20 c. Type **94**	15	10
216.	30 c. Native Oak and bible	20	15
217.	55 c. Hibiscus and bible ..	30	30

95. Cook and Village of Staithes near Marton.

1978. 250th Birth Anniv. of Captain Cook. Multicoloured.

218.	20 c. Type **95**	35	25
219.	80 c. Cook and Whitby Harbour	1·40	1·25

96. H.M.S. "Resolution".

1979. Death Bicent. of Captain Cook. Mult.

220.	20 c. Type **96**	80	30
221.	20 c. Cook statue	80	30
222.	40 c. } "Death of Captain	90	50
223.	40 c. } Cook"	90	50

Nos. 220/1 were issued se-tenant, in horizontal pairs throughout the sheet, forming a composite design. A chart of Cook's last voyage is shown in the background. Nos. 222/3 were also issued se-tenant, the horizontal pair forming a composite design taken from an aquatint by John Clevely.

97. Assembly Building.

1979. First Norfolk Island Legislative Assembly.

224. **97.**	$1 multicoloured ..	50	50

98. Tasmania 1853 1d. Stamp and Sir Rowland Hill.

1979. Death Centenary of Sir Rowland Hill.

225. **98.**	20 c. blue and brown ..	20	10
226. –	30 c. red and grey ..	25	15
227. –	55 c. violet and indigo ..	40	30

DESIGNS: 30 c. Great Britain 1841 1d. red. 55 c. 1947 "Ball Bay" 1d. stamp.

99. I.Y.C. Emblem and Map of Pacific showing Norfolk Island as Pine Tree.

1979. International Year of the Child.

229. **99.**	80 c. multicoloured ..	40	45

100. Emily Bay.

1979. Christmas.

230. **100.**	15 c. multicoloured ..	15	15
231. –	20 c. multicoloured ..	15	15
232. –	30 c. multicoloured ..	15	15

DESIGNS: 20, 30 c. Different scenes.

Nos. 230/2 were printed together, se-tenant, in horizontal strips of 3 throughout the sheet, forming a composite design.

101. Lions International Emblem.

1980. Lions Convention.

234. **101.**	50 c. multicoloured ..	35	30

102. Rotary International Emblem.

1980. 75th Anniv. of Rotary International.
235. **102.** 50 c. multicoloured .. 35 30

103. D.H. 60 (Gypsy Moth) " Mme Elijah ".

1980. Aeroplanes. Multicoloured.
236. 1 c. Hawker Siddeley " H.S. 748 " 15 20
237. 2 c. Type **103** 15 20
238. 3 c. Curtis " P-40 Kittyhawk " 15 20
239. 4 c. Chance Vought " F4U-1 Corsair " 15 30
240. 5 c. Grumman " TBF-1c Avenger " 30 30
241. 15 c. Douglas " SBD-5 " Dauntless " 30 30
242. 20 c. Cessna " 172 " 25 30
243. 25 c. Lockheed " Hudson " 30 35
244. 30 c. Lockheed " PV-1 Ventura " 40 60
245. 40 c. Avro " York " .. 50 55
246. 50 c. Douglas " DC-3 " .. 65 65
247. 60 c. Avro " 691 Lancastrian " 75 75
248. 80 c. Douglas " DC-4 " .. 95 95
249. $1 Beechcraft " Super King Air " .. .. 1·25 90
250. $2 Fokker " F-27 Friendship " .. .. 2·50 90
251. $5 Lockheed " C-130 Hercules " .. .. 6·00 2·00

104. Queen Elizabeth the Queen Mother.

1980. 80th Birthday of The Queen Mother.
252. **104.** 22 c. multicoloured .. 30 20
253. 60 c. multicoloured .. 65 40

105. Red-tailed Tropic Birds.

1980. Christmas. Birds. Multicoloured.
254. 15 c. Type **105** 35 25
255. 22 c. White Terns .. 35 25
256. 35 c. White-capped Noddys 35 25
257. 60 c. White Terns (different) 60 45

106. " Morayshire " and View of Norfolk Island.

1981. 125th Anniv. of Pitcairn Islanders' Migration to Norfolk Island. Multicoloured.
258. 5 c. Type **106** 15 15
259. 35 c. Islanders arriving ashore 55 30
260. 60 c. View of new settlement 85 45

MINIMUM PRICE

The minimum price quoted is 10p which represents a handling charge rather than a basis for valuing common stamps. For further notes about prices see introductory pages.

107. Wedding Bouquet from Norfolk Island.

1981. Royal Wedding. Multicoloured.
262. 35 c. Type **107** 20 15
263. 55 c. Prince Charles at horse trials 35 25
264. 60 c. Prince Charles and Lady Diana Spencer .. 35 35

108. Uniting Church in Australia.

1981. Christmas. Churches. Multicoloured.
265. 18 c. Type **108** 20 10
266. 24 c. Seventh Day Adventist Church 25 15
267. 30 c. Church of the Sacred Heart 30 20
268. $1 St. Barnabas Chapel .. 70 70

109. Pair of " White-breasted Silvereyes".

1981. White-breasted Silvereye. Mult.
269. 35 c. Type **109** 35 40
270. 35 c. (White-chested White eye.) Bird on nest .. 35 40
271. 35 c. Bird with egg .. 35 40
272. 35 c. Parents with chicks 35 40
273. 35 c. Fledgelings 35 40

110. Aerial view of Philip Island.

1982. Philip and Nepean Islands. Mult.
274. 24 c. Type **110** 30 25
275. 24 c. Close-up view of Philip Island landscape 30 25
276. 24 c. Gecko (" phyllodactylus guentheri "), Philip Island 30 25
277. 24 c. Sooty Tern, Philip Island 30 25
278. 24 c. Philip Island Hibiscus (" hibiscus insuarlis ") 30 25
279. 35 c. Aerial view of Nepean Island 40 35
280. 35 c. Close-up view of Nepean Island landscape 40 35
281. 35 c. Gecko (" phyllodactylus guentheri "), Nepean Is. 40 35
282. 35 c. Blue-faced Boobies. Nepean Island 40 35
283. 35 c. " Carpobrotus glaucescens" (flower), Nepean Island 40 35

111. Sperm Whale.

1982. Whales.
284. **111.** 24 c. multicoloured .. 45 35
285. – 55 c. multicoloured .. 85 75
286. – 80 c. black, mve. & stone 1·10 1·00
DESIGNS: 55 c. Black Right Whale. 80 c. Humpback Whale.

112. " Diocet ", Wrecked 20 April 1873.

1982. Shipwrecks. Multicoloured.
287. 24 c. H.M.S. " Sirius ", wrecked 19 March 1790 50 50
288. 27 c. Type **112** 50 50
289. 35 c. " Friendship ", wrecked 17 May 1835 .. 90 80
290. 40 c. " Mary Hamilton ", wrecked 6 May 1873 .. 90 90
291. 55 c. " Fairlie ", wrecked 14 February 1840 .. 1·25 1·25
292. 65 c. " Warrigal ", wrecked 18 March 1918 .. 1·25 1·50

113. R.N.Z.A.F. " Hudson " dropping Christmas Supplies, 1942.

1982. Christmas. 40th Anniv. of First Supply-plane Landings on Norfolk Island (Christmas Day 1942). Multicoloured.
293. 27 c. Type **113** 30 35
294. 40 c. R.N.Z.A.F. " Hudson " landing Christmas supplies 1942 .. .. .. 45 65
295. 75 c. Christmas, 1942 .. 90 1·40

114. 50th (Queen's Own) Regiment.

1982. Military Uniforms. Multicoloured.
296. 27 c. Type **114** 30 35
297. 40 c. 58th (Rutlandshire) Regiment 45 75
298. 55 c. 80th (Staffordshire Volunteers) Battalion Company 65 95
299. 65 c. 11th (North Devonshire) Regiment .. 80 1·25

115. "Panaeolus papilionaceus"

1983. Fungi. Multicoloured.
300. 27 c. Type **115** 45 35
301. 40 c. "Coprinus domesticus" 70 50
302. 55 c. "Marasmius niveus" 95 70
303. 65 c. "Cymatoderma elegans var. lamellatum" .. 1·25 85

116. Beechcraft " 18 ".

1983. Bicentenary of Manned Flight. Mult.
304. 10 c. Type **116** 15 15
305. 27 c. Fokker " F 28 Fellowship " 30 35
306. 45 c. French military " DC-4 " 50 60
307. 75 c. Sikorsky helicopter .. 90 95

117. St. Matthew.

1983. Christmas. 150th Birth Anniv. of Sir Edmond Burne-Jones.
309. 5 c. Type **117** 10 10
310. 24 c. St. Mark 30 30
311. 30 c. Jesus Christ .. 40 40
312. 45 c. St. Luke 55 55
313. 85 c. St. John .. .. 1·10 1·10
DESIGNS: showing stained glass windows from St. Barnabas Chapel, Norfolk Island.

118. Cable Ship "Chantik".

1983. World Communications Year. ANZCAN Cable. Multicoloured.
314. 30 c. Type **118** 40 40
315. 45 c. " Chantik " during in-shore operations .. 55 55
316. 75 c. Cable ship " Mercury " 95 95
317. 85 c. Diagram of cable route 1·10 1·10

119. Strand Morning Glory.

1984. Flowers. Multicoloured.
318. 1 c. Popwood 20 20
319. 2 c. Type **119** 30 20
320. 3 c. Native Phreatia .. 35 20
321. 4 c. Philip Island Wisteria 35 20
322. 5 c. Norfolk Island Palm 35 20
323. 10 c. Evergreen 40 20
324. 15 c. Bastard Oak .. 50 30
325. 20 c. Devil's Guts 50 30
326. 25 c. White Oak 60 35
327. 30 c. Ti 70 40
328. 35 c. Philip Island Hibiscus 70 40
329. 40 c. Native Wisteria .. 80 45
330. 50 c. Native Jasmine .. 1·25 50
331. $1 Norfolk Island Passion-fruit .. .. .. 1·25 1·00
332. $3 Native Oberonia .. 3·00 2·75
333. $5 Norfolk Island Pine .. 4·50 4·00

120. " Cheilodactylidae ".

1984. Reef Fish. Multicoloured.
334. 30 c. Type **120** 40 45
335. 45 c. " Pseudopeneus signatus " 60 65
336. 75 c. " Acanthuridae " .. 1·00 1·10
337. 85 c. " Chaeton ancinetus " 1·25 1·40

121. Owl with eggs.

1984. Boobook Owl. Multicoloured.

338. 30 c. Type **121** 65 50
339. 30 c. Fledgling 65 50
340. 30 c. Young owl on stump 65 50
341. 30 c. Adult on branch .. 65 50
342. 30 c. Owl in flight 65 50

122. 1953 7½d. and 1974 Cook Bicent. 10 c. Stamp.

1984. "Ausipex" International Stamp Exhibition, Melbourne. Multicoloured.

343. 30 c. Type **122** 30 35
344. 45 c. John Buffett commemorative postal stationery envelope .. 45 75
345. 75 c. Design from Presentation Pack for 1982 Military Uniforms issue .. 90 1·75

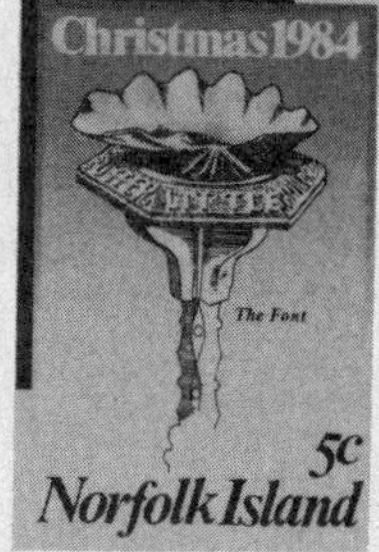

123. Font, Kingston Methodist Church.

1984. Christmas. Centenary of Methodist Church on Norfolk Island. Multicoloured.

347. 5 c. Type **123** 10 10
348. 24 c. Church service in Old Barracks, Kingston, late 1800s 35 40
349. 30 c. The Revd. & Mrs. A.H. Phelps and sailing ship 40 45
350. 45 c. The Revd. A.H. Phelps and First Congregational Church, Chester, U.S.A. 60 65
351. 85 c. Interior of Kingston Methodist Church .. 1·25 1·40

124. The Revd. Nobbs teaching Pitcairn Islanders.

1984. Death Centenary of Revd. George Hunn Nobbs (leader of Pitcairn community). Multicoloured.

352. 30 c. Type **124** 40 45
353. 45 c. The Revd. Nobbs with sick islander .. 60 65
354. 75 c. Baptising baby .. 1·00 1·10
355. 85 c. Presented to Queen Victoria, 1852 .. .. 1·25 1·40

125. "Fanny Fisher".

1985. 19th-Century Whaling Ships (1st series). Multicoloured.

356. 5 c. Type **125** 30 25
357. 33 c. "Costa Rica Packet" 85 55
358. 50 c. "Splendid" .. .. 1·25 1·25
359. 90 c. "Onward" .. .. 1·75 2·00

See also Nos. 360/3.

1985. 19th-Century Whaling Ships (2nd series). As T **125**. Multicoloured.

360. 15 c. "Waterwitch" .. 60 60
361. 20 c. "Canton" 70 70
362. 60 c. "Aladdin" .. .. 1·40 1·60
363. 80 c. "California" .. .. 1·75 2·00

126. The Queen Mother (from photo by Norman Parkinson).

1985. Life and Times of Queen Elizabeth the Queen Mother. Multicoloured.

364. 5 c. The Queen Mother (from photo by Dorothy Wilding) 10 10
365. 33 c. With Princess Anne at Trooping the Colour 35 40
366. 50 c. Type **126** 50 55
367. 90 c. With Prince Henry at his christening (from photo by Lord Snowdon) 95 1·00

127. "Swimming".

1985. International Youth Year. Children's Paintings. Multicoloured.

369. 33 c. Type **127** 75 40
370. 50 c. "A Walk in the Country" .. .. 1·50 85

128. Prize-winning Cow and Owner.

1985. 125th Anniv. of Royal Norfolk Island Agricultural and Horticultural Show. Mult.

371. 80 c. Type **128** 75 80
372. 90 c. Show exhibits .. 85 90

129. Shepherds with Flock.

1985. Christmas. Multicoloured.

374. 27 c. Type **129** 60 30
375. 33 c. Mary and Joseph with donkey 75 40
376. 50 c. The Three Wise Men 1·40 65
377. 90 c. The Nativity .. 1·75 1·25

130. Long-spined Sea Urchin.

1986. Marine Life. Multicoloured.

378. 5 c. Type **130** 10 10
379. 33 c. Blue Starfish .. 40 35
380. 55 c. Eagle Ray 60 75
381. 75 c. Moray Eel .. .. 85 1·00

131. "Giotto" Spacecraft.

1986. Appearance of Halley's Comet. Mult.

383. $1 Type **131** .. .. 1·50 1·75
384. $1 Halley's Comet .. 1·50 1·75

Nos. 383/4 were printed together, se-tenant, forming a composite design.

132. Isaac Robinson (U.S. Consul 1887–1908).

1986. "Ameripex '86" International Stamp Exhibition, Chicago. Multicoloured.

385. 33 c. Type **132** 60 35
386. 50 c. Ford "Model T" (first vehicle on island) (horiz.) 80 50
387. 80 c. Statue of Liberty .. 1·10 80

No. 387 also commemorates the Centenary of the Statue of Liberty.

133. Princess Elizabeth and Dog.

1986. 60th Birthday of Queen Elizabeth II. Multicoloured.

389. 5 c. Type **133** 10 10
390. 33 c. Queen Elizabeth II .. 50 35
391. 80 c. Opening Norfolk Island Golf Club .. 1·25 1·40
392. 90 c. With Duke of Edinburgh in carriage .. 1·50 1·60

134. Stylized Dove and Norfolk Island.

1986. Christmas.

393. **134.** 30 c. multicoloured .. 35 30
394. 40 c. multicoloured .. 50 45
395. $1 multicoloured .. 1·40 1·50

135. British Convicts, 1787.

1986. Bicentenary (1988) of Norfolk Island Settlement (1st issue). Governor Phillip's Commission. Multicoloured.

396. 36 c. Type **135** 75 35
397. 55 c. Judge passing sentence of transportation .. .. .. 1·25 65
398. 90 c. Governor Phillip meeting Home Secretary (inscr "Home Society") 2·25 1·50
399. 90 c. As No. 398, but correctly inscr "Home Secretary" (16.12) .. 2·25 1·50
400. $1 Captain Arthur Phillip 2·25 1·50

See also Nos. 401/4, 421/4, 433/5, 436/7 and 438/43.

136. Stone Tools.

1986. Bicentenary (1988) of Norfolk Island Settlement (2nd issue). Pre-European Occupation. Multicoloured.

401. 36 c. Type **136** 65 45
402. 36 c. Bananas and taro .. 65 45
403. 36 c. Polynesian outrigger canoe 65 45
404. 36 c. Maori chief 65 45

137. Philip Island from Point Ross.

1987. Norfolk Island Scenes. Multicoloured.

405. 1 c. Cockpit Creek Bridge . . 30 40
406. 2 c. Cemetery Bay Beach . . 30 40
407. 3 c. Island guesthouse . . 30 40
408. 5 c. Type **137** 20 30
409. 15 c. Cattle in pasture . . 50 55
410. 30 c. Rock fishing 30 55
411. 37 c. Old Pitcairner-style house . . . . . . 1·00 85
412. 40 c. Shopping centre . . 35 60
413. 50 c. Emily Bay 45 70
414. 60 c. Bloody Bridge . . 1·25 1·10
415. 80 c. Pitcairner-style shop 1·50 1·50
416. 90 c. Government House . . 1·25 1·60
417. $1 Melanesian Memorial Chapel . . . . . . 1·00 1·50
418. $2 Convict settlement, Kingston . . . . 1·75 2·50
419. $3 Ball Bay . . . . 4·50 4·00
420. $5 Northern cliffs . . . . 6·00 7·00

1987. Bicentenary of Norfolk Island Settlement (1988) (3rd issue). The First Fleet. As T **135**. Multicoloured.

421. 5 c. Loading supplies, Deptford 40 50
422. 55 c. Fleet leaving Spithead . . . . . . 1·40 1·75
423. 55 c. H.M.S. "Sirius" leaving Spithead . . 1·40 1·75
424. $1 Female convicts below decks . . . . . . 2·25 2·50

Nos. 422/3 were printed together, se-tenant, forming a composite design.

138. Male Red-fronted Parakeet.

1987. Red-fronted Parakeet ("Green Parrot"). Multicoloured.

425. 5 c. Type **138** 60 60
426. 15 c. Adult with fledgeling and egg . . . . 1·00 1·00
427. 36 c. Young parakeets . . 1·75 1·75
428. 55 c. Female parakeet . . 2·00 2·00

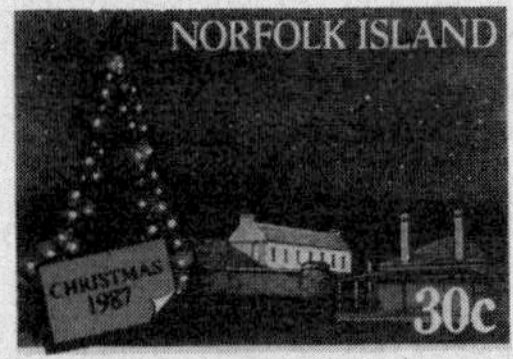

139. Christmas Tree and Restored Garrison Barracks.

1987. Christmas. Multicoloured.

429. 30 c. Type **139** 30 30
430. 42 c. Children opening presents 45 55
431. 58 c. Father Christmas with children 60 65
432. 63 c. Children's party . . 70 80

1987. Bicentenary of Norfolk Island Settlement (1988) (4th issue). Visit of La Perouse (navigator). As T **135**. Mult.

433. 37 c. La Perouse with King Louis XVI 85 55
434. 90 c. "L'Astrolabe" and "La Boussole" off Norfolk Island . . . . 2·00 2·25
435. $1 "L'Astrolabe" wrecked in Solomon Islands . . 2·25 2·75

1988. Bicentenary of Norfolk Island Settlement (5th issue). Arrival of First Fleet at Sydney. As T **135**. Multicoloured.

436. 37 c. Ship's cutter approaching Port Jackson 90 65
437. $1 Landing at Sydney Cove . . . . . . 2·10 2·10

1988. Bicentenary of Norfolk Island Settlement (6th issue). Foundation of First Settlement. As T **135**. Multicoloured.

438. 5 c. Lt. Philip Gidley King 20 20
439. 37 c. Raising the flag, March 1788 . . . . 75 75
440. 55 c. King exploring . . 1·25 1·25
441. 70 c. Landing at Sydney Bay, Norfolk Island . . 1·50 1·50
442. 90 c. H.M.S. "Supply" (brig) 1·75 1·75
443. $1 Sydney Bay Settlement, 1788 . . . . . . 1·90 1·90

140 Airliner, Container Ship and Sydney Harbour Bridge

1988. "Sydpex '88" National Stamp Exhibition, Sydney. Multicoloured.

444 37 c. Type **140** 75 75
445 37 c. Exhibition label under magnifying glass (horiz) 75 75
446 37 c. Telephone and dish aerial 75 75

141 Flowers and Decorations

1988. Christmas. Multicoloured.

448 30 c. Type **141** 40 40
449 42 c. Flowers 60 70
450 58 c. Fishes and beach . . 75 85
451 63 c. Norfolk Island . . 85 1·00

142 Pier Store and Boat Shed

1988. Restored Buildings from the Convict Era. Multicoloured.

452 39 c. Type **142** 35 40
453 55 c. Royal Engineers Building 50 55
454 90 c. Old Military Barracks 85 90
455 $1 Commissariat Store and New Military Barracks 95 1·00

143 "Lamprima aenea"

1989. Endemic Insects. Multicoloured.

456 39 c. Type **143** 45 40
457 55 c. "Insulascirtus nythos" 60 70
458 90 c. "Caedicia araucariae" 1·00 1·10
459 $1 "Thrincophora aridela" 1·10 1·25

144 H.M.S. "Bounty" off Tasmania

1989. Bicentenary of the Mutiny on the "Bounty". Multicoloured.

460 5 c. Type **144** 40 30
461 39 c. Mutineers and Polynesian women, Pitcairn Island . . 1·40 1·25
462 55 c. Lake Windermere, Cumbria (Christian's home county) . . . . 1·90 1·75
463 $1.10 "Mutineers casting Bligh adrift" (Robert Dodd) . . . . . . 2·75 2·50

145 Norfolk Island Flag

1989. 10th Anniv of Internal Self-Government. Multicoloured.

465 41 c. Type **145** 60 55
466 55 c. Old ballot box . . 70 65
467 $1 Norfolk Island Act, 1979 1·40 1·40
468 $1.10 Island crest . . 1·50 1·60

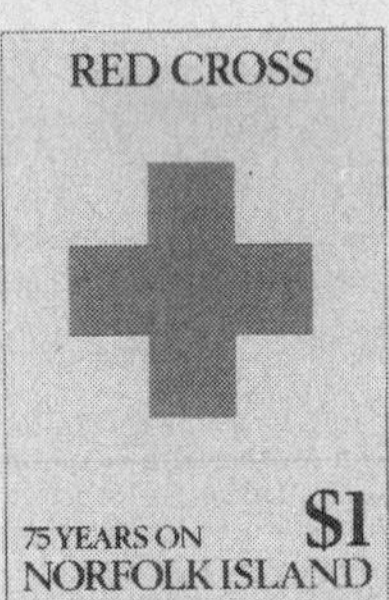

146 Red Cross

1989. 75th Anniv of Red Cross on Norfolk Island.

469 **146** $1 red and blue . . 2·50 2·00

147 "Gethsemane"

1989. Christmas. Designs showing opening lines of hymns and local scenes. Multicoloured.

470 36 c. Type **147** 80 40
471 60 c. "In the Sweet Bye and Bye" . . . . 1·40 1·40
472 75 c. "Let the Lower Lights Be Burning" . . 1·60 1·60
473 80 c. "The Beautiful Stream" . . . . 1·75 2·00

148 John Royle (first announcer)

149 H.M.S. "Bounty" on fire, Pitcairn Island, 1790

1989. 50th Anniv of Radio Australia. Designs each showing Kingston buildings. Mult.

474 41 c. Type **148** 80 55
475 65 c. Radio waves linking Australia and Norfolk Island . . . . . . 1·40 1·50
476 $1.10 Anniversary kookaburra logo . . . . 2·25 2·50

1990. History of the Norfolk Islanders (1st series). Settlement on Pitcairn Island. Mult.

477 70 c. Type **149** . . . . 1·75 1·75
478 $1.10 Arms of Norfolk Island . . . . 2·25 2·25

See also Nos. 503/4 and 516/17.

150 H.M.S. "Sirius" striking Reef

1990. Bicentenary of Wreck of H.M.S. "Sirius". Multicoloured.

479 41 c. Type **150** . . . . 1·25 1·25
480 41 c. H.M.S. "Sirius" failing to clear bay . . 1·25 1·25
481 65 c. Divers at work on wreck . . . . 1·75 1·75
482 $1 Recovered artifacts and chart of site . . . . 2·25 2·25

Nos. 479/80 were printed together, se-tenant, forming a composite design.

151 Unloading Lighter, Kingston

152 "Ile de Lumiere" (freighter)

1990. Ships.

483 **151** 5 c. brown 10 10
484 10 c. brown 10 10
485 – 45 c. multicoloured . . 40 45
486 – 50 c. multicoloured . . 45 50
487 – 65 c. multicoloured . . 60 65
488 **152** 70 c. multicoloured . . 65 70
489 – 75 c. multicoloured . . 70 75
490 – 80 c. multicoloured . . 75 80
491 – 90 c. multicoloured . . 85 90
492 – $1 multicoloured . . 95 1·00
493 – $2 multicoloured . . 2·00 2·10
494 – $5 multicoloured . . 4·75 5·00

DESIGNS—As T **152**. 45 c. "La Dunkerquoise" (French patrol vessel); 50 c. "Dmitri Mendeleev" (Russian research vessel); 65 c. "Pacific Rover" (tanker); 75 c. "Norfolk Trader" (freighter); 80 c. "Roseville" (transport); 90 c. "Kalia" (container ship); $1 "Bounty" (replica); $2 H.M.A.S. "Success" (supply ship); $5 H.M.A.S. "Whyalla" (patrol vessel).

153 Santa on House Roof

154 William Charles Wentworth

1990. Christmas. Multicoloured.

499 38 c. Type **153** 65 45
500 43 c. Santa at Kingston Post Office 70 50
501 65 c. Santa over Sydney Bay, Kingston (horiz) . . 1·25 1·25
502 85 c. Santa on Officers' Quarters (horiz) . . 1·40 1·75

1990. History of the Norfolk Islanders (2nd series). The First Generation.

503 **154** 70 c. brn & cinnamon .. 85 85
504 – $1.20 brn & cinnamon 1·40 1·40

DESIGN: $1.20, Thursday October Christian.

155 Adult Robin and Chicks in Nest — **156** Map of Norfolk Island

1990. "Birdpex '90" Stamp Exhibition, Christchurch, New Zealand. Scarlet Robin. Multicoloured.

505 65 c. Type **155** 75 75
506 $1 Hen on branch .. 1·25 1·25
507 $1.20 Cock on branch .. 1·40 1·40

1991. Ham Radio Network. Multicoloured.

509 43 c. Type **156** 75 50
510 $1 Globe showing Norfolk Island .. .. .. 1·75 2·00
511 $1.20 Map of south-west Pacific .. .. .. 2·00 2·25

157 Display in "Sirius" Museum

1991. Norfolk Island Museums. Mult.

512 43 c. Type **157** 70 50
513 70 c. 19th-century sitting room, House Museum (horiz) .. .. .. 1·25 1·25
514 $1 Carronade, "Sirius" Museum (horiz) .. 1·75 1·75
515 $1.20 Reconstructed jug and beaker, Archaeological Museum .. 1·75 2·00

158 H.M.S. "Pandora" wrecked on Great Barrier Reef (1791)

1991. History of the Norfolk Islanders (3rd series). Search for the "Bounty". Mult.

516 $1 Type **158** .. .. 1·50 1·75
517 $1.20 H.M.S. "Pandora" leaving bay .. .. 1·75 2·00

159 Hibiscus and Island Scene

1991. Christmas.

518 **159** 38 c. multicoloured .. 70 40
519 43 c. multicoloured .. 80 55
520 65 c. multicoloured .. 1·00 1·25
521 85 c. multicoloured .. 1·10 1·40

160 Tank and Soldier in Jungle

1991. 50th Anniv of Outbreak of Pacific War. Multicoloured.

522 43 c. Type **160** 65 45
523 70 c. B17 Flying Fortress on jungle airstrip .. 1·25 1·25
524 $1 Warships .. .. 1·75 2·00

161 Coat of Arms

1992. 500th Anniv of Discovery of America by Columbus. Multicoloured.

525 45 c. Type **161** 60 45
526 $1.05 "Santa Maria" .. 1·40 1·50
527 $1.20 Columbus and globe 1·90 2·00

162 Deployment Map — **163** Norfolk Pines above Ball Bay

1992. 50th Anniv of Battle of the Coral Sea. Multicoloured.

528 45 c. Type **162** .. 60 45
529 70 c. H.M.A.S. "Australia" (cruiser) .. .. 1·00 1·10
530 $1.05 U.S.S. "Yorktown" (aircraft carrier) .. 1·60 1·75

1992. 50th Anniv of Battle of Midway. As T **162**. Multicoloured.

531 45 c. Battle area 60 45
532 70 c. Catalina PBY 5 flying boat over task force .. 1·00 1·10
533 $1.05 Douglas SBD 5 Dauntless dive bomber and burning Japanese aircraft carrier .. 1·60 1·75

1992. 50th Anniv of Battle of Guadalcanal. As T **162**. Multicoloured.

534 45 c. American troops landing (horiz) 50 45
535 70 c. Machine-gun crew (horiz) .. 90 1·00
536 $1.05 Map of Pacific with Japanese and American flags (horiz) .. 1·40 1·50

1992. Christmas. Multicoloured.

537 40 c. Type **163** .. 50 40
538 45 c. Headstone Creek .. 60 45
539 75 c. South side of Ball Bay 90 90
540 $1.20 Rocky Point Reserve 1·40 1·60

164 Boat Shed and Flaghouses, Kingston

1993. Tourism. Historic Kingston. Mult.

541 45 c. Type **164** .. 65 70
542 45 c. Old Military Barracks 65 70
543 45 c. All Saints Church .. 65 70
544 45 c. Officers' Quarters .. 65 70
545 45 c. Quality Row .. 65 70

Nos. 541/5 were printed together, se-tenant forming a composite design.

165 Fire Engine

1993. Emergency Services. Multicoloured.

546 45 c. Type **165** 50 45
547 70 c. Cliff rescue squad .. 80 80
548 75 c. Ambulance 85 85
549 $1.20 Police car .. .. 1·60 1·75

166 "Glaucus atlanticus"

1993. Nudibranchs. Multicoloured.

550 45 c. Type **166** 50 45
551 45 c. "Phyllidia ocellata" 50 45
552 75 c. "Bornella sp" .. 85 85
553 85 c. "Glossodoris rubroannolata" .. 1·10 1·10
554 95 c. "Halgerda willeyi" .. 1·25 1·25
555 $1.05 "Chromodoris amoena" .. .. 1·40 1·50

167 Christmas Wreath — **168** Maori Stone Clubs

1993. Christmas.

556 **167** 40 c. multicoloured .. 50 45
557 45 c. multicoloured .. 50 45
558 75 c. multicoloured .. 85 85
559 $1.20 multicoloured .. 1·60 1·75

1993. Bicentenary of Contact with New Zealand. Multicoloured.

560 70 c. Type **168** 75 75
561 $1.20 First Maori map of New Zealand, 1793 .. 1·50 1·60

169 Alvaro de Saavedra, Route Map and "Florida"

1994. Pacific Explorers. Multicoloured.

564 5 c. Vasco Nunez de Balboa, map and "Barbara" 10 10
565 10 c. Ferdinand Magellan, map and "Vitoria" .. 10 10
566 20 c. Juan Sebastian Del Cano, map and "Vitoria" 25 25
567 50 c. Type **169** 45 50
568 70 c. Ruy Lopez de Villalobos, map and "San Juan" 65 70
569 75 c. Miguel Lopez de Legaspi, map and "San Lesmes" 70 75
574 $2 Abel Tasman, map and "Heemskerk" .. .. 2·00 2·10
575 $5 William Dampier, map and "Cygnet" .. .. 4·75 5·00

NORTH BORNEO

A territory in the N. of the Island of Borneo in the China Sea, formerly under the administration of the Br. N. Borneo Co. A Crown Colony since 1946. Joined Malaysia in 1963 and renamed Sabah in 1964.

100 cents = 1 dollar (Malayan).

1.

1883. "POSTAGE NORTH BORNEO" at top.

8 **1.** ½ c. mauve .. .. 50·00 £100
9 1 c. orange £140 £200
10 2 c. brown .. .. 15·00 17·00
11 4 c. pink .. .. 15·00 40·00
12 8 c. green .. .. .. 17·00 40·00
13 10 c. blue .. .. .. 17·00 38·00

1883. Surch. **8 Cents.** vert.

2. **1.** 8 c. on 2 c. brown £800 £550

1883. Surch. **EIGHT CENTS.**

3. **1.** 8 c. on 2 c. brown £350 £150

Where there are three price columns, prices in the second column are for postally used stamps and those in the third column are for stamps cancelled with black bars.

4. 5.

1883.

4. **4.** 50 c. violet .. 70·00 — 13·00
5. **5.** $1 red .. .. 50·00 — 8·50

1886. Optd. **and Revenue.**

14. **1.** ½ c. mauve .. .. 50·00 £110
15. 10 c. blue .. .. .. 90·00 £140

1886. Surch. in words and figures.

18. **1.** 3 c. on 4 c. pink .. 48·00 85·00
19. 5 c. on 8 c. green .. .. 60·00 85·00

9. 10.

1886. Inscr. "BRITISH NORTH BORNEO".

22. **9.** ½ c. red .. .. 2·00 10·00
24. 1 c. orange .. 1·50 6·50
25. 2 c. brown .. 1·75 7·00
26. 4 c. pink .. .. 1·50 7·00
27. 8 c. green .. 2·75 13·00
28. 10 c. blue .. 5·50 22·00

1887.

45. **10.** 25 c. blue .. 22·00 70·00 50
46. – 50 c. violet .. 42·00 £110 50
47. – $1 red .. 24·00 £100 50
48. – $2 green .. 75·00 £140 1·10
49. – $5 purple .. .. 80·00 90·00 6·00
50. – $10 brown .. £120 £160 9·00

The $5 and $10 are much larger than Type **5** and show the arms with supporters as in Type **3.**

14.

1888. Inscr. "POSTAGE & REVENUE".

36b	**14.**	½ c. red	40	2·50	30
37		1 c. orange ..	60	2·50	30
38b		2 c. brown ..	1·00	6·50	30
39		3 c. violet ..	1·75	9·00	30
40		4 c. pink ..	2·50	16·00	30
41		5 c. grey ..	2·00	11·00	30
42		6 c. deep red ..	4·75	13·00	45
43a		8 c. green ..	8·00	13·00	45
44b		10 c. blue ..	5·00	12·00	50

1890. Surch. in words.

51.	**10.**	2 c. on 25 c. blue	40·00	65·00
52.		8 c. on 25 c. blue	60·00	80·00

1891. Surch. in figures and words.

63.	**14.**	1 c. on 4 c. pink ..	14·00	14·00
64.		1 c. on 5 c. grey ..	6·00	6·00
54.	**9.**	6 c. on 8 c. green ..	£5000	£3500
55.	**14.**	6 c. on 8 c. green ..	8·00	8·50
56.	**9.**	6 c. on 10 c. blue ..	35·00	17·00
57.	**14.**	6 c. on 10 c. blue ..	75·00	24·00
65.	**10.**	8 c. on 25 c. blue ..	£110	£130

24. Dyak Chief.

25. Sambar Stag ("Cervus unicolor").

26. Sago Palm.

27. Great Argus Pheasant.

28. Arms of the Company.

29. Malay Prau.

30. Estuarine Crocodile.

31. Mt. Kinabalu.

32. Arms of the Company with Supporters.

1894.

67	**24.**	1 c. blk. & bis.	1·25	7·00	20
69	**25.**	2 c. blk. & red	3·50	4·00	30
70	**26.**	3 c. grn. & mve.	2·25	7·00	30
72	**27.**	5 c. blk. & red	7·50	11·00	40
73a	**28.**	6 c. blk. & brn.	3·50	13·00	40
74	**29.**	8 c. blk. & lilac	2·75	8·50	50
75	**30.**	12 c. blk. & bl.	24·00	65·00	2·00
78	**31.**	18 c. blk. & grn.	15·00	45·00	2·00
79	**32.**	24 c. bl. & red ..	16·00	55·00	2·00

1894. As Nos. 47, etc., but inscr. "THE STATE OF NORTH BORNEO".

81	25 c. blue	8·00	26·00	70
82	50 c. violet	9·50	45·00	70
83	$1 red	11·00	23·00	90
84	$2 green	13·00	60·00	90
85b	$5 purple	65·00	£100	3·50
86	$10 brown	£130	£190	5·00

1895. No. 83 surch. in figures and words.

87.	4 cents on $1 red	2·50	1·50	30
88.	10 cents on $1 red	5·50	1·75	30
89.	20 cents on $1 red	18·00	10·00	30
90.	30 cents on $1 red	11·00	14·00	30
91.	40 cents on $1 red	16·00	25·00	30

37. Orang-utan.

41. Sun Bear.

43. Borneo Steam Train.

1897. As 1894. issue with insertion of native inscriptions.

92a	**24.**	1 c. blk. & bis.	4·25	2·00	20
94a	**25.**	2 c. black & red	7·00	2·75	20
95		2 c. blk & grn.	25·00	1·50	20
97	**26.**	3 c. grn. & mve.	5·50	3·00	30
98	**37.**	4 c. blk. & grn.	6·00	—	40
99		4 c. black & red	17·00	5·00	30
100	**27.**	5 c. blk. & orge	45·00	3·50	30
101a	**28.**	6 c. blk. & brn.	8·50	3·00	30
102b	**29.**	8 c. blk. & lilac	16·00	2·75	40
104	**41.**	10 c. brn. & grey	48·00	27·00	1·00
106b	**30.**	12 c. blk. & bl.	48·00	28·00	1·00
107	**43.**	16 c. grn. & brn.	85·00	75·00	2·50
108	**31.**	18 c. blk. & grn.	12·00	35·00	50
110		18 c. blk. & grn.*	45·00	14·00	75
109	**32.**	24 c. bl. & red*	8·50	55·00	1·00
111		24 c. bl. & red*	38·00	32·00	1·00

* No. 110 is inscribed "POSTAGE & REVENUE" at the sides instead of "POSTAL REVENUE" as in No. 108. No. 111 has the words "POSTAGE & REVENUE" at the sides below the Arms; these words were omitted in No. 109.

1899. Stamps of 1897 and Nos. 81/6 surch. **4 CENTS.**

112a	4 c. on 5 c. black & orange	12·00	10·00
113a	4 c. on 6 c. black & brown	12·00	30·00
114	4 c. on 8 c. black and lilac	13·00	10·00
115	4 c. on 12 c. black & blue	12·00	13·00
116	4 c. on 18 c. black and green (110)	9·50	13·00
117	4c. on 24 c. bl & red (111)	11·00	12·00
118	4 c. on 25 c. blue ..	5·00	8·50
119	4 c. on 50 c. violet ..	6·00	12·00
121	4 c. on $1 red	5·00	8·50
122	4 c. on $2 green	5·00	12·00
125	4 c. on $5 purple ..	5·50	11·00
126	4 c. on $10 brown ..	5·50	11·00

1901. Stamps of 1897 and Nos. 81/6 optd. **BRITISH PROTECTORATE.**

127a	1 c. blk. & bistre ..	1·50	1·60	10
128	2 c. black & green ..	2·25	1·75	10
129	3 c. grn. & mve. ..	1·40	2·50	10
130	4 c. black and red ..	4·75	1·50	10
131a	5 c. black & orange	4·75	2·25	15
132b	6 c. black & brown	2·75	6·50	20
133	8 c. black and lilac	2·75	3·00	20
134	10 c. brown & grey	15·00	4·50	30
135	12 c. black and blue	26·00	12·00	1·00
136	16 c. green & brown	60·00	20·00	1·50
137	18 c. blk. & grn. (110)	8·00	21·00	60
138	24 c. bl. & red (111)	14·00	29·00	1·00
139	25 c. blue	2·00	10·00	30
140	50 c. violet	2·75	11·00	40
142	$1 red	6·50	32·00	2·50
143	$2 green	27·00	80·00	3·50
144	$5 purple	£140	£325	4·00
145	$10 brown	£200	£400	7·00

1904. Stamps of 1897. and Nos. 81/6 surch. **4 cents.**

146.	4 c. on 5 c. black & orange	19·00	30·00	3·00
147.	4 c. on 6 c. black & brown	6·50	17·00	2·00
148.	4 c. on 8 c. black and lilac	11·00	23·00	2·25
149.	4 c. on 12 c. black and blue	20·00	35·00	2·50
150.	4 c. on 18 c. blk. & green (110) ..	14·00	32·00	3·00
151a.	4 c. on 24 c. bl. and red (111)	16·00	45·00	3·00
152.	4 c. on 25 c. blue ..	3·50	23·00	2·50
153.	4 c. on 50 c. violet ..	3·50	32·00	2·50
154.	4 c. on $1 red ..	4·25	48·00	3·00
155.	4 c. on $2 green ..	5·50	48·00	3·25
156.	4 c. on $5 purple ..	11·00	48·00	3·50
157.	4 c. on $10 brown ..	11·00	48·00	3·50

51. Malayan Tapir. **52.** Traveller's-tree.

64.

(68.)

1909. The 18c. is surch. **20 CENTS.**

277	**51.**	1 c. black & brn	85	70	—
160	**52.**	2 c. black & grn.	75	40	10
278		2 c. blk. & red	35	55	—
161	–	3 c. black & red	2·25	1·00	10
279	–	3 c. black & grn.	2·00	1·25	—
280	–	4 c. black & red	45	10	—
281	–	5 c. black & brn.	3·00	2·00	—
282	–	6 c. black & grn.	3·25	60	—
283	–	8 c. black & red	2·00	30	—
284	–	10 c. black & bl.	1·75	60	—
285	–	12 c. black & bl.	8·00	60	—
174	–	16 c. blk. & brn.	15·00	5·50	40
175	–	18 c. blk. & grn.	65·00	27·00	50
177	–	20 c. on 18 c. black and grn.	4·75	70	10
176	–	24 c. blk. & mve.	18·00	2·75	30
178	**64.**	25 c. blk. & grn.	4·50	3·50	1·00
179		50 c. blk. & blue	6·00	3·50	1·25
180		$1 black & brn.	11·00	3·50	1·25
181		$2 black & lilac	27·00	11·00	3·00
182	–	$5 black & red	60·00	65·00	20·00
183	–	$10 blk. & orge.	£150	£180	40·00

DESIGNS—As Type **51**: 3 c. Railway at Jesselton. 4 c. Sultan of Sulu, his staff and W. C. Cowie first Chairman of the Company. 5 c. Asiatic elephant. 8 c. Ploughing with buffalo. 24 c. Dwarf Cassowary. As Type **52**: 6 c. Rhinoceros. 10 c. Wild boar. 12 c. Palm Cockatoo. 16 c. Rhinoceros Hornbill. 18 c. Wild bull. As Type **64** but Arms with supporters: $5, $10.

1916. Stamps of 1909 surch.

186.	2 c. on 3 c. black and red	11·00	8·50
187.	4 c. on 6 c. black and olive.	11·00	11·00
188.	10 c. on 12 c. black & blue	28·00	40·00

1916. Nos. 277 etc., optd with T **68**.

189.	1 c. black and brown ..	6·50	26·00
203.	2 c. black and green ..	26·00	40·00
191.	3 c. black and red	22·00	38·00
192.	4 c. black and red	5·50	24·00
193.	5 c. black and brown ..	21·00	50·00
206.	6 c. black and green ..	27·00	65·00
195.	8 c. black and red	18·00	55·00
208.	10 c. black and blue ..	32·00	60·00
197.	12 c. black and blue ..	65·00	70·00
198.	16 c. black and brown ..	65·00	70·00
199.	20 c. on 18 c. black & green	25·00	70·00
200.	24 c. black and mauve ..	65·00	70·00
201.	25 c. black and green ..	£250	£350

1918. Nos. 159, etc., surch. **RED CROSS TWO CENTS.**

214.	1 c.+2 c. black and brown	2·75	8·00
215.	2 c.+2 c. black and green	70	8·00
216.	3 c.+2 c. black and red ..	6·00	14·00
218.	4 c.+2 c. black and red ..	55	4·00
219.	5 c.+2 c. black and brown	5·00	16·00
221.	6 c.+2 c. black and olive	4·00	17·00
222.	8 c.+2 c. black and red ..	4·75	7·00
223.	10 c.+2 c. black and blue	7·00	22·00
224.	12 c.+2 c. black and blue	11·00	35·00
225.	16 c.+2 c. black & brn. ..	13·00	35·00
226.	24 c.+2 c. black & mve, ..	14·00	35·00
229.	25 c.+2 c. black and green	10·00	38·00
230.	50 c.+2 c. black and blue	12·00	38·00
231.	$1+2 c. black and brown	38·00	48·00
232.	$2+2 c. black and lilac ..	55·00	90·00
233.	$5+2 c. black and red ..	£250	£350
234.	$10+2 c. black and orange	£250	£350

The premium of 2 c. on each value was for Red Cross Funds.

1918. Nos. 159, etc., surch. **FOUR CENTS** and a red cross.

235.	1 c.+4 c. black and brown	50	4·00
236.	2 c.+4 c. black and green	65	6·50
237.	3 c.+4 c. black and red ..	80	3·25
238.	4 c.+4 c. black and red ..	40	4·50
239.	5 c.+4 c. black and brown	1·75	17·00
240.	6 c.+4 c. black and olive	1·75	11·00
241.	8 c.+4 c. black and red ..	1·10	9·00
242.	10 c.+4 c. black and blue	2·75	12·00
243.	12 c.+4 c. black and blue	7·00	12·00
244.	16 c.+4 c. black & brn. ..	5·00	16·00
245.	24 c.+4 c. black & mve. ..	5·00	20·00
246.	25 c.+4 c. black and green	3·50	42·00
248.	50 c.+4 c. black and blue	14·00	38·00
249.	$1+4 c. black and brown	14·00	50·00
250.	$2+4 c. black and lilac ..	40·00	75·00
251.	$5+4 c. black and red ..	£200	£375
252.	$10+4 c. black and orange	£200	£375

The premium of 4 c. on each value was for Red Cross Funds.

1922. Nos. 159, etc., optd. **MALAYA-BORNEO EXHIBITION 1922.**

253.	1 c. black and brown ..	6·00	40·00
255.	2 c. black and green ..	1·40	14·00
256.	3 c. black and red ..	5·50	30·00
257.	4 c. black and red ..	1·40	24·00
258.	5 c. black and brown ..	6·00	42·00
260.	6 c. black and green ..	2·75	38·00
261.	8 c. black and red ..	4·00	38·00
263.	10 c. black and blue ..	4·50	38·00
265.	12 c. black and blue ..	3·75	20·00
267.	16 c. black and brown ..	6·50	45·00
268.	20 c. on 18 c. black & green	7·00	45·00
270.	24 c. black and mauve ..	16·00	48·00
274.	25 c. black and green ..	3·75	45·00
275.	50 c. black and blue ..	6·00	35·00

1923. No. 280 surch. **THREE CENTS** and bars.

276.	–	3 c. on 4 c. black & red	1·00	4·50

73. Head of a Murut.

DESIGNS—VERT. 6 c. Orang-utan. 10 c. Dyak warrior. $1, $2, $5, Arms. HORIZ. 25 c. Clouded leopard.

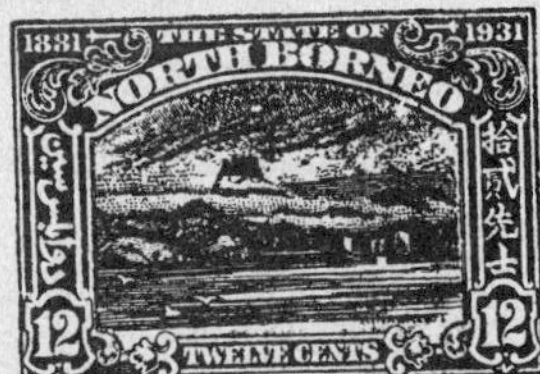

76. Mount Kinabalu.

1931. 50th Anniv. of North Borneo Company.

295.	**73.**	3 c. black and green ..	80	70
296.	–	6 c. black and orange ..	14·00	3·00
297.	–	10 c. black and red ..	2·75	9·00
298.	**76.**	12 c. black and blue ..	3·75	7·00
299.	–	25 c. black and violet ..	32·00	28·00
300.	–	$1 black and green ..	17·00	60·00
301.	–	$2 black and brown ..	38·00	80·00
302.	–	$5 black and purple ..	£110	£200

81. Buffalo Transport.

82. Palm Cockatoo.

DESIGNS—VERT 3c. Native. 4 c. Proboscis monkey. 6 c. Mounted Bajaus. 10 c. Orang-Utan. 15 c. Dyak. $1, $2, Arms. HORIZ. 8 c. Map of East Indies. 12 c. Murut with blow-pipe. 20 c. River scene. 25 c. Native boat. 50 c. Mt. Kinabalu. $5, Arms with supporters.

1939.

303. 81. 1 c. green and brown .. 40 40
304. 82. 2 c. purple and blue .. 2·50 40
305. – 3 c. blue and green .. 80 1·25
306. – 4 c. green and violet .. 1·00 30
307. – 6 c. blue and red .. 55 1·75
308. – 8 c. red .. .. 5·50 85
309. – 10 c. violet and green .. 35·00 4·75
310. – 12 c. green and blue .. 11·00 3·00
311. – 15 c. green and brown 14·00 4·50
312. – 20 c. violet and blue .. 7·50 3·25
313. – 25 c. green and brown .. 9·00 5·00
314. – 50 c. brown and violet .. 11·00 4·50
315. – $1 brown and red .. 50·00 16·00
316. – $2 violet and olive .. 75·00 65·00
317. – $5 blue £225 £160

1941. Optd. **WAR TAX.**

318. 81. 1 c. green and brown .. 30 50
319. 82. 2 c. purple and blue .. 1·50 2·50

1945. British Military Administration. Stamps of 1939 optd. **BMA.**

320. 81. 1 c. green and brown .. 3·25 60
321. 82. 2 c. purple and blue .. 7·50 1·00
322. – 3 c. blue and green .. 1·25 1·00
323. – 4 c. green and violet .. 15·00 10·00
324. – 6 c. blue and red .. 1·25 30
325. – 8 c. red .. .. 2·25 45
326. – 10 c. violet and green .. 2·50 30
327. – 12 c. green and blue .. 3·75 1·00
328. – 15 c. green and brown .. 1·50 1·00
329. – 20 c. violet and blue .. 1·75 1·00
330. – 25 c. green and brown .. 3·50 1·00
331. – 50 c. brown and violet .. 3·00 1·00
332. – $1 brown and red .. 25·00 19·00
333. – $2 violet and olive .. 25·00 19·00
334. – $5 blue .. .. .. 9·00 8·00

1947. Stamps of 1939 optd. with Crown over **GR** monogram and bars obliterating "THE STATE OF" and "BRITISH PROTECTORATE".

335. 81. 1 c. green and brown .. 15 60
336. 82. 2 c. purple and blue .. 45 70
337. – 3 c. blue and green .. 15 30
338. – 4 c. green and violet .. 20 15
339. – 6 c. blue and red .. 15 20
340. – 8 c. red 20 20
341. – 10 c. violet and green .. 40 15
342. – 12 c. green and blue .. 1·25 1·25
343. – 15 c. green and brown .. 1·50 30
344. – 20 c. violet and blue .. 45 30
345. – 25 c. green and brown .. 60 40
346. – 50 c. brown and violet .. 85 75
347. – $1 brown and red .. 70 1·00
348. – $2 violet and olive .. 2·75 5·00
349. – $5 blue .. .. .. 10·00 8·00

1948. Silver Wedding. As T **10/11** of Antigua.

350. 8 c. red 30 60
351. $10 mauve .. .. 13·00 30·00

1949. U.P.U. As T **20/23** of Antigua.

352. 8 c. red 40 30
353. 10 c. brown 70 40
354. 30 c. brown .. .. 80 1·00
355. 55 c. blue .. .. 90 1·40

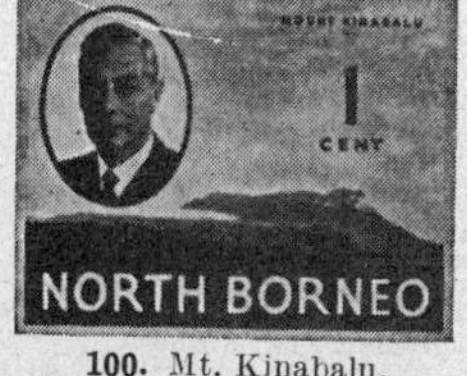

100. Mt. Kinabalu.

102. Coconut Grove.

DESIGNS—VERT. 4 c. Hemp-drying. 5 c. Cattle farm. 30 c. Sailing craft 50 c. Clock tower. $1. Horsemen. HORIZ. 2 c. Musician. 8 c. Map. 10 c. Log pond. 15 c. Malay prau, Sardakan. 20 c. Chieftain. $2, Murut with blowpipe. $5, Net fishing. $10, King George VI and arms.

1950.

356. 100. 1 c. brown 15 50
357. – 2 c. blue 15 30
358. 102. 3 c. green 15 15
359. – 4 c. purple 15 10
360. – 5 c. violet 15 10
361. – 8 c. red 50 65
362. – 10 c. purple 45 10
363. – 15 c. blue 50 60
364. – 20 c. brown 70 10
365. – 30 c. buff 70 10
366. – 50 c. red ("JESSLETON") .. 60 2·50
366a. – 50 c. red ("JESSELTON") .. 3·50 1·25
367. – $1 orange .. .. 1·25 65
368. – $2 green .. .. 2·00 6·50
369. – $5 green .. .. 10·00 13·00
370. – $10 blue .. .. 26·00 35·00

1953. Coronation. As T **13** of Aden.

371. 10 c. black and red .. 50 30

1954. As 1950 but with portrait of Queen Elizabeth II.

372. 1 c. brown 10 30
373. 2 c. blue 30 15
374. 3 c. green .. .. 30 1·75
375. 4 c. purple 30 20
376. 5 c. violet 40 10
377. 8 c. red 30 20
378. 10 c. purple 20 10
379. 15 c. blue 25 10
380. 20 c. brown 20 15
381. 30 c. buff 40 15
382. 50 c. red (No. 366a) .. 3·25 20
383. $1 orange .. .. 3·75 20
384. $2 green .. .. 10·00 1·25
385. $5 green .. .. 10·00 20·00
386. $10 blue .. .. 23·00 22·00

117. Malay Prau.

1956. 75th Anniv. of Foundation of British North Borneo Co. Inscr. "CHARTER 1ST NOVEMBER 1881".

387. – 10 c. black and red .. 1·00 30
388. 117. 15 c. black and brown .. 25 30
389. – 35 c. black and green .. 30 1·00
390. – $1 black and slate .. 65 1·75

DESIGNS—HORIZ. 10 c. Borneo Railway, 1902. 35 c. Mt. Kinabalu. VERT. $1, Arms of Chartered Company.

120. Sambar Stag.

1961.

391. 120. 1 c. green and red .. 10 10
392. – 4 c. olive and orange .. 20 40
393. – 5 c. sepia and violet .. 20 10
394. – 6 c. black and turquoise 20 30
395. – 10 c. green and red .. 20 10
396. – 12 c. brown and myrtle 20 10
397. – 20 c. turquoise and blue 3·25 10
398. – 25 c. black and red .. 60 60
399. – 30 c. sepia and olive .. 40 10
400. – 35 c. slate and brown .. 70 30
401. – 50 c. green and bistre .. 60 10
402. – 75 c. blue and purple .. 5·00 90
403. – $1 brown and green .. 7·50 70
404. – $2 brown and slate .. 13·00 3·00
405. – $5 green and purple .. 26·00 13·00
406. – $10 red and blue .. 20·00 18·00

DESIGNS—HORIZ. 4 c. Sun Bear. 5 c. Clouded leopard. 6 c. Dusun woman with gong. 10 c. Map of Borneo. 12 c. Banteng. 20 c. Butterfly orchid. 25 c. Sumatran Rhinoceros. 30 c. Murut with blow-pipe. 35 c. Mt. Kinabalu. 50 c. Dunsun and buffalo transport. 75 c. Bajau horseman. VERT. $1, Orang-utan. $2, Rhinoceros Hornbill. $5, Crested Wood Partridge. $10, Arms of N. Borneo.

1963. Freedom from Hunger. As T **28** of Aden.

407. 12 c. blue 90 20

POSTAGE DUE STAMPS

Overprinted **POSTAGE DUE**

1895. Issue of 1894.

D 2 25. 2 c. blk. & red 10·00 16·00 60
D 3 26. 3 c. grn. & mve. 3·75 9·00 75
D 4 27. 5 c. blk. & red 24·00 24·00 1·50
D 5a 28. 6 c. blk. & brn. 7·50 32·00 1·50
D 7 29. 8 c. blk. & lilac 22·00 35·00 1·50
D 8b 30. 12 c. blk. & bl. 32·00 32·00 1·50
D 10 31. 18 c. blk. & grn 38·00 45·00 3·00
D 11b 32. 24 c. bl. & red 17·00 45·00 —

1897. Issue of 1897.

D 12 25. 2 c. blk. & red 4·25 7·00 50
D 15 2 c. blk. & grn. 19·00 28·00 60
D 16b 26. 3 c. grn. & mve. 5·50 14·00 40
D 18 4 c. blk. & red 17·00 18·00 50
D 19 27. 5 c. blk. & orge. 15·00 23·00 75
D 20a 28. 6 c. blk. & brn. 3·00 15·00 40
D 21a 29. 8 c. black and lilac .. 3·00 15·00 40
D 22 30. 12 c. black and blue .. 45·00 £110 2·50
D 23 31. 18 c. black and green (No. 108) ..
D 24 18 c. black and green (No. 110) .. 26·00 £110 2·50
D 25 32. 24 c. blue and red (No. 109) — 38·00 60
D 26a 24 c. blue and red (No. 111) .. 13·00 85·00 1·00

1902. Issue of 1901.

D 47 1 c. black & bistre 3·50 50·00 —
D 36 2 c. black and green 5·00 1·75 10
D 37 3 c. grn. & mve. 1·75 1·75 10
D 38 4 c. black and red .. 4·50 4·50 20
D 39 5 c. blk. & orge 6·00 3·00 20
D 40 6 c. blk. & brn. 6·50 6·00 25
D 41 8 c. black and lilac 13·00 4·00 40
D 42b 10 c. brn. & grey 35·00 12·00 1·00
D 43 12 c. black and blue 7·00 11·00 1·00
D 44 16 c. grn. & brn. 15·00 14·00 1·00
D 45 18 c. blk. & grn. 4·00 12·00 1·00
D 46 24 c. blue and red .. 6·50 17·00 1·00

1919. Issue of 1909.

D49 2 c. black and green .. 6·50 55·00
D57 2 c. black and red .. 40 1·75
D58 3 c. black and green .. 2·50 12·00
D51 4 c. black and red .. 70 1·00
D52 5 c. black and brown .. 4·50 11·00
D61 6 c. black and olive .. 3·50 2·25
D54 8 c. black and red .. 1·25 1·25
D55 10 c. black and blue .. 7·50 13·00
D56 12 c. black and blue .. 23·00 27·00
D56ba 16 c. black and brown .. 6·00 45·00

D **2.** Crest of the Company.

1939.

D 66. D 2. 2 c. brown .. .. 5·50 65·00
D 67. 4 c. red .. .. 6·00 75·00
D 68. 6 c. violet .. .. 14·00 90·00
D 69. 8 c. green .. .. 14·00 £150
D 70. 10 c. blue .. .. 29·00 £225

For later issues see **SABAH.**

JAPANESE OCCUPATION

1942. Stamps of North Borneo optd. as T **1** of Japanese Occupation of Brunei.

(a) Issue of 1939.

J 1. 81. 1 c. green and brown .. 95·00 £140
J 2. 82. 2 c. purple and blue .. 90·00 £130
J 3. – 3 c. blue and green .. 85·00 £130
J 4. – 4 c. green and violet .. 40·00 85·00
J 5. – 6 c. blue and red .. 85·00 £130
J 6. – 8 c. red .. .. 85·00 £130
J 7. – 10 c. violet and green 85·00 £130
J 8. – 12 c. green and blue .. £110 £200
J 9. – 15 c. green and brown £110 £200
J 10. – 20 c. violet and blue .. £150 £250
J 11. – 25 c. green and brown £150 £250
J 12. – 50 c. brown and violet £200 £300
J 13. – $1 brown and red .. £190 £350
J 14. – $2 violet and olive .. £300 £450
J 15. – $5 blue £350 £550

(b) War Tax issue of 1941.

J 16. 81. 1 c. green and brown .. £300 £190
J 17. 82. 2 c purple and blue .. £700 £275

2. Mt. Kinabalu.

3. Borneo Scene.

1943.

J18 2 4 c. red .. .. .. 11·00 23·00
J19 3 8 c. blue .. .. .. 11·00 23·00

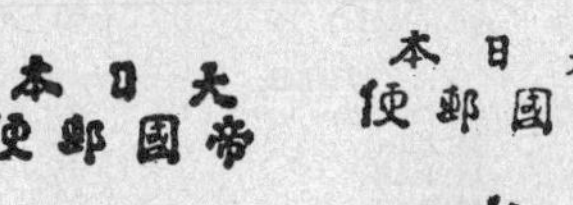

(4.) (5.)

("Imperial Japanese Postal Service, North Borneo".)

1944. Stamps of North Borneo of 1939 optd as T **4.**

J 20. 81. 1 c. green and brown .. 3·00 7·00
J 21. 82. 2 c. purple and blue .. 5·50 7·00
J 22. – 3 c. blue and green .. 2·25 4·00
J 23. – 4 c. green and violet .. 3·25 6·00
J 24. – 6 c. blue and red .. 3·00 4·00
J 25. – 8 c. red .. .. 4·50 12·00
J 26. – 10 c. violet and green .. 4·00 10·00
J 27. – 12 c. green and blue .. 4·50 10·00
J 28. – 15 c. green and brown 3·50 11·00
J 29. – 20 c. violet and blue .. 10·00 25·00
J 30. – 25 c. green and brown 10·00 25·00
J 31. – 50 c. brown and violet 40·00 65·00
J 32. – $1 brown and red .. 60·00 95·00

1944. No. J7 optd with T **4.**

J32a – 10 c. violet and green .. £160 £325

1945. No. J1 surch with T **5.**

J33 81 $2 on 1 c. green & brown £3750 £3000

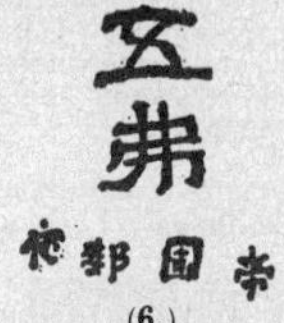

(6.)

1945. No. 315 of North Borneo surch with T **6.**

J34 $5 on $1 brown and red .. £3250 £2750

1944. Stamps of Japan optd as bottom line in T **4.**

J 35. 126. 1 s. brown .. .. 3·00 8·00
J 36. 84. 2 s. red .. .. 2·00 8·00
J 37. – 3 s. green (No. 319) .. 2·25 8·00
J 38. 129. 4 s. green .. .. 3·50 8·00
J 39. – 5 s. red (No. 396) .. 3·75 9·00
J 40. – 6 s. orange (No. 322) 3·75 9·00
J 41. – 8 s. violet (No. 324) .. 2·25 10·00
J 42. – 10 s. red (No. 399) .. 3·25 10·00
J 43. – 15 s. blue (No. 401) .. 3·25 10·00
J 44. – 20 s. blue (No. 328) .. 70·00 80·00
J 45. – 25 s. brown (No. 329) 60·00 85·00
J 46. – 30 s. blue (No. 330) .. £160 95·00
J 47. – 50 s. olive and brown (No. 331) .. .. 55·00 60·00
J 48. – 1 y. brown (No. 332) 48·00 70·00

NORTHERN NIGERIA

A British protectorate on the west coast of Africa. In 1914 incorporated into Nigeria.

12 pence = 1 shilling.
20 shillings = 1 pound.

1.

5.

1900.

1. 1. ½d. mauve and green .. 1·25 6·50
2. 1d. mauve and red .. 2·25 2·50
3. 2d. mauve and yellow .. 3·75 20·00
4. 2½d. mauve and blue .. 6·50 20·00
5. 5d. mauve and brown .. 10·00 25·00
6. 6d. mauve and violet .. 13·00 18·00
7. 1s. green and black .. 15·00 40·00
8. 2s. 6d. green and blue .. 60·00 £160
9. 10s. green and brown .. £160 £375

1902. As T **1**, but portrait of King Edward VII.

10 ½d. purple and green .. 80 60
11 1d. purple and red .. 1·00 20
12 2d. purple and yellow .. 80 1·60
13 2½d. purple and blue .. 75 3·75
14 5d. purple and brown .. 1·50 4·50
15 6d. purple and violet .. 3·50 4·50
16 1s. green and black .. 2·75 4·00
17 2s. 6d. green and blue .. 8·00 23·00
18 10s. green and brown .. 45·00 48·00

1910. As last. New colours etc.

28 ½d. green 90 50
29 1d. red 80 30
30 2d. grey .. .. 1·25 2·25
31 2½d. blue .. .. 85 3·75
32 3d. purple on yellow .. 1·50 30
34 5d. purple and green .. 2·50 4·50
35a 6d. purple .. .. 1·50 4·50
36 1s. black and green .. 1·00 65
37 2s. 6d. black & red on blue 8·50 17·00
38 5s. green and red on yellow 18·00 48·00
39 10s. green and red on green 42·00 45·00

1912.

40. 5. ½d. green 40 20
41. 1d. red 40 15
42. 2d. grey .. .. 1·50 2·75
43. 3d. purple on yellow 1·00 75
44. 4d. black & red on yellow 50 85
45. 5d. purple and olive .. 2·00 4·00
46. 6d. purple and violet .. 2·00 3·50
47. 9d. purple and red .. 1·50 7·00
48. 1s. black on green .. 2·00 1·00
49. 2s. 6d. black & red on blue 7·00 22·00
50. 5s. green & red on yellow 16·00 55·00
51. 10s. green & red on green 30·00 45·00
52. £1 purple and black on red £170 £130

NORTHERN RHODESIA

A Br. territory in C. Africa, N. of the Zambesi. From 1954 to 1963 part of the Central African Federation and using the stamps of Rhodesia and Nyasaland (q.v.). A new constitution was introduced on 3rd January, 1964, with internal self-government and independence came on 24th October, 1964, when the country was renamed Zambia (q.v.).

12 pence = 1 shilling.
20 shillings = 1 pound.

1.

1925. The shilling values are larger and the view is in first colour.

No.	Description	Unused	Used
1. 1.	½d. green	60	20
2.	1d. brown	60	10
3.	1½d. red	50	30
4.	2d. orange	80	10
5.	3d. blue	80	50
6.	4d. violet	1·40	50
7.	6d. grey	1·00	40
8.	8d. purple	3·75	20·00
9.	10d. olive	3·75	17·00
10.	1s. orange and black ..	1·00	85
11.	2s. brown and blue ..	6·00	12·00
12.	2s. 6d. black and green ..	7·00	4·75
13.	3s. violet and blue ..	16·00	9·50
14.	5s. grey and violet ..	15·00	11·00
15.	7s. 6d. purple and black ..	85·00	£130
16.	10s. green and black ..	42·00	55·00
17.	20s. red and purple ..	£150	£160

1935. Silver Jubilee. As T **13** of Antigua.

No.	Description	Unused	Used
18.	1d. blue and olive ..	50	30
19.	2d. green and blue ..	50	50
20.	3d. brown and blue ..	2·50	3·50
21.	6d. grey and purple ..	2·00	1·00

1937. Coronation. As T **2** of Aden.

No.	Description	Unused	Used
22.	1½d. red	40	35
23.	2d. brown	70	35
24.	3d. blue	1·25	1·75

1938. As 1925, but with portrait of King George VI facing right and "POSTAGE & REVENUE" omitted.

No.	Description	Unused	Used
25	½d. green	10	10
26	½d. brown	10	70
27	1d. brown	10	10
28	1d. green	60	60
29	1½d. red	32·00	30
30	1½d. orange	10	10
31	2d. brown	65·00	85
32	2d. red	30	20
33	2d. purple	45	30
34	3d. blue	30	10
35	3d. red	50	60
36	4d. violet	30	20
37	4½d. blue	40	3·00
38	6d. grey	30	10
39	9d. violet	40	2·00
40	1s. orange and black ..	1·50	30
41	2s. 6d. black and green ..	6·00	1·50
42	3s. violet and blue ..	11·00	4·00
43	5s. grey and violet ..	7·00	3·25
44	10s. green and black ..	7·00	11·00
45	20s. red and purple ..	28·00	42·00

1946. Victory. As T **9** of Aden.

No.	Description	Unused	Used
46.	1½d. orange	10	10
47.	2d. red	10	10

1948. Silver Wedding As T**10/11** of Aden.

No.	Description	Unused	Used
48.	1½d. orange	30	10
49.	20s. red	40·00	42·00

1949. U.P.U. As T **20/23** of Antigua.

No.	Description	Unused	Used
50.	2d. red	30	30
51.	3d. blue	85	1·25
52.	6d. grey	85	1·25
53.	1s. orange	85	1·00

5. Cecil Rhodes and Victoria Falls.

1953. Birth Centenary of Cecil Rhodes.

No.	Description	Unused	Used
54. 5.	½d. brown	50	50
55.	1d. green	40	40
56.	2d. mauve	40	15
57.	4½d. blue	40	3·25
58.	1s. orange and black ..	75	3·00

6. Arms of the Rhodesia and Nyasaland.

1953. Rhodes Centenary Exhibition.

No.	Description	Unused	Used
59. 6.	6d. violet	30	40

1953. Coronation. As T **13** of Antigua.

No.	Description	Unused	Used
60	1½d. black and orange ..	30	10

1953. As 1938 but with portrait of Queen Elizabeth II facing left.

No.	Description	Unused	Used
61.	½d. brown	65	10
62.	1d. green	65	10
63.	1½d. orange	70	10
64.	2d. purple	75	10
65.	3d. red	60	10
66.	4d. violet	1·25	60
67.	4½d. blue	60	1·25
68.	6d. grey	1·25	10
69.	9d. violet	60	1·25
70.	1s. orange and black ..	60	10
71.	2s. 6d. black and green ..	6·50	2·75
72.	5s. grey and purple ..	6·50	12·00
73.	10s. green and black ..	6·00	18·00
74.	20s. red and purple ..	20·00	27·00

9. Arms.

1963. Arms black, gold and blue; portrait and inscriptions black; background colours given.

No.	Description	Unused	Used
75. 9.	½d. violet	30	35
76.	1d. blue	40	10
77.	2d. brown	30	10
78.	3d. yellow	20	10
79.	4d. green	30	10
80.	6d. green	30	10
81.	9d. bistre	30	40
82.	1s. purple	30	10
83.	1s. 3d. purple	80	10
84. –	2s. orange	70	90
85. –	2s. 6d. purple	80	80
86. –	5s. mauve	3·00	3·50
87. –	10s. mauve	3·00	5·50
88. –	20s. blue	5·00	14·00

Nos. 84/88 are as Type **9** but larger 27×23 mm.).

POSTAGE DUE STAMPS

D 1.

D 2.

1929.

No.	Description	Unused	Used
D1 D 1	1d. black	2·50	2·50
D2	2d. black	3·00	3·00
D3	3d. black	3·00	21·00
D4	4d. black	6·00	26·00

1963.

No.	Description	Unused	Used
D 5. D 2.	1d. orange	40	2·25
D 6.	2d. blue	40	2·50
D 7.	3d. lake	45	3·00
D 8.	4d. blue	60	4·25
D 9.	6d. purple	1·75	5·00
D 10.	1s. green	4·50	12·00

For later issues see **ZAMBIA.**

NOVA SCOTIA

An eastern province of the Dominion of Canada, whose stamps it now uses.

Currency: As Canada.

1.

2. Emblems of the United Kingdom.

1853. Imperf.

No.	Description	Unused	Used
1 1.	1d. brown	£2000	£400
4 2.	3d. blue	£700	£130
5	6d. green	£4000	£400
8	1s. purple	£1400	£2500

3.

4.

1860. Perf.

No.	Description	Unused	Used
10. 3.	1 c. black	3·00	12·00
20.	2 c. purple	3·25	14·00
13.	5 c. blue	£250	16·00
26. 4.	8½ c. green	17·00	40·00
27.	10 c. red	3·50	20·00
17.	12½ c. black	26·00	20·00

NYASALAND PROTECTORATE

A Br. Protectorate in C. Africa. Formerly known as Br. Central Africa. From 1954 to 1963 part of the Central African Federation and using the stamps of Rhodesia and Nyasaland (q.v.). From July, 1964, independent within the Commonwealth under its new name of Malawi.

12 pence = 1 shilling.
20 shillings = 1 pound.

1891. Stamps of Rhodesia optd. **B.C.A.**

No.	Description	Unused	Used
1. 1.	1d. black	2·25	2·50
2.	2d. green and red ..	2·25	2·50
3.	4d. brown and black ..	2·00	3·75
5.	6d. blue	5·00	8·00
6.	8d. red and blue	12·00	28·00
7.	1s. brown	9·50	11·00
8.	2s. red	20·00	42·00
9.	2s. 6d. purple	45·00	65·00
10.	3s. brown and green ..	45·00	50·00
11.	4s. black and red ..	45·00	75·00
12.	5s. yellow	45·00	65·00
13.	10s. green	85·00	£120
14. –	£1 blue	£450	£450
15. –	£2 red	£650	
16. –	£5 olive	£1200	
17. –	£10 brown	£2750	

1892. Stamps of Rhodesia surch. **B.C.A.** and value in words.

No.	Description	Unused	Used
18. 1.	3s. on 4s. black and red ..	£300	£300
19.	4s. on 5s. yellow	70·00	80·00

1895. Stamp of Rhodesia surch. **B.C.A. ONE PENNY** and bar.

No.	Description	Unused	Used
20. 1.	1d. on 2d. green and red	6·00	25·00

5. Arms of the Protectorate. 7.

1895. The 2s. 6d. and higher values are larger.

No.	Description	Unused	Used
32 5.	1d. black	3·00	4·50
33	2d. black and green. ..	13·00	5·00
34	4d. black and orange ..	15·00	17·00
35	6d. black and blue ..	13·00	9·00
36	1s. black and red ..	17·00	10·00
37	2s. 6d. black and mauve ..	80·00	80·00
38	3s. black and yellow ..	60·00	38·00
39	5s. black and olive ..	80·00	95·00
29	£1 black and orange ..	£650	£375
40	£1 black and blue ..	£650	£375
30	£10 black and orange ..	£3000	£2750
31	£25 black and green ..	£5500	

1897. The 2s. 6d. and higher values are larger.

No.	Description	Unused	Used
43. 7.	1d. black and blue ..	1·00	65
57d.	1d. purple and red ..	1·00	40
44.	2d. black and yellow ..	1·40	80
45.	4d. black and red ..	5·00	1·50
57e.	4d. purple and olive ..	4·50	6·00
46.	6d. black and green ..	30·00	4·25
58.	6d. purple and brown ..	3·50	3·00
47.	1s. black and purple ..	7·00	7·00
48.	2s. 6d. black and blue ..	35·00	40·00
49.	3s. black and green ..	£160	£200
50.	4s. black and red	50·00	70·00
50a.	10s. black and olive ..	80·00	90·00
51.	£1 black and purple ..	£200	£140
52.	£10 black and yellow ..	£2750	£1500

1897. No. 49 surch **ONE PENNY**.

No.	Description	Unused	Used
53 7	1d. on 3s. black and green	5·00	8·50

10.

11.

1898.

No.	Description	Unused	Used
56. 10.	1d. red and blue (Imperf.)	—	45·00
57.	1d. red and blue (Perf.)	£1400	15·00

1903. The 2s. 6d. and higher values are larger.

No.	Description	Unused	Used
68 11.	1d. grey and red	2·00	90
60	2d. purple	3·25	1·00
61	4d. green and black ..	2·50	6·00
62	6d. grey and brown ..	2·50	2·00
62a	1s. grey and blue	2·50	7·00
63	2s. 6d. green	28·00	40·00
64	4s. purple	48·00	75·00
65	10s. green and black ..	65·00	£120
66	£1 grey and red	£180	£150
67	£10 grey and blue ..	£3500	£3250

13.

14.

1908.

No.	Description	Unused	Used
73. 13.	½d. green	1·00	75
74.	1d. red	1·50	40
75.	3d. purple on yellow ..	1·00	2·25
76.	4d. black & red on yellow	1·00	1·50
77.	6d. purple	3·75	6·50
72.	1s. black on green ..	1·60	6·50
78. 14.	2s. 6d. black & red on blue	32·00	55·00
79.	4s. red and black	60·00	75·00
80.	10s. green & red on green	75·00	£120
81.	£1 purple & black on red	£375	£425
82.	£10 purple and blue ..	£7000	£4250

1913. As 1908, but portrait of King George V.

No.	Description	Unused	Used
100	½d. green	60	30
101	1d. red	50	30
102	1½d. orange	3·25	17·00
103	2d. grey	55	30
89	2½d. blue	70	2·50
90	3d. purple on yellow ..	2·25	2·50
91	4d. black and red on yellow	2·00	2·00
107	6d. purple	3·00	3·25
93a	1s. black on green ..	2·50	1·50
109	2s. purple and blue on blue	9·00	10·00
94	2s. 6d. black & red on blue	9·50	10·00
111	4s. red and black	10·00	13·00
112	5s. green & red on yellow	27·00	48·00
96	10s. green & red on green	48·00	70·00
98	£1 purple & black on red	£150	£140
99a	£10 purple and blue ..	£2500	£1500

17. King George V and Symbol of the Protectorate.

1934.

No.	Description	Unused	Used
114. 17.	½d. green	75	55
115.	1d. brown	75	50
116.	1½d. red	75	1·25
117.	2d. grey	80	1·00
118.	3d. blue	1·50	1·50
119.	4d. mauve	2·25	2·25
120.	6d. violet	1·50	40
121	9d. olive	3·50	9·00
122.	1s. black and orange ..	3·50	8·00

1935. Silver Jubilee. As T **13** of Antigua.

No.	Description	Unused	Used
123.	1d. blue and grey ..	1·00	70
124.	2d. green and blue ..	1·00	45
125.	3d. brown and blue ..	7·00	9·50
126.	1s. grey and purple ..	16·00	22·00

1937. Coronation. As T **2** of Aden.

No.	Description	Unused	Used
127.	½d. green	30	40
128.	1d. brown	70	40
129.	2d grey	70	60

1938. As T **17,** but with head of King George VI and " POSTAGE REVENUE " omitted.

130. ½d. green 30 40
130a. ½d. brown 10 65
131. 1d. brown 30 15
131a. 1d. green 20 30
132. 1½d. red .. .. .. 75 2·75
132a. 1½d. grey .. .. .. 30 1·75
133. 2d. grey .. .. .. 1·75 50
133a. 2d. red 30 45
134. 3d. blue 40 20
135. 4d. mauve .. .. 1·25 45
136. 6d. violet .. .. .. 1·40 40
137. 9d. olive .. .. .. 2·25 2·25
138. 1s. black and orange .. 2·25 90

1938. As T **14,** but with head of King George VI facing right.

139. 2s. purple and blue on blue 10·00 7·00
140. 2s. 6d. black & red on blue 12·00 7·00
141. 5s. green & red on yellow 40·00 17·00
142. 10 s. green & red on green 55·00 22·00
143. £1 purple & black on red 29·00 23·00

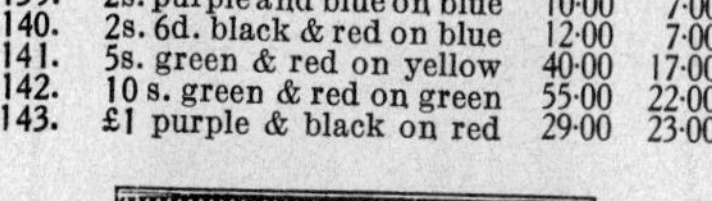

20. Lake Nyasa.

21. King's African Rifles.

DESIGNS — HORIZ. 1½d., 6d. Tea estate. 2d., 1s., 10s. Map of Nyasaland. 4d., 2s. 6d. Tobacco. 5s., 20s. Badge of Nyasaland. VERT. 1d. (No. 160), Leopard and sunrise. 3d., 2s. Fishing village.

1945.

144. **20.** ½d. black and brown .. 10 10
145. **21.** 1d. black and green .. 10 60
160. – 1d. brown and green .. 30 10
146. – 1½d. black and grey .. 15 50
147. – 2d. black and red .. 15 20
148. – 3d. black and blue .. 15 30
149. – 4d. black and red .. 75 45
150. – 6d. black and violet .. 1·00 30
151. **20.** 9d. black and olive .. 75 2·50
152. – 1s. blue and green .. 1·00 20
153. – 2s. green and purple .. 3·50 3·50
154. – 2s. 6d. green and blue .. 6·50 2·75
155. – 5s. purple and blue .. 4·50 4·00
156. – 10s. red and green .. 10·00 7·50
157. – 20s. red and black .. 17·00 17·00

1946. Victory. As T **9** of Aden.

158. 1d. green.. .. .. .. 10 10
159. 2d. red 10 10

1948. Silver Wedding. As T **10/11** of Aden.

161. 1d. green.. .. .. 15 10
162. 10s. mauve .. .. 15·00 19·00

1949. U.P.U. As T **20/23** of Antigua.

163. 1d. green.. .. .. 30 20
164. 3d. blue .. .. .. 1·00 75
165. 6d. purple .. .. .. 1·00 50
166. 1s. blue .. .. .. 1·00 50

28. Arms in 1891 and 1951.

1951. Diamond Jubilee of Protectorate.

167. **28.** 2d. black and red .. 70 45
168. 3d. black and blue .. 70 75
169. 6d. black and violet .. 70 1·00
170. 5s. black and blue .. 1·50 6·00

1953. Rhodes Centenary Exn. As T 6 of Northern Rhodesia.

171. 6d. violet 20 30

1953. Coronation. As T **13** of Aden.

172 2d. black and orange .. 40 30

29. Grading Cotton.

1953. As 1945 but with portrait of Queen Elizabeth II as in T **29.** Designs as for corresponding values except where stated.

173a **20** ½d. black and brown .. 10 70
174 – 1d. brown and green (as No. 160) 55 15
175 – 1½d. black and grey .. 20 1·60
176a – 2d. black and orange .. 30 10
177 **29** 2½d. green and black .. 20 40
178 – 3d. black & red (as 4d.) 30 10
179 – 4½d. black & blue (as 3d.) 30 40
180a – 6d. black and violet .. 30 20
181 **20** 9d. black and olive .. 70 2·50
182 – 1s. blue and green .. 80 20
183 – 2s. green and red .. 2·00 3·00
184 – 2s. 6d. green and blue 3·25 4·25
185 – 5s. purple and blue .. 6·50 4·50
186 – 10s. red and green .. 4·25 9·00
187 – 20s. red and black .. 12·00 11·00

30.

1963. Revenue stamps optd. **POSTAGE** as in T **30** or surch. also.

188. **30.** ½d. on 1d. blue.. .. 30 30
189. 1d. green 30 10
190. 2d. red 30 30
191. 3d. blue.. .. .. 30 10
192. 6d. purple 30 10
193. 9d. on 1s. red 40 25
194. 1s. purple 45 10
195. 2s. 6d. black .. .. 50 1·75
196. 5s. brown .. .. 75 1·25
197. 10s. olive .. .. 1·50 4·00
198. £1 violet .. .. 3·50 4·00

32. Mother and Child.

34. Tea Industry.

1964.

199. **32.** ½d. violet 10 30
200. – 1d. black and green .. 10 10
201. – 2d. brown 10 10
202. – 3d. brown, green & bistre 10 10
203. – 4d. blue and yellow .. 20 30
204. **34.** 6d. purple, green & blue 40 30
205. – 1s. brown, blue & yellow 15 10
206. – 1s. 3d. bronze & brown 1·50 10
207. – 2s. 6d. brown and blue 1·50 50
208. – 5s. bl., grn., yell. & blk. 1·25 1·25
209. – 10s. green, salmon & blk. 1·50 3·00
210. – £1 brown and yellow .. 6·00 4·25

DESIGNS—As Type **32.** 1d. Chambo (fish). 2d. Zebu bull. 3d. Groundnuts. 4d. Fishing. As Type **34**—HORIZ. 1s. Timber. 1s. 3d. Turkish tobacco industry. 2s. 6d. Cotton industry. 5s. Monkey Bay, Lake Nyasa. 10s. Forestry—Afzelia. VERT. £1, Nyala.

POSTAGE DUE STAMPS

1950. As Type **D 1** of Gold Coast, but inscr. "NYASALAND".

D 1. 1d. red .. .. .. 2·00 9·00
D 2. 2d. blue .. .. .. 5·00 17·00
D 3. 3d. green .. .. .. 7·50 4·75
D 4. 4d. purple .. .. .. 12·00 30·00
D 5. 6d. orange .. .. .. 20·00 65·00

For later issues see **MALAWI.**

ORANGE FREE STATE (ORANGE RIVER COLONY)

Br. possession. 1848-54. Independent 1854-99. Annexed by Great Britain, 1900. Later a province of the Union of S. Africa.

12 pence = 1 shilling.
20 shillings = 1 pound.

1.

38. King Edward VII, Springbok and Gnu.

1868.

48 1 ½d. brown 60 50
84 ½d. yellow .. .. 1·00 35
2 1d. brown .. .. 2·25 35
68 1d. purple .. .. 3·50 30
50 2d. mauve .. .. 1·00 30
51 3d. blue .. .. 1·75 2·00
19 4d. blue .. .. 4·00 2·50
7 6d. red .. .. .. 3·25 2·00
9 1s. orange .. .. 14·00 1·50
87 1s. brown .. .. 8·00 1·50
20 5s. green .. .. 8·50 10·00

1877. Surch. in figures.

75 1 ½d. on 3d. blue .. .. 2·25 2·25
36 ½d. on 5s. green .. .. 3·25 3·50
54 1d. on 3d. blue .. .. 1·10 60
57 1d. on 4d. blue .. .. 14·00 3·50
22 1d. on 5s. green .. .. 30·00 10·00
53 2d. on 3d. blue .. .. 12·00 2·00
67 "2½d." on 3d. blue .. 3·50 70
83 "2½" on 3d. blue .. 1·50 80
40 3d. on 4d. blue .. .. 25·00 16·00
12 "4" on 6d. red .. .. 85·00 25·00

1896. Surch. **Halve Penny.**

77. 1. ½d. on 3d. blue 35 50

1900. Surch. **V.R.I.** and value in figures.

112 1. ½d. on ½d. orange .. 30 20
113 1d. on 1d. purple .. 30 20
114 2d. on 2d. mauve .. 40 30
104 2½ on 3d blue (No. 83) 5·00 3·50
117 3d. on 3d. blue .. 30 30
118 4d. on 4d. blue .. 1·10 2·00
108 6d. on 6d. red .. 35·00 35·00
120 6d. on 6d. blue .. 70 40
121 1s. on 1s. brown .. 85 45
122 5s. on 5s. green .. 5·50 7·50

1900. Stamps of Cape of Good Hope optd. **ORANGE RIVER COLONY.**

133. **17.** ½d. green.. .. .. 20 10
134. 1d. red 25 10
135. **6.** 2½d. blue.. .. .. 30 35

1902. No. 120 surch. **4d** and bar.

136. 1. 4d. on 6d. blue 50 75

1902. Surch. **E.R.I.** and **6d.**

137. 1. 6d. on 6d. blue .. 1·75 5·00

1902. No. 20 surch. **V.R.I. One Shilling** and star.

138. 1. 1s. on 5s. green.. .. 4·50 6·00

1903.

148 **38.** ½d. green.. .. .. 4·25 30
140 1d. red .. .. .. 1·25 10
141 2d. brown .. .. 2·75 70
142 2½d. blue.. .. .. 1·00 50
143 3d. mauve .. .. 3·75 90
150 4d. red and green .. 4·25 1·75
145 6d. red and mauve .. 5·50 70
146 1s. red and brown .. 20·00 1·75
147 5s. blue and brown .. 65·00 20·00

MILITARY FRANK STAMP

M 1

1899.

M1 M 1 (-) black/yellow .. 10·00 40·00

POLICE FRANK STAMPS

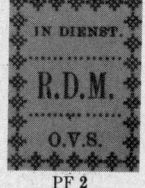

PF 1 PF 2

1896.

PF1 PF 1 (-) black .. ..

1899.

PF3 PF 2 (-) black on yellow .. £100 80·00

ORCHHA

A state of C. India. Now uses Indian stamps.

12 pies = 1 anna; 16 annas = 1 rupee.

1.

2.

1913. Imperf.

1. 1. ½ a. green .. .. .. 20·00 48·00
2. 1 a. red .. .. .. 19·00

1914. Imperf.

3a. **2.** ¼ a. blue .. .. .. 35 2·75
4. ½ a. green .. .. .. 40 2·75
5. 1 a. red .. .. .. 1·75 3·75
6. 2 a. brown .. .. 4·50 13·00
7. 4 a. bistre .. .. .. 8·00 19·00

3. Maharaja Vir Singh Deo Bahadur.

5. H.H. the Maharaja of Orchha.

1935.

8a 3 ¼ a. purple and grey .. 30 60
9 ½ a. grey and green .. 45 55
10 ¾ a. mauve and green .. 50 60
11 1 a. green and brown .. 50 55
12 3 1¼ a. grey and mauve .. 45 55
13 1½ a. brown and red .. 45 55
14 2 a. blue and orange .. 45 55
15 2½ a. brown and orange .. 65 65
16 3 a. blue and mauve .. 65 65
17 4 a. purple and green .. 65 1·25
18 6 a. black and buff .. 60 1·25
19 8 a. brown and purple .. 85 1·25
20 12 a. green and purple .. 90 1·50
21 12 a. blue and purple .. 16·00 27·00
22 1 r. brown and green .. 75 1·75
24 2 r. brown and yellow .. 1·60 3·50
25 3 r. black and blue .. 1·40 3·50
26 4 r. black and brown .. 1·75 4·00
27 5 r. blue and purple .. 2·75 5·00
28 – 10 r. green and red .. 7·00 11·00
29 – 15 r. black and green .. 10·00 22·00
30 – 25 r. orange and blue .. 13·00 26·00

DESIGN: 1 a., 10 r. to 25 r. As Type **3,** but inscr. " POSTAGE & REVENUE ". There are two different versions of the portrait for the 1 r. value.

1939.

31 **5** ¼ a. brown .. .. 1·40 30·00
32 ½ a. green .. .. 1·50 22·00
33 ¾ a. blue .. .. .. 1·50 40·00
34 1 a. red .. .. .. 1·50 8·50
35 1¼ a. blue .. .. 1·50 40·00
36 1½ a. mauve .. .. 1·75 50·00
37 2 a. red .. .. .. 1·50 30·00
38 2½ a. green .. .. 1·60 85·00
39 3 a. violet .. .. 2·25 45·00
40 4 a. slate .. .. .. 3·25 14·00
41 8 a. mauve .. .. 6·00 80·00
42 – 1 r. green .. .. 9·00
43 – 2 r. violet .. .. 22·00 £275
44 – 5 r. orange .. .. 70·00
45 – 10 r. green £250
46 – 15 r. c lilac £1800
47 – 25 r. purple £1800

The rupee values are larger (25 × 30 mm).

PAHANG

A state of the Federation of Malaya, incorporated in Malaysia in 1963.

100 cents = 1 dollar (Straits or Malayan).

1889. Nos. 52/3 and 63 of Straits Settlements optd. **PAHANG.**

4. 2 c. red .. .. .. 3·75 6·50
2. 8 c. orange £1600 £1300
3. 10 c. grey £225 £250

1891. No. 68 of Straits Settlements surch. **PAHANG Two CENTS.**

7. 2 c. on 24 c. green .. 65·00 85·00

9. Tiger.

10. Tiger.

1891.

No.	Type	Description		
11.	9.	1 c. green	3·75	2·50
12.		2 c. red	3·00	1·25
13.		5 c. blue	7·50	23·00

1895.

No.	Type	Description		
14.	10.	3 c. purple and red ..	2·75	1·40
15.		4 c. purple and red ..	11·00	5·50
16.		5 c. purple and yellow ..	18·00	12·00

1897. No. 13 divided, and each half surch.

No.	Type	Description		
18	9	2 c. on half of 5 c. blue ..	£800	£275
18d		3 c. on half of 5 c. blue ..	£800	£275

1898. Stamps of Perak optd. **Pahang.**

No.	Type	Description		
19	44	10 c. purple and orange	15·00	25·00
20		25 c. green and red ..	65·00	95·00
21		50 c. purple and black ..	£160	£170
22		50 c. green and black ..	£110	£120
23	45	$1 green	£160	£170
24		$5 green and blue ..	£500	£650

1898. Stamp of Perak surch. **Pahang Four cents.**

No.	Type	Description		
25.	44.	4 c. on 8 c. purple & blue	2·50	5·50

1899. No. 15 surch. **Four cents.**

No.	Type	Description		
28.	10.	4 c. on 5 c. purple & yellow	8·00	35·00

15. Sultan Sir Abu Bakar. **16.**

1935.

No.	Type	Description		
29.	15.	1 c. black	15	30
30.		2 c. green	60	30
31.		3 c. green	2·75	7·50
32.		4 c. orange	30	10
33.		5 c. brown	50	10
34.		6 c. red	6·50	2·25
35.		8 c. grey	50	10
36.		8 c. red	90	32·00
37.		10 c. purple	30	10
38.		12 c. blue	1·50	1·75
39.		15 c. blue	3·25	38·00
40.		25 c. purple and red ..	80	1·00
41.		30 c. purple and orange ..	80	90
42.		40 c. red and purple ..	75	1·40
43.		50 c. black on green ..	3·25	1·75
44.		$1 black and red on blue ..	2·25	5·50
45.		$2 green and red	18·00	26·00
46.		$5 green and red on green	8·00	48·00

1948. Silver Wedding. As T **10/11** of Aden.

No.	Description		
47.	10 c. violet	15	60
48.	$5 green	22·00	40·00

1949. U.P.U. As T **20/23** of Antigua.

No.	Description		
49.	10 c. purple	20	20
50.	15 c. blue	35	70
51.	25 c. orange	35	1·10
52.	50 c. black	70	2·00

1950.

No.	Type	Description		
53	16.	1 c. black	10	10
54		2 c. orange	10	10
55		3 c. green	20	25
56		4 c. brown	15	10
57a		5 c. purple	25	15
58		6 c. grey	15	10
59		8 c. red	20	1·00
60		8 c. green	85	75
61		10 c. mauve	15	10
62		12 c. red	85	1·25
63		15 c. blue	30	10
64		20 c. black and green ..	25	1·75
65		20 c. blue	75	10
66		25 c. purple and orange ..	20	10
67		30 c. red and purple ..	1·25	35
68		35 c. red and purple ..	60	25
69		40 c. red and purple ..	90	6·00
70		50 c. black and blue ..	40	10
71		$1 blue and purple ..	2·25	1·40
72		$2 green and red ..	11·00	17·00
73		$5 green and brown ..	48·00	38·00

1953. Coronation. As T **13** of Aden.

No.	Description		
74.	10 c. black and purple ..	30	10

1957. As Nos. 92/102 of Kedah but inset portrait of Sultan Sir Abu Bakar.

No.	Description		
75	1 c. black	10	10
76	2 c. red	10	10
77	4 c. sepia	10	10
78	5 c. lake	10	10
79	8 c. green	80	1·00
80	10 c. sepia	20	10
81	10 c. purple	1·75	20
82	20 c. blue	20	10
83	50 c. black and blue ..	20	10
84	$1 blue and purple ..	1·50	1·25
85	$2 green and red	3·00	6·00
86	$5 brown and green ..	6·00	8·50

INDEX
Countries can be quickly located by referring to the index at the end of this volume.

17. "Vanda hookeriana".

1965. As Nos. 115/21 of Kedah but with inset portrait of Sultan Sir Abu Bakar as in T **17.**

No.	Type	Description		
87.	17.	1 c. multicoloured ..	10	20
88.	–	2 c. multicoloured ..	10	20
89.	–	5 c. multicoloured ..	15	10
90.	–	6 c. multicoloured ..	20	20
91.	–	10 c. multicoloured ..	20	10
92.	–	15 c. multicoloured ..	80	10
93.	–	20 c. multicoloured ..	1·60	30

The higher values used in Pahang were Nos. 20/7 of Malaysia (National Issues).

18. "Precis orithya".

1971. Butterflies. As Nos. 124/30 of Kedah, but with portrait of Sultan Sir Abu Bakar as in T **18.**

No.	Type	Description		
96.	–	1 c. multicoloured ..	15	40
97.	–	2 c. multicoloured ..	40	40
98.	–	5 c. multicoloured ..	50	10
99.	–	6 c. multicoloured ..	65	50
100.	–	10 c. multicoloured ..	50	10
101.	18.	15 c. multicoloured ..	70	10
102.	–	20 c. multicoloured ..	95	30

The higher values in use with this issue were Nos. 64/71 of Malaysia (National Issues).

19. Sultan Haji Ahmad Shah.

1975. Installation of the Sultan.

No.	Type	Description		
103.	19.	10 c. green, lilac and gold	50	45
104.		15 c. black, yell. and grn.	60	10
105.		50 c. black, blue & green	1·75	2·75

1977. As Nos. 97/8, 100/102 but with portrait of Sultan Haji Ahmad Shah.

No.	Type	Description		
106.	–	2 c. multicoloured ..	25·00	25·00
107.	–	5 c. multicoloured ..	60	55
108.	–	10 c. multicoloured ..	80	20
109.	18.	15 c. multicoloured ..	80	30
110.	–	20 c. multicoloured ..	3·00	1·75

20. "Rhododendron scortechinii".

1979. Flowers. As Nos. 135/41 of Kedah but with portrait of Sultan Haji Ahmad Shah as in T **20.**

No.	Description		
111	1 c. "Rafflesia hasseltii" ..	10	20
112	2 c. "Pterocarpus indicus"	10	20
113	5 c. "Lagerstroemia speciosa"	10	10
114	10 c. "Durio zibethinus" ..	15	10
115	15 c. "Hibiscus rosa-sinensis"	15	10
116	20 c. Type **20**	20	10
117	25 c. "Etlingera elatior" (inscr "Phaeomeria speciosa")	25	20

21. Rice.

1986. As Nos. 152/8 of Kedah but with portrait of Sultan Ahmad Shah as in T **21.**

No.	Description		
125.	1 c. Coffee	10	10
126.	2 c. Coconuts	10	10
127.	5 c. Cocoa	10	10
128.	10 c. Black pepper ..	10	10
129.	15 c. Rubber	10	10
130.	20 c. Oil Palm	10	10
131.	30 c. Type **21**	15	20

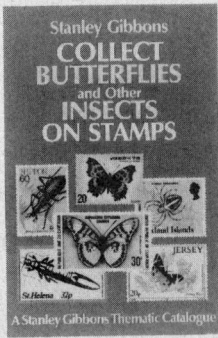

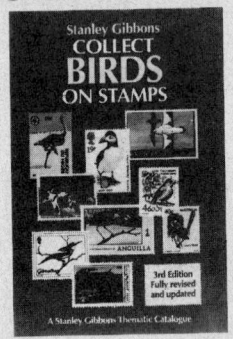

PAKISTAN

A Dominion created in 1947 from territory with predominantly Moslem population of Eastern and Western India. Became an independent Islamic Republic within the British Commonwealth in 1956. The eastern provinces declared their independence in 1971 and are now known as Bangladesh.

On 30 January 1972 Pakistan left the Commonwealth but rejoined on 1 October 1989.

1947. 12 pies = 1 anna; 16 annas = 1 rupee.
1961. 100 paisa = 1 rupee.

1947. King George VI stamps of India optd. **PAKISTAN.**

1	**100a**	3 p. slate..	10	10
2		½ a. mauve	10	10
3		9 p. green	10	10
4		1 a. red ..	10	10
5	**101**	1½ a. violet	10	10
6		2 a. red ..	10	20
7		3 a. violet	10	20
8		3½ a. blue	45	2·00
9	**102**	4 a. brown	10	10
10		6 a. green	60	40
11		8 a. violet	20	30
12		12 a. purple	1·00	20
13		14 a. purple (No. 277)	1·75	40
14	**93**	1 r. slate and brown	1·50	30
15		2 r. purple and brown	1·50	40
16		5 r. green and blue	3·50	2·00
17		10 r. purple and red	4·00	1·00
18		15 r. brown and green	48·00	70·00
19		25 r. slate and purple	48·00	35·00

3. Constituent Assembly Building, Karachi.

1948. Independence.

20.	**3.**	1½ a. blue ..	50	30
21.	–	2½ a. green	50	10
22.	–	3 a. brown	50	10
23.	–	1 r. red	50	30

DESIGNS—HORIZ. 2½ a. Entrance to Karachi Airport. 3 a. Gateway to Lahore Fort. VERT. 1 r. Crescent and Stars in foliated frame.

7. Scales of Justice.

9. Lloyd Barrage.

12. Salimullah Hostel, Dacca University.

13. Khyber Pass.

DESIGNS—VERT. As Type **7**: 1 a., 1½ a., 2 a. Star and Crescent. 6 a., 8 a., 12 a. Karachi Port Trust. HORIZ. As Type **12**: 3 a., 10 a. Karachi Airport.

1948. Designs with crescent moon pointing to right.

24	**7**	3 p. red	10	10
25		6 p. violet	30	10
26a		9 p. green	30	10
27	–	1 a. blue	10	10
28	–	1½ a. green	10	10
29	–	2 a. red	20	20
30	**9**	2½ a. green	1·50	3·50
31	–	3 a. green	1·25	20
32	**9**	3½ a. blue	1·00	2·75
33		4 a. brown	30	10
34	–	6 a. blue	30	50
35	–	8 a. black	30	30
36	–	10 a. red	1·25	4·00
37	–	12 a. red	3·00	30
38	**12**	1 r. blue	4·00	10
39		2 r. brown	18·00	30
40a		5 r. red	8·50	20
41b	**13**	10 r. mauve	13·00	30
42		15 r. green	15·00	8·50
210a		25 r. violet	2·40	3·00

1949. As 1948 but with crescent moon pointing to left.

44	–	1 a. blue	2·50	10
45	–	1½a. green	2·50	10
46	–	2 a. red ..	2·50	10
47	–	3 a. green	2·00	65
48	–	6 a. blue ..	6·00	15
49	–	8 a. black	3·25	60
50	–	10 a. red ..	7·00	80
51	–	12 a. red ..	12·00	15

16.

1949. 1st Death Anniv of Mohammed Ali Jinnah.

52	**16**	1½ a. brown	1·25	55
53		3 a. green	1·25	55
54		10 a. black	2·75	4·50

DESIGN: 10 a. inscription reads "QUAID-I-AZAM MOHAMMAD ALI JINNAH", etc.

17. Pottery.

DESIGNS—VERT. 3a., 12a. Aeroplane and hour-glass. 4a., 6a. Saracenic leaf pattern. HORIZ. 8a., 10a. Archway and lamp.

1951. 4th Anniversary of Independence.

55.	**17.**	2½ a. red ..	70	35
56.	–	3 a. purple..	40	10
57.	**17.**	3½ a. blue (A)	60	1·25
57a.		3½ a. blue (B)	2·75	60
58.	–	4 a. green ..	35	10
59.	–	6 a. orange	45	10
60.	–	8 a. sepia ..	3·75	10
61.	–	10 a. violet	80	10
62.	–	12 a. slate ..	90	10

(A) has Arabic fraction on left as in Type **17**; (B) has it on right. For similar 3½ a. see No. 88.

21. "Scinde Dawk" stamp and Ancient and Modern Transport.

1952. Cent. of "Scinde Dawk" Issue of India.

63.	**21.**	3 a. green on olive	75	50
64.		12 a. brown on salmon	1·00	15

22. Kaghan Valley.

DESIGNS — As Type **22**: HORIZ. 9 p. Mountains, Gilgit. 1 a. Badshahi Mosque, Lahore. VERT. 1½ a. Mausoleum of Emperor Jehangir, Lahore. As Type **24**: HORIZ. 1 r. Cotton plants, West Pakistan. 2 r. Jute fields and river, East Pakistan.

24. Tea Plantation, East Pakistan.

1954. 7th Anniv. of Independence.

65.	**22.**	6 p. violet	10	10
66.	–	9 p. blue ..	2·00	80
67.	–	1 a. red ..	10	10
68.	–	1½ a. red ..	10	10
69.	**24.**	14 a. myrtle	55	10
70.	–	1 r. green	10·00	10
71.	–	2 r. orange	2·00	10

29. View of K2.

1954. Conquest of K 2 (Mount Godwin-Austen).

72.	**29.**	2 a. violet	30	15

30. Karnaphuli Paper Mill, East Bengal.

DESIGNS: 6 a. Textile mill W. Pakistan. 8 a. Jute mill, E. Pakistan. 12 a. Main Sui gas plant.

1955. 8th Anniv. of Independence.

73.	**30.**	2½ a. red (A)	30	30
73a.		2½ a. red (B)	30	30
74.	–	6 a. blue ..	70	10
75.	–	8 a. violet	3·25	10
76.	–	12 a. red and orange	3·25	10

(A) has Arabic fraction on left as in Type **30**; (B) has it on right. For similar 2½ a. see No. 87.

1955. 10th Anniv. of U.N. Nos. 68 and 76 optd. **TENTH ANNIVERSARY, UNITED NATIONS 24.10.55.**

77.		1½ a red	1·75	5·00
78.		12 a. red and orange	75	4·50

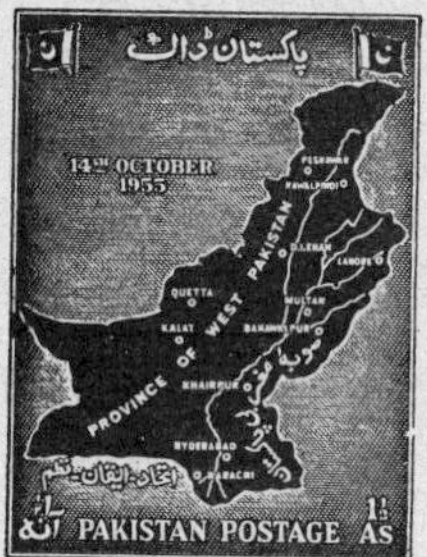

35. Map of W. Pakistan.

1955. West Pakistan Unity.

79.	**35.**	1½ a. green	15	10
80.		2 a. brown	15	10
81.		12 a. red	75	15

36. Constituent Assembly Building, Karachi.

1956. Republic Day.

82.	**36.**	2 a. green	55	10

37.

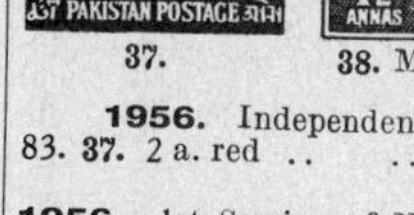

38. Map of East Pakistan.

1956. Independence. 9th Anniv.

83.	**37.**	2 a. red	40	10

1956. 1st Session of National Assembly of Pakistan at Dacca.

84.	**38.**	1½ a. green	15	90
85.		2 a. brown	15	10
86.		12 a. red	20	30

41. Orange Tree.

DESIGNS—2½ a. as Type **30** without value in Arabic at right. 3½ a. as Type **17** without value in Arabic at right.

1957. 1st Anniv. of Republic.

87	–	2½ a. red ..	20	10
88	–	3½ a. blue	30	10
89	**41.**	10 r. green and orange ..	80	20

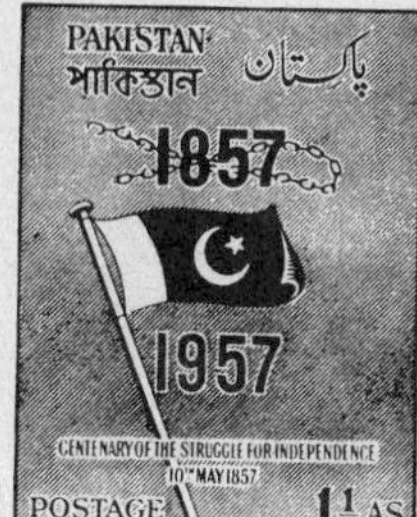

42. Pakistani Flag.

1957. Centenary of Struggle for Independence (Indian Mutiny).

90.	**42.**	1½ a. green	40	10
91.		12 a. blue	85	10

43. Pakistani Industries.

1957. 10th Anniv. of Independence.

92.	**43.**	1½ a. blue	15	20
93.		4 a. salmon	30	40
94.		12 a. mauve	30	40

1958. 2nd Anniv of Republic. As T **41**.

209		15 r. red and purple	80	1·00

DESIGNS: 15 r. Coconut tree.

45.

1958. 20th Death Anniv. of Mohammed Iqbal (poet).

96.	**45.**	1½ a. olive and black ..	45	10
97.		2 a. brown and black ..	45	10
98.		14 a. turquoise and black	75	10

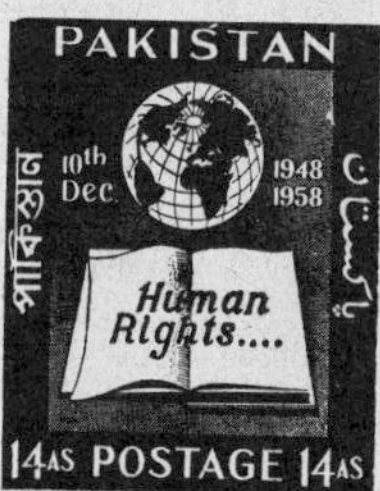

46. U.N. Charter and Globe.

1958. 10th Anniv. of Declaration of Human Rights.

99.	**46.**	1½ a. turquoise..	10	10
100.		14 a. sepia	50	10

1958. Scout Jamboree. Optd. **PAKISTAN BOY SCOUT 2nd NATIONAL JAMBOREE CHITTAGONG Dec. 58-Jan. 59.**

101.	**22.**	6 p. violet	20	10
102.	–	8 a. violet (No. 75)	40	10

1959. Revolution Day. No. 74 optd. **REVOLUTION DAY Oct. 27. 1959.**

103.	–	6a. blue	50	10

49. "Centenary of an Idea".

1959. Red Cross Commem.

104.	**49.**	2 a. red and green	30	10
105.		10 a. red and blue	55	10

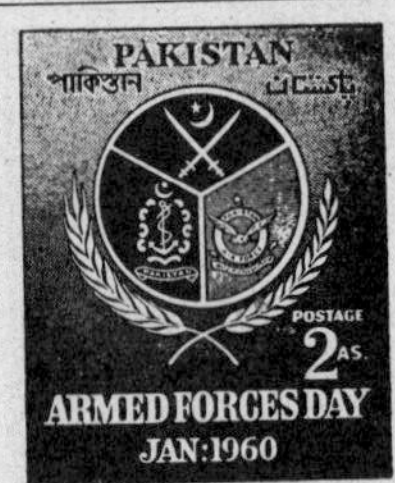

50. Armed Forces Badge.

1960. Armed Forces Day.

106. **50.** 2 a. red, blue and green 30 10
107. 14 a. red and blue .. 80 10

51. Map of Pakistan.

1960.

108. **51.** 6 p. purple 30 10
109. 2 a. red 50 10
110. 8 a. green 80 10
111. 1 r. blue .. .. 1·40 10

52. "Uprooted Tree".

1960. World Refugee Year.

112. **52.** 2 a. red 15 10
113. 10 a. green 25 10

53. Punjab Agricultural College.

1960. Golden Jubilee of Punjab Agricultural College, Lyallpur.

114. **53.** 2 a. blue and red .. 10 10
115. – 8 a. green and violet .. 20 10

DESIGN: 8 a. College Arms.

55. "Land Reforms, Rehabilitation and Reconstruction".

1960. Revolution Day.

116. **55.** 2 a. green, pink & brown 10 10
117. 14 a. green, yellow & blue 30 30

56. Caduceus.

1960. Centenary of King Edward Medical College, Lahore.

118. **56.** 2 a. yellow, black & blue 40 10
119. 14 a. green, black & red 85 20

57. "Economic Co-operation".

1960. Int. Chamber of Commerce C.A.F.E.A. Meeting, Karachi.

120. **57.** 14 a. brown 20 10

58. Zam-Zama Gun, Lahore. ("Kim's Gun" after Rudyard Kipling.)

1960. 3rd Pakistan Boy Scouts' National Jamboree, Lahore.

121. **58.** 2 a. red, yellow & green 40 10

1961. Surch. in "PAISA".

122. – 1 p. on 1½ a. red (No. 68) 30 10
123. **7.** 2 p. on 3 p. red .. 10 10
124. **51.** 3 p. on 6 p. purple .. 10 10
125. – 7 p. on 1 a. red (No. 67) 30 10
126. **51.** 13 p. on 2 a. red .. 30 10
127. **37.** 13 p. on 2 a. red .. 20 10

See also Nos. 262/4.

60. Khyber Pass.

61. Shalimar Gardens, Lahore.

62. Chota Sona Masjid (gateway).

1961.

170	**60**	1 p. violet	10	10
132		2 p. red	10	10
133		3 p. purple	30	10
173		5 p. blue	10	10
135		7 p. green	60	10
175	**61**	10 p. brown	10	10
176		13 p. violet	10	10
176a		15 p. purple	15	10
176b		20 p. green	30	10
177		25 p. blue	4·00	10
178		40 p. purple	15	10
179		50 p. turquoise	15	10
141		75 p. red	40	10
142		90 p. green	50	10
204	**62**	1 r. red	30	10
144		1 r. 25 violet	75	20
206		2 r. orange	55	15
207		5 r. green	3·50	40

1961. Lahore Stamp Exn. No. 110 optd. **LAHORE STAMP EXHIBITION 1961** and emblem.

145. **51.** 8 a. green .. .. 60 1·00

64. Warsak Dam and Power Station.

1961. Completion of Warsak Hydro-Electric Project.

146. **64.** 40 p. black and blue .. 40 10

65. Narcissus.

1961. Child Welfare Week.

147. **65.** 13 p. turquoise .. 15 10
148. 90 p. mauve 55 20

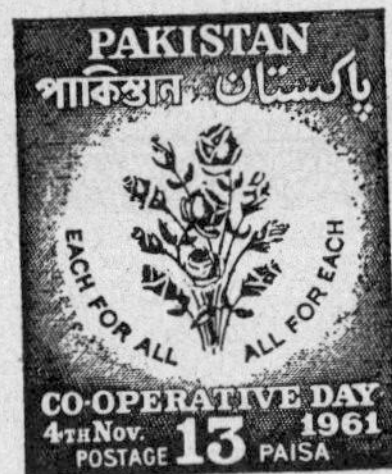

66. Ten Roses.

1961. Co-operative Day.

149. **66.** 13 p. red and green .. 30 10
150. 90 p. red and blue .. 70 30

67. Police Crest and "Traffic Control".

1961. Centenary of Police.

151. **67.** 13 p. silver, black & blue 50 10
152. 40 p. silver, black & red 1·00 20

68. Locomotive "Eagle" of 1861.

1961. Centenary of Railway.

153. **68.** 13 p. green, blk. & yell. 50 50
154. – 50 p. yell., black & green 75 75

DESIGN: 50 p. Diesel locomotive.

1962. Karachi–Dacca Flight. No. 87 surch. with 'plane and **FIRST JET FLIGHT KARACHI-DACCA 13 Paisa.**

155. 13 p. on 2½ a. red .. 70 40

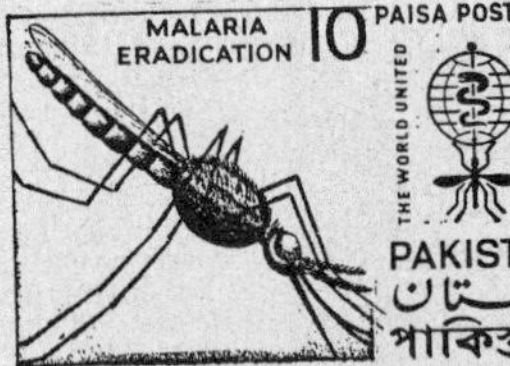

71. "Anopheles sp." (mosquito).

1962. Malaria Eradication.

156. **71.** 10 p. black, yellow & red 20 10
157. – 13 p. black, lemon & red 20 10

DESIGN: 13 p. Mosquito pierced by blade.

73. Pakistan Map and Jasmine.

1962. New Constitution.

158. **73.** 40 p. green, turq. & grey 60 10

74. Football.

1962. Sports.

159. **74.** 7 p. black and blue .. 10 10
160. – 13 p. black and green .. 10 10
161. – 25 p. black and purple .. 10 10
162. – 40 p. black and brown .. 1·40 1·40

DESIGNS: 13 p. Hockey. 25 p. Squash. 40 p. Cricket.

78. Marble Fruit Dish and Bahawalpuri Clay Flask.

DESIGNS: 13 p. Sports equipment. 25 p. Camelskin lamp and brassware. 40 p. Wooden powder - bowl and basket - work. 50 p. Inlaid cigarette-box and brassware.

1962. Small Industries.

163. **78.** 7 p. lake 10 10
164. – 13 p. green .. .. 2·75 90
165. – 25 p. violet 10 10
166. – 40 p. green 10 10
167. – 50 p. red 10 10

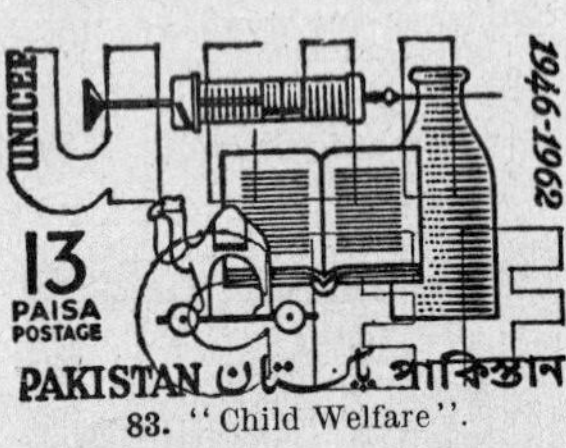

83. "Child Welfare".

1962. 16th Anniv. of U.N.I.C.E.F.

168. **83.** 13 p. blk., blue & purple 15 10
169. 40 p. blk., yell. & turq. 15 10

1963. Pakistan U.N. Force in West Irian. Optd. **U.N. FORCE W. IRIAN.**

182. **61.** 13 p. violet 10 10

85. "Dancing" Horse, Camel and Bull.

1963. Nat. Horse and Cattle Show.

183. **85.** 13 p. blue, sepia & pink 10 10

86. Wheat and Tractor.

1963. Freedom from Hunger.

184. **86.** 13 p. brown .. .. 1·00 10
185. – 50 p. bistre .. .. 2·00 40

DESIGN: 50 p. Lifting rice.

1963. 2nd Int. Stamp Exn., Dacca. Surch. **INTERNATIONAL DACCA STAMP EXHIBITION 1963 13 PAISA** and bars.

186. **51.** 13 p. on 2 a. red .. 40 10

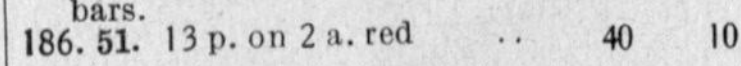

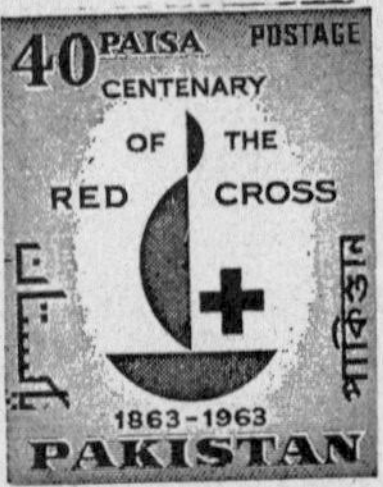

89. Centenary Emblem.

1963. Centenary of Red Cross.

187. **89.** 40 p. red and olive .. 1·25 15

90. Paharpur.

1963. Archaeological Series.

188. **90.** 7 p. blue 25 10
189. – 13 p. sepia 30 10
190. – 40 p. red 40 10
191. – 50 p. violet 45 10

DESIGNS—VERT. 13 p. Moenjodaro. HORIZ. 40 p. Taxila. 50 p. Mainamati.

1963. Pakistan Public Works Department Cent. Surch. **100 YEARS OF P.W.D. OCTOBER, 1963 13** and bars.

192. **60.** 13 p. on 3 p. purple .. 10 10

95. Ataturk's Mausoleum.

1963. 25th Death Anniv. of Kemal Ataturk.

193. **95.** 50 p. red 45 10

96. Globe and U.N.E.S.C.O. Emblem.

1963. 15th Anniv. of Declaration of Human Rights.

194. **96.** 50 p. brown, red & blue 40 10

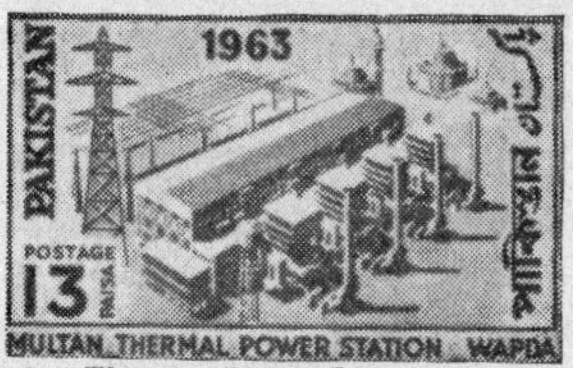

97. Thermal Power Installations.

1963. Completion of Multan Thermal Power Station.

195. **97.** 13 p. blue 10 10

99. Temple of Thot, Queen Nefertari and Maids.

1964. Nubian Monuments Preservation.

211. **99.** 13 p. blue and red .. 30 10
212. – 50 p. purple and black 70 10

DESIGN: 50 p. Temple of Abu Simbel.

101. "Unisphere" and Pakistan Pavilion.

1964. New York World's Fair.

213. **101.** 13 p. blue 10 10
214. – 1 r. 25 blue and orange 30 20

DESIGN—VERT. 1 r. 25, Pakistan Pavilion on "Unisphere".

103. Shah Abdul Latif's Mausoleum.

1964. Death Bicentenary of Shah Abdul Latif of Bhit.

215. **103.** 50 p. blue and lake .. 60 10

104. Mausoleum of "Quaid-i-Azam".

1964. 16th Death Anniv. of Mohammed Ali Jinnah ("Quaid-i-Azam").

216. **104.** 15 p. green 30 10
217. – 50 p. bronze 80 10

DESIGN: 50 p. As Type **104**, but 26½ × 31½ mm.

106. Bengali and Urdu Alphabets.

1964. "Universal Children's Day".

218. **106.** 15 p. brown 10 10

107. University Building.

1964. 1st Convocation of the West Pakistan University of Engineering and Technology, Lahore.

219. **107.** 15 p. brown 10 10

108. "Help the Blind".

1965. Blind Welfare.

220. **108.** 15 p. blue and yellow .. 20 10

109. I.T.U. Emblem and Symbols.

1965. Centenary of I.T.U.

221. **109.** 15 p. purple .. .. 1·25 30

110. I.C.Y. Emblem.

1965. Int. Co-operation Year.

222. **110.** 15 p. black and blue .. 50 15
223. 50 p. green and yellow 1·00 40

111. "Co-operation".

1965. 1st Anniversary of Regional Development Co-operation Pact. Mult.

224. 15 p. Type **111** 20 10
225. 50 p. Globe and Flags of Turkey, Iran and Pakistan (54¾ × 30¾ mm.) .. 60 10

113. Soldier and Tanks.

1965. Pakistan Armed Forces. Multicoloured.

226. 7 p. Type **113** 60 30
227. 15 p. Naval Officer and "Taghril" (destroyer) .. 1·00 10
228. 50 p. Pilot and "F–104" Starfighters .. .. 1·75 30

116. Army, Navy and Air Force Crests.

1966. Armed Forces Day.

229. **116.** 15 p. bl., grn. & buff 10 10

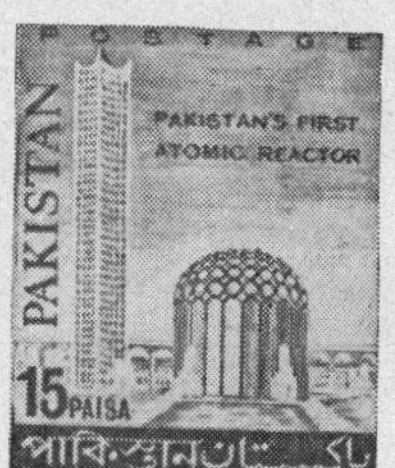

117. Atomic Reactor, Islamabad.

1966. Pakistan's 1st Atomic Reactor. Inauguration.

230. **117.** 15 p. black 10 10

118. Bank Crest.

1966. Silver Jubilee of Habib Bank.

231. **118.** 15 p. grn., orge. & sepia 10 10

119. Children.

1966. "Universal Children Day".

232. **119.** 15 p. black, red & yellow 10 10

120. U.N.E.S.C.O. Emblem.

1966. 20th Anniversary of U.N.E.S.C.O.

233. **120.** 15 p. multicoloured .. 1·75 30

121. Flag, Secretariat Building and President Ayub.

1966. Islamabad (new capital).

234. **121.** 15 p. multicoloured .. 15 10
235. 50 p. multicoloured .. 40 10

122. Avicenna.

1966. Health and Tibbi Research Institute Foundation.

236. **122.** 15 p. green and salmon 20 10

123. Mohammed Ali Jinnah. **125.** Emblem of Pakistan T.B. Association.

124. Tourist Year Emblem.

1966. 40th Birth Anniv. of Mohammed Ali Jinnah.

237. **123.** 15 p. black, orge. & blue 10 10
238. – 50 p. blk., pur. and blue 30 10

DESIGN: 50 p. Same portrait as 15 p. but different frame.

1967. Int. Tourist Year.

239. **124.** 15 p. black, blue & brn. 10 10

1967. T.B. Eradication Campaign.

240. **125.** 15 p. red, sepia & brown 10 10

126. Scout Salute and Badge.

1967. 4th National Scout Jamboree.

241. **126.** 15 p. brown and purple 15 10

127. " Justice ".

1967. Cent. of West Pakistan High Court.
242. **127.** 15 p. multicoloured .. 10 10

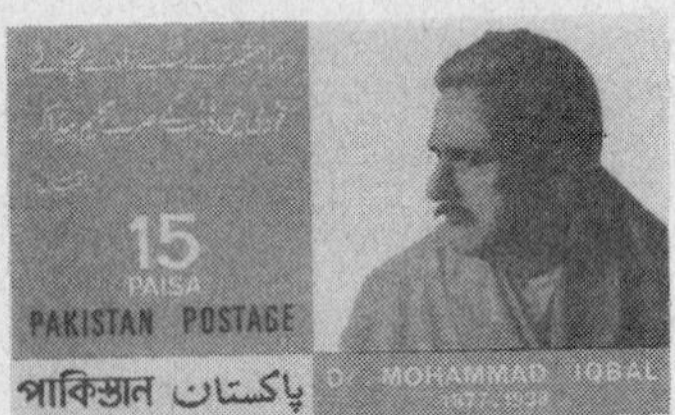

128. Dr. Mohammed Iqbal (philosopher).

1967. Iqbal Commem.
243. **128.** 15 p. sepia and red .. 10 10
244. 1 r. sepia and green .. 40 10

129. Hilal-i-Isteqlal Flag.

1967. Award of Hilal-i-Isteqlal (for Valour) to Lahore, Sialkot and Sargodha.
245. **129.** 15 p. multicoloured .. 10 10

130. "20th Anniversary".

1967. 20th Anniv. of Independence.
246. **130.** 15 p. red and green .. 10 10

131. " Rice Exports".

1967. Pakistan Exports. Multicoloured.
247. 10 p. Type **131** .. 10 15
248. 15 p. Cotton plant, yarn and textiles .. 10 10
249. 50 p. Raw jute, bale and bags .. 20 15
Nos. 248/9 are vert. and larger 27×45 mm.

134. Clay Toys.

1967. Children's Day.
250. **134.** 15 p. multicoloured .. 10 10

135. Shah and Empress of Iran and Gulistan Palace, Teheran.

1967. Coronation of Shah Mohammed Riza Pahlavi and Empress Farah of Iran.
251. **135.** 50 p. purple, blue & ochre 40 10

136. " Each For All—All for Each".

1967. Co-operative Day.
252. **136.** 15 p. multicoloured .. 10 10

137. Mangla Dam.

1967. Indus Basin Project.
253. **137.** 15 p. multicoloured .. 10 10

138. Crab Pierced by Sword.

1967. The Fight Against Cancer.
254. **138.** 15 p. red and black .. 60 10

139. Human Rights Emblem.

1968. Human Rights Year.
255. **139.** 15 p. red and blue .. 10 15
256. 50 p. red, yellow & grey 10 15

140. Agricultural University, Mymensingh.

1968. East Pakistan Agricultural University. First Convocation.
257. **140.** 15 p. multicoloured .. 10 10

141. W.H.O. Emblem.

1968. 20th Anniversary of World Health Organization.
258. **141.** 15 p. green and red .. 10 15
259. 50 p. orange and blue .. 10 15

142. Kazi Nazrul Islam (poet, composer and patriot).

1968. Nazrul Islam Commem.
260. **142.** 15 p. sepia and yellow .. 25 15
261. 50 p. sepia and red .. 50 15

1968. Nos. 56, 74 and 61 surch.
262. 4 p. on 3 a. purple .. 30 55
263. 4 p. on 6 a. blue .. 60 65
264. 60 p. on 10 a. violet .. 30 35

144. Children running with Hoops.

1968. Universal Children's Day.
265. **144.** 15 p. multicoloured .. 10 10

145. National Assembly.

1968. " A Decade of Development".
266. **145.** 10 p. multicoloured .. 10 10
267. – 15 p. multicoloured .. 15 10
268. – 50 p. multicoloured .. 70 20
269. – 60 p. blue, pur. & red 70 35
DESIGNS: 15 p. Industry and Agriculture. 50 p. Army, Navy and Air Force. 60 p. Minaret and Atomic Reactor Plant.

149. Chittagong Steel Mill.

1969. Pakistan's 1st Steel Mill, Chittagong.
270. **149.** 15 p. grey, blue and olive 10 10

150. " Family".

1969. Family Planning.
271. **150.** 15 p. purple and blue .. 10 10

151. Olympic Gold Medal and Hockey Player.

1969. Olympic Hockey Champions.
272. **151.** 15 p. multicoloured .. 75 50
273. 1 r. multicoloured .. 2·00 1·00

152. Mirza Ghalib and Lines of Verse.

1969. Death Cent. of Mirza Ghalib (poet).
274. **152.** 15 p. multicoloured .. 20 15
275. 50 p. multicoloured .. 50 15
The lines of verse on No. 275 are different from those in Type **152.**

153. Dacca Railway Station.

1969. 1st Anniversary of New Dacca Railway Station.
276. **153.** 15 p. multicoloured .. 30 10

154. I.L.O. Emblem and " 1919-1969".

1969. 50th Anniversary of I.L.O.
277. **154.** 15 p. buff and green .. 10 10
278. 50 p. brown and red .. 40 10

155. Mughal Miniature (Pakistan).

1969. 5th Anniversary of Regional Co-operation for Development. Multicoloured.
279. 20 p. Type **155** .. 15 10
280. 50 p. Safavi miniature (Iran) .. 15 10
281. 1 r. Ottoman miniature (Turkey) .. 20 10

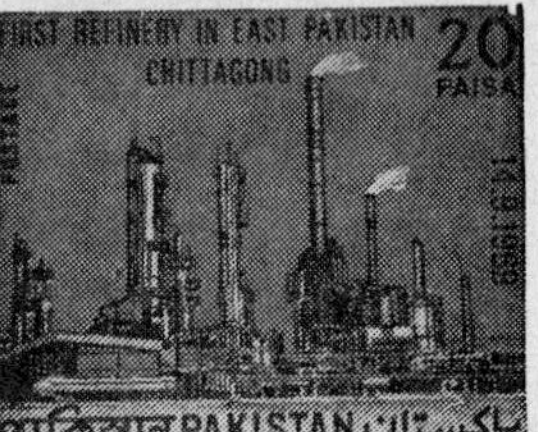

158. Eastern Refinery, Chittagong.

1969. 1st East Pakistan Oil Refinery.
282. **158.** 20 p. multicoloured .. 10 10

159. Children playing outside "School". (Reduced size Illustration—actual size 52 × 52 mm.).

1969. Universal Children's Day.
283. **159.** 20 p. multicoloured .. 10 10

160. Japanese Doll and P.I.A. Air Routes.

1969. Inauguration of P.I.A. Pearl Route, Dacca-Tokyo.
284. **160.** 20 p. multicoloured .. 40 10
285. 50 p. multicoloured .. 60 10

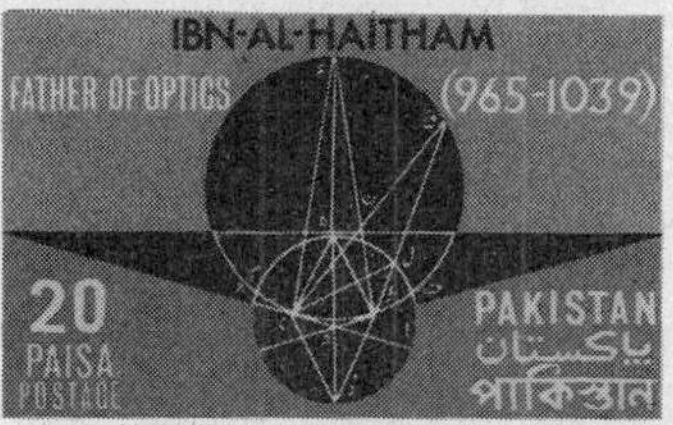

161. "Reflection of Light" Diagram.

1969. Millenary Commemorative of Ibn-al-Haitham (physicist).
286. **161.** 20 p. black, yell. & blue 10 10

162. Vickers "Vimy" and Karachi Airport.

1969. 50th Anniv. of 1st England–Australia Flight.
287. **162.** 50 p. multicoloured .. 40 35

163. Flags, Sun Tower and Expo Site Plan.

1970. World Fair, Osaka. Expo 70.
288. **163.** 50 p. multicoloured .. 20 30

164. New U.P.U. H.Q. Building.

1970. New U.P.U. Headquarters Building.
289. **164.** 20 p. multicoloured .. 15 10
290. 50 p. multicoloured .. 25 25

165. U.N. H.Q. Building.

1970. 25th Anniv. of United Nations. Mult.
291. 20 p. Type **165** 10 10
292. 50 p. U.N. Emblem .. 15 20

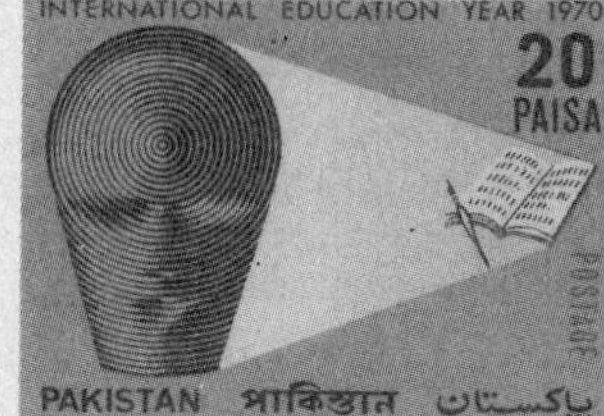

167. I.E.Y. Emblem, Book and Pen.

1970. Int. Education Year.
293. **167.** 20 p. multicoloured .. 10 10
294. 50 p. multicoloured .. 20 20

168. Saiful Malook Lake (Pakistan).

1970. 6th Anniv. of Regional Co-operation for Development. Multicoloured.
295. 20 p. Type **168** 15 10
296. 50 p. Seeyo-Se-Poi Bridge, Esfahan (Iran) .. 20 10
297. 1 r. View from Fethiye (Turkey) 20 15

171. Asian Productivity Symbol.

1970. Asian Productivity Year.
298. **171.** 50 p. multicoloured .. 20 20

172. Dr. Maria Montessori.

1970. Birth Centenary of Dr. Maria Montessori (educationalist).
299. **172.** 20 p. multicoloured .. 15 10
300. 50 p. multicoloured .. 15 30

173. Tractor and Fertilizer Factory.

1970. Near East F.A.O. Regional Conference, Islamabad.
301. **173.** 20 p. green and brown 15 20

174. Children and Open Book. **175.** Pakistan Flag and Text.

1970. Universal Children's Day.
302. **174.** 20 p. multicoloured .. 15 10

1970. Elections for National Assembly.
303. **175.** 20 p. green and violet 15 10

1970. Elections for Provincial Assemblies. As No. 303, but inscr. "PROVINCIAL ASSEMBLIES".
304. **175.** 20 p. green and red .. 15 10

176. Conference Crest and burning Al-Aqsa Mosque. (Illustration reduced, actual size 55 × 33 mm).

1970. Conference of Islamic Foreign Ministers, Karachi.
305 **176** 20 p. multicoloured .. 15 15

177. Coastal Embankments.

1971. East Pakistan Coastal Embankments Project.
306. **177.** 20 p. multicoloured .. 15 15

178. Emblem and United Peoples of the World.

1971. Racial Equality Year.
307. **178.** 20 p. multicoloured .. 10 15
308. 50 p. multicoloured .. 20 35

179. Maple Leaf Cement Factory, Daudkhel.

1971. 20th Anniversary of Colombo Plan.
309. **179.** 20 p. brn., blk. & violet 10 10

180. Chaharbagh School (Iran).

1971. 7th Anniv of Regional Co-operation for Development. Multicoloured.
310 10 p. Selimiye Mosque (Turkey) (horiz) .. 10 15
311 20 p. Badshahi Mosque, Lahore (horiz) 20 25
312 50 p. Type **180** 30 35

181. Electric Locomotive and Boy with Toy Train.

1971. Universal Children's Day.
313. **181.** 20 p. multicoloured .. 1·50 40

182. Horseman and Symbols.

1971. 2500th Anniv. of Persian Empire.
314. **182.** 10 p. multicoloured .. 25 30
315. 20 p. multicoloured .. 35 40
316. 50 p. multicoloured .. 45 50

183. Hockey-player and Trophy.

1971. World Cup Hockey Tournament, Barcelona.
317. **183.** 20 p. multicoloured .. 1·50 55

184. Great Bath, Moenjodaro.

1971. 25th Anniv. of U.N.E.S.C.O. and Campaign to save the Moenjodaro Excavations.
318. **184.** 20 p. multicoloured .. 20 30

185. U.N.I.C.E.F. Symbol.

1971. 25th Anniv. of U.N.I.C.E.F.
319. 185. 50 p. multicoloured .. 30 40

186. King Hussein and Jordanian Flag.

1971. 50th Anniv. of Hashemite Kingdom of Jordan.
320. 186. 20 p. multicoloured .. 15 15

187. Badge of Hockey Federation and Trophy.

1971. Hockey Championships Victory.
321. 187. 20 p. multicoloured .. 1·75 90

188. Reading Class.

1972. Int. Book Year.
322. 188. 20 p. multicoloured .. 20 30

189. View of Venice.

1972. U.N.E.S.C.O. Campaign to Save Venice.
323. 189. 20 p. multicoloured .. 30 30

190. E.C.A.F.E. Emblem and Discs.

1972. 25th Anniv. of E.C.A.F.E.
324. 190. 20 p. multicoloured .. 15 20

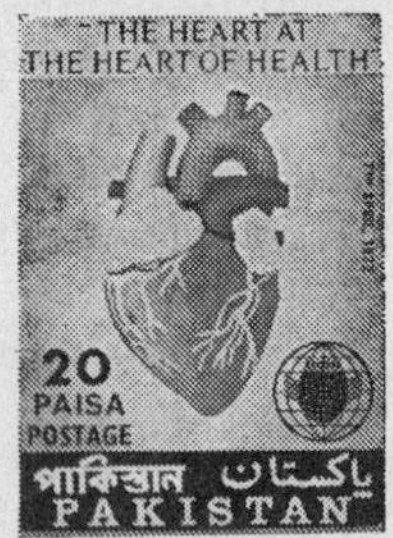
191. Human Heart.

1972. World Health Day.
325. 191. 20 p. multicoloured .. 20 30

192. "Only One Earth".

1972. U.N. Conf. on the Human Environment, Stockholm.
326. 192. 20 p. multicoloured .. 20 30

193. "Fisherman" (Cevat Dereli).

1972. 8th Anniversary of Co-operation for Regional Development. Multicoloured.
327. 10 p. Type 193 .. .. 10 20
328. 20 p. "Iranian Woman" (Behzad) 15 25
329. 50 p. "Will and Power" (A. R. Chughtai) .. 35 45

194. Mohammed Ali Jinnah and Tower.

1972. 25th Anniv. of Independence. Mult.
330. 10 p. Type 194 .. .. 10 10
331. 20 p. "Land Reform" .. 15 20
332. 20 p. "Labour Reform" 15 20
333. 20 p. "Education Policy" 15 20
334. 20 p. "Health Policy" .. 15 20
335. 60 p. National Assembly Building 25 25

The 60 p. is 46 × 28 mm.: Nos. 331/4 are 74 × 23½ mm.

195. Donating Blood.

1972. Nat. Blood Transfusion Service.
336. 195. 20 p. multicoloured .. 20 30

196. People and Squares.

1972. Centenary of Population Census.
337. 196. 20 p. multicoloured .. 20 20

197. Children from Slums.

1972. Universal Children's Day.
338. 197. 20 p. multicoloured .. 20 30

198. People and Open Book.

1972. Education Week.
339. 198. 20 p. multicoloured .. 20 20

199. Nuclear Power Plant.

1972. Inauguration of Karachi Nuclear Power Plant.
340. 199. 20 p. multicoloured .. 20 30

200. Copernicus in Observatory.

1973. 500th Birth Anniversary of Nicholas Copernicus (astronomer).
341. 200. 20 p. multicoloured .. 20 30

201. Moenjodaro Excavations.

1973. 50th Anniversary of Moenjodaro Excavations.
342. 201. 20 p. multicoloured .. 20 30

202. Elements of Meteorology.

1973. Centenary of I.M.O./W.M.O.
343. 202. 10 p. multicoloured .. 20 30

203. Prisoners-of-war.

1973. Prisoners-of-war in India.
344. 203. 1 r. 25 multicoloured .. 1·50 1·75

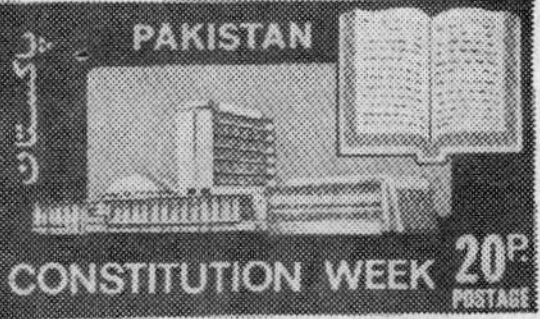
204. National Assembly Building and Constitution Book.

1973. Constitution Week.
345. 204. 20 p. multicoloured .. 40 40

205. Badge and State Bank Building.

1973. 25th Anniv. of Pakistan State Bank.
346. 205. 20 p. multicoloured .. 15 30
347. 1 r. multicoloured .. 30 50

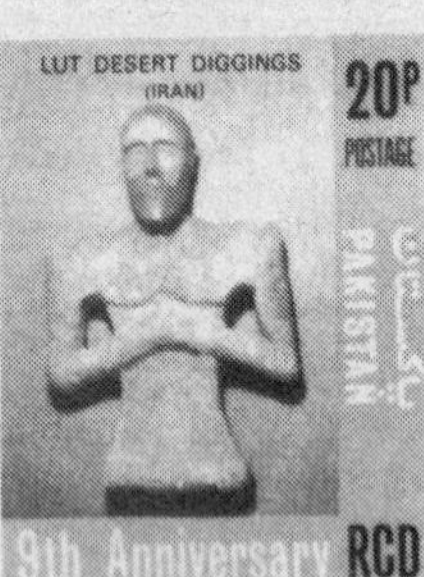
206. Lut Desert Excavations (Iran).

1973. 9th Anniversary of Regional Co-operation for Development. Multicoloured.
348. 20 p. Type 206 .. .. 30 20
349. 60 p. Main Street, Moenjodaro (Pakistan) .. 55 50
350. 1 r. 25 Mausoleum of Antiochus I (Turkey) .. 75 1·25

207. Constitution Book and Flag.

1973. Independence Day and Enforcement of the Constitution.
351. **207.** 20 p. multicoloured .. 15 30

208. Mohammed Ali Jinnah (Quaid-i-Azam).

1973. 25th Death Anniversary of Mohammed Ali Jinnah.
352. **208.** 20 p. grn., yell. & blk. 15 30

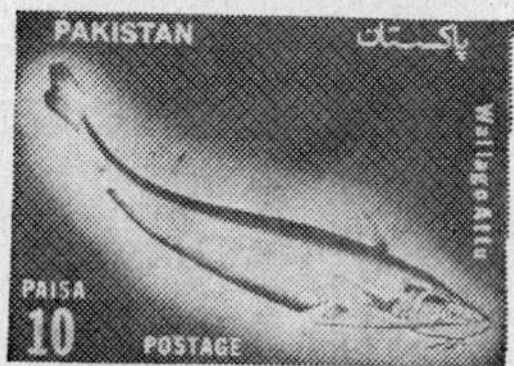

209. " Wallago attu ".

1973. Fishes. Multicoloured.
353. 10 p. Type **209** .. .. 1·00 1·00
354. 20 p. " Labeo rohita " .. 1·10 1·10
355. 60 p. " Tilapia mossambica " 1·25 1·25
356. 1 r. " Catla catla " .. 1·25 1·25

210. Children's Education.

1973. Universal Children's Day.
357. **210.** 20 p. multicoloured .. 15 30

211. Harvesting.

1973. 10th Anniversary of World Food Programme.
358. **211.** 20 p. multicoloured .. 50 40

212. Ankara and Kemal Ataturk.

1973. 50th Anniversary of Turkish Republic.
359. **212.** 50 p. multicoloured .. 45 35

213. Boy Scout. **214.** "Basic Necessities".

1973. National Silver Jubilee Jamboree.
360. **213.** 20 p. multicoloured .. 80 50

1973. 25th Anniversary of Declaration of Human Rights.
361. **214.** 20 p. multicoloured .. 30 30

215. Al-Biruni and Nandana Hill.

1973. Al-Biruni Millennium Congress.
362 215 20 p. multicoloured .. 40 20
363 1 r. 25 multicoloured .. 85 75

216. Dr. Hansen, Microscope and Bacillus.

1973. Centenary of Hansen's Discovery of Leprosy Bacillus.
364. **216.** 20 p. multicoloured .. 75 50

217. Family and Emblem.

1974. World Population Year.
365. **217.** 20 p. multicoloured .. 10 10
366. 1 r. 25 multicoloured 30 40

218. Conference Emblem.

1974. Islamic Summit Conference, Lahore. Multicoloured.
367. 20 p. Type **218** 10 10
368. 65 p. Emblem on " Sun " 25 45
No. 368 is larger, size 42 × 30 mm.

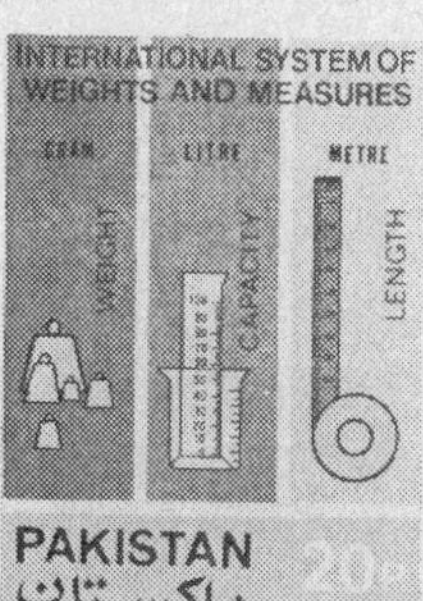

219. Units of Weight and Measurement.

1974. Adoption of Int. Weights and Measures System.
370. **219.** 20 p. multicoloured .. 15 25

220. " Chand Chauthai " Carpet, Pakistan.

1974. 10th Anniversary of Regional Co-operation for Development. Multicoloured.
371. 20 p. Type **220** 15 15
372. 60 p. Persian carpet, 16th-century 45 50
373. 1 r. 25 Anatolian carpet, 15th-century .. .. 65 1·00

221. Hands protecting Sapling.

1974. Tree Planting Day.
374. **221.** 20 p. multicoloured .. 50 40

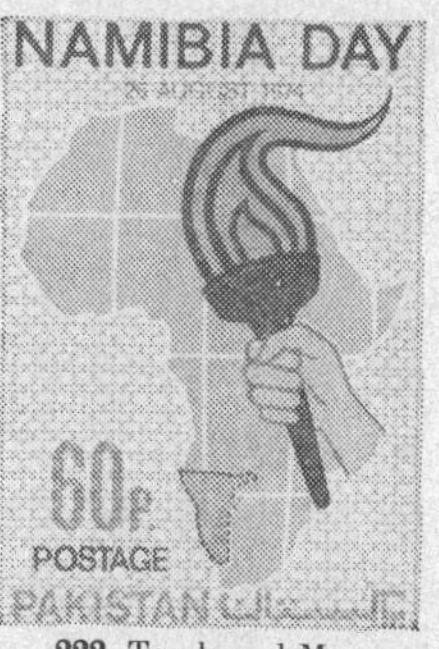

222. Torch and Map.

1974. Namibia Day.
375. **222.** 60 p. multicoloured .. 35 60

223. Highway Map.

1974. Shahrah-e-Pakistan (Pakistan Highway).
376. **223.** 20 p. multicoloured .. 65 50

224. Boy at Desk.

1974. Universal Children's Day.
377. **224.** 20 p. multicoloured .. 30 30

225. U.P.U. Emblem. **226.** Liaquat Ali Khan.

1974. Centenary of U.P.U. Multicoloured.
378. 20 p. Type **225** 20 20
379. 2 r. 25 U.P.U. emblem, aeroplane and mail-wagon 55 1·40

1974. Liaquat Ali Khan (First Prime Minister of Pakistan).
381. **226.** 20 p. black and red .. 30 30

227. Dr. Mohammed Iqbal (poet and philosopher).

1974. Birth Centenary of Dr. Iqbal. (1977) (1st issue).
382. **227.** 20 p. multicoloured .. 30 30
See also Nos. 399, 433 and 445/9.

228. Dr. Schweitzer and River Scene.

1975. Birth Cent. of Dr. Albert Schweitzer.
383. **228.** 2 r. 25 multicoloured 2·00 2·50

229. Tourism Year Symbol.

1975. South East Asia Tourism Year.
384. **229.** 2 r. 25 multicoloured 55 80

230. Assembly Hall, Flags and Prime Minister Bhutto.

1975. 1st Anniversary of Islamic Summit Conference, Lahore.

385. **230.** 20 p. multicoloured .. 35 25
386. 1 r. multicoloured .. 90 1·25

231. " Scientific Research ".

1975. International Women's Year. Mult.

387. 20 p. Type **231** 20 25
388. 2 r. 25 Girl teaching woman (" Adult Education ") 1·10 1·75

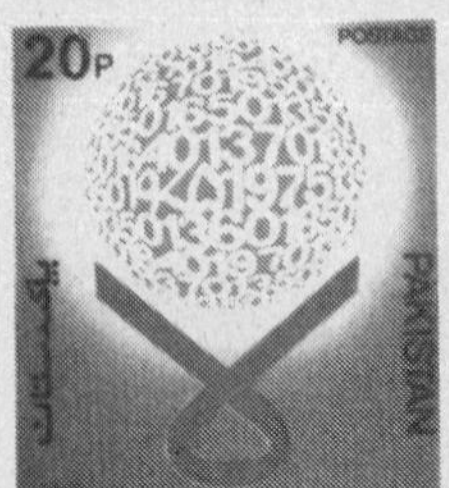

International Congress of Mathematical Sciences Karachi July 14 - 20,1975.

232. " Globe " and Algebraic Symbol.

1975. Int. Congress of Mathematical Sciences. Karachi.

389. **232.** 20 p. multicoloured .. 50 40

233. Pakistani Camel-skin Vase.

1975. 11th Anniversary of Regional Co-operation for Development. Multicoloured.

390. 20 p. Type **233** 25 30
391. 60 p. Iranian tile (horiz.) 50 70
392. 1 r. 25 Turkish porcelain vase .. .. .. 75 1·50

234. Sapling and Dead Trees.

1975. Tree Planting Year.

393. **234.** 20 p. multicoloured .. 35 30

235. Black Partridge.

1975. Wildlife Protection (1st series).

394. **235.** 20 p. multicoloured .. 1·00 35
395. 2 r. 25 multicoloured 3·75 3·75

See also Nos. 400/1, 411/12, 417/18, 493/6, 560, 572/3, 581/2, 599, 600, 605, 621/2, 691, 702, 780/3 and 853.

236. " Today's Girls ".

1975. Universal Children's Day.

396. **236.** 20 p. multicoloured .. 30 30

237. Hazrat Amir Khusrau, Sitar and Tabla.
(Reduced size illustration—actual size 74 × 23 mm.)

1975. 700th Birth Anniversary of Hazrat Amir Khusrau (poet and musician).

397. **237.** 20 p. multicoloured .. 20 45
398. 2 r. 25 multicoloured .. 75 1·60

238. Dr. Mohammed Iqbal.

1975. Birth Cent. (1977) of Dr. Iqbal. (2nd issue).

399. **238.** 20 p. multicoloured .. 30 30

239. Urial (wild sheep).

1975. Wildlife Protection (2nd series).

400. **239.** 20 p. multicoloured .. 40 30
401. 3 r. multicoloured .. 2·50 3·00

240. Moenjodaro Remains.

1976. " Save Moenjodaro " (1st issue). Multicoloured.

402. 10 p. Type **240** 65 75
403. 20 p. Remains of houses .. 75 85
404. 65 p. Citadel area and stupa 75 85
405. 3 r. Well inside a house .. 75 85
406. 4 r. The " Great Bath " .. 85 95

See also Nos. 414 and 430.

241. Dome and Minaret of the Rauza-e-Mubarak.

1976. Int. Congress on Seerat.

407. **241.** 20 p. multicoloured .. 20 20
408. 3 r. multicoloured .. 70 90

242. Alexander Graham Bell and Modern Dial.

1976. Centenary of First Telephone.

409. **242.** 3 r. multicoloured .. 1·25 2·00

243. College Arms within " Sun ".

1976. Cent. of National College of Arts, Lahore.

410. **243.** 20 p. multicoloured .. 30 40

244. Common Peafowl.

1976. Wildlife Protection (3rd series).

411. **244.** 20 p. multicoloured .. 75 35
412. 3 r. multicoloured .. 3·25 4·25

245. Human Eye.

1976. Prevention of Blindness.

413. **245.** 20 p. multicoloured .. 50 50

246. Unicorn and Ruins.

1976. " Save Moenjodaro " (2nd series).

414. **246.** 20 p. multicoloured .. 30 35

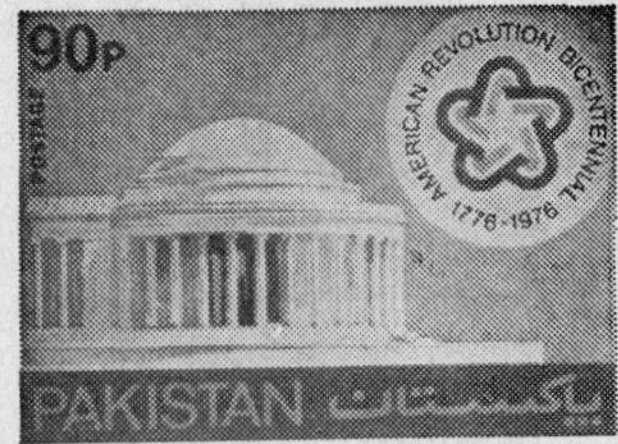

247. Jefferson Memorial.

1976. Bicent. of American Revolution. Mult.

415 90 p. Type **247** .. .. 1·00 60
416. 4 r. " Declaration of Independence " .. 3·75 5·00

No. 416 is larger, 47 × 36 mm.

248. Ibex.

1976. Wildlife Protection (4th series).

417. **248.** 20 p. multicoloured .. 30 35
418. 3 r. multicoloured .. 1·75 2·50

249. Mohammed Ali Jinnah.

1976. 12th Anniv. of Regional Co-operation for Development. Multicoloured.

419. 20 p. Type **249** 50 50
420. 65 p. Reza Shah the Great (Iran) 50 50
421. 90 p. Kemal Ataturk (Turkey) 50 50

250. Urdu Text.

251. Mohammed Ali Jinnah and Wazir Mansion.

1976. Birth Cent. of Mr. Jinnah. (1st issue).
(a) Type **250.**

422. **250.** 5 p. black, blue & yell. 20 25
423. 10 p. black, yell. & pur. 20 25
424. 15 p. black, and blue .. 20 25
425. 1 r. black, yell. & blue 30 30

(b) Type **251.** Background Buildings given. Multicoloured

426. 20 p. Type **251** 20 25
427. 40 p. Sind Madressah 20 25
428. 50 p. Minar Qarardad-e-Pakistan 20 25
429. 3 r. Mausoleum 45 50

See also No. 436.

252. Dancing-girl, Ruins and King Priest.
(Illustration reduced. Actual size 64 × 22 mm.).

1976. " Save Moenjodaro " (3rd series).
430. **252.** 65 p. multicoloured .. 35 45

253. U.N. Racial Discrimination Emblem.

1976. U.N. Decade to Combat Racial Discrimination.
431. **253.** 65 p. multicoloured .. 30 40

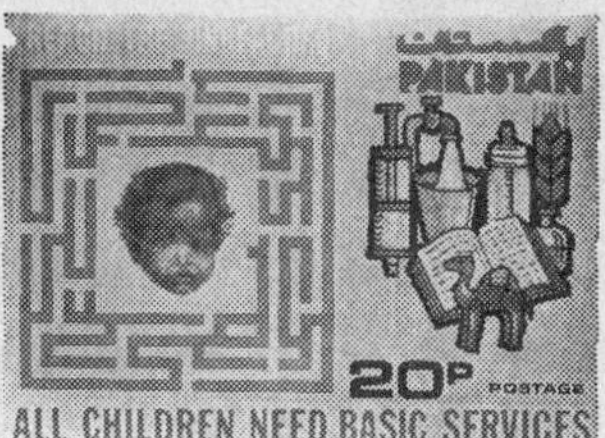

254. Child in Maze and Basic Services.

1976. Universal Children's Day.
432. **254.** 20 p. multicoloured .. 20 30

255. Verse from " Allama Iqbal ".

1976. Birth Centenary (1977) of Dr. Iqbal (3rd issue).
433. **255.** 20 p. multicoloured .. 15 30

256. Mohammed Ali Jinnah giving Scout Salute.

1976. Quaid-i-Azam Centenary Jamboree.
434. **256.** 20 p. multicoloured .. 45 30

257. Children Reading.

1976. Children's Literature.
435. **257.** 20 p. multicoloured .. 20 30

258. Mohammed Ali Jinnah.

1976. Birth Centenary of Quaid-i-Azam (Mohammed Ali Jinnah) (2nd issue).
436. **258.** 10 r. green and gold .. 2·50 3·50

259. Rural Family.

1977. Social Welfare and Rural Development Year.
437. **259.** 20 p. multicoloured .. 15 10

260. Turkish Vase, 1800 B.C.

1977. 13th Anniv. of Regional Co-operation for Development.
438. **260.** 20 p. orge., blue & blk. 25 10
43?. – 65 p. multicoloured .. 35 20
44 . – 90 p. multicoloured .. 45 40

DESIGNS: 60 p. Pakistani toy bullock cart from Moenjodaro. 90 p. Pitcher with spout from Sialk Hill, Iran.

261. Forest.

1977. Nat. Tree Plantation Campaign.
441. **261.** 20 p. multicoloured .. 10 10

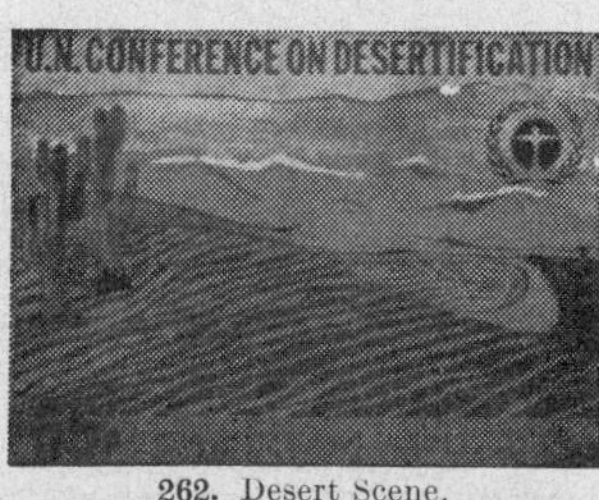

262. Desert Scene.

1977. U.N. Conf. on Desertification, Nairobi.
442. **262.** 65 p. multicoloured .. 30 20

263. " Water for Children of the World ".

1977. Universal Children's Day.
443. **263.** 50 p. multicoloured .. 40 20

264. Aga Khan III.

1977. Birth Centenary of Aga Khan III.
444. **264.** 2 r. multicoloured .. 55 85

265. Iqbal and Spirit of the Poet Roomi (from painting by Behzad).

1977. Birth Centenary of Allama Mohammed Iqbal (4th issue). Multicoloured.
445. 20 p. Type **265** 25 35
446. 65 p. " Iqbal looking at Jamaluddin Afghani and Saeed Haleem Pasha at prayer " (Behzad).. 25 35
447. 1 r. 25 Urdu verse .. 30 40
448. 2 r. 25 Persian verse .. 35 45
449. 3 r. Iqbal 40 50

266. The Holy " Khana-Kaaba " (House of God, Mecca).

1977. Haj.
450. **266.** 65 p. multicoloured .. 30 30

267. Rheumatic Patient and Healthy Man.

1977. World Rheumatism Year.
451. **267.** 65 p. blue, blk. & yell. 30 20

268. Woman in Costume of Rawalpindi-Islamabad.

1978. Indonesia-Pakistan Economic and Cultural Cooperation Organization.
452. **268.** 75 p. multicoloured .. 30 20

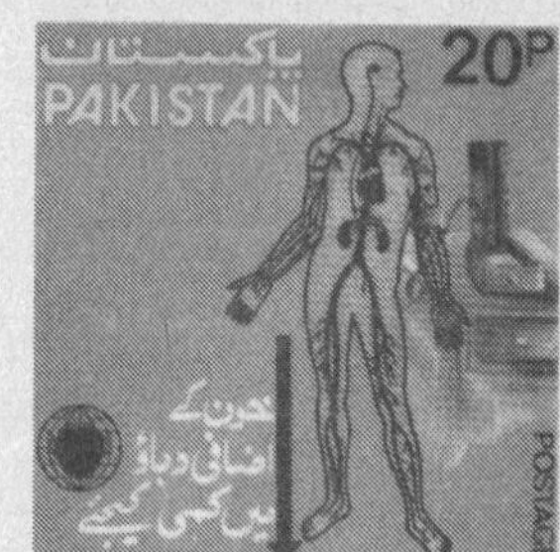

269. Human Body and Sphygmomanometer.

1978. World Hypertension Month.
453. **269.** 20 p. multicoloured .. 15 10
454. – 2 r. multicoloured .. 60 60

The 2 r. value is as Type **269**, but has the words " Down with high blood pressure " instead of the Urdu inscription at the bottom left.

270. Henri Dunant.

1978. 100th Birth Anniv. of Henri Dunant (founder of the Red Cross).
455. **270.** 1 r. multicoloured .. 65 20

271. Red Roses (Pakistan).

1978. 14th Anniv. of Regional Co-operation for Development. Roses. Multicoloured.
456. 20 p. Type **271** 35 20
457. 90 p. Pink roses (Iran) .. 50 20
458. 2 r. Yellow roses (Turkey) 75 25

272. " Pakistan, World Cup Hockey Champions ".

1978. "Riccione '78" International Stamp Fair. Multicoloured.

459. 1 r. Type **272** .. .. 1·00 25
460. 2 r. Fountain, Piazza Turismo .. .. .. 1·25 35

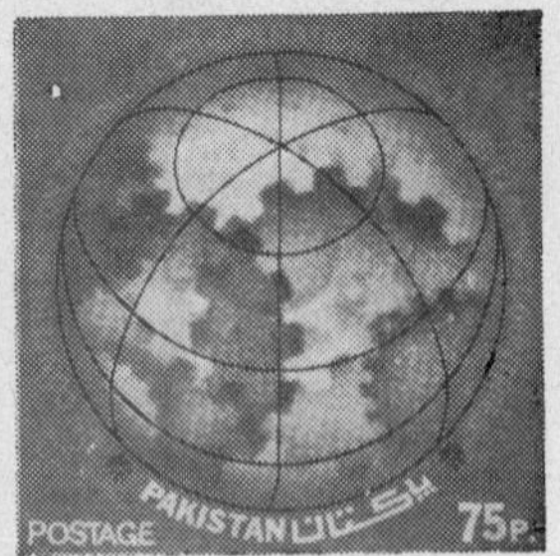

273. Cogwheels within Globe Symbol.

1978. U.N. Technical Co-operation amongst Developing Countries Conference.

461. **273.** 75 p. multicoloured .. 15 10

274. St. Patrick's Cathedral.

1978. Centenary of St. Patrick's Cathedral, Karachi. Multicoloured.

462. 1 r. Type **274** 10 10
463. 2 r. Stained glass window 25 25

275. Minar-i-Qarardad-e-Pakistan.

1978.

464.	**275.**	2 p. green	10	10
465.		3 p. black	10	10
466.		5 p. blue	10	10
467.	–	10 p. blue & turquoise	10	10
468.	–	20 p. green	50	10
469.	–	25 p. green and mauve	60	10
470.	–	40 p. blue and mauve	10	10
471.	–	50 p. lilac and green ..	30	10
472.	–	60 p. black	10	10
473b.	–	75 p. red	55	10
474.	–	90 p. mauve and blue	20	10
475.	–	1 r. green	10	10
476.	–	1 r. 50 orange	10	10
477.	–	2 r. red	10	10
478.	–	3 r. blue	15	10
479.	–	4 r. black	15	10
480.	–	5 r. brown	20	10

DESIGNS—HORIZ. (25 × 20 mm.) 10 p. to 90 p. Tractor. VERT. (21 × 25 mm.) 1 r. to 5 r. Mausoleum of Ibrahim Khan.

277. Emblem and "United Races" Symbol.

1978. International Anti-Apartheid Year.

481. **277.** 1 r. multicoloured .. 15 15

278. Maulana Mohamed Ali Jauhar.

1978. Birth Centenary of Maulana Mohamed Ali Jauhar (patriot).

482. **278.** 50 p. multicoloured .. 40 20

279. "Tornado", "Rapide" and Wright "Flyer".
(Illustration reduced, actual size 52 × 52 mm.).

1978. 75th Anniv. of Powered Flight. Mult.

483. 65 p. Type **279** .. .. 1·00 1·10
484. 1 r. "Phantom F4F", "Tristar" and Wright "Flyer" .. .. 1·10 1·25
485. 2 r. "X15", "Tu. 104" and Wright "Flyer" 1·25 1·40
486. 2 r. 25 "Mig 15", "Concorde" and Wright "Flyer" .. .. 1·50 1·75

280. "Holy Koran illuminating Globe" and Raudha-e-Mubarak (mausoleum).

1979. "12th Rabi-ul-Awwal" (Prophet Mohammed's birthday).

487. **280.** 20 p. multicoloured .. 30 15

281. "Aspects of A.P.W.A.".

1979. 30th Anniv. of A.P.W.A. (All Pakistan Women's Association.)

488. **281.** 50 p. multicoloured .. 40 15

282. Tippu Sultan Shaheed of Mysore.

1979. Pioneers of Freedom (1st series). Multicoloured.

490. 10 r. Type **282** 60 75
491. 15 r. Sir Syed Ahmad Khan 90 1·00
492. 25 r. Altaf Hussain Hali .. 1·25 1·50

See also Nos. 757, 801/27, 838/46 and 867/9.

283. Himalayan Monal Pheasant.

1979. Wildlife Protection (5th series). Pheasants. Multicoloured.

493. 20 p. Type **283** .. 1·10 50
494. 25 p. Kalij Pheasant .. 1·10 70
495. 40 p. Koklass Pheasant .. 1·40 1·25
496. 1 r. Cheer Pheasant .. 2·50 2·00

284. "Pakistan Village Scene" (Ustad Bakhsh).

1979. 15th Anniv. of Regional Co-operation for Development. Multicoloured.

497. 40 p. Type **284** 20 25
498. 75 p. "Iranian Goldsmith" (Kamal al Molk) 20 25
499. 1 r. 60 "Turkish Harvest" (Namik Ismail) .. 25 30

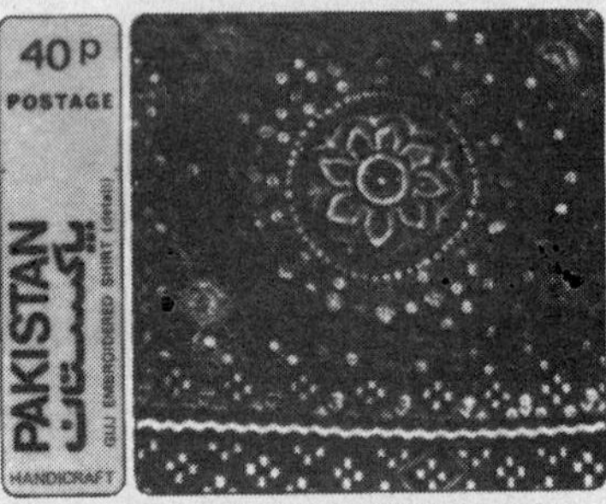

285. Guj Embroidered Shirt (detail).

1979. Handicrafts (1st series). Multicoloured.

500. 40 p. Type **285** 20 20
501. 1 r. Enamel inlaid brass plate 25 25
502. 1 r. 50 Baskets 30 30
503. 2 r. Chain-stitch embroidered rug (detail) .. 40 40

See also Nos. 578/9, 595/6 and 625/8.

286. Children playing on Climbing-frame.

1979. S.O.S. Children's Village, Lahore.

504. **286.** 50 p. multicoloured .. 30 30

287. "Island" (Z. Maloof).

1979. International Year of the Child. Children's Paintings. Multicoloured.

505. 40 p. Type **287** 15 15
506. 75 p. "Playground" (R. Akbar) 25 25
507. 1 r. "Fairground" (M. Azam) 25 25
508. 1 r. 50 "Hockey Match" (M. Tayyab) 30 30

288. Warrior attacking Crab.

1979. "Fight Against Cancer".

510. **288.** 40 p. multicoloured .. 60 40

289. Pakistan Customs Emblem. **291.** Islamic Pattern.

290. Boeing "747 (Jumbo)" and Douglas "DC-3" Airliners.

1979. Centenary of Pakistan Customs Service.

511. **289.** 1 r. multicoloured .. 30 30

1980. 25th Anniv. of Pakistan International Air Lines.

512. **290.** 1 r. multicoloured .. 90 80

1980.

513.	**291.**	10 p. green and yellow	10	10
514.		15 p. deep green & green	10	10
515.		25 p. violet and red ..	10	20
516.		35 p. red and green ..	10	20
517.	–	40 p. red and brown ..	15	10
518.	–	50 p. violet and green	10	20
519.	–	80 p. green and black ..	15	30

The 40 to 80 p. values also show different Islamic patterns, the 40 p. being horizontal and the remainder vertical.

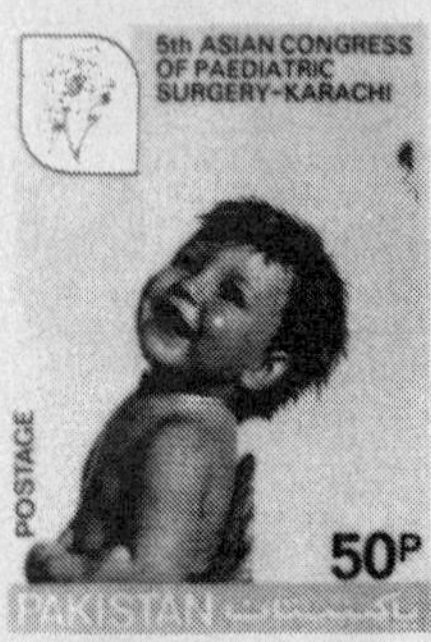

292. Young Child.

1980. Fifth Asian Congress of Paediatric Surgery, Karachi.

530. **292.** 50 p. multicoloured .. 60 60

PAKISTAN

POSTAGE Re.1

293. Conference Emblem.

1980. 11th Islamic Conference of Foreign Ministers, Islamabad.

531. **293.** 1 r. multicoloured .. 40 45

294. Karachi Port. (Illustration reduced, actual size 75 × 16 mm.)

1980. Centenary of Karachi Port Authority.

532. **294.** 1 r. multicoloured .. 90 90

1980. " Riccione 80 " International Stamp Exhibition. Nos. 505/8 optd. **RICCIONE 80.**

533. **287.** 40 p. multicoloured .. 25 25
534. – 75 p. multicoloured .. 30 30
535. – 1 r. multicoloured .. 35 35
536. – 1 r. 50 multicoloured 45 45

296. Old and New Staff College Buildings.

1980. 75th Anniv. of Quetta Staff College.

537. **296.** 1 r. multicoloured .. 10 15

1980. World Tourism Conference, Manila. No. 496 optd. **WORLD TOURISM CONFERENCE, MANILA 80.**

538. 1 r. Cheer Pheasant .. 30 20

298. Birth Centenary Emblem.

1980. Birth Cent. of Hafiz Mahmood Shairani.

539. **298.** 40 p. multicoloured .. 30 60

299. Shalimar Gardens, Lahore.

1980. Aga Khan Award for Architecture.

540. **299.** 2 r. multicoloured .. 40 75

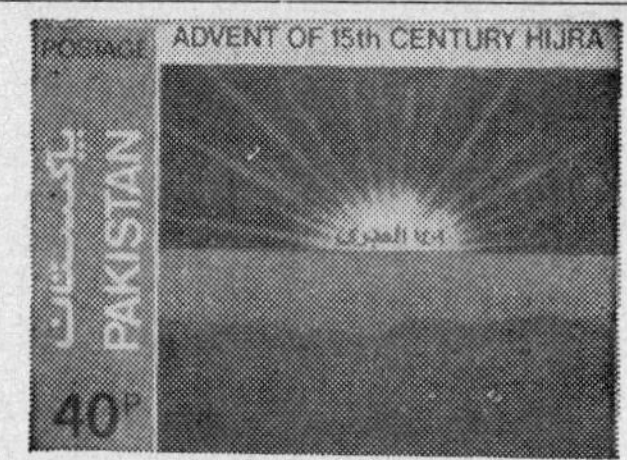

300. Rising Sun.

1980. 1400th Anniv. of Hegira (1st issue). Multicoloured.

541. 40 p. Type **300** 5 5
542. 2 r. Ka'aba and symbols of Muslim achievement (33 × 33 mm.) 25 40
543. 3 r. Koran illuminating the world (30 × 54 mm.) .. 30 60

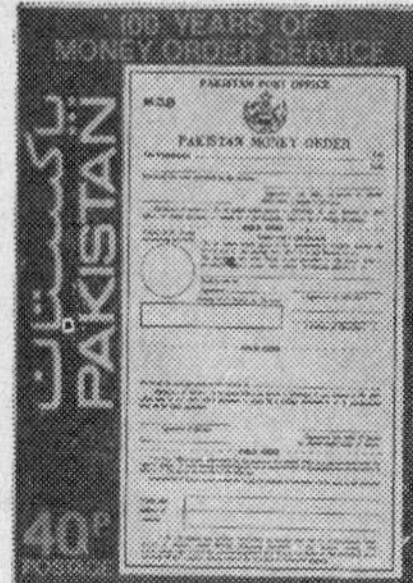

301. Money Order Form.

1980. Centenary of Money Order Service.

545. **301.** 40 p. multicoloured .. 20 50

302. Postcards encircling Globe.

1980. Centenary of Postcard Service.

546. **302.** 40 p. multicoloured .. 20 50

303. Heinrich von Stephan and U.P.U. Emblem.

1981. 150th Birth Anniv. of Heinrich von Stephan (U.P.U. founder).

547. **303.** 1 r. multicoloured .. 20 20

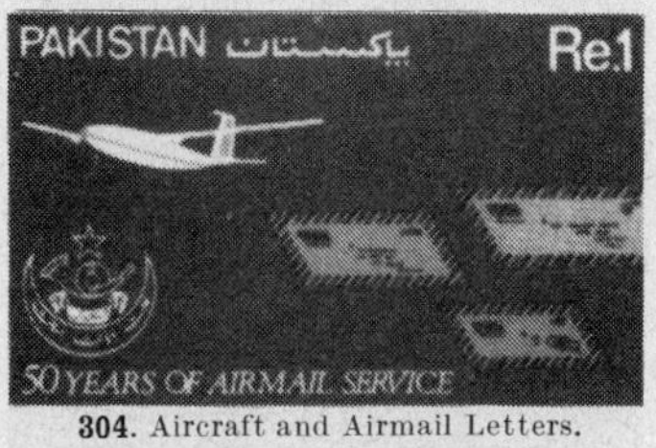

304. Aircraft and Airmail Letters.

1981. 50th Anniv. of Airmail Service.

548. **304.** 1 r. multicoloured .. 30 20

305. Mecca.

1981. 1400th Anniv. of Hegira (2nd issue).

549. **305.** 40 p. multicoloured .. 20 50

306. Conference Emblem and Afghan Refugees.

1981. Islamic Summit Conference (1st issue). Multicoloured.

550. 40 p. Type **306** 25 10
551. 40 p. Conference emblem encircled by flags and Afghan refugees (28 × 58 mm.) 25 10
552. 1 r. Type **306** 40 10
553. 1 r. As No. 551 .. .. 40 10
554. 2 r. Conference emblem and map showing Afghanistan (48 × 32 mm.) .. 55 50

307. Conference Emblem.

1981. Islamic Summit Conference (2nd issue). Multicoloured.

555. 40 p. Type **307** 10 10
556. 40 p. Conference emblem and flags (28 × 46 mm.) 10 10
557. 85 p. Type **307** 20 15
558. 85 p. As No. 556 .. .. 20 15

1981. Birth Centenary of Kemal Ataturk (Turkish statesman).

559. **308.** 1 r. multicoloured .. 20 15

309. Green Turtle.

1981. Wildlife Protection (6th series).

560. **309.** 40 p. multicoloured .. 75 40

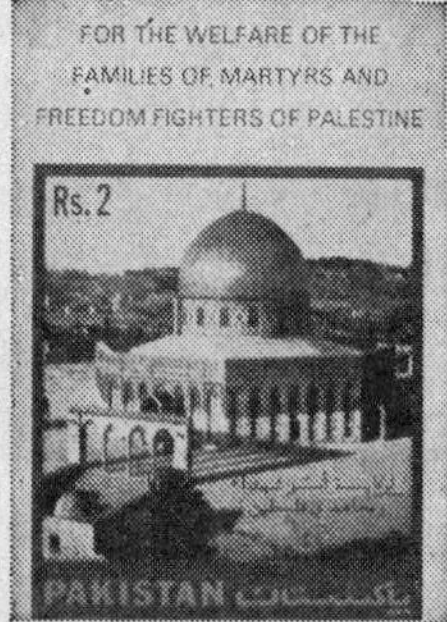

310. Dome of the Rock.

1981. Palestinian Welfare.

561. **310.** 2 r. multicoloured .. 35 35

40P KARAKORAM PAKISTAN

311. Malubiting West.

1981. Mountain Peaks (1st series). Mult.

562. 40 p. Type **311** 40 40
563. 40 p. Malubiting West (24 × 31 mm.) 40 40
564. 1 r. Haramosh 75 75
565. 1 r. Haramosh (24 × 31 mm.) 75 75
566. 1 r. 50 K6 .. .. .. 90 90
567. 1 r. 50 K6 (24 × 31 mm.) .. 90 90
568. 2 r. K2, Broad Peak, Gasherbrum 4 and Gasherbrum 2 .. .. .. 1·00 1·25
569. 2 r. K2 (24 × 31 mm.) .. 1·00 1·25

See also Nos. 674/5.

312. Pakistan Steel " Furnace No. 1 ".

1981. First Firing of Pakistan Steel " Furnace No. 1 ", Karachi.

570. **312.** 40 p. multicoloured .. 25 10
571. 2 r. multicoloured .. 55 50

313. Western Tragopan.

1981. Wildlife Protection (7th series).

572. **313.** 40 p. multicoloured .. 1·25 ·75
573. – 2 r. multicoloured .. 3·25 3·75

DESIGN: 2 r. As Type **313** but with background showing a winter view.

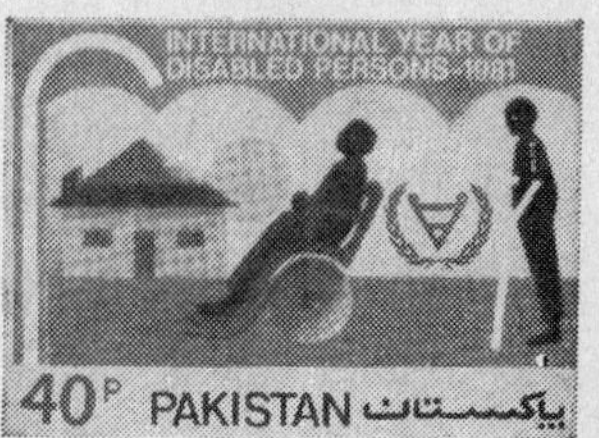

314. Disabled People and I.Y.D.P. Emblem.

1981. International Year for Disabled Persons.

574. **314.** 40 p. multicoloured .. 30 30
575. 2 r. multicoloured .. 95 1·25

315. World Hockey Cup below Flags of participating Countries.

1982. Pakistan—World Cup Hockey Champions. Multicoloured.
576. 1 r. Type **315** .. .. 1·75 1·25
577. 1 r. World Hockey Cup above flags of participating countries .. .. 1·75 1·25

316. Camel Skin Lamp.

1982. Handicrafts (2nd series). Multicoloured.
578. 1 r. Type **316** 50 50
579. 1 r. Hala pottery 50 50
See also Nos. 595/6.

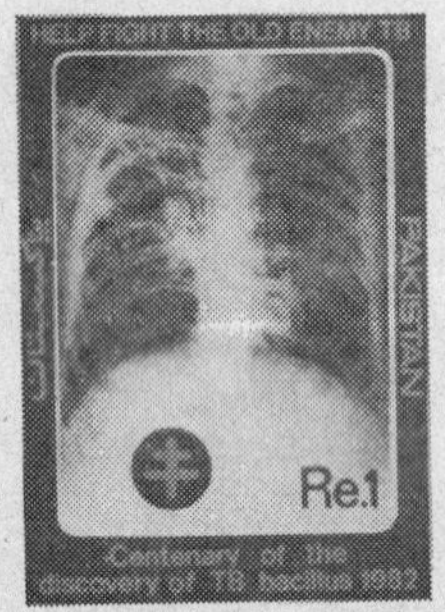

317. Chest X-Ray of Infected Person.

1982. Centenary of Robert Koch's Discovery of Tubercle Bacillus.
580. **317.** 1 r. multicoloured .. 1·00 80

318. Indus Dolphin.

1982. Wildlife Protection (8th series).
581. **318.** 40 p. multicoloured .. 1·50 1·00
582. – 1 r. multicoloured .. 2·75 2·25
DESIGN: 1 r. As Type **318** but with design reversed.

319. " Apollo-Soyuz " Linkup, 1975.

1982. Peaceful Use of Outer Space.
583. **319.** 1 r. multicoloured .. 1·75 75

320. Sukkur Barrage.

1982. 50th Anniv. of Sukkur Barrage.
584. **320.** 1 r. multicoloured .. 30 30

321. Pakistan National Flag and Stylised Sun.

1982. Independence Day. Multicoloured.
585. 40 p. Type **321** 10 30
586. 85 p. Map of Pakistan and stylised torch 20 50

1982. " Riccione 82 " Stamp Exhibition. No. 583. optd **RICCIONE-82.**
587. **320.** 1 r. multicoloured .. 20 20

323. Arabic Inscription and University Emblem.
(Illustration reduced. Actual size 67 × 23 mm.)

1982. Centenary of Punjab University.
588. **323.** 40 p. multicoloured .. 40 20

324. Scout Emblem and Tents.

1983. 75th Anniv. of Boy Scout Movement.
589. **324.** 2 r. multicoloured .. 30 30

325. Laying Pipeline.

1983. Inauguration of Quetta Natural Gas Pipeline Project.
590. **325.** 1 r. multicoloured .. 20 20

326. "Papilio polyctor".

1983. Butterflies. Multicoloured.
591 40 p. Type **326** .. .. 1·00 20
592 50 p. "Atrophaneura aristolochiae" (inscr "Polydorus") .. .. 1·00 20
593 60 p. "Danaus chrysippus" 1·25 50
594 1 r. 50 "Papilio demoleus" 2·00 1·50

1983. Handicrafts (3rd series). As T **316**. Multicoloured.
595. 1 r. Five flower motif needlework, Sind .. 15 15
596. 1 r. Straw mats 15 15

327. School of Nursing and University Emblem.

1983. Presentation of Charter to Aga Khan University, Karachi.
597. **327.** 2 r. multicoloured .. 30 30

328. Yak Caravan crossing Zindiharam-Darkot Pass, Hindu Kush.

1983. Trekking in Pakistan.
598. **328.** 1 r. multicoloured .. 80 45

329. Marsh Crocodile.

1983. Wildlife Protection (9th series).
599. **329.** 3 r. multicoloured .. 3·00 1·75

330. Goitred Gazelle.

1983. Wildlife Protection (10th series).
600. **330.** 1 r. multicoloured .. 2·25 1·75

331. Floral Design.

1983. 36th Anniv. of Independence. Mult.
601. 60 p. Type **331** 10 10
602. 4 r. Hand holding flaming torch 40 45

332. Traditional Weaving, Pakistan.

1983. Indonesian—Pakistan Economic and Cultural Co-operation Organization, 1969–1983. Multicoloured.
603. 2 r. Type **332** 20 25
604. 2 r. Traditional Weaving, Indonesia 20 25

333. "Siberian Cranes" (Great White Cranes). (Sir Peter Scott).

1983. Wildlife Protection (11th series).
605. **333.** 3 r. multicoloured .. 2·50 1·50

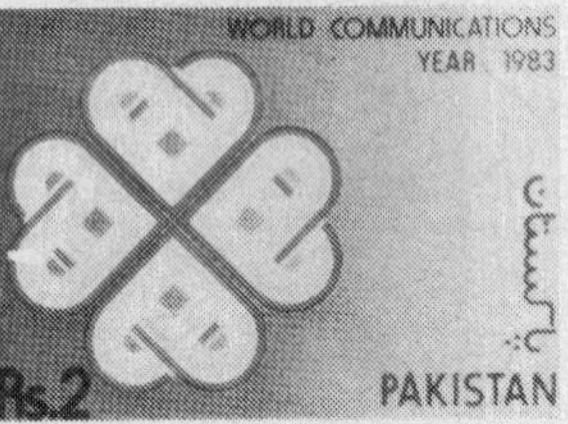

334. W.C.Y. Emblem.

1983. World Communications Year. Multicoloured.
606. 2 r. Type **334** 20 25
607. 3 r. W.C.Y. emblem (different) (33 × 33 mm.) .. 30 35

335. Farm Animals.

1983. World Food Day. Multicoloured.
608. 3 r. Type **335** .. .. 1·25 1·25
609. 3 r. Fruit .. .. .. 1·25 1·25
610. 3 r. Crops .. .. .. 1·25 1·25
611. 3 r. Sea food .. .. 1·25 1·25

336. Agriculture Produce and Fertilizer Factory.

1983. National Fertilizer Corporation.
612. **336.** 60 p. multicoloured .. 15 30

INDEX

Countries can be quickly located by referring to the index at the end of this volume.

337. Lahore, 1852

1983. National Stamp Exhibition, Lahore. Multicoloured.

613.	60 p. Musti Durwaza Dharmsala	35	35
614.	60 p. Khabgha	35	35
615.	60 p. Type 337	35	35
616.	60 p. Summan Burj Hazuri	35	35
617.	60 p. Flower Garden, Samadhi Northern Gate	35	35
618.	60 p. Budda Darya, Badshahi Masjid	35	35

338. Winner of "Enterprise" Event.

1983. Yachting Champions, Asian Games, Delhi. Multicoloured.

619.	60 p. Type 338	1·00	90
620.	60 p. Winner of "OK" Dinghy event	1·00	90

339. Snow Leopard.

1984. Wildlife Protection (12th series).

621.	339.	40 p. multicoloured ..	1·50	75
622.		1 r. 60 multicoloured ..	4·00	4·75

340. Jahangir Khan (world squash champion).

1984. Squash.

623.	340.	3 r. multicoloured ..	1·50	90

341. P.I.A. Airliner.

1984. 20th Anniv. of Pakistan International Airways Service to China.

624.	341.	3 r. multicoloured ..	3·75	3·25

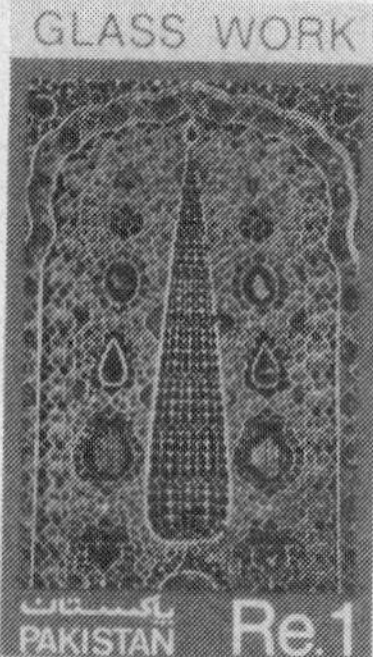

342. Glass-work.

1984. Handicrafts (4th series). Multicoloured, frame colours given.

625.	342.	1 r. blue	15	15
626.	–	1 r. red	15	15
627.	–	1 r. green	15	15
628.	–	1 r. violet	15	15

DESIGNS: showing glass-work in Sheesh Mahal, Lahore Fort. Nos. 627/8 are horizontal designs.

343. Attock Fort.

1984. Forts.

629	–	5 p. black and purple	10	10
630	–	10 p. black and red ..	10	10
631	–	15 p. violet and brown	10	10
632	343	20 p. black and violet	10	10
633	–	50 p. brown and red ..	10	10
634	–	60 p. lt brown & brown	10	10
635	–	70 p. blue	10	10
636	–	80 p. brown and red ..	10	10

DESIGNS: 5 p. Kot Diji Fort. 10 p. Rohtas Fort. 15 p. Bala Hissar Fort. 50 p. Hyderabad Fort. 60 p. Lahore Fort. 70 p. Sibi Fort. 80 p. Ranikot Fort.

344. Shah Rukn i Alam's Tomb, Multan.

1984. Aga Khan Award for Architecture.

647.	344.	60 p. multicoloured ..	1·00	1·00

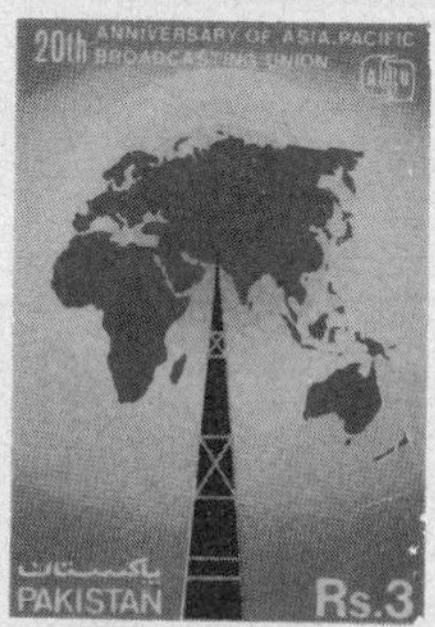

345. Radio Mast and Map of World.

1984. 20th Anniv. of Asia-Pacific Broadcasting Union.

648.	345.	3 r. multicoloured ..	80	60

346. Wrestling.

1984. Olympic Games, Los Angeles. Mult.

649.	3 r. Type 346	1·00	75
650.	3 r. Boxing	1·00	75
651.	3 r. Athletics	1·00	75
652.	3 r. Hockey	1·00	75
653.	3 r. Yachting	1·00	75

347. Jasmine (National flower) and Inscription.

1984. Independence Day. Multicoloured.

654.	60 p. Type 347	10	10
655.	4 r. Symbolic torch ..	45	50

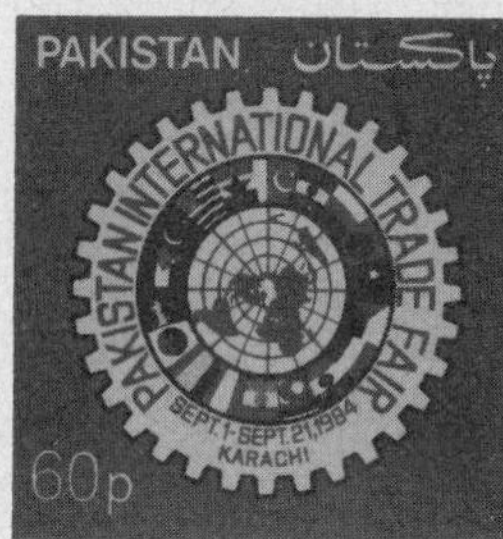

348. Gearwheel Emblem and Flags of Participating Nations.

1984. Pakistan International Trade Fair.

656.	348.	60 p. multicoloured ..	50	30

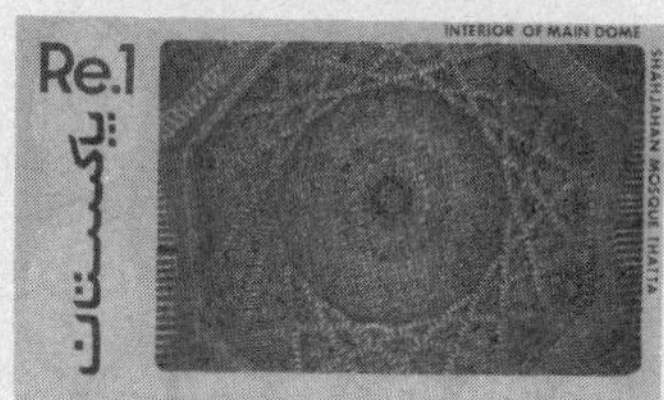

349. Interior of Main Dome.

1984. Tourism Convention. Shahjahan Mosque, Thatta. Multicoloured.

657.	1 r. Type 349	40	40
658.	1 r. Brick and glazed tile work	40	40
659.	1 r. Gateway	40	40
660.	1 r. Symmetrical archways	40	40
661.	1 r. Interior of a dome ..	40	40

350. Bank Emblem in Floral Pattern.

1984. 25th Anniv. of United Bank Ltd.

662.	350.	60 p. multicoloured ..	60	60

351. Conference Emblem.

1984. 20th United Nations Conference of Trade and Development.

663.	351.	60 p. multicoloured ..	60	40

352. Postal Life Insurance Emblem within Hands.

1984. Centenary of Postal Life Insurance. Multicoloured.

664.	60 p. Type 352	35	15
665.	1 r. "100" and Postal Life Insurance emblem ..	45	15

353. Bull (wall painting).

1984. U.N.E.S.C.O. Save Moenjadoro Campaign. Multicoloured.

666.	2 r. Type 353	1·00	1·00
667.	2 r. Bull (seal)	1·00	1·00

354. International Youth Year Emblem and "75".

1985. 75th Anniv. of Girl Guide Movement.

668.	354.	60 p. multicoloured ..	1·50	65

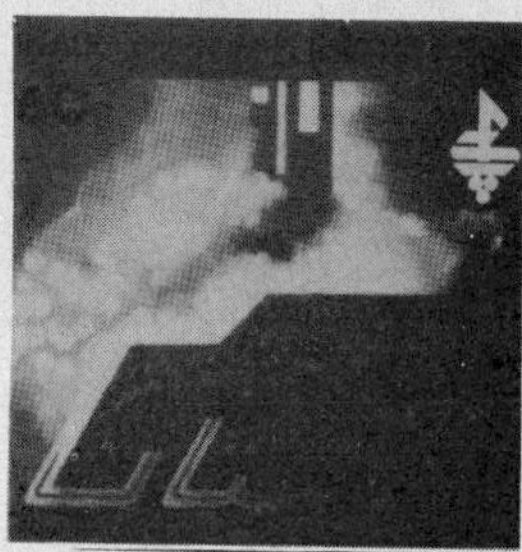

355. Smelting Ore.

1985. Inauguration of Pakistan Steel Corporation. Multicoloured.

669.	60 p. Type 355	50	25
670.	1 r. Pouring molten steel from ladle (28 × 46 mm.)	75	25

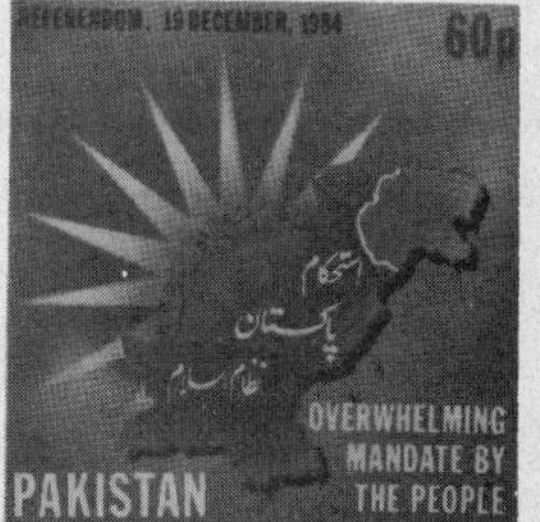

356. Map of Pakistan and Rays of Sun.

1985. Presidential Referendum of 19 December 1984.

671.	356.	60 p. multicoloured ..	60	40

357. Ballot Box and Voting Paper.

1985. March Elections. Multicoloured.

672. 1 r. Type **357** 40 15
673. 1 r. Minar-e-Qarardad-e-Pakistan Tower, and word "Democracy" (31 × 43 mm.) 40 15

1985. Mountain Peaks (2nd series). As T **311**. Multicoloured.

674. 40 p. Rakaposhi (Karakoram Range) .. 1·25 50
675. 2 r. Nangaparbat (Western Himalayas) .. .. 2·50 3·00

358. Trophy and Medals from Olympic Games 1984, Asia Cup 1985 and World Cup 1982. (Illustration reduced, actual size 58 × 28 mm.).

1985. Pakistan Hockey Team "Grand Slam" Success.

676. **358.** 1 r. multicoloured .. 1·75 1·25

359. King Edward Medical College. (Illustration reduced, actual size 57 × 27 mm.).

1985. 125th Anniv. of King Edward Medical College, Lahore.

677. **359.** 3 r. multicoloured .. 1·25 55

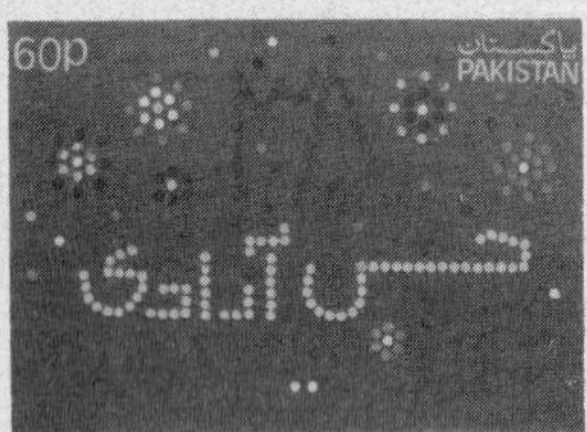

360. Illuminated Inscription in Urdu.

1985. Independence Day. Multicoloured.

678. 60 p. Type **360** 15 15
679. 60 p. Illuminated "XXXVIII" (inscr. in English) 15 15

361. Sind Madressah-tul-Islam, Karachi. (illustration reduced, actual size 56 × 27 mm).

1985. Centenary of Sind Madressah-tul-Islam (theological college), Karachi.

680. **361.** 2 r. multicoloured .. 1·25 70

362. Jamia Masjid Mosque by Day. (Illustration reduced, actual size 47 × 32 mm.).

1985. Inauguration of New Jamia Masjid Mosque, Karachi. Multicoloured.

681. 1 r. Type **362** 65 35
682. 1 r. Jamia Masjid illuminated at night .. 65 35

363. Lawrence College, Murree.

1985. 125th Anniv. of Lawrence College, Murree.

683. **363.** 3 r. multicoloured .. 1·25 55

364. United Nations Building, New York.

1985. 40th Anniv. of United Nations Organization. Multicoloured.

684. 1 r. Type **364** 15 15
685. 2 r. U.N. Building and Emblem 25 25

365. Tents and Jamboree Emblem.

1985. 10th National Scout Jamboree.

686. **365.** 60 p. multicoloured .. 1·50 1·10

366. Islamabad.

1985. 25th Anniv. of Islamabad.

687. **366.** 3 r. multicoloured .. 1·00 45

367. Map of S.A.A.R.C. Countries and National Flags.

1985. 1st Summit Meeting of South Asian Association for Regional Co-operation, Dhaka, Bangladesh. Multicoloured.

688. 1 r. Type **367** .. .. 1·75 3·00
689. 2 r. National flags (39 × 39 mm) .. .. 1·25 1·25

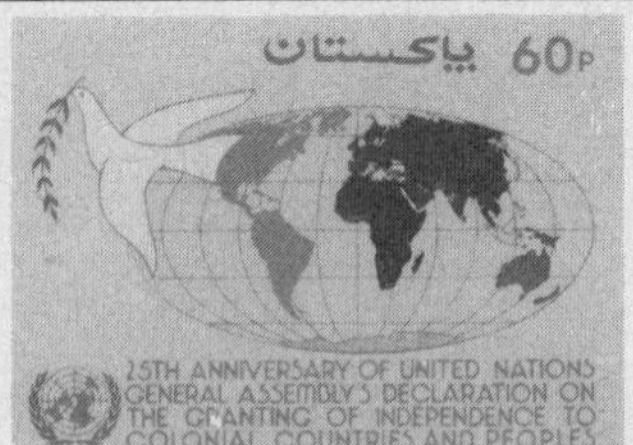

368. Globe and Peace Dove.

1985. 25th Anniv. of U.N. General Assembly's Declaration on Independence for Colonial Territories.

690. **368.** 60 p. multicoloured .. 60 50

369. Peregrine Falcon.

1986. Wildlife Protection (13th series). Peregrine Falcon.

691. **369.** 1 r. 50 multicoloured 3·00 2·75

370. A.D.B.P. Building, Islamabad.

1986. 25th Anniv. of Agricultural Development Bank of Pakistan.

692. **370.** 60 p. multicoloured .. 70 50

371. Government S.E. College.

1986. Centenary of Government Sadiq Egerton College, Bahawalpur.

693. **371.** 1 r. multicoloured .. 80 40

372. Emblem and Bar Graph.

1986. 25th Anniv. of Asian Productivity Organization.

694. **372.** 1 r. multicoloured .. 55 30

373. "1947 1986".

1986. 39th Anniv. of Independence. Multicoloured.

695. 80 p. Type **373** 15 15
696. 1 r. Illuminated inscription in Urdu 15 15

374. Open Air Class.

1986. International Literacy Day.

697. **374.** 1 r. multicoloured .. 30 30

375. Mother and Child.

1986. U.N.I.C.E.F. Child Survival Campaign.

698. **375.** 80 p. multicoloured .. 45 20

376. Aitchison College.

1986. Centenary of Aitchison College, Lahore.

699. **376.** 2 r. 50 multicoloured 30 30

377. Two Doves carrying Olive Branches.

1986. International Peace Year.

700. **377.** 4 r. multicoloured .. 50 50

378. Table Tennis Players.

1986. 4th Asian Cup Table Tennis Tournament, Karachi.

701. **378.** 2 r. multicoloured .. 85 30

379. Argali.

1986. Wildlife Protection (14th series). Argali.

702. **379.** 2 r. multicoloured .. 2·25 1·25

380. Selimiye Mosque, Erdine, Turkey.

1986. "Ecophilex '86" International Stamp Exhibition, Islamabad. Multicoloured.

703. 3 r. Type **380** 85 85
704. 3 r. Gawhar Shad Mosque, Mashhad, Iran 85 85
705. 3 r. Grand Mosque, Bhong, Pakistan 85 85

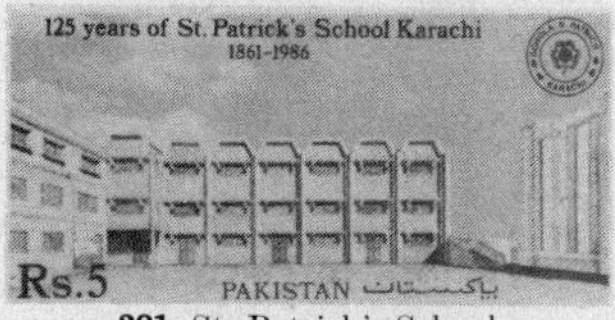

381. St. Patrick's School.

1987. 125th Anniv. of St. Patrick's School, Karachi.

706. **381.** 5 r. multicoloured .. 1·00 90

382. Mistletoe Flowerpecker and Defence Symbols.

1987. Post Office Savings Bank Week. Multicoloured.

707. 5 r. Type **382** 95 55
708. 5 r. Spotted pardalote and laboratory apparatus .. 95 55
709. 5 r. Black-throated blue warbler and agriculture symbols 95 55
710. 5 r. Red-capped manakin and industrial skyline .. 95 55

383. New Parliament House, Islamabad (illustration reduced, actual size 56 × 27 mm).

1987. Inauguration of New Parliament House, Islamabad.

711. **383.** 3 r. multicoloured .. 30 30

384. Opium Poppies and Flames.

1987. Campaign Against Drug Abuse.

712. **384.** 1 r. multicoloured .. 45 20

385. Flag and National Anthem Score.

1987. 40th Anniv. of Independence. Mult.

713. 80 p. Type **385** 10 10
714. 3 r. Text of speech by Mohammed Ali Jinnah, Minar-e-Qardad-e-Pakistan Tower and arms 20 25

386. "Tempest II".

1987. Air Force Day. Military Aircraft. Multicoloured.

715. 3 r. Type **386** 80 80
716. 3 r. Hawker "Fury" .. 80 80
717. 3 r. Supermarine "Attacker" 80 80
718. 3 r. "F86 Sabre" 80 80
719. 3 r. "F104 Star Fighter" .. 80 80
720. 3 r. "C130 Hercules" .. 80 80
721. 3 r. "F6" 80 80
722. 3 r. "Mirage III" 80 80
723. 3 r. "A5" 80 80
724. 3 r. "F16 Fighting Falcon" 80 80

387. Pasu Glacier.

1987. Pakistan Tourism Convention. Views along Karakoram Highway. Multicoloured.

725. 1 r. 50 Type **387** 30 30
726. 1 r. 50 Apricot trees .. 30 30
727. 1 r. 50 Karakoram Highway 30 30
728. 1 r. 50 View from Khunjerab Pass .. 30 30

388. Shah Abdul Latif Bhitai Mausoleum. (Illustration reduced, actual size 53 × 53 mm.).

1987. Shah Abdul Latif Bhitai (poet) Commemoration.

729. **388.** 80 p. multicoloured .. 20 20

389. D. J. Sind Science College, Karachi.

1987. Centenary of D. J. Sind Science College, Karachi.

730. **389.** 80 p. multicoloured .. 20 20

390. College Building.

1987. 25th Anniv. of College of Physicians and Surgeons.

731. **390.** 1 r. multicoloured .. 20 20

391. Homeless People, Houses and Rising Sun.

1987. International Year of Shelter for the Homeless.

732. **391.** 3 r. multicoloured .. 30 30

392. Cathedral Church of the Resurrection, Lahore.

1987. Centenary of Cathedral Church of the Resurrection, Lahore.

733. **392.** 3 r. multicoloured .. 30 30

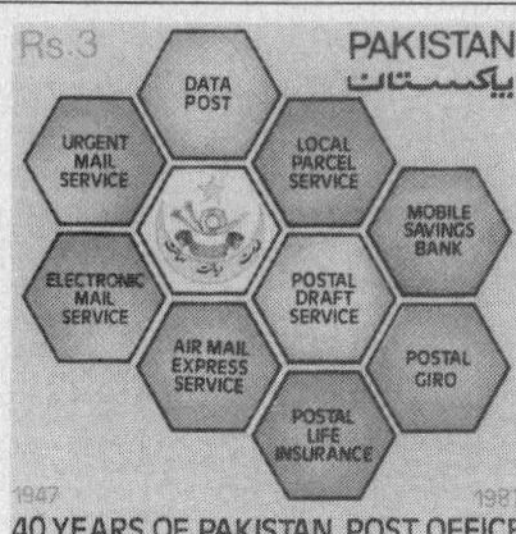

393. Honeycomb and Arms.

1987. 40th Anniv. of Pakistan Post Office.

734. **393.** 3 r. multicoloured .. 30 30

394. Corporation Emblem.

1987. Radio Pakistan's New Programme Schedules.

735. **394.** 80 p. multicoloured .. 15 15

395. Jamshed Nusserwanjee Mehta and Karachi Municipal Corporation Building.

1988. Birth Centenary (1986) of Jamshed Nusserwanjee Mehta (former President of Karachi Municipal Corporation).

736. **395.** 3 r. multicoloured .. 30 30

396. Leprosy Symbols within Flower.

1988. World Leprosy Day.

737. **396.** 3 r. multicoloured .. 35 30

397 W.H.O. Building, Geneva

1988. 40th Anniv of W.H.O.

738 **397** 4 r. multicoloured .. 35 35

398 Globe

1988. 125th Anniv of International Red Cross and Crescent.
739 **398** 3 r. multicoloured .. 30 30

399 Crescent, Leaf Pattern and Archway

1988. Independence Day.
740 **399** 80 p. multicoloured .. 10 10
741 4 r. multicoloured .. 25 30

400 Field Events

1988. Olympic Games, Seoul. Multicoloured.
742 10 r. Type **400** 75 75
743 10 r. Track events .. 75 75
744 10 r. Jumping and pole vaulting 75 75
745 10 r. Gymnastics 75 75
746 10 r. Table tennis, tennis, hockey and baseball .. 75 75
747 10 r. Volleyball, football, basketball and handball 75 75
748 10 r. Wrestling, judo, boxing and weightlifting 75 75
749 10 r. Shooting, fencing and archery 75 75
750 10 r. Water sports .. 75 75
751 10 r. Equestrian events and cycling 75 75

401 Markhor

1988. Wildlife Protection (15th series).
752 **401** 2 r. multicoloured .. 30 30

402 Islamia College, Peshawar

1988. 75th Anniv of Islamia College, Peshawar.
753 **402** 3 r. multicoloured .. 30 30

403 Symbols of Agriculture, Industry and Education with National Flags

1988. South Asian Association for Regional Co-operation, 4th Summit Meeting, Islamabad. Multicoloured.
754 25 r. Type **403** .. .. 1·40 1·50
755 50 r. National flags on globe and symbols of communications (33 × 33 mm) .. .. 3·00 3·25
756 75 r. Stamps from member countries (52 × 29 mm) .. 4·25 4·50

1989. Pioneers of Freedom (2nd series). As T **282**. Multicoloured.
757 3 r. Maulana Hasrat Mohani 15 20

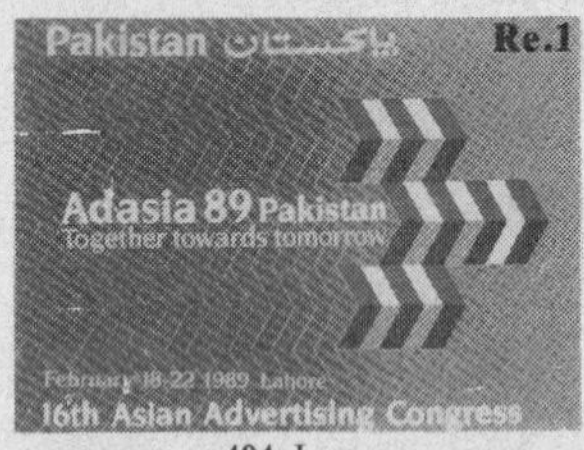

404 Logo

1989. "Adasia 89" 16th Asian Advertising Congress, Lahore.
758 **404** 1 r. multicoloured ("Pakistan" in yellow) 30 30
759 1 r. multicoloured ("Pakistan" in blue) 30 30
760 1 r. multicoloured ("Pakistan" in white) 30 30

405 Zulfikar Ali Bhutto

1989. 10th Death Anniv of Zulfikar Ali Bhutto (statesman). Multicoloured.
761 1 r. Type **405** 15 10
762 2 r. Zulfikar Ali Bhutto (different) 20 20

406 "Daphne" Class Submarine (illustration reduced, actual size 61 × 24 mm)

1989. 25 Years of Pakistan Navy Submarine Operations. Multicoloured.
763 1 r. Type **406** 40 20
764 1 r. "Fleet Snorkel" class submarine 40 20
765 1 r. "Agosta" class submarine 40 20

407 "The Oath of the Tennis Court" (David)

1989. Bicentenary of French Revolution.
766 **407** 7 r. multicoloured .. 60 70

408 Pitcher, c. 2200 B.C.

1989. Archaeological Artefacts. Terracotta pottery from Baluchistan Province. Mult.
767 1 r. Type **408** 15 15
768 1 r. Jar, c. 2300 B.C. .. 15 15
769 1 r. Vase, c. 3600 B.C. .. 15 15
770 1 r. Jar, c. 2600 B.C. .. 15 15

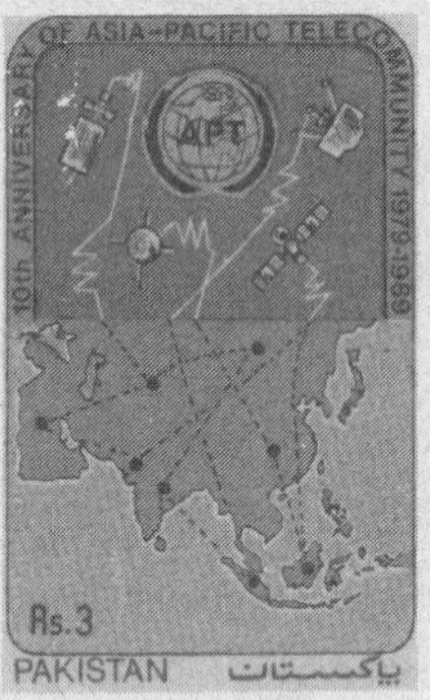

409 Satellites and Map of Asian Telecommunications Network

1989. 10th Anniv of Asia Pacific Telecommunity.
771 **409** 3 r. multicoloured .. 30 30

410 Container Ship at Wharf

1989. Construction of Integrated Container Terminal, Port Qasim.
772 **410** 6 r. multicoloured .. 1·25 1·75

411 Mohammed Ali Jinnah

1989.
773 **411** 1 r. multicoloured .. 10 10
774 1 r. 50 multicoloured .. 15 15
775 2 r. multicoloured .. 20 20
776 3 r. multicoloured .. 30 30
777 4 r. multicoloured .. 45 45
778 5 r. multicoloured .. 50 50

412 Mausoleum of Shah Abdul Latif Bhitai

1989. 300th Birth Anniv of Shah Abdul Latif Bhitai (poet).
779 **412** 2 r. multicoloured .. 20 20

COMMONWEALTH MEMBER

413 Asiatic Black Bear

1989. Wildlife Protection (15th series). Asiatic Black Bear. Multicoloured.
780 4 r. Type **413** 70 70
781 4 r. Bear among boulders 70 70
782 4 r. Standing on rock .. 70 70
783 4 r. Sitting by trees .. 70 70

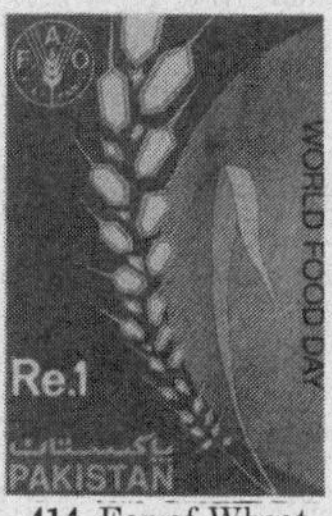

414 Ear of Wheat encircling Globe

1989. World Food Day.
784 **414** 1 r. multicoloured .. 35 35

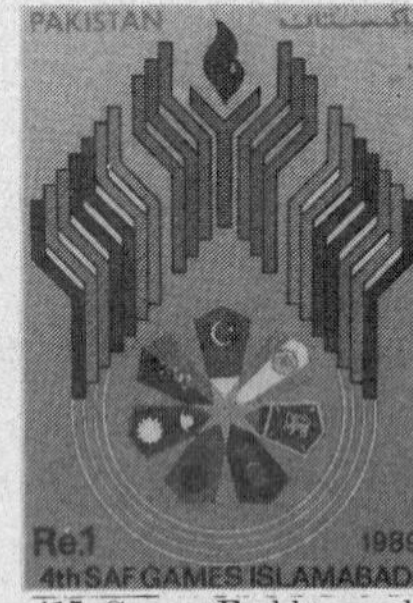

415 Games Emblem and Flags of Member Countries

1989. 4th South Asian Sports Federation Games, Islamabad.
785 **415** 1 r. multicoloured .. 35 35

416 Patchwork Kamblee (cloth) entering Gate of Heaven

1989. 800th Birth Anniv of Baba Farid (Muslim spiritual leader).
786 **416** 3 r. multicoloured .. 30 30

417 Pakistan Television Logo

1989. 25th Anniv of Television Broadcasting in Pakistan.
787 417 3 r. multicoloured .. 30 30

418 Family of Drug Addicts in Poppy Bud

1989. South Asian Association for Regional Co-operation Anti-Drugs Campaign.
788 418 7 r. multicoloured .. 55 70

419 Murray College, Sialkot

1989. Centenary of Murray College, Sialkot.
789 419 6 r. multicoloured .. 50 70

420 Government College, Lahore

1989. 125th Anniv of Government College, Lahore.
790 420 6 r. multicoloured .. 50 70

421 Fields, Electricity Pylons and Rural Buildings

1989. 10th Anniv of Centre for Asia and Pacific Integrated Rural Development.
791 421 3 r. multicoloured .. 30 40

422 Emblem and Islamic Patterns

1990. 20th Anniv of Organization of the Islamic Conference.
792 422 1 r. multicoloured .. 20 20

423 Hockey Match (illustration reduced, actual size 59 × 27 mm)

1990. 7th World Hockey Cup, Lahore.
793 423 2 r. multicoloured .. 1·25 1·25

424 Mohammed Iqbal addressing Crowd and Liaquat Ali Khan taking Oath

1990. 50th Anniv of Passing of Pakistan Resolution. Multicoloured.
794 1 r. Type 424 .. .. 40 40
795 1 r. Maulana Mohammad Ali Jauhar and Mohammed Ali Jinnah with banner 40 40
796 1 r. Women with Pakistan flag, and Mohammed Ali Jinnah taking Governor-General's oath, 1947 .. 40 40
797 7 r. Minār-i-Qarardad-e-Pakistan Monument and Resolution in Urdu and English (86 × 42 mm) 85 85
Nos. 794/6 were printed together, se-tenant, forming a composite design.

425 Pregnant Woman resting

1990. "Safe Motherhood" South Asia Conference, Lahore.
798 425 5 r. multicoloured .. 50 50

426 "Decorated Verse by Ghalib" (Shakir Ali) (illustration reduced, actual size 59 × 27mm)

1990. Painters of Pakistan (1st series). Shakir Ali.
799 426 1 r. multicoloured .. 30 30
See also Nos. 856/7.

427 Satellite in Night Sky

1990. Launch of "Badr 1" Satellite.
800 427 3 r. multicoloured .. 30 30

428 Allama Mohammed Iqbal

1990. Pioneers of Freedom (3rd series). Each brown and green.
801 1 r. Type 428 .. .. 10 10
802 1 r. Mohammed Ali Jinnah 10 10
803 1 r. Sir Syed Ahmad Khan 10 10
804 1 r. Nawab Salimullah .. 10 10
805 1 r. Mohtarma Fatima Jinnah 10 10
806 1 r. Aga Khan III .. 10 10
807 1 r. Nawab Mohammad Ismail Khan 10 10
808 1 r. Hussain Shaheed Suhrawardy 10 10
809 1 r. Syed Ameer Ali .. 10 10
810 1 r. Nawab Bahadur Yar Jung 10 10
811 1 r. Khawaja Nazimuddin 10 10
812 1 r. Maulana Obaidullah Sindhi 10 10
813 1 r. Sahibzada Abdul Qaiyum Khan 10 10
814 1 r. Begum Jahanara Shah Nawaz 10 10
815 1 r. Sir Ghulam Hussain Hidayatullah 10 10
816 1 r. Qazi Mohammad Isa 10 10
817 1 r. Sir M. Shahnawaz Khan Mamdot 10 10
818 1 r. Pir Sahib of Manki Sharif 10 10
819 1 r. Liaquat Ali Khan .. 10 10
820 1 r. Maulvi A.K. Fazl-ul-Haq 10 10
821 1 r. Allama Shabbir Ahmad Usmani .. 10 10
822 1 r. Sadar Abdur Rab Nishtar 10 10
823 1 r. Bi Amma 10 10
824 1 r. Sir Abdullah Haroon 10 10
825 1 r. Chaudhry Rahmat Ali 10 10
826 1 r. Raja Sahib of Mahmudabad 10 10
827 1 r. Hassanally Effendi .. 10 10
See also Nos. 838/46 and 870/2.

429 Cultural Aspects of Indonesia and Pakistan

1990. Indonesia–Pakistan Economic and Cultural Co-operation Organization.
828 429 7 r. multicoloured .. 50 50

430 Globe, Open Book and Pen

1990. International Literacy Year.
829 430 3 r. multicoloured .. 30 30

431 College Crests

1990. Joint Meeting between Royal College of Physicans, Edinburgh, and College of Physicians and Surgeons, Pakistan.
830 431 2 r. multicoloured .. 20 30

432 Children and Globe

1990. U. N. World Summit for Children, New York.
831 432 7 r. multicoloured .. 55 65

433 Girl within Members' Flags

1990. South Asian Association for Regional Co-operation Year of Girl Child.
832 433 2 r. multicoloured .. 20 30

434 Paper passing over Rollers

1990. 25th Anniv of Security Papers Limited.
833 434 3 r. mulitocoloured .. 30 40

435 Civil Defence Worker protecting Islamabad

1991. International Civil Defence Day.
834 **435** 7 r. multicoloured .. 60 70

436 Logo and Flags of Member Countries

1991. South and West Asia Postal Union Commemoration.
835 **436** 5 r. multicoloured .. 65 65

437 Globe and Figures

1991. World Population Day.
836 **437** 10 r. multicoloured .. 85 95

438 Mentally Handicapped Athlete

1991. Pakistan Participation in Special Olympic Games.
837 **438** 7 r. multicoloured .. 75 85

1991. Pioneers of Freedom (4th series). As T **428**. Each brown and green.
838 1 r. Maulana Zafar Ali Khan 15 15
839 1 r. Maulana Mohamed Ali Jauhar 15 15
840 1 r. Chaudhry Khaliquzzaman 15 15
841 1 r. Hameed Nizami 15 15
842 1 r. Begum Ra'ana Liaquat Ali Khan 15 15
843 1 r. Mirza Abol Hassan Ispahani 15 15
844 1 r. Raja Ghazanfar Ali Khan 15 15
845 1 r. Malik Barkat Ali .. 15 15
846 1 r. Mir Jaffer Khan Jamali 15 15

439 Habib Bank Headquarters and Emblem

1991. 50th Anniv of Habib Bank.
847 **439** 1 r. multicoloured .. 15 10
848 5 r. multicoloured .. 55 65

440 St. Joseph's Convent School

1991. 130th Anniv (1992) of St. Joseph's Convent School, Karachi.
849 **440** 5 r. multicoloured .. 60 60

441 Emperor Sher Shah Suri

1991. Emperor Sher Shah Suri (founder of road network) Commemoration.
850 **441** 5 r. multicoloured .. 60 60

442 Jinnah Antarctic Research Station

1991. Pakistan Scientific Expedition to Antarctica.
852 **442** 7 r. multicoloured .. 1·10 1·10

443 Houbara Bustard

1991. Wildlife Protection (16th series).
853 **443** 7 r. multicoloured .. 1·00 1·00

444 Mosque

1991. 300th Death Anniv of Hazrat Sultan Bahoo.
854 **444** 7 r. multicoloured .. 55 55

445 Development Symbols and Map of Asia

1991. 25th Anniv of Asian Development Bank.
855 **445** 7 r. multicoloured .. 55 55

1991. Painters of Pakistan (2nd series). As T **426**. Multicoloured.
856 1 r. "Procession" (Haji Muhammad Sharif) .. 30 30
857 1 r. "Women harvesting" (Ustad Allah Bux) .. 30 30

446 American Express Travellers Cheques of 1891 and 1991 (½-size illustration)

1991. Centenary of American Express Travellers Cheques.
858 **446** 7 r. multicoloured .. 75 75

447 Flag, Banknote and Banking Equipment

1992. 1st Anniv of Muslim Commercial Bank Privatisation. Multicoloured.
859 1 r. Type **447** 10 10
860 7 r. Flag with industrial and commercial scenes 45 45

448 Imran Khan (team captain) and Trophy

1992. Pakistan's Victory in World Cricket Championship. Multicoloured.
861 2 r. Type **448** 30 30
862 5 r. Trophy and national flags (horiz) 65 65
863 7 r. Pakistani flag, trophy and symbolic cricket ball 85 1·00

449 "Rehber-1" Rocket and Satellite View of Earth

1992. International Space Year. Mult.
864 1 r. Type **449** 15 10
865 2 r. Satellite orbiting Earth and logo 20 20

450 Surgical Instruments

1992. Industries. Multicoloured.
866 10 r. Type **450** 45 50
867 15 r. Leather goods .. 65 70
868 25 r. Sports equipment .. 1·10 1·25

451 Globe and Symbolic Family

1992. Population Day.
869 **451** 6 r. multicoloured .. 40 45

1992. Pioneers of Freedom (5th series). As T **428**. Each brown and green.
870 1 r. Syed Suleman Nadvi 15 15
871 1 r. Nawab Iftikhar Hussain Khan Mamdot 15 15
872 1 r. Maulana Muhammad Shibli Naumani .. 15 15

452 Scout Badge and Salute

1992. 6th Islamic Scout Jamboree and 4th Islamic Scouts Conference. Multicoloured.
873 6 r. Type **452** 50 50
874 6 r. Conference centre and scout salute 50 50

453 College Building

1992. Centenary of Islamia College, Lahore.
875 **453** 3 r. multicoloured .. 30 30

INDEX

Countries can be quickly located by referring to the index at the end of this volume.

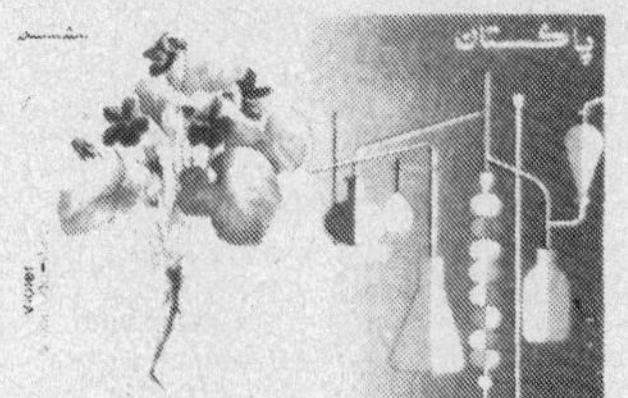

454 "Viola odorata" (flower) and Symbolic Drug Manufacture

1993. Medicinal Plants.

876	454	6 r. multicoloured ..	45	50

455 Emblem

1992. Extraordinary Ministerial Council Session of Economic Co-operation Organization, Islamabad.

877	455	7 r. multicoloured ..	50	60

456 Emblems and Field

1992. International Conference on Nutrition, Rome.

878	456	7 r. multicoloured ..	50	60

457 Alhambra Palace, Granada, Spain

1992. Cultural Heritage of Muslim Granada.

879	457	7 r. multicoloured ..	50	60

458 Baluchistan Costume

1993. Women's Traditional Costumes. Mult.

880	6 r. Type **458**	45	50
881	6 r. Punjab	45	50
882	6 r. Sindh	45	50
883	6 r. North-west Frontier Province	45	50

459 Clasped Hands and Islamic Symbols

1993. 21st Conference of Islamic Foreign Ministers, Karachi.

884	459	1 r. multicoloured ..	15	10
885		6 r. multicoloured ..	45	50

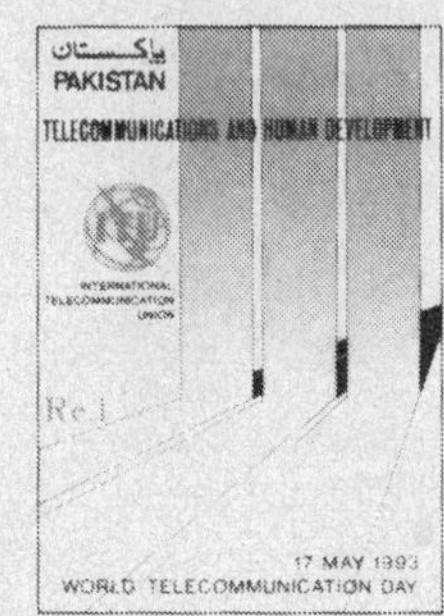

460 I.T.U. Emblem

1993. 25th Anniv of World Telecommunication Day.

886	460	1 r. multicoloured ..	15	10

OFFICIAL STAMPS

1947. King George VI official stamps of India optd. **PAKISTAN.**

O 1.	O 20.	3 p. slate	55	10
O 2.		½ a. purple	30	10
O 3.		9 p. green	2·50	2·50
O 4.		1 a. red	30	10
O 5.		1½ a. violet	30	10
O 6.		2 a. orange	30	10
O 7.		2½ a. violet	3·00	4·00
O 8.		4 a. brown	50	20
O 9.		8 a. violet	70	45
O 10.	93.	1 r. slate and brown (No. O 138)	80	60
O 11.		2 r. purple and brown (No. O 139)	3·50	1·75
O 12.		5 r. green and blue (No. O 140) ..	13·00	19·00
O 13.		10 r. purple and red (No. O 141) ..	30·00	60·00

1948. Optd. **SERVICE.** Crescent moon pointing to right.

O 14	7	3 p. red	10	10
O 15		6 p. violet	10	10
O 37		9 p. green	10	10
O 17	–	1 a. blue	2·75	10
O 18	–	1½ a. green	2·50	10
O 19	–	2 a. red	1·25	10
O 20	–	3 a. green	8·50	2·50
O 21	9	4 a. brown	80	10
O 22	–	8 a. black	80	3·50
O 23	12	1 r. blue	1·00	10
O 42		2 r. brown	2·50	10
O 61		5 r. red	3·25	15
O 26a	13	10 r. mauve	13·00	27·00

1949. Optd. **SERVICE.** Crescent moon pointing to left.

O 38	–	1 a. blue	10	10
O 39	–	1½ a. green	10	10
O 40	–	2 a. red	15	10
O 30	–	3 a. green	8·00	2·25
O 31	–	8 a. black	18·00	9·00

1951. 4th Anniv. of Independence. As Nos. 56, 58 and 60 but inscr. "SERVICE" instead of "PAKISTAN POSTAGE".

O 32.	3 a. purple	2·00	3·50
O 33.	4 a. green	75	10
O 34.	8 a. sepia	3·25	1·00

1954. 7th Anniv. of Independence. Nos. 65/71 optd. **SERVICE.**

O 53	6 p violet	10	10
O 54	9 p. blue	10	30
O 55	1 a. red	10	10
O 56	1½ a. red	10	10
O 57	14 a. myrtle	40	2·25
O 58	1 r. green	40	10
O 51	2 r. orange	1·25	15

1955. 8th Anniv. of Independence. Nos. 74/5 optd. **SERVICE.**

O 63.	6 a. blue	10	10
O 64.	8 a. violet	10	10

1959. 9th Anniv. of Independence. Optd. **SERVICE.**

O 65.	37.	2 a. red	10	10

1961. 1st Anniv. of Republic issue optd. **SERVICE.**

O 62.	41.	10 r. green and orange	6·50	7·00

1961. Optd. **SERVICE.**

O 66.	51.	8 a. green	20	10
O 67.		1 r. blue	20	10

1961. New currency. Provisional stamps, Nos. 122, etc., optd. **SERVICE.**

O 68.	–	1 p. on 1½ a. red ..	10	10
O 69.	7.	2 p. on 3 p. red ..	10	10
O 70.	51.	3 p. on 6 p. purple ..	10	10
O 71.	–	7 p. on 1 a. red ..	10	10
O 72.	51.	13 p. on 2 a. red ..	10	10
O 73.	37.	13 p. on 2 a. red ..	10	10

1961. Definitive issue optd. **SERVICE.**

O 74	60.	1 p. violet	10	10
O 75		2 p. red	10	10
O 79		3 p. purple	10	10
O 94		5 p. blue	10	10
O 81		7 p. green	10	10
O 82	61.	10 p. brown	10	10
O 83		13 p. violet	10	10
O 98		15 p. purple	10	40
O 99		20 p. green	10	30
O 100		25 p. blue	3·25	85
O 85		40 p. purple	10	10
O 102		50 p. turquoise ..	10	15
O 87		75 p. red	20	10
O 104		90 p. green	2·75	2·75
O 88	62.	1 r. red	35	10
O 89		2 r. orange	1·50	20
O 90		5 r. green	4·50	5·00

1979. Optd. **SERVICE.**

O 109.	275.	2 p. green	10	10
O 110.	–	3 p. black	10	10
O 111.	–	5 p. blue	10	10
O 112.	–	10 p. blue and turq.	10	10
O 113.	–	20 p. green (No. 468) ..	10	10
O 114.	–	25 p. green and mauve (No. 489)	10	10
O 115.	–	40 p. blue and mauve (No. 470)	30	10
O 116.	–	50 p. lilac and green (No. 471)	10	10
O 117.	–	60 p. black (No. 472)	1·00	10
O 118.	–	75 p. red (No. 473)	85	10
O 119.	–	1 r. green (No. 475)	1·25	10
O 120.	–	1 r. 50 orange (No. 476)	10	10
O 121.	–	2 r. red (No. 477) ..	15	10
O 122.	–	3 r. blue (No. 478)	20	20
O 123.	–	4 r. black (No. 479)	40	25
O 124.	–	5 r. brown (No. 480)	45	30

1980. As Nos. 513/19 but inscr. "SERVICE".

O 125.	291.	10 p. green & yellow	60	10
O 126.		15 p. deep grn. & grn.	40	10
O 127.		25 p. violet and red	15	10
O 128.		35 p. red and green	15	10
O 129.	–	40 p. red and brown	40	10
O 130.	–	50 p. red and green	20	10
O 131.	–	80 p. green and black	30	20

1984. Nos. 629/30 and 632/6 optd **SERVICE.**

O132	–	5 p. black and purple	10	10
O133	–	10 p. black and red	10	10
O135	343	20 p. black and violet	10	10
O136	–	50 p. brown and red	10	10
O137	–	60 p. lt brown & brn	10	10
O138	–	70 p. blue	10	10
O139	–	80 p. brown and red	10	10

1989. No. 773 optd **SERVICE.**

O140	411	1 r. multicoloured ..	30	20

O 7 State Bank of Pakistan Building, Islamabad

1990.

O141	O 7	1 r. red and green ..	10	10
O142		2 r. red and pink ..	15	20
O143		3 r. red and blue ..	15	20
O144		4 r. red and brown ..	15	20
O145		5 r. red and purple ..	20	25

PALESTINE

A territory at the extreme east of the Mediterranean Sea, captured from the Turks by Great Britain in 1917 and under Military Occupation till 1920. It was a British Mandate of the League of Nations from 1923 to May 1948 when the State of Israel was proclaimed.

1918. 10 milliemes = 1 piastre.
1927. 1.000 mils = £P1.

1.

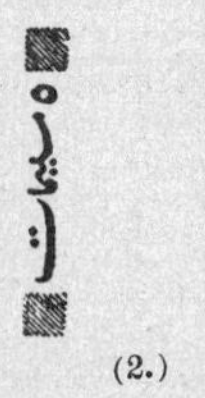

(2.)

1918.

3	1	1 p. blue	2·50	2·50

1918. Surch with T 2.

4	1	5 m. on 1 p. blue	5·00	4·00

3.
("E.E.F." = Egyptian Expeditionary Force).

فلسطين

PALESTINE

פלשתינה א״י

(4.)

1918.

5.	3.	1 m. brown	30	40
6.		2 m. green	30	35
7.		3 m. brown	35	35
8.		4 m. red	35	40
9.		5 m. orange	35	30
10.		1 p. blue	35	25
11.		2 p. olive	60	60
12.		5 p. purple	1·75	2·25
13.		9 p. ochre	2·25	4·00
14.		10 p. blue	2·25	3·00
15.		20 p. grey	9·00	15·00

Nos. 1/15 were also valid in Transjordan, Cilicia, Northern Egypt and Syria.

1920. Optd with T 4.

71	3	1 m. brown	30	30
61		2 m. green	35	30
72		2 m. yellow	35	30
62		3 m. brown	35	30
73		3 m. blue	35	15
74		4 m. red	30	20
75		5 m. orange	35	20
76		6 m. green	65	30
77		7 m. brown	65	30
78		8 m. red	65	30
79		1 p. grey	65	30
65		1 p. blue	60	35
80		13 m. blue	50	15
66		2 p. olive	70	40
67		5 p. purple	4·00	5·00
68		9 p. ochre	12·00	14·00
88		10 p. blue	7·50	2·50
26		20 p. grey	15·00	32·00
89		20 p. violet	9·00	5·50

9. Rachel's Tomb.

10. Dome of the Rock.

11. Citadel, Jerusalem.

12. Sea of Galilee.

1927.

90	9	2 m. blue	30	10
91		3 m. green	30	10
92	10	4 m. red	2·75	1·25
104		4 m. purple	30	10
93	11	5 m. orange	45	10
94a	10	6 m. green	50	20
95	11	7 m. red	4·00	1·00
105		7 m. violet	45	10
96	10	8 m. brown	11·00	5·00
106		8 m. red	60	20
97b	9	10 m. grey	40	10
98	10	13 m. blue	3·75	30
107		13 m. brown	40	10
108a		15 m. blue	50	10

99	**11**	20 m. olive	1·40	15
100a	**12**	50 m. purple	1·00	20
101		90 m. bistre	60·00	60·00
102		100 m. blue	2·00	50
103b		200 m. violet	5·50	3·00
109		250 m. brown	2·50	2·00
110		500 m. red	4·50	2·75
111		£P1 black	5·00	3·25

POSTAGE DUE STAMPS

D 1.

D 2.

1920.

D 1.	**D 1.**	1 m. brown	25·00	38·00
D 2.		2 m. green	18·00	27·00
D 3.		4 m. red	22·00	35·00
D 4.		8 m. mauve	15·00	26·00
D 5.		13 m. blue	15·00	26·00

1924.

D 6.	**D 2.**	1 m. brown	90	1·75
D 7.		2 m. yellow ..	1·00	1·75
D 8.		4 m. green	1·10	1·25
D 9.		8 m. red	2·50	90
D 10.		13 m. blue	2·50	2·50
D 11.		5 p. violet	7·00	1·75

1928. As Type D 2, but inscr. "MIL" instead of "MILLIEME".

D 12.	**D 2.**	1 m. brown	45	75
D 13.		2 m. yellow ..	55	60
D 14.		4 m. green	70	1·25
D 15.		6 m. brown	7·00	7·00
D 16.		8 m. red	1·50	70
D 17.		10 m. grey	1·25	60
D 18.		13 m. blue	1·50	1·50
D 19.		20 m. olive	1·60	1·25
D 20.		50 m. violet	2·50	1·25

PAPUA

(Formerly **BRITISH NEW GUINEA**).

The eastern portion of the island of New Guinea, to the N. of Australia, a territory of the Commonwealth of Australia, now combined with New Guinea. Australian stamps were used after the Japanese defeat in 1945 until the combined issue appeared in 1952.

12 pence = 1 shilling.
20 shillings = 1 pound.

1. Lakatoi (native canoe) with Hanuabada Village in Background.

1901.

9	**1**	½d. black and green ..	3·25	3·75
10		1d. black and red ..	3·00	2·00
11		2d. black and violet ..	6·50	4·00
12		2½d. black and blue ..	8·00	12·00
5		4d. black and brown ..	45·00	35·00
6		6d. black and green ..	42·00	35·00
7		1s. black and orange ..	60·00	65·00
8		2s. 6d. black and brown ..	£600	£550

1906. Optd. **Papua.**

40	**1.**	½d. black and green ..	4·00	5·50
41		1d. black and red ..	3·75	6·00
42		2d. black and violet ..	4·50	2·25
27		2½d. black and blue ..	3·75	13·00
43		4d. black and brown ..	25·00	45·00
29		6d. black and green ..	22·00	42·00
25		1s. black and orange ..	20·00	38·00
37		2s. 6d. black and brown ..	32·00	45·00

6.

1907.

66	**6**	½d. black and green ..	1·40	2·25
94a		1d. black and red ..	1·60	30
68		2d. black and purple ..	3·00	2·50
51a		2½d. black and blue ..	5·50	6·50
63		4d. black and brown ..	3·50	6·50
80		6d. black and green ..	5·50	7·50
81		1s. black and orange ..	5·50	15·00
82		2s. 6d. black and brown	38·00	55·00

1911.

84a.	**6.**	½d. green	30	2·00
85.		1d. red	70	40
86.		2d. mauve	70	75
87.		2½d. blue	4·75	8·50
88.		4d. olive	2·00	11·00
89.		6d. brown	3·75	5·00
90.		1s. yellow	9·00	15·00
91.		2s. 6d. red	32·00	38·00

1916.

93	**6**	½d. green and olive ..	80	80
95		1½d. blue and brown ..	1·50	70
96		2d. purple and red ..	1·50	75
97		2½d. green and blue ..	4·75	11·00
98		3d. black and turquoise	1·25	1·75
99		4d. brown and orange	2·50	4·50
100		5d. grey and brown ..	4·25	15·00
101		6d. purple	3·25	8·50
127		9d. lilac and violet ..	4·00	25·00
102		1s. brown and olive ..	3·50	6·00
128		1s. 3d. lilac and blue ..	7·00	30·00
103		2s. 6d. red and pink ..	18·00	38·00
104		5s. black and green ..	40·00	45·00
105		10s. green and blue ..	£140	£180

1917. Surch **ONE PENNY**.

106a	**6**	1d. on ½d. green ..	50	1·25
107		1d. on 2d. mauve ..	12·00	14·00
108		1d. on 2½d. blue ..	1·25	3·75
109		1d. on 4d. green ..	1·25	4·00
110		1d. on 6d. brown ..	8·00	13·00
111		1d. on 2s. 6d. red ..	1·50	8·00

1929. Air. Optd **AIR MAIL**.

114	**6**	3d. black and turquoise ..	80	7·00

(11.)

1930. Air. Optd. with **T 11.**

118.	**6.**	3d. black and turquoise ..	70	5·50
119.		6d. purple	7·00	10·00
120.		1s. brown and olive ..	4·00	15·00

1931. Surch. in words or figs. and words.

122.	**6.**	2d. on 1½d. blue & brown	1·00	2·00
125.		5d. on 1s. brown & olive	75	1·75
126.		9d. on 2s. 6d. red & pink	5·00	8·50
123.		1s. 3d. on 5d. blk. & grn.	4·00	9·00

15. Motuan Girl.

18. Raggiana Bird of Paradise.

20. Native Mother and Child.

1932.

130.	**15.**	½d. black and orange ..	55	2·50
131.	–	1d. black and green ..	80	30
132.	–	1½d. black and red ..	60	5·00
133.	**18.**	2d. red	7·00	30
134.	–	3d. black and blue ..	2·00	6·50
135.	**20.**	4d. olive	3·00	8·50
136.	–	5d. black and green ..	2·00	4·00
137.	–	6d. brown	4·25	7·00
138.	–	9d. black and violet ..	7·00	18·00
139.	–	1s. green	2·50	11·00
140.	–	1s. 3d. black and purple	8·50	20·00
141.	–	2s. black and green ..	11·00	20·00
142.	–	2s. 6d. black and mauve	24·00	38·00
143.	–	5s. black and brown ..	55·00	60·00
144.	–	10s. violet	75·00	75·00
145.	–	£1 black and grey ..	£170	£170

DESIGNS—VERT. As Type **15.** 1d. Chieftain's son. 1½d. Tree houses. 3d. Papuan dandy. 5d. Masked dancer. 9d. Shooting fish. 1s. Ceremonial platform. 1s. 3d. Lakatoi. 2s. Papuan art. 2s. 6d. Pottery-making. 5d. Native policeman. £1, Delta house. VERT. As Type **18:** 6d. Papuan mother. HORIZ. 10s. Lighting fire.

31. Hoisting the Union Jack.

1934. 50th Anniv. of Declaration of British Protectorate. Inscr. "1884 1834".

146.	**31.**	1d green	80	2·25
147.	–	2d. red	1·75	2·25
148.	**31.**	3d. blue	1·50	3·00
149.	–	5d. purple	6·50	8·00

DESIGN: 2d., 5d. Scene on H.M.S. "Nelson".

1935. Silver Jubilee. Optd. **HIS MAJESTY'S JUBILEE 1910-1935.**

150.	–	1d. black & green (No. 131)	65	1·10
151.	**18.**	2d. red	1·50	90
152.	–	3d. black & blue (No. 134)	1·50	2·50
153.	–	5d. black & green (No. 136)	2·75	2·75

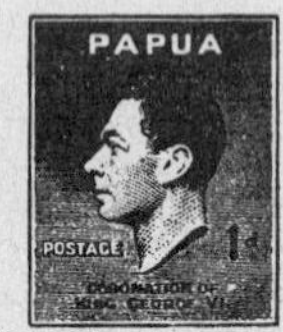

35. King George VI.

1937. Coronation.

154.	**35.**	1d. green	60	15
155.		2d. red	60	20
156.		3d. blue	60	30
157.		5d. purple	60	65

36. Port Moresby.

1938. Air. 50th Anniv. of Declaration of British Possession.

158.	**36.**	2d. red	3·75	2·25
159.		3d. blue	3·75	2·25
160.		5d. green	3·75	3·25
161.		8d. red	10·00	12·00
162.		1s. mauve	28·00	14·00

37. Natives poling Rafts.

1939. Air.

163.	**37.**	2d. red	7·00	3·25
164		3d. blue	7·00	5·00
165.		5d. green	10·00	1·50
166.		8d. red	11·00	2·50
167.		1s. mauve	13·00	5·50
168.		1s. 6d. olive	45·00	32·00

OFFICIAL STAMPS

1931. Optd. **O.S.**

O 55.	**6.**	½d. green and olive	1·00	4·50
O 56a.		1d. black and red ..	3·50	4·75
O 57.		1½d. blue and brown	1·40	11·00
O 58.		2d. brown & purple	2·25	8·50
O 59.		3d. black & turq.	2·25	15·00
O 60.		4d. brown & orange	2·25	13·00
O 61.		5d. grey and brown	6·00	35·00
O 62.		6d. purple and red	4·00	8·50
O 63.		9d. lilac and violet	35·00	50·00
O 64.		1s. brown and olive	8·00	25·00
O 65.		1s. 3d. lilac and blue	35·00	55·00
O 66.		2s. 6d. red and pink	38·00	£100

PAPUA NEW GUINEA

Combined territory on the island of New Guinea administered by Australia under trusteeship. Self-government was established during 1973.

1952. 12 pence = 1 shilling;
20 shillings = 1 pound.
1966. 100 cents = $1 Australian.
1975. 100 toea = 1 kina.

1. Tree Kangaroo. **7.** Kiriwina Chief House.

1952.

1.	**1.**	½d. green	30	10
2.	–	1d. brown	20	10
3.	–	2d. blue	35	10
4.	–	2½d. orange	1·75	40
5.	–	3d. myrtle	1·25	10
6.	–	3½d. red	60	10
6a.	–	3½d. black	11·00	4·25
18.	–	4d. red	1·75	10
19.	–	5d. green	2·25	10
7.	**7.**	6½d. purple	2·25	10
20.	–	7d. green	10·00	10
8.	–	7½d. blue	8·00	3·50
21.	–	8d. blue	1·50	2·00
9.	–	9d. brown	6·00	60
10.	–	1s. green	2·75	10
11.	–	1s. 6d. myrtle	12·00	80
22.	–	1s. 7d. brown	27·00	20·00
12.	–	2s. blue	8·00	10
23.	–	2s. 5d. red	4·75	3·25
13.	–	2s. 6d. purple	7·50	40
24.	–	5s. red and olive	13·00	1·50
14.	–	10s. slate	50·00	8·50
15.	–	£1 brown	60·00	12·00

DESIGNS—AS TYPE **1:** 1 d. Buka head-dresses. 2 d. Native youth. 2½d. Greater Bird of Paradise. 3d. Native policeman. 3½d. Papuan head-dress. 4d., 5d. Cacao plant. As Type **7.** VERT. 7½d. Kiriwina Yam house. 1s. 6d. Rubber tapping. 2s. Sepik dancing masks. 5s. Coffee beans. £1. Native shooting fish. HORIZ. 7d., 8d. Klinki plymill. 9d. Copra making. 1s. Lakatoi (trading canoe). 1s. 7d., 2s. 5d. Cattle. 2s. 6d. Native shepherd and flock. 10s. Map of Papua and New Guinea.

1957. Nos. 4, 1 and 10 surch.

16.	–	4d. on 2½d. orange ..	50	10
25.	**1.**	5d. on ½d. green	80	10
17.	–	7d. on 1s. green	40	10

23. Council Chamber, Port Moresby.

1961. Reconstitution of Legislative Council.

26.	**23.**	5d. green and yellow ..	1·50	25
27.		2s. 3d. green and salmon	4·50	1·50

24. Female, Goroka, New Guinea.

26. Female Dancer.

38. Waterfront, Port Moresby.

28. Traffic Policeman.

1961.

28. 24. 1d. lake .. .. .. 1·50 10
29. – 3d. blue 30 10
47. 38. 8d. green 40 15
30. 26. 1s. green .. .. .. 3·25 15
31. – 2s. purple 45 15
48. – 2s. 3d. blue 40 20
32. 28. 3s. green .. .. .. 2·25 1·00

DESIGNS—As Type **24**: 3d. Tribal elder, Tari, Papua. As Type **38**: 2s. 3d. Piaggio P-166 Aircraft landing at Tapini. As Type **26**: 2s. Male dancer.

29. Campaign Emblem.

1962. Malaria Eradication.

33. 29. 5d. lake and blue .. 45 15
34. 1s. red and brown .. 1·00 25
35. 2s. black and green .. 1·40 70

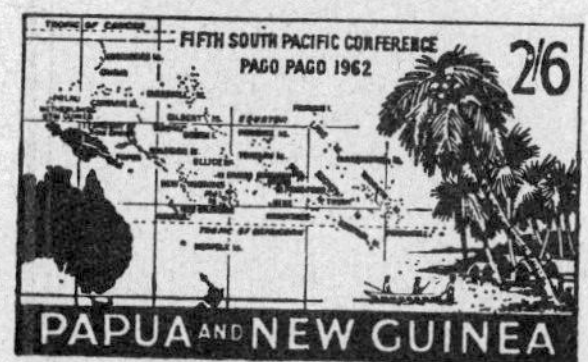

30. Map of South Pacific.

1962. 5th South Pacific Conf., Pago Pago.

36. 30. 5d. red and green .. 70 15
37. 1s. 6d. violet and yellow 2·00 60
38. 2s. 6d. green and blue .. 2·00 1·00

SPORTS: No. 40, High jump. No. 41, Runners.

31. Throwing the Javelin.

1962. 7th British Empire and Commonwealth Games, Perth.

39. 31. 5d. brown and blue .. 30 10
40. – 5d. brown and orange .. 30 10
41. – 2s. 3d. brown and green 1·75 75

34. Raggiana Bird of Paradise. 37. Queen Elizabeth II.

DESIGN—As Type **34**: 6d. Golden Opossum.

36. Rabaul.

1963.

42. 34. 5d. yellow, brown & sepia 1·75 10
43. – 6d. red, brown and grey 1·00 90
44. 36. 10s. multicoloured .. 19·00 8·00
45. 37. £1 brown, gold and green 12·00 2·50

1963. Cent. of Red Cross. As T **163** of Australia.

46. 5 d. red, grey and green .. 70 10

40. Games Emblem.

1963. 1st South Pacific Games. Suva.

49. 40. 5d. brown 10 10
50. 1s. green 30 20

41. Watam Head.

45. Casting Vote.

1964. Native Artifacts. Multicoloured.

51. 11d. Type **41** .. .. 1·00 10
52. 2s. 5d. Watam Head (diff.) 1·00 75
53. 2s. 6d. Bosmun Head .. 1·00 10
54. 5s. Medina Head .. .. 1·25 15

1964. Common Roll Elections.

55. 45. 5d. brown and drab .. 10 10
56. 2s. 3d. brown and blue 20 25

46. "Health Centres".

50. Striped Gardener Bowerbird.

1964. Health Services.

57. 46. 5d. violet 10 10
58. – 8d. green 10 10
59. – 1s. blue 10 10
60. – 1s. 2d. red 25 30

DESIGNS: 8d. "School Health". 1s. "Infant Child and Maternal Health". 1s. 2d. "Medical Training".

1964. Multicoloured.

61. 1d. Type **50** 40 10
62. 3d. Adelbert bowerbird .. 50 10
63. 5d. Blue bird of paradise .. 55 10
64. 6d. Lawes's parotia .. 75 10
65. 8d. Black-billed sicklebill .. 1·25 20
66. 1s. Emperor of Germany bird of paradise .. .. 1·25 10
67. 2s. Brown sicklebill .. 1·00 40
68. 2s. 3d. Lesser bird of paradise .. .. 1·00 85
69. 3s. Magnificent bird of paradise .. .. 1·25 1·25
70. 5s. Twelve-wired bird of paradise .. .. 16·00 2·00
71. 10s. Magnificent rifle-bird .. 11·00 5·50

Nos. 66/71 are larger (25½ × 36½ mm.).

61. Canoe Prow.

1965. Sepik Canoe Prows in Port Moresby Museum.

72. 61. 4d. multicoloured .. 40 10
73. – 1s. 3d. multicoloured .. 1·75 85
74. – 1s. 6d. multicoloured .. 50 10
75. – 4s. multicoloured .. 1·50 30

Each show different carved canoe prows as Type **61**.

1965. 50th Anniv. of Gallipoli Landing. As T **184** of Australia, but slightly larger (22 × 34½ mm.).

76. 2s. 3d. brown, black and green 20 10

65. Urban Plan and Native House.

1965. 6th South Pacific Conf., Lae.

77. 65. 6d. multicoloured .. 10 10
78. – 1s. multicoloured .. 10 10

No. 78 is similar to Type **65** but with the plan on the right and the house on the left. Also "URBANISATION" reads downwards.

66. Mother and Child.

1965. 20th Anniv. of U.N.O.

79. 66. 6d. sepia, blue & turquoise 10 10
80. – 1s. brown, blue & violet 10 10
81. – 2s. blue, green and olive 10 10

DESIGNS—VERT. 1s. Globe and U.N. Emblem. 2s. U.N. Emblem and Globes.

69. 'Papilio ulysses'.

1966. Decimal Currency. Multicoloured.

82 1 c. Type **69** 40 40
83 3 c. "Marpesia acilia" .. 40 50
84 4 c. "Graphium weiskei" .. 40 20
85 5 c. "Terinos alurgis" .. 40 10
86 10 c. "Ornithoptera priamus" 50 30
86a 12 c. "Euploea callithoe" 2·25 2·25
87 15 c. "Papilio euchenor" .. 4·25 80
88 20 c. "Parthenos sylvia" .. 2·50 25
89 25 c. "Delias aruna" .. 4·50 70
90 50 c. "Apatarina erminea" 12·00 1·25
91 $1 "Doleschallia dascylus" 3·50 1·25
92 $2 "Ornithoptera paradisea" .. .. 6·50 6·50

Nos. 86/92 are horiz.

80. "Molala Harai". 84. Throwing the Discus.

1966. Folklore. Elema Art (1st series).

93. 80. 2 c. black and red .. 10 10
94. – 7 c. black, yellow and blue 10 10
95. – 30 c. black, red and green 15 10
96. – 60 c. black, red & yellow 40 30

DESIGNS: 7 c. "Marai". 30 c. "Meavea Kivovia". 60 c. "Toivita Tapaivita".

1966. South Pacific Games, Noumea. Mult.

97. 5 c. Type **84** 10 10
98. 10 c. Football 10 10
99. 20 c. Tennis 15 10

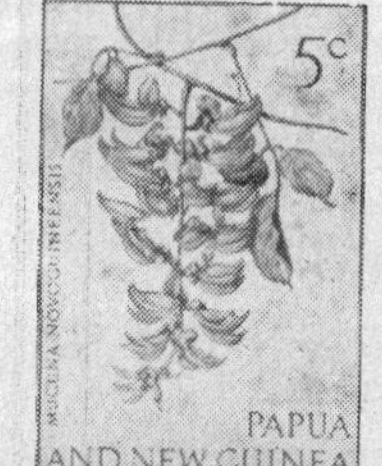

87. "Mucuna novoguineensis".

1966. Flowers. Multicoloured.

100. 5 c. Type **87** 15 10
101. 10 c. "Tecomanthe dendrophila" 15 10
102. 20 c. "Rhododendron macgregoriae" 25 10
103. 60 c. "Rhododendron konori" 55 70

91. "Fine Arts".

1967. Higher Education. Multicoloured.

104. 1 c. Type **91** 10 10
105. 3 c. "Surveying" 10 10
106. 4 c. "Civil Engineering" 10 10
107. 5 c. "Science" 10 10
108. 20 c. "Law" 10 10

96. "Sagra speciosa".

100. Laloki River.

1967. Fauna Conservation (Beetles). Mult.

109. 5 c. Type **96** 20 10
110. 10 c. "Eupholus schoenherri" 30 10
111. 20 c. "Sphingnotus albertisi" 50 10
112. 25 c. "Cyphogastra albertisi" 55 10

1967. Laloki River Hydro-Electric Scheme, and "New Industries". Multicoloured.

113. 5 c. Type **100** 10 10
114. 10 c. Pyrethrum 10 10
115. 20 c. Tea Plant 10 10
116. 25 c. Type **100** 10 10

103. Air Attack at Milne Bay.

1967. 25th Anniv. of Pacific War. Mult.

117. 2 c. Type **103** 10 30
118. 5 c. Kokoda Trail (vert.) .. 10 10
119. 20 c. The Coast Watchers .. 15 10
120. 50 c. Battle of the Coral Sea 50 40

107. Papuan Lory. 111. Chimbu Head-dress.

1967. Christmas. Territory Parrots. Mult.

121. 5 c. Type **107** 20 10
122. 7 c. Pesquet's Parrot .. 25 30
123. 30 c. Dusky Lory 60 10
124. 25 c. Edward's Fig Parrot 60 10

1968. "National Heritage". Designs showing different Head-dresses. Multicoloured.

125.	5 c. Type **111**	10	10
126.	10 c. Southern Highlands (horiz.)	10	10
127.	20 c. Western Highlands (horiz.)	15	10
128.	60 c. Chimbu (different)	40	20

115. "Hyla thesaurensis".

1968. Fauna Conservation (Frogs). Mult.

129.	5 c. Type **115**	15	20
130.	10 c. "Hyla iris"	15	10
131.	15 c. "Ceratobatrachus guentheri"	15	10
132.	20 c. "Nyctimystes narinosa"	20	20

119. Human Rights Flame and Papuan Head-dress (abstract).

1968. Human Rights Year. Multicoloured.

133.	5 c. Type **119**	10	10
134.	10 c. Human Rights in the World (abstract)	10	10

121. Leadership (abstract).

1968. Universal Suffrage. Multicoloured.

135.	20 c. Type **121**	15	10
136.	25 c. Leadership of the Community (abstract)	15	10

123. Egg Cowry.

1968. Seashells. Multicoloured.

137.	1 c. Type **123**	10	10
138.	3 c. Lancinated Conch	30	40
139.	4 c. Lithograph Cone	20	40
140.	5 c. Marbled Cone	25	10
141.	7 c. Episcopal Mitre	35	10
142.	10 c. Red Volute	45	10
143.	12 c. Areola Bonnet	1·50	1·25
144.	15 c. Scorpion Conch	80	40
145.	20 c. Fluted Clam	90	10
146.	25 c. Chocolate Flamed Venus Shell	90	30
147.	30 c. Giant Murex	1·25	65
148.	40 c. Chambered Nautilus	1·00	50
149.	60 c. Pacific Triton	1·25	20
150.	$1 Emerald Snail	3·00	50
151.	$2 Glory of the Sea	19·00	4·75

138. Tito Myth.

142. "Fireball" Class Yacht.

1969. Folklore. Elema Art (2nd series).

152.	**138.**	5 c. black, yellow & red	10	15
153.	–	5 c. black, yellow & red	10	15
154.	–	10 c. black, grey and red	15	25
155.	–	10 c. black, grey and red	15	25

DESIGNS: No. 153, Iko Myth. No. 154, Luvuapo Myth. No. 155, Miro Myth.

1969. Third South Pacific Games, Port Moresby.

156.	**142.**	5 c. black	10	10
157.	–	10 c. violet	10	10
158.	–	20 c. green	15	15

DESIGNS—HORIZ. 10 c. Swimming pool, Boroko. 20 c. Games Arena, Konedobu.

145. "Dendrobium ostrinoglossum".

149. Bird of Paradise.

1969. Flora Conservation (Orchids). Multicoloured.

159.	5 c. Type **145**	25	10
160.	10 c. "Dendrobium lawesii"	35	50
161.	20 c. "Dendrobium pseudo-frigidum"	55	70
162.	30 c. "Dendrobium conanthum"	70	50

1969. Coil Stamps.

162a.	**149.**	2 c. blue, blk. & red	10	15
163.		5 c. grn., brn. & orange	10	10

150. Native Potter.

1969. 50th Anniv. of I.L.O.

164.	**150.**	5 c. multicoloured	10	10

151. Tareko.

1969. Musical Instruments.

165.	**151.**	5 c. multicoloured	10	10
166.	–	10 c. black, grn. & yellow	10	10
167.	–	25 c. blk., yellow & brn.	15	15
168.	–	30 c. multicoloured	25	15

DESIGNS: 10 c. Garamut. 25 c. Iviliko. 30 c. Kundu.

155. Prehistoric Ambun Stone.

1970. "National Heritage". Multicoloured.

169.	5 c. Type **155**	15	10
170.	10 c. Masawa canoe of Kula Cicuit	20	15
171.	25 c. Torres' map, 1606	45	15
172.	30 c. H.M.S. "Basilisk" (paddle-sloop), 1873	60	20

159. King of Saxony Bird of Paradise.

1970. Fauna Conservation. Birds of Paradise. Multicoloured.

173.	5 c. Type **159**	1·00	15
174.	10 c. King Bird of Paradise	1·50	60
175.	15 c. Raggiana Bird of Paradise	2·25	1·00
176.	25 c. Sickle Crested Bird of Paradise	2·50	70

163. McDonnell Douglas "D.C. 6B" and Mt. Wilhelm.

1970. Australian and New Guinea Air Services. Multicoloured.

177.	5 c. Type **163**	25	10
178.	5 c. "Lockheed Electra" (turbo-prop), and Mt. Yule	25	10
179.	5 c. Boeing "727" (jet), and Mt. Giluwe	25	10
180.	5 c. Fokker "Friendship" and Manam Island	25	10
181.	25 c. "D.C. 3." and Matupi Volcano	60	40
182.	30 c. Boeing "707" and Hombrom's Bluff	70	60

169. N. Miklouho-Maclay (scientist) and Effigy.

1970. 42nd A.N.Z.A.A.S. Congress, Port Moresby. Multicoloured.

183	5 c. Type **169**	10	10
184	10 c. B. Malinowski (anthropologist) and native hut	20	10
185	15 c. T. Salvadori (ornithologist) and double-wattled cassowary	60	25
186	20 c. F. R. R. Schlechter (botanist) and flower	60	25

A.N.Z.A.A.S. = Australian–New Zealand Association for the Advance of Science.

170. Wogeo Island Food Bowl.

171. Eastern Highlands Dwelling.

1970. Native Artifacts. Multicoloured.

187.	5 c. Type **170**	10	10
188.	10 c. Lime Pot	20	10
189.	15 c. Albom Sago Storage Pot	20	10
190.	30 c. Manus Island Bowl (horiz.)	25	30

1971. Native Dwellings. Multicoloured.

191.	5 c. Type **171**	15	10
192.	7 c. Milne Bay Stilt Dwelling	15	20
193.	10 c. Purari Delta Dwelling	15	10
194.	40 c. Sepik Dwelling	35	70

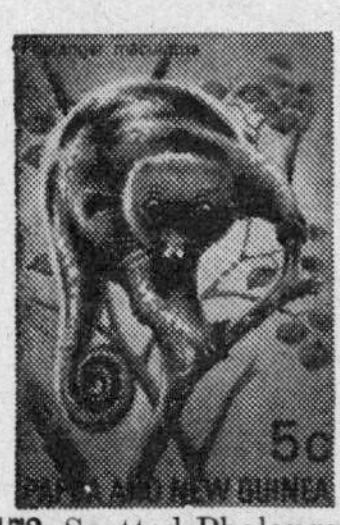

172. Spotted Phalanger.

174. Bartering Fish for Vegetables.

173. "Basketball".

1971. Fauna Conservation. Multicoloured.

195.	5 c. Type **172**	30	10
196.	10 c. Long-fingered Possum	60	15
197.	15 c. Feather-tailed Possum	1·25	1·00
198.	25 c. Long-nosed Echidna	1·75	1·00
199.	30 c. Ornate Tree Kangaroo (horiz)	1·75	70

1971. 4th South Pacific Games, Papeete. Multicoloured.

200.	7 c. Type **173**	10	10
201.	14 c. "Sailing"	15	20
202.	21 c. "Boxing"	15	30
203.	28 c. "Athletics"	15	40

1971. Primary Industries. Multicoloured.

204.	7 c. Type **174**	15	10
205.	9 c. Man stacking yams	20	30
206.	14 c. Vegetable market	30	10
207.	30 c. Highlanders cultivating garden	50	65

175. Sia Dancer.

1971. Native Dancers. Multicoloured.

208.	7 c. Type **175**	20	10
209.	9 c. Urasena dancer	30	20
210.	20 c. Siassi Tubuan dancers (horiz.)	80	90
211.	28 c. Sia dancers (horiz.)	1·00	1·10

176. Papuan Flag over Australian Flag.

1971. Constitutional Development.

212.	**176.**	7 c. multicoloured	30	10
213.	–	7 c. multicoloured	30	10

DESIGN: No. 213, Crest of Papua New Guinea and Australian coat of arms.

177. Map of Papua New Guinea and Flag of South Pacific Commission.

1972. 25th Anniv. of South Pacific Commission.

214.	**177.**	15 c. multicoloured	65	55
215.	–	15 c. multicoloured	65	55

DESIGN: No. 215, Man's face and flag of the Commission.

178. Turtle.

1972. Fauna Conservation (Reptiles). Mult.

216.	7 c. Type **178**	40	10
217.	14 c. Rainforest Dragon	1·00	1·25
218.	21 c. Green Python	1·25	1·50
219.	30 c. Salvador's Monitor	1·75	1·25

179. Curtiss "Seagull MF-6" and "Eureka" (schooner).

1972. 50th Anniv. of Aviation. Multicoloured.

No.	Description	Unused	Used
220.	7 c. Type **179**	40	10
221.	14 c. De Havilland "37" and native porters . .	1·00	1·25
222.	20 c. Junkers "G-31" and gold dredger	1·10	1·25
223.	25 c. Junkers "F-13" and mission church	1·10	1·25

180. New National Flag.

1972. National Day. Multicoloured.

No.	Description	Unused	Used
224.	7 c. Type **180**	30	10
225.	10 c. Native drum	35	25
226.	30 c. Blowing the conch-shell	60	50

181. Rev. Copland King.

1972. Christmas. Missionaries. Mult.

No.	Description	Unused	Used
227.	7 c. Type **181**	25	40
228.	7 c. Rev. Dr. Flierl . .	25	40
229.	7 c. Bishop Verjus . .	25	40
230.	7 c. Pastor Ruatoka . .	25	40

182. Mt. Tomavatur Station.

1973. Completion of Telecommunications Project, 1968-72. Multicoloured.

No.	Description	Unused	Used
231.	7 c. Type **182**	45	20
232.	7 c. Mt. Kerigomma Station	45	20
233.	7 c. Sattelburg Station . .	45	20
234.	7 c. Wideru Station	45	20
235.	9 c. Teleprinter	45	55
236.	30 c. Network map . .	1·25	1·50

Nos. 235/6 are larger, 36 × 26 mm.

183. Queen Carola's Parotia.

1973. Birds of Paradise. Multicoloured.

No.	Description	Unused	Used
237.	7 c. Type **183**	1·75	35
238.	14 c. Goldies' Bird of Paradise	3·00	1·25
239.	21 c. Ribbon-tailed Bird of Paradise . .	3·50	2·00
240.	28 c. Princess Stephanie's Bird of Paradise . .	5·00	2·50

Nos. 229/40 are size 18 × 49 mm.

184. Wood Carver.

1973. Multicoloured.

No.	Description	Unused	Used
241.	1 c. Type **184**	10	10
242.	3 c. Wig-makers	40	10
243.	5 c. Mt. Bagana	55	10
244.	6 c. Pig Exchange	70	90
245.	7 c. Coastal village . .	30	10
246.	8 c. Arawe mother . .	35	30
247.	9 c. Fire dancers	30	20
248.	10 c. Tifalmin hunter . .	55	10
249.	14 c. Crocodile hunters . .	45	70
250.	15 c. Mt. Elimbari . .	50	30
251.	20 c. Canoe-racing, Manus	1·50	40
252.	21 c. Making sago	65	80
253.	25 c. Council House . .	70	45
254.	28 c. Menyamya bowmen	80	75
255.	30 c. Shark-snaring . .	1·25	75
256.	40 c. Fishing canoes, Madang	1·50	80
257.	60 c. Tapa cloth-making . .	3·50	1·00
258.	$1 Asaro Mudmen . .	5·00	3·25
259.	$2 Enga "Sing Sing" . .	10·00	8·50

185. Stamps of German New Guinea, 1897. (Illustration reduced. Actual size 51 × 31 mm.)

1973. 75th Anniv. of Papua New Guinea Stamps.

No.	Type	Description	Unused	Used
260.	**185.**	1 c. multicoloured . .	15	15
261.	–	6 c. indigo, blue & silver	25	35
262.	–	7 c. multicoloured . .	30	35
263.	–	9 c. multicoloured . .	35	45
264.	–	25 c. orange and gold . .	60	1·00
265.	–	30 c. plum and silver . .	75	1·25

DESIGNS—As Type **185**. 6 c. 2 mark stamp of German New Guinea, 1900. 7 c. Surcharged registration label of New Guinea, 1914. 46 × 35 mm. 9 c. Papuan 1 s. stamp, 1901. 45 × 38 mm. 25 c. ½ d. stamp of New Guinea, 1925. 30 c. Papuan 10 s. stamp, 1932.

186. Native Carved Heads.

1973. Self-Government.

No.	Type	Description	Unused	Used
266	**186.**	7 c. multicoloured . .	30	15
267.		10 c. multicoloured . .	50	65

187. Queen Elizabeth II (from photo by Karsh).

1974. Royal Visit.

No.	Type	Description	Unused	Used
268.	**187.**	7 c. multicoloured . .	25	15
269.		30 c. multicoloured . .	1·00	1·75

188. Blyth's Hornbill.

1974. Bird's Heads. Multicoloured.

No.	Description	Unused	Used
270.	7 c. Type **188**	2·00	70
271.	10 c. Double-wattled Cassowary (33 × 49 mm.) . .	3·00	3·25
272.	30 c. New Guinea Harpy Eagle	7·00	8·50

189. "Dendrobium bracteosum".

1974. Flora Conservation. Multicoloured.

No.	Description	Unused	Used
273.	7 c. Type **189** . .	50	10
274.	10 c. "D. anosmum" . .	1·00	50
275.	20 c. "D. smillieae" . .	1·40	1·25
276.	30 c. "D. insigne" . .	1·75	1·75

190. Motu Lakatoi.

1974. National Heritage. Canoes. Mult.

No.	Description	Unused	Used
277.	7 c. Type **190**	30	10
278.	10 c. Tami two-mast morobe	45	60
279.	25 c. Aramia racing canoe	1·10	2·00
280.	30 c. Buka Island canoe . .	1·10	1·25

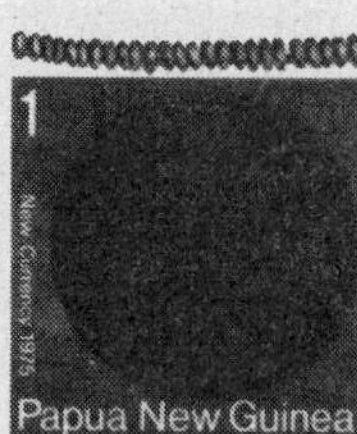

191. 1-toea Coin.

1975. New Coinage. Multicoloured.

No.	Description	Unused	Used
281.	1 t. Type **191**	10	10
282.	7 t. New 2 t. and 5 t. coins	40	10
283.	10 t. New 10 t. coin . .	60	30
284.	20 t. New 20 t. coin . .	1·00	80
285.	1 k. New 1 k. coin . .	3·50	4·00

SIZES: 10 t., 20 t. As Type **191**. 7 t., 1 k. 45 × 26 mm.

192. "Ornithoptera alexandrae". **193.** Boxing.

1975. Fauna Conservation (Birdwing Butterflies). Multicoloured.

No.	Description	Unused	Used
286.	7 t. Type **192** . .	50	10
287.	10 t. "O. victoriae regis"	80	65
288.	30 t. "O. allottei" . .	1·75	2·00
289.	40 t. "O. chimaera" . .	2·25	3·25

1975. 5th South Pacific Games, Guam. Multicoloured.

No.	Description	Unused	Used
290.	7 t. Type **193** . .	15	10
291.	20 t. Running	25	30
292.	25 t. Basketball	30	45
293.	30 t. Swimming	35	50

194. Map and National Flag.

1975. Independence. Multicoloured.

No.	Description	Unused	Used
294.	7 t. Type **194**	20	10
295.	30 t. Map and National emblem	40	65

195. M.V. "Bulolo".

1976. Ships of the 1930's. Multicoloured.

No.	Description	Unused	Used
297.	7 t. Type **195** . .	30	10
298.	15 t. M.V. "Macdhui" . .	45	30
299.	25 t. M.V. "Malaita" . .	65	65
300.	60 t. S.S. "Montoro" . .	1·75	2·50

196. Rorovana Carvings.

1976. Bougainville Artifacts. Multicoloured.

No.	Description	Unused	Used
301.	7 t. Type **196** . .	20	10
302.	20 t. Upe hats . .	40	75
303.	25 t. Kapkaps . .	50	85
304.	30 t. Canoe paddles . .	55	90

197. Rabaul House.

1976. Native Dwellings. Multicoloured.

No.	Description	Unused	Used
305.	7 t. Type **197** . .	20	10
306.	15 t. Aramia House . .	35	30
307.	30 t. Telefomin house . .	70	75
308.	40 t. Tapini house . .	80	1·25

198. Landscouts.

1976. 50th Anniv. of Survey Flight and Scouting in Papua New Guinea. Multicoloured.

No.	Description	Unused	Used
309.	7 t. Type **198** . .	30	10
310.	10 t. D.H. floatplane . .	40	30
311.	15 t. Seascouts . .	50	65
312.	60 t. Floatplane on water	1·25	2·25

199. Father Ross and New Guinea Highlands.

1976. William Ross Commemoration.

No.	Type	Description	Unused	Used
313.	**199.**	7 t. multicoloured . .	40	15

200. Clouded Rainbow Fish.

1976. Fauna Conservation (Tropical Fish). Multicoloured.

314.	5 t. Type **200**	30	10
315.	15 t. Emperor or Imperial Angel Fish	60	45
316.	30 t. Freckled Rock Cod..	1·10	70
317.	40 t. Threadfin Butterfly Fish	1·40	1·00

201. Man from Kundiawa.

202. Headdress, Wasara Tribe.

1977. Headdresses. Multicoloured.

318.	1 t. Type **201**	10	10
319.	5 t. Masked dancer, Abelam area of Maprik..	10	10
320.	10 t. Headdresses from Koiari	30	15
321.	15 t. Woman with face paint, Hanuabada	30	20
322.	20 t. Orokaiva dancer ..	50	30
323.	25 t. Haus Tambaran dancer, Abelam area of Maprik	40	30
324.	30 t. Asaro Valley head-dress	45	35
325.	35 t. Singsing costume, Garaina.. ..	70	45
326.	40 t. Waghi Valley head-dress	60	35
327.	50 t. Trobriand Island dancer	1·25	60
328.	1 k. Type **202**	1·50	1·50
329.	2 k. Headdress, Meko tribe	3·00	3·00

SIZES: 1, 5, 20 t. 25×31 mm. 35, 40 t. 23×38 mm. 1 k. 28×35 mm. 2 k. 33×23 mm. Others 26×26 mm.

203. National Flag and Queen Elizabeth II.

1977. Silver Jubilee. Multicoloured.

330.	7 t. Type **203**	25	10
331.	15 t. The Queen and national emblem.. ..	35	35
332.	35 t. The Queen and map of P.N.G.	65	70

204. White-breasted Ground Pigeon.

1977. Fauna Conservation (Birds). Mult.

333.	5 t. Type **204**	35	10
334.	7 t. Victoria Crowned Pigeon	35	10
335.	15 t. Pheasant Pigeon ..	65	65
336.	30 t. Orange-fronted Fruit Dove	1·00	1·00
337.	50 t. Banded Imperial Pigeon	1·60	2·25

205. Guides and Gold Badge.

1977. 50th Anniv. of Guiding in Papua New Guinea. Multicoloured.

338.	7 t. Type **205**	20	10
339.	15 t. Guides mapping ..	35	20
340.	30 t. Guides washing ..	55	50
341.	35 t. Guides cooking ..	60	60

206. Kari Maruppi Myth.

1977. Folklore. Elema Art (3rd series).

342. **206.**	7 t. multicoloured ..	20	10
343. –	20 t. multicoloured ..	45	35
344. –	30 t. red, blue and black	50	75
345. –	35 t. red, yellow & black	50	75

DESIGNS: 20 t. Savoripi clan myth. 30 t. Oa-Laea myth. 35 t. Oa-Iriarapo myth.

207. Blue-tailed Skink.

1978. Fauna Conservation (Skinks). Mult.

346.	10 t. Type **207**	30	10
347.	15 t. Green Tree Skink ..	35	20
348.	35 t. Crocodile Skink ..	55	55
349.	40 t. New Guinea Blue-tongued Skink.. ..	75	70

208. " Roboastra arika ".

1978. Sea Slugs. Multicoloured.

350.	10 t. Type **208**	30	10
351.	15 t. " Chromodoris fidelis "	35	30
352.	35 t. " Flabellina macassarana "	70	1·00
353.	40 t. " Chromodoris trimarginata "..	75	1·40

209. Present Day Royal Papua New Guinea Constabulary.

1978. History of Royal Papua New Guinea Constabulary. Uniformed Police and Constabulary Badges. Multicoloured.

354.	10 t. Type **209**	30	10
355.	15 t. Mandated New Guinea Constabulary, 1921–1941	40	15
356.	20 t. British New Guinea Armed Constabulary, 1890–1906	45	40
357.	25 t. German New Guinea Police, 1899–1914 ..	50	45
358.	30 t. Royal Papua and New Guinea Constabulary, 1906–1964	60	60

210. Ocarina.

1979. Musical Instruments. Multicoloured.

359.	7 t. Type **210**	15	10
360.	20 t. Musical bow (horiz.)	25	20
361.	28 t. Launut	30	30
362.	35 t. Nose flute (horiz.)..	40	45

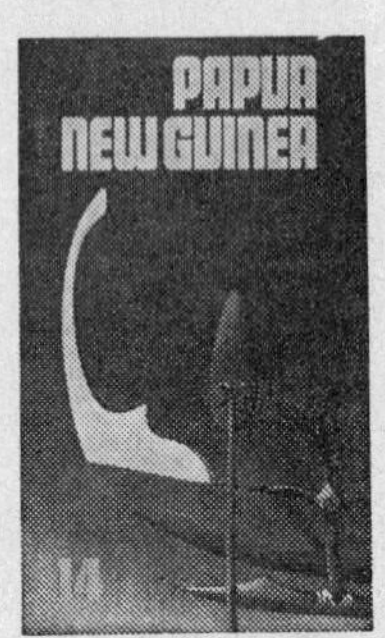

211. East New Britain Canoe Prow.

1979. Traditional Canoe Prows and Paddles. Multicoloured.

363.	14 t. Type **211**	15	15
364.	21 t. Sepik war canoe ..	25	25
365.	25 t. Trobriand Island canoe	25	30
366.	40 t. Milne Bay canoe ..	40	60

212. Katudababila (waist belt).

1979. Traditional Currency. Multicoloured.

367.	7 t. Type **212**	10	10
368.	15 t. Doga (chest ornament)	20	30
369.	25 t. Mwali (armshell) ..	35	55
370.	35 t. Soulava (necklace)..	45	75

213. "Aenetus cyanochlora".

1979. Fauna Conservation. Moths. Mult.

371	7 t. Type **213**	20	10
372	15 t. "Celerina vulgaris" ..	30	35
373	20 t. "Alcidis aurora" (vert)	40	65
374	25 t. "Phyllodes conspicillator"	45	80
375	30 t. "Lyssa patroclus" (vert)	55	90

214. " The Right to Affection and Love ".

1979. International Year of the Child. Multicoloured.

376.	7 t. Type **214**	10	10
377.	15 t. " The right to adequate nutrition and medical care "	15	15
378.	30 t. " The right to play "	20	20
379.	60 t. " The right to a free education "	45	60

215. " Post Office Service ".

1980. Admission to U.P.U. (1979). Mult.

380.	7 t. Type **215**	10	10
381.	25 t. " Wartime mail " ..	25	25
382.	35 t. " U.P.U. emblem "	35	40
383.	40 t. "Early postal services"	40	50

216. Betrothal Ceremony, Minj District, Western Highlands Province (detail).

1980. Third South Pacific Festival of Arts.

384. **216.**	20 t. yell., orge. and blk.	25	35
385. –	20 t. multicoloured ..	25	35
386. –	20 t. multicoloured ..	25	35
387. –	20 t. multicoloured ..	25	35
388. –	20 t. multicoloured ..	25	35

DESIGNS: Nos. 385/8, further details of Betrothal Ceremony. Nos. 384/8 were issued together in horizontal se-tenant strips of five within the sheet, forming a composite design.

217. Family being Interviewed.

1980. National Census. Multicoloured.

389.	7 t. Type **217**	10	10
390.	15 t. Population symbol..	15	15
391.	40 t. Papua New Guinea map	30	40
392.	50 t. Heads symbolising population growth ..	35	50

218. Donating Blood.

1980. Red Cross Blood Bank. Multicoloured.

393.	7 t. Type **218**	15	10
394.	15 t. Receiving transfusion	20	20
395.	30 t. Map of Papua New Guinea showing blood transfusion centres ..	25	25
396.	60 t. Blood and its components..	40	60

219. Dugong

1980. Mammals. Multicoloured.

397.	7 t. Type **219**	10	10
398.	30 t. New Guinea Marsupial Cat (vert.) ..	40	45
399.	35 t. Tube-nosed Bat (vert.)	40	45
400.	45 t. Rufescent Bandicoot	50	55

220. White-headed Kingfisher. **221.** Native Mask.

1981. Kingfishers. Multicoloured.

401. 3 t. Type **220** 15 20
402. 7 t. Forest Kingfisher .. 15 10
403. 20 t. Sacred Kingfisher .. 50 50
404. 25 t. White-tailed Kingfisher (26 × 46 mm.) .. 60 85
405. 60 t. Blue-winged Kookaburra .. .. .. 1·40 2·25

1981. Coil Stamps.

406 **221** 2 t. violet and orange 10 20
407 – 5 t. red and green .. 10 20
DESIGN: 5 t. Hibiscus flower.

222. Mortar Team.

1981. Defence Force. Multicoloured.

408. 7 t. Type **222** 15 10
409. 15 t. Aeroplane & aircrew 30 25
410. 40 t. "Aitape" (patrol boat) and seamen .. 60 65
411. 50 t. Medical team examining children 65 75

223. M.A.F. (Missionary Aviation Fellowship) Aeroplane.

1981. "Mission Aviation". Multicoloured.

412. 10 t. Type **223** 20 10
413. 15 t. Catholic mission aeroplane 25 25
414. 20 t. S.I.L. (Summer Institute of Linguistics) helicopter 35 35
415. 30 t. Lutheran mission aeroplane 55 55
416. 35 t. S.D.A. (Seventh Day Adventist Church) aeroplane 65 65

224. Scoop Net Fishing.

1981. Fishing. Multicoloured.

417. 10 t. Type **224** 15 10
418. 15 t. Kite fishing .. 25 30
419. 30 t. Rod fishing .. 40 50
420. 60 t. Scissor net fishing .. 75 85

225. "Forcartia buhleri".

1981. Land Snail Shells. Multicoloured.

421. 5 t. Type **225** 10 10
422. 15 t. "Naninia citrina" .. 25 25
423. 20 t. "Papuina adonis" and "papuina hermione" 30 35
424. 30 t. "Papustyla hindei" and "papustyla novaepommeraniae" .. 40 50
425. 40 t. "Rhynchotrochus strabo" 60 80

226. Lord Baden-Powell and Flag-raising Ceremony.

1981. 75th Anniv. of Boy Scout Movement. Multicoloured.

426. 15 t. Type **226** 40 25
427. 25 t. Scout leader and camp 60 50
428. 35 t. Scout, and hut building 75 65
429. 50 t. Percy Chaterton and Scouts administering first aid 90 85

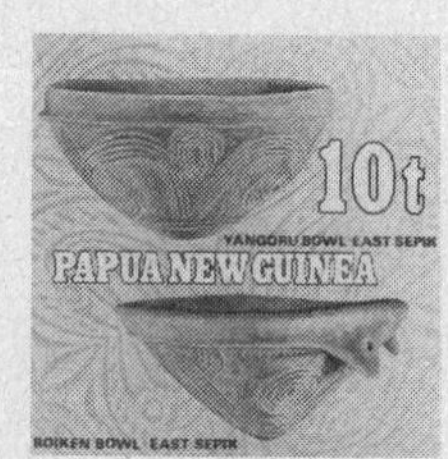

227. Yangoru and Boiken Bowls, East Sepik.

1981. Native Pottery. Multicoloured.

430. 10 t. Type **227** 15 10
431. 20 t. Utu cooking pot and small Gumalu pot, Madang 25 30
432. 40 t. Wanigela pots, Northern (37 × 23 mm.) 45 55
433. 50 t. Ramu Valley pots, Madang (37 × 23 mm.) .. 55 80

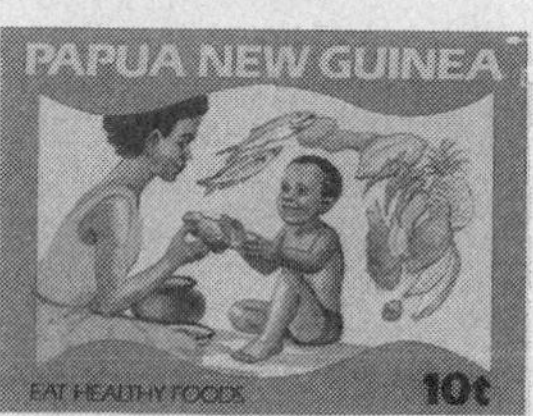

228. "Eat Healthy Foods".

1982. Food and Nutrition. Multicoloured.

434. 10 t. Type **228** 15 10
435. 15 t. Protein foods .. 30 30
436. 30 t. Protective foods .. 55 55
438. 40 t. Energy foods .. 65 70

229. "Stylophora sp.".

1982. Multicoloured.

438. 1 t. Type **229** 10 20
439. 3 t. "Dendrophyllia sp." (vert.) 60 30
440. 5 t. "Acropora humilis" .. 15 10
441. 10 t. "Dendronephthya sp." (vert.) 80 10
442. 12 t. As 10 t. .. .. 3·50 2·50
443. 15 t. "Distichopora sp." .. 30 20
444. 20 t. "Isis sp." (vert.) .. 70 25
445. 25 t. "Acropora sp." (vert.) 40 40
446. 30 t. "Dendronephthya sp." (different) (vert.) .. 1·50 80
447. 35 t. "Stylaster elegans" (vert.) 80 50
448. 40 t. "Antipathes sp." (vert.) .. .. .. 2·00 60
449. 45 t. "Turbinarea sp." (vert.) .. .. .. 2·00 60
450. 1 k. "Xenia sp." .. .. 1·25 1·25
451. 3 k. "Distichopora sp." (vert.) .. .. .. 3·75 3·50
452. 5 k. Raggiana Bird of Paradise (33 × 33 mm.). 6·00 6·50

230. Missionaries landing on Beach.

1982. Centenary of Catholic Church in Papua New Guinea. Mural on Wall of Nordup Catholic Church, East New Britain. Mult.

457 10 t. Type **230** 25 20
458 10 t. Missionaries talking to natives 25 20
459 10 t. Natives with slings and spears ready to attack .. 25 20

Nos. 457/9 were issued together, setenant, forming a compsite design.

231. Athletics.

1982. Commonwealth Games and "Anpex 82" Stamp Exhibition, Brisbane. Mult.

460. 10 t. Type **231** 15 10
461. 15 t. Boxing 20 25
462. 45 t. Rifle-shooting .. 40 70
463. 50 t. Bowls 45 75

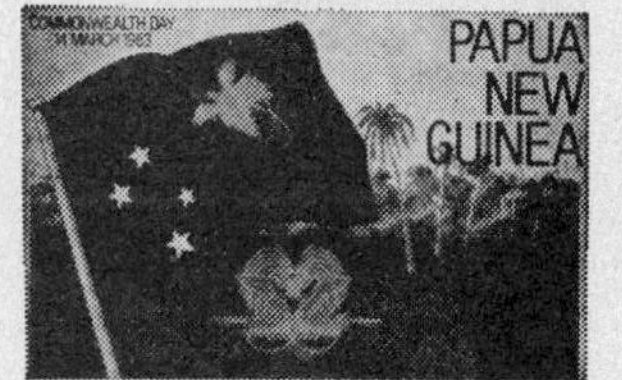

232. National Flag.

1983. Commonwealth Day. Multicoloured.

464. 10 t. Type **232** 15 10
465. 15 t. Basket-weaving and cabbage-picking .. 20 30
466. 20 t. Crane hoisting roll of material 25 35
467. 50 t. Lorries and ships .. 60 75

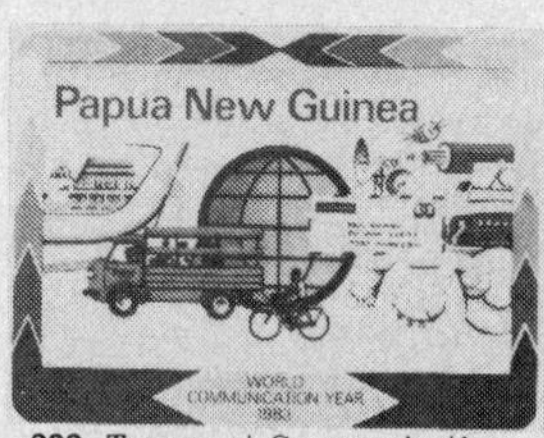

233. Transport Communications.

1983. World Communications Year. Mult.

468. 10 t. Type **233** 30 10
469. 25 t. "Postal service" .. 70 45
470. 30 t. "Telephone service" 80 50
471. 60 t. "Transport service" 1·50 90

234. "Chelonia depressa".

1984. Turtles. Multicoloured.

472. 5 t. Type **234** 20 10
473. 10 t. "Chelonia mydas" 35 10
474. 15 t. "Eretmochelys imbricata" 50 30
475. 20 t. "Lepidochelys olivacea" 65 35
476. 25 t. "Caretta caretta" .. 70 50
477. 40 t. "Dermochelys coriacea" 95 75

235. Avro "X VH-UXX" "Faith in Australia".

1984. 50th Anniv. of First Airmail Australia-Papua New Guinea. Multicoloured.

478. 20 t. Type **235** 40 30
479. 25 t. "DH86B VH-UYU" "Carmania" 50 45
480. 40 t. Westland "Widgeon VH-UGI" 90 80
481. 60 t. Consolidated "Catalina NC777" "Guba" 1·40 1·25

236. Parliament House.

1984. Opening of Parliament House.

482. **236.** 10 t. multicoloured .. 30 30

237. Ceremonial Shield and Club, Central Province. **239.** Fergusson Island.

238. H.M.S. "Nelson" at Port Moresby, 1884.

1984. Ceremonial Shields. Multicoloured.

483. 10 t. Type **237** 30 10
484. 20 t. Ceremonial shield, West New Britian .. 50 50
485. 30 t. Ceremonial shield, Madang Province .. 75 1·00
486. 50 t. Ceremonial shield, East Sepik .. .. 1·25 2·00

See also Nos. 558/61.

1984. Centenary of Protectorate Proclamations for British New Guinea and German New Guinea. Multicoloured.

487. 10 t. Type **238** 35 45
488. 10 t. Papua New Guinea flag and Port Moresby, 1984 .. .. .. 35 45
489. 45 t. Papua New Guinea flag and Rabaul, 1984 .. 1·25 1·75
490. 45 t. "Elisabeth" German warship at Rabaul, 1884 1·25 1·75

Nos. 487/8 and 489/90 were issued in se-tenant pairs, each pair forming a composite picture.

1985. Tourist Scenes. Multicoloured.

491. 10 t. Type **239** 30 10
492. 25 t. Sepik River 65 55
493. 40 t. Chimbu Gorge (horiz.) 95 80
494. 60 t. Dali Beach, Vanimo (horiz.) .. .. .. 1·40 1·40

1985. No. 408 surch.

495. **222.** 12 t. on 7 t. mult. .. 50 75

241. Dubu Platform, Central Province.

1985. Ceremonial Structures. Multicoloured.

496. 15 t. Type **241** 45 15
497. 20 t. Tamuniai House, West New Britain .. 60 50
498. 30 t. Traditional Yam Tower, Trobriand Island 85 80
499. 60 t. Huli Grave, Tari .. 1·25 1·75

242. Head of New Britain Sparrow Hawk.

1985. Birds of Prey. Multicoloured.

500. 12 t. Type **242** 55 80
501. 12 t. New Britain Sparrow Hawk in flight 55 80
502. 30 t. Doria's Goshawk .. 80 1·25
503. 30 t. Doria's Goshawk in flight .. .. .. 80 1·25
504. 60 t. Long-tailed Honey Buzzard .. .. .. 1·50 2·00
505. 60 t. Long-tailed Honey Buzzard in flight .. 1·50 2·00

243. National Flag and Parliament House.

1985. 10th Anniv. of Independence.

506. **243.** 12 t. multicoloured .. 60 70

244. Early Postcard, Aerogramme, Inkwell and Spectacles.

1985. Centenary of Papua New Guinea Post Office. Multicoloured.

507. 12 t. Type **244** 45 10
508. 30 t. Queensland 1897 1d. die with proof and modern press printing stamps 95 80
509. 40 t. Newspaper of 1885 announcing shipping service and loading mail into aircraft .. .. 1·25 1·10
510. 60 t. Friedrich-Wilhelmshafen postmark of 1892 and Port Moresby F.D.C. post-mark of 9 Oct 1985 .. 1·75 2·25

245. Figure with Eagle.

1985. Nombowai Wood Carvings. Mult.

512. 12 t. Type **245** 50 10
513. 30 t. Figure with clam shell 1·25 75
514. 60 t. Figure with dolphin 2·00 2·25
515. 80 t. Figure of woman with cockerel .. .. .. 2·50 3·00

246. "Cypraea valentia".

1986. Seashells. Multicoloured.

516. 15 t. Type **246** 55 15
517. 35 t. "Oliva buelowi" .. 1·25 1·25
518. 45 t. "Oliva parkinsoni" .. 1·50 1·60
519. 70 t. "Cypraea aurantium" 2·00 3·00

1986. 60th Birthday of Queen Elizabeth II. As T **110** of Ascension. Multicoloured.

520. 15 t. Princess Elizabeth in A.T.S. uniform, 1945 .. 20 15
521. 35 t. Silver Wedding Anniversary photograph (by Patrick Lichfield), Balmoral, 1972 .. .. 50 55
522. 50 t. Queen inspecting guard of honour, Port Moresby, 1982 .. .. 70 75
523. 60 t. On board Royal Yacht "Britannia", Papua New Guinea, 1982 85 90
524. 70 t. At Crown Agents' Head Office, London, 1983 .. .. .. 95 1·10

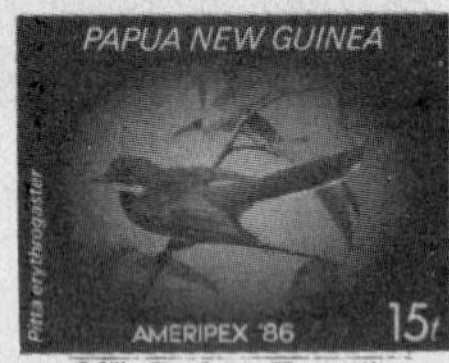

247. Rufous Fantail.

1986. "Ameripex '86" International Stamp Exhibition, Chicago. Small Birds (1st series). Multicoloured.

525. 15 t. Type **247** 70 15
526. 35 t. Streaked berrypecker 1·40 75
527. 45 t. Red-breasted pitta .. 1·50 95
528. 70 t. Olive-yellow robin (vert.) .. .. .. 2·00 2·50

See also Nos. 597/601.

248. Martin Luther nailing Theses to Cathedral Door, Wittenberg, and Modern Lutheran Pastor.

1986. Centenary of Lutheran Church in Papua New Guinea. Multicoloured.

529. 15 t. Type **248** 75 15
530. 70 t. Early church, Finschhafen, and modern Martin Luther Chapel, Lae Seminary .. 2·00 2·25

249. "Dendrobium vexillarius".

1986. Orchids. Multicoloured.

531. 15 t. Type **249** 75 15
532. 35 t. "Dendrobium lineale" 1·50 75
533. 45 t. "Dendrobium johnsoniae" .. .. 1·75 1·10
534. 70 t. "Dendrobium cuthbertsonii" .. .. 2·50 1·75

250. Maprik Dancer.

1986. Papua New Guinea Dancers. Mult.

535. 15 t. Type **250** 65 15
536. 35 t. Kiriwina .. .. 1·40 80
537. 45 t. Kundiawa .. .. 1·50 95
538. 70 t. Fasu .. .. .. 2·40 2·50

251. White Cap Anemonefish.

1987. Anemonefish. Multicoloured.

539. 17 t. Type **251** 70 25
540. 30 t. Black anemonefish .. 1·40 80
541. 35 t. Tomato clownfish .. 1·50 90
542. 70 t. Spine cheek anemone-fish .. .. .. 2·50 3·00

252. "Roebuck" (Dampier), 1700.

1987. Ships. Multicoloured.

543 1 t. "La Boudeuse" (De Bougainville), 1768 .. 20 20
544 5 t. Type **252** 40 20
545 10 t. H.M.S. "Swallow" (Philip Carteret), 1767 30 30
546 15 t. H.M.S. "Fly" (Blackwood), 1845 .. 50 40
547 17 t. As 15 t. 30 30
548 20 t. H.M.S. "Rattlesnake" (Owen Stanley), 1849 .. 50 50
549 30 t. "Vitiaz" (Maclay), 1871 .. .. .. 60 60
550 35 t. "San Pedrico" (Torres) and zabra, 1606 55 50
551 40 t. "L'Astrolabe" (D'Urville), 1872 .. 75 75
552 45 t. "Neva" (D'Albertis), 1876 .. .. .. 75 75
553 60 t. Spanish galleon (Jorge de Meneses), 1526 .. 1·00 90
554 70 t. "Eendracht" (Schouten and Le Maire), 1616 .. .. 1·25 95
555 1 k. H.M.S. "Blanche" (Simpson), 1872 .. 1·25 1·75
556 2 k. "Merrie England" (steamer), 1889 .. 3·25 2·75
557 3 k. "Samo" (German colonial steamer), 1884 4·00 4·50

1987. War Shields. As T **237**. Multicoloured.

558. 15 t. Gulf Province .. 20 25
559. 35 t. East Sepik 45 50
560. 45 t. Madang Province .. 55 60
561. 70 t. Telefomin 85 90

1987. No. 442. surch. **15 t.**

562. 15 t. on 12 t. "Dendronephthya sp." (vert.) .. 55 65

254. "Prototeaster nodosus".

1987. Starfish. Multicoloured.

563. 17 t. Type **254** 40 25
564. 35 t. "Gomophia egeriae" 75 50
565. 45 t. "Choriaster granulatus" 85 70
566. 70 t. "Neoferdina ocellata" 1·40 1·00

255. Cessna "Stationair 6" taking off, Rabaraba.

1987. Aircraft in Papua New Guinea. Multicoloured.

567. 15 t. Type **255** 55 25
568. 35 t. Britten-Norman "Islander" over Hombrum Bluff .. 1·00 60
569. 45 t. DHC "Twin Otter" Over Highlands.. .. 1·25 80
570. 70 t. Fokker "F28" over Madang .. .. .. 2·00 2·25

256 Pre-Independence Policeman on Traffic Duty and Present-day Motorcycle Patrol

1988. Centenary of Royal Papua New Guinea Constabulary. Multicoloured.

571 17 t. Type **256** 30 25
572 35 t. British New Guinea Armed Constabulary, 1890, and Governor W. MacGregor 60 50
573 45 t. Police badges .. 75 65
574 70 t. German New Guinea Police, 1888, and Dr. A. Hahl (founder) .. 1·25 1·50

257 Lagatoi (canoe) and Sydney Opera House
(Illustration reduced, actual size 53 × 26mm)

1988. "Sydpex '88" National Stamp Exhibition, Sydney.

575 **257** 35 t. multicoloured .. 80 50

258 Papua New Guinea Flag on Globe and Fireworks

1988. Bicentenary of Australian Settlement. Multicoloured.

576 35 t. Type **258** 55 65
577 35 t. Australian flag on globe and fireworks .. 55 65

Nos. 576/7 were printed together, se-tenant, forming a composite design.

259 Male and Female Butterflies in Courtship

1988. "Ornithoptera alexandrae" (butterfly). Multicoloured.

579 5 t. Type **259** 40 10
580 17 t. Female laying eggs and mature larva (vert) 80 40
581 25 t. Male emerging from pupa (vert) .. .. 1·10 1·00
582 35 t. Male feeding .. 1·40 1·75

260 Athletics

1988. Olympic Games, Seoul. Multicoloured.

583 17 t. Type **260** 20 25
584 45 t. Weightlifting .. 60 65

261 "Rhododendron zoelleri"

1989. Rhododendrons. Multicoloured.

585 3 t. Type **261** 10 10
586 20 t. "Rhododendron cruttwellii" 35 30
587 60 t. "Rhododendron superbum" .. .. 1·00 1·00
588 70 t. "Rhododendron christianae" .. .. 1·10 1·10

263 Writing Letter

1989. International Letter Writing Week. Multicoloured.

589 20 t. Type **263** 30 30
590 35 t. Stamping letter .. 55 50
591 60 t. Posting letter .. 90 1·10
592 70 t. Reading letter .. 1·10 1·40

264 Village House, Buka Island, North Solomons

1989. Traditional Dwellings. Multicoloured.

593 20 t. Type **264** 35 35
594 35 t. Tree house, Koiari, Central Province .. 60 60
595 60 t. Longhouse, Lauan, New Ireland .. .. 1·00 1·25
596 70 t. Decorated house, Basilaki, Milne Bay .. 1·25 1·50

265 Tit Berrypecker (female)

1989. Small Birds (2nd issue). Multicoloured.

597 20 t. Type **265** 70 55
598 20 t. Tit berrypecker (male) 70 55
599 35 t. Blue-capped babbler 90 75
600 45 t. Black-throated robin 1·10 1·00
601 70 t. Large mountain sericornis .. .. 1·60 1·60

1989. No. 539 surch **20 t**.

602 20 t. on 17 t. Type **251** .. 60 70

266 Motu Motu Dancer, Gulf Province

1989. Traditional Dancers. Multicoloured.

603 20 t. Type **266** 60 35
604 35 t. Baining, East New Britain 95 90
605 60 t. Vailala River, Gulf Province .. .. 1·75 2·00
606 70 t. Timbunke, East Sepik Province .. .. 1·90 2·25

267 Hibiscus, People going to Church and Gope Board

1989. Christmas. Designs showing flowers and carved panels. Multicoloured.

607 20 t. Type **267** 40 35
608 35 t. Rhododendron, Virgin and Child and mask .. 60 60
609 60 t. D'Albertis creeper, Christmas candle and warshield .. .. 1·25 1·50
610 70 t. Pacific frangipani, peace dove and flute mask .. .. 1·40 1·75

268 Guni Falls

1990. Waterfalls. Multicoloured.

611 20 t. Type **268** 50 35
612 35 t. Rouna Falls .. 75 75
613 60 t. Ambua Falls .. 1·25 1·50
614 70 t. Wawoi Falls .. 1·50 1·75

269 Boys and Census Form

1990. National Census. Multicoloured.

615 20 t. Type **269** 40 30
616 70 t. Family and census form .. .. .. 1·50 1·75

270 Gwa Pupi Dance Mask

1990. Gogodala Dance Masks. Multicoloured.

617 20 t. Type **270** 60 30
618 35 t. Tauga paiyale .. 95 70
619 60 t. A: ga .. .. 1·60 2·00
620 70 t. Owala .. .. 1·90 2·50

271 Sepik and Maori Kororu Masks

1990. "New Zealand 1990" International Stamp Exhibition, Auckland.

621 **271** 35 t. multicoloured .. 75 75

272 Dwarf Cassowary and Great Spotted Kiwi

1990. 150th Anniv of Treaty of Waitangi. Multicoloured.

622 20 t. Type **272** 70 40
623 35 t. Double-wattled cassowary and Brown kiwi .. .. .. 1·10 1·25

273 Whimbrel

1990. Migratory Birds. Multicoloured.

624 20 t. Type **273** 55 30
625 35 t. Sharp-tailed sandpiper 85 70
626 60 t. Turnstone .. .. 1·50 1·75
627 70 t. Terek sandpiper .. 1·75 2·00

274 Jew's Harp

1990. Musical Instruments. Multicoloured.

628 20 t. Type **274** 40 30
629 35 t. Musical bow .. 70 50
630 60 t. Wantoat drum .. 1·25 1·40
631 70 t. Gogodala rattle .. 1·40 1·50

275 "Rhynchotrochus weigmani"

1991. Land Shells. Multicoloured.

632 21 t. Type **275** 45 30
633 40 t. "Forcartia globula" and "Canefriula azonata" 75 60
634 50 t. "Planispira deaniana" 1·10 1·10
635 80 t. "Papuina chancel" and "Papuina xanthocheila" .. .. 1·60 1·75

276 Magnificent Riflebird

1991. Birds of Paradise. Multicoloured.

(a) Face values shown as "t" or "K".

636 1 t. Type **276** 10 10
637 5 t. Loria's bird of paradise 10 10
638 10 t. Sickle crested bird of paradise 15 20
639 20 t. Wahnes' parotia .. 25 30
640 21 t. Crinkle-collared manucode 25 30
641 30 t. Goldie's bird of paradise 40 45
642 40 t. Yellow-breasted bird of paradise 55 60
643 45 t. King bird of paradise 60 65
644 50 t. Short-tailed paradigalla bird of paradise .. 70 75
645 60 t. Queen Carola's parotia 80 85
646 90 t. Emperor of Germany bird of paradise .. 1·10 1·25
647 1 k. Magnificent bird of paradise .. .. 1·40 1·50
648 2 k. Superb bird of paradise .. .. 2·75 3·00
649 5 k. Trumpet bird .. 6·75 7·00
650 10 k. Lesser bird of paradise (32 × 32 mm) .. 13·50 14·00

(b) Face values shown as "T".

650a	21 t. Crinkle-collared manucode	35	30
650b	45 t. King bird of paradise	80	80
650c	60 t. Queen Carola's parotia	1·10	1·10
650d	90 t. Emperor of Germany bird of paradise	1·75	2·00

277 Cricket

1991. 9th South Pacific Games. Multicoloured.

651	21 t. Type **277**	60	30
652	40 t. Athletics	90	75
653	50 t. Baseball	1·25	1·25
654	80 t. Rugby Union	1·75	2·00

278 Cathedral of St. Peter and St. Paul, Dogura

1991. Cent of Anglican Church in Papua New Guinea. Multicoloured.

655	21 t. Type **278**	45	30
656	40 t. Missionaries landing, 1891, and Kaieta shrine	80	90
657	80 t. First church and Modawa tree	1·60	2·00

279 Rambusto Headdress, Manus Province

1991. Tribal Headdresses. Multicoloured.

658	21 t. Type **279**	45	30
659	40 t. Marawaka, Eastern Highlands	85	85
660	50 t. Tufi, Oro Province ..	95	95
661	80 t. Sina Sina, Simbu Province	1·75	2·00

280 "Nina"

1992. 500th Anniv of Discovery of America by Columbus and "EXPO '92" World's Fair, Seville. Multicoloured.

662	21 t. Type **280**	40	30
663	45 t. "Pinta"	90	90
664	60 t. "Santa Maria" ..	1·40	1·40
665	90 t. Christopher Columbus and ships	1·90	2·00

281 Canoe Prow Shield, Bamu

1992. Papuan Gulf Artifacts. Multicoloured.

667	21 t. Type **281**	35	30
668	45 t. Skull rack, Kerewa ..	75	75
669	60 t. Ancestral figure, Era River	1·10	1·25
670	90 t. Gope (spirit) board, Urama	1·40	1·75

282 Papuan Infantryman

1992. 50th Anniv of Second World War Campaigns in Papua New Guinea. Mult.

671	21 t. Type **282**	35	30
672	45 t. Australian militiaman	75	80
673	60 t. Japanese infantryman	1·10	1·25
674	90 t. American infantryman	1·40	1·75

283 "Hibiscus tiliaceus"

1992. Flowering Trees. Multicoloured.

675	21 t. Type **283**	50	30
676	45 t. "Castanospermum australe"	1·00	1·00
677	60 t. "Cordia subcordata"	1·50	1·60
678	90 t. "Acacia auriculiformis"	2·00	2·25

284 Three Striped Dasyure

1993. Mammals. Multicoloured.

679	21 t. Type **284**	35	30
680	45 t. Striped bandicoot ..	80	80
681	60 t. Dusky black-eared giant rat	1·10	1·10
682	90 t. Painted ringtail possum	1·60	1·75

MINIMUM PRICE

The minimum price quoted is 10p which represents a handling charge rather than a basis for valuing common stamps. For further notes about prices see introductory pages.

285 Rufous Wren Warbler

1993. Small Birds. Multicoloured.

683	21 t. Type **285**	35	30
684	45 t. Superb pitta ..	80	80
685	60 t. Mottled whistler ..	1·10	1·10
686	90 t. Slaty-chinned longbill	1·60	1·75

1993. "Taipei '93" Asian International Stamp Exhibition, Taiwan. Nos. 683/6 optd **TAIPEI '93**.

687	21 t. Type **285**	35	30
688	45 t. Superb pitta ..	80	80
689	60 t. Mottled whisker ..	1·10	1·10
690	90 t. Slaty-chinned longbill	1·60	1·75

287 Threadfin Rainbowfish

1993. Freshwater Fishes. Multicoloured.

691	21 t. Type **287**	35	30
692	45 t. Peacock gudgeon ..	80	80
693	60 t. Northern rainbowfish	1·10	1·10
694	90 t. Popondetta blue-eye	1·60	1·75

POSTAGE DUE STAMPS

1960. Stamps of 1952 surch. **POSTAL CHARGES** and value.

D 2.	1d. on 6½d. purple ..	14·00	7·00
D 3.	3d. on ½d. green ..	16·00	5·50
D 1.	6d. on 7½d. blue (A) ..	£760	£400
D 4.	6d. on 7½d. blue (B) ..	32·00	13·00
D 5.	1s. 3d. on 3½d. black ..	24·00	13·00
D 6.	3s. on 2½d. orange.. ..	40·00	26·00

In (A) value and "POSTAGE" is obliterated by a solid circle and a series of "IX's" but these are omitted in (B).

D 3.

1960.

D 7.	D 3.	1d. orange	55	75
D 8.		3d. brown	70	75
D 9.		6d. blue	75	40
D 10.		9d. red	75	1·75
D 11.		1s. green	75	50
D 12.		1s. 3d. violet ..	1·40	2·00
D 13.		1s. 6d. pale blue ..	5·50	6·00
D 14.		3s. yellow ..	6·00	1·25

PATIALA

A "convention" state in the Punjab, India.

12 pies = 1 anna; 16 annas = 1 rupee.

1884. Stamps of India (Queen Victoria) with curved opt. **PUTTIALLA STATE** vert.

1.	**23.**	½ a. turquoise	80	90
2.	–	1 a. purple	26·00	24·00
3.	–	2 a. blue	5·50	5·50
4.	–	4 a. green (No. 96) ..	28·00	28·00
5.	–	8 a. mauve	£170	£400
6.	–	1 r. grey (No. 101) ..	80·00	£200

1885. Stamps of India (Queen Victoria) optd. **PUTTIALLA STATE** horiz.

7.	**23.**	½ a. turquoise	45	20
11.	–	1 a. purple	15	15
8.	–	2 a. blue	1·40	50
9.	–	4 a. green (No. 96) ..	1·25	1·40
12.	–	8 a. mauve	8·00	16·00
10.	–	1 r. grey (No. 101) ..	5·00	30·00

Stamps of India optd. **PATIALA STATE.**

1891. Queen Victoria.

32.	**40.**	3 p. red	10	10
13.	**23.**	½ a. turquoise (No. 84)..	10	10
33.		½ a. green (No. 114) ..	30	15
14.	–	9 p. red	30	60
15.	–	1 a. purple	40	20
34.	–	1 a. red	55	30
17.	–	1½ a. brown	30	45
18.	–	2 a. blue	40	20
20.	–	3 a. orange	60	35
22.	–	4 a. green (No. 96) ..	60	40
23.	–	6 a. brown (No. 80) ..	50	2·75
26.	–	8 a. mauve	70	3·00
27.	–	12 a. purple on red ..	70	4·00
28.	**37.**	1 r. green and red ..	3·50	15·00
29.	**38.**	2 r. red and orange ..	85·00	£325
30.		3 r. brown and green ..	£110	£350
31.		5 r. blue and violet ..	£120	£375

1903. King Edward VII.

36.	3 p. grey	10	10
37.	½ a. green (No. 122) ..	50	10
38.	1 a. red (No. 123) ..	10	10
39.	2 a. lilac	40	45
40.	3 a. orange	40	25
41.	4 a. olive..	1·40	60
42.	6 a. bistre	1·00	2·75
43.	8 a. mauve	1·90	90
44.	12 a. purple on red ..	2·25	6·50
45.	1 r. green and red ..	1·25	2·25

1912. King Edward VII inscr. "INDIA POSTAGE & REVENUE".

46.	½ a. green (No. 149) ..	10	10
47.	1 a. red (No. 150) ..	30	30

1912. King George V. Optd. in two lines.

48	**55.**	3 p. grey	10	10
49	**56.**	½ a. green	25	10
50	**57.**	1 a. red	35	10
61		1 a. brown	60	15
51	**58.**	1½ a. brown (A).. ..	30	55
52	**59.**	2 a. lilac	30	20
53	**62.**	3 a. orange	50	60
62		3 a. blue	45	2·50
54	**63.**	4 a. olive..	80	1·00
55a	**64.**	6 a. bistre	60	1·50
56	**65.**	8 a. mauve	85	85
57	**66.**	12 a. red	1·00	3·00
58	**67.**	1 r. brown and green ..	2·50	6·00
59		2 r. red and orange ..	7·00	55·00
60		5 r. blue and violet ..	17·00	60·00

1928. King George V. Optd. in one line.

63.	**55.**	3 p. grey	40	10
64.	**56.**	½ a. green	15	10
75.	**79.**	½ a. green	20	10
65.	**80.**	9 p. green	30	20
66.	**57.**	1 a. brown	30	15
76.	**81.**	1 a. brown	25	10
67.	**82.**	1¼ a. mauve	75	15
77.	**59.**	2 a. red	20	20
68.	**70.**	2 a. lilac	30	20
69.	**61.**	2½ a. orange	80	1·00
70.	**62.**	3 a. blue	60	75
78.		3 a. red	1·50	1·90
71.	**71.**	4 a. green	1·00	65
79.	**63.**	4 a. olive..	50	85
72.	**65.**	8 a. mauve	1·75	1·40
73.	**66.**	1 r. brown and green ..	2·50	3·25
74.		2 r. red and orange ..	3·75	22·00

1937. King George VI. Optd. in one line.

80.	**91.**	3 p. grey	23·00	30
81.		½ a. brown	4·25	20
82.		9 p. green	1·75	40
83.		1 a. red	85	20
84.	**92.**	2 a. red	1·40	3·50
85.	–	2½ a. violet	1·60	8·00
86.	–	3 a. green	1·75	3·00
87.	–	3½ a. blue	1·90	11·00
88.	–	4 a. brown	8·50	7·50
89.	–	6 a. green	12·00	19·00
90.	–	8 a. violet	12·00	16·00
91.	–	12 a. red	12·00	22·00
92.	**93.**	1 r. grey and brown ..	17·00	26·00
93.		2 r. purple and brown ..	22·00	55·00
94.		5 r. green and blue ..	38·00	95·00
95.		10 r. purple and red ..	60·00	£170
96.		15 r. brown and green ..	£110	£275
97.		25 r. grey and purple ..	£140	£350

1943. King George VI. Optd. **PATIALA** only. (a) Issue of 1938.

98.	**94.**	3 p. grey	7·50	50
99.		½ a. brown	7·50	20
100.		9 p. green	95·00	2·00
101.		1 a. red	15·00	20
102.	**93.**	1 r. grey and brown ..	7·00	42·00

(b) Issue of 1940.

103. **92.** 3 p. grey 80 15
104. ½ a. mauve 80 15
105. 9 p. green 80 15
106. 1 a. red 60 10
107. **101.** 1 a. 3 p. bistre .. .. 1·60 1·00
108. 1½ a. violet .. .. 3·50 60
109. 2 a. red .. .. .. 3·00 20
110. 3 a. violet .. .. 2·00 70
111. 3½ a. blue .. .. 8·00 14·00
112. **102.** 4 a. brown .. .. 2·00 70
113. 6 a. green .. .. 2·00 9·00
114. 8 a. violet .. .. 2·25 5·00
115. 12 a. purple .. .. 5·00 20·00

OFFICIAL STAMPS

Overprinted **SERVICE.**

1884. Nos. 1 to 3 (Queen Victoria).

O 1. **23.** ½ a. turquoise .. .. 4·50 15
O 2. – 1 a. purple 30 10
O 3. – 2 a. blue .. .. £2250 65·00

1885. Nos. 7, 11 and 8 (Queen Victoria).

O 4 **23.** ½ a. turquoise 20 10
O 5 – 1 a. purple 30 10
O 7 – 2 a. blue 20 10

1891. Nos. 13 to 28 and No. 10 Q.V.

O 8. **23.** ½ a. turquoise (No. 13) 10 10
O 9. – 1 a. purple .. .. 2·00 10
O 20. – 1 a. red 15 10
O 10. – 2 a. blue .. .. 2·00 70
O 12. – 3 a. orange 30 95
O 13a. – 4 a. green 30 20
O 15. – 6 a. brown 65 35
O 16a. – 8 a. mauve 55 60
O 18. – 12 a. purple on red .. 45 50
O 19. – 1 r. grey 55 55
O 21. **37.** 1 r. green and red .. 5·00 9·00

1903. Nos. 36 to 45 (King Edward VII).

O22 3 p. grey 10 10
O24 ½ a. green 10 10
O25 1 a. red 10 10
O26a 2 a. lilac 20 10
O28 3 a. brown .. .. 1·25 1·50
O29 4 a. olive 30 20
O30 8 a. mauve 45 55
O32 1 r. green and red .. 70 70

1907. Nos. 46/7 (King Edward VII) inscr. "INDIA POSTAGE & REVENUE".

O 33. ½ a. green 10 10
O 34. 1 a. red 10 10

1913. Official stamps of India (King George V) optd. **PATIALA STATE** in two lines.

O 35. **55.** 3 p. grey 10 10
O 36. **56.** ½ a. green 10 10
O 37. **57.** 1 a. red 10 10
O 38. 1 a. brown .. .. 2·50 70
O 39. **59.** 2 a. mauve 35 15
O 40. **63.** 4 a. olive 25 30
O 41. **64.** 6 a. bistre .. .. 45 1·75
O 42. **65.** 8 a. purple 40 40
O 43. **67.** 1 r. brown & green 1·00 1·40
O 44. 2 r. red and brown 5·50 22·00
O 45. 5 r. blue and violet 8·00 18·00

1927. Postage stamps of India (King George V) optd. **PATIALA STATE SERVICE** in two lines.

O 47 **55.** 3 p. grey 10 10
O 48 **56.** ½ a. green 20 45
O 58 **79.** ½ a. green 10 10
O 49 **57.** 1 a. brown 10 10
O 59 **81.** 1 a. brown 10 30
O 50 **82.** 1¼ a. mauve 20 10
O 51 **70.** 2 a. purple 20 25
O 52 2 a. red 30 35
O 60 **59.** 2 a. red 15 15
O 53 **61.** 2½ a. orange 35 30
O 54 **71.** 4 a. green 30 30
O 62 **63.** 4 a. olive 40 20
O 55 **65.** 8 a. purple 50 55
O 56 **66.** 1 r. brown & green 1·60 1·10
O 57 2 r. red and orange 3·50 18·00

1938. Postage stamps of India (King George VI) optd. **PATIALA STATE SERVICE.**

O 63. **91.** ½ a. brown 75 20
O 64. 9 p. green .. .. 13·00 45·00
O 65. 1 a. red 75 20
O 66. **93.** 1 r. grey and brown 2·00 3·50
O 67. 2 r. purple & brown 8·00 5·00
O 68. 5 r. green and blue 20·00 45·00

1939. Surch. **1 A SERVICE 1 A.**

O 70. **82.** 1 a. on 1¼ a. mauve .. 1·75 1·40

1940. Official stamps of India optd. **PATIALA.**

O 71. O **20.** 3 p. grey 35 10
O 72. ½ a. brown .. .. 1·90 10
O 73. ½ a. purple 35 10
O 74. 9 p. green 35 20
O 75. 1 a. red 60 10
O 76. 1 a. 3 p. bistre 60 25
O 77. 1½ a. violet .. .. 1·50 15
O 78. 2 a. orange .. .. 3·25 15
O 79. 2½ a. violet 60 60
O 80. 4 a. brown 70 60
O 81. 8 a. violet .. .. 1·10 3·00

1940. Postage stamps of India (King George VI) optd. **PATIALA SERVICE.**

O 82. **93.** 1 r. slate and brown .. 8·00 4·50
O 83. 2 r. purple and brown 14·00 35·00
O 84. 5 r. green and blue .. 21·00 48·00

PENANG

A British Settlement which became a state of the Federation of Malaya, incorporated in Malaysia in 1963.

100 cents = 1 dollar (Straits or Malayan).

1948. Silver Wedding. As T **10/11** of Aden.

1. 10 c. violet 30 20
2. $5 brown .. .. .. 25·00 24·00

1949. As T **58** of Straits Settlements.

3. 1 c. black 10 10
4. 2 c. orange 10 10
5. 3 c. green 10 30
6. 4 c. brown 10 10
7. 5 c. purple .. .. .. 40 1·00
8. 6 c. grey 15 10
9. 8 c. red .. .. .. 30 2·75
10. 8 c. green .. .. .. 65 1·00
11. 10 c. mauve 15 10
12. 12 c. red .. .. .. 65 2·25
13. 15 c. blue 20 30
14. 20 c. black and green .. 20 1·00
15. 20 c. blue 55 20
16. 25 c. purple and orange .. 40 10
17. 35 c. red and purple .. 60 70
18. 40 c. red and purple .. 55 5·50
19. 50 c. black and blue .. 40 15
20. $1 blue and purple .. 5·00 60
21. $2 green and red .. .. 7·00 90
22. $5 green and brown .. 38·00 1·00

1949. U.P.U. As T **20/23** of Antigua.

23. 10 c. purple 20 10
24. 15 c. blue 35 50
25. 25 c. orange 35 60
26. 50 c. black .. .. .. 1·25 1·60

1953. Coronation. As T **13** of Aden.

27 10 c. black and purple .. 40 10

1954. As T **1** of Malacca but inscr. "**PENANG**".

28. 1 c. black 10 30
29. 2 c. orange 40 30
30. 4 c. brown 40 10
31. 5 c. mauve .. .. .. 1·75 1·25
32. 6 c. grey 15 10
33. 8 c. green .. .. .. 20 2·00
34. 10 c. purple 20 10
35. 12 c. red .. .. .. 30 2·50
36. 20 c. blue 40 10
37. 25 c. purple and orange .. 30 10
38. 30 c. red and purple .. 30 10
39. 35 c. red and purple .. 50 15
40. 50 c. black and blue .. 40 10
41. $1 blue and purple .. 2·00 10
42. $2 green and red .. .. 5·00 3·00
43. $5 green and brown .. 23·00 3·25

1957. As Nos. 92/102 of Kedah but inset portrait of Queen Elizabeth II.

44. 1 c. black 10 20
45. 2 c. red 10 30
46. 4 c. sepia 10 10
47. 5 c. lake 10 10
48. 8 c. green .. .. .. 1·00 1·00
49. 10 c. brown 15 10
50. 20 c. blue 20 30
51. 50 c. black and blue .. 25 20
52. $1 blue and purple .. 3·00 25
53. $2 green and red .. .. 4·25 5·00
54. $5 brown and green .. 10·00 5·00

1. Copra.

1960. As Nos. 44/54 but with inset Arms of Penang as in T **1**.

55. 1 c. black 10 15
56. 2 c. red 10 20
57. 4 c. brown 10 10
58. 5 c. lake 10 10
59. 8 c. green .. .. .. 2·00 2·25
60. 10 c. purple 15 10
61. 20 c. blue 20 10
62. 50 c. black and blue .. 20 10
63. $1 blue and purple .. 1·50 40
64. $2 green and red .. .. 3·00 2·00
65. $5 brown and green .. 8·50 4·00

2. "Vanda hookeriana".

1965. As Nos. 115/21 of Kedah but with Arms of Penang inset and inscr. "PULAU PINANG as in T **2**.

66. **2.** 1 c. multicoloured .. 10 40
67. – 2 c. multicoloured .. 10 40
68. – 5 c. multicoloured .. 20 10
69. – 6 c. multicoloured .. 30 30
70. – 10 c. multicoloured .. 20 10
71. – 15 c. multicoloured .. 1·00 10
72. – 20 c. multicoloured .. 1·60 30

The higher values used in Penang were Nos. 20/7 of Malaysia (National Issues).

3. "Valeria valeria".

1971. Butterflies. As Nos. 124/30 of Kedah but with Arms of Penang inset and inscr. "pulau pinang" as in T **3**.

75. – 1 c. multicoloured .. 15 40
76. – 2 c. multicoloured .. 40 40
77. – 5 c. multicoloured .. 55 10
78. – 6 c. multicoloured .. 65 60
79. – 10 c. multicoloured .. 65 10
80. – 15 c. multicoloured .. 65 10
81. **3.** 20 c. multicoloured .. 75 40

The higher values in use with this issue were Nos. 64/71 of Malaysia (National Issues).

4. "Etlingera elatior" (inscr "Phaeomeria speciosa").

1979. Flowers. As Nos. 135/41 of Kedah but with Arms of Penang and inscr. "pulau pinang" as in T **4**.

86. 1 c. "Rafflesia hasseltii" .. 10 20
87. 2 c. "Pterocarpus indicus" 10 20
88. 5 c. "Lagerstroemia speciosa" 10 10
89. 10 c. "Durio zibethinus" .. 15 10
90. 15 c. "Hibiscus rosa-sinensis" 15 10
91. 20 c. "Rhododendron scortechinii" 20 10
92. 25 c. Type **4** 25 10

5. Cocoa.

1986. As Nos. 152/8 of Kedah but with Arms of Penang and inscr. "PULAU PINANG" as in T **5**.

100. 1 c. Coffee 10 10
101. 2 c. Coconuts 10 10
102. 5 c. Type **5** 10 10
103. 10 c. Black pepper .. 10 10
104. 15 c. Rubber 10 10
105. 20 c. Oil palm 10 10
106. 30 c. Rice 15 20

PENRHYN ISLAND

One of the Cook Is. in the S. Pacific. A dependency of New Zealand. Used Cook Is. stamps until 1973 when further issues for use in the Northern group of the Cook Is. issues appeared.

A. NEW ZEALAND DEPENDENCY.

1902. Stamps of New Zealand (Pictorials) surch. **PENRHYN ISLAND** and value in native language.

4 **23** ½d. green .. .. 80 3·50
10 **42** 1d. red .. .. 90 2·75
1 **26** 2½d. blue (No. 253) .. 2·00 4·50
14 **28** 3d. brown .. .. 9·00 17·00
15 **31** 6d. red .. .. 15·00 30·00
16a **34** 1s. orange .. .. 45·00 48·00

1914. Stamps of New Zealand (King Edward VII) surch **PENRHYN ISLAND** and value in native language.

19c **51** ½d. green .. .. 80 4·25
22 6d. red .. .. 27·00 60·00
23 1s. orange .. .. 45·00 85·00

1917. Stamps of New Zealand (King George V) optd. **PENRHYN ISLAND.**

28 **62** ½d. green .. .. 75 1·50
29 1½d. grey .. .. 6·00 9·50
30 1½d. brown .. .. 60 9·50
24 2½d. blue .. .. 1·50 4·25
31 3d. brown .. .. 3·00 12·00
26 6d. red .. .. 5·00 15·00
27 1s. orange .. .. 12·00 27·00

1920. Pictorial types as Cook Islands (1920), but inscr. "PENRHYN".

32 **9** ½d. black and green .. 1·00 7·00
33 – 1d. black and red .. 1·25 7·00
34 – 1½d. black and violet 6·50 13·00
40 – 2½d. brown and black 2·00 16·00
35 – 3d. black and red .. 2·50 6·50
36 – 6d. brown and red .. 3·25 19·00
37 – 1s. black and blue .. 9·00 18·00

B. PART OF COOK ISLANDS.

1973. Nos. 228/9, 231, 233/6, 239/40 and 243/5 of Cook Is. optd. **PENRHYN NORTHERN** or **PENRHYN** ($1).

41. 1 c. multicoloured .. 10 10
42. 2 c. multicoloured .. 10 10
43. 3 c. multicoloured .. 20 10
44. 4 c. multicoloured .. 10 10
45. 5 c. multicoloured .. 10 10
46. 6 c. multicoloured .. 20 30
47. 8 c. multicoloured .. 30 40
48. 15 c. multicoloured .. 45 50
49. 20 c. multicoloured .. 1·50 80
50. 50 c. multicoloured .. 1·75 1·75
51. $1 multicoloured .. 2·50 2·25
52. $2 multicoloured .. 2·50 2·50

1973. Nos. 450/2 of Cook Is. optd. with **PENRHYN NORTHERN.**

53. **138.** 25 c. multicoloured .. 85 20
54. – 30 c. multicoloured .. 85 20
55. – 50 c. multicoloured .. 85 20

10. "Ostracion sp".

1974. Fishes. Multicoloured.

56. ½ c. Type **10** 50 50
57. 1 c. "Monodactylus argenteus" 70 50
58. 2 c. "Pomacanthus imperatar" 80 50
59. 3 c. "Chelmon rostratus" .. 80 50
60. 4 c. "Chaetodon ornatissimus" 80 50
61. 5 c. "Chaetodon melanotus" 80 50
62. 8 c. "Chaetodon raffessi" .. 80 50
63. 10 c. "Chaetodon ephippium" 85 50
64. 20 c. "Pygoplites diacanthus" 1·75 50
65. 25 c. "Heniochus acuminatus" 1·75 50
66. 60 c. "Plectorhynchus chaetodonoides" .. .. 2·50 90
67. $1 "Belistipus undulatus" 2·75 1·25
68. $2 Bird's-eye view of Penrhyn .. .. 6·00 11·00
69. $5 Satellite view of Australasia .. .. 6·50 6·00

Nos. 68/9 are size 63 × 25 mm.

11. Penrhyn Stamps of 1902.

1974. Centenary of Universal Postal Union. Multicoloured.

70. 25 c. Type **11** 20 20
71. 50 c. Stamps of 1920 .. 35 35

12. " Adoration of the Kings " (Memling).

1974. Christmas. Multicoloured.

72.	5 c. Type **12**	20	10
73.	10 c. "Adoration of the Shepherds" (Hugo van der Goes)	25	10
74.	25 c. "Adoration of the Magi" (Rubens)	40	15
75.	30 c. "The Holy Family" (Borianni)	50	25

13. Churchill giving "V" Sign.

1974. Birth Cent. of Sir Winston Churchill.

76. **13.**	30 c. brown and gold ..	90	70
77. –	50 c. green and gold ..	1·10	80

DESIGN: 50 c. Full-face portrait.

1975. " Apollo-Soyuz " Space Project. **Optd. KIA ORANA ASTRONAUTS and emblem.**

78.	$5 Satellite view of Australasia	3·50	4·50

15. " Virgin and Child " (Bouts).

1975. Christmas. Paintings of the "Virgin and Child" by artists given below. Mult.

79.	7 c. Type **15**	30	10
80.	15 c. Leonardo da Vinci ..	60	20
81.	35 c. Raphael	95	35

16. " Pieta ".

1976. Easter. 500th Birth Anniversary of Michelangelo.

82. **16.**	15 c. brown and gold ..	25	15
83. –	20 c. lilac and gold ..	30	20
84. –	35 c. green and gold ..	40	45

DESIGNS: Nos. 83/4 show different views of the " Pieta ".

17. " Washington crossing the Delaware " (E. Leutze).

1976. Bicent. of American Revolution.

86.	30 c. } Type **17**	50	15
87.	30 c. }	50	15
88.	30 c. }	50	15
89.	50 c. } " The Spirit of '76 "	60	20
90.	50 c. } (A. M. Willard) ..	60	20
91.	50 c. }	60	20

Type **17** shows the left-hand stamp of the 30 c. design.

18. Running.

1976. Olympic Games, Montreal. Mult.

93.	25 c. Type **18**	25	15
94.	30 c. Long jump	30	15
95.	75 c. Throwing the javelin	55	25

19. " The Flight into Egypt ".

1976. Christmas. Durer Engravings.

97. **19.**	7 c. black and silver ..	10	10
98. –	15 c. blue and silver ..	20	15
99. –	35 c. violet and silver ..	30	25

DESIGNS: 15 c. " Adoration of the Magi ". 35 c. " The Nativity ".

20. The Queen in Coronation Robes.

1977. Silver Jubilee. Multicoloured.

100.	50 c. Type **20**	50	70
101.	$1 The Queen and Prince Philip	60	75
102.	$2 Queen Elizabeth II ..	85	1·00

21. " The Annunciation ".

1977. Christmas. Illustrations by J. S. von Carolsfeld.

104. **21.**	7 c. brn., pur. and gold	30	15
105. –	15 c. red, purple & gold	50	15
106. –	35 c. deep green, green and gold	90	30

DESIGNS: 15 c. " The Announcement to the Shepherds ". 35 c. " The Nativity ".

22. Iiwi.

1978. Bicentenary of Discovery of Hawaii. Birds and Artefacts. Multicoloured.

107.	20 c. Type **22**	80	30
108.	20 c. Elgin cloak	80	30
109.	30 c. Apapane	90	40
110.	30 c. Feather image of a god	90	40
111.	35 c. Moorhen	90	45
112.	35 c. Feather cape, helmet and staff	90	45
113.	75 c. Hawaii Oo	1·50	80
114.	75 c. Feather image and cloak	1·50	80

23. " The Road to Calvary ". 24. Royal Coat of arms.

1978. Easter. 400th Birth Anniv. of Rubens. Multicoloured.

116.	10 c. Type **23**	10	10
117.	15 c. " Christ on the Cross "	15	15
118.	35 c. " Christ with Straw "	25	25

1978. 25th Anniv. of Coronation.

121. **24.**	90 c. black, gold & mauve	40	60
122. –	90 c. multicoloured ..	40	60
123. –	90 c. black, gold & green	40	60

DESIGNS: No. 122, Queen Elizabeth II. No. 123, New Zealand coat of arms.

25. " Madonna of the Pear ".

1978. Christmas. 450th Death Anniv. of Albrecht Durer. Multicoloured.

125.	30 c. Type **25**	50	30
126.	35 c. " The Virgin with St. Anne and Child " (Durer)	50	30

26. Sir Rowland Hill and G.B. Penny Black Stamp.

1979. Death Centenary of Sir Rowland Hill. Multicoloured.

128.	75 c. Type **26**	75	65
129.	75 c. 1974 U.P.U. Centenary 25 c. and 50 c. commemoratives	75	65
130.	90 c. Sir Rowland Hill ..	90	80
131.	90 c. 1978 Coronation Anniversary 90 c. commemorative	90	80

27. Max and Moritz.

INDEX

Countries can be quickly located by referring to the index at the end of this volume.

1979. Int. Year of the Child. **Illustrations from " Max and Moritz " stories by Wilhelm Busch.** Multicoloured.

133.	12 c. Type **27**	20	10
134.	12 c. Max and Moritz looking down chimney ..	20	10
135.	12 c. Max and Moritz taking food	20	10
136.	12 c. Cook about to beat dog	20	10
137.	15 c. Max sawing through bridge	25	10
138.	15 c. Pursuer approaching bridge	25	10
139.	15 c. Collapse of bridge ..	25	10
140.	15 c. Pursuer in river ..	25	10
141.	20 c. Baker locking shop ..	30	20
142.	20 c. Max and Moritz emerge from hiding	30	20
143.	20 c. Max and Moritz falling in dough	30	20
144.	20 c. Max and Moritz made into buns	30	20

28. " Christ carrying Cross " (Book of Ferdinand II).

1980. Easter. Scenes from **15th-cent.** Prayer Books. Multicoloured.

145.	12 c. Type **28** ..	10	10
146.	20 c. " The Crucifixion " (William Vrelant, Book of Duke of Burgundy) ..	15	15
147.	35 c. " Descent from the Cross " (Book of Ferdinand II)	25	25

29. "Queen Elizabeth, 1937" (Sir Gerald Kelly).

1980. 80th Birthday of The Queen Mother.

150. **29.**	$1 multicoloured ..	1·50	1·50

30. Falk Hoffman, D.D.R. (platform diving) (gold).

1980. Olympic Medal Winners. **Multicoloured.**

152.	10 c. Type **30**	10	10
153.	10 c. Martina Jaschke (platform diving) ..	10	10
154.	20 c. Tomi Polkolainen (archery)	15	15
155.	20 c. Kete Losaberidse (archery)	15	15
156.	30 c. Czechoslovakia (football)	20	20
157.	30 c. East Germany (football)	20	20
158.	50 c. Barbel Wockel (200 metres)	30	30
159.	50 c. Pietro Mennea (200 metres)	30	30

31. " The Virgin of Counsellers " (Luis Dalmau).

1980. Christmas. Multicoloured.

161. 20 c. Type **31** 15 15
162. 35 c. " Virgin and Child " (Serra Brothers) .. 20 20
163. 50 c. " The Virgin of Albocacer " (Master of the Porciuncula) .. 30 30

32. Amatasi.

1981. Sailing Ships (1st series). Mult.

166 1 c. Type **32** 20 15
167 1 c. Ndrua (canoe) .. 20 15
168 1 c. Waka (canoe) .. 20 15
169 1 c. Tongiaki (canoe) .. 20 15
170 3 c. Va'a Teu'ua (canoe) .. 40 15
171 3 c. "Vitoria" (Del Cano's ship) 40 15
172 3 c. "Golden Hind" (Drake's ship) 40 15
173 3 c. "La Boudeuse" (Bougainville's ship) .. 40 15
174 4 c. H.M.S. "Bounty" .. 50 15
175 4 c. "L'Astrolabe" (Dumont d'Urville's ship) 50 15
176 4 c. "Star of India" (full-rigged ship) .. 50 15
177 4 c. "Great Republic" (clipper) 50 15
178 6 c. "Balcutha" (clipper) .. 50 20
179 6 c. "Coonatoo" (clipper) .. 50 20
180 6 c. "Antiope" (clipper) .. 50 20
181 6 c. "Teaping" (clipper) .. 50 20
182 10 c. "Preussen" (full-rigged ship) 50 60
183 10 c. "Pamir" (barque) .. 50 60
184 10 c. "Cap Hornier" (full-rigged ship) 50 60
185 10 c. "Patriarch" (clipper) .. 50 60
186 15 c. Type **22** 50 70
187 15 c. As No. 167 .. .. 50 70
188 15 c. As No. 168 .. .. 50 70
189 15 c. As No. 169 .. .. 50 70
190 20 c. As No. 170 .. .. 50 70
191 20 c. As No. 171 .. .. 50 70
192 20 c. As No. 172 .. .. 50 70
193 20 c. As No. 173 .. .. 50 70
194 30 c. As No. 174 .. .. 50 75
195 30 c. As No. 175 .. .. 50 75
196 30 c. As No. 176 .. .. 50 75
197 30 c. As No. 177 .. .. 50 75
198 50 c. As No. 178 .. .. 1·00 1·50
199 50 c. As No. 179 .. .. 1·00 1·50
200 50 c. As No. 180 .. .. 1·00 1·50
201 50 c. As No. 181 .. .. 1·00 1·50
202 $1 As No. 182 .. .. 1·50 1·50
203 $1 As No. 183 .. .. 1·50 1·50
204 $1 As No. 184 .. .. 1·50 1·50
205 $1 As No. 185 .. .. 1·50 1·50
206 $2 "Cutty Sark" (clipper) 4·50 2·75
207 $4 "Mermerus" (clipper) .. 9·00 5·00
208 $6 H.M.S. "Resolution" and H.M.S. "Discovery" (Cook's ships) .. 14·00 11·00

Nos. 186/201 are 41 × 35 mm, Nos. 202/5 41 × 25 mm and Nos. 206/8 47 × 33 mm in size.

See also Nos. 337/55.

33. " Jesus at the Grove " (Veronese).

1981. Easter. Paintings. Multicoloured.

218. 30 c. Type **33** 25 20
219. 40 c. " Christ with Crown of Thorns " (Titian) .. 30 25
220. 50 c. " Pieta " (Van Dyck) 40 30

34. Prince Charles as Young Child.

1981. Royal Wedding. Multicoloured.

223. 40 c. Type **34** 25 35
224. 50 c. Prince Charles as schoolboy 30 40
225. 60 c. Prince Charles as young man 30 40
226. 70 c. Prince Charles in ceremonial Naval uniform 35 45
227. 80 c. Prince Charles as Colonel-in-Chief, Royal Regiment of Wales .. 35 45

1981. International Year for Disabled Persons. Nos. 223/7 surch. **+5 c.**

229. **34.** 40 c.+5 c. multicoloured 40 60
230. – 50 c.+5 c. multicoloured 45 65
231. – 60 c.+5 c. multicoloured 45 65
232. – 70 c.+5 c. multicoloured 55 75
233. – 80 c.+5 c. multicoloured 55 85

35. Footballers.

1981. World Cup Football Championships, Spain (1982). Multicoloured.

235. 15 c. Type **35** 15 15
236. 15 c. Footballer wearing orange jersey with black and mauve stripes .. 15 15
237. 15 c. Player in blue jersey 15 15
238. 35 c. Player in blue jersey 25 25
239. 35 c. Player in red jersey 25 25
240. 35 c. Player in yellow jersey with green stripes .. 25 25
241. 50 c. Player in orange jersey 35 35
242. 50 c. Player in mauve jersey 35 35
243. 50 c. Player in black jersey 35 35

36. " The Virgin on a Crescent ".

1981. Christmas. Engravings by **Durer.**

245. **36.** 30 c. violet, purple and stone 75 75
246. – 40 c. vio., pur. and stone 90 90
247. – 50 c. vio., pur. and stone 1·25 1·25

DESIGNS: 40 c. " The Virgin at the **Fence** ". 50 c. " The Holy Virgin and Child ".

37. Lady Diana Spencer as Baby.

1982. 21st Birthday of Princess of Wales. Multicoloured.

250. 30 c. Type **37** 25 30
251. 50 c. As young child .. 35 45
252. 70 c. As schoolgirl .. 50 60
253. 80 c. As teenager 60 80
254. $1·40 As young lady .. 1·00 1·25

1982. Birth of Prince William of Wales (1st issue). Nos. 223/7 optd. **BIRTH OF PRINCE WILLIAM OF WALES 21 JUNE 1982.**

256. 40 c. Type **34** 80 80
257. 50 c. Prince Charles as schoolboy 90 90
258. 60 c. Prince Charles as young man .. .. 1·00 1·00
259. 70 c. Prince Charles in ceremonial Naval Uniform .. .. 1·25 1·25
260. 80 c. Prince Charles as Colonel-in-Chief, Royal Regiment of Wales .. 1·60 1·60

1982. Birth of Prince William of Wales (2nd issue). As Nos. 250/4 but with changed inscriptions. Multicoloured.

262. 30 c. As Type **37** (inscr "21 JUNE 1982. BIRTH OF PRINCE WILLIAM OF WALES") 25 30
263. 30 c. As Type **37** (inscr "COMMEMORATING THE BIRTH OF PRINCE WILLIAM OF WALES") 25 30
264. 50 c. As No. 251 (inscr "21 JUNE 1982. BIRTH OF PRINCE WILLIAM OF WALES") 35 45
265. 50 c. As No. 251 (inscr "COMMEMORATING THE BIRTH OF PRINCE WILLIAM OF WALES") 35 45
266. 70 c. As No. 252 (inscr "21 JUNE 1982. BIRTH OF PRINCE WILLIAM OF WALES") 50 60
267. 70 c. As No. 252 (inscr "COMMEMORATING THE BIRTH OF PRINCE WILLIAM OF WALES") 50 65
268. 80 c. As No. 253 (inscr "21 JUNE 1982. BIRTH OF PRINCE WILLIAM OF WALES") 50 65
269. 80 c. As No. 253 (inscr "COMMEMORATING THE BIRTH OF PRINCE WILLIAM OF WALES") 50 65
270. $1·40 As No. 254 (inscr "21 JUNE 1982. BIRTH OF PRINCE WILLIAM OF WALES") .. .. 90 1·25
271. $1·40 As No. 252 (inscr "COMMEMORATING THE BIRTH OF PRINCE WILLIAM OF WALES") 90 1·25

39. " Virgin and Child ". (detail from painting by Joos Van Cleve).

1982. Christmas. Detail from Renaissance Paintings of " Virgin and Child ". **Mult.**

273. 25 c. Type **39** 30 40
274. 48 c. " Virgin and Child " (Filippino Lippi) .. 45 55
275. 60 c. " Virgin and Child " (Cima da Conegliano) .. 60 70

40. Red Coral.

1983. Commonwealth Day. Multicoloured.

278. 60 c. Type **40** 50 60
279. 60 c. Aerial view of Penrhyn atoll 50 60
280. 60 c. Eleanor Roosevelt on Penrhyn during Second World War 50 60
281. 60 c. Map of South Pacific 50 60

41. Scout Emblem and Blue Tropical Flower.

1983. 75th Anniv. of Boy Scout Movement. Multicoloured.

282. 36 c. Type **41** .. .. 1·25 45
283. 48 c. Emblem & pink flower 1·50 55
284. 60 c. Emblem and orange flower .. .. .. 1·75 75

1983. 15th World Scout Jamboree, Alberta, Canada. Nos 282/4 optd **XV WORLD JAMBOREE CANADA 1983.**

286. 36 c. Type **41** .. .. 1·00 40
287. 48 c. Emblem and pink flower .. .. .. 1·25 55
288. 60 c. Emblem and orange flower .. .. .. 1·40 75

43. School of Sperm Whales.

1983. Whale Conservation. **Multicoloured.**

290. 8 c. Type **43** .. .. 1·00 50
291. 15 c. Harpooner preparing to strike .. .. 1·40 75
292. 35 c. Whale attacking boat 2·00 1·25
293. 60 c. Dead whales marked with flags .. .. 3·00 1·60
294. $1 Dead whales on slipway 3·75 2·40

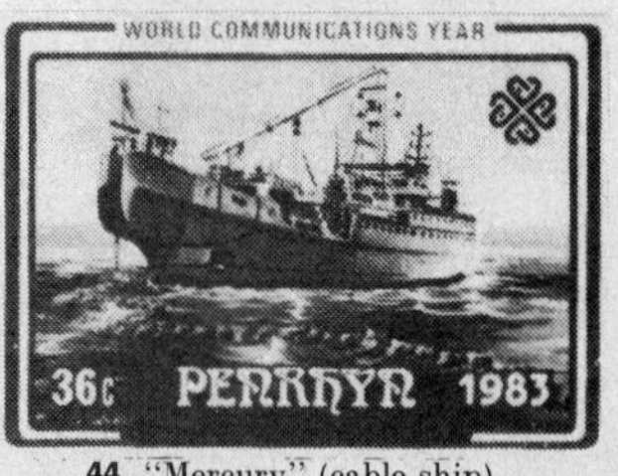

44. "Mercury" (cable ship).

1983. World Communications Year. Mult.

295. 36 c. Type **44** 40 35
296. 48 c. Men watching cable being laid 50 45
297. 60 c. "Mercury" (different) 70 60

1983. Various stamps surch. (a) Nos. 182/5, 190/7 and 206.

299 18 c. on 10 c. "Preussen", 1902 .. .. .. 20 20
300 18 c. on 10 c. "Pamir", 1902 20 20
301 18 c. on 10 c. "Cap Hornier", 1910 .. .. 20 20
302 18 c. on 10 c. "Patriarch", 1869 .. .. .. 20 20
303 36 c. on 20 c. Va'a Teu'ua 35 35
304 36 c. on 20 c. "Vitoria" .. 35 35
305 36 c. on 20 c. "Golden Hind" 35 35
306 36 c. on 20 c. "La Boudeuse" 35 35
307 36 c. on 30 c. H.M.S. "Bounty" 35 35
308 36 c. on 30 c. "L'Astrolabe" 35 35
309 36 c. on 30 c. "Star of India" 35 35
310 36 c. on 30 c. "Great Republic" 35 35
311 $1.20 on $2 "Cutty Sark" 1·40 1·40

(b) Nos. 252/3.

312 72 c. on 70 c. Princess Diana as schoolgirl .. 2·00 1·50
313 96 c. on 80 c. Princess Diana as teenager .. 2·25 1·75

1983. Nos. 225/6, 268/9, 254 and 208 surch.

314 48 c. on 60 c. Prince Charles as young man 3·50 1·50
315 72 c. on 70 c. Prince Charles in ceremonial Naval uniform 4·00 1·75
316 96 c. on 80 c. As No. 253 (inscr "21 JUNE 1982...") 2·75 1·00
317 96 c. on 80 c. As No. 253 (inscr "COMMEMORATING...") 1·75 1·00
318 $1.20 on $4.40 As young lady 3·25 1·50
319 $5.60 on $6 H.M.S. "Resolution" and "Discovery" 15·00 6·50

45. George Cayley's Airship Design, 1837.

1983. Bicentenary of Manned Flight. Mult. A. Inscr. "NORTHERN COOK ISLANS". B. Corrected spelling optd. in black on silver, over original inscription.

		A		B	
320.	36 c. Type 45	75	60	30	35
321.	48 c. Dupuy De Lome's man-powered airship, 1872	1·00	70	40	45
322.	60 c. Santos Dumont's sixth airship, 1901	1·25	1·00	45	50
323.	96 c. Lebaudy's practical airship, 1902	2·00	1·50	75	80
324.	$1.32 Graf Zeppelin "LZ 127", 1929	3·00	2·00	1·00	1·10

46. " Madonna in the Meadow ".

1983. Christmas. 500th Birth Anniv. of Raphael. Multicoloured.

326. 36 c. Type 46 35 40
327. 42 c. " Tempi Madonna " 35 40
328. 48 c. " The Smaller Cowper Madonna " 45 50
329. 60 c. " Madonna della Tenda " 55 60

1983. Nos. 266/7, 227 and 270 surch.

331. 72 c. on 70 c. As No. 252 (inscr. " 21 JUNE 1982 . . . ") 2·00 1·25
332. 72 c. on 70 c. As No. 252 (inscr. " COMMEMORATING . . . ") 1·25 90
333. 96 c. on 80 c. Prince Charles as Colonel-in-chief, Royal Regiment of Wales 2·00 1·00
334. $1.20 on $1.40 As No. 254 (inscr. " 21 JUNE 1982 . . . ") 2·25 1·25
335. $1.20 on $1.40 As No. 254 (inscr. " COMMEMORATING . . . ") 1·75 1·00

47. Waka.

1984. Sailing Craft and Ships (2nd series). Multicoloured.

337 2 c. Type 47 10 10
338 4 c. Amatasi 15 15
339 5 c. Ndrua 15 15
340 8 c. Tongiaki 20 20
341 10 c. "Vitoria" 20 20
342 18 c. "Golden Hind" 30 30
343 20 c. "La Boudeuse" 30 30
344 30 c. H.M.S. "Bounty" 40 40
345 36 c. "L'Astrolabe" 40 40
346 48 c. "Great Republic" 45 50
347 50 c. "Star of India" 45 50
348 60 c. "Coonatto" 45 50
349 72 c. "Antiope" 50 55
350 80 c. "Balcutha" 60 65
351 96 c. "Cap Hornier" 70 75
352 $1.20 "Pamir" 90 95
353 $3 "Mermerus" (41 × 31 mm) 2·25 2·40
354 $5 "Cutty Sark" (41 × 31 mm) 3·75 4·00
355 $9.60 H.M.S. "Resolution" and H.M.S. "Discovery" (41 × 31 mm) 7·00 7·25

48. Olympic Flag.

1984. Olympic Games, Los Angeles. Mult.

356. 35 c. Type 48 30 35
357. 60 c. Olympic torch and flags 50 55
358. $1.80 Ancient athletes and Coliseum 1·50 1·60

49. Penrhyn Stamps of 1978, 1979 and 1981.

1984. "Ausipex" International Stamp Exhibition, Melbourne. Multicoloured.

360. 60 c. Type 49 50 75
361. $1.20 Location map of Penrhyn 1·00 1·25

1984. Birth of Prince Henry. Nos. 223/4 and 250/1 surch. **Birth of Prince Henry 15 Sept. 1984.**

363. $2 on 30 c. Type 37 2·25 1·50
364. $2 on 40 c. Type 34 2·75 1·75
365. $2 on 50 c. Prince Charles as schoolboy 2·75 1·75
366. $2 on 50 c. Lady Diana as young child 2·25 1·50

51. "Virgin and Child" (Giovanni Bellini).

1984. Christmas. Paintings of the Virgin and Child by different artists. Multicoloured.

367. 36 c. Type 51 30 35
368. 48 c. Lorenzo di Credi 40 45
369. 60 c. Palma the Older 50 55
370. 96 c. Raphael 75 80

HAVE YOU READ THE NOTES AT THE BEGINNING OF THIS CATALOGUE?
These often provide answers to the enquiries we receive.

52. Harlequin Duck.

1985. Birth Bicentenary of John J. Audubon (ornithologist). Multicoloured.

373. 20 c. Type 52 1·00 1·00
374. 55 c. Sage grouse 1·75 1·75
375. 65 c. Solitary sandpiper 2·00 2·00
376. 75 c. Dunlin 2·50 2·50

Nos. 373/6 show original paintings.

53. Lady Elizabeth Bowes-Lyon, 1921.

1985. Life and Times of Queen Elizabeth the Queen Mother. Each violet, silver and yellow.

378. 75 c. Type 53 50 65
379. 95 c. With baby Princess Elizabeth, 1926 60 80
380. $1.20, Coronation Day, 1937 75 1·00
381. $2.80, On her 70th birthday 1·60 2·00

54. "The House in the Wood".

1985. International Youth Year. Birth Centenary of Jacob Grimm (folklorist). Multicoloured.

383. 75 c. Type 54 90 80
384. 95 c. "Snow-White and Rose-Red" 1·10 1·00
385. $1.15 "The Goose Girl" 1·40 1·25

55. "The Annunciation".

1985. Christmas. Paintings by Murillo. Mult.

386. 75 c. Type 55 90 90
387. $1.15, "Adoration of the Shepherds" 1·25 1·25
388. $1.80, "The Holy Family" 2·00 2·00

56. Halley's Comet.

1986. Appearance of Halley's Comet. Design showing details of the painting "Fire and Ice" by Camille Rendal. Multicoloured.

391 $1.50 Type 56 1·10 1·25
392 $1.50 Stylized "Giotto" spacecraft 1·10 1·25

Nos. 391/2 were printed together, forming a composite design of the complete painting.

57. Princess Elizabeth aged Three, 1929, and Bouquet.

1986. 60th Birthday of Queen Elizabeth II. Multicoloured.

394. 95 c. Type 57 80 80
395. $1.45 Profile of Queen Elizabeth and St. Edward's Crown 1·25 1·25
396. $2.50 Queen Elizabeth aged three and in profile with Imperial State Crown (56 × 30 mm.) 2·00 2·00

58. Statue of Liberty under Construction, Paris.

1986. Centenary of Statue of Liberty. Each black, gold and yellow-green.

397. 95 c. Type 58 65 70
398. $1.75 Erection of Statue, New York 1·10 1·25
399. $3 Artist's impression of Statue, 1876 2·10 2·25

59. Prince Andrew and Miss Sarah Ferguson.

1986. Royal Wedding. Multicoloured.

400. $2.50 Type 59 3·25 3·25
401. $3.50 Profiles of Prince Andrew and Miss Sarah Ferguson 3·75 3·75

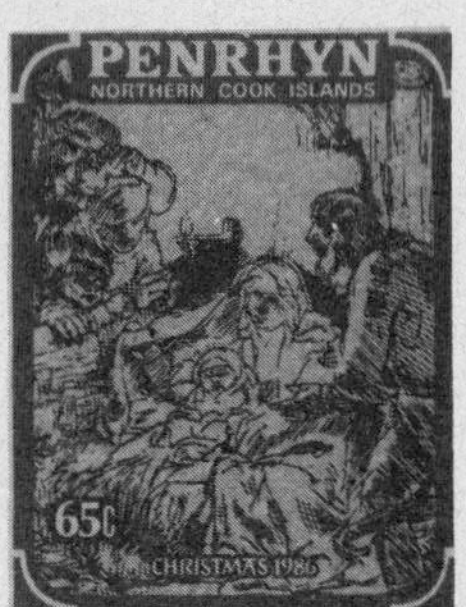

61. "Adoration of the Shepherds".

1986. Christmas. Engravings by Rembrandt. Each brown, ochre and gold.

404. 65 c. Type **61** .. .. 1·25 1·25
405. $1.75 "Virgin and Child" .. 2·50 2·50
406. $2.50 "The Holy Family" 3·50 3·50

1986. Visit of Pope John Paul II to South Pacific. Nos. 404/6 surch. **SOUTH PACIFIC VISIT 21 TO 24 NOVEMBER 1986.**

408. 65 c.+10 c. Type **61** .. 1·75 1·75
409. $1.75+10 c. "Virgin and Child" .. .. .. 3·25 3·25
410. $2.50+10 c. "The Holy Family" .. .. .. 3·75 3·75

1987. Royal Ruby Wedding. Nos. 68/9 optd. **Fortieth Royal Wedding Anniversary 1947–87.**

413. $2 Birds-eye view of Penrhyn .. .. .. 2·25 2·25
414. $5 Satellite view of Australasia .. .. 4·25 4·25

65. "The Garvagh Madonna".

1987. Christmas. Religious Paintings by Raphael. Multicoloured.

415. 95 c. Type **65** .. .. 1·00 1·00
416. $1.60 "The Alba Madonna" 1·60 1·60
417. $2.25 "The Madonna of the Fish" .. .. .. 2·25 2·25

66 Athletics

1988. Olympic Games, Seoul. Multicoloured.

420 55 c. Type **66** 55 55
421 95 c. Pole vault (vert) .. 85 85
422 $1.25 Shot put .. .. 1·10 1·10
423 $1.50 Tennis (vert) .. .. 1·50 1·50

1988. Olympic Gold Medal Winners, Seoul. Nos. 420/3 optd.

425 55 c. Type **66** (optd **CARL LEWIS UNITED STATES 100 METERS**) 40 45
426 95 c. Pole vault (optd **LOUISE RITTER UNITED STATES HIGH JUMP**) .. 65 70
427 $1.25 Shot put (optd **ULF TIMMERMANN EAST GERMANY SHOT-PUT**) 90 95
428 $1.50 Tennis (optd **STEFFI GRAF WEST GERMANY WOMEN'S TENNIS**) 1·10 1·25

67 "Virgin and Child"

1988. Christmas. Designs showing different "Virgin and Child" paintings by Titian.

430 **67** 70 c. multicoloured .. 65 65
431 – 85 c. multicoloured .. 70 70
432 – 95 c. multicoloured .. 75 75
433 – $1.25 multicoloured .. 90 95

68 Neil Armstrong stepping onto Moon

1989. 20th Anniv of First Manned Moon Landing. Multicoloured.

435 55 c. Type **68** 40 45
436 75 c. Astronaut on Moon carrying equipment .. 55 60
437 95 c. Conducting experiment on Moon 70 75
438 $1.25 Crew of "Apollo 11" 95 1·00
439 $1.75 Crew inside "Apollo 11" .. .. .. 1·40 1·50

69 Virgin Mary

1989. Christmas. Details from "The Nativity" by Durer. Multicoloured.

440 55 c. Type **69** 60 60
441 70 c. Christ Child and cherubs 70 70
442 85 c. Joseph 85 85
443 $1.25 Three women .. 1·25 1·25

70 Queen Elizabeth the Queen Mother

1990. 90th Birthday of Queen Elizabeth the Queen Mother.

445 **70** $2.25 multicoloured .. 1·75 1·75

71 "Adoration of the Magi" (Veronese)

1990. Christmas. Religious Paintings. Mult.

447 55 c. Type **71** 55 55
448 70 c. "Virgin and Child" (Quentin Metsys) .. 75 75
449 85 c. "Virgin and Child Jesus" (Hugo van der Goes) 85 85
450 $1.50 "Adoration of the Kings" (Jan Gossaert) 1·50 1·50

1990. "Birdpex '90" Stamp Exhibition, Christchurch, New Zealand. Nos 373/6 surch **Birdpex '90** and logo.

452 $1.50 on 20 c. Type **52** .. 1·50 1·50
453 $1.50 on 55 c. Sage grouse 1·50 1·50
454 $1.50 on 65 c. Solitary sandpiper .. .. 1·50 1·50
455 $1.50 on 75 c. Dunlin .. 1·50 1·50

1991. 65th Birthday of Queen Elizabeth II. No. 208 optd **COMMEMORATING 65th BIRTHDAY OF H.M. QUEEN ELIZABETH II.**

456 $6 H.M.S. "Resolution" and "Discovery", 1776–80 .. .. .. 7·00 7·00

74 "The Virgin and Child with Saints" (G. David)

1991. Christmas. Religious Paintings. Mult.

457 55 c. Type **74** 50 50
458 85 c. "Nativity" (Tintoretto) .. 75 75
459 $1.15 "Mystic Nativity" (Botticelli) .. .. 1·10 1·10
460 $1.85 "Adoration of the Shepherds" (B. Murillo) 1·60 1·60

1992. Olympic Games, Barcelona. As T **94** of Aitutaki. Multicoloured.

462 75 c. Running 65 65
463 95 c. Boxing 80 80
464 $1.15 Swimming .. .. 1·00 1·00
465 $1.50 Wrestling .. .. 1·25 1·25

75 Marquesan Canoe

1992. 6th Festival of Pacific Arts, Rarotonga. Multicoloured.

466 $1.15 Type **75** 90 90
467 $1.75 Tangaroa statue from Rarotonga .. 1·40 1·40
468 $1.95 Manihiki canoe .. 1·50 1·50

1992. Royal Visit by Prince Edward. Nos. 466/8 optd **ROYAL VISIT.**

469 $1.15 Type **75** 90 90
470 $1.75 Tangaroa statue from Rarotonga .. .. 1·40 1·40
471 $1.95 Manihiki canoe .. 1·50 1·50

76 "Virgin with Child and Saints" (Borgognone)

1992. Christmas. Religious Paintings by Ambrogio Borgognone. Multicoloured.

472 55 c. Type **76** 50 50
473 85 c. "Virgin on Throne" 75 75
474 $1.05 "Virgin on Carpet" 90 90
475 $1.85 "Virgin of the Milk" 1·50 1·50

77 Vincente Pinzon and "Nina"

1992. 500th Anniv of Discovery of America by Columbus. Multicoloured.

477 $1.15 Type **77** .. .. 1·00 1·00
478 $1.35 Martin Pinzon and "Pinta" .. .. 1·25 1·25
479 $1.75 Christopher Columbus and "Santa Maria" .. .. .. 1·60 1·60

78 Queen Elizabeth II in 1953

1993. 40th Anniv of Coronation.

480 **78** $6 multicoloured .. 5·00 5·50

79 Helmet Shell

1993. Marine Life. Multicoloured.

481 5 c. Type **79** 10 10
482 10 c. Daisy coral 10 10
483 15 c. Hydroid coral .. 10 10
484 20 c. Feather-star .. 15 20
485 25 c. Sea star 20 25
486 30 c. Nudibranch 20 25
487 50 c. Smooth sea star .. 35 40
488 70 c. Black pearl oyster .. 50 55
489 80 c. Pyjama nudibranch 60 65
490 85 c. Prickly sea cucumber 60 65
491 90 c. Organ pipe coral .. 65 70
492 $1 Aeolid nudibranch .. 70 75
493 $2 Textile cone shell .. 1·50 1·60

80 "Virgin on Throne with Child" (detail) (Tura)

1993. Christmas.

499 **80** 55 c. multicoloured .. 40 45
500 – 85 c. multicoloured .. 60 65
501 – $1.05 multicoloured .. 75 80
502 – $1.95 multicoloured .. 1·40 1·50
503 – $4.50 mult (32×47 mm) 3·25 3·50

DESIGNS: 80 c. to $4.50 Different details from "Virgin on Throne with Child" (Cosme Tura).

OFFICIAL STAMPS

1978. Optd. or surch. **O.H.M.S.**

O 1. 1 c. multicoloured (No. 57) 15 10
O 2. 2 c. multicoloured (No. 58) 15 10
O 3. 3 c. multicoloured (No. 59) 25 10
O 4. 4 c. multicoloured (No. 60) 25 10
O 5. 5 c. multicoloured (No. 61) 30 10
O 6. 8 c. multicoloured (No. 62) 35 15
O 7. 10 c. multicoloured (No. 63) 40 15
O 8. 15 c. on 60 c. mult. (No. 66) 45 25
O 9. 18 c. on 60 c. mult. (No. 66) 50 25
O 10. 20 c. multicoloured (No. 64) 50 25
O 11. 25 c. multicoloured (No. 65) 55 30
O 12. 30 c. on 60 c. mult. (No. 66) 55 35
O 13. 50 c. multicoloured (No. 89) 70 55
O 14. 50 c. multicoloured (No. 90) 70 55
O 15. 50 c. multicoloured (No. 91) 70 55
O 16. $1 multicoloured (No. 101) 2·25 1·00
O 17. $2 multicoloured (No. 102) 4·50 2·25

These stamps were originally only sold to the public cancelled-to-order and not in unused condition. They were made available to overseas collectors in mint condition during 1980.

1985. Nos. 206/8, 278/81, 337/47 and 349/55 optd. **O.H.M.S.** or surch also.

O18 2 c. Type **47** 10 10
O19 4 c. Amatasi 10 10
O20 5 c. Ndrua 10 10
O21 8 c. Tongiaki 10 10
O22 10 c. "Vitoria" 10 10
O23 18 c. "Golden Hind" .. 15 20
O24 20 c. "La Boudeuse" .. 15 20
O25 30 c. H.M.S. "Bounty" .. 20 25
O26 40 c. on 36 c. "L'Astrolabe" 30 35
O27 50 c. "Star of India" .. 35 40
O28 55 c. on 48 c. "Great Republic" 40 45
O39 65 c. on 60 c. Type **40** .. 45 50
O40 65 c. on 60 c. Aerial view of Penrhyn atoll .. 45 50
O41 65 c. on 60 c. Eleanor Roosevelt on Penrhyn during Second World War 45 50
O42 65 c. on 60 c. Map of South Pacific 45 50
O29 75 c. on 72 c. "Antiope" .. 55 60
O30 75 c. on 96 c. "Cap Hornier" 55 60
O31 80 c. "Balcutha" .. 60 65
O32 $1.20 "Pamir" 90 95
O33 $2 "Cutty Sark" .. 1·50 1·60
O34 $3 "Mermerus" .. .. 2·25 2·40
O35 $4 "Mermerus" .. .. 3·00 3·25
O36 $5 "Cutty Sark" .. 3·75 4·00
O37 $6 H.M.S. "Resolution" and H.M.S. "Discovery" .. .. 4·50 5·00
O38 $9.60 H.M.S. "Resolution" and H.M.S. "Discovery" .. .. 7·00 7·25

PERAK

A state of the Federation of Malaya, incorporated in Malaysia in 1963.

100 cents = 1 dollar (Straits or Malayan)

Stamps of Straits Settlements optd. or surch.

1878. No. 11 optd. with crescent, star and **P** in oval.

1. 2 c. brown £950 £850

1880. Optd. **PERAK.**

10. **9.** 2 c. brown .. .. 18·00 24·00
17. 2 c. red .. .. .. 1·00 90

1883. Surch. **2 CENTS PERAK.**

16. 2 c on 4 c. red £375 £225

1886. No. 63a surch. **ONE CENT PERAK.**

30 1 c. on 2 c. red .. .. 22·00 27·00

1886. No. 63a surch. **1 CENT PERAK.**

28 1 c. on 2 c. red .. .. 60·00 70·00

1886. No. 63a surch **One CENT PERAK.**

33 1 c. on 2 c. red .. .. 70 1·75

1889. Surch. **PERAK ONE CENT.**

41. 1 c. on 2 c. red .. .. £110 95·00

1891. Surch. **PERAK One CENT.**

57. 1 c. on 2 c. red .. .. 55 2·75
43. 1 c on 6 c. lilac .. .. 32·00 25·00

1891. Surch. **PERAK Two CENTS.**

48 2 c. on 24 c. green .. .. 9·00 9·00

42. Tiger. 44. Tiger.

45. Elephants.

1892.

61. **42.** 1 c. green .. .. 2·25 15
62. 2 c. red .. .. 1·75 30
63. 2 c. orange .. .. 35 3·25
64. 5 c. blue .. .. 3·00 7·50

1895. Surch. **3 CENTS.**

65. **42.** 3 c. on 5 c. red .. .. 70 1·75

1895.

66. **44.** 1 c. purple and green .. 1·00 40
67. 2 c. purple and brown 75 40
68. 3 c. purple and red .. 1·50 20
69. 4 c. purple and red .. 7·50 4·75
70. 5 c. purple and yellow .. 2·75 55
71. 8 c. purple and blue .. 30·00 65
72. 10 c. purple and orange 8·00 45
73. 25 c. green and red .. £100 12·00
74. 50 c. purple and black .. 26·00 28·00
75. 50 c. green and black .. £120 £120
76. **45.** $1 green .. .. 70·00 80·00
77. $2 green and red .. £130 £140
78. $3 green and yellow .. £130 £150
79. $5 green and blue .. £325 £300
80. $25 green and orange .. £4000 £1300

1900. Surch. in words.

81. **44.** 1 c. on 2 c. purple & brown 40 1·50
82. 1 c. on 4 c. purple and red 65 4·25
83. 1 c. on 5 c. purple & yellow 80 6·50
84. 3 c. on 8 c. purple & blue 2·50 3·50
85. 3 c. on 50 c. green & black 1·25 4·25
86. **45.** 3 c. on $1 green .. .. 55·00 £120
87. 3 c. on $2 green and red .. 28·00 75·00

50. Sultan Iskandar. 51.

1935.

88. **50.** 1 c. black 15 10
89. 2 c. green 30 10
90. 4 c. orange 30 10
91. 5 c. brown 30 10
92. 6 c. red .. .. 6·50 2·50
93. 8 c. grey 50 10
94. 10 c. purple 30 15
95. 12 c. blue 70 90
96. 25 c. purple and red .. 85 85
97. 30 c. purple and orange 90 1·50
98. 40 c. red and purple .. 2·50 4·25
99. 50 c. black on green .. 3·50 80
100. $1 blk. & red on blue 2·00 80
101. $2 green and red .. 9·50 8·50
102. $5 grn. & red on grn. 48·00 26·00

1938.

103. **51.** 1 c. black .. .. 3·50 10
104. 2 c. green .. .. 2·50 10
105. 2 c. orange .. .. 75 4·75
106. 3 c. green .. .. 1·25 1·25
107. 4 c. orange .. .. 30·00 10
108. 5 c. brown .. .. 2·75 10
109. 6 c. red .. .. 20·00 10
110. 8 c. grey .. .. 22·00 10
111. 8 c. red .. .. 1·00 40·00
112. 10 c. purple .. .. 22·00 10
113. 12 c. blue .. .. 17·00 2·00
114. 15 c. blue .. .. 1·75 13·00
115. 25 c. purple and red .. 75·00 4·25
116. 30 c. purple and orange .. 9·00 3·00
117. 40 c. red and purple .. 50·00 2·00
118. 50 c. black on green .. 24·00 75
119. $1 black and red on blue £100 14·00
120. $2 green and red .. £100 55·00
121. $5 green and red on green £170 £200

1948. Silver Wedding. As T **10/11** of Aden.

122. 10 c. violet 15 10
123. $5 green .. .. 20·00 20·00

1949. U.P.U. As T **20/23** of Antigua.

124. 10 c. purple 15 10
125. 15 c. blue 45 35
126. 25 c. orange 45 45
127. 50 c. black .. .. 1·75 1·75

52. Sultan Yussuf 'Izzuddin Shah.

1950.

128 **52.** 1 c. black 10 10
129 2 c. orange 10 10
130 3 c. green .. .. 1·00 10
131 4 c. brown 10 10
132 5 c. purple 50 50
133 6 c. grey 10 10
134 8 c. red 30 75
135 8 c. green .. .. 1·00 60
136 10 c. purple 10 10
137 12 c. red .. .. 1·00 1·25
138 15 c. blue 30 10
139 20 c. black and green .. 30 30
140 20 c. blue 75 10
141 25 c. purple and orange 30 10
142 30 c. red and purple .. 1·25 20
143 35 c. red and purple .. 70 25
144 40 c. red and purple .. 1·00 3·00
145 50 c. black and blue .. 55 10
146 $1 blue and purple .. 5·00 15
147 $2 green and red .. 9·00 2·25
148 $5 green and brown .. 35·00 10·00

1953. Coronation. As T **13** of Aden.

149. 10 c. black and purple .. 40 10

1957. As Nos. 92/102 of Kedah but portrait of Sultan Yussuf 'Izzuddin Shah.

150. 1 c. black 10 15
151. 2 c. orange 30 10
152. 4 c. brown 10 10
153. 5 c. lake 10 10
154. 8 c. green .. .. 2·00 80
155. 10 c. sepia 30 10
156. 10 c. purple 45 10
157. 20 c. blue 30 10
158a. 50 c. black and blue .. 30 10
159. $1 blue and purple .. 2·00 10
160a. $2 green and red .. 3·00 1·25
161a. $5 brown and green .. 7·00 3·00

53. Sultan Idris Shah.

1963. Installation of Sultan of Perak.

162. **53.** 10 c. multicoloured .. 10 10

54. "Vanda hookeriana".

1965. As Nos. 115/21 of Kedah but with inset portrait of Sultan Idris as in T **54.**

163. **54.** 1 c. multicoloured .. 10 30
164. – 2 c. multicoloured .. 10 30
165. – 5 c. multicoloured .. 10 10
166. – 6 c. multicoloured .. 15 10
167. – 10 c. multicoloured .. 15 10
168. – 15 c. multicoloured .. 80 10
169. – 20 c. multicoloured .. 1·25 10

The higher values used in Perak were Nos. 20/7 of Malaysia (National Issues).

55. "Delias ninus".

1971. Butterflies. As Nos. 124/30 of Kedah but with portrait of Sultan Idris as in T **55.**

172. **55.** 1 c. multicoloured .. 15 50
173. – 2 c. multicoloured .. 40 50
174. – 5 c. multicoloured .. 50 10
175. – 6 c. multicoloured .. 50 45
176. – 10 c. multicoloured .. 50 10
177. – 15 c. multicoloured .. 70 10
178. – 20 c. multicoloured .. 85 20

The higher values in use with this issue were Nos. 64/71 of Malaysia (National Issues).

56. "Rafflesia hasseltii".

1979. Flowers. As Nos. 135/41 of Kedah, but with portraits of Sultan Idris as in T **56.**

184 1 c. Type **56** 10 20
185 2 c. "Pterocarpus indicus" 10 20
186 5 c. "Lagerstroemia speciosa" 10 10
187 10 c. "Durio zibethinus" .. 15 10
188 15 c. "Hibiscus rosa-sinensis" 15 10
189 20 c. "Rhododendron scortechinii" 20 10
190 25 c. "Etlingera elatior" (inscr "Phaeomeria speciosa") 25 10

57. Coffee.

1986. As Nos. 152/8 of Kedah but with portrait of Sultan Azlan Shah as in T **57.**

198. 1 c. Type **57** 10 10
199. 2 c. Coconuts 10 10
200. 5 c. Cocoa 10 10
201. 10 c. Black pepper .. 10 10
202. 15 c. Rubber 10 10
203. 20 c. Oil palm 10 10
204. 30 c. Rice 15 20

OFFICIAL STAMPS

1889. Stamps of Straits Settlements optd. **P.G.S.**

O 1. **30.** 2 c. red .. .. 2·00 3·00
O 2. 4 c. brown .. .. 6·50 14·00
O 3. 6 c. lilac .. .. 18·00 30·00
O 4. 8 c. orange .. .. 22·00 60·00
O 5. **38.** 10 c. grey .. .. 70·00 70·00
O 6. **30.** 12 c. blue £130 £140
O 7. 12 c. purple £170 £200
O 9. 24 c. green £110 £130

1894. No. 64 optd. **Service.**

O 10. **30.** 5 c. blue .. .. 32·00 80

1895. No. 70 optd. **Service.**

O 11. **31.** 5 c. purple and yellow 1·50 35

PERLIS

A state of the Federation of Malaya, incorporated in Malaysia in 1963.

100 cents = 1 dollar (Straits or Malayan).

1948. Silver Wedding. As T **10/11** of Aden.

1	10 c. violet	30	1·50
2	$5 brown	27·00	42·00

1949. U.P.U. As T **20/23** of Antigua.

3	10 c. purple	30	60
4	15 c. blue	50	2·50
5	25 c. orange	65	2·00
6	50 c. black	1·40	3·75

1. Raja Syed Putra.

1951.

7.	**1.**	1 c. black	10	40
8.		2 c. orange	10	40
9.		3 c. green	40	1·25
10.		4 c. brown	30	20
11.		5 c. purple	30	85
12.		6 c. grey	30	60
13.		8 c. red	55	2·50
14.		8 c. green	75	1·50
15.		10 c. purple	15	20
16.		12 c. red	75	2·25
17.		15 c. blue	90	1·75
18.		20 c. black and green ..	70	3·00
19.		20 c. blue	80	65
20.		25 c. purple and orange ..	85	1·00
21.		30 c. red and purple ..	1·75	6·00
22.		35 c. red and purple ..	75	2·50
23.		40 c. red and purple ..	1·25	10·00
24.		50 c. black and blue ..	1·75	2·50
25.		$1 blue and purple ..	3·50	8·50
26.		$2 green and red ..	9·50	17·00
27.		$5 green and brown ..	45·00	48·00

1953. Coronation. As T **13** of Aden.

28	10 c. black and purple ..	40	2·00

1957. As Nos. 92/102 of Kedah but inset portrait of Raja Syed Putra.

29	1 c. black	10	30
30	2 c. red	10	30
31	4 c. brown	10	10
32	5 c. lake	10	10
33	8 c. green	2·00	1·25
34	10 c. brown	30	50
35	10 c. purple	2·00	75
36	20 c. blue	30	75
37	50 c. black and blue ..	30	75
38	$1 blue and purple ..	3·25	3·50
39	$2 green and red	3·75	5·00
40	$5 brown and green ..	6·50	7·50

2. "Vanda hookeriana".

1965. As Nos. 115/21 of Kedah but with inset portrait of Tunku Bendahara Abu Bakar as in T **2**.

41.	**2.**	1 c. multicoloured ..	10	60
42.	–	2 c. multicoloured ..	10	70
43.	–	5 c. multicoloured ..	15	15
44.	–	6 c. multicoloured ..	50	45
45.	–	10 c. multicoloured ..	55	15
46.	–	15 c. multicoloured ..	1·00	35
47.	–	20 c, multicoloured ..	1·00	95

The higher values used in Perlis were Nos. 20/7 of Malaysia (National Issues).

3. "Danaus melanippus".

1971. Butterflies. As Nos 124/30 of Kedah but with portrait of Raza Syed Putra as in T **3**.

48.	–	1 c. multicoloured ..	15	70
49.	**3.**	2 c. multicoloured ..	20	80
50.	–	5 c. multicoloured ..	55	20
51.	–	6 c. multicoloured ..	55	75
52.	–	10 c. multicoloured ..	55	20
53.	–	15 c. multicoloured ..	55	25
54.	–	20 c. multicoloured ..	65	1·00

The higher values in use with this issue were Nos. 64/71 of Malaysia (National Issues).

4. Raja Syed Putra.

1971. 25th Anniv. of Installation of Raja Syed Putra.

56.	**4.**	10 c. multicoloured ..	20	60
57.		15 c. multicoloured ..	20	35
58.		50 c. multicoloured ..	70	2·00

5. "Pterocarpus indicus".

1979. Flowers. As Nos. 135/41 of Kedah, but with portrait of Raja Syed Putra as in T **5**.

59	1 c. "Rafflesia hasseltii" ..	10	40
60	2 c. Type **5**	10	40
61	5 c. "Lagerstroemia speciosa"	10	10
62	10 c. "Durio zibethinus" ..	15	10
63	15 c. "Hibiscus rosa-sinensis"	15	10
64	20 c. "Rhododendron scortechinii"	20	10
65	25 c. "Etlingera elatior" (inscr "Phaeomeria speciosa")	25	40

6. Coconuts.

1986. As Nos. 152/8 of Kedah but with portrait of Raja Syed Putra as in T **6**.

73.	1 c. Coffee	10	10
74.	2 c. Type **6**	10	10
75.	5 c. Cocoa	10	10
76.	10 c Black pepper	10	10
77.	15 c. Rubber	10	10
78.	20 c. Oil palm	10	10
79.	30 c. Rice	15	20

PITCAIRN ISLANDS

An island group in the Pacific Ocean, nearly midway between Australia and America.

1940. 12 pence = 1 shilling;
20 shillings = 1 pound.
1967. 100 cents = 1 New Zealand dollar.

4. Lt. Bligh and the "Bounty".

1940.

1.	–	½d. orange and green ..	40	60
2.	–	1d. lilac and mauve ..	55	70
3.	–	1½d. grey and red ..	55	50
4.	**4.**	2d. green and brown ..	1·75	1·40
5.	–	3d. green and blue ..	1·25	1·40
5a.	–	4d. black and green ..	15·00	7·00
6.	–	6d. brown and blue ..	5·00	2·25
6a.	–	8d. olive and mauve ..	15·00	7·00
7.	–	1s. violet and grey ..	3·00	2·00
8.	–	2s. 6d. green and brown ..	7·50	4·25

DESIGNS—HORIZ. ½d. Oranges. 1d. Fletcher Christian, crew and Pitcairn Is. 1½d. John Adams and house. 3d. Map of Pitcairn Is. and Pacific. 4d. Bounty Bible. 6d. H.M.S. "Bounty" 8d. School, 1949. 1s. Christian and Pitcairn Is. 2s. 6d. Christian, crew and Pitcairn Coast.

1946. Victory. As T **9** of Aden.

9.	2d. brown	30	15
10.	3d. blue	30	15

1949. Silver Wedding. As T **10/11** of Aden.

11	1½d. red	2·00	1·00
12	10s. mauve	70·00	60·00

1949. U.P.U. As T **20/23** of Antigua.

13.	2½d. brown	2·00	3·00
14.	3d. blue	8·50	4·00
15.	6d. green	11·00	5·00
16.	1s. purple	11·00	5·00

1953. Coronation. As T **13** of Aden.

17	4d. black and green ..	2·00	2·75

12. Handicrafts: Bird Model.

4d. Type I is inscribed "PITCAIRN SCHOOL"; Type II is inscribed "SCHOOL-TEACHER'S HOUSE".

1957.

33	–	½d. green and mauve ..	45	60
19	–	1d. black and green ..	2·25	80
20	–	2d. brown and blue ..	75	60
21	**12**	2½d. brown and pink ..	50	40
22	–	3d. green and blue ..	80	40
23	–	4d. red and blue (I) ..	90	40
23a	–	4d. red and blue (II) ..	5·00	1·50
24	**12**	6d. buff and blue ..	1·25	55
25	–	8d. green and red ..	60	40
26	–	1s. black and brown ..	1·00	40
27	–	2s. green and orange ..	28·00	10·00
28	–	2s. 6d. blue and red ..	12·00	8·00

DESIGNS—HORIZ. ½d. "Cordyline terminalis". 3d. Bounty Bay. 4d. Pitcairn School. 6d. Map of Pacific. 8d. Inland scene. 1s. Model of the "Bounty". 2s. 6d. Launching new whaleboat. VERT. 1d. Map of Pitcairn. 2d. John Adams and "Bounty" bible. 2s. Island wheelbarrow.

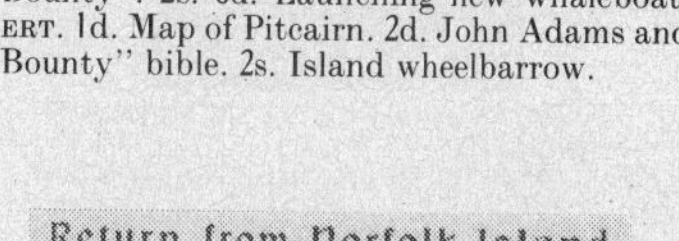

20. Pitcairn Island and Simon Young.

1961. Cent. of Return of Pitcairn Islanders.

29.	**20.**	3d. black and yellow ..	30	20
30.	–	6d. brown and blue ..	60	25
31.	–	1s. orange and green ..	70	35

DESIGNS: 6d. Maps of Norfolk and Pitcairn Is. 1s. Migrant brigantine "Mary Ann".

1963. Freedom from Hunger. As T **28** of Aden.

32.	2s. 6d. blue	18·00	3·00

1963. Cent of Red Cross. As T **33** of Antigua.

34.	2d. red and black	2·00	1·00
35.	2s. 6d. red and blue ..	11·00	5·50

23. Pitcairn Is. Longboat.

24. Queen Elizabeth II (after Anthony Buckley).

1964. Multicoloured.

36.	½d. Type **23**	10	30
37.	1d. H.M.S. "Bounty" ..	30	30
38.	2d. "Out from Bounty Bay"	30	30
39.	3d. Great frigate bird ..	30	30
40.	4d. White tern	30	30
41.	6d. Pitcairn warbler ..	30	30
42.	8d. Red-footed booby ..	30	30
43.	10d. Red-tailed tropic bird	30	30
44.	1s. Henderson Island crake	30	30
45.	1s 6d. Stephen's lory ..	5·50	1·25
46.	2s 6d. Murphy's petrel ..	5·00	1·50
47.	4s. Henderson Island fruit dove	7·00	1·75
48.	8s. Type **24**	2·50	1·75

1965. Cent of I.T.U. As T **36** of Antigua.

49.	1d. mauve and brown ..	1·00	40
50.	2s. 6d. turquoise and blue	15·00	3·50

1965. I.C.Y. As T **37** of Antigua.

51.	1d. purple and turquoise	1·00	40
52.	1s. 6d. green and lavender	14·00	4·00

1966. Churchill Commem. As T **38** of Antigua.

53.	2d. blue	1·50	60
54.	3d. green	4·50	80
55.	6d. brown	6·00	1·50
56.	1s. violet	8·00	2·00

1966. World Cup Football Championship. As T **40** of Antigua.

57.	4d. multicoloured	2·00	1·00
58.	2s. 6d. multicoloured ..	5·00	1·75

1966. Inauguration of W.H.O. Headquarters, Geneva. As T **41** of Antigua.

59.	8d. black, green and blue ..	4·50	1·25
60.	1s. 6d. black, purple & ochre	7·50	1·50

1966. 20th Anniv U.N.E.S.C.O. As T **54/6** of Antigua.

61.	½d. multicoloured	20	30
62.	10d. yellow, violet and olive	5·00	1·75
63.	2s. black, purple and orange	11·00	2·25

36. Mangarevan Canoe, c. 1325.

1967. Bicentenary of Pitcairn Islands' Discovery. Multicoloured.

64.	½d. Type **36**	10	10
65.	1d. P.F. de Quiros and "San Pedro y Pablo", 1606 ..	15	10
66.	8d. "San Pedro y Pablo" and "Los Tres Reyes" 1606	30	15
67.	1s. Carteret and H.M.S. "Swallow", 1767	25	15
68.	1s. 6d. "Hercules", 1819 ..	30	15

1967. Decimal Currency. Nos. 36/48 surch. with "Bounty" anchor and value.

69.	**23.**	½ c. on ½d. multicoloured ..	10	10
70.	–	1 c. on 1d. muiticoloured ..	30	30
71.	–	2 c. on 2d. multicoloured ..	25	30
72.	–	2½ c. on 3d. multicoloured	25	30
73.	–	3 c. on 4d. multicoloured ..	25	15
74.	–	5 c. on 6d. multicoloured	30	30
75.	–	10 c. on 8d. multicoloured	30	30
76.	–	15 c. on 10d. multicoloured	70	40
77.	–	20 c. on 1s. multicoloured	80	55
78.	–	25 c. on 1s. 6d. mult. ..	2·50	1·25
79.	–	30 c. on 2s. 6d. mult. ..	2·75	1·25
80.	–	40 c. on 4s. multicoloured	4·25	1·25
81.	**24.**	45 c. on 8s. multicoloured	4·25	1·50

42. Bligh and "Bounty's" Launch.

1967. 150th Death Anniv. of Admiral Bligh.

82. **42.**	1 c. black, ultram. & blue	10	10
83. –	8 c. black, yellow & mauve	30	15
84. –	20 c. black, brown & buff	35	20

DESIGNS: 8 c. Bligh and Followers cast adrift. 20 c. Bligh's Tomb.

45. Human Rights Emblem.

1968. Int. Human Rights Year.

85. **45.**	1 c. multicoloured	10	10
86.	2 c. multicoloured	10	10
87.	25 c. multicoloured	20	20

46. Moro Wood and Flower.

1968. Handicrafts (1st series).

88. **46.**	5 c. multicoloured	15	10
89. –	10 c. green, brown & orge.	20	20
90. –	15 c. violet, brn. & salmon	25	20
91. –	20 c. multicoloured	30	20

DESIGNS—HORIZ. 10 c. Flying Fish Model. VERT. 15 c. "Hand" Vases. 20 c. Woven Baskets.

See also Nos. 207/10.

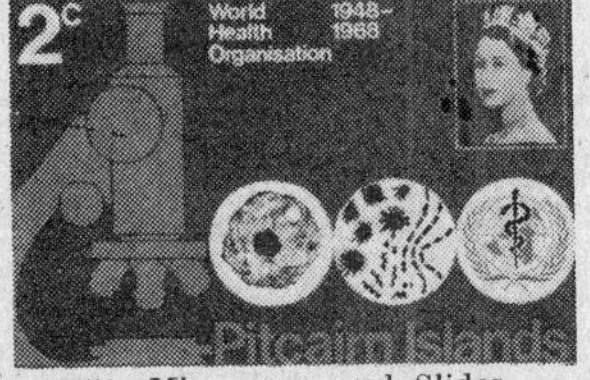

50. Microscope and Slides.

1968. 20th Anniv. of World Health Organization.

92. **50.**	2 c. black, turq. & blue	10	10
93. –	20 c. black, orange & pur.	25	20

DESIGN: 20 c. Hypodermic syringe and jars of tablets.

64b. Queen Elizabeth II.

52. Pitcairn Island.

1969. Multicoloured.

94	1 c. Type **52**	35	15
95	2 c. Captain Bligh and "Bounty" Chronometer	25	15
96	3 c. "Bounty" Anchor	25	15
97	4 c. Plans and drawing of "Bounty"	30	15
98	5 c. Breadfruit containers and plant	30	15
99	6 c. Bounty Bay	30	20
100	8 c. Pitcairn Longboat	35	20
101	10 c. Ship Landing Point	2·00	85
102	15 c. Fletcher Christian's Cave	60	50
103	20 c. Thursday October Christian's house	60	40
104	25 c. "Flying Fox" cable system	70	40
105	30 c. Radio Station, Taro Ground	55	45
106	40 c. "Bounty" Bible	75	60
106a	50 c. Pitcairn Coat-of-Arms	11·00	10·00
106b	$1 Type **64b**	16·00	15·00

The 3 c. and 25 c. are vert.

65. Lantana.

1970. Flowers. Multicoloured.

107.	1 c. Type **65**	20	30
108.	2 c. "Indian Shot"	45	30
109.	5 c. Pulau	85	45
110.	25 c. Wild Gladiolus	2·00	1·40

69. Auntie and Ann (grouper).

1970. Fishes. Multicoloured.

111.	5 c. Type **69**	2·75	70
112.	10 c. Dream Fish (rudder fish)	2·75	85
113.	15 c. Elwyn's Trousers (wrasse)	3·25	1·00
114.	20 c. Whistling Daughter (wrasse)	3·50	1·25

1971. Royal Visit. No. 101a. optd. **ROYAL VISIT 1971.**

115.	10 c. multicoloured	2·25	3·00

71. Polynesian Rock Carvings.

1971. Polynesian Pitcairn. Multicoloured.

116.	5 c. Type **71**	1·75	1·00
117.	10 c. Polynesian artifacts (horiz.)	2·25	1·25
118.	15 c. Polynesian stone fish-hook (horiz.)	2·50	1·25
119.	20 c. Polynesian stone deity	2·50	1·50

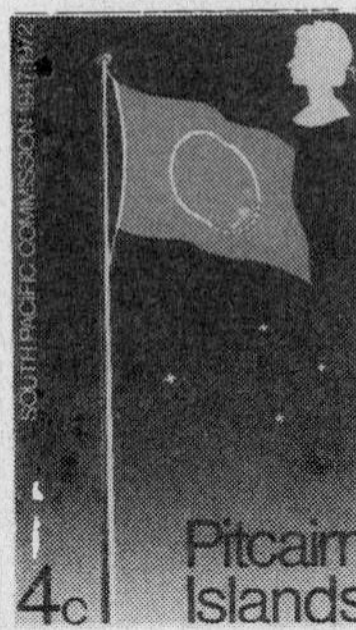

72. Commission Flag.

74. Rose-apple.

1972. 25th Anniv. of South Pacific Commission. Multicoloured.

120.	4 c. Type **72**	1·00	1·00
121.	8 c. Young and Elderly (Health)	1·00	1·00
122.	18 c. Junior School (Education)	1·50	1·50
123.	20 c. Goods Store (Economy)	2·00	2·00

1972. Royal Silver Wedding. As T **52** of Ascension, but with Red-tailed tropic birds and longboat in background.

124.	4 c. green	40	60
125.	20 c. blue	60	90

1973. Flowers. Multicoloured.

126.	4 c. Type **74**	1·25	55
127.	8 c. Mountain-apple	1·75	75
128.	15 c. "Lata"	3·00	1·00
129.	20 c. "Dorcas-flower"	3·25	1·25
130.	35 c. Guava	4·00	1·75

1973. Royal Wedding. As T **47** of Anguilla. Multicoloured, background colours given.

131.	10 c. mauve	30	15
132.	25 c. green	35	30

75. Horn-shell and Mitres.

1974. Shells. Multicoloured.

147.	4 c. Type **75**	1·50	60
148.	10 c. Dove-shell	1·75	80
149.	18 c. Limpet and False Limpet	2·00	1·00
150.	50 c. Lucine shell	2·75	1·25

76. Island Post Office.

1974. Centenary of U.P.U.

152. **76.**	4 c. multicoloured	25	30
153. –	20 c. pur., brn. & blk.	40	50
154. –	35 c. multicoloured	50	60

DESIGNS: 20 c. Pre-stamp letter, 1922. 35 c. Mailship and Pitcairn Longboat.

77. Churchill and Text "Lift up your Hearts . . .".

1974. Birth Cent. of Sir Winston Churchill.

155. **77.**	20 c. olive, grn. & grey	50	85
156. –	35 c. brn., grn. and grey	75	90

DESIGN: 35 c. Text "Give us the tools . . .".

78. H.M.S. "Seringapatam" (frigate), 1830.

1975. Mailboats. Multicoloured.

157	4 c. Type **78**	65	60
158	10 c. "Pitcairn" (missionary schooner), 1890	70	85
159	18 c. "Athenic" (liner), 1901	80	1·40
160	50 c. "Gothic" (liner), 1948	2·00	2·75

79. "Polistes jadwigae" (wasp).

1975. Pitcairn Insects. Multicoloured.

162	4 c. Type **79**	50	45
163	6 c. "Euconocephalus sp." (grasshopper)	70	55
164	10 c. "Anomis flavia" and "Chasmina tibialis" (moth)	80	70
165	15 c. "Pantala flavescens" (skimmer)	1·25	1·25
166	20 c. "Gnathothlibus erotus" (banana moth)	1·50	1·50

80. Fletcher Christian.

1976. Bicent. of American Revolution. Mult.

167.	5 c. Type **80**	40	65
168.	10 c. H.M.S. "Bounty"	50	80
169.	30 c. George Washington	75	95
170.	50 c. "Mayflower", 1620	1·00	1·50

81. Chair of Homage.

1977. Silver Jubilee. Multicoloured.

171.	8 c. Prince Philip's visit, 1971	20	20
172.	20 c. Type **81**	30	30
173.	50 c. Enthronement	50	50

82. The Island's Bell.

1977. Multicoloured.

174.	1 c. Type **82**	30	50
175.	2 c. Building a longboat	30	50
176.	5 c. Landing cargo	35	50
177.	6 c. Sorting supplies	30	50
178.	9 c. Cleaning wahoo (fish)	30	50
179.	10 c. Cultivation	30	50
179a.	15 c. Sugar Mill	1·25	1·00
180.	20 c. Grating coconut and bananas	30	50
181.	35 c. The Island church	35	70
182.	50 c. Fetching miro logs, Henderson Is.	45	80
182a.	70 c. Burning obsolete stamp issues	1·25	1·25
183.	$1 Prince Philip, Bounty Bay and Royal Yacht "Britannia"	65	1·10
184.	$2 Queen Elizabeth II (Photograph by Reginald Davis)	1·25	1·75

The 1 c., 9 c., 70 c. and $2 are vert. designs.

83. Building a "Bounty" Model.

1978. "Bounty" Day. Multicoloured.
185. 6 c. Type **83** 40 35
186. 20 c. The model at sea .. 70 60
187. 35 c. Burning the model .. 85 70

85. Harbour before Development.

1978. "Operation Pallium" (Harbour Development Project). Multicoloured.
190. 15 c. Type **85** 30 45
191. 20 c. Unloading R.F.A. "Sir Geraint" 40 55
192. 30 c. Work on the jetty .. 45 60
193. 35 c. Harbour after improvements 50 70

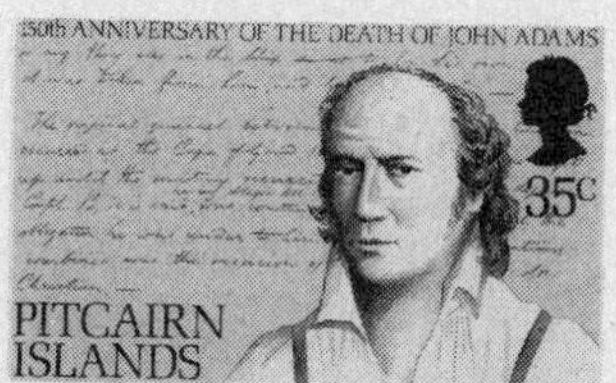

86. John Adams and Diary Extract.

1979. 150th Death Anniv. of John Adams. Multicoloured.
194. 35 c. Type **86** 40 70
195. 70 c. John Adams' grave and diary extract .. 60 90

87. Pitcairn's Island sketched from H.M.S. "Amphitrite".

1979. 19th-century Engravings.
196. **87.** 6 c. black, brown & stone 15 20
197. – 9 c. black, vio. & pale vio. 15 25
198. – 20 c. black, green & yell. 15 40
199. – 70 c. black, scarlet & red 50 1·00
DESIGNS: 9 c. Bounty Bay and Village of Pitcairn. 20 c. Lookout Ridge. 70 c. Church and School House.

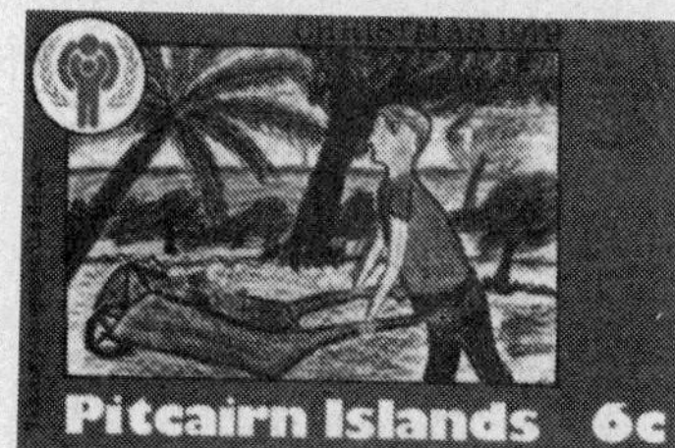

88. Taking Presents to the Square.

1979. Christmas. International Year of the Child. Multicoloured.
200. 6 c. Type **88** 15 20
201. 9 c. Decorating trees with presents 15 20
202. 20 c. Chosen men distributing gifts 25 35
203. 35 c. Carrying presents home 30 40

90. Queen Elizabeth the Queen Mother at Henley Regatta.

1980. 80th Birthday of The Queen Mother.
206. **90.** 50 c. multicoloured .. 40 70

1980. Handicrafts (2nd series). As T **46**. Multicoloured.
207. 9 c. Turtles (wood carvings) 10 10
208. 20 c. Pitcairn wheelbarrow (wood carving) 10 15
209. 35 c. Gannet (wood carving) (vert.) 15 25
210. 40 c. Woven bonnet and fan (vert.) 15 25

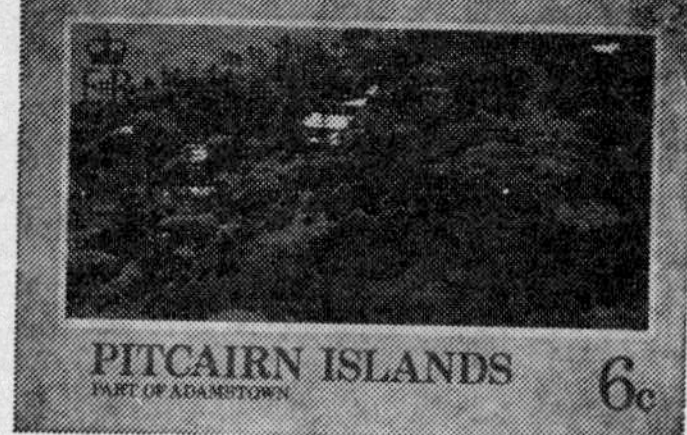

91. Part of Adamstown.

1981. Scenic Views. Multicoloured.
211. 6 c. Type **91** 10 10
212. 9 c. Big George 10 15
213. 20 c. Christian's Cave, Gannets Ridge 15 20
214. 35 c. Radio Station from Pawala Valley Ridge .. 20 30
215. 70 c. Tatrimoa 30 45

92. Islanders preparing for Departure.

1981. 125th Anniv. of Pitcairn Islanders' Migration to Norfolk Island. Multicoloured.
216. 9 c. Type **92** 15 20
217. 35 c. View of Pitcairn Island from "Morayshire" .. 30 45
218. 70 c. "Morayshire" .. 45 65

93. Prince Charles as Colonel-in-Chief, Cheshire Regiment.

1981. Royal Wedding. Multicoloured.
219. 20 c. Wedding bouquet from Pitcairn Islands .. 25 25
220. 35 c. Type **93** 40 40
221. $1·20 Prince Charles and Lady Diana Spencer .. 75 85

94. Lemon.

1982. Fruit. Multicoloured.
222. 9 c. Type **94** 10 10
223. 20 c. Pomegranate 15 20
224. 35 c. Avocado 25 30
225. 70 c. Pawpaw 50 65

95. Pitcairn Islands Coat of Arms.

1982. 21st Birthday of Princess of Wales. Multicoloured.
226. 6 c. Type **95** 10 20
227. 9 c. Princess at Royal Opera House, Covent Garden, December, 1981 10 20
228. 70 c. Balcony Kiss .. 50 75
229. $1.20 Formal portrait .. 80 1·10

96. Raphael's Angels.

1982. Christmas. Raphael's Angels.
230. **96.** 15 c. black, silver and pink 15 15
231. – 20 c. black, silver and yellow 20 20
232. – 50 c. brown, silver and stone 45 45
233. – $1 black, silver and blue 85 85
DESIGNS: 20 c. to $1 Different details, the 50 c. and $1 being vertical.

97. Radio Operator.

1983. Commonwealth Day. Multicoloured.
234. 6 c. Type **97** 10 10
235. 9 c. Postal Clerk 10 10
236. 70 c. Fisherman 50 65
237. $1 20 Artist .. .. 80 1·10

98. "Topaz" sights Smoke on Pitcairn.

1983. 175th Anniv. of Folger's Discovery of the Settlers. Multicoloured.
238. 6 c. Type **98** 20 15
239. 20 c. Three islanders approach the "Topaz" .. 30 30
240. 70 c. Capt. Mayhew Folger welcomed by John Adams 75 75
241. $1.20 Folger presented with "Bounty" chronometer 1·10 1·10

99. Hattie-Tree.

1983. Trees of Pitcairn Islands (1st series). Multicoloured.
242. 35 c. Type **99** 30 55
243. 35 c. Leaves from Hattie-Tree 30 55
244. 70 c. Pandanus 65 90
245. 70 c. Pandanus and basket weaving 65 90
See also Nos. 304/7.

100. "Pseudojuloides atavai".

1984. Fishes. Multicoloured.
246 1 c. Type **100** 20 30
247 4 c. "Halichoeres melasmopomus 30 35
248 6 c. "Scarus longipinnis" 30 35
249 9 c. "Variola louti" .. 30 35
250 10 c. "Centropyge hotumatua" 30 40
251 15 c. "Stegastes emeryi" .. 30 40
252 20 c. "Chaetodon smithi" 40 50
253 35 c. "Xanthichthys mento" 50 60
254 50 c. "Chrysiptera galba" 50 75
255 70 c. "Genicanthus spinus" 70 95
312 90 c. As 9 c. .. .. 1·75 1·75
256 $1 "Myripristis tiki" .. 90 1·25
257 $1.20 "Anthias ventralis" 1·75 2·00
258 $2 "Pseudocaranx dentex" 2·25 2·25
313 $3 "Gymnothorax eurostus" 4·25 4·25

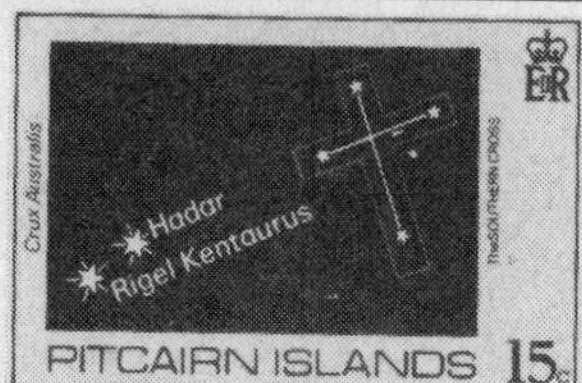

101. Southern Cross.

1984. Night Sky.
259. **101.** 15 c. blue, lilac & gold 20 20
260. – 20 c. blue, green & gold 30 30
261. – 70 c. blue, brown & gold 75 75
262. – $1 blue, lt. blue & gold 1·00 1·00
DESIGNS: 20 c. Southern Fish. 70 c. Lesser Dog. $1 The Virgin.

103. "H.M.S. "Portland" standing off Bounty Bay". (J. Linton Palmer).

1985. 19th-Century Paintings (1st series). Multicoloured.
264. 6 c. Type **103** 30 20
265. 9 c. "Christian's Look Out" (J. Linton Palmer) .. 30 20
266. 35 c. "The Golden Age" (J. Linton Palmer) .. 70 50
267. $2 "A View of the Village, 1825" (William Smyth) (48×31) mm.) .. .. 2·00 1·60
See also Nos. 308/11.

104. The Queen Mother with the Queen and Princess Margaret, 1980.

1985. Life and Times of Queen Elizabeth the Queen Mother. Multicoloured.
268 6 c. Receiving the Freedom of Dundee, 1964 .. 10 20
269 35 c. Type **104** .. 40 55
270 70 c. The Queen Mother in 1983 .. .. .. 70 90
271 $1·20 With Prince Henry at his christening (from photo by Lord Snowdon) 1·10 1·40

105. "Act 6" (container ship).

1985. Ships (1st issue). Multicoloured.
273. 50 c. Type **105** .. 1·00 1·25
274. 50 c. "Columbus Lousiana" (container ship) .. .. 1·00 1·25
275. 50 c. "Essi Gina" (tanker) (48×35 mm.) .. .. 1·00 1·25
276. 50 c. "Stolt Spirit" tanker (48×35 mm.) .. 1·00 1·25
See also Nos. 296/9.

106. "Madonna and Child" (Raphael).

1985. Christmas. Designs showing "Madonna and Child" paintings. Multicoloured.

No.	Description	Unused	Used
277.	6 c. Type **106**	30	20
278.	9 c. Krause (after Raphael)	30	20
279.	35 c. Andreas Mayer . .	65	50
280.	$2 Unknown Austrian master	2·25	2·50

107. Green Turtle.

1986. Turtles. Multicoloured.

No.	Description	Unused	Used
281.	9 c. Type **107**	75	75
282.	20 c. Green Turtle and Pitcairn Island	1·25	1·25
283.	70 c. Hawksbill Turtle . .	2·50	2·50
284.	$1.20 Hawksbill Turtle and Pitcairn Island	3·25	3·25

1986. 60th Birthday of Queen Elizabeth II. As T **110** of Ascension. Multicoloured.

No.	Description	Unused	Used
285.	6 c. Princess Elizabeth at Royal Lodge, Windsor, 1946	15	15
286.	9 c. Wedding of Princess Anne, 1973	15	15
287.	20 c. At Order of St. Michael and St. George service, St. Paul's Cathedral, 1961	30	30
288.	$1.20 At Electrical Engineering Concert, Royal Festival Hall, 1971	1·10	1·25
289.	$2 At Crown Agents Head Office, London, 1983 . .	1·75	2·00

1986. Royal Wedding. As T **112** of Ascension. Multicoloured.

No.	Description	Unused	Used
290	20 c. Prince Andrew and Miss Sarah Ferguson . .	50	50
291	$1.20 Prince Andrew aboard "Bluenose II" off Halifax, Canada, 1985 . .	1·75	1·75

108. John I. Tay (pioneer missionary) and First Church.

1986. Centenary of Seventh-Day Adventist Church on Pitcairn. Multicoloured.

No.	Description	Unused	Used
292	6 c. Type **108**	40	40
293	20 c. "Pitcairn" (missionary schooner) and second church (1907)	1·00	1·00
294	35 c. Baptism at Down Isaac and third church (1945)	1·50	1·50
295	$2 Islanders singing farewell hymn and present church (1954)	3·25	3·25

1987. Ships (2nd series). As T **105**. Multicoloured.

No.	Description	Unused	Used
296.	50 c. "Samoan Reefer" (freighter)	1·25	1·50
297.	50 c. "Brussel" (container ship)	1·25	1·50
298.	50 c. "Australian Exporter" (container ship) (48 × 35 mm.) . .	1·25	1·50
299.	50 c. "Taupo" (cargo liner) (48 × 35 mm.) . .	1·25	1·50

109. Pitcairn Island Home.

1987. Pitcairn Island Homes.

No.	Description	Unused	Used
300.	**109.** 70 c. black, deep violet and violet . .	75	60
301.	– 70 c. black, yellow and brown . .	75	60
302.	– 70 c. black, blue and deep blue . .	75	60
303.	– 70 c. black, green and deep green . .	75	60

Designs: Nos. 301/3 different houses.

1987. Trees of Pitcairn Islands (2nd series). As T **99**. Multicoloured.

No.	Description	Unused	Used
304.	40 c. Leaves and flowers from "Erythrina variegata"	70	70
305.	40 c. "Erythrina variegata" tree	70	70
306.	$1.80 Leaves from "Aleurites moluccana" and nut torch	2·00	2·00
307.	$1.80 "Aleurites moluccana" tree . .	2·00	2·00

1987. 19th-Century Paintings (2nd series). Paintings by Lt. Conway Shipley in 1848. As T **103**. Multicoloured.

No.	Description	Unused	Used
308.	20 c. "House and Tomb of John Adams"	45	45
309.	40 c. "Bounty Bay" . .	70	70
310.	90 c. "School House and Chapel"	1·25	1·25
311.	$1.80 "Pitcairn Island" (48 × 31 mm.)	2·00	2·00

111 H.M.S. "Swallow" (survey ship), 1767

1988. Ships. Multicoloured.

No.	Description	Unused	Used
315	5 c. Type **111**	10	10
316	10 c. H.M.S. "Pandora" (frigate), 1791	10	10
317	15 c. H.M.S. "Briton" and H.M.S. "Tagus" (frigates), 1814	10	15
318	20 c. H.M.S. "Blossom" (survey ship), 1825 . .	15	20
319	30 c. "Lucy Anne" (barque), 1831 . .	20	25
320	35 c. "Charles Doggett" (whaling brig), 1831 . .	25	30
321	40 c. H.M.S. "Fly" (sloop), 1838	30	35
322	60 c. "Camden" (missionary brig), 1840 . .	45	50
323	90 c. H.M.S. "Virago" (paddle-sloop), 1853 . .	65	70
324	$1.20 "Rakaia" (screw-steamer), 1867 . .	90	95
325	$1.80 H.M.S. "Sappho" (screw-sloop), 1882 . .	1·25	1·40
326	$5 H.M.S. "Champion" (corvette), 1893 . .	3·75	4·00

INDEX

Countries can be quickly located by referring to the index at the end of this volume.

112 Raising the Union Jack, 1838

1988. 150th Anniv of Pitcairn Island Constitution. Each showing different extract from original Constitution. Multicoloured.

No.	Description	Unused	Used
327	20 c. Type **112**	15	20
328	40 c. Signing Constitution on board H.M.S. "Fly", 1838	30	35
329	$1.05 Voters at modern polling station	75	80
330	$1.80 Modern classroom . .	1·25	1·40

113 Angel

1988. Christmas. Multicoloured.

No.	Description	Unused	Used
331	90 c. Type **113**	65	70
332	90 c. Holy Family . .	65	70
333	90 c. Two Polynesian Wise Men	65	70
334	90 c. Polynesian Wise Man and shepherd	65	70

114 Loading Stores, Deptford

1989. Bicentenary of Pitcairn Island Settlement (1st issue). Multicoloured.

No.	Description	Unused	Used
335	20 c. Type **114**	45	35
336	20 c. H.M.S. "Bounty" leaving Spithead . .	45	35
337	20 c. H.M.S. "Bounty" at Cape Horn . .	45	35
338	20 c. Anchored in Adventure Bay, Tasmania . .	45	35
339	20 c. Crew collecting breadfruit	45	35
340	20 c. Breadfruit in cabin . .	45	35

See also Nos. 341/7, 356/61 and 389/94.

1989. Bicentenary of Pitcairn Island Settlement (2nd issue). As T **114**. Mult.

No.	Description	Unused	Used
341	90 c. H.M.S. "Bounty" leaving Tahiti	1·50	1·50
342	90 c. Bligh awoken by mutineers	1·50	1·50
343	90 c. Bligh before Fletcher Christian	1·50	1·50
344	90 c. Provisioning "Bounty's" launch . .	1·50	1·50
345	90 c. "Mutineers casting Bligh adrift" (Robert Dodd)	1·50	1·50
346	90 c. Mutineers discarding breadfruit plants . .	1·50	1·50

115 R.N.Z.A.F. "Orion" making Mail Drop, 1985

1989. Aircraft. Multicoloured.

No.	Description	Unused	Used
348	20 c. Type **115**	35	35
349	80 c. Beechcraft "Queen Air" on photo-mission, 1983	95	95
350	$1.05 Helicopter landing diesel fuel from U.S.S. "Breton", 1969 . .	1·25	1·25
351	$1.30 R.N.Z.A.F. "Hercules" dropping bulldozer, 1983	1·40	1·40

116 Ducie Island

1989. Islands of Pitcairn Group. Mult.

No.	Description	Unused	Used
352	15 c. Type **116**	15	15
353	90 c. Henderson Island . .	90	90
354	$1.05 Oeno Island . .	1·00	1·00
355	$1.30 Pitcairn Island . .	1·25	1·25

1990. Bicentenary of Pitcairn Island Settlement (3rd issue). As T **114**. Multicoloured.

No.	Description	Unused	Used
356	40 c. Mutineers sighting Pitcairn Island . .	55	40
357	40 c. Ship's boat approaching landing . .	55	40
358	40 c. Exploring island . .	55	40
359	40 c. Ferrying goods ashore	55	40
360	40 c. Burning of H.M.S. "Bounty"	55	40
361	40 c. Pitcairn Island village	55	40

117 Ennerdale, Cumbria, and Peter Heywood

1990. "Stamp World London 90" International Stamp Exhibition, London. Designs showing English landmarks and "Bounty" crew members. Multicoloured.

No.	Description	Unused	Used
362	80 c. Type **117**	75	80
363	90 c. St. Augustine's Tower, Hackney, and John Adams	85	90
364	$1.05 Citadel Gateway, Plymouth, and William Bligh	1·00	1·25
365	$1.30 Moorland Close, Cockermouth, and Fletcher Christian . .	1·25	1·40

1990. 90th Birthday of Queen Elizabeth the Queen Mother. As T **134** of Ascension.

No.	Description	Unused	Used
378	40 c. multicoloured	50	50
379	$3 black and red	2·50	2·50

DESIGNS—21 × 36 mm. 40 c. Queen Elizabeth, 1937. 29 × 37 mm. $3 King George VI and Queen Elizabeth on way to Silver Wedding Service, 1948.

118 "Bounty" Chronometer and 1940 1d. Definitive

1990. 50th Anniv of Pitcairn Islands Stamps. Multicoloured.

380 20 c. Type **118** 30 30
381 80 c. "Bounty" Bible and 1958 4d. definitive 80 80
382 90 c. "Bounty" Bell and 1969 30 c. definitive 90 90
383 $1.05 Mutiny on the "Bounty" and 1977 $1 definitive 1·00 1·00
384 $1.30 Penny Black and 1988 15 c. definitive 1·40 1·40

119 Stephen's Lory ("Red-breast")

1990. "Birdpex '90" International Stamp Exhibition, Christchurch, New Zealand. Multicoloured.

385 20 c. Type **119** 30 30
386 90 c. Henderson Island fruit dove ("Wood pigeon") 1·10 1·10
387 $1.30 Pitcairn warbler ("Sparrow") 1·40 1·40
388 $1.80 Henderson Island crake ("Chicken bird") 1·60 1·60

1991. Bicent of Pitcairn Islands Settlement (4th issue). Celebrations. As T **114**. Mult.

389 80 c. Re-enacting landing of mutineers 1·10 1·25
390 80 c. Commemorative plaque 1·10 1·25
391 80 c. Memorial church service 1·10 1·25
392 80 c. Cricket match 1·10 1·25
393 80 c. Burning model of "Bounty" 1·10 1·25
394 80 c. Firework display 1·10 1·25

120 "Europa"

1991. Cruise Liners. Multicoloured.

395 15 c. Type **120** 30 30
396 80 c. "Royal Viking Star" 1·00 1·00
397 $1.30 "World Discoverer" 1·25 1·25
398 $1.80 "Sagafjord" 1·90 1·90

1991. 65th Birthday of Queen Elizabeth II and 70th Birthday of Prince Philip. As T **280** of Antigua. Multicoloured.

399 20 c. Prince Philip (vert) 40 30
400 $1.30 Queen in robes of the Order of St. Michael and St. George (vert) 1·60 1·25

121 Bulldozer

1991. Island Transport. Multicoloured.

401 20 c. Type **121** 30 30
402 80 c. Two-wheeled motor-cycle 1·00 1·00
403 $1.30 Tractor 1·25 1·25
404 $1.80 Three-wheeled motor-cycle 1·90 1·90

122 The Annunciation

1991. Christmas. Multicoloured.

405 20 c. Type **122** 30 30
406 80 c. Shepherds and lamb 90 90
407 $1.30 Holy Family 1·25 1·25
408 $1.80 Three Wise Men 1·75 1·75

1992. 40th Anniv of Queen Elizabeth II's Accession. As T **143** of Ascension. Mult.

409 20 c. Bounty Bay 25 25
410 60 c. Sunset over Pitcairn 70 70
411 90 c. Pitcairn coastline 90 90
412 $1 Three portraits of Queen Elizabeth 95 95
413 $1.80 Queen Elizabeth II 1·60 1·60

123 "Carcharhinus galapagensis"

1992. Sharks. Multicoloured.

414 20 c. Type **123** 25 25
415 $1 "Eugomphodus taurus" 95 95
416 $1.50 "Carcharhinus melanopterus" 1·60 1·60
417 $1.80 "Carcharhinus amblyrhynchos" 1·75 1·75

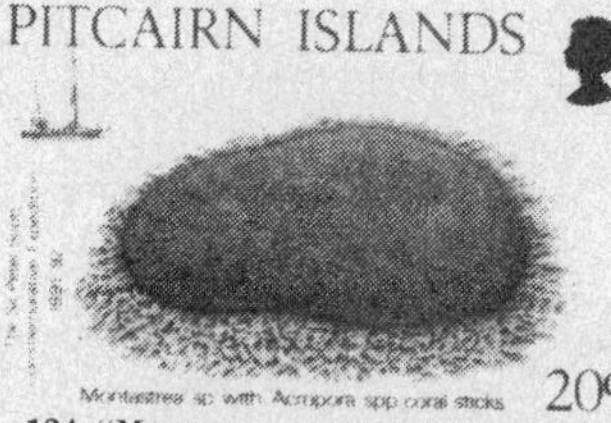

124 "Montastrea sp." and "Acropora spp." (corals)

1992. The Sir Peter Scott Memorial Expedition to Henderson Island. Multicoloured.

418 20 c. Type **124** 25 25
419 $1 Henderson sandalwood 95 95
420 $1.50 Murphy's petrel 1·60 1·60
421 $1.80 Henderson hawk-moth 1·75 1·75

125 Bligh's Birthplace at St. Tudy, Cornwall

1992. 175th Death Anniv of William Bligh. Multicoloured.

422 20 c. Type **125** 20 20
423 $1 Bligh on "Bounty" 1·00 1·00
424 $1.50 Voyage in "Bounty's" launch 1·40 1·40
425 $1.80 "William Bligh" (R. Combe) and epitaph 1·60 1·60

126 H.M.S. "Chichester" (frigate)

1993. Modern Royal Navy Vessels. Mult.

426 15 c. Type **126** 25 25
427 20 c. H.M.S. "Jaguar" (frigate) 25 25
428 $1.80 H.M.S. "Andrew" (submarine) 1·75 2·00
429 $3 H.M.S. "Warrior" (aircraft carrier) and helicopter 3·25 3·50

127 Queen Elizabeth II in Coronation Robes

1993. 40th Anniv of Coronation.

430 **127** $5 multicoloured 5·00 5·00

128 Pawala Valley Ridge

1993. Island Views. Multicoloured.

431 10 c. Type **128** 20 20
432 90 c. St. Pauls 90 90
433 $1.20 Matt's Rocks from Water Valley 1·25 1·40
434 $1.50 Ridge Rope to St. Paul's Pool 1·50 1·60
435 $1.80 Ship Landing Point 1·75 1·90

129 Indo-Pacific Tree Gecko

1993. Lizards. Multicoloured.

436 20 c. Type **129** 15 20
437 45 c. Stump-toed gecko 35 40
438 45 c. Mourning gecko 35 40
439 $1 Moth skink 70 75
440 $1.50 Snake-eyed skink 1·10 1·25
441 $1.50 White-bellied skink 1·10 1·25

1994. "Hong Kong '94" International Stamp Exhibition. Nos. 437/8 and 440/1 optd **HONG KONG '94** and emblem.

442 45 c. Stump-toed gecko 35 40
443 45 c. Mourning gecko 35 40
444 $1.50 Snake-eyed skink 1·10 1·25
445 $1.50 White-bellied skink 1·10 1·25

130 Friday October Christian

1994. Early Pitcairners. Multicoloured.

446 5 c. Type **130** 10 10
447 20 c. Moses Young 15 20
448 $1.80 James Russell McCoy 1·25 1·40
449 $3 Rosalind Amelia Young 2·25 2·40

POONCH

A state in Kashmir, India. Now uses Indian stamps.

12 pies = 1 anna; 16 annas = 1 rupee.

1.

4.

1876. Imperf.

1\. **1.** 6 pies red £2500 85·00
2\. $\frac{1}{2}$ a. red — £1400

1880. Imperf.

32\. **1.** 1 pice red 40 1·25
12 **4.** $\frac{1}{2}$ a. red 1·25 2·25
50\. 1 a. red 50 1·00
52\. 2 a. red (22×22 mm.) 70 1·10
31\. 4 a. red (28×27 mm.) 2·25 2·25

These stamps were printed on various coloured papers.

OFFICIAL STAMPS

1888. Imperf.

O 1. **1.** 1 pice black 1·10 1·25
O 2. **4.** $\frac{1}{2}$ a. black 90 1·60
O 3. 1 a. black 90 1·10
O 4. 2 a. black 1·60 1·60
O 5. 4 a. black 3·25 4·50

PRINCE EDWARD ISLAND

An island off the E. coast of Canada, now a province of that Dominion, whose stamps it uses.

1861. 12 pence = 1 shilling.
1872. 100 cents = 1 dollar.

1.

7.

1861. Queen's portrait in various frames. Values in pence.

9 **1** 1d. orange 11·00 14·00
28 2d. red 5·50 8·00
30 3d. blue 7·00 8·50
16 4d. black 12·00 15·00
18 6d. green 26·00 26·00
20 9d. mauve 22·00 22·00

1870.

32\. **7.** $4\frac{1}{2}$d. (3d. stg.) brown 22·00 32·00

8.

1872. Queen's portrait in various frames. Values in cents.

35 **8.** 1 c. orange 2·25 7·00
38 2 c. blue 8·50 26·00
37 3 c. red 7·50 10·00
40 4 c. green 3·00 11·00
41 6 c. black 2·50 11·00
42 12 c. mauve 2·50 20·00

QATAR

An independent Arab Shaikhdom with British postal administration until May 23, 1963; later issues by the Qatar Post Department. The stamps of Muscat were formerly used at the Capital, Doha and at Umm Said.

100 naye paise = 1 rupee.
Stamps of Great Britain surcharged **QATAR** and value in Indian currency.

1957. Queen Elizabeth II and pictorials.

1\. **157.** 1 n.p. on 5d. brown 10 10
2\. **154.** 3 n.p. on $\frac{1}{2}$d. orange 15 15
3\. 6 n.p. on 1d. blue 15 15
4\. 9 n.p. on $1\frac{1}{2}$d. green 15 10
5\. 12 n.p. on 2d. pale brown 20 30
6\. **155.** 15 n.p. on $2\frac{1}{2}$d. red 15 10
7\. 20 n.p. on 3d. lilac 15 10
8\. 25 n.p. on 4d. blue 40 40
9\. **157.** 40 n.p. on 6d. purple 15 10
10\. **158.** 50 n.p. on 9d. olive 40 15
11\. **159.** 75 n.p. on 1s. 3d. green 50 50
12\. 1 r. on 1s. 6d. blue 6·00 10
13\. **166.** 2 r. on 2s. 6d. brown 4·00 1·00
14\. – 5 r. on 5s. red 7·00 2·75
15\. – 10 r. on 10s. blue 8·50 8·50

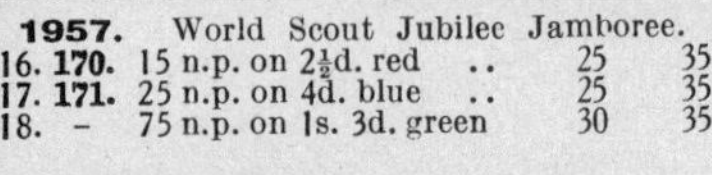

1957. World Scout Jubilee Jamboree.

16.	**170.**	15 n.p. on 2½d. red ..	25	35
17.	**171.**	25 n.p. on 4d. blue ..	25	35
18.	–	75 n.p. on 1s. 3d. green	30	35

8. Shaikh Ahmed bin Ali al Thani. **9.** Peregrine Falcon.

11. Oil Derrick.

1961.

27.	**8.**	5 n.p. red	10	10
28.		15 n.p. black	10	10
29.		20 n.p. purple	10	10
30.		30 n.p. green	10	10
31.	**9.**	40 n.p. red	85	10
32.		50 n.p. brown	1·25	10
33.	–	75 n.p. blue	60	75
34.	**11.**	1 r. red	70	10
35.		2 r. blue	2·00	25
36.	–	5 r. green	9·00	80
37.	–	10 r. black	27·00	2·50

Designs—As Type **9**; 75 n.p. Dhow. As Type **11**: 5 r., 10 r. Mosque.

For later issues see Volume 2.

QUEENSLAND

The N.E. state of the Commonwealth of Australia whose stamps it now uses.

12 pence = 1 shilling
20 shillings = 1 pound.

1.

7.

1860. Imperf.

1.	**1.**	1d. red	£2250	£800
2.		2d. blue	£5000	£1500
3.		6d. green	£3500	£800

1860. Perf.

94	**1**	1d. red	38·00	5·00
99		2d. blue	22·00	1·00
101		3d. brown	60·00	9·00
65		3d. green	80·00	5·00
53		4d. grey	£150	20·00
55		4d. lilac	90·00	16·00
103		4d. yellow	£600	20·00
27		6d. green	80·00	12·00
108		1s. purple	40·00	9·00
29		1s. grey	£130	22·00
119		2s. blue	60·00	22·00
121		2s. 6d. red	£110	40·00
58		5s. red	£200	55·00
123		5s. yellow	£150	60·00
125		10s. brown	£350	£110
127		20s. red	£700	£130

1879.

134.	**7.**	1d. brown	32·00	5·00
135.		1d. orange	15·00	3·00
136.		1d. red	12·00	1·75
138.		2d. blue	25·00	1·00
141.		4d. yellow	£100	10·00
142.		6d. green..	55·00	4·50
145.		1s. mauve	45·00	5·50

1880. No. 136 surch. **Half-penny.**

151.	**7.**	½d. on 1d. brown ..	£160	90·00

9.

13.

12.

14.

1882.

152	**9**	2s. blue	60·00	17·00
158		2s. 6d. orange	38·00	20·00
159		5s. red	35·00	28·00
160		10s. brown	95·00	40·00
161		£1 green	£170	60·00

1882. Shaded background around head.

184	**13.**	½d. green..	2·75	50
206	**12.**	1d. orange	2·00	15
204		2d. blue	3·00	20
191	**14.**	2½d. red	10·00	55
192	**12.**	3d. brown	8·50	1·40
169		4d. yellow	12·00	1·40
170		6d. green..	9·00	70
173		1s. mauve	11·00	1·40
197		2s. brown	38·00	7·50

15.

16.

17.

1895. Head on white background.

208	**15**	½d. green	1·00	45
211	**16**	1d. red	2·00	20
212		2d. blue	3·25	35
213	**17**	2½d. red	8·00	3·00
215		5d. brown	10·00	2·75

19.

21.

1896.

229.	**19.**	1d. red	8·00	40

1897. Same designs, but figures in all four corners, as T **21**.

286	½d. green	1·00	20
288	1d. red	1·25	15
234	2d. blue	1·25	15
236	2½d. red	16·00	7·50
238	2½d. purple on blue ..	8·50	85
241	3d. brown	8·00	80
244	4d. yellow	8·00	80
294	4d. black	12·00	1·50
246	5d. brown	7·00	80
250	6d. green	6·00	1·25
298	1s. mauve	11·00	1·60
300	2s. green	30·00	6·50

26.

28.

27.

1899.

287.	**26.**	½d. green	1·00	20

1900. S. African War Charity. Inscr. "PATRIOTIC FUND 1900".

264a.	**27.**	1d. (1s.) mauve ..	£100	£100
264b.	–	2d. (2s.) violet (horiz.)	£225	£225

1903.

265.	**28.**	9d. brown and blue ..	10·00	1·75

REGISTRATION STAMP

1861. Inscr. "REGISTERED".

20.	**1.**	(No value) yellow ..	45·00	35·00

RAJASTHAN

Formed in 1948 from states in Rajputana, India, which included Bundi, Jaipur and Kishangarh whose separate posts functioned until 1 April 1950. Now uses Indian stamps.

12 pies = 1 anna; 16 annas = 1 rupee.

BUNDI

सं० रा०
सरकार

(1.)

1949. Nos. 86/92 of Bundi handstamped or optd. by machine with T **1**.

1.	**21.**	¼ a. green	2·50	
2.		½ a. violet	2·25	
3.		1 a. green	2·25	
11.	–	2 a. red	2·25	30·00
12.	–	4 a. orange	2·00	30·00
6.	–	8 a. blue	2·75	
14.	–	1 r. brown	7·50	

Nos. 1, 2, 3 and 6 used are worth about three times the unused prices.

JAIPUR

राजस्थान

RAJASTHAN
(2.)

1949. Stamps of Jaipur optd. with T **2**.

15.	**7.**	¼ a. black and purple ..	3·25	10·00
16.		½ a. black and violet ..	2·75	10·00
17.		¾ a. black and orange ..	3·50	11·00
18.		1 a. black and blue ..	3·75	18·00
19.		2 a. black and orange ..	4·00	20·00
20.		2½ a. black and red ..	5·00	13·00
21.		3 a. black and green ..	5·00	30·00
22.		4 a black and green ..	5·00	35·00
23		6 a. black and blue ..	6·50	48·00
24.		8 a. black and brown ..	9·00	65·00
25.		1 r. black and bistre ..	10·00	90·00

KISHANGARH

1949. Stamps of Kishangarh handstamped with T **1**.

(a) On stamps of 1899.

26a	**2**	¼ a. pink	—	80·00
27		½ a. blue	£110	
29		1 a. lilac	14·00	30·00
30		4 a. brown	38·00	50·00
31		1 r. green	£120	£130
31a		2 r. red	£150	
32		5 r. mauve	£140	£140

(b) On stamps of 1904.

33	**13**	½ a. brown	—	55·00
33a		1 a. blue	—	75·00
34		4 a. brown	13·00	
35	**2**	8 a. grey	48·00	80·00
36	**13**	8 a. violet	11·00	
37		1 r. green	11·00	
38		2 r. yellow	18·00	
39		5 r. brown	18·00	

(c) On stamps of 1912.

40.	**14.**	½ a. green	—	65·00
41.		1 a. red	—	65·00
43.		2 a. purple	1·50	5·00
44.		4 a. blue	—	£180
45.		8 a. brown	5·00	
46.		1 r. mauve	10·00	
47.		2 r. green	10·00	
48		5 r. brown	£150	

(d) On stamps of 1928.

55	**16**	¼ a. blue	35·00	35·00
57		½ a. green	16·00	16·00
58	–	1 a. red	20·00	20·00
59	–	2 a. purple	50·00	50·00
61	**16**	4 a. brown	1·75	5·50
51		8 a. violet	6·00	42·00
63		1 r. green	6·00	
53		2 r. yellow	14·00	
54		5 r. red	15·00	

RAJPIPLA

A state of Bombay, India. Now uses Indian stamps.

12 pies = 1 anna; 12 annas = 1 rupee.

1. (1 pice).

2. (2 a.).

1880.

1.	**1.**	1 p. blue	65	14·00
2.	**2.**	2 a. green	13·00	40·00
3.		4 a. red	4·75	24·00

REDONDA

A dependency of Antigua.

The following stamps were issued in anticipation of commercial and tourist development, philatelic mail being handled by a bureau in Antigua. Since at the present time the island is uninhabited, we do not list or stock these items. It is understood that the stamps are valid for the prepayment of postage in Antigua. Miniature sheets, imperforate stamps etc., are excluded from this section.

1979.

Antigua 1976 definitive issue optd. **REDONDA.** 3, 5, 10, 25, 35, 50, 75 c., $1, 2.50, 5, 10.

Antigua Coronation Anniversary issue optd. **REDONDA.** 10, 30, 50, 90 c., $2.50.

Antigua World Cup Football Championship issue optd. **REDONDA.** 10, 15 c., $3.

Death Centenary of Sir Rowland Hill. 50, 90 c., $2.50, 3.

International Year of the Child. 25, 50 c., $1, 2.

Christmas. Paintings. 8, 50, 90 c., $3.

1980.

Marine Life. 8, 25, 50 c., $4.

Rotary International. 75th Anniv. 25, 50 c., $1, 2.

Birds of Redonda. 8, 10, 15, 25, 30, 50 c., $1, 2, 5.

Olympic Medal Winners, Lake Placid and Moscow. 8, 25, 50 c., $3.

80th Birthday of Queen Elizabeth the Queen Mother. 10 c., $2.50.

Christmas. Paintings. 8, 25, 50 c., $4.

1981.

Royal Wedding 25, 55 c., $4.

Christmas. Walt Disney Cartoon Characters. ½, 1, 2, 3, 4, 5, 10 c., $2·50, $3.

World Cup Football Championship, Spain (1982). 30 c.×2, 50 c.×2. $1×2, $2×2.

1982.

Boy Scout Annivs. 8, 25, 50 c. $3, $5.

Butterflies. 8, 30, 50 c.; $2.

21st Birthday of Princess of Wales. $2, $4.

Birth of Prince William of Wales. Optd on Princess of Wales 21st Birthday issue. $2, $4.

Christmas. Walt Disney's "One Hundred and One Dalmations". ½, 1, 2, 3, 4, 5, 10; $2.50, $3.

1983.

Easter. 500th Birth Anniv. of Raphael. 10, 50, 90 c., $5.

Bicent. of Manned Flight. 10, 50, 90 c., $2.50.

Christmas. Walt Disney Cartoon Characters. "Deck the Halls". ½, 1, 2, 3, 4, 5, 10 c., $2.50, $3.

1984.

Easter. Walt Disney Cartoon Characters. ½, 1, 2, 3, 4, 5, 10 c., $2, $4.

Olympic Games, Los Angeles. 10, 50, 90 c., $2.50.

Christmas. 50th Birthday of Donald Duck. 45, 60, 90 c., $2, $4.

1985.

Birth Bicentenary of John J. Audubon (ornithologist) (1st issue). 60, 90 c., $1, $3.

Life and Times of Queen Elizabeth the Queen Mother. $1, $1.50, $2.50.

Royal Visit. 45 c., $1, $4.

150th Birth Anniv. of Mark Twain (author). 25, 50 c., $1.50, $3.

Birth Bicentenaries of Grimm Brothers (folklorists). Walt Disney cartoon characters. 30, 60, 70 c., $4.

1986.

Birth Bicentenary of John J. Audubon (ornithologist) (2nd issue). 90 c., $1, $1.50, $3.

Appearance of Halley's Comet. 5, 15, 55 c., $4.

Centenary of Statue of Liberty (1st issue). 20, 25, 30 c., $4.

60th Birthday of Queen Elizabeth II. 50, 60 c., $4.

Royal Wedding. 60 c., $1, $4.

Christmas (1st issue). Disney characters in Hans Andersen Stories. 30, 60, 70 c., $4.

Christmas (2nd issue). "Wind in the Willows" (by Kenneth Grahame). 25, 50 c., $1.50, $3.

1987.

"Capex '87" International Stamp Exhibition, Toronto. Disney characters illustrating Art of Animation. 25, 30, 50, 60, 70 c., $1.50, $3, $4.

Birth Centenary of Marc Chagall (artist). 10, 30, 40, 60, 90 c., $1, $3, $4.

Centenary of Statue of Liberty (2nd issue). 10, 15, 25, 30, 40, 60, 70, 90 c., $1, $2, $3, $4.

250th Death Anniv. of Sir Isaac Newton (scientist) 20 c., $2.50.

750th Anniv. of Berlin. $1, $4.

Bicentenary of U.S. Constitution. 30 c., $3.

16th World Scout Jamboree, Australia. 10 c., $4.

1988.

500th Anniv. (1992) of Discovery of America by Columbus. 15, 30, 45, 60, 90 c., $1, $2, $3.

"Finlandia '88" International Stamp Exhibition, Helsinki. Disney characters in Finnish scenes. 1, 2, 3, 4, 5, 6 c., $5, $6.

Olympic Games, Seoul. 25, 60 c., $1.25, $3.

500th Birth Anniv. of Titian. 10, 25, 40, 70, 90 c., $2, $3, $4.

1989.

20th Anniv of First Manned Landing on Moon. Disney characters on moon. ½, 1, 2, 3, 4, 5 c., $5, $6.

500th Anniv (1992) of Discovery of America by Columbus (2nd issue). Pre-Columbian Societies. 15, 45, 45, 50 c., $2, $2, $3, $3.

Christmas. Disney Characters and Cars of 1950's. 25, 35, 45, 60 c., $1, $2, $3, $4.

1990.

Christmas. Disney Characters and Hollywood cars. 25, 35, 40, 60 c., $1, $2, $4, $5.

1991.

Nobel Prize Winners. 5, 15, 25, 40, 50 c., $1, $2, $4.

RHODESIA

A British territory in central Africa, formerly administered by the British South Africa Co. In 1924 divided into the territories of Northern and Southern Rhodesia which issued their own stamps (q.v). In 1964 Southern Rhodesia was renamed Rhodesia; on becoming independent in 1980 it was renamed Zimbabwe.

1890. 12 pence = 1 shilling
20 shillings = 1 pound.
1970. 100 cents = 1 dollar.

1. Arms of the Company.

1890. The pound values are larger.

18.	**1.**	½d. blue and red	2·50	1·25
1.		1d. black	9·00	1·25
20.		2d. green and red ..	9·00	1·75
21.		3d. black and green ..	8·00	1·75
22.		4d. brown and black ..	9·00	1·75
3.		6d. blue	22·00	2·50
23.		8d. red and blue	10·00	6·00
4.		1s. brown	29·00	7·50
5.		2s. red	40·00	25·00
6.		2s. 6d. purple	24·00	25·00
25.		3s. brown and green ..	95·00	65·00
26.		4s. black and red.. ..	30·00	40·00
8.	**1.**	5s. yellow	42·00	48·00
9.		10s. green	60·00	90·00
10.	–	£1 blue	£170	£130
11.	–	£2 red	£375	£150
12.	–	£5 green	£1500	£450
13.	–	£10 brown..	£2750	£700

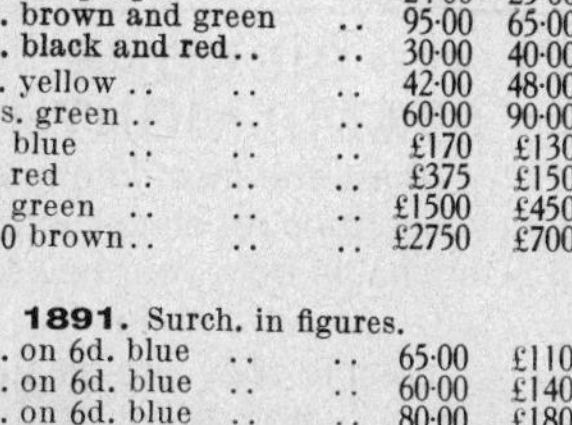

1891. Surch. in figures.

14.	**1.**	½d. on 6d. blue	65·00	£110
15.		2d. on 6d. blue	60·00	£140
16.		4d. on 6d. blue	80·00	£180
17.		8d. on 1s. brown	90·00	£250

5.

9.

1896. The ends of ribbons containing motto cross the animals' legs.

41	**5.**	½d. grey and mauve ..	1·00	1·50
42		1d. red and green ..	1·50	2·25
43		2d. brown and mauve ..	4·75	3·50
31		3d. brown and blue ..	2·25	1·00
44a		4d. blue and mauve ..	6·00	40
46		6d. mauve and red ..	4·50	45
34		8d. green & mauve on buff	4·50	45
35		1s. green and blue ..	15·00	2·25
47		2s. blue and green on buff	20·00	4·00
48		2s. 6d. brn. & pur. on yell.	55·00	38·00
36		3s. green & mauve on blue	48·00	29·00
37		4s. red and blue on green	40·00	2·00
49		5s. brown and green ..	35·00	9·00
50		10s. grey and red on rose	80·00	60·00

1896. Surch. in words.

51.	**1.**	1d. on 3d. black and green	£350	£375
52.		1d. on 4s. black and red..	£250	£225
53.		3d. on 5s. yellow ..	£150	£200

1896. Cape of Good Hope stamps optd. **BRITISH SOUTH AFRICA COMPANY.**

58.	**6.**	½d. black (No. 48) ..	6·50	11·00
59.	**17.**	1d. red (No. 58a).. ..	9·50	13·00
60.	**6.**	2d. brown (No. 60) ..	10·00	7·00
61.		3d. red (No. 40)	45·00	55·00
62.		4d. blue (No. 51) ..	12·00	12·00
63.	**4.**	6d. violet (No. 52a) ..	48·00	60·00
64.	**6.**	1s. yellow (No. 65 ..	80·00	£110

1897. The ends of motto ribbons do not cross the animals' legs.

66.	**9.**	½d. grey and mauve ..	1·60	3·00
67.		1d. red and green ..	3·00	3·75
68.		2d. brown and mauve ..	3·75	60
69.		3d. brown and blue ..	2·50	30
70.		4d. blue and mauve ..	5·00	1·25
71.		6d. mauve and red ..	5·50	3·50
72.		8d. grn. and mve. on buff	9·00	40
73.		£1 black & brown on green	£400	£225

10.

11.

1898. Nos. 90/3 are larger (24 × 28½ mm.).

75a	**10**	½d. green	85	30
77		1d. red	1·25	15
79		2d. brown	1·25	15
80		2½d. blue	3·75	40
81		3d. red	3·75	40
82		4d. olive	3·75	15
83		6d. purple	6·50	1·75
84	**11**	1s. brown	8·00	1·25
85		2s. 6d. grey	32·00	55
86		3s. violet	9·00	50
87		5s. orange	24·00	8·50
88		7s. 6d. black	45·00	14·00
89		10s. green	15·00	1·50
90		£1 purple	£150	60·00
91		£2 brown	65·00	6·50
92	–	£5 blue	£3000	£2250
93	–	£10 lilac	£3000	£2250
93a	–	£20 brown	£8500	

13. Victoria Falls.

1905. Visit of British Assn. and Opening of Victoria Falls Bridge across Zambesi.

94.	**13.**	1d. red	2·75	3·75
95.		2½d. blue	7·50	3·75
96.		5d. red	18·00	45·00
97.		1s. green	18·00	24·00
98.		2s. 6d. black	£100	£150
99.		5s. violet	85·00	40·00

1909. Optd. **RHODESIA** or surch. also.

100	**10**	½d. green	1·25	30
101		1d. red	1·25	30
102		2d. brown	1·60	2·25
103		2½d. blue	1·00	20
104		3d. red	1·60	20
105		4d. olive	2·75	45
114		5d. on 6d. purple ..	6·50	7·50
106		6d. purple	5·00	1·75
116	**11**	7½d. on 2s. 6d. grey ..	3·50	2·25
117a		10d. on 2s. violet ..	4·00	3·25
107c		1s. brown	8·50	1·50
118		2s. on 5s. orange ..	12·00	7·00
108		2s. 6d. grey	15·00	4·50
109		3s. violet	15·00	4·50
110		5s. orange	25·00	15·00
111		7s. 6d. black	65·00	11·00
112		10s. green	27·00	8·50
113	–	£1 purple	£100	60·00
113d	–	£2 brown	£3000	£300
113e	–	£5 blue	£5000	£2250

17.

1910.

119	**17.**	½d. green..	7·00	1·00
123		1d. red	10·00	60
126		2d. black and grey ..	30·00	6·00
131a		2½d. blue..	13·00	5·00
135		3d. purple and yellow ..	22·00	10·00
140		4d. black and orange ..	24·00	10·00
141		5d. purple and olive ..	20·00	32·00
145		6d. purple and mauve ..	20·00	8·00
148		8d. black and purple ..	£110	55·00
149		10d. red and purple ..	26·00	48·00
152		1s. black and green ..	28·00	9·00
153		2s. black and blue ..	55·00	50·00
157		2s. 6d. black and red ..	£275	£275
158		3s. green and violet ..	£130	£130
159		5s. red and green ..	£225	£200
160b		7s. 6d. red and blue ..	£600	£500
164		10s. green and orange ..	£375	£250
165		£1 red and black ..	£900	£375

18.

1913.

187	**18.**	½d. green	2·50	65
192		1d. red	2·75	40
197		1½d. brown	2·25	60
291		2d. black and grey ..	2·25	1·25
200		2½d. blue..	3·00	13·00
259		3d. black and yellow ..	4·00	1·40
225		4d. black and orange ..	6·50	3·50
212		5d. black and green ..	3·50	5·50
266		6d. black and mauve ..	3·50	2·25
230		8d. violet and green ..	9·50	30·00
247		10d. blue and red ..	4·25	18·00
300		1s. black and blue ..	3·00	3·75
273		2s. black and brown ..	12·00	14·00
236		2s. 6d. blue and brown..	38·00	17·0
304		3s. brown and blue ..	50·00	80·00
239		5s. blue and green ..	42·00	48·00
252		7s. 6d. mauve and grey	75·00	£130
309		10s. red and green ..	£140	£170
242		£1 black and purple ..	£350	£450

1917. Surch. **Half Penny.**

281.	**18.**	½d. on 1s. red	1·75	4·00

RHODESIA

The following stamps are for the former Southern Rhodesia, renamed Rhodesia.

59. "Telecommunications".

1965. Centenary of I.T.U.

351.	**59.**	6d. violet and olive ..	1·00	30
352.		1s. 3d. violet and lilac	1·00	35
353.		2s. 6d. violet and brown	2·00	3·25

60. Bangala Dam.

1965. Water Conservation. Multicoloured.

354.		3d. Type **60**	20	10
355.		4d. Irrigation canal	65	85
356.		2s. 6d. Cutting sugar cane	1·75	2·50

63. Sir Winston Churchill, Quill, Sword and Houses of Parliament.

1965. Churchill Commem.

357.	**63.**	1s. 3d. black and blue	50	35

64. Coat of Arms.

1965. " Independence ".

358.	**64.**	2s. 6d. multicoloured ..	15	15

1966. Optd. **INDEPENDENCE. 11th November 1965.** (a) On Nos. 92/105 of Southern Rhodesia.

359.	**45.**	½d. yellow, green & blue	10	10
360.	–	1d. violet and ochre ..	10	10
361.	–	2d. yellow and violet ..	10	10
362.	–	3d. brown and blue ..	10	10
363.	–	4d. orange and green ..	15	10
364.	**50.**	6d. red, yellow & green	15	10
365.	–	9d. brown, yellow & grn.	20	10
366.	–	1s. green and ochre ..	25	10
367.	–	1s. 3d. red, violet & grn.	80	10
368.	–	2s. blue and ochre ..	90	2·50
369.	–	2s. 6d. blue and red ..	60	30
370.	**56.**	5s. multicoloured ..	6·00	4·00
371.	–	10s. multicoloured ..	3·00	1·25
372.	–	£1 multicoloured ..	1·50	1·50

(b) Surch on No. 357.

373.	**63.**	5s. on 1s. 3d. black & blue	16·00	30·00

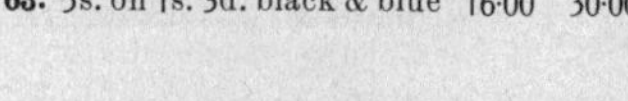

67. Emeralds.

1966. As Nos. 92/8 and 100/105 of Southern Rhodesia, but inscr. " RHODESIA " as in T **67.** Some designs and colours changed.

374.	–	1d. violet and ochre ..	10	10
375.	–	2d. orange and green (As No. 96)	10	10
376.	–	3d. brown and blue ..	10	10
377.	**67.**	4d. green and brown ..	30	10
378.	**50.**	6d. red yellow & green,	15	10
379.	–	9d. yellow and violet (As No. 94)	15	20
380.	**45.**	1s. yellow, green & blue	15	10
381.	–	1s. 3d. blue and ochre (As No. 101).. ..	25	15
382.	–	1s. 6d. brown, yellow and green (As No. 98) ..	1·00	25
383.	–	2s. red, violet and green (As No. 100).. ..	40	80
384.	–	2s. 6d. blue, red & turq.	40	20
385.	**56.**	5s. multicoloured ..	40	90
386.	–	10s. multicoloured ..	2·25	4·00
387.	–	£1 multicoloured ..	14·00	8·00

Nos. 379/80 are in larger format as Type **50.**

Stamps in these designs were later printed locally. These vary only slightly from the above in details and shade.

For Nos. 376, 380 and 382/4 in dual currency see Nos. 408/12.

68. Zeederberg Coach, c. 1895.

1966. 28th Congress of Southern Africa Philatelic Federation (" Rhopex ").
388. **68.** 3d. multicoloured .. 25 10
389. – 9d. multicoloured .. 30 35
390. – 1s. 6d. blue and black 50 50
391. – 2s. 6d. pink, grn. & blk. 55 80
DESIGNS: 9d. Sir Rowland Hill. 1s. 6d. The Penny Black. 2s. 6d. Rhodesian stamp of 1892 (No. 12).

69. De Havilland " Rapide " (1946).

1966. 20th Anniv. of Central African Airways.
393. **69.** 6d. multicoloured .. 1·00 35
394. – 1s. 3d. multicoloured .. 1·25 55
395. – 2s. 6d. multicoloured .. 3·50 1·75
396. – 5s. black and blue .. 6·00 3·50
AIRCRAFT: 1s. 3d. Douglas " D.C.3 " (1953). 2s. 6d. Vickers " Viscount " (1956). 5s. Modern jet.

70. Kudu.

1967. Dual Currency Issue. As Nos. 376, 380 and 382/4 but value in dual currency as T 70.
408. **70.** 3d./2½ c. brn. & blue .. 60 20
409. – 1s./10 c. yellow, green and blue (No. 380) .. 70 45
410. – 1s. 6d./15 c. brown, yellow & green (No. 382) 4·75 90
411. – 2s./20 c. red, violet and green (No. 383) 8·00 9·00
412. – 2s. 6d./25 c. ultram., red and blue (No. 384) .. 40·00 55·00

71. Dr. Jameson (administrator).

1967. Famous Rhodesians (1st series). 50th Death Anniv. of Dr. Jameson.
413. **71.** 1s. 6d. multicoloured .. 30 35
See also Nos. 426, 430, 457, 458, 469, 480, 488, and 513.

72. Soapstone Sculpture (Joram Mariga).

1967. 10th Anniv. of Opening of Rhodes National Gallery.
414. **72.** 3d. brn., green & black 10 10
415. – 9d. blue, brn. & black 20 20
416. – 1s. 3d. multicoloured .. 20 25
417. – 2s. 6d. multicoloured .. 25 35
DESIGNS: 9d. " The Burgher of Calais " (detail, Rodin). 1s. 3d. " The Knight " (stamp wrongly inscr.) (Roberto Crippa). 2s. 6d. " John the Baptist " (Tossini).

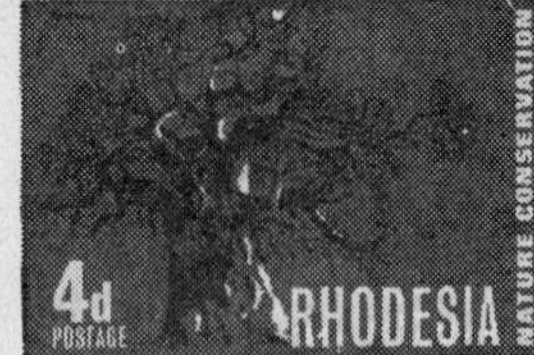

73. Baobab Tree.

1967. Nature Conservation.
418. **73.** 4d. brown and black .. 20 25
419. – 4d. green and black .. 20 25
420. – 4d. grey and black .. 20 25
421. – 4d. orange and black .. 20 25
DESIGNS—HORIZ. No. 419, White Rhinoceros No. 420, African Elephants. VERT. No. 421, Wild Gladiolus.

74. Wooden Hand Plough.

1968. 15th World Ploughing Contest, Norton, Rhodesia.
422. **74.** 3d. orange, red & brn... 10 10
423. – 9d. multicoloured .. 20 20
424. – 1s. 6d. multicoloured .. 30 45
425. – 2s. 6d. multicoloured .. 35 70
DESIGNS: 9d. Early wheel plough. 1s. 6d. Steam powered tractor, and ploughs. 2s. 6d. Modern tractor, and plough.

75. Alfred Beit (national benefactor).

1968. Famous Rhodesians. (2nd issue).
426. **75.** 1s. 6d. orge., blk. & brn. 30 30

76. Raising the Flag, Bulawayo, 1893.

1968. 75th Anniv. of Matabeleland.
427. **76.** 3d. orge., red, & black .. 10 10
428. – 9d. multicoloured .. 20 20
429. – 1s. 6d. grn., emerald & black 25 35
DESIGNS: 9d. View and coat of arms of Bulawayo. 1s. 6d. Allan Wilson (combatant in the Matabele War).

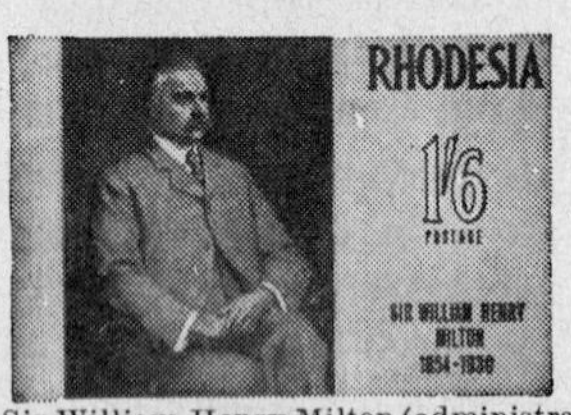

77. Sir William Henry Milton (administrator).

1969. Famous Rhodesians (3rd issue).
430. **77.** 1s. 6d. multicoloured .. 20 45

78. 2 ft. Gauge Steam Locomotive, Beira-Salisbury Line, 1899.

1969. 70th Anniv. of Opening of Beira-Salisbury Railway. Multicoloured.
431. 3d. Type **78** .. .. 1·00 10
432. 9d. Steam locomotive, 1904 1·50 75
433. 1s. 6d. Articulated steam locomotive, 1950 .. 5·50 3·25
434. 2s. 6d. Diesel locomotive, 1955 .. .. .. 7·50 6·50

79. Low Level Bridge.

1969. Bridges of Rhodesia. Multicoloured.
435. 3d. Type **79** 75 10
436. 9d. Mpudzi bridge .. 1·00 30
437. 1s. 6d. Umniati bridge .. 2·50 1·50
438. 2s. 6d. Birchenough bridge 3·50 2·00

80. Harvesting Wheat. 81. Devil's Cataract, Victoria Falls.

1970. Decimal Currency.
439. **80.** 1 c. multicoloured .. 10 10
440. – 2 c. multicoloured .. 10 10
441. – 2½ c. turquoise, bl. & blk. 10 10
441c. – 3 c. multicoloured .. 1·25 10
442. – 3½ c. multicoloured .. 10 10
442b. – 4 c. multicoloured .. 1·50 30
443. – 5 c. multicoloured .. 15 10
443b. – 6 c. multicoloured .. 4·00 3·00
443c. **81.** 7½ c. multicoloured .. 7·50 80
444. 8 c. multicoloured .. 1·25 20
445. – 10 c. multicoloured .. 60 10
446. – 12½ c. multicoloured .. 1·00 10
446a. – 14 c. multicoloured .. 15·00 90
447. – 15 c. multicoloured .. 2·50 15
448. – 20 c. multicoloured .. 1·75 15
449. – 25 c. orge., grey & blk. 3·00 80
450. – 50 c. turquoise & blue 2·25 70
451. – $1 blue, turq. & black 3·00 3·00
452. – $2 multicoloured .. 11·00 22·00
DESIGNS: Size as Type **80.** 2 c. Pouring molten metal. 2½ c. Zimbabwe Ruins. 3 c. Articulated lorry. 3½ c., 4 c. Statue of Cecil Rhodes. 5 c. Mine headgear. 6 c. Hydrofoil "Seaflight". Size as Type **81.** 10 c. Yachting on Lake Mcllwaine. 12½ c. Hippopotamus in river. 14 c., 15 c. Kariba Dam. 20 c. Irrigation canal. Larger (31 × 26 mm.). 25 c. Bateleur eagles. 50 c. Radar antenna and Vickers "Viscount". $1, "Air Rescue", $2, Rhodesian flag.

82. Despatch Rider c. 1890.

1970. Inauguration of Posts and Telecommunications Corporation. Mult.
453. 2½ c. Type **82** 25 10
454. 3½ c. Loading mail at Salisbury airport .. 40 25
455. 15 c. Constructing telegraph line, c. 1890 .. 1·25 2·00
456. 25 c. Telephone and modern telecommunications equipment .. .. .. 2·00 3·50

83. Mother Patrick (Dominican nurse and teacher).

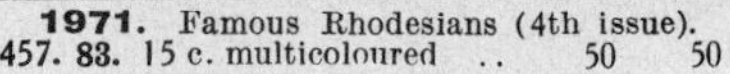
1971. Famous Rhodesians (4th issue).
457. **83.** 15 c. multicoloured .. 50 50

84. Fredrick Courteney Selous (Big-game hunter, explorer and pioneer).

1971. Famous Rhodesians (5th issue).
458. **84.** 15 c. multicoloured .. 40 40

85. Hoopoe. 86. Porphyrite Granite.

1971. Birds of Rhodesia (1st series). Mult.
459. 2 c. Type **85** .. .. 1·25 20
460. 2½ c. Half-collared kingfisher (horiz.) .. .. 1·25 20
461. 5 c. Golden-breasted bunting .. .. .. 3·50 70
462. 7½ c. Carmine bee eater .. 4·00 1·25
463. 8 c. Red-eyed bulbul .. 4·00 1·50
464. 25 c. Senegal wattled plover (horiz.) .. .. 8·50 3·25
See also Nos. 537/42.

1971. "Granite 71" Geological Symposium. Multicoloured.
465. 2½ c. Type **86** 75 10
466. 7½ c. Muscovite mica seen through microscope .. 2·00 80
467. 15 c. Granite seen through microscope .. .. 2·75 3·50
468. 25 c. Geological map of Rhodesia .. .. .. 3·25 5·00

87. Dr. Robert Moffat (missionary).

1972. Famous Rhodesians (6th issue).
469. **87.** 13 c. multicoloured .. 1·00 1·00

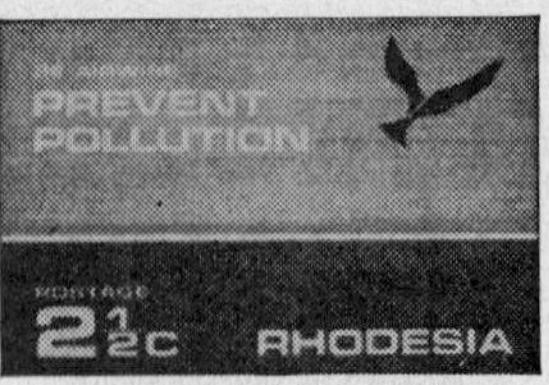

88. Bird (" Be Airwise ").

1972. " Prevent Pollution ". Mult.
470. 2½ c. Type **88** 20 10
471. 3½ c. Antelope (" Be Countrywise") 20 10
472. 7 c. Fish (" Be Waterwise") 30 45
473. 13 c. City (" Be Citywise") 45 70

89. "The Three Kings".

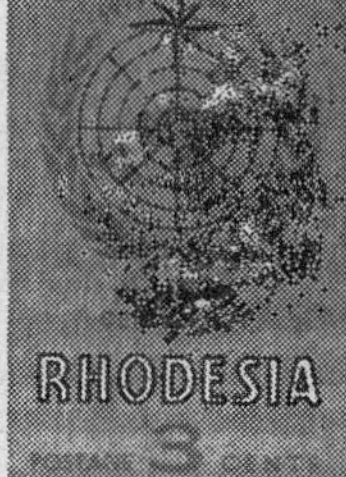

91. W.M.O. Emblem.

90. Dr. David Livingstone.

1972. Christmas.

477. 89.	2 c. multicoloured ..	10	10
478.	5 c. multicoloured ..	20	15
479.	13 c. multicoloured ..	50	55

1973. Famous Rhodesians (7th issue).

480. 90.	14 c. multicoloured ..	70	85

1973. Centenary of I.M.O./W.M.O.

481. 91.	3 c. multicoloured ..	15	10
482.	14 c. multicoloured ..	60	70
483.	25 c. multicoloured ..	1·25	2·00

92. Arms of Rhodesia.

1973. 50th Anniv. of Responsible Government.

484. 92.	2½ c. multicoloured ..	15	10
485.	4 c. multicoloured ..	20	20
486.	7½ c. multicoloured ..	35	70
487.	14 c. multicoloured ..	60	1·75

93. George Pauling (construction engineer).

1974. Famous Rhodesians (8th issne).

488. 93.	14 c. multicoloured ..	1·00	1·50

94. Greater Kudu.

95. Thunbergia.

96. "Charaxes varanes".

1974. Multicoloured.

(a) Antelopes.

489.	1 c. Type **94**	10	10
490.	2½ c. Eland	75	10
491.	3 c. Roan Antelope ..	10	10
492.	4 c. Reedbuck	20	10
493.	5 c. Bushbuck	40	10

(b) Wild Flowers.

494.	6 c. Type **95**	40	10
495.	7½ c. Flame Lily	3·00	35
496.	8 c. As 7½ c.	40	10
497.	10 c. Devil Thorn	30	10
498.	12 c. Hibiscus	70	80
499.	12½ c. Pink Sabi Star ..	4·00	50
500.	14 c. Wild Pimpernel ..	5·00	70
501.	15 c. As 12½ c.	70	60
502.	16 c. As 14 c.	70	45

(c) Butterflies.

503	20 c. Type **96**	1·75	35
504	24 c. "Precis hierta" ..	1·25	40
505	25 c. As 24 c.	6·00	3·00
506	50 c. "Colotis regina" ..	70	90
507	$1 "Papilio antheus" ..	70	1·25
508	$2 "Hamanumida daedalus"	80	1·50

97. Collecting Mail.

1974. Centenary of U.P.U. Multicoloured.

509.	3 c. Type **97**	15	10
510.	4 c. Sorting mail	20	10
511.	7½ c. Mail delivery ..	50	65
512.	14 c. Weighing parcel ..	1·00	1·75

98. Thomas Baines (artist).

1975. Famous Rhodesians (9th issue).

513. 98.	14 c. multicoloured ..	80	1·25

99. "Euphorbia confinalis".

101. Telephones, 1876 and 1976.

100. Prevention of Head Injuries.

1975. Int. Succulent Congress, Salisbury ("Aloe '75"). Multicoloured.

514.	2½ c. Type **99**	20	10
515.	3 c. "Aloe excelsa" ..	20	10
516.	4 c. "Hoodia lugardii" ..	30	15
517.	7½ c. "Aloe ortholopha"	45	40
518.	14 c. "Aloe musapana"	1·00	1·00
519.	25 c. "Aloe saponaria"	1·50	1·75

1975. Occupational Safety. Multicoloured.

520.	2½ c. Type **100**	15	10
521.	4 c. Bandaged hand and gloved hand ..	20	10
522.	7½ c. Broken glass and eye	35	20
523.	14 c. Blind man and welder with protective mask ..	50	60

1976. Centenary of Telephone.

524. 101.	3 c. grey and blue ..	10	10
525. –	14 c. black and brown ..	20	45

DESIGN: 14 c. Alexander Graham Bell.

1976. Nos. 495, 500 and 505 surch.

526.	8 c. on 7½ c. multicoloured	15	15
527.	16 c. on 14 c. multicoloured	20	25
528.	24 c. on 25 c. multicoloured	30	60

103. Roan Antelope.

1976. Vulnerable Wildlife. Multicoloured.

529.	4 c. Type **103**	20	10
530.	6 c. Brown Hyena ..	25	10
531.	8 c. Wild Dog	35	25
532.	16 c. Cheetah	45	45

104. Msasa.

1976. Trees of Rhodesia. Multicoloured.

533.	4 c. Type **104**	15	10
534.	6 c. Red Mahogany ..	15	10
535.	8 c. Mukwa	20	30
536.	16 c. Rhodesian Teak ..	25	50

105. Common Bulbul.

1977. Birds of Rhodesia (2nd series). Mult.

537.	3 c. Type **105**	20	10
538.	4 c. Yellow-mantled whydah	20	10
539.	6 c. Cape longclaw ..	25	35
540.	8 c. Eastern long-tailed shrike	35	50
541.	16 c. Lesser blue-eared glossy starling ..	55	1·00
542.	24 c. Green wood hoopoe ..	70	1·25

106. "Lake Kyle" (Joan Evans).

1977. Landscape Paintings. Multicoloured.

543.	3 c. Type **106**	15	10
544.	4 c. "Chimanimani Mountains" (Joan Evans) ..	15	10
545.	6 c. "Rocks near Bonsor Reef" (Alice Balfour) ..	15	10
546.	8 c. "A Dwala near Devil's Pass" (Alice Balfour) ..	25	10
547.	16 c. "Zimbabwe" (Alice Balfour)	35	40
548.	24 c. "Victoria Falls" (Thomas Baines) ..	40	45

107. Virgin and Child.

1977. Christmas.

549. 107.	3 c. multicoloured ..	10	10
550.	6 c. multicoloured ..	15	15
551.	8 c. multicoloured ..	30	15
552.	16 c. multicoloured ..	30	65

MORE DETAILED LISTS
are given in the Stanley Gibbons Catalogues referred to in the country headings.
For lists of current volumes see Introduction.

108. Fair Spire.

109. Morganite.

1978. Trade Fair Rhodesia, Bulawayo. Mult.

553.	4 c. Type **108**	15	10
554.	8 c. Fair Spire (different) ..	20	25

1978. Gemstones, Wild Animals and Waterfalls. Multicoloured.

555.	1 c. Type **109**	20	10
556.	3 c. Amethyst	30	10
557.	4 c. Garnet	30	10
558.	5 c. Citrine	30	10
559.	7 c. Blue Topaz	30	10
560.	9 c. White Rhinoceros ..	20	10
561.	11 c. Lion	20	15
562.	13 c. Warthog	20	15
563.	15 c. Giraffe	20	15
564.	17 c. Common Zebra ..	20	10
565.	21 c. Odzani Falls ..	20	30
566.	25 c. Goba Falls	20	40
567.	30 c. Inyangombi Falls ..	25	30
568.	$1 Bridal Veil Falls ..	50	80
569.	$2 Victoria Falls	75	1·00

Nos. 560/4 are 26 × 23 mm., and Nos. 565/9 32 × 27 mm.

112. Wright "Flyer".

1978. 75th Anniv. of Powered Flight. Mult.

570.	4 c. Type **112**	10	10
571.	5 c. Bleriot "XI"	10	10
572.	7 c. Vickers "Vimy" "Silver Queen II" ..	10	10
573.	9 c. "A.W.15 Atalanta" ..	10	10
574.	17 c. Vickers "Viking 1B"	15	15
575.	25 c. Boeing "720B" ..	20	30

POSTAGE DUE STAMPS

D 2.

D 3. Zimbabwe Bird. (soapstone sculpture).

1965. Roul.

D 8a	D 2	1d. red	2·00	5·00
D 9		2d. blue	50	8·00
D10		4d. green	60	8·00
D11		6d. plum	60	6·00

1966.

D12	D 3	1d. red	1·00	3·00
D13		2d. blue	1·50	2·75
D14		4d. green	1·50	5·00
D15		6d. violet	1·50	2·75
D16		1s. brown	1·50	3·00
D17		2s. black	2·00	6·50

1970. Decimal Currency. As Type D 3 but larger (26 × 22½ mm.).

D18	D 3	1 c. green	1·00	1·40
D19		2 c. blue	1·00	80
D20		5 c. violet	2·50	2·00
D21		6 c. yellow	4·25	3·25
D22		10 c. red	2·50	3·50

RHODESIA AND NYASALAND

Stamps for the Central African Federation of Northern and Southern Rhodesia and Nyasaland Protectorate. The stamps of the Federation were withdrawn on 19 February 1964, when all three constituent territories had resumed issuing their own stamps.

12 pence = 1 shilling.
20 shillings = 1 pound.

1. Queen Elizabeth II. 2.

1954.

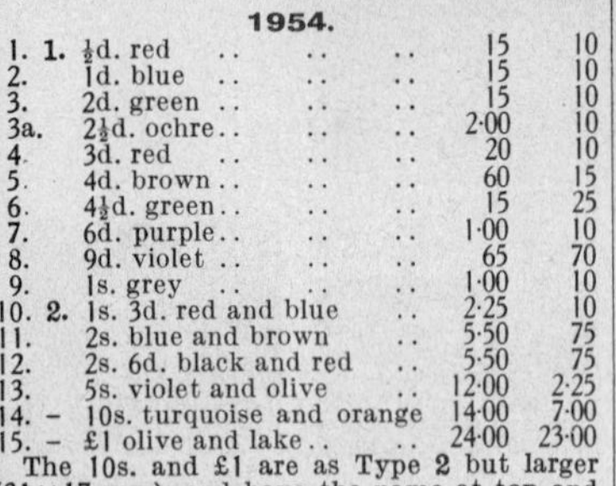

1.	1.	½d. red	15	10
2.		1d. blue	15	10
3.		2d. green	15	10
3a.		2½d. ochre	2·00	10
4.		3d. red	20	10
5.		4d. brown	60	15
6.		4½d. green	15	25
7.		6d. purple	1·00	10
8.		9d. violet	65	70
9.		1s. grey	1·00	10
10.	2.	1s. 3d. red and blue	2·25	10
11.		2s. blue and brown	5·50	75
12.		2s. 6d. black and red	5·50	75
13.		5s. violet and olive	12·00	2·25
14.	–	10s. turquoise and orange	14·00	7·00
15.	–	£1 olive and lake	24·00	23·00

The 10s. and £1 are as Type 2 but larger (31 × 17 mm). and have the name at top and foliage on either side of portrait.

4. Aeroplane over Victoria Falls. 5. Livingstone and Victoria Falls.

1955. Cent. of Discovery of Victoria Falls.

16.	4.	3d. blue and turquoise	45	30
17.	5.	1s. purple and blue	55	40

6. Tea Picking. 11. Lake Bangweulu.

17. Rhodes' Statue.

1959.

18.	6.	½d. black and green	60	30
19.	–	1d. red and black	15	10
20.	–	2d. violet and buff	75	40
21.	–	2½d. purple and blue	40	40
22.	–	3d. black and blue	15	10
23.	11.	4d. purple and olive	1·25	10
24.	–	6d. blue and green	45	10
24a.	–	9d. brown and violet	5·50	2·00
25.	–	1s. green and blue	60	10
26.	–	1s. 3d. green and brown	2·00	10
27.	–	2s. green and red	3·25	50
28.	–	2s. 6d. blue and buff	3·75	30
29.	17.	5s. brown and green	5·50	2·25
30.	–	10s. bistre and red	23·00	12·00
31.	–	£1 black and violet	38·00	26·00

DESIGNS—As Type 6: VERT. 1d. V.H.F. mast. 2d. Copper mining. 2½d. Fairbridge Memorial. HORIZ. 3d. Rhodes' grave. As Type 11: VERT. 6d. Eastern Cataract, Victoria Falls. HORIZ. 9d. Rhodesian railway trains. 1s. Tobacco. 1s. 3d. Lake Nyasa. 2s. Chirundu Bridge. 2s. 6d. Salisbury Airport. As Type 17: HORIZ. 10s. Mlanje. £1, Federal Coat of Arms.

20. Kariba Gorge, 1955.

1960. Opening of Kariba Hydro-Electric Scheme.

32.	20.	3d. green and orange	35	10
33.	–	6d. brown & bistre	70	20
34.	–	1s. blue and green	1·75	1·50
35.	–	1s.3d. blue and brown	2·50	1·50
36.	–	2s. 6d. purple and red	3·25	7·00
37.	–	5s. violet and turquoise	7·50	11·00

DESIGNS: 6d. 330 k.V. power lines. 1s. Barrage wall. 1s. 3d. Barrage and lake. 2s. 6d. Interior of power station. 5s. Queen Mother and barrage wall (inscr. "ROYAL OPENING").

26. Miner Drilling.

1961. 7th Commonwealth Mining and Metallurgical Congress.

38.	26.	6d. green and brown	40	15
39.	–	1s. 3d. black and blue	40	60

DESIGN: 1s. 3d. Surface installations, Nchanga mine.

28. D.H. "Hercules" on Rhodesian Airstrip.

1962. 30th Anniv. of 1st London-Rhodesian Airmail Service.

40.	28.	6d. green and red	35	25
41.	–	1s. 3d. blue, blk. & yell.	1·00	50
42.	–	2s. 6d. red and violet	6·50	4·25

DESIGNS: 1s. 3d. Empire "C" Class flying-boat taking-off from Zambesi. 2s. 6d. D.H. "Comet" at Salisbury Airport.

31. Tobacco Plant.

DESIGNS: 6d. Tobacco field. 1s. 3d. Auction floor. 2s. 6d. Cured tobacco.

1963. World Tobacco Congress, Salisbury.

43.	31.	3d. green and olive	15	10
44.	–	6d. green, brown & blue	20	35
45.	–	1s. 3d. brown and blue	30	45
46.	–	2s. 6d. yellow and brown	75	2·50

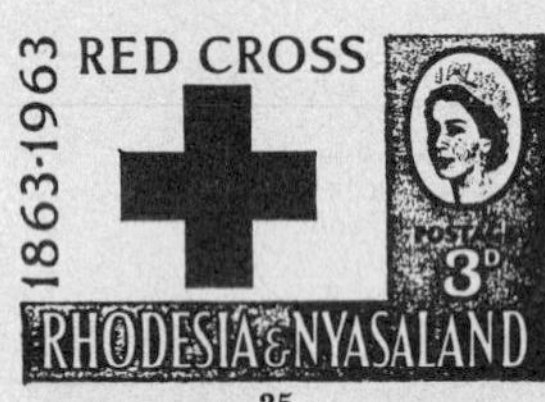

35.

1963. Centenary of Red Cross.

47.	35.	3d. red	55	10

36. African "Round Table" Emblem.

1963. World Council of Young Men's Service Clubs, Salisbury.

48.	36.	6d. black, gold and green	30	90
49.		1s. 3d. multicoloured	30	60

POSTAGE DUE STAMPS

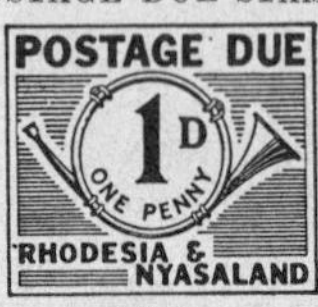

D 1.

1961.

D 1.	D 1.	1d. red	1·25	3·50
D 2.		2d. blue	1·75	3·00
D 3.		4d. green	1·75	8·00
D 4.		6d. purple	3·50	7·50

ROSS DEPENDENCY

A dependency of New Zealand in the Antarctic on the Ross Sea.

1957. 12 pence = 1 shilling.
20 shillings = 1 pound.
1967. 100 cents = 1 dollar.

DESIGNS—HORIZ. as Type 3: 3d. H.M.S. "Erebus". 4d. Shackleton and Scott.

3. Map of Ross Dependency and New Zealand. 4. Queen Elizabeth II.

1957.

1.	–	3d. blue	2·50	1·00
2.	–	4d. red	2·50	75
3.	3.	8d. red and blue	2·50	1·00
4.	4.	1s. 6d. purple	2·50	1·25

5. H.M.S. "Erebus".

1967. Nos. 1/4 with values inscr in decimal currency as T 5.

5.	5.	2 c. blue	10·00	4·75
6.	–	3 c. red	8·00	4·75
7.	3.	7 c. red and blue	12·00	7·50
8.	4.	15 c. purple	12·00	12·00

6. McCormick's Skua.

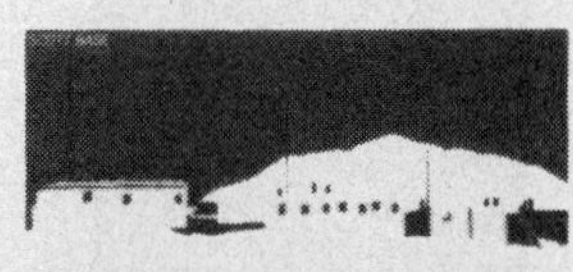

7. Scott Base.

1972.

9a.	6.	3 c. blk., grey and blue	65	1·00
10a.	–	4 c. blk., blue & violet	40	1·00
11a.	–	5 c. blk., grey and lilac	30	1·00
12a.	–	8 c. black, grey & brown	40	1·00
13a.	7.	10 c. black, green & grey	40	1·25
14a.	–	18 c. black, violet and bright violet	50	1·40

DESIGNS: Size as Type 6. 4 c. "Hercules" aeroplane at Williams Field. 5 c. Shackleton's Hut. 8 c. Supply ship H.M.N.Z.S. "Endeavour". Size as Type 7. 18 c. Tabular ice floe.

8. Adelie Penguins.

1982. Multicoloured.

15.	5 c. Type 8	75	60
16.	10 c. Tracked vehicles	40	30
17.	20 c. Scott Base	50	30
18.	30 c. Field party	50	30
19.	40 c. Vanda Station	50	30
20.	50 c. Scott's hut, Cape Evans	55	35

The post office closed on 30 September 1987.

SABAH

Formerly North Borneo, now part of Malaysia

100 cents = 1 Malaysian dollar.

1964. Nos. 391/406 of North Borneo optd. SABAH.

408.	1 c. green and red	10	10
409.	4 c. olive and orange	15	50
410.	5 c. sepia and violet	15	10
411.	6 c. black and turquoise	10	10
412.	10 c. green and red	15	10
413.	12 c. brown and myrtle	15	10
414.	20 c. turquoise and blue	2·00	10
415.	25 c. black and red	45	90
416.	30 c. sepia and olive	25	10
417.	35 c. slate and brown	30	20
418.	50 c. green and bistre	30	10
419.	75 c. blue and purple	2·25	65
420.	$1 brown and green	3·50	50
421.	$2 brown and slate	6·00	2·75
422.	$4 green and purple	8·00	11·00
423.	$10 red and blue	13·00	17·00

138. "Vanda hookeriana".

1965. As No. 115/21 of Kedah but with Arms of Sabah inset as in T 138.

424.	138.	1 c. multicoloured	10	30
425.	–	2 c. multicoloured	10	50
426.	–	5 c. multicoloured	10	10
427.	–	6 c. multicoloured	20	50
428.	–	10 c. multicoloured	20	10
429.	–	15 c. multicoloured	1·75	10
430.	–	20 c. multicoloured	2·00	40

The higher values used in Sabah were Nos. 20/7 of Malaysia.

139. "Hebomoia glaucippe".

1971. Butterflies. As Nos. 124/30 of Kedah, but with Sabah Arms inset as T 139.

432.	–	1 c. multicoloured	10	60
433.	–	2 c. multicoloured	30	60
434.	–	5 c. multicoloured	45	10
435.	–	6 c. multicoloured	45	70
436.	139.	10 c. multicoloured	45	10
437.	–	15 c. multicoloured	60	10
438.	–	20 c. multicoloured	70	60

The higher values in use with this issue were Nos. 64/71 of Malaysia.

140. "Hibiscus rosa-sinensis".

1979. As Nos. 135/41 of Kedah but with Arms of Sabah as T 140.

445	1 c. "Rafflesia hasseltii"	10	30
446	2 c. "Pterocarpus indicus"	10	30
447	5 c. "Lagerstroemia speciosa"	10	10
448	10 c. "Durio zibethinus"	20	10
449	15 c. Type 140	30	10
450	20 c. "Rhododendron scortechinii"	30	10
451	25 c. "Etlingera elatior" (inscr "Phaeomeria speciosa")	40	10

The higher values in use with this issue were Nos. 190/7 of Malaysia.

141. Coffee.

1986. As Nos. 152/8 of Kedah but with Arms of Sabah as in T 141.

459	1 c. Type 141	10	10
460	2 c. Coconuts	10	10
461	5 c. Cocoa	10	10
462	10 c. Black pepper	10	10
463	15 c. Rubber	10	10
464	20 c. Oil palm	10	10
465	30 c. Rice	15	20

ST. CHRISTOPHER

One of the Leeward Is. Stamps superseded in 1890 by Leeward Islands general issue.

12 pence = 1 shilling.

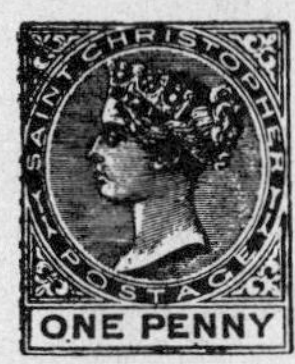

1.

1870.

11	1	½d. green	50	80
2		1d. mauve..	40·00	26·00
13		1d. red	60	70
14		2½d. brown	£170	55·00
16		2½d. blue	1·50	1·50
8		4d. blue	£150	15·00
18		4d. grey	1·25	80
9		6d. green	50·00	5·00
19		6d. olive	80·00	£250
20		1s. mauve	90·00	65·00

1885. Surch. in words.

23	1	½d. on half of 1d. red ..	24·00	35·00
26		1d. on ½d. green	28·00	38·00
28		1d. on 2½d. blue	38·00	42·00
24		1d. on 6d. green	16·00	28·00
22		4d. on 6d. green	48·00	48·00

1886. Surch. in figures.

25.	1.	4d. on 6d. green	48·00	90·00

ST. HELENA

An island in the S. Atlantic Ocean, W. of Africa.

1856. 12 pence = 1 shilling,
20 shillings = 1 pound.
1971. 100 pence = 1 pound.

1.

11.

The early stamps of St. Helena, other than the 6d. were formed by printing the 6d. in various colours and surcharging it with new values in words or (in the case of the 2½d.) in figures.

1856. Imperf.

4.	1.	1d. on 6d. red	£110	£150
5.		4d. on 6d. red	£500	£250
1.		6d. blue	£500	£180

1861. Perf.

36	1.	½d. on 6d. green ..	90	1·10
37		1d. on 6d. red	2·75	2·00
39		2d. on 6d. yellow.. ..	1·25	3·50
40		2½d. on 6d. blue	2·00	5·00
41		3d. on 6d. purple ..	2·00	2·75
14		4d. on 6d. red	75·00	48·00
43b		4d. on 6d. brown ..	14·00	8·00
25		6d. blue	£250	35·00
44		6d. grey	10·00	3·50
30		1s. on 6d. green	20·00	12·00
20		5s. on 6d. yellow ..	35·00	50·00

1890.

46.	11.	½d. green	2·75	4·50
47.		1d. red	7·50	1·00
48.		1½d. brown and green ..	4·50	6·50
49.		2d. yellow..	4·25	8·50
50.		2½d. blue	5·50	9·50
51.		5d. violet	11·00	24·00
52.		10d. brown	16·00	48·00

12.

13. Government House.

14. The Wharf.

1902. Inscr. "POSTAGE POSTAGE".

53.	12.	½d. green	1·50	90
54.		1d. red	3·75	70

1903.

55.	13.	½d. brown and green ..	2·00	2·25
56.	14.	1d. black and red ..	1·50	35
57.	13.	2d. black and green ..	6·00	1·25
58.	14.	8d. black and brown ..	14·00	32·00
59.	13.	1s. brown and orange ..	14·00	30·00
60.	14.	2s. black and violet ..	45·00	75·00

1908. Inscr. "POSTAGE & REVENUE".

64	12	2½d. blue	1·25	1·40
66a		4d. black and red on yellow	1·25	5·50
67a		6d. purple	2·75	10·00
71		10s. green & red on green	£160	£225

1912. As T **13/14**, but with medallion of King George V.

72.	13.	½d. black and green ..	1·25	6·00
73.	14.	1d. black and red ..	1·25	1·25
89.		1d. green	50	18·00
74.		1½d. black and orange ..	2·00	4·25
90.		1½d. red	6·00	25·00
75.	13.	2d. black and grey ..	2·00	1·75
76.	14.	2½d. black and blue ..	1·75	5·50
77.	13.	3d. black & purple on yell.	2·00	5·00
91.		3d. blue	12·00	40·00
78.	14.	8d. black and purple ..	5·50	45·00
79.	13.	1s. black on green ..	8·00	22·00
80.	14.	2s. black and blue on blue	27·00	60·00
81.		3s. black and violet ..	48·00	95·00

18.

22. Badge of St. Helena.

1912. Inscr. "POSTAGE & REVENUE".

83.	18.	4d. black & red on yellow	4·50	15·00
84.		6d. purple	2·50	5·00

1913. Inscr. "POSTAGE POSTAGE".

85.	18.	4d. black & red on yellow	5·50	3·50
86.		6d. purple	10·00	20·00

1916. Surch. **WAR TAX ONE PENNY.**

87.		1d. + 1d. black & red (No. 73)	85	2·75

1919. Surch. **WAR TAX 1d.**

88.		1d. + 1d. black & red (No. 73)	40	3·00

1922.

97.	22.	½d. grey and black ..	1·25	1·75
98.		1d. grey and green ..	1·75	1·40
99.		1½d. red	2·75	8·00
100.		2d. grey and brown ..	2·00	2·00
101.		3d. blue	2·00	4·00
92.		4d. grey & black on yell.	6·50	7·50
103.		5d. green & red on green	2·75	5·50
104.		6d. grey and purple ..	3·50	8·00
105.		8d. grey and violet ..	3·25	6·50
106.		1s. grey and brown ..	6·00	8·50
107.		1s. 6d. grey & grn. on grn.	13·00	42·00
108.		2s. purple & blue on blue	13·00	35·00
109.		2s. 6d. grey & red on yell.	13·00	48·00
110.		5s. grey & green on yell.	35·00	70·00
111.		7s. 6d. grey and orange..	75·00	£120
112.		10s. grey and green ..	£110	£160
113.		15s. grey & pur. on blue	£850	£1400
96.		£1 grey & purple on red..	£400	£450

23. Lot and Lots wife.

1934. Centenary of British Colonization.

114.	23.	½d. black and purple ..	65	80
115.	–	1d. black and green ..	65	85
116.	–	1½d. black and red ..	2·50	3·00
117.	–	2d. black and orange ..	1·75	1·25
118.	–	3d. black and blue ..	1·40	4·50
119.	–	6d. black and blue ..	3·25	3·00
120.	–	1s. black and brown ..	6·00	18·00
121.	–	2s. 6d. black and red ..	35·00	48·00
122.	–	5s. black and brown ..	75·00	85·00
123.	–	10s. black and purple ..	£200	£250

DESIGNS—HORIZ. 1d. "Plantation". 1½d. Map of St. Helena. 2d. Quay, Jamestown. 3d. James Valley. 6d. Jamestown. 1s. Mundens Promontory. 5s. High Knoll. 10s. Badge of St. Helena. VERT. 2s. 6d. St. Helena.

1935. Silver Jubilee. As T **13** of Antigua.

124.		1½d. blue and red ..	75	3·25
125.		2d. blue and grey ..	1·25	90
126.		6d. green and blue ..	6·50	2·50
127.		1s. grey and purple ..	7·50	11·00

1937. Coronation. As T **2** of Aden.

128.		1d. green	40	30
129.		2d. orange	75	30
130.		3d. blue..	1·25	30

33. Badge of St. Helena.

1938.

131.	33.	½d. violet	10	40
132.		1d. green	20·00	4·00
132a.		1d. orange	20	30
149.		1d. black and green ..	50	80
133.		1½d. red..	20	40
150.		1½d. black and red ..	50	80
134.		2d. orange	20	15
151.		2d. black and red ..	50	80
135.		3d. blue..	90·00	30·00
135a.		3d. grey..	30	30
135b.		4d. blue..	1·25	30
136.		6d. blue..	1·25	30
136a.		8d. green	3·00	90
137.		1s. brown	50	30
138.		2s. 6d. purple	12·00	3·50
139.		5s. brown	14·00	7·50
140.		10s. purple	14·00	15·00

1946. Victory. As T **9** of Aden.

141.		2d. orange	10	10
142.		4d. blue..	10	10

1948. Silver Wedding. As T **10/11** of Aden.

143.		3d. black	30	20
144.		10s. blue	19·00	26·00

1949. U.P.U. As T **20/23** of Antigua.

145		3d. red	75	30
146		4d. blue	1·50	90
147		6d. green	1·75	90
148		1s. black	1·75	1·10

1953. Coronation. As T **13** of Aden.

152.		3d. black and lilac ..	1·00	65

34. Badge of St. Helena.

1953.

153.	34.	½d. black and green ..	30	30
154.	–	1d. black and green ..	15	20
155.	–	1½d. black and purple..	1·50	70
156.	–	2d. black and red ..	50	30
157.	–	2½d. black and red ..	40	30
158.	–	3d. black and brown ..	3·25	30
159.	–	4d. black and blue ..	40	40
160.	–	6d. black and violet ..	40	30
161.	–	7d. black	65	1·25
162.	–	1s. black and red ..	40	40
163.	–	2s. 6d. black and violet	12·00	7·00
164.	–	5s. black and sepia ..	17·00	11·00
165.	–	10s. black and yellow..	40·00	22·00

DESIGNS—HORIZ. 1d. Flax plantation, 2d. Lace-making. 2½d. Drying flax. 3d. St. Helena Sand Plover. 4d. Flagstaff and the Barn (hills). 6d. Donkeys carrying flax. 7d. Map. 1s. The Castle. 2s. 6d. Cutting flax. 5s. Jamestown. 10s. Longwood House. VERT. 1½d. Heart-shaped Waterfall.

45. Stamp of 1856.

1956. Cent. of First St. Helena Postage Stamp.

166.	45.	3d. blue and red ..	10	10
167.		4d. blue and brown ..	10	15
168.		6d. blue and purple ..	15	25

47. East Indiaman "London" off James Bay.

1959. Tercent of Settlement.

169.	–	3d. black and red ..	10	10
170.	47.	6d. green and blue ..	40	45
171.	–	1s. black and orange ..	40	45

DESIGNS—HORIZ. 3d. Arms of East India Company. 1s. Commemoration Stone.

1961. Tristan Relief Fund. Nos. 46 and 49/51 of Tristan da Cunha surch. **ST. HELENA Tristan Relief** and premium.

172.		2½ c. + 3d. black and red..	—	£400
173.		5 c. + 6d. black and blue..	—	£400
174.		7½ c. + 9d. black and red..	—	£475
175.		10 c. + 1s. black and brown	—	£550

50. Cunning Fish.

63. Queen Elizabeth II with Prince Andrew (after Cecil Beaton).

1961.

176	50	1d. multicoloured ..	10	10
177	–	1½d. multicoloured ..	30	10
178	–	2d. red and grey ..	15	10
179	–	3d. multicoloured ..	50	20
180	–	4½d. multicoloured ..	60	30
181	–	6d. red, sepia and olive	4·00	35
182	–	7d. brown, blk. & violet	35	50
183	–	10d. purple and blue..	35	40
184	–	1s. lemon, grn. & brn.	45	40
185	–	1s. 6d. grey and blue..	9·50	3·50
186	–	2s. 6d. red, yell. & turq.	2·50	1·50
187	–	5s. yell., brown & grn.	12·00	3·00
188	–	10s. red, black & blue	17·00	8·50
189	63	£1 brown and blue ..	22·00	17·00

DESIGNS—As Type **50**—VERT. 1½d. Yellow canary. 3d. Queen Elizabeth II. 4½d. Red-wood flower. 6d. Madagascar red fody. 1s. Gum-wood flower. 1s 6d. White tern. 5s. Night-blooming Cereus. HORIZ. 2d. Brittle starfish. 7d. Trumpet fish. 10d. Feather starfish. 2s 6d. Orange starfish. 10s. Deep-water bull's-eye.

1963. Freedom from Hunger. As T **28** of Aden.

190.		1s. 6d. blue	2·00	40

1963. Cent of Red Cross. As T **33** of Antigua.

191.		3d. red and black.. ..	75	25
192.		1s. 6d. red and blue ..	3·00	75

1965. 1st Local Post. Optd. **FIRST LOCAL POST 4th JANUARY 1965.**

193.	50.	1d.	10	10
194.		3d. (No. 179)	10	10
195.		6d. (No. 181)	30	10
196.		1s. 6d. (No. 185) ..	35	15

1965. Cent of I.T.U. As T **36** of Antigua.

197.		3d. blue and brown ..	35	15
198.		6d. purple and green ..	55	15

1965. Cent of I.C.Y. As T **37** of Antigua.

199.		1d. purple and turquoise..	20	15
200.		6d. green and lavender ..	55	15

1966. Churchill Commem. As T **38** of Antigua.

201.		1d. blue	15	10
202.		3d. green	35	10
203.		6d. brown	50	10
204.		1s. 6d. violet	70	30

1966. World Cup Football Championship. As T **40** of Antigua.

205.		3d. multicoloured ..	50	15
206.		6d. multicoloured ..	75	15

1966. Inauguration of W.H.O. Headquarters, Geneva. As T **41** of Antigua.

207.		3d. black, green and blue	50	15
208.		1s. 6d. blk., purple & ochre	2·75	40

1966. 20th Anniv of U.N.E.S.C.O. As T **54/6** of Antigua.

209.		3d. multicoloured ..	1·50	20
210.		6d. yellow, violet and olive	2·50	30
211.		1s. 6d. blk., purple & orge.	4·00	1·00

65. Badge of St. Helena.

1967. New Constitution.

212.	65.	1s. multicoloured ..	10	10
213.		2s. 6d. multicoloured ..	20	20

66. Fire of London.

1967. 300th Anniv. of Arrival of Settlers after Great Fire of London.

214. 66.	1d. red and black ..	15	10
215. –	3d. blue and black ..	20	10
216. –	6d. violet and black ..	20	10
217. –	1s. 6d. green and black	20	10

DESIGNS: 3d. East Indiaman "Charles". 6d. Settlers landing at Jamestown. 1s. 6d. Settlers clearing scrub.

70. Interlocking Maps of Tristan and St. Helena.

1968. 30th Anniv. of Tristan da Cunha as a Dependency of St. Helena.

218. 70.	4d. purple and brown ..	10	10
219. –	8d. olive and brown ..	10	10
220. 70.	1s. 9d. blue and brown	10	25
221. –	2s. 3d. blue & brown	15	25

DESIGN: 8d. and 2s. 3d. Interlocking Maps of Tristan and St. Helena (different).

72. Queen Elizabeth and Sir Hudson Lowe.

1968. 150th Anniversary of Abolition of Slavery in St. Helena.

222. 72.	3d. multicoloured ..	10	10
223.	9d. multicoloured ..	10	10
224. –	1s. 6d. multicoloured ..	15	20
225. –	2s. 6d. multicoloured ..	25	20

DESIGN: Nos. 224 and 225, Queen Elizabeth and Sir George Bingham.

74. Blue Gum Eucalyptus and Road Construction.

1968. Multicoloured.

226.	½d. Type 74	10	10
227.	1d. Electricity Development	10	10
228.	1½d. Dental Unit	15	10
229.	2d. Post Control ..	15	10
230.	3d. Flats in Jamestown ..	30	10
231.	4d. Blue gum Eucalyptus and Livestock Improvement	20	10
232.	6d. Schools Broadcasting	40	10
233.	8d. County Cottages ..	30	10
234.	10d. New School Buildings	30	10
235.	1s. Reafforestation ..	30	10
236.	1s. 6d. Heavy Lift Crane ..	70	1·25
237.	2s. 6d. Lady Field Children's Home ..	80	1·40
238.	5s. Agricultural Training ..	90	1·75
239.	10s. New General Hospital	2·50	3·00
240.	£1 Lifeboat "John Dutton"	10·00	15·00

PLANTS SHOWN: 4d., 1s. 6d. Blue gum Eucalyptus. 1d., 6d., 2s. 6d. Cabbage-tree. 1½d., 8d., 5s. St. Helena Redwood. 2d., 10d., 10s. Scrubweed. 3d., 1s., £1, Tree-fern.

89. Brig "Perseverance".

1969. Mail Communications. Multicoloured.

241	4d. Type 89	20	20
242	8d. "Phoebe" (screw steamer) ..	30	30
243	1s. 9d. "Llandovery Castle" (liner)	40	40
244	2s. 3d. "Good Hope Castle" (cargo liner)	45	45

93. W.O. and Drummer of the 53rd Foot, 1815.

1969. Military Uniforms. Multicoloured.

245.	6d. Type 93	30	15
246.	8d. Officer and Surgeon, 20th Foot, 1816 ..	40	15
247.	1s. 8d. Drum Major, 66th Foot, 1816, and Royal Artillery Officer, 1920 ..	50	15
248.	2s. 6d. Private, 91st Foot, and 2nd Corporal, Royal Sappers & Miners, 1832	60	20

97. Dickens, Mr. Pickwick and Job Trotter ("Pickwick Papers").

1970. Death Cent. of Charles Dickens. Mult.

249.	4d. Type 97	30	10
250.	8d. Mr. Bumble and Oliver ("Oliver Twist") ..	40	10
251.	1s. 6d. Sairey Gamp and Mark Tapley ("Martin Chuzzlewit")	55	15
252.	2s. 6d. Jo and Mr. Turveydrop ("Bleak House")	70	30

All designs include a portrait of Dickens as Type 97.

98. "Kiss of Life".

1970. Centenary of British Red Cross.

253. 98.	6d. bistre, red and black	10	10
254. –	9d. green, red and black	15	10
255. –	1s. 9d. grey, red & black	25	10
256. –	2s. 3d. lilac, red & black	30	20

DESIGNS: 9d. Nurse with girl in wheelchair. 1s. 9d. Nurse bandaging child's knee. 2s. 3d. Red Cross emblem.

99. Officer's Shako Plate (20th Foot).

1970. Military Equipment (1st issue). Mult.

257.	4d. Type 99	70	20
258.	9d. Officer's Breast Plate (66th Foot)	1·00	30
259.	1s. 3d. Officer's Full Dress Shako (91st Foot) ..	1·25	40
260.	2s. 11d. Ensign's Shako (53rd Foot)	1·50	60

See also Nos. 281/4, 285/8 and 291/4.

100. Electricity Development.

1971. Decimal Currency. Designs as Nos. 227/39, inscr. as T 100.

261.	½p. multicoloured ..	10	10
262.	1p. multicoloured ..	10	10
263.	1½p. multicoloured ..	10	10
264.	2p. multicoloured ..	1·75	90
265.	2½p. multicoloured ..	10	10
266.	3½p. multicoloured ..	30	10
267.	4½p. multicoloured ..	10	10
268.	5p. multicoloured ..	10	10
269.	7½p. multicoloured ..	40	35
270.	10p. multicoloured ..	30	35
271.	12½p. multicoloured ..	30	50
272.	25p. multicoloured ..	60	1·25
273.	50p. multicoloured ..	1·25	2·00

101. St. Helena holding the "True Cross".

1971. Easter.

275. 101.	2p. multicoloured ..	10	10
276.	5p. multicoloured ..	15	15
277.	7½p. multicoloured ..	25	20
278.	12½p. multicoloured ..	30	25

102. Napoleon (after painting by J. L. David), and Tomb on St. Helena.

1971. 150th Death Anniv. of Napoleon. Mult.

279.	2p. Type 102	50	40
280.	34p. "Napoleon at St. Helena" (H. Delaroche)	2·00	85

1971. Military Equipment (2nd issue). As T 99. Multicoloured.

281.	1½p. Artillery Private's hanger	1·00	30
282.	4p. Baker rifle and socket bayonet	1·50	60
283.	6p. Infantry Officer's sword	1·50	80
284.	22½p. Baker rifle and sword bayonet	2·00	1·25

1972. Military Equipment (3rd issue). As T 99. Multicoloured.

285.	2p. multicoloured ..	50	20
286.	5p. lilac, blue and black ..	90	50
287.	7½p. multicoloured ..	1·10	60
288.	12½p. sepia, brn. & black ..	1·50	75

DESIGNS: 2p. Royal Sappers and Miners breast-plate, post 1823. 5p. Infantry sergeant's spontoon, c. 1830. 7½p. Royal Artillery Officer's breast-plate, c. 1830. 12½p. English military pistol, c. 1800.

1972. Royal Silver Wedding. As T 52 of Ascension but with St. Helena Sand Plover and White Tern in background.

289.	2p. green	25	35
290.	16p. brown	50	65

1973. Military Equipment (4th issue). As T 99. Multicoloured.

291.	2p. Other Rank's shako, 53rd Foot, 1815 ..	1·00	55
292.	5p. Band and Drums sword, 1830	1·75	1·00
293.	7½p. Royal Sappers and Miners Officer's hat, 1830	2·00	1·25
294.	12½p. General's sword, 1831	3·00	1·50

1973. Royal Wedding. As T 47 of Anguilla. Multicoloured, background colours given.

295.	2p. blue	15	10
296.	18p. green	25	20

104. "Westminster" and "Claudine" Beached, 1849.

1973. Tercentenary of East India Company Charter. Multicoloured.

297.	1½p. Type 104	60	45
298.	4p. "True Briton", 1790	70	70
299.	6p. "General Goddard" in action, 1795	70	70
300.	22½p. "Kent" burning in the Bay of Biscay, 1825,	1·60	2·25

105. U.P.U. Emblem and Ships.

1974. Centenary of U.P.U. Multicoloured.

301.	5p. Type 105	25	25
302.	25p. U.P.U. emblem and letters	55	55

106. Churchill in Sailor Suit and Blenheim Palace.

1974. Birth Cent. of Sir Winston Churchill.

304. 106.	5 p. multicoloured ..	25	55
305. –	25 p. black, pink & purple	55	75

DESIGN: 25 p. Churchill and River Thames.

107. Capt. Cook and H.M.S. "Resolution".

1975. Bicentenary of Capt. Cook's Return to St. Helena.

307.	5p. Type 107	50	50
308.	25p. Capt. Cook and Jamestown	1·00	1·50

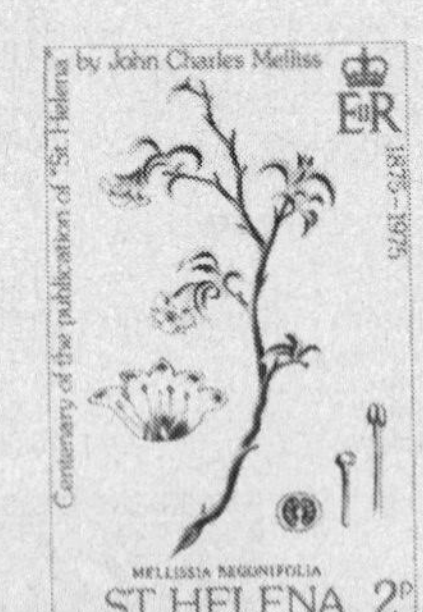

108. "Mellissia begonifolia" (tree).

1975. Centenary of Publication of "St. Helena" by J. C. Melliss. Multicoloured.

310.	2p. Type 108	25	40
311.	5p. "Mellissius adumbratus" (beetle) ..	35	60
312.	12p. St. Helena Sand Plover (bird) (horiz.) ..	90	1·50
313.	25p. "Scorpaenia mellissii" (fish) (horiz.)	1·00	1·75

109. £1 Note.

1976. Currency Notes. First Issue. Mult.

314.	8p. Type 109	40	35
315.	33p. £5 Note	85	1·25

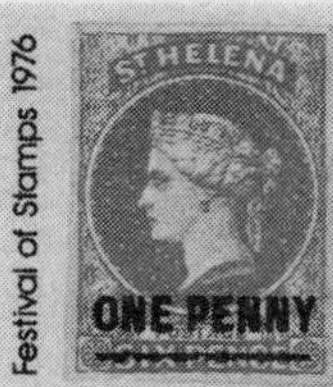

110. 1d. Stamp of 1863.

1976. Festival of Stamps, London.

316. 110.	5p. brn., blk. and pink ..	15	15
317. –	8p. blk., grn. & lt. grn.	25	30
318. –	25p. multicoloured ..	40	45

DESIGNS—VERT. 8p. 1d. stamp of 1922. HORIZ. 25p. Mail carrier "Good Hope Castle".

111. "High Knoll, 1806" (Capt. Barnett).

1976. Views of St. Helena. Multicoloured.

319.	1p. Type 111	20	50
320.	3p. "The Friar Rock. 1815" (G. Bellasis)	40	50
321.	5p. "The Column Lot, 1815" (G. Bellasis)	30	50
322.	6p. "Sandy Bay Valley, 1809" (H. Salt) ..	30	55
323.	8p. "Scene from Castle Terrace, 1815" (G. Bellasis)	40	55
324.	9p. "The Briars, 1815"	40	60
325.	10p. "Plantation House, 1821" (J. Wathen)	50	60
326.	15p. "Longwood House, 1821" ((J. Wathen) ..	45	55
327.	18p. "St. Paul's Church" (V. Brooks)	45	75
328.	26p. "St. James's Valley, 1815" (Capt. Hastings)	45	65
329.	40p. "St Matthew's Church, 1860" (V. Brooks) ..	70	1·25
330.	£1 "St. Helena, 1815" (G. Bellasis)	1·75	3·25
331.	£2 "Sugar Loaf Hill, 1821" (J. Wathen)	3·50	5·50

Nos. 330/1 are larger; 47 × 34 mm.

Nos. 319, 325 and 331 come with or without date imprint.

112. Duke of Edinburgh paying Homage.

1977. Silver Jubilee. Multicoloured.

332.	8p. Royal visit, 1947 ..	20	35
333.	15p. Queen's sceptre with dove	25	45
334.	26p. Type 112	35	50

113. Halley's Comet (from Bayeux Tapestry).

1977. Tercentenary of Halley's Visit. Mult.

335.	5p. Type 113	35	20
336.	8p. Late 17th-century sextant	50	20
337.	27p. Halley and Halley's Mount, St. Helena ..	1·00	60

114. Sea Lion.

1978. 25th Anniv. of Coronation.

338.	25p. agate, red & silver	40	50
339. –	25p. multicoloured ..	40	50
340. 114.	25p. agate, red & silver	40	50

DESIGNS: No. 338, Black Dragon of Ulster. No. 339, Queen Elizabeth II.

115. Period Engraving of St. Helena.

1978. Wreck of the "Witte Leeuw". Multicoloured.

341.	3p. Type 115	15	15
342.	5p. Chinese porcelain ..	20	20
343.	8p. Bronze cannon ..	25	30
344.	9p. Chinese porcelain ..	30	35
345.	15p. Pewter mug and ceramic flasks	50	55
346.	20p. Dutch East Indiaman	60	70

116. H.M.S. "Discovery".

1979. Bicentenary of Captain Cook's Voyages, 1768–79. Multicoloured.

347.	3p. Type 116	20	15
348.	8p. Cook's portable observatory	30	25
349.	12p. "Pharnaceum acidum" (sketch by Joseph Banks)	35	35
350.	25p. Flaxman/Wedgwood medallion of Capt. Cook	55	90

117. Sir Rowland Hill.

1979. Death Centenary of Sir Rowland Hill.

351. 117.	5p. multicoloured ..	15	15
352. –	8p. multicoloured ..	20	20
353. –	20p. multicoloured ..	40	40
354. –	32p. blk., mag. and mve.	55	55

DESIGNS—HORIZ. 8p. 1965 1d. "FIRST LOCAL POST 4th JANUARY 1965" overprinted stamp. 20p. 1863 1d. on 6d. surcharged stamp. 32p. 1902 1d. stamp.

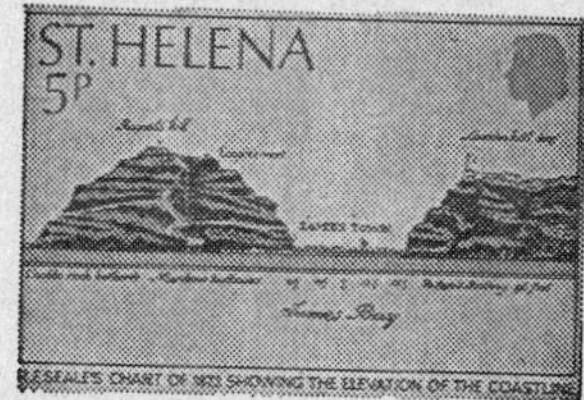

118. R. F. Seal's Chart of 1823 showing the Elevation of the Coastline.

1979. 150th Anniv. of Inclined Plane

355. 118.	5p. black, grey & stone	20	15
356. –	8p. black, grey & stone	20	20
357. –	50p. multicoloured ..	70	75

DESIGNS—HORIZ. 8p. The Inclined Plane in 1829. VERT. 50p. The Inclined Plane in 1979.

119. Napoleon's Tomb, 1848.

1980. Centenary of Visit of Empress Eugenie of France.

358. 119.	5p. brown, pink & gold	20	20
359. –	8p. brown, stone & gold	25	25
360. –	62p. brown, flesh & gold	95	1·10

DESIGNS: 8p. Landing at St. Helena. 62p. The Empress at Napoleon's Tomb.

120. East Indiaman.

1980. "London 1980" International Stamp Exhibition. Multicoloured.

362.	5p. Type 120	15	15
363.	8p. "Dolphin" Postal Stone	15	20
364.	47p. Postal Stone outside Castle entrance, Jamestown	60	80

121. Queen Elizabeth the Queen Mother in 1974.

1980. 80th Birthday of The Queen Mother.

366. 121.	24p. multicoloured ..	50	50

122. The Briars, 1815.

1980. 175th Anniv. of Wellington's Visit. Multicoloured.

367.	9p. Type 122	15	15
368.	30p. "Wellington" (Goya) (vert.)	45	45

123. Redwood.

1981. Endemic Plants. Multicoloured.

369.	5p. Type 123	15	15
370.	8p. Old Father Live Forever	20	20
371.	15p. Gumwood	25	25
372.	27p. Black Cabbage ..	45	45

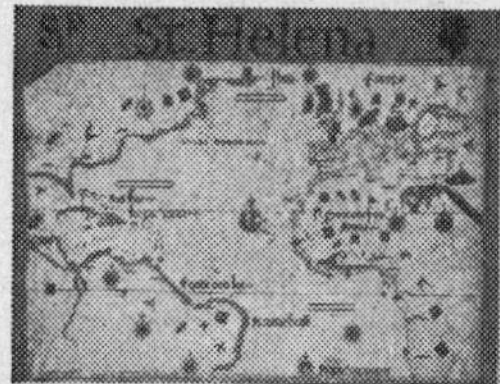

124. Detail from Reinel Portolan Chart, c. 1530.

1981. Early Maps.

373. 124.	5p. multicoloured ..	25	15
374. –	8p. black, red and grey	30	20
375. –	20p. multicoloured ..	50	35
376. –	30p. multicoloured ..	55	50

DESIGNS: 8p. John Thornton Map of St. Helena, c. 1700. 20p. Map of St. Helena, 1815. 30p. Map of St. Helena, 1817.

125. Prince Charles as Royal Navy Commander.

1981. Royal Wedding. Multicoloured.

378.	14p. Wedding bouquet from St. Helena	25	25
379.	29p. Type 125	35	35
380.	32p. Prince Charles and Lady Diana Spencer ..	50	50

126. "Charonia Variegata".

1981. Seashells. Multicoloured.

381.	7p. Type 126	35	20
382.	10p. "Cypraea spurca sanctaehelenae" ..	40	25
383.	25p. "Janthina janthina"	70	60
384.	53p. "Pinna rudis" ..	1·25	1·25

127. Traffic Duty.

1981. 25th Anniv. of Duke of Edinburgh Award Scheme. Multicoloured.

385.	7p. Type 127	15	15
386.	11p. Signposting	15	15
387.	25p. Animal care ..	35	35
388.	50p. Duke of Edinburgh in ceremonial dress, on horse-back	70	70

128. "Sympetrum dilatatum" (dragonfly).

1981. Insects (1st series). Multicoloured.

389	7p. Type 128	30	25
390	10p. "Aplothorax burchelli" (beetle) ..	40	35
391	25p. "Ampulex compressa" (wasp)	70	60
392	32p. "Labidura herculeana" (earwig) ..	80	75

See also Nos. 411/14.

129. Charles Darwin.

1982. 150th Anniv. of Charles Darwin's Voyage. Multicoloured.

393.	7p. Type 129 ..	30	30
394.	14p. Flagstaff Hill and Darwin's hammer ..	45	60
395.	25p. Ring-necked Pheasant and Chukar Partridge ..	75	1·00
396.	29p. H.M.S. "Beagle" off St. Helena	95	1·25

130. Prince and Princess of Wales at Balmoral, Autumn, 1981.

1982. 21st Birthday of Princess of Wales. Multicoloured.

397. 7p. St. Helena coat of arms 15 20
398. 11p. Type **130** 25 30
399. 29p. Bride on Palace balcony 55 80
400. 55p. Formal portrait .. 1·00 1·50

1982. Commonwealth Games, Brisbane. Nos. 326 and 328 optd. **1st PARTICIPATION COMMONWEALTH GAMES 1982.**

401. 15p. "Longwood House, 1821" (G. Wathen) .. 25 25
402. 26p. "St. James's Valley 1815" (Capt. Hastings) 45 45

132. Lord Baden-Powell.

1982. 75th Anniv. of Boy Scout Movement.

403. **132.** 3p. brn., grey and yellow 15 15
404. – 11p. brn., grey and green 35 25
405. – 29p. brn., grey and orge. 70 60
406. – 59p. brn., grey and green 1·25 1·25

DESIGNS—HORIZ. 11p. Boy Scout (drawing by Lord Baden Powell). 59p. Camping at Thompsons Wood. VERT—29p. Canon Walcott.

133. King and Queen Rocks.

1982. Views of St. Helena by Roland Svensson. Multicoloured.

407. 7p. Type **133** 20 20
408. 11p. "Turks' Cap" .. 25 25
409. 29p. Coastline from Jamestown (horiz.) 65 65
410. 59p. "Mundens Point" (horiz.) .. .. 1·40 1·40

1983. Insects (2nd series). As T **128**. Mult.

411 11p. "Acherontia atropos" (hawk moth) .. 35 30
412 15p. "Helenasaldula aberrans" (shore-bug) .. 40 35
413 29p. "Anchastus compositarum" (click beetle) .. 65 55
414 59p. "Lamprochrus cossonoides" (weevil) .. 1·40 1·25

134. "Coriolus versicolor". 135. Java Sparrow.

1983. Fungi. Multicoloured.

415. 11p. Type **134** 20 25
416. 15p. "Pluteus brunneisucus" 30 40
417. 29p. "Polyporus induratus" (horiz.) 55 75
418. 59p. "Coprinus angulatus" .. .. 1·25 1·60

1983. Birds. Multicoloured.

419. 7p. Type **135** 30 20
420. 15p. Madagascar red fody 45 35
421. 33p. Common waxbill .. 80 70
422. 59p. Yellow canary .. 1·50 1·40

136. Birth of St. Helena.

1983. Christmas. Life of St. Helena (1st series). Multicoloured.

423. 10p. Type **136** 25 35
424. 15p. St. Helena being taken to convent .. 30 35

See also Nos. 450/3 and 468/71.

137. 1934 Centenary ½d. Stamp.

1984. 150th Anniv. of St. Helena as a British Colony. Multicoloured.

425. 1p. Type **137** 10 20
426. 3p. 1934 1d. stamp .. 10 20
427. 6p. 1934 1½d. stamp .. 10 30
428. 7p. 1934 2d. stamp .. 15 30
429. 11p. 1934 3d. stamp .. 20 40
430. 15p. 1934 6d. stamp .. 25 45
431. 29p. 1934 1s. stamp .. 50 95
432. 33p. 1934 5s. stamp .. 55 1·25
433. 59p. 1934 10s. stamp .. 1·10 2·00
434. £1 1934 2s. 6d. stamp .. 1·75 3·25
435. £2 St. Helena Coat of Arms 3·50 5·00

138. Prince Andrew and H.M.S. "Invincible" (aircraft carrier).

1984. Visit of Prince Andrew. Mult.

436. 11p. Type **138** 25 25
437. 60p. Prince Andrew and H.M.S. "Herald" (survey ship) .. .. 1·25 1·40

139. "St. Helena" (schooner).

1984. 250th Anniv. of "Lloyd's List" (newspaper). Multicoloured.

438. 10p. Type **139** .. 20 20
439. 18p. Solomons Facade (local agent) 35 35
440. 25p. Lloyd's Coffee House, London 50 55
441. 50p. "Papanui" (freighter) 1·00 1·00

140. Twopenny Coin and Donkey.

1984. New Coinage. Multicoloured.

442. 10p. Type **140** 35 35
443. 15p. Five pence coin and St. Helena sand plover 45 45
444. 29p. Penny coin and yellowfin tuna 75 75
445. 50p. Ten pence coin and arum lily .. .. 1·25 1·25

141. Mrs. Rebecca Fuller (Former Corps Secretary).

1984. Centenary of Salvation Army on St. Helena. Multicoloured.

446. 7p. Type **141** 35 40
447. 11p. Meals-on-wheels service (horiz.) 45 60
448. 25p. Salvation Army Citadel, Jamestown (horiz.) .. .. .. 80 1·00
449. 60p. Salvation Army band at Jamestown Clock Tower .. .. .. 1·75 2·25

1984. Christmas. Life of St. Helena (2nd series). As T **136**. Multicoloured.

450. 6p. St. Helena visits prisoners 20 20
451. 10p. Betrothal of St. Helena 30 30
452. 15p. Marriage of St. Helena to Constantius 40 40
453. 33p. Birth of Constantine 70 70

142. Queen Elizabeth the Queen Mother aged Two.

1985. Life and Times of Queen Elizabeth the Queen Mother. Multicoloured.

454 11p. Type **142** 20 25
455 15p. At Ascot with the Queen 30 35
456 29p. Attending Gala Ballet at Covent Garden 60 65
457 55p. With Prince Henry at his christening .. 1·10 1·25

143. Rock Bullseye.

1985. Marine Life. Multicoloured.

459. 7p. Type **143** 25 25
460. 11p. Mackerel 30 30
461. 15p. Skipjack Tuna .. 40 40
462. 33p. Yellowfin Tuna .. 75 75
463. 50p. Stump .. .. 1·25 1·25

144. John J. Audubon.

1985. Birth Bicentenary of John J. Audubon (ornithologist).

464. **144.** 11p. black and brown 45 25
465. – 15p. multicoloured .. 55 35
466. – 25p. multicoloured .. 75 55
467 – 60p. multicoloured .. 1·40 1·40

DESIGN—HORIZ (from original Audubon paintings). 15p. Common gallinule (moorhen). 25p. White-tailed tropic bird. 68p. Common noddy.

1985. Christmas. Life of St Helena (3rd series). As T **136**. Multicoloured.

468. 7p. St. Helena journeys to the Holy Land 25 25
469. 10p. Zambres slays the bull 30 30
470. 15p. The bull restored to life: conversion of St. Helena 40 40
471. 60p. Resurrection of the corpse: the true Cross identified .. .. 1·50 1·50

145. Church Provident Society for Women Banner.

1986. Friendly Societies Banners. Mult.

472. 10p. Type **145** 25 25
473. 11p. Working Men's Christian Association .. 25 25
474. 25p. Church Benefit Society for Children .. 55 55
475. 29p. Mechanics and Friendly Benefit Society 65 65
476. 33p. Ancient Order of Foresters 70 70

1986. 60th Birthday of Queen Elizabeth II. As T **110** of Ascension. Multicoloured.

477. 10p. Princess Elizabeth making 21st birthday broadcast, South Africa, 1947 .. .. .. 20 25
478. 15p. Silver Jubilee photograph, 1977 .. .. 30 35
479. 20p. Princess Elizabeth on board H.M.S. "Implacable" 1947 .. 40 45
480. 50p. In the U.S.A., 1976 .. 1·00 1·10
481. 65p. At Crown Agents Head Office, London, 1983 .. .. .. 1·25 1·40

146. Plaque at Site of Halley's Observatory on St. Helena.

1986. Appearance of Halley's Comet. Multicoloured.

482. 9p. Type **146** 25 25
483. 12p. Edmond Halley .. 30 30
484. 20p. Halley's planisphere of the southern stars .. 45 45
485. 65p. "Unity" on passage to St. Helena, 1676 .. 1·40 1·40

1986. Royal Wedding. As T **112** of Ascension. Multicoloured.

486. 10p. Prince Andrew and Miss Sarah Ferguson .. 20 25
487. 40p. Prince Andrew with Governor J. Massingham on St. Helena 80 85

147. James Ross and H.M.S. "Erebus".

1986. Explorers.

No.	Type	Description	Unused	Used
488.	147.	1p. brown and pink ..	20	20
489.	–	3p. deep blue and blue	20	20
490.	–	5p. deep grn. & grn.	30	30
491.	–	9p. brown and red ..	40	40
492.	–	10p. deep brn. & brn.	40	40
493.	–	12p. green & light grn.	50	50
494.	–	15p. brown and pink	60	60
495.	–	20p. blue and lt. blue	70	70
496.	–	25p. sepia and pink ..	70	70
497.	–	40p. deep grn. & grn.	1·10	1·10
498.	–	60p. deep brn. & brn.	1·25	1·60
499.	–	£1 deep blue and blue	2·00	2·40
500.	–	£2 deep lilac & lilac ..	4·00	4·75

DESIGNS: 3p. Robert FitzRoy and H.M.S. "Beagle". 5p. Adam Johann von Krusenstern and "Nadezhda". 9p. William Bligh and H.M.S. "Resolution". 10p. Otto von Kotzebue and "Rurik". 12p. Philip Carteret and H.M.S. "Swallow". 15p. Thomas Cavendish and "Desire". 20p. Louis-Antoine de Bougainville and "La Boudeuse" 25p. Fyodor Petrovich Lütke and "Senyavin". 40p. Louis Isidore Duperrey and "La Coquille" 60p. John Byron and H.M.S. "Dolphin". £1 James Cook and H.M.S. "Endeavour". £2 Jules Dumont d'Urville and L'Astrolabe".

148. Prince Edward and H.M.S. "Repulse" (battle cruiser), 1925.

1987. Royal Visits to St. Helena. Mult.

No.	Description	Unused	Used
501.	9p. Type **148**	60	50
502.	13p. King George VI and H.M.S. "Vanguard" (battleship), 1947 ..	85	75
503.	38p. Prince Philip and Royal Yacht "Britannia", 1957 ..	1·75	2·00
504.	45p. Prince Andrew and H.M.S. "Herald" (survey ship), 1984 ..	2·00	2·25

149. St. Helena Tea Plant.

1987. Rare Plants (1st series). Multicoloured.

No.	Description	Unused	Used
505.	9p. Type **149**	65	40
506.	13p. Baby's toes	80	50
507.	38p. Salad plant	1·50	1·10
508.	45p. Scrubwood	1·75	1·40

See also Nos. 531/4.

150. Lesser Rorqual.

1987. Marine Mammals. Multicoloured.

No.	Description	Unused	Used
509.	9p. Type **150**	90	35
510.	13p. Risso's dolphin ..	95	50
511.	45p. Sperm whale ..	2·25	1·40
512.	60p. Euphrosyne dolphin	2·25	1·60

1987. Royal Ruby Wedding. Nos. 477/81 optd.. **40TH WEDDING ANNIVERSARY.**

No.	Description	Unused	Used
514.	10p. Princess Elizabeth making 21st birthday broadcast, South Africa, 1947	20	25
515.	15p. Silver Jubilee photograph, 1977	30	35
516.	20p. Princess Elizabeth on board H.M.S. "Implacable", 1947 ..	40	45
517.	50p. In the U.S.A., 1976 ..	1·00	1·10
518.	65p. At Crown Agents Head Office, London, 1983	1·25	1·40

151. "Defence" and Dampier's Signature, 1691.

1988. Bicentenary of Australian Settlement. Ships and signatures. Multicoloured.

No.	Description	Unused	Used
519.	9p. Type **151**	1·25	90
520.	13p. H.M.S. "Resolution" (Cook), 1775	1·75	1·40
521.	45p. H.M.S. "Providence" (Bligh), 1792	3·00	2·75
522.	60p. H.M.S. "Beagle" (Darwin), 1836	3·75	3·25

152 "The Holy Virgin with the Child"

1988. Christmas. Religious paintings. Mult.

No.	Description	Unused	Used
523	5p. Type **152**	10	15
524	20p. "Madonna"	40	45
525	38p. "The Holy Family with St. John"	75	80
526	60p. "The Holy Virgin with the Child" ..	1·25	1·40

1988. 300th Anniv of Lloyd's of London. As T **123** of Ascension.

No.	Description	Unused	Used
527	9p. deep brown and brown	20	25
528	20p. multicoloured ..	40	45
529	45p. multicoloured ..	90	95
530	60p. multicoloured ..	1·25	1·40

DESIGNS: VERT—9p. Lloyd's Underwriting Room, 1886; 60p. "Spangereid" (full-rigged ship) on fire, St. Helena, 1920. HORIZ—20p. "Edinburgh Castle" (liner); 45p. "Bosun Bird" (freighter).

153 Ebony

1989. Rare Plants (2nd series). Multicoloured.

No.	Description	Unused	Used
531	9p. Type **153**	30	30
532	20p. St. Helena lobelia ..	55	55
533	45p. Large bellflower ..	1·10	1·10
534	60p. She cabbage tree ..	1·40	1·40

INDEX

Countries can be quickly located by referring to the index at the end of this volume.

154 Private, 53rd Foot

1989. Military Uniforms of 1815. Mult.

No.	Description	Unused	Used
535	9p. Type **154**	35	35
536	13p. Officer, 53rd Foot ..	40	40
537	20p. Royal Marine ..	55	55
538	45p. Officer, 66th Foot ..	1·25	1·25
539	60p. Private, 66th Foot ..	1·50	1·50

1989. "PHILEXFRANCE 89" International Stamp Exhibition, Paris. Nos. 535/9 optd **PHILEXFRANCE 89**.

No.	Description	Unused	Used
540	9p. Type **154**	35	35
541	13p. Officer, 53rd Foot ..	40	40
542	20p. Royal Marine ..	55	55
543	45p. Officer, 66th Foot ..	1·25	1·25
544	60p. Private, 66th Foot ..	1·50	1·50

156 Agricultural Studies

1989. New Prince Andrew Central School. Multicoloured.

No.	Description	Unused	Used
545	13p. Type **156**	35	35
546	20p. Geography lesson ..	55	55
547	25p. Walkway and classroom block	65	65
548	60p. Aerial view of School	1·50	1·50

157 "The Madonna with the Pear" (Durer)

1989. Christmas. Religious Paintings. Mult.

No.	Description	Unused	Used
549	10p. Type **157**	40	30
550	20p. "The Holy Family under the Appletree" (Rubens)	65	55
551	45p. "The Virgin in the Meadow" (Raphael) ..	1·40	1·25
552	60p. "The Holy Family with St. John" (Raphael)	1·75	1·60

158 Chevrolet "6" 30 cwt Lorry, 1930

1989. Early Vehicles. Multicoloured.

No.	Description	Unused	Used
553	9p. Type **158**	50	40
554	20p. Austin "Seven", 1929	70	60
555	45p. Morris "Cowley" 11.9 h.p., 1929 ..	1·40	1·25
556	60p. Sunbeam 25 h.p., 1932	1·75	1·60

159 Sheep

1990. Farm Animals. Multicoloured.

No.	Description	Unused	Used
558	9p. Type **159**	30	30
559	13p. Pigs	35	35
560	45p. Cow and calf ..	1·00	1·25
561	60p. Geese	1·40	1·60

160 1840 Twopence Blue

1990. "Stamp World London 90" International Stamp Exhibition, London.

No.	Type	Description	Unused	Used
562	**160**	13p. black and blue ..	40	40
563	–	20p. multicoloured ..	65	75
564	–	38p. multicoloured ..	1·10	1·25
565	–	45p. multicoloured ..	1·40	1·60

DESIGNS: 20p. 1840 Penny Black and 19th-century St. Helena postmark; 38p. Delivering mail to sub post office; 45p. Mail van and Post Office, Jamestown.

161 Satellite Dish

1990. Modern Telecommunications Links. Multicoloured.

No.	Description	Unused	Used
566	20p. Type **161**	60	70
567	20p. Digital telephone exchange	60	70
568	20p. Public card phone ..	60	70
569	20p. Facsimile machine ..	60	70

1990. 90th Birthday of Queen Elizabeth the Queen Mother. As T **134** of Ascension.

No.	Description	Unused	Used
570	25p. multicoloured ..	75	75
571	£1 black and brown ..	2·50	3·00

DESIGNS—21 × 36 mm. 25p. Lady Elizabeth Bowes-Lyon, April 1923. 29 × 37 mm. £1 Queen Elizabeth visiting communal kitchen, 1940.

1990. Maiden Voyage of "St. Helena II". As T **137** of Ascension. Multicoloured.

No.	Description	Unused	Used
572	13p. "Dane" (mail ship), 1857	40	40
573	20p. "St. Helena I" offloading at St. Helena ..	65	75
574	38p. Launch of "St. Helena II"	1·10	1·25
575	45p. The Duke of York launching "St. Helena II"	1·25	1·50

163 Baptist Chapel, Sandy Bay

1990. Christmas. Local Churches. Mult.

577 10p. Type **163** 30 30
578 13p. St. Martin in the Hills Church 35 35
579 20p. St. Helena and the Cross Church 55 65
580 38p. St. James Church .. 1·00 1·25
581 45p. St. Paul's Cathedral, Jamestown .. .. 1·25 1·50

164 "Funeral Cortege, Jamestown Wharf" (detail, V. Adam)

1990. 150th Anniv of Removal of Napoleon's Body.

582 **164** 13p. black, brn & grn 40 40
583 – 20p. black, brown & bl 70 75
584 – 38p. black, brn & mve 1·25 1·50
585 – 45p. multicoloured .. 1·50 1·75

DESIGNS: 20p. "Coffin being conveyed to the 'Belle Poule' " (detail, V. Adam); 38p. "Transfer of the Coffin to the 'Normandie', Cherbourg", (detail, V. Adam); 45p. "Napoleon's Tomb, St. Helena" (T. Sutherland).

165 Officer, Leicestershire Regiment

1991. Military Uniforms of 1897. Mult.

586 13p. Type **165** 50 50
587 15p. Officer, York & Lancaster Regiment .. 55 55
588 20p. Colour-sergeant, Leicestershire Regiment 75 75
589 38p. Bandsman, York & Lancaster Regiment .. 1·40 1·60
590 45p. Lance-corporal, York & Lancaster Regiment 1·60 1·75

1991. 65th Birthday of Queen Elizabeth II and 70th Birthday of Prince Philip. As T **139** of Ascension. Multicoloured.

591 25p. Queen Elizabeth II .. 80 1·00
592 25p. Prince Philip in naval uniform .. .. 80 1·00

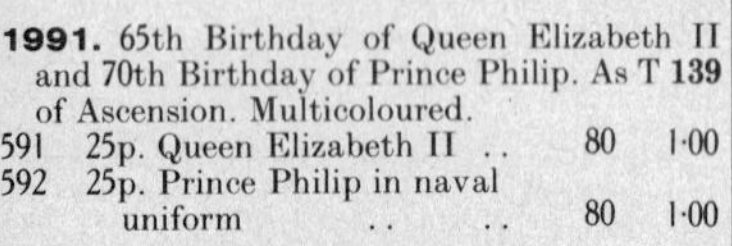

166 "Madonna and Child" (T. Vecellio)

1991. Christmas. Religious Paintings. Mult.

593 10p. Type **166** 35 35
594 13p. "The Holy Family" (A. Mengs) 45 45
595 20p. "Madonna and Child" (W. Dyce) 65 75
596 38p. "The Two Trinities" (B. Murillo) .. .. 1·10 1·25
597 45p. "The Virgin and Child" (G. Bellini) .. 1·60 1·75

167 Matchless (346cc) Motorcycle, 1947

1991. "Phila Nippon '91" International Stamp Exn, Tokyo. Motorcycles. Mult.

598 13p. Type **167** 35 35
599 20p. Triumph "Tiger 100" (500cc), 1950 .. .. 55 60
600 38p. Honda "CD" (175cc), 1967 .. .. .. 95 1·10
601 45p. Yamaha "DTE 400", 1976 .. .. .. 1·40 1·60

168 "Eye of the Wind" (cadet brig) and Compass Rose

1992. 500th Anniv of Discovery of America by Columbus and Re-enactment Voyages. Multicoloured.

603 15p. Type **168** 60 60
604 25p. "Soren Larsen" (cadet brigantine) and map of re-enactment voyages .. 90 90
605 35p. "Santa Maria", "Nina" and "Pinta" .. 1·40 1·40
606 50p. Columbus and "Santa Maria" .. .. .. 1·75 1·75

1992. 40th Anniv of Queen Elizabeth II's Accession. As T **143** of Ascension. Mult.

607 11p. Prince Andrew Central School 35 35
608 15p. Plantation House .. 50 50
609 25p. Jamestown 75 85
610 35p. Three portraits of Queen Elizabeth .. 95 1·10
611 50p. Queen Elizabeth II .. 1·25 1·40

169 H.M.S. "Ledbury" (minesweeper)

1992. 10th Anniv of Liberation of Falkland Islands. Ships. Multicoloured.

612 13p. Type **169** 50 50
613 20p. H.M.S. "Brecon" (minesweeper) 70 70
614 38p. "St. Helena I" (mail ship) off South Georgia 1·10 1·10
615 45p. Launch collecting first mail drop, 1982 .. 1·60 1·60

170 Shepherds and Angel Gabriel

1992. Christmas. Children's Nativity Plays. Multicoloured.

617 13p. Type **170** 40 40
618 15p. Shepherds and Three Kings 50 50
619 20p. Mary and Joseph .. 65 65
620 45p. Nativity scene .. 1·40 1·40

171 Disc Jockey, Radio St. Helena (25th anniv)

1992. Local Anniversaries. Multicoloured.

621 13p. Type **171** 40 40
622 20p. Scout parade (75th anniv of Scouting on St. Helena) 60 60
623 38p. H.M.S. "Providence" (sloop) and breadfruit (bicentenary of Capt. Bligh's visit) .. 1·00 1·25
624 45p. Governor Brooke and Plantation House (bicentenary) .. .. 1·25 1·50

172 Moses in the Bulrush

1993. Flowers. Multicoloured.

625 9p. Type **172** 40 40
626 13p. Periwinkle 50 50
627 20p. Everlasting flower .. 70 70
628 38p. Cigar plant .. .. 1·40 1·40
629 45p. "Lobelia erinus" .. 1·60 1·60

173 Adult St. Helena Sand Plover and Eggs

1993. Endangered Species. St. Helena Sand Plover ("Wirebird"). Multicoloured.

630 3p. Type **173** 15 15
631 5p. Male attending brooding female .. 15 15
632 12p. Adult with downy young 40 40
633 25p. Two birds in immature plumage .. 70 70
634 40p. Adult in flight .. 1·10 1·10
635 60p. Young bird on rocks 1·50 1·50

Nos. 634/5 are without the W.W.F. emblem.

174 Yellow Canary ("Swainson's Canary")

1993. Birds. Multicoloured.

636 1p. Type **174** 10 10
637 3p. Chukar partridge .. 10 10
638 11p. Rock dove 20 25
639 12p. Common waxbill .. 25 30
640 15p. Common mynah .. 30 35
641 18p. Java sparrow .. 35 40
642 25p. Red-billed tropic bird (horiz) 50 55
643 35p. Madeiran storm petrel (horiz) 70 75
644 75p. Madagascar red fody 1·50 1·60
645 £1 Common fairy tern (horiz) .. .. 2·00 2·10
646 £2 Giant petrel (horiz) .. 4·00 4·25
647 £5 St. Helena sand plover ("Wirebird") .. .. 10·00 10·50

175 Football and Teddy Bear

1993. Christmas. Toys. Multicoloured.

648 12p. Type **175** 35 35
649 15p. Yacht and doll .. 40 40
650 18p. Palette and rocking horse 45 45
651 25p. Model airplane and kite 70 70
652 60p. Guitar and roller skates .. .. .. 1·50 1·50

176 Arum Lily

1994. Flowers and Children's Art. Mult.

653 12p. Type **176** 25 30
654 12p. "Arum Lily" (Delphia Mittens) 25 30
655 25p. Ebony 50 55
656 25p. "Ebony" (Jason Rogers) 50 55
657 35p. Shell ginger 70 75
658 35p. "Shell Ginger" (Jeremy Moyce) .. 70 75

177 Abyssinian Guinea Pig

1994. "Hong Kong '94" International Stamp Exhibition. Pets. Multicoloured.

659 12p. Type **177** 25 30
660 25p. Common tabby cat .. 50 55
661 53p. Plain white and black rabbits .. .. 1·10 1·25
662 60p. Golden labrador .. 1·25 1·40

POSTAGE DUE STAMPS

D **1.** Outline Map of St. Helena.

1986.

D 1. D **1.** 1p. deep brn. & brn. 10 10
D 2. 2p. brown & orange 10 10
D 3. 5p. brown and red .. 10 15
D 4. 7p. black & violet .. 10 10
D 5. 10p. black & blue .. 20 25
D 6. 25p. black & green .. 50 55

ST. KITTS

On 23 June 1980 separate postal administrations were formed for St. Kitts and for Nevis, although both islands remained part of the State of St. Kitts–Nevis.

100 cents = 1 West Indian dollar.

1980. As Nos. 394/406 of St. Kitts–Nevis optd. **St. Kitts.**

29.	5 c. multicoloured	10	10
30.	10 c. multicoloured ..	10	10
31.	12 c. multicoloured ..	80	80
32.	15 c. multicoloured ..	10	10
33.	25 c. multicoloured ..	10	10
34.	30 c. multicoloured ..	10	10
35.	40 c. multicoloured ..	10	15
36.	45 c. multicoloured ..	15	15
37.	50 c. multicoloured ..	15	15
38.	55 c. multicoloured ..	15	15
39.	$1 multicoloured	25	25
40.	$5 multicoloured	80	1·00
41.	$10 multicoloured	1·40	1·75

9. H.M.S. " Vanguard ", 1762.

1980. Ships. Multicoloured.

42.	4 c. Type **9**	10	10
43.	10 c. H.M.S. "Boreas", 1787	10	10
44.	30 c. H.M.S. "Druid", 1827	15	10
45.	55 c. H.M.S. "Winchester", 1831	20	15
46.	$1.50 Harrison Line "Philosopher", 1857	40	30
47.	$2 Harrison Line "Contractor", 1930 ..	50	40

10. Queen Elizabeth the Queen Mother at Royal Variety Performance, 1978.

1980. 80th Birthday of The Queen Mother.

48. **10.**	$2 multicoloured	45	60

11. The Three Wise Men.

1980. Christmas. Multicoloured.

49.	5 c. Type **11**	10	10
50.	15 c. The Shepherds ..	10	10
51.	30 c. Bethlehem	10	10
52.	$4 Nativity scene	60	60

12. Purple-throated Carib.

13. Bananaquit.

1981. Birds. Multicoloured.

53	1 c. Magnificent frigate bird	15	15
54	4 c. Wied's crested flycatcher	25	15
55	5 c. Type **12**	25	15
56	6 c. Burrowing owl ..	35	25
57	8 c. Caribbean martin ..	30	25
58	10 c. Yellow-crowned night heron	25	15
59	15 c. Type **13**	25	15
60	20 c. Scaly-breasted thrasher	30	15
61	25 c. Grey kingbird ..	30	15
62	30 c. Green-throated carib	30	15
63	40 c. Turnstone	35	20
64	45 c. Black-faced grassquit	35	25
65	50 c. Cattle egret	40	30
66	55 c. Brown pelican ..	40	30
67	$1 Lesser Antillean bullfinch	60	50
68	$2.50 Zenaida dove ..	1·25	1·50
69	$5 American kestrel ..	2·25	2·75
70	$10 Antillean crested hummingbird	4·50	5·50

The 1 c. to 10 c. are vertical as Type **12**. The remainder are horizontal as Type **13**.

14. Battalion Company Sergeant, 3rd Regt. of Foot (" The Buffs "), c. 1801.

1981. Military Uniforms. Multicoloured.

71.	5 c. Type **14**	10	10
72.	30 c. Battalion Company Officer, 45th Regt. of Foot, 1796-97	20	10
73.	55 c. Battalion Company Officer, 9th Regt. of Foot, 1790	30	10
74.	$2.50 Grenadier, 38th Regt. of Foot, 1751	90	35

1981. Royal Wedding. Royal Yachts. As T **26/27** of Kiribati. Multicoloured.

75	55 c. " Saudadoes " ..	10	10
82	55 c. Prince Charles and Lady Diana Spencer ..	20	30
77	$2.50 " Royal George " ..	25	30
78	$2.50 As No. 76	70	70
79	$4 " Britannia "	35	50
80	$4 As No. 76	1·00	1·00

15. Miriam Pickard (first Guide Commissioner).

1981. 50th Anniv. of St. Kitts Girl Guide Movement. Multicoloured.

84.	5 c. Type **15**	10	10
85.	30 c. Lady Baden-Powell's visit, 1964	15	10
86.	55 c. Visit of Princess Alice, 1960	30	10
87.	$2 Thinking-Day parade, 1980's	60	35

16. Stained-glass Windows.

1981. Christmas.

88. **16.**	5 c. multicoloured ..	10	10
89. –	30 c. multicoloured ..	20	10
90. –	55 c. multicoloured ..	30	10
91. –	$3 multicoloured ..	1·00	50

DESIGNS: 30 c. to $3, Various designs showing stained-glass windows.

17. Admiral Samuel Hood.

1982. Bicentenary of Brimstone Hill Siege.

92. **17.**	15 c. multicoloured ..	10	10
93. –	55 c. multicoloured ..	20	10

DESIGNS—55 c. Marquis De Bouille.

18. Alexandra, Princess of Wales, 1863.

1982. 21st Birthday of Princess of Wales. Multicoloured.

95.	15 c. Type **18**	10	10
96.	55 c. Coat of arms of Alexandra of Denmark ..	30	35
97.	$6 Diana, Princess of Wales	1·00	1·25

1982. Birth of Prince William of Wales. Nos. 95/7 optd. **ROYAL BABY.**

98.	15 c. Type **18**	10	10
99.	55 c. Coat of arms of Alexandra of Denmark	30	35
100.	$6 Diana, Princess of Wales	1·00	1·25

20. Naturalist Badge.

1982. 75th Anniv. of Boy Scout Movement. Multicoloured.

101.	5 c. Type **20**	10	10
102.	55 c. Rescuer badge ..	40	15
103.	$2 First Aid badge ..	1·10	80

21. Santa with Christmas Tree and Gifts.

1982. Christmas. Children's Paintings. Multicoloured.

104.	5 c. Type **21**	10	10
105.	55 c. The Inn	15	10
106.	$1.10 Three Kings ..	30	15
107.	$3 Annunciation	80	40

22. Cruise Ship "Stella Oceanis" at Basseterre.

1983. Commonwealth Day. Multicoloured.

108.	55 c. Type **22**	20	10
109.	$2 "Queen Elizabeth 2" at Basseterre	50	40

1983. Military Uniforms (2nd series). As T **14**. Multicoloured.

110.	15 c. Light Company Private, 15th Regt. of Foot, c. 1814	20	10
111.	30 c. Battalion Company Officer, 15th Regt. of Foot, c. 1780	35	15
112.	55 c. Light Company Officer, 5th Regt. of Foot, c. 1822	55	20
113.	$2.50 Battalion Company Officer, 11th Regt. of Foot, c. 1804	1·40	1·60

23. Sir William Smith (founder).

1983. Centenary of Boys' Brigade. Mult.

114.	10 c. Type **23**	25	10
115.	45 c. B.B. members on steps of Sandy Point Methodist Church	55	20
116.	50 c. Brigade drummers ..	65	25
117.	$3 Boys' Brigade badge ..	2·50	3·25

1983. Nos. 55, 59/63 and 66/70 optd. **INDEPENDENCE 1983.**

118	5 c. Type **12**	15	10
119	15 c. Type**13**	20	10
120	20 c. Scaly-breasted thrasher	25	10
121	25 c. Grey kingbird ..	30	10
122	30 c. Green-throated carib	35	15
123	40 c. Turnstone ..	40	20
124	55 c. Brown pelican ..	45	30
125	$1 Lesser Antillean bullfinch	80	50
126	$2.50 Zenaida dove ..	1·50	1·25
127	$5 American kestrel ..	2·50	2·50
128	$10 Antillean crested hummingbird	5·00	5·00

25. Montgolfier Balloon, 1783.

1983. Bicentenary of Manned Flight. Mult.

129.	10 c. Type **25**	10	10
130.	45 c. Sikorsky " Russian Knight " biplane (horiz.)	15	10
131.	50 c. Lockheed " Tristar " (horiz.)	20	15
132.	$2.50 Bell " XS–1 " (horiz.)	60	75

26. Star over West Indian Town.

1983. Christmas. Multicoloured.

134.	15 c. Type **26**	10	10
135.	30 c. Shepherds watching Star	10	10
136.	55 c. Mary and Joseph ..	15	10
137.	$2.50 The Nativity ..	40	40

27. Parrot in Tree.

1984. Batik Designs. (1st series).

No.	Type	Description		
139.	27.	45 c. multicoloured ..	20	10
140.	–	50 c. multicoloured ..	20	10
141.	–	$1.50 blue, yell & pur.	55	60
142.	–	$3 multicoloured ..	85	1·25

DESIGNS: 50 c. Man under coconut tree. $1.50, Women with fruit. $3 Butterflies.

See also Nos 169/72.

28. Cushion Star.

1984. Marine Life. Multicoloured.

No.	Description		
143	5 c. Type **28**	30	20
144	10 c. Rough file shell ..	35	20
145	15 c. Red-lined cleaning shrimp	35	15
146	20 c. Bristleworm	35	15
147	25 c. Flamingo tongue ..	40	15
148	30 c. Christmas tree worm	40	20
149	40 c. Pink-tipped anemone	55	25
150	50 c. Smallmouth grunt ..	55	30
151	60 c. Glasseye snapper ..	1·25	60
152	75 c. Reef squirrelfish ..	90	55
153	$1 Sea fans and flamefish (vert.)	1·00	60
154	$2·50 Reef butterflyfish (vert.)	2·25	3·00
155	$5 Blackbar soldierfish (vert.)	5·50	7·50
156	$10 Cocoa damselfish (vert.)	9·00	12·00

The 10 c., 60 c., $5 and $10 come with or without imprint date.

29. Agriculture.

1984. 25th Anniv. of The 4-H Organisation. Multicoloured.

No.	Description		
157.	30 c. Type **29**	30	10
158.	55 c. Animal husbandry ..	40	15
159.	$1.10 The 4-H Pledge ..	70	60
160.	$3 On parade	1·25	1·25

30. Construction of Royal St. Kitts Hotel.

1984. First Anniv. of Independence of St. Kitts-Nevis. Multicoloured.

No.	Description		
161.	15 c. Type **30**	20	10
162.	30 c. Independence celebrations	30	15
163.	$1.10 National Anthem and aerial view (vert.) ..	70	60
164.	$3 "Dawn of a New Day" (vert.)	1·60	1·40

31. Opening Presents.

1984. Christmas. Multicoloured.

No.	Description		
165.	15 c. Type **31**	15	10
166.	60 c. Singing carols ..	45	35
167.	$1 Nativity play	75	60
168.	$2 Leaving church on Christmas Day	1·40	1·10

1985. Batik Designs (2nd series). Horiz. designs as T **27**.

No.	Description		
169.	15 c. black, green and light green	15	10
170.	40 c. black, blue and light blue	30	15
171.	60 c. black, orange and red	45	20
172.	$3 black, brown and light brown	1·75	2·00

DESIGNS: 15 c. Country bus. 40 c. Donkey cart. 60 c. Rum shop and man on bicycle. $3 "Polynesia" (cruise schooner).

32. Container Ship "Tropic Jade".

1985. Ships. Multicoloured.

No.	Description		
173.	40 c. Type **32**	75	30
174.	$1.20 "Atlantic Clipper" (schooner)	1·50	1·25
175.	$2 "Mandalay" (schooner)	2·25	2·25
176.	$2. "Cunard Countess" (liner)	2·25	2·25

33. James Derrick Cardin (leading Freemason).

1985. 150th Anniv. of Mount Olive S. C. Masonic Lodge. Multicoloured.

No.	Description		
177.	15 c. Type **33**	40	20
178.	75 c. Banner of Mount Olive Lodge	1·00	1·10
179.	$1·20 Masonic symbols (horiz.)	1·50	2·25
180.	$3 Lodge Charter, 1835 ..	2·25	3·75

34. Map of St. Kitts.

1985. Christmas. 400th Anniv. of Sir Francis Drake's Visit. Multicoloured.

No.	Description		
181.	10 c. Type **34**	20	15
182.	40 c. "Golden Hind" ..	55	35
183.	60 c. Sir Francis Drake ..	60	50
184.	$3 Drake's heraldic shield	1·75	2·25

35. Queen Elizabeth and Prince Philip on St. Kitts.

1986. 60th Birthday of Queen Elizabeth. Multicoloured.

No.	Description		
185.	10 c. Type **35**	15	10
186.	20 c. Queen Elizabeth on St. Kitts	25	15
187.	40 c. At Trooping the Colour	50	30
188.	$3 In Sweden	2·00	2·25

1986. Royal Wedding. As T **112** of Ascension. Multicoloured.

No.	Description		
189	15 c. Prince Andrew and Miss Sarah Ferguson ..	15	10
190	$2.50 Prince Andrew ..	1·50	2·00

36. Family on Smallholding.

1986. Agriculture Exhibition. Multicoloured.

No.	Description		
191.	15 c. Type **36**	20	10
192.	$1.20 Hands holding people, computers and crops	1·25	1·40

1986. 40th Anniv. of U.N. Week. Nos. 185/8 optd. **40th ANNIVERSARY U.N. WEEK 19–26 OCT.**

No.	Description		
207.	10 c. Type **35**	20	15
208.	20 c. Queen Elizabeth on St. Kitts	30	20
209.	40 c. At Trooping the Colour	40	30
210.	$3 In Sweden	2·25	2·75

38. Adult Green Monkey with Young.

1986. Green Monkeys on St. Kitts. Multicoloured.

No.	Description		
211.	15 c. Type **38**	35	15
212.	20 c. Adult on ground ..	40	20
213.	60 c. Young monkey in tree	1·10	1·00
214.	$1 Adult grooming young monkey	1·75	2·25

39. Frederic Bartholdi (sculptor).

1986. Centenary of Statue of Liberty. Mult.

No.	Description		
215	40 c. Type **39**	40	30
216	60 c. Torch (1876) and head (1878) on exhibition (horiz)	65	50
217	$1.50 "Isere" (French warship) carrying statue (horiz)	1·50	1·50
218	$3 Statue of Liberty, Paris, 1884	2·40	2·50

40. Officer, 9th Regt (East Norfolk), 1792.

1987. Military Uniforms (3rd series). Mult.

No.	Description		
220	15 c. Type **40**	40	30
221	15 c. Officer, Regt de Neustrie, 1779	40	30
222	40 c. Sergeant, 3rd Regt of Foot ("The Buffs"), 1801	75	45
223	40 c. Officer, French Artillery, 1812	75	45
224	$2 Light Company Private, 5th Regt, 1778	2·25	2·50
225	$2 Grenadier of the Line, 1796	2·25	2·50

41. Sugar Cane Warehouse.

1987. Sugar Cane Industry. Multicoloured (colour of panel behind "ST. KITTS" given).

No.	Type	Description		
227.	**41.**	15 c. yellow	20	20
228.	–	15 c. brown	20	20
229.	–	15 c. lilac	20	20
230.	–	15 c blue	20	20
231.	–	15 c. turquoise ..	20	20
232.	–	75 c. bright geeen ..	75	75
233.	–	75 c. lilac	75	75
234.	–	75 c. dull green ..	75	75
235.	–	75 c. yellow	75	75
236.	–	75 c. turquoise ..	75	75

DESIGNS: Nos. 227/31, Sugar cane factory. Nos. 232/6, Loading sugar train.

Nos. 227/31 and 232/6 were each printed together, se-tenant, forming composite designs.

42. B.W.I.A. "L-1011-500 TriStar".

1987. Aircraft visiting St. Kitts. Mult.

No.	Description		
237.	40 c. Type **42**	75	30
238.	60 c. L.I.A.T. BAe "Super 748"	95	60
239.	$1.20 W.I.A. "DHC-6 Twin Otter"	1·50	1·75
240.	$3 American Eagle Aerospatiale "ATR-42" ..	2·75	3·50

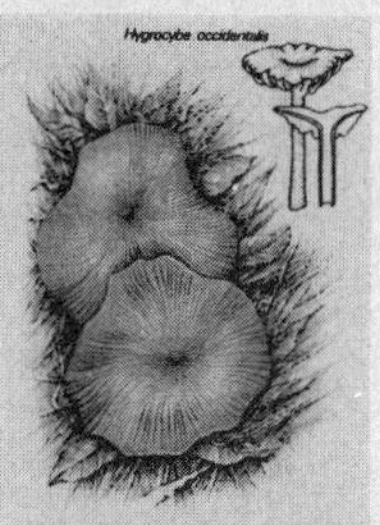

43. "Hygrocybe occidentalis".

1987. Fungi. Multicoloured.

241. 15 c. Type **43** 55 20
242. 40 c. "Marasmius haematocephalus" 85 40
243. $1.20 "Psilocybe cubensis" 1·75 1·75
244. $2 "Hygrocybe acutoconica" .. .. 2·50 2·50
245. $3 "Boletellus cubensis" .. 2·75 3·25

44. Carnival Clown.

1987. Christmas. Designs showing different clowns.

246. **44.** 15 c. multicoloured .. 25 15
247. – 40 c. multicoloured .. 55 30
248. – $1 multicoloured .. 1·25 80
249. – $3 multicoloured .. 2·50 3·00

See also Nos. 266/9.

45. Ixora.

1988. Flowers. Multicoloured.

250. 15 c. Type **45** 30 15
251. 40 c. Shrimp plant .. 55 30
252. $1 Poinsettia .. .. 1·00 75
253. $3 Honolulu rose .. .. 2·50 3·50

46. Fort Thomas Hotel.

1988. Tourism (1st series). Hotels. Mult.

254. 60 c. Type **46** 40 40
255. 60 c. Fairview Inn .. 40 40
256. 60 c. Frigate Bay Beach Hotel 40 40
257. 60 c. Ocean Terrace Inn .. 40 40
258. $3 The Golden Lemon .. 1·75 2·00
259. $3 Royal St. Kitts Casino and Jack Tar Village .. 1·75 2·00
260. $3 Rawlins Plantation Hotel and Restaurant .. 1·75 2·00

See also Nos. 270/5.

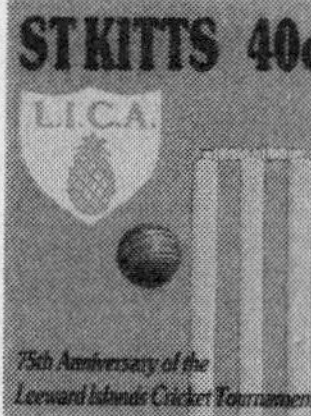

47 Ball, Wicket and Leeward Islands Cricket Association Emblem

1988. 75th Anniv of Leeward Islands Cricket Tournament. Multicoloured.

261 40 c. Type **47** 75 30
262 $3 Cricket match at Warner Park .. .. 3·25 3·75

48 Flag of St. Kitts–Nevis

1988. 5th Anniv of Independence. Mult.

263 15 c. Type **48** 15 10
264 60 c. Arms of St. Kitts .. 50 50

1988. Christmas. As T **44** showing carnival masqueraders.

266 15 c. multicoloured .. 10 10
267 40 c. multicoloured .. 20 25
268 80 c. multicoloured .. 40 45
269 $3 multicoloured .. 1·25 1·75

1989. Tourism (2nd series). Colonial Architecture. As T **46**. Multicoloured.

270 20 c. Georgian house .. 20 15
271 20 c. Colonial-style house 20 15
272 $1 Romney Manor .. 70 75
273 $1 Lavington Great House 70 75
274 $2 Government House .. 1·25 1·40
275 $2 Treasury Building .. 1·25 1·40

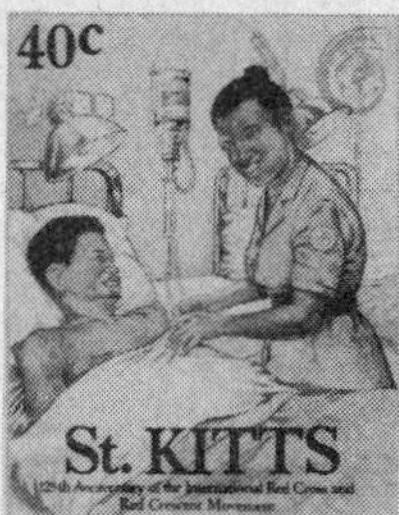

49 Red Cross Nurse with Hospital Patient

1989. 125th Anniv of International Red Cross.

276 **49** 40 c. multicoloured .. 30 30
277 – $1 multicoloured .. 65 65
278 – $3 red and black .. 1·75 2·00

DESIGNS: $1 Loading patient into ambulance; $3 125th anniversary logo.

1989. 20th Anniv of First Manned Landing on Moon. As T **126** of Ascension. Multicoloured.

280 10 c. Lunar rover on Moon 10 10
281 20 c. Crew of "Apollo 13" (30 × 30 mm) 10 10
282 $1 "Apollo 13" emblem (30 × 30 mm) 45 60
283 $2 "Apollo 13" splash-down, South Pacific .. 95 1·25

51 Outline Map of St. Kitts

1989.

285 **51** 10 c. mauve and black 10 10
286 15 c. red and black .. 10 10
287 20 c. orange and black 15 10
288 40 c. yellow and black 20 20
289 60 c. blue and black .. 30 30
290 $1 green and black .. 50 60

52 "Santa Mariagallante" passing St. Kitts, 1493

1989. 500th Anniv (1992) of Discovery of America by Columbus. Multicoloured.

291 15 c. Type **52** 45 20
292 80 c. Arms of Columbus and map of fourth voyage, 1502–04 .. 1·25 1·25
293 $1 Navigation instruments, c. 1500 .. .. .. 1·50 1·50
294 $5 Columbus and map of second voyage, 1493–96 4·50 5·50

53 Poinciana Tree

1989. "World Stamp Expo '89" International Stamp Exhibition, Washington. Multicoloured.

295 15 c. Type **53** 30 10
296 40 c. Fort George Citadel, Brimstone Hill .. 65 30
297 $1 Private, Light Company, 5th Foot, 1778 1·40 1·00
298 $3 St. George's Anglican Church .. .. .. 3·00 3·50

54 "Junonia evarete"

1990. Butterflies. Multicoloured.

299 15 c. Type **54** 25 15
300 40 c. "Anartia jatrophae" 25 25
301 60 c. "Heliconius charitonia" 65 45
302 $3 "Biblis hyperia" .. 2·25 2·75

1990. "Expo '90" International Garden and Greenery Exhibition, Osaka. Nos. 299/302 optd **EXPO '90** and logo.

303 15 c. Type **54** 25 15
304 40 c. "Anartia jatrophae" 45 30
305 60 c. "Heliconius charitoia" 65 55
306 $3 "Biblis hyperia" .. 2·25 3·00

56 Brimstone Hill

1990. 300th Anniv of English Bombardment of Brimstone Hill. Multicoloured.

307 15 c. Type **56** 20 10
308 40 c. Restored Brimstone Hill fortifications .. 35 30
309 60 c. 17th-century English marine and Fort Charles under attack 50 75
310 $3 English sailors firing cannon .. .. .. 2·25 2·50

No. 309 exists se-tenant, as a horizontal pair, with No. 310, each pair showing a composite design.

58 "Romney" (freighter)

1990. Ships. Multicoloured.

312 10 c. Type **58** 10 10
313 15 c. "Baralt" (freighter) 10 10
314 20 c. "Wear" (mail steamer) 10 10
315 25 c. "Sunmount" (freighter) 10 15
316 40 c. "Inanda" (cargo liner) 20 25
317 50 c. "Alcoa Partner" (freighter) 25 30
318 60 c. "Dominica" (freighter) 30 35
319 80 c. "C.G.M. Provence" (container ship) .. 40 45
320 $1 "Director" (freighter) .. 50 55
321 $1.20 Barque 60 65
322 $2 "Chignecto" (packet steamer) .. .. 95 1·00
323 $3 "Berbice" (mail steamer) .. .. 1·40 1·50
324 $5 "Vamos" (freighter) .. 2·40 2·50
325 $10 "Federal Maple" (freighter) .. .. 5·00 5·25

59 Single Fork Game

1990. Christmas. Traditional Games. Mult.

326 10 c. Type **59** 15 10
327 15 c. Boulder breaking .. 15 10
328 40 c. Double fork .. 30 30
329 $3 The run up .. .. 1·75 2·00

60 White Periwinkle

1991. Flowers. Multicoloured.

330 10 c. Type **60** 20 10
331 40 c. Pink oleander .. 30 25
332 60 c. Pink periwinkle (vert) 55 50
333 $2 White oleander (vert) .. 1·25 1·75

61 Census Logo

1991. Nationl Census.

334 **61** 15 c. multicoloured .. 15 10
335 $2.40 multicoloured .. 1·60 2·00

The $2.40 differs from Type **61** by showing "ST. KITTS" in a curved panel.

1991. 65th Birthday of Queen Elizabeth II and 70th Birthday of Prince Philip. As T **139** of Ascension. Multicoloured.

336 $1.20 Prince Philip .. 75 1·00
337 $1.80 Queen holding bouquet of flowers .. 1·00 1·10

62 Nassau Grouper

1991. Fishes. Multicoloured.

338 10 c. Type **62** 20 10
339 60 c. Hogfish 50 45
340 $1 Red hind 80 90
341 $3 Porkfish .. .. 2·00 2·50

63 School of Continuing Studies, St. Kitts, and Chancellor Sir Shridath Ramphal

1991. 40th Anniv of University of West Indies. Multicoloured.

342 15 c. Type **63** 20 10
343 50 c. Administration Building, Barbados .. 45 35
344 $1 Engineering Building, Trinidad and Tobago .. 80 85
345 $3 Mona Campus, Jamaica, and Sir Shridath Ramphal .. .. 2·25 2·75

64 Whipping The Bull

1991. Christmas. "The Bull" (Carnival play). Multicoloured.

346 10 c. Type **64** 15 10
347 15 c. Death of The Bull .. 15 10
348 60 c. Cast of characters and musicians 45 50
349 $3 The Bull in procession 1·60 1·90

1992. 40th Anniv of Queen Elizabeth II's Accession. As T **143** of Ascension. Mult.

350 10 c. St. Kitts coastline .. 20 10
351 40 c. Warner Park Pavilion 35 25
352 60 c. Brimstone Hill .. 50 40
353 $1 Three portraits of Queen Elizabeth .. 75 85
354 $3 Queen Elizabeth II .. 1·90 2·50

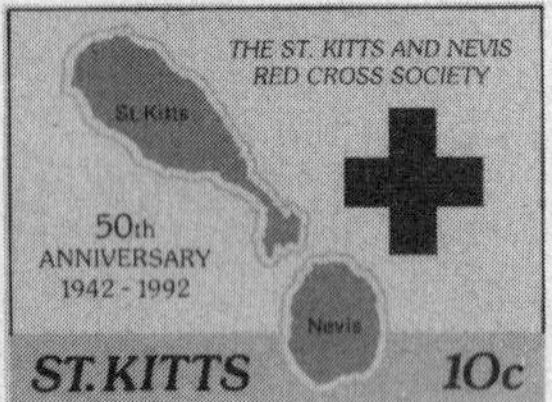

65 Map of St. Kitts-Nevis

1992. 50th Anniv of St. Kitts-Nevis Red Cross Society. Multicoloured.

355 10 c. Type **65** 20 20
356 20 c. St. Kitts-Nevis flag 25 20
357 50 c. Red Cross House, St. Kitts 45 40
358 $2.40 Henri Dunant .. 1·50 2·00

66 Columbus meeting Amerindians

1992. Organization of East Caribbean States. 500th Anniv of Discovery of America by Columbus. Multicoloured.

359 $1 Type **66** 75 70
360 $2 Ships approaching island .. .. .. 1·25 1·60

67 Fountain, Independence Square

1992. Local Monuments. Multicoloured.

361 25 c. Type **67** 25 20
362 50 c. Berkeley Memorial Drinking Fountain .. 35 35
363 80 c. Sir Thomas Warner's Tomb 55 65
364 $2 War Memorial .. 1·10 1·40

68 Joseph and Mary travelling to Bethlehem

1992. Christmas. Multicoloured.

365 20 c. Type **68** 30 20
366 25 c. Shepherds and star .. 30 20
367 80 c. Wise Men with gifts 65 55
368 $3 Mary, Joseph and Holy Child .. .. 1·75 2·00

1993. 75th Anniv of Royal Air Force. Aircraft. As T **166** of Montserrat. Multicoloured.

369 25 c. Short Singapore III 20 15
370 50 c. Bristol Beaufort .. 35 30
371 80 c. Westland Whirlwind helicopter 70 65
372 $1.60 English Electric Canberra .. .. 1·25 1·40

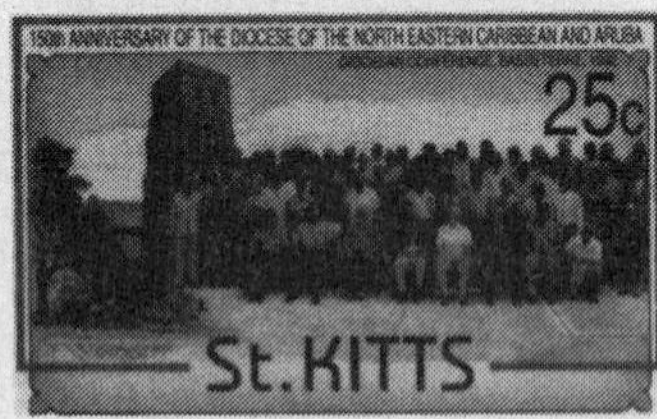

69 Members of Diocesan Conference, Basseterre, 1992

1993. 150th Anniv of Anglican Diocese of North-eastern Caribbean and Aruba. Mult.

374 25 c. Type **69** 15 10
375 50 c. Cathedral of St. John the Divine (vert) .. 40 35
376 80 c. Coat of arms and motto 70 65
377 $2 The Right Revd. Daniel Davis (first bishop) (vert) .. .. .. 1·50 1·60

70 1953 Coronation 2 c. Stamp and Ampulla

1993. 40th Anniv of Coronation. Mult.

378 10 c. Type **70** 10 10
379 25 c. 1977 Silver Jubilee $1.50 stamp and anointing spoon .. 15 10
380 80 c. 1977 Silver Jubilee 55 c. stamp and tassels 55 55
381 $2 1978 25th anniv of Coronation stamps and sceptre .. .. .. 1·25 1·40

71 Flags of Girls Brigade and St. Kitts-Nevis

1993. Centenary of Girls Brigade. Mult.

382 80 c. Type **71** 70 65
383 $3 Girls Brigade badge and coat of arms .. .. 2·25 2·40

72 Aspects of St. Kitts on Flag

1993. 10th Anniv of Independence. Mult.

384 20 c. Type **72** 15 10
385 80 c. Coat of arms and Independence anniversary logo 65 60
386 $3 Coat of arms and map 2·00 2·25

73 "Hibiscus sabdariffa"

1993. Christmas. Flowers. Multicoloured.

387 25 c. Type **73** 15 10
388 50 c. "Euphorbia pulcherrima" 45 35
389 $1.60 "Euphorbia leucocephala" .. .. 1·50 1·60

74 Mesosaurus

1994. Prehistoric Aquatic Reptiles. Mult.

390 $1.20 Type **74** 60 65
391 $1.20 Placodus 60 65
392 $1.20 Liopleurodon .. 60 65
393 $1.20 Hydrotherosaurus .. 60 65
394 $1.20 Caretta 60 65

Nos. 390/4 were printed together, se-tenant, with background forming a composite design.

1994. "Hong Kong '94" International Stamp Exhibition. Nos. 390/4 optd **HONG KONG '94** and emblem.

395 $1.20 Type **74** 60 65
396 $1.20 Placodus 60 65
397 $1.20 Liopleurodon .. 60 65
398 $1.20 Hydrotherosaurus .. 60 65
399 $1.20 Caretta 60 65

OFFICIAL STAMPS

1980. Nos. 32/41 optd. **OFFICIAL.**

O 1. 15 c. multicoloured .. 10 10
O 2. 25 c. multicoloured .. 10 10
O 3. 30 c. multicoloured .. 10 10
O 4. 40 c. multicoloured .. 10 15
O 5. 45 c. multicoloured .. 15 15
O 6. 50 c. multicoloured .. 15 15
O 7. 55 c. multicoloured .. 15 15
O 8. $1 multicoloured .. 25 25
O 9. $5 multicoloured .. 1·00 1·50
O 10. $10 multicoloured .. 1·75 2·50

1981. Nos. 59/70 optd. **OFFICIAL.**

O 11. 15 c. Bananaquit .. 20 10
O 12. 20 c. Scaly-breasted Thrasher 20 10
O 13. 25 c. Grey Kingbird .. 25 10
O 14. 30 c. Green-throated Carib 25 10
O 15. 40 c. Turnstone .. 35 15
O 16. 45 c. Black-faced Grassquit 40 20
O 17. 50 c. Cattle-Egret .. 40 20
O 18. 55 c. Brown Pelican .. 50 25
O 19. $1 Lesser Antillean Bullfinch 75 45
O 20. $2.50 Zenaida Dove .. 1·60 1·00
O 21. $5 American Kestrel .. 2·75 2·00
O 22. $10 Antillean Crested Hummingbird .. 5·00 4·25

1983. Nos. 75/80 optd. **OFFICIAL** and surch.

O 23. 45 c. on $2.50 " Royal George " 25 25
O 24. 45 c. on $2.50 Prince Charles and Lady Diana Spencer 25 25
O 25. 55 c. " Saudadoes " .. 30 30
O 26. 55 c. Prince Charles and Lady Diana Spencer .. 30 30
O 27. $1.10 on $4 " Britannia " 60 70
O 28. $1.10 on $4 Prince Charles and Lady Diana Spencer 60 70

1984. Nos. 145/56 optd. **OFFICIAL.**

O29. 15 c. Red-lined Cleaning Shrimp 25 25
O30. 20 c. Bristleworm .. 30 30
O31. 25 c. Flamingo Tongue .. 35 35
O32. 30 c. Christmas Tree Worm 40 40
O33. 40 c. Pink-tipped Anemone 50 50
O34. 50 c. Smallmouth Grunt 60 60
O35. 60 c. Glasseye Snapper .. 70 70
O36. 75 c. Reef Squirrelfish .. 80 80
O37. $1 Sea Fans and Flamefish (vert.) .. .. 1·00 1·00
O38. $2.50 Reef Butterflyfish (vert.) .. .. 2·25 2·75
O39. $5 Blackbar Soldierfish (vert.) .. .. .. 4·00 5·00
O40. $10 Cocoa Damselfish (vert.) .. .. .. 7·50 9·50

ST. KITTS-NEVIS

Islands of the Leeward Is., Br. W. Indies. The general issues for Leeward Is. were in concurrent use until 1 July 1956. From 1952 the stamps are inscribed "St. Christopher, Nevis and Anguilla". Achieved Associated Statehood on 27 February 1967. St. Kitts and Nevis had separate postal administrations from 23 June 1980.

1903. 12 pence = 1 shilling;
20 shillings = 1 pound.
1951. 100 cents = 1 West Indian dollar.

1. Christopher Columbus.

2. Medicinal Spring.

1903.

No.	Type	Description		Unused	Used
1	1	½d. purple and green	..	1·50	70
12		½d. green ..	..	30	35
13	2	1d. grey and red ..	..	1·00	25
14a		1d. red ..	..	35	20
15a	1	2d. purple and brown	..	1·50	2·50
4		2½d. black and blue	..	11·00	3·50
17		2½d. blue ..	..	1·00	40
18a	2	3d. green and orange	..	1·00	2·25
6	1	6d. black and purple	..	3·25	19·00
20		1s. green and orange	..	7·00	15·00
8		2s. green and black	..	12·00	16·00
9	1	2s. 6d. black and violet	..	18·00	32·00
21	2	5s. purple and green	..	28·00	65·00

1916. Optd **WAR TAX.**

No.	Type	Description		Unused	Used
22a	1	½d. green	.. ..	10	30

1918. Optd **WAR STAMP.**

No.	Type	Description		Unused	Used
23	1	1½d. orange	.. ..	15	30

4.

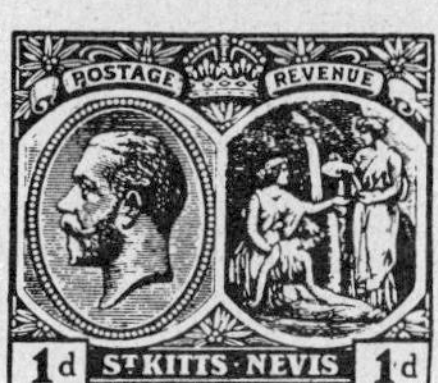

5.

1920.

No.	Type	Description		Unused	Used
37	4	½d. green	.. ..	70	80
38	5	1d. red ..	.. ..	30	15
39		1d. violet	.. ..	2·00	35
26	4	1½d. yellow	.. ..	1·25	80
40		1½d. red	.. ..	1·50	2·50
40a		1½d. brown	.. ..	50	15
41	5	2d. grey	.. ..	40	60
42	4	2½d. blue	.. ..	3·00	2·25
43		2½d. brown	.. ..	1·00	5·00
45a	5	3d. purple on yellow	..	50	2·50
45		3d. blue	.. ..	55	2·50
46	4	6d. purple and mauve	..	2·00	4·50
31	5	1s. black on green	..	1·75	3·00
47	4	2s. purple & blue on blue		5·50	15·00
33	5	2s. 6d. black & red on bl		5·00	25·00
34	4	5s. green & red on yellow		5·00	35·00
35	5	10s. green & red on green		12·00	45·00
36	4	£1 purple & black on red		£200	£275

6. Old Road Bay and Mount Misery.

1923. Tercent. Commem.

No.	Type	Description		Unused	Used
48.	6.	½d. black and green	..	2·00	6·00
49.		1d. black and violet	..	2·25	1·50
50.		1½d. black and red	..	4·25	8·00
51.		2d. black and grey	..	2·00	1·50
52.		2½d. black and brown	..	3·75	22·00
53.		3d. black and blue	..	3·25	12·00
54.		6d. black and purple	..	8·00	24·00
55.		1s. black and green	..	12·00	27·00
56.		2s. black and blue on blue		29·00	48·00
57.		2s. 6d. black & red on blue		38·00	65·00
59.		5s. black and red on yellow		60·00	£150
58.		10s. black and red on green		£225	£325
60.		£1 black and purple on red		£750	£1200

1935. Silver Jubilee. As T **13** of Antigua.

No.	Description		Unused	Used
61	1d. blue and red	.. ..	1·00	40
62	1½d. blue and grey ..	..	75	75
63	2½d. brown and blue	..	1·00	80
64	1s. grey and purple	..	5·50	11·00

1937. Coronation. As T **2** of Aden.

No.	Description		Unused	Used
65.	1d. red	.. .. ..	30	15
66.	1½d. brown	.. ..	40	10
67.	2½d. blue	.. ..	60	35

Nos. 61/7 are inscribed "ST. CHRISTOPHER NEVIS".

7. King George VI. 8. King George VI and Medicinal Spring.

10. King George VI and Anguilla Island.

1938.

No.	Type	Description		Unused	Used
68a	7	½d. green	.. ..	10	10
69a		1d. red ..	.. ..	40	40
70		1½d. orange	.. ..	20	30
71b	8	2d. red and grey	..	70	1·00
72a	7	2½d. blue	.. ..	20	30
73g	8	3d. purple and red	..	1·75	2·25
74d	–	6d. green and purple ..		2·00	2·00
75c	8	1s. black and green	..	1·25	1·50
76ab		2s. 6d. black and red ..		8·50	3·75
77b	–	5s. green and red	..	19·00	7·50
77d	10	10s. black and blue	..	12·00	19·00
77e		£1 black and brown	..	15·00	23·00

The 6d. and 5s. are as Type **8,** but with the Christopher Columbus device as in Type **4.**

1946. Victory. As T **9** of Aden.

No.	Description		Unused	Used
78.	1½d. orange	.. ..	10	10
79.	3d. red ..	.. ..	10	10

1949. Silver Wedding. As T **10/11** of Aden.

No.	Description		Unused	Used
80.	2½d. blue ..	.. ..	10	10
81.	5s. red	.. ..	4·50	2·50

1949. U.P.U. As T **20/23** of Antigua.

No.	Description		Unused	Used
82	2½d. blue	.. ..	35	20
83	3d. red	.. ..	40	30
84	6d. mauve	.. ..	40	30
85	1s. green	.. ..	40	30

1950. Tercent. Br. Settlement in Anguilla. Optd. **ANGUILLA TERCENTENARY 1650-1950.**

No.	Type	Description		Unused	Used
86.	7.	1d. red	.. ..	10	10
87.		1½d. orange	.. ..	10	10
88.		2½d. blue ..	..	10	10
89.	8.	3d. purple and red	..	10	10
90.	–	6d. green & purple (No. 74ab)		10	10
91.	8.	1s. black and green	..	10	10

1951. Inauguration of B.W.I. University College. As T **24/25** of Antigua.

No.	Type	Description		Unused	Used
92.	22.	3 c. black and orange ..		30	15
93.	23.	12 c. green and mauve..		30	30

ST. CHRISTOPHER, NEVIS AND ANGUILLA

13. Bath House and Spa.

1952.

No.	Type	Description		Unused	Used
94.	13.	1 c. green and ochre	..	15	45
95.	–	2 c. green	.. ..	20	40
96.	–	3 c. red and violet	..	30	40
97.	–	4 c. red ..	.. ..	20	20
98.	–	5 c. blue and grey	..	20	10
99.	–	6 c. blue ..	.. ..	20	15
100.	–	12 c. blue and brown	..	20	10
101.	–	24 c. black and red	..	20	10
102.	–	48 c. olive and brown	..	1·50	1·50
103.	–	60 c. ochre and green	..	1·50	1·75
104.	–	$1.20 green and blue	..	5·00	2·00
105.	–	$4.80 green and red	..	12·00	18·00

DESIGNS—HORIZ. 2 c. Warner Park. 4 c. Brimstone Hill. 5 c. Nevis from the sea, North. 6 c. Pinney's Beach, Nevis. 24 c. Old Road Bay. 48 c. Sea Island cotton, Nevis. 60 c. The Treasury. $1.20, Salt pond, Angullia. $4.80, Sugar factory. VERT. Map of the islands. 12 c. Sir Thomas Warner's tomb.

1953. Coronation. As T **13** of Aden.

No.	Description		Unused	Used
106	2 c. black and green	..	15	10

1954. As 1952 but with portrait of Queen Elizabeth II.

No.	Description		Unused	Used
106a	½ c. olive (as $1.20)	..	30	10
107	1 c. green and ochre	..	20	10
108	2 c. green ..	.. ..	45	10
109	3 c. red and violet	..	65	10
110	4 c. red	.. .. ..	15	10
111	5 c. blue and grey	..	15	10
112	6 c. blue ..	.. ..	40	10
112b	8 c. black ..	.. ..	4·50	10
113	12 c. blue and brown	..	15	10
114	24 c. black and red	..	15	10
115	48 c. olive and brown	..	60	50
116	60 c. ochre and green	..	2·50	85
117	$1.20 green and blue	..	11·00	90
117b	$2.40 black and orange ..		8·50	11·00
118	$4.80 green and red	..	12·00	11·00

DESIGNS (new values)—VERT. 8 c. Sombrero Lighthouse. HORIZ. $2.40 Map of Anguilla and Dependencies.

27. Alexander Hamilton and View of Nevis.

1956. Birth Bicent. of Alexander Hamilton.

No.	Type	Description		Unused	Used
119.	27.	24 c. green and blue ..		30	15

1958. British Caribbean Federation. As T **28** of Antigua.

No.	Description		Unused	Used
120.	3 c. green ..	.. ..	60	15
121.	6 c. blue ..	.. ..	1·00	1·50
122.	12 c. red	.. ..	1·50	30

28. 1d. Stamp of 1861.

1961. Centenary of Nevis Stamp.

No.	Type	Description		Unused	Used
123.	28.	2 c. dp. red and green..		15	20
124.		8 c. red and blue	..	20	10
125.		12 c. lilac and red	..	30	15
126.		24 c. green and orange..		35	15

The 8 c., 12 c. and 24 c. show the original 4d., 6d. and 1s. stamps of Nevis respectively.

1963. Cent of Red Cross. As T **33** of Antigua.

No.	Description		Unused	Used
127	3 c. red and black	..	10	10
128	12 c. red and blue	..	20	40

33. Loading Sugar Cane, St. Kitts.

1963. Multicoloured.

No.	Description		Unused	Used
129.	½ c. New Lighthouse Sombrero	.. ..	10	10
130.	1 c. Type **33**	.. ..	10	10
131.	2 c. Pall Mall Square, Basseterre	.. ..	10	10
132.	3 c. Gateway, Brimstone Hill Fort, St. Kitts	..	10	10
133.	4 c. Nelson's Spring, Nevis		10	10
134.	5 c. Grammar School, St. Kitts	.. .. ..	60	10
135.	6 c. Crater, Mt. Misery, St. Kitts	.. .. ..	10	10
136.	10 c. Hibiscus	.. ..	15	10
137.	15 c. Sea Island cotton, Nevis	.. .. ..	35	10
138.	20 c. Boat-building, Anguilla		20	10
139.	25 c. White-crowned pigeon		65	10
140.	50 c. St. George's Church Tower, Basseterre	..	40	25
141.	60 c. Alexander Hamilton		1·00	30
142.	$1 Map of St. Kitts-Nevis		2·25	40
143.	$2.50 Map of Anguilla	..	2·25	2·50
144.	$5 Arms of St. Christopher, Nevis and Anguilla	..	3·50	3·00

The ½, 2, 3, 15, 25, 60 c., $1 and $5 are vert. the rest horiz.

1964. Arts Festival. Optd. **ARTS FESTIVAL ST. KITTS 1964.**

No.	Description		Unused	Used
145.	3 c. mult. (No. 132)	..	10	10
146.	25 c. mult. (No. 139)	..	20	10

1965. Cent of I.T.U. As T **36** of Antigua.

No.	Description		Unused	Used
147.	2 c. bistre and red		10	10
148.	50 c. blue and olive	..	40	35

1965. I.C.Y. As T **37** of Antigua.

No.	Description		Unused	Used
149	2 c. purple and green	..	10	20
150	25 c. green and violet	..	20	10

1966. Churchill Commem. As T **38** of Antigua.

No.	Description		Unused	Used
151.	½ c. blue ..	.. ..	10	15
152.	3 c. green ..	.. ..	15	10
153.	15 c. brown	.. ..	30	20
154.	25 c. violet	.. ..	35	20

1966. Royal Visit. As T **39** of Antigua.

No.	Description		Unused	Used
155.	3 c. black and blue	..	10	15
156.	25 c. black and mauve	..	30	15

1966. World Cup Football Championship. As T **40** of Antigua

No.	Description		Unused	Used
157	6 c. multicoloured	..	20	20
158	25 c. multicoloured	..	40	10

49. Festival Emblem.

1966. Arts Festival.

No.	Type	Description		Unused	Used
159.	49.	3 c. multicoloured	..	10	10
160.		25 c. multicoloured	..	20	10

1966. Inauguration of W.H.O. Headquarters, Geneva. As T **41** of Antigua.

No.	Description		Unused	Used
161	3 c. black, green and blue		10	10
162	40 c. black, purple & brown		20	20

1966. 20th Anniv of U.N.E.S.C.O. As T **54/6** of Antigua.

No.	Description		Unused	Used
163.	3 c. multicoloured	..	10	10
164.	6 c. yellow, violet and olive		10	10
165.	40 c. black, purple & orge.		30	35

50. Government Headquarters, Basseterre.

1967. Statehood. Multicoloured.

No.	Description		Unused	Used
182.	3 c. Type **50**	..	10	10
183.	10 c. National Flag	..	10	10
184.	25 c. Coat of Arms	..	15	10

53. John Wesley and Cross.

1967. West Indies Methodist Conf.

No.	Type	Description		Unused	Used
185.	53.	3 c. black, red and violet		10	10
186.	–	25 c. black, turq. & blue		15	10
187.	–	40 c. black, yell. & orge.		15	15

DESIGNS: 25 c. Charles Wesley and cross. 40 c. Thomas Coke and cross.

56. "Herald" Aircraft over "Jamaica Producer" (freighter).

1968. Caribbean Free Trade Area.

No.	Type	Description		Unused	Used
188.	56.	25 c. multicoloured	..	15	10
189.		50 c. multicoloured	..	15	20

57. Dr. Martin Luther King.

1968. Martin Luther King Commem.
190. 57. 50 c. multicoloured .. 10 10

58. " Mystical Nativity " (Botticelli).

1968. Christmas.
191. 58. 12 c. multicoloured .. 10 10
192. – 25 c. multicoloured .. 10 10
193. 58. 40 c. multicoloured .. 15 10
194. – 50 c. multicoloured .. 15 10
DESIGN: 25 c., 50 c. " The Adoration of the Magi " (Rubens).

60. Tarpon.

1968. Fishes.
195. 60. 6 c. multicoloured .. 10 10
196. – 12 c. black, green & blue 15 10
197. – 40 c. multicoloured .. 25 10
198. – 50 c. multicoloured .. 30 15
FISHES: 12 c. Garfish. 40 c. Horse-eye Jack. 50 c. Redsnapper.

64. The Warner Badge and Islands.

1969. Sir Thomas Warner Commem. Mult.
199. 20 c. Type 64 .. .. 10 10
200. 25 c. Sir Thomas Warner's tomb 10 10
201. 40 c. Charles I's Commission 15 15

67. " The Adoration of the Kings " (Mostaert).

1969. Christmas. Multicoloured.
202. 10 c. Type 67 .. .. 10 10
203. 25 c. As 10 c. 10 10
204. 40 c. " The Adoration of the Kings " (Geertgen) .. 10 10
205. 50 c. As 40 c. 10 10

73. Portuguese Caravels (16th-cent.).

1970. Multicoloured (except ½ c.).
206. ½ c. Pirates and treasure at Frigate Bay (black, orge. and green) 10 10
207. 1 c. English Two-decker warship, 1650 .. .. 30 10
208. 2 c. Naval flags of colonising nations 15 10
209. 3 c. Rapier hilt (17th-cent.) 15 10
210. 4 c. Type 73 .. .. 20 10
211. 5 c. Sir Henry Morgan and fireships, 1669 .. .. 30 10
212. 6 c. L'Ollonois and pirate carrack 16th-cent. .. 30 10
213. 10 c. 17th-century smugglers' ship 30 10
214a. 15 c. " Piece of Eight " .. 50 10
215. 20 c. Cannon (17th-cent.) .. 35 10
216. 25 c. Humphrey Cole's astrolabe, 1574 .. .. 40 10
217. 50 c. Flintlock pistol (17th-cent). 85 80
218. 60 c. Dutch Flute (17th-cent.) .. .. .. 2·25 70
219. $1 Capt. Bartholomew Roberts and his crew's death sentence .. .. 2·50 75
220. $2.50 Railing Piece (gun) (16th-cent.) .. .. 2·00 3·00
221. $5 Drake, Hawkins and sea battle .. .. .. 2·50 4·25
280. $10 The Apprehension of Blackbeard (Edward Teach) .. .. .. 20·00 13·00
The ½ c. to 3 c., 15 c., 25 c., 60 c. and $1 are vert. designs.

85. Graveyard Scene (" Great Expectations ").

1970. Death Cent. of Charles Dickens.
222. 85. 4 c. brown, gold & green 10 10
223. – 20 c. brn., gold and purple 10 10
224. – 25 c. brown, gold & green 10 10
225. – 40 c. brown, gold & blue 10 15
DESIGNS—HORIZ. 20 c. Miss Havisham and Pip (" Great Expectations "). VERT. 25 c. Dickens' Birthplace. 40 c. Charles Dickens.

86. Local Steel Band.

1970. Festival of Arts. Multicoloured.
226. 20 c. Type 86 .. .. 10 10
227. 25 c. Local string band .. 10 10
228. 40 c. Scene from " A Midsummer Night's Dream " 15 15

87. 1d. Stamp of 1870 and Post Office, 1970.

1970. Stamp Cent.
229. 87. ½ c. green and red .. 10 10
230. – 20 c. blue, green & red 10 10
231. – 25 c. purple, grn. & red 10 10
232. – 50 c. red, green and blk. 30 45
DESIGNS: 20 c., 25 c., 1d. and 6d. stamps of 1870. 50 c. 6d. stamp of 1870 and early postmark.

88. " Adoration of the Shepherds " (Frans van Floris).

1970. Christmas. Multicoloured.
233. 3 c. Type 88 .. .. 10 10
234. 20 c. " The Holy Family " (Van Dyck) 10 10
235. 25 c. As 20 c. 10 10
236. 40 c. Type 88 .. .. 15 30

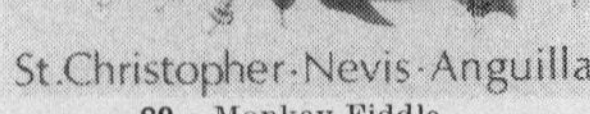

89. Monkey Fiddle.

1971. Flowers. Multicoloured.
237. ½ c. Type 89 .. .. 10 10
238. 20 c. Tropical Mountain Violet 20 10
239. 30 c. Trailing Morning Glory 20 10
240. 50 c. Fringed Epidendrum 40 65

90. Royal Poinciana.

1971. Philippe de Poincy Commem. Mult.
241. 20 c. Type 90 .. .. 10 10
242. 30 c. Chateau de Poincy .. 10 10
243. 50 c. De Poincy's badge (vert.) 20 15

91. The East Yorks.

1971. Siege of Brimstone Hill, 1782. Mult.
244. ½ c. Type 91 .. .. 10 10
245. 20 c. Royal Artillery .. 45 10
246. 30 c. French infantry .. 55 10
247. 50 c. The Royal Scots .. 75 20

92. " Crucifixion " (Massys).

1972. Easter.
248. 92. 4 c. multicoloured .. 10 10
249. 20 c. multicoloured .. 10 10
250. 30 c. multicoloured .. 10 10
251. 40 c. multicoloured .. 10 10

93. " Virgin and Child " (Borgognone).

1972. Christmas. Multicoloured.
252. 3 c. Type 93 .. .. 10 10
253. 20 c. " Adoration of the Kings " (J. Bassano) (horiz.) 15 10
254. 25 c. " Adoration of the Shepherds " (Domenichino) 15 10
255. 40 c. " Virgin and Child " (Fiorenzo di Lorenzo) .. 20 10

1972. Royal Silver Wedding. As T 52 of Ascension, but with Brown Pelicans in background.
256. 20 c. red 15 15
257. 25 c. blue 15 15

95. Landing on St. Christopher 1623.

1973. 300th Anniv. of Sir Thomas Warner's Landing on St. Christopher. Multicoloured.
258. 4 c. Type 95 .. .. 15 10
259. 25 c. Growing tobacco .. 15 10
260. 40 c. Building fort at Old Road 20 10
261. £2.50 "Concepcion" .. 80 1·10

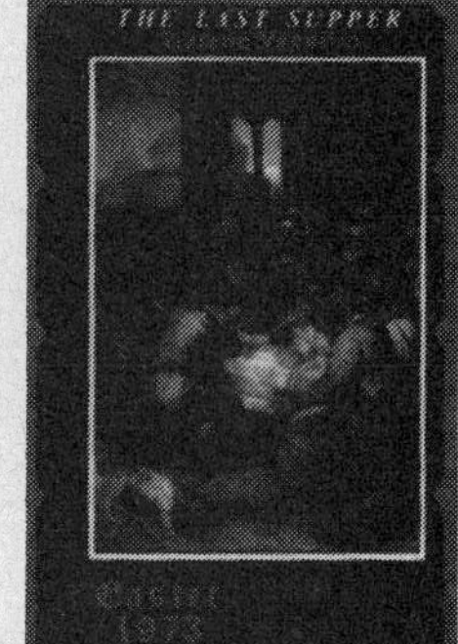

96. " The Last Supper " (Titian).

1973. Easter. Paintings of "The Last Supper" by the artists listed. Mult.
262. 4 c. Type 96 .. .. 10 10
263. 25 c. Ascribed to Roberti .. 10 10
264. $2. 50 Juan de Juanes (horiz.) 70 60

1973. Royal Visit Nos. 258/61 optd. **VISIT OF HRH THE PRINCE OF WALES 1973.**
265. 95. 4 c. multicoloured .. 10 15
266. – 25 c. multicoloured .. 10 15
267. – 40 c. multicoloured .. 15 15
268. – $2.50 multicoloured .. 45 50

99. Harbour Scene and 2d. Stamp of 1903.

1973. 70th Anniv. of 1st St. Kitts-Nevis Stamps. Multicoloured.
285. 4 c. Type 99 .. .. 10 10
286. 25 c. Sugar-mill and 1d. stamp of 1903 .. .. 15 10
287. 40 c. Unloading boat and ½d. stamp of 1903 .. 35 10
288. $2.50 Rock-carvings and 3d. stamp of 1903 .. 2·00 1·00

1973. Royal Wedding. As T 47 of Anguilla. Multicoloured, background colours given.
290. 25 c. green 15 10
291. 40 c. brown 15 10

100. " Madonna and Child " (Murillo).

1973. Christmas. Paintings of " The Holy Family " by the artists listed. Mult.
292. 4 c. Type 100 .. .. 10 10
293. 40 c. Mengs 20 10
294. 60 c. Sassoferrato 25 15
295. $1 Filippino Lippi (horiz.) 35 30

101. " Christ Carrying the Cross " (S. del Piombo).

1974. Easter. Multicoloured.

296.	4 c. Type **101**	10	10
297.	25 c. "The Crucifixion" (Goya)	15	10
298.	40 c. "Trinity" (Ribera) ..	15	10
299.	$2.50 "The Deposition" (Fra Bartolomeo) (horiz.)	1·00	75

102. University Centre, St. Kitts.

1974. 25th Anniv. of University of West Indies. Multicoloured.

300.	10 c. Type **102**	10	10
301.	$1 As Type **102** but showing different buildings ..	20	25

103. Hands reaching for Globe.

1974. Family Planning.

303. **103.**	4 c. brn., blue & black ..	10	10
304. –	25 c. multicoloured ..	10	10
305. –	40 c. multicoloured ..	10	10
306. –	$2.50 multicoloured ..	35	55

DESIGNS—HORIZ. 25 c. Instruction by nurse. $2.50, Emblem and globe on scales. VERT 40 c. Family group.

104. Churchill as Army Lieutenant.

1974. Birth Centenary of Sir Winston Churchill. Multicoloured.

307.	4 c. Type **104**	10	10
308.	25 c. Churchill as Prime Minister	15	10
309.	40 c. Churchill as Knight of the Garter	25	10
310.	60 c. Churchill's statue, London	35	15

106. "The Last Supper" (Dore).

1975. Easter. Paintings by Dore. Mult.

314.	4 c. Type **106**	10	10
315.	25 c. "Christ Mocked" ..	10	10
316.	40 c. "Jesus Falling beneath the Cross" ..	10	10
317.	$1 "The Erection of the Cross"	25	30

INDEX

Countries can be quickly located by referring to the index at the end of this volume.

107. E.C.C.A. H.Q. Buildings, Basseterre.

1975. Opening of East Caribbean Currency Authority's Headquarters.

318. **107.**	12 c. multicoloured ..	10	10
319. –	25 c. multicoloured ..	10	10
320. –	40 c. red, silver and grey	15	10
321. –	45 c. multicoloured ..	15	15

DESIGNS: 25 c. Specimen one-dollar banknote. 40 c. Half-dollar of 1801 and current 4-dollar coin. 45 c. Coins of 1801 and 1960.

108. Evangeline Booth (Salvation Army General).

1975. International Women's Year. Mult.

338.	4 c. Type **108**	10	10
339.	25 c. Sylvia Pankhurst ..	30	10
340.	40 c. Marie Curie	90	50
341.	$2.50 Lady Annie Allen (teacher and guider) ..	2·00	3·00

109. Golfer.

1975. Opening of Frigate Bay Golf Course.

342. **109.**	4 c. black and red ..	30	10
343.	25 c. black and yellow ..	55	10
344.	40 c. black and green ..	70	10
345.	$1 black and blue ..	1·00	70

110. "St. Paul" (Pier Francesco Sacchi).

1975. Christmas. Religious Paintings. Mult.

346.	25 c. Type **110**	25	10
347.	40 c. "St. James" (Bonifazio di Pitati) ..	40	10
348.	45 c. "St. John the Baptist" (Mola)	40	10
349.	$1 "St. John" (Raphael)	95	60

111. "Crucifixion" (detail).

1976. Easter. Stained Glass Windows. Mult.

350.	4 c. } Type **111**	10	10
351.	4 c. }	10	10
352.	4 c. }	10	10
353.	25 c. "Last Supper" ..	30	10
354.	40 c. "Last Supper" ..	35	10
355.	$1 "Baptism of Christ"	60	55

Type **111** shows the left-hand stamp of the 4 c. design.

Nos. 353/5 are size 27 × 35 mm.

1976. West Indian Victory in World Cricket Cup. As Nos 559/60 of Barbados.

356.	12 c. Map of the Caribbean	60	20
357.	40 c. Prudential Cup ..	1·40	50

112. Crispus Attucks and the Boston Massacre.

1976. Bicent. of American Revolution. Mult.

359.	20 c. Type **112**	20	10
360.	40 c. Alexander Hamilton and Battle of Yorktown	35	10
361.	45 c. Jefferson and Declaration of Independence ..	35	10
362.	$1 Washington and the Crossing of the Delaware	70	80

113. "The Nativity" (Storza Book of Hours).

1976. Christmas. Multicoloured.

363.	20 c. Type **113**	10	10
364.	40 c. "Virgin and Child with St. John" (Pintoricchio)	15	10
365.	45 c. "Our Lady of Good Children" (Ford Maddox-Brown)	15	10
366.	$1 "Little Hands Outstretched to Bless" (M. Tarrant)	35	50

114. Royal Visit, 1966.

1977. Silver Jubilee. Multicoloured.

367.	50 c. Type **114**	15	10
368.	55 c. The Sceptre	15	10
369.	$1.50 Bishops paying homage	30	50

115. "Christ on the Cross" (Niccolo di Liberatore).

1977. Easter. Paintings from National Gallery, London. Multicoloured.

370.	25 c. Type **115**	10	10
371.	30 c. "The Resurrection" (imitator of Mantegna)	10	10
372.	50 c. "The Resurrection" (Ugolino da Siena) (horiz.)	15	10
373.	$1 "Christ Rising from the Tomb" (Gaudenzio Ferrari)	25	30

116. Estridge Mission.

1977. Bicentenary of Moravian Mission.

374. **116.**	4 c. black, green & blue	10	10
375. –	20 c. blk., mauve & violet	10	10
376. –	40 c. blk., yell. & orge.	15	15

DESIGNS: 20 c. Mission symbol. 40 c. Basseterre Mission.

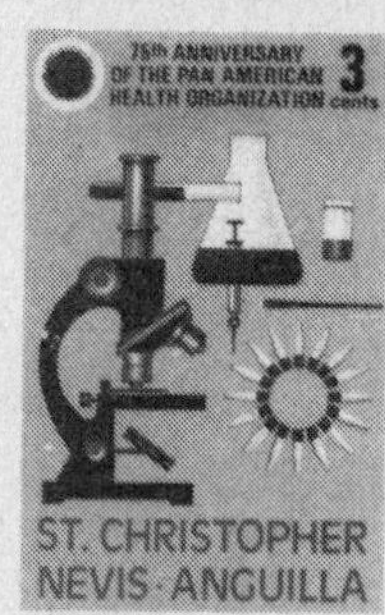

117. Laboratory Instruments.

1977. 75th Anniv. of Pan-American Health Organisation.

377. **117.**	3 c. multicoloured ..	10	10
378. –	12 c. multicoloured ..	15	10
379. –	20 c. multicoloured ..	20	10
380. –	$1 brn., orge. and black	70	40

DESIGNS: 12 c. Fat cells, blood cells and nerve cells. 20 c. "Community participation in health". $1, Inoculation.

118. "Nativity" (West Window).

1977. Christmas. Stained-glass windows from Chartres Cathedral. Multicoloured.

381.	4 c. Type **118**	10	10
382.	6 c. "Three Magi" (west window)	10	10
383.	40 c. "La Belle Verriere"	35	10
384.	$1 "Virgin and Child" (Rose window)	75	45

119. Savanna Monkey with Vervet.

120. Falcon of Edward III.

1978. The Savanna Monkey.

385. **119.**	4 c. brown, red & black	10	10
386. –	5 c. multicoloured ..	10	10
387. **119.**	55 c. brn., green and blk.	30	10
388. –	$1.50 multicoloured ..	75	60

DESIGN: 5 c., $1.50, Savanna Monkeys on branch.

1978. 25th Anniv. of Coronation.

389. **120.**	$1 brown and red ..	20	20
390. –	$1 multicoloured ..	20	20
391. –	$1 brown and red ..	20	20

DESIGNS: No. 390, Queen Elizabeth II. No. 391, Brown pelican.

121. Tomatoes.

1978. Multicoloured.

392.	1 c. Type **121**	10	15
393.	2 c. Defence Force band	10	15
394.	5 c. Radio and T.V. station	10	10
395.	10 c. Technical college	10	10
396.	12 c. T.V. assembly plant	10	20
397.	15 c. Sugar cane harvesting	15	10
398.	25 c. Crafthouse (craft centre)	15	10
399.	30 c. "Europa" (liner)	60	45
400.	40 c. Lobster and sea crab	30	10
401.	45 c. Royal St. Kitts Hotel and golf course	1·75	65
402.	50 c. Pinney's Beach, Nevis	30	10
403.	55 c. New runway at Golden Rock	30	10
404.	$1 Cotton picking	35	30
405.	$5 Brewery	1·00	1·25
406.	$10 Pineapples and peanuts	2·25	2·50

122. Investiture.

1978. 50th Anniv. of Boy Scout Movement on St. Kitts and Nevis. Multicoloured.

407.	5 c. Type **122**	10	10
408.	10 c. Map reading	10	10
409.	25 c. Pitching tent	20	15
410.	40 c. Cooking	35	25
411.	50 c. First Aid	40	35
412.	55 c. Rev. W. A. Beckett (founder of Scouting in St. Kitts)	45	45

123. Wise Man with Gift of Gold.

1978. Christmas. Multicoloured.

413.	5 c. Type **123**	10	10
414.	15 c. Wise Man with gift of Frankincense	10	10
415.	30 c. Wise Man with gift of Myrrh	10	10
416.	$2.25 Wise Man paying homage to the infant Jesus	35	50

124. "Canna coccinea".

1979. Local Flowers (1st series). Multicoloured.

417.	5 c. Type **124**	10	10
418.	30 c. "Heliconia bihai"	30	20
419.	55 c. "Ruellia tuberosa"	50	30
420.	$1.50 "Gesneria ventricosa"	1·10	1·40

See also Nos. 430/3.

125. St. Christopher 1870–76 1d. Stamp and Sir Rowland Hill.

1979. Death Centenary of Sir Rowland Hill. Multicoloured.

421.	5 c. Type **125**	10	10
422.	15 c. 1970 Stamp Centenary 50 c. commemorative	10	10
423.	50 c. Great Britain 1841 2d. blue	35	35
424.	$2.50, St. Kitts–Nevis 1923 300th Anniv. of Colony £1 commemorative	90	1·10

126. "The Woodman's Daughter".

1979. Christmas. International Year of the Child. Paintings by Sir John Millais. Multicoloured.

425.	5 c. Type **126**	10	10
426.	25 c. "Cherry Ripe"	25	20
427.	30 c. "The Rescue"	25	20
428.	55 c. "Bubbles"	30	25

1980. Local Flowers (2nd series). As T **124**. Multicoloured.

430.	4 c. "Clerodendrum aculeatum"	30	10
431.	55 c. "Inga laurina"	40	20
432.	$1. 50 "Epidendrum difforme"	1·00	50
433.	$2 "Salvia serotina"	1·10	90

127. Nevis Lagoon.

1980. "London 1980" International Stamp Exhibition. Multicoloured.

434.	5 c. Type **127**	10	10
435.	30 c. Fig Tree Church (vert.)	20	10
436.	55 c. Nisbet Plantation	45	25
437.	$3 "Nelson" (Fuger) (vert.)	1·00	1·00

OFFICIAL STAMPS

1980. Nos. 396, 398 and 400/6 optd. **OFFICIAL.**

O 1.	12 c. multicoloured	1·25	1·00
O 2.	25 c. multicoloured	15	20
O 3.	40 c. multicoloured	50	50
O 4.	45 c. multicoloured	45	45
O 5.	50 c. multicoloured	30	40
O 6.	55 c. multicoloured	30	40
O 7.	$1 multicoloured	1·25	2·25
O 8.	$5 multicoloured	1·00	2·50
O 9.	$10 multicoloured	2·50	3·50

ST. LUCIA

One of the Windward Is., Br. W. Indies Achieved Associated Statehood on 1 March 1967.

1860. 12 pence = 1 shilling;
20 shillings = 1 pound.
1949. 100 cents = 1 West Indian dollar.

1.

HALFPENNY
(3.)

1860. No value on stamps.

5.	1.	(1d.) red	55·00	80·00
11a.		(1d.) black	15·00	11·00
7.		(4d.) blue	£100	£100
16.		(4d.) yellow	60·00	18·00
8.		(6d.) green	£200	£200
17a.		(6d.) violet	60·00	18·00
14c.		(1s.) orange	£150	25·00

1881. With value added by surch. as T **2.**

25.	1.	½d. green	12·00	22·00
26.		1d. black	18·00	8·00
24.		2½d. red	20·00	18·00
27.		4d. yellow	£170	17·00
28.		6d. violet	22·00	25·00
29.		1s. orange	£250	£160

5. 9.

1882.

43.	5.	½d. green	50	30
32.		1d. red	24·00	7·50
46.		2½d. blue	2·00	30
48.		4d. brown	1·60	2·25
35.		6d. lilac	£250	£200
36.		1s. brown	£350	£140

1886.

44.	5.	1d. mauve	1·00	15
45.		2d. blue and orange	70	1·00
47.		3d. mauve and green	3·25	5·50
41.		6d. mauve and blue	3·25	7·00
50.		1s. mauve and red	3·00	5·00
51.		5s. mauve and orange	28·00	80·00
52.		10s. mauve and black	60·00	80·00

1891. Surch. in words.

56.	5.	½d. on 3d. mauve & green	32·00	15·00
55.		1d. on 4d. brown	3·00	3·00

1891. Surch. in figures.

54.	5.	½d. on half 6d. (No. 41)	14·00	3·25

1902.

64a	9	½d. purple and green	1·50	65
65		½d. green	1·50	55
66a		1d. purple and red	1·75	40
67		1d. red	2·00	20
68a		2½d. purple and blue	3·50	2·50
69		2½d. blue	3·50	1·25
70		3d. purple and yellow	3·50	3·00
71		3d. purple on yellow	1·75	8·00
72		6d. purple and violet	8·00	6·50
72ab		6d. purple	4·50	13·00
62		1s. green and black	9·50	14·00
75		1s. black on green	3·50	5·00
76		5s. green and red	40·00	85·00
77		5s. green & red on yell	45·00	48·00

11. The Pitons.

12.

13. 14.

1902. 400th Anniv. of Discovery.

63.	11.	2 d. green and brown	6·50	1·75

1912.

91	12	½d. green	30	15
79		1d. red	1·90	10
93		1d. brown	40	15
94	14	1½d. red	50	1·50
95	13	2d. grey	30	15
96	12	2½d. blue	1·75	2·00
97		2½d. orange	6·50	32·00
82		3d. purple on yellow	60	2·00
99a		3d. blue	1·00	10·00
83a	14	4d. black & red on yellow	70	1·50
102	12	6d. purple	1·50	4·75
85		1s. black on green	2·50	4·25
103		1s. brown	1·75	4·00
87	13	2s. 6d. black & red on blue	15·00	20·00
88	12	5s. green & red on yellow	18·00	60·00

1916. No. 79a optd. **WAR TAX** in two lines.

89.	12.	1d. red	3·75	3·25

1916. No. 79a optd. **WAR TAX** in one line.

90.	12.	1d. red	20	20

1935. Silver Jubilee. As T **13** of Antigua.

109.	½d. black and green	15	25
110.	2d. blue and grey	45	25
111.	2½d. brown and blue	90	65
112.	1s. grey and purple	3·75	4·00

19. Port Castries.

1936. King George V.

113.	19.	½d. black and green	30	45
114.	–	1d. black and brown	40	10
115.	–	1½d. black and red	55	30
116.	19.	2d. black and grey	40	15
117.	–	2½d. black and blue	40	15
118.	–	3d. black and green	1·25	70
119.	19.	4d. black and brown	30	1·00
120.	–	6d. black and orange	85	1·00
121.	–	1s. black and blue	1·25	2·00
122.	–	2s. 6d. black and blue	5·00	14·00
123.	–	5s. black and violet	8·00	20·00
124.	–	10s. black and red	42·00	50·00

DESIGNS—HORIZ. 1d., 2½d., 6d. Columbus Square, Castries. 1s. Fort Rodney, Pigeon Island. 5s. Govt. House. 10s. Badge of Colony. VERT. 1½d., 3d. Ventine Falls. 2s. 6d. Inniskilling Monument.

1937. Coronation. As T **2** of Aden.

125.	1d. violet	30	30
126.	1½d. red	55	20
127.	2½d. blue	55	40

26. King George VI.

DESIGNS — HORIZ. As Type **27**: 1s. Govt. House. 2s. The Pitons. 5s. Loading bananas. VERT. 10s. Device of St. Lucia as Type **33**.

27. Columbus Square.

1938. King George VI.

128a	26	½d. green	10	10
129a		1d. violet	10	15
129b		1d. red	10	10
130a		1½d. red	15	35
131a		2d. grey	10	10
132a		2½d. blue	10	10
132b		2½d. violet	20	10
133a		3d. orange	10	10
133b		3½d. blue	30	15
134b	27	6d. red	85	45
134c	26	8d. brown	2·25	30
135a	–	1s. brown	40	20
136	–	2s. blue and red	3·50	1·25
136a	26	3s. purple	8·00	2·75
137	–	5s. black and purple	14·00	6·00
138	–	10s. black on yellow	4·50	9·00
141	26	£1 brown	11·00	8·00

1946. Victory. As T **9** of Aden.

142.	1d. violet	10	10
143.	3½d. blue	10	10

1948. Silver Wedding. As T **10/11** of Aden.

144	1d. red	15	10
145	£1 purple	12·00	35·00

33. Device of St. Lucia.

34. Phoenix rising from Burning Buildings.

1949. New Currency.

146.	26.	1 c. green	10	10
147.		2 c. mauve	10	10
148.		3 c. red	10	40
149.		4 c. grey	10	10
150.		5 c. violet	10	10
151.		6 c. orange	15	30
152.		7 c. blue	80	55
153.		12 c. red	1·75	30
154.		16 c. brown	1·50	20
155.	33.	24 c. blue	30	10
156.		48 c. olive	1·50	85
157.		$1.20 purple	2·25	4·25
158.		$2.40 green	3·00	17·00
159.		$4.80 red	7·00	18·00

1949. U.P.U. As T **20/23** of Antigua.

160	5 c. violet	20	20
161	6 c. orange	45	40
162	12 c. mauve	30	20
163	24 c. green	65	20

1951. Inauguration of B.W.I. University College. As T **24/25** of Antigua.

164	3 c. black and red	45	20
165	12 c. black and red	45	20

1951. Reconstruction of Castries.

166.	34.	12 c. red and blue	15	30

1951. New Constitution. Optd. **NEW CONSTITUTION 1951.**

167.	**26.**	2 c. mauve	15	20
168.		4 c. grey	15	20
169.		5 c. violet	15	20
170.		12 c. red	15	40

1953. Coronation. As T **13** of Aden.

171.		3 c. black and red	40	10

1953. As 1949 but portrait of Queen Elizabeth II facing left and new Royal Cypher.

172.	**26.**	1 c. green	10	10
173.		2 c. purple	10	10
174.		3 c. red	10	10
175.		4 c. grey	10	10
176.		5 c. violet	10	10
177.		6 c. orange	15	10
178.		8 c. red	20	10
179.		10 c. blue	10	10
180.		15 c. brown	30	10
181.	**33.**	25 c. blue	30	10
182.		50 c. olive	4·50	50
183.		$1 green	4·00	95
184.		$2.50 red	5·00	4·00

1958. British Caribbean Federation. As T **28** of Antigua.

185		3 c. green	50	20
186		6 c. blue	85	1·00
187		12 c. red	1·10	75

38. Columbus's "Santa Maria" off the Pitons.

1960. New Constitution for the Windward and Leeward Islands.

188.	**38.**	8 c. red	35	30
189.		10 c. orange	35	30
190.		25 c. blue	50	35

39. Stamp of 1860.

1960. Stamp Cent.

191.	**39.**	5 c. red and blue	15	10
192.		16 c. blue and green	30	50
193.		25 c. green and red	30	20

1963. Freedom from Hunger. As T **28** of Aden.

194.		25 c. green	30	10

1963. Cent of Red Cross. As T **33** of Antigua.

195		4 c. red and black	15	20
196		25 c. red and blue	50	1·00

40. Queen Elizabeth II. **41.** (after A. C. Davidson-Houston).

42 Fishing Boats.

1964.

197.	**40.**	1 c. red	10	10
198.		2 c. violet	30	20
199.		4 c. green	35	20
200.		5 c. blue	30	10
201.		6 c. brown	45	20
202.	**41.**	8 c. multicoloured	10	10
203.		10 c. multicoloured	40	10
204.	**42.**	12 c. multicoloured	20	20
205.	–	15 c. multicoloured	20	10
206.	–	25 c. multicoloured	20	10
207.	–	35 c. blue and buff	1·25	10
208.	–	50 c. multicoloured	1·10	10
209.	–	$1 multicoloured	1·25	30
210.	–	$2.50 multicoloured	2·00	1·50

DESIGNS—As Type **42**: HORIZ. 15 c. Pigeon Island. 25 c. Reduit Beach. VERT. $1, Vigie Beach. As Type **42** but "E. II R" in place of portrait. HORIZ. 35 c. Castries Harbour. 50 c. The Pitons. As Type **41**: $2·50, Queen Elizabeth II, head and shoulders.

1964. 400th Birth Anniv of Shakespeare. As T **34** of Antigua.

211.	**42a.**	10 c. green	10	10

1965. Cent of I.T.U. As T **36** of Antigua.

212.		2 c. mauve and purple	10	10
213.		50 c. lilac and green	90	45

1965. I.C.Y. As T **37** of Antigua.

214		1 c. purple and green	10	10
215		25 c. green and violet	20	20

1966. Churchill Commem. As T **38** of Antigua.

216.		4 c. blue	10	10
217.		6 c. green	15	30
218.		25 c. brown	20	15
219.		35 c. violet	30	20

1966. Royal Visit. As T **39** of Antigua.

220		4 c. black and blue	10	10
221		25 c. black and mauve	50	50

1966. World Cup Football Championship. As T **40** of Antigua.

222		4 c. multicoloured	10	10
223		25 c. multicoloured	40	30

1966. Inauguration of W.H.O. Headquarters, Geneva. As T **41** of Antigua.

224		4 c. black, green and blue	10	10
225		25 c. black, purple & brown	25	20

1966. 20th Anniv of U.N.E.S.C.O. As T **54/6** of Antigua.

226.		4 c. multicoloured	10	10
227.		12 c. yellow, violet & olive	20	30
228.		25 c. black, purple & orge.	35	35

51. Map of St. Lucia.

1967. Statehood. Nos. 198, 202/9 and 257 optd. **STATEHOOD 1st MARCH 1967.**

(a) Postage.

229.	**40.**	2 c. violet	20	15
230.		5 c. blue	10	10
231.		6 c. brown	10	10
232.	**41.**	8 c. multicoloured	20	10
233.		10 c. multicoloured	25	10
234.	**42.**	12 c. multicoloured	20	10
235.	–	15 c. multicoloured	25	30
236.	–	25 c. multicoloured	30	30
237.	–	35 c. blue and buff	50	35
238.	–	50 c. multicoloured	50	55
239.	–	$1 multicoloured	50	55

(b) Air.

240.	**51.**	15 c. blue	10	10

52. "Madonna and Child with the Infant Baptist" (Raphael).

1967. Christmas.

241.	**52.**	4 c. multicoloured	10	10
242.		25 c. multicoloured	30	10

53. Batsman and Sir Frederick Clarke (Governor).

1968. M.C.C.'s West Indies Tour.

243.	**53.**	10 c. multicoloured	20	20
244.		35 c. multicoloured	45	50

54. "The Crucified Christ with the Virgin Mary, Saints and the Angels". (Raphael.) **56.** Dr. Martin Luther King.

1968. Easter Commem.

245.	**54.**	10 c. multicoloured	10	10
246.	–	15 c. multicoloured	10	10
247.	**54.**	25 c. multicoloured	15	10
248.	–	35 c. multicoloured	15	10

DESIGN: 15 c., 35 c. "Noli me tangere" (detail by Titian).

1968. Martin Luther King Commem.

250.	**56.**	25 c. blue, black & flesh	15	15
251.		35 c. blue, black & flesh	15	15

57. "Virgin and Child in Glory" (Murillo).

1968. Christmas.

252.	**57.**	5 c. multicoloured	10	10
253.	–	10 c. multicoloured	10	10
254.	**57.**	25 c. multicoloured	15	10
255.	–	35 c. multicoloured	15	10

DESIGN: 10 c., 35 c. "Madonna and Child" (Murillo).

59. Purple-throated Carib.

1969. Birds. Multicoloured.

256.		10 c. Type **59**	55	25
257.		15 c. St. Lucia amazon	70	30
258.		25 c. Type **59**	90	35
259.		35 c. As 15 c.	1·25	45

HAVE YOU READ THE NOTES AT THE BEGINNING OF THIS CATALOGUE?
These often provide answers to the enquiries we receive.

61. "Head of Christ Crowned with Thorns" (Reni).

1969. Easter Commem. Multicoloured.

260.		10 c. Type **61**	10	10
261.		15 c. "Resurrection of Christ" (Sodoma)	10	10
262.		25 c. Type **61**	15	15
263.		35 c. As the 15 c.	15	15

63. Map showing "CARIFTA" Countries.

1969. 1st Anniv. of "CARIFTA".

264.	**63.**	5 c. multicoloured	10	10
265.		10 c. multicoloured	10	10
266.	–	25 c. multicoloured	15	15
267.	–	35 c. multicoloured	15	15

DESIGN: 25 c., 35 c. Handclasp and names of "CARIFTA" countries.

65. Emperor Napoleon and Empress Josephine.

1969. Birth Bicent. of Napoleon Bonaparte.

268.	**65.**	15 c. multicoloured	10	10
269.		25 c. multicoloured	10	10
270.		35 c. multicoloured	10	10
271.		50 c. multicoloured	15	35

66. "Virgin and Child" (P. Delaroche).

1969. Christmas. Paintings. Multicoloured; background colours given.

272.	**66.**	5 c. gold and purple	10	10
273.	–	10 c. gold and blue	10	10
274.	**66.**	25 c. gold and red	20	10
275.	–	35 c. gold and green	20	10

DESIGN: 10 c. and 35 c. "Holy Family" (Rubens).

68. House of Assembly.

1970. Multicoloured.

276.		1 c. Type **68**	10	10
277.		2 c. Roman Catholic Cathedral	15	10
278.		4 c. The Boulevard, Castries	40	10
279.		5 c. Castries Harbour	40	10
280.		6 c. Sulphur Springs	15	10
281.		10 c. Vigie Airport	30	10
282.		12 c. Reduit Beach	20	10
283.		15 c. Pigeon Island	30	10

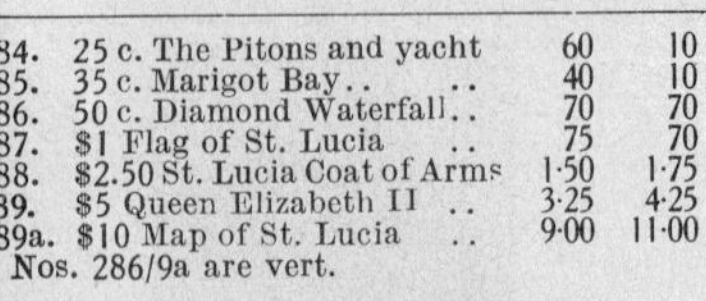

284.	25 c. The Pitons and yacht	60	10
285.	35 c. Marigot Bay.. ..	40	10
286.	50 c. Diamond Waterfall..	70	70
287.	$1 Flag of St. Lucia ..	75	70
288.	$2.50 St. Lucia Coat of Arms	1·50	1·75
289.	$5 Queen Elizabeth II ..	3·25	4·25
289a.	$10 Map of St. Lucia ..	9·00	11·00

Nos. 286/9a are vert.

69. "The Sealing of the Tomb" (Hogarth).

1970. Easter. Multicoloured.

290.	25 c. Type 69	15	20
291.	35 c. "The Three Marys at the Tomb" (Hogarth) ..	15	20
292.	$1 "The Ascension (Hogarth)	30	40

The $1 is larger (39×54 mm.).

Nos. 290/2 were issued in a triptych, with the $1 value 10 mm. higher than the other values.

72. Charles Dickens and Dickensian Characters.

1970. Death Cent. of Charles Dickens.

293.	72.	1 c. multicoloured ..	10	10
294.		25 c. multicoloured ..	20	10
295.		35 c. multicoloured ..	25	10
296.		50 c. multicoloured ..	35	40

73. Nurse and Emblem.

1970. Cent. of British Red Cross. Mult.

297.	10 c. Type 73	15	10
298.	15 c. Flags of Great Britain, Red Cross and St. Lucia	25	10
299.	25 c. Type 73	35	15
300.	35 c. As 15 c.	40	15

74. "Madonna with the Lilies" (Luca della Robbia).

1970. Christmas.

301.	74.	5 c. multicoloured ..	10	10
302.		10 c. multicoloured ..	15	10
303.		35 c. multicoloured ..	30	10
304.		40 c. multicoloured ..	30	20

75. "Christ on the Cross" (Rubens).

1971. Easter. Multicoloured.

305.	10 c. Type 75	10	10
306.	15 c. "Descent from the Cross" (Rubens) ..	15	10
307.	35 c. Type 75	30	10
308.	40 c. As 15 c.	30	20

76. Moule a Chique Lighthouse.

1971. Opening of Beane Field Airport. Mult.

309.	5 c. Type 76	30	15
310.	25 c. Aircraft landing at Beane Field	45	15

77. Morne Fortune.

78. Morne Fortune, Modern View.

1971. Old and New Views of St. Lucia. Multicoloured.

311.	5 c. Type 77	10	10
312.	5 c. Type 78	10	10
313.	10 c. } Castries City ..	10	10
314.	10 c. } ..	10	10
315.	25 c. } Pigeon Island ..	25	20
316.	25 c. } ..	25	20
317.	50 c. } View from grounds	50	55
318.	50 c. } of Govt. House ..	50	55

Each value of this issue was printed horizontally and vertically se-tenant in two designs showing respectively old and new views of St. Lucia.

The old views are taken from printings by J. H. Caddy.

79. "Virgin and Child with two Angels". (Verrocchio).

1971. Christmas. Multicoloured.

319.	5 c. Type 79	10	10
320.	10 c. "Virgin and Child, St. John the Baptist and an Angel". (Morando)..	10	10
321.	35 c. "Madonna and Child" (Battista)	15	10
322.	40 c. Type 79	20	25

80. "St. Lucia" (Dolci School) and Coat of Arms.

1971. National Day.

323.	80.	5 c. multicoloured ..	10	10
324.		10 c. multicoloured ..	15	10
325.		25 c. multicoloured ..	25	10
326.		50 c. multicoloured ..	45	40

81. "The Dead Christ Mourned" (Carracci).

1972. Easter. Multicoloured.

327.	10 c. Type 81	10	10
328.	25 c. "Angels weeping over the dead Christ" (Guercino)	20	10
329.	35 c. Type 81	30	10
330.	50 c. As 25 c.	40	40

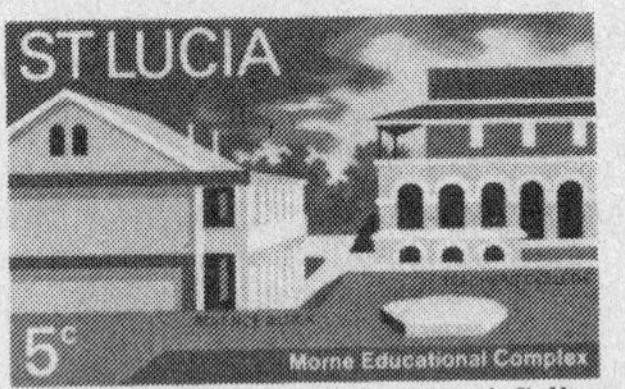

82. Science Block and Teachers' College.

1972. Morne Educational Complex. Mult.

331.	5 c. Type 82	10	10
332.	15 c. University Centre ..	10	10
333.	25 c. Secondary School ..	10	10
334.	35 c. Technical College ..	15	10

83. Steamship Stamp and Map.

1972. 1st Postal Service by St. Lucia Steam Conveyance Co. Ltd. Cent.

335.	83.	5 c. multicoloured ..	15	10
336.	–	10 c. blue, mauve & blk.	20	10
337.	–	35 c. red, blue and black	60	10
338.	–	50 c. multicoloured ..	1·00	1·00

DESIGNS: 10 c. Steamship stamp and Castries Harbour. 35 c. Steamship stamp and Soufriere. 50 c. Steamship stamps.

84. "The Holy Family" (Sebastiano Ricci).

1972. Christmas.

339.	84.	5 c. multicoloured ..	10	10
340.		10 c. multicoloured ..	10	10
341.		35 c. multicoloured ..	20	10
342.		40 c. multicoloured ..	25	15

1972. Royal Silver Wedding. As T **52** of Ascension but with Arms and St. Lucia Amazon.

343	85	15 c. red	20	15
344		35 c. green	20	15

86. Week-day Headdress.

87. Coat of Arms.

1973. Local Headdresses. Multicoloured.

345.	5 c. Type 86	10	10
346.	10 c. Formal style ..	10	10
347.	25 c. Unmarried girl's style	15	10
348.	50 c. Ceremonial style ..	25	40

1973.

349	87	5 c. green	10	35
350		10 c. blue	15	35
953		10 c. green	30	30
351		25 c. brown	15	35

88. H.M.S. "St. Lucia", 1830.

1973. Historic Ships. Multicoloured.

352.	15 c. Type 88	20	10
353.	35 c. H.M.S. "Prince of Wales", 1765	25	10
354.	50 c. "Oliph Blossom", 1605	40	20
355.	$1 H.M.S. "Rose", 1757 ..	55	65

89. Plantation and Flower.

1973. Banana Industry. Multicoloured.

357.	5 c. Type 89	10	10
358.	15 c. Aerial spraying ..	15	10
359.	35 c. Boxing plant ..	20	10
360.	50 c. Loading a boat ..	40	40

90. "The Virgin with Child" (Maratta).

1973. Christmas. Multicoloured.

361.	5 c. Type 90	10	10
362.	15 c. "Madonna in the Meadow" (Raphael) ..	10	10
363.	35 c. "The Holy Family" (Bronzino)	20	10
364.	50 c. "Madonna of the Pear" (Durer)	30	35

1973. Royal Wedding. As T **47** of Anguilla. Multicoloured, background colours given.

365	40 c. green	10	10
366	50 c. lilac	10	10

91. "The Betrayal".

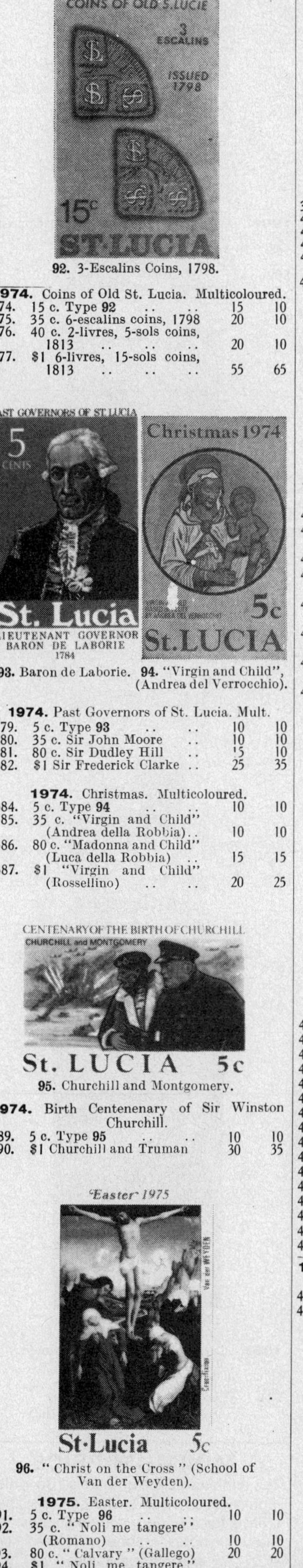

1974. Easter. Paintings by Ugolino da Siena. Multicoloured.

369.	5 c. Type **91**	10	10
370.	35 c. " The Way to Calvary "	15	10
371.	80 c. " The Deposition "	15	15
372.	$1 " The Resurrection "	20	25

92. 3-Escalins Coins, 1798.

1974. Coins of Old St. Lucia. Multicoloured.

374.	15 c. Type **92**	15	10
375.	35 c. 6-escalins coins, 1798	20	10
376.	40 c. 2-livres, 5-sols coins, 1813	20	10
377.	$1 6-livres, 15-sols coins, 1813	55	65

93. Baron de Laborie. **94.** "Virgin and Child", (Andrea del Verrocchio).

1974. Past Governors of St. Lucia. Mult.

379.	5 c. Type **93**	10	10
380.	35 c. Sir John Moore ..	10	10
381.	80 c. Sir Dudley Hill ..	15	10
382.	$1 Sir Frederick Clarke ..	25	35

1974. Christmas. Multicoloured.

384.	5 c. Type **94**	10	10
385.	35 c. "Virgin and Child" (Andrea della Robbia) ..	10	10
386.	80 c. "Madonna and Child" (Luca della Robbia) ..	15	15
387.	$1 "Virgin and Child" (Rossellino)	20	25

95. Churchill and Montgomery.

1974. Birth Centenary of Sir Winston Churchill.

389.	5 c. Type **95**	10	10
390.	$1 Churchill and Truman	30	35

96. " Christ on the Cross " (School of Van der Weyden).

1975. Easter. Multicoloured.

391.	5 c. Type **96**	10	10
392.	35 c. " Noli me tangere " (Romano)	10	10
393.	80 c. " Calvary " (Gallego)	20	20
394.	$1 " Noli me tangere " (Correggio)	30	35

97. " Nativity " (French Book of Hours).

1975. Christmas. Multicoloured.

399.	5 c. Type **97**	10	10
400.	10 c. } " Epiphany scene "	10	10
401.	10 c. } (stained glass	10	10
402.	10 c. } window) ..	10	10
403.	40 c. " Nativity " (Hastings Book of Hours) ..	30	20
404.	$1 " Virgin and Child with Saints " (Borgognone) ..	70	50

98. American Schooner "Hanna".

1975. Bicentenary of American Revolution. Ships. Multicoloured.

406	½ c. Type **98**	10	10
407	1 c. "Prince of Orange" (British sailing packet)	10	10
408	2 c. H.M.S. "Edward" (sloop)	10	10
409	5 c. "Millern" (British merchantman)	30	10
410	15 c. "Surprise" (American lugger)	60	10
411	35 c. H.M.S. "Serapis" (frigate)	1·10	20
412	50 c. "Randolph" (American frigate) ..	1·25	40
413	$1 "Alliance" (American frigate)	2·25	1·00

99. Laughing Gull.

1976. Birds. Multicoloured.

415	1 c. Type **99**	30	60
416	2 c. Little blue heron ..	30	60
417	4 c. Belted kingfisher ..	35	60
418	5 c. St. Lucia amazon ..	1·25	60
419	6 c. St. Lucia oriole ..	1·25	70
420	8 c. Brown trembler ..	1·25	75
421	10 c. American kestrel ..	1·25	35
422	12 c. Red-billed tropic bird	1·25	1·00
423	15 c. Moorhen	1·25	15
424a	25 c. Common noddy ..	1·00	30
425	35 c. Sooty tern	1·75	70
426	50 c. Osprey	4·00	1·50
427	$1 White-breasted trembler	3·25	1·75
428	$2.50 St. Lucia black finch	4·50	4·00
429	$5 Red-necked pigeon ..	5·00	4·00
430a	$10 Caribbean elaenia ..	5·00	7·50

1976. West Indian Victory in World Cricket Cup. As Nos. 599/60 of Barbados. Mult.

431	50 c. Caribbean map ..	1·00	1·00
432	$1 Prudential Cup ..	1·50	2·25

100. H.M.S. " Ceres ".

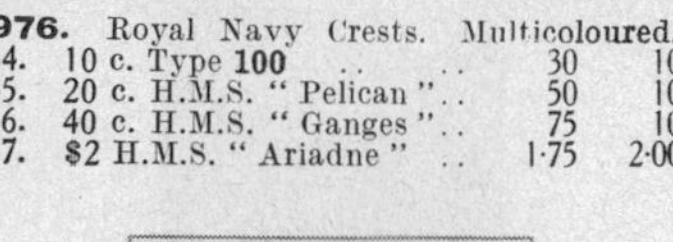

1976. Royal Navy Crests. Multicoloured.

434.	10 c. Type **100**	30	10
435.	20 c. H.M.S. " Pelican " ..	50	10
436.	40 c. H.M.S. " Ganges " ..	75	10
437.	$2 H.M.S. " Ariadne " ..	1·75	2·00

101. " Madonna and Child " (Murillo).

1976. Christmas. Multicoloured.

438.	10 c. Type **101**	10	10
439.	20 c. " Madonna and Child with Angels " (Costa) ..	10	10
440.	50 c. " Madonna and Child Enthroned " (Isenbrandt)	15	10
441.	$2 " Madonna and Child with St. John " (Murillo)	50	65

102. Queen Elizabeth II.

1977. Silver Jubilee.

443. **102.**	10 c. multicoloured ..	10	10
444.	20 c. multicoloured ..	15	15
445.	40 c. multicoloured ..	20	25
446.	$2 multicoloured	60	90

103. Scouts from Tapion School.

1977. Caribbean Boy Scout Jamboree. Multicoloured.

448.	½ c. Type **103**	10	10
449.	1 c. Sea scouts	10	10
450.	2 c. Scout from Micoud ..	10	10
451.	10 c. Two scouts from Tapion School	15	10
452.	20 c. Venture scout ..	20	15
453.	50 c. Scout from Gros Islet	45	55
454.	$1 Sea scouts in motor boat	75	1·25

104. " Nativity " (Giotto).

1977. Christmas. Multicoloured.

456.	½ c. Type **104**	10	10
457.	1 c. " Perugia triptych " (Fra Angelico)	10	10
458.	2 c. " Virgin and Child " (El Greco)	10	10
459.	20 c. " Madonna of the Rosary " (Caravaggio)	15	10
460.	50 c. " Adoration of the Magi " (Velazquez) ..	25	15
461.	$1 " Madonna of Carmel " (Tiepolo)	40	50
462.	$2.50 " Adoration of the Magi " (Tiepolo) ..	65	1·00

105. " Susan Lunden ".

1977. 400th Birth Anniv. of Rubens. Mult.

463.	10 c. Type **105**	10	10
464.	35 c. " The Rape of the Sabine Women " (detail)	15	10
465.	50 c. " Ludovicus Nonnius "	30	10
466.	$2·50 " Minerva protects Pax from Mars " (detail)	85	80

106. Yeoman of the Guard and Life Guard.

1978. 25th Anniv. of Coronation. Mult.

468.	15 c. Type **106**	10	10
469.	20 c. Groom and postillion	10	10
470.	50 c. Footman and coachman	15	10
471.	$3 State trumpeter and herald	60	80

107. Queen Angelfish.

1978. Fish. Multicoloured.

473.	10 c. Type **107**	15	10
474.	20 c. Foureye Butterflyfish	30	10
475.	50 c. French Angelfish ..	60	30
476.	$2 Yellowtail Damselfish	1·10	1·50

108. French Grenadier and Map of the Battle.

1978. Bicentenary of Battle of Cul-de-Sac. Multicoloured.

478.	10 c. Type **108**	20	10
479.	30 c. British Grenadier Officer and Map of St. Lucia (Bellin), 1762 ..	40	10
480.	50 c. Coastline from Gros Islet to Cul-de-Sac and British Fleet opposing French landings ..	55	15
481.	$2.50 General James Grant, 1798 and Light Infantrymen of the 46th Regiment	1·50	1·25

109. The Annunciation.

1978. Christmas. Multicoloured.

482.	30 c. Type **109**	10	10
483.	50 c. Type **109**	15	10
484.	55 c. The Nativity ..	15	10
485.	80 c. As 55 c.	20	20

110. Hewanorra International Air Terminal.

1979. Independence. Multicoloured.

486. 10 c. Type **110** 10 10
487. 30 c. New coat of arms .. 10 10
488. 50 c. Government House and Sir Allen Lewis (first Governor-General) .. 15 10
489. $2 French, St. Lucia and Union flags on map of St. Lucia 30 45

111. Popes Paul VI and John Paul I.

1979. Pope Paul VI Commemoration. Mult.

491. 10 c. Type **111** 10 10
492. 30 c. Pres. Sadat of Egypt with Pope Paul .. 20 10
493. 50 c. Pope Paul with Secretary-General U Thant .. 35 20
494. 55 c. Pope Paul and Prime Minister Golda Meir of Israel 40 25
495. $2 Martin Luther King received in audience by Pope Paul .. .. 1·00 80

112. Dairy Farming.

1979. Agricultural Diversification. Mult.

496. 10 c. Type **112** 10 10
497. 35 c. Fruit and vegetables 10 10
498. 50 c. Water conservation 10 10
499. $3 Copra industry .. 35 70

113. Lindbergh and Flying-boat.

1979. 50th Anniv. of Lindbergh's Inaugural Airmail Flight via St. Lucia.

500. **113.** 10 c. blk., red & orge.. .. 10 10
501. – 30 c. multicoloured .. 10 10
502. – 50 c. multicoloured .. 10 10
503. – $2 multicoloured .. 30 40

DESIGNS: 30 c. Flying-boat and route map. 50 c. Arrival at La Toc, September, 1929. $2, First flight covers.

114. " A Prince of Saxony " (Cranach the Elder).

1979. International Year of the Child. Famous Paintings. Multicoloured.

504. 10 c. Type **114** 10 10
505. 50 c. " The Infanta Margarita " (Velazquez) 15 10
506. $2 " Girl playing Badminton " (Chardin) .. 40 40
507. $2.50 " Mary and Francis Wilcox " (Stock) .. 45 45

115. Notice of Introduction of Penny Post.

1979. Death Centenary of Sir Rowland Hill. Multicoloured.

509. 10 c. Type **115** 10 10
510. 50 c. Wyon essay 20 10
511. $2 First St. Lucia stamp .. 45 50
512. $2.50 G.B. 1840 Penny Black 55 60

116. " Madonna and Child " (Bernardino Fungai).

1979. Christmas. Int. Year of the Child. Paintings of the " Madonna and Child " by artists named. Multicoloured.

514. 10 c. Type **116** 10 10
515. 50 c. Carlo Dolci 25 10
516. $2 Titian 70 40
517. $2.50 Giovanni Bellini .. 75 50

117. St. Lucia Steam Conveyance Co. Ltd. Cover of 1873.

1980. " London 1980 " International Stamp Exhibition. Multicoloured.

519. 10 c. Type **117** 10 10
520. 30 c. 1879 S.S. " Assistance " 1d. postmark 10 10
521. 50 c. 1929 Postage Due handstamp 15 10
522. $2 1844 Crown Circle Paid stamp 40 55

118. Mickey Mouse astride Rocket.

1980. 10th Anniv. (1979) of Moon Landing. Disney Characters in Space Scenes. Mult.

524. ½ c. Type **118** 10 10
525. 1 c. Donald Duck being towed by rocket (horiz.) 10 10
526. 2 c. Minnie Mouse on Moon 10 10
527. 3 c. Goofy hitching lift to Mars 10 10
528. 4 c. Goofy and Moondog (horiz.) 10 10
529. 5 c. Pluto burying bone on Moon (horiz.) 10 10
530. 10 c. Donald Duck and love-sick Martian (horiz.) 10 10
531. $2 Donald Duck paddling spaceship (horiz.) .. 1·75 1·00
532. $2·50 Mickey Mouse driving moonbuggy (horiz.) .. 2·00 1·10

119. Queen Elizabeth the Queen Mother.

1980. 80th Birthday of The Queen Mother.

534. **119.** 10 c. multicoloured .. 15 10
535. $2·50 multicoloured .. 70 1·00

120. Hawker Siddeley " HS 748 ".

1980. Transport. Multicoloured.

537 5 c. Type **120** 25 10
538 10 c. McDonnell Douglas "DC-10" airliner .. 35 10
539 15 c. Local bus 35 20
540 20 c. Refrigerated freighter 35 20
541 25 c. "Islander" airplane 50 10
542 30 c. "Charles" (pilot boat) 40 30
543 50 c. Boeing "727" airliner 65 50
544 75 c. "Cunard Countess" (liner) 65 85
545 $1 Lockheed "Tristar" airliner .. .. .. 85 1·00
546 $2 Cargo liner .. .. 1·25 1·75
547 $5 Boeing "707" airliner .. 4·50 5·00
548 $10 "Queen Elizabeth 2" (liner) .. .. .. 5·50 7·00

121. Shot-putting.

1980. Olympic Games, Moscow. Mult.

549. 10 c. Type **121** 10 10
550. 50 c. Swimming 15 10
551. $2 Gymnastics 60 50
552. $2·50 Weight-lifting .. 70 60

122. Coastal Landscape within Cogwheel.

1980. 75th Anniv. of Rotary International. Different coastal landscapes within cogwheels.

554. **122.** 10 c. multicoloured .. 10 10
555. – 50 c. multicoloured .. 15 10
556. – $2 black, red and yellow 40 40
557. – $2.50 multicoloured .. 50 55

123. Sir Arthur Lewis.

1980. Nobel Prize Winners. Multicoloured.

559. 10 c. Type **123** 10 10
560. 50 c. Martin Luther King Jnr. 20 15
561. $2 Ralph Bunche 50 60
562. $2.50 Albert Schweitzer .. 70 80

1980. Hurricane Relief. Nos. 538/9 and 542 surch. **1980 $1·50 HURRICANE RELIEF.**

564. $1·50 on 15 c. mult. .. 30 40
565. $1·50 on 20 c. mult. .. 30 40
566. $1·50 on 50 c. mult. .. 30 40

125. " The Nativity " (Giovanni Battista).

1980. Christmas. Paintings. Multicoloured.

567. 10 c. Type **125** 10 10
568. 30 c. " Adoration of the Kings " (Pieter the Elder) 10 10
569. $2 " Adoration of the Shepherds " (ascribed to Murillo) 40 60

126. Brazilian Agouti.

1981. Wildlife. Multicoloured.

571. 10 c. Type **126** .. 15 10
572. 50 c. St. Lucia Amazon .. 75 10
573. $2 Purple-throated Carib 1·25 80
574. $2.50 Fiddler Crab .. 1·25 1·00

127. Prince Charles at Balmoral.

1981. Royal Wedding. Multicoloured.

576. 25 c. Prince Charles and Lady Diana Spencer .. 10 10
577. 50 c. Clarence House .. 10 10
578. $4 Type **127** 40 55

128. Lady Diana Spencer.

1981. Royal Wedding. Booklet stamps. Multicoloured. Self-adhesive.

580. 50 c. Type **128** 15 30
581. $2 Prince Charles .. 30 60
582. $5 Prince Charles and Lady Diana Spencer .. .. 1·25 1·75

MINIMUM PRICE

The minimum price quoted is 10p which represents a handling charge rather than a basis for valuing common stamps. For further notes about prices see introductory pages.

129. " The Cock ".

1981. Birth Bicentenary of Picasso. Mult.

583. 30 c. Type **129** 25 10
584. 50 c. " Man with an Ice-cream " 35 10
585. 55 c. " Woman dressing her Hair " 35 10
586. $3 " Seated Woman " .. 95 85

130. " Industry ".

1981. 25th Anniv. of Duke of Edinburgh Award Scheme. Multicoloured.

588. 10 c. Type **130** 10 10
589. 35 c. " Community service " 15 10
590. 50 c. " Physical recreation " 20 10
591. $2.50 Duke of Edinburgh speaking at Caribbean Conference, 1975 .. 70 70

131. Louis Braille.

1981. International Year of Disabled People. Famous Disabled People. Multicoloured.

592. 10 c. Type **131** 10 10
593. 50 c. Sarah Bernhardt .. 20 10
594. $2 Joseph Pulitzer .. 60 70
595. $2.50 Henri de Toulouse-Lautrec 65 85

132. " Portrait of Fanny Travis Cochran " (Cecilia Beaux).

1981. Decade for Women. Paintings. Mult.

597. 10 c. Type **132** 10 10
598. 50 c. " Women with Dove " (Marie Laurencin) .. 20 10
599. $2 " Portrait of a Young Pupil of David " (Aimee Duvivier) 60 70
600. $2.50 " Self-portrait " (Rosalba Carriera) .. 65 85

133. "Adoration of the Magi" (Sfoza).

1981. Christmas. Paintings. Multicoloured.

602. 10 c. Type **133** 15 10
603. 30 c. " The Adoration of the Kings " (Orcanga) 30 10
604. $1.50 " The Adoration of the Kings " (Gerard) .. 1·10 60
605. $2.50 " The Adoration of the Kings " (Foppa) .. 1·75 1·25

134. 1860 1d. Stamp.

1981. 1st Anniversary of U.P.U. Membership. Multicoloured.

606. 10 c. Type **134** 10 10
607. 30 c. 1969 First anniversary of Caribbean Free Trade Area 25 c. commemorative 20 10
608. 50 c. 1979 Independence $2 commemorative .. 25 30
609. $2 U.P.U. emblem with U.P.U. and St. Lucia flags 80 1·50

135. Scene from Football Match.

1982. World Cup Football Championship, Spain.

611. **135.** 10 c. multicoloured .. 20 10
612. – 50 c. multicoloured .. 70 15
613. – $2 multicoloured .. 1·75 90
614. – $2.50 multicoloured .. 2·00 1·00

DESIGNS: 50 c. to $2.50, Scenes from different matches.

136. Pigeon Island National Park.

1982. Bicentenary of Battle of the Saints. Multicoloured.

616. 10 c. Type **136** 25 15
617. 35 c. Battle scene 80 15
618. 50 c. Rodney (English admiral) and De Grasse (French admiral) .. 1·10 45
619. $2.50 Map of the Saints, Martinique and St. Lucia 3·25 3·75

137. Map-reading.

1982. 75th Anniv. of Boy Scout Movement. Multicoloured.

621. 10 c. Type **137** 10 10
622. 50 c. First Aid practice .. 30 15
623. $1.50 Camping 75 80
624. $2.50 Campfire singsong .. 1·25 1·50

138. Leeds Castle.

1982. 21st Birthday of Princess of Wales. Multicoloured.

625. 50 c. Type **138** 30 20
626. $2 Princess Diana boarding aircraft 90 75
627. $4 Wedding .. .. 1·60 1·40

139. " Adoration of the Kings " (detail, Jan Breughel).

1982. Christmas. Multicoloured.

629. 10 c. Type **139** 10 10
630. 30 c. " Nativity " (Lorenzo Costa) 15 10
631. 50 c. " Virgin and Child " (Fra Filippo Lippi) .. 25 15
632. 80 c. " Adoration of the Shepherds " (Nicolas Poussin) 40 55

140. The Pitons.

1983. Commonwealth Day. Multicoloured.

633. 10 c. Type **140** 10 10
634. 30 c. Tourist Beach .. 15 10
635. 50 c. Banana harvesting .. 20 15
636. $2 Flag of St. Lucia .. 60 1·00

141. Crown Agents Headquarters, Millbank, London.

1983. 150th Anniv. of Crown Agents. Mult.

637. 10 c. Type **141** 10 10
638. 15 c. Road construction .. 10 10
639. 50 c. Road network map .. 20 25
640. $2 First St. Lucia stamp .. 60 1·00

142. Communications at Sea.

1983. World Communications Year. Mult.

641. 10 c. Type **142** 15 10
642. 50 c. Communications in the air 40 15
643. $1.50 T.V. transmission via satellite 90 75
644. $2.50 Computer communications .. .. .. 1·40 1·25

143. Longspine Squirrelfish.

1983. Coral Reef Fishes. Multicoloured.

646. 10 c. Type **143** 10 10
647. 50 c. Banded Butterflyfish 20 15
648. $1.50 Blackbar Soldierfish 70 75
649. $2.50 Yellowtail Snapper 1·10 1·25

144. " Duke of Sutherland " (1930).

1983. Leaders of the World. Railway Locomotives (1st series).

651. **144.** 35 c. multicoloured .. 25 20
652. – 35 c. multicoloured .. 25 20
653. – 35 c. multicoloured .. 25 20
654. – 35 c. multicoloured .. 25 20
655. – 50 c. multicoloured .. 35 30
656. – 50 c. multicoloured .. 35 30
657. – 50 c. multicoloured .. 35 30
658. – 50 c. multicoloured .. 35 30
659. – $1 multicoloured .. 50 50
660. – $1 multicoloured .. 50 50
661. – $1 multicoloured .. 50 50
662. – $1 multicoloured .. 50 50
663. – $2 multicoloured .. 70 70
664. – $2 multicoloured .. 70 70
665. – $2 multicoloured .. 70 70
666. – $2 multicoloured .. 70 70

DESIGNS: (The first in each pair shows technical drawings and the second the locomotive at work). Nos. 651/2, "Duke of Sutherland", Great Britain (1930). 653/4, "City of Glasgow", Great Britain (1940). 655/6, "Lord Nelson", Great Britain (1926). 657/8, "Leeds United", Great Britain (1928). 659/60, "Bodmin", Great Britain (1945). 661/2, "Eton", Great Britain (1930). 663/4, "Flying Scotsman", Great Britain (1923). 665/6, "Rocket", Great Britain (1923).

See also Nos. 715/26, 761/76, 824/31 and 858/73.

145. " The Niccolini-Cowper Madonna ".

1983. Christmas. 500th Birth Anniversary of Raphael. Multicoloured.

667. 10 c. Type **145** 10 10
668. 30 c. " The Holy Family with a Palm Tree " .. 20 10
669. 50 c. "The Sistine Madonna" 35 20
670. $5 " The Alba Madonna " 2·50 2·25

146. George III.

1984. Leaders of the World. British Monarchs. Multicoloured.

671. 5 c. Battle of Waterloo .. 10 10
672. 5 c. Type **146** 10 10
673. 10 c. George III at Kew .. 10 10
674. 10 c. Kew Palace 10 10
675. 35 c. Coat of Arms of Elizabeth I 20 20
676. 35 c. Elizabeth I 20 20
677. 60 c. Coat of Arms of George III 30 30
678. 60 c. George III (different) 30 30
679. $1 Elizabeth I at Hatfield 40 40
680. $1 Hatfield Palace .. 40 40
681. $2.50 Spanish Armada .. 75 75
682. $2.50 Elizabeth I (different) 75 75

147. Clarke & Co's Drug Store.

1984. Historic Buildings. Multicoloured.

683. 10 c. Type **147** 10 10
684. 45 c. Colonial architecture (horiz.) 30 25
685. 65 c. Colonial "chattel" house (horiz.) 45 35
686. $2.50 Treasury after 1906 earthquake (horiz.) .. 1·75 1·60

148. Logwood.

1984. Forestry Resources. Multicoloured.

699. 10 c. Type **148** 10 10
700. 45 c. Calabash 40 30
701. 65 c. Gommier (vert.) .. 55 55
702. $2.50 Raintree .. .. 1·25 2·75

149. Bugatti Type "578C Atlantic Coupe".

1984. Leaders of the World. Automobiles (1st series) the first in each pair showing technical drawings and the second paintings.

703 **149** 5 c. blk., lav. & yell. 10 10
704 – 5 c. multicoloured .. 10 10
705 – 10 c. black, bl. & red 10 10
706 – 10 c. multicoloured .. 10 10
707 – $1 black, grn. & brn. 25 25
708 – $1 multicoloured .. 25 25
709 – $2.50 black, pink & bl. 40 40
710 – $2.50 multicoloured .. 40 40

DESIGNS: Nos. 703/4, Bugatti Type "578C Atlantic Coupe". 705/6, Chevrolet "Bel Air Convertible". 707/8, Alfa Romeo "1750 GS (Zagato)". 709/10, Dusenberg "SJ Roadster".

See also Nos. 745/60, 789/96 and 902/13.

150. Pygmy Gecko.

1984. Endangered Wildlife. Multicoloured.

711. 10 c. Type **150** 30 10
712. 45 c. Maria Island Ground Lizard 70 50
713. 65 c. Green Iguana .. 75 85
714. $2.50 Couresse Snake .. 1·60 3·50

1984. Leaders of the World. Railway Locomotives (2nd series). As T **144**, the first in each pair showing technical drawings and the second the locomotive at work.

715. 1 c. multicoloured 10 10
716. 1 c. multicoloured 10 10
717. 15 c. multicoloured .. 15 15
718. 15 c. multicoloured .. 15 15
719. 50 c. multicoloured .. 20 20
720. 50 c. multicoloured .. 20 20
721. 75 c. multicoloured .. 25 25
722. 75 c. multicoloured .. 25 25
723. $1 multicoloured 30 30
724. $1 multicoloured 30 30
725. $2 multicoloured 50 50
726. $2 multicoloured 50 50

DESIGNS: Nos. 715/16, "Taw", Great Britain (1897). 717/18, "Crocodile I.C.C.I.", Switzerland (1920). 719/20, "The Countess", Great Britain (1903). 721/2, Class "GE6/6 C.C.", Switzerland (1921). 723/4, Class "P8", Germany (1906). 725/6, "Der Adler", Germany (1835).

151. Men's Volleyball.

1984. Leaders of the World. Olympic Games, Los Angeles. Multicoloured.

727. 5 c. Type **151** 10 10
728. 5 c. Women's volleyball .. 10 10
729. 10 c. Women's hurdles .. 10 10
730. 10 c. Men's hurdles .. 10 10
731. 65 c. Show jumping .. 15 15
732. 65 c. Dressage 15 15
733. $2.50 Women's gymnastics 40 40
734. $2.50 Men's gymnastics .. 40 40

152. Glass of Wine and Flowers.

1984. Christmas. Multicoloured.

735. 10 c. Type **152** 10 10
736. 35 c. Priest and decorated altar 10 10
737. 65 c. Nativity scene .. 20 25
738. $3 Holy Family .. .. 1·00 1·50

153. Slaves preparing Manioc.

1984. 150th Anniv. of Abolition of Slavery. Each black and brown.

740. 10 c. Type **153** 10 10
741. 35 c. Sifting and cooking cassava flour 10 10
742. 55 c. Cooking pot, and preparing tobacco .. 15 20
743. $5 Stripping tobacco leaves for twist tobacco .. 1·10 1·50

1984. Leaders of the World. Automobiles (2nd series). As T **149**, the first in each pair showing technical drawings and the second paintings.

745. 10 c. black green & brn. .. 10 10
746. 10 c. multicoloured .. 10 10
747. 30 c. black, blue and green 15 15
748. 30 c. multicoloured .. 15 15
749. 55 c. black, yellow & brn. 30 30
750. 55 c. multicoloured .. 30 30
751. 65 c. black, grey and lilac 35 35
752. 65 c. multicoloured .. 35 35
753. 75 c. black, brown and red 35 35
754. 75 c. multicoloured .. 35 35
755. $1 black, brown and blue 40 40
756. $1 multicoloured 40 40
757. $2 black, green and red .. 50 50
758. $2 multicoloured 50 50
759. $3 black, brown and red .. 60 60
760. $3 multicoloured 60 60

DESIGNS: Nos. 754/6, Panhard and Levassor. 747/8, N.S.U. "RO-80" Saloon. 749/50, Abarth "Bialbero". 751/2, TVR "Vixen 2500M". 753/4, Ford "Mustang" Convertible. 755/6, Ford "Model T". 757/8, Aston Martin DB35". 759/60, Chrysler "Imperial CG Dual Cowl" Phaeton.

1985. Leaders of the World. Railway Locomotives (3rd series). As T **144**, the first in each pair showing technical drawings and the second the locomotive at work.

761. 5 c. multicoloured 10 10
762. 5 c. multicoloured 10 10
763. 15 c. multicoloured .. 15 15
764. 15 c. multicoloured .. 15 15
765. 35 c. multicoloured .. 15 15
766. 35 c. multicoloured .. 15 15
767. 60 c. multicoloured .. 15 15
768. 60 c. multicoloured .. 15 15
769. 75 c. multicoloured .. 20 20
770. 75 c. multicoloured .. 20 20
771. $1 multicoloured .. 20 20
772. $1 multicoloured .. 20 20
773. $2 multicoloured .. 40 40
774. $2 multicoloured .. 40 40
775. $2.50 multicoloured .. 55 55
776. $2.50 multicoloured .. 55 55

DESIGNS: Nos. 761/2, Class "C53", Japan (1928). 763/4, Class "Heavy L", India (1885). 765/6, Class "B18¼", Australia (1926). 767/8, "Owain Glyndwr", Great Britain (1923). 769/70, "Lion", Great Britain (1838). 771/2, Coal engine, Great Britain (1873). 773/4, No. 2238, Class "Q6", Great Britain (1921). 775/6, Class "H", Great Britain (1920).

154. Girl Guide Badge in Shield and Crest of St. Lucia.

1985. 75th Anniv. of Girl Guide Movement and 60th Anniv. of Guiding in St. Lucia.

777. **154.** 10 c. multicoloured .. 20 10
778. 35 c. multicoloured .. 80 15
779. 65 c. multicoloured .. 1·25 35
780. $3 multicoloured .. 3·25 2·75

155. "Clossiana selene".

1985. Leaders of the World. Butterflies. Multicoloured.

781 15 c. Type **155** 10 10
782 15 c. "Inachis io" .. 10 10
783 40 c. "Philaethria dido" .. 15 15
784 40 c. "Callicore sorana" .. 15 15
785 60 c. "Kallima inachus" .. 15 15
786 60 c. "Hypanartia paullus" 15 15
787 $2.25 "Morpho helena" .. 50 50
788 $2.25 "Ornithoptera meridionalis" 50 50

1985. Leaders of the World. Automobiles (3rd series). As T **149**, the first in each pair showing technical drawings and the second paintings.

789 15 c. black, blue and red .. 10 10
790 15 c. multicoloured .. 10 10
791 50 c. black, orange and red 15 15
792 50 c. multicoloured .. 15 15
793 $1 black, green and orange 20 20
794 $1 multicoloured .. 20 20
795 $1.50 black, green & brown 30 30
796 $1.50 multicoloured .. 30 30

DESIGNS: Nos. 789/90, Hudson "Eight" (1940). 791/2, KdF (1937). 793/4, Kissel "Goldbug" (1925). 795/6, Ferrari "246 GTS" (1973).

156. Grenadier, 70th Regiment c. 1775.

1985. Military Uniforms. Multicoloured.

797 5 c. Type **156** 25 15
798 10 c. Officer, Grenadier Company, 14th Regiment, 1780 .. .. 25 15
930 15 c. Private, Battalion Company, 2nd West India Regiment, 1803 .. 35 35
799 20 c. Officer, Battalion Company, 46th Regiment, 1781 .. .. 40 15
800 25 c. Officer, Royal Artillery, c. 1782 .. 40 15
801 30 c. Officer, Royal Engineers, 1782 .. .. 60 15
802 35 c. Officer, Battalion Company, 54th Regiment, 1782 .. .. 50 20
935 45 c. Private, Grenadier Company, 14th Regiment, 1782 .. .. 50 50
936 50 c. Gunner, Royal Artillery, 1796 .. .. 60 60
937 60 c. Officer, Battalion Company, 5th Regiment, 1778 .. .. .. 70 70
805 65 c. Private, Battalion Company, 85th Regiment, c. 1796 .. .. 70 50
806 75 c. Private, Battalion Company, 76th Regiment, 1796 .. .. 75 55
940 80 c. Officer, Battalion Company, 27th Regiment, c. 1780 .. .. 90 90
807 90 c. Private, Battalion Company, 81st Regiment, c. 1796 .. .. 85 60
808 $1 Sergeant, 74th (Highland) Regiment, 1796 .. 90 60
943 $2.50 Private, Light Company, 93rd Regiment, 1803 .. .. 3·00 3·50
944 $5 Private, Battalion Company, 1st West India Regiment, 1803 .. 5·50 7·00
811 $15 Officer, Royal Artillery, 1850 .. .. 11·00 14·00
1003 $20 Private, Grenadier Company, 46th Regiment, 1778 .. .. 17·00 20·00

157. Messerschmitt "109-E".

1985. Leaders of the World. Military Aircraft. The first in each pair shows paintings and the second technical drawings.

812. **157.** 5 c. multicoloured .. 10 10
813. – 5 c. blk., bl. & yell. 10 10
814. – 55 c. multicoloured .. 40 35
815. – 55 c. blk., bl. & yell. 40 35
816. – 60 c. multicoloured .. 40 40
817. – 60 c. blk., bl. & yell. 40 40
818. – $2 multicoloured .. 80 80
819. – $2 blk., bl. & yell. 80 80

DESIGNS: Nos. 812/13, Messerschmitt "109-E". 814/15, Avro "683 Lancaster Mark I". 816/17, North American "P.51-D Mustang". 818/19, Supermarine "Spitfire Mark II".

158. Magnificent Frigate Birds, Frigate Island Bird Sanctuary.

1985. Nature Reserves. Multicoloured.

820. 10 c. Type **158** 35 20
821. 35 c. Mangrove cuckoo, Scorpion Island, Savannes Bay 85 45
822. 65 c. Lesser yellowlegs, Maria Island Reserve .. 1·25 85
823. $3 Audubon's shearwaters; Lapins Island Reserve .. 2·25 5·00

1985. Leaders of the World Railway Locomotives (4th series). As T **144**. The first in each pair shows technical drawings and the second the locomotive at work.

824. 10 c. multicoloured .. 10 10
825. 10 c. multicoloured .. 10 10
826. 30 c. multicoloured .. 15 15
827. 30 c. multicoloured .. 15 15
828. 75 c. multicoloured .. 20 20
829. 75 c. multicoloured .. 20 20
830. $2.50 multicoloured .. 55 55
831. $2.50 multicoloured .. 55 55

DESIGNS: Nos. 824/5, No. 28 Tank locomotive, Great Britain (1897). 826/7, No. 1621 Class "M", Great Britain (1893). 828/9, Class "Dunalastair", Great Britain (1896). 830/1, No. 2290 "Big Bertha" type, Great Britain (1919).

159. Queen Elizabeth the Queen Mother.

1985. Leaders of the World. Life and Times of Queen Elizabeth the Queen Mother. Various portraits.

832. **159.** 40 c. multicoloured .. 15 20
833. – 40 c. multicoloured .. 15 20
834. – 75 c. multicoloured .. 15 25
835. – 75 c. multicoloured .. 15 25
836. – $1.10 multicoloured .. 25 35
837. – $1.10 multicoloured .. 25 35
838. – $1.75 multicoloured .. 40 55
839. – $1.75 multicoloured .. 40 55

Each value issued in pairs showing a floral pattern across the bottom of the portraits which stops short of the left-hand edge on the first stamp and of the right-hand edge on the second.

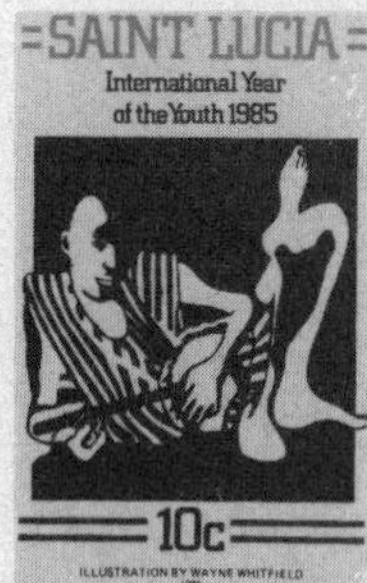

160. "'Youth playing Banjo" (Wayne Whitfield).

1985. International Youth Year. Paintings by Young St. Lucians.

841. **160.** 10 c. black, blue & mauve 10 10
842. – 45 c. multicoloured .. 30 25
843. – 75 c. multicoloured .. 50 40
844. – $3.50 multicoloured .. 2·00 1·75

DESIGNS—VERT. (as T **160**). 45 c. "Motorcyclist" (Mark Maragh). 75 c. "Boy and Girl at Pitons" (Bartholomew Eugene). $3.50 "Abstract" (Lyndon Samuel). HORIZ. (80×55 mm). $5 Young people and St. Lucia landscapes.

1985. Royal Visit Nos. 649, 685/6, 702, 713, 778 amd 836/7 optd. **CARIBBEAN ROYAL VISIT–1985.**

846. **154.** 35 c. multicoloured .. 3·50 2·50
847. – 65 c. mult. (685) .. 3·00 3·00
848. – 65 c. mult. (713) .. 3·00 3·00
849. – $1.10 mult. (836) .. 4·00 4·00
850. – $1.10 mult. (837) .. 4·00 4·00
851. – $2.50 mult. (649) .. 4·00 4·00
852. – $2.50 mult. (686) .. 3·50 3·50
853. – $2.50 mult. (702) .. 3·50 3·50

161. "Papa Jab".

1985. Christmas. Masqueraders. Mult.

854. 10 c. Type **161** 10 10
855. 45 c. "Paille Bananne" .. 20 25
856. 65 c. "Cheval Bois" .. 30 35

1986. Leaders of the World. Railway Locomotives (5th series). As T **144**. The first in each pair shows technical drawings and the second the locomotive at work.

858. 5 c. multicoloured 15 15
859. 5 c. multicoloured 15 15
860. 15 c. multicoloured .. 15 15
861. 15 c. multicoloured .. 15 15
862. 30 c. multicoloured .. 30 30
863. 30 c. multicoloured .. 30 30
864. 60 c. multicoloured .. 45 45
865. 60 c. multicoloured .. 45 45
866. 75 c. multicoloured .. 50 50
867. 75 c. multicoloured .. 50 50
868. $1 multicoloured 65 65
869. $1 multicoloured 65 65
870. $2.25 multicoloured .. 1·25 1·25
871. $2.25 multicoloured .. 1·25 1·25
872. $3 multicoloured .. .. 1·60 1·60
873. $3 multicoloured .. .. 1·60 1·60

DESIGNS: Nos. 858/9, Rack loco "Tip Top", U.S.A (1983). 860/1, "Stephenson", Great Britain (1975). 862/3, No. 737 Class "D", Great Britain (1901). 864/5, No. 13 Class "2-CO2", Great Britain (1922). 866/7, "Electra", Great Britain (1954). 868/9, "City of Newcastle", Great Britain (1922). 870/1, Von Kruckenburg propeller-driven railcar, Germany (1930). 872/3, No. 860, Japan (1893).

1986. 60th Birthday of Queen Elizabeth II (1st issue). As T **167** of British Virgin Islands. Multicoloured.

876. 5 c. Queen Elizabeth II .. 10 10
877. $1 Princess Elizabeth .. 30 30
878. $3.50 Queen Elizabeth II (different) .. .. 75 1·10
879. $6 In Canberra, 1982 (vert.) 1·25 1·75

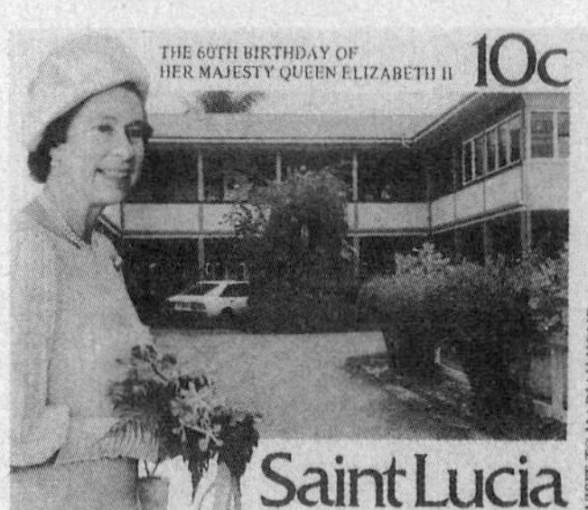

163. Queen Elizabeth and Marian Home.

1986. 60th Birthday of Queen Elizabeth II (2nd issue). Multicoloured.

881. 10 c. Type **163** 15 15
882. 45 c. Queen addressing rally, Mindoo Phillip Park, 1985 .. .. 35 35
883. 50 c. Queen opening Leon Hess Comprehensive School, 1985 .. .. 40 40
884. $5 Queen Elizabeth and Government House, Castries .. .. .. 2·50 2·75

164. Pope John Paul II kissing Ground, Castries Airport.

1986. Visit of Pope John Paul II. Multicoloured.

886. 55 c. Type **164** 70 60
887. 60 c. Pope and St. Joseph's Convent 70 60
888. 80 c. Pope and Castries Catholic Cathedral (vert.) .. .. .. 1·10 95

1986. Royal Wedding (1st issue). As T **168** of British Virgin Islands. Multicoloured.

890. 80 c. Miss Sarah Ferguson 45 50
891. 80 c. Prince Andrew .. 45 50
892. $2 Prince Andrew and Miss Sarah Ferguson (horiz.) 1·25 1·40
893. $2 Prince Andrew with Mrs Nancy Reagan (horiz.) 1·25 1·40

See also Nos. 897/900.

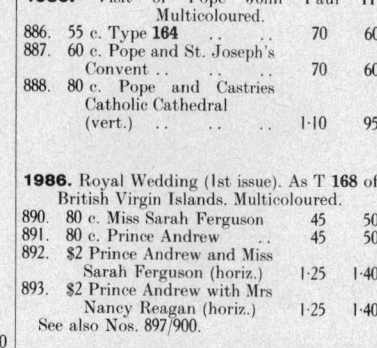

165. Peace Corps Teacher with Students.

1986. 25th Anniv. of United States Peace Corps. Multicoloured.

894. 80 c. Type **165** 35 40
895. $2 President John Kennedy (vert.) .. 1·10 1·25
896. $3.50 Peace Corps emblem between arms of St. Lucia and U.S.A. .. 1·60 2·00

166. Prince Andrew in Carriage.

1986. Royal Wedding (2nd issue). Mult.

897. 50 c. Type **166** 30 30
898. 80 c. Miss Sarah Ferguson in coach 40 40
899. $1 Duke and Duchess of York at altar 45 50
900. $3 Duke and Duchess of York in carriage .. 1·25 1·75

1986. Automobiles (4th series). As T **149**, the first in each pair showing technical drawings and the second paintings.

902. 20 c. multicoloured .. 10 10
903. 20 c. multicoloured .. 10 10
904. 50 c. multicoloured .. 15 15
905. 50 c. multicoloured .. 15 15
906. 60 c. multicoloured .. 15 15
907. 60 c. multicoloured .. 15 15
908. $1 multicoloured 15 15
909. $1 multicoloured 15 15
910. $1.50 multicoloured .. 20 20
911. $1.50 multicoloured .. 20 20
912. $3 multicoloured 45 45
913. $3 multicoloured 45 45

DESIGNS: Nos. 902/3, AMC "AMX" (1969). 904/5, Russo-Baltique (1912). 906/7, Lincoln "K.B." (1932). 908/9, Rolls Royce "Phantom II Continental" (1933). 910/11, Buick "Century" (1939). 912/13, Chrysler "300 C" (1957).

167. Chak-Chak Band.

1986. Tourism (1st series). Multicoloured.

914. 15 c. Type **167** 10 10
915. 45 c. Folk dancing .. 20 15
916. 80 c. Steel band 40 50
917. $5 Limbo dancing .. .. 1·10 2·00

See also Nos. 988/91.

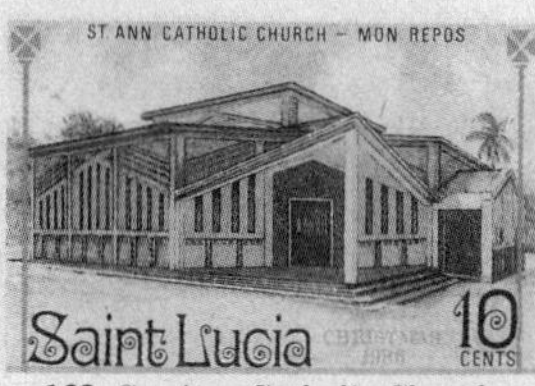

168. St. Ann Catholic Church, Mon Repos.

1986. Christmas. Multicoloured.

919. 10 c. Type **168** 10 10
920. 40 c. St. Joseph the Worker Catholic Church, Gros Islet 20 15
921. 80 c. Holy Trinity Anglican Church, Castries 40 40
922. $4 Our Lady of the Assumption Catholic Church, Soufriere (vert.) 1·25 2·00

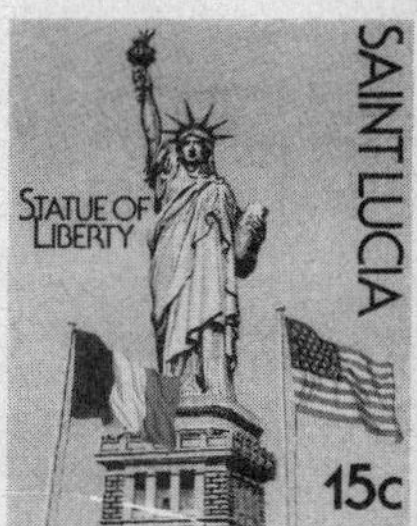

169. Outline Map of St. Lucia. **170.** Statue of Liberty and Flags of France and U.S.A.

1987.

924. **169.** 5 c. black and brown 15 15
925. 10 c. black and green 15 15
926. 45 c. black & orange 45 45
927. 50 c. black and blue .. 45 45
927c. $1 black and red .. 65 65

1987. Centenary of Statue of Liberty (1986). Multicoloured.

947 15 c. Type **170** 15 10
948 80 c. Statue and "Mauretania I" (liner) 75 55
949 $1 Statue and "Concorde" 1·10 75
950 $5 Statue and flying boat at sunset .. .. 3·00 3·50

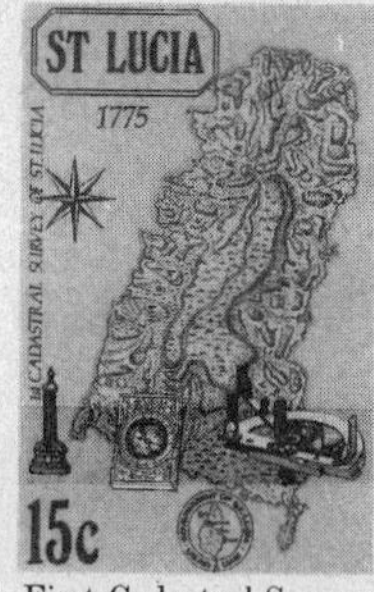

171. First Cadastral Survey Map and Surveying Instruments, 1775.

1987. New Cadastral Survey of St. Lucia. Multicoloured.

955 15 c. Type **171** 40 15
956 60 c. Map and surveying instruments, 1814 .. 80 60
957 $1 Map and surveying instruments, 1888 .. 1·00 1·00
958 $2.50 Cadastral survey map and surveying instruments, 1987 .. .. 2·50 2·75

172. Ambulance and Nurse, 1987.

1987. Centenary of Victoria Hospital, Castries. Multicoloured.

959. **172.** $1 multicoloured .. 1·25 1·25
960. – $1 blue .. .. 1·25 1·25
961. – $2 multicoloured .. 1·75 1·75
962. – $2 blue .. .. 1·75 1·75

DESIGNS: No. 960, Nurse and carrying hammock, 1913. No. 961, $2 Victoria Hospital, 1987. No. 962, Victoria Hospital, 1887.

173. "The Holy Family".

1987. Christmas. Paintings. Multicoloured.

964	15 c. Type **173**	30	10
965	50 c. "Adoration of the Shepherds"	60	30
966	60 c. "Adoration of the Magi"	70	55
967	90 c. "Madonna and Child"	1·25	1·50

174. St. Lucia Amazon perched on Branch.

1987. St. Lucia Amazon. Multicoloured.

969	15 c. Type **174**	55	20
970	35 c. Pair in flight	1·25	35
971	50 c. Perched on branch (rear view)	1·75	1·25
972	$1 Emerging from tree ..	2·75	3·50

175. Carib Clay Zemi.

1988. Amerindian Artefacts. Multicoloured.

973	25 c. Type **175**	15	10
974	30 c. Troumassee cylinder	20	15
975	80 c. Three pointer stone ..	55	45
976	$3.50 Dauphine petroglyph	2·25	3·00

176. East Caribbean Currency.

1988. 50th Anniv. of St. Lucia Co-operative Bank. Multicoloured.

977.	10 c. Type **176**	20	10
978.	45 c. Castries branch ..	55	35
979.	60 c. As 45 c.	75	80
980.	80 c. Vieux Fort branch ..	1·25	1·50

177 Rural Telephone Exchange

1988. 50th Anniv of Cable and Wireless (West Indies) Ltd. Multicoloured.

981	15 c. Type **177**	10	10
982	25 c. Early and modern telephones	15	15
983	80 c. St. Lucia Teleport dish aerial	40	45
984	$2.50 Map showing Eastern Caribbean Microwave System	1·00	1·10

178 Stained Glass Window

1988. Centenary of Methodist Church in St. Lucia. Multicoloured.

985	15 c. Type **178**	10	10
986	80 c. Church interior ..	40	45
987	$3.50 Methodist Church, Castries	1·50	1·60

179 Garnished Lobsters

1988. Tourism (2nd series). Designs showing local delicacies. Multicoloured.

988	10 c. Type **179**	40	50
989	30 c. Cocktail and tourists at buffet	55	65
990	80 c. Fresh fruits and roasted breadfruit ..	90	1·00
991	$2.50 Barbecued red snappers (fish)	2·00	2·25

Nos. 988/91 were printed together, se-tenant, forming a composite design of tourists at beach barbecue.

1988. 300th Anniv of Lloyd's of London. As T **123** of Ascension.

1004	10 c. black, lilac & brown	30	10
1005	60 c. multicoloured ..	80	55
1006	80 c. multicoloured ..	1·10	90
1007	$2.50 multicoloured ..	2·50	3·00

DESIGNS: VERT—10 c. San Francisco earthquake, 1906; $2.50, Castries fire, 1948. HORIZ—60 c. Castries Harbour; 80 c. "Lady Nelson" (hospital ship), 1942.

180 Snow on the Mountain

181 Princess Alexandra presenting Constitution Document to Prime Minister

1988. Christmas. Flowers. Multicoloured.

1008	15 c. Type **180**	30	10
1009	45 c. Christmas candle ..	55	40
1010	60 c. Balisier	70	70
1011	80 c. Poinsettia	1·00	1·25

1989. 10th Anniv of Independence. Mult.

1013	15 c. Type **181**	10	10
1014	80 c. Geothermal well ..	40	45
1015	$1 Sir Arthur Lewis Community College ..	45	50
1016	$2.50 Pointe Seraphine shopping centre ..	1·00	1·10

182 "Gerronema citrinum"

1989. Fungi. Multicoloured.

1022	15 c. Type **182**	55	15
1023	25 c. "Lepiota spiculata"	70	15
1024	50 c. "Calocybe cyanocephala" ..	1·25	75
1025	$5 "Russula puiggarii"	5·50	6·50

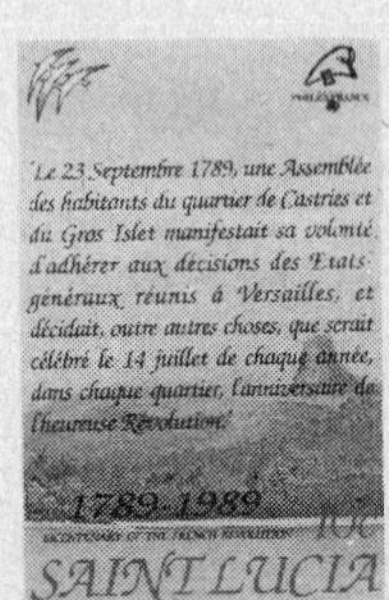

183 Local Revolutionary Declaration, 1789 and View of St. Lucia

1989. Bicentenary of the French Revolution. Designs include the "PHILEXFRANCE" International Stamp Exhibition logo. Mult.

1026	10 c. Type **183**	25	15
1027	60 c. Hoisting Revolutionary flag, Morne Fortune, 1791 (horiz) ..	1·00	70
1028	$1 Declaration of Rights of Man and view of St. Lucia	1·40	1·10
1029	$3.50 Arrival of Capt. La Crosse, Gros Islet, 1792 (horiz)	4·00	4·50

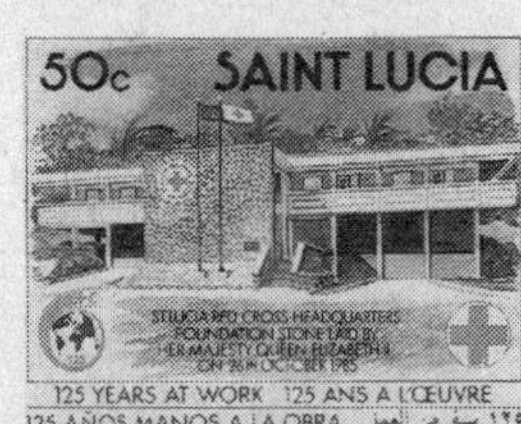

184 Red Cross Headquarters, St. Lucia

1989. 125th Anniv of International Red Cross. Multicoloured.

1030	50 c. Type **184**	1·00	1·00
1031	80 c. Red Cross seminar, Castries, 1987	1·50	1·50
1032	$1 Red Cross ambulance	1·75	1·75

185 Christmas Lantern

1989. Christmas.

1033	**185**	10 c. multicoloured ..	10	10
1034	–	50 c. multicoloured ..	35	35
1035	–	90 c. multicoloured ..	60	60
1036	–	$1 multicoloured ..	70	70

DESIGNS: 50c. to $1 various decorative "building" lanterns.

HAVE YOU READ THE NOTES AT THE BEGINNING OF THIS CATALOGUE?
These often provide answers to the enquiries we receive.

186 Gwi Gwi

1990. Endangered Trees. Multicoloured.

1081	10 c. Chinna	10	10
1082	15 c. Latanier	10	10
1039	20 c. Type **186**	10	10
1040	25 c. L'Encens	10	15
1085	50 c. Bois Lele	20	25
1042	80 c. Bois D'Amande ..	40	45
1043	95 c. Mahot Piman Grand Bois	45	50
1044	$1 Balata	50	55
1045	$1.50 Pencil cedar ..	70	75
1046	$2.50 Bois Cendre ..	1·25	1·40
1047	$5 Lowye Cannelle ..	2·40	2·50
1048	$25 Chalantier Grand Bois	12·00	12·50

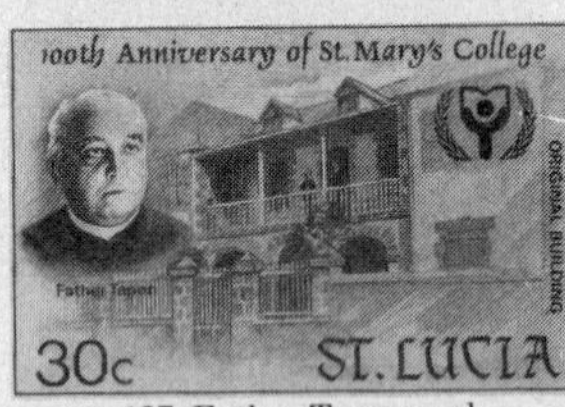

187 Father Tapon and Original College Building

1990. International Literacy Year. Cent of St. Mary's College, Castries. Multicoloured.

1049	30 c. Type **187**	15	15
1050	45 c. Brother M. C. Collins and St. Mary's College	25	25
1051	75 c. Literacy class ..	45	45
1052	$2 Children approaching "door to knowledge" ..	1·50	1·50

1990. 90th Birthday of Queen Elizabeth the Queen Mother. As T **134** of Ascension.

1053	50 c. multicoloured ..	35	35
1054	$5 black and blue ..	2·75	3·00

DESIGNS—21 × 36 mm. 50 c. Crowning of Queen Consort, 1937. 29 × 37 mm. $5 Queen Elizabeth arriving at New Theatre, London, 1949.

1990. "EXPO 90" International Garden and Greenery Exhibition, Osaka. No. 1047 optd **EXPO '90** and logo.

1055	$5 Lowye cannelle ..	2·75	3·00

189 "Adoration of the Magi" (Rubens)

1990. Christmas. Religious Painting. Mult.

1056	10 c. Type **189**	20	10
1057	30 c. "Adoration of the Shepherds" (Murillo) ..	25	15
1058	80 c. "Adoration of the Magi" (Rubens) (different)	65	65
1059	$5 "Adoration of the Shepherds" (Philippe de Champaigne)	3·00	3·50

190 "Vistafjord" (liner)

1991. Cruise Ships. Multicoloured.

1060	50 c. Type **190**	45	30
1061	80 c. "Windstar" (schooner)	70	60
1062	$1 "Unicorn" (brig) ..	90	80
1063	$2.50 Game-fishing launch	2·50	2·75

191 "Battus polydamas"

1991. Butterflies. Multicoloured.

1065	60 c. Type **191**	70	55
1066	80 c. "Strymon simaethis"	95	75
1067	$1 "Mestra cana" ..	1·25	1·00
1068	$2.50 "Allosmaitia piplea"	2·50	2·75

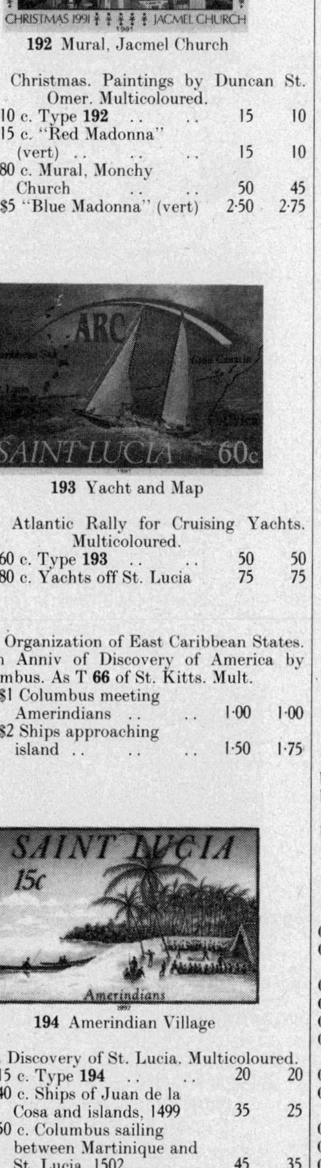

192 Mural, Jacmel Church

1991. Christmas. Paintings by Duncan St. Omer. Multicoloured.

1069	10 c. Type **192**	15	10
1070	15 c. "Red Madonna" (vert)	15	10
1071	80 c. Mural, Monchy Church	50	45
1072	$5 "Blue Madonna" (vert)	2·50	2·75

193 Yacht and Map

1991. Atlantic Rally for Cruising Yachts. Multicoloured.

1073	60 c. Type **193**	50	50
1074	80 c. Yachts off St. Lucia	75	75

1992. Organization of East Caribbean States. 500th Anniv of Discovery of America by Columbus. As T **66** of St. Kitts. Mult.

1075	$1 Columbus meeting Amerindians	1·00	1·00
1076	$2 Ships approaching island	1·50	1·75

194 Amerindian Village

1992. Discovery of St. Lucia. Multicoloured.

1077	15 c. Type **194**	20	20
1078	40 c. Ships of Juan de la Cosa and islands, 1499	35	25
1079	50 c. Columbus sailing between Martinique and St. Lucia, 1502	45	35
1080	$5 Legendary shipwreck of Gimie	3·50	4·00

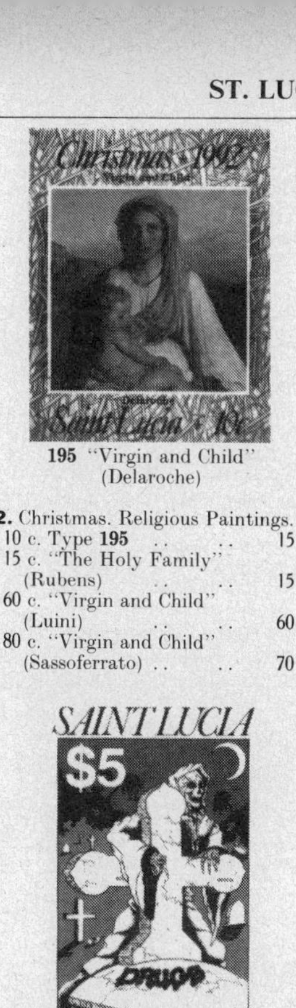

195 "Virgin and Child" (Delaroche)

1992. Christmas. Religious Paintings. Mult.

1092	10 c. Type **195**	15	10
1093	15 c. "The Holy Family" (Rubens)	15	10
1094	60 c. "Virgin and Child" (Luini)	60	65
1095	80 c. "Virgin and Child" (Sassoferrato)	70	75

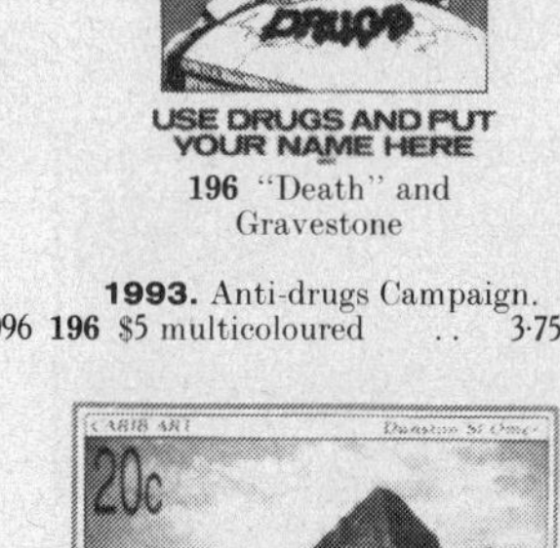

196 "Death" and Gravestone

1993. Anti-drugs Campaign.

1096	**196** $5 multicoloured ..	3·75	4·00

197 "Gros Piton from Delcer, Choiseul" (Dunstan St. Omer)

1993. Carib Art. Multicoloured.

1097	20 c. Type **197**	15	10
1098	75 c. "Reduit Bay" (Derek Walcott) ..	50	45
1099	$5 "Woman and Child at River" (Nancy Cole Auguste)	3·50	3·75

198 "The Madonna of the Rosary" (Murillo)

1993. Christmas. Religious Paintings. Mult.

1100	15 c. Type **198**	10	10
1101	60 c. "The Madonna and Child" (Van Dyck) ..	30	35
1102	95 c. "The Annunciation" (Champaigne)	45	50

OFFICIAL STAMPS.

1983. Nos. 537/48 optd **OFFICIAL**.

O 1	5 c. Type **120**	15	10
O 2	10 c. McDonnell Douglas "DC-10"	15	10
O 3	15 c. Local bus ..	20	15
O 4	20 c. Refrigerated freighter	30	20
O 5	25 c. "Islander" airplane	35	20
O 6	30 c. "Charles" (pilot boat)	40	25
O 7	50 c. Boeing "727" ..	55	35
O 8	75 c. "Cunard Countess" (liner)	75	20
O 9	$1 Lockhead "Tristar" ..	95	75
O10	$2 Cargo liner ..	1·75	1·75
O11	$5 Boeing "707" airliner	3·50	3·50
O12	$10 "Queen Elizabeth 2" (liner)	6·50	7·50

1985. Nos. 797/811 optd. **OFFICIAL.**

O 13.	5 c. Type **156**	30	30
O 14.	10 c. Officer, Grenadier Company, 14th Regiment, 1780	30	30
O 15.	20 c. Officer, Battalion Company, 46th Regiment 1781	30	30
O 16.	25 c. Officer, Royal Artillery, c 1782 ..	30	30
O 17.	30 c. Officer, Royal Engineers, 1782	40	40
O 18.	35 c. Officer, Battalion Company, 54th Regiment, 1782	40	40
O 19.	45 c. Private, Grenadier Company, 14th Regiment, 1782	50	50
O 20.	50 c. Gunner, Royal Artillery, 1796 ..	50	50
O 21.	65 c. Private, Battalion Company, 85th Regiment, c 1796	60	60
O 22.	75 c. Private, Battalion Company, 76th Regiment, 1796	70	70
O 23.	90 c. Private, Battalion Company, 81st Regiment, c. 1796	80	80
O 24.	$1 Sergeant, 74th (Highland) Regiment, 1796	90	90
O 25.	$2.50, Private, Light Company, 93rd Regiment, 1803	2·00	2·00
O 26.	$5 Private, Battalion Company, 1st West India Regiment, 1803	4·00	5·00
O 27.	$15 Officer, Royal Artillery, 1850 ..	9·00	10·00

1990. Nos. 1081/2, 1039/40, 1085 and 1042/48 optd **OFFICIAL**.

O28	10 c. Chinna	10	10
O29	15 c. Latanier	10	10
O30	20 c. Type **186**	10	10
O31	25 c. L'Encens	10	10
O32	50 c. Bois Lele	25	30
O33	80 c. Bois D'Amande ..	40	45
O34	95 c. Mahot Piman Grand Bois	45	50
O35	$1 Balata	50	55
O36	$1.50 Pencil cedar ..	75	80
O37	$2.50 Bois Cendre ..	1·25	1·40
O38	$5 Lowye Cannelle ..	2·40	2·50
O39	$25 Chalantier Grand Bois	12·00	12·50

POSTAGE DUE STAMPS

D 1.

1930.

D 1. D 1.	1d. black on blue ..	2·75	9·00
D 2.	2d. black on yellow ..	7·00	30·00

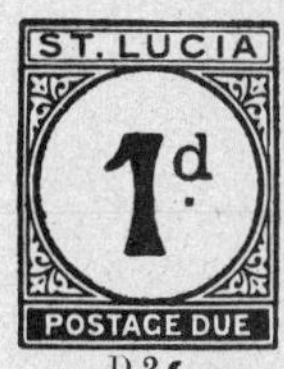

D 2.

D 3.

1933.

D 3. D 2.	1d. black	4·00	4·50
D 4.	2d. black	11·00	6·50
D 5.	4d. black	3·75	23·00
D 6.	8d. black	3·75	29·00

1949.

D 7a D 2	2 c. black	10	4·50
D 8a	4 c. black	30	6·00
D 9a	8 c. black	1·75	19·00
D10a	16 c. black	2·75	26·00

D 4. St. Lucia Coat of Arms.

1981.

D13 D 4	5 c. purple	10	15
D17	5 c. red	10	10
D18	15 c. green	10	10
D19	25 c. orange	10	15
D20	$1 blue	50	55

ST. VINCENT

One of the Windward Is., Br. W. Indies.

1861. 12 pence = 1 shilling;
20 shillings = 1 pound.
1949. 100 cents = 1 West Indian dollar.

7.

1.

3.

1861.

36 **7.**	½d. orange	7·00	2·50
47	½d. green	55	20
48b **1.**	1d. red	1·60	65
18	1d. black	40·00	7·50
29	1d. olive	85·00	3·25
39	1d. drab	35·00	1·40
61	2½d. blue	2·50	2·25
43	4d. blue	£325	18·00
56	4d. yellow	1·60	4·75
51	4d. brown	38·00	75
62	5d. sepia	5·50	17·00
4	6d. green	50·00	18·00
57	6d. violet	2·00	6·00
11	1s. grey	£225	£120
13	1s. blue	£325	90·00
14	1s. brown	£425	£160
45	1s. red	80·00	48·00
58	1s. orange	5·50	9·00
53 **3.**	5s. red	27·00	50·00

1880. Surch. in figures.

33. **1.**	½d. on half 6d. green ..	£160	£160
28.	1d. on half 6d. green ..	£400	£275

1881. Surch. in words.

34. **1.**	1d. on 6d. green	£400	£275
63.	3d. on 1d. mauve ..	6·00	15·00
60a.	5d. on 6d. red	1·00	1·75

1881. Surch. in figures.

54. **1.**	2½d. on 4d. brown ..	50·00	75·00
35.	4d. on 1s. orange	£1300	£700

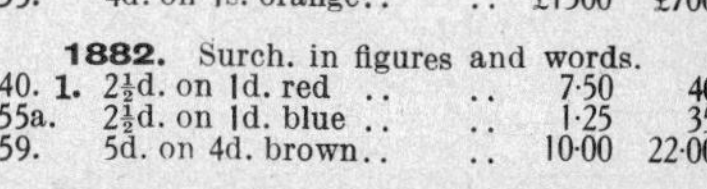

1882. Surch. in figures and words.

40. **1.**	2½d. on 1d. red	7·50	40
55a.	2½d. on 1d. blue	1·25	35
59.	5d. on 4d. brown	10·00	22·00

1885. No. 40 surch. **1d.** and bars.

46. **1.**	1d. on 2½d. on 1d. red ..	14·00	12·00

13.

17. Seal of the Colony.

1899.

67. **13.**	½d. mauve and green ..	1·75	85
68.	1d. mauve and red ..	3·25	45
69.	2½d. mauve and blue ..	4·00	2·00
70.	3d. mauve and green ..	4·00	8·50
71.	4d. mauve and orange ..	4·00	13·00
72.	5d. mauve and black ..	7·00	13·00
73.	6d. mauve and brown ..	13·00	27·00
74.	1s. green and red	13·00	42·00
75.	5s. green and blue ..	70·00	£120

1902. As T **13**, but portrait of King Edward VII.

76	½d. purple and green ..	1·50	60
77	1d. purple and red ..	1·75	20
78	2d. purple and black ..	1·75	2·25
79	2½d. purple and blue ..	2·50	3·25
80	3d. purple and green ..	2·25	2·25
81	6d. purple and brown ..	9·50	26·00
90a	1s. green and red	9·00	32·00
83	2s. green and violet ..	23·00	50·00
91	2s. purple & blue on blue	22·00	42·00
84	5s. green and blue ..	48·00	95·00
92	5s. green and red on yellow	17·00	45·00
93	£1 purple and black on red	£250	£300

1907.

94. **17.**	½d. green	1·25	90
95.	1d. red	2·75	15
96.	2d. orange	1·00	6·00
97.	2½d. blue	13·00	8·50
98.	3d. violet	4·75	14·00

18. Seal of the Colony.

19.

1909.

102	18	½d. green..	1·50	40
99		1d. red	1·25	25
104		2d. grey	2·50	8·00
105		2½d. blue..	6·50	2·50
106		3d. purple on yellow ..	2·50	3·75
107		6d. purple	2·50	5·00
101		1s. black on green ..	3·75	7·50
139		2s. blue and purple ..	4·50	13·00
140		5s. red and green ..	12·00	32·00
141		£1 mauve and black ..	70·00	£110

1913.

131	19.	½d. green..	55	20
132a		1d. red	55	15
132b		1½d. brown	75	15
133		2d. grey	75	30
111		2½d. blue..	35	40
135		3d. purple on yellow ..	60	1·50
134		3d. blue	90	6·00
113		4d. red on yellow ..	80	2·00
136		5d. green..	70	6·00
137		6d. red	80	3·50
116		1s. black on green ..	1·50	3·25
138a		1s. brown	1·50	10·00

1915. Surch. **ONE PENNY.**

121.	19.	1d. on 1s. black on green	5·50	18·00

1916. Optd. **WAR STAMP** in two lines.

122	19	1d. red	1·75	3·50

1916. Optd. **WAR STAMP** in one line.

128.	19.	1d. red	30	60

1935. Silver Jubilee. As T **13** of Antigua.

142.	1d. blue and red ..	40	65
143.	1½d. blue and grey ..	1·00	1·00
144.	2½d. brown and blue ..	1·90	85
145.	1s. grey and purple ..	2·00	3·50

1937. Coronation. As T **2** of Aden.

146.	1d. violet	35	15
147.	1½d. red	55	10
148.	2½d. blue	65	65

25.

26. Young's Island and Fort Duvernette.

1938.

149.	25.	½d. blue and green ..	10	10
150.	26.	1d. blue and brown ..	10	10
151.	–	1½d. green and red ..	20	10
152.	25.	2d. green and black ..	40	35
153.	–	2½d. black and green..	20	40
153a.	–	2½d. green and brown..	20	20
154.	25.	3d. orange and purple	20	10
154a.	–	3½d. blue and green ..	40	85
155.	25.	6d. black and red ..	1·00	40
156.	–	1s. purple and green ..	1·00	50
157.	25.	2s. blue and purple ..	6·00	75
157a.		2s. 6d. brown and blue	1·00	3·50
158.		5s. red and green ..	10·00	2·50
158a.		10 s. violet and brown	3·75	7·50
159.		£1 purple and black ..	16·00	15·00

DESIGNS—HORIZ. 1½d. Kingstown and Fort Charlotte. 2½d. (No. 153) and 3½d. Bathing Beach at Villa. 2½d. (No. 153a) and 1s. Victoria Park, Kingstown.

1946. Victory. As T **9** of Aden.

160.	1½d. red	10	10
161.	3½d. blue	10	10

1948. Silver Wedding. As T **10/11** of Aden.

162.	1½d. red	10	10
163.	£1 mauve	15·00	14·00

1949. As 1938 issue, but values in cents and dollars.

164.	25.	1 c. blue and green ..	20	20
164a.		1 c. green and black ..	30	80
165.	26.	2 c. blue and brown ..	15	20
166.	–	3 c. green and red ..	40	20
166a.	25.	3 c. orange and purple..	30	65
167.		4 c. green and black ..	35	20
167a.		4 c. blue and green ..	30	15
168.		5 c. green and brown ..	15	10
169.		6 c. orange and purple..	40	40
169a.	–	6 c. green and red ..	30	45
170.	–	7 c. black and blue ..	2·75	30
170a.	–	10 c. black & turquoise	50	20
171.	25.	12 c. black and red ..	35	15
172.	–	24 c. purple and green..	35	45
173.	25.	48 c. blue and purple ..	1·50	1·50
174.		60 c. brown and blue ..	1·75	1·75
175.		$1.20 red and green ..	4·25	4·00
176.		$2.40 violet and brown	6·50	9·00
177.		$4.80 purple and black	11·00	18·00

DESIGNS—HORIZ. 3 c. (No. 166), 6 c. (No. 169a) Kingstown and Fort Charlotte. 5 c., 24 c. Victoria Park, Kingstown. 7 c., 10 c. Bathing Beach at Villa.

1949. U.P.U. As T **20/23** of Antigua.

178.	5 c. blue	25	15
179.	6 c. purple	30	60
180.	12 c. mauve	30	55
181.	24 c. green	50	25

1951. Inauguration of B.W.I. University College. As T **24/25** of Antigua.

182.	18.	3 c. green and red ..	30	15
183.	19.	12 c. black and purple	30	15

1951. New Constitution. Optd. **NEW CONSTITUTION 1951.**

184.	–	3 c. green and red (No. 166)	15	15
185.	25.	4 c. green and black ..	15	15
186.	–	5 c. grn. & brn. (No. 168)	15	15
187.	25.	12 c. black and red ..	15	15

1953. Coronation. As T **13** of Aden.

188.	4 c. black and green ..	30	20

30.

31.

1955.

189	30.	1 c. orange	10	10
190		2 c. blue	10	10
191		3 c. grey	30	10
192		4 c. brown	15	10
215		5 c. red	15	10
216		10 c. lilac	15	10
195		15 c. blue	55	30
218		20 c. green	45	10
197		25 c. sepia	50	10
198a	31.	50 c. brown	3·50	85
199		$1 green	6·00	1·00
200		$2.50 blue	14·00	7·00

1958. British Caribbean Federation. As T **28** of Antigua.

201.	3 c. green	40	20
202.	6 c. blue	55	50
203.	12 c. red	80	45

1963. Freedom from Hunger. As T **28** of Aden.

204.	8 c. violet	60	50

1963. Cent of Red Cross. As T **33** of Antigua.

205.	4 c. red and black	15	20
206.	8 c. red and blue	35	50

32. Scout Badge and Proficiency Badges.

1964. 50th Anniversary of St. Vincent Boy Scouts Association.

221.	32.	1 c. green and brown ..	10	10
222.		4 c. blue and purple ..	10	10
223.		20 c. yellow and violet..	30	10
224.		50 c. red and green ..	45	30

33. Tropical Fruits.

1965. Bicent of Botanic Gardens. Mult.

225	1 c. Type **33**	10	10
226	4 c. Breadfruit and H.M.S. "Providence" (sloop), 1793	10	10
227	25 c. Doric Temple and Pond (vert)	15	10
228	40 c. Talipot Palm and Doric Temple (vert) ..	30	50

1965. Cent of I.T.U. As T **36** of Antigua.

229.	4 c. blue and green ..	25	10
230.	48 c. ochre and orange ..	1·00	45

37. Boat-building, Bequia (inscr. "BEOUIA").

1965. Multicoloured.

231	1 c. Type **37**	10	75
231a	1 c. Type **37** (inscr. "BEQUIA") ..	10	10
232	2 c. Friendship Beach, Bequia	10	10
233	3 c. Terminal Building, Arnos Vale Airport ..	15	10
261	4 c. Woman with Bananas	30	30
235	5 c. Crater Lake	15	10
236	6 c. Carib Stone	15	40
237	8 c. Arrowroot	30	10
238	10 c. Owia Salt Pond ..	30	10
239	12 c. Deep Water Wharf..	40	10
240	20 c. Sea Island Cotton ..	30	10
241	25 c. Map of St. Vincent and Islands	35	10
242	50 c. Breadfruit	50	30
243	$1 Baleine Falls	4·00	30
244	$2.50 St. Vincent Amazon	16·00	4·00
245	$5 Arms of St. Vincent ..	7·00	6·50

Nos. 234, 236/7 and 240/5 vert.

1966. Churchill Commem. As T **38** of Antigua.

246.	1 c. blue	10	10
247.	4 c. green	35	10
248.	20 c. brown	75	45
249.	40 c. violet	1·50	1·25

1966. Royal Visit. As T **39** of Antigua.

250.	4 c. black and blue ..	1·50	25
251.	25 c. black and mauve ..	4·00	1·25

1966. Inauguration of W.H.O. Headquarters, Geneva. As T **41** of Antigua.

252.	4 c. black, green and blue..	30	10
253.	25 c. black, purple & ochre	95	80

1966. 20th Anniv of U.N.E.S.C.O. As T **54/6** of Antigua.

254.	4 c. multicoloured ..	40	10
255.	8 c. yellow, violet & olive	75	10
256.	25 c. black, purple & orge.	1·50	60

38. Coastal View of Mount Coke Area.

1967. Autonomous Methodist Church. Mult.

257.	2 c. Type **38** .. .	10	10
258.	8 c. Kingstown Methodist Church	10	10
259.	25 c. First Licence to perform Marriages.. ..	25	10
260.	35 c. Conference Arms ..	25	10

39. Meteorological Institute.

1968. World Meteorological Day.

262.	39.	4 c. multicoloured ..	10	10
263.		25 c. multicoloured ..	10	10
264.		35 c. multicoloured ..	15	10

40. Dr. Martin Luther King and Cotton Pickers.

1968. Dr. Martin Luther King Commem.

265.	40.	5 c. multicoloured ..	10	10
266.		25 c. multicoloured ..	10	10
267.		35 c. multicoloured ..	10	10

41. Speaker addressing Demonstrators.

1968. Human Rights Year.

268.	41.	3 c. multicoloured ..	10	10
269.	–	35 c. blue	20	10

DESIGN—VERT. 35 c. Scales of Justice and Human Rights Emblem.

43. Male Masquerader.

1969. St. Vincent Carnival.

270.	43.	1 c. multicoloured ..	10	10
271.	–	5 c. red and brown ..	10	10
272.	–	8 c. multicoloured ..	10	10
273.	–	25 c. multicoloured ..	15	15

DESIGNS—VERT. 5 c. Steel Bandsman. 25 c. Queen of Bands. HORIZ. 8 c. Carnival Revellers.

1969. Methodist Conf. Nos. 241, 257/8 and 260 optd. **METHODIST CONFERENCE MAY 1969.**

274	38	2 c. multicoloured ..	10	15
275	–	8 c. multicoloured ..	30	40
276	–	25 c. multicoloured ..	35	40
277	–	35 c. multicoloured ..	1·50	3·00

48. "Strength in Unity".

1969. 1st Anniv. of "CARIFTA".

278.	48.	2 c. black, buff and red	10	10
279.	–	5 c. multicoloured ..	10	10
280.	48.	8 c. black, buff & green	10	10
281.	–	25 c. multicoloured ..	25	15

DESIGN—VERT. 5 c., 25 c. Map.

50. Flag of St. Vincent.

1969. Statehood.

282.	50.	4 c. multicoloured ..	10	10
283.	–	10 c. multicoloured ..	10	10
284.	–	50 c. grey, black & orange	35	20

DESIGNS: 10 c. Battle scene with insets of Petroglyph and Carib Chief Chatoyer. 50 c. Carib House with maces and scales.

51. Green Heron.

1970. Multicoloured.

285.	½ c. House Wren	10	75
286a.	1 c. Type **51**	30	1·50
287.	2 c. Lesser Antillean Bullfinches	15	40
288.	3 c. St. Vincent Amazon..	15	30
289.	4 c. Rufous-throated Solitaire	20	30
364.	5 c. Red-necked Pigeon ..	50	20
291.	6 c. Bananaquit	30	30
292.	8 c. Purple-throated Carib	40	20
293.	10 c. Mangrove Cuckoo ..	30	10
294.	12 c. Common Black Hawk	40	10
295.	20 c. Bare-eyed Thrush ..	60	15
296.	25 c. Hooded Tanager (Prince)	70	20
297.	50 c. Blue Hooded Euphonia	1·75	75
298.	$1 Barn Owl	6·50	3·50
299.	$2.50 Yellow-bellied Elaenia	7·00	4·00
300.	$5 Ruddy Quail Dove ..	11·00	5·50

Nos. 285, 289, 364, 293/4, and 298/9 are vert.

52. "DHC-6" Twin Otter.

1970. 20th Anniv. of Regular Air Services. Multicoloured.

301.	5 c. Type **52**	10	10
302.	8 c. "Grumman Goose" ..	15	10
303.	10 c. Hawker Siddeley "HS-748"	20	10
304.	25 c. Douglas "DC-3" ..	65	30

53. "Children's Nursery".

1970. Cent. of British Red Cross. Mult.

305. 3 c. Type **53** 10 10
306. 5 c. "First Aid" 15 10
307. 12 c. "Voluntary Aid Detachment" 35 20
308. 25 c. "Blood Transfusion" 55 20

54. "Angel and the two Marys at the tomb" (stained-glass window).

1970. 150th Anniv. of St. George's Cathedral, Kingstown. Multicoloured.

309. ½ c. Type **54** 10 10
310. 5 c. St. George's Cathedral 10 10
311. 25 c. Tower, St. George's Cathedral 10 10
312. 35 c. Interior, St. George's Cathedral 15 10
313. 50 c. Type **54** 20 30

Nos. 310 and 312 are horiz.

55. "The Adoration of the Shepherds" (Le Nain).

1970. Christmas. Multicoloured.

314. 8 c. "The Virgin and Child" (G. Bellini) (vert.) 10 10
315. 25 c. Type **55** 10 10
316. 35 c. As 8 c. 10 10
317. 50 c. Type **55** 15 20

56. New Post Office and 6d. Stamp of 1861.

1971. 110th Anniv. of 1st St. Vincent Stamps. Multicoloured.

318. 2 c. Type **56** 10 10
319. 4 c. 1d. stamp of 1861 and new Post Office 10 10
320. 25 c. Type **56** 10 10
321. $1 As 4 c. 35 45

57. Trust Seal and Wildlife.

1971. St. Vincent's National Trust. Mult.

322. 12 c. Type **57** 25 10
323. 30 c. Old Cannon, Fort Charlotte 40 15
324. 40 c. Type **57** 55 25
325. 45 c. As 30 c. 55 30

58. "Madonna appearing to St. Anthony" (Tiepolo).

1971. Christmas. Multicoloured.

326. 5 c. Type **58** 10 10
327. 10 c. "The Holy Family on the flight into Egypt" (detail, Pietro da Cortona) 10 10
328. 25 c. Type **58** 10 10
329. $1 As 10 c... .. .. 40 35

59. Careening.

1971. The Grenadines of St. Vincent. Multicoloured.

330. 1 c. Type **59** 10 10
331. 5 c. Seine fishermen .. 10 10
332. 6 c. Map of the Grenadines 10 10
333. 15 c. Type **59** 25 10
334. 20 c. As 5 c. 20 10
335. 50 c. As 6 c. 40 60

60. Private, Grenadier Company, 32nd Foot (1764).

1972. Military Uniforms.

337. **60.** 12 c. multicoloured .. 90 15
338. – 30 c. multicoloured .. 1·75 65
339. – 50 c. multicoloured .. 2·50 1·00

DESIGNS: 30 c. Officer, Battalion Company, 31st. Foot (1772). 50 c. Private, Grenadier Company, 6th Foot (1772).

61. Breadnut Fruit.

1972. Fruit. Multicoloured.

340. 3 c. Type **61** 10 10
341. 5 c. Pawpaw 10 10
342. 12 c. Plumrose or Roseapple 30 30
343. 25 c. Mango 70 70

62. Candlestick Cassia.

1972. Flowers. Multicoloured.

344. 1 c. Type **62** 10 10
345. 30 c. Lobster Claw .. 20 10
346. 40 c. White Trumpet .. 25 15
347. $1 Soufriere tree .. 70 80

63. Sir Charles Brisbane and Coat of Arms.

1972. Birth Bicent. of Sir Charles Brisbane.

348. **63.** 20 c. brn., gold & red .. 15 10
349. – 30 c. yellow, mauve & blk. 40 10
350. – $1 multicoloured .. 1·40 70

DESIGNS: 30 c. H.M.S. "Arethusa", 1807. $1 H.M.S. "Blake", 1808.

1972. Royal Silver Wedding. As T **52** of Ascension, but with Arrowroot and Bread-fruit in background.

352. 30 c. brown 10 10
353. $1 green 40 20

65. Sighting of St. Vincent.

1973. 475th Anniv. of Columbus's Visit to the West Indies. Multicoloured.

354. 5 c. Type **65** 25 15
355. 12 c. Caribs watching Columbus's fleet .. 45 20
356. 30 c. Christopher Columbus 1·00 80
357. 50 c. "Santa Maria" .. 1·50 1·40

66. "The Last Supper" (French stained-glass Window).

1973. Easter.

358. **66.** 15 c. multicoloured .. 10 10
359. – 60 c. multicoloured .. 20 20
360. – $1 multicoloured .. 20 20

Nos. 358/60 are in the form of a **triptych** which make a composite design depicting "The Last Supper".

67. William Wilberforce and Poster.

1973. 140th Death Anniv. of William Wilberforce. Multicoloured.

369. 30 c. Type **67** 15 10
370. 40 c. Slaves cutting cane .. 20 15
371. 50 c. Wilberforce and medallion 20 15

68. P.P.F. Symbol.

1973. 21st Anniv. of International Planned Parenthood Federation. Multicoloured.

372. 12 c. Type **68** 10 10
373. 40 c. "IPPF" and symbol 20 20

1973. Royal Wedding. As T **47** of Anguilla. Multicoloured, background colours given.

374. 50 c. blue 15 10
375. 70 c. green 20 10

69. Administration Block, Mona.

1973. 25th Anniv. of West Indies University. Multicoloured.

376. 5 c. Type **69** 10 10
377. 10 c. University Centre, Kingstown 10 10
378. 30 c. Aerial view, Mona University 15 10
379. $1 University coat of arms (vert.) 50 60

1973. Nos. 297, 292 and 298 **surch.**

380. 30 c. on 50 c. multicoloured 2·00 90
381. 40 c. on 8 c. multicoloured 2·00 90
382. $10 on $1 multicoloured .. 10·00 6·50

71. "The Descent from the Cross" (Sansovino).

1974. Easter. Multicoloured.

383. 5 c. Type **71** 10 10
384. 30 c. "The Deposition" (English, 14th-century) 10 10
385. 40 c. "Pieta" (Fernandez) 10 10
386. $1 "The Resurrection" (French, 16th-century) 20 25

72. "Istra".

1974. Cruise Ships. Multicoloured.

No.	Description		
387.	15 c. Type 72	20	10
388.	20 c. "Oceanic"	25	10
389.	30 c. "Aleksandr Pushkin"	25	10
390.	$1 "Europa"	50	30

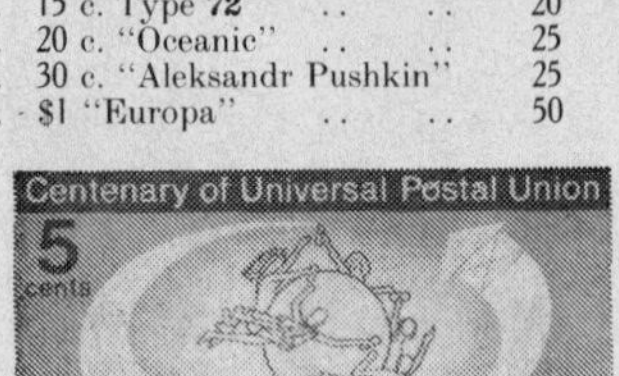

73. U.P.U. Emblem.

1974. Centenary of U.P.U. Multicoloured.

No.	Description		
392.	5 c. Type 73	10	10
393.	12 c. Globe within posthorn	10	10
394.	60 c. Map of St. Vincent and hand-cancelling	20	10
395.	90 c. Map of the World	25	30

74. Royal Tern.

1974. Multicoloured.

No.	Description		
396.	30 c. Type 74	2·00	75
397.	40 c. Brown pelican	2·00	75
398.	$10 Magnificent Frigate Bird	18·00	9·50

75. Scout Badge and Emblems.

1974. Diamond Jubilee of Scout Movement in St. Vincent.

No.	Description		
399. 75.	10 c. multicoloured	10	10
400.	25 c. multicoloured	20	10
401.	45 c. multicoloured	35	25
402.	$1 multicoloured	75	60

76. Sir Winston Churchill.

1974. Birth Cent. of Sir Winston Churchill. Multicoloured.

No.	Description		
403.	25 c. Type 76	15	10
404.	35 c. Churchill in military uniform	20	10
405.	45 c. Churchill in naval uniform	25	10
406.	$1 Churchill in air force uniform	45	50

77. The Shepherds.

1974. Christmas.

No.	Description		
407. 77.	3 c. blue and black	10	10
408. –	3 c. blue and black	10	10
409. –	3 c. blue and black	10	10
410. –	3 c. blue and black	10	10
411. 77.	8 c. green and black	10	10
412. –	35 c. pink and black	20	10
413. –	45 c. brown and black	20	10
414. –	$1 mauve and black	40	50

DESIGNS: Nos. 408, 411, Mary and crib. Nos. 409, 413, Joseph, ox and ass. Nos. 410, 414, The Magi.

78. Faces.

1975. Kingstown "Carnival '75". Mult.

No.	Description		
415.	1 c. Type 78	10	10
416.	15 c. Pineapple women	20	15
417.	25 c. King of the Bands	20	15
418.	35 c. Carnival dancers	25	15
419.	45 c. Queen of the Bands	25	20
420.	$1.25 "African Splendour"	35	55

79. French Angelfish.

1975. Multicoloured.

No.	Description		
422.	1 c. Type 79	15	60
423.	2 c. Spotfin Butterfly-fish	15	70
424.	3 c. Horse-eyed Jack	15	30
425.	4 c. Mackerel	20	10
426.	5 c. French Grunt	20	30
427.	6 c. Spotted Goatfish	20	60
428.	8 c. Ballyhoo	20	60
429.	10 c. Sperm Whale	30	10
430.	12 c. Humpback Whale	40	90
431.	15 c. Cowfish	80	75
432.	15 c. Skipjack	3·00	35
433.	20 c. Queen Angelfish	40	10
434.	25 c. Princess Parrotfish	45	20
435.	35 c. Red Hind	50	60
436.	45 c. Atlantic Flying-fish	65	65
437.	50 c. Porkfish	65	70
438.	70 c. "Albacore" or Yellow-fin Tuna	4·25	70
439.	90 c. Pompano	4·25	70
440.	$1 Queen Triggerfish	90	20
441a.	$2.50 Sailfish	3·50	1·50
442.	$5 Dolphin Fish	5·00	2·50
443.	$10 Blue Marlin	5·00	8·50

80. Cutting Bananas.

1975. Banana Industry. Multicoloured.

No.	Description		
447	25 c. Type 80	15	10
448	35 c. Packaging Station, La Croix	15	10
449	45 c. Cleaning and boxing	20	15
450	70 c. Shipping bananas aboard "Geestide" (freighter)	40	30

81. Snorkel Diving.

1975. Tourism. Multicoloured.

No.	Description		
451.	15 c. Type 81	25	15
452.	20 c. Aquaduct Golf Course	40	15
453.	35 c. Steel Band at Mariner's Inn	45	15
454.	45 c. Sunbathing at Young Island	45	25
455.	$1.25 Yachting marina	1·25	1·75

82. George Washington, John Adams, Thomas Jefferson and James Madison.

1975. Bicentenary of American Revolution.

No.	Description		
456. 82.	½ c. black and mauve	10	10
457. –	1 c. black and green	10	10
458. –	1½ c. black and mauve	10	10
459. –	5 c. black and green	10	10
460. –	10 c. black and blue	10	10
461. –	25 c. black and yellow	15	10
462. –	35 c. black and blue	15	15
463. –	45 c. black and red	20	15
464. –	$1 black and orange	40	40
465. –	$2 black and green	60	75

PRESIDENTS: 1 c. Monroe, Quincy Adams, Jackson, van Buren. 1½ c. W. Harrison, Tyler, Polk, Taylor. 5 c. Fillmore, Pierce, Buchanan, Lincoln. 10 c. Andrew Johnson, Grant, Hayes, Garfield. 25 c. Arthur, Cleveland, B. Harrison, McKinley. 35 c. Theodore Roosevelt, Taft, Wilson, Harding. 45 c. Coolidge, Hoover, Franklin Roosevelt, Truman, $1, Eisenhower, Kennedy, Lyndon Johnson, Nixon. $2, Pres. Ford and White House.

83/4. "Shepherds".

1975. Christmas.

No.	Description		
467. –	3 c. black and mauve	10	10
468. –	3 c. black and mauve	30	30
469. –	3 c. black and mauve	10	10
470. –	3 c. black and mauve	10	10
471. –	8 c. black and blue	10	10
472. –	8 c. black and blue	10	10
473. –	35 c. black and yellow	20	20
474. –	35 c. black and yellow	20	20
475. 83.	45 c. black and green	30	30
476. 84.	45 c. black and green	30	30
477. –	$1 black and purple	65	65
478. –	$1 black and purple	65	65

DESIGNS: No. 467, "Star of Bethlehem". No. 468, "Holy Trinity". No. 469, As Type 83. No. 470, "Three Kings". No. 471/2, As No. 467. No. 473/4, As No. 468. No. 475/6, Types 83/4. No. 477/8, As No. 470. The two designs of each value (Nos. 471/8) differ in that the longest side is at the foot and at the top respectively, as in Types 83/4.

85. Carnival Dancers.

1976. Kingstown "Carnival '76". Mult.

No.	Description		
479.	1 c. Type 85	10	10
480.	2 c. Humpty-Dumpty people	10	10
481.	5 c. Smiling faces	10	10
482.	35 c. Dragon worshippers	20	10
483.	45 c. Carnival tableau	25	15
484.	$1.25 Bumble-bee dancers	45	45

1976. Nos. 424 and 437 surch.

No.	Description		
485.	70 c. on 3 c. Horse-eyed Jack	90	1·25
486.	90 c. on 50 c. Porkfish	90	1·40

87. Blue-headed Hummingbird and Yellow Hibiscus.

1976. Hummingbirds and Hibiscuses. Mult.

No.	Description		
487.	5 c. Type 87	35	10
488.	10 c. Antillean Crested Hummingbird and Pink Hibiscus	60	15
489.	35 c. Purple-throated Carib and White Hibiscus	1·40	55
490.	45 c. Blue-headed Hummingbird and Red Hibiscus	1·50	65
491.	$1.25 Green-throated Carib and Peach Hibiscus	9·50	5·50

1976. West Indian Victory in World Cricket Cup. As Nos. 431/2 of St. Lucia.

No.	Description		
492.	15 c. Map of the Caribbean	75	25
493.	45 c. Prudential Cup	1·75	1·00

88. St. Mary Church, Kingstown.

1976. Christmas. Multicoloured.

No.	Description		
494.	35 c. Type 88	15	10
495.	45 c. Anglican Church, Georgetown	15	10
496.	50 c. Methodist Church, Georgetown	20	10
497.	$1.25 St. George's Cathedral, Kingstown	40	60

89. Barrancoid Pot-stand.

1977. National Trust. Multicoloured.

No.	Description		
498.	5 c. Type 89	10	10
499.	45 c. National Museum	15	10
500.	70 c. Carib sculpture	25	20
501.	$1 Ciboney petroglyph	45	50

90. William I, William II, Henry I and Stephen.

1977. Silver Jubilee. Multicoloured.

No.	Description		
502.	½ c. Type 90	10	10
503.	1 c. Henry II, Richard I, John, Henry III	10	10
504.	1½ c. Edward I, Edward II, Edward III, Richard II	10	10
505.	2 c. Henry IV, Henry V, Henry VI, Edward IV	10	10
506.	5 c. Edward V, Richard III, Henry VII, Henry VIII	10	10
507.	10 c. Edward VI, Lady Jane Grey, Mary I, Elizabeth I	10	10
508.	25 c. James I, Charles I, Charles II, James II	15	10
509.	35 c. William III, Mary II, Anne, George I	15	10
510.	45 c. George II, George III, George IV	15	10
511.	75 c. William IV, Victoria, Edward VII	20	25
512.	$1 George V, Edward VIII, George VI	30	40
513.	$2 Elizabeth II leaving Westminster Abbey	45	60

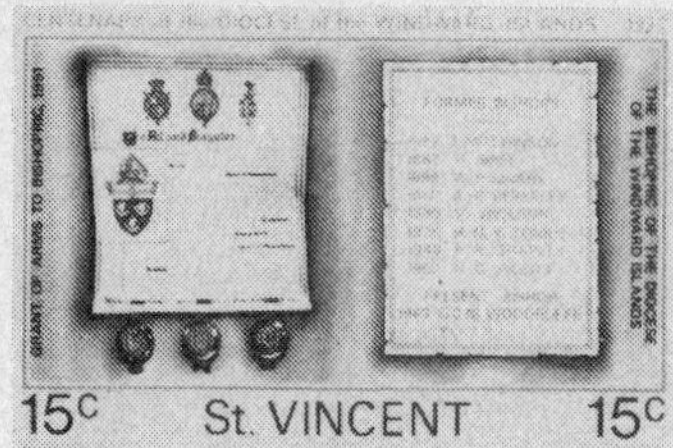

91. Grant of Arms.

1977. Centenary of Windward Islands Diocese. Multicoloured.

527. 15 c. Type **91** 10 10
528. 35 c. Bishop Berkeley and mitres 10 10
529. 45 c. Map and arms of diocese 10 10
530. $1.25 St. George's Cathedral and Bishop Woodroffe .. 30 45

1977. Carnival '77. Nos. 426, 429, 432/3 and 440 optd. **CARNIVAL 1977 JUNE 25th. — JULY 5th.**

531. 5 c. French Grunt .. 10 10
532. 10 c. Sperm Whale .. 10 10
533. 15 c. Skipjack .. 10 10
534. 20 c. Queen Angelfish .. 10 10
535. $1 Queen Triggerfish .. 40 50

93. Guide and Emblem.

1977. 50th Anniv. of St. Vincent Girl Guides. Multicoloured.

536. 5 c. Type **93** 10 10
537. 15 c. Early uniform, ranger, guide and brownie .. 15 10
538. 20 c. Early uniform and guide 15 10
539. $2 Lady Baden-Powell .. 70 80

1977. Royal Visit. No. 513 optd. **CARIBBEAN VISIT 1977.**

540. $2 Queen Elizabeth leaving Westminster Abbey .. 40 30

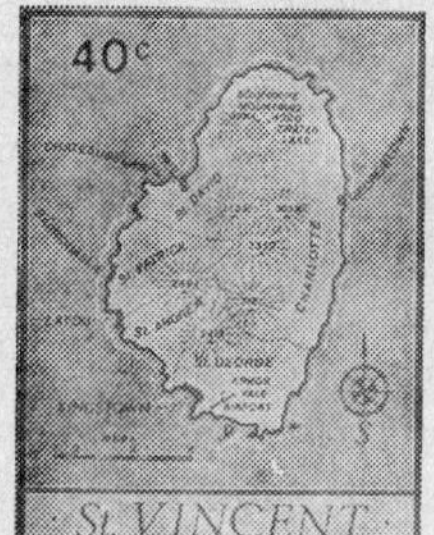

95. Map of St. Vincent.

1977. Surch. as in T **95**.

541. **95.** 20 c. pale blue and blue 15 15
542. 40 c. pale orange & orge. 25 20
543. 40 c. pink and mauve .. 20 15

Nos. 541/3 were originally printed without face values.

96. Opening Verse and Scene.

1977. Christmas. Scenes and Verses from the carol " While Shepherds Watched their Flocks by Night ". Multicoloured.

544. 5 c. Type **96** 10 10
545. 10 c. Angel consoling shepherds 10 10
546. 15 c. View of Bethlehem .. 10 10
547. 25 c. Nativity scene .. 10 10
548. 50 c. Throng of Angels .. 10 10
549. $1.25 Praising God .. 30 55

97. "Vanessa cardui" and "Bougainvillea glubra var. alba".

1978. Butterflies and Bougainvilleas. Mult.

551 5 c. Type **97** 10 10
552 25 c. "Dione juno" and (Golden Glow) 15 10
553 40 c. "Anartia amathea" and "Mrs McLean" .. 25 10
554 50 c. "Hypolimnas misippus" and "Cyphen" .. 30 10
556 $1.25 "Pseudolycaena marsyas" and "Thomasii" 65 55

1978. 25th Anniv. of Coronation. Horiz. designs as Nos. 422/5 of Montserrat. Multicoloured.

556. 40 c. Westminster Abbey 10 10
557. 50 c. Gloucester Cathedral 10 10
558. $1.25 Durham Cathedral 20 15
559. $2.50 Exeter Cathedral .. 30 25

98. Rotary International Emblem and Motto.

1978. International Service Clubs. Emblems and mottos. Multicoloured.

561. 40 c. Type **98** 25 10
562. 50 c. Lions International 25 10
563. $1 Jaycees 50 50

99. " Co-operation in Education Leads to Mutual Understanding and Respect ".

1978. 10th Anniv. of Project School to School (St. Vincent–Canada school twinning project). Multicoloured.

564. 40 c. Type **99** 10 10
565. $2 " Co-operation in Education Leads to the Elimination of Racial Intolerance " (horiz.) .. 40 50

100. Arnos Vale Airport.

1978. Powered Flight. 75th Anniv. Mult.

566. 10 c. Type **100** 10 10
567. 40 c. Wilbur Wright and " Flyer " 15 10
568. 50 c. " Flyer " 15 10
569. $1.25 Orville Wright and " Flyer " 45 35

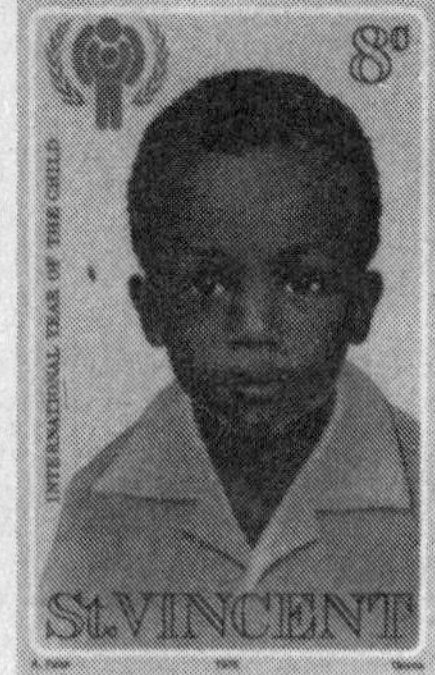

101. Young Child.

1979. International Year of the Child.

570. **101.** 8 c. black, gold and green 10 10
571. – 20 c. black, gold and lilac 15 10
572. – 50 c. black, gold and blue 25 10
573. – $2 black, gold and flesh 75 50

DESIGNS: 20 c., 50 c., $2, Different portraits of young children.

1979. Soufriere Eruption Relief Fund. As T **95**, but surch. **SOUFRIERE RELIEF FUND 1979** and premium.

574. **95.** 10 c.+5 c. blue and lilac 10 15
575. 50 c.+25 c. brn. & buff 20 20
576. $1+50 c. brown & grey 30 30
577. $2+$1 green and light green 50 50

103. Sir Rowland Hill.

1979. Death centenary of Sir Rowland Hill. Multicoloured.

578. 40 c. Type **103** 15 10
579. 50 c. Penny Black and Two Penny Blue stamps .. 20 15
580. $3 1861 1d. and 6d. stamps 75 1·10

104. First and latest Buccament Postmarks and Map of St. Vincent.

1979. Post Offices of St. Vincent. Early and modern postmarks. Multicoloured.

582. 1 c. Type **104** 10 10
583. 2 c. Sion Hill 10 10
584. 3 c. Cumberland 10 10
585. 4 c. Questelles 10 10
586. 5 c. Layou 10 10
587. 6 c. New Ground 10 10
588. 8 c. Mesopotamia 10 10
589. 10 c. Troumaca 10 10
590. 12 c. Arnos Vale 15 10
591. 15 c. Stubbs 15 10
592. 20 c. Orange Hill 15 10
593. 25 c. Calliaqua 15 10
594. 40 c. Edinboro 25 20
595. 50 c. Colonarie 30 25
596. 80 c. Biabou 40 35
597. $1 Chateaubelair 50 50
598. $2 Head P.O., Kingstown 60 80
599. $3 Barrouallie .. .. 75 1·25
600. $5 Georgetown .. .. 1·25 2·00
601. $10 Kingstown .. .. 2·25 4·00

1979. Opening of St. Vincent and the Grenadines Air Service. Optd. **ST. VINCENT AND THE GRENADINES AIR SERVICE 1979.**

602. 10 c. Type **100** 10 10

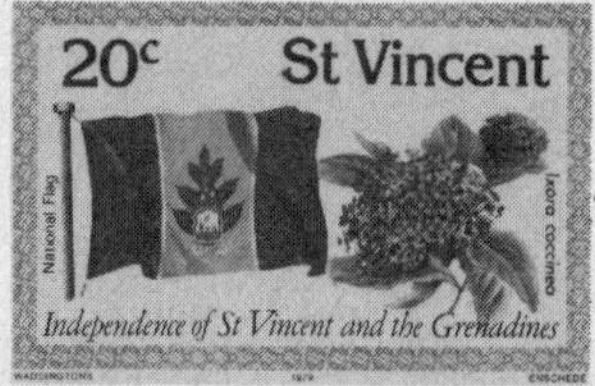

106. National Flag and " Ixora coccinea " (flower).

1979. Independence. Multicoloured.

603. 20 c. Type **106** 15 10
604. 50 c. House of Assembly and " ixora stricta " (flower) 20 10
605. 80 c. Prime Minister R. Milton Cato and " ixora williamsii " (flower) .. 25 20

1979. Independence. Nos. 422, 425/30, 432 437/41 and 443. Optd. **INDEPENDENCE, 1979.**

606. 1 c. Type **79** 10 10
607. 4 c. Mackerel 10 10
608. 5 c. French Grunt .. 10 10
609. 6 c. Spotted Goatfish .. 10 10
610. 8 c. Ballyhoo 10 10
611. 10 c. Sperm Whale .. 15 15
612. 12 c. Humpback Whale .. 15 15
613. 15 c. Skipjack 15 15
614. 25 c. Princess Parrotfish .. 20 20
615. 50 c. Porkfish 35 35
616. 70 c. " Albacore " or Yellowfin Tuna .. 45 45
617. 90 c. Pompano 60 50
618. $1 Queen Triggerfish .. 60 50
619. $2.50, Sailfish .. .. 1·75 1·00
620. $10 Blue Marlin .. .. 4·75 4·25

108. Virgin and Child.

1979. Christmas. Scenes and quotations from " Silent Night " (carol). Multicoloured.

621. 10 c. Type **108** 10 10
622. 20 c. Jesus sleeping .. 10 10
623. 25 c. Shepherds 10 10
624. 40 c. Angel 10 10
625. 50 c. Angels holding Jesus 10 10
626. $2 Nativity 40 30

109. "Polistes cinctus" (wasp) and Oleander.

1979. Flowers and Insects. Designs showing different varieties of oleander. Multicoloured.

628 5 c. Type **109** 10 10
629 10 c. "Pyrophorus noctiluca" (click beetle) .. 10 10
630 25 c. "Stagmomantis limbata" (mantid) .. 10 10
631 50 c. "Psiloptera lampetis" (beetle) 10 10
632 $2 "Diaprepies abbreviatus" (weevil) 30 30

110. Queen Elizabeth II.

1980. " London 1980 " International Stamp Exhibition. Multicoloured.

634. 80 c. Type **110** 15 20
635. $1 Great Britain 1954 3d. and St. Vincent 1954 5 c. definitives 20 30
636. $2 Unadopted postage stamp design, 1971 .. 50 60

111. Steel Band.

1980. Kingstown Carnival. Multicoloured.

638. 20 c. Type **111** 15 15
639. 20 c. Steel band (different) 15 15

112. Football.

1980. " Sport for All ". Multicoloured.

640. 10 c. Type **112** 10 10
641. 60 c. Cycling 20 15
642. 80 c. Basketball 30 30
643. $2.50 Boxing 40 90

1980. Hurricane Relief. Nos. 640/3 surch. **HURRICANE RELIEF 50 c.**

644. **112.** 10 c.+50 c. mult. .. 15 15
645. – 60 c.+50 c. mult. .. 25 25
646. – 80 c.+50 c. mult. .. 35 35
647. – $2.50+50 c. mult. .. 60 60

114. Brazilian Agouti.

1980. Wildlife. Multicoloured.

648. 25 c. Type **114** 10 10
649. 50 c. Giant Toad 15 10
650. $2 Small Indian Mongoose 40 55

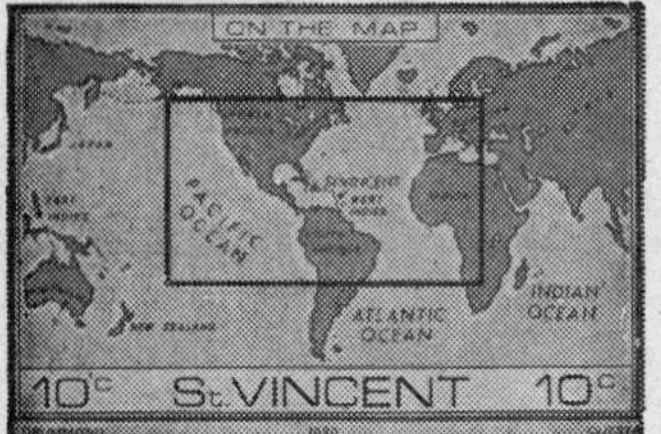

115. Map of World showing St. Vincent.

1980. St. Vincent " On the Map ". Maps showing St. Vincent. Multicoloured.

651. 10 c. Type **115** 10 10
652. 50 c. Western hemisphere 15 10
653. $1 Central America .. 30 15
654. $2 St. Vincent 50 30

116. "Ville de Paris" (French ship of the line), 1782.

1981. Sailing Ships. Multicoloured.

656 50 c. Type **116** 40 20
657 60 c. H.M.S. Ramillies" (ship of the line), 1782 45 30
658 $1.50 H.M.S. "Providence" (sloop), 1793 .. .. 1·00 1·50
659 $2 "Dee" (paddle-steamer packet) .. .. 1·25 1·75

117. Arrowroot Cultivation.

1981. Agriculture. Multicoloured.

660. 25 c. Type **117** 10 15
661. 25 c. Arrowroot processing 10 15
662. 50 c. Banana cultivation 20 25
663. 50 c. Banana export packaging station 20 25
664. 60 c. Coconut plantation .. 25 30
665. 60 c. Copra drying frames 25 30
666. $1 Cocoa cultivation .. 50 45
667. $1 Cocoa beans and sun drying frames 50 45

1981. Royal Wedding. Royal Yachts. As T **26/27** of Kiribati. Multicoloured.

668. 60 c. " Isabella " 15 15
669. 60 c. Prince Charles and Lady Diana Spencer .. 30 30
670. $2.50 " Alberta " (Tender) 30 30
671. $2.50 As No. 669 .. .. 70 70
672. $4 " Britannia " 40 40
673. $4 As No. 669 .. .. 1·25 1·25

118. Kingstown General Post Office. 119.
(Actual size 85 × 24 mm.)

1981. U.P.U. Membership.

677. **118.** $2 multicoloured .. 70 90
678. **119.** $2 multicoloured .. 70 90

Nos. 677/8 were printed together, se-tenant, in horizontal pairs throughout the sheet, forming a composite design.

120. St. Vincent Flag with Flags of other U.N. Member Nations.

1981. 1st Anniv. of U.N. Membership. Mult.

679. $1.50 Type **120** 55 25
680. $2.50 Prime Minister Robert Milton Cato 85 50

Nos. 679/80 are inscribed " ST VINCENT and the GRENADINES ".

121. Silhouettes of Figures at Old Testament Reading, and Bible Extract.

1981. Christmas. Designs showing silhouettes of Figures. Multicoloured.

681. 50 c. Type **121** 15 10
682. 60 c. Madonna and angel 15 10
683. $1 Madonna and Bible extract 25 25
684. $2 Joseph and Mary travelling to Bethlehem .. 50 50

122. Sugar Boilers.

1982. 1st Anniv. of Re-introduction of Sugar Industry. Multicoloured.

686. 50 c. Type **122** 25 15
687. 60 c. Sugar drying plant .. 25 20
688. $1.50 Sugar mill machinery 70 75
689. $2 Crane loading suger cane 95 1·00

123. Butterfly Float.

1982. Carnival 1982. Multicoloured.

690. 50 c. Type **123** 20 15
691. 60 c. Angel dancer (vert.) 20 15
692. $1.50 Winged dancer (vert) 50 80
693. $2 Eagle float .. .. 70 1·25

INDEX
Countries can be quickly located by referring to the index at the end of this volume.

124. Augusta of Saxe-Gotha, Princess of Wales, 1736.

1982. 21st Birthday of Princess of Wales. Multicoloured.

694. 50 c. Type **124** 20 20
695. 60 c. Coat of arms of Augusta of Saxe-Gotha 20 25
696. $6 Diana, Princess of Wales 1·25 1·50

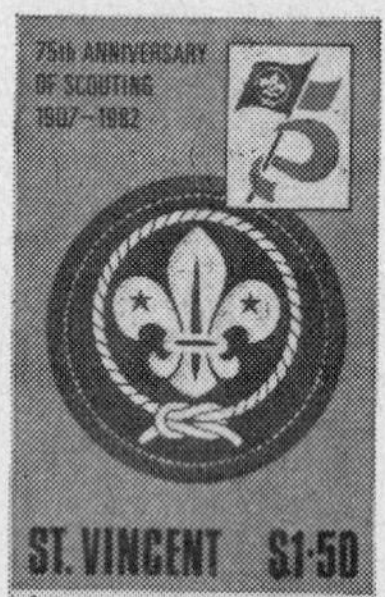

125. Scout Emblem.

1982. 75th Anniv. of Boy Scout Movement. Multicoloured.

697. $1.50 Type **125** .. .. 70 1·00
698. $2.50 75th anniversary emblem .. .. 90 1·25

1982. Birth of Prince William of Wales. Nos. 694/6 optd. **ROYAL BABY.**

699. 50 c. Type **124** 20 20
700. 60 c. Coat of arms of Augusta of Saxe-Gotha 20 25
701. $6 Diana, Princess of Wales 1·25 1·75

126. De Havilland " Moth ", 1932.

1982. 50th Anniv. of Airmail Service. Mult.

702. 50 c. Type **126** 45 30
703. 60 c. Grumman " Goose ", 1952 .. .. .. 50 40
704. $1.50 Hawker-Siddeley " 748 ", 1968 .. .. 95 1·00
705. $2 Britten-Norman " Trislander ", 1982 .. 1·10 1·60

127. "Geestport" (freighter).

1982. Ships. Multicoloured.

706 45 c. Type **127** 25 25
707 60 c. "Stella Oceanis" (liner) 30 35
708 $1.50 "Victoria" (liner) .. 70 1·00
709 $2 "Queen Elizabeth 2" (liner) .. .. .. 95 1·50

128. " Pseudocorynactis caribbeorum ".

1983. Marine Life. Multicoloured.

710. 50 c. Type **128** 55 25
711. 60 c. " Actinoporus elegans " (vert.) 65 35
712. $1.50 " Arachnanthus nocturnus " (vert.) .. 1·25 75
713. $2 " Hippocampus reidi " (vert.) .. .. 1·50 1·00

129. Satellite View of St. Vincent.

1983. Commonwealth Day. Multicoloured.

714. 45 c. Type **129** 20 20
715. 60 c. Flag of St. Vincent 20 25
716. $1·50 Prime Minister R. Milton Cato 40 65
717. $2 Harvesting bananas .. 60 90

Nos. 714/17 are inscribed "ST. VINCENT and the GRENADINES".

1983. No. 681 surch.

718. 45 c. on 50 c. Type **121** .. 40 30

131. Symbolic Handshake. 132. William A. Smith (founder).

1983. 10th Anniv. of Treaty of Chaguaramas. Multicoloured.

719. 45 c. Type **131** 25 20
720. 60 c. Commerce emblem .. 30 25
721. $1.50 Caribbean map .. 60 65
722. $2 Flags of member countries and map of St. Vincent 85 90

1983. Centenary of Boy's Brigade. Mult.

723. 45 c. Type **132** 25 25
724. 60 c. On parade 30 35
725. $1.50 Craftwork .. .. 70 1·10
726. $2 Community service .. 95 1·60

133. Ford " Model T " (1908).

1983. Leaders of the World. Automobiles (1st series).

727. **133.** 10 c. multicoloured .. 10 10
728. – 10 c. multicoloured .. 10 10
729. – 60 c. multicoloured .. 15 15
730. – 60 c. multicoloured .. 15 15
731. – $1.50 multicoloured .. 20 20
732. – $1.50 multicoloured .. 20 20
733. – $1.50 multicoloured .. 20 20
734. – $1.50 multicoloured .. 20 20
735. – $2 multicoloured .. 30 30
736. – $2 multicoloured .. 30 30
737. – $2 multicoloured .. 30 30
738. – $2 multicoloured .. 30 30

DESIGNS: (the first in each pair shows technical drawings and the second, paintings of the cars). Nos. 727/8, Ford "Model T" (1908). 729/30, "Supercharged" Cord "812" (1937). 731/2, Citroen "Open Tourer" (1937). 733/4, Mercedes Benz "300SL Gull-Wing" (1954). 735/6, Rolls Royce "Phantom I" (1925). 737/8, Ferrari "Boxer 512BB" (1967).

See also Nos. 820/9, 862/7, 884/91 and 952/63.

134. Shepherds see Nativity Star.

1983. Christmas.

No.	Description	Unused	Used
739.	10 c. Type **134**	10	10
740.	50 c. Message of the Angel	20	10
741.	$1.50 The Heavenly Host	45	45
742.	$2.40 Shepherds worship Jesus	65	75

135. " King Henry VIII ".

1983. Leaders of the World. Railway Locomotives (1st series). First in each pair shows technical drawings and the second the locomotive at work.

No.	Description	Unused	Used
744.	10 c. multicoloured ..	10	10
745.	10 c. multicoloured ..	10	10
746.	10 c. multicoloured ..	10	10
747.	10 c. multicoloured ..	10	10
748.	25 c. multicoloured ..	10	10
749.	25 c. multicoloured ..	10	10
750.	50 c. multicoloured ..	20	20
751.	50 c. multicolured ..	20	20
752.	60 c. multicoloured ..	20	20
753.	60 c. multicoloured ..	20	20
754.	75 c. multicoloured ..	25	25
755.	75 c. multicoloured ..	25	25
756.	$2.50 multicoloured ..	55	55
757.	$2.50 multicoloured ..	55	55
758.	$3 multicoloured	70	70
759.	$3 multicoloured	70	70

Designs: Nos. 744/5, "King Henry VIII", Great Britain (1927). 746/7, "Royal Scots Greys", Great Britain (1961). 748/9, "Hagley Hall", Great Britain (1928). 750/1, "Sir Lancelot", Great Britain (1926). 752/3, Class "B12", Great Britain (1912). 754/5, Deeley "Compound" type, Great Britain (1902). 756/7, "Cheshire", Great Britain (1927). 758/9, Bullied "Austerity" Class Q1, Great Britain (1942).

See also Nos. 792/807, 834/41, 872/83, 893/904 and 1001/8.

136. Fort Duvernette.

1984. Fort Duvernette. Multicoloured.

No.	Description	Unused	Used
760.	35 c. Type **136**	20	30
761.	45 c. Soldiers on fortifications	25	30
762.	$1 Canon facing bay ..	40	60
763.	$3 Map of St. Vincent and mortar	1·25	1·75

137. White Frangipani.

1984. Flowering Trees and Shrubs. Mult.

No.	Description	Unused	Used
764.	5 c. Type **137**	15	10
765.	10 c. Genip	20	10
766.	15 c. Immortelle	25	10
767.	20 c. Pink Poui	30	10
768.	25 c. Buttercup	40	10
769.	35 c. Sandbox	55	20
770.	45 c. Locust	70	25
771.	60 c. Colville's Glory ..	85	40
772.	75 c. Lignum Vitae ..	95	55
773.	$1 Golden Shower	1·25	90
774.	$5 Angelin	5·00	7·00
775.	$10 Roucou	7·50	10·00

138. Trench Warfare, First World War.

1984. Leaders of the World. British Monarchs. Multicoloured.

No.	Description	Unused	Used
776.	1 c. Type **138**	10	10
777.	1 c. George V and trenches	10	10
778.	5 c. Battle of Bannockburn	10	10
779.	5 c. Edward II and battle	10	10
780.	60 c. George V	20	20
781.	60 c. York Cottage, Sandringham	20	20
782.	75 c. Edward II	20	20
783.	75 c. Berkeley Castle ..	20	20
784.	$1 Coat of Arms of Edward II	25	25
785.	$1 Edward II (different) ..	25	25
786.	$4 Coat of Arms of George V	75	75
787.	$4 George V and Battle of Jutland	75	75

Nos. 776/7, 778/9, 780/1, 782/3, 784/5 and 786/7 were printed together, se-tenant, each pair forming a composite design.

139. Musical Fantasy Costume.

1984. Carnival 1984. Costumes. Mult.

No.	Description	Unused	Used
788.	35 c. Type **139**	15	15
789.	45 c. African princess ..	20	20
790.	$1 Market woman	40	40
791.	$3 Carib hieroglyph ..	1·25	1·40

1984. Leaders of the World. Railway Locomotives (2nd series). As T **135**, the first in each pair shows technical drawings and the second the locomotive at work.

No.	Description	Unused	Used
792.	1 c. multicoloured	10	10
793.	1 c. multicoloured	10	10
794.	2 c. multicoloured	10	10
795.	2 c. multicoloured	10	10
796.	3 c. multicoloured	10	10
797.	3 c. multicoloured	10	10
798.	50 c. multicoloured ..	30	30
799.	50 c. multicoloured ..	30	30
800.	75 c. multicoloured ..	35	35
801.	75 c. multicoloured ..	35	35
802.	$1 multicoloured	40	40
803.	$1 multicoloured	40	40
804.	$2 multicoloured	55	55
805.	$2 multicoloured	55	55
806.	$3 multicoloured	65	65
807.	$3 multicoloured	65	65

Designs: Nos. 792/3, "Liberation" Class, France (1945). 794/5, "Dreadnought", Great Britain (1967). 796/7, No. 242A1, France (1946). 798/9, Class "Dean Goods", Great Britain (1883). 800/1, Hetton colliery No. 1, Great Britain (1822). 802/3, "Penydarren", Great Britain (1804). 804/5, "Novelty", Great Britain (1829). 806/7, Class "44" Germany (1925).

140. Slaves tilling Field.

1984. 150th Anniv. of Emancipation of Slaves on St. Vincent. Multicoloured.

No.	Description	Unused	Used
808.	35 c. Type **140**	20	20
809.	45 c. Sugar-cane harvesting	25	25
810.	$1 Cutting sugar-cane ..	45	45
811.	$3 William Wilberforce and African slave caravan ..	1·25	1·40

141. Weightlifting

1984. Leaders of the World. Olympic Games, Los Angeles. Multicoloured.

No.	Description	Unused	Used
812.	1 c. Judo	10	10
813.	1 c. Type **141**	10	10
814.	3 c. Pursuit cycling ..	10	10
815.	3 c. Cycle road-racing ..	10	10
816.	60 c. Women's backstroke swimming	15	15
817.	60 c. Men's butterfly swimming	15	15
818.	$3 Sprint start	55	55
819.	$3 Finish of long distance race	55	55

1984. Leaders of the World. Automobiles (2nd series). As T **133**, the first in each pair shows technical drawings and the second paintings.

No.	Description	Unused	Used
820.	5 c. black, drab and green	10	10
821.	5 c. multicoloured	10	10
822.	20 c. black, pink and blue	15	15
823.	20 c. multicoloured ..	15	15
824.	55 c. black, green & brn. ..	25	25
825.	55 c. multicoloured ..	25	25
826.	$1.50 black, light turquoise and turquoise	35	35
827.	$1.50 multicoloured ..	35	35
828.	$2.50 black, turq. & lilac ..	40	40
829.	$2.50 multicoloured ..	40	40

Designs: Nos. 820/1, Austin-Healey "Sprite" (1958). 822/3, Maserati "Ghibli Coupe" (1971). 824/5, Pontiac "GTO" (1964). 826/7, Jaguar "D-Type" (1957). 828/9, Ferrari "365 GTB4 Daytona" (1970).

142. Grenadier, 70th Regt of Foot, 1773.

1984. Military Uniforms. Multicoloured.

No.	Description	Unused	Used
830.	45 c. Type **142**	30	30
831.	60 c. Grenadier, 6th Regt of Foot, 1775	40	35
832.	$1.50 Grenadier, 3rd Regt of Foot, 1768	85	1·00
833.	$2 Battalion Company officer, 14th Regt of Foot, 1780	1·25	1·40

1984. Leaders of the World. Railway Locomotives (3rd series). As T **135**, the first in each pair shows technical drawings and the second the locomotive at work.

No.	Description	Unused	Used
834.	5 c. multicoloured	10	10
835.	5 c. multicoloured	10	10
836.	40 c. multicoloured ..	15	20
837.	40 c. multicoloured ..	15	20
838.	75 c. multicoloured ..	20	30
839.	75 c. multicoloured ..	20	30
840.	$2.50 multicoloured ..	70	1·00
841.	$2.50 multicoloured ..	70	1·00

Designs: Nos. 834/5, Class "20", Rhodesia (1954). 836/7, "Southern Maid", Great Britain (1928). 838/9, "Prince of Wales", Great Britain (1911). 840/1, German "05", Germany (1935).

143. N. S. Taylor.

1985. Leaders of the World. Cricketers. The first in each pair shows a head portrait and the second the cricketer in action.

No.	Description	Unused	Used
842.	5 c. multicoloured	10	10
843.	5 c. multicoloured	10	10
844.	35 c. multicoloured ..	25	20
845.	35 c. multicoloured ..	25	20
846.	50 c. multicoloured ..	35	30
847.	50 c. multicoloured ..	35	30
848.	$3 multicoloured	1·50	1·25
849.	$3 multicoloured	1·50	1·25

Designs: Nos. 842/3, N. S. Taylor. 844/5, T. W. Graveney. 846/7, R. G. D. Willis. 848/9, S. D. Fletcher.

144. Eye Lash Orchid.

1985. Orchids. Multicoloured.

No.	Description	Unused	Used
850.	35 c. Type **144**	30	30
851.	45 c. "Ionopsis utricularioides"	30	30
852.	$1 "Epidendrum secundum"	50	65
853.	$3 "Oncidium altissimum"	1·25	2·00

145. Brown Pelican.

1985. Leaders of the World. Birth Bicentenary of John J. Audubon (ornithologist). Multicoloured.

No.	Description	Unused	Used
854.	15 c. Type **145**	15	10
855.	15 c. Green heron	15	10
856.	40 c. Pileated woodpecker	30	20
857.	40 c. Common flicker ..	30	20
858.	60 c. Painted bunting ..	40	30
859.	60 c. White-winged crossbill	40	30
860.	$2.25 Red-shouldered hawk	1·50	1·25
861.	$2.25 Common caracara ..	1·50	1·25

1985. Leaders of the World. Automobiles (3rd series). As T **133**, the first in each pair shows technical drawings and the second paintings.

No.	Description	Unused	Used
862.	1 c. black, yellow & green	10	10
863.	1 c. multicoloured	10	10
864.	55 c. black, blue and grey	15	15
865.	55 c. multicoloured ..	15	15
866.	$2 black, yellow and purple	40	40
867.	$2 multicoloured	40	40

Designs: Nos. 862/3, Lancia "Aprilia", (1937). 864/5, Pontiac "Firebird Trans Am", (1973). 866/7, Cunningham "C-5R", (1953).

146. Pepper.

1985. Herbs and Spices. Multicoloured.

No.	Description	Unused	Used
868.	25 c. Type **146**	10	10
869.	35 c. Sweet Marjoram ..	10	15
870.	$1 Nutmeg	25	40
871.	$3 Ginger	85	1·50

1985. Leaders of the World. Railway Locomotives (4th series). As T **135**, the first in each pair shows technical drawings and the second the locomotive at work.

872. 1 c. multicoloured 10 10
873. 1 c. multicoloured 10 10
874. 10 c. multicoloured .. 10 10
875. 10 c. multicoloured .. 10 10
876. 40 c. multicoloured .. 20 30
877. 40 c. multicoloured .. 20 30
878. 60 c. multicoloured .. 20 30
879. 60 c. multicoloured .. 20 30
880. $1 multicoloured 30 40
881. $1 multicoloured 30 40
882. $2.50 multicoloured .. 60 75
883. $2.50 multicoloured .. 60 75

DESIGNS: Nos. 872/3, "Glen Douglas", Great Britain (1913). 874/5, "Fenchurch", Great Britain (1872). 876/7, No. 1 "Stirling Single", Great Britain (1870). 878/9, No. 158A, Great Britain (1866). 880/1, No. 103 Class "Jones Goods", Great Britain (1893). 882/3, "The Great Bear", Great Britain (1908).

1985. Leaders of the World. Automobiles (4th series). As T **133**, the first in each pair shows technical drawings and the second paintings.

884. 25 c. black, grey and red .. 10 10
885. 25 c. multicoloured .. 10 10
886. 60 c. black, pink & orange 15 15
887. 60 c. multicoloured .. 15 15
888. $1 black, blue and violet .. 20 20
889. $1 multicoloured 20 20
890. $1.50 black, blue and red 25 25
891. $1.50 multicoloured .. 25 25

DESIGNS: Nos. 884/5, Essex "Coach" (1922). 886/7, Nash "Rambler" (1950). 888/9, Ferrari "Tipo 156" (1961). 890/1, Eagle-Weslake "Type 58" (1967).

1985. Leaders of the World. Railway Locomotives (5th series). As T **135**. The first in each pair shows technical drawings and the second the locomotive at work.

893. 5 c. multicoloured 10 10
894. 5 c. multicoloured 10 10
895. 30 c. multicoloured .. 15 20
896. 30 c. multicoloured .. 15 20
897. 60 c. multicoloured .. 20 30
896. 60 c. multicoloured .. 20 30
899. 75 c. multicoloured .. 20 30
900. 75 c. multicoloured .. 20 30
901. $1 multicoloured 30 40
902. $1 multicoloured 30 40
903. $2.50 multicoloured .. 60 75
904. $2.50 multicoloured .. 60 75

DESIGNS: Nos. 893/4, Tank locomotive "Loch", Great Britain (1874). 895/6, Class "47XX", Great Britain (1919). 897/8, P.L.M. Class "121", France (1876). 899/900, Class "24", Germany (1927). 90/2, No. 1008 tank locomotive, Great Britain (1889). 903/4, Class "PS-4", U.S.A. (1926).

147. Bamboo Flute.

1985. Traditional Musical Instruments. Mult.

905. 25 c. Type **147** 15 15
906. 35 c. Quatro (four-stringed guitar) 20 25
907. $1 Ba-ha (bamboo pipe) (vert.) 50 55
908. $2 Goat-skin drum (vert.) 1·00 1·10

148. Queen Elizabeth the Queen Mother.

1985. Leaders of the World. Life and Times of Queen Elizabeth the Queen Mother. Various portraits.

910. **148.** 35 c. multicoloured .. 15 20
911. – 35 c. multicoloured .. 15 20
912. – 85 c. multicoloured .. 20 30
913. – 85 c. multicoloured .. 20 30
914. – $1.20 multicoloured .. 25 35
915. – $1.20 multicoloured .. 25 35
916. – $1.60 multicoloured .. 30 45
917. – $1.60 multicoloured .. 30 45

Each value issued in pairs showing a floral pattern across the bottom of the portraits which stops short of the left-hand edge on the first stamp and of the right-hand edge on the second.

149. Elvis Presley.

1985. Leaders of the World. Elvis Presley (entertainer). Various portraits Mult., background colours given.

919. **149.** 10 c. multicoloured .. 30 10
920. – 10 c. mult. (blue) .. 30 10
921. – 60 c. mult. (brown) .. 50 35
922. – 60 c. mult. (grey) .. 50 35
923. – $1 mult. (brown) .. 75 55
924. – $ mult. (blue) .. 75 55
925. – $5 mult. (light blue) 2·00 2·75
926. – $5 mult. (blue) .. 2·00 2·75

150. Silos and Conveyor Belt.

1985. St. Vincent Flour Milling Industry. Multicoloured.

928. 20 c. Type **150** 10 15
929. 30 c. Roller mills 15 20
930. 75 c. Administration building 25 35
931. $3 Bran finishers .. .. 90 1·40

1985. Royal Visit. Nos. 672/3, 697/8, 711, 724 and 912/3 optd. **CARIBBEAN ROYAL VISIT 1985** or surch. also.

932. – 60 c. mult. (711) .. 2·50 2·00
933. – 60 c. mult. (724) .. 3·00 2·50
934. – 85 c. mult. (912) .. 4·00 3·50
935. – 85 c. mult. (913) .. 4·00 3·50
936. **125.** $1.50 multicoloured .. 4·00 4·00
937. – $1.60 on $4 mult. (672) 2·00 2·50
938. – $1.60 on $4 mult. (673) 9·00 9·00
939. – $2.50 mult. (698) .. 5·50 4·50

No. 938 shows a new face value only; "Caribbean Royal Visit—1985" is omitted from the surcharge.

151. Michael Jackson.

1985. Leaders of the World. Michael Jackson (entertainer). Various portraits. Mult.

940. 60 c. multicoloured .. 25 30
941. 60 c. multicoloured .. 25 30
942. $1 multicoloured 40 45
943. $1 multicoloured 40 45
944. $2 multicoloured 70 90
945. $2 multicoloured 70 90
946. $5 multicoloured .. .. 1·50 2·25
947. $5 multicoloured .. .. 1·50 2·25

Each value issued in pairs, the left-hand design showing the face value at top left (as on Type **151**) and the right-hand design at top right.

152. "The Serenaders" (Kim de Freitas).

1985. Christmas. Children's Paintings. Mult.

949. 25 c. Type **152** 15 15
950. 75 c. "Poinsettia" (Jackie Douglas) 35 40
951. $2.50 "Jesus our Master" (Bernadette Payne) .. 1·25 1·40

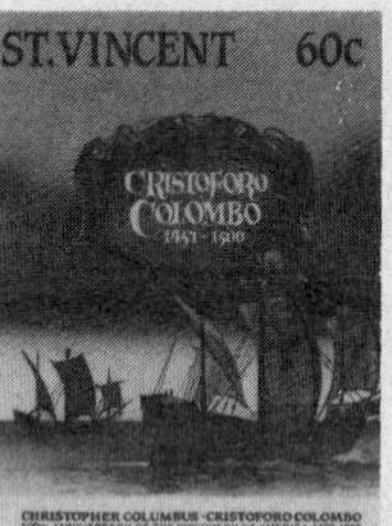

153. "Santa Maria".

1986. 500th Anniv. (1992) of Discovery of America by Columbus (1st issue). Mult.

952. 60 c. Type **153** 30 35
953. 60 c. Christopher Columbus 30 35
954. $1.50 Columbus at Spanish Court 75 80
955. $1.50 King Ferdinand and Queen Isabella of Spain 75 80
956. $2.75 "Santa Maria" and fruits .. .. .. 1·40 1·50
957. $2.75 Maize and fruits .. 1·40 1·50

See also Nos. 1125/31, 1305/24, 1639/56, 1677/84, 1895/1900 and 1981/2.

1986. Leaders of the World. Automobiles (5th series). As T **133**, the first in each pair shows technical drawings and the second paintings.

959. 30 c. black, blue & orange 15 15
960. 30 c. multicoloured .. 15 15
961. 45 c. black, grey and blue 15 15
962. 45 c. multicoloured .. 15 15
963. 60 c. black, blue and red .. 15 15
964. 60 c. multicoloured .. 15 15
965. 90 c. black, yellow and blue 20 20
966. 90 c. multicoloured .. 20 20
967. $1.50 black, lilac & mauve 25 25
968. $1.50 multicoloured .. 25 25
969. $2.50 black, blue & lt. blue 30 30
970. $2.50 multicoloured .. 30 30

DESIGNS: Nos. 959/60, Cadillac "Type 53" (1916). 961/2, Triumph "Dolomite" (1939). 963/4, Panther "J-72" (1972). 965/6, Ferrari "275 GTB/4" (1967). 967/8, Packard "Caribbean" (1953). 969/70, Bugatti "Type 41 Royale" (1931).

155. Halley's Comet.

1986. Appearance of Halley's Comet. Multicoloured.

973. 45 c. Type **155** 25 20
974. 60 c. Edmond Halley .. 30 30
975. 75 c. Newton's telescope and astronomers .. 40 45
976. $3 Amateur astronomer on St. Vincent .. .. 1·50 2·00

1986. 60th Birthday of Queen Elizabeth II (1st issue). As T **117a** of Montserrat. Mult.

978. 10 c. Queen Elizabeth II .. 10 10
979. 90 c. Princess Elizabeth .. 30 30
980. $2·50 Queen gathering bouquets from crowd .. 75 75
981. $8 In Canberra, 1982 (vert.) 2·00 2·50

See also Nos. 996/9.

156. Mexican Player.

1986. World Cup Football Championship, Mexico. Multicoloured.

983. 1 c. Football and world map (horiz.) 10 10
984. 2 c. Type **156** 10 10
985. 5 c. Mexican player (different) 10 10
986. 5 c. Hungary v Scotland .. 10 10
987. 10 c. Spain v Scotland .. 10 10
988. 30 c. England v U.S.S.R. (horiz.) 20 20
989. 45 c. Spain v France .. 30 30
990. 75 c. Mexican team (56 × 36 mm.) 45 40
991. $1 England v Italy .. 75 55
992. $2 Scottish team (56 × 36 mm.) .. .. 1·40 1·10
993. $4 Spanish team (56 × 36 mm.) .. .. 2·50 2·10
994. $5 English team (56 × 36 mm.) .. .. 3·00 2·75

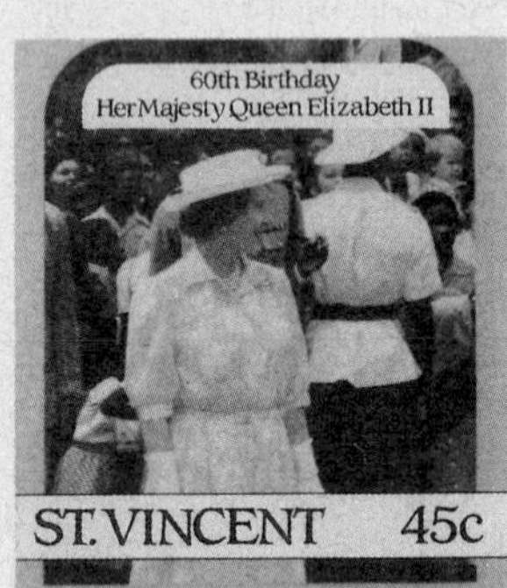

157. Queen Elizabeth at Victoria Park, Kingstown.

1986. 60th Birthday of Queen Elizabeth II (2nd issue). Scenes from 1985 Royal Visit. Multicoloured.

996. 45 c. Type **157** 35 30
997. 60 c. Queen and Prime Minister James Mitchell, Bequia 45 35
998. 75 c. Queen, Prince Philip and Mr. Mitchell, Port Elizabeth, Bequia .. 50 40
999. $2·50 Queen, Prince Philip and Mr Mitchell watching Independence Day parade, Victoria Park .. 1·50 1·75

1986. Leaders of the World. Railway Locomotives (6th series). As T **135**. Mult.

1001. 30 c. multicoloured .. 10 10
1002. 30 c. multicoloured .. 10 10
1003. 50 c. multicoloured .. 15 15
1004. 50 c. multicoloured .. 15 15
1005. $1 multicoloured .. 20 20
1006. $1 multicoloured .. 20 20
1007. $3 multicoloured .. 60 60
1008. $3 multicoloured .. 60 60

DESIGNS: Nos. 1001/2, Class "ED41 BZZB" rack and adhesion locomotive, Japan (1926). 1003/4, Locomotive "The Judge", Chicago Railroad Exposition, U.S.A. (1883). 1005/6, Class "E60C" electric locomotive, U.S.A. (1973). 1007/8, Class "SD40-2" diesel locomotive, U.S.A. (1972).

1986. Royal Wedding (1st issue). As T **168** of British Virgin Islands. Multicoloured.

1009. 60 c. Profile of Prince Andrew 20 25
1010. 60 c. Miss Sarah Ferguson 20 25
1011. $2 Prince Andrew with Mrs. Nancy Reagan (horiz.) 65 85
1012. $2 Prince Andrew in naval uniform (horiz.) 65 85

See aslo Nos. 1022/5.

158. "Acrocomia aculeata".

1986. Timber Resources of St. Vincent. Multicoloured.

1014. 10 c. Type **158** 30 15
1015. 60 c. "Pithecellobium saman" .. .. 1·00 60
1016. 75 c. White cedar .. .. 1·40 75
1017. $3 "Andira inermis" .. 3·25 3·50

159. Cadet Force Emblem and Cadets of 1936 and 1986.

1986. 50th Anniv. of St. Vincent Cadet Force (45 c., $2) and 75th Anniv. of St. Vincent Girls' High School (others). Multicoloured.

1018. 45 c. Type **159** 30 30
1019. 60 c. Grimble Building, Girls' High School (horiz.) 35 35
1020. $1.50 High School pupils (horiz.) .. .. 90 1·00
1021. $2 Cadets on parade (horiz.) .. .. 1·40 1·50

1986. Royal Wedding (2nd issue). Nos. 1009/12 optd. **Congratulations to T.R.H. The Duke and Duchess of York.**

1022. 60 c. Profile of Prince Andrew 30 35
1023. 60 c. Miss Sarah Ferguson 30 35
1024. $2 Prince Andrew with Mrs. Nancy Reagan (horiz.) .. .. 1·00 1·10
1025. $2 Prince Andrew in naval uniform (horiz.) 1·00 1·10

160. King Arthur.

1986. The Legend of King Arthur. Multicoloured.

1026. 30 c. Type **160** 40 40
1027. 45 c. Merlin taking baby Arthur 50 50
1028. 60 c. Arthur pulling sword from stone .. 60 60
1029. 75 c. Camelot 70 70
1030. $1 Arthur receiving Excalibur from the Lady of the Lake .. 80 80
1031. $1.50 Knights at the Round Table .. .. 1·25 1·25
1032. $2 The Holy Grail .. 1·50 1·50
1033. $5 Sir Lancelot jousting 2·75 2·75

MINIMUM PRICE

The minimum price quoted is 10p which represents a handling charge rather than a basis for valuing common stamps. For further notes about prices see introductory pages.

161. Statue of Liberty Floodlit.

1986. Centenary of Statue of Liberty. Designs showing aspects of the Statue.

1034. **161.** 15 c. multicoloured .. 10 10
1035. – 25 c. multicoloured .. 15 15
1036. – 40 c. multicoloured .. 20 25
1037. – 55 c. multicoloured .. 25 30
1038. – 75 c. multicoloured .. 35 40
1039. – 90 c. multicoloured .. 45 50
1040. – $1.75 multicoloured 90 95
1041. – $2 multicoloured .. 1·00 1·10
1042. – $2.50 multicoloured 1·25 1·40
1043. – $3 multicoloured .. 1·50 1·60

162. Fishing for Tri Tri.

1986. Freshwater Fishing. Multicoloured.

1045. 75 c. Type **162** 30 40
1046. 75 c. Tri Tri 30 40
1047. $1.50 Crayfishing .. 45 80
1048. $1.50 Crayfish 45 80

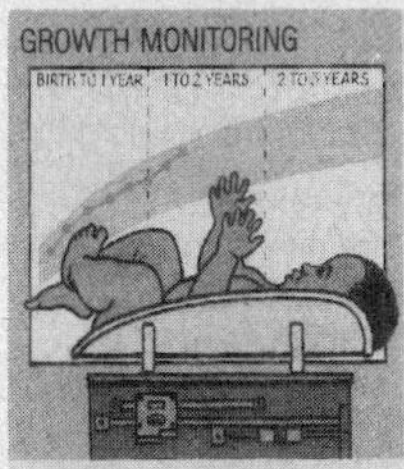

163. Baby on Scales.

1987. Child Health Campaign. Multicoloured.

1049. 10 c. Type **163** 10 10
1050. 50 c. Oral rehydration therapy 45 40
1051. 75 c. Breast feeding .. 60 55
1052. $1 Nurse giving injection 85 80

1987. World Population Control. Nos. 1049/52 optd. **WORLD POPULATION 5 BILLION 11TH JULY 1987.**

1053. 10 c. Type **163** 10 10
1054. 50 c. Oral rehydration therapy 50 40
1055. 75 c. Breast feeding .. 65 55
1056. $1 Nurse giving injection 90 70

165. Hanna Mandlikova.

1987. International Lawn Tennis Players. Multicoloured.

1057. 40 c. Type **165** 25 25
1058. 60 c. Yannick Noah .. 35 35
1059. 80 c. Ivan Lendl .. 40 40
1060. $1 Chris Evert 45 50
1061. $1.25 Steffi Graf 50 60
1062. $1.50 John McEnroe .. 60 75
1063. $1.75 Martina Navratilova with Wimbledon trophy 65 85
1064. $2 Boris Becker with Wimbledon trophy .. 70 95

166. Miss Prima Donna, Queen of the Bands, 1986.

1987. 10th Anniv. of Carnival. Multicoloured.

1066. 20 c. Type **166** 10 15
1067. 45 c. Donna Young, Miss Carnival, 1985 .. 20 25
1068. 55 c. Miss St. Vincent and the Grenadines, 1986 .. .. .. 25 30
1069. $3.70 "Spirit of Hope" costume, 1986 .. .. 1·60 1·75

The 45 c. value is inscribed "Miss Carival" in error.

1987. 10th Death Anniv. of Elvis Presley (entertainer). Nos. 919/26 optd. **THE KING OF ROCK AND ROLL LIVES FOREVER AUGUST 16th 1977-1987.**

1070. **149.** 10 c. mult. 10 10
1071. – 10 c. mult. (blue) .. 10 10
1072. – 60 c. mult. brown .. 25 30
1073. – 60 c. mult. (grey) .. 25 30
1074. – $1 mult. (brown) .. 40 45
1075. – $1 mult. (blue) .. 40 45
1076. – $5 mult. (light blue) 2·10 2·25
1078. – $5 mult. (blue) .. 2·10 2·25

168. Queen Victoria, 1841.

1987. Royal Ruby Wedding and 150th Anniv. of Queen Victoria's Accession. Mult.

1079. 15 c. Type **168** 15 10
1080. 75 c. Queen Elizabeth and Prince Andrew, 1960 .. .. .. 45 40
1081. $1 Coronation, 1953 .. 60 50
1082. $2.50 Duke of Edinburgh, 1948 .. 1·40 1·50
1083. $5 Queen Elizabeth II, c. 1980 .. .. .. 2·50 2·75

MORE DETAILED LISTS

are given in the Stanley Gibbons Catalogues referred to in the country headings.

For lists of current volumes see Introduction.

169. Karl Benz and Benz Three-wheeler (1886). (Illustration reduced. Actual size 60 × 40 mm.).

1987. Century of Motoring. Multicoloured.

1085. $1 Type **169** 60 60
1086. $2 Enzo Ferrari and Ferrari "Dino 206SP" (1966) .. .. .. 1·25 1·25
1087. $4 Charles Rolls and Sir Henry Royce and Rolls-Royce "Silver Ghost" (1907) .. .. 2·00 2·00
1088. $5 Henry Ford and Ford "Model T" (1908) .. 2·50 2·50

170. Everton Football Team. (Illustration reduced. Actual size 60 × 40 mm.).

1987. English Football Teams. Mult.

1090. $2 Type **170** .. .. 1·25 1·25
1091. $2 Manchester United .. 1·25 1·25
1092. $2 Tottenham Hotspur 1·25 1·25
1093. $2 Arsenal .. .. 1·25 1·25
1094. $2 Liverpool .. .. 1·25 1·25
1095. $2 Derby County .. 1·25 1·25
1096. $2 Portsmouth .. 1·25 1·25
1097. $2 Leeds United .. 1·25 1·25

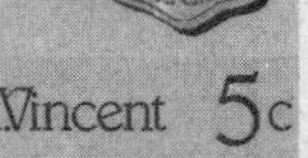

171. Five Cent Coins. 172. Charles Dickens.

1987. East Caribbean Currency. Mult.

1098 5 c. Type **171** 10 10
1099 6 c. Two cent coins .. 10 10
1100 10 c. Ten cent coins .. 10 10
1101 12 c. Two and ten cent coins 10 10
1102 15 c. Five cent coins .. 10 10
1103 20 c. Ten cent coins .. 10 10
1104 25 c. Twenty-five cent coins 10 15
1105 30 c. Five and twenty-five cent coins 10 15
1106 35 c. Twenty-five and ten cent coins 15 20
1107 45 c. Twenty-five and two ten cent coins 30 30
1108 50 c. Fifty cent coins .. 30 30
1109 65 c. Fifty, ten and five cent coins 40 45
1110 75 c. Fifty and twenty-five cent coins .. 45 50
1111 $1 One dollar note (horiz) 60 65
1112 $2 Two one dollar notes (horiz) .. .. 1·00 1·25
1113 $3 Three one dollar notes (horiz) .. .. 1·25 1·40
1114 $5 Five dollar note (horiz) 2·75 3·00
1115 $10 Ten dollar note (horiz) 4·25 4·50
1115s $20 Twenty-dollar note (horiz) .. .. 9·50 9·75

1987. Christmas. 175th Birth Anniv. of Charles Dickens. Multicoloured.

1116. 6 c. Type **172** 10 10
1117. 6 c. Mr. Fezziwig's Ball 10 10
1118. 25 c. Type **172** 15 15
1119. 25 c. Scrooge's Third Visitor 15 15

1120. 50 c. Type **172** 30 30
1121. 50 c. The Cratchits' Christmas 30 30
1122. 75 c. Type **172** 45 45
1123. 75 c. "A Christmas Carol" 45 45

Nos. 1116/17, 1118/19, 1120/1 and 1122/3 were printed together, se-tenant, each pair forming a composite design showing an open book. The first design in each pair shows Type **172** and the second a scene from "A Christmas Carol".

173. "Santa Maria".

1988. 500th Anniv. (1992) of Discovery of America by Columbus (2nd issue). Mult.
1125. 15 c. Type **173** 15 15
1126. 75 c. "Nina" and "Pinta" 50 50
1127. $1 Compass and hour-glass 70 70
1128. $1.50 Claiming the New World for Spain .. 90 90
1129. $3 Arawak village .. 1·50 1·50
1130. $4 Parrot, hummingbird, pineapple and maize .. 2·00 2·00

St. VINCENT 10c WINDSURFING

174. Brown Pelican. **175.** Windsurfing.

1988.
1132. **174.** 45 c. multicoloured .. 30 30

1988. Tourism. Multicoloured.
1133 10 c. Type **175** 10 10
1134 45 c. Scuba diving .. 20 25
1135 65 c. Aerial view of Young Island (horiz) .. 30 35
1136 $5 Cruising yacht (horiz) 2·10 2·35

176 "Nuestra Senora del Rosario" (Spanish galleon) and Spanish Knight's Cross
(Illustration reduced, actual size 56 × 36 mm)

1988. 400th Anniv of Spanish Armada. Mult.
1137 15 c. Type **176** 15 10
1138 75 c. "Ark Royal" (galleon) and English Armada medal .. 30 35
1139 $1.50 English fleet and Drake's dial 60 65
1140 $2 Dismasted Spanish galleon and 16th-century shot .. 80 85
1141 $3.50 Attack of English fireships at Calais and 16th-century grenade 1·50 1·60
1142 $5 "Revenge" (English galleon) and Drake's Drum .. .. .. 2·10 2·25

177 D. K. Lillee

1988. Cricketers of 1988 International Season. Multicoloured.
1144 15 c. Type **177** 30 30
1145 50 c. G. A. Gooch .. 50 50
1146 75 c. R. N. Kapil Dev .. 70 70
1147 $1 S. M. Gavaskar .. 85 85
1148 $1.50 M. W. Gatting .. 1·25 1·25
1149 $2.50 Imran Khan .. 1·75 1·75
1150 $3 I. T. Botham .. 2·00 2·00
1151 $4 I. V. A. Richards .. 2·25 2·25

178 Athletics

1988. Olympic Games, Seoul. Multicoloured.
1153 10 c. Type **178** 10 10
1154 50 c. Long jumping (vert) 20 25
1155 $1 Triple jumping .. 40 45
1156 $5 Boxing (vert) .. 2·10 2·25

179 Babe Ruth

1988. Famous Baseball Players (1st series).
1158 **179** $2 multicoloured .. 1·10 1·10
See also Nos. 1264/75, 1407, 1408/88, 2152/4, 2155/6 and 2426.

1988. Christmas. "Mickey's Christmas Train". As T **246** of Antigua. Multicoloured.
1160 1 c. Minnie Mouse in railway van loaded with candy (horiz) 10 10
1161 2 c. Mordie and Ferdie in wagon with toys (horiz) 10 10
1162 3 c. Chip n'Dale in wagon with Christmas trees (horiz) 10 10
1163 4 c. Donald Duck's nephews riding with reindeer (horiz) .. 10 10
1164 5 c. Donald and Daisy Duck in restaurant car (horiz) 10 10
1165 10 c. Grandma Duck, Uncle Scrooge McDuck, Goofy and Clarabelle carol singing in carriage (horiz) 10 10
1166 $5 Mickey Mouse driving locomotive (horiz) .. 2·50 2·75
1167 $6 Father Christmas in guard's van (horiz) .. 3·00 3·25

181 Mickey Mouse as Snake Charmer

1989. "India-89" International Stamp Exhibition, New Delhi. Multicoloured.
1169 1 c. Type **181** 10 10
1170 2 c. Goofy with chowsingha antelope .. 10 10
1171 3 c. Mickey and Minnie Mouse with common peafowl 10 10
1172 5 c. Goofy with Briolette Diamond and Mickey Mouse pushing mine truck 10 10
1173 10 c. Clarabelle with Orloff Diamond .. 10 10
1174 25 c. Mickey Mouse as tourist and Regent Diamond, Louvre, Paris 15 15
1175 $4 Minnie and Mickey Mouse with Kohinoor Diamond .. .. 2·40 2·40
1176 $5 Mickey Mouse and Goofy with Indian rhinoceros .. .. 2·40 2·40

182 Harry James

1989. Jazz Musicians. Multicoloured.
1178 10 c. Type **182** 10 10
1179 15 c. Sidney Bechet .. 10 10
1180 25 c. Benny Goodman .. 20 15
1181 35 c. Django Reinhardt .. 30 20
1182 50 c. Lester Young .. 40 25
1183 90 c. Gene Krupa .. 65 55
1184 $3 Louis Armstrong .. 1·75 1·75
1185 $4 Duke Ellington .. 2·25 2·50

183 Birds in Flight

1989. Wildlife Conservation. Noah's Ark. Multicoloured.
1187 40 c. Type **183** 20 20
1188 40 c. Rainbow (left side) 20 20
1189 40 c. Noah's Ark on mountain 20 20
1190 40 c. Rainbow (right side) 20 20
1191 40 c. Birds in flight (different) 20 20
1192 40 c. Cow elephant .. 20 20
1193 40 c. Bull elephant .. 20 20
1194 40 c. Top of eucalyptus tree 20 20
1195 40 c. Kangaroos 20 20
1196 40 c. Hummingbird .. 20 20
1197 40 c. Lions 20 20
1198 40 c. White-tailed deer .. 20 20
1199 40 c. Koala in fork of tree 20 20
1200 40 c. Koala on branch .. 20 20
1201 40 c. Hummingbird approaching flower .. 20 20
1202 40 c. Keel-billed toucan and flower 20 20
1203 40 c. Keel-billed toucan facing right 20 20
1204 40 c. Camels 20 20
1205 40 c. Giraffes 20 20
1206 40 c. Mountain sheep .. 20 20
1207 40 c. Ladybirds on leaf .. 20 20
1208 40 c. Swallowtail butterfly 20 20
1209 40 c. Swallowtail butterfly behind leaves 20 20
1210 40 c. Pythons 20 20
1211 40 c. Dragonflies 20 20

Nos. 1187/1211 were printed together, se-tenant, forming a composite design showing Noah's Ark and animals released after the Flood.

1989. Easter. 500th Birth Anniv of Titian (artist). As T **238** of Antigua. Multicoloured.
1212 5 c. "Baptism of Christ" (detail) 10 10
1213 30 c. "Temptation of Christ" 15 15
1214 45 c. "Ecce Homo" .. 25 25
1215 65 c. "Noli Me Tangere" (fragment) 30 30
1216 75 c. "Christ carrying the Cross" (detail) .. 35 35
1217 $1 "Christ crowned with Thorns" (detail) .. 50 50
1218 $4 "Lamentation over Christ" (detail) .. 2·00 2·00
1219 $5 "The Entombment" (detail) .. .. 2·50 2·50

184 "Ile de France"

1989. Ocean Liners. Multicoloured.
1221 10 c. Type **184** 20 10
1222 40 c. "Liberte" 40 20
1223 50 c. "Mauretania I" (launched 1906) .. 45 25
1224 75 c. "France" 65 55
1225 $1 "Aquitania" 80 65
1226 $2 "United States" .. 1·50 1·50
1227 $3 "Olympic" .. .. 1·90 2·00
1228 $4 "Queen Elizabeth" .. 2·25 2·50

185 Space Shuttle deploying West German Satellite, 1983

1989. International Co-operation in Space. Multicoloured.
1230 40 c. Type **185** 15 20
1231 60 c. Vladimir Remek (Czech cosmonaut) and "Soyuz 28", 1978 .. 25 30
1232 $1 Projected "Hermes" space plane and "Columbus" Space Station 40 45
1233 $4 Ulf Merbold (West German astronaut), 1983, and proposed European Spacelab .. 1·75 1·90

186 "Mercury 9" Capsule and Astronaut L. Gordon Cooper

1989. 25th Anniv of Launching of "Telstar II" Communications Satellite (1988). Each showing satellite and T.V. screen. Mult.
1235 15 c. Type **186** 10 10
1236 35 c. Martin Luther King addressing crowd, 1963 15 20
1237 50 c. Speed skater, Winter Olympic Games, Innsbruck, 1964 .. 20 25
1238 $3 Pope John XXIII blessing crowd .. 1·25 1·40

187 Head of St. Vincent Amazon

1989. Wildlife Conservation. St. Vincent Amazon ("St. Vincent Parrot"). Mult.

1240 10 c. Type **187** 20 10
1241 20 c. St. Vincent amazon in flight 30 20
1242 40 c. Feeding (vert) .. 60 40
1243 70 c. At entrance to nest (vert) .. .. .. 1·10 1·00

188 Blue-hooded Euphonia

1989. Birds of St. Vincent. Multicoloured.

1244 25 c. Type **188** 10 15
1245 75 c. Common black hawk ("Crab hawk") .. 30 35
1246 $2 Mangrove cuckoo ("Coucou") 85 90
1247 $3 Hooded tanager ("Prince bird") .. 1·25 1·40

1989. Japanese Art. As T **250** of Antigua. Multicoloured.

1249 10 c. "Autumn Flowers in Front of the Full Moon" (Hiroshige) .. 10 10
1250 40 c. "Hibiscus" (Hiroshige) 20 20
1251 50 c. "Iris" (Hiroshige) .. 25 25
1252 75 c. "Morning Glories" (Hiroshige) 35 35
1253 $1 "Dancing Swallows" (Hiroshige) 45 45
1254 $2 "Sparrow and Bamboo" (Hiroshige) 90 90
1255 $3 "Yellow Bird and Cotton Rose" (Hiroshige) .. .. 1·50 1·50
1256 $4 "Judos Chrysanthemums in a Deep Ravine in China" (Hiroshige) 2·00 2·00

189 Schooner

1989. "Philexfrance 89" International Stamp Exhibition, Paris, and Bicentenary of French Revolution. 18th-century French Naval Vessels. Multicoloured.

1258 30 c. Type **189** 20 15
1259 55 c. Corvette 35 35
1260 75 c. Frigate 55 50
1261 $1 Ship of the line .. 65 60
1262 $3 "Ville de Paris" (ship of the line) .. .. 1·75 2·00

190 Johnny Bench

1989. Famous Baseball Players (2nd series). Multicoloured.

1264 $2 Type **190** .. .. 1·00 90
1265 $2 Red Schoendienst .. 1·00 90
1266 $2 Carl Yastrezmski .. 1·00 90
1267 $2 Ty Cobb .. .. 1·00 90
1268 $2 Willie Mays .. .. 1·00 90
1269 $2 Stan Musial .. .. 1·00 90
1270 $2 Ernie Banks .. .. 1·00 90
1271 $2 Lou Gehrig .. .. 1·00 90
1272 $2 Jackie Robinson .. 1·00 90
1273 $2 Bob Feller .. .. 1·00 90
1274 $2 Ted Williams .. .. 1·00 90
1275 $2 Al Kaline .. .. 1·00 90

191 Dante Bichette, 1989

1989. Major League Baseball Rookies. Mult.

1276 60 c. Type **191** 30 30
1277 60 c. Carl Yastrzemski, 1961 .. .. .. 30 30
1278 60 c. Randy Johnson, 1989 30 30
1279 60 c. Jerome Walton, 1989 30 30
1280 60 c. Ramon Martinez, 1989 .. .. .. 30 30
1281 60 c. Ken Hill, 1989 .. 30 30
1282 60 c. Tom McCarthy, 1989 30 30
1283 60 c. Gaylord Perry, 1963 30 30
1284 60 c. John Smoltz, 1989 .. 30 30
1285 60 c. Bob Milacki, 1989 .. 30 30
1286 60 c. Babe Ruth, 1915 .. 30 30
1287 60 c. Jim Abbott, 1989 .. 30 30
1288 60 c. Gary Sheffield, 1989 30 30
1289 60 c. Gregg Jeffries, 1989 30 30
1290 60 c. Kevin Brown, 1989 30 30
1291 60 c. Cris Carpenter, 1989 30 30
1292 60 c. Johnny Bench, 1968 30 30
1293 60 c. Ken Griffey Jr, 1989 30 30

192 Chris Sabo

1989. Major League Baseball Award Winners. Multicoloured.

1294 60 c. Type **192** 30 30
1295 60 c. Walt Weiss 30 30
1296 60 c. Willie Mays 30 30
1297 60 c. Kirk Gibson 30 30
1298 60 c. Ted Williams 30 30
1299 60 c. Jose Canseco 30 30
1300 60 c. Gaylord Perry 30 30
1301 60 c. Orel Hershiser .. 30 30
1302 60 c. Frank Viola 30 30

194 St. Vincent Amazon

1989.

1304 **194** 55 c. multicoloured .. 30 35

195 Queen Conch and West Indian Purpura Shells

1989. 500th Anniv (1992) of Discovery of America by Columbus (3rd issue).

1305 – 50 c. multicoloured .. 25 25
1306 – 50 c. multicoloured .. 25 25
1307 – 50 c. ultram, blk & bl 25 25
1308 – 50 c. ultram, blk & bl 25 25
1309 – 50 c. multicoloured .. 25 25
1310 – 50 c. multicoloured .. 25 25
1311 – 50 c. multicoloured .. 25 25
1312 – 50 c. black and blue 25 25
1313 – 50 c. multicoloured .. 25 25
1314 – 50 c. multicoloured .. 25 25
1315 – 50 c. multicoloured .. 25 25
1316 – 50 c. multicoloured .. 25 25
1317 – 50 c. multicoloured .. 25 25
1318 – 50 c. multicoloured .. 25 25
1319 – 50 c. multicoloured .. 25 25
1320 – 50 c. multicoloured .. 25 25
1321 – 50 c. multicoloured .. 25 25
1322 – 50 c. multicoloured .. 25 25
1323 – 50 c. multicoloured .. 25 25
1324 – 50 c. multicoloured .. 25 25

DESIGNS: No. 1305, Type **195**; 1306, Caribbean reef fishes; 1307, Sperm whale; 1308, Fleet of Columbus; 1309, Remora (fish); 1310, Columbus planting flag; 1311, Navigational instruments; 1312, Sea monster; 1313, Kemp's ridley turtle; 1314, Magnificent frigate bird; 1315, Caribbean manatee; 1316, Caribbean monk seal; 1317, Mayan Chief, dugout canoe and caravel; 1318, Blue-footed boobies; 1319, Venezuelan pile village; 1320, Atlantic wing oyster and lion's paw scallop; 1321, Great hammerhead and mako sharks; 1322, Brown pelican and hyacinth macaw; 1323, Venezuelan bowmen; 1324, Capuchin and squirrel monkeys.

Nos. 1305/24 were printed together, se-tenant, forming a composite design of a map of the Caribbean showing the voyages of Columbus.

196 Command Module "Columbia" returning to Earth

1989. 20th Anniv of First Manned Landing on Moon. Multicoloured.

1325 35 c. Type **196** 15 20
1326 75 c. Lunar module "Eagle" landing .. 30 35
1327 $1 "Apollo 11" launch .. 40 45
1328 $2 Buzz Aldrin on Moon 85 90
1329 $2 Lunar module "Eagle" 85 90
1330 $2 Earth rise from the Moon 85 90
1331 $2 Neil Armstrong .. 85 90
1332 $3 "Eagle" and "Columbia" in Moon orbit .. .. .. 1·25 1·40

197 Jay Howell and Alejandro Pena

1989. Centenary of the Los Angeles Dodgers (1st issue). Baseball Players. Multicoloured.

1334 60 c. Type **197** 25 30
1335 60 c. Mike Davis and Kirk Gibson 25 30
1336 60 c. Fernando Valenzuela and John Shelby .. 25 30
1337 60 c. Jeff Hamilton and Franklin Stubbs .. 25 30
1338 60 c. Aerial view of Dodger Stadium (no inscription) 25 30
1339 60 c. Ray Searage and John Tudor 25 30
1340 60 c. Mike Sharperson and Mickey Hatcher .. 25 30
1341 60 c. Coaching staff .. 25 30
1342 60 c. John Wetteland and Ramon Martinez .. 25 30
1343 60 c. Tim Belcher and Tim Crews 25 30
1344 60 c. Orel Hershiser and Mike Morgan 25 30
1345 60 c. Mike Scioscia and Rick Dempsey 25 30
1346 60 c. Dave Anderson and Alfredo Griffin .. 25 30
1347 60 c. Anniversary emblem 25 30
1348 60 c. Kal Daniels and Mike Marshall .. 25 30
1349 60 c. Eddie Murray and Willie Randolph .. 25 30
1350 60 c. Tom Lasorda and Jose Gonzalez .. 25 30
1351 60 c. Lenny Harris, Chris Gwynn and Billy Bean 25 30

See also Nos. 1541/58.

198 "Eurema venusta"

1989. Butterflies. Multicoloured.

1352 6 c. Type **198** 10 10
1353 10 c. "Historis odius" .. 10 10
1354 15 c. "Cynthia virginiensis" 10 10
1355 75 c. "Leptotes cassius" 35 40
1356 $1 "Battus polydamas" 50 55
1357 $2 "Astraptes talus" .. 95 1·00
1358 $3 "Danaus gilippus" .. 1·40 1·50
1359 $5 "Myscelia antholia" .. 2·40 2·50

199 Young Footballers

1989. World Cup Football Championship, Italy (1990) (1st issue). Multicoloured.

1361 10 c. Type **199** 10 10
1362 55 c. Youth football teams 25 30
1363 $1 St. Vincent team in training 40 45
1364 $5 National team with trophies .. .. 2·10 2·25

See also Nos. 1559/62.

200 St. Vincent Amazon

1989. Wildlife. Multicoloured.

1366 65 c. Type **200** 55 50
1367 75 c. Whistling warbler .. 70 60
1368 $5 Black snake .. .. 3·75 4·00

1989. California Earthquake Relief Fund. Nos. 1276/302 surch **+10 CALIF. EARTHQUAKE RELIEF.**

1370 60 c. + 10 c. Type **191** .. 35 35
1371 60 c. + 10 c. Carl Yastrzemski 35 35
1372 60 c. + 10 c. Randy Johnson 35 35
1373 60 c. + 10 c. Jerome Walton 35 35
1374 60 c. + 10 c. Ramon Martinez 35 35
1375 60 c. + 10 c. Ken Hill .. 35 35
1376 60 c. + 10 c. Tom McCarthy 35 35
1377 60 c. + 10 c. Gaylord Perry 35 35
1378 60 c. + 10 c. John Smoltz 35 35
1379 60 c. + 10 c. Bob Milacki 35 35
1380 60 c. + 10 c. Babe Ruth .. 35 35
1381 60 c. + 10 c. Jim Abbott .. 35 35
1382 60 c. + 10 c. Gary Sheffield 35 35
1383 60 c. + 10 c. Gregg Jeffries 35 35
1384 60 c. + 10 c. Kevin Brown 35 35
1385 60 c. + 10 c. Cris Carpenter 35 35
1386 60 c. + 10 c. Johnny Bench 35 35
1387 60 c. + 10 c. Ken Griffey Jr 35 35
1388 60 c. + 10 c. Type **192** .. 35 35
1389 60 c. + 10 c. Walt Weiss .. 35 35
1390 60 c. + 10 c. Willie Mays 35 35
1391 60 c. + 10 c. Kirk Gibson 35 35
1392 60 c. + 10 c. Ted Williams 35 35
1393 60 c. + 10 c. Jose Canseco 35 35
1394 60 c. + 10 c. Gaylord Perry 35 35
1395 60 c. + 10 c. Orel Hershiser 35 35
1396 60 c. + 10 c. Frank Viola 35 35

1989. "World Stamp Expo '89" International Stamp Exhibition, Washington (1st issue). As T **256** of Antigua showing Walt Disney cartoon characters and U.S. monuments. Multicoloured.

1397 1 c. Mickey and Minnie Mouse by Seagull Monument, Utah (vert) 10 10
1398 2 c. Mickey Mouse and Goofy at Lincoln Memorial (vert) .. 10 10
1399 3 c. Mickey and Minnie Mouse at Crazy Horse Memorial, South Dakota (vert) 10 10
1400 4 c. Mickey Mouse saluting "Uncle Sam" Wilson statue, New York (vert) 10 10
1401 5 c. Goofy and Mickey Mouse at Benjamin Franklin Memorial, Philadelphia (vert) .. 10 10
1402 10 c. Goofy and Mickey Mouse at George Washington statue, New York (vert) .. 10 10
1403 $3 Mickey Mouse at John F. Kennedy's birth-place, Massachusetts (vert) .. .. .. 1·40 1·40
1404 $6 Mickey and Minnie Mouse at Mount Vernon, Virginia (vert) 2·75 2·75

202 Nolan Ryan

1989. Famous Baseball Players (3rd series).
1407 **202** $2 multicoloured .. 85 90

203 Early Wynn

1989. Famous Baseball Players (4th series).
1408/88 30 c. × 81 mult Set of 81 .. .. 10·00 10·50

204 Arms and 1979 Independence 50 c. Stamp

1989. 10th Anniv of Independence.
1489 **204** 65 c. multicoloured .. 30 35

1989. Christmas. Paintings by Botticelli and Da Vinci. As T **259** of Antigua. Multicoloured.

1491 10 c. Holy Family (detail, "The Adoration of the Magi") (Botticelli) .. 10 10
1492 25 c. Crowd (detail, "The Adoration of the Magi") (Botticelli) 10 15
1493 30 c. "The Madonna of the Magnificat" (detail) (Botticelli) 10 15
1494 40 c. "The Virgin and Child with St. Anne and St. John the Baptist" (detail) (Da Vinci) .. 15 20
1495 55 c. Angel (detail, "The Annunciation") (Da Vinci) 25 30
1496 75 c. Virgin Mary (detail, "The Annunciation") (Da Vinci) 30 35
1497 $5 "Madonna of the Carnation" (detail) (Da Vinci) .. .. .. 2·10 2·25
1498 $6 "The Annunciation" (detail) (Botticelli) .. 2·50 2·75

205 Boy Scout, 1989

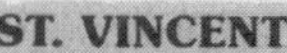

1989. 75th Anniv of Boy Scout and 60th Anniv of Girl Guide Movements in St. Vincent. Mult.

1500 35 c. Type **205** 25 20
1501 35 c. Guide, ranger and brownie 25 20
1502 55 c. Boy scout in original uniform 35 30
1503 55 c. Mrs. Jackson (founder of St. Vincent Girl Guides) 35 30
1504 $2 Scouts' 75th Anniv logo .. .. .. 1·10 1·25
1505 $2 Mrs. Russell (Girl Guide leader, 1989) .. 1·10 1·25

206 Man and Blind Girl

1990. 25th Anniv (1989) of Lions Club of St. Vincent. Multicoloured.

1507 10 c. Type **206** 10 10
1508 65 c. Handing out school books (horiz) 30 35
1509 75 c. Teacher explaining diabetes (horiz) 35 40
1510 $2 Blood sugar testing machine (horiz) .. 95 1·00
1511 $4 Distributing book on drugs (horiz) .. .. 2·00 2·10

1990. 50th Anniv of Second World War. As T **98** of Grenada Grenadines. Mult.

1512 5 c. Scuttling of "Admiral Graf Spee" (German pocket battleship), 1939 10 10
1513 10 c. General de Gaulle and French resistance, 1940 .. .. .. 10 10
1514 15 c. British tank, North Africa, 1940 .. .. 10 10
1515 25 c. U.S.S. "Reuben James" (destroyer) in periscope sight, 1941 .. 10 15
1516 30 c. General MacArthur and map of S.W. Pacific, 1942 .. .. 15 20
1517 40 c. American parachute drop on Corregidor, 1945 20 25
1518 55 c. H.M.S. "King George V" (battleship), engaging "Bismarck" (German battleship), 1941 .. .. .. 30 35
1519 75 c. American battleships entering Tokyo Bay, 1945 .. .. .. 35 40
1520 $5 Hoisting the Soviet flag on the Reichstag, Berlin, 1945 .. .. 2·40 2·50
1521 $6 American aircraft carriers, Battle of Philippines Sea, 1944 .. 3·00 3·25

207 Two Pence Blue

1990. 150th Anniv of the Penny Black.
1523 **207** $2 black, green & mve 95 1·00
1524 – $4 black and mauve 2·00 2·10
DESIGN: $4, Penny Black.

1990. "Stamp World London 90" International Stamp Exhibition. British Uniforms. As T **193** of Gambia showing Walt Disney cartoon characters. Multicoloured.

1526 5 c. Scrooge McDuck as 18th-century Admiral 10 10
1527 10 c. Huey as Light Infantry bugler, 1854 .. 10 10
1528 15 c. Minnie Mouse as Irish Guards drummer, 1900 .. .. .. 10 10
1529 25 c. Goofy as Seaforth Highlanders lance-corporal, 1944 .. .. 10 15
1530 $1 Mickey Mouse as 58th Regiment ensign, 1879 50 55
1531 $2 Donald Duck as Royal Engineers officer, 1813 95 1·00
1532 $4 Mickey Mouse as Duke of Edinburgh's Royal Regiment drum major 2·00 2·10
1533 $5 Goofy as Cameronians sergeant piper, 1918 .. 2·40 2·50

1990. Nolan Ryan—Sixth No-hitter. No. 1407 optd **Sixth No-Hitter 11 June 90 Oakland Athletics**.
1535 **202** $2 multicoloured .. 95 1·00

1990. 90th Birthday of Queen Elizabeth the Queen Mother. As T **99** of Grenada Grenadines.
1536 $2 black, green & mauve 95 1·00
1537 $2 black, green & mauve 95 1·00
1538 $2 black, green & mauve 95 1·00
DESIGNS: No. 1536, Queen Elizabeth signing visitors' book; 1537, Queen Elizabeth in evening dress; 1538, Queen Elizabeth the Queen Mother in Coronation robes, 1953.

1990. Nolan Ryan—300th Win. No. 1407 optd **300th Win Milwaukee Brewers July 31, 1990**.
1540 **202** $2 multicoloured .. 95 1·00

1990. Cent of Los Angeles Dodgers (2nd issue). Baseball Players. As T **197**. Multicoloured.

1541 60 c. Mickey Hatcher and Jay Howell 30 35
1542 60 c. Juan Samuel and Mike Scioscia 30 35
1543 60 c. Lenny Harris and Mike Hartley 30 35
1544 60 c. Ramon Martinez and Mike Morgan 30 35
1545 60 c. Aerial view of Dodger Stadium (inscr "DODGER STADIUM") 30 35
1546 60 c. Stan Javier and Don Aase 30 35
1547 60 c. Ray Searage and Mike Sharperson .. 30 35
1548 60 c. Tim Belcher and Pat Perry 30 35
1549 60 c. Dave Walsh, Jose Vizcaino, Jim Neidlinger, Jose Offerman and Carlos Hernandez 30 35
1550 60 c. Hubie Brooks and Orel Hershiser .. 30 35
1551 60 c. Tom Lasorda and Tim Crews 30 35
1552 60 c. Fernando Valenzuela and Eddie Murray .. 30 35
1553 60 c. Kal Daniels and Jose Gonzalez 30 35
1554 60 c. Dodgers emblem .. 30 35
1555 60 c. Chris Gwynn and Jeff Hamilton .. 30 35
1556 60 c. Kirk Gibson and Rick Dempsey .. 30 35
1557 60 c. Jim Gott and Alfredo Griffin .. 30 35
1558 60 c. Ron Perranoski, Bill Russell, Joe Ferguson, Joe Amalfitano, Mark Cresse, Ben Hines and Manny Mota 30 35

210 Maradona, Argentina

1990 World Cup Football Championship, Italy (2nd issue). Multicoloured.

1559 10 c. Type **210** 10 10
1560 75 c. Valderrama, Colombia 35 40
1561 $1 Francescoli, Uruguay 50 55
1562 $5 Beulemans, Belgium .. 2·40 2·50

1990. 95th Anniv of Rotary International. Nos. 1230/7 optd with Rotary emblem.

1564 10 c. Type **186** 10 10
1565 40 c. "Liberte" 20 25
1566 50 c. "Mauretania I" (launched 1906) .. 25 30
1567 75 c. "France" 35 40
1568 $1 "Aquitania" 50 55
1569 $2 "United States" .. 95 1·00
1570 $3 "Olympic" .. .. 1·40 1·50
1571 $4 "Queen Elizabeth" .. 2·00 2·10

1990. Olympic Medal Winners, Seoul. Nos. 1153/6 optd.

1573 10 c. Type **178** (optd **JOE DELOACH U.S.A STEVE LEWIS U.S.A. PAUL ERANG KENYA**) .. 10 10
1574 50 c. Long jumping (optd **CARL LEWIS U.S.A.**) 25 30
1575 $1 Triple jumping (optd **HRISTO MARKOV BULGARIA**) .. 50 55
1576 $5 Boxing (optd **HENRY MASKE E. GERMANY**) .. 2·40 2·50

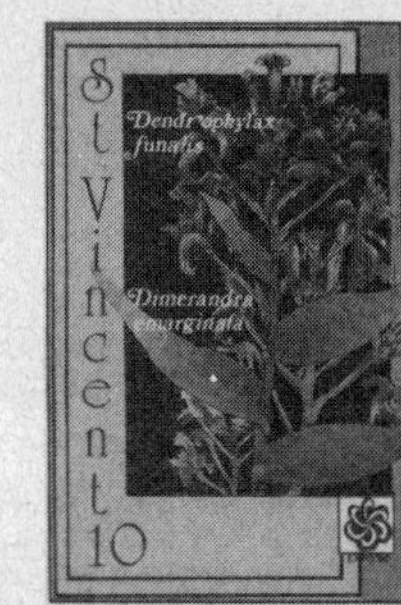

213 "Dendrophylax funalis" and "Dimerandra emarginata"

1990. "EXPO 90" International Garden and Greenery Exposition, Osaka. Orchids. Mult.

1578 10 c. Type **213** 10 10
1579 15 c. "Epidendrum elongatum" 10 10
1580 45 c. "Comparettia falcata" 20 25
1581 60 c. "Brassia maculata" 25 30
1582 $1 "Encyclia cochleata" and "Encyclia cordigera" 45 50
1583 $2 "Cyrtopodium punctatum" 85 90
1584 $4 "Cattleya labiata" .. 1·75 1·90
1585 $5 "Bletia purpurea" .. 2·25 2·40

214 "Miraculous Draught of Fishes" (detail, Rubens)

1990. Christmas. 350th Death Anniv of Rubens. Multicoloured.
1587 10 c. Type **214** 10 10
1588 45 c. "Crowning of Holy Katherine" (detail) .. 20 25
1589 50 c. "St. Ives of Treguier" (detail) .. 25 30
1590 65 c. "Allegory of Eternity" (detail) .. 30 35
1591 $1 "St. Bavo receives Monastic Habit of Ghent" (detail) .. 50 55
1592 $2 "Crowning of Holy Katherine" (different detail) .. .. 95 1·00
1593 $4 "St. Bavo receives Monastic Habit of Ghent" (different detail) .. .. 2·00 2·10
1594 $5 "Communion of St. Francis" (detail) .. 2·40 2·50

215 Geoffrey Chaucer

1990. International Literacy Year (1st issue). Chaucer's "Canterbury Tales" Mult.
1596 40 c. Type **215** 20 25
1597 40 c. "When April with his showers..." .. 20 25
1598 40 c. "When Zephyr also has..." 20 25
1599 40 c. "And many little birds..." 20 25
1600 40 c. "And palmers to go seeking out..." .. 20 25
1601 40 c. Quill in ink well and open book 20 25
1602 40 c. Green bird in tree .. 20 25
1603 40 c. Brown bird in tree and franklin's head .. 20 25
1604 40 c. Purple bird in tree and banner 20 25
1605 40 c. Canterbury 20 25
1606 40 c. Knight's head .. 20 25
1607 40 c. Black bird in tree and squire's head .. 20 25
1608 40 c. Friar 20 25
1609 40 c. Franklin 20 25
1610 40 c. Prioress and monk holding banner .. 20 25
1611 40 c. Summoner, Oxford clerk and parson .. 20 25
1612 40 c. Serjeant-at-Law and knight on horseback .. 20 25
1613 40 c. Squire 20 25
1614 40 c. "In fellowship..." .. 20 25
1615 40 c. Cockerel and horse's legs 20 25
1616 40 c. Hens 20 25
1617 40 c. Hen and rabbit .. 20 25
1618 40 c. Horses' legs and butterfly 20 25
1619 40 c. "And briefly, when the sun..." 20 25

Nos. 1596/1619 were printed together, se-tenant, forming a composite design.

See also Nos. 1777/88 and 1790/1801.

1990. Death Centenary of Vincent van Gogh (artist). As T **278** of Antigua. Multicoloured.
1620 1 c. Self-portrait, 1889 .. 10 10
1621 5 c. Self-portrait, 1886 .. 10 10
1622 10 c. Self-portrait with hat and pipe, 1888 .. 10 10
1623 15 c. Self-portrait at easel, 1888 .. .. .. 10 10
1624 20 c. Self-portrait, 1887 .. 10 10
1625 45 c. Self-portrait, 1889 (different) .. 20 25
1626 $5 Self-portrait with pipe, 1889 .. .. 2·40 2·50
1627 $6 Self-portrait wearing straw hat, 1887 .. 3·00 3·25

1990. Hummel Figurines. As T **256** of Maldive Islands. Multicoloured.
1628 10 c. "The Photographer" 10 10
1629 15 c. "Ladder and Rope" 10 10
1630 40 c. "Druggist" .. 20 25
1631 60 c. "Hello" 30 35
1632 $1 "Boots" 50 55
1633 $2 "The Artist" .. .. 95 1·00
1634 $4 "Waiter" .. .. 2·00 2·10
1635 $5 "The Postman" .. 2·40 2·50

218 U.S.A. 1893 1 c. Columbus Stamp

1991. 500th Anniv (1992) of Discovery of America by Columbus (4th issue). Designs showing U.S.A 1893 Columbian Exposition, Chicago, stamps (Nos.1639/54) or ships (others). Multicoloured.
1639 1 c. Type **218** 10 10
1640 2 c. Columbus 2 c. .. 10 10
1641 3 c. Columbus 3 c. .. 10 10
1642 4 c. Columbus 4 c. .. 10 10
1643 5 c. Columbus 5 c. .. 10 10
1644 6 c. Columbus 6 c. .. 10 10
1645 8 c. Columbus 8 c. .. 10 10
1646 10 c. Columbus 10 c. .. 10 10
1647 15 c. Columbus 15 c. .. 10 10
1648 30 c. Columbus 30 c. .. 15 20
1649 50 c. Columbus 50 c. .. 25 30
1650 $1 Columbus $1 .. .. 50 55
1651 $2 Columbus $2 .. .. 95 1·00
1652 $3 Columbus $3 .. .. 1·40 1·50
1653 $4 Columbus $4 .. .. 2·00 2·10
1654 $5 Columbus $5 .. .. 2·40 2·50
1655 $10 "Santa Maria", scarlet macaw and tropical flower .. .. .. 5·00 5·25
1656 $10 Logo, "Santa Maria" and Amerindian hut .. 5·00 5·25

219 Pebbles and Hoppy boxing

1991. Sports. Characters from the "Flintstones" cartoons. Multicoloured.
1658 10 c. Type **219** 10 10
1659 15 c. Fred Flintstone and Dino playing football 10 10
1660 45 c. Fred losing rowing race to Barney Rubble 20 25
1661 55 c. Betty Rubble, Wilma Flintstone and Pebbles in dressage competition 30 35
1662 $1 Fred playing basketball .. 50 55
1663 $2 Bamm Bamm wrestling Barney with Fred as referee .. 95 1·00
1664 $4 Fred and Barney playing tennis .. 2·00 2·10
1665 $5 Fred, Barney and Dino cycling .. .. 2·40 2·50

220 Board Meeting

1991. "The Jetsons" (cartoon film). Mult.
1667 5 c. Type **220** 10 10
1668 20 c. Jetsons with Dog .. 10 10
1669 45 c. Judy and Apollo Blue 20 25
1670 50 c. Cosmo Spacely and George Jetson .. 25 30
1671 60 c. George and Elroy catching cogs (horiz) .. 30 35
1672 $1 Judy, Apollo, Elroy and Teddy in cavern (horiz) 50 55
1673 $2 Drill destroying the cavern (horiz) .. 95 1·00
1674 $4 Jetsons celebrating with the Grungees .. 2·00 2·10
1675 $5 The Jetsons returning home .. .. .. 2·40 2·50

1991. 500th Anniv (1992) of Discovery of America by Columbus, (5th issue). History of Exploration. As T **64** of Nevis. Mult.
1677 5 c. "Sanger 2" (projected space shuttle) 10 10
1678 10 c. "Magellan" satellite, 1990 .. .. .. 10 10
1679 25 c. "Buran" space shuttle 10 15
1680 75 c. Projected "Freedom" space station 35 40
1681 $1 Projected Mars mission space craft 50 55
1682 $2 "Hubble" telescope, 1990 .. .. .. 95 1·00
1683 $4 Projected Mars mission "sailship" .. .. 2·00 2·10
1684 $5 Projected "Craf" satellite .. .. 2·40 2·50

1991. 65th Birthday of Queen Elizabeth II. As T **280** of Antigua. Multicoloured.
1686 5 c. Queen and Prince Philip during visit to Spain, 1988 .. .. 10 10
1687 60 c. Queen and Prince Philip in landau .. 30 35
1688 $2 Queen at Caen Hill Waterway, 1990 .. 95 1·00
1689 $4 Queen at Badminton, 1983 .. .. .. 2·00 2·10

1991. 10th Wedding Anniv of the Prince and Princess of Wales. As T **280** of Antigua. Multicoloured.
1691 20 c. Prince and Princess in hard hats, 1987 .. 10 10
1692 25 c. Portraits of Prince and Princess and sons 10 15
1693 $1 Prince Henry and Prince William, both in 1988 .. .. .. 50 55
1694 $5 Princess Diana in France and Prince Charles in 1987 .. 2·40 2·50

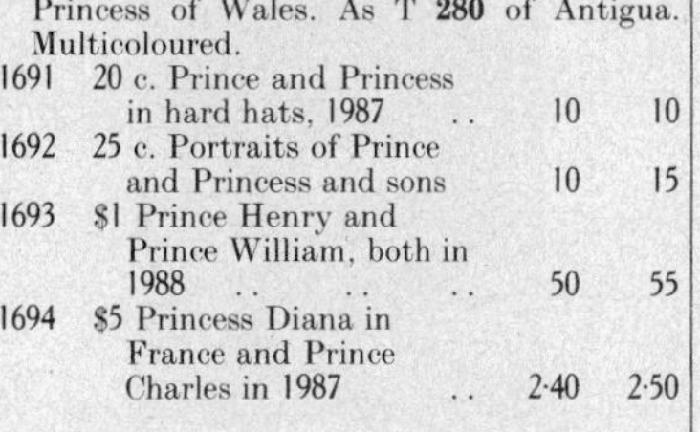

221 Class "D 51" Steam Locomotive

1991. "Phila Nippon '91" Interntional Stamp Exhibition, Tokyo. Japanese Trains. Mult.
1696 75 c. Type **221** 35 40
1697 75 c. Class "9600" steam locomotive 35 40
1698 75 c. Goods wagons and chrysanthemum emblem 35 40
1699 75 c. Passenger coach .. 35 40
1700 75 c. Decorated class "C 57" steam locomotive 35 40
1701 75 c. Oil tanker wagon .. 35 40
1702 75 c. Class "C 53" steam locomotive 35 40
1703 75 c. First Japanese steam locomotive 35 40
1704 75 c. Class "C 11" steam locomotive 35 40
1705 $1 Class "181" electric train 50 55
1706 $1 Class "EH-10" electric locomotive 50 55
1707 $1 Passenger coaches and Special Express symbol 50 55
1708 $1 Sendai City class "1" tram 50 55
1709 $1 Class "485" electric train 50 55
1710 $1 Sendai City street cleaning tram 50 55
1711 $1 Hakari "Bullet" train 50 55
1712 $1 Class "ED-11" electric locomotive 50 55
1713 $1 Class "EF-66" electric locomotive 50 55

INDEX

Countries can be quickly located by referring to the index at the end of this volume.

222 Marcello Mastroianni (actor)

1991. Italian Entertainers. Multicoloured.
1715 $1 Type **222** 50 55
1716 $1 Sophia Loren (actress) 50 55
1717 $1 Mario Lanza (singer) 50 55
1718 $1 Federico Fellini (director) 50 55
1719 $1 Arturo Toscanini (conductor) 50 55
1720 $1 Anna Magnani (actress) 50 55
1721 $1 Giancarlo Giannini (actor) 50 55
1722 $1 Gina Lollobrigida (actress) 50 55
1723 $1 Enrico Caruso (operatic tenor) 50 55

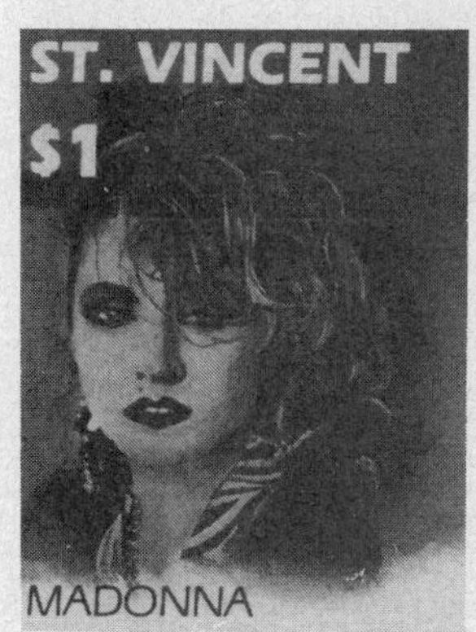

223 Madonna

1991. Madonna (American singer). Mult.
1725 $1 Type **223** 50 55
1726 $1 In strapless dress .. 50 55
1727 $1 Wearing necklaces, looking right 50 55
1728 $1 In green dress .. 50 55
1729 $1 Wearing necklaces, looking to front .. 50 55
1730 $1 With wrist bangles .. 50 55
1731 $1 With hand to face .. 50 55
1732 $1 In purple dress .. 50 55
1733 $1 With microphone .. 50 55

224 John Lennon

1991. John Lennon (British musician). Mult.
1735 $1 + 2 c. Type **224** .. 50 55
1736 $1 + 2 c. With Beatle hair cut 50 55
1737 $1 + 2 c. In cap 50 55
1738 $1 + 2 c. In red polka-dot shirt 50 55
1739 $1 + 2 c. In green polo-neck jumper and jacket 50 55
1740 $1 + 2 c. In glasses and magenta jacket .. 50 55
1741 $1 + 2 c. With long hair and glasses 50 55
1742 $1 + 2 c. In black jumper 50 55
1743 $1 + 2 c. In polo-neck jumper 50 55

225 Free French Resistance Fighters, 1944

1991. Anniversaries and Events. Mult.

1744 10 c. Type **225** 10 10
1745 45 c. De Gaulle with Churchill, 1944 .. 20 25
1746 50 c. Protestor with banner 25 30
1747 65 c. Tales around the camp fire (vert) .. 30 35
1748 75 c. Liberation of Paris, 1944 .. .. .. 35 40
1749 75 c. Building Berlin Wall 35 40
1750 90 c. German flag and protestors' shadows .. 45 50
1751 $1 Presidents Bush and Gorbachev shaking hands 50 55
1752 $1 "Marriage of Figaro" 50 55
1753 $1.50 British trenches and Mafeking Siege 3d. stamp 70 75
1754 $1.50 Modern Trans-Siberian steam locomotive 70 75
1755 $1.50 Map of Switzerland and woman in traditional costume .. 70 75
1756 $1.65 Lilienthal's signature and "Flugzeug Nr. 13 Doppeldecker" .. 75 80
1757 $2 Street fighting, Kiev 95 1·00
1758 $2 Gottfried Leibniz (mathematician) .. 95 1·00
1759 $3 "The Clemency of Titus" .. .. 1·40 1·50
1760 $3.50 Angelfish and scout diver .. .. 1·75 2·00

ANNIVERSARIES AND EVENTS: Nos. 1744/5, 1748, Birth centenary of Charles de Gaulle (French statesman); Nos. 1746, 1749/51, Bicentenary of Brandenburg Gate, Berlin; Nos. 1747, 1753, 1760, 50th death anniv of Lord Baden-Powell and World Scout Jamboree, Korea; Nos. 1752, 1759, Death bicentenary of Mozart; No. 1754, Centenary of Trans-Siberian Railway; No. 1755, 700th anniv of Swiss Confederation; No. 1756, Centenary of Otto Lilienthal's gliding experiments; No. 1757, 50th anniv of capture of Kiev; No. 1758, 750th anniv of Hanover.

226 Myrvyn Bennion

1991. 50th Anniv of Japanese Attack on Pearl Harbor. Recipients of Congressional Medal of Honor. Multicoloured.

1762 $1 Type **226** 50 55
1763 $1 George Cannon 50 55
1764 $1 John Finn 50 55
1765 $1 Francis Flaherty .. 50 55
1766 $1 Samuel Fuqua 50 55
1767 $1 Edwin Hill 50 55
1768 $1 Herbert Jones 50 55
1769 $1 Issac Kidd 50 55
1770 $1 Jackson Pharris .. 50 55
1771 $1 Thomas Reeves .. 50 55
1772 $1 Donald Ross 50 55
1773 $1 Robert Scott 50 55
1774 $1 Franklin van Valkenburgh 50 55
1775 $1 James Ward 50 55
1776 $1 Cassin Young 50 55

1991. International Literacy Year (1990) (2nd issue). As T **269** of Antigua but horiz, showing scenes from Disney cartoon film. Multicoloured. (a) "The Prince and The Pauper".

1777 5 c. Mickey Mouse, Goofy and Pluto as pauper pals 10 10
1778 10 c. Mickey as the bored prince 10 10
1779 15 c. Donald Duck as the valet 10 10
1780 25 c. Mickey as the prince and the pauper .. 10 10
1781 60 c. Exchanging clothes 30 35
1782 75 c. Prince and pauper with suit of armour .. 35 40
1783 80 c. Throwing food from the battlements .. 40 45
1784 $1 Pete as Captain of the Guard 50 55
1785 $2 Mickey and Donald in the dungeon .. .. 95 1·00
1786 $3 Mickey and Donald at dungeon window .. 1·40 1·50
1787 $4 Goofy rescuing Mickey and Donald .. .. 2·00 2·10
1788 $5 Crowning the real prince .. .. 2·40 2·50

(b) "The Rescuers Down Under".

1790 5 c. Miss Bianca 10 10
1791 10 c. Bernard 10 10
1792 15 c. Matre d'Francoise .. 10 10
1793 25 c. Wilbur the Albatross 10 10
1794 60 c. Jake the Kangaroo Mouse 30 35
1795 75 c. Bernard, Bianca and Jake in the outback 35 40
1796 80 c. Bianca and Bernard to the rescue 40 44
1797 $1 Marahute the Eagle .. 50 55
1798 $2 Cody and Marahute with eggs .. .. 95 1·00
1799 $3 McLeach and his pet Joanna the Goanna .. 1·40 1·50
1800 $4 Frank the Frill-necked Lizard .. .. 2·00 2·10
1801 $5 Red Kangaroo, Krebbs Koala and Polly Platypus .. .. .. 2·40 2·50

227 Hans-Dietrich Genscher and "Winged Victory" Statue

1991. European History. Multicoloured.

1803 $1 Type **227** 45 50
1804 $1 Destruction of Berlin Wall 45 50
1805 $1 Churchill, De Gaulle and Appeal to the French, 1940 .. .. 45 50
1806 $1 Eisenhower, De Gaulle and D-Day, 1944 .. 45 50
1807 $1 Brandenburg Gate, Berlin (bicentenary) .. 45 50
1808 $1 Chancellor Helmut Kohl and meeting of Berlin mayors, 1989 .. 45 50
1809 $1 De Gaulle with Chancellor Adenauer .. 45 50
1810 $1 Pres. Kennedy's visit to Europe, 1961, Washington and Lafayette .. 45 50

1991. Famous Golfers. As T **227**. Mult.

1812 $1 Gary Player 50 55
1813 $1 Nick Faldo 50 55
1814 $1 Severiano Ballesteros 50 55
1815 $1 Ben Hogan 50 55
1816 $1 Jack Nicklaus 50 55
1817 $1 Greg Norman 50 55
1818 $1 Jose-Maria Olazabal .. 50 55
1819 $1 Bobby Jones 50 55

1991. Famous Entertainers. As T **277**. Mult.

1820 $2 Michael Jackson .. 95 1·00
1821 $2 Madonna .. .. 95 1·00
1822 $2 Elvis Presley .. .. 95 1·00
1823 $2 David Bowie .. .. 95 1·00
1824 $2 Prince .. .. 95 1·00
1825 $2 Frank Sinatra .. .. 95 1·00
1826 $2 George Michael .. 95 1·00
1827 $2 Mick Jagger .. .. 95 1·00

1991. Famous Chess Masters. As T **227**. Mult.

1829 $1 Francoise Philidor .. 50 55
1830 $1 Karl Anderssen .. 50 55
1831 $1 Wilhelm Steinitz .. 50 55
1832 $1 Alexandrovich Alekhine 50 55
1833 $1 Boris Spassky 50 55
1834 $1 Robert Fischer 50 55
1835 $1 Anatoly Karpov .. 50 55
1836 $1 Garry Kasparov .. 50 55

1991 Nobel Prize Winners. As T **227**. Mult.

1837 $1 Albert Einstein (mathematical physicist) 50 55
1838 $1 Wilhelm Rontgen (physicist) 50 55
1839 $1 William Shockley (chemist) 50 55
1840 $1 Charles Townes (physicist) 50 55
1841 $1 Lev Landau (physicist) 50 55
1842 $1 Guglielmo Marconi (applied physicist) .. 50 55
1843 $1 Willard Libby (chemist) 50 55
1844 $1 Ernest Lawrence (nuclear physicist) .. 50 55

228 Walt Disney Characters decorating Christmas Tree, 1982

1991. Christmas. Walt Disney Christmas Cards. Multicoloured.

1845 10 c. Type **228** 10 10
1846 45 c. Mickey and Moose, 1980 .. .. .. 20 25
1847 55 c. Mickey, Pluto and Donald carrying bauble, 1970 .. .. 30 35
1848 75 c. Duckling and egg shell, 1943 .. .. 35 40
1849 $1.50 Walt Disney characters decorating globe, 1941 .. .. 70 75
1850 $2 The Lady and the Tramp by Christmas tree, 1986 .. .. 95 1·00
1851 $4 Walt Disney characters carol singing, 1977 .. 2·00 2·10
1852 $5 Mickey in fairy-tale castle, 1965 .. .. 2·40 2·50

229 Kings Hill

1992. Preserving the Environment. Mult.

1854 10 c. Type **229** 10 10
1855 55 c. Planting sapling .. 30 35
1856 75 c. Doric Temple, Botanic Gardens .. 35 40
1857 $2 18th-century map of Kings Hill .. .. 95 1·00

1992. 40th Anniv of Queen Elizabeth II's Accession. As T **288** of Antigua. Mult.

1858 10 c. Kingstown from the cliffs 10 10
1859 20 c. Deep water wharf, Kingstown 10 10
1860 $1 Residential suburb, Kingstown 50 55
1861 $5 Kingstown from the interior .. .. 2·40 2·50

230 Women's Luge

1992. Winter Olympic Games. Albertville (1st issue). Multicoloured.

1863 10 c. Type **230** 10 10
1864 15 c. Women's figure skating (vert) 10 10
1865 25 c. Two-man bobsleigh 10 10
1866 30 c. Mogul skiing (vert) 15 20
1867 45 c. Nordic combination 20 25
1868 55 c. Ski jumping .. 30 35
1869 75 c. Men's giant slalom 35 40
1870 $1.50 Women's slalom (vert) 70 75
1871 $5 Ice hockey .. .. 2·40 2·50
1872 $8 Biathlon (vert) .. 4·00 4·25

See also Nos. 1966/79.

231 Women's Synchronized Swimming

1992. Olympic Games, Barcelona. Mult.

1874 10 c. Type **231** 10 10
1875 15 c. Men's high jump (vert) 10 10
1876 25 c. Men's small-bore rifle shooting 10 10
1877 30 c. Men's 200 metres (vert) 15 20
1878 45 c. Men's judo (vert) .. 20 25
1879 55 c. Men's 200 metres freestyle swimming .. 25 30
1880 75 c. Men's javelin (vert) 35 40
1881 $1.50 Men's 4000 metre pursuit cycling (vert) .. 75 80
1882 $5 Boxing (vert) .. 2·40 2·50
1883 $8 Women's basketball (vert) .. .. 4·00 4·25

1992. International Stamp Exhibitions. As T **215** of Lesotho showing Walt Disney cartoon characters. Multicoloured.

(a) "Granada '92", Spain. The Three Pigs in Spanish Uniforms.

1885 15 c. The wolf as general of Spanish Moors .. 10 10
1886 40 c. Pig as captain of infantry 20 25
1887 $2 Pig as halberdier .. 95 1·00
1888 $4 Pig as nobleman .. 2·00 2·10

(b) "World Columbian Stamp Expo '92". Chicago Landmarks

1890 10 c. Mickey Mouse and Goofy looking at Picasso sculpture (horiz) 10 10
1891 50 c. Mickey and Donald Duck admiring Robie House (horiz) .. 25 30
1892 $1 Calder sculpture in Sears Tower (horiz) .. 50 55
1893 $5 Goofy in Buckingham Memorial Fountain (horiz) .. .. 2·40 2·50

232 "Nina"

1992. 500th Anniv of Discovery of America by Columbus (6th issue). "World Columbian Stamp Expo '92", Chicago. Multicoloured.

1895 5 c. Type **232** 10 10
1896 10 c. "Pinta" 10 10
1897 45 c. "Santa Maria" .. 20 25
1898 55 c. Fleet leaving Palos, 1492 .. .. .. 25 30
1899 $4 Christopher Columbus (vert) .. .. 2·00 2·10
1900 $5 Arms of Columbus (vert) .. .. 2·40 2·50

1992. 15th Death Anniv of Elvis Presley (1st issue). As T **298** of Antigua. Multicoloured.

1902 $1 Elvis looking pensive 50 55
1903 $1 Wearing black and yellow striped shirt .. 50 55
1904 $1 Singing into microphone 50 55
1905 $1 Wearing wide-brimmed hat 50 55
1906 $1 With microphone in right hand .. 50 55
1907 $1 In Army uniform .. 50 55
1908 $1 Wearing pink shirt .. 50 55
1909 $1 In yellow shirt .. 50 55
1910 $1 In jacket and bow tie 50 55

See also Nos. 2029/37, 2038/45 and 2047/9.

234 Bonnie Blair

1992. Bonnie Blair's Victories in 500 metres Speed Skating at Calgary and Albertville Olympic Games.

1912	**234**	$3 multicoloured ..	1·40	1·50

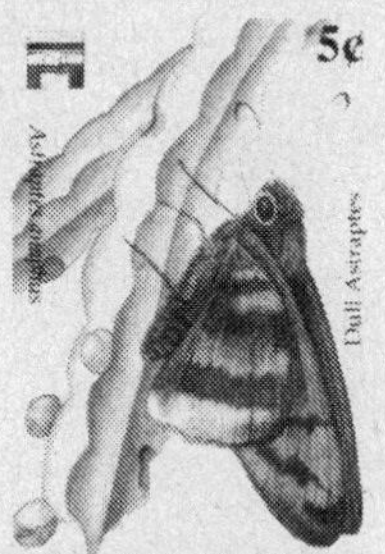

235 "Astraptes anaphus"

1992. "Genova '92" International Thematic Stamp Exhibition (1st issue). Butterflies. Multicoloured.

1914	5 c. Type **235**	10	10
1915	10 c. "Anartia jatrophae" (horiz)	10	10
1916	35 c. "Danaus eresimus"	15	20
1917	45 c. "Battus polydamus"	20	25
1918	55 c. "Junonia evarete" (horiz)	25	30
1919	65 c. "Urbanus proteus"	30	35
1920	75 c. "Pyrgus oileus" (horiz)	35	40
1921	$1 "Biblis hyperia" ..	50	55
1922	$2 "Eurema daira" ..	95	1·00
1923	$3 "Leptotes cassius" (horiz)	1·40	1·50
1924	$4 "Ephyriades brunnea" (horiz)	2·00	2·10
1925	$5 "Victorina stelenes" ..	2·40	2·50

See also Nos. 1940/51.

236 "Collybia subpruinosa"

1992. Fungi. Multicoloured.

1927	10 c. Type **236**	10	10
1928	15 c. "Gerronema citrinum"	10	10
1929	20 c. "Amanita antillana"	10	10
1930	45 c. "Dermoloma atrobrunneum" ..	15	20
1931	50 c. "Inopilus maculosus"	25	30
1932	65 c. "Pulveroboletus brachyspermus" ..	30	35
1933	75 c. "Mycena violacella"	35	40
1934	$1 "Xerocomus brasiliensis"	50	55
1935	$2 "Amanita ingrata" ..	95	1·00
1936	$3 "Leptonia caeruleocapitata" ..	1·40	1·50
1937	$4 "Limacella myochroa"	2·00	2·10
1938	$5 "Inopilus magnificus"	2·40	2·50

No. 1936 is inscribed "Leptonia caeruleocaptata" in error.

237 Rufous-breasted Hermit

1992. "Genova '92" International Thematic Stamp Exhibition (2nd issue). Hummingbirds. Multicoloured.

1940	5 c. Type **237**	10	10
1941	15 c. Hispaniolan emerald	10	10
1942	45 c. Green-throated carib	15	20
1943	55 c. Jamaican mango ..	25	30
1944	65 c. Vervain hummingbird	30	35
1945	75 c. Purple-throated carib	35	40
1946	90 c. Green mango ..	45	50
1947	$1 Bee hummingbird ..	50	55
1948	$2 Cuban emerald ..	95	1·00
1949	$3 Puerto Rican emerald	1·40	1·50
1950	$4 Antillean mango ..	2·00	2·10
1951	$5 Streamertail	2·40	2·50

238 Coral Vine

1992. Medicinal Plants. Multicoloured.

1953	75 c. Type **238**	35	40
1954	75 c. Cocoplum	35	40
1955	75 c. Angel's trumpet ..	35	40
1956	75 c. Lime	35	40
1957	75 c. White ginger ..	35	40
1958	75 c. Pussley	35	40
1959	75 c. Sea grape	35	40
1960	75 c. Indian mulberry ..	35	40
1961	75 c. Plantain	35	40
1962	75 c. Lignum vitae ..	35	40
1963	75 c. Periwinkle	35	40
1964	75 c. Guava	35	40

239 Kristi Yamaguchi (U.S.A.) (figure skating)

1992. Winter Olympic Games, Albertville (2nd issue). Gold Medal Winners. Multicoloured.

1966	$1 Type **239**	50	55
1967	$1 Pernilla Wiberg (Sweden) (giant slalom skiing)	50	55
1968	$1 Lyubov Yegorova (C.I.S.) (10 kms cross-country skiing) ..	50	55
1969	$1 Josef Polig (Italy) (combined alpine skiing)	50	55
1970	$1 Fin Christian-Jagge (Norway) (slalom skiing)	50	55
1971	$1 Kerrin Lee-Gartner (Canada) (downhill skiing)	50	55
1972	$1 Steffania Belmondo (Italy) (30 kms cross-country skiing) ..	50	55
1973	$1 Alberto Tomba (Italy) (giant slalom skiing) ..	50	55
1974	$1 Fabrice Guy (France) (nordic combined skiing)	50	55
1975	$1 Patrick Ortlieb (Austria) (downhill skiing)	50	55
1976	$1 Vegard Ulvang (Norway) (nordic cross-country skiing) ..	50	55
1977	$1 Edgar Grospiron (France) (freestyle mogul skiing) ..	50	55
1978	$1 Andre Aamodt (Norway) (super giant slalom skiing)	50	55
1979	$1 Viktor Petrenko (C.I.S.) (figure skating)	50	55

No. 1968 is inscribed "LYUBOV EGOROVA" in error.

1992. 500th Anniv of Discovery of America by Columbus (7th issue). Organization of East Caribbean States. As Nos. 1670/1 of Antigua. Multicoloured.

1981	$1 Columbus meeting Amerindians	50	55
1982	$2 Ships approaching island	95	1·00

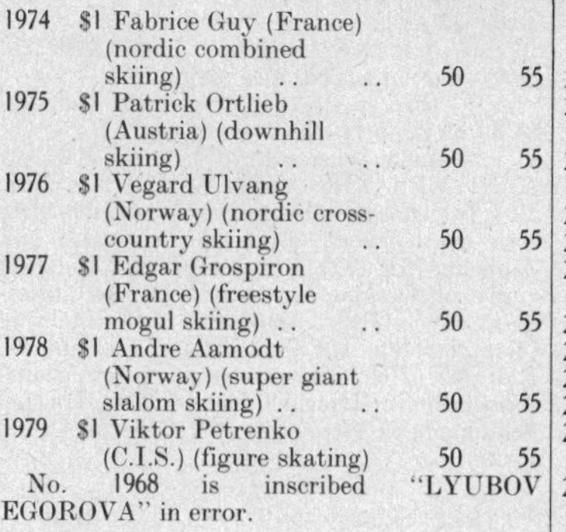

240 "Pinocchio"

1992. Opening of Euro-Disney Resort, Paris. Multicoloured.

1983	$1 Type **240**	50	55
1984	$1 "Alice in Wonderland"	50	55
1985	$1 "Bambi"	50	55
1986	$1 "Cinderella"	50	55
1987	$1 "Snow White and the Seven Dwarfs" ..	50	55
1988	$1 "Peter Pan"	50	55

1992. Christmas. Religious Paintings. As T **218** of Lesotho. Multicoloured.

1992	10 c. "Hospitality refused to the Virgin Mary and Joseph" (detail) (Metsys)	10	10
1993	40 c. "The Nativity" (detail) (Durer) ..	20	25
1994	45 c. "The Nativity" (Geertgen Tot Sint Jans)	20	25
1995	50 c. "The Nativity" (Jacopo Tintoretto) ..	25	30
1996	55 c. "The Nativity" (detail) (Follower of Calcar)	25	30
1997	65 c. "The Nativity" (Workshop of Fra Angelico)	30	35
1998	75 c. "The Nativity" (Master of the Louvre Nativity)	35	40
1999	$1 "The Nativity" (detail) (Lippi)	50	55
2000	$2 "The Nativity" (Petrus Christus)	95	1·00
2001	$3 "The Nativity" (detail) (Edward Burne-Jones)	1·40	1·50
2002	$4 "The Nativity" (detail) (Giotto)	2·00	2·10
2003	$5 "Birth of Christ" (detail) (Domenico Ghirlandaio)	2·40	2·50

242 Gaston

1992. Walt Disney's "Beauty and the Beast" (cartoon film). Multicoloured.

2005	2 c. Type **242**	10	10
2006	3 c. Belle and her father, Maurice	10	10
2007	5 c. Lumiere, Mrs. Potts and Cogsworth ..	10	10
2008	10 c. Philippe	10	10
2009	15 c. Beast and Lumiere	10	10
2010	20 c. Lumiere and Feather Duster	10	10
2011	60 c. Belle and Gaston ..	30	35
2012	60 c. Maurice	30	35
2013	60 c. The Beast	30	35
2014	60 c. Mrs. Potts	30	35
2015	60 c. Belle and enchanted vase	30	35
2016	60 c. Belle discovers enchanted rose ..	30	35
2017	60 c. Belle with wounded Beast	30	35
2018	60 c. Belle	30	35
2019	60 c. Household objects alarmed	30	35
2020	60 c. Belle and Chip (vert)	30	35
2021	60 c. Lumiere (vert) ..	30	35
2022	60 c. Cogsworth (vert) ..	30	35
2023	60 c. Armoire (vert) ..	30	35
2024	60 c. Belle and Beast (vert)	30	35
2025	60 c. Feather Duster (vert)	30	35
2026	60 c. Footstool (vert) ..	30	35
2027	60 c. Belle sitting on stone (vert)	30	35

1992. 15th Death Anniv of Elvis Presley (2nd issue). Nos. 1902/10 optd **15th Anniversary**. Multicoloured.

2029	$1 Elvis looking pensive	50	55
2030	$1 Wearing black and yellow striped shirt ..	50	55
2031	$1 Singing into microphone	50	55
2032	$1 Wearing wide-brimmed hat	50	55
2033	$1 With microphone in right hand	50	55
2034	$1 In Army uniform ..	50	55
2035	$1 Wearing pink shirt ..	50	55
2036	$1 In yellow shirt ..	50	55
2037	$1 In jacket and bow tie	50	55

1992. 15th Death Anniv of Elvis Presley (3rd issue). Nos. 1820/7 optd **15th Anniversary Elvis Presley's Death August 16, 1977**.

2038	$2 Michael Jackson ..	95	1·00
2039	$2 Madonna	95	1·00
2040	$2 Elvis Presley	95	1·00
2041	$2 David Bowie	95	1·00
2042	$2 Prince	95	1·00
2043	$2 Frank Sinatra ..	95	1·00
2044	$2 George Michael ..	95	1·00
2045	$2 Mick Jagger	95	1·00

1992. 15th Death Anniv of Elvis Presley (4th issue). As Nos. 1666/8 of Dominica. Mult.

2047	$1 Elvis Presley	50	55
2048	$1 Elvis with guitar ..	50	55
2049	$1 Elvis with microphone	50	55

245 Fifer Pig building House of Straw

1992. Walt Disney Cartoon Films.

2050/2138	60 c. × 89 mult .. Set of 89	24·00	28·00

Nos. 2050/2138 were printed as ten se-tenant sheetlets, each of nine different designs except for that for "Darkwing Duck" which contains eight vertical designs (Nos. 2131/8). The other nine sheetlets depict scenes from "The Three Little Pigs", "Thru the Mirror", "Clock Cleaners", "Orphans Benefit", "The Art of Skiing", "Symphony Hour", "How to Play Football", "The Small One" and "Chip N' Dale Rescue Rangers".

246 Scottie Pippen

1992. Olympic Gold Medal Winners, Barcelona. Members of U.S.A. basketball team. Multicoloured.

2140	$2 Type **246**	95	1·00
2141	$2 Earvin "Magic" Johnson	95	1·00
2142	$2 Larry Bird	95	1·00
2143	$2 Christian Laettner ..	95	1·00
2144	$2 Karl Malone	95	1·00
2145	$2 David Robinson ..	95	1·00
2146	$2 Michael Jordan ..	95	1·00
2147	$2 Charles Barkley ..	95	1·00
2148	$2 John Stockton ..	95	1·00
2149	$2 Chris Mullin	95	1·00
2150	$2 Clyde Drexler ..	95	1·00
2151	$2 Patrick Ewing ..	95	1·00

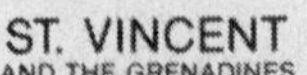

247 Tom Seaver

1992. Famous Baseball Players (5th issue). Multicoloured.

2152	$2 Type **247**	95	1·00
2153	$2 Roberto Clemente ..	95	1·00
2154	$2 Hank Aaron	95	1·00

248 Don Mattingly

1992. Famous Baseball Players (6th issue). Multicoloured.

2155	$5 Type **248**	2·40	2·50
2156	$5 Howard Johnson ..	2·40	2·50

249 Earth and U.N. Emblem

1992. Anniversaries and Events. Mult.

2157	10 c. Type **249**	10	10
2158	45 c. "Viktoria Luise" over Kiel Regatta, 1912 (vert)	20	25
2159	75 c. Adenauer and German flag	35	40
2160	75 c. Trophy and Bill Koch (skipper) of "America III", 1992 ..	35	40
2161	$1 Konrad Adenauer ..	50	55
2162	$1 Snow leopard and emblem	50	55
2163	$1.50 Caribbean manatee	70	75
2164	$2 Humpback whale ..	95	1·00
2165	$3 Adenauer and Pres. Kennedy, 1962 ..	1·40	1·50
2166	$3 Doctor checking patient's eye	1·40	1·50
2167	$4 "Discovery" space shuttle (vert)	2·00	2·10
2168	$4 Adenauer and Pope John XXIII, 1960 ..	2·00	2·10
2169	$5 Schumacher and racing car	2·40	2·50
2170	$6 Zeppelin No. 1 over Lake Constance, 1900 ..	3·00	3·25

ANNIVERSARIES AND EVENTS: Nos. 2157, 2167, International Space Year; Nos. 2158, 2170, 75th death anniv of Count Ferdinand von Zeppelin; Nos. 2159, 2161, 2165, 2168, 25th death anniv of Konrad Adenauer (German statesman); No. 2160, Americas Cup Yachting Championship; Nos. 2162/4, Earth Summit '92, Rio; No. 2166, 75th anniv of International Association of Lions Clubs; No. 2169, Michael Schumacher's Victory in 1992 Belgium Grand Prix.

1992. Ecology. As T **71** of Nevis. Mult.

2172	75 c. Care Bear and pelican	35	40

250 Farmer, Fisherman and Emblem

1993. International Conference on Nutrition, Rome.

2174	**250** 65 c. multicoloured ..	30	35

251 Coastal Village

1993. "Uniting the Windward Islands". Mult.

2175	10 c. Type **251**	10	10
2176	40 c. Children from different islands ..	20	25
2177	45 c. Chidren and palm tree	20	25

252 Fisherman holding Catch

1993. Fishing. Multicoloured.

2178	5 c. Type **252**	10	10
2179	10 c. Fish market ..	10	10
2180	50 c. Fishermen landing catch	25	30
2181	$5 Fishing with nets ..	2·40	2·50

253 Brown Pelican

1993. Migratory Birds. Multicoloured.

2182	10 c. Type **253**	10	10
2183	25 c. Red-necked grebe (horiz)	10	10
2184	45 c. Belted kingfisher (horiz)	20	25
2185	55 c. Yellow-bellied sapsucker	25	30
2186	$1 Great blue heron ..	50	55
2187	$2 Common black hawk ("Crab Hawk") (horiz)	95	1·00
2188	$4 Yellow warbler ..	2·00	2·10
2189	$5 Northern oriole (horiz)	2·40	2·50

254 Sergeant Major

1993. Fishes. Multicoloured.

2191	5 c. Type **254**	10	10
2192	10 c. Rainbow parrotfish	10	10
2193	55 c. Hogfish	25	30
2194	75 c. Porkfish	35	40
2195	$1 Spotfin butterflyfish ..	50	55
2196	$2 Trunkfish	95	1·00
2197	$4 Queen triggerfish ..	2·00	2·10
2198	$5 Queen angelfish ..	2·40	2·50

1993. Bicentenary of the Louvre, Paris. As T **305** of Antigua.

2200/39	$1 × 40 multicoloured Set of 40	18·00	20·00

Nos. 2200/39 were printed as five se-tenant sheetlets showing paintings by Gericault, Ingres, Le Sueur and Poussin, Poussin, and Boucher, Brueghel, Dumont, Gainsborough, Goya and Van Eyck.

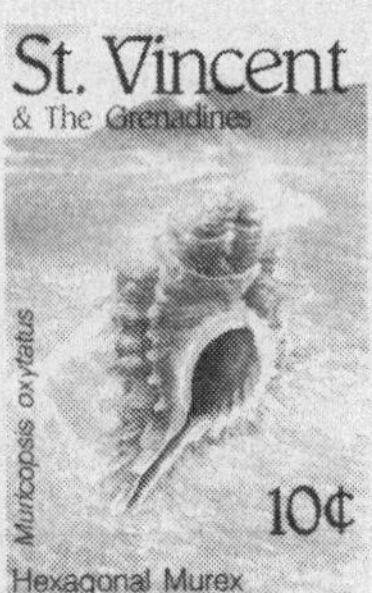

255 "Muricopsis oxytatus"

1993. Shells. Multicoloured.

2241	10 c. Type **255**	10	10
2242	15 c. "Vasum muricatum"	10	10
2243	30 c. "Cypraea zebra" ..	15	20
2244	45 c. "Diodora dysoni" ..	20	25
2245	50 c. "Cymatium pileare"	25	30
2246	65 c. "Hyalina avena" ..	30	35
2247	75 c. "Nerita peloranta"	35	40
2248	$1 "Strombus gigas" ..	50	55
2249	$2 "Strombus raninus" ..	95	1·00
2250	$3 "Voluta musica" ..	1·40	1·50
2251	$4 "Conus spurius" ..	2·00	2·10
2252	$5 "Conus cedonulli" ..	2·40	2·50

256 Ishihara holding Tennis Racket

1993. 7th Death Anniv of Yujiro Ishihara (Japanese actor)

2254	**256**	55 c. black, grey & bl	25	30
2255	–	55 c. black, grey & bl	25	30
2256	–	55 c. black, grey & bl	25	30
2257	–	55 c. multicoloured ..	25	30
2258	–	55 c. multicoloured ..	25	30
2259	–	$1 multicoloured ..	50	55
2260	–	$1 multicoloured ..	50	55
2261	–	$1 multicoloured ..	50	55
2262	–	$1 multicoloured ..	50	55

DESIGNS—As T **256**: No. 2255, Ishihara holding camera; No. 2256, In striped shirt; No. 2257, Holding drink and cigarette; No. 2258, On board yacht; No. 2259, In naval uniform; No. 2260, In jacket and tie; No. 2261, Wearing sunglasses; No. 2262, Wearing pink shirt.

1993. 40th Anniv of Coronation. As T **307** of Antigua.

2264	45 c. multicoloured ..	20	25
2265	65 c. multicoloured ..	30	35
2266	$2 green and black ..	95	1·00
2267	$4 multicoloured ..	2·00	2·10

DESIGNS: 45 c. Queen Elizabeth II at Coronation (photograph by Cecil Beaton); 65 c. Queen Elizabeth opening Parliament; $2 Queen Elizabeth during Coronation; $4 Queen Elizabeth with corgi.

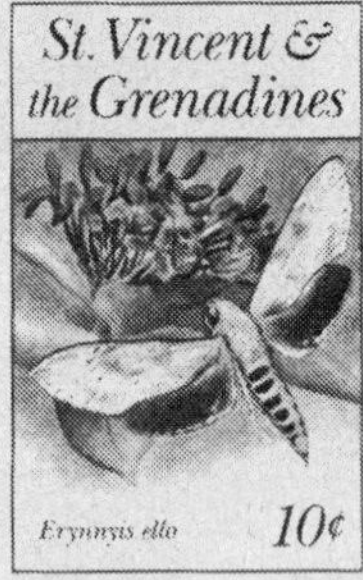

257 "Erynnyis ello"

1993. Moths. Multicoloured.

2269	10 c. Type **257**	10	10
2270	50 c. "Aellopos tantalus"	25	30
2271	65 c. "Erynnyis alope" ..	30	35
2272	75 c. "Manduca rustica"	35	40
2273	$1 "Xylophanes pluto" ..	50	55
2274	$2 "Hyles lineata" ..	95	1·00
2275	$4 "Pseudosphinx tetrio"	2·00	2·10
2276	$5 "Protambulyx strigilis"	2·40	2·50

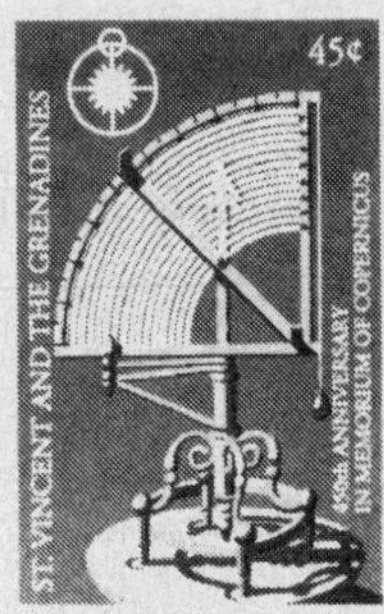

258 Early Astronomical Quadrant

1993. Anniversaries and Events. Red and black (Nos. 2281, 2293) or multicoloured (others).

2278	45 c. Type **258**	20	25
2279	45 c. "Massacre in Korea" (Picasso) (horiz) ..	20	25
2280	45 c. Marc Girardelli (Luxembourg) (giant slalom) (horiz) ..	20	25
2281	45 c. Willy Brandt and Pres. Nixon, 1971 (horiz)	20	25
2282	45 c. Count Johannes and Countess Gloria of Thurn and Taxis ..	20	25
2283	65 c. Count and Countess of Thurn and Taxis with children (horiz) ..	30	35
2284	65 c. Masako Owada and engagement photographs (horiz) ..	30	35
2285	$1 "Family of Saltimbanques" (Picasso) (horiz) ..	50	55
2286	$1 Princess Stephanie of Monaco	50	55
2287	$1 "Deux Tetes" (left detail) (S. Witkiewicz)	50	55
2288	$2 Countess Gloria of Thurn & Taxis ..	95	1·00
2289	$3 "Deux Tetes" (right detail) (S. Witkiewicz)	1·40	1·50
2290	$4 Launch of American space shuttle ..	2·00	2·10
2291	$4 "La Joie de Vivre" (Picasso) (horiz) ..	2·00	2·10
2292	$5 Paul Accola (Switzerland) (downhill skiing) (horiz) ..	2·40	2·50
2293	$5 Willy Brandt and Robert F. Kennedy, 1967 (horiz) ..	2·40	2·50
2294	$5 Prince Naruhito in tradtional dress and engagement photographs (horiz)	2·40	2·50
2295	$5 Pres. Clinton with school children (horiz)	2·40	2·50
2296	$6 Bogusz Church, Gozlin (horiz)	3·00	3·25

ANNIVERSARIES AND EVENT: Nos. 2278, 2290, 450th death anniv of Copernicus (astronomer); Nos. 2279, 2285, 2291, 20th death anniv of Picasso (artist); Nos. 2280, 2292, Winter Olympic Games '94, Lillehammer; Nos. 2281, 2293, 80th birth anniv of Willy Brandt (German politician); Nos. 2282/3, 2288, 500th anniv (1990) of Thurn and Taxis postal service; Nos. 2284, 2294, Marriage of Crown Prince Naruhito of Japan; No. 2286, Marriage of Princess Stephanie of Monaco; Nos. 2287, 2289, 2296, "Polska '93" International Stamp Exhibition, Poznan; No. 2295, Inauguration of U.S. President William Clinton.

259 Supermarine Spitfire

1993. Aviation Anniversaries. Multicoloured.

2298	50 c. Type **259**	25	30
2299	$1 Eckener, and "Graf Zeppelin" over Egypt, 1931	50	55
2300	$1 Blanchard and Pres. Washington with balloon, 1793	50	55
2301	$2 De Havilland Mosquito	95	1·00
2302	$2 Eckener and "Graf Zeppelin" over New York, 1928	95	1·00
2303	$3 Eckener and "Graf Zeppelin" over Tokyo, 1929	1·40	1·50
2304	$4 Blanchard's balloon ascending from Walnut St. Prison, Philadelphia	2·00	2·10

ANNIVERSARIES: Nos. 2298, 2301, 75th anniv of Royal Air Force; Nos. 2299, 2302/3, 125th birth anniv of Hugo Eckener (airship commander); Nos. 2300, 2304, Bicentenary of first airmail flight.

260 First Ford Car, Model "T" and "V8"

1993. Centenaries of Henry Ford's First Petrol Engine (Nos. 2306, 2309) and Karl Benz's First Four-wheeled car (others). Mult.

2306	$1 Type **260**	50	55
2307	$2 Benz racing car, 1908, "Stuttgart" and "540K"	95	1·00
2308	$3 Benz car, 1894, "Tourenwagen" and "Blitzen Benz" ..	1·40	1·50
2309	$4 Ford "Runabout", 1903, Model "T" Tourer and saloon, 1935 ..	2·00	2·10

261 Pope John Paul II and Denver Skyline

1993. Papal Visit to Denver, Colorado, U.S.A.

2311 **261**	$1 multicoloured ..	50	55

262 Corvette of 1953

1993. 40th Anniv of Corvette Range of Cars. Multicoloured.

2313	$1 Type **262**	50	55
2314	$1 1993 model	50	55
2315	$1 1958 model	50	55
2316	$1 1960 model	50	55
2317	$1 "40" and symbolic chequered flag emblem	50	55
2318	$1 1961 model	50	55
2319	$1 1963 model	50	55
2320	$1 1968 model	50	55
2321	$1 1973 model	50	55
2322	$1 1975 model	50	55
2323	$1 1982 model	50	55
2324	$1 1984 model	50	55

1993. Asian International Stamp Exhibitions. Multicoloured designs as T **268** of Dominica.

(a) "Indopex '93", Surabaya, Indonesia. Horiz designs.

2325/54	5, 10, 20, 45, 55, 75 c., $1 × 2, $1.50 × 18, $2, $4, $5 × 2 Set of 30	20·00	21·00

Nos. 2325/32 and 2351/4 show Indonesian scenes, Nos. 2333/50 masks (Nos. 2333/8) or paintings (Nos 2339/50).

(b) "Taipei '93", Taiwan. Horiz designs.

2356/85	5, 10, 20, 45, 55, 75 c., $1 × 2, $1.50 × 18, $2, $4, $5 × 2 Set of 30	20·00	21·00

Nos. 2356/63 and 2382/5 show Chinese scenes, Nos. 2364/81 kites (Nos. 2364/9) or paintings (Nos. 2370/81).

(c) "Bangkok '93", Thailand. Vert (5, 55 c., $2, 4) or horiz (others).

2387/2416	5, 10, 20, 45, 55, 75 c., $1 × 2, $1.50 × 18, $2, $4, $5 × 2 Set of 30	20·00	21·00

Nos. 2387/4 and 2413/16 show Thai scenes. Nos. 2395/2412 murals from Buddhaisawan Chapel (Nos. 2395/2400) paintings (Nos. 2401/6) or sculptures (Nos. 2407/12).

264 Players from St. Vincent and Mexico

1993. Qualifying Rounds for World Cup Football Championship, U.S.A. Multicoloured.

2418	5 c. Type **264**	10	10
2419	10 c. Honduras match ..	10	10
2420	65 c. Costa Rica match ..	30	35
2421	$5 St. Vincent goalkeeper	2·40	2·50

265 Fish Delivery Van

1993. Japanese Aid for Fishing Industry. Multicoloured.

2422	10 c. Type **265**	10	10
2423	50 c. Fish aggregation device (vert)	25	30
2424	75 c. Game fishing launch	35	40
2425	$5 Fish market	2·40	2·50

1993. Famous Baseball Players (7th issue). As T **247**. Multicoloured.

2426	$2 Reggie Jackson ..	95	1·00

266 "Adoration of the Magi" (detail) (Durer)

1994. Christmas. Religious Paintings. Black, yellow and red (Nos. 2427/9, 2434) or multicoloured (others).

2427	10 c. Type **266**	10	10
2428	35 c. "Adoration of the Magi" (different detail) (Durer)	15	20
2429	40 c. "Adoration of the Magi" (different detail) (Durer)	20	25
2430	50 c. "Holy Family with Saint Francis" (detail) (Rubens)	25	30
2431	55 c. "Adoration of the Shepherds" (detail) (Rubens)	25	30
2432	65 c. "Adoration of the Shepherds" (different detail) (Rubens) ..	30	35
2433	$1 "Holy Family" (Rubens)	50	55
2434	$5 "Adoration of the Magi" (different detail) (Durer)	2·40	2·50

OFFICIAL STAMPS.

1982. Nos. 668/73 optd. **OFFICIAL.**

O 1.	60 c. "Isabella"	20	20
O 2.	60 c. Prince Charles and Lady Diana Spencer ..	50	50
O 3.	$2.50 "Alberta" (tender)	40	40
O 4.	$2.50 Prince Charles and Lady Diana Spencer ..	80	80
O 5.	$4 "Britannia"	60	60
O 6.	$4 Prince Charles and Lady Diana Spencer	1·25	1·25

SAMOA

Islands in the W. Pacific administered jointly from 1889–99 by Gt. Britain, Germany and the U.S.A. In 1889 the eastern islands were assigned to the U.S.A. and the western to Germany (for issues see Vol. 2). The latter were occupied by British forces in 1914 and were taken over by New Zealand, under mandate, in 1920. W. Samoa was under United Nations trusteeship but became independent on 1 January 1962.

1877. 12 pence = 1 shilling,
20 shillings = 1 pound.
1967. 100 sene or cents = 1 tale or dollar.

INDEPENDENT KINGDOM.

1.

2. Palm trees.

3. King Malietoa Laupepa.

8.

1877.

15. **1.**	1d. blue	24·00	40·00
16.	3d. red	45·00	65·00
17.	6d. violet	40·00	48·00
20.	9d. brown	60·00	£120
7b.	1s. yellow	70·00	85·00
18.	2s. brown	£130	£200
19a.	5s. green	£375	£550

The majority of the stamps of T **1** found in old collections are worthless reprints. A 2d. stamp exists but was never issued.

1886.

57a **2**	2½d. brown	65	1·75
88	½d. green	65	1·40
58	1d. green	1·75	1·75
89	1d. brown	55	1·25
59c	2d. orange	4·50	1·00
60 **3**	2½d. red	70	4·50
81	2½d. black	90	3·00
61 **2**	4d. blue	5·75	2·00
72a **8**	5d. red	1·25	3·00
62 **2**	6d. lake	5·50	3·00
63	1s. red	6·00	3·75
64b	2s. 6d. violet	4·75	9·50

1893. Surch. **FIVE PENCE** and bar.

65. **2.**	5d. on 4d. blue	48·00	42·00

1893. Surch. **5d.** and bar.

69. **2.**	5d. on 4d. blue	17·00	25·00

1895. Surch. **Surcharged** and value in figures.

75. **2.**	1½d. on 2d. orange ..	1·50	3·50
84.	2½d. on 1d. green	55	2·00
85.	2½d. on 1s. red	3·50	8·50
87.	2½d. on 2s. 6d. violet ..	4·75	11·00

1895. Surch. R **3d.**

76 **2**	3d. on 2d. orange	5·50	7·50

1899. Optd. **PROVISIONAL GOVT.**

90 **2**	½d. green	30	1·25
91	1d. brown	1·00	2·75
92	2d. orange	80	3·00
93	4d. blue	45	2·75
94a **8**	5d. red	90	4·50
95 **2**	6d. lake	1·10	3·75
96	1s. red	1·50	11·00
97	2s. 6d. violet	4·75	17·00

NEW ZEALAND DEPENDENCY.
(under Mandate from League of Nations and United Nations).

1914. "Yacht" key-types as German Cameroons, but inscr "Samoa" surch **G.R.I.** and value in British currency.

101. N.	½d. on 3 pf. brown ..	18·00	8·50
102.	½d. on 5 pf. green ..	40·00	10·00
103.	1d. on 10 pf. red ..	95·00	40·00
104.	2½d. on 20 pf. blue ..	30·00	10·00
105.	3d. on 25 pf. black and red on yellow	50·00	35·00
106.	4d. on 30 pf. black and orange on buff ..	£110	60·00
107.	5d. on 40 pf. black & red	£110	70·00
108.	6d. on 50 pf. black and purple on buff ..	55·00	35·00
109.	9d. on 80 pf. black and red on rose	£200	95·00
110. O.	1s. on 1 m. red ..	£3000	£3250
112.	2s. on 2 m. blue	£3000	£2750
113.	3s. on 3 m. black ..	£1400	£1200
114.	5s. on 5 m. red and black	£1000	£950

1914. Stamps of New Zealand (King Edward VII) optd. **SAMOA.**

No.	Type	Description		
115.	**50.**	½d. green	30	30
116.	**51.**	1d. red	30	10
117.	**50.**	2d. mauve	60	95
118.	**27.**	2½d. blue	1·50	1·75
119.	**50.**	6d. red	1·50	1·75
121.		1s. red	3·50	9·50

1914. Large stamps of New Zealand (Queen Victoria) optd. **SAMOA.**

No.	Type	Description		
127	F 4	2s. blue	4·00	5·50
123		2s. 6d. brown	4·50	8·50
129		3s. violet	12·00	30·00
124		5s. green	10·00	11·00
125		10s. brown	20·00	28·00
126		£1 red	60·00	45·00

1916. Stamps of New Zealand (King George V) overprinted **SAMOA.**

No.	Type	Description		
134.	**60a.**	½d. green	30	45
135.		1½d. grey	30	25
136.		1½d. brown	20	45
137.		2d. yellow	50	20
139a.		2½d. blue	35	35
140.		3d. brown	35	90
141.		6d. red	1·25	90
142a.		1s. red	1·25	1·25

1920. Stamps of New Zealand (Victory issue. Nos. 511/16) optd. **SAMOA.**

No.	Type	Description		
143.	**62.**	½d. green	1·75	2·75
144.	**63.**	1d. red	1·50	1·50
145.	–	1½d. orange	1·50	4·25
146.	–	3d. brown	5·00	7·00
147.	–	6d. violet	4·00	6·50
148.	–	1s. orange	13·00	11·00

16. Native Hut.

1921.

No.	Type	Description		
153	**16.**	½d. green	1·50	1·75
150		1d. lake	60	20
151		1½d. brown	50	6·00
152		2d. yellow	90	2·00
157		2½d. blue	70	4·00
158		3d. sepia	75	3·00
159		4d. violet	80	3·00
160		5d. blue	75	5·00
161		6d. red	80	3·50
162		8d. brown	1·25	9·00
163		9d. olive	1·25	12·00
164		1s. red	1·25	13·00

1926. Stamps of New Zealand (King George V) overprinted **SAMOA.**

No.	Type	Description		
167.	**71.**	2s. blue	4·50	12·00
168.		3s. mauve	7·00	24·00

1932. Stamps of New Zealand (Arms type) optd. **SAMOA.**

No.	Type	Description		
171.	F **6.**	2s. 6d. brown	15·00	28·00
172.		5s. green	20·00	35·00
173.		10 s. red	45·00	75·00
174.		£1 pink	60·00	90·00
175.		£2 violet	£700	
176.		£5 blue	£1800	

1935. Silver Jubilee. Stamps of 1921 optd. **SILVER JUBILEE OF KING GEORGE V 1910-1935.**

No.	Type	Description		
177.	**16.**	1d. lake	30	30
178.		2½d. blue	60	65
179.		6d. red	2·75	2·50

18. Samoan Girl

19. Apia.

1935.

No.	Type	Description		
180.	**18.**	½d. green	10	35
181.	**19.**	1d. black and red ..	10	10
182.	–	2d. black and orange ..	2·75	2·00
183.	–	2½d. black and blue ..	10	10
184.	–	4d. grey and brown ..	40	15
205.	–	5d. brown and blue ..	20	50
185.	–	6d. mauve	40	10
186.	–	1s. violet and brown ..	30	10
187.	–	2s. green and purple ..	50	50
188.	–	3s. blue and orange ..	1·50	3·50

DESIGNS—HORIZ. 2d. River scene. 4d. Samoan canoe and house. 5d. Apia post office. 6d. R. L. Stevenson's home, "Vailima". 1s. Stevenson's tomb. VERT. 2½d. Samoan chief and wife. 2s. Lake Lanuto'o. 3s. Falefa Falls.

1935. Stamps of New Zealand (Arms types) optd. **WESTERN SAMOA.**

No.	Type	Description		
207.	F **6.**	2s. 6d. brown	2·25	5·50
208.		5s. green	5·00	7·50
209.		10s. red	16·00	17·00
234.		£1 pink	27·00	35·00
211.		30s. brown	£140	£250
235.		£2 violet	75·00	£140
213.		£3 green	£170	£325
214.		£5 blue	£250	£375

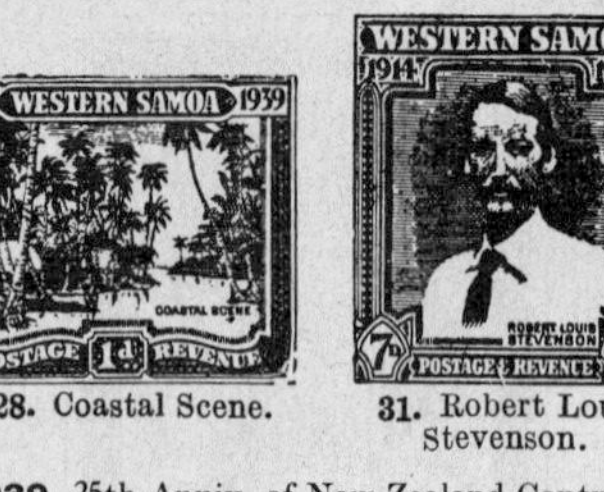

28. Coastal Scene. **31.** Robert Louis Stevenson.

1939. 25th Anniv. of New Zealand Control.

No.	Type	Description		
195.	**28.**	1d. olive and red ..	30	10
196.	–	1½d. blue and brown ..	45	30
197.	–	2½d. brown and blue ..	90	65
198.	**31.**	7d. violet and green ..	6·50	2·00

DESIGNS—HORIZ. 1½d. Map of Western Samoa. 2½d. Samoan dancing party.

32. Samoan Chief.

35. Making Siapo Cloth.

36. Native Houses and Flags.

1940. Surch.

No.	Type	Description		
199.	**32.**	3d. on 1½d. brown ..	10	10

1946. Peace stamps of New Zealand optd. **WESTERN SAMOA.**

No.	Type	Description		
215.	**132.**	1d. green	10	10
216.	–	2d. purple (No. 670) ..	10	10
217.	–	6d. brown and red (674)	10	10
218.	**139.**	8d. black and red ..	10	10

1952.

No.	Type	Description		
219.	**35.**	½d. red and brown ..	10	75
220.	**36.**	1d. olive and green ..	10	15
221.	–	2d. red	10	10
222.	–	3d. blue and indigo ..	40	10
223.	–	5d. brown and green ..	4·00	70
224.	–	6d. blue and mauve ..	50	10
225.	–	8d. red	30	30
226.	–	1s. sepia and blue ..	15	10
227.	–	2s. brown	1·40	60
228.	–	3s. brown and olive ..	3·00	2·50

DESIGNS: As Type **35**—VERT. 2d. Seal of Samoa. 5d. Tooth-billed Pigeon. HORIZ. 1s. Thatching native hut. As Type **36**—HORIZ. 3d. Malifa Falls, wrongly inscr. on stamp "Aleisa Falls". 6d. Bonito fishing canoe. 8d. Cacao harvesting. 2s. Preparing copra. VERT. 3s. Samoan chieftainess.

1953. Coronation. As Types of New Zealand.

No.	Type	Description		
229.	**164.**	2d. brown	1·00	15
230.	**166.**	6d. grey	1·00	35

48. Map of Samoa, and the Mace.

1958. Inaug. of Samoan Parliament. Inscr. "FONO FOU 1958" and SAMOA I SISIFO".

No.	Type	Description		
236.	–	4d. red (As T **36**) ..	15	10
237.	–	6d. violet (As No. 221)	15	15
238.	**48.**	1s. blue	35	15

INDEPENDENT STATE.

49. Samoan Fine Mat.

DESIGNS — HORIZ. 2d. Samoa College. 3d. Public library. 4d. Fono house. 6d. Map of Samoa. 8d. Airport. 1s. 3d. "Vailima". 2s. 6d. Samoan flag. 5s. Samoan Seal. VERT. 1s. Samoan orator.

1962. Independence.

No.	Type	Description		
239.	**49.**	1d. brown and red ..	10	10
240.	–	2d multicoloured ..	10	10
241.	–	3d. brown, green & blue	10	10
242.	–	4d. multicoloured ..	15	10
243.	–	6d. yellow and blue ..	20	10
244.	–	8d. turq., green & blue	20	10
245.	–	1s. brown and green ..	20	10
246.	–	1s. 3d. green and blue ..	75	35
247.	–	2s. 6d. red and blue ..	1·50	1·25
248.	–	5s. multicoloured ..	3·25	2·50

59. Seal and Joint Heads of State.

1963. 1st Anniv. of Independence.

No.	Type	Description		
249.	**59.**	1d. sepia and green ..	10	10
250.		4d. sepia and blue ..	10	10
251.		8d. sepia and pink ..	10	10
252.		2 s. sepia and orange ..	20	15

60. Signing the Treaty.

1964. 2nd Anniv. of New Zealand-Samoa Treaty of Friendship.

No.	Type	Description		
253.	**60.**	1d. multicoloured ..	10	10
254.		8d. multicoloured ..	10	10
255.		2s. multicoloured ..	20	10
256.		3s. multicoloured ..	20	30

62. Red-tailed Tropic Bird.

1965. Air.

No.	Type	Description		
263.	**62.**	8d. black, orge & blue	40	10
264.	–	2s. black and blue ..	55	20

DESIGN: 2s. Flying Fish.

64. Aerial View of Deep Sea Wharf.

1966. Opening of 1st Deep Sea Wharf, Apia. Multicoloured.

No.	Description		
265.	1d. Type **64**	10	10
266.	8d. Aerial View of Wharf and Bay	15	10
267.	2s. Aerial View of Wharf and Bay	25	20
268.	3s. Type **64**	30	20

66. W.H.O. Building.

1966. Inaug. of W.H.O. Headquarters, Geneva.

No.	Type	Description		
269.	**66.**	3d. ochre ,blue and slate	35	10
270.	–	4d. multicoloured ..	40	10
271.	**66.**	6d. lilac, green & olive ..	45	15
272.	–	1s. multicoloured ..	80	20

DESIGNS: 4d. and 1s. W.H.O. Building on flag.

1966. Huuricane Relief Fund. No. 244 surch **HURRICANE RELIEF** and value.

No.	Description		
273	8d. + 6d. turqoise, grn & bl	10	10

69. Hon. Tuatagaloa L.S. (Minister of Justice).

1967. 5th Anniv. of Independence.

No.	Type	Description		
274.	**69.**	3d. sepia and violet ..	10	10
275.	–	8d. sepia and blue ..	10	10
276.	–	2s. sepia and olive ..	10	10
277.	–	3s. sepia and mauve .	15	15

DESIGNS: 8d. Hon. F. C. F. Nelson (Minister of Works, Marine and Civil Aviation). 2s. Hon. To'omata T.L. (Minister of Lands). 3s. Hon. Fa'alava'au G. (Minister of Post Office, Radio and Broadcasting).

73. Samoan Fales (houses), 1890.

1967. Cent. of Mulinu'u as Seat of Government.

No.	Type	Description		
278.	**73.**	8d. multicoloured ..	15	10
279.	–	1s. multicoloured ..	15	10

DESIGN: 1s. Fono (Parliament) House, 1967.

74. Caruncalated Honeyeater.

1967. Decimal Currency. Multicoloured.

No.	Description		
280.	1 s. Type **74**	10	10
281.	2 s. Pacific Pigeon ..	10	10
282.	3 s. Samoan Starling ..	10	10
283.	5 s. White-vented Fly-catcher	15	10
284.	7 s. Red-headed Parrot Finch	15	10
285.	10 s. Purple Swamphen ..	20	10
286.	20 s. Barn Owl	2·25	40
287.	25 s. Tooth-billed Pigeon	1·50	15
288.	50 s. Island Thrush ..	1·50	25
289.	$1 Samoan Fantail ..	1·75	1·75
289a.	$2 Black-breasted Honey-eater	5·50	7·00
289b.	$4 Savaii White eye ..	40·00	45·00

85. Nurse and Child.

1967. South Pacific Health Service. Mult.

No.	Description		
290.	3 s. Type **85**	10	10
291.	7 s. Leprosarium	15	10
292.	20 s. Mobile X-ray Unit ..	25	20
293.	25 s Apia Hospital ..	30	25

89. Thomas Trood.

1968. 6th Anniv. of Independence. Mult.

No.	Description		
294.	2 s. Type **89** ..	10	10
295.	7 s. Dr. Wilhelm Solf ..	10	10
296.	20 s. J. C. Williams ..	10	10
297.	25 s. Fritz Marquardt ..	15	10

HAVE YOU READ THE NOTES AT THE BEGINNING OF THIS CATALOGUE?

These often provide answers to the enquiries we receive.

93. Cocoa.

1968. Agricultural Development.

298.	93. 3 s. brown, green & black	10	10
299.	– 5 s. green, yellow & brn.	10	10
300.	– 10 s. red, brown & yellow	10	10
301.	– 20 s. bistre, yell. & olive	15	15

DESIGNS: 5 s. Breadfruit. 10 s. Copra. 20 s. Bananas.

97. Women Weaving Mats.

1968. 21st Anniv. of South Pacific Commission. Multicoloured.

302.	7 s. Type **97**	10	10
303.	20 s. Palm trees and bay ..	15	10
304.	25 s. Sheltered cove ..	15	15

1968. Kingsford-Smith's Trans-Pacific Flight. 40th Anniv. No. 285 surch. **1928-1968 KINGSFORD-SMITH TRANS-PACIFIC FLIGHT** and new value.

305.	20 s. on 10 s. multicoloured	10	10

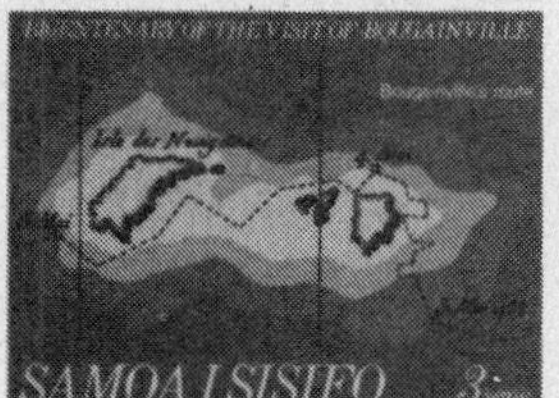
101. Bougainville's Route.

1968. Bicent. of Bougainville's Visit to Samoa.

306.	101. 3 s. blue and black ..	10	10
307.	– 7 s. ochre and black ..	15	10
308.	– 20 s. multicoloured ..	45	20
309.	– 25 s. multicoloured ..	60	30

DESIGNS: 7 s. Louis de Bougainville. 20 s. Bougainvillea flower. 25 s. Ships "La Boudeuse" and "L'Etoile".

105. Globe and Human Rights Emblem.

1968. Human Rights Year.

310.	105. 7 s. blue, brown & gold	10	10
311.	20 s. orge., green & gold	10	10
312.	25 s. violet, grn. & gold	15	10

106. Dr. Martin Luther King. 107. Polynesian Version of Madonna and Child.

1968. Martin Luther King. Commem.

313.	106. 7 s. black and green ..	10	10
314.	20 s. black and purple ..	10	10

1968. Christmas.

315.	107. 1 s. multicoloured ..	10	10
316.	3 s. multicoloured ..	10	10
317.	20 s. multicoloured ..	10	10
318.	30 s. multicoloured ..	15	15

108. Frangipani—"Plumeria acuminata".

1969. 7th Anniv. of Independence. Mult.

319.	2 s. Type **108**	10	10
320.	7 s. Hibiscus (vert.) ..	25	10
321.	20 s. Red-Ginger (vert.) ..	65	10
322.	30 s. Moso'oi	80	55

109. R. L. Stevenson and "Treasure Island".

1969. 75th Death Anniv. of Robert Louis Stevenson. Multicoloured.

323.	3 s. Type **109**	15	10
324.	7 s. R. L. Stevenson and "Kidnapped"	20	10
325.	20 s. R. L. Stevenson and "Dr. Jekyll and Mr. Hyde"	45	20
326.	22 s. R. L. Stevenson and "Weir of Hermiston" ..	55	20

110. Weightlifting.

1969. 3rd South Pacific Games, Port Moresby.

327.	110. 3 s. black and green ..	10	10
328.	– 20 s. black and blue ..	10	10
329.	– 22 s. black and orange ..	15	15

DESIGNS: 20 s. Yachting. 22 s. Boxing.

113. U.S. Astronaut on the Moon and the Splashdown near Samoan Islands.

1969. 1st Man on the Moon.

330.	113. 7 s. multicoloured ..	15	15
331.	20 s. multicoloured ..	15	15

114. "Virgin with Child" (Murillo).

1969. Christmas. Multicoloured.

332.	1 s. Type **114**	10	10
333.	3 s. "The Holy Family" (El Greco)	10	10
334.	20 s. "The Nativity" (El Greco)	30	10
335.	30 s. "The Adoration of the Magi" (detail) (Velazquez)	35	15

115. Seventh Day Adventists' Sanatorium, Apia.

1970. 8th Anniv. of Independence.

337.	115. 2 s. brown, slate & black	10	10
338.	– 7 s. violet, buff & black	10	10
339.	– 20 s. rose, lilac & black	15	10
340.	– 22 s. green, buff & black	15	15

DESIGNS—HORIZ. 7 s. Rev. Father Violette and Roman Catholic Cathedral, Apia. 22 s. John Williams, 1797-1839, and London Missionary Society Church. Sapapali'i. VERT. 20 s. Mormon Church of Latter Day Saints, Tuasivi-on-Safotulafai.

119. Wreck of "Adler" (German steam gunboat).

1970. Great Apia Hurricane of 1889. Mult.

341	5 s. Type **119**	45	10
342	7 s. U.S.S. "Nipsic" (steam sloop)	50	10
343	10 s. H.M.S. "Calliope" (screw corvette) ..	65	25
344	20 s. Apia after the hurricane	2·00	1·25

120. Sir Gordon Taylor's "Frigate Bird III".

1970. Air. Multicoloured.

345.	3 s. Type **120**	45	10
346.	7 c. Polynesian Airlines "DC-3"	70	10
347.	20 s. Pan-American Airways "Samoan Clipper"	2·00	60
348.	30 s. Air Samoa Britten-Norman "Islander" ..	2·25	1·25

121. Kendal's Chronometer and Cook's Sextant.

1970. Cook's Exploration of the Pacific.

349.	121. 1 s. red, silver and black	20	15
350.	– 2 s. multicoloured ..	35	25
351.	– 10 s. black, blue & gold	1·75	1·00
352.	– 30 s. multicoloured ..	2·75	1·75

DESIGNS—VERT. 2 s. Cook's statue, Whitby. 10 s. Cook's head. HORIZ. 30 s. Cook, H.M.S. "Endeavour" and island (83 × 25 mm.).

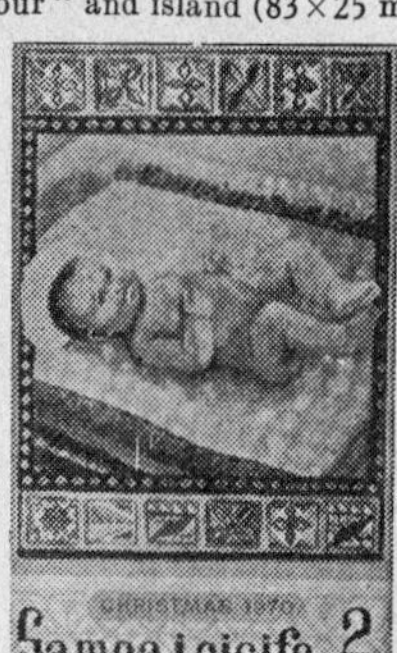
122. "Peace for the World" (F. B. Eccles).

1970. Christmas. Multicoloured.

353.	2 s. Type **122**	10	10
354.	3 s. "The Holy Family" (W. E. Jahnke) ..	10	10
355.	20 s. "Mother and Child" (F. B. Eccles)	15	10
356.	30 c. "Prince of Peace" (Meleane Fe'ao) ..	20	15

123. Pope Paul VI.

1970. Visit of Pope Paul to Samoa.

358.	123. 8 s. black and blue ..	15	15
359.	20 s. black and red ..	35	15

124. Native and Tree.

1971. Timber Industry. Multicoloured.

360.	3 s. Type **124**	10	10
361.	8 s. Bulldozer in clearing ..	15	10
362.	20 s. Log in Sawmill ..	30	10
363.	22 s. Floating Logs, and Harbour.	30	15

The 8 s. and 20 s. are horiz.

126. Siva Dance.

1971. Tourism. Multicoloured.

365.	5 s. Type **126** ..	40	10
366.	7 s. Samoan cricket ..	1·00	60
367.	8 s. Hideaway Hotel ..	1·00	35
368.	10 s. Aggie Grey and her hotel	1·00	60

127. "Queen Salamasina".

1971. Myths and Legends of Old Samoa (1st series). Multicoloured.

369.	3 s. Type **127**	10	10
370.	8 s. "Lu and his Sacred Hens"	15	10
371.	10 s. "God Tagaloa fishes Samoa from the sea" ..	20	10
372.	22 s. "Mount Vaea and the Pool of Tears" ..	35	30

See also Nos. 426/9.

128. "The Virgin and Child" (Bellini).

1971. Christmas.

373. 128. 2 s. multicoloured .. 10 10
374. 3 s. multicoloured .. 10 10
375. – 20 s. multicoloured .. 25 10
376. – 30 s. multicoloured .. 35 20

DESIGN: 20 s., 30 s. "The Virgin and Child with St. Anne and John the Baptist" (Leonardo da Vinci).

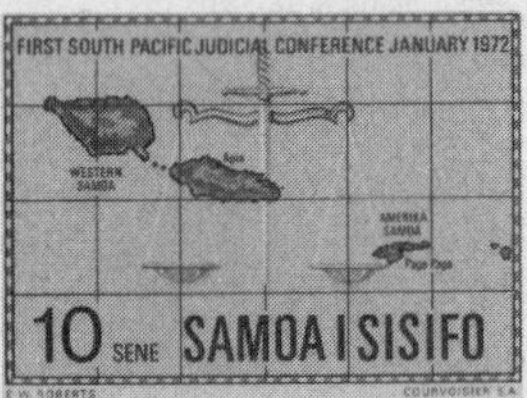

129. Map and Scales of Justice.

1972. First South Pacific Judicial Conference.

377. 129. 10 s. multicoloured .. 15 15

130. Asau Wharf, Savaii.

1972. 10th Anniv. of Independence. Mult.

378. 1 s. Type 130 .. .. 10 10
379. 8 s. Parliament Building 10 10
380. 10 s. Mothers' Centre .. 10 10
381. 22 s. "Vailima" Residence and Rulers 20 25

131. Flags of Member Countries.

1972. 25th Anniv. of South Pacific Commission. Multicoloured.

382. 3 s. Type 131 .. .. 10 15
383. 7 s. Flag and Afoafouvale Misimoa (Sec. Gen.) .. 10 15
384. 8 s. H.Q. building, Noumea (horiz.) 15 15
385. 10 s. Flags and area map (horiz.) 15 15

132. Expedition Ships.

1972. 250th Anniv. of Sighting of Western Samoa by Jacob Roggeveen. Multicoloured.

386. 2 c. Type 132 .. .. 15 10
387. 8 s. Ships in storm (horiz.) 45 10
388. 10 s. Ships passing island (horiz.) 50 10
389. 30 s. Route of Voyage (horiz.) (85 × 25 mm.) .. 1·75 1·50

133. Bull Conch.

1972. Multicoloured.

390 1 s. Type 133 .. .. 20 15
391 2 s. "Oryctes rhinoceros" (beetle) 20 15
392 3 s. Skipjack (fish) .. 30 30
393 4 s. Painted crab .. 30 10
394 5 s. Butterfly fish .. 35 10
395 7 s. "Danaus neomelissia" (butterfly) .. .. 1·40 40
396 10 s. Triton shell .. 1·50 50
397 20 s. "Cyphogastra abodominali" (beetle) 1·25 30
398 50 s. Spiny lobster .. 2·00 2·25
399 $1 "Gnathothlibus erotus" (moth) (29 × 45 mm) .. .. .. 7·00 3·75
399a $2 Green turtle (29 × 45 mm) .. .. .. 8·00 4·00
399b $4 Black marlin (29 × 45 mm) .. .. .. 5·00 7·00
399c $5 Green tree lizard (29 × 45 mm) .. .. 5·50 7·50

134. "The Ascension".

1972. Christmas. Multicoloured.

400. 1 s. Type 134 .. .. 10 10
401. 4 s. "The Blessed Virgin, and Infant Christ" .. 10 10
402. 10 s. "St. Andrew blessing Samoan canoe" 10 10
403. 30 s. "The Good Shepherd" 40 30

135. Erecting a Tent.

1973. Boy Scout Movement. Multicoloured.

405. 2 s. Saluting the flag .. 10 10
406. 3 s. First-aid 10 10
407. 8 s. Type 135 .. .. 25 10
408. 20 s. Samoan action-song 90 85

136. Hawker Siddeley "748".

1973. Air. Multicoloured.

409. 8 s. Type 136 .. .. 45 15
410. 10 s. Hawker Siddeley "748" in flight .. 55 15
411. 12 s. Hawker Siddeley "748" on runway .. 65 35
412. 22 s. "B.A.C. 1-11" aircraft .. .. .. 1·00 60

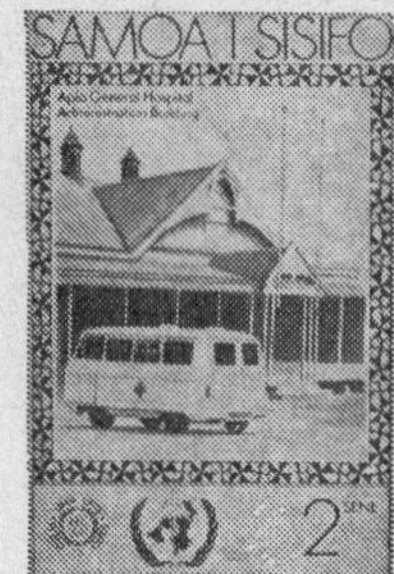

137. Apia General Hospital.

1973. 25th Anniv. of W.H.O. Multicoloured.

413. 2 s. Type 137 .. .. 10 10
414. 8 s. Baby clinic 20 10
415. 20 s. Filariasis research .. 45 20
416. 22 s. Family welfare .. 45 30

138. Mother and Child, and Map.

1973. Christmas. Multicoloured.

417. 3 s. Type 138 .. .. 10 10
418. 4 s. Mother and Child, and village 10 10
419. 10 s. Mother and child, and beach 10 10
420. 30 s. Samoan stable .. 45 50

139. Boxing.

1973. Commonwealth Games, Christchurch. Multicoloured.

422. 8 s. Type 139 .. .. 10 10
423. 10 s. Weight-lifting .. 10 10
424. 20 s. Bowls 20 10
425. 30 s. Athletics stadium .. 35 45

1974. Myths and Legends of Old Samoa (2nd series). As T 127. Multicoloured.

426. 2 s. Tigilau and sacred dove 10 10
427. 8 s. Pili, his sons and fishing net 10 10
428. 20 s. Sina and the origin of the coconut 30 10
429. 30 s. The warrior, Nafanua 45 45

140. Mail-van at Faleolo Airport.

1974. Centenary of U.P.U. Multicoloured.

430 8 s. Type 140 .. .. 15 10
431 20 s. "Mariposa" (cargo liner) at Apia Wharf .. 35 15
432 22 s. Early Post Office, Apia and letter .. 40 25
433 50 s. William Willis and "Age Unlimited" (raft) (87 × 29 mm) .. .. 80 1·00

141. "Holy Family" (Sebastiano).

1974. Christmas. Multicoloured.

435. 3 s. Type 141 .. .. 10 10
436. 4 s. "Virgin and Child with Saints" (Lotto) 10 10
437. 10 s. "Madonna and Child with St. John" (Titian) 15 10
438. 30 s. "Adoration of the Shepherds" (Rubens) .. 45 45

142. Winged Passion Flower.

1975. Tropical Flowers. Multicoloured.

440. 8 s. Type 142 .. .. 20 10
441. 20 s. Gardenia (vert.) .. 50 45
442. 22 s. "Barringtonia samoensis" (vert.) .. 55 50
443. 30 s. Malay apple 85 85

143. "Joyita" (inter-island coaster) loading at Apia.

1975. "Interpex 1975" Stamp Exhibition, New York, and "Joyita" Mystery. Mult.

444. 1 s. Type 143 .. .. 10 10
445. 8 s. "Joyita" sails for Tokelau Islands .. 15 10
446. 20 s. Taking to rafts .. 35 25
447. 25 s. "Joyita" abandoned 40 30
448. 50 s. Discovery of "Joyita" north of Fiji .. .. 1·00 1·25

144. "Pate" Drum.

1975. Musical Instruments. Multicoloured.

450. 8 s. Type 144 .. .. 10 10
451. 20 s. "Lali" drum .. 20 10
452. 22 s. "Logo" drum .. 20 10
453. 30 s. "Pu" shell horn .. 35 30

145. "Mother and Child" (Meleane Fe'ao).

1975. Christmas. Multicoloured.

454. 3 s. Type 145 .. .. 10 10
455. 4 s. "The Saviour" (Polataia Tuigamala) .. 10 10
456. 10 s. "A Star is Born" (Iosua Tovafa) 10 10
457. 30 s. "Madonna and Child" (Ernesto Coter) .. 30 45

146. "The Boston Massacre, 1770" (Paul Revere).

1976. Bicent. of American Revolution. Mult.

No.	Description	Unused	Used
459.	7 s. Type **146**	20	15
460.	8 s. "The Declaration of Independence" (John Trumbull)	20	15
461.	20 s. "The Ship that Sank in Victory, 1779" (J. L. G. Ferris)	60	35
462.	22 s. "Pitt addressing the Commons, 1782" (R. A. Hickel)	60	35
463.	50 s. "Battle of Princeton" (William Mercer)	1·50	1·75

147. Mullet Fishing.

1976. Fishing. Multicoloured.

No.	Description	Unused	Used
465.	10 s. Type **147**	10	10
466.	12 s. Fish traps	15	10
467.	22 s. Samoan fisherman	30	10
468.	50 s. Net fishing	85	70

149. Boxing.

1976. Olympic Games, Montreal. Mult.

No.	Description	Unused	Used
470.	10 s. Type **149**	10	10
471.	12 s. Wrestling	10	10
472.	22 s. Javelin	15	10
473.	50 s. Weightlifting	45	50

150. Mary and Joseph going to Bethlehem.

1976. Christmas. Multicoloured.

No.	Description	Unused	Used
474.	3 s. Type **150**	10	10
475.	5 s. The Shepherds	10	10
476.	22 s. The Holy Family	15	10
477.	50 s. The Magi	55	65

151. Queen Elizabeth and View of Apia.

1977. Silver Jubilee and Royal Visit. Mult.

No.	Description	Unused	Used
479.	12 s. Type **151**	15	10
480.	26 s. Presentation of Spurs of Chivalry	25	20
481.	32 s. Queen and Royal Yacht "Britannia"	35	25
482.	50 s. Queen leaving Abbey	40	80

152. Map of Flight Route.

1977. 50th Anniv. of Lindbergh's Transatlantic Flight. Multicoloured.

No.	Description	Unused	Used
483.	22 s. Type **152**	25	10
484.	24 s. In flight	35	15
485.	26 s. Landing	35	15
486.	50 s. Col. Lindbergh	80	75

Designs show the "Spirit of St. Louis".

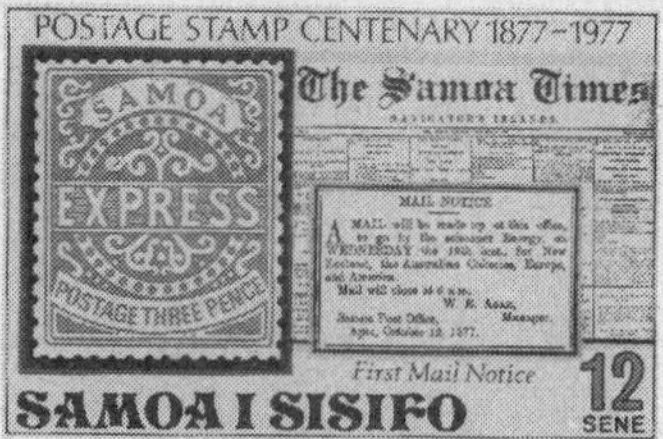

153. 3d. Express Stamp and First Mail Notice.

1977. Stamp Centenary.

No.	Description	Unused	Used
488. **153.**	12 s. yell., red and brn.	20	10
489. –	13 s. multicoloured	20	15
490. –	26 s. multicoloured	45	30
491. –	50 s. multicoloured	80	1·00

DESIGNS: 13 s. Early cover and 6d. Express. 26 s. Apia P.O. and 1d. Express. 50 s. Schooner "Energy" (1877) and 6d. Express.

154. Apia Automatic Telephone Exchange.

1977. Telecommunications Project. Mult.

No.	Description	Unused	Used
492	12 s. Type **154**	15	10
493	13 s. Mulinuu radio terminal	15	10
494	26 s. Old and new telephones	30	20
495	50 s. "Global communication"	50	70

155. "Samoan Nativity" (P. Feata).

1977. Christmas. Multicoloured.

No.	Description	Unused	Used
496	4 s. Type **155**	10	10
497	6 s. "The Offering" (E. Saofaiga)	10	10
498	26 s. "Madonna and Child" (F. Tupou)	20	10
499	50 s. "Emmanuel" (M. Sapa'u)	35	40

156. Polynesian Airlines Boeing "737".

1978. Aviation Progress. Multicoloured.

No.	Description	Unused	Used
501.	12 s. Type **156**	20	10
502.	24 s. Wright brothers' "Flyer"	40	20
503.	26 s. Kingsford Smith's "Southern Cross"	40	20
504.	50 s. "Concorde"	1·10	85

157. Hatchery, Aleipata.

1978. Hawksbill Turtle Conservation Project. Multicoloured.

No.	Description	Unused	Used
506.	24 s. Type **157**	35	30
507.	$1 Hawksbill turtle	1·60	1·60

158. Pacific Pigeon.

1978. 25th Anniv. of Coronation.

No.	Description	Unused	Used
508. –	26 s. blk., brn. and mve.	25	30
509. –	26 s. multicoloured	25	30
510. **158.**	26 s. blk., brn. and mve.	25	30

DESIGNS: No. 508, King's Lion. No. 509, Queen Elizabeth II.

160. Captain Cook.

1978. 250th Birth Anniv. of Captain Cook. Multicoloured.

No.	Description	Unused	Used
512.	12 s. Type **160**	30	15
513.	24 s. Cook's Cottage, Gt. Ayton, Yorkshire	60	35
514.	26 s. Old drawbridge over the river Esk, Whitby, 1766–1833	70	35
515.	50 s. H.M.S. "Resolution"	1·25	1·50

161. Thick-edged Cowry.

1978. Shells. Multicoloured.

No.	Description	Unused	Used
516.	1 s. Type **161**	15	10
517.	2 s. Isabella cowry	15	10
518.	3 s. Money cowry	25	10
519.	4 s. Eroded cowry	30	10
520.	6 s. Honey cowry	30	10
521.	7 s. Banded cowry	35	10
522.	10 s. Globe cowry	40	10
523.	11 s. Mole cowry	40	10
524.	12 s. Children's cowry	40	10
525.	13 s. Flag cone	40	10
526.	14 s. Soldier cone	40	10
527.	24 s. Cloth-of-gold cone	40	10
528.	26 s. Lettered cone	45	10
529.	50 s. Tiled cone	50	15
530.	$1 Black Marble cone	95	60
530a.	$2 Marlin-spike auger	1·50	90
530b.	$3 Scorpion Spider Conch	2·25	1·50
530c.	$5 Common harp	3·75	3·00

162. "Madonna on the Crescent".

1978. Christmas. Woodcuts by Durer. Multicoloured.

No.	Description	Unused	Used
531. **162.**	4 s. black and brown	10	10
532. –	6 s. black and green	10	10
533. –	26 s. black and blue	15	10
534. –	50 s. black and violet	35	50

DESIGNS: 6 s. "Nativity". 26 s. "Adoration of the Kings". 50 s. "Annunciation".

163. Boy with Coconuts.

1979. International Year of the Child. Multicoloured.

No.	Description	Unused	Used
536.	12 s. Type **163**	15	10
537.	24 s. White Sunday	30	15
538.	26 s. Children at pump	35	15
539.	50 s. Girl with ukulele	70	80

164. "Charles W. Morgan."

1979. Sailing Ships (1st series). Whalers. Multicoloured.

No.	Description	Unused	Used
540.	12 s. Type **164**	40	10
541.	14 s. "Lagoda"	45	10
542.	24 s. "James T. Arnold"	60	20
543.	50 s. "Splendid"	1·10	85

See also Nos. 561/4 and 584/7.

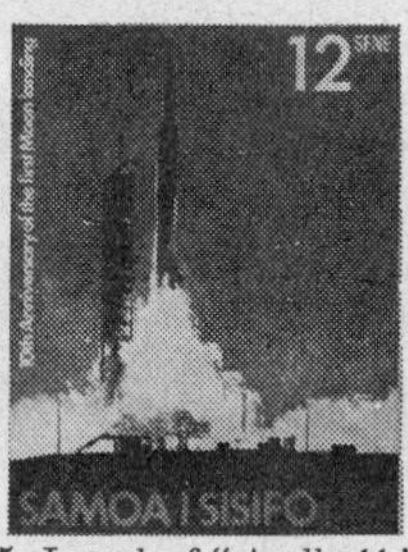

165. Launch of "Apollo 11".

1979. 10th Anniv. of Moon Landing.

No.	Description	Unused	Used
544. **165.**	12 s. brown and red	20	10
545. –	14 s. multicoloured	25	10
546. –	24 s. multicoloured	30	15
547. –	26 s. multicoloured	30	15
548. –	50 s. multicoloured	55	55
549. –	$1 multicoloured	1·25	1·50

DESIGNS—HORIZ. 14 s. Lunar module and astronaut on Moon. 26 s. Astronaut on Moon. $1 Command module after splash-down. VERT. 24 s. View of Earth from Moon. 50 s. Lunar and Command modules in Space.

166. Sir Rowland Hill (statue) and Penny Black.

1979. Death Centenary of Sir Rowland Hill. Multicoloured.

No.	Description	Unused	Used
551.	12 s. Type **166**	15	10
552.	24 s. Two-penny Blue with "Maltese Cross" postmark	20	15
553.	26 s. Sir Rowland Hill and Penny Black	20	15
554.	$1 Two-penny Blue and Sir Rowland Hill	60	75

167. Anglican Church, Apia.

1979. Christmas. Churches.

No.	Description	Unused	Used
556. **167.**	4 s. black and blue	10	10
557. –	6 s. black and yellow	10	10
558. –	26 s. black and brown	15	10
559. –	50 s. black and lilac	30	30

DESIGNS: 6 s. Congregational Christian, Leulumoega. 26 s. Methodist, Piula. 50 s. Protestant, Apia.

1980. Sailing Ships (2nd series). Whalers. As T **164**.

No.	Description	Unused	Used
561.	12 s. "William Hamilton"	40	10
562.	14 s. "California"	45	15
563.	24 s. "Liverpool II"	60	25
564.	50 s. "Two Brothers"	1·10	70

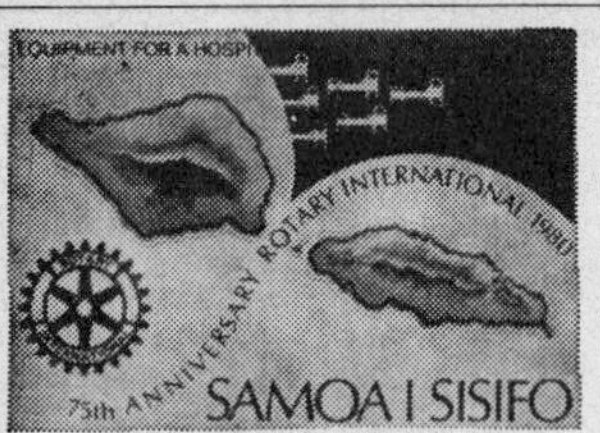

168. " Equipment for a Hospital ".

1980. Anniversaries. Multicoloured.

565. 12 s. Type **168** 40 10
566. 13 s. John Williams, dove with olive twig and commemorative inscription 40 15
567. 14 s. Dr. Wilhelm Solf (instigator), flag and commemorative inscription 45 15
568. 24 s. Cairn Monument .. 60 25
569. 26 s. Williams Memorial, Savai'i 65 25
570. 50 s. Paul P. Harris (founder) 1·10 60

COMMEMORATIONS: 12 s., 50 s. Rotary International. 75th Anniv. 13 s., 26 s. John Williams' (missionary) arrival in Samoa. 150th Anniv. 14 s., 24 s. Raising of German flag. 80th Anniv.

170. Queen Elizabeth the Queen Mother in 1970.

1980. 80th Birthday of The Queen Mother.

572. **170.** 50 s. multicoloured .. 50 35

172. Afiamalu Satellite Earth Station.

1980. Afiamalu Satellite Earth Station. Multicoloured.

574. 12 s. Type **172** 15 10
575. 14 s. Satellite station (different) 20 10
576. 24 s. Satellite station and map of Savai'i and Upolu 30 15
577. 50 s. Satellite and globe .. 60 60

174. " The Saviour " (J. Poynton).

1980. Christmas. Paintings. Multicoloured.

579. 8 s. Type **174** 10 10
580. 14 s. " Madonna and Child " (Lealofi F. Siaopo) 10 10
581. 27 s. " Nativity " (Pasila Feata) 15 10
582. 50 s. " Yuletide " (R. P. Aiono) 25 40

1981. Sailing Ships (3rd series). As T **164**. Multicoloured.

584 12 s. "Ocean" (whaling ship) 20 10
585 18 s. "Horatio" (whaling ship) 30 15
586 27 s. H.M.S. "Calliope" (screw corvette) .. 45 25
587 32 s. H.M.S. "Calypso" (screw corvette) .. 50 50

175. President Franklin D. Roosevelt and Hyde Park (family home).

1981. International Year for Disabled Persons. President Franklin D. Roosevelt Commemoration. Multicoloured.

588. 12 s. Type **175** 15 10
589. 18 s. Roosevelt's Inauguration, 4 March 1933 .. 25 15
590. 27 s. Franklin and Eleanor Roosevelt 35 20
591. 32 s. Roosevelt's Lend-lease Bill (Atlantic convoy, 1941) 40 30
592. 38 s. Roosevelt the philatelist 45 35
593. $1 Campobello House (summer home) .. 1·00 1·00

176. Hotel Tusitala.

1981. Tourism. Multicoloured.

594. 12 s. Type **176** 15 10
595. 18 s. Apia Harbour .. 25 15
596. 27 s. Aggie Grey's Hotel 25 20
597. 32 s. Preparation for Ceremonial Kava 30 30
598. 54 s. Piula water pool .. 55 55

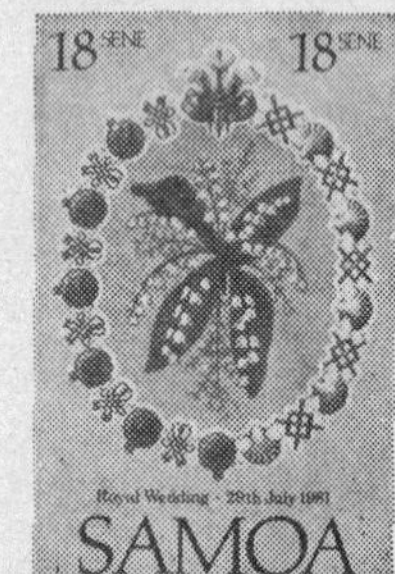

177. Wedding Bouquet from Samoa.

1981. Royal Wedding. Multicoloured.

599. 18 s. Type **177** 20 10
600. 32 s. Prince Charles as Colonel-in-Chief, Gordon Highlanders 25 15
601. $1 Prince Charles and Lady Diana Spencer 45 70

178. Tattooing Instruments.

1981. Tattooing. Multicoloured.

602. 12 s. Type **178** 20 20
603. 18 s. First stage of tattooing 25 25
604. 27 s. Progressive stage .. 30 30
605. $1 Completed tattoo .. 70 70

180. " Thespesia populnea ".

1981. Christmas. Flowers. Multicoloured.

607. 11 s. Type **180** 15 10
608. 15 s. Copper Leaf .. 20 15
609. 23 s. " Allamanda cathartica " 30 25
610. $1 Mango .. .. .. 1·00 1·00

181. George Washington's Pistol.

1982. 250th Birth Anniversary of George Washington.

612. **181.** 23 s. blk., brn. and stone 30 30
613. – 25 s. blk., brn. and stone 30 30
614. – 34 s. blk., brn. and stone 40 40

DESIGNS: 25 s. Mount Vernon (Washington's home). 34 s. George Washington.

182. "Forum Samoa" (container ship).

1982. 20th Anniv. of Independence. Mult.

616. 18 s. Type **182** 30 20
617. 23 s. " Air services " .. 40 30
618. 25 s. N.P.F. (National Provident Fund) Building, Apia 40 30
619. $1 " Telecommunications " 1·10 1·00

183. Scouts Map-reading and " 75 ".

1982. 75th Anniv. of Boy Scout Movement. Multicoloured.

620. 5 s. Type **183** 10 10
621. 38 s. Scout salute and " 75 " 40 40
622. 44 s. Scout crossing river by rope, and " 75 " .. 50 50
623. $1 " Tower " of Scouts and " 75 " .. .. .. 1·00 1·00

184. Boxing.

1982. Commonwealth Games. Brisbane. Multicoloured.

625. 23 s. Type **184** 25 20
626. 25 s. Hurdling 25 20
627. 34 s. Weightlifting .. 35 40
628. $1 Bowling .. .. 95 1·75

185. " Mary and Joseph " (Emma Dunlop).

1982. Christmas. Children's Pictures. Mult.

629. 11 s. Type **185** 15 10
630. 15 s. " Mary, Joseph and Baby Jesus " (Marie Tofaeono) 15 15
631. 38 s. " Madonna and Child " (Ralph Laban and Fetalaiga Fareni) .. 40 30
632. $1 " Mother and Child " (Panapa Pouesi) .. 90 1·40

186. Satellite View of Australasia.

1983. Commonwealth Day. Multicoloured.

634. 14 s. Type **186** 10 10
635. 29 s. Flag of Samoa .. 15 20
636. 43 s. Harvesting copra .. 25 25
637. $1 Head of State Malietoa Tanumafili II 50 80

188. Pole Vaulting.

189. Lime.

1983. South Pacific Games. Multicoloured.

639. 8 s. Type **188** 35 10
640. 15 s. Netball 45 20
641. 25 s. Tennis 70 50
642. 32 s. Weightlifting .. 70 50
643. 35 s. Boxing 75 75
644. 46 s. Football 90 90
645. 48 s. Golf .. .. .. 1·00 1·10
646. 56 s. Rugby .. .. 1·10 1·25

1983. Fruit. Multicoloured.

647. 1 s. Type **189** 10 20
648. 2 s. Star fruit 10 30
649. 3 s. Mangosteen 10 30
650. 4 s. Lychee 10 30
651. 7 s. Passion fruit 10 30
652. 8 s. Mango 10 30
653. 11 s. Pawpaw 15 30
654. 13 s. Pineapple 20 30
655. 14 s. Breadfruit 20 30
656. 15 s. Banana 30 40
657. 21 s. Cashew Nut .. .. 1·25 55
658. 25 s. Guava .. .. 1·25 40
659. 32 s. Water Melon .. .. 1·25 50
660. 48 s. Sasalapa .. .. 1·50 80
661. 56 s. Avocado .. .. 1·50 80
662. $1 Coconut .. .. 1·75 1·50
663. $2 Vi Apple .. .. 1·50 2·25
664. $4 Grapefruit .. .. 2·00 3·50
665. $5 Orange .. .. 2·50 3·75

191. Togitogiga Falls, Upolu.

1984. Scenic Views. Multicoloured.

669. 25 s. Type **191** 30 15
670. 32 s. Lano Beach, Savai'i .. 50 60
671. 48 s. Mulinu'u Point, Upolu 75 95
672. 56 s. Nu'utele Island .. 80 1·25

192. Apia Harbour.

1984. 250th Anniv of "Lloyd's List" (newspaper). Multicoloured.

673 32 s. Type **192** 25 20
674 48 s. Apia hurricane, 1889 50 45
675 60 s. "Forum Samoa" (container ship) .. 45 50
676 $1 "Matua" (inter-island freighter) 75 80

1984. Universal Postal Union Congress, Hamburg. No. 662 optd. **19th U.P.U. CONGRESS HAMBURG 1984.**

677. $1 Coconut .. .. .. 1·10 80

194. Olympic Stadium.

1984. Olympic Games, Los Angeles. Multicoloured.

678. 25 s. Type **194** 20 20
679. 32 s. Weightlifting .. 25 25
680. 48 s. Boxing 40 45
681. $1 Running 75 80

196. "Faith".

1984. Christmas. "The Three Virtues" (Raphael). Multicoloured.

684. 25 s. Type **196** 25 15
685. 35 s. "Hope" 30 25
686. $1 "Charity" .. .. 1·00 1·10

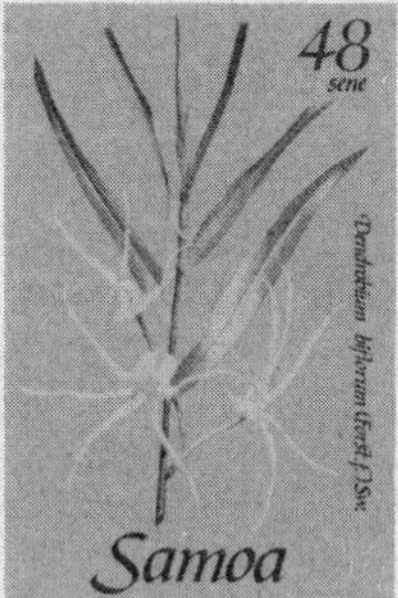

197. "Dendrobium biflorum".

1985. Orchids (1st series). Multicoloured.

688. 48 s. Type **197** 55 35
689. 56 s. "Dendrobium vaupelianum Kraenzl" 65 45
690. 67 s. "Glomera montana" .. 80 60
691. $1 "Spathoglottis plicata" 1·10 1·10

See also Nos. 818/21.

198. Ford "Model A", 1903.

1985. Veteran and Vintage Cars. Mult.

692. 48 s. Type **198** 60 35
693. 56 s. Chevrolet "Tourer", 1912 .. .. .. 70 40
694. 67 s. Morris "Oxford", 1913 80 45
695. $1 Austin "Seven", 1923 .. 1·00 70

199. "Dictyophora indusiata".

1985. Fungi. Multicoloured.

696. 48 s. Type **199** 55 45
697. 56 s. "Ganoderma tornatum" 70 55
698. 67 s. "Mycena chlorophos" 90 85
699. $1 "Mycobonia flava" .. 1·40 1·50

200. The Queen Mother at Liverpool Street Station.

1985. Life and Times of Queen Elizabeth the Queen Mother. Multicoloured.

700. 32 s. At Glamis Castle, aged 9 .. .. .. 20 25
701. 48 s. At Prince Henry's Christening with other members of the Royal Family 30 35
702. 56 s. Type **200** 35 40
703. $1 With Prince Henry at his christening (from photo by Lord Snowdon) .. 65 70

202. I.Y.Y. Emblem and Map (Alaska–Arabian Gulf).

1985. International Youth Year. Designs showing background map and emblem (Nos. 706 and 710) or raised arms (others). Multicoloured.

706. 60 s. Type **202** 40 45
707. 60 s. Raised arms (Pakistan–Mexico) .. 40 45
708. 60 s. Raised arms (Central America–China) .. 40 45
709. 60 s. Raised arms (Japan–Greenland) 40 45
710. 60 s. Type **202** (Iceland–Siberia) 40 45

Nos. 706/10 were printed together in horizontal strips of 5, the background forming a composite design of three continuous world maps.

203. "System".

1985. Christmas. Designs showing illustrations by Millicent Sowerby for R. L. Stevenson's "A Child's Garden of Verses". Multicoloured.

711. 32 s. Type **203** 20 25
712. 48 s. "Time to Rise" .. 30 35
713. 56 s. "Auntie's Skirts" .. 35 40
714. $1 "Good Children" .. 65 70

204. "Hypolimnas bolina".

1986. Butterflies. Multicoloured.

716 25 s. Type **204** 30 15
717 32 s. "Belenois java" .. 35 20
718 48 s. "Deudorix epijarbas" 55 35
719 56 s. "Badamia exclamationis" 60 40
720 60 s. "Danaus hamata" .. 60 40
721 $1 "Catochrysops taitensis" 90 65

205. Halley's Comet over Apia.

1986. Appearance of Halley's Comet. Mult.

722. 32 s. Type **205** 15 20
723. 48 s. Edmond Halley .. 30 35
724. 60 s. Comet passing Earth 35 40
725. $2 Preparing "Giotto" spacecraft .. .. 1·10 1·25

1986. 60th Birthday of Queen Elizabeth II. As T **110** of Ascension. Multicoloured.

726. 32 s. Engagement photograph, 1947 .. .. 15 20
727. 48 s. Queen with Liberty Bell, U.S.A., 1976 .. 30 35
728. 56 s. At Apia, 1977 .. 35 40
729. 67 s. At Badminton Horse Trials, 1978 .. .. 40 45
730. $2 At Crown Agents Head Office, London, 1983 .. 1·10 1·25

206. U.S.S. "Vincennes" (frigate).

1986. "Ameripex '86" International Stamp Exhibition, Chicago. Multicoloured.

731 48 s. Type **206** 30 35
732 56 s. Sikorsky "S-42" flying boat 35 40
733 60 s. U.S.S. "Swan (patrol boat) 35 40
734 $2 "Apollo 10" descending 1·10 1·25

208. Spotted Grouper.

1986. Fishes. Multicoloured.

736. 32 s. Type **208** 30 20
737. 48 s. Sabel squirrelfish .. 50 35
738. 60 s. Lunartail grouper .. 55 40
739. 67 s. Longtail snapper .. 60 45
740. $1 Berndt's soldierfish .. 85 65

209. Samoan Prime Ministers, American Presidents and Parliament House.

1986. Christmas, 25th Anniv. of United States Peace Corps. Multicoloured.

741. 45 s. Type **209** 25 30
742. 60 s. French and American Presidents, Samoan Prime Minister and Statue of Liberty .. 35 40

210. "Hibiscus rosa-sinensis" and Map of Samoa.

1987. 25th Anniv of Independence. Mult.

744 15 s. Type **210** 30 10
745 45 s. Parliament Building, Apia 50 30
746 60 s. Longboat race at Independence celebration 65 40
747 70 s. Peace dove and laurel wreath 75 50
748 $2 Head of State Malietoa Tanumafili II and national flag (horiz) .. 1·60 1·75

211. Gulper.

1987. Deep Ocean Fishes. Multicoloured.

749. 45 s. Type **211** 25 30
750. 60 s. Hatchet fish 30 35
751. 70 s. Angler fish 40 45
752. $2 Gulper .. .. .. 1·10 1·25

213. Lefaga Beach, Upolu.

1987. Coastal Scenery. Multicoloured.

754. 45 s. Type **213** 25 30
755. 60 s. Vaisala Beach, Savaii 30 35
756. 70 s. Solosolo Beach, Upolu 40 45
757. $2 Neiafu Beach, Savaii .. 1·10 1·25

214. Abel Tasman.

1987. Bicentenary of Australian Settlement (1988) (1st issue). Explorers of the Pacific. Multicoloured.

758. 40 s. Type **214** 20 25
759. 45 s. Capt. James Cook .. 25 30
760. 80 s. Comte Louis-Antoine de Bougainville 40 45
761. $2 Comte Jean de la Perouse .. .. .. 1·10 1·25

See also Nos. 768/72.

216. Christmas Tree.

1987. Christmas. Multicoloured.

764. 40 s. Type **216** 20 25
765. 45 s. Family going to church 25 30
766. 50 s. Bamboo fire-gun .. 25 30
767. 80 s. Inter-island transport 40 45

217. Samoa Coat of Arms and Australia Post Logo.

1988. Bicentenary of Australian Settlement (2nd issue). Postal Services. Multicoloured.

768.	45 s. Type **217**	25	30
769.	45 s. Samoan mail van and aircraft	25	30
770.	45 s. Loading mail plane ..	25	30
771.	45 s. Australian mail van and aircraft	25	30
772.	45 s. "Congratulations Australia" message on airmail letter	25	30

Nos. 768/72 were printed together, se-tenant, Nos. 769/71 forming a composite design.

218. Airport Terminal and Airliner taking off.

1988. Opening of Faleolo Airport. Mult.

773.	40 s. Type **218**	20	25
774.	45 s. Boeing "727" ..	25	30
775.	60 s. DHC "Twin Otter" ..	30	35
776.	70 s. Boeing "737" ..	40	45
777.	80 s. Boeing "727" and control tower	40	45
778.	$1 "DC9" over "fale" (house)	50	55

219. "Expo '88" Pacific Islands Village.

1988. "Expo '88" World Fair, Brisbane. Multicoloured.

779.	45 s. Type **219**	25	30
780.	70 s. Expo Complex and monorail	40	45
781.	$2 Map of Australia showing Brisbane ..	1·10	1·25

221 Athletics

1988. Olympic Games, Seoul. Multicoloured.

783	15 s. Type **221**	10	10
784	60 s. Weightlifting ..	30	35
785	80 s. Boxing	40	45
786	$2 Olympic stadium ..	1·10	1·25

222 Spotted Triller

1988. Birds. Multicoloured.

788	10 s. Type **222**	10	10
789	15 s. Samoan wood rail ..	10	10
790	20 s. Flat-billed kingfisher	10	10
791	25 s. Samoan fantail ..	10	10
792	35 s. Scarlet robin ..	20	25
793	40 s. Black-breasted honeyeater ("Mao") ..	20	25
794	50 s. Cardinal honeyeater	25	30
795	65 s. Yellow-fronted whistler ..	35	40
796	75 s. Many-coloured fruit dove	40	45
798	75 s. Silver gull (45 × 28mm)	40	45
797	85 s. White-throated pigeon	45	50
799	85 s. Great frigate bird (45 × 28 mm) ..	45	50
800	90 s. Eastern reef heron (45 × 28 mm) ..	45	50
801	$3 Short-tailed albatross (45 × 28 mm)	1·50	1·60
802	$10 White tern (45 × 28 mm)	5·25	5·50
803	$20 Shy albatross (45 × 28 mm)	10·50	11·00

223 Forest

1988. National Conservation Campaign. Mult.

807	15 s. Type **223**	20	10
808	40 s. Samoan handicrafts	35	25
809	45 s. Forest wildlife ..	40	30
810	50 s. Careful use of water (horiz)	45	30
811	60 s. Fishing (horiz) ..	50	35
812	$1 Coconut plantation (horiz)	75	60

224 Congregational Church of Jesus, Apia

1988. Christmas. Samoan Churches. Mult.

813	15 s. Type **224**	10	10
814	40 s. Roman Catholic Church, Leauva'a ..	25	25
815	45 s. Congregational Christian Church, Moataa	30	30
816	$2 Baha'i Temple, Vailima	1·25	1·25

225 "Phaius flavus"

1989. Orchids (2nd series). Multicoloured.

818	15 s. Type **225**	10	10
819	45 s. "Calanthe triplicata"	25	30
820	60 s. "Luisia teretifolia" ..	30	35
821	$3 "Dendrobium mohlianum"	1·50	1·60

226 "Eber" (German gunboat)

1989. Cent of Great Apia Hurricane. Mult.

822	50 s. Type **226**	25	30
823	65 s. "Olga" (German corvette)	35	40
824	85 s. H.M.S. "Calliope" (screw corvette) ..	45	50
825	$2 U.S.S. "Vandalia" (corvette)	1·10	1·25

227 Samoan Red Cross Youth Group on Parade

1989. 125th Anniv of International Red Cross. Multicoloured.

826	50 s. Type **227**	25	30
827	65 s. Blood donors ..	35	40
828	75 s. Practising first aid ..	40	50
829	$3 Red Cross volunteers carrying patient ..	1·50	1·60

1989. 20th Anniv of First Manned Landing on Moon. As T **126** of Ascension. Multicoloured.

830	18 s. Saturn rocket on mobile launcher ..	10	10
831	50 s. Crew of "Apollo 14" (30 × 30 mm)	25	30
832	65 s. "Apollo 14" emblem (30 × 30 mm)	35	40
833	$2 Tracks of lunar transporter	1·10	1·25

228 Virgin Mary and Joseph

1989. Christmas. Multicoloured.

835	18 s. Type **228**	10	10
836	50 s. Shepherds	25	30
837	55 s. Donkey and ox ..	30	35
838	$2 Three Wise Men ..	1·10	1·25

229 Pao Pao Outrigger

1990. Local Transport. Multicoloured.

840	18 s. Type **229**	10	10
841	55 s. Fautasi (large canoe)	30	35
842	60 s. Polynesian Airlines aircraft	30	35
843	$3 "Lady Samoa" (ferry)	1·50	1·60

230 Bismarck and Brandenburg Gate, Berlin

1990. Treaty of Berlin, 1889, and Opening of Berlin Wall, 1989. Multicoloured.

844	75 s. Type **230**	40	45
845	$3 "Adler" (German steam gunboat)	1·50	1·60

Nos. 844/5 were printed together, se-tenant, forming a composite design showing Berliners on the Wall near the Brandenburg Gate.

231 Penny Black and Alexandra Palace, London

(Illustration reduced, actual size 78 × 24 mm)

1990. "Stamp World London 90" International Stamp Exhibition.

846	**231** $3 multicoloured ..	1·50	1·60

232 Visitors' Bureau

1990. Tourism. Multicoloured.

847	18 s. Type **232**	10	10
848	50 s. Village resort ..	25	30
849	65 s. Aggie's Hotel ..	35	40
850	$3 Swimming pool, Tusitala Hotel	1·50	1·60

234 "Virgin and Child" (Bellini)

1990. Christmas. Paintings. Multicoloured.

852	18 s. Type **234**	10	10
853	50 s. "Virgin and Child with St. Peter and St. Paul" (Bouts)	25	30
854	55 s. "School of Love" (Correggio)	30	35
855	$3 "Virgin and Child" (Cima)	1·50	1·60

The 55 s. value should have shown "The Madonna of the Basket" by the same artist and is so inscribed.

235 William Draper III (administrator) and 40th Anniv Logo

1990. 40th Anniv of United Nations Development Programme.

856 **235** $3 multicoloured .. 1·50 1·60

236 Black-capped Lory

1991. Parrots. Multicoloured.

857 18 s. Type **236** 10 10
858 50 s. Eclectus parrot .. 25 30
859 65 s. Scarlet macaw .. 35 40
860 $3 Palm cockatoo .. 1·50 1·60

1991. 65th Birthday of Queen Elizabeth II and 70th Birthday Of Prince Philip. As T **139** of Ascension. Multicoloured.

861 75 s. Prince Philip in the countryside 40 45
862 $2 Queen wearing yellow lei .. .. .. 1·10 1·25

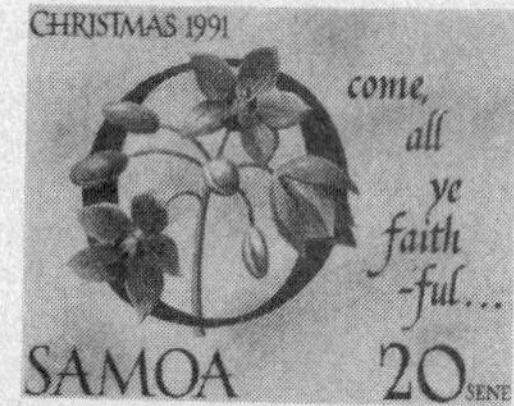

238 "O Come All Ye Faithful"

1991. Christmas. Carols (1st series). Mult.

864 20 s. Type **238** 10 10
865 60 s. "Joy to the World" 30 35
866 75 s. "Hark the Herald Angels sing" .. 40 45
867 $4 "We wish you a Merry Christmas" .. 2·00 2·10

See also Nos. 886/9 and 907/11.

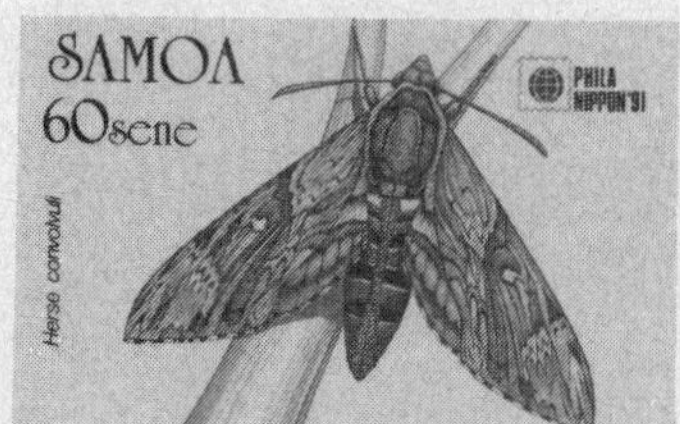

239 "Herse convolvuli"

1991. "Phila Nippon '91" Int Stamp Exn, Tokyo. Samoan Hawkmoths. Mult.

868 60 s. Type **239** 30 35
869 75 s. "Gnathothlibus erotus" 40 45
870 85 s. "Hippotion celerio" 45 50
871 $3 "Cephonodes armatus" 1·50 1·60

240 Head of State inspecting Guard of Honour

1992. 30th Anniv of Independence. Mult.

872 50 s. Type **240** 25 30
873 65 s. Siva ceremony .. 35 40
874 $1 Commemorative float 50 55
875 $3 Raising Samoan flag .. 1·50 1·60

1992. 40th Anniv of Queen Elizabeth II's Accession. As T **143** of Ascension. Mult.

876 20 s. Queen and Prince Philip with umbrellas .. 10 10
877 60 s. Queen and Prince Philip on Royal Yacht 30 35
878 75 s. Queen in multi-coloured hat 40 45
879 85 s. Three portraits of Queen Elizabeth .. 45 50
880 $3 Queen Elizabeth II .. 1·50 1·60

242 Weightlifting

1992. Olympic Games, Barcelona. Mult.

882 60 s. Type **242** 30 35
883 75 s. Boxing 40 45
884 85 s. Running 45 50
885 $3 Montjuic Olympic Stadium, Barcelona .. 1·50 1·60

1992. Christmas. Carols (2nd series). As T **238**. Multicoloured.

886 50 s. "God rest you Merry Gentle-men" 25 30
887 60 s. "While Shepherds watched their Flocks by Night" 30 35
888 75 s. "Away in a Manger, no Crib for a Bed" .. 40 45
889 $4 "O little Town of Bethlehem" .. .. 2·00 2·10

243 Batfish

1993. Fishes. Multicoloured.

890 60 s. Type **243** 30 35
891 75 s. Lined surgeonfish .. 40 45
892 $1 Red tail snapper .. 50 55
893 $3 Long nosed emperor .. 1·50 1·60

244 Samoan Players performing Traditional War Dance

1993. Rugby World Cup Seven-a-Side Championship, Edinburgh. Multicoloured.

894 60 s. Type **244** 30 35
895 75 s. Two players (vert) .. 40 45
896 85 s. Player running with ball and badge (vert) .. 45 50
897 $3 Edinburgh Castle .. 1·50 1·60

245 Flying Foxes hanging from Branch

1993. Endangered Species. Flying Foxes. Multicoloured.

898 20 s. Type **245** 10 10
899 50 s. Flying fox with young 25 30
900 60 s. Flying foxes hunting for food 30 35
901 75 s. Flying fox feeding from plant 40 45

247 Globe, Letter and Flowers

1993. World Post Day. Multicoloured.

903 60 s. Type **247** 30 35
904 75 s. Post Office counter .. 40 45
905 85 s. Hands exchanging letter 45 50
906 $4 Globe, national flags and letter .. .. 2·00 2·10

1993. Christmas Carols. Multicoloured.

907 20 s. "Silent Night" .. 10 10
908 60 s. "As with Gladness Men of Old" 30 35
909 75 s. "Mary had a Baby—yes, Lord!" .. 40 45
910 $1.50 "Once in Royal David's City" .. 75 80
911 $3 "Angels from the Realms of Glory" .. 1·50 1·60

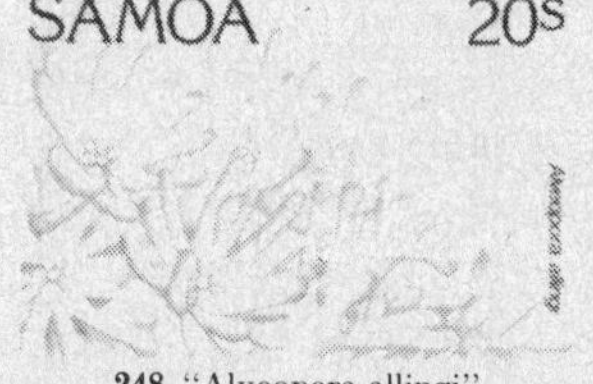

248 "Alveopora allingi"

1994. Corals. Multicoloured.

912 20 s. Type **248** 10 10
913 60 s. "Acropora polystoma" 30 35
914 90 s. "Acropora listeri" .. 45 50
915 $4 "Acropora grandis" .. 2·00 2·10

1994. "Hong Kong '94" International Stamp Exhibition. Nos. 912/15 optd **HONG KONG '94** and emblem.

916 20 s. Type **248** 10 10
917 60 s. "Acropora polystoma" 30 35
918 90 s. "Acropora listeri" .. 45 50
919 $4 "Acropora grandis" .. 2·00 2·10

249 Samoan Rugby Management Team

1994. Samoan National Rugby Team. Mult.

920 70 s. Type **249** 40 45
921 90 s. Test match against Wales 45 50
922 95 s. Test match against New Zealand .. 50 55
923 $4 Apia Park Stadium .. 2·00 1·90

SARAWAK

Formerly an independent state on the N. coast of Borneo under British protection. Under Japanese occupation from 1941 until 1945. A Crown Colony from 1946 until September 1963, when it became a state of the Federation of Malaysia.

100 cents = 1 dollar (Malayan or Malaysian).

1. Sir James Brooke. **2.** Sir Charles Brooke.

1869.

1. **1.** 3 c. brown on yellow .. 40·00 £200

1871.

3. **2.** 2 c. mauve on lilac .. .. 2·50 13·00
2. 3 c. brown on yellow .. 1·40 3·00
4. 4 c. brown on yellow .. 2·75 3·00
5. 6 c. green on green .. .. 2·75 3·50
6. 8 c. blue on blue .. .. 2·50 3·50
7. 12 c. red on red .. .. 6·50 6·50

4. Sir Charles Brooke. **11.**

1888.

8. **4.** 1 c. mauve and black .. 90 45
9. 2 c. mauve and red .. 85 65
10. 3 c. mauve and blue .. 1·25 1·25
11. 4 c. mauve and yellow .. 9·50 27·00
12. 5 c. mauve and green .. 8·00 1·50
13. 6 c. mauve and brown .. 7·00 32·00
14. 8 c. green and red .. 4·75 2·50
15. 10 c. green and violet .. 24·00 14·00
16. 12 c. green and blue .. 4·50 7·00
17. 16 c. green and orange .. 32·00 48·00
18. 25 c. green and brown .. 30·00 32·00
19. 32 c. green and black .. 24·00 35·00
20. 50 c. green .. .. 25·00 60·00
21. $1 green and black .. 40·00 55·00

1889. Surch. in words or figures.

27 **2** 1 c. on 3 c. brown on yell. 50 90
23 **4** 1 c. on 3 c. mauve & blue 2·75 2·75
24 2 c. on 8 c. green and red 2·25 5·00
25a 5 c. on 12 c. green & blue 17·00 27·00

1895. Various frames.

28c. **11.** 2 c. red .. .. .. 4·50 4·50
29. 4 c. black .. .. .. 4·50 2·50
30. 6 c. violet .. .. 3·75 7·50
31. 8 c. green .. .. .. 15·00 6·00

1899. Surch. in figures and words.

32. **2.** 2 c. on 3 c. brown on yell. 80 90
33. 2 c. on 12 c. red on red .. 2·50 3·00
34. 4 c. on 6 c. green on green 15·00 40·00
35. 4 c. on 8 c. blue on blue .. 3·00 5·50

1899. As T **4**, but inscr. "POSTAGE POSTAGE".

36. 1 c. blue and red .. 40 70
37. 2 c. green 75 50
38. 3 c. purple .. .. 3·00 30
39a. 4 c. red .. .. .. 1·75 15
40. 8 c. yellow and black .. 1·75 70
41. 10 c. blue .. .. .. 1·75 50
42. 12 c. mauve .. .. 2·25 2·00
43. 16 c. brown and green .. 1·75 1·50
44. 20 c. olive and mauve .. 4·00 2·25
45. 25 c. brown and blue .. 2·75 3·50
46. 50 c. olive and red .. 12·00 18·00
47. $1 red and green .. 28·00 55·00

17. Sir Charles Vyner Brooke. **19.**

1918.

50 **17** 1 c. blue and red .. 60 75
51 2 c. green .. .. .. 1·25 75
77 2 c. purple 50 50
52 3 c. purple .. .. 2·50 1·75
64 3 c. green 75 75
53a 4 c. red .. .. .. 2·50 1·40

No.	Type	Description	Unused	Used
65	17	4 c. purple	80	30
66		5 c. orange	1·00	90
81		6 c. red	1·00	30
54		8 c. yellow and black	5·50	26·00
82		8 c. red	1·75	6·00
55		10 c. blue	2·25	2·25
83		10 c. black	1·75	1·25
56		12 c. purple	7·00	11·00
84		12 c. blue	1·75	10·00
85		16 c. brown and green	1·75	2·75
86		20 c. olive and lilac	1·75	3·25
87		25 c. brown and blue	3·00	6·00
71		30 c. brown and blue	3·75	3·75
89		50 c. olive and red	4·00	6·00
90		$1 red and green	11·00	18·00

1923. Surch. in words.

No.	Type	Description	Unused	Used
72.	17.	1 c. on 10 c. blue	12·00	45·00
73.		2 c. on 12 c. purple	5·00	25·00

1932.

No.	Type	Description	Unused	Used
91.	19.	1 c. blue	70	40
92.		2 c. green	70	40
93.		3 c. violet	2·25	70
94.		4 c. orange	80	15
95.		5 c. red	2·25	70
96.		6 c. red	3·50	5·00
97.		8 c. yellow	3·00	5·50
98.		10 c. black	2·25	2·50
99.		12 c. blue	2·75	5·50
100.		15 c. brown	3·50	6·00
101.		20 c. orange and violet	3·00	6·50
102.		25 c. yell. and brown	5·50	9·00
103.		30 c. brown and red	4·75	13·00
104.		50 c. red and olive	5·00	7·00
105.		$1 green and red	8·00	20·00

21. Sir Charles Vyner Brooke.

1934.

No.	Type	Description	Unused	Used
106.	21.	1 c. purple	15	10
107.		2 c. green	15	10
107a.		2 c. black	80	1·40
108.		3 c. black	15	10
108a.		3 c. green	90	2·00
109.		4 c. purple	15	15
110.		5 c. violet	20	10
111.		6 c. red	15	50
111a.		6 c. brown	2·25	6·00
112.		8 c. brown	15	10
112a.		8 c. red	1·75	10
113.		10 c. red	75	40
114.		12 c. blue	45	25
114a.		12 c. orange	80	4·00
115.		15 c. orange	65	3·50
115a.		15 c. blue	2·25	6·00
116.		20 c. green and red	90	70
117.		25 c. violet and orange	90	1·00
118.		30 c. brown and violet	90	1·25
119.		50 c. violet and red	90	75
120.		$1 red and brown	60	50
121.		$2 purple and violet	5·00	6·00
122.		$3 red and green	17·00	15·00
123.		$4 blue and red	17·00	18·00
124.		$5 red and brown	17·00	24·00
125.		$10 black and yellow	17·00	30·00

1945. Optd. **BMA.**

No.	Type	Description	Unused	Used
126.	21.	1 c. purple	20	40
127.		2 c. black	30	40
128.		3 c. green	30	30
129.		4 c. purple	30	30
130.		5 c. violet	30	70
131.		6 c. brown	60	75
132.		8 c. red	9·00	9·00
133.		10 c. red	60	60
134.		12 c. orange	80	3·75
135.		15 c. blue	1·00	40
136.		20 c. green and red	1·50	1·40
137.		25 c. violet and orange	1·50	2·00
138.		30 c. brown and violet	1·50	2·75
139.		50 c. violet and red	1·25	35
140.		$1 red and brown	2·50	1·25
141.		$2 purple and violet	9·00	4·50
142.		$3 red and green	17·00	26·00
143.		$4 blue and red	25·00	26·00
144.		$5 red and brown	85·00	90·00
145.		$10 black and yellow	90·00	£110

23. Sir James Brooke, Sir Chas. Vyner Brooke and Sir Charles Brooke.

1946. Centenary Issue.

No.	Type	Description	Unused	Used
146.	23.	8 c. red	30	30
147.		15 c. blue	30	1·25
148.		50 c. black and red	40	1·00
149.		$1 black and brown	55	8·00

1947. Optd. with the Royal Cypher.

No.	Type	Description	Unused	Used
150.	21.	1 c. purple	15	30
151.		2 c. black	15	15
152.		3 c. green	15	15
153.		4 c. purple	15	15
154.		6 c. brown	20	70
155.		8 c. red	30	10
156.		10 c. red	20	20
157.		12 c. orange	20	90
158.		15 c. blue	20	40
159.		20 c. green and red	40	50
160.		25 c. violet and orange	40	30
161.		50 c. violet and red	40	40
162.		$1 red and brown	75	90
163.		$2 purple and violet	1·25	3·25
164.		$5 red and brown	2·50	3·25

1948. Silver Wedding. As T **10/11** of Aden.

No.	Type	Description	Unused	Used
165.		8 c. red	30	30
166.		$5 brown	23·00	27·00

1949. U.P.U. As T **20/23** of Antigua.

No.	Type	Description	Unused	Used
167		8 c. red	1·00	50
168		15 c. blue	1·60	2·25
169		25 c. green	1·60	1·50
170		50 c. violet	2·00	3·50

25. "Trogonoptera brookiana".

26. Western Tarsier.

27. Kayan Tomb.

1950.

No.	Type	Description	Unused	Used
171.	25.	1 c. black	30	30
172.	26.	2 c. orange	20	40
173.	27.	3 c. green	10	60
174.	–	4 c. brown	10	20
175.	–	6 c. blue	10	15
176.	–	8 c. red	10	30
177.	–	10 c. orange	50	2·75
186.	–	10 c. orange	30	40
178.	–	12 c. violet	1·75	1·50
179.	–	15 c. blue	85	15
180.	–	20 c. brown and orange	60	30
181.	–	25 c. green and red	70	30
182.	–	50 c. brown and violet	85	15
183.	–	$1 green and brown	6·00	1·50
184.	–	$2 blue and red	16·00	6·50
185.	–	$5 multicoloured	18·00	9·00

DESIGNS—VERT. 4 c. Kayan boy and girl. 6 c. Beadwork. 50 c. Iban woman. HORIZ. 8 c. Dayak dancer. 10 c. (No. 177) Malayan Pangolin. 10 c. (No. 186), Map of Sarawak. 12 c. Kenyah boys. 15 c. Fire making. 20 c. Kelemantan rice barn. 25 c. Pepper vines. $1, Kelabit smithy. $2 Map of Sarawak. $5 Arms of Sarawak.

1953. Coronation. As T **13** of Aden.

No.	Type	Description	Unused	Used
187		10 c. black and blue	85	85

47. Barong Panau (sailing prau).

51. Queen Elizabeth II.

52. Queen Elizabeth II (after Annigoni).

1955.

No.	Type	Description	Unused	Used
188.	–	1 c. green	10	30
189.	–	2 c. orange	30	55
190.	–	4 c. brown	45	30
191.	–	6 c. blue	3·00	75
192.	–	8 c. red	30	30
193.	–	10 c. green	20	10
194.	47.	12 c. plum	3·00	55
195.	–	15 c. blue	1·00	30
196.	–	20 c. olive and brown	1·00	10
197.	–	25 c. sepia and green	6·00	20
198.	51.	30 c. brown and lilac	2·00	20
199.		50 c. black and red	2·00	15
200.	52.	$1 myrtle and brown	2·25	40
201.		$2 violet and green	6·00	2·25
202.	–	$5 multicoloured	14·00	6·00

DESIGNS—As Type **47**—VERT. 1 c. Logging. 2 c. Young Orang-Utan. 4 c. Kayan dancing. HORIZ. 6 c. Malabar Pied Hornbill. 8 c. Shield with spears. 10 c. Kenyah ceremonial carving. 15 c. Turtles. 20 c. Melanan basket-making. 25 c. Astana, Kuching. $5, Arms of Sarawak.

1963. Freedom from Hunger. As T **28** of Aden.

No.	Type	Description	Unused	Used
203.		12 c. sepia	1·50	35

53. "Vanda hookeriana".

1965. As Nos. 155/21 of Kedah, but with Arms of Sarawak inset as in T **53**.

No.	Type	Description	Unused	Used
212.	53.	1 c. multicoloured	10	60
213.	–	2 c. multicoloured	15	60
214.	–	5 c. multicoloured	45	10
215.	–	6 c. multicoloured	60	60
216.	–	10 c. multicoloured	65	10
217.	–	15 c. multicoloured	1·50	10
218.	–	20 c. multicoloured	1·75	50

The higher values used in Sarawak were Nos. 20/7 of Malaysia (National Issues).

54. "Precis orithya".

1971. Butterflies. As Nos. 124/30 of Kedah, but with Sarawak Arms as in T **54**.

No.	Type	Description	Unused	Used
219.	–	1 c. multicoloured	15	65
220.	–	2 c. multicoloured	35	75
221.	–	5 c. multicoloured	65	10
222.	–	6 c. multicoloured	80	70
223.	–	10 c. multicoloured	80	10
224.	54.	15 c. multicoloured	1·25	10
225.	–	20 c. multicoloured	1·50	80

The higher values in use with this issue were Nos. 64/71 of Malaysia (National Issues).

55. "Precis orithya" (different crest at right).

1977. As Nos. 219/21 and 223/5, but showing new State Crest.

No.	Type	Description	Unused	Used
226.		1 c. multicoloured	7·00	8·00
227.	–	2 c. multicoloured	1·75	3·50
228.	–	5 c. multicoloured	80	70
230.	–	10 c. multicoloured	65	30
231.	55.	15 c. multicoloured	1·75	20
232.	–	20 c. multicoloured	1·50	2·25

56. "Rhododendron scortechinii".

1979. As Nos. 135/41 of Kedah, but with Arms of Sarawak as in T **56**.

No.	Description	Unused	Used
233	1 c. "Rafflesia hasseltii"	10	30
234	2 c. "Pterocarpus indicus"	10	30
235	5 c. "Lagerstroemia speciosa"	10	10
236	10 c. "Durio zibethinus"	10	10
237	15 c. "Hibiscus rosa-sinensis"	20	10
238	20 c. Type **56**	25	10
239	25 c. "Etlingera elatior" (inscr "Phaeomeria speciosa")	25	10

57. Coffee.

1986. As Nos. 152/8 of Kedah, but with Arms of Sarawak as in T **57**.

No.	Description	Unused	Used
247.	1 c. Type **57**	10	10
248.	2 c. Coconuts	10	10
249.	5 c. Cocoa	10	10
250.	10 c. Black pepper	10	10
251.	15 c. Rubber	10	10
252.	20 c. Oil palm	10	10
253.	30 c. Rice	15	20

Nos. 247/53 exist with slightly different versions to state arms at right.

JAPANESE OCCUPATION

府政國帝本日大

(**1.** "Imperial Japanese Government".)

1942. Stamps of Sarawak optd. with T **1**.

No.	Type	Description	Unused	Used
J 1.	21.	1 c. purple	24·00	29·00
J 2.		2 c. green	65·00	85·00
J 3.		2 c. black	40·00	55·00
J 4.		3 c. black	£130	£150
J 5.		3 c. green	35·00	40·00
J 6.		4 c. purple	26·00	35·00
J 7.		5 c. violet	30·00	32·00
J 8.		6 c. red	50·00	60·00
J 9.		6 c. brown	32·00	40·00
J 10.		8 c. brown	£110	£140
J 11.		8 c. red	90·00	£110
J 12.		10 c. red	32·00	40·00
J 13.		12 c. blue	80·00	85·00
J 14.		12 c. orange	80·00	£100
J 15.		15 c. orange	£140	£150
J 16.		15 c. blue	45·00	50·00
J 17.		20 c. green and red	30·00	42·00
J 18.		25 c. violet and orange	38·00	40·00
J 19.		30 c. brown and violet	35·00	48·00
J 20.		50 c. violet and red	35·00	45·00
J 21.		$1 red and brown	42·00	60·00
J 22.		$2 purple and violet	£100	£120
J 23.		$3 red and green	£550	£650
J 24.		$4 blue and red	£110	£140
J 25.		$5 red and brown	£110	£140
J 26.		$10 black and yellow	£120	£160

SELANGOR

A state of the Federation of Malaya, incorporated in Malaysia in 1963.

100 cents = 1 dollar (Straits or Malayan).

1881. Stamps of Straits Settlements optd. **SELANGOR.**

3.	5.	2 c. brown	60·00	65·00
35.		2 c. red	4·00	2·25

1882. Straits Settlements stamp optd. **S.**

8.	5.	2 c. brown	—	£1300

1891. Stamp of Straits Settlements surch. **SELANGOR Two CENTS.**

44.	5.	2 c. on 24 c. green ..	14·00	38·00

40.

42.

43.

1891.

49.	40.	1 c. green	70	25
50.		2 c. red	3·25	70
51.		2 c. orange	1·00	60
52.		5 c. blue	12·00	4·25

1894. Surch. **3 CENTS.**

53.	40.	3 c. on 5 c. red	1·25	40

1895.

54	42	3 c. purple and red ..	5·00	20
55		5 c. purple and yellow ..	1·50	30
56		8 c. purple and blue ..	60·00	7·00
57		10 c. purple and orange ..	7·50	80
58		25 c. green and red ..	70·00	40·00
60		50 c. green and black ..	£170	90·00
59		50 c. purple and black ..	25·00	17·00
61	43	$1 green	38·00	60·00
62		$2 green and red ..	£110	£110
63		$3 green and yellow ..	£250	£170
64		$5 green and blue ..	£100	£150
65		$10 green and purple ..	£275	£325
66		$25 green and orange ..	£1400	

1900. Surch. in words.

66a.	2.	1 c. on 5 c. purple & yell...	55·00	80·00
66b.		1 c. on 50 c. green & black	1·00	16·00
67.		3 c. on 50 c. green & black	6·00	17·00

46. Mosque at Palace, Klang.

47. Sultan Suleiman.

1935.

68.	46.	1 c. black	20	10
69.		2 c. green	50	10
70.		2 c. orange	1·25	1·10
71.		3 c. green	7·00	2·75
72.		4 c. orange	30	10
73.		5 c. brown	50	10
74.		6 c. red	4·25	10
75.		8 c. grey	40	10
76.		10 c. purple	40	10
77.		12 c. blue	1·50	10
78.		15 c. blue	5·50	24·00
79.		25 c. purple and red ..	1·50	60
80.		30 c. purple and orange ..	1·25	85
81.		40 c. red and purple ..	1·75	1·25
82.		50 c. black on green ..	1·50	15
83.	47.	$1 black and red on blue	4·25	40
84.		$2 green and red	17·00	7·50
85.		$5 green and red on green	48·00	23·00

48. Sultan Hisamud-din Alam Shah. 49.

1941.

86.	48.	$1 black and red on blue ..	8·00	5·00
87.		$2 green and red ..	48·00	27·00

1948. Silver Wedding. As T **10/11** of Aden.

88.		10 c. violet	20	10
89.		$5 green	23·00	14·00

1949.

90	49	1 c. black	10	10
91		2 c. orange	10	10
92		3 c. green	30	75
93		4 c. brown	10	10
94a		5 c. purple	30	10
95		6 c. grey	10	10
96		8 c. red	25	65
97		8 c. green	65	50
98		10 c. purple	10	10
99		12 c. red	80	1·50
100		15 c. blue	45	10
101		20 c. black and green	30	10
102		20 c. blue	80	10
103		25 c. purple and orange	40	10
104		30 c. red and purple ..	1·25	50
105		35 c. red and purple ..	70	80
106		40 c. red and purple ..	1·75	2·00
107		50 c. black and blue ..	50	10
108		$1 blue and purple ..	2·50	10
109		$2 green and red ..	6·00	15
110		$5 green and brown ..	40·00	1·00

1949. U.P.U. As T **20/23** of Antigua.

111		10 c. purple	30	10
112		15 c. blue	45	45
113		25 c. orange	50	1·25
114		50 c. black	1·60	80

1953. Coronation. As T **13** of Aden.

115		10 c. black and purple ..	40	10

1957. As Nos. 92/102 of Kedah but inset portrait of Sultan Hisamud-din Alam Shah.

116.		1 c. black	10	50
117.		2 c. red	10	40
118.		4 c. sepia	10	10
119.		5 c. lake	10	10
120.		8 c. green	1·10	25
121.		10 c. sepia	15	10
122.		10 c. purple	2·00	10
123.		20 c. blue	25	10
124a.		50 c. black and blue ..	25	10
125.		$1 blue and purple ..	1·50	10
126.		$2 green and red ..	2·50	85
127a.		$5 brown and green ..	4·75	1·00

50. Sultan Salahuddin Abdul Aziz Shah.

1961. Installation of the Sultan.

128.	50.	10 c. multicoloured ..	20	10

51. Sultan Salahuddin Abdul Aziz Shah.

1961. As Nos. 116, etc., but with inset portrait of Sultan Salahuddin Abdul Aziz as in T **51.**

129.		1 c. black	10	30
130.		2 c. red	10	30
131.		4 c. sepia	10	10
132.		5 c. lake	10	10
133.		8 c. green	1·50	1·50
134.		10 c. purple	30	10
135.		20 c. blue	1·00	10

52. "Vanda hookeriana".

1965. As Nos. 115/21 of Kedah, but with inset portrait of Sultan Salahuddin Abdul Aziz Shah as in T **52.**

136.	52.	1 c. multicoloured ..	10	10
137.	–	2 c. multicoloured ..	10	40
138.	–	5 c. multicoloured ..	15	10
139.	–	6 c. multicoloured ..	15	10
140.	–	10 c. multicoloured ..	15	10
141.	–	15 c. multicoloured ..	1·25	10
142.	–	20 c. multicoloured ..	1·60	30

The higher values used in Selangor were Nos. 20/7 of Malaysia (National Issues).

INDEX
Countries can be quickly located by referring to the index at the end of this volume.

53. "Parthenos sylvia".

1971. Butterflies. As Nos 124/30 of Kedah, but with portrait of Sultan Salahuddin Abdul Aziz Shah as in T **53.**

146.	–	1 c. multicoloured ..	15	40
147.	–	2 c. multicoloured ..	40	50
148.	53.	5 c. multicoloured ..	50	10
149.	–	6 c. multicoloured ..	50	45
150.	–	10 c. multicoloured ..	50	10
151.	–	15 c. multicoloured ..	55	10
152.	–	20 c. multicoloured ..	90	30

The higher values in use with this issue were Nos. 64/71 of Malaysia (National Issues).

54. "Lagerstroemia speciosa".

1979. Flowers. As Nos. 135/41 of Kedah, but with portrait of Sultan Salahuddin Abdul Shah as in T **54.**

158	1 c. "Rafflesia hasseltii" ..	10	20
159	2 c. " Pterocarpus indicus"	10	20
160	5 c. Type **54**	10	10
161	10 c. "Durio zibethinus" ..	15	10
162	15 c. "Hibiscus rosa-sinensis"	15	10
163	20 c. "Rhododendron scortechinii"	20	10
164	25 c. "Etlingera elatior" (inscr "Phaeomeria speciosa")	25	10

55. Sultan Salahuddin Abdul Aziz Shah and Royal Crest.

1985. 25th Anniv. of Sultan's Coronation.

173.	55.	15 c. multicoloured ..	70	10
174.		20 c. multicoloured ..	85	15
175.		$1 multicoloured ..	2·50	3·25

56. Black Pepper.

1986. As Nos. 152/8 of Kedah, but with portrait of Sultan Salahuddin Abdul Aziz Shah as in T **56.**

176.	1 c. Coffee	10	10
177.	2 c. Coconuts	10	10
178.	5 c. Cocoa	10	10
179.	10 c Type **56**	10	10
180.	15 c. Rubber	10	10
181.	20 c. Oil palm	10	10
182.	30 c. Rice	15	20

SEYCHELLES

A group of islands in the Indian Ocean, E. of Africa.

100 cents = 1 rupee.

1.

6.

1890.

9.	1.	2 c. green and red ..	75	90
28.		2 c. brown and green ..	55	45
22.		3 c. purple and orange ..	85	30
10.		4 c. red and green ..	90	85
29.		6 c. red	2·25	40
11.		8 c. purple and blue ..	3·00	1·60
12.		10 c. blue and brown ..	3·25	2·50
23.		12 c. brown and green ..	85	50
13.		13 c. grey and black ..	85	1·50
24.		15 c. olive and lilac ..	3·25	2·00
30.		15 c. blue	2·75	2·50
6.		16 c. brown and blue ..	2·00	2·75
31.		18 c. blue	1·60	90
32.		36 c. brown and red ..	15·00	4·00
25.		45 c. brown and red ..	22·00	27·00
7.		48 c. bistre & grn. ..	17·00	16·00
33.		75 c. yellow and violet ..	38·00	60·00
8.		96 c. mauve and red ..	38·00	48·00
34.		1 r. mauve and red ..	8·50	3·50
35.		1 r. 50 grey and red ..	48·00	75·00
36.		2 r. 25 mauve and green ..	60·00	75·00

1893. Surch. in figures and words in two lines.

15	1	3 c. on 4 c. red and green	95	1·25
17		12 c. on 16 c. brn. & blue	2·75	1·25
19		15 c. on 16 c. brn. & blue	7·00	2·00
20		45 c. on 48 c. brn. & grn.	9·00	4·25
21		90 c. on 96 c. mauve & red	24·00	25·00

1896. Surch. in figures and words in one line.

26.	1.	18 c. on 45 c. brown & red	8·00	2·50
27.		36 c. on 45 c. brown & red	10·00	38·00

1901. Surch. in figures and words.

41.	1.	2 c. on 4 c. red and green	1·00	2·75
37.		3 c. on 10 c. blue & brown	30	60
38.		3 c. on 16 c. brown & blue	50	1·25
39.		3 c. on 36 c. brown and red	30	50
40.		6 c. on 8 c. purple and blue	30	1·50
42.		30 c. on 75 c. yellow & vio.	80	1·40
43.		30 c. on 1 r. mauve and red	3·50	18·00
44.		45 c. on 1 r. mauve and red	3·50	18·00
45.		45 c. on 2 r. mve. & green	23·00	40·00

1903.

46	6	2 c. brown and green ..	80	40
61		3 c. green	80	40
62		6 c. red	1·25	15
49		12 c. brown and green ..	1·75	1·25
64		15 c. blue	1·75	2·00
65		18 c. olive and red ..	3·00	5·50
66		30 c. violet and green ..	6·00	7·50
67		45 c. brown and red ..	3·00	5·00
54		75 c. yellow and violet ..	9·00	18·00
69		1 r. 50 black and red ..	40·00	38·00
70		2 r. 25 purple and green ..	30·00	38·00

1903. Surch. **3 cents.**

57.	6.	3 c. on 15 c. blue.. ..	75	1·50
58.		3 c. on 18 c. olive and red	1·75	24·00
59.		3 c. on 45 c. brown and red	1·00	1·50

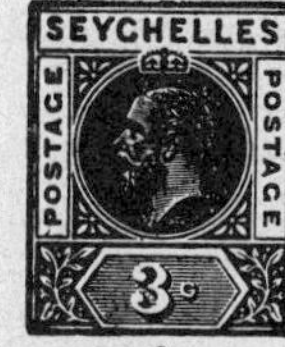

9.

11.

1912. Inscr. "POSTAGE POSTAGE."

71.	9.	2 c. brown and green ..	30	1·40
72.		3 c. green	45	40
73a.		6 c. red	2·50	45
74.		12 c. brown and green ..	1·00	3·50
75.		15 c. blue	1·50	40
76.		18 c. olive and red ..	1·50	3·50
77.		30 c. violet and green ..	5·00	1·25
78.		45 c. brown and red ..	2·50	24·00
79.		75 c. yellow and violet ..	2·50	5·50
80.		1 r. 50 black and red ..	5·50	85
81a.		2 r. 25 purple and green ..	30·00	2·50

1917. Inscr. "POSTAGE & REVENUE".

98	11.	2 c. brown and green ..	15	15
99		3 c. green	40	15
100		3 c. black	50	30
101		4 c. green	80	80
102		4 c. olive and red ..	3·50	11·00
84		5 c. brown	1·00	3·00
86		6 c. red	85	60
105		6 c. mauve	40	10
106		9 c. red	1·50	2·75
107		12 c. grey	60	20
108		12 c. red	45	20
87		15 c. blue	30	85
111		15 c. yellow	60	2·50
112		18 c. purple on yellow ..	2·00	7·50
113		20 c. blue	1·25	45
89b		25 c. blk. & red on yell.	1·00	6·50
90		30 c. purple and olive ..	1·50	5·50
116		45 c. purple and orange	1·00	5·00
117		50 c. purple and black ..	1·10	2·25
93		75 c. black on green ..	1·25	9·00
119		1 r. purple and red ..	7·00	17·00
121		1 r. 50 pur. & bl. on bl.	8·00	15·00
122		2 r. 25 green & violet ..	8·00	13·00
123		5 r. green and blue ..	48·00	£100

1935. Silver Jubilee. As T **13** of Antigua.
128. 6 c. blue and black .. 70 60
129. 12 c. green and blue .. 2·00 40
130. 20 c. brown and blue .. 2·00 40
131. 1 r. grey and purple .. 3·00 8·00

1937. Coronation. As T **2** of Aden.
132. 6 c. olive 35 15
133. 12 c. orange 50 30
134. 20 c. blue 70 65

14. Coco-de-mer Palm.

DESIGNS—VERT. 3, 12, 15, 30, 75 c., 2 r. 25, Giant Tortoise. HORIZ. 6, 20, 45 c., 1 r., 5 r. Fishing Pirogue.

1938.
135a **14** 2 c. brown 20 55
136 – 3 c. green .. .. 5·50 1·25
136a – 3 c. orange 75 40
137 – 6 c. orange .. .. 5·00 2·50
137ab – 6 c. green 55 65
138 **14** 9 c. red .. .. 9·00 2·00
138ab – 9 c. blue 90 90
139 – 12 c. mauve .. .. 35·00 1·00
139ab – 15 c. red .. .. 1·25 70
139c **14** 18 c. red .. .. 2·75 60
140 – 20 c. blue .. .. 40·00 5·50
140ab – 20 c. yellow .. .. 1·50 75
141 **14** 25 c. brown .. .. 55·00 13·00
142 – 30 c. red .. .. 60·00 7·00
142ab – 30 c. blue .. .. 60 1·50
143a – 45 c. brown .. .. 1·25 1·50
144a **14** 50 c. violet .. .. 40 1·25
145 – 75 c. blue .. .. 85·00 38·00
145ab – 75 c. mauve .. .. 70 1·50
146 – 1 r. green .. .. 95·00 48·00
146ab – 1 r. black .. .. 1·25 1·75
147a **14** 1 r. 50 blue .. .. 2·50 1·75
148a – 2 r. 25 olive .. .. 5·50 5·50
149 – 5 r. red .. .. 5·50 3·25

1946. Victory. As T **9** of Aden.
150 9 c. blue 10 10
151 30 c. blue 10 10

1948. Silver Wedding. As T **10/11** of Aden.
152. 9 c. blue 15 25
153. 5 r. red .. .. .. 8·00 14·00

1949. U.P.U. As T **20/23** of Antigua.
154. 18 c. mauve 30 15
155. 50 c. purple 45 50
156. 1 r. grey 40 15
157. 2 r. 25 olive 50 60

17. Sail-fish.

21. " La Pierre de Possession ".

1952. Full-face portrait.
158. **17.** 2 c. lilac 50 70
159. – 3 c. orange 50 30
160. – 9 c. blue 50 60
161. – 15 c. green 40 75
162. – 18 c. lake 65 20
163. – 20 c. yellow 90 60
164. – 25 c. red 70 70
165. **17.** 40 c. blue 70 90
166. – 45 c. brown 70 30
167. – 50 c. violet .. .. 1·25 60
168. – 1 r. black .. .. 2·50 1·75
169. – 1 r. 50 blue .. .. 5·00 7·50
170. – 2 r. 25 olive .. .. 5·50 9·00
171. – 5 r. red .. .. .. 5·50 12·00
172. **17.** 10 r. green .. .. 12·00 16·00

DESIGNS—VERT. 2 c., 25 c., 2 r. 25, Giant tortoise. 9 c., 50 c., 1 r. 50, Coco-de-Mer Palm. HORIZ. 15 c., 20 c., 45 c. Fishing pirogue. 18 c., 1 r., 5 r. Map of Indian Ocean.

1953. Coronation. As T **13** of Aden.
173. 9 c. black and blue .. 20 30

1954. Designs as 1952 but with portrait of Queen Elizabeth II.
174. 2 c. lilac 10 10
175. 3 c. orange 10 10
175a. 5 c. violet 30 30
176. 9 c. blue 10 10
176a. 10 c. blue (as 9 c.) .. 30 50
177. 15 c. green 20 15
178. 18 c. lake 10 10
179. 20 c. yellow 30 20
180. 25 c. red 60 85
180a. 35 c. lake (as 18 c.) .. 1·75 90
181. 40 c. blue 30 25
182. 45 c. brown 20 15
183. 50 c. violet 30 20
183a. 70 c. brown (as 45 c.) .. 1·75 1·25
184. 1 r. black 50 40
185. 1 r. 50 blue .. .. 3·50 2·75
186. 2 r. 25 olive .. .. 3·50 7·00
187. 5 r. red .. .. .. 15·00 8·00
188. 10 r. green .. .. 26·00 18·00

NEW DESIGN: 5 c. Seychelles Flying Fox.

1956. Bicent. of La Pierre de Possession.
189. **21.** 40 c. blue 15 10
190. 1 r. black 15 10

1957. No. 182 surch. **5 cents** and bars.
191. 5 c. on 45 c. brown .. 15 10

23. Mauritius 6d. Stamp with Seychelles "B 64" Cancellation.

1961. Cent. of First Seychelles Post Office.
193. **23.** 10 c. blue, black & purple 20 10
194. 35 c. blue, black & green 35 10
195. 2 r. 25 blue, black & brown 70 35

24. Black Parrot. **40.** Colony's Badge.

1962. Multicoloured.
196 5 c. Type **24** 30 10
234 10 c. Vanilla Vine .. 30 15
198 15 c. Fisherman 20 10
199 20 c. Denis Is. Lighthouse 20 10
200 25 c. Clock Tower, Victoria 20 10
200a 30 c. Anse Royal Bay .. 2·25 1·25
201 35 c. Anse Royal Bay .. 1·75 2·00
202 40 c. Government House .. 20 50
203 45 c. Fishing Pirogue .. 3·50 3·50
204 50 c. Cascade Church .. 40 25
236 60 c. red, blue and brown (Flying Fox) .. .. 1·75 45
205 70 c. Sail-fish .. .. 6·00 3·00
206 75 c. Coco-de-mer Palm .. 2·25 3·25
237 85 c. ultramarine and blue (Sail-fish) 90 40
207 1 r. Cinnamon 30 10
208 1 r. 50 Copra .. .. 4·50 5·50
209 2 r. 25 Map .. .. 4·50 3·50
210 3 r. 50 Land Settlement .. 2·25 5·00
211 5 r. Regina Mundi Convent 3·50 2·50
212 10 r. Type **40** .. .. 11·00 4·50

The 30 c., 35 c., 40 c., 85 c., 1 r., 1 r. 50, 2 r. 25, 3 r. 50 and 5 r. are horiz.
No. 236 is 23×25 mm.

1963. Freedom from Hunger. As T **28** of Aden.
213. 70 c. violet 60 25

1963. Cent of Red Cross. As T **33** of Antigua.
214. 10 c. red and black .. 25 10
215. 75 c. red and blue .. 75 40

1965. Surch.
216. 45 c. on 35 c. (No. 201) .. 10 15
217. 75 c. on 70 c. (No. 205) .. 20 15

1965. Cent of I.T.U. As T **34** of Antigua.
218. 5 c. orange and blue .. 15 10
219. 1 r. 50 mauve and green .. 65 25

1965. I.C.Y. As T **36** of Antigua.
220. 5 c. purple and turquoise .. 10 10
221. 40 c. green and lavender .. 20 20

1966. Churchill Commem. As T **37** of Antigua.
222. 5 c. blue 15 10
223. 15 c. green 40 10
224. 75 c. brown 80 10
225. 1 r. 50 violet .. .. 1·25 60

1966. World Cup Football Championship. As T **40** of Antigua.
226. 15 c. multicoloured .. 10 10
227. 1 r. multicoloured .. 20 20

1966. Inauguration of W.H.O. Headquarters, Geneva. As T **41** of Antigua.
228. 20 c. black, green and blue 15 10
229. 50 c. black, purple & ochre 25 20

1966. 20th Anniv of U.N.E.S.C.O. As T **54/6** of Antigua.
230. 15 c. multicoloured .. 25 10
231. 1 r. yellow, violet and olive 45 10
232. 5 r. black, purple & orange 1·25 1·00

1967. Universal Adult Suffrage. Nos. 198, 203, 206 and 210 optd. **UNIVERSAL ADULT SUFFRAGE 1967.**
238. 15 c. multicoloured .. 10 10
239. 45 c. multicoloured .. 10 10
240. 75 c. multicoloured .. 10 10
241. 3 r. 50 multicoloured .. 20 15

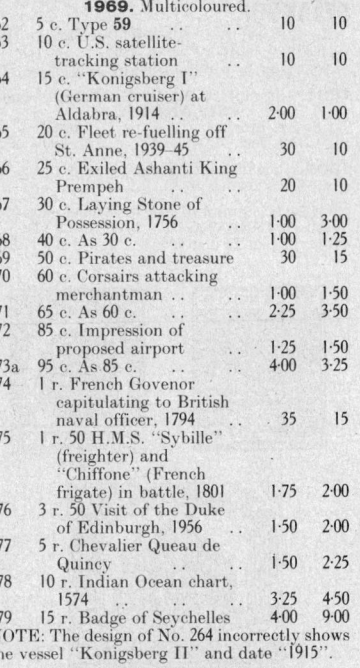

44. Cowrie Shells.

1967. Int. Tourist Year. Multicoloured.
242. 15 c. Type **44** 15 10
243. 40 c. Cone Shells 20 10
244. 1 r. Arthritic Spider Conch 25 10
245. 2 r. 25 "Subulate auger" and Triton Shells .. 55 50

1968. Nos. 202/3 and 206 surch.
246. 30 c. on 40 c. multicoloured 10 10
247. 60 c. on 45 c. multicoloured 15 10
248. 85 c. on 75 c. multicoloured 20 15

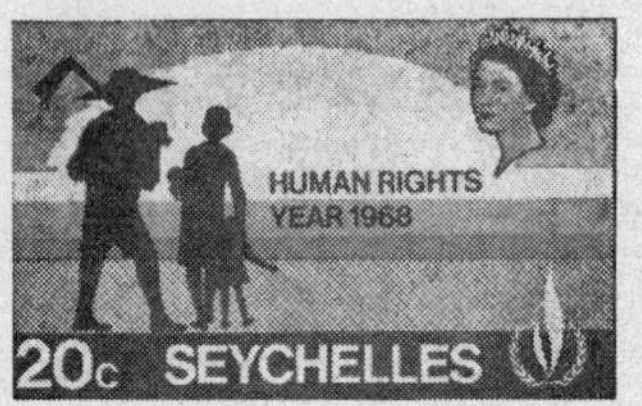

49. Farmer with Wife and Children at Sunset.

1968. Human Rights Year.
249. **49.** 20 c. multicoloured .. 10 10
250. 50 c. multicoloured .. 10 10
251. 85 c. multicoloured .. 10 10
252. 2 r. 25 multicoloured .. 20 30

50. Expedition landing at Anse Possession.

1968. Bicentenary of First Landing on Praslin. Multicoloured.
253. 20 c. Type **50** 30 10
254. 50 c. French warships at Anchor 35 15
255. 85 c. Coco-de-mer and Black Parrot 70 20
256. 2 r. 25 French warships under Sail 70 60

54. Apollo Launch.

1969. 1st Man on the Moon. Multicoloured.
257. 5 c. Type **54** 10 10
258. 20 c. Module leaving mother-ship for the moon .. 15 10
259. 50 c. Astronauts and Space Module on the moon .. 20 15
260. 85 c. Tracking Station .. 25 15
261. 2 r. 25 Moon craters with Earth on the "Horizon" 45 65

59. Picault's Landing, 1742.

1969. Multicoloured.
262 5 c. Type **59** 10 10
263 10 c. U.S. satellite-tracking station .. 10 10
264 15 c. "Konigsberg I" (German cruiser) at Aldabra, 1914 .. .. 2·00 1·00
265 20 c. Fleet re-fuelling off St. Anne, 1939–45 .. 30 10
266 25 c. Exiled Ashanti King Prempeh 20 10
267 30 c. Laying Stone of Possession, 1756 .. 1·00 3·00
268 40 c. As 30 c. .. .. 1·00 1·25
269 50 c. Pirates and treasure 30 15
270 60 c. Corsairs attacking merchantman .. .. 1·00 1·50
271 65 c. As 60 c. .. .. 2·25 3·50
272 85 c. Impression of proposed airport .. 1·25 1·50
273a 95 c. As 85 c. .. .. 4·00 3·25
274 1 r. French Govenor capitulating to British naval officer, 1794 .. 35 15
275 1 r. 50 H.M.S. "Sybille" (freighter) and "Chiffone" (French frigate) in battle, 1801 1·75 2·00
276 3 r. 50 Visit of the Duke of Edinburgh, 1956 .. 1·50 2·00
277 5 r. Chevalier Queau de Quincy .. .. 1·50 2·25
278 10 r. Indian Ocean chart, 1574 .. .. .. 3·25 4·50
279 15 r. Badge of Seychelles 4·00 9·00

NOTE: The design of No. 264 incorrectly shows the vessel "Konigsberg II" and date "1915".

74. White Tern, French Warship and Island.

1970. Bicentenary of 1st Settlement, St. Anne Island. Multicoloured.
280. 20 c. Type **74** 30 10
281. 50 c. Flying Fish, ship and island 30 10
282. 85 c. Compass and chart .. 30 10
283. 3 r. 50 Anchor on sea-bed .. 40 55

78. Girl and Optician's Chart.

1970. Cent. of British Red Cross. Mult.
284. 20 c. Type **78** 20 10
285. 50 c. Baby, scales and milk bottles 25 10
286. 85 c. Woman with child and umbrella (vert.) .. 25 10
287. 3 r. 50 Red Cross local headquarters building .. 1·25 1·00

79. Pitcher Plant. **81.** Piper "Navajo".

1970. Flowers. Multicoloured.
288. 20 c. Type **79** 45 15
289. 50 c. Wild Vanilla .. 55 15
290. 85 c. Tropic-Bird Orchid .. 1·40 30
291. 3 r. 50 Vare Hibiscus .. 2·50 1·50

1971. Airport Completion. Multicoloured.
294. 5 c. Type **81** 15 10
295. 20 c. Westland "Wessex" 30 10
296. 50 c. "Catalina" flying-boat (horiz.) 50 10
297. 60 c. Grumman "Albatross" 55 10
298. 85 c. Short "G" Class Flying-boat (horiz.) .. 75 10
299. 3 r. 50 Vickers Supermarine "Walrus" (horiz.) .. 3·50 3·00

82. Santa Claus delivering Gifts (Jean-Claude Waye Hive).

1971. Christmas. Multicoloured.
300. 10 c. Type **82** 10 10
301. 15 c. Santa Claus seated on turtle (Edison Theresine) 10 10
302. 3 r. 50 Santa Claus landing on island (Isabelle Tirant) 40 70

1971. Nos. 267, 270 and 272 surch.
303. 40 c. on 30 c. multicoloured 30 55
304. 65 c. on 60 c. multicoloured 40 75
305. 95 c. on 85 c. multicoloured 45 1·00

1972. Royal Visit. Nos. 265a and 277 optd. **ROYAL VISIT, 1972.**
306. 20 c. multicoloured .. 15 20
307. 5 r. multicoloured.. .. 1·50 2·50

85. Seychelles Brush Warbler.

1972. Rare Seychelles Birds. Multicoloured.
308. 5 c. Type **85** 30 10
309. 20 c. Bare-legged Scops Owl 1·00 20
310. 50 c. Seychelles Blue Pigeon .. .. 1·25 65
311. 65 c. Seychelles Magpie Robin .. .. 1·50 75
312. 95 c. Seychelles Paradise Flycatcher .. .. 2·25 2·00
313. 3 r. 50 Seychelles Kestrel 6·50 8·00

86. Fireworks Display.

1972. "Festival '72". Multicoloured.
315. 10 c. Type **86** 10 10
316. 15 c. Pirogue race (horiz.) 10 10
317. 25 c. Floats and costumes 10 10
318. 5 r. Water skiing (horiz.) .. 60 80

1972. Royal Silver Wedding. As T **52** of Ascension, but with Giant Tortoise and Sailfish in background.
319. 95 c. blue 15 10
320. 1 r. 50 brown 15 10

1973. Royal Wedding. As T **47** of Anguilla. Multicoloured, background colours given.
321. 95 c. brown 10 10
322. 1 r. 50 blue 10 10

88. Soldier Fish.

1974. Fishes. Multicoloured.
323. 20 c. Type **88** 15 10
324. 50 c. File Fish 25 10
325. 95 c. Butterfly Fish .. 30 20
326. 1 r. 50 Gaterin .. .. 75 1·00

89. Globe and Letter.

1974. Centenary of U.P.U. Multicoloured.
327. 20 c. Type **89** 10 10
328. 50 c. Globe and radio beacon 20 10
329. 95 c. Globe and postmark 35 40
330. 1 r. 50 Emblems within "UPU" 50 70

90. Sir Winston Churchill.

1974. Birth Centenary of Sir Winston Churchill. Multicoloured.
331. 95 c. Type **90** 20 15
332. 1 r. 50 Profile portrait .. 35 40

1975. Visit of Liner "Queen Elizabeth II". Nos. 265, 269, 273a and 275 optd **VISIT OF Q.E. II.**
334. 20 c. multicoloured .. 15 15
335. 50 c. multicoloured .. 20 20
336. 95 c. multicoloured .. 25 35
337. 1 r. 50 multicoloured .. 35 60

1975. Internal Self-Government. Nos. 265, 271, 274 and 276 optd **INTERNAL SELF-GOVERNMENT OCTOBER 1975.**
338. 20 c. multicoloured .. 15 15
339. 65 c. multicoloured .. 25 30
340. 1 r. multicoloured .. 30 35
341. 3 r. 50 multicoloured .. 1·00 1·50

93. Queen Elizabeth I.

1975. International Women's Year. Mult.
342. 10 c. Type **93** 10 10
343. 15 c. Gladys Aylward .. 10 10
344. 20 c. Elizabeth Fry .. 10 10
345. 25 c. Emmeline Pankhurst 10 10
346. 65 c. Florence Nightingale 25 20
347. 1 r. Amy Johnson.. .. 40 35
348. 1 r. 50 Joan of Arc.. .. 50 60
349. 3 r. 50 Eleanor Roosevelt 1·50 2·25

94. Map of Praslin and Postmark.

1976. Seychelles Rural Posts. Multicoloured.
350. 20 c. Type **94** 15 10
351. 65 c. La Digue 25 20
352. 1 r. Mahe with Victoria postmark 30 25
353. 1 r. 50 Mahe Anse Royale postmark 45 70
Nos. 350/53 show maps and postmarks.

95. First Landing, 1609 (Inset portrait of Premier James Mancham).

1976. Independence. Multicoloured.
355. 20 c. Type **95** 10 10
356. 25 c. The possession Stone 10 10
357. 40 c. First settlers, 1770.. 15 15
358. 75 c. Chevalier Queau de Quincy 20 20
359. 1 r. Sir Bickham Sweet-Escott 25 20
360. 1 r. 25 Legislative Building 40 50
361. 1 r. 50 Seychelles badge.. 45 60
362. 3 r. 50 Seychelles flag .. 90 1·40

96. Flags of Seychelles and U.S.A.

1976. Bicent. of Seychelles Independence and American Independence. Multicoloured.
363. 1 r. Type **96** 25 15
364. 10 r. Statehouses of Seychelles and Philadelphia 1·25 1·50

97. Swimming.

1976. Olympic Games, Montreal.
365. **97.** 20 c. blue, light blue and brown 10 10
366. – 65 c. dark green, green and grey 20 10
367. – 1 r. brown, blue & grey 25 10
368. – 3 r. 50 light red, red and grey .. .. .. 50 1·25
DESIGNS: 65 c. Hockey. 1 r. Basketball. 3 r. 50 Football.

98. Seychelles Paradise Flycatcher.

1976. 4th Pan-African Ornithological Congress, Seychelles. Multicoloured.
369. 20 c. Type **98** 15 10
370. 1 r. 25 Seychelles Sunbird (horiz.) 65 65
371. 1 r. 50 Seychelles Brown White Eye (horiz.) .. 80 80
372. 5 r. Black Parrot .. .. 2·00 2·00

1976. Independence. Nos. 265, 269, 271, 273a, 274, 276 and 277/9 optd **Independence 1976** or surch also.
374. 20 c. Fleet re-fuelling at St. Anne, 1939–45 .. 30 85
375. 50 c. Pirates and treasure 40 1·00
376. 95 c. Impressions of proposed airport .. .. 55 1·25
377. 1 r. French Governor capitulating to British naval officer, 1794 .. .. 55 1·25
378. 3 r. 50 Visit of the Duke of Edinburgh, 1956 .. 2·75 3·50
379. 5 r. Chevalier Queau de Quincy .. .. .. 3·00 4·00
380. 10 r. Indian Ocean chart, 1574 .. .. .. 5·50 9·00
381. 15 r. Badge of Seychelles 7·50 9·00
382. 25 r. on 65 c. Corsairs attacking merchantmen 11·00 16·00

100. Inauguration of George Washington.

1976. Bicentenary of American Revolution.
383. **100.** 1 c. deep red and red .. 10 10
384. – 2 c. violet and lilac .. 10 10
385. – 3 c. light blue and blue 10 10
386. – 4 c. brown and yellow.. 10 10
387. – 5 c. green and yellow .. 10 10
388. – 1 r. 50 brown and light brown 60 35
389. – 3 r. 50 blue and green.. 80 80
390. – 5 r. brown and yellow.. 1·00 1·00
391. – 10 r. blue and light blue 1·75 1·75
DESIGNS: 2 c. Jefferson and Louisiana Purchase. 3 c. William Seward and Alaska Purchase. 4 c. Pony express, 1860. 5 c. Lincoln's Emancipation Proclamation. 1 r. 50, Transcontinental Railroad, 1869. 3 r. 50, Wright Brothers flight, 1903. 5 r. Henry Ford's assembly-line, 1913. 10 r. J. F. Kennedy and 1969 Moon-landing.

101. Silhouette of the Islands.

1977. Silver Jubilee. Multicoloured.
393. 20 c. Type **101** 10 10
394. 40 c. Silhouette (different) 10 10
395. 50 c. The Orb 10 10
396. 1 r. St. Edward's Crown.. 15 10
397. 1 r. 25 Ampulla and Spoon 20 15
398. 1 r. 50 Sceptre with Cross 20 20
399. 5 r. Silhouette (different) 40 40
400. 10 r. Silhouette (different) 60 70
The 50 c. to 1 r. 50 are vertical designs.

102. Cruiser "Aurora" and Flag.

1977. 60th Anniv. of Russian Revolution.
402. **102.** 1 r. 50 milticoloured .. 45 30

103. Coral Stone.

1977. Marine Life. Rupee face value shown as "Re" or "Rs". Multicoloured.
404 5 c. Reef fish 10 20
405 10 c. Hawksbill turtle .. 10 10
406 15 c. Coco-de-Mer .. 15 15
407 20 c. Wild vanilla orchid .. 40 30
408 25 c. "Hypolimnas misippus" (butterfly) .. 40 30
409 40 c. Type **103** 15 10
410 50 c. Giant tortoise .. 20 10
411 75 c. Crayfish 20 10
412 1 r. Madagascar red fody 1·25 10
413 1 r. 25 White tern .. 1·25 15
414 1 r. 50 Seychelles flying fox 1·50 15
736 3 r. Green gecko .. .. 85 1·10
415 3 r. 50 As 3 r. .. .. 75 1·25
416 5 r. Octopus .. .. 2·00 40
417 10 r. Giant tiger cowrie .. 2·25 2·50
418 15 r. Pitcher plant .. 2·25 2·50
419 20 r. Coat of arms .. 2·50 2·50

The 40 c. 1 r., 1 r.25 and 1 r.50 values are horizontal, 31 × 27 mm. The 5, 10, 15 and 20 r. are vertical, 28 × 36 mm. The others are horizontal, 29 × 25 mm.

Nos. 405/12 and 414 exist with or without imprint date at foot.

For similar designs with rupee face values shown as "R" see Nos. 487a/94.

104. St. Roch Roman Catholic Church, Bel Ombre.

1977. Christmas. Multicoloured.

420.	20 c. Type **104**	10	10
421.	1 r. Anglican cathedral, Victoria	10	10
422.	1 r. 50 Roman Catholic cathedral, Victoria ..	15	10
423.	5 r. St. Mark's Anglican church, Praslin ..	30	45

105. Liberation Day ringed on Calendar.

1978. Liberation Day. Multicoloured.

424.	40 c. Type **105**	10	10
425.	1 r. 25 Hands holding bayonet, torch and flag	15	10
426.	1 r. 50 Fisherman and farmer	15	15
427.	5 r. Soldiers and rejoicing people	35	40

106. Stamp Portraits of Edward VII, George V and George VI.

1978. 25th Anniv. of Coronation. Mult.

428.	40 c. Type **106**	10	10
429.	1 r. 50 Queen Victoria and Elizabeth II	10	10
430.	3 r. Queen Victoria Monument	20	25
431.	5 r. Queen's Building, Victoria	30	35

107. Gardenia.

1978. World Wildlife. Multicoloured

433.	40 c. Type **107** ..	10	10
434.	1 r. 25 Seychelles Magpie Robin	55	25
435.	1 r. 50 Seychelles Paradise Flycatcher	60	35
436.	5 r. Green Turtle	70	85

108. Possession Stone.

1978. Bicentenary of Victoria. Multicoloured.

437	20 c. Type **108**	10	10
438	1 r. 25 Plan of 1782 "L'Etablissement" ..	15	15
439	1 r. 50 Clock Tower ..	15	15
440	5 r. Bust of Pierre Poivre	40	50

109. Seychelles Fody.

1979. Birds (1st series). Multicoloured.

441.	2 r. Type **109**	55	50
442.	2 r. Green heron	55	50
443.	2 r. Thick-billed Bulbul ..	55	50
444.	2 r. Seychelles cave swiftlet	55	50
445.	2 r. Grey-headed lovebird	55	50

See also Nos. 463/7, 500/4 and 523/7.

110. Patrice Lumumba.

1979. African Liberation Heroes.

446.	**110.**	40 c. blk., violet & lilac	10	10
447.	–	2 r. blk., blue & pale blue	25	25
448.	–	2 r. 25 blk., brn. & orge.	30	30
449.	–	5 r. black, olive & green	65	80

DESIGNS: 2 r. Kwame Nkrumah. 2 r. 25, Dr. Eduardo Mondlane. 5 r. Hamilcar Cabral.

111. 1978 5 r. Liberation Day Commemorative and Sir Rowland Hill.

1979. Death Centenary of Sir Rowland Hill. Multicoloured.

450.	40 c. Type **111**	10	10
451.	2 r. 25 1972 50 c. Seychelles Blue Pigeon commemorative	45	40
452.	3 r. 1962 50 c. definitive ..	50	55

112. Child with Book.

1979. International Year of the Child Multicoloured.

454.	40 c. Type **112**	10	10
455.	2 r. 25 Children of different races	20	30
456.	3 r. Young child with ball (vert.)	30	45
457.	5 r. Girl with glove-puppet (vert.)	40	65

113. The Herald Angel.

1979. Christmas. Multicoloured.

458.	20 c. Type **113**	10	10
459.	2 r. 25 The Virgin and Child	30	40
460.	3 r. The Three Kings (horiz.)	40	55

1980. No. 415 surch.

462.	1 r. 10 on 3 r. 50 Green Gecko	30	30

115. Seychelles Kestrel.

1980. Birds (2nd series). Seychelles Kestrel. Multicoloured.

463.	2 r. Type **115**. ..	60	50
464.	2 r. Pair of Seychelles Kestrels	60	50
465.	2 r. Seychelles Kestrel with eggs ..	60	50
466.	2 r. Seychelles Kestrel on nest with chick ..	60	50
467.	2 r. Seychelles Kestrel chicks in nest ..	60	50

116. 10 Rupees Banknote.

1980. " London 1980 " International Stamp Exhibition. Currency Notes. Multicoloured.

468.	40 c. Type **116**	10	10
469.	1 r. 50 25 rupees ..	25	15
470.	2 r. 25 50 rupees (vert.) ..	35	25
471.	5 r. 100 rupees (vert.) ..	65	55

117. Sprinting.

1980. Olympic Games, Moscow. Mult.

473.	40 c. Type **117** ..	10	10
474.	2 r. 25 Weightlifting ..	20	20
475.	3 r. Boxing	30	30
476.	5 r. Yachting	60	40

118. " Jumbo Jet " Airliner.

1980. International Tourism Conference, Manila. Multicoloured.

478.	40 c. Type **118**	10	10
479.	2 r. 25 Bus	35	35
480.	3 r. Cruise liner	50	50
481.	5 r. "La Belle Caralline" (tourist launch)	70	75

119. Female Palm.

1980. Coco-de-Mer (palms). Multicoloured.

482.	40 c. Type **119**.	10	10
483.	2 r. 25 Male Palm ..	25	20
484.	3 r. Artefacts	40	35
485.	5 r. Fisherman's gourd ..	55	55

1981. As Nos. 412/14, 415 (with new value), and 416/19, but face values redrawn as "R" instead of "Re" or "Rs".

487a	1 r. Madagascar red fody	50	50
488	1 r. 10 Green gecko ..	40	50
735	1 r. 25 White tern ..	85	85
490	1 r. 50 Seychelles flying fox	45	60
738	5 r. Octopus	1·75	2·25
492	10 r. Giant tiger cowrie ..	2·75	3·25
493	15 r. Pitcher plant ..	3·75	4·40
494	20 r. Seychelles coat of arms	5·00	6·00

120. Vasco da Gama's "Sao Gabriel", 1497.

1981. Ships. Multicoloured.

495.	40 c. Type **120**	15	10
496.	2 r. 25 Mascarenhas' caravel, 1505 ..	60	55
497.	3 r. 50 Darwin's H.M.S. "Beagle", 1831 ..	90	1·00
498.	5 r. "Queen Elizabeth 2" (liner), 1968	1·10	1·40

121. White Tern.

1981. Birds (3rd series). White Tern. Multicoloured.

500.	2 r. Type **121**	85	65
501.	2 r. Pair of White Terns ..	85	65
502.	2 r. Female White Tern ..	85	65
503.	2 r. Female White Tern on nest, and egg ..	85	65
504.	2 r. White Tern and chick	85	65

1981. Royal Wedding, Royal Yachts. As T **26/27** of Kiribati. Multicoloured.

505 1 r. 50 "Victoria and Albert I" 20 25
506 1 r. 50 Prince Charles and Lady Diana Spencer .. 50 50
507 5 r. "Cleveland" 60 60
513 5 r. As No. 506 .. .. 1·00 1·60
509 10 r. "Britannia" .. .. 1·00 1·50
510 10 r. As No. 506 .. .. 2·25 2·25

122. Britten-Norman "Islander".

1981. 10th Anniv. of Opening of Seychelles International Airport. Aircraft. Mult.

514. 40 c. Type **122** 15 10
515. 2 r. 25 Britten-Norman "Trislander" 55 45
516. 3 r. 50 BAC (Vickers) "VC10" airliner .. 80 70
517. 5 r. Boeing "747" airliner 1·00 1·00

123. Seychelles Flying Foxes in Flight.

1981. Seychelles Flying Fox (Roussette). Multicoloured.

518. 40 c. Type **123** 10 10
519. 2 r. 25 Flying Fox eating 45 45
520. 3 r. Flying Fox climbing across tree branch .. 70 70
521. 5 r. Flying Fox hanging from tree branch .. 1·00 1·00

124. Chinese Little Bittern (male).

1982. Birds (4th series). Chinese Bittern. Multicoloured.

523. 3 r. Type **124** .. .. 1·75 80
524. 3 r. Chinese Little Bittern (female) .. .. 1·75 80
525. 3 r. Hen on Nest .. .. 1·75 80
526. 3 r. Nest and eggs .. 1·75 80
527. 3 r. Hen and chicks .. 1·75 80

125. Silhouette Island and La Digue.

1982. Modern Maps. Multicoloured.

528. 40 c. Type **125** 15 10
529. 1 r. 50 Denis and Bird Islands .. 40 25
530. 2 r. 75 Praslin 65 65
531. 7 r. Mahe .. .. 1·60 2·00

126. "Education".

1982. 5th Anniv. of Liberation. Mult.

533. 40 c. Type **126** 10 10
534. 1 r. 75 "Health" .. 25 25
535. 2 r. 75 "Agriculture" .. 45 45
536. 7 r. "Construction" .. 1·40 1·40

127. Tourist Board Emblem.

1982. Tourism. Multicoloured.

538. 1 r. 75 Type **127** 40 35
539. 1 r. 75 Northolme Hotel .. 40 35
540. 1 r. 75 Reef Hotel .. 40 35
541. 1 r. 75 Barbarons Beach Hotel 40 35
542. 1 r. 75 Coral Strand Hotel 40 35
543. 1 r. 75 Beau Vallon Bay Hotel 40 35
544. 1 r. 75 Fisherman's Cove Hotel 40 35
545. 1 r. 75 Mahe Beach Hotel 40 35

128. Tata Bus.

1982. Land Transport. Multicoloured.

546. 20 c. Type **128** 10 10
547. 1 r. 75 Mini-moke 30 25
548. 2 r. 75 Ox-cart 50 55
549. 7 r. Truck .. .. 1·40 1·75

129. Radio Seychelles Control Room.

1983. World Communications Year. Mult

550. 40 c. Type **129** 10 10
551. 2 r. 75 Satellite Earth station 45 50
552. 3 r. 50 Radio Seychelles televison control .. 70 75
553. 5 r. Postal services sorting office .. .. 1·00 1·25

130. Agricultural Experimental Station.

1983. Commonwealth Day. Multicoloured.

554. 40 c. Type **130** 10 10
555. 2 r. 75 Food processing plant 45 50
556. 3 r. 50 Unloading fish catch 70 75
557. 7 r. Seychelles flag .. 1·40 1·50

131. Denis Island Lighthouse.

1983. Famous Landmarks. Multicoloured.

558. 40 c. Type **131** 10 10
559. 2 r. 75 Victoria Hospital .. 40 45
560. 3 r. 50 Supreme Court .. 60 65
561. 7 r. State House .. .. 1·25 1·40

132. "Royal Vauxhall" Balloon, 1836.

1983. Bicentenary of Manned Flight. Mult.

563. 40 c. Type **132** 15 10
564. 1 r. 75 De Havilland "D.H.50J" 50 30
565. 2 r. 75 Grumman "Albatross" 75 55
566. 7 r. Swearingen "Merlin" 1·60 1·75

133. Jet Plane.

1983. 1st International Flight of Air Seychelles.

567. **133.** 2 r. multicoloured .. 1·00 1·00

134. Swamp Plant and Moorhen.

1983. Centenary of Marianne North's Visit. Multicoloured.

568. 40 c. Type **134** 15 10
569. 1 r. 75 "Wormia flagellaria" 50 30
570. 2 r. 75 Asiatic Pancratium 65 60
571. 7 r. Pitcher Plant .. .. 1·50 1·60

1983. Nos. 505/7, 509/10 and 513 surch.

573. 50 c. on 1 r. 50 "Victoria and Albert I" 15 15
574. 50 c. on 1 r. 50 Prince Charles and Lady Diana Spencer 40 45
575. 2 r. 25 on 5 r. "Cleveland" 45 50
576. 2 r. 25 on 5 r. As No. 574 1·00 1·25
577. 3 r. 75 on 10 r. "Britannia" 75 80
578. 3 r. 75 on 10 r. As No. 574 1·40 1·75

136. Coconut Vessel.

1984. Traditional Handicrafts. Multicoloured.

579. 50 c. Type **136** 15 10
580. 2 r. Scarf and doll .. 50 60
581. 3 r. Coconut-fibre roses .. 70 80
582. 10 r. Carved fishing boat and doll .. .. 2·00 3·00

137. Victoria Port.

1984. 250th Anniv. of "Lloyd's List" (newspaper). Multicoloured.

583 50 c. Type **137** 20 10
584 2 r. Cargo liner 55 55
585 3 r. "Sun Viking" (liner) .. 80 80
586 10 r. Loss of R.F.A. "Ennerdale II" (tanker) 2·25 2·75

138. Old S.P.U.P. Office.

1984. 20th Anniv. of Seychelles Peoples' United Party. Multicoloured.

587. 50 c. Type **138** 15 10
588. 2 r. Liberation statue (vert.) 40 50
589. 3 r. New S.P.U.D. office .. 60 80
590. 10 r. President Rene (vert.) 2·00 3·00

140. Long jumping.

1984. Olympic Games, Los Angeles. Mult.

592. 50 c. Type **140** 10 10
593. 2 r. Boxing 40 45
594. 3 r. Swimming 60 75
595. 10 r. Weightlifting .. 1·75 2·50

141. Sub-aqua Diving.

1984. Water Sports. Multicoloured.

597. 50 c. Type **141** 20 10
598. 2 r. Paragliding 60 45
599. 3 r. Sailing 80 75
600. 10 r. Water-skiing .. .. 2·25 2·50

142. Humpback Whale.

1984. Whale Conservation. Multicoloured.

601. 50 c. Type **142** .. .. 1·00 15
602. 2 r. Sperm Whale .. .. 2·25 1·25
603. 3 r. Black Right Whale .. 2·50 1·75
604. 10 r. Blue Whale .. .. 4·75 6·00

143. Two Bare-legged Scops Owls in Tree.

1985. Birth Bicentenary of John J. Audubon (ornithologist). Bare-legged Scops Owl. Multicoloured.

605. 50 c. Type **143** 85 15
606. 2 r. Owl on branch .. 1·75 1·25
607. 3 r. Owl in flight .. .. 2·00 1·75
608. 10 r. Owl on ground .. 3·75 6·00

144. Giant Tortoises.

1985. "Expo '85" World Fair, Japan. Multicoloured.

609. 50 c. Type **144** 40 10
610. 2 r. White terns .. .. 1·50 75
611. 3 r. Windsurfing .. .. 1·50 95
612. 5 r. Coco-de-Mer .. .. 1·60 1·75

145. The Queen Mother with Princess Anne and Prince Andrew, 1970.

1985. Life and Times of Queen Elizabeth the Queen Mother. Multicoloured.

614. 50 c. The Queen Mother in 1930 .. .. .. 10 10
615. 2 r. Type **145** 45 50
616. 3 r. On her 75th Birthday 65 70
617. 5 r. With Prince Henry at his christening (from photo by Lord Snowdon) 1·10 1·25

146. Boxing.

1985. 2nd Indian Ocean Islands Games. Multicoloured.

619. 50 c. Type **146** 15 10
620. 2 r. Football 55 50
621. 3 r. Swimming 75 70
622. 10 r. Windsurfing .. .. 2·40 2·40

1985. Acquisition of 1st Air Seychelles "Airbus" As No. 735, but additionally inscribed "AIR SEYCHELLES FIRST AIRBUS".

623. 1 r. 25 White Tern .. 1·00 1·00

147. Agriculture Students.

1985. International Youth Year. Mult.

624. 50 c. Type **147** 10 10
625. 2 r. Construction students building wall 45 50
626. 3 r. Carpentry students .. 65 70
627. 10 r. Science students .. 2·25 2·40

148. Ford "Model T" (1919).

1985. Vintage Cars. Multicoloured.

628. 50 c. Type **148** 30 10
629. 2 r. Austin "Seven" (1922) 1·00 50
630. 3 r. Morris "Oxford" (1924) 1·25 70
631. 10 r. Humber "Coupe" (1929) .. .. .. 2·75 2·40

149. Five Foot Transit Instrument.

1986. Appearance of Halley's Comet. Mult.

632. 50 c. Type **149** 30 10
633. 2 r. Eight foot quadrant .. 1·00 50
634. 3 r. Comet's orbit .. .. 1·25 75
635. 10 r. Edmond Halley .. 2·75 2·40

150. Ballerina.

1986. Visit of Ballet du Louvre Company. "Giselle". Multicoloured.

636. 2 r. Type **150** 75 60
637. 3 r. Male dancer .. .. 1·00 90

1986. 60th Birthday of Queen Elizabeth II. As T **110** of Ascension. Multicoloured.

639. 50 c. Wedding photograph, 1947 .. .. .. 10 10
640. 1 r. 25 At State Opening of Parliament, 1982 .. 30 35
641. 2 r. Queen accepting bouquet, Seychelles, 1972 45 50
642. 3 r. On board Royal Yacht "Britannia", Qatar, 1979 70 75
643. 5 r. At Crown Agents Head Office, London, 1983 .. 1·10 1·25

151. Ferry to La Digue.

1986. "Ameripex '86" International Stamp Exhibition, Chicago. Inter-island Communication. Multicoloured.

644. 50 c. Type **151** 50 10
645. 2 r. Telephone kiosk (vert.) 1·10 60
646. 3 r. Post Office Counter, Victoria (vert.) .. .. 1·40 85
647. 7 r. Air Seychelles Britten-Norman "Trislander" aircraft .. .. .. 3·00 2·00

152. Crests of Seychelles and Knights of Malta.

1986. Seychelles Knights of Malta Day.

648. **152.** 5 r. multicoloured .. 1·10 1·25

1986. Royal Wedding. As T **112** of Ascension. Multicoloured.

651. 2 r. Prince Andrew and Miss Sarah Ferguson .. 45 50
652. 10 r. Prince Andrew boarding Wessex helicopter, 1983 .. .. 2·25 2·40

1986. International Creole Day. No. 487 optd. **LAZOURNEN ENTERNASYONAL KREOL.**

653. 1 r. Madagascar red fody 1·50 70

154. Pope John Paul at Seychelles Airport.

1986. Visit of Pope John Paul II. Designs showing Pope and Seychelles scene. Multicoloured.

654. 50 c. Type **154** 60 10
655. 2 r. Catholic Cathedral, Victoria .. .. .. 1·75 60
656. 3 r. Baie Lazare Parish Church .. .. .. 2·25 90
657. 10 r. Aerial view of Peoples' Stadium .. 3·75 2·75

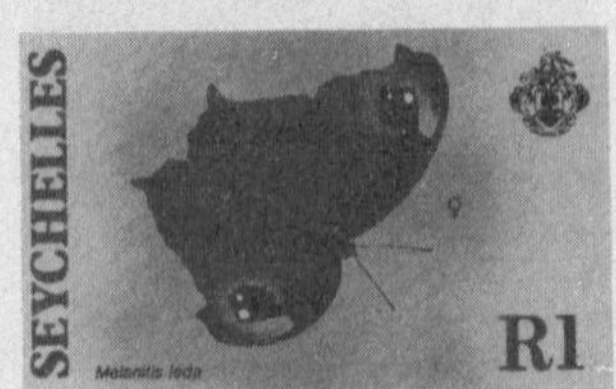

155. "Melanitis leda".

1987. Butterflies. Multicoloured.

659. 1 r. Type **155** 80 25
660. 2 r. "Phalanta philiberti" 1·40 75
661. 3 r. "Danaus chrysippus" 1·60 1·25
662. 10 r. "Euploea mitra" .. 4·50 4·50

156. "Gloripallium pallium".

1987. Seashells. Multicoloured.

663. 1 r. Type **156** 80 25
664. 2 r. "Spondylus aurantius" 1·40 75
665. 3 r. "Harpa ventricosa" and "Lioconcha ornata" 1·60 1·25
666. 10 r. "Strombus lentiginosus" .. .. 4·50 4·50

157. Statue of Liberation.

1987. 10th Anniv. of Liberation. Mult.

667. 1 r. Type **157** 20 25
668. 2 r. Seychelles hospital (horiz.) 45 50
669. 3 r. Orphanage village (horiz.) 70 75
670. 10 r. Proposed sail-fish monument .. .. 2·25 2·50

158. Seychelles Savings Bank, Praslin.

1987. Centenary of Banking in Seychelles.

671. **158.** 1 r. dp. grn. & grn. .. 20 25
672. – 2 r. brown and orange 45 50
673. – 10 r. dp. bl. & bl. .. 2·25 2·50

DESIGNS: 2 r. Development bank. 10 r. Central bank.

1987. Royal Ruby Wedding. Nos. 639/43 optd. **40TH WEDDING ANNIVERSARY.**

674. 50 c. Wedding photograph, 1947 .. .. .. 15 15
675. 1 r. 25 At State Opening of Parliament, 1982 .. 30 40
676. 2 r. Queen accepting bouquet, Seychelles, 1972 45 60
677. 3 r. On board Royal Yacht "Britannia", Qatar, 1979 70 85
678. 5 r. At Crown Agents Head Office, London, 1983 .. 1·10 1·40

159. Tuna Canning Factory.

1987. Seychelles Fishing Industry. Mult.

679. 50 c. Type **159** 15 15
680. 2 r. Trawler 45 50
681. 3 r. Weighing catch .. 70 75
682. 10 r. Unloading net .. 2·25 2·40

160. Water Sports.

1988. Tourism. Multicoloured.

683.	1 r. Type **160**	30	25
684.	2 r. Speedboat and yachts	55	65
685.	3 r. Yacht at anchor ..	80	80
686.	10 r. Hotel at night ..	2·50	3·00

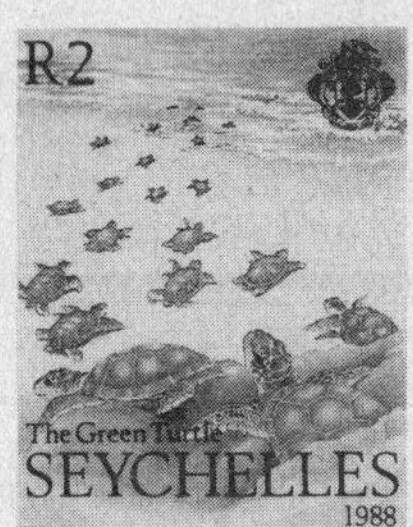

161. Young Turtles making for Sea.

1988. The Green Turtle. Multicoloured.

687.	2 r. Type **161**	1·50	1·75
688.	2 r. Young turtles hatching	1·50	1·75
689.	3 r. Female turtle leaving sea	1·75	2·00
690.	3 r. Female laying eggs ..	1·75	2·00

Nos. 687/8 and 689/90 were printed together, se-tenant, each pair forming a composite design.

162 Shot Put

1988. Olympic Games, Seoul. Multicoloured.

691	1 r. Type **162**	30	25
692	2 r. Type **162**	55	60
693	2 r. High jump	55	60
694	2 r. Gold medal winner on podium	55	60
695	2 r. Athletics	55	60
696	2 r. Javelin	55	60
697	3 r. As No. 694	60	65
698	4 r. As No. 695	80	85
699	5 r. As No. 696	1·00	1·10

1988. 300th Anniv of Lloyd's of London. As T **123** of Ascension. Multicoloured.

701	1 r. Leadenhall Street, London, 1928 ..	60	25
702	2 r. "Cinq Juin" (travelling post office) (horiz) ..	1·25	55
703	3 r. "Queen Elizabeth 2" (liner) (horiz)	1·75	80
704	10 r. Loss of "Hindenburg" (airship), 1937	4·50	3·25

163 Police Motorcyclists

1988. 1st Anniv of Defence Forces Day. Mult.

705	1 r. Type **163**	80	25
706	2 r. Air Wing helicopter ..	1·40	1·40
707	3 r. "Andromanche" (patrol boat)	1·75	1·75
708	10 r. BRDM armoured car	5·00	6·00

164 Father Christmas with Basket of Presents

1988. Christmas. Multicoloured.

709	50 c. Type **164**	15	10
710	2 r. Bird and gourd filled with presents	60	60
711	3 r. Father Christmas basket weaving ..	80	80
712	10 r. Christmas bauble and palm tree	2·25	2·50

165 "Dendrobium sp."

1988. Orchids (1st series). Multicoloured.

713	1 r. Type **165**	45	25
714	2 r. "Arachnis" hybrid (horiz)	75	55
715	3 r. "Vanda caerulea" ..	95	75
716	10 r. "Dendrobium phalaenopsis" (horiz)	2·75	3·50

See also Nos. 767/70 and 795/8.

166 India 1976 25 p. Nehru Stamp

1989. Birth Centenary of Jawaharlal Nehru (Indian statesman). Each showing flags of Seychelles and India. Multicoloured.

724	2 r. Type **166**	60	50
725	10 r. Jawaharlal Nehru ..	2·50	3·00

167 Pres. Rene addressing Rally at Old Party Office

1989. 25th Anniv of Seychelles People's United Party. Multicoloured.

742	1 r. Type **167**	20	25
743	2 r. Women with Party flags and Maison Du Peuple	40	45
744	3 r. President Rene making speech and Torch of Freedom	60	65
745	10 r. President Rene, Party flag and Torch of Freedom	2·00	2·50

1989. 20th Anniv of First Manned Landing on Moon. As T **126** of Ascension. Multicoloured.

746	1 r. Lift off of "Saturn 5" rocket	20	25
747	2 r. Crew of "Apollo 15" (30 × 30 mm)	40	50
748	3 r. "Apollo 15" emblem (30 × 30 mm)	60	70
749	5 r. James Irwin saluting U.S. flag on Moon ..	1·00	1·25

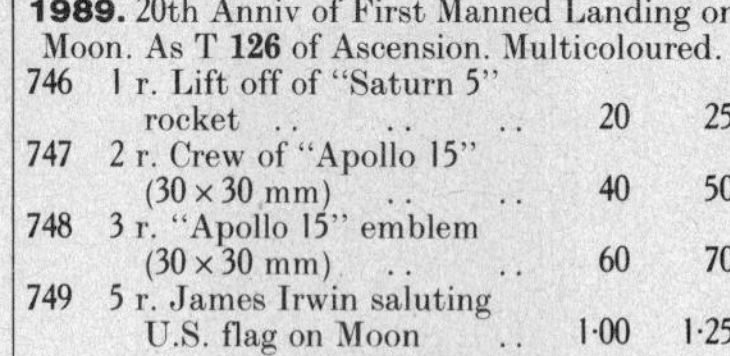

168 British Red Cross Ambulance, Franco-Prussian War, 1870

1989. 125th Anniv of International Red Cross.

751	**168** 1 r. black and red ..	65	25
752	– 2 r. black, green & red	1·10	1·00
753	– 3 r. black and red ..	1·60	1·50
754	– 10 r. black and red ..	4·50	5·50

DESIGNS: 2 r. "Liberty" (hospital ship), 1914–18; 3 r. Sunbeam "Standard" army ambulance, 1914–18; 10 r. "White Train", South Africa, 1899–1902.

169 Black Parrot and Map of Praslin

1989. Island Birds. Multicoloured.

755	50 c. Type **169**	75	15
756	2 r. Sooty tern and Ile aux Vaches	1·60	1·25
757	3 r. Seychelles magpie robin and Fregate ..	1·90	1·60
758	5 r. Roseate tern and Aride	2·50	3·00

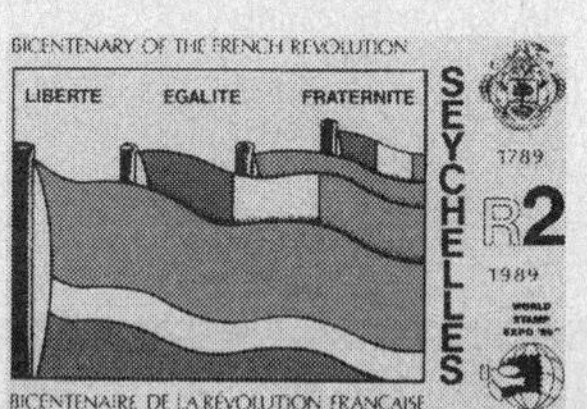

170 Flags of Seychelles and France

1989. Bicentenary of French Revolution and "World Stamp Expo '89", International Stamp Exhibition, Washington.

760	**170** 2 r. multicoloured ..	1·25	1·25
761	– 5 r. black, blue and red	2·50	3·00

DESIGN: 5 r. Storming the Bastille, Paris, 1789.

171 Beau Vallon School

1989. 25th Anniv of African Development Bank. Multicoloured.

763	1 r. Type **171**	45	25
764	2 r. Seychelles Fishing Authority Headquarters	80	70
765	3 r. "Variola" (fishing boat) (vert)	1·75	1·40
766	10 r. "Deneb" (fishing boat) (vert)	4·75	5·50

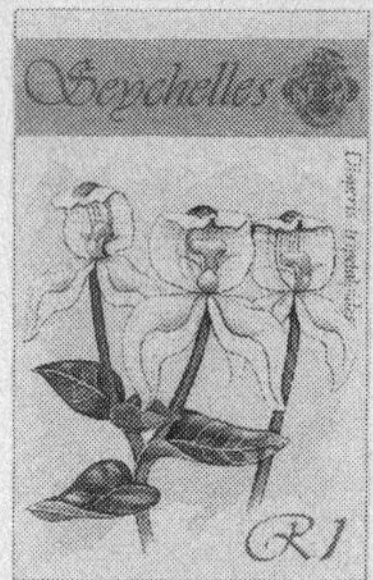

172 "Disperis tripetaloides"

1990. Orchids (2nd series). Multicoloured.

767	1 r. Type **172**	75	25
768	2 r. "Vanilla phalaenopsis"	1·25	1·00
769	3 r. "Angraecum eburneum" subsp. "superbum"	1·60	1·25
770	10 r. "Polystachya concreta"	4·25	5·00

173 Seychelles 1903 2 c. and Great Britain 1880 1½d. Stamps

1990. "Stamp World London 90" International Stamp Exhibition. Each showing stamps. Multicoloured.

771	1 r. Type **173**	55	25
772	2 r. Seychelles 1917 25 c. and G.B. 1873 1s. ..	95	1·00
773	3 r. Seychelles 1917 2 c. and G.B. 1874 6d. ..	1·40	1·50
774	5 r. Seychelles 1890 2 c. and G.B. 1841 1d. brown ..	2·00	2·50

174 Fumiyo Sako

1990. "EXPO 90" International Garden and Greenery Exhibition, Osaka. Multicoloured.

776	2 r. Type **174**	75	75
777	3 r. Male and female coco-de-mer palms ..	1·00	1·00
778	5 r. Pitcher plant and aldabra lily	1·60	1·75
779	7 r. Arms of Seychelles and gardenia	2·25	2·50

175 Air Seychelles Boeing "767-200ER" over Island

1990. Air Seychelles "Boeing 767-200ER" World Record-breaking Flight (1989).

781	**175** 3 r. multicoloured ..	1·60	1·60

1990. 90th Birthday of Queen Elizabeth the Queen Mother. As T **134** of Ascension.

782	2 r. multicoloured ..	75	60
783	10 r. black and violet ..	2·75	3·25

DESIGNS—21 × 36 mm. 2 r. Queen Elizabeth in Coronation robes, 1937. 29 × 37 mm. 10 r. Queen Elizabeth visiting Lord Roberts Workshops, 1947.

176 Adult Class

1990. International Literacy Year. Mult.
784 1 r. Type **176** 50 25
785 2 r. Reading a letter .. 85 80
786 3 r. Following written instructions .. .. 1·25 1·25
787 10 r. Typewriter, calculator and crossword .. .. 3·50 4·00

177 Sega Dancers

1990. Kreol Festival. Sega Dancing. Mult.
788 2 r. Type **177** .. .. 95 1·00
789 2 r. Dancing couple (girl in yellow dress) .. .. 95 1·00
790 2 r. Female Sega dancer .. 95 1·00
791 2 r. Dancing couple (girl in floral pattern skirt) .. 95 1·00
792 2 r. Dancing couple (girl in red patterned skirt) .. 95 1·00

178 Beach

1990. 1st Indian Ocean Regional Seminar on Petroleum Exploration. Multicoloured.
793 3 r. Type **178** .. .. 1·25 1·00
794 10 r. Geological map .. 3·50 4·00

1991. Orchids (3rd series). As T **172**. Mult.
795 1 r. "Bulbophyllum intertextum" 50 25
796 2 r. "Agrostophyllum occidentale" 90 75
797 3 r. "Vanilla planifolia" .. 1·25 1·10
798 10 r. "Malaxis seychellarum" .. .. 3·50 4·00

1991. 65th Birthday of Queen Elizabeth II and 70th Birthday of Prince Philip. As T **139** of Ascension. Multicoloured.
799 4 r. Queen in evening dress 1·40 1·75
800 4 r. Prince Philip in academic robes .. 2·75 3·50

179 "Precis rhadama"

1991. "Phila Nippon '91" Int Stamp Exn, Tokyo. Butterflies. Mult.
801 1 r. 50 Type **179** .. 80 40
802 3 r. "Lampides boeticus" 1·40 1·25
803 3 r. 50 "Zizeeria knysna" 1·60 1·50
804 10 r. "Phalanta phalanta" 4·50 5·00

180 "The Holy Virgin, Joseph, The Holy Child and St. John" (S. Vouillemont after Raphael)

1991. Christmas. Woodcuts.
806 **180** 50 c. black, brn & red 25 15
807 – 1 r. black, brown & grn 45 25
808 – 2 r. black, brown & bl 80 70
809 – 7 r. black, brown & bl 2·50 3·00
DESIGNS: 1 r. "The Holy Virgin, the Child and Angel" (A. Blooting after Van Dyck); 2 r. "The Holy Family, St. John and St. Anna" (L. Vorsterman after Rubens); 7 r. "The Holy Family, Angel and St. Cathrin" (C. Bloemaert).

1992. 40th Anniv of Queen Elizabeth II's Accession. As T **143** of Ascension. Mult.
810 1 r. Seychelles coastline .. 45 25
811 1 r. 50 Clock Tower, Victoria 60 40
812 3 r. Victoria harbour .. 1·10 1·10
813 3 r. 50 Three portraits of Queen Elizabeth .. 1·25 1·50
814 5 r. Queen Elizabeth II .. 1·50 2·00

181 Brush Warbler

1993. Flora and Fauna. Multicoloured.
815 10 c. Type **181** 10 10
816 25 c. Bronze gecko (vert) 10 10
817 50 c. Seychelles tree frog 15 20
818 1 r. Seychelles splendid palm (vert) 25 30
819 1 r. 50 Seychelles skink (vert) 40 45
820 2 r. Giant tenebrionid beetle 50 55
821 3 r. Seychelles sunbird .. 75 80
822 3 r. 50 Seychelles killifish 90 95
823 4 r. Magpie robin .. 1·00 1·10
824 5 r. Seychelles vanilla (plant) (vert) .. .. 1·25 1·40
825 10 r. Tiger chameleon .. 2·50 2·75
826 15 r. Coco-de-mer (vert) .. 4·00 4·25
827 25 r. Paradise flycatcher (vert) .. .. .. 6·50 6·75
828 50 r. Giant tortoise .. 13·00 13·50

182 Archbishop George Carey and Anglican Cathedral, Victoria

1993. 1st Visit of an Archbishop of Canterbury to Seychelles. Multicoloured.
834 3 r. Type **182** .. .. 1·00 1·00
835 10 r. Archbishop Carey with Air France and Air Seychelles airliners .. 3·25 3·50

183 Athletics

1993. 4th Indian Ocean Island Games. Mult.
836 1 r. 50 Type **183** 55 55
837 3 r. Football .. .. 1·00 1·00
838 3 r. 50 Cycling .. .. 1·25 1·25
839 10 r. Yachting .. .. 3·25 3·50

184 "Scotia" (cable ship) off Victoria, 1893

1993. Cent of Telecommunications. Mult.
840 1 r. Type **184** 50 50
841 3 r. Eastern Telegraph Co office, Victoria, 1904 .. 1·00 1·00
842 4 r. HF Transmitting Station, 1971 .. .. 1·40 1·40
843 10 r. New Telecoms House, Victoria, 1993 .. .. 3·25 3·50

1994. "Hong Kong '94" International Stamp Exhibition. Nos. 62, 64 and 66/7 of Zil Elwannyen Sesel surch **HONG KONG '94**, emblem and value.
844 1 r. on 2 r. 10 Souimanga sunbird 25 30
845 1 r. 50 on 2 r. 75 Sacred ibis 40 45
846 3 r. 50 on 7 r. Seychelles kestrel (vert) 90 95
847 10 r. on 15 r. Comoro blue pigeon (vert) .. .. 2·50 2·75

POSTAGE DUE STAMPS

D 1.

1951. Value in red.
D 1. **D 1.** 2 c. red and carmine 80 1·50
D 2. 3 c. red and green 1·25 1·50
D 3. 6 c. red and bistre 1·25 1·25
D 4. 9 c. red and orange 1·50 1·25
D 5. 15 c. red and violet 1·75 7·50
D 6. 18 c. red and blue .. 1·75 7·50
D 7. 20 c. red and brown 1·75 7·50
D 8. 30 c. red and claret 1·75 7·50

1980. As D 1 but 18 × 22 mm.
D 11. **D 1.** 5 c. red and mauve 15 40
D 12. 10 c. red and green .. 15 40
D 13. 15 c. red and bistre 20 40
D 14. 20 c. red and brown 20 50
D 15. 25 c. red and violet 20 50
D 16. 75 c. red and maroon 30 50
D 17. 80 c. red and blue .. 30 50
D 18. 1 r. red and purple .. 30 60

SHAHPURA

One of the Indian Feudatory States. Now uses Indian stamps.

12 pies = 1 anna; 12 annas = 1 rupee.

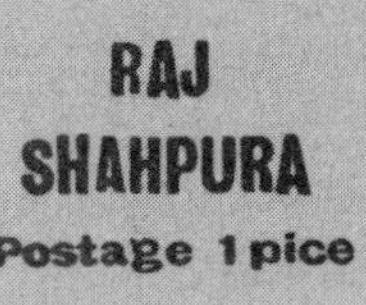

1

1914. Perf (No. 1) or imperf (No. 2).
1 **1** 1 p. red/grey .. .. — £130
2 1 p. red/brown .. .. — £200

1920. As T **1** but "Postage" omitted. Imperf.
3 1 p. red/brown .. .. — £275
4 1 a. black/pink .. .. — £275

SIERRA LEONE

A Br. colony on the W. coast of Africa. Achieved independence within the Br. Commonwealth in 1961. By vote of the Assembly on 19 April, 1971, Sierra Leone was proclaimed a Republic.

1859. 12 pence = 1 shilling.
20 shillings = 1 pound.
1964. 100 cents = 1 leone.

1.

2.

1859.
16 **2** ½d. brown .. .. .. 2·00 4·75
27 ½d. green 40 50
28 1d. red .. .. .. 2·00 55
29 1½d. lilac .. .. .. 2·00 5·00
25 2d. mauve .. .. .. 38·00 6·50
30 2d. grey .. .. .. 20·00 2·00
31 2½d. blue .. .. .. 7·00 75
32 3d. yellow .. .. .. 1·75 4·50
21 4d. blue .. .. .. £100 6·50
33 4d. brown .. .. .. 1·50 1·00
37 **1** 6d. purple .. .. .. 2·00 6·50
22 **2** 1s. green .. .. .. 50·00 6·00
34 1s. brown .. .. .. 12·00 10·00

1893. Surch. **HALF PENNY**
39. **2.** ½d. on 1½d. lilac .. .. 2·75 3·00

4.

15

6.

1896.
41. **4.** ½d. mauve and green .. 85 1·25
42. 1d. mauve and red .. 85 65
43. 1½d. mauve and black .. 2·75 8·00
44. 2d. mauve and orange .. 2·25 5·00
45. 2½d. mauve and blue .. 1·40 80
46. 3d. mauve and grey .. 7·00 7·00
47. 4d. mauve and red .. 7·00 13·00
48. 5d. mauve and black .. 8·00 11·00
49. 6d. mauve .. .. 7·00 14·00
50. 1s. green and black .. 6·00 15·00
51. 2s. green and blue .. 20·00 27·00
52. 5s. green and red .. .. 40·00 85·00
53. £1 purple on red £140 £300

1897. T **6** optd. **POSTAGE AND REVENUE**
54. **6.** 1 d. purple and green .. 1·75 2·00

1897. T **6** optd. **POSTAGE AND REVENUE** and surch. **2½d.** and bars.
55. **6.** 2½d. on 3d. purple & green 11·00 12·00
59. 2½d. on 6d. purple & green 8·50 12·00
63. 2½d. on 1s. purple .. .. 80·00 60·00
67. 2½d. on 2s. purple £1300 £1600

1903.

73 15 ½d. purple and green .. 3·00 2·75
87 1d. purple and red .. 80 35
75 1½d. purple and black .. 1·25 4·25
89 2d. purple and orange .. 4·25 3·50
90 2½d. purple and blue .. 4·50 2·00
78 3d. purple and grey .. 6·50 8·50
92 4d. purple and red .. 4·50 5·00
80 5d. purple and black .. 7·00 16·00
94 6d. purple .. .. 4·00 3·25
95 1s. green and black .. 7·50 8·50
96 2s. green and blue .. 14·00 20·00
97 5s. green and red .. 28·00 48·00
85 £1 purple on red .. £200 £225

1907.

99 15 ½d. green.. .. .. 35 30
100a 1d. red .. .. .. 2·50 20
101 1½d. orange .. .. 40 2·00
102 2d. grey .. .. .. 80 1·50
103 2½d. blue.. .. .. 2·00 1·40
104 3d. purple on yellow .. 6·00 2·75
105 4d. black and red on yell. 2·25 1·10
106 5d. purple and olive .. 5·50 4·25
108 1s. black on green .. 5·50 4·50
109 2s. purple & blue on blue 15·00 13·00
110 5s. grn. and red on yellow 27·00 40·00
111 £1 purple & black on red £170 £180

17

20

1912.

131 17 ½d. green 80 15
113 1d. red .. .. 1·25 10
132a 1d. violet .. .. 2·00 10
114 1½d. orange .. .. 1·00 95
133 1½d. red 60 30
134 2d. grey 50 10
116a 2½d. blue .. .. 1·00 65
116b 20 3d. purple on yellow 3·00 2·50
136 17 3d. blue 50 30
137 4d. blk. & red on yell. 1·75 1·75
138 5d. purple and olive.. 60 60
139 6d. purple .. .. 1·25 2·00
120 7d. purple and orange 2·00 4·50
141 9d. purple and black 2·50 8·50
142 10d. purple and red .. 2·00 15·00
124a 20 1s black on green .. 4·25 2·75
125 2s. blue & pur. on bl. 8·50 3·75
126 5s. red & grn. on yell. 11·00 18·00
127 10s. red & grn. on grn. 48·00 80·00
128 £1 blk. & pur. on red £120 £150
147 £2 blue and purple .. £425 £600
130 £5 orange and green £1200 £1400

21 Rice Field

22 Palms and Cola Tree

1932.

155 21 ½d. green.. .. .. 15 20
156 1d. violet 20 10
157 1½d. red .. .. .. 20 1·25
158 2d. brown 20 10
159 3d. blue 60 95
160 4d. orange .. .. 60 2·50
161 5d. green.. .. .. 75 1·60
162 6d. blue .. .. .. 50 1·50
163 1s. red .. .. .. 90 2·75
164 22 2s. brown .. .. 3·00 3·75
165 5s. blue .. .. .. 8·50 15·00
166 10s. green .. .. 50·00 90·00
167 £1 purple.. .. .. 80·00 £140

23 Arms of Sierra Leone

DESIGNS VERT. 1d. "Freedom". 1½d. Map of Sierra Leone. 4d. Government Sanatorium. 5s. African Elephant. HORIZ. 2d. Old Slave Market, Freetown. 3d. Native Fruitseller. 5d. Bullom canoe. 6d. Punting near Banana Is. 1s. Govt. Buildings, Freetown. 2s. Bunce Is. 10s. King George V. £1, Freetown Harbour.

1933. Cent. of Abolition of Slavery and Death of William Wilberforce. Dated "1833 1933".

168 23 ½d. green 45 85
169 – 1d. black and brown .. 40 10
170 – 1½d. brown .. .. 4·00 4·25
171 – 2d. purple .. .. 2·75 20
172 – 3d. blue.. .. .. 2·50 1·50
173 – 4d. brown .. .. 6·50 10·00
174 – 5d. green and brown .. 7·00 16·00
175 – 6d. black and orange .. 7·00 8·00
176 – 1s. violet .. .. 4·75 15·00
177 – 2s. brown and blue .. 20·00 28·00
178 – 5s. black and purple .. £130 £150
179 – 10s. black and olive .. £130 £180
180 – £1 violet and orange .. £325 £375

1935. Silver Jubilee. As T **13** of Antigua.

181 1d. blue and black .. 70 65
182 3d. brown and blue .. 1·00 4·25
183 5d. green and blue .. 1·40 5·50
184 1s. grey and purple .. 4·75 2·75

1937. Coronation. As T **2** of Aden.

185. 1d. orange 70 30
186. 2d. purple 90 30
187. 3d. blue.. .. .. 2·00 2·00

30. Freetown from the Harbour.

1938. King George VI.

188. 30. ½d. black and green .. 15 30
189. 1d. black and red .. 40 15
190. – 1½d. red .. .. 20·00 30
190a. – 1½d. mauve 20 20
191. – 2d. mauve .. .. 40·00 1·40
191a. – 2d. red 20 50
192. 30. 3d. black and blue .. 40 30
193. 4d. black and brown .. 80 85
194. – 5d. olive .. .. 5·00 2·75
195. – 6d. grey 75 30
196. 30. 1s. black and olive .. 1·25 30
196a. – 1s. 3d. orange .. 40 30
197. 30. 2s. black and brown .. 3·50 1·00
198. – 5s. brown .. .. 7·50 3·50
199. – 10s. green .. .. 13·00 7·00
200. 30. £1 blue .. .. 17·00 12·00

DESIGN: 1½d., 2d., 5d., 6d., 1s. 3d., 5s., 10s. Rice harvesting.

1946. Victory. As T **9** of Aden.

201. 1½d. lilac 15 10
202. 3d. blue 15 10

1948. Silver Wedding. As T **10/11** of Aden.

203 1½d. mauve 15 15
204 £1 blue .. .. .. 16·00 16·00

1949. 75th Anniv of U.P.U. As T **20/23** of Antigua.

205 1½d. purple 15 30
206 3d. blue .. .. .. 35 1·00
207 6d. grey .. .. .. 35 1·00
208 1s. green .. .. .. 35 1·00

1953. Coronation. As T **13** of Aden.

209. 1½d. black and lilac .. 20 20

32. Cape Lighthouse.

1956. Centres in black.

210. 32. ½d. lilac.. .. .. 70 1·00
211. – 1d. olive 70 30
212. – 1½d. blue .. .. 1·40 2·50
213. – 2d. brown 50 10
214. – 3d. blue.. .. .. 1·00 10
215. – 4d. slate .. .. 2·50 85
216. – 6d. violet 80 20
217. – 1s. red 80 10
218. – 1s. 3d. sepia .. .. 6·50 10
219. – 2s. 6d. brown .. .. 8·00 3·25
220. – 5s. green .. .. 1·25 1·00
221. – 10s. mauve .. .. 3·25 2·50
222. – £1 orange .. .. 9·00 16·00

DESIGNS—HORIZ. 1d. Queen Elizabeth II Quay. 1½d. Piassava workers. 4d. Iron ore production, Marampa. 6d. Whale Bay, York Village. 1s. 3d. Aeroplane and map. 10s. Law Courts, Freetown. £1 Government House. VERT. 2d. Cotton tree, Freetown. 3d. Rice harvesting. 1s. Bullom canoe. 2s. 6d. Orugu railway bridge. 5s. Kuranko chief.

46. Licensed Diamond Miner.

1961. Independence.

223. – ½d. brown and turquoise 20 10
224. 46. 1d. brown and green .. 1·25 10
225. – 1½d. black and green .. 20 10
226. – 2d. black and blue .. 20 10
227. – 3d. brown and blue .. 20 10
228. – 4d. blue and red .. 20 10
229. – 6d. black and purple .. 20 10
230. – 1s. brown and orange.. 20 10
231. – 1s. 3d. blue and violet.. 20 10
232. 46. 2s. 6d. green and black 2·50 20
233. – 5s. black and red .. 1·00 1·00
234. – 10s. black and green .. 1·00 1·25
235. – £1 red and yellow .. 7·00 4·50

DESIGNS—VERT. ½d., 1s. Palm fruit gathering. 1½d., 5s. Bundu mask. 2d., 10s. Bishop Crowther and Old Fourah Bay College. £1, Forces bugler. HORIZ. 3d., 6d. Sir Milton Margai. 4d., 1s. 3d. Lumley Beach, Freetown.

53. Royal Charter, 1799.

DESIGNS—As Type **53**: 4d. King's Yard Gate, Freetown, 1817. As Type **55**: 1s. 3d. Royal Yacht "Britannia" at Freetown.

55. Old House of Representatives, Freetown, 1924.

1961. Royal Visit.

236. 53. 3d. black and red .. 15 10
237. – 4d. black and violet .. 15 40
238. 55. 6d. black and orange .. 15 10
239. – 1s. 3d. black and blue.. 2·00 40

57. Campaign Emblem.

58. Fireball Lily.

1962. Malaria Eradication.

240. 57. 3d. red 10 10
241. 1s. 3d. green 20 10

1963. Flowers in natural colours; background colours given below.

242. 58. ½d. bistre 10 10
243. – 1d. red 10 10
244. – 1½d. green 10 10
245. – 2d. olive 10 10
246. – 3d. green 10 10
247. – 4d. blue.. .. .. 15 10
248. – 6d. blue.. .. .. 30 10
249. – 1s. green 40 10
250. – 1s. 3d. green .. .. 1·25 20
251. – 2s. 6d. purple .. .. 1·25 30
252. – 5s. violet .. .. 1·25 80
253. – 10s. purple .. .. 2·25 1·50
254. – £1 blue .. .. .. 7·50 7·00

FLOWERS—VERT. 1½d. Stereospermum. 3d. Beniseed. 4d. Blushing Hibiscus. 1s. Beautiful Crinum. 2s. 6d. Broken Hearts. 5s. Ra-ponthi. 10s. Blue Plumbago. HORIZ. 1d. Jina-gbo. 2d. Black-eyed Susan. 6d. Climbing Lily. 1s. 3d. Blue Bells. £1, African Tulip Tree.

71. Threshing Machine and Corn Bins.

1963. Freedom from Hunger.

255. 71. 3d. black and ochre .. 15 10
256. – 1s. 3d. sepia and green.. 35 10

DESIGN: 1s. 3d. Girl with onion crop.

1963. 2nd Anniv. of Independence. Stamp of 1956 surch. **2nd Year of Independence Progress Development 1963** and value in various types (except 2s. 6d.). Centres in black. (a) Postage.

257. 3d. on ½d. lilac 30 10
258. 4d. on 1½d. blue 15 10
259. 6d. on ½d. lilac 30 10
260. 10d. on 3d. blue 50 10
261. 1s. 6d. on 3d. blue .. 30 20
262. 3s. 6d. on 3d. blue .. 40 20

(b) Air. Optd. **AIRMAIL** in addition.

263. 7d. on 1½d. blue 20 10
264. 1s. 3d. on 1½d. blue .. 20 10
265. 2s. 6d. brown 50 20
266. 3s. on 3d. blue 40 20
267. 6s. on 3d. blue .. .. 1·00 20
268. 11s. on 10s. mauve .. 1·40 85
269. 11s. on £1 orange.. .. £500 £180

75. Centenary Emblem.

DESIGNS: 6d. Red Cross emblem. 1s. 3d. As Type **75** but with lined background and value on left.

1963. Centenary of Red Cross.

270. 75. 3d. red and violet .. 30 10
271. – 6d. red and black .. 45 15
272. – 1s. 3d. red and green .. 65 20

1963. Postal Commemorations. (a) Postage. Optd. or surch. **1853-1859-1963 Oldest Postal Service Newest G.P.O. in West Africa** and value.

273. – 3d. (No. 214) 10 10
274. – 4d. on 1½d. (No. 212) .. 10 10
275. – 9d. on 1½d. (No. 212) .. 10 10
276. – 1s. on 1s. 3d. (No. 231) 10 10
277. 32. 1s. 6d. on ½d. 15 10
278. – 2s. on 3d. (No. 214) .. 15 10

(b) Air. Optd. or surch. as above but **Postage Stamp** instead of **Postal Service** and **AIRMAIL** in addition.

279. 53. 7d. on 3d. 20 40
280. – 1s. 3d. (No. 239) .. 1·25 65
281. – 2s. 6d. on 4d. (No. 228) 65 20
282. 53. 3s. on 3d. .. .. 1·50 1·50
283. 55. 6s. on 6d. 85 70
284. – £1 (No. 222) .. .. 14·00 13·00

Commemoration dates:—
1853—"First Post Office".
1859—"First Postage Stamps".
1963—"Newest G.P.O." in West Africa.

80. Lion Emblem and Map.

81. Globe and Map.

1964. World's Fair, New York. Imperf. Self-adhesive.

285. **80.** 1d. mult. (postage) .. 10 10
286. 3d. multicoloured .. 10 10
287. 4d. multicoloured .. 10 10
288. 6d. multicoloured .. 10 10
289. 1s. multicoloured .. 10 10
290. 2s. multicoloured .. 15 10
291. 5s. multicoloured .. 30 20
292. **81.** 7d. multicoloured (air) 10 10
293. 9d. multicoloured .. 10 10
294. 1s. 3d. multicoloured .. 10 10
295. 2s. 6d. multicoloured .. 20 10
296. 3s. 6d. multicoloured .. 20 10
297. 6s. multicoloured .. 30 25
298. 11s. multicoloured .. 45 50

Warning.—These self-adhesive stamps should be kept mint on their backing paper and used on cover or piece.

82. Inscription and Map.

83. Pres. Kennedy and Map.

1964. President Kennedy Memorial Issue. Imperf. Self-adhesive.

299. **82.** 1d. mult. (postage) .. 10 10
300. 3d. multicoloured .. 10 10
301. 4d. multicoloured .. 10 10
302. 6d. multicoloured .. 10 10
303. 1s. multicoloured .. 10 10
304. 2s. multicoloured .. 10 10
305. 5s. multicoloured .. 25 20
306. **83.** 7d. multicoloured (air) 10 10
307. 9d. multicoloured .. 10 10
308. 1s. 3d. multicoloured .. 10 10
309. 2s. 6d. multicoloured .. 20 20
310. 3s. 6d. multicoloured .. 20 20
311. 6s. multicoloured .. 40 40
312. 11s. multicoloured .. 60 60

The note below No. 298 applies also to the above issue.

1964. Decimal Currency. Various stamps surch.

(i) 1st issue. Surch. in figures.

(a) Postage.

313. – 1 c. on 6d. (No. 248) .. 10 10
314. **53.** 2 c. on 3d. (No. 236) .. 10 10
315. – 3 c. on 3d. (No. 246) .. 10 10
316. – 5 c. on ½d. (No. 223) .. 10 10
317. **71.** 8 c. on 3d. (No. 255) .. 10 10
318. – 10 c. on 1s. 3d. (No. 250) 10 10
319. – 15 c. on 1s. (No. 249) .. 15 10
320. **55.** 25 c. on 6d. (No. 238) .. 30 25
321. **46.** 50 c. on 2s. 6d. (No. 232) 60 50

(b) Air. Nos. 322/5 additionally optd. AIRMAIL.

322. – 7 c. on 1s. 3d. (No. 256) 10 10
323. – 20 c. on 4d. (No. 228) .. 25 15
324. – 30 c. on 10s. (No. 234) 40 30
325. – 40 c. on 5s. (No. 233) .. 50 40
326. **83.** 1 l. on 1s. 3d. (No. 308) 75 80
327. 2 l. on 11s. (No. 312) .. 1·25 1·40

(ii) 2nd issue. Surch. in figures or figures and words (Nos. 332/3).

328. – 1 c. on 3d. (No. 227) (postage) 10 10
329. **82.** 2 c. on 1d. (No. 299) 10 10
330. 4 c. on 3d. (No. 300) 10 10
331. – 5 c. on 2d. (No. 245) 10 10
332. – 1 l. on 5s. (No. 252) .. 1·25 1·25
333. – 2 l. on £1 (No. 235) .. 2·25 2·25
334. **83.** 7 c. on 7d. (No. 306) (air) 10 10
335. 60 c. on 9d. (No. 307) 50 45

(iii) Third issue. Surch. in figures.

336. – 1 c. on 1½d. (No. 225) (postage) 10 10
337. **82.** 2 c. on 3d. (No. 300) .. 10 10
338. **80.** 2 c. on 4d. (No. 287) .. 10 10
339. – 3 c. on 1d. (No. 243) .. 10 10
340. – 3 c. on 2d. (No. 226) .. 10 10
341. 5 c. on 1s. 3d. (No. 231) 10 10
342. **82.** 15 c. on 6d. (No. 302) .. 80 50
343. 15 c. on 1s. (No. 303) .. 1·25 90
344. – 20 c. on 6d. (No. 229) .. 30 15
345. – 25 c. on 6d. (No. 248) .. 35 20
346. – 50 c. on 3d. (No. 227) .. 80 55
347. **80.** 60 c. on 5s. (No. 291) .. 3·25 1·75
348. **82.** 1 l. on 4d. (No. 301) .. 3·75 2·75
349. – 2 l. on £1 (No. 235) .. 6·00 3·75
350. **81.** 7 c. on 9d. (air) .. 15 10

(iv) Fourth issue. Surch in figures.

351. **80.** 1 c. on 6d. (postage) .. 2·75 7·00
352. 1 c. on 2s. .. .. 2·75 7·00
353. **82.** 1 c. on 2s. .. .. 2·75 7·00
354. 1 c. on 5s. .. .. 2·75 7·00
355. **81.** 2 c. on 1s. 3d. (air) .. 2·75 7·00
356. **83.** 2 c. on 1s. 3d. .. .. 2·75 7·00
357. 2 c. on 3s. 6d. .. .. 2·75 7·00
358. **81.** 3 c. on 7d. .. .. 2·75 7·00
359. **83.** 3 c. on 9d. .. .. 2·75 7·00
360. **81.** 5 c. on 2s. 6d. .. .. 2·75 7·00
361. **83.** 5 c. on 2s. 6d. .. .. 2·75 7·00
362. **81.** 5 c. on 3s. 6d. .. .. 2·75 7·00
363. 5 c. on 6s. .. .. 2·75 7·00
364. **83.** 5 c. on 6s. .. .. 2·75 7·00

(v) Fifth issue. No. 374 further surch. TWO Leones.

365. – 2 l. on 30 c. on 6d. (air) 2·50 2·00

(**91.** Margai and Churchill).

1965. Sir Milton Margai and Sir Winston Churchill Commem. Flower stamps of 1963 surch. as T **91** on horiz. designs or with individual portraits on vert. designs as indicated. Multicoloured.

(a) Postage.

366. – 2 c. on 1d. 10 10
367. – 3 c. on 3d. Margai .. 10 10
368. – 10 c. on 1s. Churchill .. 20 10
369. – 20 c. on 1s. 3d. .. 40 10
370. – 50 c. on 4d. Margai .. 90 35
371. – 75 c. on 5s. Churchill .. 2·25 1·25

(b) Air. Additionally optd. AIR MAIL.

372. – 7 c. on 2d. 20 10
373. **58.** 15 c. on ½d. Margai .. 35 10
374. – 30 c. on 6d. .. 1·25 25
375. – 1 l. on £1 .. .. 4·00 1·50
376. – 2 l. on 10s. Churchill .. 11·00 5·00

92. Cola Plant and Nut.

1965. Various shapes, backed with paper bearing advertisements. Imperf. Self-adhesive.

A. Printed in green, yellow and red on silver foil. Values in colours given.

377. **92.** 1 c. green (postage) .. 25 10
378. 2 c. red 25 10
379. 3 c. yellow 25 10
380. 4 c. silver on green .. 30 10
381. 5 c. silver on red .. 30 10

B. Designs 45×49 mm. showing Arms of Sierra Leone.

382. – 20 c. mult. on cream (postage) .. .. 1·25 40
383. – 50 c. mult. on cream .. 2·75 2·00
384. – 40 c. mult. on cream (air) 2·50 2·00

C. Designs 48×44½ mm. showing inscription and necklace.

385. – 7 c. multicoloured post.) 55 15
386. – 15 c. multicoloured .. 1·00 60

1966. 5th Anniv. of Independence. Surch. **FIVE YEARS INDEPENDENCE 1961-1966** and value.

(a) Postage.

387. – 1 c. on 6d. (No. 248) .. 10 10
388. – 2 c. on 4d. (No. 247) .. 10 10
389. – 3 c. on 1½d. (No. 212) .. 10 10
390. – 8 c. on 1s. (No. 249) .. 15 10
391. – 10 c. on 2s. 6d. (No. 251) 15 10
392. – 20 c. on 2d. (No. 213) .. 20 10

(b) Air. Surch. **AIRMAIL** also.

393. **75.** 7 c. on 3d. 10 10
394. – 15 c. on 1s. (No. 249) .. 20 10
395. – 25 c. on 2s. 6d. (No. 251) 55 60
396. – 50 c. on 1½d. (No. 244) .. 75 80
397. – 1 l. on 4d. (No. 247) .. 1·40 1·60

97. Lion's Head.

1966. 1st Sierra Leone Gold Coinage Commem. Circular designs, embossed on gold foil, backed with paper bearing advertisements. Imperf. (a) Postage.

(i) ¼ golde coin. Diameter 1½ in.

398. **97.** 2 c. mauve and orange 10 10
399. – 3 c. green and purple .. 10 10

(ii) ½ golde coin. Diameter 2⅛ in.

400. **97.** 5 c. red and blue .. 10 10
401. – 8 c. turquoise and black 15 15

(ii) 1 golde coin. Diameter 3¼ in.

402. **97.** 25 c. violet and green .. 35 35
403. – 1 l. orange and red .. 2·25 2·25

(b) Air (i) ¼ golde coin. Diameter 1½ in.

404. **97.** 7 c. orange and red .. 10 10
405. – 10 c. red and blue .. 15 15

(ii) ½ golde coin. Diameter 2⅛ in.

406. **97.** 15 c. orange and red .. 25 25
407. – 30 c. purple and black .. 40 45

(iii) 1 golde coin. Diameter 3¼ in.

408. **97.** 50 c. green and purple .. 75 75
409. – 2 l. black and green .. 3·50 3·50

DESIGN: Nos. 399, 401, 403, 405, 407 and 409 Map of Sierra Leone.

1967. Decimal Currency Provisionals. Nos. 347/8, 369/71 and 383/4 surch.

410. 6½ c. on 75 c. on 5s. (post) 15 15
411. 7½ c. on 75 c. on 5s. .. 15 15
412. 9½ c. on 50 c. on 4d. .. 20 20
413. 12½ c. on 20 c. on 1s. 3d. .. 25 25
414. 17½ c. on 50 c. .. 1·40 1·40
415. 17½ c. on 1 l. on 4d. .. 1·40 1·40
416. 18½ c. on 1 l. on 4d. .. 1·40 1·40
417. 18½ c. on 60 c. on 5s. .. 4·00 4·00
418. 25 c. on 50 c. 60 60
419. 11½ c. on 40 c. (air) .. 20 20
420. 25 c. on 40 c. 60 60

1967. Decimal Currency. Imperf. Self-adhesive. As T **92**, but embossed on white paper, backed with paper bearing advertisements. Background colours given first, and value tablet colours in brackets.

421. **92.** ½ c. red (red on white) .. 10 10
422. 1 c. red (red on white) 15 10
423. 1½ c. yellow (grn. on white) 20 15
424. 2 c. red (grn. on white) 35 10
425. 2½ c. grn. (yell. on white) 50 40
426. 3 c. red (white on red) .. 30 10
427. 3½ c. pur. (white on grn.) 50 40
428. 4 c. red (white on green) 50 15
429. 4½ c. grn. (grn. on white) 50 40
430. 5 c. red (yell. & white) 50 15
431. 5½ c. red (grn. on white) 50 50

102. Eagle.

1967. T **102** Embossed on black paper, backed with paper bearing advertisements; or, (No. 433/a), as No. 382, also with advertisements.

432. **102.** 9½ c. red & gold on black 60 60
432a. 9½ c. blue & gold on blk. 4·00 4·00
433. 10 c. mult. (red frame) 65 65
433b. 10 c. mult. (black frame) 4·50 4·00
434. **102.** 15 c. green & gold on blk. 85 85
434a. 15 c. red and gold on black 5·00 5·00

See also Nos. 538/44.

1968. No advertisements on back, and colours in value tablet reversed. Background colours given first, and value tablet colours in brackets.

435. **92.** ½ c. red (white on green) 10 10
436. 1 c. red (white on red) .. 15 10
437. 2 c. red (white in green) 4·25 4·25
438. 2½ c. grn. (white on yell.) 4·75 4·75
439. 3 c. red (red on white) .. 1·75 65

On Nos. 435 and 438, the figure "½" is larger than in Nos. 421 and 425.

1968. No advertisements on back, colours changed and new value (7 c.). Background colours given.

440. **92.** 2 c. pink (postage) .. 1·75 1·25
441. 2½ c. green .. 1·75 1·25
442. 3½ c. yellow .. 2·25 1·40
442a. 7 c. yellow (air) .. 6·50 3·25

On Nos. 441/2 the fraction "½" is larger than on Nos. 425 and 427.

103. Outline Map of Africa.

1968. Human Rights Year. Each value comes in six types, showing the following territories: Portuguese Guinea; South Africa: Mozambique; Rhodesia; South West Africa and Angola. Imperf. Self-adhesive.

443 **103** ½ c. multicoloured (post) 10 10
444 2 c. multicoloured .. 10 10
445 2½ c. multicoloured .. 10 10
446 3½ c. multicoloured .. 10 10
447 10 c. multicoloured .. 15 15
448 11½ c. multicoloured .. 20 20
449 15 c. multicoloured .. 25 25
450 **103** 7½ c. multicoloured (air) 15 15
451 9½ c. multicoloured .. 20 20
452 14½ c. multicoloured .. 25 25
453 18½ c. multicoloured .. 30 30
454 25 c. multicoloured .. 40 40
455 1 l. multicoloured .. 6·50 5·50
456 2 l. multicoloured .. 14·00 12·00

Set of 84 (6 different territories) £120 £100

Nos. 443/56 were issued in sheets of 30 (6 × 5) on backing paper depicting diamonds or the coat-of-arms on the reverse. The six types occur once in each horiz. row.

1968. Mexico Olympics Participation. Nos. 383/4 surch. or optd. (Nos. 461 and 466) **OLYMPIC PARTICIPATION 1968 MEXICO** etc.

457. 6½ c. on 50 c. mult. (post.) 20 15
458. 17½ c. on 50 c. mult. .. 25 20
459. 22½ c. on 50 c. mult. .. 40 30
460. 28½ c. on 50 c. mult. .. 50 40
461. 50 c. multicoloured .. 80 60
462. 6½ c. on 40 c. mult. (air) .. 20 15
463. 17½ c. on 40 c. mult. .. 25 20
464. 22½ c. on 40 c. mult. .. 40 30
465. 28½ c. on 40 c. mult. .. 50 40
466. 40 c. multicoloured .. 80 60

105. 1859 6d. Stamp.

111. 1965 15 c. Self-adhesive.

1969. 5th Anniv. of World's First Self-adhesive Postage Stamps. Stamp Multicoloured. Self-adhesive. Imperf.

No.	Description		
467	1 c. Type **105** (postage)	10	10
468	2 c. 1965 2 c. self-adhesive	10	10
469	3½ c. 1961 Independence £1	10	10
470	5 c. 1965 20 c. self-adhesive	10	10
471	12½ c. 1948 Royal Silver Wedding £1	30	15
472	1 l. 1923 £2	4·25	2·75
473	7½ c. Type **111** (air)	20	10
474	9½ c. 1967 9½ c. self-adhesive	20	10
475	20 c. 1964 1s. 3d. self-adhesive	40	25
476	30 c. 1964 President Kennedy Memorial 6s. self-adhesive	55	35
477	50 c. 1933 Centenary of Abolition of Slavery £1	2·00	1·00
478	2 l. 1963 2nd Anniv of Independence 11s.	16·00	13·00

Designs—As Type **105**, Nos. 468/72. As Type **111**, Nos. 474/8.

All values are on white backing paper with advertisement printed on the reverse.

117. Ore Carrier, Globe and Flags of Sierra Leone and Japan.

118. Ore Carrier, Map of Europe and Africa and Flags of Sierra Leone and Netherlands.

1969. Pepel Port Improvements. Imperf. Self-adhesive, backed with paper bearing advertisements.

No.	Description		
479. **117.**	1 c. mult. (postage)	10	10
480. **118.**	2 c. multicoloured	10	10
481. –	3½ c. multicoloured	10	10
482. –	10 c. multicoloured	10	10
483. **118.**	18½ c. multicoloured	20	25
484. –	50 c. multicoloured	70	85
485. **117.**	7½ c. multicoloured (air)	10	10
486.	9½ c. multicoloured	15	10
487. **117.**	15 c. multicoloured	20	25
488. **118.**	25 c. multicoloured	30	35
489. –	1 l. multicoloured	1·25	1·75
490. –	2 l. multicoloured	2·50	4·00

The 3½, 9½ c., 2 l. and 10, 50 c., 1 l. show respectively the flags of Great Britain and West Germany instead of the Netherlands.

119. African Development Bank Emblem.

1969. 5th Anniv. of African Development Bank. Imperf. Self-adhesive, backed with paper bearing advertisements.

No.	Description		
491. **119.**	3½ c. green, gold and black (post.)	25	20
492.	9½ c. violet, gold and green (air)	30	45

120. Boy Scouts Emblem in "Diamond".

1969. Boy Scouts Diamond Jubilee. Imperf. Self-adhesive.

No.	Description		
493. **120.**	1 c. multicoloured (postage)	10	10
494.	2 c. multicoloured	10	10
495.	3½ c. multicoloured	15	10
496.	4½ c. multicoloured	15	15
497.	5 c. multicoloured	15	15
498.	75 c. multicoloured	9·00	5·00
499. –	7½ c. multicoloured (air)	35	30
500. –	9½ c. multicoloured	45	35
501. –	15 c. multicoloured	70	50
502. –	22 c. multicoloured	1·25	70
503. –	55 c. multicoloured	7·50	4·00
504. –	3 l. multicoloured	85·00	60·00

Design—Octagonal (65 × 51 mm.): Nos. 499/504, Scout saluting, Baden-Powell and badge.

1970. Air. No. 443 surch. **AIRMAIL** twice and new value.

No.	Description		
505. **103.**	7½ c. on ½ c. mult.	20	10
506.	9½ c. on ½ c. mult.	20	10
507.	15 c. on ½ c. mult.	40	25
508.	28 c. on ½ c. mult.	70	55
509.	40 c. on ½ c. mult.	1·25	1·40
510.	2 l. on ½ c. mult.	6·00	9·00
	Set of 36 (6 different territories)	45·00	55·00

122. Expo Symbol and Maps of Sierra Leone and Japan.

1970. World Fair, Osaka. Imperf. Self-adhesive.

No.	Description		
511. **122.**	2 c. mult. (postage)	10	10
512.	3½ c. multicoloured	10	10
513.	10 c. multicoloured	15	10
514.	12½ c. multicoloured	15	10
515.	20 c. multicoloured	20	10
516.	45 c. multicoloured	45	45
517. –	7½ c. multicoloured (air)	10	10
518. –	9½ c. multicoloured	15	10
519. –	15 c. multicoloured	20	10
520. –	25 c. multicoloured	40	20
521. –	50 c. multicoloured	55	50
522. –	3 l. multicoloured	3·00	4·00

Design—Chrysanthemum (43 × 42 mm.): Nos. 517/22, Maps of Sierra Leone and Japan.

123. Diamond.

124. Palm Nut.

1970. Imperf. Self-adhesive.

No.	Description		
523. **123.**	1 c. multicoloured	10	10
524.	1½ c. multicoloured	10	10
525.	2 c. multicoloured	10	10
526.	2½ c. multicoloured	10	10
527.	3 c. multicoloured	15	10
528.	3½ c. multicoloured	15	10
529.	4 c. multicoloured	15	10
530.	5 c. multicoloured	20	10
531. **124.**	6 c. multicoloured	25	10
532.	7 c. multicoloured	30	15
533.	8½ c. multicoloured	40	15
534.	9 c. multicoloured	40	15
535.	10 c. multicoloured	45	15
536.	11½ c. multicoloured	55	20
537.	18½ c. multicoloured	75	45

1970. Air. As T **102**, but on white paper.

No.	Description		
538. **102.**	7½ c. gold and red (air)	35	10
539.	9½ c. silver and green	40	10
540.	15 c. silver and blue	55	20
541.	25 c. gold and purple	90	50
542.	50 c. green and orange	2·00	1·50
543.	1 l. blue and silver	5·00	7·00
544.	2 l. blue and gold	10·00	16·00

126. "Jewellery Box" and Sewa Diadem.

1970. Diamond Industry. Imperf. Self-adhesive.

No.	Description		
545. **126.**	2 c. mult. (postage)	30	10
546.	3½ c. multicoloured	30	10
547.	10 c. multicoloured	55	15
548.	12½ c. multicoloured	75	25
549.	40 c. multicoloured	1·75	1·00
550.	1 l. multicoloured	10·00	8·50
551. –	7½ c. multicoloured (air)	50	10
552. –	9½ c. multicoloured	60	10
553. –	15 c. multicoloured	95	30
554. –	25 c. multicoloured	1·40	60
555. –	75 c. multicoloured	5·50	4·50
556. –	2 l. multicoloured	24·00	20·00

Design—Horiz. (63 × 61 mm.) Nos. 551/6 Diamond and curtain.

127. "Traffic Changeover".

1971. Changeover to Driving on the Right of the Road. Imperf. Self-adhesive.

No.	Description		
557. **127.**	3½ c. orange, blue and black (postage)	1·50	50
558.	9½ c. blue, orange and black (air)	2·00	1·75

1971. Air. Various stamps surch. **AIRMAIL** and value (Nos. 559/61) or value only (Nos. 562/3).

No.	Description		
559.	10 c. on 2d. (No. 226)	40	20
560.	20 c. on 1s. (No. 230)	70	45
561.	50 c. on 1d. (No. 243)	1·25	1·10
562.	70 c. on 30 c. (No. 476)	2·00	2·75
563.	1 l. on 30 c. (No. 476)	3·00	3·75

129. Flag and Lion's Head.

1971. 10th Anniv. of Independence. Imperf. Self-adhesive.

No.	Description		
564. **129.**	2 c. mult. (postage)	10	10
565.	3½ c. multicoloured	10	10
566.	10 c. multicoloured	15	10
567.	12½ c. multicoloured	20	10
568.	40 c. multicoloured	70	40
569.	1 l. multicoloured	1·50	2·50
570. –	7½ c. multicoloured (air)	15	10
571. –	9½ c. multicoloured	15	10
572. –	15 c. multicoloured	25	10
573. –	25 c. multicoloured	35	35
574. –	75 c. multicoloured	1·25	1·50
575. –	2 l. multicoloured	4·00	6·50

Design: "Map" shaped as Type **129.** Nos. 570/5, Bugles and lion's head.

130. Pres. Siaka Stevens.

1972. Multicoloured. Background colour given.

No.	Description		
576. **130.**	1 c. lilac	10	10
577.	2 c. lavender	10	10
578.	4 c. blue	10	10
579.	5 c. brown	10	10
580.	7 c. pink	15	10
581.	10 c. brown	15	10
582.	15 c. green	25	15
583.	18 c. yellow	25	15
584.	20 c. blue	30	15
585.	25 c. orange	35	15
586.	50 c. green	1·00	55
587.	1 l. mauve	1·50	1·00
588.	2 l. pink	3·50	3·50
589.	5 l. cream	8·00	8·50

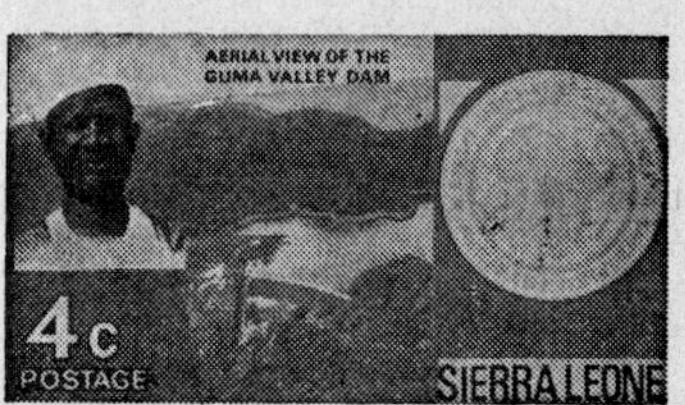

131. Guma Valley Dam and Bank Emblem.

1975. 10th Anniv. of African Development Bank.

No.	Description		
590. **131.**	4 c. multicoloured (postage)	45·00	28·00
591.	15 c. multicoloured (air)	1·00	80

132. Opening Ceremony.

1975. New Congo Bridge Opening and 70th Birthday of President Stevens.

No.	Description		
592. **132.**	5 c. multicoloured (postage)	4·00	1·75
593.	20 c. multicoloured (air)	70	25

133. Presidents Tolbert and Stevens, and Handclasp.

1975. 1st Anniv. of Mano River Union.
594. **133.** 4 c. multicoloured (postage) 75 50
595. 15 c. multicoloured (air) 35 25

134. "Quaid-i-Azam" (Mohammed Ali Jinnah).

1977. Birth Centenary of Mohammed Ali Jinnah (Quaid-i-Azam).
596. **134.** 30 c. multicoloured .. 75 30

135. Queen Elizabeth II.

1977. Silver Jubilee.
597. **135.** 5 c. multicoloured .. 10 10
598. 1 l. multicoloured .. 65 80

136. College Buildings.

1977. 150th Anniv. of Fourah Bay College. Multicoloured.
599. 5 c. Type **136** 10 10
600. 20 c. The old college (vert.) 35 30

137. St. Edward's Crown and Sceptres.

1978. 25th Anniv. of Coronation. Mult.
601. 5 c. Type **137** 10 10
602. 50 c. Queen Elizabeth II in Coronation Coach .. 30 40
603. 1 l. Queen Elizabeth II and Prince Philip .. 40 60

138. "Myrina silenus".

1979. Butterflies (1st series). Multicoloured.
604 5 c. Type **138** 10 10
605 15 c. "Papilio nireus" .. 25 15
606 25 c. "Catacroptera cloanthe" 40 15
607 1 l. "Papilio antimachus" 2·00 1·50
See also Nos. 646/9.

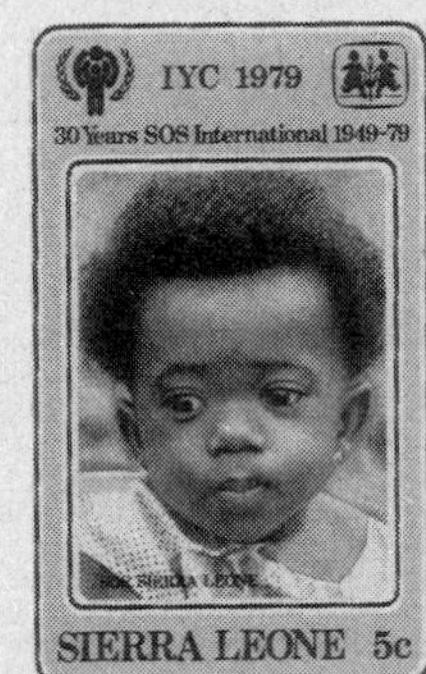

139. Young Child's Face.

1979. International Year of the Child. 30th Anniv. of S.O.S. International. Multicoloured.
608. 5 c. Type **139** 10 10
609. 27 c. Young child with baby 20 25
610. 1 l. Mother with young child .. .. .. 50 1·10

140. Presidents Stevens (Sierra Leone) and Tolbert (Liberia), Dove with Letter and Bridge.

1979. 5th Anniv. of Mano River Union and 1st Anniv. of Postal Union.
612. **140.** 5 c. brn., orge. & yell. 10 10
613. 22 c. brn., yell. & violet 10 15
614. 27 c. brn., blue & orge. 10 15
615. 35 c. brown, green & red 15 20
616. 1 l. brown, violet & blue 50 1·00

141. Great Britain 1848 10d. Stamp.

1979. Death Centenary of Sir Rowland Hill.
618. **141.** 10 c. black, brn. & blue 15 10
619. – 15 c. black, brn. & blue 25 15
620. – 50 c. black, red & yell. 60 70
DESIGNS: 15 c. 1872 4d. stamp. 50 c. 1961 £1 Independence commemorative.

142. Knysna Turaco.

1980. Birds. Multicoloured.
622 1 c. Type **142** 20 50
623 2 c. Olive-bellied sunbird .. 20 50
624 3 c. Western Black-headed oriole 50 50
625 5 c. Spur-winged goose .. 50 30
626 7 c. Didric cuckoo 40 30
627 10 c. Grey parrot (vert.) .. 30 55
628 15 c. Blue quail (vert.) .. 75 80
629 20 c. African wood owl (vert.) .. .. .. 40 1·25
630 30 c. Greater blue turaco (vert.) .. .. .. 50 1·50
631 40 c. Blue-breasted kingfisher (vert.) .. .. 60 1·50
632 50 c. Black crake (vert.) .. 60 1·75
633 1 l. Hartlaub's duck .. 60 2·75
634 2 l. Black bee eater .. 2·50 3·50
635 5 l. Barrow's bustard .. 4·25 10·00

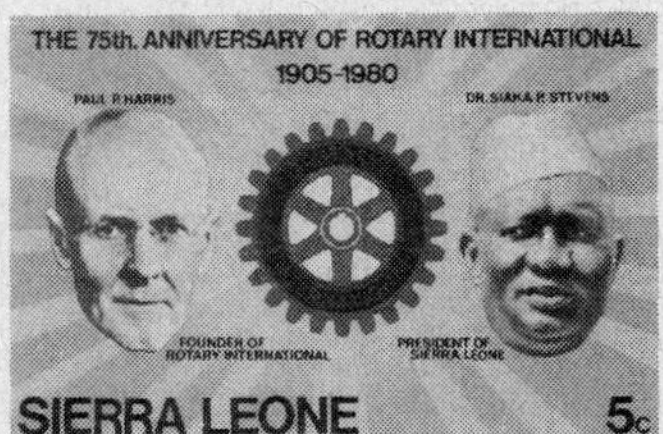

143. Paul P. Harris (founder), President Stevens of Sierra Leone and Rotary Emblem.

1980. 75th Anniv. of Rotary International
636. **143** 5 c. multicoloured .. 10 10
637. 27 c. multicoloured .. 10 10
638. 50 c. multicoloured .. 20 25
639. 1 l. multicoloured .. 40 55

144. "Maria", 1884.

1980. "London 1980" International Stamp Exhibition. Multicoloured.
640. 6 c. Type **144** 15 10
641. 31 c. "Tarquah", 1902 .. 30 30
642. 50 c. "Aureol", 1951 .. 50 60
643. 1 l. "Africa Palm", 1974 70 95

145. Organization for African Unity Emblem.

1980. African Summit Conference, Freetown.
644. **145.** 20 c. black, bl. & purple 10 10
645. 1 l. black, purple & blue 45 45

146. "Graphium policenes".

1980. Butterflies (2nd series). Multicoloured.
646 5 c. Type **146** 10 10
647 27 c. "Charaxes varanes" 30 15
648 35 c. "Charaxes brutus" .. 35 25
649 1 l. "Euphaedra zaddachi" 1·10 1·40

147. Arrival at Freetown Airport.

1980. Tourism. Multicoloured.
650. 6 c. Type **147** 10 10
651. 26 c. Welcome to tourists 20 20
652. 31 c. Freetown cotton tree 25 25
653. 40 c. Beinkongo Falls .. 30 30
654. 50 c. Sports facilities .. 40 40
655. 1 l. African Elephant .. 95 95

148. Servals.

1981. Wild Cats. Multicoloured.
656. 6 c. Type **148** 10 10
657. 6 c. Serval cubs 10 10
658. 31 c. African Golden Cats 30 30
659. 31 c. African Golden Cat cubs 30 30
660. 50 c. Leopards 45 45
661. 50 c. Leopard cubs .. 45 45
662. 1 l. Lions 80 80
663. 1 l. Lion cubs 80 80
The two designs of each value were printed together, se-tenant, in horizontal pairs, forming composite designs.

149. Soldiers (Defence).

1981. 20th Anniv of Independence and 10th Anniv of Republic. National Services. Mult.
664. 6 c. Type **149** 40 10
665. 31 c. Nurses administering first aid, and ambulance (health) (horiz.) .. 1·00 20
666. 40 c. Traffic (Police Force) 1·75 30
667. 1 l. Patrol boat (coastguard) (horiz.) .. .. .. 2·50 1·25

150. Wedding Bouquet from Sierra Leone.

1981. Royal Wedding (1st issue). Mult.
668. 31 c. Type **150** 20 20
669. 45 c. Prince Charles as helicopter pilot 25 30
670. 1 l. Prince Charles and Lady Diana Spencer .. 45 1·10

151. Sandringham.

1981. Royal Wedding (2nd issue). **Mult.**

No.	Description	Unused	Used
671.	35 c. Type 151	20	25
672.	60 c. Prince Charles in out-door clothes	30	40
675.	70 c. Type 151	75	90
676.	1 l. 30 As 60 c.	75	90
673.	1 l. 50 Prince Charles and Lady Diana Spencer ..	70	90
677.	2 l. As 1 l. 50	1·75	2·00

152. "Physical Recreation".

1981. 25th Anniv. of Duke of Edinburgh Award Scheme and President's Award Scheme Publicity. Multicoloured.

No.	Description	Unused	Used
678.	6 c. Type 152	10	10
679.	31 c. "Community service"	15	10
680.	1 l. Duke of Edinburgh ..	40	40
681.	1 l. President Siaka Stevens	40	40

153. Pineapples.

1981. World Food Day. Multicoloured.

No.	Description	Unused	Used
682.	6 c. Type 153	10	10
683.	31 c. Groundnuts	15	10
684.	50 c. Cassava fruits ..	20	15
685.	1 l. Rice plants	50	50

154. Groundnut.

1981. World Food Day (2nd issue). Agricultural Industry. Multicoloured.

No.	Description	Unused	Used
686.	6 c. Type 154	10	10
687.	31 c. Cassava	25	10
688.	50 c. Rice	45	25
689.	1 l. Pineapple	90	70

155. Scouts with Cattle.

1982. 75th Anniv. of Boy Scout Movement. Multicoloured.

No.	Description	Unused	Used
690.	20 c. Type 155	25	10
691.	50 c. Scouts picking flowers	50	40
692.	1 l. Lord Baden-Powell ..	90	1·00
693.	2 l. Scouts fishing	1·90	2·00

1982. Nos. 668/74 surch.

No.	Description	Unused	Used
695.	50 c. on 31 c. Type **150** ..	40	40
696.	50 c. on 35 c. Type **151** ..	40	40
697.	50 c. on 45 c. Prince Charles as helicopter pilot	40	40
698.	50 c. on 60 c. Prince Charles in outdoor clothes	40	40
699.	90 c. on 1 l. Prince Charles and Lady Diana Spencer ..	75	75
699a.	1 l. 30 on 60 c. Prince Charles in outdoor clothes	1·75	1·75
699b.	2 l. on 35 c. Type **151** ..	2·75	2·75
700.	2 l. on 1 l. 50 Prince Charles and Lady Diana Spencer ..	1·50	1·50
700a.	8 l. on 1 l. 50 Prince Charles and Lady Diana Spencer ..	8·75	8·75

157. Heading.

1982. World Cup Football Championship, Spain. Multicoloured.

No.	Description	Unused	Used
702.	20 c. Type **157**	45	15
703.	30 c. Dribbling	70	20
704.	1 l. Tackling	2·25	2·00
705.	2 l. Goalkeeping	3·50	3·25

158. Prince and Princess of Wales.

1982. 21st Birthday of Princess of Wales. Multicoloured.

No.	Description	Unused	Used
707.	31 c. Caernarvon Castle ..	25	15
708.	50 c. Type **158**	30	25
709.	2 l. Princess of Wales ..	80	1·10

1982. Birth of Prince William of Wales. Nos. 707/9 optd. **ROYAL BABY 21.6.82.**

No.	Description	Unused	Used
711.	31 c. Caernarvon Castle ..	25	15
712.	50 c. Type **158**	30	25
713.	2 l. Princess of Wales ..	80	1·10

159. Washington with Troops.

1982. 250th Birth Anniv. of George Washington. Multicoloured.

No.	Description	Unused	Used
715.	6 c. Type **159**	10	10
716.	31 c. Portrait of Washington (vert.)	20	20
717.	50 c. Washington with horse	35	35
718.	1 l. Washington standing on battlefield (vert.) ..	65	80

160. Temptation of Christ.

1982. Christmas. Stained-Glass Windows. Multicoloured.

No.	Description	Unused	Used
720.	6 c. Type **160**	10	10
721.	31 c. Baptism of Christ ..	15	20
722.	50 c. Annunciation ..	20	40
723.	1 l. Nativity	55	90

1982. World Cup Football Championship Winners. Nos. 702/5 optd. **WORLD CUP WINNERS ITALY 3 W. GERMANY 1.**

No.	Description	Unused	Used
725.	20 c. Type **157**	15	20
726.	30 c. Dribbling	20	30
727.	1 l. Tackling	55	85
728.	2 l. Goalkeeping	1·00	1·75

162. Long Snouted Crocodile.

1982. Death Centenary of Charles Darwin. Multicoloured.

No.	Description	Unused	Used
730.	6 c. Type **162**	40	15
731.	31 c. Rainbow Lizard ..	1·10	75
732.	50 c. River Turtle ..	1·60	1·40
733.	1 l. Chameleon	2·75	3·00

163. Diogenes.

1983. 500th Birth Anniv. of Raphael. Details from painting "The School of Athens". Multicoloured.

No.	Description	Unused	Used
735.	6 c. Type **163**	10	10
736.	31 c. Euclid, Ptolemy, Zoroaster, Raphael and Sodoma	20	30
737.	50 c. Euclid and his pupils	35	45
738.	2 l. Pythagoras, Francesco Maria della Rovere and Heraclitus	1·25	1·40

164. Agricultural Training.

1983. Commonwealth Day. Multicoloured.

No.	Description	Unused	Used
740.	6 c. Type **164**	10	10
741.	10 c. Tourism development	10	10
742.	50 c. Broadcasting training	45	45
743.	1 l. Airport services ..	90	90

165. Map of Africa and Flag of Sierra Leone.

1983. 25th Anniv. of Economic Commission for Africa.

No.	Description	Unused	Used
744.	**165.** 1 l. multicoloured ..	80	1·10

166. Chimps in Tree.

1983. Endangered Species. Multicoloured.

No.	Description	Unused	Used
745.	6 c. Type **166**	65	20
746.	10 c. Three chimps (vert.)	80	20
747.	31 c. Chimps swinging in tree (vert.)	1·90	80
748.	60 c. Group of chimps ..	3·50	4·00

167. Traditional Communications.

1983. World Communications Year. Mult.

No.	Description	Unused	Used
750.	6 c. Type **167**	10	10
751.	10 c. Mail via Mano River	10	10
752.	20 c. Satellite ground station	10	10
753.	1 l. British packet, circa 1805	75	65

168. Montgolfier Balloon, Paris, 1783.

1983. Bicentenary of Manned Flight. Mult.

No.	Description	Unused	Used
755.	6 c. Type **168**	25	10
756.	20 c. "Deutschland" airship, Berlin, 1879 (horiz.)	45	20
757.	50 c. "Norge I", North Pole, 1926 (horiz.) ..	90	90
758.	1 l. "Cape Sierra" sport balloon, Freetown, 1983	1·25	1·60

169. Mickey Mouse.

1983. Space Ark Fantasy. Multicoloured.

No.	Description	Unused	Used
774.	1 c. Type **169**	10	10
775.	1 c. Huey, Dewey and Louie	10	10
776.	3 c. Goofy in spaceship ..	10	10
777.	3 c. Donald Duck	10	10
778.	10 c. Ludwig Von Drake ..	10	10
779.	10 c. Goofy	10	10
780.	2 l. Mickey Mouse and Giraffe in spaceship ..	1·10	1·25
781.	3 l. Donald Duck floating in space	1·60	1·75

MORE DETAILED LISTS

are given in the Stanley Gibbons Catalogues referred to in the country headings.
For lists of current volumes see Introduction.

170. Graduates from Union Training Programme.

1984. 10th Anniv of Mano River Union. Mult.

783. 6 c. Type **170** 10 10
784. 25 c. Intra-Union trade .. 10 10
785. 31 c. Member Presidents on map 10 10
786. 41 c. Signing ceremony marking Guinea's accession 15 15

171. Gymnastics.

1984. Olympic Games, Los Angeles. Mult.

788. 90 c. Type **171** 30 40
789. 1 l. Hurdling 30 40
790. 3 l. Javelin throwing .. 75 1·25

172. "Apollo II" Liftoff.

1984. 15th Anniv. of First Moonwalk. Mult.

792. 50 c. Type **172** 20 20
793. 75 c. Lunar module .. 30 30
794. 1 l.25 First Moonwalk .. 45 45
795. 2 l.50 Lunar exploration .. 85 85

173. Concorde.

1984. Universal Postal Union Congress, Hamburg.

797 **173** 4 l. multicoloured .. 2·75 1·75

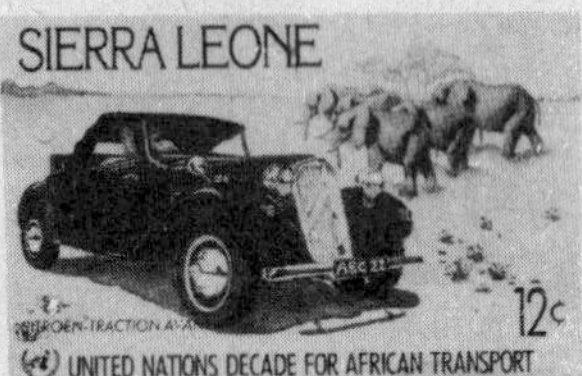

174. Citroen "Traction Avante".

1984. United Nations Decade of African Transport. Multicoloured.

799. 12 c. Type **174** 20 10
800. 60 c. Locomobile 40 25
801. 90 c. A.C. "Ace" 55 35
802. 1 l. Vauxhall "Prince Henry" 55 35
803. 1 l. 50 Delahaye "135" .. 70 50
804. 2 l. Mazda "1105" 90 65

1984. Nos. 625, 627 and 634 surch.

811. 25 c. on 10 c. Grey Parrot (vert.) 75 85
812. 40 c. on 10 c. Grey Parrot (vert.) 50 70
813. 50 c. on 2 l. Black Bee Eater 50 70
814. 70 c. on 5 c. Spur-winged Goose 50 70
815. 10 l. on 5 c. Spur-winged Goose .. .. .. 3·00 3·50

1984. "Ausipex" International Stamp Exhibition. Melbourne. Nos. 632 and 635 optd. **AUSIPEX 84.**

818. 50 c. Black Crake (vert.) .. 1·00 75
819. 5 l. Barrow's Bustard .. 2·25 2·00

177. Portuguese Caravel.

1984. History of Shipping. Multicoloured.

820. 2 c. Type **177** 20 40
821. 5 c. "Merlin" of Bristol .. 25 30
822. 10 c "Golden Hind" .. 35 30
823. 15 c. "Mordauant" .. 75 50
824. 20 c. "Atlantic" (sail transport) 50 30
825. 25 c. H.M.S. "Lapwing" (frigate), 1785 .. .. 50 30
826. 30 c. "Traveller" (brig) .. 50 35
827. 40 c. "Amistad" (schooner) 60 35
828. 50 c. H.M.S. "Teazer" (gun vessel), 1868 .. .. 70 35
829. 70 c. "Scotia" (cable ship) 85 50
830. 1 l. H.M.S. "Alecto" (paddle-steamer), 1882 .. 90 50
831. 2 l. H.M.S. "Blonde" (cruiser), 1889 .. .. 1·25 75
832. 5 l. H.M.S. "Fox" (cruiser), 1895 .. .. .. 1·75 1·50
833. 10 l. "Accra" (liner) .. 2·25 2·00
833c. 15 l. H.M.S. "Favourite" (sloop), 1829 .. .. 2·00 2·25
833d. 25 l. H.M.S. "Euryalus" (screw frigate), 1883 .. 2·75 3·00

Nos. 820/2 and 824/33 come both with and without imprint dates.

178. Mail Runner approaching Mano River Depot, c1843.

1984. 125th Anniv. of First Postage Stamps. Multicoloured.

834. 50 c. Type **178** 35 15
835. 2 l. Isaac Fitzjohn, first Postmaster, receiving letters, 1855 .. .. 1·25 85
836. 3 l. 1859 packet franked with four 6d. stamps .. 1·75 1·50

179. "Madonna and Child" (Pisanello).

1984. Christmas. Madonna and Child paintings by artist named. Multicoloured.

838. 20 c. Type **179** 10 10
839. 1 l. Memling 40 40
840. 2 l. Raphael 75 75
841. 3 l. Van der Werff .. 1·10 1·10

180. Donald Duck in "The Wise Little Hen" (Illustration reduced, actual size 50×38 mm.).

1984. 50th Birthday of Donald Duck. Walt Disney Cartoon Characters. Multicoloured.

843. 1 c. Type **180** 10 10
844. 2 c. Mickey Mouse and Donald Duck in "Boat Builders" 10 10
845. 3 c. Panchito, Donald Duck and Jose Carioca in "The Three Caballeros" 10 10
846. 4 c. Donald Duck meeting Pythagoras in "Mathmagic Land" 10 10
847. 5 c. Donald Duck and nephew in "The Mickey Mouse Club" 10 10
848. 10 c. Mickey Mouse, Goofy and Donald Duck in "Donald on Parade" .. 10 10
849. 1 l. Donald Duck riding donkey in "Don Donald" 75 75
850. 2 l. Donald Duck in "Donald Gets Drafted" 1·75 1·50
851. 4 l. Donald Duck meeting children in Tokyo Disneyland .. .. 2·75 2·50

181. Fischer's Whydah.

1985. Birth Bicentenary of John J. Audubon (ornithologist). Songbirds of Sierra Leone. Multicoloured.

853. 40 c. Type **181** .. .. 1·25 55
854. 90 c. Spotted Flycatcher .. 2·25 1·40
855. 1 l. 30 Garden Warbler .. 2·50 2·50
856. 3 l. Speke's Weaver .. 4·00 5·00

182. Fishing.

1985. International Youth Year. Mult.

858. 1 l. 15 Type **182** 45 45
859. 1 l. 50 Sawing timber .. 60 60
860. 2 l. 15 Rice farming .. 75 75

183. Eddie Rickenbacker and Spad "XIII", 1918.

1985. 40th Anniv. of International Civil Aviation Organization. Multicoloured.

862. 70 c. Type **183** .. .. 1·25 75
863. 1 l. 25 Samuel P. Langley and "Aerodrome No. 5", 1903 .. .. .. 1·75 1·50
864. 1 l. 30 Orville and Wilbur Wright with "Flyer No. 1", 1903 .. .. 1·75 1·50
865. 2 l. Charles Lindberg and "Spirit of St. Louis", 1927 .. .. .. 2·00 2·50

184. "Temptation of Christ" (Botticelli).

1985. Easter. Religious Paintings. Mult.

867. 45 c. Type **184** 30 15
868. 70 c. "Christ at the Column" (Velasquez) .. 55 25
869. 1 l. 55 "Pieta" (Botticelli) (vert.) 90 45
870. 10 l. "Christ on the Cross" (Velasquez) (vert.) .. 4·75 3·25

185. The Queen Mother at St. Paul's Cathedral.

1985. Life and Times of Queen Elizabeth the Queen Mother. Multicoloured.

872. 1 l. Type **185** 20 25
873. 1 l. 70 With her racehorse, "Double Star", at Sandown (horiz.) .. 30 40
874. 10 l. At Covent Garden, 1971 .. .. .. 2·00 2·50

1985. 75th Anniv. of Girl Guide Movement. Nos. 690/3 surch. **75th ANNIVERSARY OF GIRL GUIDES.**

876. 70 c. on 20 c. Type **155** .. 30 30
877. 1 l. 30 on 50 c. Scouts picking flowers 55 55
878. 5 l. on 1 l. Lord Baden-Powell .. .. .. 1·60 1·60
879. 7 l. on 2 l. Scouts fishing .. 2·25 2·25

1985. Olympic Gold Medal Winners, Los Angeles. Nos. 788/90 surch.

881. 2 l. on 90 c. Type **171** (surch. **MA YANHONGJ CHINA GOLD MEDAL**) 50 55
882. 4 l. on 1 l. Hurdling (surch. **E. MOSES U.S.A. GOLD MEDAL**) .. .. .. 1·00 1·25
883. 8 l. on 3 l. Javelin-throwing (surch. **A. HAERKOENEN FINLAND GOLD MEDAL**) .. .. .. 2·00 2·10

188. Chater-Lea (1905) at Hill Station House.

1985. Centenary of Motor Cycle and Decade for African Transport. Multicoloured.

885. 1 l. 40 Type **188** .. .. 1·00 1·00
886. 2 l. Honda "XR 350 R" at Queen Elizabeth II Quay, Freetown .. 1·40 1·40
887. 4 l. Kawasaki "Vulcan" at Bo Clock Tower .. 2·50 2·50
888. 5 l. Harley-Davidson "Electra-Glide" in Makeni village .. .. 2·75 2·75

1985. 300th Birth Anniv of Johann Sebastian Bach (composer). As T **206** of Antigua. Mult.

890. 70 c. Viola pomposa .. 40 25
891. 3 l. Spinet .. .. .. 1·10 80
892. 4 l. Lute .. .. .. 1·40 1·10
893. 5 l. Oboe .. .. .. 1·60 1·40

1985. Nos. 707/9 and 711/13 surch.

895. 70 c. on 31 c. Caernarvon Castle (707) 30 30
899. 1 l. 30 on 31 c. Caernarvon Castle (711) 80 80
896. 4 l. on 50 c. Type **158** (708) 2·50 2·50
897. 5 l. on 2 l. Princess of Wales (709) .. .. 3·00 3·00
900. 5 l. on 50 c. Type **158** (712) 3·00 3·00
901. 7 l. on 2 l. Princess of Wales (713) .. .. 4·00 4·00

190. "Madonna and Child" (Crivelli).

1985. Christmas. "Madonna and Child" Paintings by artists named. Multicoloured.
903. 70 c. Type **190** 25 10
904. 3 l. Bouts 80 40
905. 4 l. Da Messina 95 55
906. 5 l. Lochner .. .. 1·10 65

1985. 150th Birth Anniv of Mark Twain (author). As T **118** of Anguilla showing Walt Disney cartoon characters illustrating Mark Twain quotations. Multicoloured.
908. 1 l. 50 Snow White and Bashful 40 30
909. 3 l. Three Little Pigs .. 60 50
910. 4 l. Donald Duck and nephew 70 65
911. 5 l. Pinocchio and Figaro the cat 85 75

1985. Birth Bicentenaries of Grimm Brothers (folklorists). Walt Disney cartoon characters in scenes from "Rumpelstiltskin". As T **119** of Anguilla. Multicoloured.
913. 70 c. The Miller (Donald Duck) and his daughter (Daisy Duck) meet the King (Uncle Scrooge) .. 20 25
914. 1 l. The King puts the Miller's daughter to work 35 40
915. 2 l. Rumpelstiltskin demands payment .. 50 55
916. 10 l. The King with gold spun from straw .. 2·75 3·25

1985. 40th Anniv of U.N.O. As T **208** of Antigua showing United Nations (New York) stamps. Multicoloured.
918 2 l. John Kennedy and 1954 Human Rights 8 c. stamp 70 70
919 4 l. Albert Einstein (scientist) and 1958 Atomic Energy 3 c. .. 1·40 1·40
920 7 l. Maimonides (physician) and 1956 W.H.O. 8 c. .. .. 3·75 3·75

191. Player kicking Ball.

1986. World Cup Football Championship, Mexico. Multicoloured.
922. 70 c. Type **191** 25 10
923. 3 l. Player controlling ball 70 50
924. 4 l. Player chasing ball .. 85 70
925. 5 l. Player kicking ball (different) .. .. 1·25 80

1986. Centenary of Statue of Liberty. As T **163b** of Lesotho. Multicoloured.
927. 40 c. Times Square, 1905 (vert.) 10 10
928. 70 c. Times Square, 1986 (vert.) 15 10
929. 1 l. "Tally Ho" coach, c 1880 .. .. .. 25 15
930. 10 l. Express bus, 1986 .. 1·75 1·90

1986. Appearance of Halley's Comet (1st issue). As T **123** of Anguilla. Multicoloured.
932. 15 c. Johannes Kepler (astronomer) and Paris Observatory 10 10
933. 50 c. N.A.S.A. Space Shuttle landing, 1985 .. 10 10
934. 70 c. Halley's Comet (from Bayeux Tapestry) .. 10 10
935. 10 l. Comet of 530 A.D. and Merlin predicting coming of King Arthur .. .. 1·25 1·40
See also Nos. 988/91.

1986. 60th Birthday of Queen Elizabeth II. As T **125** of Anguilla.
937. 10 c. black and yellow .. 10 10
938. 1 l. 70 multicoloured .. 35 30
939. 10 l. multicoloured .. 1·40 1·75
Designs: 10 c. Princess Elizabeth inspecting guard of honour, Cranwell, 1951. 1 l. 70, In Garter robes. 10 l. Braemar Games, 1970.

192. Chicago-Milwaukee "Hiawatha Express".

1986. "Ameripex" International Stamp Exhibition, Chicago. American Trains. Multicoloured.
941. 50 c. Type **192** 70 30
942. 2 l. Rock Island Line "The Rocket" .. .. 1·40 1·00
943. 4 l. Rio Grande "Prospector" .. .. 2·25 2·00
944. 7 l. Southern Pacific "Daylight Express" .. 2·75 2·75

1986. Royal Wedding. As T **213** of Antigua. Multicoloured.
946. 10 c. Prince Andrew and Miss Sarah Ferguson .. 10 10
947. 1 l. 70 Prince Andrew at clay pigeon shoot .. 30 35
948. 10 l. Prince Andrew in naval uniform .. .. 1·40 1·75

193. "Monodora myristica".

1986. Flowers of Sierra Leone. Multicoloured.
950. 70 c. Type **193** 15 10
951. 1 l. 50 "Gloriosa simplex" 20 15
952. 4 l. "Mussaenda erythrophylla" 35 25
953. 6 l. "Crinum ornatum" .. 50 40
954. 8 l. "Bauhinia purpurea" 60 60
955. 10 l. "Bombax costatum" 70 70
956. 20 l. "Hibiscus rosasinensis" .. .. 1·25 1·50
957. 30 l. "Cassia fistula" .. 1·75 2·00

194. Handshake and Flags of Sierra Leone and U.S.A.

1986. 25th Anniv. of United States Peace Corps.
959. **194.** 4 l. multicoloured .. 70 70

195. Transporting Goods by Canoe.

1986. International Peace Year. Mult.
960. 1 l. Type **195** 15 15
961. 2 l. Teacher and class .. 20 20
962. 5 l. Rural post office .. 40 40
963. 10 l. Fishermen in longboat 75 75

1986. Various stamps surch.
968. 70 c. on 10 c. Princess Elizabeth inspecting guard of honour, Cranwell (No. 937) .. 10 10
971. 70 c. on 10 c. Prince Andrew and Miss Sarah Ferguson (No. 946) .. 10 10
964. 30 l. on 2 c. Type **177** (No. 820) .. .. .. 1·50 1·60
965. 40 l. on 30 c. "Traveller" (brig) (No. 826) .. 2·10 2·25
969. 45 l. on 10 l. Queen at Braemar Games, 1970 (No. 934) .. .. .. 2·40 2·50
972. 45 l. on 10 l. Prince Andrew in naval uniform (No. 948) .. .. .. 2·40 2·50
966. 45 l. on 40 c. "Amistad" (schooner) (No. 827) .. 2·40 2·50
967. 50 l. on 70 c. "Scotia" (cable ship) (No. 829) .. 2·75 2·75

1986. World Cup Football Championship Winners, Mexico. Nos. 922/5 optd. **WINNERS Argentina 3 W. Germany 2** or surch. also.
974. 70 c. Type **191** 20 10
975. 3 l. Player controlling ball 40 30
976. 4 l. Playing chasing ball .. 50 40
977. 40 l. on 5 l. Player kicking ball (different) .. .. 4·00 4·00

198. Mickey and Minnie Mouse as Jack and Jill.

1986. "Stockholmia '86" International Stamp Exhibition, Sweden. Walt Disney cartoon characters in scenes from nursery rhymes. Multicoloured.
979. 70 c. Type **198** 10 10
980. 1 l. Donald Duck as Wee Willie Winkie 15 15
981. 2 l. Minnie Mouse as Little Miss Muffet 20 20
982. 4 l. Goofy as Old King Cole 40 40
983. 5 l. Clarabelle as Mary Quite Contrary 50 50
984. 10 l. Daisy Duck as Little Bo Peep 90 90
985. 25 l. Daisy Duck and Minnie Mouse in "Polly put the Kettle on" .. 2·00 2·00
986. 35 l. Goofy, Mickey Mouse and Donald Duck as the Three Men in a Tub .. 2·50 2·50

1986. Appearance of Halley's Comet (2nd issue). Nos. 932/5 optd as T **218** of Antigua.
988. 50 c. N.A.S.A. Space Shuttle landing, 1985 .. 10 10
989. 70 c. Halley's Comet (from Bayeux Tapestry) .. 10 10
990. 1 l. 50 on 15 c. Johannes Kepler (astronomer) and Paris Observatory .. 10 10
991. 45 l. on 10 l. Comet of 530 A.D. and Merlin predicting coming of King Arthur .. .. 3·00 3·50

199. "Virgin and Child with St. Dorothy".

1986. Christmas. Paintings by Titian. Mult.
993. 70 c. Type **199** 10 10
994. 1 l. 50 "The Gypsy Madonna" (vert.) .. 15 10
995. 20 l. "The Holy Family" .. 2·25 2·25
996. 30 l. "Virgin and Child in an Evening Landscape" (vert.) .. .. .. 2·75 2·75

200. Nomoli (soapstone figure).

1987. Bicentenary of Sierra Leone. Mult.
998. 2 l. Type **200** 10 15
999. 5 l. King's Yard Gate, Royal Hospital, 1817 .. 20 30

201. Removing Top of Statue's Torch.

1987. Centenary of Statue of Liberty (1986) (2nd issue). Multicoloured.
1001. 70 c. Type **201** 10 10
1002. 1 l. 50 View of statue's torch and New York harbour (horiz.) .. 10 10
1003. 2 l. Crane lifting torch .. 10 10
1004. 3 l. Workman steadying torch 10 15
1005. 4 l. Statue's crown (horiz.) 15 20
1006. 5 l. Statue of Liberty (side view) and fireworks 20 25
1007. 10 l. Statue of Liberty and fireworks 40 45
1008. 25 l. Bedloe Island, statue and fireworks (horiz.) .. .. 1·00 1·25
1009. 30 l. Statue's face .. 1·25 1·60

202. Emblem, Mother and Child and Syringe.

1987. 40th Anniv. of U.N.I.C.E.F.
1010. **202.** 10 l. multicoloured .. 40 55

MINIMUM PRICE

The minimum price quoted is 10p which represents a handling charge rather than a basis for valuing common stamps. For further notes about prices see introductory pages.

203. "U.S.A.", 1987.

1987. America's Cup Yachting Championship. Multicoloured.

1011 1 l. Type **203** 10 10
1012 1 l. 50 "New Zealand II", 1987 (horiz) 10 10
1013 2 l. 50 "French Kiss", 1987 10 10
1014 10 l. "Stars and Stripes", 1987 (horiz) 40 45
1015 15 l. "Australia II", 1983 60 65
1016 25 l. "Freedom", 1980 .. 1·00 1·10
1017 30 l. "Kookaburra", 1987 (horiz) .. .. 1·25 1·40

204. Mickey Mouse as Mountie and Parliament Building, Ottawa (Illustration reduced. Actual size 50 × 37 mm.).

1987. "Capex '87" International Stamp Exhibition, Toronto. Walt Disney cartoon characters in Canada. Multicoloured.

1019. 2 l. Type **204** 10 10
1020. 5 l. Goofy dressed as Mountie and totem poles 20 25
1021. 10 l. Goofy windsurfing and Donald Duck fishing off Perce Rock 40 45
1022. 20 l. Goofy with mountain goat in Rocky Mountains 80 85
1023. 25 l. Donald Duck and Mickey Mouse in Old Quebec .. .. 1·00 1·10
1024. 45 l. Goofy emerging from igloo and "Aurora Borealis" .. 1·75 1·90
1025. 50 l. Goofy as gold prospector and post office, Yukon .. .. .. 2·00 2·10
1026. 75 l. Dumbo flying over Niagara Falls .. .. 3·25 3·25

205. "Salamis temora".

1987. Butterflies. Multicoloured, "Sierra Leone" in black.

1028 10 c. Type **205** 10 10
1029 20 c. "Stugeta marmorea" 10 10
1030 40 c. "Graphium ridleyanus" 10 10
1031 1 l. "Papilio bromius" .. 10 10
1032 2 l. "Iterus zalmoxis" .. 10 10
1033 3 l. "Cymothoe sangaris" 10 10
1033e 3 l. As 40 c. 10 10
1034 5 l. "Graphium tynderaeus" 10 10
1034e 9 l. As 3 l. (No. 1033) .. 10 10
1035 10 l. "Graphium policenes" 20 20
1035e 12 l. Type **205** 10 10
1035f 16 l. As 20 c. 10 10
1036 20 l. "Tanuetheira timon" 30 30
1037 25 l. "Danaus limniace" 10 10
1038 30 l. "Papilio hesperus" 30 30
1039 45 l. "Charaxes smaragdalis" .. 15 15
1040 60 l. "Charaxes lucretius" .. 40 40
1041 75 l. "Antanartia delius" 25 25
1042 100 l. "Abisara talantus" 75 75

For similar stamps but with "Sierra Leone" in blue, see Nos. 1658/72.

206. Cycling.

1987. Olympic Games, Seoul (1988) (1st series). Multicoloured.

1043. 5 l. Type **206** 20 25
1044. 10 l. Three day eventing 40 45
1045. 45 l. Athletics .. .. 1·75 1·90
1046. 50 l. Tennis .. .. 2·00 2·10

See also Nos. 1137/41.

1987. Birth Centenary of Marc Chagall (artist). As T **225** of Antigua. Multicoloured.

1048 3 l. "The Quarrel" .. 15 15
1049 5 l. "Rebecca giving Abraham's Servant a Drink" 20 25
1050 10 l. "The Village" .. 40 45
1051 20 l. "Ida at the Window" 80 85
1052 25 l. "Promenade" .. 1·00 1·10
1053 45 l. "Peasants" .. 1·75 1·90
1054 50 l. "Turquoise Plate" (ceramic) .. .. 2·00 2·10
1055 75 l. "Cemetery Gate" .. 3·00 3·25

1987. Milestones of Transportation. As T **226** of Antigua. Multicoloured.

1057 3 l. "Apollo 8" spacecraft (first manned Moon orbit), 1968 .. .. 15 15
1058 5 l. Blanchard's balloon (first U.S. balloon flight), 1793 .. .. 20 20
1059 10 l. Amelia Earhart's Lockheed "Vega" (first solo transatlantic flight by woman), 1932 .. 40 40
1060 15 l. Vicker's "Vimy" (first non-stop transatlantic flight), 1919 .. 60 60
1061 20 l. British "Mk 1" tank (first combat tank), 1916 .. .. .. 80 80
1062 25 l. Sikorsky "VS-300" (first U.S. helicopter flight), 1939 .. .. 90 90
1063 30 l. Wright brothers' "Flyer I" (first powered flight), 1903 .. .. 1·10 1·10
1064 35 l. Bleriot "XI" (first cross Channel flight), 1909 .. .. .. 1·25 1·25
1065 40 l. Paraplane (first flexible-wing ultra-light), 1983 .. .. 1·50 1·50
1066 50 l. Daimler's first motorcycle, 1885 .. 1·75 1·75

Nos. 1058/64 are horiz.

207 Evonne Goolagong

1987. Wimbledon Tennis Champions. Mult.

1068 2 l. Type **207** 20 20
1069 5 l. Martina Navratilova 35 35
1070 10 l. Jimmy Connors .. 60 60
1071 15 l. Bjorn Borg 90 90
1072 30 l. Boris Becker .. 1·75 1·75
1073 40 l. John McEnroe .. 2·00 2·00
1074 50 l. Chris Evert Lloyd .. 2·25 2·25
1075 75 l. Virginia Wade .. 3·00 3·00

208 Ducats, "Santa Maria" and Issac Abravanel (financier)

1987. 500th Anniv (1992) of Discovery of America by Columbus. Multicoloured.

1077 5 l. Type **208** 25 20
1078 10 l. Astrolabe, "Pinta" and Abraham Zacuto (astronomer) 40 35
1079 45 l. Maravedis (coins), "Nina" and Luis de Santangel (financier) .. 1·50 1·60
1080 50 l. Carib and Spaniard with tobacco plant and Luis de Torres (translator) .. .. 1·75 2·00

209 Cotton Tree

1987. Flora and Fauna. Multicoloured.

1082 3 l. Type **209** 15 15
1083 5 l. Dwarf crocodile .. 20 20
1084 10 l. Kudu 35 35
1085 20 l. Yellowbells .. 65 65
1086 25 l. Hippopotamus and calf 90 90
1087 45 l. Comet orchid .. 1·75 1·75
1088 50 l. Baobab tree .. 1·75 1·75
1089 75 l. Elephant and calf 2·75 2·75

210 Scouts at Ayers Rock

1987. World Scout Jamboree, Australia. Mult.

1091 5 l. Type **210** 20 20
1092 15 l. Scouts sailing yacht 55 60
1093 40 l. Scouts and Sydney skyline .. .. 1·50 1·60
1094 50 l. Scout, Sydney Harbour Bridge and Opera House .. .. 1·75 1·90

1987. Bicentenary of U.S. Constitution. As T **232** of Antigua. Multicoloured.

1096 5 l. White House .. 15 20
1097 10 l. George Washington (Virginia delegate) (vert) 30 35
1098 30 l. Patrick Henry (statesman) (vert) .. 90 95
1099 65 l. State Seal, New Hampshire .. .. 1·90 2·00

1987. 60th Anniv of Mickey Mouse (Walt Disney cartoon character). Cartoon characters at Tokyo Disneyland. As T **220** of Dominica. Multicoloured.

1101 20 c. Mickey and Minnie Mouse on Space Mountain 10 10
1102 40 c. Mickey Mouse at Country Bear Jamboree 10 10
1103 80 c. Mickey Mouse as bandleader and Minnie Mouse, Goofy and Pluto as musicians .. 10 10
1104 1 l. Goofy, Mickey Mouse and children in canoe and Mark Twain's river boat 10 10
1105 2 l. Mickey Mouse, Goofy and Chip n'Dale on Western River Railroad 10 10
1106 3 l. Goofy and Mickey Mouse as Pirates of the Caribbean 15 15
1107 10 l. Mickey Mouse, Goofy and children aboard "Big Thunder Mountain" train .. 45 45
1108 20 l. Mickey Mouse, Morty and Ferdie in boat and Goofy on flying carpet 85 85
1109 30 l. Mickey and Minnie Mouse in kimonos at Disneyland entrance .. 1·40 1·40

211 "The Annunciation" (detail) (Titian)

1987. Christmas. Religious Paintings by Titian. Multicoloured.

1111 2 l. Type **211** 15 10
1112 10 l. "Madonna and Child with Saints" 50 35
1113 20 l. "Madonna and Child with Saints Ulfus and Brigid" 90 90
1114 35 l. "The Madonna of the Cherries" .. .. 1·60 1·75

1988. Royal Ruby Wedding. As T **234** of Antigua.

1116 2 l. brown, black and grey 10 10
1117 3 l. multicoloured .. 10 10
1118 10 l. brown, black & orge 30 35
1119 50 l. multicoloured .. 1·75 2·00

DESIGNS: 2 l. Wedding of Princess Elizabeth and Duke of Edinburgh; 3 l. Prince Charles's christening photograph, 1949; 10 l. Queen Elizabeth II with Prince Charles and Princess Anne, c. 1951; 50 l. Queen Elizabeth, c. 1960.

212 "Russula cyanoxantha"

1988. Fungi. Multicoloured.

1121 3 l. Type **212** 35 30
1122 10 l. "Lycoperdon perlatum" 90 60
1123 20 l. "Lactarius deliciosus" .. .. 1·50 1·50
1124 30 l. "Boletus edulis" .. 2·00 2·25

213 Golden Pheasant Fish

1988. Fishes of Sierra Leone. Multicoloured.

1126 3 l. Type **213** 10 10
1127 10 l. Banded toothcarp .. 20 30
1128 20 l. Jewel fish 40 55
1129 35 l. Butterfly fish .. 75 90

1988. Stamp Exhibitions. Nos. 1016, 1072 and 1079 optd.

1131 25 l. Freedom, 1980 (optd **Independence 40**, Israel) 90 90
1132 30 l. Boris Becker (optd **OLYMPHILEX '88**, Seoul) .. .. 1·10 1·10
1133 45 l. Maravedis (coins), "Nina" and Luis de Santangel (financier) (optd **PRAGA 88**, Prague) .. .. 1·50 1·50

214 Hands holding Coffee Beans and Woman with Cocoa

1988. International Fund for Agricultural Development. Multicoloured.

No.	Description	Unused	Used
1134	3 l. Type **214**	15	15
1135	15 l. Tropical fruits and man climbing palm tree	60	70
1136	25 l. Sheaf of rice and harvesters	1·00	1·10

215 Basketball

1988. Olympic Games, Seoul (2nd issue). Mult.

No.	Description	Unused	Used
1137	3 l. Type **215**	10	10
1138	10 l. Judo	30	35
1139	15 l. Gymnastics ..	45	50
1140	40 l. Synchronized swimming	1·25	1·40

216 Swallow-tailed Bee Eater

1988. Birds. Multicoloured.

No.	Description	Unused	Used
1142	3 l. Type **216**	20	20
1143	5 l. Double-toothed barbet	30	30
1144	8 l. African golden oriole	45	45
1145	10 l. Red bishop	50	50
1146	12 l. Red-billed shrike ..	55	55
1147	20 l. European bee eater	95	95
1148	35 l. Common gonolek ("Barbary Shrike") ..	1·60	1·60
1149	40 l. Western black-headed oriole	1·75	1·75

217 "Aureol" (liner)

1988. Ships. Multicoloured.

No.	Description	Unused	Used
1151	3 l. Type **217**	30	30
1152	10 l. "Dunkwa" (freighter)	80	80
1153	15 l. "Melampus" (container ship) ..	1·10	1·10
1154	30 l. "Dumbaia" (freighter)	1·90	1·90

1988. 500th Birth Anniv of Titian (artist). As T **238** of Antigua. Multicoloured.

No.	Description	Unused	Used
1156	1 l. "The Concert" (detail)	10	10
1157	2 l. "Philip II of Spain"	10	10
1158	3 l. "Saint Sebastian" (detail)	15	15
1159	5 l. "Martyrdom of St. Peter Martyr" ..	25	25
1160	15 l. "St. Jerome" ..	60	60
1161	20 l. "St. Mark enthroned with Saints"	75	75
1162	25 l. "Portrait of a Young Man"	90	90
1163	30 l. "St. Jerome in Penitence"	1·10	1·10

218 Helicopter lowering "Mercury" Capsule to Flight Deck

1988. 25th Death Anniv of John F. Kennedy (American statesman). U.S. Space Achievements. Multicoloured.

No.	Description	Unused	Used
1165	3 l. Type **218**	10	10
1166	5 l. "Liberty Bell 7" capsule descending (vert)	15	20
1167	15 l. Launch of first manned American capsule (vert)	45	50
1168	40 l. "Freedom 7" orbiting Earth)	1·25	1·40

219 Famine Relief Convoy crossing Desert

1988. 125th Anniv of Int Red Cross. Mult.

No.	Description	Unused	Used
1170	3 l. Type **219**	30	30
1171	10 l. Rifle and map of Battle of Solferino, 1859	75	75
1172	20 l. World War II hospital ship in Pacific	1·25	1·25
1173	40 l. Red Cross tent and World War I German biplanes	2·25	2·25

1988. Christmas. "Mickey's Christmas Dance". As T **228** of Dominica showing Walt Disney cartoon characters. Multicoloured.

No.	Description	Unused	Used
1175	10 l. Donald Duck's nephews playing as band	45	45
1176	10 l. Clarabelle	45	45
1177	10 l. Goofy	45	45
1178	10 l. Scrooge McDuck and Grandma Duck ..	45	45
1179	10 l. Donald Duck ..	45	45
1180	10 l. Daisy Duck ..	45	45
1181	10 l. Minnie Mouse ..	45	45
1182	10 l. Mickey Mouse ..	45	45

Nos. 1175/82 were printed together, se-tenant, forming a composite design.

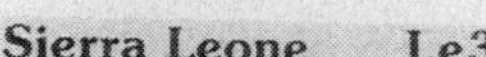

220 "Adoration of the Magi" (detail)

1988. Christmas. Religious Paintings by Rubens. Multicoloured.

No.	Description	Unused	Used
1184	3 l. Type **220**	10	10
1185	3 l. 60 "Adoration of the Shepherds" (detail) ..	10	10
1186	5 l. "Adoration of the Magi" (detail)	20	20
1187	10 l. "Adoration of the Shepherds" (diff detail)	35	35
1188	20 l. "Virgin and Child surrounded by Flowers"	65	65
1189	40 l. "St. Gregory the Great and Other Saints" (detail) ..	1·40	1·40
1190	60 l. "Adoration of the Magi" (detail) ..	1·90	1·90
1191	80 l. "Madonna and Child with Saints" (detail)	2·40	2·40

222 Brazil v. Sweden, 1958

1989. World Cup Football Championship, Italy. Designs showing action from previous World Cup finals. Multicoloured.

No.	Description	Unused	Used
1194	3 l. Type **222**	15	15
1195	6 l. West Germany v. Hungary, 1954 ..	20	20
1196	8 l. England v. West Germany, 1966 ..	20	20
1197	10 l. Argentina v. Netherlands, 1978 ..	25	25
1198	12 l. Brazil v. Czechoslovakia, 1962 ..	25	25
1199	20 l. West Germany v. Netherlands, 1974 ..	35	35
1200	30 l. Italy v. West Germany, 1982 ..	45	45
1201	40 l. Brazil v. Italy, 1970	60	60

223 Decathlon (Gold, C. Schenk, East Germany)

1989. Olympic Medal Winners, Seoul (1988). Multicoloured.

No.	Description	Unused	Used
1203	3 l. Type **223**	15	15
1204	6 l. Men's heavyweight judo (Gold, H. Saito, Japan)	20	20
1205	10 l. Women's cycle road race (Silver, J. Niehaus, West Germany) ..	20	20
1206	15 l. Men's single sculls (Gold, T. Lange, East Germany)	20	20
1207	20 l. Men's 50 metres freestyle swimming (Gold, M. Biondi, U.S.A.)	30	30
1208	30 l. Men's 100 metres (Gold, C. Lewis, U.S.A.)	35	35
1209	40 l. Dressage (Gold, West Germany)	45	45
1210	50 l. Greco-Roman wrestling (57 kg) (Gold, A. Sike, Hungary) ..	60	60

224 Map of Union States, Mail Lorry and Post Office

1989. 15th Anniv of Mano River Union. Mult.

No.	Description	Unused	Used
1212	1 l. Type **224**	10	10
1213	3 l. Map of West Africa and Presidents Momoh, Conte and Doe	15	15
1214	10 l. Construction of Freetown–Monrovia Highway	40	40

225 "Richard III" (illustration reduced, actual size 49 × 36 mm)

1989. 425th Birth Anniv of Shakespeare. Mult.

No.	Description	Unused	Used
1216	15 l. Type **225**	40	40
1217	15 l. "Othello" (Iago) ..	40	40
1218	15 l. "Two Gentlemen of Verona"	40	40
1219	15 l. "Macbeth" (Lady Macbeth)	40	40
1220	15 l. "Hamlet"	40	40
1221	15 l. "The Taming of the Shrew"	40	40
1222	15 l. "The Merry Wives of Windsor"	40	40
1223	15 l. "Henry IV" (Sir John Falstaff) ..	40	40
1224	15 l. "Macbeth" (The Witches)	40	40
1225	15 l. "Romeo and Juliet"	40	40
1226	15 l. "Merchant of Venice"	40	40
1227	15 l. "As You Like It" ..	40	40
1228	15 l. "The Taming of the Shrew" (banquet scene)	40	40
1229	15 l. "King Lear" ..	40	40
1230	15 l. "Othello" (Othello and Desdemona) ..	40	40
1231	15 l. "Henry IV" (Justice Shallow)	40	40

226 Centenary Logo

1989. Cent of Ahmadiyya Muslim Society.

No.	Description	Unused	Used
1233	**226** 3 l. black and blue ..	20	20

1989. Japanese Art (1st series). Paintings by Seiho. As T **250** of Antigua. Multicoloured.

No.	Description	Unused	Used
1234	3 l. "Lapping Waves" ..	15	15
1235	6 l. "Hazy Moon" (vert)	20	20
1236	8 l. "Passing Spring" (vert)	20	20
1237•	10 l. "Mackerels" ..	20	20
1238	12 l. "Calico Cat" ..	20	20
1239	30 l. "The First Time to be a Model" (vert) ..	35	35
1240	40 l. "Kingly Lion" ..	45	45
1241	75 l. "After a Shower" (vert)	80	80

See also Nos. 1321/50.

227 Robespierre and Bastille

1989. "Philexfrance 89" International Stamp Exhibition, Paris, and Bicentenary of French Revolution. Multicoloured.

No.	Description	Unused	Used
1243	6 l. Type **227**	25	25
1244	20 l. Danton and Louvre	45	45
1245	45 l. Queen Marie Antoinette and Notre Dame	65	65
1246	80 l. Louis XVI and Palace of Versailles ..	1·00	1·00

228 "Sputnik" Satellite in Orbit, 1957

1989. History of Space Exploration.

No.	Description	Unused	Used
1248/1301	10 l. × 27, 15 l. × 27 mult Set of 54	7·00	7·00

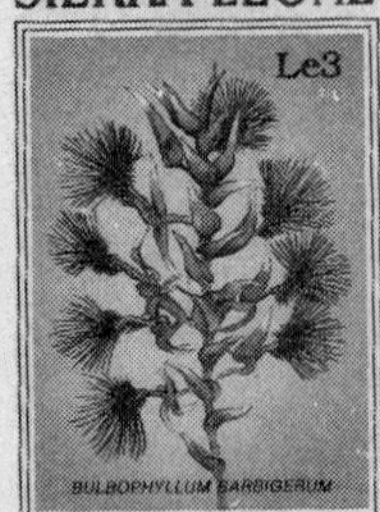

229 "Bulbophyllum barbigerum"

1989. Orchids of Sierra Leone. Multicoloured.

1303 3 l. Type **229** 25 25
1304 6 l. "Bulbophyllum falcatum" 40 40
1305 12 l. "Habenaria macrara" 60 60
1306 20 l. "Eurychone rothchildiana" .. 80 80
1307 50 l. "Calyptrochilum christyanum" .. .. 1·40 1·40
1308 60 l. "Bulbophyllum distans" .. .. 1·50 1·50
1309 70 l. "Eulophia guineensis" .. .. 1·60 1·60
1310 80 l. "Diaphananthe pellucida" .. .. 1·75 1·75

230 "Salamis temora"

1989. Butterflies. Multicoloured.

1312 6 l. Type **230** 30 30
1313 12 l. "Pseudacraea lucretia" 55 55
1314 18 l. "Charaxes boueti" (vert) 75 75
1315 30 l. "Graphium antheus" (vert) .. .. .. 1·25 1·25
1316 40 l. "Colotis protomedia" 1·40 1·40
1317 60 l. "Asterope pechueli" (vert) .. .. .. 1·50 1·50
1318 72 l. "Coenura aurantiaca" .. .. .. 1·60 1·60
1319 80 l. "Precis octavia" (vert) .. .. .. 1·75 1·75

1989. Japanese Art (2nd series). Paintings by Hiroshige of "The Fifty-three Stations on the Tokaido Road". As T **250** of Antigua. Mult.

1321 25 l. "Ferry-boat to Kawasaki" 30 30
1322 25 l. "The Hilly Town of Hodogaya" 30 30
1323 25 l. "Lute Players at Fujisawa" 30 30
1324 25 l. "Mild Rainstorm at Oiso" 30 30
1325 25 l. "Lake Ashi and Mountains of Hakone" 30 30
1326 25 l. "Twilight at Numazu" 30 30
1327 25 l. "Mount Fuji from Hara" 30 30
1328 25 l. "Samurai Children riding through Yoshiwara" 30 30
1329 25 l. "Mountain Pass at Yui" 30 30
1330 25 l. "Harbour at Ejiri" 30 30
1331 25 l. "Halt at Fujieda" .. 30 30
1332 25 l. "Misty Kanaya on the Oi River" 30 30
1333 25 l. "The Bridge to Kakegawa" 30 30
1334 25 l. "Teahouse at Fukuroi" 30 30
1335 25 l. "The Ford at Mistuke" 30 30
1336 25 l. "Coolies warming themselves at Hamamatsu" 30 30
1337 25 l. "Imakiri Ford at Maisaka" 30 30
1338 25 l. "Pacific Ocean from Shirasuka" 30 30
1339 25 l. "Futakawa Street-singers" 30 30
1340 25 l. "Repairing Yoshida Castle" 30 30
1341 25 l. "The Inn at Akasaka" 30 30
1342 25 l. "The Bridge to Okazaki" 30 30
1343 25 l. "Samurai's Wife entering Narumi" .. 30 30
1344 25 l. "Harbour at Kuwana" 30 30
1345 25 l. "Autumn in Ishiyakushi" .. 30 30
1346 25 l. "Snowfall at Kameyama" .. 30 30
1347 25 l. "The Frontier-station of Seki" 30 30
1348 25 l. "Teahouse at Sakanoshita" .. 30 30
1349 25 l. "Kansai Houses at Minakushi" 30 30
1350 25 l. "Kusatsu Station" 30 30

231 Formosan Sika Deer

1989. "World Stamp Expo '89" International Stamp Exhibition, Washington (2nd issue). Endangered Fauna. Multicoloured.

1353 6 l. Humpback whale .. 20 20
1354 9 l. Type **231** .. 20 20
1355 16 l. Spanish lynx .. 30 30
1356 20 l. Goitred gazelle .. 30 30
1357 30 l. Japanese sea lion .. 40 40
1358 50 l. Long-eared owl .. 70 70
1359 70 l. Lady Amherst's ("Chinese Copper") pheasant 85 85
1360 100 l. Siberian tiger .. 1·25 1·25

1989. Christmas. Walt Disney cartoon characters with cars. As T **183** of Gambia Multicoloured.

1362 3 l. Mickey Mouse and Goofy in Rolls-Royce "Phantom II Roadster", 1934 .. 15 15
1363 6 l. Mickey and Minnie Mouse in Mercedes-Benz "500K", 1935 .. 20 20
1364 10 l. Mickey and Minnie Mouse with Jaguar "SS-100", 1938 .. 20 20
1365 12 l. Mickey Mouse and Goofy with U.S. army jeep, 1941 .. 25 25
1366 20 l. Mickey and Minnie Mouse with Buick Roadmaster Sedan "Model 91", 1937 .. 35 35
1367 30 l. Mickey Mouse driving 1948 Tucker .. 45 45
1368 40 l. Mickey and Minnie Mouse in Alfa Romeo, 1933 .. 55 55
1369 50 l. Mickey and Minnie Mouse with 1937 Cord 65 65

1989. Christmas. Paintings by Rembrandt. As T **259** of Antigua. Multicoloured.

1371 3 l. "The Adoration of the Magi" 15 15
1372 6 l. "The Holy Family with a Cat" .. 20 20
1373 10 l. "The Holy Family with Angels" 20 20
1374 15 l. "Simeon in the Temple" 20 20
1375 30 l. "The Circumcision" 35 35
1376 90 l. "The Holy Family" 95 95
1377 100 l. "The Visitation" .. 1·10 1·10
1378 120 l. "The Flight into Egypt" .. .. 1·25 1·25

232 Johann Kepler (astronomer)

1990. Exploration of Mars. Designs showing astronomers, spacecraft and Martian landscapes.

1380/1415 175 l. × 36 mult Set of 36 .. .. 35·00 40·00

1990. 50th Anniv of Second World War. American Aircraft. As T **188** of Gambia. Multicoloured.

1417 1 l. Dolittle's B-25 "Ruptured Duck", 1942 10 10
1418 2 l. B-24 Liberator .. 10 10
1419 3 l. A-20 Boston attacking Japanese convoy, Bismark Sea, 1943 .. 10 10
1420 9 l. P-38 Lightning .. 10 10
1421 12 l. B-26 bomber .. 10 10
1422 16 l. Two B-17 F bombers 10 10
1423 50 l. B-25 D bomber .. 10 10
1424 80 l. B-29 Superfortress .. 20 25
1425 90 l. B-17 G bomber .. 20 25
1426 100 l. B-29 Superfortress "Enola Gay" 25 30

233 Mickey Mouse at Bauxite Mine

1990. Sierra Leone Sites and Scenes. Walt Disney cartoon characters. Multicoloured.

1428 3 l. Type **233** 10 10
1429 6 l. Scrooge McDuck panning for gold .. 10 10
1430 10 l. Minnie Mouse at Lungi Airport .. 10 10
1431 12 l. Mickey Mouse at Old Fourah Bay College .. 10 10
1432 16 l. Mickey Mouse mining bauxite 10 10
1433 20 l. Huey, Dewey and Louie harvesting rice .. 10 10
1434 30 l. Mickey and Minnie Mouse admire the Freetown Cotton Tree 10 15
1435 100 l. Mickey Mouse flying over Rutile Mine .. 25 30
1436 200 l. Mickey Mouse fishing at Goderich .. 50 55
1437 225 l. Mickey and Minnie Mouse at Bintumani Hotel 55 60

234 Olivier as Antony in "Antony and Cleopatra", 1951

1990. Sir Laurence Olivier (actor) Commemoration. Multicoloured.

1439 3 l. Type **234** 10 10
1440 9 l. As King Henry V in "Henry V", 1943 .. 10 10
1441 16 l. As Oedipus in "Oedipus", 1945 .. 10 10
1442 20 l. As Heathcliffe in "Wuthering Heights", 1939 .. .. .. 10 10
1443 30 l. As Szell in "Marathon Man", 1976 10 15
1444 70 l. As Othello in "Othello", 1964 .. 15 20
1445 175 l. As Michael in "Beau Geste", 1929 .. .. 40 45
1446 200 l. As King Richard III in "Richard III", 1956 50 55

235 Penny Black

1990. 150th Anniv of the Penny Black.

1448 **235** 50 l. blue 10 10
1449 100 l. brown 25 30

236 Cameroons World Cup Team

1990. World Cup Football Championship, Italy. Finalists. Multicoloured.

1451/74 15 l. × 8 (Type **236**, Colombia, Costa Rica, Egypt, Rumania, South Korea, U.A.E., Yugoslavia), 30 l. × 8 (Austria, Belgium, Czechoslovakia, Netherlands, Scotland, Sweden, Uruguay, U.S.S.R.), 45 l. × 8 (Argentina, Brazil, England, Ireland, Italy, Spain, U.S.A., West Germany) Set of 24 .. 2·10 2·25

237 Great Crested Grebe

1990. Birds. Multicoloured.

1475 3 l. Type **237** 10 10
1476 6 l. Green wood hoopoe .. 10 10
1477 10 l. African jacana .. 10 10
1478 12 l. Avocet 10 10
1479 20 l. Peters's finfoot .. 10 15
1480 80 l. Glossy ibis .. 20 25
1481 150 l. Hammerkop .. 35 40
1482 200 l. Black-throated honeyguide 50 55

1990. "Stamp World London 90" International Stamp Exhibition. British Costumes. As T **193** of Gambia showing Walt Disney cartoon characters. Multicoloured.

1484 3 l. Mickey Mouse as a Yeoman Warder .. 10 10
1485 6 l. Scrooge McDuck as a lamplighter .. 10 10
1486 12 l. Goofy as a medieval knight 10 10
1487 15 l. Clarabell as Ann Boleyn 10 10
1488 75 l. Minnie Mouse as Queen Elizabeth I .. 20 25
1489 100 l. Donald Duck as a chimney sweep .. 25 30
1490 125 l. Pete as King Henry VIII 30 35
1491 150 l. Clarabell, Minnie Mouse and Daisy Duck as May dancers .. 35 40

1990. 90th Birthday of Queen Elizabeth the Queen Mother. As T **99** of Grenada Grenadines. Multicoloured.

1493 75 l. Queen Mother on Remembrance Sunday 20 25
1494 75 l. Queen Mother in yellow hat 20 25
1495 75 l. Waving to crowds on 85th birthday .. 20 25

238 Golden Cat

1990. Wildlife. Multicoloured.

1497	25 l. Type **238**	10	10
1498	25 l. White-backed night heron	10	10
1499	25 l. Bateleur	10	10
1500	25 l. Marabou stork	10	10
1501	25 l. White-faced whistling duck	10	10
1502	25 l. Aardvark	10	10
1503	25 l. Royal antelope	10	10
1504	25 l. Pygmy hippopotamus	10	10
1505	25 l. Leopard	10	10
1506	25 l. Sacred ibis	10	10
1507	25 l. Mona monkey	10	10
1508	25 l. African darter	10	10
1509	25 l. Chimpanzee	10	10
1510	25 l. African elephant	10	10
1511	25 l. Potto	10	10
1512	25 l. African manatee	10	10
1513	25 l. African fish eagle	10	10
1514	25 l. African spoonbill	10	10

239 Rabbit

1990. Fairground Carousel Animals. Mult.

1516	5 l. Type **239**	10	10
1517	10 l. Horse with panther saddle	10	10
1518	20 l. Ostrich	10	10
1519	30 l. Zebra	10	10
1520	50 l. Horse	10	10
1521	80 l. Sea monster	20	25
1522	100 l. Giraffe	25	30
1523	150 l. Armoured horse	35	40
1524	200 l. Camel	50	55

1990. Olympic Games, Barcelona (1992). As T **268** of Antigua.

1526	5 l. Start of Men's 100 metres	10	10
1527	10 l. Men's 4 × 400 metres relay	10	10
1528	20 l. Men's 100 metres in progress	10	10
1529	30 l. Weightlifting	10	15
1530	40 l. Freestyle wrestling	10	15
1531	80 l. Water polo	20	25
1532	150 l. Women's gymnastics	35	40
1533	200 l. Cycling	50	55

240 Morty assembling Bicycle by Christmas Tree

1990. Christmas. "The Night before Christmas". Walt Disney cartoon characters in scenes from Clement Moore's poem.

1535/58	50 l. × 8, 75 l. × 8, 100 l. × 8 mult Set of 24	4·00	4·75

241 "Holy Family with St. Elizabeth" (Mantegna)

1990. Christmas. Paintings. Multicoloured.

1560	10 l. "Holy Family resting" (Rembrandt)	10	10
1561	20 l. Type **241**	10	10
1562	30 l. "Virgin and Child with an Angel" (Correggio)	10	10
1563	50 l. "Annunciation" (Bernardo Strozzi)	10	10
1564	100 l. "Madonna and Child appearing to St. Anthony" (Lippi)	25	30
1565	175 l. "Virgin and Child" (Giovanni Boltraffio)	40	45
1566	200 l. "Esterhazy Madonna" (Raphael)	50	55
1567	300 l. "Coronation of Mary" (Andrea Orcagna)	70	75

1990. 350th Death Anniv of Rubens (1st issue). As T **273** of Antigua but vert. Mult.

1569	5 l. "Helena Fourment as Hagar in the Wilderness" (detail)	10	10
1570	10 l. "Isabella Brant"	10	10
1571	20 l. "Countess of Arundel and her Party" (detail)	10	10
1572	60 l. "Countess of Arundel and her Party" (different detail)	15	20
1573	80 l. "Nicolaas Rockox"	20	25
1574	100 l. "Adriana Perez"	25	30
1575	150 l. "George Villiers, Duke of Buckingham" (detail)	35	40
1576	300 l. "Countess of Buckingham"	70	75

See also Nos. 1595/602.

242 "Chlorophyllum molybdites"

1990. Fungi. Multicoloured.

1578	3 l. Type **242**	10	10
1579	5 l. "Lepista nuda"	10	10
1580	10 l. "Clitocybe nebularis"	10	10
1581	15 l. "Cyathus striatus"	10	10
1582	20 l. "Bolbitius vitellinus"	10	10
1583	25 l. "Leucoagaricus naucinus"	10	10
1584	30 l. "Suillus luteus"	10	10
1585	40 l. "Podaxis pistillaris"	10	10
1586	50 l. "Oudemansiella radicata"	10	10
1587	60 l. "Phallus indusiatus"	15	20
1588	80 l. "Macrolepiota rhacodes"	20	25
1589	100 l. "Mycena pura"	25	30
1590	150 l. "Volvariella volvacea"	35	40
1591	175 l. "Omphalotus olearius"	40	45
1592	200 l. "Sphaerobolus stellatus"	50	55
1593	250 l. "Schizophyllum commune"	60	65

243 "The Flight of St. Barbara" (detail) (Rubens)

1991. Easter. 350th Death Anniv (1990) of Rubens (2nd issue). Multicoloured.

1595	10 l. Type **243**	10	10
1596	20 l. "The Last Judgement" (detail)	10	10
1597	30 l. "St. Gregory of Nazianzus"	10	10
1598	50 l. "Doubting Thomas"	10	10
1599	80 l. "The Way to Calvary" (detail)	20	25
1600	100 l. "St. Gregory with Sts. Domitilla, Maurus and Papianus"	25	30
1601	175 l. "Sts. Gregory, Maurus and Papianus"	40	45
1602	300 l. "Christ and the Penitent Sinners"	70	75

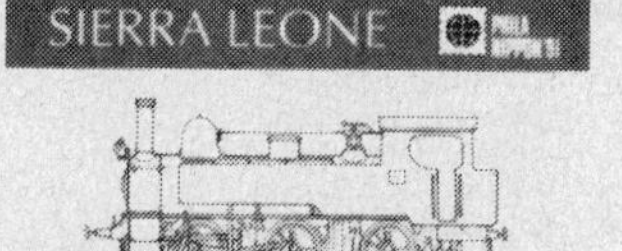

244 Class "1400" Steam Locomotive

1991. "Phila Nippon '91" International Stamp Exhibition, Tokyo. Japanese Trains. Multicoloured.

1604	10 l. Type **244**	10	10
1605	20 l. Class "C 55" streamline steam locomotive	10	10
1606	30 l. Class "ED 17" electric locomotive	10	10
1607	60 l. Class "EF 13" double-ended electric locomotive	15	20
1608	100 l. Baldwin Class "Mikado" steam locomotive	25	30
1609	150 l. Class "C 62" steam locomotive	35	40
1610	200 l. Class "KiHa 81" diesel train	50	55
1611	300 l. Class "8550" steam locomotive	70	75

245 "Aphyosemion spurrelli"

1991. Fishes. Multicoloured.

1613	10 l. Type **245**	10	10
1614	20 l. "Epiplatys dageti"	10	10
1615	30 l. "Aphyosemion petersi"	10	10
1616	60 l. "Fundulosoma thierryi"	15	20
1617	100 l. "Pantodon bulcholzi peters"	25	30
1618	150 l. "Epiplatys spilargyreius"	35	40
1619	200 l. "Epiplatys sexfasciatus"	50	55
1620	300 l. "Tetraodon lineatus"	70	75

1991. Death Centenary of Vincent van Gogh (artist). As T **278** of Antigua. Mult.

1622	10 c. "The Langlois Bridge at Arles" (horiz)	10	10
1623	50 c. "Tree in Garden at Saint-Paul Hospital"	10	10
1624	1 l. "Wild Flowers and Thistles in a Vase"	10	10
1625	2 l. "Still Life: Vase with Oleanders and Books" (horiz)	10	10
1626	5 l. "Farmhouses in a Wheatfield near Arles" (horiz)	10	10
1627	10 l. "Self-portrait, September 1889"	10	10
1628	20 l. "Patience Escalier"	10	10
1629	30 l. "Doctor Felix Rey"	10	10
1630	50 l. "The Iris"	10	10
1631	60 l. "The Shepherdess"	15	20
1632	80 l. "Vincent's House in Arles" (horiz)	20	25
1633	100 l. "The Road Menders" (horiz)	25	30
1634	150 l. "The Garden of Saint-Paul Hospital"	35	40
1635	200 l. "View of the Church, Saint-Paul-de-Mausole" (horiz)	50	55
1636	250 l. "Seascape at Saintes-Maries" (horiz)	60	65
1637	300 l. "Pieta"	70	75

1991. 65th Birthday of Queen Elizabeth II. As T **280** of Antigua. Multicoloured.

1639	10 l. The Queen and Prince Charles at polo match	10	10
1640	30 l. The Queen at Windsor, 1989	10	10
1641	200 l. The Queen and Princess Diana in Nigeria, 1989	50	55
1642	250 l. The Queen and Prince Philip	60	65

1991. 10th Wedding Anniv of Prince and Princess of Wales. As T **280** of Antigua. Multicoloured.

1644	20 l. Prince and Princess of Wales in August 1987	10	10
1645	80 l. Separate photographs of Prince, Princess and sons	20	25
1646	100 l. Prince Henry in Majorca and Prince William on his first day at school	25	30
1647	300 l. Prince Charles at Caister, April 1988, and Princess Diana in Hyde Park, May 1989	70	75

246 "Graphium latreillianus" and "Ancistrochilus rothschildianus"

1991. Butterflies and Flowers. Multicoloured.

1649	10 l. Type **246**	10	10
1650	30 l. "Euphraedra eleus" and "Clitoria ternatea"	10	10
1651	50 l. "Graphium antheus" and "Gloriosa simplex"	10	10
1652	60 l. "Salamis cacta" and "Stenandriopsis guineensis"	15	20
1653	80 l. "Kallima rumia" and "Cassia fistula"	20	25
1654	100 l. "Hypolimnas salmacis" and "Amorphophallus abyssinicus"	25	30
1655	200 l. "Danaus formosa" and "Nephthytis afzelii"	50	55
1656	300 l. "Graphium leonidas" and "Clappertonia ficifolia"	70	75

1991. Butterflies. As Nos. 1028/42 but "Sierra Leone" in blue. Multicoloured.

1658	10 c. "Danaus limniace"	—	10
1660	50 c. "Graphium ridleyanus"	—	10
1661	1 l. "Papilio bromius"	—	10
1662	2 l. "Iterus zalmoxis"	—	10
1663	5 l. "Graphium tynderaeus"	—	10
1665	10 l. "Graphium policenes"	—	10
1666	20 l. "Tanuetheira timon"	—	10
1667	30 l. "Cymothoe sangaris"	—	10
1668	50 l. Type **205**	10	—
1069	60 l. "Charaxes lucretius"	—	25
1670	80 l. "Stugeta marmorea"	20	—
1671	100 l. "Abisara talantus"	—	35
1672	300 l. "Papilio hesperus"	70	—

247 Audie Murphy in "To Hell and Back"

1991. Films of Second World War. Mult.

1675 2 l. Type **247** 10 10
1676 5 l. Jack Palance in "Attack" 10 10
1677 10 l. Greer Garson and Walter Pidgeon in "Mrs. Miniver" .. 10 10
1678 20 l. Heavy artillery from "The Guns of Navarone" 10 10
1679 30 l. Charlie Chaplin and Paulette Goddard in "The Great Dictator" 10 10
1680 50 l. Steam locomotive from "The Train" .. 10 10
1681 60 l. Diary and fountain pen from "The Diary of Anne Frank" 15 20
1682 80 l. William Holden in "The Bridge on the River Kwai" 20 25
1683 100 l. Tallulah Bankhead in "Lifeboat" and Alfred Hitchcock (director) 25 30
1684 200 l. John Wayne in "Sands of Iwo Jima" .. 50 55
1685 300 l. Van Johnson and Spencer Tracy in "Thirty Seconds over Tokyo" 70 75
1686 350 l. Humphrey Bogart and Ingrid Bergman in "Casablanca" 85 90

248 Meissen China Parrot Ornament, Munich Botanic Garden

1991. Botanical Gardens of the World.

1688/1735 60 l. × 48 mult ..
Set of 48 6·50 8·50

Issued in 3 sheetlets of 16 stamps, depicting features and plants from Munich (Nos. 16881/1703), Kyoto (Nos. 1704/19) and Brooklyn (Nos. 1720/35).

1991. Christmas. Drawings and Paintings by Albrecht Durer. As T **291** of Antigua.

1737 6 l. black and mauve .. 10 10
1738 60 l. black and blue .. 15 20
1739 80 l. multicoloured .. 20 25
1740 100 l. multicoloured .. 25 30
1741 200 l. multicoloured .. 50 55
1742 300 l. multicoloured .. 70 75
1743 700 l. multicoloured .. 1·75 1·90

DESIGNS: 6 l. "Mary being Crowned by Two Angels"; 60 l. "St. Christopher"; 80 l. "Virgin and Child with St. Anne" (detail); 100 l. "Virgin with the Pear" (detail); 200 l. "Madonna and Child" (detail); 300 l. "The Virgin in Half-Length" (detail); 700 l. "The Madonna with the Siskin" (detail).

1991. Anniversaries and Events. As T **285** of Antigua. Multicoloured.

1745 50 l. National Theatre, Prague 10 10
1746 100 l. St. Peter's Abbey, Salzburg 25 30
1747 250 l. Sea scouts learning sailing 60 65
1748 300 l. Sierra Leone scouts emblem and Lord Baden-Powell 70 75
1749 400 l. Scouts playing baseball at Mt. Sorak Jamboree .. .. 95 1·00
1750 500 l. Scene from "Idomeneo" .. .. 1·25 1·40

ANNIVERSARIES AND EVENTS: Nos. 1745/6, 1750, Death bicentenary of Mozart; Nos. 1747/9, 50th death anniv of Lord Baden-Powell and World Scout Jamboree, Korea.

250 Aichi D3A1 "Val" Dive Bomber

1991. 50th Anniv of Japanese Attack on Pearl Harbor. Multicoloured.

1752 75 l. Type **250** 20 25
1753 75 l. Japanese bomber and smoke 20 25
1754 75 l. Battleship Row burning 20 25
1755 75 l. Planes and burning dockyard 20 25
1756 75 l. Burning installations 20 25
1757 75 l. Two Japanese dive bombers 20 25
1758 75 l. Burning ships and hangars 20 25
1759 75 l. Airfield under attack 20 25
1760 75 l. American fighter .. 20 25
1761 75 l. Japanese torpedo bombers 20 25
1762 75 l. Japanese bombers over suburb 20 25
1763 75 l. Japanese bombers attacking ships .. 20 25
1764 75 l. Japanese aircraft on fire 20 25
1765 75 l. Japanese torpedo bombers over jungle .. 20 25
1766 75 l. Nakasima B5N2 "Kate" torpedo bomber 20 25

1991. Christmas. Walt Disney Christmas Cards. As T **228** of St. Vincent. Mult.

1767 12 l. Mickey Mouse, Donald Duck and characters from "Peter Pan", 1952 (horiz) .. 10 10
1768 30 l. Disney characters reading "Alice in Wonderland", 1950 (horiz) 10 10
1769 60 l. Sleepy and animals, 1938 (horiz) 15 20
1770 75 l. Mickey, Minnie, Donald and Pluto posting card, 1936 (horiz) 20 25
1771 100 l. Disney cartoon characters, 1984 (horiz) 25 30
1772 125 l. Mickey and Donald singing carols with Donald's nephews and Pluto reading, 1954 (horiz) 30 35
1773 150 l. "101 Dalmatians", 1960 (horiz) 35 40
1774 200 l. Mickey and Donald opening presents, 1948 (horiz) 50 55
1775 300 l. Mickey, Minnie, Morte and Ferde decorating tree, 1983 (horiz) 70 75
1776 400 l. Donald decorating tree and nephews watching television, 1956 (horiz) .. .. 95 1·00
1777 500 l. Characters from Disney films, 1972 (horiz) .. .. 1·25 1·40
1778 600 l. Mickey, Donald, Pluto and friends singing, 1964 (horiz) .. 1·50 1·60

1992. Mickey's World Tour. As T **270** of Maldive Islands showing Walt Disney cartoon characters in different countries. Multicoloured.

1780 6 l. Minnie Mouse as Chiquita with Pluto, Cuba 10 10
1781 10 l. Goofy as Olympic discus champion, Greece 10 10
1782 20 l. Donald and Daisy Duck as flamenco dancers, Spain .. 10 10
1783 30 l. Goofy and Donald as guardsman, England .. 10 10
1784 50 l. Mickey and Minnie at Paris fashion show, France 10 10
1785 100 l. Goofy in the Alps, Switzerland 25 30
1786 200 l. Daisy and Minnie in grass skirts, Hawaii .. 50 55
1787 350 l. Mickey, Donald and Goofy as ancient Egyptians (horiz) .. 85 90
1788 500 l. Daisy and Minnie as cancan dancers, France (horiz) .. .. 1·25 1·40

1992. 40th Anniv of Queen Elizabeth II's Accession. As T **288** of Antigua. Mult.

1790 60 l. State House .. 15 20
1791 100 l. Beach 25 30
1792 300 l. Parliament Building 70 75
1793 400 l. Canoe on beach .. 95 1·00

1992. "Granada '92" International Stamp Exhibition, Spain. Paintings by Francisco Zurbaran. As T **292** of Antigua. Mult.

1795 1 l. "Visit of St. Thomas Aquinas to St. Bonaventure" .. 10 10
1796 10 l. "St Gregory" .. 10 10
1797 30 l. "St. Andrew" .. 10 10
1798 50 l. "St. Gabriel the Archangel" 10 10
1799 60 l. "The Blessed Henry Suso" 15 20
1800 100 l. "St. Lucy" .. 25 30
1801 300 l. "St. Casilda" .. 70 75
1802 400 l. "St. Margaret of Antioch" .. .. 95 1·00
1803 500 l. "St. Apollonia" .. 1·25 1·40
1804 600 l. "St. Bonaventure at Council of Lyons" .. 1·50 1·60
1805 700 l. "St. Bonaventure on his Bier" .. .. 1·75 1·90
1806 800 l. "The Martyrdom of St. James" (detail) .. 1·90 2·00

1992. Prehistoric Animals. As T **290** of Antigua. Multicoloured.

1808 50 l. Rhamphorhynchus 10 10
1809 50 l. Pteranodon .. 10 10
1810 50 l. Dimorphodon .. 10 10
1811 50 l. Pterodactyl .. 10 10
1812 50 l. Archaeopteryx .. 10 10
1813 50 l. Iguanodon .. 10 10
1814 50 l. Hypsilophodon .. 10 10
1815 50 l. Nothosaurus .. 10 10
1816 50 l. Brachiosaurus .. 10 10
1817 50 l. Kentrosaurus .. 10 10
1818 50 l. Plesiosaurus .. 10 10
1819 50 l. Trachodon 10 10
1820 50 l. Hesperornis .. 10 10
1821 50 l. Henodus 10 10
1822 50 l. Steneosaurus .. 10 10
1823 50 l. Stenopterygius .. 10 10
1824 50 l. Eurhinosaurus .. 10 10
1825 50 l. Placodus 10 10
1826 50 l. Mosasaurus .. 10 10
1827 50 l. Mixosaurus .. 10 10

Nos. 1808/27 were printed together, se-tenant, forming a composite design.

251 Greater Flamingo

1992. Birds. Multicoloured.

1829 30 l. Type **251** 10 10
1830 50 l. White-crested hornbill 10 10
1831 100 l. Verreaux's touraco 25 30
1832 170 l. Yellow-spotted barbet 40 45
1833 200 l. African spoonbill .. 50 55
1834 250 l. Saddle-bill stork .. 60 65
1835 300 l. Red-faced lovebird ("Red headed lovebird") 70 75
1836 600 l. Yellow-billed barbet 1·50 1·60

1992. Olympic Games, Albertville and Barcelona. As T **216** of Lesotho. Mult.

1838 10 l. Marathon 10 10
1839 20 l. Men's parallel bars .. 10 10
1840 30 l. Men's discus .. 10 10
1841 50 l. Men's 110 metres hurdles (horiz) .. 10 10
1842 60 l. Women's long jump 15 20
1843 100 l. Men's floor exercise (horiz) 25 30
1844 200 l. Windsurfing .. 50 55
1845 250 l. Women's biathlon 60 65
1846 300 l. Cycle road race .. 70 75
1847 400 l. Weightlifting .. 95 1·00
1848 500 l. Men's speed skating 1·25 1·40
1849 600 l. Men's downhill skiing (horiz) .. .. 1·50 1·60

252 Minnie Mouse and Chip decorating Christmas Tree

1992. Christmas. Walt Disney Cartoon Characters. Multicoloured.

1851 10 l. Type **252** 10 10
1852 20 l. Goofy as Father Christmas 10 10
1853 30 l. Daisy Duck and Minnie decorating Christmas tree .. 10 10
1854 50 l. Mickey Mouse, and Goofy lighting candle 10 10
1855 80 l. Big Pete as Father Christmas 20 25
1856 100 l. Donald Duck as Father Christmas .. 25 30
1857 150 l. Morty and Ferdie decorating cake .. 35 40
1858 200 l. Mickey and bauble 50 55
1859 300 l. Goofy and toy Father Christmas .. 70 75
1860 500 l. Chip and Dale with sledge .. .. 1·25 1·40
1861 600 l. Donald and Dale with musical instruments .. .. 1·50 1·60
1862 800 l. Huey, Dewey and Louie making patterns in snow .. .. 1·90 2·00

253 Toy Pennsylvannia Railroad GG-1 Electric Locomotive No. 6-18306, 1992

1992. "Genova '92" International Thematic Stamp Exhibition. Toy Trains. Designs showing electric locomotives and rolling stock manufactured by Lionel. Mult.

1864 150 l. Type **253** 35 40
1865 150 l. Wabash Railroad Hudson locomotive No. 8610, 1985 .. .. 35 40
1866 150 l. Locomotive No. 1911, 1911 .. .. 35 40
1867 150 l. Chesapeake & Ohio locomotive No. 6-18627, 1992 .. .. 35 40
1868 150 l. Gang car No. 50, 1954 .. .. 35 40
1869 150 l. Rock Island & Peoria locomotive No. 8004, 1980 .. .. 35 40
1870 150 l. Western Maryland Railroad Shay locomotive No. 6-18023, 1992 35 40
1871 150 l. Boston & Albany Railroad Hudson locomotive No. 784, 1986 .. 35 40
1872 150 l. Locomotive No. 6, 1906 .. .. 35 40
1873 170 l. Special F-3 diesel locomotive, 1947 .. 40 45
1874 170 l. Pennsylvania Railroad switcher locomotive No.6-18905, 1992 40 45
1875 170 l. No. 1 Trolley, 1913 40 45
1876 170 l. Seaboard Railroad freight diesel locomotive, 1958 .. 40 45
1877 170 l. Pennsylvania S-2 turbine locomotive, 1991 40 45
1878 170 l. Western Pacific diesel locomotive No. 6-18822, 1992 .. .. 40 45
1879 170 l. Locomotive No. 10, 1929 .. .. 40 45
1880 170 l. Locomotive No. 400E, 1931 .. .. 40 45
1881 170 l. Locomotive No. 384E, 1928 .. .. 40 45

1882	170 l. Pennsylvannia Railroad Torpedo locomotive No. 238EW, 1936	40	45
1883	170 l. Denver & Rio Grande Western Alco locomotive No. 6-18107, 1992	40	45
1884	170 l. Locomotive No. 408E, 1930	40	45
1885	170 l. Mickey Mouse 60th Birthday boxcar No. 19241, 1991	40	45
1886	170 l. Polished brass locomotive No. 54, 1913	40	45
1887	170 l. Broadway Limited locomotive No. 392E, 1936	40	45
1888	170 l. Great Northern EP-5 locomotive No. 18302, 1988	40	45
1889	170 l. Locomotive No. 6, 1918	40	45
1890	170 l. Locomotive No. 400E, 1933	40	45

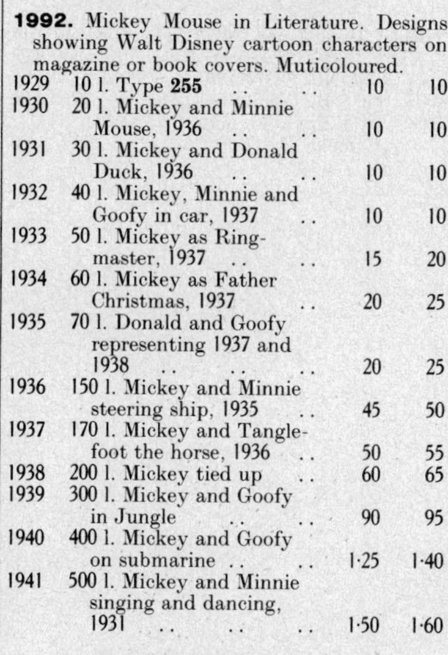

254 African Pygmy Goose

1992. Birds. Multicoloured.

1892	50 c. Type **254**	10	10
1893	1 l. Spotted eagle owl	10	10
1894	2 l. Verreaux's touraco	10	10
1895	5 l. Saddle-bill stork	10	10
1896	10 l. African golden oriole	10	10
1897	20 l. Malachite kingfisher	10	10
1898	30 l. Red-crowned bishop ("Fire-crowned bishop")	10	10
1899	40 l. Fire-bellied woodpecker	10	10
1900	50 l. Red-billed fire finch	10	10
1901	80 l. Blue fairy flycatcher	20	25
1902	100 l. Crested malimbe	25	30
1903	150 l. Vitelline masked weaver	35	40
1904	170 l. Great blue turaco ("Blue plantain-eater")	40	45
1905	200 l. Superb sunbird	50	55
1906	250 l. Swallow-tailed bee eater	60	65
1907	300 l. Cabani's yellow bunting	70	75
1908	500 l. Egyptian plover ("Crocodile bird")	1·25	1·40
1909	750 l. White-faced scops owl	1·75	1·90
1910	1000 l. African blue cuckoo shrike	2·50	2·75
1911	2000 l. Bare-headed rock fowl	5·00	5·25
1912	3000 l. Red-tailed buzzard	7·50	7·75

1992. Christmas. Religious Paintings. As T **218** of Lesotho. Multicoloured.

1916	1 l. "Virgin and Child" (Fiorenzo di Lorenzo)	10	10
1917	10 l. "Madonna and Child on a Wall" (School of Bouts)	10	10
1918	20 l. "Virgin and Child with the Flight into Egypt" (Master of Hoogstraeten)	10	10
1919	30 l. "Madonna and Child before Firescreen" (Robert Campin)	10	10
1920	50 l. "Mary in a Rose-garden" (detail) (Hans Memling)	10	10
1921	100 l. "Virgin Mary and Child" (Lucas Cranach the Elder)	25	30
1922	170 l. "Virgin and Child" (Rogier van der Weyden)	40	45
1923	200 l. "Madonna and Saints" (detail) (Perugino)	50	55
1924	250 l. "Madonna Enthroned with Sts Catherine and Barbara" (Master of Hoogstraeten)	60	65
1925	300 l. "The Virgin in a Rose Arbour" (Stefan Lochner)	70	75
1926	500 l. "Madonna with Child and Angels" (Botticelli)	1·25	1·40
1927	1000 l. "Madonna and Child with young St. John the Baptist" (Fra Bartolommeo)	2·50	2·75

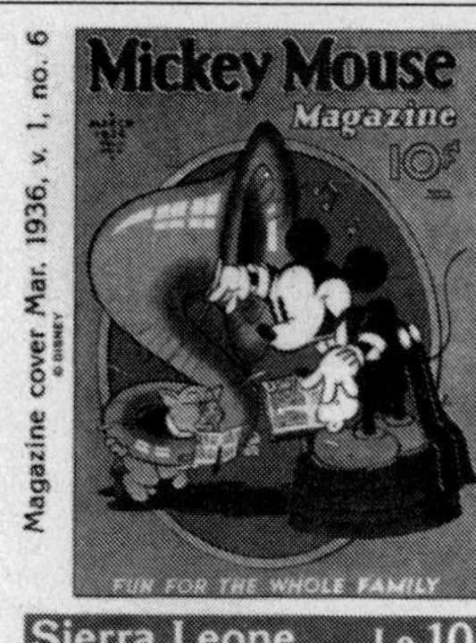

255 Mickey Mouse and Sousaphone (magazine cover, 1936)

1992. Mickey Mouse in Literature. Designs showing Walt Disney cartoon characters on magazine or book covers. Muticoloured.

1929	10 l. Type **255**	10	10
1930	20 l. Mickey and Minnie Mouse, 1936	10	10
1931	30 l. Mickey and Donald Duck, 1936	10	10
1932	40 l. Mickey, Minnie and Goofy in car, 1937	10	10
1933	50 l. Mickey as Ring-master, 1937	15	20
1934	60 l. Mickey as Father Christmas, 1937	20	25
1935	70 l. Donald and Goofy representing 1937 and 1938	20	25
1936	150 l. Mickey and Minnie steering ship, 1935	45	50
1937	170 l. Mickey and Tangle-foot the horse, 1936	50	55
1938	200 l. Mickey tied up	60	65
1939	300 l. Mickey and Goofy in Jungle	90	95
1940	400 l. Mickey and Goofy on submarine	1·25	1·40
1941	500 l. Mickey and Minnie singing and dancing, 1931	1·50	1·60

256 Emblems

1993. Anniversaries and Events. Mult.

1943	150 l. Type **256**	35	40
1944	170 l. Cow and cereal with emblems	40	45
1945	170 l. "Graf Zeppelin"	40	45
1946	200 l. Starving child with W.H.O. emblem	50	55
1947	250 l. Summit emblem and cottonwood tree	60	65
1948	250 l. Lions Club emblem and World map	70	75
1949	300 l. Emblem and African elephant	70	75
1950	300 l. Columbus, King Ferdinand and Queen Isabella	70	75
1951	500 l. Landing in the New World	1·25	1·40
1952	600 l. American space shuttle	1·50	1·60
1953	700 l. Construction drawings of "Graf Zeppelin"	1·75	1·90

ANNIVERSARIES AND EVENTS: Nos. 1943/4, International Conference on Nutrition, Rome; Nos. 1945, 1953, 75th death anniv of Count Ferdinand von Zeppelin (airship pioneer); No. 1946, United Nations World Health Organization Projects; Nos. 1947, 1949, Earth Summit '92, Rio; No. 1948, 75th anniv of International Association of Lions Clubs; Nos. 1950/1, 500th anniv of discovery of America by Columbus; No. 1952, International Space Year.

257 Joe Louis

1993. Centenary of Modern Boxing (1st issue) World Champions. Multicoloured.

1955	200 l. Type **257**	50	55
1956	200 l. Archie Moore	50	55
1957	200 l. Muhammad Ali	50	55
1958	200 l. George Foreman	50	55
1959	200 l. Joe Frazier	50	55
1960	200 l. Marvin Hagler	50	55
1961	200 l. Sugar Ray Leonard	50	55
1962	200 l. Evander Holyfield	50	55

1993. Centenary of Modern Boxing (2nd issue). Boxing Films. As T **257**. Mult.

1964	200 l. Wallace Beery ("The Champ")	50	55
1965	200 l. William Holden ("Golden Boy")	50	55
1966	200 l. John Garfield ("Body and Soul")	50	55
1967	200 l. Kirk Douglas ("Champion")	50	55
1968	200 l. Robert Ryan ("The Set-Up")	50	55
1969	200 l. Anthony Quinn ("Requiem for a Heavyweight")	50	55
1970	200 l. Elvis Presley ("Kid Galahad")	50	55
1971	200 l. Jeff Bridges ("Fat City")	50	55

1993. Bicentenary of the Louvre, Paris. Paintings by Delacroix. As T **305** of Antigua. Multicoloured

1973	70 l. "Young Orphan at a Cemetery"	15	20
1974	70 l. "Algerian Women in their Apartment" (left detail)	15	20
1975	70 l. "Algerian Women in their Apartment" (right detail)	15	20
1976	70 l. "Dante and Virgil"	15	20
1977	70 l. "Self-portrait"	15	20
1978	70 l. "Massacre of Chios" (left detail)	15	20
1979	70 l. "Massacre of Chios" (right detail)	15	20
1980	70 l. "Frederic Chopin"	15	20
1981	70 l. "Entry of the Crusaders into Constantinople" (left detail)	15	20
1982	70 l. "Entry of the Crusaders into Constantinople" (right detail)	15	20
1983	70 l. "Jewish Wedding, Morocco" (left detail)	15	20
1984	70 l. "Jewish Wedding, Morocco" (right detail)	15	20
1985	70 l. "Death of Sardanopoulous" (left detail)	15	20
1986	70 l. "Death of Sardanopoulous" (right detail)	15	20
1987	70 l. "Liberty leading the People" (left detail)	15	20
1988	70 l. "Liberty leading the People" (right detail)	15	20

258 "Amanita flammeola"

1993. Mushrooms. Multicoloured.

1990	30 l. Type **258**	10	10
1991	50 l. "Cantharellus pseudocibarius"	10	10
1992	100 l. "Volvariella volvacea"	25	30
1993	200 l. "Termitomyces microcarpus"	50	55
1994	300 l. "Auricularia auricula"	70	75
1995	400 l. "Pleurotus tuberregium"	95	1·00
1996	500 l. "Schizophyllum commune"	1·25	1·40
1997	600 l. "Termitomyces robustus"	1·50	1·60

259 "Pseudacraea boisduvali"

1993. Butterflies. Multicoloured.

1999	20 l. Type **259**	10	10
2000	30 l. "Salamis temora"	10	10
2001	50 l. "Charaxes jasius"	10	10
2002	100 l. "Amblypodia anita"	25	30
2003	150 l. "Papilio nireus"	35	40
2004	170 l. "Danaus chrysippus"	40	45
2005	200 l. "Meneris tulbaghia"	50	55
2006	250 l. "Precis octavia"	60	65
2007	300 l. "Palla ussheri"	70	75
2008	500 l. "Catacroptera cloanthe"	1·25	1·40
2009	600 l. "Cynthia cardui"	1·50	1·60
2010	700 l. "Euphaedra neophron"	1·75	1·90

260 Black Persian

1993. Cats. Multicoloured.

2012	150 l. Type **260**	35	40
2013	150 l. Blue-point Siamese	35	40
2014	150 l. American wirehair	35	40
2015	150 l. Birman	35	40
2016	150 l. Scottish fold	35	40
2017	150 l. American shorthair red tabby	35	40
2018	150 l. Blue and white Persian bicolour	35	40
2019	150 l. Havana brown	35	40
2020	150 l. Norwegian forest cat	35	40
2021	150 l. Brown tortie Burmese	35	40
2022	150 l. Angora	35	40
2023	150 l. Exotic shorthair	35	40
2024	150 l. Somali	35	40
2025	150 l. Egyptian mau smoke	35	40
2026	150 l. Chocolate-point Siamese	35	40
2027	150 l. Mi-Ke Japanese bobtail	35	40
2028	150 l. Chinchilla	35	40
2029	150 l. Red Burmese	35	40
2030	150 l. British shorthair brown tabby	35	40
2031	150 l. Blue Persian	35	40
2032	150 l. British silver classic tabby	35	40
2033	150 l. Oriental ebony	35	40
2034	150 l. Red Persian	35	40
2035	150 l. British calico shorthair	35	40

261 Gorilla

1993. Wildlife. Multicoloured.

2037	30 l. Type **261**	10	10
2038	100 l. Bongo	25	30
2039	150 l. Potto	35	40
2040	170 l. Chimpanzee ..	40	45
2041	200 l. Dwarf galago ..	50	55
2042	300 l. African linsang ..	70	75
2043	500 l. Banded duiker ..	1·25	1·40
2044	750 l. Diana monkey ..	1·90	2·00

262 "Clerodendrum thomsonae"

1993. Flowers. Multicoloured.

2046	30 l. Type **262**	10	10
2047	40 l. "Passiflora quadrangularis" ..	10	10
2048	50 l. "Hydrangea macrophylla" ..	10	10
2049	60 l. "Begonia semperflorens"	15	20
2050	100 l. "Hibiscus rosa-sinensis"	25	30
2051	150 l. "Lagerstroemia indica" ..	35	40
2052	170 l. "Bougainvillea glabra"	40	45
2053	200 l. "Plumbago capensis"	50	55
2054	250 l. "Gerbera jamesonae"	60	65
2055	300 l. "Thunbergia alata"	70	75
2056	500 l. "Gloriosa superba"	1·25	1·40
2057	900 l. "Viola odorata" ..	2·25	2·40

263 Royal Family

1993. Anniversaries and Events. Black (No. 2061) or multicoloured (others).

2059	100 l. Type **263**	25	30
2060	170 l. "Woman with Hat" (Picasso)	40	45
2061	200 l. Coronation procession	50	55
2062	200 l. "Buste de Femme" (Picasso)	50	55
2063	250 l. Early telescope ..	60	65
2064	600 l. Queen Elizabeth II in Coronation robes (from photograph by Cecil Beaton)	1·50	1·60
2065	800 l. "Maya with a Doll" (Picasso)	1·90	2·00
2066	800 l. Craters on Moon ..	1·90	2·00

ANNIVERSARIES AND EVENTS: Nos. 2059, 2061, 2064, 40th anniv of Coronation: Nos. 2060, 2062, 2065, 20th death anniv of Picasso (artist); Nos. 2063, 2066, 450th death anniv of Copernicus (astronomer).

264 "Madonna of the Fish" (detail) (Raphael)

1993. Christmas. Religious Paintings. Black, yellow and red (Nos. 2071/4) or multicoloured (others).

2068	50 l. Type **264**	10	10
2069	100 l. "Madonna of the Fish" (different detail) (Raphael)	25	30
2070	150 l. "Madonna and Child enthroned with Five Saints" (detail) (Raphael)	35	40
2071	200 l. "The Circumcision" (detail) (Durer) ..	50	55
2072	250 l. "The Circumcision" (different detail) (Durer)	60	65
2073	300 l. "The Circumcision" (different detail) (Durer)	70	75
2074	500 l. "Holy Family with Saints and Two Angels playing Music" (detail) (Durer)	1·25	1·40
2075	800 l. "The Holy Family with the Lamb" (detail) (Raphael)	1·90	2·00

265 Donald Duck and Toy Train

1993. Christmas. Walt Disney cartoon characters in Christmas scenes. Mult.

2077	50 l. Type **265**	10	10
2078	100 l. Disney carol singers	25	30
2079	170 l. Mickey drinking punch	40	45
2080	200 l. Pluto with cream-covered bones ..	50	55
2081	250 l. Goofy eating angel cakes	60	65
2082	500 l. Donald's nephews decorating Christmas tree	1·25	1·40
2083	600 l. Donald dropping Christmas cake on foot	1·50	1·60
2084	800 l. Uncle Scrooge and Daisy under mistletoe	1·90	2·00

1993. World Cup Football Championship, U.S.A (1994). As T **278** of Maldive Islands. Multicoloured.

2086	30 l. Jose Brown with goalkeeper (Argentina)	10	10
2087	50 l. Gary Lineker (England)	10	10
2088	100 l. Carlos Valderrama (Colombia)	25	30
2089	250 l. Tomas Skuhravy (Czechoslovakia) and Hector Marchena (Costa Rica)	60	65
2090	300 l. Butragueno (Spain)	70	75
2091	400 l. Roger Milla (Cameroun)	95	1·00
2092	500 l. Roberto Donadoni (Italy)	1·25	1·40
2093	700 l. Enzo Scifo (Belgium)	1·75	1·90

1994. "Hong Kong '94" International Stamp Exhibition (1st issue). As T **293** of Maldive Islands. Multicoloured.

2095	200 l. Hong Kong 1985 $1.70 Bauhinia stamp and Pagoda, Tiger Baum Garden ..	50	55
2096	200 l. Sierra Leone 1989 70 l. Orchid stamp and Aw Par Gardens ..	50	55

See also Nos. 2097/3002 and 3003/4.

1994. "Hong Kong '94" International Stamp Exhibition (2nd issue). Ching Dynasty Carved Lacquerware. As T **294** of Maldive Islands, but horiz. Multicoloured.

2097	2 r. Bowl	50	55
2098	2 r. Four-wheeled box ..	50	55
2099	2 r. Flower container ..	50	55
3000	2 r. Box with human figure design	50	55
3001	2 r. Shishi dog	50	55
3002	2 r. Box with persimmon design	50	55

1994. "Hong Kong '94" International Stamp Exhibition (3rd issue). Nos. 2013 and 2025 optd **HONG KONG '94** and emblem.

3003	150 l. Blue-point Siamese	35	40
3004	150 l. Egyptian mau smoke	35	40

SINGAPORE

An island at the south of the Malay peninsula, formerly part of the Straits Settlements but became a Crown Colony on 1 April, 1946, when the stamps of Malaya were used until 1948. From 1 August, 1958, an internally self-governing territory designated the State of Singapore. From 16 September, 1963, part of the Malaysian Federation until 9th August, 1965, when it became an independent republic within the Commonwealth.

100 cents = 1 dollar.

1948. As T **58** of Straits Settlements, but inscr. "MALAYA SINGAPORE".

1	1 c. black	15	10
2	2 c. orange..	15	10
3	3 c. green	40	10
4	4 c. brown	20	50
19a	5 c. purple..	2·50	55
5	6 c. grey	30	15
6	8 c. red	30	15
21a	8 c. green	4·00	2·50
7	10 c. mauve	20	10
22a	12 c. red	4·00	4·25
8	15 c. blue	3·75	10
9	20 c. black and green ..	2·75	20
24a	20 c. blue	4·00	10
25	25 c. purple and orange ..	80	10
25a	35 c. red and purple ..	4·00	90
11	40 c. red and purple ..	4·75	5·00
12	50 c. black and blue ..	3·25	10
13	$1 blue and purple ..	10·00	75
14	$2 green and red	48·00	2·75
15	$5 green and brown ..	£100	3·00

1948. Silver Wedding. As T **10/11** of Aden.

31.	10 c. violet	75	30
32.	$5 brown	95·00	27·00

1949. U.P.U. As T **20/23** of Antigua.

33.	10 c. purple	75	30
34.	15 c. blue	3·50	1·75
35.	25 c. orange	4·75	1·75
36.	50 c. black	6·00	1·75

1953. Coronation. As T **13** of Aden.

37.	10 c. black and purple ..	1·50	10

1. Chinese Sampan.

3. Singapore River.

1955.

38.	**1.**	1 c. black	10	40
39.	–	2 c. orange	70	1·00
40.	–	4 c. brown..	55	15
41.	–	5 c. purple	45	15
42.	–	6 c. grey	45	30
43.	–	8 c. turquoise	70	70
44.	–	10 c. lilac	2·50	10
45.	–	12 c. red	2·25	2·50
46.	–	20 c. blue	1·40	10
47.	–	25 c. orange and violet ..	1·00	20
48.	–	30 c. violet and lake ..	2·50	10
49.	–	50 c. blue and black ..	1·50	10
50.	–	$1 blue and purple ..	22·00	10
51.	**3.**	$2 green and red.. ..	30·00	75
52.	–	$5 yell., red, brn. & black	35·00	3·25

DESIGNS—As Type **1** (2 c. to 20 c. are sailing craft); 2 c. Malay kolek. 4 c. Twa-kow lighter. 5 c. Lombok sloop. 6 c. Trengganu pinas. 8 c. Palari. 10 c. Timber tongkong. 12 c. Hainan junk. 20 c. Cocos-Keeling schooner. 25 c. "Argonaut" aircraft. 30 c. Oil tanker. 50 c. "Chusan III" (liner). As Type **3**—VERT. $1, Raffles statue. $5, Arms of Singapore.

16. The Singapore Lion.

1959. New Constitution. Lion in yellow and sepia.

53.	**16.**	4 c. red	45	40
54.		10 c. purple	65	30
55.		20 c. blue	1·75	2·25
56.		25 c. green	2·00	1·50
57.		30 c. violet	1·75	2·50
58.		50 c. slate	2·50	2·50

17. State Flag.

1960. National Day.

59. 17. 4 c. red, yellow and blue .. 40 40
60. 10 c. red, yellow and grey 85 10

18. Clasped Hands.

1961. National Day.

61. 18. 4 c. black, brown & yellow 40 40
62. 10 c. black, green & yellow 50 10

19. "Arachnis—Maggie Oei" (orchid).

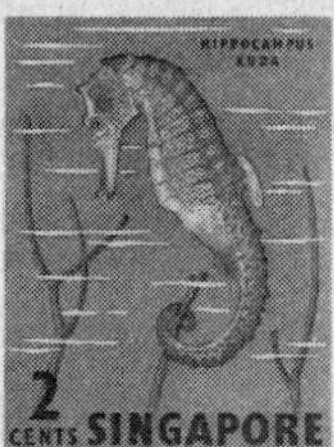

20. Sea-Horse.

1962. Orchids, Fishes and Birds.

63 19 1 c. multicoloured .. 10 75
64 20 2 c. brown and green .. 10 1·00
65 – 4 c. black and red .. 10 30
66 – 5 c. red and black .. 10 10
67 – 6 c. black and yellow .. 45 60
68 – 8 c. multicoloured .. 55 2·75
69 – 10 c. orange and black 15 10
70 – 12 c. multicoloured .. 55 2·50
70a – 15 c. multicoloured .. 80 10
71 – 20 c. orange and blue .. 30 10
72 – 25 c. black and orange 55 10
73 – 30 c. multicoloured .. 1·00 10
74 – 50 c. multicoloured .. 95 10
75 – $1 multicoloured .. 10·00 45
76 – $2 multicoloured .. 13·00 75
77 – $5 multicoloured .. 27·00 3·75

DESIGNS—VERT. (As Type 19). 8 c. "Vanda-Tan Chay Yan" (orchid). 12 c. "Grammatophyllum speciosum" (orchid). 15 c. Black-naped tern. 30 c. "Vanda-Miss Joaquim" (orchid). $2 Yellow-bellied sunbird. $5 White-bellied sea eagle. (As Type 20). 6 c. Archer fish. 20 c. Butterfly fish. HORIZ. (as Type 19). 50 c. White-rumped shama. $1 White-breasted kingfisher. (As Type 20). 4 c. Six-banded barb. 5 c. Clown fish. 10 c. Harlequin. 25 c. Two-spot gourami.

34. "The Role of Labour in Nation-Building".

1962. National Day.

78. 34. 4 c. yellow, red & black .. 15 50
79. 10 c. yellow, blue & black 35 20

35. Blocks of Flats, Singapore.

1963. National Day.

80. 35. 4 c. multicoloured .. 15 50
81. 10 c. multicoloured .. 35 10

36. Dancers in National Costume.

1963. South East Asia Cultural Festival.

82. 36. 5 c. multicoloured .. 20 30

37. Workers.

1966. 1st Anniv. of Republic.

89. 37. 15 c. multicoloured .. 40 30
90. 20 c. multicoloured .. 60 80
91. 30 c. multicoloured .. 80 1·10

38. Flag Procession.

1967. National Day.

92. 38. 6 c. red, brown & slate 30 50
93. 15 c. purple, brn. & slate 60 10
94. 50 c. blue, brown & slate 90 1·50

Nos. 92/4 are respectively inscr. "Build a Vigorous Singapore" in Chinese, Malay, and Tamil, in addition to the English inscr.

39. Skyscrapers and Afro-Asian Map.

1967. 2nd Afro-Asian Housing Congress.

95. 39. 10 c. multicoloured .. 30 10
96. 25 c. multicoloured .. 55 1·00
97. 50 c. multicoloured .. 1·10 1·60

40. Symbolical Figure wielding Hammer, and Industrial outline of Singapore.

45. Sword Dance.

43. Mirudhangam.

1968. National Day. Inscription at top in Chinese (6 c.), Malay (15 c.) or Tamil (50 c.).

98. 40. 6 c. red, black and gold 25 40
99. 15 c. green, black & gold 30 15
100. 50 c. blue, black & gold 85 85

1968.

101. 43. 1 c. multicoloured .. 15 1·75
102. – 4 c. multicoloured .. 40 2·00
103. 45. 5 c. multicoloured .. 50 60
104. – 6 c. blk., lemon & orge. 30 85
105. – 10 c. multicoloured .. 20 10
106. – 15 c. multicoloured .. 40 10
107. – 20 c. multicoloured .. 20 30
108. – 25 c. multicoloured .. 50 50
109. – 30 c. multicoloured .. 30 50
110. – 50 c. black, red & brown 50 40
111. – 75 c. multicoloured .. 1·75 80
112. – $1 multicoloured .. 2·75 80
113. – $2 multicoloured .. 3·50 1·00
114. – $5 multicoloured .. 9·00 2·00
115. – $10 multicoloured .. 30·00 13·00

DESIGNS—As Type 43—VERT. 4 c. Pi Pa. $2 Rebab. $10 Ta Ku. HORIZ. $5 Vina. As Type 45—VERT. 6 c. Lion Dance. 10 c. Bharatha Natyam. 15 c. Tari Payong. 20 c. Kathak Kali. 25 c. Lu Chih Shen and Lin Chung. 50 c. Tari Lilin. 75 c. Tarian Kuda Kepang. $1, Yao Chi. HORIZ. 30 c. Dragon Dance.

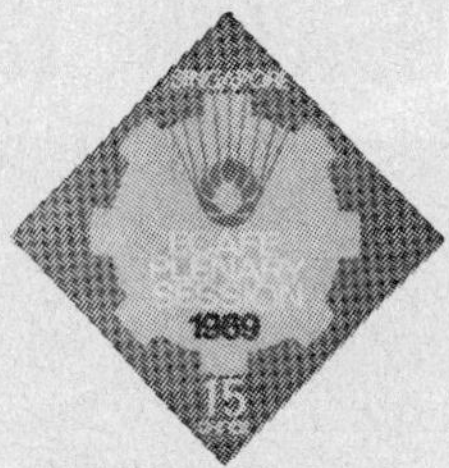

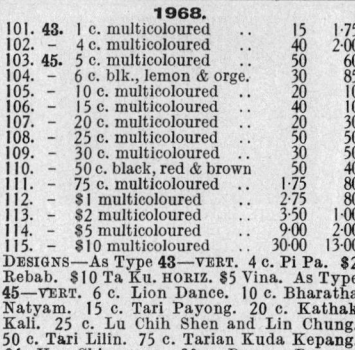

58. E.C.A.F.E. Emblem.

1969. Plenary Session of Economic Commission for Asia and the Far East.

116. 58. 15 c. black, silver & blue 40 20
117. 30 c. black, silver & red 85 1·10
118. 75 c. black, silver & violet 1·40 2·00

59. "100000" and Slogan as Block of Flats.

60. Aircraft over Silhouette of Singapore Docks.

1969. Completion of "100,000 Homes for the People" Project.

119. 59. 25 c. black and green .. 70 50
120. 50 c. black and blue .. 90 1·00

1969. 150th Anniv. of Founding of Singapore.

121. 60. 15 c. black, red & yellow 1·25 30
122. – 30 c. black and blue .. 2·00 1·00
123. – 75 c. multicoloured .. 3·50 2·00
124. – $1 black and red .. 4·50 4·50
125. – $5 red and black .. 35·00 45·00
126. – $10 black and green .. 48·00 48·00

DESIGNS: 30 c. U.N. Emblem and outline of Singapore. 75 c. Flags and outline of Malaysian Federation. $1, Uplifted hands holding crescent and stars. $5, Tail of Japanese aircraft and searchlight beams. $10, Bust from statue of Sir Stamford Raffles.

61. Sea Shells.

1970. World Fair, Osaka. Multicoloured.

128. 15 c. Type 61 .. .. 90 15
129. 30 c. Tropical fish .. 2·00 90
130. 75 c. Greater Flamingo and Helmeted Horn-bill .. 5·00 3·75
131. $1 Orchid .. .. .. 5·50 6·00

INDEX

Countries can be quickly located by referring to the index at the end of this volume.

62. "Kindergarten".

1970. 10th Anniv. of People's Assn.

133. 62. 15 c. agate and orange .. 50 15
134. – 50 c. blue and orange .. 1·40 1·60
135. – 75 c. purple and black .. 2·25 3·00

DESIGNS: 50 c. "Sport". 75 c. "Culture".

63. Soldier Charging.

1970. National Day. Multicoloured.

136. 15 c. Type 63 .. .. 70 15
137. 50 c. Soldier on assault course .. .. .. 2·75 2·75
138. $1 Soldier jumping .. 3·75 6·00

64. Sprinters.

1970. Festival of Sports.

139. 64. 10 c. mve., blk. and blue 1·25 1·75
140. – 15 c. black and orange 1·60 2·00
141. – 25 c. blk., orge. and grn. 1·75 2·25
142. – 50 c. blk., grn. and mve. 2·00 2·25

DESIGNS: 15 c. Swimmers. 25 c. Tennis-players. 50 c. Racing-cars.

65. "Neptune Aquamarine" (freighter).

1970. Singapore Shipping.

143. 65. 15 c. multicoloured .. 1·40 55
144. – 30 c. yellow and blue .. 3·75 4·50
145. – 75 c. yellow and red .. 5·50 6·00

DESIGNS: 30 c. Container berth. 75 c. Ship-building.

66. Country Names in Circle.

1971. Commonwealth Heads of Government Meeting, Singapore. Multicoloured.

146. 15 c. Type 66 .. .. 70 15
147. 30 c. Flags in Circle .. 1·25 65
148. 75 c. Commonwealth Flags 2·75 3·00
149. $1 Commonwealth Flags linked to Singapore (63×61 mm.) .. .. 3·50 4·00

DESIGNS SQUARE: 20 c. Houseboat "Village" and boats. 30 c. Bazaar. HORIZ. (68 × 18 mm.): 50 c. Modern harbour Skyline. 75 c. Religious buildings.

67. Bicycle Rickshaws.

1971. Tourism. ASEAN Year. (ASEAN = Association of South East Asian Nations).

150. 67. 15 c. black, violet & orge. 40 25
151. – 20 c. indigo, orge. & blue 55 40
152. – 30 c. red and purple .. 80 1·00
153. – 50 c. multicoloured .. 2·75 4·50
154. – 75 c. multicoloured .. 3·50 6·00

68. Chinese New Year.

1971. Singapore Festivals. Multicoloured.

155. 15 c. Type 68 .. .. 70 15
156. 30 c. Hari Raya .. .. 2·00 2·00
157. 50 c. Deepavali .. .. 2·75 4·50
158. 75 c. Christmas .. .. 3·25 5·50

69. "Dish" Aerial.

1971. Opening of Satellite Earth Station.

160. 69. 15 c. multicoloured .. 2·75 75
161. – 30 c. multicoloured .. 10·00 8·00
162. – 30 c. multicoloured .. 10·00 8·00
163. – 30 c. multicoloured .. 10·00 8·00
164. – 30 c. multicoloured .. 10·00 8·00

DESIGNS: Nos. 161/4 were printed in se-tenant blocks of four throughout the sheet, the four stamps forming a composite design similar to Type 69. They can be identified by the colour of the face value which is: yellow (No. 161), green (No. 162), red (No. 163) or orange (No.164).

SINGAPORE 10c
Scene of Singapore River & Fort Canning in 1843-7

70. "Singapore River and Fort Canning, 1843–7" (Lieut. E. A. Porcher).
(Illustration reduced. Actual size 53 × 46 mm.)

1971. Art. Multicoloured.

165 10 c. Type 70 .. .. 2·00 1·75
166 15 c. "The Padang, 1851" (J.T. Thomson) .. 2·75 3·00
167 20 c. "Singapore Waterfront, 1848–9" .. 3·50 3·25
168 35 c. "View from Fort Canning, 1846" (J.T. Thomson) .. 7·00 6·00
169 50 c. "View from Mt. Wallich, 1857" (P. Carpenter) .. 10·00 11·00
170 $1 "Singapore Waterfront, 1861" (W. Gray) .. 13·00 16·00

The 50 c. and $1 are larger, 69 × 47 mm.

71. One Dollar of 1969.

1972. Coins.

171. – 15 c. orange, blk. & grn. 55 25
172. 71. 35 c. black and red .. 1·25 1·75
173. – $1 yellow, black & blue 3·50 5·00

DESIGNS: 15 c. One-cent coin of George V. $1 One hundred and fifty dollar gold coin of 1969.

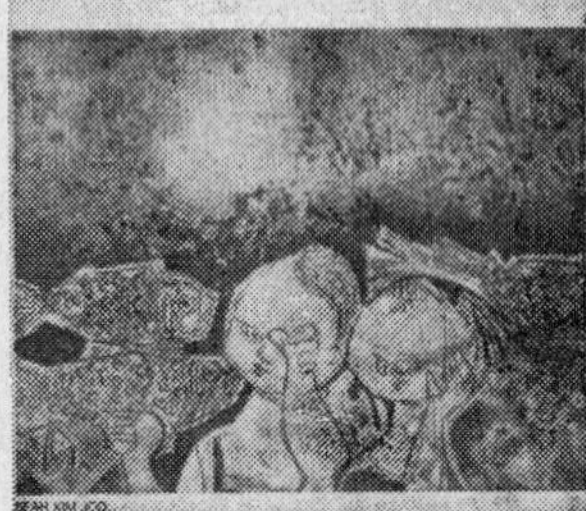

72. "Moon Festival" (Seah Kim Joo).

1972. Contemporary Art. Multicoloured.

174. 15 c. Type 72 .. .. 50 20
175. 35 c. "Complimentary Forces" (Thomas Yeo) 1·40 2·25
176. 50 c. "Rhythm in Blue" (Yusman Aman) .. 2·25 2·50
177. $1 "Gibbons" (Chen Wen Hsi) .. 4·00 5·00

Nos. 175/6 are 36 × 54 mm.

73. Lanterns and Fish.

1972. National Day. Designs symbolising Festivals. Multicoloured.

178. 15 c. Type 73 .. .. 55 20
179. 35 c. Altar and candles .. 1·10 1·75
180. 50 c. Jug, bowl and gifts 1·60 3·00
181. 75 c. Candle .. .. 2·50 4·25

74. Student Welding.

1972. Youth.

182. 74. 15 c. multicoloured .. 50 20
183. – 35 c. multicoloured .. 1·50 2·50
184. – $1 orge., violet & green 3·00 6·00

DESIGNS: 35 c. Sport. $1, Dancing.

75. "Maria Rickmers" (barque).

1972. Shipping. Multicoloured.

185. 15 c. "Neptune Ruby" (container ship) (42 × 29 mm.) 75 50
186. 75 c. Type 75 .. .. 5·00 6·00
187. $1 Chinese junk .. .. 5·50 6·50

76. P.Q.R. Slogan.

1973. "Prosperity Through Quality and Reliability" Campaign. Multicoloured.

189. 15 c. Type 76 .. .. 40 15
190. 35 c. Badge .. .. 1·40 1·50
191. 75 c. Text (diff.) .. .. 1·60 3·00
192. $1 Seal .. .. .. 1·90 4·00

77. Jurong Bird Park.

1973. Singapore Landmarks.

193. 77. 15 c. black and orange 55 15
194. – 35 c. black and green 1·75 2·00
195. – 50 c. black and brown 2·50 3·00
196. – $1 black and purple .. 3·50 4·50

DESIGNS: 35 c. National Theatre. 50 c. City Hall. $1, Fullerton Building and Singapore River.

78. Aircraft Tail-fins.

1973. Aviation. Multicoloured.

197. 10 c. Type 78 .. .. 30 10
198. 35 c. Emblems of Singapore Airlines and destinations 1·00 1·25
199. 75 c. Emblem on tail-fin .. 1·50 1·75
200. $1 Emblems encircling the globe .. .. .. 2·00 3·00

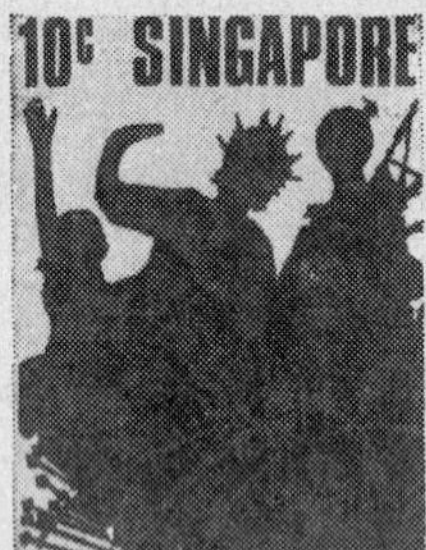

79. "Culture".

1973. National Day.

201. 79. 10 c. orange and black 1·50 1·00
202. – 35 c. orange and black 1·75 1·50
203. – 50 c. orange and black 2·00 1·75
204. – 75 c. orange and black 2·25 2·00

Nos. 201/204 were printed in se-tenant blocks of four within the sheet, and form a composite design representing Singapore's culture.

80. Athletics, Judo and Boxing.

1973. Seventh S.E.A.P.* Games.

205. 80. 10 c. gold, silver and blue 35 20
206. – 15 c. gold and black .. 70 80
207. – 25 c. gold, silver and blk. 80 1·00
208. – 35 c. gold, silver and blue 1·60 1·75
209. – 50 c. multicoloured .. 1·75 2·50
210. – $1 silver, blue and green 3·25 5·50

DESIGNS—As Type 80. 15 c. Cycling, weight-lifting, pistol-shooting and sailing. 25 c. Foot-balls. 35 c. Table-tennis bat, shuttlecock, tennis ball and hockey stick. HORIZ. (41 × 25 mm.). 50 c. Swimmers. $1, Stadium.

*S.E.A.P. = South East Asian Peninsular.

81. Agave.

82. Mangosteen.

1973. Multicoloured.

(a) Flowers and plants as T 81.

212. 1 c. Type 81 .. .. 30 55
213. 5 c. "Coleus blumei" .. 10 35
214. 10 c. "Vinca rosea" .. 15 10
215. 15 c. "Helianthus angustifolius" .. 35 10
216. 20 c. "Licuala grandis" .. 35 50
217. 25 c. "Wedelia trilobata" 70 45
218. 35 c. "Chrysanthemum frutescens" .. 60 70
219. 50 c. "Costus malortieanus" 1·00 40
220. 75 c. "Gerbera jamesonii" 1·75 90

(b) Fruits as T 82.

221. $1 Type 82 .. .. 1·50 30
222. $2 Jackfruit .. .. 3·25 1·25
223. $5 Coconut .. .. 6·00 6·00
224. $10 Pineapple .. .. 12·00 16·00

83. Tiger and Orang-Utans.

1973. Singapore Zoo. Multicoloured.

225. 5 c. Type 83 .. .. 40 35
226. 10 c. Leopard and Waterbuck 65 35
227. 35 c. Leopard and Thamin 2·75 3·25
228. 75 c. Horse and Lion .. 3·50 3·25

84. Multicolour Guppy.

86. U.P.U. Emblem and Multiple "Centenary".

85. Scout Badge within "9".

1974. Tropical Fish. Multicoloured.

229. 5 c. Type 84 .. .. 30 25
230. 10 c. Half Black Guppy .. 50 15
231. 35 c. Multicolour Guppy (different) .. .. 1·40 2·25
232. $1 Black Guppy .. .. 3·00 4·00

1974. Ninth Asia-Pacific Scout Conference.

233. 85. 10 c. multicoloured .. 40 10
234. 75 c. multicoloured .. 1·60 1·75

1974. Centenary of U.P.U.

235. 86. 10 c. brn., pur. & gold .. 20 10
236. – 35 c. bl., dark bl. & gold 55 1·00
237. – 75 c. multicoloured .. 1·25 2·75

DESIGNS: 35 c. U.P.U. emblem and multiple U.N. symbols. 75 c. U.P.U. emblem and multiple peace doves.

87. Family Emblem.

1974. World Population Year. Multicoloured.

238. 10 c. Type 87 .. .. 20 10
239. 35 c. Male and female symbols 80 1·25
240. 75 c. World Population Map 1·75 3·25

88. "Tree and Sun" (Chia Keng San).

1974. Universal Children's Day. Mult.
241. 5 c. Type **88** 20 30
242. 10 c. "My Daddy and Mummy" (Angeline Ang) 35 20
243. 35 c. "A Dump Truck" (Si-Hoe Yeen Joong) .. 1·75 3·00
244. 50 c. "My Aunt" (Raymond Teo) .. .. .. 2·25 3·75

89. Street Scene.

1975. Singapore Views. Multicoloured.
246. 15 c. Type **89** 55 20
247. 20 c. Singapore River .. 75 1·00
248. $1 "Kelong" (fish-trap) .. 3·25 6·00

90. Emblem and Lighters' Prows.

1975. 9th Biennial Conference of Int., Association of Ports and Harbours, Singapore. Multicoloured.
249. 5 c. Type **90** 20 15
250. 25 c. Freighter and ship's wheel .. .. .. 1·00 1·25
251. 50 c. Oil-tanker and flags .. 1·50 2·25
252. $1 Container-ship and propellers .. .. 2·50 4·50

91. Satellite Earth Station, Sentosa.

1975. "Science and Industry". Mult.
253. 10 c. Type **91** 25 10
254. 35 c. Oil refineries (vert.) .. 1·25 1·50
255. 75 c. "Medical Sciences" 1·75 3·00

92. "Homes and Gardens".

1975. 10th National Day. Multicoloured.
256. 10 c. Type **92** 20 10
257. 35 c. "Shipping and Ship-building" .. .. 1·00 1·25
258. 75 c. "Communications and Technology" .. 1·90 3·25
259. $1 "Trade, Commerce and Industry" .. 2·10 3·75

93. South African Crowned Cranes. **94.** "Equality".

1975. Birds. Multicoloured.
260. 5 c. Type **93** .. .. 1·00 30
261. 10 c. Great Indian Hornbill 1·50 20
262. 35 c. White-breasted Kingfishers and White-collared Kingfisher .. .. 4·00 4·25
263. $1 Sulphur-crested Cockatoo, and Blue and Yellow Macaw .. .. 10·00 13·00

1975. International Women's Year. Mult.
264. 10 c. Type **94** 25 10
265. 35 c. "Development" .. 1·50 2·00
266. 75 c. "Peace" .. .. 2·75 5·00

95. Yellow Flame. **96.** "Arachnis hookeriana x Vanda" Hilo Blue.

1976. Wayside Trees. Multicoloured.
268. 10 c. Type **95** 50 10
269. 35 c. Cabbage Tree .. 1·75 2·00
270. 50 c. Rose of India .. 2·25 2·75
271. 75 c. Variegated Coral Tree 2·50 4·50

1976. Singapore Orchids. Multicoloured.
272. 10 c. Type **96** 80 10
273. 35 c. "Arachnis Maggie Oei x Vanda insignis" .. 2·50 2·00
274. 50 c. "Arachnis Maggei Oei x Vanda" Rodman .. 3·75 3·50
275. 75c. "Arachnis hookeriana x Vanda" Dawn Nishimura .. .. .. 4·00 6·00

97. Festival Symbol and Band.

1976. 10th Anniv. of Singapore Youth Festival. Multicoloured.
276. 10 c. Type **97** 20 10
277. 35 c. Athletes .. .. 80 1·10
278. 75 c. Dancers .. .. 1·40 1·60

98. "Queen Elizabeth Walk".

1976. Paintings of Old Singapore. Mult.
279. 10 c. Type **98** 30 10
280. 50 c. "The Padang" .. 2·25 2·25
281. $1 "Raffles Place" .. 3·25 3·50

99. Chinese Costume.

1976. Bridal Costumes. Multicoloured.
283. 10 c. Type **99** 25 10
284. 35 c. Indian costume .. 1·25 1·25
285. 75 c. Malay costume .. 2·00 4·00

100. Radar, Missile and Soldiers.

1977. 10th Anniv. of National Service. Multicoloured.
286. 10 c. Type **100** 30 10
287. 50 c. Tank and soldiers .. 1·25 1·25
288. 75 c. Soldiers, wireless operators, pilot and aircraft 2·00 2·25

101. Lyrate Cockle. **102.** Spotted Hermit Crab.

1977. Multicoloured.
(a) Shells as T **101.**
289. 1 c. Type **101** 30 85
290. 5 c. Folded Scallop .. 20 10
291. 10 c. Marble cone .. 20 10
292. 15 c. Scorpion Conch .. 45 10
293. 20 c. Amplustre Bubble .. 70 10
294. 25 c. Spiral Babylon .. 80 60
295. 35 c. Regal Thorny Oyster 1·00 1·00
296. 50 c. Winged Frog Shell .. 1·25 10
297. 75 c. Troschel's Murex .. 2·00 20
(b) Fish and Crustaceans as T **102.**
298. $1 Type **102** .. .. 1·75 15
299. $2 Stingray .. .. 1·75 50
300. $5 Cuttlefish .. .. 4·00 2·25
301. $10 Lionfish .. .. 7·50 5·50

103. Shipbuilding.

1977. Labour Day. Multicoloured.
302. 10 c. Type **103** 15 10
303. 50 c. Building construction 75 60
304. 75 c. Road construction .. 1·00 1·00

104. Keyhole and Banknotes. **105.** Flags of Member Nations.

1977. Centenary of Post Office Savings Bank. Multicoloured.
305. 10 c. Type **104** 15 10
306. 35 c. On-line banking service 85 50
307. 75 c. GIRO service .. 1·75 1·50

1977. 10th Anniv. of ASEAN (Assn. of South-East Asian Nations). Multicoloured.
308. 10 c. Type **105** 15 10
309. 35 c. "Agriculture" .. 60 50
310. 75 c. "Industry" .. 1·25 1·10

106. "Chingay Procession" (Liang Yik Yin).

1977. Children's Art. Multicoloured.
311. 10 c. Type **106** 20 10
312. 35 c. "At the Bus Stop" (Chong Khing Ann) (horiz.) 75 50
313. 75 c. "Playground" (Yap Li Hwa) (horiz.) .. 1·60 2·00

10c SINGAPORE

107. "Life Sciences".

1977. Singapore Science Centre. Mult.
315. 10 c. Type **107** .. 10 10
316. 35 c. "Physical sciences" 45 30
317. 75 c. "Science and technology" .. .. 1·00 1·50
318. $1 Singapore Science Centre 1·25 1·50

108. Botanical Gardens and Esplanade, Jurong Bird Park.

1978. Park and Gardens. Multicoloured.
319. 10 c. Type **108** 15 10
320. 35 c. Lagoon, East Coast Park (vert.) 60 60
321. 75 c. Botanical Gardens (vert.) .. .. .. 90 1·40

109. Red-whiskered Bulbul.

1978. Singing Birds. Multicoloured.
322. 10 c. Type **109** 35 10
323. 35 c. Oriental white eye .. 1·00 75
324. 50 c. White-rumped shama 1·25 1·40
325. 75 c. White-crested laughing thrush and hwamei 1·50 2·50

110. Thian Hock Keng Temple.

1978. National Monuments. Multicoloured.
326. 10 c. Type **110** 20 30
327. 10 c. Hajjah Fatimah Mosque 20 30
328. 10 c. Armenian Church .. 20 30
329. 10 c. Sri Mariamman Temple 20 30

111. Map of South East Asia showing Cable Network.

1978. A.S.E.A.N. Submarine Cable (1st issue). Philippines–Singapore Section.
331. **111.** 10 c. multicoloured .. 10 10
332. 35 c. multicoloured .. 50 40
333. 50 c. multicoloured .. 70 70
334. 75 c. multicoloured .. 80 1·00

See also Nos. 385/8 and 458/61.

112. "Neptune Spinel" (bulk carrier).

1978. 10th Anniv. of Neptune Orient Shipping Lines. Multicoloured.

335 10 c. Type **112** 20 10
336 35 c. "Neptune Aries" (tanker) 70 60
337 50 c. "Anro Temasek" (container ship) .. 80 1·25
338 75 c. "Neptune Pearl" (container ship) .. 1·00 1·75

113. "Concorde".

1978. Aviation. Multicoloured.

339. 10 c. Type **113** 35 15
340. 35 c. Boeing "747B" .. 70 60
341. 50 c. Vickers "Vimy" .. 80 1·25
342. 75 c. Wright Brothers' "Flyer I" .. .. 1·00 2·00

114. 10-Kilometre Marker.

1979. Metrication. Multicoloured.

343. 10 c. Type **114** 15 10
344. 35 c. Tape measure .. 30 50
345. 75 c. Weighing scales .. 60 1·25

115. Vanda Hybrid.

1979. Orchids.

346. **115.** 10 c. multicoloured .. 20 10
347. – 35 c. multicoloured .. 55 55
348. – 50 c. multicoloured .. 70 80
349. – 75 c. multicoloured .. 1·00 1·25

DESIGNS—HORIZ. 35 c. VERT. 50, 75 c. Different varieties of Vanda Hybrid.

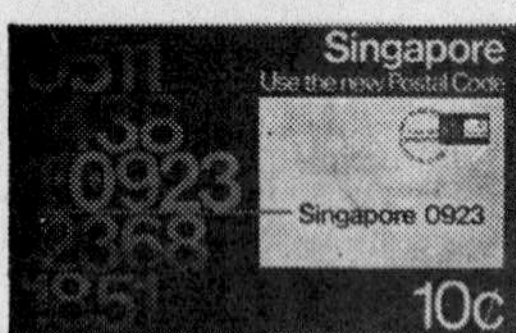

116. Envelope with new Singapore Postcode.

1979. Postal Code Publicity.

350. **116.** 10 c. multicoloured .. 10 10
351. – 50 c. multicoloured .. 60 80

The 50 c. design is as Type **116**, but the envelope is addressed to the Philatelic Bureau, General Post Office and has the postcode "Singapore 0104".

117. Early Telephone and Overhead Cables.

1979. Centenary of Telephone Service.

352. **117.** 10 c. brown and blue .. 15 10
353. – 35 c. orange and violet 30 40
354. – 50 c. blue, turq. & grn. 45 70
355. – 75 c. green and orange .. 65 1·25

DESIGNS: 35 c. Telephone dial and world map. 50 c. Modern telephone and city scene. 75 c. Latest computerised telephone and circuit diagram.

118. "Lantern Festival" (Eng Chun-Ngan).

1979. International Year of the Child. Children's Drawings. Multicoloured.

356. 10 c. Type **118** 10 10
357. 35 c. "Singapore Harbour" (Wong Chien Chien) .. 30 40
358. 50 c. "Use Your Hands" (Leong Choy Yeen) .. 40 70
359. 75 c. "Soccer" (Tan Cheong Hin) .. .. 60 1·25

119. View of Gardens.

1979. 120th Anniv. of Botanic Gardens.

361. **119.** 10 c. multicoloured .. 15 10
362. – 50 c. multicoloured .. 60 1·25
363. – $1 multicoloured .. 1·10 2·25

DESIGNS: 50 c., $1, Different views of Botanic Gardens.

120. Hainan Junk.

1980. Ships. Multicoloured.

364 1 c. Type **120** 30 70
365 5 c. Full-rigged clipper .. 10 45
366 10 c. Fujian junk .. 10 10
367 15 c. Golekkan (sailing craft) 15 15
368 20 c. Palari (sailing craft) 20 30
369 25 c. East Indiaman .. 25 40
370 35 c. Galleon 30 40
371 50 c. Caravel 50 40
372 75 c. Jiangsu trading junk 65 75
373 $1 "Kedah" (coaster) .. 70 45
374 $2 "Murex" (tanker) .. 1·25 90
375 $5 "Chusan" (screw steamer) .. .. 3·00 3·00
376 $10 "Braganza" (paddle-steamer) .. .. 6·00 6·00

Nos. 373/6 are 42 × 25 mm.

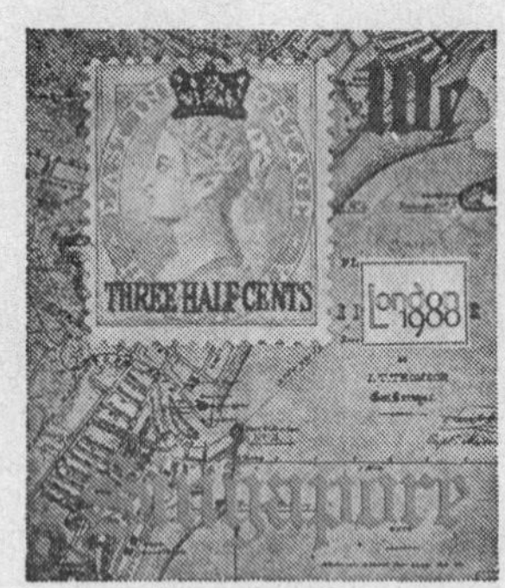

121. Straits Settlements 1867 1½ c. Stamp and Map of Singapore, 1843.

1980. "London 1980" International Stamp Exhibition. Multicoloured.

377. 10 c. Type **121** 20 10
378. 35 c. Straits Settlements 1906 $500 stamp and treaty between Johore and British Colony of Singapore 35 25
379. $1 1948 $2 stamp and map of Malaysia .. .. 70 1·10
380. $2 1969 150th Anniv. of Singapore $10 commemorative and letter to Col. Addenbrooke from Sir Stamford Raffles .. 1·25 2·25

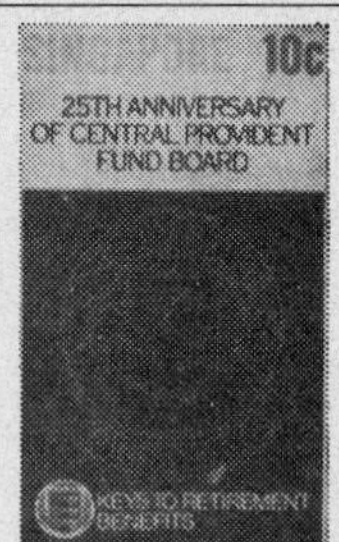

122. C.P.F. Emblem and "Keys to Retirement Benefits".

1980. 25th Anniv. of Central Provident Fund Board. Multicoloured.

382. 10 c. Type **122** 10 10
383. 50 c. "C.P.F. savings for home ownership" .. 40 40
384. $1 "C.P.F. savings for old-age" .. .. .. 75 1·25

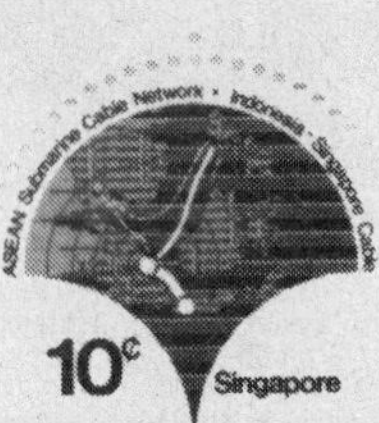

123. Map of South East Asia showing Cable Network.

1980. A.S.E.A.N. (Association of South-East Asian Nations) Submarine Cable Network (2nd issue). Completion of Indonesia—Singapore Section.

385. **123.** 10 c. multicoloured .. 10 10
386. 35 c. multicoloured .. 40 30
387. 50 c. multicoloured .. 50 75
388. 75 c. multicoloured .. 65 1·25

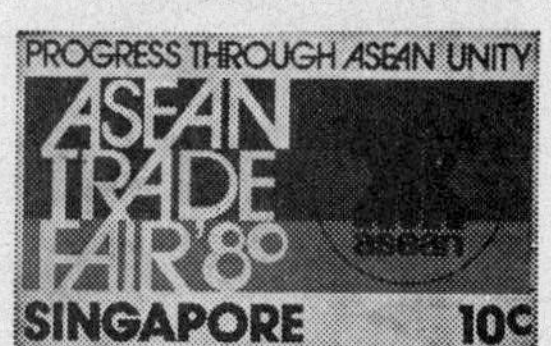

124. A.S.E.A.N. Trade Fair Emblem.

1980. A.S.E.A.N. (Association of South-East Asian Nations) Trade Fair.

389. **124.** 10 c. multicoloured .. 10 10
390. 35 c. multicoloured .. 30 30
391. 75 c. multicoloured .. 60 1·00

125. Ixora.

1980. National Tree Planting Day. Flowers. Multicoloured.

392. 10 c. Type **125** 10 10
393. 35 c. Allamanda 40 35
394. 50 c. Sky Vine 50 60
395. 75 c. Bougainvillea .. 60 90

126. International Currency Symbols.

1981. 10th Anniv. of Singapore Monetary Authority.

396. **126.** 10 c. blk., red & yell. .. 10 10
397. 35 c. multicoloured .. 30 30
398. 75 c. multicoloured .. 55 1·25

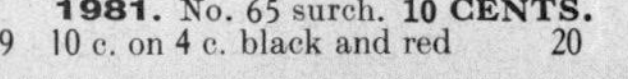

1981. No. 65 surch. **10 CENTS.**

399 10 c. on 4 c. black and red 20 40

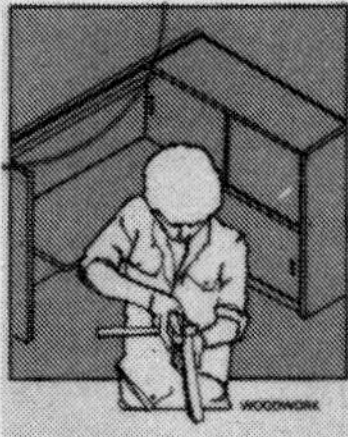

128. Woodwork.

1981. Technical Training. Multicoloured.

400. 10 c. Type **128** 10 10
401. 35 c. Building construction 25 25
402. 50 c. Electronics 40 60
403. 75 c. Precision machining 50 1·10

129. Figures representing various Sports. 130. "The Right to Environmental Aids".

1981. "Sports for All".

404. **129.** 10 c. multicoloured .. 15 10
405. – 75 c. multicoloured .. 1·50 2·00
406. – $1 multicoloured .. 1·75 2·75

DESIGNS: 75 c. and $1 Figures representing different sports.

1981. International Year for Disabled Persons. Multicoloured.

407. 10 c. Type **130**. 10 10
408. 35 c. "The right to social integration" 40 25
409. 50 c. "The right to education" 60 50
410. 75 c. "The right to work" 80 90

131. Control Tower and Passenger Terminal Building, Changi Airport.

1981. Opening of Changi Airport.

411. **131.** 10 c. multicoloured .. 10 10
412. 35 c. multicoloured .. 35 20
413. 50 c. multicoloured .. 45 60
414. 75 c. multicoloured .. 70 1·00
415. $1 multicoloured .. 80 1·25

The background emblem differs for each value.

132. "Parthenos sylvia".

1982. Butterflies. Multicoloured.

417 10 c. Type **132** 20 10
418 50 c. "Danaus vulgaris" .. 80 50
419 $1 "Trogonoptera brookiana" .. .. 1·25 1·40

133. A.S.E.A.N. Emblem.

1982. 15th Anniv. of A.S.E.A.N. (Association of South-East Asian Nations).

420 **133** 10 c. multicoloured .. 10 10

421 35 c. multicoloured .. 30 35

422 – 50 c. multicoloured .. 40 65

423 – 75 c. multicoloured .. 60 1·00

The 50 and 75 c. values are as Type **133** but inscribed "15th ASEAN Ministerial Meeting".

134. Football and Stylised Player.

1982. World Cup Football Championship, Spain.

424. **134.** 10 c. black, bright blue and blue 20 10

425. – 75 c. multicoloured .. 75 1·50

426. – $1 multicoloured .. 95 1·50

DESIGNS: 75 c. Football and World Cup, Asian Four emblem. $1 Football and globe.

135. Sultan Shoal Lighthouse, 1896.

1982. Lighthouses of Singapore. Mult.

427. 10 c. Type **135** 10 10

428. 75 c. Horsburgh Lighthouse, 1855 .. .. 75 1·40

429. $1 Raffles Lighthouse, 1855 .. .. .. 85 1·50

136. Yard Gantry Cranes.

1982. 10th Anniv. of Container Terminal. Multicoloured.

431. 10 c. Type **136** 10 10

432. 35 c. Computer .. 25 30

433. 50 c. Freightlifter .. 35 50

434. 75 c. Straddle carrier .. 65 70

137. Scouts on Parade.

1982. 75th Anniv. of Boy Scout Movement. Multicoloured.

435. 10 c. Type **137** 15 10

436. 35 c. Scouts hiking .. 45 25

437. 50 c. Scouts building tower 65 35

438. 75 c. Scouts canoeing .. 95 80

138. Productivity Movement Slogans.

1983. Productivity Movement.

439. **138.** 10 c. orange and green 10 10

440. – 35 c. brown and blue .. 35 40

441. – 50 c. red, yellow & grey 55 80

442. – 75 c. red and yellow .. 75 1·10

DESIGNS: 35 c. Family and housing (" Benefits of Productivity "). 50 c. Works meeting (" Quality Control Circles "). 75 c. Aspects of Singapore business (" Everybody's Business ").

139. Commonwealth Logo and Country Names.

1983. Commonwealth Day.

443. **139.** 10 c. multicoloured .. 10 10

444. 35 c. multicoloured .. 20 25

445. 75 c. multicoloured .. 45 85

446. $1 multicoloured .. 65 1·00

140. Soccer.

1983. 12th South-East Asia Games. Mult.

447. 10 c. Type **140** 10 10

448. 35 c. Racket games .. 20 25

449. 75 c. Athletics 45 50

450. $1 Swimming 65 70

141. Policeman and Family.

1983. Neighbourhood Watch Scheme. Mult.

451. 10 c. Type **141** 15 10

452. 35 c. Policeman and children 55 35

453. 75 c. Policeman and inhabitants with linked arms .. 1·00 1·00

142. 1977 A.S.E.A.N. Stamps and Statue of King Chulalongkorn.

1983. Bangkok International Stamp Exn. Multicoloured.

454. 10 c. Type **142** 10 10

455. 35 c. 1980 A.S.E.A.N. stamps and map of south-east Asia 25 45

456. $1 1982 A.S.E.A.N. stamps and signatures of Heads of State .. .. .. 65 1·40

143. Map of South-East Asia showing Cable Network.

1983. A.S.E.A.N. (Association of South-East Asian Nations) Submarine Cable Network (3rd issue). Completion of Malaysia–Singapore–Thailand section.

458. **143.** 10 c. multicoloured .. 15 10

459. 35 c. multicoloured .. 35 40

460. 50 c. multicoloured .. 50 65

461. 75 c. multicoloured .. 75 1·00

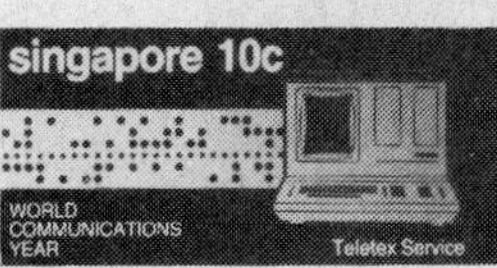

144. Teletex Service (Illustration reduced, actual size 74 × 24 mm.).

1983. World Communications Year.

463. **144.** 10 c. yell., grn. & blk. 10 10

464. – 35 c. yellow, red & brn. 25 35

465. – 75 c. grn., bl. & dp. bl. 65 90

466. – $1 yellow, brn. & blk. 80 1·25

DESIGNS: 35 c. World telephone numbering plan. 75 c. Satellite transmission. $1 Sea communications.

145. Blue-breasted Banded Rail.

1984. Coastal Birds. Multicoloured.

467. 10 c. Type **145** 30 10

468. 35 c. Black bittern .. 80 85

469. 50 c. Brahminy kite .. 95 1·10

470. 75 c. Moorhen .. .. 1·25 1·75

146. House of Tan Yeok Nee.

1984. National Monuments. Multicoloured.

471. 10 c. Type **146** 10 10

472. 35 c. Thong Chai building 30 35

473. 50 c. Telok Ayer market .. 40 60

474. $1 Nagore Durgha shrine 80 1·40

147. 1970 $1 National Day Stamp.

1984. "25 Years of Nation Building". Multicoloured.

475. 10 c. Type **147** 10 10

476. 35 c. 1981 $1 "Sports for All" stamp 30 35

477. 50 c. 1969 25 c. "100,000 Homes for the People" stamp 40 55

478. 75 c. 1976 10 c. Wayside Trees stamp 60 80

479. $1 1981 $1 Opening of Changi Airport stamp .. 80 1·25

480. $2 1981 10 c. Monetary Authority stamp .. 1·75 3·00

148. School children.

1984. "Total Defence".

482. **148.** 10 c. brown and red .. 15 20

483. – 10 c. brn., olive & bl. 15 20

484. – 10 c. brown, violet and salmon .. 15 20

485. – 10 c. brown, light brown and mauve 15 20

486. – 10 c. brn., yell. & olive 15 20

DESIGNS: No. 483, People of Singapore. 484, Industrial workers. 485, Civil Defence first aid worker. 486, Anti-aircraft gun crew.

149. Coleman Bridge.

1985. Bridges of Singapore.

487. 10 c. black (Type **149**) .. 15 10

488. 35 c. blk. (Cavenagh Bridge) 30 30

489. 75 c. black (Elgin Bridge) 55 55

490. $1 black (Benjamin Sheares Bridge) 70 70

150. "Ceriagrion cerinorubellum" (damselfly).

1985. Insects. Multicoloured.

491 5 c. Type **150** 45 10

492 10 c. "Apis javana" (bee) 55 10

493 15 c. "Delta arcuata" (wasp) 60 20

494 20 c. "Xylocopa caerulea" (bee) 80 10

495 25 c. "Donacia javana" (water beetle) .. 80 30

496 35 c. "Heteroneda reticulata" (ladybird) .. 90 30

497 50 c. "Catacanthus nigripes" (bug) .. 1·25 45

498 75 c. "Chremistica pontianaka" (cicadu) .. 1·25 60

499 $1 "Homoexipha lycoides" (cricket) .. 1·25 60

500 $2 "Traulia azureipennis" (grasshopper) .. .. 1·50 1·25

501 $5 "Trithemis aurora" (dragonfly) .. .. 2·75 3·25

502 $10 "Scambophyllum sanguinolentum" (grasshopper) .. .. 5·75 6·00

Nos. 499/502 are larger, 35 × 30 mm.

151. Tennis, canoeing, Judo and Children Playing (Illustration reduced, actual size 50 × 20 mm.)

1985. 25th Anniv. of People's Association. Multicoloured.

503. 10 c. Type **151** 15 10

504. 35 c. Lion dance, martial arts and athletes with flags 30 30

505. 50 c. Tae-kwon-do, Indian dance and Dragon dance 40 40

506. 75 c. Boxing, table tennis, basketball and dancing 55 55

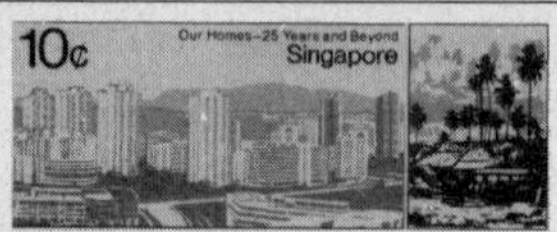

152. Modern Housing Estate and Squatter Settlement (Illustration reduced, actual size 50 × 20 mm.)

1985. 25th Anniv. of Housing and Development Board. Designs show different aspects of housing at left. Multicoloured.

507.	10 c. Type **152**	15	10
508.	35 c. Singapore family (Home-ownership)	30	30
509.	50 c. Group of residents (Community development)	40	40
510.	75 c. Construction workers (Building technology)	55	55

153. Brownies.

1985. 75th Anniv. of Girl Guide Movement. Multicoloured.

512.	10 c. Type **153**	10	10
513.	35 c. Guides practising first aid	30	30
514.	50 c. Senior Branch	40	40
515.	75 c. Adult leaders and guides	55	55

154. Badges and Emblems of Singapore Youth Organizations.

1985. International Youth Year. Mult.

516.	10 c. Type **154**	10	10
517.	75 c. Hand protecting sapling	55	55
518.	$1 Stylised figures and dove	70	70

155. Guava.

1986. Singapore Fruits. Multicoloured.

519.	10 c. Type **155**	15	10
520.	35 c. Jambu Air	35	35
521.	50 c. Rambutan	45	45
522.	75 c. Ciku	60	65

156. Laboratory Technician and Salesmen with Bar Graph.

1986. 25th Anniv. of National Trades Union Congress. Multicoloured.

523.	10 c. Type **156**	20	20
524.	10 c. Computer operator and welder	20	20
525.	10 c. Draughtsmen and surveyors	20	20
526.	10 c. Group of workers	20	20

157. Calligraphy.

1986. "Expo '86" World Fair, Vancouver. Multicoloured.

528.	50 c. Type **157**	45	65
529.	75 c. Garland maker	60	85
530.	$1 Batik printer	75	1·10

158. Industrial Automation.

1986. 25th Anniv. of Economic Development Board. Multicoloured.

531.	10 c. Type **158**	10	10
532.	35 c. Manufacture of aircraft components	25	30
533.	50 c. Electronics industry	30	40
534.	75 c. Biotechnology industry	50	70

159. Map showing Route of Cable and "Vercors" (cable ship).

1986. SEA-ME-WE Submarine Cable Project.

535.	**159.**	10 c. multicoloured	15	10
536.		35 c. multicoloured	50	35
537.		50 c. multicoloured	70	70
538.		75 c. multicoloured	85	1·10

160. Stylized Citizens.

1986. 21st Anniv. of Citizens' Consultative Committees.

539.	**160.**	10 c. multicoloured	20	20
540.	–	35 c. multicoloured	35	35
541.	–	50 c. multicoloured	40	40
542.	–	75 c. multicoloured	60	60

DESIGNS: 35 c. to 75 c. Citizens.

Nos. 539/42 were printed together, se-tenant, forming a composite design.

161. Peace Doves and People of Different Races.

1986. International Peace Year. Mult.

543.	10 c. Type **161**	10	10
544.	35 c. Doves and map of ASEAN countries	30	30
545.	$1 Doves and globe	70	1·10

162. Orchard Road.

1987. Singapore Skyline. Multicoloured.

546.	10 c. Type **162**	15	10
547.	50 c. Central Business District	40	50
548.	75 c. Marina Centre and Raffles City	60	90

163. Flags of Members Nations and Logo.

164. Soldier with Rocket Launcher

1987. 20th Anniv. of Association of South-east Asian Nations.

549.	**163.**	10 c. multicoloured	10	10
550.		35 c. multicoloured	30	30
551.		50 c. multicoloured	45	45
552.		75 c. multicoloured	55	55

1987. 20th Anniv. of National Service. Multicoloured.

553.	10 c. Type **164**	20	30
554.	10 c. Radar operator and patrol boat	20	30
555.	10 c. Fighter pilot and aircraft	20	30
556.	10 c. Servicemen pledging allegiance	20	30

165. Singapore River and Dragon Boats.

1987. River Conservation. Multicoloured.

558.	10 c. Type **165**	15	10
559.	50 c. Kallang Basin, canoe and fishing punt	55	50
560.	$1 Kranji Reservoir, athletes and cyclist	1·00	90

166. Majapahit Gold Bracelet and Museum.

1987. Centenary of National Museum. Each showing different drawings of Museum. Multicoloured.

561.	10 c. Type **166**	10	10
562.	75 c. Ming fluted kendi (water vessel)	50	60
563.	$1 Patani hulu pekakak keris (sword)	65	75

167. Omni-theatre.

1987. 10th Anniv. of Singapore Science Centre. Multicoloured.

564.	10 c. Type **167**	15	10
565.	35 c. Omni-planetarium	50	30
566.	75 c. Model of body cell	70	70
567.	$1 Physical sciences exhibits	90	90

168 Modern Anti-aircraft Gun

1988. Cent of Singapore Artillery. Mult.

568	10 c. Type **168**	30	10
569	35 c. 25-pounder field gun firing salute	75	35
570	50 c. Gunner and 12-pounder gun, c. 1920	1·00	60
571	$1 Gunner and Maxim gun, 1889	1·75	1·10

169 Route Map

1988. Singapore Mass Rapid Transit System. Multicoloured.

572	10 c. Type **169**	20	10
573	50 c. Train on elevated section	90	70
574	$1 Train in tunnel	1·40	90

170 Camera, Film and Outside Broadcast Van

1988. 25th Anniv of Television in Singapore. Multicoloured.

575	10 c. Type **170**	10	10
576	35 c. Camera, studio lights and microphone	20	25
577	75 c. Television set and transmitter	40	45
578	$1 Globe on TV screen and dish aerial	55	60

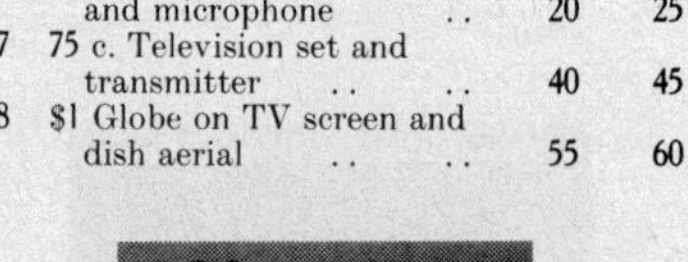

171 Water Droplet and Blocks of Flats

1988. 25th Anniv of Public Utilities Board. Multicoloured.

579	10 c. Type **171**	10	10
580	50 c. Electric light bulb and city centre	60	45
581	$1 Gas flame and factories	95	85

172 Greeting Neighbours

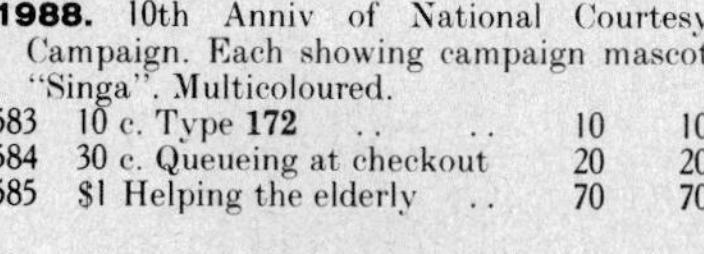

1988. 10th Anniv of National Courtesy Campaign. Each showing campaign mascot "Singa". Multicoloured.

583 10 c. Type **172** 10 10
584 30 c. Queueing at checkout 20 20
585 $1 Helping the elderly .. 70 70

173 Modern 30 Metre Turntable Fire Appliance

1988. Centenary of Fire Service. Mult.

586 10 c. Type **173** 30 15
587 $1 Steam fire engine, c. 1890 .. .. .. 1·75 1·75

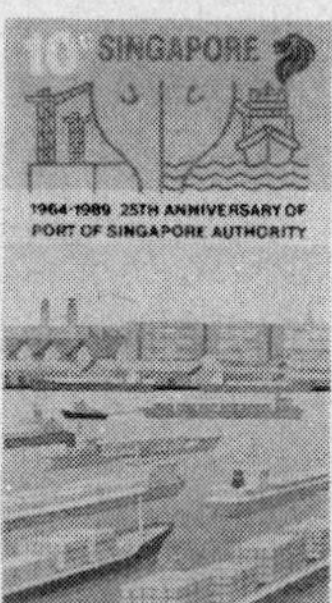

174 Container Ships and Warehouses

1989. 25th Anniv of Singapore Port Authority. Multicoloured.

588 10 c. Type **174** 15 10
589 30 c. Shipping and oil storage depot 35 30
590 75 c. Container ships and Singapore skyline .. 80 75
591 $1 Container port at night 90 90

175 "Sago Street"

1989. Paintings of Chinatown by Choo Keng Kwang. Multicoloured.

592 10 c. Type **175** 20 10
593 35 c. "Pagoda Street" .. 65 40
594 75 c. "Trengganu Street" 1·25 90
595 $1 "Temple Street" .. 1·50 1·00

176 North-west Singapore City, 1920

1989. Maps of Singapore. Multicoloured.

596 15 c. Type **176** (top left) .. 30 30
597 15 c. North-east Singapore (top right) 30 30
598 15 c. South-west Singapore (bottom left) 30 30
599 15 c. South-east Singapore (bottom right) 30 30
600 50 c. Singapore Island and Dependencies, 1860's .. 85 85
601 $1 British Settlement of Singapore, 1820's .. 1·40 1·40

Nos. 596/9 were printed together, se-tenant, forming a composite design. Individual stamps can be identified by the position of the lion emblem which is quoted in brackets.

177 Clown Triggerfish

1989. Fishes. Multicoloured.

602 15 c. Type **177** 40 10
603 30 c. Majestic angelfish .. 75 40
604 75 c. Emperor angelfish .. 1·60 1·60
605 $1 Royal empress angel-fish .. .. .. 1·75 1·75

178 "Hari Raya Puasa" (Loke Yoke Yun)

1989. Festivals of Singapore. Children's Drawings. Multicoloured.

606 15 c. Type **178** 20 10
607 35 c. "Chinese New Year" (Simon Koh) 40 30
608 75 c. "Thaipusam" (Henry Setiono) 85 70
609 $1 "Christmas" (Wendy Ang Lin Min) .. .. 1·10 1·00

179 North Entrance of Stadium

1989. Opening of Singapore Indoor Stadium. Multicoloured.

611 30 c. Type **179** 50 30
612 75 c. Arena .. .. 1·10 80
613 $1 East entrance .. 1·25 1·10

180 "Singapore River, 1839" (Louis le Breton)

1990. Lithographs of 19th-century Singapore. Multicoloured.

615 15 c. Type **180** 20 10
616 30 c. "Chinatown, 1837" (Barthelemy Lauvergne) 40 30
617 75 c. "Singapore Harbour, 1837" (Barthelemy Lauvergne) 85 70
618 $1 "View from the French Resident's House, 1824" (Deroy) .. .. 1·00 90

181 1969 150th Anniv of Singapore Stamp Issue

1990. 150th Anniv of the Penny Black. Mult.

619 50 c. Type **181** 65 40
620 75 c. Indian stamps, including bisect, used from Singapore in 1859 90 80
621 $1 Indian stamps used from Singapore in 1854 1·40 1·10
622 $2 Penny Black and Two Pence Blue .. .. 2·25 2·25

182 Zoological Gardens

183 Chinese Opera Singer and Siong Lim Temple

1990. Tourism. Multicoloured.

(a) As T **182**

624 5 c. Type **182** 10 10
625 15 c. Sentosa Island .. 10 10
626 20 c. Singapore River .. 15 20
627 25 c. Dragon Boat Festival 20 25
628 30 c. Raffles Hotel .. 25 30
629 35 c. Coffee shop bird singing contest .. 30 35
630 40 c. Jurong Bird Park .. 35 40
631 50 c. Chinese New Year boat float 40 45
632 75 c. Peranakan Place .. 65 70

(b) As T **183**

633 $1 Type **183** 85 90
634 $2 Malay dancer and Sultan Mosque .. .. 1·60 1·75
635 $5 Indian dancer and Sri Mariamman Temple .. 4·25 4·50
636 $10 Ballet dancer and Victoria Memorial Hall 8·50 9·00

184 Armed Forces Personnel

1990. 25th Anniv of Independence. Mult.

637 15 c. Type **184** 30 15
638 35 c. Inhabitants of Singapore 60 45
639 75 c. Workers and technological achievements .. .. 1·10 90
640 $1 Cultural activities .. 1·25 1·10

185 Stag's Horn Fern

1990. Ferns. Multicoloured.

641 15 c. Type **185** 15 10
642 35 c. Maiden Hair fern .. 35 35
643 75 c. Bird's Nest fern .. 70 70
644 $1 Rabbit's Foot fern .. 90 90

186 Carved Dragon Pillar, Hong San See Temple

1991. National Monuments. Multicoloured.

645 20 c. Type **186** 30 30
646 20 c. Hong San See Temple (40 × 25 mm) .. 30 30
647 50 c. Interior of dome, Abdul Gaffoor Mosque 55 55
648 50 c. Abdul Gaffoor Mosque (40 × 25 mm) .. 55 55
649 75 c. Statue of Vishnu, Sri Perumal Hindu Temple 80 80
650 75 c. Sri Perumal Temple (40 × 25 mm) 80 80
651 $1 Stained glass window, St. Andrew's Cathedral 90 90
652 $1 St. Andrew's Cathedral (40 × 25 mm) 90 90

187 "Vanda Miss Joaquim"

1991. "Singapore '95" International Stamp Exhibition. Orchids (1st issue). Mult.

653 $2 Type **187** .. .. 1·90 1·90
654 $2 "Dendrobium anocha" 1·90 1·90

See also Nos. 674/5, 725/6 and 755/6.

188 Changi Airport Terminal II, 1991, and "B747-400"

1991. Singapore Civil Aviation. Mult.

656 20 c. Type **188** 35 20
657 75 c. Changi Airport Terminal I, 1981, and "B747-200" .. .. 1·00 75
658 $1 Paya Lebar Airport, 1955–1981, and "Concorde" .. .. 1·40 95
659 $2 Kallang Airport, 1937–1955, and "DC-2" 2·25 1·90

189 "Arachnopsis Eric Holttum"

1991. Orchid Dress Motifs. Multicoloured.

660 20 c. Type **189** 40 15
661 30 c. "Cattleya meadii" .. 60 50
662 $1 "Calanthe vestita" .. 1·75 2·00

INDEX

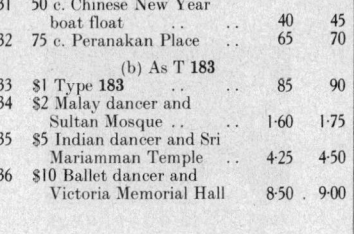

Countries can be quickly located by referring to the index at the end of this volume.

190 Long-tailed Tailor Bird

1991. Garden Birds. Multicoloured.

663	20 c. Type **190**	30	20
664	35 c. Scarlet-backed flower-pecker	60	40
665	75 c. Black-naped oriole	1·10	1·10
666	$1 Common iora	1·40	1·60

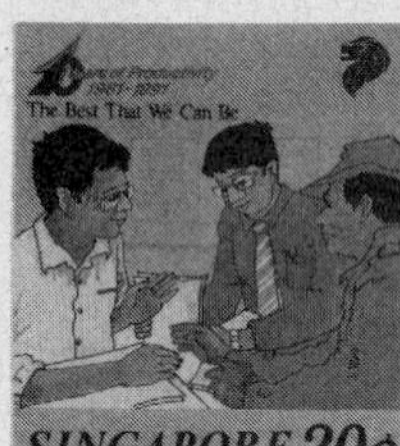

191 Productivity Discussion

1991. 10th Anniv of Productivity Movement. Multicoloured.

667	20 c. Type **191**	30	20
668	$1 Construction workers	95	1·40

192 Railway Creeper

1991. "Phila Nippon '91" Int Stamp Exn, Tokyo. Wild Flowers. Mult.

669	30 c. Type **192**	30	25
670	75 c. Asystasia	60	60
671	$1 Singapore rhododendron	80	90
672	$2 Coat buttons	1·60	1·75

1992. "Singapore '95" International Stamp Exhibition. Orchids (2nd issue). As T **187**. Multicoloured.

674	$2 "Dendrobium Sharifah Fatimah"	1·75	1·75
675	$2 "Phalaenopsis Shim Beauty"	1·75	1·75

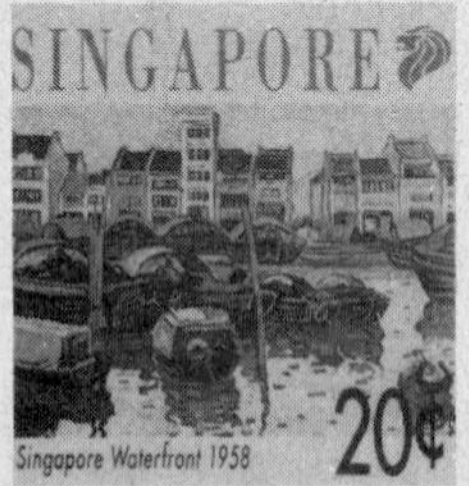

193 "Singapore Waterfront" (Georgette Chen Liying)

1992. Local Artists. Multicoloured.

677	20 c. Type **193**	30	20
678	75 c. "Kampung Hut" (Lim Cheng Hoe)	75	80
679	$1 "The Bridge" (Poh Siew Wah)	95	1·10
680	$2 "Singapore River" (Lee Boon Wang)	1·90	2·25

194 Football

1992. Olympic Games, Barcelona. Mult.

681	20 c. Type **194**	25	20
682	35 c. Athletics	35	30
683	50 c. Swimming	55	55
684	75 c. Basketball	75	75
685	$1 Tennis	95	95
686	$2 Sailing	1·90	2·00

195 Chinese Family and Samfu Pattern

1992. Singapore Costumes of 1910. Mult.

688	20 c. Type **195**	25	20
689	35 c. Malay family and sarong pattern	35	35
690	75 c. Indian family and sari pattern	80	80
691	$2 Straits Chinese family and belt pattern	1·90	1·90

196 Infantryman, Air Force Pilot and Navy Gunner

1992. 25th Anniv of National Service. Mult.

692	20 c. Type **196**	25	20
693	35 c. Navy diver, F-16 Fighting Falcon and FH-88 155 mm howitzer	35	35
694	$1 F-16 in flight, corvette and AMX-13SM1 tank	1·25	1·40

197 Crafts from A.S.E.A.N. Countries

1992. 25th Anniv of A.S.E.A.N (Association of South East Asian Nations). Multicoloured.

695	20 c. Type **197**	20	20
696	35 c. National dances	30	40
697	$1 National landmarks	1·10	1·25

198 Mosaic Crab

1992. Crabs. Multicoloured.

698	20 c. Type **198**	20	20
699	50 c. Johnson's freshwater crab	50	65
700	75 c. Singapore freshwater crab	80	90
701	$1 Swamp forest crab	1·10	1·25

199 Coins

1992. 25th Anniv of Singapore Currency. Mult.

702	20 c. Type **199**	25	35
703	75 c. Currency note from "orchid" series	80	90
704	$1 Currency note from "ship" series	95	1·10
705	$2 Currency note from "bird" series	1·75	1·75

Nos. 702/5 were printed together, se-tenant, forming a composite design.

200 Sun Bear

1993. South-East Asian Mammals. Mult.

706	20 c. Type **200**	25	20
707	30 c. Orang-utan	35	35
708	75 c. Slow loris	95	1·00
709	$2 Greater Malay chevrotain ("Large mouse deer")	2·10	2·25

201 "Thank You"

1993. Greetings Stamps. Multicoloured.

710	20 c. Type **201**	25	35
711	20 c. "Congratulations"	25	35
712	20 c. "Best Wishes"	25	35
713	20 c. "Happy Birthday"	25	35
714	20 c. "Get Well Soon"	25	35

202 Shophouses

1993. Conservation of Tanjong Pagar District. Multicoloured.

715	20 c. Type **202**	25	20
716	30 c. Jinrikisha Station	40	40
717	$2 View of Tanjong Pagar	2·40	2·50

203 "Cranes" (painting) (Chen Wen Hsi)

1993. "Indopex '93" International Stamp Exhibition, Surabaya.

718	**203** $2 multicoloured	2·00	2·25

204 Football

1993. 17th South-East Asian Games. Mult.

719	20 c. Type **204**	20	20
720	35 c. Basketball	45	45
721	50 c. Badminton	60	60
722	75 c. Athletics	80	80
723	$1 Water polo	1·10	1·10
724	$2 Yachting	1·90	1·90

1993. "Singapore '95" International Stamp Exhibition. Orchids (3rd issue). As T **187**, but 25 × 35 mm. Multicoloured.

725	$2 "Phalaenopsis amabilis"	2·00	2·25
726	$2 "Vanda sumatrana"	2·00	2·25

205 "Danaus chrysippus"

1993. Butterflies. Multicoloured.

728	20 c. Type **205**	20	20
729	50 c. "Cethosia hypsea"	55	55
730	75 c. "Amathusia phidippus"	85	85
731	$1 "Papilio demolion"	1·25	1·25

206 Papaya

1993. "Bangkok '93" International Stamp Exhibition. Local Fruits. Multicoloured.

732	20 c. Type **206**	20	20
733	35 c. Pomegranate	40	40
734	75 c. Starfruit	85	85
735	$2 Durian	2·00	2·00

207 Egrets Drinking

1993. Endangered Species. Swinhoe's Egret ("Chinese Egret"). Multicoloured.

737	20 c. Type **207**	25	25
738	25 c. Egrets eating	30	30
739	30 c. Egrets searching for fish	40	40
740	35 c. Egrets in flight	45	45

Nos. 737/40 were printed together, se-tenant, with the background forming a composite design.

MINIMUM PRICE

The minimum price quoted is 10p which represents a handling charge rather than a basis for valuing common stamps. For further notes about prices see introductory pages.

208 Palm Tree

1993. Self-adhesive. Imperf.

No.	Type	Description	Unused	Used
741	**208**	(–) multicoloured	15	20

No. 741 was only valid for use on mail to local addresses and was initially sold at 20 c., which will be increased to reflect future postage rates.

209 Tiger Cowrie

1994. Reef Life. Multicoloured.

No.	Type	Description	Unused	Used
742		5 c. Type **209**	10	10
743		20 c. Sea-fan	15	20
744		25 c. Tunicate	20	25
745		30 c. Clownfish	25	30
746		35 c. Nudibranch	30	35
747		40 c. Sea-urchin	35	40
748		50 c. Soft coral	40	45
749		75 c. Pin cushion star	65	70
750		$1 Knob coral	85	90
751		$2 Mushroom coral	1·60	1·75
752		$5 Bubble coral	4·25	4·50
753		$10 Octopus coral	8·50	8·75

Nos. 750/3 are size 32 × 27 mm.

1994. "Singapore '95" International Stamp Exhibition. Orchids (4th issue). As T **187**, but each 25 × 35 mm. Multicoloured.

No.	Type	Description	Unused	Used
755		$2 "Paphiopedilum victoriaregina"	1·60	1·75
756		$2 "Dendrobium smillieae"	1·60	1·75

210 Dancers

1994. Singapore Festival of Arts. Mult.

No.	Type	Description	Unused	Used
758		20 c. Type **210**	15	20
759		30 c. Actors and puppet	25	30
760		50 c. Musicians	40	45
761		$1 Artists	85	90

POSTAGE DUE STAMPS

The postage due stamps of Malayan Postal Union were in use in Singapore from 1948 until replaced by the following issue.

D 1.

D 2.

1968.

No.	Type	Description	Unused	Used
D 1.	**D 1.**	1 c. green	40	1·50
D 2.		2 c. red	40	2·00
D 3.		4 c. orange	55	2·50
D 4.		8 c. brown	50	90
D 5.		10 c. mauve	50	90
D 6.		12 c. violet	1·00	1·50
D 7.		20 c. blue	2·00	3·25
D 8.		50 c. green	6·00	5·00

1978.

No.	Type	Description	Unused	Used
D16a.	**D 2.**	1 c. green	15	55
D17a.		4 c. orange	20	75
D18a.		10 c. blue	50	80
D19a.		20 c. blue	65	1·25
D20a.		50 c. green	90	1·75

D 3

1989.

No.	Type	Description	Unused	Used
D21	**D 3**	5 c. mauve	10	10
D22		10 c. red	10	10
D23		20 c. blue	15	20
D24		50 c. green	40	45

SIRMOOR

A state of the Punjab, India. Now uses Indian stamps.

12 pies = 1 anna; 16 annas = 1 rupee.

1.

2.

1876.

No.	Type	Description	Unused	Used
1.	**1.**	1 pice green	5·00	
2.		1 pice blue	4·00	80·00

1892.

No.	Type	Description	Unused	Used
3b.	**2.**	1 pice green	35	40
4.		1 pice blue	45	45

3. Raja Sir Shamsher Parkash.

4.

1885.

No.	Type	Description	Unused	Used
6.	**3.**	3 p. brown	25	30
8.		3 p. orange	25	20
12.		6 p. green	35	25
14.		1 a. blue	85	1·10
20.		2 a. red	3·50	3·00

1895.

No.	Type	Description	Unused	Used
22.	**4.**	3 p. orange	75	30
23.		6 p. green	65	30
24.		1 a. blue	1·60	35
25.		2 a. red	1·10	1·00
26.		3 a. green	10·00	17·00
27.		4 a. green	4·75	7·00
28.		8 a. blue	6·50	11·00
29.		1 r. red	15·00	30·00

5. Raja Sir Surendar Bikram Parkash.

1899.

No.	Type	Description	Unused	Used
30.	**5.**	3 a. green	1·50	13·00
31.		4 a. green	1·75	7·00
32.		8 a. blue	2·50	8·50
33.		1 r. red	4·75	20·00

OFFICIAL STAMPS

1890. Optd. **ON S.S.S.**

No.	Type	Description	Unused	Used
60	**3.**	3 p. orange	50	40
79		6 p. green	40	45
80		1 a. blue	35	50
63		2 a. red	9·00	10·00

SOLOMON ISLANDS

A group of islands in the W. Pacific, E. of New Guinea, under Br. protection.

1907. 12 pence = 1 shilling;
20 shillings = 1 pound.
1966. 100 cents = $1 Australian.

1.

1907.

No.	Type	Description	Unused	Used
1.	**1.**	½d. blue	6·50	13·00
2.		1d. red	22·00	30·00
3.		2d. blue	26·00	30·00
4.		2½d. yellow	32·00	35·00
5.		5d. green	50·00	65·00
6.		6d. brown	55·00	60·00
7.		1s. purple	75·00	75·00

2.

3.

1908.

No.	Type	Description	Unused	Used
8.	**2.**	½d. green	70	80
9.		1d. red	1·00	50
10.		2d. grey	1·25	1·00
11.		2½d. blue	2·50	2·50
11a.		4d. red on yellow	3·00	11·00
12.		5d. olive	8·50	9·00
13.		6d. red	8·50	7·50
14.		1s. black on green	9·50	12·00
15.		2s. purple on blue	30·00	50·00
16.		2s. 6d. red on blue	45·00	70·00
17.		5s. green on yellow	75·00	£100

1913. Inscr. "POSTAGE POSTAGE".

No.	Type	Description	Unused	Used
18.	**3.**	½d. green	80	3·50
19.		1d. red	80	10·00
42.		1½d. red	2·00	30
20.		3d. purple on yellow	80	4·00
21.		11d. purple and red	3·00	14·00

1914. Inscr. "POSTAGE REVENUE".

No.	Type	Description	Unused	Used
39	**3**	½d. green	30	2·00
24		1d. red	1·25	1·00
41		1d. violet	1·00	5·50
26		2d. grey	1·75	9·00
27		2½d. blue	2·00	5·00
28		3d. purple on yellow	18·00	70·00
44		3d. blue	70	2·75
29		4d. black & red on yellow	2·00	2·50
45a		4½d. brown	3·00	16·00
46		5d. purple and green	2·75	20·00
47		6d. purple	3·75	17·00
33		1s. black on green	3·00	7·00
34		2s. purple and blue on blue	6·50	10·00
35		2s. 6d. black & red on blue	7·50	20·00
36		5s. green and red on yellow	25·00	42·00
37		10s. green and red on green	75·00	80·00
38		£1 purple & black on red	£200	£130

1935. Silver Jubilee. As T **13** of Antigua.

No.	Type	Description	Unused	Used
53		1½d. blue and red	1·00	50
54		3d. brown and blue	3·00	4·25
55		6d. blue and green	7·00	9·00
56		1s. grey and purple	7·00	7·50

1937. Coronation. As T **2** of Aden.

No.	Type	Description	Unused	Used
57.		1d. violet	30	50
58.		1½d. red	30	60
59.		3d. blue	50	50

5. Spears and Shield.

1939. Portrait of King George VI.

No.	Type	Description	Unused	Used
60.	**5.**	½d. blue and green	15	70
61.	–	1d. brown and violet	15	50
62.	–	1½d. green and red	35	1·00
63.	–	2d. brown and black	30	1·25
64.	–	2½d. mauve and olive	80	85
65.	–	3d. black and blue	45	85
66.	–	4½d. green and brown	8·00	13·00
67.	–	6d. violet and purple	35	90
68.	–	1s. green and black	85	55
69.	–	2s. black and orange	6·00	3·00
70.	–	2s. 6d. black and violet	25·00	4·50
71.	–	5s. green and red	28·00	9·00
72	–	10s. green and mauve	7·00	8·00

DESIGNS—VERT. 1d. Native constable and Chief. 4½d., 10s. Native house, Reef Islands. 6d. Coconut plantation. HORIZ. 1½d. Artificial Is., Malaita. 2½d. Roviana canoe. 1s. Breadfruit. 5s. Malaita canoe. LARGER—35½ × 22 mm. 2d. Canoe house. 3d. Roviana canoes. 2s. Tinakula Volcano. 2s. 6d. Common Scrub Hen.

1946. Victory. As T **9** of Aden.

No.	Type	Description	Unused	Used
73		1½d. red	15	50
74		3d. blue	15	10

1949. Silver Wedding. As T **10/11** of Aden.

No.	Type	Description	Unused	Used
75		2d. grey	50	30
76		10s. mauve	13·00	8·50

1949. U.P.U. As T **20/23** of Antigua.

No.	Type	Description	Unused	Used
77.		2d. brown	1·00	70
78.		3d. blue	1·25	80
79.		5d. green	1·25	95
80.		1s. black	1·75	70

1953. Coronation. As T **13** of Aden.

No.	Type	Description	Unused	Used
81.		2d. black and grey	40	65

17. Ysabel Canoe.

1956. Portrait of Queen Elizabeth II.

No.	Type	Description	Unused	Used
82	**17**	½d. orange and purple	15	50
83	–	1d. grn. & brn. (As No. 65)	15	15
84	–	1½d. slate & red (No. 62)	15	50
105	–	2d. sepia & green (No. 63)	20	30
86	–	2½d. black and blue	40	45
87	–	3d. green and red (No. 71)	40	15
88	–	5d. black and blue	30	55
89	–	6d. black and green	50	25
90	–	8d. blue and black	25	15
108	–	9d. green and black	20	35
91	–	1s. slate and brown	50	50
109	–	1s. 3d. black and blue	60	70
110	–	2s. black and red (No. 69)	1·00	5·50
93	–	2s. 6d. grn. & pur. (No. 66)	7·50	45
94	–	5s. brown	12·00	2·50
95	–	10s. sepia (No. 61)	17·00	3·00
96	–	£1 black and blue	42·00	35·00

DESIGNS—VERT. 2½d. Prow of Roviana canoe. HORIZ. 5d., 1s. 3d. Map. 6d. Trading schooner. 8d., 9d. Henderson Airfield, Guadalcanal. 1s. Chart showing voyage of H.M.S. "Swallow" in 1767. 5s. Mendana and Ship. 10s. Similar to No. 61, but constable in different uniform, without rifle. £1, Arms.

32. Great Frigate Bird.

1961. New Constitution, 1960.

No.	Type	Description	Unused	Used
97.	**32.**	2d. black and turquoise	10	20
98.		3d. black and red	10	10
99.		9d. black and purple	15	20

1963. Freedom from Hunger. As T **28** of Aden.

No.	Type	Description	Unused	Used
100.		1s. 3d. blue	2·50	35

1963. Cent of Red Cross. As T **33** of Antigua.

No.	Type	Description	Unused	Used
101.		2d. red and black	60	20
102.		9d. red and blue	1·40	70

33. Makira Food Bowl.

1965. Central design in black; background colours given.

No.	Type	Description	Unused	Used
112.	**33.**	½d. slate and blue	10	30
113.	–	1d. orange and yellow	50	20
114.	–	1½d. blue and green	35	35
115.	–	2d. ultramarine and blue	50	30
116.	–	2½d. brown & light brown	10	35
117.	–	3d. green and light green	10	10
118.	–	6d. mauve and orange	35	20
119.	–	9d. turquoise and yellow	40	15
120.	–	1s. brown and mauve	80	15
121.	–	1s. 3d. red	3·50	2·25
122.	–	2s. purple and lilac	5·50	2·75
123.	–	2s. 6d. olive and brown	1·00	70
124.	–	5s. blue and violet	10·00	5·00
125.	–	10s. olive and yellow	13·00	4·00
126.	–	£1 violet and pink	11·00	5·00

DESIGNS: 1d. "Dendrobium veratrifolium" (orchid). 1½d. Scorpion shell. 2d. Blyth's Hornbill. 2½d. Ysabel shield. 3d. Rennellese club. 6d. Moorish Idol (fish). 9d. Lesser Frigate Bird. 1s. "Dendrobium macrophyllum" (orchid). 1s. 3d. "Dendrobium spectabilis" (orchid). 2s. Sanford's Sea Eagle. 2s. 6d. Malaita belt. 5s. "Ornithoptera victoreae" (butterfly). 10s. Ducorp's Cockatoo. £1, Western Canoe Figurehead.

1965. Cent of I.T.U. As T **36** of Antigua.

No.	Type	Description	Unused	Used
127.		2d. red and turquoise	20	10
128.		3d. turquoise and drab	20	10

1965. I.C.Y. As T **37** of Antigua.

No.	Type	Description	Unused	Used
129.		1d. purple and turquoise	15	10
130.		2s. 6d. green and lavender	60	15

1966. Churchill Commem. As T **38** of Antigua.

No.	Type	Description	Unused	Used
131.		2d. blue	15	10
132.		9d. green	25	10
133.		1s. 3d. brown	35	10
134.		2s. 6d. violet	40	25

1966. Decimal Currency. Nos. 112/26 surch.

No.	Type	Description	Unused	Used
135.		1 c. on ½d.	10	10
136.		2 c. on 1d.	10	10
137.		3 c. on 1½d.	10	10
138.		4 c. on 2d.	15	10
139.		5 c. on 6d.	15	10
140.		6 c. on 2½d.	10	10
141.		7 c. on 3d.	10	10
142.		8 c. on 9d.	15	10
143.		10 c. on 1s.	30	10
144.		12 c. on 1s. 3d.	65	10
145.		13 c. on 1s. 3d.	1·50	15
146.		14 c. on 3d.	40	10
147.		20 c. on 2s.	75	25
148.		25 c. on 2s. 6d.	60	40
149.		35 c. on 2d.	1·75	25
150.		50 c. on 5s.	6·50	2·75
151.		$1 on 10s.	4·25	1·25
152.		$2 on £1	5·00	3·00

1966. World Cup Football Championship. As T **40** of Antigua.

No.	Type	Description	Unused	Used
153.		8 c. multicoloured	15	10
154.		35 c. multicoloured	30	10

1966. Inauguration of W.H.O. Headquarters, Geneva. As T **41** of Antigua.
155. 3 c. black, green and blue 25 10
156. 50 c. black, purple & ochre 1·00 20

1966. 20th Anniv of U.N.E.S.C.O. As T **54/6** of Antigua.
157. 3 c. multicoloured .. 20 10
158. 25 c. yellow, violet & olive 55 15
159. $1 black, purple & orange 1·50 70

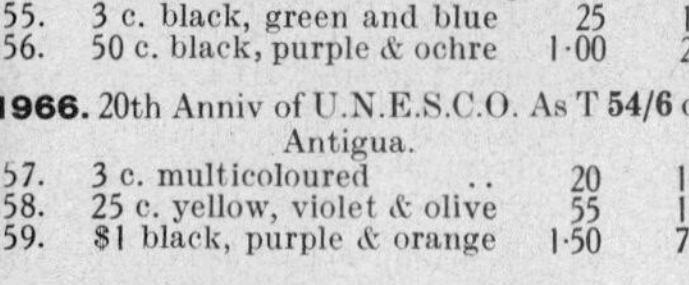

49. Henderson Field.

1967. 25th Anniv. of Guadalcanal Campaign (Pacific War). Multicoloured.
160. 8 c. Type **49** 10 10
161. 35 c. Red Beach Landings 10 10

51. Mendana's "Todos los Santos" off Point Cruz.

1968. 400th Anniv. of Discovery of the Solomon Is. Multicoloured.
162. 3 c. Type **51** 15 10
163. 8 c. Arrival of missionaries 15 10
164. 35 c. Pacific Campaign, World War II 30 10
165. $1 Proclamation of the Protectorate .. .. 50 1·25

55. Vine Fishing.

1968.
166. **55.** 1 c. blue, black & brown 10 10
167. – 2 c. green, black & brown 10 10
168. – 3 c. grn., myrtle & black 10 10
169. – 4 c. purple, black & brn. 15 10
170. – 6 c. multicoloured .. 30 10
171. – 8 c. multicoloured .. 25 10
172. – 12 c. ochre, red & black 65 40
173. – 14 c. red, brn. & black 1·75 1·00
174. – 15 c. multicoloured .. 80 50
175. – 20 c. blue, red & black 2·25 1·25
176. – 24 c. red, black & yellow 2·00 1·50
177. – 35 c. multicoloured .. 1·75 70
178. – 45 c. multicoloured .. 1·50 75
179. – $1 blue, green and black 2·50 2·00
180. – $2 multicoloured .. 4·50 5·00

DESIGNS: 2 c. Kite Fishing. 3 c. Platform Fishing. 4 c. Net Fishing. 6 c. Gold Lip Shell Diving. 8 c. Night Fishing. 12 c. Boat Building. 14 c. Cocoa. 15 c. Road Building. 20 c. Geological Survey. 24 c. Hauling Timber. 35 c. Copra. 45 c. Harvesting Rice. $1, Honiara Port. $2, Internal Air Service.

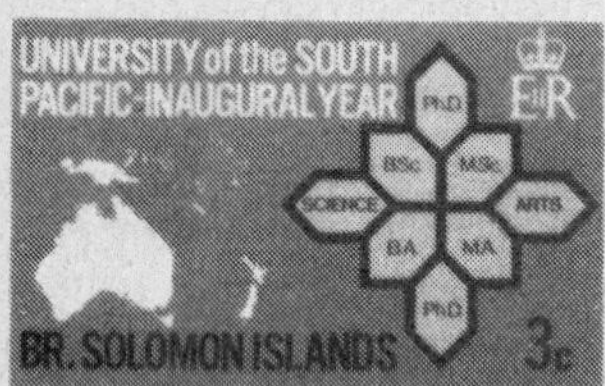

70. Map of Australasia and Diagram.

1969. Inaugural Year of South Pacific University.
181. **70.** 3 c. multicoloured .. 10 10
182. 12 c. multicoloured .. 10 10
183. 35 c. multicoloured .. 15 10

71. Basketball Player. **75.** South Sea Island with Star of Bethlehem.

1969. 3rd South Pacific Games, Port Moresby. Multicoloured.
184. 3 c. Type **71** 10 10
185. 8 c. Footballer 10 10
186. 14 c. Sprinter 10 10
187. 45 c. Rugby player .. 20 15

1969. Christmas.
189. **75.** 8 c. black, violet & green 10 10
190. – 35 c. multicoloured .. 20 20

DESIGN: 35 c. Southern Cross, "PAX" and Frigate Bird (stained glass window).

77. "Paid" Stamp, New South Wales 1896–1906 2d. Stamp and 1906–07 Tulagi Postmark.

1970. New G.P.O., Honiara.
191. **77.** 7 c. mve., blue and black 20 15
192. – 14 c. green, blue & black 25 15
193. – 18 c. multicoloured .. 25 15
194. – 23 c. multicoloured .. 30 20

DESIGNS: 14 c. 1906–07 2d. stamp and C. M. Woodford. 18 c. 1910–14 5s. stamp and Tulagi Postmark, 1913. 23 c. New G.P.O., Honiara.

81. Coat of Arms.

1970. New Constitution.
195. **81.** 18 c. multicoloured .. 15 10
196. – 35 c. green, blue & ochre 30 20

DESIGN—HORIZ. 35 c. Map.

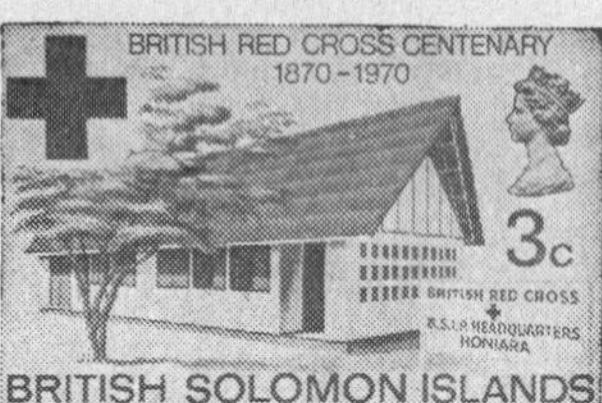

83. British Red Cross H.Q., Honiara.

1970. Centenary of British Red Cross.
197. **83.** 3 c. multicoloured .. 10 10
198. – 35 c. blue, red & blk. 25 20

DESIGN—VERT. 35 c. Wheelchair and map.

86. Reredos (Altar Screen).

1970. Christmas.
199. – 8 c. ochre and violet .. 10 10
200. **86.** 45 c. chestnut, orange and brown 25 20

DESIGN—HORIZ. 8 c. Carved angel.

87. La Perouse and "La Boussole".

1971. Ships and Navigators (1st series). Multicoloured.
201. 3 c. Type **87** 55 20
202. 4 c. Astrolabe and Polynesian reed map 65 20
203. 12 c. Abel Tasman and "Heemskerk" .. .. 1·50 45
204. 35 c. Te puki canoe .. 3·00 75

See also Nos. 215/18, 236/9, 254/7 and 272/5.

88. J. Atkin, Bishop Patteson and S. Taroaniara.

1971. Death Cent. of Bishop Patteson. Mult.
205. 2 c. Type **88** 10 10
206. 4 c. Last landing at Nukapu 10 10
207. 14 c. Memorial Cross and Nukapu (vert.) 10 10
208. 45 c. Knotted leaf and canoe (vert.) 20 10

89. Torch Emblem and Boxers.

1971. South Pacific Games, Tahiti. Mult.
209. 3 c. Type **89** 10 10
210. 8 c. Emblem and Footballers 10 10
211. 12 c. Emblem and Runner 10 10
212. 35 c. Emblem and Skin-diver 15 15

90. Melanesian Lectern.

1971. Christmas. Multicoloured.
213. 9 c. Type **90** 10 10
214. 45 c. "United we Stand" (Margarita Bara) .. 20 20

1972. Ships and Navigators (2nd series). As T **87.** Multicoloured.
215. 4 c. Bougainville and "La Boudeuse" 30 10
216. 9 c. Horizontal planisphere and ivory backstaff .. 60 10
217. 15 c. Philip Carteret and H.M.S. "Swallow" .. 85 15
218. 45 c. Malaita canoe .. 3·75 1·25

91. "Cupha woodfordi".

1972. Multicoloured.
219 1 c. Type **91** 15 30
220 2 c. "Ornithoptera priamus" 25 40
221 3 c. "Vindula sapor" .. 25 40
222 4 c. "Papilio ulysses" .. 25 40
223 5 c. Great trevally .. 25 30
224 8 c. Little bonito .. 40 50
225 9 c. Sapphire demoiselle 50 55
226 12 c. "Costus speciosus" 1·25 80
227 15 c. Orange anenome fish 1·25 1·00
228 20 c. "Spathoglottis plicata" .. .. 3·25 1·75
229 25 c. "Ephemerantha comata" .. .. 3·25 1·50
230 35 c. "Dendrobium cuthbertsonii" .. 3·50 2·25
231 45 c. "Heliconia salomonica" .. .. 3·50 3·00
232 $1 Blue finned triggerfish 6·00 4·50
233 $2 "Ornithoptera alottei" 13·00 12·00
233a $5 Great frigate bird .. 11·00 11·00

The 2, 3, 4 c and $2 are butterflies; the 5, 8, 9, 15 c. and $1 are fishes, and the 12, 20, 25, 35, 45 c. are flowers.

1972. Royal Silver Wedding. As T **52** of Ascension, but with Greetings and Message Drum in background.
234. 8 c. red 10 10
235. 45 c. green 20 20

1973. Ships and Navigators (3rd series). As T **87.** Multicoloured.
236 4 c. D'Entrecasteaux and "La Recherche" .. 30 15
237 9 c. Ship's hour-glass and chronometer 60 15
238 15 c. Lt. Shortland and H.M.S. "Alexander" .. 75 20
239 35 c. Tomoko (war canoe) 3·25 1·75

93. Pan Pipes.

1973. Musical Instruments. Multicoloured.
240. 4 c. Type **93** 10 10
241. 9 c. Castanets 10 10
242. 15 c. Bamboo flute .. 15 10
243. 35 c. Bauro gongs .. 35 25
244. 45 c. Bamboo band .. 35 30

1973. Royal Wedding. As T **47** of Anguilla.
245. 4 c. blue 10 10
246. 35 c. blue 15 10

94. "Adoration of the Kings" (Jan Brueghel).

1973. Christmas. "Adoration of the Kings" by the artists listed. Multicoloured.
247. 8 c. Type **94** 10 10
248. 22 c. Peter Brueghel .. 30 25
249. 45 c. Botticelli (49 × 35 mm.) 60 50

95. Queen Elizabeth II and Map.

1974. Royal Visit.
250. **95.** 4 c. multicoloured .. 25 10
251. 9 c. multicoloured .. 50 10
252. 15 c. multicoloured .. 60 20
253. 35 c. multicoloured .. 1·10 1·25

1974. Ships and Navigators (4th series). As T **87.** Multicoloured.
254. 4 c. Commissioner landing from "S.S. Titus" .. 20 10
255. 9 c. Radar scanner .. 25 10
256. 15 c. Natives being transported to a "Blackbirder" 40 15
257. 45 c. Lieut. John F. Kennedy's "P.T. 109" .. 2·00 1·25

96. "Postman".

1974. Centenary of U.P.U.

258. 96.	4 c. grn., dp. grn. & blk.	10	10
259. –	9 c. lt. brn., brn. & blk.	10	10
260. –	15 c. mauve, pur. & blk.	15	10
261. –	45 c. bl., dp. bl. & blk..	35	70

DESIGNS (Origami figures)—HORIZ. 9 c. Carrier-pigeon. 45 c. Pegasus. VERT. 15 c. St. Gabriel.

97. "New Constitution" Stamp of 1970.

1974. New Constitution.

262. 97.	4 c. multicoloured ..	10	10
263. –	9 c. red, black & brown	10	10
264. –	15 c. red, blk. & brown	15	10
265. 97.	35 c. multicoloured ..	45	50

DESIGN: 9 c., 15 c. "New Constitution" stamp of 1961 (inscr. "1960").

98. Golden Whistler.

1975. Birds. Multicoloured.

267.	1 c. Type 98	45	55
268.	2 c. Common Kingfisher ..	50	70
269.	3 c. Red-bibbed Fruit Dove	55	75
270.	4 c. Little Button Quail ..	55	75
271.	$2 Duchess Lorikeet ..	11·00	9·50

See also Nos. 305/20.

1975. Ships and Navigators (5th series). As T 87. Multicoloured.

272.	4 c. M.V. " Walande " ..	30	10
273.	9 c. M.V. " Melanesian "..	35	10
274.	15 c. M.V. " Marsina " ..	45	15
275.	45 c. S.S. " Himalaya " ..	1·10	1·50

99. 800 Metres Race.

1975. South Pacific Games. Multicoloured.

276.	4 c. Type 99	10	10
277.	9 c. Long jump	10	10
278.	15 c. Javelin-throwing ..	15	10
279.	45 c. Football	45	45

100. Nativity Scene and Candles.

1975. Christmas. Multicoloured.

281.	15 c. Type 100 ..	20	10
282.	35 c. Shepherds, angels and candles	40	15
283.	45 c. The Magi and candles	50	40

1975. Nos. 267/70, 223/32, 271 and 233a with obliterating bar over " BRITISH ". Mult.

285.	1 c. Type 98	25	45
286.	2 c. Common Kingfisher ..	30	45
287.	3 c. Red-bibbed Fruit Dove	30	45
288.	4 c. Little Button Quail ..	35	45
289.	5 c. Great Trevally ..	35	45
290.	8 c. Little Bonito ..	50	60
291.	9 c. Sapphire Demoiselle..	50	60
292.	12 c. " Costus speciosus "	1·50	1·00
293.	15 c. Orange Anemone Fish	1·50	1·25
294.	20 c. " Spathoglottis plicata "	2·75	1·50
295.	25 c. " Ephemerantha comata "	2·75	1·75
296.	35 c. " Dendrobium cuthbertsonii " ..	3·50	1·75
297.	45 c. " Heliconia salomonica "	3·50	3·00
298.	$1 Blue Finned Triggerfish	3·00	2·50
299.	$2 Duchess Lorikeet ..	8·00	10·00
300.	$5 Great Frigate Bird ..	15·00	18·00

102. Ceremonial Food-bowl.

1975. Artefacts (1st series). Multicoloured.

301.	4 c. Type 102	10	10
302.	15 c. Chieftains' money ..	10	10
303.	35 c. Nguzu-nguzu (canoe protector spirit) (vert.)	25	20
304.	45 c. Nguzu-nguzu canoe prow	30	25

See also Nos. 337/40, 353/6 and 376/9.

103. Golden Whistler.

1976. Multicoloured.

305.	1 c. Type 103	30	50
306.	2 c. Common kingfisher ..	30	60
307.	3 c. Red-bibbed fruit dove	30	50
308.	4 c. Little button quail ..	30	50
309.	5 c. Willie wagtail.. ..	30	60
310.	6 c. Golden cowrie ..	60	50
311.	10 c. Glory-of-the-sea cone	60	60
312.	12 c. Rainbow lory ..	60	80
313.	15 c. Pearly nautilus ..	65	40
314.	20 c. Venus comb murex ..	1·00	45
315.	25 c. Commercial trochus	85	50
316.	35 c. Melon or baler shell	1·00	70
317.	45 c. Orange spider conch	1·50	1·25
318.	$1 Pacific triton	3·25	3·00
319.	$2 Duchess lorikeet ..	6·50	4·75
320.	$5 Great frigate bird ..	6·50	6·00

104. Coastwatchers, 1942.

1976. Bicent of American Revolution. Mult.

321	6 c. Type 104	20	10
322	20 c. "Amagiri" (Japanese destroyer) ramming U.S.S. "PT109" and Lt. J. F. Kennedy ..	60	30
323	35 c. Henderson Airfield	1·00	40
324	45 c. Map of Guadalcanal	1·10	70

105. Alexander Graham Bell.

1976. Centenary of Telephone.

326. 105.	6 c. multicoloured ..	10	10
327. –	20 c. multicoloured ..	15	10
328. –	35 c. brown, orge. & red	30	15
329. –	45 c. multicoloured ..	40	35

DESIGNS: 20 c. Radio telephone via satellite. 35 c. Ericson's magneto telephone. 45 c. Stick telephone and first telephone.

106. B.A.C. " 1-11 ".

1976. 50th Anniv. of 1st Flight to Solomon Is. Multicoloured.

330.	6 c. Type 106	20	10
331.	20 c. Britten-Norman " Islander "	35	10
332.	35 c. " Dakota DC3 " ..	65	15
333.	45 c. De Havilland " DH50A "	75	45

107. The Communion Plate.

1977. Silver Jubilee. Multicoloured.

334.	6 c. Queen's Visit, 1974..	10	10
335.	35 c. Type 107	15	20
336.	45 c. The Communion ..	25	45

108. Carving from New Georgia.

1977. Artefacts (2nd series). Carvings.

337. 108.	6 c. multicoloured ..	10	10
338. –	20 c. multicoloured ..	10	10
339. –	35 c. black, grey and red	20	15
340. –	45 c. multicoloured ..	25	30

DESIGNS: 20 c. Sea adaro (spirit). 35 c. Shark-headed man. 45 c. Man from Ulawa or Malaita.

109. Spraying Roof and Mosquito.

1977. Malaria Eradication. Multicoloured.

341.	6 c. Type 109	10	10
342.	20 c. Taking blood samples	20	10
343.	35 c. Microscope and map	30	15
344.	45 c. Delivering drugs ..	40	40

110. The Shepherds.

1977. Christmas. Multicoloured.

345.	6 c. Type 110	10	10
346.	20 c. Mary and Jesus in stable..	10	10
347.	35 c. The Three Kings ..	20	15
348.	45 c. " The Flight into Egypt "	25	25

111. Feather Money.

1977. New Currency. Multicoloured.

349.	6 c. Type 111	10	10
350.	6 c. New currency coins ..	10	10
351.	45 c. New currency notes	35	25
352.	45 c. Shell money	35	25

112. Figure from Shortland Is.

1977. Artefacts (3rd series).

353. 112.	6 c. multicoloured ..	10	10
354. –	20 c. multicoloured ..	10	10
355. –	35 c. brn., blk. and orge.	20	15
356. –	45 c. multicoloured ..	25	30

DESIGNS: 20 c. Ceremonial shield. 35 c. Santa Cruz ritual figure. 45 c. Decorative combs.

113. Sandford's Sea Eagle. 114. National Flag.

1978. 25th Anniv. of Coronation. Mult.

357. –	45 c. black, red & silver	25	30
358. –	45 c. multicoloured ..	25	30
359. 113.	45 c. black, red & silver	25	30

DESIGNS: No. 357, King's Dragon. No. 358, Queen Elizabeth II.

1978. Independence. Multicoloured.

360.	6 c. Type 114	10	10
361.	15 c. Governor-General's flag	20	10
362.	35 c. The Cenotaph, Honiara	35	30
363.	45 c. National coat of arms	40	50

115. John.

1978. 450th Death Anniv. of Durer. Mult.

364.	6 c. Type 115	10	10
365.	20 c. Peter	10	10
366.	35 c. Paul..	15	15
367.	45 c. Mark	20	30

116. Firelighting.

1978. 50th Anniv. of Scouting in Solomon Islands. Multicoloured.

368.	6 c. Type 116	15	10
369.	20 c. Camping	20	20
370.	35 c. Solomon Islands Scouts	40	40
371.	45 c. Canoeing	50	70

117. " Discovery ".

1979. Bicentenary of Captain Cook's Voyages, 1768–79.

372. 117. 8 c. multicoloured .. 30 10
373. – 18 c. multicoloured .. 40 15
374. – 35 c. black, green & grey 55 25
375. – 45 c. multicoloured .. 60 40

DESIGNS: 18 c. Portrait of Captain Cook by Nathaniel Dance. 35 c. Sextant. 45 c. Flaxman/Wedgwood medallion.

118. Fish Net Float.

1979. Artefacts (4th series).

376. 118. 8 c. multicoloured .. 10 10
377. – 20 c. multicoloured .. 10 10
378. – 35 c. black, grey and red 15 15
379. – 45 c. blk., brn. and grn. 20 30

DESIGNS—VERT. 20 c. Armband of shell money. 45 c. Forehead ornament. HORIZ. 35 c. Ceremonial food bowl.

119. Running.

1979. South Pacific Games, Fiji. Multicoloured.

380. 8 c. Type 119 .. .. 10 10
381. 20 c. Hurdling 10 10
382. 35 c. Football 15 15
383. 45 c. Swimming 25 35

120. 1908 6d. Stamp.

1979. Death Centenary of Sir Rowland Hill.

384. 120. 8 c. red and pink .. 10 10
385. – 20 c. mauve & pale mauve 20 30
386. – 35 c. multicoloured .. 35 45

DESIGNS: 20 c. Great Britain 1856 6d. Stamp. 35 c. 1978 45 c. Independence commemorative.

121. Sea Snake.

1979. Animals. Multicoloured.

388. 1 c. Type 121 .. .. 10 30
389. 3 c. Red-banded tree snake 10 30
390. 4 c. Whip snake 10 30
391. 6 c. Pacific boa 10 20
392. 8 c. Skink 10 10
393. 10 c. Gecko 10 30
394. 12 c. Monitor 20 60
395. 15 c. Anglehead 30 25
396. 20 c. Giant toad 30 30
397. 25 c. Marsh frog 30 70
398. 30 c. Horned frog .. 1·50 60
399. 35 c. Tree frog 30 40
399a. 40 c. Burrowing snake .. 45 1·50
400. 45 c. Guppy's snake .. 30 70
400a. 50 c. Tree gecko 50 60
401. $1 Large skink .. .. 1·50 90
402. $2 Guppy's frog .. .. 1·25 2·00
403. $5 Estuarine crocodile .. 4·00 4·00
403a. $10 Hawksbill turtle .. 6·50 6·75

122. " Madonna and Child " (Morando).

1979. International Year of the Child. " Madonna and Child " paintings by various artists. Multicoloured.

404. 4 c. Type 122 .. .. 10 10
405. 20 c. Luini 20 15
406. 35 c. Bellini 30 15
407. 50 c. Raphael 35 50

123. H.M.S. "Curacoa" (frigate), 1839.

1980. Ships and Crests (1st series). Mult.

409 8 c. Type 123 .. .. 20 10
410 20 c. H.M.S. "Herald" (survey ship), 1854 .. 35 15
411 35 c. H.M.S. "Royalist" (screw corvette), 1889 .. 55 40
412 45 c. H.M.S. "Beagle" (survey schooner), 1878 70 80

See also Nos. 430/3.

124. "Solomon Fisher" (fishery training vessel).

1980. Fishing. Ancillary Craft. Mult.

413 8 c. Type 124 .. .. 15 10
414 20 c. "Solomon Hunter" (fishery training vessel) 20 15
415 45 c. "Ufi Na Tasi" (refrigerated fish transport) 35 40
416 80 c. Research vessel .. 60 1·00

125. "Comliebank" (cargo-ship) and 1935 Tulagi Registered Letter Postmark.

1980. "London 1980" International Stamp Exhibition. Mail-carrying Transport. Mult.

417. 45 c. Type 125 .. .. 25 40
418. 45 c. Douglas "C-47" aeroplane (U.S. Army Postal Service, 1943) 25 40
419. 45 c. B.A.C. "1-11" airliner and 1979 Honiara postmark .. 25 40
420. 45 c. "Corabank" (container ship) and 1979 Auki postmark 25 40

126. Queen Elizabeth the Queen Mother.

1980. 80th Birthday of The Queen Mother.

421. 126. 45 c. multicoloured .. 40 35

127. Angel with Trumpet.

1980. Christmas. Multicoloured.

422. 8 c. Type 127 .. .. 10 10
423. 20 c. Angel with fiddle .. 10 10
424. 45 c. Angel with trumpet (different) 25 25
425. 80 c. Angel with lute .. 40 45

128. " Parthenos sylvia ".

1980. Butterflies (1st series). Multicoloured.

426. 8 c. Type 128 .. .. 10 10
427. 20 c. " Delias schoenbergi " 25 20
428. 45 c. " Jamides cephion " 40 40
429. 80 c. " Ornithoptera victoriae " 1·00 1·00

See also. Nos. 456/9 and 610/13.

1981. Ships and Crests (2nd series). As T 123. Multicoloured.

430 8 c. H.M.S. "Mounts Bay" (frigate), 1959 .. .. 15 10
431 20 c. H.M.S. "Charybdis" (frigate), 1970 .. .. 25 15
432 45 c. H.M.S. "Hydra" (survey ship), 1972 .. 50 35
433 $1 Royal Yacht "Britannia", 1974 .. 1·40 1·00

129. Francisco Antonio Maurelle.

1981. Bicentenary of Maurelle's Visit and Bauche's Chart.

434. 129. 8 c. brown, yellow & blk. 15 10
435. – 10 c. yellow, black & red 20 10
436. – 45 c. multicoloured .. 60 65
437. – $1 multicoloured .. 1·00 1·10

DESIGNS—VERT. $1, Spanish compass cards, 1745. HORIZ. 10 c. Map by Belling of 1742 showing Maurelle's route. 45 c. " La Princesa ".

130. Netball.

1981. Mini South Pacific Games. Multicoloured.

439. 8 c. Type 130 .. .. 10 10
440. 10 c. Tennis 15 15
441. 25 c. Running 25 25
442. 30 c. Football 25 25
443. 45 c. Boxing 40 40

131. Prince Charles as Colonel-in-Chief, Royal Regiment of Wales.

1981. Royal Wedding. Multicoloured.

445. 8 c. Wedding bouquet from Solomon Islands .. 10 10
446. 45 c. Type 131 .. .. 30 40
447. $1 Prince Charles and Lady Diana Spencer .. 60 1·00

132. " Music ".

1981. 25th Anniv. of Duke of Edinburgh Award Scheme. Multicoloured.

448. 8 c. Type 132 .. .. 10 10
449. 25 c. " Handicrafts " .. 10 10
450. 45 c. " Canoeing " .. 20 20
451. $1 Duke of Edinburgh .. 50 70

133. Primitive Church.

1981. Christmas. Churches.

452. 133. 8 c. black, buff and blue 10 10
453. – 10 c. multicoloured .. 10 10
454. – 25 c. black, buff and grn. 15 10
455. – $2 multicoloured .. 1·00 1·25

DESIGNS: 10 c. St. Barnabas Anglican Cathedral, Honiara. 25 c. Early church. $2, Holy Cross Cathedral, Honiara.

1982. Butterflies (2nd series). As T 128. Mult.

456 10 c. "Doleschallia bisaltide" 15 10
457 25 c. "Papilio bridgei" .. 35 25
458 35 c. "Taenaris phorcas" 40 30
459 $1 "Graphium sarpedon" 1·50 1·50

1982. Cyclone Relief Fund. No. 447 surch. **50 CENTS SURCHARGE CYCLONE RELIEF FUND 1982.**

460. $1+50 c. Prince Charles and Lady Diana Spencer 2·00 2·50

135. Pair of Sanford's Sea Eagles constructing Nest.

1982. Sanford's Sea Eagle. Multicoloured.

461. 12 c. Type 135 .. .. 35 40
462. 12 c. Egg and chick .. 35 40
463. 12 c. Hen feeding chicks .. 35 40
464. 12 c. Fledgelings 35 40
465. 12 c. Young bird in flight 35 40
466. 12 c. Pair of birds and village dwellings .. 35 40

136. **Wedding Portrait.**

1982. 21st Birthday of Princess of Wales. Multicoloured.

No.	Description		
467.	12 c. Solomon Islands coat of arms	15	10
468.	40 c. Lady Diana Spencer at Broadlands, May 1981	30	30
469.	50 c. Type **136**	35	35
470.	$1 Formal portrait ..	65	65

137. Flags of Solomon Islands and United Kingdom.

1982. Royal Visit. (Nos. 471/2) and Commonwealth Games, Brisbane. (Nos. 473/4. Multicoloured.

No.	Description		
471.	12 c. Type **137**	15	20
472.	12 c. Queen and Prince Philip	15	20
473.	25 c. Running	30	45
474.	25 c. Boxing	30	45

138. Boy Scouts.

1982. 75th Anniv. of Boy Scout Movement. (Nos. 477, 479, 481, 483) and Centenary of Boys Brigade (others). Multicoloured.

No.	Description		
477.	12 c. Type **138**	20	15
478.	12 c. Boys Brigade cadets	20	15
479.	25 c. Lord Baden-Powell	35	40
480.	25 c. Sir William Smith ..	35	40
481.	35 c. Type **138**	40	50
482.	35 c. As No. 478	40	50
483.	50 c. As. No. 479	60	1·10
484.	50 c. As No. 480	60	1·10

139. Leatherback Turtle.

1983. Turtles. Multicoloured.

No.	Description		
485.	18 c. Type **139**	25	25
486.	35 c. Loggerhead turtle ..	45	45
487.	45 c. Pacific Ridley turtle	60	60
488.	50 c. Green turtle	65	65

140. "Oliva vidum, Conus generalis and Murex tribulus".

1983. Commonwealth Day. Shells. Mult.

No.	Description		
489.	12 c. Type **140**	15	15
490.	35 c. Romu, Kurila, Kakadu and money belt	35	40
491.	45 c. Shells from " Bride-price " necklaces	50	60
492.	50 c. " Trochus niloticus " polished and in natural state	55	65

141. Montgolfier Balloon.

1983. Bicentenary of Manned Flight. Mult.

No.	Description		
493.	30 c. Type **141**	55	40
494.	35 c. R.A.A.F. Lockheed " Hercules "	60	45
495.	40 c. Wright brothers' " Flyer III "	70	55
496.	45 c. Space shuttle " Columbia "..	75	60
497.	50 c. Beechcraft " Baron–Solair "	80	65

142. Weto Dancers.

1983. Christmas. Multicoloured.

No.	Description		
498.	12 c. Type **142**	10	10
499.	15 c. Custom wrestling ..	15	20
500.	18 c. Girl dancers	15	20
501.	20 c. Devil dancers ..	15	20
502.	25 c. Bamboo band ..	25	35
503.	35 c. Gilbertese dancers ..	30	45
504.	40 c. Pan pipers	35	55
505.	45 c. Girl dancers	40	65
506.	50 c. Cross surrounded by flowers	40	70

143. Earth Satellite Station.

1983. World Communications Year. Mult.

No.	Description		
508.	12 c. Type **143**	20	15
509.	18 c. Ham radio operator	25	20
510.	25 c. 1908 2½d. Canoe stamp	35	30
511.	$1 1908 6d. Canoe stamp ..	1·25	1·40

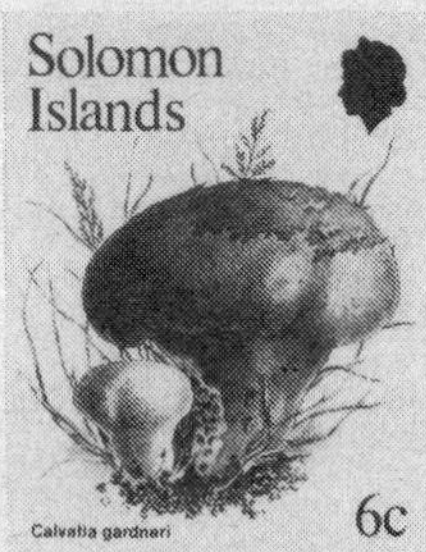

144. " Calvatia gardneri ".

1984. Fungi. Multicoloured.

No.	Description		
513.	6 c. Type **144**	10	10
514.	18 c. " Marasmiellus inoderma "	20	25
515.	35 c. " Pycnoporus sanguineus "	35	45
516.	$2 " Filoboletus manipularis "	2·25	2·50

145. Cross surrounded by Flowers.

1984. Visit of Pope John Paul II.

No.	Description		
517. **145.**	12 c. multicoloured ..	20	10
518.	50 c. multicoloured ..	65	80

146. "Olivebank" (barque), 1892

1984. 250th Anniv of "Lloyd's List" (newspaper). Multicoloured.

No.	Description		
519	12 c. Type **146**	55	15
520	15 c. "Tinhow" (freighter), 1906	60	40
521	18 c. "Oriana" (liner) at Point Cruz, Honiara ..	70	50
522	$1 "Silwyn Range" (container ship), Point Cruz, Honiara	1·75	2·75

147. Village Drums.

1984. 20th Anniv. of Asia–Pacific Broadcasting Union. Multicoloured.

No.	Description		
524.	12 c. Type **147**	15	15
525.	45 c. Radio City, Guadalcanal	60	60
526.	60 c. S.I.B.C. studios, Honiara	75	80
527.	$1 S.I.B.C. Broadcasting House	1·25	1·40

148. Solomon Islands Flag and Torch-bearer.

1984. Olympic Games, Los Angeles. Multicoloured.

No.	Description		
528.	12 c. Type **148**	15	20
529.	25 c. Lawson Tama stadium, Honiara (horiz.) ..	30	35
530.	50 c. Honiara community centre (horiz.)	65	70
531.	95 c. Alick Wickham inventing crawl stroke, Bronte Baths, New South Wales, 1898 (horiz.)	2·25	3·00
532.	$1 Olympic stadium, U.S.A. (horiz.)	1·25	1·40

149. Little Pied Cormorant.

1984. "Ausipex" International Stamp Exhibition, Melbourne. Birds. Multicoloured.

No.	Description		
533.	12 c. Type **149**	20	15
534.	18 c. Spotbill duck ..	30	30
535.	35 c. Rufous night heron ..	50	50
536.	$1 Eastern broad-billed roller	1·25	2·00

150. The Queen Mother with Princess Margaret at Badminton Horse Trials.

1985. Life and Times of Queen Elizabeth the Queen Mother. Multicoloured.

No.	Description		
538.	12 c. With Winston Churchill at Buckingham Palace, VE Day 1945	10	10
539.	25 c. Type **150**	25	30
540.	35 c. At St. Patrick's Day parade	30	35
541.	$1 With Prince Henry at his christening (from photo by Lord Snowdon)	90	95

151. Japanese Memorial Shrine, Mount Austen, Guadalcanal.

1985. "Expo '85" World Fair, Japan. Multicoloured.

No.	Description		
543.	12 c. Type **151**	10	10
544.	25 c. Digital telephone exchange equipment ..	25	30
545.	45 c. Fishing vessel "Soltai No. 7"	40	45
546.	85 c. Coastal village scene	75	80

152. Titiana Village.

1985. Christmas. "Going Home for the Holiday". Multicoloured.

No.	Description		
547.	12 c. Type **152**	10	10
548.	25 c. Sigana, Santa Isabel	25	30
549.	35 c. Artificial Island and Langa Lagoon	30	35

153. Girl Guide Activities.

1985. 75th Anniv. of Girl Guide Movement (12, 45 c.) and International Youth Year (others). Multicoloured.

No.	Description		
550.	12 c. Type **153**	40	10
551.	15 c. Boys playing and child in wheelchair (Stop Polio)	45	30
552.	25 c. Runners and Solomon Island scenes	70	40
553.	35 c. Runners and Australian scenes ("Run Round Australia") ..	85	45
554.	45 c. Guide colour party and badges	95	60

INDEX

Countries can be quickly located by referring to the index at the end of this volume.

156. Building Red Cross Centre, Gizo.

1986. Operation Raleigh (volunteer project). Multicoloured.

558 18 c. Type **156** 60 20
559 30 c. Exploring rainforest 90 45
560 60 c. Observing Halley's Comet .. .. .. 1·50 1·10
561 $1 "Sir Walter Raleigh" (support ship) and "Zebu" (brigantine) .. 2·00 1·60

1986. 60th Birthday of Queen Elizabeth II. As T **110** of Ascension. Multicoloured.

562. 5 c. Princess Elizabeth and Duke of Edinburgh at Clydebank Town Hall, 1947 .. .. .. 10 10
563. 18 c. At St. Paul's Cathedral for Queen Mother's 80th birthday service, 1980 .. .. .. 15 20
564. 22 c. With children, Solomon Islands, 1982 .. 20 25
565. 55 c. At Windsor Castle on 50th birthday, 1976 .. 40 45
566. $2 At Crown Agents Head Office, London, 1983 .. 1·40 1·50

1986. Royal Wedding. As T **112** of Ascension. Multicoloured.

568. 55 c. Prince Andrew and Miss Sarah Ferguson .. 40 45
569. 60 c. Prince Andrew at helm of yacht "Bluenose II" off Nova Scotia, 1985 45 50

158. "Freedom" (winner 1980).

1986. America's Cup Yachting Championship (1987).

570. **158.** 18 c. multicoloured .. 15 20
571. – 30 c. multicoloured .. 50 70
572. – $1 multicoloured .. 75 80

Nos. 570/2 were issued as a sheet of 50, each horizontal strip of 5 being separated by gutter margins. The sheet contains 20 different designs at 18 c., 10 at 30 c. and 20 at $1. Individual stamps depict yachts, charts, the America's Cup or the emblem of the Royal Perth Yacht Club.

1986. Cyclone Relief Fund. No. 541 surch. **+ 50c Cyclone Relief Fund 1986.**

573. $1 + 50 c. Queen Mother with Prince Henry at his christening .. .. 1·10 1·25

160. Dendrophyllia gracilis".

1987. Corals. Multicoloured.

576. 18 c. Type **160** 20 15
577. 45 c. "Dendronephthya sp." 60 50
578. 60 c. "Clavularia sp." .. 80 80
579. $1.50 "Melithaea squamata" .. .. 1·60 1·75

161. "Cassia fistula".

1987. Flowers. Multicoloured.

580. 1 c. Type **161** 10 10
581. 5 c. "Allamanda cathartica" 15 10
582. 10 c. "Catharanthus roseus" 15 10
583. 18 c. "Mimosa pudica" .. 20 10
584. 20 c. "Hibiscus rosa-sinensis" 20 15
585. 22 c. "Clerodendrum thomsonae" 20 15
586. 25 c. "Bauhinia variegata" 20 20
587. 28 c. "Gloriosa rothschildiana" 20 20
588. 30 c. "Heliconia solomonensis" 25 20
589. 40 c. "Episcia" hybrid .. 25 20
590. 45 c. "Bougainvillea" hybrid 30 25
591. 50 c. "Alpinia purpurata" 30 25
592. 55 c. "Plumeria rubra" .. 35 35
593. 60 c. "Acacia farnesiana" 40 40
594. $1 "Ipomea purpurea" .. 65 50
595. $2 "Dianella ensifolia" .. 1·25 1·40
596. $5 "Passiflora foetida" .. 3·00 3·50
597. $10 "Hemigraphis sp." .. 6·00 7·00

162. Mangrove Kingfisher on Branch.

1987. Mangrove Kingfisher. Multicoloured.

598. 60 c. Type **162** .. .. 1·40 1·75
599. 60 c. Kingfisher diving .. 1·40 1·75
600. 60 c. Entering water .. 1·40 1·75
601. 60 c. Kingfisher with prey 1·40 1·75

Nos. 598/601 were printed together, se-tenant, forming a composite design.

163. "Dendrobium conanthum".

1987. Christmas. Orchids (1st series). Mult.

602. 18 c. Type **163** 55 10
603. 30 c. "Spathoglottis plicata" 85 20
604. 55 c. "Dendrobium gouldii" .. .. .. 1·10 50
605. $1.50 "Dendrobium goldfinchii" .. .. 2·40 1·75

See also Nos. 640/3 and 748/51.

164. Telecommunications Control Room and Satellite.

1987. Asia–Pacific Transport and Communications Decade. Multicoloured

606. 18 c. Type **164** 15 15
607. 30 c. De Havilland "Twin Otter" mail plane .. 20 20
608. 60 c. Guadalcanal road improvement project .. 45 50
609. $2 Beechcraft "Queen Air" and Henderson Control Tower .. .. .. 1·25 1·50

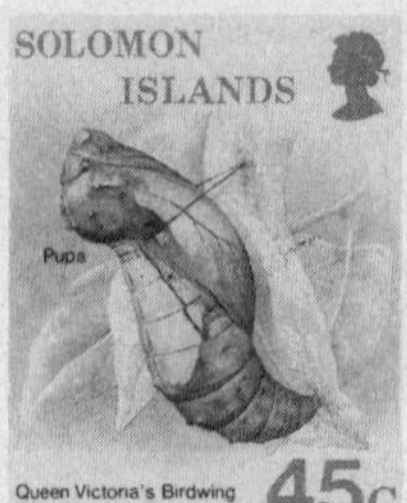

165. Pupa of "Ornithoptera victoriae".

1987. Butterflies (3rd series). "Ornithoptera victoriae" (Queen Victoria's Birdwing). Mult.

610. 45 c. Type **165** .. .. 1·50 1·25
611. 45 c. Larva.. .. .. 1·50 1·25
612. 45 c. Female butterfly .. 1·50 1·25
613. 45 c. Male butterfly .. 1·50 1·25

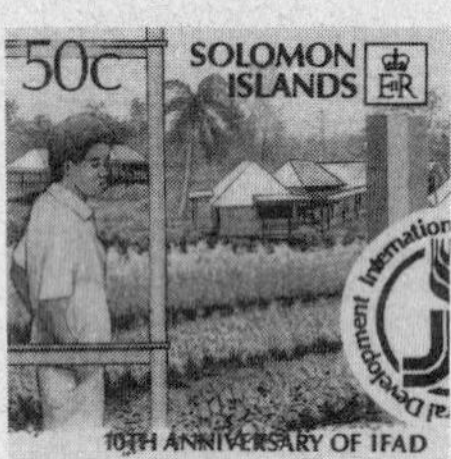

166. Student and National Agriculture Training Institute.

1988. 10th Anniv. of International Fund for Agricultural Development. Multicoloured.

614. 50 c. Type **166** 30 35
615. 50 c. Students working in fields 30 35
616. $1 Transport by lorry .. 55 60
617. $1 Canoe transport .. 55 60

Nos. 614/15 and 616/17 were printed together, se-tenant, each pair forming a composite design.

167 Building Fishing Boat

1988. "Expo '88" World Fair, Brisbane. Mult.

618 22 c. Type **167** 15 15
619 80 c. War canoe 40 45
620 $1.50 Traditional village .. 80 85

168 "Todos los Santos" in Estrella Bay, 1568

1988. 10th Anniv of Independence. Mult.

622 22 c. Type **168** 35 15
623 55 c. Raising the Union Jack, 1893 .. .. 65 40
624 80 c. High Court Building 85 60
625 $1 Dancers at traditional celebration .. .. 1·00 90

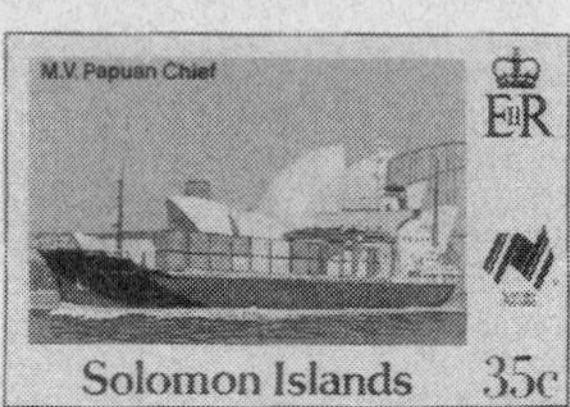

169 "Papuan Chief" (container ship)

1988. "Sydpex '88" National Stamp Exhibition, Sydney and Bicentenary of Australian Settlement. Multicoloured.

626 35 c. Type **169** 30 25
627 60 c. "Nimos" (container ship) 45 35
628 70 c. "Malaita" (liner) .. 55 45
629 $1.30 "Makambo" (inter-island freighter) .. 90 75

170 Archery

1988. Olympic Games, Seoul. Multicoloured.

631 22 c. Type **170** 30 15
632 55 c. Weightlifting .. 50 40
633 70 c. Athletics 60 55
634 80 c. Boxing 70 60

1988. 300th Anniv of Lloyd's of London. As T **123** of Ascension.

636 22 c. black and brown .. 30 15
637 50 c. multicoloured .. 50 30
638 65 c. multicoloured .. 60 55
639 $2 multicoloured .. 2·00 1·75

DESIGNS—VERT: 22 c. King George V and Queen Mary laying foundation stone of Leadenhall Street Building, 1925; $2 "Empress of China" (liner), 1911. HORIZ: 50 c. "Forthbank" (container ship); 65 c. Soltel satellite communications station.

171 "Bulbophyllum dennisii"

1989. Orchids (2nd series). Multicoloured.

640 22 c. Type **171** 35 15
641 35 c. "Calanthe langei" .. 45 30
642 55 c. "Bulbophyllum blumei" 65 45
643 $2 "Grammatophyllum speciosum" .. .. 1·60 1·75

172 Red Cross Workers with Handicapped Children

1989. 125th Anniv of International Red Cross. Multicoloured.

644 35 c. Type **172** 30 35
645 35 c. Handicapped Children Centre minibus .. 30 35
646 $1.50 Blood donor .. 1·10 1·25
647 $1.50 Balance test .. 1·10 1·25

Nos. 644/5 and 646/7 were each printed together, se-tenant, each pair forming a composite design.

173 "Phyllidia varicosa"

1989. Nudibranchs (Sea Slugs). Multicoloured.

648 22 c. Type **173** 25 10
649 70 c. "Chromodoris bullocki" 70 60
650 80 c. "Chromodoris leopardus" 75 70
651 $1.50 "Phidiana indica" .. 1·50 1·60

1989. 20th Anniv of First Manned Landing on Moon. As T **126** of Ascension. Multicoloured.

652 22 c. "Apollo 16" descending by parachute .. 20 10
653 35 c. Launch of "Apollo 16" (30 × 30 mm) .. 35 30
654 70 c. "Apollo 16" emblem (30 × 30 mm) 70 60
655 80 c. Ultra-violet colour photograph of Earth .. 75 70

174 Five Stones Catch

1989. "World Stamp Expo '89", International Stamp Exhibition, Washington. Children's Games. Multicoloured.

657 5 c. Type **174** 10 10
658 67 c. Blowing soap bubbles (horiz) 60 50
659 73 c. Coconut shell game (horiz) 60 50
660 $1 Seed wind sound .. 95 85

175 Fishermen and Butterfly

1989. Christmas. Multicoloured.

662 18 c. Type **175** 20 10
663 25 c. The Nativity .. 25 20
664 45 c. Hospital ward at Christmas 45 30
665 $1.50 Village tug-of-war .. 1·40 1·40

176 Man wearing Headband, Necklace and Sash

1990. Personal Ornaments. Multicoloured.

666 5 c. Type **176** 10 15
667 12 c. Pendant 15 15
668 18 c. Man wearing medallion, nose ring and earrings 15 15
669 $2 Forehead ornament .. 1·60 2·00

177 Spindle Cowrie

1990. Cowrie Shells. Multicolored.

670 4 c. Type **177** 15 10
671 20 c. Map cowrie 20 20
672 35 c. Sieve cowrie .. 35 25
673 50 c. Egg cowrie 50 50
674 $1 Prince cowrie .. .. 90 1·10

1990. 90th Birthday of Queen Elizabeth the Queen Mother. As T **134** of Ascension.

675 25 c. multicoloured .. 25 25
676 $5 black and red .. .. 3·00 3·00

DESIGNS—21 × 36 mm. 25 c. Queen Mother, 1987. 29 × 37 mm. $5 King George VI and Queen Elizabeth inspecting bomb damage to Buckingham Palace, 1940.

178 Postman with Mail Van

1990. 150th Anniv of the Penny Black. Mult.

677 35 c. Type **178** 30 20
678 45 c. General Post Office .. 40 35
679 50 c. 1907 ½d. Stamp .. 40 40
680 55 c. Child collecting stamps 45 50
681 60 c. Penny Black and Solomon Islands 1913 1d. stamp 45 55

179 Purple Swamphen

1990. "Birdpex '90" Stamp Exhibition, Christchurch, New Zealand. Multicoloured.

682 10 c. Type **179** 15 10
683 25 c. Mackinlay's cuckoo dove ("Rufous brown pheasant dove") .. 20 15
684 30 c. Superb fruit dove .. 25 20
685 45 c. Cardinal honeyeater 35 30
686 $2 Finsch's pygmy parrot 1·25 1·50

180 "Cylas formicarius" (weevil)

1991. Crop Pests. Multicoloured.

687 7 c. Type **180** 15 10
688 25 c. "Dacus cucurbitae" (fruit-fly) 25 15
689 40 c. "Papuana uninodis" (beetle) 35 25
690 90 c. "Pantorhytes biplagiastus" (weevil) 70 70
691 $1.50 "Scapanes australis" (beetle) .. .. 1·10 1·25

1991. 65th Birthday of Queen Elizabeth II and 70th Birthday of Prince Philip. As T **139** of Ascension. Multicoloured.

692 90 c. Prince Philip in evening dress 70 80
693 $2 Queen Elizabeth II .. 1·40 1·60

181 Child drinking from Coconut

1991. Health Campaign. Multicoloured.

694 5 c. Type **181** 10 10
695 75 c. Mother feeding child 45 55
696 80 c. Breast feeding .. 50 60
697 90 c. Local produce .. 60 70

182 Volley Ball

1991. 9th South Pacific Games. Multicoloured.

698 25 c. Type **182** 25 10
699 40 c. Judo 35 30
700 65 c. Squash 60 65
701 90 c. Bowling 75 90

183 Preparing Food for Christmas

1991. Christmas. Multicoloured.

703 10 c. Type **183** 15 10
704 25 c. Christmas Day church service 20 15
705 65 c. Christmas Day feast 50 40
706 $2 Cricket match .. .. 1·25 1·50

184 Yellowfin Tuna

1991. "Phila Nippon '91" International Stamp Exn, Tokyo. Tuna Fishing. Mult.

708 5 c. Type **184** 10 10
709 30 c. Pole and line tuna fishing boat 20 20
710 80 c. Pole and line fishing 60 70
711 $2 Processing "arabushi" (smoked tuna) .. .. 1·10 1·25

1992. 40th Anniv of Queen Elizabeth II's Accession. As T **143** of Ascension. Mult.

713 5 c. Aerial view of Honiara 10 10
714 20 c. Sunset across lagoon 15 15
715 40 c. Honiara harbour .. 30 30
716 60 c. Three portraits of Queen Elizabeth .. 50 50
717 $5 Queen Elizabeth II .. 3·00 3·25

185 Mendana's Fleet in Thousand Ships Bay, 1568

1992. "Granada '92" International Stamp Exhibition, Spain. Mendana's Discovery of Solomon Islands. Multicoloured.

718 10 c. Type **185** 15 10
719 65 c. Map of voyage .. 45 45
720 80 c. Alvaro Mendana de Niera 70 70
721 $1 Settlement at Graciosa Bay 90 90
722 $5 Mendana's fleet at sea 3·00 3·25

186 Sgt-Major Jacob Vouza

1992. Birth Centenary of Sgt-major Jacob Vouza (war hero). Multicoloured.

723 25 c. Type **186** 15 10
724 70 c. Vouza in U.S. Marine corps battle dress .. 50 50
725 90 c. Vouza in U.S. Marine corps uniform 60 60
726 $2 Statue of Vouza .. 1·25 1·40

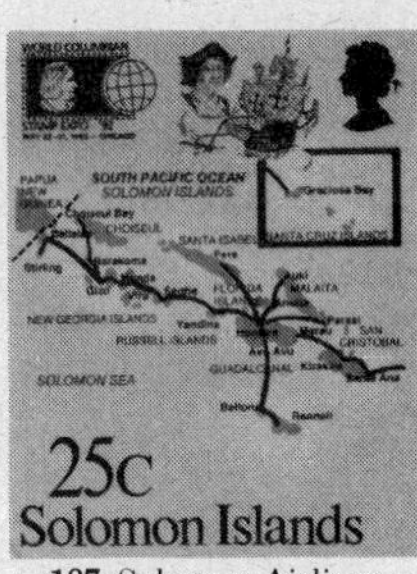

187 Solomon Airlines Domestic Routes

1992. 500th Anniv of Discovery of America by Columbus and "World Columbian Stamp Expo '92" Exhibition, Chicago. Mult.

728 25 c. Type **187** 15 10
729 80 c. Solomon Airlines Boeing 737-400 "Guadalcanal" .. 55 55
730 $1.50 Solomon Airlines international routes .. 95 95
731 $5 Columbus and "Santa Maria" .. .. .. 3·00 3·25

188 Japanese Troops landing at Esperance

1992. 50th Anniv of Battle of Guadalcanal. Multicoloured.

733 30 c. Type **188** 20 20
734 30 c. American troops in landing-craft 20 20
735 30 c. Australian cruiser .. 20 20
736 30 c. U.S. Navy post office 20 20
737 30 c. R.N.Z.A.F Catalina flying boat 20 20
738 80 c. U.S. Marine Corps Wildcat fighters .. 55 55
739 80 c. Henderson Field .. 55 55
740 80 c. U.S.S. "Quincy" (heavy cruiser) .. 55 55
741 80 c. H.M.A.S. "Canberra" (heavy cruiser) .. 55 55
742 80 c. U.S. Marine Corps landing craft 55 55
743 80 c. "Ryujo" (Japanese aircraft carrier) .. 55 55
744 80 c. Japanese Zeke fighters 55 55
745 80 c. Japanese bombers .. 55 55
746 80 c. Japanese destroyer .. 55 55
747 80 c. "Chockai" (Japanese heavy cruiser) 55 55

189 "Dendrobium" hybrid

1992. Orchids (3rd series). Multicoloured.

748 15 c. Type **189** 15 10
749 70 c. "Vanda Amy Laycock" 55 55
750 95 c. "Dendrobium mirbelianum" 65 65
751 $2.50 "Dendrobium macrophyllum" .. 1·75 1·90

190 Stalk-eyed Ghost Crab

1993. Crabs. Multicoloured.

752 5 c. Type **190** 10 10
753 10 c. Red-spotted crab .. 10 10
754 25 c. Flat crab 10 10
755 30 c. Land hermit crab .. 10 10
756 40 c. Grapsid crab .. 15 20
757 45 c. Red and white painted crab 20 25
758 55 c. Swift-footed crab .. 25 30
759 60 c. Spanner crab .. 25 30
760 70 c. Red Hermit crab .. 30 35
761 80 c. Red-eyed crab .. 35 40
762 90 c. Rathbun red crab .. 35 40
763 $1 Coconut crab 40 45
764 $1.10 Red-spotted white crab 50 55
765 $4 Ghost crab .. .. 1·75 1·90
766 $10 Mangrove fiddler crab 4·25 4·50

191 U.S. War Memorial, Skyline Ridge

1993. 50th Anniv of Second World War. Multicoloured.

767 30 c. Type **191** 10 10
768 80 c. National flags at half mast 35 40
769 95 c. Major-general Alexander Vandegrift and map 40 45
770 $4 Aerial dogfight, U.S. carrier and Solomon Islands scouts .. .. 1·75 1·90

1993. 14th World Orchid Conference, Glasgow. As Nos 748 and 751, but different face values, additionally inscr "World Orchid Conference". Multicoloured.

771 20 c. Type **189** 10 10
772 $3 "Dendrobium macrophyllum" .. .. 1·10 1·25

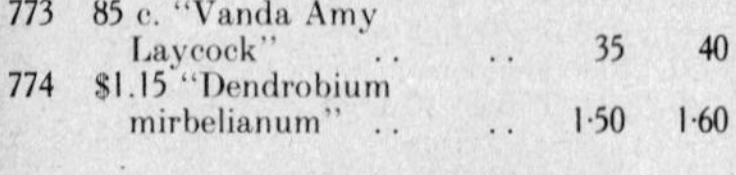

1993. "Indopex '93" International Stamp Exhibition, Surabaya. As Nos. 749/50, but different face values, additionally inscr "Indopex'93 Exhibition". Multicoloured.

773 85 c. "Vanda Amy Laycock" 35 40
774 $1.15 "Dendrobium mirbelianum" .. .. 1·50 1·60

192 U.S.S. "PT 109" being rammed by "Amagiri" (Japanese destoyer)

1993. 50th Anniv of Sinking of U.S.S. "PT 109" (motor torpedo-boat commanded by John F. Kennedy). Multicoloured.

775 30 c. Type **192** 10 10
776 50 c. Kennedy thanking islander 20 25
777 95 c. Message in coconut shell and islanders in canoe 35 40
778 $1.10 Pres. Kennedy and medal 40 45

193 Nicobar Pigeon

1993. Endangered Species. Nicobar Pigeon. Multicoloured.

781 30 c. Type **193** 10 10
782 50 c. Pigeon on ground .. 20 25
783 65 c. Pair of pigeons perched on branches .. 30 35
784 70 c. Pigeon on branch looking left 30 35
785 $1.10 Pigeon on branch looking right 40 45
786 $3 Pigeons in flight .. 1·25 1·40

194 Pair of Dachshunds

1994. "Hong Kong '94" Int Stamp Exn. Chinese New Year ("Year of the Dog"). Mult.

787 30 c. Type **194** 10 10
788 80 c. German shepherd dog 35 40
789 95 c. Pair of dobermann pinschers 35 40
790 $1.10 Australian cattle dog 40 45

195 Striped Dolphin

1994. Dolphins. Multicoloured.

792 75 c. Type **195** 30 35
793 85 c. Risso's dolphin .. 35 40
794 $1.15 Common dolphin .. 50 55
795 $2.50 Spinner dolphin .. 95 1·00
796 $3 Bottlenose dolphin .. 1·25 1·40

POSTAGE DUE STAMPS

D 1.

1940.

D 1. D **1.** 1d. green .. .. 3·75 6·50
D 2. 2d. red .. .. 4·25 6·50
D 3. 3d. brown .. .. 4·50 10·00
D 4. 4d. blue .. .. 7·00 11·00
D 5. 5d. olive .. .. 8·00 14·00
D 6. 6d. purple .. .. 8·50 15·00
D 7. 1s. violet .. .. 12·00 26·00
D 8. 1s. 6d. green .. .. 22·00 45·00

SOMALILAND PROTECTORATE

A British protectorate in north-east Africa on the Gulf of Aden. Amalgamated with the Somalia Republic on 1st July, 1960, whose stamps it now uses (see volume 2).

1903. 16 annas = 1 rupee.
1951. 100 cents = 1 shilling.

1903. Stamps of India (Queen Victoria) optd. **BRITISH SOMALILAND.**

1. **23.** ½ a. green .. .. 1·75 2·25
2. – 1 a. red .. .. .. 1·75 2·00
3. – 2 a. lilac .. .. .. 1·50 50
4. – 2½ a. blue .. .. .. 2·00 1·75
5. – 3 a. orange .. .. 1·75 1·75
6. – 4 a. green (No. 96) .. 2·00 2·75
19. – 6 a. brown (No. 80) .. 2·50 4·25
8. – 8 a. mauve .. .. 1·75 5·00
9. – 12 a. purple on red .. 2·00 7·00
21. **37.** 1 r. green and red .. 2·00 10·00
11. **38.** 2 r. red and orange .. 23·00 38·00
12. 3 r. brown and green .. 17·00 40·00
13. 5 r. blue and violet .. 20·00 48·00

1903. Stamps of India of 1902 (King Edward VII) with same opt.

25. ½ a. green (No. 122) .. 95 55
26. 1 a. red (No. 123) 75 30
27. 2 a. lilac .. .. .. 1·00 2·50
28. 3 a. orange .. .. .. 1·00 2·50
29. 4 a. olive .. .. .. 1·00 4·00
30. 8 a. mauve .. .. .. 1·25 2·25

2.

1904.

32 **2** ½ a. green .. .. .. 30 2·50
33 1 a. black and red .. 2·50 1·75
59 1 a. red .. .. .. 2·50 75
34 2 a. purple .. .. 1·50 1·00
35 2½ a. blue .. .. 1·75 3·00
36 3 a. brown and green .. 1·00 2·25
37 4 a. green and black .. 1·50 2·75
38 6 a. green and violet .. 3·00 9·00
39 8 a. black and blue .. 2·75 5·50
53 12 a. black and orange .. 3·00 10·00
41 1 r. green .. .. .. 12·00 30·00
42 2 r. purple .. .. 28·00 55·00
43 3 r. green and black .. 28·00 65·00
44 5 r. black and red .. 30·00 65·00

The rupee values are larger (26 × 31 mm.)

1912. As 1904, but portrait of King George V.

60 ½ a green .. .. .. 40 4·50
61 1 a. red 90 50
75 2 a. purple .. .. .. 2·00 1·00
76 2½ a blue .. .. .. 1·00 3·50
64 3 a. brown and green .. 90 3·75
78 4 a. green and black .. 2·50 4·25
66 6 a. green and violet .. 1·00 3·25
80 8 a. black and blue .. 1·75 5·00
68 12 a. black and orange .. 1·50 14·00
69 1 r. green .. .. .. 6·00 9·00
83 2 r. purple .. .. .. 16·00 35·00
84 3 r. green and black .. 27·00 90·00
72 5 r. black and red .. .. 48·00 £120

1935. Silver Jubilee. As T **13** of Antigua.

86. 1 a. blue and red .. .. 1·75 1·50
87. 2 a. blue and grey .. .. 1·75 1·50
88. 3 a. brown and blue .. 2·00 5·50
89. 1 r. grey and purple .. 5·00 7·50

1937. Coronation. As T **2** of Aden.

90. 1 a. red 15 10
91. 2 a. grey 55 70
92. 3 a. blue 70 55

6. Berbera Blackhead Sheep. **9.**

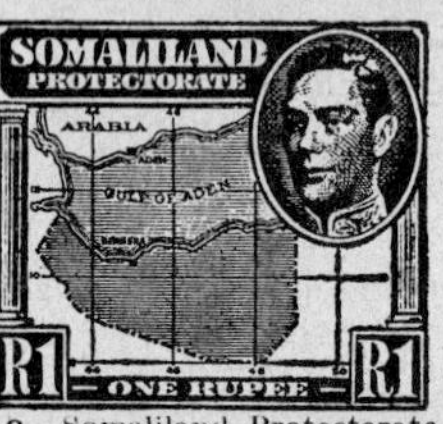

8. Somaliland Protectorate.

DESIGN—As T **6**; 4 a. to 12 a. Greater Kudu Antelope.

1938. Portrait faces left.

93. **6.** ½ a. green .. .. 15 1·90
94. 1 a. red 15 20
95. 2 a. purple 20 30
96. 3 a. blue .. .. 5·00 5·00
97. – 4 a. brown .. .. 1·75 2·50
98. – 6 a. violet .. .. 3·25 7·00
99. – 8 a. grey .. .. .. 85 6·50
100. – 12 a. orange .. .. 1·00 7·50
101. **8.** 1 r. green .. .. 8·50 24·00
102. 2 r. purple .. .. 8·50 24·00
103. 3 r. blue .. .. .. 13·00 17·00
104. 5 r. black .. .. 13·00 17·00

1942. As Nos. 93/104 but with full-face portraits as in T **9**.

105. **9.** ½ a. green 10 10
106. 1 a. red 10 10
107. 2 a. purple 40 10
108. 3 a. blue 60 10
109. – 4 a. brown 75 10
110. – 6 a. violet .. .. 1·25 10
111. – 8 a. grey 70 10
112. – 12 a. orange .. .. 1·75 10
113. – 1 r. green 60 30
114. – 2 r. purple .. .. 1·00 2·50
115. – 3 r. blue .. .. .. 1·10 6·50
116. – 5 r. black .. .. 3·25 4·00

1946. Victory. As T **9** of Aden.

117. 1 a. red 10 10
118. 3 a. blue 10 10

1949. Silver Wedding. As T **10/11** of Aden.

119. 1 a. red 10 10
120. 5 r. black .. .. .. 3·50 3·25

1949. U.P.U. As T **20/23** of Antigua.

121. 1 a. on 10 c. red .. 30 15
122. 3 a. on 30 c. blue .. 40 40
123. 6 a. on 50 c. purple .. 40 40
124. 12 a. on 1 s. orange .. 55 40

1951. 1942. issue surch. with figures and **Cents** or **Shillings.**

125. 5 c. on ½ a. green 10 10
126. 10 c. on 2 a. purple .. 10 10
127. 15 c. on 3 a. blue 30 10
128. 20 c. on 4 a. brown .. 50 10
129. 30 c. on 6 a. violet .. 70 10
130. 50 c. on 8 a. grey 55 10
131. 70 c. on 2 a. orange .. 1·00 2·00
132. 1 s. on 1 r. green 50 20
133. 2 s. on 2 r. purple .. .. 1·25 4·00
134. 2 s. on 3 r. blue .. .. 1·50 2·50
135. 5 s. on 5 r. black .. .. 2·50 4·00

1953. Coronation. As T **13** of Aden.

136. 15 c. black and green .. 30 20

12. Camel and Gurgi. **13.** Askari.

1953.

137. **12.** 5 c. black 15 30
138. **13.** 10 c. orange .. .. 1·75 30
139. **12.** 15 c. green 50 30
140. 20 c. red 50 30
141. **13.** 30 c. brown .. .. 2·00 30
142. – 35 c. blue .. .. 1·50 90
143. – 50 c. brown and red .. 1·75 35
144. – 1 s. blue 50 20
145. – 1 s. 30 blue and black 5·50 3·00
146. – 2 s. brown and violet 12·00 2·25
147. – 5 s. brown and green .. 12·00 5·50
148. – 10 s. brown and violet 7·50 13·00

DESIGNS—HORIZ. 35 c., 2 s. Somali Stock Dove. 50 c., 5 s. Martial Eagle. 1 s. Berbera Blackhead Sheep. 1 s. 30, Sheikh Isaaq's Tomb, Mait. 10 s. Taleh Fort.

1957. Opening of Legislative Council. Optd. **OPENING OF THE LEGISLATIVE COUNCIL 1957.**

149. **12.** 20 c. red 10 15
150. 1 s. blue (No. 144) .. 30 15

1960. Legislative Council's Unofficial Majority Optd. **LEGISLATIVE COUNCIL UNOFFICIAL MAJORITY. 1960.**

151. **12.** 20 c. red 10 15
152. - 1 s. 30, bl. & blk. (No. 145) 20 15

OFFICIAL STAMPS

1903. Official stamps of India (Queen Victoria) (optd **On H.M.S.**) further optd **BRITISH SOMALILAND**.

O 1. **23.** ½ a. turquoise .. .. 3·50 48·00
O 2. – 1 a. red .. .. .. 10·00 7·50
O 3. – 2 a. lilac .. .. 8·00 48·00
O 4. – 8 a. mauve .. .. 10·00 £375
O 5. **37.** 1 r. green and red .. 10·00 £550

1904. Stamps of 1904 optd. **O.H.M.S.**

O 10.	2.	½ a. green	3·25	48·00
O 11.		1 a. black and red	3·25	7·00
O 12.		2 a. purple	£130	48·00
O 13.		8 a. black and blue	60·00	£130
O 15.	–	1 r. green (No. 41)	£160	£475

SORUTH

A state of India. In 1948 the Saurashtra Union was formed which included Jasdan, Morvi, Nawanagar and Wadhwan as well as Soruth. Now uses Indian stamps.

12 pies = 1 anna; 16 annas = 1 rupee.

JUNAGADH

1.

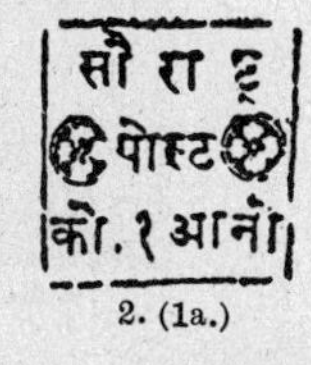

2. (1a.)

1864 (?) On paper of various colours. Imperf.

1.	1.	1 a. black	£650	42·00

1867. (Nos. 11 and 13 are on paper of various colours.) Imperf.

11	2	1 a. black	55·00	8·00
13		1 a. red	13·00	16·00
14		4 a. black	£100	£150

6.

7.

1877. Imperf. or perf.

40	7.	3 p. green	35	35
24	6.	1 a. green	15	15
41		1 a. red	60	60
26	7.	4 a. red	1·00	60

1913. Surch. in words in English and in native characters.

34.	6.	3 p. on 1 a. green	15	20
39.	7.	1 a. on 4 a. red	90	2·50

ત્રણ પાઇ

(14.)

13. Nawab Mahabat Khan III.

1923. Surch. as T **14.**

43.	13.	3 p. on 1 a. red	2·75	7·00

1924. Imperf. or perf.

44	13	3 p. mauve	35	40
46		1 a. red	3·25	4·25

The 1 a. is smaller.

15. Junagadh City.

17. Nawab Mahabat Khan III.

DESIGNS—HORIZ. ½ a., 4 a. Gir lion. 2 a., 8 a. Kathi horse.

1929. (a) Inscr. "POSTAGE".

49.	15.	3 p. black and green	50	10
50.	–	½ a. black and blue	4·50	10
51.	17.	1 a. black and red	2·75	85
52.	–	2 a. black and orange	6·50	1·75
53.	15.	3 a. black and red	2·00	3·25
54.	–	4 a. black and purple	9·00	12·00
55.	–	8 a. black and green	10·00	14·00
56.	17.	1 r. black and blue	2·75	13·00

1936. (b) Inscr. "POSTAGE AND REVENUE".

57.	17.	1 a. black and red	3·25	90

OFFICIAL STAMPS

1929. Nos. 49/56 optd. **SARKARI.**

O 1.	15.	3 p. black and green	55	10
O 2.	–	½ a. black and blue	1·25	10
O 3.	17.	1 a. black and red	1·25	20
O 4.	–	2 a. black and orange	2·00	35
O 5.	15.	3 a. black and red	60	20
O 6.	–	4 a. black and purple	1·50	40
O 7.	–	8 a. black and green	1·75	90
O 8.	17.	1 r. black and blue	2·25	9·00

1938. No. 57 optd **SARKARI.**

O13a	17	1 a. black and red	5·00	1·00

UNITED STATE OF SAURASHTRA

1949. Surch. **POSTAGE & REVENUE ONE ANNA.**

61.	15.	1 a. on 3 p. black & green	35·00	35·00
58.	–	1 a. on ½ a. black and blue (No. 50)	6·00	3·00

Surch. **Postage and Revenue ONE ANNA.**

59.		1 a. on 2 a. grey and yellow (No. 52)	6·00	14·00

21.

1949.

60	21	1 s. purple	6·00	6·50

OFFICIAL STAMPS

1948. Official stamps of 1929 surch **ONE ANNA.**

O 14	1 a. on 2 a. grey & yellow	£2750	18·00
O 15	1 a. on 3 a. black & red	£1700	35·00
O 16	1 a. on 4 a. black & purple	£180	28·00
O 17	1 a. on 8 a. black & green	£190	24·00
O 19	1 a. on 1 r. black & blue	£190	30·00

1949. No. 59 optd. **SARKARI.**

O 22.	1 a. on 2 a. grey & yellow	40·00	14·00

SOUTH AFRICA

The Union of S. Africa consists of the provinces of the Cape of Good Hope, Natal, the Orange Free State and the Transvaal. Became an independent republic on 31st May, 1961.

1910. 12 pence = 1 shilling;
20 shillings = 1 pound.
1961. 100 cents = 1 rand.

1. 2.

1910.

2.	1.	2½d. blue	2·00	1·25

1913.

3.	2.	½d. green	1·00	20
4.		1d. red	70	10
5.		1½d. brown	30	10
6.		2d. purple	1·25	10
7.		2½d. blue	2·50	1·25
8.		3d. black and red	6·50	30
9.		3d. blue	4·50	1·75
10a.		4d. orange and green	7·50	45
11.		6d. black and violet	5·50	30
12.		1s. orange	15·00	70
13.		1s. 3d. violet	12·00	7·00
14.		2s. 6d. purple and green	55·00	1·00
15.		5s. purple and blue	£130	6·50
16.		10s. blue and olive	£225	5·50
17.		£1 green and red	£650	£350

5.

1925. Air.

26.	5.	1d. red	4·50	8·00
27.		3d. blue	8·00	9·50
28.		6d. mauve	10·00	14·00
29.		9d. green	18·00	48·00

NOTE—"Bilingual" in heading indicates that the stamps are inscribed alternately in English and Afrikaans throughout the sheet.

Our prices for such issues are for mint bilingual pairs and used single stamps of either inscription.

6. Springbok.

7. Van Riebeeck's Ship.

8. Orange Tree.

11. Union Buildings, Pretoria.

12. Groot Schuur.

10. "Hope".

1926. Bilingual Pairs. No. 33 is imperf.

114	6	½d. black and green	50	10
135	7	1d. black and red	65	10
34	11	2d. grey and purple	11·00	60
44		2d. grey and lilac	15·00	20
58		2d. blue and violet	60·00	1·00
35	12	3d. black and red	20·00	60
45b		3d. blue	8·00	20
33	10	4d. blue	1·00	60
118	–	4d. brown	1·00	10
119	8	6d. green and orange	1·50	10
120	–	1s. brown and blue	10·00	10
121	–	2s. 6d. green and brown	10·00	30
49a	–	2s. 6d. blue and brown	16·00	20
64a	–	5s. black and green	35·00	50
39	–	10s. blue and brown	£150	9·00

DESIGNS—As Type **11**: 4d. (No. 118) A native kraal. 1s. Gnus. 2s. 6d. Ox-wagon crossing river. 5s. Ox-wagon outspanned. 10s. Cape Town and Table Bay.

On No. 33 the English and Afrikaans inscriptions are on separate sheets, and our price is for single stamps of either language.

For ½d., 1d., 2d. 3d. and 10s. in similar designs see Nos. 105/6, 107a, 116/7 and 64ba respectively.

17. D.H. "Moth".

1929. Air.

40.	17.	4d. green	5·00	2·50
41.		1s. orange	11·00	11·00

18. Church of the Vow.

1933. Voortrekker Memorial Fund. Inscr. as in T **18.** Bilingual pairs.

50.	18.	½d.+½d. green	3·75	50
51.	–	1d.+½d. black and pink	3·25	25
52.	–	2d.+1d. green & purple	4·00	55
53.	–	3d.+1½d. green and blue	6·50	70

DESIGNS: 1d. The "Great Trek". 2d Voortrekker man. 3d. Voortrekker woman.

24.

1935. Silver Jubilee. Bilingual pairs.

65	24	½d. black and green	2·50	10
66		1d. black and red	2·75	10
67		3d. blue	19·00	2·25
68		6d. green and orange	35·00	3·25

The positions of Afrikkaans and English inscriptions are transposed on alternate stamps.

22. Gold Mine.

25. King George VI.

1936. Bilingual pair.

57.	22.	1½d. green and gold	1·50	10

1937. Coronation. Bilingual pairs.

71.	25.	½d. grey and green	25	10
72.		1d. grey and red	35	10
73.		1½d. orange and green	50	10
74.		3d. blue	3·75	10
75.		1s. brown and blue	6·00	15

27. Wagon crossing Drakensberg.

28. Signing of Dingaan-Retief Treaty

1938. Voortrekker Centenary Fund. Dated "1838 1938". Bilingual pairs.

76.	–	½d.+½d. blue and green	10·00	30
77.	27.	1d.+1d. blue and red	11·00	40
78.	28.	1½d.+1½d. brown & grn.	15·00	80
79.	–	3d.+3d. blue	17·00	1·00

DESIGNS—As T **27**: ½d. Voortrekker ploughing. As T **28**: Voortrekker Monument.

31. Voortrekker Family.

1938. Voortrekker Commem. Bilingual pairs.

80.	–	1 d. blue and red	4·00	25
81.	31.	1½d. blue and brown	6·00	25

DESIGN: 1d. Wagon wheel.

22a. Groot Schuur.

23. Groot Constantia.

1939. Bilingual pairs.

117a	22a	3d. blue	2·00	10
64ba	23	10s. blue and brown	40·00	30

32. Old Vicarage, Paarl, now a Museum.

33. Symbol of the Reformation.

34. Huguenot Dwelling, Drakenstein Mountain Valley.

1939. 250th Anniv. of Landing of Huguenots in S. Africa. Bilingual pairs.

82.	32.	½d.+½d. brown and green	4·75	30
83.	33.	1d.+1d. green and red..	11·00	30
84.	34.	1½d.+1½d. green and pur.	22·00	90

34a. Gold Mine.

1941. Bilingual pair.

87.	34a.	1½d. green and buff	40	10

35. Infantry.

38. Sailor, Destroyer and Lifebelts.

39. Women's Auxiliary Services.

1941. War Effort. Bilingual pairs except the 2d. and 1s. which are inscr. in both languages on each stamp.

88.	35.	½d. green	75	10
89.	–	1d. red	1·50	10
90.	–	1½d. green	1·25	10
95.	38.	2d. violet	55	20
91.	39.	3d. blue	16·00	50
92.	–	4d. brown	13·00	15
93.	–	6d. orange	8·50	15
96.	–	1s. brown	2·50	50
94a.	–	1s. 3d. brown	5·50	20

DESIGNS—As Type **35**: 1d. Nurse and ambulance. 1½d. Airman. 1s. 3d. Signaller. As Type **38**: 4d. Artillery. 6d. Welding. As Type **39**: 1s. Tank corps.

43. Infantry.

DESIGNS—As Type **43**. VERT. 1d. Nurse. 1½d. Airman. 2d. Sailor. 6d. Welder. HORIZ. 3d. Women's Auxiliary Services. 6d. Heavy gun. 1s. Tanks.

1942. War Effort. Bilingual except 4d. and 1s., which are inscr. in both languages on each stamp.

97.	43.	½d. green	70	10
98.	–	1d. red	1·00	10
99.	–	1½d. brown	65	10
100.	–	2d. violet	90	10
101.	–	3d. blue	7·00	10
103.	–	4d. green	14·00	10
102.	–	6d. orange	2·00	10
104.	–	1s. brown	12·00	10

Our prices for Nos. 97, 98, 101 and 103 are for units of three. The other stamps are in units of two.

1943. As 1926, but in single colours and with plain background to central oval. Bilingual pairs.

105.	6.	½d. green	75	20
106.	7.	1d. red	1·50	15

54. Union Buildings, Pretoria.

1945. Type 11 redrawn. Bilingual pairs.

107a	54	2d. slate and violet	2·25	15
116		2d. blue and purple	40	10

55. "Victory".

58. King George VI.

59. King George VI and Queen Elizabeth.

1945. Victory. Bilingual pairs.

108.	55.	1d. brown and red	20	10
109.	–	2d. blue and violet	20	10
110.	–	3d. blue	20	10

DESIGNS: 2d. Man and oxen ploughing ("Peace"). 3d. Man and woman gazing at a star ("Hope").

1947. Royal Visit. Bilingual pairs.

111.	58.	1d. black and red	10	10
112.	59.	2d. violet	15	10
113.	–	3d. blue	15	10

DESIGN—As Type **59**: 3d. Queen Elizabeth II when Princess and Princess Margaret.

61. Gold Mine.

62. King George VI and Queen Elizabeth.

1948. Bilingual.

124.	61.	1½d. green and buff	1·25	10

The price for No. 124 is for a unit of four stamps.

1948. Royal Silver Wedding. Bilingual pair.

125.	62.	3d. blue and silver	50	10

63. "Wanderer" (emigrant ship) entering Durban.

1949. Centenary of Arrival of British Settlers in Natal. Bilingual pair.

127.	63.	1½d. brown	30	10

64. Hermes.

1949. U.P.U. 75th Anniv. Bilingual pairs.

128.	64.	½d. green	60	10
129.		1½d. red	75	10
130.		3d. blue	1·40	10

65. Wagons approaching Bingham's Berg.

1949. Inauguration of Voortrekker Monument, Pretoria.

131.	65.	1d. mauve	10	10
132.	–	1½d. green	10	10
133.	–	3d. blue	10	10

DESIGNS: 1½d. Voortrekker Monument, Pretoria. 3d. Bible, candle and Voortrekkers.

68. Union Bldgs., Pretoria.

1950. Bilingual pair.

134.	68.	2d. blue and violet	30	10

INSCRIPTIONS. In all later issues except Nos. 167 and 262/5, the stamps are inscribed in both Afrikaans and English. Our prices are for single copies, unused and used.

70. "Maria de la Quellerie" (D. Craey).

76. Queen Elizabeth II.

1952. Tercentenary of Landing of Van Riebeck. Dated "1652–1952".

136.	–	½d. purple and sepia	10	10
137.	70.	1d. green	10	10
138.	–	2d. violet	30	10
139.	–	4½d. blue	10	10
140.	–	1s. brown	20	10

DESIGNS—HORIZ. ½d. Seal and monogram. 2d. Arrival of Van Riebeeck's ships. 1s. Landing at the Cape. VERT. 4½d. Jan Van Riebeeck.

1952. S. African Tercentenary Stamp Exn., Cape Town. No. 137 optd. **SATISE** and No. 138 optd. **SADIPU**.

141.	70.	1d. green	15	1·25
142.	–	2d. violet	20	60

1953. Coronation.

143.	76.	2d. blue	30	10

77. 1d. Cape Triangular Stamp.

1953. Stamp Cent. of Cape of Good Hope.

144.	77.	1d. sepia and red	10	10
145.	–	4d. indigo and blue	20	20

DESIGN: 4d. as Type **77** but reproducing "Triangular".

79. Merino Ram.

1953.

146.	79.	4½d. purple and yellow	20	10
147.	–	1s. 3d. brown	1·25	10
148.	–	1s. 6d. red and green	80	30

DESIGNS: 1s. 3d. Springbok. 1s. 6d. Aloes.

82. Arms of Orange Free State and Scroll.

1954. Centenary of Orange Free State.

149.	82.	2d. sepia and red	10	10
150.		4½d. purple and grey	20	50

83. Warthog.

87. Rhinoceros.

1954. Wild Animals.

151.	83.	½d. turquoise	10	10
152.	–	1d. lake	10	10
153.	–	1½d. sepia	10	10
154.	–	2d. plum	10	10
155.	87.	3d. brown and blue	15	10
156.	–	4d. blue and green	40	10
157.	–	4½d. indigo and blue	60	1·50
158.	–	6d. sepia and orange	50	10
159.	–	1s. brown and red	80	10
160.	–	1s. 3d. brown and green	1·00	10
161.	–	1s. 6d. brown and pink	1·75	60
162.	–	2s. 6d. sepia & light green	3·50	20
163.	–	5s. sepia and buff	10·00	1·25
164.	–	10s. black and blue	17·00	4·50

DESIGNS: As Type **83**—VERT. 1d. Black Wildebeest. 1½d. Leopard. 2d Mountain Zebra. As Type **87**—VERT. 4d. African Elephant. 4½d. Hippopotamus. 1s. Greater Kudu 1s. 6d. Gemsbok. 2s. 6d. Nyala. 5s. Giraffe. 10s. Sable Antelope. HORIZ. 6d. Lion. 1s. 3d. Springbok.

97. President Kruger.

99. A. Pretorius, Church of the Vow and Flag.

1955. Cent. of Pretoria.

165.	97.	3d. green	10	10
166.	–	6d. pur. (Pres. Pretorius)	10	20

1955. Voortrekker Covenant Celebrations Pietermaritzburg. Bilingual pair.

167.	99.	2d. blue and red	45	10

100. Settlers' Block-wagon and House.

1958. Centenary of Arrival of German Settlers in S. Africa.

168.	**100.**	2d. brown and purple ..	10	10

101. Arms of the Academy.

1959. 50th Anniv. S. African Academy of Science and Art. Pretoria.

169.	**101.**	3d. blue and turquoise ..	10	10

103. Globe and Antarctic Scene. **104.** Union Flag.

1959. S. African National Antarctic Expedition.

178.	**103.**	3d. turquoise & orange	20	10

1960. 50th Anniv. of Union of S. Africa.

179.	**104.**	4d. orange and blue ..	30	10
180.	–	6d. red, brown & green	30	10
181.	–	1s. blue and yellow	30	10
182.	–	1s. 6d. black and blue ..	1·10	2·00

DESIGNS—VERT. 6d. Union Arms. HORIZ. 1s. "Wheel of progress". 1s. 6d. Union Festival emblem.

See also Nos. 190 and 192/3.

108. Locomotives of 1860 and 1960.

1960. Centenary of S. African Railways.

183.	**108.**	1s. 3d. blue	2·50	30

109. Prime Ministers Botha, Smuts Hertzog, Malan, Strijdom and Verwoerd.

1960. Union Day.

184.	**109.**	3d. brown & light brown	10	10

1961. Types as before but new currency

185.	**83.**	½ c. turquoise	10	10
186.	–	1 c. lake (as No. 152) ..	10	10
187.	–	1½ c. sepia (as No. 153)	10	10
188.	–	2 c. plum (as No. 154)	10	10
189.	**109.**	2½ c. brown	10	10
190.	**104.**	3½ c. orange and blue ..	15	90
191.	–	5 c. sep. & orge. (as 158)	20	10
192.	–	7½ c. red, brown and green (as No. 180) ..	20	1·25
193.	–	10 c. bl. & yell. (as 181)	30	20
194.	–	12½ c. brn. & grn. (as 160)	1·00	1·75
195.	–	20 c. brn. & pk. (as 161)	2·25	3·00
196.	–	50 c. sep. & buff (as 163)	6·00	10·00
197.	–	1 r. blk. & blue (as 164)	18·00	25·00

For later issues see Volume 2.

OFFICIAL STAMPS

1926. Optd. **OFFICIAL OFFISIEEL.**

(a) On Stamp of 1913.

O1.	**3.**	2d. purple	18·00	1·75

(b) On various pictorial issues.

O35b	**6**	½d. black and green	70	15
O25	**7**	1d. black and red ..	65	15
O26	**22**	1½d. green and gold	12·00	1·50
O37	**34a**	1½d. green and buff	1·40	25
O 6	**11**	2d. grey and purple	3·50	1·50
O15		2d. grey and lilac ..	6·00	1·50
O27		2d. blue and violet	55·00	2·25
O27a	**54**	2d. slate and violet	2·25	1·75
O38	**68**	2d. blue and violet ..	1·00	20
O39	**8**	6d. green and orange	1·00	35
O40	–	1s. brown & blue. (No.120) ..	5·50	1·75
O41	–	2s. 6d. green & brown (No. 121) ..	8·50	3·50
O20a	–	2s. 6d. blue & brown (No. 49a) ..	25·00	6·50
O41b	–	5s. black and green (No. 122) ..	28·00	6·00
O42	**23**	10s. blue and brown	55·00	18·00

POSTAGE DUE STAMPS

D 1. **D 2.**

1914. Perf. or roul.

D 11.	**D 1.**	½d. black and green	30	1·75
D 12.		1d. black and red ..	45	15
D 13.		1½d. black & brown	60	1·25
D 14.		2d. black and violet ..	55	70
D 4.		3d. black and blue ..	2·25	40
D 5.		5d. black and brown	3·75	14·00
D 16.		6d. black and grey ..	9·00	6·00
D 7.		1s. red and black ..	60·00	£120

1927.

D 17	**D 2.**	½d. black and green ..	40	2·00
D 18		1d. black and red ..	40	30
D 19		2d. black and mauve	1·25	30
D 23		2d. black and purple	4·00	1·40
D 20		3d. black and blue ..	5·50	14·00
D 28		3d. indigo and blue ..	4·50	30
D 21		6d. black and grey ..	12·00	6·00
D 29		6d. green and brown	20·00	6·00
D 29a		6d. green and orange	8·50	2·75

D 3. **D 5.**

1943.

D 30.	**D 3.**	½d. green	7·00	30
D 31.		1d. red	7·00	10
D 32.		2d. violet	6·50	15
D 33.		3d. blue	40·00	1·25

The above mint prices are for horiz units of three.

1948. Frame as Type **D 2**, but with bolder figures of value and capital "D".

D 34.		½d. black and green	6·00	6·50
D 39.		1d. black and red ..	70	30
D 40.		2d. black and violet ..	50	20
D 41.		3d. indigo and blue ..	4·00	1·75
D 42.		4d. turquoise and green ..	7·50	7·50
D 43.		6d. green and orange ..	7·00	7·00
D 44.		1s. brown and purple ..	10·00	9·00

1961.

D 45.	**D 5.**	1 c. black and red ..	20	2·75
D 46.		2 c. black and violet ..	35	2·75
D 47.		4 c. turquoise & green	80	5·50
D 48.		5 c. indigo and blue ..	1·75	6·00
D 49.		6 c. green and orange	7·50	6·00
D 50.		10 c. sepia and brown	8·50	9·00

SOUTH ARABIAN FEDERATION

Comprising Aden and most of the territories of the former Western Aden Protectorate plus one from the Eastern Aden Protectorate. The South Arabian Federation became fully independent on 30 November 1967.

1963. 100 cents = 1 shilling.
1965. 1000 fils = 1dinar.

1963. Cent of Red Cross. As T **30** of Antigua, but without portrait. Value in English and Arabic.

1.		15 c. red and black ..	30	20
2.		1s. 25 c. red and blue ..	60	40

2. Federal Crest.

3. Federal Flag.

1965.

3.	**2.**	5 f. blue	10	10
4.		10 f. lavender	10	10
5.		15 f. green	10	10
6.		20 f. green	10	10
7.		25 f. brown	10	10
8.		30 f. bistre	10	10
9.		35 f. brown	10	10
10.		50 f. red	10	10
11.		65 f. green	30	30
12.		75 f. red	30	10
13.	**3.**	100 f. multicoloured ..	30	10
14.		250 f. multicoloured ..	1·25	25
15.		500 f. multicoloured ..	3·25	50
16.		1 d. multicoloured ..	7·00	4·00

4. I.C.Y. Emblem.

1965. Int. Co-operation Year.

17.	**4.**	5 f. purple and turquoise ..	20	10
18.		65 f. green and lavender ..	70	20

5. Sir Winston Churchill and St. Paul's Cathedral in Wartime.

1966. Churchill Commem. Designs in black, cerise and gold with background in colours given.

19.	**5.**	5 f. blue	10	10
20.		10 f. green	25	10
21.		65 f. brown	65	10
22.		125 f. violet	90	1·25

6. Footballer's Legs, Ball and Jules Rimet Cup.

1966. World Cup Football Championships.

23.	**6.**	10 f. multicoloured ..	40	10
24.		50 f. multicoloured ..	1·10	20

7. W.H.O. Building.

1966. Inaug. of W.H.O. Headquarters, Geneva.

25.	**7.**	10 f. black, green and blue	40	10
26.		75 f. black, purple & brown	70	45

8. "Education".

1966. 20th Anniv. of U.N.E.S.C.O.

27.	**8.**	10 f. multicoloured ..	30	15
28.	–	65 f. yellow, violet & olive	80	80
29.	–	125 f. blk., purple & orge.	2·50	3·00

DESIGNS: 65 f. "Science". 125 f. "Culture".

For later issues see **SOUTHERN YEMEN**, and **YEMEN PEOPLE'S DEMOCRATIC REPUBLIC** in Volume 2.

SOUTH AUSTRALIA

A state of the Australian Commonwealth whose stamps it now uses.

12 pence = 1 shilling.
20 shillings = 1 pound.

1.

1855. Imperf.

1.	**1.**	1d. green	£2500	£350
9.		2d. red	£650	40·00
3.		6d. blue	£2000	£150
12.		1s. orange	£3750	£325

3. **4.**

1858. Roul. or perf.

20	**1**	1d. green	40·00	23·00
26		2d. red	38·00	2·75
112	**3**	3d. on 4d. blue	50·00	15·00
138		4d. violet	35·00	2·00
141	**1**	6d. blue	35·00	1·75
118	**4**	8d. on 9d. brown ..	50·00	5·00
124		9d. purple	10·00	3·25
35		10d. on 9d. orange ..	£100	24·00
38	**1**	1s. yellow	£450	28·00
130		1s. brown	24·00	3·00
151	**3**	2s. red	22·00	8·00

The 3d., 8d. and 10d. are formed by surcharges: **3-PENCE, 8 PENCE** and **TEN PENCE** (curved).

15. **11.** **12.**

1868. Various frames.

183	**15.**	½d. brown	2·00	35
238	**11.**	1d. green	3·00	20
294a		1d. red	1·75	10
251	**12.**	2d. orange	3·50	10
295a		2d. violet	1·75	10
230	–	2½d. on 4d. green ..	8·00	1·75
255	–	3d. green	5·00	50
256	–	4d. violet	6·00	40
232	–	5d. on 6d. brown ..	16·00	3·25
260	–	6d. blue	7·00	50

Nos. 230 and 231 are surch. in figures over straight or curved line.

1882. Surch. **HALF-PENNY** in two lines.

181.	**11.**	½d. on 1d. green	9·50	3·25

19. **24.** G.P.O., Adelaide.

22. Red Kangaroo. **23.**

1886.

195a.	**19.**	2s. 6d. mauve	24·00	6·00
196.		5s. pink	32·00	12·00
197.		10s. green	80·00	35·00
198.		15s. brown	£300	£120
199.		£1 blue	£150	80·00

1894.

262.	**24.**	½d. green	1·50	20
253.	**22.**	2½d. violet	6·00	70
266.		2½d. blue	4·50	30
258.	**23.**	5d. purple	6·50	45

1902. Inscr. "POSTAGE" at top.

268	**19.**	3d. green	3·25	45
269		4d. orange	5·00	70
284		6d. green	5·50	70
285		8d. blue	7·00	2·00
273		9d. red	8·00	1·00
274		10d. orange	10·00	3·25
303b		1s. brown	10·00	1·00
276a		2s. 6d. violet	20·00	7·00
290		5s. red	40·00	20·00
278		10s. green	£110	60·00
292a		£1 blue	£130	80·00

OFFICIAL STAMPS

1874. Various postage issues optd. **O.S.**

A. Issue of 1858.

O 6.	**1.**	1d. green	£1000	16·00
O 7.	**3.**	3d. on 4d. blue	£1000	£400
O 17.		4d. violet	25·00	2·50
O 19.	**1.**	6d. blue	35·00	4·00
O 26.	**4.**	8d. on 9d. brown	£750	£300
O 11.		9d. purple	£500	£225
O 33.	**1.**	1s. brown	25·00	4·00
O 35.	**3.**	2s. red	60·00	8·00

B. Issues of 1868-82.

O55	15	½d. brown	6·00	3·00
O50	11	½d. on 1d. green	50·00	14·00
O67		1d. green	7·00	40
O81		1d. red	7·00	50
O74		2d. orange	7·00	25
O82		2d. violet	7·00	50
O58	–	2½d. on 4d. green	32·00	4·50
O84	–	4d. violet	40·00	1·50
O61	–	5d. on 6d. brown	38·00	11·00
O62	–	6d. blue	12·00	1·25

C. Issue of 1886.

O 86.	**19.**	2s. 6d. mauve	£2000	£1600
O 87.		5s. pink	£2000	£1600

D. Issue of 1894.

O 80.	**24.**	½d. green	6·00	2·75
O 83.	**22.**	2½d. blue	50·00	9·00
O 77.	**23.**	5d. purple	50·00	5·00

SOUTH GEORGIA

An island in the Antarctic. From May 1980 to 1985 used stamps inscribed FALKLAND ISLANDS DEPENDENCIES and thereafter those of South Georgia and the South Sandwich Islands (q.v.).

1963. 12 pence = 1 shilling,
20 shillings = 1 pound.
1971. 100 pence = 1 pound.

1. Reindeer.

1963.

1.	**1.**	½d. red	50	30
2.	–	1d. blue	70	15
3.	–	2d. turquoise	70	15
4.	–	2½d. black	3·50	80
5.	–	3d. bistre	1·25	15
6.	–	4d. bronze	3·25	50
7.	–	5½d. violet	1·25	15
8.	–	6d. orange	75	15
9.	–	9d. blue	3·75	30
10.	–	1s. purple	75	15
11.	–	2s. olive and blue	11·00	4·00
12.	–	2s. 6d. blue	15·00	4·00
13.	–	5s. brown	16·00	4·00
14.	–	10s. mauve	38·00	10·00
15.	–	£1 blue	95·00	48·00
16.	–	£1 black	10·00	16·00

DESIGNS—HORIZ. 2½d. King penguin and chinstrap penguin. 4d. Fin whale. 5½d. Elephant seal. 9d. Whale-catcher. 1s. Leopard seal. 2s. Shackleton's Cross. 2s 6d. Wandering albatross. 5s. Elephant and fur seal. £1 (No. 15), Blue whale. VERT. 1d. South Sandwich Islands. 2d. Sperm whale. 3d. Fur seal. 6d. Light-mantled sooty albatross. 10s. Plankton and krill. £1, (No. 16) King penguins.

1971. Decimal Currency. Nos 1/14 surch.

18a	½p. on ½d. red	1·00	90
19	1p. on 1d. blue	1·50	55
55	1½p. on 5½d. violet	90	1·75
21	2p. on 2d. turquoise	70	50
22	2½p. on 2½d. black	1·50	40
23	3p. on 3d. bistre	1·00	50
24	4p. on 4d. bronze	90	50
25	5p. on 6d. orange	90	30
26	6p. on 9d. blue	1·50	70
27	7½p. on 1s. purple	2·00	70
63	10p. on 2s. olive and blue	4·00	8·00
64	15p. on 2s. 6d. blue	4·00	8·00
65	25 p. on 5s. brown	4·50	8·00
66	50p. on 10s. mauve	3·00	8·50

6. "Endurance" beset in Weddell Sea.

1972. 50th Death Anniv. of Sir Ernest Shackleton. Multicoloured.

32.	1½p. Type **6**	1·00	60
33.	5p. Launching of the long-boat "James Caird"	1·25	85
34.	10p. Route of the "James Caird"	1·75	1·00
35.	20p. Sir Ernest Shackleton and the "Quest"	2·00	1·25

1972. Royal Silver Wedding. As T **52** of Ascension, but with Elephant Seal and King Penguins in background.

36.	5p. green	1·00	35
37.	10p. violet	1·00	35

1973. Royal Wedding. As T **47** of Anguilla. Background colours given. Multicoloured.

38.	5p. brown	25	10
39.	15 p. lilac	35	20

8. Churchill and Westminster Skyline.

1974. Birth Cent. of Sir Winston Churchill. Multicoloured.

40.	15p. Type **8**	1·75	1·00
41.	25p. Churchill and warship	2·00	1·00

9. Captain Cook.

1975. Bicentenary of Possession by Captain Cook.

43.	2p. Type **9**	1·60	1·25
44.	8p. H.M.S. "Resolution"	2·75	1·75
45.	16p. Possession Bay	3·25	2·00

Nos 44/5 are horiz.

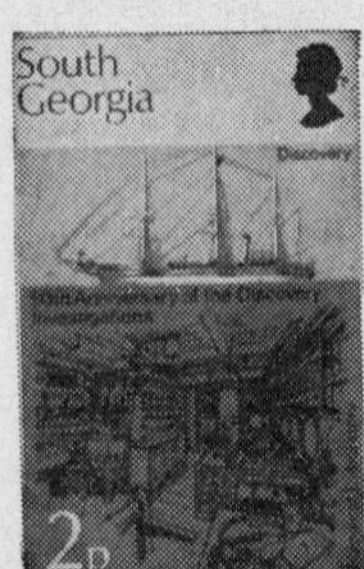

10. "Discovery" and Biological Laboratory.

1976. 50th Anniv. of "Discovery" Investigations. Multicoloured.

46.	2p. Type **10**	1·00	35
47.	8p. "William Scoresby" and water-sampling bottles	1·40	50
48.	11p. "Discovery 11" and plankton net	1·75	55
49.	25p. Biological Station and krill	2·50	85

11. The Queen and Retinue after Coronation.

1977. Silver Jubilee. Multicoloured.

50.	6p. Visit by Prince Philip, 1957	80	30
51.	11p. The Queen and Westminster Abbey	90	35
52.	33p. Type **11**	1·25	50

12. Fur Seal.

1978. 25th Anniv. of Coronation.

67.	–	25p. deep blue, blue and silver	75	1·00
68.	–	25p. multicoloured	75	1·00
69.	**12.**	25p. deep blue, blue and silver	75	1·00

DESIGNS: No. 67, Panther of Henry VI. No. 68, Queen Elizabeth II.

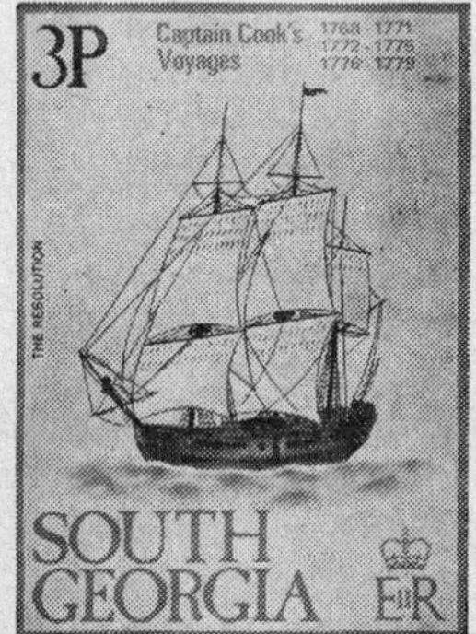

13. H.M.S. "Resolution".

1979. Bicentenary of Captain Cook's Voyages, 1768–79. Multicoloured.

70.	3p. Type **13**	1·50	1·00
71.	6p. "Resolution" and Map of South Georgia and S. Sandwich Isles showing route	1·50	80
72.	11p. King Penguin (from drawing by George Forster)	2·50	2·25
73.	25p. Flaxman/Wedgwood medallion of Capt. Cook	2·75	2·50

SOUTH GEORGIA AND THE SOUTH SANDWICH ISLANDS

Under the new constitution, effective 3 October 1985, South Georgia and the South Sandwich Islands ceased to be dependencies of the Falkland Islands.

100 pence = 1 pound.

1986. 60th Birthday of Queen Elizabeth II. As T **110** of Ascension. Multicoloured.

153.	10p. Four generations of Royal Family at Prince Charles's christening, 1948	25	25
154.	24p. With Prince Charles and Lady Diana Spencer, Buckingham Palace, 1981	55	55
155.	29p. In robes of Order of the British Empire, St. Paul's Cathedral, London	60	60
156.	45p. At banquet, Canada, 1976	95	95
157.	58p. At Crown Agents Head Office London, 1983	1·25	1·25

1986. Royal Wedding. As T **153** of Falkland Islands. Multicoloured.

158	17p. Prince Andrew and Miss Sarah Ferguson at Ascot	75	85
159	22p. Wedding photograph	85	1·00
160	29p. Prince Andrew with Lynx helicopter on board H.M.S. "Brazen"	1·00	1·25

26. Southern Black-backed Gull.

1987. Birds. Multicoloured.

161.	1p. Type **26**	15	20
162.	2p. Blue-eyed cormorant	20	20
163.	3p. Snowy sheathbill (vert.)	20	20
164.	4p. Great skua (vert.)	20	20
165.	5p. Pintado petrel	20	30
166.	6p. Georgian diving petrel	20	30
167.	7p. South Georgia pipit (vert.)	30	40
168.	8p. Georgian teal (vert.)	30	40
169.	9p. Fairy prion	40	45
170.	10p. Bearded penguin	40	45
171.	20p. Macaroni penguin (vert.)	50	70
172.	25p. Light-mantled sooty albatross (vert.)	60	75
173.	50p. Giant petrel (vert.)	1·00	1·40
174.	£1 Wandering albatros	2·00	2·40
175.	£3 King penguin (vert.)	6·00	7·00

1987. 30th Anniv of Int. Geophysical Year. As T **39** of British Antarctic Territory.

176	24p. black and blue	50	55
177	29p. multicoloured	55	60
178	58p. multicoloured	1·10	1·25

DESIGNS: 24p. I.G.Y. Logo; 29p. Grytviken; 58p. Glaciologist using hand-drill to take core sample.

27. "Gaimardia trapesina".

1988. Sea Shells. Multicoloured.

179.	10p. Type **27**	30	30
180.	24p. "Margarella tropidophoroides"	50	60
181.	29p. "Trophon scotianus"	55	65
182.	58p. "Chlanidota densesculpta"	1·10	1·25

1988. 300th Anniv of Lloyd's of London. As T **123** of Ascension.

183	10p. black and brown	30	30
184	24p. multicoloured	50	55
185	29p. black and green	60	65
186	58p. black and red	1·10	1·25

DESIGNS—VERT. 10p. Queen Mother at opening of new Lloyd's building, 1957; 58p. "Horatio" (tanker) on fire, 1916. HORIZ. 24p. "Lindblad Explorer" (cruise liner); 29p. Whaling station, Leith Harbour.

28 Glacier Headwall

1989. Glacier Formations. Multicoloured.

187	10p. Type **28**	35	35
188	24p. Accumulation area	70	70
189	29p. Ablation area	80	80
190	58p. Calving front	1·40	1·40

29 Retracing Shackleton's Trek

1989. 25th Anniv of Combined Services Expedition to South Georgia. Multicoloured.
191 10p. Type **29** 35 35
192 24p. Surveying at Royal Bay 70 70
193 29p. H.M.S. "Protector" (ice patrol ship) .. 80 80
194 58p. Raising Union Jack on Mount Paget .. 1·40 1·40

1990. 90th Birthday of Queen Elizabeth the Queen Mother. As T **134** of Ascension.
195 26p. multicoloured .. 75 75
196 £1 black and blue .. 2·75 2·75
DESIGNS—21 × 36 mm. 26p. Queen Mother. 29 × 37 mm. King George VI and Queen Elizabeth with A.R.P. wardens, 1940.

30 "Brutus", Prince Olav Harbour

1990. Wrecks and Hulks. Multicoloured.
197 12p. Type **30** 40 40
198 26p. "Bayard", Ocean Harbour 80 80
199 31p. "Karrakatta", Husvik 95 95
200 62p. "Louise", Grytviken 1·75 1·75

1991. 65th Birthday of Queen Elizabeth II and 70th Birthday of Prince Philip. As T **139** of Ascension. Multicoloured.
201 31p. Queen Elizabeth II .. 1·00 1·00
202 31p. Prince Philip in Grenadier Guards uniform .. .. .. 1·00 1·00

31. Contest between two Bull Elephant Seals.

1991. Elephant Seals. Multicoloured.
203 12p. Type **31** 40 40
204 26p. Adult elephant seal .. 85 85
205 29p. Seal throwing sand .. 95 95
206 31p. Head of elephant seal 1·00 1·00
207 34p. Seals on beach .. 1·10 1·25
208 62p. Cow seal with pup .. 1·75 1·90

1992. 40th Anniv of Queen Elizabeth II's Accession. As T **143** of Ascension. Mult.
209 7p. Ice-covered mountains 30 30
210 14p. Zavodovski Island .. 55 55
211 29p. Gulbrandsen Lake .. 95 95
212 34p. Three portraits of Queen Elizabeth .. 1·10 1·10
213 68p. Queen Elizabeth II 1·75 1·75

32 Adult Teal and Young Bird

1992. Endangered Species. Georgian Teal ("South Georgia Teal"). Multicoloured.
214 2p. Type **32** 15 15
215 6p. Adult with eggs .. 20 20
216 12p. Teals swimming .. 40 40
217 20p. Adult and two chicks 80 80

1992. 10th Anniv of Liberation. As T **169** of St. Helena. Multicoloured.
218 14p. + 6p. King Edward Point 60 70
219 29p. + 11p. "Queen Elizabeth 2" (liner) in Cumberland Bay .. 1·10 1·25
220 34p. + 16p. Royal Marines hoisting Union Jack on South Sandwich Islands 1·40 1·60
221 68p. + 32p. H.M.S. "Endurance" (ice patrol ship) and Wasp helicopter .. 2·75 3·00

33 Disused Whale Factory, Grytviken

1993. Opening of South Georgia Whaling Museum. Multicoloured.
223 15p. Type **33** 45 45
224 31p. Whaler's lighter and whale bones 90 90
225 36p. Aerial view of King Edward Cove .. .. 1·10 1·10
226 72p. Museum building .. 2·00 2·25

34 Pair of Swimming Penguins

1993. Macaroni Penguin. Multicoloured.
227 16p. Type **34** 30 35
228 34p. Group of penguins .. 70 75
229 39p. Two juvenile penguins 80 85
230 78p. Two adult penguins .. 1·60 1·75

35 Hourglass Dolphin

1994. Whales and Dolphins. Multicoloured.
231 1p. Type **35** 10 10
232 2p. Southern right whale dolphin 10 10
233 5p. Long-finned pilot whale 10 10
234 8p. Southern bottlenose whale 15 20
235 9p. Killer whale 20 25
236 10p. Minke whale .. 20 25
237 20p. Sei whale 40 45
238 25p. Humpback whale .. 50 55
239 50p. Southern right whale 1·00 1·10
240 £1 Sperm whale .. .. 2·00 2·10
241 £3 Fin whale .. .. 6·00 6·25
242 £5 Blue whale .. .. 10·00 10·50

1994. "Hong Kong '94" International Stamp Exhibition. Nos. 227/30 optd **HONG KONG '94** and emblem.
243 16p. Type **34** 30 35
244 34p. Group of penguins .. 70 75
245 39p. Two juvenile penguins 80 85
246 78p. Two adult penguins .. 1·50 1·60

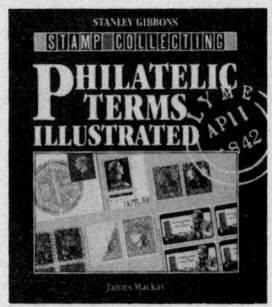

SOUTH WEST AFRICA

A territory in S.W. Africa, formerly the German Colony of German South West Africa (q.v. in Volume 1). Administered by South Africa until 1990 when it became independent as Namibia.

1923. 12 pence = 1 shilling;
20 shillings = 1 pound.
1961. 100 cents = 1 rand.

NOTE.—Stamps overprinted for South West Africa are always South African Stamps, except where otherwise indicated.
"Bilingual" in heading indicates that the stamps are inscribed alternately in English and Afrikaans throughout the sheet. "Bilingual" is not repeated in the heading where bilingual stamps of South Africa are overprinted.
Our prices for such issues are for mint bilingual pairs and used single stamps of either inscription.

1923. Optd. alternately **South West Africa** or **Zuidwest Afrika.**

No.	Type	Description	Mint	Used
1	2	½d. green	1·75	1·00
2		1d. red	2·00	1·00
3		2d. purple	2·75	1·50
19		3d. blue	4·00	1·25
20		4d. orange and green ..	5·00	2·75
34		6d. black and violet ..	7·00	4·50
35		1s. yellow	11·00	4·50
36		1s. 3d. violet	14·00	5·00
37		2s. 6d. purple and green	35·00	10·00
38		5s. purple and blue ..	55·00	14·00
39		10 s. blue and green ..	85·00	20·00
40a		£1 green and red	£250	90·00

1926. Optd. **South West Africa** or **Suidwes Afrika** alternately.

No.	Type	Description	Mint	Used
45.	6.	½d. black and green ..	1·40	80
46.	7.	1d. black and red ..	1·40	50
49.	11.	2d. grey and purple ..	3·75	1·75
50.	–	3d. black and red ..	3·75	2·50
47.	8.	6d. green and orange ..	13·00	3·00
51.	–	1s. brown and blue ..	14·00	4·00
52.	–	2s. 6d. green and brown	45·00	12·00
53.	–	5s. black and green ..	75·00	20·00
54.	–	10s. blue and brown ..	85·00	20·00

1926. Triangular optd. **SOUTH WEST AFRIKA** in two lines (E), or **SUIDWES-AFRIKA** in one line (A). Imperf. or perf.

No.	Type	Description	E. Mint	E. Used	A. Mint	A. Used
44.	10.	4d. blue ..	65	2·00	65	2·00

1927. Triangular optd. **SOUTH WEST AFRIKA** in one line. Imperf.

No.	Type	Description	Mint	Used
48.	10.	4d. blue	7·50	19·00

1927. Optd. **S.W.A.**

No.	Type	Description	Mint	Used
56.	2.	1s. 3d. violet	1·25	6·00
57.		£1 olive and red ..	£120	£180

1927. Optd. **S.W.A.**

No.	Type	Description	Mint	Used
58.	6.	½d. black and green ..	1·50	70
59.	7.	1d. black and red ..	1·25	55
60.	11.	2d. grey and purple ..	4·50	1·10
61.	–	3d. black and red ..	6·00	3·25
62.	–	4d. brown	18·00	7·00
63.	8.	6d. green and orange ..	13·00	2·75
64.	–	1s. brown and blue ..	24·00	5·00
65.	–	2s. 6d. green and brown	45·00	10·00
66.	–	5s. black and green ..	65·00	18·00
67.	–	10s. blue and brown ..	£120	28·00

1930. Air. Optd. **S.W.A.**

No.	Type	Description	Mint	Used
72.	17.	4d. green..	1·25	6·00
73.		1s. orange	1·50	15·00

12 Kori Bustard

1931. Bilingual pairs.

No.	Type	Description	Mint	Used
74.	12.	½d. black and green ..	1·40	10
75.	–	1d. blue and red ..	1·40	10
76.	–	2d. blue and brown ..	50	15
77.	–	3d. dull blue and blue ..	50	15
78.	–	4d. green and purple ..	90	20
79.	–	6d. blue and brown ..	60	20
80.	–	1s. brown and blue ..	1·00	25
81.	–	1s. 3d. violet and yellow..	8·50	50
82.	–	2s. 6d. red and grey ..	20·00	1·75
83.	–	5s. green and brown ..	20·00	2·75
84.	–	10s. brown and green ..	55·00	7·00
85.	–	£1 red and green ..	£110	12·00

DESIGNS: 1d. Cape Cross. 2d. Begenfels. 3d. Windhoek. 4d. Waterberg. 6d. Luderitz Bay. 1s. Bush scene. 1s. 3d. Elands. 2s. 6d. Mountain Zebra and Wildebeests. 5s. Herero huts. 10s. Welwitschia plant. £1, Okuwahaken Falls.

24 Monoplane over Windhoek

1931. Air. Bilingual pairs.

No.	Type	Description	Mint	Used
86.	24.	3d. brown and blue ..	32·00	3·50
87.	–	10d. black and brown ..	55·00	9·00

DESIGN: 10d. Biplane over Windhoek.

26

1935. Silver Jubilee.

No.	Type	Description	Mint	Used
88.	26.	1d. black and red ..	75	25
89.		2d. black and brown ..	1·00	25
90.		3d. black and blue ..	12·00	14·00
91.		6d. black and purple ..	5·50	3·50

1935. Voortrekker Memorial. As Nos. 50/3 of South Africa optd **S.W.A.**

No.	Type	Description	Mint	Used
92		½d.+½d. black and green ..	1·00	65
93		1d.+½d. black and pink ..	1·50	40
94		2d.+1d. green and purple ..	5·00	80
95		3d.+1½d. green and blue ..	15·00	3·50

27 Mail Transport

1937. Bilingual pair.

No.	Type	Description	Mint	Used
96	27	1½d. brown	11·00	20

28

1937. Coronation. Bilingual pairs.

No.	Type	Description	Mint	Used
97.	28.	½d. black and green ..	60	15
98.		1d. black and red ..	70	15
99.		1½d. black and orange	70	15
100.		2d. black and brown ..	70	15
101.		3d. black and blue ..	70	15
102.		4d. black and purple ..	70	20
103.		6d. black and yellow ..	80	20
104.		1s. black and grey ..	1·25	20

1938. Cent. of Voortrekker. Fund. Optd. **S.W.A.**

No.	Type	Description	Mint	Used
105.	–	½d.+½d. blue and green	7·00	1·25
106.	27.	1d.+1d. blue and red	15·00	75
107.	28.	1½d.+1½d. brown & grn.	20·00	2·50
108.	–	3d.+3d. blue	40·00	5·00

1938. Voortrekker Commem. Optd. **S.W.A.**

No.	Type	Description	Mint	Used
109.	–	1d. blue and red ..	8·50	1·00
110.	31.	1½d. blue and brown ..	11·00	1·40

1939. 250th Anniv. of Landing of Huguenots in S. Africa. Optd. **S.W.A.**

No.	Type	Description	Mint	Used
111.	32.	½d.+½d. brown & green	6·50	80
112.	33.	1d.+1d. green and red	11·00	1·10
113.	34.	1½d.+1½d. grn. & purple	14·00	1·25

1941. War Effort. Optd. **S W A.**

(a) Bilingual pairs.

No.	Type	Description	Mint	Used
114a	35.	½d. green	65	15
115	–	1d. red	55	15
116	–	1½d. green	55	15
117	39.	3d. blue	17·00	85
118	–	4d. brown	6·50	1·00
119	–	6d. orange	2·50	50
120	–	1s. 3d. brown	9·00	1·00

(b) Inscr. in both English and Afrikaans.

No.	Type	Description	Mint	Used
121.	38.	2d. violet	40	30
122.	–	1s. brown	60	40

1943. War Effort. Optd. **S W A.**

No.	Type	Description	Mint	Used
123.	43.	½d. green (T)	40	10
124.	–	1d. red (T)	90	10
125.	–	1½d. brown (P) ..	45	10
126.	–	2d. violet (P)	3·00	10
127.	–	3d. blue (T)	3·00	40
129.	–	4d. green (T)	2·00	40
128.	–	6d. orange (P)	3·00	30
130b.	–	1s. brown (P)	3·50	30

The units referred to above consist of pairs (P), or triplets (T).

1945. Victory. Optd. **S W A.**

No.	Type	Description	Mint	Used
131.	55.	1d. brown and red ..	25	10
132.	–	2d. blue and violet ..	30	10
133.	–	3d. blue..	65	10

1947. Royal Visit. Optd. **S W A.**

No.	Type	Description	Mint	Used
134.	58.	1d. black and red ..	10	10
135.	59.	2d. violet	10	10
136.	–	3d. blue..	15	10

1948. Silver Wedding Optd. **S W A.**

No.	Type	Description	Mint	Used
137.	62.	3d. blue and silver ..	1·50	10

1949. 75th Anniv. of U.P.U. Optd. **S.W.A.**

No.	Type	Description	Mint	Used
138.	64.	½d. green	1·25	25
139.		1½d. red	1·25	15
140.		3d. blue..	1·75	25

1949. Inaug. of Voortrekker Monument Pretoria. Optd. **S W A.**

No.	Type	Description	Mint	Used
141.	65.	1d. mauve	10	10
142.	–	1½d. green	10	10
143.	–	3d. blue..	10	20

1952. Tercentenary of Landing of Van Riebeeck. Optd. **S W A.**

No.	Type	Description	Mint	Used
144.	–	½d. purple and sepia ..	10	40
145.	70.	1d. green	10	10
146.	–	2d. violet	50	10
147.	–	4½d. blue	30	1·50
148.	–	1s. brown	1·25	20

33 Queen Elizabeth II and "Catophracies alexandri"

1953. Coronation. Native Flowers.

No.	Type	Description	Mint	Used
149.	33.	1d. red	75	10
150.	–	2d. green ("Banhinia machrantha")	75	10
151.	–	4d. mauve ("Caralluma nebrownii") ..	1·60	55
152.	–	6d. blue ("Gloriosa virescens") ..	1·75	1·25
153.	–	1s. brown ("Rhigozum tricholotum" ..	1·75	40

34 "Two Bucks" (rock painting)

1954.

No.	Type	Description	Mint	Used
154	34	1d. red	30	10
155	–	2d. brown	35	10
156	–	3d. purple	2·25	10
157	–	4d. black	2·50	10
158	–	4½d. blue	1·25	15
159	–	6d. green	1·25	10
160	–	1s. mauve	1·25	40
161	–	1s.3d. red	6·00	40
162	–	1s.6d. purple	6·00	40
163	–	2s. 6d. brown	10·00	60
164	–	5s. blue	15·00	2·75
165	–	10s. green	48·00	15·00

DESIGNS—VERT. 2d. "White Lady" (rock painting). 4½d. Karakul lamb. 6d. Ovambo woman blowing horn. 1s. Ovambo woman. 1s. 3d. Herero woman. 1s. 6d. Ovambo girl. 2s. 6d. Lioness. 5s. Gemsbok. 10s. African elephant. HORIZ. 3d. "Rhinoceros Hunt" (rockpainting). 4 d. "White Elephant and Giraffe" (rock painting).

46 G.P.O., Windhoek

59 "Agricultural Development"

1961.

No.	Type	Description	Mint	Used
171	46.	½ c. brown and blue ..	60	10
172	–	1 c. sepia and mauve ..	15	10
173	–	1½ c. violet and salmon ..	20	10
174	–	2 c. green and yellow ..	75	10
175	–	2½ c. brown and blue ..	35	10
176	–	3 c. blue and red ..	3·75	15
177	–	3½ c. blue and green ..	70	15
209	–	4 c. brown and blue ..	1·50	1·75
178	–	5 c. red and blue ..	3·75	10
211	–	6 c. sepia and yellow ..	8·00	9·50
179	–	7½ c. sepia and lemon ..	70	15
213	–	9 c. blue and yellow ..	8·00	9·50
180	–	10 c. blue and yellow ..	1·75	15
181	–	12½ c. blue and lemon ..	85	30
182	–	15 c. brown and blue ..	14·00	3·25
183	–	20 c. brown and orange ..	8·00	30
184	–	50 c. green and orange ..	11·00	1·50
185	–	1 r. yellow, purple & blue	22·00	14·00

DESIGNS—VERT. 1 c. Finger Rock. 1½ c. Mounted Soldier Monument. 2 c. Quivertree. 3 c. Greater flamingoes and Swakopmund Lighthouse. 3½ c. Fishing industry. 5 c. Greater flamingo. 6 c., 7½ c. German Lutheran Church, Windhoek. 10 c. Diamond. 20 c. Topaz. 50 c. Tourmaline. 1 r. Heliodor. HORIZ. 2½ c., 4 c. S.W.A. House, Windhoek. 9 c., 12½ c. Fort Namutoni, 15 c. Hardap Dam.
See also Nos. 224/26.

1963. Opening of Hardap Dam.

No.	Type	Description	Mint	Used
192.	59.	3 c. brown and green ..	30	15

61 Centenary Emblem and part of Globe

62 Interior of Assembly Hall

1963. Centenary of Red Cross.

No.	Type	Description	Mint	Used
193.	–	7½ c. red, black & blue	7·00	5·00
194.	61.	15 c. red, blk. & salmon	10·00	8·00

DESIGN: 7½ c. Centenary emblem and Map.

1964. Opening of Legislative Assembly Hall, Windhoek.

No.	Type	Description	Mint	Used
195.	62.	3 c. blue and salmon ..	50	30

63 Calvin

64 Mail Runner of 1890

1965. 400th Death Anniv. of Calvin (Protestant reformer).

No.	Type	Description	Mint	Used
196.	63.	2½ c. purple and gold ..	50	15
197.		15 c. green and gold ..	2·75	2·25

1965. 75th Anniv. of Windhoek.

No.	Type	Description	Mint	Used
198.	64.	3 c. sepia and red ..	50	15
199.	–	15 c. brown and green..	1·25	1·40

DESIGN: 15 c. Kurt von Francois (founder).

66 Dr. H. Vedder

70 Pres. Swart

67 Camelthorn Tree

1966. 90th Birth Anniv of Vedder (philosopher and writer).

No.	Type	Description	Mint	Used
200	66	3 c. green and pink ..	50	15
201		15 c. brown and blue ..	1·25	65

1967. Verwoerd Commemoration.
217 **67** 2½ c. black and green .. 20 10
218 – 3 c. brown and blue .. 30 10
219 – 15 c. brown and purple 1·10 45
DESIGNS—VERT. 3 c. Waves breaking against rock. 15 c. Dr. H. F. Verwoerd.

1968. Swart Commem. Inscr. in German, Afrikaans or English.
220. **70.** 3 c. red, blue and black 45 15
221. – 15 c. red, green and olive 1·50 1·75
DESIGN: 15 c. Pres. and Mrs. Swart.

1970. Water 70 Campaign. As Nos. 299/300 of South Africa, but inscr "SWA".
222. 2½ c. green, blue & brown 75 30
223. 3 c. blue and buff .. 75 30

1970. As Nos. 171 etc., but with "POSGELD" "INKOMSTE" omitted and larger figure of value.
224. **46.** ½ c. brown and blue .. 1·50 30
225. – 1½ c. violet and salmon.. 13·00 15·00
226. – 2 c. green and yellow .. 5·00 40

1970. 150th Anniv. of Bible Soc. of South Africa. As Nos. 301/2 of South Africa.
228. 2½ c. multicoloured .. 1·50 10
229. 12½ c. gold ,black and blue 8·00 6·50

1971. "Interstex" Stamp Exhibition, Cape Town. As No. 303 of South Africa. Inscr. "SWA".
230. 5 c. blue black and yellow 4·75 1·50

1971. 10th Anniv of Antarctic Treaty. As No. 401 of South Africa. Inscr "SWA".
231. 12½ c. black, blue and red 45·00 25·00

1971. 10th Anniv. of South African Republic As Nos. 305/6 of South Africa. Inscr. "SWA".
232 2 c. flesh and red .. .. 3·25 75
233 4 c. green and black .. 3·25 75

1972. Centenary of S.P.C.A. As No. 312 of South Africa. Inscr. "SWA".
234. 5 c. multicoloured.. .. 3·50 55

73 "Red sand-dunes, Eastern South-West Africa"

1973. Scenery. Paintings by Adolph Jentsch. Multicoloured.
235. 2 c. Type **73** 75 75
236. 4 c. "After the Rain" .. 1·25 1·25
237. 5 c. "Barren Country" .. 1·50 1·50
238. 10 c. "Schaap River" (vert.) .. .. 2·75 2·75
239. 15 c. "Namib Desert" (vert.) .. .. .. 4·00 4·00

74 "Sarcocaulon rigidum"

75 "Euphorbia virosa"

1973. Multicoloured.
(a) As T **74.**
241 1 c. Type **74** 15 10
242a 2 c." Lapidaria margaretae" 20 10
243 3 c." Titanopsis schwantesii" 20 10
244 4 c."Lithops karasmontana" 25 10
245b 5 c." Caralluma lugardii" 40 20
246 6 c. "Dinteranthus microspermus" .. 1·00 60
247 7 c." Conophytum gratum" 70 80
248 9 c." Huernia oculata" .. 65 70
249b 10 c. " Gasteria pillansii" 40 30
250 14c."Stapelia pedunculata" 1·50 90
251 15c."Fenestraria aurantiaca" 65 30
252 20c."Decabelone grandiflora" 4·00 1·50
253 25 c." Hoodia bainii" .. 2·50 1·25
(b) As T **75.**
254 30 c. Type **75** .. .. 1·00 80
255a 50 c. "Pachypodium namaquanum" (vert.) 1·50 1·50
256 1 r. "Welwitschia bainesii" 2·00 5·00

1973. Coil Stamps. As Nos 241/2a and 245. Colours changed.
257a **18** 1 c. black and mauve.. 80 40
258 – 2 c. black and yellow.. 50 50
259a – 5 c. black and red .. 1·25 60

76 Chat-shrikes

77 Giraffe, Antelope and Spoor

1974. Rare Bird Species of South West Africa. Multicoloured.
260. 4 c. Type **76** .. .. 3·00 1·00
261. 5 c. Peach-faced Lovebirds 4·00 1·50
262. 10 c. Damaraland Rock Jumper .. .. .. 10·00 5·50
263. 15 c. Ruppell's Parrots .. 14·00 9·50

1974. Twyfelfontein Rock Engravings. Mult.
264. 4 c. Type **77** .. .. 1·50 50
265. 5 c. Elephant, hyena, antelope and spoor .. .. 1·50 80
266. 15 c. Kudu cow .. .. 7·00 6·00
No. 266 is horizontal, size 38×21 mm.

78 Cut Diamond

80 Peregrine Falcon

79 Wagons and Map of the Trek

1974. Diamond Mining. Multicoloured.
267. 10 c. Type **78** .. .. 4·50 4·00
268. 15 c. Diagram of shore workings .. .. 5·00 5·00

1974. Centenary of Thirstland Trek.
269 **79** 4 c. multicoloured .. 1·00 1·00

1975. Protected Birds of Prey. Mult.
270. 4 c. Type **80** .. .. 2·00 1·25
271. 5 c. Verreaux's Eagle .. 2·25 1·75
272. 10 c. Martial Eagle .. 6·00 5·00
273. 15 c. Egyptian Vulture .. 7·50 7·50

81 Kolmannskop (ghost town)

1975. Historic Monuments. Multicoloured.
274. 5 c. Type **81** 30 15
275. 9 c. "Martin Luther" (steam tractor) .. 50 50
276. 15 c. Kurt von Francois and Old Fort, Windhoek 1·00 80

82 "View of Luderitz"

1975. Otto Schroder (painter). Multicoloured.
277. 15 c. Type **82** 55 45
278. 15 c. "View of Swakopmund" 55 45
279. 15 c. "Harbour Scene" .. 55 45
280. 15 c. "Quayside, Walvis Bay" 55 45

83 Elephants

1976. Prehistoric Rock Paintings. Mult.
282. 4 c. Type **83** 40 10
283. 10 c. Rhinoceros 65 30
284. 15 c. Antelope 80 60
285. 20 c. Man with bow and arrow .. .. .. 1·10 85

84 Schwerinsburg

1976. Castles. Multicoloured.
287. 10 c. Type **84** 50 30
288. 15 c. Schloss Duwisib .. 70 50
289. 20 c. Heynitzburg .. 1·00 80

85 Large-toothed Rock Hyrax

1976. Fauna Conservation. Multicoloured.
290. 4 c. Type **85** 50 20
291. 10 c. Kirk's Dik-Dik .. 1·50 90
292. 15 c. Kahl's Tree Squirrel 2·25 2·25

86 The Augustineum, Windhoek

1976. Modern Buildings.
293. **86.** 15 c. black and yellow.. 50 65
294. – 20 c. black and yellow.. 60 75
DESIGN: 20 c. Katutura Hospital, Windhoek.

87 Ovambo Water Canal System

1976. Water and Electricity Supply. Mult.
295. 15 c. Type **87** 30 30
296. 20 c. Ruacana Falls Power Station 40 40

88 Coastline, near Pomona. (illustration reduced, actual size 57×21 mm)

1977. Namib Desert. Multicoloured.
297. 4 c. Type **88** 20 15
298. 10 c. Bush and Dunes, Sossusvlei 30 30
299. 15 c. Plain near Brandberg 50 50
300. 20 c. Dunes, Sperr Gebiet 60 60

89 Kraal

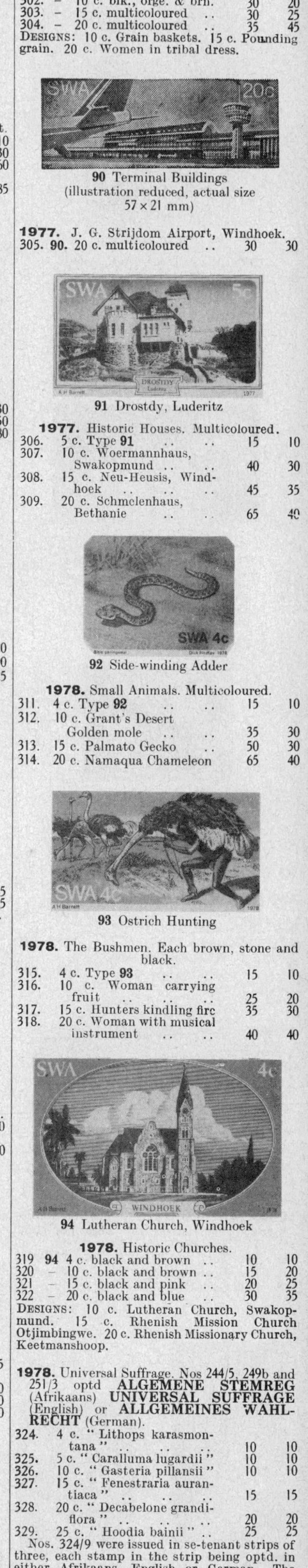

1977. The Ovambo People.
301. **89.** 4 c. multicoloured .. 10 10
302. – 10 c. blk., orge. & brn. 30 20
303. – 15 c. multicoloured .. 30 25
304. – 20 c. multicoloured .. 35 45
DESIGNS: 10 c. Grain baskets. 15 c. Pounding grain. 20 c. Women in tribal dress.

90 Terminal Buildings (illustration reduced, actual size 57×21 mm)

1977. J. G. Strijdom Airport, Windhoek.
305. **90.** 20 c. multicoloured .. 30 30

91 Drostdy, Luderitz

1977. Historic Houses. Multicoloured.
306. 5 c. Type **91** 15 10
307. 10 c. Woermannhaus, Swakopmund 40 30
308. 15 c. Neu-Heusis, Windhoek 45 35
309. 20 c. Schmelenhaus, Bethanie 65 40

92 Side-winding Adder

1978. Small Animals. Multicoloured.
311. 4 c. Type **92** 15 10
312. 10 c. Grant's Desert Golden mole 35 30
313. 15 c. Palmato Gecko .. 50 30
314. 20 c. Namaqua Chameleon 65 40

93 Ostrich Hunting

1978. The Bushmen. Each brown, stone and black.
315. 4 c. Type **93** 15 10
316. 10 c. Woman carrying fruit 25 20
317. 15 c. Hunters kindling fire 35 30
318. 20 c. Woman with musical instrument 40 40

94 Lutheran Church, Windhoek

1978. Historic Churches.
319 **94** 4 c. black and brown .. 10 10
320 – 10 c. black and brown .. 15 20
321 – 15 c. black and pink .. 20 25
322 – 20 c. black and blue .. 30 35
DESIGNS: 10 c. Lutheran Church, Swakopmund. 15 c. Rhenish Mission Church Otjimbingwe. 20 c. Rhenish Missionary Church, Keetmanshoop.

1978. Universal Suffrage. Nos 244/5. 249b and 251/3 optd **ALGEMENE STEMREG** (Afrikaans) **UNIVERSAL SUFFRAGE** (English) or **ALLGEMEINES WAHLRECHT** (German).
324. 4 c. "Lithops karasmontana" 10 10
325. 5 c. "Caralluma lugardii" 10 10
326. 10 c. "Gasteria pillansii" 10 10
327. 15 c. "Fenestraria aurantiaca" 15 15
328. 20 c. "Decabelone grandiflora" 20 20
329. 25 c. "Hoodia bainii" .. 25 25
Nos. 324/9 were issued in se-tenant strips of three, each stamp in the strip being optd. in either Afrikaans, English or German. The same prices apply for any of the three languages

96 Greater Flamingo

1979. Water Birds. Multicoloured.

330. 4 c. Type **96** 20 10
331. 15 c. White-breasted cormorant 45 25
332. 20 c. Chestnut-banded sand plover 50 35
333. 25 c. Eastern white pelican 55 40

97 Silver Topaz

1979. Gemstones. Multicoloured.

334. 4 c. Type **97** 25 10
335. 15 c. Aquamarine .. 55 20
336. 20 c. Malachite 60 25
337. 25 c. Amethyst 60 30

98 Killer Whale

1980. Whales. Multicoloured.

338. 4 c. Type **98** 35 10
339. 5 c. Humpback Whale (38 × 22 mm.) 40 10
340. 10 c. Black Right Whale (38 × 22 mm.) 55 30
341. 15 c. Sperm Whale (58 × 22 mm.) .. .. .. 1·00 60
342. 20 c. Fin Whale (58 × 22 mm.) .. .. .. 1·25 80
343. 25 c. Blue Whale (88 × 22 mm.) .. .. .. 1·60 1·10

99 Impala

1980. 25th Anniv. of Division of Nature Conservation and Tourism. Antelopes. Mult.

345. 5 c. Type **99** 15 10
346. 10 c. Topi 20 10
347. 15 c. Roan Antelope .. 40 15
348. 20 c. Sable Antelope .. 50 20

100 Black-backed Jackal

101 Meerkat

1980. Wildlife. Multicoloured.

349 1 c. Type **100** 15 10
350 2 c. Hunting dog 30 10
351 3 c. Brown hyena 20 10
352 4 c. Springbok 20 10
353 5 c. Gemsbok 20 10
354 6 c. Greater kudu 20 10
355 7 c. Mountain zebra (horiz.) 40 20
356 8 c. Cape porcupine (horiz.) 30 10
357 9 c. Ratel (horiz.) 30 10
358 10 c. Cheetah (horiz.) .. 30 10
358a 11 c. Blue wildebeest .. 40 30
358b 12 c. African buffalo (horiz.) 50 80
358c 14 c. Caracal (horiz.) .. 2·25 1·40
359 15 c. Hippopotamus (horiz.) 30 10
359ba 16 c. Warthog (horiz.) .. 1·25 1·25
360 20 c. Eland (horiz.) .. 30 10
361 25 c. Black rhinoceros (horiz.) 40 20
362 30 c. Lion (horiz.) 70 20
363 50 c. Giraffe 50 30
364 1 r. Leopard 90 55
365 2 r. African elephant .. 1·00 90

1980. Coil stamps. Wildlife.

366. **101.** 1 c. brown 15 15
367. – 2 c. blue 15 15
368. – 5 c. green 20 20

DESIGNS: 2 c. Savanna Monkey 5 c. Chacma Baboon.

102 Von Bach
(Illustration reduced, actual size 57 × 21 mm)

1980. Water Conservation. Dams. Mult.

369. 5 c. Type **102** 10 10
370. 10 c. Swakoppoort .. 15 10
371. 15 c. Naute 20 20
372. 20 c. Hardap 25 25

103 View of Fish River Canyon

1981. Fish River Canyon.

373. – 5 c. multicoloured .. 10 10
374. – 15 c. multicoloured .. 20 20
375. – 20 c. multicoloured .. 25 25
376. **103.** 25 c. multicoloured .. 30 30

DESIGNS: 5 c. to 20 c. Various views of canyon.

104 "Aloe erinacea"

1981. Aloes. Multicoloured.

377. 5 c. Type **104** 15 10
378. 15 c. "Aloe viridiflora" .. 35 25
379. 20 c. "Aloe pearsonii" .. 40 25
380. 25 c. "Aloe littoralis" .. 50 30

105 Paul Weiss-Haus

1981. Historic Buildings of Luderitz. Mult.

381. 5 c. Type **105** 10 10
382. 15 c. Deutsche Afrika Bank 20 20
383. 20 c. Schroederhaus .. 30 30
384. 25 c. Altes Postamt .. 30 35

106 Salt Plain

1981. Salt Industry. Multicoloured.

386. 5 c. Type **106** 10 10
387. 15 c. Dumping and washing 20 20
388. 20 c. Loading by conveyor 25 30
389. 25 c. Dispatch to refinery 30 35

107 Kalahari Starred Tortoise ("psammobates oculifer")

1982. Tortoises. Multicoloured.

390. 5 c. Type **107** 15 10
391. 15 c. Leopard Tortoise ("geochelone pardalis") 25 25
392. 20 c. Angulate Tortoise ("chersina angulata") 30 35
393. 25 c. Speckled Padloper ("homopus signatus") 40 45

108 Mythical Sea-monster

1982. Discoverers of South West Africa (1st series). Multicoloured.

394. 15 c. Type **108** 20 20
395. 20 c. Bartolomeu Dias and map of Africa showing voyage 30 30
396. 25 c. Dias' caravel .. 55 40
397. 30 c. Dias erecting commemorative cross, Angra das Voltas, 25 July, 1488 55 45

See also Nos. 455/8.

109 Brandberg

1982. Mountains of South West Africa. Mult.

398. 6 c. Type **109** 10 10
399. 15 c. Omatako 20 20
400. 20 c. Die Nadel 25 30
401. 25 c. Spitzkuppe 30 35

110 Otjikaeva Head-dress of Herero Woman

1982. Traditional Head-dresses of South Africa (1st series). Multicoloured.

402. 6 c. Type **110** 10 10
403. 15 c. Ekori head-dress of Himba 25 35
404. 20 c. Oshikoma hair-piece and iiponda plaits of Ngandjera 35 45
405. 25 c. Omhatela head-dress of Kwanyama 35 60

See also Nos 427/30.

111 Fort Vogelsang

1983. Centenary of Luderitz.

406 **111** 6 c. black and red .. 10 10
407 – 20 c. black and brown 25 30
408 – 25 c. black and brown 30 35
409 – 30 c. black and purple 35 40
410 – 40 c. black and green 50 55

DESIGNS—VERT. (23 × 29 mm.) 20 c. Chief Joseph Fredericks. 30 c. Heinrich Vogelsang (founder). 40 c. Adolf Luderitz (colonial promoter). HORIZ. (As T **111**) 25 c. Angra Pequena.

112 Searching for Diamonds, Kolmanskop, 1908

1983. 75th Anniv. of Discovery of Diamonds.

411. **112.** 10 c. dp. brn. & brn... 15 15
412. – 20 c. red and brown .. 30 30
413. – 25 c. blue and brown .. 35 35
414. – 40 c. black and brown 55 55

DESIGNS—HORIZ. (34 × 19 mm.). 20 c. Digging for diamonds, Kolmanskop, 1908. VERT. (19 × 26 mm.). 25 c. Sir Ernest Oppenheimer (industrialist). 40 c. August Stauch (prospector).

113 "Common Zebras drinking" (J. van Ellinckhuijzen)

1983. Painters of South West Africa. Mult.

415. 10 c. Type **113** 15 15
416. 20 c. "Rossing Mountain" (H. Henckert) 25 30
417. 25 c. "Stampeding African buffalo" (F. Krampe) .. 30 35
418. 40 c. "Erongo Mountains" (J. H. Blatt) 50 55

114 The Rock Lobster

1983. The Lobster Industry. Multicoloured.

419. 10 c. Type **114** 15 15
420. 20 c. Mother ship and fishing dinghies 25 30
421. 25 c. Netting lobsters from a dinghy 30 35
422. 40 c. Packing lobsters .. 50 55

115 Hohenzollern House

1984. Historic Buildings of Swakopmund.

423. **115.** 10 c. black & brown .. 15 15
424. – 20 c. black and blue .. 30 25
425. – 25 c. black & green .. 30 30
426. – 30 c. black & brown .. 35 30

DESIGNS: 20 c. Railway Station. 25 c. Imperial District Bureau. 30 c. Ritterburg.

1984. Traditional Head-dresses of South West Africa (2nd series). As T **110**. Mult.

427. 11 c. Eendjushi head-dress of Kwambi 25 15
428. 20 c. Bushman woman .. 40 25
429. 25 c. Omulenda head-dress of Kwaluudhi 45 30
430. 30 c. Mbukushu women .. 45 30

116 Map and German Flag

1984. Centenary of German Colonisation. Multicoloured.

431	11 c. Type **116**	25	15
432	25 c. Raising the German flag, 1884	50	50
433	30 c. German Protectorate boundary marker . .	50	60
434	45 c. "Elizabeth" and "Leipzig" (German Corvettes	1·25	1·75

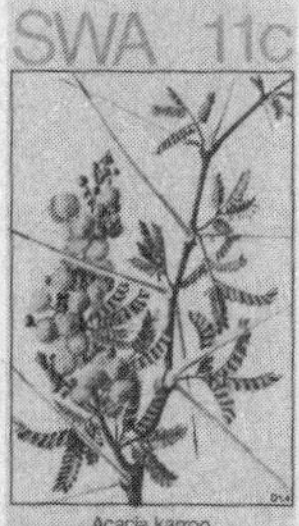

117 Sweet Thorn

1984. Spring in South West Africa. Mult.

435.	11 c. Type **117**	25	15
436.	25 c. Camel Thorn . .	50	35
437.	30 c. Hook Thorn	55	45
438.	45 c. Candle-pod Acacia . .	70	70

118 Head of Ostrich

1985. Ostriches. Multicoloured.

439.	11 c. Type **118**	40	10
440.	25 c. Ostrich on eggs . .	70	30
441.	30 c. Newly-hatched chick and eggs	80	50
442.	50 c. Mating dance . .	1·10	75

119 Kaiserstrasse

1985. Historic Buildings of Windhoek.

443.	**119.** 12 c. black and brown	25	10
444.	– 25 c. black and green	45	25
445.	– 30 c. black and brown	45	30
446.	– 50 c. black and brown	90	70

DESIGNS: 25 c. Turnhalle. 30 c. Old Supreme Court Building. 50 c. Railway Station.

120 Zwilling Locomotive

1985. Narrow-gauge Railway Locomotives. Multicoloured.

447.	12 c. Type **120**	30	10
448.	25 c. Feldspur side-tank locomotive	60	25
449.	30 c. Jung and Henschel side-tank locomotive . .	70	35
450.	50 c. Henschel Hd locomotive	90	60

121 Lidumu-dumu (keyboard instrument)

1985. Traditional Musical Instrument. Mult.

451.	12 c. Type **121**	10	10
452.	25 c. Ngoma (drum) . .	20	20
453.	30 c. Okambulumbumbwa (stringed instrument) . .	25	25
454.	50 c. Gwashi (stringed instrument)	35	35

122 Erecting Commemorative Pillar at Cape Cross, 1486

1986. Discoverers of South West Africa (2nd series). Diogo Cao.

455.	**122.** 12 c. black, grey and green	35	10
456.	– 20 c. black, grey and brown	55	25
457.	– 25 c. black, grey and blue	70	35
458.	– 30 c. black, grey & purple	85	60

DESIGNS: 20 c. Diogo Cao's coat of arms. 25 c. Caravel. 30 c. Diogo Cao.

123 Ameib Erongo Mountains

1986. Rock Formations. Multicoloured.

459.	14 c. Type **123**	60	15
460.	20 c. Vingerklip, near Outjo	70	25
461.	25 c. Petrified sand dunes, Kuiseb River . .	85	40
462.	30 c. Orgelpfeifen, Twyfelfontein	95	55

124 Model wearing Swakara Coat

1986. Karakul Industry. Multicoloured.

463.	14 c. Type **124**	35	15
464.	20 c. Weaving karakul wool carpet	55	30
465.	25 c. Flock of karakul ewes in veld	55	45
466.	30 c. Karakul rams . .	75	60

125 Pirogue, Lake Liambezi

1986. Life in the Caprivi Strip. Mult.

467.	14 c. Type **125**	50	15
468.	20 c. Ploughing with oxen	80	65
469.	25 c. Settlement in Eastern Caprivi	1·00	90
470.	30 c. Map of Caprivi Strip	1·25	1·25

126 "Gobabis Mission Station", 1863

1987. Paintings by Thomas Baines. Multicoloured.

471.	14 c. Type **126**	50	15
472.	20 c. "Outspan at Koobie". 1861	90	75
473.	25 c. "Outspan under Oomahaama Tree", 1862	1·25	1·25
474.	30 c. "Swakop River", 1861	1·50	1·50

127 "Garreta nitens" (beetle)

1987. Useful Insects. Multicoloured.

475	16 c. Type **127**	60	15
476	20 c. "Alcimus stenurus" (fly)	95	75
477	25 c. "Anthophora caerulea" (bee) . .	1·25	1·25
478	30 c. "Hemiempusa capensis" (mantid) . .	1·60	1·60

128 Okaukuejo

1987. Tourist Camps. Multicoloured.

479.	16 c. Type **128**	55	15
480.	20 c. Daan Viljoen . .	70	70
481.	25 c. Ai-Ais	80	85
482.	30 c. Hardap	85	95

129 Wreck of "Hope" (Dutch whaling schooner, 1804)

1987. Shipwrecks. Multicoloured.

483	16 c. Type **129**	60	15
484	30 c. "Tilly" (brig), 1885	1·00	1·00
485	40 c. "Eduard Bohlen" (steamer), 1909	1·25	1·50
486	50 c. "Dunedin Star" (liner), 1942	1·50	1·75

130 Bartolomeu Dias

1988. 500th Anniv. of Discovery of Cape of Good Hope by Bartolomeu Dias. Mult.

487.	16 c. Type **130**	45	15
488.	30 c. Caravel	85	55
489.	40 c. Map of South West Africa, c. 1502	1·00	70
490.	50 c. King Joao II of Portugal	1·00	75

131 Sossusvlei

1988. Landmarks of South West Africa. Multicoloured.

491.	16 c. Type **131**	45	15
492.	30 c. Sesriem Canyon . .	80	55
493.	40 c. Hoaruseb "clay castles"	95	70
494.	50 c. Hoba meteorite . .	1·00	75

132 1st Postal Agency, Otyimbingue, 1888

1988. Centenary of Postal Service in South West Africa. Multicoloured.

495	16 c. Type **132**	45	15
496	30 c. Post Office, Windhoek, 1904 . .	80	55
497	40 c. Mail-runner and map	90	70
498	50 c. Camel mail, 1904 . .	1·00	75

133 Herero Chat

1988. Birds of South West Africa. Mult.

499	16 c. Type **133**	55	15
500	30 c. Gray's lark	85	60
501	40 c. Ruppell's bustard . .	1·10	75
502	50 c. Monteiro's hornbill . .	1·25	80

134 Dr. C. H. Hahn and Gross-Barmen Mission

1989. Missionaries. Multicoloured.

503	16 c. Type **134**	40	10
504	30 c. Revd. J. G. Kronlein and Berseba Mission . .	70	50
505	40 c. Revd. F. H. Kleinschmidt and Rehoboth Mission . .	80	65
506	50 c. Revd. J. H. Schmelen and Bethanien Mission	85	70

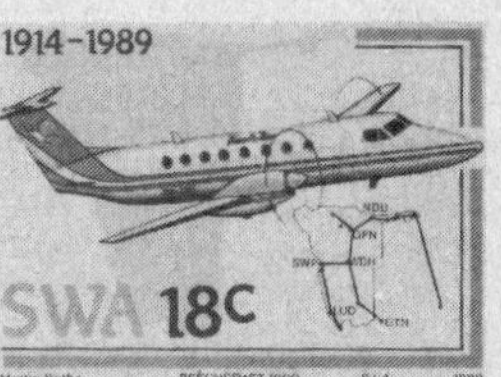

135 Beechcraft "1900"

1989. 75th Anniv of Aviation in South West Africa. Multicoloured.

507	18 c. Type **135**	40	15
508	30 c. Ryan "Navion" . .	70	50
509	40 c. Junkers "F13" . .	80	55
510	50 c. Pfalz "Otto" biplane	90	70

136 Barchan Dunes
(illustration reduced, actual size 57 × 21 mm)

1989. Namib Desert Sand Dunes. Mult.

511		18 c. Type **136**	35	15
512		30 c. Star dunes (36 × 20 mm)	65	40
513		40 c. Transverse dunes ..	75	60
514		50 c. Crescentic dunes (36 × 20 mm)	1·00	80

137 Ballot Box and Outline Map of South West Africa

1989. South West Africa Constitutional Election.

515	**137**	18 c. brown and orange	35	15
516		35 c. blue and green ..	60	40
517		45 c. purple and yellow	80	60
518		60 c. green and ochre	95	80

138 Gypsum

140 Arrow Poison

139 Oranjemund Alluvial Diamond Field

1989. Minerals. Multicoloured

519	1 c. Type **138**	10	10
520	2 c. Fluorite	10	10
521	5 c. Mimetite	10	10
522	7 c. Cuprite	10	10
523	10 c. Azurite	10	10
524	18 c. Boltwoodite ..	20	10
525	20 c. Dioptase	30	15
526	25 c. Type **139**	30	15
527	30 c. Tsumeb lead and copper complex ..	45	20
528	35 c. Rosh Pinah zinc mine	45	20
529	40 c. Diamonds	60	30
530	45 c. Wulfenite	60	30
531	50 c. Uis tin mine ..	70	30
532	1 r. Rossing uranium mine	1·25	80
533	2 r. Gold	1·75	1·50

The 1, 2, 5, 7, 10, 18, 20, 40, 45 c. and 2 r. are vert as T **138**, and the 25, 30, 35, 50 c. and 1 r. horiz as T **139**.

1990. Flora. Multicoloured.

534	18 c. Type **140** ..	45	10
535	35 c. Baobab flower ..	85	40
536	45 c. Sausage tree flowers	95	50
537	60 c. Devil's claw ..	1·10	90

MINIMUM PRICE

The minimum price quoted is 10p which represents a handling charge rather than a basis for valuing common stamps. For further notes about prices see introductory pages.

OFFICIAL STAMPS

1927. Pictorial and portrait (2d.) stamps alternately optd. **OFFICIAL South West Africa** or **OFFISIEEL Suidwes Afrika.**

O 1.	**6.**	½d. black and green ..	65·00	30·00
O 2.	**7.**	1d. black and red ..	65·00	30·00
O 3.	**2.**	2d. purple	£150	45·00
O 4.	**8.**	6d. green and orange ..	85·00	30·00

Mint prices are for pairs.

1929. Pictorial stamps alternately optd **OFFICIAL S.W.A.** or **OFFISIEEL, S.W.A.** horizontally or vertically

O 9.	**6.**	½d. black and green ..	65	2·75
O 10.		1d. black and red ..	75	2·75
O 11.	**11.**	2d. grey and purple ..	90	3·25
O 12.	**8.**	6d. green and orange	3·00	6·50

1931. Optd. alternately **OFFICIAL** or **OFFISIEEL** in small capital letters.

O 13.	**12.**	½d. black and green ..	7·50	3·50
O 14.	–	1d. blue and red ..	75	3·50
O 15.	–	2d. blue and brown ..	70	3·25
O 16.	–	6d. blue and brown ..	2·25	3·25

1938. Optd. alternately **OFFICIAL** or **OFFISIEEL** in large capital letters.

O18	**12**	½d. black and green ..	8·00	4·50
O24	–	1d. blue & red (No. 75)	1·50	1·75
O25	**27**	1½d. brown	22·00	4·75
O26	–	2d. blue & brn. (No. 76)	1·00	3·25
O22	–	6d. blue & brn. (No. 79)	7·50	5·00

POSTAGE DUE STAMPS

1923. Postage Due stamps of Transvaal optd. **South West Africa**, or **Zuidwest Afrika.**

D 25.	D **1.**	5d. black and violet	2·50	3·25
D 2.		6d. black and brown	17·00	10·00

1923. Postage Due stamps of S. Africa optd as last.

D23	D **1.**	½d. black and green ..	2·25	6·00
D28		1d. black and red ..	1·40	1·50
D 8		1½d. black and brown	1·00	2·75
D30		2d. black and violet ..	2·50	3·00
D31		3d. black and blue ..	3·00	3·25
D20		6d. black and grey ..	2·25	9·00

1927. Postage Due stamp of Transvaal optd. **Suidwes Afrika.***

D33	D **1**	5d. black and violet ..	18·00	22·00

*The corresponding English overprint used here is the same, for the purposes of this catalogue, as that on No. D 25.

1927. Postage Due Stamps of S. Africa optd as last*.

D 39.	D **2.**	1d. black and red ..	1·00	2·25
D 34.	D **1.**	1½d. black and brown	80	3·00
D 35.		2d. black and violet ..	2·75	3·00
D 37.		3d. black and blue ..	11·00	10·00
D 38.		6d. black and grey ..	7·00	8·00

*The corresponding English overprint used here is the same, for the purposes of this catalogue, as that on Nos. D 28, D 7, D 30/1 and D 20.

1928. Postage Due stamps of S. Africa (Type D 1) optd. **S.W.A.**

D 40.	D **1.**	3d. black and blue	50	11·00
D 41.		6d. black and grey ..	8·00	23·00

1928. Postage Due stamps of S. Africa (Type D 2) optd. **S.W.A.**

D 42.	D **2.**	½d. black and green ..	40	7·00
D 43.		1d. black and red ..	40	3·25
D 44.		2d. black and mauve	40	3·50
D 45.		3d. black and blue ..	1·75	18·00
D 46.		6d. black and grey ..	1·00	18·00

D 3

1931. Size 19 × 23½ mm.

D 47.	D **3.**	½d. black and green	60	6·00
D 48.		1d. black and red ..	60	1·25
D 49.		2d. black and violet	70	2·50
D 50.		3d. black and blue ..	2·50	14·00
D 51.		6d. black and slate ..	10·00	22·00

1959. As Type D **3** but smaller (17⅛ × 21 mm.).

D55	1d. black and red ..	2·75	4·50
D53	2d. black and violet ..	1·25	11·00
D56	3d. black and blue ..	2·75	6·50

1961. As Nos. D 52, etc., but value in cents.

D 57.	1 c. black and turquoise	60	3·00
D 58.	2 c. black and red ..	60	3·00
D 59.	4 c. black and violet ..	60	3·00
D 60.	5 c. black and blue ..	1·00	3·50
D 61.	6 c. black and green ..	1·00	5·00
D 62.	10 c. black and yellow ..	2·25	6·50

1972. As Type D **8** of South Africa. Inscr. "SWA".

D 63.	1 c. green	75	3·75
D 64.	8 c. blue	3·00	7·00

For subsequent issues see NAMIBIA.

SOUTHERN CAMEROONS

The southern area of that part of the Cameroun which was formerly under British trusteeship. Following a plebiscite it became an autonomous state on 1st October 1960, but after another plebiscite it became part of the independent republic of Cameroun (see volume 1) on 30th September 1961.

12 pence = 1 shilling.
20 shillings = 1 pound.

1960. Stamps of Nigeria of 1953 optd. **CAMEROONS U.K.T.T.**

1	**18**	½d. black and orange ..	10	20
2	–	1d. black and bronze ..	10	10
3	–	1½d. turquoise	10	15
4	–	2d. slate	10	15
5	–	3d. black and lilac ..	15	10
6	–	4d. black and blue ..	10	40
7	–	6d. brown and black ..	20	10
8	–	1s. black and purple ..	15	10
9	**26**	2s. 6d. black and green ..	80	80
10	–	5s. black and red ..	90	2·75
11	–	10s. black and brown ..	2·25	3·00
12	**29**	£1 black and violet ..	6·50	11·00

This issue was also on sale in Northern Cameroons.

SOUTHERN NIGERIA

A British possession on the west coast of Africa. In 1914 joined with Northern Nigeria to form Nigeria (q.v.).

12 pence = 1 shilling.
20 shillings = 1 pound.

1.

1901.

1a	**1**	½d. brown and green ..	75	60
2		1d. black and red ..	85	60
3		2d. black and brown ..	1·75	3·50
4		4d. black and green ..	1·75	7·00
5		6d. black and purple ..	1·75	3·75
6		1s. green and black ..	7·00	16·00
7		2s. 6d. black and brown ..	32·00	60·00
8		5s. black and yellow ..	38·00	80·00
9		10s. black & purple on yell	65·00	£130

2.

3.

1903.

21	**2**	½d. black and green ..	40	10
11		1d. black and red ..	1·25	15
23		2d. black and brown ..	2·50	45
24		2½d. black and blue ..	1·00	95
25		3d. brown and purple ..	8·50	1·25
14		4d. black and green ..	1·75	3·50
27		6d. black and purple ..	6·00	1·00
28		1s. green and black ..	2·75	1·75
29		2s. 6d. black and brown ..	15·00	9·00
30		5s. black and yellow ..	30·00	55·00
19		10s. black & pur. on yellow	25·00	65·00
32ab		£1 green and violet ..	£100	£140

1907.

33b	**2.**	½d. green	50	20
34ab		1d. red	50	10
35		2d. grey	1·00	70
36		2½d. blue	1·00	3·75
37		3d. purple on yellow ..	1·00	30
38		4d. black & red on yellow	70	80
39		6d. purple	12·00	3·00
40		1s. black on green ..	7·00	40
41		2s. 6d. black & red on blue	4·50	90
42		5s. green & red on yellow	26·00	48·00
43		10s. green & red on green	55·00	85·00
44		£1 purple & black on red	£140	£150

1912.

45.	**3.**	½d. green	80	10
46.		1d. red	70	10
47.		2d. grey	60	85
48.		2½d. blue	2·50	2·75
49.		3d. purple on yellow ..	75	30
50.		4d. black & red on yellow	70	2·00
51.		6d. purple	75	1·25
52.		1s. black on green ..	2·25	75
53.		2s. 6d. blk. & red on bl.	5·00	13·00
54.		5s. green & red on yellow	13·00	48·00
55.		10s. green & red on grn.	35·00	75·00
56.		$1 purple & blk. on red	£140	£150

SOUTHERN RHODESIA

A Br. territory in the N. part of S. Africa, S. of the Zambesi. In 1954 became part of the Central African Federation which issued its own stamps inscribed "Rhodesia and Nyasaland" (q.v.), until 1964 when it resumed issuing its own stamps after the break-up of the Federation. In October, 1964, Southern Rhodesia was renamed Rhodesia.

12 pence = 1 shilling.
20 shillings = 1 pound.

1.

1924.

1.	**1.**	½d. green	1·00	10
2.		1d. red	1·40	10
3.		1½d. brown	1·00	45
4.		2d. black	1·00	30
5.		3d. blue	2·00	2·00
6.		4d. black and red ..	1·50	2·75
7.		6d. black and mauve ..	1·40	2·25
8.		8d. purple and green ..	11·00	32·00
9.		10d. blue and red ..	11·00	35·00
10.		1s. black and blue ..	4·25	3·50
11.		1s. 6d. black and yellow ..	18·00	27·00
12.		2s. black and brown ..	17·00	17·00
13.		2s. 6d. blue and brown ..	35·00	50·00
14.		5s. blue and green ..	55·00	85·00

2. King George V.

3. Victoria Falls.

1931.

15a	**2.**	½d. green	40	10
16		1d. red	65	10
16d		1½d. brown	1·50	55
17	**3.**	2d. black and brown ..	3·25	70
18		3d. blue	9·00	11·00
19	**2.**	4d. black and red ..	1·10	70
20		6d. black and mauve ..	2·00	85
21		8d. violet and green ..	1·75	3·25
21b		9d. red and green ..	6·00	8·00
22		10d. blue and red ..	6·00	3·00
23		1s. black and blue ..	1·75	2·25
24		1s 6d. black and yellow ..	10·00	16·00
25		2s. black and brown ..	14·00	4·50
26a		2s. 6d. blue and brown ..	28·00	30·00
27		5s. blue and green ..	48·00	48·00

4.

1932.

29.	**4.**	2d. green and brown ..	2·50	40
30.		3d. blue	3·25	1·75

5. Victoria Falls.

1935. Silver Jubilee.

31.	**5.**	1d. green and red ..	3·00	1·00
32.		2d. green and brown ..	5·00	4·00
33.		3d. violet and blue ..	5·00	10·00
34.		6d. black and purple ..	8·00	10·00

1935. As Nos. 29/30, but inscr. "POSTAGE AND REVENUE".

35a.	**4.**	2d. green and brown ..	30	10
35b.		3d. blue	1·75	10

6. Victoria Falls and Railway Bridge.

1937. Coronation.

36.	**6.**	1d. olive and red	80	30
37.		2d. green and brown ..	80	85
38.		3d. violet and blue ..	3·75	6·00
39.		6d. black and purple ..	2·25	3·00

7. King George VI.

10. Cecil John Rhodes (after S. P. Kendrick).

8. British South Africa Co's Arms.

1937.

40. **7.** ½d. green 50 10
41. 1d. red 30 10
42. 1½d. brown .. .. 1·00 10
43. 4d. orange.. .. .. 1·50 10
44. 6d. black .. .. .. 1·50 10
45. 8d. green .. .. .. 2·00 90
46. 9d. blue .. .. .. 1·25 20
47. 10d. purple .. .. 1·75 1·75
48. 1s. black and green .. 1·50 10
49. 1s. 6d. black and yellow.. 6·50 1·25
50. 2s. black and brown .. 9·50 55
51. 2s. 6d. blue and purple .. 7·50 3·00
52. 5s. blue and green .. 26·00 2·00

1940. Golden Jubilee of British South Africa Company.

53. **8.** ½d. violet and green .. 10 20
54. – 1d. blue and red 10 10
55. **10.** 1½d. black and brown .. 15 30
56. – 2d. green and violet .. 30 30
57. – 3d. black and blue .. 30 50
58. – 4d. green and brown .. 1·60 1·25
59. – 6d. brown and green .. 30 85
60. – 1s. blue and green .. 45 1·50

Designs—Horiz. 1d. Hoisting the flag; Fort Salisbury, 1890. 2d. Pioneer Fort and mail coach, Fort Victoria. 3d. Rhodes makes peace, 1896. 1s. Queen Victoria, King George VI, Lobengula's kraal and Govt. House, Salisbury. **Vert.** 4d. Victoria Falls Bridge. 6d. Statue of Sir Charles Coghlan.

16. Mounted Pioneer.

20. King George VI.

17. Queen Elizabeth II when Princess, and Princess Margaret.

1943. 50th Anniv. of Occupation of Matabeleland.

61. **16.** 2d. brown and green .. 10 30

1947. Royal Visit.

62. **17.** ½d. black and green .. 10 30
63. – 1d. black and red .. 10 30

Design: 1d. King George VI and Queen Elizabeth.

1947. Victory.

64. – 1d. red 10 10
65. **20.** 2d. slate 10 10
66. – 3d. blue 40 30
67. – 6d. orange 20 30

Portraits: 1d. Queen Elizabeth. 3d. Queen Elizabeth II when Princess. 6d. Princess Margaret.

1949. U.P.U. As T 18/21 of Antigua.

68. 2d. green.. .. .. 80 20
69. 3d. blue .. .. .. 1·10 2·75

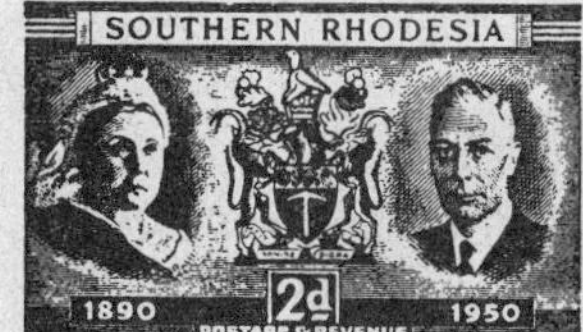

23. Queen Victoria, Arms and King George VI.

1950. Diamond Jubilee of S. Rhodesia.

70. **23.** 2d. green and brown .. 30 30

24. "Medical Services".

27. "Water Supplies".

1953. Birth Cent. of Cecil Rhodes. Inscr. "RHODES CENTENARY".

71. **24.** ½d. blue and sepia .. 15 70
72. – 1d. chestnut and green .. 15 10
73. – 2d. green and violet .. 15 10
74. **27.** 4½d. green and blue .. 75 1·75
75. – 1s. black and brown .. 3·00 70

Designs: 1d. Agricultural scene and wild animals. 2d. Township and Rhodes. 1s. Ox-cart, train and aeroplane. No. 74 also commemorates the Diamond Jubilee of Matabeleland.

1953. Rhodes Centenary Exhibition, Bulawayo. As No. 59 of Northern Rhodesia.

76. 6d. violet 30 30

30. Queen Elizabeth II.

1953. Coronation.

77. **30.** 2s. 6d. red .. .. 5·50 5·50

31. Sable Antelope.

33. Rhodes's Grave.

43. Balancing Rocks.

1953.

78. **31.** ½d. grey and claret .. 30 30
79. – 1d. green and brown .. 20 10
80. **33.** 2d. brown and violet .. 20 10
81. – 3d. brown and red .. 55 60
82. – 4d. red, green and blue.. 2·25 10
83. – 4½d. black and blue .. 2·00 2·00
84. – 6d. olive and turquoise.. 2·50 30
85. – 9d. blue and brown .. 3·50 1·75
86. – 1s. violet and blue .. 1·00 10
87. – 2s. purple and red .. 8·00 3·25
88. – 2s. 6d. olive and brown.. 6·50 3·75
89. – 5s. brown and green .. 14·00 7·50
90. **43.** 10s. brown and olive .. 16·00 35·00
91. – £1 red and black .. 25·00 35·00

Designs—As Type **31**: 1d. Tobacco planter. As Type **33**—**Horiz.** 3d. Farm worker. 4d. Flame lily. 4½d. Victoria Falls. 9d. Lion. 1s. Zimbabwe Ruins. 2s. Birchenough Bridge. 2s. 6d. Kariba Gorge. **Vert** 6d. Baobab tree. 5s. Basket maker. As Type **43**: £1, Coat of Arms.

45. Maize.

50. Flame Lily.

56. Cattle.

1964.

92. **45.** ½d. yell., green & blue.. 20 60
93. – 1d. violet and ochre .. 15 10
94. – 2d. yellow and violet .. 30 10
95. – 3d. brown and blue .. 20 10
96. – 4d. orange and green .. 30 10
97. **50.** 6d. red, yellow and green 40 10
98. – 9d. brown, yell. & green 2·00 80
99. – 1s. green and ochre .. 2·50 10
100. – 1s. 3d. red, violet & grn. 3·50 10
101. – 2s. blue and ochre .. 2·50 85
102. – 2s. 6d. blue and red .. 4·25 70
103. **56.** 5s. multicoloured .. 4·50 2·00
104. – 10s. multicoloured .. 11·00 6·50
105. – £1 multicoloured .. 7·00 13·00

Designs—As Type **45**: 1d. African buffalo. 2d. Tobacco. 3d. Greater kudu. 4d. Citrus. As Type **50**: 9d. Ansellia orchid. 1s. Emeralds. 1s. 3d. Aloe. 2s. Lake Kyle. 2s. 6d. Tiger fish. As Type **56**: 10s. Helmet guineafowl. £1 Coat of Arms.

Similar designs inscribed "RHODESIA" are listed under that heading.

POSTAGE DUE STAMPS

1951. Postage due stamps of Great Britain optd. **SOUTHERN RHODESIA.**

D 1. **D 1.** ½d. green .. .. 3·25 10·00
D 2. 1d. blue .. .. 2·50 75
D 3. 2d. black .. .. 4·00 1·75
D 4. 3d. violet .. .. 2·75 1·25
D 5. 4d. blue .. .. 1·50 2·25
D 6. 4d. green £130 £350
D 7. 1s. blue .. .. 3·00 1·75

For later issues see **RHODESIA.**

SRI LANKA

Ceylon became a republic within the British Commonwealth in 1972 and changed its name to Sri Lanka (="Resplendent Island").

100 cents = 1 rupee.

208. National Flower and Mountain of the Illustrious Foot.

1972. Inaug. of Republic of Sri Lanka.

591. **208.** 15 c. multicoloured .. 30 30

209. Map of World with Buddhist Flag.

1972. 10th World Fellowship of Buddhists. Conference.

592. **209.** 5 c. multicoloured .. 30 50

210. Book Year Emblem.

1972. Int. Book Year.

593. **210.** 20 c. orange & brown 20 30

211. Imperial Angelfish.

1972. Fish. Multicoloured.

594. 2 c. Type **211** 10 60
595. 3 c. Green Chromide .. 10 60
596. 30 c. Skipjack .. .. 1·00 30
597. 2 r. Black Ruby Barb .. 3·25 4·00

212. Memorial Hall.

1973. Opening of Bandaranaike Memorial Hall.

598. **212.** 15 c. cobalt and blue.. 30 30

213. King Vessantara giving away his Children.

1973. Rock and Temple Paintings. Mult.

599. 35 c. Type **213** 30 10
600. 50 c. The Prince and the Grave-digger 35 10
601. 90 c. Bearded old man .. 50 75
602. 1 r. 55 Two female figures 65 1·50

214. Bandaranaike Memorial Conference Hall.

1974. 20th Commonwealth Parliamentary Conf., Colombo.

604. **214.** 85 c. multicoloured .. 30 30

215. Prime Minister Bandaranaike.

1974.

605. **215.** 15 c. multicoloured .. 15 10

216. "UPU" and "100".

1974. Centenary of U.P.U.
606. **216.** 50 c. multicoloured .. 75 75

217. Sri Lanka Parliament Building.

1975. Inter-Parliamentary Meeting.
607. **217.** 1 r. multicoloured .. 30 50

218. Sir Ponnambalam Ramanathan (politician).

1975. Ramanathan Commem.
608. **218.** 75 c. multicoloured .. 30 50

219. D. J. Wimalasurendra (engineer).

1975. Wimalasurendra Commemoration.
609. **219.** 75 c. black and blue .. 30 50

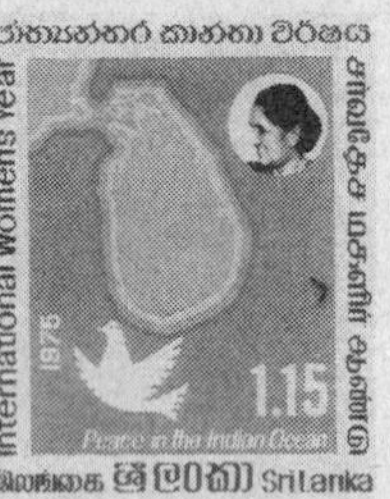

220. Mrs. Bandaranaike, Map and Dove.

1975. International Women's Year.
610. **220.** 1 r. 15 multicoloured .. 1·50 1·25

221. Ma-ratmal

1976. Indigenous Flora. Multicoloured.
611. 25 c. Type **221** 10 10
612. 50 c. Binara 10 10
613. 75 c. Daffodil orchid .. 15 15
614. 10 r. Diyapara .. .. 3·00 4·00

222. Mahaweli Dam.

1976. Mahaweli River Diversion.
616. **222.** 85 c. turq., blue & violet 30 60

223. Dish Aerial.

1976. Opening of Satellite Earth Station, Padukka.
617. **223.** 1 r. multicoloured .. 65 75

224. Conception of the Buddha.

1976. Vesek. Multicoloured.
618. 5 c. Type **224** 10 10
619. 10 c. King Suddhodana and the astrologers .. 10 10
620. 1 r. 50 The astrologers being entertained .. 30 40
621. 2 r. The Queen in a palanquin 35 45
622. 2 r. 25 Royal procession .. 40 80
623. 5 r. Birth of the Buddha .. 90 1·60
Nos. 618/23 show paintings from the Dambava Temple.

225. Blue Sapphire.

1976. Gems of Sri Lanka. Multicoloured.
625. 60 c. Type **225** .. .. 2·25 30
626. 1 r. 15 Cat's Eye .. .. 3·50 1·25
627. 2 r. Star sapphire .. 4·00 3·25
628. 5 r. Ruby .. .. .. 6·50 6·00

226. Prime Minister Mrs. S. Bandaranaike.

1976. Non-aligned Summit Conf., Colombo.
630. **226.** 1 r. 15 multicoloured .. 25 20
631. 2 r. multicoloured .. 40 35

227. Statue of Liberty.

1976. Bicent. of American Revolution.
632. **227.** 2 r. 25 light blue and deep blue 65 85

228. Bell, Early Telephone and Telephone lines.

229. Maitreya (pre-carnate Buddha).

1976. Centenary of Telephone.
633. **228.** 1 r. multicoloured .. 40 20

1976. Cent. of Colombo Museum. Mult.
634. 50 c. Type **229** 20 15
635. 1 r. Sundra Murti Swami (Tamil psalmist) .. 30 30
636. 5 r. Tara (goddess) .. 1·40 2·50

230. Kandyan Crown.

1977. Regalia of the Kings of Kandy. Multicoloured.
637. 1 r. Type **230** 35 40
638. 2 r. Throne and footstool 75 2·00

231. Sri Rahula Thero (poet).

1977. Sri Rahula Commemoration.
639. **231.** 1 r. multicoloured .. 50 55

232. Sir Ponnambalam Arunachalam.

1977. Sir Ponnambalam Arunachalam (social reformer). Commemoration.
640. **232.** 1 r. multicoloured .. 30 55

233. Brass Lamps.

1977. Handicrafts. Multicoloured.
641. 20 c. Type **233** 15 15
642. 25 c. Jewellery box .. 15 15
643. 50 c. Caparisoned elephant 30 20
644. 5 r. Mask .. .. .. 1·60 3·00

234. Siddi Lebbe (author and educationalist).

1977. Siddi Lebbe Commemoration.
646. **234.** 1 r. multicoloured .. 30 60

235. Girl Guide.

1977. 60th Anniv. of Sri Lanka Girl Guides Association.
647. **235.** 75 c. multicoloured .. 85 30

236. Parliament Building and "Wheel of Life".

1978. Election of New President.
648. **236.** 15 c. gold, grn. & emer. 20 10
For similar design in a smaller format, see Nos. 680/c.

237. Youths Running.

1978. National Youth Service Council.
649. **237.** 15 c. multicoloured .. 20 30

238. Prince Siddhartha's Renunciation.

1978. Vesak. Rock Carvings from Borobudur Temple.
650. **238.** 15 c. buff, brn. & blue 30 10
651. – 50 c. buff, brn. & blue 70 60
DESIGN: 50 c. Prince Siddhartha shaving his hair.

1978. Surch.
652 5 c. on 90 c. Beared old man (No. 601) 30 75
653 10 c. on 35 c. Type **213** .. 30 50
654 25 c. on 15 c. Type **215** .. 2·50 2·00
655 25 c. on 15 c. Type **236** .. 2·50 2·00
656 25 c. on 15 c. Type **237** .. 2·50 2·00
657 1 r. on 1 r. 55 Two female figures (No. 602) .. 75 45

240. Veera Puran Appu.

241. "Troides helena".

1978. 130th Death Anniv. of Veera Puran Appu (revolutionary).

658. **240.** 15 c. multicoloured .. 15 20

1978. Butterflies. Multicoloured.

659 25 c. Type **241** 20 10
660 50 c. "Cethosia nietneri" .. 50 10
661 5 r. "Kallima horsfieldi" 1·25 1·25
662 10 r. "Papilio polymnestor" .. .. 1·50 1·75

1979. No. 486 of Ceylon surch. **SRI LANKA 15.**

664. 15 c. on 10 c. green .. 80 65

243. Prince Danta and Princess Hema Mala bringing the Sacred Tooth Relic from Kalinga. **244.** Piyadasa Sirisena.

1979. Vesak. Kelaniya Temple Paintings. Multicoloured.

665. 25 c. Type **243** 10 10
666. 1 r. Theri Sanghamitta bringing the Bodhi Tree branch to Sri Lanka .. 15 15
667. 10 r. King Kirti Sri Rajasinghe offering fan of authority to the Sangha Raja .. .. .. 95 1·40

1979. Piyadasa Sirisena (writer) Commem.

669. **244.** 1 r. 25 multicoloured .. 20 20

245. Wrestlers. **246.** Dudley Senanayake.

1979. Wood Carvings from Embekke Temple.

670. **245.** 20 r. brn., ochre & grn. 1·25 1·50
671. – 50 r. agate, yell. & grn. 2·50 3·25

DESIGN: 50 r. Dancer.

1979. Dudley Senanayake (former Prime Minister) Commemoration.

672. **246.** 1 r. 25 green 15 20

247. Mother with Child.

1979. International Year of the Child. Multicoloured.

673. 5 c. Type **247** 10 10
674. 3 r. Superimposed heads of children of different races 30 70
675. 5 r. Children playing .. 40 80

248. Ceylon 1857 6d. Stamp and Sir Rowland Hill.

1979. Death Centenary of Sir Rowland Hill.

676. **248.** 3 r. multicoloured .. 25 45

249. Conference Emblem and Parliament Building.

1979. International Conference of Parliamentarians on Population and Development, Colombo.

677. **249.** 2 r. multicoloured .. 40 60

250. Airline Emblem on Aircraft Tail-fin. **251.** Coconut Tree.

1979. Inauguration of "Airlanka" Airline.

678. **250.** 3 r. blk., blue and red 40 75

1979. 10th Anniv. of Asian and Pacific Coconut Community.

679. **251.** 2 r. multicoloured .. 50 75

1979. As No. 648, but 20 × 24 mm.

680. **236.** 25 c. gold, green and emerald 15 20
680a. 50 c. gold, green and emerald .. .. 1·50 10
680b. 60 c. gold, green and emerald .. .. 3·25 1·25
680c. 75 c. gold, green and emerald 10 10

252. Swami Vipulananda.

1979. Swami Vipulananda (philosopher). Commemoration.

681. **252.** 1 r. 25 multicoloured .. 20 30

253. Inscription and Crescent.

1979. 1500th Anniv. of Hegira (Mohammedan Religion).

682. **253.** 3 r. 75 black, green and blue-green .. .. 35 1·00

254. "The Great Teacher" (Institute emblem). **255.** Ceylon Blue Magpie.

1979. 50th Anniv. of Institute of Ayurveda (school of medicine).

683. **254.** 15 c. multicoloured .. 30 40

1979. Birds (1st series). Multicoloured.

684. 10 c. Type **255** 10 10
685. 15 c. Ceylon Hanging Parrot 10 10
686. 75 c. Ceylon Whistling Thrush 15 15
687. 1 r. Ceylon Spurfowl .. 15 15
688. 5 r. Yellow fronted Barbet 60 1·25
689. 10 r. Yellow tufted Bulbul 75 1·75

See also Nos. 827/30 and 985/8.

256. Rotary International Emblem and Map of Sri Lanka.

1980. 75th Anniv. of Rotary International and 50th Anniv. of Sri Lanka Rotary Movement.

691. **256.** 1 r. 50 multicoloured 40 65

257. A. Ratnayake.

1980. 80th Birth Anniv. of A. Ratnayake (politician).

692. **257.** 1 r. 25 green 20 30

1980. No. 680 surch.

693. **236.** 35 c. on 25 c. gold, green and emerald .. 15 15

259. Tank and Stupa (symbols of Buddhist culture).

1980. 60th Anniv. of All Ceylon Buddhist Congress. Multicoloured.

694. 10 c. Type **259** 10 30
695. 35 c. Bo-leaf wheel and Fan 10 20

260. Colonel Olcott.

1980. Centenary of Arrival of Colonel Olcott (campaigner for Buddhism).

696. **260.** 2 r. multicoloured .. 60 75

261. Patachara's Journey through Forest.

1980. Vesak. Details from Temple Paintings, Purvaramaya, Kataluwa. Multicoloured.

697. 35 c. Type **261** 15 15
698. 1 r. 60 Patachara crossing river .. .. .. 50 1·00

262. George E. de Silva.

1980. George E. de Silva (politician). Commemoration.

699. **262.** 1 r. 60 multicoloured .. 20 30

263. Dalada Maligawa.

1980. U.N.E.S.C.O. – Sri Lanka Project.

700. **263.** 35 c. claret 10 15
701. – 35 c. grey 10 15
702. – 35 c. red 10 15
703. – 1 r. 60 olive 30 40
704. – 1 r. 60 green 30 40
705. – 1 r. 60 brown 30 40

DESIGNS: No. 701, Dambulla. No. 702, Alahana Pirivena. No. 703, Jetavanarama. No. 704, Abhayagiri. No. 705, Sigiri.

264. Co-operation Symbols.

1980. 50th Anniv. of co-operative Department.

707. **264.** 20 c. multicoloured .. 10 20

265. Lanka Mahila Samiti Emblem.

1980. 50th Anniv. of Lanka Mahila Samiti (Rural Women's Movement).

708. **265.** 35 c. vio., red & yellow 10 20

266. The Holy Family.

1980. Christmas. Multicoloured.

709. 35 c. Type **266** 10 10
710. 3 r. 75 The Three Wise Men 35 60

267. Colombo Public Library.

1980. Opening of Colombo Public Library.

712. **267.** 35 c. multicoloured .. 10 10

268. Flag of Walapane Disawa.

1980. Ancient Flags.

713. **268.** 10 c. blk., grn. & pur. 10 10
714. – 25 c. blk., yell. & pur. 10 10
715. – 1 r. 60 blk., yell. & pur. 15 20
716. – 20 r. blk., yell. & pur. 1·25 2·50

DESIGNS: 25 c. Flag of the Gajanayaka, Huduhumpola, Kandy. 1 r. 60, Sinhala royal flag. 20 r. Sinhala royal flag, Ratnapura.

269. Fishing Cat.

1981. Animals. Multicoloured.

718. 2 r. 50 on 1 r. 60 Type **269** 15 15
719. 3 r. on 1 r. 50 Golden palm civet 15 20
720. 4 r. on 2 r. Indian spotted chevrotain 25 30
721. 5 r. on 3 r. 15 Rusty-spotted cat 35 45

Nos. 718/21 are previously unissued stamps surcharged as in T **269**.

For stamps with revised face values see Nos. 780/3.

270. Heads and Houses on Map of Sri Lanka.

1981. Population and Housing Census.

723. **270.** 50 c. multicoloured .. 30 50

271. Sri Lanka Light Infantry Regimental Badge.

1981. Centenary of Sri Lanka Light Infantry.

724. **271.** 2 r. multicoloured .. 80 50

272. Panel from " The Great Stupa " in Honour of the Buddha, Sanci, India, 1st-century A.D.

1981. Vesak. Festival.

725. **272.** 35 c. blk., dk. gn. & grn. 10 10
726. – 50 c. multicoloured .. 10 10
727. – 7 r. black and pink .. 40 1·40

DESIGNS: 50 c. Silk banner representing a Bodhisattva from " Thousand Buddhas ", Tun-Huang, Central Asia. 7 r. Bodhisattva from Fondukistan, Afghanistan.

273. St. John Baptist de la Salle.

1981. 300th Anniv. of De La Salle Brothers (Religious Order of the Brothers of the Christian Schools).

729. **273.** 2 r. pink, light bl. & bl. 70 80

274. Rev. Polwatte Sri Buddadatta

1981. National Heroes.

730. **274.** 50 c. brown 40 55
731. – 50 c. pink 40 55
732. – 50 c. mauve 40 55

DESIGNS: No. 731, Rev. Mohottiwatte Gunananda. No. 732, Dr. Gnanaprakasar. **(each a scholar, writer and Buddhist campaigner).**

275. Dr. Al-Haj T. B. Jayah.

1981. Dr. Al-Haj T. B. Jayah (statesman) Commemoration.

733. **275.** 50 c. green 30 50

276. Dr. N. M. Perera.

1981. Dr. N. M. Perera (campaigner for social reform) Commemoration.

734. **276.** 50 c. red 30 50

277. Stylised Disabled Person and Globe.

1981. International Year for Disabled Persons.

735. **277.** 2 r. red, black and grey 60 75

278. Hand placing Vote into Ballot Box.

1981. 50th Anniv. of Universal Franchise. Multicoloured.

736. 50 c. Type **278** 15 10
737. 7 r. Ballot box, and people forming map of Sri Lanka (vert.) .. .. .. 1·00 90

279. T. W. Rhys Davids (founder).

1981. Centenary of Pali Text Society.

738. **279.** 35 c. stone, dp. brn. & brn. 50 20

MINIMUM PRICE

The minimum price quoted is 10p which represents a handling charge rather than a basis for valuing common stamps. For further notes about prices see introductory pages.

280. Federation Emblem and " 25 ".

1981. 25th Anniv. of All-Ceylon Buddhist Students' Federation.

739. **280.** 2 r. blk. yellow and red 60 30

281. " Plan for Happiness ".

1981. Population and Family Planning.

740. **281.** 50 c. multicoloured .. 50 30

282. Dove Symbol with Acupuncture Needle and " Yin-Yang " (Chinese universe duality emblem).

1981. World Acupuncture Congress.

741. **282.** 2 r. blk. yell., and orge. 2·00 2·25

283. Union and Sri Lanka Flags.

1981. Royal Visit.

742. **283.** 50 c. multicoloured .. 30 25
743. 5 r. multicoloured .. 1·50 2·00

284. " Conserve our Forests ".

1981. Forest Conservation.

745. **284.** 35 c. multicoloured .. 10 10
746. – 50 c. brown and stone. 10 15
747. – 5 r. multicoloured .. 1·50 2·25

DESIGN: 50 c. " Plant a tree ", 5 r. Jak (tree).

285. Sir James Peiris.

1981. Birth Centenary of Sir James Peiris (politician).

749. **285.** 50 c. brown 45 50

286. F. R. Senanayaka.

1982. Birth Centenary of F. R. Senanayaka (national hero).

750. **286.** 50 c. brown 45 55

287. Philip Gunawardhane.

1982. 10th Death Anniv. of Philip Gunawardhane (politician).

751. **287.** 50 c. red 45 55

288. Department of Inland Revenue Building, Colombo.

1982. 50th Anniv. of Department of Inland Revenue.

752. **288.** 50 c. blue, blk. & orge. 45 55

289. Rupavahini Emblem.

1982. Inauguration of Rupavahini (national television).

753. **289.** 2 r. 50 yell., brn. and grey 1·75 2·25

290. Cricketer and Ball.

1982. First Sri Lanka—England Test Match, Colombo.

754. **290.** 2 r. 50 multicoloured 3·50 3·50

291. " Obsbeckia wightiana ".

1982. Flowers. Multicoloured.

755.	35 c. Type **291**	10	10
756.	2 r. " Mesua nagassarium "	20	20
757.	7 r. " Rhodomyrtus tomentosa "	50	90
758.	20 r. " Phaius tancarvilleae "	1·40	2·50

292. Mother breast-feeding Child.

1982. Food and Nutrition Policy Planning.

760. **292.** 50 c. multicoloured .. 75 75

293. Conference Emblem.

1982. World Hindu Conference.

761. **293.** 50 c. multicoloured .. 75 75

294. King Vessantara giving away Magical, Rain-making White Elephant.

1982. Vesak. Legend of Vessantara Jataka. Details of Cloth Painting from Arattana Rajamaha Vihara (temple), Hanguranketa, District of Nuwara Eliya. Multicoloured.

762.	35 c. Type **294**	35	10
763.	50 c. King Vessantara with family in Vankagiri Forest	45	15
764.	2 r. 50 Vessantara giving away his children as slaves	1·75	2·00
765.	5 r. Vessantara and family arriving back in Jetuttara in royal chariot ..	2·50	3·25

295. Parliament Buildings, Sri Jayawardanapura.

1982. Opening of Parliament Building Complex, Sri Jayawardanapura, Kotte.

767. **295.** 50 c. multicoloured .. 75 75

296. Dr. C. W. W. Kannangara.

1982. Dr. C. W. W. Kannangara (" Father of Free Education ") Commemoration.

768. **296.** 50 c. olive 75 75

297. Lord Baden-Powell.

1982. 125th Birth Anniv. of Lord Baden-Powell.

769. **297.** 50 c. multicoloured .. 1·50 75

298. Dr. G. P. Malalasekara.

1982. Dr. G. P. Malalasekara (founder of World Fellowship of Buddhists). Commem.

770. **298.** 50 c. green 75 75

299. Wheel encircling Globe.

1982. World Buddhist Leaders Conference.

771. **299.** 50 c. multicoloured .. 75 75

300. Wildlife.

1982. World Environment Day.

772. **300.** 50 c. multicoloured .. 1·25 75

301. Sir Waitialingam Duraiswamy.

1982. Sir Waitialingam Duraiswamy (statesman and educationalist) Commemoration.

773. **301.** 50 c. deep brown and brown 75 75

302. Y.M.C.A. Emblem.

1982. Centenary of Colombo Y.M.C.A.

774. **302.** 2 r. 50 multicoloured 2·50 2·75

303. Rev. Weliwita Sri Saranankara Sangharaja.

1982. Rev. Weliwita Sri Saranankara Sangharaja (Buddhist leader) Commemoration.

775. **303.** 50 c. brown and orange 75 75

304. Maharagama Sasana Sevaka Samithiya Emblem.

1982. 25th Anniv. of Maharagama Sasana Sevaka Samithiya (Buddhist Social Reform Movement).

776. **304.** 50 c. multicoloured .. 75 75

305. Dr. Robert Koch.

1982. Centenary of Robert Koch's Discovery of Tubercle Bacillus.

777. **305.** 50 c. multicoloured .. 1·75 85

306. Sir John Kotelawala.

1982. 2nd Death Anniv. of Sir John Kotelawala.

778. **306.** 50 c. olive 75 75

307. Eye Donation Society and Lions Club Emblems.

1982. World-wide Sight Conservation Project.

779. **307.** 2 r. 50 multicoloured 2·00 2·50

1982. As Nos. 718/21, but without surcharges and showing revised face values.

780	2 r. 50 Type **269**	10	10
781	3 r. Golden palm civet ..	90	90
782	4 r. Indian spotted chevrotain	15	15
783	5 r. Rusty-spotted cat ..	20	20

308. 1859 4 d. Rose and 1948 15 c. Independence Commemorative.

1982. 125th Anniv. of First Postage Stamps. Multicoloured.

784.	50 c. Type **308**	25	25
785.	2 r. 50 1859 1 s. 9 d. green and 1981 50 c. " Just Society " stamps ..	1·00	1·50

309. Sir Oliver Goonetilleke.

1983. 4th Death Anniv. of Sir Oliver Goonetilleke (statesman).

787. **309.** 50 c. grey, brn. & blk. 40 60

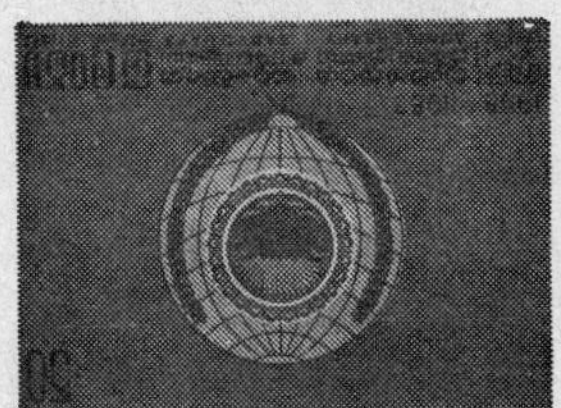

310. Sarvodaya Emblem.

1983. 25th Anniv. of Sarvodaya Movement.

788. **310.** 50 c. multicoloured .. 70 70

311. Morse Key, Radio Aerial and Radio Amateur Society Emblem.

1983. Radio Amateur Society.

789. **311.** 2 r. 50 multicoloured 2·50 3·00

312. Customs Co-operation Council Emblem and Sri Lanka Flag.

1983. 30th Anniv. of International Customs Day.

790.	**312.** 50 c. multicoloured ..	30	30
791.	5 r. multicoloured ..	2·75	3·25

313. Bottle-nosed Dolphin.

1983. Marine Mammals.

792. **313.** 50 c. blk., blue & grn. 30 15
793. – 2 r. multicoloured .. 55 60
794. – 2 r. 50 blk., bl. & grey 80 80
795. – 10 r. multicoloured .. 2·50 3·00

DESIGNS: 2 r. Dugongs. 2 r. 50, Humpback whale. 10 r. Sperm whale.

314. "Lanka Athula" (container ship).

1983. Ships of the Ceylon Shipping Corporation. Multicoloured.

796. 50 c. Type **314** 10 10
797. 2 r. 50 Map of routes .. 15 30
798. 5 r. "Lanka Kalyani" (freighter) 25 65
799. 20 r. "Tammanna" (tanker) .. .. .. 1·10 2·50

315. Wŏman with I.W.D. Emblem and Sri Lanka Flag.

1983. International Women's Day. Mult.

800. 50 c. Type **315** 10 25
801. 5 r. Woman, emblem, map and symbols of progress 40 1·00

316. Waterfall.

1983. Commonwealth Day. Multicoloured.

802. 50 c. Type **316** 10 10
803. 2 r. 50, Tea plucking .. 15 25
804. 5 r. Harvesting rice .. 25 40
805. 20 r. Decorated elephants 80 2·00

317. Lions Club International Badge.

1983. 25th Anniv. of Lions Club International in Sri Lanka.

806. **317.** 2 r. 50 multicoloured 1·75 1·75

318. " The Dream of Queen Mahamaya ".

1983. Vesak. Life of Prince Siddhartha from murals by George Keyt and Gotami Vihara. Multicoloured.

807. 35 c. Type **318** 10 10
808. 50 c. " Prince Siddhartha given to Maha Brahma " 10 10
809. 5 r. " Prince Siddhartha and the Sleeping Dancers " 25 60
810. 10 r. " The Meeting with Mara " .. .. .. 55 1·50

319. First Telegraph Transmission, Colombo to Galle, 1858.

1983. 125th Anniv. of Telecommunications in Sri Lanka (2 r.), and World Communications Year (10 r.). Multicoloured.

812. 2 r. Type **319** 25 35
813. 10 r. World Communications Year emblem .. 1·00 2·00

320. Henry Woodward Amarasuriya (philanthropist).

1983. National Heroes.

814. **320.** 50 c. green 25 45
815. – 50 c. blue 25 45
816. – 50 c. magenta .. 25 45
817. – 50 c. green 25 45

DESIGNS: No. 815, Father Simon Perera (historian). No. 816, Charles Lorenz (lawyer and newspaper editor). No. 817. Noordeen Abdul Cader (first President of All-Ceylon Muslim League).

321. Family and Village.

1983. Gam Udawa (Village Re-awakening Movement). Multicoloured.

818. 50 c. Type **321** 10 25
819. 5 r. Village view .. .. 40 1·00

322. Caravan of Bulls.

1983. Transport. Multicoloured.

820. 35 c. Type **322** 10 10
821. 2 r. Steam train 75 85
822. 2 r. 50 Ox and cart .. 75 1·00
823. 5 r. Ford motor car .. 1·25 2·25

323. Sir Tikiri Banda Panabokke.

1983. 20th Death Anniv. of Adigar Sir Tikiri Banda Panabokke.

824. **323.** 50 c. red 75 75

324. C. W. Thamotheram Pillai.

1983. C. W. Thamotheram Pillai (Tamil scholar).

825. **324.** 50 c. brown 75 75

325. Arabi Pasha.

1983. Centenary of Banishment of Arabi Pasha (Egyptian nationalist).

826. **325.** 50 c. green 75 75

326. Sri Lanka Wood Pigeon.

1983. Birds (2nd series). Multicoloured.

827. 25 c. Type **326** 10 10
828. 35 c. Large Sri Lanka white eye 10 10
829. 2 r. Sri Lanka Dusky blue flycatcher 20 10
829a. 7 r. As 35 c. 20 25
830. 20 r. Ceylon coucal .. 1·00 1·00

327. Pelene Siri Vajiragnana.

1983. Reverend Thero (scholar).

832. **327.** 50 c. brown 80 80

328. Mary praying over Jesus and St. Joseph welcomes Shepherds.

1983. Christmas.

833. **328.** 50 c. multicoloured .. 10 15
834. 5 r. multicoloured .. 25 60

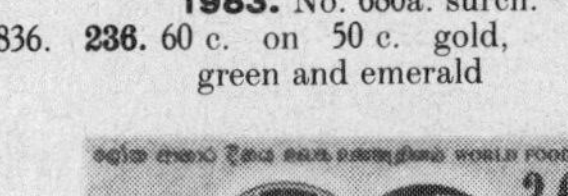

1983. No. 680a. surch.

836. **236.** 60 c. on 50 c. gold, green and emerald 70 70

331. Paddy Field, Globe and F.A.O. Emblem.

1984. World Food Day.

838. **331.** 3 r. multicoloured .. 40 1·00

332. Modern Tea Factory.

1984. Centenary of Colombo Tea Auctions. Multicoloured.

839 1 r. Type **332** 10 15
840 2 r. Logo 20 45
841 5 r. Girl picking tea .. 40 90
842 10 r. Auction in progress .. 90 1·75

333. Students and University.

1984. 4th Anniv. of Mahapola Scheme for Development and Education. Multicoloured.

843. 60 c. Type **333** 10 15
844. 1 r. Teacher with Gnana Darsana class 10 15
845. 5 r. 50 Student with books and microscope .. .. 35 1·00
846. 6 r. Mahapola lamp symbol 40 1·25

334. King Daham Sonda instructing Angels.

1984. Vesak. The Story of King Daham Sonda from Ancient Casket Paintings. Multicoloured.

847. 35 c. Type **334** 10 10
848. 60 c. Elephant paraded with gift of gold .. 15 25
849. 5 r. King Daham Sonda leaps into mouth of God Sakra .. .. .. 40 1·00
850. 10 r. God Sakra carrying King Daham Sonda .. 70 1·75

335. Development Programme Logo.

1984. Sri Lanka Lions Clubs' Development Programme.

852. **335.** 60 c. multicoloured .. 80 80

336. Dodanduwe Siri Piyaratana Tissa Mahanayake Thero (Buddhist scholar).

1984. National Heroes.

853.	**336.**	60 c. bistre	15	30
854.	–	60 c. green	15	30
855.	–	60 c. green	15	30
856.	–	60 c. red	15	30
857.	–	60 c. brown	15	30

DESIGNS: No. 854, G. P. Wickremarachchi (physician). 855, Sir Mohamed Macan Markar (politician). 856, Dr. W. Arthur de Silva (philanthropist). 857, K. Balasingham (lawyer).

337. Association Emblem.

1984. Centenary of Public Service Mutual Provident Association.

858. **337.** 4 r. 60 multicoloured 45 1·25

338. Sri Lanka Village.

1984. 6th Anniv. of "Gam Udawa" (Village Reawakening Movement).

859. **338.** 60 c. multicoloured .. 30 55

339. World Map showing A.P.B.U. Countries.

1984. 20th Anniv. of Asia-Pacific Broadcasting Union.

860. **339.** 7 r. multicoloured .. 1·40 2·00

340. Drummers and Elephant carrying Royal Instructions.

1984. Esala Perahera (Procession of the Tooth), Kandy. Multicoloured.

861.	4 r. 60 Type **340**	70	90
862.	4 r. 60 Dancers and elephants	70	90
863.	4 r. 60 Elephant carrying Tooth Relic	70	90
864.	4 r. 60 Custodian of the Sacred Tooth and attendants	70	90

Nos. 861/4 were printed together, se-tenant, in horizontal strips of 4 throughout the sheet, forming a composite design.

341. "Vanda Memoria Ernest Soysa" (orchid).

1984. 50th Anniv. of Ceylon Orchid Circle. Multicoloured.

866.	60 c. Type **341**	25	70
867.	4 r. 60 "Acanthephippium bicolor"	65	2·25
868.	5 r. "Vanda tessellata var. rufescens"	45	2·25
869.	10 r. "Anectochilus setaceus"	2·25	3·50

342. Symbolic Athletes and Stadium.

1984. 1st National School Games.

871 **342** 60 c. black, grey & blue 75 75

343. D.S. Senanayake, Temple and Fields.

1984. Birth Centenary of D.S. Senanayake (former Prime Minister). Multicoloured.

872.	35 c. Type **343**	10	10
873.	60 c. Senanayake and statue	10	10
874.	4 r. 60 Senanayake and irrigation project ..	35	50
875.	6 r. Senanayake and House of Representatives ..	40	60

344. Lake House.

1984. 150th Anniv. of "Observer" Newspaper.

876. **344.** 4 r. 60 multicoloured 75 1·60

345. Agricultural Workers and Globe.

1984. 20th Anniv. of World Food Programme.

877. **345.** 7 r. multicoloured .. 1·00 1·00

346. College Emblem. **347.** Dove and Stylised Figures.

1984. Centenary of Baari Arabic College, Weligama.

878. **346.** 4 r. 60 grn., turq. & bl. 1·00 1·50

1985. International Youth Year. Mult.

879.	4 r. 60 Type **347**	40	50
880.	20 r. Dove, stylised figures and flower	1·50	2·00

348. Religious Symbols.

1985. World Religion Day.

881. **348.** 4 r. 60 multicoloured 50 70

349. College Crest.

1985. 150th Anniv. of Royal College, Colombo.

882.	**349.**	60 c. yellow and blue	10	25
883.	–	7 r. multicoloured ..	70	1·75

DESIGN: 7 r. Royal College.

350. Banknotes, Buildings, Ship and "Wheel of Life".

1985. 5th Anniv. of Mahapola Scheme.

884. **350.** 60 c. multicoloured .. 60 75

351. Wariyapola Sri Sumangala Thero.

1985. Wariyapola Sri Sumangala Thero (Buddhist priest and patriot). Commem.

885. **351.** 60 c. brn., yell. & blk. 50 70

352. Victoria Dam.

1985. Inauguration of Victoria Hydroelectric Project. Multicoloured.

886.	60 c. Type **352**	60	40
887.	7 r. Map of Sri Lanka enclosing dam and power station (vert.) ..	2·25	3·00

353. Cover of 50th Edition of International Buddhist Annual, "Vesak Sirisara". **354.** Ven. Waskaduwe Sri Subhuthi (priest and scholar).

1985. Centenary of Vesak Poya Holiday. Multicoloured.

888.	35 c. Type **353**	10	10
889.	60 c. Buddhists worshipping at temple ..	10	10
890.	6 r. Buddhist Theosophical Society Headquarters, Colombo	30	35
891.	9 r. Buddhist Flag ..	50	55

1985. Personalities.

893.	**354.**	60 c. brn., orge. & blk.	15	20
894.	–	60 c. mve., orge & blk.	15	20
895.	–	60 c. brn., orge. & blk.	15	20
896.	–	60 c. grn., orge. & blk.	15	20

DESIGNS: 894, Revd. Fr. Peter A. Pillai (educationist and social reformer). 895. Dr. Senarath Paranavitane (scholar). 896. A. M. Wapche Marikar (architect and educationist).

355. Stylised Village and People.

1985. Gam Udawa '85 (Village Re-awakening Movement).

897. **355.** 60 c. multicoloured .. 75 85

356. Emblem.

1985. 50th Anniv. of Colombo Young Poets' Association.

898. **356.** 60 c. multicoloured .. 30 55

357. Kothmale Dam and Reservoir.

1985. Inauguration of Kothmale Hydroelectric Project. Multicoloured.

899.	60 c. Type **357**	30	15
900.	6 r. Kothmale Power Station	95	1·10

358. Federation Logo.

1985. 10th Asian and Oceanic Congress of Obstetrics and Gynaecology.
901. **358.** 7 r. multicoloured .. 2·25 2·25

359. Breast Feeding.

1985. U.N.I.C.E.F. Child Survival and Development Programme. Multicoloured.
902. 35 c. Type **359** 10 10
903. 60 c. Child and oral rehydration salts .. 20 30
904. 6 r. Weighing child (growth monitoring) .. 1·25 1·75
905. 9 r. Immunization .. 1·75 2·25

360. Blowing Conch Shell.

1985. 10th Anniv. of World Tourism Organization. Multicoloured.
907. 1 r. Type **360** 10 10
908. 6 r. Parliamentary Complex, Jayawardhanapura, Kotte .. 40 60
909. 7 r. Tea plantation .. 50 75
910. 10 r. Ruwanveliseya (Buddhist shrine), Anuradhapura .. .. 70 1·00

361. Casket containing Land Grant Deed.

1985. 50th Anniv. of Land Development Ordinance.
912. **361.** 4 r. 60 multicoloured 1·25 1·60

362. Koran and Map of Sri Lanka.

1985. Translation of The Koran into Sinhala.
913. **362.** 60 c. violet and gold 50 70

363. "Our Lady of Matara" Statue.

1985. Christmas. Multicoloured.
914. 60 c. Type **363** 25 15
915. 9 r. "Our Lady of Madhu" Statue .. .. .. 1·00 1·25

1985. Nos. 608b, 780, 828, 860 and 879 surch.
917. **236.** 75 c. on 60 c. gold, green and emerald 10 10
918. **347.** 1 r. on 4 r. 60 mult. .. 80 70
919. **339.** 1 r. on 7 r. mult. .. 1·25 70
920. **269.** 5 r. 75 on 2 r. 50 mult. 1·50 45
921. – 7 r. on 35 c. multicoloured (No. 828) 1·60 65

365. Linked Arms and Map of S.A.A.R.C. Countries.

1985. 1st Summit Meeting of South Asian Association for Regional Co-operation, Dhaka, Bangladesh. Multicoloured.
922. 60 c. Type **363** .. .. 1·25 2·50
923. 5 r. 50 Logo and flags of member countries .. 1·25 1·50

366. "Viceroy Special" Train.

1986. Inaugural Run of "Viceroy Special" Train from Colombo to Kandy.
924. **366.** 1 r. multicoloured .. 2·50 1·25

367. Girl and Boy Students.

1986. 6th Anniv. of Mahapola Scheme.
925. **367.** 75 c. multicoloured .. 40 60

368. Wijewardena.

1986. Birth Centenary of D. R. Wijewardena (newspaper publisher).
926. **368.** 75 c. brown and green 30 60

369. Ven. Welitara Gnanatilake Maha Nayake Thero.

1986. Ven. Welitara Gnanatillake Maha Nayake Thero (scholar) Commemoration.
927. **369.** 75 c. multicoloured .. 70 70

370. Red Cross Flag and Personnel.

1986. 50th Anniv. of Sri Lanka Red Cross Society.
928. **370.** 75 c. multicoloured .. 1·50 85

371. Comet depicted as Goddess visiting Sun-god.

1986. Appearance of Halley's Comet. Multicoloured.
929. 50 c. Type **371** 10 10
930. 75 c. Comet and constellations of Scorpius and Sagittarius 10 20
931. 6 r. 50 Comet's orbit .. 30 90
932. 8 r. 50 Edmond Halley .. 55 1·40

372. Woman lighting Lamp.

1986. Sinhalese and Tamil New Year. Multicoloured.
934. 50 c. Type **372** 10 10
935. 75 c. Woman and festive foods 10 15
936. 6 r. 50 Women playing drum .. .. .. 30 1·25
937. 8 r. 50 Anointing and making offerings at temple .. .. .. 55 1·60

373. The King donating Elephant to the Brahmin.

1986. Vesak. Wall paintings from Samudragiri Temple, Mirissa. Multicoloured.
939. 50 c. Type **373** 10 10
940. 75 c. The Bodhisattva in the Vasavarthi heaven 10 20
941. 5 r. The offering of milk rice by Sujatha .. .. 45 1·00
942. 10 r. The offering of parched corn and honey by Thapassu and Bhalluka .. .. 75 1·50

374. Ven. Kalukondayave Sri Prajnasekhara Maha Nayake Thero (Buddhist leader and social reformer).

1986. National Heroes. Multicoloured.
943. 75 c. Type **374** 20 35
944. 75 c. Brahmachari Walisinghe Harischandra (social reformer) (birth centenary) 20 35
945. 75 c. Martin Wickramasinghe (author and scholar) 20 35
946. 75 c. G. G. Ponnambalam (politician) 20 35
947. 75 c. A. M. A. Azeez (Islamic scholar) (75th birth anniv.) 20 35

375. Stylized Village and People.

1986. Gam Udawa '86 (Village Re-awakening Movement).
948. **375.** 75 c. multicoloured .. 70 50

376. Co-op Flag and Emblem.

1986. 75th Anniv. of Sri Lanka Co-operative Movement.
949. **376.** 1 r. multicoloured .. 1·25 1·25

377. Arthur V. Dias.

1986. Birth Centenary of Arthur V. Dias (philanthropist).
950. **377.** 1 r. brown and blue .. 75 75

378. Bull Elephant.

1986. Sri Lanka Wild Elephants. Mult.

951.	5 r. Type **378**	2·00	2·25
952.	5 r. Cow elephant and calf	2·00	2·25
953.	5 r. Cow elephant	2·00	2·25
954.	5 r. Elephants bathing ..	2·00	2·25

379. Congress Logo.

1986. 2nd Indo-Pacific Congress on Legal Medicine and Forensic Sciences.

955. **379.** 8 r. 50 multicoloured 1·25 1·25

380. Map showing Route of Cable and Telephone Receiver.

1986. SEA-ME-WE Submarine Cable Project.

956. **380.** 5 r. 75 multicoloured 1·00 1·25

381. Anniversary Logo.

1986. 25th Anniv. of Dag Hammarskjold Award.

957. **381.** 2 r. multicoloured .. 50 65

382. Logo on Flag.

1986. 2nd National School Games.

958. **382.** 1 r. multicoloured .. 1·25 75

383. Logo.

1986. 60th Anniv. of Surveyors' Institute of Sri Lanka.

959. **383.** 75 c. brn. & lt. brn. 40 55

384. College Building and Crest.

1986. Centenary of Ananda College, Colombo.

960.	**384.**	75 c. multicoloured ..	10	10
961.	–	5 r. multicoloured ..	30	40
962.	–	5 r. 75 multicoloured	30	40
963.	–	6 r. red, gold and lilac	35	45

DESIGNS: 5 r. Sports field and college crest. 5 r. 75, Col. H. S. Olcott (founder), Ven. Migettuwatte Gunananda, Ven. Hikkaduwe Sri Sumangala (Buddhist leaders) and Buddhist flag, 6 r. College flag.

385. Mangrove Swamp.

1986. Mangrove Conservation. Multicoloured.

964.	35 c. Type **385**	20	10
965.	50 c. Mangrove tree ..	25	15
966.	75 c. Germinating mangrove flower	25	15
967.	6 r. Fiddler crab	1·75	2·25

386. Family and Housing Estate.

1987. International Year of Shelter for the Homeless.

968. **386.** 75 c. multicoloured .. 80 30

387. Ven. Ambagahawatte Indasabhawaragnanasamy Thero.

1987. Ven. Ambagahawatte Indasabhawaragnanasamy Thero (Buddhist monk) Commemoration.

969. **387.** 5 r. 75 multicoloured 1·00 65

388. Proctor John de Silva.

1987. Proctor John de Silva (playwright) Commemoration.

970. **388.** 5 r. 75 multicoloured 60 50

389. Mahapola Logo and Aspects of Communication.

1987. 7th Anniv. of Mahapola Scheme.

971. **389.** 75 c. multicoloured .. 50 50

390. Dr. R. L. Brohier.

1987. Dr Richard L. Brohier (historian and surveyor) Commemoration.

972. **390.** 5 r. 75 multicoloured 70 45

391. Tyre Corporation Building, Kelaniya, and Logo.

1987. 25th Anniv. of Sri Lanka Tyre Corporation.

973. **391.** 5 r. 75 black, red and orange 45 45

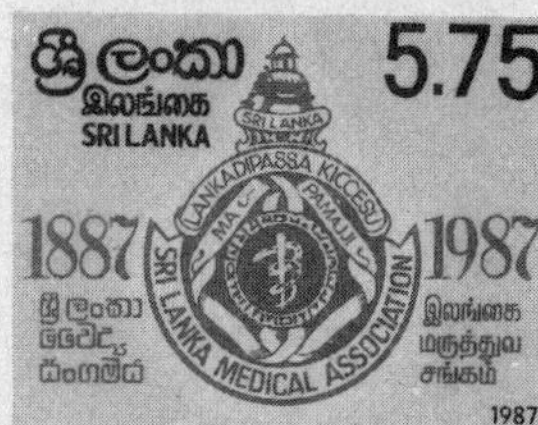
392. Logo.

1987. Centenary of Sri Lanka Medical Association.

974. **392.** 5 r. 75 brown, yellow and black 55 55

MINIMUM PRICE

The minimum price quoted is 10p which represents a handling charge rather than a basis for valuing common stamps. For further notes about prices see introductory pages.

393. Clasped Hands, Farmer and Paddy Field.

1987. Inauguration of Farmers' Pension and Social Security Benefit Scheme.

975. **393.** 75 c. multicoloured .. 30 30

394. Exhibition Logo.

1987. Mahaweli Maha Goviya Contest and Agro Mahaweli Exhibition.

976. **394.** 75 c. multicoloured .. 30 30

395. Young Children with W.H.O. and Immunization Logos.

1987. World Health Day.

977. **395.** 1 r. multicoloured .. 1·25 40

396. Girls playing on Swing.

1987. Sinhalese and Tamil New Year. Multicoloured.

978.	75 c. Type **396**	10	10
979.	5 r. Girls with oil lamp and sun symbol	50	50

397. Lotus Lanterns.

1987. Vesak. Multicoloured.

980.	50 c. Type **397**	10	10
981.	75 c. Octagonal lanterns ..	10	10
982.	5 r. Star lanterns	30	30
983.	10 r. Gok lanterns	45	55

398. Emerald-collared Parakeet.

1987. Birds (3rd series). Multicoloured.

985.	50 c. Type **398**	10	10
986.	1 r. Legge's flowerpecker ..	10	10
987.	5 r. Ceylon white-headed starling	25	25
988.	10 r. Ceylon jungle babbler	45	45

399. Ven. Heenatiyana Sri Dhammaloka Maha Nayake Thero (Buddhist monk).

1987. National Heroes. Multicoloured.

990.	75 c. Type **399**	30	25
991.	75 c. P. de S. Kularatne (educationist)	30	25
992.	75 c. M. C. Abdul Rahuman (legislator) ..	30	25

400. Peasant Family and Village.

1987. Gam Udawa '87 (Village Re-awakening Movement).

993.	**400.** 75 c. multicoloured ..	20	20

401. "Mesua nagassarium".

1987. Forest Conservation. Multicoloured.

994.	75 c. Type **401**	10	10
995.	5 r. Elephants in forest ..	80	50

402. Dharmaraja College, Crest and Col. H. Olcott (founder).

1987. Centenary of Dharmaraja College, Kandy.

996.	**402.** 75 c. multicoloured ..	85	30

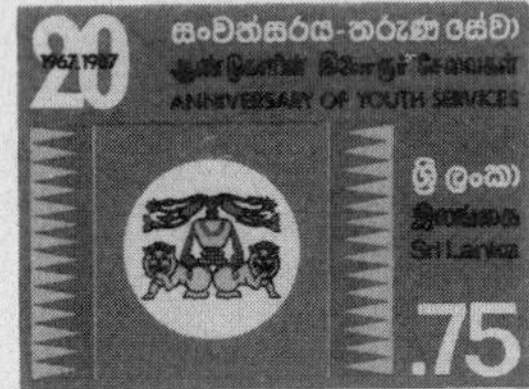

403. Youth Services Logo.

1987. 20th Anniv. of National Youth Services.

997.	**403.** 75 c. multicoloured ..	20	20

404. Arm holding Torch and Mahaweli Logo.

1987. Mahaweli Games.

998.	**404.** 75 c. multicoloured ..	85	85

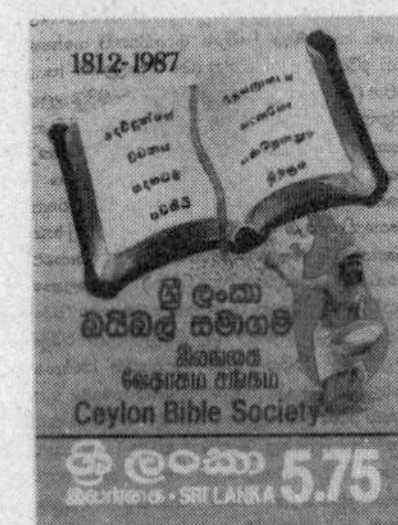

405. Open Bible and Logo.

1987. 175th Anniv. of Ceylon Bible Society.

999.	**405.** 5 r. 75 multicoloured	30	30

406. Hurdler and Committee Symbol.

1987. 50th Anniv. of National Olympic Committee.

1000.	**406.** 10 r. multicoloured ..	85	60

407. Madonna and Child, Flowers and Oil Lamp.

1987. Christmas. Multicoloured.

1001.	75 c. Type **407**	10	10
1002.	10 r. Christ Child in manger, star and dove	35	40

408. Sir Ernest de Silva.

1987. Birth Centenary of Sir Ernest de Silva (philanthropist and philatelist).

1004.	**408.** 75 c. multicoloured	20	20

409. Society Logo.

1987. 150th Anniv. of Kandy Friend-in Need Society.

1005.	**409.** 75 c. multicoloured ..	20	20

410. University Flag and Graduates.

1987. 1st Convocation of Buddhist and Pali University.

1006.	**410.** 75 c. multicoloured ..	20	20

411. Father Joseph Vaz.

1987. 300th Anniv. of Arrival of Father Joseph Vaz in Kandy.

1007.	**411.** 75 c. multicoloured ..	20	20

412. Wheel of Dhamma, Dagaba and Bo Leaf.

1988. 30th Anniv. of Buddhist Publication Society, Kandy.

1008.	**412.** 75 c. multicoloured ..	20	20

413. Dharmayatra Lorry.

1988. 5th Anniv. of Mahapola Dharmayatra Service.

1009.	**413.** 75 c. multicoloured ..	20	20

414. Society Logo.

1988. Centenary of Ceylon Society of Arts.

1010.	**414.** 75 c. multicoloured ..	20	20

415. National Youth Centre, Maharagama.

1988. Opening of National Youth Centre, Maharagama.

1011.	**415.** 1 r. multicoloured ..	90	30

416. Citizens with National Flag and Map of Sri Lanka.

1988. 40th Anniv. of Independence. Mult.

1012.	75 c. Type **416**	10	10
1013.	8 r. 50 "40" in figures and lion emblem	50	50

417. Graduates, Clay Lamp and Open Book.

1988. 8th Anniv. of Mahapola Scheme.

1014.	**417.** 75 c. multicoloured ..	20	20

418. Bus and Logo.

1988. 30th Anniv. of Sri Lanka Transport Board.

1015. **418.** 5 r. 75 multicoloured 30 30

419. Ven. Weligama Sri Sumangala Maha Nayake Thero.

1988. Ven. Weligama Sri Sumangala Maha Nayake Thero (Buddhist monk). Commemoration.

1016. **419.** 75 c. multicoloured . . 20 20

420. Regimental Colour.

1988. Centenary of Regiment of Artillery.

1017. **420.** 5 r. 75 multicoloured 90 40

421 Chevalier I.X. Pereira

1988. Birth Centenary of Chevalier I.X. Pereira (politician).

1018 **421** 5 r. 75 multicoloured 30 30

422 Invitation to the Deities and Brahmas

1988. Vesak. Paintings from Narendrarama Rajamaha Temple, Suriyagoda. Multicoloured.

1019 50 c. Type **422** 15 15

1020 75 c. Bodhisathva at the Seventh Step 15 15

423 Father Ferdinand Bonnel (educationist)

1988. National Heroes. Multicoloured.

1022 75 c. Type **423** 15 15

1023 75 c. Sir Razik Fareed (politician) 15 15

1024 75 c. W. F. Gunawardhana (scholar) . . 15 15

1025 75 c. Edward Nugawela (politician) 15 15

1026 75 c. Chief Justice Sir Arthur Wijeyewardene 15 15

424 Stylized Figures and Reawakened Village

1988. 10th Anniv of Gam Udawa (Village Reawakening Movement).

1027 **424** 75 c. multicoloured . . 20 20

425 Maliyadeva College, Kurunegala, and Crest

1988. Centenary of Maliyadeva College, Kurunegala.

1028 **425** 75 c. multicoloured . . 20 20

426 M.J.M. Lafir, Billiard Game and Trophy

1988. Mohamed Junaid Mohamed Lafir (World Amateur Billiards Champion, 1973) Commemoration.

1029 **426** 5 r. 75 multicoloured 30 30

427 Flags of Australia and Sri Lanka, Handclasp and Map of Australia

1988. Bicentenary of Australian Settlement.

1030 **427** 8 r. 50 multicoloured 30 35

428 Ven. Kataluwe Sri Gunaratana Maha Nayake Thero

1988. Ven. Kataluwe Sri Gunaratana Maha Nayake Thero (Buddhist monk) Commem.

1031 **428** 75 c. multicoloured . . 20 20

429 Athlete, Rice and Hydro-electric Dam

1988. Mahaweli Games.

1032 **429** 75 c. multicoloured . . 20 20

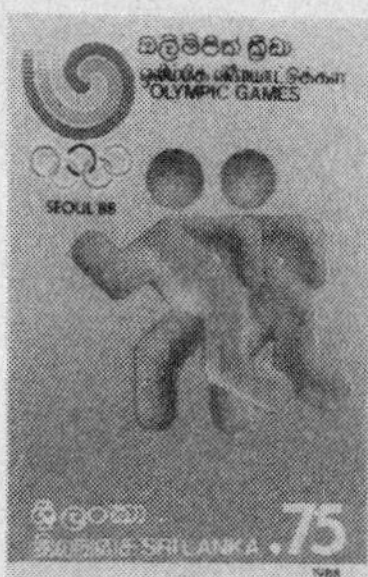

430 Athletics

1988. Olympic Games, Seoul. Multicoloured.

1033 75 c. Type **430** 10 10

1034 1 r. Swimming 10 10

1035 5 r. 75 Boxing 20 25

1036 8 r. 50 Map of Sri Lanka and logos of Olympic Committee and Seoul Games 30 35

431 Outline Map of Sri Lanka and Anniversary Logo

1988. 40th Anniv of W.H.O.

1038 **431** 75 c. multicoloured . . 20 20

432 Games Logo

1988. 3rd National School Games.

1039 **432** 1 r. black, gold & mve 75 15

433 Mahatma Gandhi

1988. 40th Death Anniv of Mahatma Gandhi.

1040 **433** 75 c. multicoloured . . 30 15

434 Globe with Forms of Transport and Communications

1988. Asia–Pacific Transport and Communications Decade.

1041 **434** 75 c. multicoloured . . 10 10

1042 – 5 r. 75 mve, bl & blk 60 30

DESIGN: 5 r. 75, Antenna tower with dish aerials and forms of transport.

435 Woman with Rice Sheaf and Hydro-electric Project

1988. Commissioning of Randenigala Project. Multicoloured.

1043 75 c. Type **435** 10 10

1044 5 r. 75 Randenigala Dam and reservoir 30 30

436 Handicrafts and Centre Logo in Cupped Hands

1988. Opening of Gramodaya Folk Art Centre, Colombo.

1045 **436** 75 c. multicoloured . . 20 20

437 Angel, Dove, Olive Branch and Globe

1988. Christmas. Multicoloured.

1046 75 c. Type **437** 10 10

1047 8 r. 50 Shepherds and Star of Bethlehem 30 35

438 Dr. E. W. Adikaram

1988. Dr. E. W. Adikaram (educationist) Commemoration.

1049 **438** 75 c. multicoloured . . 20 20

439 Open Book in Tree and Children reading

1989. 10th Anniv of Free Distribution of School Text Books.

1050 **439** 75 c. multicoloured .. 20 20

440 Wimalaratne Kumaragama

1989. Poets of Sri Lanka. Multicoloured.

1051 75 c. Type **440** 10 10
1052 75 c. G. H. Perera 10 10
1053 75 c. Sagara Palansuriya 10 10
1054 75 c. P. B. Alwis Perera 10 10

441 Logo and New Chamber of Commerce Building

1989. 150th Anniv of Ceylon Chamber of Commerce.

1055 **441** 75 c. multicoloured .. 20 20

442 Bodhisatva at Lunch and Funeral Pyre

1989. Vesak. Wall Paintings from Medawala Monastery, Harispattuwa. Multicoloured.

1056 50 c. Type **442** 10 10
1057 75 c. Rescue of King Vessantara's children by god Sakra .. 10 10
1058 5 r. Bodhisatva ploughing and his son attacked by snake 20 25
1059 5 r. 75 King Vessantara giving away his children 20 25

443 Parawahera Vajiragnana Thero (Buddhist monk)

1989. National Heroes. Multicoloured.

1061 75 c. Type **443** 15 15
1062 75 c. Fr. Maurice Jacques Le Goc (educationist) 15 15
1063 75 c. Hemapala Munidasa (author) 15 15
1064 75 c. Ananda Samarakoon (composer) 15 15
1065 75 c. Simon Casie Chitty (scholar) (horiz) .. 15 15

444 College Crest

1989. 150th Anniv of Hartley College, Point-Pedro (1988).

1066 **444** 75 c. multicoloured .. 20 20

445 Dramachakra, Lamp, Buddhist Flag and Map

1989. Establishment of Ministry of Buddha Sasana.

1067 **445** 75 c. multicoloured .. 20 20

446 Hands holding Brick and Trowel, House and Family

1989. Gam Udawa '89 (Village Re-awakening Movement).

1068 **446** 75 c. multicoloured .. 20 20

447 Two Families and Hand turning Cogwheel

1989. Janasaviya Development Programme.

1069 **447** 75 c. multicoloured .. 20 20
1070 1 r. multicoloured .. 20 20

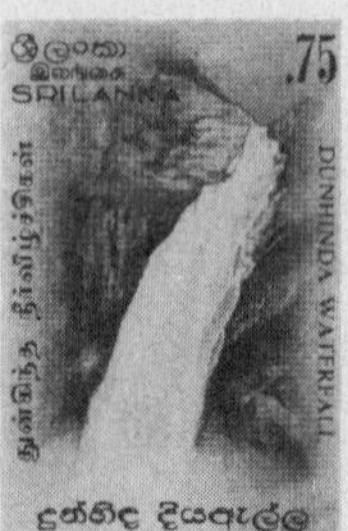

448 Dunhinda Falls

1989. Waterfalls. Multicoloured.

1071 75 c. Type **448** 10 10
1072 1 r. Rawana Falls .. 10 10
1073 5 r. 75 Laxapana Falls .. 15 20
1074 8 r. 50 Diyaluma Falls .. 20 25

449 Rev. James Chater (missionary) and Baptist Church

1989. 177th Anniv of Baptist Church in Sri Lanka.

1075 **449** 5 r. 75 multicoloured 30 30

450 Bicentenary Logo

1989. Bicentenary of French Revolution.

1076 **450** 8 r. 50 black, bl & red 40 40

451 Old and New Bank Buildings and Logo

1989. 50th Anniv of Bank of Ceylon. Mult.

1077 75 c. Type **451** 10 10
1078 5 r. "Bank of Ceylon" orchid and logo .. 30 30

452 Water Lily, Dharma Chakra and Books

1989. State Literary Festival.

1079 **452** 75 c. multicoloured .. 20 20

453 Wilhelm Geiger

1989. Wilhelm Geiger (linguistic scholar) Commemoration.

1080 **453** 75 c. multicoloured .. 20 20

454 H. V. Perera, Q.C.

1989. Constitutional Pioneers. Multicoloured.

1082 75 c. Type **454** 20 20
1083 75 c. Prof. Ivor Jennings 20 20

455 Sir Cyril de Zoysa

1989. Sir Cyril de Zoysa (Buddhist philanthropist) Commemoration.

1084 **455** 75 c. multicoloured .. 20 20

456 Map of South-east Asia and Telecommunications Equipment

1989. 10th Anniv of Asia-Pacific Telecommunity.

1085 **456** 5 r. 75 multicoloured 30 30

457 Members with Offerings and Water Lily on Map of Sri Lanka

1989. 50th Anniv of Sri Sucharitha Welfare Movement.

1086 **457** 75 c. multicoloured .. 20 20

458 "Apollo 11" Blast-off and Astronauts

1989. 20th Anniv of First Manned Landing on Moon. Multicoloured.

1087 75 c. Type **458** .. 10 10
1088 1 r. Armstrong leaving lunar module "Eagle" 10 10
1089 2 r. Astronaut on Moon .. 15 15
1090 5 r. 75 Lunar surface and Earth from Moon .. 25 25

459 Shepherds

1989. Christmas. Multicoloured.

1092 75 c. Type **459** 10 10

1093 8 r. 50 Magi with gifts .. 20 55

460 Ven. Sri Devananda Nayake Thero

1989. Ven. Sri Devananda Nayake Thero (Buddhist monk) Commemoration.

1095 **460** 75 c. multicoloured .. 20 20

461 College Building, Crest and Revd. William Ault (founder)

1989. 175th Anniv of Methodist Central College, Batticaloa.

1096 **461** 75 c. multicoloured .. 20 20

462 Golf Ball, Clubs and Logo

1989. Cent of Nuwara Eliya Golf Club. Mult.

1097 75 c. Type **462** 15 10

1098 8 r. 50 Course and club house 40 40

463 "Raja"

1989. "Raja" Royal Ceremonial Elephant, Kandy, Commemoration.

1099 **463** 75 c. multicoloured .. 40 20

464 College Building and G. Wickremarachchi (founder)

1989. 60th Anniv of Gampaha Wickremarachchi Institute of Ayurveda Medicine.

1100 **464** 75 c. multicoloured .. 20 20

465 Ven. Udunuwara Sri Saranada Thero

1989. Ven. Udunuwara Sri Saranada Thero (Buddhist monk) Commemoration.

1101 **465** 75 c. multicoloured .. 20 20

466 Diesel Train on Viaduct, Ella-Demodara

1989. 125 Years of Sri Lanka Railways. Mult.

1102 75 c. Type **466** 10 10

1103 2 r. Diesel train at Maradana Station .. 15 15

1104 3 r. Steam train 20 20

1105 7 r. Steam train, 1864 .. 40 40

467 Cardinal Thomas Cooray

1989. Cardinal Thomas Cooray Commem.

1106 **467** 75 c. multicoloured .. 45 20

468 Farmer and Wife with Dagaba and Dam

1989. Agro Mahaweli Development Programme.

1107 **468** 75 c. multicoloured .. 20 20

469 Justin Wijayawardena

1990. Justin Wijayawardena (scholar) Commemoration.

1108 **469** 1 r. multicoloured .. 70 20

1990. Surch.

1108a 25 c. on 5 r. 75 King Vessantara giving away his children (No. 1059) 10 10

1109a 1 r. on 75 c. Type **447** .. 10 10

470 Ven. Induruwe Uttarananda Mahanayake Thero

1990. 4th Death Anniv of Ven. Induruwe Uttarananda Mahanayake Thero (Buddhist theologian).

1109 **470** 1 r. multicoloured .. 30 40

471 Two Graduates, Lamp and Open Book

1990. 9th Anniv of Mahapola Scheme.

1110 **471** 75 c. multicoloured .. 20 20

472 Traditional Drums

1990. 25th Anniv of Laksala Traditional Handicrafts Organization. Multicoloured.

1111 1 r. Type **472** 10 10

1112 2 r. Silverware 15 15

1113 3 r. Lacquerware .. 20 20

1114 8 r. Dumbara mats .. 40 40

473 King Maha Prathapa visiting Queen Chandra

1990. Vesak. Wall Paintings from Buduraja Maha Viharaya, Wewurukannala. Mult.

1115 75 c. Type **473** 10 10

1116 1 r. Execution of Prince Dharmapala 10 10

1117 2 r. Prince Mahinsasaka with the Water Demon 15 15

1118 8 r. King Dahamsonda with the God Sakra disguised as a demon .. 35 35

474 Father T. Long (educationist)

1990. National Heroes. Multicoloured.

1120 1 r. Type **474** 10 10

1121 1 r. Prof. M. Ratnasuriya (37 × 25 mm) 10 10

1122 1 r. D. Wijewardene (patriot) (37 × 25 mm) 10 10

1123 1 r. L. Manjusri (artist) (37 × 25 mm) 10 10

475 Janasaviya Workers

1990. 12th Anniv of Gam Udawa and Opening of Janasaviya Centre, Pallekele.

1124 **475** 1 r. multicoloured .. 40 15

476 Gold Reliquary

1990. Cent of Department of Archaeology.

1125 **476** 1 r. black and yellow 10 10

1126 – 2 r. black and grey .. 15 15

1127 – 3 r. black, grn & brn 15 20

1128 – 8 r. black and brown 30 35

DESIGNS: 2 r. Statuette of Ganesh; 3 r. Terrace of the Bodhi-tree, Isurumuniya Vihara; 8 r. Inscription of King Nissankamalla.

477 Male Tennis Player at Left

1990. 75th Anniv of Sri Lanka Tennis Association. Multicoloured.

1129 1 r. Type **477** 20 20

1130 1 r. Male tennis player at right 20 20

1131 8 r. Male tennis players .. 65 65

1132 8 r. Female tennis players 65 65

Nos. 1129/30 and 1131/2 were each printed together, se-tenant, each pair forming a composite design of a singles (1 r.) or doubles (8 r.) match.

478 Spotted Loach

1990. Endemic Fishes. Multicoloured.

1133 25 c. Type **478** 10 10

1134 2 r. Ornate paradise fish 10 10

1135 8 r. Mountain labeo .. 20 25

1136 20 r. Cherry barb .. 50 55

479 Rukmani Devi

1990. 12th Death Anniv of Rukmani Devi (actress and singer).
1138 **479** 1 r. multicoloured .. 70 40

480 Innkeeper turning away Mary and Joseph

1990. Christmas. Multicoloured.
1139 1 r. Type **480** 15 10
1140 10 r. Adoration of the Magi 55 65

481 Health Worker talking to Villagers

1990. World AIDS Day. Multicoloured.
1142 1 r. Type **481** 10 10
1143 8 r. Emblem and Aids virus 45 60

482 Main College Building and Flag

1990. 50th Anniv of Dharmapala College, Pannipitiya.
1144 **482** 1 r. multicoloured .. 30 30

483 Peri Sundaram

1990. Birth Centenary of Peri Sundaram (lawyer and politician).
1145 **483** 1 r. brown and green 40 40

484 Letter Box, Galle, 1904

1990. 175th Anniv of Sri Lanka Postal Service. Multicoloured.
1146 1 r. Type **484** 15 10
1147 2 r. Mail runner, 1815 .. 25 15
1148 5 r. Mail coach, 1832 .. 50 50
1149 10 r. Nuwara-Eliya Post Office, 1894 .. .. 80 1·00

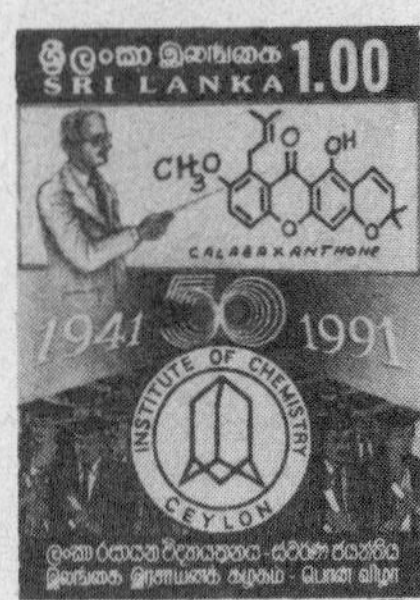

485 Chemical Structure Diagram, Graduating Students and Emblem

1991. 50th Anniv of Institute of Chemistry.
1150 **485** 1 r. multicoloured .. 55 40

486 Kastavahana on Royal Elephant

1991. Vesak. Temple Paintings from Karagampitiya Subodarama. Mult.
1151 75 c. Type **486** 10 10
1152 1 r. Polo Janaka in prison 10 10
1153 2 r. Two merchants offering food to Buddha .. 15 15
1154 11 r. Escape of Queen .. 75 85

487 Narada Thero (Buddhist missionary)

1991. National Heroes. Multicoloured.
1156 1 r. Type **487** 15 20
1157 1 r. Wallewatta Silva (novelist) 15 20
1158 1 r. Sir Muttu Coomaraswamy (lawyer and politician) 15 20
1159 1 r. Dr. Andreas Nell (ophthalmic surgeon) .. 15 20

488 Society Building

1991. Centenary of Maha Bodhi Society.
1160 **488** 1 r. multicoloured .. 40 40

489 Women working at Home

1991. 13th Anniv of Gam Udawa Movement.
1161 **489** 1 r. multicoloured .. 40 40

490 Globe and Plan Symbol

1991. 40th Anniv of Colombo Plan.
1162 **490** 1 r. violet and blue .. 40 40

491 17th-century Map and Modern Satellite Photo of Sri Lanka

1991. 190th Anniv of Sri Lanka Survey Department.
1163 **491** 1 r. multicoloured .. 40 40

492 Ven. Henpitagedera Gnanaseeha Nayake Thero

1991. 10th Death Anniv of Ven. Nayak Henpitagedera Gnanaseeha Nayake Thero (Buddhist theologian).
1164 **492** 1 r. multicoloured .. 40 40

493 Police Officers of 1866 and 1991 with Badge

1991. 125th Anniv of Sri Lankan Police Force.
1165 **493** 1 r. multicoloured .. 20 20
40 40

494 Kingswood College

1991. Centenary of Kingswood College, Kandy.
1166 **494** 1 r. multicoloured .. 30 30

495 The Annunciation

1991. Christmas. Multicoloured.
1167 1 r. Type **495** 20 20
1168 10 r. The Presentation of Jesus in the Temple .. 60 60

496 Early Magneto Telephone

1991. Inauguration of Sri Lankan Telecom Co-rporation. Multicoloured.
1170 1 r. Type **496** 15 10
1171 2 r. Manual switchboard and telephonist .. 20 15
1172 8 r. Satellite communications system .. 40 45
1173 10 r. Fibre optics cable and mobile phone .. 50 60

497 S.A.A.R.C. Logo and Bandaranaike Memorial Hall

1991. 6th South Asian Association for Regional Co-operation Summit, Colombo. Multicoloured.
1174 1 r. Type **497** 15 10
1175 8 r. Logo and hall surrounded by national flags 45 50

498 "Pancha" (Games mascot)

1991. 5th South Asian Federation Games. Multicoloured.
1176 1 r. Type **498** 15 10
1177 2 r. Games logo 20 15
1178 4 r. Sugathadasa Stadium 35 35
1179 11 r. Asia map on globe and national flags .. 75 75

499 Crate, Airliner and Container Ship

1992. Exports Year.
1180 **499** 1 r. multicoloured .. 30 30

500 Plucking Tea

1992. 125th Anniv of Tea Industry. Mult.

1181 1 r. Type **500** 15 10
1182 2 r. Healthy family, tea and tea estate . . 20 15
1183 5 r. Ceylon tea symbol . . 45 45
1184 10 r. James Taylor (founder) 70 80

501 General Ranjan Wijeratne

1992. 1st Death Anniv of General Ranjan Wijeratne.

1185 **501** 1 r. multicoloured . . 20 20

502 Olcott Hall, Mahinda College

1992. Centenary of Mahinda College, Galle.

1186 **502** 1 r. multicoloured . . 20 20

503 Newstead College and Logo

1992. 175th Anniv (1991) of Newstead Girls' College, Negombo.

1187 **503** 1 r. multicoloured . . 20 20

504 Student and Oil Lamp

1992. 11th Anniv of Mahapola Scholarship Fund.

1188 **504** 1 r. multicoloured . . 20 20

HAVE YOU READ THE NOTES AT THE BEGINNING OF THIS CATALOGUE?
These often provide answers to the enquiries we receive.

505 Sama's Parents leaving for Forest

1992. Vesak Festival. Sama Jataka Paintings from Kottimbulwala Cave Temple. Mult.

1189 75 c. Type **505** 10 10
1190 1 r. Sama and parents in forest 10 10
1191 8 r. Sama leading blind parents 45 55
1192 11 r. Sama's parents grieving for wounded son 70 80

506 Ven. Devamottawe Amarawansa (Buddhist missionary)

1992. National Heroes. Multicoloured.

1194 1 r. Type **506** 10 10
1195 1 r. Richard Mirando (Buddhist philanthropist) 10 10
1196 1 r. Gate Mudaliyar N. Canaganayagam (Buddhist social reformer) 10 10
1197 1 r. Abdul Azeez (Moorish social reformer) . . 10 10

507 Map of Sri Lanka, Flag and Symbol

1992. 2300th Anniv of Arrival of Buddhism in Sri Lanka.

1198 **507** 1 r. multicoloured . . 15 15

508 Family in House

1992. 14th Anniv of Gam Udawa Movement.

1199 **508** 1 r. multicoloured . . 15 15

509 Postal Activities and Award

1992. Postal Service Awards. Multicoloured.

1200 1 r. Type **509** 15 10
1201 10 r. Medals and commemorative cachet 50 55

510 Narilata Mask

1992. Kolam Dance Masks. Multicoloured.

1202 1 r. Type **510** 10 10
1203 2 r. Mudali mask . . 10 10
1204 5 r. Queen mask . . 20 25
1205 10 r. King mask . . 35 45

511 19th and 20th-century Players and Match of 1838

1992. 160th Anniv of Cricket in Sri Lanka.

1207 **511** 5 r. multicoloured . . 30 40

512 Running

1992. Olympic Games, Barcelona. Mult.

1208 1 r. Type **512** 10 10
1209 11 r. Shooting 45 60
1210 13 r. Swimming 50 65
1211 15 r. Weightlifting . . 55 70

513 Vijaya Kumaratunga

1992. Vijaya Kumaratunga (actor) Commem.

1213 **513** 1 r. multicoloured . . 15 15

514 College Building and Crest

1992. Cent of Al-Bahjathhul Ibraheemiyyah Arabic College.

1214 **514** 1 r. multicoloured . . 15 15

515 Official Church Seal

1992. 350th Anniv of Dutch Reformed Church in Sri Lanka.

1215 **515** 1 r. black, green & yell 15 15

516 Nativity

1992. Christmas. Multicoloured.

1216 1 r. Type **516** 10 10
1217 9 r. Family going to church 25 30

517 Fleet of Columbus

1992. 500th Anniv of Discovery of America by Columbus. Multicoloured.

1219 1 r. Type **517** 10 10
1220 11 r. Columbus landing in New World 35 40
1221 13 r. Wreck of "Santa Maria" 40 45
1222 15 r. Columbus reporting to Queen Isabella and King Ferdinand . . 45 50

1992. No. 684 surch **2.00**.

1224 **255** 2 r. on 10 c. mult . . 10 10

519 Ven. Sumedhankara Thero and Dagoba

1992. Birth Centenary of Ven. Dambagasare Sumedhankara Nayake Thero.

1225 **519** 1 r. multicoloured . . 15 15

520 University Logo, Students and Building

1992. 50th Anniv of University Education in Sri Lanka (1st issue).

1226 **520** 1 r. multicoloured . . 15 15

See also No. 1227.

521 University of Colombo Building and Logo

1993. 50th Anniv of University Education in Sri Lanka (2nd issue).
1227 **521** 1 r. multicoloured .. 15 15

522 College Building and Crest

1993. Centenary of Zahira College, Colombo.
1228 **522** 1 r. multicoloured .. 15 15

523 Magandiya being presented to Buddha

1993. Vesak Festival. Verses from the "Dhammapada". Multicoloured.
1229 75 c. Type **523** 10 10
1230 1 r. Kisa Gotami carrying her dead baby .. 10 10
1231 3 r. Patachara and her dying family 10 10
1232 10 r. Angulimala praying 25 30

524 Girl Guide, Badge and Camp

1993. 75th Anniv of Sri Lanka Girl Guides Association. Multicoloured.
1234 1 r. Type **524** 10 10
1235 5 r. Girl Guide activities 15 20

525 Ven. Yagirala Pagnananda Maha Nayaka Thero (scholar)

1993. National Heroes. Multicoloured.
1236 1 r. Type **525** 10 10
1237 1 r. Charles de Silva (politician) 10 10
1238 1 r. Wilmot A. Perera (politician) 10 10
1239 1 r. Abdul Caffoor (philanthropist) .. 10 10

526 Family arriving at New Home

1993. "Gam Udawa '93".
1240 **526** 1 r. multicoloured .. 15 15

527 Consumer Movement Flag and Logo

1993. 50th Anniv (1992) of Co-operative Consumer Movement.
1241 **527** 1 r. multicoloured .. 15 15

528 Ashy-headed Laughing Thrush

1993. Birds. Multicoloured.
1242 3 r. Type **528** 10 10
1243 4 r. Brown-capped jungle babbler 10 10
1244 5 r. Red-faced malkoha .. 15 20
1245 10 r. Ceylon grackle ("Ceylon Hill-Mynah") 25 30

529 Talawila Church

1993. 150th Anniv of Talawila Church.
1247 **529** 1 r. multicoloured .. 10 10

530 Rosette and Mail Delivery

1993. Sri Lanka Post Excellent Service Awards.
1248 **530** 1 r. multicoloured .. 10 10

531 College and Flag

1993. Centenary of Musaeus College.
1249 **531** 1 r. multicoloured .. 10 10

532 Presentation of Jesus in the Temple

1993. Christmas. Multicoloured.
1250 1 r. Type **532** 10 10
1251 17 r. Boy Jesus with the Jewish teachers .. 45 50

533 Healthy Youth and Drug Addict

1993. Youth and Health Campaign.
1253 **533** 1 r. multicoloured .. 10 10

534 Maradana Technical College Building and Emblems

1993. Centenary of Technical Education.
1254 **534** 1 r. multicoloured .. 10 10

535 Trinity College Logo

1994. Centenary of Trinity College, Kandy, Old Boys' Association.
1255 **535** 1 r. multicoloured .. 10 10

536 College Flag

1994. 150th Anniv of St. Thomas' College, Matara.
1256 **536** 1 r. brown and blue .. 10 10

537 Ven. Siyambalangamuwe Sri Gunaratana Thero

1994. Ven. Siyambalangamuwe Sri Gunaratana Thero (educationist) Commem.
1257 **537** 1 r. multicoloured .. 10 10

538 College Building and Arms

1994. 125th Anniv of St. Joseph's College, Trincomalee.
1258 **538** 1 r. multicoloured .. 10 10

STELLALAND

A temporary Boer republic annexed by the British in 1885 and later incorporated in Br. Bechuanaland.

12 pence = 1 shilling.
20 shillings = 1 pound.

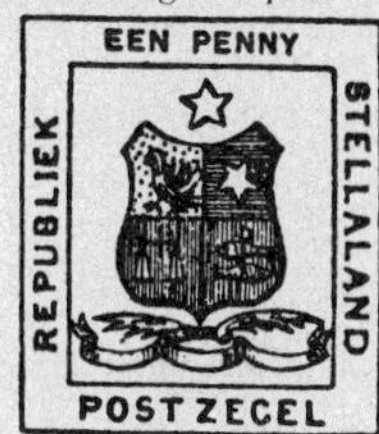

1. Arms of the Republic.

1884.

1.	1.	1d. red	£170	£275
2.		3d. orange	17·00	£275
3.		4d. blue	17·00	£300
4.		6d. mauve	17·00	£300
5.		1s. green	38·00	

1885. Surch. **Twee.**

6	1	2d. on 4d. blue	£3500	

STRAITS SETTLEMENTS

A Br. Crown colony which included portions of the mainland of the Malay Peninsula and islands off its coasts, and the island of Labuan off the N. coast of Borneo.

100 cents = 1 dollar (Straits).

1867. Stamps of India surch. with crown and value.

1.	11.	1½ c. on ½ a. blue	55·00	£150
2.		2 c. on 1 a. brown ..	60·00	55·00
3.		3 c. on 1 a. brown.. ..	70·00	60·00
4.		4 c. on 1 a. brown.. ..	£130	£170
5.		6 c. on 2 a. orange ..	£275	£160
6.		8 c. on 2 a. orange ..	90·00	32·00
7.		12 c. on 4 a. green ..	£400	£190
8.		24 c. on 8 a. red	£190	65·00
9.		32 c. on 2 a. orange ..	£190	70·00

1869 (?). No. 1 with "THREE HALF" deleted and "2" written above in manuscript.

10.	11.	2 on 1½ c. on ½ a. blue ..	£5500	£3000

5.

8. **9.**

1867.

11	5.	2 c. brown	13·00	2·00
98		4 c. red	3·00	1·25
66a		6 c. lilac	1·60	2·00
52		8 c. orange	2·00	45
15		12 c. blue	65·00	4·50
68a		24 c. green	3·00	3·50
69	8.	30 c. red	7·00	4·50
70	9.	32 c. red	5·50	1·50
71		96 c. grey	75·00	35·00

1879. Surch. in words.

20.	5.	5 c. on 8 c. orange ..	55·00	85·00
21.	9.	7 c. on 32 c. red	60·00	75·00

1880. Surch. in figures and words.

47.	5.	5 c. on 4 c. red	£160	£180
42.		5 c. on 8 c. orange ..	55·00	75·00
44.		10 c. on 6 c. lilac.. ..	35·00	6·00
45a.		10 c. on 12 c. blue ..	26·00	9·00
23.	8.	10 c. on 30 c. red.. ..	£110	42·00

1880. Surch in figures only.

33	8	"10" on 30 c. red ..	75·00	35·00

18. **19.**

1882.

63a.	5.	2 c. red	2·25	15
64.		4 c. brown	15·00	1·25
99.	18.	5 c. brown	2·50	90
65.		5 c. blue	6·50	40
100.		5 c. purple	1·75	2·00
101.	5.	8 c. blue	4·50	40
53.	19.	10 c. grey	2·50	55
102.	5.	12 c. purple	7·50	8·50

1883. Surch in words in one line horiz (No. 109) or vert.

57	5	2 c. on 8 c. orange ..	60·00	45·00
59	9	2 c. on 32 c. orange ..	£325	£100
109	18	4 c. on 5 c. red	45	30

1883. Surch. with figures over words in two lines.

61.	5.	2 c. on 4 c. red ..	50·00	60·00
62.		2 c. on 12 c. blue ..	£130	70·00
82.	18.	3 c. on 5 c. blue.. ..	75·00	£180
84.		3 c. on 5 c. purple ..	£110	£120
106.		4 c. on 5 c. brown ..	1·00	4·25
73.		4 c. on 5 c. blue (A)* ..	75·00	70·00
107.		4 c. on 5 c. blue (B)* ..	1·25	6·00
108b.	5.	4 c. on 8 c. blue.. ..	70	80
74.		8 c. on 12 c. blue ..	£160	85·00
75.		8 c. on 12 c. purple ..	£140	95·00

* (A) "Cents" in italics (B) "cents" (with small "c") in roman type.

1884. Surch. **TWO CENTS** vert.

76.	18.	2 c. on 5 c. blue.. ..	75·00	90·00

1884. Nos. 73 and 75 surch. with large figure.

80.	5.	"8" on 8 c. on 12 c. purple	£150	£160

1885. Surch. with words in one line and thick bar.

93.	5.	1 c. on 8 c. green.. ..	60	1·25
83a.	9.	3 c. on 32 c. purple ..	1·00	90
94.		3 c. on 32 c. red ..	2·25	70

1887. Surch. **2 Cents** in one line.

85.	18.	2 c. on 5 c. blue.. ..	14·00	32·00

1891. Surch. **10 CENTS** in one line and thin bar.

86.	5.	10 c. on 24 c. green ..	1·50	1·25

1891. Surch. with words in two lines and thin bar.

88.	5.	1 c. on 2 c. red ..	1·25	1·50
89.		1 c. on 4 c. brown ..	3·75	4·00
90.		1 c. on 6 c. lilac ..	1·00	2·50
91.		1 c. on 8 c. orange ..	1·00	60
92.		1 c. on 12 c. purple ..	4·00	9·00
87.	9.	30 c. on 32 c. orange ..	5·00	3·50

33. **37.**

1892.

95	33	1 c. green	50	20
96		3 c. red	7·50	30
97		3 c. brown	2·75	55
103b		25 c. purple and green ..	13·00	4·25
104		50 c. olive and red ..	17·00	2·50
105		$5 orange and red ..	£275	£275

1902.

110	37	1 c. green	65	1·25
111		3 c. purple and orange ..	1·25	15
112		4 c. purple on red ..	2·50	30
113		5 c. purple	1·75	65
157		5 c. orange	2·75	50
114		8 c. purple on blue ..	3·00	20
132		10 c. pur. and blk. on yell.	3·00	40
159		10 c. purple on yellow ..	1·75	30
116		25 c. purple and green ..	8·00	3·75
161		25 c. purple	7·50	3·00
117		30 c. grey and red ..	12·00	8·00
162		30 c. purple and yellow	24·00	1·75
135a		50 c. green and red ..	16·00	8·50
164		50 c. black on green ..	4·00	2·00
136a		$1 green and black ..	20·00	9·50
165		$1 black and red on blue	10·00	3·50
120		$2 purple and black ..	45·00	45·00
166		$2 green & red on yellow	17·00	17·00
138		$5 green and orange ..	95·00	95·00
167		$5 green and red on green	70·00	48·00
139		$25 green and black ..	£800	£800

39. **42.**

47. **46.**

1903.

127	39	1 c. green	1·50	10
128		3 c. purple	1·00	30
153		3 c. red	1·25	10
125		4 c. purple on red ..	1·50	30
154		4 c. red	5·50	1·50
155		4 c. purple	2·25	10
131	42	8 c. purple on blue ..	7·50	70
158		8 c. blue	1·75	30
160	47	21 c. purple	6·00	26·00
163		45 c. black on green ..	2·50	3·50
168	46	$25 purple and blue ..	£750	£550

1907. Stamps of Labuan (Crown type) optd. **STRAITS SETTLEMENTS** or surch. in words also.

141.	18.	1 c. black and purple ..	40·00	80·00
142.		2 c. black and green ..	£150	£170
143.		3 c. black and brown ..	14·00	75·00
144.		4 c. on 12 c. black & yell.	1·75	6·00
145.		4 c. on 16 c. green & brn.	1·75	5·00
146.		4 c. on 18 c. black & brn.	1·25	4·50
147.		8 c. black and orange ..	1·25	6·50
148.		10 c. brown and blue ..	3·50	4·25
149.		25 c. green and blue ..	4·50	22·00
150.		50 c. purple and lilac ..	9·50	48·00
151.		$1 red and orange ..	40·00	75·00

48. **54.**

52. **53.**

1912.

193	48	1 c. green	3·25	65
196a		3 c. red	60	10
197		4 c. purple	80	30
225a	54	5 c. orange	1·00	15
227	52	6 c. purple	2·00	15
201		8 c. blue	80	30
202a	54	10 c. purple on yellow..	75	50
204	53	21 c. purple	4·00	7·00
234b	54	25 c. purple and mauve	3·25	1·60
235a		30 c. purple and orange	2·00	60
208a	53	45 c. black on green ..	3·25	11·00
238	54	50 c. black on green ..	1·50	40
239		$1 black and red on blue	5·00	45
240		$2 green & red on yell.	10·00	8·00
212a		$5 green & red on green	50·00	27·00
240b	–	$25 pur. & blue on blue	£325	80·00

No. 240b is as Type **46** but with head of King George V.

1917. Surch. **RED CROSS 2c.**

216.	48.	2 c. on 3 c. red ..	1·75	22·00
217.		2 c. on 4 c. purple ..	1·75	22·00

1919.

218	48.	1 c. black	30	10
219	52.	2 c. green	30	10
220		2 c. brown	6·50	2·25
221	48.	3 c. green	1·50	70
222		4 c. red	2·00	3·25
223		4 c. violet	40	10
224		4 c. orange	1·00	10
226	54.	5 c. brown	1·25	10
229	52.	6 c. red	2·25	10
230	54.	10 c. blue	1·75	50
232	52.	12 c. blue	80	10
236a	53.	35 c. purple and orange	3·50	5·50
237		35 c. red and purple ..	8·50	7·00

1922. Optd. **MALAYA-BORNEO EXHIBITION.**

250	48.	1 c. black	80	7·00
251	52.	2 c. green	1·40	11·00
252	48.	4 c. red	1·75	16·00
243	54.	5 c. orange	3·75	12·00
244	52.	8 c. blue	1·75	6·50
254	54.	10 c. blue	2·25	18·00
245		25 c. purple and mauve	3·00	19·00
246	53.	45 c. black on green ..	3·00	16·00
255	54.	$1 black and red on blue	15·00	75·00
248		$2 green & red on yellow	22·00	85·00
249		$5 green & red on green	£190	£275

1935. Silver Jubilee. As T **13** of Antigua.

256.		5 c. blue and grey ..	80	20
257.		8 c. green and blue ..	2·00	1·40
258.		12 c. brown and blue ..	2·75	1·75
259.		25 c. grey and purple ..	2·75	3·50

57. **58.**

1936.

260.	57.	1 c. black	40	20
261.		2 c. green	40	30
262.		4 c. orange	75	30
263.		5 c. brown	40	10
264.		6 c. red	80	60
265.		8 c. grey	65	30
266.		10 c. purple	1·25	30
267.		12 c. blue	2·00	2·00
268.		25 c. purple and red ..	1·00	30
269.		30 c. purple and orange	1·25	2·00
270.		40 c. red and purple ..	1·25	2·50
271.		50 c. black and green..	1·75	80
272.		$1 black & red on blue	10·00	80
273.		$2 green and red ..	17·00	10·00
274.		$5 green & red on green	35·00	10·00

1937. Coronation. As T **2** of Aden.

275.		4 c. orange	30	10
276.		8 c. grey	65	10
277.		12 c. blue	90	60

1937.

278.	58.	1 c. black	3·00	10
279.		2 c. green	15·00	10
294.		2 c. orange	1·25	6·00
295.		3 c. green	3·00	2·50
280.		4 c. orange	11·00	10
281.		5 c. brown	19·00	20
282.		6 c. red	10·00	30
283.		8 c. grey	40·00	10
284.		10 c. purple	6·50	10
285.		12 c. blue	6·50	10
298.		15 c. blue	3·50	7·50
286.		25 c. purple and red ..	40·00	85
287.		30 c. purple and orange	40·00	1·50
288.		40 c. red and purple ..	10·00	2·00
289		50 c. black on green	8·00	10
290.		$1 black and red on blue	9·00	15
291.		$2 green and red ..	20·00	3·75
292.		$5 green & red on green	24·00	3·00

For subsequent issues see "Malaya".
For Japanese issues see "Japanese Occupation of Malaya".

POSTAGE DUE STAMPS

D 1.

1924.

D 1.	D 1.	1 c. violet	3·75	5·50
D 2.		2 c. black	3·00	1·25
D 3.		4 c. green	2·00	4·75
D 4.		8 c. red	4·50	55
D 5.		10 c. orange ..	5·00	85
D 6.		12 c. blue	7·00	65

For later issues see Malayan Postal Union.

SUDAN

A territory in Africa, extending S. from Egypt towards the equator, jointly administered by Gt. Britain and Egypt until 1954 when the territory was granted a large measure of self-government. Became independent 1 Jan. 1956.

1000 milliemes = 100 piastres = £1 Sudanese.

1897. Stamps of Egypt optd. **SOUDAN** in English and Arabic.

1.	18.	1 m. brown..	1·50	2·00
3.		2 m. green	1·25	1·75
4.		3 m. yellow	1·40	1·50
5.		5 m. red	2·00	70
6.	10.	1 pi. blue	7·00	2·00
7.	–	2 pi. orange	45·00	12·00
8.	–	5 pi. grey	42·00	12·00
9.	18.	10 pi. mauve	30·00	40·00

2. Arab Postman. **6.**

1898.

18	2	1 m. brown and red ..	40	10
19		2 m. green and brown ..	1·25	10
20		3 m. mauve and green ..	1·50	25
21		4 m. blue and brown ..	1·50	2·50
22		4 m. red and brown ..	1·50	75
13		5 m. red and black ..	1·00	60
24		1 pi. blue and brown ..	1·60	20
15		2 pi. black and blue ..	16·00	7·00
44		2 pi. purple and orange ..	40	10
44b		3 pi. brown and blue ..	2·75	10
44c		4 pi. blue and black ..	2·75	10
45		5 pi. brown and green ..	80	10
45b		6 pi. blue and black ..	2·75	20
45c		8 pi. green and black ..	4·00	1·40
46		10 pi. black and mauve ..	1·00	10
46b		20 pi. blue	2·00	10

1903. Surch. **5 Milliemes.**

29.	2.	5 m. on 5 pi. brown & grn.	6·50	9·00

1921.

37.	6.	1 m. black and orange ..	20	10
38.		2 m. yellow and brown ..	20	10
39.		3 m. mauve and green ..	20	10
40.		4 m. green and brown ..	30	10
41.		5 m. brown and black ..	30	10
42.		10 m. red and black ..	50	10
43.		15 m. blue and brown ..	40	10

For stamps as Type **2** and **6** with different Arabic inscriptions see issue of 1948.

1931. Air. Optd. **AIR MAIL.**

47.	6.	5 m. brown and black ..	35	70
48.		10 m. red and black ..	85	4·00
49.	2.	2 pi. purple and yellow ..	85	4·00

10. Statue of General Gordon.

1931. Air.

No.	Description	Mint	Used
49b **10.**	3 m. green and brown ..	2·50	5·50
50	5 m. black and green ..	1·00	20
51	10 m. black and red ..	1·00	35
52	15 m. brown	40	10
53	2 pi. black and orange ..	30	10
53c	2½ pi. mauve and blue ..	1·75	15
54	3 pi. black and grey ..	60	15
55	3½ pi. black and violet ..	1·50	80
56	4½ pi. brown and grey ..	10·00	15·00
57	5 pi. black and blue ..	1·00	40
57b	7½ pi. green	6·50	4·00
57d	10 pi. brown and blue ..	8·00	40

1932. Air. Surch. **AIR MAIL** and value in English and Arabic figures.

No.	Description	Mint	Used
58. **2.**	2½ pi. on 2 pi. pur. & orge.	2·00	3·50

12. General Gordon (after C. Ouless).

13. Gordon Memorial College, Khartoum.

1935. 50th Death Anniv. of Gen. Gordon.

No.	Description	Mint	Used
59. **12.**	5 m. green	35	10
60.	10 m. brown	75	25
61.	13 m. blue	85	6·00
62.	15 m. red	1·50	25
63.	2 pi. blue	1·25	20
64.	5 pi. orange	1·25	40
65. **13.**	10 pi. purple	7·00	7·00
66. –	20 pi black	22·00	45·00
67. –	50 pi. brown	65·00	80·00

DESIGN—(44 × 20 mm.): **20 pi., 50 pi. Gordon** Memorial Service, Khartoum.

1935. Air. Stamps of 1931 surch. in English and Arabic.

No.	Description	Mint	Used
74 **10**	5 m. on 2½ pi. mauve & bl	3·00	10
68	15 m. on 10 m. blk & red	40	10
69	2½ pi. on 3 m. grn & brn	85	5·50
70	2½ pi. on 5 m. blk & grn	40	2·00
75	3 pi. on 3½ pi. black & vio	28·00	35·00
71	3 pi. on 4½ pi. brn & grey	1·75	10·00
76	3 pi. on 7½ pi. green ..	6·50	6·00
77	5 pi. on 10 pi. brown & bl	1·75	4·75
72	7½ pi. on 4½ pi. brown and grey	6·00	35·00
73	10 pi. on 4½ pi. brown and grey	5·00	35·00

1940. Surch. **5 mills** and in Arabic.

No.	Description	Mint	Used
78. **6.**	5 m. on 10 m. red & black	50	30

1940. Surch. **4½ Piastres.**

No.	Description	Mint	Used
79. **6.**	4½ p. on 5 m. brown & blk.	42·00	2·50
80. **2.**	4½ p. on 8 p. green & black	28·00	5·50

20. Tuti Island, R. Nile, near Khartoum.

1941.

No.	Description	Mint	Used
81. **20.**	1 m. black and orange ..	30	1·50
82.	2 m. orange and brown ..	50	1·40
83.	3 m. mauve and green ..	50	10
84.	4 m. green and brown ..	30	20
85.	5 m. brown and black ..	30	10
86.	10 m. red and black ..	6·00	1·75
87.	15 m. blue and brown ..	40	10
88.	2 pi purple and yellow ..	3·50	60
89.	3 pi. brown and blue ..	70	10
90.	4 pi. blue and black ..	70	10
91.	5 pi. brown and green ..	4·50	7·00
92.	6 pi. blue and black ..	17·00	40
93.	8 pi. green and black ..	13·00	45
94.	10 pi. black and violet ..	48·00	75
95.	20 pi. blue	48·00	24·00

The piastre values are larger (30 × 25 mm.).

22. Arab Postman. 23.

1948.

No.	Description	Mint	Used
96. **22.**	1m. black and orange ..	35	1·25
97.	2 m. orange and brown ..	80	1·50
98.	3 m. mauve and green ..	30	1·25
99.	4 m. green and brown ..	30	10
100.	5 m. brown and black ..	1·75	70
101.	10 m. red and black ..	2·25	10
102.	15 m. blue and brown ..	1·75	10
103. **23.**	2 p. purple and yellow ..	3·75	45
104.	3 p. brown and blue ..	3·00	10
105.	4 p. blue and black ..	2·75	75
106.	5 p. orange and green ..	3·00	50
107.	6 p. blue and black ..	3·00	1·75
108.	8 p. green and black ..	3·00	1·75
109.	10 p. black and mauve ..	6·00	1·50
110.	20 p. blue	4·00	20
111.	50 p. red and blue ..	5·00	55

In this issue the Arabic inscriptions below the camel differ from those in Types **2** and **6**.

24. Arab Postman.

1948. Golden Jubilee of "Camel Postman" design.

No.	Description	Mint	Used
112. **24.**	2 p. black and blue ..	10	10

25. Arab Postman.

1948. Legislative Assembly.

No.	Description	Mint	Used
113. **25.**	10 m. red and black ..	10	10
114.	5 p. orange and green ..	10	30

26. Blue Nile Bridge, Khartoum.

1950. Air.

No.	Description	Mint	Used
115. **26.**	2 p. black and green ..	3·75	40
116. –	2½ p. blue and orange ..	50	65
117. –	3 p. purple and blue ..	3·00	10
118. –	3½ p. sepia and brown	75	2·50
119. –	4 p. brown and blue ..	70	1·00
120. –	4½ p. black and blue ..	2·25	3·25
121. –	6 p. black and red ..	60	1·00
122. –	20 p. black and purple	1·75	2·75

DESIGNS: 2½ p. Kassala Jebel. 3 p. Sagia (water wheel). 3½ p. Port Sudan. 4 p. Gordon Memorial College. 4½ p. "Gordon Pasha" (Nile mail boat). 6 p. Suakin. 20 p. G.P.O. Khartoum.

34. Ibex.

35. Cotton Picking.

1951.

No.	Description	Mint	Used
123 **34**	1 m. black and orange	15	90
124 –	2 m. black and blue ..	70	20
125 –	3 m. black and green ..	2·75	1·75
126 –	4 m. black and green ..	50	1·40
127 –	5 m. black and purple	50	10
128 –	10 m. black and blue ..	15	10
129 –	15 m. black and brown	75	10
130 **35**	2 p. blue	15	10
131 –	3 p. brown and blue ..	2·00	10
132 –	3½ p. green and brown	30	10
133 –	4 p. blue and black ..	30	10
134 –	5 p. brown and green	30	10
135 –	6 p. blue and black ..	3·50	1·10
136 –	8 p. blue and brown ..	4·50	85
137 –	10 p. black and green	1·00	10
138 –	20 p. turquoise & black	3·75	65
139 –	50 p. red and black ..	10·00	55

DESIGNS—As Type **34**: 2 m. Whale-headed Stork. 3 m. Giraffe. 4 m. Baggara girl. 5 m. Shilluk warrior. 10 m. Hadendowa. 15 m. Policeman. As Type **35**—HORIZ. 3 p. Ambatch canoe 3½ p. Nuba wrestlers. 4 p. Weaving. 5 p. Saluka farming. 6 p. Gum tapping. 8 p. Darfur Chief. 10 p. Stack medical Laboratory. 20 p. Nile Lechwe (antelope). VERT. 50 p. Camel postman.

51. Camel Postman.

1954. Self-Government.

No.	Description	Mint	Used
140. **51.**	15 m. brown & green ..	50	60
141.	3 p. blue and indigo ..	50	85
142.	5 p. black and purple ..	50	60

Stamps as Type **51**, but dated "1953" were released in error at the Sudan Agency in London. They had no postal validity.

For later issues see Volume 2.

ARMY SERVICE STAMPS

1905. Optd. **ARMY OFFICIAL.**

No.	Description	Mint	Used
A 1. **2.**	1 m. brown and red ..	2·50	2·00

1906. Optd. **Army Service.**

No.	Description	Mint	Used
A 6. **2.**	1 m. brown and red ..	1·50	20
A 7.	2 m. green and brown ..	5·00	1·00
A 8.	3 m. mauve and green ..	16·00	40
A 9.	5 m. red and black ..	1·50	10
A 10.	1 pi. blue and brown ..	11·00	15
A 11.	2 pi. black and blue ..	28·00	12·00
A 12.	5 pi. brown and green	80·00	48·00
A 16.	10 pi. black and mauve	£120	£170

OFFICIAL STAMPS

1902. Optd. **O.S.G.S.**

No.	Description	Mint	Used
O 5 **2.**	1 m. brown and red ..	50	10
O 6	3 m. mauve and green ..	2·00	15
O 7	5 m. red and black ..	2·00	10
O 8	1 pi. blue and brown ..	2·00	10
O 9	2 pi. black and blue ..	16·00	20
O 10	5 pi. brown and green	2·00	·30
O 4	10 pi. black and mauve	13·00	17·00

1936. Optd. **S.G.**

No.	Description	Mint	Used
O32 **6**	1 m. black and orange ..	50	6·50
O33	2 m. yellow and brown	30	2·50
O34	3 m. mauve and green ..	1·00	10
O35	4 m. green and brown	1·50	2·25
O36	5 m. brown and black ..	40	10
O37	10 m. red and black ..	60	10
O38	15 m. blue and brown ..	3·00	10
O39	2 pi. purple and orange	5·50	10
O39b	3 pi. brown and blue ..	2·50	85
O39c	4 pi. blue and black ..	6·50	70
O40	5 pi. brown and green	4·75	10
O40b	6 pi. blue and black ..	5·50	2·75
O40c **2**	8 pi. green and black ..	4·75	16·00
O41	10 pi. black and mauve	14·00	4·50
O42	20 pi. blue	16·00	18·00

1948. Optd. **S.G.**

No.	Description	Mint	Used
O 43. **22.**	1 m. black and orange ..	10	1·50
O 44.	2 m. orange and brown	30	10
O 45.	3 m. mauve and green ..	50	2·50
O 46.	4 m. green and brown ..	50	75
O 47.	5 m. brown and black ..	30	10
O 48.	10 m. red and black ..	30	40
O 49.	15 m. blue and brown ..	30	10
O 50. **23.**	2 p. purple and yellow ..	60	10
O 51.	3 p. brown and blue ..	60	10
O 52.	4 p. blue and black ..	60	10
O 53.	5 p. orange and green ..	60	10
O 54.	6 p. blue and black ..	60	10
O 55.	8 p. green and black ..	60	70
O 56.	10 p. black and mauve	60	20
O 57.	20 p. blue	3·00	25
O 58.	50 p. red and blue ..	48·00	25·00

1950. Air. Nos. 115/22 optd. **S.G.**

No.	Description	Mint	Used
O 59.	2 p. black and green ..	10·00	1·75
O 60.	2½ p. blue and orange ..	1·25	1·00
O 61.	3 p. purple and blue ..	80	70
O 62.	3½ p. sepia and brown ..	80	4·50
O 63.	4 p. brown and blue ..	80	2·75
O 64.	4½ p. black and blue ..	2·50	10·00
O 65.	6 p. black and red ..	1·00	3·75
O 66.	20 p. black and purple ..	5·00	11·00

1951. Nos. 123/39 optd. **S.G.**

No.	Description	Mint	Used
O 67.	1 m. black and orange ..	30	2·50
O 68.	2 m. black and blue ..	30	30
O 69.	3 m. black and green ..	2·00	9·50
O 70.	4 m. black and green ..	10	2·75
O 71.	5 m. black and purple ..	10	10
O 72.	10 m. black and blue ..	10	10
O 73.	15 m. black and brown ..	10	10
O 74.	2 p. blue	10	10
O 75.	3 p. brown and blue ..	1·00	10
O 76.	3½ p. green and brown ..	25	10
O 77.	4 p. blue and black ..	25	10
O 78.	5 p. brown and green ..	25	10
O 79.	6 p. blue and black ..	30	1·50
O 80.	8 p. blue and brown ..	45	10
O 81.	10 p. black and green ..	50	10
O 82.	20 p. turquoise and black	1·25	30
O 83.	50 p. red and black ..	3·50	1·25

POSTAGE DUE STAMPS

1897. Postage Due stamps of Egypt optd. **SOUDAN** in English and Arabic.

No.	Description	Mint	Used
D 1. D **23.**	2 m. green	1·75	8·00
D 2.	4 m. purple	1·75	8·00
D 3.	1 pi. blue	9·50	5·00
D 4.	2 pi. orange	9·50	11·00

D 1. . Gunboat "Zafir". D 2.

1901.

No.	Description	Mint	Used
D 5. D **1.**	2 m. black and brown	55	60
D 10.	4 m. brown and green	90	80
D 11.	10 m. green and mauve	1·25	1·60
D 8.	20 m. blue and red ..	3·25	3·25

1948.

No.	Description	Mint	Used
D 12. D **2.**	2 m. black and brown	80	16·00
D 13.	4 m. brown and green	2·00	20·00
D 394.	10 m. green & mauve	15	15
D 395.	20 m. blue and red ..	15	15

The Arabic inscription in Type D **2** differs from that in Type D **1**.

SUNGEI UJONG

A native state of the Malay Peninsula, later incorporated in Negri Sembilan.

100 cents = 1 dollar (Straits).

1878. Stamp of Straits Settlements optd. with Crescent, Star and **SU** in an oval.

No.	Description	Mint	Used
1. **5.**	2 c. brown	£1600	£1400

1881. Stamps of Straits Settlements optd **SUNGEI UJONG.**

No.	Description	Mint	Used
28. **5.**	2 c. brown	32·00	85·00
43.	2 c. red	4·75	6·50
22.	4 c. red	£750	£800
34.	4 c. brown	£130	£160
24.	8 c. orange	£950	£800
26. **19.**	10 c. grey	£350	£350

1882. Stamps of Strait Settlements optd **S.U.** (2 c. with or without stops).

No.	Description	Mint	Used
13 **5**	2 c. brown	£200	£250
14	4 c. red	£1700	£1700

1891. Stamp of Straits Settlements surch. **SUNGEI UJONG Two CENTS.**

No.	Description	Mint	Used
49. **5.**	2 c. on 24 c. green	80·00	£110

16. Tiger.

17. Tiger.

1891.

No.	Description	Mint	Used
50. **16.**	2 c. red	24·00	27·00
51.	2 c. orange	1·40	4·25
55. **17.**	3 c. purple and red ..	5·50	90
52. **16.**	5 c. blue	4·50	5·50

1894. Surch. in figures and words.

No.	Description	Mint	Used
53. **16.**	1 c. on 5 c. green	65	70
54.	3 c. on 5 c. red	2·00	4·75

SWAZILAND

A kingdom in the E. part of S. Africa. Its early stamps were issued under joint control of G. Britain and the S. Africa Republic. Incorporated into the latter state in 1895 it was transferred in 1906 to the High Commissioner for S. Africa. Again issued stamps in 1933. Achieved Independence in 1968.

1961. 100 cents = 1 rand.
1974. 100 cents = 1 lilangeni (plural-emalangeni).

1889. Stamps of Transvaal optd. **Swazieland.**

10. **18.** ½d. grey 7·00 13·00
1. 1d. red 15·00 15·00
5. 2d. pale brown 13·00 14·00
6. 6d. blue 16·00 30·00
3. 1s. green 10·00 13·00
7. 2s. 6d. yellow £120 £160
8. 5s. blue £120 £160
9. 10s. brown £4500 £2750

2. King George V. **7.** Swazi Married Woman.

1933.

11. **2.** ½d. green 30 30
12. 1d. red 30 10
13. 2d. brown 30 45
14. 3d. blue 45 60
15. 4d. red 1·00 1·40
16. 6d. mauve 1·00 80
17. 1s. olive 1·50 2·75
18. 2s. 6d. violet 15·00 28·00
19. 5s. grey 35·00 50·00
20. 10s. brown £100 £120

1935. Silver Jubilee. As T **13** of Antigua.

21. 1d. blue and red 40 20
22. 2d. blue and black 40 30
23. 3d. brown and blue 55 1·75
24. 6d. grey and purple 65 1·00

1937. Coronation. As T **2** of Aden.

25. 1d. red 75 50
26. 2d. brown 75 10
27. 3d. blue 75 50

1938. As T **2**, but with portrait of King George VI and inscr. "SWAZILAND" only below portrait.

28a. ½d. green 20 1·00
29a. 1d. red 30 60
30b. 1½d. blue 20 45
31a. 2d. brown 30 40
32b. 3d. blue 1·00 2·50
33a. 4d. orange 45 1·40
34b. 6d. purple 2·50 85
35a. 1s. olive 45 55
36a. 2s. 6d. violet 4·50 2·50
37b. 5s. grey 17·00 10·00
38a. 10s. brown 6·50 6·00

1945. Victory, Victory stamps of South Africa optd. **SWAZILAND.** Inscr. alternately in English or Afrikaans.

39. **55.** 1d. brown and red 55 40
40. – 2d. blue & vio. (No. 109) 55 40
41. – 3d. blue (No. 110) 55 1·60

Prices are for pairs.

1947. Royal Visit. As Nos. 32/5 of Basutoland.

42. 1d. red 10 10
43. 2d. green 10 10
44. 3d. blue 10 10
45. 1s. mauve 10 10

1948. Silver Wedding. As T **10/11** of Aden.

46. 1½d. blue 50 10
47. 10s. purple 22·00 18·00

1949. U.P.U. As T **20/23** of Antigua.

48. 1½d. blue 20 10
49. 3d. blue 50 60
50. 6d. mauve 60 60
51. 1s. olive 60 60

1953. Coronation. As T **13** of Aden.

52. 2d. black and brown 20 20

1956.

53. – ½d. black and orange 10 10
54. – 1d. black and green 10 10
55. **7.** 2d. black and brown 30 10
56. – 3d. black and red 20 10
57. – 4½d. black and blue 60 10
58. – 6d. black and mauve 45 10
59. – 1s. black and olive 20 10
60. – 1s. 3d. black and sepia 1·00 1·00
61. – 2s. 6d. green and red 1·00 1·25
62. – 5s. violet and grey 4·50 1·25
63. **7.** 10s. black and violet 11·00 4·00
64. – £1 black and turquoise 28·00 24·00

DESIGNS—HORIZ. ½d., 1s. Havelock asbestos mine. 1d., 2s. 6d. Highveld view. VERT. 3d., 1s. 3d. Swazi courting couple. 4½d., 5s. Swazi warrior. 6d., £1 Greater Kudu.

1961. Stamps of 1956 surch. in new currency.

65. ½ c. on ½d. black & orange 3·00 3·00
66. 1 c. on 1d. black & green 10 20
67. 2 c. on 2d. black & brown 10 20
68. 2½ c. on 2d. black & brown 10 10
69. 2½ c. on 3d. black and red 10 10
70. 3½ c. on 2d. black & brown 10 10
71. 4 c. on 4½d. black and blue 10 10
72. 5 c. on 6d. black & mauve 10 10
73. 10 c. on 1s. black & olive 16·00 3·00
74. 25 c. on 2s. 6d. green & red 30 65
75. 50 c. on 5s. violet & grey 30 60
76. 1 r. on 10s. black & violet 1·50 60
77a. 2 r. on £1 black & turquoise 4·50 5·50

1961. As 1956 but values in new currency.

78. ½ c. black and orange (as ½d.) 10 20
79. 1 c. black and green (as 1d.) 10 10
80. 2 c. black and brown (as 2d.) 10 60
81. 2½ c. black and red (as 3d.) 15 10
82. 4 c. black and blue (as 4½d.) 15 60
83. 5 c. black & mauve (as 6d.) 30 15
84. 10 c. black and olive (as 1s.) 15 10
85. 12½ c. blk. & sep. (as 1s. 3d.) 90 40
86. 25 c. green & red (as 2s. 6d.) 1·50 2·00
87. 50 c. violet and grey (as 5s.) 2·00 1·40
88. 1 r. black & violet (as 10s.) 3·00 4·50
89. 2 r. blk. & turquoise (as £1) 9·00 11·00

15. Swazi Shields. **31.** Steam Train and Map.

1962.

90. **15.** ½ c. black, brown & buff 10 10
91. – 1 c. orange and black 10 10
92. – 2 c. green, black and olive 10 30
93. – 2½ c. black and red 10 10
94. – 3½ c. green and grey 10 30
95. – 4 c. black and turquoise 10 10
96. – 5 c. black, red & deep red 30 10
97. – 7½ c. brown and buff 30 15
98. – 10 c. black and blue 70 10
99. – 12½ c. red and olive 50 80
100. – 15 c. black and mauve 1·25 60
101. – 20 c. black and green 40 80
102. – 25 c. black and blue 50 60
103. – 50 c. black and red 6·00 2·75
104. – 1 r. green and ochre 3·25 2·25
105. – 2 r. red and blue 11·00 6·00

DESIGNS—VERT. 1 c. Battle axe. 2 c. Forestry. 2½ c. Ceremonial head-dress. 3½ c. Musical instrument. 4 c. Irrigation. 5 c. Long-tailed Whydah. 7½ c. Rock paintings. 10 c. Secretary Bird. 12½ c. Pink Arum. 15 c. Swazi married woman. 20 c. Malaria control. 25 c. Swazi warrior. 1 r. Aloes. HORIZ. 50 c. Southern Ground Hornbill. 2 r. Msinsi in flower.

1963. Freedom from Hunger. As T **28** of Aden.

106. 15 c. violet 40 15

1963. Cent of Red Cross. As T **33** of Antigua.

107. 2½ c. red and black 10 10
108. 15 c. red and blue 40 20

1964. Opening of the Swaziland Railway.

109. **31.** 2½c. green and purple 35 10
110. 3½ c. blue and olive 35 25
111. 15 c. orange and brown 50 45
112. 25 c. yellow and blue 60 60

1965. Cent of I.T.U. As T **36** of Antigua.

113. 2½ c. blue and bistre 10 10
114. 15 c. purple and red 25 20

1965. I.C.Y. As T **37** of Antigua.

115. ½ c. purple and turquoise 10 10
116. 15 c. green and lavender 40 20

1966. Churchill Commem. As T **38** of Antigua.

117. ½ c. blue 10 30
118. 2½ c. green 20 10
119. 15 c. brown 35 20
120. 25 c. violet 50 55

1966. 20th Anniv of U.N.E.S.C.O. As T **54/6** of Antigua.

121. 2½ c. multicoloured 10 10
122. 7½ c. yellow, violet & olive 20 25
123. 15 c. black, purple & orge. 35 40

32. King Sobhuza II and Map.

1967. Protected State.

124. **32.** 2½ c. multicoloured 10 10
125. – 7½ c. multicoloured 15 10
126. **32.** 15 c. multicoloured 15 15
127. – 25 c. multicoloured 20 20

DESIGN—VERT. 7½ c., 25 c. King Sobhuza II.

1967. First Conferment of University Degrees. As T **66** of Botswana.

128. 2½ c. sepia, blue & orange 10 10
129. 7½ c. sepia, blue & turq. 10 10
130. 15 c. sepia, blue and red 15 15
131. 25 c. sepia, blue and violet 20 20

35. Incwala Ceremony.

1968. Traditional Customs.

132. **35.** 3 c. silver, red and black 10 10
133. – 10 c. multicoloured 10 10
134. **35.** 15 c. gold, red and black 15 15
135. – 25 c. multicoloured 15 15

DESIGN—VERT. 10 c., 25 c. Reed Dance.

1968. No. 96 Surch.

136. – 3 c. on 5 c. black, red and deep red 20 10

38. Cattle Ploughing.

1968. Independence.

137. **38.** 3 c. multicoloured 10 10
138. – 4½ c. multicoloured 10 10
139. – 17½ c. multicoloured 15 10
140. – 25 c. slate, black & gold 45 65

1968. Nos. 90/105 optd **INDEPENDENCE 1968** and No. 93 additionally surch **3 c.**

142 **15** ½ c. black, brn & lt brn 10 10
143 – 1 c. orange and black 10 10
144 – 2 c. green, black & olive 10 10
145a – 2½ c. black and red 40 10
146 – 3 c. on 2½ c. blk & red 10 10
147 – 3½ c. green and grey 15 10
148 – 4 c. black and green 10 10
149 – 5 c. black, red & verm 1·50 10
150 – 7½ c. brown and buff 20 10
151 – 10 c. black and blue 1·50 10
152 – 12½ c. red and green 25 30
153 – 15 c. black and purple 25 30
154 – 20 c. black and green 75 1·00
155 – 25 c. black and blue 35 40
159 – 50 c. black and red 2·75 2·50
157 – 1 r. green and brown 2·50 3·00
160 – 2 r. red and blue 5·50 5·00

43. Porcupine.

1969. Multicoloured.

161. ½ c. Caracal 10 10
162. 1 c. Type **43** 10 10
163. 2 c. Crocodile 20 10
164. 3 c. Lion 60 10
165. 3½ c. African elephant 60 10
166. 5 c. Bush pig 30 10
167. 7½ c. Impala 35 10
168. 10 c. Chacma baboon 45 10
169. 12½ c. Ratel 70 1·60
170. 15 c. Leopard 1·25 70
171. 20 c. Blue wildebeest 95 60
172. 25 c. White rhinoceros 1·40 1·50
173. 50 c. Common zebra 1·50 2·50
174. 1 r. Waterbuck 3·00 5·00
175. 2 r. Giraffe 7·00 8·50

Nos. 174/5 are vert. Nos. 164/5 are larger (35 × 24½ mm.).

For designs as Nos. 174/5, but in new currency, see Nos. 219/20.

44. King Sobhuza II and Flags.

1969. Swaziland's Admission to the U.N. Multicoloured.

176. 3 c. Type **44** 10 10
177. 7½ c. King Sobhuza II, U.N. building and emblem 25 10
178. 12½ c. As Type **44** 35 10
179. 25 c. As 7½ c. 55 40

46. Athlete, Shield and Spears. **47.** "Bauhinia galpinii".

1970. 9th Commonwealth Games. Multicoloured.

180. 3 c. Type **46** 10 10
181. 7½ c. Runner 25 10
182. 12½ c. Jumper 35 10
183. 25 c. Procession of Swaziland competitors 55 40

1971. Flowers. Multicoloured.

184. 3 c. Type **47** 20 10
185. 10 c. "Crocosmia aurea" 35 10
186. 15 c. "Gloriosa superba" 50 15
187. 25 c. "Watsonia densiflora 70 35

48. King Sobhuza II in Ceremonial Dress.

1971. Golden Jubilee of King Sobhuza II's Accession. Multicoloured.

188. 3 c. Type **48** 10 10
189. 3½ c. Sobhuza II in medallion 10 10
190. 7½ c. Sobhuza II attending Incwala ceremony 15 10
191. 25 c. Sobhuza II and aides at opening of Parliament 30 35

49. U.N.I.C.E.F. Emblem.

1972. 25th Anniv. of U.N.I.C.E.F.

192. **49.** 15 c. black and lilac 15 15
193. – 25 c. black and green 20 30

DESIGN: 25 c. As Type **49**, but inscription rearranged.

50. Local Dancers.

1972. Tourism. Multicoloured.

194. 3½ c. Type **50** 10 10
195. 7½ c. Swazi beehive hut 15 15
196. 15 c. Ezulwini Valley 30 30
197 25 c. Fishing, Usutu River 95 60

51. Spraying Mosquitoes.

1973. 25th Anniv. of W.H.O. Multicoloured.

198. 3½ c. Type **51** 25 10
199. 7½ c. Anti-malaria vaccination 40 40

52. Mining.

1973. Natural Resources Multicoloured.

No.	Description		
200.	3½ c. Type **52**	30	10
201.	7½ c. Cattle	30	15
202.	15 c. Water	40	20
203.	25 c. Rice	45	40

53. Coat of arms.

1973. 5th Anniv. of Independence.

No.	Description		
204. **53.**	3 c. pink and black ..	10	10
205. –	10 c. multicoloured ..	20	10
206. –	15 c. multicoloured ..	45	45
207. –	25 c. multicoloured ..	55	65

DESIGNS: 10 c. King Sobhuza II saluting. 15 c. Parliament buildings. 25 c. National Somhlolo stadium.

54. Flags and Mortarboard.

1973. 10th Anniv. of University of Botswana, Lesotho and Swaziland. Multicoloured.

No.	Description		
208.	7½ c. Type **54**	20	10
209.	12½ c. University campus	25	10
210.	15 c. Map of Southern Africa	30	20
211.	25 c. University badge ..	40	35

55. King Sobhuza as College Student.

1974. 75th Birth Anniv. of King Sobhuza II. Multicoloured.

No.	Description		
212.	3 c. Type **55**	10	10
213.	9 c. King Sobhuza in middle-age	10	10
214.	50 c. King Sobhuza at 75 years of age	70	60

56. New Post Office, Lobamba.

1974. Centenary of U.P.U. Multicoloured.

No.	Description		
215.	4 c. Type **56**	10	10
216.	10 c. Mbabane Temporary Post Office, 1902 ..	25	15
217.	15 c. Carrying mail by cableway	45	50
218.	25 c. Mule-drawn mail-coach	55	70

1975. As Nos. 174/5, but in new currency.

No.	Description		
219.	1 e. Waterbuck	2·00	2·50
220.	2 e. Giraffe	4·00	4·50

57. Umcwasho Ceremony.

1975. Swazi Youth. Multicoloured.

No.	Description		
221.	3 c. Type **57**	10	10
222.	10 c. Butimba (ritual dance)	15	10
223.	15 c. Lusekwane (preparation) (horiz.)	30	30
224.	25 c. Goina Regiment on parade	40	50

58. Control Tower Matsapa Airport.

1975. 10th Anniv. of Internal Air Service. Multicoloured.

No.	Description		
225.	4 c. Type **58**	30	10
226.	5 c. Fire engine	70	20
227.	15 c. Douglas " Dakota "	2·00	1·10
228.	25 c. Hawker Siddeley "748"	2·75	1·75

1975. Nos. 167 and 169 surch.

No.	Description		
230.	3 c. on 7½ c. Impala ..	1·75	1·25
231.	6 c. on 12½ c. Ratel ..	2·25	1·50

60. Elephant Symbol.

1975. International Women's Year.

No.	Description		
232. **60.**	4 c. grey, black and blue	15	10
233. –	5 c. multicoloured ..	15	10
234. –	15 c. multicoloured ..	40	40
235. –	25 c. multicoloured ..	60	70

DESIGNS—HORIZ. 5 c. Queen Labotsibeni. VERT. 15 c. Craftswoman. 25 c. " Women in Service ".

61. African Black-headed Oriole.

1976. Birds. Multicoloured.

No.	Description		
236.	1 c. Type **61**	60	45
237.	2 c. African Green Pigeon (vert.)	65	40
238.	3 c. Green-winged Pytilla	80	45
239.	4 c. Violet Starling (vert.)	80	15
240.	5 c. Black-headed Heron (vert.)	90	40
241.	6 c. Stonechat (vert.) ..	1·25	40
242.	7 c. Chorister Robin Chat (vert.)	90	40
243.	10 c. Four-coloured Bush-Shrike (vert.) ..	1·25	30
244.	15 c. Black-collared Barbet (vert.)	1·25	55
245.	20 c. Grey Heron (vert.) ..	2·25	1·25
246.	25 c. Giant Kingfisher (vert.)	2·50	1·25
247.	30 c. Verreaux's Eagle (vert.)	2·25	1·40
248a.	50 c. Red Bishop (vert.) ..	90	1·00
249a.	1 e. Pin-tailed Whydah (vert.)	1·75	2·50
250a.	2 e. Lilac-breasted Roller	3·00	5·00

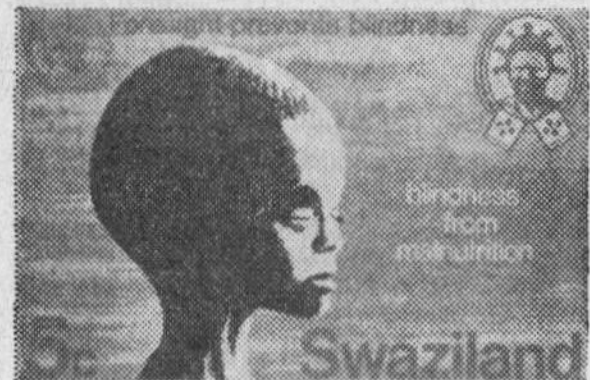

62. Blindness from Malnutrition.

1976. Prevention of Blindness. Mult.

No.	Description		
251.	5 c. Type **62**	25	10
252.	10 c. Infected retina ..	30	10
253.	20 c. Blindness from trachoma	60	35
254.	25 c. Medicines	65	40

63. Marathon.

1976. Olympic Games, Montreal. Mult.

No.	Description		
255.	5 c. Type **63**	10	10
256.	6 c. Boxing	15	10
257.	20 c. Football	40	25
258.	25 c. Olympic torch and flame	50	35

64. Footballer Shooting.

1976. F.I.F.A. Membership. Multicoloured.

No.	Description		
259.	4 c. Type **64**	15	10
260.	6 c. Heading	15	10
261.	20 c. Goalkeeping ..	50	25
262.	25 c. Player about to shoot	55	30

65. Alexander Graham Bell and Telephone.

1976. Centenary of Telephone.

No.	Description		
263. **65.**	4 c. multicoloured ..	10	10
264. –	5 c. multicoloured ..	10	10
265. –	10 c. multicoloured ..	10	10
266. –	15 c. multicoloured ..	30	20
267. –	20 c. multicoloured ..	40	30

Nos. 264/7 as Type **65**, but showing different telephones.

66. Queen Elizabeth II and King Sobhuza II.

1977. Silver Jubilee. Multicoloured.

No.	Description		
268.	20 c. Type **66**	20	20
269.	25 c. Coronation Coach at Admiralty Arch ..	20	20
270.	50 c. Queen in coach ..	30	45

67. Matsapa College.

1977. 50 Years of Police Training. Mult.

No.	Description		
271.	5 c. Type **67**	10	10
272.	10 c. Policemen and women on parade	30	10
273.	20 c. Royal Swaziland Police badge (vert.)	45	40
274.	25 c. Dog handling	50	55

68. Animals and Hunters.

1977. Rock Paintings. Multicoloured.

No.	Description		
275.	5 c. Type **68**	25	10
276.	10 c. Four dancers in a procession	30	10
277.	15 c. Man with cattle ..	40	20
278.	20 c. Four dancers	45	30

69. Timber, Highveld Region.

1977. Maps of the Regions. Multicoloured.

No.	Description		
280.	5 c. Type **69**	10	10
281.	10 c. Pineapple, Middleveld	20	10
282.	15 c. Orange and lemon, Lowveld	30	30
283.	20 c. Cattle, Lubombo region	40	50

71. Cabbage Tree.

1978. Trees of Swaziland.

No.	Description		
285. **71.**	5 c. grn., brn. and blk.	15	10
286. –	10 c. multicoloured ..	35	10
287. –	20 c. multicoloured ..	55	70
288. –	25 c. multicoloured ..	60	85

DESIGNS: 10 c. Marula. 20 c. Kiaat. 25 c. Lucky bean-tree.

72. Rural Electrification at Lobamba.

1978. Hydro-electric Power.

No.	Description		
289. **72.**	5 c. black and brown ..	10	10
290. –	10 c. black and green ..	15	10
291. –	20 c. black and blue ..	25	30
292. –	25 c. black and purple ..	30	35

DESIGNS: 10 c. Edwaleni Power Station. 20 c. Switchgear, Magudza Power Station. 25 c. Turbine Hall, Edwaleni.

MORE DETAILED LISTS

are given in the Stanley Gibbons Catalogues referred to in the country headings.

For lists of current volumes see Introduction.

73. Elephant.

1978. 25th Anniv. of Coronation.

No.	Description	Unused	Used
293.	– 25 c. blue, black & green	20	30
294.	– 25 c. multicoloured ..	20	30
295.	**73.** 25 c. blue, black & green	20	30

DESIGNS: No. 293, Queen's Lion. No. 294, Queen Elizabeth II.

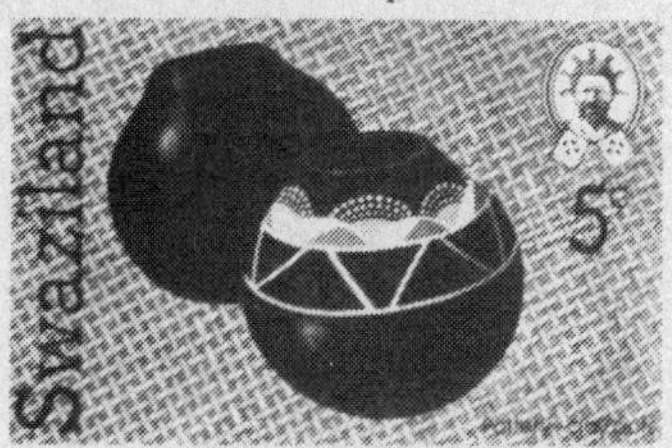

74. Clay Pots.

1978. Handicrafts (1st series). Multicoloured.

No.	Description	Unused	Used
296.	5 c. Type **74**	10	10
297.	10 c. Basketwork	10	10
298.	20 c. Wooden utensils ..	15	15
299.	30 c. Wooden pot ..	25	30

See also Nos. 310/13.

75. Defence Force.

1978. 10th Anniv. of Independence. Mult.

No.	Description	Unused	Used
300.	4 c. Type **75**	15	10
301.	6 c. The King's Regiment	15	10
302.	10 c. Tinkabi tractor (agricultural development) ..	15	10
303.	15 c. Water-pipe laying (self-help scheme)	25	10
304.	25 c. Sebenta adult literacy scheme	30	25
305.	50 c. Fire emergency service	80	50

76. Archangel Gabriel appearing before Shepherds.

1978. Christmas. Multicoloured.

No.	Description	Unused	Used
306.	5 c. Type **76**	10	10
307.	10 c. Wise Men paying homage to infant Jesus ..	10	10
308.	15 c. Archangel Gabriel warning Joseph ..	10	10
309.	25 c. Flight into Eygpt ..	20	20

1979. Handicrafts (2nd series). As T **74**. Multicoloured.

No.	Description	Unused	Used
310.	5 c. Sisal bowls	10	10
311.	15 c. Pottery	15	10
312.	20 c. Basket work ..	20	15
313.	30 c. Hide shield	30	20

77. Prospecting at Phophonyane.

1979. Centenary of Discovery of Gold in Swaziland.

No.	Description	Unused	Used
314.	**77.** 5 c. gold and blue ..	20	10
315.	– 15 c. gold and brown ..	40	20
316.	– 25 c. gold and green ..	55	30
317.	– 50 c. gold and red ..	80	90

DESIGNS: 15 c. Early 3-stamp battery mill. 25 c. Cyanide tanks at Piggs Peak. 50 c. Pouring off molten gold.

78. " Girls at the Piano ".

1979. International Year of the Child. Paintings by Renoir. Multicoloured.

No.	Description	Unused	Used
318.	5 c. Type **78**	10	10
319.	15 c. " Madame Charpentier and her Children "	25	10
320.	25 c. " Girls Picking Flowers "	35	15
321.	50 c. " Girl with Watering Can "	70	55

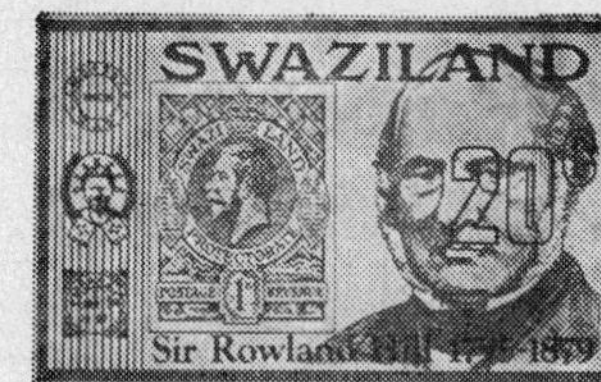

79. 1933 1d. Carmine Stamp and Sir Rowland Hill.

1979. Death Centenary of Sir Rowland Hill. Multicoloured.

No.	Description	Unused	Used
323.	10 c. 1945 3d. Victory commemorative ..	15	10
324.	20 c. Type **79**	25	25
325.	25 c. 1968 25 c. Independence commemorative ..	25	30

80. Obverse and Reverse of 5 Cents.

1979. Coins.

No.	Description	Unused	Used
327.	**80.** 5 c. black and brown ..	10	10
328.	– 10 c. black and blue ..	15	10
329.	– 20 c. black and green ..	25	20
330.	– 50 c. black and orange ..	45	45
331.	– 1 e. black and cerise ..	75	80

DESIGNS: 10 c. Obverse and reverse of 10 cents. 20 c. Obverse and reverse of 20 cents. 50 c. Reverse of 50 cents. 1 e. Reverse of 1 lilangeni.

81. Big Bend Post Office.

1979. Post Office Anniversaries.

No.	Description	Unused	Used
332.	**81.** 5 c. multicoloured ..	10	10
333.	– 15 c. multicoloured ..	15	10
334.	– 20 c. black, green & red	20	15
335.	– 50 c. multicoloured ..	40	60

DESIGNS AND COMMEMORATIONS—HORIZ. 5 c. Type 81 (25th anniversary of Posts and Telecommunications Services). 20 c. 1949 1s. 75th anniversary of U.P.U. stamp (10th anniversary of U.P.U. membership). 50 c. 1974 25 c. centenary of U.P.U. stamp (10th anniversary of U.P.U. membership). VERT. 15 c. Microwave antenna, Mount Ntondzi (25th anniversary of Posts and Telecommunications Services).

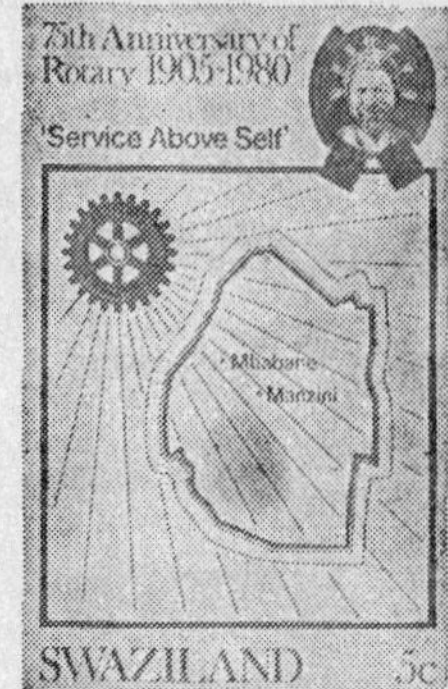

82. Map of Swaziland.

1980. 75th Anniv. of Rotary International.

No.	Description	Unused	Used
336.	**82.** 5 c. blue and gold ..	15	10
337.	– 15 c. blue and gold ..	30	10
338.	– 50 c. blue and gold ..	50	55
339.	– 1 e. blue and gold ..	85	1·25

DESIGNS: 15 c. Vitreous cutter and optical illuminator. 50 c. Scroll. 1 e. Rotary Headquarters, Evanston, U.S.A.

83. " Brunsvigia radulosa ".

1980. Flowers. Multicoloured.

No.	Description	Unused	Used
340.	1 c. Type **83**	15	10
341.	2 c. " Aloe suprafoliata " ..	15	10
342.	3 c. " Haemanthus magnificus "	15	10
343.	4 c. " Aloe marlothii " ..	20	10
344.	5 c. " Dicoma zeyheri " ..	15	10
345.	6 c. " Aloe kniphofioides "	20	20
346.	7 c. " Cyrtanthus bicolor "	15	10
347.	10 c. " Eucomis autumnalis " (horiz.)	25	10
348.	15 c. " Leucospermum gerrardii " (horiz.) ..	15	10
349.	20 c. " Haemanthus multiflorus " (horiz.) ..	40	25
350.	30 c. " Acridocarpus natalitius " (horiz.) ..	20	20
351.	50 c. " Adenium swazicum " (horiz.)	30	30
352.	1 e. " Protea simplex " ..	55	60
353.	2 e. " Calodendrum capense "	1·10	1·25
354.	5 e. " Gladiolus ecklonii " ..	2·75	3·00

Nos. 347/51 are 42 × 45 mm. and Nos. 352/4 28 × 38 mm.

Nos. 340/1, 343, 345, 347 and 349 come with and without date imprint.

84. Mail Runner.

1980. " London 1980 " International Stamp Exhibition. Multicoloured.

No.	Description	Unused	Used
355.	10 c. Type **84**	15	10
356.	20 c. Post Office mail truck	25	15
357.	25 c. Mail sorting office ..	30	20
358.	50 c. Ropeway conveying mail at Bulembu ..	70	70

85. Yellow Fish.

1980. River Fishes. Multicoloured.

No.	Description	Unused	Used
359.	5 c. Type **85**	10	10
360.	10 c. Silver Barbel ..	15	10
361.	15 c. Tiger Fish ..	20	15
362.	30 c. Squeaker Fish ..	40	30
363.	1 e. Bream	1·10	1·40

86. Oribi.

1980. Wildlife Conservation. Multicoloured.

No.	Description	Unused	Used
364.	5 c. Type **86**	10	10
365.	10 c. Nile crocodile (vert.)	15	10
366.	50 c. Temminck's ground pangolin	70	70
367.	1 e. Leopard (vert.) ..	1·25	1·50

87. Public Bus Service.

1981. Transport. Multicoloured.

No.	Description	Unused	Used
368.	5 c. Type **87**	10	10
369.	25 c. Royal Swazi National Airways	25	15
370.	30 c. Swaziland United Transport	30	20
371.	1 e. Swaziland Railway ..	1·75	1·75

88. Mantenga Falls.

1981. Tourism. Multicoloured.

No.	Description	Unused	Used
372.	5 c. Type **88**	10	10
373.	15 c. Mananga Yacht Club	15	10
374.	30 c. White Rhinoceros in Mlilwane Game Sanctuary	40	30
375.	1 e. Gambling equipment (casinos)	1·40	1·60

89. Prince Charles on Hike.

1981. Royal Wedding. Multicoloured.

No.	Description	Unused	Used
376.	10 c. Wedding bouquet from Swaziland ..	15	10
377.	25 c. Type **89**	15	10
378.	1 e. Prince Charles and Lady Diana Spencer ..	60	70

90. Installation of King Sobhuza II, 22 December 1921.

1981. Diamond Jubilee of King Sobhuza II. Multicoloured.

No.	Description	Unused	Used
379.	5 c. Type **90**	10	10
380.	10 c. Royal Visit, 1947 ..	15	10
381.	15 c. King Sobhuza II and Coronation of Queen Elizabeth II, 1953 ..	20	15
382.	25 c. King Sobhuza taking Royal Salute, Independence, 1968	25	25
383.	30 c. King Sobhuza in youth	30	30
384.	1 e. King Sobhuza and Parliament Buildings ..	90	1·25

91. "Physical Recreation".

1981. 25th Anniv. of Duke of Edinburgh Award Scheme. Multicoloured.

No.	Description		
385.	5 c. Type **91**	10	10
386.	20 c. "Expeditions" ..	15	10
387.	50 c. "Skills"	40	25
388.	1 e. Duke of Edinburgh in ceremonial dress ..	80	80

92. Disabled Person in Wheelchair.

1981. International Year for the Disabled. Multicoloured.

No.	Description		
389.	5 c. Type **92**	30	10
390.	15 c. Teacher with disabled child (vert.)	50	15
391.	25 c. Disabled craftsman (vert.) ..	75	20
392.	1 e. Disabled driver in invalid carriage ..	2·00	1·75

93. "Papilio demodocus".

1981. Butterflies. Multicoloured.

No.	Description		
393	5 c. Type **93**	40	10
394	10 c. "Charaxes candiope"	50	10
395	50 c. "Papilio nireus"	1·75	85
396	1 e. "Eurema desjardinsii"	2·25	2·00

94. Man holding a Flower, after discarding Cigarettes.

1982. Pan-African Conference on Smoking and Health. Multicoloured.

No.	Description		
397.	5 c. Type **94**	60	60
398.	10 c. Smoker and non-smoker	80	80

95. Male Pel's Fishing Owl.

1982. Wildlife Conservation (1st series). Pel's Fishing Owl. Multicoloured.

No.	Description		
399.	35 c. Type **95**	1·60	1·75
400.	35 c. Female Pel's Fishing Owl at nest ..	1·60	1·75
401.	35 c. Pair of Pel's Fishing Owls	1·60	1·75
402.	35 c. Pel's Fishing Owl, nest and eggs	1·60	1·75
403.	35 c. Adult Pel's Fishing Owl with youngster ..	1·60	1·75

See also Nos. 425/29 and 448/52.

96. Swaziland Coat of Arms.

1982. 21st Birthday of Princess of Wales. Multicoloured.

No.	Description		
404.	5 c. Type **96**	10	10
405.	20 c. Princess leaving Eastleigh Airport, Southhampton	15	10
406.	50 c. Bride at Buckingham Palace	35	35
407.	1 e. Formal Portrait ..	80	80

97. Irrigation.

1982. Sugar Industry. Multicoloured.

No.	Description		
408.	5 c. Type **97**	10	10
409.	20 c. Harvesting	25	15
410.	30 c. Mhlume mills ..	35	25
411.	1 e. Sugar transportation by train	1·00	1·40

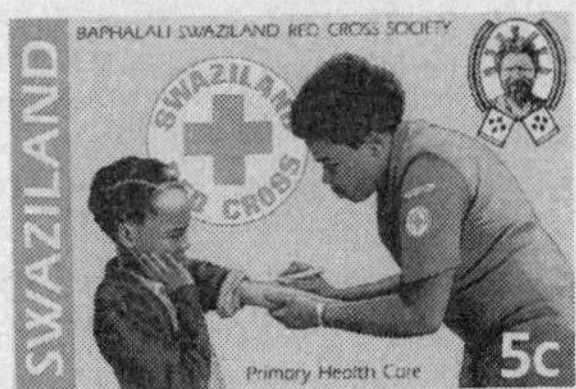

98. Doctor with Child.

1982. Swaziland Red Cross Society (Baphaladi). Multicoloured.

No.	Description		
412.	5 c. Type **98**	10	10
413.	20 c. Juniors carrying stretcher	25	15
414.	50 c. Disaster relief ..	55	60
415.	1 e. Henri Dunant (founder of Red Cross) ..	1·25	1·40

99. Taking the Oath.

1982. 75th Anniv. of Boy Scout Movement. Multicoloured.

No.	Description		
416.	5 c. Type **99**	10	10
417.	10 c. Hiking and exploration	15	10
418.	25 c. Community development	30	30
419.	75 c. Lord Baden-Powell	1·00	1·25

MINIMUM PRICE

The minimum price quoted is 10p which represents a handling charge rather than a basis for valuing common stamps. For further notes about prices see introductory pages.

100. Satellite View of Earth.

1982. Commonwealth Day. Multicoloured.

No.	Description		
421.	6 c. Type **100**	10	10
422.	10 c. King Sobhuza II ..	10	10
423.	50 c. Swazi woman and beehive huts (horiz.) ..	35	55
424.	1 e. Spraying sugar crops (horiz.)	70	1·00

1983. Wildlife Conservation (2nd series). Lammergeier. As T **95**. Multicoloured.

No.	Description		
425.	35 c. Adult male	1·00	1·00
426.	35 c. Pair	1·00	1·00
427.	35 c. Nest and egg ..	1·00	1·00
428.	35 c. Female at nest ..	1·00	1·00
429.	35 c. Adult bird with fledgeling	1·00	1·00

102. Montgolfier Balloon.

1983. Bicentenary of Manned Flight. Mult.

No.	Description		
431.	5 c. Type **102**	10	10
432.	10 c. Wright brothers' "Flyer" (horiz.) ..	15	10
433.	25 c. Fokker "Fellowship" (horiz.)	30	35
434.	50 c. Bell "X-1" (horiz.)	60	65

103. Dr. Albert Schweitzer (Peace Prize, 1952).

1983. 150th Birth Anniv. of Alfred Nobel. Multicoloured.

No.	Description		
436.	6 c. Type **103**	30	10
437.	10 c. Dag Hammarskjold (Peace Prize, 1961) ..	30	10
438.	50 c. Albert Einstein (Physics Prize, 1921) ..	1·75	70
439.	1 e. Alfred Nobel	2·00	1·50

104. Maize.

1983. World Food Day. Multicoloured.

No.	Description		
440.	6 c. Type **104**	10	10
441.	10 c. Rice	10	10
442.	50 c. Cattle herding ..	55	65
443.	1 e. Ploughing	1·10	1·40

105. Women's College.

1984. Education. Multicoloured.

No.	Description		
444.	5 c. Type **105**	10	10
445.	15 c. Technical Training School	15	15
446.	50 c. University	45	60
447.	1 e. Primary school ..	90	1·10

106. Male on Ledge.

1984. Wildlife Conservation (3rd series). Bald Ibis. Multicoloured.

No.	Description		
448.	35 c. Type **106**	1·75	2·00
449.	35 c. Male and female ..	1·75	2·00
450.	35 c. Bird and egg ..	1·75	2·00
451.	35 c. Female on nest of eggs	1·75	2·00
452.	35 c. Adult and fledgling ..	1·75	2·00

107. Mule-drawn Passenger Coach.

1984. Universal Postal Union Congress Hamburg. Multicoloured.

No.	Description		
453.	7 c. Type **107**	20	10
454.	15 c. Ox-drawn post wagon	35	15
455.	50 c. Mule-drawn mail coach	80	60
456.	1 e. Bristol to London mail coach	1·25	1·10

108. Running.

1984. Olympic Games, Los Angeles. Multicoloured.

No.	Description		
457.	7 c. Type **108**	10	10
458.	10 c. Swimming	10	10
459.	50 c. Shooting	45	60
460.	1 e. Boxing	90	1·25

109. "Suillus bovinus".

1984. Fungi. Multicoloured.

No.	Description		
462.	10 c. Type **109**	50	10
463.	15 c. "Langermannia gigantea" (vert.) ..	75	30
464.	50 c. "Coriolus versicolor" (vert.)	1·40	1·25
465.	1 e. "Boletus edulis" ..	1·90	2·00

110. King Sobhuza opening Railway, 1964.

1984. 20th Anniv. of Swaziland Railways. Multicoloured.

No.	Description		
466.	10 c. Type **110**	25	10
467.	25 c. Type "15A" locomotive at Siweni Yard	55	30
468.	30 c. Container loading, Matsapha Station ..	55	30
469.	1 e. Locomotive No. 268 leaving Alto Tunnel ..	1·50	1·40

1985. Nos. 340, 342, 343, 345 and 346 surch.

471a. 10 c. on 4 c. "Aloe marlothii" 30 10
472. 15 c. on 7 c. "Cyrtanthus bicolor" 40 10
473. 20 c. on 3 c. "Haemanthus magnificus" 50 15
474. 25 c. on 6 c. "Aloe kniphofioides" 60 20
475. 30 c. on 1 c. Type **83** .. 70 20
476. 30 c. on 2 c. "Aloe suprafoliata" .. .. .. 1·00 1·25

112. Rotary International Logo and Map of World.

1985. 80th Anniv. of Rotary International. Multicoloured.

477. 10 c. Type **112** 30 10
478. 15 c. Teacher and handicapped children 45 20
479. 50 c. Youth exchange .. 1·00 55
480. 1 e. Nurse and children .. 1·50 1·10

113. Male Southern Ground Hornbill.

1985. Birth Bicentenary of John J. Audubon (ornithologist). Southern Ground Hornbills. Multicoloured.

481. 25 c. Type **113** .. .. 1·00 1·25
482. 25 c. Male and female Ground hornbills .. 1·00 1·25
483. 25 c. Female at nest .. 1·00 1·25
484. 25 c. Ground hornbill in nest, and egg .. .. 1·00 1·25
485. 25 c. Adult and fledgeling 1·00 1·25

114. The Queen Mother in 1975.

1985. Life and Times of Queen Elizabeth the Queen Mother. Multicoloured.

486 10 c. The Queen Mother in South Africa, 1947 .. 10 10
487 15 c. With the Queen and Princess Margaret, 1985 (from photo by Norman Parkinson) 10 10
488 50 c. Type **114** 30 35
489 1 e. With Prince Henry at his christening (from photo by Lord Snowdon) 65 70

115. Buick "Tourer"

1985. Century of Motoring. Multicoloured.

491. 10 c. Type **115** 40 10
492. 15 c. Four cylinder Rover 60 20
493. 50 c. De Dion Bouton .. 1·50 1·25
494. 1 e. "Model T" Ford .. 2·00 2·50

116. Youths building Bridge over Ravine.

1985. International Youth Year (10, 50 c.) and 75th Anniv. of Girl Guide Movement (others). Multicoloured.

495. 10 c. Type **116** 15 10
496. 20 c. Girl Guides in camp 20 15
497. 50 c. Youth making model from sticks 45 60
498. 1 e. Guides collecting brushwood .. .. 80 1·25

117. Halley's Comet over Swaziland.

1986. Appearance of Halley's Comet.

499. **117.** 1 e. 50 multicoloured 2·75 2·75

1986. 60th Birthday of Queen Elizabeth II. As T **110** of Ascension. Multicoloured.

500. 10 c. Christening of Princess Anne, 1950 .. 10 10
501. 30 c. On Palace balcony after wedding of Prince and Princess of Wales, 1981 .. .. 20 25
502. 45 c. Royal visit to Swaziland, 1947 .. .. 25 30
503. 1 e. At Windsor Polo Ground, 1984 .. .. 55 60
504. 2 e. At Crown Agents Head Office, London, 1983 .. 1·10 1·25

118 King Mswati III

1986. Coronation of King Mswati III

505. **118.** 10 c. black and gold .. 35 10
506. – 20 c. multicoloured .. 70 30
507. – 25 c. multicoloured .. 80 35
508. – 30 c. multicoloured .. 90 50
509. – 40 c. multicoloured .. 1·00 90
510. – 2 e. multicoloured .. 3·25 4·50

DESIGNS—HORIZ. 20 c. Prince with King Sobhuza II at Incwala ceremony. 25 c. At primary school. 30 c. At school in England. 40 c. Inspecting guard of honour at Matsapha Airport. 2 e. Dancing the Simemo.

119. Emblems of Round Table and Project Orbis (eye disease campaign).

1986. 50th Anniv. of Round Table Organization. Designs showing branch emblems. Multicoloured.

511. 15 c. Type **119** 10 10
512. 25 c. Ehlanzeni 51 .. .. 20 20
513. 55 c. Mbabane 30 .. .. 40 40
514. 70 c. Bulembu 54 .. .. 55 50
515. 2 e. Manzini 44 .. .. 1·40 1·75

120. "Junonia hierta".

1987. Butterflies (1st series). Multicoloured.

516 10 c. Type **120** 15 10
517 15 c. "Hamanumida daedalus" 20 20
518 20 c. "Charaxes boueti" .. 30 30
519 25 c. "Abantis paradisea" 30 30
520 30 c. "Acraea anemosa" .. 30 40
521 35 c. "Graphium lepridas" 35 50
522 45 c. "Graphium antheus" 40 60
523 50 c. "Junonia orithya" .. 45 60
524 55 c. "Pinacopteryx eriphia" 45 60
525 70 c. "Precis octavia" .. 55 70
526 1 e. "Mylothris chloris" .. 70 90
527 5 e. "Colotis regina" .. 2·00 2·25
528 10 e. "Spindasis natalensis" .. .. .. 4·00 4·25

For these designs and similar 5 c. with different portrait of King Mswati III, see Nos. 606/17.

121. Two White Rhinoceroses.

1987. White Rhinoceros. Multicoloured.

529. 15 c. Type **121** 65 15
530. 25 c. Female and calf .. 1·00 65
531. 45 c. Rhinoceros charging 1·75 1·75
532. 70 c. Rhinoceros wallowing 2·25 2·75

122. Hybrid Tea Rose "Blue Moon".

1987. Garden Flowers. Multicoloured.

533. 15 c. Type **122** 55 15
534. 35 c. Rambler rose "Danse du feu" .. .. 1·00 60
535. 55 c. Pompon dahlia "Odin" .. .. .. 1·50 1·00
536. 2 e. "Lilium davidii var. willmottiae" .. .. 4·25 5·00

1987. Royal Ruby Wedding. Nos. 501/4 optd. **40th WEDDING ANNIVERSARY.**

537. 30 c. On Palace balcony after wedding of Prince and Princess of Wales, 1981 .. .. .. 20 20
538. 45 c. Royal visit to Swaziland, 1947 .. 30 30
539. 1 e. At Windsor Polo Ground, 1984 .. .. 80 85
540. 2 e. At Crown Agents Head Office, London, 1983 .. 1·50 1·75

123. "Zabalius aridus".

1988. Insects. Multicoloured.

541. 15 c. Type **123** 45 15
542. 55 c. "Callidea bohemani" 1·25 85
543. 1 e. "Phymateus viridipes" 2·25 2·25
544. 2 e. "Nomadacris septemfasciata" .. .. .. 3·75 4·00

124 Athlete with Swazi Flag and Olympic Stadium

1988. Olympic Games, Seoul. Multicoloured.

545 15 c. Type **124** 25 10
546 35 c. Taekwondo 70 35
547 1 e. Boxing .. .. 1·25 1·25
548 2 e. Tennis .. .. 2·50 3·00

125 Savanna Monkey

1989. Small Mammals. Multicoloured.

549 35 c. Type **125** 75 25
550 55 c. Large-toothed rock hyrax .. .. .. 1·00 75
551 1 e. Zorilla .. .. 2·00 2·00
552 2 e. African wild cat .. 3·50 3·75

126 Dr. David Hynd (founder of Swazi Red Cross)

1989. 125th Anniv of International Red Cross. Multicoloured.

553 15 c. Type **126** 20 15
554 60 c. First aid training .. 55 40
555 1 e. Sigombeni Clinic .. 90 80
556 2 e. Refugee camp .. 1·40 1·40

127 King Mswati III with Prince of Wales, 1987

1989. 21st Birthday of King Mswati III. Mult.

557 15 c. Type **127** 10 10
558 60 c. King with Pope John Paul II, 1988 .. .. 30 35
559 1 e. Introduction of Crown Prince to people, 1983 .. 50 55
560 2 e. King Mswati III and Queen Mother .. .. 95 1·00

128 Manzini to Mahamba Road

1989. 25th Anniv of African Development Bank. Multicoloured.

561 15 c. Type **128** 10 10
562 60 c. Microwave Radio Receiver, Mbabane .. 30 35
563 1 e. Mbabane Government Hospital 50 75
564 2 e. Ezulwini Power Station switchyard .. 95 1·50

129 International Priority Mail Van

1990. "Stamp World London 90" International Stamp Exhibition. Multicoloured.

565 15 c. Type **129** 15 10
566 60 c. Facsimile Service operators 40 40
567 1 e. Rural post office .. 75 75
568 2 e. Ezulwini Earth Station 1·40 1·40

1990. 90th Birthday of Queen Elizabeth the Queen Mother. As T **134** of Ascension.

570 75 c. multicoloured .. 50 50
571 4 e. black and green .. 2·25 2·25

DESIGNS—21 × 36 mm. 75 c. Queen Mother. 29 × 37 mm. 4 e. King George VI and Queen Elizabeth visiting Civil Resettlement Unit, Hatfield House.

130 Pictorial Teaching

1990. International Literacy Year. Mult.

572 15 c. Type **130** 10 10
573 75 c. Rural class 45 45
574 1 e. Modern teaching methods 60 60
575 2 e. Presentation of certificates .. .. 1·10 1·10

131 Rural Water Supply

1990. 40th Anniv of United Nations Development Programme. "Helping People to Help Themselves". Multicoloured.

576 60 c. Type **131** 35 35
577 1 e. Seed multiplication project 60 60
578 2 e. Low-cost housing project .. .. .. 1·25 1·25

1990. Nos. 519/20, 522 and 524 surch.

579 10 c. on 25 c. "Abantis paradisea" 15 15
580 15 c. on 30 c. "Acraea anemosa" 20 20
580a 15 c. on 45 c. "Graphium antheus" .. ..
581 20 c. on 45 c. "Graphium antheus" 20 20
582 40 c. on 55 c. "Pinacopteryx eriphia" .. 30 30

133 Lobamba Hot Spring

1991. National Heritage. Multicoloured.

583 15 c. Type **133** 15 10
584 60 c. Sibebe Rock .. 40 40
585 1 e. Jolobela Falls .. 70 70
586 2 e. Mantjolo Sacred Pool 1·25 1·40

134 King Mswati III making Speech

1991. 5th Anniv of King Mswati III's Coronation. Multicoloured.

588 15 c. Type **134** 15 10
589 75 c. Butimba Royal Hunt 50 50
590 1 e. King and visiting school friends, 1986 .. 70 70
591 2 e. King opening Parliament .. .. 1·25 1·40

1991. 65th Birthday of Queen Elizabeth II and 70th Birthday of Prince Philip. As T **139** of Ascension. Multicoloured.

592 1 e. Prince Philip .. 70 70
593 2 e. Queen Elizabeth II .. 1·25 1·40

135 "Xerophyta retinervis"

1991. Indigenous Flowers. Multicoloured.

594 15 c. Type **135** 15 10
595 75 c. "Bauhinia galpinii" 60 60
596 1 e. "Dombeya rotundifolia" 80 80
597 2 e. "Kigelia africana" .. 1·75 1·75

136 Father Christmas arriving with Gifts

1991. Christmas. Multicoloured.

598 20 c. Type **136** 15 10
599 70 c. Singing carols .. 65 50
600 1 e. Priest reading from Bible 80 90
601 2 e. The Nativity .. 1·50 1·75

137 Lubombo Flat Lizard

1992 Reptiles. Multicoloured.

602 20 c. Type **137** 25 10
603 70 c. Natal hinged tortoise 75 55
604 1 e. Swazi thick-toed gecko 1·00 1·00
605 2 e. Nile monitor .. .. 1·75 2·00

138 "Junonia hierta"

1992. Butterflies (2nd series). Nos. 516/26 and new value (5 c.) showing different portrait of King Mswati III. Multicoloured.

606 5 c. "Colotis antevippe" .. 10 10
607 10 c. Type **138** 10 10
608 15 c. "Hamanumida daedalus" 10 10
609 20 c. "Charaxes boueti" .. 10 10
610 25 c. "Abantis paradisea" 10 10
611 30 c. "Acraea anemosa" .. 15 20
612 35 c. "Graphium leonidas" 15 20
613 45 c. "Graphium antheus" 20 25
614 50 c. "Precis orithya" .. 20 25
615 55 c. "Pinacopteryx eriphia" 20 25
616 70 c. "Precis octavia" .. 30 35
617 1 e. "Mylothris chloris" .. 40 45

139 Missionaries visiting King Sobhuza II and Queen Lomawa

1992. Centenary of Evangelical Alliance Missions. Multicoloured.

620 20 c. Type **139** 20 10
621 1 e. Pioneer missionaries .. 80 1·10

140 Calabashes

1993. Archaeological and Contemporary Artifacts. Multicoloured.

622 20 c. Type **140** 15 10
623 70 c. Contemporary cooking pot 45 45
624 1 e. Wooden bowl and containers 65 65
625 2 e. Quern for grinding seeds .. .. .. 1·25 1·40

141 King Mswati III as Baby

1993. 25th Birthday of King Mswati III and 25th Anniv of Independence. Mult.

626 25 c. Type **141** 15 10
627 40 c. King Mswati III addressing meeting .. 20 20
628 1 e. King Sobhuza II receiving Instrument of Independence 65 65
629 2 e. King Mswati III delivering Coronation speech .. .. .. 1·25 1·40

142 Male and Female Common Waxbills

1993. Common Waxbill. Multicoloured.

630 25 c. Type **142** 15 10
631 40 c. Waxbill and eggs in nest 25 25
632 1 e. Waxbill on nest .. 65 65
633 2 e. Waxbill feeding chicks 1·25 1·40

143 Classroom and Practical Training

1994. 25th Anniv of U.S. Peace Corps in Swaziland. Multicoloured.

634 25 c. Type **143** 10 10
635 40 c. Rural water supply 15 20
636 1 e. Americans and Swazis in traditional costumes 40 45
637 2 e. Swazi–American co-operation 80 85

POSTAGE DUE STAMPS

D 1.

D 6.

1933.

D 1. D **1.** 1d. red .. .. 30 4·75
D 2. 2d. violet .. .. 1·25 14·00

1961. Surch. **Postage Due 2d.**

D 3. **7.** 2d. on 2d. blk. & brown 3·00 5·50

These prices apply to stamps with large figure measuring 4½ mm. high.

1961. As Type D **1** but with value in cents.

D 4. 1 c. red 15 75
D 5. 2 c. violet .. .. 15 1·10
D 6. 5 c. green .. .. .. 20 1·10

1961. Surch. **Postage Due** and value in cents.

D 10. **7.** 1 c. on 2d. black & brown 90 2·75
D 11. 2 c. on 2d. black & brown 65 2·75
D 12. 5 c. on 2d. black & brown 1·25 2·75

1971.

D19 D **6** 1 c. red 30 50
D23 2 c. purple 10 10
D24 5 c. green 10 10
D25 10 c. blue 10 10
D26 25 c. brown 10 15

TANGANYIKA

Formerly the German colony of German East Africa. After the 1914–18 War it was under British mandate until 1946 and then administered by Britain under United Nations trusteeship until 1961 when it became independent within the British Commonwealth. It had a common postal service with Kenya and Uganda from 1935 to 1961 (for these issues see under Kenya, Uganda and Tanganyika). Renamed Tanzania in 1965.

1915. 16 annas = 1 rupee.
1917. 100 cents = 1 rupee.
1922. 100 cents = 1 shilling.

BRITISH OCCUPATION

1915. Stamps of the Indian Expeditionary Forces optd. **G.R. POST MAFIA.**

M 33	**55.**	3 p. grey	20·00	42·00
M 34	**56.**	½ a. green	32·00	45·00
M 35	**57.**	1 a. red	35·00	45·00
M 36	**59.**	2 a. lilac	48·00	75·00
M 37	**61.**	2½ a. blue	65·00	90·00
M 38	**62.**	3 a. orange	65·00	90·00
M 39	**63.**	4 a. olive	85·00	£120
M 40	**65.**	8 a. mauve	£150	£200
M 41	**66.**	12 a. red	£225	£300
M 42	**67.**	1 r. brown and green	£250	£325

1916. Stamps of Nyasaland (King George V) optd. **N.F.**

N 1.	½d. green	80	4·50
N 2.	1d. red	70	2·50
N 3.	3d. purple on yellow	5·00	14·00
N 4.	4d. black and red on yellow	20·00	30·00
N 5.	1s. black on green	23·00	32·00

1917. Stamps of Kenya and Uganda (King George V, 1912) optd. **G.E.A.**

45.	1 c. black	15	70
47.	3 c. green	15	15
48.	6 c. red	15	10
49.	10 c. orange	15	30
50.	12 c. grey	15	1·25
51.	15 c. blue	20	1·75
52.	25 c. black and red on yellow	30	2·25
53.	50 c. black and lilac	50	2·75
54.	75 c. black on green	65	3·00
55.	1 r. black on green	1·25	5·50
56.	2 r. red and black on blue	4·50	25·00
57.	3 r. violet and green	8·50	42·00
58.	4 r. red and green on yellow	15·00	60·00
59.	5 r. blue and purple	26·00	60·00
60.	10 r. red and green on green	48·00	£130
61.	20 r. black and purple on red	£150	£250
62.	50 r. red and green	£475	£750

BRITISH MANDATE

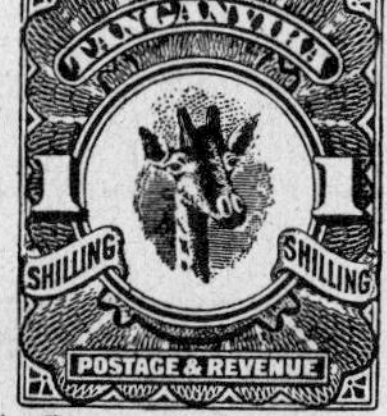

4. Giraffe. 5.

1922.

74.	**4.**	5 c. black and purple	85	20
89.		5 c. black and green	30	90
75.		10 c. black and green	40	30
90.		10 c. black and yellow	1·75	1·25
76.		15 c. black and red	90	10
77.		20 c. black and orange	60	10
78.		25 c. black	3·25	5·50
91.		25 c. black and blue	2·25	14·00
79.		30 c. black and blue	3·25	2·75
92.		30 c. black and purple	1·00	8·00
80.		40 c. black and brown	1·50	3·50
81.		50 c. black and grey	1·25	1·50
82.		75 c. black and yellow	2·75	13·00
83.	**5.**	1 s. black and green	1·25	7·00
84.		2 s. black and purple	4·25	10·00
85.		3 s. black	7·50	22·00
86.		5 s. black and red	8·50	50·00
87.		10 s. black and blue	38·00	75·00
88.		£1 black and orange	£110	£200

6. 7.

1927.

93.	**6.**	5 c. black and green	30	10
94.		10 c. black and yellow	40	10
95.		15 c. black and red	30	10
96.		20 c. black and orange	70	10
97.		25 c. black and blue	90	90
98.		30 c. black and purple	90	2·50
98a.		30 c. black and blue	16·00	30
99.		40 c. black and brown	1·00	2·75
100.		50 c. black and grey	1·00	55
101.		75 c. black and olive	1·75	8·50
102.	**7.**	1 s. black and green	2·25	1·50
103.		2 s. black and purple	7·00	2·50
104.		3 s. black	8·00	35·00
105.		5 s. black and red	9·00	14·00
106.		10 s. black and blue	42·00	75·00
107.		£1 black and orange	85·00	£130

INDEPENDENT WITHIN THE COMMONWEALTH

8. Teacher and Pupils. 15. Freedom Torch over Mt. Kilimanjaro.

1961. Independence. Inscr. "UHURU 1961"

108.	**8.**	5 c. sepia and green	10	10
109.	–	10 c. turquoise	10	10
110.	–	15 c. sepia and blue	10	10
111.	–	20 c. brown	10	10
112.	–	30 c. blk., grn. & yell.	10	10
113.	–	50 c. black and yellow	10	10
114.	–	1 s. brown, bl. & yell.	15	10
115.	**15.**	1 s. 30 multicoloured	1·50	10
116.	–	2 s. multicoloured	40	10
117.	–	5 s. turquoise and red	50	40
118.	–	10 s. black, pur. & bl.	11·00	3·50
119.	**15.**	20 s. multicoloured	3·00	7·50

DESIGNS—As Type **8.** VERT. 10 c. District nurse and child. 15 c. Coffee-picking. 20 c. Harvesting maize. 50 c. Serengeti lions. HORIZ. 30 c. Tanganyikan Flag. As Type **15.** HORIZ. 1 s. "Maternity" (mother with nurse holding baby). 2 s. Dar-es-Salaam waterfront. 5 s. Land tillage. 10 s. Diamond mine.

19. Mr. Nyerere inaugurating Self-help Project.

DESIGNS: 50 c. Hoisting flag on Mt. Kilimanjaro. 1 s. 30, Presidential emblem. 2 s. 50, Independence monument.

1962. Inauguration of Republic.

120.	**19.**	30 c. green	10	10
121.	–	50 c. multicoloured	10	10
122.	–	1 s. 30 multicoloured	10	10
123.	–	2 s. 30 black, red & bl.	15	30

23. Map of Republic.

1964. United Republic of Tanganyika and Zanzibar Commem.

124.	**23.**	20 c. green and blue	10	10
125.	–	30 c. blue and sepia	10	10
126.	–	1 s. 50 purple and blue	10	10
127.	**23.**	2 s. 50 purple and blue	65	40

DESIGN: 30 c., 1 s. 30, Torch and Spear Emblem.

Despite the inscription on the stamps the above issue was only on sale in Tanganyika and had no validity in Zanzibar.

OFFICIAL STAMPS

1961. Independence stamps of 1961 optd. **OFFICIAL.**

O 1.	5 c. brown and green	10	10
O 2.	10 c. turquoise	10	10
O 3.	15 c. brown and blue	10	10
O 4.	20 c. brown	10	10
O 5.	30 c. black, green & yell.	10	10
O 6.	50 c. black and yellow	10	10
O 7.	1 s. brn., blue and yellow	10	10
O 8.	5 s. turquoise and red	65	75

For later issues see **TANZANIA**.

TANZANIA

A republic within the Br. Commonwealth formerly known as Tanganyika and incorporating Zanzibar.

100 cents = 1 shilling.

NOTE.—Stamps inscribed "UGANDA KENYA TANGANYIKA & ZANZIBAR" (or "TANZANIA UGANDA KENYA") will be found listed under Kenya, Uganda and Tanganyika.

A. For use in Tanzania and also valid for use in Kenya and Uganda.

25. Hale Hydro-Electric Scheme.

33. Dar-es-Salaam Harbour.

1965.

128.	**25.**	5 c. blue and orange	10	10
129.	–	10 c. multicoloured	10	10
130.	–	15 c. multicoloured	10	10
131.	–	20 c. sepia, grn. & bl.	10	10
132.	–	30 c. black and brown	10	10
133.	–	40 c. multicoloured	30	20
134.	–	50 c. multicoloured	30	10
135.	–	65 c. grn, brn. & bl.	2·25	1·25
136.	**33.**	1 s. multicoloured	60	10
137.	–	1 s. 30 multicoloured	5·00	60
138.	–	2 s. 50 blue and brown	2·75	90
139.	–	5 s. brn., grn. & bl.	80	20
140.	–	10 s. yell., grn. & bl.	1·00	1·75
141.	–	20 s. multicoloured	3·75	10·00

DESIGNS—As Type **25**—HORIZ. 10 c. Tanzania flag. 20 c. Road-building. 50 c. Common Zebras, Manyara National Park. 65 c. Mt. Kilimanjaro. VERT. 15 c. National Servicemen. 30 c. Drum, Spear, Shield and Stool. 40 c. Giraffes, Mikumi National Park. As Type **33**—HORIZ. 1 s. 30, Skull of "Zinjanthropus" and Excavations, Olduvai Gorge. 2 s. 50, Fishing 5 s. Sisal Industry. 10 s. State House, Dar-es-Salaam. VERT. 20 s. Arms of Tanzania.

39. Cardinal.

1967. Fishes. Multicoloured.

142	**39.**	5 c. mauve, grn. & blk.	10	40
143	–	10 c. brown and bistre	10	10
144	–	15 c. grey, blue & black	10	40
145	–	20 c. brown and green	10	10
146	–	30 c .green and black	10	10
147	–	40 c. yell., brn. & green	20	10
148	–	50 c. multicoloured	15	10
149	–	65 c. yell., grn. & black	3·50	4·00
150	–	70 c. multicoloured	1·00	2·50
151	–	1 s. brn., blue & purple	30	10
152	–	1 s. 30 multicoloured	5·00	10
153	–	1 s. 50 multicoloured	3·00	50
154	–	2 s. 50 multicoloured	3·25	90
155a	–	5 s. yell., black & green	3·25	10
156a	–	10 s. multicoloured	2·50	10
157a	–	20 s. multicoloured	8·00	15

DESIGNS—As Type **39**: 10 c. Mud skipper. 15 c. White spotted puffer. 20 c. Sea horses. 30 c. Bat fish. 40 c. Sweetlips. 50 c. Blue clubnosed wrasse. 65 c. Bennett's butterfly. 70 c. Striped grouper. 42 × 25 mm. 1 s. Scorpion fish. 1 s. 30. Powder blue surgeon. 1 s. 50, Fusilier. 2 s. 50, Red snapper. 5 s. Moorish idol. 10 s. Picasso fish. 20 s. Squirrel fish.

53. "Papilio hornimani". 54. "Euphaedra neophron".

1973.

(a) As T **53.**

158.	**53.**	5 c. green, blue & blk.	30	20
159.	–	10 c. multicoloured	40	15
160.	–	15 c. lavender and black	40	15
161.	–	20 c. brn., yellow & blk.	50	15
162.	–	30 c. yellow, orge. & blk.	50	10
163.	–	40 c. multicoloured	60	15
164.	–	50 c. multicoloured	70	15
165.	–	60 c. brown, yell. & lake	1·00	20
166.	–	70 c. green, orge. & blk.	1·00	20

(b) As T **54.**

167.	**54.**	1 s. multicoloured	1·00	15
168.	–	1 s. 50 multicoloured	2·00	45
169.	–	2 s. 50 multicoloured	2·50	80
170.	–	5 s. multicoloured	2·75	85
171.	–	10 s. multicoloured	3·75	4·00
172.	–	20 s. multicoloured	5·50	9·00

BUTTERFLIES: 10 c. "Colotis ione". 15 c. "Amauris makuyuensis". 20 c. "Libythea laius". 30 c. "Danaus chrysippus." 40 c. "Sallya rosa". 50 c. "Axiocerses styx". 60 c. "Eurema hecabe" 70 c. "Acraea insignis". 1 s. "Euphaedra neophron". 1 s. 50, "Precis octavia". 2 s. 50, "Charaxes eupale". 5 s. "Charaxes pollux". 10 s. "Salamis parhassus". 20 s. "Papilio ophidicephalus".

1975. Nos. 165 and 172 surch.

173.	80 c. on 60 c. "Eurema hecabe"	1·75	1·25
174.	2 s. on 1 s. 50 "Precis octavia"	3·25	4·00
175.	3 s. on 2 s. 50 "Charaxes eupale"	13·00	22·00
176.	40 s. on 20 s. "Papilio ophidicephalus"	6·00	9·00

1976. Telecommunications Development As Nos. 56/9 of Kenya.

177.	50 c. Microwave Tower	10	10
178.	1 s. Cordless switchboard	15	10
179.	2 s. Telephones	25	30
180.	3 s. Message Switching Centre	30	40

1976. Olympic Games, Montreal. As Nos. 61/4 of Kenya.

182.	50 c. Akii Bua, Ugandan hurdler	15	10
183.	1 s. Filbert Bayi, Tanzanian runner	15	10
184.	2 s. Steve Muchoki, Kenyan boxer	35	40
185.	3 s. Olympic flame and East African flags	45	55

1976. Railway Transport. As Nos. 66/9 of Kenya.

187.	50 c. Tanzania-Zambia Railway	20	10
188.	1 s. Nile Bridge, Uganda	30	10
189.	2 s. Nakuru Station, Kenya	75	40
190.	3 s. Class "A" loco, 1896	90	65

1977. Game Fish of East Africa. As Nos. 71/4 of Kenya.

192.	50 c. Nile Perch	35	10
193.	1 s. Tilapia	40	10
194.	3 s. Sailfish	1·75	60
195.	5 s. Black Marlin	1·90	80

1977. Second World Black and African Festival of Arts and Culture. As Nos. 76/9 of Kenya.

197.	50 c. Maasai Manyatta (village), Kenya	15	10
198.	1 s. "Heartbeat of Africa" (Ugandan dancers)	20	10
199.	2 s. Makonde sculpture	45	70
200.	3 s. "Early Man and Technology" (skinning hippopotamus)	55	1·00

1977. 25th Anniv. of Safari Rally. As Nos. 81/4 of Kenya. Multicoloured.

202.	50 c. Rally-car and villagers	15	10
203.	1 s. Starting line	20	10
204.	2 s. Car fording river	50	60
205.	5 s. Car and elephants	1·25	1·75

1977. Centenary of Ugandan Church. As Nos. 86/9 of Kenya. Multicoloured.

207.	50 c. Canon Kivebulaya	10	10
208.	1 s. Modern Namirembe Cathedral	15	10
209.	2 s. Old Namirembe Cathedral	30	40
210.	5 s. Early congregation Kigezi	60	90

1977. Endangered Species. As Nos. 96/100 of Kenya. Multicoloured.

212. 50 c. Pancake Tortoise .. 20 10
213. 1 s. Nile Crocodile.. .. 25 10
214. 2 s. Hunter's Hartebeest .. 1·00 55
215. 3 s. Red Colobus .. .. 1·75 1·00
216. 5 s. Dugong .. .. 2·00 2·00

56. Prince Philip and President Nyerere.

1977. Silver Jubilee. Multicoloured.

218. 50 c. Type **56** 10 10
219. 5 s. Pres. Nyerere with Queen and Prince Philip .. 25 25
220. 10 s. Jubilee emblem and Commonwealth flags .. 40 40
221. 20 s. The Crowning .. 60 60

57. Improvements in Rural Living Standards.

1978. "Chama Cha Mapinduzi" (New Revolutionary Party). 1st Anniv.

223. **57.** 50 c. multicoloured .. 10 10
224. – 1 s. multicoloured .. 10 10
225. – 3 s. multicoloured .. 35 60
226. – 5 s. black, green & yellow 55 85

DESIGNS: 1 s. Flag-raising ceremony, Zanzibar. 3 s. Handing over of TANU headquarters, Dodoma. 5 s. Chairman Julius Nyerere.

1978. World Cup Football Championships. As Nos. 122/5 of Kenya. Multicoloured.

228. 50 c. Joe Kadenge and forwards 10 10
229. 1 s. Mohamed Chuma and cup presentation .. 10 10
230. 2 s. Omari S. Kidevu and goalmouth scene .. 30 60
231. 3 s. Polly Ouma and three forwards 40 75

1978. 25th Anniv. of Coronation. Nos. 218/21 optd. **25th ANNIVERSARY CORONATION 2nd JUNE 1953.**

233. 50 c. Type **56** 10 10
234. 5 s. Pres. Nyerere with Queen and Prince Philip 20 30
235. 10 s. Jubilee emblem and Commonwealth flags .. 25 40
236. 20 s. The Crowning .. 40 70

60. "Do not Drink and Drive."

1978. Road Safety.

238. **60.** 50 c. multicoloured .. 15 10
239. – 1 s. multicoloured .. 20 10
240. – 3 s. orange, black & brn. 70 60
241. – 5 s. multicoloured .. 1·00 90

DESIGNS: 1 s. "Show courtesy to young, old and crippled". 3 s. "Observe the Highway Code". 5 s. "Do not drive a faulty vehicle"

61. Lake Manyara Hotel.

1978. Game Lodges. Multicoloured.

243. 50 c. Type **61** 10 10
244. 1 s. Lobo Wildlife Lodge 15 10
245. 3 s. Ngorongoro Crater Lodge 30 35
246. 5 s. Ngorongoro Wildlife Lodge 45 55
247. 10 s. Mafia Island Lodge 80 90
248. 20 s. Mikumi Wildlife Lodge .. .. .. 1·75 2·50

62. "Racial Suppression".

1978. International Anti-Apartheid Year.

250. **62.** 50 c. multicoloured .. 10 10
251. – 1 s. black, green & yell. 15 10
252. – 2 s. 50 multicoloured .. 40 40
253. – 5 s. multicoloured .. 70 85

DESIGNS: 1 s. "Racial division". 2 s. 50, "Racial Harmony". 5 s. "Fall of suppression and rise of freedom".

63. Fokker "Friendship".

1978. 75th Anniv. of Powered Flight. Mult.

255. 50 c. Type **63** 20 10
256. 1 s. "Dragon" on Zanzibar Island, 1930's .. 25 10
257. 2 s. Supersonic "Concorde" .. .. .. 1·00 45
258. 5 s. Wright brothers "Flyer", 1903 .. 1·25 85

64. Corporation Emblem.

1979. 1st Anniv. of Tanzania Posts and Telecommunications Corporation. Mult.

260. 50 c. Type **64** 10 10
261. 5 s. Headquarters buildings 50 70

65. Pres. Nyerere (patron of National I.Y.C. Committee) with Children.

1979. Int. Year of the Child. Mult.

263. 50 c. Type **65** 10 10
264. 1 s. Day Care Centre .. 15 10
265. 2 s. "Immunisation" (child being vaccinated) 25 45
266. 5 s. National I.Y.C. Committee emblem.. .. 40 80

1979. Nos. 159 and 166 surch.

268 10 c.+30 c. multicoloured 75 60
269 50 c. on 70 c. green, orange and black .. .. 1·75 1·75

No. 268 was used as a 40 c. value.

67. Planting Young Trees.

1979. Forest Preservation. Multicoloured.

270. 50 c. Type **67** 10 10
271. 1 s. Replacing dead trees with saplings 20 10
272. 2 s. Rainfall cycle .. 65 65
273. 5 s. Forest fire warning .. 95 1·75

68. Mwenge Earth Satellite Station.

1979. Inauguration of Mwenge Earth Satellite Station.

274. **68.** 10 c. multicoloured .. 10 10
275. 40 c. multicoloured .. 15 10
276. 50 c. multicoloured .. 15 10
277. 1 s. multicoloured .. 25 20

69. Tabata Dispensary, Dar-es-Salaam.

1980. 75th Anniv. of Rotary International. Multicoloured.

278. 50 c. Type **69** 10 10
279. 1 s. Ngomvu Village water project 15 10
280. 5 s. Flying Doctor service (plane donation) .. 55 70
281. 20 s. Torch and 75th Anniversary emblem .. 1·75 2·50

70. Zanzibar 1896 2 r. Stamp and 1964 25 c. Definitive.

1980. Death Centenary of Sir Rowland Hill. Multicoloured.

283. 40 c. Type **70** 10 10
284. 50 c. Tanganyika 1962 Independence 50 c. commemorative and man attaching stamp to letter (vert.) .. 10 10
285. 10 s. Tanganyika 1922 25 c. stamp and 1961 1 s. 30 definitive.. .. 80 1·25
286. 20 s. Penny Black and Sir Rowland Hill (vert.) 1·25 2·00

1980. "London 1980" International Stamp Exhibition. Nos. 283/6 optd. **'LONDON 1980' PHILATELIC EXHIBITION.**

288. **70.** 40 c. multicoloured .. 10 10
289. – 50 c. multicoloured .. 10 10
290. – 10 s. multicoloured .. 75 1·25
291. – 20 s. multicoloured .. 1·10 1·75

1980. Annual Conference of District 920, Rotary International, Arusha. Nos. 278/81 optd. **District 920—55th Annual Conference, Arusha, Tanzania.**

293. **69.** 50 c. multicoloured .. 20 10
294. – 1 s. multicoloured .. 25 10
295. – 5 s. multicoloured .. 70 70
296. – 20 s. multicoloured .. 2·25 2·50

73. Conference, Tanzanian Posts and Telecommunications Corporation and U.P.U. Emblems.

1980. P.A.P.U. (Pan-African Postal Union) Plenipotentiary Conference, Arusha.

298. **73.** 50 c. black and violet .. 10 10
299. 1 s. black and blue .. 15 10
300. 5 s. black and red .. 65 65
301. 10 s. black and green .. 1·25 1·40

74. Gidamis Shahanga (marathon).

1980. Olympic Games, Moscow. Multicoloured.

302. 50 c. Type **74** 10 15
303. 1 s. Nzael Kyomo (sprints) 15 15
304. 10 s. Zakayo Malekwa (javelin) .. .. .. 80 1·25
305. 20 s. William Lyimo (boxing) 1·50 2·00

75. Spring Hare.

1980. Wildlife. Multicoloured.

307. 10 c. Type **75** 10 15
308. 20 c. Large-spotted Genet 15 15
309. 40 c. Banded Mongoose .. 20 10
310. 50 c. Ratel 20 10
311. 75 c. Large-toothed Rock Hyrax 20 15
312. 80 c. Leopard 30 15
313. 1 s. Impala.. .. .. 20 10
314. 1 s. 50 Giraffe 30 20
315. 2 s. Common Zebra .. 30 20
316. 3 s. Buffalo 30 20
317. 5 s. Lion 40 30
318. 10 s. Black Rhinoceros .. 75 85
319. 20 s. African Elephant .. 1·25 1·25
320. 40 s. Cheetah .. .. 1·50 2·75

Nos. 313/20 are larger, 40 × 24 mm.

77. Ngorongoro Conservation Area Authority Emblem.

1981. 60th Anniv. of Ngorongoro and Serengeti National Parks.

321. **77.** 50 c. multicoloured .. 10 10
322. – 1 s. black, gold and green 10 10
323. – 5 s. multicoloured .. 45 60
324. – 20 s. multicoloured .. 1·75 2·25

DESIGNS: 1 s. Tanzania National Parks emblem. 5 s. Friends of the Serengeti emblem. 20 s. Friends of Ngorongoro emblem.

1981. Royal Wedding. Nos. 220/1 optd. **ROYAL WEDDING H.R.H. PRINCE CHARLES 29th JULY 1981.**

325. 10 s. Jubilee emblem and Commonwealth flags .. 50 60
326. 20 s. Crowning 75 80

79. Mail Runner.

1981. Commonwealth Postal Administrations Conference, Arusha. Multicoloured.

328.	50 c. Type **79**	10	10
329.	1 s. Letter sorting ..	15	15
330.	5 s. Letter Post symbols	65	1·00
331.	10 s. Flags of Commonwealth nations	1·25	2·00

80. Morris Nyunyusa (blind drummer).

1981. International Year for Disabled Persons. Multicoloured.

333.	50 c. Type **80**	20	10
334.	1 s. Mgulani Rehabilitation Centre, Dar-es-Salaam	25	10
335.	5 s. Aids for disabled persons	1·75	2·00
336.	10 s. Disabled children cleaning school compound	2·50	3·00

81. Mwalimu Julius K. Nyerere (President).

1981. 20th Anniv. of Independence. Mult.

337.	50 c. Type **81**	10	10
338.	1 s. Electricity plant, Mtoni	15	10
339.	3 s. Sisal industry ..	45	80
340.	10 s. " Universal primary education "	1·10	2·00

82. Ostrich.

1982. Birds. Multicoloured.

342.	50 c. Type **82**	50	10
343.	1 s. Secretary Bird ..	60	10
344.	5 s. Kori Bustard ..	2·25	2·75
345.	10 s. Saddle-bill Stork ..	3·25	4·00

83. Jella Mtaga.

1982. World Cup Football Championship, Spain, Multicoloured.

346.	50 c. Type **83**	30	10
347.	1 s. Football stadium ..	35	10
348.	10 s. Diego Maradona ..	2·75	3·00
349.	20 s. FIFA emblem ..	4·50	5·00

84. "Jade" of Seronera (cheetah) with Cubs.

1982. Animal Personalities. Multicoloured.

351.	50 c. Type **84**	20	10
352.	1 s. Wild dog featured in film, " Havoc " ..	30	10
353.	5 s. " Fiji " and two sons of " Gombe " (chimpanzees)	1·00	2·00
354.	10 s. " Bahati " of Lake Manyara with twins, " Rashidi " and " Ramadhani "	1·90	3·00

85. Brick-laying.

1982. 75th Anniv. of Boy Scout Movement. Multicoloured.

356.	50 c. Type **85**	15	10
357.	1 s. Camping	20	10
358.	10 s. Tracing signs ..	1·50	2·25
359.	20 s. Lord Baden-Powell ..	2·50	3·75

86. Ploughing Field.

1982. World Food Day. Multicoloured.

361.	50 c. Type **86**	10	10
362.	1 s. Dairy farming ..	15	10
363.	5 s. Maize farming ..	60	75
364.	10 s. Grain storage ..	1·00	1·60

87. Immunization.

1982. Centenary of Robert Koch's Discovery of Tubercle Bacillus. Multicoloured.

366.	50 c. Type **87**	15	10
367.	1 s. Dr. Robert Koch ..	20	10
368.	5 s. International Union against TB emblem ..	65	1·25
369.	10 s. World Health Organization emblem	1·25	2·25

88. Letter Post.

1982. 5th Anniv. of Posts and Telecommunications Corporation. Mult.

370.	50 c. Type **88**	10	10
371.	1 s. Training institute ..	10	10
372.	5 s. Satellite communications	55	90
373.	10 s. U.P.U., I.T.U. and T.P.T.C.C. (Tanzania Post and Telecommunications Corporation) emblems	1·10	2·00

89. Pres. Mwalimu Julius Nyerere.

1982. Commonwealth Day. Multicoloured.

375.	50 c. Type **89**	10	10
376.	1 s. Athletics and boxing	15	10
377.	5 s. Flags of Commonwealth countries	60	80
378.	10 s. Pres. Nyerere and members of British Royal Family	1·25	1·75

INDEX

Countries can be quickly located by referring to the index at the end of this volume.

90. Eastern and Southern African Management Institute, Arusha, Tanzania.

1983. 25th Anniv. of Economic Commission for Africa. Multicoloured.

380.	50 c. Type **90**	15	10
381.	1 s. 25th Anniversary inscription and U.N. logo	20	10
382.	5 s. Mineral collections ..	2·50	2·50
383.	10 s. E.C.A. Silver Jubilee logo and O.A.U. flag ..	2·50	3·25

91. Telephone cables.

1983. World Communications Year. Mult.

385.	50 c. Type **91**	15	10
386.	1 s. W.C.Y. logo	20	10
387.	5 s. Postal service.. ..	1·25	1·40
388.	10 s. Microwave tower ..	1·75	2·25

92. Bagamoya Boma.

1983. Historical Buildings of Tanzania. Multicoloured.

390.	1 s. Type **92**	10	10
391.	1 s. 50 Beit El Ajaib, Zanzibar	15	25
392.	5 s. Anglican Cathedral Church, Zanzibar ..	55	1·00
393.	10 s. Original German Government House and present State House, Dar Es Salaam	1·10	2·00

93. Sheikh Abeid Amani Karume (founder of Afro-Shirazi Party).

1984. 20th Anniv. of Zanzibar Revolution. Multicoloured.

395.	1 s. Type **93**	10	10
396.	1 s. 50 Clove farming ..	15	25
397.	5 s. Symbol of Industrial Development	55	1·00
398.	10 s. New housing schemes	1·10	2·00

94. Boxing.

1984. Olympic Games, Los Angeles. Multicoloured.

400.	1 s. Type **94**	10	10
401.	1 s. 50 Running	15	10
402.	5 s. Basketball	45	60
403.	20 s. Football	1·50	2·25

95. Icarus in Flight.

1984. 40th Anniv. of International Civil Aviation Organization. Multicoloured.

405.	1 s. Type **95**	10	10
406.	1 s. 50 Aircraft and air traffic controller ..	15	20
407.	5 s. Aircraft undergoing maintenance	55	1·25
408.	10 s. I.C.A.O. Badge ..	1·10	2·00

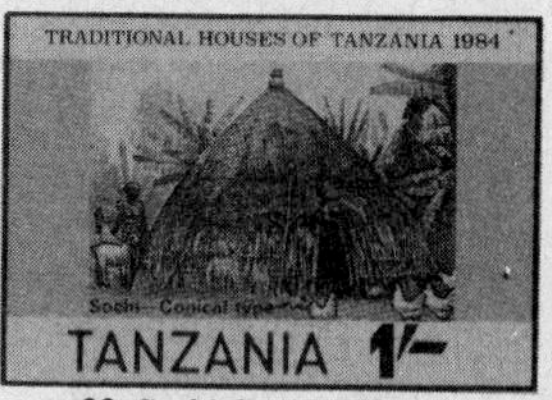

96. Sochi-Conical House.

1984. Traditional Houses. Multicoloured.

410.	1 s. Type **96**	10	10
411.	1 s. 50 Isyenga-circular type	15	20
412.	5 s. Tembe-flatroof type ..	45	1·25
413.	10 s. Banda-coastal type ..	90	2·00

97. Production of Cotton Textiles.

1985. 5th Anniv. of Southern African Development Co-ordination Conference. Multicoloured.

415.	1 s. 50 Type **97**	30	15
416.	4 s. Diamond mining ..	2·00	1·25
417.	5 s. Map of member countries and means of communication	2·00	1·25
418.	20 s. Flags and signatures of member countries ..	2·75	3·00

98. Tortoise.

1985. Rare Animals of Zanzibar. Mult.

420.	1 s. Type **98**	25	10
421.	4 s. Leopard	1·00	90
422.	10 s. Civet cat	1·75	2·75
423.	17 s. 50 Red colobus monkey (vert.)	2·50	3·50

99. The Queen Mother.

1985. Life and Times of Queen Elizabeth the Queen Mother. Multicoloured.

425.	20 s. Type **99**	15	20
426.	20 s. Queen Mother waving to crowd	15	20
427.	100 s. Oval portrait with flowers	40	80
428.	100 s. Head and shoulders portrait	40	80

100. Locomotive No. 3022.

1985. Tanzanian Railway Steam Locomotives (1st issue). Multicoloured

430. 5 s. Type **100** 10 15
431. 10 s. Locomotive No. 3107 15 30
432. 20 s. Locomotive No. 6004 30 50
433. 30 s. Locomotive No. 3129 55 80

See also Nos. 445/9.

1985. Olympic Games Gold Medal Winners, Los Angeles. Nos. 400/3 optd.

435. 1 s. Type **94** (optd. **GOLD MEDAL HENRY TILLMAN USA**) .. 10 10
436. 1 s. 50 Running (optd. **GOLD MEDAL USA**) .. 15 20
437. 5 s. Basketball (optd. **GOLD MEDAL USA**) .. 45 1·00
438. 20 s. Football (optd. **GOLD MEDAL FRANCE**) .. 1·75 2·75

102. Cooking and Water Pots.

1985. Pottery. Multicoloured.

440. 1 s. 50 Type **102** 15 10
441. 2 s. Large pot and frying pot with cover 20 10
442. 5 s. Trader selling pots .. 50 30
443. 40 s. Beer pot .. .. 2·00 2·25

103. Class "64" Locomotive.

1985. Tanzanian Railway Locomotives (2nd series).

445. **103.** 1 s. 50 multicoloured 30 10
446. – 2 s. multicoloured .. 40 20
447. – 5 s. multicoloured .. 70 60
448. – 10 s. multicoloured .. 1·25 1·40
449. – 30 s. black, deep brown and red .. 2·75 3·00

DESIGNS: 2 s. Class "36" locomotive. 5 s. "DFH1013" shunting locomotive. 10 s. "DE 1001" diesel-electric locomotive. 15 s. Class "30" steam locomotive. 20 s. Class "11" steam locomotive. 30 s. Steam locomotive, Zanzibar, 1906.

104. Young Pioneers.

1986. International Youth Year.

451. **104.** 1 s. 50 multicoloured 15 15
452. – 4 s. brown, light brown and black .. 30 45
453. – 10 s. multicoloured .. 70 1·10
454. – 20 s. brown, light brown and black .. 1·40 2·00

DESIGNS: 4 s. Youth health care. 10 s. Uhuru torch race. 20 s. Young workers and globe.

105. Rolls-Royce "20/25" (1936).

1986. Centenary of Motoring. Multicoloured.

456. 1 s. 50 Type **105** 15 10
457. 5 s. Rolls-Royce "Phantom II" (1933) 20 25
458 10 s. Rolls-Royce "Phantom I" (1926) 35 50
459. 30 s. Rolls-Royce "Silver Ghost" (1907) .. .. 80 1·10

106. Rotary Logo and Staunton Queen.

1986. World Chess Championship, London and Leningrad.

461 **106** 20 s. blue and mauve 50 50
462 – 100 s. multicoloured .. 1·50 2·25

DESIGN: 100 s. Hand moving rook on board. No. 461 also commemorates Rotary International.

107. Mallard.

1986. Birth Bicentenary (1985) of John J. Audubon (ornithologist). Multicoloured.

464. 5 s. Type **107** 15 25
465. 10 s. Eider 25 40
466. 20 s. Scarlet ibis 45 80
467. 30 s. Roseate spoonbill .. 55 1·10

108. Pearls.

1986. Tanzanian Minerals. Multicoloured.

469. 1 s. 50 Type **108** 50 15
470. 2 s. Sapphire 65 50
471. 5 s. Tanzanite .. .. 1·25 85
472. 40 s. Diamonds .. .. 5·50 6·00

110. "Hibiscus calyphyllus".

1986. Flowers of Tanzania. Multicoloured.

474. 1 s. 50 Type **110** 10 10
475. 5 s. "Aloe graminicola" .. 15 15
476. 10 s. "Nersium oleander" 25 25
477. 30 s. "Nymphaea caerulea" 65 65

111. Oryx.

1986. Endangered Animals of Tanzania. Multicoloured.

479. 5 s. Type **111** 15 15
480. 10 s. Giraffe 25 35
481. 20 s. Rhinoceros 45 60
482. 30 s. Cheetah .. .. 55 1·00

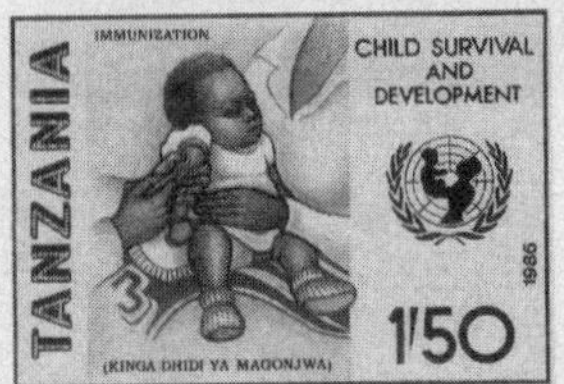

112. Immunization.

1986. U.N.I.C.E.F. Child Survival Campaign. Multicoloured.

484. 1 s. 50 Type **112** 10 10
485. 2 s. Growth monitoring .. 10 10
486. 5 s. Oral rehydration therapy 15 20
487. 40 s. Breast feeding .. 1·00 1·50

113. Butterfly Fish.

1986. Marine Life. Multicoloured.

489. 1 s. 50 Type **113** 30 10
490. 4 s. Parrot fish 55 40
491. 10 s. Turtle .. .. 1·10 1·10
492. 20 s. Octopus .. .. 1·75 1·90

114. Team Captains shaking Hands.

1986. World Cup Football Championship, Mexico. Multicoloured.

494. 1 s. 50 Type **114** 15 10
495. 2 s. Referee sending player off 15 10
496. 10 s. Goalkeeper and ball in net 60 60
497. 20 s. Goalkeeper saving ball .. .. .. 1·00 1·40

115 Pres. Nyerere receiving Beyond War Award

1986. International Peace Year. Mult.

499 1 s. 50 Type **115** 30 10
500 2 s. Children of many races 50 20
501 10 s. African cosmonaut and rocket launch .. 1·25 1·60
502 20 s. United Nations Headquarters, New York .. 1·75 2·25

116 Mobile Bank Service

1987. 20th Anniv of National Bank of Commerce. Multicoloured.

504 1 s. 50 Type **116** 30 10
505 2 s. National Bank of Commerce Head Office 50 20
506 5 s. Pres. Mwinyi laying foundation stone .. 80 80
507 20 s. Cotton harvesting .. 2·00 3·00

117 Parade of Young Party Members

1987. 10th Anniv of Chama Cha Mapinduzi Party and 20th Anniv of Arusha Declaration. Multicoloured.

508 2 s. Type **117** 15 10
509 3 s. Harvesting coffee .. 20 10
510 10 s. Pres. Nyerere addressing Second Peace Initiative Reunion .. 30 20
511 30 s. Presidents Julius Nyerere and Ali Hassan Mwinyi 50 60

118 Nungu Nungu Hair Style

1987. Traditional Hair Styles. Multicoloured.

512 1 s. 50 Type **118** 30 10
513 2 s. Upanga wa jogoo style 45 20
514 10 s. Morani style .. 80 1·00
515 20 s. Twende kilioni style 1·50 2·25

120 Royal Family on Buckingham Palace Balcony after Trooping the Colour

1987. 60th Birthday (1986) of Queen Elizabeth II. Multicoloured.

517 5 s. Type **120** 10 10
518 10 s. Queen and Prince Philip at Royal Ascot .. 15 20
519 40 s. Queen Elizabeth II .. 50 65
520 60 s. Queen Elizabeth with crowd .. .. .. 70 1·00

121 "Apis mellifera" (bee)

1987. Insects. Multicoloured.

522 1 s. 50 Type **121** 40 10
523 2 s. "Prostephanus truncatus" (grain borer) 50 20
524 10 s. "Glossina palpalis" (tsetse fly) .. .. 1·00 1·00
525 20 s. "Polistes sp." (wasp) 1·75 2·25

122 Crocodile

1987. Reptiles. Multicoloured.

527 2 s. Type **122** 20 10
528 3 s. Black-striped grass-snake 25 15
529 10 s. Adder 45 45
530 20 s. Green mamba 75 85

123 Emblems of Posts/ Telecommunications and Railways

1987. 10th Anniv of Tanzania Communications and Transport Corporations. Mult.

532 2 s. Type **123** 10 10
533 8 s. Emblems of Air Tanzania and Harbours Authority 20 20

124 Basketry

1987. Traditional Handicrafts. Multicoloured.

535 2 s. Type **124** 15 10
536 3 s. Decorated gourds 15 15
537 10 s. Stools 25 20
538 20 s. Makonde carvings 40 45

1987. 10th Anniv of Tanzania–Zambia Railway (1986). Nos. 445/9 optd **10th Anniversary of TANZANIA ZAMBIA RAILWAY AUTHORITY 1976–1986**.

540 **103** 1 s. 50 multicoloured 10 10
541 – 2 s. multicoloured 15 15
542 – 5 s. multicoloured 25 25
543 – 10 s. multicoloured 40 40
544 – 30 s. black, brn & red 70 70

126 Mdako (pebble game)

1988. Traditional Pastimes. Multicoloured.

545 2 s. Type **126** 10 10
546 3 s. Wrestling 10 10
547 8 s. Bullfighting, Zanzibar 15 15
548 20 s. Bao (board game) 35 35

127 Plateosaurus
(illustration reduced, actual size 57 × 29 mm)

1988. Prehistoric and Modern Animals. Mult.

550 2 s. Type **127** 20 15
551 3 s. Pteranodon 20 15
552 5 s. Apatosaurus ("Brontosaurus") 20 15
553 7 s. Lion 30 20
554 8 s. Tiger 30 20
555 12 s. Orang-utan 35 20
556 20 s. Elephant 70 45
557 100 s. Stegosaurus 1·75 1·50

128 Marchers with Party Flag

1988. National Solidarity Walk. Mult.

558 2 s. + 1 s. Type **128** 15 15
559 3 s. + 1 s. Pres. Mwinyi leading Walk 15 15

129 Population Symbols on Map

1988. 3rd National Population Census. Mult.

561 2 s. Type **129** 10 10
562 3 s. Census official at work 10 10
563 10 s. Community health care 15 15
564 20 s. Population growth 1967–1988 30 30

130 Javelin

1988. Olympic Games, Seoul (1st issue). Mult.

566 2 s. Type **130** 10 10
567 3 s. Hurdling 10 10
568 7 s. Long distance running 25 15
569 12 s. Relay racing 45 25

131 Football

1988. Olympic Games, Seoul (2nd issue). Mult.

571 10 s. Type **131** 10 10
572 20 s. Cycling 20 25
573 50 s. Fencing 45 50
574 70 s. Volleyball 60 65

1988. Winter Olympic Games, Calgary. As T **131**. Multicoloured.

576 5 s. Cross-country skiing 15 10
577 25 s. Figure skating 40 25
578 50 s. Downhill skiing 65 50
579 75 s. Bobsleighing 85 70

132 Goat

1988. Domestic Animals. Multicoloured.

581 4 s. Type **132** 15 15
582 5 s. Rabbit (horiz) 15 15
583 8 s. Cows (horiz) 20 20
584 10 s. Kitten (horiz) 25 25
585 12 s. Pony 30 30
586 20 s. Puppy 55 55

133 "Love You, Dad" (Pinocchio)
(illustration reduced, actual size 50 × 38 mm)

1988. Greetings Stamps. Showing Walt Disney cartoon characters. Multicoloured.

588 4 s. Type **133** 10 10
589 5 s. "Happy Birthday" (Brer Rabbit and Chip n'Dale) 10 10
590 10 s. "Trick or Treat" (Daisy and Donald Duck) 15 15
591 12 s. "Be kind to Animals" (Ferdie and Mordie with Pluto) 15 15
592 15 s. "Love" (Daisy and Donald Duck) 20 20
593 20 s. "Let's Celebrate" (Mickey Mouse and Goofy) 30 30
594 30 s. "Keep in Touch" (Daisy and Donald Duck) 55 55
595 50 s. "Love you, Mom" (Minnie Mouse with Ferdie and Mordie) 90 90

134 "Charaxes varanes"

1988. Butterflies. Multicoloured.

597 8 s. Type **134** 30 10
598 30 s. "Neptis melicorta" 65 30
599 40 s. "Mylothris chloris" 75 40
600 50 s. "Charaxes bohemani" 90 50
601 60 s. "Myrina silenus" 1·00 70
602 75 s. "Papilio phorcas" 1·50 90
603 90 s. "Cyrestis camillus" 1·75 1·10
604 100 s. "Salamis temora" 2·00 1·25

135 Independence Torch and Mt. Kilimanjaro

1988. National Monuments. Multicoloured.

606 5 s. Type **135** 10 10
607 12 s. Arusha Declaration Monument 10 10
608 30 s. Askari Monument 25 30
609 60 s. Independence Monument 55 60

136 Eye Clinic

1988. 25th Anniv of Dar es Salaam Lions Club. Multicoloured.

611 2 s. Type **136** 10 10
612 3 s. Family at shallow water well 10 10
613 7 s. Rhinoceros and outline map of Tanzania 15 15
614 12 s. Club presenting school desks 15 15

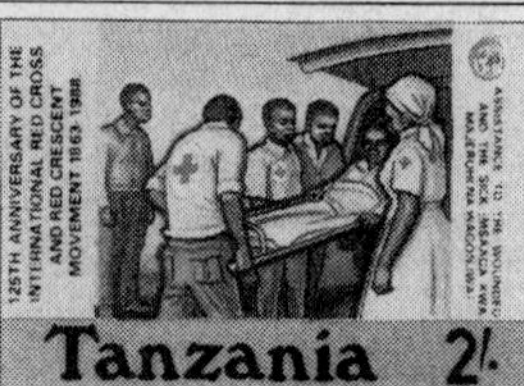

137 Loading Patient into Ambulance

1988. 125th Anniv of International Red Cross and Red Crescent. Multicoloured.

616 2 s. Type **137** 10 10
617 3 s. Mother and baby health clinic 10 10
618 7 s. Red Cross flag 15 15
619 12 s. Henri Dunant (founder) 25 25

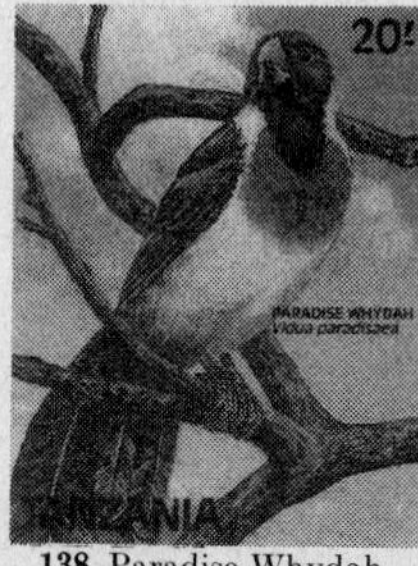

138 Paradise Whydah

1989. Birds. Multicoloured.

621 20 s. Type **138** 40 40
622 20 s. Black-collared barbet 40 40
623 20 s. Bateleur 40 40
624 20 s. Lilac-breasted roller and African open-bill storks in flight 40 40
625 20 s. Red-tufted malachite sunbird and African open-bill stork in flight 40 40
626 20 s. Dark chanting goshawk 40 40
627 20 s. White-fronted bee eater, carmine bee eater and little bee eaters 40 40
628 20 s. Narina trogon and marabou stork in flight 40 40
629 20 s. Grey parrot 40 40
630 20 s. Hoopoe 40 40
631 20 s. Masked lovebird ("Yellow-collared lovebird") 40 40
632 20 s. Yellow-billed hornbill 40 40
633 20 s. Hammerkop 40 40
634 20 s. Violet-crested turaco and flamingos in flight 40 40
635 20 s. Malachite kingfisher 40 40
636 20 s. Greater flamingos 40 40
637 20 s. Yellow-billed storks 40 40
638 20 s. Whale-headed stork ("Shoebill stork") 40 40
639 20 s. Saddle-bill stork and blacksmith plover 40 40
640 20 s. South African crowned crane 40 40

Nos. 622/40 were printed together, se-tenant, forming a composite design of birds at a waterhole.

139 Bushbaby

1989. Fauna and Flora. Multicoloured.

642 5 s. Type **139** 10 10
643 10 s. Bushbaby holding insect (horiz) 15 15
644 20 s. Bushbaby on forked branch 25 25
645 30 s. Black cobra on umbrella acacia 30 30
646 45 s. Bushbaby at night (horiz) 40 40
647 70 s. Red-billed tropic bird and tree ferns 90 90
648 100 s. African tree frog on cocoa tree 1·10 1·10
649 150 s. Black-headed heron and Egyptian papyrus 1·75 1·75

Nos. 646 and 648/50 are without the World Wildlife Fund logo.

140 Juma Ikangaa (marathon runner)

1989. International Sporting Personalities. Multicoloured.

651	4 s. Type **140**	15	15
652	8 s. 50 Steffi Graf (tennis player)	30	30
653	12 s. Yannick Noah (tennis player)	40	40
654	40 s. Pelé (footballer) . .	65	65
655	100 s. Erhard Keller (speed skater)	80	80
656	125 s. Sadanoyama (sumo wrestler)	90	90
657	200 s. Taino (sumo wrestler)	1·75	1·75
658	250 s. I. Aoki (golfer) . .	2·25	2·25

141 Drums

1989. Musical Instruments. Multicoloured.

660	2 s. Type **141**	10	10
661	3 s. Xylophones	10	10
662	10 s. Thumbpiano . .	15	20
663	20 s. Fiddles	30	40

142 Chama Cha Mapinduzi Party Flag

1989. National Solidarity Walk. Mult.

665	5 s.+1 s. Type **142** . .	10	10
666	10 s.+1 s. Marchers with party flag and President Mwinyi	10	10

143 Class "P36" Locomotive, U.S.S.R.

1989. Steam Locomotives. Multicoloured.

668	10 s. Type **143**	15	15
669	25 s. Class "12", Belgium	20	20
670	60 s. Class "C62", Japan . .	45	45
671	75 s. Pennsylvania Railroad Class "T1", U.S.A.	55	55
672	80 s. Class "WP", India . .	60	60
673	90 s. East African Railways Class "59" . .	70	70
674	150 s. Class "People", China	1·25	1·25
675	200 s. Southern Pacific "Daylight Express" U.S.A.	1·40	1·40

HAVE YOU READ THE NOTES AT THE BEGINNING OF THIS CATALOGUE?
These often provide answers to the enquiries we receive.

144 "Luna 3" Satellite orbiting Moon, 1959

1989. History of Space Exploration and 20th Anniv of First Manned Landing on Moon. Multicoloured.

678	20 s. Type **144**	10	15
679	30 s. "Gemini 6" and "7", 1965	15	20
680	40 s. Astronaut Edward White in space, 1965 . .	20	25
681	60 s. Astronaut Aldrin on Moon, 1969	30	35
682	70 s. Aldrin performing experiment, 1969 . .	35	40
683	100 s. "Apollo 15" astronaut and lunar rover, 1971	50	55
684	150 s. "Apollo 18" and "Soyuz 19" docking in space, 1975	75	80
685	200 s. Spacelab, 1983 . .	1·00	1·10

1989. Olympic Medal Winners, Calgary and Seoul. Various stamps optd.

(a) Nos. 571/4

687	10 s. Type **131** (optd **Gold-USSR Silver-Brazil Bronze-W.Germany**) . .	20	20
688	20 s. Cycling (optd **Men's Match Sprint, Lutz Hesslich, DDR**)	30	30
689	50 s. Fencing (optd **Epee, Schmitt, W.Germany**)	65	65
690	70 s. Volleyball (optd **Men's Team, USA**) . .	85	85

(b) Nos. 576/9

692	5 s. Cross-country skiing (optd **Biathlon, Peter-Roetsch, DDR**) . .	10	10
693	25 s. Figure skating (optd **Pairs, Gordeeva & Grinkov, USSR**) . .	25	25
694	50 s. Downhill skiing (optd **Zubriggen, Switerland**)	50	50
695	75 s. Bobsleighing (optd **Gold—USSR Silver—DDR Bronze—DDR**)	70	70

146 Tiger Tilapia

1989. Reef and Freshwater Fishes of Tanzania. Multicoloured.

697	9 s. Type **146**	15	15
698	13 s. Picasso fish . .	15	15
699	20 s. Powder-blue surgeonfish	20	20
700	40 s. Butterflyfish . .	35	35
701	70 s. Guenther's notho . .	60	60
702	100 s. Ansorge's neolebias	80	80
703	150 s. Lyretail panchax . .	1·25	1·25
704	200 s. Regal angelfish . .	1·50	1·50

147 Rural Polling Station

1989. Cent of Inter-Parliamentary Union.

706	**147**	9 s. multicoloured . .	10	10
707	–	13 s. multicoloured . .	10	10
708	–	80 s. multicoloured . .	40	45
709	–	100 s. blk, ultram & bl	50	55

DESIGNS: 13 s. Parliament Building, Dar-es-Salaam; 40 s. Sir William Randal Cremer and Frederic Passy (founders); 80 s. Tanzania Parliament in session; 100 s. Logo.

148 Logo

1990. 10th Anniv of Pan-African Postal Union.

711	**148**	9 s. yellow, green & blk	10	10
712	–	13 s. multicoloured . .	10	10
713	–	70 s. multicoloured . .	20	25
714	–	100 s. multicoloured . .	30	35

DESIGNS: 13 s. Collecting mail from post office box; 40 s. Logos of Tanzania Posts and Telecommunications Corporation, P.A.P.U. and U.P.U.; 70 s. Taking mail to post office; 100 s. Mail transport.

149 Admiral's Flag and "Nina"

1990. 500th Anniv (1992) of Discovery of America by Columbus (50, 60, 75, 200 s.) and Modern Scientific Discoveries (others). Multicoloured.

716	9 s. Bell X-1 aircraft (first supersonic flight, 1947 . .	10	10
717	13 s. "Trieste" (bathyscaphe) (first dive to depth of 35,000 ft, 1960)	10	10
718	50 s. Type **149**	15	20
719	60 s. Fleet flag and "Pinta"	20	25
720	75 s. Standard of Castile and Leon and "Santa Maria"	20	25
721	150 s. Transistor technology	45	50
722	200 s. Arms of Columbus and map of First Voyage	60	65
723	250 s. DNA molecule . .	75	80

150 Tecopa Pupfish

1990. Extinct Species. Multicoloured.

725	25 s. Type **150**	10	10
726	40 s. Thylacine	10	15
727	50 s. Quagga	15	20
728	60 s. Passenger pigeon . .	20	25
729	75 s. Rodriguez saddleback tortoise	20	25
730	100 s. Toolache wallaby . .	30	35
731	150 s. Texas red wolf . .	45	50
732	200 s. Utah Lake sculpin	60	65

151 Camping

1990. 60th Anniv of Girl Guides Movement in Tanzania. Multicoloured.

734	9 s. Type **151**	15	15
735	13 s. Guides planting sapling	15	15
736	50 s. Guide teaching woman to write . .	40	40
737	100 s. Guide helping at child-care clinic . .	65	65

152 Fishing

1990. 25th Anniv of Union of Tanganyika and Zanzibar. Multicoloured.

739	9 s. Type **152**	15	15
740	13 s. Vineyard	15	15
741	50 s. Cloves	30	30
742	100 s. Presidents Nyerere and Karume exchanging Union instruments (vert)	55	55

153 Footballer

1990. World Cup Football Championship, Italy (1st issue). Multicoloured.

744	25 s. Type **153** . .	20	20
745	60 s. Player passing ball . .	45	45
746	75 s. Player turning . .	55	55
747	200 s. Player kicking ball	1·25	1·25

See also Nos. 789/92 and 794/7.

154 Miriam Makeba

1990. Famous Black Entertainers. Mult.

749	9 s. Type **154**	10	10
750	13 s. Manu Dibango . .	10	10
751	25 s. Fela	10	10
752	70 s. Smokey Robinson . .	20	25
753	100 s. Gladys Knight . .	30	35
754	150 s. Eddie Murphy . .	45	50
755	200 s. Sammy Davis Jnr.	60	65
756	250 f. Stevie Wonder . .	75	80

155 Ring of People round Party Flag

1990. Solidarity Walk, 1990. Multicoloured.

758	9 s.+1 s. Type **155** . .	10	10
759	13 s.+1 s. President Mwinyi	10	10

156 Passenger Train

1990. 10th Anniv of Southern African Development Co-ordination Conf. Mult.

761	8 s. Type **156**	10	10
762	11 s. 50 Paper-making plant	10	10
763	25 s. Tractor factory and ploughing	10	10
764	100 s. Map and national flags	30	35

157 Pope John Paul II

1990. Papal Visit to Tanzania. Multicoloured.

766	10 s. Type **157**	10	10
767	15 s. Pope in ceremonial robes	10	10
768	20 s. Pope giving blessing	10	10
769	100 s. Papal coat of arms	30	35

158 Mickey and Minnie Mouse in Herby the Love Bug

1990. Motor Cars from Disney Films. Mult.

771	20 s. Type **158**	10	10
772	30 s. The Absent-minded Professor's car	10	10
773	45 s. Chitty-Chitty Bang-Bang	15	20
774	60 s. Mr. Toad's car	20	25
775	75 s. Scrooge's limousine	20	25
776	100 s. The Shaggy Dog's car	30	35
777	150 s. Donald Duck's nephews cleaning car	45	50
778	200 s. Fire engine from "Dumbo"	60	65

159 "St. Mary Magdalen in Penitence" (detail)

1990. Paintings by Titian. Multicoloured.

780	5 s. Type **159**	10	10
781	10 s. "Averoldi Polyptych" (detail)	10	10
782	15 s. "Saint Margaret" (detail)	10	10
783	50 s. "Venus and Adonis" (detail)	15	20
784	75 s. "Venus and the Lutenist" (detail)	20	25
785	100 s. "Tarquin and Lucretia" (detail)	30	35
786	125 s. "Saint Jerome" (detail)	40	45
787	150 s. "Madonna and Child in Glory with Saints" (detail)	45	50

160 Klinsmann of West Germany

1990. World Cup Football Championship, Italy (2nd issue). Multicoloured.

789	10 s. Type **160**	10	10
790	60 s. Serena of Italy	20	25
791	100 s. Nicol of Scotland	30	35
792	300 s. Susic of Yugoslavia	90	95

161 Throw-in

1990 World Cup Football Championship, Italy (3rd issue). Multicoloured.

794	9 s. Type **161**	10	10
795	13 s. Penalty kick	10	10
796	25 s. Dribbling	10	10
797	100 s. Corner kick	30	35

162 Canoe

1990. Marine Transport. Multicoloured.

799	9 s. Type **162**	10	10
800	13 s. Sailing canoe	10	10
801	25 s. Dhow	10	10
802	100 s. Freighter	30	35

163 Lesser Masked Weaver

164 Lesser Flamingo

1990. Birds. Designs as T **163** (5 s. to 30 s.) or T **164** (40 s. to 500 s.). Multicoloured.

804	5 s. Type **163**	10	10
805	9 s. African emerald cuckoo	10	10
806	13 s. Little bee eater	10	10
807	15 s. Red bishop	10	10
808	20 s. Bateleur	10	10
809	25 s. Scarlet-chested sunbird	10	10
809a	30 s. African wood pigeon	10	10
810	40 s. Type **164**	10	15
811	70 s. Helmet guineafowl	20	25
812	100 s. Eastern white pelican	30	35
813	170 s. Saddle-bill stork	50	55
814	200 s. South African crowned crane	60	65
814a	300 s. Pied crow	90	95
814b	400 s. White-headed vulture	1·25	1·40
815	500 s. Ostrich	1·50	1·60

165 Athletics

1990. 14th Commonwealth Games, Auckland, New Zealand. Multicoloured.

817	9 s. Type **165**	10	10
818	13 s. Netball (vert)	10	10
819	25 s. Pole vaulting	10	10
820	100 s. Long jumping (vert)	30	35

166 Former German Post Office, Dar-es-Salaam

1991. 150th Anniv of the Penny Black and "Stamp World London 90" International Stamp Exhibition. Multicoloured.

822	50 s. Type **166**	15	20
823	50 s. "Reichstag" (German mail steamer), 1890	15	20
824	75 s. Dhows, Zanzibar	20	25
825	75 s. Cobham's "Singapore I" (flying boat), Mwanza, Lake Victoria, 1928	20	25
826	100 s. Air Tanzania Fokker over Livingstone's house, Zanzibar	30	35
827	100 s. Mail train at Moshi station	30	35
828	100 s. English mail coach, 1840	30	35
829	150 s. Stephenson's "Rocket" and mail coach, 1838	45	50
830	200 s. Imperial Airways Handley Page "HP.42" at Croydon	60	65

167 Petersberg Railway, West Germany

1991. Cog Railways. Multicoloured.

832	8 s. Type **167**	10	10
833	25 s. "Waumbek" (locomotive), Mt. Washington Railway, U.S.A.	10	10
834	50 s. Dubrovnik–Sarajevo line, Yugoslavia	15	20
835	100 s. Cog railway, Budapest, Hungary	30	35
836	150 s. Steam locomotive, Vordenberg–Eisenerz line, Austria	45	50
837	200 s. Last train on Rimutaka Incline, New Zealand, 1955	60	65
838	250 s. John Stevens's cog locomotive, U.S.A., 1825	75	80
839	300 s. Pilatusbahn cog railcar, Switzerland	90	95

1991. International Literacy Year (1st issue). As T **269** of Antigua but horiz showing Walt Disney cartoon characters illustrating the Alphabet. Multicoloured.

841/67	1, 2, 3, 5, 10, 15, 18, 20, 25, 30, 35, 40, 45, 50, 55, 60, 75, 80, 90, 100, 120, 125, 145, 150, 160, 175, 200 s. Set of 27	2·75	3·00

See also Nos. 905/8.

1991. Olympic Games, Barcelona (1st issue). As T **268** of Antigua. Multicoloured.

869	5 s. Archery	10	10
870	10 s. Women's gymnastics	10	10
871	25 s. Boxing	10	10
872	50 s. Canoeing	15	20
873	100 s. Volleyball	30	35
874	150 s. Men's gymnastics	45	50
875	200 s. 4 × 100 metres relay	60	65
876	300 s. Judo	90	95

See also Nos. 1309/12 and 1404/11.

1991. "EXPO '90" International Garden and Greenery Exhibition, Osaka. Orchids. As T **198** of Lesotho. Multicoloured.

878	10 s. "Phalaenopsis Lipperose" (vert)	10	10
879	25 s. "Lycoste Aquila" (vert)	10	10
880	30 s. "Vuylstekeara Cambria Plush" (vert)	10	10
881	50 s. "Vuylstekeara Monica Burnham" (vert)	15	20
882	90 s. "Odontocidium Crowborough Plush" (vert)	25	30
883	100 s. "Oncidioda Crowborough Chelsea" (vert)	30	35
884	250 s. "Sophrolaeliocattleya Phena Saturn" (vert)	75	80
885	300 s. "Laeliocattleya Lykas" (vert)	90	95

168 Olympic "Soling" Class Yacht Racing

1991. Record-breaking Sports Events. Mult.

887	5 s. Type **168**	10	10
888	20 s. Olympic downhill skiing	10	10
889	30 s. "Tour de France" cycle race	10	10
890	40 s. Le Mans 24-hour endurance motor race	10	15
891	75 s. Olympic two-man bobsleighing	20	25
892	100 s. Belgian Grand Prix motor cycle race	30	35
893	250 s. Indianapolis 500 motor race	75	80
894	300 s. Gold Cup power boat championship	90	95

169 Mickey Mouse as Cowboy

1991. Mickey Mouse in Hollywood. Walt Disney cartoon characters as actors. Mult.

896	5 s. Type **169**	10	10
897	10 s. Mickey as boxer	10	10
898	15 s. Mickey as astronaut	10	10
899	20 s. Mickey and Minnie as lovers	10	10
900	100 s. Mickey as pirate rescuing Minnie	30	35
901	200 s. Mickey and Donald Duck as policemen arresting Big Pete	60	65
902	350 s. Mickey and Donald with Goofy in historical drama	1·10	1·25
903	450 s. Mickey, Donald and Goofy as sailors	1·40	1·50

170 Women learning to Read

1991. International Literacy Year (2nd issue). Multicoloured.

905	9 s. Type **170**	10	10
906	13 s. Teacher with blackboard	10	10
907	25 s. Literacy aids	10	10
908	100 s. Reading newspaper	30	35

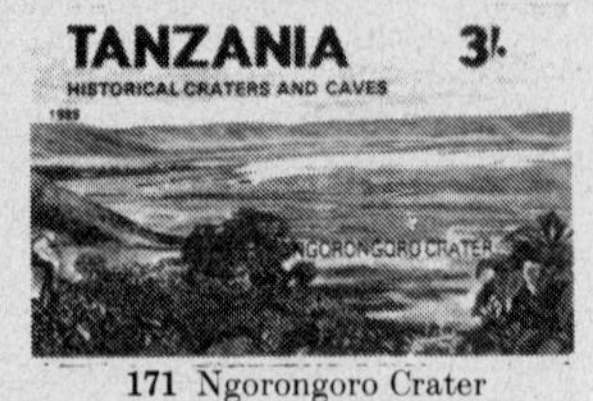

171 Ngorongoro Crater

1991. Historical Craters and Caves. Mult.

910 3 s. Type **171** 15 15
911 5 s. Prehistoric rock painting, Kondoa Caves 15 15
912 9 s. Inner crater, Mt. Kilimanjaro 20 20
913 12 s. Olduvai Gorge 25 25

1991. 350th Death Anniv of Rubens. Cartoons for Decius Mus Tapestries. As T **273** of Antigua. Multicoloured.

915 85 s. "Proclamation of the Vision" 25 30
916 85 s. "Divining of the Entrails" 25 30
917 85 s. "Dispatch of the Lictors" 25 30
918 85 s. "Dedication to Death" 25 30
919 85 s. "Victory and Death of Decius Mus" .. 25 30
920 85 s. "Funeral Rites" .. 25 30

172 Stegosaurus

1991. Prehistoric Creatures. Multicoloured.

922 10 s. Type **172** 10 10
923 15 s. Triceratops 10 10
924 25 s. Edmontosaurus .. 10 10
925 30 s. Plateosaurus .. 10 10
926 35 s. Diplodocus .. 10 10
927 100 s. Iguanodon 30 35
928 200 s. Silviasaurus .. 60 65

173 Dairy Farming

1991. 20th Anniv of Tanzania Investment Bank. Multicoloured.

930 10 s. Type **173** 10 10
931 13 s. Industrial development 10 10
932 25 s. Engineering .. 10 10
933 100 s. Tea picking .. 30 35

174 Pres. Mwinyi leading Walk

1991. National Solidarity Walk. Mult.

935 4 s.+1 s. Type **174** .. 10 10
936 30 s.+1 s. Pres. Mwinyi planting sapling .. 10 10

1991. "Phila Nippon '91" International Stamp Exhibition, Tokyo. Japanese Railway Locomotives. As T **257** of Maldive Islands. Multicoloured.

938 10 s. First steam locomotive in Japan (horiz) 10 10
939 25 s. Class "4500" steam locomotive (horiz) .. 10 10
940 35 s. Class "C 62" steam locomotive (horiz) .. 10 10
941 50 s. Class "Mikado" steam locomotive (horiz) .. 15 20
942 75 s. Class "6250" steam locomotive (horiz) .. 20 25
943 100 s. Class "C 11" steam locomotive (horiz) .. 30 35
944 200 s. Class "E 10" steam locomotive (horiz) .. 60 65
945 300 s. Class "8550" steam locomotive (horiz) .. 90 95

175 Zebra and Golden-winged Sunbird, Ngorongoro Crater

1991. National Game Parks. Multicoloured.

947 10 s. Type **175** 10 10
948 25 s. Greater kudu and elephant, Ruaha Park .. 10 10
949 30 s. Sable antelope and red and yellow barbet, Mikumi Park 10 10
950 50 s. Leopard and wildebeest, Serengeti Park .. 15 20
951 90 s. Giraffe and starred robin, Ngurdoto Park .. 25 30
952 100 s. Eland and Abbot's duiker, Kilimanjaro Park 30 35
953 250 s. Lion and impala, Lake Manyara Park .. 75 80
954 300 s. Black rhinoceros and ostrich, Tarangire Park 90 95

176 "Eronia cleodora"

1991. Butterflies. Multicoloured.

956 10 s. Type **176** 10 10
957 15 S. "Precis westermanni" 10 10
958 35 s. "Antanartia delius" 10 10
959 75 s. "Bematistes aganice" 20 25
960 100 s. "Kallima jacksoni" 30 35
961 150 s. "Apaturopsis cleochartis" 45 50
962 200 s. "Colotis aurigineus" 60 65
963 300 s. "Iolaus crawshayi" 90 95

177 Microwave Tower and Dish Aerial

1991. 25th Anniv of Intelsat Satellite System. Multicoloured.

965 10 s. Type **177** 10 10
966 25 s. Satellite picture of Earth 10 10
967 100 s. Mwenge "B" Earth station 30 35
968 500 s. Mwenge "A" Earth station .. .. .. 1·50 1·60

178 Rice Cultivation

1991. 40th Anniv of United Nations Development Programme. Multicoloured.

970 10 s. Type **178** 10 10
971 15 s. Vocational and Civil Service training .. 10 10
972 100 s. Terrace farming .. 30 35
973 500 s. Renovated Arab door (vert) .. .. 1·50 1·60

179 Netball

1991. All-Africa Games, Cairo. Mult.

975 10 s. Type **179** 10 10
976 15 s. Football (horiz) .. 10 10
977 100 s. Tennis 30 35
978 200 s. Athletics .. 60 65
979 500 s. Baseball (horiz) .. 1·50 1·60

180 "TELECOM '91" Logo

1991. "TELECOM '91" International Telecommunication Exhibition, Geneva (10, 15 s.) and World Telecommunications Day (others). Multicoloured.

981 10 s. Type **180** 10 10
982 15 s. "TELECOM '91" logo and address on envelope (horiz) 10 10
983 35 s. Symbolic telecommunication signals .. 10 10
984 100 s. Symbolic telecommunication signals (horiz) 30 35

1991. Death Centenary (1990) of Vincent van Gogh (artist). As T **278** of Antigua. Mult.

985 10 s. "Peasant Woman Sewing" 10 10
986 15 s. "Head of Peasant Woman with Greenish Lace Cap" 10 10
987 35 s. "Flowering Orchard" 10 10
988 75 s. "Portrait of a Girl" 20 25
989 100 s. "Portrait of a Woman with Red Ribbon" 30 35
990 150 s. "Vase with Flowers" 45 50
991 200 s. "Houses in Antwerp" 60 65
992 400 s. "Seated Peasant Woman with White Cap" .. .. 1·25 1·40

181 Japanese Bobtail Cat

1991. Cats. Multicoloured.

994 50 s. Type **181** 15 20
995 50 s. Cornish rex .. 15 20
996 50 s. Malayan 15 20
997 50 s. Tonkinese 15 20
998 50 s. Abyssinian 15 20
999 50 s. Russian blue .. 15 20
1000 50 s. Cymric 15 20
1001 50 s. Somali 15 20
1002 50 s. Siamese 15 20
1003 50 s. Himalayan 15 20
1004 50 s. Singapura 15 20
1005 50 s. Manx 15 20
1006 50 s. Oriental shorthair .. 15 20
1007 50 s. Maine coon .. 15 20
1008 50 s. Persian 15 20
1009 50 s. Birman 15 20

182 Shire Horse

1991. Horses and Ponies. Multicoloured.

1010 50 s. Type **182** 15 20
1011 50 s. Thoroughbred .. 15 20
1012 50 s. Kladruber 15 20
1013 50 s. Appaloosa 15 20
1014 50 s. Hanoverian .. 15 20
1015 50 s. Arab 15 20
1016 50 s. Breton 15 20
1017 50 s. Exmoor 15 20
1018 50 s. Connemara .. 15 20
1019 50 s. Lipizzaner 15 20
1020 50 s. Shetland 15 20
1021 50 s. Percheron 15 20
1022 50 s. Pinto 15 20
1023 50 s. Orlov 15 20
1024 50 s. Palomino 15 20
1025 50 s. Welsh cob 15 20

Nos. 1010/25 were printed together, se-tenant, as a sheetlet of 16 with the backgrounds of each horizontal strip of 4 forming a composite design.

183 Jewel Tetra

1991. Aquarium Fish. Multicoloured.

1026 75 s. Type **183** 20 25
1027 75 s. Five-banded barb .. 20 25
1028 75 s. Simpson platy .. 20 25
1029 75 s. Guppy 20 25
1030 75 s. Zebra danio .. 20 25
1031 75 s. Neon tetra 20 25
1032 75 s. Siamese fighting fish 20 25
1033 75 s. Tiger barb 20 25
1034 75 s. Red lyretail .. 20 25
1035 75 s. Goldfish 20 25
1036 75 s. Pearl gourami .. 20 25
1037 75 s. Angelfish 20 25
1038 75 s. Clown loach .. 20 25
1039 75 s. Red swordtail .. 20 25
1040 75 s. Brown discus .. 20 25
1041 75 s. Rosy barb 20 25

Nos. 1026/41 were printed together, se-tenant, with the backgrounds of each stamp forming a composite design.

Loxodonta africana

184 African Elephant

1991. African Elephants. Multicoloured.

1042 75 s. Type **184** 20 25
1043 75 s. Two elephants fighting 20 25
1044 75 s. Elephant facing forward and tree .. 20 25
1045 75 s. Elephant facing left and tree 20 25
1046 75 s. Cow elephant and calf facing right standing in water .. 20 25
1047 75 s. Cow watching over calf in water 20 25
1048 75 s. Two adults and calf in water 20 25
1049 75 s. Cow and calf facing left standing in water 20 25

1050	75 s. Elephant facing right	20	25
1051	75 s. Elephants feeding ..	20	25
1052	75 s. Elephant feeding ..	20	25
1053	75 s. Elephant and zebra	20	25
1054	75 s. Cow and calf drinking	20	25
1055	75 s. Calf suckling ..	20	25
1056	75 s. Bull elephant ..	20	25
1057	75 s. Cow with small calf	20	25

Nos. 1042/57 were printed together, se-tenant, as a sheetlet of 16 with each horizontal strip of 4 forming a composite design.

185 Buderigar

1991. Pet Birds. Multicoloured.

1058	75 s. Type **185**	20	25
1059	75 s. Rainbow bunting ..	20	25
1060	75 s. Golden-fronted leafbird	20	25
1061	75 s. Black-headed caique	20	25
1062	75 s. Java sparrow ..	20	25
1063	75 s. Diamond sparrow ..	20	25
1064	75 s. Peach-faced lovebird	20	25
1065	75 s. Golden conure ..	20	25
1066	75 s. Military macaw ..	20	25
1067	75 s. Celestial parrotlet ..	20	25
1068	75 s. Sulphur-crested cockatoo	20	25
1069	75 s. Spectacled amazon parrot	20	25
1070	75 s. Paradise tanager ..	20	25
1071	75 s. Gouldian finch ..	20	25
1072	75 s. Masked lovebird ..	20	25
1073	75 s. Hill mynah ..	20	25

Nos. 1058/73 were printed together, se-tenant, forming a composite design.

186 Indian Elephant

1991. Elephants. Multicoloured.

1074	10 s. Type **186**	10	10
1075	15 s. Indian elephant uprooting tree ..	10	10
1076	25 s. Indian elephant with calf	10	10
1077	30 s. African elephant ..	10	10
1078	35 s. Head of African elephant (horiz) ..	10	10
1079	100 s. African elephant and calf bathing (horiz)	30	35
1080	200 s. Two African elephants (horiz) ..	60	65

187 Russian Steam Locomotive, 1930

1991. Locomotives of the World. Mult.

1082	10 s. Type **187**	10	10
1083	15 s. Japanese electric locomotive, 1964 ..	10	10
1084	25 s. Russian steam locomotive, 1834 (vert) ..	10	10
1085	35 s. French electric locomotive, 1979	10	10
1086	60 s. French diesel railcar, 1972	20	25
1087	100 s. U.K. diesel locomotive, 1972	30	35
1088	300 s. Russian steam locomotive, 1837 (vert) ..	90	95

1991. Christmas. Walt Disney Christmas Cards. As T **228** of St. Vincent. Mult.

1090	10 s. Disney characters in "JOY", 1968 (horiz) ..	10	10
1091	25 s. Mickey, Donald, Pluto and Goofy hanging up stockings, 1981 (horiz)	10	10
1092	35 s. Characters from Disney film "Robin Hood", 1973 (horiz) ..	10	10
1093	75 s. Mickey looking at Christmas tree, 1967 (horiz)	20	25
1094	100 s. Goofy, Mickey, Donald and Chip n' Dale on film set, 1969	30	35
1095	150 s. Mickey on giant bauble, 1976	45	50
1096	200 s. Clarabelle Cow with electric cow bell, 1935	60	65
1097	300 s. Mickey's nephews with book, 1935 ..	90	95

188 Bruce Lee

1992. Entertainers.

1099/1134	75 s. × 36 mult Set of 36	6·50	8·00

Nos. 1099/1134 were issued as four sheetlets, each of nine different designs, as Type **188** depicting Bruce Lee, Marilyn Monroe, Elvis Presley and black entertainers (Scott Joplin, Sammy Davis Jnr, Joan Armatrading, Louis Armstrong, Miriam Makeba, Lionel Ritchie, Whitney Houston, Bob Marley, Tina Turner).

189 "Malacanthus latovittatus"

1992. Fishes. Multicoloured.

1136	10 s. Type **189**	10	10
1137	15 s. "Lamprologus tretocephalus" ..	10	10
1138	25 s. "Lamprologus calvus"	10	10
1139	35 s. "Hemichromis bimaculatus" ..	10	10
1140	60 s. "Aphyosemion bivittatum" ..	20	25
1141	100 s. "Synanceia verrucosa"	30	35
1142	300 s. "Aphyosemion ahli"	90	95

190 Chimpanzee in Tree

1992. Common Chimpanzee. Multicoloured.

1144	10 s. Type **190**	10	10
1145	15 s. Feeding	10	10
1146	35 s. Two chimpanzees ..	10	10
1147	75 s. Adult male with arms folded ..	20	25
1148	100 s. Breaking branch ..	30	35
1149	150 s. Young chimpanzee in tree	45	50
1150	200 s. Female holding young	60	65
1151	300 s. Chimpanzee sitting in tree	90	95

191 Pope John Paul II in Dominican Republic, 1979

1992. Papal Visits.

1153/1272	100 s. × 120 mult Set of 120 ..	32·00	38·00

DESIGNS: Nos. 1154/1272, Various scenes on Papal visits as Type **191**.

192 Balcony

1992. Zanzibar Stone Town. Multicoloured.

1273	10 s. Type **192**	10	10
1274	20 s. Bahlnara Mosque ..	10	10
1275	30 s. High Court Building	10	10
1276	200 s. National Museum (horiz)	60	65

193 Gogo Costume

1992. Traditional Costumes. Multicoloured.

1278	3 s. Type **193**	10	10
1279	5 s. Swahili	10	10
1280	9 s. Hehe and Makonde ..	10	10
1281	12 s. Maasai	10	10

194 Melisa and Mike (chimpanzees)

1992. Chimpanzees of the Gombe. Mult.

(a) Horiz designs as T **194**.

1283	10 s. Type **194**	10	10
1284	15 s. Leakey and David Greybeard	10	10
1285	30 s. Fifi termiting ..	10	10
1286	35 s. Galahad	10	15

(b) Vert designs showing individual chimpanzees

1288	10 s. Leakey	10	10
1289	15 s. Fifi	10	10
1290	20 s. Faben	10	10
1291	30 s. David Greybeard ..	10	10
1292	35 s. Mike	10	10
1293	50 s. Galahad	15	20
1294	100 s. Melisa	30	35
1295	200 s. Flo	60	65

195 Sorghum Farming, Serena

1992. 25th Anniv of National Bank of Commerce. Multicoloured.

1296	10 s. Type **195**	10	10
1297	15 s. Samora Avenue branch and computer operator (vert) ..	10	10
1298	35 s. Training centre ..	10	10
1299	40 s. Women dyeing textiles	10	15

196 "Lambis truncata"

1992. Shells. Multicoloured.

1301	10 s. Type **196**	10	10
1302	15 s. "Cypraecassis rufa"	10	10
1303	25 s. "Vexillum rugosum"	10	10
1304	30 s. "Conus litteratus" ..	10	10
1305	35 s. "Corculum cardissa"	10	10
1306	50 s. "Murex ramosus" ..	15	20
1307	250 s. "Melo melo" ..	75	80

197 Basketball

1992. Olympic Games, Barcelona (2nd issue). Multicoloured.

1309	40 s. Type **197**	10	15
1310	100 s. Billiards ..	30	35
1311	200 s. Table tennis ..	60	65
1312	400 s. Darts	1·25	1·40

198 British-designed Radar, Pearl Harbor

1992. 50th Anniv of Japanese Attack on Pearl Harbor. Multicoloured.

1314	75 s. Type **198**	20	25
1315	75 s. Winston Churchill ..	20	25
1316	75 s. Sinking of H.M.S. "Repulse" (battle cruiser)	20	25
1317	75 s. Sinking of H.M.S. "Prince of Wales" (battleship)	20	25
1318	75 s. Surrender of Singapore	20	25
1319	75 s. Sinking of H.M.S. "Hermes" (aircraft carrier)	20	25
1320	75 s. Japanese attack on Malayan airfield	20	25
1321	75 s. Japanese gun crew, Hong Kong ..	20	25
1322	75 s. Japanese landing craft	20	25
1323	75 s. "Haguro" (Japanese cruiser)	20	25

199 French Resistance Monument and Medal

1992. Birth Centenary (1990) of Charles de Gaulle (French statesman). Multicoloured.

1324 25 s. Type **199** 10 10
1325 30 s. Free French tank on Omaha beach, D-Day 10 10
1326 150 s. "Concorde" at Charles de Gaulle Airport 45 50

200 Scout Badge, Giraffe and Elephant

1992. 50th Death Anniv (1991) of Lord Baden-Powell (founder of Boy Scout movement). Multicoloured.

1328 10 s. Type **200** 10 10
1329 15 s. Scouts in boat .. 10 10
1330 400 s. John Glenn's space capsule .. .. 1·25 1·40

201 Marcella Sembrich as Zerlina in "Don Giovanni"

1992. Death Bicentenary of Mozart.

1332 **201** 10 s. black and mauve 10 10
1333 – 50 s. multicoloured .. 15 20
1334 – 300 s. black & mauve 90 95

DESIGNS: 50 s. Planet Jupiter (Symphony No. 41); 300 s. Luciano Pavarotti as Idamente in "Idomeneo".

1992. "Granada '92" International Stamp Exn, Spain. Paintings. As T **292** of Antigua.

1336 25 s. red and black .. 10 10
1337 35 s. multicoloured .. 10 10
1338 50 s. multicoloured .. 15 20
1339 75 s. multicoloured .. 20 25
1340 100 s. black, brown & pink 30 35
1341 150 s. red and black .. 45 50
1342 200 s. red and black .. 60 65
1343 300 s. multicoloured .. 90 95

DESIGNS—HORIZ: 25 s. "A Picador, mounted on a Chulo's Shoulders, spears a Bull" (Goya); 150 s. "Another Madness (of Martincho) in the Plaza de Zaragoza" (Goya); 200 s. "Recklessness of Martincho in the Plaza de Zaragoza" (Goya). VERT: 35 s. "Philip IV at Fraga" (Velazquez); 50 s. "Head of a Stag" (Velazquez); 75 s. "The Cardinal-Infante Ferdinand as a Hunter" (Velazquez); 100 s. "The Dream of Reason brings forth Monsters" (Goya); 300 s. "Pablo de Valladolid" (Velazquez).

202 Lucky Omens

1992. 500th Anniv of Discovery of America by Columbus. Multicoloured.

1345 10 s. Type **202** 10 10
1346 15 s. Map and compass .. 10 10
1347 25 s. Look-out in crow's nest 10 10
1348 30 s. Amerindians sighting ships (horiz) 10 10
1349 35 s. "Pinta" and "Nina" (horiz) 10 10
1350 75 s. "Santa Maria" (horiz) 20 25
1351 250 s. Wreck of "Santa Maria" 75 80

203 Superb Starling

1992. Birds. Multicoloured.

1353 5 s. Type **203** 10 10
1354 10 s. Canary 10 10
1355 15 s. Four-coloured bush shrike 10 10
1356 25 s. Grey-headed kingfisher 10 10
1357 30 s. Common kingfisher 10 10
1358 35 s. Yellow-billed oxpecker 10 10
1359 150 s. Black-throated honeyguide 45 50

1992. 15th Death Anniv of Elvis Presley. Nos. 1117/25 optd **15th Anniversary**.

1361 75 s. Looking pensive .. 20 25
1362 75 s. Wearing black and yellow striped shirt .. 20 25
1363 75 s. Singing into microphone 20 25
1364 75 s. Wearing wide-brimmed hat 20 25
1365 75 s. With microphone in right hand 20 25
1366 75 s. In Army uniform .. 20 25
1367 75 s. Wearing pink shirt 20 25
1368 75 s. In yellow shirt .. 20 25
1369 75 s. In jacket and bow tie 20 25

205 Iguanodon

1992. African Dinosaurs. Multicoloured.

1370 100 s. Type **205** 30 35
1371 100 s. Saltasaurus .. 30 35
1372 100 s. Cetiosaurus .. 30 35
1373 100 s. Camarasaurus .. 30 35
1374 100 s. Spinosaurus .. 30 35
1375 100 s. Stegosaurus .. 30 35
1376 100 s. Allosaurus .. 30 35
1377 100 s. Ceratosaurus .. 30 35
1378 100 s. Lesothosaurus .. 30 35
1379 100 s. Anchisaurus .. 30 35
1380 100 s. Ornithomimus .. 30 35
1381 100 s. Baronyx 30 35
1382 100 s. Pachycephalosaurus 30 35
1383 100 s. Heterodontosaurus 30 35
1384 100 s. Dryosaurus .. 30 35
1385 100 s. Coelophysis .. 30 35

Nos. 1370/85 were printed together, se-tenant, forming a composite design.

206 "Tilapia mariae"

1992. Fishes. Multicoloured.

1386 100 s. Type **206** 30 35
1387 100 s. "Capoeta hulstaerti" 30 35
1388 100 s. "Tropheus moorii" 30 35
1389 100 s. "Synodotis angelicus" 30 35
1390 100 s. "Julidochromis dickfeldi" 30 35
1391 100 s. "Tilapia nilotica" 30 35
1392 100 s. "Nothobranchius rachovii" 30 35
1393 100 s. "Pseudotropheus crabro" 30 35
1394 100 s. "Lamprologus leleupi" 30 35
1395 100 s. "Pseudotropheus zebra" 30 35
1396 100 s. "Julidochromis marlieri" 30 35
1397 100 s. "Chalinochromis brichardi" 30 35

Nos. 1386/97 were printed together, se-tenant, forming a composite design.

207 Hunting Birds with Catapults

1992. Traditional Hunting. Multicoloured.

1399 20 s. Type **207** 10 10
1400 70 s. Hunting antelope with bow and arrow .. 20 25
1401 100 s. Hunting antelopes with dogs 30 35
1402 150 s. Hunting lion with spears and shields .. 45 50

1992. Olympic Games, Albertville and Barcelona (3rd issue). As T **216** of Lesotho. Multicoloured.

1404 20 s. Men's 4000 metre pursuit cycling .. 10 10
1405 40 s. Men's double sculls rowing (horiz) .. 10 10
1406 50 s. Waterpolo (horiz) .. 15 20
1407 70 s. Women's single luge (horiz) .. 20 25
1408 100 s. Marathon (horiz) .. 30 35
1409 150 s. Women's asymmetrical bars gymnastics (horiz) .. 45 50
1410 200 s. Ice hockey .. 60 65
1411 400 s. Men's rings gymnastics .. .. 1·25 1·40

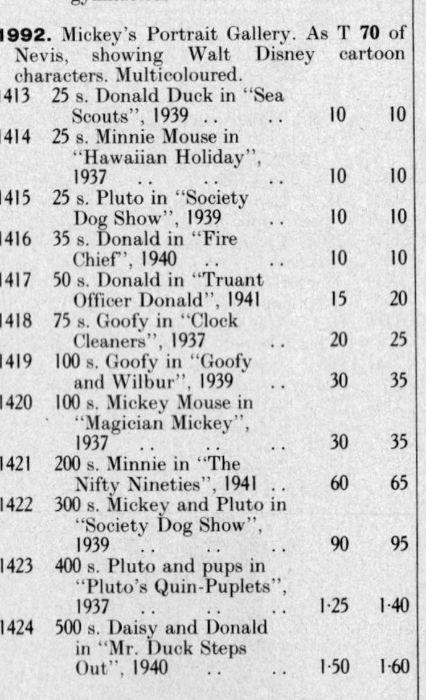

1992. Mickey's Portrait Gallery. As T **70** of Nevis, showing Walt Disney cartoon characters. Multicoloured.

1413 25 s. Donald Duck in "Sea Scouts", 1939 .. .. 10 10
1414 25 s. Minnie Mouse in "Hawaiian Holiday", 1937 .. .. .. 10 10
1415 25 s. Pluto in "Society Dog Show", 1939 .. 10 10
1416 35 s. Donald in "Fire Chief", 1940 .. .. 10 10
1417 50 s. Donald in "Truant Officer Donald", 1941 15 20
1418 75 s. Goofy in "Clock Cleaners", 1937 .. 20 25
1419 100 s. Goofy in "Goofy and Wilbur", 1939 .. 30 35
1420 100 s. Mickey Mouse in "Magician Mickey", 1937 .. .. .. 30 35
1421 200 s. Minnie in "The Nifty Nineties", 1941 .. 60 65
1422 300 s. Mickey and Pluto in "Society Dog Show", 1939 .. .. .. 90 95
1423 400 s. Pluto and pups in "Pluto's Quin-Puplets", 1937 .. .. .. 1·25 1·40
1424 500 s. Daisy and Donald in "Mr. Duck Steps Out", 1940 .. .. 1·50 1·60

208 "Couroupita guianensis"

1993. Botanical Gardens of the World. Rio de Janeiro. African Plants.

1426/45 70 s. × 20 multicoloured Set of 20 3·50 4·50

209 Abyssinian Cat

1992. Cats. Multicoloured.

1447 20 s. Type **209** 10 10
1448 30 s. Havana cat .. 10 10
1449 50 s. Persian black cat .. 15 20
1450 70 s. Persian blue cat .. 20 25
1451 100 s. European silver tabby cat 30 35
1452 150 s. Persian silver tabby cat 45 50
1453 200 s. Maine coon cat .. 60 65

1992. "Genova '92" International Stamp Exhibition. Toy Trains manufactured by Lionel. As T **257** of Dominica. Multicoloured.

1455 10 s. B. & O. Tunnel Locomotive No. 5, 1904 10 10
1456 20 s. "Liberty Bell" locomotive, 1930 .. 10 10
1457 30 s. Armoured rail car, 1917 .. .. .. 10 10
1458 50 s. Open trolley No. 202, 1910–14 .. .. 15 20
1459 70 s. "Macy Special" electric locomotive .. 20 25
1460 100 s. "Milwaukee Road" bi-polar electric locomotive, 1929 .. 30 35
1461 200 s. New York Central "S" type locomotive, 1912 .. .. .. 60 65
1462 300 s. Locomotive No. 7, 1914 .. .. 90 95

210 Count Ferdinand von Zeppelin

1992. Anniversaries and Events. Mult.

1464 30 s. Type **210** 10 10
1465 70 s. "Santa Maria" .. 20 25
1466 70 s. "Apollo-Soyuz" link-up, 1975 .. .. 20 25
1467 150 s. African elephant .. 45 50
1468 150 s. Child being offered apple 45 50
1469 200 s. Zebra 60 65
1470 200 s. Trying on glasses .. 60 65
1471 300 s. "Graf Zeppelin", 1929 .. .. .. 90 95
1472 300 s. Christopher Columbus 90 95
1473 400 s. Space shuttle .. 1·25 1·40
1474 400 s. Wolfgang Amadeus Mozart (vert) .. 1·25 1·40

ANNIVERSARIES AND EVENTS: Nos. 1464, 1471, 75th death anniv of Count Ferdinand von Zeppelin; Nos. 1465, 1472, 500th anniv of discovery of America by Columbus; Nos. 1466, 1473, International Space Year; Nos. 1467, 1469, Earth Summit '92, Rio; No. 1468, International Conference on Nutrition, Rome; No. 1470, 75th anniv of International Association of Lions Clubs; Nos. 1474, Death bicentenary of Mozart.

1992. Bicentenary of the Louvre, Paris. Paintings by Jean Chardin. As T **305** of Antigua. Multicoloured.

1476	100 s. "Young Draughts-man sharpening Pencil"	30	35
1477	100 s. "The Buffet" ..	30	35
1478	100 s. "Return from the Market"	30	35
1479	100 s. "The Hard-working Mother"	30	35
1480	100 s. "Grace"	30	35
1481	100 s. "The Copper Water Urn"	30	35
1482	100 s. "The House of Cards"	30	35
1483	100 s. "Boy with a Top"	30	35

211 Carved Head

1992. Makonde Art.

1485	**211**	20 s. multicoloured ..	10	10
1486	–	30 s. multicoloured ..	10	10
1487	–	50 s. multicoloured ..	15	20
1488	–	70 s. multicoloured ..	20	25
1489	–	100 s. multicoloured	30	35
1490	–	150 s. multicoloured	45	50
1491	–	200 s. multicoloured	60	65

DESIGNS: 30 s. to 200 s. Various carvings.

212 Russian Cycle, 1813

1992. Bicycles of the World. Multicoloured.

1493	20 s. Type **212**	10	10
1494	30 s. German, 1840 ..	10	10
1495	50 s. German, 1818 ..	15	20
1496	70 s. German, 1850 ..	20	25
1497	100 s. Italian, 1988 ..	30	35
1498	150 s. Swedish, 1982 ..	45	50
1499	300 s. Italian, 1989 ..	90	95

213 Seal

1993. Large Sea Creatures. Multicoloured.

1501	20 s. Type **213**	10	10
1502	30 s. Whale	10	10
1503	70 s. Shark	20	25
1504	100 s. Walrus	30	35

214 Boxing

1993. Sports. Multicoloured.

1506	20 s. Type **214**	10	10
1507	50 s. Hockey	15	20
1508	70 s. Show jumping ..	20	25
1509	100 s. Marathon running	30	35
1510	150 s. Football	45	50
1511	200 s. Diving	60	65
1512	400 s. Basketball ..	1·25	1·40

1993. 40th Anniv of Coronation. As T **307** of Antigua.

1514	100 s. multicoloured ..	30	35
1515	150 s. multicoloured ..	45	50
1516	200 s. lilac and black ..	60	65
1517	300 s. multicoloured ..	90	95

DESIGNS: 100 s. Queen Elizabeth II at Coronation (photograph by Cecil Beaton); 150 s. Gold salt-cellar; 200 s. Prince Philip at Coronation; 300 s. Queen Elizabeth II and Prince Andrew.

215 "Macrolepiota rhacodes"

1993. Fungi. Multicoloured.

1519	20 s. Type **215**	10	10
1520	40 s. "Mycena pura" ..	10	10
1521	50 s. "Chlorophyllum molybdites" ..	15	20
1522	70 s. "Agaricus campestris" ..	20	25
1523	100 s. "Volvariella volvacea"	30	35
1524	150 s. "Leucoagaricus naucinus" ..	45	50
1525	200 s. "Oudemansiella radicata" ..	60	65
1526	300 s. "Clitocybe nebularis" ..	90	95

216 "Geochelone elephantopus" (tortoise)

1993. Reptiles. Multicoloured.

1528	20 s. Type **216**	10	10
1529	50 s. "Iguana iguana" ..	15	20
1530	70 s. "Varanus salvator" (lizard) (horiz) ..	20	25
1531	100 s. "Naja oxiana" (cobra)	30	35
1532	150 s. "Chamaeleo jacksoni" (horiz) ..	45	50
1533	200 s. "Eunectes murinus" (snake) (horiz) ..	60	65
1534	250 s. "Alligator mississippensis" (horiz)	75	80

217 Pancake Tortoise on Rock

1993. Endangered Species. Pancake Tortoise. Multicoloured.

1536	20 s. Type **217**	10	10
1537	30 s. Drinking	10	10
1538	50 s. Under rock	15	20
1539	70 s. Tortoise hatching ..	20	25

218 Elephant

1993. Wildlife.

1540/87	100 s. × 48 multicoloured Set of 48	13·00	15·00

Nos. 1540/87 were issued together, se-tenant, as four sheetlets each of twelve different vertical designs. The species depicted are, in addition to Type **218**, Gazelle, Hartebeest, Duiker, Genet, Civet, Eastern white pelican, Waterbuck, Blacksmith plover, Lesser pied kingfisher, Black-winged stilt, Bush pig, Brown-hooded kingfisher, Sable antelope, Impala, Buffalo, Leopard, Aardvark, Hippopotamus, Spotted hyena, Crowned crane, Crocodile, Greater flamingo, Baboon, Potto, Lesser flamingo, Grey-headed kingfisher, Red colobus monkey, Dik-dik, Aardwolf, Black-backed jackal, Tree pangoliln, Serval, Yellow-billed hornbill, Pygmy mongoose, Bat-eared fox, Bushbaby, Egyptian vulture, Ostrich, Greater kudu, Diana monkey, Giraffe, Cheetah, Wildebeest, Chimpanzee, Warthog, Zebra and Rhinoceros.

219 Valentina Tereshkova (first woman in space)

1993. Famous 20th-century Women. Mult.

1589	20 s. Type **219**	10	10
1590	40 s. Marie Curie (physicist)	10	10
1591	50 s. Indira Gandhi (Prime Minister of India)	15	20
1592	70 s. Wilma Rudolph (Olympic athlete) ..	20	25
1593	100 s. Margaret Mead (anthropologist) ..	30	35
1594	150 s. Golda Meir (Prime Minister of Israel) ..	45	50
1595	200 s. Dr. Elizabeth Blackwell (first female medical doctor) ..	60	65
1596	400 s. Margaret Thatcher (Prime Minister of Great Britain) ..	1·25	1·40

OFFICIAL STAMPS

1965. Nos. 128, etc., optd. **OFFICIAL.**

O 9.	**25.**	5 c. blue & orange ..	10	20
O 10.	–	10 c. multicoloured	10	20
O 11.	–	15 c. multicoloured ..	10	20
O 12.	–	20 c. sepia, green & blue	10	20
O 13.	–	30 c. black and brown	10	20
O 14.	–	50 c. multicoloured ..	15	20
O 15.	**33.**	1s. multicoloured ..	30	20
O 16.	–	5s. brown, green & blue	1·75	3·00

1967. Nos. 142, etc., optd. **OFFICIAL.**

O 20.	5 c. mauve, grn. & blk.	10	70
O 21.	10 c. brown & bistre ..	10	30
O 22.	15 c. grey, blue & black	10	50
O 23.	20 c. brown and green ..	10	20
O 24.	30 c. green and black ..	10	20
O 36.	40 c. yell., brn. & green	—	2·25
O 25.	50 c. multicoloured ..	15	50
O 26.	1 s. brn., blue & purple	30	70
O 27.	5 s. yellow, blk. & green	2·50	5·00

1973. Nos. 158 etc. optd. **OFFICIAL.**

O 40.	**53.**	5 c. green, blue & blk.	40	75
O 41.	–	10 c. multicoloured ..	50	20
O 42.	–	20 c. brn., yell. & blk.	70	20
O 43.	–	40 c. multicoloured ..	1·00	30
O 44.	–	50 c. multicoloured ..	1·00	30
O 45.	–	70 c. grn., orge. & blk.	1·25	65
O 46.	**54.**	1 s. multicoloured ..	1·25	30
O 47.	–	1 s. 50 multicoloured ..	3·00	2·00
O 48.	–	2 s. 50 multicoloured ..	3·50	3·50
O 49.	–	5 s. multicoloured ..	4·00	4·00

1980. Nos. 307/13 and 315/17 optd. **OFFICIAL.**

O54	10 c. Type **75** ..	20	15
O55	20 c. Large-spotted genet	25	20
O56	40 c. Banded mongoose	25	20
O57	50 c. Ratel	25	20
O58	75 c. Large-toothed rock hyrax	40	40
O59	80 c. Leopard	45	45
O60	1 s. Impala	45	20
O66	1 s. 50 Giraffe	2·50	2·75
O61	2 s. Common zebra ..	75	75
O62	3 s. African buffalo ..	85	85
O63	5 s. Lion	1·25	1·25

1990. Nos. 804/12 optd **OFFICIAL**. Mult.

O70	5 s. Type **163**	10	10
O71	9 s. African emerald cuckoo	10	10
O72	13 s. Little bee eater ..	10	10
O73	15 s. Red bishop	10	10
O74	20 s. Bateleur	10	10
O75	25 s. Scarlet-chested sunbird	10	10
O76	30 s. African wood pigeon	10	10
O77	40 s. Type **164**	10	15
O78	70 s. Helmet guineafowl ..	20	25
O79	100 s. Eastern white pelican	30	35

POSTAGE DUE STAMPS

The Postage Due stamps of Kenya, Uganda and Tanganyika were used in Tanganyika until January 2nd, 1967.

D 1.

1967.

D 19.	D 1.	5 c. red	10	1·10
D 20.		10 c. green	15	1·10
D 21.		20 c. blue	20	1·40
D 22.		30 c. brown	30	2·00
D 23.		40 c. purple	35	2·50
D 24.		1 s. orange	45	3·00

D 2

1990.

D25	D 2	50 c. green	10	10
D26		80 c. blue	10	10
D27		1 s. brown	10	10
D28		2 s. green	10	10
D29		3 s. purple	10	10
D30		5 s. brown	10	10
D31		10 s. brown	10	10
D32		20 s. brown	10	10

B. For use in Zanzibar only.

Z 39. Pres. Nyerere and First Vice-Pres. Karume within Bowl of Flame.

1966. 2nd Anniv of United Republic. Mult.

Z 142.	30 c. Type Z **39**	30	30
Z 143.	50 c. Hands supporting Bowl of Flame ..	30	30
Z 144.	1 s. 30 As 50 c.	30	30
Z 145.	2 s. 50 Type Z **39** ..	45	1·25

APPENDIX

The following stamps have either been issued in excess of postal needs, or have not been made available to the public in reasonable quantities at face value.

1986.

Caribbean Royal Visit. Optd on previous issues. (a) On Nos. 425/8 20 s. × 2, 100 s. × 2. (b) On Nos. 430/3 5, 10, 20, 30 s.

"Ameripex" International Stamp Exhibition, Chicago. Optd on Nos. 425/8. 20 s. × 2, 100 s. × 2.

1988.

Cent of (1986) Statue of Liberty. 1, 2, 3, 4, 5, 6, 7, 8, 10, 12, 15, 18, 20, 25, 30, 35, 40, 45, 50, 60 s.

Royal Ruby Wedding. Optd on No. 378. 10 s.

125th Anniv of Red Cross. Optd on Nos. 486/7. 5, 40 s.

63rd Anniv of Rotary International in Africa. Optd on Nos. 422/3. 10 s., 17 s. 50.

TASMANIA

An island S. of Australia, one of the States of the Australian Commonwealth, whose stamps it now uses.

12 pence = 1 shilling.
20 shillings = 1 pound.

1.

2.

1853. Imperf.

3. **1.** 1d. blue £3000 £600
8. **2.** 4d. orange.. .. .. £1800 £325

3.

7.

8.

1855. Imperf.

28 **3** 1d. red .. .. .. 80·00 15·00
34 2d. green .. .. £120 45·00
36 4d. blue .. .. .. £100 11·00
47 **7** 6d. purple .. .. £130 40·00
41 **8** 1s. orange .. .. £500 70·00

1864. Perf.

82 **3** 1d. red .. .. .. 25·00 6·50
71 2d. green .. .. £110 38·00
72 4d. blue .. .. .. 70·00 11·00
143 **7** 6d. purple .. .. 24·00 11·00
141 **8** 1s. orange .. .. 70·00 38·00

11.

20.

1870.

159 **11.** ½d. orange .. .. 1·90 1·40
156 1d. red .. .. .. 2·75 25
157 2d. green.. .. .. 3·00 25
165 3d. brown .. .. 8·00 2·00
130 4d. blue £700 £400
226 4d. yellow .. .. 12·00 5·50
158 8d. purple .. .. 14·00 3·50
256 9d. blue .. .. .. 7·00 2·50
131 10d. black .. .. 23·00 16·00
149b 5s. mauve .. .. £120 38·00

1889. Surch. **Halfpenny.**

167. **11.** ½d. on 1d. red .. .. 8·00 8·00

1889. Surch. **2½d.**

169. **11.** 2½d. on 9d. blue .. 5·00 2·50

1892. Various frames.

216. **20.** ½d. orange and mauve .. 1·25 50
217. 2½d. purple .. .. 2·50 1·00
218. 5d. blue and brown .. 4·50 1·40
219. 6d. violet and black .. 5·50 1·75
220. 10d. lake and green .. 9·00 6·50
221. 1s. red and green .. 6·00 1·75
222. 2s. 6d. brown and blue.. 22·00 9·00
223. 5s. purple and red .. 38·00 18·00
224. 10s. mauve and brown.. 75·00 50·00
225. £1 green and yellow .. £300 £150

22. Lake Marion.

23. Mount Wellington.

DESIGNS—HORIZ. 2d. Hobart. 3d Spring River, Port Davey. 5d. Mt. Gould, Lake St. Clair. 6d. Dilston Falls, VERT. 2½d. Tasman's Arch. 4d. Russell Falls.

1899.

249 **22** ½d. green .. .. 1·25 20
250 **23** 1d. red .. .. .. 1·50 10
251b – 2d. violet .. .. 2·50 10
232 – 2½d. blue .. .. 10·00 4·50
253 – 3d. brown .. .. 6·50 1·75
247 – 4d. orange .. .. 12·00 2·00
235 – 5d. blue.. .. .. 14·00 6·50
254a – 6d. lake .. .. 15·00 9·00

1904. No. 218 surch. **1½d.**

244. **20.** 1½d. on 5d. blue & brown 1·25 60

1912. No. 251b surch **ONE PENNY**.

260 1d. on 2d. violet 90 30

TOBAGO

An island in the British West Indies, north-east of Trinidad. From 1896 to 1913 it used the stamps of Trinidad; from 1913 there were combined issues for Trinidad and Tobago.

12 pence = 1 shilling.
20 shillings = 1 pound.

1.

2.

1879.

1. **1.** 1d. red .. .. .. 70·00 55·00
2. 3d. blue .. .. .. 60·00 38·00
3. 6d. orange .. .. 24·00 38·00
4. 1s. green .. .. .. £350 60·00
5. 5s. grey £550 £500
6. £1 mauve £5000

In the above issue only stamps watermarked Crown CC were issued for postal use and our prices are for stamps bearing this watermark. Stamps with watermark Crown CA are fiscals and were never admitted to postal use.

1880. No. 3 divided vertically down the centre and surch. with pen and ink.

7. **1.** 1d. on half of 6d. orange.. £4500 £750

1880. "POSTAGE" added in design.

14. **2.** ½d. lilac .. .. .. 1·00 11·00
20. ½d. green 30 35
21. 1d. red 70 60
16a. 2½d. blue .. .. .. 2·75 75
10. 4d. green .. .. .. £180 24·00
22. 4d. grey 50 55
11. 6d. buff .. .. .. £250 90·00
23. 6d. brown .. .. .. 60 2·50
24. 1s. yellow .. .. .. 70 8·00

1883. Surch. in figures and words.

26 **2** ½d. on 2½d. blue .. .. 2·50 6·00
30 ½d. on 4d. grey .. .. 8·50 26·00
27 ½d. on 6d. buff .. .. 1·50 14·00
28 ½d. on 6d. brown .. 65·00 85·00
29 1d. on 2½d. blue .. .. 27·00 14·00
31 2½d. on 4d. grey .. .. 3·00 6·50
13 2½d. on 6d. buff .. .. 25·00 25·00

1896. Surch ½d. **POSTAGE.**

33. **1.** ½d. on 4d. lilac and red .. 28·00 25·00

TOGO

A territory in W. Africa, formerly a German Colony. Divided between France and Gt. Britain in 1919, the British portion being attached to the Gold Coast for administration and using the stamps of that country. In 1956 the French portion became an autonomous republic within the French Union. Full independence was achieved in April 1960.

100 pfennigs = 1 mark.

BRITISH OCCUPATION

1914. Nos. 7/19 (German Colonial Types) optd **TOGO Anglo-French Occupation.**

H 1 N. 3 pf. brown .. .. £110 95·00
H 2 5 pf. green .. .. £100 90·00
H 3 10 pf. red £120 £100
H 17 20 pf. blue .. .. 15·00 12·00
H 18 25 pf. blk. & red on yell. 19·00 28·00
H 19 30 pf. black & orange buff .. .. .. 19·00 28·00
H 7 40 pf. black and red .. £225 £250
H 33 50 pf. black & purple on buff £9500 £6500
H 9 80 pf. blk. & red on rose £225 £275
H 10 O. 1 m. red £5000 £2500
H 11 2 m. blue £7500 £8000
H 25 3 m. black .. .. † £32000
H 26 5 m. lake and black .. † £32000

1914. Nos. 1/2 surch. in words.

H 27. N. ½d. on 3 pf. brown .. 26·00 26·00
H 28. 1d. on 5 pf. green .. 4·00 4·25

1915. Stamps of Gold Coast (King George V) optd. **TOGO ANGLO-FRENCH OCCUPATION.**

H 47 ½d. green.. .. .. 15 85
H 48 1d. red 15 70
H 36 2d. grey 30 40
H 37 2½d. blue.. .. .. 40 80
H 51 3d. purple on yellow .. 55 70
H 52 6d. purple .. .. 55 1·00
H 53 1s. black on green .. 1·25 1·75
H 54 2s. purple & blue on blue 4·50 6·50
H 55 2s. 6d. black & red on blue 4·50 6·50
H 44 5s. green & red on yellow 8·00 13·00
H 57a 10s. green & red on green 16·00 50·00
H 58 20s. purple & black on red £120 £120

For other Togo issues see volume 2.

TOKELAU

Three islands situated north of Samoa. Formerly known as the Union Islands, they were administered as part of the Gilbert and Ellice Islands until transferred to New Zealand in 1925. Administered by Western Samoa (using stamps of Samoa) until they became a dependency of New Zealand in 1949. Adopted name of Tokelau in 1946.

1948. 12 pence = 1 shilling;
20 shillings = 1 pound.
1967. 100 cents = 1 New Zealand dollar.
1982. 100 sene or cents = 1 Samoan tola or dollar.

1. Atafu Village and Map.

1948.

1. **1.** ½d. brown and purple .. 15 20
2. – 1d. red and green 15 20
3. – 2d. green and blue.. .. 15 20

DESIGNS: 1d. Nukunonu hut and map. 2d. Fakaofo village and map.

1953. Coronation. As T **164** of New Zealand.

4. 3d. brown .. .. .. 3·00 3·00

1956. Surch. **ONE SHILLING.**

5. **1.** 1s. on ½d. brown and purple 4·00 3·50

1966. Arms types of New Zealand without value, surch. **TOKELAU ISLANDS** and value in sterling.

6. **F 6.** 6d. blue .. .. .. 65 1·25
7. 8d. green.. .. .. 75 1·00
8. 2s. pink .. .. .. 85 1·40

1967. Decimal currency. Nos 1/3 surch.

9. – 1 c. on 1d. (No. 2).. .. 60 60
10. – 2 c. on 2d. (No. 3).. .. 1·00 1·00
11. **1.** 10 c. on ½d. (No. 1) .. 2·00 2·00

1968. Arms types of New Zealand without value, surch. **TOKELAU ISLANDS** and value in decimal currency.

12. **F 6.** 3 c. lilac 50 30
13. 5 c. blue 50 30
14. 7 c. green 50 30
15. 20 c. pink 65 40

8. British Protectorate (1877).

1969. History of Tokelau Islands

16.	**8.**	5 c. blue, yellow & black	25	10
17.	–	10 c. red, yellow and black	30	10
18.	–	15 c. green, yellow & black	35	15
19.	–	20 c. brown, yellow & black	40	15

DESIGNS: 10 c. Annexed to Gilbert and Ellice Islands (1916). 15 c. New Zealand Administration (1925). 20 c. New Zealand Territory (1948).

1969. Christmas. As **T 301** of New Zealand.

20.	2 c. multicoloured	10	15

1970. Christmas. As **T 314** of New Zealand.

21.	2 c. multicoloured	10	20

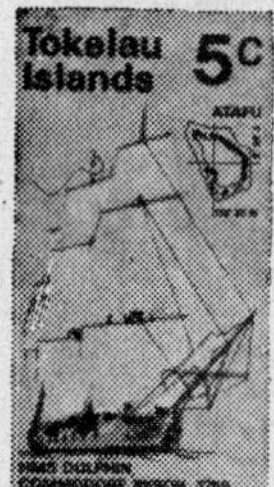

12. H.M.S. "Dolphin", 1765. **13.** Fan.

1970. Discovery of Tokelau Islands. Mult.

22	5 c. Type **12**	1·50	35
23	10 c. H.M.S. "Pandora", 1791	1·50	35
24	25 c. "General Jackson" (American whaling ship), 1835 (horiz)	3·25	70

1971. Handicrafts. Multicoloured.

25.	1 c. Type **13**	20	20
26.	2 c. Hand-bag	30	30
27.	3 c. Basket	40	40
28.	5 c. Hand-bag	50	65
29.	10 c. Shopping-bag	60	80
30.	15 c. Hand-bag	1·00	1·50
31.	20 c. Canoe	1·25	2·00
32.	25 c. Fishing hooks	1·25	2·00

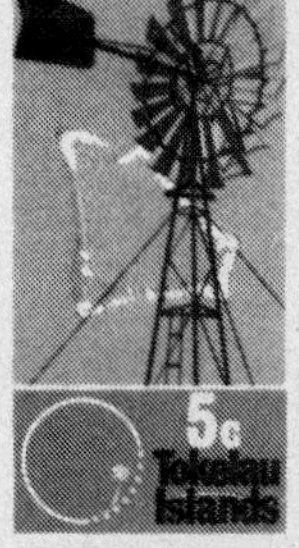

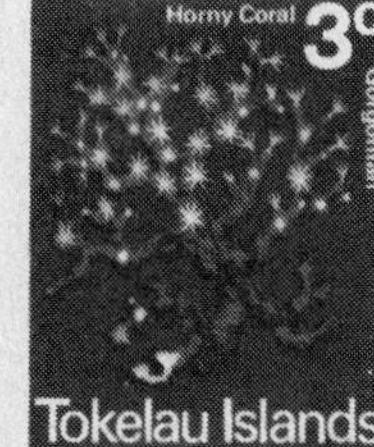

14. Windmill Pump. **15.** Horny Coral.

1972. South Pacific Commission. 25th Anniv. Multicoloured.

33.	5 c. Type **14**	35	60
34.	10 c. Community well	45	75
35.	15 c. Pest eradication	55	1·00
36.	20 c. Flags of member nations	60	1·25

In No. 35 "PACIFIC" is spelt "PACFIC".

1973. Coral. Multicoloured.

37.	3 c. Type **15**	1·00	80
38.	5 c. Soft Coral	1·00	90
39.	15 c. Mushroom Coral	1·75	1·50
40.	25 c. Staghorn Coral	2·00	1·75

16. Hump-back Cowrie.

1975. "Shells of the Coral Reef". Mult.

41.	3 c. Type **16**	1·25	1·25
42.	5 c. Tiger Cowrie	1·50	1·50
43.	15 c. Mole Cowrie	2·50	3·00
44.	25 c. Eyed Cowrie	3·00	3·50

17. Moorish Idol.

1975. Fishes. Multicoloured.

45.	5 c. Type **17**	50	1·00
46.	10 c. Long-nosed Butterfly-fish	70	1·25
47.	15 c. Lined Butterfly-fish	85	1·75
48.	25 c. Red Fire-fish	1·10	2·00

18. Canoe Building.

1976. Multicoloured.

49a	1 c. Type **18**	10	15
50	2 c. Reef fishing	20	1·25
51a	3 c. Weaving preparation	10	15
52a	5 c. Uma (kitchen)	10	15
53a	9 c. Carving	10	15
54a	20 c. Husking coconuts (vert.)	15	20
55a	50 c. Wash day (vert.)	20	20
56a	$1 Meal time (vert.)	30	30

19. White Tern.

1977. Birds of Tokelau. Multicoloured.

57.	8 c. Type **19**	30	40
58.	10 c. Turnstone	35	45
59.	15 c. White-capped Noddy	60	80
60.	30 c. Common Noddy	90	1·40

20. Westminster Abbey.

1978. Coronation. 25th Anniv. Mult.

61.	8 c. Type **20**	20	20
62.	10 c. King Edward's Chair	20	20
63.	15 c. Coronation regalia	30	35
64.	30 c. Queen Elizabeth II	50	60

21. Canoe Race.

1978. Canoe Racing.

65.	**21.**	8 c. multicoloured	20	20
66.	–	12 c. multicoloured	25	25
67.	–	15 c. multicoloured	30	30
68.	–	30 c. multicoloured	50	50

DESIGNS: 12 c. to 30 c. Different scenes of canoe racing.

22. Rugby.

1979. Local Sports. Multicoloured.

69.	10 c. Type **22**	15	15
70.	15 c. Cricket	40	60
71.	20 c. Rugby (different)	40	65
72.	30 c. Cricket (different)	60	80

23. Surfing.

1980. Water Sports. Multicoloured.

73.	10 c. Type **23**	10	10
74.	20 c. Surfing (different)	15	15
75.	30 c. Swimming	20	25
76.	50 c. Swimming (different)	25	35

24. Pole Vaulting. **25.** Wood Carving.

1981. Sports. Multicoloured.

77.	10 c. Type **24**	10	10
78.	20 c. Volleyball	20	20
79.	30 c. Athletics (different)	25	30
80.	50 c. Volleyball (different)	30	35

1982. Handicrafts. Multicoloured.

81.	10 s. Type **25**	10	10
82.	22 s. Bow-drilling sea shell	15	25
83.	34 s. Bowl finishing	20	35
84.	60 s. Basket weaving	35	50

26. Octopus Lure.

1982. Fishing Methods. Multicoloured.

85.	5 s. Type **26**	15	10
86.	18 s. Multiple-hook fishing	35	20
87.	23 s. Ruvettus fishing	40	25
88.	34 s. Netting flying fish	45	30
89.	63 s. Noose fishing	55	40
90.	75 s. Bonito fishing	60	45

27. Outrigger Canoe.

1983. Transport. Multicoloured.

91.	5 s. Type **27**	10	10
92.	18 s. Wooden whaleboat	15	15
93.	23 s. Aluminium whaleboat	15	20
94.	34 s. "Alia" (fishing catamaran)	25	25
95.	63 s. "Frysna" (freighter)	35	40
96.	75 s. McKinnon "Goose" flying-boat	45	50

28. Javelin-throwing.

1983. Traditional Pastimes. Multicoloured.

97.	5 s. Type **28**	10	10
98.	18 s. String game	15	15
99.	23 s. Fire making	15	20
100.	34 s. Shell-throwing	25	25
101.	63 s. Hand-ball game	35	40
102.	75 s. Mass wrestling	45	50

29. Planting and Harvesting.

1984. Copra Industry. Multicoloured.

103.	48 s. Type **29**	40	45
104.	48 s. Husking and splitting	40	45
105.	48 s. Drying	40	45
106.	48 s. Bagging	40	45
107.	48 s. Shipping	40	45

30. Convict Tang ("Manini").

1984. Fishes. Multicoloured.

108	1 s. Type **30**	10	10
109	2 s. Flying Fish ("Hahave")	10	10
110	5 s. Fire Wrasse ("Uloulo")	10	10
111	9 s. Unicorn Fish ("Ume iho")	10	10
112	23 s. Napoleon Fish ("Lafilafi")	15	20
113	34 s. Red Snapper ("Fag-amea")	20	25
114	50 s. Yellow Fin Tuna ("Kakahi")	35	40
115	75 s. Castor-oil Fish ("Palu po")	50	55
116	$1 Grey Shark ("Mokoha")	65	70
117	$2 Black Marlin ("Hakula")	1·25	1·40

31. "Ficus tinctoria" ("Mati").

1985. Native Trees. Multicoloured.

118.	5 c. Type **31**	10	10
119.	18 c. "Morinda citrifolia" ("Nonu")	15	15
120.	32 c. Breadfruit Tree ("Ulu")	20	25
121.	48 c. "Pandanus tectorius" ("Fala")	35	40
122.	60 c. "Cordia subcordata" ("Kanava")	40	45
123.	75 c. Coconut Palm ("Niu")	50	55

INDEX

Countries can be quickly located by referring to the index at the end of this volume.

32. Administration Centre, Atafu.

1985. Tokelau Architecture (1st series). Public Buildings. Multicoloured.

No.	Description		
124.	5 c. Type **32**	10	10
125.	18 c. Administration Centre, Nukunonu ..	15	15
126.	32 c. Administration Centre, Fakaofo ..	20	25
127.	48 c. Congregational Church, Atafu	35	40
128.	60 c. Catholic Church, Nukunonu	40	45
129.	75 c. Congregational Church, Fakaofo ..	50	55

See also Nos. 130/5.

33. Atafu Hospital.

1986. Tokelau Architecture (2nd series). Hospitals and Schools. Multicoloured.

No.	Description		
130.	5 c. Type **33**	10	10
131.	18 c. St. Joseph's Hospital, Nukunonu	10	10
132.	32 c. Fenuafala Hospital, Fakaofo	20	25
133.	48 c. Matauala School, Atafu	35	40
134.	60 c. Matiti School, Nukunonu	40	45
135.	75 c. Fenuafala School, Fakaofo	55	60

34. Coconut Crab.

1986. Agricultural Livestock. Multicoloured.

No.	Description		
136.	5 c. Type **34**	10	10
137.	18 c. Pigs	15	15
138.	32 c. Chickens	25	25
139.	48 c. Reef Hawksbill turtle	40	40
140.	60 c. Goats	45	45
141.	75 c. Ducks	60	60

35. "Scaevola taccada" ("Gahu").

1987. Tokelau Flora. Multicoloured.

No.	Description		
142.	5 c. Type **35**	45	45
143.	18 c. "Hernandia nymphaeifolia" ("Puka")	70	70
144.	32 c. "Pandanus tectorius" ("Higano")	1·00	1·00
145.	48 c. "Gardenia taitensis" ("Tialetiale")	1·25	1·25
146.	60 c. "Pemphis acidula" ("Gagie")	1·60	1·60
147.	75 c. "Guettarda speciosa" ("Puapua")	1·75	1·75

36. Javelin Throwing.

1987. Tokelau Olympic Sports. Mult.

No.	Description		
148.	5 c. Type **36**	20	20
149.	18 c. Shot putting	40	40
150.	32 c. Long jumping ..	60	60
151.	48 c. Hurdling ..	75	75
152.	60 c. Sprinting	1·00	1·00
153.	75 c. Wrestling	1·25	1·25

37 Small Boat Flotilla in Sydney Harbour

1988. Bicentenary of Australian Settlement and "Sydpex '88" National Stamp Exhibition, Sydney. Multicoloured.

No.	Description		
154	50 c. Type **37**	1·00	1·00
155	50 c. Sailing ships and liners	1·00	1·00
156	50 c. Sydney skyline and Opera House	1·00	1·00
157	50 c. Sydney Harbour Bridge	1·00	1·00
158	50 c. Sydney waterfront	1·00	1·00

Nos. 154/8 were printed together, se-tenant, forming a composite aerial view of the re-enactment of First Fleet's arrival.

38 Island Maps and Ministerial Representatives

1988. Political Development. Multicoloured.

No.	Description		
159	5 c. Type **38** (administration transferred to N.Z. Foreign Affairs Ministry, 1975)	15	15
160	18 c. General Fono (island assembly) meeting, 1977	20	20
161	32 c. Arms of New Zealand (first visit by New Zealand Prime Minister, 1985)	30	30
162	48 c. U.N. logo (first visit by U.N. representative, 1976)	45	45
163	60 c. Canoe and U.N. logo (first Tokelau delegation to U.N., 1987)	55	55
164	75 c. Secretary and N.Z. flag (first islander appointed as Official Secretary, 1987) ..	65	65

39 Three Wise Men in Canoe and Star

1988. Christmas. Designs showing Christmas in Tokelau. Multicoloured.

No.	Description		
165	5 c. Type **39**	10	10
166	20 c. Tokelau Nativity ..	20	20
167	40 c. Flight to Egypt by canoe	35	35
168	60 c. Children's presents ..	45	45
169	70 c. Christ child in Tokelauan basket ..	55	55
170	$1 Christmas parade ..	75	75

40 Launching Outrigger Canoe

1989. Food Gathering. Multicoloured.

No.	Description		
171	50 c. Type **40**	85	85
172	50 c. Paddling canoe away from shore	85	85
173	50 c. Fishing punt and sailing canoe	85	85
174	50 c. Canoe on beach ..	85	85
175	50 c. Loading coconuts into canoe	85	85
176	50 c. Tokelauans with produce	85	85

Nos. 171/3 and 174/6 were each printed together, se-tenant, forming composite designs.

41 Basketwork

1990. Womens' Handicrafts. Multicoloured.

No.	Description		
177	5 c. Type **41**	30	30
178	20 c. Preparing cloth ..	65	65
179	40 c. Tokelau fabrics ..	90	90
180	60 c. Mat weaving ..	1·40	1·40
181	80 c. Weaving palm fronds	1·90	1·90
182	$1 Basket making ..	2·00	2·00

42 Man with Adze and Wood Blocks

1990. Men's Handicrafts. Multicoloured.

No.	Description		
183	50 c. Type **42**	1·00	1·00
184	50 c. Making fishing boxes	1·00	1·00
185	50 c. Fixing handles to fishing boxes ..	1·00	1·00
186	50 c. Two men decorating fishing boxes	1·00	1·00
187	50 c. Canoe building (two men)	1·00	1·00
188	50 c. Canoe building (three men)	1·00	1·00

43 Swimming

1992. Olympic Games, Barcelona. Mult.

No.	Description		
189	40 c. Type **43**	35	35
190	60 c. Long jumping ..	50	50
191	$1 Volleyball	80	80
192	$1.80 Running	1·50	1·50

44 "Santa Maria"

1992. 500th Anniv of Discovery of America by Columbus.Multicoloured.

No.	Description		
193	40 c. Type **44**	35	35
194	60 c. Christopher Columbus	60	60
195	$1.20 Fleet of Columbus ..	1·25	1·25
196	$1.80 Columbus landing in the New World ..	2·00	2·00

45 Queen Elizabeth II in 1953

1993. 40th Anniv of Coronation. Mult.

No.	Description		
197	25 c. Type **45**	30	30
198	40 c. Prince Philip ..	50	50
199	$1 Queen Elizabeth II in 1993	1·00	1·00
200	$2 Queen Elizabeth II and Prince Philip	1·90	1·90

46 Bristle-thighed Curlew

1993. Birds of Tokelau. Multicoloured.

No.	Description		
201	25 c. Type **46**	20	25
202	40 c. Red-tailed tropic bird	30	35
203	$1 Eastern reef heron ..	70	75
204	$2 Pacific golden plover ..	1·50	1·60

TONGA

(Or Friendly Is.) A group of islands in the S. Pacific Ocean. An independent Polynesian kingdom formerly under British protection, Tonga became a member of the Commonwealth in June 1970.

1886. 12 pence = 1 shilling.
20 shillings = 1 pound.
1967. 100 seniti = 1 pa'anga.

1. King George I.

1886.

1b. 1. 1d. red .. .. .. 10·00 3·25
2b. 2d. violet .. .. .. 26·00 2·75
3ab. 6d. blue .. .. .. 20·00 2·25
9. 6d. orange .. .. .. 11·00 24·00
4ba. 1s. green .. .. .. 45·00 3·25

1891. Surch. with value in words.

5. 1. 4d. on 1d. red .. .. 2·00 11·00
6. 8d. on 2d. violet .. .. 35·00 80·00

1891. Optd. with stars in upper right and lower left corners.

7. 1. 1d. red .. .. .. 35·00 48·00
8. 2d. violet .. .. .. 48·00 38·00

5. Arms of Tonga. 6. King George I.

1892.

10. 5. 1d. red .. .. .. 12·00 17·00
11. 6. 2d. olive .. .. .. 18·00 15·00
12. 5. 4d. brown .. .. .. 38·00 55·00
13. 6. 8d. mauve .. .. .. 55·00 95·00
14. 1s. brown .. .. .. 70·00 95·00

1893. Surch in figures.

15. 5. ½d. on 1d. blue .. .. 23·00 23·00
16. 6. 2½d. on 2d. green .. .. 14·00 12·00
18. 7½d. on 6d. red .. .. 24·00 65·00

1893. Surch. in words.

17. 5. 5d. on 4d. orange .. .. 4·00 6·50

1894. Surch. vert. **SURCHARGE** and value in words.

21. 5. ½d. on 4d. brown .. .. 1·50 7·00
22. 6. ½d. on 1s. brown .. .. 1·50 11·00
25. 1d. on 2d. blue .. .. 32·00 22·00

1894. Surch. vert. **SURCHARGE** and value in figures.

26a. 6. 1½d. on 2d. blue .. .. 35·00 27·00
27. 2½d. on 2d. blue .. .. 40·00 45·00
23. 2½d. on 8d. mauve .. .. 5·00 8·00
24b. 1. 2½d. on 1s. green .. .. 15·00 30·00
28a. 6. 7½d. on 2d. blue .. .. 55·00 45·00

13. King George II. 15. Arms.

16. Ovava tree, Kana-Kubolu.

21. View of Haapai.

1895. Surch **SURCHARGE** and new value.

29 13 ½d. on 2½d. red .. .. 30·00 32·00
30 1d. on 2½d. red .. .. 40·00 28·00
31 7½d. on 2½d. red .. .. 48·00 48·00

1895.

32 13 1d. green .. .. 15·00 23·00
33 2½d. pink .. .. 20·00 20·00
34 5d. blue .. .. 15·00 40·00
35 7½d. yellow .. .. 22·00 40·00

1896. Nos. 26a and 28a surch. with typewritten **Half-Penny** and Tongan inscription

36a 6 ½d. on 1½d. on 2d. blue .. £275 £275
37 ½d. on 7½d. on 2d. blue .. 60·00 85·00

1897.

38a 15 ½d. blue .. .. .. 70 1·00
74 ½d. green .. .. .. 15 1·00
75 16 1d. black and red .. .. 40 1·00
42a – 2d. sepia and bistre .. 7·50 1·10
43b – 2½d. black and blue .. 2·75 1·25
78 – 3d. black and green .. 15 40
45 – 4d. green and purple .. 3·75 4·00
46 – 5d. black and orange .. 25·00 10·00
79 – 6d. red 50 75
48 – 7½d. black and green .. 8·50 20·00
49 – 10d. black and red .. 26·00 30·00
50 – 1s. black and brown .. 12·00 7·00
51a 21 2s. black and blue .. 18·00 24·00
81 – 2s. 6d. purple .. .. 14·00 17·00
82 – 5s. black and red .. 16·00 30·00

DESIGNS—As Type **26**: 2d., 2½d., 5d., 7½d., 10d., 1s. King George II. As Type **16**: HORIZ. 3d. Prehistoric trilith at Haamonga. 4d. Bread-fruit. VERT. 6d. Coral. As Type **21**: VERT. 2s. 6d. Red Shining Parrot. HORIZ. 5s. Vavau Harbour.

1899. Royal Wedding. Optd. **T-L 1 June, 1899.**

54. 16. 1d. black and red .. 26·00 50·00

26. Queen Salote. 29.

1920.

56. 26. 1½d. black .. .. 30 1·50
57. 2d. purple and violet .. 5·00 13·00
76. 2d. black and purple .. 60 70
58. 2½d. black and blue .. 4·25 24·00
77. 2½d. blue 15 60
60. 5d. black and orange .. 3·25 3·50
61. 7½d. black and green .. 1·75 1·75
62. 10d. black and red .. 1·50 4·50
80. 1s. black and brown .. 40 1·50

1923. Nos. 46 and 48/82 surch. **TWO PENCE PENI-E-UA.**

64 2d. on 5d. black and orange 85 85
65 2d. on 7½d. black and green 12·00 20·00
66 2d. on 10d. black and red .. 4·75 32·00
67 2d. on 1s. black and brown 27·00 22·00
68a 2d. on 2s. black and blue .. 4·50 4·50
69 2d. on 2s. 6d. purple .. 20·00 6·50
70a 2d. on 5s. black and red .. 2·50 2·50

1938. 20th Anniv of Queen Salote's Accession. Dated "1918–1938" at foot.

71. 29. 1d. black and red .. 55 2·50
72. 2d. black and purple .. 5·00 1·75
73. 2½d. black and blue .. 5·00 2·50

1944. Silver Jubilee of Queen Salote's Accession. Tablet at foot dated "1918–1943".

83. 29. 1d. black and red .. 15 30
84. 2d. black and violet .. 15 30
85. 3d. black and green .. 15 30
86. 6d. black and orange .. 30 65
87. 1s. black and brown .. 30 65

1949. U.P.U. As T **20/23** of Antigua.

88. 2½d. blue 30 20
89. 3d. olive .. .. .. 40 1·50
90. 6d. red 40 30
91. 1s. brown 40 35

31. Queen Salote.

DESIGN — VERT. 1s. Half-length portrait of Queen.

32. Queen Salote.

1950. 50th Birthday of Queen Salote.

92. 31. 1d. red 30 60
93. 32. 5d. green 30 60
94. – 1s. violet .. .. .. 30 1·25

34. Map.

DESIGNS—HORIZ. 2½d. Beach scene. 5d. Flag and island. 1s. Arms of Tonga and Great Britain. VERT., 3d. H.M.N.Z.S. "Bellona".

35. Palace, Nuku'alofa.

1951. 50th Anniv. of Treaty of Friendship with Gt. Britain.

95. 34. ½d. green 20 85
96. 35. 1d. black and red .. 10 50
97. – 2½d. green and brown .. 30 85
98. – 3d. yellow and blue .. 65 85
99. – 5d. red and green .. 50 50
100. – 1s. orange and violet .. 55 50

40. Royal Palace, Nuku'alofa.

1953.

101. 40. 1d. black and brown .. 10 10
102. – 1½d. blue and green .. 10 10
103. – 2d. turquoise and black 60 20
104. – 3d. blue and green .. 20 20
105. – 3½d. yellow and red .. 30 70
106. – 4d. yellow and red .. 45 10
107. – 5d. blue and brown .. 30 10
108. – 6d. black and blue .. 30 30
109. – 8d. green and violet .. 60 40
110. – 1s. blue and black .. 50 10
111. – 2s. olive and brown .. 1·00 60
112. – 5s. yellow and lilac .. 16·00 6·50
113. – 10s. yellow and black .. 5·50 6·00
114. – £1 yellow, red and blue 8·00 6·50

DESIGNS—HORIZ: 1½d. Shore fishing with throw-net. 2d. "Hifofua" and "Aoniu" (ketches). 3½d. Map of Tongatapu. 4d. Vava'u Harbour. 5d. P.O., Nuku'alofa. 6d. Aerodrome, Fua'amotu. 8d. "Matua" (inter-island freighter) at Nuku'alofa Wharf. 2s. Lifuka, Ha'apai. 5s. Mutiny on the "Bounty". VERT: 3d. Swallows' Cave, Vava'u. 1s. Map of Tonga Islands. 10s. Queen Salote. £1, Arms of Tonga.

54. Stamp of 1886.

1961. 75th Anniv. of Tongan Postal Service.

115. 54. 1d. red and orange .. 10 10
116. – 2d. blue 40 15
117. – 4d. turquoise 15 15
118. – 5d. violet 40 15
119. – 1s. brown 40 15

DESIGNS: 2d. Whaler and longboat. 4d. Queen Salote and Post Office, Nuku'alofa. 5d. Mail steamer. 1s. Mailplane over Tongatapu.

1962. Cent. of Emancipation. Stamps of 1953 and No. 117 optd. **1862 TAU'ATAINA EMANCIPATION 1962.** or surch. also.

120. 1d. black and brown .. 10 10
121. 4d. turquoise (No. 117) .. 10 15
122. 5d. blue and brown .. 15 15
123. 6d. black and blue .. 20 20
124. 8d. green and violet .. 40 40
125. 1s. blue and black .. 20 20
126. 2s. on 3d. blue and green .. 40 75
127. 5s. yellow and lilac .. 2·50 1·40

60. "Protein Foods".

1963. Freedom from Hunger.

128. 60. 11d. blue 65 15

61. Coat of Arms.

1963. First Polynesian Gold Coinage Commemoration. Circular designs, backed with paper, inscr. overall "TONGA THE FRIENDLY ISLANDS". Imperf.

(a) Postage. ¼ koula coin. Diameter 1⅝ in.

129. 61. 1d. red on gold .. 10 10
130. A. 2d. blue on gold .. 10 10
131. 61. 6d. green on gold .. 15 15
132. A. 9d. purple on gold .. 15 15
133. 61. 1s. 6d. violet on gold .. 20 25
134. A. 2s. green on gold .. 25 30

(b) Air. (i) ½ koula coin. Diameter 2⅛ in.

135. B. 10d. red on gold .. 20 20
136. 61. 11d. green on gold .. 20 20
137. B. 1s. 1d. blue on gold .. 20 20

(ii) 1 koula coin. Diameter 3⅛ in.

138. B. 2s. 1d. purple on gold .. 30 30
139. 61. 2s. 4d. green on gold .. 35 35
140. B. 2s. 9d. violet on gold .. 35 40

DESIGNS: A, Queen Salote (head). B. Queen Salote (full length).

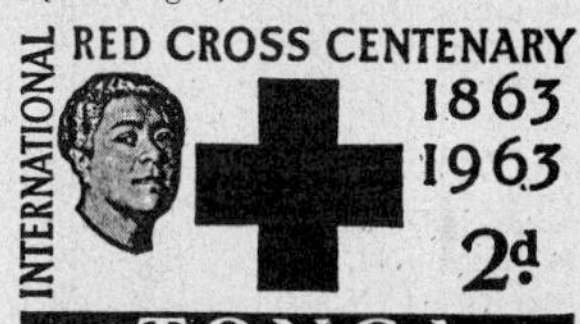

64. Red Cross Emblem.

1963. Centenary of Red Cross.

141. 64. 2d. red and black .. 15 10
142. 11d. red and blue .. 30 40

65. Queen Salote.

66. Map of Tongatapu.

1964. Pan-Pacific South-East Asia Women's Assn. Meeting, Nuku'alofa. T **65/66** backed with paper inscr. overall "TONGA THE FRIENDLY ISLANDS". Imperf.

143. 65. 3d. pink (postage) .. 10 10
144. 9d. blue 10 10
145. 2s. green 20 25
146. 5s. lilac 45 50
147. 66. 10d. turquoise (air) .. 10 10
148. 1s. 2d. black 15 15
149. 3s. 6d. red 30 35
150. 6s. 6d. violet 55 65

1965. "Gold Coin" stamps of 1963 surch. and with star over old value.

151. 61. 1s. 3d. on 1s. 6d. (post.) 15 15
152. A. 1s. 9d. on 9d. .. 15 20
153. 61. 2s. 6d. on 6d. .. 20 35
154. 5s. on 1d. .. .. 14·00 17·00
155. A. 5s. on 2d. .. .. 2·50 3·25
156. 5s. on 2s. 60 75
157. B. 2s. 3d. on 10d. (air) .. 15 25
158. 61. 2s. 9d. on 11d. .. 20 35
159. B. 4s. 6d. on 2s. 1d. .. 10·00 13·00
160. 61. 4s. 6d. on 2s. 4d. .. 10·00 13·00
161. B. 4s. 6d. on 2s. 9d. .. 7·00 8·00

1966. Tupou College and Secondary Education. Cent. Nos. 115/6 and 118/9 optd. or surch. **1866-1966 TUPOU COLLEGE & SECONDARY EDUCATION.**

162. 54. 1d. red and orge. (postage) .. 10 10
163. 3d. on 1d. red and orange 10 10
164. – 6d. on 2d. blue .. 10 10
165. – 1s. 2d. on 2d. blue .. 10 10
166. – 2s. on 2d. blue .. 20 10
167. – 3s. on 2d. blue .. 20 15

As above optd. but with additional **AIRMAIL & CENTENARY.**
168. – 5d. violet (air) 10 10
169. **54.** 10d. on 1d. red & brown 10 10
170. – 1s. brown 10 10
171. – 2s. 9d. on 2d. blue 20 15
172. – 3s. 6d. on 5d. violet .. 25 15
173. – 4s. 6d. on 1s. brown .. 30 15

1966. Queen Salote Commem. "Women's Assn." stamps optd. (a) **IN MEMORIAM QUEEN SALOTE 1900+1965.** (b) **1900 1965**+flower emblem or surch. also. Inscr. and new figures of value in first colour and obliterating shapes in second colour given.

(a) Postage.
174. **65.** 3d. (silver and blue) .. 10 10
175. 5d. on 9d. (silver and black) 10 10
176. 9d. (silver and black) .. 15 10
177. 1s. 7d. on 3d. (silver and blue) 20 15
178. 3s. 6d. on 9d. (silver and black 35 20
179. 6s. 6d. on 3d. (silver and blue) 60 30

(b) Air.
180. **66.** 10d. (silver and black) .. 10 10
181. 1s. 2d. (black and gold) 15 10
182. 4s. on 10d. (silver & black) 40 20
183. 5s. 6d. on 1s. 2d. (black and gold) .. 55 30
184. 10s. 6d. on 1s. 2d. (gold and black) 75 45

1967. Various stamps surch. **SENITI** or **Seniti** and value.

(a) Postage.
185 1s. on 1d. (No. 101) .. 10 10
186 2s. on 4d. (No. 106) .. 10 10
230 3s. on 3d. (No. 104) .. 10 10
187 3s. on 5d. (No. 107) .. 10 10
231 4s. on 5d. (No. 107) .. 10 10
232 5s. on 2d. (No. 108) .. 10 10
189 5s. on 3½d. (No. 105) .. 10 10
233 6s. on 6d. (No. 108) .. 10 10
190 6s. on 8d. (No. 109) .. 10 10
191 7s. on 1½d. (No. 102) .. 10 10
192 8s. on 6d. (No. 108) .. 10 10
235 8s. on 8d. (No. 109) .. 10 10
193 9s. on 3d. (No. 104) .. 15 15
236 9s. on 3½d. (No. 105) .. 20 20
194 10s on 1s. (No. 110) .. 15 15
195 11s. on 3d. on 1d. (No. 163) 15 20
238 20s. on 5s. (No. 112) .. 40 40
196 21s. on 3s. on 2d. (No. 167) 25 35
197 23s on 1d. (No. 101) .. 25 35
198 30s. on 2s. (No. 111) .. 1·25 1·75
199 30s. on 2s. (No. 111) .. 1·50 2·00
200 50s. on 6d. (No. 108) .. 85 1·25
201 60s. on 2d (No. 103) .. 1·25 1·75
239 2p. on 2s. (No. 111) .. 1·50 1·50

(b) Air. Surch. with **AIRMAIL** added.
240. 11s. on 10s. (No. 113) .. 25 25
241. 21s. on 10s. (No. 113) .. 40 40
242. 23s. on 10s. (No. 113) .. 40 40

74. Coat of Arms (reverse).

1967. Coronation of King Taufa'ahau IV. Circular designs, backed with paper inscr. overall "TONGA, THE FRIENDLY ISLANDS" etc. Imperf.

Sizes:
(a) Diameter 1½ in. (d) Diameter 2 3/10 in.
(b) Diameter 1 7/10 in. (e) Diameter 2 7/10 in.
(c) Diameter 2 in. (f) Diameter 2 6/10 in.

202. **74.** 1 s. orge. & bl. (b) (post.) 10 10
203. A. 2 s. blue and mauve (c) 10 10
204. **74.** 4 s. green and purple (d) 10 10
205. A. 15 s. turq. & violet (e) .. 25 25
206. **74.** 28 s. black & purple (a) 50 50
207. A. 50 s. red and blue (c) .. 85 85
208. **74.** 1 p. blue and red (f) .. 1·50 1·75
209. A. 7 s. red & black (b) (air) 10 10
210. **74.** 9 s. purple and green (c) 10 10
211. A. 11 s. blue & orange (d) 15 15
212. **74.** 21 s. black and green (e) 30 30
213. A. 23 s. purple and green (a) 40 40
214. **74.** 29 s. blue and green (c) 50 50
215. A. 2 p. purple & orge. (f) .. 2·00 2·25
DESIGN: A King Taufa'ahau IV (obverse).

The commemorative coins depicted in reverse (type **74**) are inscribed in various denominations as follows: 1 s. – "20 SENITI"; 4 s. – "PA'ANGA"; 9 s. – "50 SENITI"; 21 s. – "TWO PA'ANGA"; 28 s. – "QUARTER HAU"; 29 s. "HALF HAU"; 1 p. "HAU".

1967. Arrival of U.S. Peace Corps in Tonga. As Nos. 101/13 but imperf. in different colours and surch. **The Friendly Islands welcome the United States Peace Corps** and new value (or $ only).
216. 1 s. on 1d. black & yellow (postage) 10 10
217. 2 s. on 2d. blue and red .. 10 10
218. 3 s. on 3d. brown & yellow 10 10
219. 4 s. on 4d. violet & yellow 10 10
220. 5 s. on 5d. green and yellow 10 10
221. 10 s. on 1s. red and yellow 10 10
222. 20 s. on 2s. red and blue .. 15 15
223. 50 s. on 5s. sepia and yellow 30 35
224. 1 p. on 10s. yellow .. 50 55
225. 11 s. on 3½d. blue (air) .. 10 10
226. 21 s. on 1½d. green .. 20 20
227. 23 s. on 3½d. blue .. 20 20

1968. 50th Birthday of King Taufa'ahua IV. Nos. 202/15 optd. **H.M.'s BIRTHDAY 4 JULY 1968.**
243. **74.** 1 s. orange and blue (post.) 10 10
244. A. 2 s. blue and mauve .. 10 10
245. **74.** 4 s. green and purple .. 10 10
246. A. 15 s. turquoise & violet 25 15
247. **74.** 28 s. black and purple .. 55 30
248. A. 50 s. red and blue .. 1·00 70
249. **74.** 1 p. blue and red .. 2·25 1·75
250. A. 7 s. red and black (air) .. 10 10
251. **74.** 9 s. purple and green .. 15 10
252. A. 11 s. blue and orange .. 15 10
253. **74.** 21 s. black and green .. 40 25
254. A. 23 s. purple and green .. 40 25
255. **74.** 29 s. blue and green .. 65 35
256. A. 2 p. purple and orange .. 4·50 3·00

1968. South Pacific Games Field and Track Trials. Port Moresby, New Guinea. As Nos. 101/13 surch. **Friendly Islands Field & Track Trials South Pacific Games, Port Moresby 1969** and value.
257. 5 s. on 5d. grn. & yell. (post.) 10 10
258. 10 s. on 1s. red and yellow 10 10
259. 15 s. on 2s. red and blue .. 15 15
260. 25s. on 2d. blue and red .. 15 15
261. 50 s. on 1d. black & yellow 30 30
262. 75 s. on 10s. orge. & yellow 45 45
263. 6 s. on 6d. blk. & yell. (air) 10 10
264. 7 s. on 4d. violet & yellow 10 10
265. 8 s. on 8d. black & yellow 10 10
266. 9 s. on 1½d. green .. 10 10
267. 11 s. on 3d. brown & yellow 10 10
268. 21 s. on 3½d. blue .. 15 15
269. 38 s. on 5s. sepia and yellow 20 20
270. 1 p. on 10s. yellow .. 50 50

1969. Emergency Provisionals. Various stamps (Nos. 273/6 are imperf. and in different colours), surch. (a) Postage.
271. 1 s. on 1s. 2d. blue (No. 165) .. .. .. 1·25 1·00
272. 1 s. on 2s. on 2d. blue (No. 166) .. .. .. 1·25 1·00
273. 1 s. on 6d. black and yellow (No. 108) 40 30
274. 2 s. on 3½d. blue (No. 105) 45 30
275. 3 s. on 1½d. green (No. 102) 45 30
276. 4 s. on 8d. black and yellow (No. 109) 70 50

(b) Air. Nos. 171/3 surch.
277. 1 s. on 2s. 9d. on 2d. blue 1·25 1·00
278. 1 s. on 3s. 6d. on 5d. violet 1·25 1·00
279. 1 s. on 4s. 6d. on 1s. brown 1·25 1·00

83. Banana.

1969. Coil stamps. Self-adhesive.
280. **83.** 1 s. red, black & yellow 50 50
281. 2 s. green, black & yellow 60 60
282. 3 s. violet, black & yellow 70 70
283. 4 s. blue, black & yellow 80 80
284. 5 s. green, black & yell. 90 90
See also Nos. 325/9, 413/17, 657/89, O 45/9, O 82/6 and O 169/83.

84. Putting the Shot.

1969. 3rd South Pacific Games, Port Moresby. Imperf., Self-adhesive.
285. **84.** 1 s. blk., red & buff (post.) 10 10
286. 3 s. green, red and buff .. 10 10
287. 6 s. blue, red and buff .. 10 10
288. 10s. violet, red & buff .. 10 10
289. 30 s. blue, red and buff .. 15 20
290. – 9 s. black, violet and orange (air) 10 10
291. – 11 s. black, blue, & orge. 10 10
292. – 20 s. blk., grn. & orange 15 15
293. – 60 s. black, red & orge. 45 55
294. – 1 p. black, green & orge. 70 80
DESIGN: Nos. 290/4, Boxing.

86. Oil Derrick and Map.

1969. Oil Search. Imperf. Self-adhesive.
295. **86.** 3 s. multicoloured (post.) 10 10
296. 7 s. multicoloured .. 15 15
297. 20 s. multicoloured .. 40 40
298. 25 s. multicoloured .. 45 45
299. 35 s. multicoloured .. 70 70
300. – 9 s. multicoloured (air) 20 20
301. – 10 s. multicoloured .. 20 20
302. – 24 s. multicoloured .. 45 45
303. – 29 s. multicoloured .. 50 50
304. – 38 s. multicoloured .. 70 70
DESIGN: Nos. 300/4, Oil Derrick and island of Tongatapu.

87. Members of the British and Tongan Royal Families.
(Reduced size illustration. Actual size 54 × 49 mm.)

1970. Royal Visit. Imperf., Self-adhesive.
305. **87.** 3 s. multicoloured (postage) 20 10
306. 5 s. multicoloured .. 25 10
307. 10 s. multicoloured .. 40 20
308. 25 s. multicoloured .. 1·00 65
309. 50 s. multicoloured .. 1·75 1·25
310. – 7 s. multicoloured (air) 35 15
311. – 9 s. multicoloured .. 40 20
312. – 24 s. multicoloured .. 1·00 65
313. – 29 s. multicoloured .. 1·25 70
314. – 38 s. multicoloured .. 1·50 90
DESIGN: Nos. 310/14, Queen Elizabeth II and King Taufu'aha Tupou IV.

89. Book, Tongan Rulers and Flag.
(Reduced size illustration. Actual size 69 × 38 mm.)

1970. Entry into British Commonwealth. Imperf. Self-adhesive.
315. **89.** 3 s. multicoloured (post.) 10 10
316. 7 s. multicoloured .. 15 15
317. 15 s. multicoloured .. 25 20
318. 25 s. multicoloured .. 35 25
319. 50 s. multicoloured .. 60 50
320. – 9 s. blue, gold & red (air) 15 15
321. – 10 s. pur., gold & blue 15 15
322. – 24 s. yell., gold & green 35 30
323. – 29 s. blue, gold and red 40 30
324. – 38 s. yell., gold & green 50 40
DESIGN: ("Star" shape. Size 44×51 mm.). Nos. 320/24, Star and King Taufa'ahua Tupou IV.

90. Coconut.

1970. Coil stamps. Imperf. Self-adhesive.
(a) As T **83** but colours changed.
325. **83.** 1 s. yell., pur. and black 25 25
326. 2 s. yellow, blue & black 35 35
327. 3 s. yellow, brn. & blk. 35 35
328. 4 s. yell., green & black 35 35
329. 5 s. yell., red and black 40 40
(b) Multicoloured; colour of face values given.
330. **90.** 6 s. red 50 50
331. 7 s. purple 55 55
332. 8 s. violet 65 65
333. 9 s. green 75 75
334. 10 s. orange 75 75

91. "Red Cross".

1970. Centenary of British Red Cross. Imperf. Self-adhesive.
335. **91.** 3 s. red, black & green (postage) 10 10
336. 7 s. red, black and blue 15 15
337. 15 s. red, black & pur. 40 40
338. 25 s. red, black & blue 70 70
339. 75 s. red, black & brown 4·00 4·00
340. – 9 s. red and turq. (air) 20 20
341. – 10 s. red and purple .. 20 20
342. – 18 s. red and green .. 50 50
343. – 38 s. red and blue .. 2·00 2·00
344. – 1 p. red and silver .. 5·00 5·00
DESIGN: As Type **91.** Nos. 340/4 as Nos. 335/9 but with inscription rearranged and coat of arms omitted.

1971. 5th Death Anniv. of Queen Salote. Nos. 174/80, 182/4 with part of old surch. obliterated and further surch, **1965† 1970** and value in seniti. On air values the surch. includes two laurel leaves.
345. **65.** 2 s. on 5d. on 9d. (post.) 10 10
346. 3 s. on 9d. 10 10
347. 5 s. on 3d. 15 15
348. 15 s. on 3s. 6d. on 9d. .. 60 35
349. 25 s. on 6s. 6d. on 3d. .. 1·00 65
350. 50 s. on 1s. 7d. on 3d. .. 2·00 1·25
351. **66.** 9 s. on 10d. (air) .. 40 20
352. 24 s. on 4s. on 10d. .. 1·00 60
353. 29 s. on 5s. 6d. on 1s. 2d. 1·25 80
354. 38 s. on 10s. 6d. on 1s. 2d. 1·75 1·00

1971. Philatokyo '71 Stamp Exhib., Japan. As Nos. 101, etc., but imperf. with colours changed and surch **PHILATOKYO '71,** emblem and value or **HONOURING JAPANESE POSTAL CENTENARY 1871-1971** (Nos. 357, 362, 364) Nos. 360/4 also surch. **AIRMAIL.**
355. 3 s. on 8d. blk. & yell. (postage) 10 10
356. 7 s. on 4d. violet and yellow 10 10
357. 15 s. on 1s. red and yellow 20 20
358. 25 s. on 1d. black & yellow 30 30
359. 75 s. on 2s. red and blue .. 1·00 85
360. 9 s. on 1½d. green (air) .. 10 10
361. 10 s. on 4d. violet & yellow 10 10
362. 18 s. on 1s. red and yellow 20 20
363. 38 s. on 1d. black & yellow 40 40
364. 1 p. on 2s. red and blue .. 1·25 1·00

96. Wristwatch.

1971. Air. Imperf. Self-adhesive.
365. **96.** 14 s. multicoloured .. 75 75
365a. 17 s. multicoloured .. 85 85
366. 21 s. multicoloured .. 1·00 1·00
366a. 38 s. multicoloured .. 1·60 1·60
See also Nos. 065/6a.

97. Pole-vaulter.

1971. 4th South Pacific Games, Tahiti. Imperf. Self-adhesive.
367. **97.** 3 s. multicoloured (postage) 10 10
368. 7 s. multicoloured .. 10 10
369. 15 s. multicoloured .. 20 20
370. 25 s. multicoloured .. 30 35
371. 50 s. multicoloured .. 50 70
372. – 9 s. multicoloured (air) 10 10
373. – 10 s. multicoloured .. 10 10
374. – 24 s. multicoloured .. 30 35
375. – 29 s. multicoloured .. 40 50
376. – 38 s. multicoloured .. 45 60
DESIGN—HORIZ. Nos. 372/6 High-jumper.

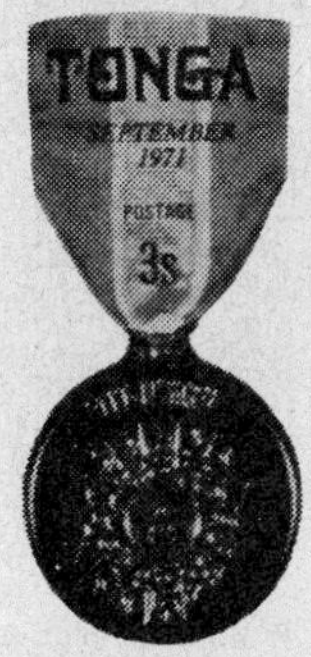

98. Medal of Merit (reverse).

1971. Investiture of Royal Tongan Medal of Merit. Multicoloured, colour of medal given. Imperf. Self-adhesive.
377. **98.** 3 s. gold (postage) .. 10 10
378. 24 s. silver 25 25
379. – 38 s. brown 40 40
380. – 10 s. gold (air) 15 15
381. – 75 s. silver 80 80
382. **98.** 1 p. brown 95 95
DESIGN—As Type **98.** Nos. 379/81, Obverse of the Medal of Merit.

1971. 25th Anniv. of U.N.I.C.E.F. Imperf. Self-adhesive.
383. **99.** 2 s. multicoloured (postage) 10 10
384. 4 s. multicoloured .. 10 10
385. 8 s. multicoloured .. 10 10
386. 16 s. multicoloured .. 25 25
387. 30 s. multicoloured .. 40 40
388. – 10 s. multicoloured (air) 15 15
389. – 15 s. multicoloured .. 25 25
390. – 25 s. multicoloured .. 40 40
391. – 50 s. multicoloured .. 75 75
392. – 1 p. multicoloured .. 1·50 1·50
DESIGN—VERT. (21 × 42 mm.). Nos. 388/92. Woman.

100. Map of South Pacific, and " Olovaha ". (Illustration reduced. Actual size 53 × 47 mm.)

1972. Merchant Marine Routes. Imperf. Self-adhesive.
393. **100.** 2 s. mult. (postage) .. 15 10
394. 10 s. multicoloured .. 40 10
395. 17 s. multicoloured .. 60 25
396. 21 s. multicoloured .. 70 35
397. 60 s. multicoloured .. 3·00 1·75
398. – 9 s. mult. (air) .. 40 10
399. – 12 s. multicoloured .. 50 15
400. – 14 s. multicoloured .. 60 15
401. – 75 s. multicoloured .. 3·25 2·00
402. – 90 s. multicoloured .. 3·75 3·00
DESIGN: Nos. 398/402, Map of South Pacific, and " Niuvakai ".

101. ½ Hau Coronation Coin. (Illustration reduced. Actual size 60 × 40 mm.)

1972. 5th Anniv. of Coronation. Imperf. Self-adhesive.
403. **101.** 5 s. multicoloured (post.) 10 10
404. 7 s. multicoloured .. 10 10
405. 10 s. multicoloured .. 15 10
406. 17 s. multicoloured .. 25 15
407. 60 s. multicoloured .. 85 40
408. – 9 s. multicoloured (air) 15 10
409. – 12 s. multicoloured .. 20 10
410. – 14 s. multicoloured .. 25 15
411. – 21 s. multicoloured .. 30 15
412. – 75 s. multicoloured .. 1·10 45
DESIGNS—(47 × 41 mm). Nos. 408/12. As T **101**, but with coins above inscription instead of beneath it.

102. Water Melon.

1972. Imperf. Self-adhesive.
(a) As T **83**, but inscription altered, omitting " Best in the Pacific ", and colours changed.
413. **83.** 1 s. yellow, red & black 20 10
414. 2 s. yellow, blue & black 25 15
415. 3 s. yellow, green & blk. 30 20
416. 4 s. yellow, blue & black 30 20
417. 5 s. yellow, brown & blk. 30 20
(b) As T **90** but colours changed. Multicoloured. Colour of face-value given.
418. **90.** 6 s. orange 35 20
419. 7 s. blue 40 25
420. 8 s. purple 40 25
421. 9 s. orange 40 25
422. 10 s. blue 50 30
(c) Type **102.** Multicoloured. Colour of face-value given.
423. **102.** 15 s. blue 85 45
424. 20 s. orange .. .. 1·00 60
425. 25 s. brown .. .. 1·10 70
426. 40 s. orange .. .. 2·25 1·50
427. 50 s. lemon .. .. 2·50 1·75

1972. Inaug. of Int. Airmail. No. 398 surch. **NOVEMBER 1972 INAUGURAL Internal Airmail Nuku'alofa – Vava'u** and value.
428. 7 s. on 9 s. multicoloured .. 1·40 2·25

104. Hoisting Tongan Flag. (Illustration reduced. Actual size 60 × 41 mm.)

1972. Proclamation of Sovereignty over Minerva Reefs. Imperf. Self-adhesive.
429. **104.** 5 s. multicoloured (post.) 10 10
430. 7 s. multicoloured .. 10 10
431. 10 s. multicoloured .. 15 10
432. 15 s. multicoloured .. 25 20
433. 40 s. multicoloured .. 80 50
434. – 9 s. multicoloured (air) 15 10
435. – 12 s. multicoloured .. 20 10
436. – 14 s. multicoloured .. 25 15
437. – 38 s. multicoloured .. 75 55
438. – 1 p. multicoloured .. 2·00 1·50
DESIGN—SPHERICAL (52 mm. diameter). Nos. 434/8, Proclamation in Govt. Gazette.

105. Coins around Bank. (Illustration reduced. Actual size 53 × 48 mm.)

1973. Bank of Tonga. Foundation. Imperf. Self-adhesive.
439. **105.** 5 s. multicoloured (post.) 10 10
440. 7 s. multicoloured .. 10 10
441. 10 s. multicoloured .. 15 10
442. 20 s. multicoloured .. 35 20
443. 30 s. multicoloured .. 45 30
444. – 9 s. multicoloured (air) 20 10
445. – 12 s. multicoloured .. 20 10
446. – 17 s. multicoloured .. 30 15
447. – 50 s. multicoloured .. 1·00 55
448. – 90 s. multicoloured .. 2·00 1·40
DESIGN—HORIZ. (64 × 52 mm.). Nos. 444/8, Bank and banknotes.

106. Handshake and Scout in Outrigger Canoe. (Illustration reduced. Actual size 61 × 43 mm.)

1973. Silver Jubilee of Scouting in Tonga. Imperf. Self-adhesive.
449. **106.** 5 s. multicoloured (post.) 20 10
450. 7 s. multicoloured .. 30 15
451. 15 s. multicoloured .. 95 40
452. 21 s. multicoloured .. 1·25 50
453. 50 s. multicoloured .. 4·50 2·00
454. – 9 s. multicoloured (air) 50 20
455. – 12 s. multicoloured .. 60 30
456. – 14 s. multicoloured .. 85 50
457. – 17 s. multicoloured .. 95 60
458. – 1 p. multicoloured .. 15·00 6·00
DESIGN—SQUARE (53 × 53 mm.). Nos. 454/8, Scout badge.

107. Excerpt from Cook's Log-book. (Illustration reduced. Actual size 69 × 38 mm.)

1973. Bicentenary of Capt. Cook's Visit to Tonga. Imperf. Self-adhesive.
459. **107.** 6 s. multicoloured (post.) 40 30
460. 8 s. multicoloured .. 40 35
461. 11 s. multicoloured .. 60 40
462. 35 s. multicoloured .. 4·00 1·90
463. 40 s. multicoloured .. 4·00 1·90
464. – 9 s. multicoloured (air) 70 30
465. – 14 s. multicoloured .. 1·25 40
466. – 29 s. multicoloured .. 4·00 1·75
467. – 38 s. multicoloured .. 4·50 2·00
468. – 75 s. multicoloured .. 8·50 3·50
DESIGNS—VERT. Nos. 464/8, H.M.S. "Resolution".

1973. Commonwealth Games, Christchurch. Various stamps optd. **COMMONWEALTH GAMES CHRISTCHURCH 1974** and No. 474 is optd. **AIRMAIL** in addition.
469. **97.** 5 s. on 50 s. multicoloured (No. 371) (post.) 15 10
470. – 12 s. on 38 s. multicoloured (No. 379) .. 30 15
471. – 14 s. on 75 s. multicoloured (No. 381) .. 30 15
472. **98.** 20 s. on 1 p. multicoloured (No. 382) .. 50 30
473. 50 s. on 24 s. multicoloured (No. 378) .. 1·25 75
474. **97.** 7 s. on 25 s. multicoloured (No. 370) (air) .. 15 10
475. – 9 s. on 38 s. multicoloured (No. 376) .. 20 10
476. – 24 s. multicoloured (No. 374) 60 30
477. – 29 s. on 9s. multicoloured (No. 454) 70 40
478. – 40 s. on 14 s. multicoloured (No. 456) .. 1·00 70

109. Red Shining Parrot

1974. Air. Imperf. Self-adhesive.
479. **109.** 7 s. multicoloured .. 50 20
480. 9 s. multicoloured .. 55 25
481. 12 s. multicoloured .. 60 30
482. 14 s. multicoloured .. 65 35
483. 17 s. multicoloured .. 75 50
484. 29 s. multicoloured .. 1·25 80
485. 38 s. multicoloured .. 1·75 1·00
486. 50 s. multicoloured .. 2·25 2·25
487. 75 s. multicoloured .. 3·00 3·00

110. "Stamped Letter".

1974. Centenary of U.P.U. Imperf. self-adhesive.
488. **110.** 5 s. mult. (postage) .. 10 10
489. 10 s. multicoloured .. 15 10
490. 15 s. multicoloured .. 25 15
491. 20 s. multicoloured .. 30 25
492. 50 s. multicoloured .. 1·25 1·00
493. – 14 s. multicoloured (air) 25 15
494. – 21 s. multicoloured .. 35 30
495. – 60 s. multicoloured .. 1·40 1·00
496. – 75 s. multicoloured .. 1·60 1·10
497. – 1 p. multicoloured .. 1·90 1·50
DESIGNS—HORIZ. Nos. 493/7, Carrier pigeon scattering letters over Tonga.

111. Girl Guides Badges.

1974. Tongan Girl Guides. Imperf. Self-adhesive.
498. **111.** 5 s. mult. (postage) .. 40 10
499. 10 s. multicoloured .. 60 20
500. 20 s. multicoloured .. 1·50 55
501. 40 s. multicoloured .. 3·25 1·25
502. 60 s. multicoloured .. 4·00 2·00
503. – 14 s. multicoloured (air) 1·00 35
504. – 16 s. multicoloured .. 1·00 35
505. – 29 s. multicoloured .. 2·00 80
506. – 31 s. multicoloured .. 2·25 90
507. – 75 s. multicoloured .. 5·50 2·50
DESIGNS—VERT. Nos. 503/7, Girl Guide leaders.

112. H.M.S. "Resolution".

1974. Establishment of Royal Marine Institute. Imperf. Self-adhesive.

508. **112.** 5 s. mult. (postage) .. 55 20
509. 10 s. multicoloured .. 75 25
510. 25 s. multicoloured .. 1·40 70
511. 50 s. multicoloured .. 2·50 2·00
512. 75 s. multicoloured .. 3·50 2·75
513. – 9 s. multicoloured (air) 90 25
514. – 14 s. multicoloured .. 1·25 40
515. – 17 s. multicoloured .. 1·40 50
516. – 60 s. multicoloured .. 3·50 2·50
517. – 90 s. multicoloured .. 5·00 3·75

DESIGNS—HORIZ. (53×47 mm.). Nos. 513/17, "James Cook" (bulk carrier).

113. Dateline Hotel, Nuku'alofa.
(Illustration reduced. Actual size 60×38 mm.)

1975. South Pacific Forum and Tourism. Imperf. Self-adhesive.

518. **113.** 5 s. multicoloured (postage) 10 10
519. 10 s. multicoloured .. 10 10
520. 15 s. multicoloured .. 20 20
521. 30 s. multicoloured .. 45 45
522. 1 p. multicoloured .. 1·60 1·50
523. – 9 s. multicoloured (air) 10 10
524. – 12 s. multicoloured .. 15 15
525. – 14 s. multicoloured .. 20 20
526. – 17 s. multicoloured .. 20 20
527. – 38 s. multicoloured .. 55 55

DESIGNS (46×60 mm.): 9, 12, 14 s. Beach. 17, 38 s. Surf and sea.

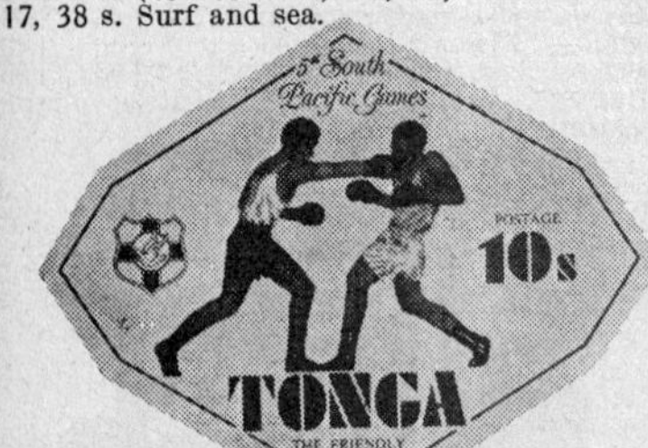

114. Boxing.
(Illustration reduced. Actual size 60×47 mm.)

1975. 5th South Pacific Games, Guam. Imperf. Self-adhesive.

528. **114.** 5s. multicoloured (post.) 10 10
529. 10 s. multicoloured .. 15 10
530. 20 s. multicoloured .. 25 20
531. 25 s. multicoloured .. 30 25
532. 65 s. multicoloured .. 70 75
533. – 9 s. multicoloured (air) 15 10
534. – 12 s. multicoloured .. 20 15
535. – 14 s. multicoloured .. 20 15
536. – 17 s. multicoloured .. 25 20
537. – 90 s. multicoloured .. 90 90

DESIGN: (37×43 mm.): Nos. 533/7, Throwing the discus.

115. Commemorative Coin.

1975. F.A.O. Commemoration. Imperf. Self-adhesive.

538. **115.** 5 s. mult. (postage) .. 10 10
539. – 20 s. multicoloured .. 30 15
540. – 50 s. blue, black & silver 65 35
541. – 1 p. blue, black & silver 1·25 1·00
542. – 2 p. black and silver .. 2·25 2·00
543. – 12 s. multicoloured (air) 25 15
544. – 14 s. multicoloured .. 25 15
545. – 25 s. red, black & silver 35 20
546. – 50 s. pur., black & silver 60 40
547. – 1 p. black and silver .. 1·25 1·00

DESIGNS: Nos. 539/47 are as T 52 but showing different coins. Nos. 542 and 544 are horiz., size 75×42 mm.

116. Commemorative Coin.
(Illustration reduced. Actual size 58×58 mm.)

1975. Centenary of Tongan Constitution. Multicoloured. Imperf. Self-adhesive.

548. 5 s. Type **116** (postage) .. 10 10
549. 10 s. King George I .. 15 10
550. 20 s. King Taufa'ahau IV 30 20
551. 50 s. King George II .. 60 35
552. 75 s. Tongan arms .. 1·00 80
553. 9 s. King Taufa'ahau IV (air) 15 10
554. 12 s. Queen Salote .. 20 10
555. 14 s. Tongan arms .. 20 10
556. 38 s. King Taufa'ahau IV 40 25
557. 1 p. Four monarchs .. 1·25 1·00

SIZES: 60×40 mm., Nos. 549 and 551. 76×76 mm., Nos. 552 and 557. 57×56 mm., others.

117. Montreal Logo.

1976. First Participation in Olympic Games. Imperf. Self-adhesive.

(a). Type **117**.

558. 5 s. red, blk. & blue (postage) 15 10
559. 10 s. red, black and green 25 10
560. 25 s. red, black and brown 75 35
561. 35 s. red, black and mauve 85 40
562. 70 s. red, black and green 2·25 90

(b). Montreal logo optd. on Nos. 500/1, 504, 507.

563. **111.** 12 s. on 20 s. multicoloured (air) 30 15
564. – 14 s. on 16 s. mult. .. 30 15
565. – 16 s. multicoloured .. 35 15
566. **111.** 38 s. on 40 s. mult. .. 1·25 45
567. – 75 s. multicoloured .. 2·50 95

118. Signatories of Declaration of Independence.

1976. Bicentenary of American Revolution. Imperf. Self-adhesive.

568. **118.** 9 s. multicoloured (postage) 40 15
569. – 10 s. multicoloured .. 40 15
570. – 15 s. multicoloured .. 70 35
571. – 25 s. multicoloured .. 1·25 60
572. – 75 s. multicoloured .. 3·75 1·75
573. – 12 s. multicoloured (air) 50 15
574. – 14 s. multicoloured .. 60 20
575. – 17 s. multicoloured .. 80 35
576. – 38 s. multicoloured .. 1·90 75
577. – 1 p. multicoloured .. 4·50 2·00

DESIGNS: Nos. 569/77 show the signatories to the Declaration of Independence.

119. Nathaniel Turner and John Thomas (Methodist Missionaries).

1976. 150th Anniv. of Christianity in Tonga. Imperf. Self-adhesive.

578. **119.** 5 s. mult. (postage) .. 20 15
579. 10 s. multicoloured .. 30 25
580. 20 s. multicoloured .. 50 40
581. 25 s. multicoloured .. 55 45
582. 85 s. multicoloured .. 2·25 1·90
583. – 9 s. multicoloured (air) 30 25
584. – 12 s. multicoloured .. 35 30
585. – 14 s. multicoloured .. 40 35
586. – 17 s. multicoloured .. 50 40
587. – 38 s. multicoloured .. 1·25 1·00

DESIGNS: Nos. 583/7 show Missionary Ship "Triton".

120. Emperor Wilhelm I and King George Tupou I.

1976. Centenary of Treaty of Friendship with Germany. Imperf. Self-adhesive.

588. **120.** 9 s. mult. (postage) .. 20 20
589. 15 s. multicoloured .. 30 30
590. 22 s. multicoloured .. 40 45
591. 50 s. multicoloured .. 90 1·10
592. 73 s. multicoloured .. 1·40 1·60
593. – 11 s. multicoloured (air) 25 25
594. – 17 s. multicoloured .. 40 45
595. – 18 s. multicoloured .. 40 45
596. – 31 s. multicoloured .. 60 70
597. – 39 s. multicoloured .. 70 80

DESIGNS—CIRCULAR: (52 mm. diameter). Nos. 593/7 show Treaty signing.

121. Queen Salote and Coronation Procession.

1977. Silver Jubilee. Imperf. Self-adhesive.

598. **121.** 11 s. mult. (postage) .. 1·50 30
599. 20 s. multicoloured .. 75 30
600. 30 s. multicoloured .. 1·00 30
601. 50 s. multicoloured .. 1·75 65
602. 75 s. multicoloured .. 2·25 85
603. – 15 s. multicoloured (air) 80 25
604. – 17 s. multicoloured .. 90 30
605. – 22 s. multicoloured .. 12·00 1·75
606. – 31 s. multicoloured .. 90 40
607. – 39 s. multicoloured .. 95 40

DESIGN—SQUARE: (59×59 mm.). Nos. 603/7 show Queen Elizabeth and King Taufa'ahau.

HAVE YOU READ THE NOTES AT THE BEGINNING OF THIS CATALOGUE?

These often provide answers to the enquiries we receive.

122. Tongan Coins.
(Illustration reduced. Actual size 53×48 mm.)

1977. 10th Anniv. of King's Coronation. Imperf. Self-adhesive.

608. **122.** 10 s. mult. (postage) .. 20 20
609. 15 s. multicoloured .. 25 25
610. 25 s. multicoloured .. 35 45
611. 50 s. multicoloured .. 75 85
612. 75 s. multicoloured .. 1·00 1·25
613. – 11 s. multicoloured (air) 25 20
614. – 17 s. multicoloured .. 30 30
615. – 18 s. multicoloured .. 30 30
616. – 39 s. multicoloured .. 45 55
617. – 1 p. multicoloured .. 1·50 1·75

DESIGN—OVAL: (64×46 mm.). Nos. 613/17 show 1967 Coronation Coin.

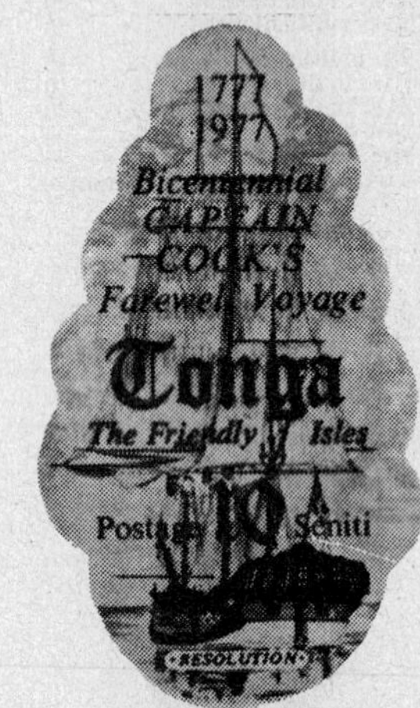

123. H.M.S. "Resolution".

1977. Bicentenary of Capt. Cook's Last Voyage. Imperf. Self-adhesive.

618. **123.** 10 s. mult. (postage) .. 1·75 75
619. 17 s. multicoloured .. 2·25 1·10
620. 25 s. multicoloured .. 3·75 2·00
621. 30 s. multicoloured .. 3·75 2·50
622. 40 s. multicoloured .. 4·50 4·00
623. – 15 s. multicoloured (air) 1·75 1·25
624. – 22 s. multicoloured .. 2·75 2·25
625. – 31 s. multicoloured .. 3·25 2·50
626. – 50 s. multicoloured .. 4·50 4·25
627. – 1 p. multicoloured .. 8·00 8·00

DESIGN: (52×46 mm.) Nos. 623/7 show Coin and extract from Cook's Journal.

124. Humpback Whale.
(Illustration reduced. Actual size 55×29 mm.)

1977. Whale Conservation. Imperf. Self-adhesive.

628. **124.** 15 s. black, grey and blue (postage) .. .. 1·25 50
629. 22 s. blk., grey and grn. 1·50 80
630. 31 s. blk., grey & orange 2·00 1·00
631. 38 s. blk., grey and lilac 2·25 1·50
632. 64 s. blk., grey and brn. 3·75 2·50
633. – 11 s. multicoloured (air) 1·25 40
634. – 17 s. multicoloured .. 1·50 60
635. – 18 s. multicoloured .. 1·50 70
636. – 39 s. multicoloured .. 2·25 1·50
637. – 50 s. multicoloured .. 3·00 2·00

DESIGN—HEXAGONAL: (66×51 mm.). Nos. 633/7 show Sei and Fin Whales.

1978. Various stamps surch.

638. **115.** 15 s. on 5 s. mult. (post.) 1·00 1·60
639. **119.** 15 s. on 5 s. mult. .. 1·00 1·60
640. **117.** 15 s. on 10 s. red, black and green .. .. 1·00 1·60
641. **119.** 15 s. on 10 s. mult. .. 1·00 1·60
642. **121.** 15 s. on 11 s. mult. .. 3·00 3·50
643. **114.** 15 s. on 20 s. mult. .. 1·00 1·60
644. – 15 s. on 38 s. mult. (No. O 133) .. .. 1·00 1·60
645. – 17 s. on 9 s. mult. (No. 533) (air) .. .. 1·00 1·60
646. – 17 s. on 9 s. mult. (No. 583) .. .. .. 1·00 1·60
647. – 17 s. on 12 s. mult. (No. 534) .. .. .. 1·00 1·60
648. – 17 s. on 12 s. mult. (No. 573) .. .. .. 1·00 1·60
649. – 17 s. on 18 s. mult. (No. 595) .. .. .. 1·00 1·60

650. – 17 s. on 38 s. mult. (No. 527) .. .. 1·00 1·60
651. – 17 s. on 38 s. mult. (No. 556) .. .. .. 1·00 1·60
652. – 1 p. on 35 s. mult. (No. O 151) .. .. 24·00 24·00
653. – 1 p. on 38 s. mult. (No. 576) .. .. .. 6·50 8·50
654. – 1 p. on 75 s. mult. (No. 572) .. .. .. 6·50 8·50

The surcharges on Nos. 638/9 are formed by adding a " 1 " to the existing face value.

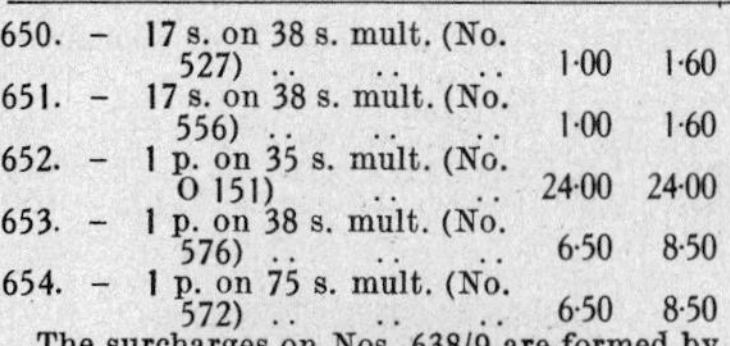

126. Flags of Canada and Tonga.

1978. 11th Commonwealth Games, Edmonton. Imperf. Self-adhesive.
655.**126.** 10 s. blue, red and black (postage) 15 15
656. 15 s. multicoloured .. 25 25
657. 20 s. green, black & red 35 35
658. 25 s. red, blue and black 40 40
659. 45 s. black and red .. 90 1·00
660. – 17 s. black and red (air) 30 30
661. – 35 s. black, red and blue 60 65
662. – 38 s. black, red & green 75 85
663. – 40 s. black, red & green 80 90
664. – 65 s. black, red & brown 1·40 1·60
DESIGN—LEAF-SHAPED (39×40 mm.). Nos. 660/664, Maple Leaf.

127. King Taufa'ahau Tupou IV.

1978. 60th Birthday of King Taufa'ahau Tupou IV. Imperf. Self-adhesive.
665.**127.** 2 s. black, deep blue and pale blue (postage).. 10 10
666. 5 s. black, blue and pink 10 10
667. 10 s. blk., blue & mauve 20 20
668. 25 s. black, blue & grey 45 35
669. 75 s. black, blue & yell. 1·10 1·00
670. – 11 s. black, blue and yellow (air) 20 20
671. – 15 s. black, blue & brn. 30 25
672. – 17 s. black, blue & lilac 35 25
673. – 39 s. black, blue & green 60 55
674. – 1 p. black, blue & pink 1·75 1·40
DESIGNS—STAR-SHAPED (44×51 mm.). Nos. 670/674, Portrait of King.

128. Bananas.

1978. Coil Stamps. Imperf. Self-adhesive.
675.**128.** 1 s. black and yellow .. 10 10
676. – 2 s. blue and yellow .. 15 15
677. – 3 s. brown and yellow .. 20 20
678. – 4 s. blue and yellow .. 20 20
679. – 5 s. red and yellow .. 20 20
680. – 6 s. pur., green & brown 30 30
681. – 7 s. blue, green & brown 30 30
682. – 8 s. red, green & brown 30 30
683. – 9 s. mve., green & brn. 30 30
684. – 10 j. green and brown .. 30 30
684a. – 13 s. mve., green & brn. 3·00 3·00
685. – 15 s. green and brown .. 60 60
686. – 20 s. brown and green .. 70 70
687. – 30 s. mve., brn. & grn... 80 80
688. – 50 s. blk., brn. and grn. 1·25 1·25
689. – 1 p. pur., brn. and grn. 1·90 1·90
689a. – 2 p. multicoloured .. 7·50 7·50
689b. – 3 p. multicoloured .. 9·50 9·50
DESIGNS—As Type 128. 2 s. to 5 s. Bananas, the number shown coinciding with the face value. 18×26 mm. 6 s. to 10 s. Coconuts. 17×30 mm. 13 s. to 1 p. Pineapples. 55×29 mm. 2 p., 3 p. Mixed fruit.

INDEX
Countries can be quickly located by referring to the index at the end of this volume.

129. Humpback Whale.

1978. Endangered Wildlife. Multicoloured. Self-adhesive.
690. 15 s. Type **129** (postage) .. 1·00 40
691. 18 s. Insular Flying Fox .. 1·00 45
692. 25 s. Turtle .. .. 1·25 60
693. 28 s. Red Shining Parrot .. 1·50 75
694. 60 s. Type **129** .. .. 2·50 2·00
695. 17 s. Type **129** (air) .. 1·00 45
696. 22 s. As 18 s. .. .. 1·00 55
697. 31 s. As 25 s. .. .. 1·50 75
698. 39 s. As 28 s. .. .. 2·00 1·25
699. 45 s. As Type **129** .. 2·50 1·75

130. Metrication.

1979. Decade of Progress. Self-adhesive.
700.**130.** 5 s. multicoloured (postage) 10 10
701. – 11 s. multicoloured .. 15 15
702. – 18 s. multicoloured .. 25 20
703. – 22 s. multicoloured .. 35 25
704. – 50 s. multicoloured .. 80 50
705. – 15 s. multicoloured (air) 20 20
706. – 17 s. multicloured .. 25 20
707. – 31 s. gold and blue .. 45 35
708. – 39 s. multicoloured .. 60 45
709. – 1 p. multicloured .. 1·60 1·25
DESIGNS:—VERT (58×55 mm.) 11 s., 17 s. Shipping routes. 22 s. New Churches. 50 s. 15 s. Air routes. 39 s. Government buildings. 1 p. Communications. TEAR-DROP, (35×52 mm.). 18 s. People building globe (U.S. Peace Corps). As Type **130**. 31 s. Rotary International.

131. Various Envelopes bearing Self-adhesive Stamps.

1979. Death Centenary of Sir Rowland Hill and 10th Anniv of Tongan Self-adhesive Stamps. Self-adhesive.
710.**131.** 5 s. multicoloured (post.) 10 10
711. 10 s. multicoloured .. 20 15
712. 25 s. multicoloured .. 55 35
713. 50 s. multicoloured .. 1·00 60
714. 1 p. multicoloured .. 2·00 1·25
715. – 15 s. multicoloured (air) 30 20
716. – 17 s. multicoloured .. 35 25
717. – 18 s. multicoloured .. 35 25
718. – 31 s. multicoloured .. 60 40
719. – 39 s. multicoloured .. 75 45
DESIGN—MULTI-ANGULAR (53×53 mm.). 15 s. to 39 s. Self-adhesive stamps.

132.

1979. Air. Coil stamps. Self-adhesive.
720.**132.** 5 s. black and blue .. 15 15
721. 11 s. black and blue .. 25 25
722. 14 s. black and violet .. 25 25
723. 15 s. black and mauve 30 30
724. 17 s. black and mauve 30 30
725. 18 s. black and red .. 30 30
726. 22 s. black and red .. 35 35
726a. 29 s. black and red .. 4·50 4·50
727. 31 s. black and yellow.. 55 55
727a. 32 s. black and brown.. 5·00 5·00
728. 39 s. black and green .. 70 70
728a. 47 s. black and brown .. 6·00 6·00
729. 75 s. black and green .. 1·25 1·50
730. 1 p. black and green .. 1·75 2·00

133. Rain Forest, Island of Eua.

1979. Views as seen through the Lens of a Camera. Self-adhesive.
731.**133.** 10 s. multicoloured (post.) 25 25
732. 18 s. multicoloured .. 30 30
733. 31 s. multicoloured .. 40 40
734. 50 s. multicoloured .. 70 70
735. 60 s. multicoloured .. 80 80
736. – 5 s. multicoloured (air) 15 15
737. – 15 s. multicoloured .. 30 30
738. – 17 s. multicoloured .. 30 30
739. – 39 s. multicoloured .. 60 60
740. – 75 s. multicoloured .. 90 90
DESIGN: 5 s. to 75 s. Isle of Kao.

134. King Tupou I, Admiral du Bouzet and Map of Tonga.

1979. 125th Anniv of France–Tonga Friendship Treaty. Self-adhesive.
741.**134.** 7 s. multicoloured (post.) 15 15
742. 10 s. multicoloured .. 20 20
743. 14 s. multicoloured .. 30 30
744. 50 s. multicoloured .. 90 90
745. 75 s. multicoloured .. 1·40 1·40
746. – 15 s. multicoloured (air) 30 30
747. – 17 s. multicoloured .. 35 35
748. – 22 s. multicoloured .. 45 45
749. – 31 s. multicoloured .. 60 60
750. – 39 s. multicoloured .. 70 70
DESIGN: 15 s. to 39 s. King Tupou II, Napoleon III and "L'Aventure" (French warship).

1980. Olympic Games, Moscow. Nos. 710/19 surch. or optd. only (Nos. 753 and 755) **1980 OLYMPIC GAMES**, Olympic mascot and symbol.
751.**131.** 13 s. on 5 s. multicoloured (postage) 30 30
752. – 20 s. on 10 s. multicoloured 40 40
753. – 25 s. multicoloured .. 45 45
754. – 33 s. on 50 s. multicoloured 55 65
755. – 1 p. multicoloured .. 2·50 3·00
756. – 9 s. on 15 s. multicoloured (air) 25 25
757. – 16 s. on 17 s. multicoloured 40 40
758. – 29 s. on 18 s. multicoloured 60 60
759. – 32 s. on 31 s. multicoloured 65 70
760. – 47 s. on 39 s. multicoloured 1·00 1·25

136. Scout at Camp-fire. (Illustration reduced. Actual size 60×50 mm.)

1980. South Pacific Scout Jamboree, Tonga and 75th Anniv of Rotary International. Self-adhesive.
761.**136.** 9 s. multicoloured (Postage) 30 15
762. 13 s. multicoloured .. 40 20
763. 15 s. multicoloured .. 40 20
764. 30 s. multicoloured .. 75 40
765. – 29 s. multicoloured (air) 75 45
766. – 32 s. multicoloured .. 80 45
767. – 47 s. multicoloured .. 1·10 70
768. – 1 p. multicoloured .. 2·00 1·25
DESIGN: 29 s. to 1p. Scout activities and Rotary emblem.

1980. Various stamps surch.
769.**117.** 9 s. on 35 s. red, black and mauve (postage) .. 30 30
770.**119.** 13 s. on 20 s. multicoloured 45 45
771. 13 s. on 25 s. multicoloured 45 45
772. – 19 s. on 25 s. multicoloured (No. 571) 65 65
773.**114.** 1 p. on 65 s. multicoloured 2·75 2·75
773a. – 5 p. on 25 s. multicoloured (No. O 213) .. .. 9·50 9·50
773b. – 5 p. on 2 p. multicoloured (No. O 214) .. .. 9·50 9·50
774. – 29 s. on 14 s. multicoloured (No. 585) (air) .. 80 80
775. – 29 s. on 39 s. multicoloured (No. 597) 80 80
776. – 32 s. on 12 s. multicoloured (No. 554) 95 95
777. – 32 s. on 14 s. multicoloured (No. 574) 95 95
778. – 47 s. on 12 s. multicoloured (No. 524) .. .. 1·40 1·40
779. – 47 s. on 12 s. multicoloured (No. 584) .. .. 1·40 1·40

138. Red Cross and Tongan Flags, with Map of Tonga.

1981. International Year for Disabled Persons. Self-adhesive.
780.**138.** 2 p. multicoloured (postage) .. .. 1·50 1·00
781. 3 p. multicoloured .. 1·75 1·25
782. – 29 s. multicoloured (air) 30 20
783. – 32 s. multicoloured .. 35 25
784. – 47 s. multicoloured .. 45 30
DESIGN: Nos. 782/4, Red Cross Flag and Map depicting Tongatapu and Eua.

139. Prince Charles and King Taufa'ahau Tupou IV.

1981. Royal Wedding and Centenary of Treaty of Friendship between Tonga and Great Britain. Multicoloured. Self-adhesive.
785. 13 s. Type **139** 30 20
786. 47 s. Prince Charles and Lady Diana Spencer .. 45 30
787. 1 p. 50 Prince Charles and Lady Diana (different) 1·10 90
788. 3 p. Prince and Princess of Wales after wedding ceremony .. .. 2·00 1·40

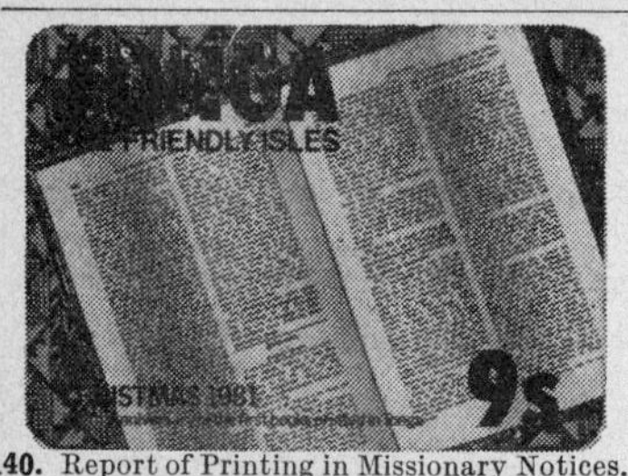

140. Report of Printing in Missionary Notices.

1981. Christmas. 150th Anniv of First Books Printed in Tonga. Multicoloured. Self-adhesive.

789. 9 s. Type **140** .. 25 15
790. 13 s. Missionary Notice report (different) .. 30 20
791. 32 s. Type in chase .. 85 40
792. 47 s. Bible class .. 1·40 70

141. Landing Scene.

1981. Bicentenary of Maurell's Discovery of Vava'u. Multicoloured. Self-adhesive.

793. 9 s. Type **141** .. 30 20
794. 13 s. Map of Vava'u .. 50 25
795. 47 s. " La Princesa " .. 2·50 1·25
796. 1 p. " La Princesa " (different) .. 4·50 3·00

142. Battle Scene.

1981. 175th Anniv of Capture of "Port au Prince" (ship). Each black and blue. Self-adhesive.

798. 29 s. Type **142** .. 55 25
799. 32 s. Battle scene (different) 65 30
800. 47 s. Map of the Ha'Apai Group .. 80 50
801. 47 s. Native canoes preparing to attack .. 80 50
802. 1 p. " Port au Prince " .. 1·75 75

143. Baden Powell at Brownsea Island, 1907.

1982. 75th Anniv of Boy Scout Movement and 125th Birth Anniv of Lord Baden-Powell (founder). Multicoloured. Self-adhesive.

803. 29 s. Type **143** .. 55 30
804. 32 s. Baden-Powell on his charger " Black Prince " 65 35
805. 47 s. Baden-Powell at Imperial Jamboree, 1924 90 45
806. 1 p. 50 Cover of first " Scouting for Boys " journal .. 2·40 1·25
807. 2 p. 50 Newsboy, 1900 and Mafeking Siege 3d. stamp 4·00 2·75

1982. No. 788 optd. **CYCLONE RELIEF T$1+50s POSTAGE & RELIEF.**

808. 1 p.+50 s. on 3 p. Prince and Princess of Wales after wedding ceremony 2·25 1·60

145. Ball Control.

1982. World Cup Football Championship, Spain. Multicoloured. Self-adhesive.

809. 32s. Type **145** 45 45
810. 47 s. Goalkeeping 60 60
811. 75 s. Heading .. .. 1·00 95
812. $1.50 Shooting .. .. 1·75 1·75

146. "Olovaha II" (inter-island freighter).

1982. Inter-Island Transport. Multicoloured. Self-adhesive.

813. 9 s. Type **146** 15 15
814. 13 s. Type **146** 20 20
815. 47 s. SPIA " Twin Otter " 75 75
816. 1 p. As 47 s. .. .. 1·75 1·75

147. Mail Canoe.

1982. Centenary of Tin Can Mail. Self-adhesive.

817. **147.** 13 s. multicoloured .. 15 15
818. – 32 s. multicoloured .. 25 25
819. – 47 s. multicoloured .. 35 35
820. – 2 p. black and green .. 1·40 1·40

DESIGNS: 32 s. Mail canoe and ship. 47 s. Collecting Tin Can Mail. 2 p. Map of Niua Fo'ou.

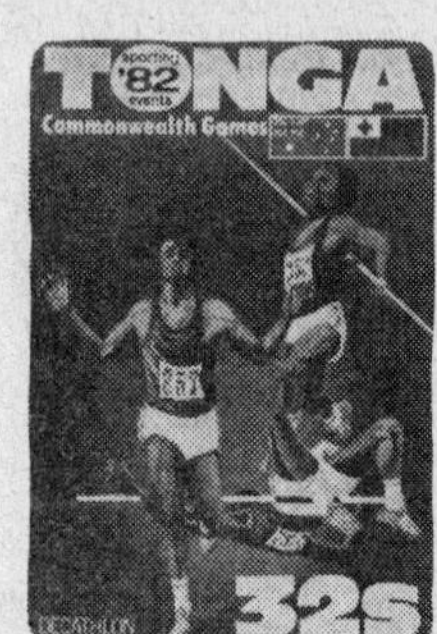

148. Decathlon.

1982. Commonwealth Games, Brisbane. Multicoloured. Self-adhesive.

823. 32 s. Type **148** 50 30
824. $1.50 Tongan Police band at opening ceremony (horiz.) .. .. 3·00 1·50

149. Pupils.

1982. Centenary of Tonga College. Multicoloured. Self-adhesive.

825. 5 s. Type **149** (Tongan inscription) 50 40
826. 5 s. Type **149** (Ringlish inscription) 50 40
827. 29 s. School crest and monument (Tongan incsr.) (29 × 22 mm.) .. 1·75 1·40
828. 29 s. As No. 827 but inscr. in English .. 1·75 1·40
829. 29 s. King George Tupou I (founder) and school (Tongan inscr.) (29 × 22 mm.) .. .. 1·75 1·40
830. 29 s. As No. 829 but inscr. at English .. 1·75 1·40

1982. Christmas. Nos. 817/9 optd. with **Christmas Greetings 1982.**

831. 13 s. Type **147** 15 15
832. 32 s. Mail boat and ship .. 45 45
833. 47 s. Collecting Tin Can Mail 55 55

151. H.M.S. " Resolution " and S.S. " Canberra ".

1983. Sea and Air Transport. Multicoloured. Self-adhesive.

834. 29 s. Type **151** .. .. 1·25 1·00
835. 32 s. Type **151** .. .. 1·40 1·10
836. 47 s. Montgolfier's balloon and " Concorde " .. 2·25 1·75
837. 1 p. 50 As No. 836 .. .. 4·00 3·50

152. Globe and Inset of Tonga.

1983. Commonwealth Day. Multicoloured. Self-adhesive.

839. 29 s. Type **152** 35 30
840. 32 s. Tongan dancers .. 6·00 2·50
841. 47 s. Trawler 50 50
842. 1 p. 50 King Taufa'ahau Tupou IV and flag .. 1·75 2·00

153. SPIA " DH Twin Otter ".

1983. Inauguration of Niuafo'ou Airport. Multicoloured. Self-adhesive.

843. 32 s. Type **153** 20 20
844. 47 s. Type **153** 25 25
845. 1 p. SPIA Boeing " 707 " 60 70
846. 1 p. 50 As No. 845 .. .. 80 1·25

154. " Intelsat IV " satellite.

1983. World Communications Year. Multicoloured. Self-adhesive.

847. 29 s. Type **154** 20 20
848. 32 s. " Intelsat IVA " satellite 25 25
849. 75 s. " Intelsat V " satellite 50 50
850. 2 p. Moon post cover (45 × 32 mm.) .. .. 1·10 1·40

155. Obverse and reverse of 1 p. Banknote.

1983. 10th Anniv of Bank of Tonga. Self-adhesive.

851. **155.** 1 p. multicoloured .. 60 65
852. 2 p. multicoloured .. 1·10 1·25

156. Early Printing Press.

1983. Printing in Tonga. Multicoloured. Self-adhesive.

853. 13 s. Type **156** 15 15
854. 32 s. Arrival of W. Woon .. 30 30
855. 1 p. Early Tongan print .. 70 70
856. 2 p. " The Tonga Chronicle " 1·25 1·50

157. Yacht off Coast.

1983. Christmas. Yachting off Vava'u. Multicoloured. Self-adhesive.

857. 29 s. Type **157** 35 35
858. 32 s. View of yacht from cave 35 35
859. 1 p. 50 Anchored yacht .. 1·25 1·25
860. 2 p. 50 Yacht off coast (different) .. .. 2·00 2·00

158. Abel Tasman and "Zeehan".

1984. Navigators and Explorers of the Pacific (1st series). Self-adhesive.

861. **158.** 32 s. green and black .. 90 90
862. – 47 s. violet and black 1·40 1·40
863. – 90 s. brown and black 2·75 2·75
864. – 1 p. 50 blue and black 4·00 4·00

DESIGNS: 47 s. Capt. Samuel Wallis and H.M.S. "Dolphin". 90 s. Capt. William Bligh and H.M.S. "Bounty". 1 p. 50, Capt. James Cook and H.M.S. "Resolution".

See also 896/9.

159. "Swainsonia casta". **160.** Printer checking Newspaper.

1984. Marine Life. Size 38 × 23 mm (878/81) or 25 × 28 mm (others). Mult. Self-adhesive.

865. 1 s. Type **159** 15 15
866. 2 s. "Porites sp" 25 25
867. 3 s. "Holocentrus ruber" .. 30 30
868. 5 s. "Cypraea mappa viridis" 30 30
869. 6 s. "Dardanus megistos" (crab) 35 35
870. 9 s. "Stegostoma fasciatum" 35 35
871. 10 s. "Conus bullatus" .. 50 45
872. 13 s. "Pterois volitans" .. 55 45
873. 15 s. "Conus textile" .. 60 50
874. 20 s. "Dascyllus aruanus" 70 60
875. 29 s. "Conus aulicus" .. 85 70
876. 32 s. "Acanthurus leucosternon" .. .. 1·00 80
877. 47 s. "Lambis truncata" .. 1·40 1·40
878. 1 p. "Millepora dichotama" .. .. 3·25 3·25
879. 2 p. "Biggus latro" (crab)
880. 3 p. "Chicoreus palmarosea" .. .. 5·50 5·50 / 6·50 6·50
881. 5 p. "Thunnus albacares" 8·50 8·50

The 10 and 32 s. also exist with normal gum.

For these designs with normal gum but different size see Nos. 999/1017a and 1087/95. For similar designs but with face value at foot see Nos. 1218/29.

1984. 20th Anniv of "Tonga Chronicle" (newspaper). Self-adhesive.

882. **160.** 3 s. brown and blue .. 10 10
883. 32 s. brown and red .. 40 45

161. U.S.A. Flag and Running.

1984. Olympic Games, Los Angeles. Each in black, red and blue. Self-adhesive.

884.	29 s. Type **161**	25	25
885.	47 s. Javelin-throwing ..	30	30
886.	1 p. 50 Shot-putting ..	85	85
887.	3 p. Olympic torch ..	1·60	1·60

162. Sir George Airy and Dateline on World Map.

1984. Centenary of International Dateline. Multicoloured. Self-adhesive.

888.	47 s. Type **162**	1·00	1·00
889.	2 p. Sir Sandford Fleming and Map of Pacific time zones	3·50	4·00

163. Australia 1914 Kookaburra 6d. Stamp.

1984. "Ausipex" International Stamp Exhibition, Melbourne. Multicoloured. Self-adhesive.

890.	32 s. Type **163**	75	60
891.	1 p. 50 Tonga 1897 Parrot 2s. 6d. stamp	2·50	2·50

164. Beach at Sunset ("Silent Night").

1984. Christmas. Carols. Mult. Self-adhesive.

893.	32 s. Type **164**	60	45
894.	47 s. Hut and palm trees ("Away in a Manger") ..	85	65
895.	1 p. Sailing boats ("I Saw Three Ships") ..	1·75	2·25

1985. Navigators and Explorers of the Pacific (2nd series). As T **158**. Self-adhesive.

896.	32 s. black and blue ..	1·75	75
897.	47 s. black and green ..	2·00	1·00
898.	90 s. black and red ..	3·00	3·00
899.	1 p. 50 black and brown ..	4·50	4·50

DESIGNS: 32 s. Willem Schouten and "Eendracht". 47 s. Jacob Le Maire and "Hoorn". 90 s. Fletcher Christian and "Bounty". 1 p. 50 Francisco Maurelle and "La Princessa".

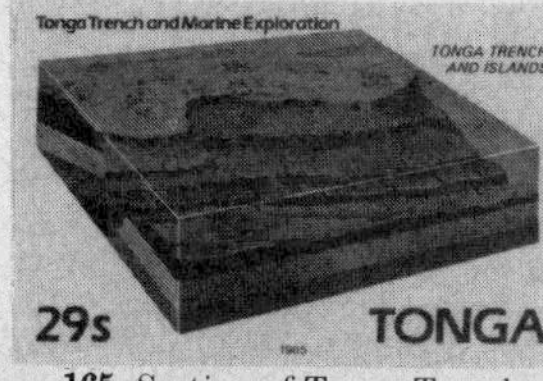

165. Section of Tonga Trench.

1985. Geological Survey of the Tonga Trench. Multicoloured. Self-adhesive.

900.	29 s. Type **165**	1·25	1·00
901.	32 s. Diagram of marine seismic survey	1·25	1·00
902.	47 s. Diagram of aerial oil survey (vert.)	1·50	1·25
903.	1 p. 50, Diagram of sea bed survey (vert.)	4·75	5·00

166. "Port au Prince" at Gravesend, 1805.

1985. 175th Anniv of Will Mariner's Departure for England. Multicoloured. Self-adhesive.

905.	29 s. Type **166**	40	40
906.	32 s. Capture of "Port au Prince", Tonga, 1806 ..	40	40
907.	47 s. Will Mariner on Tongan canoe, 1807 ..	60	60
908.	1 p. 50 Mariner boarding brig "Favourite", 1810 ..	1·75	2·00
909.	2 p. 50 "Cuffnells" in English Channel, 1811 ..	3·00	3·25

167. Quintal (Byron Russell) and Captain Bligh (Charles Laughton).

1985. 50th Anniv of Film "Mutiny on the Bounty". Multicoloured. Self-adhesive.

910.	47 s. Type **167**	2·75	2·75
911.	47 s. Captain Bligh and prisoners	2·75	2·75
912.	47 s. Fletcher Christian (Clark Gable)	2·75	2·25
913.	47 s. Mutineers threatening Bligh	2·75	2·25
914.	47 s. Bligh and Roger Byam (Franchot Tone) in boat	2·75	2·75

168. Lady Elizabeth Bowes-Lyon, 1910.

1985. Life and Times of Queen Elizabeth the Queen Mother and 75th Anniv of Girl Guide Movement. Self-adhesive.

915. **168.**	32 s. black, pink and brown	50	55
916. –	47 s. black, lilac and brown	80	90
917. –	1 p. 50 black, yellow and brown	2·50	2·75
918. –	2 p. 50 multicoloured	4·25	4·75

DESIGNS: 47 s. Duchess of York at Hadfield Girl Guides' Rally, 1931. 1 p. 50 Duchess of York in Girl Guide uniform. 2 p. 50 Queen Mother in 1985 (from photo by Norman Parkinson).

169. Mary and Joseph arriving at Inn.

1985. Christmas. Mult. Self-adhesive.

919.	32 s. Type **169**	35	30
920.	42 s. The shepherds ..	45	40
921.	1 p. 50 The Three Wise Men	1·75	2·00
922.	2 p. 50 The Holy Family ..	2·50	3·00

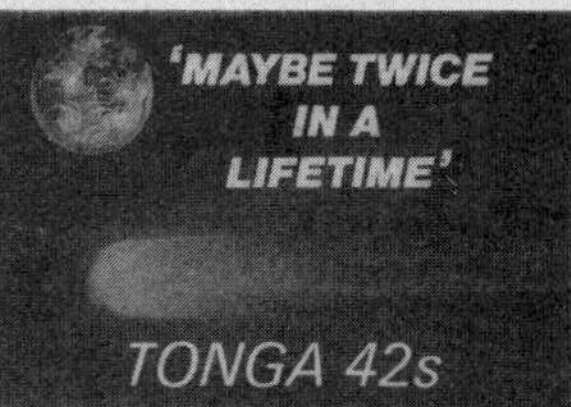

170. Comet and Slogan "Maybe Twice in a Lifetime".

1986. Appearance of Halley's Comet. Multicoloured.

923.	42 s. Type **170**	1·40	1·40
924.	42 s. Edmond Halley ..	1·40	1·40
925.	42 s. Solar System ..	1·40	1·40
926.	42 s. Telescope	1·40	1·40
927.	42 s. "Giotto" spacecraft ..	1·40	1·40
928.	57 s. Type **170**	1·60	1·60
929.	57 s. As No. 924	1·60	1·60
930.	57 s. As No. 925	1·60	1·60
931.	57 s. As No. 926	1·60	1·60
932.	57 s. As No. 927	1·60	1·60

Nos. 923/7 and 928/32 were each printed together, se-tenant, forming composite designs.

1986. Nos. 866/7, 869/70, 872, 874, 879 and 881 surch.

933.	4 s. on 2 s. "Porites sp." ..	20	20
934.	4 s. on 13 s. "Pterois volitans"	20	20
935.	42 s. on 3 s. "Holocentrus ruber"	45	45
936.	42 s. on 9 s. "Stegostoma fasciatum"	45	45
937.	57 s. on 6 s. "Dardanus megistos"	75	75
938.	57 s. on 20 s. "Dascyllus aruanus"	75	75
939.	2 p. 50 on 2 p. "Birgus latro"	3·00	3·50
940.	2 p. 50 on 5 p. "Thunnus albacares"	3·00	3·50

172. King Taufa 'ahau Tupou IV of Tonga.

1986. Royal Links with Great Britain and 60th Birthday of Queen Elizabeth II.

941. **172.**	57 s. multicoloured ..	65	80
942. –	57 s. multicoloured ..	65	80
943. –	2 p. 50 brown, black and blue	2·25	2·75

DESIGNS—HORIZ (as T **172**). No. 942, Queen Elizabeth II. Square (40×40 mm.). No. 943, Queen Elizabeth II and King Taufa'ahau Tupou IV, Tonga, 1970.

173. Peace Corps Nurse giving Injection.

1986. "Ameripex '86" International Stamps Exhibition, Chicago. 25th Anniv. of United States Peace Corps. Multicoloured.

944.	57 s. Type **173**	60	60
945.	1 p. 50 Peace Corps teacher and pupil	1·50	1·75

174. Hockey.

1986. Sporting Events. Multicoloured.

947.	42 s. Type **174** (World Hockey Cup for Men, London)	75	75
948.	57 s. Handball (13th Commonwealth Games, Edinburgh	85	85
949.	1 p. Boxing (13th Commonwealth Games, Edinburgh)	1·60	1·60
950.	2 p. 50 Football (World Cup Football Championship, Mexico)	4·00	4·00

175. 1886 1 d. King George I Definitive.

1986. Cent of First Tonga Stamps. Mult.

951	32 s. Type **175**	75	75
952	42 s. 1897 $7\frac{1}{2}$d. King George II inverted centre error	90	90
953	57 s. 1950 Queen Salote's 50th Birthday 1d. ..	1·25	1·25
954	2 p. 50 1986 Royal Links with Great Britain 2p. 50	3·25	3·25

176. Girls wearing Shell Jewellery.

1986. Christmas. Multicoloured.

956.	32 s. Type **176**	60	45
957.	42 s. Boy with wood carvings (vert.)	85	60
958.	57 s. Children performing traditional dance (vert.)	1·10	75
959.	2 p. Children in dugout canoe	3·25	4·00

1986. Scout Jamboree, Tongatapu. Nos. 957/8 optd. **BOY SCOUT JAMBOREE 5th–10th DEC '86.**

960.	42 s. Boy with wood carvings (vert.)	1·75	1·75
961.	57 s. Children performing traditional dance (vert.)	2·25	2·25

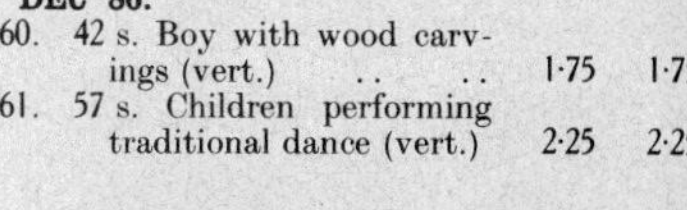

178. Dumont D'Urville and "L'Astrolabe".

1987. 150th Anniv. of Dumont D'Urville's Second Voyage. Multicoloured.

962.	32 s. Type **178**	1·60	1·10
963.	42 s. Tongan girls (from "Voyage au Pole et dans l'Oceanie")	1·90	1·40
964.	1 p. Contemporary chart ..	3·75	3·50
965.	2 p. 50 Wreck of "L'Astrolabe"	7·00	7·00

180. Two Paddlers in Canoe.

TONGA 1s

181. King Taufa'ahau Tupou IV.

1987. "Siv'a'alo" (Tonga–Fiji–Samoa) Canoe Race. Multicoloured.

967. 32 s. Type **180** 30 30
968. 42 s. Five paddlers .. 40 40
969. 57 s. Paddlers and canoe bow 50 50
970. 1 p. 50 Two paddlers (different) .. .. 1·40 1·60

1987. 20th Anniv. of Coronation of King Taufa'ahau Tupou IV. Self-adhesive.

972. **181.** 1 s. black and green .. 10 10
972d. 2 s. black and orange 10 10
973. 5 s. black and mauve 10 10
974. 10 s. black and lilac .. 10 10
975. 15 s. black and red .. 15 20
976. 32 s. black and blue .. 30 35

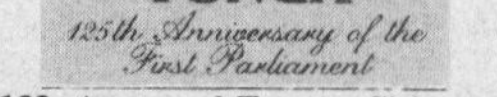

182. Arms and Tongan Citizens.

1987. 125th Anniv. of 1st Parliament.

977. **182.** 32 s. multicoloured .. 30 30
978. 42 s. multicoloured .. 40 40
979. 75 s. multicoloured .. 75 75
980. 2 p. multicoloured .. 2·00 2·25

183 Father Christmas Octopus and Rat with Sack of Presents

1987. Christmas. Cartoons. Multicoloured.

981 42 s. Type **183** 50 45
982 57 s. Delivering presents by outrigger canoe .. 70 65
983 1 p. Delivering presents by motorized tricycle .. 1·40 1·60
984 3 p. Drinking cocktails .. 3·50 3·75

184 King Taufa'ahau Tupou IV, "Olovaha II" (inter-island freighter), Oil Rig and Pole Vaulting
(Illustration reduced, actual size 59 × 43 mm)

1988. 70th Birthday of King Taufa'ahau Tupou IV. Designs each show portrait. Mult.

985 32 s. Type **184** 30 35
986 42 s. Banknote, coins, Ha'amonga Trilithon and woodcarver .. 40 45
987 57 s. Rowing, communications satellite and Red Cross worker .. 60 65
988 2 p.50 Scout emblem, 1982 47 s. Scout stamp and Friendly Island Airways aircraft .. .. 2·40 2·50

See also Nos. 1082/5.

186 Athletics

187 Traditional Tongan Fale

1988. Olympic Games, Seoul. Multicoloured.

990 57 s. Type **186** 60 65
991 75 s. Yachting 70 75
992 2 p. Cycling .. .. 1·90 2·00
993 3 p. Tennis .. .. 2·75 3·00

1988. Music in Tonga. Multicoloured.

994 32 s. Type **187** 30 35
995 42 s. Church choir .. 40 45
996 57 s. Tonga Police Band outside Royal Palace .. 55 60
997 2 p.50 "The Jets" pop group .. .. .. 2·40 2·50

1988. Designs as Nos. 865/6, 868/9, 871/6 and 879/81 and new values, all with normal gum. Size 41 × 22 mm (1013/17), 26 × 41 mm (1017a) or 27 × 33 mm (others). Multicoloured.

999 1 s. Type **159** 15 15
1000a 2 s. "Porites sp" .. 10 10
1001 4 s. "Pterois volitans" 20 20
1002a 5 s. "Cypraea mappa viridis" 30 30
1003 6 s. "Dardanus megistos" (crab) 10 10
1004 7 s. Wandering albatross 10 10
1005a 10 s. "Conus bullatus" .. 30 30
1006 15 s. "Conus textile" .. 15 20
1007 20 s. "Dascyllus aruanus" 30 30
1008a 32 s. "Acanthurus leucosternon" 30 35
1009 35 s. Sea horse 35 40
1010 42 s. Lesser frigate bird .. 40 45
1011 50 s. "Conus aulicus" .. 60 60
1012 57 s. Brown booby .. 55 60
1013 1 p. "Chelonia mydas" (turtle) .. .. 95 1·00
1014 1 p. 50 Humpback whale 1·40 1·50
1015 2 p. "Birgus latro" (crab) 2·00 2·25
1016 3 p. "Chicoreus palmarosae" .. .. 2·75 3·00
1017 5 p. "Thunnus albacares" 4·75 5·00
1017a 10 p. "Stegostoma fasciatum" .. .. .. 9·50 10·00

For smaller designs, 19 × 22 mm, see Nos. 1087/95.

188 Capt. Cook's H.M.S. "Resolution"

1988. Centenary of Tonga–U.S.A. Treaty of Friendship. Multicoloured.

1018 42 s. Type **188** 60 50
1019 57 s. "Santa Maria" .. 75 70
1020 2 p. Capt. Cook and Christopher Columbus 2·25 2·50

190 Girl in Hospital Bed

1988. Christmas. 125th Anniv of International Red Cross and 25th Anniv of Tongan Red Cross. Multicoloured.

1022 15 s. Type **190** (A) .. 15 20
1023 15 s. Type **190** (B) .. 15 20
1024 32 s. Red Cross nurse reading to young boy (A) 30 35
1025 32 s. Red Cross nurse reading to young boy (B) 30 35
1026 42 s. Red Cross nurse taking pulse (A) .. 40 45
1027 42 s. Red Cross nurse taking pulse (B) .. 40 45
1028 57 s. Red Cross nurse with sleeping child (A) .. 55 60
1029 57 s. Red Cross nurse with sleeping child (B) .. 55 60
1030 1 p. 50 Boy in wheelchair (A) .. .. .. 1·40 1·50
1031 1 p. 50 Boy in wheelchair (B) .. .. .. 1·40 1·50

Nos. 1022/3, 1024/5, 1026/7, 1028/9 and 1030/1 were printed together, se-tenant, in horizontal pairs throughout the sheets with the first stamp in each pair inscribed "INTERNATIONAL RED CROSS 125th ANNIVERSARY" (A) and the second "SILVER JUBILEE OF TONGAN RED CROSS" (B).

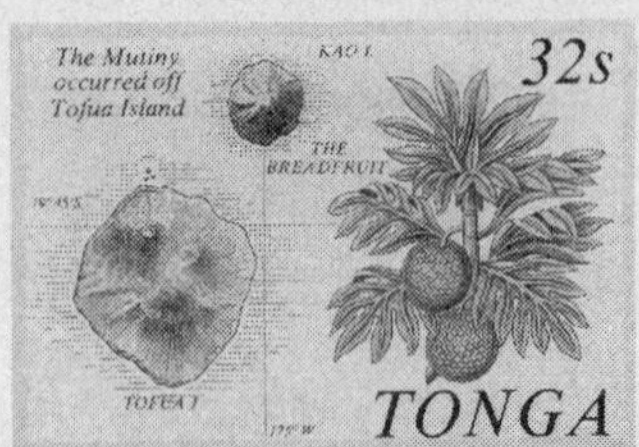

191 Map of Tofua Island and Breadfruit

1989. Bicent of Mutiny on the "Bounty". Multicoloured.

1032 32 s. Type **191** .. .. 1·00 90
1033 42 s. H.M.S. "Bounty" and chronometer .. 1·40 1·10
1034 57 s. Captain Bligh and "Bounty's" launch cast adrift .. .. 2·00 2·00

192 "Hypolimnas bolina"

1989. Butterflies. Multicoloured.

1036 42 s. Type **192** 70 70
1037 57 s. "Jamides bochus" .. 90 90
1038 1 p. 20, "Melanitis leda solandra" .. .. 1·50 1·50
1039 2 p. 50 "Danaus plexippus" .. .. 3·50 3·50

193 Football at Rugby School, 1870

1989. Inauguration of National Sports Stadium and South Pacific Mini Games, Tonga. Designs showing development of rugby, tennis and cricket. Multicoloured.

1040 32 s. Type **193** 50 50
1041 32 s. D. Gallaher (All Black's captain, 1905) and Springboks rugby match, 1906 .. .. 50 50
1042 32 s. King George V with Cambridge team, 1922 and W. Wakefield (England captain, 1926) 50 50
1043 32 s. E. Crawford (Ireland captain, 1926) and players on cigarette cards 50 50
1044 32 s. S. Mafi (Tonga captain, 1970's) and modern rugby match .. 50 50
1045 42 s. Royal tennis, 1659 .. 70 70
1046 42 s. Major Wingfield and lawn tennis, 1873 .. 70 70
1047 42 s. Oxford and Cambridge tennis teams, 1884 .. .. 70 70
1048 42 s. Bunny Ryan, 1910, and players on cigarette cards 70 70
1049 42 s. Boris Becker and modern tennis match .. 70 70
1050 57 s. Cricket match, 1743, and F. Pilch memorial 90 90
1051 57 s. W. G. Grace (19th-century cricketer) .. 90 90
1052 57 s. "Boys Own Paper" cricket article, 1909 .. 90 90
1053 57 s. Australian cricket team, 1909, and players on cigarette cards .. 90 90
1054 57 s. The Ashes urn, and modern cricket match 90 90

194 Short "S30" Flying Boat, 1939 (50th anniv of first flight)

1989. Aviation in Tonga. Multicoloured.

1055 42 s. Type **194** 90 80
1056 57 s. Vought "F4U Corsair", 1943 .. .. 1·40 1·25
1057 90 s. Boeing "737" at Fua'amotu Airport .. 2·00 1·75
1058 3 p. Montgolfier balloon, Wright biplane, "Concorde" and space shuttle (97 × 26 mm) .. 6·50 6·00

195 Aircraft landing

1989. Christmas. "Flying Home".

1059 **195** 32 s. grn, brn & orge 60 50
1060 – 42 s. grn, brn & lt grn 70 60
1061 – 57 s. green, brn & red 90 80
1062 – 3 p. green, brn & mve 4·25 4·50

DESIGNS: 42 s. Villagers waving to aircraft; 57 s. Outrigger canoe and aircraft; 3 p. Aircraft over headland.

197 1989 U.P.U. Congress Stamps

1989. "World Stamp Expo '89" International Stamp Exhibition, Washington.

1064 **197** 57 s. multicoloured .. 1·00 1·00

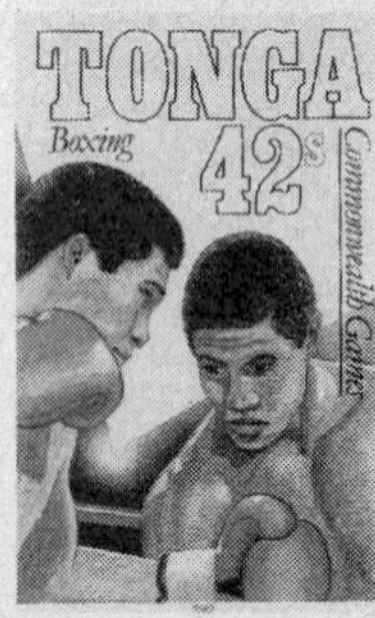

198 Boxing

1990. 14th Commonwealth Games, Auckland. Multicoloured.

1065 42 s. Type **198** 80 70
1066 57 s. Archery .. .. 1·00 85
1067 1 p. Bowls .. .. 1·75 1·75
1068 2 p. Swimming .. .. 3·00 3·25

MINIMUM PRICE

The minimum price quoted is 10p which represents a handling charge rather than a basis for valuing common stamps. For further notes about prices see introductory pages.

199 Wave Power Installation

1990. Alternative Sources of Electricity. Multicoloured.

1069 32 s. Type **199** 70 50
1070 57 s. Wind farm .. .. 1·10 90
1071 1 p. 20 Experimental solar cell vehicle .. .. 2·50 3·00

200 Penny Black

1990. 150th Anniv of the Penny Black.

1073 **200** 42 s. multicoloured .. 90 90
1074 – 42 s. multicoloured .. 90 90
1075 – 57 s. red and black .. 1·10 90
1076 – 1 p. 50 multicoloured 2·50 2·50
1077 – 2 p. 50 multicoloured 4·00 4·00

DESIGNS: 42 s. (1074) Great Britain 1840 Twopence Blue; 57 s. Tonga 1886 1d.; 1 p. 50, 1980 South Pacific Scout Jamboree and Rotary 75th anniv 2 p. official stamp; 2 p. 50, 1990 Alternative Sources of Electricity 57 s.

201 Departure of Canoe

1990. Polynesian Voyages of Discovery.

1078 **201** 32 s. green 65 55
1079 – 42 s. blue 90 80
1080 – 1 p. 20 brown .. 2·50 2·50
1081 – 3 p. violet .. 5·50 6·00

DESIGNS: 42 s. Navigating by night; 1 p. 20, Canoe and sea birds; 3 p. Landfall.

1990. Silver Jubilee of King Taufa'ahau Tupou IV. As Nos. 985/8, but inscr "Silver Jubilee of His Majesty King Taufa'ahau Tupou IV. 1965–1990" and with "TONGA" and values in silver.

1082 32 s. Type **184** 50 35
1083 42 s. Banknote, coins, Ha'amonga Trilithon and woodcarver .. 60 45
1084 57 s. Rowing, communications satellite and Red Cross worker .. 75 60
1085 2 p. 50 Scout emblem, 1982 47 s. Scout stamp and Friendly Island Airways aircraft .. 3·50 4·00

1990. As Nos. 1000, 1002a, 1003 (value changed), 1005a and 1008a redrawn smaller, 19 × 22 mm. Multicoloured.

1087 2 s. "Porites sp." .. 10 10
1089 5 s. "Cypraea mappa viridis" 10 10
1092 10s. "Conus bullatus" .. 15 15
1093 15 s. "Dardanus megistos" (crab) 25 25
1095 32 s. "Acanthurus leucosternon" 40 40

202 Iguana searching for Food

1990. Endangered Species. Banded Iguana. Multicoloured.

1105 32 s. Type **202** 65 45
1106 42 s. Head of male .. 80 55
1107 57 s. Pair of iguanas during courtship .. 1·10 80
1108 1 p. 20 Iguana basking .. 2·50 3·00

203 Tourism

1990. 40th Anniv of United Nations Development Programme. Multicoloured.

1109 57 s. Type **203** .. .. 1·00 1·00
1110 57 s. Agriculture and Fisheries .. .. 1·00 1·00
1111 3 p. Education .. .. 4·50 4·50
1112 3 p. Healthcare .. .. 4·50 4·50

204 Boy

1990. Christmas. Rotary International Interact Project. Multicoloured.

1113 32 s. Type **204** 50 40
1114 42 s. Young boys .. 70 55
1115 2 p. Girls in western clothes .. .. 2·75 2·75
1116 3 p. Girls in traditional costumes .. .. 4·00 4·25

205 Safety at Work

1991. Accident Prevention. Multicoloured.

1117 32 s. Type **205** (English inscription) 50 50
1118 32 s. Safety at home (English inscription) .. 50 50
1119 32 s. As No. 1118 (Tongan inscription) 50 50
1120 32 s. As Type **205** incorrect inscr ("Ngauo tokanga") 50 50
1120a 32 s. As Type **205** inscr corrected to ("Ngaue tokanga") .. .. 9·50 9·50
1121 42 s. Safety in cars (English inscription) .. 70 70
1122 42 s. Safety on bikes (English inscription) .. 70 70
1123 42 s. As No. 1122 (Tongan inscription) 70 70
1124 42 s. As No. 1121 (Tongan inscription) 70 70
1125 57 s. Safety at sea (English inscription) .. 90 90
1126 57 s. Safety on the beach (English inscription) .. 90 90
1127 57 s. As No. 1126 (Tongan inscription) 90 90
1128 57 s. As No. 1125 (Tongan inscription) 90 90

No. 1120 is incorrectly inscr in Tongan "Nagauo tokanga".

207 Fishes in the Sea

1991. Heilala Week. Multicoloured.

1130 42 s. Type **207** 55 45
1131 57 s. Island and yacht .. 70 55
1132 2 p. Pile of fruit .. .. 2·40 2·50
1133 3 p. Turtle on beach .. 3·00 3·25

208 Tonga Temple

1991. Centenary of Church of Latter Day Saints in Tonga. Multicoloured.

1134 42 s. Type **208** 60 60
1135 57 s. Temple at night .. 65 65

209 Making T.V. Childcare Programme

1991. Telecommunications in Tonga. Mult.

1136 15 s. Type **209** 25 25
1137 15 s. T.V. satellite .. 25 25
1138 15 s. Mothers watching programme 25 25
1139 32 s. Man on telephone and woman with computer 50 50
1140 32 s. Telecommunications satellite 50 50
1141 32 s. Overseas customer on telephone .. 50 50
1142 42 s. Sinking coaster .. 65 65
1143 42 s. Coastguard controller 65 65
1144 42 s. Maritime rescue .. 65 65
1145 57 s. Weather satellite above Southern Hemisphere .. 80 80
1146 57 s. Meteorologists collecting data .. 80 80
1147 57 s. T.V. weather map and storm 80 80

210 Women's Rowing Eight

1991. "Siu'a'alo" Rowing Festival. Mult.

1148 42 s. Type **210** 55 45
1149 57 s. Longboat 70 55
1150 1 p. Outrigger canoe .. 1·40 1·40
1151 2 p. Stern of fautasi (large canoe) .. .. 2·50 2·75
1152 2 p. Bow of fautasi .. 2·50 2·75

Nos. 1151/2 were printed together, se-tenant, forming a composite design

211 Turtles pulling Santa's Sledge

1991. Christmas. Multicoloured.

1153 32 s. Type **211** 55 3
1154 42 s. Santa Claus on roof of fala (Tongan house) 65 4
1155 57 s. Family opening presents 80 6
1156 3 p. 50 Family waving goodbye to Santa .. 4·50 5·0

212 "Pangai" (patrol boat)

1991. Royal Tongan Defence Force. Mult.

1157 42 s. Type **212** 70 7
1158 42 s. Marine in battle dress 70 7
1159 57 s. Tonga Royal Guards 80 8
1160 57 s. Raising the ensign on "Neiafu" (patrol boat) 80 8
1161 2 p. "Savea" (patrol boat) (horiz) .. .. 2·50 3·0
1162 2 p. King Taufa'ahau Tupou IV inspecting parade (horiz) .. 2·50 3·0

1992. No. 1007 surch **1s**.

1163 1 s. on 20 s. "Dascyllus aruanus" 20 2

215 U.S.S. "Arizona" under attack, Pearl Harbor, 1941

1992 50th Anniv of Outbreak of Pacific War. Multicoloured.

1165 42 s. Type **215** 60 60
1166 42 s. Japanese invasion of the Philippines .. 60 60
1167 42 s. U.S. landings in the Gilbert Islands .. 60 60
1168 42 s. Landing on Iwo Jima 60 60
1169 42 s. Admiral Nimitz and Battle of Midway map 60 60
1170 42 s. General MacArthur and liberation of Philippines map .. 60 60
1171 42 s. Lt-Gen. Holland Smith and map of landings on Saipan and Tinian 60 60
1172 42 s. Major-Gen. Curtis Lemay and bombing of Japan map .. 60 60
1173 42 s. Japanese Mitsubishi A6M Zero 60 60
1174 42 s. Douglas SBD Dauntless 60 60
1175 42 s. Grumman FM-2 Wildcat 60 60
1176 42 s. Supermarine Seafire Mk.3 .. .. .. 60 60

Nos. 1165/76 were printed together, se-tenant, forming a composite design.

INDEX

Countries can be quickly located by referring to the index at the end of this volume.

216 Boxing

1992. Olympic Games, Barcelona. Mult.
1177 42 s. Type **216** 65 40
1178 57 s. Diving 85 55
1179 1 p. 50 Tennis .. .. 2·75 2·75
1180 3 p. Cycling .. .. 4·25 4·50

217 King Taufa'ahau Tupou IV and Queen Halaevalu

1992. 25th Anniv of the Coronation of King Tupou IV.
1181 **217** 45 s. multicoloured .. 65 45
1182 – 80 s. multicoloured .. 1·25 1·25
1183 – 80 s. black & brown .. 1·25 1·25
1184 – 80 s. multicoloured .. 1·25 1·25
1185 – 2 p. multicoloured .. 3·25 3·25
DESIGNS—48 × 35 mm: No. 1182, King Tupou IV and Crown; 1183, Extract from Investiture ceremony; 1184, King Tupou IV and 1967 Coronation 2 p. commemorative; 1185, As Type **217**, but larger.
Nos. 1181/5 show the King's first name incorrectly spelt as "Taufʻahau".

1992. No. 1095 surch **45 s 45 s**.
1186 45 s. on 32 s. "Acanthurus leucosternon" 80 80

1992. Nos. 1121/4 surch **60**.
1187 60 s. on 42 s. Safety in cars (English inscr) .. 1·00 1·00
1188 60 s. on 42 s. Safety on bikes (English inscr) .. 1·00 1·00
1189 60 s. on 42 s. As No. 1187 (Tongan inscr) .. 1·00 1·00
1190 60 s. on 42 s. As No. 1188 (Tongan inscr) .. 1·00 1·00

220 Bats flying Home

1992. Sacred Bats of Kolovai. Multicoloured.
1191 60 s. Type **220** 85 85
1192 60 s. Tongan fruit bat .. 85 85
1193 60 s. Bats alighting on branches 85 85
1194 60 s. Bats hanging from tree 85 85
1195 60 s. Tongan fruit bat in tree 85 85
Nos. 1191/5 were printed together, se-tenant, forming a composite design.

221 Tongan Pearls

1992. Christmas. Multicoloured.
1197 60 s. Type **221** 70 55
1198 80 s. Reef fish 90 80
1199 2 p. Pacific orchids .. 2·50 2·50
1200 3 p. Parrots from Eua .. 3·75 3·75

222 Tonga Flag and Rotary Emblem (25th anniv of Rotary International in Tonga)

1992. Anniversaries and Events.
1201 **222** 60 s. multicoloured .. 70 55
1202 – 80 s. multicoloured .. 90 80
1203 – 1 p. 50 vio, lilac & blk 2·00 2·00
1204 – 3 p. 50 multicoloured 4·25 4·25
DESIGNS: 80 s. Pres. Kennedy and Peace Corps emblem (25th anniv of Peace Corps in Tonga); 1 p. 50, F.A.O. and W.H.O. emblems (International Conference); 3 p. 50, Globe and Rotary Foundation emblem (75th anniv of Rotary Foundation).

223 Mother and Child

1993. Family Planning.
1205 **223** 15 s. black, blue & mve (Tongan inscr) 15 20
1206 – 15 s. black, blue & mve (English inscr) 15 20
1207 – 45 s. black, yellow & grn (Tongan inscr) 40 45
1208 – 45 s. black, yellow & grn (English inscr) 40 45
1209 – 60 s. black, red & yell (Tongan inscr) .. 50 55
1210 – 60 s. black, red & yell (English inscr) .. 50 55
1211 – 2 p. black, yellow & orge (Tongan inscr) 1·75 1·90
1212 – 2 p. black, yellow & orge (English inscr) 1·75 1·90
DESIGNS: 45 s. Child on bike; 60 s. Girl with cats; 2 p. Old man and boy playing chess.

224 Anti-smoking and Anti-drugs Symbols with Healthy Food (½-size illustration)

1993. Health and Fitness Campaign. Mult.
1213 60 s. Type **224** 50 55
1214 80 s. Anti-smoking symbol and weight training .. 70 75
1215 1 p. 50 Anti-drugs symbol and water sports .. 1·25 1·40
1216 2 p. 50 Healthy food with cyclist and jogger .. 2·10 2·25

1993. No. 1087 surch **10s**.
1217 10 s. on 2 s. "Porites sp"

226 "Swainsonia casta"

1993. As Nos. 867, 877, 999, 1001/2a, 1005a, 1007, 1011, 1013 and 1015/6, some with new face values, redrawn as in T **226**. Multicoloured.
1218 1 s. Type **226** 10 10
1219 3 s. "Holocentrus ruber" 10 10
1220 5 s. "Cyprae mappa viridis" 10 10
1221 10 s. "Conus bullatus" .. 10 10
1223 20 s. "Dascyllus aruanus" .. 20 25
1225 45 s. "Lambis truncata" (as No. 877) 40 45
1227 60 s. "Conus aulicus" (as No. 1011) 55 60
1229 80 s. "Pterois volitans" (as No. 1001) 75 80
1230 1 p. "Chelonia mydas" (turtle) .. .. 95 1·00
1231 2 p. "Birgus latro" (crab) 2·00 2·10
1232 3 p. "Chicoreus palma-rosae" .. .. 2·75 3·00
Nos. 1230/2 are 38 × 23 mm.

227 Fire Brigade Badge

1993. 25th Annivs of Police Training College and Fire Service. Multicoloured.
1235 45 s. Type **227** 40 45
1236 45 s. Police badge and van 40 45
1237 60 s. Police band .. 55 60
1238 60 s. Fire engine at fire .. 55 60
1239 2 p. Fire engine at station 2·00 2·10
1240 2 p. Policeman and dog handler .. .. 2·00 2·10

228 Old Map of Islands

1993. 300th Anniv of Abel Tasman's Discovery of Eua. Multicoloured.
1241 30 s. Type **228** 30 35
1242 60 s. "Heemskirk" and "Zeehaan" at sea .. 55 60
1243 80 s. Tongan canoes welcoming ships .. 75 80
1244 3 p. 50 Tasman landing on Eua .. .. .. 3·25 3·50

229 King Taufa'ahau Tupou IV and Musical Instruments

1993. 75th Birthday of King Taufa'ahau Tupou IV. Multicoloured.
1245 45 s. Type **229** 40 45
1246 80 s. King Tupou IV and sporting events .. 75 80
1247 80 s. King Tupou IV and ancient landmarks .. 75 80
1248 80 s. King Tupou IV and Royal Palace 75 80
1249 2 p. As Type **229**, but larger .. .. .. 2·00 2·10
Nos. 1246/9 are larger, 38½ × 51 mm.

230 Christmas Feast

1993. Christmas. Multicoloured.
1250 60 s. Type **230** 55 60
1251 80 s. Firing home-made cannon 75 80
1252 1 p. 50 Band playing carols .. .. .. 1·40 1·50
1253 3 p. Going to church .. 3·00 3·25

231 "Land of Sun, Sea and Sand" (Kiley and Peter Moala)

1993. Winners of Children's Painting Competition.
1254 **231** 10 s. multicoloured .. 10 10
1255 – 10 s. multicoloured .. 10 10
1256 – 10 s. multicoloured .. 10 10
1257 – 10 s. multicoloured .. 10 10
1258 – 10 s. black and grey .. 10 10
1259 – 10 s. black and grey .. 10 10
1260 **231** 80 s. multicoloured .. 75 80
1261 – 80 s. multicoloured .. 75 80
1262 – 80 s. multicoloured .. 75 80
1263 – 80 s. multicoloured .. 75 80
1264 – 80 s. multicoloured .. 75 80
1265 – 80 s. multicoloured .. 75 80
DESIGNS: Nos. 1255 and 1261, "Maui, Fisher God of Tonga" (Kiley and Peter Moala); Nos. 1256 and 1262, "Traditional Island Transport" (Kiley and Peter Moala); Nos. 1257 and 1263, "Young Girl making Kava" (Pulotu Pole'o); Nos. 1258 and 1264, "Maui and his Hook" (Salome Tapou); Nos. 1259 and 1265, "Communications in the South Pacific" (Fe'ofa'aki Taufa).

233 Tiger Shark

1994. Game Fishing. Multicoloured.
1267 60 s. Type **233** 10 10
1268 80 s. Dolphin fish .. 75 80
1269 1 p. 50 Yellow fin tuna 1·40 1·50
1270 2 p. 50 Pacific blue marlin 2·40 2·50

234 Hands holding World cup

1994. World Cup Football Championship, U.S.A. Multicoloured.
1271 80 s. Type **234** 75 80
1272 80 s. Player's legs .. 75 80
1273 2 p. German player (black shorts) .. .. 2·00 2·10
1274 2 p. American player .. 2·00 2·10

AIRMAIL EXPRESS STAMPS

E 1 Short-eared Owl in Flight
(Illustration reduced, actual size 57 × 42 mm)

1990.
E1 **E 1** 10 p. black, red and blue 9·50 10·00

OFFICIAL STAMPS

1893. Optd. **G.F.B.**
O 1. **5.** 1d. blue.. .. .. 9·50 40·00
O 2. **6.** 2d. blue.. .. .. 25·00 45·00
O 3. **5.** 4d. blue.. .. .. 42·00 85·00
O 4. **6.** 8d. blue.. .. .. 80·00 £150
O 5. 1s. blue.. .. .. 90·00 £170

1893. Nos. O 1/5 variously surch.
O 6. **5.** ½d. on 1d. blue .. 14·00 45·00
O 7. **6.** 2½d. on 2d. blue .. 20·00 38·00
O 8. **5.** 5d on 4d. blue .. 20·00 38·00
O 9. **6.** 7½d. on 8d. blue .. 20·00 60·00
O 10. 10d. on 1s. blue .. 24·00 65·00

1962. Air. Stamps of 1953 and 1961 optd. as Nos. 120/7 but with **OFFICIAL AIR MAIL** in addition.
O 11. 2d. blue .. .. .. 11·00 6·00
O 12. 5d. violet .. .. 12·00 6·50
O 13. 1s. brown .. .. 7·50 3·75
O 14. 5s. yellow and lilac .. 90·00 55·00
O 15. 10s. yellow and black .. 42·00 22·00
O 16. £1 yellow, red and blue.. 70·00 35·00

1963. Air. First Polynesian Gold Coinage Commemoration. As No. 138 but additionally inscr. "OFFICIAL". 1 koula coin. Diameter 3⅛ in. Imperf.
O 17. B. 15s. black on gold .. 3·50 5·50

1965. Air. Surch. as Nos. 151/61.
O 18. B. 30s. on 15s. (No. O 17) 3·00 3·75

1966. Air. Tupou College and Secondary Education Cent. No. 117 surch. **OFFICIAL AIRMAIL** and new value, with commem. inscr. as Nos. 168/73.
O 19. 10s. on 4d. green .. 50 35
O 20. 20s. on 4d. green .. 75 50

1967. Air. No. 112 surch. **OFFICIAL AIRMAIL ONE PA'ANGA.**
O 21. 1 p. on 5s. yellow & lilac 1·75 2·25

1967. Air. No. 114 surch. **OFFICIAL AIRMAIL** and new value.
O 22. 40 s. on £1 yell., red & blue 50 50
O 23. 60 s. on £1 yell., red & blue 70 70
O 24. 1 p. on £1 yell., red & blue 90 90
O 25. 2 p. on £1 yell., red & blue 1·50 1·50

1967. Air. Arrival of U.S. Peace Corps in Tonga. As No. 114, but imperf. and background colour changed, surch. as Nos. 216/27 but with **Official Airmail** in addition.
O 26. 30 s. on £1 multicoloured 20 25
O 27. 70 s. on £1 multicoloured 40 45
O 28. 1 p. 50, on £1 multicoloured 70 85

1968. 50th Birthday of King Taufa'ahua IV. No. 207 surch. **"HIS MAJESTY'S 50th BIRTHDAY OFFICIAL AIRMAIL"** and new value.
O 29. 40s. on 50s. red & blue.. 1·00 70
O 30. 60s. on 50s. red & blue.. 1·50 1·25
O 31. 1 p. on 50s. red & blue.. 2·25 2·00
O 32. 2 p. on 50s. red & blue.. 4·00 2·75

1968. Air. South Pacific Games Field and Track Trials, Port Moresby, New Guinea. As No. 114, but imperf., background colour changed, surch.
O 33. 20 s. on £1 multicoloured 15 15
O 34. 1 p. on £1 multicoloured 40 40

1969. Air. 3rd South Pacific Games, Port Moresby. As Nos. 290/4 surch. **OFFICIAL AIRMAIL.**
O 35. 70 s. red, green & turquoise 45 60
O 36. 80 s. red, orge. & turquoise 55 70

1969. Air. Oil Search. As No. 114, but imperf., background colour changed, and optd. **1969 OIL SEARCH** and new value.
O 37. 90 s. on £1 multicoloured 2·75 2·00
O 38. 1 p. 10 on £1 mult. .. 2·75 2·00
No. O 37 is additionally optd. **OFFICIAL AIRMAIL.**

1969. Air. Royal Visit. As No. 110, but imperf., colour changed, and surch. **Royal Visit MARCH 1970 OFFICIAL AIRMAIL** and new value.
O 39. 75 s. on 1s. red and yellow 3·00 2·00
O 40. 1 p. on 1s. red and yellow 3·50 2·50
O 41. 1 p. 25 on 1s. red & yellow 4·25 3·25

1970. Commonwealth Membership. As No. 112, but imperf and surch **Commonwealth Member, June, 1970** and **OFFICIAL AIRMAIL.**
O42 50 s. on 5 s. yellow & brn 60 50
O43 90 s. on 5 s. yellow & brn 80 70
O44 1p. 50 on 5 s. yell & brn 1·50 1·25

1970. Imperf. Self-adhesive. Colour of "TONGA" given for 6s to 10s.
O 45. **83.** 1 s. yell., pur. & blk. 15 15
O 46. 2 s. yell., blue & black 20 20
O 47. 3 s. yell., brn. & black 25 25
O 48. 4 s. yell., green & black 25 25
O 49. 5 s. yell., red and black 30 30
O 50. **90.** 6 s. blue 35 35
O 51. 7 s. mauve 40 40
O 52. 8 s. gold 45 45
O 53. 9 s. red 55 55
O 54. 10 s. silver 55 55
On the official issues Nos. O 45 to O 54, the value tablet is black (banana issue) or green (coconut issue). On the postage issues the colour is white.
See also Nos. O 82/91.

1970. Air. Cent. of British Red Cross. As No. 102 and 112, but imperf. in different colours and surch. **Centenary British Red Cross 1870-1970 OFFICIAL AIRMAIL** and value.
O 55. 30 s. on 1½d. green .. 1·50 1·50
O 56. 80 s. on 5s. yellow & brn. 3·75 3·75
O 57. 90 s. on 5s. yellow & brn. 3·75 3·75

1971. Air. 5th Death Anniv. of Queen Salote. As No. 113, but imperf. and colour changed surch. **OFFICIAL AIRMAIL 1965 IN MEMORIAM 1970** and value.
O 58. 20 s on 10s. orange .. 80 60
O 59. 30 s. on 10s. orange .. 1·00 80
O 60. 50 s. on 10s. orange .. 2·00 1·25
O 61. 2 p. on 10s. orange .. 7·00 5·00

1971. Air. Philatokyo '71 Stamp Exhib., Japan. Nos. O 55/7 optd. **PHILATOKYO '71** and Emblem.
O 62. 30 s. on 5d. green & yellow 50 40
O 63. 80 s. on 5d. green & yellow 1·25 1·00
O 64. 90 s. on 5d. green & yellow 1·50 1·25

1971. Air. As T **96** but inscr. "OFFICIAL AIRMAIL".
O 65. 14 s. multicoloured .. 75 75
O 65a. 17 s. multicoloured .. 85 85
O 66. 21 s. multicoloured .. 1·00 1·00
O 66a. 38 s. multicoloured .. 1·60 1·60

O **13.** Football.

1971. Air. 4th South Pacific Games, Tahiti. Imperf. Self-adhesive.
O 67. O **13.** 50 s. multicoloured 50 65
O 68. 90 s. multicoloured 75 1·10
O 69. 1 p. 50 multicoloured 1·00 1·40

1971. Air. Investiture of Royal Tongan Medal of Merit. surch. **INVESTITURE 1971. OFFICIAL AIRMAIL.**
O 70. **89.** 60 s. on 3 s. mult. 60 60
O 71. 80 s. on 25 s. mult. 80 80
O 72. 1 p. **10.** on 7 s. mult. 90 90

O **15.** "U.N.I.C.E.F." and Emblem.

1971. Air 25th Anniv. of U.N.I.C.E.F. Imperf. Self-adhesive.
O 73. O **15.** 70 s. multicoloured 1·10 1·10
O 74. 80 s. multicoloured 1·25 1·25
O 75. 90 s. multicoloured 1·40 1·40

1972. Air. Merchant Marine Routes. As T **100**, but inscr "OFFICIAL AIRMAIL". Imperf. Self-adhesive.
O76 20 s. multicoloured .. 75 50
O77 50 s. multicoloured .. 2·25 1·50
O78 1 p. 20 multicoloured .. 4·25 3·25
DESIGNS: Nos. O76/8, Map of South Pacific and "Aoniu".

1972. Air. 5th Anniv. of Coronation. Design similar to T **101**, but inscr. "OFFICIAL AIRMAIL".
O 79. 50 s. multicoloured .. 80 45
O 80. 70 s. multicoloured .. 1·10 60
O 81. 1 p. 50 multicoloured .. 2·40 1·00
DESIGN: (47 × 57 mm.). Nos. O 79/81, As Type **101**, but with different background.

1972. As Nos. 413/27, but inscr. "OFFICIAL POST".
(a) As. 413/17.
O 82. **83.** 1 s. yellow, red & blk. 20 10
O 83. 2 s. yellow, green & blk. 25 15
O 84. 3 s. yellow, green & blk. 30 20
O 85. 4 s. yellow and black.. 30 20
O 86. 5 s. yellow and black.. 30 20
(b) As Nos. O 50/4, but colours changed. Multicoloured. Colour of "TONGA" given.
O 87. **90.** 6 s. green 35 20
O 88. 7 s. green 40 25
O 89. 8 s. green 40 25
O 90. 9 s. green 40 25
O 91. 10 s. green 50 30
(c) As Nos. 423/7. Multicoloured. Colour of face-value given.
O 92. **102.** 15 s. blue 85 45
O 93. 20 s. orange .. 1·00 60
O 94. 25 s. brown .. 1·10 70
O 95. 40 s. orange .. 2·25 1·50
O 96. 50 s. blue .. 2·50 1·75

1972. Air. Proclamation of Sovereignty over Minerva Reefs. As T **104**, but inscr. "OFFICIAL AIRMAIL".
O 97. 25 s. multicoloured .. 40 35
O 98. 75 s. multicoloured .. 1·25 90
O 99. 1 p. 50 multicoloured .. 2·50 1·50

1973. Air. Foundation of Bank of Tonga. No. 396 surch. **TONGA 1973 ESTABLISHMENT BANK OF TONGA OFFICIAL AIRMAIL,** star and value.
O 100. **100.** 40 s. on 21 s. mult. .. 1·25 75
O 101. 85 s. on 21 s. mult. .. 2·25 1·40
O 102. 1 p. 25 on 21 s. mult. 3·00 1·90

1973. Silver Jubilee of Scouting in Tonga. Nos. O 76, O 74 and 319 surch. or optd.
O 103. – 30 s. on 20 s. mult. 15·00 3·50
O 104. O **15.** 80 s. multicoloured 32·00 12·00
O 105. **89.** 1 p. 40 on 50 s. mult. 48·00 25·00
OVERPRINT AND SURCHARGES: 30 s. **SILVER JUBILEE TONGAN SCOUTING 1948-1973,** scout badge and value. 80 s. **SILVER-JUBILEE 1948-1973** and scout badge. 1 p. 40 **OFFICIAL AIRMAIL 1948-1973 SILVER JUBILEE TONGAN SCOUTING** and value.

1973. Air. Bicentenary of Capt. Cook's Visit. Design similar to T **107**, but inscr. "OFFICIAL AIRMAIL".
O 106. 25 s. multicoloured .. 3·25 1·50
O 107. 80 s. multicoloured .. 8·50 3·50
O 108. 1 p. 30 multicoloured .. 10·00 5·50
DESIGN—HORIZ. (52 × 45 mm.). Nos. O 106/108, (bulk carrier) "James Cook".

1973. Air. Commonwealth Games, Christchurch. Nos. O67/9 optd **1974 COMMONWEALTH GAMES, CHRISTCHURCH.**
O 109. O **13** 50 s. multicoloured 1·00 75
O 110. 90 s. multicoloured 1·75 1·25
O 111. 1 p. 50 multicoloured 2·50 2·00

O **19.** Dove of Peace.

1974. Air.
O 112. O **19.** 7 s. grn., vio. & red 50 20
O 113. 9 s. grn., vio. & brn. 55 25
O 114. 12 s. grn., vio. & brn. 60 30
O 115. 14 s. grn., vio. & yell. 65 35
O 116. 17 s. multicoloured 75 30
O 117. 29 s. multicoloured 1·25 80
O 118. 38 s. multicoloured 1·75 1·00
O 119. 50 s. multicoloured 2·25 2·25
O 120. 75 s. multicoloured 3·00 3·00

1974. Centenary of U.P.U. As Nos. 488/97 but inscr. "OFFICIAL AIRMAIL".
O 121. 25 s. orange, grn. & blk. 60 45
O 122. 35 s. yell., red & blk. .. 75 60
O 123. 70 s. orge., bl. & blk. .. 1·75 1·40
DESIGNS—HORIZ. (43 × 40 mm.). Nos. O 121/3, Letters "UPU".

1974. Air. Tongan Girl Guides. As Nos. 498/507 inscr. "OFFICIAL AIRMAIL".
O 124. 45 s. multicoloured .. 4·00 1·75
O 125. 55 s. multicoloured .. 4·25 2·00
O 126. 1 p. multicoloured .. 7·50 3·75
DESIGNS—OVAL (36 × 52 mm.). Nos. O 124/6, Lady Baden-Powell.

1974. Air. Establishment of Royal Marine Institute. Nos. 446 and 451 surch. **Establishment Royal Marine Institute Official Airmail** and new value (Nos. O 127/8 also optd **Tonga Tonga**)
O 127. 30 s. on 15 s. mult. 2·25 1·25
O 128. **106.** 35 s. on 16 s. mult. 2·50 1·50
O 129. 80 s. on 17 s. mult. 4·25 3·25

1975. Air. South Pacific Forum and Tourism. As T **113.** Imperf. Self-adhesive.
O 130. 50 s. multicoloured .. 1·10 80
O 131. 75 s. multicoloured .. 1·75 1·25
O 132. 1 p. 25 multicoloured .. 2·50 1·75
DESIGNS (49 × 43 mm.): 50 s. Jungle arch. 75 s., 1 p. 25 Sunset scene.

1975. Air. 5th South Pacific Games. As T 114. Imperf. Self-adhesive.
O 133. 38 s. multicoloured .. 45 40
O 134. 75 s. multicoloured .. 80 75
O 135. 1 p. 20 multicoloured .. 1·40 1·50
DESIGN—OVAL (51 × 27 mm.). Nos. O 133/5, Runners on track.

O **21.** Tongan Monarchs.
(Illustration reduced. Actual size 69 × 39 mm.)

1975. Air. Centenary of Tongan Constitution. Imperf. Self-adhesive.
O 136. O **21.** 17 s. multicoloured 30 25
O 137. 60 s. multicoloured 80 70
O 138. 90 s. multicoloured 1·25 1·00

1976. Air. First Participation in Olympic Games. As Nos. 558/67 but inscr. "OFFICIAL AIRMAIL".

O 139. 45 s. multicoloured .. 2·25 85
O 140. 55 s. multicoloured .. 2·50 1·00
O 141. 1 p. multicoloured .. 4·00 1·90
DESIGN—OVAL (36 × 53 mm.). Montreal logo.

1976. Air. Bicentenary of American revolution. As Nos. 568/77 but inscr. "OFFICIAL AIRMAIL".

O 142. 20 s. multicoloured .. 1·00 40
O 143. 50 s. multicoloured .. 2·25 1·00
O 144. 1 p. 15 multicoloured .. 4·75 2·50

1976. 150th Anniv. of Christianity in Tonga.

O 145. 65 s. multicoloured .. 1·75 1·40
O 146. 85 s. multicoloured .. 2·00 1·75
O 147. 1 p. 15 multicoloured .. 2·75 2·50
DESIGNS—HEXAGONAL (65 × 52 mm.). Lifuka Chapel.

1976. Air. Centenary of Treaty of Friendship with Germany.

O 148. 30 s. multicoloured .. 60 70
O 149. 60 s. multicoloured .. 1·40 1·60
O 150. 1 p. 25 multicoloured .. 2·75 3·00
DESIGN—RECTANGULAR (51 × 47 mm.). Text.

1977. Air. Silver Jubilee.

O 151. 35 s. multicoloured .. 3·00 50
O 152. 45 s. multicoloured .. 80 30
O 153. 1 p. multicoloured .. 1·10 50
DESIGN: 57 × 66 mm. Flags of Tonga and the U.K.

1977. Air. 10th Anniv. of King's Coronation.

O 154. 20 s. multicoloured .. 40 45
O 155. 40 s. multicoloured .. 80 90
O 156. 80 s. multicoloured .. 1·75 2·00
DESIGN—SQUARE: (50 × 50 mm.), 1967 Coronation Coin.

1977. Air. Bicent. of Capt. Cook's Last Voyage.

O 157. 20 s. multicoloured .. 2·75 2·50
O 158. 55 s. multicoloured .. 6·00 5·50
O 159. 85 s. multicoloured .. 8·50 8·00
DESIGN—RECTANGULAR: (52 × 46 mm.), Text.

1977. Air. Whale Conservation.

O 160. 45 s. multicoloured .. 2·75 2·00
O 161. 65 s. multicoloured .. 3·75 2·75
O 162. 85 s. multicoloured .. 4·75 3·25
DESIGN—HEXAGONAL: (66 × 51 mm.), Blue Whale.

1978. Air. Commonwealth Games, Edmonton.

O 163. 30 s. black, blue and red 45 50
O 164. 60 s. black, red and blue 1·00 1·25
O 165. 1 p. black, red and blue 1·60 1·75
DESIGN—"TEAR-DROP" (35 × 52 mm.). Games Emblem.

1978. 60th Birthday of King Taufa'ahau Tupou IV.

O 166. 26 s. black, red & yellow 35 30
O 167. 85 s. blk., brn. and yell. 1·10 1·00
O 168. 90 s. blk., violet & yell. 1·25 1·10
DESIGN—MEDAL-SHAPED (21 × 45 mm.). Portrait of King.

1978. Coil Stamps. As Nos. 675/89 but inscr. "OFFICIAL POST".

O 169. 1 s. purple and yellow .. 10 10
O 170. 2 s. brown and yellow .. 10 10
O 171. 3 s. red and yellow .. 10 10
O 172. 4 s. brown and yellow .. 10 10
O 173. 5 s. green and yellow .. 10 10
O 174. 6 s. brown and green .. 15 15
O 175. 7 s. black, green & brn. 20 20
O 176. 8 s. red, green & brown 20 20
O 177. 9 s. brown and green .. 25 25
O 178. 10 s. green and brown .. 25 25
O 179. 15 s. blk., brn. and grn. 45 45
O 180. 20 s. red, brown & green 50 50
O 181. 30 s. green and brown .. 60 60
O 182. 50 s. blue, brown & green 1·10 1·10
O 183. 1 p. violet, brn. & green 2·00 2·00

1978. Air. Endangered Wildlife. Mult.

O 184. 40 s. Type **129** .. 2·25 1·40
O 185. 50 s. Insular Flying Fox .. .. 2·25 1·50
O 186. 1 p. 10 Turtle .. .. 3·75 3·25

1979. Air. Decade of Progress, inscr. "OFFICIAL AIRMAIL".

O 187. G. 38 s. multicoloured .. 65 45
O 188. E. 74 s. multicoloured .. 1·25 75
O 189. A. 80 s. multicoloured .. 1·40 80
DESIGN—As Type **130**, G. Tonga Red Cross.

1979. Air. Death Centenary of Sir Rowland Hill and 10th Anniv. of Tongan self-adhesive Stamps.

O 190. 45 s. multicoloured .. 90 60
O 191. 65 s. multicoloured .. 1·25 85
O 192. 80 s. multicoloured .. 1·60 1·10
DESIGN—HAND-SHAPED (45 × 53 mm.) 45 s. to 80 s. Removing self-adhesive stamp from backing paper.

O **22.** Blue-crowned Lory (with foliage).

1979. Air. Coil Stamps.

O 193. O **21.** 5 s. multicoloured 20 20
O 194. 11 s. multicoloured 30 30
O 195. 14 s. multicoloured 30 30
O 196. 15 s. multicoloured 40 40
O 197. 17 s. multicoloured 40 40
O 198. 18 s. multicoloured 40 40
O 199. 22 s. multicoloured 45 45
O 200. 31 s. multicoloured 65 65
O 201. 39 s. multicoloured 80 80
O 202. 75 s. multicoloured 1·50 1·75
O 203. 1 p. multicoloured .. 2·00 2·25

1979. Air. Views as seen through the lens of a camera.

O 204. 35 s. multicoloured .. 55 55
O 205. 45 s. multicoloured .. 65 65
O 206. 1 p. multicoloured .. 1·40 1·40
DESIGN: 35 s. to 1 p. Niuatoputapu and Tafahi.

1980. Air. 125th Anniv. of Tonga–France Friendship Treaty.

O 207. 40 s. multicoloured .. 70 70
O 208. 55 s. multicoloured .. 90 90
O 209. 1 p. 25 multicoloured .. 2·00 2·00
DESIGN: 40 s. to 1 p. 25, Basilica of Tonga.

1980. Air. Olympic Games, Moscow. Nos. O 190/2 surch.

O 210. 26 s. on 45 s. multicoloured 55 55
O 211. 40 s. on 65 s. multicoloured 90 90
O 212. 1 p. 10 on 1 p. mult. 2·75 3·00

O **23.** Blue-crowned Lory (without foliage).

1980. No. O 193 redrawn without foliage as Type O **23**.

O 213. O **23.** 5 s. multicoloured .. £100

1980. Air. South Pacific Scout Jamboree, Tonga and 75th Anniv. of Rotary International.

O 214. 25 s. multicoloured .. 70 40
O 215. 2 p. multicoloured .. 3·50 3·00
DESIGN: 25 s., 2 p. Scout camp and Rotary emblem.

1980. Air. No. O 145 surch.

O 216. 2 p. on 65 s. multicoloured 4·00 4·50

1983. Nos. 834/6 optd. **OFFICIAL**.

O 217. 29 s. Type **151** .. .. 2·75 2·75
O 218. 32 s. Type **151** .. .. 3·50 3·50
O 219. 47 s. Montgolfier's balloon and "Concorde" 5·00 5·00

1984. Nos. 865/79 and 881 optd. **OFFICIAL**.

O 220. 1 s. Type **159** 10 10
O 221. 2 s. "Porites sp" 10 10
O 222. 3 s. "Holocentrus ruber" .. 10 10
O 223. 5 s. "Cypraea mappa viridis" .. 10 10
O 224. 6 s. "Dardanus megistos" .. 10 10
O 225b. 9 s. "Stegostoma fasciatum" .. 10 10
O 226. 10 s. "Conus bullatus" 10 10
O 227. 13 s. "Pterois volitans" 15 20
O 228. 15 s. "Conus textile" .. 15 20
O 229. 20 s. "Dascyllus aruanus" .. 15 20
O 230. 29 s. "Conus aulicus" .. 25 30
O 231. 32 s. "Acanthurus leucosternon" 25 30
O 232. 47 s. "Lambis truncata" 40 45
O 233. 1 p. "Millepora dichotama" .. 85 90
O 234. 2 p. "Birgus latro" .. 1·75 1·90
O 235. 5 p. "Thunnus albacares" .. 4·25 4·50

1986. Nos. 933/9 optd. **OFFICIAL**.

O 236. 4 s. on 2 s. "Porites sp." 20 20
O 237. 4 s. on 13 s. "Pterois volitans" .. 20 20
O 238. 42 s. on 3 s. "Holocentrus ruber" .. 80 80
O 239. 42 s. on 9 s. "Stegostoma fasciatum" .. 80 80
O 240. 57 s. on 6 s. "Dardanus megistos" .. 1·00 1·00
O 241. 57 s. on 20 s. "Dascyllus aruanus" .. 1·00 1·00
O 242. 2 p. 50 on 2 p. "Birgus latro" .. 3·50 3·50

TRANSVAAL

Formerly South African Republic under Boer rule, annexed by Gt. Britain in 1877, restored to the Boers in 1881 and again annexed in 1900, and since 1919 a province of the Union of S. Africa.

12 pence = 1 shilling.
20 shillings = 1 pound.

1.

1870. Imperf or roul.

61. **1.** 1d. red .. .. .. 20·00 14·00
22. 1d. black .. .. .. 15·00 25·00
53. 3d. lilac .. .. .. 45·00 38·00
54a. 6d. blue .. .. .. 45·00 38·00
32. 1s. green .. .. .. 70·00 38·00

1874. Perf.

38a. **1.** 1d. red .. .. .. 75·00 35·00
171. 1d. deep grey .. .. 3·25 1·00
172. 3d. black on red .. 14·00 2·75
173. 3d. red .. .. .. 6·00 1·00
173b. 3d. brown .. .. .. 20·00 2·25
39. 6d. blue .. .. .. £120 50·00
174. 1s. green .. .. .. 25·00 2·50

1877. Optd. **V. R. TRANSVAAL.** Imperf. or roul.

101. **1.** 1d. red .. .. .. 20·00 20·00
102. 3d. lilac .. .. .. 70·00 35·00
103. 6d. blue .. .. .. 85·00 30·00
113. 6d. blue on red .. .. 70·00 45·00
104. 1s. green .. .. .. 85·00 40·00

1877. Optd. **V. R. Transvaal.** Imperf. or roul.

116 1 1d. red on blue .. 45·00 24·00
117 1d. red on orange .. 15·00 16·00
118 3d. lilac on brown .. 38·00 24·00
119d 3d. lilac on green .. 95·00 32·00
147 3d. lilac on blue .. 40·00 25·00
126 6d. blue on green .. 70·00 22·00
121 6d. blue on blue .. 48·00 22·00

9.

18.

1878. Perf.

156. **9.** ½d. red .. .. .. 16·00 45·00
157a. 1d. brown .. .. .. 6·00 2·25
158. 3d. red .. .. .. 8·00 3·25
159. 4d. olive .. .. .. 11·00 4·25
160. 6d. black .. .. .. 5·00 3·25
161. 1s. green .. .. .. 90·00 32·00
162. 2s. blue .. .. .. £120 65·00

1879. Surch. **1 Penny.**

168. **9.** 1d. on 6d. black .. 35·00 22·00

1882. Surch. **EEN PENNY.**

170. **9.** 1d. on 4d. olive .. 6·00 3·75

1885.

175. **18.** ½d. grey 30 10
176. 1d. red 30 10
177. 2d. purple .. .. .. 1·25 1·00
178. 2d. pale brown 40 10
179. 2½d. mauve .. .. .. 1·25 40
180. 3d. mauve .. .. .. 1·50 70
181. 4d. deep olive .. .. 2·25 50
182. 6d. blue .. .. .. 3·25 2·00
183. 1s. green .. .. .. 2·50 35
184. 2s. 6d. yellow .. .. 3·50 1·40
185. 5s. grey .. .. .. 4·75 2·50
186. 10s. brown .. .. .. 24·00 5·00
187. £5 green £3000 £170

1885. Surch. **HALVE PENNY** vert., reading up or down.

188 1 ½d. on 3d. red (No. 173) 2·50 5·00
192 18 ½d. on 3d. mauve .. 1·50 1·50
189 1 ½d. on 1s. green (No.174) 7·00 17·00

1885. Surch. with value in words and **Z.A.R.** both vert.

190 9 ½d. on 6d. black.. .. 10·00 24·00
191 2d. on 6d. black .. .. 2·00 2·25

1887. Surch. **2d.** and thick bar.

194. **18.** 2d. on 3d. mauve .. 60 1·00

1893. Surch. **Halve Penny** and bars.

196 18 ½d. on 2d. pale brown .. 60 50

1893. Surch. in figures and words between bars. (A) in one line, (B) in two.

197. **18.** 1d. on 6d. blue (A) .. 40 30
198. 2½d. on 1s. green (A) .. 70 1·00
199. 2½d. on 1s. green (B) .. 2·00 1·75

29. (Wagon with shafts)

30. (Wagon with pole)

1894.

200. **29.** ½d. grey 20 10
201. 1d. red 20 10
202. 2d. pale brown 20 10
203. 6d. blue 90 40
204. 1s. green .. .. .. 4·50 6·00

1895.

205. **30.** ½d. grey 20 10
206. 1d. red 20 10
207. 2d. pale brown 20 10
208. 3d. mauve 30 10
209. 4d. black .. .. .. 1·10 60
210. 6d. blue .. .. .. 1·00 40
211. 1s. green .. .. .. 1·10 75
212. 5s. grey .. .. .. 8·00 12·00
212a. 10s. brown .. .. .. 8·00 2·25

1895. Surch. **Halve Penny** and bar.

213. **30.** ½d. on 1s. green 30 10

1895. Surch. **1d** and thick bar.

214. **18.** 1d. on 2½d. mauve .. 30 10

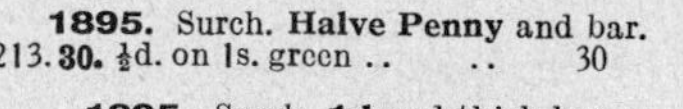

33.

1895. Fiscal stamp optd. **POSTZEGEL.**

215. **33.** 6d. red 50 75

34.

1895. Penny Postage Commem.

215b. **34.** 1d. red 75 50

1896.

216. **30.** ½d. green 20 10
217. 1d. red and green .. 20 10
218. 2d. brown and green .. 20 10
219. 2½d. blue and green .. 30 10
220. 3d. purple and green .. 60 60
221. 4d. olive and green .. 60 60
222. 6d. lilac and green .. 30 55
223. 1s. pale brown and green 45 15
224. 2s. 6d. violet and green 1·00 1·00

1900. Optd. **V.R.I.**

226. **30.** ½d. green 15 15
227. 1d. red and green .. 15 15
228. 2d. brown and green .. 1·25 50
229. 2½d. blue and green .. 50 55
230. 3d. purple and green .. 50 55
231. 4d. olive and green .. 85 20
232. 6d. lilac and green .. 85 50
233. 1s. pale brown and green 85 90
234. 2s. 6d. violet and green .. 1·75 2·75
235. 5s. grey .. .. .. 3·00 4·75
236. 10s. brown .. .. .. 5·00 6·00
237. **18.** £5 green £1800 £750

The majority of the £5 stamps, No. 237, on the market, are forgeries.

1901. Optd. **E.R.I.**

238. **30.** ½d. green 25 15
239. 1d. red and green .. 25 10
240. 3d. purple and green .. 1·25 1·25
241. 4d. olive and green .. 1·25 1·50
242. 2s. 6d. violet and green .. 4·50 5·50

1901. Surch. **E.R.I. Half Penny.**

243. **30.** ½d. on 2d. brown & green 25 25

38.

1902.

244 38 ½d. black and green .. 80 20
273 ½d. green .. .. .. 1·25 10
245 1d. black and red .. 75 15
274 1d. red .. .. .. 1·00 10
246 2d. black and purple .. 1·40 25
275 2d. purple .. .. .. 3·00 20
247 2½d. black and blue .. 2·50 85
276 2½d. blue .. .. .. 7·50 2·25
264 3d. black and green .. 2·75 30

265		4d. black and brown ..	2·25	30
266a		6d. black and orange ..	1·75	40
251	38	1s. black and green ..	8·00	3·50
267		1s. grey and brown	2·75	30
252		2s. black and brown ..	14·00	17·00
268		2s. grey and yellow ..	12·00	3·00
253		2s. 6d. mauve & black	10·00	7·00
270		5s. black & pur on yell	9·50	1·50
271		10s. black & pur on red	23·00	2·25
272a		£1 green and violet ..	£120	11·00
259		£5 brown and violet ..	£1200	£425

Nos. 267, 268 and all values of 2s. 6d. and above have the inscription "POSTAGE" on both sides. The rest are inscribed "POSTAGE" at left and "REVENUE" at right.

POSTAGE DUE STAMPS

D1.

1907.

D 1.	D 1.	½d. black and green ..	2·00	1·25
D 2.		1d. black and red ..	2·75	85
D 3.		2d. brown	2·75	1225
D 4.		3d. black and blue ..	3·50	3·00
D 5.		5d. black and violet ..	1·75	9·00
D 6.		6d. black and brown..	4·00	11·00
D 7.		1s. red and black	7·50	5·00

TRAVANCORE

A state of south-east India. In 1949 formed part of Travancore-Cochin.

16 cash = 1 chuckram.
28 chuckrams = 1 rupee.

3. Conch or Chank Shell. **1.**

1888. Various frames.

9	3	4 cash pink	15	10
24	–	5 cash olive	35	10
34	–	5 cash brown	1·40	20
10	1	6 cash brown	30	10
11a		½ ch. purple	30	10
27	–	10 cash pink	35	10
13	–	¾ ch. black	50	10
39	–	¾ ch. mauve	30	10
14c	1	1 ch. blue	50	10
15		1¼ ch. purple	30	20
42		1½ ch. red	1·25	10
16a		2 ch. red	40	10
17	–	3 ch. violet	1·50	15
18a	1	4 ch. green	1·10	35
19	–	7 ch. purple	1·60	40
20	–	14 ch. orange	2·40	1·00

1906. Surch. in figures.

21	1	¼ on ½ ch. purple.. ..	20	10
22		⅜ on ½ ch. purple.. ..	20	30

1921. Surch. in figures.

31	3	1 c. on 4 cash pink ..	15	15
57	–	1 c. on 5 cash brown ..	15	15
58	–	1 c. on 5 cash purple ..	60	15
50	1	1 c. on 1¼ ch. purple ..	15	30
59	–	2 c. on 10 cash pink ..	15	15
51	1	2 c. on 1¼ ch. purple ..	15	15
32		5 c. on 1 ch. blue ..	40	10

11. Sri Padmanabha Shrine.

13. Maharaja Sir Bala Rama Varma.

DESIGN — As Type **11**: 10 cash, State chariot.

1931. Coronation.

47.	11.	6 cash black and green ..	35	45
48.	–	10 cash black and blue ..	35	30
49.	13.	3 ch. black and purple ..	65	75

16. Maharaja Sir Bala Rama Varma and Subramania Shrine.

1937. Temple Entry Proclamation.

60.	16.	6 cash red..	40	50
61.	–	12 cash blue	80	20
62.	–	1½ ch. green	55	30
63.	–	3 ch. violet	1·50	75

DESIGNS: Portraits of the Maharaja and the temples of Sri Padmanabha (12 cash), Mahadeva (1½ ch.) and Kanyakumari (3 ch.)

17. Lake Ashtamudi.

18. Maharaja Sir Bala Rama Varma.

DESIGNS—As Type **18**. 1½ ch., 3 ch. Bust of Maharaja. As Type **17**: Sri Padmanabha Shrine (4 ch.). Bust of Maharaja and Cape Comorin (7 ch.) and Pachipari Irrigation Reservoir (14 ch.).

1939. 27th Birthday of Maharaja.

64.	17.	1 ch. green	1·50	10
65.	–	1½ ch. red	75	85
66.	18.	2 ch. orange	1·75	30
67.	–	3 ch. brown	2·50	10
68.	–	4 ch. red	1·60	40
69.	–	7 ch. blue	3·50	7·50
70.	–	14 ch. green	4·25	20·00

19. Maharaja and Aruvikara Falls.

1941. 29th Birthday of Maharaja.

71.	19.	6 cash violet	2·50	10
72.	–	¾ ch. brown	2·75	15

DESIGN: ¾ ch. Maharaja and Marthanda Varma Bridge, Alwaye.

1943. Stamps of 1939 and 1941 surch. in figures and capital letters.

73e	–	2 cash on 1½ ch. red (65)..	30	20
74a	–	4 cash on ¾ ch. brown (72)	1·50	15
75a	19	8 cash on 6 cash red (as No. 71)	1·00	10

21. Maharaja Sir Bala Rama Varma.

1946. 34th Birthday of Maharaja.

76a.	21.	8 cash red	65	50

1946. No. O 103 optd. **SPECIAL.**

77.	19.	6 cash violet	5·50	1·50

OFFICIAL STAMPS

1911. Optd. **On S.S.**

O 1	3	4 cash pink	20	10
O 14	–	5 cash olive	35	10
O 29	–	5 cash brown	20	30
O 15	1	6 cash brown	20	10
O 54		½ ch. purple	20	10
O 18	–	10 cash pink	35	10
O 39	–	¾ ch. black	30	15
O 56	–	¾ ch. mauve	30	15
O 5	1	1 ch. blue	40	10
O 21		1¼ ch. purple	35	10
O 59		1½ ch. red	40	10
O 6		2 ch. red	30	10
O 8	–	3 ch. violet	30	10
O 10	1	4 ch. green	55	10
O 64	–	7 ch. purple	1·10	30
O 65	–	14 ch. orange	1·60	40

1932. Official stamps surch. in figures.

O 74	–	6 c. on 5 cash olive ..	1·40	70
O 75	–	6 c. on 5 cash brown ..	20	20
O 83	–	12 c. on 10 cash pink ..	20	15
O 84	1	1 ch. 8 cash on 1¼ ch. red	35	25

1939. Optd. **SERVICE**.

O 85	1.	6 cash brown ..	70	15
O 94	–	¾ ch. mauve (No. 39)	7·00	20
O 96	17.	1 ch. green ..	50	10
O 97b	–	1½ ch. red (No. 65)	1·00	15
O 95a	1.	1½ ch. red ..	3·50	1·00
O 98	17.	2 ch. orange ..	1·00	30
O 99	–	3 ch. brown (No. 67)	60	10
O100	–	4 ch. red (No. 68)	1·00	45
O101	–	7 ch. blue (No. 69)	3·00	35
O102	–	14 ch. green (No. 70)	6·00	70

1942. Optd. **SERVICE.**

O 103.	19.	6 cash violet	40	20
O 104.	–	¾ ch. brown (No. 72)..	1·75	10

1942. Nos. 73/5 optd. **SERVICE.**

O 106a	–	2 cash on 1½ ch. red	40	15
O 107a	–	4 cash on † ch. brown	70	20
O 105a	19	8 cash on 6 cash red	1·25	10

1947. Optd. **SERVICE.**

O 108.	21.	8 cash red	1·40	70

TRAVANCORE—COCHIN

In 1949 the states of Cochin and Travancore in S.E. India were united under the name of the United States of Travancore and Cochin. Now uses stamps of India.

12 pies = 1 anna; 16 annas = 1 rupee.

ONE ANNA
ഒരണ
(1.)

1949. Stamps of Travancore surch. as T **1**.

1e	19	2 p. on 6 cash violet ..	35	20
2c	21	4 p. on 8 cash red ..	70	20
3e	17	½ a. on 1 ch. green ..	50	20
4a	18	1 a. on 2 ch. orange ..	50	20
5c	11	2 a. on 4 ch. brown ..	1·25	50
6a	–	3 a. on 7 ch. blue (No. 69)	4·50	1·50
7b	–	6 a. on 14 ch. grn. (No. 70)	5·00	9·00

1949. No. 106 of Cochin optd. **U.S.T.C.**

8.	21.	1 a. orange..	4·50	45·00

1950. No. 106 of Cochin optd. **T.-C.**

9.	21.	1 a. orange..	5·50	42·00

1950. No. 9 surch with new value.

10.	21.	6 p. on 1 a. orange ..	1·60	16·00
11.		9 p. on 1 a. orange ..	1·40	16·00

5. Conch or Chank Shell. **6.** Palm Trees.

1950.

12.	5.	2 p. red	75	1·10
13.	6.	4 p. blue	1·25	5·50

OFFICIAL STAMPS

1949. Stamps of Travancore surch. as T **1**.

O 8	19.	2 p. on 6 cash (No. 71)	30	65
O 10	21.	4 p. on 8 cash (No. 76a)	30	20
O 11b	17.	½ a. on 1 ch. (No. 64)	30	15
O 12c	18.	1 a. on 2 ch. (No. 66)	40	20
O 9a	–	2 a. on 4 ch. (No. 68)	60	55
O 14e	–	3 a. on 7ch. (No. 69)	1·40	1·00
O 15	–	6 a. on 14 ch. (No. 70)	1·40	2·40

TRENGGANU

A state of the Federation of Malaya, incorporated in Malaysia in 1963.

100 cents = 1 dollar (Straits or Malayan).

1. Sultan Zain ul ab din. **2.**

1910.

1.	1.	1 c. green	50	1·00
2.		2 c. brown and purple ..	40	90
3.		3 c. red	1·75	1·50
4.		4 c. orange	3·25	5·00
5.		4 c. brown and green ..	2·00	3·75
5a.		4 c. red	60	1·75
6.		5 c. grey	1·25	2·50
7.		5 c. grey and brown ..	2·25	2·00
8.		8 c. blue	1·25	6·50
9a.		10 c. purple on yellow ..	3·00	1·75
10.		10 c. grn. and red on yell.	1·00	2·25
11.		20 c. mauve and purple	2·50	3·25
12.		25 c. green and purple ..	5·00	22·00
13.		30 c. purple and black ..	6·50	32·00
14.		50 c. black on green ..	4·50	5·50
15.		$1 black and red on blue	11·00	16·00
16.		$3 green and red on green	75·00	£150
17.	2.	$5 green and purple ..	90·00	£275
18.		$25 red and green	£650	

1917. Surch. **RED CROSS 2 c.**

19	1.	2 c. on 3 c. red	30	2·75
20		2 c. on 4 c. orange ..	80	11·00
21		2 c. on 4 c. brown & green	1·10	23·00
22		2 c. on 8 c. blue	50	23·00

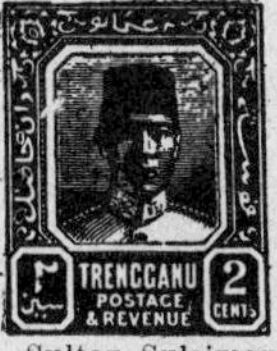

4. Sultan Suleiman. **7.** Sultan Ismail.

1921. (a) T **4**.

48.	4.	1 c. black	80	50
26.		2 c. green	1·00	50
49.		3 c. green	90	75
50.		3 c. brown	15·00	7·00
27.		4 c. red	1·00	20
28.		5 c. grey and brown ..	2·00	2·75
51.		5 c. purple on yellow ..	1·25	55
52.		6 c. orange	2·25	30
53.		8 c. grey	15·00	2·00
29.		10 c. blue	2·00	30
54.		12 c. blue	3·75	3·25
30.		20 c. purple and orange ..	2·00	1·50
31.		25 c. green and purple ..	2·25	2·00
32.		30 c. purple and black ..	3·25	1·00
55.		35 c. red on yellow ..	3·75	8·00
33.		50 c. green and red ..	5·00	1·00
56.		$1 purple and blue on blue	9·00	3·50
57.		$3 green and red on green	35·00	70·00

(b) Larger type, as T **2**, but portrait of Sultan Suleiman.

25.		$5 green and red on yellow	65·00	£160
34.		$25 purple and blue ..	£450	£650
35.		$50 green and yellow ..	£1000	£1500
36.		$100 green and red ..	£3500	

1922. Optd. **MALAYA-BORNEO EXHIBITION.**

37.	4.	2 c. green	75	24·00
38.		4 c. red	3·50	24·00
39.		5 c. grey and brown ..	2·50	25·00
40.	1.	10 c. green & red on yellow	2·50	30·00
41.		20 c. mauve and purple ..	2·00	35·00
42.		25 c. green and purple ..	2·00	35·00
43.		30 c. purple and black ..	2·25	35·00
44.		50 c. black on green ..	2·50	35·00
45.		$1 black and red on blue	10·00	65·00
46.		$3 green and red on green	£110	£350
47.	2.	$5 green and purple ..	£190	£600

1941. Surch.

59.	4.	2 c. on 5 c. purple on yellow	6·00	4·50
60.		8 c. on 10 c. blue ..	7·00	4·50

1948. Silver Wedding. As T **10/11** of Aden.

61		10 c. violet	15	50
62		$5 red	20·00	32·00

1949. U.P.U. As T **20/23** of Antigua.

63.		10 c. purple	20	35
64.		15 c. blue	55	1·60
65.		25 c. orange	55	2·25
66.		50 c. black	1·40	2·50

1949.

67	7	1 c. black	10	20
68		2 c. orange	10	20
69		3 c. green	20	1·00
70		4 c. brown	10	15
71		5 c. purple	30	50
72		6 c. grey	15	15
73		8 c. red	20	1·25
74		8 c. green	65	1·00
75		10 c. purple	15	10
76		12 c. red	65	1·75

77 7 15 c. blue 30 25
78 20 c. black and green 30 1·25
79 20 c. blue 80 25
80 25 c. purple and orange 40 55
81 30 c. red and purple 1·25 1·25
82 35 c. red and purple 70 1·00
83 40 c. red and purple 1·50 8·50
84 50 c. black and blue 40 70
85 $1 blue and purple 2·50 3·00
86 $2 green and red 11·00 13·00
87 $5 green and brown 45·00 38·00

1953. Coronation. As T **13** of Aden.
88 10 c. black and purple 30 30

1957. As Nos. 92/102 of Kedah but inset portrait of Sultan Ismail.
89 1 c. black 10 20
90 2 c. red 50 30
91 4 c. brown 10 10
92 5 c. red 10 10
93 8 c. green 3·75 60
94 10 c. brown 30 10
94a 10 c. purple 2·25 10
95 20 c. blue 30 40
96a 50 c. black and blue 30 60
97 $1 blue and purple 3·50 3·25
98 $2 green and red 6·50 6·00
99 $5 brown and green 7·50 8·00

8. "Vanda hookeriana".

1965. As Nos. 115/21 of Kedah, but inset portrait of Sultan Ismail Nasiruddin Shah, as in T **8**.
100. 8. 1 c. multicoloured 10 40
101. – 2 c. multicoloured 10 40
102. – 5 c. multicoloured 10 10
103. – 6 c. multicoloured 15 50
104. – 10 c. multicoloured 20 10
105. – 15 c. multicoloured 1·00 10
106. – 20 c. multicoloured 1·50 50
The higher values used in Trengganu were Nos. 20/7 of Malaysia (National Issues).

9. Sultan of Trengganu.

1970. 25th Anniv. of Installation of H.R.H. Tuanku Ismail Nasiruddin Shah as Sultan of Trengganu.
107. 9. 10 c. multicoloured 40 65
108. 15 c. multicoloured 40 60
109. 50 c. multicoloured 75 1·75

10. "Papilio demoleus".

1971. Butterflies. As Nos. 124/30 of Kedah but with portrait of Sultan Ismail Nasiruddin Shah as in T **10**.
110. – 1 c. multicoloured 15 70
111. – 2 c. multicoloured 30 70
112. – 5 c. multicoloured 50 10
113. 10. 6 c. multicoloured 50 50
114. – 10 c. multicoloured 50 10
115. – 15 c. multicoloured 65 10
116. – 20 c. multicoloured 75 60
The high values in use with this issue were Nos. 64/71 of Malaysia (National Issues).

11. "Durio zibethinus".

1979. Flowers. As Nos. 135/41 of Kedah, but with portrait of Sultan Ismail Nasiruddin Shah as in T **11**.
118 1 c. "Rafflesia hasseltii" 10 30
119 2 c. "Pterocarpus indicus" 10 30
120 5 c. "Largerstroemia speciosa" 10 10
121 10 c. Type **11** 15 10
122 15 c. "Hibiscus rosa-sinensis" 15 10
123 20 c. "Rhododendron scortechinii" 20 10
124 25 c. "Etlingera elatior" (inscr "Phaeomeria speciosa") 25 10

12. Sultan Mahmud.

1981. Installation of Sultan Mahmud.
125. 12. 10 c. black, blue and gold 20 55
126. 15 c. black, yell. and gold 25 30
127. 50 c. black, purple & gold 55 1·75

13. Rubber.

1986. As Nos. 152/8 of Kedah but with portrait of Sultan Mahmud and inscr. "TERENGGANU" as in T **13**.
135. 1 c. Coffee 10 10
136. 2 c. Coconuts 10 10
137. 5 c. Cocoa 10 10
138. 10 c. Black pepper 10 10
139. 15 c. Type **13** 10 10
140. 20 c. Oil palm 10 10
141. 30 c. Rice 15 20

POSTAGE DUE STAMPS

D 1.

1937.
D 1. D 1. 1 c. red 7·00 50·00
D 2. 4 c. green 7·00 55·00
D 3. 8 c. yellow 50·00 £250
D 4. 10 c. brown £100 90·00

TRINIDAD

An island in the Br. W. Indies off the coast of Venezuela. Now uses stamps of Trinidad and Tobago.

12 pence = 1 shilling.
20 shillings = 1 pound.

2. Britannia. **4.**

1851. Imperf.
2 2 (1d.) purple 5·00 55·00
3 (1d.) blue 5·00 35·00
5 (1d.) grey 30·00 50·00
8 (1d.) red £120 50·00
25 4 4d. lilac 55·00 £275
28 6d. green — £425
29 1s. deep blue 60·00 £275

3.

1852. Imperf.
18. 3. (1d.) blue £4000 £650
19. (1d.) grey £4000 £400
20. (1d.) red 11·00 £450

1859. Perf.
75 2 (1d.) red 11·00 50
70 4 4d. lilac 70·00 8·00
76 4d. grey 75·00 70
72b 6d. green 40·00 3·00
63 1s. blue £650 65·00
73b 1s. purple 65·00 4·25
78 1s. yellow 75·00 2·50

5. **10.**

1869.
113. 5. 5s. red 28·00 55·00

1879. Surch. in words.
98. 2. ½d. lilac 7·00 4·75
101. 1d. red 17·00 30

1882. No. 95 surch. **1d.** with pen.
104. 4. 1d. on 6d. green 3·50 3·25

1883.
106. 10. ½d. green 40 40
107. 1d. red 2·50 10
108. 2½d. blue 6·00 15
110. 4d. grey 2·25 20
111. 6d. black 2·25 1·50
112. 1s. orange 2·25 1·50

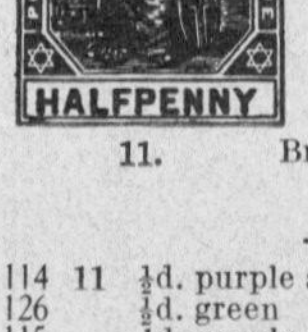

11. Britannia. **12.**

1896.
114 11 ½d. purple and green 1·00 15
126 ½d. green 45 75
115 1d. purple and red 3·25 10
127 1d. black on red 1·00 10
135 1d. red 1·00 10
117 2½d. purple and blue 2·50 15
128 2½d. pur. & blue on blue 6·50 25
137 2½d. blue 1·50 15
118 4d. purple and orange 4·50 8·50
129 4d. grn. & blue on buff 1·75 6·50
138 4d. grey & red on yell. 1·00 5·50
119 5d. purple and mauve 5·50 8·00
120 6d. purple and black 4·25 4·50

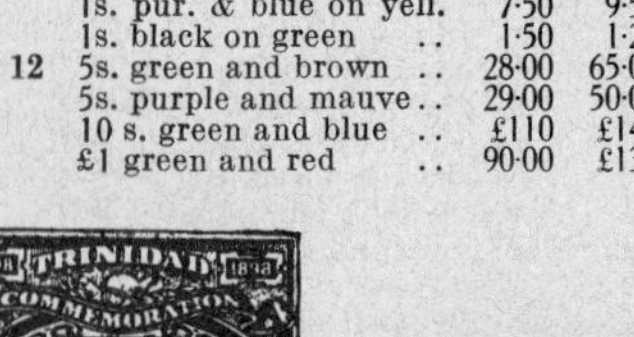
140 11 6d. purple and mauve 3·75 5·50
121 1s. green and brown 6·00 5·00
130 1s. blk. & blue on yell. 16·00 4·00
142 1s. pur. & blue on yell. 7·50 9·50
143 1s. black on green 1·50 1·25
122 12 5s. green and brown 28·00 65·00
131 5s. purple and mauve 29·00 50·00
123 10 s. green and blue £110 £140
124 £1 green and red 90·00 £130

13. Landing of Columbus. **14.**

1898. 4th Cent. of Discovery of Trinidad.
125. **13.** 2d. brown and violet 1·50 70

1909. Figures in corners.
146. 14. ½d. green 1·25 10
147. – 1d. red 75 10
148. – 2½d. blue 5·50 1·75
On the 1d. figures are in lower corners only.

POSTAGE DUE STAMPS

D 1.

1885.
D 1 D 1 ½d. black 22·00 35·00
D18 1d. black 30 80
D19 2d. black 30 75
D20 3d. black 30 1·50
D21 4d. black 1·50 9·50
D14 5d. black 8·00 9·00
D15 6d. black 6·00 9·50
D16 8d. black 12·00 14·00
D17 1s. black 12·00 24·00
For stamps in Type D 1 but with value in cents see under Trinidad and Tobago.

OFFICIAL STAMPS

1894. Optd. **O.S.**
O 1. 10. ½d. green 30·00 48·00
O 2. 1d. red 32·00 50·00
O 3. 2½d. blue 42·00 75·00
O 4. 4d. grey 42·00 80·00
O 5. 6d. black 42·00 80·00
O 6. 1s. orange 55·00 95·00
O 7. 5. 5s. red £130 £225

1909. Optd. **OFFICIAL.**
O 8. 11. ½d. green 40 3·00
O 9. 1d. red 40 3·00

1910. Optd. **OFFICIAL.**
O 10. 14. ½d. green 1·40 2·50

TRINIDAD AND TOBAGO

Combined issues for Trinidad and Tobago, administratively one colony. Part of the British Caribbean Federation from 1958 until 31 August 1962, when it became independent within the British Commonwealth.

1913. 12 pence = 1 shilling;
20 shillings = 1 pound.
1935. 100 cents = 1 West Indian dollar.

17. **18.**

1913.

149 17 ½d. green.. .. .. 1·50 10
207 1d. red 30 20
208 1d. brown 30 40
209 2d. grey .. .. 1·00 1·25
151a 2½d. blue .. .. 2·25 30
211 3d. blue .. .. .. 1·75 1·75
152a 4d. black & red on yellow 70 3·50
153a 6d. purple and mauve .. 2·50 3·75
154 1s. black on green .. 1·00 2·75
155d 18 5s. purple and mauve .. 28·00 70·00
156 £1 green and red .. 90·00 £110

1915. Optd. cross over **21.10.15.**
174.**17.** 1d. red 60 60

1916. Optd. **19.10.16.** over cross.
175.**17.** 1d. red 10 40

1917. Optd **WAR TAX** in one line (No. 176) or two lines (others)
177 17 ½d. green 10 10
176 1d. red .. .. 40 1·00
180 1d. red 10 10

27.

1922.

218.**27.** ½d. green.. .. .. 15 10
219. 1d. brown 20 10
220a. 1½d. red 50 10
222. 2d. grey 40 50
223. 3d. blue 40 50
216. 4d. black & red on yellow 1·25 1·50
225. 6d. purple and mauve 2·00 14·00
226. 6d. green & red on green 1·00 30
227. 1s. black on green .. 2·25 90
228. 5s. purple and mauve .. 15·00 22·00
229. £1 green and red .. 85·00 £170

28. First Boca.

1935.

230a. **28.** 1 c. blue and green .. 15 10
231. – 2 c. blue and brown .. 30 10
232. – 3 c. black and red .. 30 10
233. – 6 c. brown and blue .. 1·50 60
234. – 8 c. green and orange.. 1·00 1·00
235. – 12 c. black and violet.. 1·50 70
236. – 24 c. black and green.. 60 65
237. – 48 c. green .. .. 4·50 12·00
238. – 72 c. green and red .. 22·00 20·00

Designs: 2 c. Imperial College of Tropical Agriculture. 3 c. Mt. Irvine Bay, Tobago. 6 c. Discovery of Lake Asphalt. 8 c. Queen's Park, Savannah. 12 c. Town Hall, San Fernando. 24 c. Govt. House. 40 c. Memorial Park. 72 c. Blue Basin.

1935. Silver Jubilee. As T **13** of Antigua.
239. 2 c. blue and black .. 30 20
240. 3 c. blue and red 30 30
241. 6 c. brown and blue .. 1·50 1·75
242. 24 c. grey and purple .. 4·00 6·00

1937. Coronation. As T **2** of Aden.
243. 1 c. green 15 10
244. 2 c. brown 35 10
245. 8 c. orange.. .. .. 1·25 40

37. First Boca.

1938. Designs as 1935 issue but with portrait of King George VI as in T **37** and without "POSTAGE & REVENUE".
246. **37.** 1 c. blue and green .. 30 20
247. – 2 c. blue and brown .. 30 20
248. – 3 c. black and red .. 11·00 70
248a. – 3 c. green and purple .. 30 20
249. – 4 c. brown .. .. 28·00 1·00
249a. – 4 c. red 40 60
249b. – 5 c. mauve 30 15
250. – 6 c. brown and blue .. 50 40
251. – 8 c. olive and red .. 1·00 40
252a. – 12 c. black and purple.. 2·50 10
253. – 24 c. black and olive .. 50 10
254. – 60 c. green and red .. 8·50 70

New Designs: 4 c. Memorial Park. 5 c. G.P.O. and Treasury. 60 c. as No. 238.

47. King George VI.

1940.

255. **47.** $1.20 green .. .. 7·00 40
256. $4.80 red .. .. 20·00 14·00

1946. Victory. As T **9** of Aden.
257. 3 c. brown 10 10
258. 6 c. blue 10 50

1948. Silver Wedding. As T **10/11** of Aden.
259. 3 c. brown 10 10
260. $4.80 red .. .. 17·00 17·00

1949. U.P.U. As T **20/23** of Antigua.
261 5 c. purple 40 20
262 6 c. blue 40 45
263 12 c. violet 40 55
264 24 c. green 40 30

1951. B.W.I. University College. As T **24/25** of Antigua, but inscr "TRINIDAD" only.
265. **22.** 3 c. green and brown .. 20 20
266. **23.** 12 c. black and violet.. 20 20

48. First Boca.

1953. Designs as 1938 and 1940 issues but with portrait of Queen Elizabeth in place of King George VI as in T **48** (1 c., 2 c., 12 c.) or facing left (others).
267. **48.** 1 c. blue and green .. 20 20
268. – 2 c. blue and brown .. 20 20
269. – 3 c. green and purple .. 20 10
270. – 4 c. red 20 20
271. – 5 c. mauve 30 20
272. – 6 c. brown and blue .. 30 20
273. – 8 c. olive and red .. 70 30
274. – 12 c. black and purple 30 10
275. – 24 c. black and olive .. 75 10
276. – 60 c. green and red .. 11·00 60
277. – $1.20 green 90 75
278a. – $4.80 red .. .. 6·50 9·50

1953. Coronation. As T **13** of Aden.
279. 3 c. black and green .. 15 10

1956. No. 268 surch. **ONE CENT.**
280. 1 c. on 2 c. blue & brown 40 60

1958. British Caribbean Federation. As T **28** of Antigua.
281. 5 c. green 20 10
282. 6 c. blue 25 30
283. 12 c. red 25 10

51. Cipriani Memorial.

53. Copper-rumped Hummingbird.

1960.

284. **51.** 1 c. stone and black .. 10 10
285. – 2 c. blue 10 10
286. – 5 c. blue 10 10
287. – 6 c. brown 10 10
288. – 8 c. green 10 10
289. – 10 c. lilac 10 10
290. – 12 c. red 10 10
291. – 15 c. orange (A) .. 90 45
291a. – 15 c. orange (B) .. 1·25 10
292. – 25 c. red and blue .. 50 10
293. – 35 c. green and black.. 1·75 10
294. – 50 c. yell., grey and blue 35 20
295. – 60 c. red, green and blue 55 30
296. **53.** $1.20 multicoloured .. 9·00 1·50
297. – $4.80 green and blue.. 5·00 6·00

Designs—As Type **51**—**Horiz.** 2c. Queen's Hall. 5 c. Whitehall. 6 c. Treasury Building. 8 c. Governor-General's House. 10 c. General Hospital, San Fernando. 12 c. Oil refinery. 15 c. (A) Crest, (B) Coat of Arms. 25 c. Scarlet Ibis. 35 c. Pitch Lake. 50 c. Mohammed Jinnah Mosque. **Vert.** 60 c. Anthurium lilies. As Type **53**: $4.80, Map of Trinidad and Tobago.

65. Scouts and Gold Wolf Badge.

1961. 2nd Caribbean Scout Jamboree. Design multicoloured. Background colours given.
298. **65.** 8 c. green 15 10
299. 25 c. blue 15 10

66. "Buccoo Reef" (painting by Carlisle Chang).

1962. Independence.
300. **66.** 5 c. turquoise 10 10
301. – 8 c. grey 10 10
302. – 25 c. violet 15 10
303. – 35 c. multicoloured .. 1·50 15
304. – 60 c. red, black and blue 2·00 1·50

Designs: 8 c. Piarco Air Terminal. 25 c. Hilton Hotel, Port-of-Spain. 35 c. Greater Bird of Paradise and map. 60 c. Scarlet Ibis and map.

71. "Protein Foods".

1963. Freedom from Hunger.
305. **71.** 5 c. red 10 10
306. 8 c. bistre 10 15
307. 25 c. blue 20 15

72. Jubilee Emblem.

1964. Golden Jubilee of Trinidad and Tobago Girl Guides' Assn.
308. **72.** 6 c. yellow, blue and red 10 15
309. 25 c. yell., ultram. & blue 15 15
310. 35 c. yell., blue & green 15 15

73. I.C.Y. Emblem.

1965. Int. Co-operation Year.
311. **73.** 35 c. brown, grn. & yell. 30 20

74. Eleanor Roosevelt, Flag and U.N. Emblem.

1965. Eleanor Roosevelt Memorial Foundation.
312. **74.** 25 c. black, red & blue.. 15 10

HAVE YOU READ THE NOTES AT THE BEGINNING OF THIS CATALOGUE?
These often provide answers to the enquiries we receive.

75. Parliament Building.

1966. Royal Visit. Multicoloured.
313. 5 c. Type **75** 15 10
314. 8 c. Map, Royal Yacht "Britannia" and arms .. 1·50 70
315. 25 c. Map and flag.. .. 1·50 55
316. 35 c. Flag and panorama .. 1·50 70

1967. 5th Year of Independence. Nos. 288, 289, 291a and 295 optd. **FIFTH YEAR OF INDEPENDENCE 31st AUGUST 1967.**
318. 8 c. green 10 10
319. 10 c. lilac 10 10
320. 15 c. orange 10 10
321. 60 c. blue, green and red.. 25 10

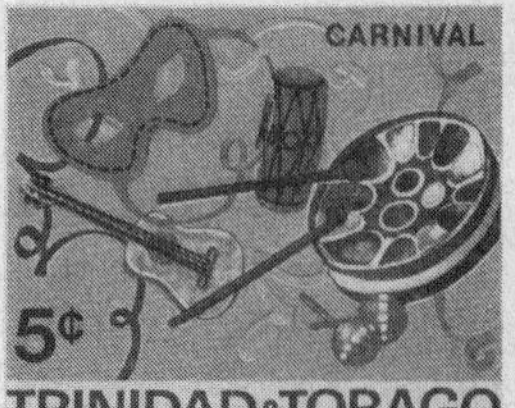

80. Musical Instruments.

1968. Trinidad Carnival. Multicoloured.
322. 5 c. Type **80** 10 10
323. 10 c. Calypso King .. 10 10
324. 15 c. Steel band 10 10
325. 25 c. Carnival procession 20 10
326. 35 c. Carnival King .. 20 10
327. 60 c. Carnival Queen .. 35 50

The 10, 35 and 60 c. are vert.

86. Doctor giving Eye-Test.

1968. 20th Anniv. of World Health Organization.
328. **86.** 5 c. red, brown and gold 10 10
329. 25 c. orange, brown & gold 25 10
330. 35 c. blue, black & gold 30 15

87. Peoples of the World and Emblem.

1968. Human Rights Year.
331. **87.** 5 c. red, black & yellow 10 10
332. 10 c. blue, black & yell. 15 10
333. 25 c. green, black & yell. 30 15

88. Cycling.

1968. Olympic Games, Mexico. Mult.
334. 5 c. Type **88** 10 10
335. 15 c. Weightlifting .. 10 10
336. 25 c. Relay-Racing .. 15 10
337. 35 c. Sprinting 20 10
338. $1.20 Maps of Mexico and Trinidad.. .. .. 70 30

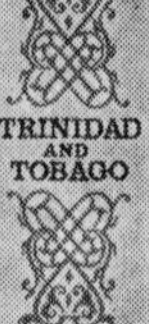

93. Cocoa Beans.

1969. Multicoloured.

339.	1 c. Type **93**	10	10
340.	3 c. Sugar Refinery	10	10
341.	5 c. Rufous-vented Chachalaca.	75	10
342.	6 c. Oil Refinery	10	10
343.	8 c. Fertiliser Plant	55	10
344.	10 c. Green Hermit	75	10
345.	12 c. Citrus Fruit	15	40
346.	15 c. Arms of Trinidad and Tobago	10	10
347.	20 c. Flag and outline of Trinidad and Tobago	15	10
348.	25 c. As 20 c.	15	15
349.	30 c. Chaconia	30	10
350.	40 c. Scarlet Ibis	3·00	10
351.	50 c. Maracas Bay	30	50
352.	$1 Poui Tree	60	15
353.	$2.50 Fishing	80	2·50
354.	$5 Red House	1·50	3·00

Nos. 344/9 and 352 are vert.

108. Captain A. A. Cipriani (labour leader), and Entrance to Woodford Square.

1969. 50th Anniv. of Int. Labour Organization

355. **108.**	6 c. black, gold and red	15	10
356. –	15 c. black, gold & blue	15	10

DESIGN: 15 c. Arms of Industrial Court and entrance to Woodford Square.

110. Cornucopia and Fruit.

1969. 1st Anniv. of C.A.R.I.F.T.A. Mult.

357.	6 c. Type **110**	10	10
358.	10 c. Flags of Britain and member-nations	10	10
359.	30 c. Map showing C.A.R.I.F.T.A. countries	25	10
360.	40 c. Boeing "727" in flight	30	20

The 10 c. and 40 c. are horiz.

114. Space Module landing on Moon.

1969. 1st Man on the Moon. Multicoloured.

361.	6 c. Type **114**	10	10
362.	40 c. Space module and astronauts on Moon's surface	15	10
363.	$1 Astronauts seen from inside space module	45	20

The 40 c. is vert.

117. Parliamentary Chamber, Flags and Emblems.

1969. 15th Commonwealth Parliamentary Assn. Conf., Port of Spain. Multicoloured.

364.	10 c. Type **117**	10	10
365.	15 c. J. F. Kennedy College	10	10
366.	30 c. Parliamentary Maces	25	20
367.	40 c. Cannon and emblem	25	20

121. Congress Emblem. 124. "Man in the Moon".

1969. Int. Congress of the Junior Chamber of Commerce.

368. **121.**	6 c. black, red and gold	10	10
369. –	30 c. gold, lake and blue	25	25
370. –	40 c. black, gold & blue	25	25

DESIGNS: (both incorporating the Congress emblem). HORIZ. 30 c. Islands at daybreak, VERT. 40 c. Palm trees and ruin.

1970. Carnival Winners. Multicoloured.

371.	5 c. Type **124**	10	10
372.	6 c. "City beneath the sea"	10	10
373.	15 c. "Antelope" God Bamibara	15	10
374.	30 c. "Chanticleer Pheasant Queen of Malaya"	25	10
375.	40 c. Steel-band of the year	25	20

129. Statue of Gandhi.

1970. Gandhi Centenary Year (1969). Multicoloured.

376.	10 c. Type **129**	25	10
377.	30 c. Head of Gandhi and flag of India (horiz.)	45	20

131. Symbols of Culture, Science, Arts and Technology.

1970. 25th Anniv. of U.N.

378. **131.**	5 c. multicoloured	10	10
379. –	10 c. multicoloured	15	10
380. –	20 c. multicoloured	35	20
381. –	30 c. multicoloured	35	20

DESIGNS AND SIZES: 10 c. Children of different races, map and flag (34 × 25 mm.). 20 c. Noah's Ark, rainbow and dove (34×23 mm.). 30 c. New U.P.U. H.Q. Building (46×27½ mm.).

1970. Inaug. of National Commercial Bank. No. 341 optd. **NATIONAL COMMERCIAL BANK ESTABLISHED 1.7.70.**

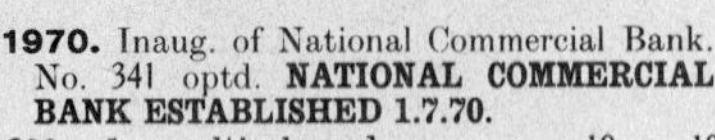

382.	5 c. multicoloured	10	10

134. " East Indian Immigrants " (J. Cazabon).

1970. 125th Anniv. of San Fernando. Paintings by Cazabon.

383. **134.**	3 c. multicoloured	10	20
384. –	5 c. black, blue & ochre	10	10
385. –	40 c. black, blue & ochre	60	20

DESIGNS—HORIZ. 5 c. " San Fernando Town Hall ". 40 c. " San Fernando Harbour, 1860 " (J. Cazabon).

135. " The Adoration of the Shepherds " (detail, School of Seville).

1970. Christmas. Multicoloured.

386.	3 c. Type **135**	10	10
387.	5 c. " Madonna and Child with Saints " (detail, Titian)	10	10
388.	30 c. " The Adoration of the Shepherds " (detail, Le Nain)	25	15
389.	40 c. " The Virgin and Child, St. John and an Angel " (Morando)	25	10
390.	$1 " The Adoration of the Kings " (detail, Veronese)	1·00	85

136. Red Brocket.

1971. Trinidad Wildlife. Multicoloured.

392.	3 c. Type **136**	20	20
393.	5 c. Collared Peccary	25	15
394.	6 c. Paca	30	40
395.	30 c. Brazilian Agouti	1·50	3·25
396.	40 c. Ocelot	1·75	2·75

137. A. A. Cipriani. 138. "Virgin and Child with St. John" (detail Bartolommeo).

1971. 9th Anniv. of Independence. Mult.

397.	5 c. Type **137**	10	10
398.	30 c. Chaconia medal	30	40

1971. Christmas.

399. **138.**	3 c. multicoloured	15	15
400. –	5 c. multicoloured	20	10
401. –	10 c. multicoloured	25	10
402. –	15 c. multicoloured	30	20

DESIGNS: 5 c. Local Creche. 10 c. " Virgin and Child with Saints Jerome and Dominic " (detail, Lippi). 15 c. " Virgin and Child with St. Anne " (detail, Gerolamo dai Libri).

139. Satellite Earth Station, Matura.

1971. Satellite Earth Station. Mult.

403.	10 c. Type **139**	10	10
404.	30 c. Dish antennae	20	20
405.	40 c. Satellite and the Earth	30	30

140. "Morpho peleides x achilleana".

1972. Butterflies. Multicoloured.

407	3 c. Type **140**	40	10
408	5 c. "Eryphanis polyxena"	50	10
409	6 c. "Phoebis philea"	55	10
410	10 c. "Prepona laertes"	80	15
411	20 c. "Eurytides telesilaus"	1·25	1·40
412	30 c. "Eurema proterpia"	1·75	2·25

141. "Lady McLeod" (paddle-steamer) and McLeod Stamp.

1972. 125th Anniv. of 1st Trinidad Postage Stamp.

413. **141.**	5 c. multicoloured	15	10
414. –	10 c. multicoloured	25	10
415. –	30 c. blue, brn. & blk.	70	45

DESIGNS: 10 c. Lady McLeod stamp and Map. 30 c. Lady McLeod and inscription.

142. Trinity Cross.

1972. 10th Anniv. of Independence. Mult.

417.	5 c. Type **142**	10	10
418.	10 c. Chaconia Medal	10	10
419.	20 c. Humming-bird Medal	15	15
420.	30 c. Medal of Merit	15	20

See also Nos. 440/3.

143. Bronze Medal, 1964 Relay.

1972. Olympic Games, Munich. Multicoloured.

422.	10 c. Type **143**	15	10
423.	20 c. Bronze, 1964 200 metres	35	20
424.	30 c. Silver, 1952 weight-lifting	45	20
425.	40 c. Silver, 1964 400 metres	45	20
426.	50 c. Silver, 1948 weight-lifting	50	80

144. " Adoration of the Kings " (detail, Dosso).

1972. Christmas. Multicoloured.

428.	3 c. Type **144**	10	10
429.	5 c. " The Holy Family and a Shepherd " (Titian)	10	10
430.	30 c. As 5 c.	70	55

MINIMUM PRICE

The minimum price quoted is 10p which represents a handling charge rather than a basis for valuing common stamps. For further notes about prices see introductory pages.

145. E.C.L.A. Building, Chile.

1973. Anniversaries. Events described on stamps. Multicoloured.

435.	10 c. Type **145**	10	10
436.	20 c. Interpol emblem ..	45	20
437.	30 c. W.M.O. emblem ..	45	20
438.	40 c. University of the West Indies	45	20

1973. 11th Anniv. of Independence. Medals as T **142**. Multicoloured.

440.	10 c. Trinity Cross ..	10	10
441.	20 c. Medal of Merit ..	20	15
442.	30 c. Chaconia medal ..	20	20
443.	40 c. Humming-bird medal	30	30

146. G.P.O., Port of Spain.

1973. 2nd Commonwealth Conference of Postal Administrations, Trinidad. Mult.

445.	30 c. Type **146**	20	25
446.	40 c. Conference Hall, Chaguaramas (wrongly inscr. "Chagaramas" ..	30	35

147. " Madonna with Child " (Murillo).

1973. Christmas.

448. **147.**	5 c. multicoloured ..	10	10
449.	$1 multicoloured ..	75	60

148. Berne H.Q. within U.P.U. Emblem.

1974. Centenary of Universal Postal Union. Multicoloured.

451.	40 c. Type **148**	45	25
452.	50 c. Map within emblem ..	45	75

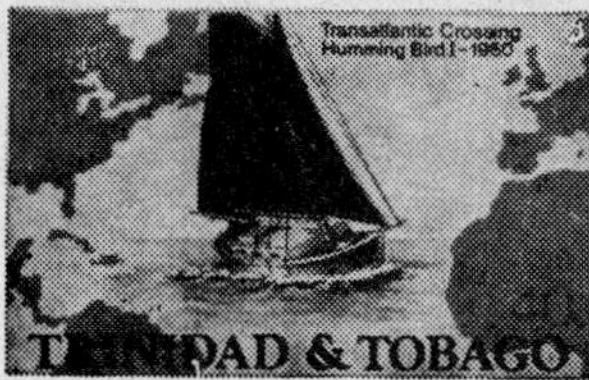

149. "Humming Bird I" (ketch) crossing Atlantic Ocean (1960).

1974. 1st Anniv of World Voyage by H. and K. La Borde. Multicoloured.

454	40 c. Type **149**	45	15
455	50 c. "Humming Bird II" (ketch) crossing globe ..	55	35

150. " Sex Equality ".

1975. International Women's Year.

457. **150.**	15 c. multicoloured ..	15	10
458.	30 c. multicoloured ..	35	55

151. Common Vampire Bat, Microscope and Syringe.

1975. Isolation of Rabies Virus. Mult.

459.	25 c. Type **151**	40	30
460.	30 c. Dr. Pawan, instruments and book ..	50	35

152. Route-map and Tail of Boeing " 707 ".

1975. 35th Anniv. of British West Indies Airways. Multicoloured.

461.	20 c. Type **152**	25	10
462.	30 c. " 707 " on ground ..	40	45
463.	40 c. " 707 " in flight ..	55	65

153. " From the Land of the Humming Bird ".

1975. Carnival. 1974 Prizewinning Costumes. Multicoloured.

465.	30 c. Type **153**	10	10
466.	$1 " The Little Carib " ..	40	50

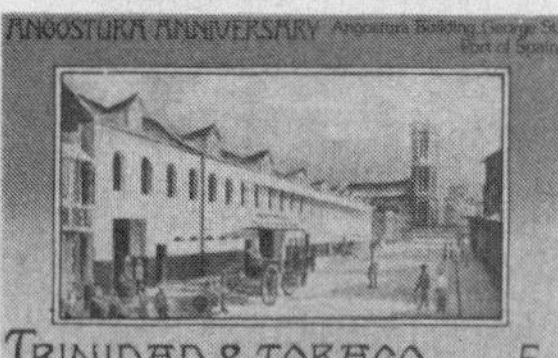

154. Angostura Building, Port of Spain.

1976. 150th Anniv. of Angostura Bitters. Multicoloured.

468.	5 c. Type **154**	10	10
469.	35 c. Medal, New Orleans 1885/6	20	25
470.	45 c. Medal, Sydney 1879	25	40
471.	50 c. Medal Brussels 1897	25	50

1976. West Indian Victory in World Cricket Cup. As T **126** of Barbados.

474.	35 c. Caribbean map ..	45	30
475.	45 c. Prudential Cup ..	55	40

155. " Columbus Sailing Through the Bocas " (Campins).

1976. Paintings, Hotels and Orchids. Mult.

479.	5 c. Type **155**	80	10
480.	6 c. Robinson Crusoe Hotel	20	60
482.	10 c. " San Fernando Hill " (J. Cazabon)	20	10
483.	12 c. " Paphinia cristata "	1·50	70
484.	15 c. Turtle Beach Hotel ..	50	70
485.	20 c. " East Indians in a Landscape " (J. Cazabon)	50	10
486.	25 c. Mt. Irvine Hotel ..	50	10
487.	30 c. " Caularthron bicornutum "	1·50	55
488.	35 c. " Los Gallos Point " (J. Cazabon)	85	10
489.	40 c. " Miltassia " ..	1·50	10
490.	45 c. " Corbeaux Town " (J. Cazabon)	1·00	10
491.	50 c. " Oncidium ampliatum "	1·75	20
492.	70 c. Beach facilities, Mt. Irvine Hotel	70	1·00
494.	$2.50 " Oncidium papilio "	2·25	1·00
495.	$5 Trinidad Holiday Inn	1·75	5·50

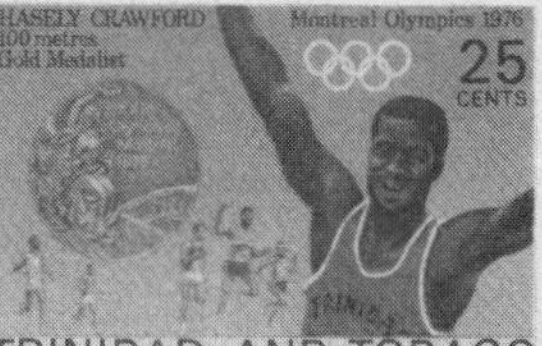

156. Hasely Crawford and Olympic Gold Medal.

1977. Hasely Crawford Commemoration.

501. **156.**	25 c. multicoloured ..	20	40

157. Lindbergh's Sikorsky " S-38 ", 1929.

1977. 50th Anniv. of Airmail Service. Mult.

503.	20 c. Type **157**	25	20
504.	35 c. Arrival of Charles and Anne Lindbergh ..	35	35
505.	45 c. Boeing " 707 ", c. 1960	45	50
506.	50 c. Boeing " 747 ", 1969	1·10	2·50

158. National Flag.

1977. Inauguration of Republic. Mult.

508.	20 c. Type **158**	25	10
509.	35 c. Coat-of-arms ..	45	45
510.	45 c. Government House ..	55	65

159. White Poinsettia.

1977. Christmas. Multicoloured.

512.	10 c. Type **159**	20	10
513.	35 c. Type **159**	35	10
514.	45 c. Red Poinsettia ..	45	30
515.	50 c. As 45 c.	55	75

160. Miss Janelle (Penny) Commissiong with Trophy.

1978. " Miss Universe 1977 " Commemoration. Multicoloured.

517.	10 c. Type **160**	15	10
518.	35 c. Portrait	40	50
519.	45 c. In evening dress ..	55	75

161. Tayra.

1978. Wildlife. Multicoloured.

521.	15 c. Type **161**	20	10
522.	25 c. Ocelot	30	20
523.	40 c. Brazilian tree porcupine	50	30
524.	70 c. Tamandua	65	1·25

162. " Burst of Beauty ".

1979. Carnival, 1978.

526. **162.**	5 c. multicoloured ..	10	10
527. –	10 c. multicoloured ..	10	10
528. –	35 c. multicoloured ..	10	10
529. –	45 c. multicoloured ..	10	10
530. –	50 c. brown, red & lilac	10	15
531. –	$1 multicoloured ..	20	55

DESIGNS: 10 c. Rain worshipper. 35 c. " Zodiac ". 45 c. Praying mantis. 50 c. " Eye of the Hurricane ". $1, Steel orchestra.

163. Day Care.

1979. International Year of the Child. Multicoloured.

532.	5 c. Type **163**	10	10
533.	10 c. School feeding programme	10	10
534.	35 c. Dental care	30	15
535.	45 c. Nursery school ..	30	20
536.	50 c. Free bus transport ..	30	35
537.	$1 Medical care	65	1·00

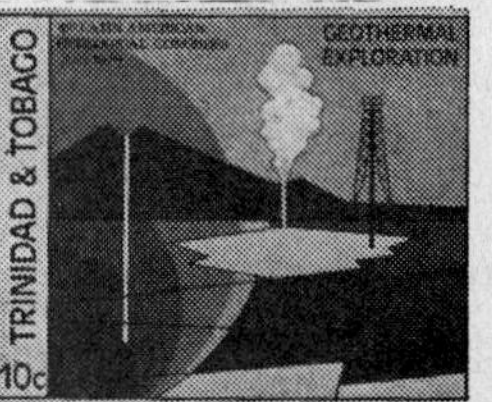

164. Geothermal Exploration.

1979. 4th Latin American Geological Congress. Multicoloured.

539. 10 c. Type **164** 20 10
540. 35 c. Hydrogeology .. 35 40
541. 45 c. Petroleum exploration 40 40
542. 70 c. Environmental preservation .. .. 55 1·25

165. 1879 1d. Stamp and Map of Tobago.

1979. Tobago Stamp Centenary.

544. **165.** 10 c. multicoloured .. 10 10
545. – 15 c. multicoloured .. 15 10
546. – 35 c. multicoloured .. 45 30
547. – 45 c. multicoloured .. 50 30
548. – 70 c. multicoloured .. 65 1·25
549. – $1 black, lilac & orange 80 1·75

DESIGNS: 15 c. 1879 3d. and 1880 ½d. surcharged on half of 6d. 35 c. 1879 6d. and 1886 ½d. surcharged on 6d. 45 c. 1879 1s. and 1886 ½d. surcharged on 2½d. 70 c. 1879 5s. and Great Britain 1856 1s. with "A14" (Scarborough, Tobago) postmark. $1, 1879 £1 and General Post Office, Scarborough, Tobago.

166. 1962 60 c. Independence Commemorative Stamp and Sir Rowland Hill.

1979. Death Centenary of Sir Rowland Hill. Multicoloured.

551. 25 c. Type **166** 30 15
552. 45 c. 1977 35 c. Inauguration of Republic commemorative 40 20
553. $1 1879 Trinidad ½d. surcharge and Tobago 1880 4d. .. .. .. 65 1·25

167. Poui Tree in Churchyard.

1980. Centenary of Princes Town. Mult.

555 5 c. Type **167** 10 10
556 10 c. Princes Town Court House 10 10
557 50 c. Steam locomotive of the Royal Train, 1880 .. 60 90
558 $1.50 H.M.S. "Bacchante" (screw corvette) .. 1·00 1·60

1980. Population Census. Nos. 479/80 and 482 optd. **1844-1980 POPULATION CENSUS 12th MAY 1980.**

560. 5 c. Type **155** 20 20
561. 6 c. Robinson Crusoe Hotel, Tobago 20 60
562. 10 c. " Old View " (Cazabon) 20 20

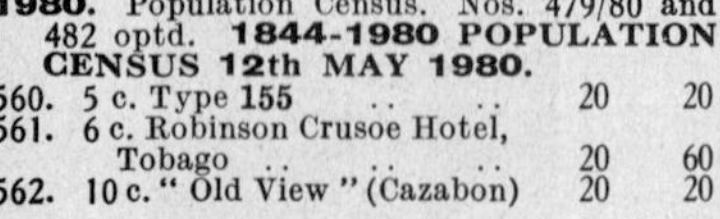

169. Scarlet Ibis (male).

1980. Scarlet Ibis. Multicoloured.

563. 50 c. Type **169** 85 95
564. 50 c. Male and female .. 85 95
565. 50 c. Hen and nest .. 85 95
566. 50 c. Nest and eggs .. 85 95
567. 50 c. Chick in nest .. 85 95

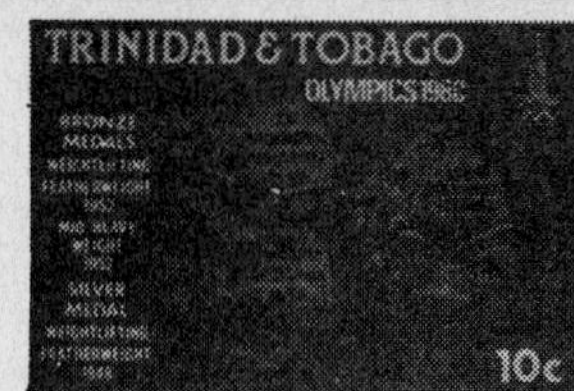

170. Silver and Bronze Medals for Weightlifting, 1948 and 1952.

1980. Olympic Games, Moscow. Multicoloured.

568. 10 c. Type **170** 10 10
569. 15 c. Hasely Crawford (100 metres sprint winner, 1976) and gold medal .. 10 10
570. 70 c. Silver medal for 400 metres and bronze medals for 4×400 metres relay, 1964 .. .. .. 30 45

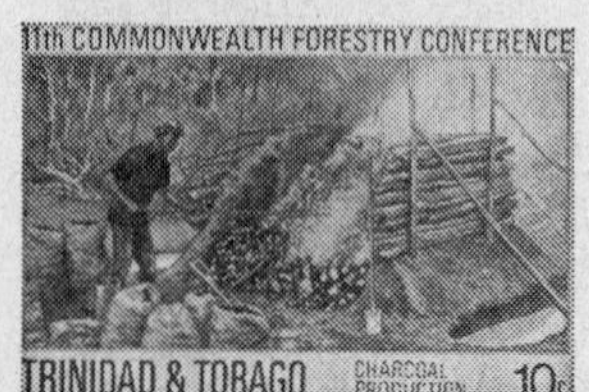

171. Charcoal Production.

1980. 11th Commonwealth Forestry Conference. Multicoloured.

572. 10 c. Type **171** 10 10
573. 55 c. Logging 45 25
574. 70 c. Teak plantation .. 55 50
575. $2.50 Watershed management .. .. .. 1·40 2·00

172. Beryl McBurnie (dance and culture) and Audrey Jeffers (social worker).

1980. Decade for Women (1st issue). Mult.

577. $1 Type **172** 55 55
578. $1 Elizabeth Bourne (judiciary) and Isabella Teshier (government) .. 55 55
579. $1 Dr. Srella Abidh (public health) and Louise Horne (nutrition) 55 55

See also Nos. 680/2.

173. Netball Stadium.

1980. World Netball Tournament.

580. **173.** 70 c. multicoloured .. 30 45

174. I.Y.D.P. Emblem, Athlete and Disabled Person.

1981. International Year for Disabled Persons.

581. **174.** 10 c. green, black & red 15 10
582. – 70 c. orge., black & red 50 70
583. – $1.50 blue, blk. & red 90 1·40
584. – $2 flesh, black and red 1·00 1·75

DESIGNS: 70 c. Man with crutch. $1.50, Blind people. $2, I.Y.D.P. emblem.

175. " Our Land Must Live ".

1981. Environmental Preservation. Mult.

585. 10 c. Type **175** 15 10
586. 55 c. " Our seas must live " 45 30
587. $3 " Our skies must live " 1·60 1·60

176. " Food or Famine ".

1981. World Food Day. Multicoloured.

589. 10 c. Type **176** 10 10
590. 15 c. " Produce more " (threshing and milling rice) 10 10
591. 45 c. " Fish for food " (Bigeye) 30 20
592. 55 c. " Prevent hunger " 35 25
593. $1.50 " Fight malnutrition " 85 90
594. $2 " Fish for food " (Smallmouth Grunt) .. .. 1·10 1·25

177. " First Aid Skills ".

1981. President's Award Scheme. Mult.

596. 10 c. Type **177** 20 10
597. 70 c. " Motor mechanics " 55 45
598. $1 " Expedition " .. 70 55
599. $2 Presenting an award .. 1·10 1·40

178. Pharmacist at Work.

1982. Commonwealth Pharmaceutical Conference. Multicoloured.

600. 10 c. Type **178** 15 10
601. $1 Gerritoute (plant) .. 1·75 2·00
602. $2 Rachette (plant) .. 2·75 3·25

179. " Production ".

1982. 75th Anniv. of Boy Scout Movement. Multicoloured.

603. 15 c. Type **179** 55 10
604. 55 c. " Tolerance " .. 1·25 25
605. $5 " Discipline " .. .. 4·75 4·50

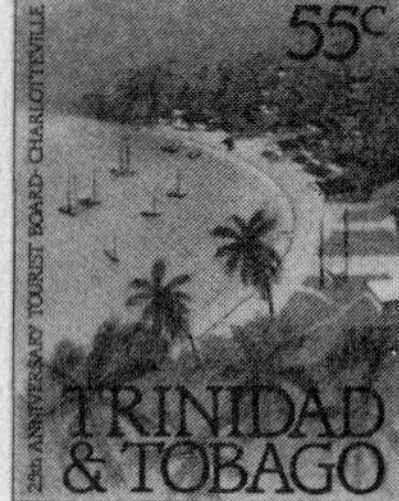

180. Charlotteville.

1982. 25th Anniv. of Tourist Board. Mult.

606. 55 c. Type **180** 35 25
607. $1 Boating 55 55
608. $3 Fort George .. .. 1·75 1·90

181. " Pa Pa Bois ".

1982. Folklore. Local Spirits and Demons. Multicoloured.

609. 10 c. Type **181** 10 10
610. 15 c. "La Diablesse" .. 10 10
611. 65 c. "Lugarhoo", "Phantom" and "Soucouyant" 35 30
612. $5 "Bois de Soleil", "Davens" and "Mamma de l'Eau" .. .. 2·50 3·25

182. Cane Harvesting.

1982. Centenary of Canefarmers' Association. Multicoloured.

614. 30 c. Type **182** 20 15
615. 70 c. Farmers loading bullock cart 50 50
616. $1.50 Cane field in bloom 95 1·10

183. National Stadium.

1982. 20th Anniv. of Independence. Mult.

618. 10 c. Type **183** 10 10
619. 35 c. Caroni water treatment plant 20 15
620. 50 c. Mount Hope maternity hospital 30 25
621. $2 National Insurance Board Mall, Tobago .. 80 1·25

184. Commonwealth Flags.

1983. Commonwealth Day. Multicoloured.

622. 10 c. Type **184** 10 10
623. 55 c. Satellite view of Trinidad and Tobago .. 25 20
624. $1 "Nodding Donkey" oil pump (vert.) .. 40 50
625. $2 Map of Trinidad and Tobago (vert.) .. 85 1·00

185. BWIA "Tristar".

1983. 10th Anniv. of Caricom.

626. **185.** 35 c. multicoloured .. 1·00 1·00

186. V.D.U. Operator.

1983. World Communications Year. Mult.

627. 15 c. Type **186** 20 10
628. 55 c. Scarborough Post Office, Tobago 80 20
629. $1 Textel building .. 1·40 70
630. $3 Morne Blue E.C.M.S. station .. .. .. 2·75 2·50

187. Financial Complex.

1983. Conference of Commonwealth Finance Ministers.

631. **187.** $2 multicoloured .. 1·50 1·00

188. Kingfish.

1983. World Food Day. Multicoloured.

632. 10 c. Type **188** 20 10
633. 55 c. Flying Fish .. .. 1·00 40
634. 70 c. Queen Conch .. 1·25 1·00
635. $4 Red Shrimp .. .. 4·50 6·00

189. Bois pois. **190.** Rooks in Staunton and 17th-century Styles.

1983. Flowers. Multicoloured.

686 5 c. Type **189** 30 15
687 10 c. Maraval lily .. 30 15
638 15 c. Star grass 40 15
639 20 c. Bois caco 30 15
640 25 c. Strangling fig .. 50 35
641 30 c. "Cassia moschata" .. 40 15
642 50 c. Chalice flower .. 30 20
643 65 c. Black stick 55 25
644 80 c. "Columnea scandens" 65 35
695 95 c. Cat's claw 50 40
696 $1 Bois l'agli 50 30
647 $1.50 "Eustoma exaltatum" .. .. 1·25 75
648 $2 Chaconia (39 × 29 mm) 1·50 1·25
649 $2.50 "Chrysothemis pulchella" (39 × 29 mm) 1·25 1·50
700 $5 "Centratherum punctatum" (39 × 29 mm) .. 1·75 1·75
701 $10 Savanna flower (39 × 29 mm) .. .. .. 3·50 3·50

1984. 60th Anniv of International Chess Federation. Multicoloured.

652 50 c. Type **190** .. .. 2·00 35
653 70 c. Bishops in Staunton and 12th-century Lewis styles .. .. .. 2·25 1·25
654 $1.50 Queens in Staunton and 13th-century Swedish styles .. .. 3·25 3·50
655 $2 Kings in Staunton and 19th-century Chinese styles .. .. .. 4·00 4·50

191. Swimming. **192.** Slave Schooner and Shackles.

1984. Olympic Games, Los Angeles. Multicoloured.

656. 15 c. Type **191** 10 10
657. 55 c. Track and field events 30 20
658. $1.50 Sailing 70 80
659. $4 Cycling .. .. .. 2·00 2·75

1984. 150th Anniv. of Abolition of Slavery. Multicoloured.

661. 35 c. Type **192** 75 20
662. 55 c. Slave and "Slave Triangle" map .. .. 1·00 40
663. $1 "Capitalism and Slavery" (book by Dr. Eric Williams) .. .. 1·75 1·00
664. $2 Toussaint l'Ouverture (Haitian revolutionary) 2·25 2·50

193. Children's Band.

1984. 125th Anniv. of St. Mary's Children's Home. Multicoloured.

666. 10 c. Type **193** 10 10
667. 70 c. St. Mary's Children's Home 40 40
668. $3 Group of children .. 2·00 2·25

194. Parang Band.

1984. Parang Festival. Multicoloured.

669. 10 c. Type **194** 15 10
670. 30 c. Music and poinsettia 30 15
671. $1 Bandola, bandolin and cuatro (musical instruments) 85 65
672. $3 Double bass, fiddle and guitar (musical instruments) .. .. .. 2·00 2·00

195. Capt. A. A. Cipriani and T. U. B. Butler

1985. Labour Day. Labour Leaders.

673. **195.** 55 c. black and red .. 55 55
674. – 55 c. black and yellow 55 55
675. – 55 c. black and green 55 55

DESIGNS: No. 674, C. P. Alexander and Q. O'Connor. 675, A. Cola Rienzi and C. T. W. E. Worrell.

196. "Lady Nelson" (1928).

1985. Ships. Multicoloured.

676. 30 c. Type **196** 70 15
677. 95 c. "Lady Drake" (1928) 1·50 1·25
678. $1.50 "Federal Palm" (1961) .. .. .. 2·00 2·50
679. $2 "Federal Maple" (1961) 2·50 3·00

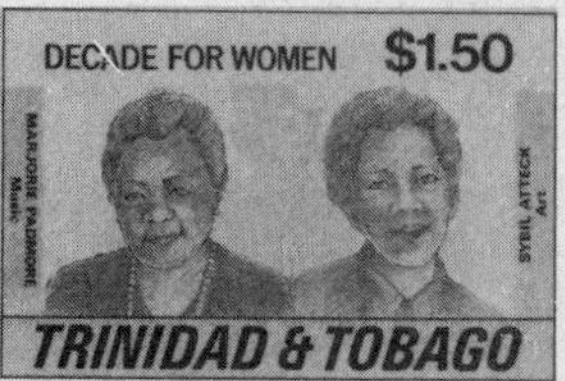

197. Marjorie Padmore (music) and Sybil Atteck (art).

1985. Decade for Women (2nd issue). Multicoloured.

680. $1.50 Type **197** .. .. 1·10 1·40
681. $1.50, May Cherrie (medical social worker) and Evelyn Tracey (social worker) .. .. .. 1·10 1·40
682. $1.50 Umilta McShine (education) and Jessica Smith-Phillips (public service) .. .. .. 1·10 1·40

198. Badge of Trinidad and Tobago Cadet Force (75th Anniv.)

1985. International Youth Year. Mult.

683. 10 c. Type **198** 25 10
684. 65 c. Guide badges (75th anniv of Girl Guide movement) .. .. 1·25 1·40
685. 95 c. Young people of Trinidad .. .. .. 1·75 2·00

199. Anne-Marie Javouhey (foundress).

1986. 150th Anniv. of Arrival of Sisters of St. Joseph de Cluny. Multicoloured.

702. 10 c. Type **199** 10 10
703. 65 c. St. Joseph's Convent, Port-of-Spain 45 65
704. 95 c. Children and statue of Anne-Marie Javouhey .. 65 90

200. Tank Locomotive "Arima".

1986. "Ameripex '86" International Stamp Exhibition, Chicago. Trinidad Railway Locomotives. Multicoloured.

705. 65 c. Type **200** 25 30
706. 95 c. Canadian-built locomotive No. "22" .. 35 40
707. $1.10 Tender engine .. 40 65
708. $1.50 Saddle tank 60 90

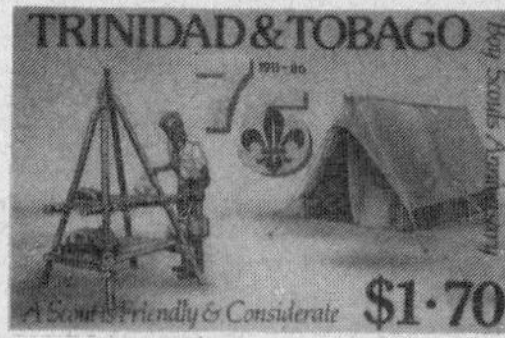

201. Scout Camp.

1986. 75th Anniv. of Trinidad and Tobago Boy Scouts. Multicoloured.

710. $1.70 Type **201** .. .. 1·00 1·25
711. $2 Scouts of 1911 and 1986 1·25 1·50

202. Queen and Duke of Edinburgh laying Wreath at War Memorial.

1986. 60th Birthday of Queen Elizabeth II. Multicoloured.

712. 10 c. Type **202** 15 10
713. 15 c. Queen with Trinidadian dignitaries aboard "Britannia" .. 30 15
714. 30 c. With President Ellis Clarke 40 20
715. $5 Receiving bouquet .. 2·75 3·75

203. Eric Williams at Graduation, 1935.

1986. 75th Birth Anniv. of Dr. Eric Williams. Multicoloured.

716. 10 c. Type **203** 15 10
717. 30 c. Premier Eric Williams (wearing red tie) .. 30 15
718. 30 c. As No. 717, but wearing black and orange tie 30 15
719. 95 c. Arms of University of West Indies and Dr. Williams as Pro-Chancellor (horiz.) 60 55
720. $5 Prime Minister Williams and Whitehall (horiz.) .. 2·00 2·50

204. "PEACE" Slogan and Outline Map of Trinidad and Tobago.

1986. International Peace Year. Mult.

722. 95 c. Type **204** 40 50
723. $3 Peace dove with olive branch .. .. .. 1·25 2·00

205. Miss Giselle La Ronde and "BWIA" Airliner.

1987. Miss World 1986. Multicoloured.

724. 10 c. Type **205** 25 10
725. 30 c. In swimsuit on beach 65 20
726. 95 c. Miss Giselle La Ronde 1·25 1·00
727. $1.65 Wearing Miss World sash .. .. .. 2·00 2·50

206. Colonial Bank, Port of Spain.

1987. 150th Anniv. of Republic Bank. Mult.

728. 10 c. Type **206** 10 10
729. 65 c. Cocoa plantation .. 50 60
730. 95 c. Oil field .. .. 1·00 1·25
731. $1.10 Belmont Tramway Company tramcar .. 1·25 1·75

207. Sergeant in Parade Order and Soldiers in Work Dress and Battle Dress.

1988. 25th Anniv. of Defence Force. Mult.

732. 10 c. Type **207** 35 10
733. 30 c. Women soldiers .. 1·00 30
734. $1.10 Defence Force officers 2·00 2·00
735. $1.50 Naval ratings and patrol boat .. .. 2·25 2·25

1988. West Indian Cricket. As T **186** of Barbados, each showing portrait, cricket equipment and early belt buckle. Mult.

736 30 c. George John .. 65 20
737 65 c. Learie Constantine 1·25 65
738 95 c. Sonny Ramadhin .. 1·40 1·10
739 $1.50 Gerry Gomez .. 2·00 2·25
740 $2.50 Jeffrey Stollmeyer 3·00 3·25

208 Uriah Butler (labour leader)

1988. 50th Anniv (1987) of Oilfield Workers Trade Union. Multicoloured.

741 10 c. Type **208** 10 10
742 30 c. Adrian Rienzi (O.W.T.U. president, 1937–42) 10 10
743 65 c. John Rojas (O.W.T.U. president, 1943–62) .. 15 20
744 $5 George Weekes (O.W.T.U. president, 1962–87) .. 1·25 1·40

209 Mary Werges and Santa Rosa Church

1988. Centenary of Borough of Arima. Mult.

745 20 c. Type **209** 15 10
746 30 c. Governor W. Robinson and Royal Charter 15 10
747 $1.10 Arrival of Governor Robinson 60 75
748 $1.50 Mayor J.F. Wallen and Centenary logo .. 90 1·10

1988. 300th Anniv of Lloyd's of London. As T **123** of Ascension. Multicoloured.

749 30 c. Queen Mother at topping-out of new building, 1984 .. .. 30 10
750 $1.10 BWIA Tristar "500" airliner (horiz) .. 1·10 90
751 $1.55 Steel works, Trinidad (horiz) .. .. 1·50 1·40
752 $2 "Atlantic Empress" (tanker) on fire off Tobago, 1979 .. .. 2·00 2·00

210 Colonial Arms of Trinidad & Tobago and 1913 1d. Stamp

1989. Centenary of Union of Trinidad and Tobago. Multicoloured.

753 40 c. Type **210** 30 10
754 $1 Pre-1889 Tobago emblem and Tobago 1896 ½d. on 4d. stamp .. 85 70
755 $1.50 Pre-1889 Trinidad emblem and Trinidad 1883 4d. stamp .. .. 1·25 1·25
756 $2.25 Current Arms of Trinidad and Tobago and 1977 45 c. Republic commemorative .. 1·60 1·75

211 Common Piping Guan

1989. Rare Fauna of Trinidad and Tobago. Multicoloured.

757 $1 Type **211** .. .. 1·50 1·50
758 $1 "Phyllodytes auratus" (frog) .. .. .. 1·50 1·50
759 $1 "Cebus albifrons trinitatis" (monkey) .. 1·50 1·50
760 $1 Tamandua .. .. 1·50 1·50
761 $1 "Lutra longicaudis" (otter) .. .. .. 1·50 1·50

Nos. 757/61 were printed together, se-tenant, forming a composite background design.

212 Blind Welfare

1989. Anniversaries. Multicoloured.

762 10 c. Type **212** (75th anniv) 10 10
763 40 c. Port-of-Spain City Hall (75th anniv) .. 25 15
764 $1 Guides and Brownies (75th anniv) 85 40
765 $2.25 Red Cross members (50th anniv) .. .. 1·75 1·40

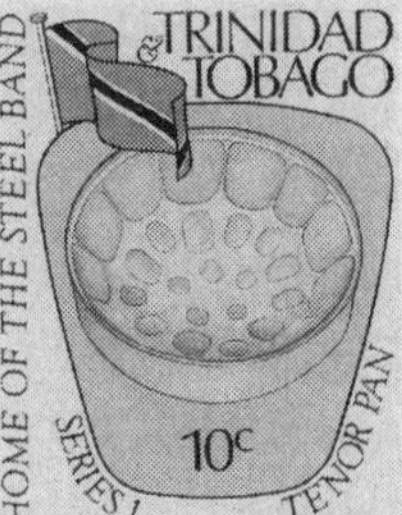

213 Tenor Pan

1989. Steel Pans (1st series). Multicoloured.

766 10 c. Type **213** 10 10
767 40 c. Guitar pans 15 15
768 $1 Cello pans 45 55
769 $2.25 Bass pans .. .. 85 1·00

See also Nos. 828/31.

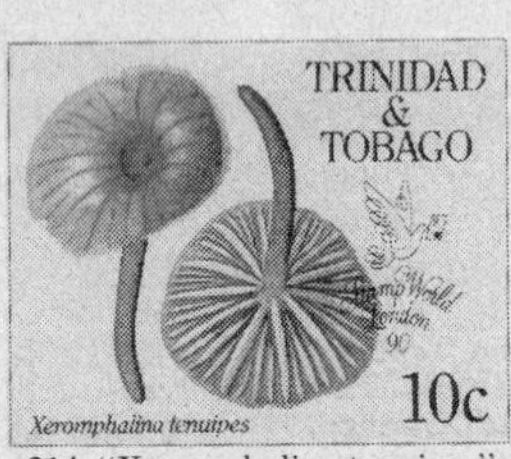

214 "Xeromphalina tenuipes"

1990. "Stamp World London 90" International Stamp Exhibition. Fungi. Mult.

770 10 c. Type **214** 15 10
771 40 c. "Dictyophora indusiata" 35 20
772 $1 "Leucocoprinus birnbaumii" 95 85
773 $2.25 "Crinipellis perniciosa" .. .. 2·00 2·75

215 Scarlet Ibis in Immature Plumage

1990. Scarlet Ibis. Multicoloured.

774 40 c. Type **215** 40 20
775 80 c. Pair in pre-nuptial display 65 60
776 $1 Male in breeding plumage 80 70
777 $2,25 Adult on nest with chick .. .. .. 1·60 2·00

216 Princess Alice and Administration Building

1990. 40th Anniv of University of West Indies. Multicoloured.

778 40 c. Type **216** 30 15
779 80 c. Sir Hugh Wooding and Library 50 50
780 $1 Sir Allen Lewis and Faculty of Engineering 70 70
781 $2.25 Sir Shridath Ramphal and Faculty of Medical Sciences .. 1·75 2·00

217 Lockheed Lodestar

1990. 50th Anniv of British West Indies Airways. Multicoloured.

782 40 c. Type **217** 40 15
783 80 c. Vickers Viking 1A .. 65 60
784 $1 Vickers Viscount 702 .. 75 70
785 $2.25 Boeing 707 .. .. 1·75 2·00

218 Yellow Oriole

1990. Birds. Multicoloured.

787 20 c. Type **218** 10 10
788 25 c. Green-rumped parrotlet 10 10
789 40 c. Fork-tailed flycatcher 10 15
790 50 c. Copper-rumped hummingbird 15 20
791 $1 Bananaquit 25 30
792 $2 Violaceous euphonia .. 50 55
793 $2.25 Channel-billed toucan 55 60
794 $2.50 Bay-headed tanager 60 65
795 $5 Green honeycreeper .. 1·25 1·40
796 $10 Cattle egret .. .. 2·40 2·50
797 $20 Golden olive woodpecker .. .. 4·75 5·00
798 $50 Peregrine falcon .. 12·00 12·50

219 "Lygodium volubile"

1991. Ferns. Multicoloured.

799 40 c. Type **219** 25 15
800 80 c. "Blechnum occidentale" 45 40
801 $1 "Gleichenia bifida" .. 55 55
802 $2.25 "Polypodium lycopodioides" .. .. 1·40 2·00

220 Trinidad and Tobago Regiment Anti-aircraft Battery

1991. 50th Anniv of Second World War. Multicoloured.

803 40 c. Type **220** 20 10
804 80 c. Fairey Barracuda attacking U-boat .. 35 35
805 $1 Avro Lancaster .. 45 45
806 $2.25 H.M.S. "Wye" (frigate) escorting convoy .. .. .. 1·00 1·60

221 H. E. Rapsey (founder)

1992. Anniversaries. Multicoloured.
808 40 c. Type **221** (centenary of Trinidad Building and Loan Assoc) 15 10
809 80 c. "Inca clathrata quesneli" (beetle) (Trinidad & Tobago Field Naturalists' Club) 35 40
810 $1 Holy Name Convent (centenary) 50 60

222 Baptism (Baptist)

1992. Religions of Trinidad and Tobago. Mult.
811 40 c. Type **222** 20 20
812 40 c. Minaret with star and crescent (Islam) .. 20 20
813 40 c. Logo (Hinduism) .. 20 20
814 40 c. Cross (Christian) .. 20 20
815 40 c. Logo (Baha'i) .. 20 20

223 MD83 Aircraft

1992. Aircraft. Multicoloured.
816 $2.25 Type **223** .. .. 90 1·00
817 $2.25 L1011 aircraft .. 90 1·00

224 "Trinidad Guardian" Title (75th anniv of newspaper)

1992. Anniversaries. Multicoloured.
818 40 c. Type **224** 10 10
819 40 c. Nativity scene (Christmas) (vert) .. 10 10
820 $1 National Museum and Art Gallery (centenary) 30 35
821 $2.25 Cover to St. James Internment Camp, 1942 (50th anniv of Trinidad and Tobago Philatelic Society) 65 70

225 Derek Walcott, Sir Shridath Ramphal and William Demas with Caribbean Maps (⅖-size illustration)

1994. 20th Anniv of CARICOM (Caribbean Economic Community). Recipients of Order of the Caribbean Community.
822 **225** 50 c. multicoloured .. 15 20
823 $1.50 multicoloured .. 35 40
824 $2.75 multicoloured .. 65 70
825 $3 multicoloured .. 75 80

226 Aldwyn Roberts Kitchener (bass player)

1994. "Land of Calypso".
827 **226** 50 c. multicoloured .. 15 20

227 Quadrophonic Pans

1994. Steel Pans (2nd series). Multicoloured.
828 50 c. Type **227** 15 20
829 $1 Tenor base pans .. 25 30
830 $2.25 Six pans 55 60
831 $2.50 Rocket pans 60 65

1994. "Hong Kong '94" International Stamp Exhibition. Nos. 788/9, 792 and 796 optd **HONG KONG '94** and emblem.
832 25 c. Green-rumped parrotlet 10 10
833 40 c. Fork-tailed flycatcher 10 10
834 $2 "Violaceous euphonia" 50 55
835 $10 Cattle egret .. .. 2·40 2·50

OFFICIAL STAMP

1913. Optd **OFFICIAL**.
O 14 **17** ½d. green 40 75

POSTAGE DUE STAMPS

1947. As Type D **1** of Trinidad, but value in cents.
D26a 2 c. black .. .. 20 2·00
D27a 4 c. black .. .. 75 2·75
D28a 6 c. black .. .. 30 4·25
D29a 8 c. black .. .. 35 8·00
D30 10 c. black .. .. 85 2·75
D31a 12 c. black .. .. 40 7·50
D32 16 c. black .. .. 2·00 22·00
D33 24 c. black .. .. 4·00 7·50

D **2.**

1969. Size 19 × 24 mm.
D 34. D **2.** 2 c. green .. .. 15 1·75
D 35. 4 c. red .. .. 25 2·50
D 36. 6 c. brown .. .. 50 3·50
D 37. 8 c. violet .. .. 65 4·00
D 38. 10 c. red .. .. 65 4·00
D 39. 12 c. yellow .. .. 70 4·50
D 40. 16 c. green .. .. 40 2·00
D 41. 24 c. grey .. .. 40 2·25
D 42. 50 c. blue .. .. 55 2·75
D 43. 60 c. green .. .. 55 2·75

1976. Smaller design, 17 × 21 mm.
D 44. D **2.** 2 c. green 15 75
D 45. 4 c. red 20 75
D 46. 6 c. brown 20 85
D 47. 8 c. lilac 20 85
D 48. 10 c. red 20 85
D 49. 12 c. orange .. .. 40 1·25

TRISTAN DA CUNHA

An island in the S. Atlantic Ocean west of So. Africa. Following a volcanic eruption the island was evacuated on 10 October 1961, but resettled in 1963.

1952. 12 pence = 1 shilling;
20 shillings = 1 pound.
1961. 100 cents = 1 rand.
1963. Reverted to sterling currency.

1952. Stamps of St. Helena optd. **TRISTAN DA CUNHA.**
1. **33.** ½d. violet 15 85
2. 1d. black and green .. 30 1·25
3. 1½d. black and red .. 30 1·25
4. 2d. black and red .. 30 1·50
5. 3d. grey .. .. .. 40 1·25
6. 4d. blue .. .. .. 1·75 2·00
7. 6d. blue .. .. .. 3·25 2·50
8. 8d. green .. .. .. 3·00 3·00
9. 1s. brown .. .. .. 3·50 2·00
10. 2s. 6d. purple .. .. 19·00 14·00
11. 5s. brown .. .. 26·00 27·00
12. 10s. purple .. .. 48·00 55·00

1953. Coronation. As T **13** of Aden.
13. 3d. black and green .. 90 1·50

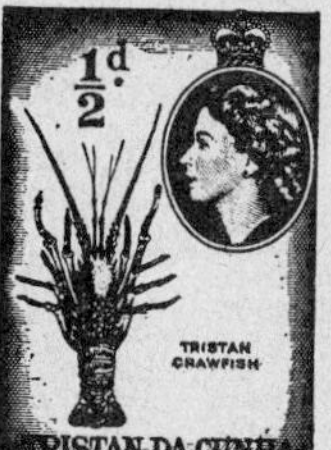

2. Tristan Crawfish.

DESIGNS—HORIZ. 1d. Carting flax. 2d. Big Beach Factory. 2½d. Yellow-nosed Albatross (sea birds). 4d. Tristan from S.W. 5d. Girls on donkeys. 6d. Inaccessible Is. from Tristan. 9d. Nightingale Is. 1s. St. Mary's Church. 2s. 6d. Southern elephant seal at Gough Is. 5s. Inaccessible Island Rail (bird). 10s. Spinning wheel. VERT. 1½d. Rockhopper Penguin. 3d. Island longboat.

1954.
14. **2.** ½d. red and brown .. 10 10
15. – 1d. sepia and green .. 10 20
16. – 1½d. black and purple .. 2·50 50
17. – 2d. violet and orange .. 30 20
18. – 2½d. black and red .. 2·00 50
19. – 3d. blue and olive .. 1·00 20
20. – 4d. turquoise and blue .. 1·25 65
21. – 5d. green and black .. 1·25 65
22. – 6d. green and violet .. 1·25 65
23. – 9d. lilac and red .. .. 1·25 45
24. – 1 s. green and sepia .. 1·25 45
25. – 2s. 6d. sepia and blue .. 26·00 10·00
26. – 5s. black and red .. .. 48·00 16·00
27. – 10s. orange and purple .. 32·00 20·00

16. Starfish.

FISH: 1d. Concha Fish. 1½d. Klip Fish. 2d. Heron Fish. 2½d. Swordfish. 3d. Tristan Crawfish. 4d. Soldier Fish. 5d. "Five Finger" Fish. 6d. Mackerel. 9d. Stumpnose Fish. 1s. Blue Fish. 2s. 6d. Snoek. 5s. Shark. 10s. Black Right Whale.

1960. Value, fish and inscriptions in black.
28. **16.** ½d. orange 15 30
29. – 1d. purple 15 15
30. – 1½d. turquoise 15 30
31. – 2d. green 20 30
32. – 2½d. sepia 25 30
33. – 3d. red 25 20
34. – 4d. olive 30 30
35. – 5d. yellow 45 30
36. – 6d. blue 50 25
37. – 9d. red 55 30
38. – 1s. brown 75 25
39. – 2s. 6d. blue .. .. 11·00 15·00
40. – 5s. green .. .. .. 28·00 22·00
41. – 10s. violet .. .. .. 55·00 40·00

1961. As 1960 issue but values in new currency. Value, fish and inscriptions black.
42. **16.** ½ c. orange 10 15
43. – 1 c. purple (as 1d.) .. 15 15
44. – 1½ c. turquoise (as 1½d.) .. 35 20
45. – 2 c. sepia (as 2½d.) .. 40 20
46. – 2½ c. red (as 3d.) .. 50 20
47. – 3 c. olive (as 4d.) .. 65 20
48. – 4 c. yellow (as 5d.) .. 80 20
49. – 5 c. blue (as 6d.) .. 85 20
50. – 7½ c. red (as 9d.) .. 90 20
51. – 10 c. brown (as 1s.) .. 1·00 20
52. – 25 c. blue (as 2s. 6d.) .. 6·00 11·00
53. – 50 c. green (as 5s.) .. 28·00 23·00
54. – 1 r. violet (as 10s.) .. 48·00 42·00

1963. Tristan Resettlement. Nos. 176/88 of St. Helena optd. **TRISTAN DA CUNHA RESETTLEMENT 1963.**
55. **50.** 1d. multicoloured .. 15 20
56. – 1½d. multicoloured .. 20 20
57. – 2d. red and grey 25 20
58. – 3d. multicoloured .. 30 30
59. – 4½d. multicoloured .. 50 40
60. – 6d. red, sepia and olive .. 85 20
61. – 7d. brown, black & violet 50 30
62. – 10d. purple and blue .. 50 20
63. – 1s. lemon, green & brown 50 20
64. – 1s. 6d. grey, black and blue .. .. .. 2·00 60
65. – 2s. 6d. red, yell. & turq. 1·00 45
66. – 5s. yellow, brown & green 6·00 1·25
67. – 10s. red, black and blue .. 6·50 1·25

1963. Freedom from Hunger. As T **28** of Aden.
68. 1s. 6d. red 90 3

1964. Cent of Red Cross. As T **33** of Antigua.
69. 3d. red and black 35
70. 1s. 6d. red and blue .. 65 2

31. South Atlantic Map.

1965.
71. **31.** ½d. black and blue .. 15 1
72. – 1d. black and green .. 30 1
73. – 1½d. black and blue .. 30 1
74. – 2d. black and purple .. 30 1
75. – 3d. black & turquoise .. 30 1
75a. – 4d. black and orange .. 5·50 4·0
76. – 4½d. black and brown .. 30 1
77. – 6d. black and green .. 30 1
78. – 7d. black and red .. 30 3
79. – 10d. black and brown .. 30 3
80. – 1s. black and red 30 3
81. – 1s. 6d. black and olive .. 2·50 2·5
82. – 2s. 6d. black and brown .. 2·75 2·7
83. – 5s. black and violet .. 4·00 3·5
84. – 10s. blue and red .. .. 1·75 1·2
84a. – 10s. black and blue .. 17·00 11·0
84b. – £1 blue and brown .. 17·00 12·0

DESIGNS—HORIZ: 1d. Flagship of Tristao da Cunha, 1506. 1½d. "Heemstede" (Dutch East Indiaman), 1643. 2d. "Edward" (American whaling ship), 1864. 3d. "Shenandoah" (Confederate warship), 1862. 4d. H.M.S "Challenger" (survey ship), 1873. 4½d. H.M.S "Galatea" (screw frigate), 1867. 6d. H.M.S "Cilicia" (transport), 1942. 7d. Royal Yacht "Britannia". 10d. H.M.S. "Leopard" (frigate) 1s. "Tjisadane" (liner). 1s. 6d. "Tristania" (crayfish trawler). 2s. 6d. "Boissevain" (cargo liner). 5s. "Bornholm" (liner). 10s. (No. 84a) "R.S.A." (research vessel). VERT: 10s. (No. 84b) £1 Queen Elizabeth II (portrait as in T **31** but larger).

1965. Cent of I.T.U. As T **36** of Antigua.
85. 3d. red and grey 50 15
86. 6d. violet and orange .. 60 15

1965. I.C.Y. As T **37** of Antigua.
87. 1d. purple and turquoise .. 40 15
88. 6d. green and lavender .. 1·50 25

1966. Churchill Commem. As T **38** of Antigua
89. 1d. blue 50 25
90. 3d. green .. .. .. 2·50 40
91. 6d. brown .. .. .. 3·50 45
92. 1s. 6d. violet .. .. 4·00 60

45. H.M.S. "Falmouth" (frigate) at Tristan and Soldier of 1816.

1966. 150th Anniv. of Tristan Garrison.
93. **45.** 3d. multicoloured 20 10
94. 6d. multicoloured .. 20 10
95. 1s. 6d. multicoloured .. 30 20
96. 2s. 6d. multicoloured .. 30 20

1966. World Cup Football Championship. As T **40** of Antigua.
97. 3d. multicoloured 25 10
98. 2s. 6d. multicoloured .. 65 20

1966. Inauguration of W.H.O. Headquarters, Geneva. As T **41** of Antigua.
99. 6d. black, green and blue .. 1·00 30
100. 5s. black, purple and ochre 1·25 70

1966. 20th Anniv of U.N.E.S.C.O. As T **54/6** of Antigua.
101. 10d. multicoloured .. 60 15
102. 1s. 6d. yell., violet & olive 65 20
103. 2s. 6d. black, pur. & orge. 80 25

46. Calshot Harbour.

1967. Opening of Calshot Harbour.
104. **46.** 6d. multicoloured .. 10 10
105. 10d. multicoloured .. 10 10
106. 1s. 6d. multicoloured .. 10 10
107. 2s. 6d. multicoloured .. 15 15

1967. No. 76 surch. 4d and bars.
108. – 4d. on 4½d. black & brn. 10 10

48. Prince Alfred, First Duke of Edinburgh.

1967. Centenary of 1st Duke of Edinburgh's Visit to Tristan.
109. 48. 3d. multicoloured .. 10 10
110. 6d. multicoloured .. 10 10
111. 1s. 6d. multicoloured .. 10 10
112. 2s. 6d. multicoloured .. 15 10

49. Wandering Albatross.

1968. Birds. Multicoloured.
113. 4d. Type **49** 40 10
114. 1s. Wilkin's Finch .. 45 10
115. 1s. 6d. Tristan Thrush .. 50 20
116. 2s. 6d. Great Shearwater .. 90 25

53. Union Jack and Dependency Flag.

1968. 30th Anniv. of Tristan da Cunha as a Dependency of St. Helena.
117. 53. 6d. multicoloured .. 10 10
118. – 9d. sepia and blue .. 10 10
119. 53. 1s. 6d. multicoloured .. 15 15
120. – 2s. 6d. red and blue .. 20 15
DESIGN: 9d. and 2s. 6d. St. Helena and Tristan on chart.

55. Frigate.

1969. Clipper Ships.
121. 55. 4d. blue 40 10
122. – 1s. red 40 20
123. – 1s. 6d. green 45 40
124. – 2s. 6d. brown 50 45
DESIGNS: 1s. Full-rigged ship. 1s 6d. Barque. 2s 6d. Full-rigged clipper.

59. Sailing Ship off Tristan da Cunha.

1969. United Society for the Propagation of the Gospel. Multicoloured.
125. 4d. Type **59** 10 10
126. 9d. Islanders going to First Gospel Service .. 10 10
127. 1s. 6d. Landing of the First Minister 10 20
128. 2s. 6d. Procession outside St. Mary's Church .. 15 25

63. Globe and Red Cross Emblem.

1970. Centenary of British Red Cross.
129. 63. 4d. deep green, red and green 10 10
130. 9d. bistre, red and green 10 10
131. – 1s. 9d. drab, red and blue 20 15
132. – 2s. 6d. pur., red & blue 25 30
DESIGNS—VERT. Nos. 131/2 "Union Jack" and Red Cross Flag.

64. Crawfish and Longboat.

1970. Crawfish Industry. Multicoloured.
133. 4d. Type **64** 20 10
134. 10d. Packing and storing crawfish 25 10
135. 1s. 6d. Type **64** 35 25
136. 2s. 6d. As 10d. 40 30

1971. Decimal Currency. Nos. 72, etc. surch with new values.
137. 31. ½p. on 1d. black & green 15 15
138. – 1p. on 2d. black & purple 15 15
139. – 1½p. on 4d. blk. & orange 30 15
140. – 2½p. on 6d. blk. & green 30 15
141. – 3p. on 7d. black and red 30 15
142. – 4p. on 10d. blk. & brown 30 20
143. – 5p. on 1s. black and red 30 20
144. – 7½p. on 1s. 6d. blk. & olive 1·75 95
145. – 12½p. on 2s. 6d. blk. & brn. 2·00 2·50
146. – 15p. on 1½d. black & blue 3·50 3·00
147. – 25p. on 5s. black & violet 3·50 5·00
148. – 50p. on 10s. black and blue (No. 84a) .. 8·00 11·00

66. "Quest".

1971. 50th Anniv. of Shackleton–Rowett Expedition.
149. 66. 1½p. multicoloured .. 90 30
150. – 4p. brown, green and light green .. .. 1·00 40
151. – 7½p. black, pur. & green 1·00 40
152. – 12½p. multicoloured .. 1·40 45
DESIGNS—HORIZ. 4p. Presentation of Scout Troop flag. 7½p. Cachet on pair of 6d. G.B. stamps. 12½p. Shackleton, postmarks, and longboat taking mail to the "Quest".

67. H.M.S. "Victory" at Trafalgar and Thomas Swain catching Nelson.

1971. Island Families. Multicoloured.
153 1½p. Type **67** 25 30
154 2½p. "Emily of Stonington" (American schooner) (P.W. Green) 35 40
155 4p. "Italia" (barque) (Lavarello and Repetto) 40 50
156 7½p. H.M.S. "Falmouth" (frigate) (William Glass) 55 65
157 12½p. American whaling ship (Rogers and Hagan) 65 80

68. Cow-Pudding.

1972. Multicoloured.
158. ½p. Type **68** 20 10
159. 1p. Peak Berry 40 10
160. 1½p. Sand Flower (horiz.) 40 15
161. 2½p. N.Z. Flax (horiz.) .. 40 15
162. 3p. Island Tree 40 15
163. 4p. Bog Fern 40 15
164. 5p. Dog Catcher 60 15
165. 7½p. Celery .. .. 2·50 30
166. 12½p. Pepper Tree .. 1·75 60
167. 25p. Foul Berry (horiz.) .. 1·75 1·50
168. 50p. Tussock .. .. 6·00 1·75
169. £1 Tussac (horiz.) .. 5·00 3·00

69. Launching.

1972. Tristan Longboats. Multicoloured.
170. 2½p. Type **69** 15 10
171. 4p. Under oars 20 10
172. 7½p. Coxswain. Arthur Repetto (vert.) .. 25 15
173. 12½p. Under Sail for Nightingale Island (vert.) 30 20

1972. Royal Silver Wedding. As T **52** of Ascension, but with Tristan Thrushes and Wandering Albatrosses in background.
174. 2½p. brown 35 40
175. 7½p. blue 15 40

71. Church Altar.

1973. Golden Jubilee of St. Mary's Church.
176. 71. 25 p. multicoloured .. 60 50

72. H.M.S. "Challenger's" Laboratory.

1973. Centenary of H.M.S. "Challenger's" Visit. Multicoloured.
177. 4p. Type **72** 30 25
178. 5p. H.M.S. "Challenger" off Tristan 30 25
179. 7½p. "Challenger's" pinnace off Nightingale Is. 30 30
180. 12½p. Survey route .. 40 40

73. Approaching English Port.

1973. 10th Anniv. of Return to Tristan da Cunha.
182. 73. 4p. brn., yellow & gold 25 25
183. – 5p multicoloured .. 25 25
184. – 7½p. multicoloured .. 35 35
185. – 12½p. multicoloured .. 45 45
DESIGNS: 5p. Survey party. 7½p. Embarking on "Bornholm". 12½p. Approaching Tristan.

1973. Royal Wedding. As T **47** of Anguilla. Multicoloured, background colours given.
186 7½p. blue 15 10
187 12½p. green 15 10

74. Rockhopper Penguin and Egg.

1974. Penguins. Multicoloured.
188. 2½p. Type **74** .. .. 3·00 75
189. 5p. Rockhopper Penguins Colony Inaccessible Island .. .. .. 3·50 1·00
190. 7½p. Rockhopper Penguins fishing .. .. .. 4·00 1·25
191. 25p. Rockhopper Penguin and fledgling .. .. 4·50 1·50

76. Blenheim Palace.

1974. Birth Centenary of Sir Winston Churchill.
193. 76. 7½p. yellow and black .. 15 10
194. – 25p. black, brn. & grey 40 25
DESIGN: 25p. Churchill with Queen Elizabeth II.

77. "Plocamium fuscorubrum".

1975. Sea Plants.
196. 77. 4p. red, lilac and black 15 10
197. – 5p. green, blue and turq. 15 15
198. – 10p. orge., brn. & pur. 20 15
199. – 20p. multicoloured .. 30 25
DESIGNS: 5p. "Ulva lactua". 10p. "Epymeniai flabellata". 20p. "Macrocystis pyrifera".

78. Killer Whale.

1975. Whales. Multicoloured.
200. 2p. Type **78** 40 25
201. 3p. Rough-toothed dolphin 40 25
202. 5p. Black right whale .. 45 30
203. 20p. Fin whale .. .. 1·00 70

79. ½d. Stamp of 1952.

1976. Festival of Stamps.
204. 79. 5p. black, violet & lilac 15 20
205. – 9p. black, green & blue 15 25
206. – 25p. multicoloured .. 40 50
DESIGNS—VERT. 9p. 1953 Coronation stamp. HORIZ. 25p. Mail carrier "Tristania II".

80. Island Cottage.

1976. Paintings by Roland Svensson (1st series). Multicoloured.
207. 3p. Type **80** 15 15
208. 5p. The potato patches (horiz.) 15 20
209. 10p. Edinburgh from the sea (horiz.) 20 25
210. 20p. Huts, Nightingale Is. 30 35
See also Nos. 234/7 and 272/5.

81. The Royal Standard.

1977. Silver Jubilee. Multicoloured.
212. 10p. Royal Yacht "Britannia" 25 30
213. 15p. Type **81** 15 20
214. 25p. Royal Family .. 25 25

82. H.M.S. "Eskimo" (frigate).

1977. Ship's Crests. Multicoloured.
215 5p. Type **82** 15 15
216 10p. H.M.S. "Naiad" (frigate) 20 15
217 15p. H.M.S. "Jaguar" (frigate) 25 25
218 20p. H.M.S. "London" (destroyer) 30 30

83. Great-winged Petrel.

1977. Birds. Multicoloured.
220. 1p. Type **83** 15 10
221. 2p. White-faced storm petrel 20 15
222. 3p. Hall's giant petrel .. 20 15
223. 4p. Soft-plumaged petrel .. 60 20
224. 5p. Wandering albatross .. 60 20
225. 10p. Kerguelen petrel .. 60 30
226. 15p. Swallow-tailed tern .. 60 50
227. 20p. Greater shearwater .. 1·00 55
228. 25p. Broad-billed prion .. 1·25 65
229. 50p. Great skua .. .. 1·50 1·00
230. £1 Common diving petrel 2·00 1·75
231. £2 Yellow-nosed albatross 4·50 3·25
The 3p. to £2 designs are vertical.

1978. Nos. 213/14 surch.
232. 4p. on 15p. Type **81** .. 1·75 5·50
233. 7½p. on 25p. Royal Family 1·75 5·50

1978. Paintings by Roland Svensson (2nd series). As T **80**. Multicoloured.
234. 5p. St. Mary's Church .. 15 15
235. 10p. Longboats 20 25
236. 15p. A Tristan home .. 25 30
237. 20p. The harbour, 1970 .. 30 40

85. King's Bull.

1978. 25th Anniv. of Coronation.
239. **85.** 25p. brn., violet & silver 35 35
240. – 25p. multicoloured .. 35 35
241. – 25p. brn., violet & silver 35 35
DESIGNS: No. 240, Queen Elizabeth II. No. 241, Tristan crawfish.

86. Sodalite.

1978. Local Minerals.
242. 3p. Type **86** 25 10
243. 5p. Aragonite 30 15
244. 10p. Sulphur 45 25
245. 20p. Lava containing pyroxene crystal 65 35

87. Klipfish.

1978. Fishes.
246. **87.** 5p. blk., brown & green 10 10
247. – 10p. blk., brown & green 15 15
248. – 15p. multicoloured .. 20 20
249. – 20p. multicoloured .. 30 25
DESIGNS: 10p. "Fivefinger". 15p. "Concha". 20p. "Soldier".

88. R.F.A. "Orangeleaf" (tanker).

1978. Royal Fleet Auxillary Vessels. Mult.
250 5p. Type **88** 15 10
251 10p. "R.F.A. Tarbatness" (store carrier) 20 10
252 20p. "R.F.A. Tidereach" (tanker) 35 25
253 25p. "R.F.A. Reliant" (store carrier) 45 30

89. Southern Elephant-Seal.

1978. Wildlife Conservation. Multicoloured.
255. 5p. Type **89** 10 10
256. 10p. Afro-Australian fur seal 15 15
257. 15p. Tristan thrush .. 25 20
258. 20p. Nightingale finch .. 35 25

90. Tristan Longboat.

1978. Visit of "Queen Elizabeth 2". Mult.
259 5p. Type **90** 15 20
260 10p. "Queen Mary" (liner) 20 30
261 15p. "Queen Elizabeth" (liner) 25 35
262 20p. "Queen Elizabeth 2" (liner) 25 40

91. 1952 "TRISTAN DA CUNHA" overprint on St. Helena 10s. Definitive.

1979. Death Centenary of Sir Rowland Hill.
264. **91.** 5p. black, lilac & yellow 10 15
265. – 10p. black, red & green 15 20
266. – 25p. multicoloured .. 30 30
DESIGNS—HORIZ. 10p. 1954 5s. definitive. VERT.—25p. "TRISTAN DA CUNHA RESETTLEMENT 1963" overprint on St. Helena 3d. definitive.

92. "The Padre's House".

1979. International Year of the Child Children's Drawings. Multicoloured.
268. 5p. Type **92** 10 10
269. 10p. "Houses in the Village" 15 15
270. 15p. "St. Mary's Church" 15 15
271. 20p. "Rockhopper Penguins" 20 25

1980. Paintings by Roland Svensson (3rd series). As T **80**. Multicoloured.
272. 5p. "Stoltenhoff Island" (horiz.) 10 10
273. 10p. "Nightingale from the East" (horiz.) .. 15 20
274. 15p. "The Administrator's abode" 15 25
275. 20p. "Ridge where the goat jump off" 20 30

93. "Tristania II" (crayfish trawler).

1980. "London 1980" International Stamp Exhibition. Multicoloured.
277. 5p. Type **93** 10 15
278. 10p. Mail being unloaded at Calshot Harbour .. 15 15
279. 15p. Tractor transporting mail to Post Office .. 15 25
280. 20p. Ringing the "dong" to summon people to Post Office 20 30
281. 25p. Distributing mail .. 25 30

94. Queen Elizabeth the Queen Mother at Royal Opera House, 1976.

1980. 80th Birthday of The Queen Mother.
282. **94.** 14p. multicoloured .. 25 25

95. "Golden Hind".

1980. 400th Anniv. of Sir Francis Drake's Circumnavigation of the World. Multicoloured.
283. 5p. Type **95** 10 10
284. 10p. Drake's route .. 15 15
285. 20p. Sir Francis Drake .. 20 20
286. 25p. Queen Elizabeth I .. 25 25

96. "Humpty Dumpty".

1980. Christmas. Scenes from Nursery Rhymes. Multicoloured.
287. 15p. Type **96** 15 25
288. 15p. "Mary had a little Lamb" 15 25
289. 15p. "Little Jack Horner" 15 25
290. 15p. "Hey Diddle Diddle" 15 25
291. 15p. "London Bridge" .. 15 25
292. 15p. "Old King Cole" .. 15 25
293. 15p. "Sing a Song of Sixpence" 15 25
294. 15p. "Tom, Tom the Piper's Son" 15 25
295. 15p. "The Owl and the Pussy Cat" 15 25

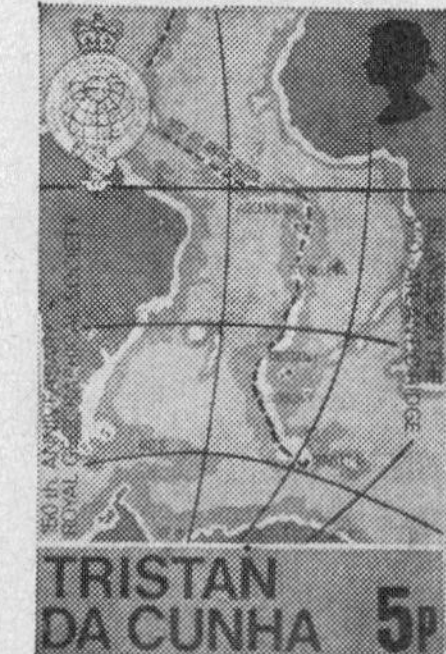

97. South Atlantic Ocean showing Islands on Mid-Atlantic Ridge.

1980. 150th Anniv. of Royal Geographical Society. Maps. Multicoloured.
296. 5p. Type **97** 15 20
297. 10p. Tristan da Cunha group 20 25
298. 15p. Tristan Island .. 30 40
299. 20p. Gough Island .. 35 50

98. Revd. Dodgson as Young Man.

1981. Centenary of Revd. Edwin Dodgson's Arrival on Tristan da Cunha. Multicoloured.
300. 10p. Type **98** 20 15
301. 20p. Dodgson and view of Tristan da Cunha (horiz.) 30 30
302. 30p. Dodgson with people of Tristan da Cunha .. 45 45

99. Detail from Captain Denham's Plan, 1853.

1981. Early Maps. Multicoloured.
304. 5p. Type **99** 15 10
305. 14p. From map by A. Dalrymple, 17 March 1781 30 20
306. 21p. From Captain Denham's plan, 1853 (different) .. 40 30

100. Wedding Bouquet from Tristan da Cunha.

1981. Royal Wedding. Multicoloured.
308. 5p. Type **100** 10 10
309. 20p. Investiture of Prince of Wales 25 25
310. 50p. Prince Charles and Lady Diana Spencer .. 65 65

101. Explorer with Rucksack.

1981. 25th Anniv. of Duke of Edinburgh Award Scheme. Multicoloured.

311. 5p. Type **101** 10 10
312. 10p. Explorer at campsite 15 15
313. 20p. Explorer map reading 25 25
314. 25p. Duke of Edinburgh .. 30 30

102. Inaccessible Island Rail on Nest.

1981. Inaccessible Island Rail. Multicoloured.

315. 10p. Type **102** 25 30
316. 10p. Inaccessible Island Rail eggs 25 20
317. 10p. Rail chicks 25 30
318. 10p. Adult Rail 25 30

103. Six-gilled Shark.

1982. Sharks. Multicoloured.

319. 5p. Type **103** 20 10
320. 14p. Porbeagle Shark .. 35 20
321. 21p. Blue Shark 50 35
322. 35p. Hammerhead Shark 60 50

104. "Marcella" (barque).

1982. Sailing Ships (1st series). Multicoloured.

323 5p. Type **104** 30 35
324 15p. "Eliza Adams" (full-rigged ship) .. 35 50
325 30p. "Corinthian" (American whaling ship) 60 80
326 50p. "Samuel and Thomas" (American whaling ship) .. .. 1·00 1·10

See also Nos. 341/4.

105. Lady Diana Spencer at Windsor, July 1981.

1982. 21st Birthday of Princess of Wales. Multicoloured.

327. 5p. Tristan da Cunha coat of arms 15 15
328. 15p. Type **105** 20 25
329. 30p. Prince and Princess of Wales in wedding portrait 35 45
330. 50p. Formal portrait .. 60 75

106. Lord Baden-Powell.

1982. 75th Anniv. of Boy Scout Movement. Multicoloured.

331. 5p. Type **106** 20 15
332. 20p. First Scout camp, Brownsea, 1907 .. 40 35
333. 50p. Local Scouts on parade (horiz.) 80 75

1982. Commonwealth Games, Brisbane, Nos. 224 and 228 optd. **1st PARTICIPATION COMMONWEALTH GAMES 1982.**

335. 5p. Wandering Albatross 10 10
336. 25p. Broad-billed Prion .. 35 30

108. Formation of Island.

1982. Volcanoes. Multicoloured.

337. 5p. Type **108** 15 15
338. 15p. Plan showing surface cinder cones and cross-section of volcano showing feeders .. 30 35
339. 25p. Eruption 45 50
340. 35p. 1961 Tristan eruption 65 70

1983. Sailing Ships (2nd series). As T **104.** Multicoloured.

341 5p. "Islander" (barque) (vert) 25 15
342 20p. "Roscoe" (full-rigged ship) 45 35
343 35p. "Columbia" (whaling ship) 60 55
344 50p. "Emeline" (schooner) (vert) 80 80

109. Tractor pulling Trailer.

1983. Land Transport. Multicoloured.

345. 5 p. Type **109** 15 15
346. 15 p. Pack donkeys .. 25 25
347. 30 p. Bullock cart .. 50 50
348. 50 p. Landrover 75 75

110. Early Chart of South Atlantic.

1983. Island History. Multicoloured.

349. 1p. Type **110** 30 30
350. 3p. Tristao da Cunha's caravel 40 30
351. 4p. Notice left by Dutch on first landing, 1643 .. 40 30
352. 5p. 17th-century views of the island 40 30
353. 10p. British army landing party, 1815 .. .. 45 40
354. 15p. 19th-century view of the settlement 55 50
355. 18p. Governor Glass's house 55 50
356. 20p. The Revd. W. F. Taylor and Peter Green 65 65
357. 25p. "John and Elizabeth" (American whaling ship) 85 75
358. 50p. Letters Patent declaring Tristan da Cunha dependency of St. Helena 1·40 1·25
359. £1 Commissioning of H.M.S. "Atlantic Isle", 1944 .. 2·50 2·50
360. £2 Evacuation, 1961 .. 3·75 4·00

111. "Christ's Charge to St. Peter" (detail).

1983. 500th Birth Anniv. of Raphael.

361 **111** 10p. multicoloured .. 20 20
362 – 25p. multicoloured .. 35 35
363 – 40p. multicoloured .. 60 60

DESIGNS: 25p., 40p. Different details of "Christ's Charge to St. Peter".

112. 1938 6d. Stamp.

1984. 150th Anniv. of St. Helena as British Colony. Multicoloured.

365. 10p. Type **112** 15 20
366. 15p. 1938 1s. stamp .. 25 30
367. 25p. 1938 2s. stamp .. 35 40
368. 60p. 1938 10s. stamp .. 85 95

113. "Agrocybe praecox var. cutefracta".

1984. Fungi. Multicoloured.

369. 10p. Type **113** 55 65
370. 20p. "Laccaria tetraspora" 85 95
371. 30p. "Agrocybe cylindracea" (horiz.) .. .. 1·00 1·25
372. 50p. "Sacoscypha coccinea" (horiz.) .. .. 1·40 1·60

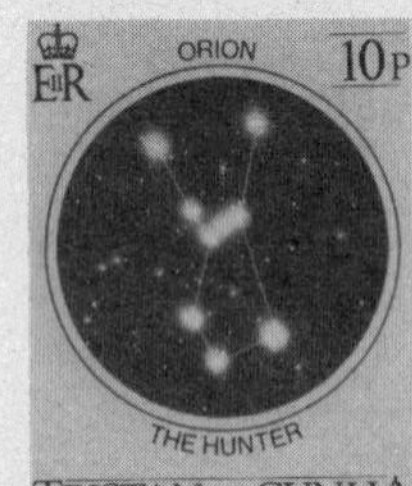

114. Constellation of "Orion".

1984. The Night Sky. Multicoloured.

373. 10p. Type **114** 45 55
374. 20p. "Scorpius" 65 75
375. 25p. "Canis Major" .. 75 85
376. 50p. "Crux" .. .. 1·10 1·25

115. Sheep-shearing.

1984. Tristan Woollens Industry. Mult.

377. 9p. Type **115** 20 30
378. 17p. Carding wool 30 40
379. 29p. Spinning 50 70
380. 45p. Knitting 75 90

116. "Christmas Dinner-table".

1984. Christmas. Children's Drawings. Multicoloured.

382. 10p. Type **116** 20 25
383. 20p. "Santa Claus in Ox Cart" 30 35
384. 30p. "Santa Claus in Longboat" 50 60
385. 50p. "The Nativity" .. 85 1·00

117. "H.M.S. 'Julia' Ashore, 1817" (Midshipman C. W. Browne).

1985. Shipwrecks (1st series).

386. **117.** 10p. bl. & light blue .. 60 80
387. – 25p. brown and green 1·10 1·40
388. – 35p. brown and yellow 1·40 1·60

DESIGNS—VERT. 25p. Bell from "Mabel Clark", St. Mary's Church. HORIZ. 35p. "Barque 'Glenhuntley' foundering, 1898" (John Hagan).

See also Nos. 411/14 and 426/8.

118. The Queen Mother at Ascot with Princess Margaret.

1985. Life and Times of Queen Elizabeth the Queen Mother. Multicoloured.

390. 10p. The Queen Mother and Prince Charles, 1954 20 30
391. 20p. Type **118** 40 60
392. 30p. Queen Elizabeth the Queen Mother 60 85
393. 50p. With Prince Henry at his christening .. .. 1·00 1·25

119. Jonathan Lambert and "Isles of Refreshment" Flag, 1811.

1985. Flags. Multicoloured.

395 10p. Type **119** 70 70
396 15p. 21st Light Dragoons guidon and cannon from Fort Malcolm (1816–17) (vert) 90 90
397 25p. White Ensign and H.M.S. "Falmouth" (frigate) offshore, 1816 (vert) .. .. .. 1·25 1·40
398 60p. Union Jack and Tristan da Cunha (vert) 2·50 2·75

120. Lifeboat heading for Barque "West Riding".

1985. Centenary of Loss of Island Lifeboat. Multicoloured.

399. 10p. Type **120** 35 60
400. 30p. Map of Tristan da Cunha .. .. 80 1·25
401. 50p. Memorial plaque to lifeboat crew .. .. 1·25 1·75

121. Halley's Comet, 1066, from Bayeux Tapestry.

1986. Appearance of Halley's Comet. Mult.

402 10p. Type **121** 40 55
403 20p. Path of Comet .. 65 80
404 30p. Comet over Inaccessible Island .. .. 85 1·10
405 50p. H.M.S. "Paramour" (pink) and map of South Atlantic .. .. 1·40 1·75

1986. 60th Birthday of Queen Elizabeth II. As T **110** of Ascension. Multicoloured.

406. 10p. With Prince Charles, 1950 .. .. 20 25
407. 15p. Queen at Trooping the Colour 30 35
408. 25p. In robes of Order of the Bath, Westminster Abbey, 1972 .. .. 50 55
409. 45p. In Canada, 1977 .. 90 95
410. 65p. At Crown Agents Head Office, London, 1983 .. .. 1·25 1·40

122. "S.V. 'Allanshaw' wrecked on East Beach, 1893" (drawing by John Hagan).

1986. Shipwrecks (2nd series).

411. **122.** 9p. blue, deep blue and black 30 40
412. – 20p. green, yellow and black 60 90
413. – 40p. blue, violet and black .. .. 1·10 1·50

Designs: 20p. Church font from wreck of "Edward Vittery", 1881. 40p. Ship's figurehead.

1986. Royal Wedding. As T **112** of Ascension. Multicoloured.

415 10p. Prince Andrew and Miss Sarah Ferguson .. 20 35
416 40p. Prince Andrew piloting helicopter, Digby, Canada, 1985 .. 80 1·25

123. Wandering Albatross.

1986. Flora and Fauna of Inaccessible Island. Multicoloured.

417 5p. Type **123** 20 35
418 10p. "Lagenophora nudicaulis" (daisy) 30 45
419 20p. "Cynthia virginiensis" (buttefly) 65 85
420 25p. Wilkin's finch .. 75 95
421 50p. White-chinned petrel 1·25 1·25

124. "Dimorphinoctua cunhaensis" (moth) and Edinburgh.

1987. Island Flightless Insects and Birds. Multicoloured.

422 10p. Type **124** 25 40
423 25p. "Tristanomyia frustilifera" (fly) and Crater Lake 55 80
424 35p. Inaccessible Island rail and Inaccessible Island 1·00 1·50
425 50p. Gough Island coot and Gough Island .. .. 1·50 1·75

125. Castaways from "Blenden Hall" attacking Sea Elephant, 1821.

1987. Shipwrecks (3rd series).

426. **125.** 11p. black and brown 40 45
427. – 17p. black and lilac .. 55 65
428. – 45p. black and green 1·00 1·10

Designs—horiz. 17p. Barquentine "Henry A. Paull" stranded at Sandy Point, 1879. vert. 45p. Gustav Stoltenhoff, 1871, and Stoltenhoff Island.

126. Rockhopper Penguin swimming.

1987. Rockhopper Penguins. Multicoloured.

430. 10p. Type **126** 35 40
431. 20p. Adult with egg .. 55 65
432. 30p. Adult with juvenile .. 75 85
433. 50p. Head of rockhopper penguin .. .. .. 1·25 1·40

127. Microscope and Published Report.

1987. 50th Anniv. of Norwegian Scientific Expedition. Multicoloured.

434. 10p. Type **127** 70 70
435. 20p. Scientists ringing yellow-nosed albatross .. 1·40 1·40
436. 30p. Expedition hut, Little Beach Point .. .. 1·75 1·75
437. 50p. S.S. "Thorshammer" (whale factory ship) .. 2·50 2·50

1988. Royal Ruby Wedding. Nos. 406/10 optd. **40TH WEDDING ANNIVERSARY.**

438. 10p. Princess Elizabeth with Prince Charles, 1950 20 25
439. 15p. Queen Elizabeth II at Trooping the Colour .. 30 35
440. 25p. In robes of Order of the Bath, Westminster Abbey, 1972 .. .. 50 55
441. 45p. In Canada, 1977 .. 90 95
442. 65p. At Crown Agents Head Office, London, 1983 .. .. .. 1·25 1·40

128. Nightingale Finch.

1988. Fauna of Nightingale Island. Mult.

443. 5p. Type **128** 20 15
444. 10p. Tristan thrush (immature) 30 25
445. 20p. Yellow-nosed albatross (chick) .. 50 45
446. 25p. Greater shearwater .. 60 55
447. 50p. Elephant seal .. 1·10 1·10

129. Painted Penguin Eggs.

1988. Tristan da Cunha Handicrafts. Mult.

448. 10p. Type **129** 25 25
449. 15p. Moccasins 35 35
450. 35p. Knitwear 75 75
451. 50p. Model longboat .. 1·10 1·10

130 Processing Blubber

1988. 19th-century Whaling. Multicoloured.

452 10p. Type **130** .. 25 25
453 20p. Harpoon guns .. 45 45
454 30p. Scrimshaw (carved whale bone) 65 65
455 50p. Whaling ships .. 1·10 1·10

1988. 300th Anniv of Lloyd's of London. As T **123** of Ascension.

457 10p. multicoloured .. 25 25
458 25p. multicoloured .. 55 55
459 35p. black and green .. 80 80
460 50p. black and red .. 1·25 1·25

DESIGNS—VERT. 10p. New Lloyd's building, 1988; 50p. "Kobenhavn" (cadet barque). HORIZ. 25p. "Tristania II" (crayfish trawler); 35p. "St. Helena" (mail ship).

131 "Government House"

1988. Augustus Earle's Paintings, 1824. Mult.

461 1p. Type **131** 10 10
462 3p. "Squall off Tristan" .. 10 10
463 4p. "Rafting Blubber" .. 10 10
464 5p. "View near Little Beach" 10 15
465 10p. "Man killing Albatross" 20 25
466 15p. "View on The Summit" 30 35
467 20p. "Nightingale Island" .. 40 45
468 25p. "Earle on Tristan" .. 50 55
469 35p. "Solitude—Watching the Horizon" 70 75
470 50p. "Northeaster" .. 1·00 1·10
471 £1 "Tristan Village" .. 2·00 2·10
472 £2 "Governor Glass at Dinner" .. .. 4·00 4·25

132 Hall's Giant Petrel

1989. Fauna of Gough Island. Multicoloured.

473 5p. Type **132** 15 15
474 10p. Gough Island moorhen 20 25
475 20p. Gough Island finch ("Gough Bunting") .. 40 45
476 25p. Sooty albatross .. 50 55
477 50p. Amsterdam fur seal 1·00 1·10

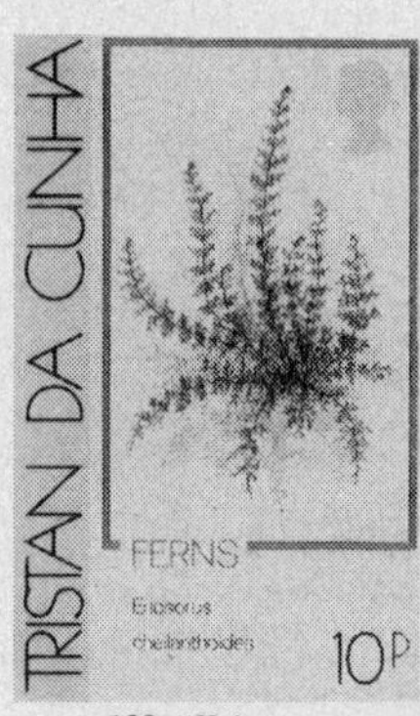

133 "Eriosorus cheilanthoides"

1989. Ferns. Multicoloured.

478 10p. Type **133** 35 35
479 25p. "Asplenium alvarezense" 75 75
480 35p. "Elaphoglossum hybridum" 85 85
481 50p. "Ophioglossum opacum" .. .. 1·40 1·40

134 Surgeon's Mortar

1989. Nautical Museum Exhibits. Mult.

482 10p. Type **134** 35 35
483 20p. Parts of darting-gun harpoon 60 60
484 30p. Ship's compass with binnacle-hood 80 80
485 60p. Rope-twisting device 1·60 1·60

135 Cattle Egret

1989. Vagrant Birds. Multicoloured.

486 10p. Type **135** 55 35
487 25p. Spotted sandpiper .. 90 70
488 35p. Purple gallinule .. 1·10 90
489 50p. Barn swallow .. 1·40 1·40

136 "Peridroma saucia"

1990. Moths. Multicoloured.

490 10p. Type **136** 30 35
491 15p. "Ascalapha odorata" 40 45
492 35p. "Agrius cingulata" .. 80 90
493 60p. "Eumorpha labruscae" .. .. 1·50 1·60

137 Sea Urchin

1990. Echinoderms.

494 **137** 10p. multicoloured .. 40 30
495 – 20p. multicoloured .. 60 50
496 – 30p. multicoloured .. 85 75
497 – 60p. multicoloured .. 1·50 1·50

DESIGNS: 20p. to 60p. Different starfish.

1990. 90th Birthday of Queen Elizabeth the Queen Mother. As T **134** of Ascension.

498 25p. multicoloured .. 75 60
499 £1 brown and blue .. 2·50 2·40

DESIGNS—21 × 36 mm. 25p. Queen Mother at the London Coliseum. 29 × 37 mm. £1 Queen Elizabeth broadcasting to women of the Empire, 1939.

1990. Maiden Voyage of "St. Helena II". As T **137** of Ascension. Multicoloured.

500 10p. "Dunnottar Castle" (liner), 1942 .. .. 35 35
501 15p. "St. Helena I" (mail ship) at Tristan .. 50 50
502 35p. Launch of "St Helena II" (mail ship) .. .. 1·00 1·00
503 60p. Duke of York launching "St. Helena II" .. 1·75 1·75

138 H.M.S. "Pyramus" (frigate), 1829

1990. Ships of the Royal Navy (1st series). Multicoloured.

505 10p. Type **138** 35 35
506 25p. H.M.S. "Penguin" (sloop), 1815 .. .. 80 80
507 35p. H.M.S. "Thalia" (screw corvette), 1886 .. 1·00 1·00
508 50p. H.M.S. "Sidon" (paddle frigate), 1858 .. 1·60 1·60

See also Nos. 509/12 and 565/8.

1991. Ships of the Royal Navy (2nd series). As T **138**. Multicoloured.

509 10 p. H.M.S. "Milford" (sloop), 1938 .. .. 35 35
510 25 p. H.M.S. "Dublin" (cruiser), 1923 .. .. 80 80
511 35 p. H.M.S. "Yarmouth" (cruiser), 1919 .. .. 1·00 1·00
512 50 p. H.M.S. "Carlisle" (cruiser), 1938 .. .. 1·60 1·60

140 Prince Alfred and H.M.S. "Galatea" (screw frigate), 1867

1991. 70th Birthday of Prince Philip, Duke of Edinburgh.

514 **140** 10p. black, lt blue & bl 60 60
515 – 25p. black, lt grn & grn 1·00 1·00
516 – 30p. black, brn & yell 1·25 1·25
517 – 50p. multicoloured .. 1·75 1·75

DESIGNS: 25p. Prince Philip meeting local inhabitants, 1957; 30p. Prince Philip and Royal Yacht "Britannia", 1957; 50p. Prince Philip and Edinburgh settlement.

141 Pair of Gough Island Moorhens

1991. Endangered Species. Birds. Mult.

518 8p. Type **141** 45 45
519 10p. Gough Island finch .. 50 50
520 12p. Gough Island moorhen on nest 55 55
521 15p. Gough Island finch feeding chicks 65 65

1992. 500th Anniv of Discovery of America by Columbus and Re-enactment Voyages. As T **168** of St. Helena. Multicoloured.

522 10p. Map of re-enactment voyages and "Eye of the Wind" (cadet brig) .. 50 50
523 15p. Compass rose and "Soren Larsen" (cadet brigantine) 75 75
524 35p. Ships of Columbus .. 1·40 1·40
525 60p. Columbus and "Santa Maria" .. .. .. 1·75 1·75

1992. 40th Anniv of Queen Elizabeth II's Accession. As T **143** of Ascension. Mult.

526 10p. Tristan from the sea 35 35
527 20p. Longboat under sail 60 60
528 25p. Aerial view of Edinburgh 70 70
529 35p. Three portraits of Queen Elizabeth .. 90 90
530 65p. Queen Elizabeth II .. 1·75 1·75

142 "Caesioperca coatsii"

1992. Fishes. Multicoloured.

531 10p. Type **142** 35 35
532 15p. "Mendosoma lineatum" 55 55
533 35p. "Physiculus karrerae" 1·40 1·40
534 60p. "Decapterus longimanus" .. .. 1·90 1·90

143 "Italia" leaving Greenock

1992. Centenary of the Wreck of Barque "Italia". Multicoloured.

535 10p. Type **143** 35 35
536 45p. In mid-Atlantic .. 1·40 1·40
537 65p. Driving ashore on Stony Beach .. .. 1·75 1·90

144 "Stenoscelis hylastoides"

1993. Insects. Multicoloured.

539 15p. Type **144** 45 50
540 45p. "Trogloscaptomyza brevilamellata" .. 1·40 1·50
541 60p. "Senilites tristanicola" 1·75 1·90

145 Ampulla and Spoon

1993. 40th Anniv of Coronation.

542 **145** 10p. green and black 30 30
543 – 15p. mauve and black 45 45
544 – 35p. violet and black 95 95
545 – 60p. blue and black .. 1·60 1·60

DESIGNS: 15p. Orb; 35p. Imperial State Crown; 60p. St. Edward's Crown.

146 "Tristania" and "Frances Repetto" (crayfish trawlers)

1993. 30th Anniv of Resettlement of Tristan. Multicoloured.

546 35p. Type **146** 95 95
547 35p. "Boissevain" (cargo liner) 95 95
548 50p. "Bornholm" (liner) and longboat .. .. 1·50 1·50

147 "Madonna with Child" (School of Botticelli)

1993. Christmas. Religious Paintings. Mult.

549 5p. Type **147** 15 15
550 15p. "The Holy Family" (Daniel Gran) 45 45
551 35p. "The Holy Virgin and Child" (Rubens) .. 95 95
552 65p. "The Mystical Marriage of St. Catherine with the Holy Child" (Jan van Balen) .. 1·60 1·60

148 "Duchess of Atholl" (liner)

1994. Ships. Multicoloured.

553 1p. Type **148** 10 10
554 3p. "Empress of Australia" (liner) 10 10
555 5p. "Anatolia" (freighter) 10 10
556 8p. "Viceroy of India" (liner) 15 20
557 10p. "Rangitata" (transport) 20 25
558 15p. "Caronia" (liner) .. 30 35
559 20p. "Rotterdam" (liner) 40 45
560 25p. "Leonardo da Vinci" (liner) 50 55
561 35p. "Vistafjord" (liner) .. 70 75
562 £1 "World Discoverer" (liner) .. .. .. 2·00 2·10
563 £2 "Astor" (liner) .. 4·00 4·25
564 £5 "St. Helena II" (mail ship) .. .. .. 10·00 10·50

1994. Ships of the Royal Navy (3rd series). As T **138**. Multicoloured.

565 10p. H.M.S. "Nigeria" (cruiser), 1948 .. .. 20 25
566 25p. H.M.S. "Phoebe" (cruiser), 1949 .. .. 50 55
567 35p. H.M.S. "Liverpool" (cruiser), 1949 .. .. 70 75
568 50p. H.M.S. "Magpie" (frigate), 1955 .. .. 1·00 1·10

POSTAGE DUE STAMPS

1957. As Type D **1** of Barbados.

D 1. 1d. red .. .. .. 1·75 7·00
D 2. 2d. yellow .. .. .. 2·25 4·75
D 3. 3d. green .. .. .. 3·50 5·50
D 4. 4d. blue .. .. .. 6·00 7·00
D 5. 5d. lake .. .. .. 5·00 20·00

D **2**.

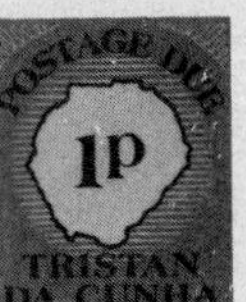

D **3**. Outline Map of Tristan da Cunha.

1976.

D 11.	D 2.	1p. purple	10	50
D 12.		2p. green	15	55
D 13.		4p. violet	20	65
D 14.		5p. blue	20	75
D 15.		10p. brown	20	95

1986.

D 16.	D 3.	1p. brown and light brown	10	10
D 17.		2p. brown & orange	10	10
D 18.		5p. brown and red ..	10	15
D 19.		7p. black and violet	15	20
D 20.		10p. black and blue	20	25
D 21.		25p. black and green	50	55

TRUCIAL STATES

Seven Arab Shaikhdoms on the Persian Gulf and Gulf of Oman, in treaty relations with Great Britain. The following stamps were issued at the British Postal Agency at Dubai until it closed on 14 June 1963.

Individual issues were later made by Abu Dhabi, Ajman, Dubai, Fujeira, Ras al Khaima, Sharjah and Umm al Qiwain.

100 naye paise = 1 rupee.

1. Palms.

2. Dhow.

1961.

1.	1.	5 n.p. green	30	10
2.		15 n.p. brown	30	10
3.		20 n.p. blue	40	10
4.		30 n.p. orange	40	10
5.		40 n.p. violet	40	10
6.		50 n.p. bistre	40	10
7.		75 n.p. grey	60	10
8.	2.	1 r. green	3·00	50
9.		2 r. black	3·00	7·00
10.		5 r. red	4·50	11·00
11.		10 r. blue	12·00	20·00

TURKS ISLANDS

A group of islands in the Br. W. Indies, S.E. of the Bahamas, now grouped with the Caicos Islands and using the stamps of Turks and Caicos Islands. A dependency of Jamaica until August, 1962, when it became a Crown Colony.

12 pence = 1 shilling.

1.

1867.

55.	1.	1d. brown	45·00	30·00
63.		1d. red	1·50	2·25
2.		6d. black	70·00	90·00
59.		6d. brown	2·00	2·75
3.		1s. blue	65·00	55·00
6.		1s. lilac	£5000	£2000
60.		1s. brown	3·00	2·75
52.		1s. green	£100	£100

1881. Surch. with large figures.

17	1	½ on 1d. red	50·00	70·00
7		½ on 6d. black	65·00	80·00
9		½ on 1s. blue	75·00	£110
19		½ on 1s. lilac	80·00	£110
34		2½ on 1d. red	£550	
28		2½ on 6d. black	£130	£180
29		2½ on 1s. lilac	£550	£700
38		2½ on 1s. blue	£600	
47		4 on 1d. red	£600	£450
42		4 on 6d. black	£250	£300
45		4 on 1s. lilac	£375	

31.

34.

1881.

70.	31.	½d. green	60	90
56.		2½d. brown	12·00	13·00
65.		2½d. blue	1·25	75
50.		4d. blue	80·00	60·00
57.		4d. grey	7·50	2·00
71.		4d. purple and blue ..	6·00	11·00
72.	34.	5d. olive and red	2·50	10·00

1889. Surch. **One Penny.**

61.	31.	1d. on 2½d. brown ..	4·75	9·50

1893. Surch ½d. and bar.

68	31	½d. on 4d. grey	£120	£120

INDEX

Countries can be quickly located by referring to the index at the end of this volume.

TURKS AND CAICOS ISLANDS

(See TURKS ISLANDS.)

1900. 12 pence = 1 shilling.
20 shillings = 1 pound.
1969. 100 cents = 1 dollar.

35.

Salt-raking. 36.

1900.

110.	35.	½d. green	75	15
102.		1d. red	2·75	75
103.		2d. brown	75	1·25
104a.		2½d. blue	1·25	1·00
112.		3d. purple on yellow ..	1·00	6·00
105.		4d. orange	3·50	7·00
106.		6d. mauve	1·25	6·00
107.		1s. brown	1·75	12·00
108.	36.	2s. purple	40·00	55·00
109.		3s. red	50·00	70·00

37. Turk's-head Cactus.

38.

1909.

115.	37.	¼d. mauve	65	1·00
116.		¼d. red	30	30
162.		¼d. black	20	60
117.	38.	½d. green	30	30
118.		1d. red	30	30
119.		2d. grey	90	1·40
120.		2½d. blue	1·25	3·75
121.		3d. purple on yellow ..	1·75	2·00
122.		4d. red on yellow ..	3·00	7·00
123.		6d. purple	6·00	7·00
124.		1s. black on green ..	3·50	8·50
125.		2s. red on green ..	22·00	40·00
126.		3s. black on red ..	22·00	35·00

39.

1913.

129	39	½d. green	30	1·00
130		1d. red	75	1·25
131		2d. grey	1·10	1·75
132		2½d. blue	1·90	2·50
133d		3d. purple on yellow ..	2·00	4·50
134		4d. red on yellow ..	1·00	6·50
135		5d. green	3·75	12·00
136		6d. purple	2·25	3·25
137		1s. orange	1·50	4·00
138		2s. red on green ..	6·50	18·00
139		3s. black on red ..	15·00	25·00

1917. Optd. **WAR TAX** in one line.

143.	39.	1d. red	10	50
144.		3d. purple on yellow ..	45	1·50

1918. Optd **WAR TAX** in two lines.

150	39	1d. red	10	60
153		3d. purple on yellow ..	10	1·25

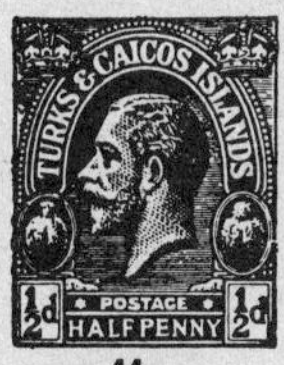

44.

45.

1922. Inscr. "POSTAGE".

163.	44.	½d. green	30	90
164.		1d. brown	40	3·00
165.		1½d. red	3·00	6·50
166.		2d. grey	40	2·75
167.		2½d. purple on yellow ..	40	75
168.		3d. blue	40	2·00
169.		4d. red on yellow ..	85	6·50
170.		5d. green	65	10·00
171.		6d. purple	60	3·00
172.		1s. orange	70	6·50
173.		2s. red on green ..	2·00	5·00
175.		3s. black on red ..	5·00	14·00

1928. Inscr. "POSTAGE & REVENUE".

176.	45.	½d. green	60	40
177.		1d. brown	60	70
178.		1½d. red	50	1·40
179.		2d. grey	45	30
180.		2½d. purple on yellow ..	45	1·75
181.		3d. blue	45	2·50
182.		6d. purple	45	3·75
183.		1s. orange	3·25	4·00
184.		2s. red on green ..	3·50	22·00
185.		5s. green on yellow ..	11·00	30·00
186.		10s. purple on blue ..	40·00	85·00

1935. Silver Jubilee. As T **13** of Antigua.

187	½d. black and green ..	20	40
188	3d. brown and blue ..	1·75	2·50
189	5d. blue and green ..	1·75	2·75
190	1s. grey and purple ..	1·75	3·25

1937. Coronation. As T **2** of Aden.

191	½d. green	10	10
192	2d. grey	60	40
193	3d. blue	80	40

46. Raking Salt. 47. Salt Industry.

1938.

194	46	¼d. black	10	10
195a		½d. green	30	60
196		1d. brown	30	10
197		1½d. red	30	15
198		2d. grey	40	30
199a		2½d. orange	1·25	90
200		3d. blue	30	30
201		6d. mauve	7·00	1·25
201a		6d. brown	15	20
202		1s. brown	3·00	7·50
202a		1s. olive	15	20
203a	47	2s. red	17·00	11·00
204a		5s. green	32·00	14·00
205		10s. violet	7·50	5·50

1946. Victory. As T **9** of Aden.

206.	2d. grey	10	10
207.	3d. blue	15	10

1948. Silver Wedding. As T **10/11** of Aden.

208.	1d. brown	15	10
209.	10s. violet	5·50	6·50

50. Badge of the Islands.

DESIGNS — HORIZ. 6d. Map of Turks and Caicos Is. 2s., 5s., 10s. Queen Victoria and King George VI.

51. Blue Ensign bearing Dependency Badge.

1948. Centenary of Dependency's Separation from the Bahamas.

210.	50.	½d. green	15	15
211.		2d. red	30	15
212.	51.	3d. blue	·50	15
213.	–	6d. violet	40	20
214	–	2s. black and blue ..	45	45
215.	–	5s. black and green ..	90	1·00
216.		10s. black and brown ..	90	3·25

1949. U.P.U. As T **20/23** of Antigua.

217.	2½d. orange	40	55
218.	3d. blue	50	50
219.	6d. brown	50	50
220.	1s. olive	50	35

MORE DETAILED LISTS

are given in the Stanley Gibbons Catalogues referred to in the country headings.

For lists of current volumes see Introduction.

65. Bulk Salt Loading.

66. Dependency's Badge.

1950.

221. **65.** ½d. green 15 40
222. – 1d. brown 15 75
223. – 1½d. red 20 55
224. – 2d. orange 15 40
225. – 2½d. olive 20 50
226. – 3d. blue 20 40
227. – 4d. black and pink .. 2·50 70
228. – 6d. black and blue .. 1·50 50
229. – 1s. black and turquoise 70 40
230. – 1s. 6d. black and red .. 2·75 3·25
231. – 2s. green and blue .. 1·50 3·50
232. – 5s. blue and black .. 7·00 3·75
233. **66.** 10s. black and violet .. 14·00 13·00

DESIGNS—As Type **65**: 1d. Salt Cay. 1½d. Caicos mail. 2d. Grand Turk. 2½d. Diving for sponges. 3d. South Creek. 4d. Map. 6d. Grand Turk Light. 1s. Government House. 1s. 6d. Cockburn Harbour. 2s. Govt. Offices. 5s. Loading salt.

1953. Coronation. As T **13** of Aden.
234. 2d. black and orange .. 20 80

1955. As 1950 but with portrait of Queen Elizabeth II.
235. 5d. black and green .. 30 30
236. 8d. black and brown .. 1·75 30

DESIGNS—HORIZ. As Type **65**. 5d. M.V. "Kirksons". 8d. Greater Flamingoes in flight.

69. Queen Elizabeth II (after Annigoni).

70. Bonefish.

1957.

237. **69.** 1d. blue and red .. 15 20
238. **70.** 1½d. grey and orange .. 15 30
239. – 2d. brown and olive .. 15 15
240. – 2½d. red and green .. 15 15
241. – 3d. turquoise & purple 15 15
242. – 4d. lake and black .. 20 15
243. – 5d. green and brown .. 30 40
244. – 6d. red and blue .. 1·00 40
245. – 8d. red and black .. 3·00 20
246. – 1s. blue and black .. 30 10
247. – 1s. 6d. sepia and blue .. 2·25 50
248. – 2s. blue and brown .. 3·50 2·25
249. – 5s. black and red .. 85 2·00
250. – 10s. black and purple .. 10·00 8·00

DESIGNS—HORIZ. As Type **70**: 2d. Red grouper. 2½d. Spiny lobster. 3d. Albacore. 4d. Muttonfish snapper. 5d. Permit. 6d. Conch. 8d. Greater flamingoes. 1s. Spanish mackerel. 1s. 6d. Salt Cay. 1s. "Uakon" (Caicos sloop). 5s. Cable Office. As Type **84**: 10s. Dependency's badge.

83. Map of the Turks and Caicos Is.

1959. New Constitution.
251. **83.** 6d. olive and orange .. 35 20
252. 8d. violet and orange .. 35 20

84. Brown Pelican.

1960.
253 **84** £1 brown and red .. 32·00 16·00

1963. Freedom from Hunger. As T **28** of Aden.
254. 8d. red 30 15

1963. Cent of Red Cross. As T **33** of Antigua.
255 2d. red and black .. 15 20
256 8d. red and blue 30 30

1964. 400th Birth Anniv of Shakespeare. As T **34** of Antigua.
257. 8d. green 10 10

1965. Cent of I.T.U. As T **36** of Antigua.
258. 1d. red and brown .. 10 10
259. 2s. green and blue .. 20 20

1965. I.C.Y. As T **37** of Antigua.
260. 1d. purple and turquoise 10 15
261. 8d. green and lavender .. 20 15

1966. Churchill Commem. As T **38** of Antigua.
262. 1d. blue 10 10
263. 2d. green 15 10
264. 8d. brown 15 10
265. 1s. 6d. violet 25 35

1966. Royal Visit. As T **39** of Antigua.
266. 8d. black and blue .. 25 10
267. 1s. 6d. black and mauve .. 45 20

86. Andrew Symmer and Royal Warrant.

1966. Bicent. of "Ties with Britain".
268. – 1d. blue and orange .. 10 10
269. **86.** 8d. red, blue and yellow 15 10
270. – 1s. 6d. multicoloured .. 20 15

DESIGNS: 1d. Andrew Symmer going ashore. 1s. 6d. Arms and Royal Cypher.

1966. 20th Anniv of U.N.E.S.C.O. As T **54/6** of Antigua.
271. 1d. multicoloured .. 10 10
272. 8d. yellow, violet and olive 15 10
273. 1s. 6d. black, purple & orge. 20 40

88. Turk's Head Cactus.

DESIGNS—HORIZ. 1½d. Boat-building. 4d. Conch Industry. 1s. Fishing. 2s. Crawfish Industry. 3s. Maps of Turks and Caicos Islands and (inset) West Indies. 5s. Fishing Industry. 10s. Arms of Turks and Caicos Islands. VERT. 2d. Donkey Cart. 3d. Sisal Industry. 6d. Salt Industry. 8d. Skin-diving. 1s. 6d. Water-skiing. £1, Queen Elizabeth II.

1967.

274. **88.** 1d. yellow, red and violet 10 10
275. – 1½d. brown and yellow 10 10
276. – 2d. grey and yellow .. 15 10
277. – 3d. agate and green .. 20 10
278. – 4d. mauve, blk. & turq. 30 10
279. – 6d. brown and blue .. 30 10
280. – 8d. yell., turq. & blue .. 20 10
281. – 1s. purple and turquoise 20 10
282. – 1s. 6d. yell., brn. & blue 50 20
283. – 2s. multicoloured .. 60 1·25
284. – 3s. mauve and blue .. 55 40
285. – 5s. ochre, blue and light blue .. .. .. 1·25 2·25
286. – 10s. multicoloured .. 1·75 2·75
287. – £1 blue, silver and red .. 3·25 5·50

102. Turks Islands 1d. Stamp of 1867.

1967. Stamp Cent.
288. **102.** 1d. black and mauve .. 10 10
289. – 6d. black and grey .. 20 10
290. – 1s. black and blue .. 20 10

DESIGNS: 6d. Queen Elizabeth "Stamp" and Turks Islands 6d. Stamp of 1867. 1s. As Type **102** but shows the 1s. stamp of 1867 in place of the 1d.

104. Human Rights Emblem and Charter.

1968. Human Rights Year.
291. **104.** 1d. multicoloured .. 10 10
292. 8d. multicoloured .. 15 15
293. 1s. 6d. multicoloured .. 15 15

105. Dr. Martin Luther King and "Freedom March".

1968. Martin Luther King. Commem.
294. **105.** 2d. brown and blue .. 10 10
295. 8d. brown and lake .. 15 15
296. 1s. 6d. brn. and violet .. 15 15

1969. Decimal Currency. Nos. 274/87 **surch.**, and new value in old design (¼ c.).
297. ¼ c. mult. (as No. 286) .. 10 10
298. 1 c. on 1d. yell., red & vio. 10 10
299. 2 c. on 2d. grey & yellow .. 10 10
300. 3 c. on 3d. agate and green 10 10
301. 4 c. on 4d. mve., blk. & turq. 10 10
302. 5 c. on 6d. brown and blue 10 10
303. 7 c. on 8d. yell., turq. & bl. 10 10
304. 8 c. on 1½d. brown & yell. 10 10
305. 10 c. on 1s. purple & turq. 20 10
306. 15 c. on 1s. 6d. yell., brn. & blue 25 10
307. 20 c. on 2s. multicoloured 30 25
308. 30 c. on 3s. mauve & blue 55 35
309. 50 c. on 5s. ochre, blue and light blue .. .. 1·00 45
310. $1 on 10s. multicoloured .. 2·00 1·00
311a. $2 on £1 blue, silver & red 2·00 1·00

107. "The Nativity with John the Baptist".

1969. Christmas. Scenes from 16th-cent. "Book of Hours". Multicoloured.
312. 1 c. Type **107** 10 10
313. 3 c. "The Flight into Egypt" 10 10
314. 15 c. Type **107** 15 10
315. 30 c. As 3 c. 25 10

109. Coat of Arms.

1970. New Constitution.
316. **109.** 7 c. multicoloured .. 20 15
317. 35 c. multicoloured .. 35 25

For similar $10 design but without commemorative inscription, see No. 946.

110. "Christ bearing the Cross".

1970. Easter. Details from the "Small Engraved Passion".
318. **110.** 5 c. grey and blue .. 10 10
319. – 7 c. grey and red .. 10 10
320. – 50 c. grey and brown .. 50 50

DESIGNS: 7 c. "Christ on the Cross" (Durer). 50 c. "The Lamentation for Christ" (Durer).

113. Dickens and Scene from "Oliver Twist".

1970. Death Cent. of Charles Dickens.
321. **113.** 1 c. blk. & brn. on yell. 10 10
322. – 3 c. blk. & blue on flesh 10 10
323. – 15 c. blk. & blue on flesh 20 10
324. – 30 c. blk. & drab on blue 40 20

DESIGNS (showing Dickens and scene): 3 c. "A Christmas Carol". 15 c. "Pickwick Papers". 30 c. "The Old Curiosity Shop".

114. Ambulance – 1870.

1970. Cent. of British Red Cross. Mult.
325. 1 c. Type **114** 10 10
326. 5 c. Ambulance – 1970 .. 10 10
327. 15 c. Type **114** 20 10
328. 30 c. As 5 c. 30 10

115. Duke of Albemarle and Coat-of-Arms.

1970. Tercentenary of Issue of Letters Patent. Multicoloured.
329. 1 c. Type **115** 10 10
330. 8 c. Arms of Charles II and Elizabeth II .. 20 20
331. 10 c. Type **115** .. 20 15
332. 35 c. As 8 c. 40 65

116. Boat-building.

1971. Designs as Nos. 274/87, but values in decimal currency as T **116**.

333. **88.** 1 c. yellow, red and violet .. 10 10
334. – 2 c. slate and yellow (as No. 276) 10 10
335. – 3 c. agate and green (as No. 277) 15 10
336. – 4 c. mauve, black and turquoise (as No. 278) 65 10
337. – 5 c. sepia and blue (as No. 279) 30 10
338. – 7 c. yellow, turquoise & blue (as No. 280) .. 30 10
339. **116.** 8 c. brown and yellow .. 50 10
340. – 10 c. purple and turq. (as No. 281) 50 10
341. – 15 c. yellow, brown and blue (as No. 282) .. 1·00 65
342. – 20 c. mult. (as No. 283) 1·25 2·00
343. – 30 c. purple and blue (as No. 284) .. .. 1·75 1·00
344. – 50 c. ochre, blue and light blue (as No. 285) 2·50 2·00
345. – $1 mult. (as No. 286) .. 2·75 3·00
346. – $2 blue, silver and red (as No. 287) .. .. 4·00 7·50

117. Seahorse.

1971. Tourist Development. Multicoloured.

347. 1 c. Type **117** 10 10
348. 3 c. Queen Conch shell .. 10 10
349. 15 c. Oyster catcher .. 30 10
350. 30 c. Blue Marlin 30 15

Nos. 348/50 are horiz.

118. Pirate Sloop.

1971. Pirates. Multicoloured.

351. 2 c. Type **118** 10 10
352. 3 c. Pirate Treasure .. 10 10
353. 15 c. Marooned sailor .. 45 15
354. 30 c. Buccaneers 70 45

119. The Wilton Diptych (Left Wing).

1971 Christmas. Multicoloured.

355. 2 c. Type **119** 10 10
356. 2 c. The Wilton Diptych (Right Wing) 10 10
357. 8 c. Type **119** 10 10
358. 8 c. As No. 356 .. .. 10 10
359. 15 c. Type **119** 20 10
360. 15 c. As No. 356 .. .. 20 10

120. Cape Kennedy Launching Area.

1972. 10th Anniv. of Colonel Glenn's Splashdown. Multicoloured.

361. 5 c. Type **120** 10 10
362. 10 c. "Friendship 7" space capsule 10 10
363. 15 c. Map of Islands and splashdown 15 10
364. 20 c. N.A.S.A. Space Medal (vert.) 15 10

121. "Christ before Pilate" (Rembrandt).

1972. Easter.

365. **121.** 2 c. black and lilac .. 10 10
366. – 15 c. black and pink .. 20 10
367. – 30 c. black and yellow .. 30 15

DESIGNS—HORIZ. 15 c. "The Three Crosses" (Rembrandt). VERT. 30 c. "The Descent from the Cross" (Rembrandt).

122. Christopher Columbus.

1972. Discoverers and Explorers. Mult.

368. ¼ c. Type **122** 10 10
369. 8 c. Sir Richard Grenville (horiz.) 40 10
370. 10 c. Capt. John Smith .. 45 10
371. 30 c. Juan Ponce de Leon (horiz.) .. .. .. 1·00 75

1972. Royal Silver Wedding. As T **52** of Ascension, but with Turk's-head Cactus and Spiny Lobster in backgroud.

372. 10 c. blue 10 10
373. 20 c. green 15 10

124. Treasure Hunting, c. 1700.

1973. Treasure.

374. **124.** 3 c. multicoloured .. 10 10
375. – 5 c. pur., silver & black 10 10
376. – 10 c. pur., silver & black 20 10
377. – 30 c. multicoloured .. 60 30

DESIGNS: 5 c. Silver Bank medallion (obverse). 10 c. Silver Bank medallion (reverse). 30 c. Treasure hunting, 1973.

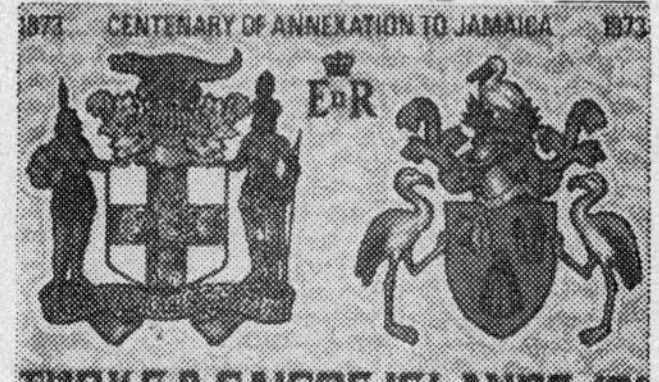

125. Arms of Jamaica and Turks and Caicos Islands.

1973. Cent. of Annexation by Jamaica.

379. **125.** 15 c. multicoloured .. 30 10
380. 35 c. multicoloured .. 60 20

126. Sooty Tern.

1973.

381 ¼ c. Type **126** 10 20
382 1 c. Magnificent frigate-bird 30 40
383 2 c. Common noddy .. 30 40
384 3 c. Blue-grey gnatcatcher 85 40
385 4 c. Little blue heron .. 35 80
386 5 c. Catbird 30 30
387 7 c. Black whiskered vireo 3·50 30
388 8 c. Osprey .. .. .. 4·50 1·25
389 10 c. Greater flamingo .. 70 60
390 15 c. Brown pelican .. 1·25 50
459 20 c. Parula warbler .. 1·50 75
392 30 c. Northern mocking-bird .. .. .. 1·75 90
461 50 c. Ruby-throated hummingbird .. .. 1·50 2·25
462 $1 Bananaquit .. .. 2·25 2·75
463 $2 Cedar waxwing .. 3·75 4·50
464 $5 Painted bunting .. 3·50 4·00

127. Bermuda Sloop.

1973. Vessels. Multicoloured

396 2 c. Type **127** 15 10
397 5 c. H.M.S. "Blanche" (screw sloop) 25 10
398 8 c. "Grand Turk" (American privateer) and "Hinchinbrook II" (British packet), 1813 .. 30 15
399 10 c. H.M.S. "Endymion" (frigate), 1790 .. .. 30 15
400 15 c. "Medina" (paddle-steamer) 35 70
401 20 c. H.M.S. "Daring" (brig), 1804 .. .. 45 75

1973. Royal Wedding. As T **47** of Anguilla.

403. 12 c. blue 10 10
404. 18 c. blue 10 10

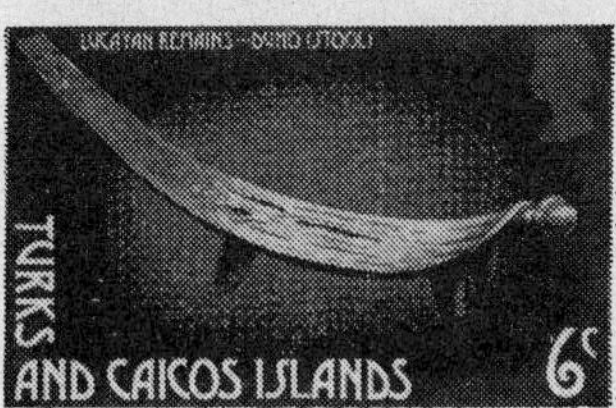

128. Duho (stool).

1974. Lucayan Remains. Multicoloured.

405. 6 c. Type **128** 10 10
406. 10 c. Broken wood bowl .. 15 10
407. 12 c. Greenstone axe .. 15 10
408. 18 c. Wood bowl 15 10
409. 35 c. Fragment of duho .. 20 20

129. G.P.O. Grand Turk.

1974. Centenary of U.P.U. Multicoloured.

426. 4 c. Type **129** 10 10
427. 12 c. Sloop and island map 20 10
428. 18 c. "UPU" and globe .. 20 10
429. 55 c. Posthorn and emblem 35 35

130. Churchill and Roosevelt.

1974. Birth Centenary of Sir Winston Churchill. Multicoloured.

430. 12 c. Type **130** 15 15
431. 18 c. Churchill and vapour-trails 15 15

131. Spanish Captain, circa 1492. **132.** Ancient Windmill, Salt Cay.

1975. Military Uniforms. Multicoloured.

433. 5 c. Type **131** 10 10
434. 20 c. Officer, Royal Artillery 1783 .. .. .. 30 15
435. 25 c. Officer, 67th Foot, 1798 .. .. .. 35 15
436. 35 c. Private, 1st West India Regiment, 1833 .. 45 25

1975. Salt-raking Industry. Multicoloured.

438. 6 c. Type **132** 15 10
439. 10 c. Salt pans drying in sun (horiz.) 15 10
440. 20 c. Salt-raking (horiz.) 25 15
441. 25 c. Unprocessed salt heaps 30 20

133. Star Coral.

1975. Island Coral. Multicoloured.

442. 6 c. Type **133** 15 10
443. 10 c. Elkhorn coral .. 20 10
444. 20 c. Brain coral .. 35 15
445. 25 c. Staghorn coral .. 40 20

134. American Schooner.

1976. Bicent. of American Revolution Mult.

446. 6 c. Type **134** 30 10
447. 20 c. British ship of the line 60 15
448. 25 c. American privateer "Grand Turk" 60 20
449. 55 c. British ketch .. .. 1·00 60

135. 1s. 6d. Royal Visit Stamp of 1966.

1976. 10th Anniv. of Royal Visit. Mult.

466. 20 c. Type **135** 50 30
467. 25 c. 8d. Royal Visit stamp 60 30

136. " The Virgin and Child with Flowers " (C. Dolci).

1976. Christmas. Multicoloured.
468. 6 c. Type **136** 10 10
469. 10 c. " Virgin and Child " with St. John and an Angel ". (Studio of Botticelli) 10 10
470. 20 c. " Adoration of the Magi " (Master of Paraiso) 30 15
471. 25 c. " Adoration of the Magi " (French miniature) 30 20

137. Balcony Scene, Buckingham Palace.

1977. Silver Jubilee. Multicoloured.
472. 6 c. Queen presenting O.B.E. to E. T. Wood.. 10 10
473. 25 c. Queen with regalia.. 20 25
474. 55 c. Type **137** 40 55

138. Col. Glenn's " Mercury " Capsule.

1977. 20th Anniv. of U.S. Tracking Station. Multicoloured.
476. 1 c. Type **138** 10 10
477. 3 c. Moon buggy " Rover " (vert.) 10 10
478. 6 c. Tracking Station, Grand Turk 10 10
479. 20 c. Moon landing craft (vert.) 15 15
480. 25 c. Col. Glenn's rocket launch (vert.) 20 20
481. 50 c. " Telstar 1 " satellite 30 40

139. " Flight of the Holy Family " (Rubens).

1977. Christmas. 400th Birth Anniv. of Rubens. Multicoloured.
482. ½ c. Type **139** 10 10
483. ½ c. " Adoration of the Magi " (1634) 10 10
484. 1 c. " Adoration of the Magi " (1624) 10 10
485. 6 c. " Virgin within Garland " 10 10
486. 20 c. " Madonna and Child Adored by Angels " .. 15 10
487. $2 " Adoration of the Magi " (1618) .. .. 1·25 1·25

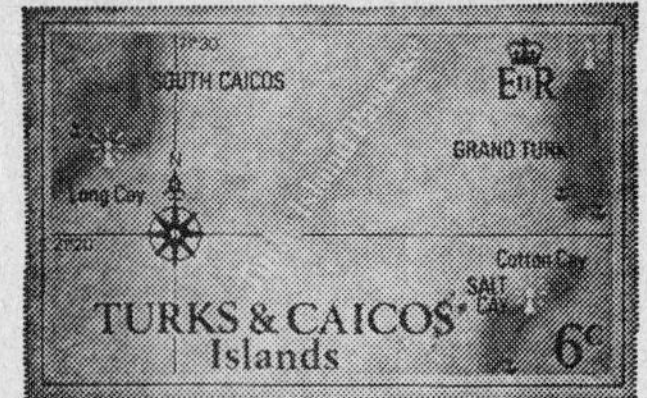

140. Map of Passage.

1978. Turks Island Passage. Multicoloured.
489. 6 c. Type **140** 10 10
490. 20 c. Caicos sloop passing Grand Turk Lighthouse 35 55
491. 25 c. Motor cruiser .. 40 65
492. 55 c. "Jamaica Planter" (freighter) .. .. 85 1·60

141. " Queen Victoria ". (Sir George Hayter).

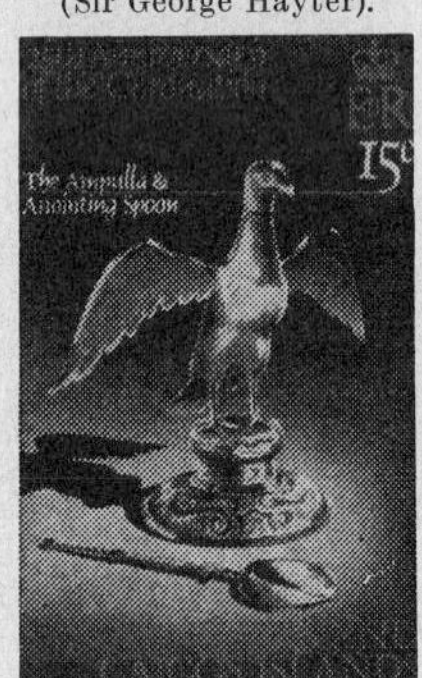

142. Ampulla and Anointing Spoon.

1978. 25th Anniv. of Coronation. Mult.

(a) Monarchs in Coronation robes.
494. 6 c. Type **141** 10 10
495. 10 c. " King Edward VII " (Sir Samuel Fields) .. 10 10
496. 25 c. King George V. .. 20 10
497. $2 King George VI .. 50 70

(b) Coronation regalia. Self-adhesive.
499. 15 c. Type **142** 15 30
500. 25 c. St. Edward's Crown 15 30
501. $2 Queen Elizabeth II in Coronation robes .. 1·00 2·25

Nos. 499/501 come from booklets.

143. Wilbur Wright and " Flyer III ".

1978. 75th Anniv. of Powered Flight. Mult.
502. 1 c. Type **143** 10 10
503. 6 c. Wright brothers and Cessna " 337 " 10 10
504. 10 c. Orville Wright and " Electra " 10 10
505. 15 c. Wilbur Wright and " C-47 " 15 15
506. 35 c. Wilbur Wright and " Islander " 35 35
507. $2 Wilbur Wright and Wright biplane .. 1·25 1·50

144. Hurdling.

1978. 11th Commonwealth Games, Edmonton. Multicoloured.
509. 6 c. Type **144** 10 10
510. 20 c. Weightlifting .. 15 15
511. 55 c. Boxing 30 30
512. $2 Cycling .. .. 1·00 1·00

145. Indigo Hamlet.

1978. Fishes. Multicoloured.
514. 1 c. Type **145** 10 25
515. 2 c. Tobacco Fish .. 40 10
516. 3 c. Passing Jack.. .. 15 10
517. 4 c. Porkfish 40 20
518. 5 c. Spanish Grunt .. 20 20
519. 7 c. Yellowtail Snapper .. 50 15
520. 8 c. Foureye Butterflyfish 60 10
521. 10 c. Yellowfin Grouper.. 30 15
522. 15 c. Beau Gregory .. 50 30
523. 20 c. Queen Angelfish .. 30 30
524. 30 c. Hogfish .. .. 1·00 40
525. 50 c. Fairy Basslet .. 1·00 65
526. $1 Clown Wrasse.. .. 1·75 1·60
527. $2 Stoplight Parrotfish .. 3·25 2·50
528. $5 Queen Triggerfish .. 3·25 6·50

Some values exist both with or without imprint date at foot.

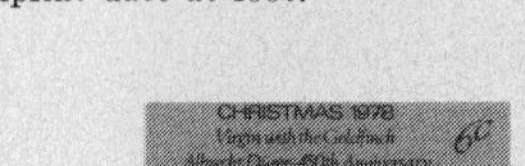

146. " Madonna of the Siskin ".

1978. Christmas Paintings by Durer. Mult.
529. 6 c. Type **146** 10 10
530. 20 c. " The Virgin and Child with St. Anne ".. 15 10
531. 35 c. " Paumgartner Nativity " (horiz.) 20 15
532. $2 " Praying Hands " .. 85 1·00

147. Osprey.

1979. Endangered Wildlife. Multicoloured.
534. 6 c. Type **147** 40 10
535. 20 c. Green Turtle.. .. 45 20
536. 25 c. Queen Conch .. 50 25
537. 55 c. Rough-toothed Dolphin 90 50
538. $1 Humpback Whale .. 1·50 1·25

148. " The Beloved " (painting by D. G. Rossetti).

1979. International Year of the Child. Multicoloured.
540. 6 c. Type **148** 10 10
541. 25 c. " Tahitian Girl " (P. Gauguin) 15 10
542. 55 c. " Calmady Children " (Sir Thomas Lawrence) 25 20
543. $1 " Mother and Daughter " (detail, P. Gauguin) .. 45 45

149. "Medina" (paddle-steamer) and Handstamped Cover.

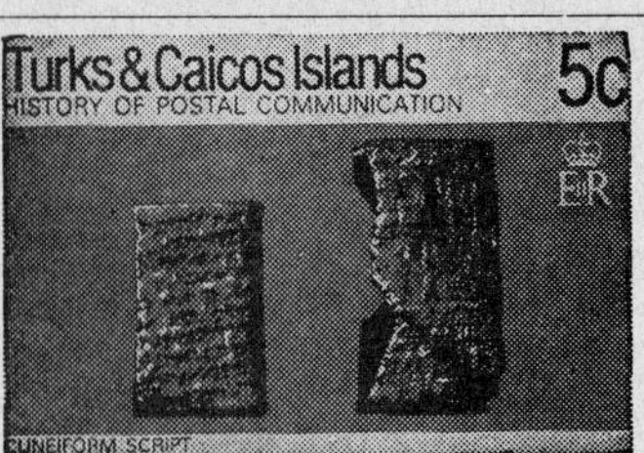

150. Cuneiform Script.

1979. Death Centenary of Sir Rowland Hill.

(a) As T **149**. Multicoloured.
545 6 c. Type **149** 10 10
546 20 c. Sir Rowland Hill and map of Caribbean .. 15 15
547 45 c. "Orinoco I", (mail paddle-steamer) and cover bearing Penny Black stamp 20 20
548 75 c. "Shannon" (screw-steamer) and letter to Grand Turk .. 30 30
549 $1 "Trent I" (paddle-steamer) and map of Caribbean 35 35
550 $2 Turks Islands 1867 and Turks and Caicos Islands 1900 1d. stamps .. 70 70

(b) As T **150**. Self-adhesive (from booklets).
552. **150.** 5 c. black and green .. 10 10
553. – 5 c. black and green .. 10 10
554. – 5 c. black and green .. 10 10
555. – 15 c. black and blue .. 20 20
556. – 15 c. black and blue .. 20 20
557. – 15 c. black and blue .. 20 20
558. – 25 c. black and blue .. 30 30
559. – 25 c. black and blue .. 60 45
560. – 25 c. black and blue .. 30 30
561. – 40 c. black and red .. 45 45
562. – 40 c. black and red .. 45 45
563. – 40 c. black and red .. 45 45
564. – $1 black and yellow .. 1·10 1·25

DESIGNS—HORIZ. No. 553, Egyptian papyrus. No. 554, Chinese paper. No. 555, Greek runner. No. 556, Roman post horse. No. 557. Roman post ship. No. 558, Pigeon post. No. 559, Railway post No. 560, Packet paddle-steamer, No. 561. Balloon post. No. 562, First airmail. No. 563, Supersonic airmail. VERT. No. 564, Original stamp press.

152. " St. Nicholas ", Prikra, Ukraine.

1979. Christmas. Religious Art. Multicoloured.
566. 1 c. Type **152** 10 10
567. 3 c. " Emperor Otto II with Symbols of Empire " (Master of the Registrum Gregorii) 10 10
568. 6 c. " Portrait of St. John " (Book of Lindisfarne).. 10 10
569. 15 c. " Adoration of the Majestas Domini " (prayer book of Otto II) 10 10
570. 20 c. " Christ attended by Angels " (Book of Kells) 15 15
571. 25 c. " St. John the Evangelist " (Gospels of St. Medard of Soissons), Charlemagne 20 15
572. 65 c. " Christ Pantocrator ", Trocany, Ukraine .. 30 25
573. $1 " Portrait of St. John " (Canterbury Codex Aureus) 45 45

153. Pluto and Starfish.

1979. International Year of the Child. Walt Disney Cartoon Characters. At the Seaside. Multicoloured.

575. ½ c. Type **153** 10 10
576. ½ c. Minnie Mouse in summer outfit 10 10
577. 1 c. Mickey Mouse underwater 10 10
578. 2 c. Goofy and turtle .. 10 10
579. 3 c. Donald Duck and dolphin 10 10
580. 4 c. Mickey Mouse fishing 10 10
581. 5 c. Goofy surfing .. 10 10
582. 25 c. Pluto and crab .. 45 20
583. $1 Daisy water-skiing .. 2·00 1·10

154. "Christina's World" (painting by Andrew Wyeth).

1979. Works of Art. Multicoloured.

585. 6 c. Type **154** 10 10
586. 10 c. Ivory Leopards, Benin (19th-cent.) .. 10 10
587. 20 c. "The Kiss" (painting by Gustav Klimt) (vert.) .. 15 15
588. 25 c. "Portrait of a Lady" (painting by R. van der Weyden) (vert.) .. 15 15
589. 80 c. Bull's head harp, Sumer c. 2600 B.C. (vert.) .. 30 30
590. $1 "The Wave" (painting by Hokusai) 45 45

155. Pied-billed Grebe.

1980. Birds. Multicoloured.

592. 20 c. Type **155** 60 15
593. 25 c. Ovenbirds at nest .. 65 20
594. 35 c. Hen Harrier 90 30
595. 55 c. Yellow-bellied Sapsucker .. .. 1·10 35
596. $1 Blue-winged Teal .. 1·40 80

156. Stamp, Magnifying Glass and Perforation Gauge.

1980. "London 1980" International Stamp Exhibition. Multicoloured.

598. **156.** 25 c. black and yellow .. 15 15
599. – 40 c. black and green .. 15 25

DESIGN: 40 c. Tweezers, stamp and perforation gauge.

157. Trumpet Triton.

1980. Shells. Multicoloured.

601. 14 c. Type **157** 20 20
602. 20 c. Measled Cowry .. 25 25
603. 30 c. True Tulip 35 35
604. 45 c. Lion's Paw 45 45
605. 55 c. Sunrise Tellin .. 55 55
606. 70 c. Crown Cone 70 70

158. Queen Elizabeth the Queen Mother.

1980. 80th Birthday of The Queen Mother.

607. **158.** 80 c. multicoloured .. 70 1·25

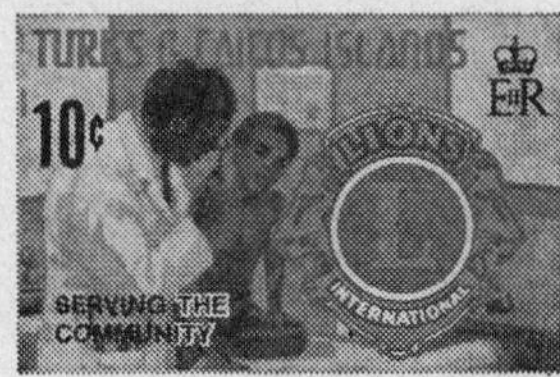

159. Doctor examining Child and Lions International Emblem.

1980. "Serving the Community". Mult.

609. 10 c. Type **159** 15 10
610. 15 c. Students receiving scholarships and Kiwanis International emblem .. 20 10
611. 45 c. Teacher with students and Soroptimist emblem 50 35
612. $1 Lobster trawler and Rotary International emblem .. .. .. 1·00 80

1980. Christmas. Scenes from Walt Disney's "Pinocchio". As T **153**. Multicoloured.

614. ½ c. Scene from "Pinocchio" 10 10
615. ½ c. As puppet 10 10
616. 1 c. Pinocchio changed into a boy 10 10
617. 2 c. Captured by fox .. 10 10
618. 3 c. Pinocchio and puppeteer 10 10
619. 4 c. Pinocchio and bird's nest nose 10 10
620. 5 c. Pinocchio eating .. 10 10
621. 75 c. Pinocchio with ass ears 60 90
622. $1 Pinocchio underwater 80 1·00

160. Martin Luther King Jr.

1980. Human Rights. Personalities. Mult.

624. 20 c. Type **160** 15 10
625. 30 c. John F. Kennedy .. 30 25
626. 45 c. Roberto Clemente (baseball player) .. 45 35
627. 70 c. Sir Frank Worrel (cricketer) 90 90
628. $1 Harriet Tubman .. 1·10 1·25

161. Yachts.

1980. South Caicos Regatta. Multicoloured.

630. 6 c. Type **161** 10 10
631. 15 c. Trophy and yachts .. 15 15
632. 35 c. Spectators watching speedboat race 25 20
633. $1 Caicos sloops 60 50

162. Night Queen Cactus.

1981. Flowering Cacti. Multicoloured.

635. 25 c. Type **162** 25 25
636. 35 c. Ripsaw Cactus .. 35 35
637. 55 c. Royal Strawberry Cactus 40 50
638. 80 c. Caicos Cactus .. 60 75

1981. 50th Anniv. of Walt Disney's Pluto (cartoon character). As T **153**. Multicoloured.

640. 10 c. Pluto listening to conch shell 10 10
641. 75 c. Pluto on raft and porpoise 75 90

1981. Easter. Walt Disney Cartoon Characters. As T **153**. Multicoloured.

643. 10 c. Donald Duck and Louie 20 20
644. 25 c. Goofy and Donald Duck 40 40
645. 60 c. Chip and Dale .. 85 1·00
646. 80 c. Scrooge McDuck and Huey .. .. .. 1·25 1·40

163. "Woman with Fan".

1981. Birth Centenary of Picasso. Mult.

648. 20 c. Type **163** 20 15
649. 45 c. "Woman with Pears" 35 30
650. 80 c. "The Accordionist" 60 50
651. $1 "The Aficionado" .. 80 80

164. Kensington Palace.

1981. Royal Wedding. Multicoloured.

653. 35 c. Prince Charles and Lady Diana Spencer .. 15 15
654. 65 c. Type **164** 25 25
655. 90 c. Prince Charles as Colonel of the Welsh Guards 35 35

165. Lady Diana Spencer.

1981. Royal Wedding. Booklet stamps. Multicoloured. Self-adhesive.

657. 20 c. Type **165** 25 30
658. $1 Prince Charles 35 70
659. $2 Prince Charles and Lady Diana Spencer .. 1·50 2·50

165. Marine Biology Observation.

1981. Diving. Multicoloured.

660. 15 c. Type **166** 20 15
661. 40 c. Underwater photography 50 35
662. 75 c. Wreck diving .. 90 70
663. $1 Diving with dolphins .. 1·25 1·00

1981. Christmas. As T **153** showing scenes from Walt Disney's cartoon film "Uncle Remus".

665. ¼ c. multicoloured .. 10 10
666. ½ c. multicoloured .. 10 10
667. 1 c. multicoloured .. 10 10
668. 2 c. multicoloured .. 10 10
669. 3 c. multicoloured .. 10 10
670. 4 c. multicoloured .. 10 10
671. 5 c. multicoloured .. 10 10
672. 75 c. multicoloured .. 80 80
673. $1 multicoloured .. 1·00 1·00

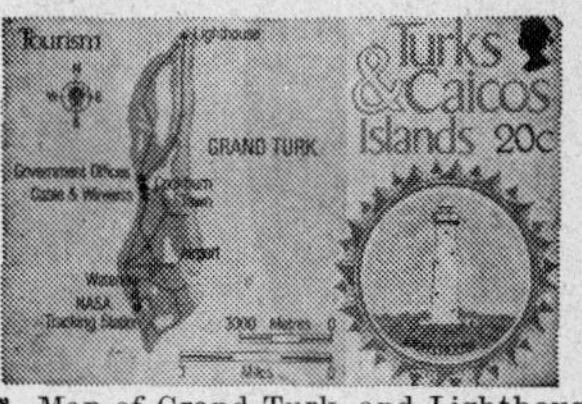

167. Map of Grand Turk, and Lighthouse.

1981. Tourism. Multicoloured.

675. 20 c. Type **167** .. 35 40
676. 20 c. Map of Salt Cay, and "industrial archaeology" 35 40
677. 20 c. Map of South Caicos, and "island flying" .. 35 40
678. 20 c. Map of East Caicos, and "beach combing" 35 40
679. 20 c. Map of Central Grand Caicos, and cave exploring 35 40
680. 20 c. Map of North Caicos, and camping and hiking 35 40
681. 20 c. Map of North Caicos, Parrot Cay, Dellis Cay, Fort George Cay, Pine Cay and Water Cay, and "environmental studies" 35 40
682. 20 c. Map of Providenciales, and scuba diving .. 35 40
683. 20 c. Map of West Caicos, and "cruising and bird sanctuary" .. 35 40
684. 20 c. Turks and Caicos Islands flag 35 40

168. "Junonia evarete"

1982. Butterflies. Multicoloured.

685 20 c. Type **168** .. 30 30
686 35 c. "Strymon maesites" 50 55
687 65 c. "Agraulis vanillae" .. 90 1·00
688 $1 "Eurema dina" .. 1·40 2·00

169. Flag Salute on Queen's Birthday.

1982. 75th Anniv. of Boy Scout Movement. Multicoloured.

690. 40 c. Type **169** .. 50 50
691. 50 c. Raft building .. 50 60
692. 75 c. Sea scout cricket match 1·10 1·40
693. $1 Nature study .. 1·50 1·60

170. Footballer.

1982. World Cup Football Championship, Spain.

695. 170. 10 c. multicoloured .. 15 15
696. – 25 c. multicoloured .. 20 20
697. – 45 c. multicoloured .. 25 25
698. – $1 multicoloured .. 80 80

DESIGNS: 25 c. to $1. various footballers.

171. Washington crossing the Delaware and Phillis Wheatley (poetess).

1982. 250th Birth Anniv. of George Washington and Birth Centenary of Franklin D. Roosevelt.

700. 20 c. Type **171** 30 30
701. 35 c. George Washington and Benjamin Banneker (surveyor) 45 45
702. 65 c. Franklin D. Roosevelt meeting George Washington Carver (agricultural researcher) 80 80
703. 80 c. Roosevelt as stamp collector .. .. 1·00 1·00

172. " Second Thoughts ".

1982. Norman Rockwell (painter) Commemoration. Multicoloured.

705. 8 c. Type **172** 15 10
706. 15 c. " The Proper Gratuity " 20 20
707. 20 c. " Before the Shot " 25 25
708. 25 c. " The Three Umpires " 25 25

173. Princess of Wales.

1982. 21st Birthday of Princess of Wales. Multicoloured.

713. 8 c. Sandringham 20 35
714. 35 c. Prince and Princess of Wales .. .. .. 45 1·00
709. 55 c. As 8 c. 45 55
710. 70 c. As 35 c. 50 70
711. $1 Type **173** .. .. 70 1·25
715. $1.10 Type **173** .. .. 75 2·00

174. " Skymaster " over Caicos Cays.

1982. Aircraft. Multicoloured.

716. 8 c. Type **174** 15 15
717. 15 c. " Jetstar " over Grand Turk 20 25
718. 65 c. Helicopter over South Caicos 65 80
719. $1.10 Seaplane over Providenciales .. 1·10 1·25

1982. Christmas. Scenes from Walt Disney's Cartoon film " Mickey's Christmas Carol ". As T **153**. Multicoloured.

721. 1 c. Donald Duck, Mickey Mouse and Scrooge .. 10 10
722. 1 c. Goofy (Marley's ghost) and Scrooge 10 10
723. 2 c. Jiminy Cricket and Scrooge 10 10
724. 2 c. Huey, Dewy and Louie 10 10
725. 3 c. Daisy Duck and youthful Scrooge 10 10
726. 3 c. Giant and Scrooge .. 10 10
727. 4 c. Two bad wolves, a wise pig and a reformed Scrooge 10 10
728. 65 c. Donald Duck and Scrooge .. .. 1·00 65
729. $1.10 Mortie and Scrooge 1·60 1·10

175. West Caicos Trolley Tram.

1983. Trams and Locomotives. Mult.

731. 15 c. Type **175** 20 25
732. 55 c. West Caicos steam locomotive 65 70
733. 90 c. East Caicos sisal locomotive .. .. 90 1·00
734. $1.60 East Caicos steam locomotive .. .. 1·75 1·90

176. Policewoman on Traffic Duty.

1983. Commonwealth Day. Multicoloured.

736. 1 c. Type **176** 15 20
737. 8 c. Stylized sun and weather vane 15 20
738. 65 c. Yacht 85 90
739. $1 Cricket .. .. 1·50 1·60

177. " St. John and the Virgin Mary " (detail).

1983. Easter. Designs showing details from the " Mond Crucifixion " by Raphael. Multicoloured.

740. 35 c. Type **177** 25 25
741. 50 c. " Two Women " .. 35 35
742. 95 c. " Angel with two jars " 55 60
743. $1.10 " Angel with one jar " 75 80

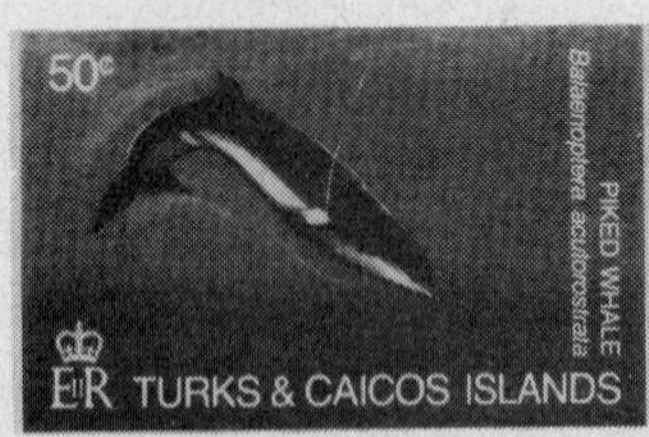

178. Minke Whale.

1983. Whales. Multicoloured.

745. 50 c. Type **178** .. .. 1·25 1·25
746. 65 c. Black Right Whale .. 1·50 1·50
747. 70 c. Killer Whale .. 1·75 1·75
748. 95 c. Sperm Whale .. 2·00 2·00
749. $1.10 Cuvier's Beaked Whale .. .. .. 2·25 2·25
750. $2 Blue Whale .. .. 4·00 4·00
751. $2.20 Humpback Whale .. 4·50 4·50
752. $3 Long-finned Pilot Whale .. .. .. 5·50 5·50

179. First Hydrogen Balloon, 1783.

1983. Bicentenary of Manned Flight. Mult.

754. 25 c. Type **179** 25 25
755. 35 c. " Friendship 7 " .. 35 35
756. 70 c. First hot-air balloon, 1783 .. .. .. 70 70
757. 95 c. Space shuttle " Columbia " 90 90

180. Fiddler Pig.

1983. Christmas. Walt Disney Cartoon Characters. Multicoloured.

759. 1 c. Type **180** 10 10
760. 1 c. Fifer Pig 10 10
761. 2 c. Practical Pig 10 10
762. 2 c. Pluto 10 10
763. 3 c. Goofy 10 10
764. 3 c. Micky Mouse 10 10
765. 35 c. Gyro Gearloose .. 35 35
766. 50 c. Ludwig von Drake .. 50 50
767. $1.10 Huey, Dewey and Louie .. .. .. 1·00 1·00

181. Bermudan Sloop.

1983. Ships. Multicoloured.

769 4 c. Arawak dug-out canoe 40 40
770 5 c. "Santa Maria" .. 50 40
771 8 c. British and Spanish ships in battle .. .. 1·00 60
772 10 c. Type **181** .. .. 1·00 60
773 20 c. U.S. privateer "Grand Turk" 50 50
774 25 c. H.M.S. "Boreas" (frigate) 50 50
775 30 c. H.M.S. "Endymion" (frigate) attacking French ship, 1790s .. 1·50 65
776 35 c. "Caesar" (barque) .. 60 60
777 50 c. "Grapeshot" (American schooner) .. 60 70
778 65 c. H.M.S. "Invincible" (battle cruiser) .. .. 1·50 1·40
779 95 c. H.M.S. "Magicienne" (cruiser) .. .. .. 2·50 1·75
780 $1.10 H.M.S. "Durban" (cruiser) .. .. .. 3·25 2·50
781 $2 "Sentinel" (cable ship) 2·50 3·00
782 $3 H.M.S. "Minerva" (frigate) .. .. .. 7·50 5·50
783 $5 Caicos sloop .. .. 7·50 9·00

182. Pres. Kennedy and Signing of Civil Rights Legislation.

1983. 20th Death Anniv. of J. F. Kennedy (U.S. President).

784. **182.** 20 c. multicoloured .. 20 15
785. $1 multicoloured .. 1·10 1·25

183. Clarabelle Cow Diving.

1984. Olympic Games, Los Angeles. Multicoloured.

A. Inscr. " **1984 LOS ANGELES** ". B. Inscr. " **1984 OLYMPICS LOS ANGELES** " and Olympic Emblem.

		A		B	
786.	1 c. Type **183** ..	10	10	10	10
787.	1 c Donald Duck in 500m kayak race	10	10	10	10
788.	2 c. Huey, Dewey and Louie in 1000m kayak race	10	10	10	10
789.	2 c. Mickey Mouse in single kayak	10	10	10	10
790.	3 c. Donald Duck highboard diving	10	10	10	10
791.	3 c. Minnie Mouse in kayak slalom	10	10	10	10
792.	25 c. Mickey Mouse freestyle swimming	40	45	40	45
793.	Donald Duck playing water-polo	1·25	1·40	1·50	1·40
794.	$1 Uncle Scrooge & Donald Duck yachting ..	1·60	1·75	1·75	1·75

184. " Cadillac V–16 ", 1933.

1984. Classic Cars and 125th Anniv. of first Commercial Oil Well. Multicoloured.

796. 4 c. Type **184** 10 10
797. 8 c. Rolls-Royce " Phantom III ", 1937 .. .. 15 15
798. 10 c. Saab " 99 ", 1969 .. 15 15
799. 25 c. Maserati " Bora ", 1973 .. .. 40 40
800. 40 c. Datsun " 260Z ", 1970 .. .. 65 65
801. 55 c. Porsche " 917 ", 1971 80 80
802. 80 c. Lincoln " Continental " 1939 .. .. 90 90
803. $1 Triumph " TR3A ", 1957 .. .. 1·25 1·25

185. " Rest during the Flight to Egypt, with St. Francis ".

1984. Easter 450th Death Anniv. of Correggio (painter). Multicoloured.

805. 15 c. Type **185** 20 15
806. 40 c. "St. Luke and St. Ambrose" 45 40
807. 60 c. "Diana and her Chariot" 65 65
808. 95 c. "The Deposition of Christ" 80 80

1984. Universal Postal Union Congress, Hamburg. Nos. 748/9 optd. **19TH UPU CONGRESS, HAMBURG, WEST GERMANY. 1874-1984.** Multicoloured.

810. 95 c. Sperm Whale .. 2·00 1·50
811. $1.10 Goosebeak Whale .. 2·00 1·60

187. "The Adventure of the Second Stain".

1984. 125th Birth Anniv. of Sir Arthur Conan Doyle (author). Multicoloured.

813. 25 c. Type **187** .. .. 2·00 1·25
814. 45 c. "The Adventure of the Final Problem" .. 2·75 2·00
815. 70 c. "The Adventure of the Empty House" .. 4·25 3·25
816. 85 c. "The Adventure of the Greek Interpreter" 5·00 3·25

188. Clown-Fish.

1984. "Ausipex" International Stamp Exhibition, Melbourne. 175th Birth Anniv. of Charles Darwin. Multicoloured.

818. 5 c. Type **188** 40 30
819. 35 c. Monitor lizard .. 1·75 1·75
820. 50 c. Rainbow lory .. 2·50 2·50
821. $1.10 Koalas .. .. 3·25 3·25

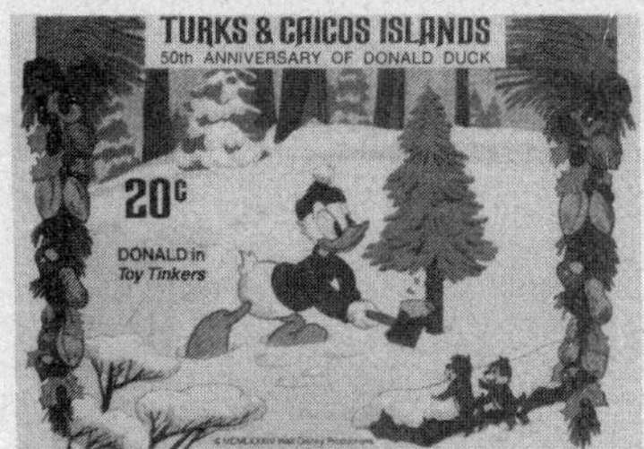

189. Donald Duck cutting down Christmas Tree.

1984. Christmas. Walt Disney Cartoon Characters. Designs showing scenes from "Toy Tinkers". Multicoloured.

823. 20 c. Type **189** 85 45
824. 35 c. Donald Duck and Chip n'Dale playing with train set .. .. 1·10 65
825. 50 c. Donald Duck and Chip n'Dale playing with catapult .. .. 1·60 85
826. 75 c. Donald Duck, Chip n'Dale and Christmas tree .. .. 2·25 1·40
827. $1.10 Donald Duck, toy soldier and Chip n'Dale 2·50 1·90

190. Magnolia Warbler.

1985. Birth Bicentenary of John J. Audubon (ornithologist). Multicoloured.

829. 25 c. Type **190** .. .. 1·50 45
830. 45 c. Short-eared owl .. 2·25 80
831. 70 c. Mourning dove and eggs .. .. 2·50 1·50
832. 85 c. Caribbean martin .. 2·75 1·75

191. Leonardo da Vinci and Illustration of Glider Wing (15th century).

1985. 40th Anniv. of International Civil Aviation Organization. Pioneers. Mult.

834. 8 c. Type **191** 40 15
835. 25 c. Sir Alliott Verdon Roe and "C.102" jetliner (1949) 85 40
836. 65 c. Robert H. Goddard and first liquid fuel rocket (1926) .. .. 2·00 95
837. $1 Igor Sikorsky and Sikorsky "VS300" helicopter (1939) .. .. 2·50 1·50

192. Benjamin Franklin and Marquis de Lafayette.

1985. Centenary of Statue of Liberty's Arrival in New York. Multicoloured.

839 20 c. Type **192** 80 50
840 30 c. Frederic Bartholdi (designer) and Gustave Eiffel (engineer) .. 90 60
841 65 c. "Isere" (French screw warship) arriving in New York with statue, 1885 2·25 1·50
842 $1.10 United States fund raisers Louis Agassiz, Charles Sumner, H. W. Longfellow and Joseph Pulitzer .. .. 2·50 1·75

193. Sir Edward Hawke and H.M.S. "Royal George" (ship of the line), 1782.

1985. Salute to the Royal Navy. Mult.

844 20 c. Type **193** .. .. 1·75 1·50
845 30 c. Lord Nelson and H.M.S. "Victory" (ship of the line), 1805 .. 2·25 2·00
846 65 c. Admiral Sir George Cockburn and H.M.S. "Albion" (ship of the line), 1802 .. .. 3·00 2·75
847 95 c. Admiral Sir David Beatty and H.M.S. "Indefatigable" (battle cruiser), 1916 .. .. 4·00 3·75

194. Mark Twain riding on Halley's Comet.

1985. International Youth Year. Birth Annivs of Mark Twain (150th) and Jakob Grimm (Bicentenary). Multicoloured.

849 25 c. Type **194** 85 40
850 35 c. "Grand Turk" (Mississippi river steamer) .. .. 1·25 55
851 50 c. Hansel and Gretel and gingerbread house (vert) .. .. 1·50 75
852 95 c. Rumpelstiltskin (vert) 2·25 1·50

195. The Queen Mother outside Clarence House. **196.** King George II and Score of "Zadok the Priest" (1727).

1985. Life and Times of Queen Elizabeth the Queen Mother. Multicoloured.

854. 30 c. Type **195** 45 45
855. 50 c. Visiting Biggin Hill airfield (horiz.) 75 75
856. $1.10 80th birthday portrait .. .. .. 1·90 1·90

1985. 300th Birth Anniv. of George Frederick Handel (composer). Multicoloured.

858. 4 c. Type **196** 65 40
859. 10 c. Queen Caroline and score of "Funeral Anthem" (1737) .. 1·00 50
860. 50 c. King George I and score of "Water Music" (1714) .. .. 2·75 1·75
861. $1.10 Queen Anne and score of "Or la Tromba" from "Rinaldo" (1711) .. 4·75 4·00

1985. 300th Birth Anniv of Johann Sebastian Bach (composer). As T **206** of Antigua. Multicoloured.

863 15 c. Bassoon .. .. 1·00 40
864 40 c. Natural Horn .. 1·75 85
865 60 c. Viola d'amore .. 2·25 1·25
866 95 c. Clavichord .. .. 2·75 2·25

197. Harley-Davidson Dual Cylinder (1915) on Middle Caicos.

1985. Centenary of the Motor Cycle. Mult.

868. 8 c. Type **197** 45 30
869. 25 c. Triumph "Thunderbird" (1950) on Grand Turk .. .. 1·00 70
870. 55 c. BMW "K100RS" (1985) on North Caicos .. 2·00 1·50
871. $1.20 Honda "1100 Shadow" (1985) on South Caicos .. .. .. 3·25 3·00

198. Pirates in Prison (Illustration reduced, actual size 50 × 37 mm.).

1985. 30th Anniv. of Disneyland, U.S.A. Designs showing scenes from "Pirates of the Caribbean" exhibition. Multicoloured.

873. 1 c. Type **198** 10 10
874. 1 c. The fate of Captain William Kidd 10 10
875. 2 c. Bartholomew Roberts 10 10
876. 2 c. Two buccaneers .. 10 10
877. 3 c. Privateers looting .. 10 10
878. 3 c. Auction of captives .. 10 10
879. 35 c. Singing pirates .. 1·50 80
880. 75 c. Edward Teach–"Blackbeard" .. .. 2·75 2·25
881. $1.10 Sir Henry Morgan .. 3·25 2·50

MINIMUM PRICE

The minimum price quoted is 10p which represents a handling charge rather than a basis for valuing common stamps. For further notes about prices see introductory pages.

199. Brownies from China, Turks and Caicos and Papua New Guinea.

1985. 75th Anniv. of Girl Guide Movement and 35th Anniv. of Grand Turk Company Multicoloured.

883. 10 c. Type **199** 75 3
884. 40 c. Brownies from Surinam, Turks and Caicos and Korea .. .. 1·75 1·2
885. 70 c. Guides from Australia, Turks and Caicos and Canada .. .. 2·50 2·0
886. 80 c. Guides from West Germany, Turks and Caicos and Israel .. 2·75 2·2

200. Iguana and Log.

1986. Turks and Caicos Ground Iguana. Multicoloured.

888. 8 c. Type **200** .. .. 1·50 1·0
889. 10 c. Iguana on beach .. 1·75 1·1
890. 20 c. Iguana at nest .. 2·25 2·2
891. 35 c. Iguana eating flowers 4·00 4·2

201. Duke and Duchess of York after Wedding.

1986. Royal Wedding. Multicoloured.

893. 35 c. Type **201** 75 5
894. 65 c. Miss Sarah Ferguson in wedding carriage .. 1·25 1·25
895. $1.10 Duke and Duchess of York on Palace balcony after wedding .. .. 2·00 2·25

202. "Prophecy of Birth of Christ to King Achaz".

1987. Christmas. Illuminated illustrations by Giorgio Clovio from "Farnese Book of Hours". Multicoloured.

897. 35 c. Type **202** .. .. 1·25 85
898. 50 c. "The Annunciation" 1·75 1·75
899. 65 c. "The Circumcision" 2·25 2·25
900. 95 c. "Adoration of the Kings" .. .. .. 3·25 4·00

203. H.M.S. "Victoria" (ship of the line), 1859, and Victoria Cross.

1987. 150th Anniv. of Accession of Queen Victoria. Multicoloured.

02. 8 c. Type **203** .. .. 1·00 70
03. 35 c. "Victoria" (paddle-steamer) and gold sovereign.. .. .. 2·00 1·75
04. 55 c. Royal Yacht "Victoria and Albert I" and 1840 Penny Black stamp .. 2·25 2·25
05. 95 c. Royal Yacht "Victoria and Albert II" and Victoria Public Library 3·25 3·75

1987. Bicentenary of U.S. Consitution. As T **232** of Antigua. Multicoloured.

07. 10 c. State Seal, New Jersey 20 15
08. 35 c. 18th-century family going to church ("Freedom of Worship") (vert.) 55 55
09. 65 c. U.S. Supreme Court, Judicial Branch, Washington (vert.) .. 1·00 1·00
10. 80 c. John Adams (statesman) (vert.) .. .. 1·25 1·40

204 "Santa Maria"

1988. 500th Anniv (1992) of Discovery of America by Columbus (1st issue). Mult.

12 4 c. Type **204** 20 15
13 25 c. Columbus meeting Tainos Indians .. 85 60
14 70 c. "Santa Maria" anchored off Indian village .. .. .. 2·25 2·50
15 $1 Columbus in field of grain .. .. .. 2·50 2·75

See also Nos. 947/50, 1028/35, 1072/9 and 1166/75.

205 Arawak Artifact and Scouts in Cave, Middle Caicos

1988. World Scout Jamboree, Australia. Mult.

917 8 c. Type **205** 20 15
918 35 c. "Santa Maria", scouts and Hawks Nest Island (horiz) 55 55
919 65 c. Scouts diving to wreck of galleon .. 95 95
920 95 c. Visiting ruins of 19th-century sisal plantation (horiz) .. 1·40 1·40

1988. Royal Ruby Wedding. Nos. 772, 774 and 781 optd **40TH WEDDING ANNIVERSARY H.M. QUEEN ELIZABETH II H.R.H. THE DUKE OF EDINBURGH**.

922 10 c. Type **181** 30 30
923 25 c. H.M.S. "Boreas" (frigate) 55 55
924 $2 "Sentinel" (cable ship) 3·25 3·25

207 Football

1988. Olympic Games, Seoul. Multicoloured.

925 8 c. Type **207** 20 15
926 30 c. Yachting 45 40
927 70 c. Cycling .. .. 1·00 1·10
928 $1 Athletics .. .. 1·40 1·75

208 Game-fishing Launch and Swordfish

1988. Billfish Tournament. Multicoloured.

930 8 c. Type **208** 30 15
931 10 c. Competitors with swordfish catch .. 35 15
932 70 c. Game-fishing launch 1·75 1·75
933 $1 Blue marlin .. .. 2·40 2·50

1988. Christmas. 500th Birth Anniv of Titian (artist). As T **238** of Antigua inscr "CHRISTMAS 1988" and with royal cypher at top right. Multicoloured.

935 15 c. "Madonna and Child with Saint Catherine" .. 40 30
936 25 c. "Madonna with a Rabbit" 50 40
937 35 c. "Virgin and Child with Saints" 60 50
938 40 c. "The Gypsy Madonna" 70 60
939 50 c. "The Holy Family and a Shepherd" .. 80 70
940 65 c. "Madonna and Child" 95 85
941 $3 "Madonna and Child with Saints" .. 4·25 5·00

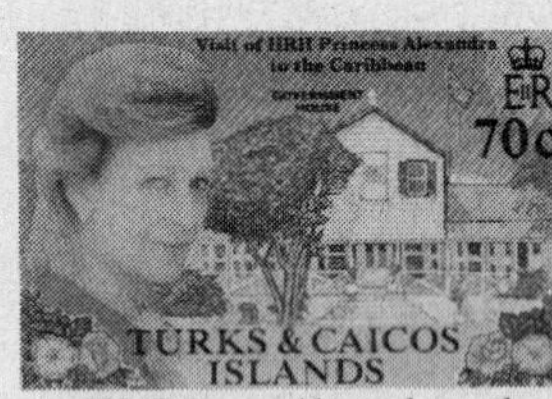

209 Princess Alexandra and Government House

1988. Visit of Princess Alexandra. Mult.

943 70 c. Type **209** .. .. 1·50 1·50
944 $1.40 Princess Alexandra and map of islands .. 2·50 2·50

210 Coat of Arms

1988.

946 **210** $10 multicoloured .. 11·00 13·00

1989. 500th Anniv (1992) of Discovery of America by Columbus (2nd issue). Pre-Columbian Carib Society. As T **247** of Antigua. Multicoloured.

947 10 c. Cutting tree bark for canoe (vert) 10 15
948 50 c. Body painting .. 60 65
949 65 c. Religious ceremony 75 80
950 $1 Canoeing (vert) .. 1·25 1·40

1989. "World Stamp Expo '89" International Stamp Exhibition, Washington. Bicentenary of the U.S. Presidency. As T **238** of Dominica. Multicoloured.

953 50 c. Andrew Jackson and "DeWitt Clinton" railway locomotive .. 60 65
954 50 c. Martin van Buren, Moses Walker and early baseball game 60 65
955 50 c. William H. Harrison and campaign parade .. 60 65
956 50 c. John Tyler, Davy Crockett and the Alamo, Texas 60 65
957 50 c. James K. Polk, California gold miner and first U.S. postage stamp 60 65
958 50 c. Zachary Taylor and Battle of Buena Vista, 1846 .. .. .. 60 65
959 50 c. Rutherford B. Hayes and end of Confederate Reconstruction .. 60 65
960 50 c. James A. Garfield and Battle of Shiloh .. 60 65
961 50 c. Chester A. Arthur and opening of Brooklyn Bridge, 1883 .. .. 60 65
962 50 c. Grover Cleveland, Columbian Exposition, Chicago, 1893, and commemorative stamp 60 65
963 50 c. Benjamin Harrison, Pan-American Union Building and map of Americas 60 65
964 50 c. William McKinley and Rough Rider Monument 60 65
965 50 c. Herbert Hoover, Sonya Heine (skater) and Ralph Metcalf (athlete) 60 65
966 50 c. Franklin D. Roosevelt with dog and in wheelchair 60 65
967 50 c. Statue of Washington by Frazer and New York World's Fair, 1939 .. 60 65
968 50 c. Harry S. Truman, Veterans Memorial Building, San Francisco, and U.N. emblem .. 60 65
969 50 c. Dwight D. Eisenhower and U.S. troops landing in Normandy, 1944 .. .. .. 60 65
970 50 c. John F. Kennedy and "Apollo 11" astronauts on Moon, 1969 .. .. 60 65

1989. Christmas. Paintings by Bellini. As T **259** of Antigua. Multicoloured.

971 15 c. "Madonna and Child" 30 30
972 25 c. "The Madonna of the Shrubs" 40 40
973 35 c. "The Virgin and Child" 50 50
974 40 c. "The Virgin and Child with a Greek Inscription" 60 60
975 50 c. "The Madonna of the Meadow" 70 70
976 65 c. "The Madonna of the Pear" 90 90
977 70 c. "The Virgin and Child" (different) .. 1·00 1·00
978 $1 "Madonna and Child" (different) .. .. 1·60 1·60

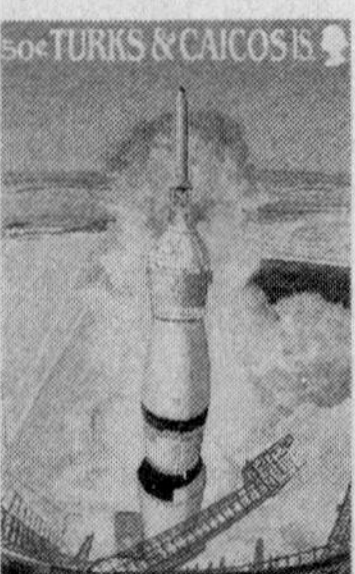

211 Lift-off of "Apollo 11"

1990. 20th Anniv of First Manned Landing on Moon. Multicoloured.

980 50 c. Type **211** 60 65
981 50 c. Lunar module "Eagle" on Moon .. 60 65
982 50 c. Aldrin gathering dust sample 60 65
983 50 c. Neil Armstrong with camera 60 65
984 50 c. "Eagle" re-united with command module "Columbia" 60 65

Nos. 980/4 were printed together, se-tenant, with Nos. 981/3 forming a composite design.

212 "Zephyranthes rosea"

1990. Island Flowers. Multicoloured.

985 8 c. Type **212** 10 10
986 10 c. "Sophora tomentosa" 10 15
987 15 c. "Coccoloba uvifera" 20 25
988 20 c. "Encyclia gracilis" 25 30
989 25 c. "Tillandsia streptophylla" 30 35
990 30 c. "Maurandella antirrhiniflora" 40 45
991 35 c. "Tillandsia balbisiana" 45 50
992 50 c. "Encyclia rufa" .. 65 70
993 65 c. "Aechmea lingulata" 85 90
994 80 c. "Asclepias curassavica" .. .. .. 1·00 1·10
995 $1 "Caesalpinia bahamensis" .. .. .. 1·25 1·40
996 $1.10 "Capparis cynophallophora .. .. 1·25 1·40
997 $1.25 "Stachytarpheta jamaicensis" .. .. 1·60 1·75
998 $2 "Cassia biflora" .. 2·50 2·75
999 $5 "Clusia rosea" .. 6·50 6·75
1000 $10 "Opuntia bahamana" 13·00 13·50

213 Queen Parrotfish

1990. Fishes. Multicoloured.

1001 8 c. Type **213** 20 15
1002 10 c. Queen triggerfish .. 20 20
1003 25 c. Sergeant major .. 50 45
1004 40 c. Spotted goatfish .. 75 65
1005 50 c. Neon goby 90 80
1006 75 c. Nassau grouper .. 1·25 1·25
1007 80 c. Jawfish .. .. 1·40 1·50
1008 $1 Blue tang .. .. 1·50 1·60

214 Yellow-billed Cuckoo

1990. Birds (1st series). Multicoloured.

1010 10 c. Type **214** 30 20
1011 15 c. White-tailed tropic bird 45 30
1012 20 c. Kirtland's warbler 55 45
1013 30 c. Yellow-crowned night heron .. 65 50
1014 50 c. Black-billed whistling duck ("West Indian tree duck") .. 1·00 90
1015 80 c. Yellow-bellied sapsucker .. .. 1·50 1·50
1016 $1 American kestrel .. 1·75 1·75
1017 $1.40 Northern mockingbird .. .. .. 2·50 2·50

See also Nos. 1050/7.

215. "Anartia jatrophae".

1990. Butterflies (1st series). Multicoloured.
1019 15 c. Type **215** 30 30
1020 25 c. "Phoebis sennae" (horiz) 50 50
1021 35 c. "Euptoieta hegesia" (horiz) 65 65
1022 40 c. "Hylephila phylaeus" (horiz) .. 70 70
1023 50 c. "Eurema chamberlaini" (horiz) .. 80 80
1024 60 c. "Brephidium exilis" .. 95 95
1025 90 c. "Papilio aristodemus" (horiz) .. 1·60 1·60
1026 $1 "Marpesia eleuchea" .. 1·75 1·75
See also Nos. 1081/8.

1990. 500th Anniv (1992) of Discovery of America by Columbus (3rd issue). New World Natural History–Fishes. As T **260** of Antigua. Multicoloured.
1028 10 c. Rock beauty .. 20 20
1029 15 c. Coney 25 25
1030 25 c. Red hind 45 45
1031 50 c. Banded butterflyfish 85 85
1032 60 c. French angelfish .. 90 90
1033 75 c. Blackbar soldierfish 1·10 1·10
1034 90 c. Stoplight parrotfish 1·50 1·50
1035 $1 French grunt .. 1·60 1·60

216 Penny "Rainbow Trial" in Blue

1990. 150th Anniv of the Penny Black.
1037 **216** 25 c. blue 55 55
1038 – 75 c. brown .. .. 1·40 1·40
1039 – $1 blue .. .. 1·75 1·75
DESIGNS: 75 c. 1d. red-brown colour trial of December, 1840; $1 2d. blue of 1840.

217 Pillar Box No. 1, 1885

1990. "Stamp World London 90" Int. Stamp Exhibition. British Pillar Boxes.
1041 **217** 35 c. brown and grey 65 65
1042 – 50 c. blue and grey .. 90 90
1043 – $1.25 blue and grey .. 2·25 2·50
DESIGNS: 50 c. Penfold box, 1866; $1.25, Air mail box, 1935.

1990. 90th Birthday of Queen Elizabeth the Queen Mother. As T **266** of Antigua.
1045 10 c. multicoloured .. 20 15
1046 25 c. multicoloured .. 50 50
1047 75 c. multicoloured .. 1·25 1·25
1048 $1.25 multicoloured .. 2·00 2·25
DESIGNS: 25, 75 c. $1.25 Recent photographs of the Queen Mother.

219 Stripe-headed Tanager

1990. Birds (2nd series). Multicoloured.
1050 8 c. Type **219** 20 20
1051 10 c. Black-whiskered vireo (horiz) .. 20 20
1052 25 c. Blue-grey gnatcatcher (horiz) .. 50 50
1053 40 c. Lesser scaup (horiz) 70 70
1054 50 c. Bahama pintail (horiz) 80 80
1055 75 c. Black-necked stilt (horiz) .. .. 1·25 1·25
1056 80 c. Oystercatcher .. 1·40 1·40
1057 $1 Louisiana heron (horiz) 2·10 2·10

220 "Triumph of Christ over Sin and Death" (detail, Rubens)

1990. Christmas. 350th Death Anniv of Rubens. Multicoloured.
1059 10 c. Type **220** .. 20 20
1060 35 c. "St. Theresa Praying" (detail) .. 60 60
1061 45 c. "St. Theresa Praying" (different detail) 70 70
1062 50 c. "Triumph of Christ over Sin and Death" (different detail) .. 80 80
1063 65 c. "St. Theresa Praying" (different detail) .. .. 1·00 1·00
1064 75 c. "Triumph of Christ over Sin and Death" (different detail) .. 1·25 1·25
1065 $1.25 "St. Theresa Praying" (different detail) .. .. 1·90 1·90

221 Canoeing

1991. Olympic Games, Barcelona (1992). Mult.
1067 10 c. Type **221** 20 20
1068 25 c. 100 metre sprint .. 50 50
1069 75 c. Pole vaulting .. 1·25 1·25
1070 $1.25 Javelin .. 1·90 1·90

1991. 500th Anniv (1992) of Discovery of America by Columbus (4th issue). History of Exploration. As T **64** of Nevis. Mult.
1072 5 c. Henry Hudson in Hudson's Bay, 1611 .. 10 10
1073 10 c. Roald Amundsen's airship "Norge", 1926 15 20
1074 15 c. Amundsen's "Gjoa" in the Northwest Passage, 1906 .. .. 20 25
1075 50 c. Submarine U.S.S. "Nautilus" under North Pole, 1958 .. 65 70
1076 75 c. Robert Scott's "Terra Nova", 1911 .. 95 1·00
1077 $1 Byrd and Bennett's Fokker aircraft over North Pole, 1926 .. 1·25 1·40
1078 $1.25 Lincoln Ellsworth's "Polar Star" on trans-Antarctic flight, 1935 1·60 1·75
1079 $1.50 Capt. James Cook in the Antarctic, 1772–75 2·00 2·10

222 "Anartia jatrophae"

1991. Butterflies (2nd series). Multicoloured.
1081 5 c. Type **222** 10 10
1082 25 c. "Historis osius" .. 30 35
1083 35 c. "Agraulis vanillae" 45 50
1084 45 c. "Junonia evarete" 60 65
1085 55 c. "Dryas julia" .. 70 75
1086 65 c. "Siproeta stelenes" 85 90
1087 70 c. "Appias drusilla" .. 90 95
1088 $1 "Ascia monuste" .. 1·25 1·40

223 Protohydrochoerus

1991. Extinct Species of Fauna. Mult.
1090 5 c. Type **223** 10 10
1091 10 c. Phororhacos .. 15 20
1092 15 c. Prothylacynus .. 20 25
1093 50 c. Borhyaena 65 70
1094 75 c. Smilodon .. .. 95 1·00
1095 $1 Thoatherium .. .. 1·25 1·40
1096 $1.25 Cuvieronius .. 1·60 1·75
1097 $1.50 Toxodon .. .. 2·00 2·10

1991. 65th Birthday of Queen Elizabeth II. As T **280** of Antigua. Multicoloured.
1099 25 c. Queen and Prince Philip at St. Paul's Cathedral, 1988 .. 30 35
1100 35 c. Queen and Prince Philip 45 50
1101 65 c. Queen and Prince Philip at Garter Ceremony, 1988 .. 85 90
1102 80 c. Queen at Windsor, May 1988 .. .. 1·00 1·10

224 "Pluteus chrysophlebius"

1991. Fungi. Multicoloured.
1104 10 c. Type **224** 10 10
1105 15 c. "Leucopaxillus gracillimus" 20 25
1106 20 c. "Marasmius haematocephalus" .. 25 30
1107 35 c. "Collybia subpruinosa" 45 50
1108 50 c. "Marasmius atrorubens" (vert) .. 65 70
1109 65 c. "Leucocoprinus birnbaumii" (vert) .. 85 90
1110 $1.10 "Trogia cantharelloides" (vert) .. 1·25 1·40
1111 $1.25 "Boletellus cubensis" (vert) .. 1·60 1·75

1991. 10th Wedding Anniv of the Prince and Princess of Wales. As T **280** of Antigua. Multicoloured.
1113 10 c. Prince and Princess of Wales, 1987 .. 10 10
1114 45 c. Separate photographs of Prince, Princess and sons .. 60 65
1115 50 c. Prince Henry in fire engine and Prince William applauding .. 65 70
1116 $1 Princess Diana in Derbyshire, 1990, and Prince Charles .. 1·25 1·40

1991. Death Centenary (1990) of Vincent van Gogh (artist). As T **278** of Antigua. Mult.
1118 15 c. "Weaver with Spinning Wheel" .. 20 25
1119 25 c. "Head of a Young Peasant with Pipe" (vert) 30 35
1120 35 c. "Old Cemetery Tower at Nuenen" (vert) 45 50
1121 45 c. "Cottage at Nightfall" 60 65
1122 50 c. "Still Life with Open Bible" 65 70
1123 65 c. "Lane, Jardin du Luxembourg" .. 85 90
1124 80 c. "Pont du Carrousel and Louvre, Paris" .. 1·00 1·10
1125 $1 "Vase with Poppies, Cornflowers, Peonies and Chrysanthemums" (vert) .. .. .. 1·25 1·40

225 Series "8550" Steam Locomotive

1991 "Phila Nippon '91" International Stamp Exhibition, Tokyo. Japanese Steam Locomotives. Multicoloured.
1127 8 c. Type **225** 10 10
1128 10 c. Class "C 57" .. 15 20
1129 45 c. Series "4110" .. 60 65
1130 50 c. Class "C 55" .. 65 70
1131 65 c. Series "6250" .. 85 90
1132 80 c. Class "E 10" .. 1·00 1·10
1133 $1 Series "4500" .. 1·25 1·40
1134 $1.25 Class "C 11" .. 1·60 1·75

1991. Christmas. Religious Paintings by Gerard David. As T **211** of Lesotho. Mult.
1136 8 c. "Adoration of the Shepherds" (detail) .. 10 10
1137 15 c. "Virgin and Child Enthroned with Two Angels" 20 25
1138 35 c. "The Annunciation" (outer wings) 45 50
1139 45 c. "The Rest on the Flight to Egypt" .. 60 65
1140 50 c. "The Rest on the Flight to Egypt" (different) 65 70
1141 65 c. "Virgin and Child with Angels" 85 90
1142 80 c. "Adoration of the Shepherds" .. 1·00 1·10
1143 $1.25 "Perussis Altarpiece" (detail) .. 1·60 1·75

1992. 40th Anniv of Queen Elizabeth II's Accession. As T **288** of Antigua. Mult.
1145 10 c. Garden overlooking sea 10 10
1146 20 c. Jetty 25 30
1147 25 c. Small bay 30 35
1148 35 c. Island road .. 45 50
1149 50 c. Grand Turk .. 65 70
1150 65 c. Beach 85 90
1151 80 c. Marina .. .. 1·00 1·10
1152 $1.10 Grand Turk (different) .. .. 1·25 1·40

1992. "Granada '92" International Stamp Exhibition, Spain. Religious Paintings. As T **292** of Antigua. Multicoloured.
1154 8 c. "St. Monica" (Luis Tristan) 10 10
1155 20 c. "The Vision of Ezekiel: The Resurrection of the Flesh" (detail) (Francisco Collantes) 25 30
1156 45 c. "The Vision of Ezekiel: The Resurrection of the Flesh" (different detail) (Collantes) 60 65
1157 50 c. "The Martyrdom of St. Phillip" (Jose de Ribera) 65 70
1158 65 c. "St. John the Evangelist" (Juan Ribalta) 85 90
1159 80 c. "Archimedes" (De Ribera) .. .. 1·00 1·10

No.	Description	Unused	Used
1160	$1 "St. John the Baptist in the Desert" (De Ribera)	1·25	1·40
1161	$1.25 "The Martyrdom of St. Phillip" (detail) (De Ribera)	1·60	1·75

226 Boy Scout on Duty at New York World's Fair, 1964

1992. 17th World Scout Jamboree, Korea. Multicoloured.

No.	Description	Unused	Used
1163	$1 Type **226**	1·25	1·40
1164	$1 Lord Baden-Powell (vert)	1·25	1·40

227 "Nina" and Commemorative Coin

1992. 500th Anniv of Discovery of America by Columbus (5th issue). Multicoloured.

No.	Description	Unused	Used
1166	10 c. Type **227**	15	20
1167	15 c. Departure from Palos	20	25
1168	20 c. Coat of Arms of Columbus	25	30
1169	25 c. Ships of Columbus ..	30	35
1170	30 c. "Pinta"	40	45
1171	35 c. Landfall in the New World	45	50
1172	50 c. Christopher Columbus	65	70
1173	65 c. "Santa Maria"	85	90
1174	80 c. Erecting commemorative cross	1·00	1·10
1175	$1.10 Columbus meeting Amerindian	1·25	1·40

1992. Christmas. Religious Paintings. As T **218** of Lesotho. Multicoloured.

No.	Description	Unused	Used
1177	8 c. "Nativity" (detail) (Simon Bening)	10	10
1178	15 c. "Circumcision" (detail) (Bening)	20	25
1179	35 c. "Flight to Egypt" (detail) (Bening)	45	50
1180	50 c. "Massacre of the Innocents" (detail) (Bening)	65	70
1181	65 c. "The Annunciation" (Dieric Bouts)	85	90
1182	80 c. "The Visitation" (Bouts)	1·00	1·10
1183	$1.10 "Adoration of the Angels" (Bouts)	1·25	1·40
1184	$1.25 "Adoration of the Wise Men" (Bouts)	1·60	1·75

228 American Astronaut repairing Satellite

1993. Anniversaries and Events. Mult.

No.	Description	Unused	Used
1186	25 c. Type **228**	30	35
1187	50 c. Dead and flourishing trees	65	70
1188	65 c. Food and World map	85	90
1189	80 c. Polluted and clean seas	1·00	1·10
1190	$1 Lions Club emblem ..	1·25	1·40
1191	$1.25 Projected orbiting quarantine modules ..	1·60	1·75

ANNIVERSARIES AND EVENTS: Nos. 1186, 1191, International Space Year; Nos. 1187, 1189, Earth Summit '92, Rio; No. 1188, International Conference on Nutrition, Rome; No. 1190, 75th anniv of International Association of Lions Clubs.

1993. Visit of the Duke of Edinburgh. Nos. 1100/1 optd **Royal Visit HRH Duke of Edinburgh 20th March 1993**.

No.	Description	Unused	Used
1193	35 c. Queen and Prince Philip	45	50
1194	65 c. Queen and Prince Philip at Garter Ceremony, 1988 ..	85	90

1993. 40th Anniv of Coronation. As T **307** of Antigua.

No.	Description	Unused	Used
1196	15 c. multicoloured ..	20	25
1197	50 c. multicoloured ..	65	70
1198	$1 green and black ..	1·25	1·40
1199	$1.25 multicoloured ..	1·60	1·75

DESIGNS: 15 c. Communion Chalice and Plate; 50 c. Queen Elizabeth II at Coronation (photograph by Cecil Beaton); $1 Queen Elizabeth during Coronation ceremony; $1.25, Queen Elizabeth and Prince Philip.

229 Omphalosaurus

1993. Prehistoric Animals. Multicoloured.

No.	Description	Unused	Used
1201	8 c. Type **229**	10	10
1202	15 c. Coelophysis ..	20	25
1203	20 c. Triceratops ..	25	30
1204	35 c. Dilophosaurus ..	45	50
1205	50 c. Pterodactylus ..	65	70
1206	65 c. Elasmosaurus ..	85	90
1207	80 c. Stegosaurus ..	1·00	1·10
1208	$1.25 Euoplocephalus ..	1·60	1275

1993. Christmas. Religious Paintings. As T **266** of St. Vincent. Black, yellow and red (Nos. 1210/12, 1217) or multicoloured (others).

No.	Description	Unused	Used
1210	8 c. "Mary, Queen of the Angels" (detail) (Durer)	10	10
1211	20 c. "Mary, Queen of the Angels" (different detail) (Durer) ..	25	30
1212	35 c. "Mary, Queen of the Angels" (different detail) (Durer) ..	45	50
1213	50 c. "Virgin and Child with St. John the Baptist" (Raphael) ..	65	70
1214	65 c. "The Canagiani Holy Family" (detail) (Raphael)	85	90
1215	80 c. "The Holy Family with the Lamb" (detail) (Raphael)	1·00	1·10
1216	$1 "Virgin and Child with St. John the Baptist" (different detail) (Raphael)	1·25	1·40
1217	$1.25 "Mary, Queen of the Angels" (different detail) (Durer) ..	1·60	1·75

231 Bluehead Wrasse

1993. Fishes. Multicoloured.

No.	Description	Unused	Used
1219	10 c. Type **231**	15	20
1220	20 c. Honeycomb cowfish	25	30
1221	25 c. Glasseye snapper ..	30	35
1222	35 c. Spotted drum ..	45	50
1223	50 c. Jolthead porgy ..	65	70
1224	65 c. Smallmouth grunt ..	85	90
1225	80 c. Peppermint bass ..	1·00	1·10
1226	$1.10 Indigo hamlet ..	1·25	1·40

232 Killdeer

1993. Birds. Multicoloured.

No.	Description	Unused	Used
1228	10 c. Type **232**	15	20
1229	15 c. Yellow-crowned night heron (vert) ..	20	25
1230	35 c. Northern mockingbird	45	50
1231	50 c. Eastern kingbird (vert)	65	70
1232	65 c. Magnolia warbler ..	85	90
1233	80 c. Cedar waxwing (vert)	1·00	1·10
1234	$1.10 Ruby-throated hummingbird	1·25	1·40
1235	$1.25 Painted bunting (vert)	1·60	1·75

TUVALU

Formerly known as the Ellice Islands and sharing a joint administration with the Gilbert group. On 1st January 1976 the two island-groups separated and the Ellice Is. were renamed Tuvalu.

100 cents = $1 Australian.

1. Tuvaluan and Gilbertese.

1976. Separation. Multicoloured.

No.	Description	Unused	Used
1.	4 c. Type **1**	45	80
2.	10 c. Map of the Islands (vert.)	55	1·00
3.	35 c. Gilbert and Ellice canoes	75	1·50

1976. Nos. 173/87 of the Gilbert and Ellice Islands optd. **TUVALU.**

No.	Description	Unused	Used
14.	1 c. Cutting toddy	30	20
20.	2 c. Lagoon fishing	80	40
21.	3 c. Cleaning pandanus leaves	80	30
22.	4 c. Casting nets	80	45
5.	5 c. Gilbertese canoe ..	80	60
15.	6 c. De-husking coconuts ..	80	40
6.	8 c. Weaving pandanus fronds	80	60
7.	10 c. Weaving a basket ..	80	80
16.	15 c. Tiger shark	80	50
23.	20 c. Beating a rolled pandanus leaf	80	75
24.	25 c. Loading copra ..	80	75
25.	35 c. Fishing at night ..	1·25	1·00
17.	50 c. Local handicrafts ..	1·00	65
18.	$1 Weaving coconut screen	1·50	85
19.	$2 Coat of Arms	2·00	85

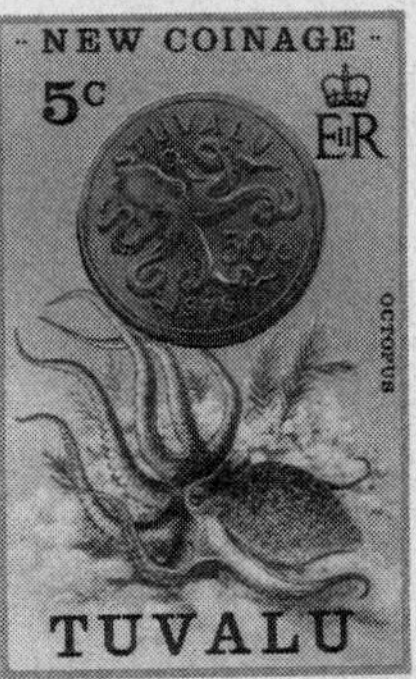

3. 50 c. Coin and Octopus.

1976. New Coinage. Multicoloured.

No.	Description	Unused	Used
26.	5 c. Type **3**	25	15
27.	10 c. 10 c. coin and Red-eyed Crab	35	20
28.	15 c. 20 c. coin and Flying Fish	45	25
29.	35 c. $1 coin and Green Turtle	60	45

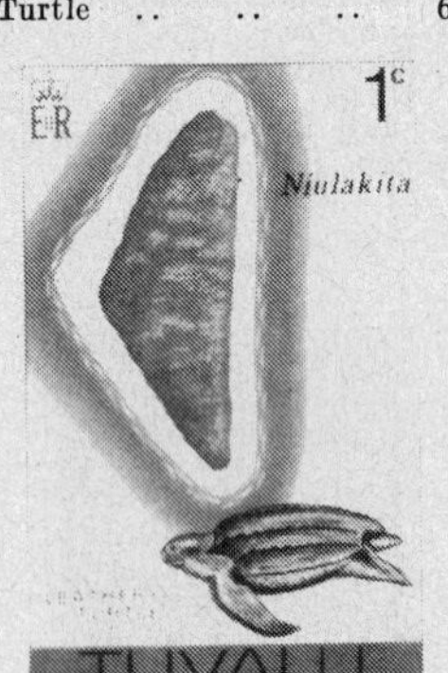

4. Niulakita and Seven-ridged Leathery Turtle.

1976. Multicoloured.

No.	Description	Unused	Used
58	1 c. Type **4**	20	15
59	2 c. Nukulaelae and sleeping mat	20	25
60	4 c. Nui and talo (vegetable)	20	15
61	5 c. Nanumanga and grass skirt	25	15
62	6 c. Nukufetau and Coconut Crab	20	35
63	8 c. Funafuti and Banana tree	20	25
64	10 c. Map of Tuvalu ..	20	20
37	15 c. Niutao and Flying fish	1·00	20
38	20 c. Vaitupu and Naneapa (house)	70	20
66	25 c. Nanumea and fish-hook	1·25	20
67	30 c. Fatele (local dancing)	30	20
40	35 c. Te Ano (game) ..	60	20
68	40 c. Screw Pine	30	15
41	50 c. Canoe pole fishing ..	75	30
42	$1 Reef fishing by flare ..	80	40
43	$2 Living house	1·10	60
69	$5 M.V. "Nivanga" ..	5·50	4·00

5. Title Page of New Testament.

1976. Christmas. Mulicoloured.

45.	5 c. Type 5	40	30
46.	20 c. Lotolelei Church, Nanumea	40	30
47.	25 c. Kelupi Church, Nui ..	40	30
48.	30 c. Mataloa o Tuvala Church, Vaitupu ..	50	30
49.	35 c. Dalataise o Keliso Church, Nanumanga ..	50	30

6. The Queen and Duke of Edinburgh after Coronation.

1977. Silver Jubilee. Multicoloured.

50.	15 c. Type 6	35	20
51.	35 c. Prince Philip carried ashore at Vaitupu ..	40	25
52.	50 c. The Queen leaving Buckingham Palace ..	50	35

7. "Health".

1977. 30th Anniv. of South Pacific Commission. Multicoloured.

54.	5 c. Type 7	20	20
55.	20 c. "Education" ..	25	20
56.	30 c. "Fruit-growing" ..	25	20
57.	35 c. Map of S.P.C. area ..	30	25

8. Scout Promise.

1977. 50th Anniv. of Scouting in the Central Pacific. Multicoloured.

73.	5 c. Type 8	20	25
74.	20 c. Canoeing	20	25
75.	30 c. Scout shelter	25	30
76.	35 c. Lord Baden-Powell ..	25	30

9. Hurricane Beach (Expedition photo).

1977. Royal Society Expeditions.

77. 9.	5 c. multicoloured ..	20	15
78. –	20 c. black and blue ..	20	20
79. –	30 c. black and blue ..	25	20
80. –	35 c. multicoloured ..	25	20

DESIGNS—VERT. 20 c. Boring apparatus on H.M.S. "Porpoise". 30 c. Dredging chart. HORIZ. 35 c. Charles Darwin and H.M.S. "Beagle".

10. Pacific Pigeon.

1978. Wild Birds. Multicoloured.

81.	8 c. Type 10	75	35
82.	20 c. Eastern Reef Heron ..	1·00	50
83.	30 c. White Tern	1·25	60
84.	40 c. Lesser Frigate Bird ..	1·25	65

11. "Lawedua" (inter-island coaster).

1978. Ships. Multicoloured.

85.	8 c. Type 11	15	15
86.	20 c. "Wallacia" (tug) ..	15	15
87.	30 c. "Cenpac Rounder" (freighter)	20	20
88.	40 c. "Pacific Explorer" (freighter)	25	20

1978. 25th Anniv. of Coronation. As Nos. 422/5 of Montserrat. Multicoloured.

89.	8 c. Canterbury Cathedral	10	10
90.	30 c. Salisbury Cathedral ..	10	10
91.	40 c. Wells Cathedral ..	10	10
92.	$1 Hereford Cathedral ..	30	30

1978. Independence. Nos. 63/4, 37/8, 68/40 and 69 optd. **INDEPENDENCE 1ST OCTOBER 1978.**

94.	8 c. Funafuti and Banana tree	10	10
95.	10 c. Map of Tuvalu ..	10	10
96.	15 c. Niutao and Flying fish	10	10
97.	20 c. Vaitupu and Maneapa (house)	15	15
98.	30 c. Fatele (local dancing)	15	15
99.	35 c. Te Ano (game) ..	20	20
100.	40 c. Screw Pines ..	20	20

13. White Frangipani.

1978. Wild Flowers. Multicoloured.

101.	8 c. Type 13	10	10
102.	20 c. Susana	10	10
103.	30 c. Tiale	15	15
104.	40 c. Inato	20	25

14. Squirrelfish.

1979. Fishes. Multicoloured.

105.	1 c. Type 14	10	10
106.	2 c. Yellow-banded Goat-fish	10	10
107.	4 c. Imperial Angelfish ..	10	10
108.	5 c. Rainbow Butterfly ..	15	10
109.	6 c. Blue Angelfish ..	15	10
110.	8 c. Blue-striped Snapper	15	10
111.	10 c. Orange Clownfish ..	25	10
112.	15 c. Chevroned Coralfish	25	10
113.	20 c. Fairy Cod	35	15
114.	25 c. Clown Triggerfish ..	35	20
115.	30 c. Long-nosed Butter-fly	35	10
116.	35 c. Yellowfin Tuna ..	40	20
117.	40 c. Spotted Eagle Ray ..	40	10
117a.	45 c. Black-tipped Rock Cod	1·50	2·00
118.	50 c. Hammerhead Shark	40	20
119.	70 c. Lionfish (vert.) ..	50	30
120.	$1 White-barred Trigger-fish (vert.)	55	55
121.	$2 Beaked Coralfish (vert.)	1·25	60
122.	$5 Tiger Shark (vert.) ..	2·00	80

15. "Explorer of the Pacific".

1979. Death Bicentenary of Capt. James Cook. Multicoloured.

123.	8 c. Type 15	20	20
124.	30 c. Claiming a new island	30	25
125.	40 c. Observing the transit of Venus, 1769	30	25
126.	$1 Cook's death	40	35

16. Flying Boat and Nukulaelae Island.

1979. Internal Air Service. Multicoloured.

127.	8 c. Type 16	15	15
128.	20 c. Flying boat and Vaitupu Island ..	15	20
129.	30 c. Flying boat and Nui Island	20	30
130.	40 c. Flying boat and Funafuti Island	25	35

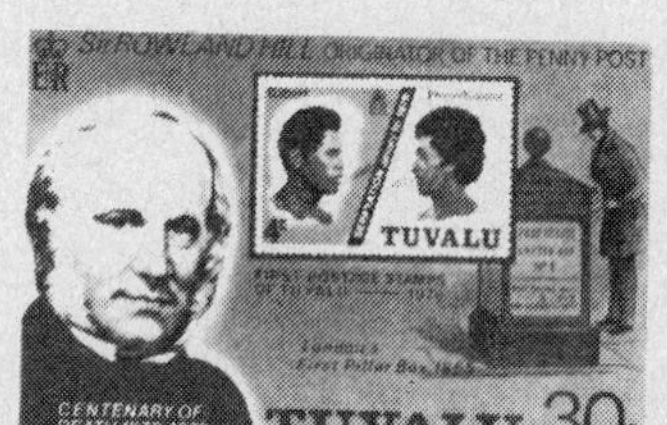

17. Sir Rowland Hill, 1976 4 c. Separation of the Islands Commemorative and London's First Pillar Box, 1855.

1979. Death centenary of Sir Rowland Hill. Multicoloured.

131.	30 c. Type 17	15	15
132.	40 c. Sir Rowland Hill, 1976 10 c. Separation commemorative and Penny Black	15	15
133.	$1 Sir Rowland Hill, 1976 35 c. Separation commemorative and mail coach	35	30

18. Child's Face.

1979. International Year of the Child.

135. 18.	8 c. multicoloured ..	10	10
136. –	20 c. multicoloured ..	10	10
137. –	30 c. multicoloured ..	10	15
138. –	40 c. multicoloured ..	15	25

DESIGNS: 20 c. to 40 c. Children's Faces.

19. "Cypraea argus".

1980. Cowrie Shells. Multicoloured.

139.	8 c. Type 19	10	10
140.	20 c. "Cypraea scurra" ..	10	10
141.	30 c. "Cypraea carneola" ..	15	15
142.	40 c. "Cypraea aurantium"	25	20

20. Philatelic Bureau, Funafuti and 1976 8 c. Definitive.

1980. "London 1980" International Stamp Exhibition. Multicoloured.

143.	10 c. Type 20	10	10
144.	20 c. Nukulaelae postmark and 1976 2 c. definitive	15	15
145.	30 c. Fleet Post Office, U.S. Navy, airmail cover, 1943	15	20
146.	$1 Map and arms of Tuvalu	35	40

21. Queen Elizabeth the Queen Mother at Royal Variety Performance, 1978.

1980. 80th Birthday of The Queen Mother.

148. 21.	15 c. multicoloured ..	25	20

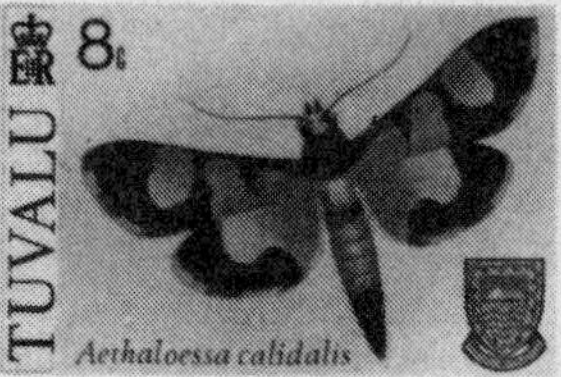

22. "Aethaloessa calidalis".

1980. Moths. Multicoloured.

149.	8 c. Type 22	10	10
150.	20 c. "Parotis suralis" ..	15	10
151.	30 c. "Dudua aprobola"	20	15
152.	40 c. "Decadarchis simulans"	20	15

23. Air Pacific. "Heron".

1980. Aviation Commemorations. Mult.

153.	8 c. Type 23	10	10
154.	20 c. Hawker Siddeley "748"	15	10
155.	30 c. "Sunderland" flying-boat	15	15
156.	40 c. Orville Wright and "Flyer"	20	15

COMMEMORATIONS: 8 c. 1st regular air service to Tuvalu, 1964. 20 c. Air service to Tuvalu. 30 c. War-time R.N.Z.A.F. flying-boat service to Funafuti, 1945. 40 c. Wright Brothers' 1st flight, 17 December, 1903.

1981. No. 118 surch. **45 CENTS.**

157.	45 c. on 50 c. Hammerhead Shark	25	40

25. "Hypolimnas bolina" (male).

1981. Butterflies. Multicoloured.

158. 8 c. Type **25** 15 10
159. 20 c. "Hypolimnas bolina elliciana" (female) .. 20 15
160. 30 c. "Hypolimnas bolina elliciana" (female) (different) 20 20
161. 40 c. "Junonia vallida" (male) 25 20

26. "Elizabeth" (brig), 1809.

1981. Ships (1st series). Multicoloured.

162 10 c. Type **26** 20 20
163 25 c. "Rebecca" (brigantine), 1819 .. 20 30
164 35 c. "Independence II" (whaling ship), 1821 .. 25 35
165 40 c. H.M.S. "Basilisk" (paddle-sloop), 1872 .. 30 40
166 45 c. H.M.S. "Royalist" (screw-corvette), 1890 .. 35 50
167 50 c. "Olivebank" (barque), 1920 .. .. 35 50

See also Nos. 235/40, 377/80 and 442/5.

1981. Royal Wedding. Royal Yachts. As T **26/7** of Kiribati. Multicoloured.

168. 10 c. "Carolina" 10 15
169. 10 c. Princes Charles and Lady Diana Spencer .. 35 35
170. 45 c. "Victoria and Albert III" 10 15
171. 45 c. As No. 169 .. .. 30 30
172. $2 "Britannia" 35 50
173. $2 As No. 169 .. .. 1·00 1·25

27. U.P.U. Emblem.

1981. U.P.U. Membership.

177. **27.** 70 c. blue 20 30
178. $1 brown 30 45

28. Map of Funafuti, and Anchor.

1982. Amatuku Maritime School. Mult.

180. 10 c. Type **28** 10 10
181. 25 c. Motor launch .. 20 20
182. 35 c. School buildings and jetty 25 30
183. 45 c. School flag, and freighter 30 35

29. Caroline of Brandenburg-Ansbach, Princess of Wales, 1714.

1982. 21st Birthday of Princess of Wales. Multicoloured.

184. 10 c. Type **29** 10 10
185. 45 c. Coat of arms of Caroline of Brandenburg-Ansbach 10 10
186. $1.50 Diana, Princess of Wales 45 45

1982. Tonga Cyclone Relief. Nos. 170/1 optd. **TONGA CYCLONE RELIEF 1982 +20 c.**

187. 45 c.+20 c. "Victoria and Albert III" 30 50
188. 45 c.+20 c. Prince Charles and Lady Diana Spencer 50 75

1982. Birth of Prince William of Wales. Nos. 184/6 optd. **ROYAL BABY.**

189. 10 c. Type **29** 10 10
190. 45 c. Coat of arms of Caroline of Brandenburg-Ansbach 10 10
191. $1.50 Diana, Princess of Wales 45 45

31. Tuvalu and World Scout Badges.

1982. 75th Anniv. of Boy Scout Movement. Multicoloured.

192. 10 c. Type **31** 15 15
193. 25 c. Camp-fire 40 40
194. 35 c. Parade 45 45
195. 45 c. Boy Scout 55 55

32. Tuvalu Crest and Duke of Edinburgh's Standard.

1982. Royal Visit. Multicoloured.

196. 25 c. Type **32** 15 20
197. 45 c. Tuvalu flag and Queen's Royal Standard .. 25 30
198. 50 c. Portrait of Queen Elizabeth II 25 30

33. Fisherman's Hat and Equipment.

1983. Handicrafts. Multicoloured.

200. 1 c. Type **33** 30 10
201. 2 c. Cowrie shell handbags 30 10
202. 5 c. Wedding and baby food baskets 30 10
203. 10 c. Model canoe .. 30 10
203a. 15 c. Ladies' sun hats .. 1·50 90
204. 20 c. Palm climbing rope and platform with toddy pot 30 20
205. 25 c. Pandanus baskets .. 30 20
205a. 30 c. Basket tray and coconut stand .. .. 1·75 1·00
206. 35 c. Pandanus pillows and shell necklaces .. 30 30
207. 40 c. Round baskets and fans 30 35
208. 45 c. Reef sandals and fish trap 35 40
209. 50 c. Rat trap (vert.) .. 40 45
209a. 60 c. Fisherman's waterproof boxes (vert.) .. 2·75 1·25
210. $1 Pump drill and adze (vert.) 75 70
211. $2 Fisherman's hat and canoe bailers (vert.) .. 1·25 1·10
212. $5 Fishing rod, lures and scoop nets (vert.) .. 2·75 2·00

34. "Te Tautai" (trawler).

1983. Commonwealth Day. Multicoloured.

213. 20 c. Type **34** 15 15
214. 35 c. Traditional dancing, Motufoua School .. 20 25
215. 45 c. Satellite view of Pacific 25 30
216. 50 c. "Morning Star" (container ship) .. 30 40

35. "Pantala flavescens".

1983. Dragonflies. Multicoloured.

217. 10 c. Type **35** 15 10
218. 35 c. "Anax guttatus" .. 35 35
219. 40 c. "Tholymis tillarga" 35 40
220. 50 c. "Diplacodes bipunctata" 40 50

36. Brigade Members Racing.

1983. Centenary of Boy's Brigade. Mult.

221. 10 c. Type **36** 10 10
222. 35 c. B.B. members in outrigger canoe 25 30
223. $1 On parade .. .. 65 1·00

1983. No. 210 surch.

224. 60 c. on $1 Pump drill and adze 70 70

38. Montgolfier Balloon, 1783.

1983. Bicentenary of Manned Flight. Mult.

225. 25 c. Type **38** 20 20
226. 35 c. McKinnon (Grumman) "Turbogoose" (horiz.) 25 25
227. 45 c. Beechcraft "Super King Air 200" (horiz.) 30 30
228. 50 c. "Double Eagle II", balloon 35 35

39. Early Communications.

1983. World Communications Year. Mult.

230. 25 c. Type **39** 20 20
231. 35 c. Radio operator .. 25 25
232. 45 c. Modern teleprinter .. 25 25
233. 50 c. Funafuti transmitting station 30 30

1984. No. 208 surch.

234. 30 c. on 45 c. Reef sandals and fish trap 35 40

1984. Ships (2nd series). As T **26**. Mult.

235 10 c. "Titus" (freighter), 1897 .. .. .. 15 15
236 20 c. "Malaita" (freighter), 1905 .. .. .. 15 15
237 25 c. "Aymeric" (freighter), 1096 .. .. .. 15 15
238 35 c. "Anshun" (freighter), 1965 .. .. .. 20 25
239 45 c. "Beaverbank" (freighter), 1970 .. 25 30
240 50 c. "Benjamin Bowring" (freighter), 1981 .. 25 30

41. Class "GS-4".

1984. Leaders of the World. Railway Locomotives (1st series). As T **41**. The first in each pair shows technical drawings and the second the locomotives at work.

241. 1 c. multicoloured 10 10
242. 1 c. multicoloured 10 10
243. 15 c. multicoloured .. 20 25
244. 15 c. multicoloured .. 20 25
245. 40 c. multicoloured .. 25 35
246. 40 c. multicoloured .. 25 35
247. 60 c. multicoloured .. 35 45
248. 60 c. multicoloured .. 35 45

DESIGNS: Nos. 241/2, Class "GS-4", U.S.A. (1941). 243/4, Class "AD 60", Australia (1952). 245/6, Class "C 38", Australia (1943). 247/8, "Lord of the Isles", Great Britain (1892).

See also Nos. 253/68, 273/80, 313/20 and 348/55.

42. "Ipomoea pes-caprae".

1984. Beach Flowers. Multicoloured.

249. 25 c. Type **42** 25 25
250. 45 c. "Ipomoea macrantha" 40 40
251. 50 c. "Triumfetta procumbens" 45 45
252. 60 c. "Portulaca quadrifida" 50 50

1984. Leaders of the World. Railway Locomotives (2nd series). As T **41**. The first design in each pair shows technical drawings and the second the locomotive at work.

253. 10 c. multicoloured. .. 10 10
254. 10 c. multicoloured .. 10 10
255. 15 c. multicoloured .. 10 15
256. 15 c. multicoloured .. 10 15
257. 20 c. multicoloured .. 10 15
258. 20 c. multicoloured .. 10 15
259. 25 c. multicoloured .. 10 15
260. 25 c. multicoloured .. 10 15
261. 40 c. multicoloured .. 15 20
262. 40 c. multicoloured .. 15 20
263. 50 c. multicoloured .. 15 20
264. 50 c. multicoloured .. 15 20
265. 60 c. multicoloured .. 15 25
266. 60 c. multicoloured .. 15 25
267. $1 multicoloured 20 30
268. $1 multicoloured 20 30

DESIGNS: Nos. 253/4, "Casey Jones" type locomotive, U.S.A. (1896). 255/6, "Triplex" type locomotive, U.S.A. (1914). 257/8, Class "370" Advanced Passenger Train, Great Britain (1981). 259/60, Class "4F" locomotive, Great Britain (1924). 261/2, Class "Tornado Rover" locomotive, Great Britain (1888). 263/4, "Broadlands" locomotive, Great Britain (1967). 265/6, Locomotive "Locomotion No. 1", Great Britain (1825). 267/8, Class "C57" locomotive, Japan (1937).

43. Exhibition Emblem.

1984. "Ausipex" International Stamp Exhibition, Melbourne. Multicoloured.

269.	60 c. Type **43**	25	30
270.	60 c. Arms of Tuvalu ..	25	30
271.	60 c. Tuvalu flag	25	30
272.	60 c. Royal Exhibition Building, Melbourne ..	25	30

1984. Leaders of the World. Railway Locomotives (3rd series). As T **41**. The first in each pair shows technical drawings and the second the locomotive at work.

273.	1 c. multicoloured	10	10
274.	1 c. multicoloured	10	10
275.	15 c. multicoloured ..	15	20
276.	15 c. multicoloured ..	15	20
277.	30 c. multicoloured ..	35	40
278.	30 c. multicoloured ..	35	40
279.	$1 multicoloured	70	1·00
280.	$1 multicoloured	70	1·00

Designs: Nos. 273/4, Class "9700", Japan (1897). 275/6, Class "231" C/K, France. 277/8, Class "640", Italy (1907). 279/80, Class "4500", France (1906).

44. A. Shrewsbury.

1984. Leaders of the World. Cricketers. As T **44**. The first in each pair shows the cricketer in action and the second a head portrait.

281.	5 c. multicoloured	10	10
282.	5 c. multicoloured	10	10
283.	30 c. multicoloured ..	30	40
284.	30 c. multicoloured ..	30	40
285.	50 c. multicoloured ..	40	50
286.	50 c. multicoloured ..	40	50
287.	60 c. multicoloured ..	50	55
288.	60 c. multicoloured ..	50	55

Designs: 281/2, A. Shrewsbury. 283/4 H. Verity. 285/6, E. H. Hendren. 287/8, J. Briggs.

45. Trees and Stars.

1984. Christmas. Children's Drawings. Multicoloured.

289.	15 c. Type **45**	10	10
290.	40 c. Fishing from outrigger canoes	20	20
291.	50 c. Three Wise Men bearing gifts	25	25
292.	60 c. The Holy Family ..	35	35

46. Morris Minor.

1984. Leaders of the World. Automobiles (1st series). As T **46**. The first in each pair shows technical drawings and the second paintings.

293.	1 c. blk, brown & yellow ..	10	10
294.	1 c. multicoloured	10	10
295.	15 c. black, pink and lilac	10	15
296.	15 c. multicoloured ..	10	15
297.	50 c. blk., brown & mauve	20	20
298.	50 c. multicoloured ..	20	20
299.	$1 black, green and blue ..	30	40
300.	$1 multicoloured	30	40

Designs: Nos. 293/4, "Morris Minor". 295/6, Studebaker "Avanti". 297/8, Chevrolet "International Six". 299/300, Allard "J2".

See also Nos. 321/8, 356/71, 421/32 and 446/69.

47. Common Flicker.

1985. Leaders of the World. Birth Bicentenary of John J. Audubon (ornithologist). Multicoloured.

301.	1 c. Type **47**	10	10
302.	1 c. Say's phoebe	10	10
303.	25 c. Townsend's warbler	20	25
304.	25 c. Bohemian waxwing ..	20	25
305.	50 c. Prothonotary warbler	35	45
306.	50 c. Worm-eating warbler	35	45
307.	70 c. Broad-winged hawk	50	70
308.	70 c. Hen harrier	50	70

48. Black-naped Tern.

1985. Birds and their Eggs. Multicoloured.

309.	15 c. Type **48**	35	20
310.	40 c. White-capped noddy	75	50
311.	50 c. White-tailed tropicbird	85	60
312.	60 c. Sooty tern	1·00	70

1985. Leaders of the World. Railway Locomotives (4th series). As T **41**. The first in each pair shows technical drawings and the second the locomotive at work.

313.	5 c. multicoloured	10	10
314.	5 c. multicoloured	10	10
315.	10 c. multicoloured ..	10	10
316.	10 c. multicoloured ..	10	10
317.	30 c. multicoloured ..	30	35
318.	30 c. multicoloured ..	30	35
319.	$1 multicoloured	75	1·00
320.	$1 multicoloured	75	1·00

Designs: Nos. 313/14, Class "Churchward 28XX", Great Britain (1905). 315/16, Class "KF", China (1935). 317/18, Class "99.77", East Germany (1952). 319/20, Pearson, Great Britain (1835).

1985. Leaders of the World. Automobiles (2nd series). As T **46**. The first in each pair shows technical drawings and the second paintings.

321.	1 c. black, green and deep green	10	10
322.	1 c. multicoloured	10	10
323.	20 c. black, pink and red ..	15	20
324.	20 c. multicoloured ..	15	20
325.	50 c. black, blue and violet	20	30
326.	50 c. multicoloured ..	20	30
327.	70 c. black, pink & brown	20	35
328.	70 c. multicoloured ..	20	35

Designs: Nos. 321/2, Rickenbacker (1923). 323/4, Detroit-Electric two door Brougham (1914). 325/6, Packard "Clipper" (1941). 327/8, Audi "Quattro" (1982).

49. Curtiss "P-40N".

1985. World War II Aircraft. Multicoloured.

329.	15 c. Type **49**	60	20
330.	40 c. Consolidated "B-24 Liberator"	1·00	45
331.	50 c. Lockheed "PV-1 Ventura"	1·10	55
332.	60 c. Douglas "C-54 Skymaster"	1·10	65

50. Queen Elizabeth the Queen Mother.

1985. Leaders of the World. Life and Times of Queen Elizabeth the Queen Mother. Various portraits.

334.	**50.**	5 c. multicoloured ..	10	10
335.	–	5 c. multicoloured ..	10	10
336.	–	30 c. multicoloured ..	10	15
337.	–	30 c. multicoloured ..	10	15
338.	–	60 c. multicoloured ..	15	20
339.	–	60 c. multicoloured ..	15	20
340.	–	$1 multicoloured ..	25	35
341.	–	$1 multicoloured ..	25	35

Each value issued in pairs showing a floral pattern across the bottom of the portraits which stops short of the left-hand edge on the first stamp and of the right-hand edge on the second.

51. Guide playing Guitar.

1985. 75th Anniv. of Girl Guide Movement. Multicoloured.

343.	15 c. Type **51**	15	20
344.	40 c. Building camp-fire ..	40	45
345.	50 c. Patrol leader with Guide flag	50	55
346.	60 c. Guide saluting ..	60	65

1985. Leaders of the World. Railway Locomotives (5th series). As T **41**. The first in each pair shows technical drawings and the second the locomotive at work.

348.	10 c. multicoloured ..	10	15
349.	10 c. multicoloured ..	10	15
350.	40 c. multicoloured ..	30	40
351.	40 c. multicoloured ..	30	40
352.	65 c. multicoloured ..	45	65
353.	65 c. multicoloured ..	45	65
354.	$1 multicoloured	70	1·00
355.	$1 multicoloured	70	1·00

Designs: Nos. 348/49, "Green Arrow", Great Britain (1936). 350/1, Class "SD-50" diesel locomotive, U.S.A. (1982). 352/3, "Flying Hamburger", Germany (1932). 354/5, Class "1070", Japan (1908).

1985. Leaders of the World. Automobiles (3rd series). As T **46**. The first in each pair shows technical drawings and the second paintings.

356.	5 c. black, grey and mauve	10	10
357.	5 c. multicoloured	10	10
358.	10 c. black, pink and red ..	10	15
359.	10 c. multicoloured ..	10	15
360.	15 c. black, brown and red	10	15
361.	15 c. multicoloured ..	10	15
362.	35 c. black, red and blue ..	20	30
363.	35 c. multicoloured ..	20	30
364.	40 c. black, lt. green & green	20	30
365.	40 c. multicoloured ..	20	30
366.	55 c. black, stone and green	20	30
367.	55 c. multicoloured ..	20	30
368.	$1 black, dp. brown & brn.	30	45
369.	$1 multicoloured	30	45
370.	$1.50 black, pink and red	40	60
371.	$1.50 multicoloured ..	40	60

Designs: Nos. 356/7, Cord "L-29" (1929). 358/9, Horch "670 V-12" (1932). 360/1, Lanchester (1901). 362/3, Citroen "2 CV" (1950). 364/5, MGA (1957). 366/7, Ferrari "250 GTO" (1962). 368/9, Ford "V-8" (1932). 370/1, Aston Martin "Lagonda" (1977).

52. Stalk-eyed Ghost Crab.

1986. Crabs. Multicoloured.

372.	15 c. Type **52**	20	25
373.	40 c. Red and white painted crab	45	55
374.	50 c. Red-spotted crab ..	55	70
375.	60 c. Red hermit crab ..	70	90

1986. Ships (3rd series). Missionary Vessels. As T **26**. Multicoloured.

377	15 c. "Messenger of Peace" (schooner)	15	15
378	40 c. "John Wesley" (brig)	35	40
379	50 c. "Duff" (full rigged-ship)	40	45
380	60 c. "Triton" (brigantine)	50	55

1986. 60th Birthday of Queen Elizabeth II. As T **167** of British Virgin Islands. Mult.

381.	10 c. Queen wearing ceremonial cloak, New Zealand, 1977	10	10
382.	90 c. Before visit to France, 1957	35	50
383.	$1.50 Queen in 1982 ..	55	75
384.	$3 In Canberra, 1982 (vert.)	1·00	1·40

54. Peace Dove carrying Wreath and Rainbow.

1986. 25th Anniv. of United States Peace Corps.

386.	**54.**	50 c. multicoloured ..	80	80

55. Island and Flags of Tuvalu and U.S.A.

1986. "Ameripex" International Stamp Exhibition, Chicago.

387.	**55.**	60 c. multicoloured ..	85	85

56. South Korean Player.

1986. World Cup Football Championship, Mexico. Multicoloured.

388.	1 c. Type **56**	10	10
389.	5 c. French player ..	10	10
390.	10 c. West German captain with World Cup trophy, 1974	10	10
391.	40 c. Italian player ..	50	40
392.	60 c. World Cup final, 1974 (59 × 39 mm.)	65	55
393.	$1 Canadian team (59 × 39 mm.)	80	80
394.	$2 Northern Irish team (59 × 39 mm.)	1·50	1·50
395.	$3 English team (59 × 39 mm.)	2·50	2·50

1986. Royal Wedding (1st issue). As T **168** of British Virgin Islands. Multicoloured.

397.	60 c. Prince Andrew and Miss Sarah Ferguson	25	30
398.	60 c. Prince Andrew with prizewinning bull	25	30
399.	$1 Prince Andrew at horse trials (horiz.)	40	55
400.	$1 Miss Sarah Ferguson and Princess Diana (horiz.)	40	55

See also Nos. 433/6.

57. Mourning Gecko.

1986. Lizards. Multicoloured.

402.	15 c. Type **57**	55	55
403.	40 c. Oceanic stump-toed gecko	1·00	1·00
404.	50 c. Azure-tailed skink	1·25	1·25
405.	60 c. Moth skink	1·50	1·50

1986. "Stampex '86" Stamp Exhibition, Adelaide. No. 386 optd. **STAMPEX 86 ADELAIDE** and Kangaroo.

406.	**54.** 50 c. multicoloured	40	45

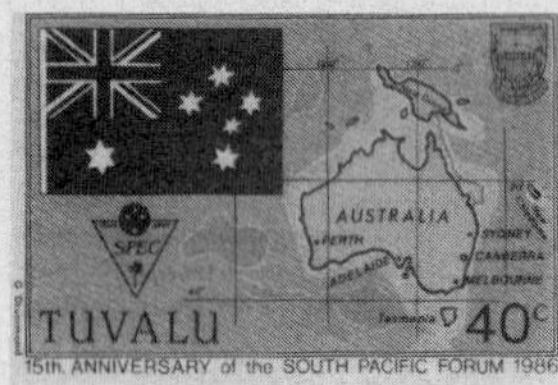

59. Map and Flag of Australia.

1986. 15th Anniv. of South Pacific Forum. Maps and national flags. Multicoloured.

407.	40 c. Type **59**	45	45
408.	40 c. Cook Islands	45	45
409.	40 c. Micronesia	45	45
410.	40 c. Fiji	45	45
411.	40 c. Kiribati	45	45
412.	40 c. Western Samoa	45	45
413.	40 c. Nauru	45	45
414.	40 c. Vanuatu	45	45
415.	40 c. New Zealand	45	45
416.	40 c. Tuvalu	45	45
417.	40 c. Tonga	45	45
418.	40 c. Solomon Islands	45	45
419.	40 c. Papua New Guinea	45	45
420.	40 c. Niue	45	45

1986. Automobiles (4th series). As T **46**. The first in each pair show technical drawings and the second paintings.

421.	15 c. multicoloured	10	15
422.	15 c. multicoloured	10	15
423.	40 c. multicoloured	15	25
424.	40 c. multicoloured	15	25
425.	50 c. multicoloured	20	30
426.	50 c. multicoloured	20	30
427.	60 c. multicoloured	25	35
428.	60 c. multicoloured	25	35
429.	90 c. multicoloured	30	40
430.	90 c. multicoloured	30	40
431.	$1.50 multicoloured	45	65
432.	$1.50 multicoloured	45	65

DESIGNS: Nos. 421/2, Copper "500" (1953). 423/4, Rover "2000" (1964). 425/6, Ruxton (1930). 427/8, Jowett "Jupiter" (1950). 429/30, Cobra "Daytona Coupe" (1964). 431/2, Packard Model F "Old Pacific" (1903).

1986. Royal Wedding (2nd issue). Nos. 397/400 optd. **Congratulations to TRH The Duke and Duchess of York**.

433.	60 c. Prince Andrew and Miss Sarah Ferguson	70	70
434.	60 c. Prince Andrew with prizewinning bull	70	70
435.	$1 Prince Andrew at horse trials (horiz.)	1·00	1·00
436.	$1 Miss Sarah Ferguson and Princess Diana (horiz.)	1·00	1·00

60. Sea Star.

1986. Coral Reef Life (1st series). Mult.

437.	15 c. Type **60**	45	45
438.	40 c. Pencil urchin	1·00	1·00
439.	50 c. Fragile coral	1·10	1·10
440.	60 c. Pink coral	1·25	1·25

See also Nos. 498/501 and 558/62.

1987. Ships (4th series). Missionary Steamers. As T **26**. Multicoloured.

442.	15 c. "Southern Cross IV"	50	50
443.	40 c. "John Williams VI"	1·00	1·00
444.	50 c. "John Williams IV"	1·25	1·25
445.	60 c. M.S. "Southern Cross"	1·40	1·40

1987. Automobiles (5th series). As T **46**. The first in each pair shows technical drawings and the second paintings.

446.	1 c. multicoloured	10	10
447.	1 c. multicoloured	10	10
448.	2 c. multicoloured	10	10
449.	2 c. multicoloured	10	10
450.	5 c. multicoloured	10	10
451.	5 c. multicoloured	10	10
452.	10 c. multicoloured	10	15
453.	10 c. multicoloured	10	15
454.	20 c. multicoloured	15	20
455.	20 c. multicoloured	15	20
456.	30 c. multicoloured	20	25
457.	30 c. multicoloured	20	25
458.	40 c. multicoloured	20	30
459.	40 c. multicoloured	20	30
460.	50 c. multicoloured	20	35
461.	50 c. multicoloured	20	35
462.	60 c. multicoloured	20	35
463.	60 c. multicoloured	20	35
464.	70 c. multicoloured	25	40
465.	70 c. multicoloured	25	40
466.	75 c. multicoloured	25	40
467.	75 c. multicoloured	25	40
468.	$1 multicoloured	40	55
469.	$1 multicoloured	40	55

DESIGNS: Nos. 446/7, Talbot-Lago (1938). 448/9, Du Pont "Model G" (1930). 450/1, Riley "RM" (1950). 452/3, Chevrolet "Baby Grand" (1915). 454/5, Shelby "Mustang GT 500 KR" (1968). 456/7, Ferrari "212 Export Barchetta" (1952). 458/9, Peerless "Model 48-Six" (1912). 460/1, Sunbeam "Alpine" (1954). 462/3, Matra-Ford "MS 80" (1969). 464/5, Squire 1½ Litre (1934). 466/7, Talbot "105" (1931). 468/9, Plymouth "Model Q" (1928).

61. "Nephrolepis saligna".

1987. Ferns. Multicoloured.

471.	15 c. Type **61**	40	40
472.	40 c. "Asplenium nidus"	70	70
473.	50 c. "Microsorum scolopendria"	85	85
474.	60 c. "Pteris tripartita"	95	95

62. Floral Arrangement.

1987. Flowers and "Fous". Designs showing either floral arrangements or "fous" (women's headdresses). Multicoloured.

476.	15 c. Type **62**	15	15
477.	15 c. "Fou"	15	15
478.	40 c. "Fou"	35	40
479.	40 c. Floral arrangement	35	40
480.	50 c. Floral arrangement	45	50
481.	50 c. "Fou"	45	50
482.	60 c. "Fou"	55	60
483.	60 c. Floral arrangement	55	60

63. Queen Victoria, 1897 (photo by Downey).

1987. Royal Ruby Wedding and 150th Anniv of Queen Victoria's Accession.

484.	**63.**	40 c. brown, black and green	35	40
485.	–	60 c. purple, black and green	55	60
486.	–	80 c. brown, black and blue	70	75
487.	–	$1 brown, black and purple	90	95
488.	–	$2 multicoloured	1·75	1·90

DESIGNS: 60 c. Wedding of Princess Elizabeth and Duke of Edinburgh, 1947. 80 c. Queen, Duke of Edinburgh and Prince Charles, 1950. $1 Queen with Princess Anne, 1950. $2 Queen Elizabeth II, 1970.

64. Coconut Crab.

1987. Crustaceans. Multicoloured.

490.	40 c. Type **64**	55	55
491.	50 c. Painted crayfish	70	70
492.	60 c. Ocean crayfish	80	80

65. Aborigine and Ayers Rock. (Illustration reduced. Actual size 60 × 40 mm.).

1987. World Scout Jamboree, Australia. Multicoloured.

493.	40 c. Type **65**	40	40
494.	60 c. Capt. Cook and H.M.S. "Endeavour"	80	80
495.	$1 Scout saluting and Scout Park entrance	1·10	1·10
496.	$1.50 Koala and kangaroo	1·40	1·40

1988. Coral Reef Life (2nd series). As T **60**. Multicoloured.

498.	15 c. Spanish dancer	50	50
499.	40 c. Hard corals	90	90
500.	50 c. Feather stars	1·00	1·00
501.	60 c. Staghorn corals	1·10	1·10

66. Red Junglefowl.

1988. Birds. Multicoloured.

502.	5 c. Type **66**	10	10
503.	10 c. White tern	15	15
504.	15 c. Common noddy	20	20
505.	20 c. Phoenix petrel	30	25
506.	25 c. American golden plover	35	30
507.	30 c. Crested tern	40	35
508.	35 c. Sooty tern	40	35
509.	40 c. Bristle-thighed curlew	45	40
510.	45 c. Bar-tailed godwit	55	45
511.	50 c. Eastern Reef heron	60	50
512.	55 c. Great frigate bird	70	55
513.	60 c. Red-footed booby	75	60
514.	70 c. Rufous-necked sandpiper	85	70
515.	$1 Long-tailed koel	1·25	95
516.	$2 Red-tailed tropic bird	2·40	2·00
517.	$5 Banded rail	5·00	4·75

67 Jean-Henri Dunant (founder)

1988. 125th Anniv of International Red Cross.

518	**67**	15 c. red and brown	10	15
519	–	40 c. red and blue	20	35
520	–	50 c. red and green	25	40
521	–	60 c. red and purple	35	60

DESIGNS: 40 c. Junior Red Cross members on parade; 50 c. Red Cross worker with boy in wheelchair; 60 c. First aid training.

68 H.M.S. "Endeavour" (Illustration reduced, actual size 56 × 37 mm)

1988. Voyages of Captain Cook. Mult.

523	20 c. Type **68**	40	55
524	40 c. Stern of H.M.S. "Endeavour"	60	80
525	50 c. Cook preparing to land at Tahiti (vert)	70	90
526	60 c. Maori chief (vert)	80	1·00
527	80 c. H.M.S. "Resolution" and Hawaiian canoe	90	1·25
528	$1 "Captain Cook" (after Nathaniel Dance) (vert)	1·25	1·50

69 "Ganoderma applanatum"

1988. Fungi (1st series). Multicoloured.

530	40 c. Type **69**	75	65
531	50 c. "Pseudoepicoccum cocos" (brown leaf spot)	80	70
532	60 c. "Rigidoporus zonalis"	90	80
533	90 c. "Rigidoporus microporus"	1·40	1·10

See also Nos. 554/7.

70 Rifle-shooting (Illustration reduced, actual size 60 × 40 mm)

1988. Olympic Games, Seoul. Multicoloured.

534	10 c. Type **70**	10	15
535	20 c. Judo	20	25
536	40 c. Canoeing	40	45
537	60 c. Swimming	55	60
538	80 c. Yachting	75	80
539	$1 Gymnastics	95	1·00

71 Queen Elizabeth II in Ceremonial Canoe

1988. 10th Anniv of Independence. Designs showing scenes from Royal Visit of 1982.

540 **71**	60 c. multicoloured	60	60
541	90 c. multicoloured	90	90
542	$1 multicoloured (horiz)	1·00	1·00
543	$1.20 multicoloured	1·25	1·25

72 Virgin Mary

1988. Christmas. Multicoloured.

545	15 c. Type **72**	15	20
546	40 c. Christ Child	40	45
547	60 c. Joseph	55	60

73 Dancing Skirt and Dancer

1989. Traditional Dancing Skirts. Designs showing skirts and dancer silhouettes.

549 **73**	40 c. multicoloured	70	70
550 –	50 c. multicoloured	80	80
551 –	60 c. multicoloured	90	90
552 –	90 c. multicoloured	1·40	1·40

1989. Fungi (2nd series). As T **69**. Mult.

554	40 c. "Trametes muelleri"	1·25	1·25
555	50 c. "Pestalotiopsis palmarum" (grey leaf spot)	1·40	1·40
556	60 c. "Trametes cingulata"	1·40	1·40
557	90 c. "Schizophyllum commune"	2·00	2·00

1989. Coral Reef Life (3rd series). As T **60**. Multicoloured.

558	40 c. Pennant coralfish	1·00	1·00
559	50 c. Anemone fish	1·25	1·25
560	60 c. Batfish	1·40	1·40
561	90 c. Threadfin coralfish	1·75	1·75

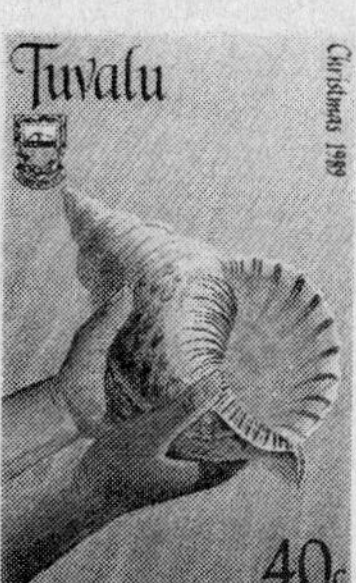

75 Conch Shell

1989. Christmas. Multicoloured.

564	40 c. Type **75**	65	65
565	50 c. Posy of flowers	80	80
566	60 c. Germinating coconut	85	85
567	90 c. Jewellery	1·50	1·50

76 "Cocus nucifera"

1990. Tropical Trees. Multicoloured.

568	15 c. Type **76**	40	40
569	30 c. "Rhizophora samoensis"	70	70
570	40 c. "Messerschmidia argentea"	85	85
571	50 c. "Pandanus tectorius"	95	95
572	60 c. "Hernandia nymphaeifolia"	1·10	1·10
573	90 c. "Pisonia grandis"	1·50	1·50

77 Penny Black with "Stamp World London 90" Emblem

1990. 150th Anniv of the Penny Black, and "Stamp World London 90" International Stamp Exhibition.

574 **77**	15 c. multicoloured	55	55
575	40 c. multicoloured	1·25	1·25
576	90 c. multicoloured	2·25	2·25

78 Japanese Camouflaged Freighter

1990. Second World War Ships (1st series). Multicoloured.

578	15 c. Type **78**	45	45
579	30 c. U.S.S. "Unimack" (seaplane tender)	70	70
580	40 c. "Amagiri" (Japanese destroyer)	80	80
581	50 c. U.S.S. "Platte" (attack transport)	95	95
582	60 c. Japanese "Shumushu" Class escort	1·10	1·10
583	90 c. U.S.S. "Independence" (aircraft carrier)	1·75	1·75

See also Nos. 613/16.

79 "Erythrina fusca"

1990. Flowers. Multicoloured.

584	15 c. Type **79**	30	30
585	30 c. "Capparis cordifolia"	50	50
586	40 c. "Portulaca pilosa"	60	60
587	50 c. "Cordia subcordata"	75	75
588	60 c. "Scaevola taccada"	80	90
589	90 c. "Suriana maritima"	1·25	1·50

80 Land Resources Survey

1990. 40th Anniv of United Nations Development Programme. Multicoloured.

590	40 c. Type **80**	65	65
591	60 c. Satellite earth station	85	85
592	$1.20 "Te Tautai" (trawler)	1·90	1·90

81 Mary and Joseph travelling to Bethlehem

1990. Christmas. Multicoloured.

593	15 c. Type **81**	35	35
594	40 c. The Nativity	70	70
595	60 c. Shepherds with flock	1·00	1·00
596	90 c. Wise Men bearing gifts	1·50	1·50

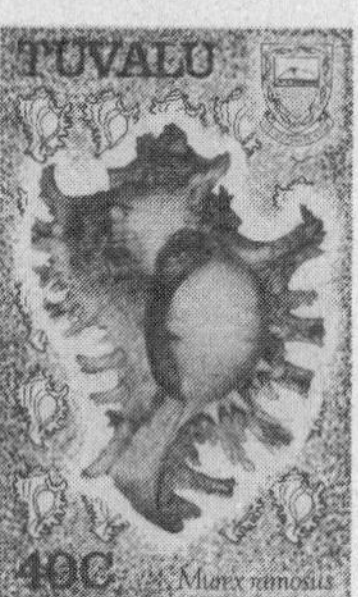

82 "Murex ramosus"

1991. Sea Shells. Multicoloured.

597	40 c. Type **82**	70	70
598	50 c. "Conus marmoreus"	80	80
599	60 c. "Trochus niloticus"	90	1·00
600	$1.50 "Cypraea mappa"	2·25	2·50

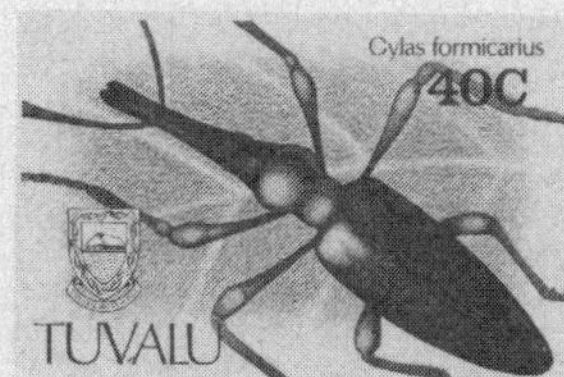

83 "Cylas formicarius" (beetle)

1991. Insects. Multicoloured.

601	40 c. Type **83**	85	85
602	50 c. "Heliothis armiger" (moth)	95	95
603	60 c. "Spodoptera litura" (moth)	1·25	1·25
604	$1.50 "Agrius convolvuli" (moth)	3·00	3·00

84 Green Turtle

1991. Endangered Marine Life. Multicoloured.

605	40 c. Type **84**	60	60
606	50 c. Humpback whale	70	70
607	60 c. Hawksbill turtle	80	90
608	$1.50 Sperm whale	2·25	2·75

85 Football

1991. 9th South Pacific Games. Multicoloured.

609	40 c. Type **85**	75	75
610	50 c. Volleyball	95	95
611	60 c. Lawn tennis	1·25	1·25
612	$1.50 Cricket	3·00	3·25

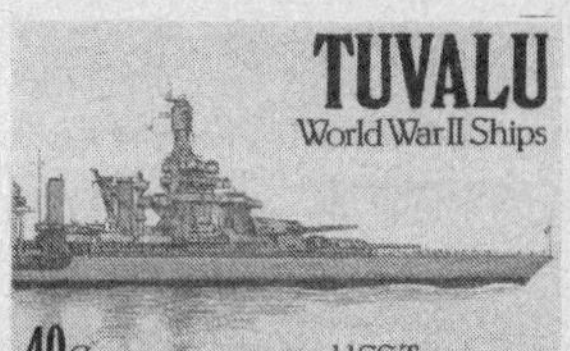

86 U.S.S. "Tennessee" (battleship)

1991. Second World War Ships (2nd series). Multicoloured.

613	40 c. Type **86**	85	85
614	50 c. "Haguro" (Japanese cruiser)	1·00	1·00
615	60 c. H.M.N.Z.S. "Achilles" (cruiser)	1·25	1·25
616	$1.50 U.S.S. "North Carolina" (battleship)	3·00	3·25

87 Traditional Dancers

1991. Christmas. Multicoloured.

617	40 c. Type **87**	80	80
618	50 c. Solo dancer	95	95
619	60 c. Dancers in green costumes	1·25	1·25
620	$1.50 Dancers in multi-coloured costumes	2·50	2·75

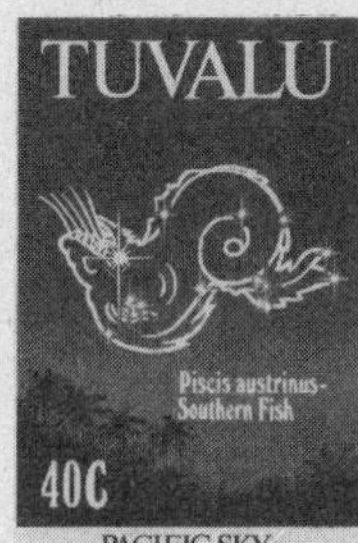

88 Southern Fish Constellation

1992. Pacific Star Constellations. Mult.

621	40 c. Type **88**	85	85
622	50 c. Scorpion	1·00	1·00
623	60 c. Archer	1·25	1·25
624	$1.50 Southern Cross	3·00	3·00

89 King George VI and Cargo Liner

1992. Centenary of British Occupation of Tuvalu. Multicoloured.

625	40 c. Type **89**	65	65
626	50 c. King George V and freighter with barges at wharf	75	75
627	60 c. King Edward VII and freighter	90	90
628	$1.50 Queen Victoria and warship	2·25	2·50

90 Columbus with King Ferdinand and Queen Isabella of Spain

1992. 500th Anniv of Discovery of America by Columbus.

629	**90**	40 c. blue and black . .	45	45
630	–	50 c. purple and black	55	55
631	–	60 c. green and black . .	70	70
632	–	$1.50 purple and black	1·75	2·25

DESIGNS: 50 c. Columbus and Polynesians; 60 c. Columbus and South American Indians; $1.50, Columbus and North American Indians.

91 "Chaetodon plebeius"

1992. Fishes. Multicoloured.

633	15 c. Type **91**	15	20
634	20 c. "Scarus frenatus" . .	20	25
635	25 c. "Acanthurus lineatus"	25	30
636	30 c. "Thalassoma lunare"	30	35
637	35 c. "Oxymonocanthus longirostis"	35	40
638	40 c. "Gomphosus varius"	40	45
639	45 c. "Bodianus loxo-zonus"	40	45
640	50 c. "Chromis viridis" . .	45	50
641	60 c. "Cheilinus undulatus"	55	60
642	70 c. "Chaetodon ornatissimus" (vert) . .	65	70
643	90 c. "Chaetodon ephippium" (vert) . .	85	90
644	$1 "Chaetodon vaga-bundus" (vert) . .	95	1·00
645	$2 "Heniochus acumi-natus" (vert)	2·00	2·10
646	$3 "Zanclus cornutus" (vert)	3·00	3·25

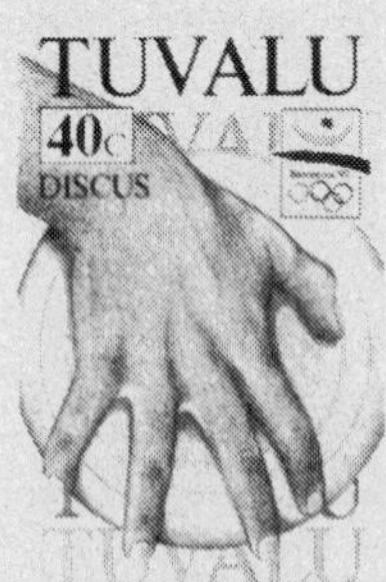

92 Discus Throwing

1992. Olympic Games, Barcelona. Mult.

647	40 c. Type **92**	40	40
648	50 c. Javelin throwing . .	50	50
649	60 c. Shotput	55	55
650	$1.50 Competitor's foot . .	1·50	1·75

93 Blue Coral

1992. Endangered Species. Blue Coral.

652	**93**	10 c. multicoloured . .	20	25
653	–	25 c. multicoloured . .	45	55
654	–	30 c. multicoloured . .	45	55
655	–	35 c. multicoloured . .	55	65

DESIGNS: 25 c. to 35 c. Different coral formations.

1992. "Kuala Lumpur '92" International Philatelic Exhibition. As Nos. 636, 638 and 640/1 optd **KL92** and symbol. Multicoloured.

656	30 c. "Thalassoma lunare"	45	45
657	40 c. "Gomphosus varius"	55	55
658	50 c. "Chromis viridis" . .	65	65
659	60 c. "Cheilinus undulatus"	75	75

95 Fishermen and Angel

1992. Christmas. Multicoloured.

660	40 c. Type **95**	35	40
661	50 c. Fishing canoes following star . .	45	50
662	60 c. Nativity scene . .	50	55
663	$1.50 Christmas gifts . .	1·25	1·40

96 "Calophyllum inophyllum"

1993. Flowers. Multicoloured.

664	40 c. Type **96**	35	40
665	50 c. "Hibiscus tiliaceus"	45	50
666	60 c. "Lantana camara" . .	50	55
667	$1.50 "Plumeria rubra" . .	1·25	1·40

97 Japanese Aircraft attacking Island

1993. 50th Anniv of War in the Pacific. Mult.

668	40 c. Type **97**	55	55
669	50 c. Japanese anti-aircraft gun (vert)	65	65
670	60 c. American troops storming beach . .	75	75
671	$1.50 Map of Funafuti Atoll (vert)	1·75	2·00

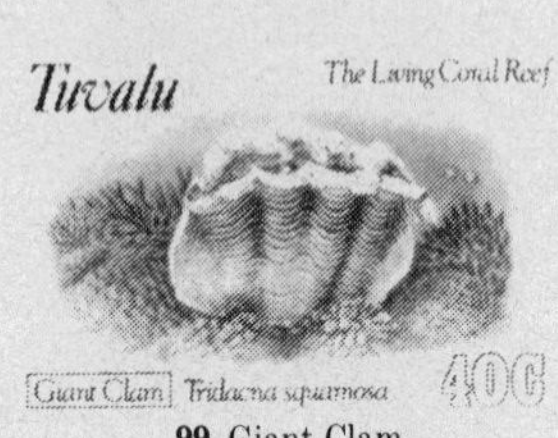

99 Giant Clam

1993. Marine Life. Multicoloured.

673	40 c. Type **99**	55	55
674	50 c. Anemone crab . .	65	65
675	60 c. Octopus	75	75
676	$1.50 Green turtle . .	1·75	2·00

100 Queen Elizabeth II and Prince Philip in Land Rover

1993. 40th Anniv of Coronation. Mult.

677	40 c. Type **100**	55	55
678	50 c. Queen Elizabeth drinking kava	65	65
679	60 c. Queen Elizabeth with parasol	75	75
680	$1.50 Ceremonial welcome	1·75	2·00

101 Hermit Crab and Shells on Beach

1993. Environmental Protection. Mult.

684	40 c. Type **101**	55	55
685	50 c. Conch shell and starfish	65	65
686	60 c. Crab, seaweed and shells	75	75
687	$1.50 Seabird and human footprint on beach . .	1·75	2·00

102 Virgin and Child with Christmas Tree

1993. Christmas. Multicoloured.

689	40 c. Type **102**	40	45
690	50 c. Candle	45	50
691	60 c. Angel	55	60
692	$1.50 Decorated palm tree	1·40	1·50

103 Beach

1994. Island Scenery. Multicoloured.

694	40 c. Type **103**	40	45
695	50 c. Lagoon	45	50
696	60 c. Distant island . .	55	60
697	$1.50 Launch and outrigger canoes on beach . .	1·40	1·50

104 Irish Red Setter

1994. Chinese New Year ("Year of the Dog"). Multicoloured.

698	40 c. Type **104**	40	45
699	50 c. Golden retriever . .	45	50
700	60 c. West highland terrier	55	60
701	$1.50 German shepherd . .	1·40	1·50

105 World Cup, Australian Player and Sydney Opera House

1994. World Cup Football Championship, U.S.A. Multicoloured.

702	40 c. Type **105**	40	45
703	50 c. English player and Big Ben, London . .	45	50
704	60 c. Argentinian player and House of Assembly, Buenos Aires . .	55	60
705	$1.50 German player and Brandenburg Gate, Berlin	1·40	1·50

OFFICIAL STAMPS

1981. Nos. 105/22 optd. **OFFICIAL.**

No.	Type	Description	Mint	Used
O 1.	14.	1 c. multicoloured ..	10	10
O 2.	–	2 c. multicoloured ..	10	10
O 3.	–	4 c. multicoloured ..	10	10
O 4.	–	5 c. multicoloured ..	10	10
O 5.	–	6 c. multicoloured ..	10	10
O 6.	–	8 c. multicoloured ..	10	10
O 7.	–	10 c. multicoloured ..	15	15
O 8.	–	15 c. multicoloured ..	20	20
O 9.	–	20 c. multicoloured ..	25	25
O 10.	–	25 c. multicoloured ..	30	30
O 11.	–	30 c. multicoloured ..	30	30
O 12.	–	35 c. multicoloured ..	35	35
O 13.	–	40 c. multicoloured ..	40	40
O 14.	–	45 c. multicoloured ..	45	45
O 15.	–	50 c. multicoloured ..	50	50
O 16.	–	70 c. multicoloured ..	75	75
O 17.	–	$1 multicoloured ..	1·10	1·10
O 18a.		$2 multicoloured ..	2·25	2·25
O 19.	–	$5 multicoloured ..	4·50	4·75

1983. Nos. 202/3a, 205/12, 224 and 234 optd. **OFFICIAL.**

No.	Description	Mint	Used
O 20.	5 c. Wedding and baby food baskets ..	10	15
O 21.	10 c. Hand-carved model of canoe	10	15
O 22.	15 c. Ladies sun hats ..	15	20
O 23.	25 c. Pandanus baskets	25	30
O 24.	30 c. on 45 c. Reef sandals and fish trap ..	50	60
O 25.	30 c. Basket tray and coconut stand ..	30	40
O 26.	35 c. Pandanus pillows and shell necklaces ..	40	45
O 27.	40 c. Round baskets and fan	45	50
O 28.	45 c. Reef Sandals and fish trap	45	50
O 29.	50 c. Rat trap	50	60
O 30.	60 c. on $1 Pump drill and adze ..	75	85
O 31.	60 c. Fisherman's waterproof boxes	60	80
O 32.	$1 Pump drill and adze	1·00	1·00
O 33.	$2 Fisherman's hat and canoe bailers	1·75	2·00
O 34.	$5 Fishing rod, lures and scoop nets	4·25	4·75

1989. Nos. 502/17 optd **OFFICIAL.**

No.	Description	Mint	Used
O 35	5 c. Type **66**	10	10
O 36	10 c. White tern ..	10	15
O 37	15 c. Common noddy	15	20
O 38	20 c. Phoenix petrel ..	15	20
O 39	25 c. American golden plover	25	30
O 40	30 c. Crested tern ..	25	30
O 41	35 c. Sooty tern ..	30	35
O 42	40 c. Bristle-thighed curlew	35	40
O 43	45 c. Bar-tailed godwit	40	45
O 44	50 c. Eastern reef heron	45	50
O 45	55 c. Great frigate bird	45	50
O 46	60 c. Red-footed booby	50	55
O 47	70 c. Rufous-necked sandpiper	60	65
O 48	$1 Long-tailed koel ..	85	90
O 49	$2 Red-tailed tropic bird	1·75	1·90
O 50	$5 Banded rail ..	4·25	4·50

POSTAGE DUE STAMPS

D 1. Tuvalu Crest.

1981.

No.	Type	Description	Mint	Used
D 1	D 1	1 c. black and purple	10	10
D 2		2 c. black and blue ..	10	10
D 3		5 c. black and brown	10	10
D 13		10 c. black and green	10	10
D 14		20 c. black and brown	15	20
D 15		30 c. black and orange	25	30
D 16		40 c. black and blue	35	40
D 17		50 c. black and green	45	50
D 18		$1 black and mauve ..	85	90

Some values exist with or without the imprint date at foot.

APPENDIX

The following stamps for individual islands of Tuvalu have either been issued in excess of postal needs, or have not been made available to the public in reasonable quantities at face value.

FUNAFUTI
1984.

Leaders of the World. Railway Locomotives (1st series). Two designs for each value, the first showing technical drawings and the second the locomotive at work. 15, 20, 30, 40, 50, 60 c., each ×2.

Leaders of the World. Automobiles (1st series). Two designs for each value, the first showing technical drawings and the second the car in action. 1, 10, 40 c., $1, each ×2.

Leaders of the World. Railway Locomotives (2nd series). Two designs for each value, the first showing technical drawings and the second the locomotive at work. 5, 15, 25, 35, 40, 55, 60 c. $1, each ×2.

1985

Leaders of the World. Automobiles (2nd series). Two designs for each value, the first showing technical drawings and the second the car in action. 1, 30, 55, 60 c., each ×2.

Leaders of the World. Railway Locomotives (3rd series). Two designs for each value, the first showing technical drawings and the second the locomotive at work. 5, 15, 35, 40, 50 c., $1, each ×2.

Leaders of the World. Life and Times of Queen Elizabeth the Queen Mother. Two designs for each value, showing different portraits. 5, 25, 80 c., $1.05, each ×2.

1986.

60th Birthday of Queen Elizabeth II. 10, 50 c., $1.50, $3.50.

Royal Wedding (1st issue). 60 c., $1, each ×2.

Royal Wedding (2nd issue). Previous Royal Wedding stamps optd. **Congratulations T.R.H. The Duke & Duchess of York.** 60 c., $1, each ×2

Railway Locomotives (4th series). Two designs for each value, the first showing technical drawings and the second the locomotive at work. 20, 40, 60 c., $1.50, each ×2.

1987.

Automobiles (3rd series). Two designs for each value, the first showing technical drawings and the second the car in action. 10, 20, 40, 60, 75, 80 c., $1, $1.50, each ×2.

Royal Ruby Wedding. 20, 50, 75 c., $1.20, $1.75.

1988.

Olympic Games, Seoul. 10, 20, 40, 50, 80, 90 c.

NANUMAGA
1984.

Leaders of the World. Automobiles (1st series). Two designs for each value, the first showing technical drawings and the second the car in action. 5, 10, 25, 30, 40 c., each ×2.

Leaders of the World. British Monarchs. Two designs for each value, forming a composite picture. 10, 20, 30, 40, 50 c., $1, each ×2.

Leaders of the World. Automobiles (2nd series). Two designs for each value, the first showing technical drawings and the second the car in action. 5, 10, 50 c., $1, each ×2.

1985

Leaders of the World. Railway Locomotives. Two designs for each value, the first showing technical drawings and the second the locomotive at work. 10, 25, 50, 60 c., each ×2.

Leaders of the World. Flowers. 25, 30, 40, 50 c., each ×2.

Leaders of the World. Automobiles (3rd series). Two designs for each value, the first showing technical drawings and the second the car in action. 10, 25, 75 c., $1, each ×2.

Leaders of the World. Life and Times of Queen Elizabeth the Queen Mother. Two designs for each value, showing different portraits. 15, 55, 65, 90 c., each ×2.

1986.

60th Birthday of Queen Elizabeth II. 5 c., $1, $1.75, $2.50.

World Cup Football Championship, Mexico. 1, 2, 5, 10, 20, 35, 50, 60, 75 c., $1, $2, $4.

Royal Wedding (1st issue). 60 c., $1, each ×2.

Royal Wedding (2nd issue). Previous Royal Wedding stamps optd. as for Funafuti. 60 c., $1, each ×2.

1987.

Automobiles (4th series). Two designs for each value, the first showing technical drawings and the second the car in action. 5, 10, 15, 20, 25, 40, 60 c., $1, each ×2.

Royal Ruby Wedding. 15, 35, 60 c., $1.50, $1.75.

NANUMEA
1984.

Leaders of the World. Railway Locomotives (1st series). Two designs for each value, the first showing technical drawings and the second the locomotive at work. 15, 20, 30, 40, 50, 60 c., each ×2.

Leaders of the World. Famous Cricketers. Two designs for each value, the first showing a portrait and the second the cricketer in action. 1, 10, 40 c., $1, each ×2.

1985.

Leaders of the World. Automobiles (1st series). Two designs for each value, the first showing technical drawings and the second the car in action. 5, 40, 50, 60 c., each ×2.

Leaders of the World. Railway Locomotives (2nd series). Two designs for each value, the first showing technical drawings and the second the locomotive at work. 1, 35, 50, 60 c., each ×2.

Leaders of the World. Automobiles (2nd series). Two designs for each value, the first showing technical drawings and the second the car in action. 15, 20, 50, 60 c., each ×2

Leaders of the World. Cats. 5, 30, 50 c., $1, each ×2.

Leaders of the World. Life and Times of Queen Elizabeth the Queen Mother. Two designs for each value, showing different portraits. 5, 30, 75 c., $1.05, each ×2.

1986.

60th Birthday of Queen Elizabeth II. 10, 80 c., $1.75, $3.

World Cup Football Championship, Mexico. 1, 2, 5, 10, 25, 40, 50, 75, 90 c., $1, $2.50, $4.

Royal Wedding (1st issue). 60 c., $1, each ×2.

Royal Wedding (2nd issue). Previous Royal Wedding stamps optd. as for Funafuti. 60 c., $1, each ×2.

Automobiles (3rd series). Two designs for each value, the first showing technical drawings and the second the car in action. 10, 20, 35, 50, 75 c., $2, each ×2.

1987.

Royal Ruby Wedding. 40, 60, 80 c., $1, $2.

NIUTAO
1984.

Leaders of the World. Automobiles (1st series). Two designs for each value, the first showing technical drawings and the second the car in action. 15, 30, 40, 50 c., each ×2.

1984.

Leaders of the World. Railway Locomotives (1st series). Two designs for each value, the first showing technical drawings and the second the locomotive at work. 5, 10, 20, 40, 50 c., $1, each ×2.

1985.

Leaders of the World. Famous Cricketers. Two designs for each value, the first showing a portrait and the second the cricketer in action. 1, 15, 50 c., $1, each ×2.

Leaders of the World. Birth Bicent. of John J. Audubon (ornithologist). Birds. 5, 15, 25 c., $1, each ×2.

Leaders of the World. Automobiles (2nd series). Two designs for each value, the first showing technical drawings and the second the car in action. 20, 25, 40, 60 c., each ×2.

Leaders of the World. Railway Locomotives (2nd series). Two designs for each value, the first showing technical drawings and the second the locomotive at work. 10, 30, 45, 60, 75 c., $1.20, each ×2.

Leaders of the World. Life and Times of Queen Elizabeth the Queen Mother. Two designs for each value, showing different portraits. 15, 35, 70, 95 c., each ×2.

1986.

60th Birthday of Queen Elizabeth II. 5, 60 c., $1.50, $3.50.

Royal Wedding (1st issue). 60 c., $1, each ×2.

Royal Wedding (2nd issue). Previous Royal Wedding stamps optd. as for Funafuti. 60 c., $1, each ×2.

1987.

Royal Ruby Wedding. 60th Birthday of Queen Elizabeth II issue of 1986 optd. **40th WEDDING ANNIVERSARY OF H. M. QUEEN ELIZABETH II.** 5, 60 c., $1.50, $3.50.

NUI
1984.

Leaders of the World. Railway Locomotives (1st series). Two designs for each value, the first showing technical drawings and the second the locomotive at work. 15, 25, 30, 50 c., each ×2.

Leaders of the World. British Monarchs. Two designs for each value, forming a composite picture. 1, 5, 15, 40, 50 c., $1, each ×2.

1985.

Leaders of the World. Railway Locomotives (2nd series). Two designs for each value, the first showing technical drawings and the second the locomotive at work. 5, 15, 25 c., $1, each ×2.

Leaders of the World. Automobiles (1st series). Two designs for each value, the first showing technical drawings and the second the car in action. 25, 30, 40, 50 c., each ×2.

Leaders of the World. Famous Cricketers. Two designs for each value, the first showing a portrait and the second the cricketer in action. 1, 40, 60, 70 c., each ×2.

Leaders of the World. Life and Times of Queen Elizabeth the queen Mother. Two designs for each value, showing different portraits. 5, 50, 75, 85 c., each ×2.

Leaders of the World. Automobiles (2nd series). Two designs for each value, the first showing technical drawings and the second the car in action. 5, 15, 40, 60, 90 c., $1.10, each ×2.

1986.

60th Birthday of Queen Elizabeth II. 10, 80 c., $1.75, $3.

Royal Wedding (1st issue). 60 c., $1, each ×2.

Royal Wedding (2nd issue). Previous Royal Wedding stamps optd. as for Funafuti. 60 c., $1, each ×2.

1987.

Railway Locomotives (3rd series). Two designs for each value, the first showing technical drawings and the second the locomotive at work. 10, 25, 35, 40, 60, 75 c., $1, $1.25, each ×2.

Royal Ruby Wedding. 20, 50, 75 c., $1.20, $1.75.

1988.

Railway Locomotives (4th series). Two designs for each value, the first showing technical drawings and the second the locomotive at work. 5, 10, 20, 25, 40, 50, 60, 75 c., each ×2.

NUKUFETAU
1984.

Leaders of the World. Automobiles (1st series). Two designs for each value, the first showing technical drawings and the second the car in action. 10, 25, 30, 50, 60 c., each ×2.

Leaders of the World. British Monarchs. Two designs for each value, forming a composite picture. 1, 10, 30, 50, 60 c., $1, each ×2.

1985.

Leaders of the World. Famous Cricketers. Two designs for each value, the first showing a portrait and the second the cricketer in action. 1, 10, 55 c., $1, each ×2.

Leaders of the World. Railway Locomotives (1st series). Two designs for each value, the first showing technical drawings and the second the locomotive at work. 1, 10, 60, 70 c., each ×2.

Leaders of the World. Automobiles (2nd series). Two designs for each value the first showing technical drawings and the second the car in action. 5, 10, 15, 20, 50, 60, 75 c., $1.50, each ×2.

Leaders of the World. Life and Times of Queen Elizabeth the Queen Mother. Two designs for each value, showing different portraits. 10, 45, 65 c., $1, each ×2.

1986.

Leaders of the World. Railway Locomotives (2nd series). Two designs for each value, the first showing technical drawings and the second the locomotive at work. 20, 40, 60 c., $1.50, each ×2.

60th Birthday of Queen Elizabeth II. 5, 40 c., $2, $4.

Royal Wedding (1st issue). 60 c., $1, each ×2.

Royal Wedding (2nd issue). Previous Royal Wedding stamps optd. as for Funafuti. 60 c., $1, each ×2.

1987.

Railway Locomotives (3rd series). Two designs for each value, the first showing technical drawings and the second the locomotive at work. 5, 10, 15, 25, 30, 50, 60 c., $1, each ×2.

Royal Ruby Wedding. 60th Birthday of Queen Elizabeth II issue of 1986 optd. as for Niutao. 5, 40 c., $2, $4.

NUKULAELAE
1984.

Leaders of the World. Railway Locomotives (1st series). Two designs for each value, the first showing technical drawings and the second the locomotive at work. 5, 15, 40 c., $1 each ×2.

Leaders of the World. Famous Cricketers. Two designs for each value, the first showing a portrait and the second the cricketer in action. 5, 15, 30 c., $1, each ×2.

Leaders of the World. Railway Locomotives (2nd series). Two designs for each value, the first showing technical drawings and the second the locomotive at work. 5, 20, 40 c., $1, each ×2.

1985.

Leaders of the World. Automobiles (1st series). Two designs for each value, the first showing technical drawings and the second the car in action. 5, 35, 50, 70 c., each ×2.

Leaders of the World. Dogs. 5, 20, 50, 70 c., each ×2.

Leaders of the World. Railway Locomotives (3rd series). Two designs for each value, the first showing technical drawings and the second the locomotive at work. 10, 25, 50 c., $1, each ×2.

Leaders of the World. Automobiles (2nd series). Two designs for each value, the first showing technical drawings and the second the car in action. 10, 25, 35, 50, 75 c., $1, each ×2.
Leaders of the World. Life and Times of Queen Elizabeth the Queen Mother. Two designs for each value, showing different portraits. 5, 25, 85 c., $1, each ×2.

1986.

60th Birthday of Queen Elizabeth II. 10 c., $1, $1.50, $3.
Railway Locomotives (4th series). Two designs for each value, the first showing technical drawings and the second the locomotive at work. 10, 15, 25, 40, 50, 80 c., $1, $1.50, each ×2.
Royal Wedding (1st issue). 60 c., $1, each ×2.
Royal Wedding (2nd issue). Previous Royal Wedding stamps optd. as for Funafuti. 60 c., $1, each ×2.

1987.

Royal Ruby Wedding. 15, 35, 60 c., $1.50, $1.75.

VAITUPU

1984.

Leaders of the World. Automobile (1st series). Two designs for each value, the first showing technical drawings and the second the car in action. 15, 25, 30, 50 c., each ×2.
Leaders of the World. British Monarchs. Two designs for each value, forming a composite picture. 1, 5, 15, 40, 50 c., $1, each ×2.
Leaders of the World. Automobiles (2nd series). Two designs for each value, the first showing technical drawings and the second the car in action. 5, 15, 25, 30, 40, 50, 60 c., $1, each ×2.

1985.

Leaders of the World. Railway Locomotives (1st series). Two designs for each value, the first showing technical drawings and the second the locomotive at work. 10, 25, 50, 60 c., each ×2.
Leaders of the World. Butterflies. 5, 15, 50, 75 c., each ×2.
Leaders of the World. Automobiles (3rd series). Two designs for each value, the first showing technical drawings and the second the car in action. 15, 30, 40, 60 c., each ×2.
Leaders of the World. Life and Times of Queen Elizabeth the Queen Mother. Two designs for each value, showing different portraits. 15, 40, 65, 95 c., each ×2.

1986.

Leaders of the World. Railway Locomotives (2nd series). Two designs for each value, the first showing technical drawings and the second the locomotive at work. 5, 25, 80 c., $1, each ×2.
60th Birthday of Queen Elizabeth II. 5, 60 c., $2, $3.50.
Royal Wedding (1st issue). 60 c., $1, each ×2.
Royal Wedding (2nd issue). Previous Royal Wedding stamps optd. as for Funafuti. 60 c., $1, each ×2.

1987.

Railway Locomotives (3rd series). Two designs for each value, the first showing technical drawings and the second the locomotive at work. 10, 15, 25, 35, 45, 65, 85 c., $1, each ×2.
Royal Ruby Wedding. 60th Birthday of Queen Elizabeth II issue of 1986 optd. as for Niutao. 5, 60 c., $2, $3.50.

UGANDA

A Br. Protectorate in Central Africa until it attained independence within the British Commonwealth 1962. From 1903 to 1962 used the stamps we list under " Kenya, Uganda and Tanganyika ".

1895. 1,000 cowries = 2 rupees.
1896. 16 annas = 1 rupee.
1962. 100 cents = 1 shilling.

U G
20
L
2.

V.96.R
25
Uganda
3.

1895. Typewritten in black.

17	2	5 (c.) black	£1100	£850
18		10 (c.) black	£1100	£950
19		15 (c.) black	£800	£850
20		20 (c.) black	£900	£600
21		25 (c.) black	£750	£800
6		30 (c.) black	£1100	£1100
7		40 (c) black	£1800	£1100
8		50 (c.) black	£1000	£950
9		60 (c.) black	£1300	£1300

1895. Typewritten in violet.

35.	2.	5 (c.) violet	£350	£400
36.		10 (c.) violet	£325	£350
37.		15 (c.) violet	£375	£325
38.		20 (c.) violet	£300	£275
39.		25 (c.) violet	£450	£450
40.		30 (c.) violet	£550	£450
41.		40 (c.) violet	£450	£450
42.		50 (c.) violet	£450	£500
43.		100 (c.) violet	£2250	£2250

1896. Typewritten in violet

44.	3.	5 (c.) violet	£300	£375
45.		10 (c.) violet	£300	£300
46.		15 (c.) violet	£300	£350
47.		20 (c.) violet	£250	£190
48.		25 (c.) violet	£325	
49.		30 (c.) violet	£350	£475
50.		40 (c.) violet	£350	£475
51.		50 (c.) violet	£350	£475
52.		60 (c.) violet	£1200	
53.		100 (c.) violet	£1200	£1200

4.

8.

1896.

55.	4.	1 a. black	8·50	9·50
56.		2 a. black	11·00	12·00
57.		3 a. black	12·00	14·00
58.		4 a. black	12·00	14·00
59.		8 a. black	18·00	22·00
60.		1 r. black	48·00	55·00
61.		5 r. black	£140	£180

1896. Optd. with large L.

70.	4.	1 a. black	£100	85·00
71.		2 a. black	45·00	70·00
72.		3 a. black	£100	£120
73.		4 a. black	60·00	95·00
74.		8 a. black	£100	£130
75.		1 r. black	£200	£250
76.		5 r. black	£5500	£5500

1898.

84a.	8.	1 a. red	50	55
86.		2 a. brown	55	2·75
87a.		3 a. grey	4·50	8·00
88.		4 a. green	1·75	5·50
89.		8 a. green	3·75	20·00

Larger type with lions at either side of portrait.

90.	–	1 r. blue	22·00	25·00
91.	–	5 r. brown	50·00	65·00

1902. Stamps of British East Africa optd. UGANDA.

92.	11.	½ a. green	80	55
93.		2½ a. blue	80	2·00

11. Ripon falls and Speke Memorial.

1962. Centenary of Speke's Discovery of Source of Nile.

95.	11.	30 c. black and red	10	10
96.		50 c. black and violet	10	10
97.		1 s. 30 black and green	15	10
98.		2 s. 50 black and blue	50	55

12. Murchison Falls.

Designs—As Type **12**: 10 c. Tobacco-growing. 15 c. Coffee-growing. 20 c. Ankole cattle. 30 c. Cotton. 50 c. Mountains of the moon. As Type **14**: 1 s. 30, Cathedrals and Mosque. 2 s. Copper mining. 10 s. Cement industry. 20 s. Parliamentary Buildings.

14. Mulago Hospital.

1962. Independence.

99.	12.	5 c. turquoise	10	10
100.	–	10 c. brown	10	10
101.	–	15 c. black, red & green	10	10
102.	–	20 c. plum and buff	10	10
103.	–	30 c. blue	10	10
104.	–	50 c. black & turquoise	10	10
105.	14.	1 s. sepia, red & turq.	15	10
106.	–	1 s. 30 orange & violet	20	10
107.	–	2 s. black, red and blue	40	30
108.	–	5 s. red and deep green	3·00	75
109.	–	10 s. slate and brown	1·75	1·50
110.	–	20 s. brown and blue	4·50	11·00

15. South African Crowned Crane.

16. Black Bee-eater.

18. Ruwenzori Turaco.

1965. Int. Trade Fair, Kampala.

111.	15.	30 c. multicoloured	10	10
112.		1 s. 30 multicoloured	20	10

1965. Birds.

113.	16.	5 c. multicoloured	10	10
114.	–	10 c. brn., blk. & blue	10	10
115.	–	15 c. yellow and brown	20	10
116.	–	20 c. multicoloured	20	10
117.	–	30 c. black and brown	1·50	10
118.	–	40 c. multicoloured	90	30
119.	–	50 c. blue and violet	25	10
120.	–	65 c. red, blk. & grey	2·50	1·25
121.	18.	1 s. multicoloured	50	10
122.	–	1 s. 30 brn., blk. & yell.	4·50	30
123.	–	2 s. 50 multicoloured	4·25	65
124.	–	5 s. multicoloured	7·00	2·00
125.	–	10 s. multicoloured	9·50	6·50
126.	–	20 s. multicoloured	21·00	25·00

Designs: As Type **16**—horiz. 10 c. African jacana. 30 c. Sacred ibis. 65 c. Red-crowned bishop. vert. 15 c. Orange weaver. 20 c. Narina trogon. 40 c. Blue-breasted kingfisher. 50 c. Whale-headed stork. As Type **18**—vert. 1 s. 30, African fish eagle. 5 s. Lilac-breasted roller. horiz. 2 s. 50, Great blue turaco. 10 s, Black-collared lovebird. 20 s. South African crowned crane.

19. Carved Screen.

1967. 13th Commonwealth Parliamentary Assn. Conf. Multicoloured.

127.	30 c. Type **19**	10	10
128.	50 c. Arms of Uganda	10	10
129.	1 s. 30 Parliamentary Bldg.	10	10
130.	2 s. 50 Conference Chamber	15	70

20. " Cordia abyssinica ". **21.** " Acacia drepanolobium ".

1969. Flowers.

131a	20	5 c. brn., grn. & yell.	40	10
132	–	10 c. multicoloured	10	10
133	–	15 c. multicoloured	40	10
134	–	20 c. vio., olive & grn.	15	10
135	–	30 c. multicoloured	20	10
136	–	40 c. vio., grn. & grey	20	10
137	–	50 c. multicoloured	20	10
138	–	60 c. multicoloured	45	90
139	–	70 c. multicoloured	35	30
140	21	1 s. multicoloured	20	10
141	–	1 s. 50 multicoloured	35	10
142a	–	2 s. 50 multicoloured	1·25	10
143a	–	5 s. multicoloured	1·75	10
144a	–	10 s. multicoloured	3·75	10
145	–	20 s. multicoloured	5·00	4·50

Designs—As Type **20**: 10 c. "Grewiasimilis". 15 c. "Cassia didymobotrya". 20 c. "Coleus barbatus". 30 c. "Ochna ovata". 40 c. "Ipomea spathulata". 50 c. "Spathodea nilotica". 60 c. "Oncoba spinosa". 70 c. "Carissa edulis". As Type **21**: 1 s. 50, "Clerodendrum myricoides". 2 s. 50, "Avanthus arboreus". 5 s. "Kigelia aethiopium". 10 s. "Erythrina abyssinica". 20 s. "Monodora myristica".

1975. Nos. 140a, 142a and 145a surch.

146.	2 s. on 1 s. multicoloured	2·00	1·50
147.	3 s. on 2 s. 50 multicoloured	20·00	35·00
148.	40 s. on 20 s. multicoloured	5·50	3·50

23. Millet.

24. Maize.

1975. Ugandan Crops.

149.	23.	10 c. blk., grn. & brn.	10	10
150.	–	20 c. multicoloured	10	10
151.	–	30 c. multicoloured	10	10
152.	–	40 c. multicoloured	10	10
153.	–	50 c. multicoloured	10	10
154.	–	70 c. blk., grn. & turq.	15	15
155.	–	80 c. multicoloured	15	15
156.	24.	1 s. multicoloured	15	15
157.	–	2 s. multicoloured	30	30
158.	–	3 s. multicoloured	50	45
159.	–	5 s. multicoloured	75	75
160.	–	10 s. multicoloured	1·25	1·25
161.	–	20 s. grn., blk. & pur.	1·75	2·50
162.	–	40 s. grn., bl. & orge.	3·00	4·75

Designs: As Type **23**. 20 c. Sugar. 30 c. Tobacco. 40 c. Onions. 50 c. Tomatoes. 70 c. Tea. 80 c. Bananas. As Type **24**. 2 s. Pineapples. 3 s. Coffee. 5 s. Oranges. 10 s. Groundnuts. 20 s. Cotton. 40 s. Runner Beans.

Face value colours: 5 s. green. 10 s. brown. 20 s. mauve. 40 s. orange.

For these values with colours changed, see Nos. 220/3.

1976. Telecommunications Development. As Nos 56/60 of Kenya.

163.	50 c. Microwave tower	10	10
164.	1 s. Cordless switchboard	10	10
165.	2 s. Telephones	20	25
166.	3 s. Message Switching Centre	30	45

1976. Olympic Games, Montreal. As Nos. 61/5 of Kenya.

168.	50 c. Akii Bua, hurdler	15	10
169.	1 s. Filbert Bayi, runner	20	10
170.	2 s. Steve Muchoki, boxer	40	30
171.	3 s. East African flags	55	45

1976. Railway Transport. As Nos. 66/70 of Kenya.

173. 50 c. Tanzania-Zambia railway 20 10
174. 1 s. Nile Bridge, Uganda .. 35 10
175. 2 s. Nakuru Station, Kenya 75 45
176. 3 s. Class "A" loco, 1896 .. 95 55

1977. Game Fish of East Africa. As Nos. 71/5 of Kenya. Multicoloured.

178. 50 c. Nile Perch 15 10
179. 1 s. Tilapia 20 10
180. 3 s. Sailfish 70 40
181. 5 s. Black Marlin .. .. 1·00 60

1977. Second World Black and African Festival of Arts and Culture. As Nos. 76/80 of Kenya. Multicoloured.

183. 50 c. Maasai Manyatta Village, Kenya 15 10
184. 1 s. "Heartbeat of Africa" (Ugandan dancers) .. 20 10
185. 2 s. Makonde sculpture, Tanzania 45 55
186. 3 s. "Early man and technology" (skinning hippopotamus) 60 85

1977. 25th Anniv. of Safari Rally. As Nos. 81/5 of Kenya. Multicoloured.

188. 50 c. Rally-car & villagers 15 10
189. 1 s. Starting-line 15 10
190. 2 s. Car fording river .. 35 35
191. 5 s. Car and elephants .. 90 1·00

1977. Centenary of Ugandan Church. As Nos. 86/90 of Kenya. Multicoloured.

193. 50 c. Canon Kivebulaya .. 10 10
194. 1 s. Modern Namirembe Cathedral 15 10
195. 2 s. Old Namirembe Cathedral 30 40
196. 5 s. Early congregation Kigezi 60 90

1977. As No. 155, surch.

198. 80 c. on 60 c. multicoloured 30 20

1977. Endangered Species. As Nos. 96/101 of Kenya. Multicoloured.

199. 50 c. Pancake Tortoise .. 30 10
200. 1 s. Nile Crocodile 45 10
201. 2 s. Hunter's Hartebeest .. 2·00 40
202. 3 s. Red Colobus monkey 2·25 75
203. 5 s. Dugong .. .. 2·25 1·00

1978. World Cup Football Championship. Argentina (1st issue). As Nos. 122/6 of Kenya. Multicoloured.

205. 50 c. Joe Kadenge and forwards 15 10
206. 1 s. Mohamed Chuma and cup presentation .. 15 10
207. 2 s. Omari Kidevu and goalmouth scene .. 40 35
208 5 c. Polly Ouma and forwards 70 85

26. Shot Putting.

1978. Commonwealth Games, Edmonton. Multicoloured.

210. 50 c. Type **26** 15 10
211. 1 s. Long jumping .. 15 10
212. 2 s. Running 30 30
213. 5 s. Boxing 55 70

1978. World Cup Football Championship, Argentina (2nd issue). As Nos. 205/8, but additionally inscr. " WORLD CUP 1978 ".

215. 50 c. Polly Ouma and forwards 15 10
216. 2 s. Omari Kidevu and goalmouth scene .. 15 10
217. 5 s. Joe Kadenge and forwards .. .. 1·00 90
218. 10 s. Mohamed Chuma and cup presentation .. 1·75 1·60

1978. As Nos. 159/62 but colours changed.

220. 5 s. mult. (face value in blue) 70 70
221. 10 s. mult. (face value in mauve) .. .. .. 80 1·25
222. 20 s. mult. (face value in brown) .. .. .. 1·00 1·25
223. 40 s. mult. (face value in red) .. .. .. 1·75 2·00

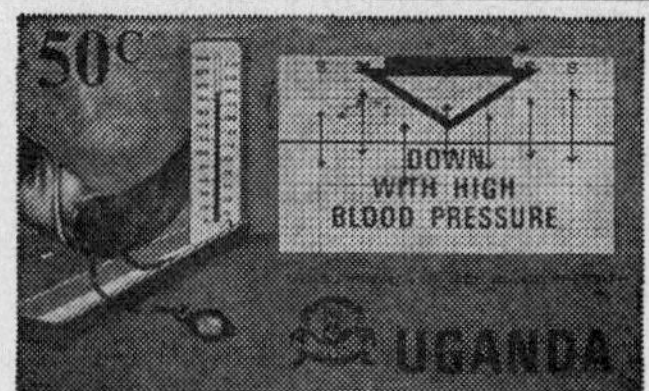

27. Measurements of High Blood Pressure.

1978. " Down with High Blood Pressure ". Multicoloured.

224. 50 c. Type **27** 15 10
225. 1 s. Human heart .. 15 10
226. 2 s. Fundus of the eye .. 40 35
227. 5 s. Human kidneys .. 75 80

28. Off Loading Cattle.

1978. 75th Anniv. of First Powered Flight. Multicoloured.

229. 1 s. Type **28** 15 10
230. 1 s. 50, Passengers boarding " Islander " .. 20 15
231. 2 s. 70, Loading Coffee .. 30 35
232. 10 s. Wright " Flyer " and " Concorde " .. .. 80 1·25

29. Queen Elizabeth II leaving Owen Falls Dam.

1979. 25th Anniv. of Coronation. (1978) Multicoloured.

234. 1 s. Type **29** 15 10
235. 1 s. 50 Regalia 20 10
236. 2 s. 70 Coronation ceremony 45 20
237. 10 s. Royal family on balcony of Buckingham Palace .. .. 1·00 60

30. Dr. Joseph Kiwanuka (first Ugandan bishop).

1979. Centenary of Catholic Church in Uganda. Multicoloured.

239. 1 s. Type **30** 15 10
240. 1 s. 50 Lubaga Cathedral 15 10
241. 2 s. 70 Ugandan pilgrimage to Rome, Holy Year, 1975 .. .. .. 20 25
242. 10 s. Friar Lourdel-Mapeera (early missionary) .. 60 80

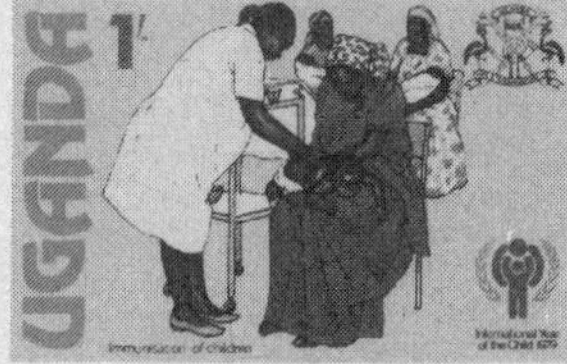

31. Immunisation of Children.

1979. International Year of the Child. Multicoloured.

244. 1 s. Type **31** 10 10
245. 1 s. 50 Handicapped children at play .. 15 20
246. 2 s. 70 Ugandan I.Y.C. emblem 20 35
247. 10 s. Children in class .. 60 90

1979. Liberation. Optd. **UGANDA LIBERATED 1979.** (a) Nos. 149/62.

249. **23.** 10 c. blk., grn. and brn. 10 10
250. – 20 c. multicoloured .. 10 10
251. – 30 c. multicoloured .. 10 10
252. – 40 c. multicoloured .. 10 10
253. – 50 c. multicoloured .. 10 10
254. – 70 c. blk., grn. and turq. 10 10
255. – 80 c. multicoloured .. 10 10
256. **24.** 1 s. multicoloured .. 15 15
257. – 2 s. multicoloured .. 20 25
258. – 3 s. multicoloured .. 35 40
259. – 5 s. multicoloured .. 55 60
260. – 10 s. multicoloured .. 1·10 1·25
261. – 20 s. grn., blk. and pur. 2·25 2·40
262. – 40 s. grn., black & orge. 4·50 4·75

(b) Nos. 210/13.

263. 50 c. Type **26** 10 10
264. 1 s. Long jumping .. 15 20
265. 2 s. Running 25 30
266. 5 s. Boxing 60 65

(c) Nos. 207, 215, 217/18.

267. 50 c. Polly Ouma and forwards 15 10
268. 2 s. Omari Kidevu and goalmouth scene .. 30 30
269. 5 s. Joe Kadenge and forwards 80 65
270. 10 s. Mohamed Chuma and cup presentation .. 1·50 1·40

(d) Nos. 220/3.

271. 5 s. multicoloured .. 55 60
272. 10 s. multicoloured .. 1·10 1·25
273. 20 s. multicoloured .. 2·25 2·40
274. 40 s. multicoloured .. 4·50 4·75

(e) Nos. 229/32.

275. 1 s. Type **28** 15 20
276. 1 s. 50 Passengers boarding " Islander " light aircraft 25 25
277. 2 s. 70 Loading coffee .. 50 55
278. 10 s. Wright " Flyer " and " Concorde " .. .. 1·75 1·75

(f) Nos. 234/7.

279. 1 s. Type **29** 10 20
280. 1 s. 50 Regalia 15 20
281. 2 s. 70 Coronation Ceremony 20 30
282. 10 s. Royal family on balcony of Buckingham Palace .. .. .. 85 1·50

(g) Nos. 239/42.

284. 1 s. Type **30** 15 20
285. 1 s. 50 Lubaga Cathedral 20 25
286. 2 s. 70 Ugandan pilgrimage to Rome, Holy Year, 1975 .. .. .. 40 45
287. 10 s. Friar Lourdel-Mapeera (early missionary) .. 1·25 1·60

(h) Nos. 244/8.

289. 1 s. Type **31** 15 20
290. 1 s. 50 Handicapped children at play .. 20 25
291. 2 s. 70 Ugandan I.Y.C. emblem 40 45
292. 10 s. Children in class .. 1·25 1·40

35. Radio Wave Symbol.

1979. 50th Anniv. of International Consultative Radio Committee and International Telecommunications Union.

294. **35.** 1 s. multicoloured .. 10 10
295. 1 s. 50 multicoloured .. 15 10
296. 2 s. 70 multicoloured .. 20 35
297. 10 s. multicoloured .. 60 90

36. 20 s. Definitive Stamp of 1965 and Sir Rowland Hill.

1979. Death Centenary of Sir Rowland Hill. Multicoloured.

298. 1 s. Type **36** 10 10
299. 1 s. 50 1967 Commonwealth Parliamentary Association Conference 50 c. commemorative 15 10
300. 2 s. 70 1962 Independence 20 s. commemorative .. 20 30
301. 10 s. Uganda Protectorate 1898 1 a. .. .. 60 1·10

37. Impala.

38. Lions with Cub.

1979. Wildlife. Multicoloured.

303. 10 c. Type **37** 10 10
304. 20 c. Large-spotted Genet 10 10
305. 30 c. Thomson's Gazelle .. 15 10
306. 50 c. Lesser Bushbaby .. 15 10
307. 80 c. Hunting Dog .. 20 10
308. 1 s. Type **38** 15 10
309. 1 s. 50 Gorilla 45 10
310. 2 s. Common Zebra .. 25 20
311. 2 s. 70 Leopard with cub .. 60 15
312. 3 s. 50 Black Rhinoceros .. 70 20
313. 5 s. Waterbuck 40 40
314. 10 s. African Buffalo .. 70 60
315. 20 s. Hippopotamus .. 80 1·25
316. 40 s. African Elephant .. 1·50 2·50

SIZES: As Type **37**, 10 c. to 80 c. As Type **38**, 1 s. to 40 s.

See also Nos. 433/9.

1980. " London 1980 " International Stamp Exhibition. Nos. 298/301 optd. **LONDON 1980**

317. **36.** 1 s. multicoloured .. 15 10
318. – 1 s. 50 multicoloured .. 20 10
319. – 2 s. 70 multicoloured .. 35 25
320. – 10 s. multicoloured .. 80 80

40. Rotary Emblem.

1980. 75th Anniv. of Rotary International. Multicoloured.

322. 1 s. Type **40** 10 10
323. 20 s. Paul P. Harris (founder) with wheel-barrow containing " Rotary projects " (horiz.) .. .. .. 1·00 1·50

41. Football.

1980. Olympic Games, Moscow. Multicoloured.

325. 1 s. Type **41** 10 10
326. 2 s. Relay 10 10
327. 10 s. Hurdles 40 60
328. 20 s. Boxing .. .. 80 1·25

1981. Olympic Medal Winners. Nos. 325/8 optd.

330. **41.** 1 s. multicoloured .. 10 10
331. – 2 s. multicoloured .. 10 15
332. – 10 s. multicoloured .. 40 50
333. – 20 s. multicoloured .. 80 1·00

OVERPRINTS: 1 s. **FOOTBALL GOLD MEDALISTS C.S.S.R.** 2 s. **RELAY GOLD MEDALIST U.S.S.R.** 10 s. **HURDLES 110m GOLD MEDALIST THOMAS MUNKLET, D.D.R.** 20 s. **BOXING WELTERWEIGHT SILVER MEDALIST JOHN MUGABI, UGANDA.**

44. Heinrich von Stephan and U.P.U. Emblem.

1981. 150th Birth Anniv. of Heinrich von Stephan (founder of U.P.U.) Multicoloured.

336. 1 s. Type **44** 10 10
337. 2 s. U.P.U. Headquarters 15 15
338. 2 s. 70 Air mail, 1935 .. 20 20
339. 10 s. Mail transport by steam, 1927 .. .. 80 80

45. Tower of London.

1981. Royal Wedding. Multicoloured.
(a) Previously unissued stamps surch.

341. 10 s. on 1 s. Prince Charles and Lady Diana Spencer 15 20
342. 50 s. on 5 s. Type **45** .. 25 30
343. 200 s. on 20 s. Prince Charles at Balmoral .. 60 80

(b) Stamps reissued with new face values.

345. 10 s. As No. 341 .. .. 10 15
346. 50 s. As Type **45** .. 15 20
347. 200 s. As No. 343 .. 30 40

48. " Sleeping Woman before Green Shutters ".

1981. Birth Centenary of Picasso. Mult.

349. 10 s. Type **48** 10 10
350. 20 s. " Bullfight " .. 20 20
351. 30 s. " Detail of a Nude asleep in a Landscape " 25 25
352. 200 s. " Interior with a Girl Drawing " .. 2·25 2·25

49. Deaf People using Sign Language.

1981. International Year for Disabled Persons. Multicoloured.

354. 1 s. Type **49** .. 10 10
355. 10 s. Disabled teacher in classroom .. 15 10
356. 50 s. Teacher and disabled children 70 50
357. 200 s. Blind person with guide dog .. .. 2·00 2·00

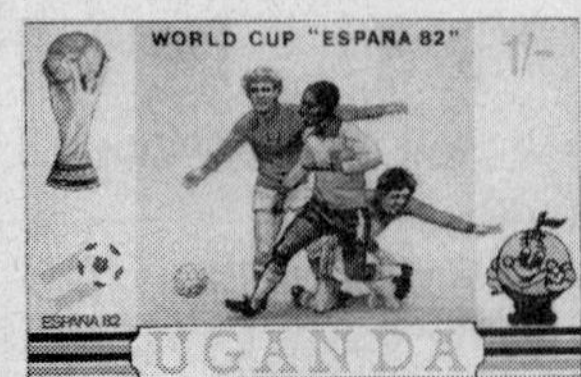

50. Footballers.

1981. World Cup Football Championships, Spain (1982).

359. **50.** 1 s. multicoloured .. 10 10
360. – 10 s. multicoloured .. 15 10
361. – 50 s. multicoloured .. 70 50
362. – 200 s. multicoloured .. 2·00 2·00

DESIGNS: Nos. 360/62, various football scenes.

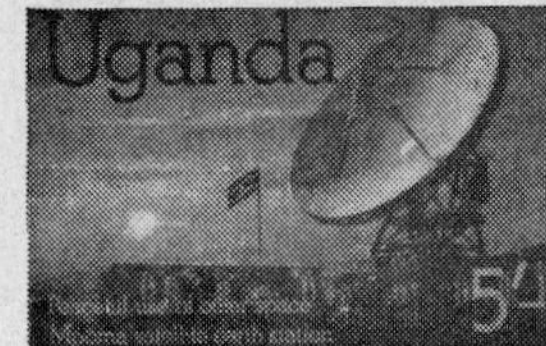

51. Mpoma Satellite Earth Station.

1982. " Peaceful Use of Outer Space ". Multicoloured.

364. 5 s. Type **51** 25 15
365. 10 s. " Pioneer II " (satellite) 35 25
366. 50 s. Space Shuttle .. 1·75 1·75
367. 100 s. " Voyager 2 " (satellite) .. .. 2·75 2·75

52. Dr. Robert Koch.

1982. Centenary of Robert Koch's Discovery of Tubercle Bacillus. Multicoloured.

369. 1 s. Type **52** 30 10
370. 10 s. Microscope .. .. 1·25 40
371. 50 s. Ugandans receiving vaccinations .. .. 3·00 2·50
372. 100 s. Tubercle virus .. 4·50 4·25

1982. Princess of Wales. 21st Birthday. Nos. 345/7 optd. **21st BIRTHDAY HRH** Princess of Wales.

374. 10 s. Prince Charles and Lady Diana Spencer .. 20 15
375. 50 s. Type **45** 60 50
376. 200 s. Prince Charles at Balmoral .. .. 2·00 1·60

54. Yellow-billed Hornbill.

1982. Birds. Multicoloured.

378. 1 s. Type **54** 15 10
379. 20 s. Superb Starling .. 60 35
380. 50 s. Bateleur .. .. 1·25 1·50
381. 100 s. Saddle-bill stork .. 2·00 2·50

55. Scout Band.

1982. 75th Anniv. of Boy Scout Movement. Multicoloured.

383. 5 s. Type **55** 40 10
384. 20 s. Scout receiving Bata Shoe trophy .. .. 1·10 45
385. 50 s. Scouts with wheelchair patient .. .. 2·25 2·00
386. 100 s. First aid instruction 3·00 3·25

56. Swearing-in of Roosevelt.

1982. 250th Birth Anniv. of George Washington and Birth Centenary of Franklin D. Roosevelt. Multicoloured.

388. 50 s. Type **56** 30 30
389. 200 s. Swearing-in of Washington .. .. 1·00 1·25

57. Italy v West Germany.

1982. World Cup Football Championship Winners. Multicoloured.

392. 10 s. Type **57** 50 25
393. 200 s. Victorious Italian team .. .. .. 3·00 3·25

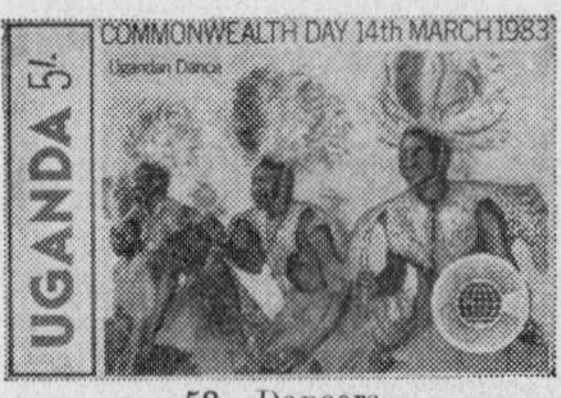

58. Dancers.

1983. Commonwealth Day. Cultural Art. Multicoloured.

395. 5 s. Type **58** 10 10
396. 20 s. Traditional currency 20 20
397. 50 s. Homestead 45 45
398. 100 s. Drums 85 85

59. " St. George and the Dragon " (Raphael).

1983. 500th Birth Anniv. of Raphael (painter). Multicoloured.

399. 5 s. Type **59** 10 10
400. 20 s. " St. George and the Dragon " (different) .. 40 30
401. 50 s. " Crossing the Red Sea " (detail) 80 70
402. 200 s. " The Expulsion of Heliodorus " (detail) .. 2·50 3·00

60. Map showing Namibia and U.N. Flag.

1983. Commemorations. Multicoloured.

404. 5 s. Type **60** 10 10
405. 200 s. 7th Non-aligned Summit Conference logo 1·40 2·25

61. Elephants in Grassland.

1983. Endangered Species (1st series). Mult.

406 5 s. Elephants in "Elephants' Graveyard" .. 70 20
407 10 s. Type **61** .. .. 1·00 35
408 30 s. Elephants at water-hole .. .. .. 2·25 1·75
409 70 s. Elephants having dust bath .. .. 3·50 3·00

See also Nos. 642 and 970/3.

1983. Centenary of Boy's Brigade. Nos. 383/6 optd **BOY'S BRIGADE CENTENARY 1833–1983**, or surch also.

411 5 s. Type **55** 10 10
412 20 s. Scout receiving Bata Shoe trophy 15 15
413 50 s. Scouts with wheel-chair patient 25 30
414 400 s. on 100 s. First aid instruction .. .. 2·40 2·75

63. Mpoma Satellite Earth Station.

1983. World Communications Year. Mult.

416. 20 s. Type **63** 25 15
417. 50 s. Railroad computer and operator 65 65
418. 70 s. Cameraman filming lions 75 80
419. 100 s. Aircraft cockpit .. 95 1·25

1983. Nos. 303, 305/9 and 313 surch.

421 100 s. on 10 c. Type **37** .. 65 55
422 135 s. on 1 s. Type **38** .. 80 70
423 175 s. on 30 c. Thomson's gazelle 95 85
424 200 s. on 50 c. Lesser bush-baby .. .. .. 1·10 1·00
425 400 s. on 80 c. Hunting dog 2·00 1·75
426 700 s. on 5 s. Waterbuck .. 3·25 3·25
427 1000 s. on 1 s. 50 Gorilla .. 4·50 4·50

65. The Nativity.

1983. Christmas. Multicoloured.

428. 10 s. Type **65** 10 10
429. 50 s. Shepherds and Angels 25 30
430. 175 s. Flight into Egypt .. 80 1·00
431. 400 s. Angels blowing trumpets .. .. .. 1·90 2·25

1983. Nos. 308/12 and 315/16 but with face values in revalued currency.

433. 100 s. Type **38** 75 35
434. 135 s. Gorilla 85 50
435. 175 s. Common Zebra .. 1·10 70
436. 200 s. Leopard with cub .. 1·50 80
437. 400 s. Black Rhinoceros .. 2·50 2·50
438. 700 s. African Elephant .. 4·00 4·25
439. 1000 s. Hippopotamus .. 4·75 5·50

66. Ploughing with Oxen.

1984. World Food Day. Multicoloured.

440. 10 s. Type **66** 15 10
441. 300 s. Harvesting bananas 4·00 4·50

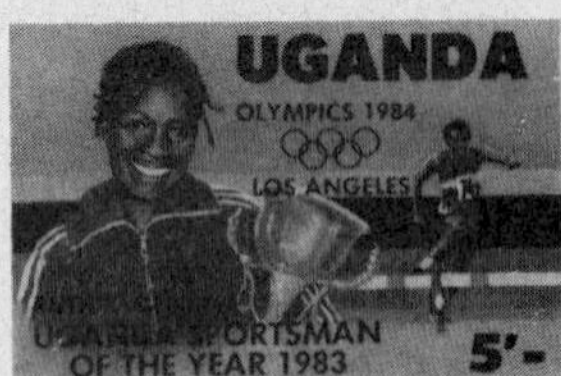

67. Ruth Kyalisiima, Sportsman of the Year 1983.

1984. Olympic Games, Los Angeles. Mult.

442. 5 s. Type **67** 10 10
443. 115 s. Javelin-throwing .. 50 60
444. 155 s. Wrestling 60 70
445. 175 s. Rowing 70 80

68. Entebbe Airport.

1984. 40th Anniv. of International Civil Aviation Organization. Multicoloured.

447. 5 s. Type **68** 15 10
448. 115 s. Loading cargo plane 1·50 1·50
449. 155 s. Uganda police helicopter .. .. .. 2·50 2·50
450. 175 s. East African Civil Flying School, Soroti .. 2·75 2·75

69. "Charaxes druceanus".

1984. Butterflies. Multicoloured.

452 5 s. Type **69** 30 10
453 115 s. "Papilio lormieri" .. 2·25 1·75
454 155 s. "Druryia antimachus" .. .. 2·75 2·00
455 175 s. "Salamis temora" .. 3·75 2·75

70. "Nothobranchius taeniopygus".

1985. Lake Fishes. Multicoloured.

457. 5 s. Type **70** 30 30
458. 10 s. "Bagrus dogmac" .. 30 30
459. 50 s. "Polypterus senegalus" 60 30
460. 100 s. "Clarias" 70 30
461. 135 s. "Mormyrus kannume" 70 45
462. 175 s. "Synodontis victoriae" .. .. 1·10 1·10
463. 205 s. "Haplochromis brownae" .. .. 1·25 1·25
464. 400 s. "Lates niloticus" .. 1·50 1·50
465. 700 s. "Protopterus aethiopicus" .. .. 1·75 1·75
466. 1000 s. "Barbus radcliffii" 2·00 2·00
467. 2500 s. "Malapterus electricus" .. .. 2·00 2·00

71. The Last Supper.

1985. Easter. Multicoloured.

468. 5 s. Type **71** 10 10
469. 115 s. Christ showing the nail marks to Thomas .. 90 60
470. 155 s. The raising of the Cross .. .. .. 1·00 70
471. 175 s. Pentecost .. .. 1·40 90

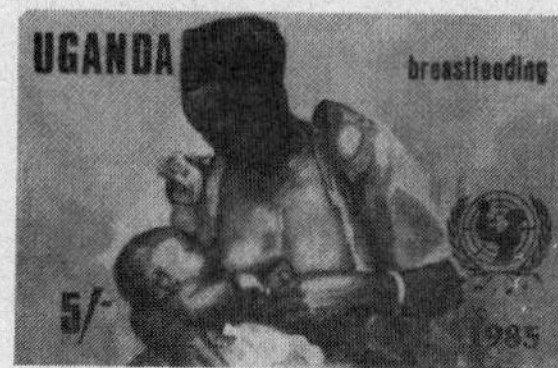

72. Breast Feeding.

1985. U.N.I.C.E.F. Child Survival Campaign. Multicoloured.

473. 5 s. Type **72** 10 10
474. 115 s. Growth monitoring 1·25 1·25
475. 155 s. Immunisation .. 1·75 1·75
476. 175 s. Oral re-hydration therapy .. .. .. 2·00 2·00

73. Queen Elizabeth the Queen Mother.

1985. Life and Times of Queen Elizabeth the Queen Mother and Decade for Women.

478 **73** 1000 s. multicoloured .. 2·00 2·10

74. Sedge Warbler.

1985. Birth Bicentenary of John J. Audubon (ornithologist) (1st issue). Multicoloured.

480. 115 s. Type **74** .. .. 1·25 1·25
481. 155 s. Cattle Egret .. 1·50 1·50
482. 175 s. Crested Lark .. 1·75 1·75
483. 500 s. Tufted Duck .. 2·50 2·50

See also Nos. 494/7.

1985. Olympic Gold Medal Winners, Los Angeles, Nos. 442/5 optd. or surch. also.

485. 5 s. Type **67** (optd. **GOLD MEDALIST BENITA BROWN-FITZGERALD USA**) 10 10
486. 115 s. Javelin-throwing (optd. **GOLD MEDALIST ARTO HAERKOENEN FINLAND**) .. 25 30
487. 155 s. Wrestling (optd. **GOLD MEDALIST ATSUJI MIYAHARA JAPAN**) 30 35
488. 1000 s. on 175 s. Rowing (surch. **GOLD MEDALIST WEST GERMANY**) .. .. 1·90 2·00

76. Women carrying National Women's Day Banner.

1985. Decade for Women. Multicoloured.

490. 5 s. Type **76** 10 10
491. 115 s. Girl Guides (horiz.) 1·50 1·50
492. 155 s. Mother Teresa (Nobel Peace Prize winner, 1979) .. .. 2·75 2·75

No. 491 also commemorates the 75th anniversary of Girl Guide movement.

1985. Birth Bicentenary of John J. Audubon (ornithologist) (2nd issue). As T **198** of Antigua. Multicoloured.

494 5 s. Rock ptarmigan .. 45 10
495 155 s. Sage grouse .. 1·75 1·50
496 175 s. Lesser yellowlegs .. 2·00 2·00
497 500s. Brown-headed cowbird .. .. 3·00 3·00

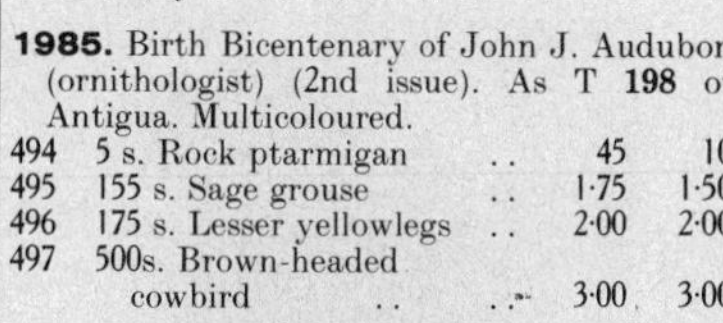

77. Man beneath Tree laden with Produce (F.A.O.).

1986. 40th Anniv. of U.N.O.

499. **77.** 10 s. multicoloured .. 10 10
500. – 180 s. multicoloured .. 60 30
501. – 200 s. blue, brn. & grn. 65 35
502. – 250 s. blue, blk. & red 70 40
503. – 2000 s. multicoloured .. 3·00 4·00

DESIGNS—HORIZ. 180 s. Soldier of U.N. Peace-Keeping Force. 250 s. Hands releasing peace dove. VERT. 200 s. U.N. emblem. 2000 s. Flags of U.N. and Uganda.

78. Goalkeeper catching Ball.

1986. World Cup Football Championship, Mexico. Multicoloured.

505. 10 s. Type **78** 10 10
506. 180 s. Player with ball .. 85 45
507. 250 s. Two players competing for ball .. 1·00 55
508. 2500 s. Player running with ball .. .. .. 4·50 5·00

1988. Liberation by National Resistance Army. Nos. 462 and 464/7 optd **NRA LIBERATION 1986**.

510 175 s. "Synodontis victoriae" 60 60
511 400 s. "Lates niloticus" .. 1·00 1·00
512 700 s. "Protopteris aethiopicus" .. .. 1·75 1·75
513 1000 s. "Barbus radcliffii" 2·00 2·50
514 2500 s. "Malapterus electricus" .. .. 3·75 4·25

1986. Appearance of Halley's Comet (1st issue). As T **123** of Anguilla. Multicoloured.

515. 50 s. Tycho Brahe and Arecibo Radio Telescope, Puerto Rico .. 20 10
516. 100 s. Recovery of astronaut John Glenn from sea, 1962 .. .. .. 35 15
517. 140 s. "The Star in the East" (painting by Giotto) 50 30
518. 2500 s. Death of Davy Crockett at the Alamo, 1835 .. .. .. 3·50 4·50

See also Nos. 544/7.

80. Niagara Falls.

1986. "Ameripex '86" International Stamp Exhibition, Chicago. American Landmarks. Multicoloured.

520. 50 s. Type **80** 15 10
521. 100 s. Jefferson Memorial, Washington D.C. .. 25 15
522. 250 s. Liberty Bell, Philadelphia 50 35
523. 1000 s. The Alamo, San Antonio, Texas .. .. 1·75 1·75
524. 2500 s. George Washington Bridge, New York–New Jersey .. .. .. 3·25 3·50

1986. 60th Birthday of Queen Elizabeth II. As T **125** of Anguilla.

526 100 s. black and yellow .. 25 15
527 140 s. multicoloured .. 30 20
528 2500 s. multicoloured .. 3·25 3·50

DESIGNS: 100 s. Princess Elizabeth at London Zoo. 140 s. Queen Elizabeth at race meeting, 1970. 2500 s. With Prince Philip at Sandringham, 1982.

81. "Gloria" (Colombia).

1986. Centenary of Statue of Liberty. Cadet sailing ships. Multicoloured.

530. 50 s. Type **81** 45 10
531. 100 s. "Mircea" (Rumania) 75 30
532. 140 s. "Sagres II" (Portugal) (horz.) .. 1·25 90
533. 2500 s "Gazela Primiero" (U.S.A.) (horiz.) .. 6·50 8·00

No. 533 is inscribed "Primero" in error.

1986. Royal Wedding. As T **213** of Antigua. Multicoloured.

535. 50 s. Prince Andrew and Miss Sarah Ferguson (horiz.) 10 10
536. 140 s. Prince Andrew with Princess Anne at shooting match (horiz.) 20 20
537. 2500 s. Prince Andrew and Miss Sarah Ferguson at Ascot (horiz.) .. .. 2·75 3·25

1986. World Cup Football Championship Winners, Mexico. Nos. 505/8 optd. **WINNERS Argentina 3 W. Germany 2** or surch. also.

539. 50 s. on 10 s. Type **78** .. 10 10
540. 180 s. Player with ball .. 25 25
541. 250 s. Two players competing for ball .. 35 35
542. 2500 s. Player running with ball .. .. .. 2·75 3·25

1986. Appearance of Halley's Comet (2nd issue). Nos. 515/18 optd as T **218** of Antigua.

544. 50 s. Tycho Brahe and Arecibo Radio Telescope, Puerto Rico .. 20 15
545. 100 s. Recovery of astronaut John Glenn from sea, 1962 .. .. .. 35 20
546. 140 s. "The Star in the East" (painting by Giotto) 55 40
547. 2500 s. Death of Davy Crockett at the Alamo, 1835 .. .. .. 4·75 5·50

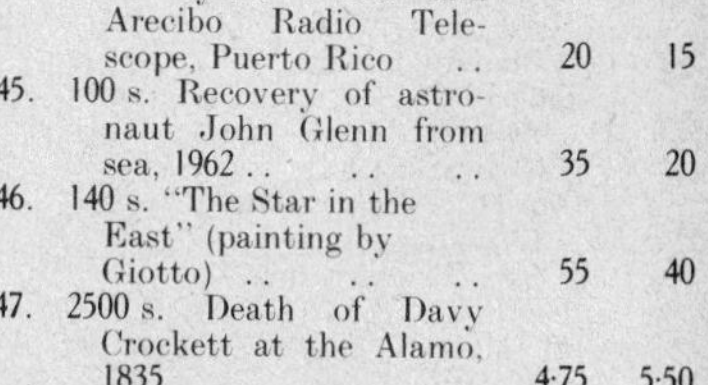

83. St. Kizito.

1986. Christian Martyrs of Uganda. Mult.

549. 50 s. Type **83** 10 10
550. 150 s. St. Kizito instructing converts 20 20
551. 200 s. Martyrdom of Bishop James Hannington, 1885 25 25
552. 1000 s. Burning of Bugandan Christians, 1886 .. .. .. 1·25 1·75

84. "Madonna of the Cherries" (Titian).

1986. Christmas. Religious Paintings. Mult.

554. 50 s. Type **84** 20 15
555. 150 s. "Madonna and Child" (Durer) (vert.) 50 30
556. 200 s. "Assumption of the Virgin" (Titian) (vert.) .. 60 40
557. 2500 s. "Praying Hands" (Durer) (vert.) .. .. 5·00 6·00

85. Red-billed Fire Finch and Glory Lily.

1987. Flora and Fauna. Multicoloured.

559. 2 s. Type **85** 15 10
560. 5 s. African pygmy kingfisher and nandi flame .. 20 15
561. 10 s. Scarlet-chested sunbird and crown of thorns 25 25
562. 25 s. White rhinoceros and yellow-billed oxpecker .. 65 60
563. 35 s. Lion and elephant grass 80 80
564. 45 s. Cheetahs and doum palm .. .. .. 1·00 1·00
565. 50 s. Cordon bleu and desert rose .. .. 1·10 1·25
566. 100 s. Giant eland and acacia .. .. .. 2·00 2·40

86. Tremml's "Eagle" (longest man-powered flight), 1987.

1987. Milestones of Transportation. Mult.

568 2 s. Type **86** 10 10
569 3 s. Junkers "W-33L" "Bremen" (first east–west transatlantic flight), 1928 .. .. 10 10
570 5 s. Lockheed "Winnie Mae" (Post's first solo round-the-world flight), 1933 .. .. .. 20 20
571 10 s. "Voyager" (first non-stop round-the-world flight), 1986 .. 40 40
572 15 s. Chanute biplane glider, 1896 .. .. 60 60
573 25 s. Airship "Norge" and polar bear (first transpolar flight), 1926 90 90
574 35 s. Curtis biplane and U.S.S. "Pennsylvania" (battleship) (first take-off and landing from ship), 1911 .. .. 1·25 1·25
575 45 s. Shepard and "Freedom 7" spacecraft (first American in space), 1961 .. .. .. 1·40 1·40
576 100 s. "Concorde" (first supersonic passenger flight), 1976 .. .. 3·50 3·50

87. Olympic Torch-bearer.

1987. Olympic Games, Seoul (1988) (1st issue). Multicoloured.

577. 5 s. Type **87** 10 10
578. 10 s. Swimming 20 25
579. 50 s. Cycling .. .. 1·00 1·10
580. 100 s. Gymnastics .. .. 2·00 2·10

See also Nos. 628/31.

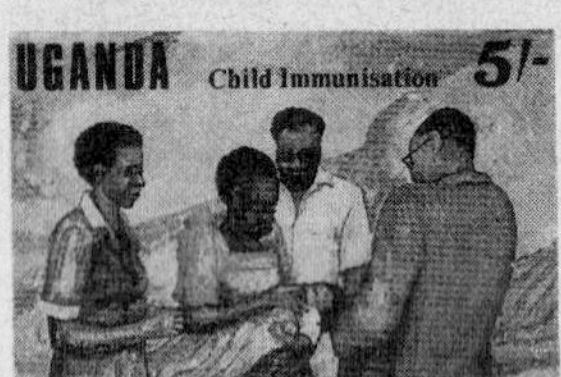

88. Child Immunization.

1987. 25th Anniv. of Independence. Mult.

582. 5 s. Type **88** 15 10
583. 10 s. Mulago Hospital, Kampala 30 25
584. 25 s. Independence Monument, Kampala City Park 70 70
585. 50 s. High Court, Kampala 1·25 1·50

89. Golden-backed Weaver.

1987. Birds of Uganda. Multicoloured.

587 5 s. Type **89** 30 30
588 10 s. Hoopoe 55 55
589 15 s. Red-throated bee eater 75 75
590 25 s. Lilac-breasted roller 1·10 1·10
591 35 s. African pygmy goose 1·40 1·40
592 45 s. Scarlet-chested sunbird .. .. 1·75 1·75
593 50 s. South African crowned crane .. .. 1·75 1·75
594 100 s. Long-tailed fiscal .. 2·75 2·75

90. Hippocrates (physician) and Surgeons performing Operation.

1987. Great Scientific Discoveries. Mult.

596. 5 s. Type **90** 40 30
597. 25 s. Einstein and deep space (Theory of Relativity) .. .. 1·50 1·50
598. 35 s. Isaac Newton and diagram from "Opticks" (Theory of Colour and Light) .. .. 1·75 2·00
599. 45 s. Karl Benz, and early Benz and modern Mercedes car .. .. 2·25 2·50

91. Scout with Stamp Album and Uganda Stamps.

1987. World Scout Jamboree, Australia. Multicoloured.

601. 5 s. Type **91** 10 10
602. 25 s. Scouts planting tree 50 55
603. 35 s. Canoeing, Lake Victoria 70 75
604. 45 s. Hiking 90 95

92. "The Annunciation".

1987. Christmas. Scenes from French diptych, c. 1250. Multicoloured.

606. 5 s. Type **92** 10 10
607. 10 s. "Nativity" 20 25
608. 50 s. "Flight into Egypt" 1·00 1·10
609. 100 s. "Adoration of the Magi" .. .. .. 2·00 2·10

93. Class "12" Light Shunter Locomotive.

1988. Locomotives of East Africa Railways. Multicoloured.

611 5 s. Type **93** 30 30
612 10 s. Class "92" diesel-electric 40 40
613 15 s. Locomotive No. 2506 55 55
614 25 s. Tank locomotive No. 126 .. .. .. 75 75
615 35 s. Class "31" locomotive 95 95
616 45 s. Class "31" locomotive (different) .. .. 1·25 1·25
617 50 s. Class "59" Double Garratt locomotive .. 1·40 1·40
618 100 s. Class "87" diesel-electric shunter .. 2·00 2·00

94. Columbite-tantalite.

1988. Minerals. Multicolured.

620. 1 s. Type **94** 10 10
621. 2 s. Galena 15 15
622. 5 s. Malachite 25 25
623. 10 s. Cassiterite 40 40
624. 35 s. Ferberite .. .. 1·25 1·25
625. 50 s. Emerald .. .. 1·75 1·75
626. 100 s. Monazite .. .. 2·50 2·50
627. 150 s. Microcline .. .. 3·50 3·50

95 Hurdling

1988. Olympic Games, Seoul (2nd issue). Mult.

628 5 s. Hurdling 10 10
629 25 s. High jumping .. 30 35
630 35 s. Javelin throwing .. 35 40
631 45 s. Long jumping .. 40 50

96 "Spathodea campanulata"

1988. Flowers. Multicoloured.

633 5 s. Type **96** 10 10
634 10 s. "Gloriosa simplex" .. 10 10
635 20 s. "Thevetica peruviana" (vert) .. 15 15
636 25 s. "Hibiscus schizopetalus" 15 25
637 35 s. "Aframomum sceptrum" 20 30
638 45 s. "Adenium obesum" 25 35
639 50 s. "Kigelia africana" (vert) 30 40
640 100 s. "Clappertonia ficifolia" 50 75

97 Elephants in Grassland (Type **61** redrawn)

1988. Endangered Species (2nd series).

642 **97** 10 s. multicoloured ..

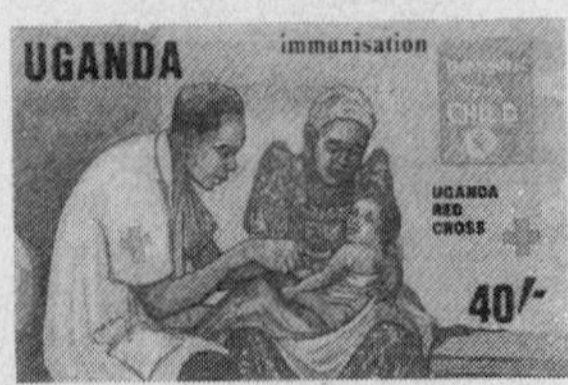

98 Red Cross Worker vaccinating Baby

1988. 125th Anniv of International Red Cross.

643 **98** 10 s. red, yellow & black 20 15
644 – 40 s. multicoloured .. 60 60
645 – 70 s. multicoloured .. 1·25 1·50
646 – 90 s. multicoloured .. 1·75 2·00

DESIGNS: 10 s. "AIDS" with test tube as "I"; 70 s. Distributing food to refugees; 90 s. Red Cross volunteers with accident victim.

1988. 500th Birth Anniv of Titian (artist). As T **238** of Antigua. Multicoloured.

648 10 s. "Portrait of a Lady" 10 10
649 20 s. "Portrait of a Man" 15 15
650 40 s. "Isabella d'Este" .. 30 30
651 50 s. "Vincenzo Mosti" .. 40 40
652 70 s. "Pope Paul III Farnese" 50 50
653 90 s. "Violante" .. 65 65
654 100 s. "Titian's Daughter Lavinia" 75 75
655 250 s. "Dr. Parma" .. 1·90 1·90

99 Giraffes, Kidepo Valley National Park

1988. National Parks of Uganda. Mult.

657 10 s. Type **99** 40 20
658 25 s. Zebras, Lake Mburo National Park 75 30
659 100 s. African buffalo, Murchison Falls National Park .. .. 1·75 2·00
660 250 s. Eastern white pelicans, Queen Elizabeth National Park 4·50 4·75

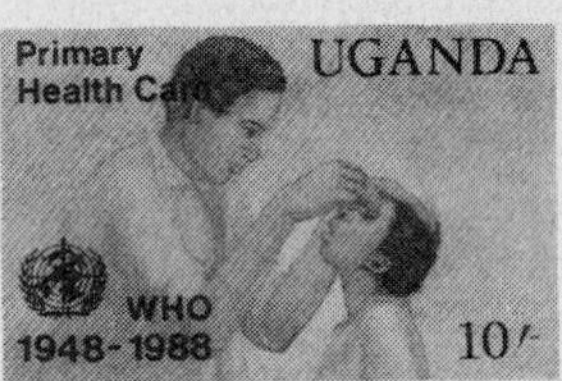

100 Doctor examining Child's Eyes

1988. 40th Anniv of W.H.O. Multicoloured.

662 10 s. Type **100** 15 10
663 25 s. Mental health therapist with patient .. 30 25
664 45 s. Surgeon performing operation 45 45
665 100 s. Dentist treating girl 90 1·25
666 200 s. Doctor examining child .. .. 1·75 2·25

1988. Christmas. "Santa's Helpers". As T **228** of Dominica showing Walt Disney cartoon characters. Multicoloured.

668 50 c. Father Christmas with list 60 60
669 50 c. Goofy carrying presents 60 60
670 50 c. Mickey Mouse on toy train 60 60
671 50 c. Reindeer at window 60 60
672 50 c. Donald Duck's nephew with building blocks 60 60
673 50 c. Donald Duck holding sack 60 60
674 50 c. Chip n'Dale on conveyor belt 60 60
675 50 c. Donald Duck's nephew operating conveyor belt 60 60

Nos. 668/75 were printed together, se-tenant, as a composite design.

1989. Olympic Gold Medal Winners, Seoul. Nos. 628/31 optd.

677 5 s. Type 95 (optd **110 M HURDLES R KINGDOM USA**) .. 10 10
678 25 s. High jumping (optd **HIGH JUMP G. AVDEENKO USSR**) 20 25
679 35 s. Javelin throwing (optd **JAVELIN T. KORJUS FINLAND**) 25 30
680 300 s. on 45 s. Long jumping (optd **LONG JUMP C. LEWIS USA**) .. .. .. 2·25 2·40

102 Goalkeeper with Ball

1989. World Cup Football Championship, Italy (1990) (1st issue). Multicoloured.

682 10 s. Type **102** 20 15
683 25 s. Player kicking ball (horiz) 40 25
684 75 s. Heading ball towards net (horiz) 70 60
685 200 s. Tackling .. .. 1·40 1·60

See also Nos. 849/52.

1989. Japanese Art. Paintings by Hokusai. As T **250** of Antigua. Multicoloured.

687 10 s. "Fuji and the Great Wave off Kanagawa" .. 20 20
688 15 s. "Fuji from Lake Suwa" 30 30
689 20 s. "Fuji from Kajikazawa" 30 30
690 60 s. "Fuji from Shichirigahama" .. 70 70
691 90 s. "Fuji from Ejiri in Sunshu" 90 90
692 120 s. "Fuji above Lightning" .. .. 1·00 1·00
693 200 s. "Fuji from Lower Meguro in Edo" .. 1·75 1·75
694 250 s. "Fuji from Edo" .. 1·90 1·90

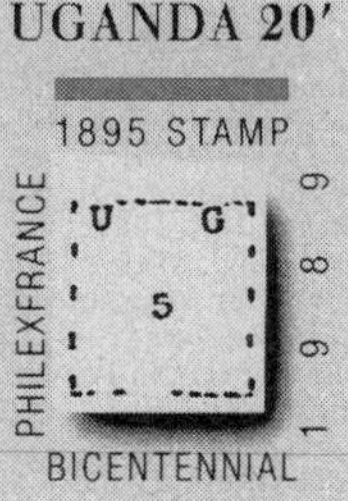

103 1895 5 Cowries Stamp

1989. "Philexfrance 89" International Stamp Exhibition, Paris.

696 **103** 20 s. black, red & brn 25 25
697 – 70 s. black, green & bl 70 70
698 – 100 s. black, vio & pink 90 90
699 – 250 s. blk, yell & lt yell 1·60 1·60

DESIGNS: 70 s. 1895 10 on 50 cowries stamp; 100 s. 1896 25 cowries stamp; 250 s. 1896 1 rupee stamp.

104 Scout advising on Immunization

1989. 2nd All African Scout Jamboree, Uganda, and 75th Anniv of Ugandan Scout Movement. Multicoloured.

701 10 s. Type **104** 15 15
702 70 s. Poultry keeping .. 60 60
703 90 s. Scout on crutches leading family to immunization centre .. 80 80
704 100 s. Scouts making bricks 90 90

105 "Suillus granulatus"

1989. Fungi. Multicoloured.

706 10 s. Type **105** 20 20
707 15 s. "Omphalotus olearius" 30 30
708 45 s. "Oudemansiella radicata" 70 70
709 50 s. "Clitocybe nebularis" 75 75
710 60 s. "Macrolepiota rhacodes" 80 80
711 75 s. "Lepista nuda" .. 85 85
712 150 s. "Suillus luteus" .. 1·50 1·50
713 200 s. "Agaricus campestris" .. .. 1·75 1·75

106 Saddle-bill Stork

1989. Wildlife at Waterhole. Multicoloured.

715 30 s. Type **106** 35 35
716 30 s. Eastern white pelican 35 35
717 30 s. Marabou stork .. 35 35
718 30 s. Egyptian vulture .. 35 35
719 30 s. Bateleur 35 35
720 30 s. African elephant .. 35 35
721 30 s. Giraffe 35 35
722 30 s. Goliath heron .. 35 35
723 30 s. Black rhinoceros .. 35 35
724 30 s. Common zebra and oribi 35 35
725 30 s. African fish eagle .. 35 35
726 30 s. Hippopotamus .. 35 35
727 30 s. Black-backed jackal and Eastern white pelican 35 35
728 30 s. African buffalo .. 35 35
729 30 s. Olive baboon .. 35 35
730 30 s. Bohar reedbuck .. 35 35
731 30 s. Lesser flamingo and serval 35 35
732 30 s. Whale-headed stork ("Shoebill stork") .. 35 35
733 30 s. South African crowned crane 35 35
734 30 s. Impala 35 35

Nos. 715/34 were printed together, se-tenant, forming a composite design showing wildlife at a waterhole.

107 Rocket on Launch Pad

1989. 20th Anniv of First Manned Landing on Moon. Multicoloured.

736 10 s. Type **107** 20 20
737 20 s. Lunar module "Eagle" on Moon .. 30 30
738 30 s. "Apollo 11" command module 40 40
739 50 s. "Eagle" landing on Moon 55 55
740 70 s. Astronaut Aldrin on Moon 75 75
741 250 s. Neil Armstrong alighting from "Eagle" (vert) .. .. .. 2·00 2·00
742 300 s. "Eagle" over Moon 2·00 2·00
743 350 s. Astronaut Aldrin on Moon (vert) .. .. 2·25 2·25

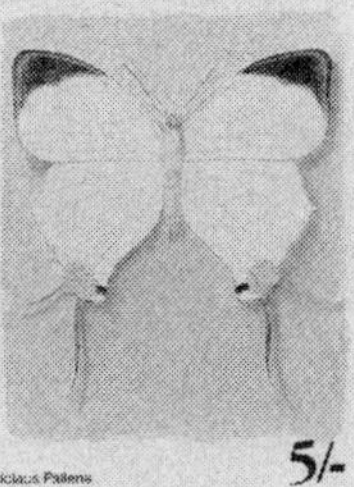

108 "Iolaus pallene"

1989. Butterflies. T **108** and similar vert designs showing "UGANDA" in black. Multicoloured.

745 5 s. Type **108** 15 15
746 10 s. "Hewitsonia boisduvali" 20 20
747 20 s. "Euxanthe wakefieldi" 30 20
748 30 s. "Papilio echerioides" 35 25
749 40 s. "Acraea semivitrea" 40 30
750 50 s. "Colotis antevippe" 40 30
751 70 s. "Acraea perenna" .. 45 40
752 90 s. "Charaxes cynthia" 50 40
753 100 s. "Euphaedra neophron" 50 40
754 150 s. "Cymothoe beckeri" 75 75
755 200 s. "Vanessula milca" 90 90
756 400 s. "Mimacraea marshalli" .. .. 1·40 1·40
757 500 s. "Axiocerses amanga" .. .. 1·75 1·75
758 1000 s. "Precis hierta" .. 1·75 2·00

For these, and similar designs showing "UGANDA" in blue see Nos. 864/80.

109 John Hanning Speke and Map of Lake Victoria

1989. Exploration of Africa. Multicoloured.

760 10 s. Type **109** 20 20
761 25 s. Sir Richard Burton and map of Lake Tanganyika 30 30
762 40 s. Richard Lander and Bakota bronze 40 40
763 90 s. Rene Caillie and mosque, Timbuktu .. 65 65
764 125 s. Sir Samuel Baker and Dorcas gazelle .. 80 80
765 150 s. Pharaoh Necho and ancient Phoenician merchant ship .. .. 1·00 1·00
766 250 s. Vasco da Gama and 15th-century caravel .. 1·25 1·25
767 300 s. Sir Henry Morton Stanley and "Lady Alice" (sectional boat) 1·50 1·50

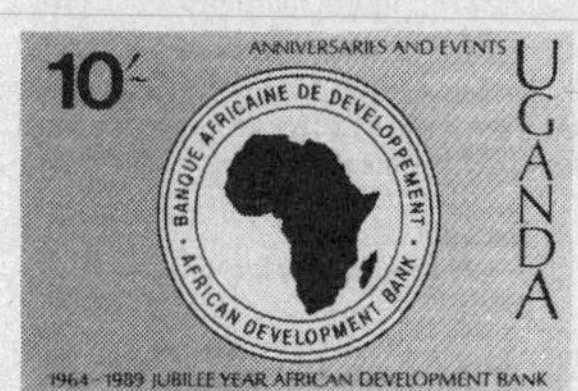

110 Logo (25th anniv of African Development Bank)

1989. Anniversaries. Multicoloured.

769 10 s. Type **110** 15 15
770 20 s. Arrows and dish aerials (World Telecommunication Day) .. 20 20
771 75 s. Nehru and Gandhi (birth cent of Nehru) .. 75 75
772 90 s. Pan Am "Dixie Clipper" flying boat (50th anniv of first scheduled trans-Atlantic airmail flight) 80 80
773 100 s. George Stephenson and "Locomotion", 1825 (175th anniv of first practical steam locomotive) 85 85
774 150 s. "Concorde" cockpit (20th anniv of first test flight) .. .. 1·50 1·50
775 250 s. "Wapen von Hamburg" and "Leopoldus Primus" (galleons) (800th anniv of Port of Hamburg) .. .. 1·75 1·75
776 300 s. "Concorde" and cockpit interior (20th anniv of first test flight) 2·00 2·00

MINIMUM PRICE

The minimum price quoted is 10p which represents a handling charge rather than a basis for valuing common stamps. For further notes about prices see introductory pages.

111 "Aerangis kotschyana"

1989. Orchids. Multicoloured.

778 10 s. Type **111** 20 20
779 15 s. "Angraecum infundibulare" 25 25
780 45 s. "Cyrtorchis chailluana" 55 55
781 50 s. "Aerangis rhodosticta" 60 60
782 100 s. "Eulophia speciosa" 90 90
783 200 s. "Calanthe sylvatica" 1·40 1·40
784 250 s. "Vanilla imperialis" 1·50 1·50
785 350 s. "Polystachya vulcanica" .. .. 1·75 1·75

1989. Christmas. Paintings by Fra Angelico. As T **259** of Antigua. Multicoloured.

787 10 s. "Madonna and Child" 10 10
788 20 s. "Adoration of the Magi" 15 15
789 40 s. "Virgin and Child enthroned with Saints" 30 30
790 75 s. "The Annunciation" 55 55
791 100 s. "Virgin and Child" (detail, "St. Peter Martyr" triptych) .. 70 70
792 150 s. "Virgin and Child enthroned with Saints" (different) 85 85
793 250 s. "Virgin and Child enthroned" .. .. 1·25 1·25
794 350 s. "Virgin and Child" (from Annalena altarpiece) .. .. .. 1·50 1·50

112 "Thevetia peruviana"

1990. "Expo '90" International Garden and Greenery Exhibition, Osaka (1st issue). Flowering Trees. Multicoloured.

796 10 s. Type **112** 10 10
797 20 s. "Acanthus eminens" 10 10
798 90 s. "Gnidia glauca" .. 10 15
799 150 s. "Oncoba spinosa" .. 15 20
800 175 s. "Hibiscus rosasinensis" 20 25
801 400 s. "Jacaranda mimosifolia" 45 50
802 500 s. "Erythrina abyssinica" 60 65
803 700 s. "Bauhinia purpurea" 80 85

See also Nos. 820/7.

1990. 50th Anniv of Second World War. As T **98** of Grenada Grenadines. Multicoloured.

805 5 s. Allied penetration of German West Wall, 1944 10 10
806 10 s. Flags of the Allies, VE Day, 1945 .. .. 10 10
807 20 s. Capture of Okinawa, 1945 .. .. .. 10 10
808 75 s. Appointment of Gen. De Gaulle to command all Free French forces, 1944 .. .. .. 10 15
809 100 s. Invasion of Saipan, 1944 .. .. .. 10 15
810 150 s. Airborne landing, Operation Market Garden, 1944 .. .. 15 20
811 200 s. MacArthur's return to Philippines, 1944 .. 25 30

812 300 s. Japanese attack on U.S. carrier, Coral Sea, 1942 .. .. .. 35 40
813 350 s. First Battle of El Alamein, 1942 .. .. 40 45
814 500 s. Naval Battle of Guadalcanal, 1942 .. 60 65

1990. 90th Birthday of Queen Elizabeth the Queen Mother. As T **99** of Grenada Grenadines.

816 250 s. black, mauve & blue 30 35
817 250 s. black, mauve & blue 30 35
818 250 s. black, mauve & blue 30 35

DESIGNS: No. 816, Queen Elizabeth with corgi; 817, Queen Elizabeth wearing feathered hat; 818 Queen Elizabeth at wartime inspection.

1990. "EXPO 90" International Garden and Greenery Exhibition, Osaka (2nd issue). Nos. 778/85 optd **EXPO '90** and logo.

820 10 s. Type **111** 10 10
821 15 s. "Angraecum infundibulare" 10 10
822 45 s. "Cyrtorchis chailluana" 10 10
823 50 s. "Aerangis rhodosticta" 10 10
824 100 s. "Eulophia speciosa" 10 15
825 200 s. "Calanthe sylvatica" 25 30
826 250 s. "Vanilla imperialis" 30 35
827 350 s. "Polystachya vulcanica" 40 45

114 P.A.P.U. Emblem

1990. 10th Anniv of Pan-African Postal Union.

829 **114** 80 s. multicoloured .. 10 15

115 Unissued G. B. "V R" Penny Black

1990. 150th Anniv of the Penny Black.

831 **115** 25 s. multicoloured .. 10 10
832 – 50 s. red, black & green 10 10
833 – 100 s. multicoloured .. 10 15
834 – 150 s. multicoloured .. 15 20
835 – 200 s. multicoloured .. 25 30
836 – 300 s. multicoloured .. 35 40
837 – 500 s. multicoloured .. 60 65
838 – 600 s. multicoloured .. 70 75

DESIGNS: 50 s. Canada 1858–59 3d. Beaver; 100 s. Baden 1851 9 k. on green error; 150 s. Basel 1845 2½ r. Dove; 200 s. U.S.A. 1918 24 c. Inverted "Jenny" error; 300 s. Western Australia 1854 1d. Black Swan; 500 s. Uganda 1895 20 c. "narrow" typewritten stamp; 600 s. G. B. Twopenny blue.

116 African Jacana

1990. Wild Birds of Uganda. Multicoloured.

840 10 s. Type **116** 10 10
841 15 s. Southern ground hornbill 10 10
842 45 s. Kori bustard (vert) .. 10 10
843 50 s. Secretary bird .. 10 10
844 100 s. Egyptian geese .. 10 15
845 300 s. Goliath heron (vert) 35 40
846 500 s. Ostrich with chicks (vert) 60 65
847 650 s. Saddle-bill stork (vert) 75 80

117 Roger Milla of Cameroon

1990. World Cup Football Championship, Italy (2nd issue). Multicoloured.

849 50 s. Type **117** 10 10
850 100 s. Ramzy of Egypt .. 10 15
851 250 s. David O'Leary of Ireland 30 35
852 600 s. Littbarsky of West Germany 70 75

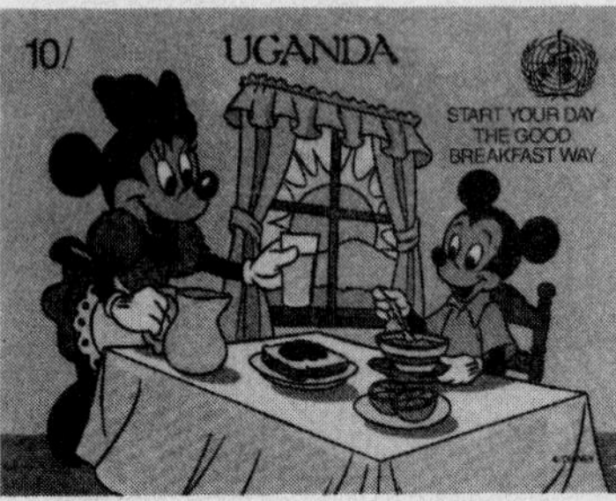

118 Mickey and Minnie Mouse at Breakfast

1990. Health and Safety Campaign. Designs showing Walt Disney cartoon characters. Multicoloured.

854 10 s. Type **118** 10 10
855 20 s. Donald Duck's nephews doing kerb drill 10 10
856 50 s. Donald and Mickey stopping Big Pete smoking 10 10
857 90 s. Mickey stopping Donald choking .. 10 15
858 100 s. Mickey and Goofy using seat belts .. 10 15
859 250 s. Mickey and Minnie dancing 30 35
860 500 s. Donald Duck's fitness class .. 60 65
861 600 s. Mickey's nephews showing lights at night 70 75

1990. As Nos. 746/55 and new values, showing butterflies, as T **108** with "UGANDA" in blue. Multicoloured.

864 10 s. "Hewitsonia boisduvali" 10 10
865 20 s. "Euxanthe wakefieldi" 10 10
866 30 s. "Papilio echerioides" 10 10
867 40 s. "Acraea semivitrea" 10 10
868 50 s. "Colotis antevippe" 10 10
869 70 s. "Acraea perenna" .. 10 10
870 90 s. "Charaxes cynthia" 10 10
871 100 s. "Euphaedra neophron" 10 10
872 150 s. "Cymothoe beckeri" 15 20
873 200 s. "Vanessula milca" 25 30
874 400 s. "Mimacraea marshalli" .. 45 50
875 500 s. "Axiocerses amanga" 60 65
876 1000 s. "Precis hierta" .. 1·10 1·25
877 2000 s. "Precis hierta" .. 2·25 2·40
878 3000 s. "Euphaedra eusemoides" .. .. 3·25 3·50
879 4000 s. "Acraea natalica" 4·50 4·75
880 5000 s. "Euphaedra themis" .. .. 5·50 5·75

1990. Christmas. 350th Death Anniv of Rubens. As T **273** of Antigua, but inscr "CHRISTMAS 1990". Multicoloured.

881 10 s. "Baptism of Christ" (detail) (vert) .. 10 10
882 20 s. "St. Gregory the Great and other Saints" (detail) (vert) .. 10 10
883 100 s. "Saints Nereus, Domitilla and Achilleus" (detail) (vert) .. 10 15
884 150 s. "St. Gregory the Great and other Saints" (different detail) (vert) 15 20
885 300 s. "Saint Augustine" (detail) (vert) .. 35 40
886 400 s. "St. Gregory the Great and other Saints" (different detail) (vert) 45 50
887 500 s. "Baptism of Christ" (different detail) (vert) 60 65
888 600 s. "St. Gregory the Great and other Saints (different detail) (vert) 70 75

119 Census Emblem

1990. National Population and Housing Census.

890 **119** 20 s. multicoloured .. 10 10

120 Damselfly

1991. Fauna of Uganda's Wetlands. Mult.

892 70 s. Type **120** 10 10
893 70 s. Purple swamphen ("Gallinule") 10 10
894 70 s. Sitatunga 10 10
895 70 s. Western reef-heron ("Purple heron") .. 10 10
896 70 s. Bushpig 10 10
897 70 s. Vervet monkey .. 10 10
898 70 s. Long reed frog .. 10 10
899 70 s. Malachite kingfisher 10 10
900 70 s. Marsh mongoose .. 10 10
901 70 s. Painted reed frog .. 10 10
902 70 s. African jacana .. 10 10
903 70 s. Charaxes butterfly .. 10 10
904 70 s. Nile crocodile .. 10 10
905 70 s. Herald snake .. 10 10
906 70 s. Dragonfly 10 10
907 70 s. Lungfish 10 10

Nos. 892/907 were printed together, se-tenant, forming a composite design.

121 "Haplochromis limax"

1991. Fishes of Uganda. Multicoloured.

909 10 s. Type **121** 10 10
910 20 s. "Nothobranchius palmqvisti" 10 10
911 40 s. "Distichodus affinis" 10 10
912 90 s. "Haplochromis sauvagei" 10 15
913 100 s. "Aphyosemion calliurum" 10 15
914 350 s. "Haplochromis johnstoni" 40 45
915 600 s. "Haplochromis dichrourus" 70 75
916 800 s. "Hemichromis bimaculatus" .. .. 95 1·00

1991. Olympic Games, Barcelona (1992). As T **268** of Antigua. Multicoloured.

918 20 s. Women's 100 metres hurdles 10 10
919 40 s. Long jump 10 10
920 125 s. Table tennis .. 15 20
921 250 s. Football .. 30 35
922 500 s. Men's 800 metres .. 60 65

122 Class "10" Steam Locomotive, Zimbabwe

1991. African Railway Locomotives. Mult.

924 10 s. Type **122** 10 10
925 20 s. Class "12" steam locomotive, Zimbabwe 10 10
926 80 s. Class "Tribal" steam locomotive, Tazara Railway 10 10
927 200 s. 4-6-0 type steam locomotive, Egypt .. 25 30
928 300 s. Mikado type steam locomotive, Sudan .. 35 40
929 400 s. Class "Mountain" Garrat steam locomotive, Uganda .. 45 50
930 500 s. Mallet type steam locomotive, Uganda .. 60 65
931 1000 s. 5 F 1 electric locomotive, South Africa 1·10 1·25

123 Lord Baden-Powell and Scout Emblem

1991. World Scout Jamboree, Mount Sorak, Korea.

933 **123** 20 s. multicoloured .. 10 10
934 – 80 s. multicoloured .. 10 15
935 – 100 s. multicoloured .. 10 15
936 – 150 s. black and green 15 20
937 – 300 s. multicoloured .. 35 40
938 – 400 s. multicoloured .. 45 50
939 – 500 s. multicoloured .. 60 65
940 – 1000 s. multicoloured 1·10 1·25

DESIGNS: 80 s. Scouts and Uganda 1982 100 s. anniversary stamp; 100 s. Scout encampment, New York World's Fair, 1939; 150 s. Cover and illustration from "Scouting for Boys"; 300 s. Cooking on campfire; 400 s. Aldrin and Armstrong on Moon; 500 s. Scout salutes; 1000 s. Statue to the Unkown Scout, Gillwell Park.

1991. "Phila Nippon '91" International Stamp Exhibition, Tokyo. As T **204** of Lesotho showing Walt Disney cartoon characters and Japanese traditions. Mult.

942 10 s. Uncle Scrooge celebrating Ga-No-Iwai 10 10
943 20 s. Mickey Mouse removing shoes .. 10 10
944 70 s. Goofy leading carthorse 10 10
945 80 s. Daisy Duck and Minnie Mouse exchanging gifts .. 10 15
946 300 s. Minnie kneeling at doorway 35 40
947 400 s. Donald Duck and Mickey taking a hot volcanic sand bath 45 50
948 500 s. Clarabella Cow burning incense .. 60 65
949 1000 s. Mickey and Minnie writing New Year cards 1·10 1·25

1991. Death Cent (1990) of Vincent van Gogh (artist). As T **195** of British Virgin Islands. Multicoloured.

951 10 s. "Snowy Landscape with Arles" 10 10
952 20 s. "Peasant Woman binding Sheaves" (vert) 10 10
953 60 s. "The Drinkers" .. 10 10
954 80 s. "View of Auvers" .. 10 10
955 200 s. "Mourning Man" (vert) 25 30
956 400 s. "Still Life: Vase with Roses" 45 50
957 800 s. "The Raising of Lazarus" .. .. 95 1·00
958 1000 s. "The Good Samaritan" (vert) .. 1·10 1·25

1991. 65th Birthday of Queen Elizabeth II. As T **280** of Antigua. Multicoloured.

960 70 s. Queen and Prince Charles after polo match 10 10
961 90 s. Queen at Balmoral, 1976 .. .. .. 10 10
962 500 s. Queen with Princess Margaret, August 1980 60 65
963 600 s. Queen and Queen Mother leaving St. George's Chapel, Windsor 70 75

1991. 10th Wedding Anniv of Prince and Princess of Wales. As T **280** of Antigua. Multicoloured.

965 20 s. Prince and Princess of Wales in July 1986 .. 10 10
966 100 s. Separate photographs of Prince, Princess and sons .. 10 10

967 200 s. Prince Henry and Prince William .. 25 30
968 1000 s. Separate photographs of Prince and Princess in 1988 .. 1·10 1·25

124 General Charles de Gaulle

1991. Birth Centenary (1990) of Charles de Gaulle (French statesman). Multicoloured.
970 20 s. Type **124** 10 10
971 70 s. Liberation of Paris, 1944 .. .. .. 10 10
972 90 s. De Gaulle with King George VI, 1940 .. 10 10
973 100 s. Reviewing free French troops, 1940 (horiz) 10 10
974 200 s. Broadcasting to France, 1940 (horiz) .. 25 30
975 500 s. De Gaulle in Normandy, 1944 (horiz) 60 65
976 600 s. De Gaulle at Albert Hall, 1940 (horiz) .. 70 75
977 1000 s. Inauguration as President, 1959 .. 1·10 1·25

125 "Volvariella bingensis"

1991. Fungi. Multicoloured.
979 20 s. Type **125** 10 10
980 70 s. "Agrocybe broadwayi" 10 10
981 90 s. "Camarophyllus olidus" 10 10
982 140 s. "Marasmius arborescens" 15 20
983 180 s. "Marasmiellus subcinereus" 25 30
984 200 s. "Agaricus campestris" 25 30
985 500 s. "Chlorophyllum molybdites" 60 65
986 1000 s. "Agaricus bingensis" .. .. 1·10 1·25

1991. Endangered Species (3rd series). As Nos. 406/9, but with changed face values, and additional horiz designs as T **61**. Mult.
988 100 s. Elephants in "Elephants' Graveyard" 10 10
989 140 s. Type **61** 15 20
990 200 s. Elephants at waterhole 25 30
991 600 s. Elephants having dust bath 70 75

126 "Anigozanthos manglesii"

1991. Botanical Gardens of the World. Mult.
993/1032 90 s. × 20, 100 s. × 20
Set of 40 .. .. 3·50 3·50

Nos. 993/1032 were issued together, se-tenant, as two sheetlets of 20 containing designs as Type **126**. The 90 s. values show "Anigozanthos manglesii", "Banksia grandis", "Clianthus formosus", "Gossypium sturtianum", "Callistemon lanceolatus", "Saintpaulia ionantha", "Calodendrum capense", "Aloe ferox × arborescens", "Bolusanthus speciousus", "Lithops schwantesii", "Protea repens", "Plumbago capensis", "Clerodendrum thomsoniae", "Thunbergia alata", "Schotia latifolia", "Epacris impressa", "Acacia pycnantha", "Telopea speciosissima", "Wahlenbergia gloriosa", "Eucalyptus globulus" from Melbourne, and the 100 s. "Cypripedium calceolus", "Rhododendron thomsonii", "Ginkgo biloba", "Magnolia campbellii", "Wisteria sinensis", "Clerodendrum ugandense", "Eulophia horsfallii", "Aerangis rhodosticta", "Abelmoschus moschatus", "Gloriosa superba", "Carissa edulis", "Ochna kirkii", "Canarina abyssinica", "Nymphaea caerulea", "Ceropegia succulenta", "Strelitzia reginae", "Strongylodon macrobotrys", "Victoria amazonica", "Orchis militaris" and "Sophora microphylla" from Kew.

1991. Nos. 573, 597 and 614 surch **20/-**.
1034 20 s. on 25 s. Airship "Norge" and polar bear (first transpolar flight) 1926
1035 20 s. on 25 s. Einstein and deep space (Theory of Relativity)
1035a 20 s. on 25 s. Tank locomotive No. 126

1991. Christmas. Paintings by Piero della Francesca. As T **291** of Antigua. Mult.
1036 20 s. "Madonna with Child and Angels" .. 10 10
1037 50 s. "The Baptism of Christ" 10 10
1038 80 s. "Polyptych of Mercy" 10 10
1039 100 s. "Polyptych of Mercy" (detail) .. 10 10
1040 200 s. "The Annunciation" from "The Legend of the True Cross" 25 30
1041 500 s. "Pregnant Madonna" 60 65
1042 1000 s. "The Annunciation" from "Polyptych of St. Anthony" .. 1·10 1·25
1043 1500 s. "The Nativity" .. 1·75 1·90

128 Boy Scout Monument, New York, and Ernest Thompson (first Chief Scout of U.S.A.)

1992. Anniversaries and Events. Mult.
1045 20 s. Type **128** 10 10
1046 50 s. Treehouse design and Daniel Beard (vert) 10 10
1047 400 s. Lilienthal's signature and "Flugzeug Nr. 8" .. 45 50
1048 500 s. Demonstrator demolishing Berlin Wall 60 65
1049 700 s. "The Magic Flute" 80 85

ANNIVERSARIES AND EVENTS: Nos. 1045/6, 50th death anniv of Lord Baden-Powell and World Scout Jamboree, Korea; No. 1047, Centenary of Otto Lilienthal's first gliding experiments; No. 1048, Bicentenary of Brandenburg Gate, Berlin; No. 1049, Death bicentenary of Mozart.

129 U.S.S. "Vestal" (transpsort) under Attack

1992. 50th Anniv of Japanese Attack on Pearl Harbor. Multicolouresd.
1051 200 s. Type **129** 25 30
1052 200 s. Japanese Zero .. 25 30
1053 200 s. U.S.S. "Arizona" (battleship) on fire .. 25 30
1054 200 s. U.S.S. "Nevada" (battleship) passing burning ships 25 30
1055 200 s. "Val" bomber attacking 25 30
1056 200 s. Dauntless bombers attacking "Hiryu" (carrier) at Midway .. 25 30
1057 200 s. Japanese aircraft attacking Midway Island 25 30
1058 200 s. U.S. Marine Buffalo (fighter) defending Midway 25 30
1059 200 s. American Wildcat aircraft and carrier .. 25 30
1060 200 s. U.S.S. "Yorktown" (carrier) torpedoed .. 25 30

130 Three Modern Hot Air Balloons

1992. 120th Anniv (1990) of Paris Balloon Post. Multicoloured.
1061 200 s. Type **130** 25 30
1062 200 s. Sport balloons and top of "Double Eagle II" 25 30
1063 200 s. Pro Juventute balloon and top of Branson's "Virgin" .. 25 30
1064 200 s. Blanchard's balloon 25 30
1065 200 s. Nadar's "Le Geant" and centre of "Double Eagle II" 25 30
1066 200 s. Branson's "Virgin" 25 30
1067 200 s. Montgolfier balloon 25 30
1068 200 s. "Double Eagle II" basket and Paris balloon of 1870 .. 25 30
1069 200 s. Early captive balloon 25 30

Nos. 1061/9 were printed together, se-tenant, forming a composite design.

1992. Mickey's World Tour. As T **264** of Maldive Islands showing Walt Disney cartoon charaters in different countries. Multicoloured.
1070 20 s. Mickey Mouse and Goofy on African safari (horiz) 10 10
1071 50 s. Mickey charming Pluto's tail, India (horiz) 10 10
1072 80 s. Minnie Mouse, Donald and Daisy Duck as Caribbean calypso band (horiz) 10 10
1073 200 s. Goofy pulling Donald and Daisy in rickshaw, China (horiz) 25 30
1074 500 s. Mickey and Minnie on camel, Egypt (horiz) 60 65
1075 800 s. Donald and Pete sumo wrestling, Japan (horiz) .. .. 95 1·00
1076 1000 s. Goofy bullfighting, Spain (horiz) .. .. 1·10 1·25
1077 1500 s. Mickey playing football, Italy (horiz) .. 1·75 1·90

1992. 40th Anniv of Queen Elizabeth II's Accession. As T **280** of Antigua. Mult.
1079 100 s. Lake Victoria .. 10 10
1080 200 s. Lake and mountains 25 30
1081 500 s. Lakeside fields .. 60 65
1082 1000 s. River Nile .. 1·10 1·25

1992. Prehistoric Animals. As T **290** of Antigua but horiz. Multicoloured.
1084 50 s. Kentrosaurus .. 10 10
1085 200 s. Iguanodon .. 25 30
1086 250 s. Hypsilophodon .. 30 35
1087 300 s. Brachiosaurus .. 35 40
1088 400 s. Peloneustes .. 45 50
1089 500 s. Pteranodon .. 60 65
1090 800 s. Tetralophodon .. 95 1·00
1091 1000 s. Megalosaurus .. 1·10 1·25

131 "The Entry into Jerusalem" (detail) (Giotto)

1992. Easter. Religious Paintings. Mult.
1093 50 s. Type **131** 10 10
1094 100 s. "Pilate and the Watch" (Psalter of Robert de Lisle) .. 10 10
1095 200 s. "The Kiss of Judas" (detail) (Giotto) 25 30
1096 250 s. "Christ washing the Feet of the Disciples" (Vita Christi manuscript) 30 35
1097 300 s. "Christ Seized in the Garden" (Melissende Psalter) .. 35 40
1098 500 s. "Doubting Thomas" (Vita Christi manuscript) 60 65
1099 1000 s. "The Marys at the Tomb" (detail) (anon) 1·10 1·25
1100 2000 s. "The Ascension" (Florentine manuscript) 2·25 2·40

132 Adungu

1992. Traditional Musical Instruments. Mult.
1102 50 s. Type **132** 10 10
1103 100 s. Endingidi 10 10
1104 200 s. Akogo 25 30
1105 250 s. Nanga 30 35
1106 300 s. Engoma 35 40
1107 400 s. Amakondere .. 45 50
1108 500 s. Akakyenkye .. 60 65
1109 1000 s. Ennanga .. .. 1·10 1·25

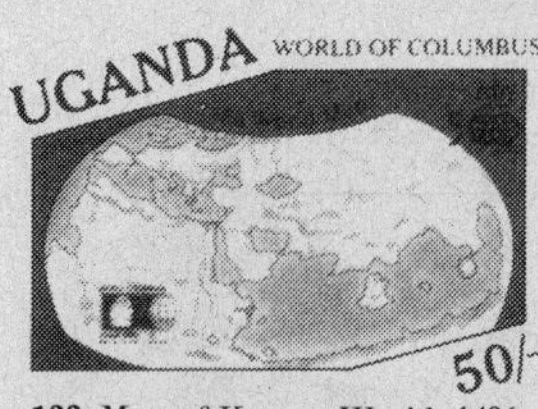

133 Map of Known World, 1486

1992. 500th Anniv of Discovery of America by Columbus and "World Columbian Stamp Expo'92" Exhibition, Chicago. Mult.
1110 50 s. Type **133** 10 10
1111 100 s. Map of Africa, 1508 10 10
1112 150 s. Map of West Indies, 1500 .. .. 15 20
1113 200 s. "Nina" and astrolabe 25 30
1114 600 s. "Pinta" and quadrant 70 75
1115 800 s. Sand glass .. 95 1·00
1116 900 s. 15th-century compass .. .. 1·00 1·10
1117 2000 s. Map of World, 1492 2·25 2·40

1992. Hummel Figurines. As T **256** of Maldive Islands. Multicoloured.
1119 50 s. Girl with washing 10 10
1120 200 s. Girl scrubbing floor 25 30
1121 250 s. Girl sweeping floor 30 35
1122 300 s. Girl with baby 35 40
1123 600 s. Boy mountaineer .. 70 75
1124 900 s. Girl knitting .. 1·00 1·10
1125 1000 s. Boy on stool .. 1·10 1·25
1126 1500 s. Boy with telescope 1·75 1·90

134 Spotted Hyena

1992. Wildlife. Multicoloured.

1128 50 s. Type **134** 10 10
1129 100 s. Impala 10 10
1130 200 s. Giant forest hog .. 25 30
1131 250 s. Pangolin 30 35
1132 300 s. Golden monkey .. 35 40
1133 800 s. Serval .. .. 95 1·00
1134 1000 s. Small-spotted genet ("Bush genet") 1·10 1·25
1135 3000 s. Waterbuck .. 3·25 3·50

1992. Olympic Games, Barcelona. As T **216** Lesotho. Multicoloured.

1137 50 s. Men's javelin .. 10 10
1138 100 s. Men's high jump (horiz) 10 10
1139 200 s. Fencing (pentathlon) 25 30
1140 250 s. Men's volleyball .. 30 35
1141 300 s. Women's platform diving 35 40
1142 500 s. Men's team cycling 60 65
1143 1000 s. Women's tennis .. 1·10 1·25
1144 2000 s. Boxing (horiz) .. 2·25 2·40

135 Red-headed Falcon

1992. Birds. Multicoloured.

1146 20 s. Type **135** 10 10
1147 30 s. Yellow-billed hornbill 10 10
1148 50 s. Purple heron .. 10 10
1149 100 s. Regal sunbird .. 10 10
1150 150 s. White-browed robin chat 15 20
1151 200 s. Shining-blue kingfisher 25 30
1152 250 s. Great blue turaco 30 35
1153 300 s. African emerald cuckoo 35 40
1154 500 s. Abyssinian roller .. 60 65
1155 800 s. South African crowned crane .. 95 1·00
1156 1000 s. Doherty's bush shrike .. .. 1·10 1·25
1157 2000 s. Splendid glossy starling .. .. 2·25 2·40
1158 3000 s. Little bee eater .. 3·25 3·50
1159 4000 s. Red-faced lovebird ("Red-headed lovebird") .. .. 4·50 4·75

136 Goofy in "Hawaiian Holiday", 1937

1992. 60th Anniv of Goofy. Multicoloured.

1161 50 s. Type **136** 10 10
1162 100 s. Riding penny-farthing cycle, 1941 .. 10 10
1163 200 s. Goofy and Mickey Mouse as firemen, 1935 25 30
1164 250 s. Skiing, 1941 (horiz) 30 35
1165 300 s. One man band, 1937 (horiz) 35 40
1166 1000 s. Asleep against boat, 1938 (hroiz) .. 1·10 1·25
1167 1500 s. Ancient Olympic champion, 1942 .. 1·75 2·00
1168 2000 s. Pole vaulting, 1942 2·25 2·40

137 "The Annunciation"

1992. Christmas. Religious Paintings by Francisco Zurbaran. Multicoloured.

1170 50 s. Type **137** 10 10
1171 200 s. "The Annunciation" (different) .. 25 30
1172 250 s. "The Virgin of the Immaculate Conception" 30 35
1173 300 s. "The Virgin of the Immaculate Conception" (detail) .. 35 40
1174 800 s. "Holy Family with Saints Anne, Joachim and John the Baptist" 95 1·00
1175 900 s. "Holy Family with Saints Anne, Joachim and John the Baptist" (detail) .. .. 1·00 1·10
1176 1000 s. "Adoration of the Magi" .. .. .. 1·10 1·25
1177 2000 s. "Adoration of the Magi" (detail) .. 2·25 2·40

138 Man cleaning Granary

1992 Anniversaries and Events. Mult.

1179 50 s. Type **138** 10 10
1180 200 s. Mother breast feeding 25 30
1181 250 s. Mother feeding baby 30 35
1182 300 s. Boy collecting water from pump .. 35 40
1183 300 s. "Voyager 2" passing Jupiter .. 35 40
1184 800 s. Mother and baby .. 95 1·00
1185 800 s. Impala .. .. 95 1·00
1186 1000 s. Mountain zebra .. 1·10 1·25
1187 1000 s. Count Ferdinand von Zeppelin and airship .. .. 1·10 1·25
1188 2000 s. "Voyager 2" passing Neptune .. 2·25 2·40
1189 3000 s. Count Ferdinand von Zeppelin and airship (different) .. 3·25 3·50

ANNIVERSARIES AND EVENTS: Nos. 1179/82, 1184, United Nations World Health Organization Projects; Nos. 1183, 1188, International Space Year; Nos. 1185/6, Earth Summit '92, Rio; Nos. 1187, 1189, 75th death anniv of Count Ferdinand von Zeppelin (airship pioneer).

139 Hands releasing Dove with Lubaga and Kampala Catholic Cathedrals

1993. Visit of Pope John Paul II. Mutl.

1191 50 s. Type **139** 10 10
1192 200 s. Pope and Kampala Cathedral .. 25 30
1193 250 s. Pope and Catholic worshipper .. 30 35
1194 300 s. Ugandan bishops and Pope .. 35 40
1195 800 s. Pope John Paul II waving .. .. 95 1·00
1196 900 s. Pope and Kampala Cathedral (different) .. 1·00 1·10
1197 1000 s. Pope, national flag and Kampala Cathedral 1·10 1·25
1198 2000 s. Pope and national flag .. .. .. 2·25 2·40

1993. Bicentenary of the Louvre, Paris. Paintings by Rembrandt. As T **305** of Antigua. Multicoloured.

1200 500 s. "Self Portrait at Easel" 60 65
1201 500 s. "Birds of Paradise" 60 65
1202 500 s. "The Carcass of Beef" 60 65
1203 500 s. "The Supper at Emmaus" 60 65
1204 500 s. "Hendrickje Stoffels" 60 65
1205 500 s. "The Artist's Son, Titus" 60 65
1206 500 s. "The Holy Family" (left detail) 60 65
1207 500 s. "The Holy Family" (right detail) 60 65

140 Afghan Hound

1993. Dogs of the World. Multicoloured.

1209 50 s. Type **140** 10 10
1210 100 s. Newfoundland .. 10 10
1211 200 s. Siberian huskies .. 25 30
1212 250 s. Briard 30 35
1213 300 s. Saluki 35 40
1214 800 s. Labrador guide-dog (vert) .. .. 95 1·00
1215 1000 s. Greyhound .. 1·10 1·25
1216 1500 s. Pointer .. 1·75 1·90

1993. 40th Anniv of Coronation. As T **307** of Antigua. Multicoloured.

1218 50 s. Queen Elizabeth II at Coronation (photograph by Cecil Beaton) 10 10
1219 200 s. Orb and Sceptre .. 25 30
1220 500 s. Queen Elizabeth during Coronation .. 60 65
1221 1500 s. Queen Elizabeth II and Princess Margaret 1·75 1·90

POSTAGE DUE STAMPS

The Postage Due stamps of Kenya, Uganda and Tanganyika were used in Uganda until 2nd January, 1967.

D 1.

D 3. Lion.

1967.

D 7 D 1. 5 c. red .. .. 15 1·75
D 8 10 c. green .. .. 15 1·75
D 9 20 c. blue .. .. 25 2·25
D 10 30 c. brown .. .. 35 2·75
D 11 40 c. purple .. .. 55 3·50
D 17 1 s. orange .. .. 2·50 8·50

These stamps exist in limited quantities overprinted **UGANDA LIBERATED 1979.**

1979. Liberation. As Nos. D12/17 optd. **LIBERATED 1979**

D 18. D 1. 5 c. red 20 35
D 19. 10 c. green 20 35
D 20. 20 c. blue 25 35
D 21. 30 c. brown 25 50
D 22. 40 c. purple 30 50
D 23. 1 s. orange 30 50

1985. Animals.

D 24. D 3. 5 s. black and turquoise 10 10
D 25. – 10 s. black and lilac 15 15
D 26. – 20 s. black and orange 25 25
D 27. – 40 s. black and lilac 40 45
D 28. – 50 s. black and blue 45 50
D 29. – 100 s. black and mauve .. .. 85 1·00

DESIGNS: 10 s. African Buffalo. 20 s. Kob. 40 s. African Elephant. 50 s. Common Zebra. 100 s. Black Rhinoceros.

VANUATU

The New Hebrides became the Republic of Vanuatu on 30 July 1980.

1980. 100 centimes = 1 franc (Vanuatu).
1981. Vatus.

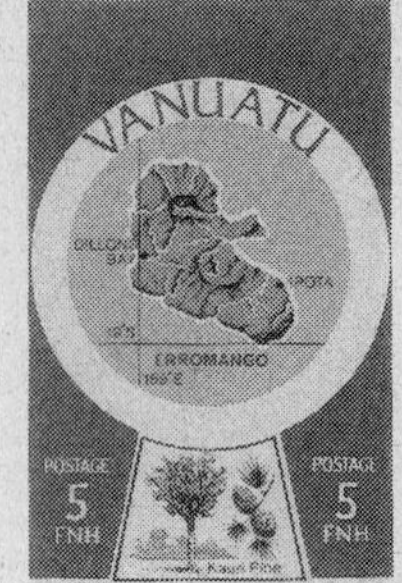

99. Island of Erromango and Kauri Pine.

1980. As Nos. 242/54 of New Hebrides but inscr. "VANUATU" and without royal and republican cyphers.

(a) Inscr. in English.

287E. 5 f. Type **99** 15 15
288E. 10 f. Territory map and copra making 15 15
289E. 15 f. Espiritu Santo and cattle 25 25
290E. 20 f. Efate and Vila P.O. 30 30
291E. 25 f. Malakula and headdresses 35 35
292E. 30 f. Aoba, Maewo and pigs tusks 45 45
293E. 35 f. Pentecost and land diver 50 50
294E. 40 f. Tanna and John Frum cross 60 60
295E. 50 f. Shepherd Is. and outrigger canoe .. 65 70
296E. 70 f. Banks Is. and custom dancers .. 1·00 1·00
297E. 100 f. Ambrym and idols 1·25 80
298E. 200 f. Aneityum and baskets .. .. 1·40 1·40
299E. 500 f. Torres Is. and archer fisherman .. 2·50 3·00

(b) Inscr. in French.

287F. Type **99** 35 15
288F. 10 f. Territory map and copra making 40 15
289F. 15 f. Espiritu Santo and cattle 45 25
290F. 20 f. Efate and Vila P.O. 50 30
291F. 25 f. Malakula and headdresses 55 35
292F. 30 f. Aoba, Maewo and pigs tusks 55 45
293F. 35 f. Pentecost and land diver 60 50
294F. 40 f. Tanna and John Frum cross 90 60
295F. 50 f. Shepherd Is. and outrigger canoe .. 1·00 70
296F. 70 f. Banks Is. and custom dancers .. 1·40 1·00
297F. 100 f. Ambrym and idols 1·50 1·10
298F. 200 f. Aneityum and baskets .. .. 1·75 1·75
299F. 500 f. Torres Is. and archer fisherman .. 4·00 3·50

100. Rotary International.

1980. 75th Anniv. of Rotary International. Multicoloured.

(a) Inscr. in English.

300E. 10 f. Type **100** 10 10
301E. 40 f. Rotary emblem (vert.) 30 20

(b) Inscr. in French.

300F. 10 f. Type **100** 10 10
301F. 40 f. Rotary emblem (vert.) 30 20

101. Kiwanis Emblem and Globe.

1980. Kiwanis International (service club), New Zealand District Convention, Port Vila.

(a) Inscr. in English.

302E. 101.	10 f. gold, blue & brown	10	10
303E. –	40 f. green and blue ..	30	20

(b) Inscr. in French.

302F. 101.	10 f. gold, blue & brn.	20	10
303F. –	40 f. green and blue ..	50	25

DESIGN: 40 f. Kiwanis and Convention emblems.

102. " The Virgin and Child enthroned with Saints and Angels " (Umkreis Michael Pacher).

1980. Christmas. Details from Paintings. Multicoloured.

304.	10 f. Type 102	10	10
305.	15 f. " The Virgin and Child with Saints, Angels and Donors " (Hans Memling)	10	10
306.	30 f. " The Rest on the Flight to Egypt " (Adriaen van der Werff)	20	20

103. Blue-faced Parrot Finch.

1981. Birds (1st series). Multicoloured.

307.	10 f. Type 103	40	20
308.	20 f. Emerald Dove ..	60	40
309.	30 f. Golden Whistler ..	80	60
310.	40 f. Silver-shouldered Fruit Dove	90	75

See also Nos. 327/30.

104. Tribesman with Portrait of Prince Philip.

105. Prince Charles with his Dog, Harvey.

1981. 60th Birthday of Prince Philip, Duke of Edinburgh. Multicoloured.

311.	15 v. Type 104	20	15
312.	25 v. Prince Philip in casual dress	30	20
313.	35 v. Queen and Prince Philip with Princess Anne and Master Peter Phillips	40	25
314.	45 v. Prince Philip in ceremonial dress ..	50	35

1981. Royal Wedding. Multicoloured.

315.	15 v. Wedding bouquet from Vanuatu	15	15
316.	45 v. Type 105	25	25
317.	75 v. Prince Charles and Lady Diana Spencer ..	45	45

106. National Flag and Map of Vanuatu.

1981. 1st Anniv. of Independence.

318. 106.	15 v. multicoloured ..	20	15
319. –	25 v. multicoloured ..	25	20
320. –	45 v. yellow and brown	35	30
321. –	75 v. multicoloured ..	60	70

DESIGNS – HORIZ. 25 v. Vanuatu emblem. 45 v. Vanuatu national anthem. VERT. 75 v. Vanuatu Coat of Arms.

107. Three Shepherds.

1981. Christmas. Children's Paintings. Mult.

322.	15 v. Type 107	10	10
323.	25 v. Vanuatu girl with lamb (vert.) ..	15	15
324.	35 v. Angel as butterfly ..	15	20
325.	45 v. Boy carrying torch and gifts (vert.)	25	30

108. New Caledonian Myiagra Flycatchers.

1982. Birds (2nd series). Multicoloured.

327	15 v. Type 108	45	20
328	20 v. Rainbow lorys ..	50	30
329	25 v. Buff-bellied fly-catchers	55	35
330	45 v. Collared grey fantails	80	65

109. " Flickingeria comata ".

1982. Orchids. Multicoloured.

331.	1 v. Type 109	10	30
332.	2 v. "Calanthe triplicata"	10	30
333.	10 v. "Dendrobium sladei"	15	20
334.	15 v. "Dendrobium mohlianum"	20	20
335.	20 v. "Dendrobium macrophyllum"	25	30
336.	25 v. "Dendrobium purpureum"	30	35
337.	30 v. "Robiquetia mimus"	35	40
338.	35 v. "Dendrobium mooreanum" (horiz.) ..	40	50
339.	45 v. "Spathoglottis plicata" (horiz.) ..	55	70
340.	50 v. "Dendrobium seemannii" (horiz.) ..	60	80
341.	75 v. "Dendrobium conanthum" (horiz.) ..	95	1·50
342.	100 v. "Dendrobium macrantham"	1·25	1·50
343.	200 v. "Coelogyne lamellata"	2·25	2·50
344.	500 v. "Bulbophyllum longioscapum"	5·00	6·00

110. Scouts round Camp-fire.

1982. 75th Anniv. of Boy Scout Movement. Multicoloured.

345.	15 v. Type 110	45	20
346.	20 v. First aid	50	25
347.	25 v. Constructing tower	55	40
348.	45 v. Constructing raft ..	80	70
349.	57 v. Scout saluting ..	1·25	1·25

111. Baby Jesus.

1982. Christmas, Nativity Scenes. Mult.

350.	15 v. Type 111	30	35
351.	25 v. Mary and Joseph ..	45	45
352.	35 v. Shepherds (vert.) ..	55	80
353.	45 v. Kings bearing gifts (vert.)	70	1·10

112. " Euploea sylvester ".

1983. Butterflies. Multicoloured.

355.	15 v. Type 112	30	25
356.	15 v. " Hypolimnas octocula "	30	25
357.	20 v. " Papilio canopus hypsicles "	45	35
358.	20 v. " Polyura sacco " ..	45	35
359.	25 v. " Luthrodes cleotas "	50	40
360.	25 v. " Paranitica pumila "	50	40

113. President Afi George Sokomanu.

1983. Commonwealth Day. Multicoloured.

361.	15 v. Type 113	15	10
362.	20 v. Fisherman and liner "Oriana"	20	15
363.	25 v. Herdsman and cattle	25	15
364.	75 v. World map showing position of Vanuatu with Commonwealth and Vanuatu flags	50	70

115. Montgolfier Balloon of De Rozier and D'Arlandes, 1783.

1983. Bicentenary of Manned Flight. Mult.

366.	15 v. Type 115	15	15
367.	20 v. J. A. C. Charles balloon (first use of hydrogen, 1783)	25	25
368.	25 v. Blanchard and Jeffries crossing English Channel, 1785	30	30
369.	35 v. Giffard's airship, 1852 (horiz.)	40	40
370.	40 v. " La France " (airship of Renard and Krebs, 1884) (horiz.)	45	45
371.	45 v. " Graf Zeppelin " (first aerial circumnavigation, 1929) (horiz.)	55	55

116. Mail at Bauefield Airport.

1983. World Communications Year. Mult.

372.	15 v. Type 116	20	25
373.	20 v. Switchboard operator	30	35
374.	25 v. Telex operator ..	35	40
375.	45 v. Satellite Earth station	65	70

117. " Cymatoderma elegans var. lamellatum ".

1984. Fungi. Multicoloured.

377.	15 v. Type 117 ..	60	35
378.	25 v. "Lignosus rhinoceros"	80	60
379.	35 v. "Stereum ostrea" (horiz.)	1·00	90
380.	45 v. "Ganoderma boninense	1·40	1·40

118. Port Vila.

1984. 250th Anniv. of "Lloyd's List" (newspaper). Multicoloured.

381.	15 v. Type 118	20	25
382.	20 v. "Induna" (container ship)	30	35
383.	25 v. Air Vanuatu aircraft	35	40
384.	45 v. "Brahman Express" (container ship)	65	70

1984. Universal Postal Union Congress, Hamburg. As No. 371, but inscribed "UPU CONGRESS HAMBURG" and U.P.U. logo.

385.	45 v. multicoloured ..	80	80

119. Charolais.

1984. Cattle. Multicoloured.

386. 15 v. Type **119** 20 25
387. 25 v. Charolais-afrikander 35 40
388. 45 v. Friesian 65 70
389. 75 v. Charolais-brahman .. 1·10 1·25

120. "Makambo".

1984. "Ausipex" International Stamp Exn, Melbourne. Inter-island freighters. Mult.

390 25 v. Type **120** 70 50
391 45 v. "Rockton" .. .. 1·10 90
392 100 v. "Waroonga" .. .. 2·00 3·00

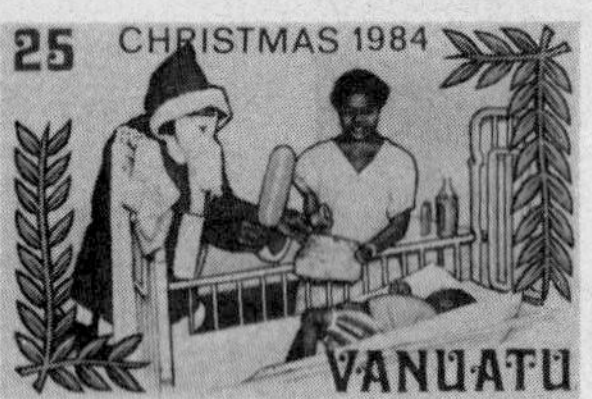

121. Father Christmas in Children's Ward.

1984. Christmas. Multicoloured.

394. 25 v. Type **121** 40 40
395. 45 v. Nativity play .. 70 70
396. 75 v. Father Christmas distributing presents .. 1·25 1·25

1985. No. 331 surch.

397. 5 v. on 1 v. Type **109** .. 50 50

123. Ambrym Island Ceremonial Dance.

1985. Traditional Costumes. Multicoloured.

398. 20 v. Type **123** 30 35
399. 25 v. Pentecost Island marriage ceremony .. 35 40
400. 45 v. Women's grade ceremony, South West Malakula 65 70
401. 75 c. Ceremonial dance, South West Malakula .. 1·10 1·25

124. Peregrine Falcon Diving.

1985. Birth Bicentenary of John J. Audubon (ornithologist). Peregrine Falcon. Mult.

402. 20 v. Type **124** 60 35
403. 35 v. Peregrine Falcon in flight 75 50
404. 45 v. Peregrine Falcon perched on branch .. 90 80
405. 100 v. "Peregrine Falcon" (John J. Audubon) .. 1·60 1·75

125. The Queen Mother with the Queen on her 80th Birthday.

1985. Life and Times of Queen Elizabeth the Queen Mother. Multicoloured.

406 5 v. Duke and Duchess of York on Wedding Day, 1923 .. .. .. 10 10
407 20 v. Type **125** 35 35
408 35 v. At Ancona, Italy .. 55 50
409 55 v. With Prince Henry at his christening (from photo by Lord Snowdon) 85 80

126. "Mala" (patrol boat).

1985. 5th Anniv. of Independence and "Expo '85" World Fair, Japan. Multicoloured.

411. 35 v. Type **126** 45 50
412. 45 v. Japanese fishing fleet 65 70
413. 55 v. Vanuatu Mobile Force Band 75 80
414. 100 v. Prime Minister Fr. Walter H. Lini .. .. 1·40 1·50

127. "Youth Activities" (Alain Lagaliu).

1985. International Youth Year. Children's Paintings. Multicoloured.

416. 20 v. Type **127** 45 35
417. 30 v. "Village" (Peter Obed) 55 45
418. 50 v. "Beach and 'PEACE' Slogan" (Mary Estelle) 95 75
419. 100 v. "Youth Activities" (different) (Abel Merani) 1·60 1·50

128. Map of Vanuatu with National and U.N. Flags.

1985. 4th Anniv. of United Nations Membership.

420. **128.** 45 v. multicoloured .. 70 70

129. "Chromodoris elisabethina".

1985. Marine Life (1st series). Sea Slugs. Multicoloured.

421. 20 v. Type **129** 30 35
422. 35 v. "Halgerda aurantiomaculata" (horiz.) .. 45 50
423. 55 v. "Chromodoris kuniei" (horiz.) 75 80
424. 100 v. "Notodoris minor" 1·40 1·50

See also Nos. 442/5 and 519/22.

130. Scuba Diving.

1986. Tourism. Multicoloured.

425. 30 v. Type **30** 70 40
426. 35 v. Yasur volcano, Tanna 1·00 45
427. 55 v. Land diving, Pentecost Island .. .. .. 1·00 70
428. 100 v. Windsurfing .. 1·40 1·25

1986. 60th Birthday of Queen Elizabeth II. As T **110** of Ascension. Multicoloured.

429. 20 v. With Prince Charles and Princess Anne, 1951 25 30
430. 35 v. Prince William's christening, 1982 .. 40 45
431. 45 v. In New Hebrides, 1974 .. .. .. 55 60
432. 55 v. On board Royal Yacht "Britannia", Mexico, 1974 .. .. 65 70
433. 100 v. At Crown Agents Head Office, London, 1983 .. .. .. 1·10 1·25

131. Liner S.S. "President Coolidge" leaving San Francisco.

1986. "Ameripex '86" International Stamp Exhibition, Chicago. Sinking of S.S. "President Coolidge". Multicoloured.

434. 45 v. Type **131** 65 60
435. 55 v. S.S. "President Coolidge" as troopship, 1942 .. .. .. 75 70
436. 135 v. Map of Espiritu Santo showing site of sinking, 1942 .. .. 1·60 1·60

132. Halley's Comet and Vanuatu Statue.

1986. Appearance of Halley's Comet. Multicoloured.

438. 30 v. Type **132** 90 50
439. 45 v. Family watching Comet .. .. .. 1·25 1·00
440. 55 v. Comet passing Earth .. .. .. 1·40 1·25
441. 100 v. Edmond Halley .. 2·00 2·75

133. Daisy Coral.

1986. Marine Life (2nd series). Corals. Multicoloured.

442. 20 v. Type **133** 50 30
443. 45 v. Organ pipe coral .. 80 70
444. 55 v. Sea fan 90 90
445. 135 v. Soft coral .. .. 2·00 2·50

134. Children of Different Races.

1986. Christmas. International Peace Year. Multicoloured.

446. 30 v. Type **134** 80 50
447. 45 v. Church and boy praying .. .. .. 1·10 85
448. 55 v. U.N. discussion and Headquarters Building, New York .. .. 1·25 1·25
449. 135 v. People of different races at work .. .. 2·50 4·00

135. Datsun "240Z" (1969).

1987. Motor Vehicles. Multicoloured.

450. 20 v. Type **135** 30 30
451. 45 v. Ford "Model A" (1927) 60 60
452. 55 v. Unic lorry (1924–5) .. 70 70
453. 135 v. Citroen "DS19" (1975) .. .. .. 1·60 1·90

1987. Hurricane Relief Fund. No. 332, already surch., and Nos. 429/33, all surch. **Hurricane Relief Fund** and premium.

454. 20 v.+10 v. on 2 v. "Calanthe triplicata" .. 35 40
455. 20 v.+10 v. Queen Elizabeth II with Prince Charles and Princess Anne, 1951 .. .. 35 40
456. 35 v.+15 v. Prince William's christening, 1982 .. .. .. 60 70
457. 45 v.+20 v. Queen in New Hebrides, 1974 .. .. 75 90
458. 55 v.+25 v. Queen on board Royal Yacht "Britannia", Mexico, 1974 .. .. .. 95 1·25
459. 100 v.+50 v. Queen at Crown Agents Head Office, London, 1983 .. 1·75 2·25

The surcharge on No. 454 also includes the word "Surcharge".

137. Young Coconut Plants.

1987. 25th Anniv. of I.R.H.O. Coconut Research Station. Multicoloured.

460. 35 v. Type **137** 40 45
461. 45 v. Coconut flower and fronds 55 60
462. 100 v. Coconuts .. .. 1·10 1·25
463. 135 v. Research station .. 1·60 1·75

The inscriptions on Nos. 462/3 are in French.

138. Spotted Hawkfish.

1987. Fishes. Multicoloured.
464 1 v. Type **138** 10 10
465 5 v. Moorish idol 15 10
466 10 v. Black-saddled puffer 15 15
467 15 v. Anemone fish .. 20 20
468 20 v. Striped surgeon .. 25 25
469 30 v. Six-barred wrasse .. 35 35
470 35 v. Purple queenfish .. 40 40
471 40 v. Long-jawed squirrelfish 45 45
472 45 v. Clown triggerfish .. 55 50
473 50 v. Scribed wrasse .. 60 55
474 55 v. Regal angelfish .. 65 60
475 65 v. Lionfish 80 70
476 100 v. Foresters hawkfish 1·25 1·10
477 300 v. Vermiculated triggerfish .. .. 3·50 3·50
478 500 v. Saddled butterfly fish .. .. .. 5·50 6·00

139. "Xylotrupes gideon" (beetle).

1987. Insects. Multicoloured.
479 45 v. Type **139** 55 60
480 55 v. "Phyllodes imperialis" (moth) 65 70
481 65 v. "Cyphogastra sp." (beetle) 75 80
482 100 v. "Othreis fullonia" (moth) .. .. .. 1·10 1·25

140. "Away in a Manger".

1987. Christmas. Christmas Carols. Mult.
483. 20 v. Type **140** 25 30
484. 45 v. "Once in Royal David's City" 55 60
485. 55 v. "While Shepherds watched their Flocks" .. 65 70
486. 65 v. "We Three Kings of Orient Are" 75 80

1987. Royal Ruby Wedding. Nos. 429/33 optd. **40TH WEDDING ANNIVERSARY.**
487. 20 v. Princess Elizabeth II with Prince Charles and Princess Anne, 1951 .. 30 30
488. 35 v. Prince William's christening, 1982 .. 45 45
489. 45 v. Queen Elizabeth II in New Hebrides, 1974 .. 60 60
490. 55 v. On board Royal Yacht "Britannia", Mexico, 1974 .. .. 70 70
491. 100 v. At Crown Agents Head Office, London, 1983 .. .. .. 1·25 1·25

141. Dugong Cow and Calf.

1988. Dugong. Multicoloured.
492. 5 v. Type **141** 40 25
493. 10 v. Dugong underwater 60 25
494. 20 v. Two dugongs surfacing to breathe .. 90 80
495. 45 v. Four dugongs swimming .. .. 1·50 2·00

142 "Tambo"

1988. Bicentenary of Australian Settlement. Freighters. Multicoloured.
496 20 v. Type **142** 20 25
497 45 v. "Induna" 50 55
498 55 v. "Morinda" 60 65
499 65 v. "Marsina" 70 75

143 Captain James Cook

144 Boxer in Training

1988. "Sydpex '88" National Stamp Exhibition, Sydney.
500 **143** 45 v. black and red .. 75 75

1988. Olympic Games, Seoul. Multicoloured.
502 20 v. Type **144** 20 25
503 45 v. Athletics 50 55
504 55 v. Signing Olympic agreement 60 65
505 65 v. Soccer 70 75

1988. 300th Anniv of Lloyd's of London. As T **123** of Ascension. Multicoloured.
507 20 v. Interior of new Lloyd's building, 1988 .. 30 25
508 55 v. "Shirrabank" (freighter) (horiz) .. 75 65
509 65 v. "Adela" (ferry) (horiz) 85 75
510 145 v. "General Slocum" (excursion paddle-steamer) on fire, New York, 1904 .. .. 2·00 1·75

145 Agricultural Crops

1988. Food and Agriculture Organization. Multicoloured.
511 45 v. Type **145** 50 55
512 55 v. Fisherman with catch (vert) 60 65
513 65 v. Livestock on smallholding (vert) .. 70 75
514 120 v. Market women with produce .. .. 1·25 1·40

146 Virgin and Child ("Silent Night")

1988. Christmas. Carols. Multicoloured.
515 20 v. Type **146** 20 25
516 45 v. Angels ("Angels from the Realms of Glory") 50 55
517 65 v. Shepherd boy with lamb ("O Come all ye Faithful") 70 75
518 155 v. Baby ("In that Poor Stable how Charming Jesus Lies") .. .. 1·75 1·90

147 "Periclimenes brevicarpalis"

1989. Marine Life (3rd series). Shrimps. Mult.
519 20 v. Type **147** 20 25
520 45 v. "Lysmata grabhami" 50 55
521 65 v. "Rhynchocinetes sp" 70 75
522 150 v. "Stenopus hispidus" 1·75 1·90

148 Consolidated "Catalina" Flying Boat

1989. Economic and Social Commission for Asia and the Pacific. Aircraft.
523 **148** 20 v. black and blue .. 40 30
524 – 45 v. black and green 75 65
525 – 55 v. black and yellow 90 80
526 – 200 v. black and red .. 3·00 3·00
DESIGNS: 45 v. Douglas "DC-3"; 55 v. Embraer "EMB110 Bandeirante"; 200 v. Boeing "737-300".

149 Porte de Versailles Hall No. 1

1989. "Philexfrance '89" International Stamp Exhibition, Paris. Multicoloured.
527 100 v. Type **149** .. .. 1·75 1·40
528 100 v. Eiffel Tower .. 1·75 1·40
Nos. 527/8 were printed together, se-tenant, forming a composite design.

1989. 20th Anniv of First Manned Landing on Moon. As T **126** of Ascension. Multicoloured.
530 45 v. Command module seen from lunar module 75 70
531 55 v. Crew of "Apollo 17" (30 × 30 mm) 85 80
532 65 v. "Apollo 17" emblem (30 × 30 mm) .. .. 1·00 90
533 120 v. Launch of "Apollo 17" .. .. .. 1·75 1·60

1989. "Melbourne Stampshow '89". No. 332 surch with Stampshow emblem.
535 100 v. on 2 v. "Calanthe triplicata" .. .. 2·25 2·50

151 New Hebrides 1978 "Concorde" 30 f. (French inscr) Stamp

1989. "World Stamp Expo '89", International Stamp Exhibition, Washington.
536 **151** 65 v. multicoloured .. 1·00 1·00

152 "Alocasia macrorrhiza"

1990. Flora. Multicoloured.
538 45 v. Type **152** 65 65
539 55 v. "Acacia spirorbis" .. 75 75
540 65 v. "Metrosideros collina" 85 85
541 145 v. "Hoya australis" .. 2·00 2·25

153 Kava (National plant)

1990. "Stamp World London 90" International Stamp Exhibition. Multicoloured.
542 45 v. Type **153** 85 75
543 65 v. Luganville Post Office .. .. .. 1·25 1·00
544 100 v. Mail plane and sailing packet .. .. 2·00 2·00
545 200 v. Penny Black and Vanuatu 1980 10 f. definitive .. .. .. 3·25 3·50

154 National Council of Women Logo

1990. 10th Anniv of Independence.
547 **154** 25 v. black and blue .. 40 40
548 – 50 v. multicoloured .. 75 75
549 – 55 v. purple, blk & buff 75 75
550 – 65 v. multicoloured .. 90 90
551 – 80 v. multicoloured .. 1·40 1·40
DESIGNS: 50 v. President Frederick Kalomuana Timakata; 55 v. Preamble to the Constitution; 65 v. Vanuaaku Pati party flag; 80 v. Reserve Bank of Vanuatu.

155 General De Gaulle at Bayeux, 1944

1990. Birth Centenary of General de Gaulle (French statesman). Multicoloured.
553 20 v. Type **155** .. .. 1·25 1·25
554 25 v. Generals De Lattre de Tassigny, De Gaulle, Devers and Patch in Alsace, 1945 .. .. 1·25 1·25
555 30 v. De Gaulle as President of the French Republic 85 85
556 45 v. De Gaulle at Biggin Hill, 1942 .. .. 90 90
557 55 v. Roosevelt, De Gaulle and Churchill, Casablanca, 1943 .. 1·00 1·00
558 65 v. General De Gaulle and Liberation of Paris, 1944 .. .. .. 1·00 1·00

156 Angel facing Right

1990. Christmas. Multicoloured.
559 25 v. Type **156** 45 55
560 50 v. Shepherds 75 85
561 65 v. Nativity 85 95
562 70 v. Three Kings .. 90 1·00
563 80 v. Angel facing left .. 1·00 1·00
Nos. 559/63 were printed together, se-tenant, forming a composite design.

157 "Parthenos sylvia"

1991. Butterflies. Multicoloured.

No.	Description	Mint	Used
564	25 v. Type **157**	40	30
565	55 v. "Euploea leuco-stictus"	80	60
566	80 v. "Lampides boeticus"	1·10	1·25
567	150 v. "Danaus plexippus"	2·40	2·75

158 Dance Troupe from South West Malakula

1991. 2nd National Art Festival, Luganville. Multicoloured.

No.	Description	Mint	Used
568	25 v. Type **158**	55	35
569	65 v. Women weavers and baskets	1·25	1·00
570	80 v. Woodcarver and carved animals, masks, dish and ceremonial figures	1·60	1·75
571	150 v. Musicians playing bamboo flute, youtatau and pan pipes	3·00	3·50

1991. Nos. 332/4 and 337 surch.

No.	Description	Mint	Used
572	20 v. on 2 v. "Calanthe triplicata"	40	40
573	60 v. on 10 v. "Dendrobium sladei"	1·00	1·00
574	70 v. on 15 v. "Dendrobium mohlianum"	1·10	1·25
575	80 v. on 30 v. "Robiquetia mimus"	1·10	1·25

1991. 65th Birthday of Queen Elizabeth II and 70th Birthday of Prince Philip. As T **139** of Ascension. Multicoloured.

No.	Description	Mint	Used
576	65 v. Queen Elizabeth II	1·10	1·25
577	70 v. Prince Philip	1·10	1·25

160 White-collared Kingfisher

1991 "Phila Nippon '91" International Stamp Exhibition, Tokyo. Birds. Multicoloured.

No.	Description	Mint	Used
578	50 v. Type **160**	75	75
579	55 v. Palm lorikeet	80	80
580	80 v. Scarlet robin	1·25	1·25
581	100 v. Pacific swallow	1·40	1·40

161 Group of Islanders

1991. World AIDS Day. Multicoloured.

No.	Description	Mint	Used
583	25 v. Type **161**	40	30
584	65 v. Caring for AIDS victim	85	85
585	80 v. AIDS shark	1·25	1·25
586	150 v. Children's play-ground	2·50	2·75

1992. 40th Anniv of Queen Elizabeth II's Accession. As T **143** of Ascension. Mult.

No.	Description	Mint	Used
587	20 v. Reserve Bank of Vanuatu building, Port Vila	35	30
588	25 v. Port Vila	40	40
589	60 v. Mural, Parliament House	85	85
590	65 v. Three portraits of Queen Elizabeth	90	90
591	70 v. Queen Elizabeth II	1·25	1·40

162 Grumman F4F-4 "Wildcat"

1992. 50th Anniv of Outbreak of the Pacific War (1st issue). Multicoloured.

No.	Description	Mint	Used
592	50 v. Type **162**	90	90
593	55 v. Douglas SBD-3 Dauntless	1·00	1·00
594	65 v. Consolidated PBY-5A Catalina	1·25	1·25
595	80 v. U.S.S. "Hornet" (aricraft carrier)	1·40	1·40

See also Nos. 622/5.

163 Meteorological Station, Port Vila

1992. 10th Anniv of Vanuatu's Membership of World Meteorological Organization. Mult.

No.	Description	Mint	Used
597	25 v. Type **163**	45	35
598	60 v. Satellite picture of tropical cyclone	95	85
599	80 v. Weather chart of Pacific showing cyclone	1·25	1·25
600	105 v. Radio Vanuatu broadcasting cyclone warning	1·60	1·75

164 Vanuatu National Football Team

1992. Vanuatu's Participation in Melanesian Football Cup and Olympic Games, Barcelona. Multicoloured.

No.	Description	Mint	Used
601	20 v. Type **164**	35	25
602	65 v. Melanesian Cup Final, 1990	95	85
603	70 v. Baptiste Firiam (800 metres)	1·10	1·10
604	80 v. Mary Estelle Kapalu (400 hurdles, 400 and 800 metres)	1·25	1·50

165 Breast Feeding

1992. World Food Day. Each brown and green.

No.	Description	Mint	Used
605	20 v. Type **165**	30	25
606	70 v. Central Hospital, Port Vila	90	90
607	80 v. Children eating	1·10	1·10
608	150 v. Nutritious food	2·25	2·50

166 Leatherback Turtle

1992. Turtles. Multicoloured.

No.	Description	Mint	Used
609	55 v. Type **166**	1·00	1·00
610	65 v. Loggerhead turtle laying eggs	1·10	1·10
611	70 v. Hawksbill turtle swimming	1·40	1·40
612	80 v. Green turtle under water	1·75	1·75

167 "Hibiscus rosa-sinensis" "Agnes Goult"

1993. Hibiscus Flowers. Multicoloured.

No.	Description	Mint	Used
614	25 v. Type **167**	35	30
615	55 v. "Hibiscus tiliaceus"	80	80
616	80 v. "Hibiscus rosa-sinensis linnaeus"	1·25	1·25
617	150 v. "Hibiscus rosa-sinensis" "Rose of China"	2·50	2·75

1993. 14th World Orchid Conference, Glasgow. Nos. 339 and 341/3 surch **WORLD ORCHID CONFERENCE 1993** and value.

No.	Description	Mint	Used
618	40 v. on 45 v. "Spathoglottis plicata" (horiz)	55	55
619	55 v. on 75 v. "Dendrobium conanthum" (horiz)	70	70
620	65 v. on 100 v. "Dendrobium macranthum"	85	85
621	150 v. on 200 v. "Coelogyne lamellata"	2·25	2·25

1993. 50th Anniv of Outbreak of the Pacific War (2nd issue). As T **162**. Multicoloured.

No.	Description	Mint	Used
622	20 v. Grumman F6F-3 Hellcat	30	25
623	55 v. Lockheed P-38F Lightning	80	80
624	65 v. Grumman TBF-1 Avenger	1·00	1·00
625	80 v. U.S.S. "Essex" (aircraft carrier)	1·40	1·40

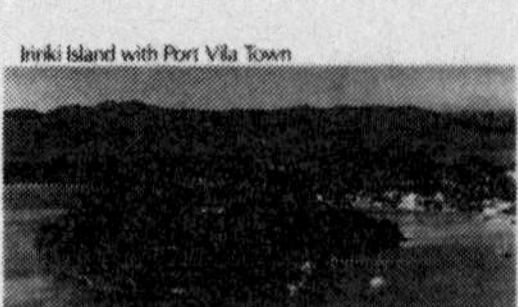

169 Port Vila and Iririki Island

1993. Local Scenery. Multicoloured.

No.	Description	Mint	Used
627	5 v. Type **169**	10	10
628	10 v. Yachts and Iririki Island	10	10
629	15 v. Court House, Port Vila	10	10
630	20 v. Two girls, Pentecost Island	20	25
631	25 v. Women dancers, Tanna Island	25	30
632	30 v. Market, Port Vila	30	35
633	45 v. Man in canoe, Erakor Island (vert)	50	55
634	50 v. Coconut trees, Champagne Beach	55	60
635	55 v. Coconut trees, North Efate Islands	60	65
636	60 v. Underwater shoal of fishes, Banks Group	65	70
637	70 v. Sea fan, Tongoa Island (vert)	75	80
638	75 v. Santo Island	80	85
639	80 v. Sunset, Port Vila harbour (vert)	85	90
640	100 v. Mele Waterfall (vert)	1·10	1·25
641	300 v. Yasur Volcano, Tanna Island (vert)	3·25	3·50
642	500 v. Aerial view of Erakor Island	5·25	5·50

170 "Trochus niloticus"

1993. Shells. Multicoloured.

No.	Description	Mint	Used
643	55 v. Type **170**	80	80
644	65 v. "Lioconcha castrensis"	95	95
645	80 v. "Turbo petholatus"	1·25	1·25
646	150 v. "Pleuroploca trapezium"	2·25	2·25

171 "St. Joseph the Carpenter" (detail) (De la Tour)

1993. Christmas. Bicentenary of the Louvre, Paris. Religious Paintings by Georges de la Tour. Multicoloured.

No.	Description	Mint	Used
647	25 v. Type **171**	35	30
648	55 v. "Holy Child" (detail)	80	80
649	80 v. "Adoration of the Shepherds" (detail)	1·25	1·25
650	150 v. "Adoration of the Shepherds" (different detail)	2·25	2·25

1993. South Pacific Mini Games, Port Vila. Nos. 602, 604, 630 and 632 surch **SOUTH PACIFIC MINI GAMES PORT VILA DECEMBER 1993** and new value.

No.	Description	Mint	Used
651	15 v. on 20 v. Two girls, Pentecost Island	15	20
652	25 v. on 30 v. Market, Port Vila	25	30
653	55 v. on 65 v. Melanesian Cup Final, 1990	60	65
654	70 v. on 80 v. Mary Estelle Kapalu (400, 400 hurdles and 800 metres)	75	80

173 Charity Horse Race and Kiwanis Emblem

174 Silhouetted Family

1994. "Hong Kong '94" International Stamp Exhibition. Charitable Organizations. Mult.

No.	Description	Mint	Used
655	25 v. Type **173**	25	30
656	60 v. Twin Otter airplane and Lions Club emblem (horiz)	60	65
657	75 v. Mosquito and Rotary International emblem	80	85
658	150 v. Blood donor service ambulance and Red Cross emblem (horiz)	1·60	1·75

1994. International Year of the Family.

No.	Type	Description	Mint	Used
660	**174**	25 v. brown and violet	25	30
661		60 v. green and red	60	65
662		90 v. brown and green	90	95
663		150 v. violet & brown	1·60	1·75

VICTORIA

The S.E. state of the Australian Commonwealth, whose stamps it now uses.

12 pence = 1 shilling.
20 shillings = 1 pound.

1. Queen Victoria ("half length").

2. Queen on throne.

1850. Imperf.

28	**1**	1d. red to brown ..	£375	32·00
6		2d. lilac to grey ..	£1100	80·00
17		2d. brown	£500	95·00
31a		3d. blue	£350	30·00

1852. Imperf.

38	**2**	2d. brown to lilac ..	£110	22·00

3.

4.

1854. Imperf.

25	**3**	1s. blue	£650	22·00

1854. Imperf.

32a	**4**	6d. orange	£150	18·00
35		2s. green	£1100	£110

7. Queen on Throne.

8. Emblems in corners.

1856. Imperf.

40	**7**	1d. green	£120	90·00

1857. Imperf.

41	**8**	1d. green	95·00	13·00
45		2d. lilac	£170	10·00
43		4d. red	£160	7·50

1857. Rouletted.

62	**8**	1d. green	£300	14·00
70		2d. lilac	£150	5·50
49a	**1**	3d. blue	—	£170
71c	**8**	4d. red	£120	3·25
53a	**4**	6d. orange	—	35·00
54	**3**	1s. blue	—	80·00
56	**4**	2s. green on yellow ..	—	£350

1858. Rouletted.

73	**7**	6d. blue	£100	12·00

1859. Perf.

98	**8**	1d. green	65·00	4·50
100a		2d. lilac	£110	4·75
100		2d. grey	£100	4·75
78	**1**	3d. blue	£750	£110
87		4d. red	£120	7·50
102	**4**	6d. black	£150	35·00
81a	**3**	1s. blue	£120	12·00
82	**4**	2s. green on yellow ..	£225	25·00
129b		2s. blue on green ..	£140	4·25

9.

10.

1860. Perf.

90	**9**	3d. blue	£120	7·00
91		3d. red	£100	25·00
92a		4d. red	80·00	3·00
93		6d. orange	£2000	£200
94		6d. black	95·00	5·50

1861.

104	**10**	1d. green	60·00	4·50

11. 15.

1862.

107	**11**	6d. black	70·00	4·50

1863.

131c	**15**	1d. green	65·00	2·10
132b		2d. lilac	50·00	3·25
135c		4d. red	70·00	3·00
112		8d. orange	£300	50·00
137c		8d. brown on red ..	75·00	5·00

16.

17.

18.

19.

1865.

118	**16**	3d. lilac	£110	20·00
134a		3d. yellow	16·00	1·90
136c	**17**	6d. blue	14·00	1·25
119		10d. grey	£450	£100
123		10d. brown on red ..	85·00	5·00
124	**18**	1s. blue on blue ..	55·00	2·50
139	**19**	5s. blue on yellow ..	£1600	£300
148		5s. blue and red ..	£130	12·00

1871. Surch. in figures and words.

174	**15.**	½d. on 1d. grn. (No. 122b)	42·00	11·00
171	**17.**	9d. on 10d. brn. on rose	£200	10·00

24.

1870.

169a	**24**	2d. lilac	42·00	1·00

25.

26.

27.

29.

30.

1873.

176b	**25**	½d. red	4·25	60
195		½d. red on red ..	20·00	9·00
177b	**26**	1d. green	13·00	55
196		1d. green on yellow ..	55·00	11·00
197		1d. green on grey ..	£100	40·00
179	**27**	2d. mauve	13·00	35
199		2d. mauve on green ..	£130	10·00
198		2d. mauve on lilac ..	—	£400
200		2d. mauve on brown ..	£120	10·00
172a	**29**	9d. brown on red ..	55·00	7·50
302		9d. green	20·00	9·00
338		9d. red	11·00	1·75
180	**30**	1s. blue on blue ..	48·00	3·00

1876. Surch **8d.. 8d.. EIGHTPENCE**.

191	**29**	8d. on 9d. brown on pink	£130	15·00

36.

33.

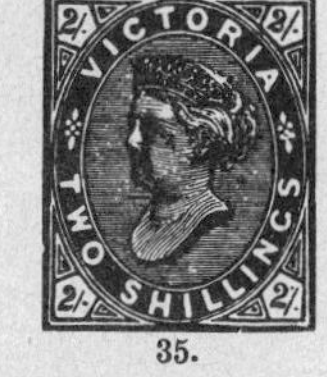

35.

1880. Frame differs in 4d.

209b	**36.**	1d. green	12·00	1·25
210	**33.**	2d. brown	13·00	50
211		2d. mauve	7·50	25
206a		4d. red	40·00	3·50
190	**35.**	2s. blue on green ..	£120	18·00

38.

39.

40.

41.

42.

43.

1884. Inscr. " STAMP DUTY ".

243	**38**	½d. red	5·00	65
244	**39**	1d. green	5·50	50
245	**40**	2d. mauve	4·00	25
334	**39**	3d. yellow	5·50	55
247	**41**	4d. mauve	30·00	3·00
249a	**39**	6d. blue	26·00	2·10
239	**42**	8d. red on red ..	20·00	5·50
240	**40**	1s. blue on yellow ..	40·00	6·00
251	**42**	2s. green on green ..	25·00	3·00
341		2s. green on white ..	16·00	4·75
254b	**43**	2s. 6d. orange ..	75·00	11·00

1885. Optd. **STAMP DUTY.**

237.	**16.**	3d. yellow	60·00	22·00
238.	**33.**	4d. red	55·00	22·00
234.	**30.**	1s. blue on blue ..	95·00	20·00
236.	**35.**	2s. blue on green ..	80·00	18·00

60.

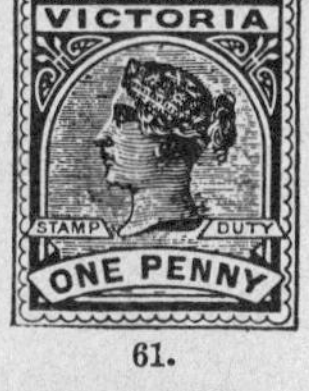

61.

62.

63.

64.

65. 66.

1886. Insc r. " STAMP DUTY ".

283	**60.**	½d. lilac	17·00	3·00
304		½d. red	2·75	15
330		½d. green	4·75	40
285a	**61.**	1d. green	5·25	20
307	**62.**	2d. purple	2·50	10
335	**63.**	4d. red	4·75	95
288b	**64.**	6d. blue	7·00	50
289	**65.**	1s. brown	22·00	2·00
339		1s. red	12·00	1·60
290	**66.**	1s. 6d. blue	£120	65·00
340		1s. 6d. orange	14·00	5·50

68.

71.

69.

70.

1890. Insc r. " STAMP DUTY ", except T **71.**

297	**68.**	1d. brown on red ..	3·50	1·50
298c		1d. brown	2·25	15
305a		1d. red	2·25	10
306	**71.**	1½d. green	4·00	1·50
327		1½d. red on yellow ..	3·00	1·75
300a	**69.**	2½d. red on yellow ..	6·00	70
333		2½d. blue	5·50	1·50
336	**70.**	5d. brown	6·50	95

73.

74.

1897. Charity

325.	**73.**	1d. (1s.) blue ..	18·00	18·00
326.	**74.**	2½d. (2s. 6d.) brown ..	85·00	70·00

76.

77.

1900. Charity.

346.	**76.**	1d. (1s.) brown ..	35·00	28·00
347.	**77.**	2d. (2s.) green ..	£110	95·00

1901.

349	25	½d. green	2·00	85
361	68	1d. olive	5·00	4·00
351	16	3d. orange	15·00	1·25
362	39	3d. green	21·00	5·00
352	33	4d. yellow	25·00	7·00
353	17	6d. green	9·00	5·50
354	30	1s. orange	32·00	22·00
348	35	2s. blue on red	40·00	11·00
355	19	5s. red and blue	45·00	20·00

1901. As previous types, but inscr. "POSTAGE" instead of "STAMP DUTY".

399	25	½d. green	1·60	15
400	36	1d. red	80	10
366a	71	1½d. red on yellow	2·10	55
367a	33	2d. mauve	2·50	30
359a	69	2½d. blue	3·00	35
403	16	3d. brown	4·50	65
369	33	4d. yellow	4·75	55
360a	70	5d. brown	4·50	40
370	71	6d. green	8·50	80
407a	29	9d. red	11·00	1·25
408	30	1s. orange	8·00	2·00
374	35	2s. blue on red	22·00	2·00
375a	19	5s. red and blue	65·00	9·00

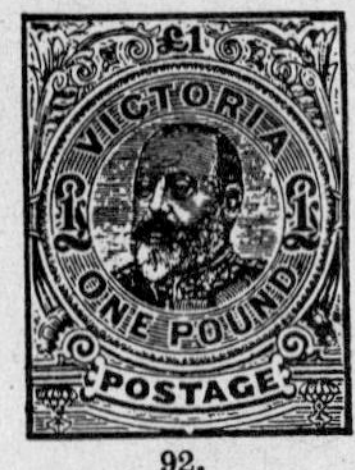

92.

1901. Frame differs for £2.

410	92.	£1 red	£225	£100
377	–	£2 blue	£550	£250

1912. Surch. **ONE PENNY.**

454.	33.	1d. on 2d. mve. (No. 367a)	70	45

POSTAGE DUE STAMPS

D 1.

1890.

D 11.	D 1.	½d. blue and red	2·50	2·25
D 12.		1d. blue and red	4·00	1·10
D 13.		2d. blue and red	6·00	90
D 4.		4d. blue and red	7·00	1·75
D 5.		5d. blue and red	6·50	2·00
D 6.		6d. blue and red	7·50	1·75
D 7.		10d. blue and red	70·00	35·00
D 8.		1s. blue and red	40·00	6·50
D 9.		2s. blue and red	£110	45·00
D 10.		5s. blue and red	£160	90·00

1895.

D15	D 1	½d. red and green	2·10	1·60
D16		1d. red and green	1·75	40
D17		2d. red and green	2·50	30
D32		4d. red and green	5·00	1·25
D49		5d. red and green	5·50	2·75
D20		6d. red and green	5·50	3·00
D21		10d. red and green	14·00	10·00
D22		1s. red and green	7·50	3·25
D23		2s. red and green	60·00	20·00
D24		5s. red and green	£100	40·00

REGISTRATION STAMP

6.

1854. Imperf.

34	6	1s. red and blue	£800	85·00

1857. Roul.

55	6	1s. red and blue	£3500	£180

TOO LATE STAMP

1855. As Type **6** but inscr "TOO LATE". Imperf.

33	6d. lilac and green	£650	£120

VICTORIA LAND

Stamps issued in connection with Capt. Scott's Antarctic Expedition.

12 pence = 1 shilling.

1911. Scott Expedition. Stamps of New Zealand optd. **VICTORIA LAND.**

A 2.	50.	½d. green	£500	£500
A 3.	52.	1d. red	45·00	75·00

WADHWAN

A state of Kathiawar India. Now uses Indian stamps.

4 pice = 1 anna.

1.

1888.

5	1	½ pice black	4·00	4·50

WESTERN AUSTRALIA

The Western State of the Australian Commonwealth, whose stamps it now uses.

12 pence = 1 shilling.
20 shillings = 1 pound.

1. 2.

3.

1854. Imperf. or roul.

1.	1.	1d. black	£800	£180
25.		2d. orange	65·00	50·00
3.	2.	4d. blue	£225	£150
26.	1.	4d. blue	£180	£1200
28.		6d. green	£1100	£400
4c.	3.	1s. brown	£325	£275

5.

7.

1857. Imperf. or roul.

15.	5.	2d. brown on red	£1700	£500
18.		6d. bronze	£1800	£600

1861. Perf.

103	1	1d. red	12·00	60
76		1d. yellow	14·00	50
39		2d. blue	50·00	25·00
77		2d. yellow	18·00	50
104		2d. grey	26·00	1·00
56		4d. red	50·00	4·00
105		4d. brown	80·00	18·00
42		6d. brown	£140	32·00
57		6d. violet	60·00	6·00
61		1s. green	85·00	12·00

1871.

141	7	3d. brown	6·00	50

1874. Surch **ONE PENNY**.

67	1	1d. on 2d. yellow	£150	45·00

1884. Surch. in figures.

90.	1.	"½" on 1d. yellow	9·00	12·00
91a.	7.	1d. on 3d. brown	30·00	7·50

12.

13.

14.

15.

1885.

94	12	½d. green	2·00	10
139a	13	1d. red	3·00	10
96a	14	2d. grey	11·00	25
113		2d. yellow	8·50	60
97	15	2½d. blue	6·00	35
98		4d. brown	6·00	35
99		5d. yellow	8·00	1·25
100		6d. violet	14·00	1·00
102		1s. green	17·00	2·50

1893. Surch. in words.

110a	7	½d. on 3d. brown	5·50	12·00
107		1d. on 3d. brown	9·00	2·75

23.

19.

24.

21.

28.

29.

30.

31.

32.

1901.

140	23.	2d. yellow	2·75	65
119	19.	2½d. blue	5·00	30
114	24.	4d. brown	6·00	90
143	15.	5d. olive	11·00	2·00
168	19.	6d. violet	9·50	3·25
121	12.	8d. green	18·00	2·50
145	24.	9d. orange	22·00	3·50
146	19.	10d. red	22·00	11·00
116	21.	1s. green	18·00	3·50
124b	28.	2s. red on yellow	40·00	8·50
125	29.	2s. 6d. blue on red	40·00	8·00
126	30.	5s. green	60·00	19·00
127	31.	10s. mauve	£140	48·00
128	32.	£1 orange	£300	£150

1906. Surch. **ONE PENNY.**

172.	23.	1d. on 2d. yellow	80	30

ZAMBIA

Formerly Northern Rhodesia, attained independence on 24 October 1964, and changed its name to Zambia.

1964. 12 pence = 1 shilling;
20 shillings = 1 pound.
1968. 100 ngwee = 1 kwacha.

11. Pres. Kaunda and Victoria Falls.

1964. Independence.

91. 11.	3d. sepia, green and blue	10	10
92. –	6d. violet and yellow	15	10
93. –	1s. 3d. multicoloured	20	15

DESIGNS—HORIZ. 6d. College of Further Education, Lusaka. VERT. 1s. 3d. Barotse Dancer.

14. Maize—Farmer and Silo.

22. Tobacco Worker.

1964.

94. 14.	½d. red, black and green	10	20
95. –	1d. brown, black & blue	10	10
96. –	2d. red, brown & orange	10	10
97. –	3d. black and red	10	10
98. –	4d. black, brown & orge.	15	10
99. –	6d. orange, brown and turquoise	15	10
100. –	9d. red, black and blue	15	10
101. –	1s. black, bistre and blue	15	10
102. 22.	1s. 3d. multicoloured	20	10
103. –	2s. multicoloured	25	10
104. –	2s. 6d. black and yellow	60	35
105. –	5s. black, yellow & green	1·25	45
106. –	10s. black and orange	3·25	3·25
107. –	£1 multicoloured	3·25	4·25

DESIGNS—As Type **14**: VERT. 1d. Health—Radiographer. 2d. Chinyau Dancer. 3d. Cotton-picking. HORIZ. 4d. Angoni Bull. As Type **22**: HORIZ. 6d. Communications, Old and New. 9d. Zambezi Sawmills and Redwood Flower. 1s. Fishing at Mpulungu. 2s. 6d. Luangwa Game Reserve. 5 s. Education — Student. 10 s. Copper Mining. VERT. 2s. Tonga Basket-making. £1, Makishi Dancer.

28. I.T.U. Emblem and Symbols.

1965. Centenary of I.T.U.

108. 28.	6d. violet and gold	15	10
109.	2s. 6d. grey and gold	70	1·25

29. I.C.Y. Emblem.

1965. Int. Co-operation Year.

110. 29.	3d. turquoise and gold	10	10
111.	1s. 3d. blue and gold	35	45

30. State House, Lusaka.

1965. 1st Anniv. of Independence. Mult.
112. 3d. Type **30** 10 10
113. 6d. Fireworks, Independence Stadium 10 10
114. 1s. 3d. Clematopsis (vert.) 10 10
115. 2s. 6d. " Tithonia diversifolia " (vert.) 25 60

34. W.H.O. Building and U.N. Flag.

1966. Inauguration of W.H.O. Headquarters, Geneva.
116. **34.** 3d. brown, gold and blue 15 10
117. 1s. 3d. violet, gold & blue 30 30

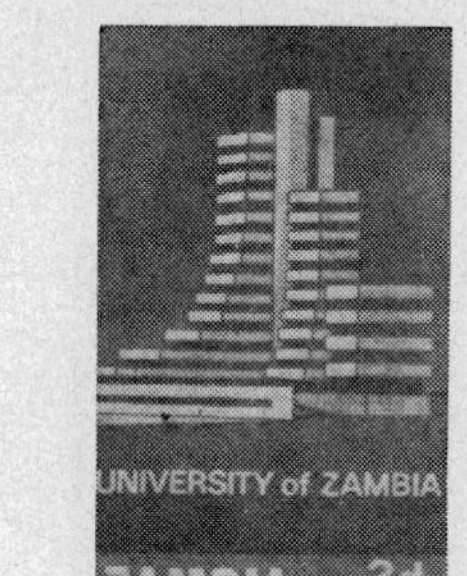

35. University Building.

1966. Opening of Zambia University.
118. **35.** 3d. green and bronze . . 10 10
119. 1s. 3d. violet and bronze 10 10

36. National Assembly Building.

1967. Inaug. of National Assembly Building.
120. **36.** 3d. black and gold . . 10 10
121. 6d. green and gold . . 10 10

37. Airport Scene.

1967. Opening of Luska Int. Airport.
122. **37.** 6d. blue and bronze . . 10 10
123. 2s. 6d. brown & bronze 40 60

38. Youth Service Badge.

43. Lusaka Cathedral.

1967. National Development.
124. **38.** 4d. black, red and gold 10 10
125. – 6d. black, gold and blue 10 10
126. – 9d. black, blue & silver 15 25
127. – 1s. multicoloured . . 40 10
128. – 1s. 6d. multicoloured . . 60 1·25
DESIGNS—HORIZ. 6d. " Co-operative Farming". 1s. 6d. Road link with Tanzania. VERT. 9d. "Communications". 1s. Coalfields.

1968. Decimal Currency.
129. **43.** 1 n. multicoloured . . 10 10
130. – 2 n. multicoloured . . 10 10
131. – 3 n. multicoloured . . 10 10
132. – 5 n. brown and bronze 10 10
133. – 8 n. multicoloured . . 15 10
134. – 10 n. multicoloured . . 25 10
135. – 15 n. multicoloured . . 2·75 10
136. – 20 n. multicoloured . . 2·50 10
137. – 25 n. multicoloured . . 25 10
138. – 50 n. brown, orange and bronze 30 15
139. – 1 k. blue and bronze . . 3·25 20
140. – 2 k. black and bronze . . 2·25 1·25
DESIGNS—As T **43**: VERT. 2 n. Baobab tree. 5 n. National Museum, Livingstone. 8 n. Vimbuza dancer. 10 n. Tobacco picking. HORIZ. 3 n. Zambia Airways jetliner. LARGER (32 × 26 mm): 15 n. "Imbrasia zambesina" (moth). 1 k. Kafue Railway Bridge. 2 k. Eland. (26 × 22 mm): 20 n. South African crowned cranes. 25 n. Angoni warrior. 50 n. Chokwe dancer.

55. Ndola on Outline of Zambia.

1968. Trade Fair, Ndola.
141. **55.** 15 n. green and gold . . 10 10

56. Human Rights Emblem and Heads.

1968. Human Rights Year.
142. **56.** 3 n. blue, violet and gold 10 10

57. W.H.O. Emblem.

1968. 20th Anniv. of World Health Organization.
143. **57.** 10 n. gold and violet . . 10 10

58. Group of Children.

1968. 22nd Anniv. of U.N.I.C.E.F.
144. **58.** 25 n. black, gold & blue 15 70

59. Copper Miner.

1969. 50th Anniv. of Int. Labour Organization.
145. **59.** 3 n. gold and violet . . 15 10
146. – 25 n. yellow, gold & brn. 85 80
DESIGN—HORIZ. 25 n. Poling a furnace.

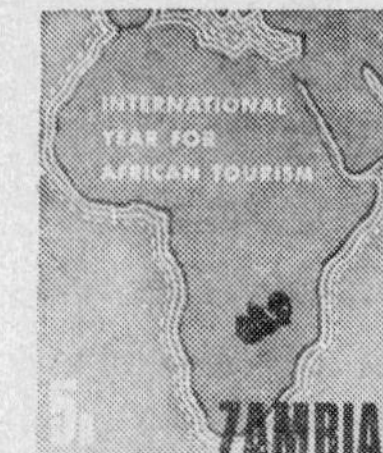

61. Zambia outlined on Map of Africa.

1969. Int. African Tourist Year. Mult.
147. 5 n. Type **61** 10 10
148. 10 n. Waterbuck 15 10
149. 15 n. Golden Perch . . 35 40
150. 25 n. Carmine Bee-Eater . . 1·00 1·00
Nos. 148/50 are horiz.

65. Satellite " Nimbus III " orbiting the Earth.

1970. World Meteorological Day.
151. **65.** 15 n. multicoloured . . 20 50

66. Woman collecting Water from Well.

1970. Preventive Medicine.
152. **66.** 3 n. multicoloured . . 10 10
153. – 15 n. multicoloured . . 25 15
154. – 25 n. blue, red and sepia 50 30
DESIGNS: 15 n. Child on scales. 25 n. Child being immunized.

67. " Masks " (mural by Gabriel Ellison).

1970. Conference of Non-Aligned Nations.
155. **67.** 15 n. multicoloured . . 45 30

68. Ceremonial Axe.

1970. Traditional Crafts. Multicoloured.
156. 3 n. Type **68** 10 10
157. 5 n. Clay Smoking-Pipe Bowl 15 10
158. 15 n. Makishi Mask . . 35 40
159. 25 n. Kuomboka Ceremony 70 1·25
SIZES—HORIZ. 5 n. as T **68**. 25 n. 72 × 19 mm. VERT. 15 n. 30 × 47 mm.

69. Dag Hammarskjold and U.N. General Assembly.

1971. 10th Death Anniv. of Dag Hammarskjold. Multicoloured.
161. 4 n. Type **69** 10 10
162. 10 n. Tail of aircraft . . 10 10
163. 15 n. Dove of Peace . . 15 25
164. 25 n. Memorial tablet . . 35 1·50

70. Red-breasted Bream.

1971. Fish. Multicoloured.
165. 4 n. Type **70** 30 10
166. 10 n. Green-headed Bream 55 30
167. 15 n. Tiger fish . . . . 90 1·75

71. North African Crested Porcupine.

1972. Conservation Year (1st issue). Mult.
168. 4 n. Cheetah (horiz.) . . 20 25
169. 10 n. Lechwe (horiz.) . . 50 60
170. 15 n. Type **71** 80 85
171. 25 n. African elephant . . 2·00 2·25
Nos. 168/9 are size 58 × 21 mm.

1972. Conservation Year (2nd issue). As T **71**. Multicoloured.
172. 4 n. Soil conservation . . 20 20
173. 10 n. Forestry 40 45
174. 15 n. Water 60 70
175. 25 n. Maize . . . . 1·25 1·40
Nos. 174/5 are size 58 × 21 mm.

73. Zambian Flowers.

1972. Conservation Year (3rd issue). Mult.
177 4 n. Type **73** 30 30
178 10 n. "Papilio demodocus" (butterfly) 70 70
179 15 n. "Apis mellifera" (bees) . . . . . . 1·25 1·25
180 25 n. "Nomadacris septemfasciata" (locusts) . . 2·00 2·00

74. Mary and Joseph.

1972. Christmas. Multicoloured.

No.	Description		
181.	4 n. Type **74**	10	10
182.	9 n. Mary, Joseph and Jesus	10	10
183.	15 n. Mary, Jesus and the shepherds	10	10
184.	25 n. The Three Wise Men	20	40

75 Oudenodn and Rubidgea

1973. Zambian Prehistoric Animals. Mult.

No.	Description		
185	4 n. Type **75**	85	85
186	9 n. Broken Hill Man ..	90	90
187	10 n. Zambiasaurus ..	1·00	1·50
188	15 n. Luangwa drysdalli ..	1·10	2·00
189	25 n. Glossopteris ..	1·25	3·00

Nos. 186/9 are smaller 38 × 21 mm and show fossils.

76. " Dr. Livingstone I Presume ".

1973. Death Cent. of Livingstone. Mult.

No.	Description		
190.	3 n. Type **76**	35	15
191.	4 n. Scripture Lesson ..	35	15
192.	9 n. Victoria Falls ..	80	40
193.	10 n. Scattering slavers ..	80	45
194.	15 n. Healing the sick ..	1·00	1·50
195.	25 n. Burial place of Livingstone's heart	1·40	2·50

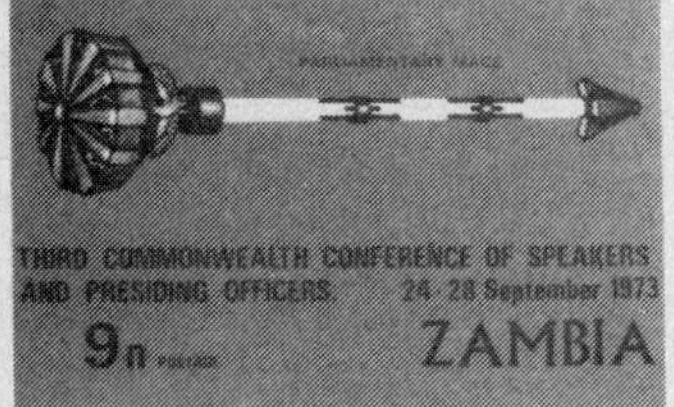

77. Parliamentary Mace.

1973. 3rd Commonwealth Conf., of Speakers and Presiding Officers, Lusaka.

No.	Type	Description		
196.	**77.**	9 n. multicoloured ..	80	65
197.		15 n. multicoloured ..	1·00	1·75
198.		25 n. multicoloured ..	1·50	2·50

78. Inoculation.

1973. 25th Anniv. of W.H.O. Multicoloured.

No.	Description		
199.	4 n. Mother washing baby (vert.)	48·00	23·00
200.	9 n. Nurse weighing baby (vert.)	45	2·00
201.	10 n. Type **78**	50	2·75
202.	15 n. Child eating meal ..	90	4·50

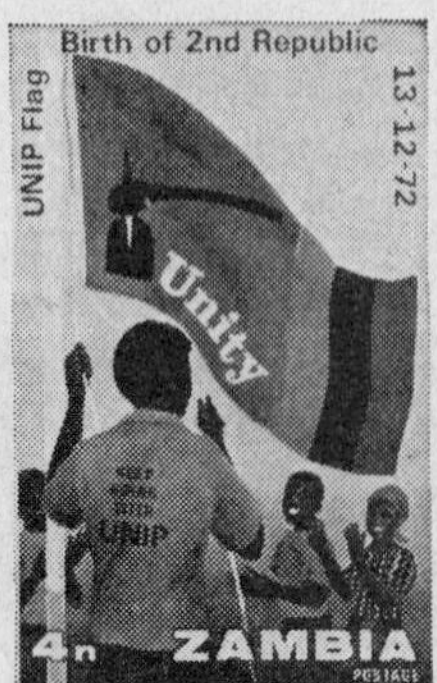

79. U.N.I.P. Flag.

1974. 1st Anniv. of Second Republic. Mult.

No.	Description		
203.	4 n. Type **79**	10·00	8·00
204.	9 n. Freedom House ..	40	1·75
205.	10 n. Army band	40	2·25
206.	15 n. "Celebrations" (dancers)	70	3·75
207.	25 n. Presidential chair ..	1·40	6·00

80. President Kaunda at Mulungushi.

1974. 50th Birthday of President Kaunda. Multicoloured.

No.	Description		
208.	4 n. Type **80**	1·00	1·00
209.	9 n. President's former residence	50	50
210.	15 n. President holding Independence flame ..	1·40	2·50

81. Nakambala Sugar Estate.

1974. 10th Anniv. of Independence. Mult.

No.	Description		
211.	3 n. Type **81**	20	15
212.	4 n. Local market	20	15
213.	9 n. Kapiri glass factory ..	35	45
214.	10 n. Kafue hydro-electric scheme	40	50
215.	15 n. Kafue railway bridge	70	1·50
216.	25 n. Non-aligned Conference, Lusaka, 1970 ..	1·10	1·75

82. Mobile Post-van.

1974. Centenary of U.P.U. Multicoloured.

No.	Description		
218.	4 n. Type **82**	20	15
219.	9 n. Aeroplane on tarmac	40	30
220.	10 n. Chipata Post Office ..	40	40
221.	15 n. Modern training centre	65	1·75

83. Dish Aerial.

1974. Opening of Mwembeshi Earth Station. Multicoloured.

No.	Description		
222.	4 n. Type **83**	30	20
223.	9 n. View at dawn ..	65	50
224.	15 n. View at dusk ..	1·00	1·25
225.	25 n. Aerial view	1·50	2·25

84. Rhinoceros and Calf.

85. Independence Monument.

1975. Multicoloured.

No.	Description		
226.	1 n. Type **84**	40	30
227.	2 n. Helmet Guinea fowl ..	30	30
228.	3 n. National Dancing Troupe	15	30
229.	4 n. African Fish Eagle ..	40	10
230.	5 n. Knife-edge Bridge ..	65	30
231.	8 n. Sitatunga (antelope) ..	65	30
232.	9 n. African Elephant, Kasaba Bay	85	20
233.	10 n. Temminck's Ground Pangolin	20	10
234.	15 n. Type **85**	30	10
235.	20 n. Harvesting groundnuts	75	85
236.	25 n. Tobacco-growing ..	85	30
237.	50 n. Flying Doctor service	90	1·60
238.	1 k. Lady Ross's Turaco ..	2·50	1·75
239.	2 k. Village scene	3·00	4·50

Nos. 234/239 are as Type **85**.

86. Map of Namibia.

1975. Namibia Day.

No.	Type	Description		
240.	**86.**	4 n. green and yellow	20	20
241.		9 n. blue and green ..	30	30
242.		15 n. orange & yellow	65	75
243.		25 n. red and orange ..	85	1·25

87. Erection of Sprinkler Irrigation.

1975. Silver Jubilee of Int. Commission on Irrigation and Drainage. Multicoloured.

No.	Description		
244.	4 n. Type **87**	15	15
245.	9 n. Sprinkler irrigation ..	30	40
246.	15 n. Furrow irrigation ..	65	1·25

88. Mutondo.

1976. World Forestry Day. Multicoloured.

No.	Description		
247.	3 n. Type **88**	25	10
248.	4 n. Mukunyu	25	10
249.	9 n. Mukusi	45	25
250.	10 n. Mopane	45	25
251.	15 n. Musuku	70	1·40
252.	25 n. Mukwa	85	1·75

MINIMUM PRICE

The minimum price quoted is 10p which represents a handling charge rather than a basis for valuing common stamps. For further notes about prices see introductory pages.

89. Passenger Train.

1976. Opening of Tanzania-Zambia Railway. Multicoloured.

No.	Description		
253.	4 n. Type **89**	30	30
254.	9 n. Copper exports ..	55	55
255.	15 n. Machinery imports ..	90	95
256.	25 n. Goods train	1·40	1·75

90. Kayowe Dance.

1977. Second World Black and African Festival of Arts and Culture, Nigeria. Multicoloured.

No.	Description		
258.	4 n. Type **90**	15	10
259.	9 n. Lilombola dance ..	25	25
260.	15 n. Initiation ceremony	45	50
261.	25 n. Munkhwele dance ..	75	1·25

91. Grimwood's Longclaw.

1977. Birds of Zambia. Multicoloured.

No.	Description		
262.	4 n. Type **91**	40	10
263.	9 n. Shelly's Sunbird ..	70	60
264.	10 n. Black Cheeked Lovebird	70	60
265.	15 n. Locust Finch ..	1·40	2·00
266.	20 n. Black-Chinned Tinker bird	1·60	2·25
267.	25 n. Chaplin's Barbet ..	2·00	2·75

92. Girls with Building Blocks.

1977. Decade of Actions to Combat Racism and Racial Discrimination. Mult.

No.	Description		
268.	4 n. Type **92**	10	10
269.	9 n. Women dancing ..	15	20
270.	15 n. Girls with dove ..	25	60

93. Angels and Shepherds.

1977. Christmas. Multicoloured.

No.	Description		
271.	4 n. Type **93**	10	10
272.	9 n. The Holy Family ..	10	10
273.	10 n. The Magi	10	15
274.	15 n. Jesus presented to Simeon	20	60

94. African Elephant and Road Check.

1978. Anti-poaching. Multicoloured.

No.	Description		
275.	8 n. Type **94**	25	10
276.	18 n. Lechwe and canoe patrol	40	65
277.	28 n. Warthog	60	95
278.	32 n. Cheetah and game guard patrol	75	1·25

1979. Various stamps surch.

No.	Description		
279. –	8 n. on 9 n. multicoloured (No. 232)	40	10
280. –	10 n. on 3 n. multicoloured (No. 228)	10	10
281. –	18 n. on 25 n. multicoloured (No. 236)	15	15
282. **85.**	28 n. on 15 n. multicoloured	20	25

96. Kayowe Dance.

1979. Commonwealth Summit Conference, Lusaka. Multicoloured.

No.	Description		
283.	18 n. Type **96**	15	25
284.	32 n. Kutambala dance ..	20	40
285.	42 n. Chitwansombo drummers	20	60
286.	58 n. Lilombola dance ..	25	80

97. " Kalulu and the Tug of War ".

1979. International Year of the Child. **Mult.**

No.	Description		
287.	18 n. Type **97**	40	30
288.	32 n. " Why the Zebra has no Horns "	55	55
289.	42 n. " How the Tortoise got his Shell " ..	60	85
290.	58 n. " Kalulu and the Lion "	80	1·00

98. Children of different races holding Anti-Apartheid Emblem.

1979. International Anti-Apartheid **Year.** Multicoloured.

No.	Description		
292.	18 n. Type **98**	15	25
293.	32 n. Children with toy car	25	40
294.	42 n. Young children with butterfly	35	60
295.	58 n. Children with microscope	50	80

99. Sir Rowland Hill and 2s. Definitive Stamp of 1964.

1979. Death Centenary of Sir Rowland Hill. Multicoloured.

No.	Description		
296.	18 n. Type **99**	20	25
297.	32 n. Sir Rowland Hill and mailman	40	55
298.	42 n. Sir Rowland Hill and Northern Rhodesia 1963 ½d. definitive stamp ..	50	70
299.	58 n. Sir Rowland Hill and mail-carrying oxwaggon	65	1·10

1980. " London 1980 " International Stamp Exhibition. Nos. 296/299 optd. **LONDON 1980.**

No.	Description		
301. **99.**	18 n. multicoloured ..	35	40
302. –	32 n. multicoloured ..	55	70
303. –	42 m. multicoloured ..	70	90
304. –	58 m. multicoloured ..	90	1·10

101. Rotary Anniv. Emblem.

1980. 75th Anniv. of Rotary International.

No.	Description		
306. **101.**	8 n. multicoloured ..	10	10
307.	32 n. multicoloured ..	40	55
308.	42 n. multicoloured ..	45	80
309.	58 n. multicoloured ..	70	1·00

102. Running.

1980. Olympic Games, Moscow. Multicoloured.

No.	Description		
311.	18 n. Type **102**	25	25
312.	32 n. Boxing	35	45
313.	42 n. Football	40	80
314.	58 n. Swimming	70	1·25

103. "Euphaedra zaddachi".

1980. Butterflies. Multicoloured.

No.	Description		
316	18 n. Type **103**	15	15
317	32 n. "Aphnaeus questiauxi"	25	40
318	42 n. "Abantis zambesiaca"	40	80
319	58 n. "Spindasis modesta"	60	1·10

104. Zambia Coat of Arms.

1980. 26th Commonwealth Parliamentary Association Conference, Lusaka.

No.	Description		
321. **104.**	18 n. multicoloured ..	15	25
322.	32 n. multicoloured ..	25	45
323.	42 n. multicoloured ..	30	65
324.	58 n. multicoloured ..	40	90

105. Nativity and St. Francis of Assisi (stained glass window, Ndola Church).

1980. 50th Anniv. of Catholic Church on the Copperbelt.

No.	Description		
325. **105.**	8 n. multicoloured ..	10	10
326.	28 n. multicoloured ..	40	60
327.	32 n. multicoloured ..	40	60
328.	42 n. multicoloured ..	60	75

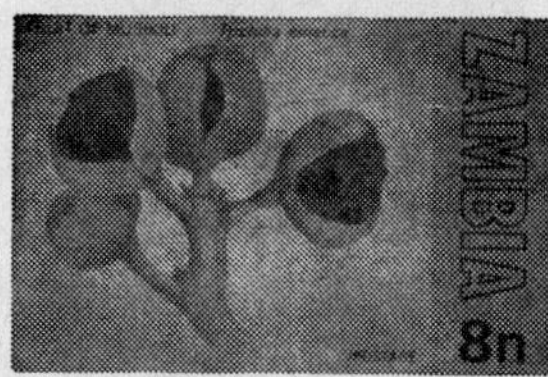

106. " Musikili ".

1981. World Forestry Day. Seedpods. **Mult.**

No.	Description		
329.	8 n. Type **106**	10	10
330.	18 n. Mupapa	20	45
331.	28 n. Mulunguti	25	80
332.	32 n. Mulama	25	1·25

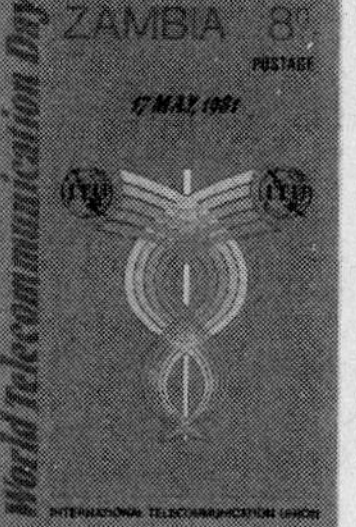

107. I.T.U. Emblems.

108. Mask Maker.

1981. World Telecommunications and Health Day. Multicoloured.

No.	Description		
333.	8 n. Type **107**	20	10
334.	18 n. W.H.O. emblems ..	45	35
335.	28 n. Type **107**	80	60
336.	32 n. As 18 n.	95	75

1981. Native Crafts. Multicoloured.

No.	Description		
337.	1 n. Type **108.**	10	10
338.	2 n. Blacksmith	10	10
339.	5 n. Pottery making ..	10	10
340.	8 n. Straw-basket fishing	10	10
341.	10 n. Thatching	10	10
342.	12 n. Mushroom picking	2·00	1·10
343.	18 n. Millet grinding on stone	30	10
344.	28 n. Royal Barge paddler	50	10
345.	30 n. Makishi tight rope dancer	50	10
346.	35 n. Tonga Ila granary and house	55	10
347.	42 n. Cattle herding ..	55	60
348.	50 n. Traditional healer (38 × 26 mm.)	55	10
349.	75 n. Women carrying water (38 × 26 mm.)	55	60
350.	1 k. Pounding maize (38 × 26 mm.)	55	60
351.	2 k. Pipe smoking, Gwembe Valley Belle (38 × 26 mm.)	55	60

109. Kankobele.

1981. Traditional Musical Instruments. **Mult.**

No.	Description		
356.	8 n. Type **109.**	30	10
357.	18 n. Inshingili	65	55
358.	28 n. Ilimba	90	1·25
359.	32 n. Bango	1·00	1·75

110. Banded Ironstone.

1982. Minerals (1st series). Multicoloured.

No.	Description		
360.	8 n. Type **110.**	40	10
361.	18 n. Cobaltocalcite ..	1·00	80
362.	28 n. Amazonite	1·25	1·25
363.	32 n. Tourmaline ..	1·40	1·75
364.	42 n. Uranium ore ..	1·75	2·25

See also Nos. 370/4.

111. Zambian Scouts.

1982. 75th Anniv. of Boy Scout Movement. Multicoloured.

No.	Description		
365.	8 n. Type **111.**	30	10
366.	18 n. Lord Baden-Powell and Victoria Falls	70	40
367.	28 n. Buffalo and Zambian Scout patrol pennant ..	70	50
368.	1 k. African Fish Eagle and Zambian Conservation badge	2·00	3·25

1982. Minerals (2nd series). As **T 110. Mult.**

No.	Description		
370.	8 n. Bornite	70	10
371.	18 n. Chalcopyrite ..	1·75	85
372.	28 n. Malachite	2·25	2·50
373.	32 n. Azurite	2·25	2·50
374.	42 n. Vanadinite	2·75	3·75

112. Drilling Rig, 1926.

1983. Early Steam Engines. Multicoloured.

No.	Description		
375.	8 n. Type **112**	50	10
376.	18 n. Fowler road locomotive, 1900	70	60
377.	28 n. Borsig ploughing engine, 1925	1·10	2·00
378.	32 n. Class "7" railway locomotive, 1900 ..	1·40	2·25

113. Cotton Picking.

1983. Commonwealth Day. Multicoloured.

No.	Description		
379.	12 n. Type **113**	20	10
380.	18 n. Mining	30	30
381.	28 n. Ritual pot and traditional dances	30	50
382.	1 k. Violet-crested Turaco and Victoria Falls ..	2·50	4·00

114. " Eulophia cucullata ".

1983. Wild Flowers. Multicoloured.

No.	Description		
383.	12 n. Type **114** ..	20	10
384.	28 n. " Kigelia africana "	35	40
385.	35 n. " Protea gaguedi " ..	45	70
386.	50 n. " Leonotis nepetifolia "	65	1·40

115. Giraffe.

1983. Wildlife of Zambia. Multicoloured.

388. 12 n. Type **115** 70 10
389. 28 n. Blue Wildebeest .. 90 70
390. 35 n. Lechwe .. .. 1·25 90
391. 1 k. Yellow Backed Duiker 2·50 4·00

116. Tiger Fish.

1983. Fishes of Zambia. Multicoloured.

392. 12 n. Type **116** 20 15
393. 28 n. Silver Barbel .. 40 60
394. 35 n. Spotted Squeaker .. 45 1·00
395. 38 n. Red-breasted Bream 50 1·00

117. The Annunciation.

1983. Christmas. Multicoloured.

396. 12 n. Type **117** 10 10
397. 28 n. The Shepherds .. 25 40
398. 35 n. Three Kings .. 30 90
399. 38 n. Flight into Egypt .. 35 1·25

118. Boeing " 737 ".

1984. Air. Transport Multicoloured.

400. 12 n. Type **118** 15 10
401. 28 n. Beaver aircraft .. 30 40
402. 35 n. Short " Solent " flying boat 35 70
403. 1 k. D.H. " 66 Hercules " 85 2·25

119. Receiving Flowers.

1984. 60th Birthday of President Kaunda. Multicoloured.

404. 12 n. Type **119** 40 10
405. 28 n. Swearing-in ceremony (vert.) 65 40
406. 60 n. Planting cherry tree 1·50 2·00
407. 1 k. Opening of 5th National Assembly (vert.) .. 2·00 2·75

120. Football.

1984. Olympic Games, Los Angeles. Multicoloured.

408. 12 n. Type **120** 25 10
409. 28 n. Running 35 50
410. 35 n. Hurdling 50 75
411. 50 n. Boxing .. .. 60 1·10

121. Gaboon Viper.

1984. Reptiles. Multicoloured.

412. 12 n. Type **121** 15 10
413. 28 n. Chameleon 30 40
414. 35 n. Nile Crocodile .. 40 60
415. 1 k. Blue-headed Agama .. 85 2·50

122. Pres. Kaunda and Mulungushi Rock.

1984. 26th Anniv. of United National Independence Party and 20th Anniv. of Independence (1st issue). Multicoloured.

417. 12 n. Type **122** 40 10
418. 28 n. Freedom statue .. 60 50
419. 1 k. Pres. Kaunda and agricultural produce ("Lima Programme") .. .. 1·50 2·75

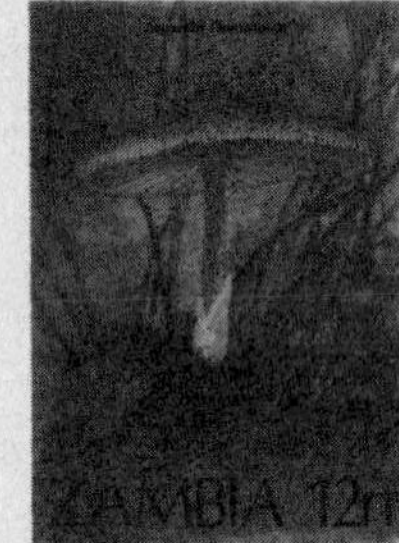

123. "Amanita flammeola".

1984. Fungi. Multicoloured.

420. 12 n. Type **123** 65 15
421. 28 n. "Amanita zambiana" 85 70
422. 32 n. "Temitomyces letestui" 1·25 1·10
423. 75 n. "Cantharellus minatescens" .. .. .. 2·25 2·75

1985. No. 237 surch.

424. 5 k. on 50 n. Flying-doctor service .. .. .. 1·25 1·75

125. Chacma Baboon.

1985. Zambian Primates. Multicoloured.

425. 12 n. Type **125** 35 10
426. 20 n. Diademed monkey .. 55 40
427. 45 n. Diademed monkey (different) .. .. 1·00 1·25
428. 1 k. Savanna Monkey .. 1·75 2·75

126. Map showing S.A.D.C.C. Member States.

1985. 5th Anniv. of Southern African Development Co-ordination Conference.

429. **126.** 20 n. multicoloured .. 60 15
430. – 45 n. black, blue and light blue .. .. 1·50 1·10
431. – 1 k. multicoloured .. 2·00 3·00

DESIGNS: 45 n. Mining. 1 k. Flags of member states and Mulungushi Hall.

127. The Queen Mother in 1980.

1985. Life and Times of Queen Elizabeth the Queen Mother.

432. **127.** 25 n. multicoloured .. 10 10
433. – 45 n. blue and gold .. 10 15
434. – 55 n. blue and gold .. 15 25
435. – 5 k. multicoloured .. 1·25 2·25

DESIGNS—VERT. 45 n. The Queen Mother at Clarence House, 1963. HORIZ. 55 n. With the Queen and Princess Margaret, 1980. 5 k. At Prince Henry's christening, 1984.

1985. Nos. 340 and 342 surch.

436 20 n. on 12 n. Mushroom picking .. .. .. 1·75 30
437 25 n. on 8 n. Straw-basket fishing 75 65

1985. 26th Anniv. of United National Independence Party (No. 438) and 20th Anniv. of Independence (2nd issue). As Nos. 417/19 but larger (55 × 34 mm.) On gold foil.

438. 5 k. As Type **122** .. .. 1·75 2·75
439. 5 k. Freedom Statue .. 1·75 2·75
440. 5 k. Pres. Kaunda and agricultural produce ("Lima Programme") .. 1·75 2·75

129. Postman and Lusaka Post Office, 1958.

1985. 10th Anniv. of Posts and Telecommunication Corporation. Multicoloured.

441. 20 n. Type **129** 45 10
442. 45 n. Postman and Livingstone Post Office, 1950. 75 25
443. 55 n. Postman and Kalomo Post Office, 1902 .. 85 65
444. 5 k. Africa Trans-Continental Telegraph Line under construction, 1900 .. .. .. 2·75 4·50

130. Boy in Maize Field.

1985. 40th Anniv. of United Nations Organization.

445 **130** 20 n. multicoloured .. 40 10
446 – 45 n. black, bl. & brn. 65 20
447 – 1 k. multicoloured .. 1·25 1·75
448 – 2 k. multicoloured .. 2·00 2·75

DESIGNS: 45 n. Logo and "40". 1 k. President Kaunda addressing U.N. General Assembly, 1970. 2 k. Signing of U.N. Charter, San Francisco, 1945.

131. "Mylabris tricolor".

1986. Beetles. Multicoloured.

449. 35 n. Type **131** 15 10
450. 1 k. "Phasgonocnema melanianthe" 20 20
451. 1 k. 70 "Amaurodes passerinii" 30 50
452. 5 k. "Ranzania petersiana" 85 2·00

1986. 60th Birthday of Queen Elizabeth II. As T **110** of Ascension. Multicoloured.

453. 35 n. Princess Elizabeth at Flower Ball, Savoy Hotel, 1951 .. .. 10 10
454. 1 k. 25 With Prince Andrew, Lusaka Airport, 1979 .. .. 15 20
455. 1 k. 70 With President Kaunda 20 25
456. 1 k. 95 In Luxembourg, 1976 .. .. .. 25 30
457. 5 k. At Crown Agents Head Office, London, 1983. .. .. .. 60 85

1986. Royal Wedding. As T **112** of Ascension. Multicoloured.

458. 1 k. 70 Prince Andrew and Miss Sarah Ferguson .. 30 35
459. 5 k. Prince Andrew in Zambia, 1979 .. .. 80 1·40

132. Goalkeeper saving Goal.

1986. World Cup Football Championship, Mexico. Multicoloured.

460. 35 n. Type **132** 70 15
461. 1 k. 25 Player kicking ball 1·75 1·40
462. 1 k. 70 Two players competing for ball .. .. 2·00 1·75
463. 5 k. Player scoring goal .. 3·25 4·50

133. Sculpture of Edmond Halley by Henry Pegram.

1986. Appearance of Halley's Comet.

464. **133.** 1 k. 25 multicoloured 75 55
465. – 1 k. 70 multicoloured 95 80
466. – 2 k. multicoloured .. 1·40 1·40
467. – 5 k. blue and black .. 3·25 4·00

DESIGNS: 1 k. 70, "Giotto" spacecraft approaching nucleus of Comet; 2 k. Studying Halley's Comet in 1682 and 1986; 5 k. Part of Halley's chart of southern sky.

134. Nativity.

1986. Christmas. Children's Paintings. Mult.

468. 35 n. Type **134** 40 10
469. 1 k. 25 Visit of the Three Kings .. .. .. 1·25 75
470. 1 k. 60 Holy Family with shepherd and king .. 1·50 1·10
471. 5 k. Angel and christmas tree .. .. .. 3·50 4·50

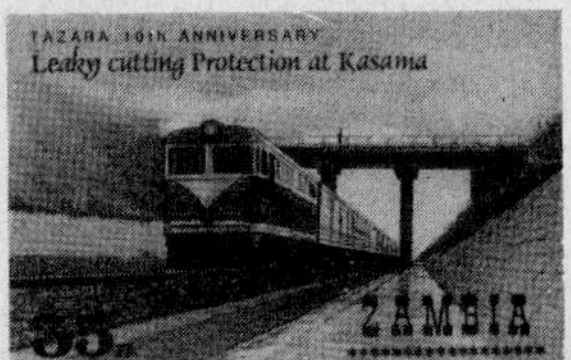

135. Train in Kasama Cutting.

1986. 10th Anniv. of Tanzania–Zambia Railway. Multicoloured.

No.	Description		
472	35 n. Type **135**	25	10
473	1 k. 25 Train leaving Tunnel No. 21	45	50
474	1 k. 70 Train between Tunnels No. 6 and 7	50	70
475	5 k. Trains at Mpika Station	1·00	2·25

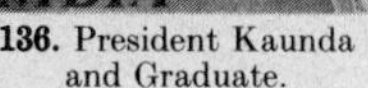

136. President Kaunda and Graduate.

1987. 20th Anniv. of University of Zambia. Multicoloured.

No.	Description		
476.	35 n. Type **136**	25	10
477.	1 k. 25 University Badge (vert.)	75	60
478.	1 k. 60 University Statue	85	85
479.	5 k. President Kaunda laying foundation stone (vert.)	2·50	4·00

137. Arms of Kitwe.

138. Chestnut-headed Crake.

1987. Arms of Zambian Towns. Mult.

No.	Description		
480.	35 n. Type **137**	10	10
481.	1 k. 25 Ndola	15	10
482.	1 k. 70 Lusaka	20	25
483.	20 k. Livingstone	2·40	4·00

1987. Birds (1st series). Multicoloured.

No.	Description		
484	5 n. Cloud-scraping cisticola	10	10
485	10 n. White-winged starling	10	10
486a	20 n. on 1 n. Yellow swamp warbler	20	20
487	25 n. Type **138**	65	40
488	30 n. Red-fronted barbet ("Miombo pied barbet")	10	10
489	35 n. Black and rufous swallow	75	50
490	40 n. Wattled crane	10	10
491	50 n. Red-throated heron ("Slaty egret")	10	10
492	75 n. on 2 n. Olive-flanked robin chat	30	50
493	1 k. Bradfield's hornbill	80	20
494	1 k. 25 Boulton's puff-backed flycatcher ("Margaret's Batis")	80	70
495	1 k. 60 Anchieta's sunbird	80	70
496	1 k. 65 on 30 n. Red-fronted barbet	30	60
497	1 k. 70 Boehm's bee eater	1·00	85
498	1 k. 95 Perrin's bush shrike	1·00	85
499	2 k. Whale-headed stork ("Shoebill")	35	35
500	5 k. Taita falcon	1·25	70
501	10 k. on 50 n. Red-throated heron	1·10	1·75
502	20 k. on 2 k. Whale-headed stork	2·10	3·00

Nos. 491, 493/5 and 497/502 are larger, size 24 × 39 mm.

No. 502 is surcharged "K20". For No. 499 surcharged "K20.00" see No. 594.

139. Look-out Tree, Livingstone.

1987. Tourism. Multicoloured.

No.	Description		
503	35 n. Type **139**	30	15
504	1 k. 25 Rafting on Zambezi	30	25
505	1 k. 70 Tourists photographing lions, Luangwa Valley	1·25	90
506	10 k. Eastern white pelicans	5·00	5·00

1987. Various stamps surch. with new value.

(a) Nos. 432/5.

No.	Description		
507. **127**.	3 k. on 25 n. mult.	55	55
508. –	6 k. on 45 n. blue and gold	1·00	1·00
509. –	10 k. on 55 n. blue and gold	1·60	1·60
510. –	20 k. on 5 k. mult.	3·25	3·75

(b) Nos. 453/7.

No.	Description		
511.	3 k. on 35 n. Princess Elizabeth at Flower Ball, Savoy Hotel, 1951	55	55
512.	4 k. on 1 k. 25 With Prince Andrew, Lusaka Airport, 1979	65	65
513.	6 k. on 1 k. 70 With President Kaunda	1·00	1·00
514.	10 k. on 1 k. 95 In Luxembourg, 1976	1·60	1·60
515.	20 k. on 5 k. At Crown Agents Head Office, London, 1983	3·25	3·75

(c) Nos. 460/3.

No.	Description		
516.	3 k. on 35 n. Type **132**	55	55
517.	6 k. on 1 k. 25 Player kicking ball	1·00	1·00
518.	10 k. on 1 k. 70 Two players competing for ball	1·60	1·60
519.	20 k. on 5 k. Player scoring goal	3·25	3·75

(d) Nos. 464/7.

No.	Description		
520. **133**.	3 k. on 1 k. 25 mult.	55	55
521. –	6 k. on 1 k. 70 mult.	1·00	1·00
522. –	10 k. on 2 k. mult.	1·60	1·60
523. –	20 k. on 5 k. blue and black	3·25	3·75

141. De Havilland "Beaver".

1987. 20th Anniv. of Zambia Airways. Aircraft. Multicoloured.

No.	Description		
524.	35 n. Type **141**	45	10
525.	1 k. 70 Douglas "DC-10"	1·25	55
526.	5 k. Douglas "DC-3 Dakota"	2·75	2·25
527.	10 k. Boeing "707"	4·50	4·75

142. Friesian/Holstein Cow.

1987. 40th Anniv. of F.A.O. Multicoloured.

No.	Description		
528.	35 n. Type **142**	10	10
529.	1 k. 25 Simmental bull	20	25
530.	1 k. 70 Sussex bull	25	30
531.	20 k. Brahman bull	2·25	3·00

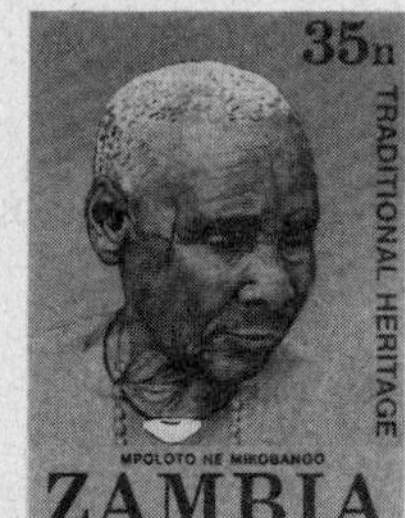

143. Mpoloto Ne Mikobango.

1987. People of Zambia. Multicoloured.

No.	Description		
532.	35 n. Type **143**	10	10
533.	1 k. 25 Zintaka	20	25
534.	1 k. 70 Mufuluhi	25	30
535.	10 k. Ntebwe	1·40	1·50
536.	20 k. Kubangwa Aa Mbulunga	2·75	3·00

144. Black Lechwe at Waterhole.

1987. Black Lechwe. Multicoloured.

No.	Description		
537.	50 n. Type **144**	40	10
538.	2 k. Black lechwe resting by pool (horiz.)	1·25	40
539.	2 k. 50 Running through water (horiz.)	1·40	70
540.	10 k. Watching for danger	3·25	3·25

145 Cassava Roots

1988. International Fund for Agricultural Development. Multicoloured.

No.	Description		
542	50 n. Type **145**	10	10
543	2 k. 50 Fishing	60	50
544	2 k. 85 Farmer and cattle	65	55
545	10 k. Picking coffee beans	1·25	1·40

146 Breast feeding

1988. U.N.I.C.E.F. Child Survival Campaign. Multicoloured.

No.	Description		
546	50 n. Type **146**	15	10
547	2 k. Growth monitoring	35	30
548	2 k. 85 Immunization	45	50
549	10 k. Oral rehydration	1·25	2·50

147 Asbestos Cement

1988. Preferential Trade Area Fair. Mult.

No.	Description		
550	50 n. Type **147**	10	10
551	2 k. 35 Textiles	25	30
552	2 k. 50 Tea	30	40
553	10 k. Poultry	1·25	2·50

148 Emergency Food Distribution

1988. 125th Anniv of International Red Cross. Multicoloured.

No.	Description		
554	50 n. Type **148**	15	10
555	2 k. 50 Giving first aid	40	50
556	2 k. 85 Practising bandaging	45	60
557	10 k. Jean Henri Dunant (founder)	1·50	2·50

149 Aardvark

1988. Endangered Species of Zambia. Mult.

No.	Description		
558	50 n. Type **149**	15	10
559	2 k. Temminck's ground pangolin	40	35
560	2 k. 85 Hunting dog	50	60
561	20 k. Black rhinoceros and calf	4·50	5·50

150 Boxing

1988. Olympic Games, Seoul. Multicoloured.

No.	Description		
562	50 n. Type **150**	15	10
563	2 k. Athletics	30	40
564	2 k. 50 Hurdling	35	50
565	20 k. Football	2·75	4·50

151 Red Toad

1989. Frogs and Toads. Multicoloured.

No.	Description		
567	50 n. Type **151**	15	10
568	2 k. 50 Puddle frog	50	50
569	2 k. 85 Marbled reed frog	55	65
570	10 k. Young reed frogs	1·60	2·75

152 Common Slit-faced Bat

1989. Bats. Multicoloured.

No.	Description		
571	50 n. Type **152**	15	10
572	2 k. 50 Little free-tailed bat	45	55
573	2 k. 85 Hildebrandt's horseshoe bat	55	70
574	10 k. Peters' epauletted fruit bat	1·50	2·75

153 Pope John Paul II and Map of Zambia

1989. Visit of Pope John Paul II. Designs each with inset portrait. Multicoloured.

No.	Description		
575	50 n. Type **153**	40	15
576	6 k. 85 Peace dove with olive branch	2·00	2·25
577	7 k. 85 Papal arms	2·25	2·75
578	10 k. Victoria Falls	3·00	3·75

1989. Various stamps surch with new value.

(a) On Nos. 339, 341/3, 345/6, 349 and 351.

579 1 k. 20 on 35 n. Tonga Ila granary and house .. 15 15
580 3 k. 75 on 5 n. Pottery making 20 20
581 8 k. 11 on 10 n. Thatching 40 40
582 9 k. on 30 n. Makishi tightrope dancer .. 40 40
583 10 k. on 75 n. Women carrying water (38 × 26 mm) 40 40
584 18 k. 50 on 2 k. Pipe-smoking Gwembe Valley Belle (38 × 26 mm) .. 90 90
585 19 k. 50 on 12 n. Mushroom picking 90 90
586 20 k. 50 on 18 n. Millet grinding on stone .. 90 90

(b) On Nos. 484, 489, 493/5 and 497/500

587 70 n. on 35 n. Black and rufous swallow 10 10
588 3 k. on 5 n. Cloud-scraping cisticola 20 20
589 8 k. on 1 k. 25 Boulton's puff-back flycatcher .. 40 40
590 9 k. 90 on 1 k. 70 Boehm's bee eater 50 50
591 10 k. 40 on 1 k. 60 Anchieta's sunbird .. 50 50
592 12 k. 50 on 1 k. Bradfield's hornbill 60 60
593 15 k. on 1 k. 95 Perrin's bush shrike 70 70
594 20 k. on 2 k. Whale-headed stork 90 90
595 20 k. 35 on 5 k. Taita falcon 90 90

No. 594 shows the surcharge as "K20.00". The previously listed 20 k. on 2 k., No. 499, is surcharged "K20" only.

156 "Parinari curatellifolia"

1989. Edible Fruits. Multicoloured.

596 50 n. Type **156** 15 10
597 6 k. 50 "Uapaca kirkiana" 1·25 1·50
598 6 k. 85 Wild fig .. .. 1·25 1·75
599 10 k. Bottle palm .. 2·25 2·75

157 "Lamarckiana sp."

1989. Grasshoppers. Multicoloured.

600 70 n. Type **157** 15 10
601 10 k. 40 "Dictyopharus sp." .. .. .. 1·25 1·50
602 12 k. 50 "Cymatomena sp." 1·50 1·75
603 15 k. "Phymateus iris" .. 2·00 2·25

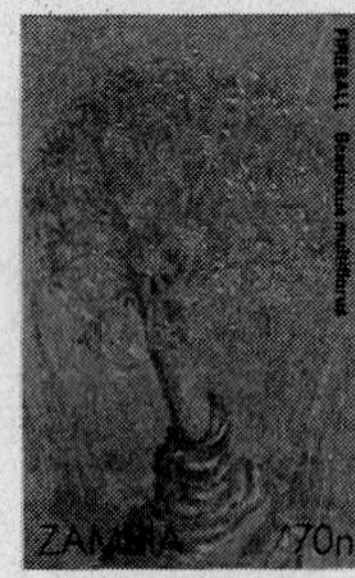

158 Fireball

1989. Christmas. Flowers. Multicoloured.

604 70 n. Type **158** 15 10
605 10 k. 40 Flame lily .. 1·00 1·25
606 12 k. 50, Foxglove lily .. 1·40 1·60
607 20 k. Vlei lily .. .. 2·40 2·75

159 Post Van, Postman on Bicycle and Main Post Office, Lusaka

1990. "Stamp World London 90" International Stamp Exhibition. Multicoloured.

608 1 k. 20 Type **159** 10 10
609 19 k. 50 Zambia 1980 18 n. butterflies stamp .. 1·75 1·75
610 20 k. 50, Rhodesia and Nyasaland 1962 9d. and Northern Rhodesia 1925 ½d. stamps .. .. 1·75 1·75
611 50 k. 1840 Penny Black and Maltese Cross cancellation .. .. .. 3·75 4·00

160 Footballer and Ball

1990. World Cup Football Championship, Italy.

612 **160** 1 k. 20 multicoloured 10 10
613 – 18 k. 50 multicoloured 1·50 1·50
614 – 19 k. 50 multicoloured 1·50 1·50
615 – 20 k. 50 multicoloured 1·50 1·50

DESIGNS: 18 k. 50 to 20 k. 50 Different football scenes.

161 Road Tanker

1990. 10th Anniv of Southern African Development Co-ordination Conference. Each showing map of Southern Africa. Multicoloured.

617 1 k. 20 Type **161** 15 10
618 19 k. 50 Telecommunications .. .. .. 1·40 1·40
619 20 k. 50 "Regional Co-operation" .. .. 1·40 1·40
620 50 k. Transporting coal by cable .. .. .. 4·50 4·50

162 Irrigation

1990. 26th Anniv of Independence. Mult.

621 1 k. 20 Type **162** 10 10
622 19 k. 50 Shoe factory .. 80 80
623 20 k. 50 Mwembeshi II satellite earth station .. 85 85
624 50 k. "Mother and Child" (statue) .. .. 2·00 2·50

1990. Birds (2nd series). As T **138**. Mult.

625 10 n. Livingstone's fly-catcher 10 10
626 15 n. Bar-winged weaver 10 10
627 30 n. Purple-throated cuckoo shrike 10 10
628 50 n. Retz's red-billed helmet shrike 10 10
629 50 n. As 10 n. 10 10
630 1 k. As 15 n. 10 10
631 1 k. 20 Western bronze-naped pigeon 10 10
632 2 k. As 30 n. 10 10
633 3 k. As 50 n. 10 10
634 5 k. As 1 k. 20 .. .. 10 10
635 15 k. Corncrake 10 10
636 20 k. Dickinson's kestrel .. 10 10
637 20 k. 50 As 20 k. 10 10
638 50 k. Barrow's bustard ("Denham's bustard") 20 25

Nos. 635/8 are larger, size 23 × 39 mm.

163 The Bird and the Snake

1991. International Literacy Year. Folklore. Multicoloured.

639 1 k. 20 Type **163** 15 10
640 18 k. 50 Kalulu and the Leopard .. .. 1·25 1·40
641 19 k. 50 The Mouse and the Lion .. .. .. 1·25 1·40
642 20 k. 50 Kalulu and the Hippopotamus .. 1·25 1·40

164 Genet

1991. Small Carnivores. Multicoloured.

643 1 k. 20 Type **164** 15 10
644 18 k. 50 Civet .. .. 1·50 1·50
645 19 k. 50 Serval .. .. 1·50 1·50
646 20 k. 50 African wild cat .. 1·50 1·50

1991. Nos. 441/4 surch **K2**.

647 2 k. on 20 n. Type **129** .. 65 55
648 2 k. on 45 n. Postman and Livingstone Post Office, 1950 .. .. .. 65 55
649 2 k. on 55 n. Postman and Kalomo Post Office, 1902 65 55
650 2 k. on 5 k. African Trans-Continental Telegraph Line under construction, 1900 .. .. .. 65 55

166 Woman Cooking

1991. Soya Promotion Campaign. Mult.

651 1 k. Type **166** 10 10
652 2 k. Soya bean and field .. 10 10
653 5 k. Mother feeding child 15 15
654 20 k. Healthy and malnourished children .. 1·00 1·25
655 50 k. President Kaunda holding child .. .. 2·00 2·25

1991. Various stamps surch **K2**.

656 **130** 2 k. on 20 n. mult ..
657 **127** 2 k. on 25 n. mult ..
658 – 2 k. on 28 n. mult (No. 344) .. ..
659 – 2 k. on 28 n. mult (No. 393) .. ..
660 – 2 k. on 28 n. mult (No. 401) .. ..
661 – 2 k. on 28 n. mult (No. 418) .. ..
662 – 2 k. on 32 n. mult (No. 422) .. ..
663 – 2 k. on 35 n. mult (No. 453) .. ..
664 **134** 2 k. on 35 n. mult ..
665 **137** 2 k. on 35 n. mult ..
666 – 2 k. on 45 n. mult (No. 427) .. ..
667 – 2 k. on 45 n. black, blue & lt bl (No. 430)
668 – 2 k. on 45 n. blue and gold (No. 433) ..
669 – 2 k. on 45 n. black, blue & brn (No. 446)
670 – 2 k. on 1 k. 60 mult (No. 470) .. ..
671 – 2 k. on 1 k. 70 mult (No. 451) .. ..
672 – 2 k. on 1 k. 70 mult (No. 482) .. ..
673 – 2 k. on 5 k. mult (No. 435) .. ..
674 – 2 k. on 5 k. mult (No. 452) .. ..
675 – 2 k. on 6 k. 50 mult (No. 597) .. ..
676 – 2 k. on 6 k. 85 mult (No. 576) .. ..
677 – 2 k. on 6 k. 85 mult (No. 598) .. ..
678 – 2 k. on 7 k. 85 mult (No. 577) .. ..

167 Chilubula Church near Kasama

1991. 500th Birth Anniv of St. Ignatius Loyola. Multicoloured.

679 1 k. Type **167** 10 10
680 2 k. Chikuni Church near Monze 10 10
681 20 k. Bishop Joseph du Pont .. .. .. 1·00 1·25
682 50 k. Saint Ignatius Loyola 2·00 2·25

168 "Adansonia digitata"

1991. Flowering Trees. Multicoloured.

683 1 k. Type **168** 10 10
684 2 k. "Dichrostachys cinerea" 10 10
685 10 k. "Stereospermum kunthianum" 50 60
686 30 k. "Azana garckeana" 1·40 1·75

No. 685 is inscribed "Sterospermum" in error.

1992. 40th Anniv of Queen Elizabeth II's Accession. As T **143** of Ascension. Mult.

687 4 k. Queen's House .. 10 10
688 32 k. Traditional village 60 55
689 35 k. Fishermen hauling nets 65 70
690 38 k. Three portraits of Queen Elizabeth .. 75 85
691 50 k. Queen Elizabeth II 90 1·50

169 "Disa hamatopetala"

1992. Orchids. Multicoloured.

692 1 k. Type **169** 10 10
693 2 k. "Eulophia paivaeana" 15 15
694 5 k. "Eulophia quartiniana" 30 30
695 20 k. "Aerangis verdickii" 1·50 2·00

170 Kasinja Mask

1992. Tribal Masks. Multicoloured.

696	1 k. Type **170**	10	10
697	2 k. Chizaluke	10	10
698	10 k. Mwanapweu ..	25	30
699	30 k. Maliya	90	1·25

171 Bushbuck

1992. Antelopes. Multicoloured.

700	4 k. Type **171**	10	10
701	40 k. Eland	40	40
702	45 k. Roan antelope ..	45	45
703	100 k. Sable antelope ..	1·10	1·40

172 DH66 Hercules

1992. 60th Anniv of Airmail Service. Mult.

704	4 k. Type **172**	10	10
705	40 k. VC10	50	50
706	45 k. "C" Class flying boat	55	55
707	100 k. DC10	1·25	1·50

173 Wise Men with Gifts

1992. Christmas. Multicoloured.

708	10 k. Type **173**	10	10
709	80 k. Nativity	80	90
710	90 k. Angelic choir ..	90	1·00
711	100 k. Angel and shepherds	1·00	1·25

174 Hurdling

1992. Olympic Games, Barcelona. Mult.

713	10 k. Type **174**	10	10
714	40 k. Boxing	40	40
715	80 k. Judo	80	90
716	100 k. Cycling	1·00	1·25

INDEX

Countries can be quickly located by referring to the index at the end of this volume.

175 Nkundalila Falls

1993. Waterfalls. Multicoloured.

717	50 k. Type **175**	25	25
718	200 k. Chishimba Falls ..	90	95
719	250 k. Chipoma Falls ..	1·10	1·25
720	300 k. Lumangwe Falls ..	1·40	1·60

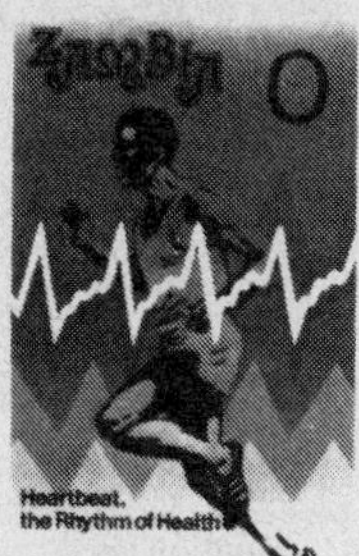

176 Athlete and Cardiograph

1993. Heartbeat Campaign. Multicoloured.

721	(O) Type **176**	20	25
722	(P) Heart and cardiograph	30	35

These stamps were initially sold at 50 k. (No. 721 for ordinary post) and 80 k. (No. 722 for priority mail). These face values may increase to reflect future postage rates.

POSTAGE DUE STAMPS

D 3.

1964.

D 11.	D 3.	1d. orange	30	1·00
D 12.		2d. blue	35	1·40
D 13.		3d. lake	45	1·60
D 14.		4d. blue	45	2·00
D 15.		6d. purple	45	2·25
D 16.		1s. green	55	4·25

APPENDIX

The following stamps have either been issued in excess of postal needs, or have not been made available to the public in reasonable quantities at face value.

1984.

Olympic Games, Los Angeles. 90 n × 5, each embossed on gold foil.

1986.

Classic Cars 1 k. 50 × 25, each embossed on gold foil.

ZANZIBAR

A Br. Protectorate consisting of several islands off the coast of Tanganyika. E. Africa. Independent in 1963 and a republic within the Br. Commonwealth in 1964. The "United Republic of Tanganyika and Zanzibar" was proclaimed in July 1964, and the country was later renamed Tanzania. Separate issues for Zanzibar ceased on 1 Jan. 1968. and Tanzania stamps became valid for the whole country.

1895. 16 annas = 1 rupee.
1908. 100 cents = 1 rupee.
1936. 100 cents = 1 shilling.

1895. Stamps of India (Queen Victoria) optd. **Zanzibar.**

3.	**23.**	½ a. turquoise	3·00	2·50
4.		1 a. purple	3·25	3·00
5.		1½ a. brown	4·00	3·00
6.	–	2 a. blue	3·75	3·50
8.	–	2½ a. green	5·00	4·25
10.	–	3 a. orange	7·50	8·50
12.	–	4 a. green (No. 96) ..	8·00	9·50
13.	–	6 a. brown (No. 80) ..	11·00	10·00
15.	–	8 a. mauve	9·00	18·00
16.	–	12 a. purple on red ..	14·00	10·00
17.	–	1 r. grey	65·00	65·00
18.	**37.**	1 r. green and red ..	10·00	17·00
19.	**38.**	2 r. red and orange ..	28·00	45·00
20.		3 r. brown and green ..	35·00	42·00
21.		5 r. biue and violet ..	30·00	48·00

1895. Nos. 4/6 surch. **2½.**

23	**23**	2½ on 1 a. purple ..	£130	£100
22		2½ on 1½ a. brown ..	32·00	30·00
26	–	2½ on 2 a. blue ..	35·00	22·00

1896. Stamps of British East Africa (Queen Victoria) optd. **Zanzibar.**

41.	**11.**	½ a. green	23·00	16·00
42.		1 a. red	22·00	15·00
43.		2½ a. blue	75·00	42·00
44.		4½ a. yellow	35·00	48·00
45.		5 a. brown	40·00	22·00
46.		7½ a. mauve	26·00	38·00

13. Sultan Seyyid Hamed-bin-Thwain

19. Sultan Seyyid Hamoud-bin-Mahommed bin Said.

1896. The Rupee values are larger.

178	**13**	½ a. green and red ..	70	35
179		1 a. blue and red ..	70	55
180		2 a. brown and red ..	1·60	75
181		2½ a. blue and red ..	1·00	30
182		3 a. grey and red ..	2·25	60
183		4 a. green and red ..	1·50	1·00
184		4½ a. orange and red ..	3·25	70
166		5 a. brown and red ..	2·25	2·25
167		7½ a. mauve and red ..	2·25	2·25
187		8 a. olive and red ..	5·00	2·25
169	–	1 r. blue and red ..	9·00	9·00
171	–	2 r. green and red ..	14·00	9·50
172	–	3 r. purple and red ..	20·00	9·50
173	–	4 r. red	14·00	13·00
174	–	5 r. brown and red ..	19·00	13·00

1896. Surch. **2½.**

175.	**13.**	2½ on 4 a. green and red	48·00	30·00

1899. The Rupee values are larger.

188.	**19.**	½ a. green and red ..	70	30
189.		1 a. blue and red ..	1·50	20
190.		1 a. red	75	10
191.		2 a. brown and red ..	1·00	40
192.		2½ a. blue and red ..	1·00	50
193.		3 a. grey and red ..	1·25	1·40
194.		4 a. green and red ..	1·25	1·00
195.		4½ a. orange and red ..	4·00	2·25
196.		4½ a. black and red ..	7·00	7·00
197.		5 a. brown and red ..	1·50	1·25
198.		7½ a. mauve and red ..	2·25	3·50
199.		8 a. olive and red ..	2·25	4·50
200.	–	1 r. blue and red ..	15·00	12·00
201.	–	2 r. green and red ..	15·00	15·00
202.	–	3 r. purple and red ..	20·00	25·00
203.	–	4 r. red	30·00	40·00
204.	–	5 r. brown and red ..	40·00	48·00

1904. Surch. in words.

205.	**19.**	1 on 4½ a. orange and red	1·40	3·25
206.		1 on 4½ a. black and red ..	4·25	15·00
207.		2 on 4 a. green and red ..	13·00	16·00
208.		2½ on 7½ a. mauve and red	12·00	18·00
209.		2½ on 8 a. olive and red ..	14·00	28·00

23. Monogram of Sultan Seyyid Ali bin Hamoud bin Naherud.

1904. The Rupee values are larger.

210.	**23.**	½ a. green	1·00	50
211.		1 a. red	1·00	10
212.		2 a. brown	1·25	40
213.		2½ a. blue	2·00	35
214.		3 a. grey	1·50	1·25
215.		4 a. green	2·25	1·25
216.		4½ a. black	3·00	2·50
217.		5 a. brown	3·25	1·25
218.		7½ a. mauve	3·75	5·50
219.		8 a. olive	3·75	2·50
220.	–	1 r. blue and red ..	16·00	8·50
221.	–	2 r. green and red ..	12·00	26·00
222.	–	3 r. violet and red ..	38·00	65·00
223.	–	4 r. deep red and red ..	42·00	80·00
224.	–	5 r. brown and red ..	42·00	85·00

25.

27. Sultan Ali bin Hamoud.

26.

28. View of Port.

1908.

225	**25**	1 c. grey	30	25
226		3 c. green	1·60	10
227		6 c. red	3·75	10
228		10 c. brown	1·50	1·75
229a		12 c. violet	4·00	60
230	**26**	15 c. blue	4·50	40
231		25 c. brown	2·50	80
232		50 c. green	3·25	3·50
233		75 c. black	6·00	9·00
234	**27**	1 r. green	15·00	6·00
235		2 r. violet	12·00	14·00
236		3 r. brown	16·00	40·00
237		4 r. red	30·00	70·00
238		5 r. blue	35·00	50·00
239	**28**	10 r. green and brown ..	65·00	£130
240		20 r. black and green ..	£160	£275
241		30 r. black and brown	£250	£400
242		40 r. black and orange ..	£400	
243		50 r. black and mauve ..	£350	
244		100 r. black and blue ..	£650	
245		200 r. black and blue ..	£950	

29. Sultan Kalif bin Harub.

30. Sailing Canoe.

31. Dhow.

1913.

246	**29.**	1 c. grey	15	20
262		3 c. green	50	10
278		3 c. orange	15	10
279		4 c. green	50	60
280		6 c. red	30	50
281		6 c. purple on blue ..	35	10
264		8 c. purple on yellow ..	60	2·50
249		10 c. brown	80	75
265		10 c. green on yellow ..	60	35
283		12 c. violet	30	30
284		12 c. red	40	35
251		15 c. blue	1·00	30
286		20 c. blue	1·00	30
252		25 c. brown	80	45
288		50 c. green	1·25	2·00
254		75 c. black	1·75	1·75
290	**30.**	1 r. green	2·00	1·60
291		2 r. violet	2·50	5·00
292		3 r. brown	4·00	6·50
293		4 r. red	10·00	25·00
259		5 r. blue	25·00	27·00
260	**31.**	10 r. green and brown ..	65·00	£100
260a		20 r. black and green ..	85·00	£180
260b		30 r. black and brown ..	£110	£250
260c		40 r. black and orange	£225	£375
260d		50 r. black and purple ..	£225	£375
260e		100 r. black and blue ..	£300	
260f		200 r. brown and black	£600	

32. Sultan Kalif bin Harub. 33.

1926.

299. 32. 1 c. brown 15 10
300. 3 c. orange 20 15
301. 4 c. green 20 30
302. 6 c. violet 20 10
303. 8 c. grey .. .. 90 3·50
304. 10 c. olive 85 40
305. 12 c. red .. .. 1·50 10
306. 20 c. blue 40 30
307. 25 c. purple on yellow .. 4·00 2·50
308. 50 c. red .. .. 1·00 35
309. 75 c. brown .. .. 4·50 8·50

1936.

310. 33. 5 c. green 10 10
311. 10 c. black 10 10
312. 15 c. red 10 15
313. 20 c. orange 10 10
314. 25 c. purple on yellow .. 10 10
315. 30 c. blue 10 10
316. 40 c. brown 15 10
317. 50 c. red 20 10
318. 30. 1 s. green 45 10
319. 2 s. violet 55 40
320. 5 s. red .. .. 2·75 4·00
321. 7 s. 50 c. blue .. .. 10·00 9·50
322. 31. 10 s. green and brown .. 7·00 9·00

In Type 33 the letters of the word "CENTS" are without serifs. In Type 32 they have serifs.

36. Sultan Kalif bin Harub.

1936. Silver Jubilee of Sultan.

323. 36. 10 c. black and olive .. 70 30
324. 20 c. black and purple .. 90 30
325. 30 c. black and blue .. 2·75 35
326. 50 c. black and red .. 3·50 90

37. "Sham Alam" (Sultan's dhow).

1944. Bicentenary of Al Busaid Dynasty.

327. 37. 10 c. blue 30 50
328. 20 c. red .. .. 30 1·00
329. 50 c. green 30 30
330. 1 s. purple 30 45

1946. Victory. Optd. **VICTORY ISSUE 8th JUNE 1946.**

331. 33. 10 c. black 20 20
332. 30 c. blue 20 40

1945. Silver Wedding. As T 10/11 of Aden.

333 20 c. orange 30 60
334 10 s. brown .. .. 16·00 22·00

1949. U.P.U. As T 20/23 of Antigua.

335. 20 c. orange 40 70
336. 30 c. blue .. .. 1·40 70
337. 50 c. mauve .. .. 1·50 85
338. 1 s. green .. .. 1·50 1·75

39. Sultan Kalif bin Harub.

40. Seyyid Khalifa Schools, Beit-el-Ras.

1952.

339. 39. 5 c. black 10 10
340. 10 c. orange 10 10
341. 15 c. green 30 60
342. 20 c. red 30 30
343. 25 c. purple 45 10
344. 30 c. green 30 10
345. 35 c. blue .. .. 30 1·00
346. 40 c. brown 30 60
347. 50 c. violet 30 10
348. 40. 1 s. green and brown .. 30 10
349. 2 s. blue and purple .. 85 50
350. 5 s. black and red .. 1·50 2·00
351. 7 s.50 black & green .. 18·00 23·00
352. 10 s. red and black .. 9·00 3·75

41. Sultan Kalif bin Harub.

1954. 75th Birthday of Sultan.

353. 41. 15 c. green 10 10
354. 20 c. red 10 10
355. 30 c. blue 10 10
356. 50 c. purple 15 10
357. 1 s. 25 red 15 60

42. Cloves. 47. Dimbani Mosque.

43. "Ummoja Wema" (dhow).

1957.

358. 42. 5 c. orange and green 10 10
359. 10 c. green and red .. 10 10
360. 43. 15 c. green and sepia 10 60
361. – 20 c. blue 10 10
362. – 25 c. brown and black 10 10
363. 43. 30 c. red and black .. 15 10
364. – 35 c. slate and green 15 15
365. – 40 c. brown and black 15 10
366. – 50 c. blue and myrtle 15 10
367. 47. 1 s. red and black .. 20 10
368. 43. 1 s. 25 c. slate and red 1·00 10
369. 47. 2 s. orange and green 75 50
370. – 5 s. blue .. .. 3·75 2·00
371. – 7 s. 50 c. green .. 3·75 4·00
372. – 10 s. red .. .. 3·75 3·25

DESIGNS—As Type 47—HORIZ. 20 c. Sultan's Barge. 25 c., 35 c., 50 c. Map of E. African coast. VERT. 40 c. Minaret Mosque. As Type 43—VERT. 5 s., 7 s. 50 c., 10 s. Kibweni Palace.

49. Sultan Seyyid Sir Abdulla bin Khalifa.

1961. As 1957 issue but with portrait of Sultan Sir Abdulla as in T 49.

373. 5 c. orange and green .. 10 10
374. 10 c. green and red .. 10 10
375. 15 c. green and sepia .. 20 80
376. 20 c. blue 15 10
377. 25 c. brown and black .. 15 10
378. 30 c. red and black .. 60 10
379. 35 c. slate and green .. 80 30
380. 40 c. brown and black .. 30 10
381. 50 c. blue and myrtle .. 30 10
382. 1 s. red and black .. 40 10
383. 1 s. 25 slate and red .. 1·00 35
384. 2 s. orange and green .. 40 40
385. 5 s. blue .. .. 90 1·60
386. 7 s. 50 green .. .. 2·25 11·00
387. 10 s. red .. .. 2·25 7·00
388. 20 s. sepia (Kibweni Palace) .. .. 17·00 27·00

50. "Protein Foods".

1963. Freedom from Hunger.

389. 50. 1 s. 30 sepia 80 30

51. Zanzibar Clove.

1963. Independence. Inscr. "UHURU 1963" Multicoloured.

390. 30 c. Type 51 .. .. 10 20
391. 50 c. "To Prosperity" (Zanzibar doorway) .. 10 30
392. 1 s. "Religious Tolerance" (mosque and churches) 10 1·75
393. 2 s. 50 "Towards the Light" (Mangapwani Cave) .. .. 15 2·75

No. 392 is horiz.

1964. Optd. **Jamhuri 1964** (a) Nos. 373/88.

414 5 c. orange and green .. 10 10
415 10 c. green and red .. 10 10
416 15 c. green and sepia .. 10 10
417 20 c. blue 10 10
418 25 c. brown and black .. 10 10
419 30 c. red and black .. 10 10
420 35 c. slate and green .. 10 10
421 40 c. brown and black .. 10 10
422 50 c. blue and myrtle .. 10 10
423 1 s. red and black .. 10 10
424 1 s. 25 slate and red .. 50 20
425 2 s. orange and green .. 30 20
426 5 s. blue 50 35
427 7 s. 50 green .. .. 65 1·50
428 10 s. red .. .. 75 1·50
429 20 s. sepia .. .. 1·50 2·25

(b) Nos. 390/3.

430. 30 c. multicoloured .. 10 10
431. 50 c. multicoloured .. 10 10
432. 1 s. 30 multicoloured .. 10 10
433. 2 s. 50 multicoloured .. 15 20

The opt. is in two lines on Nos. 421, 423, 425/429, 430, 431, 433.

NOTE. For the set inscribed "UNITED REPUBLIC OF TANGANYIKA & ZANZIBAR" see Nos. 124/7 of Tanganyika.

58. Axe, Spear and Dagger.

1964. Multicoloured.

434. 5 c. Type 58 .. .. 10 10
435. 10 c. Bow and arrow breaking chains 10 10
436. 15 c. Type 58 .. .. 10 10
437. 20 c. As 10 c. 10 10
438. 25 c. Zanzibari with rifle .. 10 10
439. 30 c. Zanzibari breaking manacles 10 10
440. 40 c. As 25 c. 10 10
441. 50 c. As 30 c. 10 10
442. 1 s. Zanzibari, flag and sun 10 10
443. 1 s. 30 Hands breaking chains (horiz.) 15 10
444. 2 s. Hand waving flag (horiz.) 20 10
445. 5 s. Map of Zanzibar and Pemba on flag (horiz.) .. 55 30
446. 10 s. Flag on map .. 1·75 1·10
447. 20 s. National flag (horiz.) 2·25 10·00

68. Soldier and Maps.

1965. 1st Anniv. of Revolution.

448. 68. 20 c. lt. grn. & grn. .. 10 10
449. – 30 c. brown & orange 10 10
450. 68. 1 s. 30 bl. & dp. bl. .. 10 10
451. – 2 s. 50 violet and red .. 10 15

DESIGNS—VERT. 30 c., 2 s. 50, Building Construction.

70. Planting Rice.

1965. Agricultural Development.

452. 70. 20 c. sepia and blue .. 10 50
453. – 30 c. sepia and mauve 10 50
454. – 1 s. 30 sepia & orange 30 1·00
455. 70. 2 s. 50 sepia and green 50 3·00

DESIGN: 30 c. and 1 s. 30, Hands holding rice.

72. Freighter, Tractor, Factory, and Open Book and Torch.

1966. 2nd Anniv. of Revolution. Mult.

456. 20 c. Type 72 .. .. 10 10
457. 50 c. Soldier 10 10
458. 1 s. 30 Type 72 .. .. 15 10
459. 2 s. 50 Soldier 20 40

74. Tree-felling.

1966.

460. 74. 5 c. purple and olive 15 30
461. – 10 c. purple and green 15 30
462. – 15 c. purple and blue 15 30
463. – 20 c. blue and orange 15 10
464. – 25 c. purple & yellow 15 10
465. – 30 c. purple & yellow 15 10
466. – 40 c. brown and red .. 30 10
467. – 50 c. green and yellow 30 10
468. – 1 s. purple and blue .. 30 10
469. – 1 s. 30 purple & turq. 30 70
470. – 2 s. purple and green 30 30
471. – 5 s. red and blue .. 80 3·50
472. – 10 s. red and yellow .. 2·25 12·00
473. 74. 20 s. brown & mauve 4·25 18·00

DESIGNS—HORIZ. 10 c. 1 s. Clove cultivation. 15 c., 40 c. Chair-making. 20 c., 5 s. Lumumba College. 25 c., 1 s. 30, Agriculture. 30 c. 2 s. Agricultural workers. VERT. 50 c., 10 s. Zanzibar Street.

81. "Education".

1966. Introduction of Free Education.

474. 81. 50 c. black, bl. & orge. 10 40
475. 1 s. 30 black, blue & green 15 65
476. 2 s. 50 black, blue and pink .. .. .. 30 3·75

82. A.S.P. Flag.

1967. 10th Anniv. of Afro-Shirazi Party.

477.	82.	30 c. multicoloured ..	10	40
478.	–	50 c. multicoloured ..	10	40
479.	–	1 s. 30 multicoloured	10	80
480.	82.	2 s. 50 multicoloured	15	2·25

DESIGN—VERT. 50 c., 1 s. 30, Vice-President M. A. Karume of Tanzania, flag and crowd.

84. Voluntary Workers.

1967. Voluntary Workers Brigade.

481.	84.	1 s. 30 multicoloured	15	75
482.		2 s. 50 multicoloured	30	4·25

POSTAGE DUE STAMPS

Insufficiently prepaid.
Postage due.
1 cent.

D 1.

1930. Roul. or roul. × imperf.

D 1	D 1	1 c. black on orange	10·00	60·00
D 18		2 c. black on orange	5·50	17·00
D 3		3 c. black on orange	3·75	26·00
D 19		3 c. black on red ..	3·00	32·00
D 21		6 c. black on yellow	3·00	19·00
D 5		9 c. black on orange	2·25	14·00
D 6		12 c. black on orange	£5500	£5500
D 7		12 c. black on green	£1000	£550
D 22		12 c. black on blue ..	4·00	15·00
D 8		15 c. black on orange	2·50	14·00
D 9		18 c. black on orange	3·00	22·00
D 11		20 c. black on orange	3·75	26·00
D 12		21 c. black on orange	3·25	16·00
D 13		25 c. black on purple	£1900	£1200
D 14		25 c. black on orange	£5500	
D 23		25 c. black on red ..	9·00	40·00
D 24		25 c. black on lilac ..	7·00	28·00
D 15		31 c. black on orange	8·00	42·00
D 16		50 c. black on orange	20·00	80·00
D 17		75 c. black on orange	65·00	£160

D 3.

1936.

D 25	D 3.	5 c. violet	90	3·50
D 26		10 c. red	80	1·40
D 27		20 c. green	75	2·75
D 28a		30 c. brown	30	5·50
D 29a		40 c. blue	40	10·00
D 30a		1 s. grey	1·00	10·00

ZIL ELWANNYEN SESEL

Beginning in June 1980 stamps were issued for use in Zil Elwagne Sesel (Seychelles Outer Islands), including Aldabra, Coetivy, Farquhar and the Amirante Islands.

100 cents = 1 rupee.

A. Inscr. "ZIL ELOIGNE SESEL".

1980. As Nos. 404/19 of Seychelles but inscr. "ZIL ELOIGNE SESEL".

1.	–	5 c. multicoloured ..	15	20
2.	–	10 c. multicoloured ..	15	20
3.	–	15 c. multicoloured ..	15	20
4.	–	20 c. multicoloured ..	20	20
5.	–	25 c. multicoloured ..	60	30
6.	103.	40 c. multicoloured ..	30	30
7.	–	50 c. multicoloured ..	30	30
8.	–	75 c. multicoloured ..	35	30
9.	–	1 r. multicoloured ..	75	40
10.	–	1 r. 10 multicoloured ..	40	40
11.	–	1 r. 25 multicoloured ..	90	45
12.	–	1 r. 50 multicoloured ..	45	35
13a.	–	5 r. multicoloured ..	65	90
14a.	–	10 r. multicoloured ..	1·00	2·00
15a.	–	15 r. multicoloured ..	1·75	2·50
16.	–	20 r. multicoloured ..	2·00	3·25

2. "Cinq Juin".

1980. Travelling Post Office. Multicoloured.

17.	1 r. 50 Type 2	25	15
18.	2 r. 10 Hand-stamping covers	30	20
19.	5 r. Map of Zil Eloigne Sesel	55	40

3. Yellowfin Tuna.

1980. Marine Life. Multicoloured.

20.	1 r. 50 Type 3	20	15
21.	2 r. 10 Blue Marlin (fish) ..	35	20
22.	5 r. Sperm Whale ..	70	50

1981. Royal Wedding. As T 26/27 of Kiribati. Multicoloured.

23	40 c. "Royal Escape" ..	10	10
24	40 c. Prince Charles and Lady Diana Spencer ..	40	40
25	5 r. "Victoria and Albert"	40	40
31	5 r. As No. 24	75	1·00
27	10 r. "Britannia"	85	85
28	10 r. As No. 24	2·00	2·50

4. Wright's Skink.

1981. Wildlife. (1st series). Multicoloured.

32.	1 r. 40 Type 4	15	15
33.	2 r. 25 Tree Frog	20	20
34.	5 r. Robber Crab	40	40

See also Nos. 45/7.

5. "Cinq Juin" ("Communications").

1982. Island Development. Ships.

35.	5.	1 r. 75 black and orange ..	50	20
36.	–	1 r. 10 black and blue ..	60	30
37.	–	5 r. black and red ..	70	50

DESIGNS: 2 r. 10 "Junon" ("fisheries protection"). 5 r. "Diamond M. Dragon" (drilling ship).

B. Inscr. "ZIL ELWAGNE SESEL".

6. "Paulette".

1982. Local Mail Vessels. Multicoloured.

38.	40 c. Type 6	20	10
39.	1 r. 75 "Janette" ..	40	30
40.	2 r. 75 "Lady Esme" ..	50	40
41.	3 r. 50 "Cinq Juin" ..	60	50

7. Birds flying over Island.

1982. Aldabra, World Heritage Site. Mult.

42.	40 c. Type 7	30	15
43.	2 r. 75 Map of the atoll ..	70	35
44.	7 r. Giant Tortoises ..	1·25	75

8. Red Land Crab.

1983. Wildlife (2nd series). Multicoloured.

45.	1 r. 75 Type 8	25	25
46.	2 r. 75 Black Terrapin ..	35	35
47.	7 r. Madagascar Green Gecko	80	80

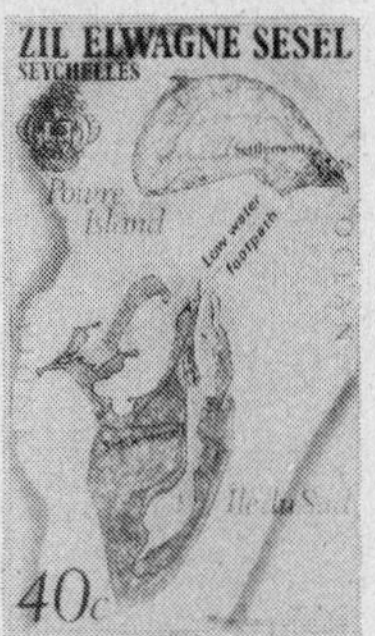

9. Map of Poivre Island and Ile du Sud.

1983. Island Maps. Multicoloured.

48.	40 c. Type 9	10	10
49.	1 r. 50 Ile des Roches ..	25	25
50.	2 r. 75 Astove Island ..	40	40
51.	7 r. Coetivy Island	1·10	1·10

10. Aldabra Warbler.

1983. Birds. Multicoloured.

53	5 c. Type 10	40	40
54	10 c. Zebra dove ("Barred ground dove") ..	80	40
55	15 c. Madagascar nightjar ..	10	10
56	20 c. Madagascar cisticola ("Malagasy grass warbler")	10	10
57	25 c. Madagascar white eye	20	30
58	40 c. Mascarene fody ..	10	10
59	50 c. White-throated rail ..	80	30
60	75 c. Black bulbul	20	25
61	2 r. Western reef heron ("Dimorphic little egret")	1·75	85
62	2 r. 10 Souimanga sunbird	50	55
63	2 r. 50 Madagascar turtle dove	60	65
64	2 r. 75 Sacred ibis	70	75
65	3 r. 50 Black coucal (vert) ..	90	95
66	7 r. Seychelles kestrel (vert)	1·75	1·90
67	15 r. Comoro blue pigeon (vert)	4·00	4·25
68	20 r. Greater flamingo (vert)	5·00	5·50

See also Nos. 165 etc. (1985).

11. Windsurfing.

1983. Tourism. Multicoloured.

69.	50 c. Type 11	10	10
70.	2 r. Hotel	25	25
71.	3 r. View of beach ..	35	35
72.	10 r. Islands at sunset ..	1·40	1·75

1983. Nos. 23/8 surch.

73	30 c. on 40 c. "Royal Escape"	25	25
74	30 c. on 40 c. Prince Charles and Lady Diana Spencer	40	50
75	2 r. on 5 r. "Victoria and Albert II"	70	70
76	2 r. on 5 r. As No. 74 ..	1·00	1·40
77	3 r. on 10 r. "Britannia" ..	85	85
78	3 r. on 10 r. As No. 74 ..	1·40	1·75

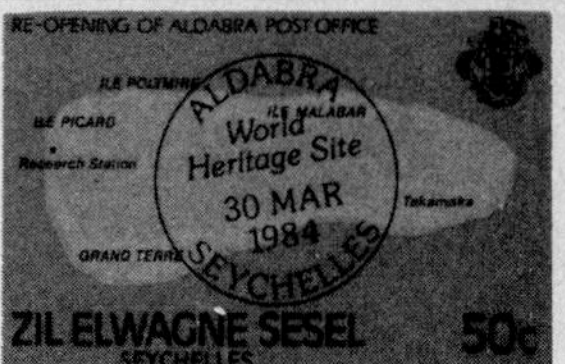

12. Map of Aldabra and Commemorative Postmark.

1984. Re-opening of Aldabra Post Office. Multicoloured.

79.	50 c. Type 12	15	25
80.	2 r. 75 White-throated rail	60	95
81.	3 r. Giant tortoise ..	60	1·10
82.	10 r. Red-footed booby ..	2·25	2·75

13. Fishing from Launch.

1984. Game Fishing. Multicoloured.

83.	50 c. Type 13	15	15
84.	2 r. Hooked fish (vert.) ..	45	55
85.	3 r. Weighing catch (vert.)	60	75
86.	10 r. Fishing from boat (different)	2·00	2·50

14. Giant Hermit Crab.

1984. Crabs. Multicoloured.

87.	50 c. Type 14	25	30
88.	2 r. Fiddler Crabs	65	85
89.	3 r. Sand Crab	80	1·25
90.	10 r. Spotted Pebble Crab ..	2·50	3·25

15. Constellation of "Orion".

1984. The Night Sky. Multicoloured.

91.	50 c. Type 15	15	15
92.	2 r. "Cygnus"	50	55
93.	3 r. "Virgo"	75	80
94.	10 r. "Scorpio"	2·00	2·25

C. Inscr. "ZIL ELWANNYEN SESEL".

16. "Lenzites elegans".

1985. Fungi. Multicoloured.

95.	50 c. Type 16	30	30
96.	2 r. "Xylaria telfairei" ..	80	80
97.	3 r. "Lentinus sajor-ceju" ..	1·10	1·10
98.	10 r. "Hexagonia tenuis" ..	3·00	3·00

1985. As Nos. 53/4, 57 and 61 but inscr. "Zil Elwannyen Sesel".

No.	Description		
165	5 c. Type **10**	10	10
166	10 c. Zebra dove ("Barred ground dove")	10	10
103	25 c. Madagascar white eye	10	10
171	50 c. White-throated rail	15	20
226	2 r. Western reef heron ("Diomorphic little egret")	50	55

17. The Queen Mother attending Royal Opera House, Covent Garden.

1985. Life and Times of Queen Elizabeth the Queen Mother. Multicoloured.

No.	Description		
115.	1 r. The Queen Mother, 1936 (from photo by Dorothy Wilding) ..	20	25
116.	2 r. With Princess Anne at Ascot, 1974	45	50
117.	3 r. Type **17**	65	70
118.	5 r. With Prince Henry at his christening (from photo by Lord Snowdon)	1·10	1·25

18. Giant Tortoise.

1985. Giant Tortoises of Aldabra (1st series). Multicoloured.

No.	Description		
120.	50 c. Type **18**	55	75
121.	75 c. Giant tortoises at stream	65	50
122.	1 r. Giant tortoises on grassland	80	55
123.	2 r. Giant tortoise (side view)	1·40	90

For stamps as Nos. 120/3, but without circular inscription around W.W.F. emblem, see Nos. 153/6.

19. Phoenician Trading Ship (600 B.C.).

1985. Famous Visitors. Multicoloured.

No.	Description		
125.	50 c. Type **19**	60	30
126.	2 r. Sir Hugh Scott and H.M.S. "Sealark", 1908	1·50	80
127.	10 r. Vasco da Gama and "Sao Gabriel", 1502 ..	3·50	2·75

1986. 60th Birthday of Queen Elizabeth II. As T **110** of Ascension. Multicoloured.

No.	Description		
128.	75 c. Princess Elizabeth at Chester, 1951	20	25
129.	1 r. Queen and Duke of Edinburgh at Falklands Service, St. Paul's Cathedral, 1985	20	25
130.	1 r. 50 At Order of St. Michael and St. George service, St. Paul's Cathedral, 1968	35	40
131.	3 r. 75 In Mexico, 1975 ..	85	90
132.	5 r. At Crown Agents Head Office, London, 1983 ..	1·10	1·25

1986. Royal Wedding. As T **112** of Ascension. Multicoloured.

No.	Description		
133.	3 r. Prince Andrew and Miss Sarah Ferguson on Buckingham Palace balcony	70	75
134.	7 r. Prince Andrew in naval uniform	1·60	1·75

20. "Acropora palifera" and "Tubastraea coccinea".

1986. Coral Formations. Multicoloured.

No.	Description		
135.	2 r. Type **20**	80	80
136.	2 r. "Echinopora lamellosa" and "Favia pallida"	80	80
137.	2 r. "Sarcophyton sp." and "Porites lutea"	80	80
138.	2 r. "Goniopora sp." and "Goniastrea retiformis"	80	80
139.	2 r. "Tubipora musica" and "Fungia fungites"	80	80

Nos. 135/9 were printed together, se-tenant, forming a composite design.

21. "Hibiscus tiliaceus".

1986. Flora. Multicoloured.

No.	Description		
140.	50 c. Type **21**	35	20
141.	2 r. "Crinum angustum" ..	1·60	1·10
142.	3 r. "Phaius tetragonus" ..	2·25	1·40
143.	10 r. "Rothmannia annae"	3·75	3·50

22. "Chaetodon unimaculatus".

1987. Coral Reef Fishes. Multicoloured.

No.	Description		
144.	2 r. Type **22**	65	65
145.	2 r. "Ostorhincus fleurieu"	65	65
146.	2 r. "Platax orbicularis" ..	65	65
147.	2 r. "Abudefduf annulatus"	65	56
148.	2 r. "Chaetodon lineolatus"	65	65

Nos. 144/8 were printed together, se-tenant, forming a composite design.

23. Coconut.

1987. Trees. Multicoloured.

No.	Description		
149.	1 r. Type **23**	60	60
150.	2 r. Mangrove	1·00	1·25
151.	3 r. Pandanus palm ..	1·50	1·75
152.	5 r. Indian almond ..	2·50	2·75

1987. Giant Tortoises of Aldabra (2nd series). Designs as Nos. 120/3 but without circular inscr. around W.W.F. emblem. Mult.

No.	Description		
153.	50 c. As Type **18**	85	85
154.	75 c. Giant tortoises at pool	1·25	1·40
155.	1 r. Giant tortoises on grassland	1·75	1·90
156.	2 r. Giant tortoise (side view)	2·75	3·00

1987. Royal Ruby Wedding. Nos. 128/32 optd. **40TH WEDDING ANNIVERSARY.**

No.	Description		
157.	75 c. Princess Elizabeth at Chester, 1951	25	20
158.	1 r. Queen and Duke of Edinburgh at Falklands Service, St. Paul's Cathedral, 1985	30	25
159.	1 r. 50 At Order of St. Michael and St. George service, St. Paul's Cathedral, 1968	45	40
160.	3 r. 75 In Mexico, 1975 ..	1·00	90
161.	5 r. At Crown Agents Head Office, London, 1983 ..	1·40	1·25

24. "Vallee de Mai" (Christine Harter).

1987. Tourism. Multicoloured.

No.	Description		
162.	3 r. Type **24**	1·75	1·50
163.	3 r. Ferns	1·75	1·50
164.	3 r. Bamboo	1·75	1·50

Nos. 162/4 were printed together, se-tenant, forming the complete picture.

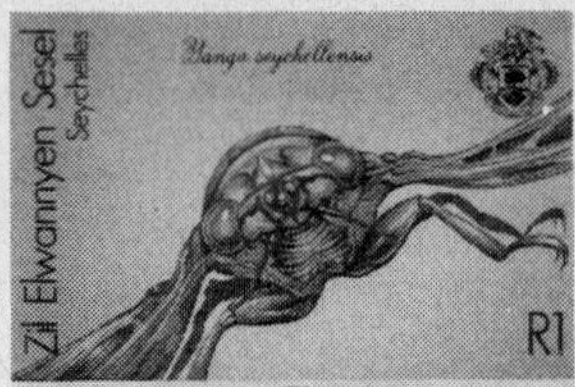

25 "Yanga seychellensis"

1988. Insects. Multicoloured.

No.	Description		
180	1 r. Type **25**	50	30
181	2 r. "Belenois aldabraensis"	75	55
182	3 r. "Polyspilota seychelliana"	85	75
183	5 r. "Polposipus herculeanus"	1·40	1·25

1988. 300th Anniv of Lloyd's of London. As T **123** of Ascension. Multicoloured.

No.	Description		
185	1 r. Modern Lloyd's Building, London ..	60	40
186	2 r. "Retriever" (cable ship) (horiz) ..	90	70
187	3 r. "Chantel" (fishing boat) (horiz)	1·50	1·25
188	5 r. Wreck of "Torrey Canyon" (tanker), Cornwall, 1967	2·00	1·60

27 "Father Christmas landing with Presents" (Jean-Claude Boniface)

1988. Christmas. Children's Paintings. Mult.

No.	Description		
189	1 r. Type **27**	25	25
190	2 r. "Church" (Francois Barra) (vert)	45	45
191	3 r. "Father Christmas flying on Bird" (Wizy Ernesta) (vert) ..	65	65
192	5 r. "Father Christmas in Sleigh over Island" (Federic Lang) ..	1·10	1·10

1989. 20th Anniv of First Manned Landing on Moon. As T **126** of Ascension. Multicoloured.

No.	Description		
193	1 r. Firing Room, Launch Control Centre	35	35
194	2 r. Crews of "Apollo–Soyuz" mission (30 × 30 mm)	60	60
195	3 r. "Apollo–Soyuz" emblem (30 × 30 mm) ..	80	80
196	5 r. "Apollo" and "Soyuz" docking in space ..	1·40	1·40

28 Dumb Cane

1989. Poisonous Plants (1st series). Mult.

No.	Description		
198	1 r. Type **28**	60	60
199	2 r. Star of Bethlehem ..	90	90
200	3 r. Indian liquorice ..	1·25	1·25
201	5 r. Black nightshade ..	1·75	1·75

See also Nos. 214/17.

29 Tec-Tec Broth

1989. Creole Cooking. Multicoloured.

No.	Description		
202	1 r. Type **29**	60	60
203	2 r. Pilaffa la Seychelloise	90	90
204	3 r. Mullet grilled in banana leaves	1·25	1·25
205	5 r. Daube	1·75	1·75

30 1980 Marine Life 5 r. Stamp

1990. "Stamp World London 90" International Stamp Exhibition. Designs showing stamps. Multicoloured.

No.	Description		
207	1 r. Type **30**	50	50
208	2 r. 1980 5 r. definitive ..	80	80
209	3 r. 1983 2 r. 75 definitive	1·10	1·10
210	5 r. 1981 Wildlife 5 r. ..	1·60	1·60

1990. 90th Birthday of Queen Elizabeth the Queen Mother. As T **134** of Ascension.

No.	Description		
212	2 r. multicoloured ..	75	75
213	10 r. black and brown ..	2·50	2·50

DESIGNS—21 × 36 mm. 2 r. Duchess of York with baby Princess Elizabeth, 1926. 29 × 37 mm. 10 r. King George VI and Queen Elizabeth visiting bombed district, London, 1940.

1990. Poisonous Plants (2nd series). As T **28**. Multicoloured.

No.	Description		
214	1 r. Ordeal plant	50	50
215	2 r. Thorn apple ..	80	80
216	3 r. Strychnine tree ..	1·00	1·00
217	5 r. Bwa zasmen ..	1·60	1·60

1991. 65th Birthday of Queen Elizabeth II and 70th Birthday of Prince Philip. As T **139** of Ascension. Multicoloured.

No.	Description		
234	4 r. Queen Elizabeth II ..	1·40	1·50
235	4 r. Prince Philip ..	1·40	1·50

31 "St. Abbs" (full-rigged ship), 1860

1991. Shipwrecks. Multicoloured.

236	1 r. 50 Type **31**	60	60
237	3 r. "Norden" (barque), 1862	1·10	1·10
238	3 r. 50 "Clan Mackay" (freighter), 1894 ..	1·25	1·25
239	10 r. "Glenlyon" (freighter), 1905 ..	3·00	3·00

1992. 40th Anniv of Queen Elizabeth II's Accession. As T **143** of Ascension. Mult.

240	1 r. Beach	35	35
241	1 r. 50 Aerial view of Desroches	50	50
242	3 r. Tree-covered coastline	95	95
243	3 r. 50 Three portraits of Queen Elizabeth II ..	1·10	1·10
244	5 r. Queen Elizabeth II ..	1·50	1·50

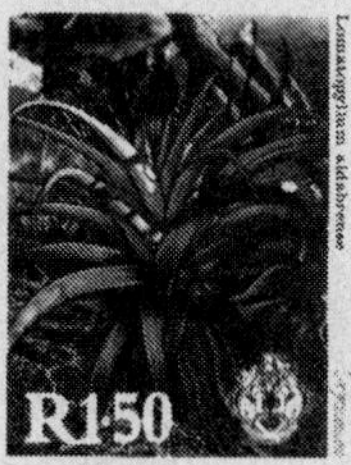

32 "Lomatopyllum aldabrense" (plant)

1992. 10th Anniv of Aldabra as a World Heritage Site. Multicoloured.

245	1 r. 50 Type **32**	65	65
246	3 r. White-throated rail ..	1·40	1·40
247	3 r. 50 Robber crab ..	1·50	1·50
248	10 r. Aldabra drongo ..	4·00	4·00

ZIMBABWE

Rhodesia became independent on 18 April 1980 and was renamed Zimbabwe.

100 cents = 1 dollar.

113. Morganite.

1980. As Nos. 555/69 of Rhodesia and new value inscr. "ZIMBABWE".

576.	1 c. Type **113**	20	20
577.	3 c. Amethyst	30	20
578.	4 c. Garnet	30	10
579.	5 c. Citrine	35	10
580.	7 c. Blue Topaz	35	10
581.	9 c. White Rhinoceros ..	15	10
582.	11 c. Lion	15	15
583.	13 c. Warthog	15	15
584.	15 c. Giraffe	15	20
585.	17 c. Common Zebra ..	15	20
586.	21 c. Odzani Falls ..	20	25
587.	25 c. Goba Falls.. ..	25	30
588.	30 c. Inyangombi Falls..	30	50
588a.	40 c. Bundi Falls ..	5·00	4·50
589.	$1 Bridal Veil Falls ..	1·10	2·00
590.	$2 Victoria Falls ..	2·00	3·75

114. Rotary Anniv. Emblem.

1980. 75th Anniv. of Rotary International.

591. **114.**	4 c. multicoloured ..	10	10
592.	13 c. multicoloured ..	20	30
593.	21 c. multicoloured ..	35	55
594.	25 c. multicoloured ..	45	80

115. Olympic Rings.

1980. Olympic Games, Moscow.

596. **115.**	17 c. multicoloured ..	30	40

116. Gatooma Post Office, 1912.

1980. 75th Anniv. of Post Office Savings Bank.

597. **116.**	5 c. black and brown ..	10	10
598. –	7 c. black and orange	10	10
599. –	9 c. black and yellow ..	10	10
600. –	17 c. black and blue ..	25	25

DESIGNS: 7 c. Salisbury Post Office, 1912. 9 c. Umtali Post Office, 1901. 17 c. Bulawayo Post Office, 1895.

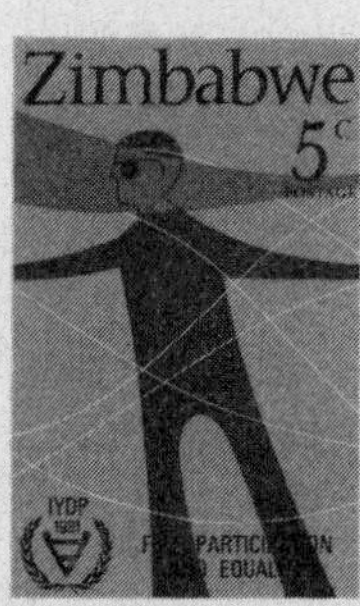

117. Stylised Blind Person.

1981. International Year for Disabled Persons. Multicoloured.

602.	5 c. Type **117**	15	10
603.	7 c. Deaf person	20	10
604.	11 c. Person with one leg..	25	15
605.	17 c. Person with one arm	35	35

118. Msasa.

1981. National Tree Day. Multicoloured.

606.	5 c. Type **118**	20	10
607.	7 c. Mopane	25	15
608.	21 c. Flat-crowned Acacia	80	70
609.	30 c. Pod Mahogany ..	1·10	1·10

119. Painting from Gwamgwadza Cave, Mtoko Area.

1982. Rock Paintings. Multicoloured.

610.	9 c. Type **119**	75	20
611.	11 c. Epworth Mission, near Harare	1·00	20
612.	17 c. Diana's Vow near Harare	1·00	65
613.	21 c. Gwamgwadza Cave, Mtoko Area (different)..	1·40	1·25
614.	25 c. Mucheka Cave, Msana Communal Land ..	1·75	2·00
615.	30 c. Chinzwini Shelter, Chiredzi Area ..	2·00	2·25

120. Scout Emblem.

1982. 75th Anniv. of Boy Scout Movement. Multicoloured.

616.	9 c. Type **120**	45	15
617.	11 c. Scouts around camp-fire	45	15
618.	21 c. Scouts map-reading	70	95
619.	30 c. Lord Baden-Powell	90	1·75

121. Dr. Robert Koch.

1982. Centenary of Dr. Robert Koch's Discovery of Tubercle Bacillus.

620. **121.**	11 c. orange, black and grey	1·00	25
621. –	30 c. multicoloured ..	2·25	2·75

DESIGN: 30 c. Man looking through microscope.

122. "Wing Woman" (Henry Mudzengerere).

1983. Commonwealth Day. Sculptures. Multicoloured.

622.	9 c. Type **122**	10	10
623.	11 c. "Telling Secrets" (Joseph Ndandarika) (horiz.)	15	10
624.	30 c. "Hornbill Man" (John Takawira) (horiz.)	35	45
625.	$1 "The Chief" (Nicholas Mukomberanwa) ..	1·00	2·00

123. Traditional Ploughing Team (moving right)

1983. World Ploughing Contest. Mult.

626.	21 c. Type **123**	25	35
627.	21 c. Traditional ploughing team (moving left) ..	25	35
628.	30 c. Tractor ploughing ..	40	65
629.	30 c. Modern plough ..	40	65

The two designs of each value were issued in horizontal se-tenant pairs, forming composite designs throughout the sheets.

124. Postman on Cycle.

1983. World Communications Year. Mult.

630.	9 c. Type **124**	20	10
631.	11 c. Aircraft controller directing aircraft ..	25	10
632.	15 c. Switchboard operator	30	30
633.	17 c. Printing works ..	35	30
634.	21 c. Road transport (horiz.)	50	60
635.	30 c. Rail transport (horiz.)	75	1·25

125. Map of Africa showing Zimbabwe.

1984. Zimbabwe International Trade Fair, 1984. Multicoloured.

636.	9 c. Type **125**	10	10
637.	11 c. Globe	15	10
638.	30 c. Zimbabwe flag and Trade Fair logo ..	45	35

126. Cycling.

1984. Olympic Games, Los Angeles. Children's Pictures. Multicoloured.

639. 11 c. Type **126** 35 15
640. 21 c. Swimming 45 40
641. 30 c. Running 65 75
642. 40 c. Hurdling .. .. 80 1·00

127. Liberation Heroes.

1984. Heroes' Day.

643 9 c. Type **127** 30 10
644 11 c. Symolic tower and flame (vert) 30 10
645 17 c. Bronze sculpture (vert) 50 30
646 30 c. Section of bronze mural 70 45

DESIGNS: 9 to 30 c. Various aspects of Heroes' Acre.

128. African Fish Eagle.

1984. Birds of Prey. Multicoloured.

647. 9 c. Type **128** 50 20
648. 11 c. Long crested eagle .. 50 20
649. 13 c. Bateleur 65 55
650. 17 c. Verreaut's eagle .. 80 55
651. 21 c. Martial eagle .. 90 1·40
652. 30 c. Bonelli's eagle .. 1·25 2·25

129. Class "9" Locomotive. No. 86.

1985. "Zimbabwe Steam Safaris". Railway Locomotives. Multicoloured.

653. 9 c. Type **129** 85 20
654. 11 c. Class "12" No. 190 .. 85 20
655. 17 c. Class "Garratt 15A" 1·50 85
656. 30 c. Class "Garratt 20A" "Gwaai" .. .. .. 2·50 2·75

130. "Intelsat V "Telecommunications Satellite.

1985. Earth Satellite Station, Mazowe. Multicoloured.

657. 26 c. Type **130** .. .. 1·75 60
658. 57 c. Earth Satellite Station, Mazowe (65 × 25 mm) .. .. 3·25 4·50

131. Tobacco.

1985. National Infrastructure. Multicoloured.

659 1 c. Type **131** 10 10
660 3 c. Maize 10 10
661 4 c. Cotton 10 10
662 5 c. Tea 10 10
663 10 c. Cattle 15 10
664 11 c. Birchenough Bridge 55 10
665 12 c. Ore stamp mill .. 90 10
666 13 c. Gold pouring .. 1·00 15
667 15 c. Dragline coal mining 1·00 15
668 17 c. Uncut amethyst .. 1·25 15
669 18 c. Electric locomotive .. 1·00 30
670 20 c. Kariba Dam .. .. 1·00 15
671 23 c. Elephants at water hole .. .. .. 1·00 15
672 25 c. Sunset over Zambezi 55 30
673 26 c. Baobab tree 55 20
674 30 c. Ruins of Great Zimbabwe 60 30
675 35 c. Traditional dancing 60 30
676 45 c. Village women crushing maize 65 40
677 57 c. Woodcarving .. 75 70
678 $1 Playing Mbira (musical instrument) .. .. 1·25 90
679 $2 Mule-drawn Scotch cart 2·00 2·75
680 $5 Zimbabwe coat-of-arms 3·75 5·50

132. Chief Mutapa Gatsi Rusere and 17th century Seal.

1985. 50th Anniv. of National Archives. Multicoloured.

681. 12 c. Type **132** 20 15
682. 18 c. Chief Lobengula, seal and 1888 Treaty .. 25 40
683. 26 c. Exhibition gallery .. 35 45
684. 35 c. National Archives building 45 75

133. Computer Operator.

1985. United Nations Decade for Women. Multicoloured.

685. 10 c. Type **133** 55 10
686. 17 c. Nurse giving injection 85 70
687. 26 c. Woman student .. 1·60 2·25

134. Harare Conference Centre.

1986. Harare International Conference Centre. Multicoloured.

688. 26 c. Type **134** 75 30
689. 35 c. Interior of conference hall .. .. .. 1·25 1·40

135. Grain Storage Silo.

1986. 6th Anniv. of Southern African Development Co-ordination Conference. Mult.

690. 12 c. Type **135** 55 20
691. 18 c. Rhinoceros and hawk at sunset .. .. 1·75 1·25
692. 26 c. Map showing S.A.D.C.C. member states, and Boeing "737" 2·00 1·75
693. 35 c. Map and national flags of S.A.D.C.C. members .. .. .. 2·25 2·00

136. "Bunaeopsis jacksoni".

1986. Moths of Zimbabwe. Multicoloured.

694 12 c. Type **136** .. .. 1·10 20
695 18 c. "Deilephila nerii" .. 1·60 80
696 26 c. "Bunaeopsis zaddachi" .. .. 2·00 1·25
697 35 c. "Heniocha apollonia" 2·40 3·25

137. Victoria Falls.

1986. 8th Non-Aligned Summit Conference. Multicoloured.

698. 26 c. Type **137** .. .. 1·25 30
699. $1 Ruins of Great Zimbabwe (62 × 24 mm.) 3·75 4·25

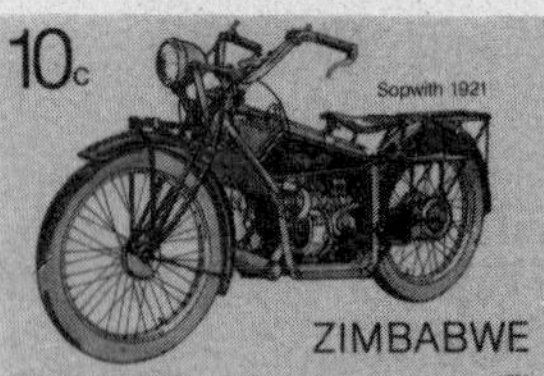

138. Sopwith Motorcycle (1921).

1986. Centenary of Motoring. Multicoloured.

700. 10 c. Type **138** 65 10
701. 12 c. Gladiator motor car (1902) 65 30
702. 17 c. Douglas motorcycle (1920) .. .. .. 1·00 40
703. 26 c. Ford "Model A" (1930) .. .. .. 1·40 70
704. 35 c. Schacht motor car (1909) .. .. .. 1·75 2·00
705. 40 c. Benz three-wheeled car (1886) .. .. 1·75 2·00

139. Growth Monitoring.

1987. Child Survival Campaign. Mult.

706. 12 c. Type **139** .. 1·40 1·50
707. 12 c. Breast-feeding .. 1·40 1·50
708. 12 c. Oral rehydration therapy .. .. 1·40 1·50
709. 12 c. Immunization .. 1·40 1·50

140. Barred Owlet.

1987. Owls (1st series). Multicoloured.

710. 12 c. Type **140** .. .. 1·50 20
711. 18 c. Pearl-spotted owlet .. 2·00 1·00
712. 26 c. White-faced scops owl 2·50 1·50
713. 35 c. African scops owl .. 3·50 4·00

See also Nos. 850/3.

141. Brownie, Guide and Ranger saluting ("Commitment").

1987. 75th Anniv. of Girl Guides Association of Zimbabwe. Multicoloured.

714. 15 c. Type **141** 40 15
715. 23 c. Guides preparing meal over campfire ("Adventure") 55 30
716. 35 c. Guide teaching villagers to read ("Service") 65 35
717. $1 Handshake and globe ("International Friendship") .. .. 1·50 1·25

142. Common Grey Duiker.

1987. Duikers of Africa Survey. Mult.

718. 15 c. Type **142** 40 15
719. 23 c. Zebra duiker 50 20
720. 25 c. Yellow-backed duiker 50 45
721. 30 c. Blue duiker 65 55
722. 35 c. Jentink's duiker .. 65 55
723. 38 c. Red duiker 75 75

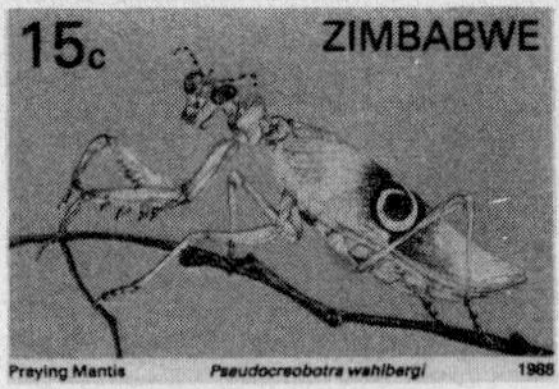

143. "Pseudocreobotra wahlberghi" (mantid).

1988. Insects. Multicoloured.

724 15 c. Type **143** 40 15
725 23 c. "Dicranorrhia derbyana" (beetle) .. 55 25
726 35 c. "Dictyophorus spumans" (grasshopper) 75 40
727 45 c. "Chalcocoris rutilus" (bug) 90 65

144 "Cockerel" (Arthur Azevedo)

1988. 30th Anniv of National Gallery of Zimbabwe. Designs showing painting (38 c.) or sculptures (others). Multicoloured.

728 15 c. Type **144** 15 10
729 23 c. "Man into Hippo" (Bernard Matemera) .. 25 20
730 30 c. "Spirit Python" (Henry Munyaradzi) .. 30 35
731 35 c. "Spirit Bird carrying People" (Thomas Mukarobgwa) (horiz) .. 30 25
732 38 c. "The Song of the Herd Boy" (George Nene) (horiz) .. 30 30
733 45 c. "War Victim" (Joseph Muzondo) (horiz) 35 40

145 "Aloe cameronii var. bondana"

1988. Aloes. Multicoloured.

734	15 c. Type **145**	20	10
735	23 c. "Orbeopsis caudata"	35	20
736	25 c. "Euphorbia wildii" . .	35	20
737	30 c. "Euphorbia fortissima"	40	30
738	35 c. "Aloe aculeata" . .	40	35
739	38 c. "Huernia zebrina" . .	45	35

146 White-faced Whistling Duck

1988. Wild Ducks and Geese of Zimbabwe. Multicoloured.

740	15 c. Type **146**	25	10
741	23 c. African pygmy goose	35	20
742	30 c. Hottentot teal . .	45	35
743	35 c. Comb duck ("Knob-billed duck") . .	50	45
744	38 c. White-backed duck	50	45
745	45 c. Maccoa duck . .	75	75

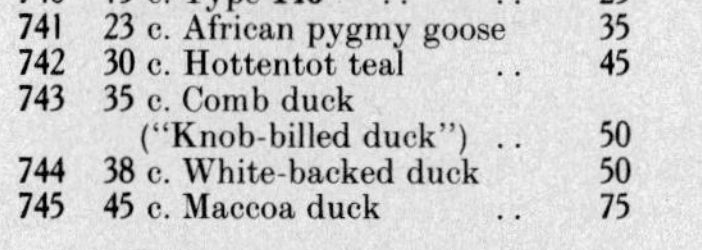

147 O'Shaughnessy's Banded Gecko

1989. Geckos. Multicoloured.

746	15 c. Type **147**	40	10
747	23 c. Tiger rock gecko . .	55	25
748	35 c. Tasman's gecko . .	75	70
749	45 c. Bibron's gecko . .	85	85

148 Spotted Leaved Arum-Lily

1989. Wild Flowers. Multicoloured.

750	15 c. Type **148**	30	10
751	23 c. Grassland vlei-lily . .	35	25
752	30 c. Manica protea . .	40	35
753	35 c. Flame lily	45	35
754	38 c. Poppy hibiscus . .	50	40
755	45 c. Blue sesbania . .	60	45

149 Red-breasted Bream

1989. Fishes (1st series). Multicoloured.

756	15 c. Type **149**	30	10
757	23 c. Chessa	45	25
758	30 c. Eastern bottle-nose	55	50
759	35 c. Vundu	55	50
760	38 c. Largemouth black bass	60	60
761	45 c. Tiger fish	80	80

See also Nos. 864/9.

150 Black Rhinoceros

1989. Endangered Species. Multicoloured.

762	15 c. Type **150**	55	20
763	23 c. Cheetah	70	35
764	30 c. Wild dog	85	75
765	35 c. Pangolin	85	80
766	38 c. Brown hyena . .	90	90
767	45 c. Roan antelope . .	1·00	1·25

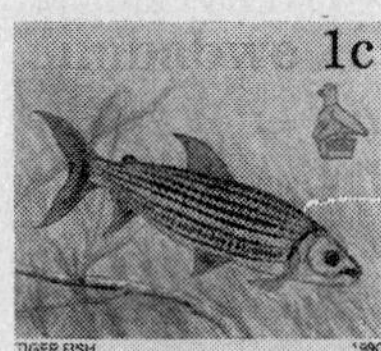

151 Tiger Fish

152 Headrest

153 Bicycles

1990. Multicoloured. (a) Wildlife. As T **151**.

768	1 c. Type **151**	10	10
769	2 c. Helmet guineafowl . .	10	10
770	3 c. Scrub hare	10	10
771	4 c. Temminck's ground pangolin	10	10
772	5 c. Greater kudu . .	10	10
773	9 c. Black rhinoceros . .	10	10

(b) Cultural Artifacts. As T **152**.

774	15 c. Type **152**	10	10
775	20 c. Hand axe and adze . .	10	10
776	23 c. Gourd and water pot	10	10
777	25 c. Snuff container . .	10	10
778	26 c. Winnowing tray and basket	10	10
779	30 c. Grinding stone . .	10	10

(c) Transport. As T **153**.

780	33 c. Type **153**	10	10
781	35 c. Buses	10	10
782	38 c. Passenger train . .	10	15
783	45 c. Mail motorcycle and trailer	10	15
784	$1 Air Zimbabwe Boeing airliner	20	25
785	$2 Lorry	40	45

154 Pres. Mugabe and Joshua Nkomo at Signing of Unity Accord, 1987

1990. 10th Anniv of Independence. Mult.

786	15 c. Type **154**	20	10
787	23 c. Conference Centre, Harare	25	20
788	30 c. Children in class . .	30	30
789	35 c. Intelsat aerial, Mazowe Earth Satellite Station	35	45
790	38 c. National Sports Stadium	35	45
791	45 c. Maize field	60	75

155 Runhare House, 1986

1990. Cent of the City of Harare. Mult.

792	15 c. Type **155**	20	10
793	23 c. Market Hall, 1894 . .	30	20
794	30 c. Charter House, 1959	35	25
795	35 c. Supreme Court, 1927	40	45
796	38 c. Standard Chartered Bank, 1911	40	50
797	45 c. The Town House, 1933	55	75

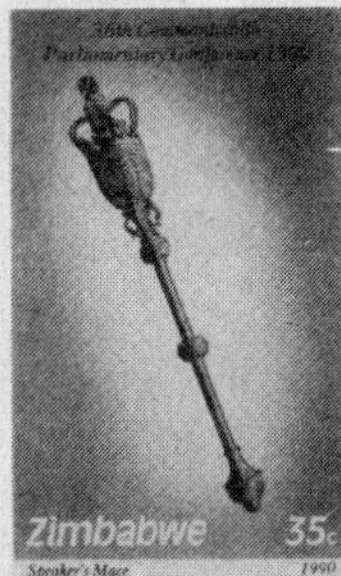

156 Speaker's Mace

1990. 36th Commonwealth Parliamentary Conference, Harare. Multicoloured.

798	35 c. Type **156**	50	25
799	$1 Speaker's chair . .	1·00	1·25

157 Small-spotted Genet

1991. Small Mammals. Multicoloured.

800	15 c. Type **157**	40	15
801	23 c. Red squirrel . .	45	20
802	35 c. Night-ape . .	65	70
803	45 c. Bat-eared fox . .	80	90

158 Hosho (rattles)

1991. Traditional Musical Instruments. Mult.

804	15 c. Type **158**	20	10
805	23 c. Mbira (thumb piano)	25	15
806	30 c. Ngororombe (pan pipes)	30	25
807	35 c. Chipendani (mouth bow)	35	35
808	38 c. Marimba (xylophone)	35	40
809	45 c. Ngoma (drum) . .	45	55

159 Snot-apple

1991. Wild Fruits. Multicoloured.

810	20 c. Type **159**	20	10
811	39 c. Marula	20	25
812	51 c. Mobola plum . .	30	40
813	60 c. Water berry . .	35	45
814	65 c. Northern dwaba berry	35	45
815	77 c. Mahobohobo . .	45	65

160 Bridal Veil Falls

1991. Commonwealth Heads of Governmen[t] Meeting, Harare. Multicoloured.

816	20 c. Type **160**	25	1[illegible]
817	39 c. Meeting logo . .	25	2[illegible]
818	51 c. Chinhoyi Caves . .	35	3[illegible]
819	60 c. Kariba Dam . .	50	5[illegible]
820	65 c. Victoria Falls . .	50	5[illegible]
821	77 c. Balancing rocks . .	60	7[illegible]

161 Lion

1992. Wildlife Conservation. Big Cats. Mult[.]

822	20 c. Type **161**	20	1[illegible]
823	39 c. Leopard	30	2[illegible]
824	60 c. Cheetah	55	6[illegible]
825	77 c. Serval	70	8[illegible]

162 "Amanita zambiana"

1992. Edible Mushrooms. Multicoloured.

826	20 c. Type **162**	20	[illegible]
827	39 c. "Boletus edulis" . .	25	[illegible]
828	51 c. "Termitomyces" . .	30	[illegible]
829	60 c. "Cantharellus densifolius"	40	4[illegible]
830	65 c. "Cantharellus longisporus"	45	5[illegible]
831	77 c. "Cantharellus cibarius"	50	6[illegible]

163 Common Bulbul

1992. Birds. Multicoloured.

832	25 c. Type **163**	15	10
833	59 c. Fiscal shrike ..	30	35
834	77 c. Forktailed drongo ..	40	50
835	90 c. Cardinal woodpecker	50	60
836	98 c. Yellow-billed hornbill	50	60
837	$1.16 Crested francolin ..	65	75

164 "Charaxes jasius"

1992. Butterflies. Multicoloured.

838	25 c. Type **164**	20	15
839	59 c. "Eronia leda" ..	40	40
840	77 c. "Princeps ophidicephalus"	45	50
841	90 c. "Junonia oenone" ..	55	60
842	98 c. "Danaus chrysippus"	60	70
843	$1.16 "Junonia octavia" ..	70	85

165 Uranium

1993. Minerals. Multicoloured.

844	25 c. Type **165**	15	10
845	59 c. Chrome	25	25
846	77 c. Copper	30	30
847	90 c. Coal	40	40
848	98 c. Gold	40	40
849	$1.16 Emerald	45	50

1993. Owls (2nd series). As T **140**. Mult.

850	25 c. Wood owl	20	15
851	59 c. Pel's fishing owl ..	35	30
852	90 c. Spotted eagle owl ..	55	55
853	$1.16 Verreaux's eagle owl ("Giant eagle owl") ..	70	80

166 Hadyana (relish pot)

1993. Household Pottery. Multicoloured.

854	25 c. Type **166**	15	10
855	59 c. Chirongo (water jar)	20	15
856	77 c. Mbiya (relish bowl) ..	25	25
857	90 c. Pfuko (water jar) ..	25	25
858	98 c. Tsaya (cooking pot)	30	35
859	$1.16 Gate (beer pot) ..	35	40

167 "Polystachya dendrobiflora"

1993. Orchids. Multicoloured.

860	35 c. Type **167**	20	15
861	$1 "Diaphananthe subsimplex"	35	40
862	$1.50 "Ansellia gigantea"	45	50
863	$1.95 "Vanilla polyepis" ..	60	65

1994. Fishes (2nd series). As T **149**. Mult.

864	35 c. Hunyani salmon ..	20	15
865	$1 Barbel	35	40
866	$1.30 Rainbow trout ..	40	45
867	$1.50 Mottled eel	45	50
868	$1.65 Mirror arp	50	55
869	$1.95 Robustus bream ..	60	65

POSTAGE DUE STAMPS

D 4. Zimbabwe Bird (soapstone sculpture).

1980. As Nos. D 11/15 of Rhodesia but inscr. "ZIMBABWE".

D23	D 4	1 c. green	30	80
D24		2 c. blue	40	90
D25		5 c. violet	50	90
D26		6 c. yellow	70	1·60
D27		10 c. red	90	2·00

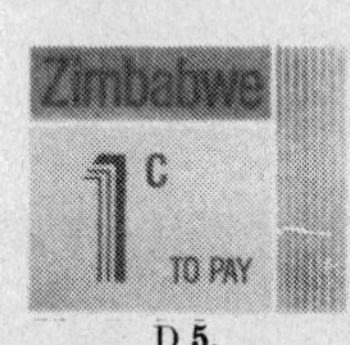

D **5.**

1985.

D28	5	1 c. orange	10	10
D29		2 c. mauve	10	10
D30		6 c. green	10	10
D31		10 c. brown	10	10
D32		13 c. blue	10	10

1990. No. D27 surch **25**.

D33	D 4	25 c. on 10 c. red ..	6·00	6·00

ZULULAND

A territory of S.E. Africa, annexed by Great Britain in 1887, and incorporated in Natal in 1897.

12 pence = 1 shilling.
20 shillings = 1 pound.

1888. Stamps of Gt. Britain (Queen Victoria) optd. **ZULULAND.**

1.	**71.**	½d. red	2·25	2·50
2.	**57.**	1d. lilac	23·00	4·75
3.	**73.**	2d. green and red ..	11·00	18·00
4.	**74.**	2½d. purple on blue ..	15·00	20·00
5.	**75.**	3d. purple on yellow ..	23·00	22·00
6.	**73.**	4d. green and brown ..	30·00	40·00
7.	**78.**	5d. purple and blue ..	80·00	£100
8.	**79.**	6d. purple on red ..	11·00	17·00
9.	**80.**	9d. purple and blue ..	70·00	75·00
10.	**82.**	1s. green	95·00	£100
11.	–	5s. red (No. 181) ..	£475	£500

1888. Natal stamps optd **ZULULAND**.

13	**23**	½d. green	20·00	30·00
16	–	6d. lilac (No. 103) ..	48·00	55·00

3.

1894.

20.	**3.**	½d. mauve and green ..	2·00	4·00
21.		1d. mauve and red ..	5·00	80
22.		2½d. mauve and blue ..	14·00	8·00
23.		3d. mauve and brown ..	8·00	3·00
24.		6d. mauve and black ..	18·00	18·00
25.		1s. green	30·00	35·00
26.		2s. 6d. green and black ..	70·00	70·00
27.		4s. green and red	95·00	£120
28.		£1 purple on red	£450	£475
29.		£5 purple & black on red	£4250	£1300

ADDENDA AND CORRIGENDA

AITUTAKI

Add to Nos. 661/70:

671	$1 "Solandra nitida" ..	70	75
672	$2 "Cordia subcordata"	1·50	1·60

Nos. 671/2 include portrait of Queen Elizabeth II at top right.

BANGLADESH

178 Discus Throwing

1993. 6th South Asian Federation Games, Dhaka. Multicoloured.

495	2 t. Type **178**	10	10
496	4 t. Running (vert) ..	10	10

179 Emblem and Mother giving Solution to Child

1994. 25th Anniv of Oral Rehydration Solution.

497	**179**	2 t. multicoloured ..	10	10

180 Interior of Chhota Sona Mosque, Nawabgonj

1994. Ancient Mosques. Multicoloured.

498	4 t. Type **180**	10	10
499	6 t. Exterior of Chhota Sona Mosque ..	20	25
500	6 t. Exterior of Baba Adam's Mosque, Munshigonj ..	20	25

181 Agricultural Workers and Emblem

1994. 75th Anniv of I.L.O. Mult.

501	4 t. Type **181**	10	10
502	10 t. Worker turning cog (vert)	30	35

182 Priest releasing Peace Doves

1994. 1500th Year of Bengali Solar Calendar.

503	**182**	2 t. multicoloured ..	10	10

BARBADOS

216 Bathsheba Beach and Logo

1994. 1st United Nations Conference of Small Island Developing States. Multicoloured.

1022	10 c. Type **216**	10	10
1023	65 c. Pico Tenneriffe ..	45	50
1024	90 c. Ragged Point Lighthouse	60	65
1025	$2.50 Consett Bay ..	1·25	1·40

BELIZE

205 "Lonchorhina aurita" (bat)

1994. Bats. Multicoloured.

1161	25 c. Type **205**	15	20
1162	60 c. "Vampyrodes caracciolí"	40	45
1163	75 c. "Noctilio leporinus" ..	50	55
1164	$2 "Desmodus rotundus"	1·25	1·40

CANADA

CORRECTION: Renumber Nos. 1469/70 to 1470/1 and 1471/2 to 1473/4.

Add to Nos. 1460/74:

1469	50 c. Snow apple ..	50	55
1472	69 c. Shagbark hickory ..	80	85
1475	88 c. Westcot apricot ..	90	95

600a Court House, Yorkton

(c) Architecture. As T **600a**.
1476 $1 Type **600a** .. .. 1·00 1·10
1477 $2 Provincial Normal School, Truro .. .. 2·00 2·10

1994. Canadian Art (7th series). As T **550**. Multicoloured.
1589 88 c. "Vera" (detail) (Frederick Varley) .. 90 95

623 Lawn Bowls

1994. 15th Commonwealth Games, Victoria. Multicoloured.
1590 43 c. Type **623** 45 50
1591 43 c. Lacrosse 45 50

CHRISTMAS ISLAND

81 Locomotive No. 4

1994. Steam Locomotives. Multicoloured.
389 85 c. Type **81** 80 85
390 95 c. Locomotive No. 9 .. 90 95
391 $1.20 Locomotive No. 1 .. 1·25 1·40

COCOS (KEELING) ISLANDS

On 1st January 1994 responsibility for Cocos (Keeling) Islands postal service passed from the territorial administration to Australia Post. In consequence Nos. 296/315 and all subsequent issues are valid for postal purposes in both Cocos (Keeling) Islands and Australia.

71 Reef Triggerfish and Coral

1994. Transfer of Postal Service to Australia Post. Multicoloured.
296 5 c. Type **71** 10 10
297 5 c. Three reef triggerfish and map section .. 10 10
298 5 c. Two reef triggerfish and map section .. 10 10
299 5 c. Two reef triggerfish, map section and red coral 10 10
300 5 c. Reef triggerfish with red and brown corals .. 10 10
301 10 c. Green turtles on beach 10 10
302 10 c. Two green turtles .. 10 10
303 10 c. Crowd of young green turtles 10 10
304 10 c. Green turtle and map section 10 10
305 10 c. Green turtle, pyramid butterflyfish and map section 10 10
306 20 c. Three pyramid butterflyfish and map section 20 25
307 20 c. Pyramid butterflyfish with brown coral .. 20 25
308 20 c. Two pyramid butterflyfish and coral 20 25
309 20 c. Three pyramid butterflyfish and coral 20 25
310 20 c. Coral, pyramid butterflyfish and map section 20 25
311 45 c. Jukongs with map of airport 40 45
312 45 c. Two jukongs with red or blue sails and map section 40 45
313 45 c. Jukong in shallows .. 40 45
314 45 c. Two jukongs with red or yellow sails and map section 40 45
315 45 c. Two jukongs, one with blue jib, and map section 40 45

Nos. 296/315 were printed together, se-tenant, with the background forming a composite map.

GAMBIA

222 "The Adoration of the Magi" (detail) (Rubens)

1993. Christmas. Religious Paintings. Black, yellow and red (Nos. 1712/13, 1715/17) multicoloured (others).
1711 25 b. Type **222** 10 10
1712 1 d. "The Holy Family with Joachim and Anna" (Durer) .. 15 20
1713 1 d. 50 "The Annunciation" (Durer) .. 25 30
1714 2 d. "The Adoration of the Magi" (different detail) (Rubens) .. 30 35
1715 2 d. "The Virgin Mary worshipped by Albrecht Bonstetten" (Durer) .. 30 35
1716 7 d. "The Holy Family with Two Angels in a Portico" (detail) (Durer) .. .. 1·00 1·10
1717 10 d. "Virgin on a Throne, crowned by an Angel" (Durer) .. .. 1·50 1·60
1718 15 d. "The Adoration of the Magi" (different deatail) (Rubens) .. 2·10 2·25

223 Mickey Mouse performing Ski Ballet

1994. Winter Sports. Walt Disney Cartoon Characters. Multicoloured.
1720 50 b. Type **223** 10 10
1721 75 b. Clarabelle and Horace ice dancing .. 10 10
1722 1 d. Donald Duck and Dale speed skating .. 15 20
1723 1 d. 25 Donald in biathlon 20 25
1724 4 d. Donald and nephews in bob-sled 55 60
1725 5 d. Goofy on luge .. 70 75
1726 7 d. Minnie Mouse figure skating .. .. 1·00 1·10
1727 10 d. Goofy downhill skiing .. .. 1·50 1·60
1728 15 d. Goofy playing ice hockey .. .. 2·10 2·25

GHANA

1993. Christmas. Religious Paintings. As T **222** of Gambia. Black, yellow and red (Nos. 1896, 1898/9 and 1903) or multicoloured (others).
1896 50 c. "Adoration of the Magi" (Durer) .. 10 10
1897 100 c. "The Virgin and Child with St. John and an Angel" (Botticelli) 20 25
1898 150 c. "Mary as Queen of Heaven" (Durer) .. 30 35
1899 200 c. "Saint Anne" (Durer) 35 40
1900 250 c. "The Madonna of the Magnificat" (Botticelli) 45 50
1901 400 c. "The Madonna of the Goldfinch" (Botticelli) 70 75
1902 600 c. "The Virgin and Child with the young St. John the Baptist" (Botticelli) .. .. 1·10 1·25
1903 1000 c. "Adoration of the Shepherds" (Durer) .. 1·75 1·90

GIBRALTAR

189 World Cup and Map of U.S.A

1994. World Cup Football Championship, U.S.A. Multicoloured.
721 26p. Type **189** 55 60
722 39p. Players and pitch in shape of U.S.A. .. 80 85
723 49p. Player's legs (vert) .. 1·00 1·10

GREAT BRITAIN

Add to Nos. X841/1024:
Y1749 **367** 19p. bistre 30 35

1154 The Old Course, St. Andrews

1994. Scottish Golf Courses. Multicoloured.
1829 19p. Type **1154** 30 35
1830 25p. The 18th Hole, Muirfield 40 45
1831 30p. The 15th Hole ("Luckyslap"), Carnoustie 45 50
1832 35p. The 8th Hole ("The Postage Stamp"), Royal Troon 55 60
1833 41p. The 9th Hole, Turnberry 65 70

Nos. 1829/33 commemorate the 250th anniversary of golf's first set of rules produced by the Honourable Company of Edinburgh Golfers.

1159 Royal Welsh Show, Llanelwedd

1994. The Four Seasons. Summertime. Mult.
1834 19p. Type **1159** 30 35
1835 25p. All England Tennis Championships, Wimbledon 40 45
1836 30p. Cowes Week .. 45 50
1837 35p. Test Match, Lord's 55 60
1838 41p. Braemar Gathering 65 70

GRENADA

1993. Christmas. Religious Paintings. A T **222** of Gambia. Black, yellow and red (Nos 2627/8, 2632 and 2634) or multicoloure (others).
2627 10 c. "The Nativity" (Durer) 10 1
2628 25 c. "The Annunciation" (Durer) 10 1
2629 35 c. "The Litta Madonna" (Da Vinci) 15 2
2630 60 c. "The Virgin and Child with St. John the Baptist and St. Anne" (Da Vinci) 30 3
2631 90 c. "The Madonna with the Carnation" (Da Vinci) 45 5
2632 $1 "Adoration of the Magi" (Durer) .. 50 5
2633 $4 "The Benois Madonna" (Da Vinci) .. .. 2·00 2·1
2634 $5 "The Virgin Mary in the Sun" (Durer) .. 2·40 2·5

Nos. 2629/31 and 2633 are inscribe "LEONARDO DI VINCI".

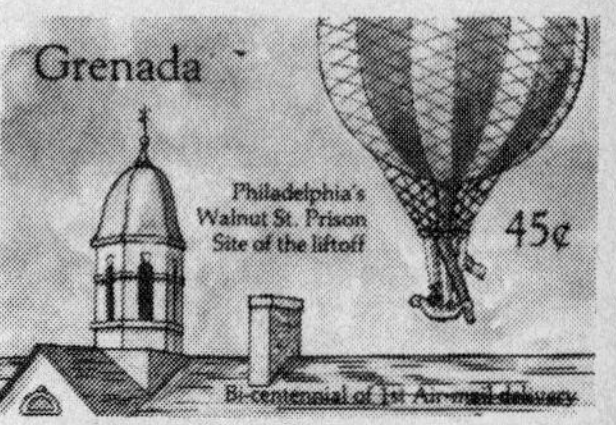

386 Blanchard's Balloon over Walnut St. Prison

1993. Aviation Anniversaries. Multicoloured
2636 35 c. "Graf Zeppelin" over Vienna at night .. 15 2
2637 45 c. Type **386** 20 2
2638 50 c. "Lysander" .. 25 3
2639 75 c. "Graf Zeppelin" over Pyramids 35 4
2640 $2 Blanchard waving hat from balloon (vert) .. 95 1·0
2641 $3 Hawker "Typhoon" .. 1·40 1·5
2642 $5 "Graf Zeppelin" over Rio de Janeiro .. 2·40 2·5

ANNIVERSARIES: Nos. 2636, 2639, 2642 125th birth anniv of Hugo Eckener (airshi commander); Nos. 2637, 2640, Bicentenary o first airmail flight; Nos. 2638, 2641, 75th anniv o Royal Air Force

387 Mercedes Benz "370 S" Cabriolet, 1932

1993. Centenaries of Henry Ford's First Petr Engine (Nos. 2645/6) and Karl Benz's Firs Four-wheeled Car (others). Multicoloured.
2644 35 c. Type **387** 15 2
2645 45 c. Ford "Mustang", 1966 .. .. .. 20 2
2646 $3 Ford "Model A" Phaeton, 1930 .. .. 1·40 1·5
2647 $4 Mercedes Benz "300 Sl" Gullwing .. .. 2·00 2·1

1993. Famous Paintings by Rembrandt an Matisse. As T **316** of Antigua. Mult.
2649 15 c. "Self-portrait", 1900 (Matisse) 10 1
2650 35 c. "Self-portrait", 1629 (Rembrandt) 15 2
2651 45 c. "Self-portrait", 1918 (Matisse) 20 2
2652 50 c. "Self-portrait", 1640 (Rembrandt) 25 3
2653 75 c. "Self-portrait", 1652 (Rembrandt) 35 4
2654 $2 "Self-portrait", 1906 (Matisse) .. .. 95 1·0
2655 $4 "Self-portrait", 1900 (different) (Matisse) .. 2·00 2·1
2656 $5 "Self-portrait", 1625–31 (Rembrandt) .. .. 2·40 2·5

INDEX

Countries can be quickly located by referring to the index at the end of this volume.

388 Fishermen with Blue Marlin

1994. 25th Anniv of Spice Island Billfish Tournament. Multicoloured.
2658 15 c. Type **388** 10 10
2659 25 c. Sailfish with angler 10 10
2660 35 c. Yellow fin tuna with angler 15 20
2661 50 c. White marlin with angler 25 30
2662 75 c. Catching a sailfish . . 35 40

389 National Flag and Ketch in Bay

1994. 25th Anniv of Independence.
2663 **389** 35 c. multicoloured . . 15 20

390 Hong Kong 1971 Scouting 50 c. Stamp and "Hong Kong Post Office, 1846" (left detail) (M. Bruce)

1994. "Hong Kong '94" International Stamp Exhibition (1st issue). Multicoloured.
2665 40 c. Type **390** 20 25
2666 40 c. Grenada 1988 Rotary $2 and "Hong Kong Post Office, 1846" (right detail) (M. Bruce) . . 20 25

Nos. 2665/6 were printed together, se-tenant, with the centre part of each pair forming the complete painting.

See also Nos. 2667/72.

Grenada 45¢
391 Vase with Dragon Decoration

1994. "Hong Kong '94" International Stamp Exhibition (2nd issue). Qing Dynasty Porcelain. Multicoloured.
2667 45 c. Type **391** 20 25
2668 45 c. Hat stand with brown base 20 25
2669 45 c. Gourd-shaped vase 20 25
2670 45 c. Rotating vase with openwork 20 25
2671 45 c. Candlestick with dogs 20 25
2672 45 c. Hat stand with orange base 20 25

GRENADINES OF GRENADA

1993. Christmas. Religious Paintings. As T **222** of Gambia. Black, yellow and red (Nos. 1717 and 1721/3) or multicoloured (others).
1717 10 c. "Adoration of the Shepherds" (detail) (Durer) 10 10
1718 25 c. "Adoration of the Magi" (detail) (Raphael) 10 10
1719 35 c. "Presentation at the Temple" (detail) (Raphael) 10 10
1720 50 c. "Adoration of the Magi" (different detail) (Raphael) 25 30
1721 75 c. "Adoration of the Shepherds" (different detail) (Durer) . . 35 40
1722 $1 "Adoration of the Shepherds" (different detail) (Durer) . . 50 55
1723 $4 "Adoration of the Shepherds" (different detail) (Durer) . . 2·00 2·10
1724 $5 "Presentation at the Temple" (different detail) (Raphael) . . 2·40 2·50

1993. Aviation Anniversaries. As T **386** of Grenada. Multicoloured.
1726 15 c. Avro "Lancaster" . . 10 10
1727 35 c. Blanchard's balloon crossing the River Delaware 10 10
1728 50 c. "Graf Zeppelin" over Rio de Janeiro . . 25 30
1729 75 c. Hugo Eckener . . 35 40
1730 $3 Pres. Washington handing passport to Blanchard . . . . 1·40 1·50
1731 $5 Short Sunderland flying boat . . . . 2·40 2·50
1732 $5 Eckener in "Graf Zeppelin" . . . . 2·40 2·50

ANNIVERSARIES: Nos. 1726, 1731, 75th anniv of Royal Air Force; Nos. 1727, 1730, Bicentenary of first airmail flight; Nos. 1728/9, 1732, 125th birth anniv of Hugo Eckener (airship commander).

1993. Centenaries of Henry Ford's First Petrol Engine (Nos. 1735/6) and Karl Benz's First Four-wheeled Car (others). As T **387** of Grenada. Multicoloured.
1734 25 c. Mercedes Benz "300 SLR", 1955 . . . . 10 10
1735 45 c. Ford "Thunderbird", 1957 . . . . 20 25
1736 $4 Ford "150-A" station wagon, 1929 . . . . 2·00 2·10
1737 $5 Mercedes Benz "540 K" 2·40 2·50

1993. Famous Paintings by Rembrandt and Matisse. As T **316** of Antigua. Multicoloured.
1739 15 c. "Hendrickje Stoffels as Flora" (Rembrandt) 10 10
1740 35 c. "Lady and Gentleman in Black" (Rembrandt) 15 20
1741 50 c. "Aristotle with the Bust of Homer" (Rembrandt) 25 30
1742 75 c. "Interior: Flowers and Parakeets" (Matisse) 35 40
1743 $1 "Goldfish" (Matisse) . . 50 55
1744 $2 "The Girl with Green Eyes" (Matisse) . . 95 1·00
1745 $3 "Still Life with a Plaster Figure" (Matisse) . . . . 1·40 1·50
1746 $5 "Christ and the Woman of Samaria" (Rembrandt) . . . . 2·40 2·50

1994. "Hong Kong '94" International Stamp Exhibition (1st issue). As T **390** of Grenada. Multicoloured.
1748 40 c. Hong Kong 1984 $5 aviation stamp and airliner at Kai Tak Airport 20 25
1749 40 c. Grenada Grenadines 1988 20 c. airships stamp and junk in Kowloon Bay 20 25

Nos. 1748/9 were printed together, se-tenant, with the centre part of each pair forming a composite design.

See also Nos. 1750/55.

1994. "Hong Kong '94" International Stamp Exhibition (2nd issue). Jade Sculptures. As T **391** of Grenada, but horiz. Multicoloured.
1750 45 c. White jade brush washer 20 25
1751 45 c. Archaic jade brush washer 20 25
1752 45 c. Dark green jade brush washer . . 20 25
1753 45 c. Green jade almsbowl 20 25
1754 45 c. Archaic jade dog . . 20 25
1755 45 c. Yellow jade brush washer 20 25

ISLE OF MAN

137 Maj-Gen. Bedell Smith and Naval Landing Force including "Ben-my-Chree IV" (ferry)

1994. 50th Anniv of D-Day. Multicoloured.
606 4p. Type **137** 10 10
607 4p. Admiral Ramsay and naval ships including "Victoria" and "Lady of Mann" (ferries) . . 10 10
608 20p. Gen. Montgomery and British landings . . 40 45
609 20p. Lt-Gen. Dempsey and 2nd Army landings . . 40 45
610 30p. Air Chief Marshal Leigh-Mallory and U.S. paratroops and aircraft 60 65
611 30p. Air Chief Marshal Tedder and British paratroops and aircraft 60 65
612 41p. Lt-Gen. Bradley and U.S. 1st Army landings 80 85
613 41p. Gen. Eisenhower and American landings . . 80 85

MALAWI

191 The Holy Family

1993. Christmas. Multicoloured.
925 20 t. Type **191** 10 10
926 75 t. Shepherds and star . . 20 25
927 95 t. Three Kings . . 30 35
928 2 k. Adoration of the Kings 60 65

192 "Pseudotropheus socolofi"

1994. Fishes. Multicoloured.
929 20 t. Type **192** 10 10
930 75 t. "Melanochromis auratus" 20 25
931 95 t. "Pseudotropheus lombardoi" 30 35
932 1 k. "Labeotropheus trewavasae" 30 35
933 2 k. "Pseudotropheus zebra" 60 65
934 4 k. "Pseudotropheus elongatus" . . . . 1·25 1·40

MALAYSIA

194 "Spathoglottis aurea"

1994. Orchids. Multicoloured.
527 20 c. Type **194** 10 10
528 30 c. "Paphiopedilum barbatum" 15 20
529 50 c. "Bulbophyllum lobbii" 25 30
530 $1 "Aerides odorata" . . 50 55

MALDIVE ISLANDS

Add to Nos. 1612/21:
1617a 6 r. 50+50 l. Egyptian vulture 80 85
1620a 30 r. Peregrine falcon 3·25 3·50
1620b 40 r. Black kite . . 4·50 4·75

Nos. 1617a and 1620a/b are larger, 23 × 32 mm.

1994. Famous Paintings by Rembrandt and Matisse. As T **316** of Antigua. Multicoloured.
1969 50 l. "Girl with a Broom" (Rembrandt) 10 10
1970 2 r. "Girl with Tulips" (Matisse) 20 25
1971 3 r. 50 "Young Girl at half-open Door" (Rembrandt) 40 45
1972 3 r. 50 "Portrait of Greta Moll" (Matisse) . . 40 45
1973 5 r. "The Prophetess Hannah" (Rembrandt) 55 60
1974 6 r. 50 "The Idol" (Matisse) 70 75
1975 7 r. "Woman with a Pink Flower" (Rembrandt) 80 85
1976 9 r. "Mme. Matisse in a Japanese Robe" (Matisse) . . . . 1·00 1·10
1977 10 r. "Portrait of Mme. Matisse" (Matisse) . . 1·10 1·25
1978 12 r. "Lucretia" (Rembrandt) . . . . 1·40 1·50
1979 15 r. "Lady with a Ostrich Feather Fan" (Rembrandt) . . . . 1·60 1·75
1980 15 r. "The Woman with the Hat" (Matisse) . . 1·60 1·75

No. 1979 is inscribed "The Lady with an Ostich Feather Fan" in error.

1994. "Hong Kong '94" International Stamp Exhibition (1st issue). As T **390** of Grenada. Multicoloured.
1982 4 r. Hong Kong 1983 $1 Space Museum stamp and Moon-lantern Festival 45 50
1983 4 r. Maldive Islands 1976 5 r. "Viking" space mission stamp and Moon-lantern Festival 45 50

Nos. 1982/3 were printed together, se-tenant, with the centre part of each pair forming a composite design.

See also Nos. 1984/9.

1994. "Hong Kong '94" International Stamp Exhibition (2nd issue). Ching Dynasty Cloisonne Enamelware. As T **391** of Grenada. Multicoloured.
1984 2 r. Vase 20 25
1985 2 r. Flower holder . . 20 25
1986 2 r. Elephant with vase on back 20 25
1987 2 r. Tibetan-style lama's teapot 20 25
1988 2 r. Fo-Dog 20 25
1989 2 r. Teapot with swing handle 20 25

295 Windischmann (U.S.A.) and Giannini (Italy)

1994. World Cup Football Championship, U.S.A. Multicoloured.

1990	7 l. Type **295**	10	10
1991	20 l. Carnevale (Italy) and Gascoigne (England) . .	10	10
1992	25 l. England players congratulating Platt . .	10	10
1993	3 r. 50 Koeman (Holland) and Klinsmann (Germany)	40	45
1994	5 r. Quinn (Ireland) and Maldini (Italy) . .	55	60
1995	7 r. Lineker (England) . .	80	85
1996	15 r. Hassam (Egypt) and Moran (Ireland) . .	1·60	1·75
1997	18 r. Canniggia (Argentina)	2·00	2·25

NIGERIA

284 Hand with Tweezers holding 1969 4d. Philatelic Service Stamp

1994. 25th Anniv of National Philatelic Service. Multicoloured.

665	1 n. Type **284**	10	10
666	1 n. 50 Philatelic Bureau . .	10	10
667	5 n. Stamps forming map of Nigeria	30	35
668	10 n. Philatelic counter . .	60	65

NIUAFO'OU

37 Stern of H.M.S. "Bounty"

1994. Sailing Ships. Multicoloured.

208	80 s. Type **37**	75	80
209	80 s. Bow of H.M.S. "Bounty"	75	80
210	80 s. H.M.S. "Pandora" (frigate)	75	80
211	80 s. Whaling ship . .	75	80
212	80 s. Trading schooner . .	75	80

NOTE The first supplement containing new issues not in this catalogue or the Addenda appeared in the October 1994 number of *Gibbons Stamp Monthly*.

INDEX